LITERARY MARKET PLACE™

LMP 2016

Literary Market Place™
76th Edition

Publisher
Thomas H. Hogan

Vice President, Content
Dick Kaser

Senior Director, ITI Reference Group
Owen O'Donnell

Managing Editor
Karen Hallard

Senior Editor
Mitra Purkayastha

Assistant Editor
Karen DiDario

Tampa Operations:

Manager, Tampa Editorial Operations
Debra James

Project Coordinator, Tampa Editorial
Carolyn Victor

Graphics & Production:

Production Manager
Tiffany Chamenko

Production
Dana Stevenson
Jackie Crawford

LITERARY MARKET PLACE™

LMP 2016

THE DIRECTORY OF THE AMERICAN BOOK PUBLISHING INDUSTRY WITH INDUSTRY INDEXES

Volume

Published by

Information Today, Inc.
143 Old Marlton Pike
Medford, NJ 08055-8750
Phone: (609) 654-6266
Fax: (609) 654-4309
E-mail (Orders): custserv@infotoday.com
Web site: www.infotoday.com

ISSN 0000-1155
ISBN 978-1-57387-509-7 (set)
Library of Congress Catalog Card Number 41-51571

Information Today, Inc.
143 Old Marlton Pike
Medford, NJ 08055-8750
Phone: 800-300-9868 (Customer Service)
800-409-4929 (Editorial)
Fax: 609-654-4309
E-mail (orders): custserv@infotoday.com
Web Site: www.infotoday.com

Printed in the United States of America

US $399.50
ISBN 13: 978-1-57387-509-7
39950
9 781573 875097

CONTENTS

VOLUME 1

VOLUME 2

SERVICES & SUPPLIERS

INDEXES

Preface

The 2016 edition marks the 76th annual publication of *Literary Market Place*™—the leading directory of the American and Canadian book publishing industry. Covering publishers and literary agents to manufacturers and shipping services, *LMP* is the most comprehensive directory of its kind. Completely revised, *LMP* 2016 contains over 9,500 entries. Of these listings 2,647 are publishers—including Canadian houses and small presses. Together with its companion publication, *International Literary Market Place*™, these directories cover the global book publishing industry.

Organization & Content

Volume 1 covers core publishing industry information: Book Publishers; Editorial Services and Agents; Associations, Events, Courses and Awards; and Books and Magazines for the Trade.

Volume 2 contains information on service providers and suppliers to the publishing industry. Advertising, Marketing and Publicity; Book Manufacturing; Sales and Distribution; and Services and Suppliers can be found in this volume.

Entries generally contain name, address, telephone and other telecommunications data, key personnel, company reportage, branch offices, brief statistics and descriptive annotations. Where applicable, Standard Address Numbers (SANs) have been included. SANs are unique numbers assigned to the addresses of publishers, wholesalers and booksellers. Publishers' entries also contain their assigned ISBN prefixes. Both the SAN and ISBN systems are administered by R.R. Bowker LLC, 630 Central Avenue, New Providence, NJ 07974.

Indexes

In addition to the numerous section-specific indexes appearing throughout, each volume of *LMP* contains four indexes that reference listings appearing in that volume. The Industry Indexes cover two distinct areas of data: a Company Index that includes the name, address, communications information and page reference for company listings and a separate Personnel Index that includes the main personnel associated with each entry as well as the page reference. Other indexes include the Index to Sections for quickly finding specific categories of information and the Index to Advertisers.

A Note to Authors

Prospective authors seeking a publisher should be aware that there are publishers who, as a condition for publishing and marketing an individual's work, may require a significant sum of money be paid to the publisher. This practice is known by a number of terms including author subsidized publishing, author investment, and co-operative publishing. Before entering an agreement involving such a payment, the author is advised to make a careful investigation to determine the standing of the publisher's imprint in the industry.

Similarly, authors seeking literary representation are advised that some agents request a nominal reading fee that may be applied to the agent's commission upon representation. Other agencies may charge substantially higher fees which may not be applicable to a future commission and which are not refundable. The recommended course is to first send a query letter with an outline, sample chapter, and a self-addressed stamped envelope (SASE). Should an agent express interest in handling the manuscript, full details of fees and commissions should be obtained in writing before the complete manuscript is sent. Should an agency require significant advance payment from an author, the author is cautioned to make a careful investigation to determine the agency's standing in the industry before entering an agreement. The author should always retain a copy of the manuscript in his or her possession.

Occasionally, the editors of *LMP* will receive complaints against publishers or agents listed in the work. If, after investigation and review, the editors determine that the complaints are significant and justified, we may exclude the company or individual in question. However, the absence of a listing in *LMP* for any particular publisher or agent should not be construed as a judgment on the legitimacy or integrity of that organization or individual.

Compilation

LMP is updated throughout the year via a number of methods. A request for updated information is sent to every current entrant at least once each year to corroborate and update the information contained on our database. All updates received are edited for the next product release. Those entrants who do not respond to our request are verified through telephone interviews. Entrants who cannot be verified or who fall short of entry criteria are dropped from the current edition.

Information for new listings is gathered in a similar method. Possible new listings are identified through ongoing research, or when a listing request is received either from the organization itself or from a third party. If sufficient information is not initially gathered to create a listing, a data collection form is provided to the organization to submit essential listing information.

Updated information or suggestions for new listings can be submitted by mail to:

Literary Market Place
Information Today, Inc.
121 Chanlon Rd, Suite G-20
New Providence, NJ 07974-2195

An updating method using the Internet is also available for *LMP* listings:

Visit the *Literary Market Place* web site to update an *LMP* listing. **Literarymarketplace.com** allows you the opportunity to provide new information for a listing by clicking on the "Update or Correct Your Entry" option. The Feedback option on the home page of the web site can be used to suggest new entries as well.

Related Services

Literary Market Place, along with its companion volume *International Literary Market Place*, is available through the Internet at **www.literarymarketplace.com**. Designed to give users simple, logical access to the information they require, the site offers users the choice of searching for data alphabetically, geographically, by type, or by subject. Continuously updated by Information Today's team of editors, this is a truly enhanced version of the *LMP* and *ILMP* databases, incorporating features that make "must-have" information easily available.

Arrangements for placing advertisements in *LMP* can be coordinated through Lauri Rimler by telephone at 800-409-4929 (press 1) or 908-219-0088, or by e-mail at lwrimler@infotoday.com.

Your feedback is important to us. We strongly encourage you to contact us with suggestions or comments on the print edition of *LMP*, or its web site. Our editorial office can be reached by telephone at 800-409-4929 (press 3) or 908-219-0277, or by e-mail at khallard@infotoday.com.

The editors would like to thank those entrants who took the time to respond to our requests for current information.

Abbreviations & Acronyms

The following is a list of acronyms & abbreviations used throughout *LMP*.

AAP - Association of American Publishers
AAR - Association of Authors' Representatives
AB - Alberta
ABA - American Booksellers Association
Acct(s) - Account(s)
Acctg - Accounting
Acq(s) - Acquisition(s)
Ad - Advertising
Admin - Administrative, Administration
Aff - Affairs
AK - Alaska
AL - Alabama
ALA - American Library Association
ALTA - American Literary Translators Association
APA - American Photographic Artists
appt - appointment
Apt - Apartment
AR - Arkansas
ASMP - American Society of Media Photographers
ASPP - American Society of Picture Professionals
Assoc(s) - Associate(s)
Asst(s) - Assistant(s)
ATA - American Translators Association
AV - Audiovisual
Ave - Avenue
AZ - Arizona

B&W - Black & White
BC - British Columbia
Bd - Board
bio - biography
BISAC - Book Industry Standards & Communications
BISG - Book Industry Study Group
Bldg - Building
Blvd - Boulevard
BMI - Book Manufacturers' Institute
Br - Branch
Busn - Business

CA - California
CEO - Chief Executive Officer
CFO - Chief Financial Officer
Chmn - Chairman
Chpn - Chairperson
CIO - Chief Information Officer
Circ - Circulation
CN - Canada
CO - Colorado
Co(s) - Company(-ies)
Co-edns - Co-editions
Coll(s) - College(s)
Comm - Committee
Commun(s) - Communication(s)
Comp - Compiler
Compt - Comptroller
Cont - Controller
Contrib - Contributing
COO - Chief Operating Officer
Coord(s) - Coordinator(s)
Corp - Corporate, Corporation
Coun - Counsel
CT - Connecticut
Ct - Court
CTO - Chief Technical / Technology Officer
Ctr - Center
Curr - Current
Cust - Customer
CZ - Canal Zone

DC - District of Columbia
DE - Delaware
Dept - Department
Devt - Development
Dir(s) - Director(s)
Dist - Distributed, Distribution, Distributor
Div - Division
Dom - Domestic
Dr - Drive

ed - edition
Ed(s) - Editor(s)
Edit - Editorial
Educ - Education, Educational
El-hi - Elementary-High School
Elem - Elementary
Ency - Encyclopedia
Eng - English
Engg - Engineering
Engr - Engineer
Equip - Equipment
ESL - English as a Second Language
Est - Established
EVP - Executive Vice President
exc - except
Exec(s) - Executive(s)
Expwy - Expressway
ext - extension

Fed - Federal
Fin - Finance, Financial
fl - floor
FL - Florida
Freq - Frequency
Fwy - Freeway

GA - Georgia
Gen - General
Govt - Government
GU - Guam

HD - High-definition
HI - Hawaii
HR - Human Resources
HS - High School
Hwy - Highway

IA - Iowa
ID - Idaho
IL - Illinois
Illus - Illustrator
IN - Indiana
indiv(s) - individual(s)
Indus - Industrial, Industry
Info - Information
Instl - Institutional
Instn(s) - Institution(s)
Instrl - Instructional
Intl - International
ISBN - International Standard Book Number
ISSN - International Standard Serial Number
IT - Information Technology

Jt - Joint
Jr - Junior
Juv - Juvenile

K - Kindergarten
KS - Kansas
KY - Kentucky

LA - Louisiana
Lang(s) - Language(s)
Lib(s) - Library(-ies)
Libn(s) - Librarian(s)
Lit - Literature

MA - Massachusetts
MB - Manitoba
MD - Maryland
Mdse - Merchandise
Mdsg - Merchandising
ME - Maine
Med - Medical
Memb(s) - Member(s)
Metro - Metropolitan
Mfg - Manufacturing
Mgmt - Management
Mgr(s) - Manager(s)
MI - Michigan
Mkt(s) - Market(s)
Mktg - Marketing
MLA - Modern Language Association
MN - Minnesota
Mng - Managing
MO - Missouri
MS - Mississippi
ms(s) - manuscript(s)
MT - Montana

Natl - National
NB - New Brunswick
NC - North Carolina
ND - North Dakota

NE - Nebraska
NH - New Hampshire
NJ - New Jersey
NL - Newfoundland and Labrador
NM - New Mexico
No - Number
NS - Nova Scotia
NT - Northwest Territories
NU - Nunavut
NV - Nevada
NY - New York

Off(s) - Office(s)
Offr - Officer
OH - Ohio
OK - Oklahoma
ON - Ontario
Oper(s) - Operation(s)
OR - Oregon

PA - Pennsylvania
Pbk(s) - Paperback(s)
PE - Prince Edward Island
Perms - Permissions
Photo - Photograph
Photog - Photographer, Photography
Pkwy - Parkway
pp - pages
PPA - Professional Photographers of America
PR - Public Relations
PR - Puerto Rico
Pres - President
Proc - Processing
Prod(s) - Product(s)
Prodn - Production
Prodr - Producer
Prof - Professional
Prog(s) - Program(s)
Proj(s) - Project(s)
Promo(s) - Promotion(s)
Prop - Proprietor
Pub Aff - Public Affairs
Publg - Publishing
Publr - Publisher
Pubn(s) - Publication(s)
Purch - Purchasing

QC - Quebec

R&D - Research & Development
Rd - Road
Ref - Reference
Reg - Region
Regl - Regional
Rel - Relations
Rep(s) - Representative(s)
Res - Research
RI - Rhode Island
Rm - Room
Rte - Route
Rts - Rights

SAN - Standard Address Number
SASE - Self-Addressed Stamped Envelope
SATW - Society of American Travel Writers
SC - South Carolina
Sci - Science
SD - South Dakota
Secy - Secretary
Serv(s) - Service(s)
SK - Saskatchewan
SLA - Special Libraries Association
Soc - Social, Sociology
Spec - Special
Sq - Square
Sr - Senior
St - Saint, Street
Sta - Station
Ste - Sainte
Subn(s) - Subscription(s)
Subs - Subsidiary
Supv - Supervisor
SVP - Senior Vice President
Synd - Syndicated, Syndication

Tech - Technical
Technol - Technology
Tel - Telephone
Terr - Terrace
TN - Tennessee
Tpke - Turnpike
Treas - Treasurer
TX - Texas

UK - United Kingdom
Univ - University
unsol - unsolicited
UT - Utah

V - Vice
VA - Virginia
VChmn - Vice Chairman
VI - Virgin Islands
vol(s) - volume(s)
VP - Vice President
VT - Vermont

WA - Washington
WI - Wisconsin
WV - West Virginia
WY - Wyoming

yr - year
YT - Yukon Territory

Book Publishers

U.S. Publishers

Listed in alphabetical order are those U.S. publishers that have reported to *LMP* that they produce an average of three or more books annually. Publishers that have appeared in a previous edition of *LMP*, but whose output currently does not meet our defined rate of activity, will be reinstated when their annual production reaches the required level. It should be noted that this rule of publishing activity does not apply to publishers of dictionaries, encyclopedias, atlases and braille books or to university presses.

The definition of a book is that used for *Books in Print* (Grey House Publishing, PO Box 56, Amenia, NY 12501-0056) and excludes charts, pamphlets, folding maps, sheet music and material with stapled bindings. Publishers that make their titles available only in electronic or audio format are included if they meet the stated criteria. In the case of packages, the book must be of equal or greater importance than the accompanying piece. With few exceptions, new publishers are not listed prior to having published at least three titles within a year.

§ before the company name indicates publishers involved in electronic publishing.

The following indexes can be found immediately after the publishers' listings:

U.S. Publishers–Geographic Index
U.S. Publishers–Type of Publications Index
U.S. Publishers–Subject Index

See **Imprints, Subsidiaries & Distributors** for additional information on the companies listed herein. This section should also be checked for apparently active companies that are no longer listed in the U.S. Publishers section. In many cases, they have been acquired as an imprint or subsidiary of a larger entity and no longer have a discrete listing.

A Better Be Write Publishing LLC
9001 Ridge Hill St, Kernersville, NC 27284
Mailing Address: PO Box 914, Kernersville, NC 27285
Tel: 336-354-7173 *Fax:* 336-993-2497
E-mail: profin@triad.rr.com
Web Site: www.abetterbewrite.com
Key Personnel
Mng Ed: William J Connor, Jr
E-mail: williamconnor@a-argusbooks.com
Founded: 2005
Subjects include the paranormal.
ISBN Prefix(es): 978-0-9767732; 978-0-9771971; 978-0-9788985
Number of titles published annually: 30 Print
Total Titles: 150 Print
Membership(s): AAP; The Independent Book Publishers Association

A Cappella Books, see Chicago Review Press

§A-R Editions Inc
1600 Aspen Commons, Suite 100, Middleton, WI 53562
Tel: 608-836-9000 *Toll Free Tel:* 800-736-0070 (North America book orders only) *Fax:* 608-831-8200
E-mail: info@areditions.com; orders@areditions.com
Web Site: www.areditions.com
Key Personnel
CEO & Pres: Patrick Wall *Tel:* 608-203-2575
E-mail: patrick.wall@areditions.com
Dir, Sales & Mktg: James L Zychowicz *Tel:* 608-203-2580 *E-mail:* james.zychowicz@areditions.com
Founded: 1962
Scholarly critical editions of music for performance & study; computer music & digital audio professional books, electronics & Internet technology, online music anthology (www.armusicanthology.com) & co-published series with MLA: Index & Bibliography, Basic Manual & Technical Reports Series.
ISBN Prefix(es): 978-0-89579
Number of titles published annually: 25 Print
Total Titles: 500 Print
Distributor for AIM (American Institute of Musicology)

§AAAI Press
Imprint of Association for the Advancement of Artificial Intelligence
2275 E Bayshore Rd, Suite 160, Palo Alto, CA 94303
Tel: 650-328-3123 *Fax:* 650-321-4457
E-mail: publications14@aaai.org
Web Site: www.aaaipress.org; www.aaai.org
Key Personnel
Exec Dir: Carol Hamilton
Pubns Dir: Mike Hamilton
Ed-in-Chief: Anthony G Cohn
Founded: 1989
Publishing books on all aspects of artificial intelligence.
ISBN Prefix(es): 978-0-929280; 978-1-57735
Number of titles published annually: 30 Print; 4 CD-ROM; 2 Online
Total Titles: 400 Print; 30 CD-ROM; 2 Online

AACC International
3340 Pilot Knob Rd, St Paul, MN 55121
Tel: 651-454-7250 *Fax:* 651-454-0766
E-mail: aacc@scisoc.org
Web Site: www.aaccnet.org
Key Personnel
Mktg Coord: Dawn Wuest *E-mail:* dwuest@scisoc.org
Dir, Pubns: Greg Grahek *E-mail:* ggrahek@scisoc.org
Founded: 1920
Source for cereal science information.
ISBN Prefix(es): 978-1-891127; 978-0-9624407
Number of titles published annually: 5 Print; 1 CD-ROM
Total Titles: 100 Print; 1 CD-ROM; 1 Online; 1 E-Book
Imprints: Eagan Press
See separate listing for:
Eagan Press

AACC Press, see AACC International

AAPC Publishing, see Autism Asperger Publishing Co

§AAPG (American Association of Petroleum Geologists)
1444 S Boulder Ave, Tulsa, OK 74119
Mailing Address: PO Box 979, Tulsa, OK 74101-0979
Tel: 918-584-2555 *Toll Free Tel:* 800-364-AAPG (364-2274) *Fax:* 918-580-2665
Toll Free Fax: 800-898-2274
E-mail: info@aapg.org
Web Site: www.aapg.org
Key Personnel
Mng Ed, Tech Pubns: Beverly Molyneux
Tel: 918-560-2670 *E-mail:* molyneux@aapg.org
Founded: 1917
Peer-reviewed geological science tomes.
ISBN Prefix(es): 978-0-89181; 978-1-58861
Number of titles published annually: 10 Print; 10 CD-ROM
Total Titles: 100 Print; 80 CD-ROM
Distributed by Affiliated East - West Press Private Ltd; Canadian Society of Petroleum Geologists; Geological Society of London
Distributor for Geological Society of London
Shipping Address: 125 W 15 St, Tulsa, OK 74119

AAVIM, see American Association for Vocational Instructional Materials

Abaris Books
Division of Opal Publishing Corp
64 Wall St, Norwalk, CT 06850
Tel: 203-838-8402 *Fax:* 203-857-0730
E-mail: abaris@abarisbooks.com
Web Site: abarisbooks.com
Key Personnel
Publr: Anthony S Kaufmann
Mng Ed: J C West *Tel:* 203-838-8625
Founded: 1973
Art, art history, art reference, philosophy & metaphysics.
ISBN Prefix(es): 978-0-913870; 978-0-89835
Number of titles published annually: 7 Print
Total Titles: 185 Print
Imprints: The Illustrated Bartsch; Janus Library

Abbeville Press
Imprint of Abbeville Publishing Group
137 Varick St, Suite 504, New York, NY 10013-1105
Tel: 212-366-5585 *Toll Free Tel:* 800-ARTBOOK (278-2665); 800-343-4499 (orders) *Fax:* 212-366-6966 *Toll Free Fax:* 800-351-5073 (orders)
E-mail: abbeville@abbeville.com; sales@abbeville.com; marketing@abbeville.com; rights@abbeville.com
Web Site: www.abbeville.com
Key Personnel
Sr Ed: Joan Strasbaugh
Cust Serv Mgr: Nadine Winns
Rts & Perms: David Fabricant
Founded: 1977
A fine arts publisher.
ISBN Prefix(es): 978-0-89659; 978-1-55859; 978-0-7892
Number of titles published annually: 25 Print

Abbeville Publishing Group
137 Varick St, Suite 504, New York, NY 10013
SAN: 211-4755
Tel: 212-366-5585 *Toll Free Tel:* 800-ART-BOOK (278-2665) *Fax:* 212-366-6966
E-mail: abbeville@abbeville.com; marketing@abbeville.com; sales@abbeville.com; rights@abbeville.com
Web Site: www.abbeville.com
Key Personnel
Pres & Publr: Robert E Abrams
Dir, Fin Analysis: John Olivieri
Warehouse Dir: Arthur Goldberg
Cust Serv Mgr: Nadine Winns *E-mail:* nwinns@abbeville.com
Rts & Perms: David Fabricant
Founded: 1977
Publishers of high-quality, fine art books, nonfiction illustrated books, children's books, limited editions, prints, gift line.
ISBN Prefix(es): 978-0-89659; 978-1-55859; 978-0-89660; 978-0-7892
Number of titles published annually: 40 Print
Total Titles: 700 Print
Imprints: Abbeville Kids; Abbeville Press; Artabras; Modern Masters
Foreign Rep(s): Book Promotions (Nicky Stubbs) (South Africa); Gilles Fauveau (Japan, Korea); Jaime Gregorio (Philippines); Sharad Mohan (Bangladesh, India, Maldives, Nepal, Pakistan, Sri Lanka); Peribo Pty Ltd (Eddie Coffey) (Australia); Perseus Books Group UK (Europe, Ireland, UK); June Poonpanich (Cambodia, Indonesia, Laos, Thailand, Vietnam); Publishers Group Canada (Canada); Steimatzky (2005) Ltd (Diane Levy) (Israel); Wei Zhao (China, Hong Kong, Taiwan)
Foreign Rights: Bookbank, SA (Latin America, Mexico, Spain); Motovun Tokyo (Japan); Ultreya srl (Italy)
Orders to: Publishers Group Worldwide, 250 W 57 St, 15th fl, New York, NY 10107 *Tel:* 212-581-7839 *E-mail:* intlorders@pgw.com
Warehouse: Client Distribution Services, 193 Edwards Dr, Jackson, TN 38301 *Toll Free Tel:* 800-343-4499 *Toll Free Fax:* 800-351-5073
See separate listing for:
Abbeville Press

§ABC-CLIO
130 Cremona Dr, Santa Barbara, CA 93117
Mailing Address: PO Box 1911, Santa Barbara, CA 93116-1911
Tel: 805-968-1911 *Toll Free Tel:* 800-368-6868 *Fax:* 805-685-9685 *Toll Free Fax:* 866-270-3856
E-mail: sales@abc-clio.com; customerservice@abc-clio.com
Web Site: www.abc-clio.com
Key Personnel
CEO & Academic Publr: Ronald Boehm
Pres: Becky Snyder *Tel:* 805-968-1911 ext 306
Founded: 1955
A privately held corporation which has for many years enjoyed an international reputation for high quality & innovation. As an educational reference publisher the company has received critical acclaim for its computer assisted abstracting & indexing services, world renowned book program & cutting-edge online products.
ISBN Prefix(es): 978-0-87436; 978-1-57607
Number of titles published annually: 300 Print; 100 E-Book
Total Titles: 900 Print; 100 Online; 150 E-Book
Imprints: Greenwood Press; Libraries Unlimited/Linworth Publishing; Praeger
Subsidiaries: ABC-CLIO Online Solutions
Warehouse: ABC-CLIO Inc, c/o Sheridan Books, 617 E Industrial Dr, Chelsea, MI 48818
See separate listing for:
Libraries Unlimited

ABDO Publishing Group
Subsidiary of Abdo Consulting Group Inc (ACGI)
8000 W 78 St, Suite 310, Edina, MN 55439
Mailing Address: PO Box 398166, Minneapolis, MN 55439-8166
Tel: 952-831-2120 *Toll Free Tel:* 800-800-1312 *Toll Free Fax:* 800-862-3480
E-mail: customerservice@abdopublishing.com
Web Site: abdopublishing.com
Key Personnel
Pres & Dir: Jill Hansen
Publr & Natl Sales Mgr: Jim Abdo
VP, Sales & Mktg: Paul Skaj *Tel:* 952-698-2403 *E-mail:* pskaj@abdopublishing.com
Mng Dir: Jennie Forsberg
Dir, Mktg: Dan Verdick *Tel:* 952-698-2404 *E-mail:* dverdick@abdopublishing.com
Mktg & Communs Mgr: BreAnn Rumsch *Tel:* 952-698-2413 *E-mail:* brumsch@abdopublishing.com
Ed-in-Chief: Paul Abdo *E-mail:* pabdo@abdopublishing.com
Founded: 1985
Children's books for the library market.
ISBN Prefix(es): 978-1-56239; 978-1-57765
Number of titles published annually: 350 Print; 350 Online
Total Titles: 3,000 Print; 2,000 Online; 500 E-Book
Imprints: A&D Xtreme (grades 3-9); Abdo & Daughters Publishing (grades 5-9); Abdo Kids (grades preK-2 beginning readers); Big Buddy Books (grades 2-5 larger trim size); Buddy Books (grades 2-5); Calico (grades 2-8 chapter books); Chapter Books; Checkerboard Library (grades 3-6); Core Library (grades 3-6); Essential Library (grades 6-12); Graphic Planet (grades 2-10 graphic novels); Looking Glass Library (grades preK-6 picture books); Magic Readers (grades K-3 leveled readers); Sandcastle (grades preK-3); Short Tales (grades 1-6 adapted stories); SportsZone (grades 2-12); Spotlight (grades preK-8 popular fiction); Super Sandcastle (grades K-4)
Distributed by Rockbottom Book Co
Warehouse: 1920 Lookout Dr, North Mankato, MN 56003

Aberdeen Bay
6285 Gentle Lane, Alexandria, VA 22310
Tel: 703-473-1392
E-mail: editor@aberdeenbay.com
Web Site: www.aberdeenbay.com
Key Personnel
Acqs Ed: Ross Murphy
Founded: 2007
Traditional publisher with focus on mainstream fiction, memoirs & motivational books.
ISBN Prefix(es): 978-0-9814725; 978-1-60830
Number of titles published annually: 20 Print; 1 Online
Total Titles: 60 Print; 1 Online

§Abingdon Press
Imprint of The United Methodist Publishing House
201 Eighth Ave S, Nashville, TN 37203-3919
SAN: 201-0046
Mailing Address: PO Box 801, Nashville, TN 37202-0801
Tel: 615-749-6000 (academic books) *Toll Free Tel:* 800-251-3320 *Fax:* 615-749-6056 (academic books) *Toll Free Fax:* 800-836-7802 (orders)
E-mail: orders@abingdonpress.com
Web Site: www.abingdonpress.com
Key Personnel
Pres & Publr: Neil M Alexander
Exec Dir, Mktg: Tamara Crabtree
Assoc Publr, Christian Fiction: Pamela Clements
Assoc Publr & Ed-in-Chief: Mary Catherine Dean
Sr Acqs Ed: Ramona Richards
Regl Sales Mgr: Bryan C Williams *Tel:* 615-749-6295 *E-mail:* bwilliams@abingdonpress.com
Mature Years Ed: Marvin Cropsey
Founded: 1789
Religion/ecumenical Christianity; general interest, children's, family, church professional, academic, reference, lay spiritual; United Methodist history, doctrine, polity.
ISBN Prefix(es): 978-0-687; 978-1-4267; 978-1-63088; 978-1-5018
Number of titles published annually: 175 Print
Total Titles: 270 Print; 10 CD-ROM; 3 Online
Imprints: Upper Room Books
Distributor for Church Publishing Inc; Judson Press; Upper Room Books
Foreign Rep(s): Ausburg Fortress Canada (Canada); Canaanland Distributors Sdn Bhd (Malaysia); Christian Connexion Methodist Publishing House (South Africa); Cross Communications Co (Hong Kong); KCBS Inc (Korea); Lion Hudson PLC (UK); MediaCom Education Inc (Australia); Rainbow Book Agencies (Australia); SKS Books (Singapore)
Orders to: Ingram Publisher Services, One Ingram Blvd, La Vergne, TN 37086 *Tel:* 615-793-5000 *Web Site:* www.ingrampublisherservices.com
Warehouse: 341 Great Circle Dr, Nashville, TN 37228-1703
Distribution Center: Ingram Publisher Services, One Ingram Blvd, La Vergne, TN 37086 *Tel:* 615-793-5000 *Web Site:* www.ingrampublisherservices.com

Harry N Abrams Inc
Subsidiary of La Martiniere Groupe
115 W 18 St, 6th fl, New York, NY 10011
SAN: 200-2434
Tel: 212-206-7715 *Toll Free Tel:* 800-345-1359 *Fax:* 212-519-1210
E-mail: abrams@abramsbooks.com
Web Site: www.abramsbooks.com

Key Personnel
CEO & Pres: Michael Jacobs *E-mail:* mjacobs@abramsbooks.com
SVP & Chief Mktg & Busn Devt Offr: Steve Tager *E-mail:* stager@abramsbooks.com
Exec Dir, Adult Mktg & Publicity: Michelle Montague
VP & Publr, Adult Trade: Michael Sand
Assoc Publr, Adult Trade: Shawna Mullen
Assoc Publr, Children's: Jody Mosley *E-mail:* jmosley@abramsbooks.com
VP & Ed-in-Chief: Eric Himmel
VP, Busn Devt: Brenda Marsh
VP, Intl & Subs Rts: Sherri Aldis
VP, Worldwide Sales: Mary Wowk *E-mail:* mwowk@abramsbooks.com
Dir & Mng Ed: David Blatty
Asst Mng Ed: Sally Knapp
Sr Dir, Adult Trade Publicity: Jennifer Brunn *E-mail:* jbrunn@abramsbooks.com
Creative Dir, Adult: John Gall
Dir, Adult Publicity & Brand Strategy: Claire Bamundo *E-mail:* cbamundo@abramsbooks.com
Dir, Children's Mktg & Publicity, Abrams Children's, Amulet & Appleseed: Nicole Russo
Dir, Digital Mktg: Jeffrey Yamaguchi
Dir, Online Mktg Opers: Chris Blank
Dir, Spec Mkts: Monica Shah
Dir, Subs & Intl Rts: Yulia Borodyanskaya
Dir, Trade Sales: Elisa Garcia *E-mail:* egarcia@abramsbooks.com
Brand Dir, Diary of a Wimpy Kid: Veronica Wasserman
Edit Dir, Gift & Paper Prods: Karrie Witkin
Mktg Dir, Adult Trade: Erin Hotchkiss *E-mail:* ehotchkiss@abramsbooks.com
Assoc Art Dir, Abrams Children's: Maria Middleton
Sr Mgr, Foreign & Subs Rts: Erica LaSala
Sr Mktg Mgr, Adult Trade: Paul Colarusso
Sr Mktg Mgr: Nancy Lambert
Sr Subs Rts Mgr: Karin Schulze
Mktg Mgr & Soc Media Specialist: Ellie Levine
Mgr, Children's Mktg & Publicity: Laura Mihalick
Digital & Soc Media Mktg Assoc: Mamie VanLangen
Publicity & Mktg Assoc, Abrams Children's: Morgan Dubin
Mgr, Corp Events & Exec Asst to CEO: Merle Brown
Gift Rep Sales Mgr, Spec Mkts: Raquel Avila
Mktg Coord: Nico Cassanetti
Sr Publicist, Adult: Marisa Dobson
Publicist, Adult Trade: Maya Bradford
Publicist: Juliana Horbachevsky
Assoc Publicist, Adult Trade: Jordan Sapiro
Exec Ed, Abrams Children's & Amulet: Traci Todd
Exec Ed, Cookbooks-Stewart, Tabori & Chang: Holly Dolce
Sr Mng Ed: Jennifer Graham
Sr Ed, Adult Trade: Eric Klopfer
Ed: Laura Dozier; Anne Heltzel
Ed, Calendars, Licensing & Custom Publg: Miriam Tribble
Assoc Ed: Erica Finkel
Asst Ed: Samantha Weiner
Trade Sales Rep: Matthew Dinda
Founded: 1949
Art & architecture, photography, natural sciences, performing arts & children's books.
ISBN Prefix(es): 978-0-8109
Number of titles published annually: 250 Print
Total Titles: 2,000 Print
Imprints: Abrams Appleseed; Abrams Books; Abrams Books for Young Readers; Abrams ComicArts; Abrams Image; Amulet Books; SelfMadeHero; STC Craft; Stewart, Tabori & Chang
Distributed by Abrams & Chronicle Books (Great Britain); Editions Alain
Distributor for Booth-Clibborn Editions; 5 Continents Editions; Royal Academy Publications; Tate Publishing; V&A Publishing; The Vendome Press
Foreign Rep(s): Canadian Manda Group
Orders to: Hachette Book Group USA (North America) *Toll Free Tel:* 800-759-0190 *Toll Free Fax:* 800-286-9471; Littlehampton Book Services Ltd, Faraday Close, Durrington, Worthing, West Sussex BN13 3RB, United Kingdom (UK, Africa, Asia, Europe & Middle East) *Tel:* (019) 0382-8500; (014) 7655-1080 (orders only) *Fax:* (019) 7654-1060; (014) 7654-1061 (orders only) *Web Site:* www.pubeasy.com
Distribution Center: Littlehampton Book Services Ltd, Faraday Close, Durrington, Worthing, West Sussex BN13 3RB, United Kingdom (UK, Africa, Asia, Europe & Middle East) *Tel:* (019) 0382-8500; (014) 7655-1080 (orders only) *Fax:* (019) 7654-1060; (014) 7654-1061 (orders only) *Web Site:* www.pubeasy.com
Membership(s): AAP
See separate listing for:
Stewart, Tabori & Chang

§Abrams Learning Trends
Subsidiary of Learning Trends LLC
16310 Bratton Lane, Suite 250, Austin, TX 78728-2403
Toll Free Tel: 800-227-9120 *Toll Free Fax:* 800-737-3322
E-mail: customerservice@abramslearningtrends.com (orders, cust serv); contactus@abramslearningtrends.com
Web Site: www.abramslearningtrends.com (orders, cust serv)
Key Personnel
CEO & Pres: Roy Mayers
VP & Cont: Peter Dunn
EVP & Publr: Erin Kinard
EVP & Gen Mgr: William Thomas
EVP, Sales: Gunnar Voltz
VP, Sales: Bruce Warren
Founded: 2008
PreK-5 educational materials.
ISBN Prefix(es): 978-0-7665; 978-0-7664
Number of titles published annually: 100 Print; 6 CD-ROM; 15 Audio
Total Titles: 1,000 Print; 36 CD-ROM; 36 Audio
Imprints: The Letter People®
Distributor for General Education Services (New Zealand)

Absey & Co Inc
23011 Northcrest Dr, Spring, TX 77389
Tel: 281-257-2340 *Toll Free Tel:* 888-41-ABSEY (412-2739) *Fax:* 281-251-4676
E-mail: info@absey.biz
Web Site: www.absey.biz
Key Personnel
Ed-in-Chief: Edward E Wilson
Founded: 1996
Small publishing house catering to the author & illustrator. We encourage end-to-end participation, e.g. author may select his or her illustrator, type of paper & type style. Queries or information about submissions can be found online. If a cover letter does not utilize conventional grammar/usage, then the ms will definitely be rejected.
ISBN Prefix(es): 978-1-888842
Number of titles published annually: 3 Print; 1 CD-ROM; 26 Online
Total Titles: 36 Print; 1 CD-ROM; 26 Online
Branch Office(s)
45 W 21 St, Suite 5, New York, NY 10010
Tel: 212-277-8028
Membership(s): Southwest Booksellers Association

§Academic Press
Imprint of Elsevier BV
225 Wyman St, Waltham, MA 02144
Tel: 781-663-5200 *Fax:* 781-663-2262
Web Site: store.elsevier.com/Academic-Press
Founded: 1942
Scientific, technical & professional information in multiple media formats.
ISBN Prefix(es): 978-0-12
Number of titles published annually: 375 Print; 8 E-Book
Total Titles: 4,700 Print; 14 CD-ROM; 175 E-Book

Academica Press LLC
PO Box 60728, Cambridge Sta, Palo Alto, CA 94306
Tel: 650-329-0685 *Fax:* 650-329-0685
E-mail: academicapress@aol.com
Web Site: www.academicapress.com
Key Personnel
Dir: Robert Redfern-West
Founded: 2002
Publish scholarly research, monographs & collections in humanities, social sciences, education & law.
ISBN Prefix(es): 978-1-933146; 978-1-930901
Number of titles published annually: 40 Print
Total Titles: 250 Print; 50 Online
Imprints: Maunsel & Co Publishers (Dublin); W B Sheridan (law books)
Foreign Rep(s): Eurospan Group (London) (Europe, Middle East, UK)
Orders to: Books International Inc, 22883 Quicksilver Dr, Dulles, VA 20166 *Tel:* 703-661-1500 *Fax:* 703-661-1501 *E-mail:* todd@booksintl.com
Returns: Books International Inc, 22883 Quicksilver Dr, Dulles, VA 20166 *Tel:* 703-661-1500 *Fax:* 703-661-1501 *E-mail:* todd@booksintl.com
Shipping Address: Books International Inc, 22883 Quicksilver Dr, Dulles, VA 20166 *Tel:* 703-661-1500 *Fax:* 703-661-1501 *E-mail:* todd@booksintl.com
Warehouse: Books International Inc, 22883 Quicksilver Dr, Dulles, VA 20166 *Tel:* 703-661-1500 *Fax:* 703-661-1501 *E-mail:* todd@booksintl.com
Distribution Center: Books International Inc, 22883 Quicksilver Dr, Dulles, VA 20166 *Tel:* 703-661-1500 *Fax:* 703-661-1501 *E-mail:* todd@booksintl.com
Membership(s): American Conference on Irish Studies

Academy Chicago
Imprint of Chicago Review Press
378 Park Ave, Suite 1E, Glencoe, IL 60022
Tel: 847-786-4224
E-mail: editors@academychicago.com
Web Site: www.chicagoreviewpress.com
Key Personnel
Ed-at-Large: Anita Miller; Jordan Miller
Founded: 1975
Fiction, nonfiction, history, mysteries, women's studies; emphasis on neglected classics & books for women.
ISBN Prefix(es): 978-0-915864; 978-0-89733
Number of titles published annually: 12 Print
Total Titles: 367 Print
Distribution Center: Independent Publishers Group, 814 N Franklin St, Chicago, IL 60610 *Tel:* 312-337-0747 *Toll Free Tel:* 800-888-4741 (orders) *Fax:* 312-337-5985 *E-mail:* frontdesk@chicagoreviewpress.com

The Academy of Northwest Writers & Publishers, see Lost Horse Press

Academy of Nutrition & Dietetics
120 S Riverside Plaza, Suite 2000, Chicago, IL 60606-6995
Tel: 312-899-0040 (ext 5000) *Toll Free Tel:* 800-877-1600
E-mail: sales@eatright.org
Web Site: www.eatright.org

Key Personnel
Publr: Cathy Iammartino
Acqs & Devt Mgr: Laura Pelehach
Prodn Ed: Carissa Vardanian
Founded: 1917
Information on food, nutrition & fitness for dieticians & other allied health professionals.
ISBN Prefix(es): 978-0-88091; 978-0-9837255 (Eat Right Press)
Number of titles published annually: 12 Print; 4 Online
Total Titles: 70 Print
Branch Office(s)
1120 Connecticut Ave NW, Suite 480, Washington, DC 20036 *Tel:* 202-775-8277 *Toll Free Tel:* 800-877-0877
Distributed by Small Press United (Eat Right Press)

§Acanthus Publishing
Division of The Ictus Group LLC
180 Lincoln St, 3rd fl, Boston, MA 02111
Tel: 617-230-2167 *Fax:* 617-995-0893
E-mail: info@acanthuspublishing.com
Web Site: www.acanthuspublishing.com
Key Personnel
CEO & Pres: Paige Stover Hague, Esq *Tel:* 508-577-0271
CTO: George Kasparian, Esq
Founded: 2004
This publisher has indicated that 100% of their product line is author subsidized.
ISBN Prefix(es): 978-0-9754810; 978-1-933631; 978-0-9815589
Number of titles published annually: 10 Print; 5 CD-ROM; 10 E-Book; 5 Audio
Total Titles: 40 Print; 20 CD-ROM; 40 E-Book; 20 Audio
Advertising Agency: The Ictus Initiative

§Accuity
Division of Reed Business Information Ltd
4709 W Golf Rd, Skokie, IL 60076
Tel: 847-676-9600 *Toll Free Tel:* 800-321-3373 *Fax:* 847-933-8101
E-mail: custserv@accuity.com; sales@accuity.com
Web Site: www.accuity.com
Key Personnel
Pres & CEO: Hugh Jones
EVP: Brent Newman
Sr Dir, HR: Patty Pickett
Founded: 1876
Leading worldwide provider of information on depository financial institutions throughout the world; specialize in Internet references/directories; software; databases.
ISBN Prefix(es): 978-1-56310
Number of titles published annually: 30 Print; 1 CD-ROM; 2 E-Book
Total Titles: 30 Print; 4 CD-ROM; 3 E-Book
Foreign Office(s): Level 10, 10 Help St, Chatswood, NSW 2067, Australia *Tel:* (02) 8006 0584 *E-mail:* asiasales@accuity.com
999 Jin Zhong Rd, 4F, Tower C, Shanghai 200335, China *Tel:* (021) 5155 1222 *Fax:* (021) 5155 0509 *E-mail:* asiasales@accuity.com
Rm 1204-6, Tai Tung Bldg, 8 Fleming Rd, Wanchai, Hong Kong *Tel:* 2280 9570 *Fax:* 2813 6357 *E-mail:* asiasales@accuity.com
1-9-15 Higashi-Azabu, Minato-ku, Tokyo 106-0044, Japan *Tel:* (03) 5561 5363 *Fax:* (065) 6544 1171 *E-mail:* asiasales@accuity.com
Killiney Rd, No 08-01, Winsland House 1, Singapore 239519, Singapore (asiasales@accuity.com) *Tel:* 6780 4814 *Fax:* 6544 1171
Proctor House, 110 High Hilborn, London WC1V 6EU, United Kingdom *Tel:* (020) 7653 3800 *Fax:* (020) 7653 3828

Acres USA
Division of Acres USA Inc
4029 Guadalupe St, Austin, TX 78751
SAN: 270-6555
Mailing Address: PO Box 301209, Austin, TX 78703-0021
Tel: 512-892-4400 *Toll Free Tel:* 800-355-5313 *Fax:* 512-892-4448
E-mail: orders@acresusa.com; editor@acresusa.com; info@acresusa.com
Web Site: www.acresusa.com
Founded: 1970
Books & a monthly periodical on organic & sustainable agriculture.
ISBN Prefix(es): 978-0-911311; 978-1-60173
Number of titles published annually: 6 Print; 1 Audio
Total Titles: 80 Print; 2 Audio
Imprints: Halcyon House Publishers

ACTA Publications
4848 N Clark St, Chicago, IL 60640
Tel: 773-271-1030 *Toll Free Tel:* 800-397-2282 *Fax:* 773-271-7399 *Toll Free Fax:* 800-397-0079
E-mail: info@actapublications.com
Web Site: www.actapublications.com
Key Personnel
Co-Owner: John Dewan
Pres & Publr: Gregory Pierce
Founded: 1957
Books, audio & video tapes for the Christian market & baseball statistics market.
ISBN Prefix(es): 978-0-87946; 978-0-914070; 978-0-915388
Number of titles published annually: 15 Print; 2 Audio
Total Titles: 150 Print; 20 Audio
Imprints: Corbey Books; In Extenso Press
Distributor for Grief Watch; Veritas
Foreign Rep(s): John Garratt Publishing (Australia); Veritas (Ireland, UK)
Membership(s): Association of Catholic Publishers Inc

ACU Press
Affiliate of Abilene Christian University
1626 Campus Ct, Abilene, TX 79601
SAN: 207-1681
Tel: 325-674-2720 *Toll Free Tel:* 877-816-4455 *Fax:* 325-674-6471
Web Site: www.acupressbooks.com; www.leafwoodpublishers.com
Key Personnel
Dir: Dr Leonard Allen *E-mail:* leonard.allen@acupressbooks.com
Dir, Opers: Duane Anderson
Founded: 1984
Religion & ethics.
ISBN Prefix(es): 978-0-915547; 978-0-89112
Number of titles published annually: 35 Print; 30 E-Book
Total Titles: 480 Print; 170 E-Book
Imprints: Leafwood Publishers (Christian trade imprint)

Adams & Ambrose Publishing
PO Box 259684, Madison, WI 53725-9684
SAN: 655-5624
Tel: 608-257-5700 *Fax:* 608-257-5700
E-mail: info@adamsambrose.com
Key Personnel
Mktg Dir & Intl Rts: Joyce Harrington *E-mail:* jharrington@adamsambrose.com
Sr Ed: Jill Robinson Wren *E-mail:* jrwren@adamsambrose.com
Edit: Roger B Oakes *E-mail:* rboakes@adamsambrose.com
Founded: 1983
Publication of nonfiction books. Specialize in academic, professional & how-to books.
ISBN Prefix(es): 978-0-916951
Number of titles published annually: 6 Print
Total Titles: 6 Print
Returns: c/o United Parcel Service, 8350 Murphy Dr, Middleton, WI 53562 (hold for pick up)

§Adams Media
Imprint of F+W, A Content + eCommerce Company
57 Littlefield St, Avon, MA 02322
Tel: 508-427-7100 *Fax:* 508-427-6790
E-mail: orders@adamsmedia.com
Web Site: www.adamsmedia.com
Key Personnel
Publr: Karen Cooper
Mktg & Publicity Dir: Beth Gissinger-Rivera *E-mail:* beth.gissinger@fwmedia.com
Natl Sales Dir: Karen Patterson
Founded: 1980
General nonfiction, including business, self-help, inspiration, careers, teen nonfiction, women's issues, cooking, parenting, reference, relationships, weddings, pets.
ISBN Prefix(es): 978-0-937860; 978-1-55850; 978-1-58062; 978-1-59337; 978-1-59869; 978-1-60550; 978-1-4405
Number of titles published annually: 200 Print
Total Titles: 800 Print; 20 CD-ROM
Imprints: Adams Business (busn); Everything (series); F+W Media Business Now; Platinum Press (mgmt & leadership); Polka Dot Press (women's nonfiction); Provenance Press (new age)
Foreign Rep(s): Advantage Quest (Malaysia); David Bateman Ltd (New Zealand); Michelle Morrow Curreri (Asia, Middle East); F+W International (Europe); IMA/Intermediaamericana (David Williams) (Caribbean, Latin America); Manda Group (Canada); Pearson Education; Peribo (Australia)
Foreign Rights: Bardon-Chinese Media Agency (China, Hong Kong, Taiwan); Graal Literary Agency (Zbigniew Kanski) (Poland); The Harris/Elon Agency (Efrat Lev) (Israel); Imprima Korea Agency (Korea); Japan Uni Agency (Japan); Alexander Korzhenevski Agency (Russia); Michael Meller Literary Agency GmbH (Germany); The Rights Agency (France); Silkroad Publishers Agency (Jane Vejjajiva) (Thailand); Julio F Yanez, Agencia Literaria S L (Spain)
Warehouse: 1140 Airport Rd, Fall River, MA 02720

ADASI Publishing Co
13 Riverdale Ave, Dover, NH 03820-4698
Tel: 603-866-9426
E-mail: info@adasi.com
Web Site: www.adasi.com
Key Personnel
Mktg Dir: Parvaneh Ghavami
Physics, math & history of those subjects.
ISBN Prefix(es): 978-0-9641295
Number of titles published annually: 6 Print
Total Titles: 12 Print
Distributor for Wall & Thompson

ADD Warehouse, see Specialty Press Inc

Addicus Books Inc
PO Box 45327, Omaha, NE 68145
Tel: 402-330-7493 *Fax:* 402-330-1707
E-mail: info@addicusbooks.com; addicusbks@aol.com
Web Site: www.addicusbooks.com
Key Personnel
Publr: Rod Colvin *E-mail:* rod@addicusbooks.com
Assoc Publr: Jack Kusler *E-mail:* jackaddicusbks@aol.com
Mng Ed: Susan Adams
Founded: 1994

Independent press, publishing high-quality trade paperbacks. Submissions by mail only, no phone inquiries.
ISBN Prefix(es): 978-1-886039; 978-1-936374; 978-1-938803; 978-1-940495
Number of titles published annually: 9 Print; 10 E-Book
Total Titles: 200 Print; 200 Online; 36 E-Book
Billing Address: IPG Books, 814 Franklin St, Chicago, IL 60610 *Tel:* 312-337-0747 *Toll Free Tel:* 800-888-4741 *Fax:* 312-337-5985 *Web Site:* ipgbook.com
Returns: IPG Warehouse, 600 N Pulaski, Chicago, IL 60624, Contact: Tom Greene
Warehouse: IPG Warehouse, 600 N Pulaski, Chicago, IL 60624, Contact: Tom Greene
Distribution Center: IPG Books, 814 Franklin St, Chicago, IL 60610 *Tel:* 312-337-0747 *Toll Free Tel:* 800-888-4741 *Fax:* 312-337-5985 *Web Site:* ipgbook.com
Membership(s): AAP; The Independent Book Publishers Association; National Association of Independent Publishers; PMA International

Adirondack Mountain Club (ADK)
814 Goggins Rd, Lake George, NY 12845-4117
SAN: 204-7691
Tel: 518-668-4447 *Toll Free Tel:* 800-395-8080 *Fax:* 518-668-3746
E-mail: info@adk.org
Web Site: www.adk.org
Key Personnel
Pres: John Gilewicz
VP: Robert Manning
Exec Dir: Neil Woodworth *Tel:* 518-449-3870 *Fax:* 518-669-0128
Founded: 1922
Calendar (wall) - trade, hiking, canoeing, skiing & climbing guidebooks & maps for New York State; natural history field guides; cultural & literary works on the Adirondacks, members journals, *Adirondac*.
ISBN Prefix(es): 978-0-935272; 978-1-931951; 978-0-9896073
Number of titles published annually: 4 Print
Total Titles: 39 Print

Adler Publishing Inc
46937 Monarch Dr, Parker, CO 80138
Tel: 303-660-2158 *Toll Free Tel:* 800-660-5107 (sales & orders)
E-mail: customerservice@adlerpublishing.com; orders@4wdbooks.com
Web Site: www.adlerpublishing.com
Key Personnel
Publr: Peter Massey
Mktg Dir: Jeanne Massey
Founded: 1999
ISBN Prefix(es): 978-0-930657; 978-0-9665675; 978-1-930193
Number of titles published annually: 5 Print
Total Titles: 70 Print
Imprints: Outdoor Books & Maps

Advance Publishing Inc
6950 Fulton St, Houston, TX 77022
SAN: 263-9572
Tel: 713-695-0600 *Toll Free Tel:* 800-917-9630 *Fax:* 713-695-8585
E-mail: info@advancepublishing.com
Web Site: www.advancepublishing.com
Key Personnel
VP: John Sommer *E-mail:* johnsommer@advancepublishing.com
Founded: 1984
Publish children's picture books, junior biographies & general nonfiction, technical books & current events.
ISBN Prefix(es): 978-1-57537; 978-0-9610810
Number of titles published annually: 20 Print
Total Titles: 150 Print; 72 CD-ROM; 75 Online
Imprints: Another Great Achiever Series (biographies of men & women of inspiring accomplishment); Number Success (online video practical mathematics program for adult & children); Phonics Adventure (motivational phonics literature-based children's reading program); Quest for Success (short stories for upper elementary & reluctant middle & high school readers); Reading Success (adult intensive phonics literature-based reading program); Sommer-Time Story Classics Series (inspirational picture books with a fun & modern take on timeless folktales & fables); Sommer-Time Story Series (character-building books for children)
Membership(s): The Children's Book Council; The Independent Book Publishers Association

Adventure House
914 Laredo Rd, Silver Spring, MD 20901
Tel: 301-754-1589
Web Site: www.adventurehouse.com
Key Personnel
Publr & Ed: John P Gunnison *E-mail:* gunnison@adventurehouse.com
Founded: 1985
Special reprints; fiction from the pulp fiction era.
ISBN Prefix(es): 978-1-886937; 978-1-59798
Number of titles published annually: 60 Print
Total Titles: 300 Print

Adventure Publications
820 Cleveland St, Cambridge, MN 55008
SAN: 212-7199
Tel: 763-689-9800 *Toll Free Tel:* 800-678-7006 *Fax:* 763-689-9039 *Toll Free Fax:* 877-374-9016
E-mail: custservice@adventurepublications.net; orders@adventurepublications.net
Web Site: www.adventurepublications.net
Key Personnel
Owner: Gerri Slabaugh *E-mail:* gerri@adventurepublications.net; Gordon Slabaugh *E-mail:* gordon@adventurepublications.net
Sales Mgr: Julie Arthur *E-mail:* julie@adventurepublications.net
Founded: 1988
General trade & regional.
ISBN Prefix(es): 978-0-934860; 978-1-885061; 978-1-59193
Number of titles published annually: 30 Print
Total Titles: 435 Print; 12 CD-ROM
Distributor for Blacklock Nature Photography; Kollath-Stensaas; Nodin Press; Pocket Guides Publishing

§Adventures Unlimited Press (AUP)
One Adventure Place, Kempton, IL 60946
Mailing Address: PO Box 74, Kempton, IL 60946-0074
Tel: 815-253-6390 *Fax:* 815-253-6300
E-mail: auphq@frontiernet.net; info@adventuresunlimitedpress.com
Web Site: www.adventuresunlimitedpress.com
Key Personnel
Pres & Intl Rts Contact: David H Childress
Mng Dir: Jennifer Bolm
Founded: 1983
Eclectic variety of books on mysteries of the past, alternative technologies & conspiracy theories.
ISBN Prefix(es): 978-0-932813; 978-1-931882; 978-1-935487; 978-1-939149
Number of titles published annually: 11 Print
Total Titles: 175 Print
Distributor for Eagle Wing Books; EDFU Books; Yelsraek Publishing
Foreign Rep(s): Brumby Books (Australia); Speaking Tree (UK)
Foreign Rights: Il Caduceo (Italy)

Aegean Publishing Co
PO Box 6790, Santa Barbara, CA 93160
Tel: 805-964-6669 *Fax:* 805-683-4798
E-mail: info@aegeanpublishing.com
Web Site: aegeanpublishing.com
Key Personnel
Gen Mgr: Mary Morgan
Founded: 1993
Book publisher.
ISBN Prefix(es): 978-0-9636178
Number of titles published annually: 3 Print
Total Titles: 4 Print
Foreign Rights: Japan UNI Agency Inc (Japan)
Membership(s): The Independent Book Publishers Association

The AEI Press
Division of American Enterprise Institute
1150 17 St NW, Washington, DC 20036
SAN: 202-4527
Tel: 202-862-5800 *Fax:* 202-862-7177
Web Site: www.aei.org
Key Personnel
Chmn of the Bd: Tully M Friedman
Pres: Arthur Brooks
Mng Ed: Sharon Kehnemui *Tel:* 202-828-6037 *E-mail:* sharon.kehnemui@aei.org
Sr Ed: Christy Sadler *Tel:* 202-862-5916 *Fax:* 202-862-7178 *E-mail:* christy.sadler@aei.org
Ed: Hilary Waterman
Founded: 1943
Public policy economics, foreign affairs & defense, government & politics, law; research on education, energy, government regulation & tax policy.
ISBN Prefix(es): 978-0-8447
Number of titles published annually: 15 Print
Total Titles: 300 Print
Distributed by MIT (selected titles)
Foreign Rep(s): Eurospan
Orders to: c/o National Book Network, 4501 Forbes Blvd, Suite 200, Lantham, MD 20706 *Toll Free Tel:* 800-462-6420 *Toll Free Fax:* 800-338-4550 *E-mail:* custserv@nbnbooks.com
Distribution Center: Client Distribution Services, 193 Edwards Dr, Jackson, TN 38301 *Toll Free Tel:* 800-343-4499 *Toll Free Fax:* 800-351-5073 *Web Site:* cdsbooks.com

§AFB Press
Imprint of American Foundation for the Blind
2 Penn Plaza, Suite 1102, New York, NY 10121
Tel: 212-502-7600 *Toll Free Tel:* 800-232-5463; 800-232-3044 (orders) *Fax:* 917-210-3979; 412-741-0609 (orders) *Toll Free Fax:* 888-545-8331
E-mail: press@afb.net; afbpress@afb.net; afbinfo@afb.net; afborder@afb.net (orders)
Web Site: www.afb.org
Key Personnel
Dir, AFB Press & Prof Devt: George Abbott
Exec Ed: Ellen Bilofski
Rts & Admin Dir: Jenese Griffiths
Mktg Mgr: Anne Durham
Founded: 1921
Text & professional books in the fields of visual impairment & blindness.
ISBN Prefix(es): 978-0-89128
Number of titles published annually: 8 Print; 4 Online
Total Titles: 200 Print; 17 Online; 5 Audio
Branch Office(s)
AFB Public Policy Center, 1660 "L" St NW, Suite 513, Washington, DC 20036, VP, Progs & Policy: Paul Schroeder *Tel:* 202-469-6831 *Fax:* 646-478-9260 *E-mail:* afbgov@afb.net
AFB Atlanta, 100 Peachtree St, Suite 2145, Atlanta, GA 30303 *Tel:* 404-525-2303 *Fax:* 646-478-9260 *E-mail:* literacy@afb.net
AFB Center on Vision Loss, 11030 Ables Lane, Dallas, TX 75229, Dir: Judy Scott *Tel:* 214-352-7222 *Fax:* 646-478-9260 *E-mail:* dallas@afb.net

AFB Huntington, 1000 Fifth Ave, Suite 350, Huntington, WV 25701 *Tel:* 304-523-8651 *Fax:* 646-478-9260
Membership(s): AAP

Africa World Press Inc
541 W Ingham Ave, Suite B, Trenton, NJ 08638
Tel: 609-695-3200 *Fax:* 609-695-6466
E-mail: customerservice@africaworldpressbooks.com
Web Site: www.africaworldpressbooks.com
Key Personnel
Owner: Kassahun Checole
Founded: 1983
Research on Latin America, the Caribbean, Africa, Afrocentric children's books.
ISBN Prefix(es): 978-0-86543; 978-1-59221
Number of titles published annually: 100 Print
Total Titles: 1,400 Print; 10 Online; 10 E-Book
Foreign Office(s): East Africa, PO Box 48, Asmara, Eritrea *Tel:* (01) 120707 *Fax:* (01) 123369
Foreign Rights: Turnaround Publisher Services Ltd (Europe, London)

§African American Images
PO Box 1799, Chicago Heights, IL 60412
Tel: 708-672-4909 (cust serv) *Toll Free Tel:* 800-552-1991 (orders) *Fax:* 708-672-0466
E-mail: customersvc@africanamericanimages.com
Web Site: www.africanamericanimages.com
Key Personnel
Pres & Intl Rts: Dr Jawanza Kunjufu, PhD
Founded: 1983
Publish & distribute books of an Africentric nature that promote self-esteem, collective values, liberation & skill development.
ISBN Prefix(es): 978-0-913543; 978-0-9749000; 978-1-934155
Number of titles published annually: 8 Print
Total Titles: 130 Print; 2 CD-ROM

Africana Homestead Legacy Publishers Inc
811 Church Rd, Suite 105, Cherry Hill, NJ 08002
SAN: 941-4811
Tel: 856-773-0694 *Fax:* 856-486-1135
E-mail: customer-service@ahlpub.com; sales@ahlpub.com; editors@ahlpub.com
Web Site: www.ahlpub.com
Key Personnel
Pres & Publr: Carolyn C Williams *E-mail:* publisher@ahlpub.com
Dir, Prodn & Design: Brian Lancaster *E-mail:* blancaster@ahlpub.com
Founded: 1996
Small independent book publisher of scholarly nonfiction, literary fiction, autobiography & memoirs focused on the experience of black people in the US & worldwide.
ISBN Prefix(es): 978-0-9653308; 978-0-9770904; 978-0-9799537; 978-0-9818939; 978-0-9825842; 978-0-9831151; 978-1-937622
Number of titles published annually: 8 Print; 2 E-Book
Total Titles: 72 Print; 21 E-Book
Imprints: AHLP Books; AHLP Communications; Nefu Books; Oyinde Publishing
Membership(s): The Independent Book Publishers Association

§Ageless Press
3759 Collins St, Sarasota, FL 34232
SAN: 297-830X
Tel: 941-365-1367 *Fax:* 941-365-1367
E-mail: irishope@comcast.net
Key Personnel
Owner: Hope Day
Ed: Iris Forrest
Founded: 1992
Publish short stories by various authors.
ISBN Prefix(es): 978-0-9635177
Number of titles published annually: 6 Print
Total Titles: 3 Print; 1 Online

AGU, see American Geophysical Union (AGU)

AHA Press
Imprint of Health Forum Inc
155 N Wacker Dr, Suite 400, Chicago, IL 60606
Tel: 312-893-6800 *Toll Free Tel:* 800-821-2039 *Fax:* 312-422-4500 *Toll Free Fax:* 866-516-5817 (orders)
Web Site: www.healthforum.com
Key Personnel
Edit Dir: Richard Hill *E-mail:* rhill@healthforum.com
Founded: 1984
Professional references for healthcare managers & textbooks for HIM (health information management) programs.
ISBN Prefix(es): 978-1-55648; 978-0-87258
Number of titles published annually: 4 Print
Total Titles: 20 Print
Orders to: AHA Services Inc, PO Box 933283, Atlanta, GA 31193-3283 *Toll Free Tel:* 800-242-2626
Returns: AHA Services Inc, Customer Returns Section, 3280 Summit Ridge Pkwy, Duluth, GA 30096 *Toll Free Tel:* 800-242-2626
Membership(s): American Hospital Association; Association Media & Publishing

Ahsahta Press
Boise State University, Mail Stop 1525, 1910 University Dr, Boise, ID 83725-1525
Tel: 208-426-3134
E-mail: ahsahta@boisestate.edu
Web Site: ahsahtapress.org
Key Personnel
Dir & Ed: Prof Janet Holmes *E-mail:* jholmes@boisestate.edu
Founded: 1974
Trade paperback books. Specialize in American poetry, Accept editorial submissions through our Submissions Manager.
ISBN Prefix(es): 978-0-916272; 978-1-934103
Number of titles published annually: 8 Print
Total Titles: 135 Print
Orders to: Small Press Distribution, 1341 Seventh St, Berkeley, CA 94710-1409, Contact: Nicole Trigg *Tel:* 510-524-1668 *Toll Free Tel:* 800-869-7553 *Fax:* 510-524-0852 *E-mail:* spd@spdbooks.org *Web Site:* www.spdbooks.org
Membership(s): Community of Literary Magazines & Presses

§AICPA Professional Publications
Subsidiary of American Institute of Certified Public Accountants
220 Leigh Farm Rd, Durham, NC 27707
SAN: 202-4578
Tel: 919-402-4500 *Toll Free Tel:* 888-777-7077 *Fax:* 919-402-4505 *Toll Free Fax:* 800-362-5066
E-mail: acquisitions@aicpa.org; service@aicpa.org
Web Site: www.aicpa.org
Key Personnel
CEO & Pres: Barry C Melancon *E-mail:* bmelancon@aicpa.org
VP, Prof Pubns: Linda Cohen *Tel:* 919-402-4500 ext 3 *E-mail:* lcohen@aicpa.org
Founded: 1959
Technical guidance for accountants & auditors, books on practice management & specialized topics, research & practice development tools, magazines, newsletters, online & downloadable products.
ISBN Prefix(es): 978-0-87051; 978-1-937350; 978-1-937351; 978-1-937352; 978-1-940235; 978-1-941651
Number of titles published annually: 150 Print; 10 CD-ROM; 20 Online; 100 E-Book
Total Titles: 600 Print; 20 CD-ROM; 50 Online; 200 E-Book
Branch Office(s)
1455 Pennsylvania Ave NW, Washington, DC 20004-1081 *Tel:* 202-737-6600 *Fax:* 202-638-4512
Princeton South Corporate Ctr, Suite 200, 100 Princeton S, Ewing, NJ 08628 *Tel:* 609-671-2902 *Fax:* 609-671-2922
1211 Avenue of the Americas, New York, NY 10036-8775 *Tel:* 212-596-6200 *Fax:* 212-596-6213
Distributed by CCH; Practitioners Publishing Co; Thomson Reuters
Distributor for Wiley
Membership(s): Association for Talent Development; EBSCO; ISO

AIMS Education Foundation
1595 S Chestnut Ave, Fresno, CA 93702-4706
Mailing Address: PO Box 8120, Fresno, CA 93747-8120
Tel: 559-255-4094 *Toll Free Tel:* 888-733-2467 *Fax:* 559-255-6396
E-mail: aimsed@aimsedu.org
Web Site: www.aimsedu.org
Key Personnel
Systems Administrator & Webmaster: Johann Weber
Founded: 1985
Provides educational enrichment for grades K-9 through hands-on activities that integrate mathematics, science, technology & other disciplines; curriculum writing for K-9.
ISBN Prefix(es): 978-1-881431
Number of titles published annually: 6 Print
Total Titles: 75 Print; 1 CD-ROM; 3 Audio
Shipping Address: 5391 E Home Ave, Fresno, CA 93727

AIP Publishing, see American Institute of Physics

Air Conditioning Contractors of America
2800 Shirlington Rd, Suite 300, Arlington, VA 22206
Tel: 703-824-8851 *Toll Free Tel:* 888-290-2220 *Fax:* 703-575-8107
Web Site: www.acca.org
Key Personnel
SVP, Busn Opers: Kevin Holland
SVP, Tech Accreditation: Glenn Hourahan
VP, Prod Devt: Christopher Hoelzel *Tel:* 703-575-4477 *E-mail:* chris.hoelzel@acca.org
Founded: 1964
Heating & air conditioning standards & systems design manuals in printed & CD formats.
ISBN Prefix(es): 978-1-892765
Number of titles published annually: 4 Print; 4 CD-ROM; 1 Online
Total Titles: 41 Print; 21 CD-ROM
Sales Office(s): ACCA Customer Service Ctr, 9050 Junction Dr, Annapolis Junction, MD 20701, Contact: Courtney Cooper *Fax:* 240-396-5698 *E-mail:* ccooper@brightkey.net
Distributed by Contractor Resource
Distributor for Cengage Learning
Orders to: ACCA Customer Service Ctr, 9050 Junction Dr, Annapolis Junction, MD 20701, Contact: Courtney Cooper *Fax:* 240-396-5698 *E-mail:* ccooper@brightkey.net
Returns: ACCA Customer Service Ctr, 9050 Junction Dr, Annapolis Junction, MD 20701, Contact: Courtney Cooper *Fax:* 240-396-5698 *E-mail:* ccooper@brightkey.net
Shipping Address: ACCA Customer Service Ctr, 9050 Junction Dr, Annapolis Junction, MD 20701, Contact: Courtney Cooper *Fax:* 240-396-5698 *E-mail:* ccooper@brightkey.net
Warehouse: ACCA Customer Service Ctr, 9050 Junction Dr, Annapolis Junction, MD 20701, Contact: Courtney Cooper *Fax:* 240-396-5698 *E-mail:* ccooper@brightkey.net

Distribution Center: ACCA Customer Service Ctr, 9050 Junction Dr, Annapolis Junction, MD 20701, Contact: Courtney Cooper *Fax:* 240-396-5698 *E-mail:* ccooper@brightkey.net

AK Press Distribution
Subsidiary of AK Press Inc
674-A 23 St, Oakland, CA 94612
Tel: 510-208-1700 *Fax:* 510-208-1701
E-mail: info@akpress.org; sales@akpress.org; orders@akpress.org
Web Site: www.akpress.org
Key Personnel
Ed: Zach Blue *Tel:* 510-208-1700 ext 3; Kate Khatib
Founded: 1990
Specialize in publishing & distribution of radical & small press nonfiction.
ISBN Prefix(es): 978-1-873176; 978-1-902593; 978-1-904859
Number of titles published annually: 20 Print; 3 Audio
Total Titles: 500 Print; 30 Audio
Distributor for AK Press; Crimethinc; Freedom Press; Payback Press; Phoenix Press; Rebel Inc; Rebel Press

Akashic Books
232 Third St, Suite A-115, Brooklyn, NY 11215
Tel: 718-643-9193 *Fax:* 718-643-9195
E-mail: info@akashicbooks.com
Web Site: www.akashicbooks.com
Key Personnel
Publr & Ed-in-Chief: Johnny Temple
Dir, Publicity & Soc Media: Susannah Lawrence
Prodn Mgr, Ebook Developer & Assoc Ed: Aaron Petrovich
Sr Ed: Ibrahim Ahmad
Mng Ed: Johanna Ingalls
Founded: 1997
Specialize in urban literary fiction & political nonfiction.
ISBN Prefix(es): 978-1-888451; 978-0-9719206; 978-1-933354; 978-1-936070; 978-1-61775
Number of titles published annually: 30 Print
Total Titles: 300 Print
Imprints: RDV Books
Orders to: Consortium Book Sales & Distribution, The Keg House, Suite 101, 34 13 Ave NE, Minneapolis, MN 55413 *Tel:* 612-746-2600 *Toll Free Tel:* 800-283-3572 (cust serv) *E-mail:* orders@cbsd.com *Web Site:* www.cbsd.com
Returns: Consortium Book Sales & Distribution, The Keg House, Suite 101, 34 13 Ave NE, Minneapolis, MN 55413 *Tel:* 612-746-2600 *Toll Free Tel:* 800-283-3572 (cust serv) *E-mail:* orders@cbsd.com *Web Site:* www.cbsd.com
Warehouse: Consortium Book Sales & Distribution, c/o Perseus, 210 American Dr, Jackson, TN 38301 *Toll Free Tel:* 800-283-3572 *Toll Free Fax:* 800-351-5073 *E-mail:* orders@cbsd.com *Web Site:* www.cbsd.com
Distribution Center: Consortium Book Sales & Distribution, The Keg House, Suite 101, 34 13 Ave NE, Minneapolis, MN 55413 *Tel:* 612-746-2600 *Toll Free Tel:* 800-283-3572 (cust serv) *E-mail:* orders@cbsd.com *Web Site:* www.cbsd.com

ALA Editions, see The American Library Association (ALA)

Aladdin, see Simon & Schuster Children's Publishing

Alaska Native Language Center
Division of University of Alaska Fairbanks
PO Box 757680, Fairbanks, AK 99775-7680
SAN: 692-9796
Tel: 907-474-7874 *Fax:* 907-474-6586
E-mail: uaf-aknativelang@alaska.edu (orders)
Web Site: www.uaf.edu/anlc
Key Personnel
Dir: Lawrence D Kaplan *Tel:* 907-474-6582 *E-mail:* ldkaplan@alaska.edu
Ed: Leon Unruh *Tel:* 907-474-6577 *E-mail:* ldunruh@alaska.edu
Founded: 1972
Publish books in & about Alaska's 20 indigenous languages, including dictionaries, grammars & collections of folktales & oral history, language maps.
ISBN Prefix(es): 978-1-55500; 978-0-933769
Number of titles published annually: 4 Print
Total Titles: 200 Print; 3 Audio

Albert Whitman & Co
250 S Northwest Hwy, Suite 320, Park Ridge, IL 60068
SAN: 201-2049
Tel: 847-232-2800 *Toll Free Tel:* 800-255-7675 *Fax:* 847-581-0039
E-mail: mail@awhitmanco.com
Web Site: www.albertwhitman.com
Key Personnel
Pres: John Quattrocchi
SVP: Pat McPartland
Edit Dir: Kelly Barrales-Saylor
Founded: 1919
Juveniles, language arts, fiction & nonfiction.
ISBN Prefix(es): 978-0-8075
Number of titles published annually: 50 Print
Total Titles: 800 Print
Distributed by Open Road

The Alexander Graham Bell Association for the Deaf & Hard of Hearing
3417 Volta Place NW, Washington, DC 20007
SAN: 203-6924
Tel: 202-337-5220 *Toll Free Tel:* 866-337-5220 (orders) *Fax:* 202-337-8314
E-mail: info@agbell.org; publications@agbell.org
Web Site: www.agbell.org
Key Personnel
Mgr, Association & Donor Rel: Gary Yates *Tel:* 202-204-4683 *E-mail:* gyates@agbell.org
Founded: 1890
Resource, support network & advocate for listening, learning, talking & living independently with hearing loss. Through publications, outreach, training, scholarships & financial aid, AG Bell promotes the use of spoken language & hearing technology. Headquarted in Washington, DC with chapters located in the US & CN & a network of international affiliates. AG Bell's global presence provides its members & the public with the support they need close to home. With over a century of service, AG Bell supports it's mission, advocating independence through listening & talking.
ISBN Prefix(es): 978-0-88200
Number of titles published annually: 9 Print
Total Titles: 70 Print

Alexander Street Press LLC
3212 Duke St, Alexandria, VA 22314
SAN: 858-5512
Tel: 703-212-8520 *Toll Free Tel:* 800-889-5937 *Fax:* 703-940-6584
E-mail: sales@alexanderstreet.com; marketing@alexanderstreet.com; info@alexanderstreet.com
Web Site: alexanderstreet.com
Key Personnel
COO: Andrea Eastman-Mullins *E-mail:* aeastmanmullins@astreetpress.com
Pres: Stephen Rhind-Tutt *E-mail:* rhindtutt@alexanderstreet.com
VP, Busn Devt: Greg Urquhart *E-mail:* gurquhart@alexanderstreet.com
VP, Licensing: Will Whalen *E-mail:* whalen@alexanderstreet.com
VP, Sales: Eileen Lawrence *E-mail:* lawrence@alexanderstreet.com
Dir: Nathalie Duval *E-mail:* nduval@astreetpress.com
Founded: 2000
Publish large-scale digital collections of works in the humanities & social sciences.
ISBN Prefix(es): 978-1-4631; 978-1-5016; 978-1-5034
Number of titles published annually: 30 Print; 6 Online; 2,000 E-Book; 4 Audio
Total Titles: 34 Online; 10,000 E-Book; 6 Audio
Imprints: Filmakers Library; Insight Media; Microtraining Associates
Foreign Office(s): 2123 Pudong Ave, Rm 805, Shanghai 200135, China *Tel:* (021) 386875
Business & Technology Ctr, Unit G04, Bessemer Dr, Stevenage SG1 2DX, United Kingdom *Tel:* (01438) 310193
Membership(s): ALA

§Alfred Music Publishing
PO Box 10003, Van Nuys, CA 91410
Tel: 818-891-5999 (dealer sales (intl)); 818-891-2452 (cust serv) *Toll Free Tel:* 800-292-6122 (dealer sales (US & CN)) *Fax:* 818-893-5560 (dealer sales); 818-830-6252 (cust serv) *Toll Free Fax:* 800-632-1928 (dealer sales)
E-mail: customerservice@alfred.com; sales@alfred.com
Web Site: www.alfred.com
Key Personnel
CEO: Ron Manus
CFO: Steven Raft
Chief Mktg Offr: Andrew Surmani
Pres: Morty Manus
Founded: 1922
Publisher of music education; music books & software, performance & instructional.
ISBN Prefix(es): 978-0-88284; 978-0-87487; 978-0-7390; 978-1-58951; 978-1-4574; 978-1-4706
Number of titles published annually: 500 Print; 4 CD-ROM
Total Titles: 18,000 Print; 20 CD-ROM
Imprints: Belwin; Highland/Etling; Kalmus; Music Inc; Warner/Chappell Music Inc
Foreign Office(s): Bankstown M5 Business Park, Units 3 & 4, 17 Willfox St, Condell Park, NSW 2200, Australia *Tel:* 8707 3600 *Toll Free Tel:* 800-257-161 *E-mail:* promo@alfredpu.com.au
Lutzerathstr 127, 51107 Cologne, Germany *Tel:* 221 93 35 3913 *Fax:* 221 93 35 3916 *E-mail:* info@alfredverlag.de *Web Site:* www.alfredverlag.de
20 Sin Ming Lane, 5th fl, 05-54 Midview City 573968, Singapore, SE Asia Mktg Mgr: Larry Bong *Tel:* 6659 8919 *Fax:* 6659 8908 *E-mail:* enquiries@alfred.com.sg
Burnt Mill, Elizabeth Way, Harlow, Essex CM20 2HX, United Kingdom *Tel:* (01279) 828960 *Fax:* (01279) 828961 *E-mail:* music@alfred.uk.com
Distributor for Daisy Rock Girl Guitars; Dover Publications; Drum Channel; Faber Music; MakeMusic Inc; Penguin; WEA
Foreign Rep(s): Dave Bolden (Australia, New Zealand); Larry Bong (Asia); Gerry Mooney (UK); Thomas Petzold (Europe)
Membership(s): MPA - The Association of Magazine Media

Algonquin Books
Division of Workman Publishing Co Inc
400 Silver Cedar Ct, Suite 300, Chapel Hill, NC 27514-1585
SAN: 282-7506
Mailing Address: PO Box 2225, Chapel Hill, NC 27515-2225
Tel: 919-967-0108 *Fax:* 919-933-0272
E-mail: inquiry@algonquin.com
Web Site: www.workman.com/algonquin

Key Personnel
Publr: Elisabeth Scharlatt
Assoc Publr: Ina Stern
Publr, Young Adult & Middle Grade: Elise Howard
Exec Dir, Publicity: Michael McKenzie
Art & Creative Dir: Anne Winslow *Tel:* 919-967-0108 ext 29
Mktg Dir: Craig Popelars *E-mail:* craig@algonquin.com
Mktg Mgr: Lauren Moseley
Online Mktg Mgr: Debra Linn
Mng Ed & ISBN Contact: Brunson Hoole *Tel:* 919-967-0108 ext 22 *E-mail:* brunson@algonquin.com
Ed: Chuck Adams
Assoc Ed, Algonquin Young Readers: Krestyna Lypen
Intl Rts: Kendra Poster *Tel:* 212-614-7506
Publicist: Emma Boyer
Founded: 1982
Trade books, fiction & nonfiction.
ISBN Prefix(es): 978-0-912697; 978-0-945575; 978-1-56512
Number of titles published annually: 38 Print
Imprints: Algonquin Young Readers; Artisan Books; The Experiment; HighBridge Audio; Shannon Ravenel Books; Storey Publishing; Timber Press
Sales Office(s): Workman Publishing Co Inc, 225 Varick St, New York, NY 10014-4381 *Tel:* 212-254-5900 *Fax:* 212-254-8098
Distributed by Workman Publishing Co Inc
Distributor for Fearless Critic Media; Greenwich Workshop Press; HighBridge Audio
Foreign Rep(s): Thomas Allen & Son Ltd (Canada)
Foreign Rights: Big Apple Agency Inc (China, Taiwan); Graal Literary Agency (Poland); The Deborah Harris Agency (Israel); Japan UNI Agency Inc (Japan); JLM Literary Agency (Greece); Katai & Bolza Literary Agency (Hungary); Korea Copyright Center Inc (KCC) (Korea); Leonhardt & Hoier (Scandinavia); Kristin Olson Literary Agency SRO (Czech Republic); Plima Literary Agency (Bulgaria, Croatia, Macedonia, Serbia, Slovenia); Sebes & Gelderen Literary Agency (Netherlands); Marco Vigevani Agenzia Letteraria (Italy); Julio F Yanez Agencia Literaria SL (Portugal, Spain)
Billing Address: Workman Publishing Co Inc, 225 Varick St, New York, NY 10014-4381 *Tel:* 212-254-5900 *Fax:* 212-254-8098
Orders to: Workman Publishing Co Inc, 225 Varick St, New York, NY 10014-4381 *Tel:* 212-254-5900 *Toll Free Tel:* 800-722-7202 *Fax:* 212-254-8098
Returns: Workman Publishing Co Inc, c/o RR Donnelly, 677 Brighton Beach Rd, Menasha, WI 54952-2998
Warehouse: Workman Publishing Co Inc, c/o RR Donnelly, 677 Brighton Beach Rd, Menasha, WI 54952-2998

Algora Publishing
222 Riverside Dr, 16th fl, New York, NY 10025-6809
Tel: 212-678-0232 *Fax:* 212-666-3682
E-mail: editors@algora.com
Web Site: www.algora.com
Key Personnel
Publr: Claudiu A Secara
Ed: Martin De Mers
Author Rel: Andrea Secara
Founded: 1992
Books on subjects of history, international affairs, current issues, political economy, philosophy, etc in the tradition of independent progressive thinking.
ISBN Prefix(es): 978-0-87586; 978-0-9646073; 978-1-892941
Number of titles published annually: 25 Print; 25 E-Book
Total Titles: 400 Print; 100 E-Book
Imprints: Agathon Press
Membership(s): AAP; The Independent Book Publishers Association

Alice James Books
Division of Alice James Poetry Cooperative Inc
114 Prescott St, Farmington, ME 04938
SAN: 201-1158
Tel: 207-778-7071 *Fax:* 207-778-7766
E-mail: info@alicejamesbooks.org
Web Site: alicejamesbooks.org
Key Personnel
Exec Dir: Carey Salerno
Mng Ed: Alyssa Neptune
Edit Asst: Nicole Wakefield
Founded: 1973
ISBN Prefix(es): 978-0-914086; 978-1-882295; 978-1-938584
Number of titles published annually: 6 Print
Total Titles: 115 Print; 3 Audio
Distribution Center: Small Press Distribution (SPD), 1341 Seventh St, Berkeley, CA 94710-1409 *Tel:* 510-524-1668 *Toll Free Tel:* 800-869-7553 *Fax:* 510-524-0852 *E-mail:* spd@spdbooks.org *Web Site:* www.spdbooks.org
Consortium Book Sales & Distribution, The Keg House, Suite 101, 34 13 Ave NE, Minneapolis, MN 55413 *Tel:* 612-746-2600 *Toll Free Tel:* 800-283-3572 (cust serv) *Fax:* 612-746-2606 *E-mail:* info@cbsd.com *Web Site:* www.cbsd.com

All About Kids Publishing
PO Box 159, Gilroy, CA 95020
Tel: 408-337-1866 *Fax:* 408-337-5192
E-mail: mail@aakp.com
Web Site: www.aakp.com
Key Personnel
Publr: Mike G Guevara
Ed: Linda L Guevara *E-mail:* lguevara@aakp.com
Founded: 2000
Strives to set the standards in children's book publishing by creating innovative books of the highest quality with beautiful art work for children of all walks of life. See submission guidelines at aakp.com.
ISBN Prefix(es): 978-0-9700863; 978-0-9710278; 978-0-9744446; 978-0-9801468
Number of titles published annually: 6 Print
Total Titles: 20 Print; 5 E-Book
Orders to: Brodart *Toll Free Tel:* 800-233-8467 *Fax:* 570-326-1479 *E-mail:* bookinfo@brodart.com; Follett School Solutions Inc, 1340 Ridgeview Dr, McHenry, IL 60050 *Tel:* 815-759-1700 *Toll Free Tel:* 888-511-5114 (cust serv) *Fax:* 815-759-9831 *Toll Free Fax:* 800-852-5458 *E-mail:* info@follettlearning.com *Web Site:* www.follettlearning.com SAN: 169-1902
Membership(s): The Independent Book Publishers Association

§All Things That Matter Press
79 Jones Rd, Somerville, ME 04348
E-mail: allthingsthatmatterpress@gmail.com
Web Site: www.allthingsthatmatterpress.com
Key Personnel
CEO: Debra Harris
Founded: 2008
Number of titles published annually: 15 Print; 15 E-Book; 10 Audio
Total Titles: 160 Print; 160 E-Book; 60 Audio

§Allium Press of Chicago
1530 Elgin Ave, Forest Park, IL 60130
SAN: 858-3331
Tel: 708-689-9323
E-mail: info@alliumpress.com
Web Site: www.alliumpress.com
Key Personnel
Publr: Emily Victorson
Founded: 2009
Small independent press publishing fiction with a Chicago connection. Publish literary fiction, historical fiction, mysteries, thrillers & young adult fiction.
ISBN Prefix(es): 978-0-9840676; 978-0-9831938; 978-0-9890535
Number of titles published annually: 5 Print; 5 E-Book
Total Titles: 14 Print; 14 E-Book
Membership(s): Historical Novel Society; The Independent Book Publishers Association; Sisters in Crime; Society of Midland Authors

Alloy Entertainment LLC
Member of Warner Bros Entertainment Group
1700 Broadway, New York, NY 10019
Web Site: alloyentertainment.com
Key Personnel
Pres & CEO: Leslie Morgenstein
Pres, East Coast: Josh Bank
SVP, Edit: Sara Shandler
Dir, Book Devt: Joelle Hobeika
Assoc Ed: Hayley Wagreich
Founded: 1987
Hardcover, trade, mass market juvenile & young adult fiction & nonfiction; adult trade fiction & mass market fiction.
ISBN Prefix(es): 978-0-9850261; 978-1-939106
Number of titles published annually: 50 Print
Distributed by Avon Books; HarperCollins; Hyperion; Little, Brown & Co; Penguin Group (USA) LLC; Random House Inc; Scholastic Books; Simon & Schuster
Foreign Rep(s): Rights People (UK)

§Allworth Press
Imprint of Skyhorse Publishing Inc
307 W 36 St, 11th fl, New York, NY 10018
Tel: 212-643-6816 *Fax:* 212-643-6819
Web Site: www.allworth.com
Key Personnel
Founder & Publr: Tad Crawford *E-mail:* crawford@allworth.com
Busn Mgr: Marrissa Jones *E-mail:* mjones@skyhorsepublishing.com
Founded: 1989
Business & self-help books for artists, crafters, designers, photographers, authors & film & performing artists; books about business & law for the general public.
ISBN Prefix(es): 978-0-927629; 978-0-9607118; 978-1-880559; 978-1-58115
Number of titles published annually: 18 Print; 3 CD-ROM; 30 E-Book
Total Titles: 400 Print; 15 CD-ROM; 38 E-Book
Distributed by W W Norton
Foreign Rep(s): Bookwise International (Australia, New Zealand); CKK Ltd (Theo Philips) (Hong Kong, Philippines, Singapore, Thailand); Windsor Books (Geoff Cowen) (Europe, UK)
Foreign Rights: Jean V Naggar Literary Agency; Jennifer Weltz (foreign lang rts)
Membership(s): The Independent Book Publishers Association

AllWrite Advertising & Publishing
241 Peachtree St NE, Suite 400, Atlanta, GA 30303
Mailing Address: PO Box 1071, Atlanta, GA 30301
Tel: 404-221-0703 *Fax:* 770-284-8986
E-mail: questions@allwritepublishing.com; support@allwritepublishing.com (orders & returns)
Web Site: allwritepublishing.com
Key Personnel
Pres & Publr: Annette R Johnson *Tel:* 770-284-8956 *E-mail:* annette@allwritepublishing.com
Founded: 2003

A conventional small press. Books that we do not decide to publish are given thorough feedback.
ISBN Prefix(es): 978-0-9744935
Number of titles published annually: 5 Print
Membership(s): Independent Book Publishing Professionals Group; Writers Guild of America East

Allyn & Bacon
Imprint of Pearson Higher Education
75 Arlington St, Suite 300, Boston, MA 02116
Tel: 617-848-6000 *Toll Free Tel:* 800-428-4466 *Fax:* 617-848-6016
Web Site: home.pearsonhighered.com
Founded: 1868
College textbook publisher focusing on a select number of social science, education & humanities disciplines.
ISBN Prefix(es): 978-0-205; 978-0-321
Number of titles published annually: 310 Print
Total Titles: 2,300 Print

Alpha Books
Imprint of Penguin Group (USA) LLC
375 Hudson St, New York, NY 10014
Tel: 212-366-2000
Key Personnel
Publr: Michael Sanders
Dir, Mktg & Publicity: Dawn Werk
Founded: 2003
ISBN Prefix(es): 978-1-61564
Number of titles published annually: 88 Print
Total Titles: 580 Print
Branch Office(s)
800 E 96 St, Indianapolis, IN 46240

ALPHA Publications of America Inc
Affiliate of Alpha Legal Forms & More
1830 E Broadway, Suite 124, Tucson, AZ 85719
Tel: 520-795-7100 *Toll Free Tel:* 800-528-3494 *Toll Free Fax:* 800-770-4329
E-mail: alphapublications@aol.com
Key Personnel
Pres: Kermit Burton
Founded: 1976
Non-lawyer self-help legal kits (books & packets).
ISBN Prefix(es): 978-0-937434; 978-1-57164
Number of titles published annually: 109 Print
Total Titles: 128 Print; 160 Online; 4 E-Book
Membership(s): The Independent Book Publishers Association

Alpine Publications Inc
38262 Linman Rd, Crawford, CO 81415
Tel: 970-921-5005 *Toll Free Tel:* 800-777-7257 *Fax:* 970-921-5081
E-mail: editorialdept@alpinepub.com; customerservice@alpinepub.com
Web Site: www.alpinepub.com
Key Personnel
Publr: Betty McKinney
Founded: 1975
Dog & horse nonfiction titles.
ISBN Prefix(es): 978-0-931866; 978-0-87714; 978-1-57779
Number of titles published annually: 6 Print; 2 E-Book
Total Titles: 70 Print; 3 E-Book
Advertising Agency: Artline
Membership(s): ABA; The Independent Book Publishers Association

AltaMira Press
Imprint of Rowman & Littlefield Publishing Group
4501 Forbes Blvd, Suite 200, Lanham, MD 20706
Tel: 301-459-3366 *Toll Free Tel:* 800-462-6420 (cust serv) *Fax:* 301-429-5748
E-mail: custserv@rowman.com
Web Site: www.altamirapress.com
Key Personnel
Exec Ed: Charles Harmon *Tel:* 212-529-3888 ext 305 *E-mail:* charmon@rowman.com
Founded: 1995
Academic & professional materials, anthropology, museum & cultural studies, religion, archeology, history & humanities.
New titles to be released under the Rowman & Littlefield imprint.
ISBN Prefix(es): 978-0-8039; 978-0-7619 (shared with Sage Publications); 978-0-930390; 978-0-910050; 978-0-942063; 978-0-7425 (shared with Rowman & Littlefield); 978-0-8039 (shared with Sage Publications); 978-1-4422 (shared with Rowman & Littlefield)
Number of titles published annually: 75 Print; 1 CD-ROM
Total Titles: 500 Print; 3 CD-ROM
Distributor for American Association for State & Local History
Foreign Rep(s): National Book Network International (Europe, UK)
Shipping Address: National Book Network, 15200 NBN Way, PO Box 191, Blue Ridge Summit, PA 17214 *Toll Free Tel:* 800-462-6420 *Toll Free Fax:* 800-338-4550 *E-mail:* customercare@rowman.com
Distribution Center: National Book Network/University Press of America, 15200 NBN Way, PO Box 191, Blue Ridge Summit, PA 17214 *Toll Free Tel:* 800-462-6420 *Toll Free Fax:* 800-338-4550 *E-mail:* customercare@rowman.com
Membership(s): AAP

Althos Publishing
1500 Piney Plains Rd, Suite 200, Carey, NC 27518
Tel: 919-557-2260 *Fax:* 919-557-2261
E-mail: info@althos.com
Web Site: www.althosbooks.com
Key Personnel
Pres & Publr: Lawrence Harte *E-mail:* lharte@althos.com
Dir: Carolyn Luck *E-mail:* carolyn@althos.com
Founded: 2002
ISBN Prefix(es): 978-0-9728053; 978-0-9742787; 978-0-9746943; 978-1-932813
Number of titles published annually: 50 Print; 45 Online; 45 E-Book
Total Titles: 140 Print; 130 Online; 130 E-Book
Returns: 106 W Vance St, Fuquay Varina, NC 27526

§AMACOM Books
Division of American Management Association (AMA)
1601 Broadway, New York, NY 10019-7420
SAN: 201-1670
Tel: 212-586-8100 *Toll Free Tel:* 800-250-5308 (cust serv) *Fax:* 212-903-8083; 518-891-2372 (orders)
E-mail: pubs_cust_serv@amanet.org
Web Site: www.amacombooks.org
Key Personnel
Pres & Publr: Nancy Roberson
VP, Mktg: Rosemary Kane Carlough *E-mail:* rcarlough@amanet.org
Dir, Publicity: Irene Majuk *Tel:* 212-903-8087 *E-mail:* imajuk@amanet.org
Dir, Subs Rts & Intl Sales: Therese Mausser *Tel:* 212-903-8084 *E-mail:* tmausser@amanet.org
Dir, Trade Sales & Mktg: Jenny Wesselmann Schwartz *Tel:* 212-903-8448 *E-mail:* jwesselmann@amanet.org
Exec Ed: Ellen Kadin *E-mail:* ekadin@amanet.org
Sr Ed: Robert Nirkind *E-mail:* rnirkind@amanet.org; Stephen S Power *E-mail:* spower@amanet.org
Founded: 1972
Publish books on business management, career growth, current events, technology & personal finance. AMACOM books help readers enhance their personal & professional growth & reach into the future to understand emerging trends & cutting-edge thinking.
ISBN Prefix(es): 978-0-8144; 978-0-7612
Number of titles published annually: 60 Print; 30 E-Book
Total Titles: 500 Print; 150 E-Book; 54 Audio
Distributed by McGraw-Hill International
Foreign Rep(s): McGraw-Hill International Distribution (Worldwide exc Canada); Publishers Group Canada (Canada)
Returns: 600 AMA Way, Saranac Lake, NY 12983
Warehouse: 600 AMA Way, Saranac Lake, NY 12983, Dist Servs Mgr: William McIntyre *E-mail:* wmcintyre@amanet.org

Amadeus Press/Hal Leonard Performing Arts Publishing Group
Imprint of Hal Leonard Performing Arts Publishing Group
33 Plymouth St, Suite 302, Montclair, NJ 07042
Tel: 973-337-5034 *Toll Free Tel:* 800-524-4425
E-mail: info@halleonardbooks.com
Web Site: www.amadeuspress.com; www.halleonardbooks.com
Key Personnel
Group Publr: John Cerullo *Tel:* 973-337-5034 ext 210 *E-mail:* jcerullo@amadeuspress.com
Founded: 1987
Full service trade publisher that produces books, book/CDs & DVDs about classical music & opera.
ISBN Prefix(es): 978-1-57467
Number of titles published annually: 20 Print; 10 E-Book
Total Titles: 150 Print; 100 E-Book
Foreign Rep(s): Publishers Group UK (Europe, UK)

Frank Amato Publications Inc
4040 SE Wister St, Milwaukie, OR 97222
Mailing Address: PO Box 82112, Portland, OR 97282
Tel: 503-653-8108 *Toll Free Tel:* 800-541-9498 *Fax:* 503-653-2766
E-mail: customerservice@amatobooks.com; info@amatobooks.com
Web Site: www.amatobooks.com
Key Personnel
Publr: Frank W Amato
Co-Publr: Nick S Amato *E-mail:* nick@amatobooks.com; Tony F Amato *E-mail:* tony@amatobooks.com
Edit Mgr: Kimberly R Callahan *E-mail:* kim@amatobooks.com
Sales: Lorraine P Guelker *E-mail:* lorraine@amatobooks.com
Founded: 1967
Fishing books & magazines, some outdoor sport titles & cookbooks.
ISBN Prefix(es): 978-0-936608; 978-1-878175; 978-1-57188
Number of titles published annually: 30 Print
Total Titles: 800 Print
Distributor for Haugen Enterprises (cooking & hunting titles)
Membership(s): Pacific Northwest Booksellers Association

§Ambassador International
Division of Emerald House Inc
427 Wade Hampton Blvd, Greenville, SC 29609
Tel: 864-235-2434 *Toll Free Tel:* 800-209-8570 *Fax:* 864-235-2491
E-mail: info@emeraldhouse.com; publisher@emeraldhouse.com (ms submissions); sales@emeraldhouse.com (orders/order inquiries)

Web Site: ambassador-international.com; www.facebook.com/AmbassadorIntl; twitter.com/ambassadorintl
Key Personnel
CEO & Pres: Dr Samuel Lowry
COO: Timothy Lowry *E-mail:* tlowry@emeraldhouse.com
Creative Dir: Hannah Nichols
Publicist: Alison Storm
Digital Prodr: Anna Riebe
Ed: Brenda Covert
Founded: 1980 (UK, 1996 US)
Christian publisher. Works with authors to create quality Christian literature of several genres - fiction, devotional & children's books. The company's vision has always been to create products that strengthen believers in their Christian walk & direct the lost to the way of salvation. New titles each year in both print & ebook format. Offices in the US & Northern Ireland, distribution partnerships on four continents & books in the hands of readers around the world.
This publisher has indicated that 90% of their product line is author subsidized.
ISBN Prefix(es): 978-1-889893; 978-1-932307; 978-1-620202
Number of titles published annually: 50 Print; 50 E-Book
Total Titles: 200 E-Book
Foreign Office(s): Ambassador Books & Media, The Mount, 2 Woodstock Link, Belfast BT6 8DD, United Kingdom *Tel:* (028) 9073 0184 *Fax:* (028) 9073 0199 *Web Site:* www.ambassadormedia.co.uk
Distribution Center: Baker & Taylor, 2550 W Tyvola Rd, Suite 300, Charlotte, NC 28217 (US dist) *Tel:* 704-998-3100 *Toll Free Tel:* 800-775-1800 *Web Site:* www.baker-taylor.com
Ingram/Spring Arbor, One Ingram Blvd, La Vergne, TN 37086 (US dist) *Tel:* 615-793-5000 *Web Site:* www.ingramcontent.com

Amber Lotus Publishing
PO Box 11329, Portland, OR 97211
SAN: 247-6819
Tel: 503-284-6400 *Toll Free Tel:* 800-326-2375 (orders only) *Fax:* 503-284-6417
E-mail: info@amberlotus.com
Web Site: www.amberlotus.com
Key Personnel
CEO & Pres: Lawson Day
Founded: 1988
Calendars, greeting cards, journals & books.
ISBN Prefix(es): 978-1-885394; 978-1-56937; 978-1-60237
Number of titles published annually: 65 Print
Returns: Ware-Pak, Amber Lotus Publishing Returns, 2427 Bond St, University Park, IL 60466

§Amber Quill Press LLC
PO Box 265, Indian Hills, CO 80454
SAN: 255-3872
E-mail: business@amberquill.com; customer_service@amberquill.com
Web Site: www.amberquill.com
Key Personnel
Owner, Edit Dir & Creative Dir: Trace Edward Zaber *E-mail:* tezaber@earthlink.net
Owner, Mktg Dir & Mng Ed: E J Gilmer
Owner & Cust Serv Dir: J Kathe
Owner & Prodn/Prepress Dir: Ingrid Arbaiza
Owner, Fin Mgr & Mng Ed: Karin Story
Ed: Catherine Snodgrass
Mktg & Promos Coord: Theresa Gallup
Mktg Consultant: Barbara Clark
Founded: 2002
An independent, royalty-paying publisher offering a varied list of fiction: young adult, romance (& all sub-genres), erotica (straight & GLBT), science fiction, mystery, thriller, suspense, horror, fantasy, vampire, historical & romantic; ebook +/or print-on-demand. Not open for submissions.
Accepts no returns.
ISBN Prefix(es): 978-1-59279; 978-1-60272; 978-1-61124
Number of titles published annually: 60 Print; 300 E-Book
Total Titles: 350 Print; 840 E-Book
Imprints: Amber Allure (GLBT fiction); Amber Heat (erotic romance); Amber Quill (genre fiction)
Membership(s): The Independent Book Publishers Association

AMC Books, see Appalachian Mountain Club Books

America West Publishers
Subsidiary of Global Insights Inc
PO Box 599, Hayden, ID 83835
Tel: 775-885-0700 *Toll Free Tel:* 800-729-4131
Web Site: www.nohoax.com
Key Personnel
Pres: George Green *E-mail:* geo@nohoax.com
Founded: 1986
New science, UFO's, healing, metaphysics, spiritual, political & economic.
ISBN Prefix(es): 978-0-922356
Number of titles published annually: 5 Print; 1 CD-ROM
Total Titles: 100 Print; 20 CD-ROM; 5 Audio
Billing Address: Global Insights Inc, 1805 N Carson St, Carson City, NV 89701
Orders to: Global Insights Inc, 1805 N Carson St, Carson City, NV 89701
Returns: Global Insights Inc, 1805 N Carson St, Carson City, NV 89701
Warehouse: 5872 Government Way, Bldg 1, No 10, Dalton Gardens, ID 83815 *E-mail:* geo@nohoax.com

American Academy of Environmental Engineers & Scientists™
147 Old Solomons Island Rd, Suite 303, Annapolis, MD 21401
Tel: 410-266-3311 *Fax:* 410-266-7653
E-mail: info@aaees.org
Web Site: www.aaees.org
Key Personnel
Exec Dir: Burk Kalweit *E-mail:* bkalweit@aaees.org
Prodn Mgr: Yolanda Moulden *E-mail:* ymoulden@aaees.org
Exec Asst: Joyce Dowen *E-mail:* jdowen@aaees.org
Founded: 1955
Journals & textbooks for the environmental engineering & science professions.
ISBN Prefix(es): 978-1-883767
Number of titles published annually: 5 Print
Total Titles: 49 Print
Distributor for The ABS Group; CRC Press; McGraw-Hill; Pearson Education; Prentice Hall; John Wiley & Sons Inc

§American Academy of Orthopaedic Surgeons (AAOS)
6300 N River Rd, Rosemont, IL 60018-4262
SAN: 228-2097
Tel: 847-823-7186 *Toll Free Tel:* 800-346-2267 *Fax:* 847-823-8125
E-mail: custserv@aaos.org
Web Site: www.aaos.org
Key Personnel
Dir, Dept of Pubns: Han Koelsch
Mgr, Pubns & Licensing: Joan Golembiewski *Tel:* 847-384-4144 *Fax:* 847-823-8033 *E-mail:* golembiewski@aaos.org
Founded: 1933
Scientific & technical books, including annual updates on orthopaedic procedures; home study programs & examinations; symposium volumes; monographs on scientific, clinical, practice management & socioeconomic topics in orthopaedics; clinical review journal.
ISBN Prefix(es): 978-0-89203
Number of titles published annually: 15 Print; 12 CD-ROM; 2 Online; 1 Audio
Total Titles: 100 Print; 38 CD-ROM; 5 Online; 5 Audio
Branch Office(s)
317 Massachusetts Ave NE, 1st fl, Washington, DC 20002 *Tel:* 202-546-4430 *Fax:* 202-546-5051
Distributed by Jones & Bartlett Publishers
Foreign Rep(s): Eurospan (Europe, Middle East); Nankodo Co Inc (Japan)
Warehouse: Dearborn Distribution Center, 940 Enterprise St, Aurora, IL 60504 *Toll Free Fax:* 800-823-8025 *E-mail:* custserv@aaos.org

American Academy of Pediatrics
141 NW Point Blvd, Elk Grove Village, IL 60007-1098
Tel: 847-434-4000 *Toll Free Tel:* 888-227-1770 *Fax:* 847-434-8000
E-mail: pubs@aap.org
Web Site: www.aap.org
Key Personnel
Pres: Dr James Perrin
Dir, Prod Devt Div: Mark Grimes *Tel:* 847-434-7822 *E-mail:* mgrimes@aap.org
Founded: 1930
Patient educational material, medical textbooks, professional textbook, patient education & practice management materials; pediatrics; family & emergency medicine.
ISBN Prefix(es): 978-0-910761; 978-0-87493; 978-0-915473; 978-0-87553; 978-0-553; 978-0-89707; 978-1-56055; 978-1-58110
Number of titles published annually: 40 Print; 5 CD-ROM; 10 Online; 120 E-Book
Total Titles: 400 Print; 10 CD-ROM; 10 Online; 120 E-Book
Branch Office(s)
601 13 St NW, Suite 400-N, Washington, DC 20005 *Tel:* 202-347-8600 *Fax:* 202-393-6137
Foreign Rights: John Scott & Co

The American Alpine Club Press
Division of The American Alpine Club
710 Tenth St, Suite 100, Golden, CO 80401
Tel: 303-384-0110 *Fax:* 303-384-0111
Web Site: www.americanalpineclub.org
Key Personnel
CFO & Opers Dir: Penn Burris *Tel:* 303-384-0110 ext 101 *E-mail:* pburris@americanalpineclub.org
Founded: 1902
Mountaineering: general, regional guides, safety, medical & scientific, annual journals & historical.
ISBN Prefix(es): 978-0-930410
Number of titles published annually: 3 Print
Total Titles: 57 Print
Distributed by Mountaineers Books
Foreign Rep(s): Mountaineers Books (Worldwide)
Foreign Rights: Mountaineers Books (Worldwide)

§American Anthropological Association (AAA)
2300 Clarendon Blvd, Suite 1301, Arlington, VA 22201
Tel: 703-528-1902 *Fax:* 703-528-3546
Web Site: www.aaanet.org
Key Personnel
Dir, Publg: Oona Schmid *Tel:* 703-528-1902 ext 1174 *E-mail:* oschmid@aaanet.org
Asst to Dir, Publg: Jennie Simpson *Tel:* 703-528-1902 ext 1181 *E-mail:* jsimpson@aaanet.org
Mng Ed: Amy Goldenberg *Tel:* 703-528-1902 ext 1184 *E-mail:* agoldenberg@aaanet.org
Founded: 1902
Publish scholarly journals.

ISBN Prefix(es): 978-0-913167; 978-1-931303; 978-0-9799094; 978-0-9826767; 978-0-9836822
Number of titles published annually: 100 Print
Total Titles: 27 Print
Distributed by Wiley-Blackwell
Membership(s): AAP; World Council of Anthropological Association

§American Association for Vocational Instructional Materials
220 Smithonia Rd, Winterville, GA 30683
Tel: 706-742-5355 *Fax:* 706-742-7005
E-mail: sales@aavim.com
Web Site: www.aavim.com
Key Personnel
Dir: Gary Farmer
Founded: 1949
Consortium formed for development, publishing & distribution of instructional materials for vocational education.
ISBN Prefix(es): 978-0-89606
Number of titles published annually: 4 Print
Total Titles: 182 Print; 10 CD-ROM
Distributor for Southeastern Cooperative Wildlife Disease Study

§American Association of Blood Banks
8101 Glenbrook Rd, Bethesda, MD 20814-2749
Tel: 301-907-6977 *Toll Free Tel:* 866-222-2498 (sales) *Fax:* 301-907-6895
E-mail: aabb@aabb.org; sales@aabb.org (ordering); publications1@aabb.org
Web Site: www.aabb.org
Key Personnel
Dir, Pubns: Laurie Munk *Tel:* 301-215-6595 *E-mail:* laurie@aabb.org
Mgr, Pubns: Jennifer Boyer *Tel:* 301-215-6596 *E-mail:* jboyer@aabb.org
Pubns Asst: Victoria Barthelmes *Tel:* 301-215-6521 *E-mail:* vbarthelmes@aabb.org
Founded: 1947
Texts in blood banking standards, transfusion medicine, transplantation & cellular therapy.
ISBN Prefix(es): 978-0-915355
Number of titles published annually: 20 Print; 14 Audio
Total Titles: 100 Print; 2 CD-ROM; 5 Online; 60 Audio

American Association of Cereal Chemists, see AACC International

American Association of Colleges for Teacher Education (AACTE)
1307 New York Ave NW, Suite 300, Washington, DC 20005
Tel: 202-293-2450 *Fax:* 202-457-8095
E-mail: aacte@aacte.org
Web Site: www.aacte.org
Key Personnel
CEO & Pres: Sharon P Robinson *Tel:* 202-478-4505
COO & CFO: Jerry D Wirth *Tel:* 202-478-4570
Ed & Mktg Communs Assoc: Kristin McCabe *Tel:* 207-899-1309 *E-mail:* kmccabe@aacte.org
Founded: 1948
Teacher education related works.
ISBN Prefix(es): 978-0-89333
Number of titles published annually: 3 Print
Total Titles: 85 Print

American Association of Collegiate Registrars & Admissions Officers (AACRAO)
One Dupont Circle NW, Suite 520, Washington, DC 20036
Tel: 202-293-9161 *Fax:* 202-872-8857
Web Site: www.aacrao.org
Key Personnel
Exec Dir: Michael Reilly *E-mail:* reillym@aacrao.org
Dir, Membership & Pubns: Martha Henebry *Tel:* 202-263-0285 ext 6812 *E-mail:* henebrym@aacrao.org
Founded: 1910
Periodicals, monograph series, higher education-general, international, technology & higher education.
ISBN Prefix(es): 978-0-929851; 978-0-910054
Number of titles published annually: 4 Print
Total Titles: 118 Print
Distribution Center: AACRAO Distribution Ctr, PO Box 231, Annapolis Junction, MD 20701 *Tel:* 301-490-7651 *Fax:* 301-206-9789 *E-mail:* pubs@aacrao.org

American Atheist Press
PO Box 158, Cranford, NJ 07016
Tel: 908-276-7300 *Fax:* 908-276-7402
Web Site: www.atheists.org
Key Personnel
Pres: David Silverman *Tel:* 908-276-7300 ext 5 *E-mail:* dsilverman@atheists.org
Mng Dir: Amanda Knief *Tel:* 908-276-7300 ext 9 *E-mail:* aknief@atheists.org
Dir, Opers: Todd Jones *E-mail:* tjones@atheists.org
PR Dir: Dave Muscato *Tel:* 908-276-7300 ext 7
Founded: 1963
Specialize in atheism, religious criticism, atheist history, religious intolerance.
ISBN Prefix(es): 978-0-910309; 978-0-911826; 978-1-57884
Number of titles published annually: 3 Print
Total Titles: 40 Print
Imprints: Gustav Broukal Press
Editorial Office(s): 1352 Hunter Ave, Columbus, OH 43201
Shipping Address: 225 Cristiani St, Cranford, NJ 07016

American Bar Association
321 N Clark St, Chicago, IL 60654
Tel: 312-988-5000 *Toll Free Tel:* 800-285-2221 (orders) *Fax:* 312-988-6281
E-mail: orders@abanet.org
Web Site: shop.americanbar.org
Key Personnel
Dir, New Prod Devt: Timothy Brandhorst *Tel:* 312-988-6082 *E-mail:* tim.brandhorst@americanbar.org
Founded: 1878
Books, magazines, journals, newsletters & AV materials.
ISBN Prefix(es): 978-1-57073; 978-1-59031; 978-1-60442
Number of titles published annually: 170 Print; 25 CD-ROM; 100 Online; 100 E-Book
Total Titles: 1,000 Print; 150 CD-ROM; 250 Online; 250 E-Book
Branch Office(s)
1050 Connecticut Ave NW, Suite 400, Washington, DC 20036 *Tel:* 202-662-1000
Warehouse: PBD, 905 Carlow Dr, Unit B, Bolingbrook, IL 60490
Distribution Center: National Book Network, 4501 Forbes Blvd, Suite 200, Lanham, MD 20706
Membership(s): The Independent Book Publishers Association

American Bible Society
1865 Broadway, New York, NY 10023-7505
SAN: 203-5189
Tel: 212-408-1200 *Toll Free Tel:* 800-322-4253; 888-596-6296 *Fax:* 212-408-1512
E-mail: info@americanbible.org
Web Site: www.americanbible.org
Key Personnel
Dir, Print & Prodn: John Greco
Dir, Publg Servs: Tom Durakis
Founded: 1816
Publisher, producer & distributor of Bibles, books, audio, video & software products emphasizing Christian, inspirational & family values.
ISBN Prefix(es): 978-1-58516
Number of titles published annually: 20 Print
Total Titles: 800 Print
Branch Office(s)
1550 Liberty Ridge Dr, Suite 330, Wayne, PA 19087 *Tel:* 610-647-8080 *Fax:* 484-654-3503

§American Carriage House Publishing
PO Box 1130, Nevada City, CA 95959
Tel: 530-432-8860 *Toll Free Tel:* 866-986-2665 *Fax:* 530-432-7379
E-mail: editor@carriagehousepublishing.com
Web Site: www.americancarriagehousepublishing.com
Founded: 2003
Focused on providing traditional & family values in a new fresh approach. Distribution Centers: Baker & Taylor Inc, FaithWorks Books, Ingram Book Group & Quality Books Inc.
ISBN Prefix(es): 978-0-970
Number of titles published annually: 8 Print; 20 CD-ROM; 8 Online; 14 E-Book; 68 Audio
Total Titles: 16 E-Book; 240 Audio
Distributed by Faith Works Books
Shipping Address: 400 Idaho Maryland Rd, Grass Valley, CA 95945
Warehouse: 400 Idaho Maryland Rd, Grass Valley, CA 95945
Membership(s): The Association of Publishers for Special Sales; The Independent Book Publishers Association

American Catholic Press (ACP)
16565 S State St, South Holland, IL 60473
SAN: 162-4989
Tel: 708-331-5485 *Fax:* 708-331-5484
E-mail: acp@acpress.org
Web Site: www.acpress.org
Key Personnel
Exec Dir: Rev Michael Gilligan, PhD
Devt Dir: Peter Ruhl
Subscriber Serv Dir: Michael Yukich
Founded: 1967
Christian liturgy, especially in the Roman Catholic Church including music resources for churches. No poetry or fiction.
ISBN Prefix(es): 978-0-915866
Number of titles published annually: 5 Print; 1 Audio
Total Titles: 25 Print; 1 CD-ROM; 4 Audio

§The American Ceramic Society
600 N Cleveland Ave, Suite 210, Westerville, OH 43082
Tel: 240-646-7054 *Toll Free Tel:* 866-721-3322 *Fax:* 240-396-5637
E-mail: customerservice@ceramics.org
Web Site: ceramics.org
Key Personnel
Exec Dir: Charles Spahr *E-mail:* cspahr@ceramics.org
Dir, Mktg & Membership: Megan Bricker *E-mail:* mbricker@ceramics.org
Dir, Tech Pubns & Meetings: Mark Mecklenborg *Tel:* 240-646-7054 ext 5829 *E-mail:* mmecklenborg@ceramics.org
Founded: 1898
Dedicated to the advancement of ceramics, serving more than 8,000 members & subscribers. Members include engineers, scientists, researchers & others in the ceramics & materials industry. Provides the latest technical, scientific & educational information.
ISBN Prefix(es): 978-0-944904; 978-1-57498; 978-0-916094
Number of titles published annually: 25 Print
Total Titles: 250 Print; 8 CD-ROM

The American Chemical Society
1155 16 St NW, Washington, DC 20036
SAN: 201-2626
Tel: 202-872-4600 *Toll Free Tel:* 800-227-5558 (US) *Fax:* 202-872-6067
E-mail: help@acs.org
Web Site: www.acs.org
Key Personnel
Pres: Bassam Z Shakhashiri *E-mail:* president@acs.org
Exec Dir: Madeleine Jacobs
Asst Dir: Joseph Graham *E-mail:* j_graham@acs.org
Founded: 1876
Serials, proceedings, reprint collections, monographs & other professional & reference books; specializes in food chemistry, environmental sciences & green chemistry, analytical, inorganic, medicinal, organic & physical chemistries, biochemistry, polymer & materials science & nanotechnology.
ISBN Prefix(es): 978-0-8412
Number of titles published annually: 31 Print
Total Titles: 500 Print; 1 CD-ROM
Distributed by Oxford University Press
Distributor for Royal Society of Chemistry
Foreign Rep(s): Maruzen Co Ltd (Japan); Sonya Nickson (UK); Andrew Pitts (UK)
Membership(s): AAP

American College
270 S Bryn Mawr Ave, Bryn Mawr, PA 19010
SAN: 240-5822
Tel: 610-526-1000 *Toll Free Tel:* 888-263-7265 *Fax:* 610-526-1310
Web Site: www.theamericancollege.edu
Key Personnel
Acting Pres: Mike Davis
VP & Dean, Academic Div: Walt Woerheide, PhD
Founded: 1927
An independent, accredited nonprofit educational institution offering financial services texts & course guides online & life insurance for students in financial services programs at colleges & universities including American College programs: CLU, ChFC, CLF, LUTCF, RHU, REBC, CASL & CFP certification curriculum & MSFS degree for professionals in the financial services industry. Subject specialties: business, finance, insurance & securities.
ISBN Prefix(es): 978-0-943590; 978-1-57996; 978-1-932819
Number of titles published annually: 42 Print; 60 Online; 11 Audio
Total Titles: 42 Print; 15 CD-ROM; 60 Online; 11 Audio

§American College of Physician Executives
400 N Ashley Dr, Suite 400, Tampa, FL 33602
SAN: 688-7449
Tel: 813-287-2000 *Toll Free Tel:* 800-562-8088 *Fax:* 813-287-8993
E-mail: acpe@acpe.org
Web Site: www.acpe.org
Key Personnel
VP, Communs & Engagement: Bill Steiger *E-mail:* bsteiger@acpe.org
Founded: 1975
Publishes books & journals.
ISBN Prefix(es): 978-0-9605218; 978-0-924674
Number of titles published annually: 6 Print; 1 CD-ROM
Total Titles: 50 Print; 6 CD-ROM; 1 Audio

American College of Surgeons
633 N Saint Clair St, Chicago, IL 60611-3211
Tel: 312-202-5000 *Fax:* 312-202-5001
E-mail: postmaster@facs.org
Web Site: www.facs.org
Key Personnel
Gen Pubns Mgr: Katie McCauley *E-mail:* kmccauley@facs.org
Founded: 1913
Publishes reference books & manuals. Specialize in surgery, trauma, cancer & professional liability. Also publishes the *Journal of the American College of Surgeons* (monthly) & the *Bulletin of the American College of Surgeons* (monthly).
ISBN Prefix(es): 978-0-9620370
Number of titles published annually: 5 Print; 10 Online
Total Titles: 20 Print; 2 CD-ROM
Distributed by Cine-Med Inc; Scientific American Medicine

American Correctional Association
206 N Washington St, Suite 200, Alexandria, VA 22314
Tel: 703-224-0000 *Toll Free Tel:* 800-222-5646 *Fax:* 703-224-0179
Web Site: www.aca.org
Key Personnel
Dir, Communs & Pubns: Susan Clayton *Tel:* 703-224-0180 *E-mail:* susanc@aca.org
Mgr, Pubns & Res: Alice Heiserman *Tel:* 703-224-0194 *E-mail:* aliceh@aca.org
Founded: 1870
Corrections professionals.
ISBN Prefix(es): 978-1-56991
Number of titles published annually: 6 Print
Total Titles: 200 Print

American Council on Education
One Dupont Circle NW, Washington, DC 20036
Tel: 202-939-9300; 301-632-6757 (orders) *Fax:* 202-939-9302
E-mail: pubs@acenet.edu
Web Site: www.acenet.edu
Key Personnel
Pres: Molly Corbett Broad
Dir, Pubns: Scott Cech
Founded: 1917
Books, directories & handbooks in higher education, monographs.
ISBN Prefix(es): 978-0-8268; 978-0-89774
Number of titles published annually: 70 Print
Total Titles: 200 Print
Distributed by Rowman & Littlefield

American Counseling Association
6101 Stevenson Ave, Suite 600, Alexandria, VA 22304
Tel: 703-823-9800 (ext 222, book orders) *Toll Free Tel:* 800-422-2648 (ext 222, book orders); 800-347-6647 *Fax:* 703-823-0252 *Toll Free Fax:* 800-473-2329
E-mail: membership@counseling.org (book orders)
Web Site: www.counseling.org
Key Personnel
Assoc Publr: Carolyn C Baker *Tel:* 703-823-9800 ext 356 *Fax:* 703-823-4786 *E-mail:* cbaker@counseling.org
Digital & Print Devt Ed & Rts & Perms: Nancy Driver *Fax:* 703-823-4786 *E-mail:* ndriver@counseling.org
Founded: 1952
More than 55,000 members from the school counseling, mental health & human development professions at all educational levels. Publishes 11 scholarly journals, a newspaper & approximately 8-10 new professional book titles a year for members & nonmembers.
ISBN Prefix(es): 978-1-55620
Number of titles published annually: 10 Print; 8 E-Book
Total Titles: 100 Print; 28 E-Book
Imprints: ACA

§American Diabetes Association
1701 N Beauregard St, Alexandria, VA 22311
Toll Free Tel: 800-342-2383
E-mail: booksinfo@diabetes.org
Web Site: www.diabetes.org
Key Personnel
Dir, Book Publg: Abe Ogden
Mgr, Mktg: Katherine Curran
Acqs Ed: Victor Van Beuren
Founded: 1945
Books, handouts & collateral materials pertaining to diabetes for patients & health-care professionals.
ISBN Prefix(es): 978-1-58040; 978-0-94544
Number of titles published annually: 20 Print; 15 E-Book
Total Titles: 180 Print; 80 E-Book
Distribution Center: Publishers Group West (PGW), 1700 Fourth St, Berkeley, CA 94710 *Toll Free Tel:* 800-788-3123 (cust serv) SAN: 202-8522

American Federation of Arts
305 E 47 St, 10th fl, New York, NY 10017
Tel: 212-988-7700 *Toll Free Tel:* 800-232-0270 *Fax:* 212-861-2487
E-mail: pubinfo@afaweb.org
Web Site: www.afaweb.org
Key Personnel
Mgr, Pubns & Communs: Audrey Walen *E-mail:* awalen@afaweb.org
Communs & Pubns Assoc: Juliet Helmke *E-mail:* jhelmke@afaweb.org
Founded: 1909
Publisher of exhibition catalogues (books) that accompany art exhibitions organized by the AFA.
ISBN Prefix(es): 978-0-917418; 978-1-885444
Number of titles published annually: 4 Print
Total Titles: 47 Print
Distributed by Harry N Abrams Inc; Distributed Art Publishers; D Giles Ltd; Hudson Hills Press Inc; Scala Publishers; Skira Rizzoli Publishers; University of Washington Press; Yale University Press

American Federation of Astrologers Inc
6535 S Rural Rd, Tempe, AZ 85283-3746
Tel: 480-838-1751 *Toll Free Tel:* 888-301-7630 *Fax:* 480-838-8293
Web Site: www.astrologers.com
Key Personnel
Exec Dir: Kris Brandt Riske
Founded: 1938
Astrology book publisher & membership organization.
ISBN Prefix(es): 978-0-86690
Number of titles published annually: 25 Print
Total Titles: 250 Print

American Fisheries Society
5410 Grosvenor Lane, Suite 110, Bethesda, MD 20814-2199
Tel: 301-897-8616; 703-661-1570 (book orders) *Fax:* 301-897-8096; 703-996-1010 (book orders)
E-mail: main@fisheries.org
Web Site: www.fisheries.org
Key Personnel
Dir, Pubns: Aaron Lerner *Tel:* 301-897-8616 ext 231 *E-mail:* alerner@fisheries.org
Off & Admin Mgr: Denise Spencer *Tel:* 301-897-8616 ext 212 *E-mail:* dspencer@fisheries.org
Founded: 1870
Fisheries science, aquaculture & management materials, aquatic ecology, fisheries law, fisheries history, conservation biology & publishing.
ISBN Prefix(es): 978-0-913235; 978-1-888569; 978-1-934874
Number of titles published annually: 10 Print
Total Titles: 100 Print
Advertising Agency: Media West Inc, 230 Kings Hwy E, Suite 316, Haddonfield, NJ 08033 (Fisheries Magazine only), Contact: Steve West *Tel:* 856-432-1501 *Fax:* 856-494-1455 *E-mail:* steve@afs-fisheries.com

American Foundation for the Blind Press, see AFB Press

American Geophysical Union (AGU)
2000 Florida Ave NW, Washington, DC 20009
SAN: 202-4489
Tel: 202-462-6900 *Toll Free Tel:* 800-966-2481 (North America) *Fax:* 202-328-0566
E-mail: service@agu.org
Web Site: www.agu.org
Founded: 1919
International scientific society with more than 50,000 members in over 135 countries. For over 80 years, AGU researchers, teachers & science administrators have dedicated themselves to advancing the understanding of earth & its environment in space. AGU now stands as a leader in the increasingly interdisciplinary global endeavor that encompasses the geophysical sciences.
ISBN Prefix(es): 978-0-87590
Number of titles published annually: 15 Print
Total Titles: 500 Print
Membership(s): AAP; Society for Scholarly Publishing

§American Geosciences Institute (AGI)
4220 King St, Alexandria, VA 22302-1502
Tel: 703-379-2480 (ext 246) *Fax:* 703-379-7563
E-mail: pubs@agiweb.org
Web Site: www.agiweb.org
Key Personnel
Exec Dir: P Patrick Leahy, PhD *Tel:* 703-379-2480 ext 202 *E-mail:* pleahy@agiweb.org
Fin & Admin Dir: Walter R Sisson *Tel:* 703-379-2480 ext 209 *E-mail:* wsisson@agiweb.org
Info Servs Dir: Sharon Tahirkheli *Tel:* 703-379-2480 ext 231 *E-mail:* snt@agiweb.org
Mktg Dir: John P Rasanen *Tel:* 703-379-2480 ext 224 *E-mail:* jr@agiweb.org
Technol & Communs Dir: Christopher Keane *Tel:* 703-379-2480 ext 219 *E-mail:* cmk@agiweb.org
Founded: 1948
Geoscience reference books.
ISBN Prefix(es): 978-0-922152; 978-0-913312; 978-1-941878
Number of titles published annually: 5 Print; 3 E-Book
Total Titles: 60 Print; 10 CD-ROM; 2 Online; 5 E-Book
Distributed by W H Freeman; It's About Time Inc; Prentice Hall
Orders to: AGI Book Center *Web Site:* www.agiweb.org/pubs

American Girl Publishing
Subsidiary of Mattel
8400 Fairway Place, Middleton, WI 53562
Mailing Address: PO Box 620497, Middleton, WI 53562-0497
Tel: 608-836-4848; 608-831-5210 (outside US & CN) *Toll Free Tel:* 800-233-0264; 800-360-1861; 800-845-0005 (US & CN) *Fax:* 608-836-1999
Web Site: www.americangirl.com
Key Personnel
Pres: Jean McKenzie
Founded: 1986
Children's fiction & nonfiction.
ISBN Prefix(es): 978-0-937295; 978-1-56247; 978-1-58485
Number of titles published annually: 40 Print; 1 CD-ROM; 6 Audio
Total Titles: 350 Print; 3 CD-ROM; 18 Audio
Imprints: A G Fiction™; American Girl Library®; The American Girls Collection®
Membership(s): The Children's Book Council

§American Historical Association (AHA)
400 "A" St SE, Washington, DC 20003
Tel: 202-544-2422 *Fax:* 202-544-8307
E-mail: aha@historians.org; awards@historians.org; info@historians.org
Web Site: www.historians.org
Key Personnel
Exec Dir: Jim Grossman
Dir, Scholarly Commun: Seth Denbo
Ed: Allen Mikaelian
Assoc Ed: Shatha Almutawa
Founded: 1884
The umbrella organization for the history profession.
ISBN Prefix(es): 978-0-87229
Number of titles published annually: 15 Print; 3 Online
Total Titles: 120 Print; 11 Online

American Hospital Association Press, see AHA Press

American Industrial Hygiene Association - AIHA
3141 Fairview Park Dr, Suite 777, Falls Church, VA 22042
Tel: 703-849-8888 *Fax:* 703-207-3561
E-mail: infonet@aiha.org
Web Site: www.aiha.org
Key Personnel
Mgr, Prod Devt: Katie Robert *Tel:* 703-846-0738 *E-mail:* krobert@aiha.org
Mgr, Cust & Career & Employment Servs: Wanda Barbour *Tel:* 703-846-0782 *E-mail:* wbarbour@aiha.org
Founded: 1939
Serves the needs of occupational & environmental health professionals practicing industrial hygiene in industry, government, labor, academic institutions & independent organizations.
ISBN Prefix(es): 978-1-931504
Number of titles published annually: 15 Print; 1 CD-ROM; 1 Online
Total Titles: 100 Print; 3 CD-ROM

§American Institute for Economic Research (AIER)
250 Division St, Great Barrington, MA 01230
Mailing Address: PO Box 1000, Great Barrington, MA 01230-1000
Tel: 413-528-1216 *Toll Free Tel:* 888-528-1216 (orders)
E-mail: info@aier.org
Key Personnel
CEO & Pres: Steven Adams
Dir, Mktg: John Sylbert
Libn: Suzanne Hermann *Tel:* 413-528-1216 ext 3116
Founded: 1933
Conducts independent, scientific, economic research to educate individuals, thereby advancing their personal interests & those of the nation.
ISBN Prefix(es): 978-0-913610
Number of titles published annually: 3 Print; 8 Online; 4 E-Book
Total Titles: 50 Print; 46 Online; 4 E-Book

American Institute of Aeronautics & Astronautics (AIAA)
1801 Alexander Bell Dr, Suite 500, Reston, VA 20191-4344
Tel: 703-264-7500 *Toll Free Tel:* 800-639-AIAA (639-2422) *Fax:* 703-264-7551
E-mail: custserv@aiaa.org
Web Site: www.aiaa.org
Key Personnel
Exec Dir: Dr Sandra Magnus *Tel:* 703-264-7512 *E-mail:* sandym@aiaa.org
Dir, Cust Serv: Aida Davis *E-mail:* aidad@aiaa.org
Ed-in-Chief, Aerospace America: Ben Iannotta *Tel:* 703-284-7528 *E-mail:* beni@aiaa.org
Mgr, Edit & Prodn: Craig Byl *Tel:* 703-264-7590 *E-mail:* craigb@aiaa.org
Mktg Strategist & Publicist: Laura Sherman
Founded: 1963
Professional technical books; archival journals & technical meeting papers in the science & technology of aerospace engineering & systems, print CD-ROMs & online delivery.
ISBN Prefix(es): 978-0-915928; 978-0-930403; 978-1-56347; 978-1-60086; 978-1-62410
Number of titles published annually: 20 Print
Total Titles: 600 Print
Foreign Rep(s): ACCUCOMS BV (Europe); ACCUCOMS India (India); ACCUCOMS MENA (Eyad Mohammad) (Middle East, North Africa); Publishers Communication Group (Rebekah Matthews) (North America, South America); Transatlantic Publishers Group (Europe)
Distribution Center: AIAA Publications Customer Service, PO Box 960, Herndon, VA 20172-0960 *Tel:* 703-661-1595 *Toll Free Tel:* 800-682-2422 *Fax:* 703-661-1501 *E-mail:* aiaamail@presswarehouse.com

American Institute of Certified Public Accountants, see AICPA Professional Publications

§American Institute of Chemical Engineers (AIChE)
120 Wall St, 23rd fl, New York, NY 10005-4020
Tel: 203-702-7660 *Toll Free Tel:* 800-242-4363 *Fax:* 203-775-5177
E-mail: customerservice@aiche.org
Web Site: www.aiche.org
Key Personnel
Pres: Otis Shelton
Exec Dir: June C Wispelwey *Tel:* 646-495-1310 *E-mail:* junew@aiche.org
Dir, Meeting & Conference Programming: Kristine Chin *Tel:* 646-495-1366 *E-mail:* krisc@aiche.org
Mktg Dir: Tim McCreight *Tel:* 646-495-1325 *E-mail:* timm@aiche.org
Pubns Dir: Stephen R Smith *Tel:* 646-495-1360 *E-mail:* steps@aiche.org
Founded: 1908
Chemical engineering books & journals, technical manuals, symposia proceedings, directories, software, CD-ROM.
ISBN Prefix(es): 978-0-8169
Number of titles published annually: 15 Print; 4 CD-ROM
Total Titles: 300 Print; 4 CD-ROM
Distributed by Dechema (selected titles)
Distributor for ASM International (selected titles); Dechema (selected titles); Engineering Foundation; IchemE (selected titles)
Foreign Rep(s): Ric Bessford (Europe, UK); Patrick Connolly (Belgium, France, Switzerland)
Distribution Center: Institution of Chemical Engineers, Davis Bldg, 165-189 Railway Terr, Rugby CV21 3HQ, United Kingdom

American Institute of Physics
1305 Walt Whitman Rd, Suite 300, Melville, NY 11747
Tel: 516-576-2200; 301-209-3165 (orders) *Fax:* 301-209-0882 (orders)
E-mail: aipinfo@aip.org
Web Site: www.aip.org
Key Personnel
CEO: John Haynes *Tel:* 516-576-2253 *E-mail:* jhaynes@aip.org
Founded: 1931
Publisher of conference proceedings, professional journals, magazines & books.
ISBN Prefix(es): 978-0-88318; 978-1-56396; 978-0-7354
Number of titles published annually: 13 Print; 8 CD-ROM; 3 Online
Total Titles: 700 Print; 200 Online
Distributed by Springer-Verlag
Membership(s): AAP

§American Law Institute
4025 Chestnut St, Philadelphia, PA 19104-3099
SAN: 204-756X
Tel: 215-243-1600 *Toll Free Tel:* 800-253-6397 *Fax:* 215-243-1664
Web Site: www.ali.org
Key Personnel
Pres: Roberta Cooper Ramo
Dir: Richard L Revesz
Deputy Dir: Stephanie Middleton
Founded: 1923
Professional & scholarly legal books & treatises.
ISBN Prefix(es): 978-0-8318
Number of titles published annually: 10 Print

§American Law Institute Continuing Legal Education (ALI CLE)
Affiliate of American Law Institute
4025 Chestnut St, Philadelphia, PA 19104
Tel: 215-243-1600 *Toll Free Tel:* 800-CLE-NEWS (253-6397) *Fax:* 215-243-1664; 215-243-1683
Web Site: www.ali-cle.org
Key Personnel
Dir, ALI: Richard Revesz
Deputy Dir, ALI: Stephanie Middleton
Dir, ALI CLE: Nancy Mulloy-Bonn
Founded: 1947 (as ALI-ABA; reconstituted as ALI CLE in 2012)
Publish law books & legal periodicals.
ISBN Prefix(es): 978-0-8318
Number of titles published annually: 2 Print; 2 Online

The American Library Association (ALA)
50 E Huron St, Chicago, IL 60611
Tel: 312-944-6780 *Toll Free Tel:* 800-545-2433 *Fax:* 312-280-5275
E-mail: editionsmarketing@ala.org
Web Site: www.alastore.ala.org
Key Personnel
Sr Ed, Lib Technol: Patrick Hogan *Tel:* 800-545-2433 ext 3240 *E-mail:* phogan@ala.org
Acqs Ed, Prof Devt & Librarianship: Jamie Santoro *Tel:* 800-545-2433 ext 5107 *E-mail:* jsantoro@ala.org
Acqs Ed, Textbooks: Rachel Chance *Tel:* 800-545-2433 ext 1548 *E-mail:* rchance@ala.org
Mktg Dir: Jill Davis *Tel:* 800-545-2433 ext 5418 *E-mail:* jdavis@ala.org
Mktg Coord: Rob Christopher *Tel:* 800-545-2433 ext 5052 *E-mail:* rchristopher@ala.org
Rts & Perms: Mary Jo Bolduc *Tel:* 312-280-5416 *E-mail:* mbolduc@ala.org
Founded: 1876
Publisher of titles for librarians & educators; library & information science, professional books.
ISBN Prefix(es): 978-0-8389; 978-1-937589
Number of titles published annually: 36 Print; 1 CD-ROM; 1 Online
Total Titles: 400 Print; 2 CD-ROM; 1 Online
Foreign Rep(s): Eurospan (Africa, Europe, Israel, UK)
Foreign Rights: Canadian Library Association (Canada); Inbooks (James Bennett) (Australia)
Orders to: ALA, PO Box 932501, Atlanta, GA 31193-2501 *Toll Free Tel:* 866-SHOP-ALA (746-7252) *Fax:* 770-280-4155 *E-mail:* ala-orders@pbd.com
Returns: ALA Distribution Center, 905 Carlow Dr, Unit B, Bolingbrook, IL 60490
See separate listing for:
Association of College & Research Libraries (ACRL)

American Map Corp
Member of Kappa Map Group
36-36 33 St, 4th fl, Long Island City, NY 11106
SAN: 202-4624
Tel: 718-784-0055 *Toll Free Tel:* 888-774-7979 *Fax:* 718-784-0640 (admin); 718-784-1216 (sales & orders)
E-mail: info@kappamapgroup.com
Web Site: www.kappamapgroup.com
Founded: 1923
Maps & atlases; charts.
ISBN Prefix(es): 978-0-8416
Number of titles published annually: 30 Print
Total Titles: 1 CD-ROM
Imprints: Cleartype American Map Corp; Colorprint American Map Corp
Subsidiaries: ADC the Map People; Arrow Maps Inc; Creative Sales Corp; Hagstrom Map Co Inc; Hammond World Atlas Corp; Trakker Maps Inc
Distributed by Arrow Maps Inc; Creative Sales Corp
Distributor for De Lorme Atlas; Kappa Map Group; RV Guides; Stubs Magazine
Advertising Agency: ATL/SD, 46-35 54 Rd, Maspeth, NY 11378, Contact: Sara Ascalon *Tel:* 718-784-0555 *Fax:* 718-784-0640 *E-mail:* sascalon@americanmap.com
See separate listing for:
Hagstrom Map

§American Marketing Association
311 S Wacker Dr, Suite 5800, Chicago, IL 60606
Tel: 312-542-9000 *Toll Free Tel:* 800-AMA-1150 (262-1150) *Fax:* 312-542-9001
E-mail: info@ama.org
Web Site: www.ama.org
Key Personnel
CEO: Dennis Dunlap *E-mail:* ceo@ama.org
Dir of Publg, Journals: Christopher Bartone *Tel:* 312-542-9029 *E-mail:* cbartone@ama.org
Founded: 1937
One of the largest professional associations for marketers, has members worldwide in every area of marketing. For 7 decades, the AMA has been an essential resource providing relevant marketing information that experienced marketers turn to every day. AMA produces forward-thinking journals catered to marketing professionals & academicians on a variety of topics.
ISBN Prefix(es): 978-0-87757
Number of titles published annually: 9 Print
Total Titles: 60 Print

American Mathematical Society
201 Charles St, Providence, RI 02904-2294
SAN: 201-1654
Tel: 401-455-4000 *Toll Free Tel:* 800-321-4267 *Fax:* 401-331-3842; 401-455-4046 (cust serv)
E-mail: ams@ams.org; cust-serv@ams.org
Web Site: www.ams.org
Key Personnel
Exec Dir: Dr Donald E McClure
Assoc Exec Dir: Dr Robert M Harrington
Assoc Exec Dir, Washington, DC: Samuel M Rankin, III
Publr: Dr Sergei Gelfand
Founded: 1888
Membership society & publisher of mathematics.
ISBN Prefix(es): 978-0-8218; 978-0-8284; 978-1-4704
Number of titles published annually: 100 Print
Total Titles: 3,400 Print; 2 CD-ROM; 28 Online
Imprints: Chelsea Publishing Co Inc
Branch Office(s)
1527 18 St NW, Washington, DC 20036-1358 (govt rels & sci policy) *Tel:* 202-588-1100 *Fax:* 202-588-1853 *E-mail:* amsdc@ams.org
Mathematical Reviews®, 416 Fourth St, Ann Arbor, MI 48103-4820 (edit) *Tel:* 734-996-5250 *Fax:* 734-996-2916 *E-mail:* mathrev@ams.org
Secretary of the AMS - Society Governance, Dept of Computer Science, North Carolina State University, Box 8206, Raleigh, NC 27695-8206 *Tel:* 919-515-7863 *Fax:* 919-515-7896 *E-mail:* secretary@ams.org
Distributor for Annales de la faculte des sciences de Toulouse mathematiques; Bar-Ilan University; Brown University; European Mathematical Society; Hindustan Book Agency; Independent University of Moscow; International Press; Mathematica Josephina; Mathematical Society of Japan; Narosa Publishing House; Ramanujan Mathematical Society; Science Press New York & Science Press Beijing; Societe Mathematique de France; Tata Institute of Fundamental Research; Theta Foundation of Bucharest; University Press; Vieweg Verlag Publications
Foreign Rep(s): Eurospan Australia (Australia, New Zealand, Oceania); Eurospan Group (Africa, Europe, Middle East, Southeast Asia); Hindustan Book Agency (India); IBH Book & Magazines Distributors Pvt Ltd (India); Maruzen Co Ltd (Japan); Neutrino Inc (Japan); Segment Book Distributors (India)
Warehouse: Pawtucket Warehouse, 35 Monticello Place, Pawtucket, RI 02861, Contact: Tom A Freitas *Tel:* 401-729-1440 *Fax:* 401-728-3564 *E-mail:* taf@ams.org
Distribution Center: Pawtucket Warehouse, 35 Monticello Place, Pawtucket, RI 02861, Contact: Tom A Freitas *Tel:* 401-729-1440 *Fax:* 401-728-3564 *E-mail:* taf@ams.org

American Medical Association
AMA Plaza, 330 N Wabash, Suite 39300, Chicago, IL 60611-5885
Tel: 312-464-5000 *Toll Free Tel:* 800-621-8335 *Fax:* 312-464-4184
Web Site: www.ama-assn.org
Key Personnel
CEO & EVP: James L Madara, MD
SVP & Publr, Periodic Pubns: Thomas J Easley *Tel:* 312-464-5000 ext 5740
SVP & Ed-in-Chief, Scientific Pubns: Howard C Bauchner, MD
VP/Exec Mng Ed, Edit Opers: Annette Flanagin
VP & Exec Dir, Scientific Pubns: Phil B Fontanarosa, MD
VP/Deputy Ed, Edit Graphics: Ronna Henry, MD
Founded: 1847
Medical profession.
ISBN Prefix(es): 978-0-89970; 978-1-57947; 978-1-60359; 978-1-62202
Number of titles published annually: 30 Print
Total Titles: 150 Print
Advertising Agency: GSP Marketing Services Inc
Warehouse: Catalog Resources Inc, 100 Enterprise Dr, Dover, DE 19901
Membership(s): AAP

American Numismatic Society
75 Varick St, 11th fl, New York, NY 10013
Tel: 212-571-4470 *Fax:* 212-571-4479
E-mail: ans@numismatics.org; orders@numismatics.org
Web Site: www.numismatics.org
Key Personnel
Exec Dir: Ute Wartenberg Kagan
Ad Ed, ANS Magazine: Joanne Isaac *Tel:* 212-571-4470 ext 112 *E-mail:* isaac@numismatics.org
Founded: 1858
Scholarly materials.
ISBN Prefix(es): 978-0-89722
Number of titles published annually: 5 Print
Total Titles: 100 Print

The American Occupational Therapy Association Inc (AOTA)
4720 Montgomery Lane, Suite 200, Bethesda, MD 20814-3449
Mailing Address: PO Box 31220, Bethesda, MD 20814
Tel: 301-652-6611 *Toll Free Tel:* 800-377-8555 (TDD); 877-404-AOTA (404-2682, orders) *Fax:* 301-652-7711; 770-238-0414 (orders)
E-mail: aotacustomerservice@pbd.com
Web Site: www.aota.org; store.aota.org

Key Personnel
Dir: Chris Davis *Tel:* 301-652-6611 ext 2653
E-mail: cdavis@aota.org
Founded: 1918
Single titles, newsletters, journals & magazines.
ISBN Prefix(es): 978-0-910317; 978-1-56900
Number of titles published annually: 25 Print
Total Titles: 150 Print
Orders to: PO Box 347036, Pittsburgh, PA 15251-4036

American Oil Chemists' Society, see AOCS Press

American Philosophical Society
104 S Fifth St, Philadelphia, PA 19106
SAN: 206-9016
Tel: 215-440-3425 *Fax:* 215-440-3450
E-mail: dianepub@comcast.net
Web Site: www.amphilsoc.org
Key Personnel
Pres: Clyde F Barker
Exec Offr: Keith Thomson
Ed: Mary McDonald *E-mail:* mmcdonald@amphilsoc.org
Founded: 1743
Nonprofit educational institution for promotion of useful knowledge in humanities & sciences.
ISBN Prefix(es): 978-0-87169; 978-1-60618
Number of titles published annually: 13 Print
Total Titles: 1,000 Print
Imprints: Lightning Rod Press; Memoirs; Proceedings; Transactions
Distributed by Diane Publishing Co
Billing Address: Diane Publishing Co, APS Fulfillment, 330 Pusey Ave, Unit 3 (rear), Collingdale, PA 19023 *Tel:* 610-461-6200 *Toll Free Tel:* 800-782-3833 *Fax:* 610-461-6130 *E-mail:* orders@dianepublishing.net
Orders to: Diane Publishing Co, APS Fulfillment, 330 Pusey Ave, Unit 3 (rear), Collingdale, PA 19023 *Tel:* 610-461-6200 *Toll Free Tel:* 800-782-3833 *Fax:* 610-461-6130 *E-mail:* orders@dianepublishing.net
Warehouse: Diane Publishing Co, Contact: Herman Baron *Tel:* 610-461-6200 *Toll Free Tel:* 800-782-3833

American Press
60 State St, Suite 700, Boston, MA 02109
SAN: 210-7007
Tel: 617-247-0022
E-mail: americanpress@flash.net
Web Site: www.americanpresspublishers.com
Key Personnel
Publr: R K Fox
Ed: Marci Taylor
Founded: 1911
College textbooks, study guides, lab manuals & handbooks.
ISBN Prefix(es): 978-0-89641
Number of titles published annually: 20 Print
Total Titles: 300 Print

§American Printing House for the Blind Inc
1839 Frankfort Ave, Louisville, KY 40206
SAN: 203-5235
Mailing Address: PO Box 6085, Louisville, KY 40206-0085
Tel: 502-895-2405 *Toll Free Tel:* 800-223-1839 (cust serv) *Fax:* 502-899-2274
E-mail: info@aph.org
Web Site: www.aph.org; shop.aph.org
Key Personnel
Pres: Tuck Tinsley, III *E-mail:* ttinsley@aph.org
VP, Pub Aff: Gary Mudd *E-mail:* gmudd@aph.org
PR Mgr: Roberta Williams *Tel:* 502-899-2357
E-mail: rwilliams@aph.org
Founded: 1858
Literature & aids for people who are visually impaired: braille text books, magazines & other items, large-type textbooks, talking books & magazines, educational & miscellaneous aids, talking PC hardware & software. Publisher of braille & reprints in braille.
ISBN Prefix(es): 978-1-61648
Number of titles published annually: 4,500 Print
Total Titles: 6,300 Print

American Products Publishing Co
Division of American Products Corp
8260 SW Nimbus Ave, Beaverton, OR 97008
Tel: 503-672-7502 *Toll Free Tel:* 800-668-8181 *Fax:* 503-672-7104
E-mail: info@american-products.com
Web Site: www.american-products.com
Key Personnel
Pres: Robert Shangle
VP: Barbara Shangle *E-mail:* barbara@american-products.com
Sales Mgr: David Mulder
Publisher of scenic books & wall calendars for the individual US states, American historic documents, books & prints.
ISBN Prefix(es): 978-1-58583; 978-1-884958; 978-1-55988
Number of titles published annually: 16 Print; 72 Online
Total Titles: 72 Print; 72 Online
Membership(s): ABA

§American Psychiatric Publishing (APP)
Division of American Psychiatric Association (APA)
1000 Wilson Blvd, Suite 1825, Arlington, VA 22209
SAN: 293-2288
Tel: 703-907-7322 *Toll Free Tel:* 800-368-5777 *Fax:* 703-907-1091
E-mail: appi@psych.org
Web Site: www.appi.org; www.psychiatryonline.org
Key Personnel
Publr: Rebecca D Rinehart *E-mail:* rrinehart@psych.org
Dir, Fin & Busn Opers: Peter Van Woerden
Dir, Sales & Mktg: Patrick Hansard
E-mail: phansard@psych.org
Edit Dir: John McDuffie *Tel:* 703-907-7871
E-mail: jmcduffie@psych.org
Edit Dir, American Journal of Psychiatry: Michael Roy
Ed-in-Chief, Books: Robert E Hales, MD
Mng Ed, Books: Greg Kuny
Opers Mgr: Debra Eubanks
Founded: 1981
Professional, reference & general trade books, college textbooks; behavioral & social sciences, psychiatry, medicine.
ISBN Prefix(es): 978-0-88048; 978-0-89042; 978-0-87318; 978-1-58562; 978-1-61537
Number of titles published annually: 30 Print; 40 Online; 30 E-Book
Total Titles: 750 Print; 3 CD-ROM; 300 Online; 300 E-Book; 1 Audio
Imprints: American Psychiatric Association (APA); American Psychiatric Publishing (APP)
Distributor for American Psychiatric Association (APA); Group for the Advancement of Psychiatry
Foreign Rep(s): Cranberry International (Latin America); Footprint Books Pty Ltd (Australia, New Zealand); iGroup (China, East Asia, India); International Publishers Representatives (Middle East); Login Brothers (Canada); Nankodo (Japan); NBN International (Europe, UK); Oxford University Press (Southern Africa)
Foreign Rights: John Scott Agency
Warehouse: Ware-Pak, 2427 Bond St, University Park, IL 60484-3170
Membership(s): AAP; American Association of University Presses

American Psychological Association
750 First St NE, Washington, DC 20002-4242
Tel: 202-336-5510 *Toll Free Tel:* 800-374-2721 *Fax:* 202-336-5502
E-mail: order@apa.org
Web Site: www.apa.org/books
Key Personnel
Publr: Jasper Simons
Exec Dir, Sci Directorate: Steven J Breckler, PhD *Tel:* 202-336-5938 *E-mail:* sbreckler@apa.org
Exec Dir, Public & Memb Communs: Rhea K Farberman *Tel:* 202-336-5709
E-mail: rfarberman@apa.org
Founded: 1892
Publish scholarly & professional works including books, journals & related materials; the PsycINFO® database & products derived from that database; the *APA Monitor*, a monthly magazine & a variety of other products including brochures & reports.
ISBN Prefix(es): 978-0-912704; 978-1-55798; 978-0-945354; 978-0-9792125; 978-1-59147; 978-1-4338
Number of titles published annually: 65 Print
Total Titles: 700 Print
Imprints: APA Books®
Warehouse: APA Order Dept, PO Box 92984, Washington, DC 20090-2984

American Public Works Association (APWA)
2345 Grand Blvd, Suite 700, Kansas City, MO 64108-2625
Tel: 816-472-6100 *Toll Free Tel:* 800-848-APWA (848-2792) *Fax:* 816-472-1610
Web Site: www.apwa.net
Key Personnel
Pubns Mgr: Connie Hartline *Tel:* 816-595-5258
E-mail: chartline@apwa.net
Ed, APWA Reporter: Kevin Clark *Tel:* 816-595-5230 *E-mail:* kclark@apwa.net
Founded: 1894
Public work related publications. Also publishes *APWA Reporter* magazine.
ISBN Prefix(es): 978-0-917084; 978-1-60675
Number of titles published annually: 12 Print
Total Titles: 12 Print
Branch Office(s)
1275 "K" St NW, Suite 750, Washington, DC 20005 *Tel:* 202-408-9541 *Fax:* 202-408-9542

American Quilter's Society
5801 Kentucky Dam Rd, Paducah, KY 42003-9323
Mailing Address: PO Box 3290, Paducah, KY 42002-3290
Tel: 270-898-7903 *Toll Free Tel:* 800-626-5420 (orders) *Fax:* 270-898-1173
E-mail: orders@americanquilter.com
Web Site: www.americanquilter.com
Key Personnel
Co-Founder & Pres: Meredith Schroeder
Mktg Dir: Katherine Rupp
Founded: 1983
Publish books & magazines, distributes books & operates quilting shows.
ISBN Prefix(es): 978-0-89145; 978-1-57432; 978-1-60460
Number of titles published annually: 20 Print; 10 CD-ROM; 4 E-Book
Total Titles: 300 Print; 20 CD-ROM; 7 E-Book
Imprints: AQS

American Society for Nondestructive Testing
1711 Arlingate Lane, Columbus, OH 43228-0518
Mailing Address: PO Box 28518, Columbus, OH 43228-0518
Tel: 614-274-6003 *Toll Free Tel:* 800-222-2768 *Fax:* 614-274-6899
Web Site: www.asnt.org
Key Personnel
Sr Mgr, Pubns: Tim Jones *Tel:* 614-274-6003 ext 204 *E-mail:* tjones@asnt.org
Founded: 1941

Nonprofit association producing educational materials for members & nonmembers engaged in nondestructive testing.
ISBN Prefix(es): 978-0-931403; 978-1-57117
Number of titles published annually: 12 Print; 6 CD-ROM
Total Titles: 250 Print; 6 CD-ROM
Distributed by American Ceramic Society (ACerS); American Society for Mechanical Engineers (ASME); American Society for Metals (ASM); The American Welding Society (AWS); ASTM; Edison Welding Institute; Mean Free Path

§American Society for Quality (ASQ)
600 N Plankinton Ave, Milwaukee, WI 53203
Mailing Address: PO Box 3005, Milwaukee, WI 53201-3005
Tel: 414-272-8575 *Toll Free Tel:* 800-248-1946 (US & CN); 800-514-1564 (Mexico) *Fax:* 414-272-1734
E-mail: help@asq.org
Web Site: www.asq.org
Key Personnel
Acq Ed: Matt Meinholz
Proj Ed: Paul O'Mara
Communs Mgr: Michael Berry
Founded: 1983
Publisher of technical books: quality, statistical process control, ISO9000, six sigma, QS9000, ISO14000, statistics, reliability, auditing, sampling, standards' supplier quality & quality costs. Also management topics: total quality management, human resources & teamwork, health care, government, education & benchmarking, quality tools.
ISBN Prefix(es): 978-0-87389
Number of titles published annually: 25 Print; 5 E-Book
Total Titles: 300 Print; 5 CD-ROM; 15 E-Book
Distributed by GOAL/QPC; IEEE Computer Society Press; McGraw-Hill Professional Publishing; Productivity Press
Distribution Center: PBD, 905 Carlow Dr, Unit B, Bolingbrook, WI 60490

American Society for Training & Development (ASTD), see Association for Talent Development (ATD)

§American Society of Agricultural & Biological Engineers (ASABE)
2950 Niles Rd, St Joseph, MI 49085-9659
Tel: 269-429-0300 *Toll Free Tel:* 800-371-2723 *Fax:* 269-429-3852
E-mail: hq@asabe.org
Web Site: www.asabe.org
Key Personnel
Exec Dir: Darrin Drollinger *Tel:* 269-932-7007 *E-mail:* drollinger@asabe.org
Dir, Pubns: Joe Walker *Tel:* 269-932-7026 *E-mail:* walker@asabe.org
Book & Journal Ed: Peg McCann *Tel:* 269-932-7019 *E-mail:* mccann@asabe.org
Journal Ed: Glenn Laing *Tel:* 269-932-7014 *E-mail:* laing@asabe.org; Melissa Miller *Tel:* 269-932-7017 *E-mail:* miller@asabe.org
Pubns Asst: Sandy Rutter *Tel:* 269-932-7004 *E-mail:* rutter@asabe.org
Founded: 1907
Agricultural, biological & food systems, books & journals.
ISBN Prefix(es): 978-0-916150; 978-0-929355; 978-1-892769
Number of titles published annually: 4 Print
Total Titles: 150 Print; 1 CD-ROM; 2 Online

American Society of Agronomy
5585 Guilford Rd, Madison, WI 53711-1086
Tel: 608-273-8080 *Fax:* 608-273-2021
E-mail: headquarters@sciencesocieties.org
Web Site: www.agronomy.org
Key Personnel
CEO: Ellen Bergfeld *Tel:* 608-268-4979 *E-mail:* ebergfeld@sciencesocieties.org
Dir, Pubns: Mark Mandelbaum *Tel:* 608-268-4974 *E-mail:* mmandelbaum@sciencesocieties.org
Founded: 1907
Technical books for professionals in agronomy; crop science, soil science, environmental sciences & related fields.
ISBN Prefix(es): 978-0-89118
Number of titles published annually: 12 Print
Total Titles: 90 Print

§American Society of Civil Engineers (ASCE)
1801 Alexander Bell Dr, Reston, VA 20191-4400
SAN: 204-7594
Tel: 703-295-6300 *Toll Free Tel:* 800-548-2723 *Fax:* 703-295-6278
E-mail: marketing@asce.org
Web Site: www.asce.org
Key Personnel
Mng Dir, Pubns: Bruce Gossett *Tel:* 703-295-6311 *E-mail:* bgossett@asce.org
Dir, Busn Opers: Gina Lindquist *E-mail:* glindquist@asce.org
Dir, Journals: Angela Cochran *Tel:* 703-295-6242
Dir, Mktg: William Nara *E-mail:* wnara@asce.org
Dir, Prodn: Matt Boyle *Tel:* 703-295-6241 *E-mail:* mboyle@asce.org
Dir, Publg Technol: Charlotte McNaughton *E-mail:* cmcnaughton@asce.org
Founded: 1852
Books, technical journals, information products on civil engineering & related fields; online & print.
ISBN Prefix(es): 978-0-87262; 978-0-7844
Number of titles published annually: 70 Print; 70 E-Book
Total Titles: 1,394 Print; 350 E-Book
Imprints: ASCE Press
Foreign Rep(s): Aditya Books (P) Ltd (India); Apex Knowledge Sdn Bhd (Brunei, Malaysia); Areesh Education & Trading Sdn Bhd (Zabedah Ahmad) (Brunei, Malaysia); Booknet Co Ltd (Suphaluck Sattabuz) (Cambodia, Laos, Myanmar, Thailand, Vietnam); ChoiceTEXTS (Asia) Pte Ltd (Philip Ang) (Indonesia, Singapore); Eurospan Group (Africa, Continental Europe, Middle East, UK); ICaves Ltd (Eddy Lam) (Hong Kong); IDC Asia (iGroup Korea) (D J Kim) (Korea); iGroup Press Co Ltd (Frank Wang) (China); MegaTEXTS Phil Inc (Jean Tiu Lim) (Philippines); Shankar's Book Agency Pvt Ltd (India); Taiwan Publishers Marketing Services Ltd (George Liu) (Taiwan)

American Society of Electroneurodiagnostic Technologists Inc, see ASET - The Neurodiagnostic Society

§American Society of Health-System Pharmacists (ASHP)
7272 Wisconsin Ave, Bethesda, MD 20814
Tel: 301-657-3000; 301-664-8700 *Toll Free Tel:* 866-279-0681 (orders) *Fax:* 301-657-1251 (orders)
E-mail: custserv@ashp.org
Web Site: www.ashp.org
Key Personnel
VP, Sales & Mktg: Dean Menke
Founded: 1943
Medical scholarly books.
ISBN Prefix(es): 978-0-930530; 978-1-879907; 978-1-58528
Number of titles published annually: 20 Print
Total Titles: 115 Print
Foreign Rep(s): APAC (Asia); L Horvath (Eastern Europe); LPR (Middle East); LR International (Brazil); R Seshadri (India)
Advertising Agency: Cunningham Associates, 180 Old Tappan Rd, Old Tappan, NJ 07675, Contact: Jim Pattis *Tel:* 201-767-4170 *E-mail:* jpattis@cunnasso.com

§American Society of Mechanical Engineers (ASME)
2 Park Ave, New York, NY 10016-5990
SAN: 201-1379
Tel: 212-591-7000 *Toll Free Tel:* 800-843-2763 (cust serv-US, CN & Mexico) *Fax:* 212-591-7674; 973-882-8113 (cust serv); 973-882-1717 (orders & inquiries)
E-mail: infocentral@asme.org
Web Site: www.asme.org
Key Personnel
Exec Dir: Thomas G Loughlin *E-mail:* execdirector@asme.org
Mng Dir, Mktg & Online Servs: Peter Hess
Mng Dir, Publg: Philip DiVietro *Tel:* 212-591-7696 *Fax:* 212-591-7292 *E-mail:* divietrop@asme.org
Dir, Media Sales & Publg Devt: Nick Ferrari *E-mail:* ferrarin@asme.org
Ad Promo Mgr: Anthony Asiaghi *Tel:* 212-591-7345 *Fax:* 212-591-7841 *E-mail:* asiaghia@asme.org
Mgr, Corp Devt: Paul Francis *Tel:* 973-244-2304 *E-mail:* francisp@asme.org
Mktg & Quality Assurance: John Yelavich *E-mail:* yelavichj@asme.org
Founded: 1880
Publisher of codes & standards, journals, conference proceedings, professional references, *Mechanical Engineering* magazine, technical papers & reports.
ISBN Prefix(es): 978-0-7918
Number of titles published annually: 185 Print
Total Titles: 1,500 Print
Imprints: ASME Press
Branch Office(s)
1828 "L" St NW, Suite 810, Washington, DC 20036-5104 *Tel:* 202-785-3756 *Fax:* 202-429-9417 *E-mail:* grdept@asme.org
Warehouse: 150 Clove Rd, Little Falls, NJ 07424-2100 *Tel:* 973-882-1170

American Society of Plant Taxonomists
University of Wyoming, Dept of Botany 3165, 1000 E University Ave, Laramie, WY 82071
SAN: 282-969X
Tel: 307-766-2556 *Fax:* 307-766-2851
E-mail: aspt@uwyo.edu
Web Site: www.aspt.net
Key Personnel
Contact: Linda Brown
Founded: 1980
Botanical monographs.
ISBN Prefix(es): 978-0-912861
Number of titles published annually: 3 Print
Total Titles: 96 Print

American Technical Publishers Inc
10100 Orland Pkwy, Suite 200, Orland Park, IL 60467-5756
SAN: 206-8141
Toll Free Tel: 800-323-3471 *Fax:* 708-957-1101
E-mail: service@atplearning.com; order@atplearning.com
Web Site: www.atplearning.com
Key Personnel
Pres: Robert D Deisinger *E-mail:* robert.deisinger@atplearning.com
SVP: J David Holloway *E-mail:* david.holloway@atplearning.com
Ed-in-Chief: Jonathan F Gosse *E-mail:* jonathan.gosse@atplearning.com
Founded: 1898
Technical, industrial & vocational textbooks, reference books & related materials.
ISBN Prefix(es): 978-0-8269
Number of titles published annually: 8 Print; 2 CD-ROM; 25 Online; 3 E-Book
Total Titles: 200 Print; 10 CD-ROM; 25 Online; 3 E-Book
Distributor for Craftsman Book Co

Orders to: Nelson Publishing, 1120 Birchmount Rd, Toronto, ON M1K 5G4, Canada (CN school orders) *Tel:* 416-752-9448 *Toll Free Tel:* 800-268-2222
Returns: 1155 W 175 St, Homewood, IL 60430, Contact: Gail Prohaska *E-mail:* gail.prohaska@atplearning.com

American Traveler Press, see Golden West Cookbooks

§American Water Works Association (AWWA)
6666 W Quincy Ave, Denver, CO 80235
Tel: 303-794-7711 *Toll Free Tel:* 800-926-7337 *Fax:* 303-347-0804
Web Site: www.awwa.org
Key Personnel
Deputy Exec Dir: Paula MacIlwaine *Tel:* 303-347-6135 *Fax:* 303-795-1440 *E-mail:* pmacilwa@awwa.org
Dir, Publg: Liz Haigh *Tel:* 303-347-6268 *E-mail:* lhaigh@awwa.org
Founded: 1881
Water works technology & management.
ISBN Prefix(es): 978-0-89867; 978-1-58321; 978-1-61300; 978-1-62576
Number of titles published annually: 50 Print
Total Titles: 500 Print; 12 CD-ROM; 2 Online
Imprints: AWWA
Distributor for CRC Press; McGraw-Hill; John Wiley & Sons
Foreign Rep(s): Australian Water Association (Australia); Canadian Water & Wastewater Association (Canada)
Membership(s): Association Media & Publishing; Publishers Association of the West

§Amherst Media Inc
175 Rano St, Suite 200, Buffalo, NY 14207
Tel: 716-874-4450 *Toll Free Tel:* 800-622-3278 *Fax:* 716-874-4508
E-mail: marketing@amherstmedia.com
Web Site: www.amherstmedia.com
Key Personnel
Publr: Craig Alesse
Assoc Publr: Kate Neaverth *E-mail:* kneaverth@amherstmedia.com
Founded: 1979
Publish how-to photography books.
ISBN Prefix(es): 978-0-936262; 978-1-58428
Number of titles published annually: 24 Print; 24 E-Book
Total Titles: 300 Print; 300 E-Book
Distributor for Firefly

Amicus
PO Box 1329, Mankato, MN 56002
Tel: 507-388-9357 *Fax:* 507-388-1779
E-mail: info@amicuspublishing.us; orders@amicuspublishing.us
Web Site: www.amicuspublishing.us
Key Personnel
Publr: Rebecca Glaser *E-mail:* rglaser@amicuspublishing.us
Dir, Opers: Cathy Stuve *E-mail:* cstuve@amicuspublishing.us
Sales Mgr: Dave Schlichte
Founded: 2010
Promotes the wonder, diversity & challenges of the modern world. From our line for grades K-2 to career advice & healthy living for middle school & everything in between, you'll find library-bound books that not only inform but also move readers past passive reading into critical thinking & deeper understanding.
ISBN Prefix(es): 978-1-60753
Number of titles published annually: 150 Print
Total Titles: 450 Print

AMMO Books LLC
1313 Foothill Blvd, La Canada, CA 91011
Mailing Address: PO Box 412402, Los Angeles, CA 90041
Tel: 323-223-AMMO (223-2666) *Fax:* 323-978-4200
E-mail: weborders@ammobooks.com; orders@ammobooks.com
Web Site: ammobooks.com
Key Personnel
Co-Founder & Pres: Paul Norton *E-mail:* paul@ammobooks.com
Publr: Steve Crist
Founded: 2006
Provocative, one-of-a-kind titles that highlight the best of the visual arts & pop culture.
ISBN Prefix(es): 978-0-9786076; 978-1-934429; 978-1-62326
Number of titles published annually: 50 Print

§Ampersand Inc/Professional Publishing Services
1050 N State St, Chicago, IL 60610
Tel: 312-280-8905 *Fax:* 312-944-1582
E-mail: info@ampersandworks.com
Web Site: www.ampersandworks.com
Key Personnel
Pres & Publr: Suzanne Talbot Isaacs *E-mail:* suzie@ampersandworks.com
Founded: 1995 (began publishing books as well as consulting in Fall 2005)
Private publisher. Work is highly customized, tailored to the author's specific objectives & developed by professionals with over 30 years of publishing experience. Able to publish from ms to finished book in a matter of weeks, on time & on budget. Also supports marketing efforts, warehouse & distributes authors' books.
This publisher has indicated that 90% of their product line is author subsidized.
ISBN Prefix(es): 978-1-4507; 978-0-9818126; 978-0-9761235; 978-0-873671; 978-1-4675; 978-0-9962525
Number of titles published annually: 10 Print; 5 E-Book
Total Titles: 47 Print; 17 E-Book
Branch Office(s)
203 Finland Place, New Orleans, LA 70131
Membership(s): Association of Independent Authors; The Association of Publishers for Special Sales; The Independent Book Publishers Association; Society of Children's Book Writers & Illustrators

AMS Press Inc
Brooklyn Navy Yard, 63 Flushing Ave, Unit 221, Brooklyn, NY 11205-1005
SAN: 201-1743
Tel: 718-875-8100 *Fax:* 718-875-3800
E-mail: editorial@amspressinc.com; orders@amspressinc.com
Web Site: www.amspressinc.com
Key Personnel
Pres: Gabriel Hornstein
Founded: 1962
Original publications & reprint editions of scholarly books & periodicals; reference works.
ISBN Prefix(es): 978-0-404
Number of titles published annually: 65 Print
Total Titles: 6,500 Print

Anaphora Literary Press
1803 Tree Hill Pkwy, Stone Mountain, GA 30088
Tel: 470-289-6395
Web Site: anaphoraliterary.com
Key Personnel
Dir: Dr Anna Faktorovich *E-mail:* director@anaphoraliterary.com
Founded: 2009
Publishes paperback & hardcover originals of creative poetry, short stories, novels & novellas & nonfiction books: critical, academic & business. Writers who are employed in the academia are especially encouraged to e-mail submissions. Offers a 50/50% split on profits, a 25-50% discount on the cover price to authors & a 55% discount to book stores & distributors. Please e-mail submissions only. Do not send submissions through the mail. Some marketing is provided, but assistance with marketing from writers is strongly encouraged. Submissions are primarily evaluated on writing quality.
ISBN Prefix(es): 978-1-937536; 978-1-68114
Number of titles published annually: 40 Print; 40 Online; 40 E-Book
Total Titles: 120 Print; 80 Online; 80 E-Book
Distribution Center: Coutts Information Services Ltd, 3 Ingram Blvd, La Vergne, TN 37086 SAN: 169-5401
Lightning Source, 1246 Heil Quaker Blvd, La Vergne, TN 37086
Membership(s): Community of Literary Magazines & Presses; Independent Book Publishing Professionals Group; MLA

Anchor Group Publishing
PO Box 551, Flushing, MI 48433
E-mail: anchorgrouppublishing@gmail.com
Web Site: anchorgrouppublishing.com
Key Personnel
Owner & CEO: Stacey Rourke
Founded: 2012
Independently owned, traditional publisher of quality literary works meant to engage & inspire readers.
ISBN Prefix(es): 978-0-9852663; 978-0-9855385; 978-0-9886334; 978-0-9882707; 978-0-9888476; 978-0-9891753; 978-0-9897073; 978-0-9915174
Number of titles published annually: 15 Print; 15 Online; 15 E-Book
Total Titles: 30 Print; 30 Online; 30 E-Book
Membership(s): The Independent Book Publishers Association

Ancient Faith Publishing
Formerly Conciliar Press
Division of Ancient Faith Ministries
2747 Bond St, University Park, IL 60484
Mailing Address: PO Box 748, Chesterton, IN 46304
Tel: 219-728-2216 *Toll Free Tel:* 800-967-7377 *Toll Free Fax:* 866-599-5208
E-mail: info@ancientfaith.com; orders@ancientfaith.com
Web Site: www.ancientfaith.com/publishing
Key Personnel
CEO: John Maddex *E-mail:* jmaddex@ancientfaith.com
Edit Dir: Katherine Hyde *E-mail:* khyde@ancientfaith.com
Mktg Dir: Matthew Dorning *E-mail:* mdorning@consiliarmedia.com
Prodn Mgr: Carla Zell *E-mail:* czell@ancientfaith.com
Founded: 1978
Books, booklets, brochures, greeting cards, icons, liturgical & quarterly magazines.
ISBN Prefix(es): 978-0-9622713; 978-0-888212; 978-0-9822770; 978-1-936270
Number of titles published annually: 12 Print
Total Titles: 120 Print
Distributed by Light & Life; St Vladimir's
Distributor for Light & Life
Foreign Rights: Rainbow Books (Australia)

Sara Anderson Children's Books
PO Box 47182, Seattle, WA 98146
Tel: 206-285-1520
Web Site: www.saranderson.com
Key Personnel
Founder & CEO: Sara Anderson *E-mail:* sara@saranderson.com
Founded: 2008
Specialize in colorful, innovatively designed early-concept books for babies & toddlers,

picture books & a line of bilingual (Spanish-English) children's books.
ISBN Prefix(es): 978-0-9702784; 978-0-9911933; 978-1-943459
Number of titles published annually: 5 Print
Total Titles: 18 Print

§Andrews McMeel Publishing LLC
Division of Andrews McMeel Universal
1130 Walnut St, Kansas City, MO 64106-2109
Toll Free Tel: 800-851-8923; 800-943-9839 (cust serv) *Toll Free Fax:* 800-943-9831 (orders)
Web Site: www.andrewsmcmeel.com
Key Personnel
Chmn: John P McMeel
VChmn: Hugh Andrews
CEO & Pres: Andy Sareyan
Pres, Book Div: Kirsty Melville
SVP: Linda Jones
VP & Ed Dir, Calendar Div & Prod Devt Group: Michael Nonbello
VP, Content & Exec Prodr, Book Div: Andrea Colvin
VP, Mktg-Book Div: Kathy Hilliard
Founded: 1973
Publish calendars & humor.
ISBN Prefix(es): 978-0-8362; 978-88-7407; 978-1-4494
Number of titles published annually: 300 Print
Imprints: Accord Publishing; Udig (ebooks)
Distributor for Gooseberry Patch (North America); Signatures Network; Sporting News; Universe Publishing Calendars; Vegan Heritage Press
Foreign Rights: Agenzia Letteraria Internazionale (Italy); Big Apple Agency Inc (China, Taiwan); The Book Publishers' Association of Israel, International Promotion & Literary Rights Department (Israel); DS Druck und Verlag (Eastern Europe); Europa Press (Scandinavia); Gamma Medya Agency (Turkey); Agence Hoffman (Germany); Japan UNI Agency Inc (Japan); JLM Literary Agents (Greece); Korea Copyright Center Inc (KCC) (Korea); Andrew Nurnberg Associates Ltd (Bulgaria); Abner Stein Agency (Australia, UK); Tuttle-Mori Agency Inc (Thailand); VVV Agency (France); Julio F Yanez Agencia Literaria SL (Brazil, Latin America, Portugal, Spain)
Orders to: c/o Simon & Schuster Inc, 100 Front St, Riverside, NJ 08075 *Toll Free Tel:* 800-943-9839 (US orders); 800-268-3216 (CN orders)
Returns: Simon & Schuster, c/o Jacobson Logistics, 4406 Industrial Park Rd, Bldg 7, Camp Hill, PA 17011; c/o Georgetown Terminal Warehouses, 34 B Armstrong Ave, Georgetown, ON L7G 4R9, Canada
Distribution Center: Simon & Schuster, Inc, 100 Front St, Riverside, NJ 08075 *Toll Free Tel:* 800-943-9839 (US orders); 800-268-3216 (CN orders)

Andrews University Press
Division of Andrews University
Sutherland House, 8360 W Campus Circle Dr, Berrien Springs, MI 49104-1700
SAN: 241-0958
Tel: 269-471-6915; 269-471-6134 (orders) *Toll Free Tel:* 800-467-6369 (Visa, MC & American Express orders only) *Fax:* 269-471-6224
E-mail: aupo@andrews.edu
Web Site: www.universitypress.andrews.edu
Key Personnel
Dir: Ronald Knott
Assoc Dir: Erno Gyeresi
Ed: Deborah L Everhart
Selected areas of theology, education, philosophy, science, faith & learning.
ISBN Prefix(es): 978-0-943872; 978-1-883925; 978-1-936337; 978-1-940980
Number of titles published annually: 7 Print
Total Titles: 100 Print; 1 CD-ROM; 1 Online

Angel City Press
2118 Wilshire Blvd, Suite 880, Santa Monica, CA 90403
Tel: 310-395-9982 *Toll Free Tel:* 800-949-8039 *Fax:* 310-395-3353
E-mail: info@angelcitypress.com
Web Site: www.angelcitypress.com
Key Personnel
CEO & Publr: Paddy Calistro
Publr & Treas: Scott McAuley
Founded: 1993
Publish books on California & Southern California social & cultural history.
ISBN Prefix(es): 978-1-883318; 978-1-62640
Number of titles published annually: 8 Print
Total Titles: 100 Print
Distributor for Los Angeles Times Books
Foreign Rep(s): Turnaround Publishing Services (London)

§Angelus Press
2915 Forest Ave, Kansas City, MO 64109
Mailing Address: PO Box 217, St Marys, KS 66536
Tel: 816-753-3150 *Toll Free Tel:* 800-966-7337 *Fax:* 816-753-3557
E-mail: support@angeluspress.org
Web Site: www.angeluspress.org
Key Personnel
Ed: James Vogel
Founded: 1978
Monthly journal of Catholic Tradition; traditional Roman Catholic books.
ISBN Prefix(es): 978-0-935952; 978-1-892331; 978-1-937843
Number of titles published annually: 10 Print
Total Titles: 100 Print
Distributed by Catholic Treasures; Fatima Crusader

Anhinga Press
PO Box 3665, Tallahassee, FL 32315
Tel: 850-577-0745
E-mail: info@anhinga.org
Web Site: www.anhinga.org; www.facebook.com/anhingapress
Key Personnel
Dir: Kristine Snodgrass *E-mail:* kristine.snodgrass@gmail.com
Founded: 1972
ISBN Prefix(es): 978-0-938078; 978-1-934695
Number of titles published annually: 8 Print
Total Titles: 70 Print
Distribution Center: SPD/Small Press Distribution Inc, 1341 Seventh St, Berkeley, CA 94710-1409 *Tel:* 510-524-1668 *Toll Free Tel:* 800-869-7553 *E-mail:* spd@spdbooks.org *Web Site:* www.spdbooks.org

Animal Media Group LLC
Subsidiary of Animal Inc
100 First Ave, Suite 1100, Pittsburgh, PA 15222-1519
Tel: 412-566-5656 *Fax:* 412-566-5656
E-mail: info@animalmediagroup.com
Web Site: www.animalmediagroup.com
Key Personnel
Dir: Howard Shapiro
Founded: 2012
ISBN Prefix(es): 978-0-9912550
Number of titles published annually: 4 Print; 4 Online; 4 E-Book; 1 Audio
Total Titles: 6 Print; 4 Online; 4 E-Book; 1 Audio
Foreign Rights: Lotus Lane Literary LLC (Priya Doraswamy)
Distribution Center: Brodart Inc, 500 Arch St, Williamsport, PA 17701-7809, Contact: Amanda Anderson
Follett School Solutions Inc, 1340 Ridgeview Dr, McHenry, IL 60050, Prog Mktg Mgr: Gina Sciore

Annual Reviews
4139 El Camino Way, Palo Alto, CA 94306
SAN: 201-1816
Mailing Address: PO Box 10139, Palo Alto, CA 94303-0139
Tel: 650-493-4400 *Toll Free Tel:* 800-523-8635 *Fax:* 650-424-0910; 650-855-9815
E-mail: service@annualreviews.org
Web Site: www.annualreviews.org
Key Personnel
Pres & Ed-in-Chief: Samuel Gubins *E-mail:* sgubins@annualreviews.org
CFO & Dir, Sales & Mktg: Steve Castro *E-mail:* scastro@annualreviews.org
Dir, HR: Lisa Wucher *E-mail:* lwucher@annualreviews.org
Dir, Prodn: Jennifer Jongsma *E-mail:* jjongsma@annualreviews.org
Dir, Technol: Paul Calvi *E-mail:* pcalvi@annualreviews.org
Mktg Mgr: Gabrielle Peterson *E-mail:* gpeterson@annualreviews.org
Mktg Specialist: Jenni Rankin *E-mail:* jrankin@annualreviews.org
Founded: 1932
Scientific review literature, in print & online, in the biomedical, life, physical & social sciences.
ISBN Prefix(es): 978-0-8243
Number of titles published annually: 40 Print; 40 Online
Foreign Rep(s): Gazelle Book Services Ltd (Africa, Continental Europe, Ireland, Middle East, UK); SARAS Books (Bangladesh, India, Pakistan, Sri Lanka)
Returns: National Distribution Services, 6118 Kingsport Hwy, Gray, TN 37615 (return authorization required)
Membership(s): ALA; International Federation of Library Associations & Institutions; Medical Library Association; National Federation of Advanced Information Services; SLA; Society for Scholarly Publishing; STM

§ANR Publications University of California
Division of Agriculture & Natural Resources, University of California
1301 S 46 St, Bldg 478 - MC 3580, Richmond, CA 94804
Mailing Address: 2801 Second St, Davis, CA 95618
Tel: 510-665-2195 (cust serv) *Toll Free Tel:* 800-994-8849 *Fax:* 510-665-3427
E-mail: anrcatalog@ucdavis.edu
Web Site: anrcatalog.ucanr.edu
Key Personnel
Pubns Mgr: Ann Senuta *Tel:* 530-750-1224 *E-mail:* aesenuta@ucanr.edu
Mktg Dir & Foreign Rts: Cynthia Kintigh *Tel:* 530-750-1217 *E-mail:* cckintigh@ucanr.edu
Fulfillment Mgr: Jon Mercy *Tel:* 510-665-2161 *E-mail:* jrmercy@ucanr.edu
Cust Serv: Mary Allen-Crowley *Tel:* 510-665-2162
Peer reviewed publications on agriculture, gardening, integrated pest management, nutrition, childhood obesity & natural resources.
ISBN Prefix(es): 978-0-931876; 978-1-879906; 978-1-60107
Number of titles published annually: 16 Print; 2 CD-ROM; 30 Online; 5 E-Book
Total Titles: 850 Print; 15 CD-ROM; 500 Online; 5 E-Book
Membership(s): Publishers Association of the West

Antique Collectors' Club Ltd
Division of Antique Collectors Club Ltd (England)
116 Pleasant St, Suite 18, East Hampton, MA 01027

Tel: 413-529-0861 *Toll Free Tel:* 800-252-5231 *Fax:* 413-529-0862
E-mail: sales@antiquecc.com
Web Site: www.antiquecollectorsclub.com; www.accdistribution.com
Key Personnel
Div Dir & Intl Rts: John Boncottie
Founded: 1966
Books on fine & decorative arts, gardening, architecture & antiques, multicultural.
ISBN Prefix(es): 978-1-85149; 978-0-907462; 978-0-902028
Number of titles published annually: 300 Print
Total Titles: 1,500 Print
Imprints: ACC Editions; Garden Art Press
Divisions: ACC Distribution
Foreign Office(s): Sandy Lane, Old Martlesham, Woodbridge, Suffolk 1P12 4SD, United Kingdom *Tel:* (01394) 389950 *Fax:* (01394) 389999 *E-mail:* sales@antique-acc.com
Foreign Rep(s): Jenny Gosling (Belgium, London, Luxembourg, Netherlands); Lilian Koe (Malaysia); Clive & Moira Malins (Northeast England, Scotland); Michael Morris (Middle East, Near East); Penny Padovani (Italy, Portugal, Spain); David Pearson (France); Ian Pringle (Brunei, Indonesia, Singapore, Thailand); Ed Summerson (China, Hong Kong, Philippines, South Korea, Taiwan); Ralph & Sheila Sumners (Japan); Robert Towers (Ireland, Northern Ireland)

Antique Trader
Imprint of Krause Publications Inc
c/o Krause Publications, 700 E State St, Iola, WI 54990-0001
Tel: 715-445-2214 *Toll Free Tel:* 888-457-2873 *Fax:* 715-445-4087
Web Site: www.krausebooks.com
Founded: 1952
Collectibles, books, magazines, trades & crafts.
ISBN Prefix(es): 978-0-930625; 978-1-58221; 978-1-4402
Number of titles published annually: 20 Print
Total Titles: 200 Print

Antrim House
21 Goodrich Rd, Simsbury, CT 06070-1804
Tel: 860-217-0023
E-mail: eds@antrimhousebooks.com
Web Site: www.antrimhousebooks.com
Key Personnel
Publr & Ed: Robert Rennie McQuilkin
Founded: 1990
Publish cloth bound editions, perfect bound paperbacks & saddle stitched chapbooks by poets & memoirists. Also a limited number of art books. On occasion, issue CDs by these poets.
This publisher has indicated that 100% of their product line is author subsidized.
ISBN Prefix(es): 978-0-9662783; 978-0-9792226; 978-0-9770633; 978-0-9762091; 978-0-9798451; 978-0-9817883; 978-0-9823970; 978-0-9843418; 978-1-936482
Number of titles published annually: 17 Print; 1 Audio
Total Titles: 140 Print; 3 E-Book; 3 Audio

AOCS Press
Division of American Oil Chemists' Society
2710 S Boulder Dr, Urbana, IL 61802-6996
Mailing Address: PO Box 17190, Urbana, IL 61803-7190
Tel: 217-359-2344 *Fax:* 217-351-8091
E-mail: general@aocs.org
Web Site: www.aocs.org
Key Personnel
CEO: Patrick Donnelly *Tel:* 217-693-4838 *Fax:* 217-693-4881 *E-mail:* patrick.donnelly@aocs.org
Founded: 1909
Journals & monographs.
ISBN Prefix(es): 978-0-935315; 978-1-893997; 978-0-9818936
Number of titles published annually: 10 Print; 5 CD-ROM
Total Titles: 100 Print; 21 CD-ROM; 2 Audio

AOTA Press, see The American Occupational Therapy Association Inc (AOTA)

APA Planners Press
Imprint of American Planning Association
205 N Michigan Ave, Suite 1200, Chicago, IL 60601
Tel: 312-431-9100 *Fax:* 312-786-6700
E-mail: customerservice@planning.org
Web Site: www.planning.org
Key Personnel
Dir, Pubns: Sylvia Lewis *Tel:* 312-786-6370 *E-mail:* slewis@planning.org
Sr Ed: Timothy Mennel *Tel:* 312-786-6378 *E-mail:* tmennel@planning.org
Founded: 1978
Books on planning.
ISBN Prefix(es): 978-0-918286; 978-1-884829; 978-1-932364
Number of titles published annually: 8 Print
Total Titles: 120 Print; 15 Audio
Warehouse: Ware-Pak, PO Box 2516, Cedar Rapids, IA 52406 *Tel:* 319-365-2518 *Fax:* 319-364-3426

Aperture Books
Division of Aperture Foundation Inc
547 W 27 St, 4th fl, New York, NY 10001
SAN: 201-1832
Tel: 212-505-5555 *Toll Free Tel:* 800-929-2323 *Fax:* 212-979-7759
E-mail: info@aperture.org
Web Site: www.aperture.org
Key Personnel
Publr: Lesley Martin
Exec Dir: Chris Boot
Dir, Sales & Mktg: Kellie McLaughlin
Intl Rts Contact: Amelia Lang
Founded: 1952
Quarterly magazine; books on photography as fine art, history of photography, photojournalism, environment.
ISBN Prefix(es): 978-0-89381
Number of titles published annually: 25 Print
Total Titles: 250 Print
Imprints: Aperture Monographs; Masters of Photography; Writers & Artists on Photography Series
Distributed by Farrar, Straus & Giroux Inc
Foreign Rep(s): General Publishing (Canada); Robert Hale Ltd (UK); InterArt (France); Nilsson & Lamm (Belgium, Netherlands); Onslow Books Ltd (Western Europe); Penny Padovani (Greece, Italy, Portugal, Spain); Southern Publisher (New Zealand); Tower (Australia); Roger Ward (East Asia)
Shipping Address: Farrar, Straus & Giroux, c/o MPS, 16365 James Madison Hwy, Gordonsville, VA 22942

The Apex Press
Imprint of Rowman & Littlefield Publishers Inc
4501 Forbes Blvd, Suite 200, Lanham, MD 20706
SAN: 281-8752
Tel: 301-459-3366 *Toll Free Tel:* 800-462-6420 *Toll Free Fax:* 800-388-4450
E-mail: customercare@rowman.com
Key Personnel
VP, Mktg & Sales: Linda May
Founded: 1990
Specialize in books on education, economics, social & political issues, human rights, corporate power.
ISBN Prefix(es): 978-0-945257; 978-0-938960 (CITE); 978-1-891843
Number of titles published annually: 8 Print
Total Titles: 100 Print

The Apocryphile Press
1700 Shattuck Ave, Suite 81, Berkeley, CA 94709
Tel: 510-290-4349
E-mail: apocryphile@earthlink.net
Web Site: www.apocryphile.org
Key Personnel
Publr & Ed: John R Mabry
Assoc Ed: Michael Asteriou
Founded: 1994
ISBN Prefix(es): 978-1-933993; 978-0-9747623; 978-0-9764025; 978-0-9771461; 978-1-937002; 978-1-940671
Number of titles published annually: 12 Print
Total Titles: 140 Print

Apogee Press
2308 Sixth St, Berkeley, CA 94710
E-mail: editors.apogee@gmail.com
Web Site: www.apogeepress.com
Key Personnel
Ed: Alice Jones; Edward Smallfield *Tel:* 510-845-8800
Founded: 1998
Publishes innovative poetry with an emphasis on West Coast writers.
ISBN Prefix(es): 978-0-9669937; 978-0-9744687; 978-0-9787667; 978-0-9851007
Number of titles published annually: 3 Print
Total Titles: 34 Print
Orders to: Small Press Distribution, 1341 Seventh St, Berkeley, CA 94710-1409, Deputy Dir: Laura Moriarty *Toll Free Tel:* 800-869-7553 *Fax:* 510-524-1563 *E-mail:* spd@spdbooks.org *Web Site:* www.spdbooks.org
Returns: Small Press Distribution, 1341 Seventh St, Berkeley, CA 94710-1409, Deputy Dir: Laura Moriarty *Toll Free Tel:* 800-869-7553 *Fax:* 510-524-1563 *E-mail:* spd@spdbooks.org *Web Site:* www.spdbooks.org
Shipping Address: Small Press Distribution, 1341 Seventh St, Berkeley, CA 94710-1409, Deputy Dir: Laura Moriarty *Toll Free Tel:* 800-869-7553 *E-mail:* spd@spdbooks.org *Web Site:* www.spdbooks.org
Warehouse: Small Press Distribution, 1341 Seventh St, Berkeley, CA 94710-1409 *Toll Free Tel:* 800-869-7553 *E-mail:* spd@spdbooks.org *Web Site:* www.spdbooks.org
Distribution Center: Small Press Distribution, 1341 Seventh St, Berkeley, CA 94710-1409, Deputy Dir: Laura Moriarty *Toll Free Tel:* 800-869-7553 *Fax:* 510-524-1563 *E-mail:* spd@spdbooks.org *Web Site:* www.spdbooks.org
Membership(s): Community of Literary Magazines & Presses

Apollo Managed Care Inc
1651 Foothill Blvd, Santa Ana, CA 92705
Tel: 805-969-2606 *Fax:* 805-969-3749
E-mail: info@apollomanagedcare.com
Web Site: www.apollomanagedcare.com
Key Personnel
CEO: Dr Margaret Bischel *E-mail:* mbischel@cox.net
Founded: 1987
Publish comprehensive evidence-based healthcare review criteria & clinical guidelines.
ISBN Prefix(es): 978-1-893826; 978-1-939209
Number of titles published annually: 35 Print; 1 CD-ROM; 5 Online
Total Titles: 40 Print; 1 CD-ROM; 40 Online
Distributed by Health Information Network; MarketResearch.com; Researchandmarkets.com

APPA: The Association of Higher Education Facilities Officers
1643 Prince St, Alexandria, VA 22314-2818
Tel: 703-684-1446 *Fax:* 703-549-2772
Web Site: www.appa.org

Key Personnel
Dir, Knowledge Mgmt: Steve Glazner
E-mail: steve@appa.org
Pubn Mgr: Anita Dosik *E-mail:* anita@appa.org
Founded: 1914
All titles seek to enhance the development of leadership & professional management applicable to the planning, design, construction & operation of higher education facilities.
ISBN Prefix(es): 978-0-913359; 978-1-890956
Number of titles published annually: 5 Print
Total Titles: 60 Print
Branch Office(s)
APPA Publications, PO Box 1201, Alexandria, VA 22313-1201
Distribution Center: 13119 Pelfrey Lane, Fairfax, VA 22033

Appalachian Mountain Club Books
Division of Appalachian Mountain Club
5 Joy St, Boston, MA 02108
SAN: 203-4808
Tel: 617-523-0655 *Toll Free Tel:* 800-262-4455 (orders) *Fax:* 617-523-0722
E-mail: amcbooks@outdoors.org
Web Site: www.outdoors.org
Key Personnel
VP, Communs & Mktg: Kevin Breunig
Founded: 1897
Guidebooks, maps, outdoor recreation & conservation, mountain history, nature & travel for Northeast US.
ISBN Prefix(es): 978-0-910146; 978-1-878239; 978-1-929173; 978-1-934028; 978-1-62842
Number of titles published annually: 20 Print
Total Titles: 110 Print
Imprints: AMC Discover Series; AMC Nature Walks Series; AMC Quiet Water Guides; AMC River Guides; AMC Trail Guides
Distributed by The Globe Pequot Press
Foreign Rep(s): Canadian Manda Group (Canada); Windsor Books Ltd (Europe)
Warehouse: The Globe Pequot Press Inc, 246 Goose Lane, Guilford, CT 06437-0480 *Tel:* 203-455-4547 *Toll Free Tel:* 800-962-0973 *Fax:* 860-395-2855 *Web Site:* www.globe-pequot.com

Appalachian Trail Conservancy
799 Washington St, Harpers Ferry, WV 25425
Mailing Address: PO Box 807, Harpers Ferry, WV 25425-0807
Tel: 304-535-6331 *Toll Free Tel:* 888-287-8673 (orders only) *Fax:* 304-535-2667
E-mail: info@appalachiantrail.org
Web Site: www.appalachiantrail.org; www.atctrailstore.org
Key Personnel
Publr: Brian B King
Founded: 1925
Books related to the Appalachian Trail.
ISBN Prefix(es): 978-0-917953; 978-1-889386
Number of titles published annually: 5 Print
Total Titles: 46 Print
Distribution Center: 179 E Burr Blvd, Unit N, Kearneysville, WV 25430 *Tel:* 304-724-8386 *E-mail:* sales@appalachiantrail.org *Web Site:* www.atctrailstore.org

Applause Theatre & Cinema Books
Imprint of Hal Leonard Performing Arts Publishing Group
33 Plymouth St, Suite 302, Montclair, NJ 07042
Tel: 973-337-5034 *Toll Free Tel:* 800-637-2852 *Fax:* 973-337-5227
E-mail: info@applausepub.com
Web Site: www.applausepub.com
Key Personnel
Group Publr: John Cerullo *E-mail:* jcerullo@halleonard.com
Founded: 1983
Plays, theatre books, cinema books, entertainment, television; including DVDs.
ISBN Prefix(es): 978-0-936839; 978-1-55783
Number of titles published annually: 25 Print; 15 E-Book
Total Titles: 1,000 Print; 500 E-Book
Sales Office(s): 7777 W Bluemound Rd, Milwaukee, WI 53213
Distributed by Hal Leonard Corporation
Distributor for The Working Arts Library; Glenn Young Books
Foreign Rep(s): Publishers Group UK (Europe, UK)
Billing Address: 960 E Mark St, Winona, MN 55987
Orders to: 7777 W Bluemound Rd, Milwaukee, WI 53213 *Toll Free Tel:* 800-554-0626
Returns: 960 E Mark St, Winona, MN 55987
Warehouse: 960 E Mark St, Winona, MN 55987 *Tel:* 507-454-2920 *Fax:* 507-454-8334

Appletree Press Inc
151 Good Counsel Dr, Suite 125, Mankato, MN 56001
Tel: 507-345-4848 *Toll Free Tel:* 800-322-5679 *Fax:* 507-345-3002
E-mail: eatwell@hickorytech.net
Web Site: www.appletreepress.com; www.appletree-press.com; www.letscookhealthymeals.com; www.appletree-press.us
Key Personnel
CEO & Publr: Linda Hachfeld *E-mail:* lindah@hickorytech.net
Founded: 1989
Independent health & nutrition publisher of cookbooks, food diaries, journaling tools & nutrition reference books. Focus on heart health, diabetes management, weight management, arthritis, vegetarian cooking, how-to cookbooks for & by people with intellectual & developmental disabilities.
ISBN Prefix(es): 978-1-891011; 978-0-962047
Number of titles published annually: 3 Print
Total Titles: 20 Print
Imprints: On My Own (pictorial cookbooks for individuals with special needs; intellectual & developmental disabilities)
Membership(s): Academy of Nutrition and Dietetics; The Association of Publishers for Special Sales; The Independent Book Publishers Association; Midwest Independent Publishers Association; Women Executives in Business; Women of Words

Applewood Books Inc
One River Rd, Carlisle, MA 01741
SAN: 210-3419
Mailing Address: PO Box 365, Bedford, MA 01730
Tel: 781-271-0055 *Toll Free Tel:* 800-277-5312 (orders) *Fax:* 781-271-0056
E-mail: bookorder@awb.com; customercare@awb.com
Web Site: www.awb.com
Key Personnel
Pres & ISBN Contact: Phil Zuckerman
E-mail: philz@awb.com
VP, Opers: Sue Cabezas *E-mail:* suec@awb.com
Founded: 1976
Americana reprints.
ISBN Prefix(es): 978-0-918222; 978-1-55709; 978-1-889833; 978-1-933212; 978-1-4290; 978-0-9819430; 978-1-60889; 978-0-9844156; 978-0-9836416; 978-1-938700; 978-0-9882885; 978-1-5162
Number of titles published annually: 500 Print
Total Titles: 2,500 Print
Imprints: Commonwealth Editions; Grab a Pencil Press
Orders to: PO Box 27, Carlisle, MA 01741
Warehouse: Ingram Publishers Services, 1280 Ingram Dr, Chambersburg, PA 17201
See separate listing for:
Commonwealth Editions

Appraisal Institute
200 W Madison, Suite 1500, Chicago, IL 60606
Tel: 312-335-4100 *Toll Free Tel:* 888-756-4624 *Fax:* 312-335-4400
Web Site: www.appraisalinstitute.org
Key Personnel
Sr Mgr, Pubns: Tep Shea-Joyce *E-mail:* tshea-joyce@appraisalinstitute.org
Founded: 1932
Professional real estate appraisal books, monographs, periodicals & videos.
ISBN Prefix(es): 978-0-911780; 978-0-922154
Number of titles published annually: 6 Print
Total Titles: 60 Print
Branch Office(s)
122 "C" St NW, Suite 360, Washington, DC 20001 *Tel:* 202-298-6449
Distributed by Dearborn Trade
Foreign Rep(s): Royal Institution of Chartered Surveyors (Africa, Caribbean, Commonwealth, Ethiopia, Europe, Far East)

Apprentice Shop Books LLC
18 Wentworth Dr, Bedford, NH 03110
Mailing Address: PO Box 375, Amherst, NH 03031
Tel: 603-472-8741 *Fax:* 603-472-2323
E-mail: info@apprenticeshopbooks.com
Web Site: www.apprenticeshopbooks.com
Key Personnel
Publr: Muriel Dubois *E-mail:* mdubois@apprenticeshopbooks.com
Art Dir: Lisa Greenleaf *Tel:* 603-566-3104
E-mail: lgreenleaf@apprenticeshopbooks.com
Dir, Mktg: Darlene Mann *Tel:* 603-244-9263
E-mail: dmann@apprenticeshopbooks.com
Photo Researcher: Sheila Brown *Tel:* 603-494-0767 *E-mail:* sbrown@apprenticeshopbooks.com
Publishes historical fiction & nonfiction books for children, teens & young adults. No unsol mss or artwork will be accepted.
ISBN Prefix(es): 978-0-9723410; 978-0-9842549; 978-0-9850144
Number of titles published annually: 3 Print
Total Titles: 12 Print; 12 Online
Distribution Center: Follett School Solutions Inc, 1340 Ridgeview Dr, McHenry, IL 60050 *Tel:* 815-759-1700 *Toll Free Tel:* 888-511-5114 (cust serv) *Fax:* 815-759-9831 *Toll Free Fax:* 800-852-5458 *E-mail:* info@follettlearning.com *Web Site:* www.follettlearning.com SAN: 169-1902
Emery Pratt, 1966 W M21, Owosso, MI 48867-9377 *Tel:* 989-723-5291 *Toll Free Tel:* 800-248-3887
Baker & Taylor, 2550 W Tyvola Rd, Suite 300, Charlotte, NC 28217 *Tel:* 704-998-3100 *Toll Free Tel:* 800-775-1800
Membership(s): ABA; The Children's Book Council; New England Independent Booksellers Association; Society of Children's Book Writers & Illustrators

Apress Media LLC
Subsidiary of Springer Science+Business Media LLC
233 Spring St, New York, NY 10013
Tel: 212-460-1500 *Fax:* 212-460-1575
E-mail: editorial@apress.com
Web Site: www.apress.com
Key Personnel
Pres & Publr: Paul Manning *E-mail:* paul.manning@apress.com
Dir, Mktg & Opers: Jeff Stonefield
E-mail: jeffstonefield@apress.com

Busn Devt: Jeff Pepper *E-mail:* jeffreypepper@apress.com
Technical publisher devoted to meeting the needs of IT professionals, software developers & programmers with books in print & electronic format.
ISBN Prefix(es): 978-1-893115; 978-1-59059; 978-1-4302
Total Titles: 1,000 Print

§APS PRESS
Imprint of The American Phytopathological Society (APS)
3340 Pilot Knob Rd, St Paul, MN 55121
Tel: 651-454-7250 *Toll Free Tel:* 800-328-7560 *Fax:* 651-454-0766
E-mail: aps@scisoc.org
Web Site: www.shopapspress.org
Key Personnel
EVP: Amy Hope *E-mail:* ahope@scisoc.org
Pubns Mktg Dir: Greg Grahek *Tel:* 651-454-7250 ext 141 *E-mail:* ggrahek@scisoc.org
Pubns Mktg Coord: Dawn Wuest *E-mail:* dwuest@scisoc.org
Founded: 1908
Publishers of key reference books, field guides, laboratory manuals & other scientific titles related to plant health.
ISBN Prefix(es): 978-0-89054
Number of titles published annually: 10 Print; 2 CD-ROM; 4 Online
Total Titles: 300 Print; 40 CD-ROM; 2 Online

Aqua Quest Publications Inc
486 Bayville Rd, Locust Valley, NY 11560-1209
Tel: 516-759-0476 *Toll Free Tel:* 800-933-8989 *Fax:* 516-759-4519
E-mail: info@aquaquest.com
Web Site: www.aquaquest.com
Key Personnel
Pres: Anthony A Bliss, Jr *E-mail:* tbliss@aquaquest.com
Founded: 1989
Publishes & distributes books on scuba diving, dive travel destinations, underwater photo/video, marine life, technical diving, marine related children's books, shipwrecks & dive related fiction.
ISBN Prefix(es): 978-0-9623389; 978-1-881652; 978-0-9752290
Number of titles published annually: 3 Print; 4 E-Book
Total Titles: 30 Print; 4 E-Book
Imprints: Watersport Books
Distribution Center: National Book Network, 15200 NBN Way, Blue Ridge Summit, PA 17214 *Tel:* 717-794-3800 *Toll Free Tel:* 800-462-6420 *Toll Free Fax:* 800-338-4550 *Web Site:* www.nbnbooks.com

§Arbordale Publishing
612 Johnnie Dodds Blvd, Suite A2, Mount Pleasant, SC 29464
SAN: 256-6109
Tel: 843-971-6722 *Toll Free Tel:* 877-243-3457 *Fax:* 843-216-3804
E-mail: customerservice@arbordalepublishing.com; info@arbordalepublishing.com
Web Site: www.arbordalepublishing.com
Key Personnel
Publr: Mr Lee German *E-mail:* leegerman@arbordalepublishing.com
Ed: Donna German *E-mail:* donna@arbordalepublishing.com
PR: Heather Williams *E-mail:* heather@arbordalepublishing.com
Bookstore & Gift Shop Sales: Jordan Fredrickson *E-mail:* jordan@arbordalepublishing.com
School & Lib Sales: Emily Gooch *E-mail:* emily@arbordalepublishing.com
Off Mgr: Elma Haley *E-mail:* elma@arbordalepublishing.com
Founded: 2005
Company on a mission to create picture books that will excite children's imagination, are artistically spectacular & have educational value. Most of our stories are fictional but relate to a nonfictional theme of science, nature or animals. Each book is seriously vetted for scientific accuracy before publication. We reserve 3-5 pages in the back of each book to add our "Creative Minds" section, loaded with fun facts, crafts & games to supplement the educational thread of the book. Ebooks with auto read, auto flip & selectable English & Spanish text in audio.
ISBN Prefix(es): 978-0-9777423; 978-1-60718; 978-1-62855; 978-1-934359; 978-0-9764943; 978-0-9768823
Number of titles published annually: 36 Print; 36 Online; 36 E-Book; 36 Audio
Total Titles: 228 Print; 228 Online; 228 E-Book; 228 Audio
Foreign Rep(s): Fitzhenry & Whiteside (Canada); Ediciones Enlace de PR (Puerto Rico)
Foreign Rights: Sylvia Hayes Literary Agency
Distribution Center: The Reading Warehouse, PO Box 41328, North Charleston, SC 29423 *E-mail:* customerservice@thereadingwarehouse.com *Web Site:* www.thereadingwarehouse.com
Bound to Stay Bound, 1880 W Morton Ave, Jacksonville, IL 62650 *Toll Free Tel:* 800-637-6586 *Toll Free Fax:* 800-747-2872 *E-mail:* btsb@btsb.com *Web Site:* www.btsb.com
Perma-Bound, 617 E Vandalia Rd, Jacksonville, IL 62650 *Tel:* 217-243-5451 *Toll Free Tel:* 800-637-9581 *Fax:* 217-243-7505 *Toll Free Fax:* 800-551-1169 *E-mail:* books@perma-bound.com *Web Site:* www.perma-bound.com
Follett School Solutions Inc, 1340 Ridgeview Dr, McHenry, IL 60050 *Tel:* 815-759-1700 *Toll Free Tel:* 888-511-5114 (cust serv) *Fax:* 815-459-9831 *Toll Free Fax:* 800-852-5458 *E-mail:* info@follettlearning.com *Web Site:* www.follettlearning.com SAN: 169-1902
Mackin Educational Resources, 3505 County Rd 42 W, Burnsville, MN 55306 *Tel:* 952-895-9540 *Toll Free Tel:* 800-245-9540 *Fax:* 952-894-8806 *Toll Free Fax:* 800-369-5490 *E-mail:* customerservice@mackin.com *Web Site:* www.mackin.com
Baker & Taylor, 2550 W Tyvola Rd, Suite 300, Charlotte, NC 28217 *Toll Free Tel:* 800-775-1800 *Fax:* 704-998-3100 *E-mail:* btinfo@baker-taylor.com *Web Site:* www.btol.com
Brodart, 500 Arch St, Williamsport, PA 17701 *Tel:* 570-326-2461 *Toll Free Tel:* 800-233-8487 *Fax:* 570-326-1479 *E-mail:* support@brodart.com *Web Site:* www.brodart.com
Davidson Titles, PO Box 3538, Jackson, TN 38303-3538 *Toll Free Tel:* 800-433-3903 *Toll Free Fax:* 800-787-7935 *E-mail:* info@davidsontitles.com *Web Site:* www.davidsontitles.com
Ingram, One Ingram Blvd, La Vergne, TN 37086 *Tel:* 615-793-5000 *Toll Free Tel:* 800-937-8200 *E-mail:* customer.service@ingrambook.com *Web Site:* www.ingrambook.com
Penworthy, 219 N Milwaukee St, Milwaukee, WI 53202 *Tel:* 414-287-4600 *Toll Free Tel:* 800-262-2665 *Fax:* 414-287-4602 *E-mail:* info@penworthy.com *Web Site:* www.penworthy.com
Membership(s): ABA; ABC; BookSense Publisher Partner; The Children's Book Council; Florida Authors & Publishers Association Inc; The Independent Book Publishers Association; International Literacy Association; MSA; NAIPR; National Association for Bilingual Education; North American Bookdealers Exchange; Northern California Independent Booksellers Association; Southern Independent Booksellers Alliance

Arbutus Press
2364 Pinehurst Trail, Traverse City, MI 49696
Tel: 231-946-7240
E-mail: info@arbutuspress.com
Web Site: www.arbutuspress.com
Key Personnel
Publr: Susan Bays
Founded: 1998
Midwest regional history & travel related.
ISBN Prefix(es): 978-0-9665316; 978-0-9766104; 978-1-933926
Number of titles published annually: 12 Print
Total Titles: 45 Print; 12 E-Book
Membership(s): Great Lakes Independent Booksellers Association; The Independent Book Publishers Association

Arcade Publishing Inc
Imprint of Skyhorse Publishing Inc
307 W 36 St, 11th fl, New York, NY 10018
Tel: 212-643-6816 *Fax:* 212-643-6819
E-mail: info@skyhorsepublishing.com (subs & foreign rts)
Web Site: www.arcadepub.com
Key Personnel
Pres & Publr: Tony Lyons
Assoc Publr: Bill Wolfsthal *E-mail:* bwolfsthal@skyhorsepublishing.com
Founded: 1988
Trade fiction & nonfiction; adult & juvenile.
ISBN Prefix(es): 978-1-61145
Number of titles published annually: 100 Print; 100 E-Book
Total Titles: 700 Print
Distributed by Perseus Books Group

Arcadia Publishing Inc
420 Wando Park Blvd, Mount Pleasant, SC 29464
SAN: 255-268X
Tel: 843-853-2070 *Toll Free Tel:* 888-313-2665 (orders only) *Fax:* 843-853-0044
E-mail: sales@arcadiapublishing.com
Web Site: www.arcadiapublishing.com
Key Personnel
Cont: Kristen Crawford
Dir, Mktg & Corp Communs: Kelly Bowen
Sales Dir: Kate Everingham *E-mail:* keveringham@arcadiapublishing.com
Founded: 1992
Local history & vintage images.
ISBN Prefix(es): 978-0-7385; 978-1-4396; 978-1-4671
Number of titles published annually: 900 Print
Total Titles: 12,000 Print; 6,000 E-Book
Imprints: History Press; Legendary Locals
Warehouse: Arcadia Distribution Center, Receiving Dock, Mount Pleasant, SC 29464 SAN: 255-2698

Arcana Publishing, see Lotus Press

Arden Press Inc
PO Box 418, Denver, CO 80201-0418
Tel: 303-697-6766 *Fax:* 303-697-3443
E-mail: ardenpress@msn.com
Key Personnel
Pres & Ed: Susan Conley
Founded: 1982
Nonfiction & primarily women's studies.
ISBN Prefix(es): 978-0-912869
Number of titles published annually: 3 Print
Total Titles: 14 Print
Returns: 20723 Seminole Rd, Indian Hills, CO 80454
Shipping Address: 20723 Seminole Rd, Indian Hills, CO 80454

§Ardent Media Inc
522 E 82 St, Suite 1, New York, NY 10028
Tel: 212-861-1501 *Fax:* 212-861-0998
E-mail: ivyboxer@aol.com; ardentmedia@hotmail.com
Key Personnel
Pres: Irving B Naiburg, Jr

Founded: 1998
Paperbacks, trade, textbooks, professional & reference books, Ardent Reprint Series (article reprints, formerly Bobbs-Merrill Reprint Series).
ISBN Prefix(es): 978-0-89197; 978-0-8422; 978-0-8290
Number of titles published annually: 10 Print
Total Titles: 4,500 Print
Distributor for Cyrco Press; Irvington Publishers; MSS Information Corp
Foreign Rep(s): Gazelle Book Services Ltd (Europe, Former USSR, Turkey, UK)

ARE Press
Division of The Association for Research & Enlightenment Inc (ARE)
215 67 St, Virginia Beach, VA 23451
Tel: 757-428-3588 *Toll Free Tel:* 800-333-4499 *Fax:* 757-491-0689
Web Site: www.edgarcayce.org
Key Personnel
Mktg Dir: Jennie Taylor Martin *Tel:* 757-457-7249 *E-mail:* jennie@edgarcayce.org
Prodn, Rts & Trade Sales Dir: Cassie McQuagge *Tel:* 757-457-7239 *E-mail:* cassie@edgarcayce.org
Founded: 1931
Holistic health & spiritual development, based on Edgar Cayce material.
ISBN Prefix(es): 978-0-87604
Number of titles published annually: 8 Print; 8 E-Book
Total Titles: 160 Print; 1 CD-ROM; 64 E-Book
Imprints: 4th Dimension Press

Ariadne Press
270 Goins Ct, Riverside, CA 92507
Tel: 951-684-9202 *Fax:* 951-779-0449
E-mail: ariadnepress@aol.com
Web Site: www.ariadnebooks.com
Key Personnel
Partner: Jorun Johns *Tel:* 951-684-6789
Founded: 1988
Studies in Austrian literature, culture & thought.
ISBN Prefix(es): 978-0-929497; 978-1-57241
Number of titles published annually: 12 Print
Total Titles: 205 Print
Foreign Rep(s): Gazelle (UK); Schaden (Austria)
Foreign Rights: Gazelle (UK)

§Ariel Press
Subsidiary of Light
3854 Mason Rd, Canal Winchester, OH 43110
Mailing Address: PO Box 249, Canal Winchester, OH 43110
Toll Free Tel: 800-336-7769
E-mail: lig201@lightariel.com
Web Site: www.lightariel.com
Key Personnel
Pres & Publr: Carl Japikse
Art Dir: Nancy Maxwell
Founded: 1976
Nonfiction hardcover & paperbound books; essays & subscription series on personal growth, creativity, holistic health & psychic phenomena; esoteric fiction; reprints.
ISBN Prefix(es): 978-0-89804
Number of titles published annually: 11 Print; 10 E-Book
Total Titles: 150 Print; 25 E-Book
Imprints: Enthea Press; Kudzu House
Distributor for Enthea Press; Kudzu House
Foreign Rep(s): Deep Books (England)

§Ariel Starr Productions Inc
PO Box 575, Woodstock, NY 12498
Tel: 201-784-9148
E-mail: arielstarrprod@aol.com
Web Site: arielstarrprod.wix.com/arielstarr
Key Personnel
Pres: Cynthia Soroka-Dunn
Founded: 1991
Publish any new & innovative projects.
ISBN Prefix(es): 978-1-889122
Number of titles published annually: 3 Print; 4 E-Book; 2 Audio
Total Titles: 20 Print; 1 Audio

The Arion Press
Division of Lyra Corp
The Presidio, 1802 Hays St, San Francisco, CA 94129
SAN: 203-1361
Tel: 415-668-2542 *Fax:* 415-668-2550
E-mail: arionpress@arionpress.com
Web Site: www.arionpress.com
Key Personnel
Publr: Andrew Hoyem
Dir, Mktg & Sales: Thomas Gladysz
Founded: 1974
Fine, limited edition illustrated books of fiction, literature & poetry.
ISBN Prefix(es): 978-0-910457
Number of titles published annually: 3 Print
Total Titles: 90 Print
Divisions: M & H Type

Arkham House Publishers Inc
PO Box 546, Sauk City, WI 53583
SAN: 206-9741
Tel: 608-643-4500 *Fax:* 608-643-5043
E-mail: sales@arkhamhouse.com
Web Site: www.arkhamhouse.com
Key Personnel
Pres: Danielle Hackett
VP: Damon Derleth
Founded: 1939
Fantasy fiction, horror, macabre, science fiction.
ISBN Prefix(es): 978-0-87054
Number of titles published annually: 3 Print
Total Titles: 50 Print; 50 Online; 50 E-Book
Imprints: Mycroft & Moran

Aro Book Publishing Co
130 S 800 W, Salt Lake City, UT 84104-1120
Tel: 801-953-1760 (office); 801-637-9115 (cell) *Fax:* 801-419-0125
E-mail: arobook@yahoo.com
Web Site: www.arobookpublishing.com
Key Personnel
Pres: Bob Reese
Founded: 1973 (sold 1985, repurchased 2006)
K-4 beginning to read.
ISBN Prefix(es): 978-0-89868
Number of titles published annually: 30 Print
Total Titles: 35 Print; 65 Online; 35 E-Book

Jason Aronson Inc
Imprint of Rowman & Littlefield Publishing Group
4501 Forbes Blvd, Suite 200, Lanham, MD 20706
SAN: 201-0127
Tel: 301-459-3366 *Toll Free Tel:* 800-462-6420 (orders) *Fax:* 301-429-5748
Web Site: www.rowman.com
Key Personnel
VP & Publr: Julie Kirsch *Tel:* 301-459-3366 ext 5309 *E-mail:* jkirsch@rowman.com
Mktg Dir: Dave Horvath
Rts & Perms: Patricia Zline *Tel:* 301-459-3366 ext 5420 *E-mail:* pzline@rowman.com
Acqs Ed, Psychotherapy/Psychoanalysis: Amy King *Tel:* 301-459-3366 ext 5305 *E-mail:* aking@rowman.com
Founded: 1965
Professional books in psychotherapy, psychoanalysis & psychology; academic, reference & trade Judaica books.
ISBN Prefix(es): 978-0-87668; 978-1-56821; 978-0-7657
Number of titles published annually: 25 Print; 25 E-Book
Total Titles: 1,700 Print
Foreign Rep(s): Academic Marketing Services Pty Ltd (Botswana, Namibia, South Africa, Zimbabwe); APD Singapore Pte Ltd (Brunei, Cambodia, Indonesia, Laos, Malaysia, Singapore, Thailand, Vietnam); Asia Publishers Service Ltd (China, Hong Kong, Korea, Philippines, Taiwan); Avicenna Partnership Ltd (Afghanistan, Algeria, Armenia, Bahrain, Cyprus, Egypt, Iran, Iraq, Jordan, Kuwait, Lebanon, Libya, Morocco, Oman, Palestine, Qatar, Saudi Arabia, Sudan, Syria, Tunisia, United Arab Emirates, Yemen); Cranbury International LLC (Caribbean, Central America, Mexico, Pakistan, Puerto Rico, South America); DA Information Services Pty Ltd (Australia, New Zealand, Papua New Guinea); Durnell Marketing Ltd (Austria, Baltic States, Belgium, Czech Republic, Denmark, Finland, France, Germany, Greece, Hungary, Iceland, Italy, Malta, Netherlands, Norway, Poland, Portugal, Slovakia, Slovenia, Spain, Sweden, Switzerland); NBN International; Overleaf (Bangladesh, Bhutan, India, Nepal, Sri Lanka); United Publishers Service Ltd (Japan, South Korea)

Art Image Publications
Division of GB Publishing Inc
PO Box 160, Derby Line, VT 05830
Toll Free Tel: 800-361-2598 *Toll Free Fax:* 800-559-2598
E-mail: info@artimagepublications.com; customer.service@artimagepublications.com
Web Site: www.artimagepublications.com
Key Personnel
Pres: Yvan Boulerice
Secy: Francois Desjardins
Founded: 1980
ISBN Prefix(es): 978-1-896876; 978-1-55292
Number of titles published annually: 12 Print
Total Titles: 52 Print

The Art Institute of Chicago
111 S Michigan Ave, Chicago, IL 60603-6404
SAN: 204-479X
Tel: 312-443-3600; 312-443-3540 (pubns) *Fax:* 312-443-1334 (pubns)
Web Site: www.artic.edu; www.artinstituteshop.org
Key Personnel
Pres & Dir: Douglas Druick *Tel:* 312-443-3632
Dir, Pubns: Sarah E Guernsey *Tel:* 312-443-3746 *E-mail:* sguernsey@artic.edu
Ed: Maia M Rigas *Tel:* 312-443-4774 *E-mail:* mrigas@artic.edu
Photog Ed: Lauren Makholm *Tel:* 312-443-3539 *E-mail:* lmakholm@artic.edu
Asst Ed: Amy Peltz *Tel:* 312-443-4963 *E-mail:* apeltz@artic.edu
Prodn Coord: Joseph Mohan *Tel:* 312-443-4955 *E-mail:* jmohan@artic.edu
Founded: 1879
Exhibition catalogues, popular & scholarly art books on the museum's permanent collection: African art & Indian art of the Americas; American art; Ancient & Byzantine art; architecture & design; Asian art; contemporary art; European painting, sculpture & decorative arts; photography; prints & drawings; textiles.
ISBN Prefix(es): 978-0-86559
Number of titles published annually: 10 Print; 1 Online
Total Titles: 60 Print
Distributed by Yale University Press

Art of Living, PrimaMedia Inc
1250 Bethlehem Pike, Suite 241, Hatfield, PA 19440
SAN: 299-8858
Tel: 215-660-5045
E-mail: primamedia4@yahoo.com

Key Personnel
Ed: Gia Carispat *E-mail:* primamedia12@yahoo.com
Billing: Joan Campo *E-mail:* primamedia40@gmail.com
Orders & Cust Serv: Sue Thomson *Tel:* 215-436-9524
Orders & Returns: Sue Timmons Thomas *Tel:* 215-640-5045
Contact: Katherine Rafter *E-mail:* primamedia9@yahoo.com
Founded: 2005
Boutique publishing company. Publisher of the award-winning book series *The Basic Art of Italian Cooking* & *The Basic Art.* Can place orders by telephone or e-mail, but prefer e-mail.
ISBN Prefix(es): 978-1-928911
Number of titles published annually: 10 Print; 6 E-Book
Total Titles: 15 E-Book
Foreign Rep(s): Rebecca Ferrone (Australia, Canada, Europe)
Distribution Center: Amazon.com
Follett School Solutions Inc, 1340 Ridgeview Dr, McHenry, IL 60050 *Tel:* 815-759-1700 *Toll Free Tel:* 888-511-5114 (cust serv) *Fax:* 815-759-9831 *Toll Free Fax:* 800-852-5458 *E-mail:* info@follettlearning.com *Web Site:* www.follettlearning.com SAN: 169-1902

ArtAge Publications
PO Box 19955, Portland, OR 97280
Tel: 503-246-3000 *Toll Free Tel:* 800-858-4998 *Fax:* 503-246-3006
Web Site: www.seniortheatre.com
Key Personnel
Pres: Bonnie L Vorenberg *E-mail:* bonniev@seniortheatre.com
Founded: 1997
The Senior Theatre Resource Center has the largest collection of plays, books & information for older performers. We help mature performers fulfill their theatrical dreams.
ISBN Prefix(es): 978-0-9669412
Number of titles published annually: 45 Print; 45 Online; 27 E-Book; 5 Audio
Total Titles: 400 Print; 300 Online; 275 E-Book; 11 Audio
Distributor for Heinemann; Hal Leonard
Returns: 7845 SW Capitol Hwy, Suite 12, Portland, OR 97219

Arte Publico Press
Affiliate of University of Houston
University of Houston, Bldg 19, Rm 10, 4902 Gulf Fwy, Houston, TX 77204-2004
Tel: 713-743-2998 (sales) *Toll Free Tel:* 800-633-2783 *Fax:* 713-743-2847 (sales)
E-mail: appinfo@uh.edu; bkorders@uh.edu
Key Personnel
Publr: Nicolas Kanellos
Asst Dir: Marina Tristan
Busn Mgr: Nellie Gonzalez
Founded: 1979
Books by American Hispanic authors.
ISBN Prefix(es): 978-0-934770; 978-1-55885
Number of titles published annually: 30 Print
Total Titles: 400 Print
Imprints: Pinata Books
Subsidiaries: The Americas Review
Distributor for Bilingual Review Press; Latin American Review Press
Foreign Rights: Raquel de la Concha (Spain); Agencia Literaria Virginia Lopez-Ballesteros (Spain)
Membership(s): AAP

§Artech House Inc
Subsidiary of Horizon House Publications Inc
685 Canton St, Norwood, MA 02062
SAN: 201-1441
Tel: 781-769-9750 *Toll Free Tel:* 800-225-9977 *Fax:* 781-769-6334
E-mail: artech@artechhouse.com
Web Site: www.artechhouse.com
Key Personnel
COO: Christopher R Ernst *E-mail:* cernst@artechhouse.com
Pres & Publr: William M Bazzy *E-mail:* wmbazzy@artechhouse.com
Edit & Prodn Dir: Darrell Judd
Dir, Sales, Mktg & Busn Devt: Kevin Danahy *E-mail:* kdanahy@artechhouse.com
Exec Ed: Judi Stone
Sr Acq Ed: Mark E Walsh *E-mail:* mwalsh@artechhouse.com
Founded: 1970
Technical & engineering.
ISBN Prefix(es): 978-0-89006; 978-1-58053; 978-1-59693; 978-1-60807; 978-1-60783; 978-1-63081
Number of titles published annually: 30 Print; 40 E-Book
Total Titles: 500 Print; 250 E-Book
Foreign Office(s): 16 Sussex St, London SW1V 4RW, United Kingdom, Sales & Mktg Mgr: Alison Hope *Tel:* (020) 7596 8750 *Fax:* (020) 7630 0166 *E-mail:* artech-uk@artechhouse.com
Foreign Rep(s): Akateeminen (Finland); Anglo-American Book Co (Italy); Asian Books Pvt Ltd (India, Pakistan); C V Toko Buku Topen (Indonesia); Clarke Associates Ltd (Pacific Basin); Computer Press (Sweden); D A Book Pty Ltd (Australia, New Zealand); Dai-Iti Publications Trading Co Ltd (Japan); Diaz de Santos (Spain); Dietmar Dreier (Germany); DK Book House Co Ltd (Thailand); Freihofer AG (Switzerland); Kumi Trading Co Ltd (South Korea); Librairie Lavoisier (France); Login Brothers (Canada); Julio Logrado de Figueiredo Lda (Portugal); The Modern Book Co (UK); Pak Book Corp (Pakistan); Polyteknisk (Denmark); Sejong (Korea); Ta Tong Book Co Ltd (Taiwan); Tapir (Norway); Tecmedd (Brazil); UBS Library Services (Singapore); United Publishers Services Ltd (Japan, South Korea); L Wouters (Belgium)
Foreign Rights: ABE Marketing (Poland); BSB Distribution (Germany); Fleet Publications (Chile); Foyles (UK); Hoepli (Italy); Kuwkab (Mideast); Livraria Canuto (Brazil); Papsotiriou (Greece)
Returns: NBN International, Airport Busn Ctr, 10 Thornbury Rd, Plymouth PL6 7PP, United Kingdom; Publishers Storage & Shipping Corp (US only), 231 Industrial Park, 46 Development Rd, Fitchburg, MA 01420 *Tel:* 978-345-2121 *Fax:* 978-348-1233
Warehouse: Publishers Storage & Shipping Corp (US only), 231 Industrial Park, 46 Development Rd, Fitchburg, MA 01420 *Tel:* 978-345-2121 *Fax:* 978-348-1233

Artisan Books
Division of Workman Publishing Co Inc
225 Varick St, New York, NY 10014-4381
Tel: 212-254-5900 *Toll Free Tel:* 800-722-7202 *Fax:* 212-677-6692
E-mail: artisaninfo@artisanbooks.com
Web Site: www.workman.com/artisanbooks
Key Personnel
Publr: Lia Ronnen
Publicity Dir: Allison McGeehon
Prodn Dir: Nancy Murray
Sr Ed: Shoshana Gutmajer
Founded: 1993
Illustrated books & calendars to the trade.
ISBN Prefix(es): 978-1-885183; 978-1-57965
Number of titles published annually: 15 Print
Distributor for Greenwich Workshop Press
Foreign Rep(s): Thomas Allen & Son Ltd (Canada); Bookreps New Zealand (New Zealand); Hardie Grant Books (Australia); Melia Publishing Services (UK)
Foreign Rights: Big Apple Agency Inc (China, Taiwan); Graal Literary Agency (Poland); The Deborah Harris Agency (Israel); Japan UNI Agency Inc (Japan); JLM Literary Agency (Greece); Katai & Bolza Literary Agents (Hungary); Korea Copyright Center Inc (KCC) (Korea); Kristin Olson Literary Agency SRO (Czech Republic); Plima Literary Agency (Bulgaria, Croatia, Macedonia, Serbia, Slovenia); Sebes & van Gelderen Literary Agency (Netherlands); Marco Vigevani Agenzia Letteraria (Italy); Julio F Yanez Agencia Literaria SL (Latin America, Portugal, Spain)
Shipping Address: RR Donnelley, 1077 Prospect Lane, Kaukauna, WI 54130

§Artisan Bookworks
921 S Third Ave, No 8, Sequim, WA 98382
Mailing Address: PO Box 1972, Sequim, WA 98382
Tel: 425-954-5277
E-mail: books@artisanbookworks.com
Web Site: www.artisanbookworks.com
Key Personnel
Publr: Kelly Lenihan
Founded: 2012
Discover, nurture, publish & promote emerging writers. Authors enjoy the advantages of self-publishing. Hand-select children's books. Services include book layout (print & digital), copyediting, proofreading & cover design for children's books, picture books & general fiction. Some nonfiction & memoirs will be considered.
This publisher has indicated that 75% of their product line is author subsidized.
ISBN Prefix(es): 978-0-9898692; 978-0-9911747
Number of titles published annually: 10 Print; 10 E-Book
Shipping Address: Ingram Books Direct Distribution Services, 1246 Heil Quaker Blvd, La Vergne, TN 37086
Membership(s): Book Publishers of the Northwest; Pacific Northwest Booksellers Association

§ASCD
1703 N Beauregard St, Alexandria, VA 22311-1714
SAN: 201-1352
Tel: 703-578-9600 *Toll Free Tel:* 800-933-2723 *Fax:* 703-575-5400
E-mail: member@ascd.org
Web Site: www.ascd.org
Key Personnel
Publr: Stefani Roth
Dir, Book Editing & Prodn: Julie Houtz *Tel:* 703-575-5706 *E-mail:* jhoutz@ascd.org
Dir, Acqs: Genny Ostertag *Tel:* 703-575-5469 *E-mail:* gostertag@ascd.org
Dir, Sales: Jean Pride *Tel:* 703-575-5634 *E-mail:* jpride@ascd.org
Founded: 1943
Professional books for educators.
ISBN Prefix(es): 978-0-87120; 978-1-4166
Number of titles published annually: 30 Print; 20 E-Book
Total Titles: 350 Print; 319 E-Book
Orders to: PO Box 17035, Baltimore, MD 21297-8431

Ascend Books LLC
12710 Pflumm Rd, Suite 200, Olathe, KS 66062
Tel: 913-948-5500
Web Site: www.ascendbooks.com
Key Personnel
CEO & Publr: Robert Snodgrass *E-mail:* bsnodgrass@ascendbooks.com
Founded: 2009
Publisher of books on sports & entertainment topics. Some childrens books.
ISBN Prefix(es): 978-0-9830619

Number of titles published annually: 12 Print; 10 E-Book
Total Titles: 35 Print; 14 E-Book
Distribution Center: Ingram Book Co, One Ingram Blvd, La Vergne, TN 37086 *Tel:* 615-793-5000 *Toll Free Tel:* 800-937-8200 *E-mail:* customer.service@ingrambook.com *Web Site:* www.ingrambook.com
Partners Books Distribution, 2325 Jarco Dr, Holt, MI 48842 *Tel:* 517-694-3205

Ascension Press
Member of Catholic Word
PO Box 1990, West Chester, PA 19380
Tel: 610-696-7795 (ext 207, edit); 484-875-4550 (admin) *Toll Free Tel:* 800-376-0520 (sales & cust serv)
E-mail: info@ascensionpress.com
Web Site: ascensionpress.com
Key Personnel
Pres: Matthew Pinto
Creative Dir: Christopher Cope *E-mail:* ccope@ascensionpress.com
Dir, Mktg: Chris Michalski *E-mail:* cmichalski@ascensionpress.com
Dir, Prodn: Mike Fontecchio *E-mail:* mfontecchio@ascensionpress.com
Dir, Sales: Lynn Klika *E-mail:* lklika@ascensionpress.com
Dir, Theology of the Body Div: Steve Motyl *E-mail:* smotyl@ascensionpress.com
Edit Supv & Sr Ed: Mike Flickinger *E-mail:* mflickinger@ascensionpress.com
Assoc Ed: Lora Brecker *E-mail:* lbrecker@ascensionpress.com
Religious educational publishers.
ISBN Prefix(es): 978-1-932645; 978-0-9742238; 978-0-9659228; 978-0-9744451; 978-1-932631; 978-1-932927; 978-1-934217; 978-1-935940
Number of titles published annually: 15 Print
Total Titles: 250 Print; 200 Online; 40 Audio
Sales Office(s): W5169 Jefferson St, Necedah, WI 54646 *Tel:* 608-565-2020 *Toll Free Tel:* 800-376-0520 *Fax:* 608-565-5025
Orders to: W5169 Jefferson St, Necedah, WI 54646 *Tel:* 608-565-2020 *Toll Free Tel:* 800-376-0520 *Fax:* 608-565-2025
Returns: W5169 Jefferson St, Necedah, WI 54646 *Tel:* 608-565-2020 *Toll Free Tel:* 800-376-0520 *Fax:* 608-565-2025
Warehouse: W5169 Jefferson St, Necedah, WI 54646 *Tel:* 608-565-2020 *Toll Free Tel:* 800-376-0520 *Fax:* 608-565-2025
Distribution Center: W5169 Jefferson St, Necedah, WI 54646 *Tel:* 608-565-2020 *Toll Free Tel:* 800-376-0520 *Fax:* 608-565-2025

ASCP Press
Subsidiary of American Society for Clinical Pathology
33 W Monroe St, Suite 1600, Chicago, IL 60603
SAN: 207-9429
Tel: 312-541-4999 *Toll Free Tel:* 800-267-2727 *Fax:* 312-541-4998
Web Site: www.ascp.org
Key Personnel
Publr: Joshua R Weikersheimer *Tel:* 312-541-4866 *E-mail:* joshua.weikersheimer@ascp.org
Founded: 1959
Books, multimedia, slide sets, atlases, audiovisual seminars, videotapes, manuals, interactive software & videodiscs for lab professionals. Subjects include continuing education.
ISBN Prefix(es): 978-0-89189
Number of titles published annually: 15 Print; 13 CD-ROM; 7 Online
Total Titles: 212 Print; 31 CD-ROM; 80 Online

ASCSA Publications
American School of Classical Studies at Athens, 6-8 Charlton St, Princeton, NJ 08540-5232
Tel: 609-683-0800 *Fax:* 609-924-0578
Web Site: www.ascsa.edu.gr/publications
Key Personnel
Dir of Pubns: Linny Schenck *Tel:* 609-683-0800 ext 21 *E-mail:* lschenck@ascsa.org
Mng Ed: Carol A Stein *Tel:* 609-683-0800 ext 16
Prodn Mgr: Sarah George Figueira *Tel:* 609-683-0800 ext 18
Founded: 1881
Publishing office for the American School of Classical Studies at Athens, an advanced research & teaching institution focused on the history & culture of Greece & the wider Greek world.
ISBN Prefix(es): 978-0-87661
Number of titles published annually: 12 Print; 1 Online
Total Titles: 300 Print; 1 Online
Imprints: American School of Classical Studies at Athens; Gennadeion Monographs; Hesperia
Billing Address: Casemate Academic, PO Box 511, 28 Main St, Oakville, CT 06779, Contact: David Brown *Tel:* 860-945-9329 *Toll Free Tel:* 800-791-9354 *Fax:* 860-945-9468 *E-mail:* jim.drenning@dbbcdist.com *Web Site:* www.oxbowbooks.com
Orders to: Casemate Academic, PO Box 511, 28 Main St, Oakville, CT 06779, Contact: David Brown *Tel:* 860-945-9329 *Toll Free Tel:* 800-791-9354 *Fax:* 860-945-9468 *E-mail:* jim.drenning@dbbcdist.com *Web Site:* www.oxbowbooks.com
Returns: Casemate Academic, PO Box 511, 28 Main St, Oakville, CT 06779, Contact: David Brown *Tel:* 860-945-9329 *Toll Free Tel:* 800-791-9354 *Fax:* 860-945-9468 *E-mail:* jim.drenning@dbbcdist.com *Web Site:* www.oxbowbooks.com
Shipping Address: Casemate Academic, PO Box 511, 28 Main St, Oakville, CT 06779, Contact: David Brown *Tel:* 860-945-9329 *Toll Free Tel:* 800-791-9354 *Fax:* 860-945-9468 *E-mail:* jim.drenning@dbbcdist.com *Web Site:* www.oxbowbooks.com
Warehouse: Casemate Academic, PO Box 511, 28 Main St, Oakville, CT 06779, Contact: David Brown *Tel:* 860-945-9329 *Toll Free Tel:* 800-791-9354 *Fax:* 860-945-9468 *E-mail:* jim.drenning@dbbcdist.com *Web Site:* www.oxbowbooks.com
Distribution Center: Casemate Academic, PO Box 511, 28 Main St, Oakville, CT 06779, Contact: David Brown *Tel:* 860-945-9329 *Toll Free Tel:* 800-791-9354 *Fax:* 860-945-9468 *E-mail:* jim.drenning@dbbcdist.com *Web Site:* www.oxbowbooks.com
Membership(s): AAP Professional & Scholarly Publishing Division; American Association of University Presses; Society for Scholarly Publishing

ASET - The Neurodiagnostic Society
402 E Bannister Rd, Suite A, Kansas City, KS 64131-3019
Tel: 816-931-1120 *Fax:* 816-931-1145
E-mail: info@aset.org
Web Site: www.aset.org
Key Personnel
Exec Dir: Arlen Reimnitz *Tel:* 816-931-1120 ext 4 *E-mail:* arlen@aset.org
Mktg & Communs Mgr: Sarah Ecker *Tel:* 816-931-1120 ext 3 *E-mail:* sarah@aset.org
Founded: 1959
Books on EEG, evoked potentials, nerve conduction & polysomnography technology.
ISBN Prefix(es): 978-1-57797
Number of titles published annually: 8 Print
Total Titles: 55 Print; 59 CD-ROM

Ash Tree Publishing
PO Box 64, Woodstock, NY 12498
Tel: 845-246-8081 *Fax:* 845-246-8081
E-mail: info@ashtreepublishing.com
Web Site: www.ashtreepublishing.com
Key Personnel
Founder & Owner: Susun Weed
Orders: Michael Dattorre *E-mail:* wisewoman@herbshealing.com
Founded: 1985
ISBN Prefix(es): 978-1-888123; 978-0-9614620
Number of titles published annually: 3 Print; 1 CD-ROM; 1 Audio
Total Titles: 14 Print; 1 CD-ROM; 2 Audio
Distributed by Ash Tree Publishing; Brumby Sunstate; Dempsey Your Distributor; New Leaf; Nutri-Books; Partners

Ashgate Publishing Co
Subsidiary of Ashgate Publishing Ltd
110 Cherry St, Suite 3-1, Burlington, VT 05401-3818
SAN: 262-0308
Tel: 802-865-7641 *Toll Free Tel:* 800-535-9544 *Fax:* 802-865-7847
E-mail: ashgate.online@ashgate.com
Web Site: www.ashgate.com
Key Personnel
Fin Cont: Burta Kelly
Head of Busn Intelligence & Data Mgmt: Brandon DeCoff
Founded: 1979
International publisher of scholarly studies in the humanities & social sciences. Covers a wide range of subject areas including law, professional, scholarly reference books, sociology, business management, philosophy, economics, art, music, literary studies, history & more.
ISBN Prefix(es): 978-0-566; 978-1-85742; 978-0-85967; 978-1-85628; 978-0-86078; 978-0-86127; 978-0-85331; 978-0-291; 978-0-7546; 978-1-85521; 978-1-85928; 978-1-84014; 978-0-85417; 978-1-4094
Number of titles published annually: 800 Print
Total Titles: 1,000 Print
Imprints: Ashgate; Gower; Lund Humphries
Distributor for Pickering & Chatto

Ashland Creek Press
2305 Ashland St, Suite C417, Ashland, OR 97520
Tel: 760-300-3620
E-mail: editors@ashlandcreekpress.com
Web Site: www.ashlandcreekpress.com
Key Personnel
Founder & Ed: Midge Raymond *E-mail:* midge@ashlandcreekpress.com; John Yunker *E-mail:* john@ashlandcreekpress.com
Founded: 2011
Small, independent publisher of books with a world view. Our mission is to publish a range of books that foster an appreciation for worlds outside our own, for nature & the animal kingdom & for the ways in which we all connect.
ISBN Prefix(es): 978-0-9796475; 978-1-61822
Number of titles published annually: 5 Print; 5 E-Book
Total Titles: 19 Print; 19 E-Book
Imprints: Ashland Creek Press; Byte Level Books
Membership(s): The Independent Book Publishers Association

Ashland Poetry Press
Affiliate of Ashland University
Ashland University, 401 College Ave, Ashland, OH 44805
Tel: 419-289-5957 *Fax:* 419-289-5255
E-mail: app@ashland.edu
Web Site: www.ashland.edu/aupoetry
Key Personnel
Dir: Dr Stephen Haven *E-mail:* shaven@ashland.edu
Mng Ed: Sarah M Wells *E-mail:* swells@ashland.edu
Ed: Dr Deborah Fleming *E-mail:* dfleming@ashland.edu
Founded: 1969

ISBN Prefix(es): 978-0-912592
Number of titles published annually: 4 Print
Total Titles: 60 Print
Distribution Center: Small Press Distribution, 1341 Seventh St, Berkeley, CA 94710-1409
Web Site: www.spdbooks.org
Membership(s): Community of Literary Magazines & Presses; The Independent Book Publishers Association

ASIS International
1625 Prince St, Alexandria, VA 22314
Tel: 703-519-6200 *Fax:* 703-519-6299
E-mail: asis@asisonline.org
Web Site: www.asisonline.org
Key Personnel
Educ Publg Mgr: Evangeline A Pappas *E-mail:* evangeline.pappas@asisonline.org
Founded: 1955
Organization for security professionals, with more than 33,000 members worldwide. Dedicated to increasing the effectiveness & productivy of security professionals by developing educational programs & materials that address broad security interests, such as the annual seminar & exhibits, as well as specific security topics. Also advocates the role & value of the security management profession to business, the media, government entities & the public.
ISBN Prefix(es): 978-1-887056
Number of titles published annually: 3 Print; 2 CD-ROM
Total Titles: 35 Print; 2 CD-ROM

Aslan Publishing
Division of Renaissance Book Services Corp
857 Post Rd, Suite 302, Fairfield, CT 06824
SAN: 242-6129
Tel: 203-372-0300; 203-374-6224 *Fax:* 203-374-4766
E-mail: information@aslanpublishing.com
Web Site: www.aslanpublishing.com
Key Personnel
Pres & Lib Sales Dir: Harold Levine *E-mail:* harold@aslanpublishing.com
Founded: 1984
Publish nonfiction books on personal growth, psychology & inspiration, parenting & education, health & cooking.
ISBN Prefix(es): 978-0-944031
Number of titles published annually: 3 Print
Total Titles: 32 Print

§ASM International
9639 Kinsman Rd, Materials Park, OH 44073-0002
SAN: 204-7586
Tel: 440-338-5151 *Toll Free Tel:* 800-336-5152; 800-368-9800 (Europe) *Fax:* 440-338-4634
E-mail: memberservicecenter@asminternational.org
Web Site: asmcommunity.asminternational.org
Key Personnel
Mgr, eDocument Prodn: Madrid Tramble *Tel:* 440-338-5151 ext 5677
Founded: 1913
Technical & reference books.
ISBN Prefix(es): 978-0-87170
Number of titles published annually: 10 Print; 3 CD-ROM; 35 Online
Total Titles: 210 Print; 1,000 Online
Foreign Rep(s): ATP (Europe); B I Publications (India); Sejong Books Inc (Korea)

§ASM Press
Division of American Society for Microbiology
1752 "N" St NW, Washington, DC 20036-2904
Tel: 202-737-3600 *Toll Free Tel:* 800-546-2416 *Fax:* 202-942-9342
E-mail: books@asmusa.org
Web Site: estore.asm.org
Key Personnel
Exec Dir: Michael Goldberg *E-mail:* mgoldberg@asmusa.org
Dir: Christine Charlip *E-mail:* ccharlip@asmusa.org
Dir, Journals Div: Barbara Goldman *E-mail:* bgoldman@asmusa.org
Mktg Mgr, Journals: Nichole Ridgeway *E-mail:* nridgeway@asmusa.org
Mktg Coord: Elena Scalerbio *E-mail:* escalerbio@asmusa.org
Edit & Rts Coord: Lindsay Williams *E-mail:* lwilliams@asmusa.org
Founded: 1899
Microbiology, cell biology, medicine, books, journals, proceedings & abstracts.
ISBN Prefix(es): 978-1-55581
Number of titles published annually: 14 Print; 1 CD-ROM; 15 Online
Total Titles: 250 Print; 3 CD-ROM; 25 Online
Foreign Rep(s): Cranbury International (Latin America); Information & Culture Korea (ICK) (South Korea); Donald MacIvor & Associates (Canada); Taylor & Francis Group (UK)
Foreign Rights: Aditya Books Pvt Ltd (Bangladesh, India, Nepal, Pakistan, Sri Lanka); Apex Knowledge Sdn Bhd (Brunei, Malaysia); Booknet Co Ltd (Cambodia, Laos, Myanmar, Thailand, Vietnam); DA Information Services (Australia, Fiji, New Zealand, Papua New Guinea); iCaves Ltd (China, Hong Kong, Macau); IG Knowledge Services Ltd (Taiwan); MegaTEXTS Phil Inc (Philippines); United Publishers Services Ltd (Japan); John Wiley & Sons Ltd (Africa, Europe, Middle East); Woodslane (Australia, Fiji, New Zealand, Papua New Guinea, Solomon Islands)
Orders to: PO Box 605, Herndon, VA 20172 *Tel:* 703-661-1593 *Fax:* 703-661-1501 *E-mail:* asmmail@presswarehouse.com
Returns: PO Box 605, Herndon, VA 20172 *Tel:* 703-661-1593 *Fax:* 703-661-1501 *E-mail:* asmmail@presswarehouse.com
Warehouse: 22883 Quicksilver Dr, Dulles, VA 20166

§Aspatore Books
Division of Thomson Reuters
610 Opperman Dr, Eagan, MN 55123
Tel: 651-687-7000 *Toll Free Tel:* 866-ASPATORE (277-2867); 888-728-7677; 800-328-4880
E-mail: customerservice@thomsonreuters.com
Web Site: legalsolutions.thomsonreuters.com; www.aspatore.com
Founded: 1999
Publish only the biggest names in the business world, including C-Level leaders (CEO, CTO, CFO, COO, CMO, Partner) from over half the world's 500 largest companies & other leading executives. By focusing on publishing only C-Level executives, we provide professionals of all levels with proven business intelligence from industry insiders, rather than relying on the knowledge of unknown authors & analysts.
ISBN Prefix(es): 978-0-314; 978-1-58762; 978-1-59622
Number of titles published annually: 150 Print
Total Titles: 500 Print
Imprints: Aspatore Thought Leadership; Bigwig Briefs; Executive Reports; Inside the Minds; Line by Line

Aspen Publishers Inc, see Wolters Kluwer Law & Business

Associated University Presses
10 Schalks Crossing Rd, Suite 501-330, Plainsboro, NJ 08536
Tel: 609-269-8094 *Fax:* 609-269-8096
E-mail: aup440@aol.com
Founded: 1968
Book publisher & licensor of intellectual property rights.
ISBN Prefix(es): 978-0-8453
Number of titles published annually: 3 Print; 3 E-Book
Total Titles: 3,000 E-Book
Distributor for Susquehanna University Press

§Association for Computing Machinery
2 Penn Plaza, Suite 701, New York, NY 10121-0701
SAN: 267-7784
Mailing Address: PO Box 30777, New York, NY 10087-0777
Tel: 212-626-0500 *Toll Free Tel:* 800-342-6626 *Fax:* 212-944-1318
E-mail: acmhelp@acm.org
Web Site: www.acm.org
Key Personnel
Publg Dir: Scott Delman *E-mail:* scott.delman@hq.acm.org
Pubns Dir: Bernard Rous *Tel:* 212-626-0660 *E-mail:* rous@acm.org
Founded: 1947
Computer science.
ISBN Prefix(es): 978-0-89791; 978-1-58113; 978-1-59593; 978-1-60558; 978-1-4503
Number of titles published annually: 150 Print
Total Titles: 500 Print
Foreign Office(s): FIT Bldg 1-118, Tsinghua University, Beijing 100084, China *Tel:* (010) 62783549 *E-mail:* acmchina@tsinghua.edu.cn
Membership(s): AAP

Association for Information Science & Technology (ASIS&T)
8555 16 St, Suite 850, Silver Spring, MD 20910
Tel: 301-495-0900 *Fax:* 301-495-0810
E-mail: asis@asis.org
Web Site: www.asis.org
Key Personnel
Exec Dir: Richard Hill *E-mail:* rhill@asis.org
Founded: 1937
Provides high-quality conference programs & publications for information systems developers, online professionals, information resource managers, librarians, records managers, academics & others who "bridge the gap".
ISBN Prefix(es): 978-0-87715
Number of titles published annually: 12 Print; 1 CD-ROM; 1 Online
Total Titles: 12 Print; 1 CD-ROM; 1 Online
Distributed by Information Today Inc; John Wiley & Sons Inc

Association for Talent Development (ATD)
Formerly American Society for Training & Development (ASTD)
1640 King St, Box 1443, Alexandria, VA 22313-1443
SAN: 224-8972
Tel: 703-683-8100 *Toll Free Tel:* 800-628-2783 *Fax:* 703-299-8723; 703-683-1523 (cust care)
E-mail: customercare@td.org
Web Site: www.astd.org; www.td.org
Key Personnel
Pres & CEO: Tony Bingham
Sr Dir, Pubns: Holly Nogas *Tel:* 703-683-8173 *E-mail:* hnogas@astd.org
Founded: 1944
Internationally renowned source of insightful & practical information on workplace learning & performance topics, including training basics, evaluation & return-on investment, instructional systems development, e-learning, leadership & career development.
ISBN Prefix(es): 978-1-56286; 978-1-60728
Number of titles published annually: 25 Print; 4 CD-ROM
Total Titles: 200 Print
Distributed by Cengage Learning Asia Pte Ltd (Asia); Eurospan Group (Europe, Middle East

& the former Soviet Bloc); Knowledge Resources (South Africa); National Book Network (NBN) (US, CN, Australia & New Zealand)

Association of College & Research Libraries (ACRL)
Division of The American Library Association (ALA)
50 E Huron St, Chicago, IL 60611
Tel: 312-280-2523 *Toll Free Tel:* 800-545-2433 (ext 2523) *Fax:* 312-280-2520
E-mail: acrl@ala.org
Web Site: www.ala.org/acrl
Key Personnel
Exec Dir: Mary Ellen K Davis *Tel:* 312-280-3248 *E-mail:* mdavis@ala.org
Founded: 1938
ISBN Prefix(es): 978-0-8389
Number of titles published annually: 8 Print
Total Titles: 60 Print

Association of Research Libraries
21 Dupont Circle NW, Suite 800, Washington, DC 20036
Tel: 202-296-2296 *Fax:* 202-872-0884
E-mail: arlhq@arl.org
Web Site: www.arl.org
Key Personnel
Pubns Prog Offr: Lee Anne George *E-mail:* leeanne@arl.org
Founded: 1932
Serial, occasional paper series & special topics of interest.
ISBN Prefix(es): 978-0-918006; 978-1-59407
Number of titles published annually: 10 Print; 14 Online
Total Titles: 600 Print; 90 Online
Distribution Center: ARL Publications Distribution Center, PO Box 531, Annapolis Junction, MD 20701-0531 *Tel:* 301-362-8196 *Fax:* 240-396-2479
Membership(s): AAP

Association of School Business Officials International
11401 N Shore Dr, Reston, VA 20190
Tel: 703-478-0405 *Toll Free Tel:* 866-682-2729 *Fax:* 703-708-7060
E-mail: asboreq@asbointl.org; asbosba@asbointl.org
Web Site: www.asbointl.org
Key Personnel
Ed: Patricia George
Pubns Mgr: Lauren Passey *E-mail:* lpassey@asbointl.org
Founded: 1910
Professional books.
ISBN Prefix(es): 978-0-910170; 978-0-810847; 978-1-1578860
Number of titles published annually: 8 Print
Total Titles: 40 Print

Asta Publications LLC
PO Box 1735, Stockbridge, GA 30281
Tel: 678-814-1320 *Toll Free Tel:* 800-482-4190 *Fax:* 678-814-1370
E-mail: info@astapublications.com
Web Site: www.astapublications.com
Key Personnel
Founder & CEO: Assuanta Howard *E-mail:* ahoward@astapublications.com
Publg Coord: Ms Rachel Schade *Tel:* 678-814-1390 *E-mail:* rschade@astapublications.com
Founded: 2004
Delivering first-class book publishing services for corporations, entrepreneurs & individuals who understand the power of being a published author.
This publisher has indicated that 30% of their product line is author subsidized.
ISBN Prefix(es): 978-0-9777060; 978-1-934947
Number of titles published annually: 200 Print; 200 Online; 200 E-Book
Total Titles: 500 Print; 500 Online; 500 E-Book
Membership(s): The Association of Publishers for Special Sales; PMA International

§ASTM International
100 Barr Harbor Dr, West Conshohocken, PA 19428-2959
Mailing Address: PO Box C-700, West Conshohocken, PA 19428
Tel: 610-832-9500; 610-832-9585 (intl) *Toll Free Tel:* 877-909-2786 (sales & cust support) *Fax:* 610-832-9555
E-mail: service@astm.org
Web Site: www.astm.org
Key Personnel
Pres: James A Thomas *Tel:* 610-832-9598 *Fax:* 610-832-9599 *E-mail:* jthomas@astm.org
VP, Pubns & Mktg: John Pace *Tel:* 610-832-9632 *E-mail:* jpace@astm.org
Mgr, Sales & Mktg: George Zajdel *Tel:* 610-832-9614 *E-mail:* gzajdel@astm.org
Founded: 1898
Standards, technical publications, data series manuals & journals on engineering, science, materials testing, safety, quality control.
ISBN Prefix(es): 978-0-8031
Number of titles published annually: 176 Print; 125 CD-ROM
Total Titles: 1,500 Print; 125 CD-ROM; 80 Online

Astragal Press
Imprint of Finney Company Inc
5995 149 St W, Suite 105, Apple Valley, MN 55124
Tel: 952-469-6699 *Toll Free Tel:* 866-543-3045 *Fax:* 952-469-1968 *Toll Free Fax:* 800-330-6232
E-mail: info@finneyco.com
Web Site: www.astragalpress.com
Key Personnel
Pres: Alan Krysan *E-mail:* akrysan@finneyco.com
Mktg Mgr: Heather McNulty
Founded: 1983
Early tools, trades & technology.
ISBN Prefix(es): 978-0-9618088; 978-1-879335; 978-1-931626
Number of titles published annually: 5 Print
Total Titles: 89 Print; 89 Online

The Astronomical Society of the Pacific
390 Ashton Ave, San Francisco, CA 94112
Tel: 415-337-1100 *Toll Free Tel:* 800-335-2624 *Fax:* 415-337-5205
Web Site: www.astrosociety.org
Key Personnel
Exec Dir: Dr Linda Shore *Tel:* 415-715-1411 *E-mail:* lshore@astrosociety.org
Founded: 1889
Books, booklets, tapes, slide sets, software & other educational materials about astronomy; conference proceedings. Mercury Magazine. PASP (Publications of the Astronomical Society of the Pacific) Journal.
ISBN Prefix(es): 978-0-937707; 978-1-886733; 978-1-58381
Number of titles published annually: 20 Print; 1 CD-ROM; 20 E-Book; 1 Audio
Total Titles: 360 Print; 1 CD-ROM; 60 E-Book; 1 Audio

Asylum Arts Press, see Leaping Dog Press/Asylum Arts Press

ATD, see Association for Talent Development (ATD)

Atheneum Books for Young Readers, see Simon & Schuster Children's Publishing

Athletic Guide Publishing
PO Box 1050, Flagler Beach, FL 32136
Tel: 386-439-2050 *Toll Free Tel:* 800-255-1050
E-mail: flaglernet@gmail.com
Web Site: www.athleticguidepublishing.com
Key Personnel
Ed: Tom Keegan
Founded: 1990
Publish hockey guides.
ISBN Prefix(es): 978-1-880941; 978-1-60179
Number of titles published annually: 35 Print
Total Titles: 120 Print
Imprints: American Sports Publishing; Old Kings Road Press
Membership(s): The Independent Book Publishers Association

Atlantic Law Book Co
Division of Peter Kelsey Publishing Inc
22 Grassmere Ave, West Hartford, CT 06110-1215
Tel: 860-231-9300 *Toll Free Tel:* 800-259-5534 *Fax:* 860-231-9242
E-mail: atlanticlawbooks@aol.com
Web Site: www.atlanticlawbooks.com
Key Personnel
VP: Richard Epstein
Founded: 1945
Law books for Connecticut legal practice. Marketed in Connecticut & other states & used by practitioners & judges in this state. The books are all written by law professors, lawyers or judges who are recognized experts in their respective fields. The material is updated regularly, usually by annual pocket supplements.
ISBN Prefix(es): 978-1-878698
Number of titles published annually: 12 Print; 2 CD-ROM
Total Titles: 12 Print; 2 CD-ROM

Atlantic Publishing Group Inc
1405 SW Sixth Ave, Ocala, FL 34471
Tel: 352-622-1825 *Toll Free Tel:* 800-814-1132 *Fax:* 352-622-1875
E-mail: sales@atlantic-pub.com
Web Site: www.atlantic-pub.com
Key Personnel
Pres: Douglas R Brown
VP: Sherri L Brown
General business, how-to, real estate, financial, education, nonprofit, restaurant management, hospitality training, videos & posters.
ISBN Prefix(es): 978-0-910627; 978-1-60138
Number of titles published annually: 100 Print; 25 CD-ROM
Total Titles: 500 Print; 150 CD-ROM
Returns: 315 E Washington St, Starke, FL 32091
Distribution Center: 315 E Washington St, Starke, FL 32091

Atria Books
Imprint of Atria Publishing Group
1230 Avenue of the Americas, New York, NY 10020
Tel: 212-698-7000 *Fax:* 212-698-7007
Web Site: www.simonandschuster.com
Key Personnel
Pres & Publr, Atria Publishing Group: Judith Curr *Tel:* 212-698-1260 *E-mail:* judith.curr@simonandschuster.com
SVP & Ed-in-Chief, Emily Bestler Books: Emily Bestler *Tel:* 212-698-7685 *E-mail:* emily.bestler@simonandschuster.com
VP & Edit Dir: Peter Borland *Tel:* 212-698-7569 *E-mail:* peter.borland@simonandschuster.com
VP & Sr Ed: Johanna Castillo *Tel:* 212-698-7339 *E-mail:* johanna.castillo@simonandschuster.com
VP & Dir, Subs Rts: Lisa Keim *Tel:* 212-698-7397 *E-mail:* lisa.keim@simonandschuster.com
VP, Publr, 37 Ink: Dawn Davis *Tel:* 212-698-2246 *E-mail:* dawn.davis@simonandschuster.com

VP & Sr Ed: Leslie Meredith *E-mail:* leslie.meredith@simonandschuster.com
Sr Dir, Art & Design: Albert Tang *Tel:* 212-698-7255 *E-mail:* albert.tang@simonandschuster.com
Ed: Sarah Branham *Tel:* 212-698-7172 *E-mail:* sarah.branham@simonandschuster.com
Founded: 2002
ISBN Prefix(es): 978-0-671; 978-0-7434; 978-0-7432
Imprints: Atria Trade Paperback; Emily Bestler Books; Beyond Words; Enliven; Keywords Press; Marble Arch; Strebor Books; 37 Ink; Washington Square Press
Foreign Rights: Akcali Copyright Agency (Turkey); Antonella Antonelli Agenzia (Italy); Bardon-Chinese Media Agency (China, Thailand); The Book Publishers' Association of Israel, International Promotion & Literary Rights Department (Israel); Japan UNI Agency Inc (Japan); JLM Literary Agency (Greece); MOHRBOOKS AG, Literary Agency (Germany); La Nouvelle Agency; Andrew Nurnberg Associates Ltd (Bulgaria, Croatia, Estonia, Hungary, Latvia, Lithuania, Montenegro, Poland, Romania, Russia, Serbia, Slovakia, Slovenia); Sane Toregard Agency (Denmark, Finland, Norway, Sweden); Sebes & Van Gelderen Literary Agency; Tuttle-Mori Agency Inc (Thailand); Eric Yang Agency

Atwood Publishing
PO Box 3185, Madison, WI 53704
Tel: 608-242-7101 *Toll Free Tel:* 888-242-7101 *Fax:* 608-242-7102
E-mail: customerservice@atwoodpublishing.com
Web Site: www.atwoodpublishing.com
Key Personnel
Publr: Linda Babler *E-mail:* lindab@atwoodpublishing.com
Founded: 1997
Book publishing for higher education market: teaching improvement, distance, education, student affairs, semiotics & administration.
ISBN Prefix(es): 978-1-891859
Number of titles published annually: 4 Print
Total Titles: 55 Print; 2 CD-ROM; 8 E-Book
Returns: 2095 Winnebago St, Suite B, Madison, WI 53704

§Augsburg Fortress Publishers, Publishing House of the Evangelical Lutheran Church in America
510 Marquette Ave S, Minneapolis, MN 55402
SAN: 169-4081
Mailing Address: PO Box 1209, Minneapolis, MN 55440-1209
Tel: 612-330-3300 *Toll Free Tel:* 800-426-0115 (ext 639, subns); 800-328-4648 (orders) *Fax:* 612-330-3455
E-mail: info@augsburgfortress.org; copyright@augsburgfortress.org (reprint permission requests); customercare@augsburgfortress.org
Web Site: www.augsburgfortress.org
Key Personnel
CEO & Pres: Beth A Lewis *E-mail:* ceo@augsburgfortress.org
CFO: John Rahja
SVP: Tim Blevins *Tel:* 612-330-3300 ext 400 *E-mail:* tim.blevins@augsburgfortress.org
VP & Publr, Fortress Press: Will Bergkamp *E-mail:* will.bergkamp@augsburgfortress.org
VP & Publr, Sparkhouse: Tim Paulson
VP, HR: Sandy Middendorf
Publr, Worship & Music: Martin Seltz
Perms, Cust: Michael Moore
Perms, Pubns: Esther Diley *E-mail:* esther.diley@augsburgfortress.org
Founded: 1855
Publishing House of the Evangelical Lutheran Church in America.
ISBN Prefix(es): 978-0-8066; 978-0-8006
Number of titles published annually: 100 Print
Total Titles: 996 Print; 10 CD-ROM; 5 Audio
Imprints: Augsburg Books; Fortress Press; Sparkhouse
Branch Office(s)
500 Trillium Dr, Unit 19, Kitchener, ON N2R 1E5, Canada *Tel:* 519-748-2200 *Fax:* 519-748-9835 *E-mail:* kitchenerstore@augsburgfortress.org
Sales Office(s): PO Box 1209, Minneapolis, MN 55440-1209
Foreign Rep(s): Asian Trading Corp (India); Australian Church Resources (Australia); Canaanland Distributors Sdn Bhd (Malaysia); Cross Communications Ltd (Hong Kong); Durnell Marketing (Israel); John Garratt Publishing (Australia); Glad Sounds Sdn Bhd (Malaysia); KCBS Inc (Korea); Kyo Bun Kwan Inc (Japan); Logos Publishers Ltd (Hong Kong); MediaCom Education (Australia); N-Online Co Ltd (Japan); NBN International (UK); Pustaka Sufes Sdn Bhd (Malaysia); Rainbow Book Agency (Australia); SKS Books Warehouse (Singapore); Soul Distributors Ltd (New Zealand); Taosheng Publishing House (Hong Kong); Tecman Management Services (Singapore)
Billing Address: PO Box 1209, Minneapolis, MN 55440-1209
Orders to: PBD Worldwide, c/o AF Distribution, 905 Carlow Dr, Unit B, Bolingbrook, IL 60490
Warehouse: PBD Worldwide, c/o AF Distribution, 905 Carlow Dr, Unit B, Bolingbrook, IL 60490
Distribution Center: PBD Worldwide, c/o AF Distribution, 905 Carlow Dr, Unit B, Bolingbrook, IL 60490

August House Inc
3500 Piedmont Rd NE, Suite 310, Atlanta, GA 30305
Tel: 404-442-4420 *Toll Free Tel:* 800-284-8784 *Fax:* 404-442-4435
E-mail: ahinfo@augusthouse.com
Web Site: www.augusthouse.com
Key Personnel
CEO: Steve Floyd *E-mail:* steve@augusthouse.com
EVP & Creative Dir: Graham Anthony *E-mail:* graham@augusthouse.com
Dir, Devt: Rob Cleveland *E-mail:* rob@augusthouse.com
Founded: 1979
Folklore, multicultural folktales & storytelling.
ISBN Prefix(es): 978-0-87483
Number of titles published annually: 15 Print; 30 Online; 15 E-Book
Total Titles: 350 Print; 300 Online; 15 E-Book; 71 Audio
Imprints: August House Audio; August House Little Folk; August House Story Cove
Foreign Rights: The Fielding Agency (Whitney Lee)

Aum Publications
86-10 Parsons Blvd, Jamaica, NY 11432-3314
SAN: 201-128X
Tel: 347-744-3199
Key Personnel
Pres: Carl Brown
Founded: 1973
Trade paperbacks; literature, Eastern philosophy, theology, occult, poetry, meditation; only books on or by Sri Chinmoy.
ISBN Prefix(es): 978-0-88497
Number of titles published annually: 5 Print
Total Titles: 53 Print; 2 CD-ROM
Distribution Center: Heart-Light Distributors, PO Box 85464, Seattle, WA 98145 *Toll Free Tel:* 800-739-2885 *Fax:* 206-523-5637

AuthorHouse
Division of Author Solutions Inc
1663 Liberty Dr, Bloomington, IN 47403
Tel: 812-339-6000 (outside US) *Toll Free Tel:* 888-519-5121
E-mail: authorsupport@authorhouse.com
Web Site: www.authorhouse.com
Key Personnel
CEO: Andrew Phillips
COO: Kevin G Gregory
CIO: Randy Davis
SVP, Mktg: Keith Ogorek
SVP, Prodn Servs & Output Opers: Bill Becher
SVP, Worldwide Sales: Don Seitz
VP, Mktg: Tracey Rosengrave
VP, Sales & Mktg: Bruce Bunner
Founded: 1997
The leading provider of indie book publishing, marketing & bookselling services for authors around the globe. Committed to providing the highest level of customer service. Assign each author personal publishing & marketing consultants who provide guidance throughout the process.
This publisher has indicated that 100% of their product line is author subsidized.
ISBN Prefix(es): 978-1-58500; 978-0-9675669; 978-1-58721; 978-1-58820; 978-0-7596; 978-1-4033; 978-1-4107; 978-1-4140; 978-1-4184; 978-1-4208
Number of titles published annually: 7,500 Print
Total Titles: 80,000 Print
Foreign Office(s): AuthorHouse UK, 500 Avebury Blvd, Milton Keynes MK9 2BE, United Kingdom *Toll Free Tel:* 800-197-4150 *Toll Free Fax:* 800-197-4151
Distribution Center: Baker & Taylor Inc, 2550 W Tyvola Rd, Suite 300, Charlotte, CA 28217
Ingram Book Group, One Ingram Blvd, La Vergne, TN 37086-1986
Membership(s): ABA; Canadian Booksellers Association

Authorlink Press
Imprint of Authorlink®
103 Guadalupe Dr, Irving, TX 75039-3334
Tel: 972-402-0101
E-mail: admin@authorlink.com
Web Site: www.authorlink.com
Key Personnel
Founder, CEO & Ed-in-Chief: Doris Booth *E-mail:* dbooth@authorlink.com
Founded: 1996
A traditional publisher specializing in true crime, books about the craft of writing, a few children's titles, books on women's issues & some self-help. Most of our titles are published as traditional runs & not as print on demand. We are an award-winning rights market-place where editors & agents buy & sell unpublished & published mss & screenplays. Provides the serious writer with access exposure to the broadest range of legitimate publishing professionals. Plus industry news, information & marketing services for publishers, literary agents, writers & readers.
ISBN Prefix(es): 978-1-928704
Number of titles published annually: 10 Print; 8 E-Book
Total Titles: 20 Print; 8 Online
Orders to: Lightning Source, 1246 Heil Quaker Blvd, La Vergne, TN 37086 *Tel:* 615-213-5815 *Fax:* 615-213-4426 *E-mail:* inquiry@lightningsource.com *Web Site:* www.lightningsource.com
Distribution Center: Lightning Source, 1246 Heil Quaker Blvd, La Vergne, TN 37086 *Tel:* 615-213-5815 *Fax:* 615-213-4426 *E-mail:* inquiry@lightningsource.com *Web Site:* www.lightningsource.com

Autism Asperger Publishing Co
11209 Strang Line Rd, Lenexa, KS 66215
Tel: 913-897-1004 *Toll Free Tel:* 877-277-8254 *Fax:* 913-681-9473
E-mail: info@aapcpublishing.net

Web Site: www.aapcpublishing.net
Key Personnel
Pres: Keith Myles *Tel:* 913-232-4500
E-mail: keith.myles@aapcpublishing.net
Dir, Opers: James Jones *Tel:* 913-232-4501
E-mail: james.jones@aapcpublishing.net
Gen Mgr: Serdar Marun *Tel:* 913-232-4505
E-mail: serdar.marun@aapcpublishing.net
Specialize in books & multimedia on autism spectrum disorders (ASD) & related exceptionalities for individuals on the spectrum, their parents, families, peers, educators & other professionals.
ISBN Prefix(es): 978-0-9672514; 978-1-931282; 978-1-937473; 978-1-934575
Number of titles published annually: 24 Print
Branch Office(s)
122 "C" St NW, Suite 360, Washington, DC 20001 *Tel:* 202-298-6449

Autumn House Press
87 1/2 Westwood St, Pittsburgh, PA 15211
Tel: 412-381-4261
Web Site: www.autumnhouse.org
Key Personnel
Assoc Ed: Christine Stroud *E-mail:* cstroud@autumnhouse.org
Founded: 1998
Nonprofit corporation with the mission of publishing poetry, fiction & nonfiction. Submissions should be through one of the annual contests. Guidelines are posted on the web site. Publish the online journal *Coal Hill Review*.
ISBN Prefix(es): 978-0-9669419; 978-1-932870
Number of titles published annually: 10 Print; 1 Online; 10 E-Book
Total Titles: 100 Print; 12 Online; 50 E-Book

Avalon Travel Publishing
Member of The Perseus Books Group
1700 Fourth St, Berkeley, CA 94710
Tel: 510-595-3664 *Fax:* 510-809-3777
Web Site: www.avalontravelbooks.com
Key Personnel
SVP & Publr: Bill Newlin
VP & Assoc Publr: Donna Galassi
VP, Prodn: Jane Musser
Edit Dir: Kevin McLain *Tel:* 510-595-3664 ext 3811
Founded: 1999
Avalon Travel Publishing, a member of the Perseus Books Group, is the largest independent travel publisher in the US. Major series include Rick Steves, Moon Handbooks, Moon Metro, Foghorn Outdoors, The Dog Lover's Companion, Living Abroad & Road Trip USA.
ISBN Prefix(es): 978-1-56261; 978-1-56691; 978-1-57354; 978-1-59880
Number of titles published annually: 211 Print
Total Titles: 700 Print
Distributed by Perseus Books Group-International Sales; Publishers Group Canada; Publishers Group West
Orders to: Publishers Group West/Perseus Books Group, 1094 Flex Dr, Jackson, TN 38301 *Toll Free Tel:* 800-788-3123 *Toll Free Fax:* 800-351-5073
Distribution Center: Publishers Group West/Perseus Books Group, 1094 Flex Dr, Jackson, TN 38301 *Toll Free Tel:* 800-788-3123 *Toll Free Fax:* 800-351-5073

Ave Maria Press
PO Box 428, Notre Dame, IN 46556
SAN: 201-1255
Tel: 574-287-2831 *Toll Free Tel:* 800-282-1865 *Fax:* 574-239-2904 *Toll Free Fax:* 800-282-5681
E-mail: avemariapress.1@nd.edu
Web Site: www.avemariapress.com
Key Personnel
CEO & Publr: Thomas Grady *Tel:* 574-287-2831 ext 212 *E-mail:* tgrady@nd.edu
VP & Creative Dir: Kristen Bonelli *Tel:* 574-287-2831 ext 240 *E-mail:* hornyak.3@nd.edu
VP & Dir, Sales & Mktg: Karey Circosta *Tel:* 574-287-2831 ext 219 *E-mail:* kcircosta@nd.edu
Edit Dir: Robert Hamma *Tel:* 574-287-2831 ext 214 *E-mail:* robert.m.hamma.1@nd.edu
Sales Mgr: Kay Luther *Tel:* 574-287-2831 ext 232 *E-mail:* k.luther.8@nd.edu
Founded: 1865
Adult paperback books of religious interest; prayer books & religious education materials, programs & textbooks.
ISBN Prefix(es): 978-0-87793 (Ave Maria Press); 978-0-939516 (Forest of Peace); 978-0-87061 (Christian Classics); 978-1-893732 (Sorin Books); 978-1-59471 (Ave Maria Press); 978-1-933495 (Sorin Books)
Number of titles published annually: 40 Print
Total Titles: 550 Print
Imprints: Ave Maria Press; Christian Classics; Forest of Peace; Sorin Books
Foreign Rep(s): Alban Books Ltd (UK); John Garratt Publishing (Australia); Joseph's Inspirational (Canada); Pleroma Christian Supplies (New Zealand)
Returns: 1865 Moreau Dr, Notre Dame, IN 46556

Avery
Imprint of Penguin Group (USA) LLC
375 Hudson St, New York, NY 10014
SAN: 282-5074
Tel: 212-366-2000 *Fax:* 212-366-2643
E-mail: online@penguinputnam.com
Web Site: www.penguinputnam.com; us.penguingroup.com
Key Personnel
VP & Publr: Megan Newman
Exec Ed: Lucia Watson
Ed: Brooke Carey
Assoc Ed: Gigi Campo
Mktg & Publicity Dir: Lindsay Gordon Bezalel
Publicity Mgr: Anne Kosmoski
Founded: 1976 (acquired by Penguin Putnam Inc in the fall of 1999)
The imprint is dedicated to publishing books on health & nutrition with a complimentary, natural, or alternative focus.
ISBN Prefix(es): 978-0-89529; 978-1-58333
Number of titles published annually: 35 Print
Total Titles: 247 Print

Avery Color Studios
511 "D" Ave, Gwinn, MI 49841
Tel: 906-346-3908 *Toll Free Tel:* 800-722-9925 *Fax:* 906-346-3015
E-mail: averycolor@averycolorstudios.com
Key Personnel
Pres: Wells Chapin
Busn Mgr: Amy Chapin
Founded: 1956
Regional publisher specializing in nautical books.
ISBN Prefix(es): 978-0-932212; 978-1-892384
Number of titles published annually: 4 Print
Total Titles: 46 Print
Distributed by Partners Book Distributing

Avisson Press Inc
3007 Taliaferro Rd, Greensboro, NC 27408
Mailing Address: PO Box 38816, Greensboro, NC 27438-8816
Tel: 336-285-6763
E-mail: avisson4@aol.com
Key Personnel
Pres & Intl Rts Contact: Martin L Hester
Contact: Michael Blood
Founded: 1994
ISBN Prefix(es): 978-1-888105
Number of titles published annually: 4 Print
Total Titles: 67 Print
Membership(s): The Independent Book Publishers Association; Society of Children's Book Writers & Illustrators

AVKO Educational Research Foundation Inc
3084 Willard Rd, Birch Run, MI 48415-9404
Tel: 810-686-9283 (orders & billing) *Toll Free Tel:* 866-AVKO612 (285-6612) *Fax:* 810-686-1101
E-mail: info@avko.org (gen inquiry)
Web Site: www.avko.org; www.avko.blogspot.org
Key Personnel
Res Dir: Don McCabe *Tel:* 810-686-9283 ext 203 *E-mail:* donmccabe@aol.com
Opers Mgr: Robert McCabe *Tel:* 810-686-9283 ext 202 *E-mail:* brian@avko.org
Accts Receivable & Accts Payable: Sue Johnson *Tel:* 810-686-9283 ext 201 *E-mail:* avkosueat@aol.com
Founded: 1974
Nonprofit organization devoted to providing free & low-cost materials for teaching language arts, keyboarding & reference. Our materials work great for dyslexics, homeschoolers & school teachers.
ISBN Prefix(es): 978-1-56400
Total Titles: 49 Print; 6 CD-ROM; 60 E-Book

AVKO Foundation, see AVKO Educational Research Foundation Inc

§Awe-Struck Publishing
Imprint of Mundania Press LLC
6457 Glenway Ave, Suite 109, Cincinnati, OH 45211-5222
Toll Free Tel: 888-402-6657 *Toll Free Fax:* 888-460-4752
E-mail: inquiry@mundania.com; orders@mundania.com; submissions@awe-struck.net; books@mundania.com
Web Site: www.awe-struck.net; www.mundania.com
Founded: 1998
Full service, royalty paying publisher of electronic books in the following formats: html, rocket, Palm, Visor, Pocket PC, Franklin, eBookman, Hiebook, pdf, MS Reader.
Subsidiary, Earthlink Press, publishes trade paperbacks; fiction (romance & science fiction) for disabled readers (Ennoble Line).
ISBN Prefix(es): 978-1-928670; 978-1-58749
Number of titles published annually: 12 Print; 42 Online; 42 E-Book
Total Titles: 104 Print; 200 Online; 200 E-Book
Subsidiaries: Earthling Press (trade quality print editions); HeatWave Romance (erotic romance/erotica)
Distribution Center: Palmdigital, 950 W Maude Ave, Sunnyvale, CA 94085 *Web Site:* www.ereader.com
ebookcorp.com, 121 Mount Vernon St, Boston, MA 02108 *Web Site:* ebookcorp.com
Fictionwise.com, 346 Main St, Chatham, NJ 07928 *Web Site:* www.fictionwise.com
Franklin E-books, Inc., One Franklin Plaza, Eight Terri Lane, Burlington, NJ 08016 *Web Site:* www.franklin.com
booksurge.com, 7290-B Investment Dr, Charleston, SC 29418 *Web Site:* www.booksurge.com
Lightning Source, 1246 Heil Quaker Blvd, La Vergne, TN 37086 *Web Site:* www.lightningsource.com
Amazon, 410 Terry Ave N, Seattle, WA 98109 *Web Site:* www.amazon.com
ebookad.com, 51 Remington Dr, Richmond Hill, ON L4S 1A1, Canada *Web Site:* www.ebookad.com
Mobipocket.com, 251 Bld Pereire, 75017 Paris, France *Web Site:* www.mobipocket.com
Membership(s): The Independent Book Publishers Association

AZ Books LLC
320 Fifth Ave, New York, NY 10001
Toll Free Tel: 888-945-7723 *Toll Free Fax:* 888-945-7724
Web Site: www.azbooksusa.com
Key Personnel
VP: Robert Tod *Tel:* 888-945-7723 ext 10
E-mail: robert@azbooksusa.com
Natl Accts Mgr: Tom Jourdane *Tel:* 801-641-3184
E-mail: tom@azbooksusa.com
Edit: Kate Kmit *E-mail:* kate.kmit@az-books.com
Sales: Anastasia Lobynko *E-mail:* anastasia.lobynko@az-books.com
ISBN Prefix(es): 978-0-938045
Number of titles published annually: 20 Print

Azro Press
1704 Llano St B, PMB 342, Santa Fe, NM 87505
Tel: 505-989-3272 *Fax:* 505-989-3832
E-mail: books@azropress.com
Web Site: www.azropress.com
Key Personnel
Pres: Gae Eisenhardt
Founded: 1997
Publish illustrated children's books with a Southwestern flavor.
ISBN Prefix(es): 978-1-929115
Number of titles published annually: 3 Print
Total Titles: 20 Print
Imprints: Green Knees

Babalu Inc
PO Box 23026, Santa Barbara, CA 93121
Toll Free Tel: 877-522-2258
E-mail: morefun@babaluinc.com
Web Site: www.babaluinc.com
Key Personnel
Pres: Blair Everett
Off Mgr: Kylie Castro
Founded: 2006
Children's books, toys & advent calendars.
ISBN Prefix(es): 978-1-56021
Number of titles published annually: 10 Print
Total Titles: 60 Print
Membership(s): ABA; Museum Store Association

Baby Tattoo Books
6045 Longridge Ave, Van Nuys, CA 91401
Tel: 818-416-5314
E-mail: info@babytattoo.com
Web Site: www.babytattoo.com
Key Personnel
Pres & Publr: Robert Self *E-mail:* bob@babytattoo.com
Founded: 2003
Publisher of art books by contemporary artists.
ISBN Prefix(es): 978-0-9729388; 978-0-9778949; 978-0-9793307; 978-0-9845210; 978-1-61404
Number of titles published annually: 4 Print
Total Titles: 30 Print
Orders to: SCB Distributors Inc, 15608 S New Century Dr, Gardena, CA 90248 *Toll Free Tel:* 800-729-6423
Returns: SCB Distributors Inc, 15608 S New Century Dr, Gardena, CA 90248 *Toll Free Tel:* 800-729-6423
Shipping Address: SCB Distributors Inc, 15608 S New Century Dr, Gardena, CA 90248 *Toll Free Tel:* 800-729-6423
Warehouse: SCB Distributors Inc, 15608 S New Century Dr, Gardena, CA 90248 *Toll Free Tel:* 800-729-6423
Distribution Center: SCB Distributors Inc, 15608 S New Century Dr, Gardena, CA 90248 *Toll Free Tel:* 800-729-6423

Back to Eden Books, see Lotus Press

Backbeat Books
Imprint of Hal Leonard Performing Arts Publishing Group
33 Plymouth St, Suite 302, Montclair, NJ 07042
Tel: 973-337-5034 *Toll Free Tel:* 800-637-2852 (Music Dispatch) *Fax:* 973-337-5227
Web Site: www.backbeatbooks.com
Key Personnel
Group Publr: John Cerullo
Founded: 1991
Books about popular music & musical instruments.
ISBN Prefix(es): 978-0-87930
Number of titles published annually: 30 Print; 20 E-Book
Total Titles: 400 Print; 300 E-Book
Foreign Rep(s): Publishers Group UK
Distribution Center: Hal Leonard Performing Arts Publishing Group, 1210 Innovation Dr, Winona, MN 55987

The Backwaters Press
3502 N 52 St, Omaha, NE 68104-3506
Tel: 402-451-4052
E-mail: thebackwaterspress@gmail.com
Web Site: www.thebackwaterspress.org
Key Personnel
Ed: James Cihlar
Founded: 1997
Nonprofit 501(c)(3) literary press.
ISBN Prefix(es): 978-0-9677149; 978-0-9726187; 978-0-9765231; 978-0-9785782; 978-0-9793934; 978-0-9816936; 978-1-935218
Number of titles published annually: 5 Print
Total Titles: 95 Print
Membership(s): Association of Writers and Writing Programs; Community of Literary Magazines & Presses

Baen Publishing Enterprises
PO Box 1188, Wake Forest, NC 27588
Tel: 919-570-1640 *Fax:* 919-570-1644
E-mail: info@baen.com
Web Site: www.baen.com
Key Personnel
Publr: Toni Weisskopf *E-mail:* toni@baen.com
Founded: 1984
Only science fiction & fantasy.
ISBN Prefix(es): 978-0-671; 978-0-7434; 978-1-4165
Number of titles published annually: 70 Print; 50 Online; 40 E-Book
Total Titles: 700 Print; 250 Online; 200 E-Book
Distributed by Simon & Schuster
Foreign Rep(s): Lora Fountain (France); Alex Korzhenevshi (Russia); Kristin Olson (Czech Republic); Thomas Schlueck (Germany)

§Bagwyn Books
Imprint of Arizona Center for Medieval & Renaissance Studies (ACMRS)
Lattie F Coor Hall, 4th fl, Rms 4426-4442, 975 S Myrtle Ave, Tempe, AZ 85281
Mailing Address: ACMRS/ASU, PO Box 874402, Tempe, AZ 85287-4402
Tel: 480-965-5900 *Fax:* 480-965-1681
E-mail: bagwynbooks@acmrs.org
Web Site: acmrs.org/publications/bagwyn
Key Personnel
Acqs Ed: Kendra TerBeek *Tel:* 480-965-8097
E-mail: kendra.terbeek@acmrs.org
Mng Ed: Roy Rukkila *Tel:* 480-727-6503
E-mail: roy.rukkila@acmrs.org
Founded: 2011
Publisher of historical fiction & fantasy from young adult to adult.
ISBN Prefix(es): 978-0-86698
Number of titles published annually: 4 Print; 7 E-Book
Total Titles: 27 Print
Orders to: Chicago Distribution Center, 11030 S Langley Ave, Chicago, IL 60628 *Tel:* 773-702-7000 *Toll Free Tel:* 800-621-2736 *Fax:* 773-702-7212 *Toll Free Fax:* 800-621-8476
E-mail: orders@press.uchicago.edu
Returns: Chicago Distribution Center, 11030 S Langley Ave, Chicago, IL 60628 *Tel:* 773-702-7000 *Toll Free Tel:* 800-621-2736 *Fax:* 773-702-7212 *Toll Free Fax:* 800-621-8476
E-mail: orders@press.uchicago.edu
Shipping Address: Chicago Distribution Center, 11030 S Langley Ave, Chicago, IL 60628 *Tel:* 773-702-7000 *Toll Free Tel:* 800-621-2736 *Fax:* 773-702-7212 *Toll Free Fax:* 800-621-8476 *E-mail:* orders@press.uchicago.edu
Warehouse: Chicago Distribution Center, 11030 S Langley Ave, Chicago, IL 60628 *Tel:* 773-702-7000 *Toll Free Tel:* 800-621-2736 *Fax:* 773-702-7212 *Toll Free Fax:* 800-621-8476
E-mail: orders@press.uchicago.edu
Distribution Center: Chicago Distribution Center, 11030 S Langley Ave, Chicago, IL 60628 *Tel:* 773-702-7000 *Toll Free Tel:* 800-621-2736 *Fax:* 773-702-7212 *Toll Free Fax:* 800-621-8476 *E-mail:* orders@press.uchicago.edu

Baha'i Publishing
Subsidiary of The National Spiritual Assembly of the Baha'is of the United States
401 Greenleaf Ave, Wilmette, IL 60091
Tel: 847-425-7950 *Toll Free Tel:* 800-999-9019 (orders) *Fax:* 847-425-7951
E-mail: bds@usbnc.org
Web Site: books.bahai.us; www.bahaibookstore.com
Key Personnel
Gen Mgr & Rts & Perms: Tim Moore
Founded: 1902
Religion (Baha'i).
ISBN Prefix(es): 978-0-87743; 978-1-931847
Number of titles published annually: 15 Print
Total Titles: 2,000 Print; 250 Audio
Shipping Address: Perseus Books Distribution, 905 Carlow Dr, Unit B, Bowling Brook, IL 60490

§Baker Books
Division of Baker Publishing Group
PO Box 6287, Grand Rapids, MI 49516-6287
SAN: 299-1500
Tel: 616-676-9185 *Toll Free Tel:* 800-877-2665; 800-679-1957 *Fax:* 616-676-9573 *Toll Free Fax:* 800-398-3111
Web Site: www.bakerpublishinggroup.com
Key Personnel
CEO & Chmn: Richard Baker
Pres: Dwight Baker
EVP & Publr: Jack Kuhatschek
EVP, Sales & Mktg: Dave Lewis
Art Dir: Cheryl Van Andel
Prodn Mgr: Bob Bol
Dist Mgr: Jack Boers
Rts & Perms: Marilyn Gordon
Founded: 1939
Religion (Protestant).
ISBN Prefix(es): 978-0-8010
Number of titles published annually: 75 Print; 1 CD-ROM; 1 Audio
Total Titles: 1,000 Print
Imprints: Hamewith; Hourglass
Foreign Rep(s): Christian Art (South Africa); Family Reading Publications (Australia); R Mitchell (Canada); Send The Light (Europe, UK); Soul Distributors (New Zealand)
Shipping Address: 6030 E Fulton Rd, Ada, MI 49301

Balance Sports Publishing LLC
195 Lucero Way, Portola Valley, CA 94028
SAN: 857-3298
Tel: 650-561-9586 *Fax:* 650-391-9850
E-mail: info@balancesportspublishing.com
Web Site: www.balancesportspublishing.com
Key Personnel
Founder & Publr: Jim Lobdell *E-mail:* jlobdell@balancesportspublishing.com

Founder & Dir, Busn Opers: Colleen Anderson *E-mail:* canderson@balancesportspublishing.com
Founder & Dir, Prod Devt: Steve Seely *E-mail:* sseely@balancesportspublishing.com
Founded: 2008
Publishes high-quality youth sports books for youth sports coaches, parents, athletes & organization leaders. Our mission is to create titles that ensure every child has a positive youth sports experience & that every coach is inspired to help youngsters achieve their goals in sports while developing important life skills & character traits.
ISBN Prefix(es): 978-0-9821317
Number of titles published annually: 3 Print
Total Titles: 12 Print
Returns: 3623 Munster St, Suite B, Hayward, CA 94545, Contact: Bill Armor *Tel:* 510-732-6521 *Fax:* 510-732-6523 *E-mail:* orders@balancesportspublishing.com
Shipping Address: 3623 Munster St, Suite B, Hayward, CA 94545, Contact: Bill Armor *Tel:* 510-732-6521 *Fax:* 510-732-6523
Warehouse: 3623 Munster St, Suite B, Hayward, CA 94545, Contact: Bill Armor *Tel:* 510-732-6521 *Fax:* 510-732-6523
Distribution Center: 3623 Munster St, Suite B, Hayward, CA 94545, Contact: Bill Armor *Tel:* 510-732-6521 *Fax:* 510-732-6523
Membership(s): The Independent Book Publishers Association

Ball Publishing, see Chicago Review Press

Ball-Stick-Bird Publications Inc
PO Box 429, Williamstown, MA 01267-0429
SAN: 222-5565
Tel: 413-664-0002 *Fax:* 413-664-0002
E-mail: info@ballstickbird.com
Web Site: www.ballstickbird.com
Key Personnel
Pres & Rts & Perms: Dr Renee Fuller, PhD
Founded: 1975
Children's reading series.
ISBN Prefix(es): 978-0-917740
Number of titles published annually: 13 Print
Total Titles: 13 Print; 13 Online

Ballinger Publishing
41 N Jefferson St, Suite 402, Pensacola, FL 32502
Mailing Address: PO Box 12665, Pensacola, FL 32591-2665
Tel: 850-433-1166 *Fax:* 850-435-9174
E-mail: info@ballingerpublishing.com
Web Site: www.ballingerpublishing.com
Key Personnel
Owner & Publr: Malcolm Ballinger *Tel:* 850-433-1166 ext 27 *E-mail:* malcolm@ballingerpublishing.com
Owner: Glenys Ballinger *Tel:* 850-433-1166 ext 22 *E-mail:* glenys@ballingerpublishing.com
Exec Ed: Kelly Oden *Tel:* 850-433-1166 ext 23 *E-mail:* kelly@ballingerpublishing.com
Founded: 2001
Publishers of local & regional magazines.
This publisher has indicated that 100% of their product line is author subsidized.
ISBN Prefix(es): 978-0-9791103
Number of titles published annually: 80 Print

BAM! Publishing, see Resilient Publishing

Bancroft Press
3209 Bancroft Rd, Baltimore, MD 21215
Mailing Address: PO Box 65360, Baltimore, MD 21209-9945
Tel: 410-358-0658 *Fax:* 410-764-1967
Web Site: www.bancroftpress.com
Key Personnel
Publr & Design Dir: Andrew Bortz *E-mail:* abortz@bancroftpress.com
Ed, Fiction & Nonfiction: Bruce L Bortz *E-mail:* bruceb@bancroftpress.com
Founded: 1995
General interest trade book publisher; has received special recognition & ranks among the nation's top 100 independent presses. Worldwide rights & distribution.
ISBN Prefix(es): 978-1-890862
Number of titles published annually: 5 Print; 1 Audio
Total Titles: 60 Print; 1 Audio
Foreign Rights: Barbara Newman
Distribution Center: Bookmasters, 30 Amberwood Pkwy, Ashland, OH 44805

Bandanna Books
1212 Punta Gorda St, No 13, Santa Barbara, CA 93103
SAN: 238-7956
Tel: 805-899-2145
E-mail: bandanna@cox.net
Web Site: www.bandannabooks.com; www.mudbornpress.us; www.betabooks.us; www.timewell.us; www.shakespeareplaybook.com; www.bookdoc.us; catandbirdiebooks.com; www.eleanorehill.com; www.castbooks.us
Key Personnel
Publr: Sasha "Birdie" Newborn *E-mail:* birdie.newborn@gmail.com
Founded: 1981 (Bandanna Books grew out of Mudborn Press in 1981, with college texts. In 2014, some MP books were reprinted & new titles have been issued)
Literary classics, translations, teacher editions, bilingual & language books, experimental book formats. Beta Books, TimeWell, the blog are resources for writers.
ISBN Prefix(es): 978-0-942208; 978-0-930012
Number of titles published annually: 8 Print; 2 Online; 8 E-Book; 2 Audio
Total Titles: 80 Print; 4 Online; 28 E-Book; 5 Audio
Imprints: Beta Books; Cast Books (experimental format: print/audio); Dictionary Series (series of little dictionaries: Italian for Opera Lovers, French for Food Lovers, Yiddish, You Say? Nu?, Doctorese for the imPatient); Gender Genre (classic transgender literature, 8 variants for third-person singular unknown or hypothetical); Mudborn Press (reprints, poetry, bilingual-Portuguese, Nahuatl, Latvian); Shakespeare Playbooks (series of playbooks designed for directors to envision a play & to keep track of production details); Supplement Editions (texts with supplementary background materials for teachers)

B&H Publishing Group
Division of LifeWay Christian Resources
One Lifeway Plaza, Nashville, TN 37234-0114
SAN: 201-937X
Tel: 615-251-2520 *Fax:* 615-251-5004
Web Site: www.bhpublishinggroup.com
Key Personnel
Pres & Publr: Tom Rainer
SVP, Mktg: John Thompson
VP, Sales: Craig Featherstone
Mktg Strategist, Christian Living, Leadership & Gift: Dave Schroeder
Founded: 1934
Religious trade publisher of nonfiction (Christian living, inspirational, devotional, contemporary issues); fiction; children's books; Bibles; Biblical reference; Biblical commentaries.
ISBN Prefix(es): 978-0-8054
Number of titles published annually: 95 Print
Total Titles: 700 Print; 5 Audio
Foreign Rights: Riggins International Rights Services (Worldwide exc USA)

Banner of Truth
63 E Louther St, Carlisle, PA 17013
Mailing Address: PO Box 621, Carlisle, PA 17013-0621
Tel: 717-249-5747 *Toll Free Tel:* 800-263-8085 (orders) *Fax:* 717-249-0604
E-mail: info@banneroftruth.org
Web Site: www.banneroftruth.co.uk; www.banneroftruth.org
Key Personnel
Mgr: Patrick Daly
Founded: 1957
Not-for-profit Evangelical Christian publisher.
ISBN Prefix(es): 978-0-85151
Number of titles published annually: 15 Print
Total Titles: 802 Print
Foreign Office(s): The Banner of Truth Trust, The Grey House, 3 Murrayfield Rd, Edinburgh EH12 6EL, United Kingdom *Tel:* (0131) 337 7310 *Fax:* (0131) 346 7484 *E-mail:* info@banneroftruth.co.uk
Membership(s): CBA: The Association for Christian Retail; Evangelical Christian Publishers Association

Baptist Spanish Publishing House, see Casa Bautista de Publicaciones

Barbour Publishing Inc
1810 Barbour Dr, Uhrichsville, OH 44683
Tel: 740-922-6045 *Fax:* 740-922-5948
E-mail: info@barbourbooks.com
Web Site: www.barbourbooks.com
Key Personnel
CEO & Pres: Tim H Martins *E-mail:* tmartins@barbourbooks.com
VP, Sales & Mktg: William Westfall *E-mail:* bwestfall@barbourbooks.com
Edit Dir: Kelly McIntosh *E-mail:* kmcintosh@barbourbooks.com
Founded: 1981
Christian books, Bibles, fiction, gift books, devotional journals, reference.
ISBN Prefix(es): 978-1-57748; 978-0-916441; 978-1-55748; 978-1-58660; 978-1-59310; 978-1-59789; 978-1-60260; 978-1-61626
Number of titles published annually: 244 Print
Total Titles: 793 Print
Imprints: Barbour Books
Foreign Rights: Christian Art Wholesale (South Africa); R G Mitchell; Nova Distributors (Canada, UK)

Barcelona Publishers
27602 Bogen Rd, New Braunfels, TX 78132-3873
Tel: 830-980-6422
E-mail: barcelonapublishers@gvtc.com; barcelonapublishers@ware-pak.com (orders)
Web Site: www.barcelonapublishers.com
Key Personnel
Prop: Kenneth E Bruscia
Founded: 1991
Music therapy books & materials.
ISBN Prefix(es): 978-0-9624080; 978-1-891278; 978-1-937440
Number of titles published annually: 3 Print
Total Titles: 72 Print

Barefoot Books
2067 Massachusetts Ave, 5th fl, Cambridge, MA 02140
Tel: 617-576-0660 *Toll Free Tel:* 866-215-1756 (cust serv); 866-417-2369 (orders) *Fax:* 617-576-0049
E-mail: help@barefootbooks.com
Web Site: www.barefootbooks.com
Key Personnel
CEO: Nancy Traversy *E-mail:* nancy.traversy@barefootbooks.com
Group Opers Dir: Karen Janson *E-mail:* karen.janson@barefootbooks.com

Ed-in-Chief (UK off): Tessa Strickland
E-mail: tessa.strickland@barefootbooks.co.uk
Founded: 1993
Publishes high quality picture books for children of all ages specializing in the work of authors & artists from many cultures, wrapping paper, artists prints & cards.
ISBN Prefix(es): 978-1-898000; 978-1-901223; 978-1-902283; 978-1-84148; 978-1-84686; 978-1-905236
Number of titles published annually: 30 Print; 12 Audio
Total Titles: 300 Print
Foreign Office(s): 294 Banbury Rd, Summertown, Oxford OX2 7ED, United Kingdom, Contact: Liz Sampson *Tel:* (01865) 311100
Returns: RR Donnelley Packaging & Fulfillment, 655 Brighton Beach Rd, Menasha, WI 54952
Warehouse: RR Donnelley Packaging & Fulfillment, 655 Brighton Beach Rd, Menasha, WI 54952
Membership(s): ALA; The Children's Book Council

Barnhardt & Ashe Publishing Inc
444 Brickell Ave, Suite 51, PMB 432, Miami, FL 33131
Toll Free Tel: 800-283-6360 (orders)
E-mail: barnhardtashe@aol.com
Web Site: barnhardtashepublishing.com
Founded: 2001
ISBN Prefix(es): 978-0-9715402; 978-0-9801744
Number of titles published annually: 10 Print
Total Titles: 9 Print
Membership(s): AAP

Barranca Press
1450 Couse St, No 10, Taos, NM 87571
Tel: 575-613-1026
E-mail: editor@barrancapress.com
Web Site: www.barrancapress.com
Key Personnel
Ed: Lisa Noudehou *E-mail:* lisa@barrancapress.com
Founded: 2012
Booklist includes photojournalism, novels, literary collections, children's books & memoirs. Unsol mss accepted March-Aug annually. E-mail submissions preferred.
ISBN Prefix(es): 978-1-939604
Number of titles published annually: 5 Print; 5 E-Book
Total Titles: 5 Print

Barricade Books Inc
2037 LeMoine Ave, Fort Lee, NJ 07024
Tel: 201-944-7600
E-mail: customerservice@barricadebooks.com
Web Site: www.barricadebooks.com
Key Personnel
Pres: Carole Stuart *E-mail:* cstuart@barricadebooks.com
Prodn Mgr: Carmela Cohen
Founded: 1992
ISBN Prefix(es): 978-1-56980; 978-0-156980
Number of titles published annually: 6 Print; 100 E-Book; 50 Audio
Total Titles: 100 Print; 200 E-Book; 50 Audio
Imprints: Barricade Books
Returns: National Book Network, 4501 Forbes Blvd, Suite 200, Lanham, MD 20706 *Tel:* 301-459-3366 *Toll Free Tel:* 800-462-6420 *Fax:* 301-429-5746
Warehouse: National Book Network, 4501 Forbes Blvd, Suite 200, Lanham, MD 20706 *Tel:* 301-459-3366 *Toll Free Tel:* 800-462-6420 *Fax:* 301-429-5746
Distribution Center: National Book Network, 4501 Forbes Blvd, Suite 200, Lanham, MD 20706 *Tel:* 301-459-3366 *Toll Free Tel:* 800-462-6420 *Fax:* 301-429-5746
Membership(s): AAP

Barringer Publishing
Division of Schlesinger Advertising & Marketing
3259 Sundance Circle, Naples, FL 34109
Tel: 239-514-7364
E-mail: schlesadv@gmail.com
Web Site: www.barringerpublishing.com
Key Personnel
Owner: Jeff Schlesinger *E-mail:* js@barringerpublishing.com
Founded: 2009
Full service: cover & book design, editing, printing, marketing, advertising & public relations, web sites, graphics, displays & illustrations.
ISBN Prefix(es): 978-0-9825109
Number of titles published annually: 15 Print
Total Titles: 120 Print
Membership(s): The Independent Book Publishers Association

Barron's Educational Series Inc
250 Wireless Blvd, Hauppauge, NY 11788
SAN: 201-453X
Tel: 631-434-3311 *Toll Free Tel:* 800-645-3476 *Fax:* 631-434-3723
E-mail: barrons@barronseduc.com
Web Site: www.barronseduc.com
Key Personnel
Chmn & CEO: Manuel H Barron
Pres & Publr: Ellen Sibley
VP, Sales & Mktg: Alex Holtz
Sr Mktg Dir: Lonny R Stein
Intl & Special Sales Dir: Jackie Raab
Dir, Rts & Digital Content: Patricia Doyle
Sales Dir, Acad & E-Trade Mkt: Frederick Glasser
Natl Sales Mgr: Jeff Goldman
Acq Ed: Wayne Barr
Founded: 1941
El-hi & college education; guidance & test review.
ISBN Prefix(es): 978-0-8120; 978-0-7641
Number of titles published annually: 300 Print
Total Titles: 3,000 Print; 125 Audio
Foreign Rep(s): Book Marketing Services Inc (Canada)
Foreign Rights: Anthea Literary Agency (Bulgaria); Big Apple Agency Inc (China); Contacts/The Rights Agency (Canada); DRT International (Korea); Lora Fountain & Associates Literary Agency (France); International Editors' Co (Latin America, Portugal, Spain); Nurcihan Kesim Literary Agency Inc (Turkey); David Matlock Agency (Russia); Montreal Contacts/The Rights Agency (Canada (French-speaking)); OA Literary Agency (Greece); Tuttle-Mori Agency Inc (Japan)
Advertising Agency: Friedman, Harris & Partners

Barrytown/Station Hill Press
120 Station Hill Rd, Barrytown, NY 12507
SAN: 214-1485
Tel: 845-758-5293
E-mail: publishers@stationhill.org
Web Site: www.stationhill.org
Key Personnel
Dir: Sam Truitt
Pubns & Ed: George Quasha
Founded: 1977
General trade books, quality paperbacks & fine editions; poetry, fiction & discourse; visual arts; studies in literature & psychology, classics, translations, theater, creative nonfiction, health/New Age.
ISBN Prefix(es): 978-0-930794; 978-0-88268
Number of titles published annually: 6 Print
Total Titles: 300 Print
Foreign Rep(s): Lora Fountain (France); Gara Media (Germany); Japanville (Japan); Kerrigan (Spain); Living Weary (Italy)
Distribution Center: Midpoint Trade Books, 1263 Southwest Blvd, Kansas City, KS 66103 *Tel:* 913-362-7400 *Fax:* 913-362-7401 *E-mail:* info@midpointtradebooks.com *Web Site:* www.midpointtradebooks.com

Bartleby Press
Subsidiary of Jackson Westgate Publishing Group
8926 Baltimore St, No 858, Savage, MD 20763
SAN: 241-2098
Tel: 301-725-3906 *Toll Free Tel:* 800-953-9929 *Fax:* 667-309-6993
E-mail: inquiries@bartlebythepublisher.com
Web Site: www.bartlebythepublisher.com
Key Personnel
Publr: Jeremy Kay *E-mail:* publisher@bartlebythepublisher.com
Proj Ed: Greg Giroux
Founded: 1981
ISBN Prefix(es): 978-0-910155; 978-0-9625963; 978-0-935437
Number of titles published annually: 4 Print; 8 E-Book
Total Titles: 52 Print; 22 E-Book
Imprints: Elstreet Educational; Eshel Books; PS&E Publications
Membership(s): The Independent Book Publishers Association

Basic Books
Member of The Perseus Books Group
250 W 57 St, 15th fl, New York, NY 10107
Tel: 212-340-8164; 212-340-8136 *Fax:* 212-340-8135
E-mail: perseus.promos@perseusbooks.com
Web Site: www.basicbooks.com; perseusbooks.com
Key Personnel
CEO & Pres, Perseus Books Group: David Steinberger
Chief Mktg Offr: Matthew Goldberg
VP & Creative Dir: Nicole Caputo
VP & Dir, Mktg & Sales: Liz Tzetzo
VP & Edit Dir, Sciences: TJ Kelleher
Dir, Publicity: Cassie Nelson
Group Publr: Susan Weinberg
Publr: Laura Heimert
Assoc Dir, Publicity: Betsy DeJesu
Sr Publicist: Carrie Majer
Sr Ed: Dan Gerstle
Ed: Ben Platt
Assoc Ed: Quynh Do; Leah Stecher
Founded: 1952
Nonfiction only. Subjects include current affairs & memoirs.
ISBN Prefix(es): 978-0-465
Number of titles published annually: 100 Print
Total Titles: 1,000 Print
Imprints: Basic Civitas; Counterpoint
Distributed by CDS Distributors
Foreign Rep(s): James Benson (North Midlands, UK, Northern England, Staffordshire, UK); Jim Chalmers (Scotland); Kemper Conseil (Belgium, Luxembourg, Netherlands); Gilles Fauveau (Japan, Korea); Bernd Feldmann (Austria, Germany, Switzerland); Colin Flint Publishers Scandinavian Consultancy (Ben Greig) (Scandinavia); Charles Gibbes (Cyprus, Greece); Jaime C Gregorio (Guam, Philippines); Laszlo Horvath (Central Europe, Eastern Europe); Natalie Jones (London); Mark Latcham (Central London, UK, Southern Wales); Vivienne Lavery (Ireland); Mare Nostrum Publishing Consultants (David Pickering) (Italy); Mare Nostrum Publishing Consultants (Sabrina Cote) (France); Mare Nostrum Publishing Consultants (Cristina de Lara) (Portugal, Spain); Barbara Martin (Buckinghamshire, UK, East Midlands, UK, Gloucestershire, UK, West Midlands, UK); Miraida Morales (Caribbean, Latin America); Ray Potts (Middle East); Publisher's Group Worldwide (Africa, Asia, Central America, Middle East, South America); Scribe International (Camilla Dorsch) (Australia, New Zealand); David Smith (East Anglia, England, Southeast

England); Wei Zhao (China, Hong Kong, Taiwan)
Foreign Rights: Bardon-Chinese Media Agency (China, Taiwan); Raquel de la Concha Agencia Literaria (Raquel de la Concha) (Brazil, Latin America, Portugal, Spain); Agence Hoffman (Germany); Duran Kim Agency (Korea); Alexander Korzhenevski Agency (Russia); I Pikarski Literary Agency (Israel); Santachiara Literary Agency (Roberto Santachiara) (Italy); Sebes & Van Gelderen Literary Agency (Netherlands); Tuttle-Mori Agency Inc (Japan)
Orders to: Perseus Books Group, 210 American Dr, Jackson, TN 38301 *Toll Free Tel:* 800-343-4499 *Toll Free Fax:* 800-351-5073
Warehouse: CDS Distributors, 193 Edwards Dr, Jackson, TN 38301
Distribution Center: Perseus Distribution, 1094 Flex Dr, Jackson, TN 38301 *Toll Free Tel:* 800-343-4499 *Toll Free Fax:* 800-351-5073

Basic Health Publications Inc
28812 Top of the World Dr, Laguna Beach, CA 92651
Tel: 949-715-7327 *Toll Free Tel:* 800-575-8890 (orders) *Fax:* 949-715-7328
E-mail: info@basichealthpub.com
Web Site: www.basichealthpub.com
Key Personnel
Pres & Publr: Norman Goldfind
Mng Ed: Cheryl Hirsch
Ed: Susan Davis; Carol Rosenberg
Sales Dir: Ken Kaiman
Prodn: Gary Rosenberg
Publicity: Courtney Dunham
Typesetter & Text Design: Gary Rosenberg
Founded: 2001
ISBN Prefix(es): 978-1-59120
Number of titles published annually: 15 Print; 15 Online; 15 E-Book
Total Titles: 250 Print; 250 Online; 250 E-Book
Imprints: Basic Health Guides; Basic Health Publications; User's Guides
Foreign Rights: Athena Productions Inc (Worldwide)
Returns: Returns Dept, 885 Claycraft Rd, Columbus, OH 43230
Warehouse: 885 Claycraft Rd, Columbus, OH 43230, Cust Serv: Alice Heigel *Tel:* 614-863-3004 *Fax:* 614-863-9007 *E-mail:* aheigel@basicmediagroup.com

Bay Tree Publishing LLC
1400 Pinnacle Ct, Suite 406, Point Richmond, CA 94801
Tel: 510-236-1475 *Toll Free Fax:* 866-552-7329
Web Site: www.baytreepublish.com
Key Personnel
Publr: David Cole *E-mail:* dcole@baytreepublish.com
Founded: 2002
ISBN Prefix(es): 978-0-9801758; 978-0-9720021; 978-0-9819577
Number of titles published annually: 4 Print; 5 E-Book
Total Titles: 20 Print; 8 E-Book
Foreign Rep(s): National Book Network (Les Petriw) (Australia, Canada, New Zealand, UK)
Orders to: National Book Network (NBN), 15200 NBN Way, Blue Ridge Summit, PA 17214 *Toll Free Tel:* 800-462-6420
Returns: National Book Network (NBN), 15200 NBN Way, Blue Ridge Summit, PA 17214
Shipping Address: National Book Network (NBN), 15200 NBN Way, Blue Ridge Summit, PA 17214
Warehouse: National Book Network (NBN), 15200 NBN Way, Blue Ridge Summit, PA 17214
Distribution Center: National Book Network (NBN), 15200 NBN Way, Blue Ridge Summit, PA 17214
Membership(s): Bay Area Independent Publishers Association; The Independent Book Publishers Association

Baylor University Press
Baylor University, One Bear Place, Waco, TX 76798-7363
SAN: 685-317X
Mailing Address: PO Box 97363, Waco, TX 76798-7363
Tel: 254-710-3164 *Fax:* 254-710-3440
Web Site: www.baylorpress.com
Key Personnel
Dir: Dr Carey C Newman
E-mail: carey_newman@baylor.edu
Prodn Mgr: Diane E Smith *E-mail:* diane_smith@baylor.edu
Founded: 1955
Scholarly books & monographs.
ISBN Prefix(es): 978-0-918954; 978-1-932792
Number of titles published annually: 30 Print
Total Titles: 110 Print
Distributed by Johns Hopkins University Press Fullfillment Service
Distribution Center: Johns Hopkins University Press Fullfillment Service, PO Box 50370, Baltimore, MD 21211-4370, Contact: Melinda Kelly *Tel:* 410-516-6956 *Fax:* 410-516-6998 *E-mail:* mrk@press.jhu.edu
Membership(s): American Political Science Association; Society of Bible Literature

Baywood Publishing Co Inc
26 Austin Ave, Amityville, NY 11701
SAN: 206-9326
Mailing Address: PO Box 337, Amityville, NY 11701-0337
Tel: 631-691-1270 *Toll Free Tel:* 800-638-7819 *Fax:* 631-691-1770
E-mail: baywood@baywood.com
Web Site: www.baywood.com
Key Personnel
Pres: Stuart Cohen
Electronic Content Mgr: Lorna Roher
Cust Rel: S Edwards
Rts & Perms & ISBN Contact: Julie Krempa
Founded: 1964
Professional journals & books: anthropology, archaeology, education, imagery, psychiatry & psychology, health services, health education, labor relations, sociology, mathematics, computers in education, thanatology, imagery, environment, technical communication, gerontology, fire science, employee rights.
ISBN Prefix(es): 978-0-89503
Number of titles published annually: 40 Print; 24 Online; 15 E-Book
Total Titles: 400 Print; 24 Online; 120 E-Book
Foreign Rep(s): Book Representation & Distribution Ltd (England, UK)

Beach Lane Books, see Simon & Schuster Children's Publishing

Beach Lloyd Publishers LLC
40 Cabot Dr, Wayne, PA 19087-5619
SAN: 255-4992
Tel: 610-407-9107 *Fax:* 775-254-0633
E-mail: beachlloyd@erols.com
Web Site: www.beachlloyd.com
Key Personnel
Owner & Mgr: Joanne S Silver
Founded: 2002
Distribution Center: Baker & Taylor.
ISBN Prefix(es): 978-0-9743158; 978-0-9792778
Number of titles published annually: 3 Print; 1 Audio
Total Titles: 18 Print
Distributed by Tralco (CN)
Distributor for Le Chambon-sur-Lignon; CIDEB (Italy); Fondation pour la Memoire de la Shoah (Paris); Kar-Ben Publishing; Kiron Editions du Felin (Paris); JP Lattes (Paris); Le Manuscrit (Paris); Oxford University Press (NYC)
Membership(s): American Association of Teachers of French

Beacon Hill Press of Kansas City
Subsidiary of Nazarene Publishing House
PO Box 419527, Kansas City, MO 64141-6527
SAN: 202-9022
Tel: 816-931-1900 *Toll Free Tel:* 800-877-0700 (cust serv) *Fax:* 816-753-4071
Web Site: www.beaconhillbooks.com
Key Personnel
Dir: Bonnie Perry
Head, Mktg: Rachel McPherson
Mgr, Rts & Perms: Janet Stapleton
ISBN Contact: Richard Buckner
Founded: 1912
Religion (Nazarene), ministry resources, Christian care & spiritual growth.
ISBN Prefix(es): 978-0-83412
Number of titles published annually: 30 Print
Total Titles: 700 Print
Imprints: Lifestream; Lillenas Publishing Co (church music); Nazarene Publishing House
Shipping Address: 2923 Troost Ave, Kansas City, MO 64109

Beacon Press
24 Farnsworth St, Boston, MA 02210-1409
SAN: 201-4483
Tel: 617-742-2110 *Fax:* 617-723-3097; 617-742-2290
Web Site: www.beacon.org
Key Personnel
Dir: Helene Atwan
Dir, Sales & Mktg & Assoc Publr: Tom Hallock
Prodn Dir: Marcy Barnes
Exec Ed: Amy Caldwell; Gayatri Patnaik
Founded: 1854
General nonfiction, religion & theology, current affairs, anthropology, women's studies, history, gay & lesbian studies, African-American studies, Latino studies, education, hardcover, paperback, ebook & audio.
ISBN Prefix(es): 978-0-8070
Number of titles published annually: 60 Print; 35 E-Book
Total Titles: 800 Print; 350 E-Book; 5 Audio
Imprints: Concord Library; The King Legacy (writings of Dr Martin Luther King Jr)
Distributed by Random House Publisher Services
Foreign Rep(s): New South Books (Australia, New Zealand); Publishers Group UK (UK)
Foreign Rights: Akcali Copyright Agency (Mustafa Urgen) (Turkey); Eliane Benisti Literary Agency (Noemie Rollet) (France); Chinese Connection Agency (Mei Yao) (China); The Deborah Harris Agency (Rene Rossner) (Israel); Agence Hoffman (Uwe Neumahr) (Germany); International Editors' Co (Isabel Monteagudo) (Portugal, Spain); Agenzia Internazionale Literaria (Stefania Fietta) (Italy); Maxima Creative Agency (Santo Manurung) (Indonesia); Prava I Prevodi Literary Agency (Milena Lukic) (Eastern Europe exc Estonia, Latvia, Lithuania & Russia, Greece); Agencia Riff (Roberto Matos) (Brazil); Serbes & Van Gelderen Literary Agency (Merijn Hollestelle) (Netherlands); Synopsis Literary Agency (Olga Zasetskaya) (Russia); Tuttle-Mori Agency Inc (Shoko Kobayashi & Youthapong Charoenpan) (Japan); Eric Yang Agency (Jackie Yang) (Korea)
Returns: Random House Returns Dept, 1019 N State Rd 47, Crawfordsville, IN 47933
Warehouse: Random House Publishing Services, 400 Hahn Rd, Westminster, MD 21157 *Toll Free Tel:* 800-733-3000 *Toll Free*

Fax: 800-659-2436 *E-mail:* customerservice@randomhouse.com
Membership(s): American Association of University Presses; New England Independent Booksellers Association

Bear & Co Inc
Imprint of Inner Traditions International Ltd
One Park St, Rochester, VT 05767
Mailing Address: PO Box 388, Rochester, VT 05767-0388
Tel: 802-767-3174 *Toll Free Tel:* 800-932-3277 *Fax:* 802-767-3726
E-mail: customerservice@InnerTraditions.com
Web Site: InnerTraditions.com
Key Personnel
Pres: Ehud C Sperling *E-mail:* prez@InnerTraditions.com
VP, Opers: Diane Shepard *E-mail:* dianes@InnerTraditions.com
Dir, Content & Consumer Sales: Rob Meadows *E-mail:* robm@InnerTraditions.com
Dir, Sales & Mktg: John Hays *E-mail:* johnh@innertraditions.com
Ed-in-Chief: Jeanie Levitan *E-mail:* jeaniel@InnerTraditions.com
Acqs Ed: Jon Graham *E-mail:* jong@InnerTraditions.com
Print Mgr: Jon Desautels *E-mail:* jond@InnerTraditions.com
Foreign Rts & Perms: Maria Murray-Urdaneta *E-mail:* mariam@InnerTraditions.com
Publicity: Manzanita Carpenter *E-mail:* manzanitac@InnerTraditions.com
Sales & Mktg: Andrea Raymond *E-mail:* andyr@InnerTraditions.com
Spec Sales: Jessica Arsenault *E-mail:* jessa@InnerTraditions.com
Founded: 1980
Mysticism, philosophy, spirituality & medieval studies, contemporary prophecy, earth sciences, indigenous wisdom, new thought, alternative healing.
ISBN Prefix(es): 978-1-879181; 978-0-939680; 978-1-59143
Number of titles published annually: 19 Print
Total Titles: 291 Print
Foreign Rights: Agenzia Letteraria Internazionale SRL (Italy); Akcali Copyright Agency (Turkey); Big Apple Agency Inc (China, Taiwan); Blackbird Literary Agency (Netherlands); The Book Publishers' Association of Israel, International Promotion & Literary Rights Department (Israel); Graal Literary Agency (Poland); International Editors' Co SA (Argentina, Spain); Simona Kessler International Copyright Agency Ltd (Romania); Alexander Korzhenevski Agency (Russia); Zvonimir Majdak (Croatia); Montreal-Contacts/The Rights Agency (Canada); Andrew Nurnberg Associates (Baltic States, Bulgaria, Czech Republic, Hungary); Read n Right Agency (Greece); Karin Schindler (Brazil); Thomas Schlueck GmbH (Germany); Agence Schweiger (France); Tuttle-Mori Agency Inc (Japan, Thailand); Eric Yang Agency (Korea)
Orders to: Inner Traditions International - Bear & Co, c/o Simon & Schuster, 100 Front St, Riverside, NJ 08075 *Toll Free Tel:* 800-223-2336 *Toll Free Fax:* 800-943-9831 *E-mail:* purchaseorders@simonandschuster.com
Returns: Simon & Schuster, c/o Jacobson Logistics, 4406 Industrial Park Rd, Bldg 7, Camp Hill, PA 17011 (truckload shipments must call for an appointment: 800-967-3914 ext 5318)
Warehouse: Inner Traditions International - Bear & Co, c/o Simon & Schuster, 100 Front St, Riverside, NJ 08075 *Toll Free Tel:* 800-943-9831 *E-mail:* purchaseorders@simonandschuster.com

Bearport Publishing Co Inc
45 W 21 St, Suite 3B, New York, NY 10010
Tel: 212-337-8577 *Toll Free Tel:* 877-337-8577 *Fax:* 212-337-8557 *Toll Free Fax:* 866-337-8557
E-mail: service@bearportpublishing.com; info@bearportpublishing.com
Web Site: www.bearportpublishing.com
Key Personnel
Pres & Publr: Kenn Goin
VP, Design & Prodn: Spencer Brinker
Sr Ed: Joyce Tavolacci
Natl Sales Mgr: Linda McGee
Founded: 2003
Curriculum-aligned, high-interest nonfiction for the library market.
ISBN Prefix(es): 978-1-59716; 978-1-936087; 978-1-61772
Number of titles published annually: 68 Print; 440 E-Book
Total Titles: 570 Print
Returns: Corporate Grapics, 2025 Lookout Dr, North Mankato, MN 56002 *Toll Free Tel:* 800-851-8767 *Fax:* 507-389-3399 *E-mail:* marketing@cgintl.com
Shipping Address: Corporate Grapics, 2025 Lookout Dr, North Mankato, MN 56002 *Toll Free Tel:* 800-851-8767 *Fax:* 507-389-3399
Warehouse: Corporate Grapics, 2025 Lookout Dr, North Mankato, MN 56002 *Toll Free Tel:* 800-851-8767 *Fax:* 507-389-3399
Membership(s): ALA; The Children's Book Council

§Beaufort Books
27 W 20 St, Suite 1102, New York, NY 10011
Tel: 212-727-0222 *Fax:* 212-727-0195
E-mail: info@beaufortbooks.com
Web Site: www.beaufortbooks.com
Key Personnel
Pres: Eric M Kampmann
Mng Ed: Megan Trank *E-mail:* megan@beaufortbooks.com
ISBN Prefix(es): 978-1-59921
Number of titles published annually: 12 Print; 12 E-Book
Total Titles: 100 Print; 100 E-Book
Imprints: Moyer Bell; Papier-Mache Press
Distribution Center: Midpoint Trade Books, 27 W 20 St, Suite 1102, New York, NY 10011 *Tel:* 212-727-0190 *Fax:* 212-727-0195

Beaver's Pond Press Inc
7108 Ohms Lane, Edina, MN 55439
Tel: 952-829-8818
E-mail: info@beaverspondpress.com
Web Site: www.beaverspondpress.com
Key Personnel
CEO & Publr: Tom Kerber *Tel:* 952-641-5250 *E-mail:* tom@beaverspondpress.com
Publg Dir: Lily Coyle *Tel:* 952-641-5254 *E-mail:* lily@beaverspondpress.com
Mktg Mgr: Heather Kerber *Tel:* 952-641-5251 *E-mail:* heather@beaverspondpress.com
Founded: 1998
Mission is to mentor authors to publish the best book possible through strategic marketing & creative collaboration, with quality, commitment & connection as the three guiding principles.
ISBN Prefix(es): 978-1-59298
Number of titles published annually: 60 Print; 50 E-Book
Total Titles: 250 Print; 100 E-Book
Branch Office(s)
Book House Fulfillment, 5120 Cedar Lake Rd S, Minneapolis, MN 55416 *Web Site:* www.bookhousefulfillment.com
Membership(s): The Independent Book Publishers Association; Midwest Independent Booksellers Association; Midwest Independent Publishers Association

Bedford, Freeman & Worth Publishing Group, LLC, see Macmillan Higher Education

Bedford/St Martin's
Imprint of Macmillan Higher Education
75 Arlington St, Boston, MA 02116
Tel: 617-399-4000 *Toll Free Tel:* 800-779-7440 *Fax:* 617-426-8582
Web Site: www.bedfordstmartins.com
Key Personnel
Ed-in-Chief, English: Karen Henry
Publr: Erika Gutierrez
Founded: 1981
Humanities publisher specializing in English composition, literature, history, communication, college success & music.
ISBN Prefix(es): 978-0-312; 978-1-457
Number of titles published annually: 200 Print; 20 CD-ROM; 50 E-Book
Branch Office(s)
33 Irving Place, New York, NY 10003 *Tel:* 212-375-7000 *Toll Free Tel:* 800-223-1715
Warehouse: MPS Distribution Center, 16365 James Madison Hwy (US Rte 15), Gordonsville, VA 22942 *Toll Free Tel:* 888-330-8477 *Fax:* 540-672-7540 (cust serv) *Toll Free Fax:* 800-672-2054 (orders)
Membership(s): AAP

Beekman Books Inc
300 Old All Angels Hill Rd, Wappingers Falls, NY 12590
Tel: 845-297-2690 *Fax:* 845-297-1002
E-mail: beekmanbooks@yahoo.com
Web Site: www.beekmanbooks.com
Key Personnel
Pres: Michael Arthur
Founded: 1972
New titles, reprints & imported titles from England, Wales, India & Russia in all subject areas, particularly music, holistic healing, homeopathic medicine, business, medical & computer books.
ISBN Prefix(es): 978-0-8464
Number of titles published annually: 3 Print
Total Titles: 3,026 Print
Distributor for C W Daniel; Gomer Press; Music Sales Corp; Kogan Page

Begell House Inc Publishers
50 North St, Danbury, CT 06810
Tel: 203-456-6161 *Fax:* 203-456-6167
E-mail: orders@begellhouse.com
Web Site: www.begellhouse.com
Key Personnel
COO & VP: Vicky Lipowski *E-mail:* vicky@begellhouse.com
Pres: Yelena Shafeyeva *E-mail:* elena@begellhouse.com
Mktg Dir: Peter White *E-mail:* peterw@begellhouse.com
Founded: 1992
Science books & journals.
ISBN Prefix(es): 978-1-56700
Number of titles published annually: 43 Print; 43 Online
Total Titles: 200 Print; 105 E-Book
Subsidiaries: Begell-Atom LLC
Membership(s): AAP

Behrman House Inc
11 Edison Place, Springfield, NJ 07081
SAN: 201-4459
Tel: 973-379-7200 *Toll Free Tel:* 800-221-2755 *Fax:* 973-379-7280
E-mail: behrmanhouse@gmail.com; customersupport@behrmanhouse.com
Web Site: www.behrmanhouse.com
Key Personnel
CEO & Pres: David Behrman
VP & Dir: Terry Kaye
Exec Ed: Dena Neusner
Founded: 1921

Synagogue school textbooks & trade books (Jewish).
ISBN Prefix(es): 978-0-87441
Number of titles published annually: 212 Print
Total Titles: 500 Print; 3 CD-ROM
Distributor for Rossel Books

Frederic C Beil Publisher Inc
609 Whitaker St, Savannah, GA 31401
Tel: 912-233-2446
E-mail: editor@beil.com
Web Site: www.beil.com
Key Personnel
Pres & Publr: Frederic C Beil *E-mail:* fcb@beil.com
Founded: 1982
Biography, history & fiction.
ISBN Prefix(es): 978-0-913720; 978-1-929490
Number of titles published annually: 6 Print
Total Titles: 221 Print
Imprints: Hypermedia Inc; The Sandstone Press
Foreign Rep(s): Gazelle Ltd (Europe, UK)
Warehouse: 609 Howard St, Savannah, GA 31401
Distribution Center: 608 Howard St, Savannah, GA 31401 *E-mail:* orders@beil.com

Bell Springs Publishing
PO Box 1240, Willits, CA 95490-1240
SAN: 209-3138
Tel: 707-459-6372
E-mail: publisher@bellsprings.com
Web Site: bellsprings.com; aboutpinball.com
Key Personnel
Publr: Sam Leandro *E-mail:* sam@bellsprings.com
Ed: Bernard Kamoroff *E-mail:* bk@bellsprings.com
Founded: 1976
Books, small business, pinball machines.
ISBN Prefix(es): 978-0-917510
Number of titles published annually: 10 Print; 10 Online; 10 E-Book
Total Titles: 20 Print; 10 Online; 10 E-Book
Shipping Address: 106 State St, Willits, CA 95490

Bella Books
PO Box 10543, Tallahassee, FL 32302
Tel: 850-576-2370 *Toll Free Tel:* 800-729-4992 *Fax:* 850-576-3498
E-mail: info@bellabooks.com; orders@bellabooks.com; ebooks@bellabooks.com
Web Site: www.bellabooks.com
Key Personnel
CEO & Publr: Linda Hill *E-mail:* linda@bellabooks.com
Founded: 1991
Publish books for, by & about women; fiction & nonfiction.
ISBN Prefix(es): 978-0-9628938; 978-1-883061
Number of titles published annually: 10 Print
Total Titles: 35 Print
Distributed by Turnaround (London)

Bellagio Press
Imprint of TAJ Books International LLC
5501 Kincross Lane, Charlotte, NC 28277
Web Site: bellagiopress.com
Key Personnel
Publr: Kay Jaitly *Tel:* 434-806-2359 *E-mail:* kay@bellagiopress.com
Founded: 2013
ISBN Prefix(es): 978-1-62732
Number of titles published annually: 22 Print
Distribution Center: Casemate Publishers & Book Distributors LLC, 908 Darby Rd, Havertown, PA 19083 *Tel:* 610-853-9131 *Fax:* 610-853-9146 *E-mail:* sean.johnston@casematepublishing.com

BelleBooks
PO Box 300921, Memphis, TN 38130
Tel: 901-344-9024 *Fax:* 901-344-9068
E-mail: bellebooks@bellebooks.com
Key Personnel
CEO & Pres: Debra Dixon
Dir, Mktg: Deborah Smith
Edit Dir, ImaJinn: Brenda Chin
Opers Mgr: Pamela Ireland
ISBN Prefix(es): 978-0-9768760
Number of titles published annually: 100 Print
Total Titles: 500 Print
Imprints: Bell Bridge Books; ImaJinn
Editorial Office(s): 1092 Ridgeway Rd, Dahlonega, GA
See separate listing for:
ImaJinn Books Inc

Bellerophon Books
PO Box 21307, Santa Barbara, CA 93121-1307
SAN: 202-392X
Tel: 805-965-7034 *Toll Free Tel:* 800-253-9943 *Fax:* 805-965-8286
E-mail: sales.bellerophon@gmail.com
Web Site: www.bellerophonbooks.com
Key Personnel
Pres: Ellen Knill
Founded: 1969
Children's art & history.
ISBN Prefix(es): 978-0-88388
Number of titles published annually: 6 Print
Total Titles: 142 Print

§Belltown Media
PO Box 980985, Houston, TX 77098
Tel: 713-344-1956 *Fax:* 713-583-7956
E-mail: subs@linuxjournal.com
Web Site: www.belltownmedia.com
Key Personnel
Publr: Carlie Fairchild *E-mail:* publisher@linuxjournal.com; Mark Irgang *E-mail:* mark@linuxjournal.com
Founded: 1968
Publish Linux Journal, a computer magazine.
ISBN Prefix(es): 978-0-916151; 978-1-57831
Number of titles published annually: 4 Print
Total Titles: 29 Print; 1 CD-ROM; 1 Online; 12 E-Book
Imprints: Linux Journal Press

Ben Yehuda Press
122 Ayers Ct, No 1B, Teaneck, NJ 07666
Tel: 201-836-0180 *Fax:* 201-917-1278
E-mail: orders@benyehudapress.com; yudel@benyehudapress.com
Web Site: www.benyehudapress.com
Key Personnel
Owner & Edit Dir: Larry Yudelson *E-mail:* larry@benyehudapress.com
Sr Ed: Eve Yudelson *E-mail:* eve@benyehudapress.com
Founded: 2005
Pluralistic Jewish publisher. We accept agented & unagented material. Prefer to see queries of a short synopsis (less than a page), the table of contents & the first 5 chapters if by mail or the complete ms by electronic submission.
ISBN Prefix(es): 978-0-9769862; 978-0-9789980
Number of titles published annually: 6 Print
Total Titles: 28 Print; 3 Online; 3 E-Book
Membership(s): The Independent Book Publishers Association

§BenBella Books Inc
10300 N Central Expwy, Suite 400, Dallas, TX 75231
Tel: 214-750-3600 *Fax:* 214-750-3645
E-mail: feedback@benbellabooks.com
Web Site: www.benbellabooks.com; www.smartpopbooks.com
Key Personnel
Publr: Glenn Yeffeth *Tel:* 214-750-3628 *E-mail:* glenn@benbellabooks.com
Admin Dir: Aida Herrera *Tel:* 214-361-7901 *E-mail:* aida@benbellabooks.com
Mktg Dir: Jennifer Canzoneri *Tel:* 214-750-3600 ext 104 *E-mail:* jennifer@benbellabooks.com
Ed-in-Chief, General Nonfiction: Debbie Harmsen *E-mail:* debbie@benbellabooks.com
Ed-in-Chief, Smart Pop: Leah Wilson *E-mail:* leah@benbellabooks.com
Founded: 2001
The best of health & nutrition, pop culture & smart nonfiction.
ISBN Prefix(es): 978-1-932100; 978-1-933771
Number of titles published annually: 30 Print
Total Titles: 150 Print
Imprints: Smart Pop
Orders to: Perseus Distribution, Cust Serv, 1049 Flex Dr, Jackson, TN 38301 *Toll Free Tel:* 800-343-4499 *Toll Free Fax:* 800-351-5073 *E-mail:* orderentry@perseusbooks.com
Returns: Perseus Distribution, Returns Dept, 193 Edwards Dr, Jackson, TN 38301 *Tel:* 731-423-1973 *Fax:* 731-422-4044
Shipping Address: 193 Edwards Dr, Jackson, TN 38301 *Toll Free Tel:* 800-343-4499 *Toll Free Fax:* 800-351-5073
Warehouse: Perseus Distribution, 193 Edwards Dr, Jackson, TN 38301 *Toll Free Tel:* 800-343-4499 *Toll Free Fax:* 800-351-5073
Distribution Center: Perseus Distribution, 193 Edwards Dr, Jackson, TN 38301 *Toll Free Tel:* 800-343-4499 *Toll Free Fax:* 800-351-5073
Membership(s): The Independent Book Publishers Association

Matthew Bender & Co Inc, see LexisNexis® Matthew Bender®

R James Bender Publishing
PO Box 23456, San Jose, CA 95153-3456
Tel: 408-225-5777 *Fax:* 408-225-4739
Web Site: www.bender-publishing.com
Key Personnel
Prop & Dir: Roger J Bender *E-mail:* rbender@bender-publishing.com
Founded: 1967
Military books & magazines.
ISBN Prefix(es): 978-0-912138
Number of titles published annually: 6 Print
Total Titles: 35 Print

John Benjamins Publishing Co
763 N 24 St, Philadelphia, PA 19130
SAN: 219-7677
Tel: 207-725-7250 *Toll Free Tel:* 800-562-5666 (orders) *Fax:* 207-725-7252
E-mail: service@benjamins.com
Web Site: www.benjamins.com
Key Personnel
Consultant: Paul Peranteau *E-mail:* paul@benjamins.com
Founded: 1981
Linguistics, language studies, English as a second language, terminology & art; translation studies; literacy; scientific study of consciousness & communication.
ISBN Prefix(es): 978-1-55619; 978-0-915027; 978-90-272; 978-1-58811
Number of titles published annually: 165 Print; 1 CD-ROM; 2 Online; 165 E-Book
Total Titles: 4,500 Print; 10 CD-ROM; 4 Online; 4,500 E-Book
Imprints: B R Gruener Publishing Co
Subsidiaries: John Benjamins North America Inc
Foreign Office(s): Box 36224, 1020 ME Amsterdam, Netherlands
Orders to: John Benjamins, PO Box 960, Herndon, VA 20172 *E-mail:* benjamins@presswarehouse.com
Returns: Books International, 22883 Quicksilver Dr, Dulles, VA 20166
Shipping Address: Books International, 22883 Quicksilver Dr, Dulles, VA 20166, Con-

tact: Todd Riggelman *E-mail:* benjamins@presswarehouse.com
Warehouse: Books International, 22883 Quicksilver Dr, Dulles, VA 20166 *Fax:* 703-661-1501
Distribution Center: Books International, 22883 Quicksilver Dr, Dulles, VA 20166

§Bentley Publishers
Division of Robert Bentley Inc
1734 Massachusetts Ave, Cambridge, MA 02138-1804
SAN: 213-9839
Tel: 617-547-4170 *Toll Free Tel:* 800-423-4595 *Fax:* 617-876-9235
E-mail: sales@bentleypublishers.com
Web Site: www.bentleypublishers.com
Key Personnel
Chmn & Pres: Michael Bentley
Dir, Publg: Janet Barnes
Sr Ed: Charlie Burke
Sales & Mktg Mgr: Maurice Iglesias
Founded: 1949
Technical automotive reference, automotive repair manuals, automotive history, automotive performance driving & motorsports.
ISBN Prefix(es): 978-0-8376
Total Titles: 400 Print; 30 CD-ROM

BePuzzled
Division of University Games
2030 Harrison St, San Francisco, CA 94110
Tel: 415-503-1600 *Toll Free Tel:* 800-347-4818 *Fax:* 415-503-0085
E-mail: info@ugames.com
Web Site: www.ugames.com
Key Personnel
Pres: Bob Moog
Sr Prods Mgr: Connie Gee
Puzzles with a plus-ages from preschool to adult.
ISBN Prefix(es): 978-1-57528; 978-1-57561
Number of titles published annually: 15 Print
Total Titles: 50 Print

R J Berg Publisher
79 Saint Paul St, Burlington, VT 05402-0369
Mailing Address: PO Box 30225, Indianapolis, IN 46230-0225
Tel: 802-557-0928
E-mail: rjberg@americanparksandresorts.com; rjberg@luxurydestinationsandresorts.com
Web Site: www.americanparksandresorts.com
Founded: 1974
Publishers of American social & cultural history of food, art & travel.
ISBN Prefix(es): 978-0-89730
Number of titles published annually: 14 Print
Total Titles: 38 Print
Imprints: American Food History; American Parks & Resorts; College Days Press; Cruise Memories; Luxury Destinations & Resorts; Luxury Destinations & Resorts Press; Luxury Destinations Press; Memorable Meetings Press; Travel Memories Press

Berghahn Books
20 Jay St, Suite 512, Brooklyn, NY 11201
Tel: 212-233-6004 *Fax:* 212-233-6007
E-mail: info@berghahnbooks.com; salesus@berghahnbooks.com; editorial@journals.berghahnbooks.com
Web Site: www.berghahnbooks.com
Key Personnel
Publr & Ed-in-Chief: Dr Marion Berghahn *E-mail:* publisher@berghahnbooks.com
Mng & Journals Edit Dir: Vivian Berghahn
Sr Ed, History & Film: Chris Chappell
Prodn Mgr: Melissa Spinelli
Sales & Mktg Mgr: Jeremy Wang-Iverson
Founded: 1994
Scholarly books & journals in humanities & social sciences.
ISBN Prefix(es): 978-1-57181; 978-1-84545
Number of titles published annually: 150 Print; 1,000 E-Book
Total Titles: 1,600 Print; 1,500 E-Book
Divisions: Berghahn Books Ltd (UK)
Foreign Office(s): 3 Newtec Place, Magdalen Rd, Oxford OX4 1RE, United Kingdom *Tel:* (01865) 250011 *Fax:* (01865) 250056
Distributor for Yad Vashem
Foreign Rep(s): The African Moon Press (Chris Reinders) (South Africa); Avicenna (Middle East exc Israel); Cranbury International LLC (Ethan Atkin) (Caribbean, Central America, Latin America); Laszlo Horvarth (Central Europe, Eastern Europe); Iberian Book Services (Peter Prout) (Portugal, Spain); Inspirees International (China); K L Books Distributor (K L Lee) (Malaysia, Southeast Asia); Flavio Marcello (Italy); Missing Link (Germany); Reimmer Book Services (Ferdinan Reimmer) (West Africa); Sara Books Pvt Ltd (Ravindra Saxena) (India); David Towle International (David Towle) (Scandinavia); UBC Press (Canada); Unifacmanu Trading Co Ltd (Celine Li) (Taiwan); UPS (Japan); Woodslane P/L (Australia, New Zealand)
Foreign Rights: Afroditi Forti (Worldwide)
Billing Address: Books International Inc, PO Box 605, Herndon, VA 20172 *Tel:* 703-661-1500 *Toll Free Tel:* 800-540-8663 *Fax:* 703-661-1501
Orders to: Books International Inc, PO Box 605, Herndon, VA 20172 *Tel:* 703-661-1500 *Toll Free Tel:* 800-540-8663 *Fax:* 703-661-1501
Returns: Books International Inc, 22883 Quicksilver Dr, Sterling, VA 20166 *Tel:* 703-661-1500 *Toll Free Tel:* 800-540-8663 *Fax:* 703-661-1501
Warehouse: Books International Inc, PO Box 605, Herndon, VA 20172 *Tel:* 703-661-1500 *Toll Free Tel:* 800-540-8663 *Fax:* 703-661-1501

Berkeley Slavic Specialties
PO Box 3034, Oakland, CA 94609-0034
SAN: 212-7245
Tel: 510-653-8048 *Fax:* 510-653-6313
E-mail: 71034.456@compuserve.com
Web Site: www.berkslav.com
Key Personnel
Owner: Gareth K Perkins
Founded: 1971
Slavic culture, literature, language & history.
ISBN Prefix(es): 978-0-933884; 978-1-57201; 978-0-936041
Number of titles published annually: 3 Print
Total Titles: 120 Print
Imprints: Scythian Books
Subsidiaries: Barbary Coast Books

Berkley Books
Imprint of Penguin Group (USA) LLC
375 Hudson St, New York, NY 10014
SAN: 282-5074
Tel: 212-366-2000 *Fax:* 212-366-2666
E-mail: online@penguinputnam.com
Web Site: www.penguinputnam.com; us.penguingroup.com
Key Personnel
Pres & Publr: Leslie Gelbman
VP & Sr Exec Ed: Natalee Rosenstein
VP & Assoc Publr: Rick Nayer
VP & Exec Creative Dir: Rich Hasselberger
VP & Dir, Prodn: Patricia King
VP, Publicity Dir, Berkley Publishing Group/NAL/Riverhead/Perigee & Mktg Dir, Riverhead/Perigee: Craig Burke
Dir, Contracts: Robin Simon
VP, Exec Ed: Cindy Hwang
Exec Ed: Jacqueline Cantor; Tom Colgan; Charles Conrad; Kendra Harpster; Kathleen Seaver; Denise Silvestro; Anne Sowards
Exec Mng Ed: Lara Robbins
Founded: 1955
ISBN Prefix(es): 978-0-425; 978-0-441; 978-0-515; 978-1-57297
Number of titles published annually: 677 Print
Total Titles: 4,433 Print
Imprints: Ace Books; Caliber; Jam; Jove; Prime Crime; Sensation
Advertising Agency: Spier NY

Berkley Publishing Group
Division of Penguin Group (USA) LLC
375 Hudson St, New York, NY 10014
SAN: 282-5074
Tel: 212-366-2000 *Fax:* 212-366-2385
E-mail: online@penguinputnam.com
Web Site: us.penguingroup.com
Key Personnel
Pres & Publr: Leslie Gelbman
VP & Sr Exec Ed: Natalee Rosenstein
VP, Assoc Publr & Exec Mng Ed: Rick Nayer
VP & Exec Creative Dir: Rich Hasselberger
VP & Dir, Prodn: Patricia King
VP & Publicity Dir, Berkley Publishing Group/NAL/Riverhead/Perigee & Mktg Dir, Riverhead/Perigee: Craig Burke
VP, Exec Ed: Cindy Hwang
Dir, Contracts: Robin Simon
Exec Mng Ed: Lara Robbins
Exec Ed: Jacqueline Cantor; Tom Colgan; Charles Conrad; Kathleen Seaver; Denise Silvestro; Anne Sowards
Founded: 1954
ISBN Prefix(es): 978-0-425; 978-0-515
Number of titles published annually: 700 Print
Imprints: Ace Books; Berkley Books; Diamond Books; HPBooks; Jove; Perigee; Prentice Hall Press; Prime Crime; Riverhead Books (Paperback); Sensation
Advertising Agency: Spier NY

Bernan
Imprint of Rowman & Littlefield Publishing Group
4501 Forbes Blvd, Suite 200, Lanham, MD 20706
Mailing Address: PO Box 191, Blue Ridge Summit, PA 17214-0191
Tel: 301-459-7666 (cust serv & orders) *Fax:* 301-459-0056
E-mail: customercare@bernan.com
Web Site: www.bernan.com
Key Personnel
Mktg Mgr: Veronica Dove *Tel:* 301-459-2255 ext 5716 *E-mail:* vdove@bernan.com
Founded: 1952
Publishes original government-related reference works & provides a wide range of services to help librarians build their government information collections.
ISBN Prefix(es): 978-1-59888
Number of titles published annually: 45 Print
Total Titles: 336 Print
Distribution Center: National Book Network, 15200 NBN Way, Blue Ridge Summit, PA 17214 *Tel:* 301-459-7666 *Toll Free Tel:* 800-865-3457 *Fax:* 301-459-6988 *Toll Free Fax:* 800-865-3450

§Berrett-Koehler Publishers Inc
1333 Broadway, Suite 1000, Oakland, CA 94612
Tel: 510-817-2277 *Fax:* 510-817-2278
E-mail: bkpub@bkpub.com
Web Site: www.bkconnection.com
Key Personnel
Pres & Publr: Steven Piersanti
VP, Design & Prodn: Rick Wilson
VP, Edit & Digital: David Marshall
VP, Intl Sales & Busn Devt: Johanna Vondeling
VP, Mktg: Kristen Frantz
Mng Dir, Edit: Jeevan Sivasubramaniam
Edit Dir: Neal Maillet
Dir, Subs Rts: Maria Jesus Aguilo
Sr Communs Mgr: Katie Sheehan
Online Mktg & Intl Sales Mgr: Zoe Mackey
Sr Sales Mgr: Marina Cook *E-mail:* mcook@bkpub.com
Assoc Ed: Anna Leinberger

Founded: 1992
Publications on business, work, stewardship, leadership, management, career development, human resources, entrepreneurship & global sustainability for the trade, scholarly, text & professional reference markets.
ISBN Prefix(es): 978-1-881052; 978-1-57675; 978-1-62656
Number of titles published annually: 40 Print
Total Titles: 320 Print
Foreign Rep(s): Eurospan Group (Australia, New Zealand, Oceania); HarperCollins Publishers India (Bangladesh, Bhutan, India, Maldives, Nepal, Pakistan, Sri Lanka); McGraw-Hill Education (Africa, Europe, Middle East, UK); McGraw-Hill Education Asia (East Asia, South Asia, Southeast Asia); Raincoast Books (Canada)
Warehouse: AIDC, 82 Winter Sport Lane, Williston, VT 05495 *Toll Free Tel:* 800-929-2929 *Toll Free Fax:* 800-864-7626
Distribution Center: Ingram Publisher Services, One Ingram Blvd, La Vergne, TN 37086 *Toll Free Tel:* 800-509-4887 *Toll Free Fax:* 800-838-1149

§Bess Press
3565 Harding Ave, Honolulu, HI 96816
Tel: 808-734-7159 *Fax:* 808-732-3627
E-mail: customerservice@besspress.com
Web Site: www.besspress.com
Key Personnel
Owner & Publr: Benjamin E Bess *Tel:* 808-734-7159 ext 123
Exec Dir: David DeLuca *Tel:* 808-734-7159 ext 124 *E-mail:* deluca@besspress.com
Cust Sales Mgr: Helene Honda *Tel:* 808-734-7159 ext 110
Founded: 1979
Books about the Pacific Islands, with a special emphasis on Hawaii. Includes elementary & secondary level textbooks in Hawaiian & Pacific Island history, geography & environment, Hawaiian & Pacific bilingual language materials, popular regional trade paperbacks, cookbooks, anthologies, humor, Christmas, guides, how-to & children's books on Hawaii & Oceania.
ISBN Prefix(es): 978-0-935848; 978-1-880188; 978-1-57306
Number of titles published annually: 17 Print
Total Titles: 285 Print; 12 Audio
Distributed by The Islander Group (TIG) (Hawaii wholesaler/book dist)

A M Best Co
One Ambest Rd, Oldwick, NJ 08858
Tel: 908-439-2200 (ext 5311-sales); 908-439-2200 *Fax:* 908-439-3385
E-mail: customer_service@ambest.com; sales@ambest.com
Web Site: www.ambest.com
Founded: 1899
Insurance industry statistics & supporting material, rate & provide financial information about insurance companies.
ISBN Prefix(es): 978-0-89408
Number of titles published annually: 3 Print
Total Titles: 17 Print
Foreign Office(s): A M Best Asia-Pacific, Central Plaza, Suite 4004, 18 Harbour Rd, Hong Kong, Hong Kong *Tel:* 2827 3400 *Fax:* 2824 1833
A M Best American Latina SA de CV, Paseo de la Reforma 412, Piso 23, Col Juarez, Mexico, DF, Mexico *Tel:* (0155) 5208-1264
A M Best MENA South & Central Asia, Off 102, Tower 2, Currency House, DIFC, PO Box 506617, Dubai, United Arab Emirates *Tel:* (04) 375 2780 *Fax:* (04) 431 3485
A M Best Europe, 12 Arthur St, 6th fl, London EC4R 9AB, United Kingdom *Tel:* (020) 7626 6264

Bethany House Publishers
Division of Baker Publishing Group
11400 Hampshire Ave S, Bloomington, MN 55438
SAN: 201-4416
Tel: 952-829-2500 *Toll Free Tel:* 800-877-2665 (orders) *Fax:* 952-829-2568 *Toll Free Fax:* 800-398-3111 (orders)
Web Site: www.bethanyhouse.com; www.bakerpublishinggroup.com
Key Personnel
EVP & Dir: Jim Parrish
VP, Edit: David Horton *Fax:* 952-829-2568
VP, Mktg: Steve Oates
Natl Sales Mgr: Rob Teigen
Pres, Baker Publishing Group: Dwight Baker
EVP, Sales & Mktg, Baker Publishing Group: Dave Lewis
Founded: 1956
Religion (Evangelical).
ISBN Prefix(es): 978-0-87123; 978-1-55661; 978-0-7642; 978-0-76428
Number of titles published annually: 90 Print; 90 E-Book
Total Titles: 500 Print
Foreign Rep(s): Challenge Bookshops Enterprises of Ghana (Nigeria); Christian Literature Center (Hong Kong); Christian Literature Crusade (Japan); David C Cook (Canada); Filadelfiaforlaget A-S (Norway, Sweden); Glad Sounds (Malaysia); International Boekencentrum Pelgrim (Netherlands); Nova Distribution (UK); Omega Distributors Ltd (New Zealand); Salvation Book Center (Malaysia); Scripture Union (Singapore); Word of Life Press (Japan, Korea)
Foreign Rights: Winfried Bluth (Europe)

Bethlehem Books
Affiliate of Bethlehem Community
10194 Garfield St S, Bathgate, ND 58216
Toll Free Tel: 800-757-6831 *Fax:* 701-265-3716
E-mail: contact@bethlehembooks.com
Web Site: www.bethlehembooks.com
Key Personnel
Pres: Jim Rasmussen
Gen Mgr & Publr: Jack Sharpe *E-mail:* jsharpe@bethlehembooks.com
Founded: 1993
Children's & youth books.
ISBN Prefix(es): 978-1-883937; 978-1-932350
Number of titles published annually: 8 Print; 10 E-Book; 1 Audio
Total Titles: 49 Print; 2 Audio
Distributed by Ignatius Press
Foreign Rights: Canadian Home Education Resources (Canada); St Andrews Books (Canada); Saint Benedicts Book Centre (Australia); Sunrise Marian Distributors (Canada)

Betterway Books
Imprint of F+W, A Content + eCommerce Company
10151 Carver Rd, Suite 200, Blue Ash, OH 45242
Tel: 513-531-2690 *Toll Free Tel:* 800-666-0963 *Fax:* 513-891-7185 *Toll Free Fax:* 888-590-4082
Web Site: www.fwmedia.com
Key Personnel
Pres: Sara Domville
Founded: 1981
Instructional & self-help books for creative people in the areas of home maintenance, repair, woodworking, home-based business, sports & recreation, theater, arts, genealogy & gardening.
ISBN Prefix(es): 978-0-932620; 978-1-55870
Number of titles published annually: 10 Print
Total Titles: 130 Print
Imprints: Family Tree Books; Horticulture Books; Numismatics Books; Popular Woodworking Books; Sports Collectors Digest
Returns: F+W, A Content + eCommerce Company, c/o Aero Fulfillment Services, 6023 Union Centre Blvd, West Chester, OH 45014
Shipping Address: F+W, A Content + eCommerce Company, c/o Aero Fulfillment Services, 6023 Union Centre Blvd, West Chester, OH 45014

Beyond Words Publishing Inc
Imprint of Simon & Schuster
20827 NW Cornell Rd, Suite 500, Hillsboro, OR 97124-9808
SAN: 666-4210
Tel: 503-531-8700 *Fax:* 503-531-8773
E-mail: info@beyondword.com
Web Site: www.beyondword.com
Key Personnel
COO: Tim Schroeder
Pres & Publr: Richard E Cohn
Mng Ed: Lindsay Brown
Mktg Mgr: Whitney Diffenderfer
Founded: 1983
Imprint of Simon & Schuster through a co-publishing agreement with Atria Books, an imprint of Simon & Schuster.
ISBN Prefix(es): 978-0-941831; 978-1-885223; 978-1-58270
Number of titles published annually: 15 Print
Total Titles: 300 Print; 25 E-Book; 10 Audio
Distributed by Simon & Schuster

§Bhaktivedanta Book Trust (BBT)
9701 Venice Blvd, Suite 3, Los Angeles, CA 90034
Mailing Address: PO Box 341445, Los Angeles, CA 90034
Tel: 310-837-5283 *Toll Free Tel:* 800-927-4152 *Fax:* 310-837-1056
E-mail: store@krishna.com
Web Site: www.krishna.com
Key Personnel
Mktg & Dist Mgr: Stuart Kadetz *E-mail:* sura108@gmail.com
Founded: 1972
Books of Vedic culture & philosophy, vegetarianism, reincarnation & karma.
ISBN Prefix(es): 978-0-89213; 978-91-7149; 978-0-912776
Number of titles published annually: 3 Print; 2 CD-ROM
Total Titles: 96 Print; 1 CD-ROM; 2 E-Book; 84 Audio
Warehouse: 705 E Gardena Blvd, Gardena, CA 90248, Contact: Efren Gonzalez *Tel:* 310-523-4533 *Fax:* 310-523-4258

BHB, see BrickHouse Books Inc

Bibliotheca Persica Press
450 Riverside Dr, Suite 4, New York, NY 10027
Tel: 212-851-9150 *Fax:* 212-749-9524
E-mail: ey4@columbia.edu
Key Personnel
Publr: Prof Ehsan Yarshater
Multi-disciplinary humanities/Iranian studies.
ISBN Prefix(es): 978-0-933273
Number of titles published annually: 3 Print
Total Titles: 40 Print
Sales Office(s): Eisenbrauns Inc, PO Box 275, Winona Lake, IN 46590-0275 *Tel:* 574-269-2011 *Toll Free Tel:* 800-736-7921 (US only) *E-mail:* orders@eisenbrauns.com *Web Site:* www.eisenbrauns.com
Billing Address: Eisenbrauns Inc, PO Box 275, Winona Lake, IN 46590-0275 *Tel:* 574-269-2011 *Toll Free Fax:* 800-736-7921 (US only) *E-mail:* orders@eisenbrauns.com *Web Site:* www.eisenbrauns.com
Returns: Eisenbrauns Inc, PO Box 275, Winona Lake, IN 46590-0275 *Tel:* 574-269-2011 *Toll Free Fax:* 800-736-7921 (US only) *E-mail:* orders@eisenbrauns.com *Web Site:* www.eisenbrauns.com

Shipping Address: Eisenbrauns Inc, PO Box 275, Winona Lake, IN 46590-0275
Distribution Center: Eisenbrauns Inc, PO Box 275, Winona Lake, IN 46590-0275 *Tel:* 574-269-2011 *Toll Free Fax:* 800-736-7921 (US only) *E-mail:* orders@eisenbrauns.com *Web Site:* www.eisenbrauns.com

Bick Publishing House
16 Marion Rd, Branford, CT 06405
Tel: 203-208-5253 *Fax:* 203-208-5253
E-mail: bickpubhse@aol.com
Web Site: www.bickpubhouse.com
Key Personnel
Owner: Dale Carlson
EVP & Ed-in-Chief: Hannah Carlson
VP & Dir, Prodn & Mktg: Jennifer Payne
Founded: 1993
Adult & young adult professional information for general audience & teens on health & recovery, adult & teenage psychology, meditation, neuroscience, general science, special needs & wildlife rehabilitation.
ISBN Prefix(es): 978-1-884158
Number of titles published annually: 4 Print
Total Titles: 32 Print
Foreign Rep(s): Bob Erdmann (Worldwide)
Foreign Rights: Bob Erdmann (Worldwide)
Distribution Center: Bookmasters, 30 Amberwood Pkwy, Ashland, OH 44805, Acct Exec: Regina Hamner *Toll Free Tel:* 800-BOOKLOG (266-5564) *E-mail:* rhamner@bookmasters.com *Web Site:* www.bookmasters.com
Membership(s): The Independent Book Publishers Association

Big Guy Books Inc
1042 N El Camino Real, Suite B-231, Encinitas, CA 92024
SAN: 253-0392
Tel: 760-652-5360 *Toll Free Tel:* 800-536-3030 (booksellers' cust serv) *Fax:* 760-652-5362
E-mail: info@bigguybooks.com
Web Site: www.bigguybooks.com
Key Personnel
Pres: Robert Gould *E-mail:* robert@bigguybooks.com
Founded: 2000
Publishes high quality adventure stories for children. Combine cutting-edge graphics & old fashioned values to increase literacy as well as confidence & self-respect in young readers.
ISBN Prefix(es): 978-1-929945
Number of titles published annually: 3 Print
Distributed by Arcturus Publishing Ltd (United Kingdom); Bookwise International (Australia); Independent Publishers Group (handles all Trade Distribution in the US); Scholastic New Zealand (New Zealand); Iwasaki Shoten (Japanese Translation)
Membership(s): ABA; ALA; The Independent Book Publishers Association

Bilingual Press/Editorial Bilingue
Arizona State Univ, Hispanic Research Ctr, Tempe, AZ 85287-2702
SAN: 208-5526
Mailing Address: PO Box 875303, Tempe, AZ 85287-5303
Tel: 480-965-3867 *Toll Free Tel:* 866-965-3867 *Fax:* 480-965-0315
E-mail: brp@asu.edu
Web Site: www.asu.edu/brp
Key Personnel
Publr: Gary D Keller *Tel:* 480-965-3990 *E-mail:* gary.keller@asu.edu
Exec Ed, Bilingual: Karen Van Hooft *Tel:* 480-727-0712 *E-mail:* karen.vanhooft@asu.edu
Founded: 1973
Publisher & distributor of US Hispanic creative literature, literary criticism & scholarship.
ISBN Prefix(es): 978-0-916950; 978-0-927534; 978-1-931010
Number of titles published annually: 6 Print
Total Titles: 200 Print; 2 CD-ROM
Shipping Address: Administration Bldg, A Wing, Rm 207, Tempe, AZ 85281

Biographical Publishing Co
95 Sycamore Dr, Prospect, CT 06712-1011
Tel: 203-758-3661 *Fax:* 253-793-2618
E-mail: biopub@aol.com
Web Site: www.biopub.us
Key Personnel
Ed: John R Guevin
Founded: 1991
Pre-print, printing & marketing services.
ISBN Prefix(es): 978-0-9637240; 978-1-929882
Number of titles published annually: 15 Print; 10 E-Book
Total Titles: 85 Print; 98 Online; 30 E-Book
Distributor for Eagles Landing Publishing; Spyglass Books LLC
Distribution Center: Pathway Book Service, PO Box 89, Gilsum, NH 03448, Serv Contact: Julie Ballough *Tel:* 603-357-0236 *Toll Free Tel:* 800-345-6665 *Fax:* 603-357-2073 *E-mail:* julie.ballough@pathwaybook.com *Web Site:* www.pathwaybook.com

BioTechniques Books
Division of Informa Business Information
52 Vanderbilt Ave, 11th fl, New York, NY 10017
Tel: 212-520-2777 *Fax:* 212-520-2705
Web Site: www.biotechniques.com
Key Personnel
Ed-in-Chief: Nathan S Blow, PhD *Tel:* 646-651-9084 *E-mail:* nathan.blow@informausa.com
Mktg Mgr: Damon Mastandrea *E-mail:* damon.mastandrea@informausa.com
Mgr, Prodn: Genevieve McCarthy *Tel:* 212-520-2752 *E-mail:* genevieve.mccarthy@informausa.com
Mng Ed: Amy Volpert *Tel:* 212-520-2719 *E-mail:* amy.volpert@informausa.com
Founded: 1996
Research monographs, laboratory manuals & reference books in biotechnology, medicine & the life sciences.
ISBN Prefix(es): 978-1-881299
Number of titles published annually: 12 Print
Total Titles: 29 Print

Birch Brook Press
PO Box 81, Delhi, NY 13753-0081
Tel: 607-746-7453 (book sales & prodn) *Fax:* 607-746-7453
E-mail: birchbrook@copper.net
Web Site: www.birchbrookpress.info
Key Personnel
Publr & Ed: Tom Tolnay
Art Dir: Leigh Eckmair *E-mail:* birchbrook@copper.net
Sales Mgr: Tim Grain
Assoc Ed: Barbara de la Cuesta
Founded: 1982
Popular culture & literary books, some of which are printed letterpress on fine stock as well as offset trade editions. Also have begun publishing hybrid print books consisting of letterpress covers & offset printed text. Books about books, fly fishing, the outdoors, baseball, fine poetry & theme-oriented anthologies of short fiction. Limited editions club for signed/numbered letterpress editions.
ISBN Prefix(es): 978-0-913559; 978-0-978997
Number of titles published annually: 3 Print; 1 E-Book
Total Titles: 100 Print; 4 E-Book
Imprints: Birch Brook Press; Brief Books (miniature handcrafted books); Persephone Press (chapbooks, handcrafted, for outside organizations)
Subsidiaries: Birch Brook Impressions (designs, typesets & prints letterpress editions for outside publishers & organizations)
Distributor for Carpenter Gothic Press; Natural Heritage Press; Persephone Press
Foreign Rep(s): Gazelle Book Services (Europe, UK); Japan UNI Agency (Japan); Multicultural Books (Canada)
Foreign Rights: Chinese Connection (Hong Kong, Mainland China, Taiwan)
Returns: 2309 County Hwy 16, Delhi, NY 13753 (returns accepted eight months after purchase if in clean saleable condition for credit on new purchases), Billing & Returns Contact: Joyce Tolnay
Warehouse: 2309 County Hwy 16, Delhi, NY 13753
Membership(s): Academy of American Poets; The Independent Book Publishers Association

Bird Dog Publishing, see Bottom Dog Press

§George T Bisel Co Inc
710 S Washington Sq, Philadelphia, PA 19106-3519
Tel: 215-922-5760 *Toll Free Tel:* 800-247-3526 *Fax:* 215-922-2235
E-mail: gbisel@bisel.com
Web Site: www.bisel.com
Key Personnel
Pres: Franklin Jon Zuch *E-mail:* fjzuch@bisel.com
VP: James L Betz *E-mail:* jbetz@bisel.com
Ed-in-Chief: Tony Di Gioia *E-mail:* tonyd@bisel.com
Ed: Frank Coyne *E-mail:* fcoyne@bisel.com
Founded: 1876
Pennsylvania, New Jersey, Florida law practice subjects.
ISBN Prefix(es): 978-1-887024
Number of titles published annually: 8 Print
Total Titles: 75 Print; 10 CD-ROM; 1 Audio

§Bisk Education
9417 Princess Palm Ave, Suite 400, Tampa, FL 33619
Tel: 813-621-6200 *Toll Free Tel:* 800-280-9718 (cust serv)
E-mail: customerservice@bisk.com
Web Site: www.bisk.com
Key Personnel
Founder & Chmn: Nathan M Bisk
CEO: Andrew Titen
CFO: William Geary, III
Pres: Michael D Bisk
EVP & COO: Joseph Smith
Chief Strategy Offr & VP, Devt: George Straschnov
VP & Chief HR Offr: Philip Kenney
VP & Corp Coun: Alison L Bisk
VP, New Busn: Blair Stobaugh
Gen Coun: Ravi Seepersad
Mktg Mgr: Kathy McDonald
Founded: 1971
One of the leading providers of online, interactive continuing professional education, including continuing education for accountants, attorneys, physicians & nurses, CPA Exam preparation materials & web-based certificate, associate's, bachelor's & master's degree programs from nationally known, regionally accredited universities, including Villanova University, Regis University, the University of South Florida, Saint Leo University & Jacksonville University.
ISBN Prefix(es): 978-1-57961
Number of titles published annually: 50 Print
Total Titles: 500 Print; 50 CD-ROM; 150 Online; 9 E-Book; 90 Audio
Distributed by Bisk Publishing Co

§Bitingduck Press LLC
1262 Sunnyoaks Circle, Altadena, CA 91001

Tel: 626-679-2494; 626-507-8033
E-mail: notifications@bitingduckpress.com
Web Site: bitingduckpress.com
Key Personnel
Ed-in-Chief: Jay Nadeau *E-mail:* jay@bitingduckpress.com
Creative Dir: Dena Eaton *E-mail:* dena@bitingduckpress.com
Technol Dir: Chris Lindensmith *E-mail:* chris@bitingduckpress.com
Ed: Susan Foster
Acqs Ed: Marie Nadeau *E-mail:* marie@bitingduckpress.com
Mktg/Contracts: Gretchen Lindensmith
Founded: 2012
Quality electronic publishing for a digital world.
ISBN Prefix(es): 978-1-938463
Number of titles published annually: 8 Print; 20 E-Book
Total Titles: 50 Print; 140 E-Book
Imprints: Boson Books
Distribution Center: Small Press Distribution, 1341 Seventh St, Berkeley, CA 94710, Opers Dir: Brent Cunningham *Toll Free Tel:* 800-869-7553 *Fax:* 510-524-0852 *E-mail:* spd@spdbooks.org *Web Site:* www.spdbooks.org
Ingram Book Group, One Ingram Blvd, La Vergne, TN *Tel:* 615-793-5000
Membership(s): The Authors Guild; Independent Book Publishing Professionals Group
See separate listing for:
Boson Books

BizBest Media Corp
860 Via de la Paz, Suite E3B, Pacific Palisades, CA 90272
E-mail: press@bizbest.com
Web Site: www.bizbest.com
Key Personnel
CEO: Daniel Kehrer *E-mail:* dkehrer@bizbest.com
Publr: Roth Savage *E-mail:* savage@bizbest.com
Founded: 1999
The only integrated media company in America delivering independently researched & rated solution & resource publications for business owners & entrepreneurs across all regions & industries. BizBest books, publications & products meet the expanding information needs of small business owners, startups, consultants, advisors & educators. BizBest is noncommercial & accepts no advertising or sponsorships.
ISBN Prefix(es): 978-0-9719045
Number of titles published annually: 6 Print; 4 CD-ROM
Subsidiaries: BizBestLocal.com; BizBriefing.com; BizLaunchPad.com; BizOwnerOnly.com; BizTaxes.com; ManagingSmart.com; MyBizDaily.com; 140Main.com (social media smarts for local business); SalesSavvy.com; SmallBusiness.tv; SocialMyBusiness.com; StartupSmarts.com; YourBusinessMinute.com; Z140.com
Divisions: BizBest Media Features (syndicates small business-related content)

§BJU Press
Unit of Bob Jones University
1700 Wade Hampton Blvd, Greenville, SC 29614-0062
SAN: 223-7512
Tel: 864-770-1317; 864-242-5100
Toll Free Tel: 800-845-5731
E-mail: bjupinfo@bjupress.com
Web Site: www.bjupress.com
Key Personnel
Chief Pubn Offr, Bob Jones Univ: Bill Apelian
Founded: 1974
El-hi textbooks & trade media.
ISBN Prefix(es): 978-0-89084; 978-1-57924; 978-1-59166
Number of titles published annually: 24 Print
Total Titles: 2,500 Print
Imprints: JourneyForth Books; ShowForth Videos; SoundForth Music
Divisions: JourneyForth Books; ShowForth Videos; SoundForth Music
Warehouse: 134 White Oak, Greenville, SC 29607-1218
Membership(s): CBA

BkMk Press - University of Missouri-Kansas City
University House, 5101 Rockhill Rd, Kansas City, MO 64110-2499
Tel: 816-235-2558 *Fax:* 816-235-2611
E-mail: bkmk@umkc.edu
Web Site: www.umkc.edu/bkmk
Key Personnel
Exec Ed: Robert Stewart *Tel:* 816-235-2610
E-mail: stewartr@umkc.edu
Mng Ed: Ben Furnish *E-mail:* furnishb@umkc.edu
Assoc Ed: Michelle Boisseau *Tel:* 816-235-2561
E-mail: boisseau@umkc.edu
Founded: 1971
Fine literature & essays.
ISBN Prefix(es): 978-0-933532; 978-1-886157
Number of titles published annually: 8 Print
Total Titles: 130 Print
Distribution Center: SPD (Small Press Distribution), 1341 Seventh St, Berkeley, CA 94710 (recent titles) *Toll Free Tel:* 800-869-7553
Membership(s): AAP; Association of Writers and Writing Programs; Community of Literary Magazines & Presses

Black Classic Press
3921 Vero Rd, Suite F, Baltimore, MD 21203-3414
SAN: 219-5836
Mailing Address: PO Box 13414, Baltimore, MD 21203-3414
Tel: 410-242-6954 *Toll Free Tel:* 800-476-8870
Fax: 410-242-6959
E-mail: email@blackclassicbooks.com; blackclassicpress@yahoo.com
Web Site: www.blackclassicbooks.com; www.bcpdigital.com
Key Personnel
Pres: W Paul Coates
Publr: Natalie Stokes-Peters
Digital Print Consultant: Damani Coates
Founded: 1978
Publishing obscure & significant works by & about people of African descent.
ISBN Prefix(es): 978-0-933121; 978-1-57478
Number of titles published annually: 20 Print
Total Titles: 100 Print
Imprints: Inprint Editions
Distributed by Publishers Group West (PGW)
Membership(s): The Independent Book Publishers Association

Black Dog & Leventhal, see Hachette Books

Black Dome Press Corp
649 Delaware Ave, Delmar, NY 12054
Tel: 518-439-6512 *Fax:* 518-439-1309
E-mail: blackdomep@aol.com
Web Site: www.blackdomepress.com
Key Personnel
Owner: Steve Hoare
Founded: 1990
Regional small press publishing New York State history & guide books.
ISBN Prefix(es): 978-1-883789; 978-0-9628523
Number of titles published annually: 5 Print
Total Titles: 80 Print

Black Heron Press
PO Box 13396, Mill Creek, WA 98082-1396
Tel: 425-355-4929 *Fax:* 425-355-4929
Web Site: blackheronpress.com
Key Personnel
Publr & Lib Sales Dir: Jerry Gold
E-mail: jgoldberon@aol.com
Founded: 1984
Literary fiction & nonfiction pertaining to independent publishing & the writing craft; literature, science fiction (not dungeons & dragons).
ISBN Prefix(es): 978-0-930773; 978-1-936364
Number of titles published annually: 4 Print
Total Titles: 80 Print
Foreign Rep(s): European-Latin American Literary Agency (Pina Von Prellwitz) (France, Italy, Latin America, Spain); International Titles (Loris Essay) (Asia, Austria, Eastern Europe, Germany, Northern Europe, Switzerland)
Foreign Rights: Europe-Latin America Literary Agency (Pina von Prellwitz) (France, Italy, Latin America, Portugal, Spain); International Titles (Loris Essay)
Warehouse: 620 112 St SE, Suite 355, Everett, WA 98208
Distribution Center: Midpoint Trade Books, 27 W 20 St, Suite 1102, New York, NY 10011
Tel: 212-727-0190 *Fax:* 212-727-0195

§Black Mountain Press
PO Box 9907, Asheville, NC 28815
Tel: 828-273-3332
Web Site: www.theblackmountainpress.com
Key Personnel
Publr: Jack Moe *E-mail:* jackmoe@theblackmountainpress.com
Sr Ed: Carlos Steward *E-mail:* carlos@theblackmountainpress.com
Ed: Joline Mechanic *E-mail:* jolene99@bellsouth.net
Founded: 1994
Literary press for emerging & established creative writers, with or without literary agents. Specialize in literary novels, short story collections, poetry & creative nonfiction.
ISBN Prefix(es): 978-0-9700165; 978-1-940605
Number of titles published annually: 12 Print; 10 E-Book
Total Titles: 25 Print; 10 E-Book

Black Rabbit Books
515 N Riverfront Dr, Suite 200, Mankato, MN 56001
Mailing Address: PO Box 3263, Mankato, MN 56002-3263
Tel: 507-388-1609 *Fax:* 507-388-1364
E-mail: info@blackrabbitbooks.com; orders@blackrabbitbooks.com
Web Site: www.blackrabbitbooks.com
Key Personnel
Natl Mktg Mgr: Ann Schwab
Assoc Publr: Jonathan Strickland
Founded: 2006
Founded on the principle that quality books produce quality readers. Our list of K-12 books has a wide variety of topics, innovative approaches & multiple reading levels to serve all facets of the school library market.
ISBN Prefix(es): 978-1-84234; 978-1-84193; 978-1-59920; 978-1-58340; 978-1-59771; 978-1-59566; 978-1-59604; 978-1-93288; 978-8-86098; 978-1-93383; 978-1-93279; 978-1-84837
Number of titles published annually: 375 Print
Total Titles: 2,000 Print
Imprints: Arcturus Publishing; Brown Bear Books; New Forest Press; Sea-to-Sea Publishing; Smart Apple Media; Stargazer Books; Zak Books
Foreign Rep(s): Saunders Book Co (Canada)

The Blackburn Press
PO Box 287, Caldwell, NJ 07006-0287
Tel: 973-228-7077 *Fax:* 973-228-7276
Web Site: www.blackburnpress.com

Key Personnel
Edit Dir & Publr: Frances Reed *E-mail:* freed@blackburnpress.com
Gen Mgr: Maryanne Kenny *E-mail:* mkenny@blackburnpress.com
Mktg & Cust Serv: Barbara R Chmiel *E-mail:* bchmiel@blackburnpress.com
Founded: 1999
Book titles, largely reprints, of classics in science & technology. Worldwide distributors.
ISBN Prefix(es): 978-1-930665; 978-1-932846
Number of titles published annually: 20 Print
Total Titles: 100 Print
Distribution Center: Baker & Taylor, 2550 W Tyrola Rd, Charlotte, NC *Toll Free Tel:* 800-775-1800 *Toll Free Fax:* 800-998-3316 *E-mail:* btinfo@baker-taylor.com *Web Site:* www.baker-tayor.com
Barnes & Noble, One Barnes & Noble Way, Monroe, NJ 08831 *Tel:* 732-656-7400
NACSCORP, 528 E Lorain St, Oberlin, OH 44074-1298, Dir, Merchandise Mktg: Joan Keehan *Tel:* 440-775-7777 *Toll Free Tel:* 800-321-3883 (orders) *E-mail:* service@nascorp.com *Web Site:* www.nascorp.com
Ingram, One Ingram Blvd, La Vergne, TN *Tel:* 615-793-5000 *Toll Free Tel:* 800-937-8200 *E-mail:* customer.service@ingrambook.com *Web Site:* www.ingrambook.com
Amazon.com, 440 Terry Ave N, Seattle, WA *E-mail:* amazonpublishing-pr@amazon.com *Web Site:* www.amazon.com
Adlibris.com, Box 3367, 103 59 Stockholm, Sweden
Mallory International Ltd, Aylesbeare Common Business Park, Exmouth Rd, Aylesbeare, Devon EX5 2DG, United Kingdom, Contact: Julian Hardinge *Tel:* (01395) 239199 *Fax:* (01395) 239168 *E-mail:* julian@malloryint.co.uk *Web Site:* www.malloryint.co.uk
Blackwell, Unipart House, Garsington Rd, Cowley, Oxford 0X4 2PG, United Kingdom *Tel:* (01865) 382 524 *Fax:* (01865) 382 790 *E-mail:* sales@blackwell.co.uk *Web Site:* bookshop.blackwell.co.uk
Gardners Books, One Whittle Dr, Eastbourne, East Sussex, United Kingdom *Tel:* (01323) 521777 *Fax:* (01323) 521666 *E-mail:* custcare@gardners.com *Web Site:* www.gardners.com
Paperback Shop, Horcott Industrial Estate, Unit 22, Horcott Rd, Fairford, Glos GL7 4BX, United Kingdom *Tel:* (01285) 712 917
Coutts & Co, 440 Stand, London WC2R 0QS, United Kingdom *Tel:* (020) 7753 1000 *Web Site:* www.coutts.com
Book Depository, PO Box 91, St Peter Port GY1 3EG, United Kingdom, Contact: Steve Potter *E-mail:* steve@bookdepository.co.uk
Aphrohead, 277-A Wennington Rd, Southport, Merseyside PR9 7TW, United Kingdom, Mng Dir: Paul Anderson *E-mail:* enquiries@aphrohead.com *Web Site:* aphrohead.com
Bertrams, Wakefield House, Pipers Way, Swindon, Wilts SN3 1RF, United Kingdom *Tel:* (0871) 803 6666 *Web Site:* www.bertrams.com

John F Blair Publisher
1406 Plaza Dr, Winston-Salem, NC 27103
SAN: 201-4319
Tel: 336-768-1374 *Toll Free Tel:* 800-222-9796 *Fax:* 336-768-9194
Web Site: www.blairpub.com
Key Personnel
Pres & Spec Projs Dir: Carolyn Sakowski *E-mail:* sakowski@blairpub.com
Dir, Design & Prodn: Debra Hampton *E-mail:* hampton@blairpub.com
Ed-in-Chief: Steve Kirk *E-mail:* kirk@blairpub.com
Founded: 1954
General trade.
ISBN Prefix(es): 978-0-910244; 978-0-89587
Number of titles published annually: 18 Print; 18 E-Book
Total Titles: 300 Print; 200 E-Book; 3 Audio
Distributor for Bandit Books; Bright Mountain Books; Canterbury House Publishing; Down Home Press; Eno Publishers; Hub City Press; Looking Glass Books; Lookout Books; New-South Books; Niche Publishing; Pennywell Press; Upper Ohio Valley Books; Walkabout Press; Willow Hill Press

§Bloch Publishing Co
10030 E W Pappy Rd, PMB 0015, Jacksonville, FL 32259
Tel: 904-880-7302 *Fax:* 904-880-7307
E-mail: info@blochpub.com
Web Site: www.blochpub.com
Key Personnel
Pres: Mitchell Bloch
Founded: 1854
Judaica.
ISBN Prefix(es): 978-0-8197
Number of titles published annually: 8 Print
Total Titles: 100 Print
Distributor for Biblio; Menorah; Scarf Press; Sephardic House; Soncino

Blood Moon Productions Ltd
75 Saint Marks Place, Staten Island, NY 10301-1606
Tel: 718-556-9410
E-mail: editors@bloodmoonproductions.com
Web Site: bloodmoonproductions.com
Key Personnel
Pres & Publr:
Danforth Prince *E-mail:* danforthprince@bloodmoonproductions.com
Founded: 2004
A New York-based publishing enterprise dedicated to researching, salvaging & indexing the oral histories of America's entertainment industry.
ISBN Prefix(es): 978-0-9748118; 978-0-9786465; 978-1-936003
Number of titles published annually: 4 Print; 4 E-Book
Total Titles: 50 Print; 50 E-Book
Imprints: The Georgia Literary Association (earlier titles)
Distribution Center: National Book Network, 4501 Forbes Blvd, Suite 200, Lanham, MD 20706 (North America, Australia, New Zealand & UK) *Tel:* 301-459-3366 *Toll Free Tel:* 800-462-6420 *Fax:* 301-429-5746 *Toll Free Fax:* 800-338-4550 *E-mail:* customercare@nbnbooks.com *Web Site:* www.nbnbooks.com
Membership(s): ABA; The Independent Book Publishers Association; NAIBA; Southern Independent Booksellers Alliance

Bloom's Literary Criticism
Imprint of Infobase Learning
132 W 31 St, 17th fl, New York, NY 10001
Toll Free Tel: 800-322-8755 *Toll Free Fax:* 800-678-3633
E-mail: custserv@factsonfile.com
Web Site: www.infobasepublishing.com
Key Personnel
Chmn, Infobase Learning: Mark McDonnell
CFO, Infobase Learning: Jim Housley
Edit Dir, Infobase Learning: Laurie Likoff
Dir, Licensing & Busn Devt, Infobase Learning: Ben Jacobs *Tel:* 212-896-4268 *E-mail:* bjacobs@factsonfile.com
Dir, Mktg, Infobase Learning: Zina Scarpulla
Dir, Opers, Infobase Learning: Mark Zielinski
Offers hundreds of volumes of literary criticism edited by Harold Bloom, focusing on the writers & works most often studied in high schools & universities.
ISBN Prefix(es): 978-0-7910; 978-1-4381
Number of titles published annually: 67 Print; 67 E-Book
Total Titles: 453 Print; 525 E-Book
Returns: c/o Maple Press Distribution Ctr, 704 Legionaire Dr, Fredericksburg, PA 17026
Warehouse: c/o Maple Press Distribution Ctr, 704 Legionaire Dr, Fredericksburg, PA 17026
Distribution Center: c/o Maple Press Distribution Ctr, 704 Legionaire Dr, Fredericksburg, PA 17026

Bloomsbury Academic
1385 Broadway, 5th fl, New York, NY 10018
SAN: 213-8220
Tel: 212-419-5300
Web Site: www.bloomsbury.com
Key Personnel
EVP, Bloomsbury USA: Derek Stordahl
Mktg Mgr: Joe Kreuser
Mktg Assoc: Laura Ewen
Conference & Events Coord: Jessica Tackett
Founded: 1999 (result of a merger between The Continuum Publishing Company of NY & the academic & religious publishing programs of Cassell plc in London)
Hardcover & paperbacks; scholary & professional & general interest; music, film, literature, media studies, the arts & popular culture; philosophy, religion, biblical studies, theology & spirituality, history, politics & contemporary issues, education; women studies & reference.
ISBN Prefix(es): 978-0-304; 978-0-7201; 978-0-8264; 978-1-56338; 978-0-7136; 978-0-86012; 978-0-225; 978-0-264; 978-0-7185; 978-0-86187; 978-1-85567; 978-0-7220; 978-0-567; 978-0-485; 978-1-84127; 978-1-85805; 978-1-84371; 978-0-8044; 978-0-223
Number of titles published annually: 1,100 Print
Total Titles: 6,000 Print
Foreign Office(s): 50 Bedford Sq, London WC1B 3DP, United Kingdom *Tel:* (020) 7631 5600
Distributor for Paragon House; Spring Publications
Foreign Rep(s): Eliane Benisti (exclusive French); Liepman AG (exclusive German); Natoli Stefan & Olivia (exclusive Italian)
Foreign Rights: Allen & Unwin Pty Ltd (Australia); APD (Brunei, Indonesia, Malaysia, Singapore, Thailand, Vietnam); APS Ltd (China, Hong Kong, Philippines, South Korea, Taiwan); Robert Barnett (USA); BCR University Bookstore (Jamaica); Eliane Benisti Literary Agency (France); Bounty Press Ltd (Nigeria); Codasat Canada Ltd (Canada); Continuum (Africa exc North & South Africa, Caribbean, Germany, Israel, Netherlands, North America); Cranbury International LLC (Central America, Mexico, South America); Durnell Marketing Ltd (Europe); Horizon Books (Botswana, Lesotho, Namibia, South Africa, Swaziland); IPS (Middle East exc Israel, North Africa); Liepman AG (Switzerland); Richard Lyle (London); Maya Publishers Pvt Ltd (Bangladesh, India, Sri Lanka); Richard McNeace (USA); Natoli Stefan & Oliva Literary Agency (Italy); Novalis (Canada); Nick Pepper (Northern England, Scotland); Publishers Consultants & Representatives (Pakistan); Jonathan Rhodes (England, Midlands); Andrew Toal (England); United Publishers Services Ltd (Japan)

Bloomsbury Publishing Inc
1385 Broadway, 5th fl, New York, NY 10018
Tel: 212-419-5300
E-mail: marketingusa@bloomsbury.com; adultpublicityusa@bloomsbury.com; askacademic@bloomsbury.com
Web Site: www.bloomsbury.com
Key Personnel
EVP & Head of Sales (Americas) & Global Academic Mktg, Bloomsbury USA: Derek Stordahl
VP, Mktg & Sales: Christina Gilbert
Sr Dir, Publicity & Communs: Marie Coolman

Publg Dir, Bloomsbury Children's Books USA: Cindy Loh
Publg Dir, Bloomsbury USA & Publr, Bloomsbury Press: George Gibson
Edit Dir, Bloomsbury Children's: Catherine Onder
Assoc Dir of Publicity, Bloomsbury USA: Summer Smith
Assoc Publicity Dir, Bloomsbury Children's Books: Lizzy Mason
Dir, Adoption Sales, Bloomsbury Academic & Professional: Melanie Sankel
Dir, Mktg Design & Opers: Alona Fryman
Dir, Trade & Digital Mktg: Laura Keefe
Dir, Children's Trade & Digital Mktg: Erica Barmash
Sales Dir, Latin America, Caribbean & Canada: Nick Parker
Mktg Mgr, Adult Trade Div: Megan Ernst
Mktg Mgr for School & Lib, Children's Trade Group: Linette Kim
US Trade Sales Opers Mgr: Doug White
Head, Academic Mktg (Americas): Abigail Naqvi
Exec Mng Ed, Bloomsbury Children's Books: Melissa Kavonic
Sr Ed, Bloomsbury Children's Books: Mary Kate Castellani
Sr Ed, Bloomsbury Children's: Sarah Shumway
Sr Ed, Bloomsbury USA: Lea Beresford
Ed: Rachel Mannheimer
Prodn Ed: Sara Kitchen
Assoc Ed, Bloomsbury Children's Books: Laura Whitaker; Brett Wright
Sr Publicist: Anthony LaSasso
Publicist, Adult Div: Theresa Collier
Publicist, Children's: Courtney Griffin
Inventory Mgr, Bloomsbury USA: Donna Gautier
Asst Mktg Mgr, Children's: Emily Ritter
Founded: 1998
No unsol mss.
ISBN Prefix(es): 978-1-58234; 978-1-61963; 978-1-62040; 978-1-63286; 978-1-68119; 978-1-59691; 978-1-59990; 978-1-60819
Number of titles published annually: 100 Print
Imprints: Bloomsbury; Bloomsbury Press (nonfiction); Bloomsbury USA (adult)
Distributed by Macmillan
Orders to: MPS Distribution Center, 16365 James Madison Hwy, Gordonsville, VA 22942-8501 *Toll Free Tel:* 888-330-8477 *Toll Free Fax:* 800-672-2054
Returns: MPS Returns Center, 14301 Litchfield Rd, Orange, VA 22960
Distribution Center: MPS Distribution Center, 16365 James Madison Hwy, Gordonsville, VA 22942-8501 *Toll Free Tel:* 888-330-8477 *Toll Free Fax:* 800-672-2054

Blue Apple Books
515 Valley St, Suite 170, Maplewood, NJ 07040
Tel: 973-763-8191 *Toll Free Tel:* 800-283-3572 (orders) *Fax:* 973-763-5944
E-mail: info@blueapplebooks.com
Web Site: blueapplebooks.com
Key Personnel
Publr: Harriet M Ziefert
Assoc Publr: Elliot Kreloff
Dir, Opers: Kip Jacobson
Founded: 2003
Publisher of innovative children's books. No unsol mss accepted at this time.
ISBN Prefix(es): 978-1-59354; 978-1-934706
Number of titles published annually: 60 Print
Total Titles: 300 Print
Distribution Center: Consortium, The Keg House, 34 13 Ave NE, Suite 101, Minneapolis, MN 55413-1007 *Tel:* 612-746-2600 *Fax:* 612-746-2606 *E-mail:* info@cbsd.com *Web Site:* www.cbsd.com

Blue Book Publications Inc
8009 34 Ave S, Suite 250, Minneapolis, MN 55425
Tel: 952-854-5229 *Toll Free Tel:* 800-877-4867 *Fax:* 925-853-1486
E-mail: support@bluebookinc.com
Web Site: www.bluebookofgunvalues.com; www.bluebookofguitarvalues.com
Key Personnel
President: Adam Burt *Tel:* 952-853-1486 ext 20 *E-mail:* adam@bluebookinc.com
Publr & Author: S P Fjestad *Tel:* 952-853-1486 ext 13 *E-mail:* stevef@bluebookinc.com
Exec Ed: Cassandra Faulkner *Tel:* 952-853-1486 ext 19 *E-mail:* cassandraf@bluebookinc.com
Founded: 1989
Industry leader in up-to-date & accurate values & information for firearms, airguns, modern black powder replicas, amplifiers & fretted instruments. Publisher of reference books, consumer pricing guides, encyclopedias & coffee table books. Online information provider/appraisals.
ISBN Prefix(es): 978-1-936120
Number of titles published annually: 20 Print; 4 CD-ROM; 8 Online; 2 E-Book
Total Titles: 36 Print; 4 CD-ROM; 8 Online; 2 E-Book
Membership(s): ABA; Midwest Independent Booksellers Association; Outdoor Writers Association of America

Blue Crane Books
PO Box 380291, Cambridge, MA 02238
Tel: 617-926-8989 *Fax:* 617-926-0982
E-mail: bluecrane@arrow1.com
Key Personnel
Publr: Mrs Alvart Badalian *Tel:* 617-926-8585 *E-mail:* alvart@arrow1.com
Art Dir: Mr Aramais Andonian
Ed: Ms Salpi H Ghazarian
Founded: 1991
Publish adult trade fiction & nonfiction, history, political & social sciences, culture & art. Special line of adult & children's books in Armenian & English translations of Armenian originals. No unsol mss.
ISBN Prefix(es): 978-0-9628715; 978-1-886434
Number of titles published annually: 3 Print
Total Titles: 20 Print

§Blue Dolphin Publishing Inc
13340-D Grass Valley Ave, Grass Valley, CA 95945
SAN: 223-2480
Mailing Address: PO Box 8, Nevada City, CA 95959-0008
Tel: 530-477-1503 *Toll Free Tel:* 800-643-0765 (orders) *Fax:* 530-477-8342
E-mail: bdolphin@bluedolphinpublishing.com
Web Site: www.bluedolphinpublishing.com
Key Personnel
Pres & Ed: Paul M Clemens *E-mail:* clemens@bluedolphinpublishing.com
Ed & Electronic Publg: Linda Maxwell
Mktg & Promo: Michael Clemens
Founded: 1985
Books, ebooks & audiotapes on health, psychology, self-help, comparative spiritual traditions, anthropology, education.
ISBN Prefix(es): 978-0-931892; 978-0-942444; 978-1-57733
Number of titles published annually: 20 Print; 20 Online; 20 E-Book; 3 Audio
Total Titles: 265 Print; 175 Online; 175 E-Book; 15 Audio
Imprints: Aura Imaging; Papillion Publishing (children's); Pelican Pond Publishing (fiction & poetry); Symposium Publishing (nonfiction)
Distributor for The Lotus Seed Press (China) (ISBN prefix: 978-962-8602)
Foreign Rep(s): Yorwerth Associates (Nigel Yorwerth) (Worldwide)
Foreign Rights: Editions Le Chaos (France); Agencia Riff (Brazil)

Blue Mountain Arts Inc
2905 Wilderness Place, Boulder, CO 80301
Mailing Address: PO Box 4549, Boulder, CO 80306-4549 SAN: 299-9609
Tel: 303-449-0536 *Toll Free Tel:* 800-525-0642 *Fax:* 303-417-6472 *Toll Free Fax:* 800-545-8573
E-mail: info@sps.com
Web Site: www.sps.com
Key Personnel
Pres: James Gurney
Sales Admin: Vicki Cornelius
Founded: 1971
Publisher of trade books: inspirational, poetry, juvenile, young adult & gift books & sidelines.
ISBN Prefix(es): 978-0-88396; 978-1-58786; 978-1-59842
Number of titles published annually: 20 Print; 20 Online
Total Titles: 120 Print; 120 Online
Imprints: Artes Monte Azul; Blue Mountain Press®; Rabbit's Foot Press™
Editorial Office(s): PO Box 1007, Boulder, CO 80301, Contact: P Wayant
Returns: 6455 Spine Rd, Boulder, CO 80301
Shipping Address: 6455 Spine Rd, Boulder, CO 80301, Contact: Wayne Ivers
Membership(s): ABA; CBA; National Association of College Stores

Blue Note Books, see Blue Note Publications Inc

Blue Note Publications Inc
721 North Dr, Suite D, Melbourne, FL 32934
Tel: 321-799-2583 *Toll Free Tel:* 800-624-0401 (orders) *Fax:* 321-799-1942
E-mail: bluenotepress@gmail.com
Web Site: www.bluenotebooks.com
Key Personnel
Pres: Paul Maluccio
Publr: Carmen Abreu
Founded: 1988
Small press book publishing, production, printing, distribution, marketing.
ISBN Prefix(es): 978-1-878398
Number of titles published annually: 10 Print; 10 Online; 10 E-Book
Total Titles: 126 Print; 2 CD-ROM; 61 Online; 34 E-Book
Imprints: Blue Note; Blue Note Books
Membership(s): The Independent Book Publishers Association

§Blue Poppy Press
Division of Blue Poppy Enterprises Inc
1990 57 Ct, Unit A, Boulder, CO 80301
Tel: 303-447-8372 *Toll Free Tel:* 800-487-9296 *Fax:* 303-245-8362
E-mail: info@bluepoppy.com
Web Site: www.bluepoppy.com
Key Personnel
Gen Mgr: Bruce Staff *E-mail:* bruce@bluepoppy.com
Founded: 1982
Books on acupuncture & Chinese medicine.
ISBN Prefix(es): 978-0-936185; 978-1-891845
Number of titles published annually: 10 Print; 3 E-Book
Total Titles: 12 Print; 100 E-Book
Distributed by China Books; New Leaf Books; Partner's Book Distributing Inc; Partner's/West Book Distributing Inc; Redwing Book Co; Satas; Tools4Healing (Scott Mieras)

Blue Rider Press
Imprint of Penguin Group (USA) LLC, a Penguin Random House company
375 Hudson St, New York, NY 10014
Tel: 212-366-2000
E-mail: blueriderpublicity@us.penguingroup.com
Key Personnel
Pres & Publr: David Rosenthal

VP, Assoc Publr & Dir, Mktg & Publicity: Aileen Boyle
Exec Ed: Sarah Hochman
Sr Ed: Brant Rumble
Ed: Vanessa Kehren
Art Dir: Jason Booher
Assoc Dir, Publicity: Brian Ulicky
Exec Publicist: Marian Brown
Sr Publicist: Eliza Rosenberry
Founded: 2011
Number of titles published annually: 28 Print
Total Titles: 32 Print

BlueBridge
Imprint of United Tribes Media Inc
PO Box 601, Katonah, NY 10536
Tel: 914-301-5901
Web Site: www.bluebridgebooks.com
Key Personnel
Founder & Publr: Jan-Erik Guerth
E-mail: janguerth@aol.com
Founded: 2004
Independent publisher of international nonfiction based near New York City. Subjects range from culture, history, biography, travel & current affairs to spirituality, self-help & inspiration. The BlueBridge Vision: Thoughtful Books for Mind & Spirit.
ISBN Prefix(es): 978-1-933346; 978-0-9742405
Number of titles published annually: 6 Print
Total Titles: 30 Print
Distribution Center: Legato Publishers Group, 814 William St, River Forest, IL 60305 *Tel:* 312-316-9618 *Web Site:* www.legatopublishersgroup.com

Bluestocking Press
3045 Sacramento St, No 1014, Placerville, CA 95667-1014
SAN: 667-2981
Mailing Address: PO Box 1014, Placerville, CA 95667-1014
Tel: 530-622-8586 *Toll Free Tel:* 800-959-8586 *Fax:* 530-642-9222
E-mail: customerservice@bluestockingpress.com; orders@bluestockingpress.com
Web Site: www.bluestockingpress.com
Key Personnel
Owner & Pres: Jane A Williams *E-mail:* jane@bluestockingpress.com
Founded: 1987
Other subjects offered: free market economics, business, finance, justice, ancient Rome, World Wars, Mideast War. Sell on nonreturnable basis (except for books received damaged) to the reseller market.
ISBN Prefix(es): 978-0-942617
Number of titles published annually: 21 Print
Total Titles: 23 Print
Sales Office(s): PO Box 1014, Placerville, CA 95667-1014, Contact: Ann Marie *E-mail:* annmarie@bluestockingpress.com
Billing Address: PO Box 1014, Placerville, CA 95667-1014, Accts Payable: Jane Williams *E-mail:* jane@bluestockingpress.com
Orders to: PO Box 1014, Placerville, CA 95667-1014, Contact: Ann Marie *E-mail:* annmarie@bluestockingpress.com

BNA Books
Division of Bloomberg BNA
1801 S Bell St, Arlington, VA 22202
SAN: 201-4262
Tel: 732-476-6397 *Toll Free Tel:* 800-372-1033; 800-960-1220 *Fax:* 732-346-1624
E-mail: books@bna.com
Web Site: www.bnabooks.com
Key Personnel
Chmn: Greg McCaffery
Publr: Margret S Hullinger *Tel:* 703-341-5742 *E-mail:* mhullinger@bna.com
Acqs Mgr: Robert Anderson *Tel:* 703-341-5765
Founded: 1929
Employment law: labor law, labor relations, employee benefits, labor arbitration, intellectual property law; health law: legal practice & reference.
ISBN Prefix(es): 978-0-87179; 978-1-57018
Number of titles published annually: 60 Print
Total Titles: 160 Print; 2 Online
Orders to: 30 Mayfield Ave, Edison, NJ 08837-3821
Returns: 30 Mayfield Ave, Edison, NJ 08837-3821
Warehouse: PO Box 7814, Edison, NJ 08818-7814

BNi Building News
990 Park Center Dr, Suite E, Vista, CA 92081-8352
Tel: 760-734-1113 *Toll Free Tel:* 888-BNI-BOOK (264-2665)
Web Site: www.bnibooks.com
Key Personnel
Dir, Sales: Bill Grote
Gen Mgr: John Moore
Founded: 1946
Construction & engineering.
ISBN Prefix(es): 978-1-55701; 978-1-878088
Number of titles published annually: 100 Print
Total Titles: 120 Print

BOA Editions Ltd
250 N Goodman St, Suite 306, Rochester, NY 14607
Tel: 585-546-3410 *Fax:* 585-546-3913
E-mail: contact@boaeditions.org
Web Site: www.boaeditions.org
Key Personnel
Publr: Peter Conners *E-mail:* conners@boaeditions.org
Devt Dir & Off Mgr: Melissa Hall *E-mail:* hall@boaeditions.org
Dir, Mktg & Prodn: Jenna Fisher
Founded: 1976
Publication of books of poetry, poetry in translation & fiction.
ISBN Prefix(es): 978-0-918526; 978-1-880238; 978-1-929918; 978-1-934414
Number of titles published annually: 10 Print
Total Titles: 205 Print
Orders to: Consortium Book Sales & Distribution, The Keg House, Suite 101, 34 13 Ave NE, Minneapolis, MN 55413-1007 *Tel:* 612-746-2600 *Toll Free Tel:* 800-283-3572 (cust serv) *Fax:* 612-746-2606 *Web Site:* www.cbsd.com
Shipping Address: Perseus Distribution, 193 Edwards Dr, Jackson, TN 38301 *Toll Free Tel:* 800-343-4499 *Toll Free Fax:* 800-351-5073 *Web Site:* www.perseusdistribution.com
Warehouse: Perseus Distribution, 1094 Flex Dr, Jackson, TN 38301 *Toll Free Tel:* 800-343-4499 *Toll Free Fax:* 800-351-5073 *Web Site:* www.perseusdistribution.com
Distribution Center: Consortium Book Sales & Distribution, The Keg House, Suite 101, 34 13 Ave NE, Minneapolis, MN 55413-1007 *Tel:* 612-746-2600 *Toll Free Tel:* 800-283-3572 (cust serv) *Fax:* 612-746-2606 *Web Site:* www.cbsd.com

§BoardSource
750 Ninth St NW, Suite 650, Washington, DC 20001-4793
Tel: 202-349-2500 *Toll Free Tel:* 877-892-6273 *Fax:* 202-349-2599
E-mail: members@boardsource.org
Web Site: www.boardsource.org
Key Personnel
CEO & Pres: Anne Lawson
Founded: 1988
Premier resource for practical information, tools & best practices, training & leadership development for board members of nonprofit organizations. Enables organizations to fulfill their missions by helping build effective nonprofit boards, offering credible support in solving tough problems.
ISBN Prefix(es): 978-0-925299; 978-1-58686
Number of titles published annually: 6 Print; 3 CD-ROM; 2 E-Book
Total Titles: 100 Print; 6 E-Book
Distributed by American Society of Association Executives

§Bolchazy-Carducci Publishers Inc
1570 Baskin Rd, Mundelein, IL 60060
SAN: 219-7685
Tel: 847-526-4344 *Toll Free Tel:* 800-392-6453 *Fax:* 847-526-2867
E-mail: info@bolchazy.com; orders@bolchazy.com
Web Site: www.bolchazy.com
Key Personnel
Owner & Pres: Dr Marie Carducci Bolchazy, PhD *E-mail:* marie@bolchazy.com
VP: Allan Bolchazy *E-mail:* abolchazy@bolchazy.com
Founded: 1978
Scholarly books, textbooks, language cassettes, CD-ROM Latin series, Latin music CDs & Slovak publications.
ISBN Prefix(es): 978-0-86516
Number of titles published annually: 15 Print; 3 CD-ROM; 5 Online; 10 E-Book; 5 Audio
Total Titles: 450 Print; 29 CD-ROM; 5 Online; 20 E-Book; 20 Audio
Advertising Agency: De Chant Hughes
Returns: 1576 Baskin Rd, Mundelein, IL 60060, Returns Coord: Betty Brendal *Tel:* 847-388-7144 *Fax:* 847-367-7684 *E-mail:* returns@bolchazy.com
Warehouse: 1576 Baskin Rd, Mundelein, IL 60060
Distribution Center: 1576 Baskin Rd, Mundelein, IL 60060 *Tel:* 847-388-7144 *Fax:* 847-367-7684

§Bold Strokes Books Inc
PO Box 249, Valley Falls, NY 12185
Tel: 518-677-5127 *Fax:* 518-677-5291
E-mail: bsb@boldstrokesbooks.com
Web Site: www.boldstrokesbooks.com
Key Personnel
Pres: Len Barot *E-mail:* publisher@boldstrokesbooks.com
Founded: 2004
Independent publishing company publishing works of gay, lesbian & feminist themed fiction in all genres, including general, genre & young adult fiction. Readership is international & all titles are released in print & multi-format ebook version. Employs conventional distribution channels to bring products to the customers.
ISBN Prefix(es): 978-1-9331100; 978-1-60282; 978-1-62639
Number of titles published annually: 110 Print; 110 Online; 110 E-Book; 25 Audio
Total Titles: 850 Print; 950 Online; 950 E-Book; 75 Audio
Orders to: Bella Distribution, 1041 Aenon Church Rd, Tallahassee, FL 32304
Returns: Bella Distribution, 1041 Aenon Church Rd, Tallahassee, FL 32304
Shipping Address: Bella Distribution, 1041 Aenon Church Rd, Tallahassee, FL 32304
Warehouse: Bella Distribution, 1041 Aenon Church Rd, Tallahassee, FL 32304
Distribution Center: Bella Distribution, 1041 Aenon Church Rd, Tallahassee, FL 32304, Contact: Becky Arbogast *Toll Free Tel:* 800-533-1973 *Fax:* 850-576-3498 *E-mail:* info@belladistribution.com

Membership(s): The Independent Book Publishers Association; Mystery Writers of America; Romance Writers of America; Science Fiction & Fantasy Writers of America

Bonasa Press
PO Box 340, Crosby, ND 58730
Tel: 701-965-3974
E-mail: new@bonasapress.com (inquiries)
Web Site: www.bonasapress.com
Key Personnel
Publr & Ed: John D Taylor *E-mail:* jdt@bonasapress.com
Sales & Mktg: Nancy E Whiting *E-mail:* new@bonasapress.com
Founded: 2002
ISBN Prefix(es): 978-0-9725594; 978-0-9772778
Number of titles published annually: 4 Print
Total Titles: 14 Print
Membership(s): Outdoor Writers Association of America; Pennsylvania Outdoors Writers Association

§Bondfire Books
7680 Goddard St, Suite 220, Colorado Springs, CO 80920
Tel: 719-260-7080
Web Site: www.bondfirebooks.com
Key Personnel
Founder: Rick Christian
ISBN Prefix(es): 978-1-939952
Number of titles published annually: 25 Print

Book Marketing Works LLC
50 Lovely St (Rte 177), Avon, CT 06001
Mailing Address: PO Box 715, Avon, CT 06001-0715
Tel: 860-675-1344
Web Site: www.bookmarketingworks.com
Key Personnel
Pres: Brian Jud *E-mail:* brianjud@bookmarketingworks.com
Founded: 1990
ISBN Prefix(es): 978-1-928782
Number of titles published annually: 10 Print
Total Titles: 26 Print
Imprints: Strong Books
Subsidiaries: Book Marketing Works

Book Peddlers
18330 Minnetonka Blvd, Deephaven, MN 55391
Tel: 952-544-1154 *Fax:* 206-339-6913
E-mail: bookpeddlers@aol.com
Web Site: www.bookpeddlers.com
Key Personnel
Owner & Publr: Vicki Lansky *E-mail:* vickilansky@aol.com
Mktg & PR: Diane Schwarze *E-mail:* diane@bookpeddlers.com
Founded: 1985
Nonfiction hardcover & CDs; gift-giving occasion books.
ISBN Prefix(es): 978-0-916773; 978-1-931863
Number of titles published annually: 1 Print; 2 E-Book
Total Titles: 20 Print; 3 CD-ROM; 15 E-Book
Orders to: Publishers Group West (PGW), 1094 Flex Dr, Jackson, TN 38301 *Toll Free Tel:* 800-788-3123 *Toll Free Fax:* 800-351-5073 *E-mail:* orderentry@perseusbooks.com
Distribution Center: Publishers Group West (PGW)/Perseus, 1700 Fourth St, Berkeley, CA 94710

Book Publishing Co
415 Farm Rd, Summertown, TN 38483
Mailing Address: PO Box 99, Summertown, TN 38483-0099
Tel: 931-964-3571 *Fax:* 931-964-3518
E-mail: info@bookpubco.com
Web Site: www.bookpubco.com
Key Personnel
Pres: Robert Holzapfel
Ed: Cynthia Holzapfel
Mktg: Anna Pope *E-mail:* annap@bookpubco.com
Founded: 1974
Community-owned independent press committed to promoting books that educate, inspire & empower. Books on vegan & vegetarian cooking & nutrition, raw food lifestyle, natural health care & Native American culture.
ISBN Prefix(es): 978-0-913990; 978-1-57067; 978-1-55312
Number of titles published annually: 10 Print
Total Titles: 250 Print; 2 Audio
Imprints: Books Alive; Botanica Press; Healthy Living; Native Voices; Norwalk Press; 7th Generation
Distributor for Cherokee Publications; Crazy Crow; CRCS Publications; Critical Path; Gentle World; Hippocrates Publications; Magni Co; Sproutman Publications
Foreign Rep(s): Brumby Books (Australia); Faradawn (South Africa); Publishers Group UK (England)

Book Sales Inc
Division of Quarto Publishing Group USA Inc
142 W 36 St, 4th fl, New York, NY 10018
SAN: 299-4062
Tel: 212-779-4971; 212-779-4972 *Toll Free Tel:* 866-483-5456 *Fax:* 212-779-6058
E-mail: sales@quartous.com; customerservice@quartous.com
Web Site: www.booksalesusa.com
Key Personnel
CEO & Pres: Melvin Shapiro
VP, Mktg & Acqs: Frank Oppel *Tel:* 212-779-4974 *E-mail:* frank.oppel@quartous.com
Dir, Opers: Joe Cella
Sales Dir: Steven Wilson *Tel:* 212-779-4973 *E-mail:* steve.wilson@quartous.com
Spec Sales: Daniel Rich *Tel:* 212-779-1816 *E-mail:* drich@quartous.com
Exec Asst: Jennifer Yee *E-mail:* jennifer.yee@quartous.com
Founded: 1952
Has been in the business of publishing & supplying books to wholesalers, mail order companies & retail stores for over 45 years. In addition to books we publish, we are one of the largest purchasers of other publishers' remainder +/or overstock titles for resale at significantly reduced prices. Categories include novels, cookbooks, history, juvenile, civil war, militaria, fine art, art instruction, how-to craft books, natural history, gardening & more.
ISBN Prefix(es): 978-0-89009; 978-1-55521; 978-0-7858
Number of titles published annually: 300 Print
Total Titles: 2,500 Print
Imprints: Blue & Gray; Castle Books; Chartwell Books; Crestline; Knickerbocker Press; Poplar Books; Wellfleet Press
Billing Address: 400 First Ave N, Suite 400, Minneapolis, MN 55401
Orders to: Hachette Book Group, 121 N Enterprise Blvd, Lebanon, IN 46052
Returns: Hachette Book Group, 121 N Enterprise Blvd, Lebanon, IN 46052
Warehouse: Hachette Book Group, 121 N Enterprise Blvd, Lebanon, IN 46052
Membership(s): ABA

The Book Tree
3316 Adams Ave, Suite A, San Diego, CA 92116
Mailing Address: PO Box 16476, San Diego, CA 92176
Tel: 619-280-1263 *Toll Free Tel:* 800-700-8733 (orders) *Fax:* 619-280-1285
E-mail: orders@thebooktree.com; titles@thebooktree.com; info@thebooktree.com
Web Site: thebooktree.com
Key Personnel
Owner: Paul Willey
Founded: 1992
Metaphysical, spiritual & controversial books; do not accept, respond to or return unsol mss.
ISBN Prefix(es): 978-1-885395; 978-1-58509
Number of titles published annually: 10 Print
Total Titles: 300 Print
Membership(s): The Independent Book Publishers Association

Bookhaven Press LLC
302 Scenic Ct, Moon Township, PA 15108
SAN: 668-7075
Tel: 412-494-6926
E-mail: info@bookhavenpress.com; orders@bookhavenpress.com
Web Site: bookhavenpress.com
Key Personnel
Pres & Publr: Dennis V Damp *E-mail:* ddamp@aol.com
Assoc Publr: Victor Richards *E-mail:* vrichards@bookhavenpress.com
Publicist: Kate Bandos *Tel:* 800-304-3269 *E-mail:* kate@ksbpromotions.com
Off Mgr: Mary McGraw
Founded: 1985
Independent publishing house dedicated to producing award winning business, career & finance books & companion web sites. *The Book of U.S. Government Jobs* was awarded "Best Career Title" by the Benjamin Franklin Awards Committee. Our 4th edition of *Health Care Job Explosion* was nominated for Best Books 2006 (Business-Career) title by USA Book News. Bookhaven's titles have been reviewed & recommended by Library Journal, Booklist, the New York Times & Washington Post, Career Opportunities News & over 100 magazines, newspapers & journals. We also publish environmental compliance books & comprehensive web sites for our titles.
ISBN Prefix(es): 978-0-943641
Number of titles published annually: 2 Print; 2 E-Book
Total Titles: 5 Print; 3 E-Book
Membership(s): The Independent Book Publishers Association

§BookLogix
1264 Old Alpharetta Rd, Alpharetta, GA 30005
SAN: 860-0376
Tel: 470-239-8547 *Toll Free Fax:* 888-564-7890
E-mail: sales@booklogix.com
Web Site: www.booklogix.com
Key Personnel
CEO & Pres: Ahmad Meradji *E-mail:* ahmad@booklogix.com
COO: Akash Mangru *E-mail:* kash@booklogix.com
Founded: 2009
This publisher has indicated that 80% of their product line is author subsidized.
ISBN Prefix(es): 978-1-61005
Number of titles published annually: 35 Print; 50 E-Book
Total Titles: 300 Print; 150 E-Book
Distribution Center: Baker & Taylor, 2550 W Tyvola Rd, Suite 300, Charlotte, NC 28217 *Tel:* 704-998-3100 *Toll Free Tel:* 800-775-1800 *Web Site:* www.btol.com

Books In Motion
Division of Classic Ventures Ltd
9922 E Montgomery, Suite 31, Spokane Valley, WA 99206
Tel: 509-922-1646 *Toll Free Tel:* 800-752-3199 *Fax:* 509-922-1445
E-mail: info@booksinmotion.com
Web Site: www.booksinmotion.com
Key Personnel
Pres: Gary Challender
Founded: 1980

Produce fiction books on CD & MP3. Does not accept unsol mss. Criteria is exceptionally high for acceptance. There is no cost to the authors. Currently seeking subsidiary audio rights on previously print published titles.
ISBN Prefix(es): 978-1-55686; 978-1-58116; 978-1-59607; 978-1-60548
Number of titles published annually: 24 Print; 60 Audio
Total Titles: 2,000 Audio

Books on Tape®
Imprint of Penguin Random House Inc
1745 Broadway, New York, NY 10019
Toll Free Tel: 800-733-3000 (cust serv) *Toll Free Fax:* 800-940-7046
Web Site: www.booksontape.com
Key Personnel
VP, Lib & Academic Sales: Skip Dye
SVP & Publr, Random House Audio: Amanda D'Acierno
Edit Dir, Listening Library®: Rebecca Waugh
Mktg Dir: Cheryl Herman
Founded: 1975
For over 30 years Books on Tape® has offered the best in unabridged audio books. Our best selling & award-winning titles are produced in NY & LA studios & read by the finest narrators in the industry. Select from over 3,000 titles available, durable library packaging & delivered with a complement of services tailored to meet special needs of librarians & educators. Flexible standing order plans, featuring the freedom to choose your titles & free lifetime replacement guarantees. Books on Tape® is proud to exclusively have Listening Library®, the premier audio book publisher of children's & young adult literature, as its children's imprint.
Number of titles published annually: 300 Audio
Total Titles: 3,000 Audio
Imprints: Listening Library®
Divisions: Listening Library®
Distributor for Listening Library®
Orders to: Random House LLC, Library & School Services, 400 Hahn Rd, Westminster, MD 21157
Returns: Random House LLC, 1019 N SR 47, Crawfordville, NJ 47933
Membership(s): AASL; ALA; ALSC; California Library Association; National Council of Teachers of English; Public Library Association; YALSA

Boom! Studios
5670 Wilshire Blvd, Suite 450, Los Angeles, CA 90036
Web Site: www.boom-studios.com
Key Personnel
Founder & CEO: Ross Richie
Pres, Publg & Mktg: Filip Sablik
VP, Licensing & Mdsg: Lance Kreiter
Ed-in-Chief: Matt Gagnon
Founded: 2005
ISBN Prefix(es): 978-1-934506; 978-1-60886; 978-1-61398; 978-1-932386; 978-1-936393; 978-1-68159; 978-1-939867
Distributed by Simon & Schuster Sales & Marketing

§Boson Books
Imprint of Bitingduck Press LLC
1262 Sunnyoaks Circle, Altadena, CA 91001
Tel: 626-507-8033; 626-395-2405
Web Site: www.bosonbooks.com; bitingduckpress.com
Key Personnel
Ed-in-Chief: Jay Nadeau *E-mail:* jay@bitingduckpress.com
Publr & Ed: Chris Lindensmith *E-mail:* chris@bitingduckpress.com
Founded: 1994
Publish ebooks & selected print books. First commercial general ebook publisher.
ISBN Prefix(es): 978-1-886420; 978-0-917990; 978-1-932482
Number of titles published annually: 8 Print; 13 E-Book
Total Titles: 25 Print; 350 E-Book
Distribution Center: Small Press Distribution (SPD), 1341 Seventh St, Berkeley, CA 94710-1409 *Tel:* 510-524-1668 *Toll Free Tel:* 800-869-7553 *Fax:* 510-524-0852 *Web Site:* www.spdbooks.org
Membership(s): The Authors Guild

Bottom Dog Press
813 Seneca Ave, Huron, OH 44839
SAN: 689-5492
Mailing Address: PO Box 425, Huron, OH 44839-0425
Tel: 419-433-3573 *Fax:* 419-616-3966
Web Site: smithdocs.net
Key Personnel
Dir & Publr: Larry Smith *E-mail:* lsmithdog@smithdocs.net
Assoc Ed: Susanna Sharp Schwacke; Laura Smith
Founded: 1985
ISBN Prefix(es): 978-0-933087; 978-1-933964
Number of titles published annually: 6 Print; 6 E-Book; 2 Audio
Total Titles: 185 Print; 2 CD-ROM; 16 E-Book; 4 Audio
Imprints: Bird Dog Publishing; Bottom Dog Press
Distributor for The Firelands Writing Center (Heartlands Magazine)
Distribution Center: Small Press Distribution, 1341 Seventh St, Berkeley, CA 94710-1409 *Tel:* 510-524-1668 *Toll Free Tel:* 800-869-7553 *Fax:* 510-524-0852 *E-mail:* spd@spdbooks.org *Web Site:* www.spdbooks.org
Baker & Taylor, 501 Gladiolus St, Momence, IL 60954
Membership(s): Community of Literary Magazines & Presses

Eddie Bowers Publishing Co Inc
PO Box 130, Peosta, IA 52068-0130
Tel: 563-582-8333 *Toll Free Tel:* 800-747-2411 *Fax:* 563-582-8555
E-mail: eddiebowerspub@aol.com
Web Site: www.eddiebowerspublishing.com
Key Personnel
Owner & Publr: Eddie Bowers
Founded: 1981
College textbooks.
ISBN Prefix(es): 978-0-912855; 978-0-945483; 978-1-57879
Number of titles published annually: 20 Print
Total Titles: 75 Print

R R Bowker LLC
Subsidiary of ProQuest LLC
630 Central Ave, New Providence, NJ 07974
SAN: 214-1191
Tel: 908-286-1090 *Toll Free Tel:* 888-269-5372 (edit & cust serv, press 2 for returns) *Fax:* 908-219-0098; (020) 7832 1710 (UK for intl) *Toll Free Fax:* 877-337-7015 (US & CN)
E-mail: orders@proquest.com (dom orders); customer_service@proquest.co.uk (intl)
Web Site: www.bowker.com
Founded: 1872
Leading provider of bibliographic information & management solutions designed to help publishers, booksellers & libraries better serve their customers. Creators of products & services that make books easier for people to discover, evaluate, order & experience, the company also generates research & resources for publishers, helping them understand & meet the interests of readers worldwide. Bowker, an affiliated business of ProQuest & the official ISBN Agency for Australia, the US & US territories, is headquartered in New Providence, NJ with additional operations in England & Australia.
ISBN Prefix(es): 978-0-8352
Number of titles published annually: 13 Print; 8 Online
Total Titles: 29 Print; 8 Online
Foreign Office(s): Thorpe - Bowker, Level One, 607 St Kilda Rd, Melbourne, Victoria 3004, Australia, Mng Dir: Gary Pengelly *Tel:* (03) 8517 8345 *Fax:* (03) 8517-8399 *E-mail:* yoursay@thorpe.com.au *Web Site:* www.thorpe.com.au
Bowker (UK) Ltd, St Andrew's House, 18-20 St Andrew St, London EC4A 3AG, United Kingdom, Mng Dir: Doug McMillan *Tel:* (020) 7832 1771 *Fax:* (020) 7832 1710 *E-mail:* sales@bowker.co.uk *Web Site:* www.bowker.co.uk
Membership(s): AAP; ALA; BISG; Canadian Booksellers Association; Evangelical Christian Publishers Association; National Association of College Stores

BowTie Press®, see I-5 Publishing LLC

Boydell & Brewer Inc
Affiliate of Boydell & Brewer Ltd (UK)
668 Mount Hope Ave, Rochester, NY 14620-2731
Tel: 585-275-0419 *Fax:* 585-271-8778
E-mail: boydell@boydellusa.net
Web Site: www.boydellandbrewer.com
Key Personnel
Mng Dir: Sue Smith *Tel:* 585-273-2817 *E-mail:* smith@boydellusa.net
Edit Dir: Sonia Kane *Tel:* 585-273-5778
Sales & Mktg Mgr: Sue Miller *Tel:* 585-273-5787
Accts Asst: Olga Reshota *Tel:* 585-273-5777
Founded: 1989
Publisher of scholarly books.
ISBN Prefix(es): 978-0-85115; 978-0-85991; 978-0-86193; 978-0-7293; 978-0-900411; 978-1-85566; 978-1-878822; 978-1-58046; 978-1-57113; 978-1-900639
Number of titles published annually: 200 Print
Total Titles: 3,100 Print
Imprints: Camden House; Companion Guides; James Curry Ltd; Early English Text Society; Plumbago Books; Royal Historical Society; Scholarly Digital Editions; Scottish Text Society; Suffolk Records Society; Tamesis Books; Toccata Press; University of Rochester Press; Victory History of the Counties of England; York Medieval Press
Foreign Office(s): Boydell & Brewer Ltd, Bridge Farm Business Park, Top St, Martlesham, Suffolk 1P12 4RB, United Kingdom, Mng Ed: Peter Clifford *Tel:* (01394) 610600 *Fax:* (01394) 610316 *E-mail:* editorial@boydell.co.uk
Orders to: Boydell & Brewer Ltd, Bridge Farm Business Park, Top St, Martlesham, Suffolk 1P12 4RB, United Kingdom *Tel:* (01394) 610600 *Fax:* (01394) 610316 *E-mail:* editorial@boydell.co.uk
Returns: c/o PSSCMA, 46 Development Rd, Fitchburg, MA 01420-6019
Warehouse: c/o PSSCMA, 46 Development Rd, Fitchburg, MA 01420-6019 *Tel:* 978-345-2121 *Fax:* 978-348-1233
College Farm, Forward Green, Stawmarket, Suffolk IP14 SEH, United Kingdom

Boyds Mills Press
Division of Highlights for Children Inc
815 Church St, Honesdale, PA 18431
Tel: 570-253-1164 *Toll Free Tel:* 800-490-5111 *Fax:* 570-253-0179
E-mail: contact@boydsmillspress.com
Web Site: www.boydsmillspress.com
Key Personnel
VP: Mary-Alice Moore
VP, Sales & Mktg: Jack Perry
Dir, Bk Mktg: Michael Eisenberg

Edit Dir, Book Publg: Elizabeth Van Doren *Tel:* 570-251-4570 *Fax:* 570-253-3110 *E-mail:* liz.vandoren@highlights.com
Natl Accts Mgr: Mr Kreig Krumpe *Fax:* 614-324-7943 *E-mail:* kreig.krumpe@boydsmillspress.com
Author & Promos Mgr: Kerry Mcmanus
Sr Ed, Wordsong & Boyds: Rebecca Davis
Mng Ed: Sarah Lozo
Founded: 1990
Books for children of all ages.
ISBN Prefix(es): 978-1-56397; 978-1-878093; 978-1-59078
Number of titles published annually: 60 Print
Total Titles: 500 Print
Imprints: Calkins Creek (history); Wordsong (poetry)
Distribution Center: INscribe Digital, 55 Francisco St, Suite 710, San Francisco, CA 94133 *Tel:* 415-489-7000 *Fax:* 415-489-7049 *Web Site:* www.inscribedigital.com

Boynton/Cook Publishers
Imprint of Heinemann
361 Hanover St, Portsmouth, NH 03801-3912
SAN: 210-5829
Mailing Address: PO Box 6926, Portsmouth, NH 03802-6926
Tel: 603-431-7894 *Toll Free Tel:* 800-225-5800 *Fax:* 603-431-2214 *Toll Free Fax:* 877-231-6980
E-mail: custserv@heinemann.com
Web Site: www.heinemann.com/boyntoncook
Key Personnel
Acting Pres: Vicky Boyd *E-mail:* vicky.boyd@heinmann.com
Founded: 1981
College composition & rhetoric textbooks.
ISBN Prefix(es): 978-0-86709
Number of titles published annually: 25 Print
Total Titles: 250 Print
Distributed by Pearson Australia-Schools Division; Pearson Education Canada; Pearson New Zealand-Schools Division
Orders to: PO Box 6926, Portsmouth, NH 03802-6926
Warehouse: 465 S Lincoln Dr, Troy, MO 63376

Boys Town Press
Division of Boys Town
14100 Crawford St, Boys Town, NE 68010
Tel: 402-498-1320 *Toll Free Tel:* 800-282-6657 *Fax:* 402-498-1310
E-mail: btpress@boystown.org
Web Site: www.boystownpress.org
Key Personnel
Dir: Erin Green *Tel:* 402-498-1422 *E-mail:* erin.green@boystown.org
Sales Mgr: Patricia Martens *Tel:* 402-498-1334 *E-mail:* patricia.martens@boystown.org
Founded: 1992
Youth care & education books, parenting books, children's books, videos & audio, sign language products, inspirational titles.
ISBN Prefix(es): 978-0-938510; 978-1-889322; 978-1-934490
Number of titles published annually: 10 Print; 3 E-Book
Total Titles: 100 Print; 2 CD-ROM; 24 E-Book; 3 Audio
Distributed by Deep Books Ltd (Europe & UK); Footprint Books (Australia & New Zealand); Monarch Books of Canada Ltd (Canada)
Foreign Rights: Amer-Asia Books (Evelyn Lee) (China, Japan, Korea, Taiwan)
Returns: 250 Monsky Dr, Boys Town, NE 68010
Warehouse: 250 Monsky Dr, Boys Town, NE 68010
Distribution Center: Follett School Solutions Inc, 1340 Ridgeview Dr, McHenry, IL 60050 *Tel:* 815-759-1700 *Toll Free Tel:* 888-511-5114 (cust serv) *Fax:* 815-759-9831 *Toll Free Fax:* 800-852-5458 *E-mail:* info@follettlearning.com *Web Site:* www.follettlearning.com SAN: 169-1902
Baker & Taylor, 2550 W Tyvola Rd, Suite 300, Charlotte, NC 28217 *Tel:* 815-802-2479 *Toll Free Fax:* 800-411-8433 *Web Site:* www.baker-taylor.com
Ingram Book Co, One Ingram Blvd, La Vergne, TN 37086-3650
Membership(s): The Independent Book Publishers Association

§Bradford Publishing Co
1743 Wazee St, Denver, CO 80202
Tel: 303-292-2590 *Toll Free Tel:* 800-446-2831 *Fax:* 303-298-5014
E-mail: marketing@bradfordpublishing.com; customerservice@bradfordpublishing.com
Web Site: www.bradfordpublishing.com
Key Personnel
Owner & Pres: Candace Boyle *E-mail:* candace@bradfordpublishing.com
Founded: 1881
Specialize in Colorado legal forms & law books.
ISBN Prefix(es): 978-1-883726
Number of titles published annually: 10 Print
Total Titles: 45 Print
Membership(s): The Independent Book Publishers Association; Publishers Association of the West

BradyGames
Member of Penguin Group (USA) LLC
800 E 96 St, 3rd fl, Indianapolis, IN 46240
Tel: 317-428-3000 *Toll Free Tel:* 800-545-5912; 800-571-5840 (cust serv)
E-mail: bradyquestions@pearsoned.com
Web Site: www.bradygames.com
Key Personnel
VP & Publr: Mike Degler
Ed-in-Chief: H Leigh Davis
Natl Accts Mgr: Jennifer Coghlan
Licensing Mgr: Christian Sumner
Mktg Mgr: Katherine Hemlock
ISBN Prefix(es): 978-1-56686; 978-0-7440
Number of titles published annually: 25 Print
Total Titles: 103 Print

Branden Books
Subsidiary of Branden Publishing Co
PO Box 812094, Wellesley, MA 02482-0013
SAN: 201-4106
Tel: 781-235-3347
E-mail: branden@brandenbooks.com
Web Site: www.brandenbooks.com
Key Personnel
Pres: Margaret Starrett
VP: Robert Caso
Ed & Treas: Adolph Caso
Founded: 1909
Publisher of fiction & nonfiction books. Distribution center in Ypsilanti, MI.
ISBN Prefix(es): 978-0-8283
Number of titles published annually: 15 Print; 4 CD-ROM; 300 E-Book
Total Titles: 400 Print; 4 CD-ROM; 410 Online; 300 E-Book
Imprints: Art Treasures; Brandon Books Cinematic Novels (cinematicnovels.com); Brashear Music Co; Four Seas; Bruce Humphries; International Pocket Library; Popular Technology
Distributor for Dante University of America Press Inc
Foreign Rep(s): Baker & Taylor (Worldwide); Gazelle (England); Ingram (Worldwide)
Advertising Agency: ADS-IPL
Returns: Publishers Storage & Shipping Corp, 660 S Mansfield, Ypsilanti, MI 48197

Brandylane Publishers Inc
5 S First St, Richmond, VA 23219
Tel: 804-644-3090 *Fax:* 804-644-3092
Web Site: brandylanepublishers.com
Key Personnel
Publr: Robert H Pruett *E-mail:* rhpruett@brandylanepublishers.com
Sr Ed: Mary A Tobey
Founded: 1985
Publisher & packager of books. Work with previously unpublished writers.
This publisher has indicated that 20% of their product line is author subsidized.
ISBN Prefix(es): 978-1-883911
Number of titles published annually: 15 Print; 15 Online; 15 E-Book
Total Titles: 60 Print; 40 Online; 7 E-Book
Imprints: Belle Isle Books
Billing Address: PO Box 274, Kilmarnock, VA 22482 *Tel:* 804-435-6900
Membership(s): The Independent Book Publishers Association

George Braziller Inc
277 Broadway, Suite 708, New York, NY 10007
SAN: 201-9310
Tel: 212-260-9256 *Fax:* 212-267-3165
E-mail: editorial@georgebraziller.com
Web Site: www.georgebraziller.com
Key Personnel
Founder: George Braziller
Pres & Ed: Michael Braziller *E-mail:* mbraziller@georgebraziller.com
Founded: 1955
Publishers of fine illustrated art books.
ISBN Prefix(es): 978-0-8076
Number of titles published annually: 12 Print
Total Titles: 300 Print
Distributed by Antique Collectors' Club Ltd
Foreign Rep(s): Antique Collectors' Club Ltd (Australia, England, Europe, India, New Zealand)
Orders to: W W Norton & Co Inc, 500 Fifth Ave, New York, NY 10110 *Toll Free Tel:* 800-233-4830 *Toll Free Fax:* 800-458-6515
Distribution Center: W W Norton & Co Inc, 500 Fifth Ave, New York, NY 10110 *Toll Free Tel:* 800-233-4830 *Toll Free Fax:* 800-458-6515

Breakaway Books
PO Box 24, Halcottsville, NY 12438-0024
Tel: 607-326-4805
E-mail: breakawaybooks@gmail.com
Web Site: www.breakawaybooks.com
Key Personnel
Publr: Garth Battista
Founded: 1994
Sports literature & books.
ISBN Prefix(es): 978-1-891369; 978-1-55821; 978-1-62124
Number of titles published annually: 10 Print
Total Titles: 100 Print; 1 E-Book
Distribution Center: Consortium, 34 13 Ave NE, Suite 101, Minneapolis, MN 55413-1007 *Toll Free Tel:* 800-283-3572 *Toll Free Fax:* 800-351-5073 *Web Site:* www.cbsd.com

Breakthrough Publications Inc
3 Iroquois St, Barn, Emmaus, PA 18049
Toll Free Tel: 800-824-5001 (ext 12) *Fax:* 610-928-4064
E-mail: dot@booksonhorses.com; ruth@booksonhorses.com
Web Site: www.booksonhorses.com
Key Personnel
Pres & Publr: Peter E Ognibene *Tel:* 914-928-4061 ext 12 *E-mail:* peter@workkplace.com
Founded: 1980
Career & equestrian.
ISBN Prefix(es): 978-0-914327
Number of titles published annually: 30 Print
Total Titles: 50 Print
Imprints: Breakthrough Publications

Nicholas Brealey Publishing
20 Park Plaza, Suite 610, Boston, MA 02116

Tel: 617-523-3801 *Toll Free Tel:* 888-BREALEY (273-2539) *Fax:* 617-523-3708
E-mail: info@nicholasbrealey.com
Web Site: www.nicholasbrealey.com
Key Personnel
Publr & Foreign Rts: Nicholas Brealey
Tel: (020) 7430 0224 *Fax:* (020) 7404 8311
E-mail: rights@nbrealey-books.com
Edit Dir: Erica Heilman
Publicity & Mktg Mgr: Jennifer Campaniolo
E-mail: marketing@nicholasbrealey.com
Sales & Mktg Mgr: Charles Dresner
Publg Coord: Bethany Sales
Founded: 1992
Professional/trade business book (hardcover & original paperback) publisher. Additional subjects include: international business & culture, training & human resources.
ISBN Prefix(es): 978-0-89106 (Davies-Black); 978-1-85788; 978-1-90483; 978-1-93193 (Intercultural Press); 978-1-87786 (Intercultural Press); 978-0-93366 (Intercultural Press)
Number of titles published annually: 200 Print
Total Titles: 270 Print
Imprints: Davies-Black Publishing
Divisions: Intercultural Press Inc
Foreign Office(s): 3-5 Spafield St, Clerkenwell, London EC1R 4QB, United Kingdom *Tel:* (020) 7239 0360 *Fax:* (020) 7239 0370 *E-mail:* sales@nicholasbrealey.com
Orders to: National Book Network, 15200 NBN Way, Blue Ridge Summit, PA 17214 *Toll Free Tel:* 800-462-6420 *Toll Free Fax:* 800-338-4550
Returns: National Book Network, 15200 NBN Way, Blue Ridge Summit, PA 17214 *Toll Free Tel:* 800-462-6420 *Toll Free Fax:* 800-338-4550
Distribution Center: National Book Network, 15200 NBN Way, Blue Ridge Summit, PA 17214 *Toll Free Tel:* 800-462-6420 *Toll Free Fax:* 800-338-4550
Membership(s): AAP; Independent Publisher's Guild; PA
See separate listing for:
Davies-Black Publishing
Intercultural Press Inc

Brenner Information Group
Division of Brenner Microcomputing Inc
9282 Samantha Ct, San Diego, CA 92129
SAN: 249-6496
Tel: 858-538-0093 *Toll Free Tel:* 800-811-4337 (orders)
E-mail: brenner@brennerbooks.com; sales@brennerbooks.com
Web Site: www.brennerbooks.com
Key Personnel
CFO: Carol Brenner
Publr: Robert Brenner
Founded: 1982 (began producing books 1987)
Collects, processes, packages & distributes information related to the pricing of desktop services.
ISBN Prefix(es): 978-0-929535; 978-1-930199
Number of titles published annually: 3 Print; 8 E-Book
Total Titles: 22 Print; 19 E-Book

Brentwood Christian Press
4000 Beallwood Ave, Columbus, GA 31904
Mailing Address: PO Box 4773, Columbus, GA 31914-4773
Toll Free Tel: 800-334-8861
E-mail: brentwood@aol.com
Web Site: www.brentwoodbooks.com
Key Personnel
Owner: U D Roberts
Founded: 1982
Publisher of Christian books.
ISBN Prefix(es): 978-1-55630
Number of titles published annually: 220 Print
Total Titles: 3,744 Print

Brethren Press
Division of Church of the Brethren
1451 Dundee Ave, Elgin, IL 60120
SAN: 201-9329
Tel: 847-742-5100 *Toll Free Tel:* 800-323-8039 *Toll Free Fax:* 800-667-8188
E-mail: brethrenpress@brethren.org
Web Site: www.brethrenpress.com
Key Personnel
Publr: Wendy McFadden *Tel:* 847-742-5100 ext 307 *E-mail:* wmcfadden@brethren.org
Dir, Mktg & Sales: Jeff Lennard *Tel:* 847-742-5100 ext 321 *E-mail:* jlennard@brethren.org
Founded: 1897
Trade books, church school curriculum, tracts & pamphlets & various media resources. Specialize in Bible study, theology, church history, practical discipleship, personal lifestyle issues, social concerns, peace & justice, devotional life & personal growth.
ISBN Prefix(es): 978-0-87178
Number of titles published annually: 6 Print
Total Titles: 100 Print
Imprints: faithQuest
Membership(s): Protestant Church-Owned Publishers Association

Brewers Publications
Division of Brewers Association
1372 Spruce St, Boulder, CO 80302
Mailing Address: PO Box 1679, Boulder, CO 80306
Tel: 303-447-0816 *Toll Free Tel:* 888-822-6273 (CN & US) *Fax:* 303-447-2825
E-mail: info@brewersassociation.org
Web Site: www.brewersassociation.org
Key Personnel
Publr: Kristi Switzer *Tel:* 720-473-7660
E-mail: kristi@brewersassociation.org
Mng Ed: Jill Redding *Tel:* 303-447-0816 ext 116
Founded: 1986
Not-for-profit educational publishing house & the foremost publisher of books on the art, science, history & culture of brewing for professional & amateur brewers & serious beer enthusiasts. Must know at least 10 brewers to query.
ISBN Prefix(es): 978-0-937381
Number of titles published annually: 2 Print; 15 E-Book
Total Titles: 50 Print
Foreign Rep(s): Gazelle Book Services Ltd (Worldwide exc North America)
Foreign Rights: Gazelle Book Services Ltd (Worldwide exc North America)
Shipping Address: National Book Network, 15200 NBN Way, Blue Ridge Summit, PA 17214 *Toll Free Tel:* 800-462-6420 *Toll Free Fax:* 800-338-4550 *E-mail:* custserv@nbnbooks.com
Warehouse: National Book Network, 15200 NBN Way, Blue Ridge Summit, PA 17214 *Tel:* 717-794-3800 *Toll Free Tel:* 800-462-6420 *Toll Free Fax:* 800-338-4550 *E-mail:* custserv@nbnbooks.com

Brick Tower Press
Imprint of J T Colby & Co Inc
1230 Park Ave, New York, NY 10128
Tel: 212-427-7139 *Toll Free Tel:* 800-68-BRICK (682-7425)
E-mail: bricktower@aol.com
Web Site: www.bricktowerpress.com
Key Personnel
Publr: John T Colby, Jr
Founded: 1993
ISBN Prefix(es): 978-1-883283; 978-0-9531737; 978-1-899694
Number of titles published annually: 20 Print; 10 E-Book
Total Titles: 125 Print; 40 E-Book
Foreign Rep(s): Gazelle Book Services (Europe, UK); Ingram Digital (Australia, New Zealand)
Foreign Rights: Bob Diforio (Worldwide); National Book Network (Canada, USA)
Warehouse: Ingram Digital, 1246 Heil Quaker Blvd., La Vergne, TN 37986 *Toll Free Tel:* 800-509-4156 *E-mail:* Inquiry@lightningsource.com
Distribution Center: Ingram Digital, 1246 Heil Quaker Blvd, La Vergne, TN 37086 *Toll Free Tel:* 800-509-4156 *E-mail:* Inquiry@lightningsource.com

BrickHouse Books Inc
306 Suffolk Rd, Baltimore, MD 21218
Tel: 410-235-7690 *Fax:* 410-235-7690
Web Site: www.brickhousebooks.wordpress.com
Key Personnel
Publr & Ed-in-Chief: Clarinda Harriss
E-mail: charriss@towson.edu
Founded: 1970
Poetry; mixed genres by gay & lesbian (Stonewall only); artistic prose, experimental, memoir, plays.
ISBN Prefix(es): 978-1-938144
Number of titles published annually: 6 Print
Total Titles: 240 Print
Imprints: Chestnut Hills Press; New Poets Series; Side Street; Stonewall
Distributed by Itasca
Foreign Rep(s): Salmon Publishing (Ireland)

Bridge-Logos Inc
Bldg 200, Suite 220, 17750 NW 115 Ave, Alachua, FL 32615
Tel: 386-462-2525 *Toll Free Tel:* 800-631-5802 (orders) *Fax:* 386-462-2535 *Toll Free Fax:* 800-935-6467
E-mail: customerservice@bridgelogos.com; info@bridgelogos.com
Web Site: www.bridgelogos.com
Key Personnel
CEO & Publr: Lloyd Hildebrand
E-mail: lhildebrand@bridgelogos.com
COO & Sales & Mktg Mgr: Mrs Shawn Myers
E-mail: shawnmyers@bridgelogos.com
Founded: 1967
Bibles, Christian classics, spirit-filled life, Christian books; parenting, family, Eschatological, evangelism, revival, children's bibles.
ISBN Prefix(es): 978-0-88270; 978-0-61036
Number of titles published annually: 20 Print
Total Titles: 216 Print
Imprints: Bridge; Haven; Logos; Open Scroll; Synergy
Distributor for New Wine Press; RoperPenberthy Publishing Ltd; Sovereign World; Warboys LLC
Foreign Rep(s): Winfred Bluth (Germany)
Foreign Rights: W M Bluth (Germany)

Bridge Publications Inc
5600 E Olympic Blvd, Commerce City, CA 90022
SAN: 208-3884
Tel: 323-888-6200 *Toll Free Tel:* 800-722-1733 *Fax:* 323-888-6202
E-mail: info@bridgepub.com
Web Site: www.bridgepub.com
Key Personnel
Pres: Blake Silber
EVP: Ann Arnow *E-mail:* annarnow@bridgepub.com
Trade Sales Mgr: Don Arnow *E-mail:* darnow@bridgepub.com
Founded: 1981
US & international nonfiction publisher of L Ron Hubbard's Dianetics & Scientology materials.
ISBN Prefix(es): 978-0-88404; 978-1-57318; 978-1-4031
Number of titles published annually: 1,100 Print; 400 CD-ROM; 8 Online; 5 Audio
Total Titles: 8,900 Print; 1,300 CD-ROM; 450 Online; 25 Audio
Imprints: BPI Records; Bridge Audio; Theta Books

Branch Office(s)
Bridge Publications Canada, 696 Yonge St, Toronto, ON M4Y-2A7, Canada, Contact: Emily Harris *Tel:* 416-964-8927 *Fax:* 416-964-3201
Foreign Office(s): Era Dinamica Editores SA de CV, Pablo U Cello, No 16, Colonia de los Deportes, 03710 Mexico, DF, Mexico, Contact: Irma Macias *Tel:* (0155) 5984487 *Fax:* (0155) 5984624
Foreign Rep(s): New Era Publications International (Copenhagen, Europe, Russia & former USSR)
Foreign Rights: New Era Publications International
Advertising Agency: Gildersleeve Inc, 3815 Shannon Rd, Los Angeles, CA, Contact: Jan Gildersleeve *Tel:* 323-663-8239 *Fax:* 323-661-8316
Membership(s): AIGA, the professional association for design; BISG; The Independent Book Publishers Association; Printing Industries of America; Printing Industries of Southern California

Brigantine Media
211 North Ave, St Johnsbury, VT 05819
Tel: 802-751-8802 *Fax:* 802-751-8804
Web Site: brigantinemedia.com
Key Personnel
Acqs Ed: Neil Raphel *E-mail:* neil@brigantinemedia.com
Edit Chief: Janis Raye
Founded: 1990
ISBN Prefix(es): 978-0-9826644
Number of titles published annually: 12 Print; 2 Online; 12 E-Book
Total Titles: 25 Print; 2 Online; 18 E-Book
Imprints: Compass (educational materials for teachers); Voyage (fiction, primarily from VT & regional suthors)

Bright Connections Media, A World Book Encyclopedia Company
233 N Michigan Ave, Suite 2000, Chicago, IL 60601
Tel: 312-729-5800 *Fax:* 312-729-5610
Web Site: www.brightconnectionsmedia.com
Key Personnel
Pres: Donald Keller
VP, Edit: Paul Kobasa *E-mail:* paul.kobasa@worldbook.com
Dir, Mktg: Nicholas Fryer *E-mail:* nick.fryer@worldbook.com
Mgr, Mktg: Erica Bruns *E-mail:* erica.bruns@worldbook.com
Founded: 2012
Nonfiction & playful educational material for young children through young adults.
ISBN Prefix(es): 978-1-62267
Number of titles published annually: 8 Print
Total Titles: 20 Print
Sales Office(s): IPG, 814 N Franklin St, Chicago, IL 60610 *Tel:* 312-337-0747 *Toll Free Tel:* 800-888-4741 *Fax:* 312-337-5985 *Web Site:* www.ipgbook.com
Orders to: IPG, 814 N Franklin St, Chicago, IL 60610 *Tel:* 312-337-0747 *Toll Free Tel:* 800-888-4741 *Fax:* 312-337-5985 *Web Site:* www.ipgbook.com
Distribution Center: IPG, 814 N Franklin St, Chicago, IL 60610 *Tel:* 312-337-0747 *Toll Free Tel:* 800-888-4741 *Fax:* 312-337-5985 *Web Site:* www.ipgbook.com
Canadian Manda Group, 165 Dufferin St, Toronto, ON M6K 3H6, Canada *Tel:* 416-516-0911 *Fax:* 416-516-0917 *E-mail:* info@mandagroup.com *Web Site:* www.mandagroup.com

§Brill Inc
Subsidiary of Koninklijke Brill NV
2 Liberty Sq, 11th fl, Boston, MA 02109
Tel: 617-263-2323 *Toll Free Tel:* 800-962-4406 *Fax:* 617-263-2324
E-mail: cs@brillusa.com
Web Site: www.brill.com
Key Personnel
Pres, Sales & Mktg: Steve Dane
Off Mgr: Rose Luongo
Founded: 1683
Publishes high level, specialized, academic titles.
ISBN Prefix(es): 978-90-04
Number of titles published annually: 600 Print
Total Titles: 6,000 Print
Orders to: Toll Free Tel: 800-337-9255
Returns: Books International Inc, c/o Brill Academic Publishers Inc, 22883 Quicksilver Dr, Sterling, VA 20166
Warehouse: PO Box 605, Herndon, VA 20172 *Tel:* 703-661-1500 *Toll Free Tel:* 800-337-9255 *Fax:* 703-661-1501
Distribution Center: Books International Inc, 22883 Quicksilver Dr, Sterling, VA 20166 *Tel:* 703-661-1500

Brilliance Audio
Subsidiary of Amazon.com
1704 Eaton Dr, Grand Haven, MI 49417
Tel: 616-846-5256 *Toll Free Tel:* 800-648-2312 (orders only) *Fax:* 616-846-0630
E-mail: customerservice@brillianceaudio.com
Web Site: www.brillianceaudio.com
Key Personnel
VP & Assoc Publr: Gary Krebs
Mng Dir: Mark Pereira *E-mail:* mpereira@brillianceaudio.com
Creative Dir: Kathlyn Miller *Tel:* 616-846-5256 ext 709
Fin Dir: Brad Dahl *Tel:* 616-846-5256 ext 750 *E-mail:* bdahl@brillianceaudio.com
Sales Dir: Steve Woessner *Tel:* 616-846-5256 ext 705 *E-mail:* swoessner@brillianceaudio.com
Acqs Ed: Sheryl Zajechowski *Tel:* 616-846-5256 ext 726 *E-mail:* szajechowski@brillianceaudio.com
Ed, Adult Nonfiction: Joe McNeely *Tel:* 616-846-5256 ext 755 *E-mail:* jmcneely@brillianceaudio.com
Ed, Waterfall Press: Tammy Faxel
Acqs, Grand Harbor Press: Amy Hofford
Founded: 1984
Country's leading independent audiobook publisher.
ISBN Prefix(es): 978-0-930435; 978-1-56100; 978-1-56740; 978-1-58788; 978-1-59086; 978-1-59355; 978-1-59600; 978-1-59710; 978-1-59737; 978-1-4233; 978-1-4418; 978-1-61106; 978-1-4558
Number of titles published annually: 700 Audio
Total Titles: 6,500 Audio
Imprints: Grand Harbor Press; Waterfall Press
Membership(s): Audio Publishers Association

Bristol Park Books
252 W 38 St, Suite 206, New York, NY 10018
Tel: 212-842-0700 *Fax:* 212-842-1771
E-mail: info@bristolparkbooks.com
Web Site: bristolparkbooks.com
Promotional hard cover reprints.
ISBN Prefix(es): 978-0-88365; 978-0-88486; 978-1-57866
Number of titles published annually: 50 Print
Total Titles: 100 Print

Broden Books LLC
3824 Sunset Dr, Spring Park, MN 55384
SAN: 920-0614
Tel: 952-471-1066
E-mail: media@brodenbooks.com
Web Site: www.brodenbooks.com
Key Personnel
CEO & Pres: Kathy La Pointe
Founded: 1999
Early childhood literacy resources for parents, schools & libraries. We are engaged in ongoing research into issues impacting literacy in the US. Our resources are sold worldwide through online & retail stores.
ISBN Prefix(es): 978-0-9832023
Number of titles published annually: 3 Print
Total Titles: 3 Print
Imprints: REAL Phonics™

§Brookes Publishing Co Inc
PO Box 10624, Baltimore, MD 21285-0624
SAN: 212-730X
Tel: 410-337-9580 (outside US & CN) *Toll Free Tel:* 800-638-3775 (US & CN) *Fax:* 410-337-8539
E-mail: custserv@brookespublishing.com
Web Site: www.brookespublishing.com
Key Personnel
Chmn of the Bd: Paul H Brookes
Pres: Jeffrey D Brookes *E-mail:* jbrookes@brookespublishing.com
EVP: Melissa A Behm *E-mail:* mbehm@brookespublishing.com
VP & Publr: George S Stamathis *E-mail:* gstamathis@brookespublishing.com
Edit Dir: Heather Shrestha *E-mail:* hshrestha@brookespublishing.com
Dir, HR & Oper: Erika Kinney *E-mail:* ekinney@brookespublishing.com
Dir, Mktg: Jessica Reighard *E-mail:* jreighard@brookespublishing.com
Sr Subs Rts & Contracts Mgr: Heather Lengyel *Tel:* 410-205-0466 *E-mail:* hlengyel@brookespublishing.com
Founded: 1978
Publishes professional books, textbooks, assessments, curricula & web-based products in the areas of: early childhood, early intervention, social-emotional development, literacy, learning disabilities, autism, behavior, special education, developmental disabilities, communication & language.
ISBN Prefix(es): 978-0-933716; 978-1-55766; 978-1-59857; 978-1-68125
Number of titles published annually: 65 Print; 5 CD-ROM; 5 Online; 50 E-Book
Total Titles: 600 Print; 20 CD-ROM; 10 Online; 50 E-Book
Subsidiaries: Health Professions Press (specialist publisher focused on the broad range of issues in gerontology, long-term care & health administration)
Foreign Rep(s): Cranbury International LLC (Caribbean, Latin America); CRW Marketing Services for Publishers Inc (Guam, Northern Mariana Islands, Palau, Philippines); Eurospan Group (Africa, Europe, Middle East, UK); Footprint Books Pty Ltd (Australia, Fiji, New Zealand, Papua New Guinea); Tahir Lodhi Publishers' Representatives (Pakistan); Sara Books Pvt Ltd (Bangladesh, India, Sri Lanka); STM Publishers Services Pte Ltd (China, Hong Kong, Macau, Malaysia, Myanmar, Singapore, Thailand, Vietnam); Unifacmanu Trading Co Ltd (Taiwan)
Returns: Maple Logistics Solutions, 60 Grumbacher Rd, I-83 Industrial Park, York, PA 17406
Warehouse: Maple Logistics Solutions, PO Box 15100, York, PA 17405 *Web Site:* www.maplelogisticssolutions.com
Membership(s): AAP PreK-12 Learning Group
See separate listing for:
Health Professions Press

§Brookhaven Press
2004 Kramer St, La Crosse, WI 54603
Tel: 608-781-0850 *Toll Free Tel:* 800-236-0850 *Fax:* 608-781-3883
E-mail: brookhaven@nmt.com
Web Site: www.brookhavenpress.com

Key Personnel
Mgr: Carol Berteotti *Tel:* 608-781-0850 ext 131
E-mail: carol.berteotti@nmt.com
Founded: 1973
Scan & reprint out-of-print county histories & genealogy books; academic microfilm & fiche.
ISBN Prefix(es): 978-1-58103; 978-1-4035
Number of titles published annually: 300 Print

§The Brookings Institution Press
Division of Brookings Institution
1775 Massachusetts Ave NW, Washington, DC 20036-2188
SAN: 201-9396
Tel: 202-536-3600 *Toll Free Tel:* 800-537-5487
Fax: 202-536-3623
E-mail: permissions@brookings.edu
Web Site: www.brookings.edu
Key Personnel
Pres: Strobe Talbott
Dir: Valentina Kalk
Edit Dir: Bill Finan
Mktg Dir: Rebecca Campany *Tel:* 202-536-2492
Mng Ed: Janet Walker *E-mail:* jwalker@brookings.edu
Dist Mgr: Terrence Melvin
Mktg Mgr: Bethany Biskey
Publicity Mgr: Carrie Engel
Libn: Cyrus Behroozi
Founded: 1916
Economics, foreign policy & government affairs.
ISBN Prefix(es): 978-0-8157
Number of titles published annually: 45 Print; 50 E-Book
Total Titles: 1,205 Print; 1 CD-ROM; 1,031 E-Book
Distributor for American Chamber of Commerce to the European Union; Asian Development Bank Institute; Aspen Institute; Bertelsmann Foundation Publishers; Carnegie Endowment for International Peace; Center for Global Development; The Centre for Economic Policy Research; Centre for European Policy Studies; The Century Foundation; Chatham House; Economica; Institute of Latin American Studies; International Labor Offices; Jamestown Foundation; Japan Center for International Exchange; Migration Policy Institute; OECD; Perseus Academic; Shorenstein Asia-Pacific Research Center; The Trilateral Commission; United Nations University Press; World Trade Organization
Foreign Rep(s): Julio E Emod (South America); Fred Hermans (Benelux, Denmark, Finland, France, Norway, Sweden); Ewa Ledochowicz (Eastern Europe); UWE Luedemann (Austria, Germany, Italy, Portugal, Spain, Switzerland); Mediamatics (India, Pakistan); NewSouth Books (Australia, New Zealand); Systematics Studies Ltd (Trinidad and Tobago); Taylor & Francis Asia Pacific (Brunei, China, Hong Kong, Korea, Malaysia, Philippines, Singapore, Taiwan); UBC Press, c/o Uni Presses (Canada); United Publishing Services Ltd (Japan); University Press Marketing (Cyprus, Greece, Ireland, Israel, Malta, UK)
Foreign Rights: Agency Literaria Internazionale (Italy); Tuttle-Mori Agency Inc (Japan)
Membership(s): AAP; American Association of University Presses

Brookline Books
8 Trumbull Rd, Suite B-001, Northampton, MA 01060
Tel: 603-669-7032 (orders) *Toll Free Tel:* 800-666-2665 (orders) *Fax:* 413-584-6184
E-mail: brbooks@yahoo.com
Founded: 1985
Education, special needs, readings, general trade.
ISBN Prefix(es): 978-0-914797; 978-1-57129
Number of titles published annually: 5 Print
Total Titles: 125 Print

Brooklyn Publishers LLC
PO Box 248, Cedar Rapids, IA 52406
Tel: 319-368-8012 *Toll Free Tel:* 888-473-8521
Fax: 319-368-8011
E-mail: customerservice@brookpub.com; editor@brookpub.com
Web Site: www.brookpub.com
Key Personnel
Sr Ed: David Burton
ISBN Prefix(es): 978-1-930961; 978-1-931000; 978-1-931805; 978-1-932404; 978-1-60003
Number of titles published annually: 100 Print
Total Titles: 600 Print

Brooks/Cole, see Wadsworth Publishing

Brown Books Publishing Group
16250 Knoll Trail, Suite 205, Dallas, TX 75248
Tel: 972-381-0009 *Fax:* 972-248-4336
E-mail: publishing@brownbooks.com
Web Site: www.brownbooks.com
Key Personnel
CEO & Publr: Milli Brown
PR: Kathy Williams
Founded: 1994
Full service independent publisher. Committed to producing high quality books of all genres for authors who choose to retain the rights to their intellectual property.
ISBN Prefix(es): 978-1-933285; 978-1-934812
Number of titles published annually: 150 Print
Total Titles: 1,000 Print
Divisions: Brown Books Agency; Brown Books Kids; Christian Press; Personal Profiles
Warehouse: Cenveo, 3210 Miller Park Dr S, Suite 100, Garland, TX 75041 *Tel:* 972-271-0591
Distribution Center: Quality Books, 1003 W Pines Rd, Oregon, IL 61061
Follett School Solutions Inc, 1340 Ridgeview Dr, McHenry, IL 60050 SAN: 169-1902
Baker & Taylor Inc, 2550 W Tyvola Rd, Suite 300, Charlotte, NC 28217
Ingram, One Ingram Blvd, La Vergne, TN 37086
Membership(s): The Independent Book Publishers Association

Karen Brown's Guides Inc
16 E Third Ave, Suite 9, San Mateo, CA 94401
Mailing Address: PO Box 70, San Mateo, CA 94401-0070
Tel: 650-342-9117 *Fax:* 650-342-9153
Web Site: www.karenbrown.com
Key Personnel
Pres: Karen Brown Herbert *E-mail:* karen@karenbrown.com
Founded: 1977
General.
ISBN Prefix(es): 978-0-930328; 978-1-928901; 978-1-933810; 978-1-63371
Number of titles published annually: 17 Print
Total Titles: 17 Print
Foreign Rep(s): National Book Network (Australia, Europe, New Zealand)
Distribution Center: National Book Network, 4501 Forbes Blvd, Suite 200, Lanham, MD 20706, Pres: Jed Lyons *Toll Free Tel:* 800-462-6420 *Toll Free Fax:* 800-338-4550 *Web Site:* www.nbnbooks.com

Bucknell University Press
6 Taylor Hall, Bucknell University, Lewisburg, PA 17837
Tel: 570-577-3674
E-mail: universitypress@bucknell.edu
Web Site: www.bucknell.edu/universitypress
Key Personnel
Dir: Greg Clingham *Tel:* 570-577-1552
E-mail: clingham@bucknell.edu
Edit Assoc: Pam Dailey *Tel:* 570-577-3674
E-mail: pad024@bucknell.edu
Founded: 1968
ISBN Prefix(es): 978-0-8387

Number of titles published annually: 35 Print
Total Titles: 700 Print
Distributed by Rowman & Littlefield

BuilderBooks.com
Division of National Association of Home Builders (NAHB)
1201 15 St NW, Washington, DC 20005
SAN: 207-7035
Tel: 202-822-0200 *Toll Free Tel:* 800-223-2665
Fax: 202-266-8096 (edit)
E-mail: builderbooks@nahb.com
Web Site: www.builderbooks.com
Key Personnel
SVP & Mktg Offr: Lakisha Campbell
E-mail: lcampbell@nahb.com
Mng Dir, Mktg: Patricia Potts
Mktg Mgr, NAHB: Jacqueline Barnes
Founded: 1943
Publish books about home construction & design, remodeling, land development, housing & construction management, sales & marketing of new homes, safety & seniors housing.
ISBN Prefix(es): 978-0-86718
Number of titles published annually: 7 Print
Total Titles: 150 Print
Distributor for National Association of Home Builders (NAHB)
Orders to: c/o Returns, National Association of Home Builders, 905 Carlow Dr, Unit B, Bolingbrook, IL 60490

Bull Publishing Co
PO Box 1377, Boulder, CO 80306
SAN: 208-5712
Tel: 303-545-6350 *Toll Free Tel:* 800-676-2855
Fax: 303-545-6354
E-mail: bullpublishing@msn.com
Web Site: www.bullpub.com
Key Personnel
CFO: Emily Sewell
Pres & Publr: James Bull
Dir, Mktg: Claire Cameron
Founded: 1974
Self-care, nutrition & health care, physical fitness, weight loss, mental health, parenting & child care, psychology, self-help.
ISBN Prefix(es): 978-0-915950; 978-0-923521; 978-1-933503
Number of titles published annually: 6 Print; 1 Audio
Total Titles: 70 Print; 6 Audio
Foreign Rep(s): Gazelle (UK & the continent)
Warehouse: A & A Quality Shipping Services, 3623 Munster Ave, Unit B, Hayward, CA 94545
Distribution Center: Independent Publishers Group, 814 N Franklin St, Chicago, IL 60610 *Toll Free Tel:* 800-888-4741 *Web Site:* www.ipgbook.com

Bunker Hill Publishing
285 River Rd, Piermont, NH 03779
Tel: 603-272-9221 *Fax:* 603-283-7240
E-mail: mail@bunkerhillpublishing.com
Web Site: www.bunkerhillpublishing.com
Key Personnel
Publr: Ib Bellew *E-mail:* ibellew@bunkerhillpublishing.com
Mng Dir: Carole Kitchel Bellew
E-mail: ckitchel@bunkerhillpublishing.com
Founded: 2001
Publishing & packaging.
ISBN Prefix(es): 978-1-59373
Number of titles published annually: 7 Print; 7 E-Book
Total Titles: 65 Print
Distribution Center: Midpoint Trade, 270 W 20 St, Suite 1102, New York, NY 10011 *Tel:* 212-727-0190 *Web Site:* www.midpointtradebooks.com

The Bureau for At-Risk Youth, see Prevention Products & Services Inc dba The Bureau for At-Risk Youth

§Bureau of Economic Geology, University of Texas at Austin
Division of University of Texas at Austin
10100 Burnet Rd, Bldg 130, Austin, TX 78758
Mailing Address: University Sta, Box X, Austin, TX 78713-8924
Tel: 512-471-1534 *Fax:* 512-471-0140
E-mail: pubsales@beg.utexas.edu
Web Site: www.beg.utexas.edu
Key Personnel
Dir: Scott W Tinker
Mgr, Pubn Sales: Amanda Masterson
E-mail: amanda.masterson@beg.utexas.edu
Founded: 1909
Scientific & technical books in geosciences.
Number of titles published annually: 6 Print; 1 CD-ROM
Total Titles: 1,700 Print; 8 CD-ROM; 1,500 E-Book
Distributor for Gulf Coast Association of Geological Societies; Gulf Coast Section; Texas Memorial Museum (selected titles)

Burford Books
101 E State St, No 301, Ithaca, NY 14850
Tel: 607-319-4373 *Fax:* 607-319-4373
Toll Free Fax: 866-212-7750
E-mail: info@burfordbooks.com
Web Site: www.burfordbooks.com
Key Personnel
Pres: Peter Burford
Founded: 1997
Publisher of books on the outdoors, sports, food & wine, fitness, nature, travel, fishing, military, Finger Lakes area.
ISBN Prefix(es): 978-1-58080
Number of titles published annually: 6 Print; 6 E-Book
Total Titles: 115 Print; 34 E-Book
Foreign Rep(s): Gazelle Book Services Ltd (UK)
Distribution Center: National Book Network, 15200 NBN Way, Blue Ridge Summit, PA 17214 *Tel:* 717-794-3800
Membership(s): Independent Publishers Association

Burns Archive Press
Imprint of Burns Archive Photographic Distributors Ltd
140 E 38 St, New York, NY 10016
Tel: 212-889-1938 *Fax:* 212-481-9113
E-mail: info@burnsarchive.com
Web Site: www.burnsarchive.com
Key Personnel
CEO & Pres: Stanley B Burns, MD
E-mail: burns@inch.com
Founded: 1979
Renowned for images of the darker side of life: death, disease, crime, racism, revolution & war. Provides a unique source of historic visual documentation containing over 700,000 vintage photographs. The Archive houses world-class holdings of African-American imagery & Judaica, as well as the foremost collection of early medical photography. More than a century of iconographic & historic photographs from the 1840s through the 1950s are available as stock photography. In addition, The Archive provides consultation, prepares exhibitions & publishes books on photographic history.
ISBN Prefix(es): 978-0-9612958; 978-0-9748688; 978-0-9748688; 978-0-9764495; 978-0-9764495; 978-1-934421; 978-1-936002
Number of titles published annually: 4 Print
Total Titles: 35 Print
Membership(s): American Book Producers Association

§Business & Legal Resources Inc
100 Winners Circle, Suite 300, Brentwood, TN 37027
Tel: 860-510-0100 *Toll Free Tel:* 800-727-5257
E-mail: service@blr.com
Web Site: www.blr.com
Key Personnel
Founder: Robert L Brady
CEO: Dan Oswald
Sr Mng Ed: Catherine Moreton Gray
Sr Ed: Celeste Blackburn
Founded: 1977
Business newsletters, books, booklets, films & CD-ROMs. Specialize in safety, human resource & environmental training & compliance.
ISBN Prefix(es): 978-1-55645
Number of titles published annually: 100 Print
Total Titles: 380 Print; 113 CD-ROM; 4 Online; 4 E-Book
Membership(s): NEPA

Business Expert Press
Subsidiary of IGroup
222 E 46 St, New York, NY 10017-2906
Tel: 630-207-5927
E-mail: charlene.kronstadt@businessexpertpress.com
Web Site: www.businessexpertpress.com
Key Personnel
EVP: Stewart Mattson *E-mail:* stewart.mattson@businessexpertpress.com
Exec Dir, Global Sales & Mktg: Sean Kaneski
Tel: 218-820-3756 *E-mail:* sean.kaneski@businessexpertpress.com
Founded: 2008
Providing MBA level students with applied, concise textbooks that can be used in & out of the classroom.
ISBN Prefix(es): 978-1-60649
Number of titles published annually: 100 Print; 100 Online; 100 E-Book
Total Titles: 300 Print; 300 Online; 300 E-Book

§Business Research Services Inc
4641 Montgomery Ave, Suite 208, Bethesda, MD 20814
SAN: 691-8522
Tel: 301-229-5561 *Toll Free Tel:* 800-845-8420
Toll Free Fax: 877-516-0818
E-mail: brspubs@sba8a.com
Web Site: www.sba8a.com; www.setasidealert.com
Key Personnel
Pres & Publr: Thomas D Johnson
E-mail: tjohnson@setasidealert.com
Founded: 1984
Directories of minority & women's businesses & marketing research firms; small business newsletters. No returns accepted.
ISBN Prefix(es): 978-0-933527
Number of titles published annually: 4 Print; 4 CD-ROM; 1 Online
Total Titles: 7 Print; 4 CD-ROM; 1 Online
Distributed by Basch; Book House; Coutts; Gale Research Inc; Midwest Library Service
Distributor for Riley & Johnson

Butte Publications Inc
PO Box 1328, Hillsboro, OR 97123-1328
SAN: 299-8866
Tel: 503-648-9791 *Toll Free Tel:* 866-312-8883
Fax: 503-693-9526 *Toll Free Fax:* 866-412-8883 (orders only)
E-mail: service@buttepublications.com
Web Site: www.buttepublications.com
Key Personnel
Pres & Publr: Matthew H Brink
E-mail: mbrink@buttepublications.com
Founded: 1992
Resources serving the deaf community.
ISBN Prefix(es): 978-1-884362; 978-1-939349
Number of titles published annually: 5 Print; 1 CD-ROM
Total Titles: 50 Print; 5 CD-ROM
Shipping Address: 149 SE Third, Suite 450, Hillsboro, OR 97123

By Design Press, see Quite Specific Media Group Ltd

Bywater Books
PO Box 3671, Ann Arbor, MI 48106-3671
Tel: 734-662-8815
Web Site: bywaterbooks.com
Key Personnel
Owner & Ed-in-Chief: Kelly Smith
Owner: Marianne K Martin
E-mail: mkmbywater@aol.com
Publr: Salem West
Dir, Creative Servs: Ann McMan
Founded: 1992
Publish top quality lesbian fiction. Our Bloody Brits imprint publishes the finest mainstream British mysteries in the US.
ISBN Prefix(es): 978-1-932859
Number of titles published annually: 10 Print
Total Titles: 42 Print
Imprints: Amble Press; Bloody Brits Press

C & T Publishing Inc
1651 Challenge Dr, Concord, CA 94520-5206
Tel: 925-677-0377 *Toll Free Tel:* 800-284-1114
Fax: 925-677-0373
E-mail: support@ctpub.com
Web Site: www.ctpub.com
Key Personnel
CEO: Todd Hensley
CFO: Tony Hensley
Edit Dir: Gailen Runge
Dir, Sales & Mktg: Sandy Balin
E-mail: sandyb@ctpub.com
Publr: Amy Marson
Founded: 1983
Specialize in fiber & paper craft books & products.
ISBN Prefix(es): 978-0-914881; 978-1-57120
Number of titles published annually: 60 Print; 2 CD-ROM
Total Titles: 300 Print; 5 CD-ROM; 10 Online
Distributed by Watson-Guptill Publications
Membership(s): Craft Hobby Association; The Independent Book Publishers Association

Caissa Editions
Affiliate of Dale A Brandreth Books
PO Box 151, Yorklyn, DE 19736-0151
Tel: 302-239-4608
Web Site: www.chessbookstore.com
Key Personnel
Owner & Pres: Dale Brandreth
E-mail: dbrandreth3@comcast.net
Founded: 1971
Publisher of books that are primarily on chess.
ISBN Prefix(es): 978-0-939433
Number of titles published annually: 3 Print
Total Titles: 23 Print

§Cambridge Educational
Imprint of Infobase Learning
132 W 31 St, 17th fl, New York, NY 10001
Toll Free Tel: 800-322-8755 *Fax:* 609-671-0266
Toll Free Fax: 800-329-6687
E-mail: custserve@infobaselearning.com
Web Site: www.infobasepublishing.com
Key Personnel
Pres, Infobase Learning: Mark McDonnell
Founded: 1980
Produce & distribute educational materials & CD-ROMs. Specialize in crime & legal studies, family & consumer science, health & guidance, social studies & vocational/technical education & career education. Cambridge Educational is a trademark of Films Media Group.
ISBN Prefix(es): 978-0-927368; 978-1-56450

Number of titles published annually: 5 Print; 20 CD-ROM
Total Titles: 35 Print; 150 CD-ROM

§Cambridge University Press
Division of University of Cambridge
32 Avenue of the Americas, New York, NY 10013-2473
SAN: 200-206X
Tel: 212-924-3900; 212-337-5000 *Fax:* 212-691-3239
E-mail: newyork@cambridge.org
Web Site: www.cambridge.org/us
Key Personnel
Mng Dir, Americas & Global Mng Dir, Eng Lang Teaching: Michael Peluse
HR Dir: Nick Correa
Press Dist Dir: Ian R Bradie
Publg Dir, Humanities & Soc Sci: Dr Beatrice Rehl *E-mail:* brehl@cambridge.org
Journals Mktg Mgr: Susan Soule
Mktg Mgr, Humanities, Law & Psychol: Michael Duncan
Mktg Communs Mgr: Carine Mitchell
Journals Ed: Mark Zadrozny
Sr Ed, Engg: Peter Gordon
Sr Ed, Law: Dr John Berger
Sr Ed, Soc Sci: Lewis Bateman; Robert Dreesen
Sr Commissioning Ed: Marigold Acland *E-mail:* mackland@cambridge.org
Ed, Math & Computer Sci: Lauren Cowles
Founded: 1534
Scholarly & trade books, college textbooks & journals.
ISBN Prefix(es): 978-0-521
Number of titles published annually: 2,400 Print
Total Titles: 45,000 Print; 160 Online
Foreign Office(s): The Edinburgh Bldg, Shaftesbury Rd, Cambridge CB2 8BS, United Kingdom *Tel:* (01223) 358331
Warehouse: One Ingram Blvd, La Vergne, TN 17202
Membership(s): AAP; Association of American University Presses; BISG

Camino Books Inc
PO Box 59026, Philadelphia, PA 19102-9026
Tel: 215-413-1917 *Fax:* 215-413-3255
E-mail: camino@caminobooks.com
Web Site: www.caminobooks.com
Key Personnel
Pres & Publr: Edward J Jutkowitz *E-mail:* ejutkowitz@caminobooks.com
Founded: 1987
Regional trade books for the Mid-Atlantic states.
ISBN Prefix(es): 978-0-940159; 978-1-933822
Number of titles published annually: 10 Print; 10 E-Book
Total Titles: 100 Print; 60 E-Book
Warehouse: Whitehurst & Clark Book Fulfillment Inc, 1200 County Rd, Rte 523, Flemington, NJ 08822 *Tel:* 908-782-2323

Campfield & Campfield Publishing
6521 Cutler St, Philadelphia, PA 19126
Toll Free Tel: 888-518-2440 *Fax:* 215-224-6696
E-mail: info@campfieldspublishing.com
Web Site: www.campfieldspublishing.com
Key Personnel
Publr: Charlene M Campfield; Leon V Campfield, Sr
Founded: 2009
Publisher of Christ-centered children's & young adult books.
ISBN Prefix(es): 978-0-9817025
Number of titles published annually: 4 Print; 4 Online
Total Titles: 6 Print; 5 Online

§Candlewick Press
Subsidiary of Walker Books Ltd (London)
99 Dover St, Somerville, MA 02144-2825
Tel: 617-661-3330 *Fax:* 617-661-0565
E-mail: bigbear@candlewick.com; salesinfo@candlewick.com
Web Site: www.candlewick.com
Key Personnel
Pres & Publr: Karen Lotz
EVP, Exec Edit Dir & Assoc Publr: Liz Bicknell
SVP, Commercial Opers: Susan Batcheller
SVP, Fin: Hilary Berkman
SVP & Group Sales Dir: John Mendelson
VP, Contracts, Rts & Royalties: Becky S Hemperly
VP, Publicity & Exec Dir, Mktg Campaigns: Jennifer Roberts
Assoc Publr & Creative Dir: Chris Paul
Exec Dir, Educ Sales & Mktg: Kathleen Rourke
Group Art Dir, Candlewick Entertainment & Walker Entertainment: Kristen Nobles
Group Edit Dir, Candlewick Entertainment & Walker Entertainment: Joan Powers
Dir, Edit Opers & Edit Dir: Mary Lee Donovan
Dir, Mass Mkt Sales: Laura Pennock
Publicity & Mktg Campaigns Dir: Tracy Miracle
Publicity, Brands & Consumer Outreach Dir: Laura Rivas
Sr Exec Ed: Sarah Ketchersid
Sr Ed: Kate Fletcher; Andrea Tompa
Sr Publicist: Erika Denn
Sr Mktg Mgr: Zoe Luderitz
Mgr, Lib Mktg & Outreach: Andie Krawczyk
Founded: 1992
Children's books.
ISBN Prefix(es): 978-1-56402; 978-0-7636
Number of titles published annually: 300 Print
Total Titles: 2,250 Print; 230 E-Book
Imprints: Big Picture Press; Candlewick Entertainment; Nosy Crow; Templar Books
Foreign Rights: Walker Books London
Returns: Penguin Random House LLC, 1019 N State Rd 47, Crawfordsville, IN 47933; Penguin Random House Canada, 6971 Columbus Rd, Mississauga, ON L5T 1K1, Canada
Distribution Center: Penguin Random House LLC, 400 Hahn Rd, Westminster, MD 21157 *Toll Free Tel:* 800-733-3000 *Toll Free Fax:* 800-659-2436 *E-mail:* customerservice@randomhouse.com
Penguin Random House of Canada Ltd, 75 Sherbourne St, 5th fl, Toronto, ON M5A 2P9, Canada *Toll Free Tel:* 888-523-9292 *Toll Free Fax:* 888-562-9924
Membership(s): The Children's Book Council

Canon Law Society of America
Hecker Ctr, Suite 111, 3025 Fourth St NE, Washington, DC 20017-1102
SAN: 237-6296
Tel: 202-832-2350 *Fax:* 202-832-2331
E-mail: coordinator@clsa.org; info@clsa.org
Web Site: www.clsa.org
Key Personnel
Exec Coord: Rev Roger H Keeler *E-mail:* rhkeeler@clsa.org
Founded: 1939
Books on canon law & marriage.
ISBN Prefix(es): 978-0-943616
Number of titles published annually: 3 Print
Total Titles: 58 Print

Cantos Para Todos
4749 Hillcrest St, Bel Aire, KS 67226
Tel: 316-239 6477
Web Site: www.cantos.org
Key Personnel
Publr: Roy Howard *E-mail:* 2rhoward@att.net
Artistic Dir: Carlene H Williams
Author: Mariana Murguia de Ferrer
Founded: 1989
Materials with multiworlds in mind. Multimedia, multicultural, multilingual materials for schools & homes.
This publisher has indicated that 100% of their product line is author subsidized.
ISBN Prefix(es): 978-0-9768650
Number of titles published annually: 2 Print; 20 CD-ROM; 5 E-Book
Total Titles: 30 Print; 75 CD-ROM; 5 E-Book
Foreign Rep(s): Mariana Murguia (Mexico)

Capital Enquiry Inc
1034 Emerald Bay Rd, No 435, South Lake Tahoe, CA 96150
Tel: 916-442-1434 *Toll Free Tel:* 800-922-7486 *Fax:* 916-244-2704
E-mail: info@capenq.com
Web Site: www.govbuddy.com
Key Personnel
Owner & Mktg Dir: Bruce Campbell
Founded: 1973
Legislative directories, information, interactive maps (CA) zip code directory, mobile apps & *US Congress Directory*.
ISBN Prefix(es): 978-0-917982
Number of titles published annually: 7 Print
Total Titles: 15 Print
Distributor for Center for Investigative Reporting

Capstone Publishers™
1710 Roe Crest Dr, North Mankato, MN 56003
Toll Free Tel: 800-747-4992 (cust serv) *Toll Free Fax:* 888-262-0705
Web Site: www.capstonepress.com
Key Personnel
Owner: Robert Coughlan
CEO: G Thomas Ahern
COO & CFO: William R Rouse
Chief Content Offr: Ashley Andersen-Zantop
Pres: Matthew A Keller
Edit Dir: Nick Healy
Book Trade Sales Mgr: Larry Dorfman
Founded: 1991
Provides new & struggling readers with a strong foundation on which to build reading success. Our broad range of nonfiction titles for grades PreK-8 easily blends a world of books with the world children experience every day.
ISBN Prefix(es): 978-1-56065; 978-0-7368
Number of titles published annually: 250 Print
Total Titles: 2,100 Print
Imprints: Capstone Press; Compass Point Books; Heinemann Raintree; Picture Window Books; Stone Arch Books
Divisions: Heinemann Raintree
Branch Office(s)
5050 Lincoln Dr, Suite 200, Edina, MN 55436
Billing Address: 3680 Momentum Place, Chicago, IL 60689-5336
Distribution Center: 1905 Lookout Dr, North Mankato, MN 56003

Captain Fiddle Music & Publications
94 Wiswall Rd, Lee, NH 03861
Tel: 603-659-2658
E-mail: cfiddle@tiac.net
Web Site: captainfiddle.com
Key Personnel
Owner: Ryan J Thomson
Founded: 1985
ISBN Prefix(es): 978-0-931877
Number of titles published annually: 3 Print
Total Titles: 24 Print

Caravan Books
Subsidiary of Academic Resources Corp
6946 E Stevens Rd, Cave Creek, AZ 85331-8677
SAN: 206-7323
Tel: 480-575-9945
E-mail: sfandr@msn.com
Web Site: www.scholarsbooklist.com
Key Personnel
Publr: Norman Mangouni
Founded: 1972
ISBN Prefix(es): 978-0-88206
Number of titles published annually: 10 Print
Total Titles: 130 Print

§Cardiotext Publishing
3405 W 44 St, Minneapolis, MN 55410
SAN: 852-2251
Tel: 612-925-2053 *Fax:* 612-922-7556
E-mail: info@cardiotextpublishing.com
Web Site: www.cardiotextpublishing.com
Key Personnel
Pres: Mike Crouchet *Tel:* 612-746-3699 *E-mail:* mike.crouchet@cardiotext.com
Founded: 2007
Independent print & digital publisher specializing in the field of cardiovascular medicine.
ISBN Prefix(es): 978-1-935395; 978-1-942909; 978-0-979016
Number of titles published annually: 10 Print; 10 Online; 10 E-Book
Total Titles: 35 Print; 35 Online; 35 E-Book
Foreign Rights: John Scott & Co (Worldwide exc North America)
Distribution Center: NBN International, 10 Thornbury Rd, Plymouth PL6 7PP, United Kingdom *Tel:* (01752) 202 301 *Fax:* (01752) 202 333 *E-mail:* orders@nbninternational.com *Web Site:* www.nbninternational.com/Home/tabid/39/Default.aspx

Cardoza Publishing
808 S Main St, Las Vegas, NV 89101
Tel: 702-870-7200 *Toll Free Tel:* 800-577-WINS (577-9467)
E-mail: cardozabooks@aol.com; info@cardozabooks.com
Web Site: www.cardozabooks.com
Key Personnel
Publr & Author: Avery Cardoza
Founded: 1981
An independent publisher specializing in gaming, gambling, poker, backgammon & chess titles.
ISBN Prefix(es): 978-1-58042
Number of titles published annually: 15 Print
Total Titles: 200 Print
Distributor for Simon & Schuster
Orders to: Simon & Schuster, 100 Front St, Riverside, NJ 08075, Order Processing Dept *Toll Free Tel:* 800-223-2336 *Toll Free Fax:* 800-943-9831 *E-mail:* order_desk@distican.com

The Career Press Inc
12 Parish Dr, Wayne, NJ 07470
Tel: 201-848-0310 *Toll Free Tel:* 800-CAREER-1 (227-3371) *Fax:* 201-848-1727
E-mail: sales@careerpress.com
Web Site: www.careerpress.com
Key Personnel
Pres: Ronald W Fry
Edit Dir: Gina Schenck *E-mail:* gschenck@careerpress.com
Dir, Sales & Publicity: Laurie Kelly-Pye *E-mail:* lkellypye@careerpress.com
Sr Acqs Ed: Michael Pye *E-mail:* mpye@careerpress.com
Acqs Ed: Adam Schwartz *E-mail:* aschwartz@careerpress.com
Founded: 1985
Reference books, careers, business & financial how-to, educational, New Age, weddings & motivational.
ISBN Prefix(es): 978-1-56414; 978-1-60163; 978-1-63265
Number of titles published annually: 75 Print
Total Titles: 400 Print
Imprints: New Page Books (www.newpagebooks.com)
Foreign Rep(s): Artemis Agency (Michelle Lin) (Taiwan); Brumby Sunstate (Australia, New Zealand); Deep Books Ltd (Europe, UK); Hornblower Group (Canada); McGraw-Hill Education (Asia); Pansing Distribution Pte Ltd (Malaysia, Singapore); Phambili Agencies (South Africa); The White Partnership (Andrew White) (Hong Kong, Indonesia, Japan, Korea, Philippines, Taiwan, Thailand)
Foreign Rights: Amo Agency (Korea); CA-Link International LLC (China); Graal Literary Agency (Zbigniew Kanski) (Poland); Grayhawk Agency (Michelle Lin) (Taiwan); Letter Soup Rights Agency (Allison Olson) (Worldwide); Tuttle Mori Agency (Manami Tamaoki) (Japan); Yu Ri Jang Literary Agency (Christine Yi) (Korea)
Returns: Books International, 22883 Quicksilver Dr, Dulles, VA 20166 *Tel:* 703-661-1516
Distribution Center: University of Toronto Press, 5201 Dufferin St, North York, ON M3H 5T8, Canada *Tel:* 416-667-7791 *Toll Free Tel:* 800-565-9523 *Fax:* 416-667-7823 *E-mail:* utpbooks@utpress.ca *Web Site:* utoronto.ca

§Caribe Betania Editores
Division of Grupo Nelson Inc
PO Box 141000, Nashville, TN 37214-1000
Tel: 615-902-1893 *Fax:* 615-883-9376
Web Site: www.caribebetania.com
Key Personnel
Mktg: Jake Salomon
Founded: 1949
Publisher of Spanish books & Bibles.
ISBN Prefix(es): 978-0-88113; 978-0-89922
Number of titles published annually: 100 Print
Total Titles: 480 Print

Carlisle Press - Walnut Creek
2673 Township Rd 421, Sugarcreek, OH 44681
Tel: 330-852-1900 *Toll Free Tel:* 800-852-4482 *Fax:* 330-852-3285
Key Personnel
Publr: Marvin Wengerd
Founded: 1992
Amish books & cookbooks, *Keeper's at Home* Magazine.
ISBN Prefix(es): 978-1-890050; 978-0-9642548; 978-1-933753
Number of titles published annually: 6 Print
Total Titles: 60 Print

Carnegie Mellon University Press
5032 Forbes Ave, Pittsburgh, PA 15289-1021
SAN: 211-2329
Tel: 412-268-2861 *Fax:* 412-268-8706
E-mail: carnegiemellonuniversitypress@gmail.com
Web Site: www.cmu.edu/universitypress
Key Personnel
Dir: Gerald Costanzo
Sr Ed: Cynthia Lamb
Prodn Mgr: Connie Amoroso *E-mail:* camoroso@andrew.cmu.edu
Founded: 1974
ISBN Prefix(es): 978-0-915604; 978-0-88748
Number of titles published annually: 15 Print
Total Titles: 280 Print
Billing Address: University Press of New England, One Court St, Suite 250, Lebanon, NH 03766 (order dept) *Toll Free Tel:* 800-421-1561 *Fax:* 603-448-9429
Orders to: University Press of New England, One Court St, Suite 250, Lebanon, NH 03766 (order dept) *Toll Free Tel:* 800-421-1561 *Fax:* 603-448-9429 *Web Site:* www.upne.com/distributed/dist_cmu.html
Returns: University Press of New England, c/o Maple Logistics Solutions, 704 Legionaire Dr, Fredericksburg, PA 17026 *Tel:* 603-448-1533 ext 503 *Fax:* 603-448-9429
Warehouse: University Press of New England, c/o Maple Logistics Solutions, 704 Legionaire Dr, Fredericksburg, PA 17026, Cust Serv Supvr: Barbara Benson *Tel:* 603-448-1533 ext 255 *Toll Free Tel:* 800-421-1561 *Fax:* 603-448-9429 *E-mail:* university.press@dartmouth.edu *Web Site:* www.upne.com

Carolina Academic Press
700 Kent St, Durham, NC 27701
SAN: 210-7848
Tel: 919-489-7486 *Toll Free Tel:* 800-489-7486 *Fax:* 919-493-5668
E-mail: cap@cap-press.com
Web Site: www.cap-press.com; www.caplaw.com
Key Personnel
Publr: Keith R Sipe *Tel:* 919-489-7486 ext 120 *E-mail:* ksipe@cap-press.com
Sr Ed: Linda M Lacy *Tel:* 919-489-7486 ext 128 *E-mail:* linda@cap-press.com
Ed: Scott Sipe *Tel:* 919-489-7486 ext 129 *E-mail:* css@cap-press.com
Prodn & Design: Tim Colton *Tel:* 919-489-7486 ext 125 *E-mail:* tim@cap-press.com
Founded: 1974
Scholarly books & journals; anthropology, archaeology, criminal justice, economics, government, political science, history, reference, law, social science, african studies.
ISBN Prefix(es): 978-0-89089; 978-1-59460; 978-1-61163
Number of titles published annually: 100 Print; 30 E-Book
Total Titles: 700 Print; 100 E-Book
Returns: 101 Tobacco Rd, Oxford, NC 27565
Warehouse: 101 Tobacco Rd, Oxford, NC 27565

Carolrhoda Books
Division of Lerner Publishing Group Inc
241 First Ave N, Minneapolis, MN 55401
SAN: 201-9671
Tel: 612-332-3344 *Toll Free Tel:* 800-328-4929 *Fax:* 612-332-7615 *Toll Free Fax:* 800-332-1132
E-mail: info@lernerbooks.com
Web Site: www.lernerbooks.com
Key Personnel
Chmn: Harry J Lerner
CFO & EVP: Margaret Wunderlich
Pres & Publr: Adam Lerner
EVP, Sales: David Wexler
EVP, Mktg & Digital Prods: Terri Soutor
VP, Ed-in-Chief: Patricia M Stockland
VP, Prodn: Gary Hansen
VP, Digital Prod Mgmt: Daniel Wallek
Edit Dir: Andrew Karre
Rts Dir: Maria Kjoller
Group Mktg Dir: Jill Braithwaite
School & Lib Mktg Dir: Lois Wallentine
Art Dir: Zach Marell
Dir, HR: Cyndi Radant
Founded: 1969
Juveniles: picture books & young adult fiction.
Number of titles published annually: 20 Print
Total Titles: 70 Print; 334 E-Book
Foreign Rep(s): INT Press Distribution (Australia); Monarch Books of Canada (Trade) (Canada); Phambili (Southern Africa); Publishers Marketing Services (Malaysia, Singapore); Saunders Book Co (Education) (Canada); South Pacific Books (New Zealand)
Foreign Rights: Japan Foreign Rights Centre (Japan); Korea Copyright Center (Korea); Michelle Lapautre Agence Junior (France); Literarische Agentur Silke Weniger (Germany)
Warehouse: Lerner Publishing Group, 1251 Washington Ave N, Minneapolis, MN 55401

Carolrhoda Lab™
Imprint of Lerner Publishing Group Inc
241 First Ave N, Minneapolis, MN 55401
Tel: 612-332-3344 *Toll Free Tel:* 800-328-4929 *Fax:* 612-332-7615 *Toll Free Fax:* 800-332-1132 (US)
E-mail: info@lernerbooks.com
Web Site: www.lernerbooks.com
Key Personnel
Chmn: Harry J Lerner
Pres & Publr: Adam Lerner
CFO & EVP: Margaret Wunderlich
EVP, Sales: David Wexler

EVP & Dir, Mktg & Digital Prods: Terri Soutor
VP, Prodn: Gary Hansen
VP, Ed-in-Chief: Patricia M Stockland
VP, Digital Prod Mgmt: Daniel Wallek
Edit Dir: Andrew Karre
Rts Dir: Maria Kjoller
Group Mktg Dir: Jill Braithwaite
School & Lib Mktg Dir: Lois Wallentine
Creative Dir: Zach Marell
Founded: 2010 (imprint launched)
Dedicated to distinctive, provocative, boundary-pushing fiction for teens & their sympathizers.
Number of titles published annually: 10 Print
Total Titles: 95 E-Book
Foreign Rep(s): INT Books Distribution (Australia); Monarch Books of Canada (Canada); Phambili Agency (Southern Africa); Publishers Marketing Services (Malaysia, Singapore); Saunders Book Co/Education (Canada); South Pacific Books (New Zealand)
Foreign Rights: Japan Foreign-Rights Centre (Japan); Korea Copyright Center (Korea); Agence Michelle Lapautre (France); Silke Weniger (Germany)
Shipping Address: Lerner Publishing Group Inc, 1251 Washington Ave N, Minneapolis, MN 55401, Contact: Ken Rued *Fax:* 612-204-9208
Warehouse: Lerner Publishing Group Inc, 1251 Washington Ave N, Minneapolis, MN 55401, Contact: Ken Rued *Fax:* 612-204-9208

Carroll Publishing
4701 Sangamore Rd, Suite S-155, Bethesda, MD 20816
SAN: 237-6334
Tel: 301-263-9800 *Toll Free Tel:* 800-336-4240 *Fax:* 301-263-9801
E-mail: info@carrollpub.com; customersvc@carrollpub.com
Web Site: www.carrollpublishing.com
Key Personnel
VP, Fin & Admin: Shirley Paris *Tel:* 301-263-9800 ext 107 *E-mail:* smparis@carrollpub.com
Founded: 1973
Number of titles published annually: 21 Print; 4 Online
Total Titles: 21 Print; 4 Online
Membership(s): National Directory Publishing Association

Carson-Dellosa Publishing LLC
PO Box 35665, Greensboro, NC 27425-5665
Tel: 336-632-0084 *Toll Free Tel:* 800-321-0943 *Fax:* 336-632-0087 *Toll Free Fax:* 800-535-2669
E-mail: custsvc@carsondellosa.com
Web Site: www.carsondellosa.com
Key Personnel
CEO: Al Greco
Founded: 1976
Publishes supplementary educational materials, including activity books, resource guides, classroom materials & reproducibles, toddler-grade 8. Topics include reading, language arts, mathematics, science, the arts, social studies, English language learners, early childhood learning, Christian books & crafts.
ISBN Prefix(es): 978-0-513; 978-0-7424; 978-1-56822; 978-0-88012; 978-0-88724; 978-1-59441; 978-1-60022; 978-1-60418
Number of titles published annually: 80 Print; 10 E-Book
Total Titles: 700 Print
Imprints: DJ Inkers; Rainbow Bridge Publishing; Kelley Wingate Publications
Branch Office(s)
8720 Orion Place, Suite 200, Columbus, OH 43240, Cust Serv Mgr: Alba Jaimes *Toll Free Tel:* 800-228-6898
Distributor for Key Education; Mark Twain Media

CarTech Inc
39966 Grand Ave, North Branch, MN 55056
Tel: 651-277-1200 *Toll Free Tel:* 800-551-4754 *Fax:* 651-277-1203
E-mail: info@cartechbooks.com
Web Site: www.cartechbooks.com
Key Personnel
Owner & Publr: David Arnold
Mktg & Sales Mgr: Molly Koecher *E-mail:* mollyk@cartechbooks.com
Founded: 1993
Automotive books.
ISBN Prefix(es): 978-1-884089; 978-1-932494; 978-1-61325
Number of titles published annually: 25 Print
Total Titles: 100 Print
Imprints: S-A Design Books
Distributor for Brooklands Books Ltd; Wolfgang Publications
Foreign Rights: Publishers Group UK (PGUK) (Australia, England)
Returns: RR Donnelley, 677 Brighton Beach Rd, Menasha, WI 54952 *Tel:* 920-751-7621
Warehouse: RR Donnelley, N9234 Lake Park Rd, Appleton, WI 54915 *Tel:* 920-969-6434

Casa Bautista de Publicaciones
Affiliate of Southern Baptist Convention
7000 Alabama Ave, El Paso, TX 79904
Tel: 915-566-9656 *Toll Free Tel:* 800-755-5958 (cust serv & orders) *Fax:* 915-562-6502; 915-565-9008 (orders)
E-mail: orders@editorialmh.org
Web Site: www.editorialmh.org
Key Personnel
Gen Dir: Raquel Contreras
Mktg & Sales Dir: Pedro Slachta
Secy: Norma C Armengol *Tel:* 915-566-9656 ext 288 *E-mail:* narmengol@editorialmh.org
Founded: 1905
Religious publications in Spanish. Foreign distributors also located in all Latin.
ISBN Prefix(es): 978-0-311
Number of titles published annually: 16 Print
Total Titles: 895 Print; 895 E-Book; 40 Audio
Imprints: CBP/EMH
Distributed by LifeWay Christian Resources

§Cascade Pass Inc
4223 Glencoe Ave, Suite C-105, Marina Del Rey, CA 90292-8801
Tel: 310-305-0210 *Toll Free Tel:* 888-837-0704 *Fax:* 310-305-7850
Web Site: www.cascadepass.com
Key Personnel
Owner & Pres: David Katz *E-mail:* dkatz@cascadepass.com
Proj Mgr: Judith Cohen *E-mail:* jlc@cascadepass.com
Founded: 1989
Science career books for children, environmental & sports.
ISBN Prefix(es): 978-1-880599
Number of titles published annually: 3 Print
Total Titles: 84 Print; 18 CD-ROM; 2 E-Book

Casemate Publishers & Book Distributors LLC
908 Darby Rd, Havertown, PA 19083
Tel: 610-853-9131 *Fax:* 610-853-9146
E-mail: casemate@casematepublishing.com
Web Site: www.casematepublishing.com
Key Personnel
CEO & Pres: David Farnsworth
VP, Busn Devt: Ms Simone Drinkwater
VP: Sarah Farnsworth
Founded: 2001
Publisher & distributor of military history, defense & travel books.
ISBN Prefix(es): 978-0-9711709; 978-1-932033; 978-1-935149; 978-1-61200
Number of titles published annually: 30 Print; 30 E-Book; 5 Audio
Total Titles: 175 Print; 175 E-Book
Distributor for AF Editions; Airfile Publications; Amber Books (UK); Amberley Publishing (UK); Birlinn Publishing (UK); CAL Books; Casemate (USA); Casemate/Flashpoint; Compendium Films; Compendium Publishing (UK); D-Day Publishing (Belgium); Eagle Editions; Earthbound Publications; Formac Publishing (Canada); Foundry; Front Street Press (USA); Frontline Books; Greenhill Books; Grub Street (UK); Harpia Publishing; Heimdal; Helion & Co Ltd (UK); Editions Charles Herissey (France); Histoire & Collections (France); Historical Archive Press; Historical Indexes (USA); History Facts; Paul Holberton Publishing; Indo Editions (France); Ironclad Publishing (USA); De Krijger (Belgium); Lancer Publishers; Lorimer; Military Illustrated; MMP (UK/ Poland); OREP; Pen & Sword Books Ltd (UK); Pen & Sword Digital; Philedition; Riebel-Roque; RZM Publishing (USA); S I Publicaties BV; Savas Beatie (USA); Scarab Miniatures; Seaforth Publishing; Tattered Flag; 30 Degrees South Publishers; Vanwell-Looking Back Press; Vanwell Publishing (Canada); WAG Books; Warlord Games; Wharncliffe
Foreign Rep(s): Casemate UK (UK & Commonwealth)
Returns: c/o Casemate, 22883 Quicksilver Dr, Dulles, VA 20166
Shipping Address: c/o Casemate, 22883 Quicksilver Dr, Dulles, VA 20166
Membership(s): PMA International

Castle Connolly Medical Ltd
42 W 24 St, 2nd fl, New York, NY 10010
Tel: 212-367-8400 *Fax:* 212-367-0964
Web Site: www.castleconnolly.com
Key Personnel
Founder & Chmn: John K Castle
Founder, Pres & CEO: John J Connolly, EdD
VP, Chief Strategy & Opers Offr: William Liss-Levinson, PhD *E-mail:* bliss-levinson@castleconnolly.com
VP, Chief Med & Res Offr: Dr Jean Morgan
Mgr, Client Rel & Res Opers: Nicki Hughes *Tel:* 212-367-8400 ext 138 *E-mail:* nhughes@castleconnolly.com
Founded: 1991
Publishing company whose mission is to help consumers find the best healthcare with its "Top Doctors" guides.
ISBN Prefix(es): 978-1-883769; 978-1-935036; 978-0-984
Number of titles published annually: 3 Print
Total Titles: 10 Print
Membership(s): The Association of Publishers for Special Sales

§Catholic Book Publishing Corp
77 West End Rd, Totowa, NJ 07512
Tel: 973-890-2400 *Toll Free Tel:* 877-228-2665 *Fax:* 973-890-2410
E-mail: info@catholicbookpublishing.com
Web Site: www.catholicbookpublishing.com
Founded: 1911
For over 90 years, the leading publisher of quality Catholic resources—including Bibles, Missals, Prayer books, liturgical books, spirituality books, Spanish titles & children's books. The company's trademark St. Joseph Editions are distinctive for their large, easy-to-read typefaces; magnificent, full-color illustrations; & helpful & plentiful guides, summaries, notes, indices & photographs. Imprint Resurrection Press is noted for spirituality & personal growth titles. Imprint World Catholic Press complements the company's rich tradition of Bible publishing.
ISBN Prefix(es): 978-0-89942; 978-1-878718 (Resurrection Press); 978-0-529 (World Catholic Press); 978-1-933066 (Resurrection Press)

Number of titles published annually: 25 Print
Total Titles: 750 Print; 9 Audio
Imprints: Resurrection Press; World Catholic Press

The Catholic Health Association of the United States
4455 Woodson Rd, St Louis, MO 63134-3797
SAN: 201-968X
Tel: 314-427-2500 *Fax:* 314-427-0029
E-mail: servicecenter@chausa.org
Web Site: www.chausa.org
Key Personnel
VP, Communs & Mktg: Edward J Giganti
E-mail: egiganti@chausa.org
Founded: 1915
Catholic health care resources, Catholic ministry, health, labor, medicine & nursing.
ISBN Prefix(es): 978-0-87125
Number of titles published annually: 3 Print; 1 CD-ROM; 2 Audio
Total Titles: 58 Print; 1 CD-ROM; 4 Audio
Branch Office(s)
1875 Eye St NW, Suite 1000, Washington, DC 20006 *Tel:* 202-296-3993 *Fax:* 202-296-3997

The Catholic University of America Press
240 Leahy Hall, 620 Michigan Ave NE, Washington, DC 20064
SAN: 203-6290
Tel: 202-319-5052 *Toll Free Tel:* 800-537-5487 (orders only) *Fax:* 202-319-4985
E-mail: cua-press@cua.edu
Web Site: cuapress.cua.edu
Key Personnel
Dir & Ed-in-Chief: Trevor C Lipscombe
E-mail: lipscombe@cua.edu
Mng Ed: Theresa Walker *E-mail:* walkert@cua.edu
Acqs Ed, Philosophy & Theology: John B Martino *E-mail:* martinoj@cua.edu
Sales & Mktg Mgr: Brian Roach *E-mail:* roach@cua.edu
Founded: 1939
ISBN Prefix(es): 978-0-8132
Number of titles published annually: 38 Print; 25 Online; 25 E-Book
Total Titles: 580 Print; 300 Online; 300 E-Book
Distributor for American Maritain Association; Institute for the Psychological Sciences Press (IPS); Sapientia Press
Foreign Rep(s): Eurospan University Press Group (Africa, Asia, Australia, Europe, Middle East, New Zealand, UK); Scholarly Book Services (Canada)
Orders to: Hopkins Fulfillment Service, PO Box 50370, Baltimore, MD 21211-4370 *Toll Free Tel:* 800-537-5487 *Fax:* 410-516-6998 *E-mail:* hfscustserv@mail.press.jhu.edu
Returns: Hopkins Fulfillment Service, c/o Maple Press Co, Lebanon Distribution Ctr, PO Box 1287, Lebanon, PA 17042-1287
Warehouse: c/o Maple Press Co, Lebanon Distribution Ctr, 704 Legionaire Dr, Fredricksburg, PA 17042
Membership(s): Association of American University Presses

Cato Institute
1000 Massachusetts Ave NW, Washington, DC 20001-5403
Tel: 202-842-0200 *Toll Free Tel:* 800-767-1241 *Fax:* 202-842-3490
E-mail: catostore@cato.org
Web Site: www.cato.org
Key Personnel
Founder: Edward H Crane
Pres: Peter Goettler
Pubns Dir: David Lampo
Founded: 1977
Non-partisan, public-policy think tank.
ISBN Prefix(es): 978-0-932790; 978-1-882577; 978-1-930865; 978-1-933995
Number of titles published annually: 15 Print
Total Titles: 150 Print
Foreign Rights: Rights & Distribution Inc (Worldwide)
Distribution Center: National Book Network, 15200 NBN Way, Blue Ridge Summit, PA 17214, VP, Opers: Mike Cornell *Tel:* 717-794-3800 *Toll Free Tel:* 800-462-6420 *Fax:* 717-794-3828 *Web Site:* www.nbnbooks.com

Caxton Press
Division of The Caxton Printers Ltd
312 Main St, Caldwell, ID 83605-3299
SAN: 201-9698
Tel: 208-459-7421 *Toll Free Tel:* 800-657-6465 *Fax:* 208-459-7450
E-mail: publish@caxtonpress.com
Web Site: www.caxtonpress.com
Key Personnel
Pres & Publr: Scott Gipson *E-mail:* sgipson@caxtonpress.com
Publg Asst/Web Site: Amanda Halverson
E-mail: ahalverson@caxtonprinters.com
Founded: 1925
Hardcover & paperback. Founded in 1925 by J H Gipson, Caxton Press is still owned & managed by the Gipson family.
ISBN Prefix(es): 978-0-87004
Number of titles published annually: 8 Print
Total Titles: 165 Print
Distributor for Hambleton Publishing; Historic Idaho Series; Photosmith Books; Snake Country Publishing; University of Idaho Asian American Comparative Collection; University of Idaho Press
Membership(s): AAP

§CCH, a Wolters Kluwer business
Subsidiary of Wolters Kluwer
2700 Lake Cook Rd, Riverwoods, IL 60015
SAN: 202-3504
Tel: 847-267-7000
Web Site: www.cch.com
Key Personnel
Pres & CEO: Teresa Mackintosh
Dir, Communs: Leslie Bonacum *Tel:* 847-267-7153 *E-mail:* mediahelp@cch.com
Founded: 1913
Current US international tax law, business, human resources, securities & health care law, tax, small business, home office human resources & health care.
ISBN Prefix(es): 978-0-8080
Number of titles published annually: 100 Print
Total Titles: 400 Print
Subsidiaries: CCH Peterson; CCH Riverwoods; CCH St Petersburg; CCH Tax Compliance; CCH Washington DC; LIS (Legal Information Services); Washington Service Bureau
Foreign Office(s): Wolters Kluwer nv, Zuidpoolsingel 2, PO Box 1030, 2400 BA Alphen aan den Rijn, Netherlands *Tel:* (0172) 641 400 *Fax:* (0172) 474 889 *E-mail:* info@wolterskluwer.com *Web Site:* www.wolterskluwer.com
Billing Address: PO Box 4307, Carol Stream, IL 60197-4307
Returns: 7201 McKinney Circle, Frederick, MD 21704-8356
Warehouse: 4025 Peterson Ave, Chicago, IL 60646-6085

CCL - Americas, see Center for Creative Leadership LLC

CDL Press
PO Box 34454, Bethesda, MD 20827
Tel: 301-762-2066 *Fax:* 253-484-5542
E-mail: cdlpress@erols.com
Web Site: www.cdlpress.com
Key Personnel
Pres: Mark E Cohen
Founded: 1981
ISBN Prefix(es): 978-1-883053
Number of titles published annually: 6 Print
Total Titles: 63 Print
Imprints: University Press of Maryland
Returns: 11903 Reynolds Ave, Potomac, MD 20827

Cedar Fort Inc
2373 W 700 S, Springville, UT 84663
Tel: 801-489-4084 *Toll Free Tel:* 800-SKY-BOOK (759-2665) *Fax:* 801-489-1097 *Toll Free Fax:* 800-388-3727
Web Site: cedarfort.com
Key Personnel
Owner & Chmn: Lyle Mortimer
Pres: Bryce Mortimer *E-mail:* brycemortimer@cedarfort.com
VP: Katriena Eden
Founded: 1986
Christian (primarily Latter-Day Saints), inspirational, motivational, LDS fiction & doctrinal.
ISBN Prefix(es): 978-1-55517
Number of titles published annually: 120 Print; 50 E-Book; 5 Audio
Total Titles: 500 Print
Imprints: Bonneville Books; CFI; Front Table Books; Hobble Creek Press; Horizon Publishers; Pioneer Press; Plain Sight Publishing; Sweetwater Books

§Cedar Grove Books
2215 High Point Dr, Carrollton, TX 75007
SAN: 255-3732
Tel: 415-364-8292 *Fax:* 415-276-9858
E-mail: queries@cedargrovebooks.com
Web Site: www.cedargrovebooks.com
Key Personnel
Publr & Mktg Dir: Rochon Perry
E-mail: rperry@cedargrovebooks.com
Edit Dir: J Cameron McClain *E-mail:* j.cameron.mcclain.stories@gmail.com
Dir, Soc Media, Children's & Young Adult Books: Rebecca Sims-Nichols
E-mail: bexisimsnichols@cedargrovebooks.com
Founded: 2010
Publish multicultural books with protagonists that overcome adversity by staying true to themselves.
ISBN Prefix(es): 978-0-9835077
Number of titles published annually: 9 Print; 9 Online; 9 E-Book
Total Titles: 6 Print; 9 Online; 6 E-Book
Imprints: The Blaxis (multicultural comics directory); CGN (graphic novels); Griot Enterprises (graphic novels); L'il Acorns (children's books); Make Prophetz (academic art & essay books); Sapling (young adult books)
Editorial Office(s): 516 Arch St, San Francisco, CA 94132
Membership(s): The Independent Book Publishers Association

Cedar Tree Books
PO Box 4256, Wilmington, DE 19807
Tel: 302-998-4171 *Fax:* 302-998-4185
E-mail: books@ctpress.com
Web Site: www.cedartreebooks.com
Founded: 1925
This publisher has indicated that 30% of their product line is author subsidized.
ISBN Prefix(es): 978-1-892142
Number of titles published annually: 8 Print
Total Titles: 48 Print

CEF Press
Subsidiary of Child Evangelism Fellowship Inc
17482 State Hwy M, Warrenton, MO 63383-0348
Mailing Address: PO Box 348, Warrenton, MO 63383-0348

Tel: 636-456-4321 *Toll Free Tel:* 800-748-7710 (cust serv); 800-300-4033 (USA ministries) *Fax:* 636-456-9935
E-mail: cefexecutiveoffices@cefonline.com
Web Site: www.cefonline.com
Key Personnel
Creative Servs: Rick Bunch *Tel:* 636-456-4321 ext 1161
Founded: 1937
Christian education curriculum.
ISBN Prefix(es): 978-1-55976
Number of titles published annually: 30 Print
Total Titles: 300 Print
Foreign Rep(s): CEFMARK (Australia)

Celebra
Imprint of Penguin Group (USA) LLC
375 Hudson St, New York, NY 10014
Tel: 212-366-2000 *Fax:* 212-366-2889
Key Personnel
Publr: Ray Garcia
Assoc Publr & Exec Mng Ed: Steve Meltzer
Number of titles published annually: 13 Print
Total Titles: 64 Print

Celebrity Profiles Publishing
Division of Edison & Kellogg
PO Box 344, Stony Brook, NY 11790
Tel: 631-862-8555 *Fax:* 631-862-0139
E-mail: celebpro4@aol.com
Web Site: www.richardgrudens.com; richardgrudensblog.blogspot.com
Key Personnel
Pres: James Snyder
Author: Richard Grudens
Founded: 1995
ISBN Prefix(es): 978-0-9763877
Number of titles published annually: 3 Print
Total Titles: 15 Print; 2 Audio
Membership(s): The Independent Book Publishers Association

§Cengage Learning
20 Channel Center St, Boston, MA 02210
Tel: 617-289-7700 *Toll Free Tel:* 800-354-9706 *Fax:* 617-289-7844 *Toll Free Fax:* 800-487-8488
E-mail: esales@cengage.com
Web Site: www.cengage.com
Key Personnel
CEO: Michael Hansen
CFO: John Leahy
CTO: George Moore
Chief Acctg Offr & SVP, Fin Planning & Analysis: Bob Gibney
Chief Mktg Offr: Sandi Kirshner
Chief People Offr & Gen Coun: Ken Carson
Chief Prod Offr: Jim Donohue
Chief Sales & Mktg Offr: Kevin Stone
Pres, Intl: Alexander Broich
EVP & Chief Strategy Offr: Fernando Bleichmar
SVP & Treas: Richard Veith
SVP, Corp Aff: Josef Blumenfeld
SVP, Corp Devt & M&A: Torsten Geers
SVP, Pub Aff: Susan Aspey
SVP, Tax: Frank Vari
Sr Dir, Corp Communs: Lindsay Stanley
Sr Educ Advisor: George Miller
Cengage Learning delivers highly-customized learning solutions for colleges, universities, instructors, students, libraries, government agencies, corporations & professionals around the world. These solutions are delivered through specialized content, applications & services that foster academic excellence & professional development, as well as provide measurable learning outcomes to its customers.
Number of titles published annually: 150 Print
Subsidiaries: Gale (www.gale.com); Heinle (www.heinle.com); Thorndike Press; Wadsworth (www.wadsworth.com)
Billing Address: Cengage Learning Distribution Center, 10650 Toebben Dr, Independence, KY 41051 *Tel:* 859-525-2230 *Fax:* 859-282-5700
Orders to: Cengage Learning Distribution Center, 10650 Toebben Dr, Independence, KY 41051 *Tel:* 859-525-2230 *Fax:* 859-282-5700
Returns: Cengage Learning Distribution Center, 10650 Toebben Dr, Independence, KY 41051 *Tel:* 859-525-2230 *Fax:* 859-282-5700
Warehouse: Cengage Learning Distribution Center, 10650 Toebben Dr, Independence, KY 41051 *Tel:* 859-525-2230 *Fax:* 859-282-5700
Distribution Center: Cengage Learning Distribution Center, 10650 Toebben Dr, Independence, KY 41051 *Tel:* 859-525-2230 *Fax:* 859-282-5700
Membership(s): AAP
See separate listing for:
Charles River Media
Gale
Milady
National Geographic Learning
Wadsworth Publishing

Center for Creative Leadership LLC
Affiliate of Smith Richardson Foundation
One Leadership Place, Greensboro, NC 27410-9427
Mailing Address: PO Box 26300, Greensboro, NC 27438-6300
Tel: 336-545-2810; 336-288-7210 *Fax:* 336-282-3284
E-mail: info@ccl.org
Web Site: www.ccl.org/publications
Key Personnel
Pres & CEO: John R Ryan
EVP & CFO: Bradley E Shumaker
EVP & Mng Dir, CCL-EMEA: David G Altman
Founded: 1970
Books on leadership & leadership development.
ISBN Prefix(es): 978-0-912879; 978-0-9638301; 978-1-882197
Number of titles published annually: 10 Print
Total Titles: 123 Print
Foreign Office(s): CCL-Europe, Rue Neerveld 101-103 Neerveldstr, 1200 Brussels, Belgium *Tel:* (02) 679 0910 *Fax:* (02) 673 6306 *E-mail:* ccl.emea@ccl.org
CCL-Asia, The Rutherford, Lobby B, No 03-07/08, 89 Science Park Dr 1, Singapore 118261, Singapore *Tel:* 6854 6000 *Fax:* 6854 6001 *E-mail:* ccl.apac@ccl.org
Distributed by Jossey-Bass; John Wiley & Sons Inc
Distributor for Free Press; Harvard Business School Press; Jossey-Bass; Lominger Inc; John Wiley & Sons Inc

Center for East Asian Studies (CEAS)
Subsidiary of Western Washington University
Western Washington University, 516 High St, Bellingham, WA 98225
Tel: 360-650-3339 *Fax:* 360-650-6110
E-mail: easpress@wwu.edu
Web Site: www.wwu.edu/eas
Key Personnel
Dir: Prof Massimiliano Tomasi *E-mail:* massimiliano.tomasi@wwu.edu
Mng Ed: Dr Scott Pearce *Tel:* 360-650-3897 *E-mail:* pearce@cc.wwu.edu
Founded: 1971
East Asia & Iran; Asia mainly monographs.
ISBN Prefix(es): 978-0-914584
Number of titles published annually: 3 Print
Total Titles: 30 Print

§Center for Futures Education Inc
345 Erie St, Grove City, PA 16127
Mailing Address: PO Box 309, Grove City, PA 16127
Tel: 724-458-5860 *Fax:* 724-458-5962
E-mail: info@thectr.com
Web Site: www.thectr.com
Key Personnel
Treas: Lyn M Sennholz *E-mail:* lyn@thectr.com
Founded: 1981
Print & online books on commodity futures & securities.
ISBN Prefix(es): 978-0-915513
Number of titles published annually: 12 Print
Total Titles: 50 Print; 15 E-Book

The Center for Learning
Division of Social Studies School Service
10200 Jefferson Blvd, Culver City, CA 90232
Mailing Address: PO Box 802, Culver City, CA 90232
Tel: 310-839-2436 *Toll Free Tel:* 800-421-4246 *Fax:* 310-839-2249 *Toll Free Fax:* 800-944-5432
E-mail: customerservice@centerforlearning.org
Web Site: www.centerforlearning.org
Key Personnel
HR Mgr: Stephanae Benson
Founded: 1965
Founded to publish values based curriculum materials. All materials are written by master teachers who integrate academic objectives & ethical values. Nonprofit educational publisher of value based curriculum units with reproducible handouts for teachers of English/Language Arts, social studies, novel/dramas, biographies & religion. Specialize in advanced placement, genres; American, British & World novels & literature; skills, supplementary topics, writing; economics, social & global issues, US government & history, world history; Catholic teaching, ministry, retreats, adult faith resources, marriage & parenting, divorce & blended families, abstinence education & chastity; publish lesson plans for elementary & secondary grades.
ISBN Prefix(es): 978-1-56077
Number of titles published annually: 20 Print
Total Titles: 600 Print

Center for the Collaborative Classroom
1250 53 St, Suite 3, Emeryville, CA 94608
Tel: 510-533-0213 *Toll Free Tel:* 800-666-7270 *Fax:* 510-464-3670
E-mail: info@collaborativeclassroom.org; clientsupport@collaborativeclassroom.org
Web Site: www.collaborativeclassroom.org
Key Personnel
Founder: Eric Schaps
SVP & CFO: Brent Welling *E-mail:* bwelling@collaborativeclassroom.org
Pres: Victor C Young *E-mail:* vyoung@collaborativeclassroom.org
VP, Dissemination: Kelly Stuart *E-mail:* kstuart@collaborativeclassroom.org
VP, IT: Mr Nazar Yousif *E-mail:* ynazar@collaborativeclassroom.org
VP, Prog Devt: Lana Costantini MFA
VP, Publg Servs: Lisa Kent Bandini *E-mail:* lbandini@collaborativeclassroom.org
Dir, Admin: Barbara Radcliffe
Founded: 1980
Books, teacher study packages, literature guides, in school & after school curricula in character education, reading & mathematics.
ISBN Prefix(es): 978-1-885603; 978-1-57621; 978-0-439
Number of titles published annually: 15 Print
Total Titles: 450 Print

Center for Women Policy Studies
4620 N Park Ave, Suite 302W, Chevy Chase, MD 20815
Tel: 301-986-0795
E-mail: cwps@centerwomenpolicy.org
Web Site: www.centerwomenpolicy.org

Key Personnel
Pres: Leslie R Wolfe, PhD *E-mail:* lwolfe@centerwomenpolicy.org
VP: Jennifer Tucker *E-mail:* jtucker@centerwomenpolicy.com
Founded: 1972
Violence against women, education, economic opportunity, work & family policy, workplace diversity, women's health policy, women & AIDS, human trafficking of women & girls.
ISBN Prefix(es): 978-1-877966
Number of titles published annually: 12 Print
Total Titles: 65 Print

Center Street, see Hachette Nashville

Centering Corp
7230 Maple St, Omaha, NE 68134
SAN: 298-1815
Tel: 402-553-1200 *Toll Free Tel:* 866-218-0101 *Fax:* 402-553-0507
E-mail: orders@centering.org
Web Site: www.centering.org
Key Personnel
Founder & Pres: Joy Johnson; Dr Marvin Johnson
Exec Dir: Janet Roberts *E-mail:* centeringcorp@aol.com
Busn Dir: Marc Roberts
Dir, Devt: Ben Schroeder
Founded: 1977
Bereavement support; specializes in divorce, grief & loss. Nonprofit organization.
ISBN Prefix(es): 978-1-56123
Number of titles published annually: 10 Print
Total Titles: 150 Print

Centerstream Publishing LLC
PO Box 17878, Anaheim Hills, CA 92817-7878
SAN: 683-8022
Tel: 714-779-9390
E-mail: centerstrm@aol.com
Web Site: www.centerstream-usa.com
Key Personnel
Owner: Ron Middlebrook
Founded: 1971
Music history, bios, music instruction books, videos & DVDs: all instruments.
ISBN Prefix(es): 978-0-931759; 978-1-57467
Number of titles published annually: 20 Print; 10 CD-ROM
Total Titles: 250 Print; 30 CD-ROM
Subsidiaries: Centerbrook Publishing
Distributed by Booklines Hawaii; Hal Leonard Corp
Membership(s): The Independent Book Publishers Association

Central Conference of American Rabbis/CCAR Press
355 Lexington Ave, 18th fl, New York, NY 10017
Tel: 212-972-3636
E-mail: info@ccarnet.org
Web Site: www.ccarpress.org
Key Personnel
Chief Exec: Steven A Fox *Tel:* 212-972-3636 ext 238 *E-mail:* sfox@ccarnet.org
Publr & Dir, Press: Hara Person *Tel:* 212-972-3636 ext 222 *E-mail:* hperson@ccarnet.org
Founded: 1889
Books on liturgy & Jewish practices from a liberal point of view.
ISBN Prefix(es): 978-0-88123; 978-0-916694
Number of titles published annually: 5 Print
Total Titles: 57 Print
Shipping Address: Mercedes Distribution Center, Brooklyn Navy Yard, Bldg 3, Brooklyn, NY 11205
Warehouse: Mercedes Distribution Center, Brooklyn Navy Yard, Bldg 3, Brooklyn, NY 11205

Central European University Press
224 W 57 St, New York, NY 10019
Web Site: www.ceupress.com
Key Personnel
Sales Mgr, US & CN: Abel Meszaros *E-mail:* meszarosa@ceu.hu
Founded: 1993
Focuses on publications relating to the humanities & social sciences. Publishes high-quality mss, interpreting the past & present history, society, culture & economy of the countries of Central & Eastern Europe, the former Soviet Union & its neighbors. In the last couple of years, the Press has expanded its list to include books in the fields of higher education policy, gender studies, media studies & art history.
ISBN Prefix(es): 978-1-85866; 978-1-61055
Number of titles published annually: 20 Print
Total Titles: 400 Print; 150 E-Book
Editorial Office(s): Oktober 6, u 14, Budapest 1051, Hungary, Dir & Ed: Krisztina Kos *Tel:* (01) 327-3844 *Fax:* (01) 327-3183 *E-mail:* kosk@ceu.hu
Foreign Office(s): Oktober 6, u 14, Budapest 1051, Hungary, Dir & Ed: Krisztina Kos *Tel:* (01) 327-3844 *Fax:* (01) 327-3183 *E-mail:* kosk@ceu.hu
Distributed by University of Toronto Press (Canada)
Distributor for Apostrofa Publishers; Baltos Lankos; Helena History Press; International Debate Education Association; Open Society Institute
Foreign Rep(s): East West Export Books (Asia, Australia, Hawaii, New Zealand); Kubon & Sagner GmbH (Germany); NBN International (UK, Western Europe); OPP (UK); Yushodo Co Ltd (Japan)
Orders to: Books International Inc, PO Box 605, Herndon, VA 20172 *Tel:* 703-661-1500 *Fax:* 703-661-1501 *E-mail:* meszarosa@ceu.hu *Web Site:* www.booksintl.com
Returns: Books International Inc, 22883 Quicksilver Dr, Dulles, VA 20166 *Tel:* 703-661-1500 *Fax:* 703-661-1501
Shipping Address: Books International Inc, PO Box 605, Herndon, VA 20172 *Tel:* 703-661-1500 *Fax:* 703-661-1501
Warehouse: Books International Inc, 22883 Quicksilver Dr, Dulles, VA 20166 *Tel:* 703-661-1500 *Fax:* 703-661-1501
Membership(s): Association of European University Presses

Central Recovery Press (CRP)
Unit of Central Recovery Treatment
3321 N Buffalo Dr, Suite 275, Las Vegas, NV 89129
Tel: 702-868-5830 *Fax:* 702-868-5831
E-mail: info@centralrecovery.com
Web Site: centralrecoverypress.com
Key Personnel
Exec Ed: Nancy Schenck *E-mail:* nschenck@centralrecovery.com
Publr: Bob Gray *E-mail:* bgray@centralrecovery.com
Mng Ed: Valerie Killeen *E-mail:* vkilleen@centralrecovery.com
Sales & Mktg Mgr: Patrick Hughes *E-mail:* phughes@centralrecovery.com
Spec Sales Mgr: John Davis
A progressive publishing company that sheds new light on an age-old problem: addiction. We hope to break the stigma of addiction by publishing quality books that holistically address the nature of this devastating disease. Offer a diverse selection of titles focused on recovery, addiction treatment & behavioral health topics. Our mission is to positively impact recovering individuals: their families, friends & allies, the behavioral health care field & the general public by creating, publishing & distributing a broad variety of unique & fresh publications that embrace best practices in addiction recovery & behavioral health care.
ISBN Prefix(es): 978-0-9799869
Number of titles published annually: 12 Print; 6 E-Book
Total Titles: 20 Print; 20 E-Book

The Century Foundation Press
Division of The Century Foundation
One Whitehall St, 15th fl, New York, NY 10004
Tel: 212-452-7700 *Fax:* 212-535-7534
E-mail: info@tcf.org
Web Site: www.tcf.org
Key Personnel
Pres: Mark Zuckerman
Edit Dir: Jason Renker *Tel:* 212-452-7715 *E-mail:* renker@tcf.org
Chief Admin Offr: Philip Li *E-mail:* li@tcf.org
Mgr, Pub Affs & Special Events: Lucy Muirhead *E-mail:* lucy@tcf.org
Founded: 1984
Reports of task forces, papers & books covering international & domestic policy issues.
ISBN Prefix(es): 978-0-87078
Number of titles published annually: 3 Print
Total Titles: 185 Print
Branch Office(s)
1333 "H" St NW, 10th fl, Washington, DC 20005 *Tel:* 202-387-0400 *Fax:* 202-483-9430
Distribution Center: The Brookings Institution, 1775 Massachusetts Ave NW, Washington, DC 20036 *Tel:* 410-516-6956 *Toll Free Tel:* 800-537-5487

§Chain Store Guide (CSG)
10117 Princess Palm Ave, Suite 375, Tampa, FL 33610
Tel: 813-627-6957 *Toll Free Tel:* 800-927-9292 (orders) *Fax:* 813-627-6888
E-mail: info@csgis.com
Web Site: www.csgis.com
Key Personnel
VP: Carmen Vasquez-Perez
Dir, Prodn: Scott Mitchell
Mkt Res Ed: Lauren McCollum
Founded: 1934
Directories of retail & wholesale companies.
ISBN Prefix(es): 978-0-86730
Number of titles published annually: 8 Print
Total Titles: 21 Print; 21 Online

Chalice Press
Division of Christian Board of Publications
483 E Lockwood Ave, Suite 100, St Louis, MO 63119
SAN: 201-4408
Tel: 314-231-8500 *Toll Free Tel:* 800-366-3383 *Fax:* 314-231-8524; 770-280-4039 (orders)
E-mail: customerservice@chalicepress.com
Web Site: www.chalicepress.com
Key Personnel
Pres & Publr: Brad Lyons *E-mail:* blyons@chalicepress.com
VP, Opers: Lynne Letchworth *E-mail:* lletchworth@chalicepress.com
Dir, Sales & Mktg: Steve Knight *E-mail:* sknight@chalicepress.com
Founded: 1911
Religion (Protestant) & hymnals.
ISBN Prefix(es): 978-0-8272
Number of titles published annually: 25 Print
Total Titles: 400 Print
Distributed by Cokesbury
Orders to: PO Box 933119, Atlanta, GA 31193-3119
Returns: 3280 Summit Ridge Pkwy, Suite 100, Duluth, GA 30096 *Fax:* 770-280-4039
Warehouse: 3280 Summit Ridge Pkwy, Suite 100, Duluth, GA 30096 *Fax:* 770-280-4039
Distribution Center: Bookmasters, 30 Amberwood Pkwy, Ashland, OH 44805

Sperlings Church Supply, 85 Bathurst Dr, Waterloo, ON N2V 1Z4, Canada *Toll Free Tel:* 888-838-6626 *Fax:* 519-725-0668
Rainbow Book Agencies, 303 Arthur St, Fairfield, Victoria 3078, Australia *Tel:* 9481-6611 *Fax:* 9481-2371 *E-mail:* rba@rainbowbooks.com.au

§Channel Photographics
980 Lincoln Ave, Suite 200-B, San Rafael, CA 94901
Tel: 415-456-2934 *Fax:* 415-456-4124
Web Site: www.channelphotographics.com
Key Personnel
Co-Publr: Adrianne Casey *E-mail:* adrianne@channelphotographics.com
Publr: Steven Goff *E-mail:* steven@channelphotographics.com
ISBN Prefix(es): 978-0-9819942; 978-0-9744029; 978-0-9766708; 978-0-9773399; 978-0-9826137; 978-0-9832983
Number of titles published annually: 10 Print
Total Titles: 50 Print
Branch Office(s)
244 Fifth Ave, Suite 2464, New York, NY 10001 *Tel:* 212-627-1400 *Toll Free Fax:* 866-729-2725
16510 203 Place NE, Woodinville, WA 98077 *Tel:* 425-354-3690; 206-390-9617 (cell) *Fax:* 425-354-3664
Foreign Office(s): 8 Commercial Tower, 30/F, Unit 06-07, 8 Sun Yip St, Chai Wan, Hong Kong
Via Meucci 24, 37036 San Martino Buon Albergo, Verona VR, Italy *Tel:* (045) 994855 *Fax:* (045) 994746

Chaosium Inc
22568 Mission Blvd, Suite 423, Hayward, CA 94541-5116
SAN: 692-6460
Tel: 510-583-1000 *Fax:* 510-583-1101
Web Site: www.chaosium.com
Key Personnel
Pres: Greg Stafford *Tel:* 510-583-1000 *Fax:* 510-583-1101
Founded: 1975
Publisher of horror anthologies & role playing games.
ISBN Prefix(es): 978-0-933635; 978-1-56882
Number of titles published annually: 15 Print; 12 E-Book
Total Titles: 241 Print; 60 E-Book
Returns: 728 "A" St, Hayward, CA 94541
Warehouse: 728 "A" St, Hayward, CA 94541

Character Publishing
6340 Kiln Delisle Rd, Unit F, Pass Christian, MS 39571
Tel: 228-234-7651 *Fax:* 228-222-3321
Web Site: www.characterpublishing.org
Key Personnel
Owner: Jerusha Bosarge *E-mail:* jbosarge@characterpublishing.org
Founded: 2010
Specialize in books that nurture a particular character trait(s) in children, listed in a gold seal on the book cover to simplify book selection.
ISBN Prefix(es): 978-0-9839355; 978-0-9890797
Number of titles published annually: 10 Print; 6 E-Book
Total Titles: 6 Print
Distribution Center: Amazon.com *Tel:* 206-266-7180 *E-mail:* amazon-pr@amazon.com *Web Site:* www.amazon.com
Baker & Taylor, 2550 W Tyvola Rd, Suite 300, Charlotte, NC 28217 *Toll Free Tel:* 800-775-1800 *E-mail:* btinfo@baker-taylor.com *Web Site:* www.btol.com
Barnes & Noble, 76 Ninth Ave, New York, NY 10011 *Toll Free Tel:* 800-843-2665 *E-mail:* info@bn.com *Web Site:* www.barnesandnoble.com
Ingram, One Ingram Blvd, La Vergne, TN 37086, Contact: Stephen Merritt *Toll Free Tel:* 800-937-8222 ext 28309 *E-mail:* stephen.merritt@ingramcontent.com *Web Site:* www.ingrambook.com
NACSCORP, 528 E Lorain St, Oberlin, OH 44074-1298 *Toll Free Tel:* 800-321-3883 *E-mail:* service@nacscorp.com *Web Site:* www.nacscorp.com
Membership(s): The Association of Publishers for Special Sales; The Independent Book Publishers Association

Charisma Media
600 Rinehart Rd, Lake Mary, FL 32746
Tel: 407-333-0600 (all imprints) *Toll Free Tel:* 800-283-8494 (Charisma Media, Siloam Press, Creation House); 800-665-1468 *Fax:* 407-333-7100 (all imprints)
E-mail: charisma@charismamedia.com
Web Site: www.charismamedia.com
Key Personnel
Owner & Pres: Stephen Strang
Founded: 1975
Christianity.
ISBN Prefix(es): 978-0-88419
Number of titles published annually: 200 Print
Total Titles: 500 Print; 2 Audio
Imprints: Casa Creation (international publishing group); Creation House (co-publishing group); Siloam Press (health publishing group)
Membership(s): CBA: The Association for Christian Retail; Evangelical Christian Publishers Association

CharismaLife Publishers
600 Rinehart Rd, Lake Mary, FL 32746
Tel: 407-333-0600 *Toll Free Tel:* 800-451-4598 *Fax:* 407-333-7100
E-mail: charismalife@charismamedia.com
Web Site: www.charismamedia.com
Key Personnel
Owner & Pres: Stephen Strang *E-mail:* steve.strang@strang.com
Founded: 1990
Christian education materials such as: Sunday school curriculum, children's church programs, youth resources, training conferences.
ISBN Prefix(es): 978-1-57405
Number of titles published annually: 20 Print
Total Titles: 40 Print
Distributor for CharismaLife

§The Charles Press, Publishers
Subsidiary of The Oxbridge Corp
230 N 21 St, Suite 202, Philadelphia, PA 19103
Tel: 215-561-2786 *Fax:* 215-561-0191
E-mail: mail@charlespresspub.com
Web Site: www.charlespresspub.com
Key Personnel
Pres & Publr: Lauren Meltzer *E-mail:* lauren@charlespresspub.com
Prodn Mgr: Brad Fisher *E-mail:* brad@charlespresspub.com
Founded: 1983
Independent publishing house that specializes in scholarly, professional & trade books on the subjects of mental & physical health for professional (doctors, nurses, psychologists, etc), those involved in health care delivery & those receiving +/or in need of health care.
ISBN Prefix(es): 978-0-914783
Number of titles published annually: 8 Print
Total Titles: 133 Print; 1 CD-ROM; 1 Online
Returns: c/o Self-Service Storage, 2000 Hamilton St, No 2884, Philadelphia, PA 19130 (permission must be requested in advance of returns)

Charles River Media
Imprint of Cengage Learning
20 Channel Center St, Boston, MA 02210
Toll Free Tel: 800-354-9706 *Toll Free Fax:* 800-487-8488
E-mail: crminfo@cengage.com
Web Site: www.cengage.com; www.delmarlearning.com/charlesriver
Founded: 1994
Publishing computer books for web development, music technology, game development, graphic design & digital video.
ISBN Prefix(es): 978-1-886801; 978-1-58450
Number of titles published annually: 50 Print; 2 CD-ROM; 150 Online; 100 E-Book
Total Titles: 200 Print; 5 CD-ROM; 150 Online; 100 E-Book
Foreign Rep(s): IPR (Middle East); Login Brothers (Canada); Thomson Learning (Asia); Transatlantic (Europe); Woodslane (Australia)
Foreign Rights: David Pallai

Charles Scribner's Sons®
Imprint of Gale
27500 Drake Rd, Farmington Hills, MI 48331-3535
Toll Free Tel: 800-877-4253 *Toll Free Fax:* 800-414-5043
E-mail: gale.galeord@cengage.com
Web Site: www.gale.com/scribners
Founded: 1846
Publishes reference books in fields of history, science & literature for audiences ranging from high school students to professional researchers.
ISBN Prefix(es): 978-0-684
Number of titles published annually: 4 E-Book

Charlesbridge Publishing Inc
85 Main St, Watertown, MA 02472
Tel: 617-926-0329 *Toll Free Tel:* 800-225-3214 *Fax:* 617-926-5720 *Toll Free Fax:* 800-926-5775
E-mail: books@charlesbridge.com
Web Site: www.charlesbridge.com
Key Personnel
Pres & Publr: Brent Farmer *E-mail:* bfarmer@charlesbridge.com
EVP & Assoc Publr: Mary Ann Sabia *E-mail:* masabia@charlesbridge.com
VP & Publr, Imagine Imprint: Charles Nurnberg
VP, Prodn: Brian Walker *E-mail:* bwalker@charlesbridge.com
Art Dir: Susan Sherman *E-mail:* ssherman@charlesbridge.com
Edit Dir: Yolanda LeRoy *E-mail:* yolanda@charlesbridge.com
Founded: 1980
Children's illustrated picture books, board books, early readers, chapter books, middle grade fiction & nonfiction. Adult general trade, cookbooks, puzzle/game, humor & supplemental educational materials K-8.
ISBN Prefix(es): 978-0-88106; 978-1-57091; 978-1-56566; 978-0-934738; 978-1-890674; 978-1-879085; 978-1-58089; 978-1-936140 (Imagine)
Number of titles published annually: 50 Print; 40 E-Book
Total Titles: 600 Print; 436 E-Book
Imprints: Imagine Publishing
Distributed by Penguin Random House Canada Limited
Distributor for American Express (travel & leisure, food & wine); EarlyLight Books
Foreign Rights: Thomas Allen & Son Ltd (Canada)
Orders to: Random House Publisher Services, 400 Hahn Rd, Westminster, MD 21157 *Toll Free Tel:* 800-733-3000
Returns: Random House Inc, 1019 N State Rd 47, Crawfordsville, IN 47933
Distribution Center: Random House Publisher Services, 400 Hahn Rd, Westminster, MD 21157 *E-mail:* distribution@randomhouse.com
Membership(s): ABA; ALA; Association of Booksellers for Children; Bookbuilders of

Boston; The Children's Book Council; Education Market Association; International Literacy Association; MSA; NAIPR; NCBA; NEBA; TLA

§Chelsea Green Publishing Co
85 N Main St, Suite 120, White River Junction, VT 05001
SAN: 669-7631
Tel: 802-295-6300 *Toll Free Tel:* 800-639-4099 (cust serv, consumer & trade orders) *Fax:* 802-295-6444
Web Site: www.chelseagreen.com
Key Personnel
Pres & Publr: Margo Baldwin *E-mail:* mbaldwin@chelseagreen.com
Busn & Dist Dir: Sandi Eaton *E-mail:* seaton@chelseagreen.com
Communs Dir: Shay Totten *E-mail:* stotten@chelseagreen.com
Prodn Dir: Patricia Stone *E-mail:* pstone@chelseagreen.com
Sr Ed & Subs Rts Mgr: Brianne Goodspeed *E-mail:* bgoodspeed@chelseagreen.com
Sr Ed: Fern Marshall Bradley *E-mail:* fbradley@chelseagreen.com; Joni Praded *E-mail:* jpraded@chelseagreen.com; Ben Watson *E-mail:* bwatson@chelseagreen.com
Author Events Mgr: Jenna Stewart *E-mail:* jstewart@chelseagreen.com
Spec & Corp Sales Mgr: Darrell Koerner *E-mail:* dkoerner@chelseagreen.com
Trade Sales Mgr: Michael Weaver *E-mail:* mweaver@chelseagreen.com
Founded: 1984
Books for sustainable living including: environment, building, nature, outdoors, sustainability, organic gardening, home, renewable energy, homesteading, politics & current events.
ISBN Prefix(es): 978-0-930031; 978-1-890132; 978-1-933392; 978-1-60358
Number of titles published annually: 35 Print; 35 E-Book
Total Titles: 300 Print; 250 E-Book
Distributor for AATEC Publications; American Council for an Energy Efficient Economy (ACEEE); Anomaly Press; Avalon House; Boye Knives Press; Cal-Earth; Earth Pledge; Eco Logic Books; Ecological Design Institute; Ecological Design Press; Empowerment Institute; Filaree Productions; Flower Press; Foundation for Deep Ecology; Fox Maple Press; Green Books; Green Building Press; Green Man Publishing; Groundworks; Hand Print Press; Holmgren Design Services; Jenkins Publishing; Knossus Project; Left To Write Press; Madison Area Community Supported Agriculture Coalition; Marion Institute; marketumbrella.org; Metamorphic Press; Moneta Publications; Ottographics; Peregrinzilla; Permanent Publications; Daniela Piazza Editore; Polyface; Rainsource Press; Raven Press; Anita Roddick Publications; Rural Science Institute; Seed Savers; Service Employees International Union; Slow Food Editore; Solar Design Association; Stonefield Publishing; Sun Plans Inc; Sustainability Press; Trailblazer Press; Trust for Public Land; Yes Books
Foreign Rep(s): Codasat: Hargreaves, Fuller, Paton (Canada)
Warehouse: c/o Claremont Ctr, 425 Washington St, No 185, Claremont, NH 03743, Warehouse Mgr: Dianna Hart *Tel:* 802-295-6300 ext 124 *E-mail:* persephone@emlot.com

Chelsea House Publishers
Imprint of Infobase Learning
132 W 31 St, 17th fl, New York, NY 10001
SAN: 169-7331
Tel: 212-967-8800 *Toll Free Tel:* 800-322-8755 *Fax:* 917-339-0325 *Toll Free Fax:* 800-678-3633
E-mail: custserv@factsonfile.com
Web Site: www.infobasepublishing.com; www.infobaselearning.com
Key Personnel
Chmn: Mark McDonnell
CFO: Jim Housley
Dir, Publicity: Laurie Katz
Dir, Opers & Sales: Mark Zielinski
Dir, Mktg: Zina Scarpulla
Edit Dir: Laurie Likoff
Dir, Licensing & Intl Sales: Ben Jacobs
Founded: 1966
Offers timely & engaging young adult sets & series ebooks spanning a wide variety of subject areas. Chelsea Clubhouse, its elementary imprint, presents easy-to-read, full-color books for young readers in grades 2-6.
ISBN Prefix(es): 978-0-87754; 978-0-7910; 978-1-55546; 978-1-60413; 978-1-4381; 978-1-61753
Number of titles published annually: 230 E-Book
Total Titles: 1,866 Print; 1,680 E-Book
Imprints: Chelsea Clubhouse
Returns: Chelsea House Publishers Returns Dept, c/o Maple Press Distribution Ctr, 704 Legionaire Dr, Fredericksburg, PA 17026
Warehouse: c/o Maple Press Distribution Ctr, 704 Legionaire Dr, Fredericksburg, PA 17026
Distribution Center: c/o Maple Press Distribution Ctr, 704 Legionaire Dr, Fredericksburg, PA 17026
Membership(s): AAP; ALA

§Cheng & Tsui Co Inc
25 West St, 2nd fl, Boston, MA 02111-1213
Tel: 617-988-2401 *Toll Free Tel:* 800-554-1963 *Fax:* 617-426-3669; 617-556-8964
E-mail: service@cheng-tsui.com; orders@cheng-tsui.com
Web Site: www.cheng-tsui.com
Key Personnel
Pres: Jill Cheng
Founded: 1979
Publisher, importer & exporter of Asian books in English. Publish & distribute Asia related books & Chinese, Japanese & Korean language learning textbooks.
ISBN Prefix(es): 978-0-917056; 978-0-88727
Number of titles published annually: 30 Print
Total Titles: 640 Print; 75 CD-ROM; 4 Online; 4 E-Book
Distributor for Action Language Learning; aha! Chinese; Bider Technology; Cengage Learning Australia; China International Book Trading Co (Beijing, selected titles only); China Soft; China Sprout; Crabtree Publishing; Curriculum Corporation; Facets Video; Ilchokak Publishers; Italian School of East Asian Studies; JPT America Inc; Oxford University Press; Pan Asian Publications; Panmun Academic Services; Panpac Education; Paradigm Busters; Pearson Australia; Royal Asiatic Society (Korea Branch); SMC Publishing; Sogang University Institute; Stone Bridge Press; SUP Publishing Logistics; Tuttle Publishing; US International Publishing; White Rabbit Press; Yale University Press; Zeitgeist Films
Warehouse: Publishers Storage & Shipping Corp, 46 Development Rd, Fitchburg, MA 01420 *Tel:* 978-345-2121 ext 223 *Fax:* 978-348-1233 *Web Site:* www.pssc.com

§Cherry Hill Publishing LLC
24344 Del Amo Rd, Ramona, CA 92065
SAN: 255-0075
Tel: 858-829-5550 *Toll Free Tel:* 800-407-1072 *Fax:* 760-203-1200
E-mail: operations@cherryhillpublishing.com; sales@cherryhillpublishing.com
Web Site: www.cherryhillpublishing.com
Key Personnel
Pres: Rick Roane *E-mail:* rick@cherryhillpublishing.com
Returns: Sharon Roane *Tel:* 858-735-5397 *E-mail:* sharon@cherryhillpublishing.com
Founded: 2002
Publisher of audiobook titles.
ISBN Prefix(es): 978-0-9843759; 978-0-9723298; 978-0-9830086; 978-1-937028; 978-1-62079
Number of titles published annually: 5 CD-ROM; 20 Online; 5 E-Book; 15 Audio
Total Titles: 1 Print; 10 CD-ROM; 125 Online; 40 E-Book; 90 Audio
Distribution Center: Baker & Taylor, 2550 W Tyvola Rd, Suite 300, Charlotte, NC 28217 *Toll Free Tel:* 800-775-1800 *Fax:* 704-998-3100 *Web Site:* www.btol.com
Midwest Tape, 6950 Hall St, Holland, OH 43528 *Toll Free Tel:* 800-875-2785 *Toll Free Fax:* 800-444-6645 *E-mail:* info@midwesttapes.com *Web Site:* www.midwesttapes.com
Membership(s): Audio Publishers Association

Chestnut Hills Press, see BrickHouse Books Inc

Chicago Review Press
814 N Franklin St, Chicago, IL 60610
Tel: 312-337-0747 *Toll Free Tel:* 800-888-4741 *Fax:* 312-337-5110
E-mail: frontdesk@chicagoreviewpress.com
Web Site: www.chicagoreviewpress.com
Key Personnel
Publr: Cynthia Sherry
Mng Ed: Allison Felus
Mktg Mgr: Mary Kravenas
Sr Ed: Jerome Pohlen; Lisa Reardon; Yuval Taylor
Founded: 1973
ISBN Prefix(es): 978-1-56976; 978-1-55652; 978-1-88305 (Ball Publishing)
Number of titles published annually: 65 Print; 65 E-Book
Total Titles: 1,000 Print; 1,000 E-Book
Imprints: A Cappella Books; Academy Chicago Publishers; Ball Publishing; Lawrence Hill Books; Zephyr Press
Divisions: Independent Publishers Group
Foreign Rights: The Susan Schulman Agency (Worldwide)
Distribution Center: Independent Publishers Group *Fax:* 312-337-5985 *E-mail:* frontdesk@ipgbook.com *Web Site:* www.ipgbook.com
See separate listing for:
Academy Chicago

Child Welfare League of America (CWLA)
1726 "M" St, Suite 500, Washington, DC 20036
SAN: 201-9876
Tel: 202-688-4200 *Fax:* 202-833-1689
E-mail: cwla@cwla.org
Web Site: www.cwla.org/publications
Key Personnel
Dir, Mktg: Karen Dunn *E-mail:* kdunn@cwla.org
Founded: 1920
Provide relevant & timely publications that enable CWLA members & the child welfare field at large to improve services to children & their families.
ISBN Prefix(es): 978-0-87868; 978-1-58760
Number of titles published annually: 9 Print
Total Titles: 167 Print
Imprints: CWLA Press
Billing Address: CWLA, PO Box 345, Mount Morris, IL 61054-9834
Orders to: CWLA, PO Box 345, Mount Morris, IL 61054-9834 *Tel:* 770-280-4164 *Toll Free Tel:* 800-407-6273 *E-mail:* order@cwla.org
Returns: PBD Inc, c/o CWLA, 420 Eagleview Blvd, Exton, PA 19341
Shipping Address: PBD Inc, c/o CWLA, 420 Eagleview Blvd, Exton, PA 19341
Warehouse: PBD Inc, c/o CWLA, 420 Eagleview Blvd, Exton, PA 19341
Distribution Center: PBD Inc, c/o CWLA, 420 Eagleview Blvd, Exton, PA 19341

Children's Book Press
Imprint of Lee & Low Books
95 Madison Ave, Suite 1205, New York, NY 10016
Tel: 212-779-4400 *Fax:* 212-683-1894
E-mail: general@leeandlow.com; orders@leeandlow.com; sales@leeandlow.com
Web Site: www.leeandlow.com
Key Personnel
Pres: Craig Low
Opers & Client Servs Mgr: John Man
Founded: 1975
Multicultural & bilingual picture books for children. Central American, African-American, Asian-American, Hispanic-American, Native American tales, folklore, contemporary fiction & nonfiction.
ISBN Prefix(es): 978-0-89239
Number of titles published annually: 6 Print
Total Titles: 30 Print
Distribution Center: Ingram Books, One Ingram Blvd, La Vergne, TN 37086 *Tel:* 615-793-5000 *Toll Free Tel:* 800-932-8200 *E-mail:* customerservice@ingrambook.com *Web Site:* www.ingrambook.com

Child's Play®
Affiliate of Child's Play (International) Ltd
250 Minot Ave, Auburn, ME 04210
Tel: 207-784-7252 *Toll Free Tel:* 800-639-6404 *Fax:* 207-784-7358 *Toll Free Fax:* 800-854-6989
E-mail: chpmaine@aol.com; cplay@earthlink.net
Web Site: www.childs-play.com
Key Personnel
VP, Sales & Mktg: Joseph Gardner *Tel:* 973-761-4555 *Fax:* 973-761-1555 *E-mail:* joe@childsplayusa.com
Gen Mgr: Laurie Reynolds *E-mail:* laurie@childsplayusa.com
Founded: 1972
Children's books, games, toys & AV materials.
ISBN Prefix(es): 978-0-85953; 978-1-904550; 978-1-84643
Number of titles published annually: 30 Print
Total Titles: 450 Print; 8 Audio

§The Child's World Inc
1980 Lookout Dr, North Mankato, MN 56003-1705
Tel: 507-385-1044 *Toll Free Tel:* 800-599-READ (599-7323) *Toll Free Fax:* 888-320-2329
E-mail: sales@childsworld.com
Web Site: childsworld.com
Key Personnel
Pres: Mike Peterson
Off Mgr: Amy Dols
Founded: 1968
K-8 library books for childhood education; social studies.
ISBN Prefix(es): 978-0-89565; 978-0-913778; 978-1-56766; 978-1-59296; 978-1-60253; 978-1-60954; 978-1-60973; 978-1-61473; 978-1-62323; 978-1-62687; 978-1-63143; 978-1-63407; 978-1-5038
Number of titles published annually: 200 Print; 100 E-Book
Total Titles: 850 Print; 1,018 E-Book
Imprints: Tradition Books
Distributor for Tradition Books

Childswork/Childsplay LLC
Subsidiary of The Guidance Group Inc
303 Crossway Park Dr, Woodbury, NY 11797
Toll Free Tel: 800-962-1141 (cust serv) *Toll Free Fax:* 800-262-1886 (orders)
Web Site: www.childswork.com
Founded: 1985
Psychological books, toys, games & counseling tools to assist counselors, therapists, teachers & parents help children cope with emotional & behavioral problems.
ISBN Prefix(es): 978-1-58815; 978-1-882732; 978-1-931704
Number of titles published annually: 85 Print
Orders to: PO Box 1246, Wilkes-Barre, PA 18703-1246
Returns: c/o Karol Media, 375 Stewart Rd, Wilkes-Barre, PA 18706-1246

§China Books
Division of Sinomedia International Group
360 Swift Ave, Suite 48, South San Francisco, CA 94080
SAN: 169-0167
Tel: 650-872-7076 *Toll Free Tel:* 800-818-2017 (US only) *Fax:* 650-872-7808
E-mail: info@chinabooks.com
Web Site: www.chinabooks.com
Key Personnel
Gen Mgr: Xin Wang
Sales Mgr: Kelly Feng *Tel:* 650-872-7076 ext 310 *E-mail:* kelly@chinabooks.com
Founded: 1960
Fiction, trade, nonfiction, dictionaries, encyclopedias, maps, atlases, periodicals, sidelines, foreign language, secondary textbooks, juvenile & young adult, subscription & mail order, hardcover & paperback trade books; government, language arts, travel.
ISBN Prefix(es): 978-0-8351
Number of titles published annually: 10 Print
Total Titles: 750 Print
Distributor for AsiaPac; CIBTC; Commercial Press; Foreign Languages Press; Joint Publishers; New World Press; Panda Books; Peace Books; Red Mansions Publishing

Chosen Books
Division of Baker Publishing Group
11400 Hampshire Ave S, Bloomington, MN 55438-2852
Tel: 616-676-9185 *Toll Free Tel:* 800-877-2665 (orders only) *Fax:* 616-676-9573 *Toll Free Fax:* 800-398-3111 (orders only)
Web Site: bakerpublishinggroup.com/chosen
Key Personnel
Pres, Baker Publishing Group: Dwight Baker
Edit Dir: Jane Campbell *E-mail:* jcampbell@chosenbooks.com
Founded: 1971
Christian.
ISBN Prefix(es): 978-0-8007
Number of titles published annually: 25 Print
Total Titles: 350 Print
Foreign Rep(s): Christian Art (South Africa); David C Cook Distribution (Canada); Family Reading Publications (Australia); Marston Book Services Ltd (Europe, UK); Soul Distributors Ltd (New Zealand)

§Christian Liberty Press
502 W Euclid Ave, Arlington Heights, IL 60004-5402
Tel: 847-259-4444 *Toll Free Tel:* 800-832-2741 (cust serv) *Fax:* 847-259-2941
E-mail: custserv@christianlibertypress.com
Web Site: www.shopchristianliberty.com
Key Personnel
Dir: Lars Johnson *E-mail:* larsj@christianlibertypress.com
Founded: 1984
Publisher of Christian education materials.
ISBN Prefix(es): 978-1-930092; 978-1-930367; 978-1-932971; 978-1-935796; 978-1-62982
Number of titles published annually: 6 Print; 3 CD-ROM; 4 Audio
Total Titles: 150 Print; 8 CD-ROM; 38 Audio
Distribution Center: STL Distribution, 100 Biblica Way, Elizabethton, TN 37643 *Toll Free Tel:* 800-289-2772 *Toll Free Fax:* 800-759-2779
Membership(s): CBA: The Association for Christian Retail

Christian Light Publications Inc
1051 Mount Clinton Pike, Harrisonburg, VA 22802
Mailing Address: PO Box 1212, Harrisonburg, VA 22803-1212
Tel: 540-434-1003 *Toll Free Tel:* 800-776-0478 *Fax:* 540-433-8896
E-mail: info@clp.org; orders@clp.org
Web Site: www.clp.org
Key Personnel
Gen Mgr: Andrew Criler
Secy, Bd of Dirs: Merna B Shank *E-mail:* mernas@clp.org
Founded: 1969
Books, booklets, tracts, Sunday school, vacation Bible school & Christian day school curriculum.
ISBN Prefix(es): 978-0-87813
Number of titles published annually: 17 Print
Total Titles: 160 Print

Christian Schools International
3350 E Paris Ave SE, Grand Rapids, MI 49512-3054
SAN: 204-1804
Tel: 616-957-1070 *Toll Free Tel:* 800-635-8288 *Fax:* 616-957-5022
E-mail: info@csionline.org
Web Site: www.csionline.org
Key Personnel
CEO & Pres: David Koetje *Tel:* 616-957-1070 ext 254 *E-mail:* dkoetje@csionline.org
VP, Corp Devt & Innovation: Darryl Shelton *Tel:* 616-957-1070 ext 257 *E-mail:* dshelton@csionline.org
VP, Mktg: Jane Mulder *Tel:* 616-957-1070 ext 235 *E-mail:* jmulder@csionline.org
Founded: 1920
Classroom curriculum resources for students & teachers.
ISBN Prefix(es): 978-0-87463; 978-1-935876
Number of titles published annually: 18 Print; 2 CD-ROM
Total Titles: 172 Print; 11 CD-ROM
Imprints: CSI Publications

§The Christian Science Publishing Society
Division of The First Church of Christ, Scientist
210 Massachusetts Ave, Boston, MA 02115
Tel: 617-450-2000 *Toll Free Tel:* 800-288-7090 *Fax:* 617-450-7334
E-mail: contact@csps.com
Web Site: christianscience.com
Key Personnel
Mgr: Michael Zanoni
Founded: 1879
Books on healing, health & spirituality; major title: *Science & Health with Key to the Scriptures* by Mary Baker Eddy, available in 16 languages & English braille.
ISBN Prefix(es): 978-0-87952
Number of titles published annually: 17 Print
Total Titles: 17 Print

Chronicle Books LLC
680 Second St, San Francisco, CA 94107
SAN: 202-165X
Tel: 415-537-4200 *Toll Free Tel:* 800-759-0190 (cust serv) *Fax:* 415-537-4460 *Toll Free Fax:* 800-858-7787 (orders); 800-286-9471 (cust serv)
E-mail: frontdesk@chroniclebooks.com
Web Site: www.chroniclebooks.com
Key Personnel
Chmn & CEO: Nion McEvoy
Pres: Jack Jensen
VP, Opers & Fin: Tom Fernald
VP, Sales & Mktg: Tyrrell Mahoney
Publr: Christine Carswell
Exec Dir, Busn Devt: Sarah Williams
Exec Dir, HR: Todd Presley
Exec Dir, Mktg & Publicity: Liza Algar

Exec Dir, Opers: John Carlson
Exec Dir, Prodn: Shona Burns
Exec Edit Dir, Entertainment: Sarah Malarkey
Exec Publg Design Dir: Sara Schneider
Publg Dir, Children's: Ginee Seo
Publg Dir, Food & Drink/Lifestyle: Lorena Jones
Edit Dir, Art Publg: Christina Amini
Edit Dir, Children's: Kelli Chipponeri
Design Dir: Kristen Hewitt
Design Dir, Mktg Communs: Liz Rico
Dir, Trade Sales: Rachel Geiger
Intl Sales & Subs Rts Dir: Johan Almqvist
Mktg Dir, Adult Trade: Albee Dalbotten
Sales Dir, Mass Mkt, Premiums & Licensing: Lynda Zuber Sassi
Assoc Dir, Online Mktg: Ali Presley
Natl Acct Mgr, Spec Mkts: Julia Carvalho
Natl Sales Mgr: Tim Wright
Sr Client Acct Mgr: Liz Marotte
Sr Mgr, Mktg & Publicity-Children's Books Div: Sally Kim
Sr Prodn Mgr, Format Devt: Erin Thacker
Foreign Rts Mgr: Jenifer Savasta
Inventory Planning Mgr: Mary O'Hara
Food & Drink Mktg & Publicity Mgr: Amy Cleary
Lifestyle Mktg & Publicity Mgr: Stephanie Wong
Mktg Mgr, Entertainment & Art: Sandy Smith
Mgr, Prodn & Creative Systems: Tim Wudurski
Assoc Mktg Mgr, Children's: Hannah Moushabeck
Assoc Sales Mgr, Spec Mkts & Mass Mkts: Erynn Im-Sato
Web Mgr: Viniita Moran
Sr Dist Client Coord: Graham Barry; Mercury Ellis
Children's Mktg Coord: Jaime Wong
Events Coord: Julia Patrick
Mng Ed, Lifestyle Group: Sara Golski
Ed: Elizabeth Yarborough
Ed, Children's Group: Naomi Kirsten; Tamra Tuller
Ed, Food & Drink Group: Sarah Billingsley
Ed, Lifestyle: Laura Lee Mattingly
Proj Ed, Entertainment Publg Group: Kim Romero
Assoc Ed, Children's Group: Ariel Richardson
Asst Ed: Courtney Drew; Caitlin Kirkpatrick
Asst Ed, Children's Group: Taylor Norman
Sr Children's Book Designer: Ryan Hayes
Sr Indus Designer: Ben Laramie
Sr Prodn Developer: Yolanda Cazares
Sr Publicist, Children's Publg: Lara Starr
Sr Publicist, Entertainment: April Whitney
Dist Fin Analyst: Barrett Hooper
Design Studio Mgr: Meghan Nowell
Sr Designer: Allison Weiner
Sr Designer, Digital Mktg: Laura Bagnato
Children's Book Designer: Tara Creehan
Designer: Anne Kenady
Jr Designer, MarCom: Alina Buevich
Visual Content Coord: Irene Kim
Founded: 1967
General nonfiction & fiction, cloth & paperbound: fine arts, gift, nature, outdoors, nationwide regional guidebooks, stationery, calendars & ancillary products.
ISBN Prefix(es): 978-0-87701; 978-0-8118; 978-0-938491; 978-1-4521
Number of titles published annually: 300 Print
Total Titles: 1,500 Print
Distributor for Blue Apple Books; Handprint Books; Laurence King Publishing; Moleskine; Princeton Architectural Press; Quadrille Publishing; SmartLab; SmartsCo
Foreign Rep(s): A-Z Africa Service (Anita Zih) (Eastern Africa, West Africa); Abrams & Chronicle Books (Europe, UK); Ampersand Inc (British Columbia, CN, Ontario, CN); Melanie Boesen (Denmark, Faroe Islands, Finland, Greenland, Iceland, Norway, Sweden); Bookreps NZ Ltd (New Zealand); Michelle Curreri & Sonja Merz (Asia exc China & Japan, India); Everest Int'l Publishing (Wei Zhao) (China); John Fitzpatrick (Ireland); Tiffany Georges (France); Hachette UK Ltd (Matthew Cowdery) (Algeria, Bahrain, Egypt, Iran, Iraq, Israel, Jordan, Kuwait, Lebanon, Libya, Morocco, Oman, Palestine, Saudi Arabia, Sudan, Syria, Tunisia, United Arab Emirates, Yemen); Hardie Grant Books (Australia); Hornblower Group Inc (Atlantic Canada, New Brunswick, CN, Nova Scotia, CN, Prince Edward Island, CN, Quebec, CN); JCC Enterprises Inc (Jerry C Carrillo) (Bermuda, Caribbean, Latin America); Cristian & Adriana Juncu (Eastern Europe, Russia); Padovani Books (Penny Padovani) (Italy, Portugal); Padovani Books (Isabella Curtis) (Greece); Padovani Books (Jenny Padovani Frias) (Spain); Publishers Group UK (Melanie Boesen) (Denmark, Faroe Islands, Finland, Greenland, Iceland, Norway, Sweden); Publishers Group UK (John Fitzpatrick) (Ireland); Publishers Group UK (Deborah Dyson) (Midlands, Northern England, Northern Wales, Scotland, Southern England, Southern Wales); Publishers Services (Gabriele Kern) (Austria, Germany, Switzerland); Raincoast Books (Canada); Real Books (South Africa); 62Damrak (Francine Siemer-Ankersmit) (Netherlands)
Foreign Rights: Bettina Nibbe (Germany); Nordin Agency (Netherlands, Scandinavia); Frederique Porretta (France); Tao Media (China)
See separate listing for:
Handprint Books Inc

Cider Mill Press Book Publishers LLC
12 Spring St, Kennebunkport, ME 04046
Mailing Address: PO Box 454, Kennebunkport, ME 04046
Tel: 207-967-8232 *Fax:* 207-967-8233
Web Site: www.cidermillpress.com
Key Personnel
Founder & Publr: John F Whalen, Jr *E-mail:* johnwhalen@cidermillpress.com
Sales & Mktg Coord: Emily Regis *E-mail:* emilyregis@cidermillpress.com
Publg Mgr: Alexandra Lewis *E-mail:* alewis@cidermillpress.com
Founded: 2005
Publish creative, innovative, inspiring & visually stunning books & gift books.
ISBN Prefix(es): 978-1-933662; 978-1-60433; 978-1-941868
Number of titles published annually: 50 Print; 4 Audio
Total Titles: 135 Print
Imprints: Applesauce Press; Cider Mill Press
Distributed by Simon & Schuster
Foreign Rights: Print Co Verlagsgesellschaft (Gabriella Scolik) (Europe)
Membership(s): ABA

Cinco Puntos Press
701 Texas Ave, El Paso, TX 79901
Tel: 915-838-1625 *Toll Free Tel:* 800-566-9072 *Fax:* 915-838-1635
E-mail: info@cincopuntos.com
Web Site: www.cincopuntos.com
Key Personnel
Co-Publr, Sr Ed & Pres: Lee Byrd *E-mail:* leebyrd@cincopuntos.com
Mktg Dir & CFO: John Byrd
Co-Publr & VP: Bobby Byrd *E-mail:* bbyrd@cincopuntos.com
Founded: 1985
Books of the Southwest US & bilingual children's literature.
ISBN Prefix(es): 978-0-938317
Number of titles published annually: 23 Print
Total Titles: 130 Print; 9 Audio
Foreign Rep(s): Publishers Group Canada (Canada)
Distribution Center: Consortium Book Sales & Distribution, The Keg House, Suite 101, 34 13 Ave NE, Minneapolis, MN 55413-1007, VP, Sales: Jim Nichols *Tel:* 612-746-2600 *Toll Free Tel:* 800-283-3572 (cust serv) *Fax:* 612-746-2606 *E-mail:* info@cbsd.com *Web Site:* www.cbsd.com SAN: 631-760X

§Circlet Press Inc
39 Hurlbut St, Cambridge, MA 02138
Toll Free Tel: 800-729-6423
E-mail: circletintern@gmail.com
Web Site: www.circlet.com
Key Personnel
Founder & Publr: Cecilia Tan *E-mail:* ctan.circletpress@gmail.com
Publicist: Ava Perry
Founded: 1992
Anthologies of erotic science fiction/fantasy, paranormal romance, alternative sexuality & fiction with transgender themes.
ISBN Prefix(es): 978-0-9633970; 978-1-885865
Number of titles published annually: 10 Print; 2 Online; 25 E-Book; 5 Audio
Total Titles: 100 Print; 2 Online; 50 E-Book; 5 Audio
Imprints: Circumflex (nonfiction & how-to on sexuality); Luster Editions (alternative sexuality fiction & erotica); The Ultra Violet Library (gay & lesbian; science fiction not erotic)
Distributed by SCB Distributors
Foreign Rep(s): Bulldog Books (Australia); Turnaround Ltd (Europe, UK)
Foreign Rights: Lawrence Schimel (all other territories)

Cistercian Publications
Imprint of Liturgical Press
Saint John's Abbey, PO Box 7500, Collegeville, MN 56321
SAN: 202-1668
Tel: 320-363-2213 *Toll Free Tel:* 800-436-8431 *Fax:* 320-363-3299 *Toll Free Fax:* 800-445-5899
E-mail: sales@litpress.org
Web Site: www.cistercianpublications.org
Key Personnel
Dir: Peter Dwyer
Founded: 1969
Religion (Roman Catholic) & history.
ISBN Prefix(es): 978-0-87907
Number of titles published annually: 15 Print
Total Titles: 212 Print
Distributed by Liturgical Press
Returns: Warepak LLC, 2427 Bond St, University Park, IL 60484 *Tel:* 708-534-2600 *Fax:* 708-534-7803 *Web Site:* www.ware-pak.com
Shipping Address: Warepak LLC, 2427 Bond St, University Park, IL 60484 *Tel:* 708-534-2600 *Fax:* 708-534-7803 *Web Site:* www.ware-pak.com

Citadel Press, see Kensington Publishing Corp

City Lights Publishers
261 Columbus Ave, San Francisco, CA 94133
SAN: 202-1684
Tel: 415-362-8193 *Fax:* 415-362-4921
E-mail: staff@citylights.com
Web Site: www.citylights.com
Key Personnel
Exec Dir & Publr: Elaine Katzenberger
PR & Mktg Dir: Stacey Lewis
Sr Ed & Subs Rts Dir: Robert Sharrard *E-mail:* sharrard@citylights.com
Open Media Series Founder & Ed: Greg Ruggiero
Publicity & Mktg Assoc: Chris Carosi
Founded: 1955
Publisher of progressive political nonfiction, innovative literature & poetry.
ISBN Prefix(es): 978-0-87286
Number of titles published annually: 15 Print
Total Titles: 200 Print
Foreign Rights: Agence Hoffman (France, Germany); Agenzia Letteraria Internazionale

(Italy); Carmen Balcells Agencia Literaria SA (Spain)
Distribution Center: Consortium Book Sales & Distribution, The Keg House, Suite 101, 34 13 Ave NE, Minneapolis, MN 55413-1007 *Tel:* 612-746-2600 *Toll Free Tel:* 800-283-3572 (cust serv) *Fax:* 612-351-5073 *E-mail:* orderentry@perseusbooks.com *Web Site:* www.cbsd.com

Clarion Books
Imprint of Houghton Mifflin Harcourt
215 Park Ave S, New York, NY 10003
Tel: 212-420-5889 *Toll Free Tel:* 800-225-3362 (orders) *Fax:* 212-420-5855 *Toll Free Fax:* 800-634-7568 (orders)
Web Site: www.hmhco.com
Key Personnel
Publr & Edit Dir: Dinah Stevenson
Sr Exec Ed: Anne Hoppe
Art Dir: Christine Kettner
Rts Mgr: Candace Finn
Assoc: Kate Green
Founded: 1965
Juvenile & young adult books, picture & chapter books, audiocassette packages.
ISBN Prefix(es): 978-0-89919; 978-0-395; 978-0-618
Number of titles published annually: 40 Print
Distributed by Houghton Mifflin Harcourt
Returns: 2700 N Richardt Ave, Indianapolis, IN 46219
Membership(s): The Children's Book Council

Clarity Press Inc
2625 Piedmont Rd NE, Suite 56, Atlanta, GA 30324
SAN: 688-9530
Toll Free Tel: 877-613-1495 (edit) *Toll Free Fax:* 877-613-7868
E-mail: claritypress@usa.net (foreign rts & perms)
Web Site: www.claritypress.com
Key Personnel
Edit Dir: Diana G Collier
Busn Mgr: Annette Gordon *E-mail:* businessmanager@claritypress.com
Founded: 1984
Scholarly works on contemporary justice & human rights issues.
ISBN Prefix(es): 978-0-932863
Number of titles published annually: 8 Print; 8 E-Book
Total Titles: 52 Print; 32 E-Book
Imprints: Clear Day Books (print-on-demand, rare books)
Foreign Rep(s): CIEL Book Distributors (Lebanon, Middle East); Marston Books (UK & the continent)
Foreign Rights: Luigi Celentano (Latin America, Spain); Chengdu Rightol Media (China)
Distribution Center: SCB Distributors, 15608 S New Century Dr, Gardena, CA 90248, Contact: Victor Duran *Tel:* 310-532-9400 *Toll Free Tel:* 800-729-6423 *Fax:* 310-532-7001 *E-mail:* victor@scbdistributors.com *Web Site:* www.scbdistributors.com
CIEL Book Co, Akef El Khoury Bldg, Dbayeh Hwy, Beirut, Lebanon (Middle East & North Africa) *Tel:* (04) 522149 ext 222 *Fax:* (04) 522144 *Web Site:* www.ciel.me
Marston Book Services Ltd, 160 Milton Park, Abingdon, Oxon OX14 4SD, United Kingdom (includes Europe) *Tel:* (01235) 465576 *Fax:* (01235) 465555 *E-mail:* trade.orders@marston.co.uk
Membership(s): AAP; Society for Scholarly Publishing

Classical Academic Press
2151 Market St, Camp Hill, PA 17011
Tel: 717-730-0711 *Fax:* 717-730-0721
E-mail: office@classicalsubjects.com
Web Site: www.classicalsubjects.com
Key Personnel
Publr: Christopher Perrin
Founded: 2001
K-12 educational textbooks & media. Focus on classical education.
ISBN Prefix(es): 978-1-60051
Number of titles published annually: 12 Print; 2 Online; 12 E-Book; 3 Audio
Total Titles: 150 Print; 1 Online; 12 E-Book; 10 Audio
Imprints: Plum Tree Books
Foreign Rep(s): Baker & Taylor (New Zealand, UK)
Shipping Address: Baker & Taylor, 2550 W Tyvola Rd, Charlotte, NC 28217 *Tel:* 704-998-3100
Membership(s): The Independent Book Publishers Association

§CLC Ministries
701 Pennsylvania Ave, Fort Washington, PA 19034
SAN: 169-7358
Mailing Address: PO Box 1449, Fort Washington, PA 19034-8499
Tel: 215-542-1240 *Toll Free Tel:* 800-659-1240 *Fax:* 215-542-7580
E-mail: orders@clcpublications.com
Web Site: www.clcpublications.com
Key Personnel
Dir: David Almack *E-mail:* dalmack@clcusa.org
Dist/Sales Dir: Charlie Hurd
Founded: 1941
English language publishing house for CLC Ministries International.
ISBN Prefix(es): 978-0-87508; 978-1-61958
Number of titles published annually: 9 Print
Total Titles: 250 Print
Distributor for Christian Fellowship
Membership(s): EFMA

Clear Light Publishers
823 Don Diego Ave, Santa Fe, NM 87505
Tel: 505-989-9590 *Toll Free Tel:* 800-253-2747 (orders) *Fax:* 505-989-9519
E-mail: market@clearlightbooks.com
Web Site: www.clearlightbooks.com
Key Personnel
Publr: Harmon Houghton
Founded: 1981
ISBN Prefix(es): 978-0-940666; 978-1-57416
Number of titles published annually: 12 Print
Total Titles: 170 Print
Foreign Rights: Harmon Houghton Clear Light Books
Membership(s): ABA; ALA; Mountains & Plains Booksellers Association; New Mexico Book Association

§Clearfield Co Inc
Subsidiary of Genealogical Publishing Co
3600 Clipper Mill Rd, Suite 260, Baltimore, MD 21211
Tel: 410-837-8271 *Toll Free Tel:* 800-296-6687 (orders & cust serv) *Fax:* 410-752-8492
E-mail: sales@genealogical.com
Web Site: www.genealogical.com
Key Personnel
Mktg Dir: Joe Garonzik *E-mail:* jgaronzi@genealogical.com
Founded: 1989
Leading publisher of genealogy how-to books, reference books & CD-ROM publications in the US.
ISBN Prefix(es): 978-0-8063
Number of titles published annually: 100 Print; 4 CD-ROM
Total Titles: 1,000 Print
Membership(s): ABA; American Name Society; National Genealogical Society

Cleis Press
Imprint of Start Publishing LLC
2246 Sixth St, Berkeley, CA 94710
Tel: 510-845-8000 *Toll Free Tel:* 800-780-2279 (US) *Fax:* 510-845-8001
E-mail: orders@cleispress.com
Web Site: www.cleispress.com; www.vivaeditions.com
Key Personnel
Publr: Karen Thomas *Tel:* 212-431-5455
Founded: 1980
Outriders. Outwriters. Outliers. Cleis Press publishes works in the areas of fiction & LGBT studies, as well as romance, erotica, how-to sex guides, human rights, memoir & women's studies. Viva Editions are books that inform, entertain & enlighten. Books contain inspiration, self-help, women's issues, lifestyle, health, parenting, reference, gift & relationship advice.
ISBN Prefix(es): 978-0-939416; 978-1-57344
Number of titles published annually: 60 Print; 60 E-Book; 150 Audio
Total Titles: 600 Print; 400 E-Book
Imprints: Midnight Editions; Viva Editions
Foreign Rep(s): PGW - New South (Australia); Turnaround (Europe, UK)
Foreign Rights: Linda Biagi (Worldwide)
Distribution Center: Publishers Group West, 1700 Fourth St, Berkeley, CA 94710, Contact: Sarah Rosenberg *Toll Free Tel:* 800-788-3123 *Fax:* 510-520-3444 *Web Site:* www.pgw.com

Clerisy Press
Imprint of Keen Communications LLC
306 Greenup St, Covington, KY 41011
Tel: 859-815-7200 *Toll Free Tel:* 800-913-9563 *Fax:* 859-291-9111
E-mail: info@clerisypress.com
Web Site: www.clerisypress.com
Key Personnel
Pres, Keen Communications: Richard Hunt *Tel:* 859-815-7204 *E-mail:* richard@clerisypress.com
Founded: 2006
Trade & custom publisher.
ISBN Prefix(es): 978-1-57860
Number of titles published annually: 10 Print; 10 E-Book
Total Titles: 100 Print; 100 E-Book
Imprints: Keen Custom Media
Billing Address: 2204 First Ave S, Suite 102, Birmingham, AL 35233, Contact: Marie Hillin *Tel:* 205-322-0439 *Fax:* 205-326-1012 *E-mail:* mhillin@menasharidge.com
Distribution Center: Publishers Group West (PGW), 1700 Fourth St, Berkeley, CA 94710
Membership(s): ABA; Great Lakes Independent Booksellers Association

§Clinical Laboratory & Standards Institute (CLSI)
950 W Valley Rd, Suite 2500, Wayne, PA 19087
Tel: 610-688-0100 *Toll Free Tel:* 877-447-1888 (orders) *Fax:* 610-688-0700
E-mail: customerservice@clsi.org
Web Site: www.clsi.org
Key Personnel
EVP: Glenn Fine
Sr Dir, Standards & Quality: Jennifer Adams *E-mail:* jadams@clsi.org
Dir, Mktg: Patrick McGinn *E-mail:* pmcginn@clsi.org
Dir, Memb Servs: Katie Barnett *E-mail:* kbarnett@clsi.org
Edit Mgr: Megan Tertel *E-mail:* mtertel@clsi.org
Founded: 1968
Voluntary consensus standards & guidelines for medical testing & in vitro diagnostic products & healthcare services.
ISBN Prefix(es): 978-1-56238
Number of titles published annually: 30 Print
Total Titles: 200 Print

Close Up Publishing
Division of Close Up Foundation
1330 Braddock Place, Suite 400, Alexandria, VA 22314
Tel: 703-706-3300 *Toll Free Tel:* 800-CLOSE-UP (256-7387) *Fax:* 703-706-3564
E-mail: info@closeup.org
Web Site: www.closeup.org
Key Personnel
Pres & CEO: Timothy S Davis, Esq
Sr Dir, Academic Outreach & Publg: Joe Geraghty
Founded: 1971
Publish supplemental texts, videos, teachers' guides & simulation activities for secondary school & college social studies, political science, government, economics, international relations & history courses & for general readership.
ISBN Prefix(es): 978-0-932765; 978-1-930810
Number of titles published annually: 1 Print; 12 Online; 3 Audio
Total Titles: 56 Print; 20 Online; 19 Audio

Closson Press
257 Delilah St, Apollo, PA 15613-1933
Tel: 724-337-4482 *Fax:* 724-337-9484
E-mail: clossonpress@comcast.net
Web Site: www.clossonpress.com
Key Personnel
Founder & Owner: Bob Closson; Marietta Closson
Founded: 1976
Printer & publisher of history, family history & genealogy books.
ISBN Prefix(es): 978-0-933227; 978-1-55856
Number of titles published annually: 40 Print
Total Titles: 800 Print
Distributed by Janaway Publishing; Masthof Press
Distributor for Hearthside Books; Darvin Martin CDs; Retrospect Publishing
Foreign Rep(s): Brian Mitchell (Ireland); Cornelia Schrader (France, Germany)

CMF Press, see Country Music Foundation Press

§CN Times Books
Imprint of CN Times Inc
501 Fifth Ave, Suite 1708, New York, NY 10017
Tel: 212-867-8666
Web Site: cntimesbooks.com
Key Personnel
Pres & Publr: George Zhu
VP & Assoc Publr: Paul Harrington
Mng Ed, Print & Digital Prodn: Heather McAdams
Sales & Mktg Mgr: Paul Myatovich
Ed: Karen Holt
Founded: 2013
ISBN Prefix(es): 978-1-62774
Number of titles published annually: 21 Print
Total Titles: 55 Print; 7 E-Book
Distributor for Bashu Publishing; Foreign Language Press; Intercontinental Press; Phoenix Publishing
Orders to: Ingram Publisher Serivces (IPS), One Ingram Blvd, La Vergne, TN 37086 *Toll Free Tel:* 855-802-8317 *Toll Free Fax:* 800-838-1149 *E-mail:* ips@ingramcontent.com *Web Site:* ipage.ingramcontent.com
Returns: Ingram Publisher Services, 1210 Ingram Dr, Chambersburg, PA 17202
Distribution Center: Ingram Publisher Serivces (IPS), One Ingram Blvd, La Vergne, TN 37086 *Toll Free Tel:* 855-802-8317 *Toll Free Fax:* 800-838-1149 *E-mail:* ips@ingramcontent.com *Web Site:* ipage.ingramcontent.com
Membership(s): ABA

Coaches Choice
514 Airport Way, Monterey, CA 93940
Mailing Address: PO Box 1828, Monterey, CA 93942-1828
Toll Free Tel: 888-229-5745 *Fax:* 831-372-6075
E-mail: info@coacheschoice.com
Web Site: www.coacheschoice.com
Key Personnel
Pres: James Peterson
Edit Mgr: Kristi Huelsing *E-mail:* kristih@coacheschoice.com
Founded: 1999
Instructional books & DVDs for coaches (football, basketball, baseball, softball, volleyball, soccer, track & field, etc); health, fitness & sports medicine professionals & camp professionals.
ISBN Prefix(es): 978-1-57167; 978-1-58518; 978-1-60679
Number of titles published annually: 40 Print

§Coachlight Press LLC
1704 Craig's Store Rd, Afton, VA 22920-2017
SAN: 254-2579
Tel: 434-823-1692
E-mail: sales@coachlightpress.com
Web Site: www.coachlightpress.com
Key Personnel
Mng Memb: Kim Murphy
Founded: 2001
ISBN Prefix(es): 978-0-9716790; 978-1-936785
Number of titles published annually: 1 Print; 2 E-Book
Total Titles: 9 Print; 8 E-Book
Membership(s): The Independent Book Publishers Association

Codhill Press
One Arden Lane, New Paltz, NY 12561
E-mail: codhillpress@aol.com
Web Site: www.codhill.com
Key Personnel
Ed: David Appelbaum *E-mail:* appelbad@gmail.com
Founded: 1998
Literary small press.
ISBN Prefix(es): 978-1-930337
Number of titles published annually: 12 Print; 2 Online; 2 E-Book
Total Titles: 100 Print; 6 Online; 6 E-Book
Distributed by SUNY Press
Orders to: SUNY Press, PO Box 960, Herndon, VA 20172 *Tel:* 703-661-1575 *Toll Free Tel:* 877-204-6073 *Fax:* 703-996-1010 *Toll Free Fax:* 877-204-6074
Warehouse: Books International, 22883 Quicksilver Dr, Dulles, VA 20166 *Tel:* 703-661-1500
Membership(s): Community of Literary Magazines & Presses

Coffee House Press
79 13 Ave NE, Suite 110, Minneapolis, MN 55413
SAN: 206-3883
Tel: 612-338-0125 *Fax:* 612-338-4004
E-mail: info@coffeehousepress.org
Web Site: coffeehousepress.org
Key Personnel
Publr: Christopher Fischbach *E-mail:* fish@coffeehousepress.org
Mng Dir: Caroline Casey *E-mail:* caroline@coffeehousepress.org
Devt Mgr: Julie Strand *E-mail:* julie@coffeehousepress.org
Publicist: Amelia Foster *E-mail:* amelia@coffeehousepress.org; Stacie Williams
Prodn Ed: Molly Fuller *E-mail:* molly@coffeehousepress.org
Devt & Publicity Asst: Ben Findlay *E-mail:* ben@coffeehousepress.org
Edit Asst: Elizabeth Ireland *E-mail:* elizabeth@coffeehousepress.org
Publg Asst: Nica Carrillo *E-mail:* nica@coffeehousepress.org
Founded: 1984
Fine editions & trade books; contemporary poetry, short fiction, novels, literary essays & memoirs.
ISBN Prefix(es): 978-0-918273; 978-1-56689
Number of titles published annually: 14 Print
Total Titles: 250 Print
Distribution Center: Consortium Book Sales & Distribution, The Keg House, 34 13 Ave NE, Minneapolis, MN 55413 *Tel:* 612-746-2600 *Toll Free Tel:* 800-283-3572 *Fax:* 612-746-2606 *E-mail:* orderentry@perseusbooks.com

Cognizant Communication Corp
18 Peekskill Hollow Rd, Putnam Valley, NY 10597-3213
Mailing Address: PO Box 37, Putnam Valley, NY 10579-0037
Tel: 845-603-6440; 845-603-6441 (warehouse & orders) *Fax:* 845-603-6442
E-mail: inquiries@cognizantcommunication.com; sales@cognizantcommunication.com
Web Site: www.cognizantcommunication.com
Key Personnel
Chmn & Publr: Robert N Miranda
Pres: Lori Miranda
Founded: 1992
STM & social science books & journals. Subjects include: tourism research & leisure studies, medical research, engineering & psychology.
ISBN Prefix(es): 978-1-882345; 978-0-971587
Number of titles published annually: 11 Print; 23 Online
Total Titles: 53 Print; 1 CD-ROM; 1 Audio
Imprints: Innovation & Tourisms (INTO); Miranda Press Trade Division; Tourism Dynamic

Cokesbury, see Abingdon Press

§Cold Spring Harbor Laboratory Press
Division of Cold Spring Harbor Laboratory
500 Sunnyside Blvd, Woodbury, NY 11797-2924
SAN: 203-6185
Tel: 516-422-4100 *Toll Free Tel:* 800-843-4388 *Fax:* 516-422-4097; 516-422-4092 (submissions)
E-mail: cshpress@cshl.edu
Web Site: www.cshlpress.com
Key Personnel
Exec Dir: John Inglis *Tel:* 516-422-4005 *E-mail:* inglis@cshl.edu
Dir, Edit Devt: Jan Argentine *E-mail:* argentin@cshl.edu
Dir, Prod Devt & Mktg: Wayne Manos *E-mail:* manos@cshl.edu
Sr Mktg Mgr: Stephanie Novara *E-mail:* novara@cshl.edu
Mktg Mgr: Robert Redmond *Tel:* 516-422-4101 *E-mail:* rredmond@cshl.edu
Opers Mgr: Nancy Hodson *E-mail:* hodson@cshl.edu
Prodn Mgr: Linda Sussman *E-mail:* sussman@cshl.edu; Denise Weiss *E-mail:* weiss@cshl.edu
Head, Ad & Sponsorship Sales: Marcie Siconolfi *Tel:* 516-422-4010 *E-mail:* siconolf@cshl.edu
Founded: 1933
Scholarly & scientific books, journals & electronic media.
ISBN Prefix(es): 978-0-87969
Number of titles published annually: 20 Print
Total Titles: 220 Print; 1 CD-ROM; 15 E-Book; 2 Audio
Foreign Rep(s): Academic Books (Austria, Europe, Germany, Switzerland); Maruzen Co Ltd (Japan); NBN International (Europe exc Austria, Germany & Switzerland, UK); Viva Books Pvt Ltd (Indian subcontinent)
Distribution Center: Oxford University Press, 2001 Evans Rd, Cary, NC 27513

College & University Professional Association for Human Resources (CUPA-HR)
1811 Commons Point Dr, Knoxville, TN 37932

Tel: 865-637-7673 *Toll Free Tel:* 877-CUPA-HR4 (287-2474) *Fax:* 865-637-7674
E-mail: communications@cupahr.org
Web Site: www.cupahr.org/publications
Key Personnel
Dir, Communs & Mktg: Gayle Kiser *Tel:* 865-637-7673 ext 111 *E-mail:* gkiser@cupahr.org
Content Mgr, Communs & Mktg: Missy Kline *Tel:* 865-637-7673 ext 118 *E-mail:* mkline@cupahr.org
Founded: 1946
Serves more than 11,000 higher education human resource professionals at nearly 1,700 colleges & universities.
ISBN Prefix(es): 978-0-910402; 978-1-878240; 978-0-9725802
Number of titles published annually: 6 Print
Total Titles: 46 Print

§The College Board
250 Vesey St, New York, NY 10281
SAN: 269-0829
Tel: 212-713-8000
Web Site: www.collegeboard.com
Key Personnel
Pres & CEO: David Coleman
Founded: 1900
Educational & trade books in the fields of college admission, continuing education, guidance, curriculum, financial aid, educational research, college-level & advanced placement examinations & school reform.
ISBN Prefix(es): 978-0-87447
Number of titles published annually: 7 Print
Total Titles: 100 Print; 7 CD-ROM; 4 E-Book; 1 Audio
Branch Office(s)
1919 "M" St NW, Suite 300, Washington, DC 20036 *Tel:* 202-741-4700
11955 Democracy Dr, Reston, VA 20190-5662 *Tel:* 571-485-3000 *Fax:* 571-485-3099
Distributed by Macmillan

College Publishing
12309 Lynwood Dr, Glen Allen, VA 23059
Tel: 804-364-8410 *Toll Free Tel:* 800-827-0723 *Fax:* 804-364-8408
E-mail: collegepub@mindspring.com
Web Site: www.collegepublishing.us
Key Personnel
Publr: Stephen R Mosberg
Founded: 2001
Publish college textbooks in engineering, literature, linguistics & scholarly journals in engineering.
ISBN Prefix(es): 978-0-9679121; 978-1-932780
Number of titles published annually: 10 Print; 2 Online
Total Titles: 30 Print; 2 Online
Orders to: c/o Port City Fulfillment Services, 35 Ash Dr, Kimball, MI 48074 *Fax:* 810-388-9502
Returns: c/o Port City Fulfillment Services, 35 Ash Dr, Kimball, MI 48074

The Colonial Williamsburg Foundation
PO Box 1776, Williamsburg, VA 23187-1776
SAN: 203-297X
Tel: 757-229-1000 *Toll Free Tel:* 800-HISTORY (447-8679) *Fax:* 757-220-7325
E-mail: cwres@cwf.org; geninfo@cwf.org
Web Site: www.colonialwilliamsburg.org/publications
Key Personnel
Chmn of the Bd & Pres: Colin G Campbell *Tel:* 757-220-7200 *Fax:* 757-220-7727 *E-mail:* ccampbell@cwf.org
SVP, Fin & Admin: Robert Taylor *Tel:* 757-220-7410 *Fax:* 757-565-8891
VP, Prodns, Pubns & Learning Ventures: William White *Tel:* 757-220-7149 *Fax:* 757-220-8916 *E-mail:* wwhite@cwf.org
Dir & Mng Ed, Pubns & Rts/Perms: Paul Aron *Tel:* 757-220-7341 *E-mail:* paron@cwf.org
Founded: 1930
Trade & scholarly nonfiction, children's, young adult, juveniles & regional books specializing in aspects of eighteenth-century history in Virginia's colonial capital.
ISBN Prefix(es): 978-0-87935; 978-0-910412
Number of titles published annually: 6 Print
Total Titles: 100 Print; 28 Audio
Imprints: Colonial Williamsburg
Distributed by Harry N Abrams Inc; John F Blair Publisher; Clarkson Potter Publishers; Lexington Books; National Geographic; Ohio University Press; Quite Specific Media Group Ltd; Random House Children's Books; Rodale; Rowman & Littlefield; Scholastic Inc; Stackpole Books; Texas Tech University Press; The University of Virginia Press; University Press of New England; Yale University Press
Shipping Address: c/o Coastal Forms & Data Products, 141 Enterprise Dr, Newport News, VA 23603 *Tel:* 757-873-8806 *Toll Free Tel:* 800-241-4067 *Fax:* 757-873-7619
Distribution Center: 201 Fifth Ave, Williamsburg, VA 23185

§Columbia Books & Information Services
4340 East-West Hwy, Suite 300, Bethesda, MD 20814
Tel: 240-235-0266 *Toll Free Tel:* 888-265-0600 (cust serv) *Fax:* 202-464-1775
E-mail: info@columbiabooks.com
Web Site: www.columbiabooks.com; www.lobbyists.info; www.associationexecs.com
Key Personnel
Pres: Joel Poznansky
EVP & COO: Frank Finn
Dir of Opers: Eric Weissmann
Dir of Sales & Mktg: Brittany Carter *Tel:* 240-235-0270 *E-mail:* bcarter@columbiabooks.com
Dir of Edit & Data Servs: Duncan Bell
Dir of Fin: Debbie Cohen
Dir of Busn Devt: Tim Teehan *E-mail:* tim@columbiabooks.com
Founded: 1965
Publish print directories, reference books, newsletters & reports. Do not accept mss.
ISBN Prefix(es): 978-0-910416; 978-1-880873; 978-0-9715487; 978-0-9747322; 978-1-938939
Number of titles published annually: 10 Print; 2 Online; 1 E-Book
Total Titles: 10 Print; 2 Online; 1 E-Book

§Columbia University Press
61 W 62 St, New York, NY 10023
SAN: 212-2472
Tel: 212-459-0600 *Toll Free Tel:* 800-944-8648 *Fax:* 212-459-3678
E-mail: cup_book@columbia.edu (orders & cust serv)
Web Site: cup.columbia.edu
Key Personnel
CFO: Richard Gehringer
Pres & Dir: Jennifer Crewe
Edit Dir: Eric Schwartz
Publicity Dir & Asst Mktg Dir: Meredith Howard
Dir, Sales & Mktg: Brad Hebel
Publr, Fin & Economics: Myles Thompson
Publr, Life Sciences: Patrick Fitzgerald
Sr Exec Ed: Wendy Lochner
Exec Ed: Jennifer Perillo
Mng Ed: Anne McCoy
Ed: Anne Routon
Founded: 1893
Books of scholarly value, including nonfiction, general interest, scientific & technical books, textbooks in special fields at the university level & reference books.
ISBN Prefix(es): 978-0-231
Number of titles published annually: 500 Print; 120 E-Book
Total Titles: 7 CD-ROM; 4 Online; 350 E-Book
Imprints: Columbia Business School Publishing (business, finance & economics titles); Wallflower Press (film titles)
Distributor for American Institute of Buddhist Studies; Austrian Film Museum Books; Auteur Publishing; Chinese University Press; Columbia University Press (Hitchcock Annual); Maria Curie-Sklodowska University Press; Dalkey Archive Press; GSAPP Books; Harrington Park Press (frontlist titles); Hong Kong University Press; ibidem Press (English-lang titles exc China & India); Jagiellonian University Press; Slovenian Cinematheque; Social Science Research Council; Transcript Verlag; University of Tokyo Press; Woodrow Wilson Center Press
Foreign Rep(s): The African Moon Press (Chris Reinders) (Botswana, Lesotho, Namibia, South Africa, Swaziland, Zimbabwe); Apex Knowledge Sdn Bhd (Simon Tay) (Brunei, Malaysia); Aromix Books Co Ltd (Nick Woon & Jane Lam) (Hong Kong); Avicenna Partnership Ltd (Claire de Gruchy) (Algeria, Cyprus, Jordan, Malta, Morocco, Palestine, Tunisia, Turkey); Avicenna Partnership Ltd (Bill Kennedy) (Bahrain, Egypt, Iran, Iraq, Kuwait, Lebanon, Libya, Oman, Qatar, Saudi Arabia, Syria, United Arab Emirates); Dominique Bartshukoff (Austria, Croatia, Czech Republic, Eastern Europe, Germany, Greece, Holland, Portugal, Russia, Slovenia, Spain); Book Marketing Services (S Janakiraman) (India); Booknet Co Ltd (Suphaluck Sattabuz) (Thailand); Everest International Publishing Services (Wei Zhao) (China); Footprints Books (Australia, New Zealand); Information & Culture Korea (Se-Yung Jun) (Korea); Peter Jacques (Belgium, Denmark, Finland, France, Italy, Norway, Poland, Sweden, Switzerland); Mega-TEXTS Phil Inc (Jean Lim) (Philippines); Mical Moser (Canada); B K Norton Ltd (Chiafeng Peng) (Singapore, Taiwan); Premium Educational Group (David R Rivera) (Caribbean, Puerto Rico); Publicaciones Educativas (Jose Rios) (Central America, Mexico); Rockbook (Akiko Iwamoto & Gilles Fauveau) (Japan); United Publishers Services Ltd (Mark Gresham) (Japan); The University Press Group Ltd (Lois Edwards) (Europe, UK); Kevin van Hasselt (Africa); Wiley Distribution Services Ltd (Africa, Europe, Middle East, South Africa, South Asia, UK); World Press (Saleem A Malik) (Pakistan)
Foreign Rights: Agencia Literaria Raquel de la Concha (Spain); Akcali Copyright Agency (Attila Akcali) (Turkey); L'Autre Agence (Corinne Marotte) (France); Bardon-Chinese Media Agency (China); Bestun Korea (Ms Yumi Chun) (Korea); The English Agency (Tsutomu Yawata) (Japan); Paul & Peter Fritz AG (Germany); Graal Literary Agency (Maria Starz-Kanska) (Poland); Danny Hong Agency (Danny Hong) (Korea); Andrew Nurnberg Associates International (Whitney Hsu & Jackie Huang) (China); Reiser Literary Agency (Roberto Gilodi) (Italy); Uli Rushby-Smith (Netherlands, UK); Karin Schindler (Portugal); Tuttle-Mori Agency Inc (Fumika Ogihara) (Japan); Eric Yang Agency (Jackie Yang) (Korea)
Advertising Agency: Columbia Advertising Group
Orders to: Perseus Distribution, 210 American Dr, Jackson, TN 38301 *Tel:* 731-988-4440 *Toll Free Tel:* 800-343-4499 *Toll Free Fax:* 800-351-5073 *E-mail:* orderentry@perseusbooks.com
Membership(s): AAP; American Association of University Presses

§Comex Systems Inc
101 Pleasant Hill Rd, Chester, NJ 07930
Tel: 973-543-2862 *Toll Free Tel:* 800-543-6959 *Fax:* 973-543-9644
E-mail: mail@comexsystems.com
Web Site: www.comexsystems.com

Key Personnel
VP: Doug Prybylowski *E-mail:* dpryb@comexsystems.com
Founded: 1973
Publish test preparation & other educational books.
ISBN Prefix(es): 978-1-56030
Number of titles published annually: 5 Print; 10 CD-ROM; 5 E-Book
Total Titles: 30 Print; 50 CD-ROM; 5 E-Book

Common Courage Press
One Red Barn Rd, Monroe, ME 04951
Mailing Address: PO Box 702, Monroe, ME 04951-0702
Tel: 207-525-0900 *Toll Free Tel:* 800-497-3207 *Fax:* 207-525-3068
Web Site: www.commoncouragepress.com
Key Personnel
Publr: Greg Bates *E-mail:* gbates@commoncouragepress.com
Founded: 1991
Books on race, feminism, gender issues, class, media, economics, ecology & foreign policy to help readers in the struggle for social justice. Accepting no new submissions.
ISBN Prefix(es): 978-0-9628838; 978-1-56751
Number of titles published annually: 20 Print
Total Titles: 90 Print
Distributor for Odonian Press; Real Story Series
Foreign Rights: James Bier (Worldwide exc USA)
Distribution Center: LPC Group, 1436 W Randolph St, Chicago, IL 60607 *Toll Free Tel:* 800-243-0138 *Toll Free Fax:* 800-334-3892

Commonwealth Editions
Imprint of Applewood Books Inc
One River Rd, Carlisle, MA 01741
Tel: 781-271-0055 *Toll Free Tel:* 800-277-5312 *Fax:* 781-271-0056
E-mail: customercare@awb.com
Web Site: www.awb.com
Key Personnel
Pres & Publr: Phil Zuckerman *E-mail:* philz@awb.com
Founded: 1988
Publisher of nonfiction books about New England & its historic places.
ISBN Prefix(es): 978-1-889833; 978-1-933212
Number of titles published annually: 12 Print
Total Titles: 125 Print
Membership(s): NEBA

Conciliar Press, see Ancient Faith Publishing

Concordia Publishing House
Subsidiary of The Luthern Church, Missouri Synod
3558 S Jefferson Ave, St Louis, MO 63118-3968
SAN: 202-1781
Tel: 314-268-1000; 314-268-1268 (bookshop) *Toll Free Tel:* 800-325-3040 (cust serv) *Toll Free Fax:* 800-490-9889 (cust serv)
E-mail: order@cph.org
Web Site: www.cph.org
Key Personnel
Pres & CEO: Dr Bruce G Kintz *Tel:* 314-268-1190 *E-mail:* bruce.kintz@cph.org
VP & Corp Coun: Jonathan D Schultz *E-mail:* jonathan.schultz@cph.org
Publr & Exec Dir: Rev Paul T McCain *E-mail:* paul.mccain@cph.org
Exec Dir, Innovation Technologies: Steve Harris *E-mail:* steve.harris@cph.org
Exec Dir, Mktg & E-Commerce: Mr Loren Pawlitz *E-mail:* loren.pawlitz@cph.org
Exec Dir, Prodn Control & Quality Systems: Karen Capps *E-mail:* karen.capps@cph.org
Dir, Facilities: Tony Shimkus *E-mail:* tony.shimkus@cph.org
Dir, Fin: Collin Bivens *E-mail:* collin.bivens@cph.org
Dir, Graphic Design: Tim Agnew *E-mail:* tim.agnew@cph.org
Dir, HR: Dana Neuhaus *E-mail:* dana.neuhaus@cph.org
Dir, Opers: Bob Rothmeyer *E-mail:* bob.rothmeyer@cph.org
Dir, Sales: Paul Brunette *E-mail:* paul.brunette@cph.org
Founded: 1869
Theological works, sacred & family, devotional music, curriculum, computer software, bulletins, envelopes.
ISBN Prefix(es): 978-0-570; 978-0-7586
Number of titles published annually: 150 Print; 2 CD-ROM
Total Titles: 1,000 Print; 10 CD-ROM
Divisions: Concordia Academic Press; Editorial Concordia; Family Films
Membership(s): CBA: The Association for Christian Retail; Evangelical Christian Publishers Association; Protestant Church-Owned Publishers Association

The Conference Board Inc
845 Third Ave, New York, NY 10022-6679
SAN: 202-179X
Tel: 212-759-0900; 212-339-0345 (cust serv) *Fax:* 212-980-7014; 212-836-9740 (cust serv)
E-mail: info@conference-board.org
Web Site: www.conference-board.org
Key Personnel
CEO: Jon Spector
Rts & Perms: Chuck Mitchell
Founded: 1916
Periodic studies in management practices, economics & public affairs.
ISBN Prefix(es): 978-0-8237
Number of titles published annually: 25 Print; 25 Online
Foreign Office(s): Chaussee de La Hulpe 130, bte 11, 1000 Brussels, Belgium

Consumer Press
13326 SW 28 St, Suite 102, Fort Lauderdale, FL 33330-1102
SAN: 297-7888
Tel: 954-370-9153 *Fax:* 954-472-1008
E-mail: info@consumerpress.com
Web Site: www.consumerpress.com
Key Personnel
Pres: Diana Gonzalez
Edit Dir: Joseph J Pappas
Publicity Dir: Linda Muzzarelli
Founded: 1989
Consumer-oriented self-help & how-to titles. Specialize in nutrition, health & homeowner issues.
ISBN Prefix(es): 978-0-9628336; 978-1-891264; 978-0-9637641
Number of titles published annually: 9 Print
Total Titles: 12 Print
Imprints: Women's Publications
Membership(s): The Independent Book Publishers Association

Consumertronics
Affiliate of Top Secret Consumertronics Global (TSC-Global)
PO Box 23097, Albuquerque, NM 87192
Tel: 505-321-1034
E-mail: wizguru@consumertronics.net
Web Site: www.consumertronics.net
Key Personnel
Pres & CEO: John J Williams
VP: Laurencia Williams
Founded: 1971
Technical books, manuals & software.
ISBN Prefix(es): 978-0-934274
Number of titles published annually: 60 Print; 60 CD-ROM
Total Titles: 150 Print

Contemporary Publishing Co of Raleigh Inc
5849 Lease Lane, Raleigh, NC 27617
Tel: 919-851-8221 *Fax:* 919-851-6666
E-mail: questions@contemporarypublishing.com
Web Site: www.contemporarypublishing.com
Key Personnel
Publr: Charles E Grantham *E-mail:* chuck246cp@aol.com
Lib Sales Dir & Prodn Mgr: Erika Kessler *E-mail:* erikacpc@aol.com
Mktg Dir: Sherri Powell
Founded: 1977
Laboratory textbooks for college.
ISBN Prefix(es): 978-0-89892
Number of titles published annually: 10 Print
Total Titles: 90 Print; 1 CD-ROM

Continental AfrikaPublishers
Division of Afrikamawu Miracle Mission, AMI Inc
182 Stribling Circle, Spartanburg, SC 29301
Tel: 864-576-7992 *Fax:* 864-576-7992
E-mail: afrikalion@aol.com; profafrikadzatadeku@facebook.com; profafrikadzatadeku@yahoo.com; afrikapharaoh@gmail.com
Web Site: www.afrikacentricity.com
Key Personnel
Publr: Prof Afrikadzata Deku, PhD
Founded: 1990
Afrikacentric books, booklets, cassettes & video documentaries, calendars, films on Continental Afrikan studies, Afrika Centricity, Pan-Continental Afrikanism, Continental Afrikan Government MIRACLE Project of the Century-its what, why, how & when.
ISBN Prefix(es): 978-1-56454
Number of titles published annually: 20 Print; 260 Online; 500 E-Book; 20 Audio
Total Titles: 260 Print; 260 Online; 638 E-Book; 20 Audio
Foreign Office(s): PO Box 209, Dansoman-Accra, Ghana, Chmn: Afrikanenyo Deku
Foreign Rep(s): Continental/Diaspora Afrikan (Worldwide)

David C Cook
4050 Lee Vance View, Colorado Springs, CO 80918
Tel: 719-536-0100 *Toll Free Tel:* 800-708-5550; 800-323-7543 (orders & cust serv) *Toll Free Fax:* 800-430-0726 (cust serv)
Web Site: www.davidccook.com
Key Personnel
CEO: Cris Doornbos
COO: Scott Miller
CIO: Sean Everhart
Chief Advancement Offr: Tim MacDonald
Chief Global Offr: Gary Hopwood
Exec Publr: Verne Kenney
Pres, Integrity Music: C Ryan Dunham
EVP, Global Dist: Greg Tombs
VP & Publr, Learning Resources Group: Dr Michelle Anthony
VP, Sales: Marilyn Largent
VP, Sales & Mktg: Chriscynethia Floyd
Sr Dir, Mktg: Tim Close
Founded: 1875
Publish & distribute leadership & discipleship resources.
ISBN Prefix(es): 978-0-912692; 978-0-89191; 978-1-55513; 978-1-56476; 978-0-89693; 978-0-7814; 978-0-88207; 978-1-4347
Number of titles published annually: 50 Print
Total Titles: 2,500 Print
Divisions: David C Cook Distribution Canada; Integrity Music (music publg & recording)
Returns: 850 N Grove, Elgin, IL 60120

Copley Custom Textbooks
Imprint of XanEdu Publishing Inc
530 Great Rd, Acton, MA 01720

Tel: 978-263-9090 *Toll Free Tel:* 800-562-2147 *Fax:* 978-263-9190
E-mail: publish@copleycustom.com; textbook@copleypublishing.com
Web Site: www.xanedu.com/copley
Key Personnel
CEO: John DeBoer
Founded: 1984
Custom publishing for the higher education market.
ISBN Prefix(es): 978-0-87411; 978-1-58152; 978-1-58390
Number of titles published annually: 85 Print; 5 CD-ROM; 10 E-Book
Total Titles: 400 Print
Imprints: Copley Editions; Copley Publishing Group

§Copper Canyon Press
Fort Worden State Park, Bldg 313, Port Townsend, WA 98368
SAN: 206-488X
Mailing Address: PO Box 271, Port Townsend, WA 98368
Tel: 360-385-4925 *Toll Free Tel:* 877-501-1393 (orders) *Fax:* 360-385-4985
E-mail: poetry@coppercanyonpress.org
Web Site: www.coppercanyonpress.org
Key Personnel
Co-Publr: Joseph Bednarik *E-mail:* joseph@coppercanyonpress.org; George Knotek *E-mail:* george@coppercanyonpress.org
Dir, Publicity: Kelly Forsythe *E-mail:* kelly@coppercanyonpress.org
Exec Ed: Michael Wiegers *E-mail:* michael@coppercanyonpress.org
Mng Ed: Tonaya Craft *E-mail:* tonaya@coppercanyonpress.org
Experimental Progs Mgr: Victoria Poling *E-mail:* victoria@coppercanyonpress.org
Fin Mgr: Randy Sturgis *E-mail:* randy@coppercanyonpress.org
Community Engagement Coord/Assoc Ed: Elaina Ellis *E-mail:* elaina@coppercanyonpress.org
Warehouse Mgr: Christopher Overman *E-mail:* christopher@coppercanyonpress.org
Fin/Opers: Margaret Kirk *E-mail:* margaret@coppercanyonpress.org
Founded: 1972
Hardcover & paperback trade books of poetry.
ISBN Prefix(es): 978-0-914742; 978-1-55659; 978-1-61932
Number of titles published annually: 32 Print
Total Titles: 400 Print
Branch Office(s)
216 First Ave, Suite 480, Seattle, WA 98104
Distributor for American Poetry Review/Honickman
Distribution Center: Consortium Book Sales & Distribution, The Keg House, Suite 101, 34 13 Ave NE, Minneapolis, MN 55413-1007 *Tel:* 612-746-2600 *Toll Free Tel:* 800-283-3572 (cust serv) *Fax:* 612-746-2606 *E-mail:* info@cbsd.com *Web Site:* www.cbsd.com

§Copywriter's Council of America (CCA)
Division of The Linick Group Inc
CCA Bldg, 7 Putter Lane, Middle Island, NY 11953-1920
Mailing Address: PO Box 102, Middle Island, NY 11953-0102
Tel: 631-924-3888 *Fax:* 631-924-8555
E-mail: cca4dmcopy@gmail.com
Web Site: www.AndrewLinickDirectMarketing.com/Copywriters-Council.html; www.NewWorldPressBooks.com
Key Personnel
Chmn, Consulting Group: Andrew S Linick, PhD *E-mail:* andrew@asklinick.com
VP: Roger Dextor
Lib Sales Dir: John Kelty
Founded: 1974
Article reprints, monographs; educational, professional & trade, fiction, nonfiction publications in direct response advertising, direct marketing, mail order, sales promotion, measurable response public relations, telemarketing, business-to-business marketing, desktop publishing, Internet marketing, e-commerce, ebooks, consulting & management. Confidential reports, newsletters, little known business secrets library of super money makers you can use tomorrow. Also 300 ebooks & e-reports available for licensing. Free 15 minute phone consultation for LMP readers - code LMP.
ISBN Prefix(es): 978-0-917098 (New World Press)
Number of titles published annually: 36 Print; 25 E-Book
Total Titles: 350 Print; 50 E-Book
Imprints: CCA; National Association of Photo Sellers; New World Press; Publishers Trade Secrets Library
Distributor for ASL; Compu-Tek; National Association of Photo Sellers; PictureProfits® Tool Kit
Advertising Agency: LK Advertising Agency, 7 Putter Lane, Middle Island, NY 11953, VP: Roger Dextor *Tel:* 631-924-3888 *Web Site:* www.AndrewLinickDirectMarketing.com/LK-Advertising.html
Membership(s): ABA; American Association of Journalists & Authors; American Association of Magazine Photographers; American Book Producers Association; American Business Women's Association; American Marketing Association; American Medical Publishers Association; American Medical Writers Association; American Publishers Association; American Society of Magazine Editors; Association of Advertising & Marketing Professionals; Association of Directory Publishers; Direct Marketing Association; Direct Marketing Club of New York; International Food, Wine and Travel Writers Association

Cornell Maritime Press Inc
Imprint of Schiffer Publishing Ltd
4880 Lower Valley Rd, Atglen, PA 19310
SAN: 203-5901
Tel: 610-593-1777 *Fax:* 610-593-2002
E-mail: info@schifferbooks.com
Web Site: www.cmptp.com
Key Personnel
Pres: Pete Schiffer
EVP: Nancy Schiffer
Founded: 1938
Professional, technical books in maritime arts & sciences; boats & boat building; related hobbies & crafts.
ISBN Prefix(es): 978-0-87033
Number of titles published annually: 15 Print
Total Titles: 300 Print
Imprints: Tidewater Publishers
Distributor for Chesapeake Bay Maritime Museum; Independent Seaport Museum; Literary House Press; Maryland Historical Trust Press; Maryland Sea Grant Program
Membership(s): ABA; Mid-Atlantic Publishers Association

Cornell University Press
Division of Cornell University
Sage House, 512 E State St, Ithaca, NY 14850
SAN: 202-1862
Tel: 607-277-2338 *Fax:* 607-277-2374
E-mail: cupressinfo@cornell.edu; cupress-sales@cornell.edu
Web Site: www.cornellpress.cornell.edu
Key Personnel
CFO & Asst Dir: Roger A Hubbs *Tel:* 607-882-2209 *E-mail:* rah9@cornell.edu
Dir: Dean J Smith *Tel:* 607-882-2226 *E-mail:* djs486@cornell.edu
Ed-in-Chief: Peter Potter *Tel:* 607-882-2254 *E-mail:* pjp33@cornell.edu
Edit Dir, ILR Press: Ms Frances Benson *Tel:* 607-882-2255 *E-mail:* fgb2@cornell.edu
Dir, Mktg: Mr Mahinder S Kingra *Tel:* 607-882-2239 *E-mail:* msk55@cornell.edu
Exec Ed: Roger Haydon *Tel:* 607-882-2236 *E-mail:* rmh11@cornell.edu
Sr Ed: James Lance *E-mail:* jml554@cornell.edu; Michael J McGandy *Tel:* 607-882-2250 *E-mail:* mjm475@cornell.edu
Assoc Ed, Comstock Publishing: Kitty Lu *Tel:* 607-882-2247 *E-mail:* khl8@cornell.edu
Asst Dir & Mng Ed: Priscilla Hurdle *Tel:* 607-277-2338 ext 244 *E-mail:* plh9@cornell.edu
Design & Prod Mgr: Karen Kerr *Tel:* 607-882-2238 *E-mail:* kg99@cornell.edu
Sales Mgr: Nathan D Gemignani *Tel:* 607-882-2234 *E-mail:* ndg5@cornell.edu
Subs Rts Mgr: Tonya Cook *Tel:* 607-882-2252 *E-mail:* tcc6@cornell.edu
Asst to the Dir: Michael A Morris *Tel:* 607-882-2256 *E-mail:* mam278@cornell.edu
Founded: 1869 (reconstituted in 1930)
General nonfiction, scholarly books & monographs; hardcover & paperbacks.
ISBN Prefix(es): 978-0-8014; 978-0-87546; 978-1-5017
Number of titles published annually: 120 Print
Total Titles: 2,200 Print
Imprints: Comstock Publishing Associates; ILR Press
Distributor for Cornell Southeast Asia Program (SEAP) Publications; Leuven University Press
Foreign Rep(s): East-West Export Books (Royden Muranaka) (Asia); Footprint Books Pty Ltd (Australia, Fiji, New Zealand, Papua New Guinea); KW Publishers Pvt Ltd (Kalpana Shukla) (Afghanistan, Bangladesh, Bhutan, India, Maldives, Myanmar, Nepal, Pakistan, Sri Lanka, Thailand); Ewa Ledochowicz (Eastern Europe); Lexa Publishers' Representatives (Mical Moser) (Canada); Uwe Luedemann (Austria, Germany, Italy, Liechtenstein, Portugal, Spain, Switzerland); University Presses Marketing (Benelux, France, Greece, Ireland, Israel, Scandinavia, UK); US PubRep Inc (Craig Falk) (Latin America)
Foreign Rights: Agencja Literacka Graal (Poland); Eulama (Dr Pina von Prellwitz) (Italy); Maya Publishers (Mr Surit Mitra) (India); La Nouvelle Agence (Vanessa King) (France); RDC Agencia Literaria (Beatriz Coll & Lukasz Wrobel) (Albania, Bulgaria, Croatia, Czech Republic, Estonia, Hungary, Latvia, Lithuania, Montenegro, Portugal, Romania, Serbia, Slovakia, Spain)
Orders to: CUP Services, 750 Cascadilla St, PO Box 6525, Ithaca, NY 14851-6525 *Tel:* 607-277-2211 *Toll Free Tel:* 800-666-2211 *Fax:* 607-277-6292 *Toll Free Fax:* 800-688-2877 *E-mail:* orderbook@cupserv.org *Web Site:* cupserv.org
Returns: CUP Services, 750 Cascadilla St, PO Box 6525, Ithaca, NY 14851-6525 *Toll Free Tel:* 800-666-2211 *Web Site:* cupserv.org
Shipping Address: CUP Services, 750 Cascadilla St, PO Box 6525, Ithaca, NY 14851-6525 *Tel:* 607-277-2211 *Toll Free Tel:* 800-666-2211 *Fax:* 607-277-6292 *Toll Free Fax:* 800-688-2877 *E-mail:* orderbook@cupserv.org *Web Site:* cupserv.org
Warehouse: CUP Services, 750 Cascadilla St, PO Box 6525, Ithaca, NY 14851-6525 *Tel:* 607-277-2211 *Toll Free Tel:* 800-666-2211 *Fax:* 607-277-6292 *Toll Free Fax:* 800-688-2877 *E-mail:* orderbook@cupserv.org *Web Site:* cupserv.org
Distribution Center: CUP Services, 750 Cascadilla St, PO Box 6525, Ithaca, NY 14851-6525 *Tel:* 607-277-2211 *Toll Free Tel:* 800-666-2211 *Fax:* 607-277-6292 *Toll Free Fax:* 800-688-2877 *E-mail:* orderbook@cupserv.org *Web Site:* cupserv.org

Footprint Books Pty Ltd, 1/6a Prosperity Parade, Warriewood, NSW 2102, Australia *Tel:* (02) 9997 3973; 1300 260 090 (toll free) *Fax:* (02) 9997 3185

NBN International, 10 Thornbury Rd, Plymouth PL6 7PP, United Kingdom *Tel:* (01752) 202301 *Fax:* (01752) 202333 *E-mail:* orders@nbninternational.com

Membership(s): AAP; Association of American University Presses

Cornell University Southeast Asia Program Publications
Unit of Cornell University
213 Kahin Ctr, 640 Stewart Ave, Ithaca, NY 14850
Tel: 607-255-4359 *Fax:* 607-255-4359
E-mail: seappublications@cornell.edu
Web Site: seapeinaudi.cornell.edu/southeastasia/publications
Key Personnel
Mng Ed: Sarah Grossman
Pubns Asst: Fred Connor *E-mail:* flc2@cornell.edu
Founded: 1951
Publish books & one semiannual journal (Indonesia) on the history, politics, culture & languages of Southeast Asian countries.
ISBN Prefix(es): 978-0-87727; 978-0-87763; 978-0-9910478; 978-0-9910479; 978-0-9910480; 978-0-991081; 978-0-991082
Number of titles published annually: 6 Print; 1 CD-ROM
Total Titles: 130 Print
Distributor for A U A Language Center
Orders to: 95 Brown Rd, Box 1004, Ithaca, NY 14850, Dist & Busn Mgr: Cynthia Dickinson *Tel:* 607-255-8038 *Fax:* 607-255-7534 *E-mail:* cld227@cornell.edu
Shipping Address: 95 Brown Rd, Box 1004, Ithaca, NY 14850, Dist & Busn Mgr: Cynthia Dickinson *Tel:* 607-255-8038 *Fax:* 607-255-7534 *E-mail:* cld227@cornell.edu
Warehouse: 95 Brown Rd, Box 1004, Ithaca, NY 14850, Dist & Busn Mgr: Cynthia Dickinson *Tel:* 607-255-8038 *Fax:* 607-255-7534 *E-mail:* cld227@cornell.edu
Distribution Center: 95 Brown Rd, Box 1004, Ithaca, NY 14850, Dist & Busn Mgr: Cynthia Dickinson *Tel:* 607-255-8038 *Fax:* 607-255-7534 *E-mail:* cld227@cornell.edu

Cornerstone Book Publishers
PO Box 24652, New Orleans, LA 70184
E-mail: info@cornerstonepublishers.com
Web Site: www.cornerstonepublishers.com
Key Personnel
Owner: Michael R Poll
Founded: 1995
Masonic, Scottish Rite, Rosicrucian, metaphysical, Louisiana themed & classic outdoor & bushcraft books.
ISBN Prefix(es): 978-1-887560
Number of titles published annually: 6 Print; 10 E-Book
Total Titles: 33 Print; 65 E-Book
Foreign Rep(s): Ingram (UK)

Cortina Institute of Languages
Division of Cortina Learning International Inc (CLI)
9 Hollyhock Rd, Wilton, CT 06897
Tel: 203-762-2510 *Toll Free Tel:* 800-245-2145 *Fax:* 203-762-2514
Web Site: www.cortina-languages.com
Key Personnel
Pres: Magdalen B Livesey *Tel:* 203-762-2510 ext 109 *E-mail:* m.livesey@cortinalearning.com
Gen Mgr: George Bollas *Tel:* 203-762-2510 ext 105 *E-mail:* g.bollas@cortinalearning.com
Founded: 1958
Learning foreign languages for English speakers; English as a second language.
ISBN Prefix(es): 978-0-8489
Total Titles: 277 Print
Warehouse: 15 Great Pasture Rd, Danbury, CT 06810 *Tel:* 203-778-9639 *Fax:* 203-778-4029

Cortina Learning International Inc (CLI)
9 Hollyhock Rd, Wilton, CT 06897
Tel: 203-762-2510 *Toll Free Tel:* 800-245-2145 *Fax:* 203-762-2514
E-mail: info@cortinalearning.com
Web Site: www.cortinalearning.com
Key Personnel
Pres: Magdalen B Livesey *Tel:* 203-762-2510 ext 109 *E-mail:* m.livesey@cortinalearning.com
Gen Mgr: George Bollas *Tel:* 203-762-2510 ext 105 *E-mail:* g.bollas@cortinalearning.com
Founded: 1882
Foreign languages, English as second language, art instruction, writing instruction, fiction & nonfiction.
ISBN Prefix(es): 978-0-8327
Total Titles: 50 Print
Divisions: Cortina Institute of Languages; Famous Artists School; Famous Writers School
Warehouse: 15 Great Pasture Rd, Danbury, CT 06810 *Tel:* 203-778-9639 *Fax:* 203-778-4029
See separate listing for:
Cortina Institute of Languages

§Corwin, a Sage Co
2455 Teller Rd, Thousand Oaks, CA 91320
Tel: 805-499-9734 *Toll Free Tel:* 800-233-9936 *Fax:* 805-499-5323 *Toll Free Fax:* 800-417-2466
E-mail: info@corwin.com; order@corwin.com
Web Site: www.corwin.com
Key Personnel
Pres: Mike Soules
VP, Mktg & Channel Devt: Elena Nikitina
VP, Publg & Prof Learning: Lisa Shaw
Dir, Prof Learning: Kristin Anderson
Sr Licensing Mgr & Foreign Rts Agent: Anna Termine *E-mail:* anna.termine@sagepub.com
Founded: 1990
Offers practical, research-based books, journals & multimedia resources specifically developed for principals, administrators, teachers, staff developers, curriculum developers, special & gifted educators & other PreK-12 education professionals.
ISBN Prefix(es): 978-0-7619; 978-0-8039; 978-1-4129; 978-1-8904; 978-1-57517; 978-1-5697; 978-1-879179
Number of titles published annually: 120 Print
Total Titles: 1,900 Print
Distributor for SAGE UK Resources for Educators
Foreign Rep(s): SAGE India (India); SAGE London (Europe, UK); SAGE Singapore (Asia-Pacific)

§Cosimo Inc
Old Chelsea Sta, PO Box 416, New York, NY 10011-0416
Tel: 212-989-3616 *Fax:* 212-989-3662
E-mail: info@cosimobooks.com
Web Site: www.cosimobooks.com
Founded: 2005
Specialty publisher for independent authors, not-for-profit organizations & innovative businesses, dedicated to publishing books that inspire, inform & engage readers around the world. We offer authors & organizations full publishing support, while using the newest technologies to present their works in the most timely & effective way.
ISBN Prefix(es): 978-1-931044 (Paraview Print on Demand titles); 978-1-4165 (Paraview Pocket Books); 978-1-59605; 978-1-60206; 978-1-60520; 978-1-61640
Number of titles published annually: 12 Print; 12 E-Book
Total Titles: 45 Print
Imprints: Cosimo Books; Cosimo Classics; Cosimo Reports; Paraview Pocket Books; Paraview Special Editions
Divisions: Paraview Press

Costume + Fashion Press, see Quite Specific Media Group Ltd

Cotsen Institute of Archaeology Press
308 Charles E Young Dr N, Fowler A163, Box 951510, Los Angeles, CA 90024
Tel: 310-206-9384 *Fax:* 310-206-4723
E-mail: ioapubs@ioa.ucla.edu
Web Site: www.ioa.ucla.edu
Key Personnel
Dir of Institute: Charles Stanish *Tel:* 310-267-5579 *E-mail:* stanish@anthro.ucla.edu
Pubns Mgr: Randi Danforth *E-mail:* cioapress@ioa.ucla.edu
Founded: 1974
Books, monographs & occasional papers in the field of archaeology.
ISBN Prefix(es): 978-0-917956
Number of titles published annually: 5 Print
Total Titles: 69 Print
Distribution Center: University of New Mexico Press, 1312 Basehart Rd SE, Albuquerque, NM *Tel:* 505-272-7777 *Toll Free Tel:* 800-249-7737 (ordering) *Toll Free Fax:* 800-622-8667 *E-mail:* unmpress@unm.edu *Web Site:* www.unmpress.com

Cottonwood Press
University of Kansas, Kansas Union, Rm 400, 1301 Jayhawk Blvd, Lawrence, KS 66045
Tel: 785-864-4520
Web Site: www.englishcw.ku.edu/cottonwood
Key Personnel
Ed: Tom Lorenz *Tel:* 785-864-2516 *E-mail:* tlorenz@ku.edu
Poetry Ed: Phil Wedge *E-mail:* pwedge@ku.edu
Founded: 1965
Poetry & fiction.
ISBN Prefix(es): 978-1-878434
Number of titles published annually: 4 Print
Total Titles: 15 Print
Membership(s): Community of Literary Magazines & Presses

Council for Exceptional Children (CEC)
2900 Crystal Dr, Suite 1000, Arlington, VA 22201
Toll Free Tel: 888-232-7733 (memb servs); 866-509-0219 *Fax:* 703-264-9494
E-mail: service@cec.sped.org
Web Site: www.cec.sped.org
Key Personnel
Exec Dir: Alex Graham *Tel:* 703-264-9404 *E-mail:* agraham@cec.sped.org
Founded: 1922
Mail order books & videos to improve the educational success of individuals with disabilities +/or gifts & talents.
ISBN Prefix(es): 978-0-86586
Number of titles published annually: 6 Print
Total Titles: 75 Print
Branch Office(s)
CEC Publications, PO Box 79026, Baltimore, MD 21279-0026
Distributed by Free Spirit Publishing Inc; LMD Inc (selected titles); Orchard House Inc
Distributor for Brooks (selected titles); Longman; Love Publishing; Pearson; Pro Ed; Sopris West

Council for Research in Values & Philosophy (RVP)
The Catholic University of America, Gibbons Hall, Rm B-12, 620 Michigan Ave NE, Washington, DC 20064

Mailing Address: PO Box 261, Cardinal Sta, Washington, DC 20064-0261
Tel: 202-319-6089 *Fax:* 202-319-6089
E-mail: cua-rvp@cua.edu
Web Site: www.crvp.org
Key Personnel
Pres: George F McLean *E-mail:* mclean@cua.edu
Dir, Opers & Treas: Hu Yeping *E-mail:* huy@cua.edu
Founded: 1982
Works on philosophy, values, education, civil society, culture.
ISBN Prefix(es): 978-1-56518
Number of titles published annually: 12 Print; 12 Online
Total Titles: 220 Print; 215 Online
Imprints: The Council for Research in Values & Philosophy
Orders to: Oblate School of Theology (OST), 285 Oblate Dr, San Antonio, TX 78216

Council Oak Books LLC
2822 Van Ness Ave, San Francisco, CA 94109
SAN: 689-5522
Tel: 415-931-7700 *Toll Free Tel:* 888-275-2596
E-mail: marketing@counciloakbooks.com
Web Site: www.counciloakbooks.com
Founded: 1984
Publisher of nonfiction titles that point the way to a richer life & a better world. Areas of special interest include world religions, Native American, Americana (especially Route 66), animals & nature.
ISBN Prefix(es): 978-0-933031 (Council Oak Books); 978-1-57178 (Council Oak Books); 978-1-885171 (Wildcat Canyon Press)
Number of titles published annually: 10 Print
Total Titles: 300 Print
Imprints: Wildcat Canyon Press (Women's relationships)
Distribution Center: Independent Publishers Group (IPG), 814 N Franklin St, Chicago, IL 60610 *Tel:* 312-337-0747 *Toll Free Tel:* 800-888-4741 *E-mail:* orders@ipgbook.com

Council of State Governments
2760 Research Park Dr, Lexington, KY 40511
Mailing Address: PO Box 11910, Lexington, KY 40578-1910
Tel: 859-244-8000 *Toll Free Tel:* 800-800-1910 *Fax:* 859-244-8001
E-mail: sales@csg.org
Web Site: www.csg.org; www.csgstore.org
Key Personnel
Exec Dir & CEO: David Adkins *E-mail:* dadkins@csg.org
Founded: 1933
Nonprofit association representing state government officials in all three branches. Publish reference guides, books, directories, journals, newsletters & conference proceedings & hold major regional & special topical conferences. Will contract or do grant-funded topic research. Specialize in corrections & public safety.
ISBN Prefix(es): 978-0-87292
Number of titles published annually: 10 Print
Total Titles: 72 Print
Branch Office(s)
1107 Ninth St, Suite 730, Sacramento, CA 95814, Exec Dir: Edgar E Ruiz *Tel:* 916-553-4423 *Fax:* 916-446-5760 *E-mail:* csgw@csg.org *Web Site:* www.csgwest.org
444 N Capitol St NW, Suite 401, Washington, DC 20001 *Tel:* 202-624-5460 *Fax:* 202-624-5452 *Web Site:* www.csgdc.org
PO Box 98129, Atlanta, GA 30359, Dir: Colleen Cousineau *Tel:* 404-633-1866 *Fax:* 404-633-4896 *E-mail:* slc@csg.org *Web Site:* www.slcatlanta.org
701 E 22 St, Suite 110, Lombard, IL 60148, Dir: Michael H McCabe *Tel:* 630-925-1922 *E-mail:* csgm@csg.org *Web Site:* www.csgmidwest.org
22 Cortlandt St, 22nd fl, New York, NY 10007, Dir: Wendell Hannaford *Tel:* 212-482-2320 *Fax:* 212-482-2344 *E-mail:* info@csg-erc.org *Web Site:* www.csg-erc.org

Council on Foreign Relations Press
Division of Council on Foreign Relations
The Harold Pratt House, 58 E 68 St, New York, NY 10065
SAN: 201-7784
Tel: 212-434-9400 *Fax:* 212-434-9800
E-mail: publications@cfr.org
Web Site: www.cfr.org
Key Personnel
Edit Dir: Patricia Dorff *Tel:* 212-434-9514 *Fax:* 212-434-9807 *E-mail:* pdorff@cfr.org
Founded: 1922
Scholarly books on foreign policy, international economics, international affairs.
ISBN Prefix(es): 978-0-87609
Number of titles published annually: 10 Print
Total Titles: 228 Print
Branch Office(s)
1777 "F" St NW, Washington, DC 20006 *Tel:* 202-509-8400 *Fax:* 202-509-8490
Distributed by Brookings Institution Press
Membership(s): AAP

Council on Social Work Education (CSWE)
1701 Duke St, Suite 200, Alexandria, VA 22314-3457
Tel: 703-683-8080 *Fax:* 703-683-8493
E-mail: publications@cswe.org; info@cswe.org
Web Site: www.cswe.org
Key Personnel
Pres & CEO: Darla Spence Coffey, PhD
Pubns Mgr: Elizabeth Simon *Tel:* 703-519-2076 *E-mail:* esimon@cswe.org
Founded: 1952
Professional books.
ISBN Prefix(es): 978-0-87293
Number of titles published annually: 6 Print
Total Titles: 75 Print
Membership(s): Association Media & Publishing

Counterpath Press
613 22 St, Denver, CO 80205
E-mail: counterpath@counterpathpress.org; editors@counterpathpress.org
Web Site: www.counterpathpress.org
Key Personnel
Assoc Dir & Co-Founder: Julie Carr
Dir: Tim Roberts
Assoc Ed: Will Skinker
Founded: 2006
Independent, nonprofit, literary publisher of poetry, fiction, drama, cross-genre work, literary & cultural theory & criticism, translations, reprints & high-quality Internet material.
ISBN Prefix(es): 978-1-933996
Number of titles published annually: 6 Print
Total Titles: 15 Print
Distribution Center: Small Press Distribution, 1341 Seventh St, Berkeley, CA 94710-1409, Deputy Dir: Laura Moriarty *Tel:* 510-524-1668 *Fax:* 510-524-0852 *E-mail:* laura@spdbooks.org *Web Site:* www.spdbooks.org
Membership(s): Community of Literary Magazines & Presses

Counterpoint Press LLC
1919 Fifth St, Berkeley, CA 94710
Tel: 510-704-0230 *Fax:* 510-704-0268
E-mail: info@counterpointpress.com
Web Site: counterpointpress.com; www.sierraclub.org/books; softskull.com
Key Personnel
CEO & Exec Ed: Charlie Winton
VP & Edit Dir: Jack Shoemaker
Publr, Counterpoint/Soft Skull: Rolph Blythe
Exec Ed: Dan Smetanka
Publicity Dir: Megan Fishmann
Busn Mgr: Kelli Adams
Founded: 2007 (through acquisition of Counterpoint, Shoemaker & Hoard, & Soft Skull Press)
Publish literary work with an emphasis on fiction, natural history, philosophy & contemporary thought, history, art, poetry, narrative & nonfiction.
ISBN Prefix(es): 978-1-887178; 978-1-58243; 978-1-61902 (Counterpoint); 978-1-933368 (Soft Skull); 978-1-57805 (Serra Club Books); 978-0-9796636 (Soft Skull); 978-1-932360 (Soft Skull); 978-1-887128 (Soft Skull)
Number of titles published annually: 60 Print
Total Titles: 60 Print
Imprints: Counterpoint; Sierra Club Books; Soft Skull Press
Foreign Rep(s): Bookwise International (Australia, New Zealand); Publishers Group Canada (Canada); Publishers Group Worldwide (Worldwide exc Australia, Canada, Ireland, New Zealand, UK & USA); Turnaround Publisher Service (Ireland, UK)
Foreign Rights: Anatolialit Agency (Amy Marie Spangler) (Turkey); Big Apple Agency (Wendy King) (China); Big Apple Agency (Chris Lin) (Taiwan); Katai Bolza Agency (Peter Bolza) (Hungary); Ersilia Literary Agency (Evangelia Avloniti) (Greece); The Foreign Office (Teresa Vilarrubla) (Brazil, Portugal, South America, Spain); Graal Agency (Parcin Biegaj) (Poland); Deborah Harris Agency (Ilana Kurshan) (Israel); Mohrbooks AG Literary Agency (Annelie Geissler) (Germany); Piergiorgio Nicolazzini Literary Agency (Maura Solinas) (Italy); La Nouvelle Agence (Anne Maizeret, Michele Kanonidis & Vanessa Kling) (France); Prava i Prevodi (Milena Kaplarevic) (Eastern Europe); Sebes & Van Gelderen Literary Agency (Jeanine Langenberg & Paul Sebes) (Netherlands); Abner Stein Agency (Anna Carmichael) (UK)
Distribution Center: Publishers Group West, 1700 Fourth St, Berkeley, CA 94710 *Toll Free Tel:* 800-788-3123 *Fax:* 510-528-3444 *Web Site:* www.pgw.com

Country Music Foundation Press
Division of Country Music Hall of Fame® & Museum
222 Fifth Ave S, Nashville, TN 37203
Tel: 615-416-2001 *Fax:* 615-255-2245
E-mail: info@countrymusichalloffame.com
Web Site: www.countrymusichalloffame.com
Key Personnel
Writer/Ed: Michael McCall
Founded: 1967
Publish books & calendars. Also author books for trade publications & co-publish with Vanderbilt University Press.
ISBN Prefix(es): 978-0-8265; 978-0-915608
Number of titles published annually: 3 Print
Total Titles: 40 Print
Distributed by Chronicle; Oxford University Press Inc; Providence Publishing; Universe; Vanderbilt University Press

§The Countryman Press
Division of W W Norton & Co Inc
c/o W W Norton & Co Inc, 500 Fifth Ave, New York, NY 10110
SAN: 206-4901
Tel: 212-354-5500 *Fax:* 212-869-0856
E-mail: countrymanpress@wwnorton.com
Web Site: www.countrymanpress.com
Key Personnel
Chmn & Pres, W W Norton: W Drake McFeely
Edit Asst: Sarah Bennett *E-mail:* sbennett@wwnorton.com
Founded: 1973
ISBN Prefix(es): 978-0-936399; 978-1-58157; 978-0-914378; 978-0-88150; 978-0-942440
Number of titles published annually: 70 Print
Total Titles: 350 Print

Distributed by Penguin Books (CN only); W W Norton & Co Inc
Foreign Rep(s): W W Norton & Co Inc
Foreign Rights: Casanovas & Lynch (Portugal, Spain)
Advertising Agency: Bennett Book Advertising
Warehouse: National Book Co Inc, 800 Keystone Industrial Park, Scranton, PA 18512-4601

Course Technology, see Wadsworth Publishing

§Covenant Communications Inc
920 E State Rd, Suite F, American Fork, UT 84003-0416
Mailing Address: PO Box 416, American Fork, UT 84003-0416
Tel: 801-756-1041
E-mail: info@covenant-lds.com
Web Site: www.covenant-lds.com
Key Personnel
VP, Mktg: Robby Nichols *Tel:* 801-756-1041 ext 106 *E-mail:* robbyn@covenant-lds.com
Mng Ed, Multimedia & Electronic Publg: Phil Reschke *Tel:* 801-756-1041 ext 114
Sales Mgr: Tammy Kolkman *Tel:* 801-756-1041 ext 122
Founded: 1958
Publish for the LDS (Mormon) market.
ISBN Prefix(es): 978-1-55503; 978-1-57734; 978-1-59156; 978-1-59811; 978-1-60681; 978-1-62108; 978-1-68047
Number of titles published annually: 60 Print; 60 E-Book; 50 Audio
Total Titles: 300 Print; 500 E-Book; 450 Audio

Coyote Press
Affiliate of Archaeological Consulting
PO Box 3377, Salinas, CA 93912-3377
Tel: 831-422-4912 *Fax:* 831-422-4913
E-mail: orders@coyotepress.com
Web Site: www.coyotepress.com
Key Personnel
Owner & Ed: Gary Breschini, PhD
Founded: 1980
Archaeology, history, pre-history, ethnography, linguistics, rock art & Native American studies of Western North America.
ISBN Prefix(es): 978-1-55567; 978-1-4044
Number of titles published annually: 50 Print
Total Titles: 3,000 Print

CQ Press
Imprint of SAGE Publications
2300 "N" St NW, Suite 800, Washington, DC 20037
Tel: 202-729-1900 *Toll Free Tel:* 866-4CQ-PRESS (427-7737) *Fax:* 202-729-1923 *Toll Free Fax:* 800-380-3810
E-mail: customerservice@cqpress.com; librarysales@cqpress.com
Web Site: www.cqpress.com
Founded: 1959
Publisher of books, directories, subscriptions & web products on American politics, federal & state government, American institutions, campaigns & elections, current events & world affairs.
ISBN Prefix(es): 978-0-87187; 978-1-56802; 978-0-9625531; 978-1-56692; 978-0-7401; 978-1-933116; 978-1-60426; 978-0-9823537; 978-1-60871
Number of titles published annually: 50 Print
Total Titles: 300 Print; 4 CD-ROM; 1 Online; 3 E-Book
Foreign Rep(s): SAGE Publications (Amanda Fox); SAGE Publications (Sarah Broomhead); SAGE Publications Asia-Pacific Pte Ltd (Rosalia da Garcia)

§Crabtree Publishing Co
350 Fifth Ave, 59th fl, PMB 59051, New York, NY 10118
Tel: 212-496-5040 *Toll Free Tel:* 800-387-7650 *Toll Free Fax:* 800-355-7166
E-mail: custserv@crabtreebooks.com
Web Site: www.crabtreebooks.com
Key Personnel
Pres: Peter A Crabtree *Tel:* 212-496-5040 ext 225 *E-mail:* peter_c@crabtreebooks.com
Publr: Ms Bobbie Kalman *E-mail:* bobbiek@crabtreebooks.com
Cont & Gen Mgr: John Siemens *Tel:* 212-496-5040 ext 229 *E-mail:* john_s@crabtreebooks.com
VP, Opers: Craig Culliford *Tel:* 212-496-5040 ext 236 *E-mail:* craig_c@crabtreebooks.com
Edit Dir: Kathy Middleton *Tel:* 212-496-5040 ext 226 *E-mail:* kathy_m@crabtreebooks.com
Mktg Mgr: Julie Alguire *Tel:* 212-496-5040 ext 235 *E-mail:* julie_a@crabtreebooks.com
Sales Dir: Andrea Crabtree *Tel:* 212-496-5040 ext 265 *E-mail:* andrea_c@crabtreebooks.com
Dir, Art & New Media: Robert MacGregor *Tel:* 212-496-5040 ext 231 *E-mail:* rob_m@crabtreebooks.com
Cust Serv Mgr: Linda Wade *Tel:* 212-496-5040 ext 223 *E-mail:* linda_w@crabtreebooks.com
Warehouse Mgr: Karl Kasper *Tel:* 212-496-5040 ext 237 *E-mail:* warehouse@crabtreebooks.com
Founded: 1978
Publisher of children's nonfiction & fiction; library binding & paperback for school & trade.
ISBN Prefix(es): 978-0-86505; 978-0-7787; 978-1-4271
Number of titles published annually: 300 Print; 150 E-Book
Total Titles: 4,375 Print; 1,400 E-Book; 105 Audio
Subsidiaries: Crabtree Publishing Co Ltd (CN)
Distributor for Bayard; Maren Green
Foreign Rep(s): INT Press (Australia, New Zealand); Roundhouse Group (European Union, UK); Titles (South Africa)
Warehouse: 2299 Kenmore Ave, Buffalo, NY 14207
Membership(s): ABA; ALA; American Alliance of Museums; Educational Book & Media Association; Museum Store Association; NAIPR; National Science Teachers Association

§Craftsman Book Co
6058 Corte Del Cedro, Carlsbad, CA 92011
SAN: 159-7000
Tel: 760-438-7828 *Toll Free Tel:* 800-829-8123 *Fax:* 760-438-0398
Web Site: www.craftsman-book.com
Key Personnel
Chmn & Intl Rts: Gary Moselle *E-mail:* gary@costbook.com
Publr, Data Licensing: Ben Moselle *Tel:* 760-438-7828 ext 122 *E-mail:* ben@costbook.com
Dir, Lib Sales & Mgr, Sales & Ad: Jennifer Johnson *Tel:* 760-438-7828 ext 105 *E-mail:* johnson@costbook.com
Edit Mgr & Rts & Perms: Laurence Jacobs *Tel:* 760-438-7828 ext 108 *E-mail:* jacobs@costbook.com
Founded: 1952
Estimating software, trade & professional, state-specific contract-writing software, subscription, mail order & download, reference; construction industry.
ISBN Prefix(es): 978-0-934041; 978-0-910460; 978-1-57218
Number of titles published annually: 10 Print; 9 CD-ROM; 150 Online; 5 E-Book
Total Titles: 150 Print; 9 CD-ROM; 150 Online; 8 E-Book
Distributed by The Aberdeen Group; BNI Publications; Builders Book Inc
Distributor for BNI Publications; Builders Book Inc; Building News Inc; Home Builders Press
Foreign Rep(s): Gauge Publications (Canada)
Distribution Center: Quality Books Inc, 103 W Pines Rd, Oregon, IL 61061-9680 *Tel:* 815-732-4450 *Toll Free Tel:* 800-323-4241 *Fax:* 815-732-4499 *E-mail:* info@quality-books.com *Web Site:* www.quality-books.com

§CRC Press LLC
Subsidiary of Taylor & Francis
6000 Broken Sound Pkwy NW, Suite 300, Boca Raton, FL 33487
Tel: 561-994-0555 *Toll Free Tel:* 800-272-7737 (orders) *Toll Free Fax:* 800-643-9428 (sales); 800-374-3401 (orders)
E-mail: orders@crcpress.com; orders@taylorandfrancis.com
Web Site: www.crcpress.com
Key Personnel
Pres: Emmett Dages
SVP, Publg & Online Prods: John Lavender *Tel:* 561-998-2579 *E-mail:* john.lavender@taylorandfrancis.com
SVP, Sales: Dennis Weiss *Tel:* 561-998-2510 *Fax:* 561-998-2580 *E-mail:* dennis.weiss@taylorandfrancis.com
VP, Mktg: Stacey Mironov *E-mail:* stacey.mironov@taylorandfrancis.com
Founded: 1913
Premier publisher of science, technology & medical reference books, textbooks & online content.
ISBN Prefix(es): 978-0-8493; 978-0-935184; 978-1-57491; 978-0-87762; 978-1-56676; 978-0-87819; 978-1-58488; 978-1-58716; 978-1-4200; 978-1-4398; 978-1-4665; 978-1-4822; 978-1-4987
Number of titles published annually: 900 Print
Total Titles: 14,000 Print
Warehouse: Taylor & Francis, 7625 Empire Dr, Florence, KY 41042

§The Creative Co
PO Box 227, Mankato, MN 56002
Tel: 507-388-6273 *Toll Free Tel:* 800-445-6209 *Fax:* 507-388-2746
E-mail: info@thecreativecompany.us; orders@thecreativecompany.us
Web Site: www.thecreativecompany.us
Key Personnel
Owner & Publr: Tom Peterson *Tel:* 507-388-6273 ext 225
VP, Retail Sales, Creative Editions & Creative Paperbacks: Anna Erikson
Founded: 1932
Gift books.
ISBN Prefix(es): 978-0-87191; 978-0-88682; 978-0-89812; 978-1-56660; 978-1-56846; 978-1-60818; 978-1-62832; 978-1-58341
Number of titles published annually: 110 Print
Total Titles: 3,500 Print
Imprints: Creative Editions; Creative Education; Creative Paperbacks
Foreign Rep(s): JCC Enterprises Inc (Jerry C Carrillo) (Canada); Raincoast Books (Canada)
Warehouse: 2140 Howard Dr W, North Mankato, MN 56003

Creative Homeowner
Imprint of Fox Chapel Publishing Co Inc
1970 Broad St, East Petersburg, PA 17520
Tel: 717-560-4703 *Toll Free Tel:* 800-475-9112 *Fax:* 717-560-4702 *Toll Free Fax:* 888-369-2885
E-mail: customerservice@foxchapelpublishing.com; sales@foxchapelpublishing.com
Web Site: www.foxchapelpublishing.com/home-and-garden/creative-homeowner
Founded: 1978
Quality trade paperbacks for kitchen & bath design & decor, gardening, landscaping, outdoor hobbies & home improvement.
ISBN Prefix(es): 978-0-932944; 978-1-880029; 978-1-58011
Number of titles published annually: 20 Print
Total Titles: 220 Print

Cricket Cottage Publishing LLC
4409 Hoffner Ave, Unit 127, Orlando, FL 32812
Tel: 407-255-7785
E-mail: cricketcottage@att.net
Web Site: www.thecricketpublishing.com
Key Personnel
Pres: Andrew Robinson *Tel:* 407-928-6215 *E-mail:* drwhoar@hotmail.com
VP: Jo Ann Robinson *Tel:* 407-923-1738 *E-mail:* jodero5325@yahoo.com
Info Technol: Alexa Robinson *Tel:* 407-412-1712 *E-mail:* dumbledoresarmyfau@gmail.com
Founded: 2012
Micro-publisher combining the best of traditional & modern publishing. Strictly royalty-based, giving authors a new chance & making use of social media to help promote the company & its books. Basic editing/proofing, book formatting & cover design. Online distribution for paperback & ebook versions.
Number of titles published annually: 15 Print; 12 Online; 15 E-Book
Total Titles: 28 Print; 24 Online; 24 E-Book

Crickhollow Books
Imprint of Great Lakes Literary LLC
3147 S Pennsylvania Ave, Milwaukee, WI 53207
Tel: 414-294-4319
E-mail: info@crickhollowbooks.com
Web Site: www.crickhollowbooks.com
Key Personnel
Edit Dir: Philip Martin
Founded: 1993
Publish books on regional heritage, with a focus on books for children, fiction & chapter books with a regional slant.
ISBN Prefix(es): 978-1-883953
Number of titles published annually: 3 Print
Total Titles: 12 Print
Membership(s): The Independent Book Publishers Association

§Cross-Cultural Communications
Division of Cross-Cultural Literary Editions Inc
239 Wynsum Ave, Merrick, NY 11566-4725
SAN: 208-6122
Tel: 516-868-5635 *Fax:* 516-379-1901
E-mail: info@cross-culturalcommunications.com; cccbarkan@optonline.net; cccpoetry@aol.com
Web Site: www.cross-culturalcommunications.com
Key Personnel
Publr & Ed-in-Chief: Stanley H Barkan
Art Ed: Bebe Barkan
Asst Ed: Mia Barkan Clarke
Founded: 1971
Traditionally neglected languages & cultures in bilingual format, primarily poetry, some fiction, drama, music & art. Cross-cultural review series of world literature & art in sound, print & motion.
ISBN Prefix(es): 978-0-89304
Number of titles published annually: 20 Print; 1 CD-ROM; 100 Online; 1 Audio
Total Titles: 420 Print; 3 CD-ROM; 300 Online; 14 Audio
Imprints: ARC (Magazine & Press) (Israel); Chlen$kiy Publishing (US & Russia); Cross-Cultural Prototypes; Expressive Editions; Fact Publishers (Ukraine); Midrashic Editions; Nightingale Editions; Ostrich Editions; The Seventh Quarry (Wales, Seventh Quarry Chapbook Series); The Seventh Quarry Press
Subsidiaries: Bulgarian-American Cultural Society ALEKO (Chicago/Sofia, Bulgaria); Varlik (Turkey)
Branch Office(s)
3131 Mott Ave, Far Rockaway, NY 11691, Contact: Roy Cravzow *Tel:* 718-327-4714
6 Pfeiffer Ridge, Big Sur, CA 93920, Contact: Patricia Holt *Tel:* 831-667-2433 *E-mail:* surph8@yahoo.com
Foreign Office(s): Antigruppo Siciliano, Via Mogia 8, 90138 Palermo, Sicily PA, Italy, Contact: Nicolo D'Alessandro *Tel:* (091) 322030 *E-mail:* nicolodalessandro@virgilio.it
Distributed by Ad Infinitum Books; Hochelaga (Canada)
Distributor for Ad Infinitum Press; Arba Sicula (Magazine, US); Center of Emigrants from Serbia (Serbia); Decalogue Books (US); The Feral Press (US); Greenfield Review Press (US); Hochelaga (Canada); Immagine&Poesia (Italy); Legas Publishers (CN); Lips (Magazine & Press) (US); Pholiota Press Inc (England); The Seventh Quarry Press (Wales); Shabdaguchha (Magazine & Press) (Bangladesh & US); Sicilia Parra (Magazine, US); Word & Quill Press (US)
Foreign Rep(s): Hassanal Abdullah (Bangladesh, USA); Karen Alkalay-Gut (Israel); Max Babi (India); Vahe Baladouni (Armenia, USA); Raymond Beauchemin (Canada); August Bover (Spain); Bohdan Boychuk (Ukraine); Gaetano Cipolla (Italy, USA); Nicolo D'Alessandro (Italy); Kristine Doll (Spain, USA); Christopher Fauske (Norway, USA); Isaac Goldemberg (Peru, USA); Theofil Halama (Czech Republic, USA); Luisa A Igloria (Philippines, USA); Vladimir Kandelaki (Georgia); Dovid Katz (UK); Naoshi Koriyama (Japan); Dariusz Thomasz Lebioda (Poland); Vladimir Levchev (Bulgaria, USA); Bijana D Obradovic (Montenegro, Serbia, USA); Ritva Poom (Estonia, Finland, USA); Kyung-Nyun "Kay" Kim Richards (South Korea, USA); Stephen A Sadow (Argentina, USA); Marco Scalabrino (Italy); Stoyan "Tchouki" Tchoukanov (Bulgaria); Peter Thabit Jones (UK); Tino Villanueva (Mexico, USA); Claire Nicolas White (Netherlands, USA); Sara Wolosker (Brazil)
Membership(s): ALTA

Crossquarter Publishing Group
PO Box 23749, Santa Fe, NM 87502
Tel: 505-690-3923 *Fax:* 214-975-9715
E-mail: sales@crossquarter.com; info@crossquarter.com
Web Site: www.crossquarter.com
Key Personnel
Exec Dir: Therese Francis
Founded: 1986
Small book press with some sidelines. Publishes books, ebooks & information packages. No longer accept fiction queries.
ISBN Prefix(es): 978-1-890109
Number of titles published annually: 25 Print; 3 E-Book
Total Titles: 57 Print; 2 E-Book
Imprints: Crossquarter Breeze; CrossTIME; Fenris Brothers; Herb & Spice; Xemplar
Membership(s): The Association of Publishers for Special Sales; The Independent Book Publishers Association

§The Crossroad Publishing Co
831 Chestnut Ridge Rd, Chestnut Ridge, NY 10977
SAN: 287-0118
Tel: 845-517-0180 *Toll Free Tel:* 800-888-4741 (orders) *Fax:* 845-517-0181
E-mail: office@crossroadpublishing.com
Web Site: www.CrossroadPublishing.com
Key Personnel
CEO & Publr: Dr Gwendolin Herder
Off Admin: Stephanie Marchese
Founded: 1980
Independent book publisher in religion, spirituality, theology, personal growth, leadership & parenting.
ISBN Prefix(es): 978-0-8245
Number of titles published annually: 30 Print; 1 CD-ROM; 1 Online; 20 E-Book; 1 Audio
Total Titles: 550 Print; 1 CD-ROM; 1 Online; 20 E-Book; 4 Audio
Imprints: Crossroad (trade secular & religious); Herder & Herder (Catholic parish & academic)
Foreign Rep(s): John Garratt (Australia); Novalis (Canada)
Billing Address: Independent Publishers Group, 814 N Franklin St, Chicago, IL 60610 *E-mail:* orders@ipgbook.com *Web Site:* www.ipgbook.com
Membership(s): Association of Catholic Publishers Inc

Crossway
Division of Good News Publishers
1300 Crescent St, Wheaton, IL 60187
SAN: 211-7991
Tel: 630-682-4300 *Toll Free Tel:* 800-635-7993 (orders); 800-543-1659 (cust serv) *Fax:* 630-682-4785
E-mail: info@crossway.org
Web Site: www.crossway.org
Key Personnel
Pres: Lane T Dennis
EVP, Bible Ministry Rel: Randy Jahns
EVP, Design Servs: Josh Dennis
SVP & Publr, Books: Justin Taylor
SVP, Bible Publg: Dane Ortlund
SVP, Fin: Paul Thomas
VP, Sales: Anthony Gosling
Edit Administrator, Perms & ISBN Contact: Jill Carter *E-mail:* jcarter@crossway.org
Intl Rts: Aaron Camp
Founded: 1969
Books with an evangelical Christian perspective aimed at the religious market.
ISBN Prefix(es): 978-0-89107; 978-1-58134; 978-1-4335
Number of titles published annually: 80 Print
Total Titles: 354 Print; 9 Audio

§Crown House Publishing Co LLC
Division of Crown House Publishing Ltd (UK Co)
6 Trowbridge Dr, Bethel, CT 06801
SAN: 013-9270
Tel: 203-778-1300 *Toll Free Tel:* 877-925-1213 (cust serv); 866-272-8497 *Fax:* 203-778-9100
E-mail: info@chpus.com
Web Site: www.crownhousepublishing.com
Key Personnel
Pres: Mark Tracten *E-mail:* mtracten@chpus.com
Founded: 1996
Publisher of quality books in psychology & education.
ISBN Prefix(es): 978-1-89983; 978-1-90442; 978-1-84590; 978-0-98235
Number of titles published annually: 30 Print; 1 CD-ROM; 6 Audio
Total Titles: 330 Print; 2 CD-ROM; 30 Audio
Distributor for Developing Press Co; Human Alchemy Publications; Institute Press; Transforming Press
Foreign Rep(s): Footprint Books Pty Ltd (Australia, New Zealand)
Foreign Rights: Anglo-American Book Co Ltd (Europe, UK)
Billing Address: PO Box 2223, Williston, VT 05495
Orders to: PO Box 2223, Williston, VT 05495, Contact: Matt Drake *Fax:* 802-864-7626 *E-mail:* mdrake@aidcvt.com
Returns: 82 Wintersport Lane, Williston, VT 05496, Contact: Matt Drake *E-mail:* mdrake@aidcvt.com
Shipping Address: PO Box 2223, Williston, VT 05495, Contact: Laurie Kenyon *Tel:* 802-862-0095 ext 113 *Fax:* 802-864-7626 *E-mail:* info@chpus.com
Warehouse: PO Box 2223, Williston, VT 05495 *E-mail:* info@chpus.com
Distribution Center: 82 Wintersport Lane, Williston, VT 05496, Contact: Laurie Kenyon *Fax:* 802-864-7626 *E-mail:* lkenyon@aidcvt.com

Crown Publishing Group
Division of Penguin Random House Inc
c/o Penguin Random House Inc, 1745 Broadway, New York, NY 10019
Tel: 212-782-9000 *Toll Free Tel:* 888-264-1745 *Fax:* 212-940-7408
E-mail: crownosm@penguinrandomhouse.com
Web Site: crownpublishing.com
Key Personnel
Pres & Publr: Maya Mavjee
EVP & Exec Dir, Mktg & Publicity: Donna Passanante
EVP & Dir, Publicity: Carisa Hays
SVP & Dir, Publg Opers: Jill Flaxman
SVP, Publg Opers: Pete Muller
SVP & Creative Dir: Whitney Cookman
SVP & Deputy Publr: David Drake
SVP & Publr, Clarkson Potter, Potter Craft & Potter Style: Lauren Shakely
SVP & Publr, Crown Business, Crown Forum & Religious Publg: Tina Constable
SVP & Publr, Crown Publishers, Crown Archetype, Broadway Books, Hogarth & Three Rivers Press: Molly Stern
VP & Publr, Ten Speed Press: Aaron Wehner
VP & Publr, WaterBrook Multnomah: Alexander Field
VP & Assoc Publr, Ed-in-Chief, Doubleday Religion: Trace Murphy
VP & Assoc Publr, Crown, Hogarth, Archetype, Tim Duggan Books, Broadway Books & Three Rivers Press: Annsley Rosner
VP & Assoc Publr, Trade Paperbacks: Catherine Pollock
VP & Exec Ed, Convergent Books: David Kopp
VP & Exec Ed, Crown Archetype: Dominick Anfuso
VP & Exec Ed, Harmony Books: Heather Jackson
VP & Edit Dir, Crown Archetype & Three Rivers Press: Tricia Boczkowski
VP & Edit Dir, WaterBrook Multnomah: Laura Barker
VP & Creative Dir: Christopher Brand
VP & Dir, Academic Mktg & Lib Sales: Skip Dye
VP & Dir, Mktg & Publicity, Clarkson Potter & Potter Style: Kate Tyler
VP & Dir, Prodn: Linnea Knollmueller
VP & Dir, Sales, Mktg & Publicity, Ten Speed Press: Patricia Kelly
VP & Dir, Subs Rts: Lance Fitzgerald
VP & Mng Ed: Amy Boorstein
Publr, Monacelli Press: Gianfranco Monacelli
Publr, Tim Duggan Books: Tim Duggan
Assoc Publr, Broadway Books & Hogart Paperbacks: Sheila O'Shea
Assoc Publr, Crown Business, Crown Forum & Convergent: Campbell Wharton
Creative Dir, Clarkson Potter & BOT: Marysarah Quinn
Dir, Community Devt: Kate Rados
Edit Dir, Crown & Hogarth: Lindsay Sagnette
Edit Dir, Crown Business: Roger Scholl
Edit Dir, Monacelli Press: Andrea Monfried
Dir of Mktg & Publicity, Crown Business: Jocelyn Cordova
Mktg Dir, Crown Archetype, Three Rivers Press & Harmony Books: Julie Cepler
Mktg Dir, Crown Publishers & Broadway Books: Patty Berg
Mktg Dir, Ten Speed Press: Michele Crim
Deputy Mktg Dir, Crown Publishing Group & Mktg Dir, Clarkson Potter, Potter Craft, Potter Style & Monacelli Press: Donna Passannante
Assoc Dir, Dom Rts: Courtney Snyder
Assoc Dir, Foreign Rts: Rachel Berkowitz
Asst Dir of Mktg, Clarkson Potter, Potter Style & Potter Craft: Carly Gorga
Exec Publicist: Sarah Breivogel
Sr Publicist, Harmony: Lauren Cook
Publicist: Lauren Kuhn; Rebecca Marsh
Publicist, Clarkson Potter: Natasha Martin
Publicist/Marketer, Convergent Books: Jessica Brown
Publicity Dir, Crown Archetype, Harmony Books, Crown Forum, Three Rivers: Tammy Blake
Publicity Dir, Crown, Hogarth, Tim Duggan Books & Broadway Books: Rachel Rokicki
Publicity Dir, Potter Craft, Watson-Guptill & Monacelli Press: Kim Small
Assoc Publicity Dir, Crown, Hogarth, Tim Duggan Books & Broadway Books: Dyana Messina
Asst Publicity Dir, Crown Archetype: Ellen Folan
Publicity Mgr, Crown Business & Crown Forum: Megan Perritt
Assoc Publicist, Crown Trade: Rebecca Welbourn
Imprint Sales Dir: Candice Chaplin
Imprint Sales Dir, Publg Brands: Jacqueline Lebow
Assoc Prodn Dir: Luisa Francaville
Publg Mgr, Crown Archetype, Harmony, Crown Business, Crown Forum: Mary Choteborsky
Publg Mgr, Crown, Crown Archetype, Hogarth, Broadway, Three Rivers Press & Tim Duggan Books: Rachel Meier
Publg Mgr, Three Rivers Press: Heather Lazare
Sr Mgr, Community Devt: Alana Buckbee
Sr Mgr, Community Opers: Chris Sigfrids
Sr Mktg Mgr, Crown Trade: Sarah Pekdemir
Sr Mktg Mgr, Harmony: Christina Foxley
Sr Prodn Mgr: Serena Sigona
Community Devt Mgr, Blogging for Books: Emma Shafer
Assoc Mgr, Foreign Rts, Ten Speed, Clarkson Potter, Potter Style, Potter Craft & Pam Krauss Books: Nidhi Berry
Mktg Mgr, Clarkson Potter & Harmony: Stephanie Davis
Mktg Mgr, Crown Business & Crown Forum: Ayelet Gruenspecht
Mktg Mgr, Hogarth, Crown & Broadway Books: Keyleigh George; Jessica Prudhomme
Mktg & Publicity Mgr, Watson-Guptill & Amphoto Books: Natalie Mulford
E-Mail Mktg Mgr: Kevin Jan
Assoc Mktg Mgr, Crown Archetype & Three Rivers Press: Gianna Antolos
Assoc Mktg Mgr, Ten Speed Press, Watson-Guptill & Amphoto Books: Daniel Wikey
Asst Mktg Mgr: Emily Davis
Asst Mktg Mgr, Clarkson Potter, Potter Style & Potter Craft: Kevin Sweeting
Prepress Mgr: Neil Spitkovsky
Exec Ed, Crown Archetype: Suzanne O'Neill
Exec Ed, Crown/Hogarth: Alexis Washam
Digital Mng Ed: Alissa Kleinman
Mng Ed, Crown, Hogarth, Broadway, Tim Duggan Books, Crown Archetype & Three Rivers Press: Aislinn Belton
Assoc Mng Ed: Hanna Glidden
Sr Ed: Julian Pavia; Hilary Rubin Teeman
Sr Ed, Convergent: Gary Jansen
Sr Ed, Crown Publishers: Kevin Doughten
Sr Ed, Crown Archetype: Talia Krohn
Sr Ed, Crown Archetype & Three Rivers Press: Matt Inman
Sr Prodn Ed/Digital Copy Chief: Patricia Shaw
Ed: Domenica Alioto
Ed, Harmony Books: Leah Miller
Assoc Ed: Miriam Chotiner-Gardiner
Assoc Ed, Clarkson Potter & Potter Style: Amanda Englander
Assoc Ed, Crown Business, Crown Forum & Convergent: Derek Reed
Assoc Ed, Crown/Hogarth: Nathan Roberson
Asst Ed: Emma Boyer; Nora Evans-Reitz; Meghan Houser; Claire Potter
Asst Ed, Crown Archetype & Three Rivers Press: Jesse Aylen
Asst Ed, Crown/Hogarth: Sarah Bedingfield
Assoc, Ad Promo: Ellyn Russo
Community Devt Assoc: Ta-Tanisha Williams
Mktg Assoc: Danielle Crabtree
Mktg Assoc, Archetype, Crown Forum & Three Rivers Press: Tommy Cabrera
Mktg Assoc, Crown Archetype: Gianna Sandri
Prodn Assoc: Shira Gluck; Virginia Rhoda; Heather Williamson
Category Specialist: Allison Devlin
Sr Web Developer: Matt Uhnjem
Assoc Web Developer: Maren Childs
Data Analyst: Patrick Lee
Mktg Data Analyst: Alex Czik
Founded: 1933
Nonfiction & fiction; illustrated books; business books.
Random House Inc & its publishing entities are not accepting unsol submissions, proposals, mss or submission queries via e-mail at this time.
ISBN Prefix(es): 978-0-553; 978-0-609; 978-0-307; 978-0-8129; 978-1-4000; 978-0-8041; 978-0-517
Number of titles published annually: 400 Print
Imprints: Amphoto Books; Broadway Books; Clarkson Potter; Convergent Books; Crown Archetype; Crown Business; Crown Forum; Crown Publishers; Doubleday Religion; Tim Duggan Books; Harmony; Hogarth; Image Books; Potter Craft; Potter Style; Ten Speed Press; Three Rivers Press; WaterBrook Multnomah; Watson-Guptill
See separate listing for:
Clarkson Potter Publishers
Ten Speed Press
Watson-Guptill Publications

Crumb Elbow Publishing
PO Box 294, Rhododendron, OR 97049-0294
Tel: 503-622-4798
Key Personnel
Publr: Michael P Jones
Founded: 1979
Send an SASE for all mss, no exceptions.
ISBN Prefix(es): 978-0-89904
Number of titles published annually: 20 Print; 5 Audio
Total Titles: 500 Print
Imprints: Bear Meadows Research Group; Cascade Expeditions; Cascade Geographic Society; Ecosystem Research Group; Elbow Books; The Final Edition; Horse Latitudes Press; Lady Fern Press; Meadow Creek Press; Oregon Fever Books; Oregon River Watch; Read'n Run Books; Research Centrex; Sealife Research Alliance; Silhouette Imprints; Timberline Productions; Trillium Mountain Productions; Tyee Press; Wildlife Research Group; Wild Mountain Press; Windflower Press

§Crystal Clarity Publishers
14618 Tyler Foote Rd, Nevada City, CA 95959
Tel: 530-478-7600 *Toll Free Tel:* 800-424-1055 *Fax:* 530-478-7610
E-mail: clarity@crystalclarity.com
Web Site: www.crystalclarity.com
Key Personnel
Pres & Publr: Richard Salva *Tel:* 530-478-7600 ext 7606
Sales Mgr: Avital Miller *Tel:* 530-478-7600 ext 7605 *E-mail:* sales@crystalclarity.com
Founded: 1968
Self-help, psychology, philosophy, religion, business, books, tapes, videos, sidelines, metaphysical, health/healing.
ISBN Prefix(es): 978-0-916124; 978-1-878265; 978-1-56589
Number of titles published annually: 6 Print
Total Titles: 104 Print; 15 Audio
Imprints: Clarity Sound & Light
Foreign Rep(s): Brumby Books (Australia); Deep Books Ltd (England, Europe); National Book Network (Canada, New Zealand); New Horizons (South Africa)
Foreign Rights: Alexandra McGilloway

Crystal Productions
5320 Carpinteria Ave, Suite K, Carpinteria, CA 93013-2107

Tel: 847-657-8144 *Toll Free Tel:* 800-255-8629 *Fax:* 847-657-8149 *Toll Free Fax:* 800-657-8149
E-mail: custserv@crystalproductions.com
Web Site: www.crystalproductions.com
Key Personnel
Pres: Amy L Woodworth *E-mail:* alwcp@aol.com
Founded: 1973
Art education resources including interactive digital software, digital downloads, DVDs, posters, prints, books & more for preK, elementary, middle, secondary & college.
ISBN Prefix(es): 978-0-924509; 978-1-56290
Number of titles published annually: 2 Print; 1 CD-ROM

Crystal Publishers Inc
3460 Lost Hills Dr, Las Vegas, NV 89122
Tel: 702-434-3037 *Fax:* 702-434-3037
Web Site: www.crystalpub.com
Key Personnel
Pres: Frank Leanza *E-mail:* leanzaent@centurylink.net
Exec Dir: Inge Allen
Founded: 1985
Music books for schools & professionals.
ISBN Prefix(es): 978-0-934687
Number of titles published annually: 15 Print
Total Titles: 45 Print

CSHL Press, see Cold Spring Harbor Laboratory Press

The CSIS Press
Division of Center for Strategic & International Studies
1616 Rhode Island Ave, Washington, DC 20036
Tel: 202-887-0200 *Fax:* 202-775-3199
E-mail: books@csis.org
Web Site: www.csis.org
Key Personnel
CEO & Pres: John J Hamre
Dir: James R Dunton *Tel:* 202-775-3160 *E-mail:* jdunton@csis.org
Founded: 1962
Public policy research organization.
ISBN Prefix(es): 978-0-89206
Number of titles published annually: 65 Print; 65 Online; 25 E-Book
Total Titles: 250 Print; 100 Online; 200 E-Book
Distributed by Rowman & Littlefield
Membership(s): AAP

§CSLI Publications
Stanford University, Cordura Hall, 220 Panama St, Stanford, CA 94305-4115
Tel: 650-723-1839 *Fax:* 650-725-2166
E-mail: pubs@csli.stanford.edu
Web Site: cslipublications.stanford.edu
Key Personnel
Dir: Dikran Karagueuzian *Tel:* 650-723-1712 *E-mail:* dikran@csli.stanford.edu
Founded: 1985
Subjects include computer science, computational linguistics, linguistics & philosophy.
ISBN Prefix(es): 978-0-937073; 978-1-881526; 978-1-57586; 978-0-226
Number of titles published annually: 10 Print
Total Titles: 339 Print; 7 Online
Distributed by University of Chicago Press
Advertising Agency: University of Chicago Press, 1427 E 60 St, Chicago, IL 60637-2954 *Tel:* 773-568-1550 *Toll Free Tel:* 800-621-2736 *Fax:* 773-660-2235 *Toll Free Fax:* 800-621-8471

CTB/McGraw-Hill
Division of McGraw-Hill Education
20 Ryan Ranch Rd, Monterey, CA 93940-5703
Tel: 831-393-0700 *Toll Free Tel:* 800-538-9547 *Fax:* 831-393-7825 *Toll Free Fax:* 800-282-0266
Web Site: www.ctb.com
Key Personnel
COO: Sandor Nagy
Pres: Ellen Haley
VP, Res: Craig N Mills *E-mail:* craig_mills@mcgraw-hill.com
VP, Sales: David Seitter *E-mail:* david_seitter@mcgraw-hill.com
Founded: 1926
Publishes nationally standardized tests, provides comprehensive scoring & reporting services & creates online solutions for managing & reporting test scores & student information to support sound accountability decisions.
ISBN Prefix(es): 978-0-9726382

Cumberland House
Imprint of Sourcebooks Inc
1935 Brookdale Rd, Suite 139, Naperville, IL 60563
Tel: 630-961-3900 *Toll Free Tel:* 800-43-BRIGHT (432-7444) *Fax:* 630-961-2168
E-mail: info@sourcebooks.com
Web Site: www.sourcebooks.com
Key Personnel
CEO & Publr, Sourcebooks: Dominique Raccah
Founded: 1996
Nonfiction books & current subjects include cooking, regional topics, humor & lifestyle books.
ISBN Prefix(es): 978-1-888952; 978-1-58182
Number of titles published annually: 60 Print
Total Titles: 240 Print
Membership(s): ABA; The Independent Book Publishers Association; Southern Independent Booksellers Alliance

Cummings & Hathaway Publishers
395 Atlantic Ave, East Rockaway, NY 11518
Tel: 516-593-3607 *Fax:* 516-593-1401
Key Personnel
Pres: William Burke
Founded: 1980
Publish paperback books only.
ISBN Prefix(es): 978-1-57981; 978-0-943025
Number of titles published annually: 5 Print
Total Titles: 48 Print

CUNY Journalism Press
Division of CUNY Graduate School of Journalism
219 W 40 St, New York, NY 10018
Tel: 646-758-7824 *Fax:* 646-758-7809
Web Site: www.journalism.cuny.edu; press.journalism.cuny.edu
Founded: 2012
Publish serious books about journalism & the news media - history, theory, criticism, craft, memoir & more.
ISBN Prefix(es): 978-1-939293
Number of titles published annually: 6 Print
Total Titles: 6 E-Book
Distributed by OR Books

§Cup of Tea Books
Imprint of PageSpring Publishing
PO Box 21133, Columbus, OH 43221
Tel: 614-264-5588
E-mail: sales@pagespringpublishing.com
Web Site: www.cupofteabooks.com
Key Personnel
Publr & Ed: Rebecca Seum
Founded: 2012
Independent publisher. Specialize in quality women's fiction.
ISBN Prefix(es): 978-1-939403
Number of titles published annually: 2 Print; 2 E-Book
Total Titles: 9 Print; 8 E-Book

Cycle Publishing LLC
1282 Seventh Ave, San Francisco, CA 94122-2526
Tel: 415-665-8214 *Fax:* 415-753-8572
Web Site: www.cyclepublishing.com
Key Personnel
Principal & Publr: Rob van der Plas *E-mail:* rvdp@vanderplas.net
Founded: 1997
Books on sports, fitness, home building & home buying; emphasis on cycling.
ISBN Prefix(es): 978-1-892495
Number of titles published annually: 3 Print
Total Titles: 30 Print
Imprints: Cycle Publishing; Van der Plas Publications
Foreign Rights: Bicycling (Australia); Fahrradbuch.de (Austria, Germany); Orca Book Services (UK)
Warehouse: PCFS, 35 Ash Dr, Kimball, MI 48074
Membership(s): The Association of Publishers for Special Sales; The Independent Book Publishers Association

Cyclotour Guide Books
160 Harvard St, Rochester, NY 14607-3174
Tel: 585-244-6157
E-mail: cyclotour@cyclotour.com
Web Site: www.cyclotour.com
Key Personnel
Publr & Author: Harvey Botzman
Founded: 1993
Books, bicycling related, bicycle (cycling), travel guides.
Publisher is a member of the League of American Bicyclists, New York Bicycling Coalition & New York State Travel Industry Association (NYSTIA).
ISBN Prefix(es): 978-1-889602
Number of titles published annually: 4 Print
Total Titles: 5 Print

Cypress House
Imprint of Comp-Type Inc
155 Cypress St, Fort Bragg, CA 95437
Tel: 707-964-9520 *Toll Free Tel:* 800-773-7782 *Fax:* 707-964-7531
E-mail: cypresshouse@cypresshouse.com
Web Site: www.cypresshouse.com
Key Personnel
Pres: Cynthia Frank *E-mail:* cynthia@cypresshouse.com
Mng Ed: Joe Shaw *E-mail:* joeshaw@cypresshouse.com
Prodn Mgr: Michael Brechner *E-mail:* unclemike@cypresshouse.com
ISBN Prefix(es): 978-1-879384
Number of titles published annually: 10 Print
Total Titles: 1 Audio
Imprints: QED Press
Membership(s): ABA; The Independent Book Publishers Association; Northern California Independent Booksellers Association; Pacific Northwest Booksellers Association

Da Capo Press & Lifelong Books
Member of The Perseus Books Group
44 Farnsworth St, 3rd fl, Boston, MA 02210
SAN: 201-2944
Tel: 617-252-5200 *Toll Free Tel:* 800-343-4499 (orders) *Fax:* 617-252-5285
Web Site: www.perseusbooksgroup.com/dacapo
Key Personnel
Dir, Mktg: Kevin Hanover *Tel:* 617-252-5262
Sr Dir, Publicity: Lissa Warren *Tel:* 617-252-5212 *Fax:* 617-252-5265 *E-mail:* lissa.warren@perseusbooks.com
Dir, Publicity: Kate Burke
Sr Ed: Dan Ambrosio
Assoc Ed: Claire Ivett
Founded: 1964

Publishes a wide-ranging list of nonfiction titles, both hardcover & paperback, focusing on history, music, the performing arts, sports & popular culture. Lifelong Books is a health & wellness imprint founded in 2003 that publishes books on pregnancy, parenting, fitness, cooking, diabetes, psychology, personal growth & sexuality.
ISBN Prefix(es): 978-0-201; 978-0-7867; 978-0-306; 978-1-55561; 978-1-56858; 978-1-56924; 978-0-7382; 978-1-60094
Number of titles published annually: 90 Print
Total Titles: 5,000 Print
Branch Office(s)
387 Park Ave S, New York, NY 10016
Distributed by The Perseus Books Group
Warehouse: 1094 Flex Dr, Jackson, TN 38301

Dalkey Archive Press
University of Houston-Victoria, 3007 N Ben Wilson, Victoria, TX 77901
E-mail: contact@dalkeyarchive.com
Web Site: www.dalkeyarchive.com
Key Personnel
Dir: John O'Brien
Assoc Dir: Jake Snyder
Prodn Mgr: Jeff Higgins
Asst Ed: Nathaniel Davis
Founded: 1984
Literary fiction, translations & criticism. We keep works of literary value in print.
ISBN Prefix(es): 978-0-916583; 978-1-56478; 978-1-62897; 978-1-943150
Number of titles published annually: 112 Print
Total Titles: 550 Print
Distributed by Columbia University Press
Foreign Rep(s): Aromix Books Co Ltd (Nick Woon & Jane Lam) (Hong Kong); Book Marketing Services (S Janakiraman) (India); Booknet Co Ltd (Ms Suphaluck Sattabuz) (Thailand); Columbia University Press (Africa, Europe, Middle East, South Africa, South Asia, UK); Everest International Publishing Services (Wei Zhao) (China); Footprint Books (Australia, New Zealand); harbra (Julio Emod) (South America); ICK-Information & Culture Korea (Se-Yung Jun) (Korea); Mical Moser (Canada); B K Norton (Chiafeng Peng) (Singapore, Taiwan); Premium Educational Group (David R Rivera) (Caribbean, Puerto Rico); Publicaciones Educativas (Jose Rios) (Central America, Mexico); Rockbook (Akiko Iwamoto & Gilles Fauveau) (Japan)

Damron Co
PO Box 422458, San Francisco, CA 94142-2458
Tel: 415-255-0404 *Toll Free Tel:* 800-462-6654 *Fax:* 415-703-9049
E-mail: info@damron.com
Web Site: www.damron.com
Key Personnel
Mng Ed: Erika O'Connor *E-mail:* erika@damron.com
Founded: 1964
Annual travel guides.
ISBN Prefix(es): 978-0-929435
Number of titles published annually: 5 Print
Total Titles: 5 Print; 1 Online
Distribution Center: SCB Distributors, 15608 S New Century Dr, Gardena, CA 90248 *Tel:* 310-532-9400 *Toll Free Tel:* 800-729-6423 *Fax:* 310-532-7001 *E-mail:* scb@scbdistributors.com

Dancing Dakini Press
77 Morning Sun Dr, Sedona, AZ 86336
Tel: 928-852-0129
E-mail: editor@dancingdakinipress.com
Web Site: www.dancingdakinipress.com
Key Personnel
CEO: Robin Weeks *Tel:* 505-699-6044 *E-mail:* robin@dancingdakinipress.com
CFO: Ben Long *Tel:* 503-415-0229 *E-mail:* ben@benllong.com
Founded: 2012
Small publisher creating well-crafted books to inspire compassionate awareness, skillful means, authentic lives & a deep respect for all.
ISBN Prefix(es): 978-0-9836333
Number of titles published annually: 3 Print; 2 E-Book
Total Titles: 5 Print; 3 E-Book
Orders to: New Leaf Distribution Co, 401 Thornton Rd, Lithia Springs, GA 30122-1557, Contact: Lenora Whitmire *Tel:* 770-948-7845 *Fax:* 770-944-2313 *E-mail:* domestic@newleaf-dist.com
Returns: New Leaf Distribution Co, 401 Thornton Rd, Lithia Springs, GA 30122-1557, Contact: Lenora Whitmire *Tel:* 770-948-7845 *Fax:* 770-944-2313 *E-mail:* lwhitmire@newleaf-dist.com
Shipping Address: New Leaf Distribution Co, 401 Thornton Rd, Lithia Springs, GA 30122-1557 *Tel:* 770-948-7845 *Fax:* 770-944-2313
Warehouse: New Leaf Distribution Co, 401 Thornton Rd, Lithia Springs, GA 30122-1557 *Tel:* 770-948-7845 *Fax:* 770-944-2313
Distribution Center: New Leaf Distribution Co, 401 Thornton Rd, Lithia Springs, GA 30122-1557, Contact: Lenora Whitmire *Tel:* 770-948-7845 *Fax:* 770-944-2313 *E-mail:* lwhitmire@newleaf-dist.com

Dancing Lemur Press LLC
PO Box 383, Pikeville, NC 27863-0383
Tel: 919-273-0939
E-mail: inquiries@dancinglemurpressllc.com
Web Site: www.dancinglemurpressllc.com
Founded: 2008
We strive to publish works that uplift & inspire, encouraging the reader to explore & discover while remaining morally grounded. At the heart of our young adult & science fiction lies positive relationship dynamics, optimistic attitudes & non-salacious material. Our nonfiction offers insightful information, uplifting ideas & real life opportunities. Our goal is to provide hope for readers.
ISBN Prefix(es): 978-0-9816210; 978-0-9827139; 978-1-939844
Number of titles published annually: 5 Print; 4 E-Book
Total Titles: 7 Print; 7 E-Book
Imprints: Freedom Fox Press
Membership(s): The Independent Book Publishers Association

John Daniel & Co
Division of Daniel & Daniel Publishers Inc
PO Box 2790, McKinleyville, CA 95519-2790
SAN: 215-1995
Tel: 707-839-3495 *Toll Free Tel:* 800-662-8351 *Fax:* 707-839-3242
E-mail: dandd@danielpublishing.com
Web Site: www.danielpublishing.com
Key Personnel
Owner & Publr: John Daniel *E-mail:* john@danielpublishing.com
Owner & Sales Mgr: Susan Daniel *E-mail:* susan@danielpublishing.com
Founded: 1985
ISBN Prefix(es): 978-0-936784; 978-1-880284
Number of titles published annually: 5 Print
Total Titles: 200 Print
Branch Office(s)
2611 Kelly Ave, McKinleyville, CA 95519
Distributor for Fithian Press; Perseverance Press
Returns: 2611 Kelly Ave, McKinleyville, CA 95519
Distribution Center: SCB Distributors, 15608 S New Century Dr, Gardena, CA 90248, Contact: Aaron Silverman *Toll Free Tel:* 800-729-6423
Membership(s): The Independent Book Publishers Association

§Dante University of America Press Inc
PO Box 812158, Wellesley, MA 02482-0014
SAN: 220-150X
Tel: 781-235-3634
E-mail: danteu@danteuniversity.org
Web Site: www.danteuniversity.org/books
Founded: 1980
Italian Americana.
ISBN Prefix(es): 978-0-937832
Number of titles published annually: 7 Print
Distributed by Branden Publishing Co
Foreign Rep(s): Baker & Taylor (Worldwide)
Foreign Rights: Gazelle (England)

Dark Horse Comics
Affiliate of Dark Horse Entertainment
10956 SE Main St, Milwaukie, OR 97222
Tel: 503-652-8815 *Fax:* 503-654-9440
E-mail: dhcomics@darkhorse.com
Web Site: www.darkhorse.com
Key Personnel
Founder & Pres: Michael Richardson
Online Mktg Mgr: Matt Parkinson
Founded: 1986
Primary area is graphic novels; pop culture; limited edition hard covers & comics.
ISBN Prefix(es): 978-1-56971
Number of titles published annually: 200 Print
Total Titles: 600 Print
Imprints: Dark Horse Books
Distributed by LPC Group Inc
Foreign Rights: Anita Nelson
Distribution Center: Random House Publisher Services, 1745 Broadway, New York, NY 10019 *E-mail:* distribution@randomhouse.com

§The Dartnell Corporation
Subsidiary of Eli Research Inc
2222 Sedwick Dr, Durham, NC 27713
Toll Free Tel: 800-223-8720; 800-472-0148 (cust serv) *Fax:* 585-292-4392 *Toll Free Fax:* 800-508-2592
E-mail: customerservice@dartnellcorp.com
Web Site: www.dartnellcorp.com
Founded: 1916
Business information, training, motivation.
ISBN Prefix(es): 978-0-85013
Number of titles published annually: 20 Print
Total Titles: 300 Print

The Darwin Press Inc
PO Box 2202, Princeton, NJ 08543
SAN: 201-2987
Tel: 609-737-1349 *Fax:* 609-737-0929
E-mail: books@darwinpress.com
Web Site: www.darwinpress.com
Key Personnel
Publr & Mng Dir: Ed Breisacher
Founded: 1970
Natural & behavioral sciences; Near Eastern studies; technical, scientific, reference.
ISBN Prefix(es): 978-0-87850
Number of titles published annually: 5 Print
Total Titles: 70 Print
Imprints: Darwin® Books
Foreign Rep(s): Gazelle (Europe)

§Data Trace Publishing Co (DTP)
110 West Rd, Suite 227, Towson, MD 21204-2316
Mailing Address: PO Box 1239, Brooklandville, MD 21022-1239
Tel: 410-494-4994 *Toll Free Tel:* 800-342-0454 (orders only) *Fax:* 410-494-0515
E-mail: info@datatrace.com; salesandmarketing@datatrace.com; editorial@datatrace.com; info@datatrace.com
Web Site: www.datatrace.com
Key Personnel
VP, Edit & Acqs: Kimberly Collignon
Dir, Mktg: Lisa Charyszyn
Ad Mgr: Frank Tufariello
Founded: 1987

Full service specialty publisher with interest in science, technical, law & medicine.
ISBN Prefix(es): 978-0-9637468; 978-1-57400
Number of titles published annually: 20 Print; 6 E-Book
Total Titles: 115 Print; 15 CD-ROM; 6 Online; 15 E-Book
Foreign Rep(s): Eurospan (Worldwide exc Canada & USA)

Daughters of St Paul, see Pauline Books & Media

May Davenport Publishers
26313 Purissima Rd, Los Altos Hills, CA 94022
Tel: 650-947-1275 *Fax:* 650-947-1373
E-mail: mdbooks@earthlink.net
Web Site: www.maydavenportpublishers.org
Key Personnel
Ed & Publr: May Davenport
Founded: 1975
Create & distribute books for children/young adults (ages 15-18). With special grants, we print & distribute literary writings, which counselors at schools give to troubled teens. Books are written by teachers, writers, social workers, mental clinicians & counselors. We sell books by direct mail. Remainders are donated to schools in depressed areas who ask for free copies for their students to take home; to penal institutions who ask for our young adult books for their teenaged inmates & to literacy projects. The company originally created comic tales to read & for the child, 3-4 yrs old, to color the illustrations. Currently working on *Comic Tales Easy Reader Anthologies* for children/young adults.
ISBN Prefix(es): 978-0-9603118; 978-0-943864; 978-0-9794140
Number of titles published annually: 3 Print; 8 Online
Total Titles: 32 Print; 32 Online
Imprints: Md Books

Davies-Black Publishing
Imprint of Nicholas Brealey Publishing
53 State St, Boston, MA 02109
Tel: 617-523-3801 *Fax:* 617-523-3708
E-mail: info@nicholasbrealey.com
Web Site: www.nicholasbrealey.com
Founded: 1995
Book publishing in leadership & management, organization development, human resources & career management.
ISBN Prefix(es): 978-0-89106
Number of titles published annually: 12 Print
Total Titles: 120 Print
Foreign Rep(s): Bacchus Books CC (South Africa); Cengage Learning Asia (Asia-Pacific); Cengage Learning India (India); Eurospan Group (Europe, Middle East, North Africa, UK); NBN Canada (Canada); NBN/Central Book Services (Australia, New Zealand)
Orders to: National Book Network, 15200 NBN Way, Blue Ridge Summit, PA 17214 *Toll Free Tel:* 800-462-6420
Warehouse: 1150 Hamilton Ct, Menlo Park, CA 94025
Distribution Center: National Book Network, 15200 NBN Way, Blue Ridge Summit, PA 17214 *Toll Free Tel:* 800-462-6420
Membership(s): BISG; The Independent Book Publishers Association

The Davies Group Publishers
PO Box 440140, Aurora, CO 80044-0140
Tel: 303-750-8374 *Fax:* 303-337-0952
E-mail: info@thedaviesgrouppublishers.com; daviesgroup@msn.com (orders)
Web Site: www.thedaviesgrouppublishers.com
Key Personnel
Ed: Victor E Taylor
Founded: 1991
Scholarly publisher; philosophy, humanities & social sciences.
ISBN Prefix(es): 978-1-888570; 978-0-9630076; 978-1-934542; 978-1-935790; 978-1-943047
Number of titles published annually: 3 Print; 10 E-Book
Total Titles: 85 Print; 85 E-Book
Imprints: Noesis Press; PenMark Press

§Davies Publishing Inc
32 S Raymond Ave, Suites 4 & 5, Pasadena, CA 91105-1961
SAN: 217-3255
Tel: 626-792-3046 *Toll Free Tel:* 877-792-0005 *Fax:* 626-792-5308
E-mail: info@daviespublishing.com
Web Site: daviespublishing.com
Key Personnel
Pres & Publr: Michael Davies *E-mail:* mikedavies@daviespublishing.com
Edit Dir: Christina Moose *E-mail:* chrismoose@daviespublishing.com
Corp Secy & Opers Mgr: Janet Heard *E-mail:* janetheard@daviespublishing.com
Prodn Mgr: Charlene Locke *E-mail:* charlenelocke@daviespublishing.com
Digital Media Specialist: Dan Liota *E-mail:* danliota@daviespublishing.com
Founded: 1981
Ultrasound education & test preparation: books, software, DVDs, mock examinations & flashcards.
ISBN Prefix(es): 978-0-941022
Number of titles published annually: 8 Print; 2 CD-ROM
Total Titles: 48 Print; 6 CD-ROM
Membership(s): AAP; The Independent Book Publishers Association

§F A Davis Co
1915 Arch St, Philadelphia, PA 19103
SAN: 200-2078
Tel: 215-568-2270; 215-440-3001 *Toll Free Tel:* 800-523-4049 *Fax:* 215-568-5065; 215-440-3016
E-mail: info@fadavis.com; orders@fadavis.com
Web Site: www.fadavis.com
Key Personnel
Chmn of the Bd: Robert H Craven, Sr
Pres: Robert H Craven, Jr
SVP: Judith Illov Neely
VP & CFO: Robert B Schenck
Exec Dir, Sales: Neil K Kelly
Dir, HR: Crystal Spraggins
Publr: Joanne DaCunha; Lisa Deitch; Robert Martone
Ed-in-Chief, Nursing: Jean Rodenberger
Founded: 1879
Publisher of nursing, medical & health profession texts, podcasts & clinical simulations.
ISBN Prefix(es): 978-0-8036
Number of titles published annually: 75 Print; 1 Online; 65 E-Book; 5 Audio
Total Titles: 399 Print; 150 E-Book; 10 Audio
Distribution Center: 404 N Second St, Philadelphia, PA 19123, Gen Mgr: John Lancaster *Tel:* 215-440-3001 *Toll Free Tel:* 800-323-3555 (orders, cust serv, returns) *Fax:* 215-440-3016

§DAW Books Inc
Imprint of Penguin Group (USA) LLC
375 Hudson St, New York, NY 10014
SAN: 282-5074
Tel: 212-366-2096 *Fax:* 212-366-2090
E-mail: daw@penguinrandomhouse.com
Web Site: us.penguingroup.com; www.dawbooks.com
Key Personnel
Publr: Sheila E Gilbert; Elizabeth R Wollheim
Submission Ed: Peter Stampfel *E-mail:* submissions@us.penguingroup.com
Founded: 1971
Science fiction; fantasy; paperbound originals & reprints; hardcover editions, trade paperbacks & ebooks.
ISBN Prefix(es): 978-0-8099; 978-0-88677; 978-0-7564
Number of titles published annually: 60 Print; 60 E-Book
Total Titles: 325 Print
Imprints: DAW/Fantasy; DAW/Fiction; DAW/Science Fiction
Distributed by Penguin Group (USA) LLC

The Dawn Horse Press
Division of Avataric Pan-Communion of Adidam
10336 Loch Lomond Rd, No 305, Middletown, CA 95461
Tel: 707-928-6590 *Toll Free Tel:* 877-770-0772 *Fax:* 707-928-6590
E-mail: dhp@adidam.org
Web Site: www.dawnhorsepress.com
Key Personnel
Publr: Neil Panico *E-mail:* npanico@adidam.org
Founded: 1972
Produces & markets books, CDs & AV materials on every aspect of authentic spiritual life & human development based upon the wisdom & teaching of Avatar Adi Da Samraj.
ISBN Prefix(es): 978-0-913922; 978-0-918801; 978-0-918801; 978-1-57097; 978-0-929929
Number of titles published annually: 8 Print; 8 CD-ROM; 12 Online; 4 Audio
Total Titles: 49 Print; 19 CD-ROM; 65 Online; 1 E-Book; 33 Audio
Shipping Address: 12312 Hwy 175, Cobb Mountain, CA 95426, Contact: Patrick Forristal
Distribution Center: New Leaf Distributing Co, 401 Thorton Rd, Lithia Springs, GA 30122-1557 *Tel:* 770-948-7845 *Fax:* 770-944-2313 *E-mail:* newleaf@newleaf-dist.com *Web Site:* www.newleaf-dist.com
Membership(s): The Independent Book Publishers Association

Dawn Publications Inc
12402 Bitney Springs Rd, Nevada City, CA 95959
Tel: 530-274-7775 *Toll Free Tel:* 800-545-7475 *Fax:* 530-274-7778
E-mail: nature@dawnpub.com; orders@dawnpub.com
Web Site: www.dawnpub.com
Key Personnel
Publr & Ed: Glenn Hovemann *E-mail:* glenn@dawnpub.com
Art Dir & Publr: Muffy Weaver *E-mail:* muffy@dawnpub.com
Mktg Dir: Sandy Philpott *E-mail:* sandy@dawnpub.com
Founded: 1979
Nature awareness nonfiction picture books for children, teachers, naturalists & parents; character value education; natural science.
ISBN Prefix(es): 978-0-916124; 978-1-883220; 978-1-58469
Number of titles published annually: 6 Print; 6 E-Book
Total Titles: 95 Print; 75 E-Book
Foreign Rep(s): Deep Books Ltd (UK); Monarch Books of Canada (Canada); John Reed Book Distribution (Australia); SULA Book Distributors (South Africa)
Membership(s): ABA; APPL; The Independent Book Publishers Association; Publishers Association of the West

DawnSignPress
6130 Nancy Ridge Dr, San Diego, CA 92121-3223
Tel: 858-625-0600 *Toll Free Tel:* 800-549-5350 *Fax:* 858-625-2336
E-mail: info@dawnsign.com
Web Site: www.dawnsign.com

Key Personnel
Founder & Pres: Joe Dannis
Mktg & Lib Sales Dir: Becky Ryan
Founded: 1979
Specialty publisher of instructional sign language & educational deaf studies materials for both children & adults.
ISBN Prefix(es): 978-0-915035; 978-1-58121
Number of titles published annually: 5 Print
Total Titles: 65 Print; 1 CD-ROM
Distributed by Gryphon House
Distributor for Gallaudet University Press; MIT Press; Random House Inc
Foreign Rights: Gloval Interprint (Hong Kong)

Day Owl Press Corp
201 W Ocean Ave, Unit 3574, Lantana, FL 33465
Mailing Address: PO Box 3574, Lantana, FL 33465
Toll Free Tel: 888-806-6981 *Toll Free Fax:* 866-854-4375
E-mail: info@dayowl.net
Web Site: www.dayowl.net
Key Personnel
Pres: Carolyn Clay
Founded: 2011
Independent publisher of offbeat unusual new works. Interested in books that are new, funny, intelligent, prophetical, unconventional, controversial, cutting edge, innovative, radical, Christian, revolutionary +/or otherwise atypical.
ISBN Prefix(es): 978-1-940401
Number of titles published annually: 30 Print; 30 Online; 30 E-Book; 5 Audio
Total Titles: 37 Print; 37 Online; 37 E-Book; 5 Audio
Membership(s): The Independent Book Publishers Association

dbS Productions
PO Box 94, Charlottesville, VA 22902
Tel: 434-293-5502 *Toll Free Tel:* 800-745-1581 *Fax:* 434-293-5502
E-mail: info@dbs-sar.com
Web Site: www.dbs-sar.com
Key Personnel
CEO & Sr Scientist: Robert J Koester *E-mail:* robert@dbs-sar.com
Founded: 1989
Search & rescue.
ISBN Prefix(es): 978-1-879471
Number of titles published annually: 5 Print; 1 CD-ROM
Total Titles: 15 Print; 2 CD-ROM
Distributed by CMC

DC Entertainment
Division of Warner Bros Entertainment Co
2900 Alameda, Burbank, CA 91505
Toll Free Tel: 800-887-6789
E-mail: dccomics@cambeywest.com
Web Site: www.dcentertainment.com; www.dccomics.com; www.madmag.com
Key Personnel
CEO: Diane Nelson
Publr: Dan Didio; Jim Lee
Ed, Vertigo: Ellie Pyle
Founded: 1935
Innovative comics publishing in periodical & book formats. In addition to the world's most popular super-heroes - Superman, Batman & Wonder Woman - DC publishes cutting edge fantasy, horror, mystery, adventure, humor, nonfiction & general interest titles & maintains a 500+ title backlist in print. *MAD* Books is based on the classic magazine featuring Alfred E Neuman, Spy vs Spy & other icons. DC/MAD properties are also licensed for various publishing formats, as well as media, promotions & consumer products. DC Comics does not accept unsol mss. For more information, visit our web site at www.dcentertainment.com.
ISBN Prefix(es): 978-0-930289; 978-1-56389
Number of titles published annually: 240 Print
Total Titles: 2,778 Print
Imprints: DC Comics; DC Nation; MAD Books; Vertigo
Distributed by Random House Publisher Services (RHPS)

§DC Press LLC
750 Powderhorn Circle, Lake Mary, FL 32746
Tel: 407-688-1156 *Toll Free Tel:* 877-203-1895
Web Site: www.dcpressbooks.com
Key Personnel
Pres & Publr: Dennis McClellan *E-mail:* dennis.dcpress@gmail.com
Founded: 2001 (name change from original organization founded in 1989)
Independent niche publisher, producing books with emphasis on ethics, character, spirit, encouragement & volition in the area of self-help & business.
ISBN Prefix(es): 978-1-929902; 978-1-932021
Number of titles published annually: 6 Print; 6 E-Book
Total Titles: 80 Print; 3 CD-ROM; 40 E-Book
Foreign Rep(s): Russo Rights LLC (Cat Russo) (Worldwide)
Foreign Rights: Russo Rights LLC (Cat Russo) (Worldwide)
Distribution Center: Midpoint Trade Books, 27 W 20 St, Suite 1002, New York, NY 10011, Contact: Eric Kampman *Tel:* 212-727-0190 *Fax:* 212-727-0195 *E-mail:* eric@midpointtrade.com *Web Site:* www.midpointtradebooks.com
Membership(s): The Association of Publishers for Special Sales; The Independent Book Publishers Association

§Walter De Gruyter Inc
Division of Walter de Gruyter GmbH & Co KG
125 Pearl St, 3rd fl, Boston, MA 02110
Tel: 857-284-7073 *Fax:* 857-284-7358
E-mail: service@degruyter.com
Web Site: www.degruyter.com
Founded: 1749
Scholarly & scientific books, journals, paperbacks & hardcover reprints.
ISBN Prefix(es): 978-0-311; 978-0-89925; 978-3-11; 978-1-56445; 978-1-934078; 978-1-61451; 978-1-5015
Number of titles published annually: 200 Print; 5 CD-ROM
Total Titles: 8,500 Print; 20 CD-ROM; 15 Online; 10 E-Book
Foreign Office(s): Walter de Gruyter GmbH & Co KG, Genthinerstr 13, 10785 Berlin, Germany *Tel:* (030) 260 05 0 *Fax:* (030) 260 05 251 *E-mail:* info@degruyter.com
Foreign Rep(s): Allied Publishers (India, Nepal, Sri Lanka); Book Club International (Bangladesh); Combined Representatives Worldwide Inc (Philippines); D A Books & Journals (Australia, New Zealand); Verlags und Kommissionsbuchhandlung Dr Franz Hain (Austria); Kumi Trading (South Korea); Kweilin Bookstore (Taiwan); Maruzen Co Ltd (Japan); Pak Book Corp (Pakistan); Parry's Book Center (Sendjrjan Berhad) (Brunei, Malaysia, Singapore); Swinden Book Co Ltd (Hong Kong)
Orders to: TriLiteral, 100 Maple Ridge Dr, Cumberland, RI 02864 *Tel:* 401-531-2800 *Toll Free Tel:* 800-405-1619 *Fax:* 401-531-2801 *Toll Free Fax:* 800-406-9145 *E-mail:* orders@triliteral.org

De Vorss & Co
553 Constitution Ave, Camarillo, CA 93012-8510
SAN: 168-9886
Mailing Address: PO Box 1389, Camarillo, CA 93011-1389
Tel: 805-322-9010 *Toll Free Tel:* 800-843-5743 *Fax:* 805-322-9011
E-mail: service@devorss.com
Web Site: www.devorss.com
Key Personnel
Pres: Gary R Peattie *Tel:* 805-322-9010 ext 14 *E-mail:* gpeattie@devorss.com
Off & Cust Serv Mgr: Debbie Krovitz *E-mail:* dkrovitz@devorss.com
Buyer: Sonia Dominguez *E-mail:* sdominguez@devorss.com
Founded: 1929
Publisher & distributor of metaphysical, spiritual, inspirational, self-help, body/mind/spirit & new thought books & sidelines since 1929.
ISBN Prefix(es): 978-0-87516
Number of titles published annually: 10 Print
Total Titles: 270 Print; 85 E-Book; 4 Audio
Distributor for Acropolis Books (Joel S Goldsmith titles); Touch for Health; White Eagle Publishing Trust (England)
Foreign Rep(s): Brumby Books (Australia); Deep Books (UK); Dempsey Canada (Canada); New Horizons (South Africa)
Billing Address: PO Box 1389, Camarillo, CA 93011-1389

Decent Hill Publishers LLC
6100 Oak Tree Blvd, Suite 200, Cleveland, OH 44131
SAN: 858-2483
Mailing Address: PO Box 1173, Hilliard, OH 43026
Toll Free Tel: 866-688-5325 *Toll Free Fax:* 866-688-5325
E-mail: support@decenthill.com
Web Site: www.decenthill.com
Key Personnel
Founder & CEO: Jude Odu
Book & music publisher.
ISBN Prefix(es): 978-1-936085
Total Titles: 25 Print; 25 Online; 25 E-Book
Imprints: Decent Hill; Felsen Press; The Lord's Press
Membership(s): The American Society of Composers, Authors and Publishers; The Independent Book Publishers Association

DeLorme Publishing Co Inc
2 DeLorme Dr, Yarmouth, ME 04096
Mailing Address: PO Box 298, Yarmouth, ME 04096
Tel: 207-846-7000; 207-846-7111 (sales) *Toll Free Tel:* 800-561-5105; 800-511-2459 (cust serv) *Fax:* 207-846-7051 *Toll Free Fax:* 800-575-2244
E-mail: reseller@delorme.com
Web Site: www.delorme.com
Key Personnel
VP, Mktg: Kim Stiver *Tel:* 207-846-7018 *E-mail:* kim.stiver@delorme.com
Mktg Mgr: Charlie Conley *Tel:* 207-846-7022 *E-mail:* charlie.conley@delorme.com
Founded: 1976
Digital maps; software; posters.
ISBN Prefix(es): 978-0-89933
Number of titles published annually: 5 Print
Total Titles: 50 Print

§Delphi Books
216 Landings Ct, Lee's Summit, MO 64064
E-mail: delphibks@yahoo.com
Web Site: www.delphibooks.us
Key Personnel
Publr: Fran Baker
Founded: 1998
ISBN Prefix(es): 978-0-9663397; 978-0-9765185; 978-0-9846015
Number of titles published annually: 10 Print; 5 E-Book

Total Titles: 18 Print
Returns: Ingram Book Co, One Ingram Blvd, La Vergne, TN 37086
Shipping Address: Ingram Book Co, One Ingram Blvd, La Vergne, TN 37086 *Tel:* 615-793-5000 *Toll Free Tel:* 800-937-8200 *E-mail:* customerservice@ingrambook.com *Web Site:* www.ingrambook.com
Warehouse: Ingram Book Co, One Ingram Blvd, La Vergne, TN 37086 *Tel:* 615-793-5000 *Toll Free Tel:* 800-937-8200 *E-mail:* customer.service@ingrambook.com *Web Site:* www.ingrambook.com
Membership(s): The Association of Publishers for Special Sales; The Authors Guild; Novelists Inc

Delphinium Books
PO Box 703, Harrison, NY 10528
Tel: 917-301-7496 (e-mail first)
E-mail: contactform@delphiniumbooks.com
Web Site: www.delphiniumbooks.com
Founded: 1986
ISBN Prefix(es): 978-1-883285
Number of titles published annually: 5 Print; 5 E-Book; 5 Audio
Total Titles: 45 Print; 30 E-Book; 7 Audio
Distributed by HarperCollins
Foreign Rights: David Marshall (Worldwide exc Canada)

Delta Publishing Co
Division of Delta Systems Co Inc
1400 Miller Pkwy, McHenry, IL 60050-7030
Tel: 815-363-3582 *Toll Free Tel:* 800-323-8270 (orders) *Fax:* 815-363-2948 *Toll Free Fax:* 800-909-9901
E-mail: custsvc@deltapublishing.com
Web Site: www.deltapublishing.com
Key Personnel
Pres: Richard R Patchin *E-mail:* d.patchin@deltapublishing.com
Founded: 1979
Publisher & distribution of English as a second language (ESL) & foreign language materials. Publisher of award-winning children's picture books in English-only, Spanish-only & bilingual formats. Returns within 90 days, no permission required for materials we distribute. Within 180 day for proprietary titles. All must be in perfect condition.
ISBN Prefix(es): 978-0-937354; 978-1-887744; 978-0-9720192; 978-0-9724973; 978-1-934960; 978-1-936299; 978-1-936402; 978-1-932748; 978-0-9794462; 978-0-9770906; 978-0-9795477; 978-1-62167
Number of titles published annually: 8 Print
Total Titles: 120 Print
Divisions: Raven Tree Press
Distributor for Alma Edizioni; Barron's; Cambridge University Press; Edilingual; Oxford University Press
See separate listing for:
Raven Tree Press

§Demos Medical Publishing
Division of Springer Publishing Co
11 W 42 St, 15th fl, New York, NY 10036
Tel: 212-683-0072
E-mail: info@demosmedpub.com; orderdept@demosmedical.com; editorial@demosmedical.com
Web Site: www.demosmedical.com
Key Personnel
CEO: Theodore C Nardin
Publr: Beth Barry *E-mail:* bbarry@demosmedical.com
Spec Sales & Foreign Rts: Reina Santana
Founded: 1985
Publish medical & nursing text & patient education titles in trade paperback.
ISBN Prefix(es): 978-1-888799; 978-0-939957; 978-1-932603; 978-1-933864; 978-1-934559; 978-1-935281; 978-1-936287; 978-1-936303; 978-1-61705; 978-1-62070
Number of titles published annually: 40 Print; 2 CD-ROM
Total Titles: 150 Print; 2 CD-ROM; 100 E-Book
Imprints: Demos Health
Foreign Rep(s): Cranbury International LLC (Caribbean, Latin America); Eurospan Group (Africa, Brunei, Cambodia, China, Europe, Hong Kong, Indonesia, Korea, Malaysia, Middle East, Philippines, Singapore, Taiwan, Thailand, UK, Vietnam); Footprint Books Pty Ltd (Australia, Fiji, New Zealand); Taylor & Francis Books Pvt Ltd (Ritesh Kumar) (India, South Asia)
Membership(s): AAP

§Deseret Book Co
Subsidiary of Deseret Management Corp
57 W South Temple, Salt Lake City, UT 84101-1511
SAN: 201-3185
Mailing Address: PO Box 30178, Salt Lake City, UT 84130
Tel: 801-517-3369 *Toll Free Tel:* 800-453-4532 (orders); 888-846-7302 (orders) *Fax:* 801-517-3126
E-mail: service@deseretbook.com
Web Site: www.deseretbook.com
Key Personnel
CEO & Pres: Sheri L Dew
Publr: Lisa Mangum *E-mail:* lmangum@deseretbook.com
Founded: 1886
Juveniles & young adults, trade paperbacks; fiction, general nonfiction, religion (Mormon).
ISBN Prefix(es): 978-0-87747; 978-1-59038; 978-1-57345; 978-0-87579; 978-1-60908; 978-1-60641; 978-1-60907; 978-1-62972; 978-1-62973
Number of titles published annually: 150 Print
Total Titles: 1,100 Print; 1 CD-ROM; 120 Audio
Imprints: Deseret Book; Ensign Peak; Shadow Mountain
Shipping Address: 2240 W 1500 S, Salt Lake City, UT 84104 *Tel:* 801-517-3285 *Fax:* 801-972-4823

§DEStech Publications Inc
439 N Duke St, Lancaster, PA 17602-4967
Tel: 717-290-1660 *Toll Free Tel:* 877-500-4337 *Fax:* 717-509-6100
E-mail: info@destechpub.com
Web Site: www.destechpub.com
Key Personnel
Pres: Anthony Deraco *E-mail:* aderaco@destechpub.com
Edit Dir: Dr Joseph Eckenrode *E-mail:* jeckenrode@destechpub.com
Prodn Dir: Stephen Spangler *E-mail:* sspangler@destechpub.com
Mktg Mgr: Michael T Hauck *E-mail:* mhauck@destechpub.com
Founded: 2001
Science, technical & medical publisher; proceedings publishing.
ISBN Prefix(es): 978-1-605950
Number of titles published annually: 12 Print; 5 CD-ROM; 2 Online
Total Titles: 115 Print; 22 CD-ROM; 3 Online
Foreign Rep(s): CRW Marketing Services for Publishers Inc (American Samoa, Guam, Philippines, Virgin Islands); DKG Info Systems (Hong Kong, India, Scandinavia, Western Europe); Tahir Lodhi Publisher's Representatives (Pakistan); LSR Libros Services (Latin America, Mexico); Transatlantic Publishers Group Ltd (Europe, Middle East, UK)

§Destiny Image Inc
Subsidiary of Nori Media Group
167 Walnut Bottom Rd, Shippensburg, PA 17257-0310
SAN: 253-4339
Mailing Address: PO Box 310, Shippensburg, PA 17257-0310
Tel: 717-532-3040 *Toll Free Tel:* 800-722-6774 (orders only) *Fax:* 717-532-9291
Web Site: www.destinyimage.com
Key Personnel
CEO & Pres: Nathan Martin
Dir, Sales & Mktg: Joel Nori
Founded: 1983
Publisher of Christian books.
ISBN Prefix(es): 978-0-914903; 978-1-56043; 978-0-938612; 978-0-7684
Number of titles published annually: 36 Print
Total Titles: 500 Print
Foreign Rep(s): Koorong (Australia); STL Ltd (UK); Word Alive (Canada)
Membership(s): ABA; CBA: The Association for Christian Retail; Evangelical Christian Publishers Association

Development Concepts Inc, see Impact Publications/Development Concepts Inc

Developmental Studies Center, see Center for the Collaborative Classroom

§Dewey Publications Inc
1840 Wilson Blvd, Suite 203, Arlington, VA 22201
SAN: 694-1451
Tel: 703-524-1355 *Fax:* 703-524-1463
E-mail: deweypublications@gmail.com
Web Site: www.deweypub.com
Key Personnel
Owner & Author: Peter Broida
Busn Mgr: Karen Troutman
Founded: 1984
ISBN Prefix(es): 978-1-878810; 978-1-932612
Number of titles published annually: 8 Print; 4 CD-ROM; 8 E-Book
Total Titles: 36 Print; 8 CD-ROM; 36 E-Book; 5 Audio

Dharma Publishing
35788 Hauser Bridge Rd, Cazadero, CA 95421
SAN: 201-2723
Tel: 707-847-3717 *Toll Free Tel:* 800-873-4276 *Fax:* 707-847-3380
E-mail: contact@dharmapublishing.com; customerservice@dharmapublishing.com
Web Site: www.dharmapublishing.com
Key Personnel
Mng Dir: Arnaud Maitland
Sales Dir: Rima Tamar *Tel:* 707-847-3717 ext 210 *E-mail:* rimat@dharmapublishing.com
Founded: 1971
Asian art, Eastern philosophy & psychology, Tibetan meditation & yoga, scholarly, history, biography, cosmology, juveniles, Asian culture.
ISBN Prefix(es): 978-0-913546; 978-0-89800
Number of titles published annually: 10 Print; 6 E-Book; 36 Audio
Total Titles: 120 Print; 12 E-Book; 48 Audio
Sales Office(s): 2210 Harold Way, Berkeley, CA 94704 *Tel:* 510-809-1540
Foreign Rep(s): Ka-Nying (India, Nepal); Nyingma Centrum Nederland (Netherlands); Nyingma Do Brazil (Brazil); Nyingma Gemeinschaft (Germany); Windhorse (Australia, UK); Wisdom Publications (UK)
Membership(s): AAP

Dial Books for Young Readers
Imprint of Penguin Group (USA) LLC
345 Hudson St, New York, NY 10014
SAN: 282-5074
Tel: 212-366-2000 *Fax:* 212-414-3396
E-mail: online@penguinputnam.com
Web Site: www.penguinputnam.com; us.penguingroup.com

Key Personnel
Pres & Publr, Dial: Lauri Hornik
Assoc Publr & Exec Mng Ed: Steve Meltzer
Assoc Publr & Exec Art Dir: Lily Malcolm
Exec Ed: Elizabeth Waniewski; Nancy Conescu
Sr Ed: Katherine Harrison; Lucia Monfried
Ed: Jessica Garrison
VP & Publr, Kathy Dawson Books: Kathy Dawson
Founded: 1961
ISBN Prefix(es): 978-0-8037
Number of titles published annually: 85 Print
Total Titles: 383 Print

Diane Publishing Co
330 Pusey Ave, Suite 3 (rear), Collingdale, PA 19023-0617
Mailing Address: PO Box 617, Darby, PA 19023-0617
Tel: 610-461-6200 *Toll Free Tel:* 800-782-3833 *Fax:* 610-461-6130
Web Site: www.dianepublishing.net
Key Personnel
Pres & Publr: Herman Baron
VP, Edit: Dorothy Perkins
Mgr, Opers & Technol: Curtis Fisher *E-mail:* cfisher@dianepublishing.net
Founded: 1987
Publishes & repackages over 45,000 books, documents & reports in law enforcement, intelligence, security, military, education, biotechnology, medicine & health & high-technology. Most titles were originally prepared by US government agencies. Also distributes 9,000 nonfiction remainder books.
ISBN Prefix(es): 978-0-941375; 978-1-56806; 978-0-7881; 978-0-7567; 978-1-4223; 978-1-4289; 978-1-4379; 978-1-4578
Number of titles published annually: 200 Print
Total Titles: 30,000 Print; 10,000 E-Book
Distributor for Academy of Natural Sciences; American Philosophical Society; American Swedish Historical Museum; Augustinian Press; Chemical Heritage Foundation; Christ Church-Philadelphia; Friends of University of Princeton; Geneological Society of Pennsylvania; Library Company of Philadelphia; University of Pennsylvania Libraries

Direct Marketing Association (DMA)
1120 Avenue of the Americas, New York, NY 10036-6700
SAN: 692-6487
Tel: 212-768-7277 *Fax:* 212-302-6714
E-mail: memberservices@the-dma.org
Web Site: thedma.org
Key Personnel
CEO: Thomas J Benton
Sr Dir, Memb Communs & Sr Ed: Susan Taplinger *Tel:* 212-790-1589
Dir, Educ & Prof Devt: Michelle Tiletnick
Founded: 1917
Directories, consumer guides, industry resource guides, statistical compilations, newsletter & council publications, quarterly magazine & electronic newsletter.
ISBN Prefix(es): 978-0-933641; 978-1-931361; 978-0-9817604; 978-0-9833791
Number of titles published annually: 5 Print
Total Titles: 5 Print
Branch Office(s)
1615 "L" St NW, Suite 1100, Washington, DC 20036 *Tel:* 202-955-5030 *Fax:* 202-955-0085

§Discovery House Publishers
Division of Our Daily Bread Ministries
3000 Kraft Ave SE, Grand Rapids, MI 49512
Mailing Address: PO Box 3566, Grand Rapids, MI 49501-3566
Tel: 616-942-2803 *Toll Free Tel:* 800-653-8333 (cust serv)
E-mail: support@dhp.org
Web Site: www.dhp.org
Key Personnel
Publr: Carol Holquist
Mng Ed: Judy Markham
Founded: 1987
Religious trade books; audio CDs (recorded music); DVDs.
ISBN Prefix(es): 978-0-929239; 978-1-57293
Number of titles published annually: 12 Print; 1 Audio
Total Titles: 3 CD-ROM; 150 Online; 1 Audio
Membership(s): CBA: The Association for Christian Retail; Evangelical Christian Publishers Association

Disney-Hyperion Books
Imprint of Disney Book Group
1101 Flower St, Glendale, CA 91201
Web Site: books.disney.com
Key Personnel
Edit Dir: Stephanie Owens Lurie
Exec Ed: Kevin Lewis
Mng Ed: Sara Liebling
Sr Ed: Rotem Moscovich; Kieran Viola
Ed: Abby Ranger; Laura Schreiber
Asst Ed: Ricardo Mejias; Julie Moody
Publg Coord: Liz Usuriello
Sr Mgr, Design: Joann Hill
Sr Designer: Maria Elias; Tyler Nevins
Founded: 1991
Publish high quality picture books, young adult fiction & nonfiction.
ISBN Prefix(es): 978-0-7868
Number of titles published annually: 250 Print
Total Titles: 2,200 Print
Imprints: Jump at the Sun; Michael di Capua Books; Volo
Foreign Rep(s): Little, Brown Canada Ltd; Little, Brown International
Foreign Rights: ACER Agencia Literaria (Spain); Agence Hoffman (Germany); Luigi Bernabo Associates SRL (Italy); Big Apple Agency Inc (China); BMSR Agencia Literaria (Brazil); The English Agency (Japan) Ltd (Japan); Harris/Elon Agency (Israel); Kooy & van Gelderen (Netherlands); Jacqueline Miller (France)
Membership(s): The Children's Book Council
See separate listing for:
Jump at the Sun

Disney Press
Division of The Walt Disney Co
1101 Flower St, Glendale, CA 91201
Web Site: books.disney.com
Key Personnel
Edit Dir: Wendy Lefkon
Exec Ed: Nachie Marsham
Sr Ed: Brooke Dworkin
Dir, Subs Rts: Molly Kong
Founded: 1990
Publish fiction & fantasy.
ISBN Prefix(es): 978-1-56282; 978-0-7868
Number of titles published annually: 55 Print
Total Titles: 1,000 Print
Distributed by Hachette Book Group USA
Foreign Rep(s): Little, Brown Canada Ltd; Little, Brown International
Foreign Rights: A M Heath & Co Ltd (England); ACER Agencia Literaria (Spain); Agence Hoffman (Germany); Luigi Bernabo Associates SRL (Italy); Big Apple Agency Inc (China); BMSR Agencia Literaria (Brazil); The English Agency Ltd (Japan); Harris/Elon Agency (Israel); Monica Heyum Agency (Denmark, Finland, Iceland, Norway, Sweden); Kooy & van Gelderen (Netherlands); Michele Lapautre (France)
Warehouse: 53 State St, Boston, MA 02109

Disney Publishing Worldwide
Subsidiary of The Walt Disney Co
1101 Flower St, Glendale, CA 91201
Web Site: books.disney.com
Key Personnel
Pres, Disney Consumer Prods: Leslie Ferraro
EVP: Andrew Sugerman
SVP & Gen Mgr, Global Magazines Div: Jeanne Mosure
SVP Fin, IT & Global Opers: Raj Murari
VP, Digital Media: Yves Saada
VP, Publg Opers: Terry Downes
Publicity Dir: Seale Ballenger
Publicity Mgr: Mary Ann Zissimos
Mng Ed: Sara Liebling
Founded: 1930
Publisher of children's books, comics & magazines.
ISBN Prefix(es): 978-1-56115
Number of titles published annually: 275 Print
Total Titles: 1,000 Print
Imprints: Disney Editions; Disney Libri; Disney Press; Hyperion Books for Children; Jump at the Sun
Divisions: Disney Children's Book Group
Branch Office(s)
500 S Buena Vista St, Burbank, CA 91521 *Tel:* 914-288-4100

Dissertation.com
Imprint of Universal-Publishers Inc
23331 Water Circle, Boca Raton, FL 33486-8540
SAN: 299-3635
Tel: 561-750-4344 *Toll Free Tel:* 800-636-8329 *Fax:* 561-750-6797
Web Site: www.dissertation.com
Key Personnel
Publr & CEO: Dr Jeffrey Young
Artistic & Edit Dir: Shereen Siddiqui
Prodn Ed: Christie Mayer
Founded: 1997
Academic books.
ISBN Prefix(es): 978-1-58112; 978-0-9658564; 978-1-59942; 978-1-61233; 978-1-62734
Number of titles published annually: 50 Print; 50 Online; 50 E-Book
Total Titles: 300 Print; 300 Online; 300 E-Book
Distributed by Bertrams UK

Diversion Books
443 Park Ave S, Suite 1008, New York, NY 10016
Tel: 212-961-6390
E-mail: info@diversionbooks.com
Web Site: www.diversionbooks.com
Key Personnel
Co-Founder: Charles Platkin
Co-Founder & CEO: Scott Waxman
VP & Edit Dir: Mary Cummings
Sr Acqs Ed: Laura Duane
Founded: 2010
An innovative indie publisher, combining decades of traditional experience with new, digital strategies. In publishing a mix of original titles & giving old titles a digital life, our high royalties, quick turnaround & tailored marketing plans are helping us to create a space between legacy publishing & the uneven field of self-publishing. We are taking advantage of the abundance of opportunities that new models of distribution & purchasing provide, while executing our core publishing capabilities, ultimately connecting great books with avid readers.
ISBN Prefix(es): 978-0-9845151; 978-0-9829050; 978-0-9838395; 978-0-9839885; 978-0-9833371; 978-1-938120
Number of titles published annually: 50 Print; 350 E-Book
Total Titles: 50 Print; 1,000 E-Book
Distributor for Zubaan Books

Distribution Center: Ingram Publisher Services, One Ingram Blvd, La Vergne, TN 37086 *Toll Free Tel:* 866-400-5351 (orders)
Membership(s): AAP; The Independent Book Publishers Association; International Thriller Writers Inc; Media Women's Association

DK Publishing
Division of Penguin Group (USA) LLC
345 Hudson St, 2nd fl, New York, NY 10014
Tel: 646-674-4000 *Toll Free Tel:* 877-342-5357 (cust serv)
Web Site: us.dk.com
Key Personnel
Dir, Sales: Tom Korman
VP, Dir, Fin & Opers: Simon Fraser
VP, Mktg & Publicity: Rachel Kempster
Edit Dir, Children's: Nancy Ellwood
Dir, Opers: Sheila Phelan
Mktg Mgr, Licensing & Children's: Kell Wilson
Asst Mktg Mgr: Kathleen Quinlan
Founded: 1974 (in UK)
Illustrated reference books on a wide range of topics for adults & children, including travel, health, history, sports, pets, atlases, dictionaries, music, art, decorating, astrology, sex & cooking.
ISBN Prefix(es): 978-1-879431; 978-1-56458; 978-0-7894; 978-0-7566
Number of titles published annually: 392 Print
Total Titles: 1,850 Print
Foreign Rep(s): Dorling Kindersley Ltd (UK)
Advertising Agency: Spier NY
Warehouse: Pearson Education, 135 S Mount Zion Rd, Lebanon, IN 46052
Membership(s): ABA; ALA; The Children's Book Council; International Association of Culinary Professionals; International Literacy Association; National Council of Teachers of English; National Science Teachers Association

Caitlyn Dlouhy Books, see Simon & Schuster Children's Publishing

Do It Now Foundation
PO Box 27568, Tempe, AZ 85285-7568
Tel: 480-736-0599 *Fax:* 480-736-0771
E-mail: e-mail@doitnow.org; orders@doitnow.org
Web Site: www.doitnow.org
Key Personnel
Exec & Creative Dir: Jim Parker *E-mail:* jimparker@doitnow.org
Founded: 1968
Drugs, alcohol & health.
ISBN Prefix(es): 978-0-89230
Number of titles published annually: 50 Print
Total Titles: 150 Print

Do-It-Yourself Legal Publishers
Affiliate of Selfhelper Law Press of America
1588 Remsen Ave, Brooklyn, NY 11236
SAN: 214-1876
Tel: 718-684-4769 *Fax:* 718-684-4769
E-mail: ba07102@yahoo.com
Key Personnel
Sr Ed: Dan Benjamin
Founded: 1978
The simplest problems can be effectively handled by anyone with average common sense & a competent guidebook. Specialists in self-help, how-to law manuals & kits for the non-lawyer.
ISBN Prefix(es): 978-0-932704
Number of titles published annually: 7 Print
Total Titles: 30 Print
Imprints: The Selfhelper Law Press of America
Distributed by Brodart Co; Midwest Library Service; Quality Books; Unique Books
Foreign Rep(s): Yeh Yeh Book Gallery Ltd (Taiwan)

§Dogwise Publishing
Division of Direct Book Service Inc
403 S Mission St, Wenatchee, WA 98801
SAN: 132-9545
Tel: 509-663-9115 *Toll Free Tel:* 800-776-2665
E-mail: mail@dogwise.com
Web Site: www.dogwise.com
Key Personnel
Owner & Publr: Charlene Woodward
Owner: Larry Woodward
Founded: 2000
Publish how-to books on dog care, training, behavior, health & competition.
ISBN Prefix(es): 978-1-929242; 978-1-61781
Number of titles published annually: 10 Print
Total Titles: 90 Print; 260 E-Book
Membership(s): Book Publishers of the Northwest; Dogwise Association of America; The Independent Book Publishers Association

Tom Doherty Associates, LLC
Subsidiary of Macmillan
175 Fifth Ave, 14th fl, New York, NY 10010
Tel: 646-307-5151 *Toll Free Tel:* 800-455-0340 *Fax:* 212-388-0191
E-mail: firstname.lastname@tor.com
Web Site: www.tor-forge.com
Key Personnel
Pres & Publr: Thomas Doherty
VP & Assoc Publr: Linda Quinton
Publr, Aerie Books: Kathleen Doherty
Exec Dir, Mktg: Phyllis Azar
Mgr, Admin: Dana Giusio
Art Dir: Irene Gallo
Art Dir, Mass Market/Forge Books: Seth Lerner
Publicity Dir: Patty Garcia
Exec Ed: Patrick Nielsen Hayden; Beth Meacham
Assoc Publicist, Tor/Forge: Desirae Friesen
Founded: 1980
Mass market & trade paperbacks; trade hardcover: fiction, horror, science fiction, fantasy, mystery, suspense, techno-thrillers, western fiction, American historicals, nonfiction, paranormal romance, true crime & biography.
ISBN Prefix(es): 978-0-8125; 978-0-7653
Number of titles published annually: 425 Print
Total Titles: 2,224 Print
Imprints: Aerie Books; Forge Books; Orb Books; Starscape; Tor; Tor Teen
Distributed by Macmillan
Foreign Rights: St Martin's Press
Advertising Agency: Slocum Advertising Agency
Distribution Center: MPS Distribution Center, 16365 James Madison Hwy, Gordonsville, VA 22942-8501 *Toll Free Tel:* 888-330-8477 *Fax:* 540-672-7540 (cust serv) *Toll Free Fax:* 800-672-2054 (orders) *E-mail:* firstinitial.lastname@mpsvirginia.com

Dominie Press
Imprint of Pearson Learning Group
145 S Mount Zion Rd, Lebanon, IN 46052
Mailing Address: c/o Pearson Learning Group, PO Box 2500, Lebanon, IN 46052
Tel: 765-483-6500 *Toll Free Tel:* 800-321-3106 (Pearson Cust Serv); 800-848-9500 *Toll Free Fax:* 877-260-2530
Web Site: www.pearsonschool.com
Founded: 1987
Educational textbooks, children's books, Spanish books.
ISBN Prefix(es): 978-1-56270; 978-0-7685
Number of titles published annually: 240 Print
Total Titles: 2,500 Print
Distributor for Cambridge University Press (limited number of titles, adult GED)

The Donning Company Publishers
Subsidiary of Walsworth Publishing Co Inc
184 Business Park Dr, Suite 206, Virginia Beach, VA 23462
SAN: 211-6316
Tel: 757-497-1789 *Toll Free Tel:* 800-296-8572 *Fax:* 757-497-2542
Web Site: www.donning.com
Key Personnel
Gen Mgr: Lex Cavanah *Tel:* 800-369-2646 ext 4320 *E-mail:* lex.cavanah@donning.com
Sr Ed: Richard Horwege *E-mail:* richard.horwege@donning.com
Founded: 1974
Specialty book publisher of limited-edition commemorative volumes, pictorial histories & contemporary portraits.
ISBN Prefix(es): 978-0-915442; 978-0-89865
Number of titles published annually: 80 Print
Imprints: Portraits of America
Branch Office(s)
306 N Kansas Ave, Marceline, MO 64658, Mktg Specialist: Tonya Hannink *Tel:* 660-376-3543 ext 3278 *Toll Free Tel:* 800-369-2646 ext 3278 *Fax:* 660-258-7798 *E-mail:* tonya.hannink@donning.com
Foreign Rights: Writers House Inc

Dordt College Press
Affiliate of Dordt College
498 Fourth Ave NE, Sioux Center, IA 51250-1606
Tel: 712-722-6420 *Toll Free Tel:* 800-343-6738 *Fax:* 712-722-1198
E-mail: dordtpress@dordt.edu; bookstore@dordt.edu
Web Site: www.dordt.edu
Key Personnel
Mng Ed: John H Kok *Tel:* 712-722-6308 *E-mail:* jkok@dordt.edu
Founded: 1978
Publishes primarily academic books & monographs, plus a quarterly journal.
ISBN Prefix(es): 978-0-932914; 978-1-940567
Number of titles published annually: 6 Print
Total Titles: 45 Print

Dorland Health
Division of DecisionHealth LLC
4 Choke Cherry Rd, 2nd fl, Rockville, MD 20850
Tel: 301-354-2000 *Toll Free Tel:* 855-225-5341 *Fax:* 301-287-2535
E-mail: customer@decisionhealth.com
Web Site: www.dorlandhealth.com
Key Personnel
VP: Carol Brault *Tel:* 301-287-2470 *E-mail:* cbrault@decisionhealth.com
Mng Ed: Richard Scott *Tel:* 301-287-2582 *E-mail:* rscott@decisionhealth.com
Founded: 1950
Directories, market research, databases & mailing lists.
ISBN Prefix(es): 978-1-880874; 978-0-9624105; 978-1-933985; 978-0-9770821
Number of titles published annually: 6 Print; 1 CD-ROM; 4 Online
Total Titles: 6 Print; 1 CD-ROM; 4 Online

Dorrance Publishing Co Inc
585 Alpha Dr, Suite 103, Pittsburgh, PA 15238
Toll Free Tel: 800-695-9599; 800-788-7654 (gen cust orders) *Fax:* 412-288-1786
E-mail: dorrinfo@dorrancepublishing.com; redleadbookorders@dorrancepublishing.com; bookorders@rosedogbooks.com
Web Site: www.dorrancepublishing.com
Key Personnel
Mng Dir: David Zeolla
Founded: 1920
Full service author services company.
This publisher has indicated that 100% of their product line is author subsidized.
ISBN Prefix(es): 978-0-8059; 978-1-4349; 978-1-4809
Number of titles published annually: 360 Print; 360 Online; 360 E-Book; 10 Audio
Total Titles: 2,500 Print; 2,500 Online; 2,200 E-Book; 5 Audio
Imprints: Red Lead Press; Rose Dog Books

Dorset House Publishing Co Inc
3143 Broadway, Suite 2-B, New York, NY 10027
SAN: 687-794X
Tel: 212-620-4053 *Toll Free Tel:* 800-DHBOOKS (342-6657, orders only) *Fax:* 212-727-1044
E-mail: info@dorsethouse.com
Web Site: www.dorsethouse.com
Key Personnel
Pres, Admin & Gen Mgr, Rts & Perms: Wendy Eakin
Founded: 1984
Professional books, management, business, consulting, geared to software engineering.
ISBN Prefix(es): 978-0-932633
Number of titles published annually: 3 Print
Total Titles: 70 Print; 23 E-Book
Foreign Rep(s): Aikem Co (S) Pvt Ltd (Brunei, Hong Kong, Indonesia, Japan, Korea, Malaysia, Myanmar, Philippines, Singapore, Taiwan, Thailand); Prism Books Pvt Ltd (Bangladesh, India, Nepal, Sri Lanka)
Foreign Rights: Chinese Connection (Hong Kong, Mainland China, Taiwan)
Membership(s): The Independent Book Publishers Association

Doubleday/Nan A Talese
Imprint of Knopf Doubleday Publishing Group
c/o Penguin Random House Inc, 1745 Broadway, New York, NY 10019
Tel: 212-751-2600 *Fax:* 212-572-2662
E-mail: ddaypub@randomhouse.com
Web Site: knopfdoubleday.com
Key Personnel
Chmn & Ed-in-Chief, Knopf Doubleday Publishing Group: Sonny Mehta
Pres: Anthony Chirico
SVP, Publr & Ed-in-Chief: William Thomas
SVP, Publr, Pres & Edit Dir, Nan A Talese Books: Nan A Talese
EVP, Dir Publg: Suzanne Herz
VP & Dir, Busn Opers: Justine LeCates
SVP & Dir, Intl Rts & Domestic: Sean Yule
Mgr, Foreign Rts: Suzanne Smith
Dir, Ad & Promos: Judy Jacoby
VP & Exec Dir, Publicity, Doubleday & Assoc Publr, Nan A Talese Books: Alison Rich
Dir, Mktg: John Pitts
Publicist: Michael Goldsmith
Group Sales Dir: Janet Cooke
Imprint Sales Dir: James Kimball
VP & Dir, Prodn/Design: Andrew W Hughes
VP & Dir, Interior Design & Desktop Publg: Peter Andersen
Dir, Art Jacket: John Fontana
VP & Mng Ed: Katherine Hourigan
Exec Ed: Gerry Howard; Jason Kaufman
Sr Ed: Melissa Ann Danaczko; Kristine Puopolo; Jennifer Jackson; Yaniv Soha
Ed: Ronit Feldman
Founded: 1897
Penguin Random House Inc & its publishing entities are not accepting unsol submissions, proposals, mss or submission queries via e-mail at this time.
ISBN Prefix(es): 978-0-385; 978-0-7679
Number of titles published annually: 100 Print
Total Titles: 2,500 Print
Foreign Rights: ALS-Agenzia Letteraria Santachiara (Roberto Santachiara) (Italy); Anthea Agency (Katalina Sabeva) (Bulgaria); Bardon-Chinese Media (Xu-Weiguang) (China); Bardon-Chinese Media Agency (Yu-Shiuan Chen) (Taiwan); The English Agency (Junzo Sawa) (Japan); Graal Literary Agency (Maria Strarz-Kanska) (Poland); The Deborah Harris Agency (Ilana Kurshan) (Israel); JLM Literary Agency (Nelly Moukakos) (Greece); Katai & Bolza Literary (Peter Bolza) (Croatia, Hungary); KCC (MiSook Hong) (Korea); Simona Kessler International (Simona Kessler) (Romania); Licht & Burr Literary Agency (Trine Licht) (Scandinavia); La Nouvelle Agence (Vanessa Kling) (France); Kristin Olson Literary Agency (Kristin Olson) (Czech Republic); Sebes & Van Gelderen Literary Agency (Paul Sebes) (Netherlands)

§Dover Publications Inc
31 E Second St, Mineola, NY 11501-3852
Tel: 516-294-7000 *Toll Free Tel:* 800-223-3130 (orders) *Fax:* 516-742-6953
E-mail: rights@doverpublications.com; service@doverpublications.com
Web Site: store.doverdirect.com; www.doverpublications.com
Key Personnel
Pres: Frank Fontana
VP, Mktg: Ken Katzman *E-mail:* kkatzman@doverpublications.com
Asst to Pres & Sr Reprint Ed: John Grafton
Founded: 1941
Trade, scientific, paperbound books; posters, language, literature & stationery items.
ISBN Prefix(es): 978-0-486; 978-1-60660
Number of titles published annually: 670 Print; 8 CD-ROM
Total Titles: 8,000 Print; 36 CD-ROM; 22 Audio
Foreign Rep(s): David & Charles (UK)
Shipping Address: 11 E Second St, Mineola, NY 11501

Down East Books
Imprint of The Globe Pequot Press
680 Commercial St (US Rte 1), Rockport, ME 04856
Mailing Address: PO Box 679, Camden, ME 04843
Tel: 207-594-9544 *Toll Free Tel:* 800-685-7962 (US only orders); 800-766-1670
E-mail: editorial@downeast.com
Web Site: www.downeast.com
Key Personnel
Pres, Publr & CEO: Bob Fernald *E-mail:* bob.fernald@downeast.com
Assoc Publr: Thomas J Giovanniello, Jr *E-mail:* tgiovanniello@downeast.com
Mktg Dir: Becca Gildred *E-mail:* bgildred@downeast.com
Ed-in-Chief: Kathleen Fleury
Sr Ed: Virginia Wright *E-mail:* vwright@downeast.com
Assoc Ed: Brian Kevin *E-mail:* bkevin@downeast.com
Founded: 1954
Tied directly to *Down East, The Magazine of Maine*, the book publishing mission is to bring Maine's excess of literary & artistic talent to the book marketplace.
ISBN Prefix(es): 978-0-924357; 978-0-89272
Number of titles published annually: 25 Print; 16 E-Book
Total Titles: 350 Print; 50 E-Book
Sales Office(s): National Book Network, 15200 NBN Way, Blue Ridge Summit, PA 17214 *Toll Free Tel:* 800-462-6420
Distributor for Nimbus Publishing Ltd (selected titles, CN sales only)
Distribution Center: National Book Network, 15200 NBN Way, Blue Ridge Summit, PA 17214 *Tel:* 717-794-3800 *Toll Free Tel:* 800-462-6420 *Fax:* 717-794-3828 *Toll Free Fax:* 800-338-4550 *E-mail:* customercare@nbnbooks.com

Down The Shore Publishing Corp
106 Stafford Forge Rd, West Creek, NJ 08092
SAN: 661-082X
Mailing Address: PO Box 100, West Creek, NJ 08092
Tel: 609-812-5076 *Fax:* 609-812-5098
E-mail: dtsbooks@comcast.net; info@down-the-shore.com
Web Site: www.down-the-shore.com
Key Personnel
Founder & Pres: Raymond G Fisk
Founded: 1984
Regional books, history; calendars; videos; note cards.
ISBN Prefix(es): 978-0-9615208; 978-0-945582; 978-1-59322
Number of titles published annually: 6 Print
Total Titles: 95 Print
Imprints: Bufflehead Books; Cormorant Books; Cormorant Calendars; Terrapin Greetings
Membership(s): The Independent Book Publishers Association

§Dragon Door Publications
5 E Country Rd B, Suite 3, Little Canada, MN 55117
Tel: 651-487-2180 *Toll Free Tel:* 800-899-5111 (orders & cust serv)
E-mail: support@dragondoor.com
Web Site: www.dragondoor.com
Key Personnel
Publr & Ed-in-Chief: John Du Cane
ISBN Prefix(es): 978-0-938045
Number of titles published annually: 5 Print

§Dragonfairy Press
Imprint of Dragonfairy Press LLC
2107 N Decatur Rd, Suite 211, Decatur, GA 30033
Tel: 404-955-8150
E-mail: info@dragonfairypress.com
Web Site: www.dragonfairypress.com
Key Personnel
Exec Ed: Alicia Wright
Sr Ed: Kenya Wright
Founded: 2012
Independent publisher of adult & young adult speculative fiction, including fantasy, science fiction, urban fantasy, paranormal romance, supernatural horror, dystopia & other subgenres.
ISBN Prefix(es): 978-0-9850230; 978-1-939452
Number of titles published annually: 8 Print; 8 E-Book
Total Titles: 10 Print; 8 E-Book
Distribution Center: Small Press United, Independent Publishers Group, 814 N Franklin St, Chicago, IL 60610 *Tel:* 312-337-0747 *Fax:* 312-337-5985 *E-mail:* frontdesk@ipgbook.com
Membership(s): The Independent Book Publishers Association

Drama Publishers, see Quite Specific Media Group Ltd

Dramatic Publishing Co
311 Washington St, Woodstock, IL 60098-3308
SAN: 201-5676
Tel: 815-338-7170 *Toll Free Tel:* 800-448-7469 *Fax:* 815-338-8981 *Toll Free Fax:* 800-334-5302
E-mail: plays@dramaticpublishing.com; customerservice@dpcplays.com
Web Site: www.dramaticpublishing.com
Key Personnel
Pres: Christopher Sergel, III
VP: Gayle Sergel; Susan Sergel
Dir: Kent Brown
Founded: 1885
Acting editions of plays & musicals & licensing productions of same.
ISBN Prefix(es): 978-0-87129; 978-1-58342; 978-1-61959
Number of titles published annually: 55 Print
Total Titles: 2,000 Print
Foreign Rep(s): DALRO Pty Ltd (Southern Africa); Origin Theatrical Pty Ltd (Australia); The Play Bureau NZ Ltd (New Zealand)

Dramatists Play Service Inc
440 Park Ave S, New York, NY 10016
Tel: 212-683-8960 *Fax:* 212-213-1539

E-mail: postmaster@dramatists.com; orders@dramatists.com; publications@dramatists.com
Web Site: www.dramatists.com
Key Personnel
Pres: Peter Hagan *E-mail:* hagan@dramatists.com
VP: Mary Harden
Mgr, Opers: Joel Rudzinski *E-mail:* rudzinski@dramatists.com
Mng Ed: Emily Kadish *E-mail:* kadish@dramatists.com; Haleh Roshan Stilwell *E-mail:* stilwell@dramatists.com
Founded: 1936
Publisher & licensor of plays & musicals.
ISBN Prefix(es): 978-0-8222
Number of titles published annually: 60 Print
Total Titles: 4,000 Print
Foreign Rights: DALRO (South Africa); Hal Leonard Australia Pty Ltd (Australia, New Zealand); Josef Weinberger (UK)

Dreaming Robot Press
Imprint of Studio Weaver
1214 San Francisco Ave, Las Vegas, NM 87701
Tel: 505-264-3830
E-mail: books@dreamingrobotpress.com
Web Site: dreamingrobotpress.com
Founded: 2013
Quality middle grade & young adult science fiction & fantasy novels.
ISBN Prefix(es): 978-1-940924
Number of titles published annually: 20 E-Book
Total Titles: 3 Print; 3 E-Book
Membership(s): The Independent Book Publishers Association

Dreamscape Media LLC
Division of Midwest Tapes
6940 Hall St, Holland, OH 43528
Tel: 419-867-6965 *Toll Free Tel:* 877-983-7326
E-mail: info@dreamscapeab.com
Web Site: www.dreamscapeab.com
Key Personnel
Publr: Tammy Faxel *Tel:* 312-757-4759 *E-mail:* tfaxel@dreamscapeab.com
VP, Content: Brad Rose
Founded: 2010
Audio & video media publisher.
ISBN Prefix(es): 978-0-9745563; 978-0-9747118; 978-0-9760996; 978-0-9761981; 978-0-9771510; 978-0-9772338; 978-0-9774680; 978-0-9776262; 978-0-9777098; 978-1-933938; 978-1-61120; 978-1-62406; 978-1-62923; 978-1-63379
Number of titles published annually: 200 Audio
Total Titles: 850 Audio
Editorial Office(s): 150 N Wacker Dr, Chicago, IL 60606
Distributor for HarperCollins; Penguin Random House
Foreign Rep(s): CVS Midwest Tape (Canada)
Membership(s): Audio Publishers Association

Dufour Editions Inc
PO Box 7, Chester Springs, PA 19425
SAN: 201-341X
Tel: 610-458-5005 *Fax:* 610-458-7103
E-mail: info@dufoureditions.com
Web Site: www.dufoureditions.com
Key Personnel
Pres & Publr: Christopher May
Publicity Dir: Larisa Werstler
Ed: Duncan May
Opers Mgr: Brad Elliott
Warehouse Mgr: Alishea Mock
Founded: 1949
Literary fiction, general nonfiction, literature, poetry, philosophy, history, drama & criticism.
ISBN Prefix(es): 978-0-8023
Number of titles published annually: 400 Print
Total Titles: 6,000 Print
Imprints: Dufour Editions' Distributed Presses
Distributor for Angel Books; Arcadia Books (London) (including Black Amber, Bliss, Eurocrime & Maia); Attic Press (including Atrium); Between the Lines; Black Amber Press; Blackstaff Press Ltd; Bliss; Bloodaxe Books Ltd; Brandon Books; Carysfort Press; Clo Iar-Chonnachta; Collins Press; Columba Books; Currach Press; Eland Books/Sickle Moon Books; Eurocrime; Flyleaf Press; Gill & Macmillan; Goblinshead; Hersilia; The Liffey Press; Lilliput Press Ltd; Little Toller Books; Y Lolfa (including Alcemi); Maia Press; Mercier; Messenger Publications; New Island Books; Norvik Press; O'Brien Press; Orpen Press; Persephone Books; Portnoy Publishing; Route; Salmon Poetry; Sandstone Press; Smokestack Books; Colin Smythe Ltd; Stinging Fly Press; University College Dublin Press; Vagabond Voices; Veritas; The Waywiser Press
Warehouse: 124 Byers Rd, Chester Springs, PA 19425

Duke University Press
905 W Main St, Suite 18B, Durham, NC 27701
SAN: 201-3436
Mailing Address: PO Box 90660, Durham, NC 27708-0660
Tel: 919-688-5134 *Toll Free Tel:* 888-651-0122 (US) *Fax:* 919-688-2615 *Toll Free Fax:* 888-651-0124
E-mail: orders@dukeupress.edu; permissions@dukeupress.edu
Web Site: www.dukeupress.edu
Key Personnel
CFO: Norris Langley
Dir: Steve Cohn
Edit Dir: Ken Wissoker *Tel:* 919-687-3648 *E-mail:* kwiss@dukeupress.edu
Books Metadata & Digital Systems Mgr: H Lee Willoughby-Harris
Direct Mktg Mgr & Sales Assoc: Julie Thomson
Edit/Admin Mgr, Journals: Rob Dilworth
Mgr, Cust Rel, Sales & Journals Mktg: Cason Lynley *E-mail:* jrnl_mktg_mgr@dukeupress.edu
Mktg Mgr, Journals: Jocelyn Dawson
Assoc Mktg & Sales Mgr: Michael McCullough *Tel:* 919-687-3600 *E-mail:* mmccullough@dukeupress.edu
Acqs Ed, Journals: Erich Staib *Tel:* 919-687-3664
Founded: 1921
Scholarly, trade & textbooks.
ISBN Prefix(es): 978-0-8223; 978-1-4780
Number of titles published annually: 100 E-Book
Total Titles: 2,000 E-Book
Distributor for Forest History Society
Foreign Rep(s): Combined Academic Publishers Ltd (Africa, Europe, Middle East, UK); East-West Export Books (Royden Muranaka) (Asia, Australia, New Zealand, The Pacific); Lexa Publishers Representatives (Mical Moser) (Canada)
Foreign Rights: Jos de Jong (Belgium, Luxembourg, Netherlands); Cristina de Lara Ruiz (Portugal, Spain); Bernd Feldmann (Austria, Germany, Switzerland); Colin Flint (Denmark, Finland, Iceland, Norway, Sweden); Charles Gibbes (Greece); Emma Hester (England, Scotland, Wales); Bill Kennedy (Middle East); Tony Moggach (Africa, Eastern Europe); David Pickering (France, Italy); Gabrielle Redmond (Ireland, Northern Ireland); Chris Reinders (South Africa)
Advertising Agency: Unabridged Advertising, Contact: Dafina Diabate *Tel:* 919-687-3649 *E-mail:* ddiabate@dukeupress.edu
Warehouse: 120 Golden Dr, Durham, NC 27705, Mgr: Don Griffin *Tel:* 919-384-0733 *Fax:* 919-384-9564
Distribution Center: Ubiquity Distributors, 607 Degraw St, Brooklyn, NY 11211 *Tel:* 718-875-5491 *Fax:* 718-875-8047

Dumbarton Oaks
1703 32 St NW, Washington, DC 20007
Tel: 202-339-6400 *Fax:* 202-339-6401; 202-298-8407
E-mail: doaksbooks@doaks.org
Web Site: www.doaks.org
Key Personnel
Dir, Pubns: Kathy Sparkes
Mng Ed, Art & Archaeology: Sara Taylor
Edit Asst: Meredith Baber
ISBN Prefix(es): 978-0-88402
Number of titles published annually: 8 Print
Total Titles: 260 Print
Distributed by Harvard University Press

§Dun & Bradstreet
103 JFK Pkwy, Short Hills, NJ 07078
Tel: 973-921-5500 *Toll Free Tel:* 800-526-0651; 800-234-3867 (cust serv)
E-mail: custserv@dnb.com
Web Site: www.dnb.com
Key Personnel
Pres, CEO & Dir: Bob Carrigan
Chief Mktg Offr: Rishi Dave
Chief Sales Offr: Mark Geneste
Business & business reference; US & international coverage, country information.
ISBN Prefix(es): 978-1-56203
Total Titles: 31 Print; 20 CD-ROM
Subsidiaries: Hoover's Inc
See separate listing for:
Hoover's Inc

Dunhill Publishing
Division of Warwick Associates
18340 Sonoma Hwy, Sonoma, CA 95476
Tel: 707-939-0570 *Fax:* 707-938-3515
E-mail: dunhill@vom.com
Web Site: www.dunhillpublishing.com
Key Personnel
Pres: Simon Warwick-Smith *E-mail:* warwick@vom.com
Founded: 1985
Handles process of editing, prepress, design, printing, distribution, book reviews, book & author promotion, media contact, Internet sales & marketing, retail sales & marketing, fulfillment & shipping.
ISBN Prefix(es): 978-1-931501
Number of titles published annually: 3 Print
Total Titles: 10 Print

Duquesne University Press
600 Forbes Ave, Pittsburgh, PA 15282
Tel: 412-396-6610 *Fax:* 412-396-5984
E-mail: dupress@duq.edu
Web Site: www.dupress.duq.edu
Key Personnel
Dir: Susan Wadsworth-Booth *E-mail:* wadsworth@duq.edu
Mktg & Busn Mgr: Lori R Crosby *E-mail:* crosbyl@duq.edu
Mng Ed: Kathleen Meyer *E-mail:* meyerk@duq.edu
Founded: 1927
Nonfiction: literary studies, ethics, philosophy, religion, philology, psychology, communication.
ISBN Prefix(es): 978-0-8207
Number of titles published annually: 10 Print
Total Titles: 120 Print
Foreign Rep(s): Gazelle (European Union)
Warehouse: CUP Services, 750 Cascadilla St, Ithaca, NY 14851-6525 *Toll Free Tel:* 800-666-2211 *Toll Free Fax:* 800-688-2877 *E-mail:* orderbook@cupserv.org
Membership(s): Association of American University Presses; Society for Scholarly Publishing

§Dustbooks
Affiliate of Associated Writing Programs
PO Box 100, Paradise, CA 95967-0100
SAN: 204-1871

Tel: 530-877-6110 *Fax:* 530-877-0222
E-mail: publisher@dustbooks.com; info@dustbooks.com
Web Site: www.dustbooks.com
Key Personnel
Publr: Kathleen Glanville
Founded: 1964
Full service publishing company founded by Len Fulton.
ISBN Prefix(es): 978-0-913218; 978-0-916685; 978-1-935742
Number of titles published annually: 3 CD-ROM
Total Titles: 4 CD-ROM; 4 Online
Distributor for American Dust Publications

Dutton
Division of Penguin Group (USA) LLC
375 Hudson St, New York, NY 10014
SAN: 282-5074
Tel: 212-366-2000 *Fax:* 212-366-2262
E-mail: online@penguinputnam.com
Web Site: www.penguinputnam.com; us.penguingroup.com
Key Personnel
Pres, Putnam & Dutton: Ivan Held
VP, Publr & Ed-in-Chief: Ben Sevier
VP, Assoc Publr & Dir, Publicity: Christine Ball
VP & Assoc Publr, Paperbacks: Benjamin Lee
VP & Exec Creative Dir: Rich Hasselberger
VP, Prodn: Pat Lyons
Exec Ed: Stephen Morrow; Jill Schwartzman
Mng Ed: Susan Schwartz
Sr Ed, Plume/Dutton: Denise Roy
Mktg Dir, Putnam/Dutton: Carrie Swetonic
Mktg Mgr, Putnam/Dutton: Katie Parry
Publicist: Emily Brock
ISBN Prefix(es): 978-0-525; 978-0-917657; 978-1-55611
Number of titles published annually: 40 Print
Total Titles: 130 Print
Advertising Agency: Spier NY

Dutton Children's Books
Imprint of Penguin Group (USA) LLC
345 Hudson St, New York, NY 10014
SAN: 282-5074
Tel: 212-366-2000
E-mail: online@penguinputnam.com
Web Site: www.penguinputnam.com; us.penguingroup.com
Key Personnel
Pres, Putnam & Dutton: Ivan Held
VP & Publr: Julie Strauss-Gabel
Assoc Publr & Exec Mng Ed: Steven Meltzer
Founded: 1852 (as Dutton)
ISBN Prefix(es): 978-0-525
Number of titles published annually: 12 Print
Total Titles: 355 Print
Imprints: Dutton

§DynaMinds Publishing®
PO Box 106, Johnston, IA 50131
Tel: 515-991-5315
Web Site: www.dynamindspublishing.com
Key Personnel
Publr: Charles Kuster *E-mail:* chuck@dynamindspublishing.com
Founded: 2002 (Parent company founded in 1980)
We are a niche publishing company that creates co-branded & custom products.
ISBN Prefix(es): 978-0-9712900
Number of titles published annually: 1 Print; 2 CD-ROM; 2 E-Book
Total Titles: 5 Print; 2 E-Book
Membership(s): The Independent Book Publishers Association; Midwest Independent Publishers Association

Eagan Press
Imprint of AACC International
3340 Pilot Knob Rd, St Paul, MN 55121
Tel: 651-454-7250 *Toll Free Tel:* 800-328-7560 *Fax:* 651-454-0766
E-mail: aacc@scisoc.org
Web Site: www.aaccnet.org
Key Personnel
VP, Opers: Amy Hope *E-mail:* ahope@scisoc.org
Dir, Pubns: Greg Grahek *E-mail:* ggrahek@scisoc.org
Founded: 1995
Food science publishing.
ISBN Prefix(es): 978-1-891127
Number of titles published annually: 5 Print; 15 E-Book
Total Titles: 200 Print; 25 E-Book

Eagle Publishing Inc, see Regnery Publishing Inc

Eagle's View Publishing
Subsidiary of Westwind Inc
6756 North Fork Rd, Liberty, UT 84310
SAN: 240-6330
Tel: 801-393-4555; 801-745-0905 (edit) *Fax:* 801-745-0903 (edit); 801-393-4647
E-mail: sales@eaglefeathertrading.com
Web Site: www.eaglesviewpub.com
Key Personnel
Pres & Publr: Monte Smith
Sales Mgr: Sue Smith *Tel:* 801-393-3991
Ed & Publicity: Denise Knight
Founded: 1982
Books on Indian arts, crafts & culture, mountain men & the early frontier, beading, historical clothing patterns, jewelry & how-to craft books in these areas.
ISBN Prefix(es): 978-0-943604
Number of titles published annually: 3 Print
Total Titles: 50 Print
Orders to: 168 W 12 St, Ogden, UT 84404
Returns: 168 W 12 St, Ogden, UT 84404
Warehouse: 168 W 12 St, Ogden, UT 84404

Eakin Press
Imprint of Wild Horse Media Group
PO Box 331779, Fort Worth, TX 76163
Tel: 817-344-7036 *Toll Free Tel:* 888-982-8270 *Fax:* 817-344-7036
Web Site: www.eakinpress.com
Key Personnel
CEO: Billy Huckaby
COO: Ronna Huckaby
Founded: 1979
ISBN Prefix(es): 978-0-89015; 978-1-57168
Number of titles published annually: 25 Print
Total Titles: 1,000 Print; 220 E-Book; 1 Audio

Earth Aware Editions, see Mandala Earth

East Asian Legal Studies Program (EALSP)
Division of University of Maryland School of Law
500 W Baltimore St, Suite 411, Baltimore, MD 21201-1786
Tel: 410-706-3870 *Fax:* 410-706-1516
E-mail: eastasia@law.umaryland.edu
Web Site: www.law.umaryland.edu/programs/international/eastasia
Key Personnel
Dir: Dr Michael Van Altine
Assoc Dir: Chih-Yu T Wu
Founded: 1977
East Asian legal studies, political, economic & legal.
ISBN Prefix(es): 978-0-942182; 978-0-925153; 978-1-932330
Number of titles published annually: 4 Print
Total Titles: 218 Print

East West Discovery Press
PO Box 3585, Manhattan Beach, CA 90266
Tel: 310-545-3730 *Fax:* 310-545-3731
E-mail: info@eastwestdiscovery.com
Web Site: www.eastwestdiscovery.com
Key Personnel
Publr & Ed: Icy Smith
Dir: Michael Smith
Founded: 2000
Independent publisher & distributor of multicultural & bilingual books in 50+ languages.
ISBN Prefix(es): 978-0-9701654; 978-0-9669437; 978-0-9799339; 978-0-9821675; 978-0-9856237; 978-0-9913454; 978-0-9832278
Number of titles published annually: 5 Print
Total Titles: 48 Print
Membership(s): APALA; The Children's Book Council; The Independent Book Publishers Association

EastBridge
70 New Canaan Ave, Norwalk, CT 06850
Tel: 203-855-9125 *Fax:* 203-857-0730
E-mail: asia@eastbridgebooks.org; ask@eastbridgebooks.org
Web Site: www.eastbridgebooks.org
Key Personnel
Founding Dir & Mng Ed: J C West *E-mail:* west@eastbridgebooks.org
Dir & Sr Ed: Anthony S Kaufmann *E-mail:* ask@eastbridgebooks.org
Ed, D'Asia Vu Reprint Lib: Chuck Hayford
Ed, The Missionary Enterprise in Asia: Kathleen Lodwick
Founded: 1997
Not-for-profit publisher in Asian studies.
ISBN Prefix(es): 978-1-891936; 978-1-59988
Number of titles published annually: 20 Print
Total Titles: 75 Print
Imprints: D'Asia Vu Reprint Library (reprints of important classical works); The Missionary Enterprise in Asia (memoirs, autobiographies & biographies of missionaries in Asia); Signature Books (Asian literature, history & analysis); Voices of Asia (current books on Asia authoritatively translated from the original language)
Distributor for China Institute; John Helde; International Christian University Foundation; Nippon Foundation; Yosifumi Taguchi
Foreign Rep(s): Royal Asiatic Society, Korea Branch (Korea)
Membership(s): Association for Asian Studies

Eastland Press
1240 Activity Dr, Suite D, Vista, CA 92081
Mailing Address: PO Box 99749, Seattle, WA 98139
Tel: 206-217-0204 (edit); 760-598-9695 (orders) *Toll Free Tel:* 800-453-3278 (orders) *Fax:* 760-598-6083 (orders) *Toll Free Fax:* 800-241-3329 (orders)
E-mail: info@eastlandpress.com; orders@eastlandpress.com (credit card orders only)
Web Site: www.eastlandpress.com
Key Personnel
Mng Ed & Lib Sales Dir: John O'Connor
Prodn Mgr: Patricia O'Connor
Author & Med Ed: Dan Bensky
Founded: 1981
Chinese medicine, osteopathic & structural medicine, yoga. Use Seattle, WA address for submitting a ms or inquiring about a publication. Use Vista, CA address for ordering books.
ISBN Prefix(es): 978-0-939616
Number of titles published annually: 5 Print; 1 CD-ROM
Total Titles: 55 Print; 4 CD-ROM
Distributor for Journal of Chinese Medicine Publications
Membership(s): Publishers Association of the West

Easy Money Press
Subsidiary of Wolford & Associates
5419 87 St, Lubbock, TX 79424
Tel: 806-543-5215

E-mail: easymoneypress@yahoo.com
Key Personnel
Creative Dir: Henry Wolford *E-mail:* hcwolford@yahoo.com
Mktg Dir: Sheri Kephart
Prodn Dir: P J Max
Founded: 1996
ISBN Prefix(es): 978-0-9654563; 978-1-929714
Number of titles published annually: 3 Print; 3 E-Book
Total Titles: 22 Print; 12 E-Book
Imprints: Big Tree Books; EMP; Haase House

Eaton Publishing, see BioTechniques Books

Ecopress
Imprint of Finney Company Inc
5995 149 St W, Suite 105, Apple Valley, MN 55124
Tel: 952-469-6699 *Toll Free Tel:* 800-846-7027 *Fax:* 952-469-1968 *Toll Free Fax:* 800-330-6232
E-mail: info@finneyco.com
Web Site: www.ecopress.com
Key Personnel
Pres: Alan E Krysan
Mktg Specialist: Krista Danielson
Founded: 1996
Produces books & art that enhance environmental awareness, offering high quality titles covering subjects such as rivers, hiking, plant & environmental guides.
ISBN Prefix(es): 978-1-89327; 978-0-96397
Number of titles published annually: 3 Print
Total Titles: 14 Print

ECS, see The Electrochemical Society (ECS)

ECS Publishing Corp
615 Concord St, Framingham, MA 01702
Tel: 508-620-7400 *Fax:* 508-620-7401
E-mail: office@ecspub.com
Web Site: ecspublishing.com
Key Personnel
Owner & Pres: Robert Schuneman
Founded: 1993
Music publishing (sheet music).
ISBN Prefix(es): 978-0-911318
Number of titles published annually: 125 Print
Total Titles: 10,200 Print
Imprints: ARSIS Audio; Galaxy Music Corp; Highgate Press; Ione Press; E C Schirmer Music Co
Distributor for Randol Bass Music; Dunstan House; Edition Delrieu; Gaudia Music & Arts; Stainer & Bell Ltd; Vireo Press
Orders to: Canticle Distributing, 1727 Larkin Williams Rd, St Louis, MO 63026-2024 *Tel:* 636-305-0100 *Toll Free Tel:* 800-647-2117 (US only) *Fax:* 636-305-0121 *E-mail:* morningstar@morningstarmusic.com
Distribution Center: Canticle Distributing, 1727 Larkin Williams Rd, St Louis, MO 63026-2024 *Tel:* 636-305-0100 *Toll Free Tel:* 800-647-2117 (US only) *Fax:* 636-305-0121 *E-mail:* morningstar@morningstarmusic.com
Membership(s): Music Publishers Association; National Music Publishers' Association

EDC Publishing
Division of Educational Development Corp
10302 E 55 Place, Tulsa, OK 74146-6515
Mailing Address: PO Box 470663, Tulsa, OK 74147-0663
Tel: 918-622-4522 *Toll Free Tel:* 800-475-4522 *Fax:* 918-665-7919 *Toll Free Fax:* 800-743-5660
E-mail: edc@edcpub.com
Web Site: www.edcpub.com
Key Personnel
CEO & Pres: Randall White *E-mail:* rwhite@edcpub.com
VP, Publg & Natl Sales Mgr: Jeanie M Crone *E-mail:* jeanie.crone@edcpub.com
VP, Info Systems: Craig M White
Cont & Corp Secy: Marilyn R Pinney
Founded: 1978
Children's books (fiction & nonfiction) & kid kits.
ISBN Prefix(es): 978-0-88110; 978-0-7460; 978-0-86020; 978-0-7945; 978-1-58086; 978-1-60130
Number of titles published annually: 200 Print
Total Titles: 1,800 Print; 22 CD-ROM
Imprints: Usborne Books
Distributor for Usborne Publishing

Edda USA
Division of Edda Publishing Ltd (Iceland)
373 Park Ave S, 6th fl, New York, NY 10016
Tel: 646-755-9210
Web Site: eddausa.com
Key Personnel
CEO: Jon Axel Olafsson *E-mail:* jax@eddausa.com
Ed-in-Chief: Tinna Proppe *E-mail:* tinna@eddausa.com
Art Dir: Johann G Olafsson *E-mail:* gassi@eddausa.com
Founded: 2013
ISBN Prefix(es): 978-1-940787
Number of titles published annually: 10 Print
Distribution Center: Midpoint Trade Books Inc, 27 W 20 St, Suite 1102, New York, NY 10011, Natl Sales Mgr: Nicholas Sinisi *Tel:* 212-727-0190 *Fax:* 212-727-0195 *E-mail:* nicholas@midpointtrade.com *Web Site:* www.midpointtrade.com

Edgewise Press Inc
24 Fifth Ave, Suite 224, New York, NY 10011
Tel: 212-982-4818 *Fax:* 212-982-1364
E-mail: epinc@mindspring.com
Web Site: www.edgewisepress.org
Key Personnel
CEO: Howard Johnson, Jr
Ed: Joy L Glass; Richard Milazzo
Founded: 1995
Publisher of serious art & literary books.
ISBN Prefix(es): 978-0-9646466; 978-1-893207
Number of titles published annually: 3 Print
Total Titles: 29 Print
Distributor for Editions d'Afrique du Nord; Libri Canali Bassi; Paolo Torti degli Alberti

ediciones Lerner
Division of Lerner Publishing Group Inc
241 First Ave N, Minneapolis, MN 55401
Tel: 612-332-3344 *Toll Free Tel:* 800-328-4929 *Fax:* 612-332-7615 *Toll Free Fax:* 800-332-1132
E-mail: info@lernerbooks.com
Web Site: www.lernerbooks.com
Key Personnel
Chmn: Harry J Lerner
Pres & Publr: Adam Lerner
CFO & EVP: Margaret Wunderlich
EVP, Sales: David Wexler
EVP & Dir, Mktg & Digital Prods: Terri Soutor
VP, Ed-in-Chief: Patricia M Stockland
VP, Prodn: Gary Hansen
VP, Digital Prod Mgmt: Daniel Wallek
Rts Dir: Maria Kjoller
Dir, HR: Cyndi Radant
Art Dir: Zach Marell
Group Mktg Dir: Jill Braithwaite
School & Lib Mktg Dir: Lois Wallentine
Publishes fiction & nonfiction books for PreK-4 in Spanish.
ISBN Prefix(es): 978-0-8225; 978-0-7613
Total Titles: 150 Print; 100 E-Book

Editions Orphee Inc
1240 Clubview Blvd N, Columbus, OH 43235-1226
Tel: 614-846-9517 *Fax:* 614-846-9794
E-mail: sales@editionsorphee.com
Web Site: www.editionsorphee.com
Key Personnel
Pres: Mr Matanya Orphee *E-mail:* m.orphee@orphee.com
Classical sheet music, books on music.
ISBN Prefix(es): 978-0-936186; 978-1-882612
Number of titles published annually: 12 Print
Total Titles: 20 Print
Distributed by Theodore Presser Co
Foreign Rep(s): Chanterelle Verlag (Germany)

Editorial Bautista Independiente
Division of Baptist Mid-Missions
3417 Kenilworth Blvd, Sebring, FL 33870-4469
Tel: 863-382-6350 *Toll Free Tel:* 800-398-7187 (US) *Fax:* 863-382-8650
E-mail: info@ebi-bmm.org; ebiweb@ebi-bmm.org
Web Site: www.ebi-bmm.org
Key Personnel
Gen Dir & Busn Mgr: Bruce Burkholder
Founded: 1950
Sunday school materials, extension materials, Bible study-all in Spanish.
ISBN Prefix(es): 978-1-879892
Number of titles published annually: 5 Print
Total Titles: 200 Print
Distributor for Casa Bautista; CLIE; Portavoz

Editorial Portavoz
Division of Kregel Publications
2450 Oak Industrial Dr NE, Grand Rapids, MI 49505
SAN: 298-9115
Toll Free Tel: 877-733-2607 (ext 206) *Fax:* 616-493-1790
E-mail: portavoz@portavoz.com
Web Site: www.portavoz.com
Key Personnel
Pres: James R Kregel *E-mail:* president@kregel.com
Publr: Tito Mantilla
Founded: 1970
Christian products.
ISBN Prefix(es): 978-0-8254
Number of titles published annually: 30 Print
Total Titles: 600 Print
Membership(s): CBA: The Association for Christian Retail; Evangelical Christian Publishers Association; SEPA

Educational Directories Inc (EDI)
1025 W Wise Rd, Suite 101, Schaumburg, IL 60193
Mailing Address: PO Box 68097, Schaumburg, IL 60168-0097
Tel: 847-891-1250 *Toll Free Tel:* 800-357-6183 *Fax:* 847-891-0945
E-mail: info@ediusa.com
Web Site: www.ediusa.com
Key Personnel
Publr: Douglas Moody
Founded: 1904
Reference publications in education.
ISBN Prefix(es): 978-0-910536; 978-0-9821099; 978-0-9771602; 978-0-9883500
Number of titles published annually: 3 Print
Total Titles: 3 Print; 1 CD-ROM

Educational Impressions Inc
785 Franklin Ave, Franklin Lakes, NJ 07417
Tel: 201-644-0908 *Toll Free Tel:* 800-451-7450 *Fax:* 201-644-0907
Web Site: www.edimpressions.com; www.awpeller.com

Key Personnel
Pres: Allan W Peller *E-mail:* awpeller@optonline.net
Dir, Sales & Mktg: Neil Peller
Founded: 1983
Supplemental textbooks, literature guides.
ISBN Prefix(es): 978-0-910857; 978-1-56644
Number of titles published annually: 30 Print
Total Titles: 450 Print
Distributed by Newbridge Communications Inc; Scholastic Inc; Scholastic-Tab Publications

Educational Insights
Subsidiary of Learning Resources
152 W Walnut St, Suite 201, Gardena, CA 90248
SAN: 282-762X
Toll Free Tel: 800-995-4436 *Toll Free Fax:* 888-892-8731
E-mail: cs@educationalinsights.com
Web Site: www.educationalinsights.com
Key Personnel
Gen Mgr: Lisa Guili *Tel:* 847-968-3719
Press & Media: Courtney Wachs *Tel:* 847-968-3722
Founded: 1962
El-hi instructional materials; teacher's aids, teaching machines & games.
ISBN Prefix(es): 978-1-56767; 978-0-88679
Number of titles published annually: 4 Print; 2 Audio
Total Titles: 92 Print
Distribution Center: Learning Resources, 380 N Fairway Dr, Vernon Hills, IL 60061

Educator's International Press Inc (EIP)
756 Linderman Ave, Kingston, NY 12401
Tel: 518-334-0276 *Fax:* 703-661-1547
E-mail: info@edint.com
Web Site: edint.presswarehouse.com
Key Personnel
Pres: William Clockel
Founded: 1997
Educational foundations, teacher research, curriculum, special education.
ISBN Prefix(es): 978-0-9658339; 978-1-891928
Number of titles published annually: 4 Print; 4 E-Book
Total Titles: 40 Print; 4 E-Book

Educators Progress Service Inc
214 Center St, Randolph, WI 53956
SAN: 201-3649
Tel: 920-326-3126 *Toll Free Tel:* 888-951-4469 *Fax:* 920-326-3127
E-mail: epsinc@centurytel.net
Key Personnel
Pres: Kathy Nehmer
Founded: 1934
Educator guides to free materials in various subject areas; video.
ISBN Prefix(es): 978-0-87708
Number of titles published annually: 16 Print
Total Titles: 16 Print

Edupress Inc
Division of Demco
4810 Forrest Run Rd, Madison, WI 53704
Toll Free Tel: 800-835-7978 *Toll Free Fax:* 800-558-9332
E-mail: edupressdealers@edupress.com
Web Site: www.edupress.com
Key Personnel
Sales Mgr: Rachel Lehmann *Tel:* 608-242-2352
Founded: 1956
Publisher of teacher resource materials.
ISBN Prefix(es): 978-1-56472
Number of titles published annually: 20 Print
Total Titles: 220 Print

Wm B Eerdmans Publishing Co
2140 Oak Industrial Dr NE, Grand Rapids, MI 49505
SAN: 220-0058
Tel: 616-459-4591 *Toll Free Tel:* 800-253-7521 *Fax:* 616-459-6540
E-mail: customerservice@eerdmans.com; sales@eerdmans.com
Web Site: www.eerdmans.com
Key Personnel
Chmn of the Bd: William B Eerdmans, Jr
Pres & Publr: Anita Eerdmans *E-mail:* aeerd@eerdmans.com
VP & Treas: Claire Vander Kam
VP & Ed-in-Chief: James Ernest
VP, Content & Technol: Klaas Wolterstorff *E-mail:* kwolter@eerdmans.com
Mktg Dir: Rachel Bomberger *E-mail:* rbomberger@rowman.com
Dir, Sales: Bob Hetico *E-mail:* bhetico@eerdmans.com
Ad Coord: Janice Myers *E-mail:* jmyers@eerdmans.com
Sales & Mktg Coord: Amy Kent *E-mail:* akent@eerdmans.com
Cust Serv & ISBN Contact: Karen Shippy *E-mail:* kshippy@eerdmans.com
Sr Acqs Ed, Gen Trade: Lil Copan
Devt Ed, Biblical Studies: Andrew Knapp
Prodn Ed: Alexander Bukovietski
Founded: 1915
Scholarly religious & religious reference, religion & social concerns, children's books.
ISBN Prefix(es): 978-0-8028; 978-1-4674
Number of titles published annually: 130 Print
Total Titles: 1,200 Print
Imprints: Eerdmans Books for Young Readers
Foreign Rep(s): Acts TCCN Bookshop (Nigeria); Alban Books Ltd (Europe, UK); Asian Trading Corp (India); Bethesda Book Centre (East Asia, Singapore); Challenge Enterprises of Ghana (Ghana); Christian Art Distributors (South Africa); Christian Book Discounters (South Africa); Co Info Pty Ltd (Australia); Cru Asia Ltd (East Asia, Singapore); Culturasia (East Asia, Singapore); Evangelical Outreach (Philippines); Foundation Distributing Inc (Canada); John Garratt Publishing (Australia); KCBS (Korea); Kyo Bun Kwan Inc (Japan); Manna Christian Stores (New Zealand); Momentum Christian Literature (Indonesia); OM Books Foundation (India); OMF Literature (Philippines); Pustaka Sufes Sdn Bhd (Malaysia); SKS Books Warehouse (East Asia, Singapore); Tien Dao Publishing House (Hong Kong)

Eisenbrauns Inc
PO Box 275, Winona Lake, IN 46590-0275
SAN: 200-7835
Tel: 574-269-2011 *Fax:* 574-269-6788
E-mail: customer_service@eisenbrauns.com; publisher@eisenbrauns.com
Web Site: www.eisenbrauns.com
Key Personnel
Pres & Publr: James E Eisenbraun *E-mail:* jeisenbraun@eisenbrauns.com
Ed: Amy Becker; Beverly McCoy
Founded: 1975
Educational books, books on the Ancient Near East.
ISBN Prefix(es): 978-0-931464; 978-1-57506
Number of titles published annually: 38 Print; 2 CD-ROM; 38 E-Book
Total Titles: 440 Print; 10 CD-ROM; 225 E-Book

§Elderberry Press Inc
1393 Old Homestead Dr, Oakland, OR 97462-9690
Tel: 541-459-6043
Web Site: www.elderberrypress.com
Key Personnel
Co-Owner & Exec Ed: Valerie St John *E-mail:* editor@elderberrypress.com
Co-Owner: Asia St John
Founded: 1997
Works closely with authors, from first reading of their ms to publishing & long after to ensure their book finds up to 50,000 or more readers.
ISBN Prefix(es): 978-0-9658407; 978-1-930859; 978-1-932762; 978-1-934956
Number of titles published annually: 12 Print; 12 Online; 12 E-Book
Total Titles: 300 Print; 120 Online; 100 E-Book; 1 Audio
Imprints: Poison Vine Books; Red Anvil Press
Distributor for Poison Vine Books; Red Anvil Press
Foreign Rep(s): Ingram Book Co (Worldwide)
Membership(s): The Independent Book Publishers Association

§The Electrochemical Society (ECS)
65 S Main St, Bldg D, Pennington, NJ 08534-2839
Tel: 609-737-1902 *Fax:* 609-737-2743
E-mail: publications@electrochem.org; customerservice@electrochem.org
Web Site: www.electrochem.org
Key Personnel
Deputy Exec Dir & Chief Content Offr: Mary E Yess *Tel:* 609-737-1902 ext 119 *E-mail:* mary.yess@electrochem.org
Exec Dir & CEO: Roque J Calvo *Tel:* 609-737-1902 ext 101 *E-mail:* roque.calvo@electrochem.org
Dir, Mktg & Digital Engagement: Rob Gerth *Tel:* 609-737-1902 ext 114 *E-mail:* rob.gerth@electrochem.org
Dir, Pubns: James Ryan *Tel:* 609-737-1902 ext 107 *E-mail:* james.ryan@electrochem.org
Dir, Pubns Prodn: Annie Goedkoop *Tel:* 609-737-1902 ext 118 *E-mail:* ann.goedkoop@electrochem.org
Edit Mgr: Paul B Cooper *E-mail:* paul.cooper@electrochem.org
Pubns Specialist: Andrea L Guenzel *E-mail:* andrea.guenzel@electrochem.org; Beth Schademann *E-mail:* beth.schademann@electrochem.org
Founded: 1902
Technical journals, members magazine, proceedings volumes, monographs, ECS Digital Library.
ISBN Prefix(es): 978-1-56677; 978-1-60768; 978-1-62332
Number of titles published annually: 30 Print; 1 CD-ROM; 4 Online
Total Titles: 300 Print; 1 CD-ROM; 4 Online
Distributed by American Institute of Physics (AIP) (journals); John Wiley & Sons (monographs)

Edward Elgar Publishing Inc
The William Pratt House, 9 Dewey Ct, Northampton, MA 01060-3815
SAN: 299-4615
Tel: 413-584-5551 *Toll Free Tel:* 800-390-3149 (orders) *Fax:* 413-584-9933
E-mail: elgarinfo@e-elgar.com; elgarsales@e-elgar.com; elgarsubmissions@e-elgar.com (edit)
Web Site: www.e-elgar.com; www.elgaronline.com (ebooks & journals)
Key Personnel
Mng Dir: Tim Williams *E-mail:* tim@e-elgar.co.uk
Sales & Mktg Mgr: Katy Wight *E-mail:* kwight@e-elgar.com
Exec Ed: Alan Sturmer *E-mail:* asturmer@e-elgar.com
Founded: 1986
Leading international publisher of academic books, ebooks & journals in economics, finance, business & management, law, environment, public & social policy.
ISBN Prefix(es): 978-1-85898; 978-1-85278; 978-1-84064; 978-1-84376; 978-1-84542; 978-1-84720; 978-1-84844; 978-1-78536; 978-

1-78471; 978-1-78347; 978-1-78100; 978-1-78254; 978-1-84980
Number of titles published annually: 350 Print; 300 E-Book
Total Titles: 5,600 Print; 3,000 E-Book
Foreign Office(s): Edward Elgar Publishing Ltd, the Lypiatts, 15 Lansdown Rd, Cheltenham, Glos GL50 2JA, United Kingdom, Mng Dir: Tim Williams *Tel:* (01242) 226934 *Fax:* (01242) 262111 *E-mail:* info@e-elgar.co.uk *Web Site:* www.e-elgar.co.uk
Warehouse: Books International Inc, 22883 Quicksilver Dr, Dulles, VA 20166, Cust Serv: Todd Riggleman *Tel:* 703-661-1596 *Toll Free Tel:* 800-390-3149 *Fax:* 703-996-1010 *E-mail:* elgar.orders@presswarehouse.com

Elite Books
Division of Author's Publishing Cooperative (APC)
PO Box 442, Fulton, CA 95439
Tel: 707-525-9292 *Toll Free Fax:* 800-330-9798
E-mail: books@authorspublishing.com
Web Site: www.elitebooksonline.com
Key Personnel
Publr: Courtney Arnold *E-mail:* courtney.elitebooks@gmail.com
Ed-in-Chief: Dawson Church *E-mail:* dawson@authorspublishing.com
Prodn Coord: Deb Tribbey *E-mail:* deb@authorspublishing.com
Ed: Stephanie Marohn *E-mail:* stephanie@stephaniemarohn.com
ISBN Prefix(es): 978-0-9720028; 978-0-9710888; 978-1-60070
Number of titles published annually: 5 Print
Total Titles: 40 Print
Distribution Center: Midpoint Trade, 27 W 20 St, Suite 1102, New York, NY 10010, Contact: Gail Kump *Tel:* 212-727-0190 *E-mail:* midpointny1@aol.com *Web Site:* www.midpointtrade.com
Membership(s): The Independent Book Publishers Association

Ellora's Cave
Imprint of Ellora's Cave Publishing Inc
1056 Home Ave, Akron, OH 44310-3302
Tel: 330-253-3521
E-mail: service@ellorascave.com; comments@ellorascave.com
Web Site: www.ellorascave.com
Key Personnel
CEO: Patty Marks
Chief Creative Offr: Darrell King
Publr & Mng Ed: Raelene Gorlinsky
Founded: 2000
Publisher of erotic romances.
ISBN Prefix(es): 978-1-84360; 978-1-4199
Number of titles published annually: 120 Print
Total Titles: 500 Print
Distribution Center: Ingram Publisher Services, One Ingram Blvd, La Vergne, TN 37086-1986 *Toll Free Tel:* 800-400-5351 *E-mail:* customerservice@ingrampublisherservices.com *Web Site:* www.ingrampublisherservices.com

Elsevier Engineering Information (Ei)
Subsidiary of Elsevier Inc
360 Park Ave S, New York, NY 10010-1710
Tel: 212-989-5800 *Toll Free Tel:* 800-221-1044 *Fax:* 212-633-6380
E-mail: eicustomersupport@elsevier.com
Web Site: www.ei.org
Key Personnel
Dir, Scopus & EV Content Mgmt: Judy Salk
Founded: 1884
Provides online information, knowledge & support to engineering researchers. Flagship platform is Engineering Village & the primary database is Compendex.
ISBN Prefix(es): 978-0-87394
Number of titles published annually: 8 Online
Total Titles: 8 Online

Elsevier, Health Sciences Division
Division of RELX Group PLC
1600 John F Kennedy Blvd, Suite 1800, Philadelphia, PA 19103-2899
Tel: 215-239-3900 *Toll Free Tel:* 800-523-1649 *Fax:* 215-239-3990
Web Site: www.elsevierhealth.com
Key Personnel
CFO, Health Sci Div: Bob Munro
SVP, US Global Medicine: Linda Belfus
VP, Sales: Jo Beth Griffin
VP, Book Prodn: Meeuwis Van Arkel
VP, Global Sales & Mktg: John Hope
Mng Dir, Nursing & Health Professions & Edit: Sally Schrefer
Founded: 1906
ISBN Prefix(es): 978-0-7506; 978-0-443; 978-0-444; 978-0-932883; 978-1-56053; 978-0-8016; 978-0-8151; 978-0-7216; 978-0-7020; 978-0-7234; 978-0-323; 978-0-7236; 978-1-4160; 978-1-55664; 978-0-920513; 978-1-898507; 978-1-932141; 978-1-4377; 978-1-4557
Number of titles published annually: 2,000 Print
Imprints: ASVP; B C Decker; Gower; Jems; Mosby; PSG; Saunders; Wolfe; Year Book
Branch Office(s)
6277 Sea Harbor Dr, Orlando, FL 32887-4800 *Tel:* 407-345-2000
3251 Riverport Lane, Maryland Heights, MO 63043 *Tel:* 314-872-8370 *Toll Free Tel:* 800-325-4177 *Fax:* 314-432-1380 SAN: 200-2280
360 Park Ave S, New York, NY 10010-1710 *Tel:* 212-989-5800 *Fax:* 212-633-3990
Foreign Office(s): 30-52 Smidmore St, Marrckville, NSW 2204, Australia
Beilstein Informationssysteme, Theodor-Heuss-Allee 108, 60486 Frankfurt, Germany
2F Higashi Azabu, One Chome Bldg, 1-9-15 Higashi Azabu, Minato-ku 106-0044, Japan
3 Killiney Rd 08-01, Winsland House I, Singapore 239519, Singapore
Linacre House, Jordan Hill, Oxford 0X2 8DP, United Kingdom
Distributor for G W Medical Publisher
Foreign Rights: John Scott & Co (Jake Scott)
Shipping Address: PO Box 437, Linn, MO 65051-0437
Distribution Center: Hwy 50 & Hwy CC, Linn, MO 65051

§Elsevier Inc
Subsidiary of RELX Group PLC
225 Wyman St, Waltham, MA 02144
Tel: 781-663-5200 *Fax:* 781-663-2262
E-mail: bookscustomerservice-usa@elsevier.com
Web Site: www.elsevier.com
Key Personnel
VP, Sales: Charles Withington
Founded: 1880
Books for professionals, researchers & students in the sciences, technology, engineering, business & media. Also research monographs, major reference works & serials.
Number of titles published annually: 2,500 Print; 400 E-Book
Total Titles: 40,000 Print
Foreign Office(s): Linacre House, Jordan Hill, Oxford OX2 8DP, United Kingdom, Contact: Duncan Enright *Tel:* (01865) 314563
Foreign Rep(s): Elsevier (UK) (Europe)
Foreign Rights: Elsevier; Linacre House (Europe)
Membership(s): AAP
See separate listing for:
Elsevier Engineering Information (Ei)
Morgan Kaufmann

Elva Resa Publishing
8362 Tamarack Village, Suite 119-106, St Paul, MN 55125
Tel: 651-357-8770 *Fax:* 501-641-0777
E-mail: staff@elvaresa.com
Web Site: www.elvaresa.com; www.almalittle.com
Founded: 1997
Books for & about military families.
ISBN Prefix(es): 978-1-934617; 978-0-9657483
Number of titles published annually: 4 Print
Total Titles: 22 Print
Imprints: Alma Little (children's books); Elva Resa (books for & about military families); Juloya (inspirational works that help people celebrate life)
Membership(s): The Independent Book Publishers Association; Midwest Independent Publishers Association

§EMC Publishing LLC
Division of New Mountain Learning LLC
875 Montreal Way, St Paul, MN 55102
SAN: 201-3800
Tel: 651-290-2800 (corp) *Toll Free Tel:* 800-328-1452 *Toll Free Fax:* 800-328-4564
E-mail: educate@emcp.com
Web Site: www.emcp.com
Key Personnel
EVP & COO: Joy Hoppe
VP, Info Technol: Chuck Bratton
VP, Sales: Joe Modzelewski
VP, Sales (Coll Div): Todd Larsen
Dir, Mktg: Peter Hodges
Gen Mgr: Michael Demakos
Cust Serv Mgr: Cheryl Monson
Founded: 1954
Paper & hardbound textbooks, audio, video, online Internet, CD-ROM, software microcomputer instructional materials in world language, business education, literature & language arts, social studies, medical, computer technology.
ISBN Prefix(es): 978-0-8219; 978-1-56118; 978-0-7638; 978-0-88436; 978-0-912022
Number of titles published annually: 100 Print; 75 CD-ROM; 20 Online; 100 E-Book; 80 Audio
Total Titles: 3,700 Print; 300 CD-ROM; 75 Online; 3,500 E-Book; 1,035 Audio
Divisions: JIST Publishing; Paradigm Publishing Inc
Distributor for Sybex Inc
Foreign Rep(s): Wolfgang Kraft (Worldwide)
Foreign Rights: Wolfgang Kraft (Worldwide)
See separate listing for:
JIST Publishing

Emerald Books
Affiliate of YWAM Publishing
PO Box 55787, Seattle, WA 98155
Tel: 425-771-1153 *Toll Free Tel:* 800-922-2143 *Fax:* 425-775-2383
E-mail: books@ywampublishing.com
Web Site: www.ywampublishing.com
Key Personnel
Publr & Intl Rts: Warren Walsh
Mktg Dir: Wenke Warren
Ed: Ryan Davis
Founded: 1992
Christian theme.
ISBN Prefix(es): 978-1-883002; 978-1-932096; 978-1-62486
Number of titles published annually: 15 Print
Total Titles: 364 Print
Distributed by YWAM Publishing
Shipping Address: 7825 230 St SW, Edmonds, WA 98026 *Web Site:* ywampublishing.com

Emmaus Road Publishing Inc
Division of St Paul Center for Biblical Theology
1468 Parkview Cir, Steubenville, OH 43952
Tel: 740-283-2880 (outside US) *Toll Free Tel:* 800-398-5470 (orders) *Fax:* 740-283-4011 (orders)
E-mail: questions@emmausroad.org
Web Site: www.emmausroad.org

Key Personnel
VP, Opers: Nate Roberts
Publr: Andrew Jones
Order Processing: Michelle Olenick
E-mail: molenick@emmausroad.org
Founded: 1998
Bible studies, biblically based apologetics & other materials faithful to the teaching of the Catholic church. Restocking fee of 20% for returns.
ISBN Prefix(es): 978-0-9663223; 978-1-931018; 978-1-937155; 978-1-941447; 978-1-940329; 978-1-63446
Number of titles published annually: 12 Print; 12 E-Book
Total Titles: 80 Print; 1 CD-ROM; 50 E-Book; 10 Audio

Empire Press Media/Avant-Guide
Unit of Empire Press Media Inc
244 Fifth Ave, Suite 2053, New York, NY 10001-7604
Tel: 917-512-3881 *Fax:* 212-202-7757
E-mail: info@avantguide.com; communications@avantguide.com; editor@avantguide.com
Web Site: www.avantguide.com
Key Personnel
Dir: Scott Walker
Founded: 1999
Publisher of nonfiction books on pop culture, travel, business & marketing, as well as handbooks for keynote speakers & trends titles by the global trends expert Daniel Levine.
ISBN Prefix(es): 978-1-891603
Number of titles published annually: 50 Print; 50 E-Book
Total Titles: 224 Print; 400 E-Book
Imprints: Avant-Guide; Empire; Keynote Speakers Today
Distributed by Publishers Group West
Foreign Rep(s): Hi Marketing (Europe, UK)
Foreign Rights: PGW (Canada)

Empire Publishing Service
Division of The Empire (media group)
PO Box 1344, Studio City, CA 91614-0344
Tel: 818-784-8918
E-mail: empirepubsvc@att.net
Web Site: www.ppeps.com
Key Personnel
Dir, Opers: Joseph W Witt
Lib Sales Dir & Busn Mgr: David Cole
Founded: 1960
Publisher & distributor of entertainment books, plays & musicals, specialty books & printed music.
ISBN Prefix(es): 978-1-58690; 978-0-934468
Number of titles published annually: 70 Print
Total Titles: 4,365 Print
Imprints: Arsis Press (music, worldwide); Classics With a Twist (world); Gaslight Publications (world); Paul Mould Publishing (world); Phantom Books & Music (world); Sisra Music Publishing (world); Spotlight Books (world); Jack Spratt Choral Music (world)
Subsidiaries: Best Books International
Foreign Office(s): EPS/Players Press Combined Trade, 20 Park Dr, Romford, Essex RM1 4LH, United Kingdom
Distributor for Arsis Press (world); Arte Publico Press (world); Ian Henry Publications (world); ISH Group (Worldwide exc Australia); Paul Mould Publishing (world)
Advertising Agency: Players Press Inc, PO Box 1132, Studio City, CA 91614-0132 *Tel:* 818-789-4980 *E-mail:* playerspress@att.net

Enchanted Lion Books
351 Van Brunt St, Ground fl-Gallery, Brooklyn, NY 11231
Tel: 646-785-9272
E-mail: enchantedlion@gmail.com
Web Site: www.enchantedlionbooks.com
Key Personnel
Publr: Claudia Bedrick
Founded: 2002
Publish illustrated nonfiction picture books for children in the categories of art, biography & history, science & nature, folktales & mythology.
ISBN Prefix(es): 978-1-59270
Number of titles published annually: 16 Print
Total Titles: 100 Print
Distributed by Consortium; Farrar, Straus & Giroux, LLC
Orders to: Perseus Distribution Services, 1094 Flex Dr, Jackson, TN 38301-5070 *Toll Free Tel:* 800-283-3572 *Toll Free Fax:* 800-351-5073 *E-mail:* orderentry@perseusbooks.com
Returns: Perseus Distribution Services, 193 Edwards Dr, Jackson, TN 38301-5070 *Toll Free Tel:* 800-343-4499
Distribution Center: Consortium Book Sales & Distribution, The Keg House, 34 13 Ave NE, Minneapolis, MN 55413-1007 *Tel:* 612-746-2600 *Fax:* 612-746-2606 *E-mail:* info@cbsd.com

Encounter Books
900 Broadway, Suite 601, New York, NY 10003
Tel: 212-871-6310 *Toll Free Tel:* 800-786-3839 *Fax:* 212-871-6311
E-mail: publicity@encounterbooks.com
Web Site: www.encounterbooks.com
Key Personnel
Pres & Publr: Roger Kimball *E-mail:* kimball@encounterbooks.com
Exec Dir, Opers: Nola Tully *E-mail:* ntully@encounterbooks.com
Dir, Mktg: Sam Schneider
Dir, Prodn: Heather Ohle *E-mail:* ohle@encounterbooks.com
Publicity Dir: Lauren Miklos *E-mail:* lmiklos@encounterbooks.com
Founded: 1998
Serious nonfiction books about history, culture, current events, religion, politics, social criticism & public policy.
ISBN Prefix(es): 978-1-893554; 978-1-59403
Number of titles published annually: 30 Print; 30 E-Book
Total Titles: 400 Print; 250 E-Book
Orders to: Perseus Books Group, 1094 Flex Dr, Jackson, TN 38301 (US, CN & Australia) *Toll Free Tel:* 800-343-4499 *Toll Free Fax:* 800-351-5073 *Web Site:* www.perseusbooks.com
Returns: PSSC-Returns, 660 S Mansfield, Ypsilanti, MI 48197
Distribution Center: Perseus Books Group, 1094 Flex Dr, Jackson, TN 38301 (US, CN & Australia) *Toll Free Tel:* 800-343-4499 *Toll Free Fax:* 800-351-5073 *Web Site:* www.perseusbooks.com
Membership(s): ABA; ALA; The Independent Book Publishers Association

§Encyclopaedia Britannica Inc
331 N La Salle St, Chicago, IL 60654
Tel: 312-347-7159 (all other countries) *Toll Free Tel:* 800-323-1229 (US & CN) *Fax:* 312-294-2104
E-mail: editor@eb.com
Web Site: www.eb.com; www.britannica.com
Key Personnel
Pres: Jorge Cauz
Gen Coun: Douglas Eveleigh
SVP, Corp Devt: Michael Ross
SVP, Intl Opers: Leah Mansoor
Founded: 1768
Reference works, print & online for consumers & institutions.
ISBN Prefix(es): 978-0-87827; 978-0-8347; 978-0-85229; 978-1-61535; 978-0-9823824; 978-1-62513; 978-1-59339; 978-1-60835; 978-0-9823823; 978-0-9823819; 978-0-7826; 978-0-9823820; 978-0-9823821; 978-0-9823822
Subsidiaries: Merriam-Webster Inc
Foreign Office(s): Encyclopaedia Britannica Australia Ltd, Level 1, 90 Mount St, North Sydney, NSW 2060, Australia (Australia & Asia Pacific) *Tel:* (02) 9923 5600 *Fax:* (02) 9929 3753 *E-mail:* sales@britannica.com.au *Web Site:* www.britannica.com.au
Encyclopaedia Britannica India Pvt Ltd, 140, Zamrudpur Shopping Complex, N-Block Rd, Greater Kailash-I, New Dehli 110048, India (Bahrain, Kuwait, Oman, Qatar, Saudi Arabia, United Arab Emirates, Yemen) *Tel:* (011) 4653-6450 *Fax:* (011) 2924-5116 *E-mail:* marketing@ebindia.com *Web Site:* www.britannicaindia.com
Britannica.com Israel Ltd, 16 Tozeret Ha'aretz St., Tel Aviv 67891, Israel (Israel) *Tel:* (03) 607 0400 *Fax:* (03) 607 0401 *Web Site:* www.britannicaindia.co.il
Britannica Japan Co Ltd, Da Vinci Nishi-Gotanda 2-F, 8-3-16 Nishi-Gotanda, Shinagawa-ku, Tokyo 141-0031, Japan (Japan) *Tel:* (03) 5436 1388 *Fax:* (03) 5436 1380 *E-mail:* info@britannica.co.jp *Web Site:* www.britannica.co.jp
Encyclopaedia Britannica (UK) Ltd, Unity Wharf, 2nd fl, Mill St, London SE1 2BH, United Kingdom (Africa, Europe, Middle East) *Tel:* (020) 7500 7800 *Fax:* (020) 7500 7878 *E-mail:* enquiries@britannica.co.uk *Web Site:* www.britannica.co.uk
See separate listing for:
Merriam-Webster Inc

Energy Information Administration (EIA)
Imprint of US Government Publishing Office
1000 Independence Ave SW, Washington, DC 20585
Tel: 202-586-8800 *Fax:* 202-586-0727
E-mail: infoctr@eia.doe.gov
Web Site: www.eia.doe.gov
Key Personnel
Dir: Gina Pearson *Tel:* 202-586-6537 *Fax:* 202-586-0114 *E-mail:* gina.pearson@eia.gov
Founded: 1977
Periodicals, analytical reports, energy statistics.
ISBN Prefix(es): 978-0-16; 978-0-18
Number of titles published annually: 37 Print
Distributed by EPO; NTIS

Energy Psychology Press
Division of Soul Medicine Institute
1490 Mark West Springs Rd, Santa Rosa, CA 95404
Mailing Address: PO Box 442, Fulton, CA 95439
Tel: 707-237-6951 *Toll Free Fax:* 800-330-9798
E-mail: books@authorspublishing.com
Web Site: www.energypsychologypress.com; www.elitebooksonline.com
Key Personnel
Publr: Courtney Arnold *E-mail:* courtney.elitebooks@gmail.com
Ed-in-Chief: Dawson Church *E-mail:* dawson@authorspublishing.com
Prodn Coord: Deb Tribbey *E-mail:* deb@authorspublishing.com
Ed: Stephanie Marohn *E-mail:* stephanie@stephaniemarohn.com
ISBN Prefix(es): 978-1-60415
Number of titles published annually: 5 Print
Total Titles: 40 Print
Distribution Center: Midpoint Trade, 27 W 20 St, Suite 1102, New York, NY 10010, Contact: Gail Kump *Tel:* 212-727-0190 *E-mail:* midpointny1@aol.com *Web Site:* www.midpointtrade.com
Membership(s): The Independent Book Publishers Association

§Enfield Publishing & Distribution Co
234 May St, Enfield, NH 03748

Mailing Address: PO Box 699, Enfield, NH 03748
Tel: 603-632-7377 *Fax:* 603-632-5611
E-mail: info@enfieldbooks.com
Web Site: www.enfieldbooks.com
Key Personnel
Mng Dir: Linda Jones
Founded: 1996
Distribute foreign publishers, regional publishers, educational titles, phonics programs grades K-2.
ISBN Prefix(es): 978-0-9656184; 978-1-893598
Number of titles published annually: 5 Print
Total Titles: 11 Print
Distributor for Athenaeum Books; Beech River Books; Cambridge Scientific Publishers; Faculty Ridge Books; Heart Path Press; Institution of Chemical Engineers; Isles of Shoals Association (Star Island); Jetty House (imprint of Peter Randall Press); Verlag Valentin Koerner; Kom Forlag; Letterland International Ltd (phonics progs grades K-2); Moose Country Press; Norwegian Petroleum Agency; Picture Book Press; Portsmouth Marine Society; Safe Harbor Books; Sights Unscene Press (photography); Singing Brook Press; Smith-Gordon; Thistle Hill Publications; Trans Tech Publications; Treeline Press; Vett og Viten Forlag (Norwegian petroleum safety titles); Vital Communities (family quests in VT & NH); Wageningen Academic Publishers
Membership(s): Independent Publishers of New England

Enigma Books
12 E 86 St, New York, NY 10028
Tel: 646-246-8010
E-mail: editor@enigmabooks.com
Web Site: www.enigmabooks.com
Key Personnel
Ed: Robert Miller
Founded: 1999
ISBN Prefix(es): 978-1-929631; 978-0-9824911; 978-1-936274; 978-0-9863764
Number of titles published annually: 10 Print; 15 E-Book
Total Titles: 200 Print; 100 E-Book
Distribution Center: Perseus Distribution, 387 Park Ave S, 12th fl, New York, NY 10016 *E-mail:* client.info@perseusbooks.com
Consortium, The Keg House, 34 13 Ave NE, Suite 101, Minneapolis, MN 55413

§Enslow Publishing LLC
101 W 23 St, Suite 240, New York, NY 10011
Tel: 908-771-9400 *Toll Free Tel:* 800-398-2504 *Fax:* 908-771-0925 *Toll Free Fax:* 877-980-4454
E-mail: customerservice@enslow.com
Web Site: www.enslow.com
Key Personnel
Pres: Mark Enslow
VP & Publr: Brian D Enslow
Founded: 1976
Educational nonfiction books for children & young adults.
ISBN Prefix(es): 978-0-89490; 978-0-7760; 978-1-59845; 978-1-4644; 978-1-4645; 978-1-4646; 978-1-62285; 978-1-62293; 978-1-62324; 978-1-62400
Number of titles published annually: 200 Print; 200 E-Book
Total Titles: 2,400 Print
Imprints: Enslow (middle & high school books); Enslow Elementary (pre-k through 5th grade); MyReportLinks.com Books (Internet supported books)
Foreign Rep(s): CrossCan Educational Services Inc (Canada); EduCan Media (Canada); Everybody's Books (Warren Halford) (South Africa); Read Pacific (New Zealand)
Membership(s): AASL; ALA; Educational Book & Media Association; TLA

Entangled Publishing
2614 S Timberline Rd, Suite 109, Fort Collins, CO 80525
Tel: 724-208-7888 (sales)
E-mail: publisher@entangledpublishing.com
Web Site: www.entangledpublishing.com
Key Personnel
Publr & Edit Dir, Covet: Liz Pelletier
Exec Publicity Dir: Melissa Bourbon Ramirez
ISBN Prefix(es): 978-1-937044; 978-1-62266; 978-1-62061
Number of titles published annually: 48 Print; 312 E-Book
Imprints: Bliss (everyday heroes, sweet romance); Brazen (where romance begins in the bedroom); Covet (put a little para in your normal); Embrace (new adult romance); Entangled Edge (digital first romance); Entangled Select (adult single title romance); Entangled Teen (young adult romance); Ignite (intrigue, passion, heart-stopping suspense); Indulgence (powerful heroes, passionate romance); Lovestruck (romantic comedy & fun, flirty romance); Scandalous (daring love, timeless romance)
Distributed by Macmillan

EntertainmentPro, see Quite Specific Media Group Ltd

Entomological Society of America
3 Park Place, Suite 307, Annapolis, MD 21401-3722
Tel: 301-731-4535 *Fax:* 301-731-4538
E-mail: esa@entsoc.org
Web Site: www.entsoc.org
Key Personnel
Exec Dir: David Gammel *E-mail:* dgammel@entsoc.org
Dir, Communs: Lisa Junker *Tel:* 301-731-4535 ext 3020 *E-mail:* ljunker@entsoc.org
Dir, Strategic Initiatives: Christopher Stelzig *E-mail:* cstelzig@entsoc.org
Founded: 1889
Professional scientific society for entomologists. Publish research journals on all areas of entomology.
ISBN Prefix(es): 978-0-938522; 978-0-9776209; 978-0-9966674
Number of titles published annually: 9 Print; 1 CD-ROM; 5 Online
Total Titles: 57 Print; 1 CD-ROM; 5 Online
Distributed by Oxford University Press

§Environmental Law Institute
1730 "M" St NW, Suite 700, Washington, DC 20036
Tel: 202-939-3800 *Toll Free Tel:* 800-433-5120 *Fax:* 202-939-3868
E-mail: law@eli.org
Web Site: www.eli.org
Key Personnel
Chmn: Edward Strohbehn
Pres & VP, Pubns: Scott Schang *E-mail:* schang@eli.org
Ed, The Environmental Forum: Stephen Dujack *E-mail:* dujack@eli.org
Founded: 1969
Environmental studies, references, online database services, monographs, policy studies.
ISBN Prefix(es): 978-0-911937; 978-1-58576
Number of titles published annually: 6 Print; 30 Online
Total Titles: 53 Print; 1 CD-ROM; 200 Online
Distributed by Island Press

Epicenter Press Inc
6524 NE 181 St, Suite 2, Kenmore, WA 98028
Tel: 425-485-6822 (edit, mktg, busn off) *Fax:* 425-481-8253
E-mail: info@epicenterpress.com
Web Site: www.epicenterpress.com
Key Personnel
COO: J Stephen Lay *E-mail:* slay@epicenterpress.com
Dir, Sales & Mktg: Phil Garrett *E-mail:* phil@epicenterpress.com
Acqs Ed: Lael Morgan *E-mail:* lael@epicenterpress.com
Managerial Asst: Aubrey Anderson *E-mail:* aubrey@epicenterpress.com
Founded: 1988
Regional nonfiction trade publisher. Specialize in titles about Alaska & the Pacific Northwest. Trade distributor of titles by other publishers. Packager, print-broker & book publishing consultant.
ISBN Prefix(es): 978-0-945397; 978-0-9708493; 978-0-9724944; 978-0-9800825; 978-1-935347
Number of titles published annually: 8 Print; 10 E-Book
Total Titles: 100 Print
Divisions: Aftershocks Media (book packager, contract publishing services, consulting, book distribution)
Distributor for Appell Publishing; Camel Press; Coastal Publishing; Coffeetown Press; Copper Raven Press; Delano Publishing; Documentary Media; Far North Press; Five Star Misadventures; Gold Fever Press; Joyful Productions; McRoy & Blackburn, Publishers; Meditation Press; Old Seattle Press; Patos Island Press; Raising Lucy Studios LLC; Raleigh Press; Reach for the Sky Publishing; RLO Media Productions; Saltry Press; Sprucehaven Publishing; Westridge Art; Winternights Publishing; Yamhill Press
Foreign Rights: Wales Literary Agency (Worldwide)
Returns: Partners West, 1901 Raymond Ave SW, Renton, WA 98057 *Toll Free Tel:* 800-563-2385
Warehouse: Partners West, 1901 Raymond Ave SW, Renton, WA 98057 *Toll Free Tel:* 800-563-2385
Distribution Center: Partners West, 1901 Raymond Ave SW, Renton, WA 98057 *Toll Free Tel:* 800-563-2385
Membership(s): Book Publishers of the Northwest; The Independent Book Publishers Association

EPS/School Specialty Literacy & Intervention
Division of School Specialty Inc
625 Mount Auburn St, 3rd fl, Cambridge, MA 02138-3039
SAN: 201-8225
Mailing Address: PO Box 9031, Cambridge, MA 02139-9031
Toll Free Tel: 800-225-5750 *Toll Free Fax:* 888-440-2665
E-mail: customerservice.eps@schoolspecialty.com
Web Site: eps.schoolspecialty.com
Key Personnel
VP & Publr: Charles Heinle
VP, Fin: Dave Ciommo
Founded: 1952
Technology & print educational materials for grades K-12, with particular emphasis on language arts, remedial reading skills, materials for the child with specific language disability, workbooks - elementary; workbooks - secondary, learning differences.
ISBN Prefix(es): 978-0-8388; 978-1-4293
Number of titles published annually: 25 Print
Total Titles: 800 Print
Imprints: Modern Learning Press
Branch Office(s)
555 Legget Dr, Suite 900, Tower B, Ottawa, ON K2K 2X3, Canada
Returns: 80 Northwest Blvd, Nashua, NH 03063

Ericson Books
1614 Redbud St, Nacogdoches, TX 75965-2936
Tel: 936-564-3625 *Fax:* 936-552-8999

E-mail: kissinkuzzins@suddenlink.net
Web Site: www.ericsonbooks.com
Key Personnel
Owner & Publr: Carolyn Reeves Ericson
Exec Asst: Kimberly Whitmore
Founded: 1975
Genealogical & East Texas history.
ISBN Prefix(es): 978-0-911317
Number of titles published annually: 5 Print
Total Titles: 95 Print
Distributed by Mountain Press; Byron Sistler
Distributor for Clearfield; Dietz Press; Southern Historical Press

Etruscan Press
Wilkes University, 84 W South St, Wilkes-Barre, PA 18766
Tel: 570-408-4546 *Fax:* 570-408-3333
E-mail: books@etruscanpress.org
Web Site: www.etruscanpress.org
Key Personnel
Exec Dir: Philip Brady
Exec Ed: Robert Mooney
Mng Ed: Bill Schneider
Founded: 2001
Book of poems, novels, short stories, creative nonfiction, criticism & anthologies.
ISBN Prefix(es): 978-0-9832944; 978-0-9797450; 978-0-9833294; 978-0-9897532; 978-0-9886922; 978-0-9903221
Number of titles published annually: 6 Print
Total Titles: 67 Print
Distribution Center: Small Press Distribution, 1341 Seventh St, Berkeley, CA 94710-1409 *Tel:* 510-524-1668 *Toll Free Tel:* 800-869-7553 *Fax:* 510-524-0852 *Web Site:* www.spdbooks.org
Consortium Book Sales & Distribution, The Keg House, 34 13 Ave NE, Suite 101, Minneapolis, MN 55413-1007 *Toll Free Tel:* 800-283-3572 *Web Site:* www.cbsd.com
Membership(s): Community of Literary Magazines & Presses; The Independent Book Publishers Association

Europa Editions
214 W 29 St, Suite 1003, New York, NY 10001
Tel: 212-868-6844 *Fax:* 212-868-6845
E-mail: info@europaeditions.com
Web Site: www.europaeditions.com
Key Personnel
Founder, Owner & Edit Dir: Sandra Ozzola Ferri; Sandro Ferri
Publr-at-Large: Kent Carroll
Ed-in-Chief: Michael Reynolds
Sales & Mktg Mgr: Christian Westermann
Publicist: Rachael Small
Founded: 2005
Publisher of international literary fiction in translation, domestic literary fiction, crime & narrative nonfiction.
ISBN Prefix(es): 978-1-933372; 978-1-60945
Number of titles published annually: 25 Print
Total Titles: 300 Print
Imprints: Tonga Books
Distribution Center: Penguin Group (USA) LLC, 405 Murray Hill Pkwy, East Rutherford, NJ 07073-2136 *Toll Free Tel:* 800-526-0275 *Toll Free Fax:* 800-227-9604 *E-mail:* orders@us.penguingroup.com

European Masterpieces
Imprint of LinguaText Ltd
103 Walker Way, Newark, DE 19711
SAN: 238-0307
Tel: 302-453-8695 *Fax:* 302-453-8601
E-mail: text@linguatextltd.com
Web Site: www.europeanmasterpieces.com
Key Personnel
Owner & Publr: Michael Bolan
Founded: 2002
Publish classics of Spanish & French literature designed for the English-speaking college student. The complete text of the classic work is included in its native language with extensive English glosses & footnotes on every page, an English introduction & a glossary of Spanish or French to English.
ISBN Prefix(es): 978-1-58977
Number of titles published annually: 5 Print
Total Titles: 120 Print
Imprints: Cervantes & Co (Spanish Classics series); Juan De La Cuesta-Hispanic Monographs; Moliere & Co (French Classics series)
Distributor for Cervantes & Co (Spanish Classics series); Juan De La Cuesta-Hispanic Monographs; Moliere & Co (French Classics series)

§Evan-Moor Educational Publishers
18 Lower Ragsdale Dr, Monterey, CA 93940-5746
Tel: 831-649-5901 *Toll Free Tel:* 800-777-4362 (orders) *Fax:* 831-649-6256 *Toll Free Fax:* 800-777-4332 (orders)
E-mail: sales@evan-moor.com; marketing@evan-moor.com
Web Site: www.evan-moor.com
Key Personnel
Founder & CEO: William Evans *E-mail:* bill@evan-moor.com
Chief Mktg Offr: Trisha Thomas
VP, Sales: Glenn Aument
Exec Ed: Lisa Vitarisi Mathews
Dir, Fin: David Miller
Founded: 1979
Supplemental educational materials in print & digital formats for parents & teachers of children ages 3-14. Subjects include reading, math, writing, science, social studies, arts & crafts & literature.
ISBN Prefix(es): 978-1-55799; 978-1-62938; 978-1-61367; 978-1-61366; 978-1-59673; 978-1-4409; 978-1-60792; 978-1-61368; 978-1-61365; 978-1-60793; 978-1-935353; 978-1-60823; 978-1-60963
Number of titles published annually: 25 Print; 60 Online; 25 E-Book
Total Titles: 450 Print; 450 Online; 450 E-Book
Membership(s): AAP PreK-12 Learning Group; ABA; ALA; Education Market Association

M Evans & Company
Imprint of Rowman & Littlefield Publishing Group
c/o Rowman & Littlefield Publishing Group, 4501 Forbes Blvd, Suite 200, Lanham, MD 20706
Tel: 301-459-3366 *Fax:* 301-429-5748
Web Site: rowman.com
Key Personnel
Ed: Rick Rinehart *E-mail:* rrinehart@rowman.com
Founded: 1963
Health, medical & business books.
ISBN Prefix(es): 978-0-87131; 978-1-59077
Number of titles published annually: 30 Print
Total Titles: 250 Print
Foreign Rights: Rights Unlimited
Shipping Address: National Book Network, 15200 NBN Way, Blue Ridge Summit, PA 17214 *Tel:* 717-794-3800 *Toll Free Tel:* 800-462-6420 *Fax:* 717-794-4801 *Toll Free Fax:* 800-338-4550
Distribution Center: National Book Network, 4720 Boston Way, Lanham, MD 20706

Evergreen Pacific Publishing Ltd
4204 Russell Rd, Suite M, Mukilteo, WA 98275-5424
Tel: 425-493-1451 *Fax:* 425-493-1453
E-mail: sales@evergreenpacific.com
Web Site: www.evergreenpacific.com
Key Personnel
Pres: Paul Hamstra
Founded: 1996
Books, charts & guides for water related recreations.
ISBN Prefix(es): 978-0-945265; 978-0-9609036; 978-1-934707
Number of titles published annually: 4 Print
Total Titles: 25 Print
Imprints: Evergreen Pacific Publishing

Everything Goes Media LLC
PO Box 1524, Milwaukee, WI 53201
Tel: 312-226-8400
E-mail: info@everythinggoesmedia.com
Web Site: www.everythinggoesmedia.com
Key Personnel
Owner & Publr: Sharon Woodhouse *E-mail:* sharon@everythinggoesmedia.com
Founded: 1994
"The book is the medium." Traditional publisher with unconventional approaches.
ISBN Prefix(es): 978-1-893121
Number of titles published annually: 5 Print; 4 E-Book
Total Titles: 40 Print; 4 E-Book
Imprints: Everything Goes Media (nonfiction-lifestyle, hobby, gift & business); Lake Claremont Press (nonfiction-Chicago guidebooks & histories); S Woodhouse Books (nonfiction-ideas, history, trends & current events)
Divisions: Conspire Creative
See separate listing for:
Lake Claremont Press

Excalibur Publications
PO Box 89667, Tucson, AZ 85752-9667
Tel: 520-575-9057
E-mail: excaliburpublications@centurylink.net
Key Personnel
Ed-in-Chief: Alan M Petrillo
Founded: 1990
ISBN Prefix(es): 978-1-880677
Number of titles published annually: 3 Print; 2 E-Book
Total Titles: 20 Print; 2 E-Book
Distribution Center: Barnes & Noble, One Barnes & Noble Way, Suite B, Monroe, NJ 08831
Baker & Taylor, 2550 W Tyvola Rd, Suite 300, Charlotte, NC 28217
Amazon.com, 1200 12 Ave S, Suite 1200, Seattle, WA 98144-2734

Excelsior Editions
Imprint of State University of New York Press
22 Corporate Woods Blvd, 3rd fl, Albany, NY 12211-2504
SAN: 760-7261
Tel: 518-472-5000 *Toll Free Tel:* 866-430-7869 *Fax:* 518-472-5038
E-mail: info@sunypress.edu
Web Site: www.sunypress.edu
Key Personnel
Co-Dir: James Peltz *Tel:* 518-641-0668 *E-mail:* james.peltz@sunypress.edu
Assoc Dir & Dir, Sales & Busn Devt: Daniel Flynn *Tel:* 518-641-0676 *E-mail:* daniel.flynn@sunypress.edu
Founded: 2008
Publish regional & trade books.
ISBN Prefix(es): 978-0-7914; 978-1-929373 (Hudson Valley region); 978-1-4384; 978-0-9722977 (Uncrowned Queens)
Number of titles published annually: 25 Print; 15 Audio
Total Titles: 200 Print; 95 E-Book; 1 Audio
Distributor for Albany Institute of History & Art; Uncrowned Queens
Foreign Rep(s): Apac Publishers Services Pte Ltd (China, Hong Kong, Indonesia, Malaysia, Singapore, Taiwan, Thailand, Vietnam); Eleanor Brasch Enterprises (Eleanor Brasch) (Australia, New Zealand); Cassidy & Associates Inc (Tom Cassidy) (China, Hong Kong, Tai-

wan); Lexa Publishers' Representatives (Elise & Mical Moser) (Canada); Mediamatics (Asoke K Ghosh) (India); NBN International (UK & the continent); United Publisher's Services Ltd (Japan); University Presses Marketing (Andrew Gilman) (Continental Europe, Ireland, Israel, UK); US PubRep Inc (Craig Falk) (Caribbean, Central America, Mexico, Puerto Rico, South America)
Orders to: SUNY Press, PO Box 960, Herndon, VA 20172-0960, Cust Serv *Tel:* 703-661-1575 *Toll Free Tel:* 877-204-6073 *Fax:* 703-996-1010 *Toll Free Fax:* 877-204-6074 *E-mail:* suny@presswarehouse.com
Returns: SUNY Press, Returns Dept, 22883 Quicksilver Dr, Dulles, VA 20166, Cust Serv *Tel:* 703-661-1575 *Toll Free Tel:* 877-204-6073 *Fax:* 703-996-1010 *Toll Free Fax:* 877-204-6074 *E-mail:* suny@presswarehouse.com
Shipping Address: SUNY Press, 22835 Quicksilver Dr, Dulles, VA 20166, Cust Serv *Tel:* 703-661-1575 *Toll Free Tel:* 877-204-6073 *Fax:* 703-996-1010 *Toll Free Fax:* 877-204-6074 *E-mail:* suny@presswarehouse.com
Warehouse: SUNY Press, PO Box 960, Herndon, VA 20172-0960, Cust Serv *Tel:* 703-661-1575 *Toll Free Tel:* 877-204-6073 *Fax:* 703-996-1010 *Toll Free Fax:* 877-204-6074 *E-mail:* suny@presswarehouse.com

The Experiment
220 East 23 St, Suite 301, New York, NY 10010-4674
Tel: 212-889-1659
E-mail: info@theexperimentpublishing.com
Web Site: www.theexperimentpublishing.com
Key Personnel
COO & CFO: Peter Burri
Pres & Publr: Matthew Lore
Assoc Publr: Dan O'Connor
Art Dir: Sarah Smith
Sales Dir: Ani Chamichian
Mktg & Publicity Mgr: Jennifer Hergenroeder
Ed: Allie Bochicchio; Nick Cizek; Sasha Tropp
Founded: 2008
ISBN Prefix(es): 978-1-61519
Number of titles published annually: 25 Print; 25 E-Book
Total Titles: 90 Print; 90 E-Book
Sales Office(s): Workman Publishing, 225 Varick St, New York, NY 10014-4381 SAN: 631-760X
Distributed by Workman Publishing
Orders to: Workman Publishing, 225 Varick St, New York, NY 10014-4381 *E-mail:* orders@workman.com
Returns: Workman Publishing Co Inc, c/o RR Donnelley, 677 Brighton Beach Rd, Menasha, WI 54952
Membership(s): AAP

Eye in the Ear Children's Audio
5 Crescent St, Portland, ME 04102
Toll Free Tel: 855-99-STORY (997-8679) *Fax:* 207-699-1380 (attn: Laurence Kelly)
E-mail: info@eyeintheear.com
Web Site: www.eyeintheear.com
Key Personnel
Owner: Frances Kelly
Pres: Laurence A Kelly *E-mail:* lk@maine.rr.com
Founded: 1985
Production & distribution of quality classic children's audio stories. Titles available from Amazon.com, Chinaberry, Landmark Audio Books & TEI Landmark Audio.
ISBN Prefix(es): 978-0-944168
Number of titles published annually: 3 Audio
Total Titles: 31 Online; 31 Audio
Editorial Office(s): c/o MBC, 415 Congress St, Portland, ME 04101
Returns: Fleetwood MultiMedia, 20 Wheeler St, St Lynn, MA 01910, Contact: Wayne Terminello *Toll Free Tel:* 800-353-1830 *Fax:* 781-599-2440 *E-mail:* wayne@fltwood.com
Shipping Address: Fleetwood MultiMedia, 20 Wheeler St, St Lynn, MA 01910, Contact: Wayne Terminello *Toll Free Tel:* 800-353-1830 *Fax:* 781-599-2440 *E-mail:* wayne@fltwood.com
Warehouse: Fleetwood MultiMedia, 20 Wheeler St, St Lynn, MA 01910, Contact: Wayne Terminello *Toll Free Tel:* 800-353-1830 *Fax:* 781-599-2440 *E-mail:* wayne@fltwood.com
Distribution Center: Christian Book Distributors, 1400 Summit St, Peabody, MA 01960 *Toll Free Tel:* 800-247-4784 *E-mail:* customer.service@christianbook.com
Fleetwood MultiMedia, 20 Wheeler St, St Lynn, MA 01910, Contact: Wayne Terminello *Toll Free Tel:* 800-353-1830 *Fax:* 781-599-2440 *E-mail:* wayne@fltwood.com

§Facts On File
Imprint of Infobase Learning
132 W 31 St, 17th fl, New York, NY 10001
SAN: 201-4696
Tel: 212-967-8800 *Toll Free Tel:* 800-322-8755 *Toll Free Fax:* 800-678-3633
E-mail: custserv@factsonfile.com
Web Site: infobasepublishing.com
Key Personnel
Pres & CEO: Mark McDonnell
CFO: Jim Housley
Dir, Book & Ebook Sales: Justyna Pawluk *E-mail:* jpawluk@infobaselearning.com
Edit Dir, Print: Laurie Likoff
Dir, Licensing & Busn Devt: Ben Jacobs *E-mail:* bjacobs@infobaselearning.com
Dir, Mktg: Zina Scarpulla
Dir, Publicity: Laurie Katz *E-mail:* lkatz@infobaselearning.com
Dir, Sales: Mark Zielinski
Founded: 1941
Award-winning publisher of authoritative curriculum-related print & online reference materials for schools & libraries.
ISBN Prefix(es): 978-0-8160; 978-0-87196; 978-1-60057; 978-1-60413; 978-1-4381; 978-1-57852; 978-1-61753
Number of titles published annually: 135 Print; 28 Online; 135 E-Book
Total Titles: 940 Print; 37 Online; 934 E-Book
Returns: Maple Logistics Solutions Distribution Center, 704 Legionaire Dr, Fredericksburg, PA 17026
Warehouse: Maple Logistics Solutions Distribution Center, 704 Legionaire Dr, Fredericksburg, PA 17026
Distribution Center: Maple Logistics Solutions Distribution Center, 704 Legionaire Dr, Fredericksburg, PA 17026

Fair Winds Press
Imprint of Quarto Publishing Group USA
100 Cummings Ctr, Suite 406-L, Beverly, MA 01915
Tel: 978-282-9590 *Fax:* 978-282-7765
E-mail: sales@quartos.com
Web Site: www.quartoknows.com
Key Personnel
VP & Group Publr: Winnie Prentiss *E-mail:* winnie.prentiss@quartous.com
Founded: 2001
Offer nonfiction books in a range of practical categories, including nutrition & cookery, fitness, parenting, beauty, treating sickness, mental health & using new medicine.
ISBN Prefix(es): 978-1-59233
Number of titles published annually: 50 Print
Total Titles: 200 Print

Fairchild Books
Division of Bloomsbury Publishing PLC
1385 Broadway, 5th fl, New York, NY 10018
SAN: 201-470X
Tel: 212-419-5300 *Toll Free Tel:* 800-932-4724; 888-330-8477 (orders) *Fax:* 212-704-5975
Web Site: bloomsbury.com/us/academic/fairchildbooks
Key Personnel
Publr: Priscilla McGeehon *E-mail:* priscilla.mcgeehon@bloomsbury.com
Dir, Sales & Sr Devt Ed: Joe Miranda *E-mail:* joseph.miranda@bloomsbury.com
Sr Acct Mgr: Allison Jones *E-mail:* allison.jones@bloomsbury.com
Sr Prodn Ed: Claire Henry
Founded: 1910
Interior design, fashion, merchandising, marketing, management, retailing, careers market, research art foundation, clothing, textiles.
Membership(s): International Textiles Apparel Association (ITAA); Interior Design Educators Council (IDEC).
ISBN Prefix(es): 978-0-87005; 978-1-56367; 978-1-60901
Number of titles published annually: 40 Print; 30 CD-ROM
Total Titles: 375 Print; 60 CD-ROM
Orders to: MPS Distribution Center, 16365 James Madison Hwy, Gordonsville, VA 22942-8501
Returns: MPS Distribution Center, 16365 James Madison Hwy, Gordonsville, VA 22942-8501
Warehouse: MPS Distribution Center, 16365 James Madison Hwy, Gordonsville, VA 22942-8501
Distribution Center: MPS Distribution Center, 16365 James Madison Hwy, Gordonsville, VA 22942-8501

Fairleigh Dickinson University Press
Affiliate of Rowman & Littlefield
M-GH2-01, 285 Madison Ave, Madison, NJ 07940
Tel: 973-443-8564 *Fax:* 974-443-8364
E-mail: fdupress@fdu.edu
Web Site: www.fdupress.org
Key Personnel
Dir: Harry Keyishian *E-mail:* harry_keyishian@fdu.edu
Founded: 1967
Publish books in the humanities & social sciences, with special strengths in history & literature.
ISBN Prefix(es): 978-0-8386; 978-1-61147
Number of titles published annually: 40 Print
Total Titles: 1,500 Print
Distributed by Rowman & Littlefield
Foreign Rep(s): Eurospan (Europe, UK); Scholarly Book Services (Canada); United Publishers Services (Japan)

The Fairmont Press Inc
700 Indian Trail, Lilburn, GA 30047
SAN: 207-5946
Tel: 770-925-9388 *Fax:* 770-381-9865
Web Site: www.fairmontpress.com
Key Personnel
VP: Linda Hutchings *E-mail:* linda@fairmontpress.com
Book Prodn Mgr: Beth Pearce *E-mail:* beth@aeecenter.org
Founded: 1973
Professional & reference books on energy, safety, environment, how-to & facility management.
ISBN Prefix(es): 978-0-915586; 978-0-88173
Number of titles published annually: 12 Print; 1 CD-ROM; 12 E-Book
Total Titles: 425 Print; 8 CD-ROM; 125 E-Book
Distributed by CRC Press; Taylor & Francis
Foreign Rep(s): CRC Press

§Faith Alive Christian Resources
Imprint of Christian Reformed Church in North America
1700 28 St SE, Grand Rapids, MI 49508-1407

Tel: 616-224-0728 *Toll Free Tel:* 800-333-8300 *Toll Free Fax:* 888-642-8606
E-mail: info@faithaliveresources.org; sales@faithaliveresources.org; orders@faithaliveresources.org
Web Site: www.faithaliveresources.org
Key Personnel
Dir: Mark Rice *Tel:* 616-224-0795 *E-mail:* mrice@crcna.org
Mng Ed: Ruth Vanderhart *E-mail:* rvanderhart@crcna.org
Founded: 1928
Publish materials for Sunday school & other children's ministries, youth ministry, adults & small groups, prayer & evangelism, church leadership, worship & disability ministry. Also publish the monthly magazine *The Banner* & the quarterly journal *Reformed Worship*.
ISBN Prefix(es): 978-0-933140; 978-0-930265; 978-1-56212; 978-1-59255; 978-1-62025
Number of titles published annually: 50 Print
Total Titles: 307 Print
Imprints: Faith Alive; Friendship Bible Studies; Libros Desafio; World Literature Ministries
Distribution Center: 3475 Mainway, PO Box 5070, CTN LCD-1, Burlington, ON L7R 3Y8, Canada
RCA Resources, 2 Sydney Ave, Mt Evelyn, Victoria 3796, Australia *Tel:* (03) 9736 2412 *Fax:* (03) 9736 2654 *E-mail:* resources@crca.org.au

Faith & Fellowship Publishing
Subsidiary of Church of the Lutheran Brethren
1020 W Alcott Ave, Fergus Falls, MN 56537
Tel: 218-736-7357 *Toll Free Tel:* 800-332-9232
E-mail: clb@clba.org
Web Site: www.clba.org
Key Personnel
Dir: Tim Mathieson
Religious books, newsletters.
ISBN Prefix(es): 978-0-943167
Number of titles published annually: 8 Print
Total Titles: 59 Print

Faith & Life Resources, see MennoMedia

§Faith Library Publications
Subsidiary of RHEMA Bible Church
PO Box 50126, Tulsa, OK 74150-0126
Tel: 918-258-1588 (ext 2218) *Toll Free Tel:* 888-258-0999 (orders) *Fax:* 918-872-7710 (orders)
E-mail: flp@rhema.org
Web Site: www.rhema.org/store
Key Personnel
Dept Head, Kenneth Hagin Ministries: Brian Cumberland
Founded: 1963
ISBN Prefix(es): 978-0-89276; 978-1-60616
Number of titles published annually: 4 Print; 15 CD-ROM
Total Titles: 185 Print; 93 CD-ROM; 50 E-Book
Distributed by Appalachian; Harrison House; Spring Arbor; Whitaker

§Faithlife Corp
Formerly Logos Bible Software
1313 Commercial St, Bellingham, WA 98225
Tel: 360-527-1700 *Toll Free Tel:* 800-875-6467 *Fax:* 360-527-1707
E-mail: sales@faithlife.com; customerservice@faithlife.com
Web Site: www.faithlife.com
Founded: 1992
Electronic & ebook publisher & technology provider.
ISBN Prefix(es): 978-1-57799
Number of titles published annually: 30 CD-ROM; 200 E-Book
Total Titles: 200 CD-ROM; 4,000 E-Book
Membership(s): CBA; Evangelical Christian Publishers Association; Society of Bible Literature

FaithWalk Publishing
Imprint of CSS Publishing Co Inc
5450 N Dixie Hwy, Lima, OH 45807
Tel: 419-227-1818 *Toll Free Tel:* 800-537-1030 (orders: non-bookstore mkts) *Fax:* 419-224-9184
E-mail: orders@csspub.com
Web Site: www.faithwalkpub.com
Key Personnel
Pres: David Runk *E-mail:* david@csspub.com
Prodn Mgr: Sue Sonntag *E-mail:* sue@csspub.com
Acctg: Patti Furr *E-mail:* pfurr@csspub.com
Founded: 2002
ISBN Prefix(es): 978-0-9724196; 978-1-932902
Number of titles published annually: 10 Print
Total Titles: 31 Print
Membership(s): The Independent Book Publishers Association

FaithWords, see Hachette Nashville

F+W, A Content + eCommerce Company
10151 Carver Rd, Suite 200, Blue Ash, OH 45242
Tel: 513-531-2690 *Toll Free Tel:* 800-289-0963 (trade accts); 800-258-0929 (orders)
E-mail: contact_us@fwmedia.com
Web Site: www.fwcommunity.com
Key Personnel
Chmn & CEO: David Nussbaum
COO & CFO: Jim Ogle
Chief Digital Offr: Chad Phelps
Cont: Rich Werner
Pres: Sara Domville
SVP, Opers: Phil Graham *E-mail:* phil.graham@fwcommunity.com
VP, Communs & PR: Stacie Berger *E-mail:* sberger@fwcommunity.com
Sales Dir: Joanne Widmer *E-mail:* joanne.widmer@fwcommunity.com
Sales Dir, Adams Media: Karen Patterson
Edit Dir, Krause Publications: Paul Kennedy
Publr: Jamie Markle
Publr & Content Strategist: Phil Sexton
Publr & Content Strategist, Adams Media: Karen Cooper
Group Publr/Community Leader, Automotive/Outdoors: Jamie Wilkinson
Spec Sales Mgr, Adams Media: Lauren Rouleau
Digital Marketer: Bethany Carland-Adams
Exec Ed, Crimson Romance: Tara Gelsomino
Ed-in-Chief, Merit Press Books: Jacquelyn Mitchard
Founded: 1913
ISBN Prefix(es): 978-0-930625; 978-0-87349; 978-0-87341; 978-0-87069; 978-0-89689; 978-1-58221; 978-0-8019; 978-1-63250
Number of titles published annually: 200 Print
Total Titles: 860 Print
Imprints: Adams Media; Antique Trader Books; Crimson Romance (digital/POD); David & Charles; HOW Books; Interweave; Krause Publications; Merit Press Books (young adult); North Light Books; Prologue Books; Tyrus Books; Warman's; Writer's Digest Books
Branch Office(s)
10901 W 120 Ave, Suite 350, Broomfield, CO 80021 *Tel:* 303-442-0427
4868 Innovation Dr, Fort Collins, CO 80525
490 Boston Post Rd, Suite 15A, Sudbury, MA 01776 *Tel:* 978-203-5444
1140 Broadway, 14th fl, New York, NY 10001 *Tel:* 212-447-1400
Foreign Office(s): Brunel House, Forde Close, Newton, Abbot, Devon TQ12 4PU, United Kingdom *Tel:* (01626) 323200
Foreign Rep(s): David Bateman Ltd (New Zealand); Canadian Manda Group (Canada); Capricorn Link (Australia); China Publishers Services Ltd (Edwin Chu) (China); F+W International (Europe, UK); IPR (Middle East); JCC Enterprises Inc (Jerry Cruz Carrilo Ortiz) (Caribbean, Latin America); Penguin Books India (South Asia); Real Books (South Africa); Trinity Books (South Africa); The White Partnership (Andrew White) (East Asia, Southeast)
Returns: Aero Fulfillment Services, 6023 Union Centre Blvd, Fairfield, OH 45014; Fraser Direct, 100 Armstrong Ave, Georgetown, ON L7G 5S4, Canada *Tel:* 905-877-4411 *Toll Free Tel:* 800-840-5220 *Fax:* 905-877-4410
See separate listing for:
Adams Media
Betterway Books
Interweave Press LLC
Krause Publications Inc
Writer's Digest Books

Farrar, Straus & Giroux Books for Young Readers
Imprint of Macmillan Children's Publishing Group
175 Fifth Ave, 7th fl, New York, NY 10010
Tel: 646-307-5151 *Fax:* 646-438-6150
Web Site: us.macmillan.com/mackids.aspx
Key Personnel
VP & Edit Dir: Joy Peskin
Founded: 1953
Preschool through young adult fiction & nonfiction, hardcover & paperback.
Number of titles published annually: 80 Print
Total Titles: 700 Print
Imprints: Margaret Ferguson Books; Frances Foster Books
Membership(s): The Children's Book Council

Farrar, Straus & Giroux, LLC
Subsidiary of Macmillan
18 W 18 St, New York, NY 10011
SAN: 206-782X
Tel: 212-741-6900
E-mail: fsg.publicity@fsgbooks.com
Web Site: us.macmillan.com/fsg.aspx
Key Personnel
Pres & Publr: Jonathan Galassi
EVP & Deputy Publr: Andrew Mandel *Tel:* 212-206-5354
SVP & Dir, Mktg & Publicity: Jeff Seroy *Tel:* 212-206-5323
SVP & Sales Dir: Spenser Lee
VP & Dir, Publicity: Sarita Varma *Tel:* 212-206-5327 *E-mail:* svarma@fsgbooks.com
VP & Ed-in-Chief: Eric Chinski
VP & Cont, Rts & Perms: Erika Seidman
Exec Mng Ed: Debra Helfand
Ad Dir: Victoria Genna
Creative Dir: Rodrigo Corral
Design Dir: Abby Kagan
Founded: 1946
General fiction, nonfiction, poetry & juveniles.
ISBN Prefix(es): 978-0-374
Number of titles published annually: 150 Print
Total Titles: 1,400 Print
Imprints: Farrar, Straus & Giroux Books for Young Readers; Hill & Wang; North Point Press; Scientific American
Distributor for Drawn & Quarterly; Gray Wolf Books
Foreign Rep(s): Pan Macmillan Ltd (UK); Raincoast Books (Canada)
Foreign Rights: ANA Baltic (Tatjana Zoldnere) (Estonia, Latvia, Lithuania); AnatoliatLit Agency (Amy Spangler & Eda Caca) (Turkey); Anthea Agency (Katalina Sabeva) (Bulgaria); L'Autre Agence (Corinne Marotte & Marie Lannurien) (France); Bardon Chinese Media (David Tsai) (China); Marcin Biegaj (Poland); Anoukh Foerg (Germany); Deborah Harris Agency (Rena Rossner) (Israel); International Copyright Agency (Simon Kessler & Marina Adriana) (Romania); Katai & Bolza (Peter Bolza) (Hungary); KCC (Kyung Kang) (Korea); Leonhardt & Hoier (Eva Haagerup) (Scandinavia); Monica Martin

(Latin America, Spain); Kristin Olson Literarni Agentura (Czech Republic); Ines Planells (Latin America, Spain); Plima Literary Agency (Vuk Perisic) (Albania, Croatia, Serbia, Slovenia); Read 'n Right Agency (Nike Davarinou) (Greece); Riff Agency (Laura & Joao Paulo Riff) (Brazil); Claire Sabatie-Garat (Italy); Sebes & van Gelderen (Paul Sebes) (Netherlands); Maria Strarz-Kanska (Poland); Synopsis Literary Agency (Olga Zasetskaya) (Russia); Tuttle-Mori Agency Inc (Asako Kawachi) (Japan)
Advertising Agency: Verso Advertising
Warehouse: MPS Distribution Center, 16365 James Madison Highway, Gordonsville, VA 22942 *Toll Free Tel:* 888-330-8477
Membership(s): The Children's Book Council
See separate listing for:
Hill & Wang
North Point Press

§Father & Son Publishing Inc
4909 N Monroe St, Tallahassee, FL 32303-7015
Tel: 850-562-2612 *Toll Free Tel:* 800-741-2712 (orders only) *Fax:* 850-562-0916
Web Site: www.fatherson.com
Key Personnel
Pres: Lance Coalson *E-mail:* lance@fatherson.com
Founded: 1982
Publishers of nonfiction, historical fiction, cookbooks, giftbooks & children's books.
ISBN Prefix(es): 978-0-942407; 978-1-935802
Number of titles published annually: 12 Print; 3 Audio
Total Titles: 212 Print; 15 Audio
Distributor for BADM Books
Membership(s): ABA; Florida Authors & Publishers Association Inc; National Association of Independent Publishers

Favorable Impressions
Affiliate of The Lincoln Library (now part of the FactCite family of databases)
9 Elm Park Blvd, Pleasant Ridge, MI 48069
Tel: 248-544-2421
Web Site: www.favimp.com
Key Personnel
Owner & SVP, Mktg & Opers: Dan R Harris *E-mail:* danh@favimp.com
Pres, Publr & Ed: Laurie Lanzen Harris *E-mail:* laurieh@favimp.com
Founded: 1995
Reference & nonfiction books, ebooks & databases for elementary school libraries & public libraries.
ISBN Prefix(es): 978-1-931360
Number of titles published annually: 5 Print
Total Titles: 40 Print; 40 Online; 40 E-Book

FC&A Publishing
103 Clover Green, Peachtree City, GA 30269
Tel: 770-487-6307 *Toll Free Tel:* 800-226-8024 *Fax:* 770-631-4357
E-mail: customer_service@fca.com
Web Site: www.fca.com
Key Personnel
Mktg: Anne Kaufmann *Tel:* 770-487-6307 ext 2151 *E-mail:* anne_kaufmann@fca.com
Founded: 1969
ISBN Prefix(es): 978-0-915099; 978-1-890957; 978-1-932470; 978-1-935574
Number of titles published annually: 3 Print; 3 Online
Total Titles: 36 Print; 30 Online

§Federal Bar Association
1220 N Filmore St, Suite 444, Arlington, VA 22201
Tel: 571-481-9100 *Fax:* 571-481-9090
E-mail: fba@fedbar.org
Web Site: www.fedbar.org
Key Personnel
Exec Dir: Karen Silberman *E-mail:* ksilberman@fedbar.org
Deputy Exec Dir: Stacy King *E-mail:* sking@fedbar.org
Founded: 1920
Publish course materials, newsletters & *The Federal Lawyer* magazine.
ISBN Prefix(es): 978-1-56986
Number of titles published annually: 15 Print; 1 CD-ROM
Total Titles: 350 Print; 1 CD-ROM; 2 Audio

Federal Street Press
Division of Merriam-Webster Inc
25-13 Old Kings Hwy N, No 277, Darien, CT 06820
Tel: 203-852-1280 *Toll Free Tel:* 877-886-2830 *Fax:* 203-852-1389
E-mail: sales@federalstreetpress.com
Web Site: www.federalstreetpress.com
Key Personnel
Publr: Deborah Hastings *E-mail:* dhastings@federalstreetpress.com
Sr Mgr, Sales & Opers: Virginia Guilfoyle *E-mail:* vguilfoyle@federalstreetpress.com
Founded: 1998
Offers up-to-date, quality, value-priced language reference titles created in cooperation with the editors of Merriam-Webster Inc.
ISBN Prefix(es): 978-1-892859; 978-1-59695
Number of titles published annually: 5 Print
Total Titles: 45 Print

Philipp Feldheim Inc, see Feldheim Publishers (Philipp Feldheim Inc)

Feldheim Publishers (Philipp Feldheim Inc)
208 Airport Executive Park, Nanuet, NY 10954
SAN: 207-0545
Tel: 845-356-2282 *Toll Free Tel:* 800-237-7149 (orders) *Fax:* 845-425-1908
E-mail: sales@feldheim.com
Web Site: www.feldheim.com
Key Personnel
Pres: Yitzchak Feldheim
Mng Dir: Elia Hollander
Sales Mgr: Moshe Grossman
Founded: 1939
Translations from Hebrew of Jewish classical works & works of contemporary authors in the field of Orthodox Jewish thought & contemporary Jewish literature for ages three & up.
ISBN Prefix(es): 978-0-87306; 978-1-58330; 978-1-59826; 978-1-68025
Number of titles published annually: 100 Print
Total Titles: 800 Print
Imprints: Feldheim Publishers USA
Foreign Office(s): Yaakov Feldheim Publishers Ltd, Box 43163, 91431 Jerusalem, Israel
Distributor for Hamadia Publishing; Jerusalem Publications

The Feminist Press at The City University of New York
365 Fifth Ave, Suite 5406, New York, NY 10016
SAN: 213-6813
Tel: 212-817-7915 *Fax:* 212-817-1593
E-mail: info@feministpress.org
Web Site: www.feministpress.org
Key Personnel
Exec Dir/Publr: Jennifer Baumgardner *Tel:* 212-817-7916 *E-mail:* jenniferbaumgardner@gmail.com
Mng Ed: Julia Berner-Tobin *E-mail:* jberner-tobin@gc.cuny.edu
Ed: Clarissa Wong
Events Mgr: Lucia Brown *E-mail:* lbrown@gc.cuny.edu
Prodn & Design Mgr: Drew Stevens *E-mail:* dstevens@gc.cuny.edu
Publicity Mgr: Kait Heacock *E-mail:* kheacock@gc.cuny.edu
Devt: Yamberlie Tavarez *E-mail:* ytavarez@gc.cuny.edu
Publicity: Kait Heacock *E-mail:* kheacock@gc.cuny.edu
Sales & Inventory: Jisu Kim *E-mail:* jkim@gc.cuny.edu
Edit Asst: Lauren Hook *E-mail:* lhook@gc.cuny.edu
Founded: 1970
Popular culture, African studies, Asian American studies, international studies, history of feminism, women's studies, working class studies, current issues & women's literature from the Middle East, Africa, Asia & Latin America & US women writers.
ISBN Prefix(es): 978-0-912670; 978-0-935312; 978-1-55861
Number of titles published annually: 18 Print; 10 E-Book
Total Titles: 400 Print; 50 E-Book
Foreign Rights: AnatoliaLit Agency (Amy Spangler) (Turkey); Japan Uni Agency (Miko Yamanouchi) (Japan); Natoli, Stefan & Oliva (Roberta Oliva) (Italy); VBMLitag (Luciana Villas-Boas) (Brazil); Literary Agent Silke Weniger (Germany)
Distribution Center: Baker & Taylor International, 652 E Main St, PO Box 6920, Bridgewater, NJ 08807-0920 (Worldwide exc Africa, Asia, Canada, Continental Europe, Middle East, UK & US) *Tel:* 908-218-0400 *Fax:* 908-707-4387 *E-mail:* btinfo@btol.com *Web Site:* btol.com/international.cfm
Consortium Book Sales & Distribution, c/o Perseus Distribution Services, 1094 Flex Dr, Jackson, TN 38301-5070 (US & CN) *Toll Free Tel:* 800-283-3572 *Toll Free Fax:* 800-351-5073 *E-mail:* info@cbsd.com *Web Site:* www.cbsd.com SAN: 631-760X
Turnaround Publisher Services Ltd, Unit 3, Olympia Trading Estate, Coburg Rd, Wood Green, London, United Kingdom (UK, Africa, Asia, Continental Europe & Middle East) *Tel:* (020) 8829 3000 *Fax:* (020) 8881 5088 *E-mail:* orders@turnaround-uk.com *Web Site:* www.turnaround-uk.com
Membership(s): AAP; Community of Literary Magazines & Presses; National Council for Research on Women (NCRW)

Fence Books
University at Albany, Science Library 320, 1400 Washington Ave, Albany, NY 12222
Tel: 518-591-8162
E-mail: fence.fencebooks@gmail.com
Web Site: www.fenceportal.org
Key Personnel
Publr & Ed: Rebecca Wolff *E-mail:* rebeccafence@gmail.com
Mng Ed: Jess Puglisi *E-mail:* jessp.fence@gmail.com
Founded: 2001
ISBN Prefix(es): 978-1-934200; 978-0-9771064; 978-0-9713189; 978-0-9663324; 978-0-9740909; 978-0-9864373
Number of titles published annually: 6 Print
Total Titles: 60 Print
Distribution Center: Small Press Distribution, 1341 Seventh St, Berkeley, CA 94710-1409 *Tel:* 510-524-1668 *Toll Free Tel:* 800-869-7553 *E-mail:* spd@spdbooks.org *Web Site:* www.spdbooks.org
Consortium Book Sales & Distribution, The Keg House, 34 13 Ave NE, Suite 101, Minneapolis, MN 55413 *Tel:* 612-746-2600 *Fax:* 612-746-2606 *E-mail:* info@cbsd.com *Web Site:* www.cbsd.com

Feral House
1240 W Sims Way, Suite 124, Port Townsend, WA 98368

Tel: 323-666-3311 *Fax:* 323-297-4331
E-mail: info@feralhouse.com
Web Site: feralhouse.com
Key Personnel
Pres & Publr: Adam Parfrey
Founded: 1989
Pop culture, alternative, art, nonfiction, religion, sociology & social sciences.
ISBN Prefix(es): 978-0-922915; 978-1-932595
Number of titles published annually: 10 Print
Total Titles: 66 Print
Imprints: Process Media
Distribution Center: Consortium Book Sales & Distribution, The Keg House, 34 13 Ave NE, Suite 101, Minneapolis, MN 55413-1007 *Tel:* 612-746-2600 *Toll Free Tel:* 800-283-3572 (cust serv) *Fax:* 612-746-2606 *Web Site:* www.cbsd.com
Turnaround Publisher Services, Olympia Trading Estate, Unit 3, Coburg Rd, London N22 6TZ, United Kingdom *Tel:* (020) 8829-3000 *Fax:* (020) 8881-5088 *E-mail:* orders@turnaround-uk.com

§Ferguson Publishing
Imprint of Infobase Learning
132 W 31 St, 17th fl, New York, NY 10001
Tel: 212-967-8800 *Toll Free Tel:* 800-322-8755 *Fax:* 917-339-0323 *Toll Free Fax:* 800-678-3633
E-mail: custserv@factsonfile.com
Web Site: infobasepublishing.com
Key Personnel
CEO & Pres: Mark McDonnell
CFO: Jim Housley
Edit Dir: Laurie Likoff
Dir, Book & Ebook Sales: Justyna Pawluk *E-mail:* jpawluk@infobaselearning.com
Dir, Licensing & Busn Devt: Ben Jacobs *E-mail:* bjacobs@infobaselearning.com
Dir, Mktg: Zina Scarpulla
Dir, Opers: Mark Zielinski
Dir, Publicity: Laurie Katz *E-mail:* lkatz@infobaselearning.com
With its acclaimed career guidance & reference materials, Ferguson Publishing is known among librarians & guidance counselors as the premier publisher in the career education field.
ISBN Prefix(es): 978-0-8160; 978-0-87196; 978-0-89434; 978-1-60413; 978-1-4381
Number of titles published annually: 74 Print; 74 E-Book
Total Titles: 333 Print; 363 E-Book

Howard Fertig, Publisher
80 E 11 St, New York, NY 10003
SAN: 201-4777
Tel: 212-982-7922 *Fax:* 212-982-1099
E-mail: enquiries@hfertigbooks.com; orders@hfertigbooks.com
Web Site: www.hfertigbooks.com
Key Personnel
Pres & Ed-in-Chief: Howard Fertig
Founded: 1966
Scholarly reprints & originals in European history, literature & social sciences.
ISBN Prefix(es): 978-0-86527
Number of titles published annually: 12 Print
Total Titles: 160 Print

Fiction Collective Two Inc (FC2)
Imprint of University of Alabama Press
c/o Dept of English, Langs & Commun Bldg, 255 S Central Campus Dr, Rm 3500, Salt Lake City, UT 84112-0494
Tel: 773-702-7000
E-mail: fc2.cmu@gmail.com
Web Site: www.fc2.org/prizes.html
Key Personnel
Chair, Bd of Dirs: Lance Olsen
Founded: 1973
Publish formally innovative fiction.
ISBN Prefix(es): 978-1-57366
Number of titles published annually: 6 Print
Total Titles: 200 Print
Distributed by University of Alabama Press
Orders to: University of Alabama Press, PO Box 870380, Tuskaloosa, AL 35487-0380 *Tel:* 773-702-7000 *Fax:* 773-702-7212 *Toll Free Fax:* 800-621-8476
Returns: University of Alabama Press, Chicago Distribution Center, 11030 S Langley Ave, Chicago, IL 60628 *Tel:* 773-702-7000 *Toll Free Tel:* 800-621-2736 *Fax:* 773-702-7212 *Toll Free Fax:* 800-621-8476
Membership(s): Community of Literary Magazines & Presses

Fifth Estate Publishing
2795 County Hwy 57, Blounstville, AL 35031
SAN: 852-6419
Toll Free Tel: 855-299-2160
E-mail: fifth-estate@hotmail.com
Web Site: fifthestatepub.com
Founded: 2003
Publisher & distributor.
ISBN Prefix(es): 978-0-9746336; 978-0-9760992; 978-0-9768233; 978-1-933580; 978-1-936533
Number of titles published annually: 6 Print; 6 Online; 6 E-Book
Total Titles: 136 Print; 136 Online; 75 E-Book

Film-Video Publications/Circus Source Publications
7944 Capistrano Ave, West Hills, CA 91304
SAN: 211-1527
Tel: 818-340-0175 *Fax:* 818-340-6620
E-mail: circussource@aol.com
Key Personnel
Pres & Publr: Alan Gadney *Tel:* 818-340-6620
VP & Exec Ed: Carolyn Porter
Ed: Nancy Gadney
Founded: 1974
Reference books, directories & audio/video cassettes on film, video, photography, TV/radio broadcasting, writing, theater, business & finance, performing arts.
ISBN Prefix(es): 978-0-930828
Number of titles published annually: 21 Print; 10 Audio
Total Titles: 25 Print; 16 Audio
Foreign Rep(s): Australia & New Zealand Book Co (Australia); Fitzhenry & Whiteside (Canada); Reed Methuen Publishers (New Zealand)
Advertising Agency: Carolyn Chadwick Advertising
Membership(s): The Association of Publishers for Special Sales; Book Publicists of Southern California; The Independent Book Publishers Association

Filter Press LLC
PO Box 95, Palmer Lake, CO 80133
SAN: 201-484X
Tel: 719-481-2420 *Toll Free Tel:* 888-570-2663 *Fax:* 719-481-2420
E-mail: info@filterpressbooks.com; orders@filterpressbooks.com
Web Site: filterpressbooks.com
Key Personnel
Pres: Doris Baker *E-mail:* doris@filterpressbooks.com
Founded: 1957
Publisher of books on the American West, Western expansion, childrens historical fiction, Colorado history & biography.
ISBN Prefix(es): 978-0-910584; 978-0-86541
Number of titles published annually: 5 Print; 1 Audio
Total Titles: 62 Print; 11 E-Book; 2 Audio
Returns: 19980 Top O'Moor W, Monument, CO 80132
Shipping Address: 19980 Top O'Moor W, Monument, CO 80132
Membership(s): Colorado Association of Libraries; Colorado Independent Publishers Association; Women Writing the West

Financial Executives Research Foundation Inc (FERF)
Affiliate of Financial Executives International (FEI)
West Tower, 7th fl, 1250 Headquarters Plaza, Morristown, NJ 07960-6837
Tel: 973-765-1000 *Fax:* 973-765-1023
Web Site: www.financialexecutives.org
Key Personnel
CEO: William Sinnett
Dir, Fin Servs & Devt: Lorna Raagas *Tel:* 973-765-1033 *E-mail:* lraagas@financialexecutives.org
Sr Mgr, Devt: Kit Hall
Sr Mgr, Res: Leena Roselli
Mgr, Res: Tom Thompson
Founded: 1944
Executive reports & full-length monographs of research related to financial topics. All publications available on PDF.
ISBN Prefix(es): 978-0-910586; 978-1-885065; 978-1-61509; 978-1-933130
Number of titles published annually: 20 Print; 20 Online
Total Titles: 120 Print; 120 Online

Financial Times Press
Imprint of Pearson
225 River St, Hoboken, NJ 07030-4772
Tel: 201-236-7000 *Toll Free Tel:* 800-922-0579 (orders)
Web Site: www.ftpress.com
Key Personnel
Publr: Amy Neidlinger *E-mail:* amy.neidlinger@pearson.com
Exec Ed: Jeanne Levine *E-mail:* jeanne.levine@pearson.com
Publisher of business, management, investment & finance books for general consumers, professionals & students.
ISBN Prefix(es): 978-0-13
Number of titles published annually: 165 Print
Total Titles: 1,200 Print
Imprints: FT Press
Foreign Office(s): 128 Long Acre, London WC2E 9AN, United Kingdom *Tel:* (020) 7447 2000 *Fax:* (020) 7240 5771

Fine Creative Media, Inc
322 Eighth Ave, 15th fl, New York, NY 10001
Tel: 212-595-3500 *Fax:* 212-595-3779
Key Personnel
Founder & CEO: Michael J Fine *E-mail:* mjf@mjfbooks.com
Dir of MJF Books: Scott Messina
Dir of Prodn: Ben Lee
Dir of Fin & Acctg: Ian Teixeira
Dir of Admin & HR: Steven Fine
Dir of Acqs, MJF Books: Roz Siegel
Sr Advisor: Stanley Last
Reprint Mgr: Colin Warnock
Acqs Ed, MJF Books: Jo Fagan; Lizz Brady
Bookkeeper: Cindy Lew
Founded: 1991
Publish hardcover & paperback reprints of fiction & nonfiction as MJF Books; develop & produce Barnes & Noble Classics.
ISBN Prefix(es): 978-1-56731 (MJF Books); 978-1-59308 (Barnes & Noble Classics); 978-1-60671 (MJF Books)
Number of titles published annually: 80 Print
Total Titles: 1,000 Print
Imprints: Barnes & Noble Classics (produced & published in conjunction with Barnes & Noble Inc); MJF Books

FineEdge.com LLC
14004 Biz Point Lane, Anacortes, WA 98221
Tel: 360-299-8500 *Fax:* 360-299-0535
E-mail: pub@fineedge.com; orders@fineedge.com
Web Site: www.fineedge.com
Key Personnel
Publr: Mark Bunzel *E-mail:* mark@fineedge.com
Founded: 1986
Publishing, wholesaling, outdoor guidebooks & maps; specializing in nautical books & mountain biking publications.
ISBN Prefix(es): 978-0-938665; 978-1-932310
Number of titles published annually: 3 Print
Total Titles: 50 Print; 2 Online
Imprints: Mountain Biking Press
Distributed by Heritage House; Sunbelt Publications Inc
Membership(s): The Independent Book Publishers Association

Finney Company Inc
5995 149 St W, Suite 105, Apple Valley, MN 55124
Tel: 952-469-6699 *Toll Free Tel:* 800-846-7027 *Fax:* 952-469-1968 *Toll Free Fax:* 800-330-6232
E-mail: info@finneyco.com
Web Site: www.finneyco.com
Key Personnel
Pres: Alan E Krysan
Mktg Specialist: Krista Danielson
Founded: 1946
Publish books with educational value; children's books, trade, travel guides & educational reference/textbooks.
ISBN Prefix(es): 978-0-9618088; 978-1-879335; 978-0-944280; 978-0-913163; 978-0-912486; 978-0-8134; 978-1-883477; 978-0-9627860; 978-0-9617767; 978-1-880654; 978-0-89317; 978-0-933855; 978-1-931626; 978-0-9616847; 978-0-911781; 978-0-9639705; 978-1-893272; 978-1-879535; 978-0-8200; 978-1-885258; 978-1-888025; 978-0-9662589
Number of titles published annually: 15 Print
Total Titles: 400 Print
Imprints: Anacus Press; Astragal Press; Bancroft-Sage Publishing; Ecopress; Great Outdoors Publishing Co; Lone Oak Press; Pogo Press; SkipJack Press; Windward Publishing
Divisions: Chester Book Co; Hobar Publications; The New Careers Center (Live Oak Publications is an imprint of The New Careers Center)
Distributor for Drache Publications; Images Unlimited Publishing; Pine Forest Publishing; Joyce Shellhart; Snaptail Press
Membership(s): Education Market Association
See separate listing for:
Astragal Press
Ecopress
Hobar Publications
Pogo Press Inc
Windward Publishing

Fire Engineering Books & Videos
Division of PennWell Books
1421 S Sheridan Rd, Tulsa, OK 74112
Tel: 918-931-9410 *Toll Free Tel:* 800-752-9764 *Fax:* 918-931-9555
E-mail: sales@pennwell.com
Web Site: www.pennwellbooks.com
Key Personnel
Dir: Mary McGee *E-mail:* marym@pennwell.com
Mktg Mgr: Sarah De Vos *E-mail:* sarahd@pennwell.com
Founded: 1877
Fire science, suppression & protection, petroleum, electric power, water, hazardous materials books & videos.
ISBN Prefix(es): 978-1-57340; 978-0-912212; 978-0-87814
Number of titles published annually: 10 Print; 5 CD-ROM
Total Titles: 120 Print; 10 CD-ROM
Distributed by David Publishing; Fire Protection Publications
Distributor for Brady; Idea Bank; IFSTA; Mosby

§Firefall Editions
27 Bath St, Lido Beach, NY 11561
Tel: 510-549-2461
E-mail: fire@firefallmedia.com
Web Site: www.firefallmedia.com
Key Personnel
Mng Dir: Robinson Joyce *E-mail:* literary@att.net
Mktg Dir: Kathryn DeLappe *E-mail:* prize@att.net
Founded: 1996
Specialize in fiction, photography, art, judicial fact, textbooks, audiobooks & documentary films.
ISBN Prefix(es): 978-0-915090; 978-1-939434
Number of titles published annually: 6 Print; 3 E-Book; 5 Audio
Total Titles: 66 Print; 6 E-Book; 24 Audio
Distribution Center: Brodart, 500 Arch St, Williamsport, PA 17701

First Avenue Editions
Imprint of Lerner Publishing Group Inc
241 First Ave N, Minneapolis, MN 55401
Tel: 612-332-3344 *Toll Free Tel:* 800-328-4929 *Fax:* 612-332-7615 *Toll Free Fax:* 800-332-1132
E-mail: info@lernerbooks.com
Web Site: www.lernerbooks.com
Key Personnel
Chmn: Harry J Lerner
Pres & Publr: Adam Lerner
CFO & EVP: Margaret Wunderlich
EVP, Sales: David Wexler
EVP & Dir, Mktg & Digital Prods: Terri Soutor
VP, Digital Prod Mgmt: Daniel Wallek
VP, Ed-in-Chief: Patricia M Stockland
VP, Prodn: Gary Hansen
Rts Dir: Maria Kjoller
Dir, HR: Cyndi Radant
Art Dir: Zach Marell
Group Mktg Dir: Jill Braithwaite
School & Lib Mktg Dir: Lois Wallentine
Social studies, picture story books, art, multicultural issues, activity books & beginning readers.
Total Titles: 240 Print; 65 E-Book
Foreign Rep(s): INT Press Distribution (Australia); Monarch Books of Canada (Trade) (Canada); Phambili (Southern Africa); Publishers Marketing Services (Malaysia, Singapore); Saunders Book Co (Education) (Canada); South Pacific Books (New Zealand)
Foreign Rights: Japan Foreign-Rights Centre (Japan); Korea Copyright Center (Korea); Michelle Lapautre Agence Junior (France); Literarische Agentur Silke Weniger (Germany)
Warehouse: 1251 Washington Ave N, Minneapolis, MN 55401

Five Star Publications Inc
4696 W Tyson St, Chandler, AZ 85226-2903
Tel: 480-940-8182 *Fax:* 480-940-8787
E-mail: fivestarpublications@gmail.com
Web Site: www.FiveStarPublications.com; www.FiveStarBookAwards.com; www.AuthorsandExperts.com
Key Personnel
Pres: Linda F Radke
Founded: 1985
Five Star Publications is dedicated to helping authors of all ages achieve their publishing dreams. We strive for excellence in every aspect of our book publishing, marketing & author consulting services, from our award-winning books to our promotional expertise.
ISBN Prefix(es): 978-0-9619853; 978-1-877749; 978-1-58985
Number of titles published annually: 10 Print
Total Titles: 36 Print; 12 E-Book
Imprints: Five Star Express Press (self-publishing plan); Five Star Legends (western books); Five Star Sleuths (mystery books); Little Five Star (children's books); School Express Press (publishing plan for schools, teachers & librarians); Six Points Press (books on Judaic culture); StoryMonsters Ink (subscription-based e-digest)
Divisions: AuthorsandExperts.com; Publishers Support Services; SchoolBookings.com
Membership(s): Arizona Authors Association; Arizona Book Publishing Association; The Independent Book Publishers Association; National Federation of Press Women; Publishers Association of the West

FJH Music Co Inc
2525 Davie Rd, Suite 360, Fort Lauderdale, FL 33317-7424
Tel: 954-382-6061 *Toll Free Tel:* 800-262-8744 *Fax:* 954-382-3073
E-mail: custserv@fjhmusic.com; sales@fjhmusic.com
Web Site: www.fjhmusic.com
Key Personnel
CEO & Pres: Frank J Hackinson
VP: Kevin Hackinson; Kyle Hackinson *E-mail:* kyleh@fjhmusic.com
Founded: 1988
Educational music publications.
ISBN Prefix(es): 978-0-929666; 978-1-56939
Number of titles published annually: 100 Print

Flashlight Press
527 Empire Blvd, Brooklyn, NY 11225
Tel: 718-288-8300 *Fax:* 718-972-6307
E-mail: editor@flashlightpress.com
Web Site: www.flashlightpress.com
Key Personnel
Publr: Harry Mauer *E-mail:* publisher@flashlightpress.com
Ed: Shari Dash Greenspan *E-mail:* editor@flashlightpress.com
Founded: 2004
Children's picture books that explore & illuminate.
ISBN Prefix(es): 978-0-9729225; 978-0-9799746; 978-1-993612
Number of titles published annually: 3 Print
Total Titles: 20 Print
Returns: Independent Publishers Group (IPG), c/o Returns Dept, 814 N Franklin St, Chicago, IL 60610 *Tel:* 312-337-0747 *Toll Free Tel:* 800-888-4741 *Fax:* 312-337-5985 *E-mail:* frontdesk@ipgbook.com *Web Site:* www.ipgbook.com
Distribution Center: Independent Publishers Group (IPG), 814 N Franklin St, Chicago, IL 60610 *Tel:* 312-337-0747 *Toll Free Tel:* 800-888-4741 *Fax:* 312-337-5985 *E-mail:* frontdesk@ipgbook.com *Web Site:* www.ipgbook.com

§FleetSeek
6190 Powers Ferry Rd, Suite 320, Atlanta, GA 30339
Tel: 540-899-9872 *Toll Free Tel:* 888-ONLY-TTS (665-9887) *Fax:* 540-899-1948
E-mail: fleetseek@fleetseek.com
Web Site: www.fleetseek.com
Founded: 1980
Directories online relating to data in the trucking industry.
ISBN Prefix(es): 978-1-880701
Number of titles published annually: 4 Online
Total Titles: 1 CD-ROM; 4 Online

Florida Academic Press
Division of FAP Books Inc
PO Box 357425, Gainesville, FL 32635
SAN: 299-3643
Tel: 352-332-5104
E-mail: fapress@gmail.com

Web Site: www.florida-academic-press.com
Key Personnel
Exec Ed: Prof Sam Decalo
Founded: 1997
Please submit only complete ms, hard copy, with SASE +/or postage for return if needed. No general query letters. 4-6 week assessment time if not interested; 5-10 weeks if interested. Best, fastest responses are by e-mail. If a contract is cut, ms must be returned to us as ready to print electronic PDF files. We can refer you to several moderately-priced graphic designers for this if needed.
ISBN Prefix(es): 978-1-890357
Number of titles published annually: 10 Print; 8 E-Book
Total Titles: 48 Print; 20 E-Book
Imprints: New Voices (primarily fiction)
Distributor for Publisher's Stone Publications

Flying Pen Press LLC
1416 S Newport St, Denver, CO 80224
Tel: 303-375-0499 *Fax:* 303-375-0499
E-mail: directory@flyingpenpress.com
Web Site: www.flyingpenpress.com
Key Personnel
Publr: David A Rozansky
Founded: 2007
Publisher of fiction & nonfiction.
ISBN Prefix(es): 978-0-9795889
Number of titles published annually: 5 Print; 5 E-Book
Total Titles: 12 Print; 1 E-Book
Imprints: Carpe Diem Professional Calendars; Flying Pen Press Colorado; Flying Pen Press Park Trek; Flying Pen Press Rocky Mountain West; Flying Pen Press Science Fiction; Flying Pen Press Southwest; Flying Pen Press Travel Guides; Flying Piggybank Press; The Press for Humanitarian Causes; Traveling Pen Press
Distribution Center: Lightning Source Inc, 1246 Heil Quaker Blvd, La Vergne, TN 37086

§Focus
Imprint of Hackett Publishing Co Inc
PO Box 44937, Indianapolis, IN 46244-0937
Tel: 317-635-9250 *Fax:* 317-635-9292
E-mail: customer@hackettpublishing.com; editorial@hackettpublishing.com
Web Site: focusbookstore.com
Key Personnel
Pres, Publr & CEO: Deborah Wilkes
Edit Dir: Brian Rak
Rts Mgr & Edit Asst: Christina Kowalewski
Founded: 1985
Classical & modern languages.
ISBN Prefix(es): 978-0-941051; 978-1-58510
Number of titles published annually: 12 Print; 1 CD-ROM; 3 E-Book; 2 Audio
Total Titles: 200 Print; 5 CD-ROM; 1 E-Book; 2 Audio
Editorial Office(s): PO Box 390007, Cambridge, MA 02139-0001 *Tel:* 617-497-6303 *Fax:* 617-661-8703
Distributor for Domus Latina Publishing
Foreign Rep(s): Accademia Vivarium Novum (Lingua Latina titles) (Continental Europe exc Portugal & Spain); Cultura Clasica SL (Lingua Latina titles) (Portugal, Spain); Gazelle Book Services (Europe, UK); NewSouth Books (Australia, New Zealand)
Returns: 3333 Massachusetts Ave, Indianapolis, IN 46218
Shipping Address: 3333 Massachusetts Ave, Indianapolis, IN 46218

Focus on the Family
8605 Explorer Dr, Colorado Springs, CO 80920-1051
Tel: 719-531-5181 *Toll Free Tel:* 800-A-FAMILY (232-6459) *Fax:* 719-531-3424
Web Site: www.focusonthefamily.com; www.facebook.com/focusonthefamily
Key Personnel
VP, Communs: Paul Batura
VP, Content Devt & Integration: Jim Mhoon
Founded: 1986
Case bound & soft cover (adult & children) dealing with family relationships & emphasizing the importance of values & Christian principles in people's lives.
ISBN Prefix(es): 978-0-929608; 978-1-56179; 978-1-58997; 978-1-60482; 978-1-62405; 978-1-62471
Number of titles published annually: 60 Print
Total Titles: 200 Print; 4 CD-ROM; 60 Audio
Imprints: Adventures in Odyssey; Brio Girls; Focus on the Family; Heritage Builders; Life on the Edge; Radio Theatre; Renewing the Heart; Ribbits; That the World May Know
Distributed by Baker Books; Cook Communications; Harvest House; Moody Press; Tommy Nelson; Standard Publishing Co; Tyndale House Publishers; Zondervan

Fodor's Travel Publications
Division of Penguin Random House Inc
1745 Broadway, 15th fl, New York, NY 10019
SAN: 204-1073
Toll Free Tel: 800-733-3000
E-mail: fodorspublicity@randomhouse.com; editors@fodors.com
Web Site: www.fodors.com
Key Personnel
SVP & Publr: Amanda D'Acierno
VP, Ed-in-Chief: Arabella Bowen
Edit Dir: Linda Cabasin
Dir, Prod Mgmt-Fodors.com: Roxanne Chen
Dir, Publicity: Katherine Fleming
Sr Map Ed: Rebbecca Baer
Sr Content Mgmt Strategist: Cate Starmer
Founded: 1936
Travel guides, foreign & domestic.
ISBN Prefix(es): 978-0-679; 978-0-307; 978-0-676; 978-1-4000
Number of titles published annually: 100 Print
Total Titles: 800 Print; 800 E-Book
Imprints: Compass American Guides; Fodor's
Warehouse: Penguin Random House, 400 Hahn Rd, Westminster, MD 21157

Fons Vitae
49 Mockingbird Valley Dr, Louisville, KY 40207-1366
Tel: 502-897-3641 *Fax:* 502-893-7373
E-mail: fonsvitaeky@aol.com
Web Site: www.fonsvitae.com
Key Personnel
Dir: Gray Henry *E-mail:* grayh101@aol.com
Proj Dir: Elena Lloyd-Sidle
Busn Mgr: Lucy Langman
Mktg & Multimedia: Paul T Carney
Founded: 1997
Fons Vitae is both an academic charity with 501(c)(3) charitable status & a peer-reviewed publishing house which ensures the highest scholarly standards for its publications. Authentic text, impeccably translated & exquisitely produced, make these volumes useful for both the university classroom & for those interested in the eternal verities with no compromise to a recent soft focus on spirituality.
ISBN Prefix(es): 978-1-887752
Number of titles published annually: 10 Print; 5 CD-ROM
Total Titles: 130 Print; 5 CD-ROM
Distributor for African American Islamic Institute; Anqa Press (UK); Aperture (NY); Archetype (UK); Broadstone Books; Dar Nun; Golganooza Press (UK); Islamic Texts Society (UK); Matheson Trust; Parabola; Paragon; Parvardigar Press; Pir Press (NY); Qiblah Books; Quilliam Press (UK); Sandala Productions; Sophia Perennis; Sri Lanka Institute of Traditional Studies; Thesaurus Islamicus Foundation; Tradigital; White Thread Press (US); Wisdom Foundation; World Wisdom (US); Zaytuna Institute Press (US)
Foreign Rep(s): American University Cairo Press (AUC) (Middle East)
Distribution Center: Independent Publishers Group (IPG), 814 N Franklin St, Chicago 60610, IL *Tel:* 312-337-0747 *Toll Free Tel:* 800-888-4741 *Fax:* 312-337-5985 *E-mail:* frontdesk@ipgbook.com *Web Site:* www.ipgbook.com

Fordham University Press
2546 Belmont Ave, University Box L, Bronx, NY 10458
SAN: 201-6516
Tel: 718-817-4795 *Fax:* 718-817-4785
Web Site: www.fordhampress.com
Key Personnel
Dir: Fredric Nachbaur *E-mail:* fnachbaur@fordham.edu
Edit Dir: Richard Morrison *E-mail:* rmorrison@fordham.edu
Mktg Dir: Kathleen O'Brien-Nicholson *Tel:* 718-817-4782 *E-mail:* bkaobrien@fordham.edu
Busn Mgr: Margaret Noonan *E-mail:* mnoonan@fordham.edu
Prodn & Design Mgr: Ann-Christine Racette *E-mail:* aracette@fordham.edu
Asst Busn Mgr: Marie Hall *E-mail:* mhall21@fordham.edu
Asst Mktg Mgr: Katie Sweeney *E-mail:* kasweeney@fordham.edu
Mng Ed: Eric Newman *Tel:* 718-817-4786 *E-mail:* ernewman@fordham.edu
Edit Assoc & Asst to Dir: Will Cerbone *E-mail:* wcerbone@fordham.edu
Acqs Ed: Tom Lay *E-mail:* tlay@fordham.edu
Founded: 1907
Scholarly books & journals, New York regional books, general trade books & videos.
ISBN Prefix(es): 978-0-8232
Number of titles published annually: 42 Print
Total Titles: 450 Print
Imprints: Empire State Editions
Sales Office(s): Oxford University Press, 2001 Evans Rd, Cary, NC 27513 *Toll Free Tel:* 800-445-9714 *Fax:* 919-677-1303 *E-mail:* custserv.us@oup.com SAN: 202-5892
Distributed by Oxford University Press (US & CN)
Distributor for Creighton University Press; Institute for Advanced Study in the Theatre Arts (IASTA); Little Room Press; The Reconstructionist Press; Rockhurst University Press; St Bede's Publications; University of San Francisco Press
Foreign Rep(s): Combined Academic Publishers Ltd (Africa, Europe, India, Middle East, UK); Cranbury International LLC (Ethan Atkin) (Latin America); East-West Export Books (EWEB) c/o University of Hawaii Press (Royden Muranaka) (Asia, The Pacific)
Orders to: Oxford University Press, 2001 Evans Rd, Cary, NC 27513 *Toll Free Tel:* 800-445-9714 *Fax:* 919-677-1303 *E-mail:* custserv.us@oup.com SAN: 202-5892
Returns: Maple Press Distribution Center, 704 Legionnaire Dr, Fredricksburg, PA 17026
Membership(s): AAP; Association of American University Presses; Association of Jesuit University Presses

Fort Ross Inc Russian-American Publishing Projects
Division of Fort Ross Inc
26 Arthur Place, Yonkers, NY 10701
Tel: 914-375-6448
Web Site: www.fortrossinc.com
Key Personnel
Pres & Exec Dir: Dr Vladimir Kartsev *E-mail:* vkartsev2000@yahoo.com

Founded: 1992
Books in Russian. Russia-related books in English, co-publishing of books of American authors in Russia, buying rights from American authors & illustrators.
ISBN Prefix(es): 978-1-57480
Number of titles published annually: 4 Print
Total Titles: 49 Print
Foreign Rep(s): Nova Littera (Baltic States, Belarus, Eastern Europe, Russia, Ukraine)

Fortress Press, see Augsburg Fortress Publishers, Publishing House of the Evangelical Lutheran Church in America

The Forum Press Inc
3100 W Warner Ave, Suite 7, Santa Ana, CA 92704
Tel: 323-244-3938
E-mail: theforumpress@cs.com
Web Site: www.theforumpress.com
Key Personnel
Publr: Kira Fulks
Founded: 2009
Also distributor.
This publisher has indicated that 25% of their product line is author subsidized.
ISBN Prefix(es): 978-0-9842752
Number of titles published annually: 10 Print
Total Titles: 4 Print

§Forum Publishing Co
383 E Main St, Centerport, NY 11721
Tel: 631-754-5000 *Toll Free Tel:* 800-635-7654 *Fax:* 631-754-0630
E-mail: forumpublishing@aol.com
Web Site: www.forum123.com
Key Personnel
CEO & Publr: Martin Stevens
Founded: 1981
Business magazines & books.
ISBN Prefix(es): 978-0-9626141
Number of titles published annually: 5 Print
Total Titles: 15 Print; 6 CD-ROM

Forward Movement
Affiliate of The Episcopal Church
412 Sycamore St, Cincinnati, OH 45202-4110
Tel: 513-721-6659 *Toll Free Tel:* 800-543-1813 *Fax:* 513-721-0729 (orders)
E-mail: orders@forwardmovement.org (orders & cust serv)
Web Site: www.forwardmovement.org
Key Personnel
Deputy Dir & Mng Ed: Richelle Thompson *E-mail:* rthompson@forwardmovement.org
Dir, Busn Opers: D Jane Paraskevopoulos *E-mail:* jparaskevo@forwardmovement.org
Mktg Mgr: Heidi Weaver-Smith *E-mail:* hweaver@forwardmovement.org
Founded: 1935
Inspires disciples & empowers evangelists around the globe through offerings that encourage spiritual growth in individuals & congregations.
ISBN Prefix(es): 978-0-88028
Number of titles published annually: 12 Print
Total Titles: 60 Print; 1 Audio
Imprints: FMP
Distributor for Anglican Book Centre
Warehouse: 10001 Alliance Rd, Cincinnati, OH 45242

Walter Foster Publishing Inc
Imprint of Quarto Publishing Group USA
6 Orchard Rd, Suite 100, Lake Forest, CA 92630
SAN: 249-051X
Tel: 949-380-7510 *Toll Free Tel:* 800-426-0099; 800-759-0190 (orders) *Fax:* 949-380-7575
E-mail: walterfoster@quartous.com
Web Site: www.quartous.com
Key Personnel
VP: Anne Landa
VP, Sales-Arts/Crafts: Dan Widner
Mktg Mgr: Angela Corpus
Founded: 1922
Instructional art books, specialty art & creative products.
ISBN Prefix(es): 978-0-929261; 978-1-56010
Number of titles published annually: 30 Print
Total Titles: 350 Print
Foreign Rep(s): Apple Press

§The Foundation Center
32 Old Slip, 24th fl, New York, NY 10005-3500
SAN: 207-5687
Tel: 212-620-4230 *Toll Free Tel:* 800-424-9836 *Fax:* 212-807-3677
E-mail: customerservice@foundationcenter.org
Web Site: foundationcenter.org
Key Personnel
Pres: Bradford K Smith *Tel:* 212-807-3602 *E-mail:* bks@foundationcenter.org
Dir, Busn Devt, Mktg & Communs: Elizabeth Bradley *Tel:* 212-807-3619 *E-mail:* eab@foundationcenter.org
Founded: 1956
Reference books on US foundations, corporations & their grant-making activities & books about philanthropy & nonprofit management.
ISBN Prefix(es): 978-0-87954; 978-1-931923; 978-1-59542
Number of titles published annually: 12 Print; 3 Online
Total Titles: 292 Print; 3 Online; 25 E-Book
Branch Office(s)
312 Sutter St, Suite 606, San Francisco, CA 94108-4314 *Tel:* 415-397-0902
1627 "K" St NW, 3rd fl, Washington, DC 20006-1708 *Tel:* 202-331-1400
133 Peachtree St NE, Lobby Suite 350, Atlanta, GA 30303-1804 *Tel:* 404-880-0094
1422 Euclid Ave, Suite 1600, Cleveland, OH 44115-2001 *Tel:* 216-861-1933

Foundation Press
Imprint of West Academic Publishing
c/o West Academic Publishing, 444 Cedar St, Suite 700, St Paul, MN 55101
Toll Free Tel: 877-888-1330
E-mail: customerservice@westacademic.com
Web Site: www.westacademic.com
Key Personnel
VP & Publr: Pamela Siege Chandler *E-mail:* pamela.siege@westacademic.com
Acct Mgr: Peter Hinsch *Tel:* 651-202-4780 *E-mail:* peter.hinsch@westacademic.org
Founded: 1931
Law, business, political science, criminal justice, curriculum books, graduate & undergraduate primarily in law.
ISBN Prefix(es): 978-0-88277; 978-1-56662; 978-1-58778; 978-1-59941
Number of titles published annually: 120 Print
Total Titles: 500 Print

Foundation Publications
900 S Euclid St, La Habra, CA 90631
Mailing Address: PO Box 2935, La Habra, CA 90632-2935
Tel: 714-879-2286 *Toll Free Tel:* 800-257-6272 *Fax:* 714-535-2164
E-mail: info@foundationpublications.com
Web Site: www.foundationpublications.com
Key Personnel
EVP: Pike Lambeth *E-mail:* pike@foundationpublications.com
Founded: 1971
Publish New American Standard Bible, La Biblia de Las Americas & Nueva Biblia Latinoamericana de Hoy.
ISBN Prefix(es): 978-0-910618; 978-1-58135; 978-1-885217
Number of titles published annually: 5 Print
Total Titles: 8 Print; 1 CD-ROM
Distribution Center: Anchor Distributors, 1030 Hunt Valley Circle, New Kensington, PA 15068 *Toll Free Fax:* 800-444-4484
STL Distribution, 212 Industrial Dr, Bristol, TN 37620 *Toll Free Tel:* 800-289-2772
Membership(s): Evangelical Christian Publishers Association; SEPA

Fox Chapel Publishing Co Inc
1970 Broad St, East Petersburg, PA 17520
Tel: 717-560-4703 *Toll Free Tel:* 800-457-9112 *Fax:* 717-560-4702
E-mail: customerservice@foxchapelpublishing.com
Web Site: www.foxchapelpublishing.com
Key Personnel
CFO: Kerry Eltman
Pres: Alan Giagnocavo *E-mail:* alan@foxchapelpublishing.com
Dir, Edit: Peg Couch *E-mail:* peg@foxchapelpublishing.com
Prodn: Troy Thorne
Intl Rts: Jane Patukas *E-mail:* patukas@foxchapelpublishing.com
Founded: 1991
Publisher of illustrated nonfiction books, magazines, patterns & videos for craft, hobby & do-it-yourself enthusiasts. Fox Chapel Publishing inspires & informs readers who enjoy woodworking, needlework, pyrography, home & garden, cooking, outdoor recreation, coloring, Zentangle®, kids crafts & more. Fox Chapel publishes two magazines, *Woodcarving Illustrated & Scroll Saw, Woodworking & Crafts.*
ISBN Prefix(es): 978-1-56523
Number of titles published annually: 120 Print
Total Titles: 1,200 Print
Imprints: Creative Homeowner; Design Originals; Heliconia Press; IMM Lifestyle Books
Distributed by Ingram Publisher Services
Distributor for Reader's Digest; Taunton Sterling Dover
Membership(s): Craft Hobby Association; Publishers Association of the West
See separate listing for:
Creative Homeowner

§Fox Run Press LLC
7840 Bullet Rd, Peyton, OH 80831
Mailing Address: PO Box 64380, Colorado Springs, CO 80962
Tel: 719-482-4035 *Fax:* 719-623-0254
E-mail: info@foxrunpress.com
Web Site: www.foxrunpress.com
Key Personnel
Ed: Ron Hardman *E-mail:* ron@foxrunpress.com
Sales: Shelly Johnson
Acctg: Kevin Cronk
Founded: 2008
Publish books, ebooks & online content for children's fiction & historical fiction titles.
ISBN Prefix(es): 978-0-9819607
Number of titles published annually: 5 Print; 5 E-Book
Total Titles: 3 Print
Distribution Center: Ingram Publisher Services, One Ingram Blvd, La Vergne, TN 37086 *Tel:* 615-793-5000 *E-mail:* orders@ingrambook.com
Membership(s): The Association of Publishers for Special Sales; The Independent Book Publishers Association

FPMI Solutions Inc
689 Discovery Dr, Suite 300, Huntsville, AL 35806
Toll Free Tel: 888-644-3764
E-mail: info@fpmi.com

Web Site: www.fpmisolutions.com; www.fpmi.com
Key Personnel
CEO: R Mark McLindon
COO: Dustin B DeFee
VP, Capture: Dawn B Winters
Founded: 1985
Government publications.
ISBN Prefix(es): 978-0-936295; 978-1-930542
Number of titles published annually: 4 Print
Total Titles: 20 Print
Branch Office(s)
66 Canal Center Plaza, Suite 305, Alexandria, VA 22314 *Tel:* 703-690-7000 *Fax:* 703-690-7009

§Franciscan Media
28 W Liberty St, Cincinnati, OH 45202
SAN: 204-6237
Tel: 513-241-5615 *Toll Free Tel:* 800-488-0488 *Fax:* 513-241-0399
E-mail: books@americancatholic.org
Web Site: www.americancatholic.org; www.franciscanmedia.org
Key Personnel
Pres: Rev Jeff Scheeler, OFM
CEO & Publr: Rev Dan Kroger, OFM *Tel:* 513-241-5615 ext 127 *E-mail:* dank@americancatholic.org
Edit Dir, Franciscan Media Books: Jon M Sweeney
Dir, Design & Prodn: Jeanne Kortekamp *Tel:* 513-241-5615 ext 113 *E-mail:* jeannek@americancatholic.org
Dir, Mktg, Sales & Internet: Barbara Baker *Tel:* 513-241-5615 ext 101 *E-mail:* bkbaker@americancatholic.org
Ad Mgr: Fred Limke *Tel:* 800-488-0488 ext 117 *E-mail:* flimke@americancatholic.org
Mng Ed: Katie Carroll *Tel:* 513-241-5615 ext 141 *E-mail:* katiec@americancatholic.org
Founded: 1970
Religion (Catholic); inspirational resources for parishes, schools & individuals; books, videos, audio books, ebooks, weekly & Sunday homily programs; monthly subscription newsletters, monthly magazine; American Catholic (web site).
ISBN Prefix(es): 978-0-912228; 978-0-86716; 978-1-61636; 978-1-63253; 978-1-63254
Number of titles published annually: 30 Print; 35 E-Book; 25 Audio
Total Titles: 550 Print; 100 E-Book; 200 Audio
Imprints: Fisher Productions; Franciscan Communications; Ikonographics; Servant Books
Distributor for Franciscan Communications (books & videos); Ikonographics (videos)
Foreign Rep(s): Pleroma Christian Supplies (New Zealand); Rainbow/Word of Life (Australia); Redemptorist Publications Book Service (UK)
Membership(s): Association of Catholic Publishers Inc; Canadian Booksellers Association; Catholic Press Association; Society of Professional Journalists

§Franklin, Beedle & Associates Inc
2154 NE Broadway, Suite 100, Portland, OR 97232
Tel: 503-284-6348 *Toll Free Tel:* 800-322-2665 *Fax:* 503-625-4434
Web Site: www.fbeedle.com
Key Personnel
Ed: Tom Sumner *E-mail:* tsumner@fbeedle.com
Founded: 1985
College textbooks in computer science, information systems & computers in education, educational software, computer engineering, computer information systems, information technology.
ISBN Prefix(es): 978-0-938661; 978-1-887902; 978-1-59028
Number of titles published annually: 10 Print; 5 E-Book
Total Titles: 50 Print; 5 E-Book
Imprints: William, James & Co (humanities publr); Xpat Fiction
Distributor for Arcus; Battlebridge; Blue Sky Gallery; Photolucida Book; Ringing Bell Press; Tayo Press; Wordstock
Foreign Rep(s): Transatlantic Publishers (Europe, Middle East, UK)
Membership(s): Association for Computing Machinery

Frederick Fell Publishers Inc
2131 Hollywood Blvd, Suite 305, Hollywood, FL 33020
SAN: 208-2365
Tel: 954-925-5242
E-mail: fellpub@aol.com (admin only)
Web Site: www.fellpub.com
Key Personnel
Pres & Publr: Donald L Lessne *E-mail:* donlessne@aol.com
Ed-in-Chief: Barbara Newman *E-mail:* felleditor@aol.com
Founded: 1943
An award-winning publisher of general trade books. The series we publish include the Know-it-All Guides, the Top 100 series & Heroes & Heroines series & So You Want To Be series.
ISBN Prefix(es): 978-0-88391
Number of titles published annually: 24 Print; 50 E-Book
Total Titles: 150 Print; 150 E-Book
Foreign Rep(s): Brumby Sunstate (Australia); Gazelle Book Services (UK & the continent); Jarir Bookstore (Tony Herold) (Saudi Arabia); Monarch Books of Canada (Canada); Parrot Reads Publishers (Indian subcontinent); Trinity Books (South Africa); USBD Distribution (Singapore)
Foreign Rights: Akcali Copyright Agency (Turkey); Balcells Agency (Latin America exc Brazil, Portugal, Spain); Lorella Belli Literary Agency (UK); Big Apple Agency (Taiwan); Big Apple Agency (Maggie Han) (China); Book Publishers Association of Israel (Beverley Levit) (Israel); Daniel Doglioli (Italy); Graal Literary Agency (Marcin Biegaj) (Poland); Imprima Korea Agency (Korea); International Copyright Agency Ltd (Simona Kessler) (Romania); Christiane Janssen (Germany); Japan UNI Agency Inc (Japan); Jarir Bookstore (Tony Herold) (Saudi Arabia); LEX Copyright Office (Norbert Uzseka) (Hungary); Maxima Creative Agency (Santo Manurung) (Indonesia); Nova Littera S L (Konstantin Paltchikov) (Russia); Andrew Nurnberg Associates Ltd (Tatjana Zoldnere) (Latvia, Lithuania, Ukraine); Andrew Nurnberg Associates Prague (Petra Tobiskova) (Czech Republic); Andrew Nurnberg Associates Sofia (Anna Droumeva) (Bulgaria); OA Literary Agency (Greece); Plima Literary Agency (Mila Perisic) (Croatia, Serbia, Slovenia); Karin Schindler (Brazil); Tuttle-Mori Agency (Thailand); Tuttle-Mori Agency Inc (Japan)
Distribution Center: Bookmasters, 30 Amberwood Pkwy, Ashland, OH 44805, Contact: Tony Proe *Tel:* 419-281-0200 *Toll Free Tel:* 800-537-6727 *Fax:* 419-281-0200 *E-mail:* tproe@bookmasters.com
Monarch Books of Canada, 5000 Dufferin St, Downsview, ON M3H 5T5, Canada, Contact: Ron Gurfinkel *Tel:* 416-663-8231 *E-mail:* ron@monarchbooks.ca
Trinity Books, PO Box 242, Randburg 2125, South Africa *Tel:* (011) 787-4010 *Fax:* (011) 781-1501 *E-mail:* trinity@iafrica.com
Gazelle Book Services Ltd, White Cross Mills, Hightown, Lancaster LA1 4XS, United Kingdom *Tel:* (01524) 68765 *Fax:* (01524) 63232 *E-mail:* sales@gazellebooks.co.uk

§Free Spirit Publishing Inc
217 Fifth Ave N, Suite 200, Minneapolis, MN 55401-1299
Tel: 612-338-2068 *Toll Free Tel:* 800-735-7323 *Fax:* 612-337-5050 *Toll Free Fax:* 866-419-5199
E-mail: help4kids@freespirit.com
Web Site: www.freespirit.com
Key Personnel
Pres & Publr: Judy Galbraith
Intl Rts Mgr: Lindsey LaBore
Founded: 1983
Offer books & learning materials for parents, educators, children & teens. Topics include: self-esteem, stress management, school success, creativity, relationships with friends & family, social action, special needs (i.e. children with LD/learning differences, gifted & talented & at-risk youth), bullying & conflict resolution.
ISBN Prefix(es): 978-0-915793; 978-1-57542; 978-0-9665988
Number of titles published annually: 25 Print; 1 CD-ROM
Total Titles: 170 Print; 2 CD-ROM; 3 Audio
Foreign Rep(s): Educational Distributors (New Zealand); Georgetown Publications (Canada); Incentive Plus (UK)

§W H Freeman
Imprint of Macmillan Higher Education
41 Madison Ave, 37th fl, New York, NY 10010
Tel: 212-576-9400 *Fax:* 212-689-2383
Web Site: www.whfreeman.com
Key Personnel
Pres: Elizabeth Widdicombe
Publr: Ruth Baruth; Peter Marshall
Founded: 1946
Science & mathematics texts for the higher education market & high school advanced courses.
ISBN Prefix(es): 978-0-312; 978-1-57259; 978-1-4292
Number of titles published annually: 25 Print; 20 Online; 20 E-Book
Total Titles: 500 Print
Foreign Rep(s): Macmillan East Asia (China, Hong Kong, Indonesia, Korea, Philippines, Singapore, Thailand, Vietnam); Macmillan Publishers (Taiwan); Palgrave Macmillan (Australia, New Zealand); Palgrave Macmillan UK (Africa, Caribbean, Europe, India, Japan, Latin America, Middle East, Pakistan, UK); UBSD Distribution SDN BHD (Malaysia)
Warehouse: MPS Distribution Center, 16365 James Madison Hwy (US Rte 15), Gordonsville, VA 22942 *Toll Free Tel:* 888-330-8477 *Fax:* 540-672-7540 (cust serv) *Toll Free Fax:* 800-672-2054 (orders)

Samuel French Inc
235 Park Ave S, 5th fl, New York, NY 10003
Tel: 212-206-8990 *Toll Free Tel:* 866-598-8449 *Fax:* 212-206-1429
E-mail: info@samuelfrench.com; publications@samuelfrench.com
Web Site: www.samuelfrench.com
Key Personnel
Pres: Nate Collins *E-mail:* ncollins@samuelfrench.com
VP & Dir, Opers: Kenneth Dingledine *E-mail:* kdingledine@samuelfrench.com
Literary Dir: Amy Rose Marsh *E-mail:* amarsh@samuelfrench.com
Pubns Mgr: David Geer *E-mail:* dgeer@samuelfrench.com
Founded: 1830
Plays.
ISBN Prefix(es): 978-0-573
Number of titles published annually: 130 Print
Total Titles: 5,000 Print
Branch Office(s)
Samuel French Bookshop, 7623 Sunset Blvd, Hollywood, CA 90046

Foreign Office(s): Samuel French Ltd, 52 Fitzroy St, London W1T 5JR, United Kingdom, Opers Dir: David Webster *Tel:* (020) 7387 9373 *Fax:* (020) 7387 2161 *E-mail:* theatre@samuelfrench-london.co.uk *Web Site:* www.samuelfrench-london.co.uk
Distributed by Baker's Plays; Samuel French Ltd (UK)
Distributor for Baker's Plays; Samuel French Ltd (UK)
Foreign Rights: DALRO Pty Ltd (Botswana, Lesotho, Namibia, South Africa, Swaziland); Drama League of Ireland (Ireland); Origin Theatrical (Australia); Play Bureau (NZ) Ltd (New Zealand)

Fresh Air Books
Imprint of Upper Room Books
1908 Grand Ave, Nashville, TN 37212
Tel: 615-340-7200 *Toll Free Tel:* 800-972-0433 (orders)
Web Site: books.upperroom.org
Key Personnel
Asst Ed & Admin Coord: Joanna Bradley *Tel:* 615-340-7256 *E-mail:* jbradley@umcdiscipleship.org
Founded: 2009
Nonprofit publisher of religious materials.
ISBN Prefix(es): 978-1-935205
Number of titles published annually: 1 Print; 2 E-Book
Total Titles: 14 Print; 10 E-Book
Returns: PBD Worldwide Fulfillment Services, Discipleship Resources, Upper Rm, Return Door 16, 1650 Bluegrass Lakes Pkwy, Alpharetta, GA 30004 *Tel:* 770-442-8633 *Fax:* 770-442-9742
Warehouse: PBD Worldwide Fulfillment Services, 1650 Bluegrass Lakes Pkwy, Alpharetta, GA 30004 *Tel:* 770-442-8633 *Fax:* 770-442-9742
Distribution Center: PBD Worldwide Fulfillment Services, 1650 Bluegrass Lakes Pkwy, Alpharetta, GA 30004 *Tel:* 770-442-8633 *Fax:* 770-442-9742

Friends United Press
Subsidiary of Friends United Meeting
101 Quaker Hill Dr, Richmond, IN 47374
SAN: 201-5803
Tel: 765-962-7573 *Fax:* 765-966-1293
E-mail: friendspress@fum.org; orders@fum.org
Web Site: shop.fum.org
Key Personnel
Communs Ed: Annie Glen *E-mail:* annieg@fum.org
Founded: 1969
Paperbound books; religion.
ISBN Prefix(es): 978-0-913408; 978-0-944350
Number of titles published annually: 3 Print; 3 Online
Total Titles: 85 Print; 67 Online
Membership(s): The Associated Church Press; The Independent Book Publishers Association; Protestant Church-Owned Publishers Association; Quakers Uniting in Publications

Frog Books
Imprint of North Atlantic Books
2526 Martin Luther King Jr Way, Berkeley, CA 94704
Tel: 510-549-4270 *Fax:* 510-549-4276
E-mail: customerservice@northatlanticbooks.com
Web Site: www.northatlanticbooks.com
Key Personnel
Publr: Richard Grossinger
Publr & Exec Dir: Doug Reil
Dir, Publg: Tim McKee
Dist & Mktg Lead: Drew Cavanaugh *E-mail:* dcavanaugh@northatlanticbooks.com
Foreign Rts Mgr: Sarah Serafimidis *Tel:* 510-549-4270 ext 16 *E-mail:* sserafimidis@northatlanticbooks.com
Founded: 1993
Internal martial arts, alternative medicine, somatic psychology, sports, science, women's topics, psychology, political/current affairs, Buddhism, gay & lesbian, environmental, art books (if bought direct), sustainable development, ecology, parenting, popular culture, body work, literary nonfiction, memoir, biography & children's picture books.
ISBN Prefix(es): 978-1-883319; 978-1-58394
Number of titles published annually: 33 Print
Total Titles: 300 Print; 7 E-Book
Distributed by North Atlantic Books; Random House
Foreign Rep(s): Bacchus Books (South Africa); Publishers Group UK (UK); John Reed Distribution (Australia, New Zealand)
Distribution Center: Random House Distribution Services, 400 Hahn Rd, Westminster, MD 21157 *Toll Free Tel:* 800-733-3000 *Toll Free Fax:* 800-659-2436 *E-mail:* csorders@randomhouse.com
Random House of Canada Limited, 2775 Matheson Blvd E, Mississauga, ON L4W 4P7, Canada *Toll Free Tel:* 888-523-9292 *Toll Free Fax:* 888-562-9924
Membership(s): Northern California Book Publicity & Marketing Association

Fulcrum Publishing Inc
4690 Table Mountain Dr, Suite 100, Golden, CO 80403
SAN: 200-2825
Tel: 303-277-1623 *Toll Free Tel:* 800-992-2908 *Fax:* 303-279-7111 *Toll Free Fax:* 800-726-7112
E-mail: info@fulcrumbooks.com; orders@fulcrumbooks.com
Web Site: www.fulcrumbooks.com
Key Personnel
Publr: Sam Scinta
Dir, Sales & Mktg: Melanie Roth *Tel:* 800-922-2908 ext 1213 *E-mail:* melanie@fulcrumbooks.com
Ed-in-Chief: Rebecca McEwen
Founded: 1984
Nonfiction trade: Western culture & history, Native American culture & history, environment & nature, popular culture, lifestyle, outdoor recreation, public policy & gardening.
ISBN Prefix(es): 978-1-55591; 978-1-56373; 978-0-912347; 978-1-936218; 978-1-938486
Number of titles published annually: 15 Print; 15 E-Book
Total Titles: 600 Print; 250 E-Book
Imprints: Speaker's Corner (public policy series)
Distribution Center: Consortium Book Sales & Distribution, The Keg House, 34 13 Ave NE, Suite 101, Minneapolis, MN 55413-1007, Contact: Jim Nichols *Tel:* 612-746-2600 *Toll Free Tel:* 800-283-3572 *Fax:* 612-746-2606 *Toll Free Fax:* 800-351-5073 *E-mail:* info@cbsd.com *Web Site:* www.cbsd.com
Membership(s): AAP; ABA; Midwest Independent Booksellers Association; Mountains & Plains Independent Booksellers Association; Pacific Northwest Booksellers Association

FurnitureCore
1389 Peachtree St NE, Suite 310, Atlanta, GA 30309
Tel: 404-961-3734 *Toll Free Tel:* 800-826-8868 *Fax:* 404-961-3749
E-mail: info@furniturecore.com
Web Site: www.furniturecore.com
Key Personnel
Owner & Pres: Bob George
Founded: 1985 (acquired in 2008)
Specialize in business, industry & statistical reports.
ISBN Prefix(es): 978-0-921577; 978-1-894330; 978-1-894960
Number of titles published annually: 12 Print; 10 Online
Total Titles: 56 Print; 30 Online
Distributor for AMA Research; Business & Research Associates

§Future Horizons Inc
721 W Abram St, Arlington, TX 76013
Tel: 817-277-0727 *Toll Free Tel:* 800-489-0727 *Fax:* 817-277-2270
E-mail: info@fhautism.com
Web Site: www.fhautism.com
Key Personnel
Pres: R Wayne Gilpin
Founded: 1996
Resources on Autism/Asperger's Syndrome, including books, CDs, DVDs, magazines & conferences.
ISBN Prefix(es): 978-1-885477; 978-1-932565; 978-1-935274
Number of titles published annually: 6 Print
Total Titles: 20 Print

Gagosian Gallery
980 Madison Ave, New York, NY 10075
Tel: 212-744-2313 *Fax:* 212-772-7962
E-mail: newyork@gagosian.com
Web Site: www.gagosian.com
Key Personnel
Publg Dir: Alison McDonald
Founded: 1989
Publish fine editions & illustrated books on contemporary & modern art.
ISBN Prefix(es): 978-1-880154
Number of titles published annually: 30 Print
Total Titles: 40 Print
Branch Office(s)
456 N Camden Dr, Beverly Hills, CA 90210 *Tel:* 310-271-9400 *Fax:* 310-271-9420 *E-mail:* losangeles@gagosian.com

§Galaxy Press
7051 Hollywood Blvd, Suite 200, Hollywood, CA 90028
SAN: 254-6906
Tel: 323-466-7815 *Toll Free Tel:* 877-8GALAXY (842-5299)
E-mail: customers@galaxypress.com; info@galaxypress.com
Web Site: www.galaxypress.com
Key Personnel
Pres: John Goodwin *Tel:* 323-466-7812 *E-mail:* jgoodwin@galaxypress.com
SVP, Intl Sales/Rts: Claude Sandoz *E-mail:* claude@asirights.com
SVP, US Sales & Rts: Kim Catalano *Tel:* 323-466-7815 ext 145 *E-mail:* kcatalano@galaxypress.com
VP, US Trade Sales: Juliet Wills *E-mail:* jwills@galaxypress.com
Consumer Sales: Sarah Toth *E-mail:* sarahc@galaxypress.com
Founded: 2002
Publisher of the fiction works of L Ron Hubbard.
ISBN Prefix(es): 978-1-59212
Number of titles published annually: 13 Print; 14 E-Book; 14 Audio
Total Titles: 60 Print; 50 E-Book; 40 Audio
Imprints: Galaxy Audio
Returns: 6121 Malburg Way, Vernon, CA 90058 *Tel:* 323-588-8777
Warehouse: 6121 Malburg Way, Vernon, CA 90058 *Tel:* 323-588-8777
Distribution Center: 6121 Malburg Way, Vernon, CA 90058 *Tel:* 323-588-8777

Galde Press Inc
PO Box 460, Lakeville, MN 55044
Tel: 952-891-5991 *Toll Free Tel:* 800-777-3454
Web Site: www.galdepress.com

Key Personnel
Founder & Pres: Phyllis Galde *E-mail:* phyllis@galdepress.com
Founded: 1991
Independent publisher of books on a variety of subjects & have over 100 titles in print.
ISBN Prefix(es): 978-1-880090; 978-1-931942
Number of titles published annually: 11 Print
Total Titles: 108 Print

§Gale
Unit of Cengage Learning
27500 Drake Rd, Farmington Hills, MI 48331-3535
SAN: 213-4373
Tel: 248-699-4253 *Toll Free Tel:* 800-877-4253 *Fax:* 248-699-8049 *Toll Free Fax:* 800-414-5043 (orders)
E-mail: gale.salesassistance@cengage.com
Web Site: www.gale.cengage.com
Key Personnel
EVP & Publr: Frank Menchaca
SVP & Gen Mgr: Paul Gazzolo
Founded: 1954
Gale, part of Cengage Learning, serves the world's information & education needs through its vast & dynamic content pools, which are used by students & consumers in their libraries, schools & on the Internet. It is best known for the accuracy, breadth & convenience of its data, addressing all types of information needs – from homework help to health questions to business profiles – in a variety of formats.
ISBN Prefix(es): 978-0-8103; 978-0-7876
Number of titles published annually: 50 Print
Imprints: Charles Scribner's Sons®; Christian Large Print; Five Star™; Greenhaven Press®; KidHaven Press™; Large Print Press™; Lucent Books®; Macmillan Reference USA™; Primary Source Media™; St James Press®; Schirmer Reference™; Scholarly Resources Inc; The TAFT Group®; Thorndike Press®; Twayne Publishers™; U X L™; Wheeler Publishing™
Branch Office(s)
10 Davis Dr, Belmont, CA 94002 *Tel:* 650-595-2350
Distribution Center: 10650 Toebben Dr, Independence, KY 41051
See separate listing for:
Charles Scribner's Sons®
Greenhaven Press®
Lucent Books®
Macmillan Reference USA™
St James Press®
Thorndike Press
Twayne Publishers™

§Galen Press Ltd
PO Box 64400-WB, Tucson, AZ 85728-4400
Tel: 520-577-8363 *Fax:* 520-529-6459
E-mail: sales@galenpress.com
Web Site: www.galenpress.com
Key Personnel
Owner, CFO & Publr: Mary Lou Iserson
VP, Mktg & Spec Sales: Mary Lou Sherk *E-mail:* ml@galenpress.com
Ed: Jennifer G Gilbert *E-mail:* jennifer@galenpress.com
Founded: 1993
Publish non-clinical health related books in medical education, death & dying & bioethics.
ISBN Prefix(es): 978-1-883620
Number of titles published annually: 2 Print; 1 CD-ROM; 3 E-Book
Total Titles: 32 Print; 1 CD-ROM; 6 E-Book
Membership(s): The Association of Publishers for Special Sales

§Gallaudet University Press
800 Florida Ave NE, Washington, DC 20002-3695
SAN: 205-261X
Tel: 202-651-5488; 773-568-1550 (orders)
Toll Free Tel: 800-621-2736 (orders)
Fax: 202-651-5489; 773-660-2235 (orders)
Toll Free Fax: 800-621-8476 (orders)
E-mail: gupress@gallaudet.edu
Web Site: gupress.gallaudet.edu
Key Personnel
Exec Dir: Gary Aller
Edit Dir: Ivey P Wallace
Founded: 1980
Reference books, scholarly, educational & general interest books on deaf studies, deaf culture & issues, sign language textbooks.
ISBN Prefix(es): 978-0-913580; 978-0-930323; 978-1-56368
Number of titles published annually: 16 Print
Total Titles: 250 Print; 4 CD-ROM
Imprints: Clerc Books; Gallaudet University Press; Kendall Green
Distributor for Signum Verlag
Warehouse: Chicago Distribution Center, 11030 S Langley Ave, Chicago, IL 60628, Contact: Karen Hyzy *Toll Free Tel:* 800-630-9347 *Fax:* 773-702-7212
Membership(s): American Association of University Presses

Gallery Books
Imprint of Gallery Publishing Group
1230 Avenue of the Americas, New York, NY 10020
Toll Free Tel: 800-456-6798 *Fax:* 212-698-7284
E-mail: consumer.customerservice@simonandschuster.com
Web Site: www.simonsays.com
Key Personnel
Pres & Publr, Gallery Books Group: Louise Burke
Assoc Publr, Gallery Books Group: Jennifer Long
VP & Publr, Gallery Books: Jennifer Bergstrom
VP & Publr, North Star Way: Michele Martin
VP & Sr Ed, Gallery Books & VP & Edit Dir, Threshold Editions: Mitchell Ivers
VP & Dir, Publicity, Gallery Books, Pocket Books & Threshold Editions: Jennifer Robinson
VP & Dir, Rts, Gallery Books & Pocket Books: Paul O'Halloran
Exec Ed, Gallery Books & Pocket Books, Edit Dir, Pocket Star: Lauren McKenna
Exec Ed, Gallery Books/Scout Press: Karen Kosztolnyik; Allison Callahan
Sr Ed, Gallery Books: Jeremie Ruby-Strauss
Sr Ed, Gallery Books & Pocket Books: Micki Nuding; Abby Zidle
Sr Ed, Media, Gallery Books & Pocket Books: Edward Schlesinger
Sr Ed, Gallery Books & Pocket Books: Adam Wilson
Sr Ed, North Star Way: Kathryn Huck
Mng Ed, Gallery Books, Pocket Books & Threshold Editions: Susan Rella
Ed, Gallery Books & Pocket Books: Kate Dresser
Sr Publg Mgr, Gallery Books, Pocket Books & Threshold Editions: Brigitte Smith
Sr Art Dir, Gallery Books, Pocket Books & Threshold Editions: Lisa Litwack
Dir, Publicity, Gallery Books, Pocket Books & Threshold Editions: Jean Anne Rose
Dir, Rts, Threshold Editions: Marie Florio
Dir, Mktg, Gallery Books, Pocket Books & Threshold Editions: Elizabeth Psaltis
Imprint Mktg Mgr: Melanie Mitzman
Online Mktg Mgr: Diana Velasquez
Subs Rts Assoc, Gallery Books: Elizabeth Lotto
Founded: 1939
Trade paperbacks & hardcovers; mass market, reprints & originals.
ISBN Prefix(es): 978-0-671; 978-0-7434; 978-1-4165
Imprints: Downtown Press; G-unit; Jeter Publishing; Karen Hunter Publishing; MTV Books; North Star Way; Pocket Star; Pocket Books Trade Paperback; Scout Press; Star Trek®; Threshold Editions; VH-1; World Wrestling Entertainment
Foreign Rights: Antonella Antonelli Agenzia (Italy); Arts & Licensing International (Mainland China, Taiwan); Book Publishers Association of Israel (Israel); Japan UNI Agency (Japan); JLM Literary Agency (Greece); Nurcihan Kesim Literary Agency Inc (Turkey); Mohrbooks Literary Agency (Germany); La Nouvelle Agence (France); Andrew Nurnberg Associates (Bulgaria, Croatia, Czech Republic, Estonia, Hungary, Latvia, Lithuania, Montenegro, Poland, Romania, Russia, Serbia, Slovakia, Slovenia); Sane Toregard Agency (Denmark, Finland, Iceland, Norway, Sweden); Sebes & Van Gelderen Literary Agency (Netherlands); Tuttle-Mori Agency Inc (Thailand); Eric Yang Agency (Korea)

§Gallopade International Inc
611 Hwy 74 S, Suite 2000, Peachtree City, GA 30269
SAN: 213-8441
Mailing Address: PO Box 2779, Peachtree City, GA 30269
Tel: 770-631-4222 *Toll Free Tel:* 800-536-2GET (536-2438) *Fax:* 770-631-4810
Toll Free Fax: 800-871-2979
E-mail: customerservice@gallopade.com
Web Site: www.gallopade.com
Key Personnel
Owner & CEO: Carole Marsh *E-mail:* carole@gallopade.com
Pres & Intl Rts: Michele Yother *E-mail:* michele@gallopade.com
VP: Michael Longmeyer *E-mail:* michael@gallopade.com
Founded: 1979
"State stuff" for all 50 states including activity books, games, maps, posters, stickies, etc. Subjects include travel, regional, school travel supply, home school, juvenile mysteries, human sex education, multicultural, preschool through adult.
ISBN Prefix(es): 978-0-935326; 978-1-55609; 978-0-7933; 978-0-635
Number of titles published annually: 500 Print; 50 CD-ROM; 200 Online; 200 E-Book
Total Titles: 15,000 Print; 200 CD-ROM; 10,050 Online; 10,050 E-Book; 13 Audio
Imprints: American Milestones; Black Heritage: Celebrating Culture; The Day That Was Different; Here & Now; Heroes & Helpers; Carole Marsh Books; Carole Marsh Mysteries; New Traditions; 1000 Readers; Smart Sex Stuff for Kids; State Experience; State Stuff
Subsidiaries: Six House; The World's Largest Publishing Co
Membership(s): Education Market Association

Gareth Stevens Publishing
Imprint of The Rosen Publishing Group Inc
111 E 14 St, Suite 349, New York, NY 10003
Mailing Address: PO Box 29088, New York, NY 10087-9088
Toll Free Tel: 800-542-2595 *Toll Free Fax:* 877-542-2596 (cust serv)
E-mail: customerservice@gspub.com
Web Site: garethstevens.com
Founded: 1983
ISBN Prefix(es): 978-0-918831; 978-1-55532; 978-0-8368; 978-1-4339
Number of titles published annually: 400 Print
Total Titles: 1,500 Print
Returns: Maple Press Distribution Center, 60 Grumbacher Rd, York, PA 17406

§Garland Science Publishing
Member of The Taylor & Francis Group
711 Third Ave, 8th fl, New York, NY 10017

Tel: 212-216-7800; 212-281-4487 *Fax:* 212-947-3027
E-mail: science@garland.com
Web Site: www.garlandscience.com
Key Personnel
Pres, Taylor & Francis US: Emmett Dages
VP, Sales, Taylor & Francis US: Dennis Weiss
VP, Garland Science: Denise Schanck *E-mail:* denise.schanck@taylorandfrancis.com
Founded: 1969
Textbooks & professional books in biology & chemistry.
ISBN Prefix(es): 978-0-8153; 978-1-5603
Number of titles published annually: 10 Print; 4 CD-ROM; 30 E-Book
Total Titles: 50 Print; 4 CD-ROM; 30 E-Book
Branch Office(s)
4133 Whitney Ave, Hamden, CT 06578 *Tel:* 203-281-4487 *Toll Free Tel:* 800-627-6273 *Fax:* 203-230-1186
Warehouse: Taylor & Francis/Garland, 7625 Empire Dr, Florence, KY 41042 *Toll Free Tel:* 800-634-7064 *Toll Free Fax:* 800-248-4724 *Web Site:* www.garlandscience.com

§Gatekeeper Press
3971 Hoover Rd, Suite 77, Columbus, OH 43123-2839
Toll Free Tel: 866-535-0913 *Fax:* 216-403-1314
E-mail: info@gatekeeperpress.com
Web Site: www.gatekeeperpress.com
Key Personnel
Pres: Robert Price *Tel:* 866-535-0913 ext 713 *Fax:* 216-803-0350 *E-mail:* rprice@gatekeeperpress.com
Founded: 2015
Full service publishing house that partners with authors & publishers to produce & distribute high quality books in digital & print formats. Authors earn 100% of their royalties. Distribution networks reach readers worldwide. Provide services for all subjects & types of books, including ebook conversion & distribution, book cover design, paperback publishing & distribution, editing & proofreading.
This publisher has indicated that 100% of their product line is author subsidized.
ISBN Prefix(es): 978-1-61984
Number of titles published annually: 50 Print
Membership(s): The Independent Book Publishers Association

§Gateways Books & Tapes
Division of Institute for the Development of the Harmonious Human Being Inc
PO Box 370, Nevada City, CA 95959
SAN: 211-3635
Tel: 530-271-2239 *Toll Free Tel:* 800-869-0658 *Fax:* 530-272-0184
E-mail: info@gatewaysbooksandtapes.com
Web Site: www.gatewaysbooksandtapes.com; www.retrosf.com (Retro Science Fiction Imprint)
Key Personnel
Sr Ed & Intl Rts: Iven Lourie *E-mail:* ilourie@oro.net
Founded: 1971
Trade & fine art book publisher. Categories include psychology, spirituality, metaphysics, Judaica, science fiction & limited editions.
ISBN Prefix(es): 978-0-89556
Number of titles published annually: 6 Print; 4 CD-ROM; 4 Audio
Total Titles: 35 Print; 8 CD-ROM; 300 Audio
Imprints: Artemis Books (2 titles); Consciousness Classics; Gateways Fine Art Series; Retro Science Fiction
Distributor for Cloister Recordings (audio & video tapes)

Gault Millau Inc/Gayot Publications
4311 Wilshire Blvd, Suite 405, Los Angeles, CA 90010
Tel: 323-965-3529 *Fax:* 323-936-2883
E-mail: info@gayot.com
Web Site: www.gayot.com
Key Personnel
Pres: Andre Gayot
Publr & Ed-in-Chief: Alain Gayot
Founded: 1986
Publish travel guides to world destinations with a rating system to the best hotels, restaurants & shops.
ISBN Prefix(es): 978-1-881066
Number of titles published annually: 12 Print
Total Titles: 16 Print; 5 E-Book
Imprints: Gault Millau; GAYOT
Subsidiaries: Tastes Newsletter
Divisions: The Food Paper
Distributed by Publishers Group West

Gauthier Publications Inc
PO Box 806241, St Clair Shores, MI 48080
SAN: 857-2119
Tel: 313-458-7141 *Fax:* 586-279-1515
E-mail: info@gauthierpublications.com
Web Site: www.gauthierpublications.com
Key Personnel
CEO: Daniel J Gauthier *E-mail:* daniel@gauthierpublications.com
Creative Dir: Elizabeth Gauthier *E-mail:* elizabeth@gauthierpublications.com
Founded: 2008
Devoted to printing high quality literary work. Our mission is simple, to introduce reading early & help promote a lifetime love for the written word by putting out captivating & unique titles that are tailored to their audience. We are proud to say all of our books are printed & bound in the USA & our Hungry Goat Press line is made with 100% post consumer recycled paper because we think a good book means more than an exciting plot-line. Distribution also by Amazon.
ISBN Prefix(es): 978-0-9820812; 978-0-9833593
Number of titles published annually: 15 Print
Total Titles: 35 Print
Imprints: DragonFish Comics (graphic novels); Frog Legs Ink (children's books); Hungry Goat Press (young adult books)
Distribution Center: Follett School Solutions Inc, 1340 Ridgeview Dr, McHenry, IL 60050 *Tel:* 815-759-1700 *Toll Free Tel:* 888-511-5114 (cust serv) *Fax:* 815-759-9831 *Toll Free Fax:* 800-852-5458 *E-mail:* info@follettlearning.com *Web Site:* www.follettlearning.com SAN: 169-1902
Diamond, 1966 Greenspring Dr, Suite 300, Timonium, MD 21093 *Toll Free Tel:* 800-452-6642
Membership(s): ABA

Gefen Books
c/o Storch, 255 Central Ave, B-206, Lawrence, NY 11559
Tel: 516-593-1234 *Toll Free Tel:* 800-477-5257 *Fax:* 516-295-2739
E-mail: gefenny@gefenpublishing.com; info@gefenpublishing.com
Web Site: www.gefenpublishing.com; www.israelbooks.com
Key Personnel
Contact: Maury Storch
Founded: 1981
General interest, mainly books from Israel. Specialize in Judaic interest, Israel, art, Holocaust & Jewish history. Can supply any books published in Israel +/or in the Hebrew language.
ISBN Prefix(es): 978-965-229; 978-0-86343
Number of titles published annually: 25 Print
Total Titles: 425 Print; 400 Online; 400 E-Book
Imprints: Gefen Publishing Ltd
Subsidiaries: IsraBook
Divisions: Medical Publishing (Gefen)
Foreign Office(s): Gefen Publishing House Ltd, 6 Hatzvi St, 94386 Jerusalem, Israel *Tel:* (02) 538-0247 *Fax:* (02) 538-8423
Distributor for Bar Ilan; Magnes Press
Shipping Address: 11 Edison Place, Springfield, NJ 07081
Warehouse: 11 Edison Place, Springfield, NJ 07081

Gem Guides Book Co
1275 W Ninth St, Upland, CA 91786
Tel: 626-855-1611 *Toll Free Tel:* 800-824-5118 (orders) *Fax:* 626-855-1610
E-mail: info@gemguidesbooks.com
Web Site: www.gemguidesbooks.com
Key Personnel
Opers Mgr: Matt Warner
Chief Ed: Nancy Fox
Off Mgr: Nannette Becerra
Sales: Michael Moran
Founded: 1965
Publisher & distributor of regional & specialty trade books; rocks, minerals, crystals, Old West, western & southwestern region & local interests.
ISBN Prefix(es): 978-0-935182; 978-1-889786
Number of titles published annually: 7 Print
Total Titles: 80 Print
Imprints: Gembooks
Distributed by Nevada Publications
Distributor for Borden Publishing; Brynmorgen Press; Clear Creek Publishing; Earth Love Publishing; Editions du Signe; Gemstone Press; Golden West Books; Grand Canyon Association; Heaven & Earth Press; Hexagon Press; International Jewelry Publications; George R Jezek Photography; Cy Johnson & Son; KC Publications Inc; Many Moons Press; Naturegraph; Nevada Publications; Out of This World Press; Pinyon Publishing; Primer Publications; Ram Publishing; Recreation Sales; Shortfuse Press; Sierra Press; Delos Toole; Trees Co; Tri-Star Boze Books; Weseanne Publications
Membership(s): ABA; The Independent Book Publishers Association; Northern California Independent Booksellers Association

§Genealogical Publishing Co
Subsidiary of Genealogical.com
3600 Clipper Mill Rd, Suite 260, Baltimore, MD 21211
Tel: 410-837-8271 *Toll Free Tel:* 800-296-6687 *Fax:* 410-752-8492 *Toll Free Fax:* 800-599-9561
E-mail: sales@genealogical.com; info@genealogical.com
Web Site: www.genealogical.com
Key Personnel
VP & Ed-in-Chief: Michael Tepper *E-mail:* mtepper@genealogical.com
Mktg Dir: Joe Garonzik *E-mail:* jgaronzi@genealogical.com
Data Processing Mgr: Roger Sherr *E-mail:* rsherr@genealogical.com
Founded: 1959
Genealogy, local history, immigration history & source records. Products are non-returnable, unless mis-shipped or damaged in shipment.
ISBN Prefix(es): 978-0-8063
Number of titles published annually: 50 Print; 2 CD-ROM
Total Titles: 352 Print; 84 CD-ROM
Subsidiaries: Clearfield Co Inc
See separate listing for:
Clearfield Co Inc

Genesis Press Inc
PO Box 101, Columbus, MS 39701
Toll Free Tel: 888-463-4461 (orders only)
Web Site: www.genesis-press.com
Key Personnel
Owner & Pres: Wilbur O Colom
Off Mgr: Diane Blair
Founded: 1993
Privately owned African-American book publisher.

ISBN Prefix(es): 978-1-885478; 978-1-58571
Number of titles published annually: 26 Print
Total Titles: 160 Print
Imprints: Black Coral; INDIGO; Indigo Love Spectrum; Indigo Vibe; Mt Blue; Obsidian; Sage Books
Membership(s): AAP

Geological Society of America (GSA)
3300 Penrose Place, Boulder, CO 80301-1806
SAN: 201-5978
Mailing Address: PO Box 9140, Boulder, CO 80301-9140
Tel: 303-357-1000 *Fax:* 303-357-1070
E-mail: pubs@geosociety.org (prodn); editing@geosociety.org (edit)
Web Site: www.geosociety.org
Key Personnel
Exec Dir: John W Hess *Tel:* 303-357-1011 *E-mail:* jhess@geosociety.org
Ad Mgr: Ann H Crawford *Tel:* 303-357-1053 *E-mail:* acrawford@geosociety.org
Founded: 1888
General earth sciences, cover such areas as geology, economic geology, engineering geology, geochemistry, geomorphology, marine geology, mineralogy, paleontology, petrology, seismology, solid earth geophysics, structural geology, tectonics & environmental geology.
ISBN Prefix(es): 978-0-8137
Number of titles published annually: 9 Print
Total Titles: 200 Print
Branch Office(s)
1200 New York Ave NW, Suite 400, Washington, DC 20005, Dir, Geoscience Policy: Kasey White *Tel:* 202-669-0466 *E-mail:* kwhite@geosociety.org
Foreign Rep(s): Geological Society of London (UK)

§GeoLytics Inc
3322 Rte 22, Suite 806, Branchburg, NJ 08876
Mailing Address: PO Box 5336, East Brunswick, NJ 08876
Tel: 908-707-1505 *Toll Free Tel:* 800-577-6717 *Fax:* 908-707-1595
E-mail: support@geolytics.com; questions@geolytics.com
Web Site: www.geolytics.com
Key Personnel
Mktg Dir: Katia Segre Cohen
Founded: 1996
Provider of census, demographic & geographic data for academic & business researchers.
ISBN Prefix(es): 978-1-892445
Number of titles published annually: 7 CD-ROM; 7 Online
Total Titles: 55 CD-ROM; 55 Online

Georgetown University Press
3240 Prospect St NW, Suite 250, Washington, DC 20007
Tel: 202-687-5889 (busn) *Fax:* 202-687-6340 (edit)
E-mail: gupress@georgetown.edu
Web Site: press.georgetown.edu
Key Personnel
Dir & Acqs: Richard Brown, PhD *Tel:* 202-687-5912 *E-mail:* reb7@georgetown.edu
Mktg & Sales Dir: Jessica Pellien *Tel:* 202-687-9856 *E-mail:* jhp73@georgetown.edu
Asst Dir of Press & Busn Mgr: Ioan Suciu *Tel:* 202-687-5641 *E-mail:* suciui@georgetown.edu
Asst Dir of Press & Langs, Linguistics & Dir, Georgetown Langs: Hope J LeGro *Tel:* 202-687-4704 *E-mail:* hjs6@georgetown.edu
Sr Acqs Ed & Intl Aff, Public Policy & Public Mgmt: Donald Jacobs *Tel:* 202-687-5218 *E-mail:* dpj5@georgetown.edu
Edit Designer & Prodn Mgr: Glenn Saltzman *Tel:* 202-687-6251 *E-mail:* gls43@georgetown.edu
Digital Publg & Rts Mgr: Laura Leichum *Tel:* 202-687-7687 *E-mail:* lal75@georgetown.edu
Founded: 1964
Bioethics; international affairs & human rights; languages & linguistics; political science, public policy & public management; religion & ethics.
ISBN Prefix(es): 978-0-87840; 978-1-58901
Number of titles published annually: 40 Print; 2 Audio
Total Titles: 500 Print; 9 Audio
Foreign Rep(s): Apex Knowledge Sdn Bhd (Simon Tay) (Brunei, Malaysia); Avicenna Partnership Ltd (Middle East); Booknet Co Ltd (Ms Suphaluck Sattabuz) (Cambodia, Laos, Myanmar, Thailand, Vietnam); ChoiceTEXTS (Asia) Pte Ltd (Philip Ang) (Indonesia, Singapore); Footprint Books (Australia, New Zealand); iCaves Ltd (Eddy Lam) (China, Hong Kong, Macau); iGroup (Asia Pacific) Ltd (Estela Suyat) (Philippines); iGroup Korea (IDC Asia) (Mr DJ Kim) (Korea); KW Publishers Pvt Ltd (India); Taiwan Publisher Marketing Service Ltd (George Liu) (Taiwan); United Publishers Services Ltd (Mark Gresham) (Japan); University Presses Marketing (Europe, UK)
Orders to: Hopkins Fulfillment Service, PO Box 50370, Baltimore, MD 21211-4370 *Tel:* 410-516-6956 *Toll Free Tel:* 800-537-5487 *Fax:* 410-516-6998 *E-mail:* hfscustserv@press.jhu.edu; NBN International Business Center, 10 Thornbury Rd, Plymouth PL6 7PP, United Kingdom (Africa, Europe, Middle East & UK) *Tel:* (01752) 202301 *Fax:* (01752) 202333 *E-mail:* orders@nbninternational.com *Web Site:* www.nbninternational.com
Returns: Hopkins Fulfillment Service, c/o Maple Press, Lebanon Distribution Ctr, 704 Legionaire Dr, Fredericksburg, PA 17026
Warehouse: c/o Maple Press Co, Lebanon Distribution Ctr, 704 Legionaire Dr, Fredericksburg, PA 17026
Distribution Center: Scholarly Book Services, 289 Bridgeland Ave, Unit 105, Toronto, ON M6A 1Z6, Canada *Toll Free Tel:* 800-847-9736 *Toll Free Fax:* 800-220-9895 *E-mail:* orders@sbookscan.com *Web Site:* www.sbookscan.com

§Gestalt Journal Press
PO Box 278, Gouldsboro, ME 04607-0278
Tel: 207-404-9954 *Fax:* 207-510-4889
E-mail: press@gestalt.org
Web Site: www.gestaltjournalpress.com
Founded: 1975
Mental health, gestalt therapy specifically.
ISBN Prefix(es): 978-0-939266
Number of titles published annually: 3 Print; 10 E-Book
Total Titles: 41 Print; 2 CD-ROM; 20 E-Book; 4 Audio

§Getty Publications
1200 Getty Center Dr, Suite 500, Los Angeles, CA 90049-1682
SAN: 208-2276
Tel: 310-440-7365 *Toll Free Tel:* 800-223-3431 (orders) *Fax:* 310-440-7758
E-mail: pubsinfo@getty.edu
Web Site: www.getty.edu/publications
Key Personnel
Publr: Kara Kirk *Tel:* 310-440-6066 *E-mail:* kkirk@getty.edu
Ed-in-Chief: Robert T Flynn *Tel:* 310-440-6486 *E-mail:* rflynn@getty.edu
Gen Mgr: Carolyn Simmons *Tel:* 310-440-7130 *E-mail:* csimmons@getty.edu
Rts Mgr: Leslie Rollins *Tel:* 310-440-7102 *E-mail:* lrollins@getty.edu
Sales & Mktg Mgr: Mark Heineke *E-mail:* mheineke@getty.edu
Founded: 1982
Produces a wide variety of books in the fields of art, photography, archaeology, architecture, conservation & the humanities for both general & specialized audiences. These award-winning publications complement & often result from the work of the J Paul Getty Museum, the Getty Conservation Institute & the Getty Research Institute. Publications include illustrated exhibition catalogues, illustrated works on single artists & art history, works on cultural history, scholarly monographs, critical editions of translated works, comprehensive studies of the Getty's collections, educational books to interest children of all ages in art & gift books.
ISBN Prefix(es): 978-0-89236; 978-1-60606
Number of titles published annually: 50 Print; 2 Online; 3 E-Book
Total Titles: 500 Print; 5 Online; 5 E-Book
Distributed by University of Chicago Press (US only)
Foreign Rep(s): Canadian Manda Group (Canada); EWEB (Asia, Pacific Rim); Orca Book Services (Europe, UK); Roundhouse Group (Europe, UK)
Distribution Center: Chicago Distribution Center, 11030 S Langley Ave, Chicago, IL 60628 *Tel:* 773-702-7000 *Toll Free Tel:* 800-621-2736 *Fax:* 773-702-7212 *Toll Free Fax:* 800-621-8476 *E-mail:* custserv@press.uchicago.edu *Web Site:* www.press.uchicago.edu
Membership(s): AAP; Association of American University Presses; CAA; International Association of Museum Publishers; International Association of Scholarly Publishers; International Group of Publishing Libraries; Society for Scholarly Publishing

GIA Publications Inc
7404 S Mason Ave, Chicago, IL 60638
Tel: 708-496-3800 *Toll Free Tel:* 800-GIA-1358 (442-1358) *Fax:* 708-496-3828
E-mail: custserv@giamusic.com
Web Site: www.giamusic.com
Key Personnel
COO & Pres: Alec Harris *E-mail:* alech@giamusic.com
Founded: 1941
Publish sacred choral music, hymnals, books, recordings & music education materials.
ISBN Prefix(es): 978-0-941050; 978-1-57999
Number of titles published annually: 200 Print
Total Titles: 6,000 Print; 250 Audio

§Gibbs Smith Publisher
1877 E Gentile St, Layton, UT 84041
Mailing Address: PO Box 667, Layton, UT 84041-0667 SAN: 201-9906
Tel: 801-544-9800 *Toll Free Tel:* 800-748-5439; 800-835-4993 (orders) *Fax:* 801-544-5582 *Toll Free Fax:* 800-213-3023 (orders only)
E-mail: info@gibbs-smith.com; tradeorders@gibbs-smith.com
Web Site: www.gibbs-smith.com
Key Personnel
CEO: Brad Farmer *E-mail:* brad.farmer@gibbs-smith.com
Gen Mgr, Trade Sales: Dan Moench *Tel:* 801-544-9800 ext 156 *E-mail:* dan.moench@gibbs-smith.com
Founded: 1969
ISBN Prefix(es): 978-0-87905; 978-1-58685
Number of titles published annually: 80 Print; 50 Online; 80 E-Book
Total Titles: 350 Print; 200 Online; 350 E-Book
Imprints: Ancient City Press; Wyrick & Co
Foreign Rep(s): Jonathan Ball & Nicky Stubbs (South Africa); Gilles Fauveau (Japan, Korea); Jaime Gregorio (Philippines); Penguin Books India Pvt Ltd (Sharad Mohan) (Bangladesh, India, Maldives, Nepal, Pakistan, Sri Lanka);

Peribo (Australia, New Zealand); Perseus Books Group UK (Europe exc UK); Perseus Intl (Suk Lee) (Malaysia, Singapore); Perseus Intl (Edison Garcia) (Caribbean, Latin America, Middle East, North Africa); June Poonpanich (Cambodia, Indonesia, Laos, Thailand, Vietnam); Publishers Group UK (UK); Raincoast Books (Canada); Wei Zhao (China, Hong Kong, Taiwan)
Returns: 570 N Sportsplex Dr, Kaysville, UT 84037
Shipping Address: 570 N Sportsplex Dr, Kaysville, UT 84037
Membership(s): AAP

Gifted Education Press
10201 Yuma Ct, Manassas, VA 20109
Mailing Address: PO Box 1586, Manassas, VA 20109-1586
Tel: 703-369-5017
Web Site: www.giftededpress.com
Key Personnel
Publr & Dir: Maurice D Fisher *E-mail:* mfisher345@comcast.net
Founded: 1981
Books, quarterly newsletter, "Gifted Education News-Page" published 6 times a year, teaching guides & supplemental materials for students. Education of gifted children.
ISBN Prefix(es): 978-0-910609
Number of titles published annually: 10 Print
Total Titles: 80 Print

Gingko Press Inc
1321 Fifth St, Berkeley, CA 94710
Tel: 510-898-1195 *Fax:* 510-898-1196
E-mail: books@gingkopress.com
Web Site: www.gingkopress.com
Key Personnel
Chmn & CEO: Mo Cohen *E-mail:* mo@gingkopress.com
VP & Ed-in-Chief: David Lopes *E-mail:* david@gingkopress.com
VP, Sales & Mktg: Rick Markell *E-mail:* rick@gingkopress.com
Admin & Edit Asst: Amy Detrich *E-mail:* amy@gingkopress.com
Founded: 1991
Publisher & distributor.
ISBN Prefix(es): 978-1-58423; 978-1-934471
Number of titles published annually: 100 Print; 1 E-Book
Total Titles: 450 Print; 2 E-Book
Imprints: Rebel Arts
Foreign Office(s): Gingko Press Verlags GmbH, Schulterblatt 58, 20357 Hamburg, Germany, Contact: Anika Heusermann *Tel:* (040) 29 14 25 *Fax:* (040) 29 10 55 *E-mail:* gingkopress@t-online.de
Distributor for All Rights Reserved; Archimap; Art Power; Basheer; Carpet Bombing Culture; Choi's Gallery; CYPI; Gingko Press; Grand Central Art Center; Rebel Arts; Sandu Publications; Sendpoints Books Co Ltd; Upper Playground; Victionary; Wax Facts Press; Zero+ Publishing

Gival Press
Imprint of Gival Press LLC
5200 N First St, Arlington, VA 22203
Mailing Address: PO Box 3812, Arlington, VA 22203 SAN: 852-9787
Tel: 703-351-0079 *Fax:* 703-351-0079 (call first)
E-mail: givalpress@yahoo.com
Web Site: www.givalpress.com
Key Personnel
Publr & Ed: Robert L Giron
Founded: 1998
Small, independent literary press.
ISBN Prefix(es): 978-1-928589
Number of titles published annually: 4 Print; 4 E-Book
Total Titles: 59 Print; 23 E-Book
Distribution Center: Follett Higher Education Group, 3 Westbrook Corporate Ctr, Suite 200, Westchester, IL 60154 *Tel:* 708-884-0000 *Toll Free Tel:* 800-FOLLETT (365-5388) *Web Site:* www.follett.com/higher-ed
Membership(s): AAP; The Association of Publishers for Special Sales; Community of Literary Magazines & Presses; The Independent Book Publishers Association; Publishing Triangle

§Glenbridge Publishing Ltd
19923 E Long Ave, Centennial, CO 80016-1969
SAN: 243-5403
Tel: 720-870-8381 *Toll Free Tel:* 800-986-4135 (orders) *Fax:* 720-230-1209
E-mail: glenbridge10@gmail.com
Web Site: www.glenbridgepublishing.com
Key Personnel
Pres & Intl Rts: Mary B Keene
VP & Ed: James A Keene
Founded: 1986
Publish nonfiction, hardcover originals, reprints & paperback originals.
ISBN Prefix(es): 978-0-944435
Number of titles published annually: 5 Print; 5 CD-ROM
Total Titles: 62 Print; 62 CD-ROM

§Peter Glenn Publications
Division of Blount Communications Corp
306 NE Second St, 2nd fl, Delray Beach, FL 33483
Tel: 561-404-4290 *Fax:* 561-892-5786
Web Site: pgdirect.com
Key Personnel
CEO & Publr: Gregory James Blount *E-mail:* gregjames@me.com
Dir: L Chip Brill; Umberto Guido, III
Ed: Todd Heustess
Founded: 1956
Directories for the world of advertising, TV & film publicity; directories & how-to books for performing arts, fashion & modeling industry.
ISBN Prefix(es): 978-0-87314
Number of titles published annually: 9 Print
Total Titles: 9 Print; 6 E-Book

Glimmer Train Press Inc
PO Box 80430, Portland, OR 97280-1430
Tel: 503-221-0836 *Fax:* 503-221-0837
E-mail: editors@glimmertrain.org
Web Site: www.glimmertrain.org
Key Personnel
Co-Ed: Susan Burmeister-Brown *E-mail:* susan@glimmertrain.org; Linda Swanson-Davies *E-mail:* linda@glimmertrain.org
Founded: 1990
In addition to books, also publishes triannual short story journal *Glimmer Train.*
ISBN Prefix(es): 978-1-880966; 978-1-59553
Number of titles published annually: 3 Print
Total Titles: 81 Print
Distributor for Glimmer Train Stories
Membership(s): Community of Literary Magazines & Presses

Glitterati Inc
630 Ninth Ave, Suite 603, New York, NY 10036
Tel: 212-362-9119 *Fax:* 646-607-4433
E-mail: info@glitteratiincorporated.com
Web Site: glitteratiincorporated.com
Key Personnel
CEO & Pres: Martha Hallett *E-mail:* mhallett@glitteratiincorporated.com
Publicity & Promos Dir: Sara Rosen *E-mail:* srosen@glitteratiincorporated.com
Mng Ed: Kiara Cobb *E-mail:* kcobb@glitteratiincorporated.com
Assoc Publicity Dir: Gayatri Mullapudi *E-mail:* gmullapudi@glitteratiincorporated.com
Sales & Prodn Mgr: Brandon Schultz *E-mail:* bschultz@glitteratiincorporated.com
Publg Asst: Sarah Schreiber *E-mail:* sschreiber@glitteratiincorporated.com
Independent producer & publisher of distinctive illustrated books, ancillary gift products & electronic media for domestic & international markets.
ISBN Prefix(es): 978-0-9721152; 978-0-9765851; 978-0-9777531; 978-0-9793384; 978-0-9801557; 978-0-9822669; 978-0-9823412; 978-0-9823799; 978-0-9832702
Number of titles published annually: 9 Print
Total Titles: 58 Print; 1 Audio
Foreign Office(s): One Rona Rd, London NW3 2HY, United Kingdom, Edit: Chris Fagg *Tel:* (020) 7267 8339 *E-mail:* cfagg@glitteratiincorporated.com

Global Authors Publications (GAP)
38 Bluegrass, Middleberg, FL 32068
Tel: 904-425-1608
E-mail: gapbook@yahoo.com
Web Site: globalauthorspublications.com
Key Personnel
Publr: Kathleen Walls
Book Ed: Barbara Sachs Sloan
Founded: 2003
Offer complete subsidy publishing services & consider any genre except pornography or text books. Books must be at least 48 pages & not more than 700. We have set a literary standard with all the books we have published already & we do not plan to change our reputation. We won't publish everything that is offered us. Provide an affordable alternative to traditional publishing.
This publisher has indicated that 100% of their product line is author subsidized.
ISBN Prefix(es): 978-0-97
Number of titles published annually: 6 Print
Total Titles: 30 Print

§Global Publishing, Sales & Distribution
980 Lincoln Ave, Suite 200 B, San Rafael, CA 94901
Tel: 415-456-2934 *Fax:* 415-456-4124
Web Site: www.globalpsd.com
Key Personnel
Publr: Adrianne Casey *E-mail:* adrianne@globalpsd.com; Steven Goff *E-mail:* steven@globalpsd.com
ISBN Prefix(es): 978-0-9819942
Number of titles published annually: 50 Print; 50 CD-ROM; 100 Online
Total Titles: 50 Print; 50 CD-ROM; 100 Online
Branch Office(s)
244 Fifth Ave, Suite 2464, New York, NY 10001 *Tel:* 212-627-1400 *Toll Free Fax:* 866-729-2725
16510 203 Place NE, Woodinville, WA 98077 *Tel:* 425-354-3690 *Fax:* 425-354-3664
Foreign Office(s): 8 Commercial Tower, 30/F, Unit 06-07, 8 Sun Yip St, Chai Wan, Hong Kong *Tel:* 3576 3239 *Fax:* 3184 0728
Via Meucci 24, 37036 San Martino Buon Albergo, Verona, Italy *Tel:* (045) 994855 *Fax:* (045) 994746

Global Training Center Inc
550 S Mesa Hills Dr, Suite E4, El Paso, TX 79912
Mailing Address: PO Box 221977, El Paso, TX 79913
Tel: 915-534-7900 *Toll Free Tel:* 800-860-5030 *Fax:* 915-534-7903
E-mail: contact@globaltrainingcenter.com
Web Site: www.globaltrainingcenter.com
Key Personnel
Pres: Elsa Solorzano
Founded: 1992
Training seminar/workshops covering International Documentation, NAFTA, Importing, etc.
ISBN Prefix(es): 978-1-891249

Number of titles published annually: 23 Print
Total Titles: 23 Print

The Globe Pequot Press
Division of Rowman & Littlefield Publishing Group
246 Goose Lane, Guilford, CT 06437
SAN: 201-9892
Tel: 203-458-4500 *Toll Free Tel:* 800-243-0495 (orders only); 888-249-7586 (cust serv) *Fax:* 203-458-4601 *Toll Free Fax:* 800-820-2329 (orders & cust serv)
E-mail: editorial@globepequot.com; info@rowman.com; orders@rowman.com
Web Site: rowman.com
Key Personnel
Publr: Jim Childs
Edit Dir: Erin Turner *Tel:* 406-442-6597 *E-mail:* eturner@rowman.com
Mgr, Dist Busn: Andrea Jacobs *Tel:* 203-458-4552 *E-mail:* ajacobs@rowman.com
Dir, Outdoor Sales: Max Phelps *Tel:* 203-458-4551 *E-mail:* mphelps@nbnbooks.com
Founded: 1947
Travel guidebooks, regional books, sports, how-to, outdoor recreation, personal finance, self-help, sports, cooking, entertaining, military history, fishing, hunting, gift books.
ISBN Prefix(es): 978-0-937959; 978-1-56044; 978-1-57380; 978-1-57540; 978-1-882997; 978-0-87842; 978-0-87106; 978-0-7627; 978-0-89933; 978-1-898323 (Bradt); 978-0-934641; 978-1-56440; 978-1-84162 (Bradt); 978-0-912367; 978-0-933469; 978-0-934802; 978-0-934318; 978-1-57034; 978-1-58592; 978-1-901970 (Sawday)
Number of titles published annually: 500 Print; 500 E-Book
Total Titles: 2,800 Print; 1,000 E-Book
Imprints: Cheap Bastards; Down East; Falcon®; Globe Pequot; Gooseberry Patch; GPP® Travel; The Lyons Press; Taylor Trade; TwoDot®; Western Horseman
Distributor for Appalachian Mountain Club Books; Boone & Crockett Club; Thomas Cook Publishing; D&B Publishing; Day Hike Books Inc; Everyman Chess; Explorer Publishing; Globetrotter; Good Sam's; Jonglez Publishing; Montana Historical Society Press; New Holland Publishers (UK) Ltd; Oval Books (UK); Alastair Sawday Publishing (co-publr); Stoecklein Publishing; 30 Words; Trailblazer Publications; Western Horseman Books
Foreign Rep(s): Faradawn (South Africa); Pansing (Singapore); Les Petriw (Canada); Woodslane NZ Ltd (New Zealand); Woodslane Pty Ltd (Australia)
Returns: National Book Network (NBN), 15200 NBN Way, Blue Ridge Summit, PA 17214
Warehouse: National Book Network (NBN), 15200 NBN Way, Blue Ridge Summit, PA 17214
Distribution Center: National Book Network (NBN), 15200 NBN Way, Blue Ridge Summit, PA 17214
Membership(s): AAP; ABA; BISG; NEBA
See separate listing for:
The Lyons Press

David R Godine Publisher Inc
15 Court Sq, Suite 320, Boston, MA 02108-4715
SAN: 213-4381
Tel: 617-451-9600 *Fax:* 617-350-0250
E-mail: info@godine.com
Web Site: www.godine.com
Key Personnel
Pres & Publr: David R Godine
Black Sparrow Publr: Aaron Kerner *E-mail:* akerner@godine.com
Dir, Sales & Mktg: David Goldberg
Prodn Mgr: Heather Tamarkin *E-mail:* htamarkin@godine.com
Publicity Mgr: Amanda Diehl *E-mail:* adiehl@godine.com
Founded: 1970
Fiction & nonfiction, history, biography, typography, art & photography, poetry, horticulture, Americana, cooking, regional, mysteries, juveniles.
ISBN Prefix(es): 978-0-87923; 978-1-56792; 978-0-87685; 978-1-57423
Number of titles published annually: 40 Print
Total Titles: 500 Print
Imprints: Black Sparrow; Imago Mundi; Nonpareil Books; Verba Mundi
Sales Office(s): 426 Nutting Rd, PO Box 450, Jaffrey, NH 03452
Foreign Rep(s): Big Apple Agency Inc (Kelly Chang) (Taiwan); Mercedes Casanovas Agencia (Maria Lynch) (Spain); The English Agency (Hamish Macaskill) (Japan); Paul & Peter Fritz Agency (Peter Fritz) (Switzerland); Graal Literary Agency (Magda Koceba) (Poland); Korea Copyright Center (Jae-Yeon Ryu) (Korea); Michelle Lapautre Agence (Michelle Lapautre) (France); Natoli Stefan & Oliva Agenzia (Roberta Oliva) (Italy); Agencia Literara SUN (Crina Chitan) (Romania)
Foreign Rights: Mercedes Casanovas (Spain); The English Agency (Japan); Paul & Peter Fritz (Germany); Korea Copyright Center (Korea); Catherine Lapautre (France); Michelle Lapautre (France); Natoli, Stefan & Oliva (Italy)
Orders to: 426 Nutting Rd, PO Box 450, Jaffrey, NH 03452 *Toll Free Tel:* 800-344-4771 *Toll Free Fax:* 800-226-0934 *E-mail:* order@godine.com
Returns: 426 Nutting Rd, PO Box 450, Jaffrey, NH 03452 *Toll Free Tel:* 800-344-4771 *Toll Free Fax:* 800-226-0934
Warehouse: 426 Nutting Rd, PO Box 450, Jaffrey, NH 03452 *Tel:* 603-532-4100 *Toll Free Tel:* 800-344-4771 *Fax:* 603-532-5940 *Toll Free Fax:* 800-226-0934 *E-mail:* order@godine.com
Membership(s): AAP

Golden West Cookbooks
Division of American Traveler Press
5738 N Central Ave, Phoenix, AZ 85012-1316
Tel: 602-234-1574 *Toll Free Tel:* 800-521-9221 *Fax:* 602-234-3062
E-mail: info@americantravelerpress.com
Web Site: www.americantravelerpress.com
Key Personnel
Gen Mgr: Bill Fessler
Founded: 1973
Cookbooks & nonfiction books on the Southwest & the Rocky Mountains.
ISBN Prefix(es): 978-0-914846; 978-1-885590
Number of titles published annually: 5 Print
Total Titles: 150 Print
Membership(s): Publishers Association of the West

Gollehon Press Inc
3655 Glenn Dr SE, Grand Rapids, MI 49546
Tel: 616-949-3515 *Fax:* 616-949-8674
Web Site: www.gollehonbooks.com
Key Personnel
Pres: John T Gollehon *E-mail:* john@gollehonbooks.com
Publr: Kathy Gollehon *E-mail:* kathy@gollehonbooks.com
Ed: Becky Anderson
Sales Mgr: Jerome K Smith
Founded: 1983
Books related to Christian religions, young adult, seniors, health, how-to, reference, collectibles & current affairs. No unsol mss. Brief book proposals are reviewed. Simultaneous submissions are encouraged.
ISBN Prefix(es): 978-0-914839
Number of titles published annually: 10 Print
Total Titles: 97 Print
Imprints: Gollehon Books; GPC/Gollehon
Warehouse: Offset/Gollehon Distribution Ctr, 10 Passan Dr, Bldg 10, Laflin, PA 18702

Goodheart-Willcox Publisher
18604 W Creek Dr, Tinley Park, IL 60477-6243
SAN: 203-4387
Tel: 708-687-5000 *Toll Free Tel:* 800-323-0440 *Fax:* 708-468-8692 *Toll Free Fax:* 888-409-3900
E-mail: custserv@g-w.com; orders@g-w.com
Web Site: www.g-w.com
Key Personnel
CEO & Pres: John F Flanagan
VP, Admin & Treas: Robert Kelly
VP, Sales & Mktg: Todd Scheffers
Ad Coord: Zak Semens *Tel:* 708-623-1826 *E-mail:* zsemens@g-w.com
Founded: 1921
Industrial technical; family & consumer sciences & career textbooks.
ISBN Prefix(es): 978-0-87006; 978-1-56637; 978-1-59070; 978-1-60525
Number of titles published annually: 50 Print
Total Titles: 150 Print; 100 CD-ROM; 150 Online
Foreign Rep(s): Baker & Taylor International (Europe); Oxford University Press (Canada)

Goose River Press
3400 Friendship Rd, Waldoboro, ME 04572-6337
Tel: 207-832-6665
E-mail: gooseriverpress@roadrunner.com
Web Site: gooseriverpress.com
Key Personnel
Owner & Ed: Deborah J Benner
Acct Exec: Meredith K Sanders *E-mail:* mksanders@roadrunner.com
Founded: 1999
Acts as a traditional publisher, but also offers self-publishing services to books that do not meet literary quality or would prefer to self-publish.
This publisher has indicated that 50% of their product line is author subsidized.
ISBN Prefix(es): 978-1-930648; 978-1-59713
Number of titles published annually: 10 E-Book
Total Titles: 70 Print; 16 E-Book
Distribution Center: Ingram Content Group, 1246 Heil Quaker Blvd, La Vergne, TN 37086, Contact: Jim Patterson *Tel:* 615-213-4475 *Fax:* 615-213-4725 *E-mail:* jim.patterson@lightningsource.com
Membership(s): Maine Writers & Publishers Alliance

Goosebottom Books
Imprint of Goosebottom Books LLC
543 Trinidad Lane, Foster City, CA 94404
SAN: 859-8029
Tel: 650-204-4076 *Toll Free Fax:* 888-407-5286
E-mail: info@goosebottombooks.com
Web Site: goosebottombooks.com
Key Personnel
Publr: Shirin Yim Bridges *E-mail:* shirin.bridges@goosebottombooks.com
Founded: 2010
A small press dedicated to stealth education through fun nonfiction.
ISBN Prefix(es): 978-0-9845098 (Real Princesses); 978-0-9834256 (Dastardly Dames); 978-1-937463 (Augmented Reality)
Number of titles published annually: 6 Print; 6 Online; 12 E-Book
Total Titles: 18 Print
Orders to: Publishers Group West (PGW), 1700 Fourth St, Berkeley, CA 94710 *Toll Free Tel:* 800-788-3123 *Toll Free Fax:* 800-351-5073 *E-mail:* orderentry@perseusbooks.com *Web Site:* www.pgw.com
Distribution Center: Publishers Group West (PGW), 1700 Fourth St, Berkeley, CA 94710 *Toll Free Tel:* 800-788-3123 *Toll Free*

Fax: 800-351-5073 *E-mail:* orderentry@perseusbooks.com *Web Site:* pgw.com
Membership(s): The Children's Book Council; Northern California Independent Booksellers Association

Gorgias Press LLC
PO Box 6939, Piscataway, NJ 08854-6939
Tel: 732-885-8900 *Fax:* 732-885-8908
E-mail: helpdesk@gorgiaspress.com
Web Site: www.gorgiaspress.com
Key Personnel
Co-Founder & Pres: George Anton Kiraz, PhD
Co-Founder & VP: Christine Kiraz, PhD
Acqs Ed: Melonie Schmierer-Lee, PhD
Founded: 2001
Academic publishers of specialty books; provides for author/small publisher's digitization & publishing services needs.
ISBN Prefix(es): 978-1-59333; 978-0-9713097; 978-0-9715986; 978-1-931956; 978-1-60724
Number of titles published annually: 70 Print
Total Titles: 320 Print
Distributor for Yeshiva University Museum Press
Membership(s): The Independent Book Publishers Association

Gospel Publishing House (GPH)
Division of General Council of the Assemblies of God
1445 Boonville Ave, Springfield, MO 65802
SAN: 206-8826
Tel: 417-862-2781; 417-831-8000 (outside US) *Toll Free Tel:* 800-641-4310 *Fax:* 417-863-1874; 417-862-5881 *Toll Free Fax:* 800-328-0294
E-mail: custsrvreps@ag.org
Web Site: www.gospelpublishing.com
Key Personnel
VP: Steve Blount
Founded: 1914
Religion (Assemblies of God); sign-language textbooks & curricular materials.
ISBN Prefix(es): 978-0-88243
Number of titles published annually: 6 Print
Total Titles: 250 Print
Imprints: Gospel Publishing House; Influence Resources; Logion Press; My Healthy Church; Radiant Life Curriculum; Salubris Resources; Vital Resources
Distribution Center: Bookmasters, 30 Amberwood Pkwy, Ashland, OH 44805 *Tel:* 419-281-5100 *Fax:* 419-281-0200 *E-mail:* info@bookmasters.com *Web Site:* www.bookmasters.com

The Graduate Group/Booksellers
86 Norwood Rd, West Hartford, CT 06117-2236
Mailing Address: PO Box 370351, West Hartford, CT 06137-0351
Tel: 860-233-2330 *Fax:* 860-233-2330
E-mail: graduategroup@hotmail.com
Web Site: www.graduategroup.com
Key Personnel
Partner: Mara Whitman
Lib Sales Dir: Robert Whitman *Tel:* 860-232-3100
Founded: 1964
Publish career oriented reference books & self-help books for libraries, career & placement offices in the US & abroad, law enforcement, career series, exam preparation.
ISBN Prefix(es): 978-0-938609
Number of titles published annually: 20 Print; 1 Online
Total Titles: 100 Print; 2 Online

Grand Central Publishing
Division of Hachette Book Group
1290 Avenue of the Americas, New York, NY 10019
Tel: 212-364-1100
Web Site: www.hachettebookgroup.com
Key Personnel
Pres, Hachette Book Group & Publr, Grand Central Publishing: Jamie Raab
VP & Ed-in-Chief, Grand Central Publishing, Publr, Twelve: Deb Futter
VP, Digital & Pbk Publr: Beth de Guzman
VP, Assoc Publr & Mktg Dir, Grand Central Publishing & Twelve: Brian McLendon
Ed-in-Chief, Forever & Forever Yours: Amy Pierpont
VP, Edit Dir, Grand Central Life & Style: Karen Murgolo
Edit Dir, Forever & Forever Yours: Leah Hultenschmidt
VP, Exec Dir, Publicity: Matthew Ballast
Sr Dir of Hachette Book Group Multicultural Publicity: Linda Duggins
Sr Publicity Dir: Jimmy Franco
VP, Creative Dir: Anne Twomey
VP, Subs Rts: Nancy Wiese
Founded: 1961
Hardcover, trade paperback & mass market paperback, reprint & original, fiction & nonfiction, audio books. Unsol/unagented mss not accepted.
ISBN Prefix(es): 978-0-445; 978-0-446; 978-0-89296
Number of titles published annually: 260 Print
Total Titles: 3,860 Print
Imprints: Forever; Forever Yours; Grand Central Life & Style; Twelve; Vision
Foreign Rights: Antonella Antonelli Agenzia (Italy); Bardon Far Eastern Agents (Taiwan); Graal Ltd (Poland); Imprima Korea Agency (Korea); Katai & Bolza Literary Agents (Hungary); Simona Kessler International Copyright Agency Ltd (Romania); La Nouvelle Agence (France); Andrew Nurnberg Associates Ltd (Baltic States, Bulgaria, Mainland China, Russia); OA Literary Agency (Greece); Kristin Olson Literary Agency SRO (Czech Republic, Slovakia); Pikarski Agency (Israel); Prava I Prevodi International Literary Agency (Croatia, Slovenia); RDC Agencia Literaria (Brazil, Latin America, Spain); Sane Toregard Agency (Denmark, Finland, Iceland, Norway, Sweden); Thomas Schlueck GmbH (Germany)
Advertising Agency: Publishers Advertising
Shipping Address: Hachette Book Group Distribution Center, 121 N Enterprise Blvd, Lebanon, IN 46052 *Tel:* 765-483-9900 *Fax:* 765-483-0706
Membership(s): AAP; BISG

Donald M Grant Publisher Inc
PO Box 187, Hampton Falls, NH 03844-0187
Tel: 603-778-7191 *Fax:* 603-778-7191
E-mail: office@grantbooks.com
Web Site: secure.grantbooks.com
Key Personnel
Pres: Robert K Wiener *E-mail:* robert@grantbooks.com
Founded: 1964
Horror, science fiction, art & fantasy illustrated books.
ISBN Prefix(es): 978-0-937986; 978-1-880418
Number of titles published annually: 6 Print
Total Titles: 50 Print
Distributor for Archival; Oswald Train

Graphic Arts Books
Unit of Ingram Content Group Inc
7820 NE Holman St, Suite B-9, Portland, OR 97218
Mailing Address: PO Box 56118, Portland, OR 97236-6618
Tel: 503-254-5591 *Fax:* 503-254-5609
E-mail: info-ga@graphicartsbooks.com
Web Site: www.graphicartsbooks.com
Key Personnel
Publg Dir: Douglas Pfeiffer
Mktg Mgr: Angela Zbornik *Tel:* 970-375-7765 *E-mail:* angela.zbornik@graphicartsbooks.com
Ed: Kathy Howard
Creative Design Specialist: Vicki Knapton *E-mail:* vicki.knapton@graphicartsbooks.com
Founded: 1967
ISBN Prefix(es): 978-1-55868; 978-0-88240; 978-0-8108; 978-1-94182; 978-0-78108
Number of titles published annually: 35 Print; 30 E-Book
Total Titles: 300 Print; 125 E-Book
Imprints: Alaska Northwest Books®; Graphic Arts Books®; WestWinds Press®
Distribution Center: Ingram Publisher Services, One Ingram Blvd, La Vergne, TN 37086 *Toll Free Tel:* 866-400-5351 *Toll Free Fax:* 800-838-1149
Membership(s): Publishers Association of the West

Graphic Universe™
Division of Lerner Publishing Group Inc
241 First Ave N, Minneapolis, MN 55401
Mailing Address: Empire State Bldg, Suite 7206, 350 Fifth Ave, New York, NY 10118
Tel: 612-332-3344 *Toll Free Tel:* 800-328-4929 *Fax:* 612-332-7615 *Toll Free Fax:* 800-332-1132
E-mail: info@lernerbooks.com
Web Site: www.lernerbooks.com
Key Personnel
Chmn: Harry J Lerner
CFO & EVP: Margaret Wunderlich
Pres & Publr: Adam Lerner
EVP, Sales: David Wexler
EVP & Dir, Mktg & Digital Prods: Terri Soutor
VP, Ed-in-Chief: Patricia M Stockland
VP, Prodn: Gary Hansen
VP, Digital Prod Mgmt: Daniel Wallek
Rts Dir: Maria Kjoller
Dir, HR: Cyndi Radant
Group Mktg Dir: Jill Braithwaite
School & Lib Mktg Dir: Lois Wallentine
Art Dir: Zach Marell
Founded: 2006
Publish graphic novel fiction & nonfiction books for children & young adults.
Total Titles: 150 Print; 520 E-Book
Foreign Rep(s): INT Press Distribution (Australia); Phambili (Southern Africa); Publishers Marketing Service (Brunei, Malaysia, Singapore); South Pacific Books (New Zealand)
Foreign Rights: Sandra Bruna Agencia Literaria (Spain); Japan Foreign-Rights Centre (JFC) (Japan); Korea Copyright Center Inc (KCC) (Korea); Agence Michelle Lapautre (France)
Distribution Center: Lerner Publishing Group, 1251 Washington Ave N, Minneapolis, MN 55401

Gray & Company Publishers
1588 E 40 St, Suite 3A, Cleveland, OH 44103
Tel: 216-431-2665 *Toll Free Tel:* 800-915-3609
E-mail: sales@grayco.com; editorial@grayco.com; support@grayco.com; publicity@grayco.com
Web Site: www.grayco.com
Key Personnel
Pres: David Gray
Mktg: Chris Andrikanich *E-mail:* promotions@grayco.com
Founded: 1991
Books about Cleveland, Northeast Ohio & Ohio.
ISBN Prefix(es): 978-1-886228; 978-0-9631738; 978-1-59851; 978-1-938441
Number of titles published annually: 8 Print
Total Titles: 85 Print

Graywolf Press
250 Third Ave N, Suite 600, Minneapolis, MN 55401
Tel: 651-641-0077 *Fax:* 651-641-0036

E-mail: wolves@graywolfpress.org
Web Site: www.graywolfpress.org
Key Personnel
Dir & Publr: Fiona McCrae
Assoc Dir: Katie Dublinski
Mng Dir: Leslie Johnson
Marketing & Publicity Dir: Erin Kottke
Exec Ed: Jeffrey Shotts
Assoc Ed: Steve Woodward
Contrib Ed: Brigid Hughes
Publicity & Events Mgr: Marisa Atkinson
Founded: 1974
Poetry, fiction, nonfiction.
ISBN Prefix(es): 978-1-55597
Number of titles published annually: 30 Print
Total Titles: 200 Print; 30 E-Book
Foreign Rights: Agence Michelle Lapautre (France); Michael Meller Literary Agency GmbH (Germany)
Billing Address: MPS Distribution Center, 16365 James Madison Hwy, Gordonsville, VA 22942
Orders to: MPS Distribution Center, 16365 James Madison Hwy, Gordonsville, VA 22942
Warehouse: MPS Distribution Center, 16365 James Madison Hwy, Gordonsville, VA 22942
Distribution Center: MPS Distribution Center, 16365 James Madison Hwy, Gordonsville, VA 22942 *Tel:* 212-206-5311 *Toll Free Tel:* 888-330-8477 *Fax:* 540-672-7703

Great Potential Press Inc
Division of Anodyne Inc
1325 N Wilmot Ave, Suite 300, Tucson, AZ 85712
Tel: 520-777-6161 *Fax:* 520-777-6217
Web Site: www.greatpotentialpress.com
Key Personnel
Pres & Publr: James T Webb
VP, Acq Ed, Devt Ed: Janet Gore *E-mail:* janet@greatpotentialpress.com
Founded: 1982
Educational guide books & books for parents & adults relating to social/emotional needs & other characteristics of gifted children & adults.
ISBN Prefix(es): 978-0-910707
Number of titles published annually: 5 Print
Total Titles: 58 Print; 4 CD-ROM; 1 Audio
Imprints: Gifted Psychology Press
Foreign Rights: Amer-Asia Book (Evelyn K Lee) (Asia)
Distribution Center: Ingram Book Co, One Ingram Blvd, La Vergne, TN 37086
Membership(s): Arizona Book Publishing Association; The Independent Book Publishers Association

Great Quotations Inc
1410 Brook Dr, Downers Grove, IL 60515
Tel: 630-985-2628 *Toll Free Tel:* 800-830-3020 *Fax:* 630-985-2610
E-mail: info@greatquotationsinc.com
Web Site: www.greatquotationsinc.com
Key Personnel
Pres: Ringo Suek
Founded: 1984
Motivation, inspiration & humor titles, also gifts.
ISBN Prefix(es): 978-1-56245; 978-0-931089
Number of titles published annually: 30 Print
Total Titles: 500 Print
Imprints: G Q Publishing

Great Source Education Group
Subsidiary of Houghton Mifflin Harcourt Publishing Company
181 Ballardvale St, Wilmington, MA 01887
Mailing Address: PO Box 7050, Wilmington, MA 01887-7050
Toll Free Tel: 800-289-4490 *Toll Free Fax:* 800-289-3994; 800-269-5232
Web Site: www.hmhco.com
Key Personnel
SVP, Fin/Opers, Planning: Steve Zukowski *E-mail:* steve.zukowski@hmhpub.com
Founded: 1996
Supplemental school instructional materials.

Green Dragon Books
2875 S Ocean Blvd, Suite 200, Palm Beach, FL 33480
Tel: 561-533-6231 *Toll Free Tel:* 800-874-8844 *Fax:* 561-533-6233 *Toll Free Fax:* 888-874-8844
E-mail: info@greendragonbooks.com
Web Site: greendragonbooks.com
Key Personnel
Chmn & Publr: Gary Wilson *E-mail:* garyw@greendragonbooks.com
Founded: 1969
Publications include Learning Center guides, early learning activity guides, children's picture books, general trade books, Legacies memoir series & SleuthHound mystery series.
ISBN Prefix(es): 978-1-63006; 978-1-62386
Number of titles published annually: 12 Print; 12 Online; 12 E-Book
Total Titles: 400 Print; 400 Online; 400 E-Book
Foreign Rights: Montreal-Contacts/The Rights Agency (Worldwide)

Green Integer
6210 Wilshire Blvd, Suite 211, Los Angeles, CA 90048
SAN: 216-3063
Tel: 323-857-1115 *Fax:* 323-857-0143
Web Site: www.greeninteger.com
Key Personnel
Publr: Douglas Messerli *E-mail:* douglas.messerli@gmail.com
Founded: 1978
Contemporary fiction, criticism, drama & poetry.
ISBN Prefix(es): 978-0-940650; 978-1-55713
Number of titles published annually: 15 Print
Total Titles: 300 Print
Imprints: New American Fiction Series; New American Poetry Series; Sun & Moon Classics
Foreign Rights: Eliane Benesti Literary Agency (France); Bookbank SA (Spain); Paul & Peter Fritz AG Literary Agency (Germany, Switzerland); Japan UNI Agency Inc (Japan); Leonhardt Literary Agency (Scandinavia); Natoli, Stefan & Oliva Literary Agency (Italy); Rogan Pikarski Literary Agency (Israel)
Distribution Center: Consortium Book Sales & Distribution, The Keg House, 34 13 Ave NE, Minneapolis, MN 55413-1007 *Tel:* 651-746-2600 *Toll Free Tel:* 800-283-3572 (cust serv) *Fax:* 612-746-2606 *E-mail:* info@cbsd.com *Web Site:* www.cbsd.com

Greenhaven Press®
Imprint of Gale
27500 Drake Rd, Farmington Hills, MI 48331
Toll Free Tel: 800-877-GALE (877-4253 - cust serv & orders) *Toll Free Fax:* 800-414-5043 (orders only)
E-mail: gale.customerservice@cengage.com; gale.galeord@cengage.com
Web Site: www.gale.cengage.com/greenhaven
Key Personnel
Dir, Prod Mgmt, Cengage Learning: Leigh Ann Cusack
Prodn Mgr: Ellen McGeagh *E-mail:* ellen.mcgeagh@cengage.com
Founded: 1970
High school, college & secondary nonfiction social studies & debate books for classrooms & libraries: social studies reference series; library & paper bound books in area studies, criminal justice, the environment, health, Literary Companion & American History series & AT Issues series.
ISBN Prefix(es): 978-0-89908; 978-1-56510; 978-0-7377
Number of titles published annually: 200 Print
Total Titles: 3,500 Print

Greenleaf Book Group LLC
Three Park Place, 4005 Banister Lane, Suite B, Austin, TX 78704
Mailing Address: PO Box 91869, Austin, TX 78709
Tel: 512-891-6100 *Toll Free Tel:* 800-932-5420 *Fax:* 512-891-6150
E-mail: contact@greenleafbookgroup.com
Web Site: www.greenleafbookgroup.com
Key Personnel
Founder: Clint Greenleaf
CEO: Tanya Hall
COO & Gen Coun: Bryan Goodwin
CFO: Brian Viktorin
Art Dir: Neil Gonzalez
Dir, Consulting: Justin Branch
Dir, Mktg & Busn Devt: Ashley Jones
Dir, Prodn: Carrie Jones
Mktg Mgr: Corrin Foster
Sr Ed: Diana Ceres; Nathan True
Founded: 1997
Publisher & distributor specializing in the development of independent authors & the growth of small presses. Our publishing model was designed to support independent authors & allow writers to retain the rights to their work & still compete with major publishing houses. We also distribute select titles from small & independent publishers to major trade outlets, including bookstores, libraries & airport retailers. We serve the small & independent publishing community by offering industry guidance, business development, production, distribution & marketing services.
ISBN Prefix(es): 978-0-9665319; 978-1-929774
Number of titles published annually: 100 Print
Total Titles: 350 Print
Imprints: Emerald Book Co; 500/5000 Press Inc; Greenleaf Book Group Press; Olive Tree Book Co; River Grove Books
Returns: Archway, 20770 Westwood Dr, Strongsville, OH 44149
Membership(s): AAP; The Association of Publishers for Special Sales; BookSense Publisher Partner; The Independent Book Publishers Association; Midwest Publishing Association; National Speakers Association; Society of Children's Book Writers & Illustrators

Greenleaf Book Group Press, see Greenleaf Book Group LLC

§Greenwoman Publishing LLC
1823 W Pikes Peak Ave, Colorado Springs, CO 80904-3844
Mailing Address: PO Box 6587, Colorado Springs, CO 80934-6587
Tel: 719-473-9237 *Fax:* 719-473-9237
Web Site: www.greenwomanpublishing.com
Key Personnel
Owner, Publr & Ed: Sandra Knauf *E-mail:* sandra@greenwomanmagazine.com
Assoc Publr & Deputy Ed: Zora Knauf
Founded: 2011
Publisher of *Greenwoman Magazine*, a biannual literary garden writing magazine in print & electronic. Publish books on subjects related to gardening, sustainability & biography. Also published its first fiction book, a young adult environmental fantasy, in 2013.
ISBN Prefix(es): 978-0-9897056
Number of titles published annually: 2 Print; 2 E-Book
Total Titles: 1 Print; 3 E-Book

§Greenwood Research Books & Software
Division of Greenwood Research

PO Box 12102, Wichita, KS 67277-2102
Tel: 316-214-5103
Web Site: greenray4ever.com (ordering)
Key Personnel
Lib Sales Dir & Gen Mgr: James A Green
E-mail: jimgreenhimself@gmail.com
Founded: 1990 (in Clearwater, FL & relocated to Wichita, KS in 1991)
Science & engineering emphasis: Medical Image Processing.
ISBN Prefix(es): 978-1-890121
Number of titles published annually: 6 Print
Total Titles: 15 Print
Distribution Center: Midwest Library Service, 11443 St Charles Rock Rd, Bridgeton, MO 63044-2789 *Tel:* 314-739-3100 *Toll Free Tel:* 800-325-8833 *Fax:* 314-739-1326 *Toll Free Fax:* 800-962-1009 *E-mail:* mail@midwestls.com *Web Site:* midwestls.com
Membership(s): The Independent Book Publishers Association

Grey House Publishing Inc™
4919 Rte 22, Amenia, NY 12501
Mailing Address: PO Box 56, Amenia, NY 12501-0056
Tel: 518-789-8700 *Toll Free Tel:* 800-562-2139 *Fax:* 518-789-0556
E-mail: books@greyhouse.com; customerservice@greyhouse.com
Web Site: www.greyhouse.com
Key Personnel
Pres: Richard Gottlieb *Fax:* 518-789-0544
E-mail: rhg@greyhouse.com
VP, Mktg: Jessica Moody *Tel:* 518-789-8700 ext 101 *E-mail:* jmoody@greyhouse.com
Publr: Leslie Mackenzie *E-mail:* lmackenzie@greyhouse.com
Edit Dir: Laura Mars *E-mail:* lmars@greyhouse.com
Founded: 1981
Directories, reference books & encyclopedias in history, business, economics, health & demographic areas.
ISBN Prefix(es): 978-1-930956; 978-1-891482; 978-0-939300; 978-1-59237; 978-1-61925
Number of titles published annually: 48 Print
Total Titles: 60 Print; 25 Online; 26 E-Book
Imprints: R R Bowker's Books in Print Series; Grey House; Financial Ratings Series; Salem Press; H W Wilson
Divisions: Grey House Publishing Canada
Returns: 5979 N Elm Ave, Suite 113, Millerton, NY 12546
Warehouse: 5979 N Elm Ave, Suite 113, Millerton, NY 12546
Membership(s): ALA

Grosset & Dunlap
Imprint of Penguin Group (USA) LLC, a Penguin Random House company
345 Hudson St, New York, NY 10014
Tel: 212-366-2000
Web Site: www.penguinrandomhouse.com
Key Personnel
Pres & Publr, Grosset & Dunlap/Price Stern Sloan: Francesco Sedita
Ed-in-Chief, Early Readers & Assoc Publr, Warne: Bonnie Bader
Ed-in-Chief, Series & Licenses: Sarah Fabiny
VP & Ed-at-Large: Jane O'Connor
Exec Ed: Rob Valois
Exec Dir, Licensing Acqs & Media: Lori Burke
Art Dir: Giuseppe Castellano
Founded: 1898
ISBN Prefix(es): 978-0-448; 978-1-58184
Number of titles published annually: 133 Print
Total Titles: 1,098 Print
Imprints: PSS; Somerville House USA

§Group Publishing Inc
1515 Cascade Ave, Loveland, CO 80538
Mailing Address: PO Box 481, Loveland, CO 80539-0481
Tel: 970-669-3836 *Toll Free Tel:* 800-447-1070 *Fax:* 970-292-4373
E-mail: info@group.com
Web Site: www.group.com
Key Personnel
Founder & Chmn: Thom Schultz
Database Mktg Mgr: Eric Dowdy
Ed & Copyright Coord: Kerri Loesche
E-mail: kloesche@group.com
Founded: 1974
Books, magazines, video & audio tapes, computer online service, curriculum.
ISBN Prefix(es): 978-1-55945; 978-0-7644; 978-0-931529
Number of titles published annually: 40 Print
Total Titles: 400 Print; 2 CD-ROM; 15 Audio
Imprints: Faith Weaver Bible Curriculum™; FW Friends™; Group Workcamps™; Group's Hands-On Bible Curriculum™; Kids Own Worship™
Foreign Rights: Canaanland (Malaysia); CLC Wholesale (UK); Group Canada (Canada); KCBS Inc (Korea); Koorung Books Pty Ltd (Australia); STL (UK)
Returns: 1615 Cascade Ave, Loveland, CO 80538
Shipping Address: 1615 Cascade Ave, Loveland, CO 80538
Membership(s): CBA; Evangelical Christian Publishers Association

Grove Atlantic Inc
154 W 14 St, 12th fl, New York, NY 10011
SAN: 201-4890
Tel: 212-614-7850 *Toll Free Tel:* 800-521-0178 *Fax:* 212-614-7886
E-mail: info@groveatlantic.com
Web Site: www.groveatlantic.com
Key Personnel
Pres & Publr: Morgan Entrekin
E-mail: mentrekin@groveatlantic.com
VP & Edit Dir: Elisabeth Schmitz
E-mail: eschmitz@groveatlantic.com
Sr Ed: Corinna Barsan; Jamison Stoltz
E-mail: jstoltz@groveatlantic.com
Ed: Peter Blackstock
Assoc Ed: Katie Raissian
Asst Ed: Allison Malecha
Dir, Publicity: Deb Seager *E-mail:* dseager@groveatlantic.com
Dir, Subs Rts & Ed: Amy Hundley
E-mail: ahundley@groveatlantic.com
Sr Publicist: John Mark Boling
Founded: 1917
General fiction & nonfiction, hardcover & paperbound.
ISBN Prefix(es): 978-0-8021; 978-1-55584; 978-0-87113; 978-1-61185
Number of titles published annually: 120 Print; 30 E-Book
Total Titles: 1,200 Print; 250 E-Book
Imprints: Atlantic Books Ltd; Atlantic Monthly Press; Black Cat; Grove Press; The Mysterious Press
Foreign Rep(s): Book Promotions (Nicky Stubbs) (South Africa); Gilles Fauveau (Japan, Korea); Jaime Gregorio (Philippines); Sharad Mohan (Bangladesh, India, Maldives, Nepal, Pakistan, Sri Lanka); NewSouth Books (Australia, New Zealand); Perseus Books Group UK (Europe, Ireland, UK); Perseus Distribution (Edison Garcia) (Latin America); Perseus International (Suk Lee) (Middle East); June Poonpanich (Cambodia, Indonesia, Laos, Thailand, Vietnam); Wei Zhao (China, Hong Kong, Taiwan)
Foreign Rights: AnatoliaLit Agency (Amy Spangler) (Turkey); Eliane Benisti Agency (Eliane Benisti) (France); Casanovas & Lynch Agencia Literaria (Maria Lynch) (Latin America, Portugal, Spain); Ersilia Literary Agency (Evangelia Avloniti) (Greece); Graal Literary Agency (Filip Wojciechowski) (Poland); International Copyright Agency (Simona Kessler) (Romania); Japan Uni Agency Inc (Miko Yamanouchi) (Japan); Katai & Bolza (Peter Bolza) (Hungary); Korea Copyright Center (Ms Kyung Kang) (Korea); Andrew Nurnberg Associates (Tatjana Zoldnere) (Estonia, Latvia, Lithuania); Andrew Nurnberg Associates, Beijing Representative Office (Jackie Huang) (China); Andrew Nurnberg Associates, Taiwan Representative Office (Whitney Hsu) (Taiwan); Kristin Olson Literary Agency (Kristin Olson) (Czech Republic); Plima Literary Agency (Vuk Perisic) (Bulgaria, Croatia, Serbia, Slovenia); The Riff Agency (Laura Riff & Joao Paulo Riff) (Brazil); Elisabeth Ruge Agentur GmbH (Elisabeth Ruge) (Germany); Synopsis Literary Agency (Natalia Sanina) (Russia); Ulf Toregard Agency (Ulf Toregard) (Netherlands, Scandinavia); Tuttle-Mori Agency Inc (Ken Mori) (Japan); Marco Vigevani Agenzia Letteraria (Claire Sabatie-Garat) (Italy)
Orders to: Publishers Group Worldwide, 250 W 57 St, 15th fl, New York, NY 10107 *Tel:* 212-581-7839; Perseus Distribution, 210 American Dr, Jackson, TN 38301; Publishers Group Canada, 559 College St, Suite 402, Toronto, ON M6G 1A9, Canada *Tel:* 416-934-9900 *Toll Free Tel:* 800-747-8147 *Fax:* 416-934-1410 *E-mail:* info@pgcbooks.ca; Grantham Book Services, Trent Rd, Grantham NG31 7XQ, United Kingdom *Tel:* (0147) 654 1080 *Fax:* (0147) 654 1061 *E-mail:* orders@gbs.tbs-ltd.co.uk
Returns: Publishers Group West, Returns Dept, 40 Carl Kirkland Dr, Jackson, TN 38301; Raincoast Books, 2440 Viking Way, Richmond, BC V6V 1N2, Canada *Toll Free Tel:* 800-663-5714 *Toll Free Fax:* 800-565-3770 *E-mail:* customerservice@raincoast.com
Distribution Center: Perseus Distribution, 210 American Dr, Jackson, TN 38301
Membership(s): AAP

Gryphon Editions
PO Box 241823, Omaha, NE 68124
Tel: 402-298-5385 (intl) *Toll Free Tel:* 888-655-0134 (US & CN)
E-mail: customerservice@gryphoneditions.com
Web Site: www.gryphoneditions.com
Founded: 1977
Reprints: medicine, law, political philosophy, science; fine editions.
Number of titles published annually: 25 Print
Total Titles: 750 Print
Distribution Center: Bindtech Distribution, 428 Harding Industrial Blvd, Nashville, TN 37211

Gryphon House Inc
Subsidiary of Kaplan Early Learning Co
6848 Leon's Way, Lewisville, NC 27023
Mailing Address: PO Box 10, Lewisville, NC 27023
Toll Free Tel: 800-638-0928 *Toll Free Fax:* 877-638-7576
E-mail: info@ghbooks.com
Web Site: www.gryphonhouse.com
Key Personnel
Gen Mgr: Jennifer Lewis *E-mail:* jennifer@ghbooks.com
Mktg Mgr: Anna Wilmoth *E-mail:* anna@ghbooks.com
Sales: Amy Acocella *E-mail:* amy@ghbooks.com
Founded: 1971
Publishes & distributes books for teachers & parents of young children.
ISBN Prefix(es): 978-0-87659
Number of titles published annually: 12 Print; 12 E-Book
Total Titles: 275 Print; 80 E-Book
Distributor for Aha Communications; Book Peddlers; Deya Brashears; Bright Ring Publishing; Building Blocks; Center for the Child Care Workforce; Chatterbox Press; Chicago Re-

view Press; Children's Resources International; Circle Time Publishers; Sydney Gurewitz Clemens; Conari Press; Council Oak Books; Dawn Sign Press; Delmar Publishers Inc; Early Educator's Press; Educators for Social Responsibility; Family Center of Nova University; Jean Feldman; Floris Books; Hawthorne Press; Hunter House Publishers; Kaplan Press; Miss Jackie Inc; Monjeu Press; National Center Early Childhood Workforce; New England AEYC; New Horizons; Nova Southeastern University; Pademelon Press; Partner Press; Pollyanna Productions; Robins Lane Press; School Renaissance; Southern Early Childhood Association; Steam Press; Syracuse University Press; Teaching Strategies; Telshare Publishing
Foreign Rep(s): Monarch Books (Canada); Pademelon Press (Australia)

Guideposts Book & Inspirational Media
16 E 34 St, 12th fl, New York, NY 10016
Tel: 212-251-8100 *Toll Free Tel:* 800-431-2344 (cust serv) *Fax:* 212-684-0689
E-mail: gpsprod@cdsfulfillment.com
Web Site: guideposts.org
Key Personnel
CEO & Pres: John F Temple
Founded: 1945
Inspirational books & videos.
ISBN Prefix(es): 978-0-9661766
Number of titles published annually: 30 Print

§The Guilford Press
72 Spring St, New York, NY 10012
SAN: 212-9442
Tel: 212-431-9800 *Toll Free Tel:* 800-365-7006 *Fax:* 212-966-6708
E-mail: info@guilford.com
Web Site: www.guilford.com
Key Personnel
Pres & Gen Mgr: Robert Matloff *E-mail:* bob.matloff@guilford.com
Lib Sales Dir & Sales Mgr: Anne Patota *Tel:* 212-431-9800 ext 217 *E-mail:* anne.patota@guilford.com
Mktg Dir: Marian Robinson *E-mail:* marian.robinson@guilford.com
Ed-in-Chief: Seymour Weingarten *E-mail:* seymour.weingarten@guilford.com
Mng Ed: Judith Grauman *E-mail:* judith.grauman@guilford.com
Acct Mgr: Estefeni Estremera *Tel:* 212-431-9800 ext 258 *E-mail:* estefeni.estremera@guilford.com
Busn Mgr: David Mitchell *E-mail:* david.mitchell@guilford.com
Credit Mgr: Vernita Hurston *Tel:* 212-431-9800 ext 230 *E-mail:* vernita.hurston@guilford.com
Fulfillment Mgr: William McEvoy *E-mail:* william.mcevoy@guilford.com
Prodn Mgr: Katya Edwards *E-mail:* katya.edwards@guilford.com
Intl Rts, Perms & ISBN Contact: Kathy Kuehl *E-mail:* kathy.kuehl@guilford.com
Founded: 1973
Professional & reference books, videos, journals & software in psychology, psychiatry & the behavioral sciences, neuroscience, research methods, education & literacy & geography.
ISBN Prefix(es): 978-0-89862; 978-1-57230; 978-1-59385; 978-1-60623; 978-1-60918; 978-1-4625
Number of titles published annually: 90 Print; 90 E-Book
Total Titles: 1,350 Print; 2 CD-ROM; 850 E-Book
Foreign Rep(s): Avicenna Partnership (Middle East); Cranbury International (Caribbean, Pakistan, South America); Disvan Enterprises (India); Footprint Books (Australia, New Zealand); Juta (South Africa); Taylor & Francis Asia Pacific (Asia, China); Taylor & Francis Informa UK (Europe, UK); Unifacmanu (Taiwan); United Publishers Services (Japan)
Returns: c/o Maple Press Distribution Ctr, I-83 Industrial Park, 60 Grumbacher Rd, York, PA 17406
Warehouse: c/o Maple Press Distribution Ctr, I-83 Industrial Park, 60 Grumbacher Rd, York, PA 17406

Guilford Publications Inc, see The Guilford Press

§Gulf Publishing Co
2 Greenway Plaza, Suite 1020, Houston, TX 77046
Mailing Address: PO Box 2608, Houston, TX 77252
Tel: 713-529-4301 *Fax:* 713-520-4433
E-mail: store@gulfpub.com
Web Site: www.gulfpub.com
Key Personnel
CEO & Pres: John T Royall
Publr, Hydrocarbon Processing: Bret Ronk
Publr, World Oil Magazine: Ron Higgins
Founded: 1916
Communications company dedicated to the petrochemical industry & related industries.
ISBN Prefix(es): 978-1-933762; 978-0-9765113
Number of titles published annually: 10 Print; 3 CD-ROM
Total Titles: 20 Print; 30 CD-ROM
Distributor for Elsevier; Pennwell; Simon & Schuster; Editions Technip; Wiley

Hachai Publishing
527 Empire Blvd, Brooklyn, NY 11225
SAN: 251-3749
Tel: 718-633-0100 *Fax:* 718-633-0103
E-mail: info@hachai.com
Web Site: www.hachai.com
Key Personnel
Pres: Yerachmiel Binyominson
Publr & Sales: Yossi Leverton *E-mail:* yossi@hachai.com
Ed: Dina Rosenfeld *E-mail:* dlr@hachai.com
Founded: 1988
Full color children's Judaica books.
ISBN Prefix(es): 978-0-922613; 978-1-929628
Number of titles published annually: 5 Print
Total Titles: 100 Print
Distributor for Attara; Kerem
Membership(s): Association of Jewish Book Publishers; Association of Jewish Libraries; The Independent Book Publishers Association

Hachette Audio
Division of Hachette Book Group
1290 Avenue of the Americas, New York, NY 10019
Tel: 212-364-1100
Key Personnel
VP, Publr, Audio & Large Print: Anthony Goff
Exec Dir, Audio & Opers: Kim Sayle
Dir, Audio Mktg & Publicity: Megan Fitzpatrick
Dir, Prodn: Michele McGonigle
Number of titles published annually: 417 Audio

Hachette Book Group
Division of Hachette Livre
1290 Avenue of the Americas, New York, NY 10019
Tel: 212-364-1100 *Toll Free Tel:* 800-759-0190 (cust serv) *Fax:* 212-364-0933 (intl orders) *Toll Free Fax:* 800-286-9471 (cust serv)
Web Site: www.HachetteBookGroup.com
Key Personnel
CEO: Michael Pietsch
EVP & COO: Joe Mangan
SVP & Communs Dir: Sophie Cottrell
EVP, Busn Aff & Gen Coun: Carol Ross
SVP, HR: Andrea Weinzimer
SVP, HBG & Publr, Little, Brown and Company: Reagan Arthur
VP, Publr, Hachette Books: Mauro DiPreta
VP, Publr, Audio & Large Print: Anthony Goff
SVP, HBG & Publr, Orbit: Tim Holman
Pres, HBG & Publr, Grand Central Publishing: Jamie Raab
SVP, HBG & Publr, Little, Brown Books for Young Readers: Megan Tingley
SVP, HBG & Publr, Nashville Div: Rolf Zettersten
SVP, Group Sales Dir: Christopher Murphy
SVP & CFO: Stephen Mubarek
VP, Distr, Sales & Servs: Todd McGarity
SVP, Strategy & Publg Opers: Dan Lubart
VP, Contracts: Andrea Shallcross
VP, Subs Rts: Nancy Wiese
SVP, Intl, Canada, Spec Mkts: Jean Griffin
EVP, HBG & CFO: Thomas Maciag
Hachette Book Group (HBG) is a leading trade publisher based in New York & a division of Hachette Livre, the third-largest trade & educational publisher in the world. HBG publishes under the divisions of Little, Brown and Company, Little Brown Books for Young Readers, Grand Central Publishing, Orbit, Hachette Books, Hachette Nashville, & Hachette Audio.
ISBN Prefix(es): 978-1-56282; 978-0-7868; 978-0-316; 978-1-4013
Divisions: Grand Central Publishing; Hachette Audio; Hachette Books; Hachette Nashville; Little, Brown and Company; Little, Brown Books for Young Readers; Orbit
Distributor for Harry N Abrams Inc; Amazing People Club; Chronicle Books; Disney Book Group; Gildan Media; Guiness World Records; Hachette UK; Hearst Books; Houghton Mifflin Harcourt; Kensington Publishing; Kids Can Press; Marvel Worldwide Inc; Octopus Books; Oxmoor House; Phaidon Press; Quarto Publishing; Quercus Books; Time Home Entertainment Inc
Orders to: Order Dept, 53 State St, Boston, MA 02109 (US orders) *Toll Free Tel:* 800-759-0190 *Toll Free Fax:* 800-286-9471
Returns: Returns Dept, 322 S Enterprise Blvd, Lebanon, IN 46052
Shipping Address: Hachette Book Group Distribution Center, 121 N Enterprise Blvd, Lebanon, IN 46052 *Tel:* 765-483-9900 *Fax:* 765-483-0706
See separate listing for:
Grand Central Publishing
Hachette Audio
Hachette Books
Hachette Nashville
Little, Brown and Company
Little, Brown Books for Young Readers
Orbit

Hachette Books
Division of Hachette Book Group
1290 Avenue of the Americas, New York, NY 10019
Tel: 212-364-1100
Web Site: www.hachettebookgroup.com
Key Personnel
VP & Publr: Mauro DiPreta
Publr, Black Dog & Leventhal: J P Leventhal
Exec Ed: Stacy Creamer
Edit Dir, Black Dog & Leventhal: Becky Koh
Mktg Dir: Betsy Hulsebosch
Exec Dir, Publicity: Michelle Aielli
Assoc Publr, Black Dog & Leventhal: Maureen Winter
ISBN Prefix(es): 978-1-884822 (Black Dog & Leventhal); 978-1-57912 (Black Dog & Leventhal); 978-1-56282; 978-0-7868; 978-0-316; 978-0-316 (Black Dog & Leventhal); 978-1-4013; 978-1-60376 (Black Dog & Leventhal); 978-1-63191 (Black Dog & Leventhal)
Number of titles published annually: 25 Print
Total Titles: 972 Print

Imprints: Black Dog & Leventhal
Orders to: Hachette Book Group, Order Dept, 53 State St, Boston, MA 02109 (US orders) *Toll Free Tel:* 800-759-0190 *Toll Free Fax:* 800-286-9471
Returns: Hachette Book Group, Returns Dept, 122 S Enterprise Blvd, Lebanon, IN 46052

Hachette Nashville
Division of Hachette Book Group
12 Cadillac Dr, Suite 480, Brentwood, TN 37027
Tel: 615-221-0996 *Fax:* 615-221-0962
Web Site: www.hachettebookgroup.com
Key Personnel
SVP & Publr, Nashville Div: Rolf Zettersten
VP, Mktg: Patsy Jones
Exec Ed: Kate Hartson
Exec Ed, FaithWords: Joseph Paul
Sr Ed, Fiction: Christina Boys
Founded: 2001
Publish books for the growing inspirational market. No unsol mss.
ISBN Prefix(es): 978-0-446
Number of titles published annually: 75 Print
Total Titles: 475 Print
Imprints: Center Street; FaithWords; Jericho Books
Orders to: Hachette Book Group, 53 State St, Boston, MA 02109 *Toll Free Tel:* 800-759-0190 *Toll Free Fax:* 800-286-9471
Membership(s): CBA; Evangelical Christian Publishers Association

Hackett Publishing Co Inc
3333 Massachusetts Ave, Indianapolis, IN 46218
SAN: 201-6044
Mailing Address: PO Box 44937, Indianapolis, IN 46244-0937
Tel: 317-635-9250 (orders & cust serv) *Fax:* 317-635-9292 *Toll Free Fax:* 800-783-9213
E-mail: customer@hackettpublishing.com
Web Site: www.hackettpublishing.com
Key Personnel
CEO, Pres & Publr: Deborah Wilkes
VP, Mktg Dir & Dir, Opers: John Persh-ing *Tel:* 617-234-0371 *E-mail:* johnp@hackettpublishing.com
Secy & Treas: Cheri Brown
Edit Asst & Off Mgr: Christina Kowalewski *Tel:* 617-234-0375 *E-mail:* christinak@hackettpublishing.com
Founded: 1972
College textbooks & scholarly books; emphasis on philosophy, political theory, political science, classics, history & literature.
ISBN Prefix(es): 978-0-915144; 978-0-915145; 978-0-87220; 978-1-60384
Number of titles published annually: 30 Print; 30 E-Book
Total Titles: 588 Print; 286 E-Book
Imprints: Focus
Editorial Office(s): Hackett Publishing Co Inc, PO Box 390007, Cambridge, MA 02139 *Tel:* 617-497-6303 *Fax:* 617-661-8703 *E-mail:* editorial@hackettpublishing.com
Sales Office(s): Hackett Publishing Co Inc, PO Box 390007, Cambridge, MA 02139
Distributor for Bryn Mawr Commentaries
Foreign Rep(s): Gazelle Book Services Ltd (Europe, UK); UNIREPS (Australia, New Zealand)
Foreign Rights: Eulama
See separate listing for:
Focus

§Hagstrom Map
Subsidiary of American Map Corp
1800 Lovering Ave, Wilmington, DE 19806
Toll Free Tel: 800-432-MAPS (432-6277) *Toll Free Fax:* 888-210-9654
Web Site: rockfordpublishing.com
Key Personnel
Pres: Patrick Keane
Founded: 1916
3,000,000 maps, atlases, guides.
ISBN Prefix(es): 978-0-88097; 978-0-910684; 978-1-59245
Total Titles: 1 CD-ROM
Distributor for ADC The Map People; American Map Corp; Arrow Maps Inc; Creative Sales Corp; De Lorme Atlas; Hammond World Atlas Corp; RV International Maps & Atlases; Stubs Guides; Trakker Maps Inc

§Haights Cross Communications®
136 Madison Ave, 8th fl, New York, NY 10016
Tel: 212-209-0500 *Fax:* 212-209-0501
E-mail: info@haightscross.com
Web Site: www.haightscross.com
Key Personnel
CEO & Pres: Rick Noble
CFO: Scott August
SVP, Fin & Planning & Treas: Melissa L Linsky
Founded: 1996
Educational & professional publishing group that creates books, instructional materials, audio products, periodicals, software & online services, serving the following markets: K-12 supplemental education, public & school library publishing, audio books & medical publishing.
Number of titles published annually: 856 Print; 10 CD-ROM; 50 Online; 10 E-Book; 787 Audio
Total Titles: 6,200 Print; 20 CD-ROM; 50 Online; 10 E-Book; 5,808 Audio
Divisions: Triumph Learning
Foreign Office(s): Recorded Books/W F Howes, Rearsby Business Park, Unit 3, Gaddesby Lane, Rearsby, Leics LE7 4YH, United Kingdom, Mng Dir: Sean Sibley *Tel:* (0116) 230-1144 *Fax:* (0116) 230-1155
Membership(s): AAP; ALA; Audio Publishers Association; International Literacy Association; Specialized Information Publishers Association
See separate listing for:
Triumph Learning LLC

§Hal Leonard Books
Imprint of Hal Leonard Performing Arts Publishing Group
33 Plymouth St, Suite 302, Montclair, NJ 07042
Toll Free Tel: 800-637-2852
E-mail: info@halleonardbooks.com; custserv@halleonardbooks.com
Web Site: www.halleonardbooks.com
Key Personnel
Group Publr: John Cerullo *E-mail:* jcerullo@halleonard.com
Founded: 1984
Publisher of songbooks & books on the music business, audio technology, instrument history & more.
ISBN Prefix(es): 978-1-4234
Number of titles published annually: 30 Print; 20 E-Book
Total Titles: 1,000 Print; 500 E-Book
Imprints: Amadeus Press (classical music & opera); Applause Theatre & Cinema Books; Backbeat Books (music trade books); Limelight Editions (instruction, ref & how-to titles)
Sales Office(s): 7777 W Bluemound Rd, Milwaukee, WI 53213, Contact: Doug Lady *Tel:* 414-774-3630
Foreign Rep(s): Publishers Group UK (Europe, UK)
Returns: Hal Leonard, 1210 Innovation Dr, Winona, MN 55987, Contact: Kim Jereczek *E-mail:* kjereczek@halleonard.com
Warehouse: Hal Leonard, 1210 Innovation Dr, Winona, MN 55987, Contact: Tony Prodzinski *E-mail:* tprodzinski@halleonard.com

§Hal Leonard Corp
7777 W Bluemound Rd, Milwaukee, WI 53213
Mailing Address: PO Box 13819, Milwaukee, WI 53213-0819
Tel: 414-774-3630 *Toll Free Tel:* 800-524-4425 *Fax:* 414-774-3259
E-mail: halinfo@halleonard.com
Web Site: www.halleonard.com
Key Personnel
Chmn & CEO: Keith Mardak
Pres: Larry Morton
Sr Sales & Mktg Mgr, Book Trade & Ebooks: Mike Hansen *E-mail:* mhansen@halleonard.com
Consumer Prods Accts Mgr: David Cywinski *E-mail:* dcywinski@halleonard.com
Founded: 1947
The world's largest music print publisher, with an incomparable selection of sheet music, songbooks, music related books, self-instruction books, CD packs & videos, music reference & special interest titles, music biographies, children's music products; CD-ROMs, DVDs, performance videos & more. Additional offices in Minnesota, New York, Nashville, Australia, Belgium, France, Germany, Holland, Italy, Switzerland & the UK.
ISBN Prefix(es): 978-1-57467; 978-0-88188; 978-0-7935; 978-0-87910; 978-0-87930; 978-0-634; 978-1-4234; 978-0-9607350; 978-1-56516; 978-1-61713; 978-1-61774; 978-1-61780; 978-1-4584; 978-1-4768; 978-1-4803; 978-0-931340; 978-1-4950
Number of titles published annually: 2,000 Print
Total Titles: 200,000 Print; 15 CD-ROM
Imprints: Berklee Press; Centerstream Publications; Cherry Lane Music Co; Ashley Mark Publishing Co; Musicians Institute Press; G Shirmer; Vintage Guitar
Divisions: Hal Leonard Performing Arts Publishing Group
Distributor for Amadeus Press; Applause Theatre & Cinema Books; Artistpro; Ashley Music; Backbeat Books; Beacon Music; Berklee Press; Fred Bock Music Company; Boosey & Hawkes; Centerstream Publications; Cherry Lane Music Co; Cinema Books; Community Music Videos; Creative Concepts; DC Publications; Devine Entertainment Corp; Editions Durand; Editions Max Eschig; Editions Salabert; EM Books; EMI Christian; Faber Music Ltd; Guitar One; Guitar World; Home Recording; Homespun Tapes; Houston Publications; Hudson Music; iSong CD-ROMs; Jawbone Press; Kenyon Publications; Limelight Editions; Ashley Mark Publishing Co; Edward B Marks Music; Meredith Music; Modern Drummer Publications; Music Sales America; Musicians Institute Press; Musikverlage Han Sikorski; Christopher Parkening; Reader's Digest; Record Research; Ricordi; Lee Roberts Publications; Rubank Publications; G Schirmer Inc (Associated Music Publishers); Second Floor Music; Sing Out Corp; Star Licks Videos; Bernard Stein Music Co; String Letter Press; Tara Publications; Transcontinental Music; 21st Century Publications; Vintage Guitar; Word Music; Writer's Digest
Foreign Rep(s): Publishers Group UK (Europe, UK)
Shipping Address: 1210 Innovation Dr, Winona, MN 55987 *Tel:* 507-454-2920 *Fax:* 507-454-4042
Warehouse: 960 E Mark St, Winona, MN 55987
Distribution Center: 1210 Innovation Dr, Winona, MN 55987

Hal Leonard Performing Arts Publishing Group, see Amadeus Press/Hal Leonard Performing Arts Publishing Group

Hamilton Books
Imprint of University Press of America Inc
4501 Forbes Blvd, Suite 200, Lanham, MD 20706

Tel: 301-459-3366 *Toll Free Tel:* 800-462-6420 (cust serv) *Fax:* 301-429-5748 *Toll Free Fax:* 800-388-4550 (cust serv)
Key Personnel
VP & Publr: Julie Kirsch *E-mail:* jkirsch@rowman.com
Acqs Ed: Nicolette Amstutz *E-mail:* namstutz@univpress.com; Stella Donovan *E-mail:* sdonovan@univpress.com
Founded: 2002
Serious nonfiction: memoirs, biographies, autobiographies, religious perspectives.
ISBN Prefix(es): 978-0-7618
Number of titles published annually: 40 Print; 40 E-Book
Total Titles: 250 Print; 125 E-Book
Membership(s): AAP

§Hamilton Stone Editions
PO Box 43, Maplewood, NJ 07040
Tel: 973-378-8361
E-mail: hstone@hamiltonstone.org
Web Site: www.hamiltonstone.org
Key Personnel
Edit Dir: Meredith Sue Willis *E-mail:* meredithsuewillis@gmail.com
Artistic Dir: Lynda Schor *E-mail:* lynda.schor@gmail.com
Dir: Halvard Johnson *E-mail:* halvard@gmail.com; Edith Konecky *E-mail:* erkonecky@verizon.net; Nathan Leslie *E-mail:* nleslie@nvcc.edu; Carole Rosenthal *E-mail:* crlrosenthal@gmail.com
Founded: 2003
Independent press for independent literary writing. Dedicated to vivid writing that probes the hidden realities of the everyday, valuing most highly the kind of writing that displays a multifaced vision. Interested in keeping new books in print & bringing forgotten, excellent old books back into print.
ISBN Prefix(es): 978-0-9654043; 978-0-9714873
Number of titles published annually: 4 Print; 4 E-Book
Total Titles: 39 Print; 115 E-Book
Imprints: Irene Weinberger Books (literary books in ebook & trade paperback format, often in collaboration with other presses)
Shipping Address: 311 Prospect St, South Orange, NJ 07079

Hampton Press Inc
307 Seventh Ave, Suite 506, New York, NY 10001
Tel: 646-638-3800 *Toll Free Tel:* 800-894-8955 *Fax:* 646-638-3802
E-mail: hamptonpr1@aol.com
Web Site: www.hamptonpress.com
Key Personnel
Pres: Barbara Bernstein
Founded: 1992
ISBN Prefix(es): 978-1-881303; 978-1-57273; 978-1-61289
Number of titles published annually: 20 Print
Total Titles: 700 Print
Foreign Rep(s): Eurospan Group (Asia, Australia, Europe, Far East, Latin America, UK)

Hampton Roads Publishing Co
65 Parker St, Suite 7, Newburyport, MA 01950-4600
Tel: 978-465-0504 *Toll Free Tel:* 800-423-7087 (orders) *Fax:* 978-465-0243 *Toll Free Fax:* 877-337-3309
E-mail: orders@rwwbooks.com
Web Site: redwheelweiser.com
Key Personnel
Dir, Mktg & Digital Content: Bonni Hamilton *E-mail:* bhamilton@rwwbooks.com
Mktg Assoc: Eryn Carter *E-mail:* ecarter@rwwbooks.com
Founded: 1989
Trade publishing. Specialize in metaphysics, self-help, integrative medicine, visionary fiction & paranormal phenomena.
ISBN Prefix(es): 978-1-878901; 978-1-57174; 978-1-61283
Number of titles published annually: 30 Print
Total Titles: 350 Print; 2 Audio
Distributed by Red Wheel/Weiser Books/Conari Press
Foreign Rep(s): Brumby Sunstate (Australia); Deep Books Ltd (Europe, UK); Georgetown Publications (Canada); Publishers International Marketing (Asia, Middle East)
Foreign Rights: Biagi Rights Management (Linda Biagi) (Worldwide)

§Hancock House Publishers
4550 Birch Bay Lynden Rd, Suite 104, Blaine, WA 98230-5005
Tel: 604-538-1114 *Toll Free Tel:* 800-938-1114 *Fax:* 604-538-2262 *Toll Free Fax:* 800-983-2262
E-mail: sales@hancockhouse.com
Web Site: www.hancockhouse.com
Key Personnel
Publr & Intl Rts: David Hancock
Founded: 1975
Specialize in natural history (world), regional northwest history & Native art.
ISBN Prefix(es): 978-0-88839
Number of titles published annually: 15 Print
Total Titles: 300 Print
Branch Office(s)
19313 Zero Ave, Surrey, BC V3S 9R9, Canada

Handprint Books Inc
Imprint of Chronicle Books LLC
413 Sixth Ave, Brooklyn, NY 11215-3310
Tel: 718-768-3696 *Toll Free Tel:* 800-722-6657 (orders) *Fax:* 718-369-0844 *Toll Free Fax:* 800-858-7787 (orders)
E-mail: info@handprintbooks.com
Web Site: www.handprintbooks.com
Key Personnel
Pres & Publr: Christopher Franceschelli *E-mail:* cmf@handprintbooks.com
Founded: 2000
Publisher of high-quality books for children.
ISBN Prefix(es): 978-1-929766; 978-1-59354
Number of titles published annually: 12 Print
Distributed by Chronicle Books
Returns: Chronicle Books, c/o Genco Fullfillment, 1585 Linda Way, Door 1, Sparks, NV 89431

Hanging Loose Press
231 Wyckoff St, Brooklyn, NY 11217
SAN: 206-4960
Tel: 347-529-4738 *Fax:* 347-227-8215
E-mail: print225@aol.com
Web Site: www.hangingloosepress.com
Key Personnel
Ed & Intl Rts: Robert Hershon
Ed: Dick Lourie; Mark Pawlak
Founded: 1966
Poetry & short fiction.
ISBN Prefix(es): 978-0-914610; 978-1-882413; 978-1-931236
Number of titles published annually: 8 Print
Total Titles: 225 Print
Membership(s): Community of Literary Magazines & Presses

Hannacroix Creek Books Inc
1127 High Ridge Rd, No 110-B, Stamford, CT 06905-1203
SAN: 299-9560
Tel: 203-968-8098 *Fax:* 203-968-0193
E-mail: hannacroix@aol.com
Web Site: www.hannacroixcreekbooks.com
Key Personnel
CEO & Pres: Dr Jan Yager
Founded: 1996
Trade publisher of quality & innovative fiction & nonfiction books & journals that entertain, educate & inform.
ISBN Prefix(es): 978-1-889262
Number of titles published annually: 7 Print; 10 E-Book
Total Titles: 38 Print; 18 E-Book
Foreign Rep(s): International Editors' Co (Flavia Sala) (Brazil)
Foreign Rights: Guiliana Bernardi Literary Agent (Italy); DS Rights (Eastern Europe); Antonia Kerrigan Literary Agency (Spain); Eric Yang Agency (Korea)
Membership(s): AAP; The Independent Book Publishers Association; Women's Media Group

§Hanser Publications LLC
Subsidiary of Carl Hanser Verlag GmbH & Co KG
6915 Valley Ave, Cincinnati, OH 45244-3029
Tel: 513-527-8977 *Toll Free Tel:* 800-950-8977; 877-751-5052 (orders) *Fax:* 513-534-7803 *Toll Free Fax:* 800-527-8801
E-mail: info@hanserpublications.com
Web Site: www.hanserpublications.com
Key Personnel
Mktg Mgr: Valerie Lauer *E-mail:* valerie.lauer@hanserpublications.com
Founded: 1993
Technical & reference books & related products in manufacturing, metalworking & products finishing. Hanser Publishers: technical, engineering & science reference books, monographs, textbooks & journals in plastics technology, polymer & materials science.
ISBN Prefix(es): 978-1-56990
Number of titles published annually: 17 Print
Total Titles: 312 Print; 250 Online
Foreign Office(s): Carl Hanser Verlag, Kolbergerstr 22, 81679 Munich, Germany *Tel:* (089) 99 93 00 *Fax:* (089) 98 48 09
Distributor for Hanser Publishers (call Hanser Verlag)
Warehouse: Ware-Pak LLC, 2427 Bond St, University Park, IL 60484 *Tel:* 708-587-4124 *Fax:* 708-534-7803 *E-mail:* hanser@ware-pak.com
Distribution Center: Ware-Pak LLC, 2427 Bond St, University Park, IL 60484 *Tel:* 708-587-4124 *Fax:* 708-534-7803 *E-mail:* hanser@ware-pak.com

§Harcourt Achieve
Division of Houghton Mifflin Harcourt
6277 Sea Harbor Dr, Orlando, FL 32887
Tel: 407-345-2000 *Toll Free Tel:* 800-531-5015 (cust serv/orders) *Toll Free Fax:* 800-699-9459 (cust serv/orders)
Web Site: www.harcourtachieve.com
Key Personnel
CEO & Pres: Linda K Zecher
CFO & COO: Eric Shuman
COO, HMH Pub Co: Joel Zucker
EVP: William Bayers
Founded: 2001
Educational materials for PreK, elementary, secondary, test preparation, ESL & professional development for educators.
ISBN Prefix(es): 978-0-8172; 978-0-8114; 978-0-7312; 978-0-7327; 978-0-7901; 978-0-7578; 978-0-7635; 978-1-4189; 978-0-7398; 978-1-4190; 978-1-5574; 978-0-4350; 978-0-9473
Total Titles: 8,000 Print; 8,000 Online

§Harcourt Inc
Division of Houghton Mifflin Harcourt
6277 Sea Harbor Dr, Orlando, FL 32887
SAN: 200-2736
Tel: 407-345-2000 *Toll Free Tel:* 800-225-5425 (cust serv/orders) *Toll Free Fax:* 800-269-5232 (cust serv/orders)
Web Site: www.hmhco.com

Key Personnel
CEO & Pres: Linda K Zecher
CFO & COO: Eric Shuman
COO, HMH Pub Co: Joel Zucker
EVP: William Bayers
Founded: 1919
ISBN Prefix(es): 978-0-15
Total Titles: 8,000 Print; 8,000 Online
Imprints: Great Source; Harcourt Achieve; Rigby; Saxon; Steck Vaughn
Membership(s): AAP; BISG; The Children's Book Council; Software & Information Industry Association

Harcourt Inc, see Houghton Mifflin Harcourt

§Hard Shell Word Factory
Imprint of Mundania Press LLC
6457 Glenway Ave, No 109, Cincinnati, OH 45211
Toll Free Tel: 888-232-0808 *Toll Free Fax:* 888-460-4752
E-mail: inquiry@mundania.com
Web Site: www.mundania.com
Founded: 1998
Royalty publisher of fiction & nonfiction books, ebooks & trade paperback.
ISBN Prefix(es): 978-1-58200; 978-0-7599
Number of titles published annually: 100 Print; 200 E-Book
Total Titles: 2,000 Print; 4,000 E-Book
Imprints: HSWF
Membership(s): Electronically Published Internet Connection; The Independent Book Publishers Association

Harlequin Enterprises Ltd
Division of HarperCollins
233 Broadway, Suite 1001, New York, NY 10279
SAN: 200-2450
Tel: 212-553-4200 *Fax:* 212-227-8969
E-mail: CustomerService@harlequin.com
Web Site: www.harlequin.com
Key Personnel
Edit Dir: Margaret Marbury
Sr Exec Ed: Glenda Howard
Exec Ed, Love Inspired: Tina James
Sr Mng Ed: Kathleen Reed
Mng Edit Coord, NY/Toronto: Beth Attwood
Asst Mng Ed: Kristin Errico
Sr Ed: Gail Chasan; Patience Bloom; Ann Leslie Tuttle; Denise Zaza
Sr Ed, Carina Press: Kerri Buckley
Ed: Rebecca Hunt
Ed, Harlequin Teen: Annie Stone
Ed, MIRA Books: Liz Stein
Assoc Ed, HQN & LUNA: Kate Dresser
Asst Ed, Desire & Romantic Suspense: Allison Carroll
Asst Ed/Edit Asst, Harlequin Historical & Love Inspired Suspense: Dina Davis
Asst Ed, Love Inspired: Emily Krupin
Ed-at-Large: Leslie Wainger
Publicity Dir: Shara Alexander
Publicity Mgr, Fiction: Emer Flounders
Asst Publicity Mgr, Harlequin Teen: Jennifer Abbots
Assoc Publicist: Sarah Hermalyn; Lauren Jackson; Jessica Rosenberg
Founded: 1980
Adult contemporary, historical romance novels & women's fiction.
ISBN Prefix(es): 978-0-373
Number of titles published annually: 1,400 Print
Imprints: Carina Press; Harlequin; HQN Books; Kimani; Luna Books; MIRA Books; Red Dress Ink; Silhouette; Steeple Hill
Distributed by Simon & Schuster Mass Merchandise Sales Co
Distribution Center: 3010 Walden Ave, Depew, NY 14043
Membership(s): AAP; Association of Canadian Publishers; BISG

HarperCollins Children's Books
Division of HarperCollins Publishers
195 Broadway, New York, NY 10007
SAN: 200-2086
Tel: 212-207-7000
Web Site: www.harpercollins.com/childrens
Key Personnel
Pres & Publr: Suzanne Murphy
SVP, Assoc Publr & Ed-in-Chief: Kate Jackson *E-mail:* Kate.Jackson@HarperCollins.com
SVP, Children's Sales: Andrea Pappenheimer *E-mail:* Andrea.Pappenheimer@HarperCollins.com
VP, Children's Mktg: Diane Naughton *E-mail:* Diane.Naughton@HarperCollins.com
VP, Fin: Randy Rosema *E-mail:* Randy.Rosema@HarperCollins.com
VP, Prodn & Creative Opers: Tracey Menzies
Exec Art Dir: Alison Donalty; Amy Ryan
Edit Dir: Rosemary Brosnan; Nancy Inteli; Erica Sussman
Dir, Children's Inventory: Sheryl Moore-Anderson
Dir, Integrated Mktg: Lauren Flower; Nellie Kurtzman
Dir, Integrated Mktg, Ad & Promo: Cheryl Rozier
Dir, Intellectual Property Devt: Dan Ehrenhaft
Sr Exec Ed, Katherine Tegen Books: Claudia Gabel
Exec Ed: Alexandra Cooper; Kristen Pettit; Sara Sargent
Exec Ed, Balzer + Bray: Kristin Rens
Exec Ed, Katherine Tegen Books: Anica Rissi
Sr Ed: Karen Chaplin; Alyson Day; Sarah Landis; Abby Ranger
Sr Ed, HarperTeen: Emilia Rhodes
Sr Ed, Katherine Tegen Books: Melissa Miller
Ed: Jocelyn Davies; Andrew Harwell
Assoc Ed: Christopher Hernandez; Stephanie Stein
Assoc Ed, Katherine Tegen Books: Alex Arnold
Asst Ed: Alice Jerman
Sr Mgr, Integrated Mktg: Alana Whitman
Asst Mgr, Integrated Mktg Opers: Alison Noll
Sr Publicity Mgr: Rosanne Romanello
Publicity Mgr: Caroline Sun
Sr Publicist: Gina Rizzo
Assoc Publicist: Stephanie Hoover
Picture books, juvenile fiction & nonfiction, young adult novels.
ISBN Prefix(es): 978-0-06; 978-0-688; 978-0-380; 978-0-694; 978-0-690
Imprints: Amistad; Balzer + Bray; Greenwillow Books; HarperAudio; HarperCollins Children's Books; HarperCollins e-books; HarperFestival; HarperTeen; HarperTeen Impulse; Rayo; Katherine Tegen Books; TOKYOPOP; Walden Pond Press
Membership(s): The Children's Book Council

HarperCollins General Books Group
Division of HarperCollins Publishers
195 Broadway, New York, NY 10007
SAN: 200-2086
Tel: 212-207-7000
Web Site: www.harpercollins.com
Key Personnel
Chief Mktg Offr: Angela Tribelli
Pres & Publr: Michael Morrison
Pres & Publr, Ecco: Daniel Halpern
SVP & Publr, Dey Street Books & Deputy Publr, Morrow/Voyager/Avon: Lynn Grady
SVP & Publr, Elixir: Claudia Boutote
SVP & Publr, Harper: Jonathan Burnham
SVP & Publr, William Morrow/Eos/Avon/Harper Paperbacks: Liate Stehlik
SVP & Dir, Dom & Foreign Rts: Brenda Segel *E-mail:* Brenda.Segel@HarperCollins.com
SVP & Exec Ed, Harper Div & Edit Dir, Harper Perennial & Harper Paperbacks: Cal Morgan
SVP & Exec Ed, Harper Wave: Karen Rinaldi
SVP, Fin & Publg: Len Marshall *E-mail:* Len.Marshall@HarperCollins.com
SVP, Morrow/Avon: Carrie Feron
SVP, Publicity: Tina Andreadis
VP: Gideon Weil
VP & Publr, Harper Busn: Hollis Heimbouch
VP & Publr, Harper Design: Marta Schooler
VP & Assoc Publr, HarperOne: Laina Adler
VP & Edit Dir Nonfiction, William Morrow: Geoff Shandler
VP & Exec Ed: Jonathan Jao
VP & Exec Ed, William Morrow: Dan Mallory
VP & Assoc Publr, Ecco & Amistad: Craig Young
VP & Art Dir, William Morrow: Jeanne Reina
VP, Deputy Gen Coun: Beth Silfin
VP, Mktg: Carrie Bloxson; Leah Wasielewski
VP, Prodn & Creative Opers: Tracey Menzies
Publr, Amistad & Exec Ed, Ecco: Dawn Davis
Publr, HarperOne: Mark Tauber
Assoc Publr, Harper Perennial & Harper Paperbacks: Amy Baker
Assoc Publr, Dey Street Books: Kevin Callahan
Exec Dir, Digital Prod Devt: Adrianna Dufay
Sr Dir, Audience Devt & Insight: Jim Hanas
Sr Dir, Mktg Digital Prod Devt, Harper Wave & Harper Business: Brian Perrin
Sr Dir, Publicity & Brand Devt, Avon/Voyager: Pamela Spengler-Jaffee
Sr Publicity Dir, HarperOne: Melinda Mullin; Suzanne Wickham
Sr Mktg Dir, William Morrow: Tavia Kowalchuk
Edit Dir, Amistad: Tracy Sherrod
Edit Dir, Broadside Books: Adam Bellow
Edit Dir, Dey Street Books: Carrie Thornton
Edit Dir, Ecco: Megan Lynch
Edit Dir, William Morrow/Avon: Erika Tsang
Dir, Prodn Edit, Harper, Harper Business & Collins Reference: John Jusino
Dir, Brand Devt, William Morrow: Kathryn Gordon
Dir, Fulfillment Opers: Joe Macavage
Dir, Publicity: Brianne Halverson
Publg Opers Dir, Willian Morrow & Ecco: Catherine Felgar
Publicity Dir: Kelly Rudolph
Publicity Dir, Ecco: Sonya Cheuse
Publicity Dir, Harper One: Darcy Cohan
Publicity Dir, Harper 360: Victoria Commella
Publicity Dir, William Morrow & Avon: Shelby Meizlik
Mktg Dir, William Morrow: Molly Birckhead; Kaitlin Harri
Assoc Dir, Mktg: Brianne Halverson; Katie O'Callaghan
Assoc Dir, Mktg, Dey Street Books & Harper Design: Michael Barrs
Assoc Dir, Online Mktg: Blaise Base
Assoc Dir, Publicity, Harper One: Julie Burton
Assoc Dir, Publicity, Dey Street Books: Heidi Metcalfe
Assoc Dir, Publicity, Morrow/Avon: Danielle Bartlett
Sr Publicity Mgr, Ecco: Ashley Garland
Sr Mktg Mgr: Penny Makras; Stephanie Selah
Sr Mktg Mgr, Dey Street Books: Kendra Newton
Sr Mgr, Digital Mktg: Dana Trombley
Exec Ed: Julie Will
Exec Ed, Creative Devt: Matt Harper
Exec Ed, Ecco: Hilary Redmon; Zack Wagman
Exec Ed, Dey Street Books: Mark Chait; Julia Cheiffetz
Exec Ed, HarperOne: Luke Dempsey; Roger Freet; Julia Pastore
Exec Ed, William Morrow: Deborah Brody; Peter Hubbard; Rachel Kahan; Adam Korn; Katherine Nintzel
Exec Ed, William Morrow/Avon: May Chen
Exec Ed, William Morrow/Harper Voyager: David Pomerico
Sr Ed: Amy Bendell; Denise Oswald; Maya Ziv
Sr Ed, Dey Street Books: Rob Kirkpatrick
Sr Ed, Harper Design: Rebecca Hunt
Sr Ed, Harper Elixir: Libby Edelson
Sr Ed, HarperOne: Genoveva Llosa; Jeanette Perez

Sr Ed, William Morrow: Cara Bedick
Sr Ed, William Morrow/Avon: Tessa Woodward
Ed, Harper Wave: Sarah Murphy
Ed, William Morrow: Jessica Williams
Ed, William Morrow/Avon: Amanda Bergeron; Emily Krump
Asst Ed: Jillian Verrillo
ISBN Prefix(es): 978-0-06
Imprints: Amistad; Avon; Avon Impulse (digital only); Avon Inspire; Avon Red; Bourbon Street Books; Broadside Books; Dey Street Books; Ecco; Harper; Harper Business; Harper Design; Harper Elixir; Harper Paperbacks; Harper Perennial; Harper Voyager; Harper Wave; HarperAudio; HarperBibles; HarperCollins; HarperCollins e-Books; HarperCollins 360; HarperLuxe (large print); HarperOne; Infinitum Nihil; Dennis Lehane Books; William Morrow; William Morrow Cookbooks; William Morrow Paperbacks; Newmarket Press for It Books; Witness Impulse

§HarperCollins Publishers
Subsidiary of News Corporation
195 Broadway, New York, NY 10007
SAN: 200-2086
Tel: 212-207-7000 *Fax:* 212-207-7145
Web Site: www.harpercollins.com
Key Personnel
CEO: Brian Murray *E-mail:* Brian.Murray@HarperCollins.com
CFO: Janet Gervasio *E-mail:* Janet.Gervasio@HarperCollins.com
Chief Digital Offr & EVP, Intl: Chantal Restivo-Alessi
CIO: Rick Schwartz *E-mail:* Rick.Schwartz@HarperCollins.com
SVP & Gen Coun: Chris Goff
SVP, Dist Opers: Joe Franceschelli
SVP, Fin & Strategic New Busn Devt: Rob Zaffiris
SVP, HR: Diane Bailey
SVP, Mkt Insight & Sales Opers: Frank Albanese
EVP, Opers & Technol: Larry Nevins
VP, Global Insight: Catherine Makk
VP, Corp Communs: Erin Crum
VP, Assoc Gen Coun: Kyran Cassidy
VP & Dir, Foreign Rts: Juliette Shapland
VP, Prodn & Creative Opers: Tracey Menzies
Affiliate Publr, HarperCollins 360: Jean Marie Kelly
Pres, Sales: Josh Marwell *E-mail:* Josh.Marwell@HarperCollins.com
Sr Dir, Audience Devt & Insight: Jim Hanas
Sr Dir, Intl Sales & Mktg: Samantha Hagerbaumer
Dir, Publicity: Kate D'Esmond; Rachel Elinsky
Assoc Dir, Mktg: Stephanie Cooper
Sr Mgr, Consumer Insight: Allison Jarvela
Asst Mgr, Corp Communs: Katie Levine
Sr Pricing Analyst: Ruchir Pandya
Founded: 1817
HarperCollins is one of the leading English-language publishers in the world & is a subsidiary of News Corp (NYSE: NWS, NWS.A; ASX: NCP, NCPDP). Headquartered in New York, the company has publishing groups in the US, Canada, Australasia & the UK. Its publishing groups (US) include the HarperCollins General Books Group, HarperCollins Children's Books Group, Zondervan; outside the US: HarperCollins Australia, HarperCollins Canada, HarperCollins India, HarperCollins New Zealand & HarperCollins UK.
ISBN Prefix(es): 978-0-06; 978-0-688; 978-0-380; 978-0-694
Number of titles published annually: 1,700 Print
Imprints: Beech Tree Books; Dey Street Books; Greenwillow Books; HarperCollins; Hearst Books; Lothrop, Lee & Shepard Books; Morrow Junior Books; Mulberry Books; Quill Trade Paperbacks
Distributed by Cynthia Publishing Co; Ingram Publisher Services/Spring Arbor (Christian market)
Distributor for Perseus (Addison Wesley Trade); Basic Books; Civitas; Counterpoint; Delphinium Books; GT Publishing; Public Affairs; TV Books
Foreign Rep(s): Publishers International Marketing Services
Foreign Rights: Kezban Akcali Agency (Turkey); Antonella Antonelli Agenzia (Italy); Bardon Far Eastern Agents (China, Taiwan); Eliane Benisti Literary Agency (France); Mercedes Casanovas (Spain); Lynn Franklin (Russia); June Hall Literary Agency; Kooy & Van Gerderen Agency (Netherlands); Licht & Licht Agency (Denmark, Finland, Norway, Sweden); Rogan Pikarski Literary Agency (Israel); Gerd Plessl Agency (Czech Republic, Greece, Hungary, Montenegro, Poland, Serbia); Tuttle-Mori Agency Inc (Japan)
Advertising Agency: Franklin Spier Inc
Membership(s): AAP; BISG
See separate listing for:
HarperCollins Children's Books
HarperCollins General Books Group

HarperCollins Publishers Sales
195 Broadway, New York, NY 10007
SAN: 200-2086
Fax: 212-207-7000
Web Site: www.harpercollins.com
Key Personnel
Pres, Sales: Josh Marwell *E-mail:* Josh.Marwell@HarperCollins.com
SVP, Children's Sales: Andrea Pappenheimer *E-mail:* Andrea.Pappenheimer@HarperCollins.com
SVP, Group Sales Dir, Gen Books: Doug Jones
SVP, Mkt Insight & Sales Opers: Frank Albanese
VP & Deputy Dir, Sales: Mary Beth Thomas
VP & Deputy Dir, Sales, Children's: Kerry Moynagh
Dir, Sales & Retail Mktg: Kristine Macrides
Natl Acct Mgr: Rachel Levenberg
Sr Mgr, Proprietary & Display Mktg Sales: Christina Tomasulo
Mgr, Sales Opers: Eric Lovaas
Asst Mgr, Sales & Retail Mktg: Lillie Walsh
Founded: 1817
Group members include: HarperCollins Trade, HarperPerennial, HarperCollins Children's Books, HarperPaperbacks, HarperPrism, HarperHorizon, HarperSanFrancisco; Harper Reference & HarperBusiness.
Imprints: Access; Amistad; Avon Books; Cademon; Ecco; Eos; Fourth Estate; HarperAudio; HarperBusiness; HarperCollins; HarperDesign; HarperEntertainment; HarperLarge Print; HarperResource; HarperSanFrancisco; HarperTorch; William Morrow; William Morrow Cookbooks; Perennial; Perennial Currents; Perennial Dark Alley; PerfectBound; Rayo; Regan Books

Harper's Magazine Foundation
666 Broadway, 11th fl, New York, NY 10012
Tel: 212-420-5720 *Toll Free Tel:* 800-444-4653 *Fax:* 212-228-5889
E-mail: harpers@harpers.org
Web Site: www.harpers.org
Key Personnel
VP & Gen Mgr: Lynn Carlson *E-mail:* lynn@harpers.org
Exec Ed: James Marcus
Ed-in-Chief: Ellen Rosenbush
Founded: 1850
General trade.
ISBN Prefix(es): 978-1-879957
Number of titles published annually: 12 Print
Total Titles: 40 Print

§Harrison House Publishers
7498 E 46 Place, Tulsa, OK 74145
SAN: 208-676X
Mailing Address: PO Box 35035, Tulsa, OK 74153-1035
Tel: 918-523-5700 *Toll Free Tel:* 800-888-4126 *Toll Free Fax:* 800-830-5688
Web Site: www.harrisonhouse.com
Founded: 1975
Charismatic/Christian publishing house.
ISBN Prefix(es): 978-1-57794; 978-0-89274
Number of titles published annually: 50 Print
Total Titles: 400 Online

Hartman Publishing Inc
1313 Iron Ave SW, Albuquerque, NM 87102
Tel: 505-291-1274 *Toll Free Tel:* 800-999-9534 *Fax:* 505-291-1284 *Toll Free Fax:* 800-474-6106
E-mail: orders@hartmanonline.com; help@hartmanonline.com
Web Site: www.hartmanonline.com
Key Personnel
Publr: Mark Hartman
Mng Ed: Susan Alvare Hedman
Founded: 1994
Publish a variety of in-service training materials & textbooks for certified nursing assistants & home health aides. Subjects include Alzheimer's disease, infection control, body mechanics, abuse & neglect, AIDS/HIV & communication skills.
ISBN Prefix(es): 978-1-888343
Number of titles published annually: 12 Print; 1 CD-ROM; 1 Audio
Total Titles: 40 Print; 1 CD-ROM; 1 Audio
Membership(s): New Mexico Book Association

Harvard Art Museums
32 Quincy St, Cambridge, MA 02138
Tel: 617-495-1440; 617-496-6529 (edit) *Fax:* 617-495-9985
E-mail: am_shop@harvard.edu
Web Site: www.harvardartmuseums.org
Key Personnel
Dir, Communs: Daron Manoogian
Founded: 1901
Art history.
ISBN Prefix(es): 978-0-916724; 978-1-891771
Number of titles published annually: 5 Print
Total Titles: 70 Print
Distributed by Yale University Press

Harvard Business Review Press
Division of Harvard Business Publishing
300 N Beacon St, Watertown, MA 02472
SAN: 202-277X
Tel: 617-783-7400 *Fax:* 617-783-7489
E-mail: custserv@hbsp.harvard.edu
Web Site: www.harvardbusiness.org
Key Personnel
Publr: Sarah McConville
Assoc Publr: Keith Pfeffer
Ed-in-Chief: Adi Ignatius
Publicity Mgr: Julie De Voll
Assoc Ed: Ania Wieckowski
Founded: 1984
Trade & professional books for the business management & academic audiences in the areas of strategy, leadership, innovation, organizational behavior/human resource management, finance management, marketing, production & operations management. *Harvard Business Review*, reference books & Internet.
ISBN Prefix(es): 978-0-87584; 978-1-57851; 978-1-4221; 978-1-59139
Number of titles published annually: 70 Print
Total Titles: 700 Print
Imprints: Harvard Business Reference
Distributed by Client Distribution Services

Foreign Rep(s): McGraw-Hill Education (Africa, Asia, Australia, Canada, Europe, Middle East, New Zealand); United Publishers Services Ltd (Japan)

The Harvard Common Press
535 Albany St, Boston, MA 02118
SAN: 208-6778
Tel: 617-423-5803 *Toll Free Tel:* 888-657-3755 *Fax:* 617-695-9794
E-mail: orders@harvardcommonpress.com; info@harvardcommonpress.com
Web Site: www.harvardcommonpress.com
Key Personnel
Pres & Publr: Bruce P Shaw
Assoc Publr: Adam Salome
Founded: 1976
General nonfiction: cookbooks, small business guides, travel guides, child care & parenting.
ISBN Prefix(es): 978-0-916782; 978-0-87645; 978-1-55832
Number of titles published annually: 10 Print
Total Titles: 150 Print
Imprints: Gambit Books
Distributed by Houghton Mifflin Harcourt
Foreign Rep(s): Gazelle; Southern Publishing Group
Foreign Rights: Dan Bial

Harvard Education Publishing Group
Division of Harvard Graduate School of Education
8 Story St, 1st fl, Cambridge, MA 02138
Tel: 617-495-3432 *Toll Free Tel:* 800-513-0763 (subns); 888-437-1437 (orders) *Fax:* 617-496-3584; 978-348-1233 (orders)
E-mail: hepg@harvard.edu
Web Site: www.hepg.org
Key Personnel
Dir: Douglas Clayton *E-mail:* douglas_clayton@gse.harvard.edu
Asst Dir & Ed-in-Chief: Caroline Chauncey *E-mail:* caroline_chauncey@gse.harvard.edu
Publisher of books & journals on education practice, research & policy.
ISBN Prefix(es): 978-1-891792; 978-1-883433; 978-0-916690
Number of titles published annually: 16 Print
Total Titles: 90 Print
Imprints: Harvard Education Letter; Harvard Education Press; Harvard Educational Review Reprint Series

Harvard Square Editions
2152 Beachwood Terr, Hollywood, CA 90068
Tel: 323-469-8932 *Fax:* 323-469-8932
Web Site: harvardsquareeditions.org
Key Personnel
Ed-in-Chief: David Landau
Outreach Dir: Simone Weingarten *E-mail:* sw@harvardsquareeditions.org
Founded: 2000
Publishing house run by Harvard alumni. Specialize in ecologically & socially conscious fiction.
ISBN Prefix(es): 978-0-9833216; 978-0-9895960; 978-1-941861
Number of titles published annually: 12 Print; 14 E-Book
Total Titles: 34 Print; 36 E-Book

Harvard Ukrainian Research Institute
Subsidiary of Harvard University
34 Kirkland St, Cambridge, MA 02138
SAN: 208-967X
Tel: 617-495-4053 *Fax:* 617-495-8097
E-mail: huri@fas.harvard.edu
Web Site: www.huri.harvard.edu
Key Personnel
Mgr, Pubns: Marika Whaley *E-mail:* mwhaley@fas.harvard.edu
Founded: 1973
ISBN Prefix(es): 978-0-916458; 978-1-932650
Number of titles published annually: 5 Print; 3 Online
Total Titles: 100 Print; 6 Online
Distributed by Harvard University Press

Harvard University Press
79 Garden St, Cambridge, MA 02138-1499
SAN: 200-2043
Tel: 617-495-2600; 401-531-2800 (intl orders) *Toll Free Tel:* 800-405-1619 (orders) *Fax:* 617-495-5898 (general); 617-496-4677 (edit & rts); 401-531-2801 (intl orders) *Toll Free Fax:* 800-406-9145 (orders)
E-mail: contact_hup@harvard.edu
Web Site: www.hup.harvard.edu
Key Personnel
CFO: Dan Wackrow *E-mail:* dan_wackrow@harvard.edu
Dir: William P Sisler *E-mail:* william_sisler@harvard.edu
Dir, Design & Prodn: Tim Jones *E-mail:* tim_jones@harvard.edu
Dir, Intellectual Property & Subs Rts: Stephanie Vyce *E-mail:* stephanie_vyce@harvard.edu
Promo & Ad Dir: Sheila Barrett *E-mail:* sheila_barrett@harvard.edu
Asst Dir, Sales & Mktg: Susan Donnelly *E-mail:* susan_donnelly@harvard.edu
Publicity Mgr: Phoebe Kosman *E-mail:* phoebe_kosman@harvard.edu
Sales Mgr & Digital Content Mgr: Vanessa Vinarub *E-mail:* vanessa_vinarub@harvard.edu
Ed-in-Chief: Susan Boehmer *E-mail:* susan_boehmer@harvard.edu
Sr Exec Ed, History & Contemporary Aff: Joyce Seltzer *E-mail:* joyce_seltzer@harvard.edu
Exec Ed, Humanities: Lindsay Waters *E-mail:* lindsay_waters@harvard.edu
Exec Ed, Life Sci: Janice Audet
Exec Ed, Soc Sci: Michael A Aronson *E-mail:* michael_aronson@harvard.edu
Exec Ed-at-Large: Thomas LeBien *E-mail:* thomas_lebien@harvard.edu; Sharmila Sen *E-mail:* sharmila_sen@harvard.edu
Exec Ed-at-Large, History: Kathleen McDermott *E-mail:* kathleen_mcdermott@harvard.edu
Mng Ed: Mary Ann Lane *E-mail:* mary_lane@harvard.edu
Ed, Human Behavior, Educ & the Humanities: Andrew Kinney *E-mail:* andrew_kinney@harvard.edu
Founded: 1913
General scholarly, medical, scientific.
ISBN Prefix(es): 978-0-674
Number of titles published annually: 200 Print
Total Titles: 8,000 Print
Imprints: Belknap Press
Foreign Office(s): Vernon House, 23 Sicilian Ave, London WC1A 2QS, United Kingdom *Tel:* (020) 3463 2350 *Fax:* (020) 7831 9261 *E-mail:* info@harvardup.co.uk
Distributor for Harvard Center for Middle Eastern Studies; Harvard Center for Population Studies; Harvard Center for the Study of World Religions; Harvard College Library (including Houghton Library Judaica division); Harvard Department of Sanskrit & Indian Studies; Harvard Department of the Classics; Harvard Ukrainian Research Institute; Harvard University Asia Center; Harvard University David Rockefeller Center for Latin American Studies; Harvard-Yenching Institute; Peabody Museum of Archaeology & Ethnology
Foreign Rep(s): Academic Book Promotions (Benelux); Aromix Books (Hong Kong); Avicenna Ltd (Bill Kennedy) (Bahrain, Egypt, Iran, Iraq, Kuwait, Lebanon, Libya, Oman, Qatar, Saudi Arabia, Sudan, Syria, United Arab Emirates, Yemen); Avicenna Ltd (Claire de Gruchy) (Algeria, Cyprus, Jordan, Malta, Morocco, Palestine, Tunisia, Turkey); Amos Bampisaki (Burundi, Rwanda, Sudan, Tanzania, Uganda); John Eklund (Canada exc British Columbia, Midwestern States); Everest International Publishing Services (Wei Zhao) (China); Harvard Business Review Press (Bangladesh, Bhutan, India, Maldives, Nepal, Pakistan, Sri Lanka); Harvard University Press London (Greece, Ireland, Israel, UK); Havilah Procurement & Library Services (Ghana, Nigeria); IMA (Tony Moggach) (Cameroon, Ethiopia, The Gambia, Ghana, Kenya, Malawi, Mauritius, Nigeria, Rwanda, Tanzania, Uganda, Zambia); InBooks/James Bennett Pty Ltd (Australia, New Zealand); Information & Culture, Korea (South Korea); Ewa Ledochiwicz (Albania, Bosnia and Herzegovina, Croatia, Czech Republic, Estonia, Hungary, Kazakhstan, Latvia, Lithuania, Poland, Romania, Russia, Serbia, Slovakia, Slovenia); Uwe Ludemann (Austria, France, Germany, Italy, Portugal, Spain, Switzerland); Patricia Nelson (British Columbia, CN, Southwest, Western USA); B K Norton (Taiwan); Palgrave (Cory Voigt) (Southern Africa); Rockbook Inc (Japan); Joan Wamae (Kenya); Yuha Associates (Malaysia); Zimpfer Global Services (Caribbean, Central America)
Foreign Rights: Akcali Agency (Turkey); L'Autre Agence (France); Bardon-Chinese Media Agency (China, Hong Kong, Taiwan); Bookman Literary Agency (Denmark, Finland, Iceland, Norway, Sweden); Dar Cherlin (Arab Middle East); The English Agency (Japan); Graal Literary Agency (Bulgaria, Macedonia, Poland, Romania, Serbia, Slovakia); The Deborah Harris Agency (Israel); International Editors' Co (Central America, Latin America, South America, Spain); Alexander Korzhenevski Agency (Russia); Liepman Agency AG (Germany, Switzerland); Ilidio Matos Agencia (Portugal); OA Literary Agency (Greece); Oxford Literary & Rights Agency (Croatia, Czech Republic, Ukraine); Seibel Publishing Services (Brazil); Suzanna Zevi Agenzia Letteraria (Italy)
Shipping Address: Triliteral LLC, 100 Maple Ridge Dr, Cumberland, RI 02864-1769
Membership(s): AAP; American Association of University Presses; BISG

Harvest Hill Press
PO Box 55, Salisbury Cove, ME 04672-0055
Tel: 207-288-8900
E-mail: shop@harvesthillpress.com
Web Site: www.harvesthillpress.com
Founded: 1994
Cookbooks & printed kitchen stationery for gift, children's & book markets.
ISBN Prefix(es): 978-1-886862
Number of titles published annually: 3 Print
Total Titles: 40 Print
Imprints: Coastal New England Publications
Distributed by University Press of New England
Membership(s): The Independent Book Publishers Association

Harvest House Publishers Inc
990 Owen Loop N, Eugene, OR 97402-9173
SAN: 207-4745
Tel: 541-343-0123 *Toll Free Tel:* 888-501-6991 *Fax:* 541-342-6410
E-mail: admin@harvesthousepublishers.com
Web Site: harvesthousepublishers.com
Key Personnel
Pres: Bob Hawkins, Jr
Sr Ed & Ms Coord: Nick Harrison
Intl Rts: Sharon Shook
Founded: 1974
Evangelical Christian books; no unsol mss.
ISBN Prefix(es): 978-0-89081; 978-1-56507; 978-0-7369
Number of titles published annually: 160 Print; 6 Audio
Total Titles: 1,100 Print; 6 Audio
Membership(s): BISG

§Hatherleigh Press Ltd
62545 State Hwy 10, Hobart, NY 13788
E-mail: info@hatherleighpress.com; publicity@hatherleighpress.com
Web Site: www.hatherleighpress.com
Key Personnel
CEO & Pres: Andrew Flach
Assoc Publr: Ryan Tumambing
Mng Ed: Anna Krusinski
Founded: 1995
Motto: "Improve your life. Change your world." Dedicated to publishing reliable & authoritative content in healthy living & sustainability. Formats include print books, ebook, audio & filmed entertainment.
ISBN Prefix(es): 978-1-886330; 978-1-57826
Number of titles published annually: 30 Print; 30 E-Book
Total Titles: 300 Print; 100 E-Book; 4 Audio
Imprints: GetFitNow.com Books; Healthy Living Books
Distribution Center: Random House Distribution Services *Toll Free Tel:* 800-733-3000; 888-523-9292 (CN sales) *Toll Free Fax:* 800-659-2436; 888-562-9924 (CN sales) *E-mail:* csorders@randomhouse.com

§Hay House Inc
2776 Loker Ave W, Carlsbad, CA 92010
SAN: 630-477X
Mailing Address: PO Box 5100, Carlsbad, CA 92018-5100
Tel: 760-431-7695 (ext 2, intl) *Toll Free Tel:* 800-654-5126 (ext 2, US) *Toll Free Fax:* 800-650-5115
E-mail: info@hayhouse.com; editorial@hayhouse.com
Web Site: www.hayhouse.com
Key Personnel
Founder & Chmn: Louise L Hay
CEO & Pres: Reid Tracy
COO: Margarete Nielsen
Founded: 1984
Self-help/New Age, health, philosophy, spiritual growth & awareness, mental & environmental harmony books; also self-healing; biography, producers & distributors of recordings & video pertaining to health of mind, body & spirit. Accept agented submissions only; SASE required.
ISBN Prefix(es): 978-0-937611; 978-1-56170; 978-1-4019
Number of titles published annually: 50 Print; 50 Audio
Total Titles: 300 Print; 350 Audio
Imprints: New Beginnings Press; Smiley Books
Divisions: Balboa Press
Branch Office(s)
250 Park Ave S, Suite 201, New York, NY 10003 *Tel:* 646-484-4950 *Fax:* 646-484-4956
Foreign Office(s): Hayhouse Australia Pty Ltd, 18/36 Ralph St, Alexandria, NSW 2015, Australia *Tel:* (02) 9669 4299 *Fax:* (02) 9669 4144 *Web Site:* www.hayhouse.com.au
Hayhouse Publishers India, Muskaan Complex, Plot No 3, B-2, Vasant Kunj, New Delhi 110070, India *Tel:* (011) 4176 1620 *Fax:* (011) 4176 1630 *Web Site:* www.hayhouse.co.in
Hayhouse SA Pty Ltd, PO Box 990, Witkoppen 2068, South Africa *Web Site:* www.hayhouse.co.za
Hayhouse UK Ltd, 292-B Kensal Rd, London W10 5BE, United Kingdom *Tel:* (020) 8962 1230 *Fax:* (020) 8962 1239 *Web Site:* www.hayhouse.co.uk
Returns: 2750 Progress St, Vista, CA 92081 *Toll Free Tel:* 800-654-5126
Warehouse: 2750 Progress St, Suite B, Vista, CA 92081 *Fax:* 760-431-6948
Distribution Center: Dempsey-Your Distributor Inc, 305-3815 First Ave, Burnaby, BC V5C 3V6, Canada *Toll Free Tel:* 800-667-3399 *E-mail:* orders@dempseycanada.com
Raincoast Books, 2440 Viking Way, Richmond, BC V6V 1N2, Canada *Toll Free Tel:* 800-663-5714 *Toll Free Fax:* 800-565-3770 *E-mail:* customerservice@raincoast.com

Haynes Manuals Inc
Division of The Haynes Publishing Group
861 Lawrence Dr, Newbury Park, CA 91320
Tel: 805-498-6703 *Toll Free Tel:* 800-4-HAYNES (442-9637) *Fax:* 805-498-2867
E-mail: cstn@haynes.com
Web Site: www.haynes.com
Key Personnel
Chmn: J Haynes
Pres: Eric Oakley
Mktg Dir: George Brueggeman
Founded: 1960
Publisher & importer of books on domestic & foreign autos & motorcycles & historical & technical motoring.
ISBN Prefix(es): 978-0-946609; 978-1-56392
Number of titles published annually: 13 Print
Total Titles: 690 Print
Distributed by Motorbooks International
Distributor for G T Foulis; Haynes Owners Workshop Manuals; Oxford Illustrated Press
Warehouse: Eastern Warehouse, 1299 Bridgestone Pkwy, La Vergne, TN 37086 *Fax:* 615-793-5325

§Hazelden Publishing
Division of Hazelden Foundation
15251 Pleasant Valley Rd, Center City, MN 55012-0011
SAN: 125-1953
Mailing Address: PO Box 176, Center City, MN 55012-0176
Tel: 651-213-4200 *Toll Free Tel:* 800-257-7810 *Fax:* 651-213-4590
E-mail: info@hazelden.org
Web Site: www.hazelden.org
Key Personnel
SVP & COO, Publg: Joel Jaksah
Exec Dir: Kristine Van Hoof-Haines
Founded: 1954
Adult trade hardcover & paperbacks; curriculum, workbooks, giftbooks, video & audio; self-help, addiction & recovery, personal & spiritual growth; computer based products, wellness products, young adult nonfiction.
ISBN Prefix(es): 978-0-89486; 978-1-56838; 978-0-89638; 978-0-942421; 978-0-935908; 978-1-56246; 978-0-934125
Number of titles published annually: 12 Print
Total Titles: 500 Print; 500 E-Book; 10 Audio
Imprints: Hazelden/Johnson Institute; Hazelden/Keep Coming Back; Hazelden-Pittman Archives Press
Distributed by Health Communications Inc (trade)
Distributor for Obsessive Anonymous
Foreign Rep(s): Eurospan (Europe, Ireland, UK); RecoverOz (Australia, New Zealand)

§HCPro Inc
75 Sylvan St, Suite A-101, Danvers, MA 01923
Toll Free Tel: 800-650-6787 *Toll Free Fax:* 800-785-9212
E-mail: customerservice@hcpro.com
Web Site: www.hcpro.com
Founded: 1986
Specialize in healthcare administration & management.
ISBN Prefix(es): 978-1-885829
Number of titles published annually: 110 Print; 4 CD-ROM; 30 Online; 5 E-Book; 60 Audio
Total Titles: 125 Print; 5 CD-ROM; 40 Online; 25 E-Book; 75 Audio
Imprints: Opus Communications
Subsidiaries: The Greeley Co
Orders to: 100 Hoods Lane, Marblehead, MA 01945
Warehouse: 100 Hoods Lane, Marblehead, MA 01945
Distribution Center: 100 Hoods Lane, Marblehead, MA 01945
Membership(s): NEPA

Health Administration Press
Division of Foundation of the American College of Healthcare Executives
One N Franklin St, Suite 1700, Chicago, IL 60606-3491
SAN: 207-0464
Tel: 312-424-2800 *Fax:* 312-424-0014
E-mail: hap1@ache.org
Web Site: www.ache.org/publications (orders)
Key Personnel
Pres: Deborah J Bowen
SVP: Maureen Glass *Tel:* 312-424-9450 *E-mail:* mglass@ache.org
Assoc Dir & Mktg Mgr: Michael Cunningham *Tel:* 312-424-9470 *E-mail:* mcunningham@ache.org
Acqs Ed: Janet Davis *Tel:* 312-424-9460 *E-mail:* jdavis@ache.org
Founded: 1972
Health administration, health care, law & medicine, medical care organization.
ISBN Prefix(es): 978-0-910701; 978-1-56793
Number of titles published annually: 20 Print
Total Titles: 200 Print; 1 E-Book
Imprints: American College of Healthcare Executives Management Series; AUPHA Press/Health Administration Press; Executive Essentials; Gateway to Healthcare Management
Branch Office(s)
PO Box 75145, Baltimore, MD 21275, Contact: Melissa Lawson *Tel:* 301-362-6905 *Fax:* 301-206-9789
Foreign Rep(s): ELEA doo (Europe); iGroup (Asia); Login Bros (Canada)
Billing Address: 9050 Junction Dr, Annapolis Junction, MD 20701
Orders to: 9050 Junction Dr, Annapolis Junction, MD 20701 *Tel:* 301-362-6905 *Fax:* 240-396-5907 *E-mail:* hap@brightkey.net
Returns: 9050 Junction Dr, Annapolis Junction, MD 20701
Shipping Address: 9050 Junction Dr, Annapolis Junction, MD 20701 *Tel:* 301-362-6905 *E-mail:* hap@brightkey.net
Warehouse: 9050 Junction Dr, Annapolis Junction, MD 20701, Contact: Melissa Lawson *Tel:* 301-362-6905 *Fax:* 301-206-9789
Distribution Center: 9050 Junction Dr, Annapolis Junction, MD 20701

§Health Communications Inc
3201 SW 15 St, Deerfield Beach, FL 33442
SAN: 212-100X
Tel: 954-360-0909 *Toll Free Tel:* 800-851-9100; 800-441-5569 (cust serv & orders) *Fax:* 954-360-0034 *Toll Free Fax:* 800-424-7652 (cust serv & orders)
Web Site: www.hcibooks.com
Key Personnel
Pres & Publr: Peter Vegso
EVP: Christian Blonshine
Art Dir: Larissa Henoch
Edit Dir: Allison Janse Collins; Candace Johnson
Sales & Mktg Dir: Kelly Maragni
Publicity & Media Contact: Kim Weiss *E-mail:* kim.weiss@hcibooks.com
Foreign Rts & Dist: Lori Golden *E-mail:* lori.golden@hcibooks.com
Foreign Rts Agent: Luc Jutras
Founded: 1977
Publisher of nonfiction paperbacks & hardcover books on self-help, personal growth, diet, fitness, inspiration, health, parenting, women's issues, teens, religion, psychology, addiction & recovery.
ISBN Prefix(es): 978-0-932194; 978-1-55874; 978-0-7573

Number of titles published annually: 50 Print; 50 E-Book
Total Titles: 500 Print; 500 E-Book; 18 Audio
Imprints: HCI Books; HCI Teens
Divisions: HCI Printing & Publishing
See separate listing for:
Simcha Press

§Health Forum Inc
Subsidiary of American Hospital Association
155 N Wacker Dr, Suite 400, Chicago, IL 60606
SAN: 216-5872
Tel: 312-893-6800 *Toll Free Tel:* 800-242-2626 *Fax:* 312-422-4500
E-mail: hfcustsvc@healthforum.com
Web Site: www.ahaonlinestore.com; www.healthforum.com
Key Personnel
Dir, Mktg: Peggy Scanlan *E-mail:* pscanlan@healthforum.com
Ed, Books: Rick Hill *Tel:* 312-893-6863 *E-mail:* rhill@healthforum.com
Founded: 1936
Publisher of professional books & textbooks for health care professionals. Specialize in books that help hospital executives & department heads manage their business better & achieve improved patient satisfaction. Also provide ICD-10-CM/PCS & data information from the AHA Central Office & the American Hospital Association annual survey of hospitals.
ISBN Prefix(es): 978-1-55648; 978-0-87258
Number of titles published annually: 10 Print; 2 CD-ROM; 2 E-Book
Total Titles: 30 Print; 2 CD-ROM; 3 E-Book
Imprints: AHA (American Hospital Association); AHA Press
Billing Address: AHA Services Inc, Contact: Francine Adcock *Tel:* 312-422-3238 *Fax:* 312-422-4597 *E-mail:* fadcock@aha.org
Orders to: AHA Services Inc, PO Box 933283, Atlanta, GA 31193-3283 *Toll Free Fax:* 866-516-5817 *E-mail:* aha-orders@pbd.com
Returns: AHA Services Inc, Cust Returns, 3280 Summit Ridge Pkwy, Duluth, GA 30096
Warehouse: AHA Services Inc, 3280 Summit Ridge Pkwy, Duluth, GA 30096 (AHA order servs) *Toll Free Fax:* 866-516-5817 *E-mail:* aha-orders@pbd.com
Distribution Center: Rittenhouse Book Distributors, 511 Feheley Dr, King of Prussia, PA 19406, Contact: Nicole Gallo *Toll Free Tel:* 800-345-6425 *Fax:* 610-277-0390 *E-mail:* n.gallo@rittenhouse.com *Web Site:* www.rittenhouse.com
Majors Education Solutions, 500 E Corporate Dr, Suite 600, Lewisville, TX 75057, Contact: Martha Yeahquo *Tel:* 972-353-1100 *Toll Free Tel:* 800-633-1851 *Fax:* 972-353-1300 *E-mail:* customerservice@majors.com *Web Site:* www.majors.com
Membership(s): American Hospital Association; The Independent Book Publishers Association
See separate listing for:
AHA Press

§Health Professions Press
Division of Paul H Brookes Publishing Co Inc
409 Washington Ave, Suite 500, Towson, MD 21204
SAN: 297-7338
Mailing Address: PO Box 10624, Baltimore, MD 21285-0624
Tel: 410-337-9585 *Toll Free Tel:* 888-337-8808 *Fax:* 410-337-8539
E-mail: custserv@healthpropress.com
Web Site: www.healthpropress.com
Key Personnel
Pres: Melissa A Behm
Dir, Pubns: Mary H Magnus *E-mail:* mmagnus@healthpropress.com
Mktg Coord: Kaitlin Konecke
Founded: 1989
Hardcover, paperback & digital professional resources & textbooks in aging, Alzheimer's disease, long-term care & health administration.
ISBN Prefix(es): 978-1-878812; 978-1-932529; 978-1-938870
Number of titles published annually: 10 Print; 2 CD-ROM
Total Titles: 100 Print; 10 CD-ROM
Distributed by The Eurospan Group (Africa, Europe & Middle East); Footprint Books Pty Ltd (Australia, Fiji, New Zealand & Papua New Guinea); Login Brothers (Canada); Unifacmanu Trading Co Ltd (Taiwan)
Foreign Rep(s): CRW Marketing Services for Publishers Inc (Guam, Philippines); Tahir Lodhi Publishers' Representatives (Pakistan); Sara Books Pvt Ltd (Bangladesh, India, Sri Lanka); STM Publishers Services Pte Ltd (China, Hong Kong, Malaysia, Myanmar, Singapore, Thailand, Vietnam)
Warehouse: Maple Logistics Solutions, 60 Grumbacher Rd I-83 Industrial Park, PO Box 15100, York, PA 17406
Membership(s): The Independent Book Publishers Association

Health Research Books
62 Seventh St, Pomeroy, WA 99347
Mailing Address: PO Box 850, Pomeroy, WA 99347
Tel: 509-843-2385 *Toll Free Tel:* 888-844-2386 *Fax:* 509-843-2387
E-mail: publish@pomeroy-wa.com
Web Site: www.healthresearchbooks.com
Key Personnel
Owner: Nikki Jones
Founded: 1952
Publish reprints of rare, hard to find, out-of-print books. Subjects include mysticism, Egyptology, divination, UFOs, hypnotism, mental & spiritual healing, acupuncture, metaphysical, palmistry & many, many more.
ISBN Prefix(es): 978-0-7873
Number of titles published annually: 300 Print
Total Titles: 2,000 Print

Healthy Learning, see Coaches Choice

§HeartMath LLC
14700 W Park Ave, Boulder Creek, CA 95006
Tel: 831-338-8700 *Toll Free Tel:* 800-450-9111 *Fax:* 831-338-9861
E-mail: inquiry@heartmath.com
Web Site: www.heartmath.com
Key Personnel
Global Dir: Bruce Cryer
EVP, Strategic Devt: Howard Martin
SVP, Sales & Mktg: Catherine Calarco
VP, Fin/COO: Chris Jacob
Founded: 1998
Publishers of The HeartMath System.
ISBN Prefix(es): 978-1-879052
Number of titles published annually: 16 Print
Total Titles: 2 CD-ROM; 7 Audio

Hearts & Tummies Cookbook Co
Division of Quixote Press
3544 Blakslee St, Wever, IA 52658
Tel: 319-372-7480 *Toll Free Tel:* 800-571-2665 *Fax:* 319-372-7485
E-mail: quixotepress@gmail.com; heartsntummies@gmail.com
Web Site: www.heartsntummies.com
Key Personnel
Pres & Intl Rts: Bruce Carlson
Founded: 1982
Cookbooks.
ISBN Prefix(es): 978-1-878488; 978-1-57166
Number of titles published annually: 28 Print
Total Titles: 400 Print
Imprints: Black Iron Cooking Co; Hearts 'n Tummies Cookbook Co; Kid Help Publishing Co; PYO (Publish Your Own Co); Quixote Press

Hebrew Union College Press
Division of Hebrew Union College
3101 Clifton Ave, Cincinnati, OH 45220
Tel: 513-221-1875 *Fax:* 513-221-0321
Web Site: press.huc.edu
Key Personnel
Chmn, Pubns Comm: Michael A Meyer
Founded: 1921
Scholarly Jewish books.
ISBN Prefix(es): 978-0-87820
Number of titles published annually: 3 Print
Total Titles: 100 Print
Distributed by Wayne State University Press

Heian
Imprint of Stone Bridge Press Inc
1393 Solono Ave, Albany, CA 94706
Tel: 510-524-8732 *Toll Free Fax:* 888-411-8527
E-mail: sbp@stonebridge.com
Web Site: www.stonebridge.com
Key Personnel
Founder & Publr: Peter Goodman
Founded: 1973 (acquired by Stone Bridge Press in 2009)
General trade, juvenile; languages, dictionaries & literature, Oriental culture, customs, philosophy & religion; classic Japanese art calendars & books.
ISBN Prefix(es): 978-0-89346
Number of titles published annually: 8 Print
Total Titles: 40 Print

Heimburger House Publishing Co
7236 W Madison St, Forest Park, IL 60130
Tel: 708-366-1973 *Fax:* 708-366-1973
E-mail: info@heimburgerhouse.com
Web Site: www.heimburgerhouse.com
Key Personnel
Publr: Donald J Heimburger
Founded: 1962
Publish books & magazines on railroad & other transportation subjects; list includes more than 300 book titles.
ISBN Prefix(es): 978-0-911581
Number of titles published annually: 3 Print
Total Titles: 75 Print
Distributor for Book Sales Inc; Boyds Mills Press; Canadian Caboose Press; Carstens; Child's Play International; Evergreen Press; Firefly Books Ltd; Fitzhenry & Whiteside Ltd; Fordham University Press; Globe Pequot Press; Golden Hill Press; Harbour Publishing; HarperCollins; Johns Hopkins University Press; Hot Box Press; Houghton Mifflin Harcourt; Howling at the Moon Press; Iconografix; Indiana University Press; Kalmbach Publishing; Krause Publications; Motorbooks International; National Book Network; New York University Press; W W Norton & Co; Penguin Putnam Inc; Pictorial Histories Publishing Co; Sono Nis Press; Steam Passages Publishing; Sterling Publishing; Sugar Cane Press; Syracuse University Press; Thunder Bay Press; University of Minnesota Press; University of Scranton; Westcliffe Publishing; John Wiley & Sons

§William S Hein & Co Inc
2350 N Forest Rd, Getzville, NY 14068
Tel: 716-882-2600 *Toll Free Tel:* 800-828-7571 *Fax:* 716-883-8100
E-mail: mail@wshein.com; marketing@wshein.com
Web Site: www.wshein.com
Key Personnel
Chmn of the Bd: William S Hein, Jr *E-mail:* whein@wshein.com

Pres: Kevin M Marmion *Tel:* 716-882-2600 ext 115 *E-mail:* kmarmion@wshein.com
SVP: Daniel Rosati *E-mail:* drosati@wshein.com
Mgr, Mktg: Miranda J Rosati *E-mail:* mrosati@wshein.com
Founded: 1961
Publish & reprint law & related materials, hard copy, micro, CDs & online products.
ISBN Prefix(es): 978-0-8377; 978-0-89941; 978-1-57588
Number of titles published annually: 30 Print; 2 CD-ROM; 1 Online
Total Titles: 5,000 Print; 5 CD-ROM; 2 Online
Distributor for Ashgate; Aspen; Butterworths; Sweet & Maxwell; John Wiley & Sons Inc
Returns: 24 E Ferry St, Buffalo, NY 14209 *E-mail:* returns@wshein.com
Membership(s): American Association of Law Libraries; Canadian Association of Law Libraries; Library Binding Institute

§Heinemann
Division of Houghton Mifflin Harcourt
361 Hanover St, Portsmouth, NH 03801-3912
SAN: 210-5829
Mailing Address: PO Box 6926, Portsmouth, NH 03802-6926
Tel: 603-431-7894 *Toll Free Tel:* 800-225-5800 (US) *Fax:* 603-431-2214 *Toll Free Fax:* 877-231-6980 (US)
E-mail: custserv@heinemann.com
Web Site: www.heinemann.com
Key Personnel
Pres: Vicki Boyd *E-mail:* vicki.boyd@heinemann.com
Founded: 1978
Education - professional books for teachers K-college. Literacy, math, social studies, drama, art & English teaching. Hardcover & paperbound. Trade - drama, world literature, education, African studies. Hardcover & paperbound class.
ISBN Prefix(es): 978-0-86709; 978-0-434; 978-0-325; 978-1-59469; 978-0-435
Number of titles published annually: 115 Print
Total Titles: 1,500 Print
Distributed by Pearson (Canada, Australia & New Zealand)
See separate listing for:
Boynton/Cook Publishers

Heinle, see Wadsworth Publishing

§Hellgate Press
Imprint of L & R Publishing
PO Box 3531, Ashland, OR 97520
Tel: 541-973-5154 *Toll Free Tel:* 800-795-4059
E-mail: sales@hellgatepress.com
Web Site: www.hellgatepress.com
Key Personnel
Owner: Harley B Patrick *E-mail:* harley@hellgatepress.com
Founded: 1975
Military history, adventure travel, veteran memoirs, historical & adventure fiction.
ISBN Prefix(es): 978-1-55571
Number of titles published annually: 15 Print
Total Titles: 80 Print
Shipping Address: Midpoint Trade Books, 27 W 20 St, New York, NY 10011 *Tel:* 212-727-0190 *Fax:* 212-727-0195 *Web Site:* www.midpointtrade.com

§Helm Book Publishing
3437 Huntington Place Dr, Sarasota, FL 34237
SAN: 254-7562
Tel: 727-623-5014
Web Site: www.helmbookpublishing.com
Key Personnel
CEO: Dianne Helm *E-mail:* dianne@helmbookpublishing.com
Founded: 1994
Specialize in new & emerging authors in fiction/nonfiction genres.
This publisher has indicated that 50% of their product line is author subsidized.
ISBN Prefix(es): 978-0-9723011; 978-0-9760919; 978-0-9769193; 978-0-0930109; 978-0-9850488; 978-0-9841397; 978-0-9820605; 978-0-9801780; 978-0-9792328; 978-0-9778205
Number of titles published annually: 8 Print; 1 CD-ROM; 15 E-Book
Total Titles: 120 Print; 1 CD-ROM; 75 E-Book
Membership(s): ABA

Hendrickson Publishers Inc
PO Box 3473, Peabody, MA 01961-3473
Tel: 978-532-6546 *Toll Free Tel:* 800-358-3111 *Fax:* 978-573-8111
E-mail: orders@hendrickson.com
Web Site: www.hendrickson.com
Key Personnel
Sales: Bobby Koduvalil *E-mail:* bkoduvalil@hendrickson.com
Contract & Licensing/Digital Publg/Systems Mgr: Kris Orlando
Founded: 1978
Religious reference, language, history & theology.
ISBN Prefix(es): 978-0-913573; 978-0-943575; 978-0-917006; 978-1-56563
Number of titles published annually: 40 Print; 3 CD-ROM
Total Titles: 450 Print
Foreign Rep(s): Alban Books Ltd (Europe, UK)
Foreign Rights: KCBS (Korea)
Orders to: David C Cook Distribution Canada, 55 Woodslee Ave, PO Box 98, Paris, ON N3L 3E5, Canada (CN) *Toll Free Tel:* 800-263-2664 *Toll Free Fax:* 800-461-8575 *E-mail:* custserv@davidccook.ca *Web Site:* www.davidccook.ca; Alban Books Ltd, 14 Belford Rd, Edinburgh, Scotland EH4 3BL, United Kingdom *Tel:* (0131) 226 2217 *Fax:* (0131) 225 5999 *E-mail:* sales@albanbooks.com *Web Site:* www.albanbooks.com

Her Own Words LLC
PO Box 5264, Madison, WI 53705-0264
Tel: 608-271-7083 *Fax:* 608-271-0209
Web Site: www.herownwords.com; www.nontraditionalcareers.com
Key Personnel
Mgr: Jocelyn Riley *E-mail:* jocelynriley@herownwords.com
Founded: 1986
Women's history, literature, arts & women in non-traditional careers.
ISBN Prefix(es): 978-1-60118
Number of titles published annually: 3 Print; 3 Audio
Total Titles: 36 Print; 36 Audio
Imprints: Women In Nontraditional Careers

Herald Press
Imprint of MennoMedia
1251 Virginia Ave, Harrisonburg, VA 22802-2434
SAN: 202-2915
Toll Free Tel: 800-245-7894 (orders-US); 800-631-6535 (orders-CN) *Toll Free Fax:* 877-271-0760
E-mail: info@MennoMedia.org
Web Site: www.heraldpress.com; store.mennomedia.org
Key Personnel
Exec Dir, MennoMedia: Russ Eanes *E-mail:* russ@mennomedia.org
Edit Dir: Amy Gingerich *E-mail:* agingerich@mpn.net
Dir, Sales & Mktg: Ben Penner
Congregational Mktg & Sales Mgr, US: Josh Byler *E-mail:* jbyler@mpn.net
Founded: 1908
General Christian trade books, family, devotional, cookbooks, juveniles, adult fiction, Bible study, theology, peace & social concerns, missions, Amish & Mennonite history & culture, songbooks.
ISBN Prefix(es): 978-0-8361
Number of titles published annually: 20 Print
Total Titles: 500 Print
Branch Office(s)
718 N Main St, Newton, KS 67114 *Tel:* 316-281-4412 *Toll Free Tel:* 800-245-7894 ext 220 *Fax:* 316-283-0454
50 Kent Ave, Suite 204, Kitchener, ON N2G 3R1, Canada *Toll Free Tel:* 800-245-7894 *Fax:* 519-747-5721 (orders)
Membership(s): CBA: The Association for Christian Retail; Evangelical Christian Publishers Association

Herald Publishing House
Division of Community of Christ
1001 W Walnut St, Independence, MO 64051
SAN: 202-2907
Mailing Address: PO Box 390, Independence, MO 64051-0390
Tel: 816-521-3015 *Toll Free Tel:* 800-767-8181 *Fax:* 816-521-3066
E-mail: sales@heraldhouse.org
Web Site: www.heraldhouse.org
Key Personnel
Fiscal Servs Specialist: Suzan Hudson
Founded: 1860
ISBN Prefix(es): 978-0-8309
Number of titles published annually: 12 Print
Total Titles: 360 Print
Imprints: Independence Press

Heritage Books Inc
5810 Ruatan St, Berwyn Heights, MD 20740
Toll Free Tel: 800-876-6103 *Toll Free Fax:* 800-876-6103
E-mail: orders@heritagebooks.com; submissions@heritagebooks.com
Web Site: www.heritagebooks.com
Key Personnel
CEO & Pres: Craig R Scott *E-mail:* crscott@heritagebooks.com
Founded: 1978
Books on local history, genealogy & Americana.
ISBN Prefix(es): 978-0-917890; 978-1-55613; 978-0-7884; 978-1-58549; 978-0-940907; 978-1-888265
Number of titles published annually: 200 Print; 5 CD-ROM; 200 E-Book
Total Titles: 5,300 Print; 1,200 CD-ROM; 2,000 E-Book
Imprints: Eagle Editions; Fireside Fiction; Heritage Books; Willow Bend Books
Distributor for Fairfax Genealogical Society; National Genealogical Society; Virginia Genealogical Society

§The Heritage Foundation
214 Massachusetts Ave NE, Washington, DC 20002-4999
Tel: 202-546-4400 *Toll Free Tel:* 800-544-4843 *Fax:* 202-546-8328
E-mail: info@heritage.org
Web Site: www.heritage.org
Key Personnel
Pres: Jim DeMint
Creative Dir: Melissa Bluey
Founded: 1973
Domestic policy, foreign policy & defense.
ISBN Prefix(es): 978-0-89195
Number of titles published annually: 10 Print; 2 CD-ROM
Total Titles: 19 Print; 2 CD-ROM; 8 E-Book

Heuer Publishing LLC
PO Box 248, Cedar Rapids, IA 52406
Tel: 319-368-8008 *Toll Free Tel:* 800-950-7529 *Fax:* 319-368-8011

E-mail: editor@hitplays.com; customerservice@hitplays.com
Web Site: www.hitplays.com
Key Personnel
Publr: Steven S Michalicek
Ed: Ms Geri Albrecht
Founded: 1928
Publishes plays, musicals, operas/operettas & guides (choreography, costume, production/staging) for amateur & professional markets including junior & senior high schools, college/university & community theatres. Focus includes comedy, drama, fantasy, mystery & holiday with special interest focus in multicultural, historic, classic literature, Shakespearian theatre, interactive, teen issues & biographies. Pays by percentage royalty or outright purchase.
ISBN Prefix(es): 978-1-61588
Number of titles published annually: 25 Print
Total Titles: 150 Print

Hewitt Homeschooling Resources
Division of Hewitt Research Foundation
2103 Main St, Washougal, WA 98671
Mailing Address: PO Box 9, Washougal, WA 98671
Tel: 360-835-8708 *Toll Free Tel:* 800-348-1750 *Fax:* 360-835-8697
E-mail: sales@hewitthomeschooling.com
Web Site: hewitthomeschooling.com
Key Personnel
Pres: April Purtell
Founded: 1964
Homeschooling, curriculum.
ISBN Prefix(es): 978-0-913717; 978-1-57896
Number of titles published annually: 6 Print
Total Titles: 150 Print

Heyday Books
1633 University Ave, Berkeley, CA 94703
SAN: 207-2351
Mailing Address: PO Box 9145, Berkeley, CA 94709-0145
Tel: 510-549-3564 *Fax:* 510-549-1889
E-mail: heyday@heydaybooks.com; orders@heydaybooks.com
Web Site: heydaybooks.com
Key Personnel
Publr: Malcolm Margolin
Founded: 1974
Nonprofit company that specializes in California Indians, California history & literature, regional conservation & ecology; women of California; literary anthologies; Asian-American; art & photography.
ISBN Prefix(es): 978-0-930588; 978-1-890771; 978-0-9666691; 978-1-59714
Number of titles published annually: 25 Print
Total Titles: 110 Print
Imprints: Sierra College Press
Returns: Heyday Books, c/o Fulfillco, 2801 Merced St, San Leandro, CA 94577
Warehouse: Heyday Books, c/o Fulfillco, 2801 Merced St, San Leandro, CA 94577

Hi Willow Research & Publishing
123 E Second Ave, Suite 1106, Salt Lake City, UT 84103
Tel: 801-532-1165
E-mail: sales@lmcsource.com
Web Site: www.lmcsource.com; www.davidvl.org
Key Personnel
Owner: David V Loertscher
Founded: 1978
Books for schools & libraries.
ISBN Prefix(es): 978-0-931510; 978-1-933170
Number of titles published annually: 8 Print
Total Titles: 35 Print

Higginson Book Co
10 Colonial Rd, Salem, MA 01970
Mailing Address: PO Box 778, Salem, MA 01970
Tel: 978-745-7170 *Fax:* 978-745-8025
Web Site: www.higginsonbooks.com
Key Personnel
Mgr: Robert Murphy *E-mail:* robert.murphy1945@yahoo.com
Founded: 1969
Publish reprints of rare & out-of-print genealogies, local history & Civil War regimentals.
ISBN Prefix(es): 978-0-8328; 978-0-7404
Number of titles published annually: 200 Print
Total Titles: 15,000 Print

High Plains Press
PO Box 123, Glendo, WY 82213
Toll Free Tel: 800-552-7819 *Fax:* 307-735-4590
E-mail: editor@highplainspress.com
Web Site: highplainspress.com
Key Personnel
Founder & Publr: Nancy Curtis
Founded: 1984
Books about Wyoming & the American West.
ISBN Prefix(es): 978-0-931271
Number of titles published annually: 3 Print; 3 E-Book
Total Titles: 64 Print; 12 E-Book; 1 Audio
Membership(s): The Independent Book Publishers Association; Publishers Association of the West

High Tide Press
Subsidiary of The Trinity Foundation
301 Veterans Pkwy, New Lenox, IL 60451
Web Site: cherryhillhightide.com/high-tide-press/
Key Personnel
Dir: Anne C Ward *Tel:* 800-235-6009 *E-mail:* award@hightidepress.com
Founded: 1995
Full service publisher of hardcover & paperback books & one quarterly magazine for the book trade & professional niche markets. Specialize in the fields of developmental & intellectual disabilities, behavioral health, nonprofit management, social enterprise, leadership. The High Tide Monograph Series imprint focuses on high quality management practices in behavioral health & developmental disability services while the Midewin Series focuses on the prevention of abuse & neglect of persons with disabilities.
ISBN Prefix(es): 978-0-9653744; 978-1-892696
Number of titles published annually: 12 Print; 4 Online; 4 E-Book
Total Titles: 46 Print; 1 E-Book
Imprints: High Tide Monograph Series; Midewin Series
Orders to: Cherry Hill Bookstore, 1805 Ferro Dr, New Lenox, IL 60451 (part of Trinity Foundation), Cust Serv: Terra Radetski *Tel:* 815-723-0898 *Toll Free Tel:* 800-235-6009 *Fax:* 815-723-2760 *E-mail:* terra@cherryhillbooks.com *Web Site:* www.cherryhillbooks.com
Membership(s): The Independent Book Publishers Association

Highlights for Children
1800 Watermark Dr, Columbus, OH 43215
Mailing Address: PO Box 269, Columbus, OH 43216-0269
Tel: 614-486-0631 *Toll Free Tel:* 800-962-3661 (Highlights Club cust serv); 800-255-9517 (Highlights Magazine cust serv)
Web Site: www.highlights.com
Key Personnel
CEO: Kent S Johnson
VP, Print & Ebook Sales: Jack W Perry
VP, Publg Strategy & Prod Devt: Mary-Alice Moore
Edit Dir, Book Publg: Liz Van Doren
Dir, Book Mktg: Michael Eisenberg
Dir, Sales: Dave Bolen
Prodn Dir: Sue Cole
Ed-in-Chief (PA off): Christine French Cully
Sr Ed: Mary Colgan
Founded: 1946
ISBN Prefix(es): 978-0-87534
Number of titles published annually: 150 Print
Editorial Office(s): 803 Church St, Honesdale, PA 18431 *Tel:* 570-253-1080 *Fax:* 570-251-7847
Distribution Center: INscribe Digital, 55 Francisco St, Suite 710, San Francisco, CA 94133 *Tel:* 415-489-7000 *Fax:* 415-489-7049 *Web Site:* www.inscribedigital.com

Hill & Wang
Division of Farrar, Straus & Giroux, LLC
18 W 18 St, New York, NY 10011
SAN: 201-9299
Tel: 212-741-6900 *Fax:* 212-633-9385
E-mail: fsg.publicity@fsgbooks.com; fsg.editorial@fsgbooks.com; sales@fsgbooks.com
Web Site: us.macmillan.com/hillandwang.aspx
Key Personnel
SVP, Mktg & Publicity, FSG: Jeff Seroy
VP & Contracts Dir, FSG: Erika Seidman
Dir, Ad & Promo, FSG: Victoria Genna
Founded: 1956
General nonfiction, history & drama.
ISBN Prefix(es): 978-0-8090
Number of titles published annually: 10 Print
Warehouse: MPS Distribution Center, 16365 James Madison Hwy, Gordonsville, VA 22942 *Toll Free Tel:* 888-330-8477

Lawrence Hill Books, see Chicago Review Press

Hillsdale College Press
Division of Hillsdale College
33 E College St, Hillsdale, MI 49242
Tel: 517-437-7341 *Toll Free Tel:* 800-437-2268 *Fax:* 517-437-3923
E-mail: news@hillsdale.edu
Web Site: www.hillsdale.edu
Key Personnel
Ed & VP, External Aff: Douglas A Jeffrey *Tel:* 517-607-2538 *E-mail:* douglas.jeffrey@hillsdale.edu
Founded: 1974
Single author books & collected essays of historical, political & economic interest.
ISBN Prefix(es): 978-0-916308

Hillsdale Educational Publishers Inc
39 North St, Hillsdale, MI 49242
SAN: 159-8759
Tel: 517-437-3179 *Fax:* 517-437-0531
E-mail: davestory@aol.com
Web Site: www.hillsdalepublishers.com; michbooks.com
Key Personnel
Pres & Author: David B McConnell
Founded: 1965
Publish & distribute regional titles for schools & libraries.
ISBN Prefix(es): 978-0-910726; 978-1-931466
Number of titles published annually: 4 Print; 1 CD-ROM; 1 Audio
Total Titles: 18 Print; 1 CD-ROM; 1 Audio

§Hilton Publishing
1630 45 St, Suite 103, Munster, IN 46321
Tel: 219-922-4868 *Fax:* 219-924-6811
E-mail: info@hiltonpub.com; orders@hiltonpub.com
Web Site: www.hiltonpub.com
Key Personnel
Dir, Mktg & Publg: Megan Lippert *E-mail:* mlippert@hiltonpub.com
Mktg Proj Mgr: Martha Jimenez
Founded: 1996
Publish books in health & wellness, minority health, religion (health-related). Consistent themes of publications include living with & preventing various disease states, illustrating & promoting components of healthy living, embracing & illuminating cultural diversity re-

lated to health & well-being & fostering health in the Christian community. Books are peer reviewed by experts in the appropriate fields to insure we have included the most current, accurate & relevant information. We publish informative & educational books for the general public as well as books aimed at the medical community.
ISBN Prefix(es): 978-0-9654553; 978-0-9675258; 978-0-9716067; 978-0-9743144; 978-0-9764443; 978-0-9773160; 978-0-9777779; 978-0-9800649; 978-0-9815381; 978-0-9841447; 978-0-9847566
Number of titles published annually: 12 Print; 3 CD-ROM; 12 Online; 7 E-Book; 3 Audio
Total Titles: 50 Print; 3 CD-ROM; 50 Online; 7 E-Book; 3 Audio
Foreign Rep(s): Gabriel Wilmoth (Canada, Germany, USA)
Foreign Rights: Nigel Yorwerth (Worldwide)
Membership(s): Indiana Minority Supplier Development Council; National Minority Supplier Development Council; North Carolina Ministry Supplier Development Council

Himalayan Institute Press
Division of Himalayan International Institute of Yoga Science & Philosophy
952 Bethany Tpke, Honesdale, PA 18431
Tel: 570-253-5551 *Toll Free Tel:* 800-822-4547
E-mail: info@himalayaninstitute.org
Web Site: www.himalayaninstitute.org
Key Personnel
Chmn & Spiritual Head: Pandit Rajmani Tigunait, PhD
Dir: Stephen Moulton
Founded: 1971
Publish CDs, DVDs & books on yoga, meditation, holistic health, philosophy, psychology & stress management.
ISBN Prefix(es): 978-0-89389
Number of titles published annually: 4 Print; 3 E-Book; 2 Audio
Total Titles: 60 Print; 10 Audio
Foreign Rights: Hagenbach & Bender GmbH (Worldwide)

§Hippocrene Books Inc
171 Madison Ave, New York, NY 10016
Tel: 212-685-4373 *Fax:* 212-779-9338
E-mail: info@hippocrenebooks.com; orderdept@hippocrenebooks.com (orders)
Web Site: www.hippocrenebooks.com
Key Personnel
Publr & Edit Dir: Priti Chitnis Gress *E-mail:* pgress@hippocrenebooks.com
Fin Offr: Awilda Alvarez *E-mail:* aalvarez@hippocrenebooks.com
Publicity Mgr & Ed: Colette Laroya *Tel:* 212-685-4371 *E-mail:* claroya@hippocrenebooks.com
Sales Acct Mgr: Melissa Santana *E-mail:* msantana@hippocrenebooks.com
Founded: 1971
Foreign language dictionaries & self-study guides in over 120 languages; international cookbooks, history & travel.
ISBN Prefix(es): 978-0-87052; 978-0-7818
Number of titles published annually: 25 Print
Total Titles: 500 Print; 150 E-Book
Foreign Rights: A B E Marketing (Poland); Bookery Pty Ltd (Australia); Gazelle Book Services (England); Publishers Group Canada (Canada)
Shipping Address: Whitehurst & Clark Book Services, 1200 County Rd, Rte 523, Flemington, NJ 08822
Warehouse: Whitehurst & Clark Book Services, 1200 County Rd, Rte 523, Flemington, NJ 08822
Membership(s): The Independent Book Publishers Association

The Historic New Orleans Collection
533 Royal St, New Orleans, LA 70130
Tel: 504-523-4662 *Fax:* 504-598-7108
E-mail: wrc@hnoc.org
Web Site: www.hnoc.org
Key Personnel
Exec Dir: Priscilla Lawrence *Tel:* 504-598-7127 *E-mail:* priscill@hnoc.org
Dir, Pubns & Mktg: Dr Jessica Dorman *Tel:* 504-598-7174 *E-mail:* jessicad@hnoc.org
Founded: 1966
Publications related to Louisiana history & to the holdings of The Historic New Orleans Collection; preservation manuals for family papers, photographs, etc.
ISBN Prefix(es): 978-0-917860
Number of titles published annually: 3 Print
Total Titles: 52 Print

History Publishing Co LLC
PO Box 700, Palisades, NY 10964
SAN: 850-5942
Tel: 845-398-8161
E-mail: info@historypublishingco.com
Web Site: www.historypublishingco.com
Key Personnel
Owner & Publr: Don Bracken *E-mail:* djb@historypublishingco.com
Assoc Publr: Carolyn Doyle Winter *Tel:* 845-548-2784 *E-mail:* cdw@historypublishingco.com
Sr Ed: Alexis Starke *E-mail:* alex@historypublishingco.com
Founded: 2007
Trade book publisher dealing in 18th-20th century history. Strong focus on history told from the first person perspective by people who participated in the making of history or were ongoing witness to the making of history.
ISBN Prefix(es): 978-19339-09; 978-19407-73
Number of titles published annually: 18 Print; 12 Online; 15 E-Book
Total Titles: 35 Print; 19 Online; 30 E-Book
Imprints: Chronology Books; Today's Books
Returns: APG Sales & Distribution, 7344 Cockrill Bend Blvd, Nashville, TN 37209, VP: Martin Flanagan *Tel:* 615-254-2482 *Fax:* 615-254-2405 *E-mail:* mflanagan@wfsllc.com *Web Site:* apgbooks.com
Warehouse: APG Sales & Distribution, 7344 Cockrill Bend Blvd, Nashville, TN 37209 *Tel:* 615-254-2482 *Toll Free Tel:* 800-327-5113 *Fax:* 615-254-2405 *E-mail:* mflanagan@wfsllc.com *Web Site:* apgbooks.com
Distribution Center: INscribe Digital, 444 Spear St, Suite 213, San Francisco, CA 94105
Midpoint Trade Books, 5701 Ranch Dr, Little Rock, AR 72223, Dir: Julie Hardison *Tel:* 913-362-1120 *Fax:* 913-362-7401 *E-mail:* julie@midpointtrade.com *Web Site:* midpointtrade.com
Membership(s): AAP; The Independent Book Publishers Association

W D Hoard & Sons Co
28 W Milwaukee Ave, Fort Atkinson, WI 53538
Mailing Address: PO Box 801, Fort Atkinson, WI 53538-0801
Tel: 920-563-5551 *Fax:* 920-563-7298
E-mail: hdbooks@hoards.com; editors@hoards.com
Web Site: www.hoards.com; www.hoardprinting.com
Key Personnel
Book Ed: Maggie Seiler
Founded: 1870
Dairy oriented & some agricultural, regional publications, catalogs & specialty projects.
ISBN Prefix(es): 978-0-932147
Number of titles published annually: 5 Print
Total Titles: 22 Print
Imprints: Hoard's Dairyman Magazine

Hobar Publications
Division of Finney Company Inc
5995 149 St W, Suite 105, Apple Valley, MN 55124
Tel: 952-469-6699 *Toll Free Tel:* 800-846-7027 *Fax:* 952-469-1968 *Toll Free Fax:* 800-330-6232
E-mail: info@finneyco.com
Web Site: www.finney-hobar.com
Key Personnel
Pres: Alan E Krysan
Mktg Specialist: Krista Danielson
Founded: 1964
Produces educational materials for grades 7-12 in the areas of agriculture, career exploration & guidance & technical education.
ISBN Prefix(es): 978-0-913163; 978-0-9616847
Number of titles published annually: 4 Print
Total Titles: 45 Print
Imprints: Agronomy Publications; K A Publishing
Divisions: National Farm Book Co
Distributor for Drache Publications
Membership(s): National Association of Agriculture Educators

§Hobbes End Publishing LLC
Subsidiary of Hobbes End Entertainment LLC
PO Box 193, Aubrey, TX 76227
Web Site: hobbesendpublishing.com
Founded: 2005
Specialize in adult fiction, children's fiction, fantasy, science fiction & horror.
ISBN Prefix(es): 978-0-9763510; 978-0-9859110
Number of titles published annually: 3 Print
Total Titles: 22 Print

Hobblebush Books
17-A Old Milford Rd, Brookline, NH 03033
Tel: 603-672-4317 *Fax:* 603-672-4317
E-mail: hobblebush@charter.net; info@hobblebush.com
Web Site: www.hobblebush.com
Key Personnel
Owner & Pres: Mr Sidney Hall, Jr
Mktg Dir: Kirsty Walker
Founded: 1993
Independent publisher of both literary & nonliterary titles.
ISBN Prefix(es): 978-0-9636413; 978-0-9760896; 978-0-9801672; 978-1-939449
Number of titles published annually: 3 Print; 3 E-Book
Total Titles: 37 Print; 3 E-Book
Orders to: Small Press Distributors, 1341 Seventh St, Berkeley, CA 94710-1409 (bookstores & libs) *Toll Free Tel:* 800-869-7553 *Fax:* 510-524-0852 *Web Site:* www.spdbooks.org; Baker & Taylor, 2550 W Tyvola Rd, Suite 300, Charlotte, NC 28217 (trade) *Tel:* 704-998-3100 *Toll Free Tel:* 800-775-1800 *E-mail:* btinfo@btol.com *Web Site:* www.btol.com
Distribution Center: Small Press Distributors, 1341 Seventh St, Berkeley, CA 94710-1409 (bookstores & libs) *Toll Free Tel:* 800-869-7553 *Fax:* 510-524-0852 *Web Site:* www.spdbooks.org
Quality Books Inc, 1003 W Pines Rd, Oregon, IL 61061 *Toll Free Tel:* 800-323-4241 *Fax:* 815-732-4499 *Web Site:* www.quality-books.com
Baker & Taylor, 2550 W Tyvola Rd, Suite 300, Charlotte, NC 28217 (trade) *Tel:* 704-998-3100 *Toll Free Tel:* 800-775-1800 *Web Site:* www.btol.com
Membership(s): Community of Literary Magazines & Presses; Independent Publishers of New England; New Hampshire Writers Project

Hogrefe Publishing
38 Chauncy St, Suite 1002, Boston, MA 02111
SAN: 293-2792
Toll Free Tel: 866-823-4726 *Fax:* 617-354-6875
E-mail: publishing@hogrefe.com
Web Site: www.hogrefe.com

Key Personnel
Publg Mgr: Robert Dimbleby *E-mail:* robert.dimbleby@hogrefe.com
Founded: 1978
Books & journals in the fields of medicine, neurosciences, psychiatry, psychology.
ISBN Prefix(es): 978-0-88937; 978-0-920887; 978-1-61676 (ebooks); 978-1-61334 (EPUB)
Number of titles published annually: 15 Print
Foreign Office(s): Hogrefe Verlag, Merkelstr 3, 37085 Goettingen, Germany *Tel:* (0551) 99950 0 *Fax:* (0551) 99950 425
Distributor for Verlag Hans Huber Hogrefe AG (Switzerland); Hogrefe Verlag (Germany)
Orders to: Bookmasters, 30 Amberwood Pkwy, Ashland, OH 44805, Dist Servs Mgr: Cheryl Householder *Tel:* 419-281-1802 *Toll Free Tel:* 800-228-3749 *Fax:* 419-281-6883
Returns: Bookmasters, 30 Amberwood Pkwy, Ashland, OH 44805, Dist Servs Mgr: Cheryl Householder *Tel:* 419-281-1802 *Toll Free Tel:* 800-228-3749 *Fax:* 419-281-6883
Distribution Center: Bookmasters, 30 Amberwood Pkwy, Ashland, OH 44805, Dist Servs Mgr: Cheryl Householder *Tel:* 419-281-1802 *Toll Free Tel:* 800-228-3749 *Fax:* 419-281-6883
Membership(s): AAP; STM

Hohm Press
Subsidiary of HSM LLC
PO Box 4410, Chino Valley, AZ 86323
Tel: 928-636-3331 *Toll Free Tel:* 800-381-2700 *Fax:* 928-636-7519
E-mail: hppublisher@cableone.net; hohmpresseditor@gmail.com
Web Site: www.hohmpress.com
Key Personnel
Gen Mgr & Publr: Dasya Anthony Zuccarello
Mng Ed: Regina Sara Ryan
Prodn Mgr: Joe Bala Zuccarello
Founded: 1975
Independent publisher of books on spirituality & consciousness studies.
ISBN Prefix(es): 978-0-934252; 978-1-890772
Number of titles published annually: 8 Print; 8 E-Book
Total Titles: 180 Print; 30 E-Book; 6 Audio
Imprints: Kalindi Press (books on natural health & nutrition, children's & family health)
Foreign Rep(s): Gazelle (Europe)
Foreign Rights: Hagenbach & Bender GmbH (Deanna Leah) (Worldwide exc USA)
Shipping Address: 860 Staley Lane, Chino Valley, AZ 86323
Warehouse: 860 Staley Lane, Chino Valley, AZ 86323
Distribution Center: SCB Distributors, 15608 S New Century Dr, Gardena, CA 90248 (US & CN) *Toll Free Tel:* 800-729-6423 *Web Site:* www.scbdistributors.com

Holiday House Inc
425 Madison Ave, New York, NY 10017
SAN: 202-3008
Tel: 212-688-0085 *Fax:* 212-421-6134
E-mail: holiday@holidayhouse.com
Web Site: www.holidayhouse.com
Key Personnel
Pres: John Briggs *E-mail:* jbriggs@holidayhouse.com
VP & Ed-in-Chief: Mary Cash *E-mail:* mcash@holidayhouse.com
VP, Mktg: Theresa M Borzumato *E-mail:* tborzumato@holidayhouse.com
VP, Rts, Perms & Digital Publg: Julia Gallagher *E-mail:* jgallagher@holidayhouse.com
VP, Sales: Barbara A Walsh *E-mail:* bwalsh@holidayhouse.com
Dir, Art & Design: Claire Counihan *E-mail:* ccounihan@holidayhouse.com
Dir, Opers: Lisa Morales *E-mail:* lisamorales@holidayhouse.com
Dir, Prodn: Lisa Lee *E-mail:* llee@holidayhouse.com
Exec Ed: Grace Maccarone *E-mail:* gmaccarone@holidayhouse.com
Consulting Ed: Julie Amper *E-mail:* jamper@holidayhouse.com
Assoc Ed: Kelly Loughman *E-mail:* kloughman@holidayhouse.com
Asst Ed: Sally Morgridge *E-mail:* smorgridge@holidayhouse.com
Mktg Assoc: Sabrina Aballe *E-mail:* saballe@holidayhouse.com
Publicity Asst: Aubrey Churchward *E-mail:* achurchward@holidayhouse.com
Cust Serv: Kathryn Hoban *E-mail:* khoban@holidayhouse.com
Founded: 1935
Juvenile & young adult books.
ISBN Prefix(es): 978-0-8234
Number of titles published annually: 90 Print
Total Titles: 800 Print; 300 E-Book
Foreign Rep(s): Thomas Allen & Son Ltd (Canada)
Foreign Rights: Big Apple Agency Inc (China, Taiwan); Caroline Hill-Trevor (Europe exc Germany, Israel, Scandinavia, Spanish languages, Turkey, UK Commonwealth); Korea Copyright Center (Korea); Tuttle-Mori (Indonesia, Japan, Thailand, Vietnam); Silke Weniger (Austria, Germany)
Shipping Address: Maple Logistics Solutions, 1000 Strickler Rd, Mount Joy, PA 17552 *Tel:* 717-653-5483
Membership(s): The Children's Book Council

Hollym International Corp
18 Donald Place, Elizabeth, NJ 07208
SAN: 211-0172
Tel: 908-353-1655 *Fax:* 908-353-0255
E-mail: contact@hollym.com
Web Site: www.hollym.com
Key Personnel
Pres: Gene S Rhie
Founded: 1977
Publish & distribute books in English on Korea related topics.
ISBN Prefix(es): 978-0-930878; 978-1-56591
Number of titles published annually: 10 Print
Total Titles: 155 Print
Foreign Office(s): Hollym Corp, 13-13 Gwancheol-dong, Jongno-gu, 110-111 Seoul, South Korea, Contact: Kim-Man Ham *Tel:* (02) 735-7551 *Fax:* (02) 730-5149 *E-mail:* info@hollym.co.kr *Web Site:* www.hollym.co.kr

Hollywood Film Archive
8391 Beverly Blvd, Los Angeles, CA 90048
Tel: 323-655-4968
Web Site: hfarchive.com
Key Personnel
Dir: D Richard Baer
Dir, Admin: Howard Schiller
Founded: 1972
Publication, sales & distribution of comprehensive movie, video & TV reference books.
ISBN Prefix(es): 978-0-913616
Number of titles published annually: 3 Print
Total Titles: 50 Print
Advertising Agency: Tartan Advertising

Holmes Publishing Group LLC
PO Box 2370, Sequim, WA 98382
Tel: 360-681-2900
E-mail: holmespub@fastmail.fm
Web Site: www.jdholmes.com
Key Personnel
CEO & Pres: J D Holmes *E-mail:* jdholmes@fastmail.fm
Founded: 1971
Specialize in antiquarian, secondhand & rare books, as well as esoteric publications.
ISBN Prefix(es): 978-1-55818; 978-0-916411
Number of titles published annually: 16 Print
Total Titles: 389 Print
Imprints: Alchemical Press; Alexandrian Press; Contra/Thought; Holmes Publishing Group; Near Eastern Press; Sure Fire Press
Distributor for Capall-Bann (UK); Edda Publishing (Sweden); Fulgur Ltd (UK); Jerusalem Press (UK); Starfire Publishing (UK); Theion Publishing (Germany); Three Hands Press (US); Xoanon Publishing (US)
Distribution Center: New Leaf Distributing Co, 401 Thornton Rd, Lithia Springs, GA 30122-1557 *Tel:* 770-948-7845 *Fax:* 770-944-2313 *Web Site:* www.newleaf-dist.com

Henry Holt and Company, LLC
Division of Macmillan
175 Fifth Ave, New York, NY 10010
SAN: 200-2108
Tel: 646-307-5151 *Toll Free Tel:* 888-330-8477 (orders) *Fax:* 646-307-5285
E-mail: firstname.lastname@hholt.com
Web Site: www.henryholt.com
Key Personnel
Pres & Publr: Stephen Rubin
Deputy Publr, VP, Sales & Mktg: Maggie Richards
VP, Dir of Publicity: Patricia Eisemann
Dir, Perms & Copyright: Mimi Ross
Art Dir: Richard Pracher
Exec Mng Ed, Adult Trade: Kenn Russell
Ed-in-Chief, NY: Gillian Blake
Publr, Metropolitan Books: Sara Bershtel
Sr Ed, Metropolitan Books: Riva Hocherman
Edit Dir, Times Books: Paul Golob
Founded: 1866
ISBN Prefix(es): 978-0-8050 (Holt)
Number of titles published annually: 56 Print
Total Titles: 3,000 Print
Imprints: Henry Holt; Holt Paperbacks; John Macrae Books; Metropolitan Books; Times Books
Foreign Rep(s): Raincoast (Canada)
Foreign Rights: A/S Bookman Literary Agency (Denmark, Finland, Iceland, Norway, Sweden); AnatoliaLit Agency (Turkey); Anthea Agency (Bulgaria); Author Rights Agency Ltd (Russia); Bardon-Chinese Media Agency (Mainland China, Taiwan); Eliane Benisti Literary Agency (France); The English Agency (Japan) Ltd (Japan); Farrar, Straus and Giroux (USA); Graal Literary Agency (Maria Strarz-Kanska) (Poland); The Deborah Harris Agency (Israel); Internationaal Literatuur Bureau BV (Netherlands); International Copyright Agency Ltd (Simona Kessler) (Romania); Katai & Bolza Literary Agents (Hungary); Korea Copyright Center Inc (KCC) (Korea); Leonhardt & Hoier (Scandinavia); Liepman Agency (Eva Koralnik & Ronit Zafran) (Germany); Literarni Aventura sro (Czech Republic, Slovakia); MB Agencia Literaria (Portugal, Spain); Plima Literary Agency (Croatia, Serbia, Slovenia); RIFF (Brazil); Marco Vigevani Agenzia Letteraria (Italy)
Advertising Agency: Verso Advertising, 50 W 17 St, New York, NY 10010 *Tel:* 212-292-2990 *Web Site:* www.versoadvertising.com
Warehouse: MPS, 16365 James Madison Hwy, Gordonsville, VA 22942, SVP, Opers: Michael Shareck *Tel:* 540-672-7698 SAN: 631-5011
Membership(s): AAP

Holy Cow! Press
PO Box 3170, Mount Royal Sta, Duluth, MN 55803
Tel: 218-724-1653
E-mail: holycow@holycowpress.org
Web Site: www.holycowpress.org
Key Personnel
Publr & Ed: Jim Perlman
Founded: 1977
ISBN Prefix(es): 978-0-930100; 978-0-9779458

Number of titles published annually: 4 Print; 3 E-Book
Total Titles: 120 Print; 8 E-Book
Distribution Center: Consortium Book Sales & Distribution, 1045 Westgate Dr, St Paul, MN 55114 *Toll Free Tel:* 800-283-3572 (cust serv) *Fax:* 651-221-0124 *Web Site:* www.cbsd.com

Holy Cross Orthodox Press
Division of Hellenic College Holy Cross
50 Goddard Ave, Brookline, MA 02445
Tel: 617-731-3500; 617-850-1200 *Fax:* 617-850-1460
E-mail: info@hchc.edu
Web Site: www.hchc.edu
Key Personnel
Dir: Dr Anton Vrame
Prodn Mgr: Sarah Parro
Founded: 1974
Books on Orthodox Christian religion.
ISBN Prefix(es): 978-0-917651; 978-1-885652; 978-0-916586; 978-1-935317
Number of titles published annually: 10 Print
Total Titles: 120 Print

§Homa & Sekey Books
140 E Ridgewood Ave, Paramus, NJ 07652
Tel: 201-261-8810 *Toll Free Tel:* 800-870-HOMA (870-4662 orders) *Fax:* 201-261-8890
E-mail: info@homabooks.com
Web Site: www.homabooks.com
Key Personnel
Publr: Shawn Ye
Founded: 1997
Publisher & distributor of books on Asia.
ISBN Prefix(es): 978-1-931907; 978-0-966542
Number of titles published annually: 15 Print
Distributor for China Encyclopedia Publishing House; China Intercontinental Press; China Zhejiang Publishing United Group
Foreign Rights: Eric Yang Agency (Korea)
Membership(s): The Independent Book Publishers Association

Homestead Publishing
Affiliate of Book Design Ltd
Box 193, Moose, WY 83012-0193
Tel: 307-733-6248 *Fax:* 307-733-6248
E-mail: orders@homesteadpublishing.net
Web Site: www.homesteadpublishing.net
Key Personnel
Publr: Carl Schreier *Tel:* 415-621-5039
Contact: Diane Henderson
Founded: 1980
Publisher of guide books.
ISBN Prefix(es): 978-0-943972
Number of titles published annually: 12 Print; 2,000 Online; 6 E-Book
Total Titles: 268 Print; 4,500 Online; 16 E-Book
Branch Office(s)
1068 14 St, San Francisco, CA 94114 *Tel:* 415-621-5039 *Fax:* 415-621-5039
Returns: 4030 W Lake Creek Dr, Wilson, WY 83014
Warehouse: 4030 W Lake Creek Dr, Wilson, WY 83014

Hoover Institution Press
Subsidiary of Hoover Institution on War, Revolution & Peace
Stanford University, 434 Galvez Mall, Stanford, CA 94305-6003
SAN: 202-3024
Tel: 650-725-7146; 650-723-3373
Toll Free Tel: 800-935-2882 *Fax:* 650-723-8626
E-mail: hooverpress@stanford.edu
Web Site: www.hoover.org; www.hooverpress.org
Key Personnel
Mng Ed, Hoover Digest: Charles Lindsey *Tel:* 650-723-1471 *E-mail:* digesteditor@stanford.edu
Mng Ed, Education Next: Carol Peterson *E-mail:* peterson@fas.harvard.edu
Book Prodn Mgr: Marshall Blanchard *Tel:* 650-725-3460
Founded: 1962
Studies on domestic & international policy, studies of nationalities in Central & Eastern Europe, history & political science; bibliographies & surveys of Hoover Institution's resources.
ISBN Prefix(es): 978-0-8179
Number of titles published annually: 20 Print
Total Titles: 675 Print; 75 Online
Foreign Rep(s): East-West Export Books (Asia, Hawaii, The Pacific); Eurospan (Europe)
Orders to: Independent Publishers Group (IPG), 814 N Franklin St, Chicago, IL 60610 *Tel:* 312-337-0747 *Toll Free Tel:* 800-888-4741 *Fax:* 312-337-5985 *E-mail:* orders@ipgbook.com *Web Site:* www.ipgbook.com
Returns: Independent Publishers Group (IPG), 814 N Franklin St, Chicago, IL 60610 *Tel:* 312-337-0747 *Toll Free Tel:* 800-888-4741 *Fax:* 312-337-5985 *E-mail:* orders@ipgbook.com *Web Site:* www.ipgbook.com
Distribution Center: Independent Publishers Group (IPG), 814 N Franklin St, Chicago, IL 60610 *Tel:* 312-337-0747 *Toll Free Tel:* 800-888-4741 *Fax:* 312-337-5985 *E-mail:* orders@ipgbook.com *Web Site:* www.ipgbook.com

Hoover's Inc
Subsidiary of Dun & Bradstreet
5800 Airport Blvd, Austin, TX 78752
Tel: 512-374-4500 *Toll Free Tel:* 866-486-8666 *Fax:* 512-374-4501
Web Site: www.hoovers.com
Founded: 1990
Business reference books & online services.
ISBN Prefix(es): 978-1-878753; 978-1-57311; 978-1-59274
Number of titles published annually: 7 Print
Total Titles: 7 Print; 3 Online
Imprints: Hoover's Business Press; Hoover's Handbooks
Foreign Office(s): William Snyder Publishing Associates, 5 Five Mile Dr, Oxford OX2 8HT, United Kingdom
Foreign Rep(s): William Snyder Publishing Associates (England)

Hope Publishing Co
380 S Main Place, Carol Stream, IL 60188
Tel: 630-665-3200 *Toll Free Tel:* 800-323-1049 *Fax:* 630-665-2552
E-mail: hope@hopepublishing.com
Web Site: www.hopepublishing.com
Key Personnel
Pres: John Shorney *E-mail:* john@hopepublishing.com
VP: Scott A Shorney *E-mail:* scott@hopepublishing.com; Steve Shorney *E-mail:* steve@hopepublishing.com
Founded: 1892
Choir music, hymnals, instrumental music books & hand bell music.
ISBN Prefix(es): 978-0-916642
Number of titles published annually: 50 Print
Divisions: Agape; Providence Press; Somerset Press; Tabernacle Publishing
Advertising Agency: Lamplighter Agency

§Hope Street Publishing
PO Box 2705, Philadelphia, PA 19120
E-mail: contact@hopestreetpublishing.com
Web Site: www.hopestreetpublishing.com
Key Personnel
Founder & CEO: Vanna B
Founded: 2012
Committed to achieving literary excellence while providing moving, thought-provoking & entertaining publications.
ISBN Prefix(es): 978-0-9853515; 978-0-9888822
Number of titles published annually: 2 Print; 3 E-Book
Total Titles: 4 Print; 6 E-Book

Horizon Publishers & Distributors Inc
191 N 650 E, Bountiful, UT 84010-3628
Tel: 801-292-7102
E-mail: ldshorizonpublishers1@gmail.com
Web Site: www.ldshorizonpublishers.com
Key Personnel
Owner & CEO: Duane S Crowther; Jean D Crowther
Founded: 1971
Christian (primarily Latter-day Saints), inspirational, health foods, self-sufficient living, music, marriage & family, children's activities, needlework, nonfiction, biography paperbacks & hardbound.
ISBN Prefix(es): 978-0-88290
Number of titles published annually: 15 Print
Total Titles: 521 Print; 35 CD-ROM; 40 Audio
Distributed by Cedar Fort Inc

Hospital & Healthcare Compensation Service
Subsidiary of John R Zabka Associates Inc
3 Post Rd, Suite 3, Oakland, NJ 07436
Mailing Address: PO Box 376, Oakland, NJ 07436-0376
Tel: 201-405-0075 *Fax:* 201-405-2110
E-mail: allinfo@hhcsinc.com
Web Site: www.hhcsinc.com
Key Personnel
Dir, Client Servs: Sharah Wallace *Tel:* 201-405-0075 ext 14 *E-mail:* swallace@hhcsinc.com
Dir, Reports: Rosanne Zabka *Tel:* 201-405-0075 ext 11 *E-mail:* rzabka@hhcsinc.com
Founded: 1971
Publisher of salary & benefits reports for hospital, nursing home, assisted living, CCRC, home care, hospice & rehabilitation employees.
ISBN Prefix(es): 978-0-939326; 978-1-934847
Number of titles published annually: 11 Print; 11 CD-ROM
Total Titles: 10 Print; 11 CD-ROM

Host Publications
3408 West Ave, Austin, TX 78705
Mailing Address: 3507 N Lamar Blvd, PO Box 302920, Austin, TX 78703
Tel: 512-236-1290 *Fax:* 512-236-1208
Web Site: www.hostpublications.com
Key Personnel
Pres: Joe W Bratcher, III *E-mail:* jbratcher@hostpublications.com
Dir, Fulfillment: Susan Lesak *E-mail:* slesak@hostpublications.com
Founded: 1987
ISBN Prefix(es): 978-0-924047
Number of titles published annually: 6 Print
Total Titles: 50 Print
Distribution Center: Small Press Distribution, 1341 Seventh St, Berkeley, CA 94710-1409, Opers Dir: Dr Brent Cunningham *Tel:* 510-524-1668 ext 308 *Toll Free Tel:* 800-869-7553 *E-mail:* spd@spdbooks.org *Web Site:* www.spdbooks.org
Membership(s): The Independent Book Publishers Association

Houghton Mifflin Company, see Houghton Mifflin Harcourt

§Houghton Mifflin Harcourt
222 Berkeley St, Boston, MA 02116
Tel: 617-351-5000 *Toll Free Tel:* 800-225-5425 (K-12 educ materials); 800-323-9540 (assessment materials); 877-219-1537 (SkillsTutor); 888-242-6747 (Destination; Earobics; Edmark; Learning Village; Riverdeep); 800-225-3362 (Houghton Mifflin Harcourt Trade & Reference Publishers) *Toll Free Fax:* 800-269-5232
E-mail: customerservice@hmhpub.com
Web Site: www.hmhco.com

Key Personnel
CEO, Pres & Dir: Linda K Zecher
Chief Content Offr & EVP, Corp Aff: Mary Cullinane
CFO: Eric Shuman
EVP & CTO: Brook Colangelo
EVP & Chief HR Offr: Joanne Karimi
EVP & Gen Coun: William Bayers
EVP & Chief, Consumer Brands & Strategy: CJ Kettler
EVP: Rita Schaefer
EVP, Content Devt & Publg Opers: Bethlam Forsa
EVP, Strategy & Alliances: Tim Cannon
SVP, Consumer Brands: Leigh Zarelli
SVP, HR & Chief People Offr: Bridgett Paradise
SVP & Head, Intl Mkts: Mark Short
SVP & Gen Mgr, Specialized Curriculum: Scott Bowker
SVP, Consumer Prods & Mktg: Wendy Bronfin
SVP, Digital Strategy: Nicole Melander
SVP, HMH Studios: Cliff Rotenberg
VP, Prog Devt & Acq: Caroline Fraser
Pres, Trade & Reference Publishers: Gary Gentel
Exec Dir, Mass Mkt & Specialty Retail Channels: Colleen Murphy
Dir, Field Sales: Jen Reynolds
Asst Dir, Mktg: Hannah Harlow
Sr Mktg Mgr: Katrina Kruse
Sr Natl Accts Mgr: Peter Cohen
Natl Accts Mgr & Dist Client Sales Mgr: Morgan Gould
Natl Acct Mgr: James Phirmam
Publicity Mgr: Stephanie Kim
Soc Media Mgr: Liz Anderson
Specialty Retail Sales Mgr: Emily Logan
Mktg Specialist, Culinary Team: Jessica Gilo
Sr Designer: Patrick Barry; Brian Moore
Publicity Assoc: Leila Meglio
Founded; 1832
With education products & services used by 57 million students throughout all 50 U.S. states & 120 countries, Houghton Mifflin Harcourt is a global education & learning company. The world's largest provider of materials for PreK-12 learning, HMH is leading the way with innovative solutions & approaches to the challenges facing education today. Through curricula excellence coupled with technology innovations & professional services, HMH collaborates with school districts, administrators, teachers, parents & students, providing interactive, results-driven learning solutions. Its Educational Consulting Services group works to increase student achievement in underperforming schools by developing, implementing & supporting education transformation through sustained district partnerships. With origins dating back to 1832, the company also publishes an extensive line of reference works & award-winning literature for adults & young readers.
ISBN Prefix(es): 978-0-395 (Houghton Mifflin/Mariner); 978-0-618 (Houghton Mifflin/Mariner/Clarion); 978-0-151 (Harcourt); 978-0-547 (Mariner); 978-0-753 (Kingfisher)
Imprints: The Learning Company; SkillsTutor
Divisions: Houghton Mifflin Harcourt K-12 Publishers; Houghton Mifflin Harcourt Trade & Reference Division
Distributor for Chambers; Harrap; Larousse Bilingual; Larousse Mexico; The Old Farmer's Almanac
Membership(s): AAP; AAP PreK-12 Learning Group; ABA; ALA; American Bar Association; Association of Booksellers for Children; Association of Catholic Publishers Inc; Association of Test Publishers; The Children's Book Council; Dictionary Society of North America; National Catholic Education Association; Society of Printers; Software & Information Industry Association
See separate listing for:
Clarion Books
Great Source Education Group
Harcourt Achieve
Harcourt Inc
Heinemann
Houghton Mifflin Harcourt K-12 Publishers
Houghton Mifflin Harcourt School Publishers
Houghton Mifflin Harcourt Trade & Reference Division
Math Solutions®
Riverside Publishing

Houghton Mifflin Harcourt K-12 Publishers
Division of Houghton Mifflin Harcourt
222 Berkeley St, Boston, MA 02116
Tel: 617-351-5000 *Toll Free Tel:* 800-225-5425 (cust serv)
Web Site: www.hmhco.com/educators; www.hmhco.com
Key Personnel
Dir, School & Lib Mktg: Lisa Di Sarro
Digital Mktg & Publicity Specialist: Roshan Nozari
Elementary school textbooks, educational materials & services.
Imprints: Rigby; Saxon
Sales Office(s): 637 Cypress Hills Dr, Encinitas, CA 92024, SVP, West Area Sales: John Sipe *Tel:* 858-535-3901
8400 E Prentice Ave, Denver, CO 80232-2550
5555 Triangle Pkwy, Suite 150, Norcross, GA 30092, VP & Regl Mgr: Deborah Sanders *Tel:* 404-449-5881
1900 S Batavia Ave, Geneva, IL 60134 *Tel:* 630-232-2550
307 Fellowship Rd, Suite 104, Mount Laurel, NJ 08054 *Tel:* 609-452-0200
13400 Midway Rd, Dallas, TX 75244, VP & Regl Mgr: Mary Lytle *Tel:* 972-980-1100

§Houghton Mifflin Harcourt School Publishers
Division of Houghton Mifflin Harcourt
9205 Southport Center Loop, Orlando, FL 32819
Tel: 407-345-2000 *Toll Free Tel:* 800-225-5425 (cust serv) *Fax:* 407-345-3016 (cust serv) *Toll Free Fax:* 800-874-6418; 800-269-5232 (cust serv)
Web Site: www.hmhco.com
Key Personnel
SVP, Corp Mktg: Margaret deBoer
VP, Math & Science: Peggy Smith-Herbst
Founded: 1919
ISBN Prefix(es): 978-0-15
Number of titles published annually: 500 Print
Total Titles: 20,000 Print; 43 CD-ROM; 3,500 E-Book; 466 Audio
Sales Office(s): 5513 N Cumberland Ave, Chicago, IL 60656 *Tel:* 773-594-5110 *Toll Free Fax:* 800-787-8707
1175 N Stemmons Fwy, Lewisville, TX 75067 *Toll Free Tel:* 800-426-6577 *E-mail:* hsplewis@harcourtschool.com
Warehouse: 1175 N Stemmons Fwy, Lewisville, TX 75067

Houghton Mifflin Harcourt Trade & Reference Division
Division of Houghton Mifflin Harcourt
222 Berkeley St, Boston, MA 02116
SAN: 200-2388
Tel: 617-351-5000 *Toll Free Tel:* 800-225-3362
Web Site: www.hmhco.com
Key Personnel
Pres: Gary Gentel
SVP & Publr: Bruce Nichols
SVP & Publr, Children's Books: Betsy Groban
SVP, Content & Prod Innovation: Cheryl Cramer Toto
SVP, Digital Mkts: Sanj Kharbanda
SVP, Edit Opers & Design: Becky Saikia-Wilson
SVP, Prodn & Creative Servs: Sandy Grebenar
SVP, Sales & Mktg: Laurie Brown
VP & Assoc Publr: Ken Carpenter
VP, Prodn: Jill Lazer
VP, Sales & Children's Mktg: Maire Gorman
VP, Publr & Edit Dir, Clarion Div: Dinah Stevenson
VP & Publr, Culinary Books: Natalie Chapman
VP & Exec Dir, Publicity: Lori Glazer
VP & Creative Dir: Michaela Sullivan
VP & Dir, Subs Rts: Deborah Engel
VP & Dir, Electronic Devt: David Jost
VP & Ed-in-Chief, Children's: Mary Wilcox
Sr Exec Ed: Rick Wolff
Exec Dir, Children's Publicity: Karen Walsh
Exec Dir, Prodn: Donna McCarthy
Natl Accts Dir: Josh Harwood
Culinary Digital Edit Dir: Allison Renzulli
Dir, Culinary Mktg: Brad Parsons
Assoc Dir, Publicity: Taryn Roeder
Sr Exec Ed: Susan Canavan; Rux Martin; Margaret Raymo; Deanne Urmy
Sr Exec Ed, Books for Young Readers: Jeannette Larson
Exec Mng Ed, Children's: Ann-Marie Pucillo
Exec Ed: Helen Atsma; Jenna Johnson; Lauren Wein
Exec Ed, Children's: Elizabeth Bewley
Exec Ed, CliffsNotes: Greg Tubach
Exec Ed, Franchise Publg, Houghton Mifflin Harcourt Children's: Elizabeth Bennett
Mng Ed: Mary Huot
Mng Ed, Cookbooks: Marina Padakis
Mng Ed, Digital Cookbooks: Rebecca Springer
Sr Ed: Alex Littlefield
Ed: Nicole Angeloro
Assoc Ed: Naomi Gibbs; Ben Hyman
Assoc Ed, Children's: Adah Nuchi
Assoc Ed, Culinary: Stephanie Fletcher
Sr Mktg Mgr: Katrina Krause
Sr Mgr, Subs Rts: Candace Finn
Sr Designer: Patrick Barry; Whitney Leader-Picone; Brian Moore
Sr Publicist: Michelle Bonanno
Sr Publicity Assoc: Simmi Aujla
Sr Publicity Mgr, Children's: Rachel Wasdyke
Culinary Publicity Mgr: Brittany Edwards
Digital Prod Mgr: Taylor Foley
Soc Media Mgr, Children's: Meredith Wilson
Sr Prodn Coord: Kim Kiefer
Edit Assoc: Laney Everson
Edit Assoc, Children's: Amy Cherrix; Anna Dobbin; Christine Krones; Anna Meier
Mktg Assoc, School & Lib Mktg: Amanda Acevedo
General literature, fiction, nonfiction, biography, autobiography, history, poetry & juvenile publications, dictionary, reference books, cookbooks & guidebooks.
ISBN Prefix(es): 978-0-89919; 978-0-395; 978-1-85697; 978-0-7534; 978-0-618; 978-1-88152
Number of titles published annually: 400 Print; 1 CD-ROM; 1 Online; 14 Audio
Total Titles: 3,300 Print; 2 CD-ROM; 2 Online; 110 Audio
Imprints: American Heritage Dictionary; Betty Crocker®; Clarion Books; CliffNotes™; Eamon Dolan Books; Graphia; Harcourt Children's; HMH Franchise; Houghton Mifflin Books for Children; Houghton Mifflin Harcourt; Mariner Books; Rux Martin Books; New Harvest; Sandpiper
Editorial Office(s): 215 Park Ave S, New York, NY 10003 *Tel:* 212-420-5800
Distributed by Hachette Book Group
Distributor for Harvard Common Press; Larausse; Old Farmers Almanac
Orders to: Houghton Mifflin Harcourt Trade Customer Service, 181 Ballardvale St, PO Box 705, Wilmington, MA 01887 *Toll Free Tel:* 800-225-3362 *Toll Free Fax:* 800-634-7568
Returns: Houghton Mifflin Harcourt Publishing Company, Trade Returns Department, 2700 N Richard Ave, Indianapolis, IN 46219
Distribution Center: Raincoast Books, 2440 Viking Way, Richmond, BC V6V 1N2, Canada *Tel:* 604-448-7100 *Fax:* 604-270-7161 *E-mail:* customerservice@raincoast.com

House of Collectibles
Imprint of Random House Information Group
1745 Broadway, New York, NY 10019
Tel: 212-782-9000
Web Site: www.houseofcollectibles.randomhouse.com; www.randomhouse.com
Publisher that collectors, dealers & investors around the world turn to for detailed reference information & current market values on all antiques & collectibles, whether they want to know the history of Gustav Stickley furniture, buy a Chinese vase, sell their grandmother's depression glass or evaluate the worth of their Star Wars memorabilia. The House of Collectibles books are compiled by experts, renowned for accuracy & completeness & profusely illustrated, many with full color. Accept unsol proposals & mss from authors who are experts in the antiques & collectibles areas, also accept mss & proposals from agents.
ISBN Prefix(es): 978-0-307; 978-0-676; 978-1-4000; 978-0-87637
Total Titles: 4 Print

House to House Publications
Division of DOVE International
11 Toll Gate Rd, Lititz, PA 17543
Tel: 717-627-1996 *Toll Free Tel:* 800-848-5892 *Fax:* 717-627-4004
E-mail: h2hp@dcfi.org
Web Site: www.dcfi.org
Key Personnel
Pubns Ed: Lou Anne Good
Founded: 1997
Provide resources for the body of Christ worldwide.
ISBN Prefix(es): 978-1-886973
Number of titles published annually: 4 Print; 5 E-Book; 1 Audio
Total Titles: 37 Print; 5 Audio
Imprints: Partnership Publications

Housing Assistance Council
1025 Vermont Ave NW, Suite 606, Washington, DC 20005
Tel: 202-842-8600 *Fax:* 202-347-3441
E-mail: hac@ruralhome.org
Web Site: www.ruralhome.org
Key Personnel
Sr Policy Analyst: Leslie R Strauss *E-mail:* leslie@ruralhome.org
Founded: 1971
Provides technical housing services, loans, program & policy assistance, training, research & information. Specialize in research reports, technical manuals & information pieces, all exclusively about low-income rural housing in the US.
ISBN Prefix(es): 978-1-58064
Number of titles published annually: 15 Print; 15 Online
Total Titles: 80 Print; 50 Online
Branch Office(s)
717 "K" St, Suite 404, Sacramento, CA 95814 *Tel:* 916-706-1836 *Fax:* 916-706-1849 *E-mail:* western@ruralhome.org
600 W Peachtree St NW, Suite 1500, Atlanta, GA 30308 *Tel:* 404-892-4824 *Fax:* 404-892-1204 *E-mail:* southeast@ruralhome.org
10100 NW Ambassador Dr, Suite 310, Kansas City, MO 64153-1362 *Tel:* 816-880-0400 *Fax:* 816-880-0500 *E-mail:* midwest@ruralhome.org
7510 Montgomery NE, Suite 205, Albuquerque, NM 87109 *Tel:* 505-883-1003 *Fax:* 505-883-1005 *E-mail:* southwest@ruralhome.org

Howard Books
Imprint of Atria Publishing Group
216 Centerview Dr, Suite 303, Brentwood, TN 37027
SAN: 298-7597
Tel: 615-873-2080 *Fax:* 615-370-3834
E-mail: howardbooks@simonandschuster.com (info)
Web Site: www.howardpublishing.com
Key Personnel
VP, Publr: Jonathan Merkh *Tel:* 615-873-2211 *E-mail:* jonathan.merkh@simonandschuster.com
VP, Dir, Subs Rts (dom): Lisa Keim
VP, Assoc Publr: Rob Birkhead *Tel:* 615-873-2090 *E-mail:* rob.birkhead@simonandschuster.com
VP, Dir of Publicity: Jennifer Smith *Tel:* 615-873-2085 *E-mail:* jennifer.smith@simonandschuster.com
VP, Ed-in-Chief: Ami McConnell *Tel:* 615-873-2195 *E-mail:* ami.mcconnell@simonandschuster.com
Sr Ed: Philis Boultinghouse *Tel:* 615-873-2196 *E-mail:* Philis.Boultinghouse@simonandschuster.com; Beth Adams *Tel:* 212-698-7329 *E-mail:* beth.adams@simonandschuster.com
Art Dir: Bruce Gore *Tel:* 615-873-2202 *E-mail:* bruce.gore@simonandschuster.com
Mng Ed: Karen Longino *Tel:* 615-873-2197 *E-mail:* karen.longino@simonandschuster.com
Imprint Mktg Mgr: Brandi Lewis *Tel:* 615-873-2191 *E-mail:* brandi.lewis@simonandschuster.com
Assoc Ed: Katie Sandell *Tel:* 615-873-2198 *E-mail:* katherine.sandell@simonandschuster.com; Amanda Demastus *Tel:* 615-873-2194 *E-mail:* amanda.demastus@simonandschuster.com
Publicist: Bonnie MacIsaac *Tel:* 615-873-2091 *E-mail:* bonnie.macisaac@simonandschuster.com
CBA Key Accts Mgr: Chris Long *Tel:* 615-873-2193 *E-mail:* christopher.long@simonandschuster.com
Founded: 1969
Inspirational books.
ISBN Prefix(es): 978-1-4165; 978-1-58229; 978-1-4391
Number of titles published annually: 50 Print
Foreign Rights: Akcali Copyright Agency (Turkey); Antonella Antonelli Agenzia; Book Publishers' Association of Israel, International Promotion & Literary Rights Dept (Israel); International Editors' Company (Latin America, Portugal, Spain); Japan UNI Agency Inc (Japan); JLM Literary Agency (Greece); Korea Copyright Center Inc (KCC) (Korea); Mohrbooks AG, Literary Agency; La Nouvelle Agence; Andrew Nurnberg Associates Ltd (Bulgaria, China, Croatia, Czech Republic, Estonia, Hungary, Latvia, Lithuania, Montenegro, Poland, Romania, Russia, Serbia, Slovakia, Slovenia, Taiwan); Sane Toregard Agency (Denmark, Finland, Norway, Sweden); Karin Schindler (Brazil); Sebes & Van Gelderen Literary Agency (Netherlands); Tuttle-Mori Agency Inc (Thailand)
Membership(s): CBA: The Association for Christian Retail; Evangelical Christian Publishers Association

HPBooks
Imprint of Penguin Group (USA) LLC
375 Hudson St, New York, NY 10014
SAN: 282-5074
Tel: 212-366-2000
E-mail: online@penguinputnam.com
Web Site: www.penguinputnam.com; us.penguingroup.com
Key Personnel
VP, Publr: John Duff
Sales Rep: Hal Holding
Founded: 1964
Automotive book publisher. High performance, restoration & racing how-to books for automotive enthusiasts. Cover domestic & foreign vehicles. Also publishes cookbooks.
ISBN Prefix(es): 978-0-89586; 978-0-912656; 978-1-55788
Total Titles: 104 Print; 72 E-Book
Advertising Agency: Spier NY

§HRD Press
22 Amherst Rd, Amherst, MA 01002-9709
SAN: 201-9213
Tel: 413-253-3488 *Toll Free Tel:* 800-822-2801 *Fax:* 413-253-3490
E-mail: info@hrdpress.com; customerservice@hrdpress.com
Web Site: www.hrdpress.com
Key Personnel
Publr: Robert W Carkhuff
Cust Rel Mgr: Donna Long
Founded: 1972
Textbooks & off-the-shelf workshops on human resource development, management & training. Packaged training materials & assessments.
ISBN Prefix(es): 978-0-914234; 978-0-87425
Number of titles published annually: 25 Print
Total Titles: 600 Print; 20 E-Book
Distributed by Training & Development Materials of Canada (Canada)
Foreign Rep(s): Eurospan Ltd (Europe); HRD Central (Australia); Human Capital Partners (Nigeria); Management Learning Resources (UK); Multimedia HRD Pvt Ltd (India); Trainco (South Africa); Training & Development Materials of Canada (Canada)
Returns: c/o ViaTech Publishing Solutions Inc, 8857 Alexander Rd, Batavia, NY 14020

Hudson Hills Press LLC
116 Pleasant St, Suite 049, Easthampton, MA 01027
Mailing Address: PO Box 205, Easthampton, MA 01027
Tel: 413-527-6450
E-mail: artbooks@hudsonhills.com; editorial@hudsonhills.com (submissions)
Web Site: www.hudsonhills.com
Key Personnel
Sales & Internet Mktg Mgr: Kristen van Breen
Founded: 1978
Renowned titles on fine art, photography, decorative arts & architecture.
ISBN Prefix(es): 978-0-933920; 978-1-55595
Number of titles published annually: 20 Print
Total Titles: 150 Print
Distributed by National Book Network
Foreign Rights: Peribo (Australia); Windsor Books International (Europe, UK)

Hudson Institute
1015 15 St NW, 6th fl, Washington, DC 20005
Tel: 202-974-2400 *Fax:* 202-974-2410
E-mail: info@hudson.org
Web Site: www.hudson.org
Key Personnel
Pres & CEO: Kenneth R Weinstein
COO: John P Walters
SVP: Lewis Libby
Sr Fellow & Dir, Pub Aff & Spec Projs: David Tell
Founded: 1961
Books, monographs, briefing papers, newsletters.
ISBN Prefix(es): 978-1-55813
Number of titles published annually: 10 Print
Total Titles: 60 Print

§Human Kinetics Inc
1607 N Market St, Champaign, IL 61820
Mailing Address: PO Box 5076, Champaign, IL 61825-5076 SAN: 211-7088
Tel: 217-351-5076 *Toll Free Tel:* 800-747-4457 *Fax:* 217-351-1549 (orders/cust serv)
E-mail: info@hkusa.com
Web Site: www.humankinetics.com
Key Personnel
Founder & Pres: Rainer Martens

CEO: Brian Holding
CFO & Opers Dir: Tina Daniel
EVP: Julie S Martens
VP & Coach Educ Dir: Ted Miller
VP, Consumer Div: Jason Muzinic
VP, Higher Educ Div: Steve Ruhlig
E-mail: stever@hkusa.com
VP, Prod Devt: Holly Gilly
Intl Devt Dir: Barry Johnson
Intl Sales & Translation Rts Mgr: Drew Tyler
Founded: 1974
Scholarly books, college textbooks, continuing education courses & trade books in physical education, sports medicine & science, coaching, sport technique & fitness, courses, CDs & DVDs.
ISBN Prefix(es): 978-0-931250; 978-0-87322; 978-0-88011; 978-0-918438; 978-0-7360; 978-0-912781; 978-1-4504
Number of titles published annually: 200 Print
Total Titles: 1,693 Print; 174 CD-ROM; 387 Online
Branch Office(s)
Human Kinetics Canada, 475 Devonshire Rd, Unit 100, Windsor, ON N8Y 2L5, Canada *Tel:* 519-971-9500 *Toll Free Tel:* 800-465-7301 (CN) *Fax:* 519-971-9797 *E-mail:* info@hkcanada.com
Foreign Office(s): Human Kinetics Australia, PO Box 80, 57 A Price Ave, Lower Mitcham, SA 5062, Australia *Tel:* (08) 8372-0999 *Fax:* (08) 8372 0998 *E-mail:* info@hkaustralia.com
Human Kinetics New Zealand Pty Ltd, PO Box 80, Mitcham, SA 5062, Australia *Tel:* (08) 8372-0999; 0800 222 062 *Fax:* (08) 8372-0998; 0800 222 064 *E-mail:* info@hknewzealand.com
Human Kinetics UK, Europe & Middle East, 107 Bradford Rd, Stanningley, Leeds LS28 6AT, United Kingdom *Tel:* (0113) 255 5665 *Fax:* (0113) 255 5885 *E-mail:* hk@hkeurope.com
Foreign Rep(s): Aditya Books (India); Africa Connection, Old School House (Angola, Benin, Cameroon, Cape Verde, Cote d'Ivoire (Ivory Coast), Gabon, The Gambia, Ghana, Liberia, Mali, Mozambique, Niger, Sao Tome and Principe, Senegal, Uganda, Zambia, Zimbabwe); Alkem Co (Bangladesh, Brunei, Indonesia, Laos, Malaysia, Philippines, Singapore, Thailand); Asian Books (Sri Lanka); Atlantic Publishers & Distributors (India); Bookport (Trade) (Croatia, Gibraltar, Greece, Italy, Malta, Montenegro, Portugal, Serbia, Slovenia, Spain); CBS Publishers & Distributors (India); Charran Publishing House (Trinidad and Tobago); Comprajato (Brazil); Cranbury International Books LLC (Caribbean, Latin America); CRW Marketing Services for Publishers Inc (Philippines, Saipan); Dasansogo Co Ltd (Korea); Disvan Enterprises (India); Eureka Press (Japan); Laszlo Horvath (Austria, Czech Republic, Hungary, Macedonia, Montenegro, Poland, Romania, Russia, Slovakia); Icon Books (Malaysia, Singapore, Vietnam); IPR (Middle East, North Africa); Kemper Conseil (Belgium, France, Germany, Switzerland); Kinemed Technologies (Chile); KinesWorld (China, Hong Kong); Libreria Medica (Colombia); Flavio Marcello (Academic) (Italy, Portugal, Spain); Research Periodicals & Book Services (Tanzania); Saras Books (India); Unifacmanu Trading Co Ltd (Taiwan)

§Human Rights Watch
350 Fifth Ave, 34th fl, New York, NY 10118-3299
Tel: 212-290-4700 *Fax:* 212-736-1300
E-mail: hrwnyc@hrw.org
Web Site: www.hrw.org
Key Personnel
Communs Dir: Emma Daly *Tel:* 212-216-1835
Founded: 1978
Nonprofit human rights organization publishing books & newsletters on human rights practices in more than 80 countries worldwide; documents arbitrary imprisonment, censorship, disappearances, due process of law, murder, prison conditions, torture, violations of laws of war & other abuses of internationally recognized human rights.
ISBN Prefix(es): 978-0-938579; 978-0-929692; 978-1-56432
Number of titles published annually: 67 Print
Total Titles: 1,000 Print; 60 E-Book
Imprints: Human Rights Watch Books

§Humanix Books LLC
Division of NewsMaxx
PO Box 20989, West Palm Beach, FL 33416
Tel: 561-459-5997 *Toll Free Tel:* 855-371-7810 *Fax:* 561-241-6448 *Toll Free Fax:* 855-371-7809
E-mail: info@humanixbooks.com
Web Site: www.humanixbooks.com
Key Personnel
Publr: Mary Glenn
Dir, Publg: Sherri Slopianka
Mng Dir: Jennifer Wilson
Sales Mgr: Gina Sinnett
Exec Ed: Pam Pantelo
Founded: 2012
Trade paperbacks, hardcover & ebooks in the following areas: finance, investing, health, wellness, lifestyle, business, leadership, management, politics, current events, success, motivation, history & military.
ISBN Prefix(es): 978-1-63006
Number of titles published annually: 8 Print; 8 Online; 8 E-Book
Total Titles: 15 Print; 15 Online; 15 E-Book; 1 Audio
Orders to: Ingram Book Co, One Ingram Blvd, La Vergne, TN 37086
Distribution Center: Ingram Book Co, One Ingram Blvd, La Vergne, TN 37086 *Tel:* 615-793-5000 *Web Site:* www.ingrambookcontent.com

Karen Hunter Publishing, see Gallery Books

§Hunter Publishing Inc
222 Clematis St, West Palm Beach, FL 33401
SAN: 695-3425
Tel: 561-835-2022
Web Site: guidestotheworld.com
Key Personnel
Founder & Pres: Michael Hunter
E-mail: michael@hunterpublishing.com
Founded: 1985
Books for travelers.
ISBN Prefix(es): 978-1-55650; 978-1-58843
Number of titles published annually: 50 E-Book
Total Titles: 640 E-Book
Imprints: Adventure Guides; Alive Guides; Best Dives Guides; Cruise Guides; Romantic Weekends; State & National Parks Guides

Huntington Library Press
Division of Huntington Library, Art Collections & Botanical Gardens
1151 Oxford Rd, San Marino, CA 91108
SAN: 202-313X
Tel: 626-405-2172 *Fax:* 626-585-0794
E-mail: booksales@huntington.org
Web Site: www.huntington.org
Key Personnel
Dir: Susan Green *E-mail:* sgreen@huntington.org
Mng Ed: Jean Patterson *E-mail:* jpatterson@huntington.org
Founded: 1920
Scholarly nonfiction in English & American history, literature & art.
ISBN Prefix(es): 978-0-87328
Number of titles published annually: 6 Print
Total Titles: 70 Print

Huntington Press Publishing
3665 Procyon St, Las Vegas, NV 89103-1907
Tel: 702-252-0655 *Toll Free Tel:* 800-244-2224 *Fax:* 702-252-0675
E-mail: sales@huntingtonpress.com
Web Site: www.huntingtonpress.com
Key Personnel
Publr: Anthony Curtis *E-mail:* publisher@huntingtonpress.com
Founded: 1983
Books relating to gambling & Las Vegas.
ISBN Prefix(es): 978-0-929712; 978-1-935396
Number of titles published annually: 8 Print
Total Titles: 105 Print; 53 Online; 53 E-Book
Imprints: Vegas Lit

Hutton Publishing
140D Heritage Village, Southbury, CT 06488
Tel: 203-558-4478
E-mail: huttonbooks@hotmail.com
Web Site: www.huttonpublishing.com
Key Personnel
Ed-in-Chief: Caroline DuBois Hutton
Founded: 2004
Digital publishing for Kindle, Nook, etc; print-on-demand. All books receive personal attention & are professionally designed & listed for distribution in the Ingram Catalog, available through Amazon, B&N Online & local bookstores. Promotion notes available for all Huttonelectronicpublishing.com authors. All royalties are split 50-50, author & publisher. Some books paid 100% by authors, others, by special arrangement with the publisher, at varying percentages subsidized by the publisher. Please inquire by e-mail for further information. Prize-winning illustrators available as needed.
ISBN Prefix(es): 978-0-9742894; 978-0-9785171
Number of titles published annually: 10 Print; 10 E-Book
Total Titles: 20 Print; 20 E-Book
Distribution Center: Lightning Source Inc, 1246 Heil Quaker Blvd, La Vergne, TN 37086

Hyperion, see Hachette Books

I-5 Publishing LLC
3 Burroughs, Irvine, CA 92618
Tel: 949-855-8822 *Toll Free Tel:* 888-738-2665 *Fax:* 949-458-3856
Web Site: www.i5publishing.com
Key Personnel
Founder & Pres: Mark Harris
Founder: David Fry
Mng Ed: April Balotro
Sales Mgr: Kim Huey-Steiner
Founded: 2013
Number of titles published annually: 18 Print

Ibex Publishers
PO Box 30087, Bethesda, MD 20824
SAN: 696-866X
Tel: 301-718-8188 *Toll Free Tel:* 888-718-8188 *Fax:* 301-907-8707
E-mail: info@ibexpub.com
Web Site: www.ibexpublishers.com
Key Personnel
Publr: Mr Farhad Shirzad *E-mail:* fs@ibex.net
Founded: 1979
English & Persian language books about Iran.
ISBN Prefix(es): 978-0-936347; 978-1-58814
Number of titles published annually: 15 Print
Total Titles: 330 Print; 3 CD-ROM; 5 Audio
Imprints: IBEX Press; Iranbooks Press
Distributor for Farhang Moaser

IBFD North America Inc (International Bureau of Fiscal Documentation)
Division of IBFD Foundation
8100 Boone Blvd, Suite 210, Vienna, VA 22182
Tel: 703-442-7757 *Fax:* 703-442-7758
Web Site: www.ibfd.org
Key Personnel
Mgr, Americas: Steven Stroschein *E-mail:* s.stroschein@ibfd.org
Founded: 1938
International taxation & investment & tax law.
Number of titles published annually: 30 Print
Total Titles: 30 Print; 1 CD-ROM; 42 Online
Foreign Office(s): HJE Wenckebachweg 210, 1096 AS Amsterdam, Netherlands *Tel:* (020) 554 0100 *E-mail:* info@ibfd.org

ICMA, see International City/County Management Association (ICMA)

Iconografix Inc
2017 O'Neil Rd, Hudson, WI 54016
Tel: 715-381-9755 *Toll Free Tel:* 800-289-3504 (orders only) *Fax:* 715-381-9756
E-mail: info@iconografixinc.com
Web Site: www.iconografixinc.com
Key Personnel
Edit Dir: David Hohman
Founded: 1992
Publish special historical interest photographic books.
ISBN Prefix(es): 978-1-882256; 978-1-58388
Number of titles published annually: 8 Print
Total Titles: 300 Print
Divisions: Enthusiast Books
Shipping Address: Motorbooks International, 729 Prospect Ave, Osceola, WI 54020
Distribution Center: Motorbooks International, PO Box 2, Osceola, WI 54020, Contact: Brad Siqueiros *Tel:* 715-294-3345 *Fax:* 715-294-4448

Idaho Center for the Book
Affiliate of Library of Congress
Boise State University, 1910 University Dr, Boise, ID 83725
Tel: 208-426-1000 *Toll Free Tel:* 800-992-8398 (outside ID)
Web Site: www.boisestatebooks.com (orders)
Key Personnel
Dir: Stephanie Bacon *E-mail:* sbacon@boisestate.edu
Founded: 1993
Idaho book history & culture.
ISBN Prefix(es): 978-0-932129
Number of titles published annually: 4 Print
Total Titles: 25 Print; 1 CD-ROM
Editorial Office(s): ICB, MS 1525 BSU, Boise, ID 83725

Ideals Publications, a Guideposts Co
6100 Tower Circle, Suite 210, Franklin, TN 37067
SAN: 213-4403
Tel: 615-932-7600 *Toll Free Tel:* 800-586-2572 (cust serv) *Fax:* 615-781-1447
Web Site: www.idealsbooks.com
Key Personnel
VP, Sales & Group Publr: Marty Flanagan
Publr: Peggy Schaefer *E-mail:* pschaefer@guideposts.org
Founded: 1944
Publisher of *IDEALS* magazine, children's books & boardbooks.
ISBN Prefix(es): 978-0-8249; 978-0-89542
Number of titles published annually: 30 Print
Total Titles: 200 Print
Imprints: CandyCane Press; Ideals; Ideals Children's Books; Williamson Books
Distributor for Hinkler Books; Rourke Publishing; Smart Ink; Smart Kidz; Someday Baby

Idyll Arbor Inc
39129 264 Ave SE, Enumclaw, WA 98022
Tel: 360-825-7797 *Fax:* 360-825-5670
E-mail: sales@idyllarbor.com
Web Site: www.idyllarbor.com
Key Personnel
Pres & Intl Rts: Tom Blaschko *E-mail:* tom@idyllarbor.com
Founded: 1984
Publish health care books, information for recreational therapists & activity directors & books on social issues. The Issues Press imprint covers important social issues such as addictions & health care for returning military personnel. Titles published under the Pine Winds Press imprint relate to discussions of the life force, including spiritual reality, Bigfoot, fairies & other strange phenomena.
ISBN Prefix(es): 978-1-882883; 978-0-937663; 978-1-930461; 978-1-61158
Number of titles published annually: 8 Print; 8 E-Book
Total Titles: 100 Print; 50 E-Book; 1 Audio
Imprints: Issues Press; Pine Winds Press
Foreign Rights: Columbine Communications (Worldwide exc Canada & USA)
Membership(s): Book Publishers of the Northwest; The Independent Book Publishers Association; Pacific Northwest Booksellers Association

§IEEE Computer Society
2001 "L" St NW, Suite 700, Washington, DC 20036-4928
SAN: 264-620X
Tel: 202-371-0101 *Toll Free Tel:* 800-272-6657 (memb info) *Fax:* 202-728-9614
E-mail: help@computer.org
Web Site: www.computer.org
Key Personnel
Exec Dir: Angela R Burgess *E-mail:* aburgess@computer.org
Dir, Sales & Mktg: Chris Jensen *E-mail:* cjensen@computer.org
Busn Analytics Mgr: John Reimer *E-mail:* jreimer@computer.org
Founded: 1980
Tutorials, reports, reprint collections, conference proceedings, textbooks & CD-ROMs.
ISBN Prefix(es): 978-0-8186; 978-0-7695
Number of titles published annually: 155 Print
Total Titles: 1,000 Print; 5 CD-ROM
Branch Office(s)
10662 Los Vaqueros Circle, Los Alamitos, CA 90720-1314 *Tel:* 714-821-8380 *Fax:* 714-821-4010
Foreign Office(s): KFK Bldg, 2-14-14 Minami-Aoyama, Minato-ku, Tokyo 107-0062, Japan *Tel:* (03) 3408 3118 *Fax:* (03) 3408 3553 *E-mail:* tokyo.ofc@computer.org

§IEEE Press
Division of Institute of Electrical & Electronics Engineers Inc (IEEE)
445 Hoes Lane, Piscataway, NJ 08854
Tel: 732-981-0060 *Fax:* 732-562-1746
E-mail: pressbooks@ieee.org (proposals & info)
Web Site: www.ieee.org/press
Key Personnel
Dir, Books & Info Servs: Kenneth Moore *E-mail:* k.moore@ieee.org
Founded: 1971
Professional books & texts in electrical & computer engineering, computer science, electrotechnology, general engineering, applied mathematics. Tutorials in technical subjects.
ISBN Prefix(es): 978-0-87942; 978-0-7803; 978-0-471
Number of titles published annually: 40 Print
Total Titles: 600 Print; 425 E-Book
Imprints: Wiley-IEEE Press
Distributed by John Wiley & Sons Inc
Foreign Rep(s): John Wiley & Sons Inc
Foreign Rights: John Wiley & Sons Inc
Membership(s): AAP

IET USA Inc
379 Thornall St, Edison, NJ 08837
Tel: 732-321-5575 *Fax:* 732-321-5702
E-mail: ietusa@theiet.org
Web Site: www.theiet.org
Key Personnel
VP & Gen Mgr: Michael Ornstein
Founded: 1871
Professional books, journals, magazines & conference proceedings in many areas of electrical & electronic engineering, including telecommunications, computing, power, control, radar, circuits, materials & more.
ISBN Prefix(es): 978-0-85296; 978-0-906048; 978-0-86341
Number of titles published annually: 30 Print
Total Titles: 500 Print; 300 E-Book
Imprints: IEE; Inspec; Peter Peregrinus Ltd
Foreign Office(s): The IET, Suite G, 10F, China Merchants Tower, No 118 Jianguo Rd, Chaoyang District, Beijing 100022, China *Tel:* (010) 6566 7697 *E-mail:* china@theiet.org *Web Site:* www.theiet.org/cn
The IET, 4405-06 Cosco Tower, 183 Queen's Rd Central, Hong Kong, Hong Kong *Tel:* 2521 2140 *Fax:* 2778 1711 *E-mail:* adminap@theiet.org
IET India, Unit No 405 & 406, 4th fl, West Wing, Raheja Towers, MG Rd, Bangalore 560 001, India *Tel:* (080) 4089 2222 *E-mail:* india@theiet.in *Web Site:* theiet.in
The Institution of Engineering & Technology, Michael Faraday House, 6 Hills Way, Stevenage, Herts SG1 2AY, United Kingdom (journal & magazine sales), Contact: Neil Dennis *Tel:* (01438) 313 311 *E-mail:* postmaster@theiet.org
Foreign Rep(s): Cranbury International (Latin America, Mexico, South America)
Orders to: c/o Books International Inc, PO Box 605, Herndon, VA 20172 *Tel:* 703-661-1573 *Toll Free Tel:* 800-230-7286 (US & CN) *Fax:* 703-661-1501 *E-mail:* ieemail@presswarehouse.com
Distribution Center: c/o Books International Inc, PO Box 605, Herndon, VA 20172 *Tel:* 703-661-1500 *Fax:* 703-661-1501
Membership(s): Association of Learned & Professional Society Publishers; STM

IFPRI, see International Food Policy Research Institute

§Ignatius Press
Division of Guadalupe Associates Inc
1348 Tenth Ave, San Francisco, CA 94122-2304
SAN: 214-3887
Toll Free Tel: 800-651-1531 (orders); 888-615-3186 (cust serv)
E-mail: info@ignatius.com
Web Site: www.ignatius.com
Key Personnel
Pres: Mark Brumley *E-mail:* mark@ignatius.com
Art Dir: Roxanne Lum
Mktg Dir: Anthony J Ryan
Ed: Fr Joseph Fessio SJ
Prodn Ed: Carolyn Lemon
Mktg Mgr: Eva Mutean *E-mail:* eva@ignatius.com
Foreign Rts: Penelope Boldrick
Founded: 1978
ISBN Prefix(es): 978-0-89870; 978-1-58617
Number of titles published annually: 30 Print
Total Titles: 510 Print; 55 Audio
Distributor for Bethlehem Books; Veritas
Foreign Rep(s): Ancoh Enterprises (Nigeria); B Broughton Co Ltd (Canada); Freedom Publishing (Australia, New Zealand); Gracewing Publishing (Europe, UK); John XXIII Fellowship Co-op Ltd (Australia, New Zealand); St

Andrew's Church Supply (Canada); Sunrise Marian Distribution (Canada); Veritas Publications (Ireland)

§IHS Jane's
Subsidiary of IHS Inc
110 N Royal St, Suite 200, Alexandria, VA 22314-1651
SAN: 286-357X
Tel: 703-683-3700 *Toll Free Tel:* 800-824-0768 (sales) *Fax:* 703-836-0297 *Toll Free Fax:* 800-836-0297
E-mail: customercare@ihs.com
Web Site: www.ihs.com
Key Personnel
America's Mktg Mgr: Jim Scanlon
Founded: 1897
Hard copy, online services, magazines, CD-ROM, electronic databases on defense aerospace, transportation & terrorism subjects.
ISBN Prefix(es): 978-0-7106; 978-0-354; 978-0-356
Number of titles published annually: 50 Print
Total Titles: 180 Print
Warehouse: ITP Distribution Center, 7625 Empire Dr, Florence, KY 41042

IHS Press
222 W 21 St, Suite F-122, Norfolk, VA 23517
Toll Free Tel: 877-447-7737 *Toll Free Fax:* 877-447-7737
E-mail: info@ihspress.com; tradesales@ihspress.com (wholesale sales); order@ihspress.com
Web Site: www.ihspress.com
Founded: 2001
ISBN Prefix(es): 978-0-9714894; 978-0-9718286; 978-1-932528; 978-1-60570
Number of titles published annually: 12 Print; 12 E-Book
Total Titles: 42 Print; 42 E-Book
Distribution Center: Intrepid Group, 1331 Red Cedar Circle, Fort Collins, CO 80524

§Illinois State Museum Society
Affiliate of Illinois State Museum
502 S Spring St, Springfield, IL 62706-5000
Tel: 217-782-7386 *Fax:* 217-782-1254
E-mail: editor@museum.state.il.us
Web Site: www.museum.state.il.us
Key Personnel
Museum Dir: Bonnie Styles *Tel:* 217-782-7011 *E-mail:* bwstyles@museum.state.il.us
Museum Ed: Andy Hanson *Tel:* 217-782-6700 *E-mail:* ahanson@museum.state.il.us
Founded: 1877
Softcover texts, quarterly magazines, quarterly newsletters, quarterly calendars of events & activities brochures, educational posters & CD-ROM.
ISBN Prefix(es): 978-0-89792
Number of titles published annually: 5 Print
Total Titles: 1 CD-ROM

§Illuminating Engineering Society of North America (IES)
120 Wall St, 17th fl, New York, NY 10005-4001
Tel: 212-248-5000 *Fax:* 212-248-5017; 212-248-5018
E-mail: ies@ies.org
Web Site: www.ies.org
Key Personnel
Mktg Mgr: Clayton Gordon *Tel:* 212-248-5000 ext 110 *E-mail:* cgordon@ies.org
Founded: 1906
ISBN Prefix(es): 978-0-87995
Number of titles published annually: 10 Print; 1 E-Book
Total Titles: 90 Print; 1 E-Book
Distributor for Taylor & Francis; Techstreet

Illumination Arts Publishing, see Inspiring Every Child dba Illumination Arts Publishing

Imagination Publishing Group
PO Box 1304, Dunedin, FL 34697
Toll Free Tel: 888-701-6481 *Fax:* 727-361-0584
E-mail: info@imaginationpublishinggroup.com
Web Site: www.imaginationpublishinggroup.com
Key Personnel
Pres: Alan Wayne
Asst: Miranda Jade
Founded: 2008
Publisher of fine quality printed products & educational apps for mobile devices.
ISBN Prefix(es): 978-0-9800
Number of titles published annually: 5 Print; 2 Audio
Total Titles: 3 Print; 1 Audio
Membership(s): ABA; Association of Booksellers for Children; Florida Association for Media in Education; Florida Association for Partners in Education; Florida Authors & Publishers Association Inc; Society of Children's Book Writers & Illustrators; Southern Independent Booksellers for Children

§Imago Press
3710 E Edison St, Tucson, AZ 85716
Tel: 520-444-2265
Web Site: www.oasisjournal.org
Key Personnel
Publr: Leila Joiner *E-mail:* ljoiner@dakotacom.net
Founded: 2002
Provide a place for older authors to present their work to appreciative audiences. Our flagship offering is the *OASIS Journal*, an annual anthology of short fiction, short nonfiction & poetry by writers over fifty, which originated with the OASIS Institute, a national nonprofit organization that promotes ongoing education for seniors.
ISBN Prefix(es): 978-0-9725303; 978-0-9799341; 978-1-935437
Number of titles published annually: 6 Print; 3 E-Book
Total Titles: 52 Print; 22 E-Book
Imprints: As Sabr; Pennywyse Press
Membership(s): The Independent Book Publishers Association

§ImaJinn Books Inc
Imprint of BelleBooks
PO Box 74274, Phoenix, AZ 85087-4274
Tel: 623-236-3361 *Toll Free Tel:* 877-625-3592 (US & CN)
E-mail: orders@imajinnbooks.com; editors@imajinnbooks.com
Web Site: www.imajinnbooks.com
Founded: 1998
Specialize in publishing & selling paranormal romance, urban fantasy, regency romance & erotica.
ISBN Prefix(es): 978-1-893896; 978-0-9759653; 978-1-933417; 978-1-61026
Number of titles published annually: 24 Print
Total Titles: 100 Print
Imprints: Forever Regency (regency line); ImaJinn Books (paranormal & urban fantasy line); Silk & Magic (erotica line)
Membership(s): The Association of Publishers for Special Sales; The Independent Book Publishers Association

Immedium
Imprint of Immedium Inc
535 Rockdale Dr, San Francisco, CA 94127
Mailing Address: PO Box 31846, San Francisco, CA 94131
Tel: 415-452-8546 *Fax:* 360-937-6272
E-mail: orders@immedium.com; sales@immedium.com
Web Site: www.immedium.com
Key Personnel
Publr: Oliver Chin *E-mail:* o.chin@comcast.net
Ed: Don Menn
Acqs Ed: Amy Ma
Graphic Design: Elaine Chu
Founded: 2005
Publish wonderfully illustrated children's picture books, Asian American topics & contemporary arts & culture.
ISBN Prefix(es): 978-1-59702
Number of titles published annually: 4 Print; 4 Online; 4 E-Book
Total Titles: 25 Print; 20 Online; 20 E-Book
Foreign Rep(s): John Reed Book Distribution (Australia, New Zealand)
Foreign Rights: HarperCollins UK (UK & Commonwealth)
Orders to: Consortium Book Sales & Distribution, 1045 Westgate Dr, Suite 90, St Paul, MN 55114-1065 *Tel:* 651-621-9035 *Toll Free Tel:* 800-283-3572 (cust serv) *Fax:* 651-221-0124 *E-mail:* info@cbsd.com *Web Site:* www.cbsd.com
Returns: Consortium Book Sales & Distribution, 1045 Westgate Dr, Suite 90, St Paul, MN 55114-1065 *Tel:* 651-621-9035 *Toll Free Tel:* 800-283-3572 (cust serv) *Fax:* 651-221-0124 *E-mail:* info@cbsd.com *Web Site:* www.cbsd.com
Shipping Address: Consortium Book Sales & Distribution, 1045 Westgate Dr, Suite 90, St Paul, MN 55114-1065 *Tel:* 651-621-9035 *Toll Free Tel:* 800-283-3572 (cust serv) *Fax:* 651-221-0124 *E-mail:* info@cbsd.com *Web Site:* www.cbsd.com
Warehouse: Consortium Book Sales & Distribution, 1045 Westgate Dr, Suite 90, St Paul, MN 55114-1065 *Tel:* 651-621-9035 *Toll Free Tel:* 800-283-3572 (cust serv) *Fax:* 651-221-0124 *E-mail:* info@cbsd.com *Web Site:* www.cbsd.com
Distribution Center: Consortium Book Sales & Distribution, 1045 Westgate Dr, Suite 90, St Paul, MN 55114-1065 *Tel:* 561-621-9035 *Toll Free Tel:* 800-283-3572 (cust serv) *Fax:* 651-221-0124 *E-mail:* info@cbsd.com *Web Site:* www.cbsd.com

§Impact Publications/Development Concepts Inc
9104 Manassas Dr, Suite N, Manassas Park, VA 20111-5211
Tel: 703-361-7300 *Toll Free Tel:* 800-361-1055 (cust serv) *Fax:* 703-335-9486
E-mail: query@impactpublications.com
Web Site: www.impactpublications.com; www.ishoparoundtheworld.com; www.veteransworld.com; www.middleeasttravellover.com
Key Personnel
Pres: Ronald Krannich, PhD
Founded: 1982
Career & travel publications.
ISBN Prefix(es): 978-1-57023
Number of titles published annually: 18 Print
Total Titles: 167 Print
Distributed by National Book Network

Impact Publishers Inc
PO Box 6016, Atascadero, CA 93423-6016
SAN: 202-6864
Tel: 805-466-5917 (opers & admin offs) *Toll Free Tel:* 800-246-7228 (orders) *Fax:* 805-466-5919 (opers & admin offs)
E-mail: info@impactpublishers.com
Web Site: www.impactpublishers.com; www.bibliotherapy.com
Key Personnel
Pres & Ed: Robert E Alberti
Publr: Melissa Froehner
Cust Serv Mgr: Cheyenne Ladd
Intl Rts: Jean Trumbull
Founded: 1970

Self-help, relationships, divorce recovery, health, families & parenting, juvenile nonfiction & systematic training for effective parenting.
ISBN Prefix(es): 978-0-915166; 978-1-886230
Number of titles published annually: 6 Print; 1 CD-ROM; 1 Audio
Total Titles: 60 Print; 1 CD-ROM; 3 Audio
Imprints: Little Imp Books; The Practical Therapist Series; Rebuilding Books
Distributor for STEP Publishers (Systematic Training for Effective Parenting)
Foreign Rep(s): Footprint Books (Australia, New Zealand); Publishers Group UK (UK)
Foreign Rights: Bardon Agency (China, Taiwan); Bookbank SL (Latin America, Spain); Japan UNI Agency (Japan); Kayi Literary Agency (Turkey); Montreal Contacts (Canada, France); O A Literary Agency (Greece); The Riff Agency (Brazil, Portugal); Livia Stoia Literary Agency (Romania)
Advertising Agency: IMP Advertising
Membership(s): AAP; The Independent Book Publishers Association

In the Garden Publishing
Division of What Would Love Do Intl
7525 Paragon Rd, No 752252, Dayton, OH 45459
Mailing Address: PO Box 752252, Dayton, OH 45475 SAN: 920-3389
Tel: 937-317-0859
E-mail: editor@inthegardenpublishing.com
Web Site: www.inthegardenpublishing.com
Key Personnel
Publr: Christine Horner *E-mail:* christine@inthegardenpublishing.com
Founded: 2012
Discover your inner guru. Conscious community & brilliant minds unite. Together, what can we create?
ISBN Prefix(es): 978-0-9855314; 978-0-9888333
Number of titles published annually: 5 Print; 5 Online; 5 E-Book
Total Titles: 9 Print; 10 Online; 8 E-Book
Distribution Center: New Leaf Distributing Co, 401 Thornton Rd, Lithia Springs, GA 30122-1557, Contact: Stephen Davenport *Tel:* 770-948-7845 *E-mail:* sdavenport@newleaf-dist.com

§Incentive Publications by World Book
233 N Michigan Ave, Suite 2000, Chicago, IL 60601
Toll Free Tel: 800-967-5325
E-mail: incentive@worldbook.com
Web Site: www.incentivepublications.com
Founded: 1968 (acquired by World Book 2013)
Preschool through high school supplementary educational materials for students, parents & teachers.
ISBN Prefix(es): 978-0-913916; 978-0-86530
Number of titles published annually: 25 Print
Total Titles: 425 Print; 1 CD-ROM

§Independent Information Publications
Division of Computing!
3357 21 St, San Francisco, CA 94110
Tel: 415-643-8600
E-mail: sharisteiner@gmail.com
Web Site: www.movedoc.com
Founded: 1982
ISBN Prefix(es): 978-0-913733
Number of titles published annually: 4 Print; 1 CD-ROM; 6 Online; 2 E-Book
Total Titles: 5 Print; 1 CD-ROM; 4 Online; 2 E-Book
Imprints: IIP Consumers Series
Branch Office(s)
IIP, 500 Kentucky Ave, Savannah, GA 31404, Contact: Cima Star *Tel:* 912-233-8873
Distributed by Pathway Book Service
Shipping Address: Pathway Book Service, PO Box 89, Gilsum, NH 03448 *Tel:* 603-357-0236 *E-mail:* pbs@pathwaybook.com *Web Site:* www.pathwaybook.com
Membership(s): Bay Area Independent Publishers Association; The Independent Book Publishers Association

§Independent Institute
100 Swan Way, Oakland, CA 94621-1428
Tel: 510-632-1366 *Toll Free Tel:* 800-927-8733 *Fax:* 510-568-6040
E-mail: orders@independent.org
Web Site: www.independent.org
Key Personnel
Founder & CEO: David J Theroux *E-mail:* dtheroux@independent.org
Acqs Dir: Roy M Carlisle *Tel:* 510-632-1366 ext 112 *E-mail:* rcarlisle@independent.org
Communs Dir: Kim Cloidt *Tel:* 510-632-1366 ext 116 *E-mail:* kcloidt@independent.org
Research Dir: William Shughart, II *E-mail:* william.shughart@usu.edu
Founded: 1986
Nonprofit research & publication. Branch office in Washington, DC.
ISBN Prefix(es): 978-0-945999; 978-1-59813
Number of titles published annually: 6 Print; 1 CD-ROM; 2 Online; 6 E-Book; 1 Audio
Total Titles: 88 Print; 40 E-Book
Distribution Center: Independent Publishers Group, 814 N Franklin St, Chicago, IL 60610 *Toll Free Tel:* 800-888-4741 *Web Site:* www.ipgbook.com
Membership(s): AAP; The Independent Book Publishers Association; Independent Publishers Group

Indiana Historical Society Press (IHS Press)
450 W Ohio St, Indianapolis, IN 46202-3269
SAN: 201-5234
Tel: 317-232-1882; 317-234-0026 (orders); 317-234-2716 (edit) *Toll Free Tel:* 800-447-1830 (orders) *Fax:* 317-234-0562 (orders); 317-233-0857 (edit)
E-mail: ihspress@indianahistory.org; orders@indianahistory.org (orders)
Web Site: www.indianahistory.org; shop.indianahistory.org (orders)
Key Personnel
CEO & Pres: John Herbst *E-mail:* jherbst@indianahistory.org
Natl Sales Coord: Becke Bolinger *Tel:* 317-234-3683 *E-mail:* bbolinger@indianahistory.org
Buyer/Mgr, Retail Opers: Phil Janes *E-mail:* pjanes@indianahistory.org
Sr Ed: Ray Boomhower *E-mail:* rboomhower@indianahistory.og
Founded: 1886
Books, journals & newsletters on Indiana history, including an illustrated history magazine & a family history magazine. Also offers videos, recordings, prints, note cards & other gift items.
ISBN Prefix(es): 978-0-87195
Number of titles published annually: 2 Print; 1 Online
Total Titles: 90 Print; 1 Online; 3 Audio

Indiana University African Studies Program
Indiana University, 221 Woodburn Hall, Bloomington, IN 47405
Tel: 812-855-8284 *Fax:* 812-855-6734
E-mail: afrist@indiana.edu
Web Site: www.indiana.edu/~afrist
Key Personnel
Dir: Samuel Obeng *E-mail:* sobeng@indiana.edu
Assoc Dir: Maria Grosz-Ngate *Tel:* 812-855-5081 *E-mail:* mgrosz@indiana.edu
Founded: 1965
Monograph & working papers, humanities, interdisciplinary study of Africa.
ISBN Prefix(es): 978-0-941934
Number of titles published annually: 50 Print
Total Titles: 52 Print

§Indiana University Press
Herman B Wells Library 350, 1320 E Tenth St, Bloomington, IN 47405-3907
SAN: 202-5647
Tel: 812-855-8817 *Toll Free Tel:* 800-842-6796 (orders only) *Fax:* 812-855-7931; 812-855-8507
E-mail: iupress@indiana.edu; iuporder@indiana.edu (orders)
Web Site: www.iupress.indiana.edu
Key Personnel
Exec Dir, Off of Scholarly Publg: Carolyn Walters
Dir: Gary Dunham
Dir, Sales & Mktg: Dave Hulsey *Tel:* 812-855-6553 *E-mail:* hulseyd@indiana.edu
Ed-in-Chief: Robert Sloan *Tel:* 812-855-7561 *E-mail:* rjsloan@indiana.edu
Dir, Prodn: Bernadette Zoss *Tel:* 812-855-5563 *E-mail:* bzoss@indiana.edu
Technol Dir: Ted Boardman *Tel:* 812-855-6468 *E-mail:* tboardma@indiana.edu
Sr Sponsoring Ed: Dee Mortensen *Tel:* 812-855-0268 *E-mail:* mortense@indiana.edu
Sponsoring Ed: Raina Polivka *Tel:* 812-855-5261 *E-mail:* rpolivka@indiana.edu; Linda Oblack *Tel:* 812-855-2175 *E-mail:* loblack@indiana.edu; Rebecca Tolen *Tel:* 812-855-2756 *E-mail:* retolen@indiana.edu
Mgr, Accts Receivable: Kimberly B Childers *Tel:* 812-855-4134 *E-mail:* kchilder@indiana.edu
Rts & Perms Mgr: Peter Froehlich *Tel:* 812-855-6314 *E-mail:* pfroehli@indiana.edu
Trade Mktg & Publicity Mgr: Mandy Hussey *Tel:* 812-855-4522 *E-mail:* mlclarke@indiana.edu
Acctg Assoc: Katie Scarlet O'Brien *Tel:* 812-855-5366 *E-mail:* kasobrie@indiana.edu
Proj Mgr/Ed: Michelle Sybert *Tel:* 812-855-5031 *E-mail:* msybert@indiana.edu
Founded: 1950
Trade & scholarly nonfiction; film & media studies, literature & music, African studies, backlist, classical studies, contemporary issues, cultural studies, folklore, international studies, Jewish studies, journals, Middle East studies, paleontology, philanthropy, politics/political science, railroads & transportation, Russian studies.
ISBN Prefix(es): 978-0-253
Number of titles published annually: 130 Print; 2 CD-ROM; 5 Audio
Total Titles: 3,000 Print; 8 CD-ROM
Imprints: Quarry Books (regional imprint for Midwest)
Foreign Rights: Agenzia Letteraria Internazionale (Maria Stefania Fietta) (Italy); Agencia Literaria Carmen Balcells SA (Maribel Luque) (Spain); Bookman Literary Agency (Ib H Lauritzen) (Denmark); The English Agency (Tsutomu Yawata) (Japan); The Deborah Harris Agency (Efrat Lev) (Israel); Liepman AG (Marc Koralnik) (Germany); La Nouvelle Agence (Anne Maizeret) (France); O A Literary Agency (Michael Avramides) (Greece)
Orders to: Ingram Publisher Services, 1210 Ingram Dr, Chambersburg, PA 17202 *Tel:* 717-262-4860 *Toll Free Tel:* 800-648-3013 *E-mail:* pubsupport@ingramcontent.com *Web Site:* ipage.ingramcontent.com
Shipping Address: Ingram Publisher Services, 1210 Ingram Dr, Chambersburg, PA 17202 *Tel:* 717-262-4860 *Toll Free Tel:* 800-648-3013 *E-mail:* pubsupport@ingramcontent.com *Web Site:* ipage.ingramcontent.com
Distribution Center: Ingram Publisher Services, 1210 Ingram Dr, Chambersburg, PA 17202 *Tel:* 717-262-4860 *Toll Free Tel:* 800-648-3013 *E-mail:* pubsupport@ingramcontent.com *Web Site:* ipage.ingramcontent.com

§Industrial Press Inc
32 Haviland St, Unit 2C, Norwalk, CT 06854
SAN: 202-6945
Tel: 212-889-6330 *Toll Free Tel:* 888-528-7852
Fax: 212-545-8327
E-mail: info@industrialpress.com
Web Site: new.industrialpress.com
Key Personnel
Owner & Pres: Alex Luchars
Cont: Peter Burri
Art Dir & Prodn Mgr: Janet Romano-Murray
Edit Dir: Tai Soda *Tel:* 212-889-6330 ext 222
E-mail: tsoda@industrialpress.com
Founded: 1883
Scientific & technical handbooks, professional & reference books for engineering, technology, manufacturing & education.
ISBN Prefix(es): 978-0-8311
Number of titles published annually: 28 Print; 10 CD-ROM; 10 E-Book
Total Titles: 320 Print; 40 CD-ROM; 40 E-Book
Foreign Rep(s): Academic Marketing Services (Botswana, Lesotho, Namibia, South Africa, Swaziland); Co Info Pty Ltd (Australia, Fiji, New Zealand); Cranbury International LLC (Central America, Mexico, Puerto Rico, South America, West Indies); Nelson Education Ltd (Canada); Tata McGraw-Hill (Pankaj Bamola) (India exc South India); Tata McGraw-Hill (VP Chandrashekhar) (South India); Transatlantic Publishers Group Ltd (Europe, Middle East); The White Partnership (Asia exc India & Japan)
Advertising Agency: Flamm Advertising Inc
Returns: Ware-Pak, 2427 Bond St, University Park, IL 60466, Contact: Tammy Cote *Tel:* 708-587-4124 *Fax:* 708-587-4167
Warehouse: Ware-Pak, 2427 Bond St, University Park, IL 60466, Contact: Tammy Cote *Tel:* 708-587-4124 *Fax:* 708-587-4167
Membership(s): AAP

Information Age Publishing Inc
PO Box 79049, Charlotte, NC 28271-7047
Tel: 704-752-9125 *Fax:* 704-752-9113
E-mail: infoage@infoagepub.com
Web Site: www.infoagepub.com
Key Personnel
Pres & Publr: George F Johnson
E-mail: george@infoagepub.com
Founded: 1999
Social science publisher of academic & scholarly book series & journals.
ISBN Prefix(es): 978-1-930608; 978-1-931576; 978-1-59311
Number of titles published annually: 240 Print; 9 Online; 120 E-Book
Total Titles: 3,500 Print; 800 E-Book
Foreign Rep(s): James Bennett Pty Ltd (Australia); Sara Book (India); Capital Book (India); Cranberry International (Latin America); DA Information Services (Australia, New Zealand); The Eurospan Group; Information Age Publishing (Europe); Logan Brothers (Canada); Taylor & Francis Asia Pacific (Singapore); United Publisher Services (Japan)

§Information Gatekeepers Inc
1340 Soldiers Field Rd, Suite 2, Boston, MA 02135
Mailing Address: PO Box 35880, Brighton, MA 02135
Tel: 617-782-5033 *Fax:* 617-507-8338
E-mail: info@igigroup.com
Web Site: www.igigroup.com
Key Personnel
CEO & Pres: Paul Polishuk, PhD
Chief Analyst & Ed-in-Chief: Dr Hui Pan
E-mail: hpan@igigroup.com
Mng Ed: Bev Wilson *E-mail:* editor@igigroup.com
Founded: 1977
Fiber optics, optical networks, wireless, ATM, XDSL & telecommunications, trade shows, conferences, newsletters, market studies & consulting.
ISBN Prefix(es): 978-0-918435; 978-1-56851
Number of titles published annually: 35 Print
Total Titles: 542 Print
Foreign Office(s): IPI Services Pty Ltd, 128 Chalmers St, Surry Hills, NSW 2010, Australia *Tel:* (02) 9319 7933 *Fax:* (02) 9319-3408 *E-mail:* ipi@ipi.com
Global Informaton Inc, A Sahi Bank Bldg, 4th fl, 151 Kamiasao, A Sno-ku, Kawasaki 215, Japan *Tel:* (044) 952 0102 *Fax:* (044) 952 0109 *E-mail:* k.endo@gii.co.jp
OIC, Sam Hwam Bldg 38-1, 3rd fl, Wonhyoru 1-9a, Yongsan-Ku, Seoul, South Korea *Tel:* (027) 49 86 40 *Fax:* (027) 49 86 41
c/o CMS, 122 High St, Chesham, Berks HP5 1EB, United Kingdom *Tel:* (01494) 771 734 *Fax:* (01494) 779 994
Foreign Rep(s): Chiltern Magazine Services (England); Chongno Book Center Co Ltd (Korea); Global Information Inc (Japan); Investment Publications Information Service (Australia); Overseas Information Services (Korea)
Membership(s): IEEE; The Optical Society; Plastic Optical Fiber Trade Organization

§Information Today, Inc
143 Old Marlton Pike, Medford, NJ 08055-8750
Tel: 609-654-6266 *Toll Free Tel:* 800-300-9868 (cust serv) *Fax:* 609-654-4309
E-mail: custserv@infotoday.com
Web Site: www.infotoday.com
Key Personnel
Pres & CEO: Thomas H Hogan, Sr
VP, Admin: John Yersak
VP, Content: Richard T Kaser *E-mail:* kaser@infotoday.com
VP, Mktg & Busn Devt: Thomas Hogan, Jr
VP, IT: Bill Spence *E-mail:* spence@infotoday.com
Ad Sales Mgr: David Panara *E-mail:* dpanara@infotoday.com
Prodn Mgr: Tiffany Chamenko
E-mail: tchamenko@infotoday.com
Mktg & Exhibits: Robert Colding
E-mail: rcolding@infotoday.com
Founded: 1980
Publisher specializing in: Books, directories, newspapers, journals, newsletters, conferences & information services for users & producers of digital information content & technologies, including professionals in the library, publishing, online information, K-12 education, business research & IT, knowledge management, customer relationship management, speech technology & streaming media industries. ITI's reference division is the publisher of *LMP, ILMP, American Book Trade Directory, Library and Book Trade Almanac* & other professional reference titles.
ISBN Prefix(es): 978-0-938734; 978-0-904933; 978-1-57387; 978-0-910965
Number of titles published annually: 28 Print; 15 E-Book
Total Titles: 460 Print; 220 E-Book
Imprints: ASI Books (books for indexing professionals from the American Society for Indexing); ASIS&T Monograph Series (scholarly monographs from the American Society for Information Science & Technology); CyberAge Books (books for tech-savvy consumers & business information users; nationally distributed to the book trade by IPG); Information Today Books (practical books for library & information professionals)
Membership(s): ALA; American Society for Indexing; Association for Independent Information Professionals; Association for Information Science & Technology; Independent Publishers Group; SLA

Infosources Publishing
140 Norma Rd, Teaneck, NJ 07666
Tel: 201-836-7072
Web Site: www.infosourcespub.com
Key Personnel
Publr & Ed: Arlene L Eis
Founded: 1981
Legal reference books, newsletters, online databases. Publisher of *The Informed Librarian Online*.
ISBN Prefix(es): 978-0-939486
Number of titles published annually: 5 Print; 4 Online
Total Titles: 10 Print

Ingalls Publishing Group Inc (IPG)
PO Box 2500, Banner Elk, NC 28604
Tel: 828-297-6884 *Fax:* 828-297-6880
E-mail: sales@ingallspublishinggroup.com
Web Site: www.ingallspublishinggroup.com
Key Personnel
Publr: Robert Ingalls
Sr Ed: Judith Geary *E-mail:* editor@ingallspublishinggroup.com
Sales & Opers Mgr: Rebecca Owen
Founded: 2001
Small publishing company focusing on historical fiction, murder mystery, romantic suspense & adventure.
ISBN Prefix(es): 978-0-9713045; 978-1-932158
Number of titles published annually: 4 Print
Total Titles: 40 Print
Imprints: Almont Books; Ingalls Publishing
Distributor for Southlore Press
Shipping Address: Ingram Book Group, One Ingram Blvd, La Vergne, TN 37086 *Tel:* 615-793-5000 *Web Site:* www.ingrambook.com
Warehouse: Ingram Book Group, One Ingram Blvd, La Vergne, TN 37086 *Tel:* 615-793-5000 *Web Site:* www.ingrambook.com
Distribution Center: Ingram Book Group, One Ingram Blvd, La Vergne, TN 37086 *Tel:* 615-793-5000 *Web Site:* www.ingrambook.com
Membership(s): The Independent Book Publishers Association; NAIBA; Southern Independent Booksellers Alliance

Ink Smith Publishing
PO Box 1086, Glendora, CA 91016
Tel: 626-415-7179
Web Site: ink-smith.com
Key Personnel
Owner: Ashley Howie
Founded: 2012
ISBN Prefix(es): 978-1-939156
Number of titles published annually: 24 Print; 24 Online; 24 E-Book
Total Titles: 17 Print; 17 Online; 17 E-Book
Imprints: Native Ink Press
Editorial Office(s): 800 Oakglade Dr, Monrovia, CA 91016
Sales Office(s): 800 Oakglade Dr, Monrovia, CA 91016
Billing Address: 800 Oakglade Dr, Monrovia, CA 91016
Orders to: 800 Oakglade Dr, Monrovia, CA 91016
Returns: 800 Oakglade Dr, Monrovia, CA 91016
Membership(s): The Independent Book Publishers Association

Inkwater Press
Imprint of Firstbooks.com Inc

6750 SW Franklin St, Suite A, Portland, OR 97223
Tel: 503-968-6777 *Fax:* 503-968-6779
E-mail: orders@inkwaterbooks.com
Web Site: www.inkwater.com
Key Personnel
Pres: Jeremy Solomon *E-mail:* jeremy@inkwater.com
Founded: 2002
Publishing services to individuals & corporations as well as author subsidized publishing.
This publisher has indicated that 95% of their product line is author subsidized.
ISBN Prefix(es): 978-0-9719414; 978-1-59299; 978-1-62901
Number of titles published annually: 70 Print; 70 E-Book
Total Titles: 430 Print; 115 E-Book; 2 Audio
Imprints: Franklin Street Books

Inner Traditions International Ltd
One Park St, Rochester, VT 05767
Mailing Address: PO Box 388, Rochester, VT 05767
Tel: 802-767-3174 *Toll Free Tel:* 800-246-8648 *Fax:* 802-767-3726
E-mail: customerservice@InnerTraditions.com
Web Site: www.InnerTraditions.com
Key Personnel
Pres: Ehud C Sperling *E-mail:* prez@InnerTraditions.com
VP, Opers: Diane Shepard *E-mail:* dianes@InnerTraditions.com
Dir, Sales & Mktg: John Hays *E-mail:* johnh@InnerTraditions.com
Ed-in-Chief: Jeanie Levitan *E-mail:* jeaniel@InnerTraditions.com
Acqs Ed: Jon Graham *E-mail:* jong@InnerTraditions.com
Print Mgr: Jon Desautels *E-mail:* jond@InnerTraditions.com
Foreign Rts & Perms: Maria Murray-Urdaneta *E-mail:* mariam@InnerTraditions.com
Publicity: Manzanita Carpenter *E-mail:* manzanitac@InnerTraditions.com
Sales & Mktg: Andrea Raymond *E-mail:* andyr@InnerTraditions.com
Spec Sales: Jessica Arsenault *E-mail:* jessa@InnerTraditions.com
Founded: 1975
Nonfiction cloth & quality trade paperbacks; audio cassettes & CDs (ethnic music & meditation aids).
ISBN Prefix(es): 978-0-89281; 978-1-59477; 978-1-62055
Number of titles published annually: 66 Print; 66 E-Book
Total Titles: 1,499 Print; 976 E-Book; 15 Audio
Imprints: Bear & Co Inc; Bear Cub Books; Bindu Books; Destiny Books; Destiny Recordings; Healing Arts Press; Inner Traditions; Inner Traditions en espanol; Inner Traditions India; Park Street Press
Foreign Rights: Agenzia Letteraria Internazionale SRL (Italy); Akcali Copyright Agency (Turkey); Big Apple Agency Inc (China, Taiwan); Blackbird Literary Agency (Netherlands); The Book Publishers' Association of Israel, International Promotion & Literary Rights Dept (Israel); Graal Literary Agency (Poland); International Editors' Co SA (Argentina, Spain); Simona Kessler International Copyright Agency Ltd (Romania); Alexander Korzhenevski Agency (Russia); Zvonimir Majdak (Croatia); Montreal Contacts/The Rights Agency (Canada); Andrew Nurnberg Associates (Baltic States, Bulgaria, Czech Republic, Hungary); Read n Right Agency (Greece); Karin Schindler (Brazil); Thomas Schlueck GmbH (Germany); Agence Schweiger (France); Tuttle-Mori Agency Inc (Japan, Thailand); Eric Yang Agency (Korea)
Orders to: Inner Traditions International - Bear & Co, c/o Simon & Schuster, 100 Front St, Riverside, NJ 08075 *Toll Free Tel:* 800-223-2336 *Toll Free Fax:* 800-943-9831 *E-mail:* purchaseorders@simonandschuster.com
Returns: Simon & Schuster, c/o Jacobson Logistics, 4406 Industrial Park Rd, Bldg 7, Camp Hill, PA 17011 (truckload shipments must call for an appointment: 800-967-3914 ext 5318)
Warehouse: Inner Traditions International - Bear & Co, c/o Simon & Schuster, 100 Front St, Riverside, NJ 08075 *Toll Free Tel:* 800-943-9831 *E-mail:* purchaseorders@simonandschuster.com
See separate listing for:
Bear & Co Inc

innovativeKids®
Division of Innovative USA® Inc
50 Washington St, Suite 201, Norwalk, CT 06854
Tel: 203-838-6400
E-mail: info@innovativekids.com
Web Site: www.innovativekids.com
Key Personnel
CEO: Michael S Levins *E-mail:* mlevins@innovativekids.com
Pres & Publr: Shari Kaufman *Tel:* 203-838-6400 ext 4305 *E-mail:* skaufman@innovativekids.com
Founded: 1989
Publishing interactive, tactile books for preschool through elementary school age children - unusual formats that foster the growth of essential learning skills.
ISBN Prefix(es): 978-1-58476
Number of titles published annually: 50 Print
Total Titles: 150 Print
Membership(s): ABA; American Book Producers Association; American Specialty Toy Retailing Association; Education Market Association; The Independent Book Publishers Association; Toy International Association

Insight Editions
800 "A" St, San Rafael, CA 94901
Tel: 415-526-1370 *Toll Free Tel:* 800-809-3792 *Toll Free Fax:* 866-509-0515
E-mail: info@insighteditions.com
Web Site: www.insighteditions.com
Key Personnel
Pres & Publr: Raoul Goff *E-mail:* raoul@palacepress.com
Head, Sales & Mktg: Terry Newell
Sales Dir: Julie Hamilton
Sales Mgr: Jacqui Goff *E-mail:* j.goff@insighteditions.com
Sr Ed: Vanessa Lopez
Founded: 2000
Renowned for creating beautiful, innovative books that excel in the marketplace. Insight Editions brings the vision & style of high-end illustrated books to the realm of the arts & entertainment.
ISBN Prefix(es): 978-1-933784
Number of titles published annually: 75 Print
Total Titles: 300 Print
Shipping Address: Publishers Group West (PGW), 1700 Fourth St, Berkeley, CA 94710 *Toll Free Tel:* 800-788-3123 *Web Site:* www.pgw.com
See separate listing for:
Mandala Earth

Inspiring Every Child dba Illumination Arts Publishing
13023 NE Hwy 99, Suite 7-8, Vancouver, WA 98686
Tel: 425-968-5097 *Fax:* 425-968-5634
E-mail: liteinfo@illumin.com
Web Site: www.illumin.com
Key Personnel
Pres: John Thompson
Founded: 1987
Publishing of uplifting/inspiring children's picture books.
ISBN Prefix(es): 978-0-935699; 978-0-9740190; 978-0-9701907
Number of titles published annually: 4 Print

§Institute of Continuing Legal Education
1020 Greene St, Ann Arbor, MI 48109-1444
Tel: 734-764-0533 *Toll Free Tel:* 877-229-4350 *Fax:* 734-763-2412 *Toll Free Fax:* 877-229-4351
E-mail: icle@umich.edu
Web Site: www.icle.org
Key Personnel
Dir: Lynn P Chard *E-mail:* lchard@umich.edu
Educ Dir: Jeffrey E Kirkley
Founded: 1959
Books, supplements, disk products, audio, web site.
ISBN Prefix(es): 978-0-88288
Number of titles published annually: 3 Print
Total Titles: 55 Print; 48 Online
Imprints: ICLE

§Institute of Environmental Sciences and Technology - IEST
2340 S Arlington Heights Rd, Suite 620, Arlington Heights, IL 60005-4510
Tel: 847-981-0100 *Fax:* 847-981-4130
E-mail: publications@iest.org
Web Site: www.iest.org
Key Personnel
Exec Dir: Roberta Burrows *Tel:* 847-981-0100 ext 6015 *E-mail:* executive@iest.org
Tech Prog Mgr: Jennifer Sklena *Tel:* 847-981-0100 ext 6011
Educ & Meetings Mgr: Heather Wooden *Tel:* 847-981-0100 ext 6014 *E-mail:* marketing@iest.org
Memb & Acctg Coord: Mara Douvris *Tel:* 847-981-0100 ext 6109 *E-mail:* membershipdept@iest.org
A multidisciplinary, international society whose members are recognized worldwide for their contributions to the environmental sciences in the area of contamination control in electronics manufacturing & pharmaceutical processes; design, test & evaluation of commercial & military equipment; product reliability issues associated with commercial & military systems.
ISBN Prefix(es): 978-0-915414; 978-1-877862; 978-0-9747313; 978-0-9787868; 978-0-9841330
Number of titles published annually: 3 Print
Total Titles: 26 CD-ROM; 48 Online

Institute of Governmental Studies
Subsidiary of University of California, Berkeley
109 Moses Hall, No 2370, Berkeley, CA 94720-2370
Tel: 510-642-1428 *Fax:* 510-642-3020; 510-642-5537 (orders)
E-mail: igspress@berkeley.edu
Web Site: www.igs.berkeley.edu
Key Personnel
Dir, Pubns: Ethan Rarick *E-mail:* erarick@berkeley.edu
Pubns Ed: Maria Wolf *E-mail:* mariaw@berkeley.edu
Public policy issues.
ISBN Prefix(es): 978-0-87772
Number of titles published annually: 6 Print
Total Titles: 54 Print

§Institute of Jesuit Sources (IJS)
3601 Lindell Blvd, St Louis, MO 63108
Tel: 314-633-4622 *Fax:* 314-633-4623
E-mail: ijs@jesuitsources.com
Web Site: www.jesuitsources.com
Key Personnel
Dir: Fr John W Padberg *Tel:* 314-633-4400
Founded: 1961

Books on history & spirituality of the society of Jesus (Jesuits) translated from non-English sources & originally in English.
ISBN Prefix(es): 978-0-912422; 978-1-880810
Number of titles published annually: 8 Print
Total Titles: 103 Print; 1 CD-ROM

§Institute of Mathematical Geography
Division of Arlinghaus Enterprises LLC
1964 Boulder Dr, Ann Arbor, MI 48104
Tel: 734-975-0246
E-mail: image@imagenet.org
Web Site: www.imagenet.com
Key Personnel
Founding Dir: Sandra Lach Arlinghaus
E-mail: sandy@almalach.com
Founded: 1986
Publish scholarly books & college textbooks, electronic journals & books.
ISBN Prefix(es): 978-1-877751
Number of titles published annually: 3 Print
Total Titles: 39 Print; 13 E-Book

§Institute of Police Technology & Management
Division of University of North Florida
University Ctr, 12000 Alumni Dr, Jacksonville, FL 32224-2678
Tel: 904-620-4786 *Fax:* 904-620-2453
E-mail: info@iptm.org; orders@iptm.org
Web Site: www.iptm.org
Key Personnel
Dir: Cameron Pucci *E-mail:* cpucci@unf.edu
Founded: 1980
In-service training for law enforcement, civilian personnel; marketing of publications, templates & videos. Specialize in traffic crash investigation & reconstruction; law enforcement management & supervision; criminal investigation; DUI & drug law enforcement; radar/laser speed enforcement; law enforcement computer training; gangs & other specialized subjects.
ISBN Prefix(es): 978-1-884566
Number of titles published annually: 7 Print; 2 CD-ROM
Total Titles: 65 Print; 6 CD-ROM
Foreign Rep(s): Paul Feenan (Australia, South Pacific)
Foreign Rights: Pacific Traffic Education Centre (Canada)

The Institutes™
720 Providence Rd, Suite 100, Malvern, PA 19355-3433
Tel: 610-644-2100 *Toll Free Tel:* 800-644-2101 *Fax:* 610-640-9576
E-mail: customerservice@theinstitutes.org
Web Site: www.theinstitutes.org
Key Personnel
Pres/CEO: Peter Miller
Property-casualty continuing insurance education.
ISBN Prefix(es): 978-0-89463; 978-0-89462
Number of titles published annually: 12 Print
Total Titles: 120 Print

The Institution of Engineering & Technology, see IET USA Inc

Inter-American Development Bank
Division of Multilateral Development Bank
1300 New York Ave NW, Washington, DC 20577
Tel: 202-623-1000 *Fax:* 202-623-3096
E-mail: pic@iadb.org
Web Site: www.iadb.org/pub
Key Personnel
Pres: Luis Alberto Moreno
EVP: Julie T Katzman
Founded: 1959
Economic development in Latin America & the Caribbean.
ISBN Prefix(es): 978-0-940602; 978-1-886938; 978-1-931003
Number of titles published annually: 30 Print
Total Titles: 160 Print
Distributed by Johns Hopkins University Press

§Inter-University Consortium for Political & Social Research (ICPSR)
Affiliate of University of Michigan Institute for Social Research
330 Packard St, Ann Arbor, MI 48104
Mailing Address: PO Box 1248, Ann Arbor, MI 48106-1248
Tel: 734-647-5000 *Fax:* 734-647-8200
E-mail: netmail@icpsr.umich.edu
Web Site: www.icpsr.umich.edu
Key Personnel
Dir: George Alter *Tel:* 734-615-7652
E-mail: altergc@umich.edu
Dir, Summer Prog in Quantitative Methods of Social Res: Saundra K Schneider *Tel:* 734-763-6281 *E-mail:* saundras@umich.edu
Asst Dir: Mary Vardigan *Tel:* 734-615-7908
E-mail: vardigan@umich.edu
Founded: 1962
Provides access to social science data collections & documentation. Additional subjects include: demography & aging/gerontology.
ISBN Prefix(es): 978-0-89138
Number of titles published annually: 300 Online
Total Titles: 7,500 Online

Intercultural Development Research Association (IDRA)
5815 Callaghan Rd, Suite 101, San Antonio, TX 78228
Tel: 210-444-1710 *Fax:* 210-444-1714
E-mail: contact@idra.org
Web Site: www.idra.org
Key Personnel
CEO & Pres: Dr Maria "Cuca" Robledo Montecel
Communs Mgr: Christie Goodman
Founded: 1973
Independent & private, nonprofit organization dedicated to creating schools that work for all children; works with people to create & apply cutting-edge educational policies & practices that value & empower all children, families & communities. Conducts research & development activities, creates, implements & administers innovative education programs & provides teacher, administrator, parent training & technical assistance.
ISBN Prefix(es): 978-1-878550
Number of titles published annually: 10 Print
Total Titles: 50 Print

Intercultural Press Inc
Division of Nicholas Brealey Publishing
20 Park Plaza, Suite 610, Boston, MA 02116
SAN: 212-6699
Tel: 617-523-3801 *Toll Free Tel:* 888-273-2539 *Fax:* 617-523-3708
E-mail: info@interculturalpress.com
Web Site: nicholasbrealey.com
Key Personnel
Dir, Prodn: Jennifer Delaney
Founded: 1980
Books, training & educational materials on international, cross-cultural & diversity subjects, including reference books, bibliographies, manuals, handbooks, nonfiction.
ISBN Prefix(es): 978-0-933662; 978-1-877864; 978-1-931930
Number of titles published annually: 12 Print
Total Titles: 150 Print
Distributed by NBN

Interlink Publishing Group Inc
46 Crosby St, Northampton, MA 01060
SAN: 664-8908
Tel: 413-582-7054 *Toll Free Tel:* 800-238-LINK (238-5465) *Fax:* 413-582-7057
E-mail: info@interlinkbooks.com
Web Site: www.interlinkbooks.com
Key Personnel
Publr & Edit Dir: Michel Moushabeck
Tel: 413-582-7054 ext 204 *E-mail:* michel@interlinkbooks.com
Lib Sales Dir: Brenda Eaton
Publicity Dir: Moira Megargee
Founded: 1987
World travel, world literature, world history/politics/current affairs, ethnic cooking & illustrated children's books.
ISBN Prefix(es): 978-0-940793; 978-1-56656
Number of titles published annually: 55 Print; 40 E-Book
Total Titles: 996 Print; 500 E-Book
Imprints: Clockroot Books; Codagen Guides USA; Crocodile Books; Interlink Books; Olive Branch Press
Distributor for Black & White Publishing (UK); Camerapix Publishers International; Georgina Campbell Guides (Ireland); Macmillan Caribbean (UK); Quartet Books (UK); Rucksack Readers (UK); Serif Publishing Ltd (UK); Sheldrake Press (UK); Signal Books (UK); Waverley Books (UK); Neil Wilson Publishing (UK)
Foreign Rep(s): Codasat Canada Ltd (Canada); Electra Media Group (Southeast Asia); Network Book Distribution Ltd (Europe, UK); Palgrave Macmillan (Australia, New Zealand); Peter Ward Book Exports (Middle East)
Distribution Center: Publishers Group West (digital dist servs via Constellation)

International Book Centre Inc
2391 Auburn Rd, Shelby Township, MI 48317
SAN: 208-7022
Mailing Address: PO Box 295, Troy, MI 48085
Tel: 586-254-7230 *Fax:* 586-254-7230
E-mail: ibc@ibcbooks.com
Web Site: www.ibcbooks.com
Key Personnel
Owner: Doris Mukalla
Founded: 1974
Publisher of foreign language books. Specialize in the language & culture of the Middle East.
ISBN Prefix(es): 978-0-86685
Number of titles published annually: 2 Print; 2 Audio
Total Titles: 28 Print; 5 Audio
Distributor for Library du Liban (Lebanon); Stacey International Ltd (London); University of Michigan

§International City/County Management Association (ICMA)
777 N Capitol St NE, Suite 500, Washington, DC 20002-4201
Tel: 202-289-4262 *Toll Free Tel:* 800-745-8780 *Fax:* 202-962-3500
E-mail: customerservice@icma.org
Web Site: icma.org
Key Personnel
Exec Dir: Robert J O'Neill, Jr *E-mail:* roneill@icma.org
Dir, Pubns: Ann Mahoney *Tel:* 202-962-3643
Founded: 1914
Local government leadership & management organization that provides member support; publications, data & information; peer & results-oriented assistance; training & professional development to more than 8,200 city, town & county experts throughout the world.
ISBN Prefix(es): 978-0-87326
Number of titles published annually: 10 Print; 2 CD-ROM; 25 Online
Total Titles: 200 Print; 7 CD-ROM; 85 Online
Warehouse: PBD, 1650 Bluegrass Lakes Pkwy, Alpharetta, GA 30004 *Tel:* 770-442-8633
Distribution Center: PBD, 1650 Bluegrass Lakes Pkwy, Alpharetta, GA 30004 *Tel:* 770-442-8633

International Code Council Inc
5360 Workman Mill Rd, Whittier, CA 90601-2256
Tel: 562-699-0541 *Toll Free Tel:* 888-422-7233 *Fax:* 562-908-5524; 562-699-8031
E-mail: es@icc-es.org
Web Site: www.iccsafe.org
Key Personnel
SVP, Busn & Prod Devt: Mark Johnson *Tel:* 562-699-0541 ext 3248 *E-mail:* mjohnson@icc-es.org
Founded: 1922
Publisher of construction codes & regulations used in US & abroad.
ISBN Prefix(es): 978-1-58001; 978-1-884590; 978-1-892395
Number of titles published annually: 60 Print; 10 CD-ROM
Total Titles: 300 Print; 20 CD-ROM

International Council of Shopping Centers (ICSC)
1221 Avenue of the Americas, 41st fl, New York, NY 10020-1099
Tel: 646-728-3800 *Fax:* 732-694-1755
E-mail: icsc@icsc.org
Web Site: www.icsc.org
Key Personnel
Dir, Pubns: Patricia Montagni *Tel:* 646-728-3494 *Fax:* 732-694-1767 *E-mail:* pmontagni@icsc.org
Founded: 1957
Books & ebooks.
ISBN Prefix(es): 978-0-927547; 978-0-913598; 978-1-58268
Number of titles published annually: 15 Print; 5 E-Book
Total Titles: 100 Print; 5 E-Book
Foreign Office(s): 29 Queen Anne's Gate, London SW1H 9BU, United Kingdom *Tel:* (020) 7976 3102 *Fax:* (020) 7976 3101 *E-mail:* info.europe@icsc.org
Warehouse: BrightKey, 9050 Junction Dr, Annapolis Junction, MD 20701 *Tel:* 301-362-6900
Distribution Center: BrightKey, 9050 Junction Dr, Annapolis Junction, MD 20701 *Tel:* 301-362-6900

International Food Policy Research Institute
Member of Consultative Group on International Agricultural Research (CGIAR)
2033 "K" St NW, Washington, DC 20006-1002
Tel: 202-862-5600 *Fax:* 202-467-4439
E-mail: ifpri@cgiar.org
Web Site: www.ifpri.org
Key Personnel
Dir Gen: Shenggen Fan
Communs Dir: Klaus von Grebmer *E-mail:* k.vongrebmer@cgiar.org
Founded: 1975
Research reports, occasional papers & newsletter series, books, briefs, abstracts.
ISBN Prefix(es): 978-0-89629
Number of titles published annually: 270 Print; 2 CD-ROM; 270 Online
Total Titles: 3,980 Print; 21 CD-ROM; 3,634 Online
Distributed by Johns Hopkins University Press

International Foundation of Employee Benefit Plans
18700 W Bluemound Rd, Brookfield, WI 53045
Mailing Address: PO Box 69, Brookfield, WI 53008-0069
Tel: 262-786-6700 *Toll Free Tel:* 888-334-3327 *Fax:* 262-786-8780
E-mail: editor@ifebp.org
Web Site: www.ifebp.org
Key Personnel
Sr Dir, Info Servs & Pubns: Kelli Kolsrud *E-mail:* kellik@ifebp.org
Assoc Dir, Book Pubns: Pat Bonner *E-mail:* patb@ifebp.org
Founded: 1954
ISBN Prefix(es): 978-0-89154
Number of titles published annually: 2 Print; 2 E-Book
Total Titles: 30 Print; 15 CD-ROM; 30 E-Book
Membership(s): Association Media & Publishing; The Independent Book Publishers Association

The International Institute of Islamic Thought
500 Grove St, Suite 200, Herndon, VA 20170
Tel: 703-471-1133 *Fax:* 703-471-3922
E-mail: iiit@iiit.org
Web Site: www.iiit.org
Key Personnel
Pres: Abusolayman Abdulhamid
Dir, Pubns: Dr Jamal Barzinji
Mgr, Pubns: Riyad Al-Yemany
Founded: 1981
Books, audiobooks & videos.
ISBN Prefix(es): 978-0-912463; 978-1-56564
Number of titles published annually: 40 Print
Total Titles: 500 Print

§International Linguistics Corp
Learnables, 12220 Blue Ridge Blvd, Suite G, Grandview, MO 64030
Tel: 816-765-8855 *Toll Free Tel:* 800-237-1830 (orders) *Fax:* 816-765-2855
E-mail: learnables@sbcglobal.net
Web Site: www.learnables.com
Key Personnel
Gen Mgr: Jennifer Elliott
Founded: 1976
Foreign & English language materials, language teaching materials.
ISBN Prefix(es): 978-0-939990; 978-1-887371
Number of titles published annually: 3 Print; 3 CD-ROM; 1 Online; 3 Audio
Total Titles: 52 Print; 10 CD-ROM; 1 Online; 50 Audio

International Literacy Association (ILA)
Formerly International Reading Association (IRA)
800 Barksdale Rd, Newark, DE 19711-3204
Mailing Address: PO Box 8139, Newark, DE 19714-8139
Tel: 302-731-1600 *Toll Free Tel:* 800-336-7323 (US & CN) *Fax:* 302-731-1057
E-mail: customerservice@reading.org
Web Site: www.literacyworldwide.org; www.reading.org
Key Personnel
Exec Ed, Pubns: Shannon Fortner *Fax:* 302-368-2449 *E-mail:* sfortner@reading.org
Content Acqs Mgr: Tori Bachman *Fax:* 302-368-2449 *E-mail:* tbachman@reading.org
Exec Asst: Kathy Baughman *Tel:* 302-731-3761 *E-mail:* kbaughman@reading.org
Founded: 1956
Books & journals related to reading instruction & literary education.
ISBN Prefix(es): 978-0-87207
Number of titles published annually: 10 Print; 5 E-Book
Total Titles: 150 Print; 15 E-Book
Branch Office(s)
444 N Capitol St NW, Suite 640, Washington, DC 20001 *Tel:* 202-624-8800 *Fax:* 202-624-8826
Foreign Rights: Academics Plus (Andrea Permel) (UK); Eurospan Group (Catherine Lawn) (Trinidad and Tobago)

§International Monetary Fund (IMF), Editorial & Publications Division
700 19 St NW, HQ1-7-124, Washington, DC 20431
SAN: 203-8188
Tel: 202-623-7430 *Fax:* 202-623-7201
E-mail: publications@imf.org
Web Site: www.imfbookstore.org; elibrary.imf.org (online collection)
Key Personnel
Publr: Jeremy Clift
Assoc Publr: Linda Griffin Kean
Founded: 1946
Publishes books, periodicals & electronic products covering international finance, monetary issues, statistics & exchange rates, which are sold worldwide by distributors, bookstores & direct mail.
ISBN Prefix(es): 978-0-939934; 978-1-55775; 978-1-58906; 978-1-61635
Number of titles published annually: 120 Print; 12 CD-ROM; 120 Online; 200 E-Book
Total Titles: 750 Print
Orders to: IMF Publications, PO Box 92780, Washington, DC 20090
Membership(s): AAP; Association of American University Presses; Association of Learned & Professional Society Publishers; CrossRef

§International Press of Boston Inc
387 Somerville Ave, Somerville, MA 02143
Mailing Address: PO Box 502, Somerville, MA 02143
Tel: 617-623-3016 *Fax:* 617-623-3101
E-mail: ipb-info@intlpress.com; ipb-orders@intlpress.com
Web Site: www.intlpress.com
Key Personnel
Gen Mgr: Brian Bianchini *Tel:* 617-623-3855 *E-mail:* ipb-mgmt@intlpress.com
Founded: 1992
Publish books, monographs, conference proceedings in advanced mathematics.
ISBN Prefix(es): 978-1-57146
Number of titles published annually: 10 Print
Total Titles: 100 Print; 3 CD-ROM
Distributed by AMS

International Publishers Co Inc
235 W 23 St, New York, NY 10011
SAN: 202-5655
Tel: 212-366-9816 *Fax:* 212-366-9820
E-mail: service@intpubnyc.com
Web Site: www.intpubnyc.com
Key Personnel
Pres & Ed: Betty Smith
Founded: 1924
Short discount titles & Marxist classics. Trade in cloth & paperback, general nonfiction, social sciences, classic & contemporary Marxism-Leninism, literature, poetry & biography, labor, women's studies.
ISBN Prefix(es): 978-0-7178
Number of titles published annually: 4 Print
Total Titles: 160 Print
Imprints: New World Paperbacks
Foreign Rep(s): Global Book Marketing (London, UK)
Returns: Whitehurst & Clark, 1200 County Rd 523, Flemington, NJ 08822
Warehouse: WC Books, 1200 County Rd, Rte 523, Flemington, NJ 08822, Contact: Brad Searles *Tel:* 908-782-2323 *Fax:* 908-237-2407
Membership(s): ABA; The Association of Publishers for Special Sales; The Independent Book Publishers Association; National Association of College Stores

International Reading Association (IRA), see International Literacy Association (ILA)

International Research Center for Energy & Economic Development
850 Willowbrook Rd, Boulder, CO 80302
Tel: 303-442-4014 *Fax:* 303-442-5042
E-mail: info@iceed.org
Web Site: www.iceed.org
Key Personnel
Dir: Dorothea H El Mallakh

Lib Sales Dir: Helen El Mallakh
Founded: 1974
Monographs & hardcover; public policy; journal.
ISBN Prefix(es): 978-0-918714
Number of titles published annually: 3 Print
Total Titles: 80 Print
Warehouse: William S Hein & Co Inc, 1285 Main St, Buffalo, NY 14209 (for back orders of earlier volumes)

§International Risk Management Institute Inc
12222 Merit Dr, Suite 1600, Dallas, TX 75251-2266
Tel: 972-960-7693 *Fax:* 972-371-5120
E-mail: info27@irmi.com
Web Site: www.irmi.com
Key Personnel
CFO: Ron Allen
Pres: Jack Gibson
Founded: 1978
Publish both print & online books on commercial & personal lines of insurance.
ISBN Prefix(es): 978-1-886813; 978-0-938358; 978-1-933686
Number of titles published annually: 20 Print; 36 Online
Total Titles: 34 Print

International Society for Technology in Education
180 W Eighth Ave, Suite 300, Eugene, OR 97401-2916
Tel: 541-302-3777 (intl) *Toll Free Tel:* 800-336-5191 (US & CN) *Fax:* 541-302-3778
E-mail: iste@iste.org
Web Site: www.iste.org; www.iste.org/bookstore (orders); www.isteconference.org
Key Personnel
CEO: Brian Lewis
Chief Mktg Offr: Tracee Aliotti *Tel:* 541-681-3805
Chief Membership Offr: Jessica Medaille
Founded: 1979
Work with experienced educators to develop & produce practical resources for classroom teachers, teacher educators & technology leaders. Home of the National Educational Technology Standards (NETS), ISTE is the trusted source for educational technology books & courseware.
ISBN Prefix(es): 978-1-56484
Number of titles published annually: 12 Print
Total Titles: 60 Print

§International Society of Automation (ISA)
67 T W Alexander Dr, Research Triangle Park, NC 27709-0185
Mailing Address: PO Box 12277, Research Triangle Park, NC 27709-2277
Tel: 919-549-8411 *Fax:* 919-549-8288
E-mail: info@isa.org
Web Site: www.isa.org
Key Personnel
Exec Dir: Patrick Gouhin
Dir, Publg, Mktg & Sales: Tim Feldman
Founded: 1945
Technical books, references, journals, video-based training programs, directories, software, standards, proceedings, CD-ROM, electronic references.
ISBN Prefix(es): 978-1-55617; 978-1-939660; 978-0-87664; 978-0-9791330; 978-1-936007; 978-1-941546; 978-0-9792343; 978-1-934394; 978-1-937560
Number of titles published annually: 20 Print
Total Titles: 139 Print; 10 CD-ROM; 20 E-Book
Foreign Rep(s): Eurospan (Europe)

§International Wealth Success Inc
PO Box 186, Merrick, NY 11566-0186
Tel: 516-766-5850 *Toll Free Tel:* 800-323-0548 *Fax:* 516-766-5919
E-mail: admin@iwsmoney.com
Web Site: www.iwsmoney.com
Key Personnel
Pres & Ed: Tyler G Hicks *E-mail:* tyghicks@aol.com
Founded: 1966
Publish a variety of business & financial titles in the fields of small business, real estate, mail order, import-export & financing.
ISBN Prefix(es): 978-0-934311; 978-0-914306; 978-1-56150
Number of titles published annually: 6 Print; 6 CD-ROM; 4 Online; 70 E-Book; 4 Audio
Total Titles: 120 Print; 120 CD-ROM; 70 Online; 100 E-Book; 12 Audio

InterVarsity Press
Division of InterVarsity Christian Fellowship/USA
430 Plaza Dr, Westmont, IL 60559-1234
SAN: 202-7089
Mailing Address: PO Box 1400, Downers Grove, IL 60515
Tel: 630-734-4000 *Toll Free Tel:* 800-843-9487 *Fax:* 630-734-4200
E-mail: email@ivpress.com
Web Site: www.ivpress.com
Key Personnel
Publr: Robert A Fryling *Tel:* 630-734-4001 *E-mail:* bfryling@ivpress.com
Edit Dir: Andrew T Le Peau *Tel:* 630-734-4036 *E-mail:* alepeau@ivpress.com
Assoc Edit Dir: Cindy Bunch *Tel:* 630-734-4078 *E-mail:* cbunch@ivpress.com
Sr Ed: Daniel Reid *Tel:* 360-379-2599 *E-mail:* dgreid@ivpress.com
Art Dir: Cindy Kiple *Tel:* 630-734-4024 *E-mail:* ckiple@ivpress.com
Dir, Busn & Fin: James Hagen *Tel:* 630-734-4005 *E-mail:* jhagen@ivpress.com
Dir, Prodn & Fulfillment: Anne Gerth *Tel:* 630-734-4027 *E-mail:* agerth@ivpress.com
Dir, Sales & Mktg: Jeff Crosby *Tel:* 630-734-4017 *E-mail:* jcrosby@ivpress.com
Rts & Perms: Ellen Hsu *Tel:* 630-734-4034 *E-mail:* ehsu@ivpress.com
Founded: 1947
Religion (interdenominational); textbooks.
ISBN Prefix(es): 978-0-87784; 978-0-8308
Number of titles published annually: 110 Print; 70 E-Book; 15 Audio
Total Titles: 1,800 Print; 2 CD-ROM; 850 E-Book; 20 Audio
Imprints: Formatio (books that follow the rich tradition of the church in the journey of spiritual formation); IVP Academic (publishing to facilitate broader conversations in the academy & the church); IVP Books (thoughtful books on church, culture & mission); IVP Connect (resources for Bible study & small groups); IVP Crescendo (women applying their vision & gifts to the good of the whole church); IVP Praxis (bringing together theory & practice for the advancement of ministry); LifeGuide Bible Studies (guides on books of the Bible & key Biblical topics)
Branch Office(s)
Port Townsend, WA 98368, Sr Ed: Dr Dan Reid *E-mail:* dgreid@ix.netcom.com
Foreign Office(s): IVP Book Centre, Norton St, Nottingham NG7 3HR, United Kingdom, Fin & Opers Mgr: George Russell *Tel:* (0115) 978 1054 *Fax:* (0115) 942 2694 *E-mail:* sales@ivpbooks.com *Web Site:* www.ivpbooks.com
Foreign Rep(s): Inter-Varsity Press - UK (Africa, Asia, Europe)
Membership(s): Evangelical Christian Publishers Association

Interweave Press LLC
Imprint of F+W, A Content + eCommerce Company
201 E Fourth St, Loveland, CO 80537
Toll Free Tel: 800-272-2193; 800-289-0963 *Fax:* 970-613-4656 *Toll Free Fax:* 888-590-4082
Web Site: www.interweave.com
Key Personnel
Founder & Creative Dir: Linda Ligon
Sr Ed: Erica Smith
Mktg: Heidi Hedger *E-mail:* hhedger@interweave.com
Founded: 1975
ISBN Prefix(es): 978-0-934026; 978-1-883010; 978-1-931499; 978-0-9796073; 978-1-4402; 978-1-63250; 978-1-59668; 978-1-62033
Number of titles published annually: 45 Print
Total Titles: 350 Print
Distributed by Keith Ainsworth Pty Ltd (Australia); David Bateman Ltd (New Zealand); Search Press (UK)
Membership(s): Publishers Association of the West

§The Intrepid Traveler
152 Staltonstall Pkwy (rear entrance), East Haven, CT 06512
Mailing Address: PO Box 531, Branford, CT 06405-0531
Tel: 203-469-0214
E-mail: admin@intrepidtraveler.com
Web Site: www.intrepidtraveler.com
Key Personnel
Publr: Kelly Monaghan
Assoc Publr: Sally Scanlon *E-mail:* sscanlon@intrepidtraveler.com
Founded: 1990
Publish travel how-to & guidebooks titles.
ISBN Prefix(es): 978-0-9627892; 978-1-887140; 978-1-937011
Number of titles published annually: 4 Print; 4 E-Book
Total Titles: 21 Print; 11 E-Book
Distribution Center: National Book Network Inc (NBN), 15200 NBN Way, Blue Ridge Summit, PA 17214 *Tel:* 717-794-3800 *Toll Free Tel:* 800-462-6420 *Fax:* 717-794-3828 *Toll Free Fax:* 800-338-4550 *E-mail:* customercare@nbnbooks.com *Web Site:* www.nbnbooks.com
Membership(s): The Independent Book Publishers Association

Iron Gate Publishing
PO Box 999, Niwot, CO 80544
Tel: 303-530-2551 *Fax:* 303-530-5273
E-mail: editor@irongate.com
Web Site: www.irongate.com
Key Personnel
Publr & Ed: Dina C Carson *E-mail:* editor@irongate.com
Founded: 1990
Genealogy, self-publishing, reference, reunion planning how-to.
ISBN Prefix(es): 978-1-879579; 978-0-9724975
Number of titles published annually: 6 Print; 6 CD-ROM; 25 Online; 25 E-Book
Total Titles: 25 Print; 6 CD-ROM; 17 Online; 25 E-Book
Membership(s): The Association of Publishers for Special Sales; Colorado Independent Publishers Association; The Independent Book Publishers Association; Publishers Association of the West

Irvington Publishers Inc, see Ardent Media Inc

ISI Books
Imprint of Intercollegiate Studies Institute Inc
3901 Centerville Rd, Wilmington, DE 19807-1938
Tel: 302-652-4600 *Toll Free Tel:* 800-526-7022 *Fax:* 302-652-1760
E-mail: info@isi.org; isibooks@isi.org
Web Site: www.isibooks.org
Key Personnel
Pres: Christopher G Long

VP & Ed-in-Chief: Jed Donahue
E-mail: jdonahue@isi.org
Founded: 1993
Publisher of serious but accessible nonfiction titles. ISI also publishes the esteemed quarterly journal *Modern Age* (founded in 1957 by Russell Kirk) & the magazine *Intercollegiate Review.*
ISBN Prefix(es): 978-1-882926; 978-1-932236
Number of titles published annually: 8 Print; 8 E-Book
Total Titles: 200 Print; 100 E-Book

Island Press
2000 "M" St NW, Suite 650, Washington, DC 20036
SAN: 212-5129
Tel: 202-232-7933 *Toll Free Tel:* 800-828-1302
Fax: 202-234-1328
E-mail: info@islandpress.org
Web Site: www.islandpress.org
Key Personnel
Pres: Charles C Savitt
EVP & Publr: David Miller
VP, Sales & Mktg: Julie Marshall
Exec Ed: Heather Boyer
Founded: 1984
Books about the environment for professionals, students & general readers, autobiography-scientific; land use planning; environmental economics; nature essays; "green" architecture.
ISBN Prefix(es): 978-0-933280; 978-1-55963; 978-1-59726; 978-1-61091
Number of titles published annually: 40 Print; 40 E-Book
Total Titles: 1,000 Print; 800 E-Book
Imprints: Shearwater Books
Distributor for IUCN; Techne Press
Shipping Address: University of Chicago Distribution Center, 11030 S Langley Ave, Chicago, IL 60628 *Tel:* 773-702-7000 *Toll Free Tel:* 800-621-2736 *Fax:* 773-702-7212 *Toll Free Fax:* 800-621-8476 *E-mail:* custserv@press.uchicago.edu
Membership(s): American Association of University Presses; BISG

ISTE, see International Society for Technology in Education

§Italica Press
595 Main St, Suite 605, New York, NY 10044
SAN: 695-1805
Tel: 917-371-0563
E-mail: info@italicapress.com
Web Site: www.italicapress.com
Key Personnel
Pres & Publr, Electronic Publg: Eileen Gardiner
E-mail: egardiner@italicapress.com
Secy & Publr, Electronic Publg: Ronald G Musto
E-mail: rgmusto@italicapress.com
Founded: 1985
English translations of Latin & Italian works from the Middle Ages to the present.
ISBN Prefix(es): 978-0-934977; 978-1-59910
Number of titles published annually: 7 Print; 20 E-Book
Total Titles: 200 Print; 60 E-Book

iUniverse
Division of Author Solutions Inc
1663 Liberty Dr, Bloomington, IN 47403
Toll Free Tel: 800-AUTHORS (288-4677)
Fax: 812-355-4085
Web Site: www.iuniverse.com
Key Personnel
CEO & Pres: Andrew Phillips
COO: Kevin G Gregory
SVP, Mktg: Keith Ogorek
SVP, Prodn Servs: Bill Becher
SVP, Worldwide Sales: Don Seitz
Founded: 1999
iUniverse is the industry's leading book marketing, editorial services & supported self-publishing company. The iUniverse management team has extensive editorial & managerial experience with traditional publishers such as Random House, Wiley, Macmillan, Chronicle Books & Addison-Wesley. iUniverse maintains a strategic alliance with Chapters Indigo in Canada & titles accepted into the iUniverse Rising Star program are featured in a special collection on www.barnesandnoble.com.
This publisher has indicated that 100% of their product line is author subsidized.
ISBN Prefix(es): 978-0-9665514; 978-1-58348; 978-0-9668591; 978-1-893652; 978-0-595
Number of titles published annually: 4,500 Print
Total Titles: 40,000 Print
Distribution Center: Baker & Taylor Inc
Ingram Book Group
Membership(s): AAP; Canadian Booksellers Association

Jade Rabbit, see Quite Specific Media Group Ltd

§Jain Publishing Co
PO Box 3523, Fremont, CA 94539
SAN: 213-6503
Tel: 510-659-8272 *Fax:* 510-659-0501
E-mail: mail@jainpub.com
Web Site: www.jainpub.com
Key Personnel
Pres & Publr: Mukesh Jain
Founded: 1989
College textbooks & supplements, professional & scholarly references, ebooks & elearning products & services.
ISBN Prefix(es): 978-0-89581; 978-0-87573
Number of titles published annually: 10 Print; 1 CD-ROM; 2 Online; 2 E-Book
Total Titles: 200 Print; 1 CD-ROM; 2 Online; 4 E-Book
Imprints: Asian Humanities Press

JayJo Books LLC
Subsidiary of The Guidance Group
One Huntington Quadrangle, Suite 1N03, Melville, NY 11747
Tel: 516-496-4863 *Toll Free Tel:* 800-999-6884
Fax: 516-496-4050 *Toll Free Fax:* 800-262-1886
E-mail: jayjobooks@guidance-group.com
Web Site: www.guidance-group.com; www.jayjo.com
Key Personnel
Publr: Ed Werz
Ed: Danielle Sensale
Founded: 1992
Educational books to help parents, teachers & children cope with chronic illness, special needs & health education.
ISBN Prefix(es): 978-0-9639449; 978-1-891383
Number of titles published annually: 4 Print
Total Titles: 26 Print

Jeter Publishing, see Gallery Books

Jewish Lights Publishing
Division of Longhill Partners Inc
Sunset Farm Offices, Rte 4, Woodstock, VT 05091
SAN: 134-5621
Mailing Address: PO Box 237, Woodstock, VT 05091
Tel: 802-457-4000 *Toll Free Tel:* 800-962-4544 (orders only) *Fax:* 802-457-4004
E-mail: sales@jewishlights.com
Web Site: www.jewishlights.com
Key Personnel
Publr & Ed-in-Chief: Stuart M Matlins
VP, Edit & Prodn: Emily Wichland
PR: Leah Brewer
Founded: 1990
General trade adult & children's books on spirituality, theology, philosophy, mysticism, women's studies, recovery/self-help/healing & history for people of all faiths & backgrounds.
ISBN Prefix(es): 978-1-879045; 978-1-58023
Number of titles published annually: 40 Print; 40 E-Book
Total Titles: 500 Print; 450 E-Book
Foreign Rep(s): Bayard-Novalis (Canada); Brumby Sunstate (Australia, New Zealand); Deep Books (Europe, UK); Disticor Direct (Canada); Brian Scheiffer Agencies (South Africa)
Foreign Rights: The Deborah Harris Agency (Israel); Alexander Korzhenevski Agency (Russia); Andrew Nurnberg Associates Ltd (Hungary); Katia Schumer (Brazil); Christian Schweiger Agency (France, Germany); Susanna Zevi Agenzia Letteraria (Italy)
Returns: 28 River St, Windsor, VT 05089
Distribution Center: Baker & Taylor, 2550 W Tyvola Rd, Suite 300, Charlotte, NC 28217
Tel: 704-998-3100 *Web Site:* www.btol.com
Ingram Book Co, One Ingram Blvd, La Vergne, TN 37086 *Tel:* 615-793-5000 *Web Site:* www.ingrambook.com
New Leaf Distributing Co, 401 Thornton Rd, Lithia Springs, GA 30122-1577 *Tel:* 770-948-7845 *Fax:* 770-944-2313 *Web Site:* www.newleaf-dist.com

Jewish Publication Society
2100 Arch St, Philadelphia, PA 19103
SAN: 201-0240
Tel: 215-832-0600 *Toll Free Tel:* 800-234-3151
Fax: 215-568-2017
Web Site: www.jps.org
Key Personnel
Dir & Acqs Ed: Barry L Schwartz
E-mail: bschwartz@jps.org
Mng Ed: Carol Hupping *Tel:* 215-832-0605
E-mail: chupping@jps.org
Off Mgr: Trisha Lubrant *Tel:* 215-832-0612
E-mail: tlubrant@jps.org
Founded: 1888
Books of Jewish interest.
ISBN Prefix(es): 978-0-8276
Number of titles published annually: 8 Print; 8 E-Book
Total Titles: 250 Print
Distributed by University of Nebraska Press
Foreign Rep(s): Eurospan (Europe, Latin America, Middle East, UK & Commonwealth); Scholarly Book Service (Canada)
Membership(s): Association of American University Presses

§Jhpiego
Affiliate of The Johns Hopkins University
1615 Thames St, Baltimore, MD 21231-3492
Tel: 410-537-1800 *Fax:* 410-537-1473
E-mail: info@jhpiego.net
Web Site: www.jhpiego.org
Key Personnel
Pres & CEO: Leslie D Mancuso, PhD
COO: Edwin J Judd
CIO: Glenn R Strachan
VP, External Aff & Communs: Melody McCoy
Founded: 1973
Reproductive health, medical texts, family planning, maternal health, HIV/AIDS & cervical cancer prevention & treatment, infection prevention.
ISBN Prefix(es): 978-0-929817; 978-1-943408
Number of titles published annually: 20 Print
Total Titles: 80 Print; 4 CD-ROM

JHU Press, see The Johns Hopkins University Press

The Jim Henson Co
1416 N La Brea Ave, Hollywood, CA 90028
Tel: 323-802-1500 *Fax:* 323-802-1825
Web Site: www.henson.com
Key Personnel
Chmn: Brian Henson
CEO: Lisa Henson, Esq
COO & Pres: Peter Schube
CFO & EVP: Laurie Don
EVP, Busn & Legal Aff: Dan Scharf
EVP, Children's Entertainment: Halle Stanford
EVP, Global Dist: Richard Goldsmith
SVP, Admin: Joe Henderson
SVP, Global Consumer Prods: Melissa Segal
SVP, Mktg & PR: Nicole Goldman
VP, New Media: Allyson Smith
VP, Prodn Fin & Physical Prodn: Brittan Brown
Creative Supv, JHCS: Peter Brooke
Founded: 1955
Humor, craft, coffee table, children's concept & storybooks, comic books, novelty books, activity & coloring books, children's book clubs, movie & TV tie-ins.
Number of titles published annually: 25 Print; 1 Audio
Total Titles: 400 Print
Branch Office(s)
37-18 Northern Blvd, Suite 400, Long Island City, NY 11101 *Tel:* 212-794-2400 *Fax:* 212-439-7452
Distributed by At a Glance; Walter Foster; Golden Books Family Entertainment; Grolier; KidsBooks; Penguin Group (USA) LLC; PK; Random House; Reader's Digest Children's Books; Running Press; Simon & Schuster
Foreign Rep(s): Bi Plano (Spain); Design Rights Intl (UK); Gaffney (Australia); Publishing Partner (Germany)

§JIST Publishing
Division of EMC Publishing LLC
875 Montreal Way, St Paul, MN 55102
SAN: 240-2351
Toll Free Tel: 800-328-1452 *Toll Free Fax:* 800-328-4564
E-mail: educate@emcp.com
Web Site: jist.emcp.com
Key Personnel
Pres & CEO: Eric Cantor
CFO: Joy Hoppe
Sr Acct Mgr: Bob Grilliot
Founded: 1981
Job search (resumes, cover letters, interviewing), career planning, job retention, occupational reference, assessment, self-help, career exploration, occupational information, character education, life skills, CD-ROMs & reference books, videos & software.
ISBN Prefix(es): 978-0-942784; 978-1-56370; 978-1-57112; 978-1-930780; 978-1-55864; 978-1-59357; 978-1-63332
Number of titles published annually: 50 Print; 2 CD-ROM; 20 E-Book; 1 Audio
Total Titles: 350 Print; 6 CD-ROM; 60 E-Book; 1 Audio
Imprints: JIST Career Solutions
Membership(s): The Independent Book Publishers Association

The JOC Group Inc
Formerly UBM Global Trade
Division of IHS Inc
2 Penn Plaza E, Newark, NJ 07105
Tel: 973-776-8660
Web Site: www.joc.com
Key Personnel
EVP, Chief Content Offr: Peter Tirschwell *E-mail:* ptirschwell@joc.com
Exec Ed: Chris Brooks *E-mail:* cbrooks@joc.com
Exec Ed, JOC.com: Mark Szakonyi *E-mail:* mszakonyi@joc.com
Ed-at-Large: Peter Leach *E-mail:* pleach@joc.com
Founded: 2000
Provider of proprietary data, news, business intelligence & analytical content supporting commercial maritime, rail, trucking, warehousing & logistics industries worldwide.
ISBN Prefix(es): 978-0-9649630; 978-1-891131
Number of titles published annually: 40 Online
Total Titles: 40 Online

John Deere Publishing
Division of Deere & Co
5440 Corporate Park Dr, Davenport, IA 52807
Toll Free Tel: 800-522-7448 (orders) *Fax:* 563-355-3690
E-mail: johndeerepublishing@johndeere.com
Web Site: www.johndeere.com/publications
Founded: 1967
ISBN Prefix(es): 978-0-86691
Number of titles published annually: 8 Print
Total Titles: 27 Print
Warehouse: Quad City Consolidation, 2900 Research Pkwy, Davenport, IA 52806

§The Johns Hopkins University Press
Affiliate of The Johns Hopkins University
2715 N Charles St, Baltimore, MD 21218-4363
SAN: 202-7348
Tel: 410-516-6900; 410-516-6987 (journal orders outside US & CN) *Toll Free Tel:* 800-537-5487 (book orders & cust serv); 800-548-1784 (journal orders) *Fax:* 410-516-6968; 410-516-3866 (journal orders)
E-mail: hfscustserv@press.jhu.edu (cust serv); jrnlcirc@press.jhu.edu (journal orders)
Web Site: www.press.jhu.edu; muse.jhu.edu
Key Personnel
Dir: Kathleen Keane *E-mail:* kk@press.jhu.edu
Edit Dir: Greg Britton *E-mail:* gb@press.jhu.edu
Dir, Fin & Admin: Erik Smist *E-mail:* eas@press.jhu.edu
Dir, Mktg & Online Book Publg: Becky Brasington Clark *E-mail:* rbc@press.jhu.edu
Sales Dir: Kerry Cahill *E-mail:* kpc@press.jhu.edu
Journals Publr: William M Breichner *E-mail:* wmb@press.jhu.edu
Exec Ed: Vincent J Burke *E-mail:* vjb@press.jhu.edu; Jacqueline C Wehmueller *E-mail:* jcw@press.jhu.edu
Mng Ed: Juliana M McCarthy *E-mail:* jmm@press.jhu.edu
Sr Acqs Ed: Elizabeth Sherburn Demers *E-mail:* ed@press.jhu.edu; Matthew McAdam *E-mail:* mxm@press.jhu.edu
Acqs Ed: Robin W Coleman *E-mail:* rwc@press.jhu.edu
Devt & Publicity Offr: Jack Holmes *E-mail:* jmh@press.jhu.edu
Design & Prodn Mgr: John Cronin *E-mail:* jgc@press.jhu.edu
Fulfillment Opers Mgr: Davida Breier *E-mail:* dgb@press.jhu.edu
Journals Mktg Mgr: Lisa Klose *E-mail:* llk@press.jhu.edu
Journals Prodn Mgr: Carol Hamblen *E-mail:* crh@press.jhu.edu
Journals Subn Mgr: Robert White Goodman *E-mail:* aha@press.jhu.edu
Rts Mgr: Kelly Rogers *E-mail:* klr@press.jhu.edu
Mktg & Sales Coord: Catherine Bergeron *E-mail:* cab@press.jhu.edu
Founded: 1878
Scholarly books, nonfiction of general interest, paperbacks, scholarly journals.
ISBN Prefix(es): 978-0-8018; 978-1-4214
Number of titles published annually: 175 Print
Total Titles: 4,200 Print; 5 Online; 3,200 E-Book
Sales Office(s): Terry & Read LLC, 2031 N Craig St, Altadena, CA 91001, Contact: Alan Read *Fax:* 626-356-4630 *E-mail:* alanread@earthlink.net
Terry & Read LLC, 247 Fourth St, Loft 402, Oakland, CA, Contact: David Terry *Tel:* 510-813-9854 *Fax:* 510-465-7668 *E-mail:* dmterry@aol.com
Miller Trade Book Marketing, 363 W Erie St, Suite 7-E, Chicago, IL 60654, Contact: Bruce Miller *Tel:* 312-423-7880 *Fax:* 312-276-8109 *E-mail:* orders@millertrade.com
Book Traveler, Box 193, 1289 N Fordham Blvd, Chapel Hill, NC 27514, Contact: Roger Sauls *Tel:* 919-490-5656 *Fax:* 919-490-0297 *E-mail:* roger_165@msn.com
Terry & Read LLC, 19216 SE 46 Place, Issaquah, WA 98027, Contact: Ted H Terry *Tel:* 425-747-3411 *Fax:* 425-747-0366 *E-mail:* colterryassoc@aol.com
Distributor for Baylor University Press; The Brookings Institution Press; Catholic University of America Press; Center for Talented Youth; Georgetown University Press; Howard University Press; Johns Hopkins Aids Service; Maryland Historical Society; Resources for the Future; University of Massachusetts Press; University of Pennsylvania Museum; University of Pennsylvania Press; University of Washington Press; The University Press of Kentucky; Urban Institute Press; The Woodrow Wilson Center Press; World Resources Institute
Foreign Rep(s): Apex Knowledge Sdn Bhd (Simon Tay) (Brunei, Malaysia); Aromix Books Co Ltd (Nick Woon) (Hong Kong); Avicenna Partnership Ltd (Bill Kennedy) (Bahrain, Egypt, Iran, Iraq, Kazakhstan, Kuwait, Kyrgyzstan, Lebanon, Oman, Qatar, Saudi Arabia, Sudan, Syria, Tajikistan, Turkmenistan, United Arab Emirates, Uzbekistan, Yemen); Avicenna Partnership Ltd (Claire de Gruchy) (Algeria, Cyprus, Greece, Israel, Jordan, Libya, Malta, Morocco, Palestine, Tunisia, Turkey); CRW Books (Tony Sagun) (Philippines); Everest International Publishing Services (Wei Zhao) (China); Footprint Books Pty Ltd (Kate O'Reilly) (Australia, Fiji, New Zealand, Papua New Guinea); ICK-Information & Culture Korea (Mr Se-Yung Jun) (Korea); Ewa Ledochowicz (Eastern Europe); Lexa Publishers' Representatives (Mical Moser) (Canada); Uwe Luedemann (Austria, France, Germany, Italy, Portugal, Spain, Switzerland); Mirjam Mayenburg (Benelux); B K Norton (Ms Meihua Sun) (Taiwan); Provider of Contents & Information (Mr P C Tham) (Singapore); Rockbook Inc (Japan); Christopher Stamp (Denmark, Iceland, Scandinavia); Robert Towers (Ireland, Northern Ireland); Kevin van Hasselt (Africa, Caribbean); The White Partnership (Andrew White) (Hong Kong, India, Indonesia, Malaysia, Thailand); John Wiley & Sons Ltd (Africa, Continental Europe, Middle East, South Asia, UK); World Press (Saleem Malik) (Pakistan); Yale Representation Ltd (Andrew Jarmain) (UK); YUHA Associates (Ahmed Zaharr Kamaruddin) (Brunei, Malaysia)
Foreign Rights: Agenzia Letteraria (Italy); The Chinese Connection Agency (China); Du Ran Kim Agency (Korea); The English Agency (Japan); Graal Literary Agency (Poland); The Deborah Harris Agency (Israel); International Editors' Co (Spain); Japan Uni Agency (Japan); The Kalem Literary Agency (Turkey); La Nouvelle Agence (France); Tuttle-Mori Agency (Japan)
Advertising Agency: Welch, Mirabile & Co Inc
Orders to: PO Box 19966, Baltimore, MD 21211-0966
Returns: Hopkins Fulfillment Service, c/o Maple Press Co, Lebanon Distribution Ctr, PO Box 1287, Lebanon, PA 17042
Warehouse: Lebanon Distribution Center, 704 Legionaire Dr, Fredricksburg, PA 17026
Membership(s): AAP; BISG

Johnson Books
Division of Big Earth Publishing
3005 Center Green Dr, Suite 225, Boulder, CO 80301

SAN: 201-0313
Tel: 303-443-9766 *Toll Free Tel:* 800-258-5830
Fax: 303-443-9687
E-mail: books@bigearthpublishing.com
Web Site: www.bigearthpublishing.com; www.johnsonbooks.com
Key Personnel
Publr & Mng Ed: Mira Perrizo *Tel:* 303-541-1511
E-mail: mperrizo@bigearthpublishing.com
Mktg Mgr: Julie Heins *Tel:* 303-541-1506
E-mail: jheins@bigearthpublishing.com
Founded: 1978
Hardcover & paperbound originals & reprints: nonfiction history, nature, archaeology, guidebooks, outdoors, travel, astronomy, American West, environment, Native American.
ISBN Prefix(es): 978-0-933472; 978-1-55566; 978-0-917895
Number of titles published annually: 20 Print
Total Titles: 160 Print
Shipping Address: 2650 S Juni St, Englewood, CO 80110
Warehouse: 2650 S Juni St, Englewood, CO 80110

§Jones & Bartlett Learning LLC
Division of Ascend Learning
5 Wall St, Burlington, MA 01803
Tel: 978-443-5000 *Toll Free Tel:* 800-832-0034
Fax: 978-443-8000
E-mail: info@jblearning.com
Web Site: www.jblearning.com
Key Personnel
CEO: Ty Field
Pres: James Homer
Founded: 1983
Academic & professional publisher.
ISBN Prefix(es): 978-0-86720; 978-0-7637; 978-1-4496; 978-1-284
Number of titles published annually: 300 Print
Total Titles: 2,500 Print; 100 CD-ROM
Foreign Office(s): Jones & Bartlett Learning International, The Exchange, Express Park, Bristol Rd, Bridgwater, Somerset TA6 4RR, United Kingdom *Tel:* (01278) 427800 *Fax:* (01278) 421077
Foreign Rep(s): Academic Marketing Services Ltd (Michael Brightmore) (South Africa); Advanced Marketing Associates (Kevin Fong) (Malaysia, Singapore); BNC Publishers Services Inc (Nanette Beramo) (Guam, Philippines); Cengage Learning Asia Pte Ltd (Cambodia, Hong Kong, Indonesia, Laos, Vietnam); Merry Chang (Taiwan); Cranbury International LLC (Caribbean, South America); Elsevier Australia (Australia, Fiji, New Zealand); Benjamin Ho (China, Thailand); Impact Korea (ChongHo Ra) (South Korea); IPR (International Publishers Representatives) (Middle East); Jones & Bartlett India Pvt Ltd (Vinod Vasishtha) (Bangladesh, India, Sri Lanka); The White Partnership (Andrew White) (Japan); World Press (Saleem Malik) (Pakistan)
Returns: 905 Carlow Dr, Unit 5, Bolingbrook, IL 60490
Warehouse: 905 Carlow Dr, Unit 5, Bolingbrook, IL 60490

Jones McClure Publishing
3131 Eastside St, Suite 300, Houston, TX 77098
Mailing Address: PO Box 3348, Houston, TX 77253-3348
Tel: 713-335-8200 *Toll Free Tel:* 800-626-6667
Fax: 713-335-8201
E-mail: comments@jonesmcclure.com
Web Site: www.jonesmcclure.com
Key Personnel
Pres: Baird Craft
Founded: 1992
Provides a comprehensive desk reference to the trial lawyer, through codes, commentaries & form covering several areas of Texas law & federal litigation, written in an easy to follow, plain English format.
ISBN Prefix(es): 978-1-884554; 978-1-59839
Number of titles published annually: 26 Print
Total Titles: 26 Print; 3 CD-ROM

§Joshua Tree Publishing
190 S LaSalle St, Suite 2100, Chicago, IL 60603
Tel: 312-893-7525
E-mail: info@joshuatreepublishing.com
Web Site: www.joshuatreepublishing.com; www.centaurbooks.com (imprint); www.chiralhouse.com (imprint)
Key Personnel
Pres & Publr: John Paul Owles *E-mail:* jpo@joshuatreepublishing.com
Founded: 1977
Believe in authors & dedicated to making the dream of being a published author a reality. Specialize in works that uplift the human spirit, inspire people to reach for higher goals & touch the hearts of readers.
ISBN Prefix(es): 978-0-9710954; 978-0-9778311; 978-0-9768677; 978-0-9845904; 978-0-9823703; 978-0-9829803; 978-1-941049
Number of titles published annually: 18 Print; 18 E-Book
Total Titles: 70 Print; 50 E-Book
Imprints: Centaur Books; Chiral House; Heroides Publishing; Joshua Tree Publishing
Membership(s): Book Publicists of Southern California; The Independent Book Publishers Association

Jossey-Bass
Imprint of John Wiley & Sons Inc
One Montgomery St, Suite 1200, San Francisco, CA 94104
Tel: 415-433-1740 *Toll Free Tel:* 800-956-7739
Fax: 415-433-0499 (edit/mktg)
Web Site: www.josseybass.com; www.pfeiffer.com
Key Personnel
Dir, HR: Susan Call
Founded: 1966
General education, higher & adult education, management & business, human resources, training, health & health administration, social & behavioral sciences, psychology, conflict resolution, mediation & negotiation, religion, nonprofit & public management.
ISBN Prefix(es): 978-1-55542; 978-0-87589; 978-0-7879; 978-0-88390; 978-0-89384
Total Titles: 5,000 Print
Imprints: Pfeiffer
Orders to: John Wiley & Sons Inc, Customer Service, One Wiley Dr, Somerset, NJ 08875-1272 *Tel:* 732-469-4400 *Toll Free Tel:* 800-225-5945 *Fax:* 732-302-2300 *E-mail:* customer@wiley.com
Returns: John Wiley & Sons Inc, Customer Service, One Wiley Dr, Somerset, NJ 08875-1272 *Tel:* 732-469-4400 *Toll Free Tel:* 800-225-5945 *Fax:* 732-302-2300 *E-mail:* customer@wiley.com

Journal of Roman Archaeology LLC
95 Peleg Rd, Portsmouth, RI 02871
Tel: 401-683-1955 *Fax:* 401-683-1975
E-mail: jra@journalofromanarch.com
Web Site: www.journalofromanarch.com
Key Personnel
Publr & Gen Ed: John H Humphrey
Founded: 1988
Annual journal & supplementary series.
ISBN Prefix(es): 978-1-887829; 978-0-9913730
Number of titles published annually: 6 Print
Total Titles: 96 Print

§Joy Publishing Co
Division of California Clock Co
PO Box 9901, Fountain Valley, CA 92708
SAN: 663-3544
Tel: 714-545-4321 *Toll Free Tel:* 800-454-8228
Fax: 714-708-2099
Web Site: www.joypublishing.com; www.kit-cat.com
Key Personnel
Pres: Woody Young *E-mail:* woody@joypublishing.com
Founded: 1986
Publish spiritual books.
ISBN Prefix(es): 978-0-939513
Number of titles published annually: 10 Print
Total Titles: 70 Print; 3 CD-ROM; 3 Online; 3 Audio
Shipping Address: 16060 Abajo Circle, Fountain Valley, CA 92708

Joyce Media Inc
3413 Soledad Canyon Rd, Acton, CA 93510-1974
Mailing Address: PO Box 57, Acton, CA 93510-0057
Tel: 661-269-1169 *Fax:* 661-269-2139
E-mail: help@joycemediainc.com
Web Site: www.joycemediainc.com
Key Personnel
Founder & Pres: John Joyce
Founded: 1968
General interest publications; specialize in sign language & newspapers.
ISBN Prefix(es): 978-0-913072
Number of titles published annually: 40 Print; 3 CD-ROM
Total Titles: 35 CD-ROM; 2 Online; 2 E-Book; 2 Audio

Judaica Press Inc
123 Ditmas Ave, Brooklyn, NY 11218
SAN: 204-9856
Tel: 718-972-6200 *Toll Free Tel:* 800-972-6201
Fax: 718-972-6204
E-mail: info@judaicapress.com; orders@judaicapress.com
Web Site: www.judaicapress.com
Key Personnel
Pres: Gloria Goldman
Mng Ed: Norman Shapiro *E-mail:* nshapiro@judaicapress.com
Founded: 1963
Classic & contemporary Jewish literature in Hebrew & English.
ISBN Prefix(es): 978-0-910818; 978-1-880582; 978-1-932443; 978-1-60763
Number of titles published annually: 25 Print; 6 E-Book
Total Titles: 400 Print; 12 E-Book
Imprints: Zahava Publications
Foreign Rep(s): Lehmanns (Europe, UK); Shanky's (Israel)

Judson Press
Division of American Baptist Churches in the USA
588 N Gulph Rd, King of Prussia, PA 19406
Mailing Address: PO Box 851, Valley Forge, PA 19482-0851 SAN: 201-0348
Toll Free Tel: 800-458-3766 *Fax:* 610-768-2107
Web Site: www.judsonpress.com
Key Personnel
Publr: Laura Alden *E-mail:* laura.alden@abhms.org
Mktg Dir: Linda Johnson-LeBlanc *Tel:* 610-768-2458 *E-mail:* linda.johnson-leblanc@abhms.org
Busn Mgr: Ronald Freeland
Ed: Rebecca Irwin-Diehl *Tel:* 610-768-2109
E-mail: rebecca.irwin-diehl@abhms.org
Founded: 1824
Religion (Baptist & nondenominational Christian), African American, women & multicultural; cloth & paperback.
ISBN Prefix(es): 978-0-8170
Number of titles published annually: 12 Print; 2 Audio
Total Titles: 350 Print; 1 CD-ROM; 2 Audio

Jump at the Sun
Imprint of Disney-Hyperion Books
125 West End Ave, 3rd fl, New York, NY 10023
Web Site: books.disney.com
Founded: 1998
Books celebrating the African-American experience & culture.
ISBN Prefix(es): 978-0-7868
Number of titles published annually: 2 Print; 2 E-Book
Total Titles: 100 Print; 100 E-Book

Jungle Wagon Press
5116 Didier Ave, Rockford, IL 61101
SAN: 920-6426
Tel: 815-988-9048
E-mail: junglewagonpress@gmail.com
Web Site: www.junglewagonpress.com
Key Personnel
Owner: Angela Malavolti
Founded: 2011
Provides publishing services including editing, professional illustrations, design, ISBN, copyright, printing & marketing. Specialize in high quality children's picture books, often with an educational element.
This publisher has indicated that 80% of their product line is author subsidized.
ISBN Prefix(es): 978-0-9834092; 978-0-9904271
Number of titles published annually: 3 Print
Total Titles: 5 Print

§Kabbalah Publishing
Division of Kabbalah Centre International
1100 S Robertson Blvd, Los Angeles, CA 90035
Tel: 310-601-1039 *Fax:* 310-657-7957
E-mail: customerservice@kabbalahpublishing.com; kcla@kabbalah.com
Web Site: publishing.kabbalah.com; www.kabbalah.com
Founded: 2002
Dedicated to bringing the world's oldest & deepest treasury of spiritual wisdom.
ISBN Prefix(es): 978-1-57189; 978-0-943688; 978-0-924457
Number of titles published annually: 15 Print; 2 CD-ROM; 2 Online; 2 E-Book; 2 Audio
Total Titles: 35 Print; 3 CD-ROM; 2 Online; 4 E-Book; 4 Audio
Foreign Rights: Kabbalah Agency (Worldwide)
Distribution Center: Publishers Group West, 1700 Fourth St, Berkeley, CA 94710 *Tel:* 510-809-3700 *Fax:* 510-809-3777

Kaeden Corp
PO Box 16190, Rocky River, OH 44116-0190
Tel: 440-617-1400 *Toll Free Tel:* 800-890-7323 *Fax:* 440-617-1403
E-mail: info@kaeden.com
Web Site: www.kaeden.com
Key Personnel
Pres: Craig Urmston *E-mail:* curmston@kaeden.com
Ed: Lisa Stenger *E-mail:* lstenger@kaeden.com
Founded: 1986
Books for emergent, early & fluent readers, grades K-3, reading recovery & guided reading programs.
ISBN Prefix(es): 978-1-879835; 978-1-57874; 978-1-61181; 978-1-61181
Number of titles published annually: 16 Print
Total Titles: 300 Print; 7 CD-ROM; 72 E-Book; 7 Audio
Imprints: Kaeden Books
Membership(s): AAP; American Educational Publishers; International Literacy Association; National Council of Teachers of English; Reading Recovery Council of North America

Kalmbach Publishing Co
21027 Crossroads Circle, Waukesha, WI 53186
Mailing Address: PO Box 1612, Waukesha, WI 53187-1612
Tel: 262-796-8776 *Toll Free Tel:* 800-533-6644 (cust serv & orders) *Fax:* 262-796-1615 (sales & cust serv); 262-798-6468 (edit)
E-mail: customerservice@kalmbach.com
Web Site: www.kalmbach.com; www.kalmbachstore.com
Key Personnel
Pres: Charles R Croft *E-mail:* ccroft@kalmbach.com
VP, Sales & Mktg: Dan Lance
Books Publr: Diane Bacha *E-mail:* dbacha@kalmbach.com
Books Ed-in-Chief: Diane Wheeler *E-mail:* dwheeler@kalmbach.com
Corp Circ Dir: Michael Barbee
Founded: 1934
Special interest books, calendars & magazines in the astronomy, jewelry making, crafts, hobby & collectibles market.
ISBN Prefix(es): 978-0-89024; 978-0-913135; 978-0-89778; 978-0-8238; 978-0-87116; 978-0-933168; 978-1-62700
Number of titles published annually: 35 Print
Total Titles: 135 Print
Imprints: Greenberg Books; Kalmbach Books
Distributed by Publishers Group West (PGW)

§Kamehameha Publishing
Division of Kamehameha Schools
567 S King St, Suite 118, Honolulu, HI 96813
Tel: 808-534-8205 *Fax:* 808-541-5305
E-mail: publishing@ksbe.edu
Web Site: kamehamehapublishing.org
Key Personnel
Dir: Ron Cox
Founded: 1933
Book, journal & poster publishing in the areas of Hawaiian history, studies, language & culture.
ISBN Prefix(es): 978-0-87336
Number of titles published annually: 12 Print
Total Titles: 100 Print
Imprints: Kamehameha Schools Press
Distributed by Islander Group
Membership(s): The Association of Publishers for Special Sales; Hawaii Book Publishers Association; The Independent Book Publishers Association

Kane Miller Books
Division of Educational Development Corp
4901 Morena Blvd, Suite 213, San Diego, CA 92117
SAN: 295-8945
E-mail: info@kanemiller.com
Web Site: www.kanemiller.com
Key Personnel
Publr: Kira Lynn
Mktg: Lynn Kelley
Founded: 1984
Juvenile board, novelty & picture books & middle grade fiction from around the world.
ISBN Prefix(es): 978-0-916291; 978-1-929132; 978-1-933605; 978-1-61067
Number of titles published annually: 60 Print
Total Titles: 250 Print
Warehouse: Educational Development Corp, 10302 E 55 Place, Tulsa, OK 74146
Distribution Center: Publishers Group Canada, 300-76 Stafford St, Toronto, ON M6J 2S1, Canada *Tel:* 416-934-9900 *E-mail:* info@pgcbooks.ca *Web Site:* www.pgcbooks.ca
Membership(s): ABA; ALA; Association of Booksellers for Children; United States Board on Books for Young People

Kane Press Inc
225 E 46 St, Suite 4D, New York, NY 10017-2924
Tel: 212-935-0246
Web Site: www.kanepress.com
Key Personnel
Publr: Joanne E Kane *E-mail:* jkane@kanepress.com
Sr Ed: Juliana Hanford
Edit Asst: Nadia DiMattia
Founded: 1996
Publishes books for children ages 3 to 11, including picture books & first chapter books.
ISBN Prefix(es): 978-1-57565
Number of titles published annually: 12 Print; 12 E-Book; 15 Audio
Total Titles: 190 Print; 175 E-Book; 41 Audio
Distributed by Lerner Publishing Group
Orders to: Lerner Publishing Group, 1251 Washington Ave N, Minneapolis, MN 55401-1036 *Toll Free Tel:* 800-328-4929 *Toll Free Fax:* 800-332-1132 *E-mail:* custserv@lernerbooks.com *Web Site:* www.lernerbooks.com
Returns: Lerner Publishing Group, 1251 Washington Ave N, Minneapolis, MN 55401-1036 *Toll Free Tel:* 800-328-4929 *Toll Free Fax:* 800-332-1132 *E-mail:* custserv@lernerbooks.com *Web Site:* www.lernerbooks.com
Shipping Address: Lerner Publishing Group, 241 First Ave N, Minneapolis, MN 55401-1607, VP & Dir, Sales: David Wexler *Toll Free Tel:* 800-328-4929 *Toll Free Fax:* 800-332-1132 *E-mail:* custserv@lernerbooks.com *Web Site:* www.lernerbooks.com
Warehouse: Lerner Publishing, 1251 Washington Ave N, Minneapolis, MN 55401 *Toll Free Tel:* 800-328-4929 *Toll Free Fax:* 800-332-1132 *E-mail:* custserv@lernerbooks.com *Web Site:* www.lernerbooks.com
Distribution Center: Lerner Publishing Group, 1251 Washington Ave N, Minneapolis, MN 55401-1036 *Toll Free Tel:* 800-328-4929 *Toll Free Fax:* 800-332-1132 *E-mail:* custserv@lernerbooks.com *Web Site:* www.lernerbooks.com
Membership(s): The Children's Book Council; Educational Book & Media Association; International Literacy Association; NAIPR; National Council for the Social Studies; National Council of Teachers of Mathematics; National Science Teachers Association

Kapp Books LLC
3602 Rocky Meadow Ct, Fairfax, VA 22033
Tel: 703-261-9171 *Fax:* 703-621-7162
E-mail: info@kappbooks.com
Web Site: www.kappbooks.com
Key Personnel
Mng Dir: Parveen Ahuja
Founded: 2006
ISBN Prefix(es): 978-1-60346
Number of titles published annually: 100 Print
Total Titles: 350 Print; 10 CD-ROM
Membership(s): The Independent Book Publishers Association

Kar-Ben Publishing
Division of Lerner Publishing Group Inc
241 First Ave N, Minneapolis, MN 55401
Tel: 612-332-3344 *Toll Free Tel:* 800-4-KARBEN (452-7236) *Fax:* 612-332-7615 *Toll Free Fax:* 800-332-1132
Web Site: www.karben.com
Key Personnel
Chmn: Harry J Lerner
Pres: Adam Lerner
Publr: Joni Sussman *E-mail:* jsussman@karben.com
Rts Dir: Maria Kjoller
Founded: 1976
Jewish books, calendars & cassettes; preschool & primary, activity books, holiday books, folktales, services.
ISBN Prefix(es): 978-1-58013
Total Titles: 240 Print; 195 E-Book

Foreign Rep(s): Bravo (UK); Mazeltov Books (Australia)
Warehouse: Lerner Publishing Group, 1251 Washington Ave N, Minneapolis, MN 55401

Kazi Publications Inc
3023 W Belmont Ave, Chicago, IL 60618
Tel: 773-267-7001 *Fax:* 773-267-7002
E-mail: info@kazi.org
Web Site: www.kazi.org
Key Personnel
Pres: Liaquat Ali
Mktg Dir: Mary Bakhtiar
Founded: 1972
Nonprofit organization; print, publish & distribute; Islamic books in Arabic, English & Urdu language.
ISBN Prefix(es): 978-0-935782; 978-1-56744; 978-0-933511; 978-1-871031; 978-1-930637
Number of titles published annually: 30 Print; 6 E-Book
Total Titles: 401 Print; 150 E-Book
Imprints: ABC International Group Inc; Abjad Books; Great Books of the Islamic World; Library of Islam

§J J Keller & Associates, Inc
3003 Breezewood Lane, Neenah, WI 54957
Mailing Address: PO Box 368, Neenah, WI 54957-0368
Tel: 920-722-2848 *Toll Free Tel:* 877-564-2333 *Toll Free Fax:* 800-727-7516
E-mail: contactus@jjkeller.com; customerservice@jjkeller.com
Web Site: www.jjkeller.com
Key Personnel
Chmn: Robert L Keller
VChmn & Treas: Jim Keller
Pres & CEO: Marne Keller-Krikava
EVP & COO: Rustin R Keller
CFO: Dana S Gilman
Dir, Creative & Promos: Tom Hines
Corp Mktg Communs Specialist: Mary Borsecnik
Founded: 1953
Publish regulatory compliance, "best practices" & training products dealing with occupational safety, job safety, environment & industry & motor-carrier (trucking) operations. On demand, print, CD-ROM, intranet & Internet formats.
ISBN Prefix(es): 978-1-57943; 978-0-934674; 978-1-877798; 978-1-59042; 978-0-9789130; 978-1-60287; 978-1-61099; 978-1-68008
Number of titles published annually: 4 Print; 12 E-Book
Total Titles: 300 Print; 100 CD-ROM
Branch Office(s)
7273 State Rd 76, Neenah, WI 54956-9614
Sales Office(s): 1315 Gillingham Rd, Neenah, WI 54956-4503
600 S Nicolet Rd, Appleton, WI 54914-8285
700 N Lynndale Dr, Appleton, WI 54914-3019
Distributed by AMACOM Books
Distributor for Chilton Book Co; International Air Transport Association; National Archives & Records Administration; National Institute of Occupational Safety & Health; Office of the Federal Register; Research & Special Programs Administration of the US Department of Transportation; John Wiley & Sons Inc

Kelsey Street Press
2824 Kelsey St, Berkeley, CA 94705
Tel: 510-845-2260 *Fax:* 510-548-9185
E-mail: info@kelseyst.com
Web Site: www.kelseyst.com
Key Personnel
Founding Ed: Patricia Dienstfrey; Rena Rosenwasser
Off Mgr: Ramsay Breslin
Founded: 1974
Nonprofit press, publish experimental poetry & short fiction by women & collaborations between poets & artists.
ISBN Prefix(es): 978-0-932716
Number of titles published annually: 3 Print
Total Titles: 45 Print
Orders to: Small Press Distribution, 1341 Seventh St, Berkeley, CA 94710 (contact Small Press Distribution for large orders) *Tel:* 510-524-1668 *Toll Free Tel:* 800-869-7553 *E-mail:* orders@spdbooks.org *Web Site:* www.spdbooks.org
Membership(s): Community of Literary Magazines & Presses

Kendall Hunt Publishing Co
4050 Westmark Dr, Dubuque, IA 52002-2624
SAN: 203-9184
Mailing Address: PO Box 1840, Dubuque, IA 52004-1840
Tel: 563-589-1000 *Toll Free Tel:* 800-228-0810 (orders) *Fax:* 563-589-1046 *Toll Free Fax:* 800-772-9165
E-mail: orders@kendallhunt.com
Web Site: www.kendallhunt.com
Key Personnel
Chmn & CEO: Mark C Falb
COO & Pres: Chad M Chandlee
VP, Opers: Tim Beitzel
VP, Higher Educ Div: David Tart
VP, K-12 Div: Charles Cook
Founded: 1969
Higher education custom publishing, K-12 math & science.
ISBN Prefix(es): 978-0-8403; 978-0-7872; 978-0-7575; 978-1-4652
Number of titles published annually: 1,500 Print; 200 Online
Total Titles: 6,500 Print; 10 CD-ROM; 5,500 Online; 6,500 E-Book
Membership(s): National Council of Supervisors of Mathematics; National Council of Teachers of Mathematics; National Science Teachers Association

Kennedy Information Inc
Division of Bloomberg BNA
24 Railroad St, Keene, NH 03431
Tel: 603-924-0900 *Toll Free Tel:* 800-531-0140 *Fax:* 603-357-8112
E-mail: customerservice@kennedyinfo.com
Web Site: www.kennedyinfo.com
Key Personnel
COO: Daniel Houder *E-mail:* dhouder@kennedyinfo.com
Founded: 1970
Newsletters, special reports, books, directories of management consultants, executive recruiters & outplacement consultants.
ISBN Prefix(es): 978-0-916654; 978-1-885922; 978-1-58673; 978-1-932079; 978-1-934717
Number of titles published annually: 15 Print; 1 CD-ROM; 3 Online
Total Titles: 50 Print; 1 CD-ROM

Kensington Publishing Corp
119 W 40 St, New York, NY 10018
SAN: 207-9860
Tel: 212-407-1500 *Toll Free Tel:* 800-221-2647 *Fax:* 212-935-0699
Web Site: www.kensingtonbooks.com
Key Personnel
CEO & Pres: Steven Zacharius
CFO: Michael Rosamilia
Edit Dir: Gary Goldstein; Audrey La Fehr; Wendy McCurdy
Edit Dir, Brava Books: Alicia Condon
Mng Dir, Lyrical Press: Renee Rocco
Ed-in-Chief, Citadel Press: Michaela Hamilton
Ed-in-Chief, Kensington: John Scognamiglio
Exec Ed: Tara Gavin; Selena James
Sr Ed: Esi Sogah
Ed: Martin Biro
Assoc Ed: Mercedes Fernandez; Peter Senftleben
Creative Dir: Janice Rossi
Dir, Mktg: Lesleigh Irish-Underwood
Dir, Publicity & PR: Karen Auerbach
Dir, Sales: Lynn Cully; Chris Grimm
Dir, Subs Rts: Jackie Dinas
Info Technol Dir: Jonathan Cohen
Prodn Dir: Joyce Kaplan
Assoc Dir, Mktg & Communs: Vida Engstrand
Assoc Dir, Sales: Darla Freeman
Assoc Dir, Soc Media & Digital Sales: Alex Nicolajsen
Communs & Mktg Mgr, Dafina & Women's Fiction: Mala Bhattacharjee
Communs & Mktg Mgr, Lyrical Press: Michelle Forde
Communs & Mktg Mgr, Mystery & Thrillers: Morgan Elwell
Mktg & Projs Mgr: Anne Marie Turner
Mktg Mgr, Ad & Promo: Sakina Williams
Gen Coun: Barbara Bennett
Cust Serv: Guy Chapman
Founded: 1975
Mass market paperback originals including thillers & men's adventure.
ISBN Prefix(es): 978-0-89083; 978-0-8217
Number of titles published annually: 500 Print
Total Titles: 9,000 Print
Imprints: Aphrodisia; Brava; Citadel; Dafina; Holloway House; Kensington Books; KTeen; KTeen Dafina; Lyrical Press; Lyrical Shine (contemporary romance); Lyrical Underground (thriller, mystery, suspense & horror); Pinnacle Books; Rebel Base Books; Lyle Stuart Books; Zebra Books
Distributed by Hachette Book Group USA; Penguin Group (USA) LLC
Distributor for Genesis Press; Marimba Books; New Horizon Press; Urban Books; Vibe Books
Foreign Rights: Agenzia Letteraria Internazionale (Italy); Big Apple Agency Inc (China); The Book Publishers' Association of Israel, International Promotion & Literary Rights Dept (Israel); Graal Literary Agency (Poland); International Editors' Co (Latin America, Mexico); International Literatuur Bureau (ILB) (Netherlands); Maxima Creative Agency (Santo Manurung) (Indonesia); La Nouvelle Agence (France); Andrew Nurnberg Associates (Tatjana Zoldnere) (Baltic States); Andrew Nurnberg Associates (Judit Hermann) (Croatia, Hungary); Andrew Nurnberg Literary Agency (Ludmilla Sushkova) (Russia); Kristin Olson Literary Agency SRO (Czech Republic, Slovakia); ONK Agency Ltd (Turkey); Read n Right Agency (Greece); Lennart Sane Agency AB (Scandinavia); Karin Schindler (Brazil); Thomas Schlueck GmbH (Germany); Shin Won Agency Co (Korea); Tuttle-Mori Agency Inc (Japan, Thailand)
Warehouse: Penguin Group (USA) LLC, Pittston, PA
Distribution Center: Pearson Canada Distribution Centre, 195 Harry Walker Pkwy N, Newmarket, ON L3Y 7B3, Canada *Tel:* 905-853-7888 *Fax:* 905-853-7865 *Web Site:* www.pearsoned.ca

Kent State University Press
1118 University Library Bldg, 1125 Risman Dr, Kent, OH 44242
SAN: 201-0437
Mailing Address: PO Box 5190, Kent, OH 44242-0001
Tel: 330-672-7913; 419-281-1802 *Fax:* 330-672-3104
E-mail: ksupress@kent.edu
Web Site: www.kentstateuniversitypress.com
Key Personnel
Dir & Rts & Perms: Will Underwood *Tel:* 330-672-8094 *E-mail:* wunderwo@kent.edu
Journals Mgr: Carol Heller *Tel:* 330-672-8090 *E-mail:* cheller1@kent.edu

Mktg Mgr: Susan L Cash *Tel:* 330-672-8097
E-mail: scash@kent.edu
Acquiring Ed: Joyce Harrison *Tel:* 330-672-8099
E-mail: jharri18@kent.edu
Founded: 1965
Scholarly nonfiction, with emphasis on Civil War, military history, literary studies, archaeology, biography & Midwest regional.
ISBN Prefix(es): 978-0-87338; 978-1-60635
Number of titles published annually: 35 Print; 35 E-Book; 5 Audio
Total Titles: 700 Print; 470 E-Book; 10 Audio
Imprints: Black Squirrel Books
Foreign Rep(s): East-West Export Books (Asia, Australia, The Pacific); Eurospan Ltd (Africa, Europe, Middle East, UK); Scholarly Book Services (Canada)
Orders to: Bookmasters, 30 Amberwood Pkwy, Ashland, OH 44805, Contact: Elaine Lattanzi *Tel:* 419-281-1802 *Toll Free Tel:* 800-247-6553 *Fax:* 419-281-6883
Returns: Bookmasters, 30 Amberwood Pkwy, Ashland, OH 44805, Contact: Elaine Lattanzi *Tel:* 419-281-1802 *Toll Free Tel:* 800-247-6553 *Fax:* 419-281-6883
Warehouse: Bookmasters, 30 Amberwood Pkwy, Ashland, OH 44805, Contact: Elaine Lattanzi *Tel:* 419-281-1802 *Toll Free Tel:* 800-247-6553 *Fax:* 419-281-6883
Distribution Center: Bookmasters, 30 Amberwood Pkwy, Ashland, OH 44805, Contact: Elaine Lattanzi *Tel:* 419-281-1802 *Toll Free Tel:* 800-247-6553 *Fax:* 419-281-6883
Membership(s): ABA; American Association of University Presses

Kessinger Publishing LLC
PO Box 1404, Whitefish, MT 59937
E-mail: books@kessingerpub.com
Web Site: www.kessinger.net
Key Personnel
Pres: Roger A Kessinger
Founded: 1988
Alchemy, free masonry, ancient civilization, astrology, Bible study, comparative religion, Egyptology, esotericism, gnosticism, health, hermetics, magic, metaphysical, mysticism, Rosicrucian.
ISBN Prefix(es): 978-0-922802; 978-1-56459; 978-0-7661; 978-1-4192; 978-1-4191
Number of titles published annually: 5,000 Print; 5,000 E-Book
Imprints: Kessinger Publishing®

Kidsbooks LLC
3535 W Peterson Ave, Chicago, IL 60659
SAN: 666-3729
Tel: 773-509-0707 *Fax:* 773-509-0404
E-mail: sales@kidsbooks.com; customerservice@kidsbooks.com
Web Site: www.kidsbooks.com
Key Personnel
CEO & Foreign Rts Agent: Dan Blau
Founded: 1987
Promotional book publishers of children, juvenile & hardcover, Search & Find®, board books, cloth books & other novelty books.
ISBN Prefix(es): 978-0-942025; 978-1-56156; 978-1-58865
Number of titles published annually: 100 Print
Total Titles: 3,000 Print
Imprints: KidsBooks; Learning Challenge; Masterwork Books
Foreign Rep(s): Trish Pugsley (Western Europe)
Foreign Rights: Dan Blau; Mauricio Placencia (Mexico, South America)

Jessica Kingsley Publishers Inc
400 Market St, Suite 400, Philadelphia, PA 19106
SAN: 256-2391
Tel: 215-922-1161 *Toll Free Tel:* 866-416-1078 (cust serv) *Fax:* 215-922-1474
E-mail: orders@jkp.com; hello.usa@jkp.com
Web Site: www.jkp.com
Key Personnel
Chmn: Jessica Kingsley
VP, Sales & Mktg: David Corey
Spec Sales Mgr: Colin McGee
Mktg Assoc: Katelynn Bartleson
Sales & Mktg Assoc: Stephanie DeMuzio
Founded: 1987 (US office opened 2004)
Publish books for the consumer on autism spectrum disorders & related developmental disorders; books for professionals in expressive arts therapies: art, music, drama & dance & social work; books on Tai Chi & Quigong.
ISBN Prefix(es): 978-1-85302; 978-1-84310; 978-1-84819; 978-1-874579; 978-1-900990; 978-0-902817; 978-1-904787; 978-1-905818; 978-1-84642; 978-1-84905; 978-1-84985; 978-0-85701; 978-0-85700; 978-1-78450
Number of titles published annually: 250 Print
Total Titles: 1,800 Print
Imprints: Singing Dragon
Foreign Office(s): 73 Collier St, London N1 9BE, United Kingdom, Contact: Mark Scott *Tel:* (020) 7833 2307 *E-mail:* hello@jkp.com
Foreign Rep(s): Avicenna Partnership Ltd (Bill Kennedy) (Bahrain, Egypt, Iran, Iraq, Kuwait, Lebanon, Libya, Oman, Qatar, Saudi Arabia, Sudan, United Arab Emirates, Yemen); Avicenna Partnership Ltd (Claire de Gruchy) (Algeria, Jordan, Morocco, Palestine, Tunisia, Turkey); Brookside Publishing Services (Ireland); Compass Academic (UK); Durnell Marketing Ltd (Europe); Footprint Books Pty Ltd (Australia, New Zealand); Taylor & Francis Asia Pacific (Brunei, China, Hong Kong, Indonesia, Japan, Macau, Malaysia, Philippines, Singapore, Taiwan, Thailand, Vietnam); UBC Press (Canada); United Publishers Services Ltd (Japan)
Distribution Center: Books International, PO Box 960, Herndon, VA 20172 *Toll Free Tel:* 866-416-1078 *Fax:* 703-611-1501
E-mail: jkpmail@presswarehouse.com

Kinship Books
305 Cedar Heights Rd, Rhinebeck, NY 12572
Tel: 845-876-4592 (orders)
E-mail: kinship@hvc.rr.com
Web Site: www.kinshipny.com
Key Personnel
Owner: Susan Kelly Fitzgerald
Founded: 1967
Books of genealogical source information, histories, directory & journals.
ISBN Prefix(es): 978-1-56012
Number of titles published annually: 5 Print
Total Titles: 330 Print

Kirk House Publishers
PO Box 390759, Minneapolis, MN 55439
Tel: 952-835-1828 *Toll Free Tel:* 888-696-1828 *Fax:* 952-835-2613
E-mail: publisher@kirkhouse.com
Web Site: www.kirkhouse.com
Key Personnel
Publr: Karen Walhof
Founded: 1994
ISBN Prefix(es): 978-1-886513; 978-1-932688; 978-1-933794; 978-1-942304
Number of titles published annually: 15 Print; 3 E-Book
Total Titles: 300 Print; 15 E-Book; 4 Audio
Imprints: Quill House Publishers
Membership(s): The Independent Book Publishers Association; Midwest Independent Publishers Association

§Kirkbride Bible Co Inc
1102 Deloss St, Indianapolis, IN 46203
Mailing Address: PO Box 606, Indianapolis, IN 46206-0606
Tel: 317-633-1900 *Toll Free Tel:* 800-428-4385 *Fax:* 317-633-1444
E-mail: sales@kirkbride.com; info@kirkbride.com
Web Site: www.kirkbride.com
Key Personnel
Pres: Michael Gage
Founded: 1915
Bible publisher, also children's Bible.
ISBN Prefix(es): 978-0-88707; 978-0-934854
Number of titles published annually: 5 Print
Total Titles: 7 Print; 3 CD-ROM
Advertising Agency: Canal Advertising

Kiva Publishing Inc
10 Bella Loma, Santa Fe, NM 87506
Tel: 909-896-0518
E-mail: kivapub@aol.com
Web Site: www.kivapub.com
Key Personnel
Publr: Stephen W Hill
Founded: 1993
Publish Native American & Southwest regional books & cards.
ISBN Prefix(es): 978-1-885772
Number of titles published annually: 3 Print
Total Titles: 40 Print
Membership(s): The Association of Publishers for Special Sales; The Independent Book Publishers Association; New Mexico Publishers Association; Publishers Association of the West

Klutz
Division of Scholastic Corp
568 Broadway, Suite 503, New York, NY 10012
Tel: 212-343-6360 *Fax:* 212-343-6366
E-mail: sales@klutz.com
Web Site: store.scholastic.com
Key Personnel
SVP & Gen Mgr: Stacy Lellos
Founded: 1977
Premium brand of book-based activity kits, committed to inspiring creativity in every kid with a unique combination of crystal clear instructions, custom tools & materials & a hearty helping of humor.
ISBN Prefix(es): 978-0-932592; 978-1-57054; 978-1-878257; 978-1-59174; 978-0-545
Number of titles published annually: 14 Print
Total Titles: 90 Print
Foreign Rep(s): Scholastic Asia (Selina Lee) (Asia); Scholastic Australia Ltd (Australia); Scholastic Canada Ltd (Canada); Scholastic Ltd (UK); Scholastic New Zealand Ltd (New Zealand)
Orders to: 2931 E McCarty St, Jefferson City, MO 65101 *Toll Free Tel:* 888-724-1872 *Toll Free Fax:* 877-724-1872 *E-mail:* orders@klutz.com
Membership(s): American Specialty Toy Retailing Association

Kluwer Law International (KLI), see Wolters Kluwer Law & Business

§Wolters Kluwer Law & Business
Subsidiary of Wolters Kluwer
76 Ninth Ave, 7th fl, New York, NY 10011-5201
SAN: 203-4999
Tel: 212-771-0600; 301-698-7100 (cust serv outside US) *Toll Free Tel:* 800-234-1660 (cust serv)
E-mail: customer.service@wolterskluwer.com; sales@kluwerlaw.com
Web Site: www.wklawbusiness.com
Key Personnel
VP, Chief Content Offr & Acting CTO: Gustavo Dobles
Exec Dir, Strategic Communs: Deborah Sauer
E-mail: deborah.sauer@wolterskluwer.com
Founded: 1959

Publisher of legal, business & health care titles for professionals. Publishes more than 500 journals, newsletters, electronic products & loose-leaf manuals & has more than 1,000 active professional & textbook titles.
ISBN Prefix(es): 978-0-89443; 978-0-912862; 978-0-8342; 978-1-56706; 978-0-87189; 978-0-8080; 978-0-444; 978-1-56542; 978-1-878375; 978-0-9625969; 978-1-56759; 978-0-7355; 978-0-7896; 978-0-87457; 978-0-87622; 978-0-916592; 978-1-4548
Number of titles published annually: 100 Print; 16 CD-ROM; 55 Online
Total Titles: 1,500 Print; 107 CD-ROM; 55 Online; 1 Audio
Foreign Rep(s): David Bartolone
Distribution Center: 7201 McKinney Circle, Frederick, MD 21704 *Tel:* 301-698-7100 *Fax:* 301-695-7931

Allen A Knoll Publishers
200 W Victoria St, Santa Barbara, CA 93101-3627
SAN: 299-0539
Tel: 805-564-3377 *Toll Free Tel:* 800-777-7623 *Fax:* 805-966-6657
E-mail: bookinfo@knollpublishers.com
Web Site: www.knollpublishers.com
Key Personnel
Lib Sales & Mktg Dir: Abby Schott
Shipping & Receiving Mgr: Lisa Carroll
Accts: Elizabeth Hanning-Yu *E-mail:* elizabeth@knollpublishers.com
Founded: 1991
Books for intelligent people who read for fun. No unsol mss.
ISBN Prefix(es): 978-0-9627297; 978-1-888310
Number of titles published annually: 5 Print
Total Titles: 50 Print
Membership(s): Independent Publishers Association

Alfred A Knopf/Everyman's Library
Imprint of Knopf Doubleday Publishing Group
c/o Random House Inc, 1745 Broadway, New York, NY 10019
Tel: 212-751-2600 *Toll Free Tel:* 800-638-6460 *Fax:* 212-572-2593
Web Site: www.knopfdoubleday.com
Key Personnel
Chmn: Sonny Mehta
Pres: Anthony Chirico
EVP & Publr, Everyman's Library: Anne Messitte
EVP & Exec Dir, Publicity, Promo & Media Rel: Paul Bogaards
SVP & Assoc Publr: Christine Gillespie
SVP & Edit Dir, Everyman's Library: LuAnn Walther
VP & Dir, Art Jacket: Carol Carson
VP & Dir, Busn Opers: Justine LeCates
VP & Dir, Creative Mktg: Anne-Lise Spitzer
VP & Dir, Interior Design & Desktop Publg: Peter Andersen
VP & Dir, Prodn/Design: Andrew W Hughes
VP & Dir, Promo & Serial Rts: Gabrielle Brooks
VP & Dir, Publicity: Nicholas Latimer
VP & Edit Dir: Robin Desser
VP & Exec Ed: Jordan Pavlin
VP & Mng Ed: Katherine Hourigan
VP & Sr Ed: Victoria Wilson; Jonathan Segal; George Andreou
VP & Ed-at-Large: Gary Fisketjon
Sr Ed: Ann Close; Jennifer Jackson; Andrew Miller
Sr Ed, Poetry: Deborah Garrison
Ed: Diana Coglianese
Ed-at-Large: Carole Baron
Dir, Ad: Stephanie Kloss
Dir, Dom Rts: Sean Yule
Dir, Mktg, Everyman's Library: Roz Parr
Group Sales Dir: Janet Cooke
Imprint Sales Dir: James Kimball
Deputy Dir, Publicity & Promotion: Kathryn Zuckerman
Assoc Dir, Publicity: Jessica Purcell
Publicity Mgr: Josie Kals
Publicist: Erica Hinsley; Elizabeth Lindsay; Brittany Morrongiello; Helen Tobin
Assoc Publicist: Erinn McGrath
Asst, Publicity: Madeline Caldwell
Mktg Mgr: Sara Eagle
Asst Mktg Mgr: Danielle Plafsky
Mgr, Foreign Rts: Suzanne Smith
Founded: 1915
Random House Inc & its publishing entities are not accepting unsol submissions, proposals, mss, or submission queries via e-mail at this time.
ISBN Prefix(es): 978-0-679; 978-0-7679; 978-1-4000; 978-0-394
Foreign Rights: ALS-Agenzia Letteraria Santachiara (Roberto Santachiara) (Italy); Anthea Agency (Katalina Sabeva) (Bulgaria); Bardon-Chinese Media (Xu Weiguang) (China); Bardon-Chinese Media Agency (Yu-Shiuan Chen) (Taiwan); The English Agency (Junzo Sawa) (Japan); Graal Literary Agency (Maria Strarz-Kanska) (Poland); The Deborah Harris Agency (Ilana Kurshan) (Israel); JLM Literary Agency (Nelly Moukakos) (Greece); Katai & Bolza Literary (Peter Bolza) (Croatia, Hungary); KCC (MiSook Hong) (Korea); Simona Kessler International (Simona Kessler) (Romania); Licht & Burr Literary Agency (Trine Licht) (Scandinavia); La Nouvelle Agence (Vanessa Kling) (France); Kristin Olson Literary Agency (Kristin Olson) (Czech Republic); Sebes & Van Gelderen Literary Agency (Paul Sebes) (Netherlands)

Kodansha USA Inc
Subsidiary of Kodansha Ltd (Japan)
451 Park Ave S, 7th fl, New York, NY 10016
SAN: 201-0526
Tel: 917-322-6200 *Fax:* 212-935-6929
E-mail: info@kodansha-usa.com
Web Site: www.kodanshausa.com
Key Personnel
CEO: Takashi Sakuda
Founded: 2008
Publishes hardcover & paperback books in English on Japanese cultures, history, art, architecture, design, craft, gardening, literature, material arts, language, cookbooks, travel & memoir.
ISBN Prefix(es): 978-0-87011; 978-1-56836; 978-1-935429; 978-1-61262; 978-1-63236
Number of titles published annually: 4 Print
Total Titles: 270 Print
Imprints: Kodansha America; Kodansha Globe; Kodansha International
Distributed by Oxford University Press
Distributor for Japan Publications Inc; Japan Publications Trading Co Inc
Foreign Rep(s): Amin Al-Abini (Middle East); Bill Bailey Publishers' Representatives (Austria, Benelux, Bosnia and Herzegovina, Croatia, Cyprus, Estonia, France, Germany, Gibraltar, Greece, Hungary, Iceland, Italy, Latvia, Lithuania, Macedonia, Malta, Montenegro, Portugal, Scandinavia, Serbia, Slovenia, Spain, Switzerland, Turkey); DIP Inc (Japan); Fitzhenry & Whiteside (Canada); Intext Book Co (Australia, New Zealand); Japan Publications Trading Co Ltd (Japan); Kinokuniya Book Stores of Singapore Pte Ltd (Indonesia, Malaysia, Singapore, Taiwan, Thailand, United Arab Emirates); Kodansha Europe Ltd (Africa, Central America, Europe, Middle East, Near East, South America); Stephan Phillips (Pty) Ltd (Botswana, Lesotho, Mozambique, Namibia, South Africa, Swaziland, Zimbabwe); Publishers Group UK (Ireland, UK)
Warehouse: Oxford University Press, 2001 Evans Rd, Cary, NC 27513 *Toll Free Tel:* 800-451-7556 *Fax:* 919-677-1303

§Kogan Page Publishers
1518 Walnut St, Suite 1100, Philadelphia, PA 19102
Tel: 215-928-9112 *Fax:* 215-928-9113
E-mail: info@koganpage.com
Web Site: www.koganpageusa.com
Key Personnel
Dir: Keith Ashfield
Founded: 1967
Publish books & e-versions of them.
ISBN Prefix(es): 978-0-7494
Number of titles published annually: 120 Print; 20 Online; 40 E-Book
Total Titles: 400 Print; 40 Online; 300 E-Book
Foreign Office(s): 120 Pentonville Rd, London N1 9JN, United Kingdom *Tel:* (020) 7278 0433 *Web Site:* www.koganpage.com
Foreign Rep(s): Kogan Page London (Worldwide exc USA)
Foreign Rights: Kogan Page London (Worldwide exc USA)
Billing Address: IPS, One Ingram Blvd, La Vergne, TN 37086
Orders to: IPS, One Ingram Blvd, La Vergne, TN 37086 *Toll Free Tel:* 800-961-2026 *Toll Free Fax:* 800-838-1149 *E-mail:* customer.service@ingrampublisherservices.com
Returns: IPS, 1210 Ingram Dr, Chambersburg, PA 17201
Distribution Center: IPS, One Ingram Blvd, La Vergne, TN 37086

§Koho Pono LLC
15024 SE Pinegrove Loop, Clackamas, OR 97015
Tel: 503-723-7392 *Toll Free Tel:* 800-937-8000 (orders) *Toll Free Fax:* 800-876-0186 (orders)
E-mail: info@kohopono.com; orders@ingrambook.com
Web Site: kohopono.com
Key Personnel
Publr: Scott Burr *Tel:* 408-689-0888; Dayna Hubenthal
Founded: 2010
Multimedia publishing company that is passionate about growth & improvement for all aspects of life: business, career, relationships & personal. Specialize in innovation, awareness, process improvement, change management & strengthening relationships for business & individuals. Support the evolution of consciousness, self-exploration & the pursuit of increasing relevance in life.
ISBN Prefix(es): 978-0-984554
Number of titles published annually: 3 Print; 3 Online; 3 E-Book; 3 Audio
Total Titles: 6 Print; 6 Online; 2 E-Book; 3 Audio
Shipping Address: Lightning Source Inc, 1246 Heil Quaker Blvd, La Vergne, TN 37086, Contact: Amy Waugh *Tel:* 615-213-5815 *Fax:* 615-213-4725 *E-mail:* inquiry@lightningsource.com
Warehouse: Lightning Source Inc, 1246 Heil Quaker Blvd, La Vergne, TN 37086, Contact: Amy Waugh *Tel:* 615-213-5815 *Fax:* 615-213-4725 *E-mail:* inquiry@lightningsource.com
Distribution Center: Ingram Book Co, One Ingram Blvd, La Vergne, TN 37086 *Tel:* 615-793-5000 *Toll Free Tel:* 800-937-8200 *E-mail:* customer.service@ingrambook.com
Lightning Source Inc, 1246 Heil Quaker Blvd, La Vergne, TN 37086, Contact: Amy Waugh *Tel:* 615-213-5815 *Fax:* 615-213-4725 *E-mail:* inquiry@lightningsource.com

Konecky & Konecky LLC
72 Ayers Point Rd, Old Saybrook, CT 06475
Tel: 860-388-0878 *Fax:* 860-388-0273
Web Site: www.koneckyandkonecky.com
Key Personnel
Publr: Sean Konecky *E-mail:* seankon@comcast.net
Founded: 1982
Hardcover art books & Civil War history, military history, biography, religion & spirituality.

ISBN Prefix(es): 978-1-56852; 978-0-914427
Number of titles published annually: 10 Print
Total Titles: 250 Print
Imprints: Konecky & Konecky (K&K); Tabard Press
Distributor for Octavo Editions

HJ Kramer Inc
Division of New World Library
PO Box 1082, Tiburon, CA 94920
Tel: 415-884-2100 (ext 10) *Toll Free Tel:* 800-972-6657 *Fax:* 415-435-5364
E-mail: hjkramer@jps.net
Web Site: www.hjkramer.com; www.newworldlibrary.com
Key Personnel
Pres: Linda Kramer
Intl Rts: Suezen Stone *Tel:* 415-499-1622 *Fax:* 415-499-1654 *E-mail:* Suezenstone@msn.com
Mktg & Publicity: Monique Muhlenkamp *E-mail:* monique@newworldlibrary.com
Founded: 1984
Personal growth, self-help, spiritual growth, trade paperbacks & hardcovers. Any correspondence regarding mss must be accompanied by an appropriately sized SASE.
ISBN Prefix(es): 978-0-915811; 978-1-932073
Number of titles published annually: 3 Print; 3 E-Book
Total Titles: 70 Print
Foreign Rep(s): Akasha Books Ltd (New Zealand); Brumby Books (Australia); Publishers Group Canada (Canada); Publishers Group UK (UK); Real Books (South Africa)
Orders to: Publisher Group West, 1700 Fourth St, Berkeley, CA 94710 *Toll Free Tel:* 800-788-3123 *Fax:* 510-528-3444

Krause Publications Inc
Subsidiary of F+W, A Content + eCommerce Company
700 E State St, Iola, WI 54990
SAN: 202-6554
Tel: 715-445-2214 *Toll Free Tel:* 800-258-0929 (cust serv); 888-457-2873 (orders) *Fax:* 715-445-4087
E-mail: bookorders@krause.com
Web Site: www.krausebooks.com
Key Personnel
Founder: Chester L Krause
CFO: Jim Ogle
Pres: David Blansfield
Publr, Books: Sara Domville
Publr, Log House & Metal Roofing: Hugh McAloon
Dir, Libr Sales: Mary Roco
Mktg: Corinne Zielke
Prodn: Marilyn McGrane
Intl Rts Contact: Laurie Smith
ISBN Prefix(es): 978-0-87349; 978-0-87341; 978-0-87069; 978-0-89689; 978-0-8019
Number of titles published annually: 150 Print
Total Titles: 1,000 Print
Imprints: Antique Trader Books; Books Americana; DBI Books; Gun Digest® Books; Warman's
Distributor for Country Bumpkin; David & Charles; Colin Gower; Quarto Books
Foreign Rep(s): David Bateman Ltd (New Zealand); Canadian Manda Group (Canada); Capricorn Link (Australia); David & Charles (Europe, UK); Real Books (Southern Africa); Marta Schooler (Asia, Latin America, Middle East)
See separate listing for:
Antique Trader

Kregel Publications
Division of Kregel Inc
2450 Oak Industrial Dr NE, Grand Rapids, MI 49505
SAN: 298-9115
Tel: 616-451-4775 *Toll Free Tel:* 800-733-2607 *Fax:* 616-451-9330
E-mail: kregelbooks@kregel.com
Web Site: www.kregel.com
Key Personnel
Pres: James R Kregel *E-mail:* president@kregel.com
VP, Publg: Jerold W Kregel
Exec Dir, Sales & Mktg: David Hill *Tel:* 616-451-4775 ext 235 *E-mail:* dave@kregel.com
Publr & Rts & Perms: Dennis Hillman
Founded: 1949
Evangelical Christian publications including devotionals, Bible study & reference.
ISBN Prefix(es): 978-0-8254
Number of titles published annually: 75 Print
Total Titles: 1,500 Print
Imprints: Editorial Portavoz; Kregel Academic & Professional; Kregel Classics; Kregel Kidzone; Kregel Publications
Distributor for Candle Books; Monarch Books
Foreign Rep(s): Christian Art Wholesale (South Africa); Christian Literature Crusade (Japan); David C Cook (Canada); Omega Distribution (New Zealand); STL Distribution (UK); Word of Life Press (Korea)
Membership(s): Evangelical Christian Publishers Association
See separate listing for:
Editorial Portavoz

Krieger Publishing Co
1725 Krieger Dr, Malabar, FL 32950
SAN: 202-6562
Tel: 321-724-9542 *Toll Free Tel:* 800-724-0025 *Fax:* 321-951-3671
E-mail: info@krieger-publishing.com
Web Site: www.krieger-publishing.com
Key Personnel
CEO: Robert E Krieger
Pres: Donald E Krieger
VP: Maxine D Krieger
Ad Mgr: Cheryl Stanton
Cust Serv: Dianne Struckman
Founded: 1969
A scientific-technical publisher serving the college textbook market. Reprints & new titles: technical, science, psychology, geology, humanities, ecology, history, social sciences, engineering, mathematics, chemistry, adult educational, herpetology, space science.
ISBN Prefix(es): 978-0-88275; 978-0-89464; 978-0-89874; 978-1-57524
Number of titles published annually: 11 Print
Total Titles: 1,000 Print; 2 CD-ROM
Imprints: Anvil Series; Exploring Community History Series; Orbit Series; Professional Practices; Public History
Foreign Rep(s): Eurospan (Middle East, UK)
Advertising Agency: Krieger Enterprises Inc

KTAV Publishing House Inc
888 Newark Ave, Jersey City, NJ 07306
Tel: 201-963-9524 *Fax:* 201-963-0102
E-mail: orders@ktav.com
Web Site: www.ktav.com
Key Personnel
Pres: Moshe Heller
Founded: 1924
Books of Jewish interest; juvenile, textbooks; scholarly Judaica & interfaith issues.
ISBN Prefix(es): 978-0-87068; 978-0-88125; 978-1-60280
Number of titles published annually: 20 Print
Total Titles: 840 Print
Distributor for Yeshiva University Press

Kumarian Press
Division of Lynne Rienner Publishers Inc
1800 30 St, Suite 314, Boulder, CO 80301
Tel: 303-444-6684 *Toll Free Tel:* 800-232-0223 (orders only) *Fax:* 303-444-0824
E-mail: questions@rienner.com
Web Site: www.kpbooks.com
Key Personnel
CEO: Lynne Rienner
Founded: 1977
Academic, professional books, college textbooks in social sciences: international development, international relations, political science, political economy, economics, globalization, women & gender studies, conflict resolution, environment, sustainability, civil society & NGO's.
ISBN Prefix(es): 978-0-931816; 978-1-56549; 978-1-887208
Number of titles published annually: 18 Print; 10 E-Book
Total Titles: 300 Print; 100 E-Book
Foreign Rep(s): Alkem Co (Brunei, Indonesia, Malaysia, Philippines, Singapore, Taiwan, Vietnam); Eurospan (Europe, Middle East, North Africa, UK); Everest Media International Services (Nepal)
Membership(s): The Association of Publishers for Special Sales; The Independent Book Publishers Association

Kumon Publishing North America
300 Frank Burr Blvd, Suite 6, Teaneck, NJ 07666
Tel: 201-836-2105 *Fax:* 201-836-1559
E-mail: books@kumon.com
Web Site: www.kumonbooks.com
Key Personnel
SVP: Brian Klingborg
Founded: 2004
Publisher of children's educational books & toys.
ISBN Prefix(es): 978-4-7743; 978-1-933241
Number of titles published annually: 20 Print
Total Titles: 105 Print

George Kurian Reference Books
3689 Campbell Ct, Yorktown Heights, NY 10598
Tel: 914-962-3287 *Fax:* 914-962-3287
Key Personnel
Pres & Ed: George Thomas Kurian *E-mail:* gtkurian@aol.com
Founded: 1972
Reference books for libraries, schools, colleges.
ISBN Prefix(es): 978-0-914746
Number of titles published annually: 7 Print
Total Titles: 102 Print
Imprints: Foreign Affairs Information Service
Foreign Rights: Gazelle Book Services (UK)

L & R Publishing, see Hellgate Press

LadybugPress
Division of NewVoices Inc
16964 Columbia River Dr, Sonora, CA 95370
SAN: 299-0377
Tel: 209-694-8340 *Toll Free Tel:* 888-892-5000 *Fax:* 209-694-8916
E-mail: ladybugpress@ladybugbooks.com
Web Site: www.ladybugbooks.com
Key Personnel
Publr: Georgia Jones
Founded: 1996
Books & audio books of particular interest to women.
This publisher has indicated that 40% of their product line (primarily fiction & poetry) is author subsidized.
ISBN Prefix(es): 978-1-889409
Number of titles published annually: 8 Print; 2 CD-ROM; 1 Audio
Total Titles: 27 Print; 15 CD-ROM; 9 Audio
Membership(s): The Independent Book Publishers Association

Lake Claremont Press
Imprint of Everything Goes Media LLC

PO Box 711, Chicago, IL 60690
Mailing Address: PO Box 1524, Milwaukee, WI 53201
Tel: 312-226-8400 *Fax:* 312-226-8420
Web Site: www.lakeclaremont.com
Key Personnel
Owner & Publr: Sharon Woodhouse *E-mail:* sharon@lakeclaremont.com
Founded: 1994
Histories & guidebooks on the Chicago area by local authors with a passion & organizations with a mission.
ISBN Prefix(es): 978-1-893121; 978-0-9642426
Number of titles published annually: 3 Print; 6 E-Book
Total Titles: 50 Print

Lake Superior Port Cities Inc
310 E Superior St, Suite 125, Duluth, MN 55802
Mailing Address: PO Box 16417, Duluth, MN 55816-0417
Tel: 218-722-5002 *Toll Free Tel:* 888-BIG-LAKE (244-5253) *Fax:* 218-722-4096
E-mail: reader@lakesuperior.com
Web Site: www.lakesuperior.com
Key Personnel
Pres & Publr: Cynthia Hayden *E-mail:* cmh@lakesuperior.com
Publr: Paul L Hayden *E-mail:* plh@lakesuperior.com
Ed: Konnie Le May *E-mail:* kon@lakesuperior.com
Founded: 1979
Began as regional magazine publisher & expanded services to include books, travel guides, calendars, maps & merchandise.
ISBN Prefix(es): 978-0-942235
Number of titles published annually: 3 Print
Total Titles: 25 Print
Membership(s): International Regional Magazine Association; Midwest Independent Booksellers Association; Midwest Independent Publishers Association; Minnesota Magazine & Publications Association

LAMA Books
2381 Sleepy Hollow Ave, Hayward, CA 94545-3429
Tel: 510-785-1091 *Toll Free Tel:* 888-452-6244 *Fax:* 510-785-1099
Web Site: www.lamabooks.com
Key Personnel
Pres, Sales & Mktg Dir: Steve Meyer *E-mail:* steve@lamabooks.com
Founded: 1970
Develop & publish books for heating, ventilating & air conditioning (HVAC) field; occupational trades, reading development, teacher preparation; directories-occupational programs in California community colleges.
ISBN Prefix(es): 978-0-88069
Number of titles published annually: 5 Print
Total Titles: 50 Print

Lanahan Publishers Inc
324 Hawthorne Rd, Baltimore, MD 21210-2303
Tel: 410-366-2434 *Toll Free Tel:* 866-345-1949 *Fax:* 410-366-8798
E-mail: lanahan@aol.com
Web Site: www.lanahanpublishers.com
Key Personnel
Pres: Donald W Fusting
Founded: 1995
College textbook publisher.
ISBN Prefix(es): 978-0-9652687; 978-1-930398
Number of titles published annually: 4 Print
Total Titles: 20 Print

Landauer Corp
3100 101 St, Suite A, Urbandale, IA 50322
Tel: 515-287-2144 *Toll Free Tel:* 800-557-2144 *Fax:* 515-276-5102
E-mail: info@landauercorp.com
Web Site: www.landauercorp.com
Key Personnel
Pres & Publr: Jeramy Landauer
Founded: 1991
Publishing & licensing for the home arts working with leading designers & artists.
ISBN Prefix(es): 978-1-890621; 978-0-9646870; 978-0-9793711; 978-0-9770166; 978-1-935726; 978-0-9825586; 978-0-9818040
Number of titles published annually: 12 Print
Total Titles: 114 Print
Foreign Rep(s): A Great Notion (Canada); Alba Patchwork (Spain); N Jefferson (Canada); Quilt Source (Canada); John Reed Book Distribution (Australia); RJR Fabrics (Europe); Roundhouse Group (England); Stallion Press (Singapore); Virka (Iceland)
Membership(s): ABA; The Independent Book Publishers Association

§Peter Lang Publishing Inc
Subsidiary of Verlag Peter Lang AG (Switzerland)
29 Broadway, 18th fl, New York, NY 10006-3223
SAN: 241-5534
Tel: 212-647-7706 *Toll Free Tel:* 800-770-5264 (cust serv) *Fax:* 212-647-7707
Web Site: www.peterlang.com
Key Personnel
SVP & Mng Dir: Christopher S Myers *E-mail:* chrism@plang.com
Sales & Mktg Dir: Patricia Mulrane Clayton
Lead Ed: Heidi Burns
Mktg Coord: Michael McFadden
Founded: 1982
Scholarly monographs & textbooks in the humanities, social sciences, media studies, Festschriften & conference proceedings.
ISBN Prefix(es): 978-0-8204; 978-1-4331
Number of titles published annually: 240 Print
Total Titles: 2,500 Print
Foreign Office(s): Verlag Peter Lang GmbH, Eschborner-Landstr 42-50, 60489 Frankfurt/Main, Germany, Mgr: Jurgen-Matthias Springer *Tel:* (069) 78 07 05 0 *Fax:* (069) 78 07 05 50
Verlag Peter Lang AG, Hochfeldstr 32, 3012 Bern, Switzerland *Tel:* (031) 306 1717 *Fax:* (031) 306 1727
Foreign Rep(s): Verlag Peter Lang GmbH (Germany)

LangMarc Publishing
PO Box 90488, Austin, TX 78709-0488
SAN: 297-519X
Tel: 512-394-0989 *Toll Free Tel:* 800-864-1648 (orders) *Fax:* 512-394-0829
E-mail: langmarc@booksails.com
Web Site: www.langmarc.com
Key Personnel
Pres & Lib Sales Dir: Lois Qualben
VP: Susan Reue
Prodn Mgr: Michael Qualben
Founded: 1991
Publisher of inspirational titles.
ISBN Prefix(es): 978-1-880292
Number of titles published annually: 3 Print; 20 E-Book
Total Titles: 75 Print
Imprints: Harbor Lights
Shipping Address: 7500 Shadowridge Run, No 28, Austin, TX 78749

Lantern Books
Division of Booklight Inc
128 Second Place, Garden Suite, Brooklyn, NY 11231
Tel: 212-414-2275
E-mail: editorial@lanternbooks.com; info@lanternmedia.net
Web Site: lanternbooks.presswarehouse.com/Home/home.aspx
Key Personnel
Pres: Gene Gollogly *E-mail:* gene@lanternbooks.com
Mng Dir: Kara Davis *E-mail:* kara@lanternbooks.com
Dir, Publg: Martin Rowe
ISBN Prefix(es): 978-1-59056; 978-1-930051
Number of titles published annually: 15 Print
Total Titles: 150 Print
Foreign Rep(s): Ceres Books (New Zealand); Deep Books (Europe, UK)
Foreign Rights: Sabine Weeke
Billing Address: Steiner Books, Quicksilver Dr, Sterling, VA 20166 *E-mail:* anthroposophicmail@presswarehouse.com
Orders to: PO Box 960, Herndon, VA 20172-0960 *Tel:* 703-661-1594 *Toll Free Tel:* 800-856-8664 *Fax:* 703-661-1501 *E-mail:* anthroposophicmail@presswarehouse.com
Returns: Steiner Books, Quicksilver Dr, Sterling, VA 20166 *E-mail:* anthroposophicmail@presswarehouse.com
Shipping Address: Steiner Books, Quicksilver Dr, Sterling, VA 20166 *Tel:* 703-661-1500 *E-mail:* anthroposophicmail@presswarehouse.com
Warehouse: Steiner Books, Quicksilver Dr, Sterling, VA 20166 *Tel:* 703-661-1500 *E-mail:* anthroposophicmail@presswarehouse.com
Distribution Center: Steiner Books, Quicksilver Dr, Sterling, VA 20166 *Tel:* 703-661-1500 *E-mail:* anthroposophicmail@presswarehouse.com
Membership(s): ABA

Laredo Publishing Co Inc
465 Westview Ave, Englewood, NJ 07631
Tel: 201-408-4048 *Fax:* 201-408-5011
E-mail: info@laredopublishing.com
Web Site: www.laredopublishing.com
Key Personnel
Pres: Sam Laredo *E-mail:* laredo@laredopublishing.com
VP & Exec Ed: Raquel Benatar *E-mail:* raquel@laredopublishing.com
ISBN Prefix(es): 978-1-56492
Number of titles published annually: 25 Print
Total Titles: 150 Print
Imprints: Renaissance House
See separate listing for:
Renaissance House

Lark Crafts
Imprint of Sterling Publishing Co Inc
1166 Avenue of the Americas, New York, NY 10036
Tel: 212-532-7160
E-mail: customerservice@sterlingpublishing.com
Web Site: larkcrafts.com; www.sterlingpublishing.com
Key Personnel
Ed: Connie Santisteban; Diana Ventimiglia
Asst Ed: Brita Vallens; Deborah Stack
Founded: 1979
How-to books in crafts & photography.
ISBN Prefix(es): 978-0-937274; 978-1-887374; 978-1-57990; 978-1-60059; 978-1-4547
Number of titles published annually: 120 Print
Total Titles: 400 Print
Foreign Rights: Sterling Publishing Co Inc
Shipping Address: Sterling Publishing Co Inc, 40 Saw Mill Pond Rd, Edison, NJ 08837 *Toll Free Tel:* 800-367-9692 *Toll Free Fax:* 800-542-7567

Larson Publications
4936 State Rte 414, Burdett, NY 14818

Tel: 607-546-9342 *Toll Free Tel:* 800-828-2197 *Fax:* 607-546-9344
E-mail: custserv@larsonpublications.com
Web Site: www.larsonpublications.com
Key Personnel
Mktg Dir & Publr: Amy Opperman Cash *E-mail:* amy@larsonpublications.com
Founded: 1982
Resources for spiritual independence & social relevance.
ISBN Prefix(es): 978-0-943914; 978-1-936012
Number of titles published annually: 6 Print; 1 CD-ROM; 1 Online; 5 E-Book
Total Titles: 90 Print; 1 CD-ROM; 25 E-Book; 3 Audio
Foreign Rep(s): Gazelle Bookservices Ltd (Europe, UK); Bokforlaget Robert Larson (Scandinavia)
Foreign Rights: Literaryventuresfund (Mary Bisbee-Beek)
Distribution Center: New Leaf Distributing Co, 401 Thornton Rd, Lithia Springs, GA 30122-1557 *Tel:* 770-948-7845 *Toll Free Tel:* 800-326-2665 *Fax:* 770-944-2313 *E-mail:* newleaf@newleaf-dist.com *Web Site:* www.newleaf-dist.com
National Book Network, 15200 NBN Way, Blue Ridge Summit, PA 17214 *Toll Free Tel:* 800-462-6420 *Toll Free Fax:* 800-338-4550 *E-mail:* custserv@nbnbooks.com *Web Site:* www.nbnbooks.com

§Lasaria Creative Publishing
4094 Majestic Lane, Suite 352, Fairfax, VA 22033
E-mail: info@lasariacreative.com
Web Site: www.lasariacreative.com
Key Personnel
Publg Analyst: Adam Lee *E-mail:* adamlee@lasariacreative.com
Founded: 2008
Author-owned independent publishing company looking for nonfiction, general fiction, short stories & juvenile fiction books. We encourage first time authors & are willing to help get your work into mainstream distribution channels. Also offer editing services for new authors.
ISBN Prefix(es): 978-0-9818367; 978-0-9836671
Number of titles published annually: 10 Print; 10 Online; 10 E-Book
Total Titles: 14 Print; 12 Online; 12 E-Book

Latin American Literary Review Press
PO Box 7530, Pittsburgh, PA 15213
Tel: 412-824-7903
E-mail: lalrp.editor@gmail.com
Web Site: www.lalrp.org
Key Personnel
Founding Ed & Pres: Dr Yvette E Miller
Founded: 1980
Publish Latin American literature in English translation. Publish Latin American Literary Review, a semiannual journal of scholarly essays & book reviews on the literatures of Spanish America & Brazil, which also distributes Spanish books on social sciences, history & art.
ISBN Prefix(es): 978-0-935480; 978-1-891270
Number of titles published annually: 3 Print
Total Titles: 146 Print
Orders to: Independent Publishers Group, 814 N Franklin St, Chicago, IL 60610 *Toll Free Tel:* 800-888-4741 *E-mail:* orders@ipgbook.com *Web Site:* www.ipgbook.com
Membership(s): Community of Literary Magazines & Presses

Laughing Elephant
3645 Interlake N, Seattle, WA 98103
Tel: 206-447-9229 *Toll Free Tel:* 800-354-0400 *Fax:* 206-447-9189
E-mail: support@laughingelephant.com
Web Site: www.laughingelephant.com
Key Personnel
Pres & Publr: Harold Darling
Ed-in-Chief: Abigail Darling
Ed: Christina Darling
Founded: 1986
Publish books, cards & printed gifts with an emphasis on imagery, especially from antique children's books, self-generating content.
ISBN Prefix(es): 978-1-883211; 978-0-9621131; 978-1-59583
Number of titles published annually: 8 Print
Total Titles: 80 Print
Imprints: Darling & Co; Green Tiger Press

§Law School Admission Council
662 Penn St, Newtown, PA 18940
Mailing Address: PO Box 40, Newtown, PA 18940
Tel: 215-968-1101
E-mail: lsacaccounts@lsac.org
Web Site: www.lsac.org
Key Personnel
Dir, Communs: Wendy Margolis *Tel:* 215-968-1219 *E-mail:* wmargolis@lsac.org
Founded: 1947
Standardized testing, legal education & law school admission activities, law school admission test preparation.
ISBN Prefix(es): 978-0-9846360
Number of titles published annually: 4 Print; 2 Online; 3 E-Book
Total Titles: 30 Print; 2 Online; 8 E-Book
Distribution Center: Ingram Publisher Services, 14 Ingram Blvd, La Vergne, TN 37086 *Toll Free Tel:* 866-400-5351 *Toll Free Fax:* 800-838-1149 *E-mail:* customer.service@ingrampublisherservices.com *Web Site:* ipage.ingramcontent.com SAN: 631-8630

Law Tribune Books
Division of American Lawyer Media
201 Ann Uccello St, 4th fl, Hartford, CT 06103
Tel: 860-527-7900 *Fax:* 860-527-7433
E-mail: lawtribune@alm.com
Web Site: www.ctlawtribune.com
Key Personnel
Publr: Jeffrey L Forte *Tel:* 860-757-6650 *E-mail:* jforte@alm.com
Ed-in-Chief: Paul Sussman *Tel:* 860-757-6640 *E-mail:* psussman@alm.com
Mng Ed: Jay Stapleton *Tel:* 860-757-6642 *E-mail:* jstapleton@alm.com
Busn Mgr: Heather Granger *Tel:* 860-757-6612 *E-mail:* hgranger@alm.com
Founded: 1974
Publisher of books, newspapers & other materials for the legal community & the public.
ISBN Prefix(es): 978-0-910051
Number of titles published annually: 20 Print
Total Titles: 20 Print; 3 E-Book
Imprints: The Connecticut Law Tribune

The Lawbook Exchange Ltd
33 Terminal Ave, Clark, NJ 07066-1321
Tel: 732-382-1800 *Toll Free Tel:* 800-422-6686 *Fax:* 732-382-1887
E-mail: law@lawbookexchange.com
Web Site: www.lawbookexchange.com
Key Personnel
Pres: Greg Talbot
Mng Ed, Pubns: Valerie Horowitz
Mgr, Antiquarian Books Dept: Michael von der Linn, PhD
Founded: 1983
Publisher of books on legal history. Also reprints of legal classics.
ISBN Prefix(es): 978-1-886363; 978-1-58477; 978-0-9630106
Number of titles published annually: 100 Print
Total Titles: 1,000 Print
Membership(s): Antiquarian Booksellers Association of America; International League of Antiquarian Booksellers

Merloyd Lawrence Inc
102 Chestnut St, Boston, MA 02108
Tel: 617-523-5895 *Fax:* 617-252-5285
Key Personnel
Pres & Ed: Merloyd Ludington Lawrence *E-mail:* merloyd.lawrence@perseusbooks.com
Intl Rts, The Perseus Books Group: Carolyn Savarese
Founded: 1982
Co-publisher with The Perseus Books Group.
Number of titles published annually: 6 Print; 5 E-Book
Total Titles: 81 Print; 39 E-Book
Distributed by The Perseus Books Group

§Lawyers & Judges Publishing Co Inc
917 N Swan Rd, Suite 300, Tucson, AZ 85711
Mailing Address: PO Box 30040, Tucson, AZ 85751-0040
Tel: 520-323-1500 *Toll Free Tel:* 800-209-7109 *Fax:* 520-323-0055 *Toll Free Fax:* 800-330-8795
E-mail: sales@lawyersandjudges.com
Web Site: www.lawyersandjudges.com
Key Personnel
Pres & Publr: Steve Weintraub *E-mail:* steve@lawyersandjudges.com
Founded: 1963
Professional, text & reference materials in law, accident reconstruction, legal economics & taxation, forensics, medicine.
ISBN Prefix(es): 978-0-88450; 978-0-913875; 978-1-930056
Number of titles published annually: 25 Print; 8 CD-ROM
Total Titles: 103 Print; 16 CD-ROM

Leadership Directories
1407 Broadway, Suite 318, New York, NY 10018
Tel: 212-627-4140 *Fax:* 212-645-0931
E-mail: info@leadershipdirectories.com
Web Site: www.leadershipdirectories.com
Key Personnel
CEO: Gretchen Teichgraeber *E-mail:* gteichgraeber@leadershipdirectories.com
SVP, Prods & Content: Sue Healy *E-mail:* shealy@leadershipdirectories.com
SVP, Sales & Mktg: Tom Silver *E-mail:* tsilver@leadershipdirectories.com
Sr Relationship Mgr: Jim Marcus *Tel:* 212-433-1408 *E-mail:* jmarcus@leadershipdirectories.com
Founded: 1969
Provider of premium contact solutions, covering the public & private sectors. Leadership Directories maintains a database of biographical & contact information on over 700,000 leaders & executives from more than 100,000 organizations. Content is available online, as datafeeds & pre-selected lists, or in print.
Number of titles published annually: 14 Print
Total Titles: 14 Print; 11 Online
Imprints: Yellow Books
Branch Office(s)
1667 "K" St NW, Suite 801, Washington, DC 20006, VP: Imogene Akins Hutchinson *Tel:* 202-347-7757 *Fax:* 202-628-3430

Leadership Ministries Worldwide/OBR
3755 Pilot Point, Chattanooga, TN 37416
Mailing Address: PO Box 21310, Chattanooga, TN 37424-0310
Tel: 423-855-2181 *Toll Free Tel:* 800-987-8790 *Fax:* 423-855-8616
E-mail: info@outlinebible.org
Web Site: www.outlinebible.org
Key Personnel
Pres: Randall Collins
Commentaries.
ISBN Prefix(es): 978-1-57407; 978-0-945863
Number of titles published annually: 12 Print

Total Titles: 275 Print
Membership(s): Evangelical Christian Publishers Association

Leaf Storm Press
PO Box 4670, Santa Fe, NM 87502-4670
Tel: 505-216-6155
E-mail: leafstormpress@gmail.com
Web Site: leafstormpress.com
Key Personnel
Publr: Andy Dudzik *E-mail:* publisher@leafstormpress.com
Founded: 2014
ISBN Prefix(es): 978-0-9914105
Number of titles published annually: 12 Print; 12 E-Book; 4 Audio
Total Titles: 1 Print; 6 E-Book
Membership(s): AAP; ABA; The Independent Book Publishers Association; New Mexico Book Association

§Leaping Dog Press/Asylum Arts Press
PO Box 90473, Raleigh, NC 27675-0473
Tel: 919-809-9045
E-mail: sales@leapingdogpress.com
Web Site: www.leapingdogpress.com
Key Personnel
Ed & Publr: Mr Jordan D Jones *E-mail:* editor@leapingdogpress.com
Founded: 1985
Publishers of contemporary literature; online only.
ISBN Prefix(es): 978-1-58775; 978-1-878580
Number of titles published annually: 4 Online
Total Titles: 4 Online
Imprints: Asylum Arts Press
Distribution Center: Bookmasters, 30 Amberwood Pkwy, Ashland, OH 44805 *Toll Free Tel:* 877-312-3520
Membership(s): Community of Literary Magazines & Presses; The Independent Book Publishers Association; Northern California Independent Booksellers Association

Learnables Foreign Language Courses, see International Linguistics Corp

§THE Learning Connection®
4100 Silverstar Rd, Suite D, Orlando, FL 32808
Tel: 407-292-2125 *Toll Free Tel:* 800-218-8489 *Fax:* 407-292-2123
E-mail: tlc@tlconnection.com
Web Site: www.tlconnection.com
Key Personnel
Gen Mgr: Ryan Handberg *E-mail:* ryan@tlconnection.com
Founded: 1991
Thematic Literacy Centers & teacher's guides for early childhood & middle school; parent involvement & family literacy; bilingual, math, science, multicultural, manipulatives, technology.
ISBN Prefix(es): 978-1-56831
Number of titles published annually: 15 Print; 15 CD-ROM; 5 Audio
Total Titles: 1,000 Print; 15 CD-ROM; 50 Audio
Imprints: Computer Connections; PAKS-Parents & Kids
Branch Office(s)
300 E 93 St, Suite 29C, New York, NY 10128, VP, NJ Accts: Timothy Sasman
Membership(s): International Literacy Association

Learning Links Inc
PO Box 326, Cranbury, NJ 08512
SAN: 175-081X
Tel: 516-437-9071 *Toll Free Tel:* 800-724-2616 *Fax:* 516-437-5392
E-mail: info@learninglinks.com
Web Site: www.learninglinks.com
Key Personnel
Owner: Linda Bradley
Founded: 1976
Publish study guides for novels for school use, grades 1-12. Distribute paperback books, audios, videos, craft kits & book-related toys.
ISBN Prefix(es): 978-0-88122; 978-1-56982; 978-0-7675
Number of titles published annually: 25 Print
Total Titles: 850 Print
Imprints: Novel-Ties Study Guides
Divisions: Swan Books
Distributor for Harcourt; HarperCollins; Houghton Mifflin Harcourt Publishing Company; Little, Brown & Company; Penguin Group (USA) LLC; Random House Inc; Scholastic; Simon & Schuster
Membership(s): International Literacy Association

LearningExpress LLC
2 Rector St, 26th fl, New York, NY 10006
Tel: 212-995-2566 *Toll Free Tel:* 800-295-9556 (ext 2) *Fax:* 212-995-5512
E-mail: customerservice@learningexpressllc.com (cust serv)
Web Site: www.learningexpressllc.com
Key Personnel
CEO & Pres: Barry Lippman
COO & CFO: Kheil McIntyre
CTO: Tammy Cunningham
VP, Busn Devt: Helen Sileno
Dir, Cust Serv: Shana Ashwood
Dir, Sales, Lib & Educ Solutions: Tom Burnosky
Founded: 1995
Publishes print & online test-preparation resources, skill building tools, study guides & career guidance materials for the trade, library, school & consumer markets.
ISBN Prefix(es): 978-1-57685
Number of titles published annually: 40 Print; 4 CD-ROM; 30 Online; 40 E-Book
Total Titles: 200 Print; 12 CD-ROM; 300 Online; 150 E-Book
Imprints: LearningExpress
Sales Office(s): National Book Network, 4501 Forbes Blvd, Suite 200, Lanham, MD 20706
Distributed by National Book Network
Orders to: National Book Network, 15200 NBN Way, Blue Ridge Summit, PA 17214 *Tel:* 717-794-3800 *Toll Free Tel:* 800-462-6420 *Toll Free Fax:* 800-338-4550 *E-mail:* customercare@nbnbooks.com
Returns: National Book Network, 15200 NBN Way, Blue Ridge Summit, PA 17214 *Tel:* 717-794-3800 *Toll Free Tel:* 800-462-6420 *Toll Free Fax:* 800-338-4550 *E-mail:* customercare@nbnbooks.com
Warehouse: National Book Network, 15200 NBN Way, Blue Ridge Summit, PA 17214

Lectorum Publications Inc
205 Chubb Ave, Lyndhurst, NJ 07071
Toll Free Tel: 800-345-5946 *Fax:* 201-559-2201 *Toll Free Fax:* 877-532-8676
E-mail: lectorum@lectorum.com
Web Site: www.lectorum.com
Key Personnel
Pres & CEO: Alex Correa *E-mail:* acorrea@lectorum.com
Opers Mgr: Fernando Febus *E-mail:* ffebus@lectorum.com
Lib & Trade Sales Mgr: Laura Bejarano *E-mail:* lbejarano@lectorum.com
Educ Sales: Hilda Viskovic *E-mail:* hviskovic@lectorum.com
Founded: 1960
Distribute children & adult books in Spanish, with over 25,000 titles from more than 500 domestic & foreign publishers. Serves schools & libraries, as well as the trade & various specialized markets, with children's books in Spanish, including works originally written in Spanish, translations from other languages & the Spanish-language editions of many popular children's books.
ISBN Prefix(es): 978-1-880507; 978-1-930332; 978-0-9625162; 978-1-933032; 978-1-941802; 978-1-63245
Number of titles published annually: 10 Print

Lederer Books
Division of Messianic Jewish Publishers
6120 Day Long Lane, Clarksville, MD 21029
Tel: 410-531-6644 *Toll Free Tel:* 800-410-7367 (orders) *Fax:* 410-531-9440
E-mail: lederer@messianicjewish.net; customerservice@messianicjewish.net
Web Site: www.messianicjewish.net
Key Personnel
Pres: Barry Rubin *E-mail:* president@messianicjewish.net
Founded: 1949
Publish & distribute Messianic Jewish books, bibles & other resources.
ISBN Prefix(es): 978-1-880226; 978-1-936716
Number of titles published annually: 6 Print
Total Titles: 100 Print
Distributor for Chosen People Ministries; First Fruits of Zion; Jewish New Testament Publications
Foreign Rep(s): Winfried Bluth (Europe)
Foreign Rights: Winfried Bluth (Europe)
Membership(s): CBA: The Association for Christian Retail; Evangelical Christian Publishers Association

Lee & Low Books Inc
95 Madison Ave, New York, NY 10016
Tel: 212-779-4400 *Toll Free Tel:* 888-320-3190 (ext 28, orders only) *Fax:* 212-683-1894 (orders only); 212-532-6035
E-mail: general@leeandlow.com
Web Site: www.leeandlow.com
Key Personnel
Pres: Craig Low *E-mail:* clow@leeandlow.com
VP & Edit Dir: Louise May
Publr: Jason Low *E-mail:* jlow@leeandlow.com
Founded: 1991
Publisher of high quality multicultural children's books. We provide for the school, library & bookstore market.
ISBN Prefix(es): 978-1-880000; 978-1-58430; 978-1-600
Number of titles published annually: 15 Print; 15 E-Book
Total Titles: 650 Print; 50 E-Book; 50 Audio
Imprints: Bebop Books; Children's Book Press; Shen's Books; Tu Books
See separate listing for:
Children's Book Press
Shen's Books

Left Coast Press Inc
1630 N Main St, Suite 400, Walnut Creek, CA 94596
Tel: 925-935-3380 *Fax:* 925-935-2916
E-mail: explore@lcoastpress.com
Web Site: www.lcoastpress.com
Key Personnel
Founder & Publr: Mitch Allen
Founded: 2005
Publisher of scholarly books & journals on social sciences & humanities.
ISBN Prefix(es): 978-1-59874; 978-1-61132; 978-1-62958
Number of titles published annually: 40 Print; 35 E-Book
Total Titles: 300 Print; 250 E-Book
Distributor for UCL Institute of Archaeology (UK)
Foreign Rep(s): Eurospan (Africa, Europe, Middle East); Footpoint Books (Australia, New Zealand)
Distribution Center: University Chicago Press, 1427 E 60 St, Chicago, IL 60637-2954

Legacy Press, see Rainbow Publishers

Lehigh University Press
Affiliate of Rowman & Littlefield Publishing Group (RLPG)
B-040 Christmas-Saucon Hall, 14 E Packer Ave, Bethlehem, PA 18015
Tel: 610-758-3933 *Fax:* 610-758-6331
E-mail: inlup@lehigh.edu
Web Site: inpress.sites.lehigh.edu
Founded: 1985
18th century American studies, East Asian studies, literary theory & criticism, history & technology, science, sociology, biography & the Arts. Submissions welcome on any topic that is intellectually substantive.
ISBN Prefix(es): 978-1-61146
Number of titles published annually: 10 Print
Total Titles: 149 Print
Distributed by Rowman & Littlefield

§Leilah Publications
510 E University Dr, No 3413, Tempe, AZ 85281
Tel: 847-275-1657
E-mail: leilah@leilahpublications.com
Web Site: facebook.com/leilahpublications
Key Personnel
CEO: Joshua Seraphim
Creative Consultant: Amany El-Ameera Daghesty
Founded: 2006
Brings a global vision of art & writing for the 21st century, publishing & investing in avantegarde artists, lyricists, writers, actors, actresses & poets.
ISBN Prefix(es): 978-0-9829992; 978-0-9963338
Number of titles published annually: 3 Print; 3 Online; 3 E-Book; 1 Audio
Total Titles: 16 Print; 16 Online; 3 E-Book; 1 Audio
Subsidiaries: Brigids Books
Warehouse: Ingram/Lightning Source, 1246 Neil Quaker Blvd, La Vergne, TN 37086
Distribution Center: Ingram/Lightning Source, 1246 Neil Quaker Blvd, La Vergne, TN 37086
Membership(s): American Academy of Religion

Leisure Arts Inc
Division of Liberty Media
104 Champs Blvd, Suite 100, Maumelle, AR 72113
SAN: 666-9565
Tel: 501-868-8800 *Toll Free Tel:* 800-643-8030 *Fax:* 501-868-8748
Web Site: www.leisurearts.com
Key Personnel
Pres & CEO: Rick Barton
VP, Retail Sales: Martha Adams
Founded: 1971
Hard & soft cover books featuring instructions for needlework, crafts, cooking & gardening.
ISBN Prefix(es): 978-0-942237; 978-1-57486; 978-1-60140
Number of titles published annually: 200 Print
Total Titles: 2,000 Print

The Lentz Leadership Institute
Imprint of The Refractive Thinker Press
7124 Glyndon Trail NW, Albuquerque, NM 87114
SAN: 857-7994
Tel: 702-719-9214
E-mail: orders@lentzleadership.com
Web Site: www.lentzleadership.com; www.refractivethinker.com
Key Personnel
The Academic Entrepreneur: Dr Cheryl Lentz *Tel:* 505-990-2274 *E-mail:* drcheryllentz@gmail.com
Founded: 2008
Publishes scholarly materials as part of The Anthology series: The Refractive Thinker Series, to include the educational seminar series for public speaking. Individual books & individual Doctoral or Graduate level publications by participating authors are also published. Offer APA Doctoral & Graduate editing services.
ISBN Prefix(es): 978-0-9823036; 978-0-9828740; 978-0-9840054
Number of titles published annually: 14 Print; 2 Online; 97 E-Book; 1 Audio
Total Titles: 12 Print; 14 Online; 97 E-Book; 1 Audio
Imprints: Pensiero Press
Distribution Center: Lightning Source Inc, 1246 Heil Quaker Blvd, La Vergne, TN 37086 *Tel:* 615-213-5815 *Fax:* 615-213-4725 *E-mail:* inquiry@lightningsource.com *Web Site:* www.lightningsource.com
Membership(s): The Independent Book Publishers Association

Lerner Publications
Division of Lerner Publishing Group Inc
241 First Ave N, Minneapolis, MN 55401
SAN: 201-0828
Tel: 612-332-3344 *Toll Free Tel:* 800-328-4929 *Fax:* 612-332-7615 *Toll Free Fax:* 800-332-1132
E-mail: info@lernerbooks.com
Web Site: www.lernerbooks.com
Key Personnel
Chmn: Harry J Lerner
Pres & Publr: Adam Lerner
EVP, Sales: David Wexler
EVP & Dir, Mktg & Digital Prods: Terri Soutor
VP, Ed-in-Chief: Patricia M Stockland
CFO & EVP: Margaret Wunderlich
VP, Prodn: Gary Hansen
VP, Digital Prod Mgmt: Daniel Wallek
Rts Dir: Maria Kjoller
Dir, HR: Cyndi Radant
Group Mktg Dir: Jill Braithwaite
School & Lib Mktg Dir: Lois Wallentine
Art Dir: Zach Marell
Founded: 1959
Juveniles: science, history, sports, fiction, art, geography, aviation, environment, ethnic, multicultural issues & activity books.
Total Titles: 1,025 Print; 920 E-Book
Foreign Rep(s): INT Press Distribution (Australia); Monarch Books of Canada (Trade) (Canada); Phambili (Southern Africa); Publishers Marketing Service (Malaysia, Singapore); Saunders Book Co (Education) (Canada); South Pacific Books (New Zealand)
Foreign Rights: Japan Foreign-Rights Centre (Japan); Korea Copyright Center (KCC) (Korea); Michelle Lapautre Agence Junior (France); Literarische Agentur Silke Weniger (Germany)
Warehouse: Lerner Publishing Group, 1251 Washington Ave N, Minneapolis, MN 55401

Lerner Publishing Group Inc
241 First Ave N, Minneapolis, MN 55401
SAN: 201-0828
Tel: 612-332-3344 *Toll Free Tel:* 800-328-4929 *Fax:* 612-332-7615 *Toll Free Fax:* 800-332-1132
E-mail: info@lernerbooks.com
Web Site: www.lernerbooks.com
Key Personnel
Chmn: Harry J Lerner
CFO & EVP: Margaret Wunderlich
Pres & Publr: Adam Lerner
EVP, Sales: David Wexler
EVP & Dir, Mktg & Digital Prods: Terri Soutor
VP, Prodn: Gary Hansen
VP, Ed-in-Chief: Patricia M Stockland
VP, Digital Prod Mgmt: Daniel Wallek
Rts Dir: Maria Kjoller
Dir, HR: Cyndi Radant
Group Mktg Dir: Jill Braithwaite
School & Lib Mktg Dir: Lois Wallentine
Art Dir: Zach Marell
School & Lib Sales Mgr: Brad Richason
Founded: 1959
ISBN Prefix(es): 978-0-87614; 978-1-58013; 978-0-8225; 978-0-7613; 978-1-57505; 978-0-92937; 978-0-93049; 978-1-58196
Number of titles published annually: 450 Print
Total Titles: 4,800 Print; 3,800 E-Book
Imprints: Carolrhoda Books Inc; Carolrhoda Lab™; Darby Creek Publishing; ediciones Lerner; First Avenue Editions; Graphic Universe™; Lerner Publications; LernerClassroom; Millbrook Press; Twenty-First Century Books
Divisions: Kar-Ben Publishing; Lerner Books UK; Lerner Publisher Services
Distributor for Andersen Press USA; Columbus Zoo; Walter Foster Publishing; Gecko Press; JR Comics; The Kane Press; Kar-Ben Partners; MVP Books; Red Chair Press; Sandy Creek; Scobre Educational; Stoke Books; We Do Listen
Foreign Rep(s): Bravo (Kar-Ben) (UK & the continent); Int Books (Australia); J Appleseed, A Division of Saunders (Canada); Mazeltov Books (Kar-Ben) (Australia); Monarch Books of Canada/Trade (Canada); Phambili Agencies (Botswana, Lesotho, Namibia, South Africa, Swaziland, Zimbabwe); Publishers Marketing Services (Brunei, Malaysia, Singapore); Saunders Book Co/Education (Canada); South Pacific Books (New Zealand)
Foreign Rights: Japan Foreign-Rights Center (Japan); Korea Copyright Center (KCC) (Korea); Michelle Lapautre Agence Junior (France); Literarische Agentur Silke Weniger (Germany)
Warehouse: 1251 Washington Ave N, Minneapolis, MN 55401
See separate listing for:
Carolrhoda Books
Carolrhoda Lab™
ediciones Lerner
First Avenue Editions
Graphic Universe™
Kar-Ben Publishing
Lerner Publications
LernerClassroom
Millbrook Press
Twenty-First Century Books

LernerClassroom
Division of Lerner Publishing Group Inc
241 First Ave N, Minneapolis, MN 55401
Tel: 612-332-3344 *Toll Free Tel:* 800-328-4929 *Fax:* 612-332-7615 *Toll Free Fax:* 800-332-1132
E-mail: info@lernerbooks.com
Web Site: www.lernerbooks.com
Key Personnel
Chmn: Harry J Lerner
CFO & EVP: Margaret Wunderlich
Pres & Publr: Adam Lerner
EVP, Sales: David Wexler
EVP & Dir, Mktg & Digital Prods: Terri Soutor
VP, Ed-in-Chief: Patricia M Stockland
VP, Prodn: Gary Hansen
VP, Digital Prod Mgmt: Daniel Wallek
Rts Dir: Maria Kjoller
Dir, HR: Cyndi Radant
Art Dir: Zach Marell
Group Mktg Dir: Jill Braithwaite
School & Lib Mktg Dir: Lois Wallentine
Nonfiction children's publications with teaching guides.
Total Titles: 860 Print; 55 E-Book
Foreign Rep(s): INT Books (Australia); Monarch Books of Canada (Canada); Phambili (Southern Africa); Publishers Marketing Services (Brunei, Malaysia, Singapore); South Pacific Books (New Zealand)
Foreign Rights: Japan Foreign-Rights Centre (Japan); Korea Copyright Center (Korea); Michelle Lapautre Agence Junior (France); Literarische Agentur Silke Weniger (Germany)
Warehouse: Lerner Publishing Group, 1251 Washington Ave N, Minneapolis, MN 55401

Lessiter Publications
16655 W Wisconsin Ave, Brookfield, WI 53005
Mailing Address: PO Box 624, Brookfield, WI 53008-0624
Tel: 262-782-4480 *Toll Free Tel:* 800-645-8455 *Fax:* 262-782-1252
E-mail: info@lesspub.com
Web Site: www.lesspub.com
Key Personnel
Chmn & Edit Dir: Frank Lessiter
Pres: Mike Lessiter
Founded: 1981
Animals, farm equipment, business, sports, veterinary science (equine hoof care).
ISBN Prefix(es): 978-0-944079
Number of titles published annually: 6 Print
Total Titles: 35 Print

Letterbox/Papyrus of London Publishers USA
10501 Broom Hill Dr, Suite 1-F, Las Vegas, NV 89134-7339
Tel: 702-256-3838
E-mail: lb27383@cox.net
Key Personnel
Mng Dir: Anthony Wade
Ed-in-Chief: Geoffrey Hutchison-Cleaves, MA
Fin Offr: Josef Kase *Tel:* 702-256-3838 ext 2
Spec Orders Mgr: Erica Neubauer *Tel:* 702-256-3838 ext 1
Rts & Perms: Mrs H Neubauer *Tel:* 702-256-3838 ext 8
Founded: 1946 (at Penley Court, 173 Strand, London EC4)
No submissions accepted.
ISBN Prefix(es): 978-0-943698
Number of titles published annually: 3 Print
Total Titles: 137 Print
Imprints: Challenges of Aging Instruction Booklets; Difficult Subjects Made Easy Instruction Booklets
Advertising Agency: ShowKase Advertising & Public Relations, 3250 S Fort Apache Rd, Suite 217, Las Vegas, NV 89117, Acct Exec: Ms Robin Lindsay
Distribution Center: Baker & Taylor Books, PO Box 8888, Momence, IL 60954 *Tel:* 908-541-7459

Letterbox Service, see Letterbox/Papyrus of London Publishers USA

Level 4 Press Inc
13518 Jamul Dr, Jamul, CA 91935-1635
Fax: 619-374-7311
E-mail: sales@level4press.com
Web Site: www.level4press.com
Key Personnel
Founder & CEO: William Roetzheim
Founded: 2006
ISBN Prefix(es): 978-0-9768001; 978-1-933769
Number of titles published annually: 1 Print; 6 Audio
Total Titles: 35 Print; 15 Audio

Lexington Books
Imprint of Rowman & Littlefield Publishing Group
4501 Forbes Blvd, Suite 200, Lanham, MD 20706
Tel: 301-459-3366 *Fax:* 301-429-5749
Web Site: www.lexingtonbooks.com
Key Personnel
VP & Publr: Julie Kirsch *E-mail:* jkirsch@rowman.com
Mktg Mgr: Dave Horvath *E-mail:* dhorvath@rowman.com
Premier publisher of scholarly monographs & textbooks. Subjects include classics, political science, political theory, philosophy, history, international relations, literary studies, public policy, sociology, anthropology, religion, communications, cultural studies, education & area studies.
ISBN Prefix(es): 978-0-7391
Number of titles published annually: 400 Print; 400 E-Book
Total Titles: 3,500 Print; 2,000 E-Book
Foreign Rep(s): Academic Marketing Services Pty Ltd (Botswana, Namibia, South Africa, Zimbabwe); APD Singapore Pte Ltd (Brunei, Cambodia, Indonesia, Laos, Malaysia, Singapore, Thailand, Vietnam); Asia Publishers Service Ltd (China, Hong Kong, Korea, Philippines, Taiwan); Avicenna Partnership Ltd (Afghanistan, Algeria, Armenia, Bahrain, Cyprus, Egypt, Iran, Iraq, Jordan, Kuwait, Lebanon, Libya, Morocco, Oman, Palestine, Qatar, Saudi Arabia, Sudan, Syria, Tunisia, United Arab Emirates, Yemen); Cranbury International LLC (Caribbean, Central America, Mexico, Pakistan, Puerto Rico, South America); DA Information Services Pty Ltd (Australia, New Zealand, Papua New Guinea); Durnell Marketing Ltd (Austria, Baltic States, Belgium, Czech Republic, Denmark, Finland, France, Germany, Greece, Hungary, Iceland, Italy, Malta, Netherlands, Norway, Poland, Portugal, Slovakia, Slovenia, Spain, Sweden, Switzerland); Overleaf (Bangladesh, India, Nepal); United Publishers Service Ltd (Japan, South Korea)
Foreign Rights: Clare Cox (Worldwide)
Orders to: Rowman & Littlefield Publishing Group, 15200 NBN Way, Blue Ridge Summit, PA 17214 *Tel:* 717-794-3800 *Toll Free Tel:* 800-462-6420 *Fax:* 717-794-3803 *E-mail:* custserv@rowman.com
Membership(s): AAP

§LexisNexis®
Division of RELX Group PLC
701 E Water St, Charlottesville, VA 22902
SAN: 202-6317
Tel: 434-972-7600 *Toll Free Tel:* 800-446-3410 *Fax:* 434-961-5576
E-mail: customer.support@lexisnexis.com
Web Site: www.lexisnexis.com
Key Personnel
CEO, US Legal Mkts: Mike Walsh
Founded: 1897
Multivolume legal reference works, state codes & single-volume legal texts, treatises & casebooks. Most material also in online versions.
ISBN Prefix(es): 978-0-409; 978-0-87215; 978-0-672; 978-0-87473; 978-0-406; 978-0-327; 978-0-88063; 978-0-930273; 978-1-55834; 978-1-56257
Imprints: Michie
Shipping Address: Broome Corp Park, 136 Carlin Rd, Conklin, NY 13748 *Tel:* 607-772-2600 *Toll Free Tel:* 800-323-9608

§LexisNexis® Matthew Bender®
Member of The LexisNexis® Group
630 Central Ave, New Providence, NJ 07974
Tel: 908-464-6800
Web Site: bender.lexisnexis.com
Founded: 1887
Treatises, text & form books, newsletters, periodicals & manuals for the legal, accounting, insurance, banking & related professions, selected libraries on CD-ROM.
Branch locations also in New York City & Dayton, OH.
ISBN Prefix(es): 978-0-8205; 978-1-4224
Total Titles: 577 Print; 277 CD-ROM; 27 Online; 277 E-Book
Branch Office(s)
Immaculata Hall, 32 S Ewing St, Helena, MT 59601 *Toll Free Tel:* 800-227-9597
630 Central Ave, New Providence, NJ 07974 *Tel:* 908-464-6800 *Toll Free Tel:* 800-526-4902
701 E Water St, Charlottesville, VA 22902 *Tel:* 434-972-7600 *Toll Free Tel:* 800-446-3410

LexisNexis/Martindale-Hubbell, see Martindale LLC

Liberty Fund Inc
8335 Allison Pointe Trail, Suite 300, Indianapolis, IN 46250-1684
SAN: 202-6740
Tel: 317-842-0880 *Toll Free Tel:* 800-955-8335; 800-866-3520; 800-368-7897 ext 6069 (cust serv) *Fax:* 317-577-9067; 317-579-6060 (cust serv); 708-534-7803
E-mail: books@libertyfund.org; info@libertyfund.org
Web Site: www.libertyfund.org
Key Personnel
VP, Publg: Patricia Gallagher
Mng Ed: Dan Kirklin
Mktg & Fulfillment Coord: Michele Roberts *Tel:* 317-842-0880 ext 0020 *E-mail:* mroberts@libertyfund.org
Founded: 1960
A publisher of print & electronic scholarly resources including new editions of classic works in American constitutional history, European history, natural law, law, modern political thought, economics & education.
ISBN Prefix(es): 978-0-913966; 978-0-86597; 978-1-61487
Number of titles published annually: 10 Print; 100 Online
Total Titles: 360 Print; 1,450 Online; 1 Audio
Foreign Rep(s): Academic Sales & Marketing (Andrew Jones) (Midlands, Northern England); Jim Biaho (Italy); Mara Cheli (Italy); Peter Couzens (Asia); Everybodys Book's (Warren Halford) (Southern Africa); Export Sales Agency (Ted Dougherty) (Austria, Germany, Switzerland); Four Corners Sales Agency (Charlotte Kelly) (Ireland, London, Scotland, Southern England, Wales); Gazelle Academic (Mark Trotter) (London); Charles Gibbes (Cyprus, Greece); Iberian Book Services (Charlotte Prout) (Gibraltar, Portugal, Spain); Iberian Book Services (Peter Prout); Marketing Solutions LLP (Andrew Wallace) (Central London, UK, East Anglia, England); Maya Publishers Pvt Ltd (India); Tony Moggach (Eastern Europe); David Towle (Baltic States, Northern Europe, Scandinavia)
Distribution Center: Scholarly Book Services, 289 Ridgeland Ave, Unit 105, Toronto, ON M6A 1Z6, Canada *Toll Free Tel:* 800-847-9736
Membership(s): AAP; ALA

Libraries Unlimited
Imprint of ABC-CLIO
130 Cremona Dr, Santa Barbara, CA 93117
Mailing Address: PO Box 1911, Santa Barbara, CA 93116-1911
Tel: 805-968-1911 *Toll Free Tel:* 800-368-6868 *Fax:* 805-685-9685 *Toll Free Fax:* 866-270-3856
E-mail: customerservice@abc-clio.com
Web Site: www.abc-clio.com
Founded: 1964
Library science textbooks, annotated bibliographies, reference books, professional books for school media specialists as well as resource & activity books for librarians & teachers; storytelling resources & collections.
ISBN Prefix(es): 978-0-87287; 978-1-56308
Number of titles published annually: 80 Print
Total Titles: 600 Print; 5 Audio
Imprints: Linworth Publishing
See separate listing for:
Linworth Publishing

The Library of America
14 E 60 St, New York, NY 10022-1006
SAN: 286-9918
Tel: 212-308-3360 *Fax:* 212-750-8352
E-mail: info@loa.org
Web Site: www.loa.org

Key Personnel
CEO & Pres: Cheryl Hurley
CFO & VP: Daniel W Baker
VP & Publr: Max Rudin
Assoc Publr: Brian McCarthy *Tel:* 212-308-3360 ext 227 *E-mail:* bmccarthy@loa.org
Ed-in-Chief: Geoffrey O'Brien
Dir, Mktg: David Cloyce Smith
Prodn Ed: Trish Hoard
Cust Serv Mgr: Laura Gazlay
Founded: 1979
Collected editions of classic American authors; literature, history, philosophy, drama, poetry & journalism.
ISBN Prefix(es): 978-0-940450; 978-1-883011; 978-1-931082; 978-1-59853
Number of titles published annually: 14 Print
Total Titles: 300 Print
Distributed by Penguin Group (USA) LLC
Foreign Rep(s): Penguin Canada (Canada); United Publishers Service (Japan)
Warehouse: Penguin Group (USA) LLC, One Grosset Dr, Kirkwood, NY 13795

Mary Ann Liebert Inc
140 Huguenot St, 3rd fl, New Rochelle, NY 10801-5215
Tel: 914-740-2100 *Toll Free Tel:* 800-654-3237 *Fax:* 914-740-2101
E-mail: info@liebertpub.com
Web Site: www.liebertonline.com
Key Personnel
SVP: Harriet I Matysko *Tel:* 914-740-2182 *E-mail:* hmatysko@liebertpub.com
Dir, Ad Prodn-Genetic Engg & Biotechnology News: Anne B Chin Aleong *Tel:* 914-740-2178 *E-mail:* achin@genengnews.com
Ad Prodn Mgr: Kathleen De Souza *Tel:* 914-740-2295 *E-mail:* kdesouza@liebertpub.com
Supv, Ad Prodn-GEN Print & Online & MAL Journals: Sherine Morris *Tel:* 914-740-2174 *E-mail:* smorris@liebertpub.com
Ad Prodn: Wanda Sanchez *Tel:* 914-740-2178 *E-mail:* wsanchez@genengnews.com
Founded: 1980
Medical & sci-tech journals, books & newspapers. Additional subjects include: biomedical research, integrative medicine (CAM), public policy, public health/policy, gender & population studies, regenerative medicine, clinical medicine, biotechnology, environmental studies, humanities, life sciences, allied health & surgery.
ISBN Prefix(es): 978-0-913113
Number of titles published annually: 3 Print; 3 Online
Total Titles: 65 Print; 70 Online
Divisions: Genetic Engineering & Biotechnology News
Foreign Office(s): Impress Media, Carrington Kirk, Carrington, Midlothian EH23 4LR, United Kingdom, Contact: Hilary Turnbull *Tel:* (01875) 825700 *Fax:* (01875) 825701 *E-mail:* hturnbull@genengnews.com

Life Cycle Books
Division of Life Cycle Books Ltd (Canada)
PO Box 799, Fort Collins, CO 80522
SAN: 692-7173
Toll Free Tel: 800-214-5849 *Toll Free Fax:* 888-690-8532
E-mail: orders@lifecyclebooks.com; support@lifecyclebooks.com
Web Site: www.lifecyclebooks.com
Key Personnel
Founder & Pres: Paul Broughton *E-mail:* paulb@lifecyclebooks.com
Founded: 1973
Books, pamphlets, brochures & audiovisuals on human life issues.
ISBN Prefix(es): 978-0-919225
Number of titles published annually: 6 Print
Total Titles: 41 Print

Light-Beams Publishing
10 Toon Lane, Lee, NH 03861
Tel: 603-659-1300
E-mail: info@light-beams.com
Web Site: www.light-beams.com
Key Personnel
Mktg Mgr: Mark Forman *E-mail:* mforman@light-beams.com
Founded: 2000
Specialize in & publishes award-winning children's books & videos for children ages 3 & up.
ISBN Prefix(es): 978-0-9708104; 978-0-9766289
Number of titles published annually: 10 Print
Distribution Center: Independent Publishers Group, 814 N Franklin St, Chicago, IL 60610 (exclusive distributor to the book trade) *Toll Free Tel:* 800-888-4741 *Web Site:* www.ipgbook.com

Light Publications
Hope Artiste Village, 1005 Main St, Suite 1212, Pawtucket, RI 02806
Mailing Address: PO Box 2462, Providence, RI 02906
Tel: 401-484-0228
E-mail: info@lightpublications.com
Web Site: lightpublications.com
Key Personnel
Pres: Stephen Brendan *E-mail:* stephen@lightpublications.com
Founded: 1999
ISBN Prefix(es): 978-0-9702642; 978-0-9824707; 978-1-940060
Number of titles published annually: 5 Print; 5 Online; 5 E-Book; 1 Audio
Total Titles: 15 Print; 15 Online; 15 E-Book; 7 Audio
Membership(s): The Independent Book Publishers Association

Light Technology Publishing
4030 E Huntington Dr, Flagstaff, AZ 86004
Mailing Address: PO Box 3540, Flagstaff, AZ 86003-3540
Tel: 928-526-1345 *Toll Free Tel:* 800-450-0985 *Fax:* 928-714-1132
E-mail: publishing@lighttechnology.net
Web Site: www.lighttechnology.com
Key Personnel
Owner & Publr: O'Ryin Swanson
Sidona Journal, metaphysical publications, mostly channelled.
ISBN Prefix(es): 978-1-891824; 978-1-929385
Number of titles published annually: 15 Print
Total Titles: 150 Print
Foreign Rights: Hagenbach & Bender GmbH (Worldwide exc USA)
Membership(s): AAP

Lighthouse Publishing of the Carolinas
2333 Barton Oaks Dr, Raleigh, NC 27614-7940
Tel: 919-562-8439
E-mail: lighthousepublishingcarolinas@gmail.com
Web Site: lighthousepublishingofthecarolinas.com
Key Personnel
Founder & CEO: Eddie Jones
ISBN Prefix(es): 978-0-9833196; 978-0-9822065; 978-0-9847655; 978-1-938499
Number of titles published annually: 40 Print
Total Titles: 132 Print; 40 E-Book

Liguori Publications
One Liguori Dr, Liguori, MO 63057-1000
Tel: 636-464-2500 *Toll Free Tel:* 866-848-2492; 800-325-9521 *Fax:* 636-464-8449 *Toll Free Fax:* 800-325-9526 (sales)
E-mail: liguori@liguori.org (sales & cust serv)
Web Site: www.liguori.org/contact-us.html
Key Personnel
Pres: Fr Byron Miller
Publr: Virgil Tipton, III
Dir, Fin & Busn Opers: Tracey Kane
Acqs Ed: Julia DiSalvo
Founded: 1947
Academic & trade books on religion (Catholic) & spirituality, inspirational & educational resources for parishes & schools, devotional music, bulletins, pamphlets, Liguorian magazine.
ISBN Prefix(es): 978-0-89243; 978-0-7648
Number of titles published annually: 50 Print
Total Titles: 600 Print; 14 CD-ROM
Imprints: Libros Liguori; Liguori/Triumph
Distributor for Redemptorist Publications
Foreign Rep(s): Majellan (Australia); Novalis (Canada); Redemptorist Publications Book Services (England)

Limelight Editions
Imprint of Hal Leonard Performing Arts Publishing Group
33 Plymouth St, Suite 302, Montclair, NJ 07042
Tel: 973-337-5034 *Fax:* 973-337-5227
Web Site: limelighteditions.com
Key Personnel
Group Publr: John Cerullo
Full service trade publisher that produces books, book/CDs & DVDs on the performing arts including cinema, dance & theater.
ISBN Prefix(es): 978-0-87910
Number of titles published annually: 8 Print; 2 Audio
Total Titles: 260 Print; 5 Audio
Sales Office(s): 7777 W Bluemound Rd, Milwaukee, WI 53213 *Toll Free Tel:* 800-554-0626
Distributed by Hal Leonard Corp
Foreign Rep(s): Publishers Group UK (Europe, UK)
Billing Address: 960 E Mark St, Winona, MN 55987 *Tel:* 507-454-2920 *Fax:* 507-454-9334
Orders to: 7777 W Bluemound Rd, Milwaukee, WI 53213 *Toll Free Tel:* 800-554-0626
Returns: 1210 Innovation Dr, Winona, MN 55987 *Tel:* 507-454-2920 *Fax:* 507-454-8334
Warehouse: 1210 Innovation Dr, Winona, MN 55987 *Tel:* 507-454-2920 *Fax:* 507-454-8334
Distribution Center: 960 E Mark St, Winona, MN 55987 *Tel:* 507-454-2920 *Fax:* 507-454-8334

Linden Publishing Co Inc
2006 S Mary St, Fresno, CA 93721
Tel: 559-233-6633 *Toll Free Tel:* 800-345-4447 (orders) *Fax:* 559-233-6933
Web Site: lindenpub.com
Key Personnel
Pres & Publr: Richard Sorsky *E-mail:* richard@lindenpub.com
Founded: 1977
ISBN Prefix(es): 978-0-941936; 978-1-933502; 978-1-884956; 978-1-884995
Number of titles published annually: 12 Print; 50 E-Book
Total Titles: 200 Print
Imprints: Craven Street Books; Quill Driver Books; Word Dancer Press
Foreign Rights: Books Crossing Borders (Worldwide)
Distribution Center: Ingram Publisher Services, One Ingram Blvd, La Vergne, TN 37086
Membership(s): ABA; The Independent Book Publishers Association

Lindisfarne Books
Imprint of SteinerBooks
610 Main St, Great Barrington, MA 01230
Mailing Address: PO Box 749, Great Barrington, MA 01230
Tel: 413-528-8233 *Fax:* 413-528-8826
E-mail: service@steinerbooks.org
Web Site: www.steinerbooks.org
Key Personnel
CEO & Pres: Eugene Gollogly *E-mail:* gene@steinerbooks.org
Ed-in-Chief: Christopher Bamford

Founded: 1979
Fine quality books in the areas of philosophy, psychology, new sciences, comparative theology, art & literature, emphasizing the synthesis of science, religion & art.
ISBN Prefix(es): 978-0-940262; 978-1-58420; 978-0-9701097
Number of titles published annually: 5 Print
Total Titles: 103 Print
Distributed by Floris Books
Foreign Rep(s): Floris Books (UK)
Orders to: PO Box 960, Herndon, VA 20172 *Tel:* 703-661-1594 *Toll Free Tel:* 800-856-8664 *Fax:* 703-661-1501
Warehouse: PO Box 960, Herndon, VA 20172 *Tel:* 703-661-1594

LinguaText Ltd
103 Walker Way, Newark, DE 19711
SAN: 238-0307
Tel: 302-453-8695 *Fax:* 302-453-8601
Web Site: www.linguatextltd.com
Key Personnel
Publr: Michael Bolan *Fax:* 302-453-8601
Ed, Juan de la Cuesta Hispanic Monographs: Michael McGrath *Tel:* 912-478-0115 *Fax:* 912-478-0652 *E-mail:* mmcgrath@georgiasouthern.edu
Founded: 1974
Publish foreign language textbooks (Portuguese), scholarly monographs on Spanish literature from medieval to modern & student editions of Spanish & French classic literature designed for English speakers.
60% subvented by institution.
ISBN Prefix(es): 978-0-936388; 978-0-942566; 978-1-58871; 978-1-58977
Number of titles published annually: 15 Print
Total Titles: 350 Print
Imprints: Juan de la Cuesta Hispanic Monographs; European Masterpieces (Cervantes & Co Spanish Classics/Moliere & Co French Classics); LinguaText (language textbooks)
Distributor for Juan de la Cuesta—Hispanic Monographs; European Masterpieces
Distribution Center: Amazon.com
Barnes & Noble Distribution, One Barnes & Noble Way, Monroe Township, NJ 08831 *Tel:* 732-656-7200 *Web Site:* www.barnesandnoble.com
Baker & Taylor Inc, 2550 W Tyvola Rd, Suite 300, Charlotte, NC 28217 *Tel:* 704-998-3100 *Toll Free Tel:* 800-775-1800 *Fax:* 704-998-3319 *E-mail:* btinfo@btol.com *Web Site:* www.btol.com
Brodart, 500 Arch St, Williamsport, PA 17701 *Toll Free Tel:* 800-474-9816 *E-mail:* support@brodart.com *Web Site:* www.brodartbooks.com
Coutts Information Services Ltd, 3 Ingram Blvd, La Vergne, TN 37086 *Toll Free Tel:* 800-263-1686
Follett School Solutions Inc, 1340 Ridgeview Dr, McHenry, IL 60050 *Toll Free Tel:* 800-621-4272 *Toll Free Fax:* 800-852-5458 *Web Site:* www.follettlearning.com
Foreign Book Source *Tel:* 773-588-5555 *Fax:* 773-588-5453 *E-mail:* info@foreignbooksource.com *Web Site:* www.foreignbooksource.com
Ideal Foreign Books, 13210 Hillside Ave, Jamaica, NY 11418 *Tel:* 718-297-7477
Ingram Book Group, One Ingram Blvd, La Vergne, TN 37086 *Tel:* 615-793-5000 *Toll Free Fax:* 800-876-0186 *Web Site:* www.ingramcontent.com
Midwest Library Services, 11443 St Charles Rock Rd, Bridgeton, MO 63044 *Toll Free Tel:* 800-325-8833 *Toll Free Fax:* 800-962-1009 *Web Site:* www.midwestlts.com
Transmedia Inc, 1101 Richmond Ave, Point Pleasant Beach, NJ 08742 *Tel:* 732-899-0577
YBP Library Services, 999 Maple St, Contoocook, NH 03229 *Tel:* 603-746-3102 *Toll Free Tel:* 800-258-3774 *Fax:* 603-746-5628 *E-mail:* sales@ybp.com *Web Site:* www.ybp.com
Membership(s): CSA; Text & Academic Authors
See separate listing for:
European Masterpieces

§The Linick Group Inc
Linick Bldg, 7 Putter Lane, Middle Island, NY 11953
Mailing Address: PO Box 102, Middle Island, NY 11953-0102
Tel: 631-924-3888; 631-924-8555 *Fax:* 631-924-8555
E-mail: linickgroup@gmail.com; andrew@AskLinick.com
Web Site: www.AndrewLinickDirectMarketing.com/Publishers-Advice.html; www.NewWorldPressBooks.com
Key Personnel
Lib Sales Dir: Jill Reynolds
Founded: 1968
Specialized health titles, health care, weight loss, exercise, fitness, martial arts/self-defense, wine & spirits, mature market, multicultural & bilingual picture; multi-media, workbooks & instructional material, public relations, restaurants & travel & tourism; confidential reports, foreign countries, newsletters, business & direct response advertising & marketing, communications, subscription & mail order, photography, psychology, e-commerce, ebooks, e-publishing, Internet interactive campaigns, targeted e-public relations on a guaranteed placement basis.
ISBN Prefix(es): 978-0-917098 (New World Press)
Number of titles published annually: 25 Print; 10 CD-ROM; 450 Online; 50 E-Book
Total Titles: 125 Print; 120 CD-ROM; 950 Online; 350 E-Book
Imprints: CCA; Isshin-Ryu Productions; LKA Inc; National Association of Photo Sellers™; New World Press
Distributed by New World Press Books; Okinawan Kobujutsu Kyokai Association (OKKA)
Distributor for Linick International; LKA Inc; National Association of Photo Sellers™
Advertising Agency: LK Advertising Agency, 7 Putter Lane, PO Box 102, Middle Island, NY 11953-0102, EVP: Roger Dextor *Tel:* 631-924-3888; 631-924-8555 *Fax:* 631-924-8555 *E-mail:* printmedia4less@gmail.com *Web Site:* www.newworldpressbooks.com
Distribution Center: Bookmasters, 30 Amberwood Pkwy, Ashland, OH 44805
See separate listing for:
Copywriter's Council of America (CCA)

Linworth Publishing
Imprint of Libraries Unlimited
130 Cremona Dr, Santa Barbara, CA 93117
Mailing Address: PO Box 1911, Santa Barbara, CA 93116-1911
Tel: 805-968-1911 *Toll Free Tel:* 800-368-6868 *Fax:* 805-685-9685 *Toll Free Fax:* 866-270-3856
E-mail: customerservice@abc-clio.com
Web Site: www.abc-clio.com
Key Personnel
Pres & Publr: Marlene Woo-Lun
Founded: 1982
Professional book & magazine publishing for school library media specialists.
ISBN Prefix(es): 978-0-938865; 978-1-58683
Number of titles published annually: 20 Print
Total Titles: 100 Print
Imprints: Linworth Learning

§Lippincott Williams & Wilkins
Unit of Wolters Kluwer Health
333 Seventh Ave, New York, NY 10001
Toll Free Tel: 800-950-2035
E-mail: orders@lww.com
Web Site: www.lww.com
Key Personnel
Dir, Corp Communs, Health Learning, Res & Practice: Connie Hughes *Tel:* 646-674-6348 *E-mail:* connie.hughes@wolterskluwer.com
Founded: 1792
Medicine, dentistry life sciences, nursing, allied health, veterinary medicine books, journals, textbooks, looseleaf, newsletters & media.
ISBN Prefix(es): 978-0-8021; 978-0-397; 978-0-316; 978-0-683; 978-0-7817; 978-1-4698; 978-1-60929; 978-1-60831; 978-0-8067; 978-1-60547; 978-1-881063; 978-0-88167; 978-0-89004; 978-0-89313; 978-0-89640; 978-0-911216
Total Titles: 4,000 E-Book
Branch Office(s)
2 Commerce Sq, 2001 Market St, Philadelphia, PA 19103 *Tel:* 215-521-8300 *Fax:* 215-521-8902
351 W Camden St, Baltimore, MD 21201 *Tel:* 410-528-4000
Foreign Office(s): Lippincott Williams & Wilkins Pty Ltd, 101 Waterloo Rd, Level 2, North Ryde, NSW 2113, Australia *Tel:* (02) 9857 1313 *Fax:* (02) 9857 1304
Lippincott Williams & Wilkins Asia Ltd, 15/F, W Sq, 314-324 Hennessy Rd, Wan Chai, Hong Kong *Tel:* 2610 7000 *Fax:* 2610 7098
250 Waterloo Rd, London SE1 8RD, United Kingdom *Tel:* (020) 7981 0600 *Fax:* (020) 7981 0601
Warehouse: 16522 Hunters Green Pkwy, Hagerstown, MD 21740 *Tel:* 301-223-2300 *Fax:* 301-223-2400
Distribution Center: 16522 Hunters Green Pkwy, Hagerstown, MD 21740 *Tel:* 301-223-2300 *Fax:* 301-223-2400

Listen & Live Audio Inc
PO Box 817, Roseland, NJ 07068-0817
Tel: 201-558-9000 *Toll Free Tel:* 800-653-9400 (orders) *Fax:* 201-558-9800
Web Site: www.listenandlive.com
Key Personnel
Pres: Alfred C Martino *E-mail:* alfred@listenandlive.com
Publr: Alisa Weberman *E-mail:* alisa@listenandlive.com
Founded: 1995
Strictly audio books, self-help, fiction, motivational & men's adventure.
ISBN Prefix(es): 978-1-885408; 978-1-931953; 978-1-59316
Number of titles published annually: 10 Audio
Total Titles: 500 Audio
Membership(s): Audio Publishers Association; The Independent Book Publishers Association

Little Bee Books
Imprint of Bonnier Publishing
853 Broadway, Suite 2014, New York, NY 10003
E-mail: info@littlebeebooks.com
Web Site: www.littlebeebooks.com
Key Personnel
Pres: Shimul Tolia
Fin & Opers Dir: Tom Morgan
Edit Dir: Sonali Fry
Assoc Ed: Jenna Pocius
Edit Asst: Charlie Ilgunas
Sr Designer: Rob Wall
Prodn Mgr: Barbara Cho
Dir, Sales & Mktg: Sarah Rucker
Mgr, Mktg & Publicity: Caitlin Casey
Sales & Mktg Asst: Shefali Lohia
Founded: 2014
Creative & fun books for busy little bees ages 0-12 designed to entertain, inspire & educate.
Agented submissions only. No unsol mss accepted.
ISBN Prefix(es): 978-1-4998
Number of titles published annually: 150 Print

Total Titles: 46 Print
Distributed by Simon & Schuster, Inc
Foreign Rep(s): Bonnier Publishing (James Tavendale) (Worldwide)
Foreign Rights: Bonnier Publishing (Nick Franklin) (Worldwide)
Billing Address: Simon & Schuster, Inc, 100 Front St, Riverside, NJ 08075
Orders to: Simon & Schuster, Inc, 100 Front St, Riverside, NJ 08075 *Toll Free Tel:* 800-223-2336
Returns: Simon & Schuster, Inc, c/o Jacobson Logistics, 4406 Industrial Park Rd, Bldg 7, Camp Hill, PA 17011
Shipping Address: Simon & Schuster, Inc, 100 Front St, Riverside, NJ 08075
Warehouse: Simon & Schuster, Inc, 100 Front St, Riverside, NJ 08075
Distribution Center: Simon & Schuster, Inc, 100 Front St, Riverside, NJ 08075
Membership(s): AAP

Little, Brown and Company
Division of Hachette Book Group
1290 Avenue of the Americas, New York, NY 10019
Tel: 212-364-1100 *Fax:* 212-364-0952
E-mail: firstname.lastname@hbgusa.com
Web Site: www.HachetteBookGroup.com
Key Personnel
SVP, Hachette Book Group & Publr, Little, Brown and Company: Reagan Arthur
SVP, Dir, Mktg Strategy & Deputy Publr: Heather Fain
VP, Ed-in-Chief: Judy Clain
VP, Publr, Digital & Pbk: Terry Adams
Edit Dir, Mulholland Books: Josh Kendall
Exec Ed: John Parsley
VP, Exec Dir of Publicity: Nicole Dewey
VP, Subs Rts, Hachette Book Group: Nancy Wiese
Dir, Intl Rts: Tracy Williams
VP, Sales & Brand Dir, James Patterson: Ned Rust
VP, Creative Dir: Mario Pulice
Founded: 1837
Little, Brown and Company, the adult trade division of Hachette Book Group, is one of the country's oldest & most distinguished publishing houses. Unsol/unagented mss not accepted.
ISBN Prefix(es): 978-0-316
Number of titles published annually: 224 Print
Total Titles: 1,738 Print
Imprints: Back Bay Books; Lee Boudreaux Books; Mulholland Books; Jimmy Patterson
Sales Office(s): Hachette Book Group, 1290 Avenue of the Americas, New York, NY 10019 (spec mkts) *Toll Free Tel:* 800-222-6747 *Toll Free Fax:* 800-477-5925
Foreign Rights: Agencia Literaria Balcells (Portugal, Spain); Bardon Chinese Media (China, Taiwan); Luigi Bernabo Associates SRL (Italy); BMSR Ag Literaria (Brazil); JLM Literary Agency (Greece); Nurcihan Kesim Literary Agency (Turkey); The KM Agency (Netherlands); Agence Michelle Lapautre (France); Mohrbooks Agency (Germany); Andrew Nurnberg Associates LTD (Baltic States, Bulgaria, Croatia, Czech Republic, Hungary, Poland, Romania, Russia & former USSR); I Pitarski Ltd Literary Agency (Israel); Sane Toregard Agency (Scandinavia); Tuttle-Mori Agency Inc (Japan); Eric Yang Agency (Korea)
Orders to: Hachette Book Group, 53 State St, Boston, MA 02109 *Toll Free Tel:* 800-759-0190 *Toll Free Fax:* 800-286-9471
Returns: Hachette Book Group, 322 S Enterprise Blvd, Lebanon, IN 46052
Shipping Address: Hachette Book Group, 121 N Enterprise Blvd, Lebanon, IN 46052

Little, Brown Books for Young Readers
Division of Hachette Book Group
1290 Avenue of the Americas, New York, NY 10019
SAN: 200-2205
Tel: 212-364-1100 *Toll Free Tel:* 800-759-0190 (cust serv)
Web Site: www.HachetteBookGroup.com
Key Personnel
EVP, Hachette Book Group & Publr, Little, Brown Books for Young Readers: Megan Tingley
SVP, Deputy Publr, Exec Dir, New Busn Devt: Andrew Smith
VP, Integrated Mktg: Melanie Chang
VP & Ed-in-Chief: Alvina Ling
Edit Dir: Andrea Spooner
Edit Dir, Poppy: Farrin Jacobs
Exec Dir, Strategic Planning & Digital Publr: Tina McIntyre
Exec Dir, School & Lib Mktg: Victoria Stapleton
Exec Edit Dir, Brand, Licensed & Media Tie-In Publg: Kara Sargent
Dir, Subs Rts: Kristin Dulaney
Creative Dir: David Caplan
Assoc Dir, Publicty: Lisa Moraleda
Founded: 1837
Specializes in board books, novelty items, picture books, middle reader, young adult fiction & nonfiction & selected media tie-ins.
ISBN Prefix(es): 978-0-316
Number of titles published annually: 270 Print
Total Titles: 1,660 Print
Imprints: LBKids; Poppy
Orders to: Hachette Book Group, 53 State St, Boston, MA 02109 *Toll Free Tel:* 800-759-0190 *Toll Free Fax:* 800-286-9471
Shipping Address: Hachette Book Group Distribution Center, 121 N Enterprise Blvd, Lebanon, IN 46052 *Tel:* 765-483-9900 *Fax:* 765-483-0706
Membership(s): AAP; ALA; The Children's Book Council; Women's National Book Association

The Little Entrepreneur
Imprint of Harper Arrington Publishing & Media
c/o Harper-Arrington, 18701 Grand River, Suite 105, Detroit, MI 48223
Toll Free Tel: 888-435-9234 *Fax:* 248-281-0373
E-mail: info@harperarringtonmedia.com
Web Site: www.thelittlee.com
Key Personnel
Founder & Publr: Jay Arrington; Michael Harper
Media Rel: John Thomas
Media Contact: Lance Smith
Founded: 2004
ISBN Prefix(es): 978-0-9764161
Number of titles published annually: 3 Print; 1 CD-ROM
Total Titles: 4 Print; 2 CD-ROM; 1 Online
Distributed by Harper Arrington Publishing

Little Simon, see Simon & Schuster Children's Publishing

§Liturgical Press
Division of The Order of St Benedict Inc
PO Box 7500, St John's Abbey, Collegeville, MN 56321-7500
SAN: 202-2494
Tel: 320-363-2213 *Toll Free Tel:* 800-858-5450 *Fax:* 320-363-3299 *Toll Free Fax:* 800-445-5899
E-mail: sales@litpress.org
Web Site: www.litpress.org
Key Personnel
Dir: Peter Dwyer *Tel:* 320-363-2533 *E-mail:* pdwyer@osb.org
Assoc Publr, Parish Mkt: Michelle Verkuilen *Tel:* 320-363-2227 *E-mail:* mverkuilen@osb.org
Fin Dir: Sandra Eiynck *Tel:* 320-363-2225 *E-mail:* seiynck@csbsju.edu
Sales & Mktg Mgr: Brian Woods *Tel:* 320-363-3953 *E-mail:* bwoods@csbsju.edu
Founded: 1926
Began publishing for the Church in 1926 & continues to sustain the original mission of proclaiming the Good News of Jesus Christ. Liturgical Press is a trusted publisher of liturgy, scripture, theology & spirituality evolving to serve the changing needs of the Church.
ISBN Prefix(es): 978-0-87907; 978-0-8146
Number of titles published annually: 90 Print; 50 E-Book
Total Titles: 1,500 Print; 10 CD-ROM; 50 E-Book; 20 Audio
Imprints: Cistercian Publications; Michael Glazier Books; Liturgical Press Books; Pueblo Books
Foreign Rep(s): B Broughton Co Ltd (Canada); The Catholic Bookshop (South Africa); Claretian Publications (Philippines); Columba Book Service (European Union, Ireland, UK); John Garratt Publishing (Australia); Katong Catholic Book Centre Pte Ltd (Malaysia, Singapore); Pleroma Christian Supplies (New Zealand); Spring Arbor/Ingram (Tennessee)
Advertising Agency: Liturgical Advertising Agency
See separate listing for:
Cistercian Publications

Liturgy Training Publications
Subsidiary of Archdiocese of Chicago
3949 S Racine Ave, Chicago, IL 60609-2523
SAN: 670-9052
Tel: 773-579-4900 *Toll Free Tel:* 800-933-1800 (US & CN only orders) *Fax:* 773-579-4929 *Toll Free Fax:* 800-933-7094 (US & CN only orders)
E-mail: orders@ltp.org
Web Site: www.ltp.org
Key Personnel
Dir: John A Thomas *Tel:* 773-579-4900 ext 3557 *E-mail:* jthomas@ltp.org
Mktg & Sales Mgr: Kathleen Sommers *Tel:* 773-579-4900 ext 3525 *E-mail:* ksommers@ltp.org
Cust Serv & Trade Rep: Irene Sanchez *Tel:* 773-579-4900 ext 3566 *E-mail:* isanchez@ltp.org
Founded: 1964
Books & periodicals on Roman Catholic liturgy, worship & prayer in the home & church.
ISBN Prefix(es): 978-0-929650; 978-1-56854; 978-1-59525
Number of titles published annually: 30 Print; 2 CD-ROM; 20 E-Book; 2 Audio
Total Titles: 500 Print; 6 CD-ROM; 80 E-Book; 7 Audio
Imprints: Catechesis of the Good Shepherd Publications; Hillenbrand Books
Distributor for United States Catholic Conference Publications
Foreign Rep(s): The Catholic Bookshop (South Africa); Katong Catholic Book Centre (Malaysia); McCrimmons Bookstore/Publisher (UK exc Ireland); Pleroma Christian Supplies (New Zealand)
Membership(s): Association of Catholic Publishers Inc

The Live Oak Press LLC
PO Box 60036, Palo Alto, CA 94306-0036
Tel: 650-853-0197 *Fax:* 815-366-8205
E-mail: info@liveoakpress.com
Web Site: www.liveoakpress.com
Key Personnel
Founder & Pres: David M Hamilton
Founded: 1982
Publishes California literary history.
ISBN Prefix(es): 978-0-931095; 978-0-931378
Number of titles published annually: 3 Print
Total Titles: 14 Print
Membership(s): ALA; Association of College & Research Libraries; The Authors Guild; The Independent Book Publishers Association; PINC; Publishing Professionals Network; Society for Scholarly Publishing

Living Language
Imprint of Penguin Random House Audio
c/o Random House Inc, 1745 Broadway, New York, NY 10019
Tel: 212-782-9000 *Toll Free Tel:* 800-733-3000 (orders) *Toll Free Fax:* 800-659-2436
E-mail: livinglanguage@randomhouse.com
Web Site: www.livinglanguage.com
Key Personnel
SVP & Publr: Amanda D'Acierno
Assoc Dir, Mng Edit: Alison Skrabek
Dir, Publicity: Katherine Fleming Punia
Mktg Dir: Heather Dalton
Sr Mgr, Subs Rts: Maren McCamley
Founded: 1946
Self-study foreign language & ESL. Online courses, apps & digital content; Sign Language & dictionaries.
Random House Inc & its publishing entities are not accepting unsol submissions, proposals, mss, or submission queries via e-mail at this time.
ISBN Prefix(es): 978-0-609; 978-0-307
Number of titles published annually: 12 Print
Total Titles: 22 Print; 122 Audio

§Living Stream Ministry (LSM)
2431 W La Palma Ave, Anaheim, CA 92801
Tel: 714-991-4681 *Fax:* 714-236-6005
E-mail: books@lsm.org
Web Site: www.lsm.org
Key Personnel
Intl Rts Contact: Yorke Warden
Lib Sales Dir: John Pester
Founded: 1963
Religious publications.
ISBN Prefix(es): 978-0-87083; 978-1-57593; 978-0-7363
Number of titles published annually: 50 Print
Total Titles: 1,500 Print

Livingston Press
Division of University of West Alabama
University of West Alabama, Sta 22, Livingston, AL 35470
SAN: 851-917X
Tel: 205-652-3470
Web Site: www.livingstonpress.uwa.edu
Key Personnel
Dir: Joe Taylor *E-mail:* jwt@uwa.edu
Founded: 1984
ISBN Prefix(es): 978-0-942979; 978-0-930501; 978-1-931982; 978-1-60489
Number of titles published annually: 8 Print; 8 E-Book; 2 Audio
Total Titles: 140 Print; 90 E-Book; 2 Audio
Imprints: Swallow's Tale Press
Distributor for Swallow's Tale Press
Distribution Center: Small Press Distribution (SPD), 1341 Seventh St, Berkeley, CA 94710-1409 *Tel:* 510-524-1668 *Toll Free Tel:* 800-869-7553 *E-mail:* spd@spdbooks.org *Web Site:* www.spdbooks.org
Membership(s): Community of Literary Magazines & Presses; The Independent Book Publishers Association

Llewellyn Publications
Division of Llewellyn Worldwide Ltd
2143 Wooddale Dr, Woodbury, MN 55125
SAN: 201-100X
Tel: 651-291-1970 *Toll Free Tel:* 800-843-6666 *Fax:* 651-291-1908
E-mail: publicity@llewellyn.com
Web Site: www.llewellyn.com
Key Personnel
Pres: Carl L Weschcke
Publr: Bill Krause
Dir, Sales & Mktg: Tom Lund
Sr Publicist: Kat Sanborn
Founded: 1901
Body, mind, spirit. Trade publisher.
ISBN Prefix(es): 978-0-87542; 978-1-56718; 978-0-7387
Number of titles published annually: 110 Print; 10 CD-ROM
Total Titles: 900 Print
Imprints: Flux (teen, fiction, children's literature, paperback); Midnight Ink (mystery, trade, fiction, paperback)
Distributor for Lo Scarabeo
Foreign Rights: Oxana Schroeder

The Local History Co
112 N Woodland Rd, Pittsburgh, PA 15232-2849
Tel: 412-362-2294 *Toll Free Tel:* 866-362-0789 (orders) *Fax:* 412-362-8192
E-mail: info@thelocalhistorycompany.com; sales@thelocalhistorycompany.com
Web Site: www.thelocalhistorycompany.com
Founded: 2001
Publishers of history & heritage.
ISBN Prefix(es): 978-0-9711835; 978-0-9744715; 978-0-9770429
Number of titles published annually: 10 Print
Total Titles: 25 Print
Imprints: Towers Maguire Publishing
Membership(s): The Independent Book Publishers Association

Locks Art Publications/Locks Gallery
Division of Locks Gallery
600 Washington Sq S, Philadelphia, PA 19106
Tel: 215-629-1000
E-mail: info@locksgallery.com
Web Site: www.locksgallery.com
Key Personnel
Dir: Sueyun Locks
Founded: 1968
Exhibition catalogue, monographs on contemporary art.
ISBN Prefix(es): 978-1-879173; 978-0-9623799
Number of titles published annually: 8 Print
Total Titles: 45 Print

Loft Press Inc
9293 Fort Valley Rd, Fort Valley, VA 22652
Tel: 540-933-6210 *Fax:* 540-933-6523
E-mail: Books@LoftPress.com
Key Personnel
Pres & Publr: Stephen R Hunter
Ed-in-Chief: Ann A Hunter
Founded: 1987
ISBN Prefix(es): 978-0-9630797; 978-1-893846
Number of titles published annually: 4 Print; 2 CD-ROM; 1 E-Book
Total Titles: 130 Print; 2 CD-ROM; 1 E-Book
Imprints: Eschat Press (religion); Far Muse Press; Merry Muse Press; Punch Press
Subsidiaries: AAH Graphics Inc
Advertising Agency: AAH Advertising *Tel:* 540-933-6211
Membership(s): Washington Book Publishers

Logos Bible Software, see Faithlife Corp

Logos Press
Imprint of thinkBiotech LLC
3909 Witmer Rd, Suite 416, Niagara Falls, NY 14305
Fax: 815-346-3514
E-mail: info@logos-press.com
Web Site: www.logos-press.com
Key Personnel
Ed: Yali Friedman
Founded: 2003
Specializes in reference & text books addressing the use of knowledge to make intelligent strategic decisions. Target audiences include college & advanced courses, business managers, directors & C-level executives. The objective is to help advanced students & decision makers implement their ideas based on solid fundamentals.
ISBN Prefix(es): 978-0-9734676; 978-1-934899
Number of titles published annually: 4 Print; 4 Online
Total Titles: 12 Print; 4 Online

Lonely Planet
150 Linden St, Oakland, CA 94607
Tel: 510-893-8555 *Toll Free Tel:* 800-275-8555 (orders) *Fax:* 510-893-8572
E-mail: info@lonelyplanet.com
Web Site: www.lonelyplanet.com
Key Personnel
CEO: Daniel Houghton
Dir, Mktg (US): Rana Freedman
Dir, Sales (Americas): Patricia Kelly
Sr Design Mgr: Gerilyn Attebery
Sr Sales Mgr & Children's Specialist: Peg O'Donnell
Global Mktg Mgr, Busn Devt: Jennifer Pentes
Founded: 1973
Create & deliver the most compelling & comprehensive travel content in the world, giving travellers trustworthy information, engaging opinions, powerful images & informed perspectives on destinations around the globe. While known primarily for its 600+ travel guidebooks, we also offer an award-winning web site, photographic image library, television production, distribution & digital travel content licensing.
ISBN Prefix(es): 978-0-908086; 978-0-86442
Number of titles published annually: 100 Print
Total Titles: 600 Print
Foreign Office(s): 90 Maribyrnong St, Footscray, Victoria 3011, Australia
240 Blackfriars Rd, London SE1 8NW, United Kingdom
Foreign Rep(s): A B E Marketing (Poland); Altair (Spain); Asia Books Co Ltd (Thailand); Asia Publishers' Services Ltd (China, Hong Kong, Taiwan); David Bateman Ltd (New Zealand); The Book Centre (Pakistan); Booktraders Ltd (Cyprus, Czech Republic, Greece, Israel, Malta, Middle East, Turkey); Brettschneider (Germany); CDE (sales: English & French editions) (France); Centralivros (Portugal); TB Clarke (Overseas Pty Ltd) (Fiji); CLB Marketing Services (Croatia, Hungary, Montenegro, Romania, Serbia, Slovenia); CV Java Books (Indonesia); Dinternal (Russia); Electra Media Group Pty Ltd (Guam, Micronesia, Philippines); Eleftheroudakis SA (Greece); Faradawn (South Africa); Freytag & Berndt U Artaria KG (Austria); Geocentre ILH (Germany); Geographical Tours Ltd (Israel); IMA Distribution (East Asia); India Book Distributors (Bombay) Ltd (India, Nepal); Intercontinental Marketing Corp (Japan); International Educational Library (Greece); Kartbutiken (Sweden); Lannoo Publishers (Belgium); Logos Art Srl (Italy); MPH Distributors (Malaysia, Singapore); Nilsson & Lamm Bv (Netherlands); Olf SA (Switzerland); Raincoast Books (Canada); Cav Giovanni Russano SAS (Italy); Scanvik Books Aps (Denmark, Finland, Iceland, Norway); Jana Seta (Latvia); Shoestring International (Korea); Sklep Podroznika (Poland); Sodis (distribution) (France); Text Book Centre Ltd (Kenya); Trak Trade Centre (Estonia); The Travel Bookshop (Switzerland); Vijitha Yapa Bookshop (Pvt) Ltd (Sri Lanka); Westland Sundries Ltd (Kenya); Yab Yay Yayimcilik Sanayi (Turkey)

§Long River Press
Imprint of Sinomedia International Group
360 Swift Ave, Suite 48, South San Francisco, CA 94080
Tel: 650-872-7718 (ext 312) *Fax:* 650-872-7808
E-mail: info@longriverpress.com
Web Site: www.chinabooks.com

Key Personnel
Exec Ed: Chris Robyn *E-mail:* chris@chinabooks.com
Founded: 2002
Trade & academic titles on any aspect of China or Chinese history, culture & society.
ISBN Prefix(es): 978-1-59265
Number of titles published annually: 10 Print; 5 E-Book
Total Titles: 120 Print; 20 E-Book
Distribution Center: China Books, 360 Swift Ave, Suite 48, South San Francisco, CA 94706 *Toll Free Tel:* 800-818-2017 *E-mail:* orders@chinabooks.com
Membership(s): Association for Asian Studies

Looseleaf Law Publications Inc
Division of Warodean Corp
43-08 162 St, Flushing, NY 11358
Mailing Address: PO Box 650042, Fresh Meadows, NY 11365-0042
Tel: 718-359-5559 *Toll Free Tel:* 800-647-5547 *Fax:* 718-539-0941
E-mail: info@looseleaf.com
Web Site: www.looseleaflaw.com
Key Personnel
Owner: Michael L Loughrey
VP & Edit: Mary Loughrey
Sales Dir: Hilary McKeon
Founded: 1967
Law books; study aids for law enforcement, students, attorneys & court personnel.
ISBN Prefix(es): 978-0-930137; 978-1-889031; 978-1-932777
Number of titles published annually: 11 Print
Total Titles: 160 Print; 25 CD-ROM

§Lorenz Educational Press
Division of The Lorenz Corp
501 E Third St, Dayton, OH 45402
Mailing Address: PO Box 802, Dayton, OH 45401-0802
Tel: 937-228-6118 *Toll Free Tel:* 800-444-1144 *Fax:* 937-223-2042
E-mail: lep@lorenz.com
Web Site: www.lorenzeducationalpress.com
Key Personnel
VP: Debra Kaiser *E-mail:* debk@lorenz.com
Founded: 2008
Educational publishing division includes visual resources, instructional guides & reproducibles, elementary supplementals.
ISBN Prefix(es): 978-1-42911
Number of titles published annually: 10 Print
Total Titles: 75 Print; 75 E-Book; 7 Audio
Membership(s): Education Market Association

Lost Classics Book Company LLC
411 N Wales Dr, Lake Wales, FL 33853-3881
Tel: 863-632-1981 (edit off)
E-mail: mgeditor@lostclassicsbooks.com
Web Site: www.lostclassicsbooks.com
Key Personnel
Owner: Michael Alan Fitterling
Founded: 1996
Republish late 19th & early 20th century literature & textbooks to aid parents & teachers in educating children.
ISBN Prefix(es): 978-0-9652735; 978-1-890623
Number of titles published annually: 8 Print
Total Titles: 43 Print
Imprints: Road Dog Publications (motorcycling books)
Distribution Center: National Book Network, 15200 NBN Way, Blue Ridge Summit, PA 17214 *Tel:* 717-794-3800 *Fax:* 717-794-3828 *E-mail:* customercare@nbnbooks.com *Web Site:* www.nbnbooks.com
Membership(s): The Independent Book Publishers Association

Lost Horse Press
105 Lost Horse Lane, Sandpoint, ID 83864
Tel: 208-255-4410
E-mail: losthorsepress@mindspring.com
Web Site: www.losthorsepress.org
Key Personnel
Publr: Christine Holbert
Founded: 1998
Nonprofit independent press that publishes poetry titles of high literary merit & makes available fine contemporary literature through cultural, educational & publishing programs & activities.
ISBN Prefix(es): 978-0-9668612; 978-0-9717265; 978-0-9762114; 978-0-9800289
Number of titles published annually: 10 Print; 1 CD-ROM; 1 Audio
Total Titles: 85 Print; 2 CD-ROM; 1 Audio
Distributed by University of Washington Press
Distribution Center: University of Washington Press, 4333 Brooklyn Ave NE, Seattle, WA 98195 *Tel:* 410-516-6956 *Toll Free Tel:* 800-537-5487 *Fax:* 410-516-6998 *E-mail:* hfscustserv@press.jhu.edu *Web Site:* www.washington.edu/uwpress
Membership(s): Community of Literary Magazines & Presses

Lotus Light Publications, see Lotus Press

Lotus Press
Division of Lotus Brands Inc
PO Box 325, Twin Lakes, WI 53181-0325
Tel: 262-889-8561 *Toll Free Tel:* 800-824-6396 (orders) *Fax:* 262-889-8591
E-mail: lotuspress@lotuspress.com
Web Site: www.lotuspress.com
Key Personnel
Pres: Santosh Krinsky *E-mail:* santosh@lotuspress.com
Founded: 1981
Health, yoga, Native American & New Age metaphysics, Vedic astrology.
ISBN Prefix(es): 978-0-941524; 978-0-910261; 978-0-914955; 978-0-940985; 978-0-940676; 978-0-930736
Number of titles published annually: 6 Print; 2 CD-ROM; 2 Online; 15 E-Book; 3 Audio
Total Titles: 325 Print; 5 CD-ROM; 10 Online; 175 E-Book; 42 Audio
Imprints: Arcana Publishing; DIPTI; Shangri-La; Specialized Software
Distributor for Back to Eden Books; Dipti; East West Cultural Center; Les Editions E T C; Inner Worlds Music; November Moon; S A B D A; Sadhana Publications; Samata Books; Sri Aurobindo Ashram; Star Sounds
Warehouse: 1100 Lotus Dr, Bldg 3, Silver Lake, WI 53170

Louisiana State University Press
338 Johnston Hall, Baton Rouge, LA 70803
Tel: 225-578-6294 *Fax:* 225-578-6461
E-mail: lsupress@lsu.edu
Web Site: lsupress.org
Key Personnel
Dir: MaryKatherine Callaway *E-mail:* mkc@lsu.edu
Asst Dir & Design & Prodn Mgr: Laura Gleason *Tel:* 225-578-6469 *E-mail:* lgleasn@lsu.edu
Mktg Mgr: Erin Rolfs *Tel:* 225-578-8282 *E-mail:* erolfs@lsu.edu
Mng Ed: Lee Sioles *Tel:* 225-578-6467 *E-mail:* lsioles@lsu.edu
Fulfillment Opers Mgr: Becky Brown *Tel:* 225-578-6415 *E-mail:* rbrown2@lsu.edu
Founded: 1935
Scholarly, regional, general; humanities & social sciences; southern history & literature; poetry; government & political science; music; paperbacks; fiction.
ISBN Prefix(es): 978-0-8071
Number of titles published annually: 85 Print
Total Titles: 1,000 Print; 4 CD-ROM
Foreign Rep(s): East-West Export Books (Asia, Australia, Japan, New Zealand, The Pacific); Scholarly Book Services (Canada)
Foreign Rights: McIntosh & Otis
Orders to: Longleaf Services, 116 S Boundery St, Chapel Hill, NC 27514-3803 *Toll Free Tel:* 800-848-6224 *Toll Free Fax:* 800-272-6817
Returns: Longleaf Services Inc, c/o Ingram Publisher Services, 1210 Ingram Blvd, Chambersburg, PA 17202
Warehouse: Longleaf Services Inc, c/o Ingram Publisher Services, 1210 Ingram Blvd, Chambersburg, PA 17202
Membership(s): American Association of University Presses

Love Inspired Books
Imprint of Harlequin Enterprises Ltd
233 Broadway, Suite 1001, New York, NY 10279
SAN: 200-2450
Tel: 212-553-4200 *Fax:* 212-227-8969
E-mail: customer_service@harlequin.ca
Web Site: www.harlequin.com
Key Personnel
CEO & Publr: Craig Swinwood
EVP, Global Publg & Strategy: Loriana Sacilotto
Exec Ed: Tina James
Ed: Emily Rodmell
Founded: 1997
Inspirational romance novels, romantic suspense & women's fiction.
ISBN Prefix(es): 978-0-373
Number of titles published annually: 192 Print
Imprints: Love Inspired; Love Inspired Historical; Love Inspired Suspense
Distribution Center: 3010 Walden Ave, Depew, NY 14043

Love Publishing Co
9101 E Kenyon Ave, Suite 2200, Denver, CO 80237
SAN: 205-2482
Tel: 303-221-7333 *Toll Free Tel:* 877-240-6396 *Fax:* 303-221-7444
E-mail: lpc@lovepublishing.com
Web Site: www.lovepublishing.com
Key Personnel
Pres & Publr: Stanley F Love
Founded: 1968
College textbooks, journals & professional books in counseling, social work & special needs education.
ISBN Prefix(es): 978-0-89108
Number of titles published annually: 8 Print; 1 E-Book
Total Titles: 125 Print; 1 E-Book
Foreign Rep(s): Eurospan (Europe, UK); Publishers Marketing Service (Malaysia, Singapore)
Membership(s): AAP

Loving Healing Press Inc
5145 Pontiac Trail, Ann Arbor, MI 48105
SAN: 255-7770
Tel: 734-417-4266 *Toll Free Tel:* 888-761-6268 (US & CN) *Fax:* 734-663-6861
E-mail: info@lovinghealing.com; info@lhpress.com
Web Site: www.lovinghealing.com; www.modernhistorypress.com (imprint)
Key Personnel
Pres: Prof Victor R Volkman
Founded: 2003
Dedicated to producing books about innovative & rapid therapies to empower authors in redefining what is possible for healing the mind & spirit.
ISBN Prefix(es): 978-1-932690
Number of titles published annually: 15 Print; 15 E-Book; 2 Audio
Total Titles: 120 Print; 15 E-Book; 2 Audio

Imprints: Modern History Press (memoirs of people who have lived through significant events); Victorian Heritage Press (showcasing the best of 19th century contemporary histories)
Foreign Rep(s): Lightning Source UK (Europe)
Membership(s): The Independent Book Publishers Association

Loyola Press
3441 N Ashland Ave, Chicago, IL 60657
SAN: 211-6537
Tel: 773-281-1818 *Toll Free Tel:* 800-621-1008 *Fax:* 773-281-0555 (cust serv); 773-281-4129 (edit)
E-mail: customerservice@loyolapress.com
Web Site: www.loyolapress.com
Key Personnel
Pres: Terry Locke
Exec Ed & Acqs: Joseph Durepos *E-mail:* durepos@loyolapress.com
Digital Rts Mgr & Foreign Rep: Andrew Yankech
Founded: 1912
Catholic publisher of books for elementary schools, parishes & the general trade.
ISBN Prefix(es): 978-0-8294
Number of titles published annually: 25 Print; 5 Audio
Total Titles: 350 Print

LPD Press
925 Salamanca NW, Los Ranchos de Albuquerque, NM 87107-5647
Tel: 505-344-9382 *Fax:* 505-345-5129
E-mail: info@nmsantos.com
Web Site: nmsantos.com
Key Personnel
Sr Partner: Barbe Awalt; Paul Rhetts
Founded: 1984
Publisher of books on the American Southwest & a quarterly magazine on the art & culture of the American Southwest.
ISBN Prefix(es): 978-0-9641542; 978-1-890689
Number of titles published annually: 18 Print; 10 E-Book
Total Titles: 125 Print; 1 CD-ROM; 50 E-Book
Imprints: Rio Grande Books
Membership(s): The Independent Book Publishers Association; New Mexico Book Association; New Mexico Book Co-op

§LRP Publications
360 Hiatt Dr, Palm Beach Gardens, FL 33418
Tel: 561-622-6520 *Toll Free Tel:* 800-341-7874 *Fax:* 561-622-2423
E-mail: custserve@lrp.com
Web Site: www.lrp.com
Key Personnel
Pres: Kenneth F Kahn
Founded: 1977
Legal & general nonfiction in the areas of education, bankruptcy, employment, disability, workers compensation, personal injury & human resources.
ISBN Prefix(es): 978-0-934753
Number of titles published annually: 500 Print; 10 CD-ROM; 95 Online; 5 Audio
Total Titles: 9,000 Print; 10 CD-ROM; 95 Online; 8 Audio
Subsidiaries: LRP Magazine Group
Divisions: Jury Verdict Research; LRP Magazine Group

LRS
Division of Library Reproduction Service
19146 Van Ness Ave, Torrance, CA 90501
Tel: 310-354-2610 *Toll Free Tel:* 800-255-5002 *Fax:* 310-354-2601
E-mail: largeprintsb@aol.com
Web Site: lrs-largeprint.com
Key Personnel
Pres: Peter Jones
Founded: 1946
Large print books for adults & children including classics & fiction.
ISBN Prefix(es): 978-1-58118
Number of titles published annually: 10 Print
Total Titles: 150 Print

Lucent Books®
Imprint of Gale
27500 Drake Rd, Farmington Hills, MI 48331
Tel: 248-699-4253 *Fax:* 248-699-8004
E-mail: gale.customerservice@cengage.com
Web Site: solutions.cengage.com/greenhaven
Founded: 1988
Curriculum-related nonfiction books aimed at the junior high level that explore current issues, historical topics, health, science/technology & biography. Active series include: *Diseases & Disorders, Hot Topics, People in the News, Technology 360 & World History.*
ISBN Prefix(es): 978-1-56006; 978-1-59018
Number of titles published annually: 85 Print; 60 E-Book
Distributed by Greenhaven Imprints
Distributor for Greenhaven Press; Kidhaven Press

§Lucky Marble Books
Imprint of PageSpring Publishing
2671 Bristol Rd, Columbus, OH 43221
Mailing Address: PO Box 21133, Columbus, OH 43221
Tel: 614-264-5588
E-mail: sales@pagespringpublishing.com
Web Site: www.luckymarblebooks.com
Key Personnel
Ed: Katherine Matthews *Tel:* 614-327-3676 *E-mail:* yaeditor@pagespringpublishing.com
Sales & Mktg Dir: Lynn Bartels
Founded: 2012
Independent publisher. Specialize in high quality fiction for young adult & middle grade readers.
ISBN Prefix(es): 978-1-939403
Number of titles published annually: 4 Print; 4 E-Book

Luminis Books Inc
1950 E Greyhound Pass, Suite 18, PMB 280, Carmel, IN 46033
Tel: 317-840-5838
E-mail: editor@luminisbooks.com
Web Site: www.luminisbooks.com
Key Personnel
Pres: Tracy Richardson
Founded: 2008
Publish young adult, middle grade & literary fiction.
ISBN Prefix(es): 978-1-935462
Number of titles published annually: 7 Print; 7 E-Book
Total Titles: 10 Print; 10 E-Book
Membership(s): Society of Children's Book Writers & Illustrators

Luna Bisonte Prods
137 Leland Ave, Columbus, OH 43214
Tel: 614-846-4126
Web Site: www.johnmbennett.net; www.lulu.com/spotlight/lunabisonteprods
Key Personnel
Head & Intl Rts: John M Bennett *E-mail:* bennettjohnm@gmail.com
Founded: 1974
Avant-garde to experimental literature & poetry.
ISBN Prefix(es): 978-0-935350; 978-1-892280
Number of titles published annually: 25 Print; 2 Audio
Total Titles: 350 Print; 50 Audio

Lutheran Braille Workers Inc
13471 California St, Yucaipa, CA 92399
Mailing Address: PO Box 5000, Yucaipa, CA 92399-1450
Tel: 909-795-8977 *Fax:* 909-795-8970
E-mail: lbw@lbwinc.org
Web Site: www.lbwinc.org
Key Personnel
Pres: Rev Dennis Stueve
Founded: 1943
Produce & distribute free braille & large print biblical & Christian literature in more than 30 languages for the blind & visually impaired in over 120 countries.
Number of titles published annually: 5 Print
Total Titles: 200 Print

Lyceum Books Inc
5758 S Blackstone Ave, Chicago, IL 60637
Tel: 773-643-1902 *Fax:* 773-643-1903
E-mail: lyceum@lyceumbooks.com
Web Site: www.lyceumbooks.com
Key Personnel
Pres & Publr: David C Follmer
Dir, Mktg: Sarah Butcher
Founded: 1988
Books for social service practitioners & social service students.
ISBN Prefix(es): 978-0-925065; 978-1-933478
Number of titles published annually: 16 Print; 5 E-Book
Total Titles: 130 Print; 18 E-Book
Foreign Rep(s): Eurospan Group (Worldwide exc North America)
Returns: 2427 Bond St, University Park, IL 60466
Warehouse: 2427 Bond St, University Park, IL 60466

Lyndon B Johnson School of Public Affairs
University of Texas at Austin, 2315 Red River St, Austin, TX 78712-1536
Mailing Address: University of Texas at Austin, PO Box Y, Austin, TX 78713-8925
Tel: 512-471-3200 *Fax:* 512-471-4697
E-mail: lbjdeansoffice@austin.utexas.edu
Web Site: www.utexas.edu/lbj
Founded: 1972
Working papers; public service monographs; policy research projects; conference proceedings.
Return policy: No refunds; replace damaged books only. All sales are final. Prepayment usually required.
ISBN Prefix(es): 978-0-89940
Number of titles published annually: 8 Print
Total Titles: 300 Print

Lynx House Press
420 W 24 St, Spokane, WA 99203
Tel: 509-624-4894
E-mail: lynxhousepress@gmail.com
Web Site: www.lynxhousepress.org
Key Personnel
Dir & Ed-in-Chief: Christopher Howell *E-mail:* cnhowell@ewu.edu
Assoc Ed: Kristina Morgan
Intl Rts: John Orr
Founded: 1972
Fiction & poetry.
ISBN Prefix(es): 978-0-89924
Number of titles published annually: 4 Print
Total Titles: 140 Print
Distributed by University of Washington Press
Distribution Center: Hopkins Fulfillment Service, 704 Legionaire Dr, Fredericksburg, PA 17026 *Tel:* 410-516-6956

The Lyons Press
Imprint of The Globe Pequot Press
246 Goose Lane, Guilford, CT 06437
Tel: 203-458-4500 *Fax:* 203-458-4668
E-mail: info@rowman.com
Web Site: www.lyonspress.com; rowman.com
Key Personnel
Edit Dir: Keith Wallman *E-mail:* kwallman@rowman.com
Founded: 1978

Outdoors, natural history, sports, fitness, cooking, military history, fishing, hunting, equine, nonfiction, fiction, practical, Americana, outdoor skills, pets, nautical, survival & adventure.
ISBN Prefix(es): 978-1-55821; 978-0-8329; 978-1-58574; 978-1-59228; 978-0-936644; 978-0-941130
Number of titles published annually: 180 Print
Total Titles: 1,500 Print

M U Press, see Marquette University Press

MAA Press, see The Mathematical Association of America

Pat MacKay Projects, see Quite Specific Media Group Ltd

Macmillan
Subsidiary of Verlagsgruppe Georg von Holtzbrinck GmbH
175 Fifth Ave, New York, NY 10010
Tel: 646-307-5151 *Fax:* 212-420-9314
E-mail: firstname.lastname@macmillan.com
Web Site: www.macmillan.com
Key Personnel
CEO: John Sargent
SVP & COO: Peter Garabedian
Pres, Macmillan Children's Publishing Group: Jonathan Yaged
SVP & Publg Dir, Macmillan Children's Publishing Group: Simon Boughton; Jean Feiwel
Pres & Publr, Audio: Mary Beth Roche
Pres & Publr, Farrar, Straus & Giroux: Jonathan Galassi
Pres & Publr, Henry Holt & Company: Stephen Rubin
Pres & Publr, St Martin's Press: Sally Richardson
Pres & Publr, Tom Doherty Associates: Thomas Doherty
Editor-at-Large: John Sterling
Pres of Sales: Alison Lazarus
SVP of Opers, MPS: Michael Shareck
SVP, Fin: Edward Garrett
VP, Fin Planning & Admin: Cathy Goodfriend
VP, Treas & Tax Dir: Michael Ross
SVP, Fin & Admin: Allan Meese
EVP, Digital Publg & Strategic Technol: Fritz Foy
SVP & COO, Group Technol Servs: Chris Kohn
VP, Academic & Lib Mktg: Peter Janssen
VP, Supply Chain & Sales Opers: Tom Stouras
SVP, Group Strategy & M&A: Kenneth Eng
SVP, Gen Coun: Paul Sleven
VP, Dir of HR: Helaine Ohl
Founded: 1986
Macmillan is the administrative, sales, distribution & information technology arm of the Macmillan group in the US, which includes Bedford, Freeman & Worth Publishing Group, LLC (W H Freeman, Worth Publishers & Bedford/St Martin's); Tom Doherty Associates, LLC (Tor & Forge Books); Faber & Faber Inc; Farrar, Straus & Giroux, LLC; Feiwel & Friends; First Second; Hayden McNeil; Henry Holt and Company, LLC; Macmillan Audio; Nature America Inc; Palgrave Macmillan; Picador; Roaring Brook Press; St Martin's Press, LLC; Scientific American Inc; Square Fish.
Distribution Center: MPS Distribution Center, 16365 James Madison Hwy, Gordonsville, VA 22942-8501 *Toll Free Tel:* 888-330-8477 *Fax:* 540-672-7540 (cust serv) *Toll Free Fax:* 800-672-2054 (orders) *E-mail:* firstinitiallastname@mpsvirginia.com
See separate listing for:
Tom Doherty Associates, LLC
Farrar, Straus & Giroux, LLC
Henry Holt and Company, LLC
Macmillan Higher Education
Picador
St Martin's Press, LLC

Macmillan Audio
Division of Macmillan
175 Fifth Ave, New York, NY 10010
Tel: 646-307-5151 *Toll Free Tel:* 888-330-8477 (cust serv) *Fax:* 917-534-0980
Web Site: www.macmillanaudio.com
Key Personnel
Pres & Publr: Mary Beth Roche
Assoc Publr: Robert Allen
Sr Art Dir: Margo Goody
Dir, Prodn: Laura Wilson
Mktg Dir: Samantha Edelson
Founded: 1987
ISBN Prefix(es): 978-1-55927; 978-0-7927; 978-0-940687; 978-1-59397; 978-1-4272
Number of titles published annually: 100 Audio
Distributed by BBC Audiobooks America (library editions)
Distributor for HighRoads Media
Orders to: MPS Order Dept, 16365 James Madison Hwy, Gordonsville, VA 22942-8501 *Toll Free Tel:* 888-330-8477 *Fax:* 540-672-7540 *Toll Free Fax:* 800-672-2054
Membership(s): Audio Publishers Association; Publishers' Publicity Association

Macmillan Higher Education
Subsidiary of Macmillan
41 Madison Ave, 37th fl, New York, NY 10010
Tel: 212-576-9400 *Fax:* 212-689-2383
Web Site: www.macmillanhighered.com
Key Personnel
CEO: Ken Michaels
COO: Ken Brooks
Pres: Joan Feinberg
Pres, W H Freeman & Worth: Elizabeth Widdicombe
SVP, Fin & Admin: Jamie Demas
VP, Communs: Kate Geraghty
Mng Dir: Susan Winslow
Dir, Content Mgmt Solutions: Susan Brown
Founded: 1999
Imprints: Bedford/St Martin's; W H Freeman; Palgrave Macmillan; Worth Publishers
See separate listing for:
Bedford/St Martin's
W H Freeman
Palgrave Macmillan
Worth Publishers

§Macmillan Reference USA™
Imprint of Gale
12 Lunar Dr, Woodbridge, CT 06525
Tel: 203-397-2600 *Toll Free Tel:* 800-444-0799 *Fax:* 203-397-8296
Web Site: www.gale.cengage.com/macmillan/
Key Personnel
EVP & Publr: Frank Menchaca
Number of titles published annually: 4 E-Book
Total Titles: 84 E-Book

Mage Publishers Inc
1408 35 St NW, Washington, DC 20007
Tel: 202-342-1642 *Fax:* 202-342-9269
Web Site: www.mage.com
Key Personnel
Art Dir: Najmieh Batmanglij *E-mail:* nb@mage.com
Publr & Ed: Mohammad Batmanglij *E-mail:* mb@mage.com
Asst to Publr & Rts Contact: Amin Sepehri *E-mail:* as@mage.com
Founded: 1985
Persian literature, art & culture in English; poetry, fiction, art & history.
ISBN Prefix(es): 978-0-934211; 978-1-933823
Number of titles published annually: 4 Print
Total Titles: 75 Print
Imprints: Mage Persian Editions
Distributed by University of Toronto Press (Canada)
Returns: Tasco, Mage Returns, 9 Jay Gould Ct, Waldorf, MD 20602
Warehouse: Tasco, 9 Jay Gould Ct, Waldorf, MD 20602
Membership(s): AAP

The Magni Co
Subsidiary of The Magni Group Inc
7106 Wellington Point Rd, McKinney, TX 75070
Tel: 972-540-2050 *Fax:* 972-540-1057
E-mail: sales@magnico.com; info@magnico.com
Web Site: www.magnico.com
Key Personnel
Pres: Evan B Reynolds
EVP: Darlene Reynolds
Founded: 1982
Health & beauty books, weight loss books, informative books, organizer books.
ISBN Prefix(es): 978-1-882330
Number of titles published annually: 5 Print; 1 CD-ROM; 3 Online; 50 E-Book; 2 Audio
Total Titles: 61 Print; 2 CD-ROM; 50 Online; 50 E-Book; 9 Audio
Imprints: MAGNI
Membership(s): ABA

Maharishi University of Management Press
Subsidiary of Maharishi University of Management
1000 N Fourth St, Dept 1155, Fairfield, IA 52557-1155
Tel: 641-472-1101 *Toll Free Tel:* 800-831-6523 *Fax:* 641-472-1122
E-mail: mumpress@mum.edu
Web Site: www.mumpress.com
Key Personnel
Dir: Harry Bright
Founded: 1974
Specialize in books about transcendental meditation.
ISBN Prefix(es): 978-0-9616944; 978-0-923569
Number of titles published annually: 5 Print
Total Titles: 50 Print; 4 Audio
Distributed by Fairfield Press; Penguin Group (USA) LLC

Maisonneuve Press
Division of Institute for Advanced Cultural Studies
6423 Adelphi Rd, Hyattsville, MD 20782
Mailing Address: PO Box 426, College Park, MD 20741-0241
Tel: 301-277-7505 *Fax:* 301-277-2467
Web Site: www.maisonneuvepress.com
Key Personnel
Dir & Ed: Robert Merrill *E-mail:* rm@maisonnuevepress.com
Assoc Ed: Dennis Crow; Thomas Wilkinson
Founded: 1988
Publish books for academic market. Not currently accepting new mss.
ISBN Prefix(es): 978-0-944624
Number of titles published annually: 8 Print
Total Titles: 32 Print
Distributed by Merlin Press (London, England)
Membership(s): The Independent Book Publishers Association

Management Advisory Services & Publications (MASP)
PO Box 81151, Wellesley Hills, MA 02481-0001
SAN: 203-8692
Tel: 781-235-2895 *Fax:* 781-235-5446
E-mail: info@masp.com
Web Site: www.masp.com
Key Personnel
Principal & Ed: Jay Kuong *E-mail:* jaykmasp@aol.com
Founded: 1972
A well established publications & advisory & training services company with a concentration in enterprise governance, internal controls, information technology security, auditing &

contingency planning & business continuity fields. This includes reference books, journals & practitioners' manuals. Under the enterprise governance field, MASP publishes books on Sarbanes-Oxley compliance. Additionally, as part of the diversification efforts, we publish a few literary fiction books.
ISBN Prefix(es): 978-0-940706
Number of titles published annually: 10 Print
Total Titles: 75 Print
Foreign Office(s): Santa Fe Ave, Buenos Aires, Argentina, Contact: D Ramos *E-mail:* dramos@satlink.com

§Management Concepts Inc
8230 Leesburg Pike, Suite 800, Vienna, VA 22182
Tel: 703-790-9595 *Toll Free Tel:* 800 506-4450 *Fax:* 703-790-1371
E-mail: info@managementconcepts.com
Web Site: www.managementconcepts.com
Key Personnel
CEO: Thomas F Dungan, III
Edit Dir: Myra Strauss
Founded: 1973
Books, newsletters, looseleafs & electronic products serving the information needs of project management, acquisition & federal financial management professionals.
ISBN Prefix(es): 978-1-56726
Number of titles published annually: 10 Print; 5 CD-ROM
Foreign Rep(s): NBN (Europe)
Warehouse: Brightkey, 1780 Crossroads Dr, Odenton, MD 21113, Contact: Sandi Hessie *Tel:* 301-604-3305 ext 1406 *Web Site:* www.managementconcepts.com

§Management Sciences for Health
200 Rivers Edge Dr, Medford, MA 02155
Tel: 617-250-9500 *Fax:* 617-250-9090
E-mail: bookstore@msh.org
Web Site: www.msh.org
Key Personnel
Deputy Dir, Pubns: Barbara K Timmons *Tel:* 617-250-9291 *E-mail:* btimmons@msh.org
Founded: 1971
Established to "assist, promote, evaluate, manage & perform research on the delivery of health care," establish "methods & procedures leading to the improvement of health & social services" & conduct education & publishing in these areas. MSH's publications unit develops & distributes books & a quarterly periodical to further MSH's mission, which is to help close the gap between knowledge about public health problems & action to solve them.
MSH currently stocks about three dozen products, most of which are books (including monographs, manuals & handbooks, some of which are available on CD-ROM). Many are available in languages other than English. Major products are The Manager continuing education quarterly; Managing Drug Supply (first published in 1981); instructional manuals (CORE, MOST, HOSPICAL, FIMAT); the Lessons from MSH & Stubbs monograph series; the series of "success stories" (20-page color booklets that present the highlights of successful programs) & books ranging from textbooks to syntheses of research.
MHS has offices in Afghanistan, Angola, Guinea, Haiti, Indonesia, Malawi, the Philippines & Senegal.
ISBN Prefix(es): 978-0-913723
Number of titles published annually: 2 Print; 1 CD-ROM
Total Titles: 39 Print; 4 CD-ROM
Branch Office(s)
4301 N Fairfax Dr, Suite 400, Arlington, VA 22203-1627, Contact: Keith Johnson *Tel:* 703-524-6575

Distributed by Kumarian Press
Membership(s): The Independent Book Publishers Association

Mandala Earth
Formerly Mandala Publishing; Earth Aware Editions
Imprint of Insight Editions
800 "A" St, San Rafael, CA 94901
Tel: 415-526-1370 *Toll Free Fax:* 866-509-0515
E-mail: info@mandalapublishing.com
Web Site: www.mandalaeartheditions.com
Key Personnel
CEO & Publr: Raoul Goff *E-mail:* raoul@insighteditions.com
Sales Dir: Julie Hamilton *E-mail:* j.hamilton@insighteditions.com
Sales Mgr: Jacqui Goff *E-mail:* j.goff@insighteditions.com
Full color coffee table books & minibooks, as well as decks, calendars, journals, greeting cards, art prints & incense. Topics include: environmental issues, women's studies, Asian art, music, philosophy, cross-cultural issues & Hinduism. Cutting-edge environmental & cultural topics that feature the unique voices & new concepts of leading thinkers, environmentalists, photojournalists, cultural commentators & artists.
ISBN Prefix(es): 978-1-886069; 978-1-932771; 978-1-60109; 978-0-945475
Number of titles published annually: 15 Print; 2 Audio
Total Titles: 300 Print; 200 Online; 10 Audio
Foreign Rep(s): Bill Bailey Publishers Representatives (Europe); Book Promotions (Jonathan Ball) (South Africa); Gilles Fauveau (Japan, Korea); Jaime Gregorio (Philippines); New-South Books (Australia, New Zealand); Penguin Books India (Bangladesh, India, Maldives, Nepal, Pakistan, Sri Lanka); Perseus International (Suk Lee) (Malaysia, Singapore); Perseus International (Edison Garcia) (Caribbean, Latin America, Middle East, North Africa); June Poonpanich (Cambodia, Indonesia, Laos, Thailand, Vietnam); Publishers Group UK (UK); Wei Zhao (China, Hong Kong, Taiwan)
Shipping Address: Publishers Group West, 210 American Dr, Jackson, TN 38301
Warehouse: Publishers Group West, 210 American Dr, Jackson, TN 38301
Distribution Center: Publishers Group West, 210 American Dr, Jackson, TN 38301

Mandala Publishing, see Mandala Earth

Manhattan Publishing Co
Division of US & Europe Books Inc
670 White Plains Rd, Scarsdale, NY 10583
Tel: 914-472-4650 *Fax:* 914-472-4316
E-mail: coe@manhattanpublishing.com
Web Site: www.manhattanpublishing.com
Key Personnel
Pres: Kenneth Polin
Lib Sales Dir: Cathy Polin
Founded: 1938
Import sales for Council of Europe, European Court of Human Rights.
Number of titles published annually: 200 Print
Total Titles: 3,000 Print; 20 CD-ROM
Distributor for Council of Europe; European Court of Human Rights

Manic D Press Inc
250 Banks St, San Francisco, CA 94110
Mailing Address: PO Box 410804, San Francisco, CA 94141
Tel: 415-648-8288
E-mail: info@manicdpress.com
Web Site: www.manicdpress.com
Key Personnel
Publr & Intl Rts: Jennifer Joseph
Founded: 1984
Poetry & unusual fiction & alternative travel books, emphasis on innovative, new & established styles, writers & artists, paperbacks, general adult books.
ISBN Prefix(es): 978-0-916397; 978-1-933149
Number of titles published annually: 6 Print
Total Titles: 200 Print
Foreign Rep(s): Perseus (Worldwide exc Canada & Europe); Publishers Group Canada (Canada); Turnaround Distribution (Europe)
Distribution Center: Consortium Book Sales & Distribution, The Keg House, 34 13 Ave NE, Suite 101, Minneapolis, MN 55413-1007 *Tel:* 612-746-2600 *Toll Free Tel:* 800-283-3572 (cust serv) *Fax:* 612-746-2606 *Web Site:* www.cbsd.com

Manning Publications Co
PO Box 761, Shelter Island, NY 11964
Tel: 203-626-1510
E-mail: sales@manning.com; support@manning.com (cust serv)
Web Site: www.manning.com
Key Personnel
Publr: Marjan Bace *Fax:* 203-629-8535 *E-mail:* maba@manning.com
Assoc Publr: Michael Stephens
Dir, Prodn: Mary Piergies
Busn Mgr: Kimberly Dickinson *Tel:* 856-375-2597 *E-mail:* kidi@manning.com
Founded: 1990
Full-scale company whose titles are distributed in the US, Europe & Asia.
ISBN Prefix(es): 978-1-884777; 978-1-930110; 978-1-932394; 978-1-933988; 978-1-61729; 978-1-935182
Number of titles published annually: 25 Print; 10 E-Book
Total Titles: 300 Print; 20 CD-ROM; 200 E-Book
Distributed by IPG; Pearson Education; Prentice Hall; TransQuest Publishers Pte Ltd
Distribution Center: O'Reilly Media Inc, 1005 Granvenstein Hwy N, Sebastopol, CA 95472 (US & CN) *Tel:* 707-829-1515 *Toll Free Tel:* 800-998-9939 *Toll Free Fax:* 800-997-9901 *E-mail:* retailics@oreilly.com *Web Site:* www.oreilly.com
Woodslane Pty Lane, Unit 7/5 Vuko Place, Warriewood, NSW 2102, Australia (Australia, New Zealand, Pacific Islands) *Tel:* 02 9970 5111 *Fax:* 02 9970 5002 *E-mail:* info@woodslane.com.au *Web Site:* www.woodslane.com.au
Pansing Distribution Pte Ltd, 438 Ang Mo Kio Industrial Park 1, Off Ang Mo Kio Ave 10, Singapore, Singapore (Hong Kong, Malaysia, Singapore, South Korea, Taiwan, Thailand) *Tel:* 6319 9939 *Fax:* 6459 4931 *E-mail:* infobooks@pansing.com
Pearson Education, Edinburgh Gate, Harlow, Essex CM20 2JE, United Kingdom (Africa, Europe, UK) *Tel:* (01279) 623928 *Fax:* (01279) 414130 *E-mail:* enq.orders@pearsoned-ema.com *Web Site:* www.pearson-books.com

MapEasy Inc
PO Box 80, Wainscott, NY 11975-0080
Tel: 631-537-6213 *Toll Free Tel:* 888-627-3279 *Fax:* 631-537-4541
E-mail: info@mapeasy.com
Web Site: www.mapeasy.com
Key Personnel
Owner: Gary Bradhering *Tel:* 631-537-6213 ext 160; Chris Harris *Tel:* 631-537-6213 ext 150 *E-mail:* charris@mapeasy.com
Founded: 1989
Guidemaps & location guides to cities in North America, Western Europe & Asia.
ISBN Prefix(es): 978-1-878979
Number of titles published annually: 4 Print
Total Titles: 72 Print

MAR*CO Products Inc
1443 Old York Rd, Warminster, PA 18974
Tel: 215-956-0313 *Toll Free Tel:* 800-448-2197 *Fax:* 215-956-9041
E-mail: help@marcoproducts.com
Web Site: www.marcoproducts.com
Key Personnel
Opers Mgr: Kathy Crocco
Founded: 1977
Educational guidance materials for elementary & secondary counselors, psychologists & social workers.
ISBN Prefix(es): 978-1-884063; 978-1-57543
Number of titles published annually: 12 Print; 20 Online; 25 E-Book
Total Titles: 300 Print; 400 Online
Distributed by ASCA; Boulden Publishing; Burnell Books; Calloway House; Career Kids FYI; CFKR Career; Character Development; Community Intervention; Courage to Change; Cress Productions Co; EDU Reference; Educational Media Corp; Incentive Plus; Jist; Mental Health Resources; National Professional Resources; National Resource Center Youth Services; NIMCO Bookstore; Paperbacks for Educators; School Speciality; SourceResource; STARS-National Center for Youths; WRS Group; YouthLight Inc
Distributor for Boulden; Center for Youth Issues/STARS; Educational Media; HarperCollins

Marathon Press
1500 Square Turn Blvd, Norfolk, NE 68701
Mailing Address: PO Box 407, Norfolk, NE 68702-0407
Tel: 402-371-5040 *Toll Free Tel:* 800-228-0629 *Fax:* 402-371-9382
Web Site: www.marathonpress.com
Key Personnel
Owner: Rex Alewel
Pres: Bruce Price
Founded: 1974
Books on professional photography.
ISBN Prefix(es): 978-0-934420
Number of titles published annually: 5 Print
Total Titles: 30 Print

Maren Green Publishing Inc
5630 Memorial Ave N, Suite 3, Oak Park Heights, MN 55082
Tel: 651-439-4500 *Toll Free Tel:* 800-287-1512 *Fax:* 651-439-4532
E-mail: info@marengreen.com
Web Site: www.marengreen.com
Key Personnel
Owner & Pres: Todd Snow *E-mail:* toddsnow@marengreen.com
Founded: 2006
Fiction & nonfiction books for children newborn to age 9.
This publisher has indicated that 100% of their product line is author subsidized.
ISBN Prefix(es): 978-1-934277
Number of titles published annually: 5 Print
Total Titles: 19 Print
Imprints: Books Good For Young Children™
Distributed by Crabtree Publishing Inc
Foreign Rights: Sylvia Hayse Literary Agency (Worldwide)
Membership(s): ABA; The Independent Book Publishers Association

Margaret K McElderry, see Simon & Schuster Children's Publishing

Marick Press
PO Box 36253, Grosse Pointe Farms, MI 48236
Tel: 313-407-9236
E-mail: orders@marickpress.com
Web Site: www.marickpress.com
Key Personnel
Publr: Mariela Griffor
A not-for-profit literary publisher founded to preserve the best work by poets around the world including many under published women poets. We seek out & publish the best new work from an eclectic range of aesthets - work that is technically accomplished, distinctive in style & thematically fresh.
ISBN Prefix(es): 978-0-9779703; 978-1-934851
Number of titles published annually: 6 Print
Total Titles: 45 Print

Marine Education Textbooks
124 N Van Ave, Houma, LA 70363-5895
SAN: 215-9651
Tel: 985-879-3866 *Fax:* 985-879-3911
E-mail: email@marineeducationtextbooks.com
Web Site: www.marineeducationtextbooks.com
Key Personnel
Mgr: Gwen M Block *E-mail:* gwen@ourmet.com
Ed: Richard A Block
Founded: 1970
Training & educational books for preparation of USCG Exams. Marine safety signs, nautical charts.
ISBN Prefix(es): 978-0-934114; 978-1-879778
Number of titles published annually: 6 Print
Total Titles: 40 Print
Imprints: Marine Survey Press

Marine Techniques Publishing
126 Western Ave, Suite 266, Augusta, ME 04330-7249
SAN: 298-7805
Tel: 207-622-7984
E-mail: info@marinetechpublishing.com; sales@marinetechpublishing.com
Web Site: marinetechpublishing.com; www.groups.yahoo.com/group/marinetechniquespublishing
Key Personnel
Owner & Pres: James L Pelletier
Founded: 1983
Industry specific directories; maritime/worldwide merchant marine; naval architecture; marine biology, chemistry, geology; civil, marine engineering; electrical, electronic marine engineering; energy, oil & gas offshore; mechanical marine engineering; transportation, marine. Commercial merchant marine - worldwide directories, *Mariner's Employment Guide* & maritime autobiographies (true maritime stories).
This publisher has indicated that 100% of their product line is author subsidized.
ISBN Prefix(es): 978-0-9644915; 978-0-9798008
Number of titles published annually: 5 Print; 245 Online; 2 E-Book; 2 Audio
Total Titles: 100 Print; 8 CD-ROM; 245 Online; 2 E-Book; 2 Audio
Distributed by Elsevier Science, Technology & Business Books; PennWell Business & Industrial Division
Distributor for Academic Press; Best Publishing Co; Butterworth-Heinemann; Clarkson Research Services Ltd; Elsevier, Science & Technology Books; Focal Press; Gulf Professional Publishers; PennWell Business & Industrial Division; W B Saunders Co; Waterfront Soundings Productions; Witherby Seamanship International Ltd
Foreign Rep(s): Chapters Inc (Canada, Ontario, CN); W H Everett & Sons Ltd (England, London, UK); Lavoisier (France)
Distribution Center: BooksXYZ.com
Follett School Solutions Inc, 1340 Ridgeview Dr, McHenry, IL 60050 *Tel:* 815-759-1700 *Toll Free Tel:* 888-511-5114 (cust serv) *Fax:* 815-759-9831 *Toll Free Fax:* 800-852-5458 *E-mail:* info@follettlearning.com *Web Site:* www.follettlearning.com SAN: 169-1902
Baker, Lyman & Co Inc, 5250 Veterans Memorial Blvd, Metairie, LA 70006 *Toll Free Tel:* 800-535-6956 *E-mail:* sales@bakerlyman.com *Web Site:* www.bakerlyman.com
The Book House Inc, 208 W Chicago St, Jonesville, MI 49250 *Toll Free Tel:* 800-248-1146 *Toll Free Fax:* 800-858-9716 *Web Site:* www.thebookhouse.com
Emery-Pratt Co, 1966 W Main St, Owosso, MI 48867 *Toll Free Tel:* 800-248-3887 *Toll Free Fax:* 800-523-6379 *Web Site:* www.emery-pratt.com
Membership(s): American Maritime Association; American Society of Naval Engineers; Association of Marine Engineers; The Association of Publishers for Special Sales; The Independent Book Publishers Association; Independent Publishers of New England; Lloyd's Maritime Information Register; Women's Maritime Association

Marion Street Press LLC
4207 SE Woodstock Blvd, No 168, Portland, OR 97206
Tel: 503-888-4624 *Toll Free Fax:* 866-571-8359
E-mail: marionbooks@outlook.com
Web Site: www.marionstreetpress.com
Key Personnel
Publr: Kel Winter
Founded: 1993
Books for writers & journalists, students, educators & financial professionals.
ISBN Prefix(es): 978-0-9665176; 978-0-9729937; 978-1-933338
Number of titles published annually: 12 Print
Total Titles: 60 Print
Foreign Rep(s): IPG (Canada)
Membership(s): The Association of Publishers for Special Sales; The Independent Book Publishers Association; National Association of Independent Publishers

Markowski International Publishers
One Oakglade Circle, Hummelstown, PA 17036-9525
Tel: 717-566-0468
E-mail: info@possibilitypress.com
Web Site: www.possibilitypress.com; www.aeronauticalpublishers.com
Key Personnel
Publr: Mike Markowski
Founded: 1981
Books on personal development, business, success, motivation, aviation & model aviation.
ISBN Prefix(es): 978-0-938716
Number of titles published annually: 6 Print
Total Titles: 40 Print
Imprints: Aeronautical Publishers; Possibility Press
Membership(s): The Independent Book Publishers Association

Marquette University Press
1415 W Wisconsin Ave, Milwaukee, WI 53233
Mailing Address: PO Box 3141, Milwaukee, WI 53201-3141
Tel: 414-288-1564 *Toll Free Tel:* 800-247-6553 (cust serv) *Fax:* 414-288-7813
Web Site: www.marquette.edu/mupress
Key Personnel
Dir: Dr Andrew Tallon *E-mail:* andrew.tallon@marquette.edu
Mgr: Maureen Kondrick *E-mail:* maureen.kondrick@marquette.edu
Founded: 1916
Publications in the humanities by scholars of international reputation. Specialize in philosophy, theology, humanities & history in addition to regional studies relating to the city of Milwaukee & the state of Wisconsin.
ISBN Prefix(es): 978-0-87462; 978-1-62600
Number of titles published annually: 18 Print; 1 CD-ROM; 15 E-Book
Total Titles: 480 Print; 3 CD-ROM; 250 E-Book
Foreign Rep(s): Scholarly Book Services (Canada)

Orders to: Bookmasters, 30 Amberwood Pkwy, Ashland, OH 44805, Contact: Elaine Lattanzi *Tel:* 419-281-1802 ext 1408 *Fax:* 419-281-6883 *E-mail:* orders@bookmasters.com
Returns: Bookmasters, 30 Amberwood Pkwy, Ashland, OH 44805, Contact: Elaine Lattanzi *Tel:* 419-281-1802 ext 1408 *Fax:* 419-281-6883
Distribution Center: Bookmasters, 30 Amberwood Pkwy, Ashland, OH 44805, Contact: Elaine Lattanzi *Tel:* 419-281-1802 ext 1408 *Fax:* 419-281-6883 *E-mail:* orders@bookmasters.com
Membership(s): American Association of University Presses; Association of Jesuit University Presses

Marquis Who's Who LLC
430 Mountain Ave, Suite 400, New Providence, NJ 07974
Tel: 908-673-1000 *Toll Free Tel:* 800-473-7020 *Fax:* 908-673-1189 (cust serv); 908-673-1179 (edit)
E-mail: info@marquiswhoswho.com; customerservice@marquiswhoswho.com (cust serv, sales)
Web Site: www.marquiswhoswho.com
Key Personnel
CEO: Fred Marks *Tel:* 908-673-1010 *E-mail:* fred.marks@marquiswhoswho.com
Founded: 1899
Publisher of comprehensive biographical references available in print, online & mailing list. Major Marquis Who's Who publications include *Who's Who in America, Who's Who in the World & Who's Who of American Women.*
ISBN Prefix(es): 978-0-8379
Number of titles published annually: 11 Print
Total Titles: 17 Print; 17 Online
Divisions: National Register Publishing
See separate listing for:
National Register Publishing

Marriage Transformation LLC
PO Box 249, Harrison, TN 37341
Tel: 423-599-0153
Web Site: www.marriagetransformation.com
Key Personnel
Pres: Susanne M Alexander *E-mail:* susanne@marriagetransformation.com
Relationship & marriage education.
This publisher has indicated that 90% of their product line is author subsidized.
ISBN Prefix(es): 978-0-9726893
Number of titles published annually: 3 Print; 6 E-Book
Total Titles: 10 Print; 6 E-Book
Distributed by Barringer; Longman
Membership(s): National Association for Relationship & Marriage Education

Marshall & Swift
777 S Fiqueroa St, 12th fl, Los Angeles, CA 90017
Tel: 213-683-9000 *Toll Free Tel:* 800-544-2678 *Fax:* 213-683-9043
E-mail: csinquiry@marshallswift.com
Web Site: www.marshallswift.com
Key Personnel
Res Supv: Gary Miller
Founded: 1932
Building cost databases for the construction market & insurance industry.
ISBN Prefix(es): 978-1-56842
Number of titles published annually: 10 Print
Total Titles: 21 Print
Imprints: Valuation Press
Distributed by McGraw-Hill Book Co
Warehouse: 1625 W Temple, Los Angeles, CA 90026

Marshall Cavendish Corp
Member of Times International Publishing Group
99 White Plains Rd, Tarrytown, NY 10591-9001
Tel: 914-332-8888 *Toll Free Tel:* 800-821-9881 *Fax:* 914-332-8102
E-mail: mce@marshallcavendish.com
Web Site: www.mceducation.us
Key Personnel
Dir, US: Vivian Cheng
Sales & Busn Devt Dir: Scott Burns
Busn Devt Mgr (Intl): Hoover Herrera
Mktg Mgr: Jennifer Feldman
Sr Accountant: Richard Moore
Accountant: Jay Lee
Accts Payable/Accts Receivable Assoc: Imelda Guarin
Sr Educ Consultant: Christopher Coyne
Educ/Sales Consultant: Thomas Corbia; Peter Iandiorio; Ellen Lauterbach; Jessica Shelley
Sr Cust Serv: Norma Palazzo
Founded: 1970
International publisher of books, directories, magazines & digital platforms. Products reach across the globe in 13 languages & our publishing network spans Asia & the US. Dedicated to the promotion of lifelong learning & self-development.
ISBN Prefix(es): 978-1-85435; 978-0-7614
Number of titles published annually: 320 Print; 10 Online; 300 E-Book
Total Titles: 1,200 Print; 57 Online; 590 E-Book
Imprints: Marshall Cavendish Adult Trade; Marshall Cavendish Benchmark; Marshall Cavendish Digital; Marshall Cavendish Education; Marshall Cavendish Reference
Distributed by Marshall Cavendish Ltd (UK)
Foreign Rep(s): Peter Pal Library Suppliers (Australia)
Warehouse: Swan Packaging, 415 Hamburg Tpke, Wayne, NJ 07470
Membership(s): ALA; The Children's Book Council

Martindale-Hubbell, see Martindale LLC

§Martindale LLC
Formerly LexisNexis/Martindale-Hubbell
121 Chanlon Rd, 1st fl, New Providence, NJ 07974
SAN: 205-8863
Mailing Address: PO Box 1001, Summit, NJ 07902-1001
Tel: 908-464-6800 *Toll Free Tel:* 800-526-4902 *Fax:* 908-464-3553
E-mail: info@martindale.com
Web Site: www.martindale.com
Founded: 1868
Publisher of the *Martindale-Hubbell Law Directory* in hardcopy, on CD-ROM & available online; containing listings of over 1 million lawyers & law firms worldwide. Other publications include *Law Digest*, a summary of laws from each of the 50 states & 80 countries; *Martindale-Hubbell International Law Directory*, designed for the international legal community & *Martindale-Hubbell Bar Register of Preeminent Lawyers*, listing of over 8,900 law practices designated as outstanding by members of the legal community.
ISBN Prefix(es): 978-1-56160
Number of titles published annually: 5 Print; 1 CD-ROM; 1 Online
Total Titles: 5 Print; 1 CD-ROM; 1 Online

Martingale®
19021 120 Ave NE, Suite 102, Bothell, WA 98011
Tel: 425-483-3313 *Toll Free Tel:* 800-426-3126 *Fax:* 425-486-7596
E-mail: info@martingale-pub.com
Web Site: www.martingale-pub.com
Key Personnel
Publr: Jennifer Kelpner
CFO: Keith Brants
Content Dir: Karen Foltys
Dir, Mktg: Karen Johnson *Tel:* 425-483-3313 ext 1387
Dir, Sales: Wendy Jacobson
Founded: 1976
Quilting, knitting & crafting.
ISBN Prefix(es): 978-1-56477; 978-0-943574; 978-1-60468
Number of titles published annually: 55 Print; 55 E-Book
Total Titles: 250 Print; 300 E-Book
Imprints: That Patchwork Place

Maryland Historical Society
201 W Monument St, Baltimore, MD 21201
Tel: 410-685-3750 *Fax:* 410-385-2105
Web Site: www.mdhs.org
Key Personnel
Dir, Pubns & Lib Servs: Patricia Anderson, PhD *Tel:* 410-685-3750 ext 317 *E-mail:* panderson@mdhs.org
Founded: 1844
Publish historical books.
ISBN Prefix(es): 978-0-938420
Number of titles published annually: 5 Print
Total Titles: 45 Print
Distributed by Alan C Hood & Co Inc
Orders to: Alan C Hood & Co Inc, PO Box 775, Chambersburg, PA 17201, Contact: Alan Hood *Tel:* 717-267-0867 *Fax:* 717-267-0572
Returns: Maple Press Distribution Ctr, I-83 Industrial Park, York, PA 17405
Shipping Address: Maple Press Distribution Ctr, I-83 Industrial Park, York, PA 17405, Contact: Alan C Hood *Tel:* 717-267-0867 *Fax:* 717-267-0572
Warehouse: Maple Press Distribution Ctr, I-83 Industrial Park, York, PA 17405
Distribution Center: Maple Press Distribution Ctr, I-83 Industrial Park, York, PA 17405

Maryland History Press
PO Box 206, Fruitland, MD 21826-0206
Tel: 410-742-2682
E-mail: sales@marylandhistorypress.com
Web Site: www.marylandhistorypress.com
Key Personnel
Pres: Elaine Patterson
Founded: 1999
Provide quality books on various topics & by various authors to help celebrate America's uniqueness-people, events, culture & environs. Services provided are publishing services, author-subsidy program, consignments, distribution services via national company, book searches & web site exposure through major online booksellers.
This publisher has indicated that 85% of their product line is author subsidized.
ISBN Prefix(es): 978-0-9703802; 978-0-9897944
Number of titles published annually: 3 Print
Total Titles: 15 Print; 10 Online
Distributor for Dogwood Ridge Books; Tapestry Press Ltd
Warehouse: 109 Clyde Ave, Fruitland, MD 21826
Distribution Center: Follett School Solutions Inc, 1340 Ridgeview Dr, McHenry, IL 60050 *Tel:* 815-759-1700 *Toll Free Tel:* 888-511-5114 (cust serv) *Fax:* 815-759-9831 *Toll Free Fax:* 800-852-5458 *E-mail:* info@follettlearning.com *Web Site:* www.follettlearning.com SAN: 169-1902
Baker & Taylor, PO Box 8888, Momemce, IL 60954

Marymark Press
45-08 Old Millstone Dr, East Windsor, NJ 08520
Tel: 609-443-0646
Key Personnel
Publr & Ed: Mark Sonnenfeld
Founded: 1994

Independent small press publishing vehicle; various size chapbooks, broadsides, writing samplers, give-out sheets, single sheets, audio sound collages. Experimental writing. Prefer automatic writing/avant-garde genre.
ISBN Prefix(es): 978-0-9632820; 978-1-887379; 978-0-9844182; 978-0-9798819
Number of titles published annually: 10 Print; 3 Audio
Total Titles: 400 Print; 35 Audio

Mason Crest Publishers
Imprint of National Highlights
450 Parkway Dr, Suite D, Broomall, PA 19008
Tel: 610-543-6200 *Toll Free Tel:* 866-MCP-BOOK (627-2665) *Fax:* 610-543-3878
Web Site: www.masoncrest.com
Key Personnel
Pres: Daniel Hilferty *E-mail:* dhilferty@masoncrest.com
Principal & Creative Dir: Louis Cohen *Tel:* 917-763-7760
Cont: Diana Daniels *E-mail:* ddaniels@masoncrest.com
Opers Mgr: Lee Wark *Tel:* 610-583-0211 *Fax:* 610-583-0212 *E-mail:* lwark@masoncrest.com
Cust Serv: Grace Baffa *Tel:* 610-543-6200 ext 113 *E-mail:* gbaffa@masoncrest.com
Founded: 2001
Mason Crest Publishers is committed to publishing the finest nonfiction school, library & curriculum products available today. Our titles are full-color & include a glossary, index, further reading section, Internet resources & are library bound. Subjects include reality shows.
ISBN Prefix(es): 978-1-59084; 978-1-4222; 978-1-59482
Number of titles published annually: 300 Print; 1,500 E-Book
Total Titles: 2,000 Print; 2,500 E-Book
Returns: 701 Ashland Ave, Bays 1 & 2, Folcroft, PA 19032, Opers Mgr: Lee Wark *Tel:* 610-583-0211 *Fax:* 610-583-0212 *E-mail:* lee6250@aol.com
Shipping Address: 701 Ashland Ave, Bays 1 & 2, Folcroft, PA 19032, Opers Mgr: Lee Wark *Tel:* 610-583-0211 *Fax:* 610-583-0212 *E-mail:* lee6250@aol.com
Warehouse: 701 Ashland Ave, Bays 1 & 2, Folcroft, PA 19032, Opers Mgr: Lee Wark *Tel:* 610-583-0211 *Fax:* 610-583-0212 *E-mail:* lee6250@aol.com
Distribution Center: 701 Ashland Ave, Bays 1 & 2, Folcroft, PA 19032, Opers Mgr: Lee Wark *Tel:* 610-583-0211 *Fax:* 610-583-0212 *E-mail:* lee6250@aol.com
Membership(s): Friends of Libraries of USA; The Independent Book Publishers Association

The Massachusetts Historical Society
1154 Boylston St, Boston, MA 02215-3695
Tel: 617-536-1608 *Fax:* 617-859-0074
E-mail: publications@masshist.org
Web Site: www.masshist.org
Key Personnel
Dir, Pubns: Ondine E Le Blanc *Tel:* 617-646-0524 *E-mail:* oleblanc@masshist.org
Founded: 1792
Scholarly historical regional publications.
ISBN Prefix(es): 978-0-934909; 978-0-9652584; 978-1-936520
Number of titles published annually: 4 Print
Total Titles: 500 Print
Distributed by University of Virginia Press

Massachusetts Institute of Technology Libraries
77 Massachusetts Ave, Bldg 14-S, Rm 0551, Cambridge, MA 02139-4307
Tel: 617-253-5671
Web Site: libraries.mit.edu/docs
Key Personnel
Dir, Libs: Chris Bourg *Tel:* 617-253-5297 *E-mail:* cbourg@mit.edu
Assoc Dir, Admin: Keith Glavash *Tel:* 617-253-7059 *E-mail:* kglavash@mit.edu
Founded: 1863
MIT theses, dissertations, technical reports & working papers.
ISBN Prefix(es): 978-0-911379
Number of titles published annually: 2,000 Print
Total Titles: 15,000 Print

§Master Books
Subsidiary of New Leaf Publishing Group
PO Box 726, Green Forest, AR 72638-0726
Tel: 870-438-5288 *Fax:* 870-438-5120
E-mail: submissions@newleafpress.net
Web Site: www.nlpg.com
Key Personnel
Edit Asst: Craig Froman
Founded: 1975
Publish Biblically-based, scientifically sound creation materials & curriculum.
ISBN Prefix(es): 978-0-89051
Number of titles published annually: 25 Print; 20 E-Book
Total Titles: 425 Print; 3 CD-ROM; 70 E-Book; 2 Audio
Shipping Address: 3142 Hwy 103 N, Green Forest, AR 72638

Materials Research Society
506 Keystone Dr, Warrendale, PA 15086-7537
SAN: 686-0125
Tel: 724-779-3003 *Fax:* 724-779-8313
E-mail: info@mrs.org
Web Site: www.mrs.org
Key Personnel
Dir, Communs: Eileen Kiley Novak *Tel:* 724-779-2742 *E-mail:* kiley@mrs.org
Pubns Mgr: Ellen Kracht *Tel:* 724-779-2766 *E-mail:* kracht@mrs.org
Pubns Edit Asst: Susan Seibel *Tel:* 724-779-2753 *E-mail:* seibel@mrs.org
Principal Devt Ed: Elizabeth Fleischer *Tel:* 724-779-2746 *E-mail:* fleischer@mrs.org
Founded: 1973
Scientific reports on leading edge topics in materials research.
ISBN Prefix(es): 978-0-931837; 978-1-55899
Number of titles published annually: 30 Print
Total Titles: 900 Print

Math Solutions®
Unit of Houghton Mifflin Harcourt
One Harbor Dr, Suite 101, Sausalito, CA 94965
Tel: 415-332-4181 *Toll Free Tel:* 800-868-9092 *Fax:* 415-331-1931 *Toll Free Fax:* 877-942-8837
E-mail: info@mathsolutions.com; orders@mathsolutions.com
Web Site: www.mathsolutions.com
Key Personnel
Founder & Math Educ Consultant: Marilyn Burns
CEO & Pres: Christine Willig
VP: Patricio Dujan
Dir, Sales & Client Rel: Jane Manning Hyatt
Exec Ed: Jamie Cross
Sr Mktg Mgr: Kelli Cook
Founded: 1994
Dedicated to improving the teaching of mathematics by providing professional development of the highest quality to teachers & administrators.
ISBN Prefix(es): 978-0-941355; 978-1-935099
Number of titles published annually: 10 Print
Total Titles: 80 Print
Shipping Address: 1805 S McDowell Blvd, Petaluma, CA 94954, Contact: Taber Auren *Tel:* 707-769-0722
Warehouse: 1805 S McDowell Blvd, Petaluma, CA 94954, Contact: Taber Auren *Tel:* 707-769-0722
Membership(s): ASCD; National Council of Teachers of Mathematics

Math Teachers Press Inc
4850 Park Glen Rd, Minneapolis, MN 55416
Tel: 952-545-6535 *Toll Free Tel:* 800-852-2435 *Fax:* 952-546-7502
E-mail: info@movingwithmath.com
Web Site: www.movingwithmath.com
Key Personnel
Founder & Pres: Caryl K Pierson *E-mail:* cpierson@movingwithmath.com
Founded: 1985
Pre K-12 manipulative-based math curriculum.
ISBN Prefix(es): 978-0-933383; 978-1-891192; 978-1-931106; 978-1-59167
Number of titles published annually: 3 Print
Total Titles: 70 Print

§The Mathematical Association of America
1529 18 St NW, Washington, DC 20036-1358
SAN: 203-9737
Tel: 202-387-5200 *Toll Free Tel:* 800-741-9415 *Fax:* 202-265-2384
E-mail: maahq@maa.org
Web Site: www.maa.org
Key Personnel
Exec Dir: Michael Pearson *E-mail:* mpearson@maa.org
Dir, Pubns: Jim Angelo *E-mail:* jangelo@maa.org
Assoc Dir, Pubns: Carol Baxter *E-mail:* cbaxter@maa.org
Founded: 1915
Mathematical books & journals.
ISBN Prefix(es): 978-0-88385
Number of titles published annually: 15 Print; 2 CD-ROM
Total Titles: 200 Print; 2 CD-ROM
Distributed by Cambridge University Press
Foreign Rep(s): Cambridge University Press (Africa, Europe, Middle East)
Orders to: MAA Service Center, PO Box 91112, Washington, DC 20090-1112 *Tel:* 301-617-7800 *Toll Free Tel:* 800-331-1622 *Fax:* 240-396-5647 *E-mail:* maaservice@maa.org

§Maven House Press
4 Snead Ct, Palmyra, VA 22963
Tel: 610-883-7988 *Toll Free Fax:* 888-894-3403
E-mail: info@mavenhousepress.com
Web Site: mavenhousepress.com
Key Personnel
Publr & Ed-in-Chief: Jim Pennypacker *E-mail:* jim@mavenhousepress.com
Desktop Publr, Ed & Indexer: Deborah Weiss
Founded: 2012
Publisher of business books for professionals.
ISBN Prefix(es): 978-1-938548
Number of titles published annually: 5 Print; 5 E-Book
Total Titles: 3 Print; 3 E-Book
Foreign Rights: Russo Rights (Worldwide)
Distribution Center: Bookmasters, 30 Amberwood Pkwy, Ashland, OH 44805 *Toll Free Tel:* 800-266-5564 *Fax:* 419-989-4047 *E-mail:* info@bookmasters.com *Web Site:* www.bookmasters.com
Legato Publishers Group, 210 American Dr, Jackson, TN 38301 *Toll Free Tel:* 800-343-4499 *Toll Free Fax:* 800-351-5073 *E-mail:* orderentry@perseusbooks.com

Mazda Publishers Inc
One Park Plaza, Suite 600, Irvine, CA 92614
SAN: 658-120X
Mailing Address: PO Box 2603, Costa Mesa, CA 92628
Tel: 714-751-5252 *Fax:* 714-751-4805
E-mail: mazdapub@aol.com

Web Site: www.mazdapub.com
Key Personnel
Founder & Pres: Dr Ahmad Jabbari
Ed-at-Large: Ann West
Founded: 1980
Publishes scholarly books dealing with the Middle East, Central Asia & North Africa; critical reviews of poetry; Central Asia including art & architecture.
ISBN Prefix(es): 978-1-56859
Number of titles published annually: 32 Print
Total Titles: 280 Print

McBooks Press Inc
ID Booth Bldg, 520 N Meadow St, Ithaca, NY 14850
Tel: 607-272-2114 *Fax:* 607-273-6068
E-mail: mcbooks@mcbooks.com
Web Site: www.mcbooks.com
Key Personnel
Publr & Intl Rts Contact: Alexander Skutt
E-mail: alex@mcbooks.com
Art Dir: Panda Musgrove *E-mail:* panda@mcbooks.com
Founded: 1979
Trade books; specialize in historical fiction, vegetarianism, NYS regional books, period nautical, military fiction, sports including boxing.
ISBN Prefix(es): 978-1-59013
Number of titles published annually: 6 Print; 6 E-Book
Total Titles: 185 Print; 145 E-Book
Foreign Rep(s): Gazelle Book Services Ltd (Europe, UK)
Orders to: Independent Publishers Group, 814 N Franklin St, Chicago, IL 60610 *Tel:* 312-337-0747 *Toll Free Tel:* 800-888-4741 *Fax:* 312-337-5985 *Toll Free Fax:* 800-338-4550 *E-mail:* orders@ipgbook.com *Web Site:* www.ipgbook.com
Distribution Center: Independent Publishers Group, 814 N Franklin St, Chicago, IL 60610 *Tel:* 312-337-0747 *Toll Free Tel:* 800-888-4741 *Fax:* 312-337-5985 *Toll Free Fax:* 800-338-4550 *E-mail:* orders@ipgbook.com *Web Site:* www.ipgbook.com

McClanahan Publishing House Inc
107 W Main, Princeton, KY 42445
Tel: 270-963-9005
E-mail: books@kybooks.com
Web Site: kybooks.com
Key Personnel
Pres & Exec Ed: Michelle Stone
E-mail: mstone@kybooks.com
Founded: 1983
Full service publisher offering art services & artist illustration, jacket design, book design & layout. Self-publishing division provides these services as well for authors who want to retain control of their work.
ISBN Prefix(es): 978-0-913383; 978-0-9758788
Number of titles published annually: 15 Print
Total Titles: 140 Print
Imprints: Four Rivers Press

McCutchan Publishing Corp
2694 Ohart Rd, Richmond, CA 94806
SAN: 203-9486
Tel: 510-758-5510 *Toll Free Tel:* 800-227-1540
Fax: 510-758-6078
E-mail: mccutchanpublish@sbcglobal.net
Web Site: www.mccutchanpublishing.com
Key Personnel
Pres & Publr: Nancy Runyon
ISBN Contact & Rts & Perms: Kim Sharrar
Founded: 1963
College textbooks & professional books in education, hotel & restaurant management & law enforcement education.
ISBN Prefix(es): 978-0-8211
Number of titles published annually: 3 Print
Total Titles: 100 Print

The McDonald & Woodward Publishing Co
695 Tall Oaks Dr, Newark, OH 43055
Tel: 740-641-2691 *Toll Free Tel:* 800-233-8787
Fax: 740-641-2692
E-mail: mwpubco@mwpubco.com
Web Site: www.mwpubco.com
Key Personnel
Publr & Intl Rts Mgr: Jerry N McDonald
E-mail: jmcd@mwpubco.com
Mktg Mgr: Trish Newcomb *E-mail:* tnewcomb@mwpubco.com
Founded: 1986
Books (primarily adult) in natural history & cultural history; co-publish with educational & governmental entities.
ISBN Prefix(es): 978-0-939923
Number of titles published annually: 8 Print
Total Titles: 70 Print

§McFarland
960 NC Hwy 88 W, Jefferson, NC 28640
Mailing Address: PO Box 611, Jefferson, NC 28640-0611
Tel: 336-246-4460 *Toll Free Tel:* 800-253-2187 (orders) *Fax:* 336-246-5018; 336-246-4403 (orders)
E-mail: info@mcfarlandpub.com
Web Site: www.mcfarlandpub.com
Key Personnel
Founder & Ed-in-Chief: Robert Franklin
E-mail: rfranklin@mcfarlandpub.com
Pres: Rhonda Herman *E-mail:* rherman@mcfarlandpub.com
VP & Edit Dir: Steve Wilson *E-mail:* swilson@mcfarlandpub.com
Dir, Sales & Mktg: Karl-Heinz Roseman
E-mail: kroseman@mcfarlandpub.com
Subs & Intl Rights: Beth Cox *E-mail:* bcox@mcfarlandpub.com
Sr Acqs Ed: Gary Mitchem *E-mail:* gmitchem@mcfarlandpub.com
Acqs Ed: Charles Perdue *E-mail:* cperdue@mcfarlandpub.com
Founded: 1979
A leading independent publisher of academic & nonfiction books, known for covering popular topics in a serious fashion & for manufacturing books to meet high library standards.
ISBN Prefix(es): 978-0-89950; 978-0-7864
Number of titles published annually: 400 Print; 390 E-Book
Total Titles: 5,200 Print; 2,600 E-Book
Subsidiaries: McFarland & Co Ltd Publishers (London, UK)
Foreign Rep(s): Eurospan (Africa, Asia-Pacific, Australia, Europe, India, Middle East)
Returns: 961 NC Hwy 88 W, Jefferson, NC 28640
Shipping Address: 961 NC Hwy 88 W, Jefferson, NC 28640

§McGraw-Hill Career Education
Division of McGraw-Hill Higher Education
1333 Burr Ridge Pkwy, Burr Ridge, IL 60527
Tel: 630-789-4000 *Toll Free Tel:* 800-338-3987 (cust serv) *Fax:* 630-789-5523; 614-755-5645 (cust serv)
Web Site: www.mhhe.com
Key Personnel
VP & Natl Sales Mgr: Alan Hensley
E-mail: alan.hensley@mheducation.com
Mng Dir: Scott Davidson *Tel:* 314-439-6862
E-mail: scott.davidson@mheducation.com
Dir, Sales: Micaela Haidle *E-mail:* micaela.haidle@mheducation.com
Founded: 2001
Provides textbooks & educational materials to post-secondary, trade & career schools.
ISBN Prefix(es): 978-0-697; 978-0-256; 978-0-07
Number of titles published annually: 100 Print; 7 CD-ROM; 50 Online; 75 E-Book
Total Titles: 2,315 Print; 250 Online; 350 E-Book
Branch Office(s)
McGraw-Hill Learning Solutions, 8900 Keystone at the Crossing, Suite 950, Indianapolis, IN 46240
Returns: 860 Taylor Station Rd, Blacklick, OH 43004-0539
Distribution Center: 860 Taylor Station Rd, Blacklick, OH 43004-0539

McGraw-Hill Contemporary Learning Series
Division of McGraw-Hill Higher Education
501 Bell St, Dubuque, IA 52001
SAN: 201-3460
Toll Free Tel: 800-243-6532
Web Site: www.mhcls.com
Key Personnel
Pres, Sci, Engg & Mathematics: Kurt Strand
Tel: 563-584-6633 *Fax:* 563-584-6600
E-mail: kurt_strand@mcgraw-hill.com
SVP, Sales MHHE: Doug Hughes
Tel: 630-789-5121 *Fax:* 630-789-6944
E-mail: doug_hughes@mcgraw-hill.com
VP, Creative Solutions: Mr Christian Perlee
Tel: 732-275-1251 *E-mail:* christian.perlee@mheducation.com
Founded: 1971
Thought-provoking series of supplements & online web sites appropriate for college-level courses or for library purchase. Materials span over 20 disciplines & cover compelling, current topics & issues. The publications include annual discipline readers, debate style readers, online readers, geographic/atlas readers & college textbooks.
ISBN Prefix(es): 978-0-07; 978-0-697; 978-0-87967; 978-1-56134; 978-0-7024; 978-0-7235; 978-1-25
Number of titles published annually: 50 Print; 50 Online; 125 E-Book
Total Titles: 350 Print; 350 Online; 246 E-Book

McGraw-Hill Create
Division of McGraw-Hill Higher Education
501 Bell St, Dubuque, IA 52001
Tel: 563-584-6000 *Fax:* 563-584-6600
E-mail: first_last@mcgraw-hill.com
Web Site: www.mhhe.com
Key Personnel
Dir, Print Solutions: Beth Kundert
Tel: 563-584-6302 *Fax:* 563-584-6301
E-mail: beth_kundert@mcgraw-hill.com
Sr Opers Mgr: Pat Koch *Tel:* 609-426-5721
Fax: 609-426-5900 *E-mail:* pat_koch@mcgraw-hill.com
Mgr, Custom Publg Reps: Shirley Grall
Tel: 563-584-6303 *Fax:* 563-584-6300
E-mail: shirley_grall@mcgraw-hill.com
Sr Mgr, Create Mktg Servs: Dudley Land
Tel: 530-621-3976 *Fax:* 775-255-9197
E-mail: dudley_land@mcgraw-hill.com
Dir, Opers & Content Mgmt: Cat Mattura
Tel: 212-904-3559 *Fax:* 212-904-2340
E-mail: cat_mattura@mcgraw-hill.com
VP: Chris Perlee *Tel:* 732-275-1251
E-mail: christian_perlee@mcgraw-hill.com
Order Fulfullment Mgr: Kathy Kilburg *Tel:* 563-584-6282 *E-mail:* kathyj_kilburg@mcgraw-hill.com
Mktg Mgr: Rachel Egan *Tel:* 614-532-5589
E-mail: rachel_egan@mcgraw-hill.com
Custom products derived from McGraw-Hill copyrighted material; college textbook & electronic book adaptations; supplemental materials.
ISBN Prefix(es): 978-0-07
Branch Office(s)
148 Princeton-Hightstown Rd, Hightstown, NJ 08520

2 Penn Plaza, 12th fl, New York, NY 10121-2298
Distribution Center: The McGraw-Hill Companies, Distribution Center, 860 Taylor Station Rd, Blacklick, OH 43004

McGraw-Hill/Dushkin, see McGraw-Hill Contemporary Learning Series

§McGraw-Hill Education
2 Penn Plaza, New York, NY 10121-2298
Tel: 212-904-2000
E-mail: customer.service@mcgraw-hill.com
Web Site: www.mheducation.com; www.mheducation.com/custserv.html
Key Personnel
CEO & Pres, McGraw-Hill Education: David Levin
Chief Communs Offr: Catherine J Mathis
Pres, McGraw-Hill Education International: Mark Dorman
Pres, CTB/McGraw-Hill: Ellen Haley *Tel:* 831-393-7757 *Fax:* 831-393-7243 *E-mail:* ellen_haley@mcgraw-hill.com
Group Pres, US Educ: Peter Cohen
Chief Digital & Info Offr: Bruce D Marcus *Tel:* 212-904-3416 *Fax:* 212-904-3391 *E-mail:* bruce_marcus@mcgraw-hill.com
EVP: William F Oldsey *Tel:* 212-904-4298 *Fax:* 212-904-4299 *E-mail:* william_oldsey@mcgraw-hill.com
SVP, Fin & Opers: Joseph Micallef *Tel:* 212-904-2485 *Fax:* 212-904-4745 *E-mail:* joseph_micallef@mcgraw-hill.com
SVP, HR: Maryellen Valaitis *Tel:* 212-904-3621 *Fax:* 212-904-3661 *E-mail:* maryellen_valaitis@mcgraw-hill.com
SVP, Pub & Govt Aff: Rosemarie Cappabianca *Tel:* 212-904-4563 *Fax:* 212-904-6664 *E-mail:* rosemarie_cappabianca@mcgraw-hill.com
SVP, R&D: Charlotte Frank *Tel:* 212-512-6512 *Fax:* 212-512-4769 *E-mail:* charlotte_frank@mcgraw-hill.com
VP, Learning Ecosystems: Vineet Madan *Tel:* 212-904-3941 *E-mail:* vineet_madan@mcgraw-hill.com
VP, Communs & Mktg: Mary Skafidas *Tel:* 212-904-2078 *Fax:* 212-904-6287 *E-mail:* mary_skafidas@mcgraw-hill.com
Sr Dir, Busn Devt: Derek Wessler *Tel:* 212-904-4311 *E-mail:* derek_wessler@mcgraw-hill.com
Assoc Ed, Intl & Prof Div: Cheryl Ringer
Founded: 1989
McGraw-Hill Education, a division of The McGraw-Hill Companies (NYSE: MHP), is a leading global provider of instructional, assessment & reference solutions that empower professionals & students of all ages. McGraw-Hill Education has offices in numerous countries & publishes in more than 40 languages. Additional information is available at mheducation.com.
ISBN Prefix(es): 978-0-07
Imprints: CTB/McGraw-Hill; Glencoe/McGraw-Hill; The Grow Network/McGraw-Hill; Macmillan/McGraw-Hill; McGraw-Hill Contemporary; McGraw-Hill Create; McGraw-Hill Education Australia, New Zealand & South Africa; McGraw-Hill Education Europe, Middle East and Africa; McGraw-Hill Education Latin America; McGraw-Hill Education - Mexico; McGraw-Hill Education - Spain; McGraw-Hill Humanities, Social Sciences, Languages; McGraw-Hill/Irwin; McGraw-Hill Professional; McGraw-Hill Professional Development; McGraw-Hill Ryerson; McGraw-Hill Science, Engineering, Mathematics; SRA/McGraw-Hill; Tata/McGraw-Hill; The Wright Group/McGraw-Hill
Distribution Center: McGraw-Hill Education Distribution Center: Norcross, 26510 Jimmy Carter Blvd, Norcross, GA 30071 *Tel:* 404-442-3347
McGraw-Hill Education Distribution Center: Gahanna, 860 Taylor Station Rd, Blacklick, OH 43004 *Tel:* 614-755-4151
McGraw-Hill Education Distribution Center: DeSoto, 220 E Danieldale Rd, DeSoto, TX 75115-2490 *Tel:* 214-224-1111
Membership(s): AAP
See separate listing for:
CTB/McGraw-Hill
McGraw-Hill Higher Education
McGraw-Hill International Publishing Group
McGraw-Hill Professional
McGraw-Hill School Education Group

§McGraw-Hill Financial
1221 Avenue of the Americas, 50th fl, New York, NY 10020
SAN: 200-2248
Tel: 212-512-2000
Web Site: www.mhfi.com
Key Personnel
Chmn, Pres & CEO: Harold W (Terry) McGraw, III
Pres, McGraw-Hill Education: Robert Bahash
Pres, Standard & Poors: Deven Sharma
Pres, Info & Media Servs: Glenn S Goldberg
CFO: Jack Callahan
EVP, HR: John Berisford *Tel:* 212-512-6544 *Fax:* 212-512-3481 *E-mail:* john_berisford@mhfi.com
SVP, Corp Aff & Exec Asst to the Chmn: Edward Smith *Tel:* 212-512-3915 *E-mail:* ted_smyth@mhfi.com
SVP, Investor Rel: Donald S Rubin
EVP, Global Strategy: Charles Teschner, Jr
Founded: 1888
A global information services provider for the financial services, education & business information markets.
ISBN Prefix(es): 978-0-8385; 978-0-07; 978-0-83
Divisions: Information & Media Services; McGraw-Hill Education; Standard & Poor's
Membership(s): AAP; American Business Media; Association of Test Publishers; Better Business Bureau; Brookings Institution; Business Roundtable; Conference Board; Copyright Clearance Center; Council for the Americas; Council of Foreign Relations; Direct Marketing Association; Emergency Committee for American Trade; Entertainment Software Rating Board; European Institute; MPA - The Association of Magazine Media; National Association of Broadcasters; National Governor's Association; Private Sector Council; Software & Information Industry Association; United States Chamber of Commerce; United States Council for International Business; US-ASEAN Business Council; US-China Business Council

§McGraw-Hill Higher Education
Division of McGraw-Hill Education
1333 Burr Ridge Pkwy, Burr Ridge, IL 60527
Tel: 630-789-4000 *Toll Free Tel:* 800-338-3987 (cust serv) *Fax:* 614-755-5645 (cust serv)
Web Site: www.mhhe.com
Key Personnel
Group Pres, US Educ: Peter Cohen
SVP, MHHE Fin: Mona Leung *E-mail:* mona.leung@mheducation.com
SVP, Prods & Mkts: Kurt Strand *Tel:* 563-584-6633 *Fax:* 563-584-6600 *E-mail:* kurt.strand@mheducation.com
SVP, Sales: Doug Hughes *Tel:* 630-789-5121 *E-mail:* doug.hughes@mheducation.com
VP, Content Prodn & Tech Servs: Kim David *Tel:* 563-584-6650 *Fax:* 563-584-6701 *E-mail:* kim.david@mheducation.com
VP, MHHE Global Publg: Michael Hays *Tel:* 212-904-5979 *Fax:* 212-904-5974 *E-mail:* michael.hays@mheducation.com
Founded: 1996
College texts.
ISBN Prefix(es): 978-0-07; 978-0-697; 978-0-256; 978-0-87; 978-1-25
Number of titles published annually: 1,100 Print; 50 CD-ROM; 750 Online; 800 E-Book; 5 Audio
Total Titles: 12,000 Print; 1,600 CD-ROM; 6,000 Online; 6,000 E-Book; 120 Audio
Imprints: McGraw-Hill Create; McGraw-Hill/Irwin; McGraw-Hill Learning Solutions; McGraw-Hill Science, Engineering, Mathematics
Divisions: McGraw-Hill Contemporary Learning Series; McGraw-Hill Humanities, Social Sciences, Languages
Orders to: The McGraw-Hill Companies, Distribution Center, 860 Taylor Station Rd, Blacklick, OH 43004-0539 *Toll Free Tel:* 800-338-3987 *Fax:* 614-755-5654
Returns: The McGraw-Hill Companies, Distribution Center, 860 Taylor Station Rd, Blacklick, OH 43004-0539 *Toll Free Tel:* 800-338-3987 *Fax:* 614-755-5654
Shipping Address: The McGraw-Hill Companies, Distribution Center, 860 Taylor Station Rd, Blacklick, OH 43004-0539 *Toll Free Tel:* 800-338-3987 *Fax:* 614-755-5654
Warehouse: The McGraw-Hill Companies, Distribution Center, 860 Taylor Station Rd, Blacklick, OH 43004-0539 *Toll Free Tel:* 800-338-3987 *Fax:* 614-755-5654
Distribution Center: The McGraw-Hill Companies, Distribution Center, 860 Taylor Station Rd, Blacklick, OH 43004-0539 *Toll Free Tel:* 800-338-3987 *Fax:* 614-755-5654
See separate listing for:
McGraw-Hill Career Education
McGraw-Hill Contemporary Learning Series
McGraw-Hill Create
McGraw-Hill Humanities, Social Sciences, Languages
McGraw-Hill/Irwin
McGraw-Hill Science, Engineering, Mathematics

McGraw-Hill Humanities, Social Sciences, Languages
Division of McGraw-Hill Higher Education
2 Penn Plaza, 21st fl, New York, NY 10121
Tel: 212-904-2000 *Toll Free Tel:* 800-338-3987 (cust serv) *Fax:* 614-755-5645 (cust serv)
Web Site: www.mhhe.com
Key Personnel
SVP, Prods & Mkts: Kurt Strand *Tel:* 563-584-6633 *Fax:* 563-584-6600 *E-mail:* kurt.strand@mheducation.com
SVP, Sales: Doug Hughes *Tel:* 630-789-5121 *Fax:* 630-789-6944 *E-mail:* doug.hughes@mheducation.com
VP & Ed-in-Chief: Mike Ryan *Tel:* 212-904-3044 *Fax:* 212-904-3813 *E-mail:* michael.ryan@mheducation.com
VP, Content Prodn & Tech Servs: Kim David *Tel:* 563-584-6650 *Fax:* 563-584-6701 *E-mail:* kim.david@mheducation.com
Founded: 1944
Publishes college textbooks & numerous ebooks.
ISBN Prefix(es): 978-0-07; 978-0-697; 978-0-87; 978-1-25
Number of titles published annually: 300 Print; 11 CD-ROM; 225 Online; 275 E-Book; 15 Audio
Total Titles: 3,500 Print; 150 CD-ROM; 2,500 Online; 2,500 E-Book; 225 Audio
Returns: 860 Taylor Station Rd, Blacklick, OH 43004-0539
Distribution Center: 860 Taylor Station Rd, Blacklick, OH 43004-0539

McGraw-Hill International Publishing Group
Division of McGraw-Hill Education
2 Penn Plaza, New York, NY 10121
Tel: 212-904-2000
Web Site: www.mcgraw-hill.com

Key Personnel
Pres, McGraw-Hill Education International: Mark Dorman
VP, Latin America (Mexico): Javier Nerya *Tel:* (55) 1473-5008 *E-mail:* andres_rodriguez@mcgraw-hill.com
SVP, IPG Canada: David Swail *Tel:* 905-430-5006 *Fax:* 905-430-5020 *E-mail:* david_swail@mcgraw-hill.com
EVP & CFO, Ryerson (Ontario, CN): Gordon Dyer *Tel:* 905-430-5032 *Fax:* 905-430-5020
VP, IBG Opers (UK): Raymond Yager *Tel:* (01628) 502962 *Fax:* (01628) 502963
VP, Fin, LHPG (Mexico): Juan Ortega *Tel:* (55) 5081-4471 *E-mail:* fernando_urresta@mcgraw-hill.com
VP & Mng Dir, India: Ajay Shukla *Tel:* (011) 204-383410 *E-mail:* ajay_shuka@mcgraw-hill.com
Mng Dir, Europe: John Donovan *Tel:* (01628) 502971 *E-mail:* john_donovan@mcgraw-hill.com
ISBN Prefix(es): 978-0-07

§McGraw-Hill/Irwin
Division of McGraw-Hill Higher Education
1333 Burr Ridge Pkwy, Burr Ridge, IL 60527
Tel: 630-789-4000 *Toll Free Tel:* 800-338-3987 (cust serv) *Fax:* 630-789-6942; 614-755-5645 (cust serv)
Web Site: www.mhhe.com
Key Personnel
VP & Chief Mktg Offr: Sharon Loeb *Tel:* 212-904-3731 *E-mail:* sharon_loeb@mcgraw-hill.com
SVP, Prods & Mkts: Kurt Strand *Tel:* 563-584-6633 *E-mail:* kurt.strand@mheducation.com
VP & Natl Sales Mgr: Doug Hughes *Tel:* 630-789-5121 *E-mail:* doug_hughes@mcgraw-hill.com
VP, Content Prodn & Tech Servs: Kim David *Tel:* 563-584-6650 *E-mail:* kim_david@mcgraw-hill.com
Founded: 1933
College textbooks & numerous ebook titles.
ISBN Prefix(es): 978-0-07; 978-0-697; 978-0-256
Number of titles published annually: 230 Print; 57 CD-ROM; 200 Online; 200 E-Book
Total Titles: 2,100 Print; 630 CD-ROM; 1,500 Online; 1,500 E-Book; 1 Audio
Returns: 860 Taylor Station Rd, Blacklick, OH 43004-0539
Distribution Center: 860 Taylor Station Rd, Blacklick, OH 43004-0539

§McGraw-Hill Professional
Division of McGraw-Hill Education
1221 Avenue of the Americas, New York, NY 10020
Tel: 212-512-2000
Web Site: www.mhprofessional.com
Key Personnel
VP, Sales: Lynda Luppino
VP, Publr - Med: Scott Grillo
Dir, STM Rts: Mary Murray
Exec Ed: Donya Dickerson
Sr Ed, Busn Group: Casey Ebro
Publishes "need-to-know" books & other products for a broad range of professional, technical & consumer/reference markets. Key subject areas include business, computing, medicine, technical & consumer reference including foreign languages, dictionaries & self-help. The company also provides online information services to the medical & other markets.
ISBN Prefix(es): 978-0-07
Number of titles published annually: 1,100 Print; 5 Online; 500 E-Book
Total Titles: 12,500 Print; 43 Online; 2,000 E-Book
Imprints: Certification Press; International Marine Publishing; Irwin Professional; Lange Medical Books; NTC Contemporary Books; Oracle Press; Ragged Mountain Press; Schaum
Branch Office(s)
McGraw-Hill Medical, 1333 Burr Ridge Pkwy, Burr Ridge, IL 60527, Ed-in-Chief: James Shanahan *Tel:* 630-789-4000
McGraw-Hill Professional, One Prudential Plaza, Suite 900, 130 E Randolph St, 9th fl, Chicago, IL 60601, Publr: Christopher Brown *Tel:* 312-233-7611
Shipping Address: 7500 Chavenelle Rd, Dubuque, IA 52002
Warehouse: 7500 Chavenelle Rd, Dubuque, IA 52002
Distribution Center: 7500 Chavenelle Rd, Dubuque, IA 52002
Membership(s): AAP; American Medical Publishers Association; International Association of Scientific, Technical & Medical Publishers

McGraw-Hill School Education Group
Division of McGraw-Hill Education
8787 Orion Place, Columbus, OH 43240
Tel: 614-430-4000 *Toll Free Tel:* 800-848-1567
Web Site: www.mheducation.com
Key Personnel
Group Pres, US Educ: Peter Cohen
Pres, School: Christine Willig
SVP, Sales: Sean Ryan
Founded: 1971
Educational materials for elementary, middle school & high school.
ISBN Prefix(es): 978-0-02; 978-0-07; 978-0-31; 978-0-39; 978-0-53; 978-0-65; 978-0-67; 978-0-80; 978-0-84; 978-0-89; 978-0-93; 978-0-96; 978-1-57; 978-1-58; 978-1-88
Imprints: Glencoe (grades 6-12); Macmillan (grades PreK-5)
Branch Office(s)
303 E Wacker Dr, Chicago, IL 60601 *Tel:* 312-233-6500
2 Penn Plaza, New York, NY 10121 *Tel:* 212-904-2000
Foreign Rep(s): The McGraw-Hill Companies (Worldwide); McGraw-Hill Ryerson Limited (Canada)
Orders to: 860 Taylor Station Rd, Blacklick, OH 43004-0543, SVP, Cust Opers: Gerald A Salters *Tel:* 614-759-3825 ext 3825 *Toll Free Tel:* 800-334-7344 *Fax:* 614-759-3670 *E-mail:* gary_salters@mcgraw-hill.com
Returns: 6405 Commerce Ct, Groveport, OH 43125
Shipping Address: 6405 Commerce Ct, Groveport, OH 43125, Sr Dir, Dist: Richard Sestrich *Tel:* 614-835-2302 *Fax:* 614-835-2303
Distribution Center: 6405 Commerce Ct, Groveport, OH 43125 *Toll Free Tel:* 800-334-7344
See separate listing for:
SRA/McGraw-Hill
Wright Group/McGraw-Hill

§McGraw-Hill Science, Engineering, Mathematics
Division of McGraw-Hill Higher Education
501 Bell St, Dubuque, IA 52001
Tel: 563-584-6000 *Toll Free Tel:* 800-338-3987 (cust serv) *Fax:* 614-755-5645 (cust serv)
Web Site: www.mhhe.com
Key Personnel
SVP, Prods & Mkts: Kurt Strand *Tel:* 563-584-6633 *Fax:* 563-584-6600 *E-mail:* kurt.strand@mheducation.com
SVP, Sales: Doug Hughes *Tel:* 630-789-5121 *Fax:* 630-789-6944 *E-mail:* doug.hughes@mheducation.com
VP & Gen Mgr: Marty Lange *Tel:* 563-584-6648 *Fax:* 563-584-6601 *E-mail:* marty.lange@mheducation.com
VP, Content Prodn & Tech Servs: Kim David *Tel:* 563-584-6650 *Fax:* 563-584-6701 *E-mail:* kim.david@mheducation.com
Founded: 1944
College textbook publisher.
ISBN Prefix(es): 978-0-07; 978-0-697; 978-1-25
Number of titles published annually: 260 Print; 8 CD-ROM; 240 Online; 240 E-Book
Total Titles: 1,790 Print; 337 CD-ROM; 2,000 Online; 2,000 E-Book
Imprints: McGraw-Hill
Branch Office(s)
1333 Burr Ridge Pkwy, Burr Ridge, IL 60527 *Tel:* 630-789-4000 *Fax:* 630-789-5030
Returns: 860 Taylor Station Rd, Blacklick, OH 43004-0539
Distribution Center: 860 Taylor Station Rd, Blacklick, OH 43004-0539

McPherson & Co
148 Smith Ave, Kingston, NY 12401
SAN: 203-0632
Mailing Address: PO Box 1126, Kingston, NY 12402-1126
Tel: 845-331-5807 *Fax:* 845-331-5807
E-mail: bmcphersonco@gmail.com
Web Site: www.mcphersonco.com
Key Personnel
Publr & Ed-in-Chief: Bruce R McPherson
Founded: 1973
Fiction, anthropology, belles lettres & avant-garde art.
ISBN Prefix(es): 978-0-914232; 978-0-929701; 978-1-878352 (Saroff Books); 978-1-62054
Number of titles published annually: 5 Print; 5 E-Book
Total Titles: 134 Print; 8 E-Book
Imprints: Documentext; Recovered Classics; Saroff Editions; Treacle Press
Foreign Rights: Agnese Incisa Agenzia Literaria (Italy); Kerigan-Moro Literary (Portugal, Spain); La Nouvelle Agence (France); Prava i Prevodi (Bulgaria, Czech Republic, Hungary, Poland, Serbia, Slovenia); Literarische Agentur Simon (Germany)
Orders to: PO Box 1126, Kingston, NY 12402-1126
Distribution Center: Central Books, 99 Wallis Rd, London E9 5LN, United Kingdom (UK only)
Membership(s): Community of Literary Magazines & Presses

McSweeney's Publishing
849 Valencia St, San Francisco, CA 94110
Tel: 415-642-5609 (cust serv)
Web Site: www.mcsweeneys.net
Key Personnel
Publr & Ed: Jordan Bass
Publicity Dir: Ruby Perez
Ed: Andi Winnette
Founded: 1998
ISBN Prefix(es): 978-1-936365
Number of titles published annually: 25 Print
Total Titles: 150 Print
Foreign Rights: The Wylie Agency (Worldwide)
Distribution Center: Publishers Group West, 1700 Fourth St, Berkeley, CA 94710 *Tel:* 510-809-3700 *Fax:* 510-809-3777 *E-mail:* info@pgw.com *Web Site:* www.pgw.com

MDR, A D&B Co
6 Armstrong Rd, Suite 301, Shelton, CT 06484
Tel: 203-926-4800 *Toll Free Tel:* 800-333-8802 *Fax:* 203-225-4603 *Toll Free Fax:* 866-532-7097
E-mail: mdrinfo@dnb.com
Web Site: schooldata.com
Key Personnel
Gen Mgr: Mike Subrizi
VP, Mktg: Moira McArdle *Tel:* 203-225-4743
VP, Sales & Mktg: Steve Gatland
Mktg Coord: Aggie Mingolello *Tel:* 203-225-4607 *E-mail:* amingo@dnb.com
Founded: 1969
First choice for marketing information & services for the K-12, higher education, library, early

childhood & related education markets. Powered by the most complete, current & accurate education databases available in the industry, MDR provides e-mail contacts & deployment, direct mail lists, sales contact & lead solutions, along with web & social media marketing services.
ISBN Prefix(es): 978-1-57953; 978-1-943664
Number of titles published annually: 51 Print
Branch Office(s)
1050 17 St, Suite 1100, Denver, CO 80265, Pres, MDR Prof Servs: Andy Lacy *Tel:* 303-209-9400 *Fax:* 303-209-9401
20 S Clark St, Suite 2100, Chicago, IL 60603 *Tel:* 312-263-4169 *Fax:* 312-345-4360
Membership(s): AAP PreK-12 Learning Group

Meadowbrook Press
6110 Blue Circle Dr, Suite 237, Minnetonka, MN 55343
SAN: 207-3404
Toll Free Tel: 800-338-2232 *Fax:* 952-930-1940
E-mail: info@meadowbrookpress.com
Web Site: www.meadowbrookpress.com
Key Personnel
Pres & Publr: Bruce Lansky
Busn Mgr: Robyn Beck
Prodn Mgr: Tami Peterson
Founded: 1975
Trade paperbacks; baby & child care, parenting, health, children's activities, humor, parties & games, children's poetry, adult light verse & business travel.
ISBN Prefix(es): 978-0-915658; 978-0-88166
Number of titles published annually: 5 Print
Total Titles: 75 Print
Distributed by Simon & Schuster
Foreign Rep(s): Chris Lloyd Sales & Marketing Services (UK); Monarch Books of Canada (Canada)
Foreign Rights: AM-USA (Seiko Uyeda) (Japan); Arrowsmith Agency (Nina Arrowsmith) (Germany); Big Apple Agency Inc (Wendy King) (China, Taiwan); The Book Publishers Association of Israel (Shoshi Grajower) (Israel); Bridge Communications Co (Pat Akkarasawrt) (Thailand); Iris Literary Agency (Catherine Fragou) (Greece); Alexander Korzhenevski Agency (Alexander Korzhenevski) (Russia); Maxima Creative Agency (Santo Manurung) (Indonesia); Montreal Contacts/The Rights Agency (Luc Jutras) (Canada); Montreal Contacts/The Rights Agency (Anne Confuron) (Canada (French-speaking), France); Kristin Olson Literary Agency (Kristin Olson) (Czech Republic); Publishing & Data Services (Sue Francis) (Australia); RDC Agencia Literaria (Beatriz Coll) (Latin America, Portugal, Spain); Margit Schaleck Literary Agency (Margit Schaleck) (Denmark); Tuttle-Mori Agency Inc (Thailand); WNET (H Katia Schumer) (Brazil); Eric Yang Agency (Henry Shin) (Korea)

me+mi publishing inc
400 S Knoll St, Suite B, Wheaton, IL 60187
Toll Free Tel: 888-251-1444 *Fax:* 630-588-9804
E-mail: rw@rosawesley.com
Web Site: www.memima.com
Key Personnel
Principal & Publr: Gladys Rosa-Mendoza; Mark Wesley
Founded: 2002
Independent publisher dedicated to creating the highest quality books available in two or more languages for infants & toddlers.
ISBN Prefix(es): 978-0-9679748; 978-1-931398
Number of titles published annually: 5 Print
Total Titles: 33 Print
Imprints: The English Spanish Foundation Series
Membership(s): The Independent Book Publishers Association

§R S Means from The Gordian Group
1099 Hingham St, Suite 201, Rockland, MA 02370
Tel: 781-422-5000 *Toll Free Tel:* 800-448-8182 *Fax:* 781-585-8814 *Toll Free Fax:* 800-632-6701
Web Site: www.rsmeans.com
Key Personnel
VP, Sales: Scott Smith
Prod Mgr, RS Means Books: Andrea Sillah
Founded: 1942
A leader in construction cost estimating data, analytics & life cycle cost analysis available in 4 convenient formats: online, books, ebooks +/or CDs.
ISBN Prefix(es): 978-0-911950; 978-0-87629; 978-1-936335
Number of titles published annually: 25 Print
Total Titles: 150 Print
Divisions: Cost Annuals
Distributed by John Wiley & Sons Inc
Advertising Agency: The Stancliff Agency

MedBooks
Division of Professional Education Workshops & Seminars
101 W Buckingham Rd, Richardson, TX 75081-4802
Tel: 972-643-1809 *Fax:* 972-643-1859
E-mail: medbooks@medbooks.com
Web Site: www.medbooks.com
Key Personnel
Owner & Pres: Patrice Morin-Spatz
Gen Mgr: Mark Lerner
Founded: 1985
Specialize in books on health insurance coding & processing for medical offices, insurance companies & other health professions.
ISBN Prefix(es): 978-0-923369; 978-0-9762699; 978-0-9822597; 978-0-9773154; 978-0-9831904; 978-0-9790318; 978-0-9797234; 978-0-9800627; 978-1-937816
Number of titles published annually: 5 Print
Total Titles: 25 Print
Distributed by JA Majors
Membership(s): The Independent Book Publishers Association; Text & Academic Authors

Medical Group Management Association (MGMA)
104 Inverness Terr E, Englewood, CO 80112-5306
Tel: 303-799-1111; 303-799-1111 (ext 1888, book orders) *Toll Free Tel:* 877-275-6462
E-mail: support@mgma.com
Web Site: www.mgma.com
Founded: 1926
Specialize in medical practice management.
ISBN Prefix(es): 978-1-56829
Number of titles published annually: 8 Print; 4 CD-ROM; 1 E-Book
Total Titles: 150 Print; 15 CD-ROM; 1 E-Book; 2 Audio
Branch Office(s)
Government Affairs, 1717 Pennsylvania Ave NW, No 600, Washington, DC 20006, Contact: Anders Gilberg *Tel:* 202-293-3450 *Fax:* 202-293-2787
Distributor for American Medical Association; Aspen Publishers; Greenbranch; HAP (Health Adminstration Press); Jones & Bartlett Learning; J Wiley & Sons

Medical Physics Publishing Corp (MPP)
555 Helgesen Dr, Madison, WI 53718
Tel: 608-262-4021 *Toll Free Tel:* 800-442-5778 (cust serv)
E-mail: mpp@medicalphysics.org
Web Site: www.medicalphysics.org
Key Personnel
Gen Mgr & Intl Rts: Ms Bobbett Shaub *E-mail:* bobbett@medicalphysics.org
Ed: Todd Hanson *E-mail:* todd@medicalphysics.org
Founded: 1985
Publish & distribute books & CD-ROMs in medical physics & related fields.
ISBN Prefix(es): 978-0-944838; 978-1-930524
Number of titles published annually: 6 Print
Total Titles: 100 Print; 3 CD-ROM

Medieval & Renaissance Texts & Studies, see MRTS

Medieval Institute Publications
Division of Medieval Institute of Western Michigan University
WMU East Campus, 100-E Walwood Hall, Kalamazoo, MI 49008
Mailing Address: 1903 W Michigan Ave, Kalamazoo, MI 49008-5432
Tel: 269-387-8755 (orders) *Fax:* 269-387-8750
Web Site: www.wmich.edu/medieval/mip
Key Personnel
Mng Ed: Patricia Hollahan *Tel:* 269-387-8754 *E-mail:* patricia.hollahan@wmich.edu
Founded: 1978
Also publish two journals.
ISBN Prefix(es): 978-1-918720; 978-1-879288; 978-1-58044
Number of titles published annually: 14 Print
Total Titles: 215 Print
Membership(s): Association of American University Presses

MedMaster Inc
3337 Hollywood Oaks Dr, Fort Lauderdale, FL 33312
Mailing Address: PO Box 640028, Miami, FL 33164-0028
Tel: 954-962-8414 *Toll Free Tel:* 800-335-3480 *Fax:* 954-962-4508
E-mail: mmbks@aol.com
Web Site: www.medmaster.net
Key Personnel
Founder & Pres: Stephen Goldberg *E-mail:* stgoldberg@aol.com
VP & Secy: Michael Goldberg
Founded: 1979
Medical book & software publishers; medical subjects for education of medical students & other health professionals.
This publisher has indicated that 100% of their product line is author subsidized.
ISBN Prefix(es): 978-0-940780; 978-1-935660
Number of titles published annually: 6 Print; 1 CD-ROM; 1 E-Book
Total Titles: 31 Print; 8 CD-ROM
Returns: 360 NE 191 St, Miami, FL 33179
Warehouse: 360 NE 191 St, Miami, FL 33179

The Russell Meerdink Co Ltd
1555 S Park Ave, Neenah, WI 54956
SAN: 249-1680
Tel: 920-725-0955 *Toll Free Tel:* 800-635-6499 *Fax:* 920-725-0709
E-mail: questions@horseinfo.com
Web Site: www.horseinfo.com
Key Personnel
Mng Dir & Intl Rts Contact: Jan Meerdink *E-mail:* jmeerdink@horseinfo.com
Founded: 1980
Equine titles & thoroughbred data services. Distribution & mail order sales of equine titles.
ISBN Prefix(es): 978-0-929346
Number of titles published annually: 8 Print; 2 CD-ROM
Total Titles: 33 Print; 4 CD-ROM

Mehring Books Inc
PO Box 48377, Oak Park, MI 48237-5977
Tel: 248-967-2924 *Fax:* 248-967-3023
E-mail: sales@mehring.com
Web Site: www.mehring.com

Key Personnel
Pres: Helen Halyard
Sales Rep: Heather Jowsey
Founded: 1998
Books & journals on contemporary events, history, political economy, Trotsky's writings.
ISBN Prefix(es): 978-0-929087; 978-1-893638
Number of titles published annually: 3 Print
Total Titles: 56 Print
Foreign Rep(s): Arbeiterpresse Verlag (Germany); Mehring Books (Australia, England)

Mel Bay Publications Inc
4 Industrial Dr, Pacific, MO 63069-0066
Tel: 636-257-3970 *Toll Free Tel:* 800-863-5229 *Fax:* 636-257-5062 *Toll Free Fax:* 800-660-9818
E-mail: email@melbay.com
Web Site: www.melbay.com
Key Personnel
Pres: Bryndon Bay *E-mail:* bryndon@melbay.com
VP, Web/IT: Tony Cornejo *E-mail:* tcornejo@melbay.com
Info Systems Supv: Sharon Feldmann *E-mail:* sharon@melbay.com
Founded: 1947
Innovative instructional & performance material for most instruments.
ISBN Prefix(es): 978-0-7866; 978-0-87166; 978-1-56222; 978-8-83206
Number of titles published annually: 500 Print
Total Titles: 4,500 Print
Imprints: Building Excellence; Cathedral Music Press; Editions Classicae; Creative Keyboard; First Lessons; Getting Into; Gig Savers; Qwikguide; School of the Blues; You Can Teach Yourself
Divisions: Cathedral Music Press; Creative Keyboard Publications
Foreign Office(s): Mel Bay Music Ltd, Fortis House, Office 512, 160 London Rd, Barking, Essex IG11 8BB, United Kingdom (sales agent for Europe), Mng Dir: Chris Statham *Tel:* (020) 8214 1222 *Fax:* (020) 8214 1328 *E-mail:* salesuk@melbay.com *Web Site:* www.melbay.com
Distributor for AcuTab Publications Inc; AMA; Chanterelle; Stefan Grossman's Guitar Workshop; Hardie Press; Learn Roots Music; Maggies Music; Malley's; Registry of Guitar Tutors (RGT); RGB Arte Visual; Scott's Highland Services; Voggenreiter Publishers; Walton's; SR Wheat
Foreign Rep(s): ATN Inc (Japan); Chorus Productions (Finland); Mel Bay Music Ltd (Belgium, Central Germany, Croatia, Czech Republic, Denmark, Eastern Africa, Eastern Europe exc Estonia, Latvia, Lithuania & Russia); Music Sales (Australia, New Zealand); People's Music Publishing House (China)
Advertising Agency: Mel Bay Licensing, Industrial Dr, No 4, Pacific, MO 63069, Dir, Music Licensing: Julie Price *Tel:* 678-772-0021 *E-mail:* licensing@melbay.com *Web Site:* www.licensing.melbay.com
Membership(s): ABA

The Mellen Poetry Press
240 Portage Rd, Lewiston, NY 14092
SAN: 207-110X
Mailing Address: PO Box 450, Lewiston, NY 14092-0450
Tel: 716-754-2266; 716-754-1400 (mktg); 716-754-2788 (order fulfillment) *Fax:* 716-754-4056; 716-754-1860 (fulfillment)
E-mail: cservice@mellenpress.com
Web Site: www.mellenpress.com
Key Personnel
Founder & CEO: Herbert Richardson
Publr: Ruth Koheil
Dir & Acqs: Dr John Rupnow *Tel:* 716-754-2266 *E-mail:* jrupnow@mellenpress.com
Fulfillment Dir: Irene Miller *E-mail:* imiller@mellenpress.com
Mktg Dir: Bradley Kaye *E-mail:* editor@mellenpress.com
Prodn Mgr & Perms Ed: Patricia Schultz *E-mail:* pschultz@mellenpress.com
Founded: 1974
Poetry & poetic theory.
ISBN Prefix(es): 978-0-88946; 978-0-7734
Number of titles published annually: 40 Print
Total Titles: 600 Print
Branch Office(s)
Box 67, Queenston, ON, Canada
Foreign Office(s): The Edwin Mellen Press Ltd UK, Mellen House, 16 College St, Lampeter, Ceredigion SA48 7DY, United Kingdom, Mgr, Wales/UK Off: Mrs Iona Williams *Tel:* (01570) 423 356 *Fax:* (01570) 423 775 *E-mail:* emp@mellenpress.co.uk
Advertising Agency: Lewiston Business Services

Menasha Ridge Press Inc
Imprint of Keen Communications
2204 First Ave S, Suite 102, Birmingham, AL 35233
Tel: 205-322-0439 *Toll Free Tel:* 888-604-4537 *Fax:* 205-326-1012
E-mail: info@menasharidge.com
Web Site: www.menasharidge.com
Key Personnel
Pres: Molly B Merkle *Tel:* 205-443-7993 *E-mail:* mmerkle@menasharidge.com
Publr: Robert W Sehlinger *Tel:* 205-443-7989 *E-mail:* bsehlinger@menasharidge.com
Mktg & Publicity Specialist: Pat LaFleur *Tel:* 859-815-7207 *E-mail:* pat@menasharidge.com
Founded: 1982
Outdoor recreation, travel, nature & reference guides.
ISBN Prefix(es): 978-0-89732
Number of titles published annually: 35 Print; 35 E-Book
Total Titles: 140 Print; 100 E-Book
Orders to: Publishers Group West, 1700 Fourth St, Berkeley, CA 94710 *Toll Free Tel:* 800-788-3123 *Toll Free Fax:* 800-351-5073 *Web Site:* www.pgw.com
Returns: Perseus Distribution Returns Dept, 193 Edwards Dr, Jackson, TN 38301 *Toll Free Tel:* 800-788-3123
Membership(s): ABA; Southern Independent Booksellers Alliance

MennoMedia
Formerly Faith & Life Resources
1251 Virginia Ave, Harrisonburg, VA 22802-2434
Toll Free Tel: 800-245-7894 (orders & cust serv US); 800-631-6535 (orders & cust serv CN)
Web Site: www.mennomedia.org
Key Personnel
Edit Dir: Amy Gingerich *Tel:* 540-908-4877 *E-mail:* amyg@mennomedia.org
Founded: 1878
An agency of Mennonite Church USA & Mennonite Church Canada. Small denominational publisher. Specialize in the production of innovative Christian education resources for children, youth, young adults, adults & intergenerational groups. Topics of interest include materials on peace & justice, evangelism, Christian service & radical Christian discipleship.
ISBN Prefix(es): 978-0-87303; 978-0-8361 (Herald Press)
Number of titles published annually: 10 Print
Imprints: Herald Press
Branch Office(s)
718 Main St, Newton, KS 67114 *Tel:* 316-281-4412 *Fax:* 316-283-0454
490 Dutton Dr, Unit C-8, Waterloo, ON N2L 6H7, Canada *Tel:* 519-747-5722 *Fax:* 519-747-5721
See separate listing for:
Herald Press

Mercer University Press
368 Orange St, Macon, GA 31201
Mailing Address: 1400 Coleman Ave, Macon, GA 31207 SAN: 220-0716
Tel: 478-301-2880 *Toll Free Tel:* 866-895-1472 *Fax:* 478-301-2585
E-mail: mupressorders@mercer.edu
Web Site: www.mupress.org
Key Personnel
Dir: Marc Jolley *Tel:* 478-301-2880 *E-mail:* jolley_ma@mercer.edu
Publg Asst: Marsha Luttrell *Tel:* 478-301-4266 *E-mail:* luttrell_mm@mercer.edu
Mktg Dir: Mary Beth Kosowski *Tel:* 478-301-4262 *E-mail:* kosowski_mb@mercer.edu
Cust Serv Assoc: Candice E Morris *Tel:* 478-301-4261 *E-mail:* morris_ce@mercer.edu
Busn Off: Jenny Toole *Tel:* 478-301-4267 *E-mail:* toole_rw@mercer.edu
Founded: 1979
History, philosophy, religion, Southern studies, Southern literature, literary studies, regional interest.
ISBN Prefix(es): 978-0-86554; 978-0-88146
Number of titles published annually: 40 Print
Total Titles: 1,200 Print
Foreign Rep(s): East-West Export Books (Royden Muranaka) (Asia, Australia, New Zealand); The Eurospan Group (Africa, Central Asia, Europe, Middle East, UK)
Warehouse: 1701 Seventh St, Macon, GA 31206
Membership(s): American Association of University Presses

Merit Publishing International Inc
6839 Villas Dr S, Boca Raton, FL 33433
Tel: 561-350-0329; 561-697-1116 (orders)
E-mail: merituk@aol.com; meritpi@aol.com
Web Site: www.meritpublishing.com
Key Personnel
Owner & Pres: Gene Evans
Owner & VP: Dr Marta Garrido
Founded: 1986 (Founded in UK 1986, US 1992)
Medical publishing & marketing in all clinical areas. Questions & answers series, visual diagnosis self-tests series, customized books, slide kits, newsletters, proceedings & monographs, new perspectives series, guides to families & children series.
ISBN Prefix(es): 978-1-873413
Number of titles published annually: 13 Print; 3 CD-ROM
Total Titles: 65 Print; 3 CD-ROM; 3 Online
Foreign Office(s): 30 Wey Barton, Byfleet, Surrey KT14 7EF, United Kingdom, Mrs Gene Evans *Tel:* (01932) 844526 *Fax:* (01932) 820419
Foreign Rep(s): Gazelle (UK); Momento Medico (Italy)
Foreign Rights: J & C Ediciones Medicas (Latin America, Spain)
Orders to: Midpoint Trade Books, 27 W 20 St, Suite 1102, New York, NY 10011; Baker & Taylor, 2550 W Tyrola Rd, Suite 300, Charlotte, NC 28217 (wholesale) *Tel:* 704-998-3100 *Toll Free Tel:* 800-775-1800 *Web Site:* www.btol.com; Ingram Book Co, One Ingram Blvd, La Vergne, TN 37086 *Tel:* 615-793-5000 *Toll Free Tel:* 800-937-8200 *E-mail:* customer.service@ingrambook.com *Web Site:* www.ingrambook.com
Distribution Center: Midpoint Trade Books, 27 W 20 St, Suite 1102, New York, NY 10011 *Tel:* 212-727-0190 *Fax:* 212-727-0195 *Web Site:* www.midpointtradebooks.com
Membership(s): The Independent Book Publishers Association

Meriwether Publishing
Division of Pioneer Drama Service Inc
c/o Pioneer Drama Service, 9707-A E Easter Lane, Englewood, CO 80112
Mailing Address: PO Box 4267, Englewood, CO 80155
Tel: 303-779-4035 *Toll Free Tel:* 800-333-7262 *Fax:* 303-779-4315
E-mail: wholesale@pioneerdrama.com
Web Site: www.pioneerdrama.com
Key Personnel
Publr: Steven Fendrich *E-mail:* steve@pioneerdrama.com
Exec Ed: Debra Fendrich *E-mail:* debra@pioneerdrama.com
Book Dept Coord: Karen Bullock *E-mail:* karen@pioneerdrama.com
Founded: 1960
Books on theater, drama, performing arts, costuming, stagecraft, theatre games, play anthologies, plays, musicals, theatre arts DVDs, theatre/drama education.
ISBN Prefix(es): 978-0-916260; 978-1-56608
Number of titles published annually: 35 Print
Total Titles: 1,500 Print
Foreign Rep(s): Gazelle Book Service (Europe, UK); Hanbury Plays (UK); Mentone Educational Centre (Australia)
Membership(s): Publishers Association of the West

§Merriam Press
133 Elm St, Suite 3R, Bennington, VT 05201-2250
Tel: 802-447-0313
E-mail: ray@merriam-press.com
Web Site: www.merriam-press.com
Key Personnel
Owner: Ray Merriam *E-mail:* ray@merriam-press.com
Founded: 1988
Primarily WWII/military history, memoirs & some fiction; also some non-military history, fiction, memoirs, poetry.
This publisher has indicated that 90% of their product line is author subsidized.
ISBN Prefix(es): 978-1-57638
Number of titles published annually: 40 Print; 20 CD-ROM; 20 E-Book
Total Titles: 250 Print; 150 CD-ROM; 20 E-Book

§Merriam-Webster Inc
Subsidiary of Encyclopaedia Britannica Inc
47 Federal St, Springfield, MA 01102
Mailing Address: PO Box 281, Springfield, MA 01102-0281
Tel: 413-734-3134 *Toll Free Tel:* 800-828-1880 (orders & cust serv) *Fax:* 413-731-5979 (sales)
E-mail: support@merriam-webster.com
Web Site: www.merriam-webster.com
Key Personnel
Pres & Publr: John M Morse
CFO: Caryl Schivley
VP & Dir, Sales: Jed Santoro *E-mail:* jsantoro@m-w.com
VP, Busn Devt: Matthew Dube
Dir, Eng Lang Learning Publg: Jane Mairs
Dir, Mktg: Meghan Lunghi *E-mail:* mlunghi@m-w.com
Founded: 1831
Dictionaries & language reference products.
ISBN Prefix(es): 978-0-87779
Number of titles published annually: 4 Print
Total Titles: 102 Print; 7 CD-ROM; 2 Online; 2 E-Book
Imprints: Federal Street Press
Divisions: Federal Street Press
See separate listing for:
Federal Street Press

Mesorah Publications Ltd
4401 Second Ave, Brooklyn, NY 11232
SAN: 213-1269
Tel: 718-921-9000 *Toll Free Tel:* 800-637-6724 *Fax:* 718-680-1875
E-mail: artscroll@mesorah.com
Web Site: www.artscroll.com; www.mesorah.com
Key Personnel
Pres & Intl Rts Contact: Meir Zlotowitz
EVP & Ed-in-Chief: Nosson Scherman
VP & Prodn Mgr: Jacob Brander *E-mail:* jacob@mesorah.com
Founded: 1976
Judaica, Bible study, liturgical materials, juvenile, history, Holocaust, Talmud, novels.
ISBN Prefix(es): 978-0-89906; 978-1-57819
Number of titles published annually: 50 Print
Total Titles: 850 Print
Imprints: Art Scroll Series; Shaar Press; Tamar Books
Distributor for NCSY Publications
Foreign Rep(s): Stephen Blitz (Israel)
Returns: 222 44 St, Brooklyn, NY 11232

Messianic Jewish Publishers
Division of Messianic Jewish Communications
6120 Day Long Lane, Clarksville, MD 21029
Tel: 410-531-6644 *Toll Free Tel:* 800-410-7367 (orders) *Fax:* 410-531-9440 (no orders)
E-mail: lederer@messianicjewish.net; rightsandpermissions@messianicjewish.net (rights & perms)
Web Site: messianicjewish.net
Key Personnel
Pres: Barry Rubin *E-mail:* president@messianicjewish.net
Mng Ed: Lisa Rubin
Founded: 1949
Publish & distribute Messianic Jewish books & other products.
ISBN Prefix(es): 978-1-880226
Number of titles published annually: 12 Print; 6 E-Book
Total Titles: 82 Print; 40 E-Book
Divisions: Lederer Books
Distributor for Chosen People Ministries; First Fruits of Zion; Jewish New Testament Publications
Foreign Rep(s): Winfried Bluth (Europe)
Foreign Rights: Winfried Bluth (Europe)
Membership(s): CBA: The Association for Christian Retail; Evangelical Christian Publishers Association
See separate listing for:
Lederer Books

§The Metropolitan Museum of Art
1000 Fifth Ave, New York, NY 10028
SAN: 202-6279
Tel: 212-879-5500; 212-570-3725 *Fax:* 212-396-5062
E-mail: editorial@metmuseum.org
Web Site: www.metmuseum.org
Key Personnel
CEO & Dir: Thomas P Campbell
Pres: Emily K Rafferty
Publr & Ed-in-Chief: Mark Polizzotti
Assoc Publr & Gen Mgr, Pubns: Gwen Roginsky
Chief Prodn Mgr: Peter Antony
Mgr, Spec Pubns: Robie Rogge
Founded: 1870
Art books, exhibition catalogs, quarterly bulletin, annual journal.
ISBN Prefix(es): 978-0-87099; 978-1-58839
Number of titles published annually: 30 Print
Total Titles: 250 Print; 5 CD-ROM
Distributed by Yale University Press
Foreign Rep(s): Yale University Press
Warehouse: Middle Village, Queens, NY 11381-0001

MFA Publications
Imprint of Museum of Fine Arts Boston
465 Huntington Ave, Boston, MA 02115
Tel: 617-369-4233 *Fax:* 617-369-3459
Web Site: www.mfa.org/publications
Key Personnel
Publr: Emiko Usui *Tel:* 617-369-4231 *E-mail:* eusui@mfa.org
Prod Mgr: Terry McAweeney
Sales & Mktg: Chris Di Pietro *E-mail:* cdipietro@mfa.org
Founded: 1877
Exhibition & collection catalogues; general interest & trade arts publications, children's books. No returns accepted.
ISBN Prefix(es): 978-0-87846
Number of titles published annually: 12 Print
Total Titles: 80 Print
Imprints: ArtWorks
Distributed by Art Books/D A P
Warehouse: c/o PSSC, 46 Development Rd, Fitchburg, MA 01420

MGI Management Institute Inc
Subsidiary of SmartPros Ltd
12 Skyline Dr, Hawthorne, NY 10532
Tel: 914-428-6500 *Toll Free Tel:* 800-932-0191 *Fax:* 914-428-0773
E-mail: mgiusa@aol.com
Web Site: www.mgi.org
Key Personnel
Mgr: Sandra Wacht
Founded: 1968
Home study guides.
Number of titles published annually: 60 Print
Total Titles: 60 Print; 5 Online; 5 E-Book

Michelin Maps & Guides
Division of Michelin North America Inc
One Parkway S, Greenville, SC 29615-5022
Tel: 864-458-5565 *Fax:* 864-458-5665 *Toll Free Fax:* 866-297-0914; 888-773-7979
E-mail: orders@americanmap.com (orders)
Web Site: www.michelintravel.com; www.michelinguide.com
Key Personnel
Dir, B&B Sales & Mktg: Christopher Aufmuth
Cust Serv Mgr: Steve Hunt
Gen Mgr: Hellan Mitchell *E-mail:* hellan.mitchell@us.michelin.com
Founded: 1900
Specialize in travel publications; hotel & restaurant guides.
ISBN Prefix(es): 978-2-06
Number of titles published annually: 50 Print
Total Titles: 175 Print
Distributed by Editions du Renouveau Pedagogique (French titles in Canada); Langenscheidt Publishing Group; MAPART Publishing (CN only); NBN (guides for North America); Penguin Canada (English titles in Canada)
Orders to: PO Box 19001, Greenville, SC 29615 *Toll Free Tel:* 800-423-0485 *Toll Free Fax:* 800-378-7471

Michigan Municipal League
Affiliate of National League of Cities
1675 Green Rd, Ann Arbor, MI 48105
Mailing Address: PO Box 1487, Ann Arbor, MI 48106-1487
Tel: 734-662-3246 *Toll Free Tel:* 800-653-2483 *Fax:* 734-663-4496
Web Site: www.mml.org
Key Personnel
Ed: Kim Cekola *Tel:* 734-669-6321 *E-mail:* kcekola@mml.org
Founded: 1899
Municipal topics & newsletters, services & publications for local governments in Michigan.
ISBN Prefix(es): 978-1-929923
Number of titles published annually: 6 Print
Distributor for Crisp Books

§Michigan State University Press (MSU Press)
Division of Michigan State University

1405 S Harrison Rd, Suite 25, East Lansing, MI 48823
SAN: 202-6295
Tel: 517-355-9543 *Fax:* 517-432-2611
Toll Free Fax: 800-678-2120
E-mail: msupress@msu.edu
Web Site: www.msupress.msu.edu
Key Personnel
Dir: Gabriel Dotto *Tel:* 517-884-6900
Asst Dir & Ed-in-Chief: Julie L Loehr *Tel:* 517-884-6905 *E-mail:* loehr@msu.edu
Mng Ed: Kristine M Blakeslee *Tel:* 517-884-6912
Prodn Mgr: Annette K Tanner *Tel:* 517-884-6910
Busn & Fin Offr: Julie Wrzesinski *Tel:* 517-884-6922
Mktg & Sales: Julie K Reaume *Tel:* 517-884-6920
Founded: 1947
Scholarly works & general nonfiction trade books.
ISBN Prefix(es): 978-1-882997; 978-0-916418; 978-0-944311; 978-0-88406; 978-0-937191; 978-1-55238; 978-0-87013
Number of titles published annually: 40 Print; 2 CD-ROM; 10 E-Book
Total Titles: 650 Print; 4 CD-ROM; 59 E-Book
Distributed by UBC Press, Canada
Distributor for Mackinac Historic Parks; MSU Museum; University of Alberta Press; University of Calgary Press; University of Manitoba Press
Foreign Rep(s): Eurospan (Europe); Raincoast Books-University of British Columbia Press (Canada)
Orders to: Chicago Distribution Center, 11030 S Langley Ave, Chicago, IL 60628 *Toll Free Tel:* 800-621-2736 *Toll Free Fax:* 800-621-8476 *Web Site:* www.press.uchicago.edu
Returns: Chicago Distribution Center, 11030 S Langley Ave, Chicago, IL 60628 *Toll Free Tel:* 800-621-2736 *Toll Free Fax:* 800-621-8476 *Web Site:* www.press.uchicago.edu
Distribution Center: Chicago Distribution Center, 11030 S Langley Ave, Chicago, IL 60628 *Toll Free Tel:* 800-621-2736 *Toll Free Fax:* 800-621-8476 *Web Site:* www.press.uchicago.edu
Membership(s): American Association of University Presses; Society for Scholarly Publishing

§Microsoft Press
Division of Microsoft Corp
One Microsoft Way, Redmond, WA 98052-6399
SAN: 264-9969
Tel: 425-882-8080 *Toll Free Tel:* 800-677-7377
Fax: 425-936-7329
Web Site: www.microsoft.com/learning/books
Key Personnel
Assoc Publr & Developer: Al Valvano
Founded: 1983
Computing, technical, professional & chess.
ISBN Prefix(es): 978-1-55615; 978-1-57231; 978-0-7356
Number of titles published annually: 160 Print
Total Titles: 400 Print; 20 CD-ROM; 100 Online; 1 E-Book
Subsidiaries: Microsoft Press France; Microsoft Press Germany
Distributed by O'Reilly Media (Asia, Australia, Europe, New Zealand, North America, UK); Shroff Publishers & Distributors (India)
Foreign Rep(s): ITP Nelson
Warehouse: 121 N Enterprise Blvd, Lebanon, IN 46052
Distribution Center: John Wiley & Sons, 111 River St, Hoboken, NJ 07030-5774 *Tel:* 201-748-6000 *Fax:* 201-748-6088 *E-mail:* info@wiley.com *Web Site:* www.wiley.com

Mid-List Press
6524 Brownlee Dr, Nashville, TN 37205-3038
Tel: 615-822-3777 *Fax:* 612-823-8387
E-mail: guide@midlist.org
Web Site: www.midlist.org
Key Personnel
Bd Pres: Dan Verdick
Exec Dir: Marianne Leslie Nora
Publr: Lane Stiles
Founded: 1989
Fiction, creative nonfiction & poetry.
ISBN Prefix(es): 978-0-922811
Number of titles published annually: 2 Print; 5 E-Book
Total Titles: 60 Print; 7 E-Book

Midmarch Arts Press
300 Riverside Dr, New York, NY 10025-5239
SAN: 200-8882
Tel: 212-666-6990
Web Site: midmarchartspress.org
Key Personnel
Dir: Cynthia Navaretta
Mgr: Lynda Hulkower
Ed: Sylvia Moore; Judy Seigel
Founded: 1975
Books.
ISBN Prefix(es): 978-1-877675
Number of titles published annually: 3 Print
Total Titles: 118 Print
Returns: 19 Deep Six Dr, East Hampton, NY 11937
Warehouse: 19 Deep Six Dr, East Hampton, NY 11937
Membership(s): College Art Association; International Association of Art Critics

Midnight Marquee Press Inc
9721 Britinay Lane, Baltimore, MD 21234
Tel: 410-665-1198
E-mail: mmarquee@aol.com
Web Site: www.midmar.com
Key Personnel
Pres: Gary Svehla
VP & Lib Sales Dir: Susan Svehla
Founded: 1995
Publisher of books, two magazines, graphic novels with the main focus on film history, biographies & mysteries.
ISBN Prefix(es): 978-1-887664
Number of titles published annually: 6 Print
Total Titles: 150 Print

§MidWest Plan Service (MWPS)
Affiliate of Iowa State University-Information Technology Services
Iowa State University, 122 Davidson Hall, Ames, IA 50011-3080
Tel: 515-294-4337 *Toll Free Tel:* 800-562-3618
Fax: 515-294-9589
E-mail: mwps@iastate.edu
Web Site: www.mwps.org
Key Personnel
Graphics & Pubns: Kathy Walker
E-mail: kjwalker@iastate.edu
Liaison: Jay Harmon *E-mail:* jharmon@iastate.edu
Founded: 1932
Educational publishing consortium located at Iowa State University that provides science-based low cost & free information & building plans to persons in agriculture & related businesses as well as to acreage & homeowners.
ISBN Prefix(es): 978-0-89373
Number of titles published annually: 3 Print; 1 CD-ROM; 2 Online; 1 E-Book
Total Titles: 77 Print; 6 CD-ROM; 19 Online; 2 E-Book
Distributed by Natural Resource Agriculture & Engineering Service
Distributor for Natural Resource Agriculture & Engineering Service

§Mighty Media Press
Formerly Scarletta
1201 Currie Ave, Minneapolis, MN 55403
Tel: 612-455-0252 *Fax:* 612-338-4817
E-mail: info@mightymedia.com
Web Site: www.mightymediapress.com
Key Personnel
Publr & Creative Dir: Nancy Tuminelly *Tel:* 612-338-2075 *E-mail:* nancy@mightymedia.com
Mktg Dir & Publicity: Sammy Bosch
E-mail: sammy@mightymedia.com
Founded: 2005
Delivers captivating books & media that ignite a child's curiosity, imagination, social awareness & sense of adventure.
ISBN Prefix(es): 978-0-9765201; 978-0-9798249; 978-0-9824584; 978-0-9830219; 978-1-938063
Number of titles published annually: 10 Print; 10 E-Book
Total Titles: 36 Print; 40 E-Book
Imprints: Mighty Media Junior Readers (middle grade literature); Mighty Media Kids (picture books & first reader/beginner books); Red Portal Press
Foreign Rights: Letter Soup Rights Agency (Allison Olson) (Worldwide)
Returns: Perseus Distribution, Returns Dept, 193 Edwards Dr, Jackson, TN
Distribution Center: Publishers Group West, 1700 Fourth St, Berkeley, CA 94710 *Tel:* 510-809-3700 *Toll Free Tel:* 800-788-3123
Membership(s): ABA; The Children's Book Council; Midwest Independent Booksellers Association; Midwest Independent Publishers Association; Minnesota Book Publishers Roundtable; Minnesota Bookbuilders; Society of Children's Book Writers & Illustrators

Mike Murach & Associates Inc
4340 N Knoll Ave, Fresno, CA 93722
SAN: 264-2255
Tel: 559-440-9071 *Toll Free Tel:* 800-221-5528
Fax: 559-440-0963
E-mail: murachbooks@murach.com
Web Site: www.murach.com
Key Personnel
Pres: Ben Murach
Mktg: Cynthia Vasquez *Tel:* 559-440-9071 ext 18
E-mail: cyndi@murach.com
Founded: 1974
Computer books.
ISBN Prefix(es): 978-0-911625; 978-1-890774
Number of titles published annually: 5 Print
Total Titles: 50 Print
Distributed by Shroff Publishers (reprints)
Foreign Rep(s): BPB Publications Ltd (India); Gazelle Book Services Ltd (Continental Europe, UK); Woodslane Pty Ltd (Australia, New Zealand)

§Milady
Division of Cengage Learning
Executive Woods, 5 Maxwell Dr, Clifton Park, NY 12065-2919
Tel: 518-348-2300 *Toll Free Tel:* 800-998-7498
Fax: 518-373-6309
Web Site: milady.cengage.com
Key Personnel
Pres: Dawn Gerrain *Tel:* 518-348-2300 ext 2409
E-mail: dawn.gerrain@cengage.com
Dir, Indus Rel: Sandra Bruce *Tel:* 518-348-2300 ext 2378
Founded: 1928
Textbooks, workbooks, exam reviews, AV materials & instructional software, newsletters, cosmetology & beauty education.
ISBN Prefix(es): 978-1-56253; 978-0-87350; 978-1-4018; 978-1-4180
Number of titles published annually: 220 Print
Total Titles: 288 Print
Foreign Office(s): Cengage Learning-Australia, 80 Dorcas St, Level 7, South Melbourne, Victoria 3205, Australia *Tel:* (03) 9685 4111 *Fax:* (03) 9685 4199
Cengage Learning-Latin America, Av Santa Fe 505 piso 12, Col Cruz Manca Sante Fe, Cuaji-

malpa CP, 05349 Mexico, DF, Mexico *Tel:* 55 1500 6000
Cengage Learning-EMEA, Cheriton House, North Way, Andover, Hampshire SP10 5BE, United Kingdom *Tel:* (01264) 332424 *Fax:* (01264) 342763
Distribution Center: 10650 Toebben Dr, Independence, KY 41051

Military Info Publishing
PO Box 41211, Plymouth, MN 55442
Tel: 763-533-8627 *Fax:* 763-533-8627
E-mail: publisher@military-info.com
Web Site: www.military-info.com
Key Personnel
Publr: Bruce A Hanesalo
Founded: 1987
Reprint historical military technology, including 34 books, 11,000 photocopies & 400 other items.
ISBN Prefix(es): 978-1-886848
Number of titles published annually: 4 Print
Total Titles: 34 Print

Military Living Publications
Division of Military Marketing Services Inc
333 Maple Ave E, Suite 3130, Vienna, VA 22180-4717
Tel: 703-237-0203 (ext 1) *Toll Free Tel:* 877-363-4677 (ext 1) *Fax:* 703-997-8861
E-mail: customerservice@militaryliving.com
Web Site: www.militaryliving.com
Key Personnel
CEO: William R Crawford, Sr
Founded: 1969
Publisher of military travel atlases, maps & directories; for military only.
ISBN Prefix(es): 978-0-914862; 978-1-931424
Number of titles published annually: 8 Print
Total Titles: 12 Print
Foreign Rep(s): US Forces Exchanges

Milkweed Editions
1011 Washington Ave S, Suite 300, Minneapolis, MN 55415-1246
Tel: 612-332-3192 *Toll Free Tel:* 800-520-6455 *Fax:* 612-215-2550
Web Site: www.milkweed.org
Key Personnel
CEO & Publr: Daniel Slager
Mng Dir: Patrick Thomas *E-mail:* patrick_thomas@milkweed.org
Devt Mgr: Kate Strickland
Mktg Assoc: Casey O'Neil
Admin Asst: Tracy Mumford
Founded: 1980
Literary, nonprofit, independent press.
ISBN Prefix(es): 978-0-915943; 978-1-57131
Number of titles published annually: 18 Print; 18 E-Book; 1 Audio
Total Titles: 250 Print; 10 E-Book; 5 Audio
Foreign Rights: Ben Barnhart (Worldwide)
Distribution Center: Publishers Group West, 1700 Fourth St, Berkeley, CA 94710 *Tel:* 510-809-3700 *Toll Free Tel:* 800-788-3123 *Fax:* 510-528-3444
Membership(s): ABA; The Children's Book Council; Community of Literary Magazines & Presses; The Independent Book Publishers Association; Midwest Independent Booksellers Association; Southern Independent Booksellers Alliance

Millbrook Press
Division of Lerner Publishing Group Inc
241 First Ave N, Minneapolis, MN 55401
Tel: 612-332-3344 *Toll Free Tel:* 800-328-4929 (US only) *Fax:* 612-332-7615 *Toll Free Fax:* 800-332-1132
Key Personnel
Chmn: Harry J Lerner
CFO & EVP: Margaret Wunderlich
Pres & Publr: Adam Lerner
EVP, Sales: David Wexler
EVP & Dir, Mktg & Digital Prods: Terri Soutor
VP, Ed-in-Chief: Patricia M Stockland
VP, Prodn: Gary Hansen
VP, Digital Prod Mgmt: Daniel Wallek
Edit Dir: Carol Hinz
Rts Dir: Maria Kjoller
Dir, HR: Cyndi Radant
Art Dir: Zach Marell
Group Mktg Dir: Jill Braithwaite
School & Lib Mktg Dir: Lois Wallentine
Founded: 1989
ISBN Prefix(es): 978-1-56294; 978-1-878841; 978-0-7613; 978-1-878137
Total Titles: 630 Print; 775 E-Book
Foreign Rep(s): INT Press Distribution (Australia); Monarch (Canada); Phambili (Southern Africa); Publishers Marketing Services (Brunei, Malaysia, Singapore); Saunders (Canada); South Pacific Books (New Zealand)
Foreign Rights: Japan Foreign-Rights Centre (Japan); Korea Copyright Center (Korea); Michelle Lapautre Agence Junior (France); Literarische Agentur Silke Weniger (Germany)
Warehouse: Lerner Publishing Group, 1251 Washington Ave N, Minneapolis, MN 55401

Richard K Miller Associates
4132 Atlanta Hwy, Suite 110, Loganville, GA 30052
Tel: 404-276-3376 *Toll Free Tel:* 888-928-RKMA (928-7562) *Toll Free Fax:* 877-928-7562
Web Site: rkma.com
Key Personnel
Pres: Richard K Miller *E-mail:* richard.miller@rkma.com
Founded: 1972
Market research reference handbooks for college & corporate libraries. Subjects include consumer behavior, marketing, retail, travel, healthcare, entertainment & restaurants.
ISBN Prefix(es): 978-1-57783
Number of titles published annually: 6 Print; 6 Online; 1 E-Book
Total Titles: 11 Print; 11 Online; 11 E-Book

Robert Miller Gallery
524 W 26 St, New York, NY 10001
Tel: 212-366-4774 *Fax:* 212-366-4454
E-mail: rmg@robertmillergallery.com
Web Site: www.robertmillergallery.com
Key Personnel
Dir: Betsy Miller
Founded: 1977
Art books on artwork by represented artists.
ISBN Prefix(es): 978-0-944680
Number of titles published annually: 3 Print
Total Titles: 30 Print

§Milliken Publishing Co
Division of The Lorenz Corp
501 E Third St, Dayton, OH 45402
Mailing Address: PO Box 802, Dayton, OH 45401-0802
Tel: 937-228-6118 *Toll Free Tel:* 800-444-1144 *Fax:* 937-223-2042
E-mail: order@lorenz.com
Web Site: www.lorenz.educationalpress.com
Key Personnel
VP, Mktg: Debra Kaiser *E-mail:* debk@lorenz.com
Founded: 1960
Educational publishing division includes visual resources, instructional guides & reproducibles; elementary supplementals.
ISBN Prefix(es): 978-0-88335; 978-1-55863; 978-1-42911
Number of titles published annually: 20 Print
Total Titles: 400 Print; 20 CD-ROM; 200 E-Book; 6 Audio
Membership(s): Education Market Association

§The Minerals, Metals & Materials Society (TMS)
Affiliate of AIME
184 Thorn Hill Rd, Warrendale, PA 15086
Tel: 724-776-9000 *Toll Free Tel:* 800-759-4867 *Fax:* 724-776-3770
E-mail: publications@tms.org (orders)
Web Site: www.tms.org (orders)
Key Personnel
Exec Dir: James J Robinson *E-mail:* robinson@tms.org
Content Specialist: Matt Baker *E-mail:* mbaker@tms.org
Founded: 1871
Leading professional society dedicated to the development & dissemination of scientific & engineering knowledge for materials-centered technology. The society is the only professional organization that encompasses the entire spectrum of materials & engineering, from minerals processing through the advanced applications of materials.
ISBN Prefix(es): 978-0-87339
Number of titles published annually: 25 Print

Minnesota Historical Society Press
Division of Minnesota Historical Society
345 Kellogg Blvd W, St Paul, MN 55102-1906
SAN: 202-6384
Tel: 651-259-3205; 651-259-3000 *Toll Free Tel:* 800-621-2736 (warehouse) *Fax:* 651-297-1345 *Toll Free Fax:* 800-621-8476 (warehouse)
E-mail: info-mnhspress@mnhs.org
Web Site: www.mnhs.org/mnhspress
Key Personnel
Dir & Intl Rts: Pamela McClanahan *Tel:* 651-259-3210 *E-mail:* pamela.mcclanahan@mnhs.org
Ed-in-Chief: Ann Regan *Tel:* 651-259-3206 *E-mail:* ann.regan@mnhs.org
Mng Ed: Shannon M Pennefeather *Tel:* 651-259-3212 *E-mail:* shannon.pennefeather@mnhs.org
Acqs Ed: Josh Leventhal
Mktg & Sales Mgr: Mary Poggione *Tel:* 651-259-3204 *E-mail:* mary.poggione@mnhs.org
Sales Mgr: Jerry Bilek; Nan Fulle
Founded: 1849
Scholarly & trade books on Upper Midwest history & prehistory.
ISBN Prefix(es): 978-0-87351
Number of titles published annually: 20 Print; 100 E-Book
Total Titles: 350 Print; 6 Audio
Imprints: Borealis Books
Foreign Rep(s): Gazelle Books Services Ltd (Europe, UK)
Warehouse: Chicago Distribution Center, 11030 S Langley Ave, Chicago, IL 60628 *Toll Free Tel:* 800-621-2736 (orders) *Toll Free Fax:* 800-621-8476 (orders)
Membership(s): American Association of University Presses

MIT List Visual Arts Center
MIT E 15-109, 20 Ames St, Cambridge, MA 02139
Tel: 617-253-4400; 617-253-4680 *Fax:* 617-258-7265
E-mail: mlinga@mit.edu
Web Site: listart.mit.edu
Key Personnel
Dir: Paul C Ha
Asst Dir: David Freilach *Tel:* 617-253-5076 *E-mail:* freilach@mit.edu
Admin Asst: Barbra Pine *Tel:* 617-253-9479 *E-mail:* barbra@media.mit.edu
Founded: 1966
Contemporary art.
ISBN Prefix(es): 978-0-938437
Number of titles published annually: 6 Print
Distributed by DAP Distributed Art Publishers

§The MIT Press
55 Hayward St, Cambridge, MA 02142
SAN: 202-6414
Tel: 617-253-5255 *Toll Free Tel:* 800-207-8354 (orders) *Fax:* 617-258-6779; 617-577-1545 (orders)
Web Site: mitpress.mit.edu
Key Personnel
Cont: Charles Hale *Tel:* 617-258-0577 *E-mail:* chale@mit.edu
Dir: Amy Brand *Tel:* 617-253-4078 *E-mail:* amybrand@mit.edu
Dir, Fin & Opers & Assoc Dir: Rebecca Schrader *Tel:* 617-253-5250 *E-mail:* recs@mit.edu
Dir, Intl Property Licensing: William Smith
Dir, Journals: Nick Lindsay *Tel:* 617-258-0594 *E-mail:* nlindsay@mit.edu
Mktg Dir: Katie Hope *Tel:* 617-258-0603 *E-mail:* khope@mit.edu
Dir, Sales: Anne Bunn *Tel:* 617-253-8838 *E-mail:* annebunn@mit.edu
Dir, Technol: Bill Trippe *Tel:* 617-452-3747 *E-mail:* trippe@mit.edu
Edit Dir: Gita Manaktala *Tel:* 617-253-3172 *E-mail:* manak@mit.edu
Mng Ed: Michael Sims *Tel:* 617-253-2080 *E-mail:* msims@mit.edu
Exec Ed: Roger L Conover *Tel:* 617-253-1677 *E-mail:* conover@mit.edu; Robert Prior *Tel:* 617-253-1584 *E-mail:* prior@mit.edu
Sr Acqs Ed: John S Covell *Tel:* 617-253-3757 *E-mail:* jcovell@mit.edu; James S De Wolf *Tel:* 617-253-1558 *E-mail:* jdewolf@mit.edu; Phil Laughlin *Tel:* 617-252-1636 *E-mail:* laughlin@mit.edu; Clay Morgan *Tel:* 617-253-4113 *E-mail:* claym@mit.edu; Douglas Sery *Tel:* 617-253-5187 *E-mail:* dsery@mit.edu
Acqs Ed: Marguerite Avery *Tel:* 617-253-1653 *E-mail:* mavery@mit.edu; Jane MacDonald *Tel:* 617-253-1605 *E-mail:* janem@mit.edu
Ad Mgr: Anar Badalov *Tel:* 617-253-3516 *E-mail:* badalov@mit.edu
Design Mgr: Yasuyo Iguchi *Tel:* 617-253-8034 *E-mail:* iguchi@mit.edu
Digital Publg Mgr: Jake Furbush *Tel:* 617-258-0583 *E-mail:* jfurbush@mit.edu
Exhibits Mgr: John Costello *Tel:* 617-258-5764 *E-mail:* jcostell@mit.edu
Prodn Mgr: Janet Rossi *Tel:* 617-253-2882 *E-mail:* janett@mit.edu
Promos & Direct Mail Mgr: Astrid Baehrecke *Tel:* 617-253-7297 *E-mail:* baehreck@mit.edu
Publicity Mgr: Colleen Lanick *Tel:* 617-253-2874 *E-mail:* colleenl@mit.edu
Subs Rts Mgr: Cristina Sanmartin *Tel:* 617-253-0629 *E-mail:* csan@mit.edu
Textbook Promos Mgr: Michelle Pullano *Tel:* 617-253-3620 *E-mail:* mpullano@mit.edu
Asst Journals Mgr & Journals Busn Mgr: June McCaull *Tel:* 617-258-0593 *E-mail:* jmccaull@mit.edu
Bookstore Mgr: John Jenkins *Tel:* 617-253-5249 *E-mail:* jjenkins@mit.edu
Founded: 1962
Scholarly & professional books, advanced textbooks, nonfiction trade books & reference books; architecture & design, cognitive sciences & linguistics, computer science & artificial intelligence, economics & management sciences, environmental studies; philosophy, neuroscience; technology studies; new media; paperbacks, journals.
ISBN Prefix(es): 978-0-262
Number of titles published annually: 250 Print
Total Titles: 3,400 Print; 5 CD-ROM; 2 Online; 1 E-Book
Imprints: Bradford Books
Foreign Office(s): The MIT Press Ltd, One Duchess St, Suite 2, London W1W 6AN, United Kingdom *Tel:* (020) 7306 0603 *Fax:* (020) 7306 0604 *E-mail:* info@mitpress.org.uk
Distributor for AAAI Press; Canadian Centre for Architecture; Zone Books
Foreign Rep(s): Academic Book Promotions (France, Scandinavia); American University Press Group (Hong Kong, Japan, Korea, Taiwan); Apac Publishers Services Pte Ltd; Cassidy & Associates (China); Rodney Franklin Agency (Israel); Christopher Humphrys; Humphrys Roberts Associates (Latin America); Uwe Ludemann (Austria, Germany, Italy, Switzerland); Mediamatics (India); MIT Press Ltd (Greece, Ireland, UK); David Stimpson (Australia, Canada, New Zealand); Cory Voigt Associates (South Africa)
Foreign Rights: Agencia Litterana Carmen Balcells (Maribel Luque) (Spain); Bardon-Chinese Media (Joanne Yang) (Taiwan); The Berlin Agency (Frauke Jung-Lindemann) (Germany); The English Agency (Tsutomu Yawata) (Japan); Graal Literary Agency (Lukasz Wrobel) (Poland); The Deborah Harris Agency (Ilana Kurshan) (Israel); Agence Hoffman (Christine Scholz) (France); The Kayi Agency (Dilek Kayi) (Turkey); KCC (Sageun Lee) (Korea); Alexander Korzheneveski Agency (Alexander Korzheneveski) (Russia); OA Literary Agency (Michael Avramides) (Greece); Reiser Literary Agency (Roberto Gilodi) (Italy); Agencia Riff (Joao Riff) (Brazil)
Warehouse: Triliteral LLC, 100 Maple Ridge Dr, Cumberland, RI 02864 *Tel:* 401-658-4226 *Fax:* 401-658-4193 *Toll Free Fax:* 800-406-9145 *E-mail:* orders@triliteral.org
Membership(s): AAP; Association of American University Presses

Mitchell Lane Publishers Inc
PO Box 196, Hockessin, DE 19707
SAN: 858-3749
Tel: 302-234-9426 *Toll Free Tel:* 800-814-5484 *Fax:* 302-234-4742 *Toll Free Fax:* 866-834-4164
E-mail: orders@mitchelllane.com
Web Site: www.mitchelllane.com
Key Personnel
Pres & Publr: Barbara J Mitchell *E-mail:* barbaramitchell@mitchelllane.com
VP, Sales & Mktg: Robert P Mitchell *Tel:* 302-250-2880 *E-mail:* robertmitchell@mitchelllane.com
Founded: 1993
Nonfiction for children & young adults.
ISBN Prefix(es): 978-1-883845; 978-1-58415; 978-1-61228; 978-1-68020
Number of titles published annually: 80 Print; 80 E-Book
Total Titles: 1,200 Print; 300 E-Book
Editorial Office(s): 1104 Kelly Dr, Newark, DE 19711
Foreign Rep(s): CrossCan Educational (Canada); Edu-Reference (Canada); David Hall (Africa, Australia, Continental Europe, Ireland, Malaysia, Singapore, South Africa)
Orders to: 1104 Kelly Dr, Newark, DE 19711
Warehouse: 20 Shea Way, Suite 205, Newark, DE 19713
Membership(s): Educational Book & Media Association

Mobility International USA
132 E Broadway, Suite 343, Eugene, OR 97401
Tel: 541-343-1284 *Fax:* 541-343-6812
E-mail: info@miusa.org
Web Site: www.miusa.org
Key Personnel
CEO & Exec Dir: Susan Sygall
Founded: 1981
The mission of Mobility International USA (MIUSA) is to empower people with disabilities through international exchange & international development to achieve their human rights.
MIUSA manages the National Clearinghouse on Disability & Exchange (NCDE), a project sponsored by the bureau of Educational & Cultural Affairs of the US Department of State.
ISBN Prefix(es): 978-1-880034
Number of titles published annually: 4 Print
Total Titles: 6 Print

§Modern Language Association of America (MLA)
26 Broadway, 3rd fl, New York, NY 10004-1789
SAN: 202-6422
Tel: 646-576-5000 *Fax:* 646-458-0030
Web Site: www.mla.org
Key Personnel
Exec Dir: Rosemary G Feal *E-mail:* rfeal@mla.org
Assoc Exec Dir & Dir of Publg Opers: Judy Goulding *E-mail:* jgoulding@mla.org
Assoc Dir of Publg Opers, Mktg & Sales: Kathleen Hansen *E-mail:* khansen@mla.org
Founded: 1883
Research & teaching tools in languages & literature; professional publications for college teachers.
ISBN Prefix(es): 978-0-87352; 978-1-60329
Number of titles published annually: 12 Print
Total Titles: 300 Print; 1 CD-ROM; 1 Online

Modern Memoirs
34 Main St, No 9, Amherst, MA 01002-2367
Tel: 413-253-2353
Web Site: www.modernmemoirs.com
Key Personnel
Founder & Pres: Kitty Axelson-Berry *E-mail:* kitty@modernmemoirs.com
Assoc Publr: Ali de Groot *E-mail:* ali@modernmemoirs.com
Founded: 1994
Private publishing services for discerning clients.
This publisher has indicated that 100% of their product line is author subsidized.
ISBN Prefix(es): 978-0-9662602
Number of titles published annually: 12 Print
Total Titles: 135 Print
Imprints: White Poppy Press
Membership(s): Association of Personal Historians; The Association of Publishers for Special Sales; The Independent Book Publishers Association

Modern Publishing
Division of Unisystems Inc
155 E 55 St, New York, NY 10022
Tel: 212-826-0850 *Fax:* 212-759-9069
Web Site: www.modernpublishing.com
Key Personnel
Pres: Andrew Steinberg *E-mail:* asteinberg@modernpublishing.com
Founded: 1969
Juvenile, reference books; general nonfiction, humor, puzzle books.
ISBN Prefix(es): 978-0-7666
Number of titles published annually: 180 Print
Total Titles: 357 Print
Imprints: Block Board Books; Bubble Books; Detect-A-Word; Early Learners; Flip N Fun; Honey Bear Books; I Love You; Look at Me; Ready Reader Storybooks
Warehouse: Lehigh Valley Industrial Park, 2410 Brodhead Rd, Bethlehem, PA 18020

MoMA, see The Museum of Modern Art (MoMA)

The Monacelli Press
236 W 27 St, 4th fl, New York, NY 10001
Tel: 212-229-9925
E-mail: contact@monacellipress.com
Web Site: www.monacellipress.com

Key Personnel
Publr: Gianfranco Monacelli
Exec Ed, Fine & Applied Arts: Victoria Craven
Mng Ed & Prodn Dir: Elizabeth White
Sr Ed, Architecture & Design: Alan Rapp
Consulting Ed, Architecture: Nancy Green
Publicity Dir: Andrea Monfried
E-mail: amonfried@monacellipress.com
Prodn Mgr: Michael Vagnetti
Mktg Assoc: Kimberly Sheu
Founded: 1994
High-quality, illustrated, hardcover & paperback books on art, architecture, decorative arts, interior design, fashion, photography, landscape, urbanism & graphic design.
ISBN Prefix(es): 978-1-58093; 978-1-885254
Imprints: Monacelli Studio (applied arts)

Mondial
203 W 107 St, Suite 6-C, New York, NY 10025
Tel: 646-807-8031 *Fax:* 208-361-2863
E-mail: contact@mondialbooks.com
Web Site: www.mondialbooks.com
Key Personnel
Owner: Uday K Dhar
Publr: Ulrich Becker
Founded: 2004
Specialize in fiction & nonfiction translated into English from other languages or originally written in English or German. All kinds of publications (fiction & nonfiction) in the international language Esperanto.
ISBN Prefix(es): 978-1-59569
Number of titles published annually: 15 Print; 15 E-Book
Total Titles: 220 Print; 1 CD-ROM; 110 E-Book

Mondo Publishing
200 Sherwood Ave, Farmingdale, NY 11735
Tel: 212-268-3560 *Toll Free Tel:* 888-88-MONDO (886-6636) *Toll Free Fax:* 888-532-4492
E-mail: info@mondopub.com
Web Site: www.mondopub.com
Key Personnel
Pres: Mark Vineis
Edit Dir: Susan Eddy
Mktg: Jackie Greenspan
Founded: 1986
K-5 literacy materials & professional development services.
ISBN Prefix(es): 978-1-879531; 978-1-57255; 978-1-58653; 978-1-59034; 978-1-59366; 978-1-60201
Number of titles published annually: 200 Print
Total Titles: 500 Print
Imprints: Mondo
Warehouse: 113 Amfesco Dr, Plainview, NY 11803
Membership(s): The Children's Book Council

Money Market Directories
Unit of Standard & Poor's
401 E Market St, Charlottesville, VA 22902
Mailing Address: PO Box 1608, Charlottesville, VA 22902-1608
Tel: 434-977-1450 *Toll Free Tel:* 800-446-2810 *Fax:* 434-979-9962
Web Site: www.mmdwebaccess.com
Key Personnel
Dir: Jay Zacter
Mng Ed: Jehu Martin
Direct Mktg Specialist: Misty Combs
E-mail: misty_combs@standardandpoors.com
Founded: 1970
Financial information regarding pension funds, nonprofits & service providers plus investment managers & consultants. Publications available as e-directories & online.
ISBN Prefix(es): 978-0-939712
Number of titles published annually: 3 Print; 2 CD-ROM; 1 Online; 4 E-Book
Total Titles: 3 Print; 2 CD-ROM; 1 Online; 4 E-Book

The Mongolia Society Inc
Indiana University, 322 Goodbody Hall, 1011 E Third St, Bloomington, IN 47405-7005
Tel: 812-855-4078 *Fax:* 812-855-4078
E-mail: monsoc@indiana.edu
Web Site: www.mongoliasociety.org
Key Personnel
Pres: Dr Alicia Campi
VP: Dr Christopher Atwood
Exec Dir: Susie Drost
Mng Ed: David Bade
Secy: Dr Peter Marsh
Treas: Tristra Newyear Yeager
Founded: 1961
Interests, culture & language of Mongolia.
ISBN Prefix(es): 978-0-910980
Number of titles published annually: 4 Print
Total Titles: 60 Print

Monkfish Book Publishing Co
22 E Market St, Suite 304, Rhinebeck, NY 12572
Tel: 845-876-4861
E-mail: monkfish@monkfishpublishing.com
Web Site: www.monkfishpublishing.com
Key Personnel
Publr: Paul Cohen *E-mail:* bookcohen@aol.com
Founded: 2002
Publisher of spirituality & religion titles. Also operates a self-publishing company.
ISBN Prefix(es): 978-0-9823246; 978-0-9766843; 978-0-9726357; 978-0-9798828; 978-0-9749359
Number of titles published annually: 4 Print; 4 Online; 4 E-Book
Total Titles: 40 Print; 32 Online; 32 E-Book
Divisions: Epigraph Publishing Service (subsidy publishers)
Orders to: Consortium Book Sales & Distribution, 3413 13 Ave NE, Suite 101, Minneapolis, MN 55413-1007 *Toll Free Tel:* 800-283-3572
Distribution Center: Consortium Book Sales & Distribution, 3413 13 Ave NE, Suite 101, Minneapolis, MN 55413-1007 *Tel:* 612-746-2600 *Toll Free Tel:* 800-283-3572 *Fax:* 612-746-2606

The Montana Council for Indian Education
1240 Burlington Ave, Billings, MT 59102-4224
SAN: 202-2117
Tel: 406-652-7598 (AM); 406-248-3465 (PM) *Fax:* 406-248-1297
E-mail: cie@cie-mt.org
Web Site: www.cie-mt.org
Key Personnel
Pres & Ed: Hap Gilliland *E-mail:* hapg@q.com
Busn Mgr & Lib Sales Dir: Sue A Clague
Founded: 1968
Publish only books giving a true picture of American Indian life & culture; for use in schools. Full refund available for undamaged books.
ISBN Prefix(es): 978-0-89992
Number of titles published annually: 3 Print
Total Titles: 130 Print; 2 Online
Imprints: Indian Culture Series

Montana Historical Society Press
Capitol Complex, 225 N Roberts St, Helena, MT 59620
Mailing Address: PO Box 201201, Helena, MT 59620-1201
Tel: 406-444-0090 (edit); 406-444-2890 (ordering/mktg); 406-444-2694 *Toll Free Tel:* 800-243-9900 *Fax:* 406-444-2696 (ordering/mktg)
Web Site: www.montanahistoricalsociety.org
Key Personnel
Ed & Dir, Pubns: Molly Holz *E-mail:* mholz@mt.gov
Membership Coord: Rebecca Baumann *Tel:* 406-444-2918 *E-mail:* mhsmembership@mt.gov
Founded: 1891
ISBN Prefix(es): 978-0-917298; 978-0-9721522; 978-0-9759196; 978-0-9801292
Number of titles published annually: 4 Print
Total Titles: 45 Print; 1 Online; 1 Audio
Distributed by Globe Pequot Press

Montemayor Press
663 Hyland Hill Rd, Washington, VT 05675
Mailing Address: PO Box 546, Montpelier, VT 05601
Tel: 802-883-5081
E-mail: montepress@aol.com
Web Site: www.montemayorpress.com
Key Personnel
Publr: Edward Myers
Exec Ed: Edith Poor
Founded: 1999
Independent publisher whose mission is to print & distribute quality fiction & nonfiction to adult, young adult & juvenile audiences.
ISBN Prefix(es): 978-0-9674477; 978-1-932727
Number of titles published annually: 2 Print; 2 E-Book
Total Titles: 20 Print; 2 E-Book
Membership(s): Community of Literary Magazines & Presses; The Independent Book Publishers Association

Monthly Review Press
Division of Monthly Review Foundation Inc
146 W 29 St, Suite 6W, New York, NY 10001
SAN: 202-6481
Tel: 212-691-2555 *Toll Free Tel:* 800-670-9499 *Fax:* 212-727-3676
E-mail: mreview@igc.org
Web Site: www.MonthlyReview.org
Key Personnel
Mng Dir: Martin Paddio
Mktg Publicity Mgr: Scott Borchert
Founded: 1949
Economics, politics, history, sociology & world affairs.
ISBN Prefix(es): 978-0-85345; 978-1-58367
Number of titles published annually: 15 Print
Total Titles: 550 Print
Distributed by New York University Press
Billing Address: New York University Press, 838 Broadway, 3rd fl, New York, NY 10003
Orders to: New York University Press, 838 Broadway, 3rd fl, New York, NY 10003 *Toll Free Tel:* 800-996-6987 *Fax:* 212-995-4798
Returns: Maple Press Distribution Ctr Lebanon, 704 Legionaire Dr, Fredericksburg, PA 17026
Warehouse: Maple Press Distribution Ctr Lebanon, 704 Legionaire Dr, Fredericksburg, PA 17026

Moody Publishers
Affiliate of Ministry of Moody Bible Institute
820 N La Salle Blvd, Chicago, IL 60610
SAN: 202-5604
Tel: 312-329-4000 *Toll Free Tel:* 800-678-8812 (cust serv) *Fax:* 312-329-2019
Web Site: www.moodypublishers.com
Key Personnel
VP & Publr: Greg Thornton
VP: Wade Koenig
Edit Dir: Dave De Wit
Dir, Mktg: John Hinkley
Publicist: Janis Backing
Founded: 1894
Religion (interdenominational).
ISBN Prefix(es): 978-0-8024; 978-1-881273 (Northfield Publishing)
Number of titles published annually: 75 Print
Total Titles: 1,000 Print; 10 Audio
Imprints: Lift Every Voice; Northfield Publishing; River North
Foreign Rep(s): Biblicum AS (Norway); Bookhouse Australia Ltd (Australia); Challenge Bookshops (Nigeria); Christian Art Wholesale (South Africa); Christian Literature Crusade (Hong Kong); David C Cook Distribution (Canada); Editeurs de Litterature Biblique (Germany); Euro-Outreach Ministries (East

Africa, Kenya, Nairobi); Hong Kong Tien Dao Publishing House Ltd (Belgium); Kesho Publications (Zimbabwe); Matopo Book Room (Philippines); Overseas Missionary Fellowship (Canada); Rhema Boekimport (Singapore); S & U Book Centre (New Zealand); S-U Wholesale; Send the Light (England)
Shipping Address: 215 W Locust St, Chicago, IL 60610

Morehouse Publishing
Imprint of Church Publishing Inc
19 E 34 St, New York, NY 10016
SAN: 202-6511
Tel: 212-592-1800 *Toll Free Tel:* 800-672-1789 (retail orders only); 800-251-3320 (wholesale orders only)
Web Site: www.morehousepublishing.com; www.churchpublishing.org
Key Personnel
VP, Prodn: Lorraine Simonello
Founded: 1884
Spirituality, religious, lay ministry, liturgy, church supplies, music cassettes & CDs, all from an Episcopal/Anglican perspective. No illustrated children's books.
ISBN Prefix(es): 978-0-8192
Number of titles published annually: 40 Print; 35 E-Book
Total Titles: 800 Print; 650 E-Book
Distributed by Cokesbury (retail orders only); Abingdon Press (wholesale orders only)
Foreign Rep(s): Novalis (Canada)
Foreign Rights: Bayard Novalis Distribution (Canada); Norwich Books & Music (UK, UK Commonwealth, Worldwide exc USA)
Warehouse: UMPH Distribution Center, Nashville, TN

Morgan James Publishing
5 Penn Plaza, 23rd fl, New York, NY 10001
Tel: 212-655-5470 *Toll Free Tel:* 800-485-4943 *Fax:* 516-908-4496
E-mail: csauer@morganjamespublishing.com
Web Site: www.morganjamespublishing.com
Key Personnel
Founder: David L Hancock *E-mail:* david@morganjamespublishing.com
Founded: 2003
Provides entrepreneurs with the vital information, inspiration & guidance they need to be successful.
ISBN Prefix(es): 978-0-9746133; 978-0-9758570; 978-0-9760901; 978-0-9768491; 978-1-933596; 978-1-60037; 978-0-9815058; 978-0-9817906; 978-0-9820750; 978-0-9823793
Number of titles published annually: 130 Print; 90 E-Book
Total Titles: 415 Print
Returns: IPS Warehouse, 1280 Ingram Dr, Chambersburg, PA 17201
Membership(s): AAP

Morgan Kaufmann
Imprint of Elsevier Inc
225 Wyman St, Waltham, MA 02451
Toll Free Tel: 866-607-1417 *Fax:* 619-699-6310
Web Site: www.mkp.com
Key Personnel
Publr: Steve Elliot
Founded: 1984
Computer science book publishers including database, networking, architecture, engineering, graphics & artificial intelligence.
ISBN Prefix(es): 978-1-55860
Number of titles published annually: 65 Print
Total Titles: 552 Print; 606 E-Book
Orders to: 3251 Riverport Lane, Maryland Heights, MO 63040
Returns: 3251 Riverport Lane, Maryland Heights, MO 63040
Warehouse: 3251 Riverport Lane, Maryland Heights, MO 63040

Morgan Reynolds Publishing
620 S Elm St, Suite 387, Greensboro, NC 27406
Tel: 336-275-1311 *Toll Free Tel:* 800-535-1504 *Fax:* 336-275-1152 *Toll Free Fax:* 800-535-5725
E-mail: editorial@morganreynolds.com
Web Site: www.morganreynolds.com
Key Personnel
Founder & Publr: John Riley
Mktg Dir: Anita Richardson *E-mail:* anita@morganreynolds.com
Mng & Acqs Ed: Sharon F Doorasamy *E-mail:* sharon@morganreynolds.com
Founded: 1993
Hardcover trade & library-bound editions.
ISBN Prefix(es): 978-1-883846; 978-1-931798; 978-1-59935
Number of titles published annually: 100 Print
Total Titles: 300 Print

Morning Sun Books Inc
PO Box 326, Kutztown, PA 19530-0326
Tel: 610-683-8566 *Fax:* 610-683-3287
E-mail: sales.morningsunbooks@gmail.com (Sales)
Web Site: www.morningsunbooks.com
Key Personnel
Pres: Robert J Yanosey
Founded: 1986
Color photography of railroads during 1940-1970 period.
ISBN Prefix(es): 978-1-878887; 978-1-58248
Number of titles published annually: 24 Print
Total Titles: 350 Print
Editorial Office(s): 9 Pheasant Lane, Scotch Plains, NJ 07076

William Morrow & Co Inc, see HarperCollins Publishers

Morton Publishing Co
925 W Kenyon Ave, Unit 12, Englewood, CO 80110
SAN: 210-9174
Tel: 303-761-4805 *Fax:* 303-762-9923
E-mail: contact@morton-pub.com
Web Site: www.morton-pub.com
Key Personnel
Chmn: Douglas Morton *E-mail:* mortond@morton-pub.com
Pres: David Ferguson *E-mail:* davidf@morton-pub.com
VP, Opers: Chrissy De Mier *E-mail:* chrissyd@morton-pub.com
VP, Sales & Mktg: Carter Fenton *E-mail:* carterf@morton-pub.com
Returns: Heather Herman *E-mail:* heatherh@morton-pub.com
Founded: 1977
Allied health, biology, pharmacy, computer information technology, speech & educational.
ISBN Prefix(es): 978-0-89582; 978-1-61731
Number of titles published annually: 10 Print
Total Titles: 50 Print
Foreign Rep(s): Northrose Associates (Canada)

Mosaic Press
4500 Witmer Industrial Estates, PMB 145, Niagara Falls, NY 14305-1386
Mailing Address: 1252 Speers Rd, Units 1 & 2, Oakville, ON L6L 5N9, Canada
Tel: 905-825-2130 *Fax:* 905-825-2130
E-mail: info@mosaic-press.com
Web Site: www.mosaic-press.com
Key Personnel
Publr: Howard Aster *E-mail:* mosaicpress@on.aibn.com
Founded: 1974
Literary scholarly books. No unsol mss.
ISBN Prefix(es): 978-0-88962
Number of titles published annually: 19 Print
Total Titles: 502 Print
Warehouse: 1252 Speers Rd, Units 1 & 2, Oakville, ON L6L 5N9, Canada
Distribution Center: Gazelle Book Services Ltd, White Cross Mills, Hightown LA1 4XS, United Kingdom
Midpoint, 5701 Ranch Dr, Little Rock, AR 72223-9633 (US) *Toll Free Tel:* 800-643-8030 *Fax:* 501-868-6321
Publishers Group of Canada, 300-76 Stafford St, Toronto, ON M6J 2S1, Canada (CN) *Tel:* 416-934-9900 *Fax:* 416-934-1410 *E-mail:* info@pgcbooks.ca

Mount Olive College Press
Affiliate of Mount Olive College
634 Henderson St, Mount Olive, NC 28365
Tel: 252-286-6851 *Fax:* 919-658-7180
Web Site: www.umo.edu
Key Personnel
Edit Dir: Dr Pepper Worthington
Founded: 1990
Poetry, drama, biography, devotional, travel, essay, novel, cookbook, photography, children's books, literary criticism.
ISBN Prefix(es): 978-0-9627087; 978-1-880994
Number of titles published annually: 5 Print
Total Titles: 75 Print

Mountain n' Air Books
2947-A Honolulu Ave, La Crescenta, CA 91214
Mailing Address: PO Box 12540, La Crescenta, CA 91224-5540
Tel: 818-248-9345 *Toll Free Tel:* 800-446-9696 *Toll Free Fax:* 800-303-5578
Web Site: www.mountain-n-air.com
Key Personnel
Pres: Gilberto d'Urso *E-mail:* gilberto@mountain-n-air.com
Publr & Ed: Mary K d'Urso
Off Mgr: Elvira Sakalenka *E-mail:* elvira@mountain-n-air.com
Founded: 1985
Outdoor guides, nonfiction, cookbooks & travel adventures, maps.
ISBN Prefix(es): 978-1-879415
Number of titles published annually: 6 Print
Total Titles: 99 Print
Imprints: Mountain Air Books
Distributor for Tom Harrison Cartography

Mountain Press Publishing Co
1301 S Third W, Missoula, MT 59801
SAN: 202-8832
Mailing Address: PO Box 2399, Missoula, MT 59806-2399
Tel: 406-728-1900 *Toll Free Tel:* 800-234-5308 *Fax:* 406-728-1635
E-mail: info@mtnpress.com
Web Site: www.mountain-press.com
Key Personnel
History Ed: Gwen McKenna
Natural History & Roadside Geology Series Ed: Jennifer Carey
Gen Mgr: John Rimel *E-mail:* johnargyle@aol.com
Busn Mgr: Rob Williams
Mktg Mgr: Anne Iverson *Tel:* 406-728-1900 ext 131 *E-mail:* anne@mtnpress.com
Graphic Design: Jeannie Painter
Founded: 1948
ISBN Prefix(es): 978-0-87842; 978-0-9632562; 978-0-9626999; 978-1-886370; 978-1-889921; 978-1-892784; 978-0-9676747; 978-0-9717748; 978-0-9724827
Number of titles published annually: 20 Print
Total Titles: 150 Print

Imprints: Geology Underfoot Series; Mountain Sports Press Series; Roadside Geology Series; Roadside History Series; Tumbleweed Series
Distributor for Bucking Horse Books; Clark City Press; Cottonwood Publishing; Hops Press; Npustin Publishing; Western Edge Press

The Mountaineers Books
Division of The Mountaineers Club
1001 SW Klickitat Way, Suite 201, Seattle, WA 98134
Tel: 206-223-6303 *Toll Free Tel:* 800-553-4453 *Fax:* 206-223-6306 *Toll Free Fax:* 800-568-7604
E-mail: mbooks@mountaineersbooks.org
Web Site: www.mountaineersbooks.org
Key Personnel
Publr: Helen Cherullo *Tel:* 206-223-6303 ext 122
Ed-in-Chief: Kate Rogers *Tel:* 206-223-6303 ext 109
Mng Ed: Margaret Sullivan *Tel:* 206-223-6303 ext 133 *E-mail:* margarets@mountaineersbooks.org
Sr Ed: Mary Metz *Tel:* 206-223-6303 ext 119 *E-mail:* marym@mountaineersbooks.org
Dir, Sales & Mktg: Doug Canfield *Tel:* 206-223-6303 ext 114
Digital Media Mgr: Ashley Knecht *E-mail:* ashleyk@mountaineersbooks.org
Publicist: Emily White *Tel:* 206-223-6303 ext 138
Founded: 1961
Mountaineering, backpacking, hiking, cross-country skiing, bicycling, canoeing, kayaking, trekking, nature, conservation, green living & sustainability; outdoor how-to, guidebooks & maps; nonfiction adventure-travel accounts; biographies of outdoor people; reprint editions of mountaineering classics; adventure narratives.
ISBN Prefix(es): 978-0-89886; 978-0-916890
Number of titles published annually: 20 Print
Total Titles: 550 Print
Imprints: Braided River; Skipstone
Distributor for The American Alpine Club Press; Colorado Mountain Club Press
Foreign Rep(s): Cordee Publishing (UK)

§De Gruyter Mouton
Imprint of Walter de Gruyter GmbH & Co KG
121 High St, 3rd fl, Boston, MA 02110
Tel: 857-284-7073 *Fax:* 857-284-7358
E-mail: degruytermail@presswarehouse.com (orders & claims)
Web Site: www.degruyter.com
Key Personnel
Mktg Mgr: Heather Anderson *Tel:* 857-284-7073 ext 106 *E-mail:* heather.anderson@degruyter.com
Founded: 1956
Scholarly books & journals.
ISBN Prefix(es): 978-0-311; 978-90-279
Number of titles published annually: 75 Print; 2 Online
Total Titles: 2,500 Print; 3 CD-ROM; 10 Online
Foreign Office(s): Walter de Gruyter GmbH & Co KG, Genthinerstr 13, 10785 Berlin, Germany *Tel:* (030) 260 05-0 *Fax:* (030) 260 05-251 *E-mail:* info@degruyter.com
Distributed by Walter de Gruyter Inc
Foreign Rep(s): Allied Publishers Ltd (India, Nepal, Sri Lanka); Book Club International (Bangladesh); Combined Representatives Worldwide Inc (Philippines); D A Books & Journals (Australia, New Zealand); Walter de Gruyter Inc (Canada, Mexico); Verlags und Kommissionsbuchhandlung Dr Franz Hain (Austria); Kumi Trading (South Korea); Kweilin Bookstore (Taiwan); Maruzen Co Ltd (Japan); Pak Book Corp (Pakistan); Parry's Book Center (Sendjrjan Berhad) (Brunei, Malaysia, Singapore); Swinden Book Co Ltd (Hong Kong)
Orders to: Walter de Gruyter, PO Box 960, Herndon, VA 20172-0960 *Tel:* 703-661-1589 *Toll Free Tel:* 800-208-8144 *Fax:* 703-661-1501
Shipping Address: 22803 Quicksilver Dr, Dulles, VA 20166-2019

Moznaim Publishing Corp
4304 12 Ave, Brooklyn, NY 11219
SAN: 214-4123
Tel: 718-438-7680 *Fax:* 718-438-1305
E-mail: sales@moznaim.com
Web Site: www.moznaim.com
Key Personnel
Pres: Menachem Wagshal
VP: Moshe Sternlicht
Founded: 1981
Judaica books in Hebrew, English & Spanish.
ISBN Prefix(es): 978-0-940118; 978-1-885220
Number of titles published annually: 7 Print
Total Titles: 200 Print
Foreign Office(s): 10 Telmie Yosef St, Mishor Adumim, Israel *Tel:* (02) 5333441 *Fax:* (02) 5354345
Distributor for Avamra Institute; Breslov Research Institute; Red Wheel-Weiser Inc

MRTS
Imprint of Arizona Center for Medieval & Renaissance Studies (ACMRS)
PO Box 874402, Tempe, AZ 85287-4402
Tel: 480-727-6503 *Toll Free Tel:* 800-621-2736 (orders) *Fax:* 480-965-1681 *Toll Free Fax:* 800-621-8476 (orders)
E-mail: mrts@asu.edu
Web Site: www.acmrs.org/pubs
Key Personnel
Mng Ed: Roy Rukkila *E-mail:* roy.rukkila@asu.edu
Scholarly/academic press. Specialize in medieval & Renaissance texts & studies.
ISBN Prefix(es): 978-0-86698
Number of titles published annually: 24 Print
Total Titles: 440 Print
Sales Office(s): Chicago Distribution Center, 11030 S Langley Ave, Chicago, IL 60628 *Tel:* 773-702-7000 *Toll Free Tel:* 800-621-2736 *Fax:* 773-702-7212 *Toll Free Fax:* 800-621-8476 *E-mail:* orders@press.uchicago.edu *Web Site:* www.press.uchicago.edu
Billing Address: Chicago Distribution Center, 11030 S Langley Ave, Chicago, IL 60628 *Tel:* 773-702-7000 *Toll Free Tel:* 800-621-2736 *Fax:* 773-702-7212 *Toll Free Fax:* 800-621-8476 *E-mail:* orders@press.uchicago.edu *Web Site:* www.press.uchicago.edu
Orders to: Chicago Distribution Center, 11030 S Langley Ave, Chicago, IL 60628 *Tel:* 773-702-7000 *Toll Free Tel:* 800-621-2736 *Fax:* 773-702-7212 *Toll Free Fax:* 800-621-8476 *E-mail:* orders@press.uchicago.edu *Web Site:* www.press.uchicago.edu
Returns: Chicago Distribution Center, 11030 S Langley Ave, Chicago, IL 60628 *Tel:* 773-702-7000 *Toll Free Tel:* 800-621-2736 *Fax:* 773-702-7212 *Toll Free Fax:* 800-621-8476 *E-mail:* orders@press.uchicago.edu *Web Site:* www.press.uchicago.edu
Distribution Center: Chicago Distribution Center, 11030 S Langley Ave, Chicago, IL 60628 *Tel:* 773-702-7000 *Toll Free Tel:* 800-621-2736 *Fax:* 773-702-7212 *Toll Free Fax:* 800-621-8476 *E-mail:* orders@press.uchicago.edu *Web Site:* www.press.uchicago.edu

§Multicultural Publications Inc
Subsidiary of Making Education Reform Imperative Today Inc (MERIT)
936 Slosson St, Akron, OH 44320
Mailing Address: PO Box 8001, Akron, OH 44320-0001
Tel: 330-865-9578 *Fax:* 330-865-9578
E-mail: multiculturalpub@prodigy.net
Web Site: www.multiculturalpub.net
Key Personnel
CEO & Pres: Bobby L Jackson
Dir, Mktg & Promos & Intl Rts: James Lynell
Lib Sales Dir: Rae Neal
Founded: 1992
Books, greeting cards, dolls & stuffed toys, multimedia.
ISBN Prefix(es): 978-0-9634932; 978-1-884242
Number of titles published annually: 1 Print; 1 CD-ROM; 1 Online
Total Titles: 28 Print; 2 CD-ROM; 28 Online; 4 Audio
Branch Office(s)
1907 Massillon Rd, Akron, OH 44312
Returns: 1939 Manchester Rd, Akron, OH 44314
Shipping Address: 1939 Manchester Rd, Akron, OH 44314

Multimedia Larga
900 S Boardman Dr, No G72, Gallup, NM 87301
Key Personnel
Dir & Publr: Minh L Perez *E-mail:* m_l_perez@yahoo.com
Ed: Jo Anne McGray
Intl Rts Contact & Lib Sales Dir: J Castillo
Founded: 1990
Publishers of books, journals, ebooks & ejournals.
ISBN Prefix(es): 978-1-879585; 978-1-931233
Number of titles published annually: 15 Print; 10 Online; 40 E-Book
Total Titles: 90 Print; 40 Online; 68 E-Book
Foreign Rep(s): W B Vasantha Kandasami; M Monu
Distribution Center: ProQuest Inc

§Mundania Press LLC
6457 Glenway Ave, Suite 109, Cincinnati, OH 45211-5222
SAN: 255-013X
Tel: 513-490-2822 *Fax:* 513-598-9220 *Toll Free Fax:* 888-460-4752
E-mail: books@mundania.com; inquiry@mundania.com
Web Site: www.mundania.com
Key Personnel
COO & Sr Ed: Skyla Dawn Cameron
Pres & Mktg Dir: Bob Sanders *Tel:* 513-404-7357 *E-mail:* bob@mundania.com
Art Dir: Niki Browning
Founded: 2002
Provides authors with publishing & distribution worldwide. Submissions are currently open & actively look for any fiction with exception being poetry. All other specifics are listed on the web site.
ISBN Prefix(es): 978-0-9723670; 978-1-59426
Number of titles published annually: 500 Print; 100 CD-ROM; 500 Online; 900 E-Book; 5 Audio
Total Titles: 700 Print; 200 CD-ROM; 700 Online; 900 E-Book; 1 Audio
Imprints: Awe-Struck; Hard Shell; Phaze Books
Foreign Rep(s): Lightning Source (UK, USA)
Membership(s): Electronically Published Internet Connection; The Independent Book Publishers Association

Municipal Analysis Services Inc
PO Box 13453, Austin, TX 78711-3453
Tel: 512-327-3328
E-mail: munilysis@gmail.com
Web Site: sites.google.com/site/gregmichels/home
Key Personnel
Pres: Greg Michels
Founded: 1983
Largest analysis of local governments.
ISBN Prefix(es): 978-1-55507; 978-0-31738
Number of titles published annually: 82 Print; 40 CD-ROM; 80 E-Book
Total Titles: 2,200 Print; 200 CD-ROM; 540 E-Book

The Museum of Modern Art (MoMA)
11 W 53 St, New York, NY 10019
SAN: 202-5809
Tel: 212-708-9443 *Fax:* 212-333-6575
E-mail: moma_publications@moma.org
Web Site: www.moma.org
Key Personnel
Prodn Dir: Marc Sapir
Publr: Christopher Hudson
Assoc Publr: Charles R Kim
Edit Dir: David Frankel
Founded: 1929
Art, architecture, design, photography, film.
ISBN Prefix(es): 978-0-87070
Number of titles published annually: 18 Print
Total Titles: 1,250 Print
Distributed by Distributed Art Publishers (DAP) (US & Canada only)
Foreign Rep(s): Thames & Hudson Ltd (Worldwide exc Canada & USA)
Warehouse: South River Distribution, South River, NJ 08882
Membership(s): American Alliance of Museums; American Association of University Presses; CAA

§Museum of New Mexico Press
Unit of New Mexico State Department of Cultural Affairs
725 Camino Lejo, Suite C, Santa Fe, NM 87505
SAN: 202-2575
Mailing Address: PO Box 2087, Santa Fe, NM 87504-2087
Tel: 505-476-1155; 505-272-7777 (orders) *Toll Free Tel:* 800-249-7737 (orders) *Fax:* 505-476-1156 *Toll Free Fax:* 800-622-8667 (orders)
Web Site: www.mnmpress.org
Key Personnel
Dir: Anna Gallegos *Tel:* 505-476-1154 *E-mail:* anna.gallegos@state.nm.us
Art Dir & Prodn Mgr: David Skolkin *Tel:* 505-476-1159 *E-mail:* david.skolkin@state.nm.us
Edit Dir: Mary Wachs *Tel:* 505-476-1161 *E-mail:* mary.wachs@state.nm.us
Mktg & Sales Dir: Renee Tambeau *E-mail:* renee.tambeau@state.nm.us
Design Assoc: Jason Valdez
Founded: 1951
Publications related to Native America, Hispanic Southwest, 20th century art, photography, folk art & folklore, nature & gardening, architecture & the Americas.
ISBN Prefix(es): 978-0-89013
Number of titles published annually: 15 Print
Total Titles: 140 Print
Distributed by University of New Mexico Press
Foreign Rep(s): Codasat Canada Ltd (Canada); East-West Export Books (Asia-Pacific); Gazelle Book Services (Europe); US PubRep (Caribbean, Latin America, Mexico, Puerto Rico)
Warehouse: University of New Mexico Press

Mutual Publishing
1215 Center St, Suite 210, Honolulu, HI 96816
Tel: 808-732-1709 *Fax:* 808-734-4094
E-mail: info@mutualpublishing.com
Web Site: www.mutualpublishing.com
Key Personnel
Dir, Sales & Mktg: Gay Wong *E-mail:* gaywong@mutualpublishing.com
Founded: 1974
Publishing, print brokering & packaging. Editorial & design services; trade, mass market paperback, coffee table & souvenir books.
ISBN Prefix(es): 978-1-56647
Number of titles published annually: 50 Print
Total Titles: 330 Print

Mystic Seaport Museum Inc
PO Box 6000, Mystic, CT 06355-0990
SAN: 213-7550
Tel: 860-572-5302; 860-572-0711 (visitor serv) *Toll Free Tel:* 800-248-1066 (wholesale orders only); 800-331-2665 (retail orders only) *Fax:* 860-572-5321
E-mail: info@mysticseaport.org
Web Site: www.mysticseaport.org
Key Personnel
Pres: Stephen C White *E-mail:* administration@mysticseaport.com
EVP: Susan Funk; Marcy Withington
Dir, Busn Devt: Mary Anne Stets
Founded: 1929
Scholarly & trade books on American maritime history & art.
ISBN Prefix(es): 978-0-913372; 978-0-939510
Number of titles published annually: 3 Print
Total Titles: 84 Print
Imprints: American Maritime Library
Distributor for Glencannon; Ten Pound Island Books
Foreign Rep(s): Nimbus (Canada); Dalton Young Assoc (UK)

NAB, see National Association of Broadcasters (NAB)

NACE International
1440 S Creek Dr, Houston, TX 77084-4906
Tel: 281-228-6200 *Toll Free Tel:* 800-797-NACE (797-6223) *Fax:* 281-228-6300
E-mail: firstservice@nace.org
Web Site: www.nace.org
Key Personnel
Exec Dir: Bob Chalker *Tel:* 281-228-6250
Dir, Pubns: Gretchen Jacobson *Tel:* 281-228-6207 *E-mail:* gretchen.jacobson@nace.org
Founded: 1943
Publishes technical books on corrosion control & prevention & materials selection, design & degradation issues. Books are developed by individual authors/editors utilizing corrosion experts to contribute text. Compilations of technical papers from NACE conferences & symposia are also issued on an annual basis.
ISBN Prefix(es): 978-1-877914; 978-0-915567; 978-1-57590
Number of titles published annually: 50 Print
Total Titles: 425 Print; 30 CD-ROM; 4 Online; 80 Audio
Foreign Office(s): Menara Hap Seng, Level 16, Suite 812, Jalan P Ramlee, 50250 Kuala Lumpur, Malaysia *Tel:* (03) 9236 7333 *Fax:* (03) 9236 7410 *E-mail:* astley.pung@nace.org
Distributed by Australasian Corrosion Association
Distributor for ASM International; ASTM; AWS; Butterworth-Heinemann; Cambridge University Press; CASTI Publishing; Compass Publications; CRC Press; Marcel Dekker Inc; E&FN Spon; Elsevier Science Publishers; Gulf Publishing; Industrial Press; Institute of Materials; ISO; McGraw-Hill; MTI; Prentice Hall; Professional Publications; SSPC; Swedish Corrosion Institute; John Wiley & Sons Inc
Foreign Rep(s): ABI (India); ATP (Europe); BI Publications (Asia); IBS (India)

NACE Press, see NACE International

NAL
Division of Penguin Group (USA) LLC
375 Hudson St, New York, NY 10014
SAN: 282-5074
Tel: 212-366-2000
E-mail: online@penguinputnam.com
Web Site: www.penguinputnam.com; us.penguingroup.com
Key Personnel
VP & Publr: Kara Welsh
VP, Prodn: Pat Lyons
VP & Exec Creative Dir: Rich Hasselberger
VP, Sr Art Dir: Anthony Ramondo
VP & Dir, Mktg: Jeanne-Marie Hudson
VP & Publicity Dir: Craig Burke
VP & Assoc Publr: Rick Nayer
VP, Edit Dir: Claire Zion
Exec Ed: Tracy Bernstein; Danielle Perez; Ellen Edwards
Exec Mng Ed: Frank Walgren
Sr Ed: Kerry Janiszewski; Brent Howard; Sandra Harding; Laurien Wade; Jennifer Schuster
Founded: 1948
ISBN Prefix(es): 978-0-451
Number of titles published annually: 415 Print
Total Titles: 2,630 Print
Imprints: New American Library; Onyx; Roc; Signet; Signet Classics; Topaz
Advertising Agency: Spier NY

The Narrative Press
2041 E "A" St, Torrington, WY 82240
Tel: 307-532-3495 *Fax:* 307-532-3495
E-mail: service@narrativepress.com
Web Site: www.narrativepress.com
Key Personnel
Ed: Vickie Zimmer
Founded: 2001
Publishes true first person accounts of historical adventure & exploration.
ISBN Prefix(es): 978-1-58976
Number of titles published annually: 4 Print; 20 E-Book
Total Titles: 104 Print; 78 E-Book

NASW Press
Division of National Association of Social Workers (NASW)
750 First St NE, Suite 700, Washington, DC 20002
SAN: 202-893X
Tel: 202-408-8600 *Fax:* 203-336-8312
E-mail: press@naswdc.org
Web Site: www.naswpress.org
Key Personnel
Publr: Cheryl Bradley *E-mail:* cbradley@naswdc.org
Mktg Mgr: Sharon Fletcher *E-mail:* sfletcher@naswdc.org
Mng Ed & ISBN Contact: John Cassels *E-mail:* jcassels@naswdc.org
Mng Ed: Kristina Campbell *E-mail:* kcampbell@naswdc.org
Founded: 1955
Professional & scholarly books & journals in the social sciences.
ISBN Prefix(es): 978-0-87101
Number of titles published annually: 10 Print; 2 CD-ROM
Total Titles: 100 Print; 2 CD-ROM; 5 Online; 6 Audio
Orders to: PBD Worldwide Fulfillment Services, 1650 Bluegrass Lakes Pkwy, Alpharetta, GA 30004 *Tel:* 770-238-0450 *Toll Free Tel:* 800-227-3590 *Fax:* 770-238-0453 *Toll Free Fax:* 866-494-1499 *E-mail:* nasw@pbd.com *Web Site:* www.pbd.com
Returns: PBD Worldwide Fulfillment Services, 1650 Bluegrass Lakes Pkwy, Alpharetta, GA 30004 *Tel:* 770-238-0450 *Toll Free Tel:* 800-227-3590 *Fax:* 770-238-0453 *Toll Free Fax:* 866-494-1499 *E-mail:* nasw@pbd.com *Web Site:* www.pbd.com
Shipping Address: PBD Worldwide Fulfillment Services, 1650 Bluegrass Lakes Pkwy, Alpharetta, GA 30004 *Tel:* 770-238-0450 *Toll Free Tel:* 800-227-3590 *Fax:* 770-238-0453 *Toll Free Fax:* 866-494-1499 *E-mail:* nasw@pbd.com *Web Site:* www.pbd.com
Warehouse: PBD Worldwide Fulfillment Services, 1650 Bluegrass Lakes Pkwy, Alpharetta, GA 30004 *Tel:* 770-238-0450 *Toll Free Tel:* 800-227-3590 *Fax:* 770-238-0453 *Toll Free Fax:* 866-494-1499 *E-mail:* nasw@pbd.com *Web Site:* www.pbd.com

Distribution Center: PBD Worldwide Fulfillment Services, 1650 Bluegrass Lakes Pkwy, Alpharetta, GA 30004 *Tel:* 770-238-0450 *Toll Free Tel:* 800-227-3590 *Fax:* 770-238-0453 *Toll Free Fax:* 866-494-1499 *E-mail:* nasw@pbd.com *Web Site:* www.pbd.com
Membership(s): Association Media & Publishing

Nataraj Books
7967 Twist Lane, Springfield, VA 22153
Tel: 703-455-4996 *Fax:* 703-455-4001
E-mail: nataraj@erols.com; orders@natarajbooks.com
Web Site: www.natarajbooks.com
Key Personnel
Pres: Vinod Mahajan
Founded: 1986
Books from South Asia.
ISBN Prefix(es): 978-1-881338
Number of titles published annually: 7 Print
Total Titles: 70 Print
Orders to: 7073 Brookfield Plaza, Springfield, VA 22150 *Fax:* 703-912-9052

Nation Books
Imprint of The Nation Institute
116 E 16 St, 8th fl, New York, NY 10003
SAN: 216-4663
Tel: 212–822–0250 *Fax:* 212-253-5356
E-mail: submissions@nationbooks.org
Web Site: www.nationbooks.org
Key Personnel
Group Publr: Susan Weinberg
Edit Dir: Alessandra Bastagli
Assoc Ed: Katy O'Donnell
Founded: 2000
Specializes in publishing books from a progressive social & political viewpoint with independent & critical thoughts on current issues of the day.
ISBN Prefix(es): 978-1-56025
Number of titles published annually: 30 Print
Total Titles: 175 Print
Foreign Rep(s): Chistra Bopardikar
Foreign Rights: Yulia Borodyanskaya
Orders to: Publishers Group West, 1700 Fourth St, Berkeley, CA 94710 *Tel:* 510-528-1444 *Toll Free Tel:* 800-788-3123
Distribution Center: Publishers Group West, c/o Advanced Marketing Services, 5045 W 79 St, Indianapolis, IN 46268

§National Academies Press (NAP)
Division of National Academies
Lockbox 285, 500 Fifth St NW, Washington, DC 20001
SAN: 202-8891
Mailing Address: PO Box 741500, Atlanta, GA 30374-1500
Tel: 202-334-3313 *Toll Free Tel:* 888-624-8373 (cust serv) *Fax:* 202-334-2451 (cust serv); 202-334-2793 (mktg dept)
E-mail: customer_service@nap.edu
Web Site: www.nap.edu
Key Personnel
Dir: Barbara Kline Pope *Tel:* 202-334-3328 *E-mail:* bkline@nas.edu
Deputy Exec Dir, Communs: Ann Merchant *Tel:* 202-334-3117 *E-mail:* amerchan@nas.edu
Exec Ed: Stephen Mautner *Tel:* 202-334-3336 *E-mail:* smautner@nas.edu
Dir, Publg Servs: Dottie Lewis *Tel:* 202-334-2409 *E-mail:* dlewis@nas.edu
Art Dir: Francesca Moghari *Tel:* 202-334-3323 *E-mail:* fmoghari@nas.edu
Founded: 1863
Science, technology & health, scholarly & trade books.
ISBN Prefix(es): 978-0-309
Number of titles published annually: 200 Print
Total Titles: 3,500 Print; 1,000 E-Book
Imprints: Joseph Henry Press
Foreign Office(s): Cumnor Hill, 12 Hid's Copse Rd, Oxford 0X2 9JJ, United Kingdom
Foreign Rep(s): Durnell Marketing Ltd (Europe, Ireland); Footprint Books Pty Ltd (Australia, New Zealand); Kinokuniya (Japan); Maruzen Co Ltd (Japan); US PubRep (Caribbean including Puerto Rico, Central America, Mexico, South America); Viva Group (India); World Scientific Publishing Co Pte Ltd (Brunei, China, Hong Kong, India, Indonesia, Korea, Malaysia, Philippines, Singapore, Taiwan, Thailand)
Orders to: Marston Book Service Ltd, PO Box 269, Abingdon, Oxon OX14 4YN, United Kingdom (for UK & Europe) *Tel:* (01235) 465500 *Fax:* (01235) 465555 *Web Site:* www.marston.co.uk
Returns: 22883 Quicksilver Dr, Dulles, VA 20166
Membership(s): AAP

The National Alliance Research Academy
Division of The National Alliance for Insurance Education & Research
3630 N Hills Dr, Austin, TX 78755
Mailing Address: PO Box 27027, Austin, TX 78755-2027
Tel: 512-345-7932 *Toll Free Tel:* 800-633-2165 *Fax:* 512-349-6194
E-mail: alliance@scic.com
Web Site: www.scis.com/academy
Key Personnel
CEO & Pres, National Alliance for Insurance Education & Research: William T Hold, PhD
Assoc Dir: William J Hold
Founded: 1983
Insurance research & education.
ISBN Prefix(es): 978-1-878204
Number of titles published annually: 4 Print
Total Titles: 15 Print; 1 CD-ROM; 1 Audio

National Association for Music Education (NAfME)
1806 Robert Fulton Dr, Reston, VA 20191
Tel: 703-860-4000 *Toll Free Tel:* 800-462-6420 (orders & returns); 800-336-3768 *Fax:* 703-860-1531
Web Site: www.menc.org; www.nafme.org
Founded: 1907
Books on all phases of music education in schools & communities; professional philosophy & practical techniques, the arts & art education as a whole; current issues in music teaching & learning; music education advocacy.
ISBN Prefix(es): 978-0-940796; 978-1-56545
Number of titles published annually: 15 Print; 3 Online
Total Titles: 151 Print; 3 Online
Editorial Office(s): Rowman & Littlefield Publishing Group Inc, 4501 Forbes Blvd, Lanham, MD 20706
Distributed by Rowman & Littlefield Education
Orders to: Rowman & Littlefield Publishing Group Inc, 15200 NBN Way, Blue Ridge Summit, PA 17214 *Tel:* 717-794-3800 *Toll Free Tel:* 800-462-6420 *Fax:* 717-794-3803 *Toll Free Fax:* 800-338-4550 *E-mail:* orders@rowman.com
Distribution Center: National Book Network, 4501 Forbes Blvd, Suite 200, Lanham, MD 20706 *Web Site:* www.nbnbooks.com

National Association of Broadcasters (NAB)
1771 "N" St NW, Washington, DC 20036
Tel: 202-429-5300 *Fax:* 202-429-4199
E-mail: nab@nab.org
Web Site: www.nab.org
Key Personnel
CEO & Pres: Gordon H Smith
EVP, Mktg & Communs: Michelle Lehman *Tel:* 202-429-5444 *E-mail:* mlehman@nab.org
EVP, Conventions & Busn Opers: Mr Chris Brown
Trade association representing radio & television stations & companies that serve the broadcasting industry.
ISBN Prefix(es): 978-0-89324
Number of titles published annually: 15 Print
Total Titles: 71 Print
Distributed by Allyn & Bacon; Lawrence Erlbaum Assoc; Focal Press; Macmillan Publishing Co; Tab Books; Wadsworth Inc

§National Association of Insurance Commissioners
2301 McGee St, Suite 800, Kansas City, MO 64108-2662
Tel: 816-842-3600; 816-783-8300 (cust serv) *Fax:* 816-783-8175; 816-460-7593 (cust serv)
E-mail: prodserv@naic.org
Web Site: www.naic.org
Key Personnel
Mgr II, PRISM: Renee Jensen *Tel:* 816-783-8305 *Fax:* 816-460-7452 *E-mail:* rjensen@naic.org
Sr Prod Devt/Prodn Mgr: William Maher *Tel:* 813-783-8301 *Fax:* 813-460-7670 *E-mail:* wmaher@naic.org
Founded: 1871
ISBN Prefix(es): 978-0-89382; 978-1-59917
Number of titles published annually: 110 Print
Total Titles: 356 Print; 110 Online; 110 E-Book
Branch Office(s)
NAIC Government Relations, Hall of the States, Suite 701, 4444 N Capitol St NW, Washington, DC 20001-1509, Dir: Ethan Sonnichsen *Tel:* 202-471-3990
Capital Markets & Investment Analysis Office, 48 Wall St, 6th fl, New York, NY 10005-2906, Dir: Chris Evangel *Tel:* 212-398-9000 *Fax:* 212-382-4207

National Association of Secondary School Principals (NASSP)
1904 Association Dr, Reston, VA 20191-1537
Tel: 703-860-0200 *Toll Free Tel:* 800-253-7746 *Fax:* 703-476-5432
E-mail: membership@principals.org; sales@principals.org; publications2@nassp.org (communs & devt)
Web Site: www.principals.org
Key Personnel
Sr Dir, Communs & Devt: Bob Farrace *Tel:* 703-860-7257 *E-mail:* farraceb@principals.org
Founded: 1916
Journals, magazines, monographs, newsletters, videos & software.
ISBN Prefix(es): 978-0-88210
Number of titles published annually: 6 Print
Total Titles: 74 Print
Imprints: NASSP
Advertising Agency: Publishers Associates

National Book Co
Division of Educational Research Associates
PO Box 8795, Portland, OR 97207-8795
SAN: 212-4661
Tel: 503-228-6345 *Fax:* 810-885-5811
E-mail: info@eralearning.com
Web Site: www.eralearning.com
Key Personnel
VP, SE Reg: Richard R Gallagher
Dir, Spec Materials: Mark R Salser
Prodn Mgr: Ward J Stroud
Founded: 1960
Individualized mastery learning programs for elementary, secondary & college levels, consisting of multimedia materials in business education, home economics, language skills, mathematics, science, shorthand skills, social studies, general & vocational education; special trade publications, particularly in subjects relating to education. Computer software; reference books; Black/Afro-American history; English as a second language.
ISBN Prefix(es): 978-0-89420
Number of titles published annually: 25 Print

Total Titles: 175 Print; 100 Audio
Imprints: Halcyon House

National Braille Press
88 St Stephen St, Boston, MA 02115-4302
Tel: 617-266-6160 *Toll Free Tel:* 800-548-7323 (cust serv); 888-965-8965 *Fax:* 617-437-0456
E-mail: orders@nbp.org
Web Site: www.nbp.org
Key Personnel
Pres: Brian A MacDonald *E-mail:* bmacdonald@nbp.org
VP, Publg & Prod Devt: Diane Croft *E-mail:* dcroft@nbp.org
VP, Braille Pubns: Tony Grima *Tel:* 617-266-6160 ext 29 *E-mail:* agrima@nbp.org
VP, Natl Mktg & Community Rel: Kimberly Ballard *E-mail:* kballard@nbp.org
Founded: 1929
Braille books & magazines.
ISBN Prefix(es): 978-0-939173
Number of titles published annually: 30 Print; 15 E-Book
Total Titles: 50 Print; 1 CD-ROM; 14 E-Book

National Catholic Educational Association
1005 N Glebe Rd, Suite 525, Arlington, VA 22201
Tel: 571-257-0010 *Toll Free Tel:* 800-711-6232 *Fax:* 703-243-0025
E-mail: nceaadmin@ncea.org
Web Site: www.ncea.org
Key Personnel
Pres: Karen M Ristau, PhD *E-mail:* president@ncea.org
Nonfiction: educational trends, methodology, innovative programs, teacher education & in-service, research, technology, financial & public relations programs, management systems all applicable to nonpublic education.
ISBN Prefix(es): 978-1-55833
Number of titles published annually: 25 Print
Total Titles: 225 Print

§National Center for Children in Poverty
Division of Mailman School of Public Health at Columbia University
215 W 125 St, 3rd fl, New York, NY 10027
Tel: 646-284-9600 *Fax:* 646-284-9623
E-mail: info@nccp.org
Web Site: www.nccp.org
Founded: 1989
Nonprofit publisher of monographs, reports, statistical updates, working papers & issue briefs concerning children under six who live in poverty in the US. Topics cover impact of poverty on child health & development; statistical profiles of poor children & their families; research programs on the effects of poverty; research on policies that could reduce the young child poverty rate; integrated social & human services (private & public) for low-income families. Welfare reform & children, research forum on children, families & the new federalism.
ISBN Prefix(es): 978-0-926582
Number of titles published annually: 24 Print
Total Titles: 40 Print; 20 E-Book

National Center For Employee Ownership (NCEO)
1736 Franklin St, 8th fl, Oakland, CA 94612-3445
Tel: 510-208-1300 *Fax:* 510-272-9510
E-mail: customerservice@nceo.org
Web Site: www.nceo.org
Key Personnel
Exec Dir: Loren Rodgers *Tel:* 510-208-1307 *E-mail:* lrodgers@nceo.org
Dir, Publg & Info Technol: Scott Rodrick *Tel:* 510-208-1315 *E-mail:* srodrick@nceo.org
Founded: 1981
Employee ownership books, pamphlets & newsletter.
ISBN Prefix(es): 978-0-926902
Number of titles published annually: 4 Print; 5 E-Book
Total Titles: 50 Print

National Conference of State Legislatures (NCSL)
7700 E First Place, Denver, CO 80230
Tel: 303-364-7700 *Fax:* 303-364-7800
E-mail: books@ncsl.org
Web Site: www.ncsl.org
Key Personnel
Exec Dir: William T Pound
Ed: Karen Hansen
Meeting Mgr: Stacy Householder *Tel:* 303-364-7700 ext 1352 *E-mail:* stacy.householder@ncsl.org
Founded: 1975
Books, magazines, series of papers & issue briefs on state public policy issues.
ISBN Prefix(es): 978-1-55516; 978-1-58024
Number of titles published annually: 100 Print
Total Titles: 200 Print
Branch Office(s)
444 N Capitol St NW, Suite 515, Washington, DC 20001 *Tel:* 202-624-5400 *Fax:* 202-737-1069

National Council of Teachers of English (NCTE)
1111 W Kenyon Rd, Urbana, IL 61801-1096
Tel: 217-328-3870 *Toll Free Tel:* 877-369-6283 (cust serv) *Fax:* 217-328-9645
E-mail: orders@ncte.org
Web Site: www.ncte.org
Key Personnel
Interim Exec Dir: Barbara Cambridge *Tel:* 217-278-3601
Deputy Exec Dir: Mila Fuller *Tel:* 217-278-3628 *E-mail:* mfuller@ncte.org
Pubns Dir: Kurt Austin *Tel:* 217-278-3619
Sr Ed: Bonny Graham *Tel:* 217-278-3618
Purch & Prodn Mgr: Charles Hartman *Tel:* 217-278-3664
Books Prog Asst: Kim Black
Perms Coord: Shellie Elson *Tel:* 217-278-3638 *Fax:* 217-328-0977 *E-mail:* permissions@ncte.org
Founded: 1911
Nonprofit professional association of educators in English studies, literacy & language arts. Specialize in the teaching of English & the language arts at all grade levels; research reports; guidelines & position statements; journals.
ISBN Prefix(es): 978-0-8141
Number of titles published annually: 10 Print
Total Titles: 240 Print; 2 CD-ROM
Imprints: Principles in Practice

§National Council of Teachers of Mathematics (NCTM)
1906 Association Dr, Reston, VA 20191-1502
SAN: 202-9057
Tel: 703-620-9840 *Toll Free Tel:* 800-235-7566 *Fax:* 703-476-2970
E-mail: nctm@nctm.org
Web Site: www.nctm.org
Key Personnel
Pres: Linda M Gojak
Exec Dir: Kichoon Yang
Assoc Exec Dir, Communs: Kenneth Krehbiel *E-mail:* kkrehbiel@nctm.org
Dir, Pubns: Joanne Hodges *Tel:* 703-620-9840 ext 2129
Founded: 1920
Professional publications, including books (printed & online), monographs & yearbooks. Members include individuals, institutions, students, teachers & educators. Multiyear plans available to individual & institutional members.
ISBN Prefix(es): 978-0-87353
Number of titles published annually: 15 Print
Total Titles: 175 Print
Distributed by Eric Armin Inc Education Ctr; Delta Education; Didax Educational Resources; Educators Outlet; ETA Cuisenaire; Lakeshore Learning Materials; NASCO; Spectrum

National Council on Radiation Protection & Measurements (NCRP)
7910 Woodmont Ave, Suite 400, Bethesda, MD 20814-3095
Tel: 301-657-2652 *Toll Free Tel:* 800-229-2652 *Fax:* 301-907-8768
E-mail: ncrppubs@ncrponline.org
Web Site: www.ncrponline.org; www.ncrppublications.org
Key Personnel
Pres: Thomas Tenforde, PhD *E-mail:* tenforde@ncrponline.org
Exec Dir: David A Schauer *E-mail:* schauer@ncrponline.org
Mng Ed: Cindy L O'Brien *E-mail:* obrien@ncrponline.org
Sr Word Processor: Luvenia J Hawkins
Edit Asst: Bonnie G Walker
Founded: 1928
NCRP reports, statements, proceedings, commentaries, news; Taylor lectures.
ISBN Prefix(es): 978-0-913392; 978-0-929600
Number of titles published annually: 4 Print
Total Titles: 150 Print

National Crime Prevention Council
2001 Jefferson Davis Hwy, Suite 901, Arlington, VA 22202
Tel: 202-466-6272 *Fax:* 202-296-1356
E-mail: ncpc@fulfills.org (orders)
Web Site: www.ncpc.org
Key Personnel
CEO & Pres: Ann M Harkins
Mng Dir, Progs, Training & Multimedia Servs: Judy Kirby *E-mail:* kirby@ncpc.org
Founded: 1982
Crime prevention publications, training & technical assistance; McGruff public service advertising campaign, conferences & on-site training & technical assistance.
ISBN Prefix(es): 978-0-934513; 978-1-929888; 978-1-59686
Number of titles published annually: 5 Print
Total Titles: 90 Print
Shipping Address: NCPC Fulfillment Center, 49 Elk St, Amsterdam, NY 12010 *Toll Free Tel:* 800-627-2911

National Education Association (NEA)
1201 16 St NW, Washington, DC 20036-3290
Tel: 202-833-4000 *Fax:* 202-822-7974
Web Site: www.nea.org
Key Personnel
Secy/Treas: Rebecca "Becky" Pringle
Pres: Dennis Van Roekel
VP: Lily Eskelsen
Exec Dir: John C Stocks
Dir, PR: Andy Linebaugh *Tel:* 202-822-7218 *E-mail:* alinebaugh@nea.org
Founded: 1857
Professional development publications for K-12 & higher education & AV materials for educators. Web site with resources & general information for educators & the general public.
ISBN Prefix(es): 978-0-8106
Number of titles published annually: 7 Print; 2 CD-ROM; 2 Online
Total Titles: 189 Print; 2 CD-ROM; 9 Online
Imprints: NEA Professional Library

§National Gallery of Art
Fourth St & Pennsylvania Ave NW, Washington, DC 20565
Mailing Address: 2000 S Club Dr, Landover, MD 20785

Tel: 202-737-4215; 202-842-6480 *Fax:* 202-842-6733
E-mail: casva@nga.gov
Web Site: www.nga.gov
Key Personnel
Deputy Publr & Prodn Mgr: Chris Vogel
Ed-in-Chief: Judy Metro
Founded: 1941
Exhibition catalogues, catalogues of the collection & scholarly monographs.
ISBN Prefix(es): 978-0-89468
Number of titles published annually: 12 Print
Total Titles: 112 Print; 2 CD-ROM; 1 Online
Distributed by Abrams; Bulfinch/Little; Cambridge University Press; Hudson Hills; Lund Humphries/Ashgate; OAP; Princeton University Press; Thames & Hudson; Yale University Press

National Geographic Books
Division of National Geographic Society
1145 17 St NW, Washington, DC 20036-4688
Tel: 202-857-7000 *Fax:* 202-857-7670
Web Site: books.nationalgeographic.com/books
Key Personnel
Chief Media Offr, NGS: Declan Moore
SVP & Gen Mgr, Book Publg Group: Hector Sierra *E-mail:* hsierra@ngs.org
Publr & Chief Creative Offr: Melinda Gerosa Bellows
SVP & Edit Dir, Adult Books: Lisa Thomas
SVP, Kids Publg & Media: Nancy Laties Feresten *E-mail:* nfereste@ngs.org
VP, Sales & Mktg: Heidi Vincent *E-mail:* hvincent@ngs.org
Sr Dir, Digital Book Publg: Rachel Graham
Dir, Mng Ed: Jennifer Thornton
Dir, Photog: Susan Blair
Founded: 1888
Nonfiction general illustrated reference, travel, photography, history, science. Children's nonfiction with emphasis on school & library markets.
ISBN Prefix(es): 978-0-7922; 978-0-87044
Number of titles published annually: 180 Print
Total Titles: 700 Print; 15 E-Book
Imprints: National Geographic Adventure Classics; National Geographic Adventure Press; National Geographic Children's Books; National Geographic Directions
Distributed by PGUK / Hi Marketing (United Kingdom); Random House (Worldwide exc UK)
Foreign Rights: Maeyee Lee (Worldwide); Rachel Love (Worldwide); Mary Jo Slazak (USA)
Membership(s): AAP

National Geographic Learning
Unit of Cengage Learning
One Lower Ragsdale Dr, Bldg 1, Suite 200, Monterey, CA 93940
Tel: 831-625-3666
Web Site: www.ngl.cengage.com
Founded: 1980
Publisher of K-12 language & literary educational materials; Spanish & English.
ISBN Prefix(es): 978-0-917837; 978-1-56334
Number of titles published annually: 10 CD-ROM; 10 Online
Membership(s): AAP

National Geographic Society
1145 17 St NW, Washington, DC 20036-4688
SAN: 202-8956
Tel: 202-857-7000 *Fax:* 202-429-5727
Web Site: www.nationalgeographic.com
Key Personnel
Pres, Books & Publg Group & EVP: Declan Moore
Pres, Magazines & Publg Admin: John Griffin
Pres, Global Media Group: Timothy T Kelly
Founded: 1888
Books for adults; nonfiction.
ISBN Prefix(es): 978-0-87044
Number of titles published annually: 75 Print
Total Titles: 450 Print
Distributed by Random House
Membership(s): AAP; The Children's Book Council
See separate listing for:
National Geographic Books

§National Golf Foundation
1150 S US Hwy One, Suite 401, Jupiter, FL 33477
Tel: 561-744-6006 *Toll Free Tel:* 888-275-4643 *Fax:* 561-744-6107
E-mail: general@ngf.org
Web Site: www.ngf.org
Key Personnel
CEO & Pres: Dr Joseph Beditz
Founded: 1936
Premier publisher of research & information for the business of golf. Over 200 publications are offered on golf consumer research, industry & market trends, golf facility development & operations, golf range development, instruction & player development.
ISBN Prefix(es): 978-0-9638647; 978-1-57701
Number of titles published annually: 4 Print
Total Titles: 100 Print; 1 CD-ROM; 2 Online; 1 Audio

National Information Standards Organization
3600 Clipper Mill Rd, Suite 302, Baltimore, MD 21211
Tel: 301-654-2512 *Fax:* 410-685-5278
E-mail: nisohq@niso.org
Web Site: www.niso.org
Key Personnel
Exec Dir: Todd Carpenter *E-mail:* tcarpenter@niso.org
Assoc Dir: Nettie Lagace *E-mail:* nlagace@niso.org
Memb Servs & Engagement Mgr: DeVonne Parks *E-mail:* dparks@niso.org
Founded: 1939
Maintain & develop technical standards for libraries, publishers & information services.
ISBN Prefix(es): 978-1-880124
Number of titles published annually: 6 Print; 6 E-Book
Total Titles: 60 Print; 3 Online; 60 E-Book
Distributor for Niso Press

National Institute for Trial Advocacy (NITA)
1685 38 St, Suite 200, Boulder, CO 80301-2735
Tel: 720-890-4860 *Toll Free Tel:* 877-648-2632; 800-225-6482 (orders & returns) *Fax:* 720-890-7069
E-mail: info@nita.org
Web Site: www.nita.org
Key Personnel
Exec Dir: John Baker *E-mail:* jbaker@nita.org
Dir, Sales & Mktg: Daniel McHugh *E-mail:* dmchugh@nita.org
Publr: Wendy Velez *E-mail:* wvelez@nita.org
Mng Ed: Eric H Sorensen *Tel:* 303-953-6823 *E-mail:* esorensen@nita.org
Founded: 1970
Legal & litigation training.
ISBN Prefix(es): 978-1-55681
Number of titles published annually: 20 Print; 1 CD-ROM
Total Titles: 350 Print; 2 CD-ROM; 12 Audio

National League of Cities
1301 Pennsylvania Ave NW, Washington, DC 20004-1763
Tel: 202-626-3100 *Fax:* 202-626-3043
E-mail: info@nlc.org
Web Site: www.nlc.org
Key Personnel
Dir, Ctr for Pub Aff & Memb Rel: Amy Elsbree *E-mail:* elsbree@nlc.org
Memb Rel Rep: Mae Davis *E-mail:* mdavis@nlc.org
Founded: 1924
ISBN Prefix(es): 978-0-933729; 978-1-886152
Number of titles published annually: 5 Print
Total Titles: 50 Print; 1 CD-ROM

National Learning Corp
212 Michael Dr, Syosset, NY 11791
Tel: 516-921-8888 *Toll Free Tel:* 800-632-8888 *Fax:* 516-921-8743
E-mail: info@passbooks.com
Web Site: www.passbooks.com
Key Personnel
Pres: Michael P Rudman
Founded: 1967
Basic competency tests for college, high school & occupations; functional literacy; career, general, vocational & technical, adult & continuing, special, cooperative & community education; professional licensure; test preparation books for civil service, postal service, government careers, armed forces, high school & college equivalency; college, graduate & professional school enhancement; certification & licensing in engineering & technical careers, teaching, law, dentistry, medicine & allied health professions.
ISBN Prefix(es): 978-0-8373
Number of titles published annually: 3 Print
Total Titles: 5,000 Print
Imprints: ACT Proficiency Examination Program; Admission Test Series; Career Examination Series; Certified Nurse Series (CN); College Level Examination Series; College Proficiency Examination Series; Dante Series; Graduate Record Examination Series; National Teacher Examination Series; Occupational Competency Examination Series; Passbooks; Regents External Degree Series; Teachers License Examination Series; Test Your Knowledge Books; Undergraduate Program Field Test Series; What Do You Know About Books
Subsidiaries: Delaney Books Inc; Frank Merriwell Inc
Membership(s): AAP

National Notary Association (NNA)
9350 De Soto Ave, Chatsworth, CA 91311
Mailing Address: PO Box 541032, Los Angeles, CA 90054-1032
Tel: 818-739-4000 *Toll Free Tel:* 800-876-6827 *Toll Free Fax:* 800-833-1211
E-mail: nna@nationalnotary.org
Web Site: www.nationalnotary.org
Key Personnel
CEO: Marc A Reiser
CFO & EVP: Jane Eagle
Pres: Milton G Valera
EVP: Debora M Thaw
SVP, Systems & Opers: Ronald Johnson
Dir, Mktg: Thomas K Hayden
Founded: 1957
Publish books, periodical, videos, seminars.
ISBN Prefix(es): 978-0-9600158; 978-0-933134; 978-1-891133
Number of titles published annually: 15 Print
Total Titles: 40 Print

National Park Service Media Services
Subsidiary of US Department of the Interior
67 Mather Place, Harpers Ferry, WV 25425
Mailing Address: PO Box 50, Harpers Ferry, WV 25425-0050
Tel: 304-535-5050 *Fax:* 304-535-6176
Web Site: www.nps.gov/hfc
Key Personnel
Dir: Don Kodak *Tel:* 304-535-6104
Ed: Diane Liggett

Pubns Supv: Melissa Cronyn
Founded: 1965
Official National Park Service handbooks, maps & brochures.
ISBN Prefix(es): 978-0-912627
Number of titles published annually: 3 Print
Total Titles: 43 Print
Warehouse: US Government Publishing Office, Superintendent of Documents, Washington, DC 20402

National Register Publishing
Division of Marquis Who's Who LLC
430 Mountain Ave, Suite 400, New Providence, NJ 07974
Toll Free Tel: 800-473-7020 *Fax:* 908-673-1189 (cust serv)
E-mail: NRPeditorial@marquiswhoswho.com (edit); NRPsales@marquiswhoswho.com (sales)
Web Site: www.nationalregisterpub.com
Founded: 1915
Publisher of business information directories available in print, online & mailing list for commercial & reference use.
ISBN Prefix(es): 978-0-87217
Number of titles published annually: 5 Print
Total Titles: 1 Online

National Resource Center for Youth Services (NRCYS)
Division of University of Oklahoma-Outreach
Schusterman Ctr, Bldg 4W, 4502 E 41 St, Tulsa, OK 74135-2512
Tel: 918-660-3700 *Toll Free Tel:* 800-274-2687 *Fax:* 918-660-3737
Web Site: www.nrcys.ou.edu
Key Personnel
Dir: Peter R Correia, III *E-mail:* pcorreia@ou.edu
Assoc Dir: Kristi Charles *E-mail:* klcharles@ou.edu
Asst Prog Dir: TeRessa Kaemmerling *E-mail:* tkaemmerling@ou.edu
Founded: 1985
Curricula & resource manuals for professionals & volunteers who work with foster care & at-risk teenagers.
ISBN Prefix(es): 978-1-878848
Number of titles published annually: 3 Print
Total Titles: 20 Print

National Science Teachers Association (NSTA)
1840 Wilson Blvd, Arlington, VA 22201-3000
Tel: 703-312-9205 *Toll Free Tel:* 800-277-5300 (orders) *Toll Free Fax:* 888-433-0526 (orders)
E-mail: orders@nsta.org; publisher@nsta.org (general info)
Web Site: www.nsta.org/store
Key Personnel
Publr & Assoc Exec Dir: David Beacom *Tel:* 703-312-9207 *Fax:* 703-841-0250 *E-mail:* dbeacom@nsta.org
Founded: 1944
Books & periodicals.
ISBN Prefix(es): 978-0-87355; 978-1-93353; 978-1-936137; 978-1-935155; 978-1-936959; 978-1-938946; 978-1-941316
Number of titles published annually: 25 Print; 25 E-Book
Total Titles: 350 Print; 350 E-Book
Imprints: NSTA Ebooks+; NSTA Kids; NSTA Press
Foreign Rep(s): Alkem (Southeast Asia); Eurospan (all other territories); University of Toronto Press (Canada)
Foreign Rights: Cat Russo (Worldwide)
Orders to: PO Box 90214, Washington, DC 20090-5300
Returns: 3280 Summit Ridge Pkwy, Duluth, GA 30096
Membership(s): AAP; AAP PreK-12 Learning Group; Association Media & Publishing; Independent Book Publishing Professionals Group

The National Underwriter Co
Division of Summit Business Media
5081 Olympic Blvd, Erlanger, KY 41018-3164
Tel: 859-692-2100 *Toll Free Tel:* 800-543-0874 *Fax:* 859-692-2289
E-mail: customerservice@nuco.com
Web Site: www.nationalunderwriter.com
Key Personnel
Interim CFO & COO: Thomas M Flynn
CIO: David MacDonald
Founded: 1897
ISBN Prefix(es): 978-0-87218
Number of titles published annually: 3 Print
Total Titles: 15 Print

The Nautical & Aviation Publishing Co of America Inc
845-A Lowcountry Blvd, Mount Pleasant, SC 29464
SAN: 213-3431
Tel: 843-856-0561 *Fax:* 843-856-3164
Web Site: www.nauticalandaviation.com
Key Personnel
Pres: Jan W Snouck-Hurgronje
Founded: 1979
Military history & aviation.
ISBN Prefix(es): 978-1-877853; 978-0-933852
Number of titles published annually: 4 Print; 2 Audio
Total Titles: 47 Print; 2 Audio
Imprints: N & A
Warehouse: REO Distribution, One Solutions Way, Waynesboro, VA 22980

§Naval Institute Press
Division of US Naval Institute
291 Wood Rd, Annapolis, MD 21402-5034
SAN: 202-9006
Tel: 410-268-6110 *Toll Free Tel:* 800-233-8764 *Fax:* 410-295-1084; 410-571-1703 (cust serv)
E-mail: webmaster@navalinstitute.org; customer@navalinstitute.org (cust serv); trade@usni.org
Web Site: www.nip.org; www.usni.org
Key Personnel
CEO: Peter H Daly *E-mail:* trade@usni.org
Press Dir: Rick Russell *E-mail:* rrussell@usni.org
Sales & Mktg Dir: Claire Noble *Tel:* 410-295-1039 *E-mail:* cnoble@usni.org
Mng Ed: Susan Corrado *Tel:* 410-295-1032 *E-mail:* scorrado@usni.org
Sr Acqs Ed: Thomas Cutler *E-mail:* tcutler@usni.org
Subs Rts Ed: Susan Todd Brook *E-mail:* sbrook@usni.org
Publicist: Judy Heise *Tel:* 410-295-1028 *E-mail:* jheise@usni.org
Cust Serv: Jaemellah Kemp
Founded: 1873
Naval & maritime subjects: professional, biography, science, history, ship & aviation references, US Naval Institute magazines; literature.
ISBN Prefix(es): 978-0-87021; 978-1-55750; 978-1-59114; 978-1-61251
Number of titles published annually: 65 Print
Total Titles: 800 Print
Distributed by Publishers Group West (digital only)
Foreign Rep(s): Eurospan Group (Africa, Asia, Australia, Europe, India, Middle East, Oceania, UK); Scholarly Book Services (Canada)
Warehouse: US Naval Institute, 2427 Bond St, University Park, IL 60466 *Toll Free Tel:* 800-233-8764
Membership(s): Association of American University Presses

NavPress Publishing Group
Division of The Navigators
3820 N 30 St, Colorado Springs, CO 80904
SAN: 211-5352
Mailing Address: PO Box 35002, Colorado Springs, CO 80935
Tel: 719-548-9222 *Toll Free Tel:* 800-366-7788 *Toll Free Fax:* 800-343-3902
E-mail: customerservice@navpress.com
Web Site: www.navpress.com
Key Personnel
Interim CEO: Charlie Dokmo
Sales & Trade Mktg Dir: Eric Helus
Founded: 1975
Paperbacks, mass market & trade, hardcovers, periodicals; religious (Protestant) materials.
ISBN Prefix(es): 978-0-89109; 978-1-57683
Number of titles published annually: 123 Print
Total Titles: 380 Print; 2 Audio
Imprints: NavPress; Think

NBM Publishing Inc
160 Broadway, E Wing, Suite 700, New York, NY 10038
SAN: 210-0835
Tel: 646-559-4681 *Toll Free Tel:* 800-886-1223 *Fax:* 212-643-1545
E-mail: admin@nbmpub.com
Web Site: www.nbmpub.com
Key Personnel
Pres & Publr: Terry Nantier
Off Mgr: May Wong *E-mail:* mayw@nbmpub.com
Founded: 1976
Graphic novels.
ISBN Prefix(es): 978-0-918348; 978-1-56163; 978-1-68112
Number of titles published annually: 20 Print; 20 E-Book
Total Titles: 250 Print; 100 E-Book
Imprints: Amerotica (erotic graphic novels from North American authors); ComicsLit (best fiction in graphic novels from around the world); Eurotica (erotic graphic novels from European authors); Forever Nuts (reprints of classic comic strips)
Foreign Rep(s): IPG (Canada); Turnaround (Europe, UK)
Orders to: IPG Distribution Center, 600 N Pulaski Rd, Chicago, IL 60624 *Toll Free Tel:* 800-888-IPG1 (888-4741)
Returns: IPG Distribution Center, 600 N Pulaski Rd, Chicago, IL 60624
Warehouse: IPG Distribution Center, 600 N Pulaski Rd, Chicago, IL 60624
Distribution Center: IPG Distribution Center, 600 N Pulaski Rd, Chicago, IL 60624
Membership(s): AAP; The Children's Book Council; The Independent Book Publishers Association

NCRP, see National Council on Radiation Protection & Measurements (NCRP)

§Neal-Schuman Publishers Inc
100 William St, Suite 2004, New York, NY 10038
SAN: 210-2455
Tel: 212-925-8650 *Toll Free Tel:* 866-NS-BOOKS (672-6657) *Fax:* 212-219-8916 *Toll Free Fax:* 877-231-6980
E-mail: info@neal-schuman.com
Web Site: www.neal-schuman.com
Key Personnel
Pres: Patricia Glass Schuman
EVP: John Vincent Neal
VP, Fin & New Busn Devt: Kathryn Suarez *E-mail:* suarez.kathryn@neal-schuman.com
Founded: 1976
How-to manuals, technology, library & information science texts.
ISBN Prefix(es): 978-0-918212; 978-1-55570
Number of titles published annually: 32 Print; 5 CD-ROM
Total Titles: 320 Print; 25 CD-ROM

Foreign Office(s): 3 Henrietta St, London WC2E 8LU, United Kingdom
Distributor for Chandos; Facet
Foreign Rep(s): James Bennett (Australia, New Zealand); Eurospan (Europe, UK); I-Group (Asia Pacific) (Asia); Ontario Library Association (Canada)
Warehouse: 1200 County Rd, Rte 523, Flemington, NJ 08822
Membership(s): ALA; Ontario Library Association

NeDeo Press
PO Box 668, Robbins, NC 27325
Web Site: www.nedeopress.com
Key Personnel
Dir: Barbara S Bane *E-mail:* bbane@nedeopress.com
Founded: 2005
Publish quality fiction & nonfiction books to entertain & inform for both regional & national markets.
ISBN Prefix(es): 978-0-9763874
Number of titles published annually: 3 Print
Total Titles: 7 Print
Membership(s): The Independent Book Publishers Association; Independent Publishers Association

Neibauer Press & ChurchSupplier.com
Division of Louis Neibauer Co Inc
20 Industrial Dr, Warminster, PA 18974
Tel: 215-322-6200 *Toll Free Tel:* 800-322-6203 *Fax:* 215-322-2495
E-mail: sales@neibauer.com; sales@churchsupplier.com
Web Site: www.churchsupplier.com
Key Personnel
Pres: Nathan Neibauer *E-mail:* nathan@neibauer.com
Founded: 1967
ISBN Prefix(es): 978-1-878259
Number of titles published annually: 5 Print
Total Titles: 30 Print
Membership(s): CBA: The Association for Christian Retail

New American Library, see NAL

New Canaan Publishing Co LLC
2384 N Hwy 341, Rossville, GA 30741
Tel: 423-285-8672
E-mail: djm@newcanaanpublishing.com
Web Site: www.newcanaanpublishing.com
Key Personnel
Pres: David J Mittelstadt
Founded: 1995
Publisher of children's books, selected Christian works for all ages & humor books confronting current trends & issues.
ISBN Prefix(es): 978-1-889658
Number of titles published annually: 4 Print
Total Titles: 23 Print
Distribution Center: Advocate Distribution Services™, 100 Biblica Way, Elizabethton, TN 37643 *Web Site:* www.advocatedistribution.com
Membership(s): The Independent Book Publishers Association

§New City Press
Division of Focolare Movement
202 Comforter Blvd, Hyde Park, NY 12538
SAN: 203-7335
Tel: 845-229-0335 *Toll Free Tel:* 800-462-5980 (orders only) *Fax:* 845-229-0351
E-mail: info@newcitypress.com
Web Site: www.newcitypress.com
Key Personnel
Publr & Gen Mgr: Gary Brandl *E-mail:* garybrandl@newcitypress.com
Accts Payable: Ms Soki Stanczyk *E-mail:* accountant@newcitypress.com
Cust Serv: Nick Cianfarani *E-mail:* orders@newcitypress.com
Founded: 1964
Publishes spiritual works of all Christian eras, including the Church Fathers, the spiritual masters of the middle-ages, as well as publications of contemporary spirituality & theology.
ISBN Prefix(es): 978-0-911782; 978-1-56548
Number of titles published annually: 25 Print
Total Titles: 215 Print
Imprints: NCP
Distributor for Ciudad Nueva (Spain/Argentina); New City (Great Britain)
Foreign Rep(s): Enderle Book Co (Japan); John Garratt Publishing (Australia); Jerome's Specialist Booksellers (New Zealand); Joseph's Inspirational (Canada); New City (China, England, Ireland, Philippines); Preca Bookshop (Malta)

§New Concepts Publishing
106-A W Hill Ave, Valdosta, GA 31636
E-mail: service@newconceptspublishing.com; submissions@newconceptspublishing.com
Web Site: www.newconceptspublishing.com
Key Personnel
Pres: Madris De Pasture *E-mail:* madris@newconceptspublishing.com
Ed-in-Chief: Andrea De Pasture *E-mail:* andrea@newconceptspublishing.com
Founded: 1996
ISBN Prefix(es): 978-1-58608
Number of titles published annually: 50 Print; 192 Online; 144 E-Book
Total Titles: 200 Print; 700 Online; 700 E-Book

New Dimensions Publishing
11248 N 11 St, Phoenix, AZ 85020
Tel: 602-861-2631 *Toll Free Tel:* 800-736-7367 *Fax:* 602-944-1235
E-mail: info@thedream.com
Web Site: www.thedream.com
Key Personnel
Pres: Keith Varnum *E-mail:* keith@thedream.com
Founded: 1989
Book & audio tape publisher.
ISBN Prefix(es): 978-0-9722699
Number of titles published annually: 3 Print; 5 Audio
Total Titles: 6 Print; 5 Audio
Membership(s): The Association of Publishers for Special Sales; The Independent Book Publishers Association

New Directions Publishing Corp
80 Eighth Ave, New York, NY 10011
SAN: 202-9081
Tel: 212-255-0230 *Fax:* 212-255-0231
E-mail: newdirections@ndbooks.com; editorial@ndbooks.com
Web Site: ndbooks.com
Key Personnel
Pres & Publr: Barbara Epler *E-mail:* bepler@ndbooks.com
EVP: Laurie Callahan *E-mail:* lcallahan@ndbooks.com
Art Dir & Prodn Mgr: Erik Rieselbach *E-mail:* erieselbach@ndbooks.com
Founded: 1936
Modern literature, poetry, criticism & belles lettres.
ISBN Prefix(es): 978-0-8112
Number of titles published annually: 30 Print
Total Titles: 930 Print
Distributed by W W Norton Co
Foreign Rep(s): Australia Pansing Distribution (Malaysia, Singapore); Everest International Publishing Services (China); Hardy Bigfoss International Co Ltd (Cambodia, Laos, Myanmar, Thailand, Vietnam); MK International Ltd (Japan); B K Norton Ltd (Korea, Taiwan); W W Norton & Co Ltd (Africa, Europe, Ireland, Middle East, UK); Penguin Books Canada Ltd (Canada); Penguin Group New Zealand (New Zealand); Transglobal Publishers Services Ltd (Hong Kong, Macau); US PubRep (Caribbean, Central America, Mexico, South America); John Wiley & Sons (Australia)
Foreign Rights: Agenzia Letteraria Internazionale (Italy); Carmen Balcells Agencia Literaria (Spain); Agence Hoffman (France, Germany); Orion Literary Agency (Japan); Laurence Pollinger Ltd (British Commonwealth)
Warehouse: National Book Co, 800 Keystone Industrial Park, Scranton, PA 18512 *Tel:* 212-790-9453 *Toll Free Tel:* 800-233-4830 *Toll Free Fax:* 800-458-6515
Distribution Center: W W Norton Co, 500 Fifth Ave, New York, NY 10110

§New Forums Press Inc
1018 S Lewis St, Stillwater, OK 74074
Mailing Address: PO Box 876, Stillwater, OK 74076-0876
Tel: 405-372-6158 *Toll Free Tel:* 800-606-3766 *Fax:* 405-377-2237
E-mail: submissions@newforums.com
Web Site: www.newforums.com
Key Personnel
Pres: Douglas Dollar *E-mail:* ddollar@newforums.com
Founded: 1981
Practical & innovative academic journals, newsletters & books for educators in two & four year colleges & universities. Textbooks are also a primary interest.
ISBN Prefix(es): 978-0-913507; 978-1-58107
Number of titles published annually: 25 Print; 1 Online; 3 E-Book
Total Titles: 201 Print; 1 Online; 5 E-Book
Advertising Agency: Copy & Art, 219 E Greenvale Ct, Stillwater, OK 74075 *Tel:* 405-377-8224
Membership(s): The Association of Publishers for Special Sales

New Harbinger Publications Inc
5674 Shattuck Ave, Oakland, CA 94609
Tel: 510-652-0215 *Toll Free Tel:* 800-748-6273 (orders only) *Fax:* 510-652-5472 *Toll Free Fax:* 800-652-1613
E-mail: nhhelp@newharbinger.com; customerservice@newharbinger.com
Web Site: www.newharbinger.com
Key Personnel
Acq Ed: Catherine Sutker *E-mail:* catherine@newharbinger.com
Gen Mgr: Matt McKay, PhD *E-mail:* matt@newharbinger.com
Intl Rts: Dorothy Smyk *E-mail:* dorothy@newharbinger.com
Prodn Mgr: Michele Waters *E-mail:* michele@newharbinger.com
Founded: 1973
We offer the best in self-help psychology & health publications for tackling real problems.
ISBN Prefix(es): 978-1-57224
Number of titles published annually: 50 Print; 1 E-Book; 1 Audio
Total Titles: 250 Print; 1 E-Book; 46 Audio
Imprints: Context Press; Instant Help; Noetic Books
Foreign Rights: Raincoast Books (UK); Real Books (South Africa); John Reed Book Distributors (Australia); Southern Publishers Group (New Zealand)
Returns: 660 S Mansfield St, Ypsilanti, MI 48197

New Horizon Press
PO Box 669, Far Hills, NJ 07931-0669
SAN: 677-119X

Tel: 908-604-6311 *Toll Free Tel:* 800-533-7978 (orders only) *Fax:* 908-604-6330
E-mail: nhp@newhorizonpressbooks.com
Web Site: www.newhorizonpressbooks.com
Key Personnel
Publr & Ed-in-Chief: Dr Joan S Dunphy *E-mail:* nhp@newhorizonpressbooks.com
VP, Fin & Mktg: Jo Anne C Thomas *E-mail:* jct@newhorizonpressbooks.com
Prodn Mgr: Charles Nasta *E-mail:* prd@newhorizonpressbooks.com
Founded: 1982
True stories of uncommon heroes, true crime, social issues, behavioral, political science & psychologically-oriented nonfiction, trade paper, children's self-help, helping children deal with crisis.
ISBN Prefix(es): 978-0-88282; 978-1-933893
Number of titles published annually: 12 Print; 12 E-Book
Total Titles: 340 Print; 62 Online
Imprints: Small Horizons
Foreign Rights: Books Crossing Borders Inc (Betty Ann Crawford) (Worldwide)
Orders to: Publishers Group West (Perseus Distribution), 1700 Fourth St, Berkeley, CA 94710 *Toll Free Tel:* 800-788-3123 *Fax:* 510-528-3614 *Toll Free Fax:* 800-351-5073 *Web Site:* www.pgw.com
Returns: Perseus Distribution Returns Dept, 1700 Fourth St, Berkeley, CA 94710 *Toll Free Tel:* 800-788-3123 *Toll Free Fax:* 800-351-5073
Distribution Center: Publishers Group West (Perseus Distribution), 1700 Fourth St, Berkeley, CA 94710 *Tel:* 510-809-3700 *Toll Free Tel:* 800-788-3123 *Fax:* 510-809-3777 *Toll Free Fax:* 800-351-5073 *E-mail:* info@pgw.com *Web Site:* www.pgw.com

New Issues Poetry & Prose
Affiliate of Western Michigan University
c/o Western Michigan University, 1903 W Michigan Ave, Kalamazoo, MI 49008-5463
Tel: 269-387-8185 *Fax:* 269-387-2562
E-mail; new-issues@wmich.edu
Web Site: www.wmich.edu/newissues
Key Personnel
Mng Ed: Kimberly Kolbe
Ed: William Olsen
Founded: 1996
ISBN Prefix(es): 978-1-930974
Number of titles published annually: 8 Print
Total Titles: 130 Print
Distribution Center: SPD/Small Press Distribution Inc, 1341 Seventh St, Berkeley, CA 94710-1409 *Toll Free Tel:* 800-869-7553 *E-mail:* spd@spdbooks.org *Web Site:* www.spdbooks.org
Partners, 2325 Jarco Dr, Holt, MI 48842 *Toll Free Tel:* 800-336-3137 *Fax:* 517-694-0617

New Leaf Press Inc
Division of New Leaf Publishing Group
3142 Hwy 103 N, Green Forest, AR 72638-2233
Mailing Address: PO Box 726, Green Forest, AR 72638-0726
Tel: 870-438-5288 *Toll Free Tel:* 800-999-3777 *Fax:* 870-438-5120
E-mail: submissions@newleafpress.net
Web Site: www.nlpg.com
Key Personnel
Asst Ed: Craig Froman
Founded: 1975
Christian living & creation books; evangelical, devotionals.
ISBN Prefix(es): 978-0-89221
Number of titles published annually: 35 Print; 25 E-Book
Total Titles: 425 Print; 200 E-Book

New Poets Series, see BrickHouse Books Inc

The New Press
38 Greene St, 4th fl, New York, NY 10013
Tel: 212-629-8802 *Toll Free Tel:* 800-343-4489 (orders) *Fax:* 212-629-8617 *Toll Free Fax:* 800-351-5073 (orders)
E-mail: newpress@thenewpress.com
Web Site: www.thenewpress.com
Key Personnel
Exec Dir: Diane Wachtell
Publr: Ellen Adler
Exec Ed: Marc Favreau
Sr Mng Ed: Maury Botton
Edit Dir: Carl Bromley
Fin Dir: Carline Yup
Prodn Dir: Fran Forte
Founded: 1990
Nonprofit publisher in the public interest; politics, education, current affairs, history, biography, economics, international fiction in translation.
ISBN Prefix(es): 978-1-56584
Number of titles published annually: 50 Print
Total Titles: 800 Print; 200 E-Book
Foreign Rep(s): MK International Ltd (Japan); W W Norton & Co Ltd (USA); I B Taurus & Co Ltd (Worldwide); University of Toronto Press (Canada)
Foreign Rights: Carmen Balcells (Spain); Ursula Bender (Germany); Ann Christine Danielsson (Scandinavia); Cristina de Mello e Souza; Beth Elon (Israel); Mary Kling (France); William Miller (Japan); Susanna Zevi (Italy)

New Readers Press
Division of ProLiteracy
1320 Jamesville Ave, Syracuse, NY 13210
SAN: 202-1064
Tel: 315-422-9121 *Toll Free Tel:* 800-448-8878 *Fax:* 315-422-6369 *Toll Free Fax:* 866-894-2100
E-mail: nrp@proliteracy.org
Web Site: www.newreaderspress.com
Key Personnel
Busn Dir: Susan Willey *Tel:* 315-422-9121 ext 260
ISBN Contact: Mike Shaffer
Founded: 1965
Books & periodical for adults & young adult reading at a 0-8 reading level, basic reading & writing materials, English as a second language, mathematics & GED prep.
ISBN Prefix(es): 978-0-88336; 978-1-56420; 978-1-56853; 978-0-929631
Number of titles published annually: 20 Print
Total Titles: 550 Print; 41 Audio
Foreign Rep(s): Frontier Books (Canada)
Foreign Rights: Frontier BookStore (Canada); Laubach Literacy Ontario (Canada)

New Rivers Press
c/o Minnesota State University Moorhead, 1104 Seventh Ave S, Moorhead, MN 56563
Tel: 218-477-5870 *Fax:* 218-477-2236
E-mail: nrp@mnstate.edu
Web Site: www.newriverspress.com; www.mnstate.edu/newriverspress
Key Personnel
Mng Ed: Dr Suzzanne Kelley *E-mail:* kelleysu@mnstate.edu
Sr Ed: Dr Alan Davis *Tel:* 218-477-4681 *E-mail:* davisa@mnstate.edu
Founded: 1968
Books of poetry, short stories & novellas, creative nonfiction, memoir.
ISBN Prefix(es): 978-0-912284; 978-0-89823
Number of titles published annually: 6 Print; 6 E-Book
Total Titles: 340 Print
Distribution Center: Consortium Books Sales & Distribution, The Keg House, Suite 101, 34 13 Ave NE, Minneapolis, MN 55413-1007 *Tel:* 612-746-2600 *Toll Free Tel:* 800-283-3572 (cust serv) *Fax:* 612-746-2606 *Web Site:* www.cbsd.com
Membership(s): Association of Writers and Writing Programs; Community of Literary Magazines & Presses

New Strategist Publications Inc
120 W State St, 4th fl, Ithaca, NY 14850
Mailing Address: PO Box 242, Ithaca, NY 14851-0242
Tel: 607-273-0913 *Toll Free Tel:* 800-848-0842 *Fax:* 607-277-5009
E-mail: demographics@newstrategist.com
Web Site: newstrategist.com
Key Personnel
Pres & Publr: Penelope Wickham
Ed-in-Chief: Cheryl Russell
Founded: 1990
Publish reference books; demographics & consumer spending.
ISBN Prefix(es): 978-1-885070; 978-1-933588; 978-1-935775
Number of titles published annually: 20 Print; 20 Online
Total Titles: 32 Print; 32 Online

New Win Publishing
Division of Academic Learning Co LLC
9682 Telstar Ave, Suite 110, El Monte, CA 91731
SAN: 217-1201
Tel: 626-448-3448 *Fax:* 626-602-3817
E-mail: info@academiclearningcompany.com
Web Site: www.newwinpublishing.com; www.wbusinessbooks.com/
Key Personnel
Publr: Arthur Chou
Founded: 1988
General nonfiction: business books for sales, marketing & entrepreneurship, crafts, reference, health & nutrition, healthy gourmet cooking, career development, outdoor sports, hunting, shooting, fishing, decoys & dogs.
ISBN Prefix(es): 978-0-8329
Number of titles published annually: 25 Print
Total Titles: 70 Print
Imprints: WBusiness Books; Winchester Press; ZHealth Books

New World Library
Division of Whatever Publishing Inc
14 Pamaron Way, Novato, CA 94949
SAN: 211-8777
Tel: 415-884-2100 *Toll Free Tel:* 800-227-3900 (ext 52, retail orders); 800-972-6657 *Fax:* 415-884-2199
E-mail: escort@newworldlibrary.com
Web Site: www.newworldlibrary.com
Key Personnel
Pres: Marc Allen *E-mail:* marc@newworldlibrary.com
Edit Dir: Georgia Hughes *E-mail:* georgia@newworldlibrary.com
Mktg Dir & Assoc Publr: Munro Magruder *E-mail:* munro@newworldlibrary.com
Prodn Dir: Tona Pearce Meyers *E-mail:* tona@newworldlibrary.com
Publicity Dir: Monique Muhlenkamp *E-mail:* monique@newworldlibrary.com
Sr Ed: Jason Gardner *E-mail:* jason@newworldlibrary.com
Submissions Ed: Jonathan Wichmann *E-mail:* jonathan@newworldlibrary.com
Foreign Rts Mgr: Danielle Galat *E-mail:* danielle@newworldlibrary.com
Soc Media Mgr & Sr Publicist: Kim Corbin *E-mail:* kim@newworldlibrary.com
Spec Sales Mgr: Ami Parkerson *E-mail:* ami@newworldlibrary.com
Founded: 1977
Publisher of books on self-improvement, personal growth & spirituality, health & wellness, pets & animals, psychology & women's interest.

ISBN Prefix(es): 978-0-915811; 978-0-931432; 978-1-880032; 978-0-945934; 978-1-57731; 978-1-882591; 978-1-930722; 978-1-932073; 978-1-60868
Number of titles published annually: 35 Print; 35 E-Book; 2 Audio
Total Titles: 550 Print; 470 E-Book; 35 Audio
Imprints: Amber-Allen Publishing; Nataraj
Divisions: H J Kramer Inc
Foreign Rep(s): Akasha Books (New Zealand); Brumby Books (Australia); Dempsey-Your Distributor (Canada); Perseus International (Continental Europe, India, Japan, Korea, Latin America, Middle East, Philippines, South America, Southeast Asia, Taiwan); Publishers Group Canada (Canada); Publishers Group UK (UK); Real Books (South Africa)
Distribution Center: Publishers Group West, 193 Edwards Dr, Jackson, TN 38301-7795 *Toll Free Tel:* 800-788-3123 *Web Site:* www.pgw.com
Membership(s): AAP; Publishers Association of the West; Publishing Professionals Network
See separate listing for:
HJ Kramer Inc

New York Academy of Sciences
7 World Trade, 40th fl, 250 Greenwich St, New York, NY 10007-2157
SAN: 203-753X
Tel: 212-298-8600 *Toll Free Tel:* 800-843-6927 *Fax:* 212-298-3644
E-mail: nyas@nyas.org; publications@nyas.org
Web Site: www.nyas.org
Key Personnel
CEO & Pres: Ellis Rubenstein *Tel:* 212-298-8686 *E-mail:* erubenstein@nyas.org
COO: Richard Baum *Tel:* 212-298-8695 *E-mail:* rbaum@nyas.org
VP, HR: Wendy Caruso Schneider *Tel:* 212-298-8680 *E-mail:* wschneider@nyas.org
Dir, Scientific Pubns & Ed-in-Chief, Annals of the NYAS: Douglas Braaten, PhD *Tel:* 212-298-8634 *E-mail:* dbraaten@nyas.org
Founded: 1817
Annals & transactions of the New York Academy of Sciences; also publish *Update Magazine*.
ISBN Prefix(es): 978-0-89072; 978-0-89766; 978-1-57331
Number of titles published annually: 32 Print
Total Titles: 333 Print
Distributed by Wiley Blackwell Publishers
Membership(s): AAP

The New York Botanical Garden Press
Division of The New York Botanical Garden
2900 Southern Blvd, Bronx, NY 10458-5126
Tel: 718-817-8721 *Fax:* 718-817-8842
E-mail: nybgpress@nybg.org
Web Site: www.nybgpress.org
Key Personnel
Mng Ed, NYBG Press: Joy Runyon *Tel:* 718-817-8574
Cust Serv: Diedra Howson *Tel:* 718-817-8918 *E-mail:* dhowson@nybg.org
Founded: 1896
Dissemination of information on the scientific study of plants.
ISBN Prefix(es): 978-0-89327
Number of titles published annually: 15 Print
Total Titles: 244 Print
Warehouse: Maple-Vail Distribution Center, PO Box 15100, York, PA 17405
Distribution Center: Maple-Vail Distribution Center, PO Box 15100, York, PA 17405
Membership(s): AAP

New York Public Library
Publications Off, 2nd fl, 188 Madison Ave, New York, NY 10016-4314
Tel: 917-275-6975
Web Site: www.nypl.org
Key Personnel
Dir, PR: Angela Montefinise
Founded: 1895
Reference books, exhibition catalogs, literature & humanities; hardcover & softcover.
ISBN Prefix(es): 978-0-87104
Number of titles published annually: 5 Print
Total Titles: 60 Print

New York State Bar Association
One Elk St, Albany, NY 12207
SAN: 226-1952
Tel: 518-463-3200 *Toll Free Tel:* 800-582-2452 *Fax:* 518-487-5517
Web Site: www.nysba.org
Key Personnel
CLE (Continuing Legal Educ) Pubns Dir: Daniel J McMahon *Tel:* 518-487-5582 *E-mail:* dmcmahon@nysba.org
Founded: 1985
Legal publications, including hardbound, loose-leaf, softbound & diskettes.
ISBN Prefix(es): 978-0-942954
Number of titles published annually: 110 Print; 6 CD-ROM
Total Titles: 600 Print; 500 Online

New York University Press
838 Broadway, 3rd fl, New York, NY 10003-4812
SAN: 658-1293
Tel: 212-998-2575 (edit) *Toll Free Tel:* 800-996-6987 (orders) *Fax:* 212-995-3833 (orders)
E-mail: information@nyupress.org; customerservice@nyupress.org; orders@nyupress.org
Web Site: www.nyupress.org
Key Personnel
Publr: Ellen Chodosh
Mktg & Sales Dir: Mary Beth Jarrad
Assoc Dir & Ed-in-Chief: Eric Zinner
Prodn Mgr: Charles Hames
Exec Ed: Ilene Kalish
Mng Ed: Despina P Gimbel
Sr Ed: Deborah Gershenowitz
Ed: Jennifer Hammer
Publicist: Betsy Steve
Order Fulfillment & Spec Sales Supv: Kevin Cooper
Founded: 1916
Publish a wide array of provocative & compelling titles, as well as works of lasting scholarly & reference value.
ISBN Prefix(es): 978-0-8147
Number of titles published annually: 100 Print
Total Titles: 2,000 Print
Distributor for Combined Academic Publishers Ltd; Footprint Books; Monthly Review Press
Returns: c/o Maple Press Lebanon Distribution Center, 704 Legionaire Dr, Fredricksburg, PA 17026 *Tel:* 717-865-7600 *Fax:* 717-865-7800
Warehouse: c/o Maple Press Lebanon Distribution Center, 704 Legionaire Dr, Fredricksburg, PA 17026 *Tel:* 717-865-7600 *Fax:* 717-865-7800
Membership(s): AAP; Association of American University Presses

Newbury Street Press
Imprint of New England Historic Genealogical Society
101 Newbury St, Boston, MA 02116
Tel: 617-536-5740 *Toll Free Tel:* 888-296-3447 (NEHGS membership) *Fax:* 617-536-7307
E-mail: sales@nehgs.org
Web Site: www.newenglandancestors.org
Key Personnel
CEO & Pres: D Brenton Simons
VP & COO: Ryan Woods *Tel:* 617-226-1205 *E-mail:* rwoods@nehgs.org
Publg Dir: Penny Stratton *Tel:* 617-226-1210 *E-mail:* pstratton@nehgs.org
Dir, Pubns: Scott C Steward *Tel:* 617-226-1208 *E-mail:* ssteward@nehgs.org
Dir, Devt: Ted MacMahon *Tel:* 617-226-1218 *E-mail:* tmacmahon@nehgs.org
Sales Coord: Rick Park *Tel:* 617-226-1212 *E-mail:* rpark@nehgs.org
Founded: 1996
A special publications division of The New England Historic Genealogical Society which publishes scholarly books & compiled genealogies.
ISBN Prefix(es): 978-0-88082
Number of titles published annually: 10 Print
Total Titles: 67 Print

NewSouth Books
Imprint of NewSouth Inc
105 S Court St, Montgomery, AL 36104
Tel: 334-834-3556 *Fax:* 334-834-3557
E-mail: info@newsouthbooks.com
Web Site: www.newsouthbooks.com
Key Personnel
Owner & Publr: Suzanne La Rosa
Owner & Ed-in-Chief: Randall Williams
Mng Ed: Brian Seidman *E-mail:* brian@newsouthbooks.com
Founded: 2000
Independent book publisher, publishing 15-20 titles per year, including literary fiction & non-fiction, with a special emphasis on books about the history & culture of the South.
ISBN Prefix(es): 978-1-58838; 978-1-60306
Number of titles published annually: 20 Print; 10 Online; 10 E-Book
Total Titles: 175 Print; 30 Online; 30 E-Book
Imprints: Junebug Books; NewSouth Books; NewSouth Classics
Distributed by John F Blair Publisher
Billing Address: 1406 Plaza Dr, Winston-Salem, NC 27103
Returns: 1406 Plaza Dr, Winston-Salem, NC 27103
Shipping Address: 1406 Plaza Dr, Winston-Salem, NC 27103
Warehouse: 1406 Plaza Dr, Winston-Salem, NC 27103
Distribution Center: 1406 Plaza Dr, Winston-Salem, NC 27103
Membership(s): Southern Independent Booksellers Alliance

§Nightingale-Conant
6245 W Howard St, Niles, IL 60714
Tel: 847-647-0306 *Toll Free Tel:* 800-572-2770; 800-557-1660 (sales); 800-560-6081 (cust serv) *Fax:* 847-647-7145; 847-647-9143 (sales)
E-mail: distributordivision@nightingale.com (orders)
Web Site: www.nightingale.com
Key Personnel
Chmn of the Bd: Vic Conant
CEO & Pres: Gary Chappell *E-mail:* garyc@nightingale.com
Founded: 1960
Audio, video books & CD-ROMs in the areas of sales, skills, wealth building, spiritual growth, foreign language & personal development.
ISBN Prefix(es): 978-1-55525
Number of titles published annually: 3 Print; 1 CD-ROM; 12 Audio
Total Titles: 190 Print; 5 CD-ROM; 400 Audio
Subsidiaries: Nightingale-Conant (UK)
Distributed by William Morrow; Simon & Schuster

§Nilgiri Press
Division of Blue Mountain Center of Meditation
3600 Tomales Rd, Tomales, CA 94971
Mailing Address: PO Box 256, Tomales, CA 94971
Tel: 707-878-2369
E-mail: info@easwaran.org
Web Site: www.easwaran.org

Key Personnel
Press Coord: Debbie McMurray *E-mail:* debbie.mcmurray@nilgiripress.org
Intl Rts: Jennifer Jones *E-mail:* jennifer.jones@nilgiripress.org
Founded: 1972
Timeless wisdom for daily living books, video & audio.
ISBN Prefix(es): 978-0-915132; 978-1-888314; 978-1-58638
Number of titles published annually: 3 Print; 10 E-Book; 10 Audio
Total Titles: 28 Print
Foreign Rep(s): Publishers Group West
Foreign Rights: Publishers Group West (Canada)

NK Publications Inc
Affiliate of Loukoumi Books
PO Box 1735, Radio City Sta, New York, NY 10101-1735
E-mail: info@nkpublications.com
Web Site: www.nkpublications.com
Key Personnel
Pres: Nick Katsoris
Founded: 2002
ISBN Prefix(es): 978-0-9705100; 978-0-9841610
Number of titles published annually: 10 Print

No Frills Buffalo
119 Dorchester Rd, Buffalo, NY 14213
Tel: 716-510-0520
E-mail: contact@nofrillsbuffalo.com
Web Site: www.nofrillsbuffalo.com
Key Personnel
Founder: Mark Pogodzinski
Founded: 2009
Publishing new & engaging authors. Provides editorial services, interior & cover design, publicity & a chance to succeed.
Number of titles published annually: 4 Print; 4 E-Book
Total Titles: 12 Print; 4 E-Book
Distributed by Aardvark
Membership(s): Independent Publishers Association

No Starch Press Inc
245 Eighth St, San Francisco, CA 94103
Tel: 415-863-9900 *Toll Free Tel:* 800-420-7240 *Fax:* 415-863-9950
E-mail: info@nostarch.com
Web Site: www.nostarch.com
Key Personnel
Pres: William Pollock
Busn Mgr: Leigh Poehler *E-mail:* leigh@nostarch.com
Founded: 1994
General computer trade; Linux.
ISBN Prefix(es): 978-1-886411; 978-1-593270
Number of titles published annually: 24 Print; 24 E-Book
Total Titles: 120 Print; 120 E-Book
Imprints: Linux Journal Press
Distributed by O'Reilly Media
Membership(s): The Independent Book Publishers Association

§NOLO
Subsidiary of Internet Brands Inc
950 Parker St, Berkeley, CA 94710
SAN: 206-7935
Web Site: www.nolo.com
Founded: 1972
A leading provider of plain-English legal information & products for consumers & businesses. Most efforts are focused on a network of web sites featuring extensive free content, do-it-yourself products including forms, software & ebooks, as well as a consumer-friendly lawyer directory. Pioneered the self-help law movement in 1972 when two legal aid attorneys set out to demystify the law for people who couldn't afford lawyers.
This publisher has indicated that 100% of their product line is author subsidized.
ISBN Prefix(es): 978-0-87337; 978-1-41330
Number of titles published annually: 60 Print; 200 Online; 200 E-Book; 7 Audio
Total Titles: 200 Print; 200 Online; 200 E-Book; 7 Audio
Distribution Center: Ingram Publisher Services, One Ingram Blvd, La Vergne, TN 37086 *Toll Free Tel:* 855-802-8230 *Toll Free Fax:* 800-838-1149 *E-mail:* customerservice@ingrampublisherservices.com *Web Site:* www.ingrampublisherservices.com
Membership(s): ALA

The Noontide Press
Imprint of Legion for the Survival of Freedom
PO Box 2719, Newport Beach, CA 92659-1319
Tel: 714-593-9725 *Fax:* 714-593-9731
E-mail: orders@noontidepress.com
Web Site: www.noontidepress.com
Key Personnel
Pres: Mark Weber
Founded: 1968
Publisher & mail-order distributor of books, disks & tapes.
ISBN Prefix(es): 978-0-939482
Number of titles published annually: 3 Print; 3 Audio
Total Titles: 3 Print; 2 CD-ROM; 50 Audio

Norilana Books
PO Box 209, Highgate Center, VT 05459-0209
SAN: 851-8556
E-mail: service@norilana.com
Web Site: www.norilana.com
Key Personnel
Owner & Publr: Vera Nazarian
Founded: 2006
Beautifully produced & packaged editions, primarily classics of world literature & quality originals.
ISBN Prefix(es): 978-1-934169; 978-1-934648; 978-1-60762
Number of titles published annually: 100 Print
Total Titles: 300 Print
Imprints: Curiosities; Leda; Spirit; The Sword of Norilana; Taleka; YA Angst

North Atlantic Books
Division of Society for the Study of Native Arts & Sciences
2526 Martin Luther King Jr Way, Berkeley, CA 94704
SAN: 203-1655
Mailing Address: PO Box 12327, Berkeley, CA 94712-3327
Tel: 510-549-4270 *Fax:* 510-549-4276
Web Site: www.northatlanticbooks.com
Key Personnel
Publr: Richard Grossinger
Assoc Publr & Mng Dir: Doug Reil *Tel:* 510-549-4270 ext 29 *E-mail:* dreil@northatlanticbooks.com
Dir, Sales & Dist: Janet Levin *Tel:* 510-549-4270 ext 35 *E-mail:* jlevin@northatlanticbooks.com
Dir, Publg: Roslyn Bullas *Tel:* 510-549-4270 ext 30 *E-mail:* rbullas@northatlanticbooks.com
Art Dir: Paula Morrison
Contracts Mgr: Susan Bumps *Tel:* 510-549-4270 ext 13 *E-mail:* sbumps@northatlanticbooks.com
Foreign Rts & Perms Mgr: Sarah Serafimidis *Tel:* 510-549-4270 ext 16 *E-mail:* sserafimidis@northatlanticbooks.com
Founded: 1974
North Atlantic Books has been located in Berkeley, California since 1977. Over this period, North Atlantic has become a leading publisher of alternative health, nutrition, bodywork, martial arts & spiritual titles.
ISBN Prefix(es): 978-1-883319; 978-0-913028; 978-0-938190; 978-1-55643; 978-1-58394 (Frog Ltd Books)
Number of titles published annually: 65 Print; 100 E-Book
Total Titles: 1,000 Print; 100 E-Book
Imprints: Blue Snake Books; Evolver Editions; Frog Books
Distributor for DharmaCafe; Energy Arts; Ergos Institute; Heaven & Earth Publications; New Pacific Press; Rangjung Yeshe Publications; Sunfood Living
Foreign Rep(s): Publishers Group UK (UK); Random House Inc International Sales Div (Africa, Asia, Australia, Caribbean, Europe, Latin America, Middle East, New Zealand, South Africa); Random House of Canada Limited (Canada)
Orders to: Random House Distribution Services, 400 Hahn Rd, Westminister, MD 21157 (bookstore orders) *Toll Free Tel:* 800-733-3000 *Toll Free Fax:* 800-659-2436 *E-mail:* csorders@randomhouse.com *Web Site:* www.randomhouse.com
Returns: Random House Returns Dept, 1019 N State Rd 47, Crawfordsville, IN 47933
Distribution Center: Random House Distribution Services, 400 Hahn Rd, Westminister, MD 21157
Membership(s): Northern California Book Publicity & Marketing Association
See separate listing for:
Frog Books

North Carolina Office of Archives & History
Historical Publications Section, 4622 Mail Service Ctr, Raleigh, NC 27699-4622
Tel: 919-733-7442 (ext 225) *Fax:* 919-733-1439
Web Site: www.ncpublications.com; nc-historical-publications.stores.yahoo.net (online store)
Key Personnel
Administrator: Donna E Kelly *Tel:* 919-733-7442 ext 223 *E-mail:* donna.kelly@ncdcr.gov
Mktg Mgr: William A Owens, Jr *E-mail:* bill.owens@ncdcr.gov
Sales Mgr: Trudy Rayfield *Tel:* 919-733-7442 ext 221 *E-mail:* trudy.rayfield@ncdcr.gov
Founded: 1903
State government agency that publishes nonfiction hardcover & trade paperback books relating to North Carolina; publishes maps, posters, facsimile documents & the *North Carolina Historical Review*, a scholarly journal of history.
ISBN Prefix(es): 978-0-86526
Number of titles published annually: 4 Print
Total Titles: 160 Print

North Country Books Inc
220 Lafayette St, Utica, NY 13502-4312
Tel: 315-735-4877 *Toll Free Tel:* 800-342-7409 (orders) *Fax:* 315-738-4342
E-mail: ncbooks@verizon.net
Web Site: www.northcountrybooks.com
Key Personnel
Owner & Pres: Robert B Igoe, Jr *E-mail:* rbigoe@verizon.net
Gen Mgr: Zach Steffen
Founded: 1965
Book publisher & distributor of New York state regional titles to bookstores, schools & libraries, booksellers & non-traditional outlets.
ISBN Prefix(es): 978-0-932052; 978-0-925168; 978-0-9629159; 978-0-8478; 978-0-9760640
Number of titles published annually: 9 Print
Total Titles: 140 Print
Imprints: North Country Books; North Country Classics

North Country Press
126 Main St, Unity, ME 04988
SAN: 247-9680
Mailing Address: PO Box 501, Unity, ME 04988

Tel: 207-948-2208 *Fax:* 207-948-9000
E-mail: info@northcountrypress.com
Web Site: www.northcountrypress.com
Key Personnel
Publr: Patricia Newell
Founded: 1977
Regional press dealing with New England (specializing in Maine) subjects. Three lines: outdoor (hunting, fishing, etc); humor, lore; literature (mysteries, essays, poetry).
ISBN Prefix(es): 978-0-945980
Number of titles published annually: 5 Print
Total Titles: 42 Print

North Point Press
Imprint of Farrar, Straus & Giroux, LLC
18 W 18 St, 8th fl, New York, NY 10011
Tel: 212-741-6900 *Toll Free Tel:* 888-330-8477 *Fax:* 212-633-9385
Web Site: www.fsgbooks.com
Key Personnel
SVP, Mktg & Publicity: Jeff Seroy *Tel:* 212-741-6900 ext 6323
VP, Contracts & Perms: Erika Seidman
Dir, Publicity & Promo: Sarita Varma
Founded: 1981
Nonfiction, environment, nature, design, food, spirituality.
ISBN Prefix(es): 978-0-86547
Number of titles published annually: 10 Print
Foreign Rep(s): HarperCollins Publishers (Canada); Jacaranda Wiley Ltd (Australia); Orion Ltd (Worldwide)
Foreign Rights: Agence Hoffman (Ursula Bender) (Germany); Agencja Literacka Graal (Maria Strarz-Kanska) (Poland); The Deborah Harris Agency (Efrat Lev) (Israel); International Copyright Agency (Simona Kessler) (Romania); International Editors' Co (Isabel Monteagudo) (Argentina, Portugal, Spain); Katai & Bolza (Peter Bolza) (Hungary); KCC (MiSook Hong) (Korea); Leonhardt & Hoier (Anneli Hoier) (Denmark, Scandinavia); Literami Agentura (Kristin Olson) (Czech Republic); Riff Agency (Laura Paulo) (Brazil); Sebes & Van Gelderen Literary Agency (Mariska Kleinhoonte van Os) (Netherlands); Tuttle-Mori Agency Inc (Asako Kawachi) (Japan); Marco Vigevani Agenzia Letteraria (Marco Vigevani) (Italy)

North River Press Publishing Corp
27 Rosseter St, Great Barrington, MA 01230
SAN: 202-1048
Mailing Address: PO Box 567, Great Barrington, MA 01230-0567
Tel: 413-528-0034 *Toll Free Tel:* 800-486-2665 *Fax:* 413-528-3163 *Toll Free Fax:* 800-BOOK-FAX (266-5329)
E-mail: info@northriverpress.com
Web Site: www.northriverpress.com
Key Personnel
Pres: Laurence Gadd
VP: Amy Gallagher
Founded: 1971
General nonfiction, business books, hardcovers & paperback.
ISBN Prefix(es): 978-0-88427
Number of titles published annually: 6 Print
Total Titles: 40 Print; 1 Audio

North Star Press of Saint Cloud Inc
PO Box 451, St Cloud, MN 56302-0451
Tel: 320-558-9062 *Toll Free Tel:* 888-820-1636 *Fax:* 320-558-9063
E-mail: info@northstarpress.com
Web Site: www.northstarpress.com
Key Personnel
Publr: Corinne A Dwyer
Busn Mgr: Cecelia Dwyer
Ed: Brandon Paumen
Founded: 1969
Regional, women's issues, Minnesota history & fiction, Finnish ethnic, nature.
ISBN Prefix(es): 978-0-87839
Number of titles published annually: 50 Print; 40 E-Book
Total Titles: 500 Print; 55 E-Book
Shipping Address: 19485 Estes Rd, Clearwater, MN 55320
Membership(s): The Independent Book Publishers Association; Midwest Independent Booksellers Association; Midwest Independent Publishers Association; Minnesota Library Association

North Star Way, see Gallery Books

Northeast-Midwest Institute
50 "F" St NW, Suite 950, Washington, DC 20001
Tel: 202-544-5200 *Fax:* 202-544-0043
E-mail: info@nemw.org
Web Site: www.nemw.org
Key Personnel
Pres: Allegra Cangelosi *Tel:* 202-464-4014 *E-mail:* acangel@nemw.org
Dir, Admin & Fin: JT Fletcher *E-mail:* jfletcher@nemw.org
Founded: 1976
Energy, environment, economic development, human resources.
ISBN Prefix(es): 978-1-882061
Number of titles published annually: 3 Print
Total Titles: 50 Print

Northern Illinois University Press
2280 Bethany Rd, DeKalb, IL 60115
SAN: 202-8875
Tel: 815-753-1826; 815-753-1075 *Fax:* 815-753-1845
Web Site: www.niupress.niu.edu
Key Personnel
Dir: J Alex Schwartz *Tel:* 815-753-1075 *E-mail:* aschwartz@niu.edu
Mng Ed: Susan Bean *Tel:* 815-753-9908 *E-mail:* sbean@niu.edu
Ed: Amy Farranto *Tel:* 815-753-9946 *E-mail:* afarranto@niu.edu; Sara Hoerdeman *Tel:* 815-753-9907 *E-mail:* shoerdeman@niu.edu
Prodn & Design Mgr: Julia Fauci *Tel:* 815-753-9904 *E-mail:* jfauci@niu.edu
Founded: 1965
Publishes nonfiction on a variety of topics in the humanities, arts & social sciences. With more than 400 books in print, each year it brings out about twenty new books on aspects of history, politics, anthropology & literature. In fulfilling its broadly educational mission, the Press publishes books for inquiring general readers as well as for specialists.
ISBN Prefix(es): 978-0-87580
Number of titles published annually: 32 Print
Total Titles: 450 Print
Imprints: Switchgrass Books (literary fiction)
Foreign Rep(s): Eurospan (Europe, Middle East, UK); United Publishers Service Ltd (Japan, South Korea)
Distribution Center: Chicago Distribution Center, 11030 S Langley Ave, Chicago, IL 60628 *Toll Free Fax:* 800-621-8476 *E-mail:* orders@press.uchicago.edu
Membership(s): American Association for the Advancement of Slavic Studies; American Association of University Presses; American Historical Association; Organization of American Historians

Northwestern University Press
629 Noyes St, Evanston, IL 60208-4210
SAN: 202-5787
Tel: 847-491-2046 *Toll Free Tel:* 800-621-2736 (orders only) *Fax:* 847-491-8150
E-mail: nupress@northwestern.edu
Web Site: www.nupress.northwestern.edu
Key Personnel
Dir: Jane Bunker
Sr Ed & Asst Dir: Henry Carrigan *Tel:* 847-491-8112 *E-mail:* h-carrigan@northwestern.edu
Mktg & Publicity Mgr: Rudy Faust *Tel:* 847-467-0319 *E-mail:* r-faust@northwestern.edu
Prodn Mgr: Dino Robinson *Tel:* 847-467-3392 *E-mail:* morris-robinson@northwestern.edu
Sales & Subs Rts Mgr: Parneshia Jones *Tel:* 847-471-7420 *E-mail:* p-jones3@northwestern.edu
Founded: 1958
Scholarly books, with emphasis on literature & language, philosophy, works in translation, theatre.
ISBN Prefix(es): 978-0-8101
Number of titles published annually: 60 Print
Imprints: Curbstone Books; The Marlboro Press; TriQuarterly Books
Distributor for Lake Forrest College Press; Third World Press; Tia Chucha Press
Distribution Center: Chicago Distribution Center, 11030 S Langley, Chicago, IL 60628 *Toll Free Fax:* 800-621-8476
Membership(s): Association of American University Presses
See separate listing for:
TriQuarterly Books

§W W Norton & Company Inc
500 Fifth Ave, New York, NY 10110-0017
SAN: 202-5795
Tel: 212-354-5500 *Toll Free Tel:* 800-233-4830 (orders & cust serv) *Fax:* 212-869-0856 *Toll Free Fax:* 800-458-6515
Web Site: www.wwnorton.com
Key Personnel
Chair & Pres: W Drake McFeely
CFO & VP: Stephen King
CIO & VP: Ray Worrell
VChair & VP, Coll Dept: Roby Harrington
VChair & VP, Trade Dept: Jeannie Luciano
EVP, National Book Co: Raymond E Worrell
VP & Exec Dir, Publicity & PR: Louise Brockett
VP & Dir, Opers: Jorie Krumpfer
VP & Edit Dir, Coll Dept: Julia Reidhead
VP & Dir, Lib Sales & Mktg: Dosier D Hammond
VP & Dir, Natl Accts: Deirdre F Dolan
VP & Dir, Prodn Dept: Tim McGuire
VP & Dir, Sales & Mktg, Coll Dept: Stephen P Dunn
VP & Dir, Sales & Mktg, Trade Dept: William F Rusin
VP & Dir, Trade Prodn: Julia Druskin
VP & Art Dir, Trade Hardcover: Ingsu Liu
VP & Corp Art Dir: Debra Morton Hoyt
VP & Assoc Publg Dir: Nomi Victor
VP & Foreign Rts Mgr: Elisabeth Kerr
VP & Mgr, Intl Sales: Dorothy M Cook
VP & Exec Ed: Alane Mason
VP & Exec Ed, Trade Dept: Jill Bialosky
VP & Mng Ed, Trade Dept: Nancy K Palmquist
VP & Ed, Coll Dept: Karl Bakeman; Carol Stiles Bemis; Jon Durbin; Stephen A Forman; Marilyn Moller; Maribeth Payne; Jack Repcheck; Peter J Simon
VP & Ed, Trade Dept: Amy Cherry; Maria Guarnaschelli; Angela von der Lippe
Sr Publicity Dir: Elizabeth Riley
Publicity Dir: Erin Lovett; Rachel Salzman
Publr & Ed-in-Chief, Liveright & Co: Robert Weil
Dir, Electronic Media: Cliff Landesman *E-mail:* c.landesman@wwnorton.com
Dir, Mktg-Trade Dept: Meredith McGinnis
Edit Dir, Prof Books Dept: Deborah A Malmud
Sales & Mktg Dir, Dist Servs: Eugenia Pakalik
Assoc Dir, Electronic Media: Steve Hoge
Assoc Dir, Electronic Media, Coll Dept: April Lange
Assoc Dir, Subs Rts: Felice Mello
Ed-in-Chief, Trade Dept: John Glusman

Assoc Mng Ed, Prof Books Dept: Andrea Costella
Sr Ed: Matt Weiland
Sr Ed, Trade Dept: Brendan Curry; Tom Mayer
Ed, Coll Dept: Erik Fahlgren; Aaron Javsicas; Ann Shin; Sheri Snavely; Betsy Twitchell
Ed, Liveright & Co: Katie Henderson Adams
Assoc Ed: Jeff Shreve
Busn Mgr, Coll Dept: Emily Turner
Contracts Mgr: Jessie Hughes
Cust Serv Mgr: Flossie Hallett
Internet Acct Mgr: John Di Bello
Mktg Mgr, Prof Books Dept: Kevin Olsen
Natl Field Sales Mgr, Trade Dept: Rick Raeber
Natl Sales Mgr, Coll Dept: Michael Wright
Perms Mgr: Elizabeth Clementson
Perms & Copyright Mgr: Claire Reinertsen
Cont: Katarzyna Kulikowski
HR: Jamie Finkelman
Sr Publicist: Alice Rha
Publicist: Lauren Opper
Founded: 1923
General nonfiction & fiction; trade paperbacks; college texts, professional books, architecture & interior design.
No unsol mss accepted.
ISBN Prefix(es): 978-0-393; 978-0-87140
Number of titles published annually: 400 Print; 110 E-Book
Total Titles: 4,800 Print; 75 CD-ROM; 600 E-Book
Imprints: Backcountry Publications; Countryman Press; Liveright & Co
Foreign Office(s): Castle House, 75/76 Wells St, London W1T 3QT, United Kingdom, Mng Dir & VP: Edward Crutchley *Tel:* (020) 7323 1579 *Fax:* (020) 7436 4553
Distributor for Airphoto International Ltd/ Odyssey Publications; Albatross Publishing House; Atlas & Co; Blue Guides Ltd; George Braziller Inc; Chess Information & Research Center; Dalkey Archive Press; Fantagraphics Books; Kales Press; New Directions Publishing Corp; Ontario Review Press; The Overlook Press; Peace Hill Press; Pegasus Books; Persea Books Inc; Pushcart Press; Quantuck Lane Press; Skyhorse Publishing; Thames & Hudson; Tin House Books
Foreign Rep(s): APAC Publishers Services (Indonesia, Malaysia, Singapore); Everest International Publishing Services (China); Hardy Bigfoss International Co Ltd (Cambodia, Laos, Myanmar, Thailand, Vietnam); M K International Ltd (Japan); B K Norton Ltd (Korea, Taiwan); W W Norton & Company Ltd (UK) (Africa, Bangladesh, Europe, India, Ireland, Middle East, Pakistan, UK); Pansing (Malaysia, Singapore); Pearson Education (New Zealand); Penguin Books Canada Ltd (Canada); Transglobal Publishers Services Ltd (Hong Kong, Macau); US PubRep (Caribbean, Central America, Mexico, South America); John Wiley & Sons Australia Ltd (Australia)
Foreign Rights: Akcali Copyright Agency (Turkey); L'Autre Agence (France); Bardon Chinese Media Agency (China, Taiwan); Casanovas & Lynch (Portugal, Spain); Graal Literary Agency (Poland); The Deborah Harris Agency (Israel); International Copyright Agency (Romania); Japan UNI Agency (Japan); Katai & Bolza (Hungary); Duran Kim Agency (Korea); Mohrbooks (Germany); Nordin Agency (Scandinavia); Andrew Nurnberg Associates (Baltic States, Bulgaria, Russia); Olson Literary Agents (Czech Republic); The Riff Agency (Brazil); Roberto Santachiara Literary Agency (Italy); Marianne Schonbach Literary Agency (Netherlands)
Advertising Agency: Verso Advertising
Shipping Address: National Book Co Inc, Keystone Industrial Park, Scranton, PA 18512
See separate listing for:
The Countryman Press

Norwood House Press
PO Box 316598, Chicago, IL 60631
Tel: 773-467-0837 *Toll Free Tel:* 866-565-2900 *Fax:* 773-467-9686 *Toll Free Fax:* 866-565-2901
E-mail: customerservice@norwoodhousepress.com
Web Site: www.norwoodhousepress.com
Founded: 2005
Publisher specializing in children's books for the school & library.
ISBN Prefix(es): 978-1-59953
Number of titles published annually: 75 Print; 50 E-Book
Total Titles: 163 Print; 50 E-Book

Nova Press
9058 Lloyd Place, West Hollywood, CA 90069
Tel: 310-275-3513 *Toll Free Tel:* 800-949-6175 *Fax:* 310-281-5629
E-mail: novapress@aol.com
Web Site: www.novapress.net
Key Personnel
Pres & Electronic Publg: Jeff Kolby
Founded: 1993
Publishes test prep books, software, phone apps & online courses for the SAT, GRE, LSAT, GMAT, MCAT & TOEFL.
ISBN Prefix(es): 978-1-889057
Total Titles: 24 Print; 6 CD-ROM; 22 Online; 24 E-Book

Nova Science Publishers Inc
400 Oser Ave, Suite 1600, Hauppauge, NY 11788-3619
Tel: 631-231-7269 *Fax:* 631-231-8175
E-mail: main@novapublishers.com
Web Site: www.novapublishers.com
Key Personnel
Pres: Nadia Columbus
Founded: 1985
Scientific, technical, medical & social sciences publishing; trade books - hardcover & softcover.
ISBN Prefix(es): 978-0-941743
Number of titles published annually: 2,000 Print; 10 CD-ROM
Total Titles: 20,000 Print
Imprints: Noel Press; Nova Biomedical Press; Nova Global Affairs Press; Nova History Press; Nova Music; Nova Science Books; Novinka Books; Snova Books; Troitsa Books

NPS, see BrickHouse Books Inc

NRP®, see National Register Publishing

nursesbooks.org, The Publishing Program of ANA
Division of American Nurses Association
8515 Georgia Ave, Suite 400, Silver Spring, MD 20910-3492
Tel: 301-628-5000 *Toll Free Tel:* 800-924-9053; 800-637-0323 (orders) *Fax:* 301-628-5001
E-mail: anp@ana.org
Web Site: www.nursesbooks.org; www.nursingworld.org
Key Personnel
Publr: Rosanne Roe
Ed & Proj Mgr: Eric Wurzbacher *E-mail:* eric.wurzbacher@ana.org
Health care & nursing.
ISBN Prefix(es): 978-1-55810
Number of titles published annually: 8 Print
Total Titles: 45 Print

NYBG Press, see The New York Botanical Garden Press

§Nystrom Herff Jones Education Division
4719 W 62 St, Indianapolis, IN 46268-2593
SAN: 203-5529
Tel: 317-612-3901 *Toll Free Tel:* 800-621-8086 (cust serv) *Fax:* 317-329-3305
E-mail: info@nystromnet.com
Web Site: www.nystromnet.com
Key Personnel
Pres: Joe Slaughter
Dir, Mktg: Don Rescigno *E-mail:* drescigno@herffjones.com
Founded: 1903
Social studies, history & geography programs, maps, globes, atlases & multimedia.
ISBN Prefix(es): 978-0-7825; 978-0-88463
Number of titles published annually: 3 Print
Total Titles: 50 Print; 5 CD-ROM; 1 E-Book

§OAG Worldwide
3025 Highland Pkwy, Suite 200, Downers Grove, IL 60515-5561
Tel: 630-515-5300 *Toll Free Tel:* 800-342-5624 (cust serv) *Fax:* 630-515-3251
E-mail: contactus@oag.com
Web Site: www.oag.com
Founded: 1929
Supplier of independent travel info.
ISBN Prefix(es): 978-0-9776295
Number of titles published annually: 11 Print; 5 CD-ROM; 5 Online
Total Titles: 11 Print; 5 CD-ROM; 5 Online
Foreign Office(s): 18F, Caroline Centre, Lee Gardens Two, 28 Yun Ping Rd, Causeway Bay, Hong Kong *Tel:* 2965 1700 *Fax:* 2965 1777 *E-mail:* custsvcaspac@oag.com
Toranomon, 40 MT Bldg 9F, 5-13-1 Toranomon, Minato-ku, Tokyo 105-0001, Japan *Tel:* 36402 7301 *Fax:* 36402 7302 *E-mail:* acustsvcjpn@oag.com
3 Lim Teck Kim Rd, No 10-01, Singapore Technologies Bldg, Singapore 088934, Singapore *Tel:* 6395-5868 *Fax:* 6293-6566 *E-mail:* custsvcsaspac@oag.com
Church St, Dunstable, Bedfordshire LU5 4HB, United Kingdom (headquarters) *Tel:* (01582) 600111 *Fax:* (01582) 695230 *E-mail:* customers@oag.com

Oak Knoll Press
310 Delaware St, New Castle, DE 19720
Tel: 302-328-7232 *Toll Free Tel:* 800-996-2556 *Fax:* 302-328-7274
E-mail: oakknoll@oakknoll.com
Web Site: www.oakknoll.com
Key Personnel
Pres: Robert D Fleck *E-mail:* bob@oakknoll.com
Publg Dir: Laura Williams *E-mail:* laura@oakknoll.com
Antiquarian & Lib Sales: Robert Fleck, III *E-mail:* rob@oakknoll.com
Founded: 1976
Publish scholarly books (books about books), bibliographies, book arts & book history.
ISBN Prefix(es): 978-1-884718; 978-1-58456
Number of titles published annually: 25 Print
Total Titles: 1,100 Print; 1 CD-ROM
Distributor for American Antiquarian Society; Bibliographical Society of America; Bibliographical Society of University of Virginia; The Bibliographical Society (UK); Block Museum; Boston College; John Carter Brown Library; Bryn Mawr College; Catalpa Press; Caxton Club; Center for Book Arts; Chapin Library; Fondation Custodia; The Grolier Club; Hes & De Graaf; Historic New Orleans Collection; Library of Congress-Center for the Book; The Manuscript Society; New England Bibliographies; Providence Athenaeum; Rivendale Press; Tate Galleries; Texas State Historical Association; Typophiles; Winterthur Museum; Yushodo Press
Membership(s): AAP; Antiquarian Booksellers Association of America; International League of Antiquarian Booksellers

Oak Tree Press
1820 W Lacey Blvd, Suite 220, Hanford, CA 93230
Tel: 217-824-6500
E-mail: publisher@oaktreebooks.com; info@oaktreebooks.com; query@oaktreebooks.com; pressdept@oaktreebooks.com; bookorders@oaktreebooks.com
Web Site: www.oaktreebooks.com; www.otpblog.blogspot.com
Key Personnel
Publr: Billie Johnson
PR Mgr: Jeana Thompson *Tel:* 217-825-4489
Ed: Marilyn Olsen *E-mail:* coptaleseditor@oaktreebooks.com
Acqs Ed: Marilyn Olsen
Off Mgr: Suzanne Yazell *E-mail:* officemanager@oaktreebooks.com
Founded: 1998
Independent press that publishes fiction & nonfiction. Emphasis on mysteries & romances with series potential, business books, self-help & how-to.
ISBN Prefix(es): 978-1-892343; 978-1-61009
Number of titles published annually: 60 Print; 60 E-Book
Total Titles: 250 Print; 250 E-Book
Imprints: Acorn (children's books); Coptales (stories by & about law enforcement professionals-cops, medical examiners, criminal defense attorneys, DAs); Dark Oak Mysteries (all mystery genres, from amateur sleuths to hard-boiled detectives); Mystic Oaks (paranormal mysteries & romances); Oak Tree Books (mainstream fiction, how-to, memoir, self-help); Timeless Love (all romance genres, from sweet to steamy); Wild Oak (western)
Membership(s): Sisters in Crime

Oaklea Press
Unit of Oaklea Press Inc
41 Old Mill Rd, Richmond, VA 23226-3111
Tel: 804-308-3906 *Fax:* 804-980-7057
Web Site: oakleapress.com
Key Personnel
Publr: Stephen H Martin *E-mail:* shmartin@oakleapress.com
Founded: 1995
Tradebook publisher.
ISBN Prefix(es): 978-1-892538; 978-0-9646601; 978-0-9664098
Number of titles published annually: 6 Print; 8 E-Book; 6 Audio
Total Titles: 45 Print; 8 E-Book; 6 Audio
Imprints: New Marketplace
Sales Office(s): Delphi Distribution, 1263 Southwest Blvd, Kansas City, KS 66103, Contact: Amanda Garcia *Toll Free Tel:* 866-463-8541 *E-mail:* agarcia@delphidistribution.com *Web Site:* www.delphidistribution.com
Distribution Center: Delphi Distribution, 1263 Southwest Blvd, Kansas City, KS 66103, Contact: Amanda Garcia *Toll Free Tel:* 866-463-8541 *E-mail:* agarcia@delphidistribution.com *Web Site:* www.delphidistribution.com
Membership(s): The Independent Book Publishers Association

§Oakstone Publishing LLC
Division of Boston Ventures
100 Corporate Pkwy, Suite 600, Birmingham, AL 35242
Toll Free Tel: 800-633-4743 *Fax:* 205-995-1926
E-mail: service@oakstonemedical.com
Web Site: www.oakstonepublishing.com; www.cmeonly.com; www.cdeonly.com
Key Personnel
CEO & Pres: Diane Munson
CFO & EVP: Donnie Parkerson
SVP, Opers & HR: Connie Fleming *Tel:* 205-437-3015
VP & Publr: Marianne Kerr
VP, Corp Devt: H Montgomery Rains
Founded: 1975
Produce board review programs for medical specialties.
Number of titles published annually: 20 CD-ROM; 4 Online; 5 Audio
Total Titles: 46 CD-ROM; 12 Online; 42 Audio
Imprints: Clinical Advances; Inservice Reviews; Journalbytes.com; MKSAP® Audio Companion; MultiMedia Reviews®; Practical Reviews®; QuickScan Reviews®; Select; SESAP Audio Companion; Topic Series
Membership(s): Specialized Information Publishers Association

Oberlin College Press
Subsidiary of Oberlin College
50 N Professor St, Oberlin, OH 44074-1091
SAN: 212-1883
Tel: 440-775-8408 *Fax:* 440-775-8124
E-mail: oc.press@oberlin.edu
Web Site: www.oberlin.edu/ocpress
Key Personnel
Mng Ed & Intl Rts Contact: Marco Wilkinson
First Ed: David Young
Ed: David Walker
Assoc Ed: Pamela Alexander; Kazim Ali; DeSales Harrison
Ed-at-Large: Martha Collins
Founded: 1969
Poetry in translation; contemporary American poetry.
ISBN Prefix(es): 978-0-932440
Number of titles published annually: 3 Print
Total Titles: 55 Print
Distributed by University Press of New England (UPNE)
Orders to: University Press of New England (UPNE), One Court St, Suite 250, Lebanon, NH 03766 *Toll Free Tel:* 800-421-1561 *Fax:* 603-448-9429 *Web Site:* www.upne.com
Returns: University Press of New England (UPNE), c/o Maple Logistics Solutions, Lebanon Distribution Ctr, 704 Legionaire Dr, Fredericksburg, PA 17026 *Tel:* 603-448-1533 ext 503 *Fax:* 603-448-9429
Membership(s): Community of Literary Magazines & Presses

Ocean Press
511 Avenue of the Americas, Suite 96, New York, NY 10011-8436
Tel: 212-260-3690
E-mail: info@oceanbooks.com.au; orders@oceanbooks.com.au (orders only)
Web Site: www.oceanbooks.com.au
Key Personnel
Dir & Publr: Deborah Shnookal
Founded: 1990
ISBN Prefix(es): 978-1-875284; 978-1-876175; 978-1-920888; 978-1-921235
Number of titles published annually: 30 Print
Total Titles: 260 Print
Foreign Office(s): PO Box 1015, North Melbourne, Victoria 3051, Australia *Tel:* (03) 9326 4280 *Fax:* (03) 9329 5040
Immobiliaria Jardines de 5ta, Avenida 5ta y 114, Apartamento 135, Playa, Havana, Cuba *Tel:* (07) 204-1324
Distributed by Consortium Book Sales & Distribution

Ocean Publishing
Division of The Gromling Group Inc
PO Box 1080, Flagler Beach, FL 32136-1080
SAN: 254-8755
Tel: 386-517-1600
E-mail: publisher@oceanpublishing.org
Web Site: www.oceanpublishing.org
Key Personnel
Publr: Frank Gromling
Founded: 2002
Traditional publisher of quality nonfiction books about nature, marine life, environment & conservation.
ISBN Prefix(es): 978-0-9717; 978-0-9767
Number of titles published annually: 4 Print
Total Titles: 26 Print; 10 E-Book
Foreign Rights: Independent Publishers Group (Worldwide)
Distribution Center: Independent Publishers Group, 814 N Franklin St, Chicago, IL 60610 *Tel:* 312-337-0747 *Fax:* 312-337-5985
Membership(s): Florida Authors & Publishers Association Inc; The Independent Book Publishers Association

Ocean Tree Books
1325 Cerro Gordo Rd, Santa Fe, NM 87501
Mailing Address: PO Box 1295, Santa Fe, NM 87504 SAN: 241-0478
Tel: 505-983-1412 *Fax:* 505-983-0899
Web Site: www.oceantree.com
Key Personnel
Dir: Richard Polese *E-mail:* richard@oceantree.com
Publicity & Mktg: Hudson White
Off Mgr: Martin Burch
Founded: 1983
General trade with emphasis on Southwestern & Southern travel, faith & spirit & peacemaking. Distribution Centers: Baker & Taylor, Books West LLC & New Leaf Distributing Co.
ISBN Prefix(es): 978-0-943734; 978-0-9712548
Number of titles published annually: 5 Print
Total Titles: 60 Print
Imprints: Adventure Roads Travel; OTB Legacy Editions; Peacewatch Editions
Distributed by Treasure Chest Books
Foreign Rep(s): Blessingway Author Services (Worldwide)
Foreign Rights: Blessingway Author Services
Membership(s): The Independent Book Publishers Association; New Mexico Book Association; Publishers Association of the West

Oceanview Publishing
CEO Center at Mediterranean Plaza, Suite 120-G, 595 Bay Isles Rd, Longboat Key, FL 34228
Tel: 941-387-8500 *Fax:* 941-387-0039
Web Site: www.oceanviewpub.com
Founded: 2006
ISBN Prefix(es): 978-1-933515; 978-1-60809
Number of titles published annually: 12 Print
Total Titles: 52 Print
Billing Address: Midpoint Trade Books, c/o Leisure Arts, 5701 Ranch Dr, Little Rock, AR 72223 *Tel:* 501-868-8800 ext 259 *Fax:* 501-877-5603 *E-mail:* customerorders@leisurearts.com
Distribution Center: Midpoint Trade Books, c/o Leisure Arts, 5701 Ranch Dr, Little Rock, AR 72223 *Tel:* 501-868-8800 ext 259 *Fax:* 501-877-5603 *E-mail:* customerorders@leisurearts.com
Membership(s): International Thriller Writers Inc; Mystery Writers of America

§OCP
5536 NE Hassalo St, Portland, OR 97213
Tel: 503-281-1191 *Toll Free Tel:* 800-548-8749 *Fax:* 503-282-3486 *Toll Free Fax:* 800-843-8181
E-mail: liturgy@ocp.org
Web Site: www.ocp.org
Key Personnel
Publr: John Limb *E-mail:* jlimb@ocp.org
Mktg Mgr: Monica Rada *E-mail:* mrada@ocp.org
Cust Serv Mgr: Tim Dooley *Tel:* 503-460-5489 *E-mail:* tdooley@ocp.org
Founded: 1922
Books of music & liturgy.
ISBN Prefix(es): 978-0-915531

Number of titles published annually: 25 Print; 25 Audio
Total Titles: 500 Print; 1 CD-ROM; 1 Online; 2,500 Audio
Imprints: Pastoral Press
Foreign Rights: Decani Music; Rainbow Book Agencies (Australia); Universal Songs (England, Europe, Ireland, UK)
Membership(s): CBA; CMPA

Octane Press
808 Kinney Ave, Austin, TX 78704
Tel: 512-334-9441 *Fax:* 512-852-4737
E-mail: info@octanepress.com
Web Site: www.octanepress.com
Key Personnel
Publr: Lee Klancher *E-mail:* lee@octanepress.com
Ed: Tobias Gros *E-mail:* tobias@octanepress.com
Designer: Tom Heffron *E-mail:* tom@octanepress.com
Print Buyer: Joe Sita *E-mail:* joe@octanepress.com
Founded: 2010
Niche book publisher.
ISBN Prefix(es): 978-0-9821733; 978-0-9829131; 978-1-937747
Number of titles published annually: 10 Print; 5 E-Book
Total Titles: 18 Print; 10 E-Book
Foreign Rep(s): Star Book Sales (Europe)
Membership(s): The Independent Book Publishers Association; Motorsports Press Guild

Odyssey Books
Division of The Ciletti Publishing Group Inc
2421 Redwood Ct, Longmont, CO 80503-8155
Tel: 720-494-1473 *Fax:* 720-494-1471
E-mail: books@odysseybooks.net
Web Site: cilettipublishinggroup.com
Key Personnel
Pres & Publr: Barbara Ciletti *E-mail:* barbaraj@odysseybooks.net
Promo: Erin Jones
Founded: 1995
Provides fiction & nonfiction for the retail trade, library, education & consumer markets.
ISBN Prefix(es): 978-0-9768655
Number of titles published annually: 20 Print
Membership(s): ABA; ALA; CMN; The Independent Book Publishers Association; International Literacy Association; National Council of Teachers of English; National Science Teachers Association

OECD Washington Center, see Organization for Economic Cooperation & Development

Ohio Genealogical Society
611 State Rte 97 W, Bellville, OH 44813-8813
Tel: 419-886-1903 *Fax:* 419-886-0092
E-mail: ogs@ogs.org
Web Site: www.ogs.org
Key Personnel
Pres: Funda Peters
Lib Dir: Thomas Stephen Neel
Founded: 1959
Family history library & society.
ISBN Prefix(es): 978-0-935057
Number of titles published annually: 3 Print
Total Titles: 25 Print

Ohio State University Foreign Language Publications
Division of Foreign Language Center
198 Hagerty Hall, 1775 College Rd, Columbus, OH 43210-1340
Tel: 614-292-3838 *Toll Free Tel:* 800-678-6999 *Fax:* 614-688-3355
E-mail: flpubs@osu.edu
Web Site: www.flpubs.osu.edu
Key Personnel
Pubns Mgr: Lauren Barrett
Founded: 1972
Foreign language individualized instruction materials for less commonly taught languages.
ISBN Prefix(es): 978-0-87415
Number of titles published annually: 5 Print
Total Titles: 280 Print

Ohio State University Press
180 Pressey Hall, 1070 Carmack Rd, Columbus, OH 43210-1002
Tel: 614-292-6930 *Fax:* 614-292-2065 *Toll Free Fax:* 800-621-8476
E-mail: info@osupress.org
Web Site: ohiostatepress.org
Key Personnel
Dir: Malcolm Litchfield *Tel:* 614-292-7818 *E-mail:* ml@osupress.org
Mng Ed: Eugene O'Connor, PhD *Tel:* 614-292-3667 *E-mail:* eugene@osupress.org
Mktg Dir: Laurie Avery *Tel:* 614-292-1462 *E-mail:* laurie.avery@osupress.org
Asst Dir: Kathy Edwards *Tel:* 614-292-3692 *E-mail:* edwards@osupress.org
Founded: 1957
General scholarly & trade nonfiction & fiction; classics.
ISBN Prefix(es): 978-0-8142
Number of titles published annually: 30 Print
Total Titles: 270 Print
Foreign Rep(s): East-West Export Books
Distribution Center: University of Chicago Distribution Center, 11030 S Langley Ave, Chicago, IL 60628 *Tel:* 773-568-1550 *Toll Free Tel:* 800-621-2736 *Fax:* 773-702-7212

Ohio University Press
215 Columbus Rd, Suite 101, Athens, OH 45701-1373
Fax: 740-593-4536
Web Site: www.ohioswallow.com
Key Personnel
Dir: Gillian Berchowitz *Tel:* 740-593-1159 *E-mail:* berchowi@ohio.edu
Acqs Ed: Ricky S Huard *Tel:* 740-593-1157 *E-mail:* huard@ohio.edu
Mng Ed: Nancy Basmajian *Tel:* 740-593-1161 *E-mail:* basmajia@ohio.edu
Busn Mgr: Omar Aziz *Tel:* 740-593-1156 *E-mail:* azizo@ohio.edu
Perms & Serv Specialist: Sally R Welch *Tel:* 740-593-1154 *E-mail:* welchs@ohio.edu
Founded: 1964
Publisher of scholarly & trade books.
ISBN Prefix(es): 978-0-8214; 978-0-8040; 978-0-89680; 978-0-940717
Number of titles published annually: 50 Print
Total Titles: 600 Print
Imprints: Swallow Press
Foreign Rep(s): East-West Export Books (Asia, Australia, New Zealand, Pacific Region); Eurospan (Africa, Continental Europe, Middle East, UK)
Orders to: Chicago Distribution Center, 11030 S Langley Ave, Chicago, IL 60628 *Tel:* 773-702-7000 *Toll Free Tel:* 800-621-2736 *Fax:* 773-702-7212 *Toll Free Fax:* 800-621-8476
Warehouse: Chicago Distribution Center, 11030 S Langley Ave, Chicago, IL 60628 *Toll Free Tel:* 800-621-2736 *Toll Free Fax:* 800-621-8476
Membership(s): American Association of University Presses
See separate listing for:
Swallow Press

Old Barn Enterprises Inc
600 Kelly Rd, Carthage, NC 28327
Tel: 910-947-2587 *Fax:* 480-287-9017
E-mail: jeffandpam@nynphotoschool.com
Web Site: www.nynphotoschool.com
Key Personnel
Pres: Jeff Farr
Founded: 1992
Publish, professional books, home study courses, photography & marketing.
ISBN Prefix(es): 978-1-879009
Number of titles published annually: 3 Print
Total Titles: 8 Print
Imprints: Old Barn Publishing; Scots Plaid Press

§Olde & Oppenheim Publishers
3219 N Margate Place, Chandler, AZ 85224
E-mail: olde_oppenheim@hotmail.com
Web Site: oldeandoppenheimpublishers.com
Key Personnel
Dir, Mktg: Mike Gratz
Animation, satire, slice-of-life.
ISBN Prefix(es): 978-0-944861
Number of titles published annually: 3 Print; 2 CD-ROM; 5 Online; 2 E-Book
Total Titles: 13 Print

The Oliver Press Inc
Charlotte Sq, 5707 W 36 St, Minneapolis, MN 55416-2510
Tel: 952-926-8981 *Toll Free Tel:* 800-8-OLIVER (865-4837) *Fax:* 952-926-8965
E-mail: orders@oliverpress.com
Web Site: www.oliverpress.com
Key Personnel
Publr & Ed: Mark Lerner *E-mail:* mark@oliverpress.com
Admin: Charles Helgesen *E-mail:* charles@oliverpress.com
Founded: 1991
Nonfiction children's books.
ISBN Prefix(es): 978-1-881508
Number of titles published annually: 10 Print
Total Titles: 100 Print
Imprints: Clara House Books
Foreign Rights: John Reed Book Distribution (Australia)

OMNI Publishers Inc
29131 Bulverde Rd, San Antonio, TX 78260
Mailing Address: PO Box 408, Bulverde, TX 78163
Tel: 210-778-4437 *Fax:* 830-438-4645
Web Site: www.omnipublishers.com; www.educatorethicsseries.com
Key Personnel
Owner: Ruth Lansing
Gen Mgr: Jim Lansing *E-mail:* jim@omnipublishers.com
Founded: 1989
Books on law & real estate, national education products, Texas law.
ISBN Prefix(es): 978-1-891172
Number of titles published annually: 25 Print
Total Titles: 65 Print

Omnibus Press
Division of Music Sales Ltd
257 Park Ave S, 20th fl, New York, NY 10010
Tel: 212-254-2100 *Toll Free Tel:* 800-431-7187 *Fax:* 212-254-2013 *Toll Free Fax:* 800-345-6842
E-mail: info-us@omnibuspress.com
Web Site: www.omnibuspress.com; www.musicsales.com
Key Personnel
Pres: Barrie Edwards
VP, Admin & Opers: Denise Maurin
Founded: 1976
Pop culture, music & film books.
ISBN Prefix(es): 978-0-8256; 978-0-7119; 978-0-86001; 978-1-84449
Number of titles published annually: 30 Print
Total Titles: 500 Print
Distributor for Big Meteor; Gramophone
Distribution Center: Music Sales Distribution Center, 445 Bellvale Rd, Chester, NY 10918 *Tel:* 845-469-4699 *Toll Free Tel:* 800-431-

7187 *Fax:* 845-469-7544 *Toll Free Fax:* 800-345-6842 *E-mail:* info@musicsales.com *Web Site:* www.musicsales.com

Omnidawn Publishing
1632 Elm Ave, Richmond, CA 94805-1614
SAN: 299-3236
Tel: 510-237-5472 *Toll Free Tel:* 800-792-4957 *Fax:* 510-232-8525
E-mail: manager@omnidawn.com
Web Site: www.omnidawn.com
Key Personnel
Founder & Publr: Kenneth Keegan *E-mail:* kkeegan@omnidawn.com; Rusty Morrison *E-mail:* rusty@omnidawn.com
Asst Ed: Rebecca Stoddard *E-mail:* rstoddard@omnidawn.com
Founded: 1996
Publishers of poetry & fabulist & new wave fabulist fiction.
ISBN Prefix(es): 978-1-890650
Number of titles published annually: 7 Print
Total Titles: 21 Print
Distribution Center: Independent Publishers Group (IPG), 814 N Franklin St, Chicago, IL 60610 *Tel:* 312-337-0747 *Toll Free Tel:* 800-888-4741 *Fax:* 312-337-5985 *E-mail:* frontdesk@ipgbook.com *Web Site:* www.ipgbook.com

Omnigraphics Inc
155 W Congress, Suite 200, Detroit, MI 48226
SAN: 249-2520
Tel: 313-961-1340 *Toll Free Tel:* 800-234-1340 (cust serv) *Fax:* 313-961-1383 *Toll Free Fax:* 800-875-1340 (cust serv)
E-mail: info@omnigraphics.com
Web Site: www.omnigraphics.com
Key Personnel
Founder & Chmn: Frederick G Ruffner, Jr
Founder & Publr: Peter E Ruffner *E-mail:* peter@omnigraphics.com
SVP: Matthew Barbour *E-mail:* matt@omnigraphics.com
Opers Mgr: Kevin Hayes
Founded: 1985
Reference books, periodicals & journals for libraries & schools, directories.
ISBN Prefix(es): 978-1-55888; 978-0-7808
Number of titles published annually: 40 Print; 1 Online
Total Titles: 400 Print; 1 Online
Advertising Agency: Marley & Cratchit
Orders to: PO Box 625, Holmes, PA 19043
Returns: 2050 Elmwood Ave, Sharon Hill, PA 19079

Omohundro Institute of Early American History & Culture (OIEAHC)
Swem Library, Ground fl, 400 Landrum Dr, Williamsburg, VA 23185
Mailing Address: PO Box 8781, Williamsburg, VA 23187-8781 SAN: 201-5161
Tel: 757-221-1110 *Fax:* 757-221-1047
E-mail: ieahc1@wm.edu
Web Site: oieahc.wm.edu
Key Personnel
Dir: Karin A Wulf *Tel:* 757-221-1133 *E-mail:* kawulf@wm.edu
Ed, Pubns: Fredrika J Teute *Tel:* 757-221-1118 *E-mail:* fjteut@wm.edu
Founded: 1943
Scholarly books on early American history culture & literature 1500-1815. Founded & still sponsored jointly by the College of William & Mary & the Colonial Williamsburg Foundation.
ISBN Prefix(es): 978-0-910776
Number of titles published annually: 4 Print
Total Titles: 205 Print
Distributed by The University of North Carolina Press

§OneSource
300 Baker Ave, Concord, MA 01742
Tel: 978-318-4300 *Toll Free Tel:* 866-354-6936 *Fax:* 978-318-4690
E-mail: sales@onesource.com
Web Site: www.onesource.com
Key Personnel
Pres: Philip Garlick
SVP, Global Sales & Serv: Colleen Honan
Founded: 1984
Database of approximately 50,000 US technicians, manufacturers, developers & services.
ISBN Prefix(es): 978-1-57114
Number of titles published annually: 5 Online
Total Titles: 5 CD-ROM; 5 Online
Foreign Office(s): Citigroup Ctr, Level 39, 2 Park St, Sydney, NSW 2000, Australia *Tel:* (02) 9004 7868 *Fax:* (02) 9004 7070
Global Business Park, MG Rd, Gurgaon 122002, India *Tel:* 987 1046415
208-A Telok Ayer St, Singapore 068642, Singapore *Tel:* 6221 7920 *Fax:* 6221 7929
55 Old Broad St, 3rd fl, London EC2M 1RX, United Kingdom *Tel:* (020) 7382 8800 *Fax:* (020) 7382 8801

Online Training Solutions Inc (OTSI)
2217 152 Ave NE, Redmond, WA 98052
Mailing Address: PO Box 874, Argyle, TX 76226-0874
Toll Free Tel: 888-308-6874 *Toll Free Fax:* 888-308-6875
E-mail: biz@otsi.com
Web Site: www.otsi.com
Key Personnel
Pres: Joan Lambert
Founded: 1987
Educational & professional book publisher.
ISBN Prefix(es): 978-1-879399; 978-1-58278
Number of titles published annually: 12 Print
Total Titles: 60 Print
Returns: 602 Bellevue Way SE, Bellevue, WA 98004
Membership(s): Women's Business Enterprise National Council

§Ooligan Press
Portland State University, 369 Neuberger Hall, 724 SW Harrison St, Portland, OR 97201
Tel: 503-725-9748 *Fax:* 503-725-3561
E-mail: ooligan@ooliganpress.pdx.edu
Web Site: ooligan.pdx.edu
Key Personnel
Publr: Abbey Gaterud
Founded: 2001
ISBN Prefix(es): 978-1-932010
Number of titles published annually: 6 Print; 6 E-Book
Total Titles: 30 Print
Orders to: Ingram Publisher Services, One Ingram Blvd, La Vergne, TN 37086-1986 *Toll Free Tel:* 866-400-5351
Membership(s): Association of Writers and Writing Programs; Publishers Association of the West

Open Court
Division of Carus Publishing Co
70 E Lake St, Suite 300, Chicago, IL 60601
Tel: 312-701-1720 *Toll Free Tel:* 800-815-2280 (orders only) *Fax:* 312-701-1728
E-mail: opencourt@caruspub.com
Web Site: www.opencourtbooks.com
Key Personnel
Edit Dir: David Ramsay Steele
Ed: Kerri Mommer
Founded: 1887
Academic philosophy, popular culture & philosophy.
ISBN Prefix(es): 978-0-87548; 978-0-912050; 978-0-89688; 978-0-8126
Number of titles published annually: 20 Print
Total Titles: 350 Print
Orders to: 30 Grove St, Suite C, Peterborough, NH 03458 *Fax:* 603-924-7380

Open Horizons Publishing Co
PO Box 2887, Taos, NM 87571
Tel: 575-751-3398 *Fax:* 575-751-3100
E-mail: info@bookmarket.com
Web Site: www.bookmarket.com
Key Personnel
Owner & Publr: John Kremer *E-mail:* johnkremer@bookmarket.com
Assoc Publr & Lib Sales Dir: Gail Berry
Mktg Dir: Bob Sanny
Founded: 1982
Books for publishers & direct marketers.
ISBN Prefix(es): 978-0-912411
Number of titles published annually: 3 Print; 3 CD-ROM; 3 Online; 40 E-Book; 3 Audio
Total Titles: 21 Print; 16 CD-ROM; 6 Online; 43 E-Book; 12 Audio
Distributed by National Book Network
Membership(s): The Association of Publishers for Special Sales; The Independent Book Publishers Association

Open Road Publishing
32 Turkey Lane, Cold Spring Harbor, NY 11724
Tel: 631-692-7172
E-mail: jopenroad@aol.com
Web Site: www.openroadguides.com
Key Personnel
Publr: Jonathan Stein
Founded: 1993
Travel, domestic & foreign, how-to, biographies, current events, sports, fantasy & commentary.
ISBN Prefix(es): 978-1-892975; 978-1-59360
Number of titles published annually: 22 Print
Total Titles: 62 Print
Imprints: Cold Spring Press
Distributed by Simon & Schuster

§OPIS/STALSBY Directories & Databases
Division of United Communications Group
3349 Hwy 138, Bldg D, Suite D, Wall, NJ 07719
Tel: 732-901-8800 *Toll Free Tel:* 800-275-0950 *Toll Free Fax:* 800-450-5864
E-mail: opisstalsbylistings@opisnet.com
Web Site: www.opisnet.com
Key Personnel
Dir, Prodn: Renee Ortner *E-mail:* rortner@opisnet.com
Supervising Ed: Bonnie Walling *Tel:* 732-730-2536 *E-mail:* bwalling@opisnet.com
Founded: 1980
ISBN Prefix(es): 978-0-911299
Number of titles published annually: 4 Print
Total Titles: 4 Print; 4 CD-ROM

The Optical Society (OSA)
2010 Massachusetts Ave NW, Washington, DC 20036-1023
Tel: 202-223-8130 *Toll Free Tel:* 800-766-4672
E-mail: custserv@osa.org
Web Site: www.osa.org
Key Personnel
Chief Publg Offr: Elizabeth Nolan *Tel:* 202-416-1949 *E-mail:* enolan@osa.org
CIO: Sean Bagshaw *Tel:* 202-416-1905 *E-mail:* sbagsh@osa.org
Sr Publr: Kelly Cohen *Tel:* 202-416-1917 *E-mail:* kcohen@osa.org
Deputy Sr Dir, Publg Sales: Keith Allen *Tel:* 202-416-1906 *E-mail:* kallen@osa.org
Dir, Sales: Alan N Tourtlotte *Tel:* 202-416-1908 *Fax:* 202-416-1408 *E-mail:* atourt@osa.org
Rts & Perms: Susannah Lehman *Tel:* 202-416-1901 *E-mail:* slehman@osa.org
Founded: 1916
Journal publishing, meetings & technical membership.
ISBN Prefix(es): 978-1-55752
Number of titles published annually: 20 Online

Total Titles: 230 Online
Foreign Rep(s): David Charles e-Licensing (Europe); Globe Publication Pvt Ltd (India); iGroup (Asia exc India & Japan, Australia, New Zealand); Kinokuniya (Japan); Shinwon Datanet (South Korea)
Membership(s): American Institute of Physics

Optometric Extension Program Foundation
1921 E Carnegie Ave, Suite 3-L, Santa Ana, CA 92705-5510
Tel: 949-250-8070 *Fax:* 949-250-8157
E-mail: oep@oep.org
Web Site: www.oepf.org
Key Personnel
Exec Dir: Robert A Williams *E-mail:* rwilliams@oep.org
Dir, Pubns: Sally Marshall Corngold *E-mail:* smcorngold@oep.org
Cust Serv Specialist: Kathleen Patterson *E-mail:* kpatterson@oep.org
Founded: 1928
Books, journals, pamphlets, catalogs & directories.
ISBN Prefix(es): 978-0-943599; 978-0-929780
Number of titles published annually: 10 Print; 1 CD-ROM
Total Titles: 150 Print; 3 CD-ROM

§OptumInsight™
12125 Technology Dr, Eden Prairie, MN 55334
Tel: 952-833-7100 *Toll Free Tel:* 888-445-8745; 800-765-6713 *Fax:* 952-833-7201
E-mail: insight@optum.com
Web Site: www.optuminsight.com
Key Personnel
CEO: Andrew Slavitt
Chief Strategy Offr: John Nackel
Founded: 1983
Books & software for health-care professionals.
ISBN Prefix(es): 978-1-56337; 978-1-56329
Number of titles published annually: 90 Print; 5 Online
Total Titles: 90 Print; 8 CD-ROM; 5 Online
Branch Office(s)
1755 Telstar Dr, Suite 400, Colorado Springs, CO 80920 *Tel:* 719-277-7545 *Toll Free Tel:* 800-341-6141 *Fax:* 719-277-0254
400 Capital Blvd, Rocky Hill, CT 06067 *Tel:* 860-221-0054 *Toll Free Tel:* 800-367-2427 *Fax:* 860-221-0209
8345 Lenexa Dr, Suite 300, Lenexa, KS 66214 *Tel:* 913-904-0515 *Toll Free Tel:* 800-457-4697 *Fax:* 913-904-0505
301 N Hurstibourne Pkwy, Suite 200, Louisville, KY 40222 *Tel:* 502-326-8900 *Toll Free Tel:* 888-452-5000 *Fax:* 502-326-5376
70 Royal Little Dr, Providence, RI 02904 *Tel:* 401-331-5300 *Fax:* 401-331-5301
2525 Lake Park Blvd, Salt Lake City, UT 84120 *Tel:* 801-982-3000 *Toll Free Tel:* 800-464-3649 *Fax:* 801-982-4000
12018 Sunrise Valley Dr, Suite 400, Reston, VA 20191 *Tel:* 571-521-7661 *Toll Free Tel:* 800-464-3649 *Fax:* 571-521-7237
10701 W Research Dr, Wauwatosa, WI 53226-3452 *Toll Free Tel:* 800-651-8313 *Fax:* 414-443-4331
Distributed by American Medical Association; Mosby
Distributor for American Medical Association; Medical Economics; Mosby
Warehouse: 3687 W Great Lake Dr, Suite C, Salt Lake City, UT 84120

Orange Frazer Press Inc
37 1/2 W Main St, Wilmington, OH 45177
Mailing Address: PO Box 214, Wilmington, OH 45177-0214
Tel: 937-382-3196 *Toll Free Tel:* 800-852-9332 (orders) *Fax:* 937-383-3159
E-mail: ofrazer@erinet.com
Web Site: www.orangefrazer.com
Key Personnel
Publr: Marcy Hawley
Ed: John Baskin
Tech & Design: Tim Fauley
Off Mgr: Sarah Hawley
Founded: 1987
Regional book publisher specializing in Ohio nonfiction (reference, sports, commentary, travel, nature, etc). Production & design is considered "high-end". Recent winner of the Ohioana 2000 Citation Award for Excellence in Publishing.
ISBN Prefix(es): 978-1-882203; 978-0-9619637; 978-1-933197
Number of titles published annually: 16 Print
Total Titles: 60 Print
Membership(s): The Association of Publishers for Special Sales; The Independent Book Publishers Association

Orbis Books
Division of Maryknoll Fathers & Brothers
Price Bldg, Box 302, Maryknoll, NY 10545-0302
Tel: 914-941-7636 *Toll Free Tel:* 800-258-5838 (orders) *Fax:* 914-941-7005
E-mail: orbisbooks@maryknoll.org
Web Site: www.orbisbooks.com
Key Personnel
Publr & Ed-in-Chief: Robert Ellsberg *E-mail:* rellsberg@maryknoll.org
Assoc Publr & Mktg Mgr: Bernadette B Price *E-mail:* bprice@maryknoll.org
Busn Mgr: William Medeot *E-mail:* bmedeot@maryknoll.org
Sales Mgr: Michael Lawrence *E-mail:* mlawrence@maryknoll.org
Ed-at-Large: Michael Leach *E-mail:* mleach@maryknoll.org
Rts & Perms: Doris Goodnough *E-mail:* dgoodnough@maryknoll.org
Founded: 1970
Offering a wide range of books on prayer, spirituality, Catholic life, theology, mission & current affairs.
ISBN Prefix(es): 978-0-88344; 978-1-57075; 978-1-60833; 978-1-62698
Number of titles published annually: 50 Print; 50 E-Book
Total Titles: 780 Print; 470 E-Book
Foreign Rep(s): Alban Books (Europe, UK); Bayard/Novalis Distribution (Canada); Catholic Book Shop (South Africa); Garratt Publishing (Australia)
Advertising Agency: Roth Advertising, PO Box 96, Sea Cliff, NY 11579-0096, Pres: Daniel Roth *Tel:* 516-674-8603 *Fax:* 516-368-3885 *E-mail:* dan@rothadvertising.com
Warehouse: Maryknoll Center Warehouse, 79 Ryder Rd, Ossining, NY 10562, Warehouse Mgr: Jim Matthieu *Tel:* 914-941-7636 ext 2613
Membership(s): Association of Catholic Publishers Inc

Orbit
Division of Hachette Book Group
1290 Avenue of the Americas, New York, NY 10019
Tel: 212-364-1100 *Toll Free Tel:* 800-759-0190
Web Site: www.orbitbooks.net
Key Personnel
SVP, Hachette Book Group & Publr, Orbit: Tim Holman
VP & Deputy Publr: Anne Clarke
VP, Publg Dir, Yen Press: Kurt Hassler
Edit Dir: Devi Pillai
Mktg & Publicity Dir: Alex Lencicki
Creative Dir: Lauren Panepinto
Founded: 2008
Orbit is a leading publisher of science fiction & fantasy with imprints in the UK, US & Australia. We publish across the spectrum of science fiction & fantasy—from action-packed urban fantasy to widescreen space opera; from sweeping epic adventures to near-future thrillers.
Number of titles published annually: 226 Print
Total Titles: 1,200 Print
Imprints: Redhook; Yen Press
Orders to: Hachette Book Group, 53 State St, Boston, MA 02109 *Toll Free Tel:* 800-759-0190 *Toll Free Fax:* 800-286-9471
Shipping Address: Hachette Book Group Distribution Center, 121 N Enterprise Blvd, Lebanon, IN 46052 *Tel:* 765-483-9900 *Fax:* 765-483-0706

Orca Book Publishers
PO Box 468, Custer, WA 98240-0468
Tel: 250-380-1229 *Toll Free Tel:* 800-210-5277 *Fax:* 250-380-1892 *Toll Free Fax:* 877-408-1551
E-mail: orca@orcabook.com
Web Site: www.orcabook.com
Key Personnel
Publr: Andrew Wooldridge *E-mail:* andrew.wooldridge@orcabook.com
Edit Dir: Robert Tyrrell *E-mail:* tyrrell@orcabook.com
Founded: 1982
Children & young adult literature.
ISBN Prefix(es): 978-1-55143; 978-0-920501
Number of titles published annually: 60 Print
Total Titles: 350 Print
Branch Office(s)
PO Box 5626, Victoria, BC V8R 6S4, Canada
Distributor for The Book Publishing Co; Coteau Books; Creative Book Publishing; Formac Publishing; Lobster Press; James Lorimer & Co; Nimbus Publishing; Polestar Calendars; Second Story Press; 7th Generation; Sono Nis Press; Sumach Press; Tradewind Books; Tuckamore Books; Tudor House
Foreign Rights: Transatlantic Literary Agency (Samantha Haywood) (Worldwide exc North America)
Warehouse: 7056 Portal Way, Bldg E, Ferndale, WA 98248
Membership(s): ABA; ALA; Association of Book Publishers of British Columbia; Association of Canadian Publishers; Canadian Booksellers Association; Canadian Library Association; Educational Book & Media Association

§Orchard Publications
39510 Paseo Padre Pkwy, Suite 315, Fremont, CA 94538
SAN: 254-1645
Tel: 510-792-6077 *Fax:* 510-792-6097
E-mail: info@orchardpublications.com; orchard@orchardpublications.com
Web Site: www.orchardpublications.com
Key Personnel
Pres: Steven T Karris
Founded: 1992
Publisher of applied math & engineering textbooks.
This publisher has indicated that 100% of their product line is author subsidized.
ISBN Prefix(es): 978-0-9709511; 978-0-9744239; 978-1-934404
Number of titles published annually: 2 Print; 2 Online; 2 E-Book
Total Titles: 11 Print; 11 Online; 11 E-Book
Membership(s): The Association of Publishers for Special Sales; The Independent Book Publishers Association

Orchises Press
PO Box 320533, Alexandria, VA 22320-4533
Tel: 703-683-1243
Web Site: mason.gmu.edu/~lathbury/
Key Personnel
Pres & Ed-in-Chief: Roger Lathbury *E-mail:* lathbury@gmu.edu

Founded: 1983
Small press.
ISBN Prefix(es): 978-0-914061; 978-1-932535
Number of titles published annually: 3 Print
Total Titles: 130 Print

Oregon Catholic Press, see OCP

Oregon State University Press
121 The Valley Library, Corvallis, OR 97331-4501
SAN: 202-8328
Tel: 541-737-3166 *Toll Free Tel:* 800-621-2736 (orders)
Web Site: osupress.oregonstate.edu
Key Personnel
Dir: Faye Chadwell *E-mail:* faye.chadwell@oregonstate.edu
Assoc Dir: Tom Booth *E-mail:* thomas.booth@oregonstate.edu
Acqs Ed: Mary Elizabeth Braun *E-mail:* mary.braun@oregonstate.edu
Edit, Design & Prodn Mgr: Micki Reaman *E-mail:* micki.reaman@oregonstate.edu
Mktg Mgr: Marty Brown *E-mail:* marty.brown@oregonstate.edu
Founded: 1961
ISBN Prefix(es): 978-0-87071
Number of titles published annually: 15 Print
Total Titles: 225 Print
Foreign Rights: East-West Export Books (Royden Muranaka) (Asia-Pacific); Eurospan Group (Africa, Europe, Middle East); US PubRep (Craig Falk) (Latin America); UTP Distribution (Canada)
Distribution Center: Chicago Distribution Center, 11030 S Langley Ave, Chicago, IL 60628 *Toll Free Tel:* 800-621-2736 *Toll Free Fax:* 800-621-8476

O'Reilly Media Inc
1005 Gravenstein Hwy N, Sebastopol, CA 95472
Tel: 707-827-7000; 707-827-7019
Toll Free Tel: 800-998-9938; 800-889-8969
Fax: 707-829-0104; 707-824-8268
E-mail: orders@oreilly.com
Web Site: www.oreilly.com
Key Personnel
Founder & CEO: Tim O'Reilly
VP: Sara Winge *Tel:* 707-827-7109 *E-mail:* sara@oreilly.com
Dir, Sales: Mike Leonard *Tel:* 707-827-7078 *E-mail:* mleonard@oreilly.com
Founded: 1978
Technical computer book publisher, conference provider.
ISBN Prefix(es): 978-0-937175; 978-1-56592; 978-0-596
Number of titles published annually: 140 Print; 65 E-Book
Total Titles: 800 Print
Branch Office(s)
O'Reilly AlphaTech Ventures (OATV), One Lombard St, Suite 303, San Francisco, CA 94111 *Tel:* 415-693-0200 *Web Site:* www.oatv.com
10 Fawcett St, Cambridge, MA 02138 *Tel:* 617-354-5800 *Toll Free Tel:* 800-775-7731 *Fax:* 617-661-1116
Foreign Office(s): O'Reilly Beijing, Cheng Ming Mansion, Bldg C, Suite 807, No 2 Xizhimen South St, Xicheng District, Beijing 100035, China, Contact: Michelle Chen *Tel:* (010) 88097475 *Fax:* (010) 88097463 *E-mail:* orb@oreilly.com *Web Site:* www.oreilly.com.cn
O'Reilly Verlag, Balthasarstr 81, 50670 Cologne, Germany, Contact: Anke Wallbrecher *Tel:* (0221) 9731600 *Fax:* (0221) 973160-8 *E-mail:* anfragen@oreilly.de *Web Site:* www.oreilly.de
Intelligent Plaza, Bldg 1-F, 26 Banchi 27, Sakamachi, Shinjuku-ku, Tokyo 160-0002, Japan, Contact: Kenji Watari *Tel:* (03) 3356 5227 *Fax:* (03) 3356 5261 *E-mail:* kenji@oreilly.com *Web Site:* www.oreilly.co.jp
Gostrey House, Union Rd, Farnham, Surrey GU9 7PT, United Kingdom *Tel:* (01252) 721284 *Fax:* (01252) 722337 *E-mail:* information@oreilly.co.uk *Web Site:* www.oreilly.uk
Distributor for Microsoft Press (North America); Packt Publishing (technol ebook prog)
Foreign Rep(s): WoodsLane (Australia, New Zealand)
Distribution Center: Les Editions Flammarion ltee, 375 Ave Laurier Ouest, Montreal, QC H2V 2K3, Canada (The Americas) *Tel:* 514-277-8807 *Fax:* 514-278-2085 *E-mail:* info@flammarion.qc.ca
WoodsLane Pty Ltd, 7/5 Vuko Place, Warriewood NSW 2102, Australia (Australia & New Zealand) *Tel:* (02) 9970 5111 *Toll Free Tel:* 800-006-723 *Fax:* (02) 9970 5002 *Toll Free Fax:* 800-006-715 *E-mail:* info@woodslane.com.au *Web Site:* www.woodslane.com.au
Sodis, 128 Ave du Marechal de Lattre de Tassigny, 77400 Lagny sur Marne, France (Austria, Germany, Liechtenstein, Luxembourg & Switzerland) *Tel:* 01 60 07 82 00 *Fax:* 01 64 30 92 22 *E-mail:* portail@sodis.fr *Web Site:* www.sodis.fr
STP Distributors Pte Ltd (TQ), 10/F, Block C, Seaview Estate, 2-8 Watson Rd, North Point, Hong Kong (Hong Kong), Contact: Ray Chan *Tel:* 2992 0878 *Fax:* 2992 0983 *E-mail:* ray@tplhk.com.hk
Shroff Publishers & Distributors Pvt Ltd, C-103, TTC Industrial Area, MIDC, Pawane, Navi Mumbai 400 701, India (India) *Tel:* (022) 2763 4290 *Fax:* (022) 2768 3337 *E-mail:* spdorders@shroffpublishers.com *Web Site:* www.shroffpublishers.com
Eastern Book Service Inc, 3-13 Hongo 3-chome, Bunkyo-ku, Tokyo 160-8480, Japan (Japan) *Tel:* (03) 3818 0861 *Fax:* (03) 3818 0864 *E-mail:* orders@svt-ebs.co.jp *Web Site:* www.svt-ebs.co.jp
Pansing Distribution Sdn Bhd, Lot 557 A & B, Jalan Subang 3, Subang Jaya Industrial Estate, 47610 Subang Jaya, Selangor, Darul Ehsan, Malaysia (Malaysia), Sales Mgr: Ms Kavitajit Kaur *Tel:* (03) 56310794 *Fax:* (03) 56384337 *E-mail:* kavitajit@my.pansing.com
Pansing Distribution Pte Ltd, Times Ctr, One New Industrial Rd 536196, Singapore (Singapore & Indonesia), Prod Specialist: Benjamin Xu *Tel:* 6319 9939 *Fax:* 6459 4930 *E-mail:* benjaminxu@pansing.com
Hanbit Media Inc, Chungmu Bldg 301, Yonnamdong 568-33, Mapo-gu, Seoul, South Korea (Korea) *Tel:* (02) 325-0397 *Fax:* (02) 325-9697 *E-mail:* thkim@hanbitbook.co.kr *Web Site:* www.hanbitbook.co.kr
Tenlong Computer Book Co Ltd, No 107 Chong Ching S Rd, Sec 1, Taipei, Taiwan (Taiwan) *Tel:* (02) 2371-7725 *Fax:* (02) 2331-1905 *E-mail:* service@tenlong.com.tw *Web Site:* www.tenlong.com.tw
Far East Publications Ltd, 253 Asoke, 12th fl, Sukhumit 21, Klongteoy Nua, Wattana District, Bangkok 10110, Thailand (Thailand), Contact: Puripat Pakavaleetorn *Tel:* (02) 2611908 *Fax:* (02) 2611912 *E-mail:* puripat@pansing.com
Wiley Distribution Services Ltd, One Oldlands Way, Bonor Regis, West Sussex P022 9SA, United Kingdom (Africa, Europe (exc Austria, Germany, Liechtenstein, Luxembourg & Switzerland), Middle East & UK) *Tel:* (01243) 843242 *Toll Free Tel:* 800-243407 *Fax:* (01243) 843302 *E-mail:* cs-books@wiley.co.uk

§Organization for Economic Cooperation & Development
Division of Organization for Economic Cooperation & Development (France)
2001 "L" St NW, Suite 650, Washington, DC 20036-4922
Tel: 202-785-6323 *Toll Free Tel:* 800-456-6323 (dist ctr/pubns orders) *Fax:* 202-785-0350
E-mail: washington.contact@oecd.org
Web Site: www.oecdwash.org; www.oecd.org
Key Personnel
Deputy Head & Sales Mgr: Kathleen Deboer *Tel:* 202-822-3870 *E-mail:* kathleen.deboer@oecd.org
Founded: 1961
Periodicals, books, magnetic tapes, diskettes & microfiche, CD-ROM, online services.
ISBN Prefix(es): 978-92-64; 978-92-821; 978-92-65; 978-0-9501741
Number of titles published annually: 300 Print; 50 CD-ROM; 300 Online; 200 E-Book
Total Titles: 3,500 Print; 50 CD-ROM; 6,500 Online; 1,200 E-Book
Foreign Office(s): 2 rue Andre-Pascal, 75775 Paris Cedex 16, France *Tel:* (01) 45 24 82 00 *Fax:* (01) 45 24 85 00
Distributor for International Energy Agency (Imprint); International Transportation Forum; Nuclear Energy Agency (Imprint)
Orders to: Turpin Distribution Services Ltd, The Bleachery, 143 West St, New Milford, CT 06776 *Toll Free Tel:* 800-456-6323 *Fax:* 781-829-9052
Distribution Center: Turpin Distribution Services Ltd, The Bleachery, 143 West St, New Milford, CT 06776 *Toll Free Tel:* 800-456-6323 *Fax:* 860-350-0039

Oriental Institute Publications
Division of University of Chicago
1155 E 58 St, Chicago, IL 60637
Tel: 773-702-5967 *Fax:* 773-702-9853
E-mail: oi-publications@uchicago.edu; oi-museum@uchicago.edu; oi-administration@uchicago.edu
Web Site: oi.uchicago.edu
Key Personnel
Mng Ed, Pubns: Thomas Urban *E-mail:* t-urban@uchicago.edu
Ed, Pubns Off: Leslie Schramer *E-mail:* leslie@uchicago.edu
Founded: 1919
Academic publications.
ISBN Prefix(es): 978-0-918986; 978-1-885923
Number of titles published annually: 10 Print; 10 Online
Total Titles: 250 Print; 250 Online
Orders to: Casemate Academic, PO Box 511, Oakville, CT 06779 *Tel:* 860-945-9329 *Toll Free Tel:* 800-791-9354 *Fax:* 860-945-9468
Distribution Center: Casemate Academic, PO Box 511, Oakville, CT 06779 *Tel:* 860-945-9329 *Toll Free Tel:* 800-791-9354 *Fax:* 860-945-9468

The Original Falcon Press
1753 E Broadway Rd, No 101-277, Tempe, AZ 85282
Tel: 602-708-1409
E-mail: info@originalfalcon.com
Web Site: www.originalfalcon.com
Key Personnel
Pres: Nicholas Tharcher *E-mail:* nick@originalfalcon.com
Founded: 1982
Books, CDs & DVDs.
ISBN Prefix(es): 978-1-935150; 978-1-61869
Number of titles published annually: 10 Print; 10 E-Book; 10 Audio
Total Titles: 50 Print; 40 E-Book; 30 Audio
Imprints: Falcon Press; Golden Dawn Publications; New Falcon Publications
Distribution Center: New Leaf Distributing Co, 401 Thornton Rd, Lithia Springs, GA 30122-1557 *Tel:* 770-948-7845 *Fax:* 770-944-2313 *E-mail:* newleaf@newleaf-dist.com *Web Site:* www.newleaf-dist.com

Quanta Distribution, 3251 Kennedy Rd, Unit 20, Toronto, ON M1V 2J9, Canada *Tel:* 416-410-9411 *Toll Free Tel:* 888-436-7962 *Fax:* 416-291-8764 *E-mail:* quantamail@quanta.ca *Web Site:* www.quanta.ca
John Reed Book Distribution, 2/11 Yandala St, Tea Garden, NSW 2324, Australia, Dir: John Reed *Tel:* (02) 4997 2936 *Fax:* (02) 4997 2937 *E-mail:* sales@johnreedbooks.com.au *Web Site:* www.johnreedbooks.com.au
Gazelle Book Services Ltd, White Cross Mills, High Town, Lancaster LA1 4XS, United Kingdom *Tel:* (0152) 468765 *Web Site:* www.gazellebookservices.co.uk

Original Publications
PO Box 236, Old Beth Page, NY 11804
SAN: 133-0225
Tel: 516-605-0547 *Toll Free Tel:* 888-622-8581 *Fax:* 516-605-0549
E-mail: originalpub@aol.com
Web Site: www.occult1.com
Key Personnel
Publr & Dist: Mark Benezra
Founded: 1962
African religion, New Age, spirituality, Santeria & occult books.
ISBN Prefix(es): 978-0-942272
Number of titles published annually: 40 Print
Total Titles: 50 Print
Distribution Center: New Leaf Distributing Co, 401 Thornton Rd, Lithia Springs, GA 30122-1557 SAN: 169-1449
AzureGreen, 16 Bell Rd, Middlefield, MA

ORO editions
31 Commercial Blvd, Suite F, Novato, CA 94949
Tel: 415-883-3300 *Fax:* 415-883-3309
E-mail: info@oroeditions.com
Web Site: www.oroeditions.com
Key Personnel
Contact: Gordon Goff *E-mail:* gordon@oroeditions.com
Founded: 2003
ISBN Prefix(es): 978-0-9746800; 978-0-9774672; 978-0-9793801; 978-0-9795395; 978-0-9814628; 978-0-9820607; 978-0-9819857; 978-0-9826226; 978-0-935935
Number of titles published annually: 25 Print; 8 E-Book

Osprey Publishing Inc
4301 21 St, Suite 220B, Long Island City, NY 11101
Tel: 718-433-4402 *Fax:* 718-433-4497
E-mail: ospreyusa@ospreypublishing.com
Web Site: www.ospreypublishing.com
Key Personnel
Dir, Mktg & New Busn Devt: Christian Waters
Sales & Mktg Mgr, Old House & Shire: Elyse Turr
Founded: 1969
Series publishing in history, military nonfiction, local interest, genre fiction: science fiction/fantasy, young adult & mysteries.
ISBN Prefix(es): 978-1-85532; 978-0-85045; 978-1-84176; 978-1-84603 (Osprey); 978-1-84908 (Osprey); 978-0-85766 (Angry Robot)
Number of titles published annually: 120 Print
Total Titles: 2,500 Print
Imprints: Aircraft of the Aces; Aviation Elite Units; Battle Orders; Campaign; Combat Aircraft; Command; Duel; Elite; Essential Histories; Field of Glory; Force on Force; Fortress; General Aviation; General Military; Graphic History; Men at Arms; Modelling Manuals; Modelling Masterclass; New Vanguard; Old House; Osprey; Osprey Modelling; Raid; Shire (local history); Wargaming; Warrior; Weapon
Foreign Office(s): Osprey Publishing Ltd, Midland House, West Way, Botley, Oxon OX2 0PH, United Kingdom, Off Mgr: Diane Hobbs *Tel:* (01865) 727022 *Fax:* (01865) 242009 *E-mail:* diane.hobbs@ospreypublishing.com
Distributed by Random House (US & CN)
Distribution Center: TBS (The Book Service), Colchester Rd, Frating Green, Colchester, Essex CO7 7DW, United Kingdom (Worldwide)

Other Press LLC
2 Park Ave, 24th fl, New York, NY 10016
Tel: 212-414-0054 *Toll Free Tel:* 877-843-6843 *Fax:* 212-414-0939
E-mail: editor@otherpress.com; rights@otherpress.com
Web Site: www.otherpress.com
Key Personnel
Publr: Judith Feher-Gurewich
CFO: Bill Foo
Mng Ed: Elana Seplow-Jolley
Ed: Marjorie De Witt
Dir, Online Mktg: Terrie Akers
Dir, Publicity: Jessica Greer
Dir, Subs Rts: Lauren Shekari
Publicist: Megan Feulner; Charlotte Kelly; Robert Wicks
Publicity & Mktg Coord: Sophia Sherry
Mktg Assoc: Christie Michel
Founded: 1998
Publish literary fiction, literature in translation, trade nonfiction, memoir, cultural studies, biographies & other subjects.
ISBN Prefix(es): 978-1-892746; 978-1-59051
Number of titles published annually: 25 Print; 25 E-Book
Distributed by Random House Inc
Foreign Rep(s): Eurospan (professional titles outside of North America); Random House International Sales; Random House of Canada Limited (Canada)
Membership(s): ABA; Community of Literary Magazines & Presses; The Independent Book Publishers Association

OTTN Publishing
16 Risler St, Stockton, NJ 08559
Tel: 609-397-4005 *Toll Free Tel:* 866-356-6886 *Fax:* 609-397-4007
E-mail: inquiries@ottnpublishing.com
Web Site: www.ottnpublishing.com
Key Personnel
Publr: Jim Gallagher *E-mail:* jgallagher@ottnpublishing.com
Founded: 1998
Provide a full range of editorial services from developing book or series ideas to providing a finished product all at a reasonable price.
ISBN Prefix(es): 978-1-59556
Number of titles published annually: 5 Print
Total Titles: 17 Print
Membership(s): The Independent Book Publishers Association

§Our Sunday Visitor Publishing
Division of Our Sunday Visitor Inc
200 Noll Plaza, Huntington, IN 46750
SAN: 202-8344
Tel: 260-356-8400 *Toll Free Tel:* 800-348-2440 (orders) *Fax:* 260-356-8472 *Toll Free Fax:* 800-498-6709
E-mail: osvbooks@osv.com (book orders)
Web Site: www.osv.com
Key Personnel
Chmn of the Bd: Bishop Kevin C Rhoades
Pres & Publr: Greg Erlandson *E-mail:* gerlandson@osv.com
Assoc Publr & Ed: Owen Campion *E-mail:* ocampion@osv.com
Exec Asst: Michelle Hogan *E-mail:* mhogan@osv.com
Founded: 1912
Religious books: trade, adult & juvenile general interest & reference, hardcover & paperback, early childhood school; newsweekly, religious magazines & newspapers, CD-ROM.
ISBN Prefix(es): 978-0-87973; 978-1-931709; 978-0-9707756
Number of titles published annually: 60 Print
Total Titles: 600 Print; 6 CD-ROM; 8 Audio
Foreign Rep(s): Baker & Taylor (Worldwide exc Canada, France, Malta, New Zealand, South Africa & UK); B Broughton (Canada); Catholic Supplies (New Zealand); Preca (Malta); Veritas (UK); Veritas Co Ltd (Ireland); Grace Wing (Canada, UK, Worldwide exc Australia); Word of Life (Australia)

OUT OF YOUR MIND...AND INTO THE MARKETPLACE™
13381 White Sand Dr, Tustin, CA 92780-4565
Tel: 714-544-0248 *Toll Free Tel:* 800-419-1513 *Fax:* 714-730-1414
Web Site: www.business-plan.com
Key Personnel
Owner & Publr: Linda Pinson *E-mail:* lpinson@business-plan.com
Asst Publr: Julie Filppi *E-mail:* jfilppi@aol.com
Mktg Dir: Ndaba Mdhlongwa *E-mail:* ndaba@business-plan.com
Founded: 1986
Publisher of entrepreneurial books & business plan software.
This publisher has indicated that 80% of their product line is author subsidized.
ISBN Prefix(es): 978-0-944205
Number of titles published annually: 2 Print; 1 CD-ROM; 6 E-Book
Total Titles: 3 Print; 1 CD-ROM; 6 E-Book
Distribution Center: Independent Publishers Group (IPG), 814 N Franklin St, Chicago, IL 60610, Title Devt Mgr: Mary Rowles *Toll Free Tel:* 800-888-4741 *E-mail:* mrowles@ipgbook.com *Web Site:* ipg.com
Membership(s): The Independent Book Publishers Association

The Overlook Press
Subsidiary of Peter Mayer Publishers Inc
141 Wooster St, Suite 4-B, New York, NY 10012
SAN: 202-8360
Tel: 212-673-2210; 845-679-6838 (orders & dist) *Fax:* 212-673-2296
E-mail: sales@overlookny.com (orders)
Web Site: www.overlookpress.com
Key Personnel
Pres & Publr: Peter Mayer
Dir, Publicity: Jack Lamplough
Sales Mgr: Jill Lichtenstadter
Assoc Ed: Erik Hane; Allyson Rudolph
Founded: 1971
Fiction, general nonfiction, theatre, biography, art, architecture, history, design, film, popular culture, hardcover reprints & trade paperbacks.
ISBN Prefix(es): 978-0-87951; 978-1-58567; 978-1-59020
Number of titles published annually: 90 Print
Total Titles: 1,000 Print
Imprints: Ardis Russian Literature; Elephant's Eye; Tusk Ivory; Tusk Paperbacks
Distributed by W W Norton & Co Inc
Foreign Rights: Agencia Literaria Carmen Balcells (Portugal, South America, Spain); The Deborah Harris Agency (Israel); Asli Karasuil (Turkey); Agence Michelle Lapautre (Belgium, France); Agenzia Letteraria (Italy); Licht & Burr Literary Agency APS (Scandinavia); Dr Ruth Liepman Agency (Germany, Switzerland); Andrew Nurnberg Associates (Bulgaria, China, Croatia, Czech Republic, Estonia, Hungary, Latvia, Lithuania, Montenegro, Poland, Romania, Russia, Serbia, Taiwan); Agencia Riff (Lucia Riff) (Brazil); Sebes & Van Gelderen Literary Agency (Netherlands); Tuttle-Mori Agency Inc (Japan)
Membership(s): AAP; National Book Foundation

The Overmountain Press
Division of Sabre Industries Inc
PO Box 1261, Johnson City, TN 37605-1261
SAN: 687-6641
Tel: 423-926-2691 *Toll Free Tel:* 800-992-2691 (orders) *Fax:* 423-232-1252
E-mail: orders@overmtn.com
Web Site: www.overmtn.com
Key Personnel
Publr: Elizabeth L Wright *E-mail:* beth@overmtn.com
Mng Ed: Daniel Lewis *E-mail:* daniel@overmtn.com
Sr Ed: Sherry Lewis *E-mail:* sherry@overmtn.com
Mktg: Karin O'Brien *E-mail:* karino@overmtn.com
Founded: 1970
Exhibit at trade shows, festivals, conventions. Subjects include Southern Appalachian nonfiction, history & children.
ISBN Prefix(es): 978-0-932807; 978-1-57072
Number of titles published annually: 10 Print
Total Titles: 300 Print
Imprints: Silver Dagger Mysteries

Richard C Owen Publishers Inc
PO Box 585, Katonah, NY 10536-0585
Tel: 914-232-3903 *Toll Free Tel:* 800-336-5588 *Fax:* 914-232-3977
Web Site: www.rcowen.com
Key Personnel
Pres & Publr: Richard C Owen *E-mail:* richardowen@rcowen.com
Founded: 1982
Education, language arts & literacy.
ISBN Prefix(es): 978-0-913461; 978-1-878450; 978-1-57274
Number of titles published annually: 5 Print
Total Titles: 378 Print
Warehouse: 243 Rte 100, Somers, NY 10589

Owl About Books Publisher Inc
1632 Royalwood Circle, Joshua, TX 76058
Mailing Address: PO Box 867, Joshua, TX 76058
Tel: 682-553-9078 *Fax:* 817-558-8983
E-mail: owlaboutbooks@gmail.com
Web Site: www.owlaboutbooks.com
Key Personnel
Pres: Dorota Harrington
Founded: 2011
Privately owned & devoted to publishing literature for children. Educational series philosophy is best described by the company's motto "Children's learning has no limits." Specialize in beautifully illustrated reading resources for parents & children with special needs. Well-placed fun facts accompany most of the stories & provide educational benefit.
ISBN Prefix(es): 978-1-937752
Number of titles published annually: 7 Print; 7 Online
Total Titles: 14 Print; 14 Online
Membership(s): The Independent Book Publishers Association

§Oxbridge® Communications Inc
39 W 29 St, Suite 301, New York, NY 10001
Tel: 212-741-0231 *Toll Free Tel:* 800-955-0231 *Fax:* 212-633-2938
E-mail: info@oxbridge.com
Web Site: www.oxbridge.com
Key Personnel
CEO: Louis Hagood
Pres: Patricia Hagood
Founded: 1964
Over the last 40 years, Oxbridge has built the largest database of information on US & Canadian periodicals & catalogs with a total of 72,000 titles. Data is available online, on CD & in print. Oxbridge publishes the *Standard Periodical Directory, the National Directory of Magazines, the National Directory of Catalogs & the Oxbridge Directory of Newsletters*.
ISBN Prefix(es): 978-1-891783
Number of titles published annually: 4 Print; 1 CD-ROM; 1 Online
Total Titles: 4 Print; 1 CD-ROM; 1 Online

§Oxford University Press USA
Division of University of Oxford
198 Madison Ave, New York, NY 10016
SAN: 202-5892
Tel: 212-726-6000 *Toll Free Tel:* 800-451-7556 (orders); 800-445-9714 (cust serv) *Fax:* 919-677-1303
E-mail: custserv.us@oup.com
Web Site: www.oup.com/us
Key Personnel
CEO: Nigel Portwood
CFO: Kevin Allison
Pres, OUP USA & Publr, Academic & Trade: Niko Pfund
VP & Publr, Clinical Medicine: Catherine Barnes
VP & Publr, Higher Educ: John Challice
VP & Dir, Dist, Cary, NC: Tom Shannon
VP, Global Mktg: Colleen Scollans
VP, Publr Rel: Casper Grathwohl
Head, Academic Publg Div: Tim Barton
Head, Design, Global Academic Busn: Linda Secondari
Head, US Content Opers: Deborah Shor
Head, US Dictionaries: Katherine Martin
Head, US Stock Planning & Pubns: Bill Haydis
Dir, Academic/Trade Mkt: Kim Craven
Edit Dir, Higher Educ: Patrick Lynch
Edit Dir, Ref Acqs: Damon Zucca
Ed-in-Chief, Academic/Trade Edit: Suzanne Ryan
Ed-in-Chief, Social Sciences: David McBride
Cust Serv Dir: Cheryl Ammons-Longtin
Dir, Direct Mktg: Rose Pintaudi-Jones
Dir, Fin: Dottie Warlick
Dir, Fin & Opers: Jim Jordan
Dir, Global Online Mktg: Sarah Ultsch
Dir, Higher Educ Mktg & Sales: Frank Mortimer
Dir, HR: Linda Rooney
Dir, HR, Cary, NC: Cherlynn Hoover
Dir, Info Systems: Raju Gadiraju
Dir, Instl Sales: Rebecca Seger
Dir, Mktg & Dist: Kurt Hettler
Dir, Medicine & Law Sales & Mktg: Greg Bussy
Opers Dir: Laurea Salvatore
Dir, Publicity: C Purdy
Divisional Systems Mgr: James Martin
Facilities/Off Servs Mgr, NY: Terese Dickerson
Publicity Mgr: Tara Kennedy
Stock Planning Proj Mgr: Nancy Wu
Warehouse Mgr: Todd Hayes
Gen Coun: Barbara Cohen
Founded: 1896 (1478 in UK)
Scholarly, professional & reference books in the humanities, science, medicine & social studies; nonfiction trade, Bibles, college textbooks, music, English as a second language, paperbacks, children's books, journals, online reference & online scholarly. Prospective authors should consult the Oxford University Press web site for submission guidelines & proposal submission policy.
ISBN Prefix(es): 978-0-19
Number of titles published annually: 3,000 Print; 6 CD-ROM; 100 Online; 400 E-Book; 23 Audio
Total Titles: 26,000 Print; 27 CD-ROM; 200 Online; 500 E-Book; 220 Audio
Imprints: Clarendon Press
Foreign Office(s): Great Clarendon St, Oxford OX2 6DP, United Kingdom (worldwide headquarters) *Tel:* (018165) 556-767
Distributor for The American Chemical Society; American University in Cairo; Arnold Clarendon; Cold Spring Harbor Laboratory Press; Engineering Press; Fordham University Press; Getty; Greenwich Medical Media; Grove Dictionaries; Hurst; IRL; Kodansha; Roxbury Publishing; Saunders; Thomson Publishing
Foreign Rights: Gersh Agency
Returns: 2001 Evans Rd, Cary, NC 27513 *Toll Free Tel:* 800-451-7556 *Web Site:* www.oup.com/us
Warehouse: 2001 Evans Rd, Cary, NC 27513 *Toll Free Tel:* 800-451-7556 *Web Site:* www.oup.com/us
Distribution Center: 2001 Evans Rd, Cary, NC 27513 *Toll Free Tel:* 800-451-7556 *Web Site:* www.oup.com/us
Membership(s): AAP; American Association of University Presses; BISG

Oxmoor House
Imprint of Time Inc Books
2100 Lakeshore Dr, Birmingham, AL 35209
SAN: 205-3462
Tel: 205-445-6000 *Toll Free Tel:* 800-366-4712; 888-891-8935 (cust serv); 800-765-6400 (orders)
Web Site: www.oxmoorhouse.com
Key Personnel
Edit Dir: Anja Schmidt
Sr Ed: Erica Sanders-Foege
Founded: 1968
General interest books; cooking, gardening, decorating, home improvement, travel, entertaining, health, motion film companions, custom products, celebrity how-to, crafts, art, hobbies; book & binder programs.
ISBN Prefix(es): 978-0-8487
Number of titles published annually: 250 Print
Total Titles: 329 Print
Imprints: Coastal Living Books; Cooking Light Books; Health Books; Southern Living Books; Sunset Books
Distributed by H B Fenn (Canada); Leisure Arts Inc
Foreign Rep(s): Beckett Sterling (New Zealand); General Publishing Co (Canada); Little, Brown & Co, UK (Europe, UK); Struik Book Distributers (South Africa); Transworld Publishers (Australia)

Ozark Mountain Publishing Inc
PO Box 754, Huntsville, AR 72740-0754
Tel: 479-738-2348 *Toll Free Tel:* 800-935-0045 *Fax:* 479-738-2448
E-mail: info@ozarkmt.com
Web Site: www.ozarkmt.com
Key Personnel
Founder & Pres: Dolores Cannon *E-mail:* decannon@msn.com
Off Mgr: Julia Degan *E-mail:* julia@ozarkmt.com
Edit Asst: Joy Newman *E-mail:* joy@ozarkmt.com
Founded: 1992
Publish nonfiction New Age/metaphysical & spiritual type books.
ISBN Prefix(es): 978-0-9632776; 978-1-886940
Number of titles published annually: 10 Print
Total Titles: 50 Print
Foreign Rights: Ajatus Publishing Co (Finland); Gazelle Books Distributor (England, Europe); Gill & Macmillan (Ireland); Helfa A W (Poland); Jaico (India); Luciernaga Oceano (Spain); Lyubka Mihailova (Bulgaria); Quanta Distribution Inc (Canada); Schriwer Forlag (Norway); Stigmarion (Russia)

Ozark Publishing Inc
PO Box 228, Prairie Grove, AR 72753-0228
Tel: 479-595-9522 *Toll Free Tel:* 800-321-5671 *Fax:* 479-846-2843
E-mail: srg304@yahoo.com
Web Site: www.ozarkpublishing.us
Key Personnel
Mng Ed: Dave Sargent
Mgr: Dave Sargent, Jr
Founded: 1988

Children & young adult books. All books have a moral; the children's books include both fact & fiction.
ISBN Prefix(es): 978-1-56763
Number of titles published annually: 60 Print
Total Titles: 700 Print; 80 Audio
Distributed by Amazon.com; Apple; Barnes & Noble; Econoclad; Gumdrop; Perma-Bound; Stay Bound
Shipping Address: 13062 Butler, Prairie Grove, AR 72753
Distribution Center: Follett School Solutions Inc, 1340 Ridgeview Dr, McHenry, IL 60050 *Tel:* 815-759-1700 *Toll Free Tel:* 888-551-5114 (cust serv) *Fax:* 815-759-9831 *Toll Free Fax:* 800-852-5458 *E-mail:* info@follettlearning.com *Web Site:* www.follettlearning.com SAN: 169-1902

P & R Publishing Co
1102 Marble Hill Rd, Phillipsburg, NJ 08865
SAN: 205-3918
Mailing Address: PO Box 817, Phillipsburg, NJ 08865
Tel: 908-454-0505 *Toll Free Tel:* 800-631-0094 *Fax:* 908-859-2390
E-mail: sales@prpbooks.com; info@prpbooks.com
Web Site: www.prpbooks.com
Key Personnel
Pres: Bryce H Craig *E-mail:* bryce@prpbooks.com
VP: Ian M Thompson *E-mail:* ian@prpbooks.com
Sr Proj Mgr: Aaron Gottier *E-mail:* aarong@prpbooks.com
Founded: 1930
Christian books for all ages (Reformed Theology).
ISBN Prefix(es): 978-0-87552; 978-1-59638
Number of titles published annually: 60 Print; 100 E-Book
Total Titles: 750 Print; 1 CD-ROM; 200 E-Book
Foreign Rights: F J Rudy & Associates (Fred Rudy) (Worldwide)
Membership(s): Evangelical Christian Publishers Association

P S M J Resources Inc
10 Midland Ave, Newton, MA 02458
Tel: 617-965-0055 *Toll Free Tel:* 800-537-7765 *Fax:* 617-965-5152
E-mail: info@psmj.com
Web Site: www.psmj.com
Founded: 1980
Books, survey reports & audio cassette programs for architects, engineers, interior designers, urban designers, planners, landscape architects on business & financial management; marketing; time & personnel management; legal topics; project management; human resources; newsletters; consulting & educational seminars.
ISBN Prefix(es): 978-1-55538
Number of titles published annually: 12 Print
Total Titles: 100 Print
Branch Office(s)
2746 Rangewood Rd, Atlanta, GA 30345 *Tel:* 770-723-9651 *Fax:* 815-461-7478 *E-mail:* dbustein@psmj.com
Foreign Office(s): PO Box 773, Artarmon, NSW 2064, Australia *Tel:* (02) 9411 4819 *Fax:* (02) 9419 6044 *E-mail:* egoullet@psmj.com
242 Dorcas St, South Melbourne, Victoria 3205, Australia *Tel:* (03) 9686-3846 *Fax:* (03) 9682-5169 *E-mail:* cnelson@psmj.com

Pace University Press
Unit of Pace University
Dept of Publishing, Rm 805-E, 551 Fifth Ave, New York, NY 10176
Tel: 212-346-1417 *Fax:* 212-346-1165
Web Site: www.pace.edu/press
Key Personnel
Dir: Sherman Raskin *E-mail:* sraskin@pace.edu
Assoc Dir: Manuela Soares *E-mail:* msoares@pace.edu
Founded: 1988
Academic books in the humanities.
ISBN Prefix(es): 978-0-944473
Number of titles published annually: 6 Print
Total Titles: 55 Print

Pacific Press Publishing Association
Division of Seventh-Day Adventist Church
1350 N Kings Rd, Nampa, ID 83687-3193
Mailing Address: PO Box 5353, Nampa, ID 83653-5353
Tel: 208-465-2500 *Toll Free Tel:* 800-447-7377 *Fax:* 208-465-2531
Web Site: www.pacificpress.com
Key Personnel
CIO: Ed Bahr *Tel:* 208-465-2630 *E-mail:* edubah@pacificpress.com
Pres & Gen Mgr: Dale Galusha *Tel:* 208-465-2501 *E-mail:* dalgal@pacificpress.com
VP, Fin: Don Upson *Tel:* 208-465-2536 *E-mail:* don.upson.sr@pacificpress.com
VP, Mktg & Sales: Doug Church *Tel:* 208-465-2505 *E-mail:* douchu@pacificpress.com
VP, Prodn: Chuck Bobst *Tel:* 208-465-2611 *E-mail:* chubob@pacificpress.com
VP, Prod Devt: Jerry Thomas *E-mail:* jertho@pacificpress.com
Magazine Sr Ed: Marvin Moore *Tel:* 208-465-2577 *E-mail:* marmoo@pacificpress.com
Magazine Juv Ed: A Sox *Tel:* 208-465-2580 *E-mail:* ailsox@pacificpress.com
Ad: Bonnie Laing *Tel:* 208-465-2524 *E-mail:* bonlai@pacificpress.com
Sales: Dave Gatten *Tel:* 208-465-2618 *E-mail:* davgat@pacificpress.com
Libn: Bonnie Tyson-Flyn *Tel:* 208-465-2582 *E-mail:* bontys@pacificpress.com
Intl Rts: Carolyn Curtis *Tel:* 208-465-2511 *E-mail:* carcur@pacificpress.com
Trade Mktg Dir: Beverly Logan *Tel:* 208-465-2550 *E-mail:* bevlog@pacificpress.com
Founded: 1874
Religion (Seventh-day Adventist).
ISBN Prefix(es): 978-0-8163
Number of titles published annually: 39 Print
Total Titles: 350 Print; 2 CD-ROM; 675 Online; 2 Audio

Paintbox Press
275 Madison Ave, Suite 600, New York, NY 10016
Tel: 212-878-6610 *Fax:* 212-202-6157
E-mail: info@paintboxpress.com
Web Site: www.paintboxpress.com
Key Personnel
Owner: Pamela Pease
PR: Kelly Smith
Founded: 1998
Pop-ups & books on art & design.
ISBN Prefix(es): 978-0-966943; 978-0-977790
Number of titles published annually: 4 Print
Total Titles: 10 Print
Membership(s): AIGA, the professional association for design; The Children's Book Council; Society of Illustrators

§Painted Pony Inc
Subsidiary of Wind River Development Fund
3 Ethete Rd, Fort Washakie, WY 82514
Mailing Address: PO Box 661, Fort Washakie, WY 82514-0661
Tel: 307-335-7330 *Toll Free Tel:* 877-253-3824 *Fax:* 307-335-7332
E-mail: ppi@wrdf.org
Web Site: www.paintedponyinc.com
Key Personnel
Pres: Scott Ratliff
Publg Mgr: Jon Cox *Tel:* 307-857-6643 *Fax:* 307-857-7050 *E-mail:* jonc@proformtech.com
Founded: 2004
ISBN Prefix(es): 978-0-9759806
Number of titles published annually: 5 Print; 3 Audio
Total Titles: 5 Print; 3 Audio

Paladin Press
Division of Paladin Enterprises Inc
5540 Central Ave, Suite 20, Boulder, CO 80301
SAN: 212-0305
Tel: 303-443-7250 *Toll Free Tel:* 800-392-2400 *Fax:* 303-442-8741
E-mail: service@paladin-press.com
Web Site: www.paladin-press.com
Key Personnel
Pres & Publr: Peder C Lund
Edit Dir & Sr Ed: Donna Duvall *E-mail:* donnad@paladin-press.com
Art Dir: Barbara Beasley
Sales & Mktg Mgr: Brad Efting
Cust Rel, Trade & Mail Order Sales: Jeanne Vaughan
Founded: 1970
New titles & reprints on military science & history, weaponry, martial arts & self-defense, survival, police science, terrorism & general interest.
ISBN Prefix(es): 978-0-87364; 978-1-58160
Number of titles published annually: 60 Print
Total Titles: 800 Print
Imprints: C E P Inc; Flying Machines Press; Sycamore Island Books
Distributed by Amazon.com; Barnes & Noble; Borders
Advertising Agency: J S O Advertising Inc
Membership(s): The Independent Book Publishers Association

Palgrave Macmillan
Imprint of Macmillan Higher Education
175 Fifth Ave, Suite 200, New York, NY 10010
Tel: 646-307-5151 *Fax:* 212-777-6359
E-mail: firstname.lastname@palgrave-usa.com
Web Site: us.macmillan.com/Palgrave.aspx
Key Personnel
Publr, Global Outreach: Farideh Koohi-Kamali
Edit Dir: Karen Wolny
Exec Ed: Laurie Harting
Prodn & Opers Dir: Alan Bradshaw
Mktg Dir: Michelle Fitzgerald
Assoc Dir, Mktg: Denise de la Rosa
Assoc Dir, Online Sales: Roohana Khan
Assoc Dir, Channel Sales: Marit Vagstad
Assoc Dir, Publicity: Gabrielle Gantz
Head of Digital Mktg, Projs & Events: Carol St Thomasino
Founded: 1952
Scholarly & trade publisher - cross market publisher.
ISBN Prefix(es): 978-0-312; 978-0-333; 978-1-4039; 978-0-230
Number of titles published annually: 3,200 Print; 2 Online; 850 E-Book
Total Titles: 28,000 Print
Distributor for Berg Publishers; British Film Institute; Manchester University Press; Pluto Press; I B Tauris & Co Ltd; Zed Books
Membership(s): AAP Professional & Scholarly Publishing Division

Palladium Books Inc
39074 Webb Ct, Westland, MI 48185
SAN: 294-9504
Tel: 734-721-2903 (orders) *Fax:* 734-721-1238
Web Site: www.palladiumbooks.com
Key Personnel
Pres: Kevin Siembieda *E-mail:* ksiembieda@palladiumbooks.com
Sr Ed: Alex Marciniszyn *E-mail:* alex@palladiumbooks.com

Founded: 1981
Role-playing game books & supplements.
ISBN Prefix(es): 978-0-916211; 978-1-57457
Number of titles published annually: 15 Print
Total Titles: 190 Print

§Palm Island Press
411 Truman Ave, Key West, FL 33040
SAN: 298-4024
Tel: 305-296-3102
E-mail: pipress2@gmail.com
Key Personnel
Gen Mgr: Donald Langille
Founded: 1994
ISBN Prefix(es): 978-0-9643434; 978-0-9743524
Number of titles published annually: 3 Print; 2 E-Book
Total Titles: 15 Print; 2 E-Book
Membership(s): Florida Authors & Publishers Association Inc; The Independent Book Publishers Association

Palmetto Bug Books
121 N Hibiscus Dr, Miami Beach, FL 33139
Tel: 305-531-9813 *Fax:* 305-604-1516
E-mail: palmettobugbooks@gmail.com
Key Personnel
Pres: Reginald Roach
Founded: 1992
Small publisher of fiction with a slant toward south Florida.
ISBN Prefix(es): 978-0-9634499
Number of titles published annually: 4 Print; 1 Online; 1 E-Book
Total Titles: 4 Print; 4 Online; 4 E-Book

Pangaea Publications
226 Wheeler St S, St Paul, MN 55105-1927
Tel: 651-226-2032 *Fax:* 651-226-2032
E-mail: info@pangaea.org
Web Site: pangaea.org
Key Personnel
Pres: Bonnie Hayskar *E-mail:* bonzi@pangaea.org
Founded: 1991
Publisher for Nature & Peoples of the Earth.
ISBN Prefix(es): 978-0-9630180; 978-1-929165
Number of titles published annually: 4 Print
Total Titles: 32 Print

§Panoptic Enterprises
PO Box 11220, Burke, VA 22009-1220
SAN: 265-3141
Tel: 703-451-5953 *Toll Free Tel:* 800-594-4766 *Fax:* 703-451-5953
E-mail: panoptic@fedgovcontracts.com
Web Site: www.fedgovcontracts.com
Key Personnel
Pres & Intl Rts: Vivina H McVay
VP: Barry McVay
Founded: 1982
Books on how-to obtain & administer federal contracts.
ISBN Prefix(es): 978-0-912481
Number of titles published annually: 6 Print
Total Titles: 12 Print
Returns: 6055 Ridge Ford Dr, Burke, VA 22015
Shipping Address: 6055 Ridge Ford Dr, Burke, VA 22015
Warehouse: 6055 Ridge Ford Dr, Burke, VA 22015
Membership(s): The Independent Book Publishers Association; Washington Book Publishers

Pantheon Books/Schocken Books
Imprint of Knopf Doubleday Publishing Group
c/o Random House Inc, 1745 Broadway, New York, NY 10019
SAN: 202-862X
Tel: 212-751-2600 *Toll Free Tel:* 800-638-6460 *Fax:* 212-572-6030
Key Personnel
EVP & Publg Dir: Patricia Johnson
VP & Dir, Edit: Daniel Frank
VP & Exec Ed: Erroll McDonald
VP & Dir, Prodn: Andy Hughes
VP & Assoc Publr: Christine Gillespie
Mng Ed & Dir, Edit, Schocken Books: Altie Karper
Sr Ed, Pantheon Books: Shelley Wanger
Sr Ed: Deborah Garrison
Ed: Diana Coglianese
Dir, Busn Opers: Justine LeCates
Dir, Dom Rts (Reprint Rts): Sean Yule
Dir, Publicity: Michiko Clark
Assoc Dir, Publicity: Michelle Somers
Asst Mgr, Dom Rts (Book Club, Serial & Performance): Thomas Dobrowolski
Asst Mgr, Foreign Rts: Suzanne Smith
Founded: 1942
Fiction & nonfiction.
Random House Inc & its publishing entities are not accepting proposals, mss or submission queries via e-mail at this time.
ISBN Prefix(es): 978-0-679; 978-0-8052; 978-0-375
Imprints: Schocken Books
Foreign Rep(s): Century Hutchinson Group (South America); Colt Associates (Africa exc South Africa); Steve Franklin (Israel); India Book Distributors (India); International Publishers Representatives (Middle East exc Israel); Pandemic Ltd (Continental Europe exc Scandinavia); Periodical Management Group Inc (Mexico); Random Century (Australia); Random House New Zealand Ltd (New Zealand); Random House of Canada Limited (Canada); Random House UK Ltd (UK); Saga Books ApS (Scandinavia); Sonrisa Book Service (Latin America exc Mexico); Yohan (Japan)
Foreign Rights: Agencia Literaria BMSR (Brazil); Arts & Licensing International (China); Carmen Balcells Agencia (Spain); DRT International (Korea); The English Agency (Japan); Graal Literary Agency (Poland); JLM Literary Agency (Greece); Katai & Bolza (Hungary); Agence Michelle Lapautre (France); Licht & Licht Agency (Scandinavia); Literarni Agentura (Czech Republic); Roberto Santachiara (Italy); Sebes & Van Gelderen Literary Agency (Netherlands)

Pants On Fire Press
2062 Harbor Cove Way, Winter Garden, FL 34787
Tel: 863-546-0760
E-mail: submission@pantsonfirepress.com
Web Site: www.pantsonfirepress.com
Key Personnel
Publr: David Powers *E-mail:* david@pantsonfirepress.com
Dir, Mktg: Cris Francet *E-mail:* cris@pantsonfirepress.com
Founded: 2007
Award-winning children's book publisher of picture, middle-grade & young adult books.
ISBN Prefix(es): 978-0-9827271
Number of titles published annually: 12 Print; 12 E-Book; 1 Audio
Total Titles: 21 Print; 21 E-Book; 1 Audio
Foreign Rights: The Gersh Agency (Joe Veltre) (Worldwide)
Distribution Center: INscribe Digital, 55 Francisco St, Suite 710, San Francisco, CA 94133 *Tel:* 415-489-7000 *Fax:* 415-489-7049
Membership(s): The Independent Book Publishers Association

Papercutz
160 Broadway, E Wing, Suite 700, New York, NY 10038
Tel: 646-559-4681 *Toll Free Tel:* 800-886-1223 *Fax:* 212-643-1545
E-mail: papercutz@papercutz.com
Web Site: www.papercutz.com
Key Personnel
CEO & Pres: Terry Nantier
VP, Mktg: Sven Larsen *E-mail:* larsen@papercutz.com
Ed-in-Chief: Jim Salicup
Founded: 2005
Graphic novels for ages 7-14.
ISBN Prefix(es): 978-1-59707; 978-1-62991
Number of titles published annually: 50 Print; 50 E-Book
Total Titles: 350 Print; 200 E-Book
Imprints: SuperGenius (graphic novels for teens & older)
Distributed by Macmillan
Orders to: MPS Distribution Center, 16365 James Madison Hwy, Gordonsville, VA 22942 *Toll Free Tel:* 888-330-8477 *Toll Free Fax:* 800-672-2054
Warehouse: MPS Distribution Center, 16365 James Madison Hwy, Gordonsville, VA 22942 *Toll Free Tel:* 888-330-8477 *Toll Free Fax:* 800-672-2054
Distribution Center: MPS Distribution Center, 16365 James Madison Hwy, Gordonsville, VA 22942 *Toll Free Tel:* 888-330-8477 *Toll Free Fax:* 800-672-2054
Membership(s): AAP; The Children's Book Council

Papyrus Publishers, see Letterbox/Papyrus of London Publishers USA

§Para Publishing LLC
PO Box 8206-240, Santa Barbara, CA 93118-8206
SAN: 215-8981
Tel: 805-968-7277 *Toll Free Tel:* 800-727-2782 *Fax:* 805-968-1379
Web Site: www.parapublishing.com
Key Personnel
Owner & Publr: Dan Poynter *E-mail:* danpoynter@parapublishing.com
Dir: Becky Carbone *E-mail:* becky@parapublishing.com
Founded: 1969
Illustrated nonfiction trade books; parachutes, skydiving & aspects of book publishing; book marketing, promotion & distribution.
ISBN Prefix(es): 978-1-56860
Number of titles published annually: 6 Print; 1 CD-ROM; 6 Online; 6 E-Book; 1 Audio
Total Titles: 33 Print; 3 CD-ROM; 15 Online; 15 E-Book; 3 Audio
Imprints: Parachuting Publications
Divisions: Global eBook Awards; Paralists; Para Publishing Seminars; Poynter Consulting; Publishing Poynters Newsletter
Distributed by NBN
Foreign Rep(s): NBN (Australia, Canada, UK)
Foreign Rights: Bob Erdmann
Advertising Agency: Chadwick Advertising
Shipping Address: 530 Ellwood Ridge, Santa Barbara, CA 93117-1407
Distribution Center: National Book Network, 4501 Forbes Blvd, Suite 200, Lanham, MD 20706
Membership(s): The Independent Book Publishers Association

Parabola Books
Subsidiary of Society for the Study of Myth & Tradition
20 W 20 St, 2nd fl, New York, NY 10011
Tel: 212-822-8806 *Toll Free Tel:* 800-592-2521 (subns) *Fax:* 212-822-8823
E-mail: info@parabola.org
Web Site: www.parabola.org
Key Personnel
Publr & Ed-in-Chief: Jeff Zaleski
Exec Ed: Tracy Cochran

Mng Ed: Dale Fuller
Founded: 1976
Classic & contemporary works exploring the human search for meaning through story, art, psychology, science, etc. Subject specialties include essays, literary analysis, interviews, mythology & multiculturalism.
ISBN Prefix(es): 978-0-930407
Number of titles published annually: 4 Print
Total Titles: 130 Print

Parachute Publishing LLC
Division of Parachute Properties LLC
322 Eighth Ave, Suite 702, New York, NY 10001
Tel: 212-691-1421 *Fax:* 212-647-9650
Web Site: www.parachutepublishing.com
Key Personnel
CEO & Chmn: Joan Waricha *E-mail:* jwaricha@parachutepublishing.com
Chair: Jane Stine *Tel:* 212-691-1421 *E-mail:* jstine@parachutepublishing.com
Founded: 1983
Children's & adult fiction & nonfiction: original books & series, books from licensed properties.
ISBN Prefix(es): 978-0-938753
Number of titles published annually: 100 Print; 2 E-Book
Total Titles: 1,000 Print
Distributed by Bantam; Bendon; Berkley; Dorling Kindersley; Grosset; Harcourt; HarperCollins; HarperEntertainment; Kensington; Little, Brown; Pocket; Random House; Running Press; Scholastic; Simon & Schuster
Membership(s): American Book Producers Association; The Children's Book Council

Paraclete Press Inc
36 Southern Eagle Cartway, Brewster, MA 02631
SAN: 282-1508
Mailing Address: PO Box 1568, Orleans, MA 02653-1568
Tel: 508-255-4685 *Toll Free Tel:* 800-451-5006 *Fax:* 508-255-5705
E-mail: mail@paracletepress.com
Web Site: www.paracletepress.com
Founded: 1981
Spirituality, personal testimonies, devotionals, literary fiction, new editions of classics & CDs.
ISBN Prefix(es): 978-1-55725; 978-0-941478
Number of titles published annually: 38 Print
Total Titles: 145 Print; 3 Audio
Distributor for Abbey of Saint Peter of Solesmes; Gloriae Dei Cantores
Membership(s): CBA; Evangelical Christian Publishers Association

§Paradigm Publications
Division of Redwing Book Co
202 Bendix Dr, Taos, NM 87571
Tel: 575-758-7758 *Toll Free Tel:* 800-873-3946 (US); 888-873-3947 (CN) *Fax:* 575-758-7768
Web Site: www.paradigm-pubs.com; www.redwingbooks.com
Key Personnel
Publr: Robert L Felt *E-mail:* bob@paradigm-pubs.com
Founded: 1980
Scholarly books on traditional Chinese medicine & acupuncture.
ISBN Prefix(es): 978-0-912111
Number of titles published annually: 2 Print
Total Titles: 60 Print; 12 E-Book; 1 Audio

§Paradigm Publishers
5589 Arapahoe Ave, Suite 206A, Boulder, CO 80303
Tel: 303-245-9054
Web Site: www.paradigmpublishers.com
Key Personnel
Pres & Publr: Dean Birkencamp
VP & Assoc Publr: Jennifer Knerr
Dir, Edit Prodn: Laura Esterman
Dir, Sales & Mktg: Annie Daniel
Sales, Mktg & Foreign Rts Mgr: Melissa Mazza
Busn Mgr & Data Opers Mgr: Maggie Faber
Founded: 2003
ISBN Prefix(es): 978-1-59451; 978-1-61205
Number of titles published annually: 80 Print
Total Titles: 500 Print
Foreign Rep(s): Brookside Publishing Services (Ireland, Northern Ireland); Compass Academic Ltd (UK exc Northern Ireland); Durnell Marketing (Europe exc Ireland); Footprint Books Pty Ltd (Australia, New Zealand); IMA (Tony Moggach) (Africa exc South Africa); Jacana Media Pty Ltd (Botswana, Lesotho, Namibia, South Africa, Swaziland); Maya Publishers Pvt Ltd (Surit Mitra) (India); Missing Link Versandbuchhandlung (Germany); Taylor & Francis Asia Pacific (Far East exc Japan); United Publishers Services Ltd (Japan); University of BC Press (Canada)
Foreign Rights: Brookside Publishing Services (Northern Ireland); Compass Academic Ltd (UK exc Ireland); Durnell Marketing (Europe exc Ireland & UK); Footprint Books Pty Ltd (Australia, New Zealand); IMA (Tony Moggach) (Africa exc South Africa); Jacana Media (Pty) Ltd (Botswana, Lesotho, Namibia, South Africa, Swaziland); Maya Publishers Pvt Ltd (Surit Mitra) (India); Missing Link Versandbuchhandlung (Germany); Taylor & Francis Asia Pacific (Far East exc Japan); United Publishers Service (Japan)
Orders to: PO Box 605, Herndon, VA 20172-0605 *Toll Free Tel:* 800-887-1591 *Fax:* 703-661-1501 *E-mail:* paradigmmail@presswarehouse.com; University of Toronto Press, 5201 Dufferin St, Toronto, ON M3H 5T8, Canada *Tel:* 416-667-7791 *Toll Free Tel:* 800-565-9523 *Fax:* 416-667-7832 *Toll Free Fax:* 800-221-9985 *E-mail:* utpbooks@utpress.utoronto.ca; Pluto Press/Marston Book Services, 345 Archway Rd, London N6 5AA, United Kingdom (UK & Europe) *Tel:* (020) 8348 2724 *Fax:* (020) 8348 9133 *E-mail:* pluto@plutobooks.com *Web Site:* www.plutobooks.com
Returns: 22883 Quicksilver Dr, Dulles, VA 20166

Paradise Cay Publications Inc
550 S "G" St, Suite 1, Arcata, CA 95521
Mailing Address: PO Box 29, Arcata, CA 95518-0029
Tel: 707-822-9063 *Toll Free Tel:* 800-736-4509 *Fax:* 707-822-9163
E-mail: info@paracay.com
Web Site: www.paracay.com
Key Personnel
Owner & Dir: Jim Morehouse *E-mail:* jim@paracay.com
Publr: Matt Morehouse *E-mail:* matt@paracay.com
Founded: 1977
Nautical books, videos, art prints, cruising guides & software.
ISBN Prefix(es): 978-0-939837; 978-0-9646036
Number of titles published annually: 6 Print
Total Titles: 82 Print; 4 Audio
Imprints: Pardey Publications
Foreign Rep(s): Boat Books (Australia); Islamorado Internacional (Panama); The Nautical Mind (Canada); Transpacific Marine (New Zealand)

Paragon House
3600 Labore Rd, Suite 1, St Paul, MN 55110-4144
Tel: 651-644-3087 *Toll Free Tel:* 800-447-3709 *Fax:* 651-644-0997
E-mail: paragon@paragonhouse.com
Web Site: www.paragonhouse.com
Key Personnel
Pres: Gordon L Anderson
Acqs Mgr & Opers Coord: Rosemary Yokoi
Founded: 1982
Nonfiction; reference, academic/scholarly monographs, trade & college paperbacks. History, religion, philosophy, New Age & government.
ISBN Prefix(es): 978-1-55778; 978-0-913729; 978-0-913757; 978-0-89226; 978-0-943852; 978-0-88702; 978-1-885118
Number of titles published annually: 10 Print
Total Titles: 400 Print
Imprints: Life Wisdom; PWPA Books
Distributed by Bloomsbury International Publishing USA (fulfillment by Macmillan)
Distributor for Professors World Peace Academy
Foreign Rep(s): Roundhouse Publishing (Europe, UK)
Foreign Rights: Paragon House (Worldwide)
Orders to: MPS, PO Box 470, Gordonsville, VA 22942-8501 *Tel:* 540-672-7600 *Toll Free Tel:* 888-330-8477 *Fax:* 540-672-7703 *Toll Free Fax:* 800-672-2054 *E-mail:* orders@mpsvirginia.com

§Parallax Press
Division of Unified Buddhist Church
2236-B Sixth St, Berkeley, CA 94710
Mailing Address: PO Box 7355, Berkeley, CA 94707-0355 SAN: 663-4494
Tel: 510-525-0101 *Toll Free Tel:* 800-863-5290 (orders) *Fax:* 510-525-7129
E-mail: info@parallax.org
Web Site: www.parallax.org
Key Personnel
Publr: Travis Masch *Tel:* 510-525-0101 ext 104 *E-mail:* travism@parallax.org
Sr Ed: Rachel Neumann *Tel:* 510-525-0101 ext 113 *E-mail:* rachel@parallax.org
Founded: 1986
Trade paperbacks; audio cassettes; subscription & mail-order books.
ISBN Prefix(es): 978-0-938077; 978-1-888375
Number of titles published annually: 15 Print
Total Titles: 7 Audio
Imprints: Plum Blossom Books (mindfulness books for children)
Foreign Rights: Cecile Barendsma (all other territories); Brother Phap Kham (Vietnam); Literaturmanufaktur (Ursula Richard) (Germany); Plum Village Foundation (Thailand); Shantum Seth (India)
Distribution Center: Publishers Group West, 1094 Flex Dr, Jackson, TN 38301 *Toll Free Tel:* 800-788-3123 *Toll Free Fax:* 800-351-5073 *E-mail:* orderentry@perseusbooks.com *Web Site:* www.pgw.com
Publishers Group Canada, 559 College St, Suite 402, Vancouver, BC M6G 1A9, Canada *Tel:* 604-323-7106 *Toll Free Tel:* 800-663-5714 *Fax:* 604-323-2600 *Toll Free Fax:* 800-565-3770 *E-mail:* customerservice@raincoast.com *Web Site:* www.pgcbooks.ca
Publishers Group UK, 8 The Arena, Mollison Ave, Enfield, Middlesex EN3 7NJ, United Kingdom *Tel:* (020) 8804 0400 *Fax:* (020) 8804 0044 *E-mail:* info@pguk.co.uk

Paramount Market Publishing Inc
950 Danby Rd, Suite 136, Ithaca, NY 14850
Tel: 607-275-8100 *Toll Free Tel:* 888-787-8100 *Fax:* 607-275-8101
E-mail: editors@paramountbooks.com
Web Site: www.paramountbooks.com
Founded: 1999
Marketing, market research, market segments & brand management.
ISBN Prefix(es): 978-0-9571439; 978-0-9725290; 978-0-9766973; 978-0-9786602; 978-0-9801745; 978-0-9819869; 978-0-9830436
Number of titles published annually: 6 Print; 6 E-Book
Total Titles: 85 Print; 60 E-Book
Imprints: PMP

Parenting Press Inc
13751 Lake City Way NE, Suite 110, Seattle, WA 98125
Mailing Address: PO Box 75267, Seattle, WA 98175-0267
Tel: 206-364-2900 *Toll Free Tel:* 800-99-BOOKS (992-6657) *Fax:* 206-364-0702
E-mail: office@parentingpress.com; marketing@parentingpress.com
Web Site: www.parentingpress.com
Key Personnel
Pres: Elizabeth Crary
Opers Mgr: Homer Henderson *Tel:* 206-364-2900 ext 101
Acqs: Carolyn Threadgill *Tel:* 206-364-2900 ext 107 *E-mail:* cthreadgill@parentingpress.com
Mktg: Linda Carlson *Tel:* 206-364-2900 ext 105
Founded: 1979
Parenting, social skill building, personal safety for children, discipline, feelings, temperament, development, boundaries, problem solving, social relations.
ISBN Prefix(es): 978-0-943990; 978-0-9602862 (co-published with Raefield-Roberts); 978-1-884734; 978-1-936903
Number of titles published annually: 6 Print; 26 Online; 2 E-Book
Total Titles: 113 Print; 5 Online; 11 E-Book
Distributor for Raefield-Roberts, Publishers
Distribution Center: IPG, 814 N Franklin St, Chicago, IL 60610 *Tel:* 312-337-0747 *Toll Free Tel:* 800-888-4741 *Fax:* 312-337-5985 *Web Site:* www.ipgbook.com
Membership(s): Book Publishers of the Northwest; The Independent Book Publishers Association; Publishers Association of the West

Park Genealogical Books
PO Box 130968, Roseville, MN 55113-0968
Tel: 651-488-4416 *Fax:* 651-488-2653
Web Site: www.parkbooks.com
Key Personnel
Owner: Mary Hawker Bakeman
E-mail: mbakeman@parkbooks.com
Founded: 1974
Minnesota genelogy.
ISBN Prefix(es): 978-0-915709; 978-1-932212
Number of titles published annually: 5 Print
Total Titles: 140 Print

Park Place Publications
591 Lighthouse Ave, Suite 10, Pacific Grove, CA 93950
SAN: 297-5238
Mailing Address: PO Box 722, Pacific Grove, CA 93950-0722
Tel: 831-649-6640
E-mail: publishingbiz@sbcglobal.net
Web Site: www.parkplacepublications.com
Key Personnel
Owner & Publr: Patricia Hamilton
Founded: 1991
Provides book publishing, graphic design & prepress services. Founded on the premise that "Books make a world of difference" (the company slogan).
This publisher has indicated that 90% of their product line is author subsidized.
ISBN Prefix(es): 978-1-935530
Number of titles published annually: 15 Print; 15 Online; 10 E-Book
Total Titles: 75 Print; 15 Online; 10 E-Book
Imprints: Alamos Press (American & Mexican culture & bilingual); At Home on the Road (travel)
Membership(s): Association of Personal Historians; The Association of Publishers for Special Sales; The Independent Book Publishers Association; Small Publishers, Artists & Writers Network

Parlay Press
301 Central Ave, No 311, Hilton Head, SC 29926
Toll Free Fax: 888-301-3116
E-mail: mail@parlaypress.com
Web Site: www.parlaypress.com
Key Personnel
Publr: Peyton Parker
Founded: 1988
Publishes textbooks on language & writing.
ISBN Prefix(es): 978-0-9644636; 978-0-9767180
Number of titles published annually: 4 Print

§Parmenides Publishing
3753 Howard Hughes Pkwy, Suite 200, Las Vegas, NV 89169
SAN: 254-4342
Tel: 702-892-3934 *Fax:* 702-892-3939
E-mail: info@parmenides.com
Web Site: www.parmenides.com
Key Personnel
Publr & CEO: Sara Hermann *E-mail:* sherman@parmenides.com
VP & Sales Dir: Gale Carr *E-mail:* gcarr@parmenides.com
Founded: 2000
Independent publishing house. Specialize in literature on philosophy, especially ancient Greek philosophy for the academic & trade markets.
ISBN Prefix(es): 978-1-930972
Number of titles published annually: 10 Print; 10 Online; 4 Audio
Total Titles: 28 Print; 15 Online; 4 Audio
Divisions: ParmenidesAudio™; ParmenidesFiction™
Foreign Rep(s): APAC (Tom Cassidy) (Brunei, Cambodia, China, Hong Kong, Indonesia, Malaysia, Myanmar, Singapore, Taiwan, Thailand, Vietnam)
Orders to: The University of Chicago Press Distribution Center, 1427 E 60 St, Chicago, IL 60637 *Toll Free Tel:* 800-621-2736 *Fax:* 773-702-9756 *E-mail:* orders@press.uchicago.edu
Returns: The University of Chicago Press Distribution Center, 11030 S Langley, Chicago, IL 60628 *Tel:* 773-702-7700 *Fax:* 773-702-9756 *Toll Free Fax:* 800-621-8476 *E-mail:* orders@press.uchicago.edu
Shipping Address: The University of Chicago Press Distribution Center, 11030 S Langley, Chicago, IL 60628 *Tel:* 773-702-7700 *Fax:* 773-702-9756 *Toll Free Fax:* 800-621-8476 *E-mail:* orders@press.uchicago.edu
Warehouse: The University of Chicago Press Distribution Center, 11030 S Langley, Chicago, IL 60628 *Tel:* 773-702-7700 *Fax:* 773-702-9756 *Toll Free Fax:* 800-621-8476 *E-mail:* orders@press.uchicago.edu
Distribution Center: The University of Chicago Press Distribution Center, 11030 S Langley, Chicago, IL 60628 *Tel:* 773-702-7700 *Toll Free Tel:* 800-621-8476 (orders) *Fax:* 773-702-9756 *Toll Free Fax:* 800-621-8476 *E-mail:* orders@press.uchicago.edu
Membership(s): AAP

§Pastoral Press
Imprint of OCP Publications Inc
5536 NE Hassalo, Portland, OR 97213-3638
Tel: 503-281-1191 *Toll Free Tel:* 800-548-8749 *Fax:* 503-282-3486 *Toll Free Fax:* 800-462-7329
E-mail: liturgy@ocp.org
Web Site: www.ocp.org
Key Personnel
Publr: John Limb
Ed: Bari Columbari
Mktg: Kelsey Markham
Founded: 1985
Association presses, professional books & scholarly books, books on religion & theology.
ISBN Prefix(es): 978-0-915531; 978-0-9602378; 978-0-912405; 978-1-56929
Number of titles published annually: 8 Print
Total Titles: 190 Print
Foreign Rep(s): Decani Music Ltd (UK); Rainbow Book Agencies (Australia)

Path Press Inc
1229 Emerson St, Evanston, IL 60201
SAN: 630-2041
Tel: 847-492-0177
E-mail: pathpressinc@aol.com
Key Personnel
Pres: Bennett J Johnson
Founded: 1962
Books for African-American & Third World people.
ISBN Prefix(es): 978-0-910671
Number of titles published annually: 3 Print
Total Titles: 43 Print
Subsidiaries: African-American Book Distributors Inc

Pathfinder Publishing Inc
120 S Houghton Rd, Suite 138, Tucson, AZ 85748
SAN: 694-2571
Tel: 520-647-0158 *Toll Free Tel:* 800-977-2282 *Fax:* 520-647-0160
Web Site: www.pathfinderpublishing.com
Key Personnel
CEO & Pres: Bill Mosbrook *E-mail:* bill@pathfinderpublishing.com
Treas: Evelyn Mosbrook *E-mail:* evelyn@pathfinderpublishing.com
Founded: 1985
Books & audiotape books. Specialize in music, psychology & military.
ISBN Prefix(es): 978-0-934793
Number of titles published annually: 3 Print; 1 Audio
Total Titles: 50 Print; 3 Audio
Membership(s): The Independent Book Publishers Association

Patria Press Inc
PO Box 752, Carmel, IN 46082
Tel: 317-577-1321 *Fax:* 413-215-8030
E-mail: moreinfo@patriapress.com
Web Site: www.patriapress.com; www.facebook.com/YoungPatriotsBooks; twitter.com/#!/kidsbios
Key Personnel
Pres & Publr: Florrie Binford Kichler
Founded: 1999
Publisher of the Young Patriots Series of children's historical fiction.
ISBN Prefix(es): 978-1-882859
Number of titles published annually: 2 Print; 2 E-Book
Total Titles: 14 Print; 14 E-Book
Imprints: Young Patriots Series
Sales Office(s): Independent Publishers Group (IPG), 814 N Franklin St, Chicago, IL 60610
Billing Address: Independent Publishers Group (IPG), 814 N Franklin St, Chicago, IL 60610
Orders to: Independent Publishers Group (IPG), 814 N Franklin St, Chicago, IL 60610 *Tel:* 312-337-0747 *Toll Free Tel:* 800-888-4741 *Fax:* 312-337-5985 *E-mail:* orders@ipgbook.com *Web Site:* www.ipgbook.com
Returns: Independent Publishers Group (IPG), 814 N Franklin St, Chicago, IL 60610
Shipping Address: Independent Publishers Group (IPG), 814 N Franklin St, Chicago, IL 60610 *Tel:* 312-337-0747 *Toll Free Tel:* 800-888-4741 *Fax:* 312-337-5985 *E-mail:* orders@ipgbook.com *Web Site:* www.ipgbook.com
Warehouse: Independent Publishers Group (IPG), 814 N Franklin St, Chicago, IL 60610
Membership(s): BISG; The Children's Book Council; The Independent Book Publishers Association; Women's National Book Association

Paul Dry Books
1616 Walnut St, Suite 808, Philadelphia, PA 19103
Tel: 215-231-9939 *Fax:* 215-231-9942
E-mail: editor@pauldrybooks.com
Web Site: www.pauldrybooks.com
Key Personnel
Owner & Publr: Paul Dry *E-mail:* pdry@pauldrybooks.com
Mng Ed: John Corenswet *E-mail:* jcorenswet@pauldrybooks.com
Assoc Ed: William Schofield
Literary publications: fiction, history & essays.
ISBN Prefix(es): 978-0-9664913; 978-0-9679675; 978-1-58988
Number of titles published annually: 6 Print
Total Titles: 6 Print

Paula Wiseman Books, see Simon & Schuster Children's Publishing

Pauline Books & Media
Division of Daughters of St Paul
50 St Paul's Ave, Boston, MA 02130
SAN: 203-8900
Tel: 617-522-8911 *Toll Free Tel:* 800-876-4463 (orders); 800-836-9723 (cust serv) *Fax:* 617-541-9805
E-mail: editorial@paulinemedia.com (ms submissions); orderentry@pauline.org (cust serv)
Web Site: www.pauline.org
Key Personnel
Publr & Edit Dir: Sr Mary Mark Wickenhiser
Promo Mgr: Sr Mary Martha Moss
Adult Acqs Ed: Sr Sean Marie David Mayer; Sr Christina Wegendt
Children's & Teen Ed: Sr Marlyn Evangelina Monge; Jaymie Stuart Wolfe
Book Center Acqs: Anthony Ruggiero
Edit Asst, Acqs: Brittany Schlorff
Digital: Sr Kathryn James Hermes
Intl Rts & Perms: Brad McCracken
Founded: 1932
Spirituality, prayer books, teachers' resources for religious education, liturgical books, church documents, adult religious instruction, saints lives, faith & culture, music & music CDs.
ISBN Prefix(es): 978-0-8198
Number of titles published annually: 60 Print; 50 E-Book; 1 Audio
Total Titles: 600 Print; 72 Audio
Imprints: Catholic Approach Series; Encounter the Saints Series (children); Faith & Culture; Pauline Comics & Graphic Novels (children & teens); Pauline Teen; The Saints Series; Theology of the Body Series
Membership(s): Association of Catholic Publishers Inc; Catholic Press Association; Society of Children's Book Writers & Illustrators

§Paulist Press
997 Macarthur Blvd, Mahwah, NJ 07430-9990
SAN: 202-5159
Tel: 201-825-7300 *Toll Free Tel:* 800-218-1903 *Fax:* 201-825-8345 *Toll Free Fax:* 800-836-3161
E-mail: info@paulistpress.com
Web Site: www.paulistpress.com
Key Personnel
Pres & Publr: Mark-David Janus, CSP *E-mail:* mdjanus@paulistpress.com
VP & Gen Mgr: Kevin Maguire
Edit Dir: Trace Murphy *E-mail:* tmurphy@paulistpress.com
Dir, Sales: Bob Byrns *Tel:* 201-825-7300 ext 231 *E-mail:* bbyrns@paulistpress.com
Dir, Mktg: Gloria A Capik *E-mail:* gcapik@paulistpress.com
Prodn Dir: Kimberly Bernard *E-mail:* kbernard@paulistpress.com
Mng Ed: Donna Crilly *E-mail:* dcrilly@paulistpress.com
Academic Ed: Nancy de Flon
Ed-at-Large: Enrique Aguilar; Christopher Bellitto; Christopher Frechette
Publicity: Mary Ann Carey *E-mail:* mcarey@paulistpress.com
Rts & Intl Rts: Angela Ekroth *E-mail:* aekroth@paulistpress.com
Founded: 1866
Resources with emphasis on biblical studies, Christian, Catholic & ecumenical formation & education, ethics & social issues, pastoral ministry, personal growth, spirituality, philosophy, theology.
ISBN Prefix(es): 978-0-8091
Number of titles published annually: 90 Print
Total Titles: 1,600 Print
Imprints: HiddenSpring; E T Nedder Publishing; The Newman Press; Stimulus Books
Foreign Rep(s): Columba Book Service (Europe); Katong Catholic Book Centre Pte Ltd (Singapore); KCBS Inc (Korea); Novalis (Canada); Pleroma Christian Supplies (New Zealand); PRECA Bookshop (Malta); Rainbow Book Agencies/Word of Life (Australia); St Paul's India (India); St Paul's Liberia (Liberia)
Warehouse: 39 Ramapo Valley Rd, Mahwah, NJ 07430

Peabody Museum Press
Unit of Peabody Museum of Archaeology & Ethnology, Harvard University
11 Divinity Ave, Cambridge, MA 02138
Tel: 617-495-4255 *Fax:* 617-495-7535
E-mail: peapub@fas.harvard.edu
Web Site: www.peabody.harvard.edu/publications
Key Personnel
Exec Ed: Joan O'Donnell *E-mail:* jkodonn@fas.harvard.edu
Proj Mgr: Donna Dickerson *E-mail:* ddickers@fas.harvard.edu
Founded: 1888
ISBN Prefix(es): 978-0-87365
Number of titles published annually: 9 Print
Total Titles: 140 Print
Distribution Center: Harvard University Press

Peace Hill Press
18021 The Glebe Lane, Charles City, VA 23030
Tel: 804-829-5043 *Toll Free Tel:* 877-322-3445 (orders) *Fax:* 804-829-5704
E-mail: info@peacehillpress.com
Web Site: www.peacehillpress.com
Key Personnel
CEO: Jay Wise
Ed-in-Chief: Susan Wise Bauer
Exec Administrator: Kim Norton
Founded: 2001
Publish educational books for home school families & schools & books for the well-trained mind.
ISBN Prefix(es): 978-0-9714129; 978-1-933339
Number of titles published annually: 5 Print
Total Titles: 12 Print
Distributed by W W Norton & Co
Foreign Rights: Richard Henshaw (Central America, South America)

Peachpit Press
Division of Pearson Education
1249 Eighth St, Berkeley, CA 94710
Tel: 510-524-2178 *Toll Free Tel:* 800-283-9444 *Fax:* 510-524-2221
E-mail: info@peachpit.com
Web Site: www.peachpit.com
Key Personnel
VP & Publr: Nancy Ruenzel *Tel:* 510-524-2178 ext 124 *Fax:* 510-524-2385 *E-mail:* nancy.ruenzel@peachpit.com
Assoc Publr: Hannah Onstad-Latham
Exec Ed: Clifford Colby
Ed-in-Chief: Nancy Davis
Dir, Mktg: Scott Cowlin *E-mail:* scott.cowlin@peachpit.com
Busn Mgr: Keasley Jones
Founded: 1986
ISBN Prefix(es): 978-0-201; 978-1-56609; 978-0-938151
Number of titles published annually: 180 Print
Total Titles: 400 Print

Peachtree Publishers
1700 Chattahoochee Ave, Atlanta, GA 30318-2112
SAN: 212-1999
Tel: 404-876-8761 *Toll Free Tel:* 800-241-0113 *Fax:* 404-875-2578 *Toll Free Fax:* 800-875-8909
E-mail: hello@peachtree-online.com
Web Site: www.peachtree-online.com
Key Personnel
Subs Rts: Kathy Landwehr
Sales: Laura Palermo *Tel:* 404-876-8761 ext 114
Founded: 1977
Children's fiction & nonfiction, self-help & health/parenting & regional guides.
ISBN Prefix(es): 978-0-931948; 978-0-934601; 978-1-56145
Number of titles published annually: 40 Print
Total Titles: 300 Print
Imprints: Freestone; Peachtree Jr
Foreign Rep(s): Fitzhenry & Whiteside Publishers (Canada); Jacqueline Miller Agency (France)
Foreign Rights: Kathy Landwehr (Worldwide)

Peanut Butter & Jelly Press LLC
PO Box 590239, Newton, MA 02459-0002
SAN: 299-7444
Tel: 617-630-0945 *Fax:* 617-630-0945 (call first)
E-mail: info@pbjpress.com
Web Site: www.publishinggame.com; www.pbjpress.com
Key Personnel
Owner: Elizabeth Harris
Off Mgr: Alyza Harris *E-mail:* alyza@publishinggame.com
Founded: 1998
General Trade Books - hardcover & softcover, including our best selling *The Infertility Diet: Get Pregnant and Prevent Miscarriage* now in it's 12th printing; BookSense selection: *Terrorism & Kids: Comforting Your Child* & *The Publishing Game* 3 in the series.
ISBN Prefix(es): 978-1-893290
Number of titles published annually: 5 Print
Total Titles: 11 Print
Membership(s): ABA; The Association of Publishers for Special Sales; Great Lakes Independent Booksellers Association; The Independent Book Publishers Association; International Association of Writers; NEBA; Pacific Northwest Booksellers Association; Southern Independent Booksellers Alliance

Pearson Arts & Sciences
Division of Pearson Education
330 Hudson St, 9th fl, New York, NY 10013-1048
Tel: 917-981-2200
Web Site: www.pearsonhighered.com
Key Personnel
Pres, ECP: Roth Wilkofsky *Tel:* 917-981-2300 *Fax:* 917-981-2210 *E-mail:* roth.wilkofsky@pearson.com
Number of titles published annually: 200 Print

Pearson Benjamin Cummings
Imprint of Pearson Higher Education
1301 Sansome St, San Francisco, CA 94111-1122
Tel: 415-402-2500 *Toll Free Tel:* 800-922-0579 (orders) *Fax:* 415-402-2590
E-mail: question@aol.com
Web Site: www.pearsonhighered.com

Key Personnel
Pres: Linda Baron Davis
VP & Dir, Mktg: Stacy Treco
Other subjects include: anatomy, physiology & microbiology.
ISBN Prefix(es): 978-0-201; 978-0-582; 978-0-8053; 978-0-321; 978-0-8465
Orders to: 75 Arlington St, Suite 300, Boston, MA 02116-3988 *Tel:* 617-848-7500

Pearson Business Publishing
Unit of Pearson Higher Education Division
225 River St, Hoboken, NJ 07030-4772
Tel: 201-236-7000
Web Site: www.pearsonhighered.com
Key Personnel
Pres: Jerome Grant

Pearson Career, Health, Education & Technology
Division of Pearson Education
225 River St, Hoboken, NJ 07030-4772
Tel: 201-236-7000 *Fax:* 201-236-7755

Pearson Education
225 River St, Hoboken, NJ 07030-4772
Tel: 201-236-7000 *Fax:* 201-236-6549
E-mail: communications@pearsoned.com
Web Site: www.pearsoned.com
ISBN Prefix(es): 978-0-582
See separate listing for:
Pearson Arts & Sciences
Pearson Career, Health, Education & Technology
Pearson ELT
Pearson Higher Education
Pearson School

Pearson Education/ELT, see Pearson ELT

§Pearson Education International Group
225 River St, Hoboken, NJ 07030-4772
Tel: 201-236-7000
Number of titles published annually: 6 Print

Pearson ELT
Formerly Pearson Education/ELT
Division of Pearson Education
10 Bank St, 9th fl, White Plains, NY 10606-1951
Tel: 914-287-8000
Web Site: www.pearsonelt.com
Key Personnel
VP & Dir, Publg-Coll ELT: Pietro Alongi
VP & Dir, Publg-School ELT: Ed Lamprich
VP, Design & Prodn: Rhea Banker
VP, Mktg: Kate McLoughlin
Mktg Dir: Oliva Fernandez
Prodn Ed: Christopher Leonowicz
Number of titles published annually: 100 Print
Foreign Office(s): Harlow Office, Edinburgh Gate, Harlow, Essex CM20 2JE, United Kingdom *Tel:* (01279) 623623 *Fax:* (01279) 431059

Pearson Higher Education
Division of Pearson Education
225 River St, Hoboken, NJ 07030-4772
Tel: 201-236-7000 *Fax:* 201-236-3381
Web Site: www.pearsonhighered.com
Key Personnel
CEO: Tim Bozik
COO: George Werner
SVP, Systems & Technol: Jack Reilly
SVP & Dir, Publg Servs: Logan Campbell
ISBN Prefix(es): 978-0-13; 978-0-205; 978-0-8428; 978-0-87618; 978-0-87619; 978-0-87628; 978-0-89303
Imprints: Pearson Addison Wesley; Pearson Allyn & Bacon; Pearson Benjamin Cummings; Pearson Longman; Pearson Prentice Hall
See separate listing for:
Allyn & Bacon
Pearson Benjamin Cummings
Pearson Business Publishing
Pearson Humanities & Social Sciences
Pearson Learning Solutions

Pearson Humanities & Social Sciences
Unit of Pearson Higher Education Division
225 River St, Hoboken, NJ 07030-4772
Tel: 201-236-7000 *Fax:* 201-236-3400
Key Personnel
Pres: Yolanda de Rooy
VP & Busn Mgr: Robert Santini
Asst VP & Dir, Prodn: Barbara Kittle
EIC & Edit Dir, Humanities & Eng: Charlyce Jones Owen
EIC, Soc Sci & Psychology: Nancy Roberts
EIC, Devt: Susanna Lesan
EIC, Modern Langs: Rosemary Bradley
Total Titles: 250 Print

Pearson Learning Solutions
Unit of Pearson Higher Education
501 Boyleston St, Suite 900, Boston, MA 02116
SAN: 214-0225
Tel: 617-848-6300 *Toll Free Tel:* 800-428-4466 (orders) *Fax:* 617-848-6358
E-mail: pcp@pearsoncustom.com
Web Site: www.pearsoned.com
Key Personnel
CEO: Donald Kilburn *Tel:* 617-671-3300
ISBN Prefix(es): 978-0-8087; 978-0-536
Branch Office(s)
Pearson Custom Publishing, 7110 Ohms Lane, Edina, MN 55439-2143 *Tel:* 952-831-1881 *Toll Free Tel:* 800-922-2579 *Fax:* 952-831-3167

Pearson School
Unit of Pearson Education
225 River St, Hoboken, NJ 07030-4772
Tel: 201-236-7000
Web Site: www.pearsonschool.com
Key Personnel
EVP, Sales: Rick Culp
EVP, Prod Devt & Solutions: Jeffrey Ikler
ISBN Prefix(es): 978-0-13; 978-0-205; 978-0-556; 978-0-8224

Pearson Scott Foresman
1900 E Lake Ave, Glenview, IL 60025
Tel: 847-729-3000 *Toll Free Tel:* 800-535-4391 (Midwest) *Fax:* 847-729-8910
Web Site: www.pearsonschool.com
Key Personnel
COO & EVP: George McGuirk
Pres, Digital: Bob Roliardi
EVP, Lit, Math, Sci & Humanities: Emily Swenson
VP, HR: Stuart G Cohn *E-mail:* stuart.cohn@pearsoned.com
Total Titles: 100 Print

T H Peek Publisher
Division of Clearweave Corp
PO Box 7406, Ann Arbor, MI 48107
SAN: 693-9708
Tel: 734-222-8205 *Fax:* 734-661-0136
E-mail: info@thpeekpublisher.com
Web Site: www.thpeekpublisher.com
Key Personnel
Owner: Colin D O'Brien
Founded: 1966
Ms acquisition, editorial, art, design, distribution, advertising & promotion.
ISBN Prefix(es): 978-0-917962; 978-1-935770
Number of titles published annually: 3 Print
Total Titles: 6 Print
Imprints: Alice Greene & Co

Peel Productions Inc
9415 NE Woodridge St, Vancouver, WA 98664
Tel: 360-326-8003 *Toll Free Tel:* 800-345-6665
Web Site: www.peelbooks.com
Key Personnel
Publr: Douglas C DuBosque
Ed: Susan Joyce DuBosque
Founded: 1985
ISBN Prefix(es): 978-0-939217
Number of titles published annually: 6 Print
Total Titles: 45 Print
Membership(s): The Children's Book Council

Pelican Publishing Co
1000 Burmaster St, Gretna, LA 70053-2246
SAN: 212-0623
Tel: 504-368-1175 *Toll Free Tel:* 800-843-1724 *Fax:* 504-368-1195
E-mail: sales@pelicanpub.com (sales); office@pelicanpub.com (permission); promo@pelicanpub.com (publicity)
Web Site: www.pelicanpub.com
Key Personnel
Pres & Publr: Kathleen Calhoun Nettleton *Tel:* 504-368-1175 ext 312
Promo Dir: Antoinette de Alteriis
Dir, Sales: Joseph Billingsley
Ed & ISBN Contact: Nina Kooij *E-mail:* editorial@pelicanpub.com
Rts & Perms: Sally Boitnott *Tel:* 504-368-1175 ext 310
Founded: 1926
General, motivational, inspirational, nostalgia, note cards, almanacs, business & children's.
ISBN Prefix(es): 978-0-911116; 978-0-88289; 978-1-56554; 978-1-58980
Number of titles published annually: 70 Print; 1 E-Book; 10 Audio
Total Titles: 2,600 Print; 1 CD-ROM; 1 E-Book; 35 Audio
Imprints: Robert L Crager & Co; Dixie Press; Dove Inspirational Press; Jackson Square Press; Louisiana Book Distributors
Subsidiaries: Pelican International Corp
Distributor for Hope Publishing House; Marmac Publishing Co; SelfHelp Success Books
Foreign Rights: Fitzhenry & Whiteside Publishers (Canada); Roundhouse Group (Europe, Ireland, UK)
Advertising Agency: Bayou Advertising
Membership(s): AAP; The Children's Book Council; Great Lakes Independent Booksellers Association; Jewish Book Publishers Association; Mid-South Booksellers Association; Midwest Independent Booksellers Association; Museum Store Association; Publishers Association of the West; Southern Independent Booksellers Alliance

Pendragon Press
Subsidiary of Camelot Publishing Co Inc
52 White Hill Lane, Hillsdale, NY 12529-5839
Mailing Address: PO Box 190, Hillsdale, NY 12529
Tel: 518-325-6100 *Toll Free Tel:* 877-656-6381 (orders) *Fax:* 518-325-6102
E-mail: editor@pendragonpress.com
Web Site: www.pendragonpress.com
Key Personnel
Mng Ed: Robert J Kessler
Founded: 1972
Reference works on books & musicology including music/aesthetics, biographies, music theory, organ, harpsichord, historic brass, 20th century music, French opera, music & religion.
ISBN Prefix(es): 978-0-918728; 978-0-945193; 978-1-57647
Number of titles published annually: 15 Print
Total Titles: 266 Print
Distributed by LIM Editrice SRL (Italy); G Ricordi (Italy)
Distributor for Croatian Musicological Society
Foreign Rep(s): Eurospan Ltd (Europe)

Penfield Books
215 Brown St, Iowa City, IA 52245

SAN: 221-6671
Tel: 319-337-9998 *Toll Free Tel:* 800-728-9998
Fax: 319-351-6846
E-mail: penfield@penfieldbooks.com
Web Site: www.penfieldbooks.com
Key Personnel
Publr: Joan Liffring-Zug Bourret
Returns Assoc: John Johnson *Tel:* 319-337-0570
Founded: 1979 (also known as Penfield Press in the past)
Ethnic (Czech, Danish, Dutch, Finnish, French, German, Irish, Italian, Mexican, Norwegian, Polish, Scandinavian, Scottish, Slovak, Swedish & Ukrainian); cookbooks; crafts & folk art; history; ethnic cultural cookbooks, cookbooks of the states. No unsol mss.
ISBN Prefix(es): 978-0-941016; 978-1-932043; 978-1-57216
Number of titles published annually: 6 Print; 6 CD-ROM; 15 E-Book
Total Titles: 168 Print; 268 Online; 70 E-Book
Distribution Center: Amazon.ca (CN)
Amazon.com
Bergquist
Book Marketing Plus
Createspace.com
Kindle
Partners

Penguin Books
Imprint of Penguin Group (USA) LLC
375 Hudson St, New York, NY 10014
SAN: 282-5074
Tel: 212-366-2000
E-mail: online@penguinputnam.com
Web Site: www.penguinputnam.com; www.penguinclassics.com; us.penguingroup.com
Key Personnel
Pres & Publr, Penguin Books, Publr, Plume & VP, Penguin Group (USA) LLC: Kathryn Court
VP, Ed-in-Chief, Assoc Publr: Patrick Nolan
VP & Exec Creative Dir: Paul Buckley
VP & Dir, Mktg, Penguin/Exec Dir, Academic Sales & Mktg: John Fagan
Assoc Publr & Edit Dir, Penguin Classics: Elda Rotor
Exec Mng Ed: Matt Giarratano
Exec Ed: Meg Leder
Exec Ed, Penguin Classics & Sr Ed, Penguin Books: John Siciliano
Sr Ed: Paul Slovak
Ed: Sarah Stein
Dir, Ad & Promo: Dennis Swaim
Founded: 1935
ISBN Prefix(es): 978-0-14
Number of titles published annually: 244 Print
Total Titles: 4,425 Print
Imprints: Penguin; Penguin Classics; Penguin Compass; Penguin 20th Century Classics
Distributor for Pearson Technology Group Canada
Advertising Agency: Spier NY

Penguin Group (USA) LLC, a Penguin Random House company
375 Hudson St, New York, NY 10014
SAN: 282-5074
Tel: 212-366-2000 *Toll Free Tel:* 800-847-5515 (inside sales); 800-631-8571 (cust serv)
Fax: 212-366-2666; 607-775-4829 (inside sales)
E-mail: online@us.penguingroup.com
Web Site: www.penguin.com; us.penguingroup.com
Key Personnel
Pres, Penguin Books for Young Readers: Don Weisberg
Pres, Putnam & Dutton: Ivan Held
Pres, Mass Market Pbks: Leslie Gelbman
Pres & Publr, Blue Rider: David Rosenthal
Pres & Publr, Penguin & Publr, Plume: Kathryn Court
Pres & Publr, Penguin Press: Ann Godoff
Pres & Publr, Portfolio & Sentinel Books: Adrian Zackheim
Pres & Publr, Viking: Brian Tart
SVP & Corp Dir, Busn Aff: John Schline
SVP & Dir, Sales for Penguin Young Readers Group: Felicia Frazier
SVP & Dir, Subs Rts: Leigh Butler
SVP, Dist: James C Clark
VP, Secy & Gen Coun: Karen Mayer
VP & Assoc Publr, Paperbacks (Putnam/Dutton): Benjamin Lee
VP & Corp Dir, HR: Carol Peterson
VP & Dir, Ad & Promos: Nancy Sheppard
VP & Dir, Bldg Admin: Heidi Kagan
VP & Dir, Opers: Yvette Dano
VP & Dir of Sales, Paperback & Berkley/NAL: Lauren Monaco
VP & Print Prodn Dir: Vincenzo Ruggiero
VP, HR: Paige McInerney
VP, Order Fulfillment: Linda Bay
Edit Dir, Plume: Philip Budnick
Dir, Mfg Procurement: Mike Gallagher
Dir, Intellectual Property Group: Peter Harris
Dir, Publicity & Assoc Dir, Mktg - Portfolio, Sentinel & Current: Tara Gilbride
Media Rel Mgr: Erica Glass
Ed-in-Chief, Avery: Caroline Sutton
Ed-in-Chief, Viking: Andrea Schulz
Exec Ed, Portfolio, Sentinel & Current: Eric Nelson
Sr Ed, Portfolio, Sentinel & Current: Stephanie Frerich
Ed, Avery: Brooke Carey
Ed, Viking: Melanie Tortoroli
Assoc Ed, Avery: Gigi Campo
Assoc Ed, Dutton: Stephanie Kelly
Asst Ed, Penguin Classics: Sam Raim
Asst Ed, Putnam: Sofie Brooks
Publicity Mgr: Meredith Burks
Founded: 1996
Publisher of consumer books in both hardcover & paperback for adults & children. Also produces maps, calendars, audio books & mass merchandise products.
Adult: hardcover, trade paperbacks & mass market paperbacks (originals & reprints)
Children: hardcover picture books, paperback picture books, board & novelty books
Young Adult: hardcover & trade paperback
Mass merchandise products.
ISBN Prefix(es): 978-0-201; 978-0-89529; 978-0-425; 978-0-441; 978-0-515; 978-1-57297; 978-0-14; 978-0-8037; 978-0-525; 978-0-452; 978-0-917657; 978-1-55611; 978-0-7232; 978-0-399; 978-0-698; 978-0-448; 978-1-58184; 978-0-89586; 978-0-912656; 978-1-55788; 978-0-87477; 978-0-451; 978-0-453; 978-0-670; 978-0-7860; 978-0-8431; 978-1-57395; 978-1-55773; 978-1-57322; 978-1-58333
Imprints: Ace (paperback); Ace/Putnam (hardcover); Alpha Books; Avery; Berkley Books (Paperback); Blue Rider (hardcover); Current; DAW (hardcover & paperback); Dial Books for Young Readers (children's); Pam Dorman Books; Dutton (hardcover); Dutton Children's Books (children's); Grosset & Dunlap (children's); Grosset/Putnam (hardcover); HPBooks (paperback); InterMix; Jove (paperback); Minedition; Onyx (paperback); PaperStar (children's); Penguin (paperback); Penguin Classics (paperback); The Penguin Press; Perigee (paperback); Philomel Books (children's); Plume (paperback); Portfolio; Price Stern Sloan Inc (hardcover, paperback & children's); Puffin (children's); Putnam (hardcover); Razorbill; Riverhead Books (hardcover & paperback); ROC (paperback); Sentinel; Signet (paperback); Signet Classics (paperback); Studio; Jeremy P Tarcher (hardcover & paperback); Topaz (paperback); Viking (hardcover); Viking Children's Books (children's); Viking Compass (hardcover); Frederick Warne (children's); Wee Sing (children's)
Subsidiaries: Frederick Warne; Grosset & Dunlap
Distributor for Arkangel; Bibli O'Phile; Consumer Guide/PIL; DAW Books Inc; Dream Works; Granta; HighBridge Audio; Kensington Publishing Corp; The Library of America; The Monacelli Press
Foreign Rights: Penguin (Australia, Canada, India, New Zealand, South Africa, UK); Penguin Putnam International Sales
Advertising Agency: Mesa Group; Spier NY
Distribution Center: One Grosset Dr, Kirkwood, NY 13795 (hardcover, juvenile & audio imprints) *Tel:* 607-775-1740 *Fax:* 607-775-5586
One Commerce Rd, Pittston Township, PA 18640 (mass market & trade paperback imprints) *Tel:* 570-655-5965 *Fax:* 570-655-3907
Membership(s): AAP
See separate listing for:
Alpha Books
Avery
Berkley Books
Berkley Publishing Group
Blue Rider Press
BradyGames
Celebra
DAW Books Inc
Dial Books for Young Readers
DK Publishing
Dutton
Dutton Children's Books
Grosset & Dunlap
HPBooks
NAL
Penguin Books
The Penguin Press
Penguin Young Readers Group
Perigee Books
Philomel
Plume
Portfolio
Prentice Hall Press
Price Stern Sloan
Puffin Books
Putnam Berkley Audio
The Putnam Publishing Group
GP Putnam's Sons (Hardcover)
Razorbill
Riverhead Books (Hardcover)
Riverhead Books (Trade Paperback)
Jeremy P Tarcher
Viking
Viking Children's Books
Viking Studio
Frederick Warne

Penguin Group (USA) LLC Sales
375 Hudson St, New York, NY 10014
SAN: 282-5074
Tel: 212-366-2000
E-mail: online@penguinputnam.com
Web Site: us.penguingroup.com
Key Personnel
SVP & Dir, Sales for Penguin Young Readers Group: Felicia Frazier
VP & Dir, Natl Accts, Adult Div: John Lawton
VP & Dir, Adult Hardcover, Field Sales: Katya Shannon
VP & Dir, Field Sales, Pbk: Patricia Weyenberg
VP, Dir, Field Sales & Mass Mkt Sales/Dir, Sales Busn Devt: Jackie Engel Steinberg
VP, Dir, Sales, Mass Mkt Mdse/Wholesale: Mary McGrath
VP, Intl Sales, Latin America, Caribbean & Mexico: Carlos Azula
VP & Dir, Premium Sales: Lisa Vitelli
VP, Dir, Spec Mkts: Jennifer Schwabinger
VP & Dir, Custom & Proprietary Sales: Sandra Dear
VP, Sr Dir, Academic Mktg & Sales: Alan Walker
Dir, Trade Pbk Sales: Hank Cochrane
Dir, Dist Client Sales: Kristen Feehan
Dir, Spec Mkts: Laura Koch
Dir, Digital Busn: Caroline Riordan
Dir, Online Sales & Mktg: Kent Anderson

Dir, Digital Sales, Children's Div: Stephanie Sabol
Natl Accts Mgr, Adult Div: Fred Huber; Paul Deykerhoff; Glenn Timony; Mark McDiarmid; Christine Mosley
Natl Accts Mgr, Children's Div: Albert Winebarger; Alexis Lunsford
Natl Accts Mgr, Mass Mdse, Children's Div: Andrea Mai
Natl Accts Mgr, Pbk: Carla Clifford; Sharon Gamboa
Educ Sales Mgr: Mary Raymond
Natl Accts Mgr & Publg Coord, Religious Mkt: William Bauers
Natl Accts Wholesale Mgr: Christina Stout
Natl Accts Mgr: Vance Lee, Jr
Natl Accts Mgr, Online Sales & Mktg: Kevin Che
Natl Accts Mgr, Apple: Lisa Pannek
Sales Rep, New England: Megan Sullivan

The Penguin Press
Imprint of Penguin Group (USA) LLC
375 Hudson St, New York, NY 10014
Key Personnel
Pres & Ed-in-Chief: Ann Godoff
VP & Publr: Scott Moyers
VP & Exec Dir, Copyediting: Tory Klose
VP, Art Dir: Darren Haggar
Publicity Dir: Sarah Hutson
Mktg Mgr: Caitlin O'Shaughnessy
Exec Mng Ed: Tricia Conley
Exec Ed: Ed Park
Sr Ed: Virginia Smith
Ed: Emily Cunningham; Lindsay Whalen
Assoc Ed: Will Heyward
Founded: 2003
Publishers of literary fiction & select nonfiction.
ISBN Prefix(es): 978-1-59420
Number of titles published annually: 38 Print
Total Titles: 127 Print

Penguin Random House Audio
Subsidiary of Penguin Random House
1745 Broadway, New York, NY 10019
E-mail: audio@randomhouse.com
Web Site: www.randomhouse.com/audio
Key Personnel
SVP & Publr: Amanda D'Acierno
VP, Opers: Sue Daulton
VP, Content Prodn: Dan Zitt
Dir, Mktg: Heather Dalton
Random House Inc & its publishing entities are not accepting unsol submissions, proposals, mss, or submission queries via e-mail at this time.
ISBN Prefix(es): 978-0-7393; 978-0-375
Number of titles published annually: 500 Print; 300 Audio
Total Titles: 2,000 Print; 894 Audio
Imprints: Living Language
See separate listing for:
Living Language

§Penguin Random House Inc
1745 Broadway, New York, NY 10019
SAN: 202-5507
Tel: 212-782-9000 *Toll Free Tel:* 800-726-0600
Web Site: www.randomhouse.com
Key Personnel
Chmn: John Makinson
CEO: Markus Dohle
COO & Pres, Sales, Opers & Digital: Madeline McIntosh
Chief HR Offr: Frank Steinert
Chmn, Knopf: Sonny Mehta
Pres & Publr, Crown Publishing Group: Maya Mavjee
Pres & Publr, Random House Children's Books: Barbara Marcus
Pres & Publr, Random House Publishing Group: Gina Centrello
Pres, Knopf Publishing Group: Tony Chirico
Pres, RH Films & VP, Ed-at-Large: Peter Gethers
EVP & Gen Coun: Katherine Trager
EVP, Dir, Publg Devt & Author Platforms: Nina von Moltke
SVP & Assoc Gen Coun: Matthew Martin; Anke Steinecke
SVP, Publr Digital Content: Scott Shannon
VP, Corp Projs: Brendan Cahill
VP, Sales Devt: Randi Rosenkranz
VP & Dir, Academic Mktg & Lib Sales: Skip Dye
VP & Dir, Intl Mktg & British Commonwealth Sales: Christopher Dufault
VP & Dir, Retail Sales: Kim Shannon
VP & Publr, Crown Books for Young Readers: Phoebe Yeh
VP, Dir Digital Strategy & Assoc Publr, Digital: Matt Schwartz
VP, Edit Dir (Digital) & Assoc Publr (Romance): Gina Wachtel
Sr Dir, Content Mktg: Kristen Fritz
Exec Ed, Crown Books for Young Readers: Emily Easton
Assoc Ed, Alibi: Randall Klein
Assoc Ed, Hydra: Sarah Peed
Ed-at-Large, Flirt & Loveswept: Sue Grimshaw
Random House Inc & its publishing entities are not accepting unsol submissions, proposals, mss, or submission queries via e-mail at this time.
ISBN Prefix(es): 978-0-307; 978-0-679; 978-0-553; 978-0-676; 978-0-375; 978-0-87665; 978-0-805
Imprints: Alibi (mystery, thriller, suspense); Anchor Bible Commentary; Anchor Bible Dictionary; Anchor Bible Reference Library; Anchor Books; AtRandom.com; Ballantine Books; Ballantine Wellspring; Bantam Books; Bantam Hardcover; Bantam Mass Market; Bantam Skylark; Bantam Starfire; Bantam Trade Paperback; BDD Audio Publishing; Bell Tower; Children's Classics; Children's Media; Clarkson Potter; Crescent Books; Crimeline; Crown Books for Young Readers; Crown Publishers Inc; CTW Publishing; Currency; David Fickling Books; Del Rey; Delacorte Books for Young Readers; Delacorte Press; Dell; Dell Laurel Leaf; Dell Yearling; Delta; Derrydale; The Dial Press; Discovery Books; Disney Books for Young Readers; Domain; Doubleday; Doubleday Bible Commentary; Doubleday Books for Young Readers; Doubleday/Galilee; Doubleday/Image; Dragonfly Books; DTP; Everyman's Library; Fanfare; Fawcett; First Choice Chapter Books; Flirt (new adult); Fodor's; Golden Books; Gramercy Books; Harmony Books; House of Collectibles; Hydra (science fiction & fantasy); Island; Ivy; Alfred A Knopf; Knopf Books for Young Readers; Knopf Guides; Laurel Leaf Books; Library of Contemporary Thought; Living Language; Loveswept (digital only romance); Main Street Books; Modern Library; The Monacelli Press; The New Jerusalem Bible; One World; Pantheon Books; Picture Yearling; The Princeton Review; Random House; Random House Books for Young Readers; Random House Children's Publishing; Random House Digital; Random House Large Print Publishing; Random House Reference & Information Publishing; Schocken Books; Schwartz & Wade Books; Shaye Areheart Books; Sierra Club Adult Books; Skylark; Spectra; Nan A Talese; Testament Books; Three Rivers Press; Times Books; Villard Books; Vintage Books; Wendy Lamb Books; Wings Books; Yearling
Branch Office(s)
WaterBrook Press, 5446 N Academy, Suite 200, Colorado Springs, CO 80918 *Tel:* 719-590-4999 *Fax:* 719-590-8977
Random House of Canada Limited, 2775 Matheson Blvd E, Mississauga, ON L4W 4P7, Canada *Tel:* 905-624-0672 *Toll Free Tel:* 888-523-9292 (orders) *Fax:* 905-624-6217 *Web Site:* www.randomhouse.ca
Bantam Books Canada Inc, One Toronto St, Suite 300, Toronto, ON M5C 2V6, Canada *Tel:* 416-364-4449 *Fax:* 416-364-6863
Doubleday Canada, One Toronto St, Suite 300, Toronto, ON M5C 2V6, Canada *Tel:* 416-364-4449 *Fax:* 416-364-6863
Editorial Office(s): One Toronto St, Suite 300, Toronto, ON M5C 2V6, Canada *Tel:* 416-777-9477 *Fax:* 416-777-9470
Foreign Office(s): Random House Australia Pty Ltd, 16 Dalmore Dr, Scoresby, Victoria 3153, Australia *Tel:* (03) 9753-4511 *Fax:* (03) 9753-3944
Random House Australia Pty Ltd, 20 Alfred St, Milsons Point, Sydney, NSW 2061, Australia *Tel:* (02) 9954-9966 *Fax:* (02) 9954-4562
Random House New Zealand Ltd, 18 Poland Rd, Glenfield, Auckland 0627, New Zealand *Tel:* (09) 444-7197 *Fax:* (09) 444-7524
Random House South Africa Pty Ltd, Endulini, East Wing, 5A Jubilee Rd, Parktown, Sandton 2193, South Africa *Tel:* (011) 484-3538 *Fax:* (011) 484-6180
Tiptree Book Services, Colchester Rd, Frating Green, Colchester, Essex C07 7DW, United Kingdom *Tel:* (01206) 256000 *Fax:* (01206) 255916
Grantham Book Services, Alma Park Industrial Estate, Isaac Newton Way, Grantham, Lincs NG31 9SD, United Kingdom *Tel:* (01476) 541000 *Fax:* (01476) 590223
Doubleday London, 61-63 Uxbridge Rd, Ealing, London W5 5SA, United Kingdom *Tel:* (020) 8231 6717 *Fax:* (020) 8231 6718
Random House UK Ltd, 20 Vauxhall Bridge Rd, London SW1V 2SA, United Kingdom *Tel:* (020) 7840 8400 *Fax:* (020) 7233 8791
Transworld Publishers Ltd, 61-63 Uxbridge Rd, Ealing, London W5 5SA, United Kingdom *Tel:* (020) 8579-2652 *Fax:* (020) 8579-5479
Transworld Publishers Ltd, Sanders Rd, Finedon Rd Industrial Estate, Wellingborough, Northamptonshire NN8 4BU, United Kingdom (dist ctr) *Tel:* (0193) 322-5761 *Fax:* (0193) 327-1235
Distributor for Karen Brown's Guides; Mondadori Spanish Language; National Geographic; Princeton Review; Rizzoli; Rugged Land; Shambhala; Smithsonian Books; Soho Press; Steerforth Press; The Taunton Press; Ten Speed Press; Wizards of the Coast
Shipping Address: Westminster Distribution Center, 400 Hahn Rd, Westminster, MD 21157 *Tel:* 410-848-1900 *Fax:* 410-386-7013
Membership(s): AAP; BISG
See separate listing for:
Books on Tape®
Crown Publishing Group
Fodor's Travel Publications
Random House Children's Books
Random House Large Print
Random House Publishing Group
Random House Reference/Random House Puzzles & Games/House of Collectibles
WaterBrook Multnomah Publishing Group

Penguin Young Readers Group
Division of Penguin Group (USA) LLC
345 Hudson St, New York, NY 10014
Tel: 212-366-2000
E-mail: online@penguinputnam.com
Web Site: www.penguinputnam.com; us.penguingroup.com
Key Personnel
Pres, Penguin Young Readers Div: Don Weisberg
Pres & Publr, Nancy Paulsen Books: Nancy Rose Paulsen
SVP & Dir, Sales for Penguin Young Readers Group: Felicia Frazier
VP, Assoc Publr: Jennifer Haller
VP, Group Sales Dir & Dir, Field Sales & Busn Devt: Jacqueline Engel

VP & Dir, Subs Rts (Penguin Children's): Helen Boomer
VP & Dir, Mfg: Ginny Anson-Turturro
VP & Dir, Contracts & Busn Aff: George Schumacher
VP, Mktg & Mktg Design Servs: Emily Romero
VP, Digital Content Devt: Adam Royce
Exec Dir, Brand Mgmt: Jocelyn Schmidt
Exec Dir, Licensing: Lori Burke
Exec Dir, Trade Mktg: Erin Berger
Dir, Preschool & Young Readers Mktg: Jed Bennett
Dir, Publicity: Shanta Newlin
Dir, School Book Fair Sales: Tanni Tytel
Assoc Digital Publicist: Rachel Lodi
Founded: 1997
Children's hardcover picture books; fiction & nonfiction; trade paperbacks; picture book paperbacks; board & novelty books; calendars.
ISBN Prefix(es): 978-0-201; 978-0-14; 978-0-8037; 978-0-525; 978-0-7232; 978-0-399; 978-0-698; 978-0-448; 978-1-58184; 978-0-670; 978-0-8431
Imprints: Kathy Dawson Books; Dial Books for Young Readers; Dutton Children's Books; Dutton Interactive; Grosset & Dunlap; Paperstar; Nancy Paulsen Books; Philomel; Price Stern Sloan; PSS; Puffin Books; G P Putnam's Sons; Viking Children's Books; Frederick Warne
Distribution Center: Penguin Group (USA) Juvenile Imprints, One Grosset Dr, Kirkwood, NY 13795 *Tel:* 607-775-1740 *Fax:* 607-775-5586
See separate listing for:
GP Putnam's Sons (Children's)

Peninsula Publishing
26666 Birch Hill Way, Los Altos Hills, CA 94022
Tel: 650-948-2511 *Fax:* 650-948-5004
E-mail: sales@peninsulapublishing.com
Web Site: www.peninsulapublishing.com
Key Personnel
Publr: Charles Wiseman *E-mail:* cwiseman@peninsulapublishing.com
Off Mgr: Hannah Wiseman
Founded: 1978
Publish new titles & reprints in the field of acoustics & sound.
ISBN Prefix(es): 978-0-932146
Number of titles published annually: 3 Print
Total Titles: 30 Print
Distributed by Scitech Publishing Inc
Membership(s): ABA; Acoustical Society of America; American Institute of Physics

Pennsylvania Historical & Museum Commission
Subsidiary of The Commonwealth of Pennsylvania
Commonwealth Keystone Bldg, 400 North St, Harrisburg, PA 17120-0053
SAN: 282-1532
Tel: 717-783-2618 *Toll Free Tel:* 800-747-7790 *Fax:* 717-787-8312
E-mail: ra-pabookstore@state.pa.us
Web Site: www.pabookstore.com; www.phmc.state.pa.us
Key Personnel
Chief, Pubns: Jean Cutler *E-mail:* jecutler@state.pa.us
Sales Mgr: Susan Lindeman *E-mail:* slindeman@state.pa.us
Founded: 1913
Books, booklets & references on Pennsylvania prehistory, history, culture & natural history, both scholarly & popular.
ISBN Prefix(es): 978-0-911124; 978-0-89271
Number of titles published annually: 5 Print
Total Titles: 145 Print

§Pennsylvania State Data Center
Subsidiary of Institute of State & Regional Affairs
Penn State Harrisburg, 777 W Harrisburg Pike, Middletown, PA 17057-4898
Tel: 717-948-6336 *Fax:* 717-948-6754
E-mail: pasdc@psu.edu
Web Site: pasdc.hbg.psu.edu
Key Personnel
Dir: Susan Copella *Tel:* 717-948-6427 *E-mail:* sdc3@psu.edu
Founded: 1981
Policy, demographical analytical reports, hard copy & computer discs.
ISBN Prefix(es): 978-0-939667; 978-1-58036
Number of titles published annually: 5 Print; 5 CD-ROM
Total Titles: 130 Print; 130 CD-ROM; 1 E-Book

The Pennsylvania State University Press
Division of The Pennsylvania State University
University Support Bldg 1, Suite C, 820 N University Dr, University Park, PA 16802-1003
SAN: 213-5760
Tel: 814-865-1327 *Toll Free Tel:* 800-326-9180 *Fax:* 814-863-1408 *Toll Free Fax:* 877-778-2665
E-mail: info@psupress.org
Web Site: www.psupress.org
Key Personnel
Dir, Press: Patrick Alexander *Tel:* 814-867-2209 *E-mail:* pha3@psu.edu
Asst Press Dir, Design & Prodn Mgr: Jennifer Norton *Tel:* 814-863-8061 *E-mail:* jsn4@psu.edu
Asst Press Dir, Mktg & Sales Dir: Tony Sanfilippo *Tel:* 814-863-5994 *E-mail:* ajs23@psu.edu
Busn Mgr: Tina Laychur *Tel:* 814-863-5993 *E-mail:* cgw3@psu.edu
Info Systems Mgr: Ed Spicer *E-mail:* res122@psu.edu
Publicity Mgr: Danny Bellet *Tel:* 814-863-0524 *E-mail:* hms7@psu.edu
Mng Ed: Laura Reed-Morrisson *Tel:* 814-865-1606 *E-mail:* lxr168@psu.edu
Exec Ed: Eleanor Goodman *Tel:* 814-867-2212 *E-mail:* ehg11@psu.edu
Prodn Coord, Books & Journals: Patricia Mitchell *Tel:* 814-867-2216 *E-mail:* pam18@psu.edu
Chief Designer: Steven Kress *Tel:* 814-867-2215 *E-mail:* srk5@psu.edu
Founded: 1956
Scholarly books & journals; art & architectural history; literature & literary criticism, philosophy, religion, social sciences, law, history, Latin American studies, regional books on mid-Atlantic area; Special Series: Literature & Philosophy; Penn State Series in the History of the Book; Re-Reading the Canon; Keystone Books (regional); American & European Philosophy; Magic in History; Rural Studies; Refiguring Modernism; Buildings, Landscapes & Societies.
ISBN Prefix(es): 978-0-271
Number of titles published annually: 60 Print
Total Titles: 1,300 Print; 3 CD-ROM; 12 Online; 100 E-Book
Imprints: Keystone Books
Foreign Rep(s): European University Press Group (Africa, Central America, Europe, Middle East, South America, UK); United Publishers Services (China); University of Toronto Press (Canada)
Membership(s): AAP; Association of American University Presses

PennWell Books
Division of PennWell
1421 S Sheridan Rd, Tulsa, OK 74112
Mailing Address: PO Box 21288, Tulsa, OK 74121-1288
Tel: 918-831-9410 *Toll Free Tel:* 800-752-9764 *Fax:* 918-831-9555
E-mail: sales@pennwell.com
Web Site: www.pennwellbooks.com
Key Personnel
CEO & Pres: Bob Biolchini
Dir: Mary McGee *E-mail:* marym@pennwell.com
Prodn Mgr: Sheila Brock
Mktg Coord: Jane Green
Cust Serv: Holly Fournier
Founded: 1973
Publish both technical & nontechnical books. Written by selected industry experts, our books will help you broaden your expertise in your current field, understand other related disciplines & provide quick-glance references as a topic arrives in your daily routine. Our products make excellent classroom, seminar & in-house training texts.
ISBN Prefix(es): 978-0-912212; 978-0-87814; 978-1-59370
Number of titles published annually: 20 Print
Total Titles: 400 Print; 5 Audio
Divisions: Fire Engineering Books & Videos
Foreign Rep(s): Cranbury Intl LLC (Ethan Atkin) (Central America, South America); Ish Dawar (India); Eurospan Group Ltd (Europe, UK); Intercontinental Marketing (Japan, South Korea); Dar Kriedieh (Brazil); STM Publishers Rep (Tony Poh) (Southeast Asia)
See separate listing for:
Fire Engineering Books & Videos

§Pentecostal Publishing House
Subsidiary of United Pentecostal Church International
8855 Dunn Rd, Hazelwood, MO 63042
SAN: 219-3817
Tel: 314-837-7300 *Fax:* 314-336-1803
E-mail: pphordersdept@upci.org (orders)
Web Site: www.pentecostalpublishing.com
Key Personnel
Administrator: Billy Babb
Purch: Terri Miller
Edit: Robin Johnson
Founded: 1945
Trade paperbacks, periodicals, bibliographies; religion (Protestant), Bibles, foreign languages, crafts, self-help.
ISBN Prefix(es): 978-0-912315; 978-0-932581; 978-1-56722; 978-0-7577
Number of titles published annually: 10 Print; 10 CD-ROM
Total Titles: 400 Print; 35 CD-ROM
Imprints: Word Aflame Press
Subsidiaries: Word Aflame Press
Distributed by Anchor Distributors; Christian Network International; Innovative Marketing; Spring Arbor

Penton Media
9800 Metcalf Ave, Overland Park, KS 66212
SAN: 204-3416
Mailing Address: PO Box 12901, Overland Park, KS 66282-2901
Tel: 913-967-1719 *Toll Free Tel:* 800-262-1954 (cust serv) *Fax:* 913-967-1901 *Toll Free Fax:* 800-633-6219
E-mail: bookorders@penton.com
Web Site: www.buypenton.com
Key Personnel
Sales Mgr: Matt Tusken
Publisher of repair manuals for motorcycles, ATV, PWC, boats, outdoor power equipment, snowmobiles & tractors, as well as valuation guides.
ISBN Prefix(es): 978-0-89287; 978-0-87288; 978-0-1599
Number of titles published annually: 25 Print
Total Titles: 532 Print
Imprints: Ac-u-Kwik; Clymer ProSeries; Clymer Publications; EC&M Books; Electrical Wholesaling; The Electronics Source Book; Equipment Watch; I&T Shop Service; Penton Price Digests
Shipping Address: Smart Warehousing, 1869 N Topping Ave, Kansas City, MO 64120

Peoples Education Inc
Subsidiary of Peoples Educational Holdings Inc

299 Market St, Suite 240, Saddle Brook, NJ 07663
Mailing Address: PO Box 513, Saddle Brook, NJ 07663-0513
Tel: 201-712-0090 *Toll Free Tel:* 800-822-1080 *Fax:* 201-712-0045
Web Site: www.peopleseducation.com; www.peoplescollegeprep.com; www.measuringuplive.com
Key Personnel
CEO & Pres: Brian Beckwith
E-mail: brianbeckwith@peoplesed.com
CFO & EVP: Michael DeMarco
E-mail: mdemarco@peoplesed.com
Founded: 1990
Publisher & marketer of print & electronic educational materials for the K-12 school market. We focus our efforts in test preparation, assessment & instruction & college preparation.
ISBN Prefix(es): 978-1-61526; 978-1-61527; 978-1-936025; 978-1-936027; 978-1-936028; 978-1-936029; 978-1-936030; 978-1-61602; 978-1-61734; 978-1-60979; 978-1-936026; 978-1-936031; 978-1-56256; 978-1-58984; 978-1-4138
Number of titles published annually: 50 Print
Total Titles: 2,000 Print
Imprints: Asante®; Measuring Up®
Distributor for New Path Learning
Membership(s): International Society for Technology in Education

Per Annum Inc
555 Eighth Ave, Suite 203, New York, NY 10018
SAN: 289-3673
Tel: 212-647-8700 *Toll Free Tel:* 800-548-1108 *Fax:* 212-647-8716
E-mail: info@perannum.com
Web Site: www.perannum.com
Key Personnel
Pres: Alicia B Settle
Acct Exec: Liz Smith *Tel:* 212-647-8700 ext 202
Founded: 1979
Guide books, agendas.
ISBN Prefix(es): 978-1-57499
Number of titles published annually: 16 Print
Total Titles: 16 Print
Distributor for New Yorker Desk Diary

Peradam Press
Subsidiary of The Center for Cultural & Naturalist Studies
PO Box 6, North San Juan, CA 95960-0006
Tel: 530-292-4266 *Fax:* 530-292-4266
E-mail: peradam@earthlink.net
Key Personnel
Pres & Sr Ed: Linda Birkholz
Exec Ed: Corinne Boyle
Ed: Patricia Hicks
Founded: 1993
General trade books hardcover & paperbacks.
ISBN Prefix(es): 978-1-885420
Number of titles published annually: 10 Print
Total Titles: 73 Print
Shipping Address: 19074 Oak Tree Rd, Nevada City, CA 95959

Perfection Learning Corp
2680 Berkshire Pkwy, Clive, IA 50325
Tel: 515-278-0133 *Toll Free Tel:* 800-762-2999 *Fax:* 515-278-2980
Web Site: perfectionlearning.com
Key Personnel
Design Dir: Randy Messer *E-mail:* rmesser@plconline.com
Edit Dir, Elem: Sue Thies *E-mail:* sthies@plconline.com
Mktg Opers Dir: Mark Hagenberg
E-mail: mhagenberg@plconline.com
Founded: 1926
Elementary & secondary product line covers such content areas as reading, literature, math, test preparation, writing, vocabulary, handwriting, spelling & more.
ISBN Prefix(es): 978-0-89598
Number of titles published annually: 30 Print
Total Titles: 500 Print
Imprints: Cover Craft; Cover-to-Cover; Literature & Thought; Passages; Retold Classics; Summit Books; Tale Blazers
Distributor for Abrams; Ace Books; Airmont; Annick Press; Archway; Atheneum; Baker Books; Ballantine; Bantam; Barrons; Berkley; Blake Books; Candlewick Press; Charlesbridge Press; Chelsea House; Children's Press; Chronicle Books; Crabtree Publishing; Crown; Disney Press; Distri Books; DK; Doubleday; Dutton; F+W, A Content + eCommerce Company; Farrar, Straus & Giroux Inc; Fawcett; Firefly; First Avenue; Free Spirit; Fulcrum; Golden Books; Greenhaven Press Inc; Hammond Pub; Harcourt Inc; Hayes; Gareth Stevens; Frederick Warne
Foreign Rep(s): Ron Grant, School Book Fairs Ltd (Canada)
Warehouse: 1000 N Second Ave, PO Box 500, Logan, IA 51546-0500 *Toll Free Tel:* 800-831-4190 *Fax:* 712-644-2392 *E-mail:* orders@perfectionlearning.com

Perigee Books
Imprint of Penguin Group (USA) LLC
375 Hudson St, New York, NY 10014
SAN: 282-5074
Tel: 212-366-2000 *Fax:* 212-366-2365
E-mail: perigeebooks@us.penguingroup.com
Web Site: www.penguin.com
Key Personnel
Publr: John Duff
Ed-in-Chief: Marian Lizzi
Sr Ed: Stephanie Bowen
Asst Ed: Amanda Shih
Publicity & Mktg Coord: Tyler Fields
Founded: 1980
Focus on prescriptive nonfiction.
ISBN Prefix(es): 978-0-399
Number of titles published annually: 73 Print
Total Titles: 517 Print
Advertising Agency: Spier NY

The Permanent Press
4170 Noyac Rd, Sag Harbor, NY 11963
Tel: 631-725-1101 *Fax:* 631-725-8215
E-mail: info@thepermanentpress.com
Web Site: www.thepermanentpress.com
Key Personnel
Co-Publr: Judith Shepard *E-mail:* judith@thepermanentpress.com; Martin Shepard
E-mail: shepard@thepermanentpress.com
Mng Ed: Cathy Suter *E-mail:* cathy@thepermanentpress.com
ISBN Prefix(es): 978-1-877946; 978-0-932966; 978-1-57962
Number of titles published annually: 16 Print
Imprints: Second Chance Press
See separate listing for:
Second Chance Press

Persea Books
277 Broadway, Suite 708, New York, NY 10007
SAN: 212-8233
Tel: 212-260-9256 *Fax:* 212-267-3165
E-mail: info@perseabooks.com
Web Site: www.perseabooks.com
Key Personnel
Pres & Publr: Michael Braziller
VP & Edit Dir: Karen Braziller
Poetry Ed: Gabriel Fried *E-mail:* poetry@perseabooks.com
Publicity: Nina Puro *E-mail:* npuro@perseabooks.com
Founded: 1975
ISBN Prefix(es): 978-0-89255
Number of titles published annually: 12 Print; 10 E-Book
Total Titles: 500 Print; 30 E-Book
Imprints: A Karen & Michael Braziller Book
Distributed by W W Norton & Co (worldwide exc Canada); Penguin Books (Canada only)
Distributor for Ontario Review Press
Orders to: W W Norton & Co, 500 Fifth Ave, New York, NY 10110 *Toll Free Tel:* 800-233-4830
Distribution Center: W W Norton c/o National Book Co, Keystone Industrial Park, Scranton, PA 18512 *Toll Free Fax:* 800-233-4830

The Perseus Books Group
387 Park Ave S, 12th fl, New York, NY 10016
Tel: 212-340-8100 *Toll Free Tel:* 800-343-4499 (cust serv) *Fax:* 212-340-8105
Web Site: www.perseusbooksgroup.com
Key Personnel
CEO & Pres: David Steinberger
COO: Charles Gallagher
Pres, Client Servs: Mark Suchomel
Pres, Publg, Client & Sales Devt: Matty Goldberg
SVP & Group Publr: Susan Weinberg
SVP, Opers: Raymond Floyd
SVP, Group Sales: Sabrina McCarthy
VP: Anjali V Jolly; J T Mauk
VP, Intl Rts: Isabelle Bleecker; Jennifer Thompson
VP, Legal Aff: Teresa Young Bernstein
VP, Mass Merchandising Sales: Mary Faria
VP, Natl Accts: Maha Khalil
VP, Perseus Imprint Sales Dir: Adam Schnitzer
VP, Supply Chain & Sales Opers: Greg Anastas
Group Publr: Bill Newlin
Sr Mng Dir: John C Fox; Sheryl Schwartz; Kenneth M Socha
Mng Dir: John M Glazer
Sr Dir, Gift Sales: Eric Green
Dir, HR: Lindsey Pullen *E-mail:* lindsey.pullen@perseusbooks.com
Dir, Intl Opers & Communs: Agustina Casal
Asst Dir, Specialty Retail Sales: Steve Quinn
Academic Mktg Mgr: Allison Finkel
Natl Acct Mgr: James Chan
Asst Mgr, Amazon: Andrea Gochnauer
Corp Communs: Kathleen Schmidt
Founded: 1997
Perseus Books, LLC does not accept unsol mss or proposals.
ISBN Prefix(es): 978-0-938289; 978-1-58097; 978-0-7382; 978-1-882810; 978-1-60286
Number of titles published annually: 50 Print
Total Titles: 530 Print
Imprints: Avalon Travel; Basic Books; Basic Civitas Books; Courage Books; Da Capo Lifelong Books; Da Capo Press; Nation Books; PublicAffairs; Running Press; Running Press Kids; Running Press Miniature Editions; Seal Press; Weinstein Books; Westview Press
Divisions: Legato Publishers Group
Distributed by NOW; Perseus Distribution Services
Orders to: 1094 Flex Dr, Jackson, TN 38301 *Toll Free Tel:* 800-343-4499 *Toll Free Fax:* 800-351-5073
Distribution Center: 1094 Flex Dr, Jackson, TN 38301 *Toll Free Tel:* 800-343-4499 *Toll Free Fax:* 800-351-5073
See separate listing for:
Avalon Travel Publishing
Basic Books
Da Capo Press & Lifelong Books
PublicAffairs
Running Press Book Publishers
Seal Press
Westview Press

Peter Pauper Press, Inc
202 Mamaroneck Ave, White Plains, NY 10601-5376
SAN: 204-9449

Tel: 914-681-0144 Fax: 914-681-0389
E-mail: customerservice@peterpauper.com; orders@peterpauper.com
Web Site: www.peterpauper.com
Key Personnel
CEO: Laurence Beilenson *E-mail:* lbeilenson@peterpauper.com
VP: John Hartley *E-mail:* jhartley@peterpauper.com
Edit Dir: Barbara Paulding *E-mail:* bpaulding@peterpauper.com
Art Dir: Heather Zschock *E-mail:* hzschock@peterpauper.com
Publr: Evelyn L Beilenson *E-mail:* ebeilenson@peterpauper.com
Sr Ed: Lois Kaufman *E-mail:* lkaufman@peterpauper.com
Founded: 1928
Decorated hardcover gift, inspirational; quotations, miniatures, journals, photo albums, children's picture books, children's activity books, travel guides.
ISBN Prefix(es): 978-0-88088; 978-1-59359; 978-1-44130
Number of titles published annually: 60 Print; 15 E-Book
Total Titles: 500 Print; 270 E-Book
Imprints: Inspire Books
Foreign Rep(s): For Arts Sake (Australia, New Zealand); Alejandra Garza (Mexico); Saskia Knobbe (Netherlands); Bara Kristinsdottir (Iceland); Peter Pauper Press UK (UK); Phambili (Southern Africa); Israel Ring (Brazil); Sunstate Books (Australia, New Zealand)
Shipping Address: Conri Services Inc, 5 Skyline Dr, Hawthorne, NY 10532, Contact: Connie Levene *Tel:* 914-592-2300 *Fax:* 914-592-2174
Warehouse: Conri Services Inc, 5 Skyline Dr, Hawthorne, NY 10532, Contact: Connie Levene *Tel:* 914-592-2300 *Fax:* 914-592-2174

§Peterson Institute for International Economics (PIIE)
1750 Massachusetts Ave NW, Washington, DC 20036-1903
SAN: 293-2865
Tel: 202-328-9000 *Toll Free Tel:* 800-522-9139 (orders) *Fax:* 202-328-5432; 202-659-3225
E-mail: orders@petersoninstitute.org
Web Site: www.petersoninstitute.org
Key Personnel
Dir: C Fred Bergsten
Edit Dir & Public Policy Fellow: Steven R Weisman *Tel:* 202-454-1331 *E-mail:* media@piie.com
Founded: 1981
Trade & textbooks on key economic, monetary, trade & investment issues.
ISBN Prefix(es): 978-0-88132
Number of titles published annually: 15 Print; 14 Online
Total Titles: 300 Print; 200 Online; 35 E-Book
Distributed by DA Information Services (Australia, New Zealand & Papua New Guinea); East West Export Books (Cambodia, China, Indonesia, Japan, Philippines, Singapore, Taiwan, Thailand & Vietnam); The Eurospan Group (Africa, Eastern & Western Europe, Iran, Israel, Russia & Turkey); Renouf Bookstore (Canada); United Publishers Services Ltd (Japan & Republic of Korea); Viva Books PVT (Bangladesh, India, Nepal & Sri Lanka)
Distributor for Center for Global Development
Orders to: Peterson Institute for International Economics, PO Box 960, Herndon, VA 20172 *Toll Free Tel:* 800-522-9139 *Fax:* 703-661-1501 *E-mail:* petersonmail@presswarehouse.com *Web Site:* bookstore.petersoninstitute.org
Returns: Peterson Institute for International Economics, 22883 Quicksilver Dr, Dulles, VA 20166
Membership(s): AAP; Society for Scholarly Publishing; Washington Book Publishers

§Peterson's, a Nelnet Company
Princeton Pike Corporate Ctr, 2000 Lenox Dr, Lawrenceville, NJ 08648
Tel: 609-896-1800
E-mail: sales@petersons.com
Web Site: www.petersons.com
Key Personnel
Mng Dir, Digital Publg: Stephen Clemente
Founded: 1966
Education, career books, software & CD-ROM, data licensing, test preparation, financial aid & adult education, online lead generation.
ISBN Prefix(es): 978-1-56079; 978-0-7689
Number of titles published annually: 50 Print; 2 E-Book
Total Titles: 120 Print; 2 E-Book
Imprints: Peterson's/Pacesetter Books
Foreign Rights: Ann-Christine Daniellsson Agency (Scandinavia); International Editors' Co (Latin America, Spain); Frederique Parretta Agency (Canada (French-speaking), France); Pikarski (Israel); Tuttle-Mori Agency Inc (Japan, Thailand)
Membership(s): BISG

Petroleum Extension Service (PETEX)
Division of University of Texas
University of Texas at Austin-PETEX, One University Sta, R8100, Austin, TX 78712-1100
Tel: 512-471-5940 *Toll Free Tel:* 800-687-4132 *Fax:* 512-471-9410 *Toll Free Fax:* 800-687-7839
E-mail: plach@www.utex.edu; petex@www.utexas.edu
Web Site: www.utexas.edu/ce/petex
Key Personnel
Sr Mgr, Publg & Communs: Debbie Denehy *E-mail:* ddenehy@austin.utexas.edu
Founded: 1944
Training reference materials for oil field personnel including ebook titles.
ISBN Prefix(es): 978-0-88698
Number of titles published annually: 10 Print
Total Titles: 400 Print
Branch Office(s)
PETEX, 2700-W W Thorne Dr, Houston, TX 77073-3410
Shipping Address: 10100 Burnet Rd, Austin, TX 78758-4445

§Pflaum Publishing Group
Division of Peter Li Inc
2621 Dryden Rd, Suite 300, Dayton, OH 45439
Tel: 937-293-1415 *Toll Free Tel:* 800-543-4383; 800-523-4625 (sales) *Fax:* 937-293-1310 *Toll Free Fax:* 800-370-4450
E-mail: service@pflaum.com
Web Site: pflaum.com
Key Personnel
VP & Dir, Sales: Michael Raffio *E-mail:* mraffio@peterli.com
VP, Mktg: Mr Terry Perkins *Tel:* 212-818-0700 *Fax:* 212-818-0708 *E-mail:* tperkins@peterli.com
Ed-in-Chief: Michael Donald Thomas *Tel:* 937-293-1415 ext 1118 *E-mail:* mthomas@peterli.com
Founded: 1885
Weekly liturgical magazines for PreK-8. Sacramental preparation for children & teens, catechetical resources for PreK-12, religious educators & youth ministers. Branch offices in Phoenix, AZ & New York, NY.
ISBN Prefix(es): 978-0-937997; 978-0-89837; 978-1-933178; 978-1-935042
Number of titles published annually: 20 Print
Total Titles: 75 Print; 15 CD-ROM; 15 Online; 10 E-Book
Membership(s): Association of Catholic Publishers Inc; National Catholic Education Association; National Catholic Educational Exhibitors

Phaidon Press Inc
Subsidiary of Phaidon Press Ltd
180 Varick St, 14th fl, New York, NY 10014
Tel: 212-652-5400 *Toll Free Tel:* 800-759-0190 (cust serv) *Fax:* 212-652-5410 *Toll Free Fax:* 800-286-9471 (cust serv)
E-mail: ussales@phaidon.com
Web Site: www.phaidon.com
Key Personnel
CEO: Keith Fox
COO: Philip Ruppel
VP: Mary Albi
VP & Group Publr: Deborah Aaronson
Publr: Emilia Terragni
Publg Dir, Children's Books: Cecily Kaiser
Art Dir, Children's Books: Meagan Bennett
Publicity & Mktg Dir: Liz Thompson *Tel:* 212-652-5217 *E-mail:* lthompson@phaidon.com
Sales Dir: James Whittaker *Tel:* 905-338-6480 *E-mail:* jwhittaker@phaidon.com
Publicist: Peter Tittiger
Sales Rep, Northeast: Richard Gregg *Tel:* 617-964-5669 *E-mail:* rgregg@phaidon.com
Exec Commissioning Ed, Food: Emily Takoudes
Proj Ed, Food: Olga Massov
Founded: 1923
Illustrated books on fine art, architecture, design, photography, decorative arts, film & music.
ISBN Prefix(es): 978-0-7148
Number of titles published annually: 70 Print
Total Titles: 525 Print
Foreign Office(s): Phaidon Sarl, 65 rue Montmartre, Paris 75002, France *Tel:* 01 55 28 38 38 *Fax:* 01 55 28 38 39
Phaidon Verlag, Grunbergerstr 81, 10245 Berlin, Germany *Tel:* (030) 28 88 64 14 *Fax:* (030) 28 04 48 79
Phaidon Srl, Corso Sempione 33, 20145 Milan MI, Italy *Tel:* (024) 399-0450 *Fax:* (024) 399-0450
Phaidon KK, AD Homes 104, 3-28-18 Yushima, Bunkyo-ku, Tokyo 113-0034, Japan *Tel:* (03) 5812 6839
Phaidon Press, C/ Buenos Aires, 54 3º 3, Barcelona 08036, Spain *Tel:* 934193833 *Fax:* 934193833
Phaidon Press Ltd, 18 Regents Wharf, All Saints St, London N1 9PA, United Kingdom *Tel:* (020) 7843 1000 *Fax:* (020) 7843 1010 *E-mail:* enquiries@phaidon.com *Web Site:* www.phaidon.com
Distributor for Mitchell Beazley; Electa

Phi Delta Kappa International®
320 W Eighth St, Suite 216, Bloomington, IN 47404
Mailing Address: PO Box 7888, Bloomington, IN 47407-7888
Tel: 812-339-1156 *Toll Free Tel:* 800-766-1156 *Fax:* 812-339-0018
E-mail: customerservice@pdkintl.org
Web Site: www.pdkintl.org
Key Personnel
Exec Dir: Joshua Starr
Dir, Mktg & Communs: Ashley McDonald Kinkaid *Tel:* 703-988-4037 *E-mail:* akinkaid@pdkintl.org
Founded: 1906
International professional association of educators.
ISBN Prefix(es): 978-0-87367
Number of titles published annually: 30 Print
Total Titles: 220 Print; 1 CD-ROM
Branch Office(s)
Phi Delta Kappa Educational Foundation, 408 N Union St, Bloomington, IN 47405-3800, Contact: Lynn Lewis *Toll Free Tel:* 800-776-1156 ext 2222 *E-mail:* llewis@pdkintl.org
Foreign Rep(s): Unifacmann Trading Co (Taiwan)

Philadelphia Museum of Art
2525 Pennsylvania Ave, Philadelphia, PA 19130
Tel: 215-684-7250 *Fax:* 215-235-8715

Web Site: www.philamuseum.org
Key Personnel
Dir, Publg: Sherry Babbitt *Tel:* 215-684-7242
E-mail: sbabbitt@philamuseum.org
Prodn Mgr: Rich Bonk
Ed: Kathleen Krattenmaker
Assoc Ed: Mary Cason; David Updike
Founded: 1901
Illustrated scholarly works on the permanent collection & exhibitions at the museum.
ISBN Prefix(es): 978-0-87633
Number of titles published annually: 7 Print
Total Titles: 80 Print
Distributed by Yale University Press

Philomel
Imprint of Penguin Group (USA) LLC
345 Hudson St, New York, NY 10014
Tel: 212-366-2000
Key Personnel
Pres & Publr: Michael Green
Exec Ed: Jill Santopolo
Assoc Publr/Exec Mng Ed: David Briggs
Art Dir: Semadar Megged
Founded: 1980
Number of titles published annually: 41 Print
Total Titles: 367 Print

Philosophical Library Inc
275 Central Park W, Suite 12D, New York, NY 10024
Tel: 212-886-1873 *Fax:* 212-873-6070
E-mail: editors@philosophicallibrary.com
Web Site: philosophicallibrary.com
Key Personnel
Mgr: Regeen Runes Najar
Founded: 1941
Comprehensive collection of mid-level reference books. A consistent source for serious readers, libraries, academic institutions & booksellers worldwide. Also have a program for Print On Demand.
ISBN Prefix(es): 978-0-8022
Number of titles published annually: 70 Print; 70 E-Book
Total Titles: 500 Print; 300 E-Book
Distributed by Open Road Integrated Media
Foreign Rights: Philosophical Library Inc (Worldwide)

Philosophy Documentation Center
PO Box 7147, Charlottesville, VA 22906-7147
Tel: 434-220-3300 *Toll Free Tel:* 800-444-2419
Fax: 434-220-3301
E-mail: order@pdcnet.org
Web Site: www.pdcnet.org
Key Personnel
Dir: George Leaman *E-mail:* leaman@pdcnet.org
Assoc Dir: Pamela K Swope *E-mail:* pkswope@pdcnet.org
Electronic Publg & Mktg: Susanne Mueller-Grote
E-mail: smg@pdcnet.org
Founded: 1966
ISBN Prefix(es): 978-0-912632; 978-1-889680
Number of titles published annually: 20 Print; 20 Online; 10 E-Book
Total Titles: 100 Print; 140 Online; 30 E-Book
Distributor for Zeta Books (online access)
Membership(s): Society for Scholarly Publishing

Phoenix Society for Burn Survivors
1835 R W Berends Dr SW, Grand Rapids, MI 49519
Tel: 616-458-2773 *Toll Free Tel:* 800-888-BURN (888-2876) *Fax:* 616-458-2831
E-mail: info@phoenix-society.org
Web Site: www.phoenix-society.org
Key Personnel
Exec Dir: Amy Acton *E-mail:* amy@phoenix-society.org
Founded: 1977
Books regarding burns.
Number of titles published annually: 3 Print
Total Titles: 35 Print; 35 E-Book

Piano Press
1425 Ocean Ave, Suite 5, Del Mar, CA 92014
Mailing Address: PO Box 85, Del Mar, CA 92014-0085
Tel: 619-884-1401 *Fax:* 858-755-1104
E-mail: pianopress@pianopress.com
Web Site: www.pianopress.com
Key Personnel
Owner & Ed: Elizabeth C Axford
E-mail: lizaxford@pianopress.com
Music Typesetter: David Murray; Mark So
Audio Engr: John Dawes; Denny Martin; Matthew Dela Pola; Peter Sprague; Kris Stone
Webmaster & Mktg: Frank Tranfaglia
Edit Asst: Kathy Alward; Carol Buckley; Katie Cook; Dee Rome; Gay Salo
Founded: 1998
Publishes songbooks & CDs as well as music-related coloring books & poetry for the educational & family markets.
ISBN Prefix(es): 978-0-9673325; 978-1-931844
Number of titles published annually: 6 Print; 1 Audio
Total Titles: 100 Print
Membership(s): The American Society of Composers, Authors and Publishers; The Recording Academy; Society of Children's Book Writers & Illustrators

Picador
Subsidiary of Macmillan
175 Fifth Ave, 19th fl, New York, NY 10010
Tel: 646-307-5151 *Fax:* 212-253-9627
E-mail: firstname.lastname@picadorusa.com
Web Site: www.picadorusa.com
Key Personnel
VP & Publr: Stephen Morrison
VP, Sales & Mktg: Darin Keesler
Exec Dir, Publicity: James Meader
Sr Ed: Anna deVries
Creative Dir: Henry Yee
Sr Designer: LeeAnn Falciani
Sr Publicist: Declan Taintor
Founded: 1995
ISBN Prefix(es): 978-0-312
Number of titles published annually: 90 Print
Total Titles: 7,000 Print
Distribution Center: MPS Distribution Center, 16365 James Madison Hwy, Gordonsville, VA 22942-8501 *Toll Free Tel:* 888-330-8477 *Fax:* 540-672-7540 (cust serv)
Toll Free Fax: 800-672-2054 (orders)
E-mail: firstinitiallastname@mpsvirginia.com

Picasso Project
Division of Alan Wofsy Fine Arts
1109 Geary Blvd, San Francisco, CA 94109
Tel: 415-292-6500 *Fax:* 415-292-6594
E-mail: editeur@earthlink.net (editorial); picasso@art-books.com (orders)
Web Site: www.art-books.com
Key Personnel
Mgr: Adios Butler
Ed: Alan Hyman
Founded: 1990
Publish & distribute comprehensive catalogues on the works of Pablo Picasso. Distribution center located in Ashland, OH.
ISBN Prefix(es): 978-1-55660
Number of titles published annually: 6 Print; 4 CD-ROM
Total Titles: 22 Print; 12 CD-ROM
Distributed by Alan Wofsy Fine Arts
Distributor for Cramer (Switzerland); Kornfeld (Switzerland); Ramie (France)
Billing Address: PO Box 2210, San Francisco, CA 94126-2110
Distribution Center: Ashland, OH 44805
Membership(s): AAP

Piccadilly Books Ltd
PO Box 25203, Colorado Springs, CO 80936-5203
SAN: 665-9969
Tel: 719-550-9887
E-mail: orders@piccadillybooks.com
Web Site: www.piccadillybooks.com
Key Personnel
Publr: Bruce Fife *E-mail:* bruce@piccadillybooks.com
Founded: 1985
Health & nutrition, entertainment, performing arts, humorous skits & sketches, writing.
ISBN Prefix(es): 978-0-941599; 978-1-936709
Number of titles published annually: 3 Print
Total Titles: 75 Print; 25 E-Book; 2 Audio
Foreign Rep(s): Gazelle Books (Europe)
Membership(s): The Independent Book Publishers Association

§Picton Press
Subsidiary of Picton Corp
814 E Elkcam Circle, Marco Island, FL 34145-2558
Mailing Address: 1637 Briarwood Ct, Marco Island, FL 34145-4007
Tel: 239-970-2442
E-mail: sales@pictonpress.com (orders)
Web Site: www.pictonpress.com
Key Personnel
Pres: Lewis Bunker Rohrbach
E-mail: lewisrohrbach@hotmail.com
Founded: 1973
Genealogical & historical books.
ISBN Prefix(es): 978-0-89725
Number of titles published annually: 15 Print; 25 CD-ROM
Total Titles: 1,000 Print; 1,000 CD-ROM; 1 E-Book
Imprints: New England History Press; Penobscot Press

Pictorial Histories Publishing Co
521 Bickford St, Missoula, MT 59801
Mailing Address: 713 S Third St, Missoula, MT 59801
Tel: 406-549-8488 *Toll Free Tel:* 888-763-8350
Fax: 406-728-9280
E-mail: phpc@montana.com
Web Site: www.pictorialhistoriespublishing.com
Key Personnel
Pres & Publr: Stan Cohen
Founded: 1976
History books.
ISBN Prefix(es): 978-0-933126; 978-0-929521; 978-1-57510
Number of titles published annually: 4 Print
Total Titles: 180 Print

Pie in the Sky Publishing LLC
8031 E Phillips Circle, Centennial, CO 80112
Tel: 303-773-0851 *Fax:* 303-773-0851
E-mail: pieintheskypublishing@msn.com
Web Site: www.pieintheskypublishing.com
Key Personnel
Pres: Ann Simmons
Publr: Nancy L Mills *Tel:* 303-221-1551
Founded: 1998
Publishers of high quality, brightly illustrated children's picture books. Most stories are written for both the reader & listener.
ISBN Prefix(es): 978-1-893815
Number of titles published annually: 5 Print; 1 Audio
Total Titles: 9 Print; 1 Audio
Distribution Center: Book West

Pieces of Learning
Division of Creative Learning Consultants Inc
1990 Market Rd, Marion, IL 62959-8976
SAN: 298-461X

Tel: 618-964-9426 *Toll Free Tel:* 800-729-5137 *Toll Free Fax:* 800-844-0455
E-mail: piecesoflearning@verizon.net
Web Site: www.piecesoflearning.com
Key Personnel
Pres: Kathy Balsamo
Busn Mgr: Stan Balsamo
Founded: 1989
Teacher supplementary educational books; mail order.
ISBN Prefix(es): 978-1-880505; 978-0-9623835; 978-0-945799; 978-0-913839; 978-1-931334
Number of titles published annually: 16 Print
Total Titles: 350 Print; 50 E-Book
Distributed by ALPS Publishing; A W Peller & Associates; Professional Associate Publishing; Prufrock Press Inc
Membership(s): Education Market Association

The Pilgrim Press/United Church Press
700 Prospect Ave, Cleveland, OH 44115-1100
Toll Free Tel: 800-537-3394 (cust serv-indivs); 800-654-5129 (cust serv-commercial accts) *Fax:* 216-736-2206 (orders)
E-mail: proposals@thepilgrimpress.com
Web Site: www.thepilgrimpress.com; www.unitedchurchpress.com
Key Personnel
Dir: Ann Poston *Tel:* 216-736-3755 *E-mail:* stavetet@ucc.org
Edit Dir: Kim Martin Sadler *Tel:* 216-736-3756 *E-mail:* sadlerk@ucc.org
Dir, Prodn: Janice W Brown *Tel:* 216-736-3763 *E-mail:* brownj@ucc.org
Dir, Dist Servs: Marie Tyson *Tel:* 216-736-3777 *E-mail:* tysonm@ucc.org
Graphic Designer: Robyn Nordstrom *Tel:* 216-736-3758 *E-mail:* nordstrr@ucc.org
Mktg Communs Assoc: Aimee Jannsohn *Tel:* 216-736-3761 *E-mail:* jannsoha@ucc.org
Mktg Communs: Tiffany French
Mktg: Darlene Grant
Mktg Asst: Juliet Dombos *Tel:* 216-736-3766 *E-mail:* dombosj@ucc.org
Founded: 1608
Alternative spiritualities; peace & justice; world religions; contemporary ministry.
ISBN Prefix(es): 978-0-8298
Number of titles published annually: 20 Print
Total Titles: 485 Print

Pilgrim Publications
PO Box 66, Pasadena, TX 77501-0066
Tel: 713-477-4261 *Fax:* 713-477-7561
E-mail: pilgrimpub@aol.com
Web Site: members.aol.com/pilgrimpub/; www.pilgrimpublications.com
Key Personnel
Dir: Bob Ross
Founded: 1969
The works & sermons of Charles H Spurgeon (1834-1892).
ISBN Prefix(es): 978-1-56186
Number of titles published annually: 4 Print
Total Titles: 200 Print
Distributor for Christian Focus; Fox River Press; Hess Publications
Warehouse: 1609 Preston, Pasadena, TX 77503
Membership(s): CBA: The Association for Christian Retail

Pine Forge Press
Subsidiary of SAGE Publications Inc
2455 Teller Rd, Thousand Oaks, CA 91320
Tel: 805-499-4224; 805-499-9774 (orders) *Fax:* 805-499-0871 (orders)
E-mail: info@sagepub.com
Web Site: www.sagepub.com; www.pineforge.com
Key Personnel
Pres & CEO, SAGE Pubns: Blaise Simqu
Founded: 1991
Texts & software for use in graduate & undergraduate social & behavioral science courses.
ISBN Prefix(es): 978-0-8039
Number of titles published annually: 25 Print
Total Titles: 150 Print

Pineapple Press Inc
PO Box 3889, Sarasota, FL 34230-3889
SAN: 631-8630
Tel: 941-706-2507 *Toll Free Tel:* 866-766-3850 (orders) *Fax:* 941-706-2509 *Toll Free Fax:* 800-838-1149 (orders)
E-mail: info@pineapplepress.com; customer.service@ingrampublisherservices.com
Web Site: www.pineapplepress.com
Key Personnel
Pres: David M Cussen *E-mail:* david@pineapplepress.com
Exec Ed: June Cussen *E-mail:* june@pineapplepress.com
Founded: 1982
ISBN Prefix(es): 978-0-910923; 978-1-56164
Number of titles published annually: 25 Print
Total Titles: 300 Print
Warehouse: Ingram Publisher Services, 1210 Ingram Dr, Chambersburg, PA 17202

Pinnacle Books, see Kensington Publishing Corp

Pioneer Publishing Co
Hwy 82 E, Carrolton, MS 38917
Mailing Address: PO Box 408, Carrolton, MS 38917-0408
Tel: 662-237-6010
E-mail: pioneerse@tecinfo.com
Web Site: www.pioneersoutheast.com
Key Personnel
Owner: Betty C Wiltshire
ISBN Prefix(es): 978-1-885480
Number of titles published annually: 6 Print
Total Titles: 100 Print

Pippin Press
229 E 85 St, New York, NY 10028
Mailing Address: PO Box 1347, Gracie Sta, New York, NY 10028
Tel: 212-288-4920 *Fax:* 908-237-2407
Key Personnel
Pres, Publr & Ed-in-Chief: Barbara Francis
Mng Ed & Rts Dir: Gregory Filling
Sr Ed: Joyce Segal
Sales Mgr & Lib Sales Dir: Alan Frese
Founded: 1987
Small chapter books for ages 7-10, humorous fiction for all ages, novels for ages 8-12 & unusual nonfiction for ages 6-12.
ISBN Prefix(es): 978-0-945912
Number of titles published annually: 4 Print
Total Titles: 55 Print
Foreign Rep(s): Baker & Taylor Books (Canada); Baker & Taylor International (Worldwide exc Canada)
Orders to: Whitehurst & Clark Book Fulfillment Inc, 1200 County Rd, Rte 523, Flemington, NJ 08822 *Tel:* 908-782-2323 *Toll Free Tel:* 800-488-8040
Returns: Whitehurst & Clark Book Fulfillment Inc, 1200 County Rd, Rte 523, Flemington, NJ 08822 *Tel:* 908-782-2323 *Toll Free Tel:* 800-488-8040
Shipping Address: Whitehurst & Clark Book Fulfillment Inc, 1200 County Rd, Rte 523, Flemington, NJ 08822 *Tel:* 908-782-2323 *Toll Free Tel:* 800-488-8040
Warehouse: Whitehurst & Clark Book Fulfillment Inc, 1200 County Rd, Rte 523, Flemington, NJ 08822 *Tel:* 908-782-2323 *Toll Free Tel:* 800-488-8040
Distribution Center: Whitehurst & Clark Book Fulfillment Inc, 1200 County Rd, Rte 523, Flemington, NJ 08822 *Tel:* 908-782-2323 *Toll Free Tel:* 800-488-8040
Membership(s): ALA

PJD Publications Ltd
PO Box 966, Westbury, NY 11590-0966
SAN: 202-0068
Tel: 516-626-0650 *Fax:* 516-626-4456
Web Site: www.pjdonline.com
Key Personnel
CEO & Pres: Siva Sankar *E-mail:* sankar@pjdonline.com
Tech: Barbara Kelly
Founded: 1968
Biomedical & educational books, philosophy, scholarly, science & social sciences, books & journals.
ISBN Prefix(es): 978-0-9600290; 978-0-915340
Number of titles published annually: 6 Print
Total Titles: 15 Print
Divisions: Institute for Research Information; Office & Print Technologies; PJD Electronic Publishing

Planert Creek Press
E4843 395 Ave, Menomonie, WI 54751
SAN: 855-7454
Tel: 715-235-4110
E-mail: publisher@planertcreekpress.com
Web Site: www.planertcreekpress.com
Key Personnel
Publr: David Tank
Founded: 2008
Specialize in 3D books & topics related to West Central Wisconsin.
This publisher has indicated that 100% of their product line is author subsidized.
ISBN Prefix(es): 978-0-9815064; 978-0-9962218
Number of titles published annually: 3 Print; 3 Online
Total Titles: 8 Print; 3 Online; 1 Audio
Membership(s): National Stereoscopic Association; Society of Children's Book Writers & Illustrators

Platinum Press LLC
281 Hicks St, Brooklyn Heights, NY 11201
Tel: 718-875-5065 *Fax:* 718-875-5065
Key Personnel
Pres: Herbert J Cohen *E-mail:* herbertjcohen@aol.com
Founded: 1990
Publish nonfiction; book producer & packager; appointment books, diaries, date books, journals, blankbooks & joke books.
ISBN Prefix(es): 978-1-879582
Number of titles published annually: 12 Print
Total Titles: 120 Print; 2 E-Book

Platypus Media LLC
Affiliate of Science, Naturally!™
725 Eighth St SE, Washington, DC 20003
Tel: 202-546-1674 *Toll Free Tel:* 877-PLATYPS (752-8977) *Fax:* 202-546-2356
E-mail: info@platypusmedia.com
Web Site: www.platypusmedia.com
Key Personnel
Pres: Dia L Michels
Founded: 2000
An independent publisher creating books for families, teachers & parenting professionals.
ISBN Prefix(es): 978-1-930775
Number of titles published annually: 4 Print; 2 Audio
Total Titles: 16 Print; 2 Audio
Warehouse: Border Mail Services, Champlain, NY
Distribution Center: National Book Network, 4501 Forbes Blvd, Lanham, MD 20706 *Tel:* 301-459-3366 *Toll Free Tel:* 800-787-6859 *Fax:* 301-459-5746 *Web Site:* www.nbnbooks.com

Membership(s): The Association of Publishers for Special Sales; The Children's Book Council; The Independent Book Publishers Association; Washington Book Publishers; Women's National Book Association

§Players Press Inc
PO Box 1132, Studio City, CA 91614-0132
Tel: 818-789-4980
E-mail: playerspress@att.net
Web Site: www.ppeps.com
Key Personnel
CEO & Pres: Robert Gordon
VP, Ed: David Wainright
VP, Opers: Chris Cordero
Busn Mgr: David Cole
Sales Mgr: M Cohen
Founded: 1965
Publisher of plays, musicals & performing arts textbooks & Sherlock Holmes. Represents world rights for other publishers of performing arts books (film, theater, television). Distributes English Speaking World for other publishers of entertainment books & Sherlockian. Publishes costume books in English & German.
ISBN Prefix(es): 978-0-88734; 978-1-85729
Number of titles published annually: 60 Print; 5 CD-ROM
Total Titles: 2,085 Print; 62 CD-ROM; 4 Audio
Imprints: Healthwatch; Players Press; Showcase
Divisions: Players Press (Canada); Player Press A/Z Ltd; Player Press Ltd (UK)
Foreign Office(s): 20 Park Dr, Romford, Essex RM1 4LH, United Kingdom
Distributor for Camelion Plays; Garland-Clark Editors; Macmillan Education (UK); Preston Editions
Foreign Rep(s): Players Press Germany GMBH; Players Press UK Ltd (UK)
Foreign Rights: Players Press International (Europe)
Advertising Agency: Empire Enterprises, PO Box 1344, Studio City, CA 91614-0344 *Tel:* 818-784-8918
Membership(s): ABA

Playhouse Publishing
PO Box 1962, Cleveland, OH 44106
Tel: 330-926-1313 *Fax:* 330-475-8579
E-mail: info@picturemepress.com
Web Site: www.picturemepress.com
Key Personnel
Pres: Deborah D'Andrea
Spec Sales Dir: Noelle Pangle *Tel:* 216-375-3544 *E-mail:* n.pangle@picturemepress.com
Founded: 1989
Children's book publisher of interactive titles.
ISBN Prefix(es): 978-1-878338; 978-1-57151
Number of titles published annually: 15 Print
Total Titles: 130 Print
Imprints: Little Lucy & Friends™; Look & Learn™; Nibble Me Books™; Picture Me Books™; Picture, Play & Tote™; Pretend & Play™; Sparkle Shapes
Membership(s): ABA; The Independent Book Publishers Association

Pleasure Boat Studio: A Literary Press
201 W 89 St, New York, NY 10024
Tel: 212-362-8563 *Fax:* 413-677-0085
E-mail: pleasboat@nyc.rr.com
Web Site: www.pleasureboatstudio.com
Key Personnel
Publr: Jack Estes
Founded: 1996
Fiction, nonfiction & poetry.
ISBN Prefix(es): 978-0-9651413; 978-1-929355; 978-0-912887
Number of titles published annually: 10 Print; 5 E-Book
Total Titles: 120 Print; 20 E-Book
Imprints: Aequitas Books (nonfiction only); Caravel Books (mysteries only)
Divisions: Empty Bowl Press
Distributor for Empty Bowl Press
Foreign Rights: Books Crossing Borders (Worldwide)
Returns: 721 Mount Pleasant Rd, Port Angeles, WA 98362, Contact: Jo Anne Hughes *Tel:* 360-457-5541
Shipping Address: 721 Mount Pleasant Rd, Port Angeles, WA 98362, Contact: Jo Anne Hughes *Tel:* 360-457-5541
Membership(s): Community of Literary Magazines & Presses; The Independent Book Publishers Association

§Plexus Publishing, Inc
Affiliate of Information Today, Inc
143 Old Marlton Pike, Medford, NJ 08055
Tel: 609-654-6500 *Fax:* 609-654-4309
E-mail: info@plexuspublishing.com
Web Site: www.plexuspublishing.com
Key Personnel
Pres & CEO: Thomas H Hogan, Sr
VP, Mktg & Busn Devt: Thomas Hogan, Jr
Mktg & Exhibits: Robert Colding *Tel:* 609-654-6500 ext 330 *E-mail:* rcolding@plexuspublishing.com
Sales & Admin: Deb Kranz *Tel:* 609-654-6500 ext 117 *E-mail:* dkranz@plexuspublishing.com
HR Dir: Mary S Hogan *E-mail:* shogan@plexuspublishing.com
Founded: 1977
Regional book publisher specializing in nature, history & fiction for readers interested in the NJ Pinelands, Atlantic City/Jersey shore, Philadelphia & surrounds. No children's books, poetry, religion, or calendars.
ISBN Prefix(es): 978-0-937548; 978-0-9666748
Number of titles published annually: 3 Print
Total Titles: 50 Print; 25 E-Book; 2 Audio
Imprints: Medford Press (trade book titles, nationally dist by IPG); Plexus Books (regional titles/NJ topics especially Southern NJ history, nature/Pinelands, fiction)
Distribution Center: Independent Publishers Group (IPG) (Medford Press imprint only)

§Plough Publishing House
151 Bowne Dr, Walden, NY 12586-2832
SAN: 202-0092
Mailing Address: PO Box 398, Walden, NY 12586-0398
Tel: 845-572-3455 *Toll Free Tel:* 800-521-8011 *Fax:* 845-572-3472
E-mail: info@plough.com
Web Site: www.plough.com
Key Personnel
Mgr: Sam Hine
Founded: 1920
Religion (Anabaptist), church history, children's education, Christian communal living; music; social justice, radical Christianity; social issues.
ISBN Prefix(es): 978-0-87486
Number of titles published annually: 10 Print; 10 Online; 10 E-Book; 1 Audio
Total Titles: 59 Print; 59 Online; 55 E-Book; 5 Audio
Foreign Office(s): 4188 Gwydir Hwy, Elsmore, NSW 2360, Australia
Brightling Rd, Robertsbridge, East Sussex TN32 5DR, United Kingdom *E-mail:* contact@ploughbooks.co.uk
Distribution Center: Ingram Publisher Services, One Ingram Blvd, La Vergne, TN 37086 *Toll Free Tel:* 866-400-5351 *E-mail:* ips@ingramcontent.com *Web Site:* www.ingramcontent.com

Ploughshares
Subsidiary of Ploughshares Inc
Emerson College, 120 Boylston St, Boston, MA 02116
Tel: 617-824-3757
E-mail: pshares@pshares.org
Web Site: www.pshares.org
Key Personnel
Dir & Ed: Ladette Randolph
Founded: 1971
Journal publishing.
ISBN Prefix(es): 978-0-933277; 978-1-933058
Number of titles published annually: 3 Print
Total Titles: 118 Print; 9 E-Book
Membership(s): Combined Book Exhibit

§Plowshare Media
405 Vincente Way, La Jolla, CA 92037
SAN: 857-2933
Mailing Address: PO Box 278, La Jolla, CA 92038
E-mail: sales@plowsharemedia.com
Web Site: plowsharemedia.com
Key Personnel
Mng Partner: Maryann Callery *E-mail:* mc@plowsharemedia.com; Thomas P Tweed *E-mail:* tt@plowsharemedia.com
Founded: 2008
Handle all aspects of book publishing including acquisition, editing, typesetting, cover design, printing, marketing & promotion.
ISBN Prefix(es): 978-0-9860428; 978-0-9821145
Number of titles published annually: 2 Print; 2 E-Book
Total Titles: 10 Print; 8 E-Book
Imprints: RELS Press (nonprofit)
Membership(s): The Independent Book Publishers Association

§Plum Tree Books
Imprint of Classical Academic Press LLC
2151 Market St, Camp Hill, PA 17011
Tel: 717-730-0711 *Fax:* 717-730-0721
E-mail: info@classicalsubjects.com
Web Site: www.plumtreebooks.com
Key Personnel
Publr: Christopher Perrin *E-mail:* cperrin@classicalsubjects.com
Founded: 2012
Old Virtues, New Stories™ - children's stories presented entirely through digital formats.
ISBN Prefix(es): 978-1-60051
Number of titles published annually: 10 Print

Plume
Division of Penguin Group (USA) LLC
375 Hudson St, New York, NY 10014
SAN: 282-5074
Tel: 212-366-2000 *Fax:* 212-366-2666
E-mail: online@penguinputnam.com
Web Site: www.penguinputnam.com; us.penguingroup.com
Key Personnel
VP, Assoc Publr & Dir, Mktg & Publicity: Aileen Boyle
VP, Prodn: Pat Lyons
Publr: Kathryn Court
Exec Mng Ed: Matt Giarratano
Edit Dir: Rachel Bressler
Dir, Art: Jaya Miceli
Assoc Mktg Dir, Blue Rider Press/Plume: Christina Hu
Mktg Assoc, Blue Rider Press/Plume: Wesley Salazar
Sr Ed: Becky Cole
Sr Ed, Plume/Dutton: Denise Roy
Exec Publicist: Marian Brown
ISBN Prefix(es): 978-0-452
Number of titles published annually: 83 Print
Total Titles: 947 Print

§Plunkett Research Ltd
PO Drawer 541737, Houston, TX 77254-1737
Tel: 713-932-0000 *Fax:* 713-932-7080

E-mail: customersupport@plunkettresearch.com
Web Site: www.plunkettresearch.com
Key Personnel
CEO & Publr: Jack W Plunkett
E-mail: jack_plunkett@plunkettresearch.com
Founded: 1985
Provider of business & industry information to corporate, library, academic & government markets. Plunkett's unique reference books are the only complete sources written in lay language for readers of all types. In many cases, these valuable resources are the only comprehensive guides covering the specific industries involved. Publish in print & electronic formats.
ISBN Prefix(es): 978-0-9638268; 978-1-891775
Number of titles published annually: 27 Print; 29 CD-ROM; 30 Online; 30 E-Book
Total Titles: 27 Print; 30 CD-ROM; 30 Online; 30 E-Book

Pocket Books, see Gallery Books

Pocket Press Inc
PO Box 25124, Portland, OR 97298-0124
Toll Free Tel: 888-237-2110 *Toll Free Fax:* 877-643-3732
E-mail: sales@pocketpressinc.com
Web Site: www.pocketpressinc.com
Key Personnel
Pres: Bruce Coorpender
Sales & Mktg: Bob Born
Founded: 1992
Reference books for law enforcement.
ISBN Prefix(es): 978-1-884493; 978-1-61371
Number of titles published annually: 40 Print
Total Titles: 40 Print

Pocket Star, see Gallery Books

Pocol Press
6023 Pocol Dr, Clifton, VA 20124-1333
SAN: 253-6021
Tel: 703-830-5862
E-mail: chrisandtom@erols.com
Web Site: www.pocolpress.com
Key Personnel
Owner & Publr: J Thomas Hetrick
Founded: 1999
Leaders in short fiction & baseball history from first-time non-agented authors. Several books used as college textbooks. All titles also ebooks available from Amazon for Kindle.
ISBN Prefix(es): 978-1-929763
Number of titles published annually: 4 Print; 4 E-Book
Total Titles: 53 Print; 53 E-Book
Membership(s): The Association of Publishers for Special Sales

Pogo Press Inc
Imprint of Finney Company Inc
5995 149 St W, Suite 105, Apple Valley, MN 55124
Tel: 952-469-6699 *Toll Free Tel:* 800-846-7027 *Fax:* 952-469-1968 *Toll Free Fax:* 800-330-6232
E-mail: info@finneyco.com
Web Site: www.pogopress.com
Key Personnel
Pres: Alan Krysan
Mktg Specialist: Krista Danielson
Founded: 1986
Popular culture.
ISBN Prefix(es): 978-0-9617767; 978-1-880654
Number of titles published annually: 3 Print
Total Titles: 41 Print
Distribution Center: SCB Distributors, 15608 S New Century Dr, Gardena, CA 90248 *Tel:* 310-532-9400 *Toll Free Tel:* 800-729-6423 *Fax:* 310-532-7001 *E-mail:* info@scbdistributors.com

Pointed Leaf Press
136 Baxter St, New York, NY 10013
Tel: 212-941-1800 *Fax:* 212-941-1822
E-mail: info@pointedleafpress.com
Web Site: www.pointedleafpress.com
Key Personnel
Publg Dir: Suzanne Slesin
Founded: 2002
This publisher has indicated that 50% of their product line is author subsidized.
ISBN Prefix(es): 978-0-9727661; 978-0-9777875; 978-0-9823585; 978-0-9833889; 978-1-938461
Number of titles published annually: 10 Print

Poisoned Pen Press
6962 E First Ave, Suite 103, Scottsdale, AZ 85251
Tel: 480-945-3375 *Toll Free Tel:* 800-421-3976 *Fax:* 480-949-1707
E-mail: info@poisonedpenpress.com
Web Site: www.poisonedpenpress.com
Key Personnel
Pres & Publr: Robert Rosenwald *E-mail:* robert@poisonedpenpress.com
Ed-in-Chief: Barbara Peters *E-mail:* barbara@poisonedpenpress.com
Ed: Annette Rogers *E-mail:* annette@poisonedpenpress.com
Mktg Coord: Tiffany White *E-mail:* tiffany@poisonedpenpress.com
Prodn Coord: Pete Zrioka *E-mail:* pete@poisonedpenpress.com
Admin Asst: Diane DiBiase *E-mail:* diane@poisonedpenpress.com
Data Entry Specialist: Ariel Amsden
E-mail: ariel@poisonedpenpress.com
Founded: 1997
Publishing high quality works in the field of mystery. Interested in publishing books that we think booksellers everywhere & especially independent mystery booksellers would want to have available to sell. Electronic submissions only. Visit www.poisonedpenpress.com, click on Publishing Information, then on Manuscript Submission Guidelines for submission information.
ISBN Prefix(es): 978-1-890208; 978-1-59058
Number of titles published annually: 40 Print; 50 E-Book
Total Titles: 600 Print; 500 E-Book
Imprints: Poisoned Pen Press (adult mystery); The Poisoned Pencil (young adult mystery)
Foreign Rep(s): Baror International (Worldwide)
Foreign Rights: Danny Baror (Worldwide)
Distribution Center: Ingram Publisher Services (IPS), One Ingram Blvd, La Vergne, TN 37086 *Tel:* 617-793-5000 *Toll Free Tel:* 866-400-5351 (orders) *E-mail:* ips@ingramcontent.com *Web Site:* www.ingramcontent.com
Membership(s): AAP; The Independent Book Publishers Association; Publishers Association of the West

Polar Bear & Co
8 Brook St, Solon, ME 04979
Mailing Address: PO Box 311, Solon, ME 04979-0311
Tel: 207-643-2795
Web Site: www.polarbearandco.com
Key Personnel
Publr & Consultant: Paul Cornell du Houx
Founded: 1991
Rebuilding our cultural heritage with words & art, we are publishers of high quality fiction & nonfiction who provide consultancy services for writers, artists & photographers who wish to bring out that spark in us all. We produce books highlighting social & environmental issues, works that grow with the readership in time.
ISBN Prefix(es): 978-1-882190
Number of titles published annually: 6 Print
Total Titles: 40 Print; 3 Audio

Foreign Office(s): 22-12 Miyamotocho Itabashiku, T174 Tokyo, Japan, Contact: Takafumi Suzuki
Distribution Center: Baker & Taylor, 2550 Tyvola Rd, Suite 300, Charlotte, NC 28217 *Tel:* 704-998-3100 *Toll Free Tel:* 800-775-1800 *Web Site:* www.btol.com

Polebridge Press
Division of Westar Institute
c/o Willamette University, 900 State St, Salem, OR 97301
Tel: 503-375-5323
E-mail: orders@westarinstitute.org
Web Site: www.polebridgepress.com
Key Personnel
Publr: Lawrence Alexander *E-mail:* lalexander@polebridgepress.com
Assoc Publr & Dir, Mktg: Cassandra Farrin
E-mail: cfarrin@polebridgepress.com
Opers Dir & Dist Mgr: Bill Lehto *E-mail:* bill.lehto@polebridgepress.com
Art Dir & Prodn Mgr: Robaire Ream
E-mail: robaire.ream@westarinstitute.org
Mng Ed: Char Matejovsky *E-mail:* char@polebridgepress.com
Accts Mgr: Alisha Beck *E-mail:* alisha.beck@westarinstitute.org
Founded: 1981
Publishes up-to-date reference works for biblical scholars, primarily in support of research on the historical Jesus & the origins of Christianity; scholarly books produced by Westar seminars, research projects & by individual scholars; books & periodicals that disseminate the results of critical scholarship on religion to the public.
ISBN Prefix(es): 978-1-59815; 978-0-944344
Number of titles published annually: 10 Print; 6 E-Book; 3 Audio
Total Titles: 110 Print; 30 E-Book; 93 Audio
Returns: 660 S Mansfield, Ypsilanti, MI 48197, Contact: Bill Lehto *Tel:* 651-605-5275 *E-mail:* bill.lehto@westarinstitute.org

Police Executive Research Forum
1120 Connecticut Ave NW, Suite 930, Washington, DC 20036
Tel: 202-466-7820 *Fax:* 202-466-7826
E-mail: perf@policeforum.org
Web Site: www.policeforum.org
Key Personnel
Dir, Communs: Craig Fischer *Tel:* 202-454-8332
Opers Admin: Rebecca Neuburger *Tel:* 202-454-8300 *E-mail:* rneuburger@policeforum.org
Chief of Staff: Andrea Luna *Tel:* 202-454-8346
Receptionist/Staff Asst: Alicia Armstrong
Founded: 1977
Community policing, POP, police research & management, police & criminal justice.
ISBN Prefix(es): 978-1-878734
Number of titles published annually: 5 Print
Total Titles: 70 Print
Distribution Center: Whitehurst & Clark, 1200 Rte 523, Flemington, NJ 08822, Contact: Brad Searles *Toll Free Tel:* 888-202-4563 *Fax:* 908-237-2407 *E-mail:* wcbooks@aol.com

Polis Books
1201 Hudson St, No 211S, Hoboken, NJ 07030
E-mail: info@polisbooks.com; submissions@polisbooks.com
Web Site: www.polisbooks.com; facebook.com/PolisBooks; twitter.com/PolisBooks
Key Personnel
Publr: Jason Pinter
Founded: 2013
Publishing primarily commercial fiction in adult, young adult & middle grade.
ISBN Prefix(es): 978-1-940610
Number of titles published annually: 30 Print; 40 Audio

Foreign Rights: The Book Publishers Association of Israel (Israel); Agentur Brauer (Austria, Germany, Switzerland); Sandra Bruna Agencia Literaria (Brazil, Latin America, Portugal, Spain); Graal Literary Agency (Croatia, Czech Republic, Estonia, Hungary, Poland, Serbia, Slovakia, Slovenia); Nova Littera Ltd (Russia); Peony Literary Agency (China, Taiwan); Ulf Toregard Agency AB (Denmark, Finland, Holland, Iceland, Norway, Scandinavia, Sweden); Tuttle-Mori Agency Inc (Japan)
Distribution Center: Publishers Group West, 1700 Fourth St, Berkeley, CA 94710 *Toll Free Tel:* 800-788-3123 SAN: 202-8522

Pomegranate Communications Inc
19018 NE Portal Way, Portland, OR 97230
Tel: 503-328-6500 *Toll Free Tel:* 800-227-1428 *Fax:* 503-328-9330 *Toll Free Fax:* 800-848-4376
E-mail: contactus@pomegranate.com
Web Site: www.pomegranate.com
Key Personnel
Pres & Intl Rts: Thomas F Burke
Publr: Katie Burke
Asst Publr: Becky Holtzman
Intl Sales Dir: Darius Burke
Founded: 1968
Fine arts publisher of books, calendars, puzzles, stationery & children's products.
ISBN Prefix(es): 978-0-87654; 978-1-56640; 978-0-7649
Number of titles published annually: 12 Print
Total Titles: 120 Print
Imprints: PomegranateKids
Foreign Rep(s): Ashton International (Far East, Middle East); Canadian Manda (Canada); Hardie Grant Books (Australia, New Zealand); Pomegranate Europe Ltd (Europe, UK); Pomegranate International Sales (Africa, Latin America)
Membership(s): American Specialty Toy Retailing Association; APPL; Art Libraries Society of North America; MSA; Pacific Northwest Booksellers Association; Publishers Association of the West; Toy International Association

Portfolio
Subsidiary of Penguin Group (USA) LLC
375 Hudson St, New York, NY 10014
Key Personnel
Pres & Publr: Adrian Zackheim
VP, Assoc Publr & Mktg Dir: William Weisser
VP & Exec Dir, Copyediting: Tory Klose
Art Dir: Christopher Sergio
Dir, Publicity & Assoc Dir, Mktg: Tara Gilbride
Dir, Publicity: Allison McLean
Exec Mng Ed: Tricia Conley
Exec Ed: Eric Nelson
Sr Ed: Stephanie Frerich; Niki Papadopoulos
Ed: Emily Angell
Assoc Ed: Natalie Horbachevsky
Founded: 2001
Specialize in management, leadership, marketing, business narrative, investing, personal finance, economics & career advice.
ISBN Prefix(es): 978-1-59184
Number of titles published annually: 78 Print
Total Titles: 286 Print

Potomac Books Inc
Imprint of University of Nebraska Press
22841 Quicksilver Dr, Dulles, VA 20166
Tel: 703-661-1548 *Fax:* 703-661-1547
E-mail: pbimail@presswarehouse.com
Web Site: www.potomacbooksinc.com
Key Personnel
Publr: Samuel R Dorrance *Tel:* 703-996-1028 *E-mail:* sam@booksintl.com
Prodn Ed: Katherine Owens
Mktg: Laura Briggs
Founded: 1984 (prior to 2005, Brassey's Inc)
ISBN Prefix(es): 978-1-57488; 978-1-59797
Number of titles published annually: 80 Print; 50 E-Book
Total Titles: 550 Print; 400 E-Book
Foreign Rep(s): International Publishers Representatives (IPR) (Middle East); Login Brothers Canada (Canada); Orca Book Services (Europe, Ireland, UK); Peribo (Australia, New Zealand); Transatlantic Publishers Group Ltd (UK)
Foreign Rights: The Asano Agency Inc (Japan); CA-LINK International LLC (China); Graal Literary Agency (Eastern Europe, Poland); Natoli, Stefan & Oliva (Italy); La Nouvelle Agence (France); Julio F Yanez Agencia Literaria SL (Spanish languages)
Distribution Center: Books International, 22883 Quicksilver Dr, Dulles, VA 20166 *Tel:* 703-661-1500 *Fax:* 703-661-1501
Membership(s): NAIPR

Clarkson Potter Publishers
Imprint of Crown Publishing Group
c/o Random House Inc, 1745 Broadway, New York, NY 10019
Tel: 212-782-9000 *Toll Free Tel:* 888-264-1745 *Fax:* 212-572-6181
Web Site: www.clarksonpotter.com; www.randomhouse.com/crown/clarksonpotter
Key Personnel
SVP & Publr, Clarkson Potter, Ten Speed Press & Harmony: Aaron Wehner
VP & Assoc Publr: Doris Cooper
VP & Dir, Mktg & Publicity: Kate Tyler
Creative Dir: Marysarah Quinn
Asst Dir, Mktg: Carly Gorga
Asst Dir, Publicity: Anna Mintz
Publicist: Sean Boyles
Assoc Publicist: Natasha Martin
Mktg Mgr, Clarkson Potter & Harmony: Stephanie Davis
Asst Mktg Mgr: Kevin Sweeting
Assoc Mgr, Foreign Rts: Nidhi Berry
Sr Ed: Aliza Fogelson
Sr Ed, Potter Style: Jay Sacher
Ed: Angelin Borsics; Ashley Phillips; Lisa Tauber
Assoc Ed: Jessica Freeman-Slade
Assoc Ed, Potter Style: Camaren Subiyah
Ed-at-Large: Francis Lam
Founded: 1959
Illustrated & non-illustrated books on style, design, architecture, cookery, gardening, crafts, fashion, health, house & home.
Random House Inc & its publishing entities are not accepting unsol submissions, proposals, mss or submission queries via e-mail at this time.
ISBN Prefix(es): 978-0-609; 978-0-307; 978-1-4000; 978-0-517
Number of titles published annually: 145 Print
Total Titles: 1,000 Print
Imprints: Clarkson Potter; Pam Krauss Books; Potter Craft; Potter Style
Distributed by Random House
Advertising Agency: Franklin Spier

powerHouse Books
Division of powerHouse Cultural Entertainment Inc
37 Main St, Brooklyn, NY 11201
Tel: 212-604-9074 *Fax:* 212-366-5247
E-mail: info@powerhousebooks.com
Web Site: www.powerhousebooks.com
Key Personnel
Publr: Daniel Power
Mng Ed: Craig Cohen *E-mail:* press@powerhousebooks.com
Founded: 1995
Contemporary art, photography & image-based cultural books.
ISBN Prefix(es): 978-1-57687
Number of titles published annually: 45 Print; 1 E-Book
Total Titles: 350 Print; 3 E-Book; 1 Audio
Imprints: Miss Rosen Edition
Distributed by Random House Publisher Services
Distributor for Antinous Press; Juno Books; MTV Press; Throckmorton Press; VH1 Press; Vice Books
Foreign Rep(s): Bookwise International Pty Ltd (Australia); Critiques Livres (France); Peter Hyde Associates (South Africa); Perseus Books Group (Canada); Shimada (Japan); Turnaround (Austria, Eastern Europe, Germany, Ireland, Mediterranean, Scandinavia, Switzerland, UK)
Foreign Rights: Bookwise International Pty Ltd (Australia); Critiques Livres (France); Turnaround (UK)
Warehouse: Random House

Practice Management Information Corp (PMIC)
4727 Wilshire Blvd, Suite 300, Los Angeles, CA 90010
SAN: 139-438X
Tel: 323-954-0224 *Fax:* 323-954-0253 *Toll Free Fax:* 800-633-6556 (orders)
E-mail: orders@medicalbookstore.com; customer.service@pmiconline.com
Web Site: www.pmiconline.com
Key Personnel
Publr & Pres: James B Davis
Founded: 1986
Books & software for physicians, hospitals, insurance companies & other healthcare professionals on medical coding, reimbursement, practice management, financial management & medical risk management.
ISBN Prefix(es): 978-1-878487 (Health Info); 978-1-57066
Number of titles published annually: 35 Print
Total Titles: 35 Print
Imprints: Health Information Press (HIP)
Branch Office(s)
PMIC Sales Office, 2001 Butterfield Rd, Suite 850, Downers Grove, IL 60515 *Tel:* 630-964-7800 *Toll Free Tel:* 800-MEDSHOP *Fax:* 630-964-8873

§Practising Law Institute
1177 Avenue of the Americas, New York, NY 10036
SAN: 203-0136
Tel: 212-824-5700 *Toll Free Tel:* 800-260-4PLI (260-4754, cust serv) *Fax:* 212-265-4742 (intl) *Toll Free Fax:* 800-321-0093 (local)
E-mail: info@pli.edu (cust serv)
Web Site: www.pli.edu
Key Personnel
CFO & Treas: Frank De Vivo *Tel:* 212-824-5709 *E-mail:* fdevivo@pli.edu
CIO: Kenneth Moskowitz *Tel:* 212-824-5766 *E-mail:* kmoskowitz@pli.edu
Pres: Victor J Rubino *Tel:* 212-824-5701 *E-mail:* vrubino@pli.edu
EVP: Sandra R Geller *Tel:* 212-824-5796 *E-mail:* sgeller@pli.edu
VP: William Cubberley *Tel:* 212-824-5761 *E-mail:* wcubberley@pli.edu
VP, Cust Rel: Kevin Kelly *Tel:* 212-824-8839 *E-mail:* kkelly@pli.edu
VP, Progs: Anita C Shapiro *Tel:* 212-824-5760 *E-mail:* ashapiro@pli.edu
Founded: 1933
Professional books for lawyers; CDs, DVDs, CD-ROMs, programs.
ISBN Prefix(es): 978-0-87224; 978-1-4024
Number of titles published annually: 181 Print
Total Titles: 233 Print; 4 CD-ROM; 206 Online; 308 Audio
Imprints: PLI
Branch Office(s)
685 Market St, Suite 100, San Francisco, CA 94105-4202 *Tel:* 415-498-2800
Distributed by PLI
Shipping Address: PMDS, 1780A Crossroads Dr, Odenton, MD 21113 *Tel:* 301-604-3305

Prayer Book Press Inc
Subsidiary of Media Judaica Inc
1363 Fairfield Ave, Bridgeport, CT 06605
SAN: 282-1796
Tel: 203-384-2284 *Fax:* 203-579-9109
Key Personnel
Pres & Ed: Jonathan D Levine
VP & Prodn Mgr: Andrew Amsel
VP & Sales & Dist Mgr: Walter B Stern
Compt: Sharon Dworkin
Founded: 1933
Religion (Jewish); prayer books, textbooks, gift editions & reference.
ISBN Prefix(es): 978-0-87677
Number of titles published annually: 5 Print; 1 Audio
Total Titles: 50 Print; 5 Audio
Imprints: Center for Contemporary Judaica

PRB Productions
963 Peralta Ave, Albany, CA 94706-2144
Tel: 510-526-0722 *Fax:* 510-527-4763
E-mail: prbprdns@aol.com
Web Site: www.prbmusic.com
Key Personnel
Prop & Publr: Peter R Ballinger; Leslie J Gold
Founded: 1989
Specialize in publishing high-quality performing editions of instrumental & vocal music from the Baroque & Classical eras, along with original contemporary works for early & contemporary instruments & voices. Customized music typesetting services available by special arrangement.
ISBN Prefix(es): 978-1-56571
Number of titles published annually: 10 Print
Total Titles: 300 Print

Prentice Hall Press
Division of Penguin Group (USA) LLC
375 Hudson St, New York, NY 10014
Tel: 212-366-2000 *Fax:* 212-366-2666
Key Personnel
Publr, Busn, Self-Help & Health: John Duff
Ed: Jeanette Shaw
Founded: 1913
Number of titles published annually: 7 Print
Total Titles: 134 Print

PREP Publishing
Subsidiary of PREP Inc
3528 Turnberry Circle, Fayetteville, NC 28303
Tel: 910-483-6611 *Toll Free Tel:* 800-533-2814
E-mail: preppub@aol.com
Web Site: www.prep-pub.com
Key Personnel
Publr: Anne McKinney
Lib Sales Dir: Frances Sweeney
Founded: 1994
Books designed to enrich people's lives & help optimize the human experience. Publisher of general trade books, fiction & nonfiction, especially books related to careers, job hunting, government jobs & business planning, marketing & entrepreneurship. Fiction titles include mysteries, Christian fiction & romance.
ISBN Prefix(es): 978-1-885288
Number of titles published annually: 8 Print
Total Titles: 52 Print
Imprints: Business Success Series; Government Jobs Series; Judeo Christian Ethics Series; Anne McKinney Career Series
Advertising Agency: McKinney Communications, PO Box 66, Fayetteville, NC 28302-0066, Contact: Pat Mack
Warehouse: 435 W Russell St, Fayetteville, NC 28301
Membership(s): Community of Literary Magazines & Presses; The Independent Book Publishers Association; Southern Independent Booksellers Alliance

Presbyterian Publishing Corp (PPC)
100 Witherspoon St, Louisville, KY 40202
Tel: 502-569-5000 *Toll Free Tel:* 800-523-1631 (US only) *Fax:* 502-569-5113
E-mail: ppcmail@presbypub.com
Web Site: www.ppcbooks.com
Key Personnel
COO: Monty Anderson *E-mail:* manderson@wjkbooks.com
Pres & Publr: Marc Lewis *E-mail:* mlewis@wjkbooks.com
Exec Dir, Publg & Edit: David Dobson *Tel:* 502-569-5394 *E-mail:* ddobson@wjkbooks.com
Exec Dir, Sales & Mktg: Gavin Stephens *E-mail:* gstephens@wjkbooks.com
Founded: 1838
Biblical studies, academic & scholarly textbooks, general trade religious books.
ISBN Prefix(es): 978-0-664; 978-0-8042
Number of titles published annually: 80 Print; 2 CD-ROM
Total Titles: 1,700 Print; 5 CD-ROM
Imprints: Geneva Press; Westminster John Knox Press (WJK)
Distributed by Spring Arbor Distributors
Distributor for Epworth; SCM
Foreign Rep(s): Alban Books Ltd (Europe, UK)
See separate listing for:
Westminster John Knox Press (WJK)

The Press at California State University, Fresno
Unit of California State University, Fresno
2380 E Keats, M/S MB 99, Fresno, CA 93740-8024
Tel: 559-278-3056 *Fax:* 559-278-6758
E-mail: press@csufresno.edu
Web Site: shop.thepressatcsufresno.com; thepressatcsufresno.com
Key Personnel
Gen Mgr: Carla Millar
Founded: 1982
Art, architecture, drama, music, film & the media, New Age politics, business, autobiography, Armenian history, Fresno history & Literary magazine. Peer reviewed multi-disciplinary victimology journal.
ISBN Prefix(es): 978-0-912201
Number of titles published annually: 4 Print; 1 Online
Total Titles: 30 Print

Prestel Publishing
900 Broadway, Suite 603, New York, NY 10003
Tel: 212-995-2720 *Toll Free Tel:* 888-463-6110 (cust serv) *Fax:* 212-995-2733
E-mail: sales@prestel-usa.com
Web Site: www.prestel.com
Key Personnel
VP: Stephen Hulburt *Tel:* 212-995-2720 ext 22 *E-mail:* shulburt@prestel-usa.com
Mktg & Spec Sales Dir: Raya Thoma *E-mail:* rthoma@prestel-usa.com
Acqs Ed: Holly La Due
Publicist: Anne Wu *E-mail:* awu@prestel-usa.com
Founded: 1999
ISBN Prefix(es): 978-3-7913
Number of titles published annually: 150 Print
Total Titles: 1,000 Print
Distributor for Die Gestalten Verlag (DGV); Loft; Lars Muller; Periscope; Schirmer/Mosel
Warehouse: Innovative Logistics, 406 Wyckoff Mills Rd, East Windsor, NJ 08520 *Tel:* 732-363-5679 *Fax:* 732-363-0338 *Toll Free Fax:* 877-372-8892

§Prevention Products & Services Inc dba The Bureau for At-Risk Youth
PO Box 170, Farmingville, NY 11738
Toll Free Tel: 800-99YOUTH (999-6884) *Fax:* 631-389-2511
Web Site: www.at-risk.com
Key Personnel
Owner: Carmine Russo
Founded: 1988
Educational materials on at-risk children's issues for educators, counselors, parents & children.
ISBN Prefix(es): 978-1-56688
Number of titles published annually: 15 Print
Total Titles: 250 Print
Returns: c/o Karol Media, 375 Stewart Rd, Wilkes-Barre, PA 18706-1246

Price Stern Sloan
Imprint of Penguin Group (USA) LLC
345 Hudson St, New York, NY 10014
SAN: 282-5074
Tel: 212-366-2000
E-mail: online@penguinputnam.com
Web Site: www.penguinputnam.com; us.penguingroup.com
Key Personnel
VP & Publr: Francesco Sedita
Founded: 1963
ISBN Prefix(es): 978-0-201; 978-0-8431
Number of titles published annually: 29 Print
Total Titles: 319 Print
Imprints: Crazy Games; Doodle Art; Serendipity; Troubador Press; Wee Sing

§Price World Publishing
3971 Hoover Rd, Suite 77, Columbus, OH 43123-2839
Toll Free Tel: 888-234-6896 *Fax:* 216-803-0350
E-mail: info@priceworldpublishing.com
Web Site: www.priceworldpublishing.com
Key Personnel
Pres & Exec Ed: Robert Price, Esq *Tel:* 888-234-6896 ext 713 *E-mail:* rprice@priceworldpublishing.com
Acqs Ed: Miss Takako Sakai
Founded: 2001
Bringing books & ebooks to global markets.
ISBN Prefix(es): 978-1-932549; 978-0-9724102; 978-1-61984; 978-1-93691
Number of titles published annually: 15 Print; 1 CD-ROM; 50 E-Book
Total Titles: 81 Print; 2 CD-ROM; 387 E-Book
Distributed by David Bateman Ltd (New Zealand); Cardinal Publishers Group (US); Fortytwo Bookz Galaxy (India)
Foreign Rep(s): Gazelle Book Services (UK); Monarch Books of Canada (Canada); John Reed Books (Australia); Rights & Distribution Inc (Brunei, Hong Kong, Malaysia, New Zealand, Philippines, Singapore, South Africa, Thailand)
Foreign Rights: Rights & Distribution Inc
Orders to: Cardinal Publishers Group, 2402 Shadeland Ave, Suite A, Indianapolis, IN 46219, Pres: Tom Doherty *Tel:* 317-352-8200 *Fax:* 317-352-8202 *E-mail:* tdoherty@cardinalpub.com *Web Site:* www.cardinalpub.com
Membership(s): American Bar Association; The Independent Book Publishers Association

Prima Games
Imprint of Random House Information Group
3000 Lava Ridge Ct, Roseville, CA 95661
SAN: 289-5609
Tel: 916-787-7000 *Fax:* 916-787-7001
Web Site: www.primagames.com
Key Personnel
Pres: Debra Kempker
Founded: 1984
Computer & video game guides.
Random House Inc & its publishing entities are not accepting unsol submissions, proposals, mss, or submission queries via e-mail at this time.
ISBN Prefix(es): 978-0-7615
Number of titles published annually: 150 Print
Total Titles: 1,100 Print

Primary Research Group Inc
2753 Broadway, Suite 156, New York, NY 10025
Tel: 212-736-2316 *Fax:* 212-412-9097
E-mail: primaryresearchgroup@gmail.com
Web Site: www.primaryresearch.com
Key Personnel
Pres: James Moses
Founded: 1989
Monographs, books, surveys & research reports on library science industry, economics, publishing (book, electronic & magazine), telecommunication, entertainment & higher education.
ISBN Prefix(es): 978-1-57440
Number of titles published annually: 35 Print
Total Titles: 175 Print
Distributed by Academic Book Center; Ambassador Books; The Book House; Coutts Library Service; Croft House Books; Eastern Book Company; MarketResearch.com; Midwest Library Service; OPAMP Technical Books; Emory Pratt; Research & Markets; Rittenhouse Book Distributors; Total Information; Yankee Book Peddler

Princeton Architectural Press
37 E Seventh St, New York, NY 10003
Tel: 212-995-9620 *Toll Free Tel:* 800-722-6657 (dist); 800-759-0190 (sales) *Fax:* 212-995-9454
E-mail: sales@papress.com
Web Site: www.papress.com
Key Personnel
Publr: Kevin C Lippert *Tel:* 212-995-9620 ext 203 *E-mail:* lippert@papress.com
Mng Ed: Tom Cho
Sr Ed: Linda Lee *Tel:* 212-995-9620 ext 226 *E-mail:* linda@papress.com
Prog Dir, Paper+Goods: Sara McKay
Publicity Dir: Diane Levinson
Publicist: Stephanie Leke
Sales & Mktg Dir: Lia Hunt
Founded: 1981
Publisher of high quality books in architecture, graphic design & visual culture.
ISBN Prefix(es): 978-0-910413; 978-1-878271; 978-1-56898
Number of titles published annually: 100 Print
Total Titles: 700 Print
Distributed by Chronicle Books
Distributor for Balcony Press; Hyphen Press
Foreign Rep(s): Abrams UK (David Gooding) (Europe, Ireland, UK); Chronicle Books (Central America, South America, USA); JCC Enterprises Inc (Bermuda, Caribbean, Latin America); Raincoast Books (Canada)
Distribution Center: Chronicle Books, 680 Second St, San Francisco, CA 94107 *Toll Free Tel:* 800-759-0190 *Toll Free Fax:* 800-286-9471 *E-mail:* order.desk@hbgusa.com *Web Site:* www.chroniclebooks.com

§Princeton Book Co Publishers
614 Rte 130, Hightstown, NJ 08520
Tel: 609-426-0602 *Toll Free Tel:* 800-220-7149 *Fax:* 609-426-1344
E-mail: pbc@dancehorizons.com; elysian@princetonbookcompany.com
Web Site: www.dancehorizons.com
Key Personnel
Pres & Rts & Perms: Charles Woodford
Dir: Connie Woodford
Ad & Internet: John McMenamin
Cust Serv: Marcia Sylvester
Founded: 1975
Specialize in dance.
ISBN Prefix(es): 978-0-916622; 978-0-87127; 978-0-903102; 978-0-85418; 978-0-932582; 978-0-7121; 978-0-8463; 978-0-340
Number of titles published annually: 6 Print; 3 E-Book
Total Titles: 150 Print; 14 E-Book
Imprints: Dance Horizons; Dance Horizons Video; Elysian Editions (adult nonfiction)
Distributed by Dance Books Ltd
Distributor for Dance Books Ltd; Dance Notation Bureau
Foreign Rep(s): Dance Books Ltd (UK); Footprint Books (Australia, New Zealand)
Shipping Address: Whitehurst & Clark, 1200 County Rd, Rte 523, Flemington, NJ 08822
Warehouse: Whitehurst & Clark, 1200 County Rd, Rte 523, Flemington, NJ 08822

§The Princeton Review
Imprint of Random House Information Group
c/o Random House Inc, 1745 Broadway, New York, NY 10019
Toll Free Tel: 800-733-3000 *Fax:* 212-782-9682
E-mail: princetonreview@randomhouse.com
Web Site: www.princetonreview.com
Key Personnel
VP & Publr: Tom Russell
Mng Ed: Alison Stoltzfus
Test preparation, college & graduate school guides, career guides & general study aids.
Random House Inc & its publishing entities are not accepting unsol submissions, proposals, mss, or submission queries via e-mail at this time.
Number of titles published annually: 75 Print; 12 CD-ROM
Total Titles: 230 Print; 15 CD-ROM

Princeton University Press
41 William St, Princeton, NJ 08540-5237
Tel: 609-258-4900 *Toll Free Tel:* 800-777-4726 (orders) *Fax:* 609-258-6305 *Toll Free Fax:* 800-999-1958
E-mail: orders@cpfsinc.com
Web Site: press.princeton.edu
Key Personnel
CIO: Dennis Langlois
Exec Ed: Seth Ditchik *Tel:* 609-258-9428; Robert Tempio *Tel:* 609-258-0843
Publr, Field Guides & Exec Ed: Robert Kirk *Tel:* 609-258-4884
Publr, Sciences, Europe: Ingrid Gnerlich
Dir: Peter Dougherty *Tel:* 609-258-6778 *E-mail:* peter_dougherty@press.princeton.edu
Dir, Contracts: Shaquona Crews
Publicity Dir: Andrew DeSio *Tel:* 609-258-5165
Sales Dir: Timothy Wilkins *Tel:* 609-258-4877
UK Intl Rts Dir: Kim Williams
Sr Publicist: Julia Haav; James Schneider
Asst Press Dir & Mktg Dir: Adam Fortgang *Tel:* 609-258-4896 *E-mail:* adam_fortgang@press.princeton.edu
Asst Dir, Ed-in-Chief & Exec Ed: Brigitta van Rheinberg *Tel:* 609-258-4935 *E-mail:* brigitta_vanrheinberg@press.princeton.edu
Assoc Dir & Cont: Patrick Carroll *Tel:* 609-258-2486 *E-mail:* patrick_carroll@press.princeton.edu
Exhibits Mgr: Melissa Burton *Tel:* 609-258-4915 *E-mail:* melissa_burton@press.princeton.edu
Proj & Systems Mgr: Steven Peter
Exec Ed, Anthropology, Music & Religion: Fred Appel *Tel:* 609-258-2484
Exec Ed, Art & Architecture: Michelle Komie
Exec Ed, Literature: Anne Savarese *Tel:* 609-258-4937
Sr Ed, Biology & Earth Sciences: Alison Kalett *Tel:* 609-258-9232
Sr Ed, Political Science & American History: Eric Crahan *Tel:* 609-258-4922
Sr Ed, Sociology & Psychology: Meagan Stacey Levinson
Assoc Ed, Physical & Earth Sciences: Eric Henney
Asst Ed: Ryan Mulligan
Founded: 1905
Scholarly, scientific & trade books on all subjects.
ISBN Prefix(es): 978-0-691
Number of titles published annually: 250 Print; 100 E-Book
Total Titles: 4,000 Print; 800 E-Book
Imprints: Bollingen Series
Foreign Office(s): 6 Oxford St, Woodstock, Oxfordshire 0X20 1TW, United Kingdom, Publg Dir, Europe: Caroline Priday *Tel:* (01993) 814500 *Fax:* (01993) 814504 *E-mail:* cpriday@pupress.co.uk
c/o John Wiley & Sons Distribution Center, One Oldlands Way, Bognor Regis, West Sussex P022 9NQ, United Kingdom
Foreign Rep(s): African Moon Press (Chris Reinders) (South Africa); APD (Singapore); Aromix Books Co Ltd (Hong Kong); Avicenna Partnership Ltd (Claire de Gruchy) (Algeria, Cyprus, Jordan, Libya, Malta, Morocco, Palestine, Tunisia); Book Promotions Ltd (South Africa); Everest International Publishing Services (Wei Zhao) (China); ICK (Information & Culture) (Korea); S Janakiraman, Book Marketing Services (Bangladesh, Sri Lanka); B K Norton (Taiwan); Rockbook (Japan); University Press Group (Africa, Europe, India, Israel, Middle East, Pakistan, UK); Kelvin van Hasselt Publishing Services (Africa exc North & South Africa); World Press (Saleem Malik) (Pakistan)
Foreign Rights: APD (Malaysia, Thailand); Mega Texts (Philippines)
Advertising Agency: Caslon
Orders to: California/Princeton Fulfillment Services Inc, 1445 Lower Ferry Rd, Ewing, NJ 08618 *Tel:* 609-883-1759 *Toll Free Tel:* 800-777-4726 *Fax:* 609-883-7413 *Toll Free Fax:* 800-999-1958 *E-mail:* orders@cpfsinc.com; University Press Group Ltd, New Era Estate, Oldlands Way, Bognor Regis, West Sussex P022 9NQ, United Kingdom (UK & Europe), Contact: Lois Edwards *Tel:* (01243) 842165 *Fax:* (01243) 842167 *E-mail:* sales@upguk.com
Warehouse: California/Princeton Fulfillment Services Inc, 1445 Lower Ferry Rd, Ewing, NJ 08618 *Tel:* 609-883-1759 *Fax:* 609-883-7413 *E-mail:* orders@cpfsinc.com
Membership(s): AAP; American Association of University Presses; BISG

§Printing Industries of America
200 Deer Run Rd, Sewickley, PA 15143-2324
Tel: 412-741-6860; 412-259-1770
E-mail: membercentral@printing.org (orders)
Web Site: www.printing.org
Key Personnel
Dir: Amy Woodall
Ed: Joe Deemer
Founded: 1924
Textbooks & reference books on graphic communications techniques & technology.
ISBN Prefix(es): 978-0-88362
Number of titles published annually: 10 Print; 5 E-Book
Total Titles: 250 Print; 10 E-Book
Divisions: Web Offset Association (WOA)

Printing Industries Press, see Printing Industries of America

Privacy Journal
PO Box 28577, Providence, RI 02908
Tel: 401-274-7861 *Fax:* 401-274-4747
E-mail: orders@privacyjournal.net
Web Site: www.privacyjournal.net
Key Personnel
Publr: Robert Ellis Smith
Founded: 1974
Monthly newsletter.
ISBN Prefix(es): 978-0-930072
Number of titles published annually: 1 Print; 1 CD-ROM; 1 E-Book
Total Titles: 12 Print; 1 CD-ROM; 5 E-Book
Membership(s): The Association of Publishers for Special Sales; The Authors Guild; The Independent Book Publishers Association; Independent Publishers of New England

PRO-ED Inc
8700 Shoal Creek Blvd, Austin, TX 78757-6897
SAN: 222-1349
Tel: 512-451-3246 *Toll Free Tel:* 800-897-3202 *Fax:* 512-451-8542 *Toll Free Fax:* 800-397-7633
E-mail: general@proedinc.com
Web Site: www.proedinc.com
Key Personnel
COO & Gen Coun: Robert Lum *Tel:* 512-451-3246 ext 664
Founded: 1977
College & professional reference books, tests, student materials, journals in education & psychology.
ISBN Prefix(es): 978-0-936104; 978-0-89079
Number of titles published annually: 50 Print
Total Titles: 1,500 Print

Pro Lingua Associates Inc
74 Cotton Mill Hill, Suite A-315, Brattleboro, VT 05301
SAN: 216-0579
Mailing Address: PO Box 1348, Brattleboro, VT 05302-1348
Tel: 802-257-7779 *Toll Free Tel:* 800-366-4775 *Fax:* 802-257-5117
E-mail: info@prolinguaassociates.com
Web Site: www.prolinguaassociates.com
Key Personnel
Pres & Publr: Arthur A Burrows *E-mail:* andy@prolinguaassociates.com
VP & Ed: Raymond C Clark
Treas & Lib Sales Dir: Elise C Burrows
Secy: Patrick R Moran
Founded: 1980
Teacher resource handbooks, language teacher training handbooks, English language & foreign language texts.
ISBN Prefix(es): 978-0-86647
Number of titles published annually: 7 Print
Total Titles: 114 Print; 8 Online; 11 Audio
Foreign Rep(s): Baja Ediciones SA (BESA) (Mexico); Bookman Books (Taiwan); English Central (Canada); English Language Bookshop (England); Foreign Language Bookshop (Australia); Foreign Language Ltd (Korea); Independent Publishers International (Japan); Nellie's Group Ltd (Japan); B K Norton (Taiwan)
Membership(s): The Children's Book Council; Teachers of English to Speakers of Other Languages

§Productivity Press
Division of Taylor & Francis Group
c/o Routledge, 711 Third Ave, New York, NY 10017
SAN: 290-036X
Tel: 212-216-7800 *Toll Free Tel:* 800-634-7064 (orders) *Fax:* 212-563-2269 *Toll Free Fax:* 800-248-4724 (orders)
E-mail: info@productivitypress.com; orders@taylorandfrancis.com
Web Site: www.productivitypress.com
Key Personnel
Sr Acqs Ed: Michael Sinocchi *Tel:* 212-216-7867 *E-mail:* michael.sinocchi@taylorandfrancis.com
Mgr, Mktg: Christopher Manion *Tel:* 800-272-7737 ext 2508 *E-mail:* chris.manion@taylorandfrancis.com
Founded: 1983
Books & AV programs. Publishes & distributes materials on productivity, quality improvement, product development, corporate management, profit management & employee involvement for business & industry. Many products are direct source materials from Japan that have been translated into English for the first time.
ISBN Prefix(es): 978-0-915299; 978-1-56327; 978-0-915801
Number of titles published annually: 12 Print
Total Titles: 200 Print; 4 CD-ROM
Imprints: Healthcare Performance Press; Productivity Press Spanish Imprint
Foreign Rep(s): Asia Pacific Research Center (Singapore); Books Aplenty (South Africa); Learning & Productivity (Australia); OCAPT Inc (Canada); Prism Books Private Ltd (India); Productivity Editorial Consultores SPD CV (Mexico)

Professional Communications Inc
20968 State Rd 22, Caddo, OK 74729
Mailing Address: PO Box 10, Caddo, OK 74729-0010
Tel: 580-367-9838 *Toll Free Tel:* 800-337-9838 *Fax:* 580-367-9989
E-mail: info@pcibooks.com
Web Site: www.pcibooks.com
Key Personnel
Pres & Publr: J Malcolm Beasley *Tel:* 631-661-2852 *Fax:* 631-661-2167 *E-mail:* jmbpci@earthlink.net
VP: Phyllis Jones Freeny
Founded: 1992
Medicine.
ISBN Prefix(es): 978-1-884735; 978-0-932610
Number of titles published annually: 5 Print
Total Titles: 41 Print
Branch Office(s)
Bulk Sales only, 400 Center Bay Dr, West Islip, NY 11795

§The Professional Education Group Inc (PEG)
Subsidiary of CredibleLaw
12401 Minnetonka Blvd, Suite 200, Minnetonka, MN 55305-3994
Tel: 952-933-9990 *Toll Free Tel:* 800-229-2531 *Fax:* 952-933-7784
E-mail: orders@proedgroup.com
Web Site: www.proedgroup.com
Key Personnel
Pres: Paul A Fogelberg *E-mail:* paul@proedgroup.com
SVP: Henry Lake *E-mail:* henry@proedgroup.com
Founded: 1981
Continuing legal education materials; audio & video programs & books.
ISBN Prefix(es): 978-0-943380; 978-1-932831
Number of titles published annually: 6 Print; 1 CD-ROM; 6 Online; 5 Audio
Total Titles: 43 Print; 40 CD-ROM; 40 Online; 43 Audio
Distributed by ALI-ABA; American Bar Association
Distributor for ALI-ABA; American Bar Association; ASPEN
Membership(s): Association for Continuing Legal Education

§Professional Publications Inc (PPI)
1250 Fifth Ave, Belmont, CA 94002
SAN: 264-6315
Tel: 650-593-9119 *Fax:* 650-592-4519
E-mail: info@ppi2pass.com
Web Site: ppi2pass.com; feprep.com
Key Personnel
Pres: Michael Lindeburg
Edit Dir: Heather Subba *Tel:* 650-593-9119 ext 139 *E-mail:* hsubba@ppi2pass.com
Dir, Mktg: Thomas Hayward *Tel:* 650-593-9119 ext 1010 *E-mail:* thayward@ppi2pass.com
Dir, Prod Devt: Sarah Hubbard *Tel:* 650-593-9119 ext 128 *E-mail:* shubbard@ppi2pass.com
Founded: 1981
Provider of exam review books, online products & live & online classes in the fields of engineering, land surveying, LEED, architecture, interior design & landscape architecture. Specialty engineering areas include civil, structural, seismic, mechanical, electrical, environmental, chemical, nuclear, geotechnical & industrial engineering fields.
ISBN Prefix(es): 978-0-932276; 978-0-912045; 978-1-888577; 978-1-59126
Number of titles published annually: 10 Print; 1 CD-ROM; 2 Online; 5 E-Book
Total Titles: 120 Print; 20 Online; 20 E-Book
Distributor for American Association of State Highway & Transportation Officials; American Wood Council (American Forest & Paper Association) (National Design Specification for Wood Construction (NDS) & others); International Code Council; McGraw-Hill Professional (green building, design & construction titles, LEED titles); National Council of Examiners for Engineering & Surveying; SmartPros; Transportation Research Board Code; US Green Building Council (LEED reference guides)
Membership(s): American Society of Civil Engineers; American Society of Engineering Educators; American Society of Mechanical Engineers; National Society of Professional Engineers; US Green Building Council

Professional Resource Press
Imprint of Professional Resource Exchange Inc
1958 Barber Rd, Sarasota, FL 34240
SAN: 240-1223
Mailing Address: PO Box 3197, Sarasota, FL 34230-3197
Tel: 941-343-9601 *Toll Free Tel:* 800-443-3364 (orders & cust serv) *Fax:* 941-343-9201 *Toll Free Fax:* 866-804-4843 (orders only)
E-mail: cs.prpress@gmail.com
Web Site: www.prpress.com
Key Personnel
Pres: Judith W Ritt *E-mail:* jwrprp@gmail.com
Mktg & Lib Sales Dir: J M Warinner *E-mail:* judew61@gmail.com
Mng Ed: Laurie Girsch
Cust Serv: Jeff Klosterman *E-mail:* jdkprp@gmail.com
Founded: 1980
Books (clinical & forensic psychology), CD-ROMs, DVDs, continuing education programs & texts for mental health & health care professionals. Includes medicine & nursing.
ISBN Prefix(es): 978-0-943158; 978-1-56887
Number of titles published annually: 15 Print; 5 CD-ROM; 4 E-Book; 3 Audio
Total Titles: 230 Print; 10 CD-ROM; 4 E-Book; 17 Audio
Advertising Agency: Ashley Ball Group, 630 Venice Lane, Sarasota, FL 34242 *Tel:* 941-993-3598
Membership(s): The Association of Publishers for Special Sales

Progressive Press
3716 37 St, San Diego, CA 92105-2409
SAN: 222-5395
Tel: 619-892-7781 *Fax:* 619-892-7781
E-mail: info@progressivepress.com
Web Site: www.progressivepress.com
Key Personnel
Owner: John-Paul Leonard
Founded: 1973
Small publisher of political trade paperbacks. Also provides distribution for one Canadian publisher & several self-published authors. Frontlist: politics, backlist: New Age.
ISBN Prefix(es): 978-0-930852; 978-1-61577
Number of titles published annually: 6 Print
Total Titles: 60 Print
Imprints: Arthritis Research; Banned Books; Collections Livrier; Leaves of Healing; Prensa Pensar; Progressive Press; Tree of Life Books
Distributor for Global Research
Foreign Rep(s): Gazelle Book Services (UK); New Horizons (South Africa); Woodslane (Australia)

Foreign Rights: Beniamino Soressi (Italy); Thinkers Library (Malaysia); Gerhard Wisnewski (Germany)
Membership(s): The Independent Book Publishers Association; PMA International

Prometheus Books
59 John Glenn Dr, Amherst, NY 14228-2119
SAN: 202-0289
Tel: 716-691-0133 *Toll Free Tel:* 800-421-0351 *Fax:* 716-691-0137
E-mail: marketing@prometheusbooks.com; editorial@prometheusbooks.com
Web Site: www.prometheusbooks.com
Key Personnel
Chmn: Paul Kurtz
Pres: Jonathan Kurtz
VP, Busn & Admin Dir: Lynette Nisbet
Edit Dir, Pyr: Rene Sears
Dir, Rts: Gretchen Kurtz *E-mail:* rights@prometheusmail.com
Dir, Publicity: Jill Maxick *Tel:* 800-853-7545 *E-mail:* jmaxick@prometheusbooks.com
Ed-in-Chief: Steven L Mitchell *E-mail:* smitchell@prometheusbooks.com
Mgr, Print-on-Demand Div: Patrick Martin
Publicist: Meghan Quinn
Founded: 1969
Philosophy, social sciences/current events, popular science, religion & politics.
ISBN Prefix(es): 978-0-87975; 978-1-57392; 978-1-59102; 978-1-61614
Number of titles published annually: 120 Print; 100 E-Book
Total Titles: 2,300 Print; 1,500 E-Book
Imprints: Humanity Books (scholarly/academic); Pyr (science fiction/fantasy)
Foreign Rep(s): Random House Publisher Services (Worldwide)
Advertising Agency: University Advertising, PO Box 924, Amhurst, NY 14226

ProQuest LLC
Subsidiary of Cambridge Information Group Inc
789 E Eisenhower Pkwy, Ann Arbor, MI 48108-3218
Mailing Address: PO Box 1346, Ann Arbor, MI 48106-1346
Tel: 734-761-4700 *Toll Free Tel:* 800-521-0600 *Fax:* 734-975-6486 *Toll Free Fax:* 800-864-0019
E-mail: info@proquest.com
Web Site: www.proquest.com
Key Personnel
CEO: Kurt Sanford
CFO: Jonathan Collins
SVP & Gen Mgr: Kevin Sayar
SVP, Global Mktg, Sales & Cust Experience & Serv: Michael Gersch
SVP, Global Sales: Simon Beale
SVP, Global Sales, Mktg & Cust Experience: Kristi Marchbanks
SVP, HR & Busn Servs: Elliot Forsyth
SVP, Info Solutions: Rafael Sidi
SVP, Mktg & Cust Care: Lynda James-Gilboe
SVP, Publg & Global Content Alliances: Rod Gauvin
SVP, Res Solutions: Boe Horton
VP, Content Opers: Vince Price
VP, Global Mktg: Clay McDaniel
VP, Global Sales: Tony Rummans
VP, Technol & Gen Mgr, Cambridge Opers: John Taylor
VP & Gen Mgr, Serials Solutions: Matthew Brine
Gen Coun & Global Content Alliances: Kevin Norris
Interim Dialog Gen Mgr: Julie Janusz
Publisher, distributor & aggregator of value-added information to libraries, government, universities & schools in over 160 countries. Access to information in periodicals, newspapers, doctoral dissertations & out-of-print books (retrospective scholarly works). Produce & publish Dissertation Abstracts International.
ISBN Prefix(es): 978-0-8357; 978-0-608; 978-0-7837; 978-0-591; 978-0-9702937; 978-0-599; 978-1-931694; 978-1-59399; 978-0-496; 978-0-542; 978-1-4247; 978-0-9778091; 978-1-4345; 978-0-549
Number of titles published annually: 56 Print
Total Titles: 56 Print
Subsidiaries: R R Bowker LLC
Branch Office(s)
Micromedia ProQuest, 20 Victoria St, Toronto, ON M5C 2N8, Canada
Foreign Office(s): The Quorum, Barnwell Rd, Cambridge CB5 8SW, United Kingdom
See separate listing for:
R R Bowker LLC

§Prospect Park Books
2359 Lincoln Ave, Altadena, CA 91001
Tel: 626-793-9796
E-mail: info@prospectparkbooks.com
Web Site: www.prospectparkbooks.com
Key Personnel
Publr & Founding Partner: Colleen Dunn Bates
Partner: Patty O'Sullivan
Founded: 2006
Trade publisher.
ISBN Prefix(es): 978-0-9753939; 978-0-9844102; 978-0-9834594; 978-1-938849
Number of titles published annually: 10 Print; 8 E-Book
Total Titles: 45 Print; 40 E-Book
Foreign Rights: Readmore Literary Management (Linda Kaplan) (Worldwide)
Warehouse: Perseus Distribution, 193 Edwards Dr, Jackson, TN 38301 *Toll Free Tel:* 800-343-4499
Distribution Center: Consortium Book Sales & Distribution, The Keg House, 34 13 Ave NE, Suite 101, Minneapolis, MN 55413-1007 *Web Site:* www.cbsd.com SAN: 200-6049
Membership(s): AAP; Community of Literary Magazines & Presses; International Association of Culinary Professionals; Publishers Association of the West

ProStar Publications Inc
3 Church Circle, Suite 109, Annapolis, MD 21401
SAN: 210-525X
Mailing Address: 8643 Hayden Place, Culver City, CA 90232
Tel: 310-280-1010 *Toll Free Tel:* 800-481-6277 *Fax:* 310-280-1025 *Toll Free Fax:* 800-487-6277
E-mail: editor@prostarpublications.com
Web Site: www.prostarpublications.com
Key Personnel
Pres & Publr: Peter L Griffes *E-mail:* peter@prostarpublications.com
Founded: 1965
Books about boating: regional guides, planning, navigation data, nautical charts, marine fauna, how-to, travel, technical, general fiction & music.
ISBN Prefix(es): 978-0-930030; 978-1-57785
Number of titles published annually: 145 Print
Total Titles: 440 Print; 30 CD-ROM
Imprints: Atlantic Boating Almanac; Lighthouse Press; Pacific Boating Almanac; US Coast Pilot

§The PRS Group Inc
6320 Fly Rd, Suite 102, East Syracuse, NY 13057-9358
Tel: 315-431-0511 *Fax:* 315-431-0200
E-mail: custserv@prsgroup.com
Web Site: www.prsgroup.com
Key Personnel
Pres: Mary Lou Walsh
Circ Mgr: Patti Davis
Asst to Pres: Dianna Spinner *E-mail:* dspinner@prsgroup.com
Founded: 1979
Over 100 reports, newsletters, journals & volumes per year for international business. No returns without prior approval.
ISBN Prefix(es): 978-1-933539
Number of titles published annually: 3 Print
Total Titles: 20 Print; 100 CD-ROM; 100 Online; 100 E-Book
Imprints: International Country Risk Guide; Political Risk Services

Prufrock Press
PO Box 8813, Waco, TX 76714-8813
SAN: 851-9188
Tel: 254-756-3337 *Toll Free Tel:* 800-998-2208 *Fax:* 254-756-3339 *Toll Free Fax:* 800-240-0333
E-mail: info@prufrock.com
Web Site: www.prufrock.com
Key Personnel
Publr & Mktg Dir: Joel McIntosh *Tel:* 254-756-3337 ext 203 *E-mail:* jmcintosh@prufrock.com
Sr Ed & Perms Coord: Jennifer Robins *E-mail:* jrobins@prufrock.com
Founded: 1977
Publish supplementary text books & teacher guides for grades K-12, including gifted educational materials.
ISBN Prefix(es): 978-1-883055; 978-0-931724
Number of titles published annually: 20 Print
Total Titles: 200 Print
Membership(s): The Independent Book Publishers Association

§Psychological Assessment Resources Inc (PAR)
16204 N Florida Ave, Lutz, FL 33549
Tel: 813-968-3003; 813-449-4065 *Toll Free Tel:* 800-331-8378 *Fax:* 813-968-2598; 813-961-2196 *Toll Free Fax:* 800-727-9329
E-mail: custsup@parinc.com
Web Site: www4.parinc.com
Key Personnel
Chmn & CEO: R Bob Smith, III *E-mail:* bsmith@parinc.com
COO & EVP: Kay Cunningham *E-mail:* kcunningham@parinc.com
VP, Cust Serv: Cynthia Lumpee *E-mail:* clumpee@parinc.com
VP, Mktg & Sales: Jim Gyurke *E-mail:* jgyurke@parinc.com
VP, R&D: Travis White *E-mail:* twhite@parinc.com
Exec Asst to CEO: Vicki King
Founded: 1978
Career, psychological, neuropsychology, educational & clinical assessments products; software.
ISBN Prefix(es): 978-0-911907
Number of titles published annually: 10 Print; 2 CD-ROM; 1 Online
Total Titles: 150 Print; 20 CD-ROM; 3 Online; 5 Audio
Distributed by ACER; Pro-Ed; The Psychological Corp; Riverside Publishing; Western Psychological Service
Distributor for American Guidance Service; Pro-Ed; The Psychological Corp; Riverside Publishing; Rorschach Workshops
Foreign Rep(s): ACER (Australia); Tea Ediciones (Spain); Testzentrale (Germany)
Returns: 16130 N Florida Ave, Lutz, FL 33549 *E-mail:* gpresson@parinc.com
Warehouse: 16130 N Florida Ave, Lutz, FL 33549 *E-mail:* gpresson@parinc.com

Psychology Press
Imprint of Taylor & Francis Group
711 Third Ave, 8th fl, New York, NY 10017

Tel: 212-216-7800 *Toll Free Tel:* 800-634-7064 *Fax:* 212-563-2269
Web Site: www.psypress.com
Key Personnel
Publr: Paul Dukes *Tel:* 917-351-7103 *E-mail:* paul.dukes@taylorandfrancis.com
Founded: 1983
Created to serve the needs of researchers, students & professionals concerned with the science of human & animal behavior, Psychology Press publishes academic psychology at all levels, including student texts, handbooks, monographs, professional books & scientific journals. Key areas include cognitive psychology, cognitive neuroscience, developmental psychology & family studies, industrial & organizational psychology, neuropsychology & language disorders, research methods & statistics, social psychology.
ISBN Prefix(es): 978-0-8058; 978-0-86377; 978-1-84169; 978-1-84872
Number of titles published annually: 102 Print; 4 CD-ROM; 90 E-Book
Total Titles: 6,000 Print; 6 CD-ROM
Sales Office(s): CRC Press/Taylor & Francis, 6000 Broken Sound Pkwy NW, Suite 300, Boca Raton, FL 33487 *Toll Free Tel:* 800-272-7737 *Toll Free Fax:* 800-374-3401 *E-mail:* orders@crcpress.com
Foreign Office(s): 27 Church Rd, Hove BN3 2FA, United Kingdom, Mng Dir: Michael Forster *Tel:* (020) 7017 6000 *Fax:* (020) 7017 6717 *E-mail:* info@psypress.co.uk
Foreign Rep(s): Ethan Atkin (Latin America)
Foreign Rights: Taylor & Francis (Worldwide)
Distribution Center: Taylor & Francis, 7625 Empire Dr, Florence, KY 41042 *Toll Free Tel:* 800-634-7064 *Toll Free Fax:* 800-248-4724 *E-mail:* orders@taylorandfrancis.com

Public Citizen
1600 20 St NW, Washington, DC 20009
Tel: 202-588-1000 *Fax:* 202-588-7798
E-mail: public_citizen@citizen.org
Web Site: www.citizen.org
Key Personnel
CFO: Joe Stoshak
Pres: Robert Weissman
Founded: 1971
Books & reports; consumer advocacy organization.
ISBN Prefix(es): 978-0-937188; 978-1-58231
Number of titles published annually: 47 Print
Total Titles: 48 Print
Divisions: Congress Watch; Critical Mass Energy Project; Global Trade Watch; Health Research GP Buyers UP; Litigation GP
Branch Office(s)
215 Pennsylvania Ave SE, Washington, DC 20003 *Tel:* 202-546-4996
1303 San Antonio St, Austin, TX 78701 *Tel:* 512-477-1155
Distributed by Addison Wesley; Simon & Schuster Pocket Books
Foreign Rights: Random House-Pantheon

PublicAffairs
Member of The Perseus Books Group
250 W 57 St, Suite 1321, New York, NY 10107
Tel: 212-397-6666 *Toll Free Tel:* 800-343-4499 (orders) *Fax:* 212-397-4277
E-mail: publicaffairs@perseusbooks.com
Web Site: www.publicaffairsbooks.com
Key Personnel
Founder & Ed-at-Large: Peter Osnos
Group Publr: Susan Weinberg
Publr: Clive Priddle
VP, Assoc Publr & Dir, Publicity: Jaime Leifer
Mktg Dir: Lindsay Fradkoff
Publicity Mgr: Emily Lavelle
Publicist: Tony Forde
Mng Ed: Melissa Raymond
Sr Ed: Ben Adams; Colleen Lawrie; Clara Platter
Ed: Brandon Proia
Contrib Ed: John Mahaney
Off Administrator: Darrell Jonas *E-mail:* darrell.jonas@publicaffairsbooks.com
Founded: 1997
Current affairs, history, biography, journalism & social criticism.
ISBN Prefix(es): 978-1-891620; 978-1-58648
Number of titles published annually: 60 Print
Total Titles: 300 Print
Orders to: Perseus Distribution Service, 1094 Flex Dr, Jackson, TN 38301 *Toll Free Fax:* 800-351-5073
Warehouse: Perseus Distribution Service, 1094 Flex Dr, Jackson, TN 38301 *Toll Free Fax:* 800-351-5073
Distribution Center: Perseus Distribution Service, 1094 Flex Dr, Jackson, TN 38301 *Toll Free Fax:* 800-351-5073

§Publication Consultants
8370 Eleusis Dr, Anchorage, AK 99502
Tel: 907-349-2424 *Fax:* 907-349-2426
E-mail: books@publicationconsultants.com
Web Site: www.publicationconsultants.com
Key Personnel
Owner & Publr: Evan Swensen *E-mail:* evan@publicationconsultants.com
Founded: 1978
This publisher has indicated that 40% of their product line is author subsidized.
ISBN Prefix(es): 978-0-9644809; 978-1-888125; 978-1-59433
Number of titles published annually: 30 Print; 30 E-Book
Total Titles: 307 Print; 154 E-Book
Membership(s): Alaska Writers Guild; Better Business Bureau

Publications International Ltd
7373 N Cicero Ave, Lincolnwood, IL 60712
Tel: 847-676-3470 *Fax:* 847-676-3671
E-mail: customer_service@pubint.com
Web Site: www.pilbooks.com
Key Personnel
CEO: Louis Weber
Founded: 1967
ISBN Prefix(es): 978-0-7853; 978-0-88176; 978-1-56173; 978-1-4127; 978-1-60553; 978-1-4508

Puffin Books
Imprint of Penguin Group (USA) LLC
345 Hudson St, New York, NY 10014
SAN: 282-5074
Tel: 212-366-2000
E-mail: online@penguinputnam.com
Web Site: www.penguinputnam.com; us.penguingroup.com
Key Personnel
Pres & Publr: Eileen Kreit
Mng Ed, Assoc Publr: Gerard Mancini
Edit Dir: Kristin Gilson
VP & Exec Art Dir, Penguin Young Readers Design Group: Deborah Kaplan
Founded: 1935
ISBN Prefix(es): 978-0-14
Number of titles published annually: 87 Print
Total Titles: 1,724 Print
Membership(s): The Children's Book Council

Purdue University Press
Stewart Ctr 370, 504 W State St, West Lafayette, IN 47907-2058
SAN: 203-4026
Tel: 765-494-2038 *Fax:* 765-496-2442
E-mail: pupress@purdue.edu
Web Site: www.thepress.purdue.edu
Key Personnel
Ed: Katherine Purple
Prodn Mgr: Bryan Shaffer
Intl Rts: Anu Hansen
Founded: 1960
Publisher of scholarly titles with emphasis on business, veterinary medicine, health issues & the humanities.
ISBN Prefix(es): 978-0-911198; 978-1-55753
Number of titles published annually: 25 Print; 3 E-Book
Total Titles: 350 Print; 10 E-Book
Imprints: Ichor Business Books; Nota Bell Books; PUP Books
Foreign Rep(s): APAC Publishers Services Pty Ltd (Asia, China, Hawaii, Pacific Islands, Singapore, Taiwan, Thailand); Cranbury International (Africa, India, Latin America, South America); The Eurospan Group (Continental Europe, Israel, Middle East, UK); Footprint Books Pty Ltd (Australia, New Zealand); Scholarly Book Services Inc (Canada); United Publishers Services Ltd (Japan)
Foreign Rights: Atmarr Agency Services; Global Rights Agent; Anu Hansen
Orders to: Bookmasters, 30 Amberwood Pkwy, Ashland, OH 44805 *Toll Free Tel:* 800-247-6553 *Fax:* 419-281-6883 *Web Site:* www.bookmasters.com/purduepress
Returns: Bookmasters, 30 Amberwood Pkwy, Ashland, OH 44805 *Toll Free Tel:* 800-247-6553 *Fax:* 419-281-6883 *Web Site:* www.bookmasters.com/purduepress
Warehouse: Bookmasters, 30 Amberwood Pkwy, Ashland, OH 44805 *Toll Free Tel:* 800-247-6553 *Fax:* 419-281-6883 *Web Site:* www.bookmasters.com/purduepress
Distribution Center: Bookmasters, 30 Amberwood Pkwy, Ashland, OH 44805 *Toll Free Tel:* 800-247-6553 *Fax:* 419-281-6883 *Web Site:* www.bookmasters.com/purduepress
Membership(s): American Association of University Presses

§Pureplay Press
195 26 Ave, No 2, San Francisco, CA 94121
Tel: 310-597-0328
E-mail: info@pureplaypress.com
Web Site: www.pureplaypress.com
Key Personnel
Publr & Ed: David Landau *E-mail:* editor@pureplaypress.com
Assoc Publr: Wakeford Gong *E-mail:* wclr@ix.netcom.com
Founded: 2001
Publish books in English & Spanish about history & culture or containing those things (as in literature).
ISBN Prefix(es): 978-0-9714366; 978-0-9765096
Number of titles published annually: 3 Print
Foreign Rights: IMC Literary Agency (all other territories)
Membership(s): The Independent Book Publishers Association; PEN Center USA

Purple House Press
Imprint of Purple House Inc
8100 US Hwy 62 E, Cynthiana, KY 41031
Mailing Address: PO Box 787, Cynthiana, KY 41031
Tel: 859-235-9970
Web Site: www.purplehousepress.com
Key Personnel
Publr: Jill Morgan *E-mail:* jill@purplehousepress.com
Dir, Cust Fulfillment, Managed Info Servs: Ray Sanders *E-mail:* ray@purplehousepress.com
Founded: 2000
Reissue of children's classics from the 1920s-1990s.
ISBN Prefix(es): 978-1-930900
Number of titles published annually: 8 Print; 3 E-Book
Total Titles: 50 Print; 10 E-Book
Warehouse: Purple House Inc, c/o Avi's Warehouse, 974-B US Hwy 62 E, Cynthiana, KY 41031

Purple Mountain Press Ltd
1060 Main St, Fleischmanns, NY 12430
Mailing Address: PO Box 309, Fleischmanns, NY 12430-0309 SAN: 222-3716
Tel: 845-254-4062 *Toll Free Tel:* 800-325-2665 (orders) *Fax:* 845-254-4476
E-mail: purple@catskill.net
Web Site: www.catskill.net/purple
Key Personnel
Pres & Publr: Wray Rominger
Founded: 1973
Publish adult nonfiction books about colonial history & New York State; history, natural history, folklore, the arts, outdoor recreation, a few regional mysteries, also maritime books.
ISBN Prefix(es): 978-0-935796; 978-0-916346; 978-1-930098
Number of titles published annually: 6 Print
Total Titles: 150 Print
Divisions: Harbor Hill Books
Distributor for Carmania Press London (North America only)

Purple Pomegranate Productions
Division of Jews for Jesus
60 Haight St, San Francisco, CA 94102
Tel: 415-864-2600 *Fax:* 415-552-8325
E-mail: sf@jewsforjesus.org
Web Site: www.jewsforjesus.org
Key Personnel
Mdse Mgr: Shannon Fischer
Jewish evangelism, books, pamphlets, music.
ISBN Prefix(es): 978-0-9616148; 978-1-881022
Number of titles published annually: 3 Print
Total Titles: 45 Print; 5 E-Book; 19 Audio

Pushcart Press
PO Box 380, Wainscott, NY 11975-0380
SAN: 202-9871
Tel: 631-324-9300
Key Personnel
Pres: Bill Henderson
Founded: 1972
Trade books, literary anthologies.
ISBN Prefix(es): 978-0-916366; 978-1-888889
Number of titles published annually: 6 Print
Total Titles: 65 Print
Distributed by W W Norton & Co Inc
Distribution Center: 500 Fifth Ave, New York, NY 10110

Putnam Berkley Audio
Imprint of Penguin Group (USA) LLC
375 Hudson St, New York, NY 10014
SAN: 282-5074
Tel: 212-366-2000 *Fax:* 212-366-2666
E-mail: online@penguinputnam.com
Web Site: www.penguinputnam.com; us.penguingroup.com
Founded: 1996
Abridged, unabridged formats; simultaneous release with hardcover.
Total Titles: 21 Audio
Distributor for Arkangel
Orders to: Penguin Group (USA) LLC, 405 Murray Hill Pkwy, East Rutherford, NJ 07073 *Toll Free Tel:* 800-788-6262
Returns: Penguin Group (USA) LLC, 405 Murray Hill Pkwy, East Rutherford, NJ 07073
Warehouse: Penguin Group (USA) LLC, One Grosset Dr, Kirkwood, NY 13795 *Fax:* 607-775-5586

The Putnam Publishing Group
Division of Penguin Group (USA) LLC
375 Hudson St, New York, NY 10014
SAN: 282-5074
Tel: 212-366-2000 *Toll Free Tel:* 800-631-8571 *Fax:* 212-366-2643
E-mail: online@penguinputnam.com
Web Site: www.penguinputnam.com; us.penguingroup.com
Key Personnel
VP & Assoc Publr, Paperbacks: Benjamin Lee
Mktg Dir, Putnam: Ashley Pattison McClay
Mktg Dir, Putnam/Dutton: Carrie Swetonic
Mktg Mgr, Putnam/Dutton: Katie Parry
Asst Mktg Mgr, Putnam: Anna Romig
Publicist: Elena Hershey
Imprints: Avery; Putnam Adult; Putnam Berkley Audio; Putnam Juvenile; Riverhead Books; Jeremy P Tarcher; Tarcher/Penguin
Advertising Agency: Mesa Group

GP Putnam's Sons (Children's)
Member of Penguin Young Readers Group
345 Hudson St, New York, NY 10014
SAN: 282-5074
Tel: 212-366-2000 *Fax:* 212-414-3393
E-mail: online@penguinputnam.com
Web Site: us.penguingroup.com
Key Personnel
Pres & Publr, Nancy Paulsen Books: Nancy Paulsen
VP & Publr, Putnam Books for Young Readers: Jennifer Besser
VP & Art Dir: Cecilia Yung
Assoc Publr & Exec Mng Ed: David Briggs
Assoc Edit Dir: Susan Kochan
Exec Ed: Arianne Lewin
Ed: Stacey Barney
Founded: 1838
ISBN Prefix(es): 978-0-399; 978-0-698
Number of titles published annually: 51 Print
Total Titles: 386 Print
Imprints: PaperStar
Membership(s): The Children's Book Council

GP Putnam's Sons (Hardcover)
Imprint of Penguin Group (USA) LLC
375 Hudson St, New York, NY 10014
SAN: 282-5074
Tel: 212-366-2000
E-mail: online@penguinputnam.com
Web Site: us.penguingroup.com
Key Personnel
Pres, Putnam & Dutton: Ivan Held
SVP & Publr: Neil Nyren
VP & Assoc Publr: Catharine Lynch
VP & Exec Ed: Christine Pepe
VP & Ed: Marian Wood
Exec Ed: Kerri Kolen; Nita Taublib; Leslie Gelbman
Sr Ed: Tara Singh Carlson; John Duff
Dir, Religious Pubns: Joel Fotinos
Dir, Publicity: Alexis Welby
VP & Prodn Dir: William Peabody
VP, Exec Creative Dir: Rich Hasselberger
Dir, Copy Ed: Linda Rosenberg
Dir, Art Interiors: Claire Vaccaro
Dir, Contracts & Copyrights: Jennifer Uram
Mktg Dir, Putnam: Ashley Pattison McClay
Mktg Dir, Putnam/Dutton: Carrie Swetonic
Mktg Mgr, Putnam/Dutton: Katie Parry
Asst Mktg Mgr, Putnam: Anna Romig
Sr Publicist: Ashley Hewlett
Assoc Publicist: Sarah Grimm
Founded: 1838
Fiction & general nonfiction.
ISBN Prefix(es): 978-0-399
Number of titles published annually: 65 Print
Total Titles: 208 Print
Imprints: Ace/Putnam; Grosset/Putnam; Putnam; Putnam Berkley Audio; Marian Wood Books
Advertising Agency: Mesa Group

Pyncheon House
6 University Dr, Suite 105, Amherst, MA 01002
SAN: 297-6269
Key Personnel
Ed-in-Chief: David R Rhodes
Founded: 1991
Fine editions & trade books; contemporary poetry, short fiction, novels & essays; member of Library of Congress CIP Program.
ISBN Prefix(es): 978-1-881119
Number of titles published annually: 4 Print
Total Titles: 16 Print

Quackenworth Publishing
PO Box 4747, Culver City, CA 90231-4747
Tel: 310-945-5634 *Toll Free Tel:* 888-701-4991 *Fax:* 310-945-5709 *Toll Free Fax:* 888-892-6339
E-mail: info@quackenworth.com
Web Site: www.quackenworth.com; www.wittybittybunch.com
Key Personnel
Pres: David Hollaway
Dir, Sales & Mktg: Damien Harvey
E-mail: damien@quackenworth.com
Dir, Online Strategy: Anthony Green
E-mail: anthony@quackenworth.com
Founded: 2003
Publisher & distributor of children's books & educational materials.
ISBN Prefix(es): 978-1-933211
Number of titles published annually: 10 Print
Total Titles: 60 Print; 12 CD-ROM; 8 E-Book
Returns: 20223 Campaign Dr, Carson, CA 90746
Warehouse: 5855 Centinela Ave, Los Angeles, CA 90045

Quail Ridge Press
101 Brooks Dr, Brandon, MS 39042
Mailing Address: PO Box 123, Brandon, MS 39043 SAN: 214-2201
Tel: 601-825-2063 *Toll Free Tel:* 800-343-1583 *Fax:* 601-825-3091 *Toll Free Fax:* 800-864-1082
E-mail: info@quailridge.com
Web Site: quailridge.com
Key Personnel
COO: Terresa Ray *E-mail:* tray@quailridge.com
Publr: Barney McKee *E-mail:* bmckee@quailridge.com
Ed-in-Chief: Gwen McKee *E-mail:* gmckee@quailridge.com
Founded: 1978
Cookbooks, general interest, regional, health.
ISBN Prefix(es): 978-0-937552
Number of titles published annually: 4 Print
Total Titles: 132 Print

§Quality Medical Publishing Inc
2248 Welsch Industrial Ct, St Louis, MO 63146-4222
Tel: 314-878-7808 *Toll Free Tel:* 800-348-7808 *Fax:* 314-878-9937
E-mail: qmp@qmp.com
Web Site: www.qmp.com
Key Personnel
Pres: Karen Berger *E-mail:* kberger@qmp.com
Founded: 1987
Medical books (especially surgery); plastic, neurological, spine & orthopaedics.
ISBN Prefix(es): 978-0-942219; 978-1-57626
Number of titles published annually: 16 Print
Total Titles: 145 Print; 2 CD-ROM
Imprints: QMP

Quarto Publishing Group USA Inc
Subsidiary of Quarto Group Inc (London, UK)
400 First Ave N, Suite 300, Minneapolis, MN 55401
SAN: 289-7148
Tel: 612-344-8100 *Toll Free Tel:* 800-328-0590 (sales); 800-458-0454 *Fax:* 612-344-8691
E-mail: sales@creativepub.com
Web Site: quartoknows.com
Key Personnel
CEO & Pres: Ken Fund
CFO: George Maspeller
VP & Sales Dir: Tara Catogge

Publr, Home Improvement: Bryan Trandem
Dir, Quayside Dist Servs: John Groton
Assoc Dir, Children's Book Mktg, Publicity & Soc Media: Michelle Bayuk
Represents a dynamic group of imprints dedicated to providing quality & excellence to its readers. Each imprint embodies the breadth & scope of its specialty topics.
ISBN Prefix(es): 978-0-86573; 978-1-58923; 978-1-61673; 978-1-61058; 978-1-61059; 978-1-61060; 978-1-62788
Number of titles published annually: 300 Print
Total Titles: 4,000 Print
Imprints: Cool Springs Press; Creative Publishing International; Fair Winds Press; Walter Foster Publishing; Moondance Press; Motorbooks; Quarry Books; QDS; Race Point Publishing; Rock Point Gift & Stationery; Rockport Publishers; Seagrass Press; Voyageur Press; Wellfleet Press; Zenith Press
Divisions: Book Sales Inc; Quayside Distribution Services
Distributed by Allen & Unwin (Australia & New Zealand)
See separate listing for:
Book Sales Inc
Fair Winds Press
Walter Foster Publishing Inc

Quicksilver Productions
PO Box 340, Ashland, OR 97520-0012
Tel: 541-482-5343 *Toll Free Fax:* 888-974-6462
E-mail: celestialcalendars@email.com
Web Site: www.quicksilverproductions.com
Key Personnel
Prop: Jim Maynard
Off Mgr: Lisa Devalin
Founded: 1972
Publisher of calendars & cookbooks.
ISBN Prefix(es): 978-0-930356 (cookbooks); 978-1-935482 (astrological calendars)
Number of titles published annually: 4 Print
Total Titles: 8 Print

Quincannon Publishing Group
PO Box 8100, Glen Ridge, NJ 07028-8100
Tel: 973-380-9942
E-mail: editors@quincannongroup.com
Web Site: www.quincannongroup.com
Key Personnel
Ed-in-Chief: Alan Quincannon
Ed: Holly Benedict
Consulting Ed: Jeanne Wilcox
Lib Sales Dir & Admin Asst: Patricia Drury
Publicity: Loretta Bolger
Intl Rts: Loris Essary
Founded: 1990
Regional mystery novels made unique by involving some element of a region's history (i.e. the story's setting & time frame or the mystery's origin); custom tailored books for local & regional museums.
ISBN Prefix(es): 978-1-878452
Number of titles published annually: 3 Print
Total Titles: 18 Print; 17 Online
Imprints: Compass Point Mysteries; Jersey Yarns; Learning & Coloring Books; Rune-Tales; Tory Corner Editions
Foreign Rep(s): International Titles

§Quintessence Publishing Co Inc
4350 Chandler Dr, Hanover Park, IL 60133
SAN: 215-9783
Tel: 630-736-3600 *Toll Free Tel:* 800-621-0387 *Fax:* 630-736-3633
E-mail: contact@quintbook.com; service@quintbook.com
Web Site: www.quintpub.com
Key Personnel
Pres: H W Haase
VP, Opers & Dir, Lib Sales: William Hartman *Tel:* 630-736-3600 ext 413 *E-mail:* whartman@quintbook.com
Founded: 1950
Professional & scholarly books, journals, medicine, dentistry, health & nutrition, medical history.
ISBN Prefix(es): 978-0-931386; 978-0-86715
Number of titles published annually: 20 Print; 2 CD-ROM
Total Titles: 410 Print; 80 CD-ROM; 250 Audio
Imprints: Quintessence Books; Quintessence of Dental Technology; Quintessence Pockets
Foreign Office(s): 2-4 Ifenpfad, 12107 Berlin, Germany *Tel:* (030) 761-805 *Fax:* (030) 761-80693 *E-mail:* info@quintessenz.de *Web Site:* www.quintessenz.de
Quint House Bldg, 326 Hongo, Bunkyo-ku Tokyo, Japan *Tel:* (03) 5842-2270 *Fax:* (03) 5800-7598 *E-mail:* info@quint-j.co.jp *Web Site:* www.quint-j.co.jp
2 Graston Rd, New Malden, Surrey KT3 3AB, United Kingdom *Tel:* (020) 8949-6087 *Fax:* (020) 8336-1484 *E-mail:* info@quintpub.co.uk *Web Site:* www.quintpub.co.uk
Distributor for Quintessence Publishing Co Ltd (Japan); Quintessence Publishing Ltd (London); Quintessence Verlags GmbH
Advertising Agency: QPC Advertising Inc

Quirk Books
215 Church St, Philadelphia, PA 19106
Tel: 215-627-3581 *Fax:* 215-627-5220
E-mail: general@quirkbooks.com
Web Site: www.quirkbooks.com
Key Personnel
Owner & CEO, Quirk Productions: David Borgenicht
Pres: Brett Cohen
Publr: Jason Rekulak
VP, Sales: Moneka Hewlett
Dir, Digital & Print Prodn: John McGurk
Assoc Dir, Publicity & Mktg: Nicole De Jackmo
Mng Ed: Mary Ellen Wilson
Publicity Mgr: Nicole de Jackmo
Mktg & Soc Media Coord: Eric Smith
Acqs Ed: Paul Stevens
Edit Asst: Margaret McGuire; Jane Morley
Founded: 2002
Publishing list focuses on irreverent pop-culture, humor, gift, self-help & "impractical" reference books. The actual subject matter of our books is quite diverse. Publish everything from childcare tips & magic tricks to advice on stain removal. All of our books have a distinct sense of style, a refreshing sense of humor & innovative production values.
ISBN Prefix(es): 978-1-931686; 978-1-59474
Number of titles published annually: 25 Print
Total Titles: 150 Print
Distributed by Random House Publisher Services

Quite Specific Media Group Ltd
7373 Pyramid Place, Hollywood, CA 90046
Tel: 323-851-5797 *Fax:* 323-851-5798
E-mail: info@quitespecificmedia.com
Web Site: www.quitespecificmedia.com
Key Personnel
Publr: Ralph Pine *E-mail:* rpine@quitespecificmedia.com
Founded: 1967
Publish original books as well as co-publish with foreign publishers. Specialize in costumes, fashion & theatre.
ISBN Prefix(es): 978-0-89676
Number of titles published annually: 8 Print
Total Titles: 80 Print
Imprints: By Design Press; Costume & Fashion Press; Drama Publishers; EntertainmentPro; Jade Rabbit; Pat MacKay Projects
Foreign Rep(s): Nick Hern Books (UK)
Warehouse: Publishers Storage & Shipping Corp, 660 S Mansfield, Ypsilanti, MI 48197, VP, Opers: Donna Moore *Tel:* 734-487-9720 ext 130

Quixote Press
3544 Black St, Wever, IA 52658
Tel: 319-372-7480 *Toll Free Tel:* 800-571-2665 *Fax:* 319-372-7485
E-mail: heartsntummies@gmail.com; potpress@gmail.com
Key Personnel
Pres: Bruce Carlson
Founded: 1985
Regional paperback books of humor or folklore & cookbooks. Consulting work for self-publishers.
ISBN Prefix(es): 978-1-878488; 978-1-57166
Number of titles published annually: 35 Print
Total Titles: 350 Print
Imprints: Black Iron Cookin' Co; Hearts & Tummies Cookbook Co; Raise the Dough in 30 Days Co
See separate listing for:
Hearts & Tummies Cookbook Co

Rada Press Inc
One Richdale Ave, Unit 10, Cambridge, MA 02140
Tel: 651-645-3304
E-mail: info@radapress.com
Web Site: www.radapress.com
Key Personnel
Publr & Ed: Irving Fang *Tel:* 651-645-3304 *E-mail:* fangx001@umn.edu
Prodn Head: Ron-Michael Pellant *E-mail:* rm@radapress.com
Mktg Dir: Daisy Pellant *E-mail:* daisy@radapress.com
Founded: 1975
ISBN Prefix(es): 978-0-9604212; 978-1-933011
Number of titles published annually: 2 Print; 1 E-Book
Total Titles: 13 Print; 1 E-Book
Imprints: Tree Frog Publications

§Radix Press
Subsidiary of UGF/OR
11715 Bandlon Dr, Houston, TX 77072
Tel: 281-879-5688
Web Site: www.specialforcesbooks.com
Key Personnel
Dir: Stephen Sherman *E-mail:* sherman1@flash.net
Founded: 1983
Directories, reference books. All unsol mss sent will be discarded.
ISBN Prefix(es): 978-0-9624009; 978-0-9623992; 978-1-929932
Number of titles published annually: 3 Print; 2 CD-ROM
Total Titles: 40 Print; 12 CD-ROM
Imprints: Electric Strawberry Press

Rainbow Books Inc
PO Box 430, Highland City, FL 33846
SAN: 221-9859
Tel: 863-648-4420 *Fax:* 863-647-5951
E-mail: info@rainbowbooksinc.com
Web Site: www.rainbowbooksinc.com
Key Personnel
Pres & Edit Dir: Betsy Lampe
Publr: Betty Wright *E-mail:* blfallot@aol.com
Opers Dir: C Marzen Lampe
Prodn Mgr: Marilyn Ratzlaff
Founded: 1979
How-to both for the adult layman & the juvenile markets, self-help, reference, resource & general books; parenting; nonfiction; also package books for other publishers & act as consultants, mystery & mainstream fiction at 50,000 or 75,000 words.
ISBN Prefix(es): 978-0-935834; 978-1-56825

Number of titles published annually: 20 Print
Total Titles: 141 Print
Foreign Rep(s): Hagenbach & Bender (Worldwide exc USA)
Foreign Rights: Hagenbach & Bender (Worldwide exc USA)
Warehouse: Publishers Storage & Shipping Corp, 660 S Mansfield St, Ypsilanti, MI 48197-5167, Contact: Donna Moore *Tel:* 734-487-9720 *Fax:* 734-487-1890 *E-mail:* dmoore@psscmi.com *Web Site:* www.pssc.com
Membership(s): AAP; Florida Authors & Publishers Association Inc; National Association of Independent Publishers

Rainbow Publishers
PO Box 261129, San Diego, CA 92196
Tel: 858-277-1167 *Toll Free Tel:* 800-323-7337 *Toll Free Fax:* 800-331-0297
E-mail: info@rainbowpublishers.com; editor@rainbowpublishers.com (edit dept)
Web Site: www.rainbowpublishers.com
Key Personnel
Publr: Daniel Miley
Founded: 1951
Christian education books.
ISBN Prefix(es): 978-0-937282; 978-1-885358; 978-1-58411
Number of titles published annually: 12 Print
Total Titles: 250 Print
Imprints: Legacy Press

Ram Publishing Co
Subsidiary of Garrett Electronics
1881 W State St, Garland, TX 75042
Tel: 972-494-6151 *Toll Free Tel:* 800-527-4011 *Fax:* 972-494-1881
E-mail: sales@garrett.com
Web Site: www.garrett.com
Key Personnel
Ed: Steve Moore
Founded: 1967
Nonfiction on treasure hunting with a metal detector & metal detector security.
ISBN Prefix(es): 978-0-915920
Number of titles published annually: 3 Print
Total Titles: 15 Print

§RAND Corp
1776 Main St, Santa Monica, CA 90407-2138
Mailing Address: PO Box 2138, Santa Monica, CA 90407-2138
Tel: 310-393-0411 *Fax:* 310-393-4818
Web Site: www.rand.org
Key Personnel
Dir, Opers: Jane Ryan *Tel:* 310-393-0411 ext 7260 *E-mail:* ryan@rand.org
Dir, Strategic Communs: Peg Schumacher *E-mail:* pege@rand.org
Mng Ed: Steve Kistler
Mgr, Publg Servs: Paul Murphy
Print & Dist Mgr: Tim Erickson
Cust Serv Supv: Amy Majczyk *Tel:* 412-683-2300 ext 4604
Founded: 1948
Public policy research.
ISBN Prefix(es): 978-0-8330
Number of titles published annually: 140 Print; 100 Online; 50 E-Book
Total Titles: 20,000 Print; 15,000 Online; 1,500 E-Book
Divisions: Office of External Affairs
Foreign Rep(s): Aditya Books Pvt Ltd (India); Booknet Co Ltd (Cambodia, Laos, Myanmar, Thailand, Vietnam); ChoiceTEXTS Ltd (Indonesia, Singapore); iCaves Ltd (Hong Kong); IG Knowledge Services Ltd (Taiwan); iGroup (Brunei, China, Hong Kong, India, Indonesia, Malaysia, Philippines, Singapore, Taiwan); iGroup Press Co Ltd (China); Inbooks (Australia); Information Development Consultancy (IDC) (Korea); MegaTEXTS Phil Inc (Philippines); NBN Canada (Canada); NBN/DA Trade (Australia, New Zealand); NBN International (Europe, Middle East, UK)
Orders to: RAND Distribution Services, 4570 Fifth Ave, Pittsburgh, PA 15213, Cust Serv Mgr: Amy Majczyk *Tel:* 412-683-2300 *Toll Free Tel:* 877-584-8642 *Fax:* 412-802-4981 *E-mail:* order@rand.org
Distribution Center: National Book Network, 4720 Boston Way, Blue Ridge Summit, PA 17214 *Tel:* 717-794-3800 *Toll Free Tel:* 800-462-6420 *Toll Free Fax:* 800-338-4550 *E-mail:* mcozy@nbnbooks.com *Web Site:* www.nbnbooks.com
Membership(s): AIGA, the professional association for design; American Association of University Presses; Public Relations Society of America; Society for Scholarly Publishing; Washington Book Publishers

§Rand McNally
9855 Woods Dr, Skokie, IL 60077
SAN: 203-3917
Mailing Address: PO Box 7600, Chicago, IL 60680-7600
Tel: 847-329-8100 *Toll Free Tel:* 800-678-7263 *Fax:* 847-329-6139
E-mail: ctsales@randmcnally.com; mediarelations@randmcnally.com
Web Site: www.randmcnally.com
Key Personnel
CEO & Pres: David Muscatel
VP, Mktg: Kendra Ensor
Founded: 1856
Road atlases & maps; world atlases; mileage & routing publications & software; educational maps, atlases; children's atlases, maps, books; electronic multimedia products; retail & online stores; online travel services, travel software.
Publisher of the *Thomas Guide* atlas series.
ISBN Prefix(es): 978-0-528
Number of titles published annually: 20 Print
Total Titles: 100 Print; 5 CD-ROM
Imprints: Rand McNally for Kids
Subsidiaries: Allmaps
Warehouse: 106 Hi-Lane, Richmond, KY 40475

Peter E Randall Publisher
5 Greenleaf Woods Dr, Suite 102, Portsmouth, NH 03801
Mailing Address: PO Box 4726, Portsmouth, NH 03802-4726
Tel: 603-431-5667 *Fax:* 603-431-3566
E-mail: media@perpublisher.com
Web Site: www.perpublisher.com
Key Personnel
Owner & CEO: Deidre C Randall *E-mail:* deidre@perpublisher.com
Founded: 1970
This publisher has indicated that 100% of their product line is author subsidized.
ISBN Prefix(es): 978-0-914339; 978-1-931807; 978-0-9817898; 978-0-9828236; 978-1-937721
Number of titles published annually: 20 Print; 5 E-Book

Random House Children's Books
Division of Random House Inc
1745 Broadway, New York, NY 10019
Tel: 212-782-9000 *Toll Free Tel:* 800-200-3552 *Fax:* 212-782-9452
Web Site: randomhousekids.com
Key Personnel
Pres & Publr: Barbara Marcus
EVP, Publg Opers: Rich Romano
SVP & Assoc Publr: Judith Haut
SVP, Mktg: John Adamo
VP & Publr, Bantam Delacorte Dell: Beverly Horowitz
VP & Publr, Crown Books for Young Readers: Phoebe Yeh
VP & Publr, Knopf Books for Young Readers: Jennifer M Brown
VP & Publg Dir, Knopf/Crown: Nancy Hinkel
VP & Publg Dir, Schwartz & Wade Books: Anne Schwartz; Lee Wade
VP & Publg Dir, Wendy Lamb Books: Wendy Lamb
VP, Assoc Publr & Art Dir, Random House/Golden Books Young Readers Group: Cathy Goldsmith
VP & Exec Mng Ed: Denise DeGennaro
VP & Ed-in-Chief, Random House Books for Young Readers & Publg Dir, Golden Group: Mallory Loehr
VP & Dir, Brand/Category Mgmt: Enid Chaban
VP & Dir, Children's Retail Sales: Becky Green
VP & Prodn Dir: Linda Palladino
VP, Group Sales Dir & Dir, Mass Mdse Sales: Mark Santella
VP, Subs Rts Mkts: Pam White
Exec Dir, Consumer Devt: Rachel Feld
Exec Dir, Mktg & Design Opers: Mary Beth Kilkelly
Exec Dir, Mktg, Licensing & Proprietary Brands: Kerri Benvenuto
Exec Dir, Mktg Prodn & Opers: Beth Conte
Exec Dir, Art & Design, Knopf Delacorte Dell Young Readers Group: Isabel Warren-Lynch
Dir, Content Devt: Lynn Kestin
Dir, Mktg: Kimberly Lauber
Dir, School & Lib Mktg: Adrienne Waintraub
Assoc Publg Dir, Random House/Golden Books Group: Michelle Nagler
Assoc Publg Dir & Exec Ed, Knopf/Crown: Nancy Siscoe
Publicity Dir: Noreen Herits
Assoc Dir, Publicity: Casey Lloyd
Art Dir, Random House Books for Young Readers: Jan Gerardi
Art Dir, Mass Mkt, Random House/Golden Books Young Readers Group: Tracy Tyler
Art Dir, KDD Art Group: Alison Impey
Assoc Art Dir, KDD Art Group: Stephanie Moss
Assoc Art Dir: Sharon Burkle; Lora Grisafi
Exec Ed, Doubleday: Francoise Bui
Exec Ed, Media & Series, Bantam Delacorte Dell: Wendy Loggia
Edit Dir, Picture Books: Maria Modugno
Sr Mktg Mgr: Stephanie O'Cain
Sr Mgr, Lib Mktg: Laura Antonacci
Publicity Mgr & Online Media Specialist: Dominique Cimina
Sr Publicist: Lydia Finn
Publicist & Online Media Specialist: Meg O'Brien
Publicist: Emily Pourciau; Jillian Vandall; Elizabeth Zajac
Assoc Dir, Subs Rts: Kim Wrubel
Edit Dir, Sesame Workshop, Random House Books for Young Readers: Naomi Kleinberg
Ed-in-Chief & Exec Dir, Licensed Publg, Golden Books: Chris Angelilli
Exec Ed: Erin Clarke
Exec Ed, Crown Books for Young Readers: Emily Easton
Exec Ed, Disney Books for Young Readers: Andrea Posner-Sanchez
Exec Ed, Random House Books for Young Readers: Heidi Kilgras
Edit Dir, Novelty, Random House/Golden Books Young Readers Group: Dennis Shealy
Creative Dir, Random House/Golden Books for Young Readers Group: Martha Rago
Dir, Mktg, New Media: Linda Leonard
Assoc Art Dir: Sarah Hokanson
Assoc Publg Dir, Knopf Children's: Melanie Cecka
Mng Ed, Knopf Children's: Dawn Ryan
Sr Ed, Knopf Books for Young Readers: Michele Burke; Allison Worchte
Sr Ed, Schwartz & Wade Books: Annie Kelley
Ed: Frank Berrios
Ed, Knopf Books for Young Readers: Julia Maguire

Assoc Ed, Golden Books: Courtney Carbone
Assoc Ed, Knopf Books for Young Readers: Katherine Harrison
Asst Ed: Jenna Lettice
Asst Ed, Knopf Books for Young Readers: Stephen Brown
Asst Ed, Schwartz & Wade: Stephanie Pitts
Soc Media Mgr: Chelsea Hassman
Assoc Mgr, Consumer Devt: Melissa Zar
Assoc Mktg Mgr: Nora MacDonald
Asst Mktg Mgr: Hannah Black; Nick Elliot; Sarah Wharton
Asst Mktg Mgr, Trade: Ashley Woodfolk
Mktg Assoc, Licensed & Proprietary Brands: Lauren Adams
Mktg Coord, Licensed & Proprietary Brands: Emily Ollis
Mktg Coord: Alissa Nigro; Danielle Rollins
Mktg Assoc: Linda Camacho
Mng Prodr, Content Devt & Mktg: Alison Folino
Prodr: Santhana Souksamrane
Prodn Assoc: Maggie Gibson; Alice Rahaeuser
Publg Consultant: Robin Corey
Sr Designer: Krister Engstrom
Jr Designer: Jinna Shin
Random House Inc & its publishing entities are not accepting unsol submissions, proposals, mss, or submission queries via e-mail at this time.
ISBN Prefix(es): 978-0-679; 978-0-307; 978-0-676; 978-0-375; 978-1-4000; 978-1-58836
Imprints: Beginner Books; Robin Corey Books; Crown Books for Young Readers; Delacorte Books for Young Readers; Doubleday Books for Young Readers; Dragonfly; Golden Books; Alfred A Knopf Books for Young Readers; Laurel-Leaf; Random House Books for Young Readers; Schwartz & Wade Books; Wendy Lamb Books; Yearling
Divisions: Knopf Delacorte Dell Young Readers Group; Random House/Golden Books Young Readers Group
Warehouse: Crawfordsville Distribution Center, 1019 N State Rd 47, Crawfordsville, IN 47933
Distribution Center: Crawfordsville Distribution Center, 1019 N State Rd 47, Crawfordsville, IN 47933
Membership(s): Association of Booksellers for Children; The Children's Book Council

Random House Large Print
Division of Random House Inc
1745 Broadway, New York, NY 10019
Tel: 212-782-9000 *Fax:* 212-782-9484
Key Personnel
Edit Dir: Amy Metsch
Founded: 1990
Acquires & publishes general interest fiction & nonfiction in large print editions.
Random House Inc & its publishing entities are not accepting unsol submissions, proposals, mss, or submission queries via e-mail at this time.
ISBN Prefix(es): 978-0-679
Number of titles published annually: 40 Print
Total Titles: 300 Print

Random House Publishing Group
Division of Random House Inc
1745 Broadway, New York, NY 10019
SAN: 214-1175
Toll Free Tel: 800-200-3552
Web Site: atrandom.com
Key Personnel
CFO, Penguin Random House: Milena Alberti
Pres & Publr: Gina Centrello
SVP & Deputy CFO, Penguin Random House: James Johnston
Publr, Random House & Dial Press: Susan Kamil
Publr, Spiegel & Grau: Julie Grau; Cindy Spiegel
Deputy Publr, Nonfiction & Publr, Modern Library: Thomas Perry
Assoc Publr & Edit Strategy: Gina Wachtel
Assoc Publr, Nonfiction, Ballantine Bantam Dell: Richard Callison
Assoc Publr, Spiegel & Grau & Dir, Mktg, Random House, Spiegel & Grau, Dial Press & Modern Library: Leigh Merchant
COO & EVP: Nihar Malaviya
Group EVP & Dir, Publg: Bill Takes
Group SVP & Creative Dir: Paolo Pepe
Group SVP & Mktg Dir: Sanyu Dillon
EVP, Assoc Publr & Exec Edit Dir: Kate Medina
SVP & Dir, Publg Opers: Lisa Feuer
SVP & Dir, Penguin Random House Intl Sales & Mktg & Dir, East Asia Busn Devt: Cyrus Kheradi
SVP & Publr, Ballantine Bantam Dell: Libby McGuire
SVP & Deputy Publr, Ballantine Bantam Dell: Kim Hovey
SVP & Sr Dir, Subs Rts: Denise Cronin
SVP & Dir, Digital Marketplace Devt: Amanda Close
SVP & Edit Dir, Ballantine: Linda Marrow
SVP & Ed-in-Chief, Ballantine Bantam Dell: Jennifer Hershey
SVP & Dir, Corp Communs: Claire von Schilling
SVP & Dir, Publicity: Theresa Zoro
SVP & Publr, Digital Content: Scott Shannon
SVP: Nina von Moltke
VP & Assoc Publr, Del Rey/VP & Assoc Publr, Mass Mkt, Ballantine Bantam Dell: Keith Clayton
VP & Sr Dir, Copy: Grant Neumann
VP & Dir, Digital Strategy: Matt Schwartz
VP & Dir, Publicity, Random House: Sally Marvin
VP & Edit Dir, Bantam Books/Delacorte Press: Kate Miciak
VP & Edit Dir, Nonfiction: Andy Ward
VP & Edit Dir, Nonfiction, Ballantine Bantam Dell: Jennifer Tung
VP & Exec Ed: David Ebershoff
VP, Assoc Publr, Random House & Dial Press: Avideh Bashirrad
Edit Dir, Fiction, Ballantine Bantam Dell: Mark Tavani
Exec Dir, Art/Design: Robbin Schiff
Sr Dir, Art/Design: Beck Stvan
Sr Art Dir: Joe Perez
Exec Ed, Ballantine: Pamela Cannon; Marnie Cochran; Susanna Porter
Exec Ed, Ballantine Bantam Dell: Tracy Devine
Exec Ed, Random House: Susan Mercandetti; Will Murphy
Dir, Ad & Promo: Stacey Witcraft
Dir, Creative Servs: Annette Melvin
Dir, Dom Rts: Rachel Bernstein
Dir, Interior Design: Carole Lowenstein
Dir, Partnerships & Busn Devt: Melissa Milsten
Dir, Spec Events: Kate Childs
Group Sales Dir: Cynthia Lasky
Imprint Sales Dir: Allyson Pearl
Deputy Dir, Digital Mktg: Susana Zialcita
Deputy Dir, Publicity: London King; David Moench; Cindy Murray
Assoc Dir, Publicity: Melanie DeNardo
Asst Dir, Publicity: Maria Braeckel; Jennifer Garza
Assoc Dir, Foreign Rts: Rachel Kind
Sr Mng Ed, Random House & Copy Chief: Benjamin Dreyer
Sr Mgr, Ad & Promos: Elizabeth Fabian
Sr Mktg Mgr: Erika Greber
Mktg Mgr: Maggie Oberrender
Sr Publicity Mgr: Michelle Jasmine; Greg Kubie
Publicity Mgr: Alison Masciovecchio
Publicity Mgr, Spec Events & Partnerships: Jenna Friedman
Publicist, Partnerships & Spec Events: Abbey Corey
Publicist: Lindsay Kennedy
Assoc Publicist: Alex Coumbis; Ella Maslin; Katie McNally
Sr Ed: Andrea Walker
Sr Ed, Ballantine Bantam Dell: Sara Weiss
Ed: Caitlin Alexander; Kate Collins; Noah Eaker; Anne Groell; Dana Isaacson; Christopher Jackson; Sam Nicholson; Tricia Pasternak; Anna Pitoniak; Shauna Summers; Paul Taunton
Ed, Spiegel & Grau: Jessica Sindler
Assoc Ed: Priyanka Krishnan; Kaela Myers; Nina Shield
Assoc Ed, Alibi: Randall Klein
Assoc Ed, Hydra: Sarah Reed
Assoc Ed, Spiegel & Grau: Laura Van der Veer
Asst Ed: Mika Kasuga; Caitlin McKenna; Sarah Murphy; Molly Turpin
Ed-at-Large, Ballantine Bantam Dell: Alino Cho
Ed-at-Large, Del Rey/Ballantine: Shelly Shapiro
Ed-at-Large, Flirt & Loveswept: Sue Grimshaw
Founded: 1925
General fiction & nonfiction hardcover, trade & mass market paperbacks.
Random House Inc & its publishing entities are not accepting unsol submissions, proposals, mss, or submission queries via e-mail at this time.
ISBN Prefix(es): 978-0-307; 978-0-679; 978-0-89141; 978-0-345; 978-0-449; 978-0-8129; 978-0-375; 978-1-4000; 978-1-58836; 978-0-8041
Number of titles published annually: 700 Print; 150 E-Book
Total Titles: 5,900 Print; 1,100 E-Book
Imprints: Alibi (mystery, thriller, suspense); Ballantine Books; Bantam Books; Del Rey; Dell; The Dial Press; Flirt (new adult); Hydra (science fiction & fantasy); Loveswept (digital only romance); Modern Library; One World; Presidio Press; Random House; Spiegel & Grau; Triumph Books; Villard; Zinc Ink
Warehouse: 400 Hahn Rd, Westminster, MD 21157

Random House Reference/Random House Puzzles & Games/House of Collectibles
Imprint of Random House Audio Publishing Group
1745 Broadway, New York, NY 10019
Toll Free Tel: 800-733-3000 *Toll Free Fax:* 800-659-2436
E-mail: words@random.com; puzzles@random.com
Key Personnel
SVP & Publr: Amanda D'Acierno
Assoc Dir, Mng Edit: Alison Skrabek
Publishes reference, crossword puzzle books & chess books & price guides for collectibles.
Random House Inc & its publishing entities are not accepting unsol submissions, proposals, mss, or submission queries via e-mail at this time.
ISBN Prefix(es): 978-0-8129; 978-0-375
Total Titles: 215 Print
Imprints: Boston Globe Puzzle Books; Chicago Tribune Crosswords; House of Collectibles; Los Angeles Times Crosswords; McKay Chess Library; Random House Websters; Washington Post Crosswords

§Rattapallax Press
217 Thompson St, Suite 353, New York, NY 10012
E-mail: info@rattapallax.com
Web Site: www.rattapallax.com
Key Personnel
Pres & Publr: Ram Devineni
Founded: 2000
ISBN Prefix(es): 978-1-892494
Number of titles published annually: 4 Print; 1 CD-ROM; 15 Online; 15 E-Book; 15 Audio
Total Titles: 15 Print; 1 CD-ROM; 15 Online; 15 E-Book; 15 Audio
Distribution Center: Small Press Distribution, 1341 Seventh St, Berkeley, CA 94710-1409 *Tel:* 510-524-1668 *Toll Free Tel:* 800-869-7553

E-mail: spd@spdbooks.org *Web Site:* www.spdbooks.org
Membership(s): Community of Literary Magazines & Presses

Raven Productions Inc
PO Box 188, Ely, MN 55731
Tel: 218-365-3375 *Fax:* 678-306-3375
E-mail: raven@ravenwords.com; order@ravenwords.com
Web Site: www.ravenwords.com
Founded: 1999
ISBN Prefix(es): 978-0-9677057; 978-0-9766264; 978-0-9794202; 978-0-9801045; 978-0-9819307; 978-0-9883508; 978-0-9835189
Number of titles published annually: 3 Print
Total Titles: 21 Print
Imprints: Rosebud Books
Distributed by Adventure Publications
Warehouse: R & R, 420 N 15 Ave E, Ely, MN 55731
Membership(s): The Independent Book Publishers Association; Midwest Independent Publishers Association

Raven Publishing Inc
125 Cherry Creek Rd, Norris, MT 59745
SAN: 254-5861
Mailing Address: PO Box 2866, Norris, MT 59745
Tel: 406-685-3545 *Toll Free Tel:* 866-685-3545 *Fax:* 406-685-3599
E-mail: info@ravenpublishing.net
Web Site: www.ravenpublishing.net
Key Personnel
Founder & Pres: Janet Muirhead Hill *E-mail:* janet@ravenpublishing.net
Founded: 2001
ISBN Prefix(es): 978-0-9714161; 978-0-9772525
Number of titles published annually: 4 Print; 3 Online
Total Titles: 17 Print; 17 Online
Billing Address: PO Box 2866, Norris, MT 59745
Membership(s): The Independent Book Publishers Association

Raven Tree Press
Division of Delta Publishing Co
1400 Miller Pkwy, McHenry, IL 60050-7030
SAN: 253-6005
Tel: 815-363-3582 *Toll Free Tel:* 800-323-8270; 877-256-0579 *Fax:* 815-363-2948 *Toll Free Fax:* 800-909-9901
E-mail: raven@raventreepress.com; raven@deltapublishing.com
Web Site: www.raventreepress.com
Key Personnel
Mktg Dir: Diane Bergeron *E-mail:* d.bergeron@deltapublishing.com
Founded: 2000
Children's bilingual (English-Spanish) picture books. Check web site for submission details.
ISBN Prefix(es): 978-0-9701107; 978-0-9720192; 978-0-9724973
Number of titles published annually: 20 Print; 10 Online
Total Titles: 50 Print; 136 Online
Membership(s): The Children's Book Council; The Independent Book Publishers Association; Society of Children's Book Writers & Illustrators

§Ravenhawk™ Books
Division of The 6DOF Group
8364 E Balfour Place, Tucson, AZ 85710
Tel: 520-296-4491 *Fax:* 520-296-4491
E-mail: ravenhawk6dof@yahoo.com
Web Site: 6dofsolutions.com
Key Personnel
Publr: Karl Lasky
Founded: 1998
Royalty publisher. Specialize in general trade, hard/softcover, fiction, nonfiction, self-help, teaching texts for professionals, crime, mystery & suspense fiction. Ebooks, CD/DVD audio books. Ms submissions are by invitation only through acknowledged literary agents.
ISBN Prefix(es): 978-1-893660
Number of titles published annually: 6 Print; 4 CD-ROM; 4 Online; 10 E-Book; 4 Audio
Total Titles: 38 Print; 1 Online; 4 E-Book
Distribution Center: Baker & Taylor Inc, 2550 W Tyvola Rd, Suite 300, Charlotte, NC 28217 *Tel:* 704-998-3100 *Fax:* 704-998-3319 *E-mail:* btinfo@baker-taylor.com *Web Site:* www.baker-taylor.com
Ingram Content Group Inc, One Ingram Blvd, La Vergne, TN 37086-1986 *Tel:* 615-793-5000 *Web Site:* www.ingramcontent.com
Membership(s): Interactive Creative Artists Network; National Writers Association; Society of Southwestern Authors

Rayve Productions Inc
PO Box 726, Windsor, CA 95492
SAN: 248-4250
Tel: 707-838-6200 *Toll Free Tel:* 800-852-4890 *Fax:* 707-838-2220
E-mail: rayvepro@aol.com
Web Site: www.rayveproductions.com; www.foodandwinebooks.com
Key Personnel
Pres: Norm Ray
VP & Ed-in-Chief: Barbara F Ray
Founded: 1989
Business guidebooks, illustrated children's books, history books, counseling, parenting, caregiving & cookbooks.
ISBN Prefix(es): 978-1-877810; 978-1-893718; 978-0-9629927
Number of titles published annually: 5 Print
Total Titles: 35 Print; 1 CD-ROM; 1 Audio
Imprints: LifeTimes; Toucan Tales
Membership(s): The Independent Book Publishers Association

Razorbill
Imprint of Penguin Group (USA) LLC
345 Hudson St, New York, NY 10014
Tel: 212-366-2000
Key Personnel
Pres & Publr: Ben Schrank
Assoc Publr: Erin Berger
Ed: Caroline Donofrio
Founded: 2004
ISBN Prefix(es): 978-1-59514
Number of titles published annually: 42 Print
Total Titles: 159 Print

The Reader's Digest Association Inc
750 Third Ave, New York, NY 10017
SAN: 212-4416
Tel: 914-238-1000; 646-293-6284 *Toll Free Tel:* 800-310-6261 (cust serv) *Fax:* 914-238-4559
Web Site: www.rd.com; www.rda.com
Key Personnel
Chmn: Randall Curran
CEO & Pres: Robert E Guth
CFO & EVP: Paul Tomkins *E-mail:* paul_tomkins@rda.com
Global CIO & SVP: Joe Held
EVP, Busn Opers: Albert L Peruzza
SVP, Gen Coun/Secy: Andrea Newborn
VP & Treas: William H Magill
VP, Global Communs: Susan Fraysse Russ *E-mail:* susan_russ@rda.com
VP & Assoc Publr: Rosanne McManus
Mng Dir & Publr, Children's Brand: Neil Wertheimer
Subsidiaries: Studio Fun International Inc
Divisions: Reader's Digest General Books; Reader's Digest Trade Books; Reader's Digest USA Select Editions
Membership(s): AAP
See separate listing for:
Reader's Digest General Books
Reader's Digest Trade Books
Reader's Digest USA Select Editions
Studio Fun International Inc

Reader's Digest General Books
Division of The Reader's Digest Association Inc
Reader's Digest Rd, Pleasantville, NY 10570-7000
SAN: 240-9720
Tel: 914-238-1000 *Toll Free Tel:* 800-304-2807 (cust serv) *Fax:* 914-244-7436
Key Personnel
Pres & CEO: Mary Berner
SVP & Gen Coun: Michael A Brizel
SVP & Pres, Intl: Thomas D Gardner
SVP & CFO: Michael S Geltzeiler
SVP & Pres, North America & Global Ed-in-Chief: Eric Schrier
VP & Circ Dir: Dawn Zier
VP & Treas: William H Magill
VP, Global Communs: William K Adler
Mgr, Rts & Perms: Lisa Garrett Smith
Founded: 1961
Direct marketed reference books on home maintenance & repair, health & fitness, crafts & hobbies, history, cooking, travel, geography, religion, nature, law, medicine, gardening, English usage & vocabulary.
ISBN Prefix(es): 978-0-89577
Number of titles published annually: 10 Print
Distributed by Simon & Schuster

Reader's Digest Trade Books
Division of Reader's Digest Association Inc
44 S Broadway, White Plains, NY 10601
SAN: 240-9720
Tel: 914-244-7503 *Fax:* 914-244-4841
Web Site: www.rd.com
Key Personnel
Pres & Publr: Harold Clarke
VP & Assoc Publr: Rosanne McManus
Exec Ed: Dolores York
VP & Dir, Sales & Mktg: Stacy Ashton
Creative Dir: Julia Sabbagh
Dir, Prodn & Prod Devt: Debbie Gagnon
Founded: 1971
Illustrated trade (retail) reference books on home maintenance & repair, gardening, home decorating, crafts, art instruction, cooking, health & fitness, pet care, photography, family reference, religion & inspiration, science & nature, travel & atlases, humor.
ISBN Prefix(es): 978-0-7621
Number of titles published annually: 100 Print
Total Titles: 350 Print
Distributed by Simon & Schuster
Foreign Rights: Biagi Rights Management

Reader's Digest USA Select Editions
Division of The Reader's Digest Association Inc
44 S Broadway, 7th fl, White Plains, NY 10601
Tel: 914-238-1000 *Toll Free Tel:* 800-304-2807 (cust serv) *Fax:* 914-831-1560
Web Site: www.rda.com/readers-digest-select-editions
Key Personnel
Pres & Publr, Books & Music: Harold Clarke *E-mail:* harold_clarke@rd.com
Exec Ed: Jim Menick *E-mail:* jim_menick@rd.com
Founded: 1950
Publishers of current fiction & general nonfiction in condensed form. Selections are licensed from original publisher.
ISBN Prefix(es): 978-0-89577

Recorded Books LLC
270 Skipjack Rd, Prince Frederick, MD 20678
SAN: 677-8887
Tel: 410-535-5590 *Toll Free Tel:* 800-638-1304; 877-732-2898 *Fax:* 410-535-5499
E-mail: customerservice@recordedbooks.com
Web Site: www.recordedbooks.com
Key Personnel
CEO & Pres: Rich Freese
COO: Edward Longo *E-mail:* elongo@recordedbooks.com
CFO: Neil Tress *E-mail:* ntress@recordedbooks.com
VP, Sales & Mktg: Matthew Walker *E-mail:* mwalker@recordedbooks.com
Dir, Acqs: Brian Sweany
Sr Acqs Ed: Bob Podrasky
Founded: 1979
Independent publisher of unabridged audiobooks & distributor of films & other media content delivered in CD & downloadable formats, to consumers, libraries & schools.
ISBN Prefix(es): 978-0-7887; 978-1-4025
Number of titles published annually: 700 Print; 250 CD-ROM; 100 Online; 50 E-Book; 787 Audio
Total Titles: 8,000 Print; 1,000 CD-ROM; 100 Online; 50 E-Book; 5,808 Audio
Imprints: Classic Library; Clipper Audio (UK); Griot Audio; Lone Star Audio; Pimlseur Language Programs; Recorded Books Audiolibros; Recorded Books Evergreen; Recorded Books Inspirational; Romantic Sounds Audio; Sci-Fi Audio; Southern Voices Audio; Your Coach in a Box
Branch Office(s)
Audio Adventures, 200 Skipjack Rd, Prince Frederick, MD 20678, Contact: Scott Williams *Toll Free Tel:* 800-580-2989 *Web Site:* www.landmarkaudio.com
Foreign Office(s): WF Howes, Unit 4, Rearsby Business Park, Gaddesby Lane, Rearsby, Leics LE7 4YH, United Kingdom (recorded books), Mng Dir: Sean Sibley *Tel:* (011) 0016-230-1144 *Fax:* (011) 0016-230-1155
Distributor for Buena Vista DVDs; The Film Movement DVDs
Distribution Center: Audio Adventures, 200 Skipjack Rd, Prince Frederick, MD 20678, Contact: Scott Williams *Toll Free Tel:* 800-580-2989 *Web Site:* www.landmarkaudio.com
Membership(s): Audio Publishers Association

Red Chair Press
PO Box 333, South Egremont, MA 01258-0333
Toll Free Tel: 888-327-2141 (ext 110) *Toll Free Fax:* 888-533-4037
E-mail: info@redchairpress.com
Web Site: www.redchairpress.com
Key Personnel
Pres & Publr: Keith Garton *E-mail:* keith@redchairpress.com
Creative Dir: Jeff Dinardo
Founded: 2009
Fiction & nonfiction books & ebook apps; social & emotional learning. Books about good decision making for children ages 4-8.
ISBN Prefix(es): 978-1-936163; 978-1-937529
Number of titles published annually: 20 Print; 12 CD-ROM; 20 E-Book
Total Titles: 54 Print; 32 CD-ROM; 54 E-Book
Distributed by Lerner Publishing
Foreign Rep(s): Lerner Publishing (Maria Kjoller)
Membership(s): AAP PreK-12 Learning Group; The Association of Publishers for Special Sales; The Independent Book Publishers Association; Society of Children's Book Writers & Illustrators

Red Dust Inc
1148 Fifth Ave, New York, NY 10128
SAN: 203-3860
Tel: 212-348-4388
Web Site: www.reddustbooks.com
Key Personnel
Pres & Publr: Joanna Gunderson *E-mail:* reddustjg@aol.com
Founded: 1961
Works by new writers; fiction, poetry, nonsequential texts.
ISBN Prefix(es): 978-0-87376
Number of titles published annually: 3 Print
Total Titles: 84 Print
Editorial Office(s): 845 Hancock St, Brooklyn, NY 11233, Mng Ed: Donald Breckenridge *Tel:* 347-721-7790 *E-mail:* dpbreckenridge@yahoo.com

Red Hen Press
PO Box 40820, Pasadena, CA 91114
Tel: 626-356-4760 *Fax:* 626-356-9974
Web Site: www.redhen.org
Key Personnel
Pres & Publr: Mark E Cull *E-mail:* mark@redhen.org
Mng Ed: Kate Gale *E-mail:* kategale@verizon.net
Founded: 1994
Publish perfect bound collections of poetry, short stories & books of a literary nature. Also sponsor several literary awards, along with the literary journal *The Los Angeles Review*.
ISBN Prefix(es): 978-0-9639528; 978-1-888996; 978-1-59709
Number of titles published annually: 20 Print
Total Titles: 350 Print
Imprints: Arktoi Books; Boreal Books; Xeno Books
Distribution Center: Chicago Distribution Center, 11030 S Langley, Chicago, IL 60628 *Toll Free Tel:* 800-621-2736 *Toll Free Fax:* 800-621-8476 *E-mail:* orders@press.uchicago.edu
Membership(s): Association of Writers and Writing Programs; Community of Literary Magazines & Presses

Red Moon Press
PO Box 2461, Winchester, VA 22604-1661
Tel: 540-722-2156
Web Site: www.redmoonpress.com
Key Personnel
Owner: Jim Kacian *E-mail:* jim.kacian@redmoonpress.com
Founded: 1993
Largest & most prestigious publisher of English-language haiku & related forms in the world.
ISBN Prefix(es): 978-1-9657818; 978-1-893959; 978-1-936848
Number of titles published annually: 10 Print
Total Titles: 110 Print
Imprints: Pond Frog Editions; Soffietto Editions

Red Rock Press
331 W 57 St, Suite 175, New York, NY 10019
Tel: 212-362-8304 *Fax:* 212-362-6216
E-mail: info@redrockpress.com
Web Site: www.redrockpress.com
Key Personnel
Creative Dir: Ilene Barth
Sales Dir: Richard Barth *E-mail:* richard@redrockpress.com
Founded: 1998
Gift books.
ISBN Prefix(es): 978-0-97143; 978-1-93317
Number of titles published annually: 3 Print
Total Titles: 50 Print

Red Sea Press Inc
541 W Ingham Ave, Suite B, Trenton, NJ 08638
Tel: 609-695-3200 *Fax:* 609-695-6466
E-mail: customerservice@africaworldpressbooks.com
Web Site: www.africaworldpressbooks.com
Key Personnel
Pres & Publr: Kassahun Checole
Opers Mgr: Senait Kassahun
Founded: 1985
Publisher of books on the Horn of Africa, Latin America; distributor of books on the Third World.
ISBN Prefix(es): 978-0-932415; 978-1-56902
Number of titles published annually: 100 Print
Total Titles: 1,200 Print
Imprints: Karnak House
Foreign Rights: Turnaround Publisher Services (Europe, London)

Red Wheel/Weiser/Conari
65 Parker St, Suite 7, Newburyport, MA 01950
Tel: 978-465-0504 *Toll Free Tel:* 800-423-7087 (orders) *Fax:* 978-465-0243
E-mail: info@rwwbooks.com
Web Site: www.redwheelweiser.com
Key Personnel
CEO & Pres: Michael Kerber *Tel:* 978-465-0504 ext 1115 *E-mail:* mkerber@rwwbooks.com
Assoc Publr: Greg Brandenburgh; Caroline Pincus
Publicity Dir: Bonni Hamilton
Publicist: Kat Salazar
Assoc Prodn Dir: Jordan Overby
Ed: Amber Guetebier
Prodn Ed: Michael Alexander
Asst Ed: Kimberly Ehart
Sales Mgr: Debra Woodward
Founded: 1956
Self-help, new consciousness, spirituality, inspiration, women's interest & esoteric subjects from many traditions.
ISBN Prefix(es): 978-0-943233 (Conari); 978-0-87728 (Weiser); 978-1-57863 (Weiser); 978-1-59003 (Red Wheel); 978-1-57324 (Conari)
Number of titles published annually: 50 Print
Total Titles: 1,000 Print
Imprints: Hampton Roads Publishing
Editorial Office(s): 665 Third Street, Suite 400, San Francisco, CA 94107
Distributor for Nicolas Hays Inc
Foreign Rep(s): Brumby Books (Australia); Deep Books (UK); ITI-Canada (Canada)
Foreign Rights: Linda Biagi (Worldwide)
Warehouse: Books International Inc, 22883 Quicksilver Dr, Dulles, VA 20166
Membership(s): ABA

RedBone Press
PO Box 15571, Washington, DC 20003
Tel: 202-667-0392 *Fax:* 301-588-0588
E-mail: info@redbonepress.com
Web Site: www.redbonepress.com
Key Personnel
Publr: Lisa C Moore
Founded: 1997
Publishes black, gay & lesbian literature.
ISBN Prefix(es): 978-0-9656659; 978-0-9786251
Number of titles published annually: 3 Print
Total Titles: 20 Print; 1 Audio
Distribution Center: Small Press Distribution, 1341 Seventh St, Berkeley, CA 94710-1409 *Tel:* 510-524-1668 *Toll Free Tel:* 800-869-7553 *E-mail:* spd@spdbooks.org *Web Site:* www.spdbooks.org
Membership(s): Community of Literary Magazines & Presses

Redleaf Press
Division of Think Small
10 Yorkton Ct, St Paul, MN 55117
SAN: 212-8691
Tel: 651-641-0508 *Toll Free Tel:* 800-423-8309 *Toll Free Fax:* 800-641-0115
Web Site: www.redleafpress.org
Key Personnel
Co-Dir: Paul Bloomer *E-mail:* pbloomer@redleafpress.org; David Heath *E-mail:* dheath@redleafpress.org
Mng Ed: Doug Schmitz *E-mail:* dschmitz@redleafpress.org
Mktg Mgr: Eric Johnson *E-mail:* ejohnson@redleafpress.org

Sales Mgr: Sue Ostfield; Inga Weberg
E-mail: iweberg@redleafpress.org
Founded: 1973
Resources for early childhood professionals including. early childhood curriculum, professional development, family child care business, record keeping & parenting.
ISBN Prefix(es): 978-0-934140; 978-1-884834; 978-1-929610; 978-1-933653; 978-1-60554
Number of titles published annually: 32 Print; 3 CD-ROM; 50 E-Book
Total Titles: 270 Print; 15 CD-ROM; 5 Online; 50 E-Book
Distributed by Pademelon Press Pty Ltd (Australia)
Foreign Rights: Perseus (Worldwide)
Distribution Center: Consortium Book Sales & Distribution, The Keg House, Suite 101, 34 13th Ave NE, Minneapolis, MN 55413 (US book trade & libs) *Tel:* 612-746-2600 *Toll Free Tel:* 800-283-3572 (cust serv) *Fax:* 612-746-2606 *Web Site:* www.cbsd.com
Monarch Books of Canada, 5000 Dufferin St, Downsview, ON M3H 5T5, Canada
Pademelon Press Pty Ltd, Unit 7/3 Packard Ave, Castle Hill, NSW 2154, Australia *Tel:* (02) 9634 4655 *Fax:* (02) 9680 4634
Eurospan Group, 3 Henrietta St, London WC2E 8LU, United Kingdom (UK, Continental Europe, Africa, Asia & Middle East) *Tel:* (01767) 604972 *Fax:* (01767) 601640 *E-mail:* eurospan@turpin-distribution.com
Membership(s): Education Market Association

Robert D Reed Publishers
PO Box 1992, Bandon, OR 97411-1192
Tel: 541-347-9882 *Fax:* 541-347-9883
E-mail: 4bobreed@msn.com
Web Site: www.rdrpublishers.com
Key Personnel
Publr: Robert D Reed
Founded: 1977
All types of publications for trade, educational institutions, individuals & corporations.
ISBN Prefix(es): 978-1-889710; 978-1-885003; 978-1-931741
Number of titles published annually: 25 Print
Total Titles: 225 Print
Foreign Rep(s): Sylvia Hayse Literary Agency

Reedswain Inc
88 Wells Rd, Spring City, PA 19475
Tel: 610-495-9578 *Toll Free Tel:* 800-331-5191 *Fax:* 610-495-6632
E-mail: orders@reedswain.com
Web Site: www.reedswain.com
Key Personnel
Pres & Foreign Rts: Richard Kentwell
Founded: 1987
Soccer coaching books.
ISBN Prefix(es): 978-1-8809; 978-1-59164
Number of titles published annually: 10 Print
Total Titles: 190 Print

The Re-evaluation Counseling Communities
719 Second Ave N, Seattle, WA 98109
Mailing Address: Main Office Sta, PO Box 2081, Seattle, WA 98111-2081
Tel: 206-284-0311 *Fax:* 206-284-8429
E-mail: ircc@rc.org
Web Site: www.rc.org
Key Personnel
Ed: Katie Kauffman
Founded: 1954
Articles about Re-evaluation Counseling (Co-Counseling) - the theory, the practice, the applications & implications.
ISBN Prefix(es): 978-0-911214; 978-0-913937; 978-1-885357; 978-1-58429
Number of titles published annually: 6 Print
Total Titles: 263 Print

Referee Books
Imprint of Referee Enterprises Inc
2017 Lathrop Ave, Racine, WI 53405
Tel: 262-632-8855 *Toll Free Tel:* 800-733-6100 *Fax:* 262-632-5460
E-mail: questions@referee.com
Web Site: www.referee.com
Key Personnel
Pres: Barry Mano *E-mail:* bmano@naso.org
Founded: 1976
Publish sports officiating publications; magazines, books, manuals & booklets on officiating, umpiring, baseball, basketball, football, soccer, softball & athletics referee books.
ISBN Prefix(es): 978-1-58208; 978-0-9660209
Number of titles published annually: 25 Print
Total Titles: 75 Print

Reference Publications Inc
218 Saint Clair River Dr, Algonac, MI 48001
SAN: 208-4392
Mailing Address: PO Box 344, Algonac, MI 48001-0344
Tel: 810-794-5722 *Fax:* 810-794-7463
E-mail: referencepub@sbcglobal.net
Key Personnel
Pres & Ed: Marie Aline Irvine
Dir, Mktg: Dominique Irvine
Legal Coun: John Somers
Founded: 1975
Mail order & reference books. Specialize in botanical & medicinal plants, Americana, Amerindian & African reference books & botanical works.
ISBN Prefix(es): 978-0-917256
Number of titles published annually: 2 Print
Total Titles: 24 Print
Imprints: Encyclopaedia Africana
Sales Office(s): PO Box 344, Algonac, MI 48001-0344

§Reference Service Press
5000 Windplay Dr, Suite 4, El Dorado Hills, CA 95762-9319
Tel: 916-939-9620 *Fax:* 916-939-9626
E-mail: info@rspfunding.com
Web Site: www.rspfunding.com
Key Personnel
Pres: Gail Schlachter, PhD
E-mail: gailschlachter@rspfunding.com
Founded: 1975
Online financial aid databases, financial aid directories & resources.
ISBN Prefix(es): 978-1-58841
Number of titles published annually: 15 Print; 56 Online; 10 E-Book
Total Titles: 25 Print; 3 CD-ROM; 56 Online; 15 E-Book
Membership(s): American Indian Library Association; California Library Association; The Independent Book Publishers Association

ReferencePoint Press Inc
17150 Via del Campo, Suite 205, San Diego, CA 92127
Mailing Address: PO Box 27779, San Diego, CA 92198
Tel: 858-618-1314 *Toll Free Tel:* 888-479-6436 *Fax:* 858-618-1730
E-mail: orders@referencepointpress.com
Web Site: www.referencepointpress.com
Key Personnel
Pres & Publr: Dan Leone *Tel:* 858-618-1314 ext 102 *E-mail:* dan@referencepointpress.com
Founded: 2006
Publish series nonfiction for young adults: current issues, health, science & paranormal.
ISBN Prefix(es): 978-1-60152
Number of titles published annually: 75 Print; 75 E-Book
Total Titles: 300 Print; 300 E-Book
Foreign Rep(s): Saunders Book Co (Canada)
Returns: Bang Fulfillment, 217 Etak Dr, Brainerd, MN 56401
Warehouse: Bang Fulfillment, 217 Etak Dr, Brainerd, MN 56401, Contact: Perry Gienger *Toll Free Tel:* 800-328-0450 *Fax:* 218-829-7145 *E-mail:* perryg@bangprinting.com

Reformation Heritage Books
2965 Leonard St NE, Grand Rapids, MI 49525
Tel: 616-977-0889 *Fax:* 616-285-3246
E-mail: orders@heritagebooks.org
Web Site: www.heritagebooks.org
Key Personnel
Chmn: Joel R Beeke
Contact: Jonathan Engelsma
Founded: 1993
Sell new & used religious books with emphasis on experiential religion. Also republish out-of-print Puritan works.
ISBN Prefix(es): 978-1-892777
Number of titles published annually: 40 Print
Total Titles: 250 Print; 70 E-Book

§Regal Books
Division of Gospel Light
1957 Eastman Ave, Ventura, CA 93003
SAN: 203-3852
Tel: 805-644-9721 *Toll Free Tel:* 800-446-7735 (orders)
Web Site: www.regalbooks.com; www.gospellight.com
Key Personnel
CFO: Todd White
Pres: Bill T Greig, III
Publg Dir: Stan Jantz *E-mail:* stan.jantz@regalbooks.com
Founded: 1933
Faith books. Christian publisher of books & DVDs, with topics ranging from worship to women's needs & from prayer to praise. No unsol mss.
ISBN Prefix(es): 978-0-8307
Number of titles published annually: 50 Print
Total Titles: 500 Print
Foreign Rep(s): Christian Art Distributors (South Africa); CRU Singapore (Singapore); Glad Sounds Sdn Bhd (Malaysia); KI Entertainment (Australia); Kingsway Communications (Ireland, UK); Koorong Books (Australia); OMF Literature Inc (Philippines); Soul Distributors (New Zealand); Trust Media (Ireland, UK)
Advertising Agency: Gospel Light Worldwide, Contact: Elaine Montefu *Toll Free Tel:* 800-737-6071 *Fax:* 805-477-4987 *Web Site:* www.glww.org

§Regal Crest Enterprises LLC
229 Sheridan Loop, Belton, TX 76513
Tel: 409-527-1188 *Toll Free Fax:* 866-294-9628
E-mail: info@regalcrestbooks.biz
Web Site: www.regalcrest.biz
Key Personnel
Owner: Cathy C Bryerose
Founded: 2003 (originally in 1999 as Renaissance Alliance Publishing Inc)
Traditional royalty publisher using innovative print technology.
ISBN Prefix(es): 978-1-932300; 978-1-935053; 978-1-61929
Number of titles published annually: 32 Print; 32 E-Book
Total Titles: 153 Print; 168 E-Book
Imprints: Blue Beacon Books (nonfiction); Mystic Books (paranormal); Quest Books (action, adventure, mystery, police procedure, detective); Regal Crest (drama & general fiction); Silver Dragon Books (science fiction/fantasy); Troubadour Books (poetry, short story, anthology); YA Books (young adult); Yellow Rose Books (romance)
Foreign Rep(s): Bella Distribution Inc (Worldwide); Ingram (Worldwide)

Distribution Center: Bella Distribution Inc, 1041 Aenon Church Rd, Tallahassee, FL 32302 *Toll Free Tel:* 800-533-1973
Ingram, One Ingram Blvd, La Vergne, TN 17202

Regnery Publishing Inc
Subsidiary of Eagle Publishing Inc
300 New Jersey Ave NW, Washington, DC 20001
Tel: 202-216-0600 *Toll Free Tel:* 888-219-4747 *Fax:* 202-216-0612
Web Site: www.regnery.com
Key Personnel
Pres & Publr: Marjory G Ross
Dir, Publicity: Patricia Jackson *E-mail:* patricia.jackson@regnery.com
Dir, Sales: Mark Bloomfield
Exec Ed: Harry W Crocker, III
Foreign Rts: Alex Novak *E-mail:* anovak@eaglepub.com
Perms: Maria Ruhl *E-mail:* mruhl@eaglepub.com
Founded: 1947
Trade book publisher.
ISBN Prefix(es): 978-0-89526; 978-1-59698; 978-1-62157
Number of titles published annually: 35 Print
Total Titles: 400 Print
Imprints: Gateway; Little Patriot Press; Regnery; Regnery History
Distribution Center: Perseus Distribution Services, 193 Edwards Dr, Jackson, TN 38301

Regular Baptist Press
Division of General Association of Regular Baptist Churches
1300 N Meacham Rd, Schaumburg, IL 60173-4806
Tel: 847-843-1600 *Toll Free Tel:* 800-727-4440 (orders only); 888-588-1600 *Fax:* 847-843-3757
E-mail: rbp@garbc.org
Web Site: www.regularbaptistpress.org
Key Personnel
Book Ed & Intl Rts Contact: Norman A Olson *E-mail:* nolson@garbc.org
Founded: 1952
Curriculum & Christian books.
ISBN Prefix(es): 978-0-87227; 978-1-59402
Number of titles published annually: 6 Print

Renaissance House
Imprint of Laredo Publishing Co Inc
465 Westview Ave, Englewood, NJ 07631
Tel: 201-408-4048 *Fax:* 201-408-5011
E-mail: info@renaissancehouse.net
Web Site: www.renaissancehouse.net
Key Personnel
Pres: Sam Laredo *E-mail:* laredo@renaissancehouse.net
VP & Exec Ed: Raquel Benatar *E-mail:* raquel@renaissancehouse.net
Founded: 1991
Book developer & publisher of high quality illustrated children's books. Specialize in Spanish bilingual market. Works with more than 60 illustrators. Offers editorial services, translations, illustrations, project development & management.
ISBN Prefix(es): 978-1-56492
Number of titles published annually: 30 Print
Total Titles: 150 Print
Distributed by SRA/McGraw-Hill

Research & Education Association (REA)
61 Ethel Rd W, Piscataway, NJ 08854
Tel: 732-819-8880 *Fax:* 732-819-8808 (orders)
E-mail: info@rea.com
Web Site: www.rea.com
Key Personnel
Pres: Rich Weisman *E-mail:* rweisman@rea.com
VP, Sales: Roger Romano *E-mail:* rromano@rea.com
VP, Publg: Pamela Weston *E-mail:* pweston@rea.com
Cust Serv Mgr: Rosemarie Hannigan *E-mail:* rhannigan@rea.com
Founded: 1959
Professional books, secondary & college study guides & test preparation books, biology, business, engineering, mathematics, general science, history, social sciences, accounting & computer science.
ISBN Prefix(es): 978-0-87891; 978-0-7386
Number of titles published annually: 50 Print; 10 CD-ROM; 5 Audio
Total Titles: 1,200 Print; 26 CD-ROM; 7 Audio

Research Press
2612 N Mattis Ave, Champaign, IL 61822
SAN: 203-381X
Mailing Address: PO Box 9177, Dept 11-W, Champaign, IL 61826-9177
Tel: 217-352-3273 *Toll Free Tel:* 800-519-2707 *Fax:* 217-352-1221
E-mail: rp@researchpress.com; orders@researchpress.com
Web Site: www.researchpress.com
Key Personnel
Chmn of the Bd: Cynthia Parkinson Martin
Pres: Judy Parkinson *E-mail:* jparkinson@researchpress.com
Mng Ed & Rts & Perms: Karen Steiner
Prodn Mgr: Jeff Helgesen
Secy: Deborah Wilcoxon
Founded: 1968
ISBN Prefix(es): 978-0-87822
Number of titles published annually: 4 Print
Total Titles: 200 Print; 2 Audio
Foreign Rep(s): Footprint Books (Australia); Incentive Plus (UK)
Foreign Rights: Books Crossing Borders

Resilient Publishing
406 S Third St, Boise, ID 83702
Tel: 208-258-9544
E-mail: submissions@resilientpublishing.com
Web Site: www.resilientpublishing.com
Key Personnel
CEO: Lynn Hardy
Mktg & PR Support: Kate Delano-Condax Decker
Tech Ed: Phil Athens; Angela Gaudioso
Graphic Designer & Tech Support: Robert Morrissey
Cover Artist: Jeff Sharpton
Founded: 2009
Commitment fee $299. Authors receive 75% of income from bound book sales & 65% of income from ebook sales.
ISBN Prefix(es): 978-1-936408; 978-0-9841902; 978-1-937703; 978-0-9843669; 978-0-9845045
Number of titles published annually: 15 Print; 15 Online; 15 E-Book; 2 Audio
Total Titles: 40 Print; 40 Online; 40 E-Book
Distributor for Anderson Design; Brynwood Publishing
Membership(s): Idaho Writers Guild

§Resource Publications Inc
160 E Virginia St, Suite 170, San Jose, CA 95112-5876
SAN: 209-3081
Tel: 408-286-8505 *Fax:* 408-287-8748
E-mail: orders@rpinet.com
Web Site: www.rpinet.com
Key Personnel
Pres & Publr: William Burns *E-mail:* billb@rpinet.com
Busn Mgr: Mary J Dent *E-mail:* maryd@rpinet.com
Mktg Mgr: Joshua P Burns *E-mail:* joshb@rpinet.com
Founded: 1973
Hardcover & paperback, reference, religious trade & general trade books, textbooks & periodicals with emphasis on peer counseling, applied storytelling, recovery & personal growth & on imagination & creative resources for leaders & artists. Resources primarily for worship & ministry.
ISBN Prefix(es): 978-0-89390
Number of titles published annually: 4 Print; 2 CD-ROM; 3 Online; 2 E-Book
Total Titles: 245 Print; 2 CD-ROM; 3 Online; 12 E-Book; 10 Audio
Foreign Rep(s): Columba Book Service (Europe); Pleroma Catholic Supplies (New Zealand); Rainbow Books (Australia, New Zealand); St Pauls India (India)

§Revell
Division of Baker Publishing Group
PO Box 6287, Grand Rapids, MI 49516-6287
SAN: 203-3801
Tel: 616-676-9185 *Toll Free Tel:* 800-877-2665; 800-679-1957 *Fax:* 616-676-9573
Web Site: www.revellbooks.com
Key Personnel
Pres: Dwight Baker
Editorial Dir: Jennifer Leep
Mktg Dir: Twila Bennett
Mng Ed: Kristin Kornoelje
Prodn & ISBN Contact: Robert Bol
Rts & Perms & Intl Rts: Marilyn Gordon
Founded: 1870
Religious.
ISBN Prefix(es): 978-0-8007
Number of titles published annually: 100 Print
Total Titles: 5 Audio
Imprints: Spire Books
Foreign Rep(s): Christian Art (South Africa); David C Cook Distribution (Canada); Marston Book Services Ltd (Europe, UK); Soul Distributors Ltd (New Zealand)
Shipping Address: 6030 E Fulton Rd, Ada, MI 49301

§Review & Herald Publishing Association
55 W Oak Ridge Dr, Hagerstown, MD 21740
Tel: 301-393-3000 *Toll Free Tel:* 800-234-7630 *Fax:* 301-393-4055 (edit); 301-393-3222 (book div)
E-mail: editorial@rhpa.org
Web Site: www.reviewandherald.com
Key Personnel
Pres: Mark B Thomas
Founded: 1849
Religion (Seventh-day Adventist), health, nutrition & education.
ISBN Prefix(es): 978-0-8280
Number of titles published annually: 43 Print
Total Titles: 1,600 Print; 2 CD-ROM; 10 Audio
Foreign Rep(s): Stanborough Press Ltd (England)

Rhemalda Publishing
PO Box 1790, Moses Lake, WA 98837
E-mail: editor@rhemalda.com; customer_service@rhemalda.com
Web Site: rhemalda.com
Key Personnel
Pres & Publr: Rhett Hoffmeister
VP: Emmaline Hoffmeister
Founded: 2009
ISBN Prefix(es): 978-0-9827437; 978-1-936850
Number of titles published annually: 15 Print; 12 Online; 12 E-Book
Total Titles: 45 Print; 45 Online; 45 E-Book

Lynne Rienner Publishers Inc
1800 30 St, Suite 314, Boulder, CO 80301
SAN: 683-1869
Tel: 303-444-6684 *Fax:* 303-444-0824
E-mail: questions@rienner.com; cservice@rienner.com
Web Site: www.rienner.com

Key Personnel
CEO & Pres: Lynne C Rienner
Dir, Mktg & Sales: Sally Glover
E-mail: sglover@rienner.com
Mgr, Cust Serv: Nancy Spohn
Rts & Perms: Alessandra Downey
Founded: 1984
Scholarly & reference books & journals, college textbooks; comparative politics, US politics, international relations, sociology, Third World literature & literary criticism.
ISBN Prefix(es): 978-0-931477; 978-1-55587; 978-1-56000; 978-1-57454; 978-0-89410; 978-1-58826; 978-1-935049 (FirstForumPress)
Number of titles published annually: 70 Print
Total Titles: 1,050 Print
Divisions: FirstForumPress (scholarly monographs); Kumarian Press
Distributor for Center for US-Mexican Studies; Ayebia Clarke Publishing Ltd (African lit); St Andrews Center for Syrian Studies
Foreign Rep(s): Apac (Asia, The Pacific); Cranbury International LLC (Latin America); Far Eastern Booksellers (Japan); Kinokuniya Co Ltd (Japan); Maruzen Co Ltd (Japan); Palgrave Macmillan (Australia); Turpin Distribution (Europe); Viva (India)
Warehouse: 22883 Quicksilver Dr, Dulles, VA 20166, Contact: Vartan Ajamian
Membership(s): AAP
See separate listing for:
Kumarian Press

Rio Nuevo Publishers
451 N Bonita Ave, Tucson, AZ 85745
Mailing Address: PO Box 5250, Tucson, AZ 85703
Tel: 520-623-9558 *Toll Free Tel:* 800-969-9558 *Fax:* 520-624-5888 *Toll Free Fax:* 800-715-5888
E-mail: info@rionuevo.com (cust serv)
Web Site: www.rionuevo.com
Founded: 1975
Publisher of fine regional southwestern photographic, cooking & historical books & quality Native American books.
ISBN Prefix(es): 978-1-887896; 978-1-933855
Number of titles published annually: 12 Print
Total Titles: 125 Print
Imprints: Rio Chico (educ & children's books)
Membership(s): Society of Children's Book Writers & Illustrators

Rising Sun Publishing
PO Box 70906, Marietta, GA 30007-0906
Tel: 770-518-0369 *Toll Free Tel:* 800-524-2813 *Fax:* 770-587-0862
E-mail: info@rspublishing.com
Web Site: www.rspublishing.com
Key Personnel
CFO: Mychal Wynn
Founded: 1982
Primary focus is educational training & materials.
ISBN Prefix(es): 978-1-880463
Number of titles published annually: 5 Print
Total Titles: 32 Print; 4 Audio

River City Publishing LLC
1719 Mulberry St, Montgomery, AL 36106
Tel: 334-265-6753 *Fax:* 334-265-8880
E-mail: sales@rivercitypublishing.com
Web Site: www.rivercitypublishing.com
Key Personnel
Publr: Carolyn Newman *E-mail:* cjnewman_seacrest@rivercitypublishing.com
Ed: Fran Norris *E-mail:* fnorris@rivercitypublishing.com
Sales Mgr: William Hicks *E-mail:* whicks@rivercitypublishing.com
Founded: 1989
Acquisition, editing, design, composition, marketing & sales of new books. Regional fiction & narrative nonfiction, especially books about the South, civil rights, folk art, contemporary fiction, regionally related travel history.
ISBN Prefix(es): 978-1-881320; 978-0-9622815; 978-1-57966; 978-0-913515
Number of titles published annually: 4 Print; 4 E-Book
Total Titles: 200 Print
Imprints: Elliott & Clark Publishing; River City Kids; Starrhill Press
Membership(s): Southern Independent Booksellers Alliance

§Riverdale Avenue Books (RAB)
5676 Riverdale Ave, Bronx, NY 10471
Tel: 212-279-6418
Web Site: www.riverdaleavebooks.com
Key Personnel
Publr: Lori Perkins
Edit Dir: Donald Weise
Edit Dir, Dagger: Joseph Pittman
Founded: 2012
Hybrid publisher of fiction & nonfiction, e-pub, print & audio.
ISBN Prefix(es): 978-1-936833 (Magnus); 978-1-62601 (RAB)
Number of titles published annually: 60 Print; 60 Online; 60 E-Book; 10 Audio
Total Titles: 43 Print; 60 Online; 60 E-Book; 5 Audio
Imprints: Dagger (mystery/thriller); RAB Desire (erotica & romance); RAB HSF (horror, science fiction & fantasy); RAB Pop (pop culture); RAB Truth (erotic memoir line); Riverdale Ave Books/Magnus Books (LGBT titles)
Foreign Rights: L Perkins Agency (Emily Keyes)

Riverhead Books (Hardcover)
Imprint of Penguin Group (USA) LLC
375 Hudson St, New York, NY 10014
SAN: 282-5074
Tel: 212-366-2000
E-mail: online@penguinputnam.com
Web Site: www.penguinputnam.com; us.penguingroup.com
Key Personnel
VP & Publr: Geoffrey Kloske
VP, Edit Dir: Rebecca Saletan
VP & Exec Ed: Sarah McGrath
Exec Ed: Jake Morrissey; Courtney Young
VP, Dir of Mktg (HC), Assoc Publr: Kate Stark
Art Dir: Helen Yentus
Dir, Publicity: Jynne Martin
Assoc Dir, Publicity: Katharine Freeman
Sr Publicity Mgr: Claire McGinnis
Publicity Mgr: Liz Hohenadel
Publicist: Glory Plata
Assoc Publicist: Margaret Delaney
Founded: 1995
ISBN Prefix(es): 978-1-57322
Number of titles published annually: 40 Print
Total Titles: 115 Print
Advertising Agency: Mesa Group

Riverhead Books (Trade Paperback)
Imprint of Penguin Group (USA) LLC
375 Hudson St, New York, NY 10014
SAN: 282-5074
Tel: 212-366-2000
E-mail: online@penguinputnam.com
Web Site: www.penguinputnam.com; us.penguingroup.com
Key Personnel
Art Dir: Helen Yentus
Founded: 1995
ISBN Prefix(es): 978-1-57322
Number of titles published annually: 37 Print
Total Titles: 400 Print
Advertising Agency: Spier NY

Riverside Publishing
Subsidiary of Houghton Mifflin Harcourt Publishing Co
3800 Golf Rd, Suite 200, Rolling Meadows, IL 60008
SAN: 213-554X
Tel: 630-467-7000 *Toll Free Tel:* 800-323-9540 *Fax:* 630-467-7192 (cust serv)
E-mail: rpc_customer_service@hmhpub.com (cust serv)
Web Site: www.riversidepublishing.com
Key Personnel
Pres: Jim Nicholson
VP, Sales & Mktg: Don Back
Regl VP, Sales (Northern Region): Jeff Squires
Regl VP, Sales (Southern Region): Ellis Tesh
Regl VP, Sales (Western Region): Darlene Hart
VP, Sales Opers: Mort Cohen
Dir, Mktg & Sales Opers: Kim Ross
Natl Dir, Prod Specialization Group: Van Mabie
Founded: 1852 (as Riverside Press)
Develops & sells print & digital assessment tools for the education & clinical markets.
ISBN Prefix(es): 978-0-8292
Number of titles published annually: 20 Print
Imprints: Wintergreen/Orchard House Inc
Foreign Rep(s): ACER (Australia); Artsberg (Hong Kong); Camera-Mundi (Puerto Rico); Nelson Canada (Canada); NFER-Nelson (UK); NZCER (New Zealand); Psicologiay Material-Tecnico (Spain); Taskmaster (UK)

Rizzoli International Publications Inc
Subsidiary of RCS Rizzoli Corp New York
300 Park Ave S, 4th fl, New York, NY 10010-5399
Tel: 212-387-3400 *Toll Free Tel:* 800-522-6657 (orders only) *Fax:* 212-387-3535
E-mail: publicity@rizzoliusa.com
Web Site: www.rizzoliusa.com
Key Personnel
CFO: Alan Rutsky
VP & Publr: Charles Miers
VP & Dir, Mktg & Sales: Jennifer Pierson
Exec Publicity Dir: Pam Sommers
Assoc Publr, HLLA, Universe & Welcome Books: Jim Muschett
Assoc Publr, Universe Books, Calendars & Licensing: Robb Pearlman
Creative Dir: Dung Ngo
Dir, Prodn: Maria Pia Gramaglia
Assoc Dir, Prodn: Kaija Markoe
Dir, Spec Sales: Tracey Petitt
Intl Sales Dir: Shanta Inshiqaq
Trade Sales Dir: John Deen
Assoc Dir, Publicity: Jessica Napp
Client Publr Sales Mgr: Sarah Carstens
Mktg Mgr, Creative Servs & Social/New Media: Linda Pricci
Intl Sales Mgr: Susan Masry
Mgr, Spec Sales & Universe Calendars: Casey Whalen
Sr Ed, Architecture: David Morton
Sr Ed, Ex Libris: Alessandra Lusardi
Dist Coord: Jerry Hoffnagle
Founded: 1976
Fine arts, architecture, photography, decorative arts, cookbooks, gardening & landscape design, fashion & sports.
ISBN Prefix(es): 978-0-8478
Number of titles published annually: 100 Print
Imprints: Ex Libris; Flammarion; Marsilio; Pie Books; RCS Libri; Rizzoli First; Rizzoli, New York; SkiraRizzoli Publishing; Universe; Welcome Books
Distributed by Random House
Distributor for Editions Flammarion; Skira Editore
Advertising Agency: Rizzoli Graphic Studios
Returns: Random House, 1019 N State Rd 47, Crawfordsville, IN 47933; Random House of Canada Ltd, 2775 Mattheson Blvd E, Mississaugua, ON L4W 4P7, Canada *Toll Free Tel:* 800-733-3000 *Toll Free Fax:* 800-659-2436

See separate listing for:
Universe Publishing
Welcome Books®

The RoadRunner Press
124 NW 32 St, Oklahoma City, OK 73118
Mailing Address: PO Box 2564, Oklahoma City, OK 73101
Tel: 405-524-6205 *Fax:* 405-524-6312
E-mail: info@theroadrunnerpress.com; orders@theroadrunnerpress.com
Web Site: www.theroadrunnerpress.com
Key Personnel
Publr & Ed: Jeanne Devlin *E-mail:* jeanne@theroadrunnerpress.com
Dir, Sales & Mktg: Michael Hollman
Founded: 2011
Small indie publishing house specializing in quality young adult fiction & regional nonfiction as well as select nonfiction & literary fiction with an emphasis on Native American voices from the American West.
ISBN Prefix(es): 978-1-937054
Number of titles published annually: 10 Print; 6 E-Book; 1 Audio
Total Titles: 29 Print; 8 E-Book
Imprints: Max Books; Red River Books; The RoadRunner Press
Foreign Rep(s): Fitzhenry & Whiteside (Canada)
Billing Address: PO Box 2564, Oklahoma City, OK 73101
Returns: Aero Corp, 1377 Tefft Ct, Saline, MI 48176
Warehouse: Aero Corp, 1377 Tefft Ct, Saline, MI 48176
Membership(s): ALA; The Children's Book Council; The Independent Book Publishers Association; Midwest Independent Publishers Association; Mountains & Plains Independent Publishers Association; New Mexico Book Association; Publishers Association of the West; Western Writers of America

Roaring Brook Press
Member of Macmillan Children's Publishing Group
175 Fifth Ave, New York, NY 10010
Tel: 646-307-5151
Web Site: us.macmillan.com/roaringbrookpressaspx
Key Personnel
Publr: Simon Boughton
Sr Ed, First Second Books: Calista Brill *Tel:* 646-307-5386
Founded: 2002
ISBN Prefix(es): 978-0-7613; 978-1-59643
Number of titles published annually: 50 Print
Imprints: First Second Books; Neal Porter Books

Roaring Forties Press
1053 Santa Fe Ave, Berkeley, CA 94706
Tel: 510-527-5461
E-mail: info@roaringfortiespress.com
Web Site: www.roaringfortiespress.com
Key Personnel
Founder & Publr: Deirdre Greene *E-mail:* dmg@roaringfortiespress.com; Nigel Quinney *E-mail:* nq@roaringfortiespress.com
Publisher of unique fiction, literary nonfiction & travel books with a twist.
ISBN Prefix(es): 978-0-9766706; 978-0-9777429; 978-0-9823410; 978-1-938901; 978-0-9843165
Number of titles published annually: 4 Print; 4 E-Book
Total Titles: 21 Print; 70 E-Book
Distribution Center: Legato Publishers Group/PGW, 1700 Fourth St, Berkeley, CA 94710 *Tel:* 510-809-3700 *Toll Free Tel:* 800-788-3123 *Fax:* 510-809-3777 *Web Site:* www.pgw.com
Perseus Books Group UK, 69-70 Temple Chambers, 3-7 Temple Ave, London EC4Y 0HP, United Kingdom *Tel:* (020) 7353 7771 *Fax:* (020) 7353 7786 *E-mail:* enquiries@perseusbooks.co.uk *Web Site:* www.perseusbooksgroup.com
Membership(s): The Independent Book Publishers Association

James A Rock & Co Publishers
900 S Irby St, Suite 508, Florence, SC 29501
Toll Free Tel: 800-411-2230 *Fax:* 843-395-5975
E-mail: jrock@rockpublishing.com
Web Site: rockpublishing.com
Key Personnel
Publr: James A Rock
Founded: 1977
ISBN Prefix(es): 978-0-918736; 978-1-59663
Number of titles published annually: 20 Print
Total Titles: 76 Print
Imprints: Aonian Press (contemporary, historical & suspense romance); Castle Keep Books (children & young adult); Seaboard Press (nonfiction); Sense of Wonder Press (science fiction, fantasy, horror); Yellowback Mysteries (mystery, detective)
Membership(s): AAP

RockBench Publishing Corp
6101 Stillmeadow Dr, Nashville, TN 37211-6518
SAN: 855-5559
Tel: 615-831-2277 *Fax:* 615-831-2212
E-mail: info@rockbench.com
Web Site: www.rockbench.com
Key Personnel
Acqs Ed: David C Baker *E-mail:* david@rockbench.com
Circ Mgr: Jane Lawrence *E-mail:* jane@recourses.com
Royalties: Julie Warren *E-mail:* info@recourses.com
Founded: 2008
Publish courageous thought leadership content for the business community.
ISBN Prefix(es): 978-1-60544
Number of titles published annually: 7 Print; 5 E-Book; 2 Audio
Total Titles: 14 Print; 5 E-Book
Advertising Agency: faceoutstudio, 520 SW Powerhouse Dr, Suite 628, Bend, OR 97702-1295, Pres: Mr Torrey Sharp *Tel:* 541-323-3220 *Fax:* 541-323-3221 *E-mail:* torrey@faceoutstudio.com *Web Site:* www.faceoutstudio.com
Membership(s): The Association of Publishers for Special Sales; The Independent Book Publishers Association

The Rockefeller University Press
Unit of Rockefeller University
1114 First Ave, 3rd fl, New York, NY 10065-8325
Tel: 212-327-7938 *Fax:* 212-327-8587
E-mail: rupress@rockefeller.edu
Web Site: www.rupress.org
Key Personnel
Fin Dir: Ray Fastiggi *Tel:* 212-327-8567 *E-mail:* fastigg@rockefeller.edu
Prodn Dir: Rob O'Donnell *Tel:* 212-327-8545 *E-mail:* odonner@rockefeller.edu
Mktg Assoc: Laraine Karl *E-mail:* lkarl@rockefeller.edu
Founded: 1906
Currently publishes biomedical journals & books.
ISBN Prefix(es): 978-0-87470
Number of titles published annually: 1 Print
Total Titles: 8 Print; 3 Online; 6 Audio
Foreign Rep(s): Charlesworth (China); iGroup Asia Pacific Ltd (Asia-Pacific)
Membership(s): AAP Professional & Scholarly Publishing Division; Association of American University Presses; Association of Learned & Professional Society Publishers; Society for Scholarly Publishing

Rocky Mountain Mineral Law Foundation
9191 Sheridan Blvd, Suite 203, Westminister, CO 80031
Tel: 303-321-8100 *Fax:* 303-321-7657
E-mail: info@rmmlf.org
Web Site: www.rmmlf.org
Key Personnel
Exec Dir: Stevia Walther *Tel:* 303-321-8100 ext 101
Assoc Dir: Frances Hartogh *Tel:* 303-321-8100 ext 118; Mark Holland *Tel:* 303-321-8100 ext 106 *E-mail:* mholland@rmmlf.org
Founded: 1955
Natural resources & legal education.
ISBN Prefix(es): 978-0-929047; 978-0-882047
Number of titles published annually: 5 Print
Total Titles: 81 Print; 1 CD-ROM

Rocky River Publishers LLC
PO Box 1679, Shepherdstown, WV 25443-1679
Tel: 304-876-1868 *Fax:* 304-263-2949
E-mail: rockyriverpublishers@citlink.net
Web Site: www.rockyriver.com
Key Personnel
Pres: Miriam J Wilson
Founded: 1987
High quality books & materials with creative approaches to help children deal with problems & needs they may have from infancy to adulthood.
ISBN Prefix(es): 978-0-944576
Number of titles published annually: 3 Print
Total Titles: 20 Print
Distributed by C E Mendez Foundation Inc
Distribution Center: Follett School Solutions Inc, 1340 Ridgeview Dr, McHenry, IL 60050 *Tel:* 815-759-1700 *Toll Free Tel:* 888-511-5114 (cust serv) *Fax:* 815-759-9831 *Toll Free Fax:* 800-852-5458 *E-mail:* info@follettlearning.com *Web Site:* www.follettlearning.com SAN: 169-1902

Rod & Staff Publishers Inc
Hwy 172, Crockett, KY 41413
Mailing Address: PO Box 3, Crockett, KY 41413-0003
Tel: 606-522-4348 *Fax:* 606-522-4896 *Toll Free Fax:* 800-643-1244 (ordering in US)
Key Personnel
Busn Mgr: John Martin
Founded: 1958
Religious-story books; church, Sunday & Christian school materials & tracts.
ISBN Prefix(es): 978-0-7399
Number of titles published annually: 20 Print
Total Titles: 700 Print

Rodale Inc
400 S Tenth St, Emmaus, PA 18098
SAN: 200-2477
Tel: 610-967-5171
Web Site: www.rodaleinc.com
Key Personnel
Chmn & CEO: Maria Rodale
Pres: Scott Schulman *Tel:* 212-697-2040
VP & Publr: Mary Ann Naples *Tel:* 212-573-0289
VP & Assoc Publr, Trade Books: Gail Gonzales
VP, Brand & Digital Communs: Allison Hobson Falkenberry
Edit Dir: Jennifer Levesque *Tel:* 212-573-0264
Asst Ed: Mollie Thomas
Founded: 1932 (by J I Rodale)
Adult trade titles in health & wellness, fitness & sports, cooking, gardening, spirituality & nature.
ISBN Prefix(es): 978-0-87857; 978-1-57954; 978-0-87596; 978-1-59486; 978-1-59486; 978-1-60529; 978-1-60961; 978-1-62336
Number of titles published annually: 75 Print

Branch Office(s)
733 Third Ave, 8th fl, New York, NY 10017-3204 *Tel:* 212-697-2040 *Fax:* 212-682-2237
Distributed by Macmillan
Foreign Rights: Bob Niegowski (Worldwide exc Canada & USA)
Shipping Address: MPS Distribution Center, 16365 James Madison Hwy, Gordonsville, VA 22942-8501 *Toll Free Tel:* 888-330-8477 *Toll Free Fax:* 800-672-2054

Roman Catholic Books
Division of Catholic Media Apostolate Inc
PO Box 2286, Fort Collins, CO 80522-2286
Tel: 970-490-2735 *Fax:* 904-212-1287
Web Site: www.booksforcatholics.com
Key Personnel
Pres: Roger A McCaffrey *E-mail:* cxpeditor@gmail.com
VP, Mktg: Maureen Williamson *E-mail:* maureen@intrepidgroup.com
Founded: 1981
Traditional Catholic books.
ISBN Prefix(es): 978-0-912141; 978-1-929291; 978-0-9793540; 978-1-934888
Number of titles published annually: 10 Print
Total Titles: 270 Print

Roncorp Music
Division of Northeastern Music Publications
PO Box 517, Glenmoore, PA 19343
Tel: 610-942-2370 *Fax:* 610-942-0660
E-mail: info@nemusicpub.com
Web Site: www.nemusicpub.com
Key Personnel
Pres: Randy Navarre
Founded: 1978
Music & music texts.
ISBN Prefix(es): 978-0-939103
Number of titles published annually: 15 Print
Total Titles: 300 Print

Ronin Publishing Inc
PO Box 22900, Oakland, CA 94609
Tel: 510-420-3669 *Fax:* 510-420-3672
E-mail: ronin@roninpub.com
Web Site: www.roninpub.com
Key Personnel
Publr: Beverly Potter *E-mail:* beverly@roninpub.com
Founded: 1983
Small, independent publisher in San Francisco Bay Area.
ISBN Prefix(es): 978-0-914171; 978-1-57951
Number of titles published annually: 6 Print; 8 E-Book
Total Titles: 110 Print; 80 E-Book; 2 Audio
Imprints: And/Or Books; Books for Independent Minds
Foreign Rep(s): Airlift (UK); PGW (Canada)
Foreign Rights: Interlicense (Worldwide)
Distribution Center: Publishers Group West, 1700 Fourth St, Berkeley, CA 94710 *Tel:* 510-809-3700 *Fax:* 510-809-3777 *E-mail:* info@pgw.com *Web Site:* www.pgw.com
New Leaf Distributing Co, 401 Thornton Rd, Lithia Springs, GA 30122 *Tel:* 770-948-7845 *Fax:* 770-944-2313 *Web Site:* www.newleaf-dist.com
Membership(s): ABA; The Association of Publishers for Special Sales; The Independent Book Publishers Association; Northern California Book Publicity & Marketing Association

The Rosen Publishing Group Inc
29 E 21 St, New York, NY 10010
SAN: 203-3720
Tel: 212-777-3017 *Toll Free Tel:* 800-237-9932 *Toll Free Fax:* 888-436-4643
E-mail: info@rosenpub.com
Web Site: www.rosenpublishing.com
Key Personnel
Pres: Roger Rosen
Founded: 1950
Hardcover, library editions, vocational guidance; personal guidance; music & art catalogs; drug abuse prevention, self-esteem development, values & ethics, new international writing, multicultural, African heritage, graphic nonfiction, curriculum related nonfiction. Grades PreK-12.
ISBN Prefix(es): 978-0-8239; 978-1-4042
Number of titles published annually: 200 Print
Total Titles: 2,000 Print
Imprints: Gareth Stevens Publishing; Power Kids Press
Divisions: Rosen Classroom Books & Materials
Warehouse: Maple Press Distribution, 60 Grumbacher Rd, York, PA 17405
See separate listing for:
Gareth Stevens Publishing

§Ross Books
PO Box 4340, Berkeley, CA 94704-0340
Tel: 510-841-2474 *Fax:* 510-295-2531
E-mail: sales@rossbooks.com
Web Site: www.rossbooks.com
Key Personnel
Owner & Pres: Franz H Ross
Sales: Benny Juarez
Founded: 1977
General trade books & ebooks.
ISBN Prefix(es): 978-0-89496
Number of titles published annually: 4 Print; 1 CD-ROM; 3 E-Book; 1 Audio
Total Titles: 26 Print; 2 CD-ROM; 2 Online; 6 E-Book; 2 Audio
Imprints: Baldar
Membership(s): Northern California Book Publicity & Marketing Association

Ross Publishing LLC
392 Central Park W, Suite 20-C, New York, NY 10025-5878
SAN: 201-8969
Tel: 212-765-8200
E-mail: info@rosspub.com
Web Site: www.rosspub.com
Key Personnel
Chmn of the Bd & Pres: Norman A Ross *E-mail:* norman@rosspub.com
Founded: 1972
Publisher of reference books (US Census reprints); Slavica, microfilms on Central America, Black Panthers, etc. Request permission for all returns.
ISBN Prefix(es): 978-0-88354
Number of titles published annually: 3 Print
Total Titles: 400 Print; 30 Audio
Warehouse: Publishers Storage & Shipping Corp, 46 Development Rd, Fitchburg, MA 01420 *Tel:* 978-345-2121 *Fax:* 978-348-1233

§Rothstein Publishing
Division of Rothstein Associates Inc
4 Arapaho Rd, Brookfield, CT 06804-3104
Tel: 203-740-7400 *Toll Free Tel:* 888-768-4783 *Fax:* 203-740-7401
E-mail: info@rothstein.com
Web Site: www.rothstein.com; www.rothsteinpublishing.com
Key Personnel
Pres: Philip Jan Rothstein *E-mail:* pjr@rothstein.com
Chief Mktg Offr: Mr Glyn Davies *Tel:* 415-457-9392 *E-mail:* glyndavies@rothstein.com
Edit Dir: Kristen Noakes-Fry *Tel:* 727-258-8389 *E-mail:* knfwriter@rothstein.com
Mktg Dir: Terri Mitchem *Tel:* 352-596-1192 *E-mail:* mtmitchem@rothstein.com
Founded: 1985
Publish books & software for business.
ISBN Prefix(es): 978-0-9641648; 978-1-931332
Number of titles published annually: 20 Print; 6 CD-ROM; 12 E-Book
Total Titles: 80 Print; 36 CD-ROM; 25 E-Book

Rough Guides
Subsidiary of Pearson PLC
375 Hudson St, New York, NY 10014
SAN: 282-5074
Toll Free Tel: 800-631-8571
E-mail: mail@roughguides.com
Web Site: www.roughguides.com
Key Personnel
Sr Mktg Mgr (US): Megan Kennedy
Founded: 1982
Travel guides; phrasebooks, music & film reference; pop culture; city & country maps; world & Internet reference.
ISBN Prefix(es): 978-1-85828; 978-1-84353
Number of titles published annually: 60 Print; 10 E-Book
Total Titles: 425 Print; 40 E-Book
Foreign Office(s): 80 Strand, London WC2R 0RL, United Kingdom *Tel:* (020) 7010 3000
Distributed by Penguin Group (USA) LLC
Orders to: 405 Murray Hill Pkwy, East Rutherford, NJ 07073 *Toll Free Tel:* 800-526-0275 *Toll Free Fax:* 800-227-9604
Returns: 199 Pearson Pkwy, Lebanon, IN 46052

§The Rough Notes Co Inc
Subsidiary of Insurance Publishing Plus Corp
11690 Technology Dr, Carmel, IN 46032-5600
Tel: 317-582-1600 *Toll Free Tel:* 800-428-4384 (cust serv) *Fax:* 317-816-1000 *Toll Free Fax:* 800-321-1909
E-mail: rnc@roughnotes.com
Web Site: www.roughnotes.com
Key Personnel
VP & Natl Sales Dir: Eric Hall *E-mail:* ehall@roughnotes.com
Opers Mgr: Sam Berman
Founded: 1878
Technical/educational reference material specific to the property/casualty insurance industry.
ISBN Prefix(es): 978-1-56461
Number of titles published annually: 10 Print
Total Titles: 40 Print; 4 Online
Advertising Agency: AdCom Group

Routledge/Taylor & Francis
Member of Taylor & Francis Group
711 Third Ave, 8th fl, New York, NY 10017
SAN: 213-196X
Tel: 212-216-7800 *Toll Free Tel:* 800-634-7064 (orders) *Fax:* 212-564-7854
Web Site: www.routledge.com
Founded: 1836
Academic books in the humanities, social & behavioral sciences. Academic reference. Professional titles in architecture, education & the behavioral sciences.
ISBN Prefix(es): 978-0-915202 (formerly Accelerated Development); 978-1-55959 (formerly Accelerated Development); 978-0-87630 (formerly Brunner-Routledge); 978-1-57958 (formerly Fitzroy Dearborn); 978-0-8240 (formerly Garland); 978-0-8153 (formerly Garland); 978-0-415 (Routledge); 978-0-87830 (Theatre Arts); 978-1-85000 (formerly RoutledgeFalmer); 978-0-7007 (formerly Routledge Curzon); 978-0-419 (formerly Spon); 978-0-946653 (formerly Europa); 978-1-85743 (formerly Europa); 978-0-7494 (formerly Kogan Page); 978-90-5701 (formerly Gordon & Breach); 978-1-58391 (formerly BrunnerRoutledge); 978-1-88496 (formerly Fitzroy Dearborn); 978-90-5702 (formerly Harwood Academic); 978-3-7186 (formerly Harwood Academic); 978-90-5823 (formerly Harwood Academic); 978-0-19713 (formerly Routledge Curzon); 978-0-72860 (formerly Routledge Curzon); 978-0-75070 (formerly RoutledgeFalmer)

Number of titles published annually: 2,000 Print; 2,000 Online; 2,000 E-Book
Total Titles: 33,000 Print; 21,000 Online; 21,000 E-Book
Imprints: CRC Press; Garland Science; Psychology Press; Routledge
Sales Office(s): Taylor & Francis, 6000 Broken Sound Pkwy, Suite 300, Boca Raton, FL 33487, VP, Sales: Dennis Weiss *Tel:* 561-994-0555 *Toll Free Tel:* 800-272-7737 *Fax:* 561-989-8732 *Toll Free Fax:* 800-374-3401
Foreign Office(s): 2 Park Sq, Milton Park, Abingdon Oxon OX14 4RN, United Kingdom, Group Sales Dir: Christoph Chesher *Tel:* (020) 7017 6000 *Fax:* (020) 7017 6699 *E-mail:* book.orders@tandf.co.uk
Distributor for David Fulton Books
Foreign Rights: Jennifer Strong (Worldwide)
Warehouse: Taylor & Francis, 7625 Empire Dr, Florence, KY 41042-2919 *Toll Free Tel:* 800-634-7064 *Toll Free Fax:* 800-248-4724 *E-mail:* orders@taylorandfrancis.com

Rowman & Littlefield Publishers Inc
4501 Forbes Blvd, Suite 200, Lanham, MD 20706
SAN: 208-5143
Tel: 301-459-3366 *Toll Free Tel:* 800-462-6420 (cust serv) *Fax:* 301-429-5748
Web Site: www.rowmanlittlefield.com
Key Personnel
Group CEO & Pres: Jed Lyons
CFO: George Franzak
EVP, Fin & Opers: Robert Marsh
SVP & Exec Ed: Jonathan Sisk *E-mail:* jsisk@rowmanlittlefield.com
Trade Publr: Jim Childs
Rts & Perms Dir: Clare Cox *Tel:* 301-459-3366 ext 308 *E-mail:* ccox@rowman.com
Sales Dir: Sheila Burnett *Tel:* 301-459-3366 ext 5606 *E-mail:* sburnett@rowmanlittlefield.com
Exec Ed: Charles Harmon
Sr Acqs Ed: Leanne Silverman
Founded: 1949
Policy studies; supplemental books & monographs, academic publisher.
ISBN Prefix(es): 978-0-8476; 978-0-7425
Number of titles published annually: 350 Print
Total Titles: 2,000 Print
Foreign Office(s): 10 Thornbury Rd, Plymouth, Devon PL6 7PP, United Kingdom, Contact: Suzanne Wheatley *Tel:* (05602) 698234 *Fax:* (05602) 698234 *E-mail:* swheatley@rowman.com
Foreign Rep(s): Academic Marketing Services Pty Ltd (Botswana, Namibia, South Africa, Zimbabwe); APD Singapore Pte Ltd (Brunei, Cambodia, Indonesia, Laos, Malaysia, Singapore, Thailand, Vietnam); Aristotle House (Simons Watts) (Cameroon, Ethiopia, The Gambia, Ghana, Kenya, Malawi, Mauritius, Nigeria, Tanzania, Uganda); Asia Publishers Service Ltd (China, Hong Kong, Korea, Philippines); Avicenna Partnership Ltd (Middle East); Cranbury International LLC (Caribbean, Central America, Mexico, Puerto Rico, South America); Durnell Marketing Ltd (Europe); Inbooks (Australia, New Zealand, Papua New Guinea); Overleaf (Bangladesh, Bhutan, India, Nepal, Sri Lanka); Publishers Representatives (Pakistan); Quantum Publishing Solutions Ltd (UK); United Publishers Services Ltd (Japan)
Warehouse: 15200 NBN Way, Warehouse C, Blue Ridge Summit, PA 17214 *Tel:* 717-794-3800 *Fax:* 717-794-3803
See separate listing for:
Down East Books

Royal Fireworks Press
PO Box 399, Unionville, NY 10988
Fax: 845-726-3824
E-mail: mail@rfwp.com
Web Site: www.rfwp.com
Key Personnel
Dir, Order Dept & Cust Rel: Margaret Foley
Founded: 1977
Educational materials for gifted children, their parents & teachers; reading materials; adult literacy/education materials; fiction series for middle school: mystery & adventure; novels of growing up; young adult science fiction; youth against violence early childhood program (K-3).
ISBN Prefix(es): 978-0-89824; 978-0-88092
Number of titles published annually: 60 Print
Total Titles: 840 Print; 40 E-Book
Distributor for KAV Books; Silk Label Books; Trillium Press

§Running Press Book Publishers
Member of The Perseus Books Group
2300 Chestnut St, Philadelphia, PA 19103-4399
SAN: 204-5702
Tel: 215-567-5080 *Toll Free Tel:* 800-343-4499 (cust serv & orders) *Fax:* 215-568-2919 *Toll Free Fax:* 800-453-2884 (cust serv & orders)
E-mail: perseus.promos@perseusbooks.com
Web Site: www.runningpress.com
Key Personnel
Pres, Publg, Client & Sales Devt: Matty Goldberg
VP & Publr: Kristin Kiser
VP & Dir, Mktg & Publicity: Kathleen Schmidt
Design Dir: Frances Soo Ping Chow
Edit Dir: Jennifer Kasius
Edit Dir, Running Press Miniature Editions: Jennifer Leczkowski
Sr Ed: Jordana Tusman; Kristen Wiewora
Sr Ed, Running Press Kids: Lisa Cheng
Ed: Cindy de la Hoz
Publicity Mgr: Seta Zink
Founded: 1972
Hardcover & paperback trade books; art, craft/how-to, general nonfiction, children's books, promotional books, notebooks, journals & Miniature Editions™, cookbooks, books & products.
ISBN Prefix(es): 978-1-56138; 978-0-7624
Number of titles published annually: 150 Print
Total Titles: 2,000 Print; 6 CD-ROM
Imprints: Courage Books (illustrated gift books, promotional titles); Running Press; Running Press Kids; Running Press Miniature Editions
Distributor for Wine Enthusiast
Foreign Rep(s): Book Promotions (Nicky Stubbs) (South Africa); Gilles Fauveau (Japan, Korea); Jaime Gregorio (Philippines); Sharad Mohan (Bangladesh, India, Maldives, Nepal, Pakistan, Sri Lanka); New South Books (Australia, New Zealand); Perseus Books Group UK (Europe, Ireland, UK); Perseus International (Suk Lee) (Middle East); Perseus International (all other territories, Caribbean, Latin America); June Poonpanich (Cambodia, Indonesia, Laos, Thailand, Vietnam); Wei Zhao (China, Hong Kong, Taiwan)
Foreign Rights: Anthea Agency (Katalina Sabeva) (Bulgaria); Bardon-Chinese Media Agency (David Tsai) (China, Taiwan); Raquel de la Concha Agencia Literaria (Raquel de la Concha & Marilu Casquero) (Brazil, Latin America, Portugal, Spain); Paul & Peter Fritz Agency (Peter Fritz, Christian Dittus & Antonia Fritz) (Germany); Deborah Harris Agency (Efrat Lev) (Israel); Anna Jarota Agency (Anna Jarota) (France); Nurcihan Kesim Literary Agency (Turkey); Duran Kim Agency (Duran Kim & Joe Moon) (Korea); Alexander Korzhenevski Agency (Alexander & Tania Korzhenevski) (Russia); Maxima Creative Agency (Santo Manurung) (Indonesia); Kristin Olson Literary Agency (Kristin Olson) (Czech Republic, Slovakia); Oxford Literary & Rights Agency (Hana Whitton) (Ukraine); Read n' Right Agency (Nike Davarinou) (Greece); Lennart Sane Agency (Philip Sane) (Scandinavia); Santachiara Literary Agency (Roberto Santachiara) (Italy); Sebes & Van Gelderen Literary Agency (Paul Sebes & Mariska Kleinhoonte van Os) (Netherlands); Livia Stoia Agency (Livia Stoia & Mirela Calota) (Albania, Bosnia and Herzegovina, Croatia, Macedonia, Montenegro, Romania, Serbia, Slovenia); Torus-Books Literary & Scouting Agency Ltd (Gynn Kalman) (Hungary); Tuttle-Mori Agency (Mr Thananchai Pandey) (Thailand, Vietnam); Tuttle-Mori Agency Inc (Manami Tamaoki & Asako Kawachi) (Japan)
Orders to: Raincoast Books, 2440 Viking Way, Richmond, BC V6V 1N2, Canada *Toll Free Tel:* 800-663-5714 *Toll Free Fax:* 800-565-3770 *E-mail:* orders@raincoastbooks.com; Grantham Book Services, Trent Rd, Grantham NG31 7XQ, United Kingdom (UK, Europe & Ireland) *Tel:* (0147) 654 1080 *Fax:* (0147) 654 1061 *E-mail:* orders@gbs.tbs-ltd.co.uk
Distribution Center: 210 American Dr, Jackson, TN 38301 *Toll Free Tel:* 800-343-4499 *Toll Free Fax:* 800-351-5073

Russell Sage Foundation
112 E 64 St, New York, NY 10065
SAN: 201-4521
Tel: 212-750-6000 *Toll Free Tel:* 800-524-6401 *Fax:* 212-371-4761
E-mail: info@rsage.org
Web Site: www.russellsage.org
Key Personnel
Pres: Eric Wanner
Dir, Pubns: Suzanne Nichols
Dir, Communs: David Haproff
Founded: 1907
Sociology, economics, political science.
ISBN Prefix(es): 978-0-87154
Number of titles published annually: 25 Print
Total Titles: 1,000 Print
Foreign Rep(s): University Presses Marketing (Continental Europe, Ireland, Israel, UK)
Advertising Agency: Verso Book Advertising Inc
Shipping Address: CUP Services, 750 Cascadilla St, Ithaca, NY 14851

Russian Information Service Inc
PO Box 567, Montpelier, VT 05601
Tel: 802-223-4955
E-mail: editors@russianlife.com
Web Site: www.russianlife.com
Key Personnel
Pres & Publr: Paul E Richardson *E-mail:* paulr@russianlife.com
Founded: 1990
Publish magazines, books, info, maps for business & independent travel to Russia.
ISBN Prefix(es): 978-1-880100
Number of titles published annually: 3 Print; 3 E-Book
Total Titles: 20 Print; 20 E-Book
Imprints: Edward & Dee

Russian Life Magazine, see Russian Information Service Inc

Rutgers University Press
Division of Rutgers, The State University of New Jersey
106 Somerset St, 3rd fl, New Brunswick, NJ 08901
SAN: 203-364X
Tel: 848-445-7762 *Toll Free Tel:* 800-848-6224 (orders only) *Fax:* 732-745-4935 (acqs, edit, mktg, perms & prodn) *Toll Free Fax:* 800-272-6817 (fulfillment)
Web Site: rutgerspress.rutgers.edu
Key Personnel
Dir: Marlie Wasserman *Tel:* 848-445-7784 *E-mail:* marlie@rutgers.edu
Assoc Dir & Ed-in-Chief: Leslie Mitchner *Tel:* 848-445-7787 *E-mail:* lmitch@rutgers.edu

Asst to the Dir, Perms & Subs Rts Mgr & Ebook Coord: Allyson Fields *Tel:* 848-445-7785 *E-mail:* amfields@rutgers.edu
Mktg & Sales Dir: Jeremy Grainger *Tel:* 848-445-7781 *E-mail:* jeremy.grainger@rutgers.edu
Prepress Dir: Marilyn A Campbell *Tel:* 848-445-7756 *E-mail:* marilync@rutgers.edu
Sr Promos Mgr: Brice Hammack *Tel:* 848-445-7765 *E-mail:* bhammack@rutgers.edu
Busn Mgr: David Flum *Tel:* 848-445-7763 *E-mail:* dflum@rutgers.edu
Cust Serv Mgr: Penny Burke *Tel:* 848-445-7788 *E-mail:* pborden@rutgers.edu
Mktg & Publicity Mgr: Lisa Fortunato *Tel:* 848-445-7775 *E-mail:* lisafort@rutgers.edu
Exec Ed: Kimberly Guinta *Tel:* 848-445-7786
Exec Ed, Clinical Health & Medicine: Dana Dreibelbis *Tel:* 848-445-7792 *E-mail:* dana.dreibelbis@rutgers.edu
Sr Ed: Peter Mickulas *Tel:* 848-445-7752 *E-mail:* mickulas@rutgers.edu
Prodn Ed: Carrie Hudak *Tel:* 848-445-7755 *E-mail:* carrie.hudak@rutgers.edu
Asst Ed: Lisa Boyajian *Tel:* 848-445-7791 *E-mail:* lmb333@rutgers.edu
Sr Prodn Coord: Ann Hegeman *Tel:* 848-445-7761 *E-mail:* hegeman@rutgers.edu
Prodn Coord: Jennifer Blanc-Tal *Tel:* 848-445-7764 *E-mail:* jfb131@scarletmail.rutgers.edu
Exhibit Coord/Mktg Asst: Victoria Verhowsky *Tel:* 848-445-7782 *E-mail:* victoria.verhowsky@rutgers.edu
Founded: 1936
Since its founding as a nonprofit publisher, Rutgers University Press has been dedicated to the advancement & dissemination of knowledge to scholars, students & the general reading public. An integral part of one of the leading public research & teaching universities in the US, the Press reflects & is essential to the University's missions of research, instruction & service. To carry out these goals, books are published in electronic & print format in a broad array of disciplines across the humanities, social sciences & sciences. Fulfilling its mandate to serve the people of New Jersey, books of scholarly & popular interest on the state & surrounding region are also published. Working with authors throughout the world, the Press seeks books that meet high editorial standards, facilitate the exchange of ideas, enhance teaching & make scholarship accessible to a wide range of readers. It celebrates & affirms its role as a major cultural institution that contributes significantly to the ideas that shape the critical issues of our day.
ISBN Prefix(es): 978-0-8135
Number of titles published annually: 90 Print; 80 Online; 80 E-Book
Total Titles: 3,500 Print; 1,600 Online; 1,600 E-Book
Foreign Rep(s): Eurospan (Europe, Ireland, UK); Scholarly Book Services Inc (Canada)
Foreign Rights: McIntosh & Otis Inc (Worldwide)
Returns: Ingram Book Group, One Ingram Blvd, La Vergne, TN 37086-1986 *Tel:* 615-793-5000 *Web Site:* www.ingramcontent.com
Warehouse: Ingram Book Group, One Ingram Blvd, La Vergne, TN 37086-1986 *Tel:* 615-793-5000 *Web Site:* www.ingramcontent.com
Membership(s): American Association of University Presses

§Saddleback Educational Publishing
3120-A Pullman St, Costa Mesa, CA 92626
SAN: 860-0902
Tel: 714-640-5200 *Toll Free Tel:* 888-SDLBACK (735-2225); 800-637-8715 *Fax:* 714-640-5297 *Toll Free Fax:* 888-734-4010
E-mail: contact@sdlback.com
Web Site: www.sdlback.com
Key Personnel
Pres: Arianne McHugh
Founded: 1982
Publish high-interest, low-readabilty material for middle school & high school. Solutions for struggling learners.
ISBN Prefix(es): 978-1-56254; 978-1-59905; 978-1-6165
Number of titles published annually: 200 Print; 10 CD-ROM; 20 E-Book; 10 Audio
Total Titles: 2,000 Print; 150 CD-ROM; 400 E-Book; 150 Audio
Distributed by Children's Plus; Delaney
Distribution Center: Follett School Solutions Inc, 1340 Ridgeview Dr, McHenry, IL 60050 *Tel:* 815-759-1700 *Toll Free Tel:* 888-511-5114 (cust serv) *Fax:* 815-759-9831 *Toll Free Fax:* 800-852-5458 *E-mail:* info@follettlearning.com *Web Site:* www.follettlearning.com SAN: 169-1902
Membership(s): American Educational Publishers; Education Market Association; Educational Book & Media Association

§William H Sadlier Inc
9 Pine St, New York, NY 10005
SAN: 204-0948
Tel: 212-227-2120 *Toll Free Tel:* 800-221-5175 (cust serv) *Fax:* 212-312-6080
E-mail: customerservice@sadlier.com
Web Site: www.sadlier.com
Key Personnel
Chmn of the Bd: Frank S Dinger
Treas: Raymond Sagan
Pres: William S Dinger
EVP & Publr, Sadlier: Rosemary Calicchio
VP & Dir, Mktg: Alexandra Rivas-Smith
VP & Natl Field Sales Mgr: John Bonenberger
VP & Natl Sales Administrator: Kevin O'Donnell
Creative Dir: Vincent Gallo
Gen Coun: Angela Dinger
Cust Serv: Melissa Gibbons
Founded: 1832
Pre-school, elementary & secondary textbooks on catechetics, sacraments, reading/language arts, mathematics; adult catechetical programs.
ISBN Prefix(es): 978-0-8215
Number of titles published annually: 4 Print
Divisions: Sadlier; Sadlier-Oxford

§SAE (Society of Automotive Engineers International)
400 Commonwealth Dr, Warrendale, PA 15096-0001
SAN: 216-0811
Tel: 724-776-4841; 724-776-4970 (outside US & CN) *Toll Free Tel:* 877-606-7323 (cust serv) *Fax:* 724-776-0790 (cust serv)
E-mail: publications@sae.org; customerservice@sae.org
Web Site: www.sae.org
Key Personnel
CEO: David L Schutt
Pres: Donald Hillebrand
Treas: Ronald Rath
Founded: 1905
Scientific & technical publications.
ISBN Prefix(es): 978-0-89883; 978-1-56091; 978-0-7680
Number of titles published annually: 150 Print
Total Titles: 650 Print; 23 CD-ROM; 1 Online; 15 E-Book; 1 Audio
Branch Office(s)
1200 "G" St NW, Suite 800, Washington, DC 20005 *Tel:* 202-463-7318
Automotive Headquarters, 755 W Big Beaver Rd, Suite 1600, Troy, MI 48084 *Tel:* 248-273-2455 *Fax:* 248-273-2494
5 Research Dr, Greenville, SC 29607 *Tel:* 724-776-4841
Foreign Office(s): SAE International China Office, Rm 3037, 3F, Silver Ct, No 85 Taoyuan Rd, Huangpu District, Shanghai 200021, China
Aerospace Standards Europe Office, One York St, London W1U 6PA, United Kingdom *Tel:* (020) 70341250
Distributor for Coordinating Research Council Inc
Foreign Rep(s): Aeromarine Vehicles (Singapore); Allied Publishers Pvt Ltd (India); Booknet Co Ltd (Thailand); China National Publications (China); China Publishers Marketing (China); EBSCO Korea (Korea); Eurospan (Marc Bedwell) (Asia-Pacific exc China); Eurospan Group (Africa, Australasia, Brazil, Europe, Oceania); Eurospan India (India); GDI Co Ltd (Korea); Kinokuniya Co Ltd (Japan); Maruzen Co Book Division (Japan); Normdocs (Russia); PB for Books (Pathumthani) Co Ltd (Thailand); SAE Australasia (Australasia, Oceania); SAE Brasil (Brazil); SAE International China Office (China); SAE of Japan (Japan); Ta Tong Book Co Ltd (Taiwan); UBS Library Services Pte Ltd (Singapore); UBSD Distrubution Sdn Bhd (Malaysia); YPJ Publications & Distributors Sdn Bhd (Malaysia)

Safari Press
15621 Chemical Lane, Bldg B, Huntington Beach, CA 92649
Tel: 714-894-9080 *Toll Free Tel:* 800-451-4788 *Fax:* 714-894-4949
E-mail: info@safaripress.com
Web Site: www.safaripress.com
Key Personnel
CEO: Ludo J Wurfbain
Chief Ed: J Neufeld
Founded: 1984
Specialize in big-game hunting, firearms, wing-shooting, Africana & sporting; hardcover trade & limited editions.
ISBN Prefix(es): 978-0-924357; 978-0-940143; 978-1-57157
Number of titles published annually: 10 Print
Total Titles: 250 Print
Distributor for Quiller

Safer Society Foundation Inc
29 Union St, Brandon, VT 05733
Mailing Address: PO Box 340, Brandon, VT 05733-0340
Tel: 802-247-3132 *Fax:* 802-247-4233
E-mail: info@safersociety.org
Web Site: www.safersociety.org
Founded: 1985
Specialize in titles relating to the prevention & treatment of sexual abuse.
ISBN Prefix(es): 978-1-884444
Number of titles published annually: 4 Print
Total Titles: 80 Print
Imprints: Safer Society Press
Foreign Rep(s): Open Leaves Books (Australia); Visions Book Store Ltd (Canada)
Membership(s): The Independent Book Publishers Association

Saga Press, see Simon & Schuster Children's Publishing

Sagamore Publishing LLC
1807 Federal Dr, Urbana, IL 61801
SAN: 292-5788
Tel: 217-359-5940 *Toll Free Tel:* 800-327-5557 (orders) *Fax:* 217-359-5975
E-mail: books@sagamorepub.com
Web Site: www.sagamorepub.com
Key Personnel
CEO & Publr: Dr Joseph J Bannon, Sr
Pres & Intl Rts: Peter L Bannon
Dir, Mktg & Sales: William Anderson
Founded: 1974
ISBN Prefix(es): 978-0-915611; 978-1-57167
Number of titles published annually: 15 Print
Total Titles: 210 Print; 6 Online

Distributor for American Academy for Park & Recreation Administration
Foreign Rep(s): Gazelle Book Services Ltd (Continental Europe, Ireland, UK); HM Leisure Planning (Australia, New Zealand)

SAGE Publications
2455 Teller Rd, Thousand Oaks, CA 91320
Toll Free Tel: 800-818-7243 *Toll Free Fax:* 800-583-2665
E-mail: info@sagepub.com
Web Site: www.sagepub.com
Key Personnel
Founder, Chmn & Publr: Sara Miller McCune
CEO & Pres: Blaise R Simqu
Founded: 1965
Professional & reference books, supplementary texts, journals, papers & newsletters in the social & behavioral sciences.
ISBN Prefix(es): 978-0-8039
Number of titles published annually: 275 Print
Total Titles: 5,731 Print
Imprints: Corwin Press; CQ Press; Learning Matters; Adam Matthew; Pine Forge Press
Subsidiaries: Corwin Press Inc
Divisions: Scolari
Foreign Office(s): Sage Publications India Pvt Ltd, B1/I-1 Mohan Cooperative Industrial Area, Mathura Rd, New Delhi 110 044, India *Tel:* (011) 4053 9222 *Fax:* (011) 4053 9234
SAGE Publications Asia-Pacific Pte Ltd, 3 Church St, Samsung Hub, Unit 10-04, Singapore 049483, Singapore *Tel:* 6220-1800 *Fax:* 6438-1008 *E-mail:* apac-librarysales@sagepub.co.uk
Sage Publications Ltd, One Oliver's Yard, 55 City Rd, London EC1Y 1SP, United Kingdom *Tel:* (020) 7324 8500 *Fax:* (020) 7324 8600
Foreign Rep(s): Astam Books Pty Ltd (Australia, New Zealand); Sage Publications India Pvt Ltd (India, South Asia); Sage Publications Ltd (Africa, Asia-Pacific, Europe, Middle East, UK); United Publishers Services Ltd (Japan, Korea)
See separate listing for:
CQ Press

St Andrews College Press
Subsidiary of St Andrews University
1700 Dogwood Mile, Laurinburg, NC 28352-5598
Tel: 910-277-5310 *Fax:* 910-277-5020
E-mail: press@sapc.edu
Web Site: www.sapc.edu/sapress
Key Personnel
Ed: Caitlin Johnson
Founded: 1968
ISBN Prefix(es): 978-0-932662; 978-1-879934
Number of titles published annually: 5 Print
Total Titles: 82 Print

St Augustine's Press Inc
PO Box 2285, South Bend, IN 46680-2285
Tel: 574-291-3500 *Toll Free Tel:* 888-997-4994 *Fax:* 574-291-3700
Web Site: www.staugustine.net
Key Personnel
Pres & Publr: Bruce Fingerhut *E-mail:* bruce@staugustine.net
Prodn: Benjamin Fingerhut *Tel:* 773-983-8471 *E-mail:* benjaminfingerhut@yahoo.com
Founded: 1996
Scholarly & trade publishing in humanities; Ad Agency, Design Promotion.
ISBN Prefix(es): 978-1-890318; 978-1-883357; 978-1-58731
Number of titles published annually: 30 Print
Total Titles: 475 Print; 4 E-Book
Imprints: Carthage Reprints; William of Moerbeke Translation (literal translations of major works in philosophy, theology & cultural history)
Editorial Office(s): 17917 Killington Way, South Bend, IN 46614-9773, Contact: Bruce Fingerhut *Tel:* 574-291-3500 *E-mail:* bruce@staugustine.net
Sales Office(s): University of Chicago Press, Sales Dept, 1429 E 60 St, Chicago, IL 60637-2954, Sales Dir: John Kessler *Tel:* 773-702-7248 *Fax:* 773-702-9756 *E-mail:* jkessler@press.uchicago.edu
Distributed by University of Chicago Press
Distributor for Dumb Ox Books (publishes the Aristotelian Commentaries of Thomas Aquinas & like works); Hardwood Press (trade books, mostly in sports & regional works); New Criterion Books (poetry prize)
Foreign Rights: Jeremy Beer (Worldwide exc USA)
Billing Address: Chicago Distribution Center, 11030 S Langley Ave, Chicago, IL 60628-3893
Orders to: Chicago Distribution Center, 11030 S Langley Ave, Chicago, IL 60628-3893, Karen Hyzy *Tel:* 773-702-7000 *Toll Free Tel:* 800-621-2736 *Fax:* 773-702-7212 *Toll Free Fax:* 800-621-8476 *E-mail:* kh@press.uchicago.edu
Returns: Chicago Distribution Center, 11030 S Langley Ave, Chicago, IL 60628-3893
Shipping Address: Chicago Distribution Center, 11030 S Langley Ave, Chicago, IL 60628-3893, Contact: Karen Hyzy *Tel:* 773-702-7000 *Toll Free Tel:* 800-621-2736 *Fax:* 773-702-7212 *Toll Free Fax:* 800-621-8476 *E-mail:* kh@press.uchicago.edu
Warehouse: Chicago Distribution Center, 11030 S Langley Ave, Chicago, IL 60628-3893
Distribution Center: Chicago Distribution Center, 11030 S Langley Ave, Chicago, IL 60628-3893 *Toll Free Tel:* 800-621-8471 *Toll Free Fax:* 800-621-8471 *E-mail:* kh@press.uchicago.edu

Saint Herman Press
Subsidiary of Brotherhood of Saint Herman of Alaska
10 Beegum Gorge Rd, Platina, CA 96076
SAN: 661-583X
Mailing Address: PO Box 70, Platina, CA 96076-0070
Tel: 530-352-4430 *Fax:* 530-352-4432
E-mail: stherman@stherman.com
Web Site: www.stherman.com
Key Personnel
CFO: Nicholas Liebmann
Pres: Abbott Hilarian
Secy: Paisius Bjerke
Founded: 1963
Publisher of books about the Orthodox Christian faith & Orthodox monasticism. Special emphasis on recent saints & spirituality, curriculum & textbooks.
ISBN Prefix(es): 978-0-938635; 978-1-887904
Number of titles published annually: 3 Print
Total Titles: 70 Print
Imprints: Brotherhood of Saint Herman of Alaska; Fr Seraphim Rose Foundation; St Herman Press; St Paisius Abbey; St Paisius Missionary School; St Xenia Skete; Valaam Society of America
Foreign Office(s): V Ivlenkov, Box 1854 Q, Melbourne, Victoria 3001, Australia
Orthodox Christian Books Ltd, Townhouse Farm, Studio 7, Alsager Rd, Audley, Staffordshire ST7 8JQ, United Kingdom, CEO: Nicholas Chapman *Fax:* (011) 178-272-3930 *E-mail:* 101600.262@compuserve.com
Distributed by Light & Life Publishing Co
Foreign Rep(s): Vladimir Ivlenkov (Australia); Orthodox Christian Books Ltd (Nicholas Chapman) (England)
Shipping Address: 4430 Hwy 36 W, Platina, CA 96076

St James Press®
Imprint of Gale
27500 Drake Rd, Farmington Hills, MI 48331-3535
Tel: 248-699-4253 *Toll Free Tel:* 800-877-4253 (orders) *Fax:* 248-699-8035 *Toll Free Fax:* 800-414-5043 (orders)
E-mail: gale.galeord@cengage.com
Web Site: www.gale.cengage.com
Founded: 1968
ISBN Prefix(es): 978-1-55862; 978-0-912289
Total Titles: 303 Print

Saint Johann Press
315 Schraalenburgh Rd, Haworth, NJ 07641
Tel: 201-387-1529 *Fax:* 201-501-0698
Web Site: www.stjohannpress.com
Key Personnel
Pres: David Biesel *E-mail:* d.biesel@verizon.net
VP: Diane Biesel
Dir, Sales & Promos: Deborah Brugger
Mgr, Acctg: Barbara Stinnett
Founded: 1990
Started as a book packager & consultant. Began publishing in 1998.
ISBN Prefix(es): 978-1-878282; 978-1-937943
Number of titles published annually: 12 Print
Total Titles: 120 Print
Distributor for MerwinAsia
Membership(s): ALA; Combined Book Exhibit; The Independent Book Publishers Association; USMC Combat Correspondents Association

St Joseph's University Press
5600 City Ave, Philadelphia, PA 19131-1395
SAN: 240-8368
Tel: 610-660-3402 *Fax:* 610-660-3412
E-mail: sjupress@sju.edu
Web Site: www.sjupress.com
Key Personnel
Dir: Mr Carmen R Croce *E-mail:* ccroce@sju.edu
Edit Dir of the Press: Rev Joseph F Chorpenning *Tel:* 610-660-1214 *E-mail:* jchorpen@sju.edu
Founded: 1971
Scholarly books on early modern Catholicism & the visual arts, regional studies (Philadelphia & environments), Jesuit studies (history, visual arts).
ISBN Prefix(es): 978-0-916101
Number of titles published annually: 5 Print
Total Titles: 60 Print
Membership(s): American Association of University Presses; Association of Jesuit University Presses

St Martin's Press, LLC
Subsidiary of Macmillan
175 Fifth Ave, New York, NY 10010
SAN: 200-2132
Tel: 646-307-5151 *Fax:* 212-420-9314
E-mail: firstname.lastname@macmillan.com
Web Site: www.stmartins.com
Key Personnel
Pres & Publr: Sally Richardson
EVP & COO, Macmillan Trade Publg: Steve Cohen
EVP, Mktg & Digital Media Strategy: Jeff Dodes
VP, Dir of Fin: Thomas Cronin
VP, Fin & Acctg: John Cusack
VP, Exec Ed & Publr: Thomas Dunne
VP, Publr of Minotaur: Andrew Martin
VP & Publr: Jennifer Enderlin
VP, Assoc Publr & Publg Dir, SMP Swerve: Anne Marie Tallberg
VP, Dir of Prodn/Mfg: Karen Gillis
VP, Mktg, Communs & Audience Devt: Brant Janeway
VP, Publicity: Dori Weintraub
VP, Creative Dir, Pbks: Michael Storrings
Div VP, Publg Opers: Sidney Conde
Div VP & Assoc Publr, Pbk/Ref Group: Lisa Senz

Div VP, Dir of Publicity: John Murphy
Div VP, Creative Dir, Trade: Stephen Snider
Div VP, Ed-in-Chief, Trade: George Witte
Exec Art Dir, SMP/Minotaur: David Rotstein
Dir, Subs Rts: Kerry Nordling
Dir, Quick & Dirty Tips: Kathy Doyle
Edit Dir & Assoc Publr, Minotaur Books: Kelley Ragland
Art Dir: Jimmy Iacobelli
Assoc Publicity Dir, Pbk/Ref Group: John Karle
Assoc Publr/Exec Ed, Thomas Dunne Books: Peter Wolverton
Sr Exec Mng Ed, Trade: Amelie Littell
Exec Mng Ed, Pbk/Ref Group: John Rounds
Exec Ed, Pbk/Ref Group: Marc Resnick
Exec Ed, Thomas Dunne Books: Marcia Markland
Exec Ed & Edit Dir, Romance: Monique Patterson
Exec Ed, Mgr of Concept Devt: Jennifer Weis
Exec Ed: Elizabeth Beier; Brenda Copeland; Hope Dellon; Elisabeth Dyssegaard; Michael Flamini; Keith Kahla; Charles Spicer; Karen Wolny
Sr Ed: Emily Carleton
Ed, Thomas Dunne Books: Anne Brewer
Assoc Ed, Thomas Dunne Books: Melanie Fried
Assoc Dir, Mktg: Christine Catarino
Assoc Dir, Publicity: Gabrielle Gantz
Mgr, SMP Swerve & Assoc Ed: Eileen Rothschild
Assoc Mktg Mgr: John Nicholas
Sr Publicist: Katie Bassel; Justin Velella
Founded: 1952
General nonfiction, fiction, reference, scholarly, mass market, travel, children's books.
For information on ordering & returns, visit www.macmillan.com.
ISBN Prefix(es): 978-0-312
Number of titles published annually: 1,000 Print
Imprints: Thomas Dunne Books; Griffin; Minotaur; SMP Swerve (romance, digital); Weight Watchers
Distributor for Berg Publishers; Bloomsbury USA; College Board; Manchester University Press; Palgrave Macmillan; Papercutz; Rodale; I B Tauris; Walker and Company; Zed Books
Foreign Rep(s): H B Fenn & Co Ltd (Canada); Macmillan India (India); Macmillan New Zealand (New Zealand); Melia UK (Ireland, UK); Pan Macmillan Australia (Australia); Pan Macmillan-Hong Kong (Asia, Middle East); Pan Macmillan South Africa (South Africa); Pan Macmillan UK (Caribbean, Latin America); Pan Macmillan UK (Europe, Israel)
Foreign Rights: Big Apple Agency Inc (China, Taiwan); The Book Publishers Association of Israel (Israel); Eliane Benisti (France); International Editors' Co (Portugal, South America, Spain); Nurcihan Kesim Literary Agency Inc (Turkey); Lex Copyright Office (Hungary); Literary Services (Italy); Prava I Prevodi (Eastern Europe, Greece); Sane Toregard Agency (Denmark, Finland, Iceland, Norway, Sweden); Thomas Schlueck GmbH (Germany); Tuttle-Mori Agency Inc (Thailand)
Distribution Center: MPS Distribution Center, 16365 James Madison Hwy, Gordonsville, VA 22942-8501 *Toll Free Tel:* 888-330-8477 *Fax:* 540-672-7540 (cust serv) *Toll Free Fax:* 800-672-2054 (orders)
Membership(s): AAP

Saint Mary's Press
Subsidiary of Christian Brothers Publications
702 Terrace Heights, Winona, MN 55987-1318
SAN: 203-073X
Tel: 507-457-7900 *Toll Free Tel:* 800-533-8095 *Fax:* 507-457-7990 *Toll Free Fax:* 800-344-9225
E-mail: smpress@smp.org
Web Site: www.smp.org
Key Personnel
CEO & Pres: John M Vitek
Exec Dir, Delivery: Caren Yang
Libn & ISBN Contact: Connie Jensen
Founded: 1943
High School curriculum, paperbound & digital; religion (Catholic); Bibles, youth ministry resources.
ISBN Prefix(es): 978-0-88489
Number of titles published annually: 25 Print
Total Titles: 483 Print
Distributor for Group Publishing
Foreign Rep(s): The Bible Society (New Zealand); B Broughton Ltd (Canada); Catholic News, Books & Media (Singapore); John Garratt Publishing (Australia); Herald Publications SDN BHD (Malaysia); Pleroma Christian Supplies (New Zealand); Redemptorist Publications (UK)

Saint Nectarios Press
10300 Ashworth Ave N, Seattle, WA 98133-9410
SAN: 159-0170
Tel: 206-522-4471 *Toll Free Tel:* 800-643-4233 *Fax:* 206-523-0550
E-mail: orders@stnectariospress.com
Web Site: www.stnectariospress.com
Key Personnel
Dir: Neketas S Palassis *E-mail:* frneketas@gmail.com
Busn Mgr: Nina S Seco *E-mail:* seco@orthodoxpress.org
Founded: 1977
Traditional Eastern Orthodox books.
ISBN Prefix(es): 978-0-913026
Number of titles published annually: 3 Print
Total Titles: 50 Print

St Pauls
Division of The Society of Saint Paul
2187 Victory Blvd, Staten Island, NY 10314-6603
SAN: 201-2405
Tel: 718-761-0047 (edit & prodn); 718-698-2759 (mktg & billing) *Toll Free Tel:* 800-343-2522 *Fax:* 718-761-0057
E-mail: sales@stpauls.us; marketing@stpauls.us
Web Site: www.stpauls.us
Key Personnel
Ed-in-Chief & Contact, ISBN & Rts & Perms: Fr Edmund C Lane *E-mail:* edmund_lane@juno.com
Copy Ed: Br Frank Sadowski
Prodn Mgr & Art Dir: Br Edward Donaher *E-mail:* edonaher@aol.com
Treas: Br Richard C Brunner
Mktg: Fr Matthew Roehrig *Tel:* 718-698-2759 *E-mail:* marketing@stpauls.us
Founded: 1961
Religion (Catholic), bible, education, pastoral care, prayer books, biography, spirituality, psychology, philosophy, theology, Spanish titles (Roman Catholic), bereavement, church, ethics, homilies, liturgy, marriage & family life, prayer, religious education, saints lives, scripture, cassettes & videos.
ISBN Prefix(es): 978-0-8189
Number of titles published annually: 24 Print; 10 CD-ROM; 20 Online; 20 E-Book
Total Titles: 425 Print; 85 CD-ROM; 33 Online; 33 E-Book
Foreign Office(s): Edizioni Paoline, Piazza Soncino 5, 520092 Cinisello Balsamo MI, Italy
Foreign Rep(s): St Paul Publications (Australia, Canada, India, Ireland, Italy, Philippines, South Africa, UK)

Sts Judes imPress
5537 Waterman Blvd, Suite 2-W, St Louis, MO 63112
Tel: 314-454-0064
E-mail: stjudes1@att.net
Key Personnel
Publr: Lawrence A Murray
Founded: 1989
Historical novels, socio-economic studies, religious history & science.
ISBN Prefix(es): 978-0-9722149; 978-0-9766599; 978-0-9801289
Number of titles published annually: 3 Print; 2 CD-ROM; 12 Online
Total Titles: 38 Print; 12 CD-ROM; 12 Online

Salem Press Inc
Division of EBSCO Information Services
2 University Plaza, Suite 310, Hackensack, NJ 07601
SAN: 208-838X
Tel: 201-968-0500 *Toll Free Tel:* 800-221-1592; 800-221-1592 *Fax:* 201-968-0511
E-mail: csr@salempress.com
Web Site: salempress.com
Key Personnel
Territory Sales Mgr: Pamela Brunke *E-mail:* pbrunke@salempress.com
Founded: 1949
Reference books & online products for middle school, secondary school, colleges & public libraries.
ISBN Prefix(es): 978-0-89356; 978-1-58765
Number of titles published annually: 25 Print; 10 Online; 15 E-Book
Total Titles: 150 Print; 35 Online; 60 E-Book
Imprints: Magill's Choice
Foreign Rep(s): Aditya Books Pvt Ltd (Bangladesh, India, Nepal, Pakistan, Sri Lanka); Alkem Co (S) Pte Ltd (Brunei, Hong Kong, Indonesia, Korea, Malaysia, Philippines, Singapore, Taiwan, Thailand, Vietnam); Eurospan Ltd (Africa, Europe, Middle East, UK); Grey House Publishing Canada (Canada); Somohano Express SA de CV (Mexico); Warner Books Pty Ltd (Australia, New Zealand); Yushodo Co Ltd (Japan)

Salina Bookshelf Inc
3120 N Caden Ct, Suite 4, Flagstaff, AZ 86004
SAN: 253-0503
Toll Free Tel: 877-527-0070 *Fax:* 928-526-0386
Web Site: www.salinabookshelf.com
Key Personnel
Pres: Eric Lockard *Tel:* 928-527-0700 ext 425 *E-mail:* elockard@salinabookshelf.com
Art Dir: Baje Whitethorne, Jr *Tel:* 928-527-0700 ext 202
Founded: 1994
Publisher of multicultural books with a strong focus on the stories of the Navajo people. Our textbooks, children's picture books & electronic media in Navajo & English are resources for the home, library & classroom. We recognize the importance of portraying traditional language & culture & of making this knowledge accessible to a broad spectrum of curious minds.
ISBN Prefix(es): 978-1-893354; 978-0-9644189
Number of titles published annually: 10 Print; 3 Audio
Total Titles: 65 Print; 1 CD-ROM; 6 Audio
Membership(s): American Indian Library Association; The Children's Book Council; The Independent Book Publishers Association; Publishers Association of the West

§Samhain Publishing Ltd
11821 Mason Montgomery Rd, Suite 4-B, Cincinnati, OH 45249
SAN: 257-7488
Tel: 513-453-4688 *Fax:* 513-583-0191
E-mail: support@samhainpublishing.com
Web Site: www.samhainpublishing.com
Key Personnel
Publr: Christina M Brashear *Tel:* 513-453-4684 *E-mail:* cbrashear@samhainpublishing.com

COO: Amanda S Brashear *Tel:* 513-774-2075 *E-mail:* amanda@samhainpublishing.com
Exec Ed, Horror: Don D'Auria *Tel:* 513-453-4688 ext 207 *E-mail:* ddauria@samhainpublishing.com
Exec Ed, Romance: Latoya Smith *Tel:* 513-774-2064 *E-mail:* lsmith@samhainpublishing.com
Content Mgmt Specialist: Jacob Hammer *Tel:* 513-774-2067 *E-mail:* jacob@samhainpublishing.com
Busn Devt: Jeff Humby *Tel:* 513-774-2071 *E-mail:* bizdev@samhainpublishing.com
Founded: 2005
Publish works of fiction in horror & all genres & heat levels of romance; contemporary, erotica & fantasy, urban fantasy & science fiction with strong romantic elements in both ebooks & trade paper.
ISBN Prefix(es): 978-1-59998; 978-1-60504; 978-1-60928; 978-1-61921; 978-1-61922; 978-1-61923; 978-1-5139
Number of titles published annually: 180 Print; 480 Online; 300 E-Book
Total Titles: 1,250 Print; 3,635 Online; 2,361 E-Book
Imprints: RetroRomance™ (classic romance novels published between the 1970s & early 2000s); Samhain Horror (dark fiction); Samhain Romance
Foreign Rights: Betty Anne Crawford (Worldwide)
Orders to: Ingram Book Co, One Ingram Blvd, La Vergne, TN 37086 *Tel:* 615-793-5000 *Toll Free Tel:* 800-937-8200 *E-mail:* customer.service@ingrambook.com *Web Site:* www.ingrambook.com
Membership(s): AAP; ABA; ALA; BISG; The Independent Book Publishers Association

SAMS Technical Publishing LLC
Division of AGS Capital LLC
9850 E 30 St, Indianapolis, IN 46229
Tel: 317-396-5336 *Toll Free Tel:* 800-428-7267 *Fax:* 317-489-3406 *Toll Free Fax:* 800-552-3910
E-mail: customercare@samswebsite.com
Web Site: www.samswebsite.com
Key Personnel
COO: Lou Hurrle *E-mail:* lhurrle@samswebsite.com
Founded: 1946
Publisher of Photofact repair manuals.
ISBN Prefix(es): 978-0-7906
Number of titles published annually: 100 Print
Total Titles: 400 Print
Imprints: Indy-Tech Publishing; Photofact®
Distributor for Butterworth Heinemann; McGraw-Hill; Prompt Publications
Orders to: Cardinal Publishers Group, 2222 Hillside Ave, Indianapolis, IN 46218, Tom Doherty *Tel:* 317-879-0871 *Fax:* 317-879-0872 *E-mail:* tdoherty@cardinalpub.com
Returns: Cardinal Publishers Group, 2222 Hillside Ave, Indianapolis, IN 46218, Tom Doherty *Tel:* 317-879-0871 *Fax:* 317-879-0872 *E-mail:* tdoherty@cardinalpub.com
Shipping Address: Cardinal Publishers Group, 2222 Hillside Ave, Indianapolis, IN 46218, Tom Doherty *Tel:* 317-879-0871 *Fax:* 317-879-0872 *E-mail:* tdoherty@cardinalpub.com
Warehouse: Cardinal Publishers Group, 2222 Hillside Ave, Indianapolis, IN 46218, Tom Doherty *Tel:* 317-879-0871 *Fax:* 317-879-0872 *E-mail:* tdoherty@cardinalpub.com
Distribution Center: Cardinal Publishers Group, 2222 Hillside Ave, Indianapolis, IN 46218, Tom Doherty *Tel:* 317-879-0871 *Fax:* 317-879-0872 *E-mail:* tdoherty@cardinalpub.com

San Diego State University Press
Division of San Diego State University Foundation
Arts & Letters 283, 5500 Campanile Dr, San Diego, CA 92182-6020
Tel: 619-594-6220 (orders)
Web Site: sdsupress.sdsu.edu
Key Personnel
Dir: Prof Harry Polkinhorn *E-mail:* hpolkinh@mail.sdsu.edu
Edit Bd: Dr Bill Nericcio *Tel:* 619-594-1524
Founded: 1959
Scholarly & trade, monographs.
ISBN Prefix(es): 978-0-916304; 978-1-879691
Number of titles published annually: 2 Print; 2 Online
Imprints: Binational Press; Hyperbole
Distributor for Institute for Regional Studies of the Californias

Sandlapper Publishing Inc
1281 Amelia St NE, Orangeburg, SC 29115-5475
SAN: 203-2678
Mailing Address: PO Box 730, Orangeburg, SC 29116-0730
Tel: 803-531-1658 *Toll Free Tel:* 800-849-7263 (orders only) *Fax:* 803-534-5223 *Toll Free Fax:* 800-337-9420
E-mail: sales@sandlapperpublishing.com
Web Site: www.sandlapperpublishing.com
Key Personnel
Owner & Pres: Amanda Gallman *E-mail:* agallman@sandlapperpublishing.com
Founded: 1982
Nonfiction material about South Carolina only. Submit query letter.
ISBN Prefix(es): 978-0-87844
Number of titles published annually: 10 Print
Total Titles: 100 Print

§Santa Monica Press LLC
215 S Hwy 101, Suite 110, Solana Beach, CA 92075
SAN: 298-1459
Mailing Address: PO Box 850, Solana Beach, CA 92075
Tel: 858-793-1890 *Toll Free Tel:* 800-784-9553 *Fax:* 858-777-0444
E-mail: books@santamonicapress.com
Web Site: www.santamonicapress.com
Key Personnel
Publr: Jeffrey Goldman *E-mail:* jgoldman@santamonicapress.com
Founded: 1994
Publish an eclectic line of books. Our critically acclaimed titles are sold in retail outlets around the world. Our authors are recognized experts who receive coverage both nationally & internationally. We're not afraid to cast a wide editorial net. Our list of lively & modern nonfiction titles includes books in such categories as popular culture, film history, photography, humor, biography, travel & reference.
ISBN Prefix(es): 978-0-9639946; 978-1-891661; 978-1-59580
Number of titles published annually: 12 Print; 12 E-Book
Total Titles: 125 Print; 75 E-Book
Foreign Rep(s): The Perseus Books Group (all other territories); Turnaround Publisher Services Ltd (Europe, UK)
Foreign Rights: The Perseus Books Group (Jennifer Thompson) (all other territories)
Orders to: Legato Publishers Group, 210 American Dr, Jackson, TN 38301 *Toll Free Tel:* 800-343-4499 *Toll Free Fax:* 800-351-5073 *E-mail:* orderentry@perseusbooks.com *Web Site:* www.legatopublishersgroup.com
Returns: The Perseus Books Group, 210 American Dr, Jackson, TN 38301 *Toll Free Tel:* 800-343-4499 *Toll Free Fax:* 800-351-5073 *Web Site:* www.legatopublishersgroup.com
Warehouse: The Perseus Books Group, 210 American Dr, Jackson, TN 38301 *Toll Free Tel:* 800-343-4499 *Toll Free Fax:* 800-351-5073 *E-mail:* orderentry@perseusbooks.com *Web Site:* www.legatopublishersgroup.com
Distribution Center: Legato Publishers Group, 210 American Dr, Jackson, TN 38301 *Toll Free Tel:* 800-343-4499 *Toll Free Fax:* 800-351-5073 *E-mail:* orderentry@perseusbooks.com *Web Site:* www.legatopublishersgroup.com

Santillana USA Publishing Co Inc
Division of The Richmond Publishing Co Inc
2023 NW 84 Ave, Doral, FL 33122
SAN: 205-1133
Tel: 305-591-9522 *Toll Free Tel:* 800-245-8584 *Fax:* 305-591-9145 *Toll Free Fax:* 888-248-9518
E-mail: customerservice@santillanausa.com
Web Site: www.santillanausa.com; www.alfaguara.net
Key Personnel
CEO & Pres: Miguel Tapia *E-mail:* mtapia@santillanausa.com
Mktg Dir: Kathy Jimenez *E-mail:* kjimenez@santillanausa.com
Dir, Children's Lit & Trade Div: Silvia Matute *E-mail:* smatute@santillanausa.com
Founded: 1972
Educational & Spanish language trade books; English as a second language & bilingual textbooks; Spanish as a foreign language.
ISBN Prefix(es): 978-0-88272; 978-1-56014; 978-1-58105; 978-1-58986; 978-1-59437
Number of titles published annually: 50 Print; 3 CD-ROM; 5 Audio
Total Titles: 1,200 Print; 3 CD-ROM; 15 Audio
Imprints: Aguilar; Alfaguara; Santillana; Taurus
Membership(s): AAP

SAR Press, see School for Advanced Research Press

Sarabande Books Inc
2234 Dundee Rd, Suite 200, Louisville, KY 40205
Tel: 502-458-4028 *Fax:* 502-458-4065
E-mail: info@sarabandebooks.org
Web Site: www.sarabandebooks.org
Key Personnel
Pres & Ed-in-Chief: Sarah Gorham
Mng Ed: Kirby Gann
Founded: 1994
Short fiction, poetry & literary nonfiction collections.
ISBN Prefix(es): 978-1-889330; 978-1-932511
Number of titles published annually: 10 Print; 1 E-Book
Total Titles: 160 Print; 1 E-Book
Branch Office(s)
112 W 27 St, Suite 607, New York, NY 10001, Mktg & Publicity Dir: Ariel Lewiton *Tel:* 917-923-3109 *E-mail:* kristen@sarabandebooks.org
Membership(s): ABA; Academy of American Poets; Association of Writers and Writing Programs; Community of Literary Magazines & Presses; PEN Center USA

SAS Publishing
Imprint of SAS Institute Inc
100 SAS Campus Dr, Cary, NC 27513-2414
Tel: 919-677-8000 *Fax:* 919-677-4444
E-mail: saspress@sas.com
Web Site: www.sas.com/publishing
Key Personnel
Ed-in-Chief: Julie M Platt *E-mail:* julie.platt@sas.com
Founded: 1976
Books about SAS or JMP software.
ISBN Prefix(es): 978-1-55544; 978-0-917382
Number of titles published annually: 50 Print
Distributed by John Wiley & Sons Inc
Distributor for AMACOM Books; Breakfast Communications; CRC Press; Duxbury;

Harcourt; Harvard Business School Press; McGraw-Hill; Oxford; Prentice-Hall; Springer; John Wiley & Sons Inc

Sasquatch Books
1904 S Main St, Suite 710, Seattle, WA 98101
SAN: 289-0208
Tel: 206-467-4300 *Toll Free Tel:* 800-775-0817 *Fax:* 206-467-4301
E-mail: custserv@sasquatchbooks.com
Web Site: www.sasquatchbooks.com
Key Personnel
Publr & Edit Dir: Gary Luke *Tel:* 206-826-4304 *E-mail:* gluke@sasquatchbooks.com
Sales & Mktg Dir: Sarah Hanson *Tel:* 206-826-4303 *E-mail:* shanson@sasquatchbooks.com
Acqs Ed: Hannah Elnan
Founded: 1986
Nonfiction of & from the West Coast.
ISBN Prefix(es): 978-0-934007; 978-0-912365; 978-1-57061
Number of titles published annually: 40 Print
Total Titles: 390 Print; 3 Audio
Imprints: Best Places® Guidebooks Series; Paws IV
Foreign Rep(s): Publishers Group Canada (Canada)
Distribution Center: Random House Publisher Services, 1700 Fourth St, Berkeley, CA 94710 *Toll Free Tel:* 800-788-3123 *Fax:* 510-528-3444

§Satya House Publications
22 Turkey St, Hardwick, MA 01037
Mailing Address: PO Box 122, Hardwick, MA 01037
Tel: 413-477-8743
E-mail: info@satyahouse.com; orders@satyahouse.com
Web Site: www.satyahouse.com
Key Personnel
Publr: Julie Murkette *E-mail:* julie@satyahouse.com
Founded: 2003
Independent publishing company.
This publisher has indicated that 25% of their product line is author subsidized.
ISBN Prefix(es): 978-0-9729191; 978-0-9818720; 978-1-9358740
Number of titles published annually: 4 Print; 4 E-Book
Total Titles: 20 Print; 1 CD-ROM; 9 E-Book
Foreign Rep(s): Gazelle (UK)
Foreign Rights: Sylvia Hayse Literary Agency LLC (Worldwide exc USA)
Distribution Center: Midpoint Trade Books, 27 W 20 St, Suite 1102, New York, NY 10011 *Tel:* 212-727-0190 *Web Site:* www.midpointtrade.com
Membership(s): The Independent Book Publishers Association; Independent Publishers of New England

Savant Books & Publications LLC
2630 Kapiolani Blvd, Suite 1601, Honolulu, HI 96826
Tel: 808-941-3927 *Fax:* 808-941-3927
E-mail: savantbooks@gmail.com
Web Site: www.savantbooksandpublications.com
Key Personnel
Owner: Daniel S Janik
Dir, Mktg & Dist: Setsuko Tsuchiya
Founded: 2007
Publishes unpublished, post-modern works of enduring value "with a twist" for English readers throughout the world. Special interest areas include: fiction (novels - all genres), nonfiction (transformative education, memoirs, academic theses & dissertations of note, single-author textbooks & workbooks).
ISBN Prefix(es): 978-0-9841175; 978-0-9845552; 978-0-9829987; 978-0-9832861
Number of titles published annually: 15 Print
Total Titles: 70 Print

SBL Press
Unit of Society of Biblical Literature
The Luce Ctr, Suite 350, 825 Houston Mill Rd, Atlanta, GA 30329
Tel: 404-727-3100 *Fax:* 404-727-3101 (corp)
E-mail: sbl@sbl-site.org
Web Site: www.sbl-site.org
Key Personnel
Exec Dir: John F Kutsko *E-mail:* john.kutsko@sbl_site.org
Dir, Pubns: Bob Buller *E-mail:* bob.buller@sbl_site.org
Mktg Mgr: Kathie Klein *Tel:* 404-727-2325 *E-mail:* kathie.klein@sbl-site.org
Sales Mgr: Heather McMurray *Tel:* 404-727-3096 *E-mail:* heather.mcmurray@sbl-site.org
Founded: 1880
Publishing program of the Society of Biblical Literature, a learned society whose purpose is to stimulate the critical investigation of Biblical literature.
ISBN Prefix(es): 978-0-89130; 978-0-7885; 978-0-88414; 978-1-58983
Number of titles published annually: 43 Print; 43 Online; 43 E-Book
Total Titles: 850 Print; 200 Online; 200 E-Book
Distributor for Brown Judaic Studies; Sheffield Phoenix Press
Orders to: PO Box 2243, Williston, VT 05495-2243 *Tel:* 802-864-6185 *Toll Free Tel:* 877-725-3334 *Fax:* 802-864-7626
Returns: 82 Winter Sport Lane, Williston, VT 05495 *Tel:* 802-864-6185 *Toll Free Tel:* 877-725-3334 *Fax:* 802-864-7626
Warehouse: 82 Winter Sport Lane, Williston, VT 05495 *Tel:* 802-864-6185 *Toll Free Tel:* 877-725-3334 *Fax:* 802-864-7626

SBPRA, see Strategic Book Publishing & Rights Agency (SBPRA)

Scarecrow Press Inc
Imprint of Rowman & Littlefield Publishing Group
4501 Forbes Blvd, Suite 200, Lanham, MD 20706
Tel: 301-459-3366 *Fax:* 301-429-5748
Web Site: www.scarecrowpress.com
Key Personnel
CEO & Pres: Jed Lyons *E-mail:* jlyons@rowman.com
Publr & Edit Dir: Marcus Boggs
VP, Mktg & Sales: Linda May
Rts & Perms Dir: Clare Cox
Sales Dir: Sheila Burnett
Exec Ed: Charles Harmon
Founded: 1950
Reference books & texts in music, film, information technology, theater, performing arts, history, religion & cultural studies. Professional & reference books in library & information sciences & government regulatory areas. Co-publishing with Rutgers Jazz Institute, Music Library Association, American Theological Library Association & Children's Literature Association.
New titles to be released under the Rowman & Littlefield imprint.
ISBN Prefix(es): 978-0-8108; 978-1-57886
Number of titles published annually: 175 Print; 2 CD-ROM; 10 Online; 5 E-Book
Total Titles: 5,000 Print; 6 CD-ROM; 100 Online; 30 E-Book
Distribution Center: 15200 NBN Way, PO Box 191, Blue Ridge Summit, PA 17214 *Toll Free Tel:* 800-462-6420 *Toll Free Fax:* 800-338-4550

Scarletta, see Mighty Media Press

Scepter Publishers
PO Box 1391, New York, NY 10802
Tel: 212-354-0670 *Toll Free Tel:* 800-322-8773 *Fax:* 212-354-0736
Web Site: www.scepterpublishers.org
Key Personnel
Pres & Publr: Nathan Davis *Tel:* 646-205-1508 *E-mail:* nathan@scepterpublishers.org
Orders & Cust Serv: Kevin Lay *E-mail:* kevin@scepterpublishers.org
Founded: 1954
Catholic Book Publishing including doctrinal works, theology & liturgy.
ISBN Prefix(es): 978-0-933932; 978-0-1889334; 978-1-594170
Number of titles published annually: 10 Print
Total Titles: 150 Print
Distribution Center: Maple-Vail Distribution, 1000 Strickler Rd, Mount Joy, PA 17552

Schaffner Press
PO Box 41567, Tucson, AZ 85717
E-mail: tim@schaffnerpress.com
Web Site: www.schaffnerpress.com
Founded: 2001
Independent publisher of books of social relevance for the discerning reader.
ISBN Prefix(es): 978-0-9710598; 978-0-9801394; 978-0-9824332; 978-1-936182
Number of titles published annually: 6 Print; 4 E-Book
Total Titles: 16 Print; 10 E-Book

§Schiel & Denver Book Publishers
10685-B Hazelhurst Dr, Suite 8575, Houston, TX 77043
Tel: 832-699-0264 *Toll Free Tel:* 888-629-4449 *Toll Free Fax:* 888-224-2721
E-mail: enquiries@schieldenver.com
Web Site: www.schieldenver.com
Key Personnel
Sr Mgr: Simon Hornby *E-mail:* simon.hornby@schieldenver.com
Acqs Mgr: Ken Hudson *E-mail:* ken.hudson@schieldenver.com
Author Servs Mgr: Hannah Bell *E-mail:* hannah.bell@schieldenver.com
Founded: 2008
Independent book publishers offering professional ISBN book publishing, editing & book marketing services to first time & veteran authors with the support of an expert book publishing team.
This publisher has indicated that 50% of their product line is author subsidized.
ISBN Prefix(es): 978-1-84903
Number of titles published annually: 90 Print
Total Titles: 100 Print; 100 Online; 50 E-Book
Imprints: Heirloom Children's Book Publishers
Foreign Office(s): Schiel & Denver Publishing Ltd, The Meridian, 4 Copthall House, Station Sq, Coventry CV1 2FL, United Kingdom *Tel:* (0844) 54 99 191 *Fax:* (0844) 507 0985 *E-mail:* enquiries@schieldenver.co.uk
Distribution Center: Baker & Taylor
Ingram
Membership(s): AAP; ATA

Schiffer Publishing Ltd
4880 Lower Valley Rd, Atglen, PA 19310
SAN: 208-8428
Tel: 610-593-1777 *Fax:* 610-593-2002
E-mail: schifferbk@aol.com
Web Site: www.schifferbooks.com
Key Personnel
Pres & Ed-in-Chief: Pete Schiffer
EVP: Nancy Schiffer
Spec Sales: Joe Langman
Founded: 1974
Collecting, art books, antiques, architecture, toys, woodcarving, hobbies, weaving, color, metaphysics, aviation, military books, automotive books, design & fashion.

ISBN Prefix(es): 978-0-916838; 978-0-88740; 978-0-7643
Number of titles published annually: 300 Print
Total Titles: 5,000 Print
Imprints: Canal Press; Cornell Maritime Press; Geared Up Publications; Kaiser-Barlow; LW Books; Para Research; Schiffer; Schiffer Fashion Press; Schiffer LTD; Schiffer Military History; Tidewater Publishers; Whitford Press
Distributor for The Donning Co
Foreign Rights: Bushwood Books (Europe)
See separate listing for:
Cornell Maritime Press Inc

Schirmer, see Wadsworth Publishing

Schirmer Trade Books
Imprint of Music Sales Corp
180 Madison Ave, 24th fl, New York, NY 10016
Tel: 212-254-2100 *Toll Free Tel:* 800-431-7187 (orders) *Fax:* 212-254-2013
Web Site: www.musicsales.com
Key Personnel
Pres: Barrie Edwards *E-mail:* be@musicsales.com
Dir, Digital Publg: Tomas Wise
Founded: 1935
Committed to intelligent, educational & entertaining books about all aspects of music, especially the recording arts, music business, genre histories & musician biographies.
ISBN Prefix(es): 978-0-8256; 978-0-7119
Number of titles published annually: 25 Print
Total Titles: 300 Print
Sales Office(s): 445 Bellvale Rd, Chester, NY 10918-0572, Contact: Steve Wilson *Toll Free Tel:* 800-431-7187 *Toll Free Fax:* 800-345-6842 *E-mail:* sw@musicsales.com
Foreign Office(s): 8/9 Frith St, London W1D 3JB, United Kingdom *Tel:* (020) 7434-0066 *Fax:* (020) 7434-2246
Distributor for Big Meteor Publishing; Independent Music Press
Billing Address: 445 Bellvale Rd, Chester, NY 10918-0572 *Toll Free Tel:* 800-431-7187 *Toll Free Fax:* 800-345-6842 *E-mail:* info@musicsales.com
Orders to: 445 Bellvale Rd, Chester, NY 10918-0572 *Toll Free Tel:* 800-431-7187 *Toll Free Fax:* 800-345-6842 *E-mail:* info@musicsales.com
Returns: 445 Bellvale Rd, Chester, NY 10918-0572 *Toll Free Tel:* 800-431-7187 *Toll Free Fax:* 800-345-6842 *E-mail:* info@musicsales.com
Shipping Address: 445 Bellvale Rd, Chester, NY 10918-0572 *Toll Free Tel:* 800-431-7187 *Toll Free Fax:* 800-345-6842 *E-mail:* info@musicsales.com
Warehouse: 445 Bellvale Rd, Chester, NY 10918-0572 *Toll Free Tel:* 800-431-7187 *Toll Free Fax:* 800-345-6842 *E-mail:* info@musicsales.com
Distribution Center: 445 Bellvale Rd, Chester, NY 10918-0572 *Toll Free Tel:* 800-431-7187 *Toll Free Fax:* 800-345-6842 *E-mail:* info@musicsales.com
Membership(s): ABA; American Society of Journalists & Authors; The Independent Book Publishers Association; Women's National Book Association

§Schlager Group Inc
325 N Saint Paul, Suite 3425, Dallas, TX 75201
Toll Free Tel: 888-416-5727 *Fax:* 214-347-9469
E-mail: info@schlagergroup.com
Web Site: www.schlagergroup.com
Key Personnel
Pres: Neil Schlager *Tel:* 888-416-5727 ext 801 *E-mail:* neil@schlagergroup.com
Creative Dir: Benjamin Painter *Tel:* 888-416-5727 ext 802 *E-mail:* benjamin@schlagergroup.com
Mng Ed: Sarah Robertson *Tel:* 888-416-5727 ext 804 *E-mail:* sarah@schlagergroup.com
Founded: 1997
Publisher of books & Internet materials for history instructors & students. Foreign Reps in Africa, Australia, Bangladesh, Canada, Europe, India, Japan, Mexico, Middle East, Nepal, New Guinea, New Zealand, Pakistan, Southeast Asia, Sri Lanka & UK, all via Salem Press Inc distributors & representatives.
ISBN Prefix(es): 978-9-797758; 978-9-35306
Number of titles published annually: 2 Print; 1 Online; 2 E-Book
Total Titles: 5 Print; 1 Online; 5 E-Book
Divisions: Milestone Documents
Distributed by Salem Press (ref books only)
Orders to: Salem Press, 2 University Plaza, Suite 121, Hackensack, NJ 07601 (ref books only)
Returns: Salem Press, 2 University Plaza, Suite 121, Hackensack, NJ 07601 (ref books only)
Shipping Address: Salem Press, 2 University Plaza, Suite 121, Hackensack, NJ 07601 (ref books only) *Toll Free Tel:* 800-221-1592 *Fax:* 201-968-1411 *E-mail:* csr@salempress.com *Web Site:* www.salempress.com
Membership(s): American Historical Association; Organization of American Historians

Scholars' Facsimiles & Reprints
Subsidiary of Academic Resources Corp
6946 E Stevens Rd, Cave Creek, AZ 85331-8677
SAN: 203-2627
Tel: 480-575-9945
E-mail: sfandr@msn.com
Web Site: www.scholarsbooklist.com
Key Personnel
Publr: Norman Mangouni
Founded: 1936
Facsimile reprints of rare books of scholarly interest, microforms, occasional originals.
ISBN Prefix(es): 978-0-8201
Number of titles published annually: 12 Print
Total Titles: 565 Print

Scholastic Education
Division of Scholastic Inc
524 Broadway, New York, NY 10012
Tel: 212-343-6100 *Fax:* 212-343-6189
Web Site: www.scholastic.com
Key Personnel
Pres, Scholastic Education: Greg Worrell
COO, Scholastic Education: Beth Polcari
SVP & Educ Advisor: Patrick Daley
VP, Literacy Initiatives/FACE: Karine Apollon
Pres, Scholastic Consumer & Professional Publishing: Hugh Roome
VP, Gen Mgr, Scholastic Library Publishing: Allison Henderson
VP, Digital Initiatives: Evan St Lifer
VP, Mktg, Classroom Magazines: Danielle Mirsky
Ed-in-Chief, Classroom Magazines: Elliot Rebhun
SVP, Sales, Scholastic Education: Jennifer Boykins
VP & Publr, Scholastic Education: Janelle Cherrington
Scholastic Education is a leading provider of comprehensive literacy solutions reinforcing student achievement through instructional reading & writing, professional learning for teacher effectiveness & family & community engagement. Scholastic Consumer & Professional Publishing is a leading print & digital publisher of Classroom Magazines & children's reference materials for schools & public libraries, which include digital brands such as BookFlix & TrueFlix & the prestigious imprints Children's Press®, Franklin Watts® & Grolier Online®.
ISBN Prefix(es): 978-0-516; 978-0-590; 978-0-531; 978-0-7172; 978-0-439; 978-0-926891; 978-1-55998; 978-1-57809; 978-1-59009; 978-0-545
Imprints: Children's Press®; Franklin Watts®; Grolier Online®
Divisions: Assessment; Curriculum Solutions; Early Childhood Education; Professional Development; Publishing Services; Research; Sales & Marketing; Technology

§Scholastic Inc
557 Broadway, New York, NY 10012
Tel: 212-343-6100 *Toll Free Tel:* 800-scholastic
Web Site: www.scholastic.com
Key Personnel
Chmn, Pres & CEO: Richard Robinson
EVP, Chief Admin Offr & CFO: Maureen O'Connell
EVP, Gen Coun: Andrew Hedden
Pres, Trade Publg: Ellie Berger
EVP, Pres, Reading Club & E-Commerce: Judith A Newman
Pres, Scholastic Book Fairs: Alan Boyko
EVP & Pres, Consumer & Prof Publg: Hugh Roome
Pres, Scholastic Education: Greg Worrell
EVP & Pres, Intl Growth Mkts: Shane Armstrong
SVP, Corp Communs & Media Rel: Kyle Good
Chief, Strategy: Iole Lucchese
Founded: 1920
Scholastic Corporation (NASDAQ: SCHL) is the world's largest publisher & distributor of children's books, a leading provider of print & digital instructional materials for Pre-K to grade 12, & a producer of educational & entertaining children's media. The company creates quality books & ebooks, print & technology-based learning materials & programs, classroom magazines & other products that, in combination, offer schools customized & comprehensive solutions to support children's learning both at school & at home. The company also makes quality, affordable books available to all children through school-based book clubs & book fairs. With a 94 year history of service to schools & families, Scholastic continues to carry out its commitment to "Open a World of Possible" for all children. Learn more at www.scholastic.com.
ISBN Prefix(es): 978-0-590; 978-0-439
Distribution Center: 2931 E McCarty St, Jefferson City, MO 65101
100 Plaza Drive W, Secaucus, NJ 07094
Membership(s): AAP; ALA; The Children's Book Council; Direct Marketing Association; International Literacy Association; National Governor's Association; Software & Information Industry Association
See separate listing for:
Scholastic Education
Scholastic International
Scholastic Trade Division

§Scholastic International
Division of Scholastic Inc
557 Broadway, New York, NY 10012
Tel: 212-343-6100; 646-330-5288 (intl cust serv) *Toll Free Tel:* 800-SCHOLASTIC (800-724-6527) *Fax:* 646-837-7878
E-mail: international@scholastic.com
Key Personnel
EVP & Pres, Intl: Shane Armstrong
VP, Intl Fin: Joe Macca
VP, Export Sales & Mktg: Anne Boynton-Trigg
VP, Global Prod Devt: Edie Perkins
VP, New Busn Devt: Carol Sakoian
Scholastic International includes the publication & distribution of products & services outside the US by the company's international operations & its export sales business. Scholastic has operations in Canada, the UK, Australia, New Zealand & Asia, & export sales representatives in the rest of the world.
ISBN Prefix(es): 978-0-590; 978-0-439; 978-0-545

Subsidiaries: Scholastic Asia (with cos in China, India, Malaysia & Singapore & sales offs in Indonesia, Philippines, Taiwan & Thailand); Scholastic Australia Pty Ltd; Scholastic Canada Ltd; Scholastic Ltd UK; Scholastic New Zealand Ltd

Scholastic Trade Division
Division of Scholastic Inc
557 Broadway, New York, NY 10012
Tel: 212-343-6100; 212-343-4685 (export sales) *Fax:* 212-343-4714 (export sales)
Web Site: www.scholastic.com
Key Personnel
Pres, Trade Publg: Ellie Berger
VP, Group Publr: Lori Benton
VP & Publr, Arthur A Levine Books: Arthur A Levine
VP, Publr & Edit Dir, Scholastic Press: David Levithan
VP, Publr: Debra Dorfman
VP & Edit Dir, The Blue Sky Press: Bonnie Verburg
VP, Ed-at-Large: Andrea Pinkney
VP, Creative Dir & Edit Dir, Graphix: David Saylor
VP, Trade Sales: Alan Smagler
VP, Trade Fin: David Ascher
VP, Edit Dir, Orchard Books, Scholastic Press Picture Books & Cartwheel Books: Ken Geist
VP, Mktg: Caitlin Friedman
VP, Publicity: Tracy van Straaten
SVP, Gen Mgr, Klutz: Stacy Lellos
VP, Consumer Prods: Gary Hymowitz
VP, Fin: Ken Yamamoto
VP, Publg Opers: JoAnne Mojica
Exec Ed & Mgr, Scholastic en espanol: Maria Dominguez
Exec Ed, Scholastic Press: Dianne Hess
Exec Dir, Creative Servs & Mktg/Sales Opers: Leslie Garych
Dir, Brand Mgmt: Julie Amitie
Dir, Global Prog Sales & Mdsg: Anthony Kosiewska
Scholastic Trade Books is an award-winning publisher of original children's books. Scholastic publishes more than 600 new hardcover, paperback & novelty books each year & brings beloved stories & characters to life beyond the printed page via virtually every platform or screen kids access.
ISBN Prefix(es): 978-0-590; 978-0-439; 978-0-545
Number of titles published annually: 600 Print
Total Titles: 6,000 Print
Imprints: Arthur A Levine Books; The Blue Sky Press; Cartwheel Books; Chicken House; David Fickling Books; Graphix; Klutz; Little Shepherd; Orchard Books; Point; PUSH; Scholastic en Espanol; Scholastic Nonfiction; Scholastic Paperbacks; Scholastic Press; Scholastic Reference
Distribution Center: 2931 E McCarty St, Jefferson City, MO 65102 *Tel:* 573-635-5881

§Scholium International Inc
151 Cow Neck Rd, Port Washington, NY 11050
Tel: 516-767-7171
E-mail: info@scholium.com
Web Site: www.scholium.com
Key Personnel
Pres: Arthur Candido
EVP & Juv Ed: Elena M Candido
Founded: 1973
Science, medicine & technology.
ISBN Prefix(es): 978-0-87936
Number of titles published annually: 10 Print; 1 CD-ROM
Total Titles: 300 Print; 5 CD-ROM
Distributor for Dechema Series; Macmillan (UK); Micelle Press; Royal Society of London; Zuckschwerdt Verlag (Munich, Germany)

Schonfeld & Associates Inc
1931 Lynn Circle, Libertyville, IL 60048
SAN: 255-2361
Tel: 847-816-4870 *Toll Free Tel:* 800-205-0030 *Fax:* 847-816-4872
E-mail: saiinfo@saibooks.com
Web Site: www.saibooks.com
Key Personnel
Pres: Carol Greenhut *E-mail:* cgreenhut@saibooks.com
Founded: 1977
Author statistical reference works.
ISBN Prefix(es): 978-1-878339; 978-1-932024; 978-0-989055; 978-0-996048; 978-0-996248
Number of titles published annually: 9 Print; 12 CD-ROM; 12 E-Book
Total Titles: 10 Print; 12 CD-ROM; 12 E-Book

School for Advanced Research Press
660 Garcia St, Santa Fe, NM 87505
Mailing Address: PO Box 2188, Santa Fe, NM 87504-2188
Tel: 505-954-7206 *Toll Free Tel:* 888-390-6070 *Fax:* 505-954-7241
E-mail: press@sarsf.org
Web Site: sarpress.sarweb.org
Founded: 1907
Scholarly & general-interest books on anthropology, archaeology, Native American art & the American Southwest.
ISBN Prefix(es): 978-1-930618; 978-0-933452
Number of titles published annually: 12 Print
Total Titles: 142 Print
Foreign Rep(s): Eurospan Ltd (Africa, Asia, Australasia, Europe, Middle East, UK); Scholarly Book Services (Canada)

School Guide Publications
210 North Ave, New Rochelle, NY 10801
Tel: 914-632-1220 *Toll Free Tel:* 800-433-7771 *Fax:* 914-632-3412
E-mail: info@religiousministries.com
Web Site: www.graduateguide.com; www.schoolguides.com; www.religiousministries.com
Key Personnel
Pres & Publr: Myles Ridder *E-mail:* mridder@schoolguides.com
Founded: 1886
Directories for colleges, institutions & religious communities.
Number of titles published annually: 5 Print; 3 Online
Total Titles: 15 Print; 3 Online
Membership(s): Copywriter's Council of America; National Association of College Admission Counseling

School of Government
Division of The University of NC Chapel Hill
University of North Carolina, CB 3330, Chapel Hill, NC 27599-3330
Tel: 919-966-4119 *Fax:* 919-962-2709
Web Site: www.sog.unc.edu
Key Personnel
Mktg & Communs Specialist: Matthew McKirahan *E-mail:* mckirahan@sog.unc.edu
Founded: 1931
Textbooks, casebooks, manuals & guidebooks, monographs, reports, ebooks & bulletins.
ISBN Prefix(es): 978-1-56011
Number of titles published annually: 20 Print; 1 CD-ROM; 5 Online; 1 E-Book
Total Titles: 200 Print

§School Zone Publishing Co
1819 Industrial Dr, Grand Haven, MI 49417
Tel: 616-846-5030 *Toll Free Tel:* 800-253-0564 *Fax:* 616-846-6181 *Toll Free Fax:* 800-550-4618 (orders only)
Web Site: www.schoolzone.com
Key Personnel
Pres: Joan Hoffman
VP, Retail Sales: Sharon Winningham *Tel:* 616-846-5030 ext 217 *E-mail:* sharonw@schoolzone.com
Founded: 1979
Instructional materials for early childhood, pre-K to 6th grade; educational workbooks, flashcards & software.
ISBN Prefix(es): 978-0-88743; 978-0-938256; 978-1-58947
Number of titles published annually: 12 Print; 12 CD-ROM
Total Titles: 300 Print; 50 CD-ROM

Schreiber Publishing Inc
PO Box 4193, Rockville, MD 20849
SAN: 203-2465
Tel: 301-725-3906 *Toll Free Tel:* 800-296-1961 (sales) *Fax:* 301-725-0333 (orders)
E-mail: schreiberpublishing@comcast.net
Web Site: schreiberlanguage.com; shengold.com
Key Personnel
Pres: Jeremy Kay
Ed & Off Asst: Greg Giroux
Founded: 1954 (as Shengold Publishers)
Books on language & translation, Judaica history, Holocaust memoirs, juveniles, reference books, fiction, art books.
ISBN Prefix(es): 978-0-88400; 978-1-887563
Number of titles published annually: 12 Print; 7 E-Book; 1 Audio
Total Titles: 145 Print; 32 E-Book; 1 Audio
Imprints: Shengold Books
Foreign Rights: Bet Alim (Israel); Gazelle (Europe, UK); Importadora Agrimen (Latin America)
Shipping Address: National Book Network, 15200 NBN Way, Blue Ridge Summit, PA 17214, Contact: Christine Wolf *Tel:* 717-794-3800 *Fax:* 717-794-3804
Warehouse: National Book Network, 15200 NBN Way, Blue Ridge Summit, PA 17214, Contact: Christine Wolf *Tel:* 717-794-3800 *Fax:* 717-794-3804
Distribution Center: National Book Network, 4720 Boston Way, Lanham, MD 20706, Contact: Eileen Judd *Tel:* 301-459-3366 *Toll Free Tel:* 800-462-6420 *Fax:* 301-459-1705

§Science & Humanities Press
Subsidiary of Banis & Associates
63 Summit Point, St Charles, MO 63301-0571
Tel: 636-394-4950
Web Site: sciencehumanitiespress.com; beachhousebooks.com; macroprintbooks.com; earlyeditionsbooks.com; heuristicsbooks.com
Key Personnel
CEO & Publr: Robert J Banis *E-mail:* banis@sciencehumanitiespress.com
Founded: 1994
Publish books with a mission. Titles include adapting to living with a disability, computer capabilities, education & specialized medical/wellness topics. Most interested in books that have enduring human value, promoting the kind of world we all want to live in. Prefer inquiries by e-mail. No unsol mss; author guidelines on web site (sciencehumanitiespress.com).
ISBN Prefix(es): 978-1-888725; 978-1-59630
Number of titles published annually: 20 Print; 20 E-Book; 1 Audio
Total Titles: 110 Print; 10 Online; 60 E-Book; 4 Audio
Imprints: BeachHouse Books; Early Editions Books; Heuristic Books; MacroPrintBooks
Membership(s): The Independent Book Publishers Association; St Louis Publishers Association

Science, Naturally!™
Affiliate of Platypus Media
725 Eighth St SE, Washington, DC 20003
Tel: 202-465-4798 *Toll Free Tel:* 866-724-9876 *Fax:* 202-558-2132
E-mail: info@sciencenaturally.com

Web Site: www.sciencenaturally.com
Key Personnel
Pres: Dia L Michels *E-mail:* dia@sciencenaturally.com
Founded: 2001
Committed to increasing science literacy by exploring & demystifying key science topics.
ISBN Prefix(es): 978-0-9678020
Number of titles published annually: 5 Print; 5 E-Book
Total Titles: 7 Print; 7 E-Book
Warehouse: Ware Pak Inc, 2427 Bond St, University Park, IL 60466 *Tel:* 708-534-2600 *Fax:* 708-534-7803 *Web Site:* www.ware-pak.com
Distribution Center: National Book Network, 4501 Forbes Blvd, Lanham, MD 20706 *Tel:* 301-459-3366 *Fax:* 301-429-5746 *E-mail:* custserv@nbnbooks.com

Science Publishers Inc
Imprint of Edenbridge Ltd
PO Box 699, Enfield, NH 03748-0699
Tel: 603-632-7377 *Fax:* 603-632-5611
E-mail: info@scipub.net
Web Site: www.scipub.net
Key Personnel
Pres & Intl Rts: Vijay Primlani
Sales Exec & Lib Sales Dir: Linda Jones
Founded: 1992
Publish scholarly & scientific books.
ISBN Prefix(es): 978-1-886106; 978-1-57808; 978-1-881570
Number of titles published annually: 50 Print; 1 CD-ROM
Total Titles: 800 Print
Foreign Office(s): c/o Plymbridge Distributors Ltd, Estover Rd, Plymouth PL6 7PY, United Kingdom *E-mail:* orders@plymbridge.com
Distributed by CRC Press
Foreign Rep(s): Academic Marketing Services Pty Ltd (South Africa); James Benson (Ireland, UK); Paulo Ceschi (Brazil); Jim Chalmers (Ireland, UK); D A Information Services (Australia); Michael Goh (Southeast Asia); IMA (North Africa); International Publishers Representatives Ltd (Middle East, North Africa); Ben Kato (Japan); Kemper Conseil Publishing (Benelux, Switzerland); Mark Latcham (Ireland, UK); Livraria Polytechnica Ltda (Brazil); Marcello s.a.s (France, Italy, Portugal, Spain); Minimax SAS (Italy); P B Foreign Book Centre LP (Cambodia, Thailand, Vietnam); P F Books (Indonesia); SHS Publishers' Consultants & Representatives (Austria, Germany, Switzerland); David Towle (Scandinavia)

ScienceThrillers Media
PO Box 601392, Sacramento, CA 95860-1392
Tel: 916-712-3334
E-mail: query@sciencethrillersmedia.com
Web Site: www.sciencethrillersmedia.com
Key Personnel
Publr: Dr Amy Rogers *E-mail:* publisher@sciencethrillersmedia.com
Founded: 2014
Specialize in page-turning stories (fiction or nonfiction) that feature science, technology, engineering, math, or medicine in the plot, or a protagonist in one of those fields.
ISBN Prefix(es): 978-1-940419
Number of titles published annually: 4 Print; 4 E-Book; 1 Audio
Membership(s): California Writers Club; The Independent Book Publishers Association; International Thriller Writers Inc; Northern California Publishers & Authors Association

Scobre Press Corp
2255 Calle Clara, La Jolla, CA 92037
Toll Free Tel: 877-726-2734 *Fax:* 858-551-1232
E-mail: info@scobre.com
Web Site: www.scobre.com
Key Personnel
Owner & Pres: Scott Blumenthal
Owner: Brett Hodus
Founded: 1999
ISBN Prefix(es): 978-0-9741692; 978-1-933423
Number of titles published annually: 6 Print
Total Titles: 12 Print

§Scott Publishing Co
Division of AMOS Publishing Co
911 S Vandemark Rd, Sidney, OH 45365
Mailing Address: PO Box 828, Sidney, OH 45365-0828
Tel: 937-498-0802 *Toll Free Tel:* 800-572-6885 (cust serv) *Fax:* 937-498-0807 *Toll Free Fax:* 800-488-5349
E-mail: cuserv@amospress.com
Web Site: www.amosadvantage.com
Key Personnel
Ed: Charles Snee
Dealers Sales Rep: Joellen Walter
Founded: 1863
Stamp collecting catalogs, reference books & stamp collecting accessories.
ISBN Prefix(es): 978-0-89487
Number of titles published annually: 8 Print
Total Titles: 8 Print

Scout Press, see Gallery Books

Scribner
Imprint of Scribner Publishing Group
1230 Avenue of the Americas, New York, NY 10020
Key Personnel
Pres: Susan Moldow *Tel:* 212-698-7182 *E-mail:* susan.moldow@simonandschuster.com
SVP, Publr: Nan Graham *Tel:* 212-632-4930 *E-mail:* nan.graham@simonandschuster.com
VP, Assoc Publr: Roz Lippel *Tel:* 212-698-7666 *E-mail:* roz.lippel@simonandschuster.com
VP, Ed-in-Chief: Colin Harrison *Tel:* 212-632-4942 *E-mail:* colin.harrison@simonandschuster.com
VP, Dir of Subs Rts: Paul O'Halloran *Tel:* 212-698-7367 *E-mail:* paul.o'halloran@simonandschuster.com
VP, Dir of Publicity: Brian Belfiglio *Tel:* 212-632-4945 *E-mail:* brian.belfiglio@simonandschuster.com
Art Dir: Jaya Miceli *Tel:* 212-632-4959 *E-mail:* jaya.miceli@simonandschuster.com
Ed, Assoc Mktg Dir: Kara Watson *Tel:* 212-632-4936 *E-mail:* kara.watson@simonandschuster.com
Deputy Dir of Publicity: Katie Monaghan *Tel:* 212-632-4950 *E-mail:* katie.monaghan@simonandschuster.com; Kate Lloyd *Tel:* 212-632-4951 *E-mail:* kate.lloyd@simonandschuster.com
Sr Ed: Shannon Welch *Tel:* 212-632-4934 *E-mail:* shannon.welch@simonandschuster.com
Ed: Liese Mayer *Tel:* 212-632-4938 *E-mail:* liese.mayer@simonandschuster.com
Asst Ed: Daniel Loedel *Tel:* 212-698-1226 *E-mail:* daniel.loedel@simonandschuster.com
Assoc Ed: John Glynn *Tel:* 212-698-1295 *E-mail:* john.glynn@simonandschuster.com
Edit Asst: Katrina Diaz *Tel:* 212-632-4903 *E-mail:* katrina.diaz@simonandschuster.com; David Lamb *Tel:* 212-698-2445 *E-mail:* david.lamb@simonandschuster.com
Online Mktg Mgr: Ashley Gilliam *Tel:* 212-698-2889 *E-mail:* ashley.gilliam@simonandschuster.com
Sr Publicist: Gwyneth Stansfield *Tel:* 212-632-4947 *E-mail:* gwyneth.stansfield@simonandschuster.com
Publicity Asst: Kyle Radler *Tel:* 212-698-2358 *E-mail:* kyle.radler@simonandschuster.com
ISBN Prefix(es): 978-0-684; 978-0-7432
Number of titles published annually: 70 Print
Imprints: Scribner Classics; Scribner Poetry

Scripta Humanistica Publishing International
Subsidiary of Brumar Communications
1383 Kersey Lane, Potomac, MD 20854
Tel: 301-294-7949 *Fax:* 301-424-9584
E-mail: info@scriptahumanistica.com
Web Site: www.scriptahumanistica.com
Key Personnel
Chmn of the Bd & Publr: Prof Bruno M Damiani *Tel:* 301-340-1095 *E-mail:* damiani@cua.edu
Founded: 1984
Publish reference books in the Humanities.
ISBN Prefix(es): 978-0-916379
Number of titles published annually: 5 Print
Total Titles: 175 Print; 175 Online
Editorial Office(s): Dept of Romance Languages, 512 Williams Hall, Philadelphia, PA 19104-6305, Gen Ed: Jose M Regueiro *Tel:* 215-898-5124 *Fax:* 215-898-0933 *E-mail:* jrequeir@sas.upenn.edu
Foreign Rep(s): Grant & Cutler Ltd (Northern Europe, UK); Leader Books SA (Greece, Middle East); Portico (Africa, Southern Europe, Spain); Scripta Humanistica (Caribbean, Latin America); Spain Shobo Co Inc (Asia, Australia, New Zealand)
Distribution Center: Baker & Taylor, 501 S Gladiolus Ave, Momence, IL 60954-1799 *Tel:* 815-472-2444
Ingram/Lightning Source, 7315 Innovation Blvd, Fort Wayne, IN 46818-1371 *E-mail:* csacademic@ingramcontent.com *Web Site:* www.ingramcontent.com
Midwest Library Service, 11443 Saint Charles Rock Rd, Bridgeton, MO 63044-2789 *Tel:* 314-739-3100 *Fax:* 314-739-1326 *E-mail:* madden@midwestls.com *Web Site:* www.midwestls.com
Yankee Book Peddler Inc, 999 Maple St, Contoocook, NH 03229-3374 *Tel:* 603-746-3102 *Fax:* 603-746-5628
Scripta Humanistica, Calle Union 657, Miramar 00907, Puerto Rico *Tel:* 809-723-2445
Leader Books SA, 62 Koniaristr, 115 21 Ampelokipi, Greece *Tel:* 210 6452825 *Fax:* 210 6449924
Spain Shobo Co Ltd, Yamoto, PO Box 12, Miyagui 981-0503, Japan *Tel:* (0225) 84-1280 *Fax:* (0225) 84-1283 *E-mail:* info@spainshobo.co.jp
Portico Librerias SA, Calle Munoz Seca 6, 50005 Zaragoza, Spain *Tel:* 976 55 70 39 *Fax:* 976 35 32 26 *E-mail:* jalcrudo@porticolibrerias.es
Grant & Cutler Ltd, 55-57 Great Marlborough St, London W1V 1DD, United Kingdom *Tel:* (0171) 734-2012

The Scriptural Research & Publishing Co Inc
344 E Johnson Ave, Cheshire, CT 06410
Mailing Address: PO Box 725, New Britain, CT 06050-0725
Tel: 203-272-1780 *Fax:* 203-272-2296
E-mail: src1@srpublish.org
Web Site: www.scripturalresearch.com
Key Personnel
Administrator: Joseph R Poulin
Founded: 1995
Religious & scripturally-based books.
ISBN Prefix(es): 978-1-57277
Number of titles published annually: 2 Print; 1 E-Book
Total Titles: 50 Print; 1 Audio

Scurlock Publishing Co Inc
1293 Myrtle Springs Rd, Texarkana, TX 75503
Tel: 903-832-4726 *Toll Free Tel:* 800-228-6389 (US & CN) *Fax:* 903-831-3177
E-mail: custserv@scurlockpublishing.com
Web Site: muzzleloadermag.com; www.scurlockpublishing.com

Key Personnel
Publr & Ed-in-Chief: Bill Scurlock
Mng Ed: Linda Scurlock
Founded: 1974
Historical nonfiction, early American nonfiction, hunting nonfiction, muzzleloading arms & shooting.
ISBN Prefix(es): 978-0-9605666; 978-1-880655
Number of titles published annually: 1 Print
Total Titles: 16 Print

Seal Press
Imprint of The Perseus Books Group
1700 Fourth St, Berkeley, CA 94710
SAN: 215-3416
Tel: 510-595-3664 *Fax:* 510-595-4228
Web Site: www.sealpress.com
Key Personnel
VP & Publr: Krista Lyons
Exec Ed: Laura Mazer
Ed: Stephanie Knapp
Founded: 1976
Publish books with the goal of informing women's lives. Our authors are radical & original thinkers, professionals with a distinct point of view, gutsy explorers, truth-tellers & writers who engender laughter, tears, inspiration & transformation.
ISBN Prefix(es): 978-0-931188; 978-1-878067; 978-1-58005
Number of titles published annually: 40 Print
Total Titles: 500 Print
Branch Office(s)
Perseus Books Group, 250 W 57 St, 15th fl, New York, NY 11216
Foreign Rep(s): Isabelle Bleecker
Distribution Center: Publishers Group West, 1700 Fourth St, Berkeley, CA *Tel:* 510-809-3700 *Toll Free Tel:* 800-788-3123 *Fax:* 510-809-3777 *Web Site:* www.pgw.com SAN: 202-8522

SEAP Publications, see Cornell University Southeast Asia Program Publications

Search Institute Press®
Division of Search Institute
The Banks Bldg, Suite 125, 615 First Ave NE, Minneapolis, MN 55413
Tel: 612-376-8955 *Toll Free Tel:* 800-888-7828 *Fax:* 612-692-5553
E-mail: si@search-institute.org
Web Site: www.search-institute.org
Key Personnel
Dir, Serv & Content Devt: Rebecca Post *E-mail:* beckyp@search-institute.org
Provide practical, hope-filled books to create a world in which young people are valued & thrive. Content is based on Search Institute's 50 years of research & focuses on the 40 Developmental Assets®, a framework of qualities, experiences & relationships youth need to succeed. Publishe resources for adults & youth that help strengthen communities by nurturing parents, concerned & caring adults, young people, educators & youth- family- & community-service professionals.
ISBN Prefix(es): 978-1-57482
Number of titles published annually: 4 Print; 4 E-Book
Total Titles: 110 Print; 50 E-Book
Distribution Center: Independent Publishers Group (IPG), 814 N Franklin St, Chicago, IL 60610 *Tel:* 312-337-0747 *Toll Free Tel:* 800-888-4741 (orders) *Fax:* 312-337-5985 *E-mail:* orders@ipgbook.com *Web Site:* www.ipgbook.com
Membership(s): ABC

Second Chance Press
Imprint of The Permanent Press
4170 Noyac Rd, Sag Harbor, NY 11963
SAN: 213-1633
Tel: 631-725-1101
E-mail: info@thepermanentpress.com
Web Site: www.thepermanentpress.com
Key Personnel
Co-Publr: Judith Shepard *E-mail:* judith@thepermanentpress.com; Martin Shepard *E-mail:* shepard@thepermanentpress.com
Mng Ed: Cathy Suter *E-mail:* cathy@thepermanentpress.com
Typesetting, Design & Prodn: Susan Ahlquist *E-mail:* susan@thepermanentpress.com
Founded: 1977
Originals & reprints of literary works in hardcover & paperback.
ISBN Prefix(es): 978-0-933256
Number of titles published annually: 16 Print
Total Titles: 450 Print
Foreign Rights: Nike Davarinou (Greece); Kira Dominguez (Australia); Lora Fountain Agency (France); Jill Hughes (Eastern Europe); Intl Editors (Jennifer Houge) (Portugal, Spain); Jane Judd (UK); Andrew Nurnberg Associates (China); ONK Agency Ltd (Turkey); Thomas Schlueck (Germany); Rita Vivian (Italy); Eric Yang (Korea)

§See-More's Workshop
325 West End Ave, Suite 12-B, New York, NY 10023
Tel: 212-724-0677 *Fax:* 212-724-0767
E-mail: sbt@shadowboxtheatre.org
Web Site: www.shadowboxtheatre.org
Key Personnel
Administrator: Elaine Brand *E-mail:* ebrand@shadowboxtheatre.org
Founded: 1992
Publishing arm of the The Shadow Box Theatre, New York's musical puppet theatre for children. Publishes children's books, audio tapes & CDs & videos based on the shows.
ISBN Prefix(es): 978-1-882601
Number of titles published annually: 3 Print; 1 Audio
Total Titles: 10 Print; 10 Online; 10 Audio
Distribution Center: Amazon.com, 1200 12 Ave, Suite 1200, Seattle, WA 98144-2734 *Toll Free Tel:* 866-216-1074 *Web Site:* www.amazon.com
Brodart Co, 500 Arch St, Williamsport, PA 17701 *Tel:* 570-326-2461 *Toll Free Tel:* 800-233-8467 *Fax:* 570-326-1479 *E-mail:* support@brodart.com *Web Site:* www.brodart.com
Follett School Solutions Inc, 1340 Ridgeview Dr, McHenry, IL 60050 *Tel:* 815-759-1700 *Toll Free Tel:* 888-511-5114 (cust serv) *Fax:* 815-759-9831 *Toll Free Fax:* 800-852-5458 *E-mail:* info@follettlearning.com *Web Site:* www.follettlearning.com SAN: 169-1902

See Sharp Press
PO Box 1731, Tucson, AZ 85702-1731
Tel: 520-338-2151
E-mail: info@seesharppress.com
Web Site: www.seesharppress.com
Key Personnel
Founder, Publr & Sr Ed: Charles Bufe
Founded: 1984
Iconoclastic trade paperbacks & pamphlets on a wide variety of nonfiction topics.
ISBN Prefix(es): 978-1-884365
Number of titles published annually: 6 Print; 1 CD-ROM
Total Titles: 45 Print; 2 CD-ROM
Foreign Rights: Independent Publishers Group (Worldwide)
Distribution Center: Independent Publishers Group, 814 N Franklin, Chicago, IL 60610 *Tel:* 312-337-0747 *Toll Free Tel:* 800-888-4741 orders *Fax:* 312-337-5985 *Web Site:* www.ipgbook.com
Membership(s): The Independent Book Publishers Association

Seedling Publications Inc
Imprint of Continental Press
520 E Bainbridge St, Elizabethtown, PA 17022
Toll Free Tel: 800-233-0759 *Toll Free Fax:* 888-834-1303
E-mail: info@continentalpress.com
Web Site: www.continentalpress.com
Key Personnel
Pres: Eric Beck *E-mail:* ebeck@continentalpress.com
Founded: 1992
Books for beginning readers in 8-16 page format; leveled readers-parental involvement materials.
ISBN Prefix(es): 978-0-8454
Number of titles published annually: 15 Print
Total Titles: 275 Print
Distributed by Kendall Hunt Publishing
Foreign Rep(s): PSI

SelectBooks Inc
One Union Sq W, Suite 909, New York, NY 10003
Tel: 212-206-1997 *Fax:* 212-206-3815
E-mail: info@selectbooks.com
Web Site: www.selectbooks.com
Key Personnel
Founder & Publr: Kenzi Sugihara *E-mail:* kenzi@selectbooks.com
Publicity Mgr: Kenichi Sugihara *E-mail:* kenichi@selectbooks.com
Founded: 2001
Book publisher.
ISBN Prefix(es): 978-1-59079
Number of titles published annually: 10 Print; 5 E-Book; 2 Audio
Total Titles: 50 Print; 5 E-Book; 3 Audio
Sales Office(s): Midpoint Trade Books, 27 W 20 St, Suite 1102, New York, NY 10011 *Tel:* 212-727-0190 *Fax:* 212-727-0195 *E-mail:* midpointny1@aol.com
Foreign Rights: Waterside Productions (Worldwide)
Orders to: Midpoint Trade Books, 27 W 20 St, Suite 1102, New York, NY 10011 *Tel:* 212-727-0190 *Fax:* 212-727-0195 *E-mail:* orders@midpt.com *Web Site:* www.midpointtrade.com
Returns: Midpoint Trade Books, 27 W 20 St, Suite 1102, New York, NY 10011 *Tel:* 212-727-0190 *Fax:* 212-727-0195 *E-mail:* orders@midpt.com *Web Site:* www.midpointtrade.com
Distribution Center: Midpoint Trade Books, 27 W 20 St, Suite 1102, New York, NY 10011 *Tel:* 212-727-0190 *Fax:* 212-727-0195 *Web Site:* www.midpointtrade.com
Baker & Taylor, 2550 W Tyvola Rd, Suite 300, Charlotte, NC 28217 *Tel:* 704-998-3100 *Toll Free Tel:* 800-775-1800 *Web Site:* www.btol.com
Ingram Content Group Inc, One Ingram Blvd, La Vergne, TN 37086 *Tel:* 615-793-5000 *E-mail:* inquiry@ingramcontent.com *Web Site:* www.ingramcontent.com
Membership(s): The Independent Book Publishers Association

§Self-Counsel Press Ltd
4152 Meridian St, Suite 105-471, Bellingham, WA 98226
SAN: 240-9925
Toll Free Tel: 800-663-3007
E-mail: orders@self-counsel.com
Web Site: www.self-counsel.com
Key Personnel
Pres: Diana R Douglas *E-mail:* drdouglas@self-counsel.com
Mng Ed: Richard Day *E-mail:* rday@self-counsel.com
Mktg Mgr: Tyler Douglas *Tel:* 604-986-3366 ext 215
Founded: 1971
Legal, business & reference books.
ISBN Prefix(es): 978-1-55180; 978-1-77040

Number of titles published annually: 15 Print; 5 CD-ROM
Total Titles: 230 Print; 100 CD-ROM
Branch Office(s)
1481 Charlotte Rd, North Vancouver, BC V7J 1H1, Canada *Tel:* 604-986-3366 *Fax:* 604-986-3947 SAN: 115-0545
Membership(s): ALA

Self-Realization Fellowship Publishers
3208 Humboldt St, Los Angeles, CA 90031
SAN: 204-5788
Tel: 323-276-6002 *Toll Free Tel:* 888-773-8680 *Fax:* 323-927-1624
Web Site: www.srfpublishers.org
Key Personnel
Sales Mgr: Phil Gray *E-mail:* philg@srfpublishers.org
Mktg: Mike Baake *E-mail:* mikeb@srfpublishers.org
Founded: 1920 (by Paramahansa Yogananda)
Publisher for the complete works of Paramahansa Yogananda.
ISBN Prefix(es): 978-0-87612
Number of titles published annually: 10 Print; 7 Audio
Returns: 3233 N San Fernando Rd, Unit 2, Los Angeles, CA 90065, Mark Russell *Tel:* 323-276-6000 *E-mail:* markr@yogananda-srf.org SAN: 204-5688
Membership(s): The Independent Book Publishers Association

Sentient Publications LLC
1113 Spruce St, Boulder, CO 80302
Tel: 303-443-2188 *Fax:* 303-381-2538
E-mail: contact@sentientpublications.com
Web Site: www.sentientpublications.com
Key Personnel
Publr: Connie Shaw *E-mail:* cshaw@sentientpublications.com
Founded: 2001
Ecology, education, health, science, spirituality. Publish quality nonfiction books that arise from the spirit of inquiry & the richness of the inherent dialogue between writer & reader.
ISBN Prefix(es): 978-0-9710786; 978-1-59181
Number of titles published annually: 5 Print; 5 E-Book
Total Titles: 105 Print; 105 E-Book; 10 Audio
Foreign Rights: ANA Sofia Ltd (Bulgaria, Romania); Asli Karasuil Telif Haklari Ajansi (Turkey); Book Publishers Association of Israel (Israel); Giro di Parole (Italy); The English Agency (Japan); International Editors' Co (Spain); JLM Literary Agency (Greece); Michelle Lapautre Literary Agency (France); Maxima Creative Agency (Indonesia); Andrew Nurnberg (China); Piper & Poppenhusen (Germany); H Katia Schumer (Brazil); Silkroad Publishers Agency (Thailand)
Orders to: National Book Network, 4720 Boston Way, Lanham, MD 20706 *Tel:* 301-459-3366 *Toll Free Tel:* 800-462-6420 *Fax:* 301-459-1705 *Web Site:* www.nbnbooks.com
Shipping Address: National Book Network, 4720 Boston Way, Lanham, MD 20706 *Tel:* 301-459-3366 *Toll Free Tel:* 800-462-6420 *Fax:* 301-459-1705 *Web Site:* www.nbnbooks.com
Distribution Center: National Book Network, 4720 Boston Way, Lanham, MD 20706 *Tel:* 301-459-3366 *Toll Free Tel:* 800-462-6420 *Fax:* 301-459-1705 *Web Site:* www.nbnbooks.com
Membership(s): Publishers Association of the West

Serindia Publications
PO Box 10335, Chicago, IL 60610-0335
Tel: 312-664-5531 *Fax:* 312-664-4389
E-mail: info@serindia.com
Web Site: www.serindia.com
Key Personnel
Publr: Shane Suvikapakornkul
Founded: 1976 (established in London)
ISBN Prefix(es): 978-1-932476
Number of titles published annually: 11 Print
Total Titles: 60 Print
Distributed by Art Media Resources Inc (US & CN)
Foreign Rep(s): Kodansha Europe (Europe, UK); Paragon Asia Co Ltd (Singapore, Southeast Asia, Thailand); United Century Book Service (Hong Kong, Mainland China); The Variety Book Depot (Bhutan, India, Nepal, South Asia)

Seven Footer Kids
Imprint of Seven Footer Press
247 W 30 St, 11th fl, New York, NY 10001-2824
Tel: 212-710-9340 *Fax:* 212-710-9344
E-mail: info@sevenfooter.com
Web Site: www.sevenfooterpress.com
Key Personnel
Pres & Publr: David Gomberg
Chief Creative Offr: Justin Heimberg
Founded: 2009
Dedicated to publishing books that, together, children & parents can learn from & enjoy.
ISBN Prefix(es): 978-0-9740439; 978-0-9788178; 978-1-934734
Number of titles published annually: 12 Print
Total Titles: 20 Print
Distribution Center: Publishers Group West, 1094 Flex Dr, Jackson, TN 38301 *Toll Free Tel:* 800-788-2123 *Toll Free Fax:* 800-351-5073 *Web Site:* www.pgw.com

Seven Footer Press
Subsidiary of Seven Footer Entertainment LLC
247 W 30 St, 2nd fl, New York, NY 10001-2824
Tel: 212-710-9340 *Fax:* 212-710-9344
E-mail: info@sevenfooter.com
Web Site: www.sevenfooterpress.com
Key Personnel
Pres & Publr: David Gomberg
Chief Creative Offr: Justin Heimberg
Founded: 2004
Publishes cutting-edge nonfiction: innovative humor, puzzle, gift & high-concept books including the enormously successful *Would You Rather...?* series.
ISBN Prefix(es): 978-0-9740439; 978-0-9788178; 978-1-934734
Number of titles published annually: 20 Print; 5 E-Book
Total Titles: 51 Print; 4 E-Book
Imprints: Seven Footer Kids
Distribution Center: Publishers Group West, 1094 Flex Dr, Jackson, TN 38301 *Toll Free Tel:* 800-788-2123 *Toll Free Fax:* 800-351-5073 *Web Site:* www.pgw.com
See separate listing for:
Seven Footer Kids

Seven Locks Press
3100 W Warner Ave, Suite 8, Santa Ana, CA 97204
Mailing Address: PO Box 25689, Santa Ana, CA 92799
E-mail: sevenlocks@aol.com
Web Site: www.sevenlockspublishing.com
Key Personnel
Publr: James C Riordan
Founded: 1973
Publishes a variety of hardcover & trade paperback books; foreign rights agents worldwide; foreign representatives in UK, European Union & South Africa.
This publisher has indicated that 30% of their product line is author subsidized.
ISBN Prefix(es): 978-0-9801270; 978-1-931643; 978-0-929
Number of titles published annually: 25 Print
Total Titles: 500 Print
Membership(s): AAP; Northern California Independent Booksellers Association; Pacific Northwest Booksellers Association; Southern California Independent Booksellers Association

Seven Stories Press
140 Watts St, New York, NY 10013
Tel: 212-226-8760 *Toll Free Tel:* 800-733-3000 (orders) *Fax:* 212-226-1411
E-mail: info@sevenstories.com
Web Site: www.sevenstories.com
Key Personnel
Publr: Daniel Simon
Opers Dir: Jon Gilbert *E-mail:* jon@sevenstories.com
Dir, Mktg & Publicity, Triangle Square Books: Ruth Weiner *E-mail:* ruth@sevenstories.com
Mng Ed: Elizabeth DeLong
Publicity Mgr: Amy L Hayden *E-mail:* amy@sevenstories.com
Publicist: Ian Dreiblatt
Founded: 1995
Publish original hardcover & paperback books for the general reader in the area of literature, literature in translation, popular culture, politics, media studies, health & nutrition & sports. No unsol mss.
ISBN Prefix(es): 978-1-58322; 978-1-888363; 978-1-60980
Number of titles published annually: 50 Print; 15 E-Book; 2 Audio
Total Titles: 380 Print
Imprints: Triangle Square Books for Young Readers
Foreign Rep(s): Random House (all other territories); Turnaround Distribution (UK)
Foreign Rights: Anatoliat Agency (Turkey); Big Apple Agency (China, Taiwan); Paul & Peter Fritz Agency (Germany); Deborah Harris Literary Agency (Israel); Japan Uni Agency Inc (Japan); Katai & Bolza Agency (Hungary); Duran Kim Agency (Korea); MB Agencia Literaria (Spain, Spanish Latin America); Piergiorgio Nicolazzini Literary Agency (Italy); Sandorf Literary Agency (Croatia, Serbia, Slovenia); Ludmilla Shuskova (Russia); Villas-Boas & Moss Agencia Literaria (Brazil, Portugal)
Distribution Center: Random House, 400 Hahn Rd, Westminster, MD 21157 *Tel:* 612-746-2600 *Toll Free Tel:* 800-283-3572 (cust serv) *Fax:* 612-746-2606 *Web Site:* www.cbsd.com

1765 Productions
PO Box 4151, Fairfax, VA 22124-8151
Tel: 703-242-1734 *Fax:* 703-242-1734
E-mail: 1765productions@gmail.com
Key Personnel
Publr: Patrick G Finegan, Jr
Founded: 1990
Subject specialties include finance, film scripts & screenplays.
ISBN Prefix(es): 978-1-878905
Number of titles published annually: 4 Print
Total Titles: 6 Print

§Shadow Mountain
PO Box 30178, Salt Lake City, UT 84130
Tel: 801-534-1515 *Fax:* 801-517-3474
E-mail: submissions@shadowmountain.com
Web Site: shadowmountain.com
Key Personnel
Acq Ed: Allison Mathews
Founded: 1985
US-based publisher committed to providing books (print, electronic & audio) that offer value-based messages for readers of all ages. Publish quality children's fantasy & numerous bestsellers in the inspiration, fiction, history & business genres.
ISBN Prefix(es): 978-0-88494; 978-1-59038; 978-1-57345; 978-1-57008; 978-0-87579; 978-1-60908

Number of titles published annually: 25 Print; 2 Online; 25 E-Book; 10 Audio
Total Titles: 200 Print; 2 Online; 70 E-Book; 80 Audio
Imprints: Proper Romance
Distribution Center: Baker & Taylor, 2550 W Tyvola Rd, Suite 300, Charlotte, NC 28217 *Tel:* 704-998-3100 *Web Site:* www.btol.com
Ingram Content Group, One Ingram Blvd, La Vergne, TN 37086 *Tel:* 615-793-5000 *Web Site:* www.ingramcontent.com
Membership(s): ABC; The Children's Book Council; The Independent Book Publishers Association; Mountains & Plains Independent Publishers Association; Romance Writers of America

§Shambhala Publications Inc
Horticultural Hall, 300 Massachusetts Ave, Boston, MA 02115
SAN: 203-2481
Tel: 617-424-0030 *Toll Free Tel:* 866-424-0030 (off); 888-424-2329 (cust serv) *Fax:* 617-236-1563
E-mail: customercare@shambhala.com
Web Site: www.shambhala.com
Key Personnel
Founder & Ed-in-Chief: Samuel Bercholz
Owner & EVP: Sara Bercholz
Owner & Ed: Ivan Bercholz
Pres: Nikko Odiseos
Publr: Julie Saidenberg
Sr Ed: David O'Neal
Mng Ed: Liz Shaw
Ed, Roost Books: Rochelle Bourgault
Ed: Beth Frankl
Acquiring Ed & Ed, Roost Books: Jennifer Urban-Brown
Ed-at-Large: Susan Piver
Sr Designer: Jim Zaccaria
Founded: 1969
Trade books; art, literature, comparative religion, philosophy, science, psychology & related subjects.
ISBN Prefix(es): 978-0-307; 978-0-87773; 978-1-56957; 978-1-57062; 978-1-59030
Number of titles published annually: 85 Print; 50 Online
Total Titles: 600 Print; 50 Online
Imprints: Roost Books; Snow Lion
Distributed by Random House Inc
Foreign Rep(s): Airlift Books (UK); Random House Australia Ltd (Australia); Random House of Canada Ltd (Canada); Random House of New Zealand (New Zealand)
Foreign Rights: ACER (Spain); The English Agency (Japan); Anoukh Foerg (Germany); La Nouvelle Agence (Vanessa Kling) (France); Karen Schindler (Brazil)
Advertising Agency: Vermillion Graphics, Boulder, CO 80302
Returns: Random House Returns Dept, 400 Bennett Dr, Westminster, MD 21157
Shipping Address: Random House Distribution Center, 400 Hahn Rd, Westminster, MD 21157
See separate listing for:
Snow Lion Publications Inc

§M E Sharpe Inc
80 Business Park Dr, Suite 202, Armonk, NY 10504
SAN: 202-7100
Tel: 914-273-1800 *Toll Free Tel:* 800-541-6563 *Fax:* 914-273-2106
E-mail: info@mesharpe.com
Web Site: www.mesharpe.com
Key Personnel
CEO: Carol Sharpe
Pres: Myron E Sharpe
VP & Edit Dir: Patricia A Kolb *E-mail:* pkolb@mesharpe.com
VP & Dir, Mktg & Sales: Diana McDermott *E-mail:* dmcdermott@mesharpe.com
VP & Dir, New Prod Devt: Donna Sanzone *E-mail:* dsanzone@mesharpe.com
Exec Ed, Mgmt, Mktg & Pub Admin: Harry Briggs *E-mail:* briggs.harry@gmail.com
Founded: 1958
Scholarly books in social sciences, international relations, area studies, management. College texts, reference, trade, business & professional books. Scholarly & professional journals.
ISBN Prefix(es): 978-0-87332; 978-1-56324; 978-0-7656
Number of titles published annually: 80 Print; 6 Online; 35 E-Book
Total Titles: 1,200 Print; 3 CD-ROM; 9 Online; 200 E-Book
Imprints: East Gate Books; North Castle Books; Sharpe Focus; Sharpe Online Reference; Sharpe Reference
Foreign Rep(s): APAC Publishers Services Pte Ltd (American Samoa, Brunei, Cambodia, Guam, Indonesia, Korea, Laos, Malaysia, Micronesia, Papua New Guinea, Philippines, Singapore, Solomon Islands, Thailand, Vietnam); Applied Media (India); J Coutts Library Services Ltd (Canada); DA Information Services (Australia, New Zealand, Pacific Basin); The Eurospan Group (Africa, Algeria, Asia, Bahrain, Caribbean, Central America, Egypt, Europe, Iran, Iraq, Israel, Jordan, Lebanon, Libya, Mexico, Morocco, Oman, Palestine, Qatar, Saudi Arabia, South America, Sudan, Tunisia, Turkey, United Arab Emirates, UK, Yemen); ITA Beijing (China, Hong Kong, Taiwan); Kinokuniya Co Ltd (Japan); PAK Book Corp (Pakistan)
Warehouse: Maple Press Distribution Center, 1000 Strickler Rd, Mount Joy, PA 17552 *Tel:* 717-653-5483 *Fax:* 717-653-8269
Distribution Center: Maple Press Distribution Center, 1000 Strickler Rd, Mount Joy, PA 17552 *Tel:* 717-653-5483 *Fax:* 717-653-8269
Membership(s): ALA; Society for Scholarly Publishing

Sheffield Publishing Co
Subsidiary of Waveland Press Inc
9009 Antioch Rd, Salem, WI 53168
Mailing Address: PO Box 359, Salem, WI 53168-0359
Tel: 262-843-2281 *Fax:* 262-843-3683
E-mail: info@spcbooks.com
Web Site: www.spcbooks.com
Key Personnel
Mng Ed: Stephen R Nelson
Busn Mgr: Jodi R Jacobsen *E-mail:* jodi@spcbooks.com
Founded: 1984
Publisher of college texts & supplements.
ISBN Prefix(es): 978-0-88133; 978-1-879215
Number of titles published annually: 10 Print
Total Titles: 17 Print

Shenanigan Books
84 River Rd, Summit, NJ 07901
Tel: 908-219-4275 *Fax:* 908-219-4485
E-mail: info@shenaniganbooks.com
Web Site: www.shenaniganbooks.com
Key Personnel
Founder & Creative Dir: Mary Watson
Children's Literature: craft/picture/board books.
ISBN Prefix(es): 978-0-9726614; 978-1-934860
Number of titles published annually: 6 Print
Membership(s): ALA; The Children's Book Council; The Independent Book Publishers Association

Shengold Publishers Inc, see Schreiber Publishing Inc

Shen's Books
Imprint of Lee & Low Books
1547 Palos Verdes Mall, Unit 291, Walnut Creek, CA 94597
SAN: 138-2926
Tel: 925-262-8108 *Toll Free Tel:* 800-456-6660 *Fax:* 925-415-6136 *Toll Free Fax:* 888-269-9092
E-mail: info@shens.com
Web Site: www.shens.com
Key Personnel
Owner & Pres: Renee Ting *E-mail:* renee@shens.com
Founded: 1985
Children's books.
ISBN Prefix(es): 978-1-885008
Number of titles published annually: 3 Print
Total Titles: 25 Print
Membership(s): ABA; The Independent Book Publishers Association

Shepard Publications
PO Box 280, Friday Harbor, WA 98250
Web Site: www.shepardpub.com
Key Personnel
Owner & Pres: Aaron Shepard
ISBN Prefix(es): 978-0-938497; 978-1-62035; 978-0-9849616
Number of titles published annually: 4 Print; 10 E-Book
Total Titles: 38 Print; 37 E-Book
Imprints: Islander Press; Shepard & Piper (literary fiction & nonfiction); Shepard Publications (practical nonfiction, alternative viewpoints & professional resources); Simple Productions (nonviolence, lifestyle alternatives, music); Skyhook Press (children's)

Sherman Asher Publishing
126 Candelario St, Santa Fe, NM 87501
Tel: 505-988-7214
E-mail: westernedge@santa-fe.net
Web Site: www.shermanasher.com; www.westernedgepress.com
Key Personnel
Owner & Publr: James Mafchir
Founded: 1995
Literary books that include Spanish, English & bilingual memoirs & Judaica.
ISBN Prefix(es): 978-0-9644196; 978-1-890932
Number of titles published annually: 3 Print
Total Titles: 29 Print
Imprints: Western Edge Press (titles: 3)
Distribution Center: SCB Distributors, 15608 S New Century Dr, Gardena, CA 90248 *Tel:* 310-532-9400 *Toll Free Tel:* 800-729-6423 *Fax:* 310-532-7001

Sheron Enterprises Inc
1035 S Carley Ct, North Bellmore, NY 11710
Tel: 516-783-5885
E-mail: contact@longislandbookpublisher.com
Web Site: www.longislandbookpublisher.com
Key Personnel
Owner & Pres: Sheryl Perry
Secy: Ronald Perry
Founded: 1996
Publish college textbooks, lab manuals & study aids for college professors with small & large print runs as well as helping unknown authors get published: poetry.
ISBN Prefix(es): 978-1-891877
Number of titles published annually: 5 Print
Total Titles: 42 Print

Shields Publications
PO Box 669, Eagle River, WI 54521-0669
Tel: 715-479-4810 *Fax:* 715-479-3905
E-mail: wormbooks@wormbooks.com
Web Site: www.wormbooks.com
Key Personnel
Owner: Lynda Bolte
Founded: 1951

Publisher of books about earthworms, vermiculture, vermicomposting, commercial worm production.
ISBN Prefix(es): 978-0-914116
Number of titles published annually: 22 Print
Total Titles: 22 Print; 1 CD-ROM

Show What You Know® Publishing, A Lorenz Company
501 E Third St, Dayton, OH 45402
Tel: 614-764-1211; 937-228-6118
Toll Free Tel: 877-PASSING (727-7464)
Fax: 937-233-2042
E-mail: info@swykonline.com
Web Site: www.swykonline.com; www.lorenzeducationalpress.com
Key Personnel
Pres: Geoff Lorenz
Educational publisher of K-12 supplemental test-preparation books & other materials.
ISBN Prefix(es): 978-1-884183; 978-1-59230
Number of titles published annually: 90 Print
Total Titles: 275 Print
Membership(s): The Independent Book Publishers Association

SIAM, see Society for Industrial & Applied Mathematics

Side Street, see BrickHouse Books Inc

Sierra Club Books
85 Second St, 2nd fl, San Francisco, CA 94105
SAN: 203-2406
Tel: 415-977-5500 *Fax:* 415-977-5794
E-mail: books.publishing@sierraclub.org
Web Site: www.sierraclubbooks.org
Key Personnel
Publr: Helen Sweetland *E-mail:* helen.sweetland@sierraclub.org
Calendar Prog Coord: Mollie Eldemir *E-mail:* mollie.eldemir@sierraclub.org
Founded: 1892
Publisher of books on nature & the environment, including children's books & calendars.
ISBN Prefix(es): 978-0-87156; 978-1-57805
Number of titles published annually: 10 Print
Total Titles: 125 Print
Divisions: Sierra Club Books for Children; Sierra Club Calendars
Distributed by Chronicle Books (Sierra Club Calendars); Gibbs Smith (Sierra Club Books for Children)
Distributor for Counterpoint Press
Distribution Center: Publishers Group West, 1700 Fourth St, Berkeley, CA 94710 *Tel:* 510-809-3700 *Fax:* 510-809-3777 *E-mail:* info@pgw.com *Web Site:* www.pgw.com

Siglio
2432 Medlow Ave, Los Angeles, CA 90041
Tel: 310-857-6935 *Fax:* 310-728-6844
E-mail: publisher@sigliopress.com
Web Site: sigliopress.com
Key Personnel
Publr: Lisa Pearson
Founded: 2008
ISBN Prefix(es): 978-0-9799562; 978-1-938221
Number of titles published annually: 6 Print

Signalman Publishing
3700 Commerce Blvd, Kissimmee, FL 34741
Tel: 407-504-4103 *Toll Free Tel:* 888-907-4423
E-mail: info@signalmanpublishing.com
Web Site: www.signalmanpublishing.com
Key Personnel
Pres: John McClure *E-mail:* john@signalmanpublishing.com
Ed: Urmila McClure *E-mail:* urmila@signalmanpublishing.com
Founded: 2008
Specialize in bringing nonfiction works to the Kindle format. Have also branched out into trade paper with both nonfiction & fiction works.
This publisher has indicated that 45% of their product line is author subsidized.
ISBN Prefix(es): 978-0-9840614; 978-1-935991; 978-1-940145
Number of titles published annually: 12 Print; 14 E-Book
Total Titles: 56 Print; 76 E-Book
Imprints: Trinity Grace Press
Orders to: Lightning Source, 1246 Heil Quaker Blvd, La Vergne, TN 37086, Contact: Justine Bylo *Tel:* 212-714-9000 *Fax:* 615-213-4725 *E-mail:* justine.bylo@ingramcontent.com
Shipping Address: Lightning Source, 1246 Heil Quaker Blvd, La Vergne, TN 37086, Contact: Justine Bylo *Tel:* 212-714-9000 *Fax:* 615-213-4725 *E-mail:* justine.bylo@ingramcontent.com
Membership(s): The Association of Publishers for Special Sales; Christian Small Publishers Association

Signature Books Publishing LLC
564 W 400 N, Salt Lake City, UT 84116-3411
SAN: 217-4391
Tel: 801-531-1483 *Fax:* 801-531-1488
E-mail: people@signaturebooks.com
Web Site: www.signaturebooks.com; www.signaturebookslibrary.org
Key Personnel
Pres & Publr: George D Smith
Mng Dir & Sr Ed: Ronald L Priddis
Mktg Dir: Tom Kimball
Busn Mgr: Keiko Jones *Tel:* 801-531-1483 ext 102 *E-mail:* keiko@signaturebooks.com
Shipping Mgr: Greg Jones
Prodn & Design: Connie Disney
Off Mgr: Jani Fleet
Founded: 1980
Western Americana.
ISBN Prefix(es): 978-0-941214; 978-1-56085
Number of titles published annually: 10 Print; 10 E-Book
Total Titles: 173 Print; 1 CD-ROM; 173 E-Book
Distribution Center: Chicago Distribution Center, 11030 S Langley Ave, Chicago, IL 60628 *Tel:* 773-702-7000 *Toll Free Tel:* 800-621-2736 *Fax:* 773-702-7212 *Toll Free Fax:* 800-621-8476 *E-mail:* orders@press.uchicago.edu *Web Site:* www.press.uchicago.edu

§SIL International
7500 W Camp Wisdom Rd, Dallas, TX 75236-5629
Tel: 972-708-7400 *Fax:* 972-708-7350
E-mail: publications_intl@sil.org
Web Site: www.ethnologue.com; www.sil.org
Key Personnel
Asst Mgr, Bookstore: Darryl Johnson
Founded: 1934
Books.
ISBN Prefix(es): 978-0-88312; 978-1-55671
Number of titles published annually: 6 Print
Total Titles: 160 Print; 2 CD-ROM; 3 Online; 3 E-Book

Silicon Press
25 Beverly Rd, Summit, NJ 07901
Tel: 908-273-8919 *Fax:* 908-273-6149
E-mail: info@silicon-press.com
Web Site: www.silicon-press.com
Key Personnel
CEO: Indu Gehani
Founded: 1987
Books about computers & technology/fiction.
ISBN Prefix(es): 978-0-929306
Number of titles published annually: 10 Print; 4 Audio
Total Titles: 45 Print

Silman-James Press
3624 Shannon Rd, Los Angeles, CA 90027
Tel: 323-661-9922 *Toll Free Tel:* 877-SJP-BOOK (757-2665) *Fax:* 323-661-9933
E-mail: info@silmanjamespress.com
Web Site: www.silmanjamespress.com
Key Personnel
Publr: Gwen Feldman *E-mail:* gwen@silmanjamespress.com; Jim Fox *E-mail:* jim@silmanjamespress.com
Founded: 1990
Publisher of books on film, filmmaking, the motion picture industry & the performing arts.
ISBN Prefix(es): 978-1-879505
Number of titles published annually: 3 Print; 12 E-Book
Total Titles: 75 Print; 12 E-Book
Divisions: Siles Press (chess & nonfiction titles)
Distributed by Codasat Canada Ltd
Foreign Rep(s): Gazelle Book Services (Continental Europe, UK)
Returns: 660 S Mansfield, Ypsilanti, MI 48197

Silver Leaf Books LLC
13 Temi Rd, Holliston, MA 01746
Mailing Address: PO Box 6460, Holliston, MA 01746
E-mail: sales@silverleafbooks.com; editor@silverleafbooks.com; customerservice@silverleafbooks.com
Web Site: www.silverleafbooks.com
Key Personnel
Mng Dir & Dir, Fin: Clifford B Bowyer *E-mail:* cbbowyer@silverleafbooks.com
Edit Mgr: Brett Fried
Sales Mgr: Marilyn Fried
Founded: 2003
ISBN Prefix(es): 978-0-9744354; 978-0-9787782; 978-1-60975
Number of titles published annually: 13 Print; 8 E-Book
Total Titles: 43 Print; 42 E-Book

Silver Moon Press
400 E 85 St, New York, NY 10028
Toll Free Tel: 800-874-3320 *Fax:* 212-988-8112
E-mail: mail@silvermoonpress.com
Web Site: www.silvermoonpress.com
Key Personnel
Publr: David Katz
Founded: 1992
Publish curriculum workbooks in mathematics, English language arts & social studies for the K-8 market.
ISBN Prefix(es): 978-1-881889; 978-1-893110
Number of titles published annually: 4 Print
Total Titles: 110 Print
Returns: c/o The Oliver Press, 5707 W 36 St, Minneapolis, MN 55416
Warehouse: c/o Metro-Pack Inc, 37 Jeanne Dr, Newburgh, NY 12550 *Tel:* 845-564-5275 *Fax:* 845-564-5305

SilverHouse Books
555 NE 15 St, Suite 2-i, Miami, FL 33132
Tel: 305-747-1258
E-mail: info@silverhousebooks.com
Web Site: www.silverhousebooks.com
Key Personnel
VP: Rebeca Del'Isola
Founded: 2010
Small publisher of children's & young adult books.
ISBN Prefix(es): 978-0-9829312; 978-0-9831038; 978-0-9847909
Number of titles published annually: 6 Print; 6 Online; 6 E-Book
Total Titles: 6 Print; 6 Online; 6 E-Book
Membership(s): The Independent Book Publishers Association

Simba Information
Division of Market Research.com

1266 E Main St, Suite 700, Stamford, CT 06902
SAN: 210-2021
Tel: 203-325-8193 *Toll Free Tel:* 888-297-4622 (cust serv)
E-mail: customerservice@simbainformation.com
Web Site: www.simbainformation.com
Key Personnel
Sr Analyst/Mng Ed: Kathy Mickey
Analyst/Ed: Valerie Chernetskyy
Prodn Coord: Farah Pierre
Founded: 1989
Newsletters & research reports for information companies. Subject specialties: publishing & media.
ISBN Prefix(es): 978-0-88709
Number of titles published annually: 15 Print; 15 Online
Total Titles: 75 Print; 75 Online
Membership(s): AAP; BISG

Simcha Press
Imprint of Health Communications Inc
3201 SW 15 St, Deerfield Beach, FL 33442-8190
Tel: 954-360-0909 ext 212 *Toll Free Tel:* 800-851-9100 ext 212 *Toll Free Fax:* 800-424-7652
E-mail: simchapress@hcibooks.com
Web Site: www.hcibooks.com
Key Personnel
Dir, Communs & Mgr: Kim Weiss
E-mail: kimw@hcibooks.com
Founded: 1999
Nonfiction titles for those on the path of Jewish enrichment. Jewish interest, spirituality, inspirational, mysticism & recovery.
ISBN Prefix(es): 978-1-55874; 978-0-7573
Number of titles published annually: 4 Print; 4 Online; 4 E-Book
Total Titles: 13 Print; 13 Online; 8 E-Book

Simon & Schuster
Imprint of Simon & Schuster Publishing Group
1230 Avenue of the Americas, New York, NY 10020
Tel: 212-698-7000 *Toll Free Tel:* 800-223-2348 (cust serv); 800-223-2336 (orders)
Toll Free Fax: 800-943-9831 (orders)
Web Site: www.simonandschuster.com
Key Personnel
Pres & Publr: Jonathan Karp
VP & Assoc Publr: Richard Rhorer
VP & Edit Dir: Alice E Mayhew
VP & Ed-in-Chief: Marysue Rucci
VP & Exec Ed: Priscilla Painton; Trish Todd
VP & Sr Ed: Robert Bender
VP & Dir, Publicity, Sr Ed: Cary Goldstein
VP & Exec Art Dir, Trade Art: Jackie Seow
Dir of Subs Rts: Marie Florio
Sr Ed: Jofie Ferrari-Adler; Ben Loehnen; Millicent Bennett; Karyn Marcus
Ed: Emily Graff; Jonathan Cox
Assoc Ed: Johanna Li; Brit Hvide
Asst Ed: Stuart Roberts
Assoc Dir, Publicity: Larry Hughes
Deputy Dir, Publicity: Julia Prosser
Sr Publicity Mgr: Sarah Reidy
Publicity Mgr: Anne Pearce
Sr Publicist: Maureen Cole; Kate Gales
Publicist: Leah Johanson; Amanda Lang
Assoc Publicist: Erin Reback
Asst Publicist: Kellyn Patterson
Mktg Mgr: Stephen Bedford; Ebony LaDelle
Online Mktg Mgr: Elina Vaysbeyn
Assoc Mktg Mgr: Dana Trocker
Mktg Coord: Pronoy Sarkar
Assoc Art Dir: Alison Forner
Mng Ed: Kristen Lemire
Asst Mng Ed: Allison Har-zvi
Subs Rts Mgr: Sandy Hill
Subs Rts Asst: Emma del Valle
Edit Asst: Julianna Haubner; Elizabeth Breeden; Kaitlin Olson; Sophia Jimenez
Publg Asst: Megan Hogan
Publicity Asst: Kelsey Donohue; Lindsay Means; Clarissa Marzan
ISBN Prefix(es): 978-0-684
Number of titles published annually: 125 Print
Imprints: Folgers Shakespeare Library; Free Press
Foreign Rights: Akali Copyright Agency (Turkey); Antonella Antonelli Agenzia (Italy); Book Publishers Association of Israel (Israel); Japan UNI Agency (Japan); JLM Literary Agency (Greece); KCC (Korea Copyright Center) (Korea); Mohrbooks Literary Agency (Germany); La Nouvelle Agence (France); Andrew Nurnberg Associates (Bulgaria, Croatia, Czech Republic, Estonia, Hungary, Latvia, Lithuania, Montenegro, Poland, Romania, Serbia, Slovakia, Slovenia); Sane Toregard Agency (Denmark, Finland, Iceland, Norway); Sebes & Van Gelderen Literary Agency (Netherlands); Tuttle-Mori Agency Inc (Thailand)
See separate listing for:
Beyond Words Publishing Inc

Simon & Schuster Audio
Division of Simon & Schuster, Inc
1230 Avenue of the Americas, New York, NY 10020
Web Site: audio.simonandschuster.com
Key Personnel
Pres & Publr: Chris Lynch
VP, Audio Prodn: Elisa Shokoff
VP, Audio Sales: Ken Oxenreider
VP & Edit Dir: Tom Spain
VP, Mktg Dir: Sarah Lieberman
Sr Publicity, Media & Mktg Mgr: Lauren Pires
Audiobooks & Pimsleur Language Programs.
ISBN Prefix(es): 978-0-684; 978-0-7435; 978-0-671; 978-1-4423
Number of titles published annually: 100 Audio
Imprints: Audioworks; Beyond Words; Encore; Pimsleur; Sound Ideas
Distributor for Monostereo
Shipping Address: Total Warehouse Services, 2207 Radcliffe St, Bristol, PA 19007

Simon & Schuster Books for Young Readers, see Simon & Schuster Children's Publishing

Simon & Schuster Children's Publishing
Division of Simon & Schuster, Inc
1230 Avenue of the Americas, New York, NY 10020
Tel: 212-698-7000
Web Site: KIDS.SimonandSchuster.com; TEEN.SimonandSchuster.com; simonandschuster.net; simonandschuster.biz
Key Personnel
Pres & Publr: Jon Anderson
VP & Publr, S&S Books for Young Readers, Atheneum, McElderry Books, Saga Press: Justin Chanda
VP & Publr, Simon Pulse, Aladdin: Mara Anastas
VP & Publr, Licensed & Novelty Pub, Simon Spotlight, Little Simon: Valerie Garfield
VP & Publr, Paula Wiseman Books: Paula Wiseman
VP & Publr, Beach Lane Books: Allyn Johnston
VP & Deputy Publr, S&S Books for Young Readers, Atheneum, McElderry, Saga Press, Paula Wiseman Books, Beach Lane Books: Anne Zafian
VP & Deputy Publr, Aladdin, Simon Pulse, Little Simon, Simon Spotlight: Mary Marotta
VP & Edit Dir, S&S Books for Young Readers: David Gale
VP & Edit Dir, Atheneum, Caitlyn Dlouhy Books: Caitlyn Dlouhy
VP, Edit Dir, McElderry Books: Karen Wojtyla
VP, Edit Dir, Simon Pulse & Assoc Edit Dir, Aladdin: Liesa Abrams
VP & Creative Dir: Dan Potash
Edit Dir, Saga Press: Joe Monti
Edit Dir, Aladdin: Fiona Simpson
Edit Dir, Little Simon: Jeffrey Salane
Edit Dir, Simon Spotlight: Siobhan Ciminera
Exec Ed, S&S Books for Young Readers: Zareen Jaffrey; Christian Trimmer
Exec Ed, Atheneum: Reka Simonsen
Exec Ed, Aladdin: Karen Nagel
Sr Ed, Beach Lane Books: Andrea Welch
Sr Ed, S&S Books for Young Readers: Kristin Ostby
Sr Ed, McElderry: Ruta Rimas
Exec Art Dir, Simon Pulse, Atheneum (Novels), McElderry (Novels): Russell Gordon
Exec Art Dir, Atheneum (Picture Books), McElderry (Picture Books), Beach Lane Books: Ann Bobco
Exec Art Dir, Little Simon, Simon Spotlight: Channi Yammer
Exec Art Dir, S&S Books for Young Readers, Paula Wiseman Books: Lizzy Bromley
Exec Art Dir, Aladdin: Karin Paprocki
VP & Exec Mng Ed: Lisa Donovan
VP, Subs Rts: Stephanie Voros
VP, Dir of Publicity: Jennifer Romanello
VP, Dir of Mktg: Lucille Rettino
VP, Dir of Educ & Lib Mktg: Michelle Leo
Dir of Children's Sales: Christina Pecorale
Assoc Mktg Dir, S&S Books for Young Readers, Atheneum, McElderry, Saga Press, Paula Wiseman, Beach Lane: Chrissy Noh
Assoc Mktg Dir, Aladdin, Simon Pulse, Simon Spotlight, Little Simon: Carolyn Swerdloff
Assoc Mktg Dir, Digital: Matt Pantoliano
Preschool through young adult, hardcover & paperback fiction, nonfiction, trade, library, mass market titles & novelty books.
ISBN Prefix(es): 978-0-02; 978-0-609; 978-0-689; 978-0-7434; 978-1-4169
Number of titles published annually: 750 Print
Total Titles: 4,329 Print
Imprints: Aladdin Paperbacks; Atheneum Books for Young Readers; Beach Lane Books; Little Simon; Margaret K McElderry Books; Saga Press (adult science-fiction/fantasy/horror); Simon & Schuster Books for Young Readers; Simon Pulse; Simon Spotlight; Paula Wiseman Books

Simon & Schuster Digital
Division of Simon & Schuster, Inc
1230 Avenue of the Americas, New York, NY 10020
Tel: 212-698-7547
Web Site: www.simonandschuster.com; kids.simonandschuster.com; www.simonandschuster.ca; www.simonandschuster.co.uk; www.simonandschuster.net; www.simonandschuster.biz; www.tipsoncareerandmoney.com; www.tipsonhealthyliving.com; www.tipsonhomeandstyle.com; www.tipsonlifeandlove.com; www.offtheshelf.com; www.simonandschuster.com/teen
Key Personnel
VP, Mktg & New Prods: Adrian Norman
Tel: 212-698-2349 *E-mail:* adrian.norman@simonandschuster.com
VP, Prod Devt: David Krivda *Tel:* 212-698-1273
E-mail: david.krivda@simonandschuster.com
VP & Exec Dir of Content & Programming: Sue Fleming *Tel:* 212-698-7641 *E-mail:* sue.fleming@simonandschuster.com
VP, Technol: Steven Morgan *Tel:* 212-698-7135
E-mail: steven.morgan@simonandschuster.com
Founded: 1996
Manages company web site (www.simonandschuster.com) & all digital content production, marketing & distribution.
Number of titles published annually: 1,500 E-Book
Imprints: www.simonandschuster.com

§Simon & Schuster, Inc
Division of CBS Corporation

1230 Avenue of the Americas, New York, NY 10020
SAN: 200-2450
Tel: 212-698-7000 *Fax:* 212-698-7007
E-mail: firstname.lastname@simonandschuster.com
Web Site: www.simonandschuster.com
Key Personnel
Pres & CEO: Carolyn K Reidy
EVP, Opers & CFO: Dennis Eulau
EVP, Sales & Mktg: Michael Selleck
Pres & Publr, Simon & Schuster Audio: Chris Lynch
Pres & Publr, Children's Publishing Div: Jon Anderson
Pres & Publr, Simon & Schuster Publishing Group: Jonathan Karp
Pres & Publr, Scribner Publishing Group: Susan Moldow
Pres & Publr, Gallery Publishing Group: Louise Burke
Pres & Publr, Atria Publishing Group: Judith Curr
Pres & Publr, Simon & Schuster Canada: Kevin Hanson
VP & Publr, Howard Books: Jonathan Merkh
Chief Exec & Publr, Simon & Schuster UK Ltd: Ian Chapman
Mng Dir, Simon & Schuster (Australia) Pty Ltd: Dan Ruffino
Mng Dir, Simon & Schuster India: Rahul Srivastava
EVP, Gen Coun: David Hillman
EVP, Chief Mktg Offr: Liz Perl
SVP, Corp Communs: Adam Rothberg
SVP, Group Cont: Dave Upchurch
SVP, HR: Carolyn Connolly
VP, Busn Opers: Frank Nunez
VP, Gen Mgr, Adult, Children's & Audio: Craig Mandeville
VP, Client Publr Servs: Stephen Black
VP, Global Ebook Mkt Devt & Strategy: Doug Stambaugh
VP, Client Mgmt & Busn Devt: Joe Bulger
VP, Exec Mng Ed, Prodn & Copy Editing: Irene Kheradi
VP, Design & Digital Content Devt: Samantha Cohen
VP, Dist & Fulfillment: Dave Schaeffer
VP, Facilities: Lee Kartsaklis
VP, Contracts & Perms: Jeff Wilson
VP, Dir, Ad & Promo: Mark Speer
VP, Dir of Mktg, Adult Trade: Wendy Sheanin
VP, Dir of Educ & Lib Mktg: Michelle Leo
Founded: 1924
ISBN Prefix(es): 978-0-02; 978-0-941831; 978-1-885223; 978-0-7867; 978-0-13; 978-1-878990; 978-0-07; 978-0-7318; 978-0-669; 978-0-86417; 978-1-85626; 978-1-56025; 978-0-88708; 978-0-7434; 978-1-58270; 978-1-86842; 978-0-7435; 978-1-4169; 978-1-4165; 978-1-904027; 978-1-84483; 978-1-904292; 978-0-89256; 978-0-9674601; 978-0-9711953; 978-1-58229; 978-1-59309; 978-1-84448; 978-1-84737; 978-1-84738; 978-1-84739; 978-0-684; 978-0-7432; 978-0-689; 978-0-671; 978-1-4391; 978-1-903650; 978-1-84293; 978-1-905857; 978-1-906787; 978-1-4423; 978-1-4424; 978-1-4516; 978-1-84983; 978-1-84938; 978-1-84970; 978-1-907486; 978-1-921470; 978-0-85720; 978-0-85707; 978-1-4215; 978-1-62266; 978-1-4711; 978-1-4767; 978-1-4814; 978-1-921997; 978-1-922052; 978-1-925030; 978-0-85783; 978-0-85941; 978-0-87605; 978-0-9586517; 978-0-9806294; 978-0-9870829; 978-1-5011; 978-1-78028; 978-1-78108; 978-1-84899; 978-1-903301; 978-1-925184; 978-1-78496; 978-1-925183; 978-1-925310
Branch Office(s)
Beach Lane Books, 5666 La Jolla Blvd, No 154, La Jolla, CA 92037 *Tel:* 858-551-0860 *Fax:* 858-551-0492
Pimsleur, 30 Monument Sq, Concord, MA 01742 *Tel:* 978-369-7525
1639 Rte 10 E, Parsippany, NJ 07054 (royalties, accts payable, fin) *Tel:* 973-656-6000 *Fax:* 973-656-6070
Howard Books, 216 Centerview Dr, Suite 303, Brentwood, TN 37027 *Tel:* 615-873-2080 *Fax:* 615-370-3834
Simon & Schuster Canada, 116 King St E, Suite 300, Toronto, ON M5A 1J3, Canada *Tel:* 647-427-8882 *Fax:* 647-430-9446
Foreign Office(s): Simon & Schuster Australia Pty Ltd, 450 Miller St, Suite 19a, Level 1, Bldg C, Cammeray, NSW 2062, Australia *Tel:* (02) 9983 6600 *Fax:* (02) 9988 4232 (sales & mktg) *E-mail:* cservice@simonandschuster.com.au *Web Site:* www.simonandschuster.com.au/
Simon & Schuster Publishers India Pvt Ltd, 2316, Tower–A, The Corenthum A -41, Sector -62, Noida, Uttar Pradesh 201301, India
Simon & Schuster UK Ltd, 222 Gray's Inn Rd, 1st fl, London WC1X 8HB, United Kingdom *Tel:* (020) 7316-1900 *Fax:* (020) 7316-0333 *E-mail:* enquiries@simonandschuster.co.uk *Web Site:* www.simonandschuster.co.uk
Distributor for Andrews McMeel Publishing LLC; Backlist LLC (div of Chicken Soup for the Soul Publishing); Baen Books; Baseball America; Beyond Words; BL Publishing (div of Games Workshop); Boom! Studios; Cardoza Publishing; Chicken Soup for the Soul Publishing; Cider Mill Press Book Publishers LLC (including Applesauce Press & Appleseed imprint); Downtown Bookworks; Frederator Books LLC; Gallup (worldwide); Games Workshop; Harlequin Enterprises Ltd (billing only); Hooked on Phonics (Sandviks HOP Inc/Sandvik Publishing); Inner Traditions/Bear & Company; Kaplan Publishing (including Manhattan Prep); Katalitix Media; Kinfolk; Little Bee Books; Meadowbrook Press; Merck Publishing; Omnific Publishing; Open Road Publishing; Permuted Press LLC; Piggyback Interactive; Pikachu Press (Pokemon Company International); Post Hill Press LLC; Reader's Digest Books; Rebellion Publishing; Regan Arts; Ripley Entertainment Inc (Ripley's Believe it or Not); Studio Fun International (formerly Reader's Digest Children's Publishing); TC Media Books; To The Stars Inc; Tuttle Publishing; Uncrate LLC; Victory Belt Publishing; VIZ Media; Weldon Owen; Wisdom Publications; World Almanac (div of Facts on File); Yilin Press (Mandarin ebooks)
Returns: Simon & Schuster, c/o Jacobson Companies, 4406 Industrial Park Rd, Bldg 7, Camp Hill, PA 17011 (by appt; to schedule call 717-730-5212 ext 5316)
Shipping Address: Riverside Distribution Center, 100 Front St, Riverside, NJ 08075 (trade, children's, audio, mass-market & dist clients) *Tel:* 856-461-6500 *Fax:* 856-824-2402; Bristol Distribution Center, 2207 Radcliffe St, Bristol, PA 19007 *Tel:* 215-785-0531 *Fax:* 215-826-3002
Membership(s): AAP; BISG
See separate listing for:
Simon & Schuster Audio
Simon & Schuster Children's Publishing
Simon & Schuster Digital
Simon & Schuster Sales Division

Simon & Schuster Sales Division
Division of Simon & Schuster, Inc
1230 Avenue of the Americas, New York, NY 10020
Tel: 212-698-7000
Key Personnel
EVP, Sales & Mktg: Michael Selleck *Tel:* 212-698-7420 *E-mail:* michael.selleck@simonandschuster.com
VP & Exec Dir, Dist Sales & Retail Mktg: Gary Urda *Tel:* 212-698-7389 *E-mail:* gary.urda@simonandschuster.com
Sr Dir, Children's Sales: Christina Pecorale *Tel:* 212-698-1126 *E-mail:* christina.pecorale@simonandschuster.com
VP & Dir, Retail Sales: Paula Amendolara *Tel:* 212-698-7069 *E-mail:* paula.amendolara@simonandschuster.com
VP & Dir, Global Digital & Online Sales: Colin Shields *Tel:* 212-698-7536 *E-mail:* colin.shields@simonandschuster.com
VP & Dir, Intl Sales: Mr Seth Russo *Tel:* 212-698-7422 *E-mail:* seth.russo@simonandschuster.com
VP & Dir, Sales & Client Communs: Eileen Gentillo *Tel:* 212-698-7470 *E-mail:* eileen.gentillo@simonandschuster.com
VP & Dir, Client Sales & Servs: Michael Perlman *Tel:* 212-698-7061 *E-mail:* michael.perlman@simonandschuster.com
Dir, Spec Mkts: Sumya Ojakli *Tel:* 212-698-7202 *E-mail:* sumya.ojakli@simonandschuster.com
Distributor for Andrews McMeel Publishing LLC; Applesauce Press (children's); Avatar Press; Baen Books; Baseball America; Boom! Studios; Cardoza; Chicken Soup for the Soul; Cider Mill Press Book Publishers; Downtown Bookworks; Frederator Books LLC; Gallup (worldwide); Games Workshop; Harlequin (billing only); Kaplan Publishing; Manhattan Prep; Meadowbrook Press; Merck; Open Road; Permuted Press LLC; Piggyback Interactive; Post Hill Press LLC; Reader's Digest Children's Books; Rebellion; Regan Arts; Ripley Entertainment; To the Stars Inc; Uncrate LLC; VIZ Media; Weldon Owen; World Almanac (div of Facts on File)

Simon Pulse, see Simon & Schuster Children's Publishing

Simon Spotlight, see Simon & Schuster Children's Publishing

§Sinauer Associates Inc
23 Plumtree Rd, Sunderland, MA 01375
SAN: 203-2392
Mailing Address: PO Box 407, Sunderland, MA 01375-0407 SAN: 203-2392
Tel: 413-549-4300 *Fax:* 413-549-1118
E-mail: publish@sinauer.com; orders@sinauer.com
Web Site: www.sinauer.com
Key Personnel
Pres & Biology Ed: Andrew D Sinauer
VP & Dir, Mktg & Dist: Dean Scudder
Mng Ed: Carol J Wigg
Biology Ed: C Azelie Fortier
Psychology Ed: Sydney Carroll
Busn Mgr: Penny Grant
Prodn Mgr: Christopher Small
Mktg Coord: Marie Scavotto *E-mail:* scavotto@sinauer.com
Rts & Perms: Sherri Ellsworth
Founded: 1969
College textbooks & reference works in the biological & behavioral sciences.
ISBN Prefix(es): 978-0-87893; 978-1-60535
Number of titles published annually: 10 Print
Total Titles: 97 Print; 23 CD-ROM; 4 Online; 37 E-Book
Foreign Rep(s): Alkem (Bangladesh, Brunei, Cambodia, Hong Kong, Indonesia, Laos, Malaysia, Myanmar, Philippines, Singapore, Taiwan, Thailand); FUNPEC-Editora (Brazil); Macmillan Publishers New Zealand Ltd (New Zealand); Palgrave Macmillan (Africa, Australia, Brazil, Caribbean, China, Europe, Japan, Korea, Latin America, Middle East, Nepal, Pakistan, Russia, Sri Lanka, UK); Shinil Books Co Ltd (Korea); World Science Publishing Co (Korea)
Warehouse: Publishers Storage & Shipping Corp, 46 Development Rd, Fitchburg, MA 01420 *Tel:* 978-345-2121 *Fax:* 978-348-1233

Six Gallery Press
PO Box 90145, Pittsburgh, PA 15224-0545
Web Site: www.sixgallerypress.com
Key Personnel
Publr & Ed: Che Elias *E-mail:* rocketsconstrue@yahoo.com; Michael Hafftka *E-mail:* michael@sixgallerypress.com
Founded: 2000
Independent press producing & marketing experimental literature. We promote these books through reviews in journals, online & through author readings as well as special events including bookfairs.
ISBN Prefix(es): 978-0-9703840; 978-0-9726301; 978-0-9810091; 978-0-9782962
Number of titles published annually: 10 Print
Total Titles: 50 Print
Imprints: Convergence
Distribution Center: Small Press Distribution, 1341 Seventh St, Berkeley, CA 94710-1409

Skandisk Inc
6667 W Old Shakapee Rd, Suite 109, Bloomington, MN 55438-2622
Tel: 952-829-8998 *Toll Free Tel:* 800-468-2424 *Fax:* 952-829-8992
E-mail: tomten@skandisk.com
Web Site: www.skandisk.com
Key Personnel
Pres: Mike Sevig *E-mail:* mike@skandisk.com
Prodn Mgr: Lisa Hamnes *E-mail:* lhamnes@skandisk.com
Founded: 1975
Publisher & distributor of books with a particularly strong selection of titles of Scandinavian interest, including children's books, mythology, historical fiction, Scandinavian culture & Scandinavian humor.
ISBN Prefix(es): 978-0-9615394; 978-1-57534
Number of titles published annually: 3 Print
Total Titles: 25 Print; 1 CD-ROM

§SkillPath Publications
Division of The Graceland University Center for Professional Development & Lifelong Learning Inc
PO Box 2768, Mission, KS 66201-2768
Tel: 913-362-3900 *Toll Free Tel:* 800-873-7545 *Fax:* 913-362-4241
E-mail: customercare@skillpath.net; products@skillpath.net
Web Site: www.skillpath.com
Key Personnel
Acct Rep: Casey Smith
Founded: 1989
Books, audio programs, computer based training.
ISBN Prefix(es): 978-1-878542; 978-1-57294; 978-1-929874; 978-1-934589
Number of titles published annually: 10 Print
Total Titles: 50 Print; 4 Audio
Divisions: CompuMaster
Branch Office(s)
100 Armstrong Ave, Georgetown, ON L7G 5S4, Canada *Fax:* 913-362-4241
Foreign Office(s): GPO Box 1747, Melbourne, Victoria 3001, Australia *Tel:* (0800) 145 231 *Fax:* (0800) 145 244 *Web Site:* www.skillpath.com.au
FreePost 105776, PO Box 742, Wellington 6140, New Zealand *Tel:* (0800) 447 301 *Fax:* (0800) 447 304 *Web Site:* www.skillpath.co.nz
PO Box 203, Chessington KT9 9BZ, United Kingdom *Tel:* (0800) 328 1140 *Fax:* (0800) 892972 *Web Site:* www.skillpath.co.uk
Distributor for Franklin Covey; Pearson Technology; Thomson Publishing; John Wiley

Skinner House Books
Imprint of Unitarian Universalist Assn
c/o Unitarian Universalist Assn, 24 Farnsworth St, Boston, MA 02210-1409
Tel: 617-742-2100 *Fax:* 617-948-6466
E-mail: skinnerhouse@uua.org
Web Site: www.skinnerhouse.org
Key Personnel
Edit Dir: Mary Benard
Edit Asst: Betsy Martin *Tel:* 617-948-4644 *E-mail:* betsymartin@uua.org
Founded: 1975
Specialize in spirituality, inspirational literature, books on church resources for religious liberals.
ISBN Prefix(es): 978-0-933840; 978-1-55896
Number of titles published annually: 15 Print; 15 E-Book
Total Titles: 265 Print
Sales Office(s): Red Wheel/Weiser/Conari, 65 Parker St, Suite 7, Newburyport, MA 01950 *Tel:* 978-465-0504 *Toll Free Tel:* 800-423-7087 *Fax:* 978-465-0243 *E-mail:* orders@redwheelweiser.com *Web Site:* redwheelweiser.com
Returns: Red Wheel/Weiser/Conari, 65 Parker St, Suite 7, Newburyport, MA 01950 *Tel:* 978-465-0504 *Toll Free Tel:* 800-423-7087 *Fax:* 978-465-0243 *E-mail:* orders@redwheelweiser.com *Web Site:* redwheelweiser.com
Distribution Center: Red Wheel/Weiser/Conari, 65 Parker St, Suite 7, Newburyport, MA 01950 *Tel:* 978-465-0504 *Toll Free Tel:* 800-423-7087 *Fax:* 978-465-0243 *E-mail:* info@redwheelweiser.com *Web Site:* redwheelweiser.com

Sky Oaks Productions Inc
19544 Sky Oaks Way, Los Gatos, CA 95030
Mailing Address: PO Box 1102, Los Gatos, CA 95031
Tel: 408-395-7600 *Fax:* 408-395-8440
E-mail: tprworld@aol.com
Web Site: www.tpr-world.com
Key Personnel
Pres: Virginia Lee Asher
Founded: 1973
ISBN Prefix(es): 978-0-940296; 978-1-56018
Number of titles published annually: 4 Print
Total Titles: 300 Print; 40 Online; 40 E-Book; 7 Audio

Sky Pony Press
Imprint of Skyhorse Publishing Inc
307 W 36 St, 11th fl, New York, NY 10018
Tel: 212-643-6816 *Fax:* 212-643-6819
E-mail: skypony@skyhorsepublishing.com; submissions@skyhorsepublishing.com; info@skyhorsepublishing.com
Web Site: www.skyponypress.com
Key Personnel
Edit Dir: Julie Matysik
Ed: Alison Weiss
Asst Ed: Adrienne Szpyrka
Founded: 2011
ISBN Prefix(es): 978-1-61145; 978-1-60239; 978-1-61608; 978-1-62087; 978-1-63220; 978-1-62914; 978-1-62873; 978-1-5107
Number of titles published annually: 80 Print
Foreign Rights: Biagi Literary Management (Linda Biagi) (Worldwide)
Orders to: Perseus Distribution, 250 W 57 St, 15th fl, New York, NY 10107 *E-mail:* orderentry@perseusbooks.com
Warehouse: 210 American Dr, Jackson, TN 38301
Distribution Center: Perseus Distribution, 250 W 57 St, 15th fl, New York, NY 10107 *E-mail:* orderentry@perseusbooks.com

Sky Publishing
90 Sherman St, Cambridge, MA 02140
Tel: 617-864-7360 *Toll Free Tel:* 866-644-1377 *Fax:* 617-864-6117
E-mail: info@skyandtelescope.com
Web Site: www.skyandtelescope.com
Key Personnel
VP & Publg Dir: Joel Toner
Ed-in-Chief: Robert Naeye
Sr Ed: Demis di Cicco; Alan M MacRobert
Assoc Ed: Tony Flanders
Founded: 1941
Astronomy books & software, maps, posters, globes, sidelines.
ISBN Prefix(es): 978-0-933346
Number of titles published annually: 15 Print
Total Titles: 20 Print

SkyLight Paths Publishing
Division of LongHill Partners Inc
Sunset Farm Offices, Rte 4, Woodstock, VT 05091
SAN: 134-5621
Mailing Address: PO Box 237, Woodstock, VT 05091-0237
Tel: 802-457-4000 *Toll Free Tel:* 800-962-4544 *Fax:* 802-457-4004
E-mail: sales@skylightpaths.com
Web Site: www.skylightpaths.com
Key Personnel
Pres & Publr: Stuart M Matlins
SVP, Admin & Fin: Amy M Wilson *E-mail:* awilson@longhillpartners.com
VP, Edit & Prodn: Emily Wichland *E-mail:* ewichland@longhillpartners.com
Founded: 1999
General trade books for seekers & believers of all faith traditions. Subject areas include spirituality, children's, self-help, crafts, interfaith, spiritual living, eastern & western religion.
ISBN Prefix(es): 978-1-893361; 978-1-59473
Number of titles published annually: 20 Print
Total Titles: 350 Print
Foreign Rep(s): Bayard/Novalis (Canada); Deep Books (Europe, UK); Rainbow Book Agencies (Australia, New Zealand); Brian Scheiffer Agencies (South Africa)
Foreign Rights: Andreas Brunner Literature Agentur (Germany); Deborah Harris Agency (Israel); International Editors' Co (IECO) (Isabel Monteagudo) (Spain); Nurnberg Associates (Judit Hermann) (Hungary); Nurnberg Associates (L Strakova) (Czech Republic); H Katia Schumer (Brazil); Susanna Zevi (Italy)
Returns: 28 River St, Suite 7, Windsor, VT 05089

§Slack Incorporated
6900 Grove Rd, Thorofare, NJ 08086-9447
SAN: 201-8632
Tel: 856-848-1000 *Toll Free Tel:* 800-257-8290 *Fax:* 856-848-6091
E-mail: sales@slackinc.com
Web Site: www.slackbooks.com
Key Personnel
SVP, Books & Journals: John H Bond *E-mail:* jbond@slackinc.com
Mktg Communs Dir: Michelle Gatt *E-mail:* mgatt@slackinc.com
Founded: 1960
Academic textbooks & professional reference books: medicine, occupational therapy, physical therapy, ophthalmology, gastroenterology, orthopedics, athletic training, pediatrics, nursing & other areas.
ISBN Prefix(es): 978-1-55642
Number of titles published annually: 35 Print; 2 CD-ROM; 10 E-Book
Total Titles: 250 Print; 15 CD-ROM; 25 E-Book
Divisions: Journal Publishing; Professional Book Publishing; Trade Book Publishing
Foreign Rep(s): EuroSpan (Europe); Login Brothers (Canada); McGraw-Hill (Asia)
Foreign Rights: John Scott Co
Advertising Agency: Alcyon Advertising
Distribution Center: 200 Richardson Ave, Bldg B, Swedesboro, NJ 08085

Sleeping Bear Press™
315 Eisenhower Pkwy, Suite 200, Ann Arbor, MI 48108

Toll Free Tel: 800-487-2323 *Fax:* 734-794-0004
E-mail: sleepingbearpress@cengage.com
Web Site: www.sleepingbearpress.com
Key Personnel
Publr: Heather Hughes
Publicity: Audrey Mitnick
Founded: 1998
Publisher of children's books infants to young adults.
ISBN Prefix(es): 978-1-886947; 978-1-58536
Number of titles published annually: 32 Print
Total Titles: 451 Print
Membership(s): ALA; Association of Children's Booksellers; International Literacy Association

§Slipdown Mountain Publications LLC
28151 Quarry Lake Rd, Lake Linden, MI 49945
Tel: 906-523-4118 *Toll Free Tel:* 866-341-3705 *Toll Free Fax:* 866-341-3705
E-mail: books@jacobsvillebooks.com
Web Site: www.jacobsvillebooks.com
Key Personnel
Publr: Walt Shiel *E-mail:* walt@jacobsvillebooks.com
Staff Libn: Lisa Shiel *E-mail:* lisa@jacobsvillebooks.com
Founded: 2003
Independent micro-publisher of fiction & nonfiction books. All new books published through Jacobsville Books imprint. Publish historical & speculative fiction, military history, alternative views of science, cryptozoology & paranormal subjects. All books are available in print & most are available in popular ebook formats (Kindle/mobi, EPUB, PDF).
ISBN Prefix(es): 978-0-9746553; 978-1-934631
Number of titles published annually: 5 Print; 6 E-Book; 2 Audio
Total Titles: 14 Print; 27 E-Book
Imprints: Jacobsville Books
Subsidiaries: Five Rainbows Services for Authors & Publishers (publishing services)
Membership(s): The Association of Publishers for Special Sales

§Small Beer Press
150 Pleasant St, No 306, Easthampton, MA 01027
Tel: 413-203-1636 *Fax:* 413-203-1636
E-mail: info@smallbeerpress.com
Web Site: smallbeerpress.com
Key Personnel
Founder & Publr: Gavin J Grant
Founder: Kelly Link
CTO: Michael J Deluca
Founded: 2000
ISBN Prefix(es): 978-1-931520; 978-1-61873
Number of titles published annually: 10 Print; 10 E-Book
Total Titles: 50 Print; 100 E-Book
Sales Office(s): Consortium, 34 13 Ave N, Suite 101, Minneapolis, MN 55413
Foreign Rights: Cooke Agency International
Billing Address: Consortium, 34 13 Ave N, Suite 101, Minneapolis, MN 55413
Orders to: Consortium, 34 13 Ave N, Suite 101, Minneapolis, MN 55413
Returns: Consortium, 34 13 Ave N, Suite 101, Minneapolis, MN 55413
Shipping Address: Consortium, 34 13 Ave N, Suite 101, Minneapolis, MN 55413
Warehouse: Consortium, 34 13 Ave N, Suite 101, Minneapolis, MN 55413
Distribution Center: Consortium, 34 13 Ave N, Suite 101, Minneapolis, MN 55413
Membership(s): Community of Literary Magazines & Presses

Small Business Advisors Inc
11 Franklin Ave, Hewlett, NY 11557
Mailing Address: PO Box 758, Armonk, NY 10504-0758
Tel: 516-374-1387; 914-260-1027 *Fax:* 516-374-1175; 720-294-3202
E-mail: info@smallbusinessadvice.com
Web Site: www.smallbusinessadvice.com
Key Personnel
Contact: Eric Gelb *E-mail:* eric@smallbusinessadvice.com; Joe Gelb *E-mail:* joe@smallbusinessadvice.com
Founded: 1991
Publisher of books, ebooks & blogs on small business, finance & marketing/copyrighting.
ISBN Prefix(es): 978-1-890158
Number of titles published annually: 4 Print
Total Titles: 15 Print; 1 Audio
Membership(s): ALA; The Independent Book Publishers Association

Smith & Kraus Publishers Inc
40 Walch Dr, Portland, ME 04103
Mailing Address: PO Box 127, Lyme, NH 03768-0127
Tel: 207-523-2585 *Toll Free Tel:* 877-668-8680 *Fax:* 207-699-3698
E-mail: editor@smithandkraus.com
Web Site: www.smithandkraus.com
Key Personnel
Pres & Publr: Marisa Smith Kraus
Founded: 1990
Drama books, monologues, books of interest to our theatrical community, play anthologies. Smith & Kraus Global: religious/political.
ISBN Prefix(es): 978-0-9622722; 978-1-880399; 978-1-57525
Number of titles published annually: 35 Print
Total Titles: 500 Print
Imprints: Smith & Kraus Books For Kids (young adult fiction)
Subsidiaries: Smith & Kraus Global (world affairs)
Foreign Rep(s): Agnes Krup Literary Agency

§M Lee Smith Publishers LLC
5201 Virginia Way, Brentwood, TN 37027
Mailing Address: PO Box 5094, Brentwood, TN 37024-5094
Tel: 615-373-7517 *Toll Free Tel:* 800-274-6774 *Fax:* 615-373-5183
E-mail: custserv@mleesmith.com
Web Site: www.mleesmith.com
Key Personnel
Chmn: M Lee Smith
CFO: Lawton Miller
Pres: Dan Oswald
VP, Mktg: Guy Crossley
VP, Content: Brad Forrister
Dir, Cust Serv & Circulation: Kim Mesecher
Founded: 1975
Legal newsletters/legal book related titles.
ISBN Prefix(es): 978-0-925773; 978-1-60029; 978-0-9605796
Number of titles published annually: 130 Print
Total Titles: 2 CD-ROM; 60 Online

Steve Smith Autosports
PO Box 11631, Santa Ana, CA 92711-1631
Tel: 714-639-7681 *Fax:* 714-639-9741
Web Site: www.stevesmithautosports.com
Key Personnel
Pres & Publr: Steve Smith *E-mail:* steve@ssapubl.com
Founded: 1971
Specialize in auto racing technical books.
ISBN Prefix(es): 978-0-936834
Number of titles published annually: 5 Print
Total Titles: 200 Print

Smithsonian Scholarly Press
Division of Smithsonian Institution
Aerospace Bldg, 704-A, MRC 957, Washington, DC 20013
Mailing Address: PO Box 37012, Washington DC, DC 20013-7012
Tel: 202-633-3017 *Fax:* 202-633-6877
E-mail: schol_press@si.edu
Web Site: www.scholarlypress.si.edu
Key Personnel
Prog Asst: Stephanie Summerhays
Founded: 1966
General trade & adult nonfiction.
ISBN Prefix(es): 978-0-87474; 978-1-56098; 978-1-58834
Number of titles published annually: 8 Print
Total Titles: 800 Print
Distributed by Random House
Distribution Center: Random House

§Smyth & Helwys Publishing Inc
6316 Peake Rd, Macon, GA 31210-3960
Tel: 478-757-0564 *Toll Free Tel:* 800-747-3016 (orders only); 800-568-1248 (orders only) *Fax:* 478-757-1305
E-mail: information@helwys.com
Web Site: www.helwys.com
Key Personnel
Pres & CEO: Cecil P Staton, Jr
Publr & EVP: Keith Gammons *E-mail:* keith@helwys.com
Founded: 1990
Christian books, literature, Sunday School books (curriculum).
ISBN Prefix(es): 978-1-880837; 978-0-9628455; 978-1-57312
Number of titles published annually: 30 Print
Total Titles: 330 Print
Foreign Rep(s): Grace Wing Publishers (England)

Snow Lion Publications Inc
Imprint of Shambhala Publications
300 Massachusetts Ave, Boston, MA 02115
Tel: 617-236-0030 *Fax:* 617-236-1563
E-mail: customercare@shambhala.com
Web Site: www.shambhala.com/snowlion
Key Personnel
VP, Sales: Julie Saidenberg
Founded: 1980
Trade & scholarly books on Tibetan Buddhism & Tibet & books by the Dalai Lama.
ISBN Prefix(es): 978-0-937938; 978-1-55939
Number of titles published annually: 18 Print; 20 E-Book
Total Titles: 300 Print; 220 E-Book; 1 Audio

Society for Human Resource Management (SHRM)
1800 Duke St, Alexandria, VA 22314
Tel: 703-548-3440 *Toll Free Tel:* 800-444-5006 (orders) *Fax:* 703-535-6490
E-mail: shrm@shrm.org; shrmstore@shrm.org
Web Site: www.shrm.org
Trade organization of human resource professional with over 170,000 members.
ISBN Prefix(es): 978-0-939900; 978-1-58644; 978-1-932132
Number of titles published annually: 14 Print
Total Titles: 100 Print

§Society for Industrial & Applied Mathematics
3600 Market St, 6th fl, Philadelphia, PA 19104-2688
Tel: 215-382-9800 *Toll Free Tel:* 800-447-7426 *Fax:* 215-386-7999
E-mail: siambooks@siam.org
Web Site: www.siam.org
Key Personnel
Cont: Lauren Steidel *E-mail:* steidel@siam.org
Publr: David K Marshall *E-mail:* marshall@siam.org
Exec Dir: James M Crowley *E-mail:* jcrowley@siam.org
Dir, Mktg & Outreach: Michelle Montgomery *Tel:* 215-382-9800 ext 368 *E-mail:* montgomery@siam.org
Mng Ed: Kelly Thomas *E-mail:* thomas@siam.org

Sr Acqs Ed: Elizabeth Greenspan
E-mail: greenspan@siam.org
Cust Serv Mgr: Arlette Liberatore
E-mail: liberatore@siam.org
Membership Mgr: Susan Whitehouse
E-mail: whitehouse@siam.org
Pubns Mgr: Mitchell Chernoff *E-mail:* chernoff@siam.org
Founded: 1952
Journals, books, conferences & reprints in mathematics/computer science/statistics/physical science.
ISBN Prefix(es): 978-0-89871
Number of titles published annually: 16 Print
Total Titles: 400 Print; 35 CD-ROM; 300 E-Book

§Society for Mining, Metallurgy & Exploration
12999 E Adam Aircraft Circle, Englewood, CO 80112
Tel: 303-948-4200 *Toll Free Tel:* 800-763-3132 *Fax:* 303-973-3845
E-mail: cs@smenet.org
Web Site: www.smenet.org
Key Personnel
Exec Dr: Dave Kanagy
Sr Ed: Bill Gleason; Georgene Renner
Pubns Ed: Steve Kral *Tel:* 303-948-4200 ext 245 *E-mail:* kral@smenet.org
Founded: 1871
Publish mining related monthly magazine, quarterly journal, trade books, hardbound & paperback.
ISBN Prefix(es): 978-0-87335
Number of titles published annually: 5 Print
Total Titles: 80 Print; 15 CD-ROM
Foreign Rep(s): Affiliated East-West Press (India); Australian Mineral Foundation (Australia)

Society of American Archivists
17 N State St, Suite 1425, Chicago, IL 60602-4061
SAN: 211-7614
Tel: 312-606-0722 *Toll Free Tel:* 866-722-7858 *Fax:* 312-606-0728
E-mail: info@archivists.org
Web Site: www.archivists.org
Key Personnel
Exec Dir: Nancy Beaumont *E-mail:* nbeaumont@archivists.org
Dir, Publg: Teresa Brinati *E-mail:* tbrinati@archivists.org
Founded: 1936
Archival literature; preservation.
ISBN Prefix(es): 978-0-931828; 978-1-931666
Number of titles published annually: 5 Print
Total Titles: 72 Print

Society of Automotive Engineers International, see SAE (Society of Automotive Engineers International)

Society of Biblical Literature, see SBL Press

Society of Environmental Toxicology & Chemistry
229 S Baylen St, 2nd fl, Pensacola, FL 32502
Tel: 850-469-1500 *Fax:* 850-469-9778
E-mail: setac@setac.org
Web Site: www.setac.org
Key Personnel
Sr Publg Mgr: Mimi Meredith *Tel:* 850-469-1500 ext 113 *E-mail:* mimi.meredith@setac.org
Founded: 1979
Supports publications of scientific value relating to environmental topics. Proceedings of technical workshops that explore current & prospective environmental issues are published as peer-reviewed technical documents. Publications are used by scientists, engineers & managers because of their technical basis & comprehensive, state-of-the-science reviews; association press; nonprofit, professional society.
ISBN Prefix(es): 978-1-880611
Number of titles published annually: 8 Print; 1 CD-ROM
Total Titles: 105 Print; 5 CD-ROM
Imprints: SETAC Press

§Society of Exploration Geophysicists
8801 S Yale Ave, Tulsa, OK 74137
Mailing Address: PO Box 702740, Tulsa, OK 74170-2740
Tel: 918-497-5500 *Fax:* 918-497-5557
E-mail: web@seg.org
Web Site: www.seg.org
Key Personnel
Dir, Pubns: Ted Bakamjian *Tel:* 918-497-5506 *E-mail:* tbakamjian@seg.org
Manuscript Tracking Specialist: Merrily Sanzalone *Tel:* 918-497-5507 *E-mail:* msanzalone@seg.org
Founded: 1930
Types of publications: textbooks; videos; technical journals & web site.
ISBN Prefix(es): 978-1-56080; 978-0-931839
Number of titles published annually: 3 Print
Total Titles: 100 Print; 9 CD-ROM

§Society of Manufacturing Engineers
One SME Dr, Dearborn, MI 48121
SAN: 203-2376
Tel: 313-425-3000 *Toll Free Tel:* 800-733-4763 (cust serv) *Fax:* 313-425-3400
E-mail: publications@sme.org
Web Site: www.sme.org
Key Personnel
CEO & Exec Dir: Mark Tomlinson *Tel:* 313-425-3100 *E-mail:* mtomlinson@sme.org
Dir, Prof Devt: Jeannine Kunz
SME Resource Ctr: Carol Selleck *Tel:* 313-425-3152
E-Libn: Carol Tower *Tel:* 313-425-3288 *E-mail:* ctower@sme.org
Founded: 1932
Professional engineering association.
ISBN Prefix(es): 978-0-87263
Number of titles published annually: 5 Print
Total Titles: 150 Print; 21 CD-ROM
Branch Office(s)
7100 Woodbine Ave, Suite 312, Markham, ON L3R 5J2, Canada *Tel:* 905-752-4415 *Toll Free Tel:* 888-322-7333 *Fax:* 905-479-0113 *E-mail:* canadasales@sme.org
Distributed by American Technical Publishers Inc; McGraw-Hill; Productivity Press
Distributor for Industrial Press; McGraw-Hill; Prentice Hall; John Wiley & Sons Inc
Foreign Rights: American Technical Publishers (UK); DA Book Pty Ltd (Australia); Elsevier Science Publishers (Netherlands)

The Society of Naval Architects & Marine Engineers
601 Pavonia Ave, Jersey City, NJ 07306-2907
SAN: 202-0572
Tel: 201-798-4800 *Toll Free Tel:* 800-798-2188 *Fax:* 201-798-4975
Web Site: www.sname.org
Key Personnel
Pubns Dir: Susan Evans Grove *E-mail:* sevans@sname.org
Reference books, directories, periodicals, technical research reports & bulletins on naval architecture, marine engineering & ocean engineering.
ISBN Prefix(es): 978-0-87033; 978-0-9603048; 978-0-939773; 978-0-7698
Number of titles published annually: 3 Print
Total Titles: 29 Print

Soho Press Inc
853 Broadway, New York, NY 10003
SAN: 202-5531
Tel: 212-260-1900 *Fax:* 212-260-1902
E-mail: soho@sohopress.com; publicity@sohopress.com
Web Site: www.sohopress.com
Key Personnel
Publr: Bronwen Hruska *E-mail:* bhruska@sohopress.com
Assoc Publr: Juliet Grames
Sr Ed: Mark Doten *E-mail:* mdoten@sohopress.com
Asst Ed: Amara Hoshijo
Publicity & Mktg: Paul Oliver *E-mail:* poliver@sohopress.com
Publicist: Abby Koski
Founded: 1986 (incorporated in 1986, published first books in 1987)
Hard & softcover trade books: fiction, mysteries, general nonfiction, history & social history.
ISBN Prefix(es): 978-0-939149; 978-1-56947; 978-1-61695
Number of titles published annually: 70 Print; 68 E-Book
Total Titles: 350 Print
Imprints: Soho Constable; Soho Crime; Soho Teen
Distributed by Random House
Foreign Rights: ACER Agencia Literaria (Latin America, Portugal, Spain); AnatoliaLit Agency (Turkey); Biagi Rights Management (UK); English Agency (Juzzo Sawa) (Japan); Grayhawk Agency (Taiwan); Deborah Harris Agency (Israel); Agence Hoffman (France); International Editors Co (Flavia Sala) (Brazil); Leonardt & Hoier Literary Agency (Scandinavia); Meller Literary Agency (Germany); Jan Michael (Belgium, Netherlands); Daniela Micura Literary Services (Italy); PLS (Publishing Language Service) (Korea); Prava i Prevodi (Bulgaria, Croatia, Czech Republic, Hungary, Montenegro, Poland, Romania, Russia, Serbia, Slovakia, Slovenia); Read N' Right Agency (Nike Davarinou) (Greece)
Orders to: Random House Customer Service, 400 Hahn Rd, Westminster, MD 21157 *Toll Free Tel:* 800-733-3000; 800-669-1536 (electronic orders) *Toll Free Fax:* 800-659-2436 *Web Site:* www.randomhouse.com/backyard/order.html SAN: 631-760X; Random House of Canada Ltd, 2775 Matheson Blvd E, Mississauga, ON L4W 4P7, Canada *Toll Free Tel:* 888-523-9292; 800-258-4233 (electronic orders) *Toll Free Fax:* 888-562-9924
Distribution Center: Random House Customer Service, 400 Hahn Rd, Westminster, MD 21157 *Toll Free Tel:* 800-733-3000; 800-669-1536 (electronic orders) *Toll Free Fax:* 800-659-2436 *Web Site:* www.randomhouse.com/backyard/order.html SAN: 631-760X
Random House of Canada Ltd, 2775 Matheson Blvd E, Mississauga, ON L4W 4P7, Canada *Toll Free Tel:* 888-523-9292; 800-258-4233 (electronic orders) *Toll Free Fax:* 888-562-9924

Soil Science Society of America
5585 Guilford Rd, Madison, WI 53711-5801
Tel: 608-273-8080 *Fax:* 608-273-2021
E-mail: headquarters@soils.org
Web Site: www.soils.org
Key Personnel
CEO: Ellen Bergfeld *E-mail:* ebergfeld@sciencesocieties.org
Founded: 1936
Technical books for professionals in soil science.
ISBN Prefix(es): 978-0-89118
Number of titles published annually: 5 Print
Total Titles: 90 Print

Solano Press Books
PO Box 773, Point Arena, CA 95468
Tel: 707-884-4508 *Toll Free Tel:* 800-931-9373 *Fax:* 707-884-4109
E-mail: spbooks@solano.com

Web Site: www.solano.com
Key Personnel
Publr: Ling-Yen Jones
Acqs Ed: Natalie Macris
Asst to Publr: Nancy McLaughlin
Founded: 1984
Professional books: law, public administration, real estate, land use, environment, urban planning, environmental analysis & management.
ISBN Prefix(es): 978-0-9614657; 978-0-923956; 978-1-938166
Number of titles published annually: 4 Print
Total Titles: 25 Print; 3 E-Book

Solution Tree
555 N Morton St, Bloomington, IN 47404
Tel: 812-336-7700 *Toll Free Tel:* 800-733-6786 *Fax:* 812-336-7790
E-mail: info@solution-tree.com
Web Site: www.solution-tree.com
Key Personnel
Dist Rel: Cindy Johnson *E-mail:* cindy.johnson@solution-tree.com
Founded: 1987
Provide tested & proven resources that help those who work with youth create safe & caring schools, agencies & communities where all children succeed.
ISBN Prefix(es): 978-1-879639; 978-1-932127
Number of titles published annually: 20 Print
Total Titles: 400 Print; 2 Audio

SOM Publishing
Subsidiary of School of Metaphysics
163 Moon Valley Rd, Windyville, MO 65783
SAN: 159-5423
Tel: 417-345-8411 *Fax:* 417-345-6668
E-mail: som@som.org; dreamschool@dreamschool.org
Web Site: www.som.org; www.dreamschool.org
Key Personnel
CEO: Dr Barbara Condron
Pres: Dr Laurel Clark
Founded: 1973
Publish books in the fields of dream interpretation, Kundalini, holistic health, visualization, interfaith studies, meditation, Religious-Christian, past life recall & spiritual enlightenment.
ISBN Prefix(es): 978-0-944386
Number of titles published annually: 4 Print
Total Titles: 30 Print
Distribution Center: New Leaf Distributing Co, 401 Thornton Rd, Lithia Springs, GA 30122-1557 *Tel:* 770-948-7845 *Fax:* 770-944-2313 *E-mail:* newleaf@newleaf-dist.com *Web Site:* www.newleaf-dist.com

Somerset Hall Press
416 Commonwealth Ave, Suite 612, Boston, MA 02215
Tel: 617-236-5126
E-mail: info@somersethallpress.com
Web Site: www.somersethallpress.com
Key Personnel
Publr: Dean Papademetriou
Founded: 2003
Independent press specializing in literary & scholarly titles with a special interest in Greek studies.
ISBN Prefix(es): 978-0-9724661; 978-0-9774610; 978-1-935244
Number of titles published annually: 3 Print
Total Titles: 20 Print

Soncino Press Ltd
123 Ditmas Ave, Brooklyn, NY 11218
Tel: 718-972-6200 *Toll Free Tel:* 800-972-6201 *Fax:* 718-972-6204
E-mail: info@soncino.com
Web Site: www.soncino.com
Key Personnel
Pres: Gloria Goldman
Mng Ed: Norman Shapiro *E-mail:* nshapiro@soncino.com
Bible, Talmud & Judaism.
ISBN Prefix(es): 978-1-871055; 978-0-900689
Number of titles published annually: 20 Print
Total Titles: 75 Print

Sophia Institute Press®
522 Donald St, Unit 3, Bedford, NH 03110
Mailing Address: PO Box 5284, Manchester, NH 03108 SAN: 657-7172
Tel: 603-836-5505 *Toll Free Tel:* 800-888-9344 *Fax:* 603-641-8108 *Toll Free Fax:* 888-288-2259
E-mail: orders@sophiainstitute.com
Web Site: www.sophiainstitute.com
Key Personnel
Pres: Charlie McKinney
Prodn Mgr: Sheila M Perry *E-mail:* production@sophiainstitute.com
Founded: 1983
Books on religion (Roman Catholicism).
ISBN Prefix(es): 978-0-918477; 978-1-928832; 978-1-933184
Number of titles published annually: 15 Print
Total Titles: 150 Print
Foreign Rep(s): Family Life International (New Zealand); John XXIII Fellowship (Australia); St Joseph's Workshops (Canada); Sunrise Marion Center (Canada)

§Sopris West Educational Services
Imprint of Cambium Learning Inc
17855 Dallas Pkwy, Suite 400, Dallas, TX 75287
Tel: 303-651-2829 *Toll Free Tel:* 800-547-6747 *Fax:* 303-776-5934 *Toll Free Fax:* 888-819-7767
E-mail: customerservice@sopriswest.com
Web Site: www.sopriswest.com
Founded: 1978
Training, development materials for educators.
ISBN Prefix(es): 978-0-944584; 978-1-57035; 978-1-59318
Number of titles published annually: 100 Print
Total Titles: 350 Print

§Soul Mate Publishing
PO Box 24, Macedon, NY 14502
Tel: 585-598-4791
E-mail: submissions@soulmatepublishing.com
Web Site: www.soulmatepublishing.com
Key Personnel
Ed-in-Chief: Deborah Gilbert
Founded: 2010
ISBN Prefix(es): 978-1-61935
Number of titles published annually: 100 E-Book
Total Titles: 15 Print; 120 E-Book
Membership(s): Romance Writers of America

§Sound Feelings Publishing
18375 Ventura Blvd, No 8000, Tarzana, CA 91356
Tel: 818-757-0600
E-mail: information@soundfeelings.com
Web Site: www.soundfeelings.com
Key Personnel
Founder & Pres: Howard Richman
This publisher has indicated that 80% of their product line is author subsidized.
ISBN Prefix(es): 978-0-9615963; 978-1-882060
Number of titles published annually: 3 Print; 3 E-Book; 2 Audio
Total Titles: 15 Print; 10 E-Book; 11 Audio
Foreign Rep(s): Gazelle (Europe)

Sounds True Inc
413 S Arthur Ave, Louisville, CO 80027
Tel: 303-665-3151 *Toll Free Tel:* 800-333-9185
E-mail: customerservice@soundstrue.com
Web Site: www.soundstrue.com
Key Personnel
Founder & Publr: Tami Simon
Founded: 1985
ISBN Prefix(es): 978-1-56455; 978-1-59179; 978-1-60407; 978-1-62203
Number of titles published annually: 24 Print

§Sourcebooks Inc
1935 Brookdale Rd, Suite 139, Naperville, IL 60563
SAN: 666-7864
Mailing Address: PO Box 4410, Naperville, IL 60567-4410
Tel: 630-961-3900 *Toll Free Tel:* 800-432-7444 *Fax:* 630-961-2168
E-mail: info@sourcebooks.com; customersupport@sourcebooks.com
Web Site: www.sourcebooks.com
Key Personnel
CEO & Publr: Dominique Raccah
COO & SVP: Barbara Briel
SVP & Dir, Technol & Content Delivery: Lynn Dilger
VP & Edit Dir: Todd Stocke *Tel:* 630-536-0543 *E-mail:* todd.stocke@sourcebooks.com
Edit Dir, Sourcebooks Casablanca: Deb Werksman *Tel:* 203-876-9790 *E-mail:* deb.werksman@sourcebooks.com
Edit Dir, Sourcebooks Children's Books: Steve Geck *Tel:* 212-414-1701 ext 2226 *E-mail:* steve.geck@sourcebooks.com
Edit Dir, Sourcebooks Landmark: Shana Drehs *Tel:* 630-536-0535 *E-mail:* shana.drehs@sourcebooks.com
Art Dir, Entertainment & Gift Group: John Aardema
Busn Devt Mgr, Put Me In The Story: Lyron Bennett *Tel:* 630-536-0540 *E-mail:* lyron.bennett@sourcebooks.com
Publg Mgr, Entertainment Group: Karen Shapiro
Edit Mgr, Sourcebooks Fire: Annette Pollert *Tel:* 212-414-1701 ext 2229 *E-mail:* annette.pollert@sourcebooks.com
Ed, Jabberwocky & Fire: Aubrey Poole
Dir, Sales & Mktg: Chris Bauerle *E-mail:* chris.bauerle@sourcebooks.com
Mktg Mgr, Retail & Libr: Valerie Pierce *Tel:* 630-961-3900 ext 233 *E-mail:* valerie.pierce@sourcebooks.com
Publicity Mgr: Heather Moore *Tel:* 630-536-0553 *E-mail:* heather.moore@sourcebooks.com
Publicity & Mktg Mgr, Sourcebooks Casablanca: Morgan Doremus
Ebook Prodn Coord: Jessica Zulli
Mktg Coord: Stephanie Graham
Founded: 1987
Nonfiction, fiction, romance novels, children's books, young adult, gift books & calendars.
ISBN Prefix(es): 978-0-942061; 978-1-57071; 978-1-57248; 978-0-913825; 978-1-883518; 978-0-9629162; 978-1-887166; 978-1-4022; 978-1-4926
Number of titles published annually: 300 Print; 270 E-Book
Total Titles: 2,000 Print; 1,400 E-Book
Imprints: Cumberland House (nonfiction gift, history & cooking); Sourcebooks Casablanca (romance novels & nonfiction relationships, sex & weddings titles); Sourcebooks Fire (young adult); Sourcebooks Jabberwocky (children's books); Sourcebooks Landmark (fiction); Sourcebooks MediaFusion (multimedia books); Sphinx Publishing (self-help law, real estate & law)
Branch Office(s)
18 Cherry St, Suite 1W, Milford, CT 06460 *Tel:* 203-876-9790
Sourcebooks New York, 232 Madison Ave, Suite 805, New York, NY 10018 *Tel:* 212-414-1701
Distributed by Raincoast Books (Canada)
Distributor for Prufrock Press

Foreign Rep(s): Eliane Benisti (France); The Deborah Harris Agency (Israel); Inter-Ko (Korea); Nurcihan Kesim Literary Agency Inc (Turkey); Maxima Creative Agency (Indonesia); Piergiorgio Nicolazzini (Italy); Nova Littera Ltd (Russia); Prava I Prevodi (Eastern Block, Slovakia); Karen Schindler (Brazil); Tuttle-Mori Agency Inc (Japan, Thailand); Yanez Agencia Literaria (Spain)
Returns: RR Donnelley, 677 Brighton Beach Rd, Menasha, WI 54952
Warehouse: RR Donnelley, N9234 Lake Park Rd, Appleton, WI 54915 *Tel:* 920-969-6400 *Fax:* 920-969-6441
See separate listing for:
Cumberland House

Sourced Media Books
29 Via Regalo, San Clemente, CA 92673
Tel: 949-813-0182
E-mail: info@sourcedmediabooks.com
Web Site: sourcedmediabooks.com
Key Personnel
Publr: Amy Cook, PhD
Sr Ed: Alden Weight, PhD
Founded: 2009
ISBN Prefix(es): 978-0-9841068; 978-1-937458
Number of titles published annually: 15 Print; 15 Online; 15 E-Book
Total Titles: 30 Print; 18 Online; 18 E-Book
Distributed by Gibbs-Smith; Many Hats Media
Distribution Center: Brigham Distributing, 110 S 800 W, Brigham City, UT 84302

South Carolina Bar
Continuing Legal Education Div, 950 Taylor St, Columbia, SC 29201
Mailing Address: PO Box 608, Columbia, SC 29202-0608
Tel: 803-799-6653 *Toll Free Tel:* 800-768-7787 *Fax:* 803-799-4118
E-mail: scbar-info@scbar.org
Web Site: www.scbar.org
Key Personnel
Pubns Dir: Alicia Hutto *E-mail:* ahutto@scbar.org
Continuing Legal Educ Dir: Terry Burnett *Tel:* 803-799-6653 ext 152 *E-mail:* tburnett@scbar.org
Founded: 1979
Law materials, legal treatises, manuals & software.
ISBN Prefix(es): 978-0-943856
Number of titles published annually: 10 Print
Total Titles: 100 Print

South Dakota Historical Society Press
900 Governors Dr, Pierre, SD 57501
Tel: 605-773-6009 *Fax:* 605-773-6041
E-mail: info@sdshspress.com
Web Site: sdshspress.com
Key Personnel
Dir: Nancy Tystad Koupal *Tel:* 605-773-4371 *E-mail:* Nancy.Koupal@state.sd.us
Mktg Dir & Assoc Ed: Jennifer McIntyre *Tel:* 605-773-8161 *E-mail:* Jennifer.McIntyre@state.sd.us
Prodn Mgr & Assoc Ed: Rodger Hartley *Tel:* 605-773-8380 *E-mail:* Rodger.Hartley@state.sd.us
Assoc Ed: Jeanne Ode *Tel:* 605-773-6008 *E-mail:* Jeanne.Ode@state.sd.us; Steve Witte *Tel:* 605-773-2904 *E-mail:* Stephen.Witte@state.sd.us
Acctg Asst: Lisa Nold *E-mail:* Lisa.Nold@state.sd.us
Edit Asst: Carol Olson *E-mail:* Carol.Olson@state.sd.us
Founded: 1997
The South Dakota Historical Society Press is committed to producing books that reflect the rich & varied history of South Dakota & the region.
ISBN Prefix(es): 978-0-9622621; 978-0-9715171; 978-0-9749195; 978-0-9777955; 978-0-9798940; 978-0-9845041; 978-0-9846505; 978-0-9852905; 978-0-9860355; 978-1-941813; 978-0-9822749; 978-0-9852817
Number of titles published annually: 7 Print
Total Titles: 55 Print
Foreign Rep(s): Eurospan Group (Worldwide exc North America)

South End Press
Affiliate of Institute for Social & Cultural Change
PO Box 382132, Cambridge, MA 02238
SAN: 211-979X
Tel: 718-874-0089 *Toll Free Fax:* 800-960-0078
E-mail: southend@southendpress.org; info@southendpress.org
Web Site: www.southendpress.org
Key Personnel
Publr & Ed: Jocelyn Burrell; Asha Tall
Founded: 1977
Collectively managed nonprofit publisher of original trade paperbacks offering nonfiction analyses of politics, culture, ecology & feminism, race & sexuality from a radical perspective.
ISBN Prefix(es): 978-0-89608
Number of titles published annually: 10 Print
Total Titles: 260 Print
Foreign Rep(s): Consortium Book Sales & Distribution (Canada)
Distribution Center: Consortium Book Sales & Distribution, The Keg House, 34 13 Ave NE, Suite 101, Minneapolis, MN 55413-1007 *Tel:* 612-746-2600 *Toll Free Tel:* 800-283-3572 (cust serv) *Fax:* 612-746-2606 *E-mail:* consortium@cbsd.com *Web Site:* www.cbsd.com SAN: 200-6049

South Platte Press
PO Box 163, David City, NE 68632-0163
Tel: 402-367-3554
E-mail: railroads@windstream.net
Web Site: www.southplattepress.net
Key Personnel
Publr: James J Reisdorff
Founded: 1982
Railroad related titles.
ISBN Prefix(es): 978-0-942035
Number of titles published annually: 5 Print
Total Titles: 25 Print

Southern Historical Press Inc
375 W Broad St, Greenville, SC 29601
Mailing Address: PO Box 1267, Greenville, SC 29602-1267
Tel: 864-233-2346 *Toll Free Tel:* 800-233-0152 *Fax:* 864-233-2349
Key Personnel
Pres: LaBruce M S Lucas
Founded: 1967
Historical & genealogical.
ISBN Prefix(es): 978-0-89308
Number of titles published annually: 20 Print
Total Titles: 370 Print

Southern Illinois University Press
Division of Southern Illinois University
1915 University Press Dr, SIUC Mail Code 6806, Carbondale, IL 62901-4323
SAN: 203-3623
Tel: 618-453-2281 *Fax:* 618-453-1221
E-mail: custserv@press.uchicago.edu; rights@siu.edu
Web Site: www.siupress.com
Key Personnel
Ed-in-Chief: Karl Kageff *Tel:* 618-453-6629 *E-mail:* kageff@siu.edu
Dir: Barbara Martin *Tel:* 618-453-6614 *E-mail:* bbmartin@siu.edu
Mktg & Sales Mgr: Amy Etcheson *Tel:* 618-453-6623 *E-mail:* aetcheson@siu.edu
Publicity Mgr: Bridget Brown *Tel:* 618-453-6633 *E-mail:* bcbrown@siu.edu
Rts & Perms Mgr: Angela Moore-Swafford *Tel:* 618-453-6619 *E-mail:* angmoore@siu.edu
Founded: 1956
Scholarly nonfiction, educational material, rhetoric & composition, aviation, history, theatre, speech communication, regional history & poetry.
ISBN Prefix(es): 978-0-8093
Number of titles published annually: 40 Print; 40 E-Book
Total Titles: 1,400 Print; 2 CD-ROM; 400 E-Book; 17 Audio
Foreign Rep(s): East West Export Books (Royden Muranaka) (Asia, Australia, Pacific Rim); Eurospan (Andrew Wong) (Europe, Middle East); Scholarly Book Services Inc (Laura Rust) (Canada)
Distribution Center: Chicago Distribution Center, 11030 S Langley Ave, Chicago, IL 60628-3830 *Toll Free Tel:* 800-621-2736 *Toll Free Fax:* 800-621-8476
Membership(s): Association of American University Presses

South-Western, see Wadsworth Publishing

Soyinfo Center
PO Box 234, Lafayette, CA 94549-0234
SAN: 212-8411
Tel: 925-283-2991
E-mail: info@soyinfocenter.com
Web Site: www.soyinfocenter.com
Key Personnel
Pres & Ed-in-Chief: William Shurtleff
Founded: 1976
Books & bibliographies on all aspects of soybeans & soyfoods; industry & marketing studies. All books since 2008 published in PDF format on the web free of charge.
ISBN Prefix(es): 978-0-933332; 978-1-928914
Number of titles published annually: 3 Print; 10 Online
Total Titles: 62 Print; 60 Online
Shipping Address: 1021 Dolores Dr, Lafayette, CA 94549

Specialty Press Inc
300 NW 70 Ave, Suite 102, Plantation, FL 33317
SAN: 251-6977
Tel: 954-792-8100 *Toll Free Tel:* 800-233-9273 *Fax:* 954-792-8545
E-mail: websales@addwarehouse.com
Web Site: addwarehouse.com
Key Personnel
CEO & Intl Rts: Harvey Parker *E-mail:* hparker@addwarehouse.com
Founded: 1990
Selections related to children with special needs.
ISBN Prefix(es): 978-0-9621629; 978-1-886941; 978-1-937761
Number of titles published annually: 3 Print
Total Titles: 40 Print; 4 E-Book
Distributed by Boys Town Press; Child Play; MHS
Distributor for Bantam; Guilford Press; Plenum; Simon & Schuster; Slossen; Woodbine House

§SPIE
1000 20 St, Bellingham, WA 98225-6705
Mailing Address: PO Box 10, Bellingham, WA 98227-0010
Tel: 360-676-3290 *Toll Free Tel:* 888-504-8171 *Fax:* 360-647-1445
E-mail: spie@spie.org
Web Site: www.spie.org
Key Personnel
Pres: Bill Arnold
Dir, Pubns & Intl Rts Contact: Eric Pepper
Founded: 1955

Scientific, technical books & journals, proceedings of symposia.
ISBN Prefix(es): 978-0-8194
Number of titles published annually: 380 Print; 30 CD-ROM
Total Titles: 7,075 Print; 450 CD-ROM
Imprints: SPIE Press

Spinsters Ink
Division of Spinsters Ink Publishing Co
PO Box 242, Midway, FL 32343
E-mail: info@spinstersink.com; editorialdirector@spinstersink.com
Web Site: www.spinstersink.com
Key Personnel
Publr: Linda Hill *E-mail:* linda@spinstersink.com
Founded: 1978
Novels & nonfiction by women about women, including social justice.
ISBN Prefix(es): 978-1-935226; 978-1-883523
Number of titles published annually: 8 Print; 12 E-Book
Total Titles: 100 Print; 24 E-Book
Imprints: Grave Issues
Sales Office(s): Bella Distribution, PO Box 10543, Tallahassee, FL 32302, Linda Hill *Toll Free Tel:* 800-729-4992
Foreign Rep(s): Airlift Book Co (Europe); Bulldog Distribution (Australia)
Distribution Center: Bella Distribution, PO Box 10543, Tallahassee, FL 32302 *Toll Free Tel:* 800-729-4992

Spizzirri Publishing Inc
PO Box 9397, Rapid City, SD 57709-9397
Tel: 605-348-2749 *Toll Free Tel:* 800-325-9819 *Fax:* 605-348-6251 *Toll Free Fax:* 800-322-9819
E-mail: spizzpub@aol.com
Web Site: www.spizzirri.com
Key Personnel
Pres: Linda Spizzirri
Founded: 1978
Educational coloring books, book-cassette packages, activity books, work books & how-to-draw books. PreK-5th grade featuring realistic illustrations & museum curator approved texts on topics, including everything from dinosaurs to space.
ISBN Prefix(es): 978-0-86545
Number of titles published annually: 3 Print
Total Titles: 200 Print

§Springer
Subsidiary of Springer Science+Business Media
233 Spring St, New York, NY 10013-1578
Tel: 212-460-1500 *Toll Free Tel:* 800-SPRINGER (777-4643) *Fax:* 212-460-1575
E-mail: service-ny@springer.com
Web Site: www.springer.com
Key Personnel
Pres, Springer Science+Business Media LLC & EVP, Medicine, Biomedicine & Life Sci, Springer: William F Curtis, PhD
Pres, STM Sales, Global Academic & Govt, Springer: Syed Hasan
Pres, Apress & EVP, Computer Sci: Paul Manning
CFO, Springer Americas: Christian Staral
CFO, Springer US: Ned Woods
VP, Cust Serv & Fulfillment-Secaucus: Richard Sabol
VP, HR: Eileen Purelis
VP, Prodn: Henry Krell
Dir, Edit Opers-Clinical Medicine: Lori Holland
Edit Dir, Biomed & Life Sci: Carolyn Honour
Edit Dir, Busn Law, Statistics: Nicholas Phillipson
Edit Dir, Clinical Medicine: Antoinette Cimino; Richard Lansing
Edit Dir, Computer Sci: Jennifer Evans
Edit Dir, Engg: Alexander Greene
Edit Dir, Human Sci: Dieter Merkle
Edit Dir, Mathematics: Mark Strauss
Edit Dir, Physics: Harry Blom
Dir, Lib Mktg & Acct Devt: Jason Marcakis
Founded: 1842 (1964 NY office)
Scientific, medical, technical, research, reference books & periodicals.
ISBN Prefix(es): 978-0-387
Number of titles published annually: 6,500 Print; 6,000 E-Book
Total Titles: 70,000 Print; 36,000 Online; 38,000 E-Book
Imprints: Apress; BioMed Central; Birkhauser Science; Copernicus; Current Medicine Group; Humana Press; Springer; Springer Healthcare
Foreign Office(s): Heidelberger Platz 3, 14197 Berlin, Germany
Tiergartenstr 17, 69121 Heidelberg, Germany
Van Godewijckstr 30, 3311 GX Dordrecht, Netherlands
Membership(s): International Association of Scientific, Technical & Medical Publishers

§Springer Publishing Co
11 W 42 St, 15th fl, New York, NY 10036-8002
SAN: 203-2236
Tel: 212-431-4370 *Toll Free Tel:* 877-687-7476 *Fax:* 212-941-7842
E-mail: marketing@springerpub.com; cs@springerpub.com (orders); editorial@springerpub.com
Web Site: www.springerpub.com
Key Personnel
CEO & Pres: Theodore C Nardin *E-mail:* tnardin@springerpub.com
VP, Sales & Mktg: Jason Roth *E-mail:* jroth@springerpub.com
Edit Dir: Nancy Hale *E-mail:* nhale@springerpub.com
Dir, Journal Pubns: James C Costello *E-mail:* jcostello@springerpub.com
Dir, Spec Sales & Rts: Annette Imperati *E-mail:* aimperati@springerpub.com
Sr Sales Dir: Matt Conmy *E-mail:* mconmy@springerpub.com
Nursing Publr: Margaret Zuccarini *E-mail:* mzuccarini@springerpub.com
Exec Ed: Sheri W Sussman *E-mail:* swsussman@springerpub.com
Exec Ed, Nursing: Elizabeth Nieginski *E-mail:* enieginski@springerpub.com
Sr Acqs Ed: Joseph Morita *E-mail:* jmorita@springerpub.com
Acqs Ed: Stephanie Drew *E-mail:* sdrew@springerpub.com
Founded: 1950 (Feb 2004, acquired by Mannheim Holdings, LLC, subsidiary of Mannheim Trust)
Professional books, encyclopedias, college textbooks & journals; nursing, psychology, gerontology/geriatrics, medical education, public health, rehabilitation, social work & scholarly health sciences.
ISBN Prefix(es): 978-0-8261
Number of titles published annually: 100 Print
Total Titles: 700 Print
Divisions: Demos Medical Publishing
Foreign Rep(s): Cranbury International LLC (Argentina, Brazil, Chile, Colombia, Costa Rica, Ecuador, El Salvador, Guatemala, Guyana, Jamaica, Mexico, Panama, Paraguay, Peru, Puerto Rico, Trinidad and Tobago, Venezuela, Virgin Islands); Elsevier-Australia (Australia, New Zealand); The Eurospan Group (Europe, Middle East); Login Brothers Canada (Canada); Taylor & Francis Asia Pacific (China, Hong Kong, Indonesia, Korea, Malaysia, Singapore, Taiwan, Thailand, Vietnam); Taylor & Francis Books India Pvt Ltd (Bangladesh, India, Pakistan, Sri Lanka)
Shipping Address: Ingram Publishers Services, One Ingram Blvd, La Vergne, TN 37006 *Tel:* 978-345-2121 *Toll Free Tel:* 877-687-7476 *Fax:* 978-348-1233 *Web Site:* www.ingrampublisherservices.com
Warehouse: Ingram Publishers Services, One Ingram Blvd, La Vergne, TN 37006 *Tel:* 978-345-2121 *Toll Free Tel:* 877-687-7476 *Fax:* 978-348-1233 *Web Site:* www.ingrampublisherservices.com
Membership(s): AAP; American Medical Publishers Association; STM
See separate listing for:
Demos Medical Publishing

Spry Publishing
2500 S State St, Ann Arbor, MI 48104
Tel: 734-913-1700 *Toll Free Tel:* 877-722-2264 *Fax:* 734-913-1249
E-mail: info@sprypub.com
Web Site: www.sprypub.com
Key Personnel
Assoc Publr: Lynne Johnson *E-mail:* ljohnson@aaeditions.com
Dir, Busn Devt: Jeremy Sterling
Mktg & Publicity Mgr: Sally Feller
Founded: 1999
ISBN Prefix(es): 978-1-58726
Number of titles published annually: 20 Print
Total Titles: 120 Print
Imprints: Mitten Press
Membership(s): Great Lakes Independent Booksellers Association; The Independent Book Publishers Association; Midatlantic Book Publishers Association

Square One Publishers Inc
115 Herricks Rd, Garden City Park, NY 11040
Tel: 516-535-2010 *Toll Free Tel:* 877-900-BOOK (900-2665) *Fax:* 516-535-2014
E-mail: sq1publish@aol.com
Web Site: www.squareonepublishers.com
Key Personnel
Pres & Publr: Rudy Shur
Art Dir: Jeannie Tudor
Dir, Publicity & Mktg: Anthony Pomes
Sales Dir: Ken Kaiman
Mgr, Opers: Robert Love
Exec Ed: Joanne Abrams
Sr Ed: Marie Caratozzolo
Founded: 2000
Specialize in adult nonfiction books. Topics covered include collectibles, cooking, general interest, history, how-to, parenting, self-help & health.
ISBN Prefix(es): 978-0-7570
Number of titles published annually: 25 Print
Total Titles: 500 Print; 1 Audio
Distributed by Thomas Allen & Son
Distributor for InnoVision Health Media; Rainbow Ridge Books
Foreign Rep(s): Thomas Allen & Son (Canada); Brumby Books (Australia, New Zealand); G D Daby (Southeast Asia); Deep Books (Europe, UK); Trinity Books (South Africa)
Membership(s): ABA; ALA; The Association of Publishers for Special Sales; The Independent Book Publishers Association

§SRA/McGraw-Hill
Division of McGraw-Hill School Education Group
8787 Orion Place, Columbus, OH 43240
Tel: 614-430-4000 *Fax:* 614-430-4303
E-mail: sra@mcgraw-hill.com
Web Site: www.sraonline.com
Key Personnel
SVP & Natl Sales Mgr: Sean Ryan
SVP, Fin & Opers: Bill Hess
Founded: 1938
Supplemental & curriculum materials for kindergarten through high school & direct instruction programs. Online instruction & assessment.
ISBN Prefix(es): 978-0-307; 978-0-8126; 978-0-383

Number of titles published annually: 2,000 Print; 100 CD-ROM; 100 Online; 200 Audio
Total Titles: 18,000 Print; 500 CD-ROM; 500 Online; 10,000 Audio
Membership(s): AAP; AAP PreK-12 Learning Group; International Literacy Association; National Council of Supervisors of Mathematics; National Council of Teachers of Mathematics; National Science Teachers Association

SSPC: The Society for Protective Coatings
40 24 St, 6th fl, Pittsburgh, PA 15222-4656
Tel: 412-281-2331 *Toll Free Tel:* 877-281-7772 (US only) *Fax:* 412-281-9992
E-mail: info@sspc.org
Web Site: www.sspc.org
Key Personnel
Exec Dir: William Shoup *Tel:* 412-281-2331 ext 2230 *E-mail:* shoup@sspc.org
Pubns Fulfillment Coord: Jeannine Bodack *Tel:* 412-281-2331 ext 2204 *E-mail:* bodack@sspc.org
Mktg Specialist: Michael Kline *Tel:* 412-281-2331 ext 2207 *E-mail:* kline@sspc.org
Founded: 1950
Technical publications; CD-ROMs, standards for industry.
ISBN Prefix(es): 978-0-938477; 978-1-889060
Number of titles published annually: 12 Print
Total Titles: 80 Print
Distributed by Technology Publishing Co

§ST Media Group Book Division
Division of ST Media Group Intl
11262 Cornell Park Dr, Cincinnati, OH 45242
SAN: 204-5974
Tel: 513-421-2050 *Toll Free Tel:* 866-265-0954 *Fax:* 513-421-5144
E-mail: books@stmediagroup.com
Web Site: www.stmediagroup.com
Key Personnel
Dir: Mark Kissling *Tel:* 800-925-1110 ext 399 *E-mail:* mark.kissling@stmediagroup.com
Founded: 1906
Books, magazines, buyers' guides: sign, screen printing, visual merchandising & store design industries, large format digital printing & package design.
ISBN Prefix(es): 978-0-911380; 978-0-944094
Number of titles published annually: 3 Print
Total Titles: 44 Print

§Stackpole Books
5067 Ritter Rd, Mechanicsburg, PA 17055
SAN: 202-5396
Tel: 717-796-0411 *Toll Free Tel:* 800-732-3669 *Fax:* 717-796-0412
Web Site: www.stackpolebooks.com
Key Personnel
Publr & Acting CEO: Judith Schnell *E-mail:* jschnell@stackpolebooks.com
VP & Dir, Creative Servs & Prodn: Tracy Patterson
Fulfillment Mgr & Warehouse Supv: Anne Lodge
Ed & Rts: Mark Allison *Tel:* 717-796-0411 ext 153
Ed: Kyle Weaver
Founded: 1933
Trade book publisher with a proud, 80 plus year history of publishing titles in the categories of outdoor sports, nature, crafts, history, military reference & regional. Strong in fly fishing, nature guides, military history & military reference, we publish deep in our niche areas. Presently expanding into the fast-growing world of ebooks while continuing to produce alternative, high-quality hardcovers, trade paperbacks & ebooks.
ISBN Prefix(es): 978-0-8117
Number of titles published annually: 100 Print; 5 CD-ROM
Total Titles: 2,000 Print; 5 CD-ROM
Distributor for The Army War College Foundation Press; Headwater Books; Historical Society of Western Pennsylvania; Quiller Press Ltd; Ryton Publications; The Sausage Maker; Stackpole Magazines; Swan Hill
Foreign Rights: Bardon Chinese Media Agency (Phillip Chen) (China); Alex Korzheneuski (Russia); Hana Whitton (Eastern Europe)

Standard International Media Holdings
568 Ninth St S, Suite 201, Naples, FL 34102-7336
Tel: 239-248-5550 *Fax:* 239-649-5832 *Toll Free Fax:* 866-948-7883
E-mail: sales@standardinternationalmedia.com
Web Site: www.standardinternationalmedia.com
Key Personnel
CFO: Connie Miller *E-mail:* connie@standardinternationalmedia.com
Pres: Simon Bailey *Tel:* 844-502-6657 *E-mail:* simon@standardinternationalmedia.com
Intl Sales Dir: Elaine Evans *Tel:* 844-502-6657 *E-mail:* elaine@standardinternationalmedia.com
Founded: 1994
Book publisher & distributor.
ISBN Prefix(es): 978-1-888777; 978-1-58279; 978-1-86091
Number of titles published annually: 7 Print
Total Titles: 200 Print
Imprints: Chef Express; Chef Success; Trident Reference

Standard Publications Inc
PO Box 2226, Champaign, IL 61825-2226
SAN: 912-9251
Tel: 217-898-7825 *Fax:* 630-214-0564
E-mail: spi@standardpublications.com
Web Site: standardpublications.com
Founded: 2001
ISBN Prefix(es): 978-0-9709788; 978-0-9722691; 978-1-59462; 978-1-60424; 978-1-60597; 978-1-4385; 978-1-61742
Number of titles published annually: 3 Print
Total Titles: 10,000 Print

Standard Publishing
8805 Governors Hill Dr, Suite 400, Cincinnati, OH 45249
SAN: 110-5515
Tel: 513-931-4050 *Toll Free Tel:* 800-543-1353 *Fax:* 513-931-0950 *Toll Free Fax:* 877-867-5751
E-mail: customerservice@standardpub.com
Web Site: www.standardpub.com
Key Personnel
VP, Prod Devt: Matt Lockhart
Dir, Adult & Teen: Lindsay Black
Dir, Sales: Ken Lorenz
Mng Ed: James Nieman
Sr Ed: Jon Underwood
Ed: Shawn McMullen; Ron Nickelson; Margie Redford; Margaret K Williams
Ed, Children's: Karen Cain
Ed, Christian Standard: Mark Taylor
Asst Ed, The Lookout: Sheryl Overstreet
Magazine Prodn Coord, Christian Standard: Diane Jones
Rts Coord: Joann VanMeter
Sr Designer: Andrew Quach; Sandy Wimmer
Book Designer: Steve Clark
Graphic Designer: Bob Korth
Graphic Designer & Prodn Technician: Dale Meyers
Founded: 1866
Religious children's books, Sunday school literature & supplies, helps for Sunday school teachers, youth & adult trade books.
ISBN Prefix(es): 978-0-87239; 978-0-87403; 978-0-7847
Number of titles published annually: 75 Print
Total Titles: 700 Print; 30 CD-ROM
Imprints: Happy Day Books
Foreign Rights: Foundation Distributing Inc (Canada); Omega (New Zealand); Salvation Book Centre (Malaysia); Scripture Press Foundation Ltd (UK)

§Standard Publishing Corp
155 Federal St, 13th fl, Boston, MA 02110
Tel: 617-457-0600 *Toll Free Tel:* 800-682-5759 *Fax:* 617-457-0608
Web Site: www.spcpub.com
Key Personnel
Pres & Publr: John C Cross, Esq
Edit Dir: Katherine Allnutt Panikian, Esq
Ad Sales Mgr: Barbara Crockett
Circ Mgr & Cust Serv: Kelly Cotter
Classified Ad Mgr & Prodn Mgr: Nakeesha Warner
Mktg Mgr: Susanne Edes Dillman *Tel:* 617-457-0600 ext 229 *E-mail:* s.dillman@spcpub.com
Founded: 1865
Information for insurance professionals.
ISBN Prefix(es): 978-0-923240
Number of titles published annually: 10 Print
Total Titles: 10 Print; 3 CD-ROM
Subsidiaries: John Liner Organization
Branch Office(s)
Insurance Record, 9601 White Rock Trail, Suite 213, Dallas, TX 75238
Distributed by LexisNexis®; Silverplume, a Vertafore Co

Stanford University Press
1450 Page Mill Rd, Palo Alto, CA 94304-1124
SAN: 203-3526
Tel: 650-723-9434 *Fax:* 650-725-3457
E-mail: info@sup.org
Web Site: www.sup.org
Key Personnel
Publr: Michael Keller
Publg Dir & Ed-in-Chief: Kate Wahl *E-mail:* kwahl@stanford.edu
Dir: Dr Alan Harvey *E-mail:* aharvey@stanford.edu
Dir, Edit, Design & Prodn: Patricia Myers *E-mail:* pmyers@stanford.edu
Dir, Fin & Opers: Jean H Kim *E-mail:* plcmnkim@stanford.edu
Dir, Sales & Mktg: David B Jackson *E-mail:* david.jackson@stanford.edu
Art Dir: Robert Ehle *E-mail:* ehle@stanford.edu
Exec Ed: Dr Geoffrey R H Burn *E-mail:* grhburn@stanford.edu
Sr Ed, Busn Economics & Organizational Studies: Margo Beth Fleming *E-mail:* mbfleming@stanford.edu
Sr Ed, History, Jewish & Asian Studies: Stacy Wagner *E-mail:* swagner@stanford.edu
Sr Ed, Literature, Philosophy & Religion: Dr Emily-Jane Cohen
Acqs Ed, Anthropology, Asian Studies & Law: Michelle Lipinski *E-mail:* mlipinski@stanford.edu
Contracts & Rts Mgr: Ariane de Pree-Kajfez
Prodn Mgr: Harold Moorehead *E-mail:* hmoorehead@stanford.edu
Exhibits Mgr: Christie Cochrell *E-mail:* cochrell@stanford.edu
Founded: 1925
ISBN Prefix(es): 978-0-8047
Number of titles published annually: 150 Print; 40 E-Book
Total Titles: 2,500 Print; 400 E-Book
Imprints: Redwood Press; Stanford Business Books; Stanford General Books; Stanford Law Books; Stanford Security Studies; Stanford University Press
Foreign Rep(s): East-West Export Books (Asia, Australia, Hawaii, New Zealand, The Pacific); Eurospan Group (Africa, Central Asia, Europe, Middle East, UK)
Returns: Chicago Distribution Center, 11030 S Langley Ave, Chicago, IL 60628 *Tel:* 773-568-1550 *Toll Free Tel:* 800-621-2736 *Fax:* 773-

660-2235 *Toll Free Fax:* 800-621-8471
E-mail: custserv@press.uchicago.edu
Warehouse: Chicago Distribution Center, 11030 S Langley Ave, Chicago, IL 60628 *Tel:* 773-568-1550 *Toll Free Tel:* 800-621-2736 *Fax:* 773-660-2235 *Toll Free Fax:* 800-621-8471
E-mail: custserv@press.uchicago.edu
Distribution Center: Chicago Distribution Center, 11030 S Langley Ave, Chicago, IL 60628 *Tel:* 773-568-1550 *Toll Free Tel:* 800-621-2736 *Fax:* 773-660-2235 *Toll Free Fax:* 800-621-8471 *E-mail:* custserv@press.uchicago.edu
Membership(s): AAP; Association of American University Presses

Star Bright Books Inc
13 Landsdowne St, Cambridge, MA 02139
Tel: 617-354-1300 *Fax:* 617-354-1399
E-mail: info@starbrightbooks.com; orders@starbrightbooks.com
Web Site: www.starbrightbooks.com
Key Personnel
Publr: Deborah Shine
Founded: 1995
Independent children's book publisher.
ISBN Prefix(es): 978-1-887734; 978-1-932065; 978-1-59572
Number of titles published annually: 16 Print
Total Titles: 400 Print
Membership(s): ABA; ALA; The Independent Book Publishers Association

Star Publishing Co Inc
650 El Camino Real, Redwood City, CA 94063
SAN: 212-6958
Tel: 650-591-3505 *Fax:* 650-591-3898
E-mail: mail@starpublishing.com
Web Site: www.starpublishing.com
Key Personnel
Publr: Stuart A Hoffman *E-mail:* stuart@starpublishing.com
Founded: 1978
College/university textbooks, laboratory manuals; reference books; professional books; California history/local history.
ISBN Prefix(es): 978-0-89863
Number of titles published annually: 14 Print
Total Titles: 205 Print
Imprints: Encore Editions

STARbooks Press
Affiliate of Florida Literary Foundation (FLF)
PO Box 711612, Herndon, VA 20171
E-mail: contact@starbookspress.com
Web Site: www.starbookspress.com
Key Personnel
Sr Edit Dir: Eric Summers
Founded: 1980
ISBN Prefix(es): 978-1-877978; 978-1-891855
Number of titles published annually: 8 Print
Total Titles: 30 Print; 1 Audio
Imprints: Florida Literary Foundation (FLF) Press; Starbooks

§Starcrafts LLC
334-A Calef Hwy, Epping, NH 03042
SAN: 208-5380
Tel: 603-734-4300 *Toll Free Tel:* 866-953-8458 (24/7 message ctr) *Fax:* 603-734-4311
E-mail: astrosales@astrocom.com; starcrafts@comcast.net
Web Site: www.astrocom.com; starcraftspublishing.com; acspublications.com
Key Personnel
Owner & Publr: Maria K Simms *E-mail:* maria@starcraftpublishing.com
Cust Serv: Thomas Canfield *E-mail:* tom@starcraftpublishing.com
Founded: 1973
Astrology: ephemerides, chart interpretation.
ISBN Prefix(es): 978-0-935127; 978-0-917086; 978-0-9762422; 978-1-934976
Number of titles published annually: 8 Print; 1 CD-ROM
Total Titles: 60 Print; 5 CD-ROM; 1 Audio
Imprints: ACS Publications; Starcrafts LLC
Foreign Rep(s): The Rights Agency (Canada)
Distribution Center: New Leaf Distributing Co, 401 Thornton Rd, Lithia Springs, GA 30122-1557 *Tel:* 770-948-7845 *Fax:* 770-944-2313 *E-mail:* newleaf@newleaf-dist.com *Web Site:* www.newleaf-dist.com

Stargazer Publishing Co
958 Stanislaus Dr, Corona, CA 92881
Mailing Address: PO Box 77002, Corona, CA 92877-0100
Tel: 951-898-4619 *Toll Free Tel:* 800-606-7895 (orders) *Fax:* 951-898-4633
E-mail: stargazer@stargazerpub.com; orders@stargazerpub.com
Web Site: www.stargazerpub.com
Founded: 1995
ISBN Prefix(es): 978-0-9643853; 978-1-933277; 978-0-9713756
Number of titles published annually: 10 Print; 5 CD-ROM; 5 E-Book
Total Titles: 40 Print; 5 CD-ROM; 5 E-Book
Warehouse: Publishers Storage & Shipping Corp, 660 S Mansfield, Ypsilanti, MI 48197
Membership(s): The Independent Book Publishers Association; National Association of College Stores; Publishers Association of Los Angeles

StarGroup International Inc
1194 Old Dixie Hwy, Suite 201, West Palm Beach, FL 33413
Tel: 561-547-0667 *Fax:* 561-843-8530
E-mail: info@stargroupinternational.com
Web Site: www.stargroupinternational.com
Key Personnel
CEO & Pres: Brenda Star *E-mail:* brenda@stargroupinternational.com
Creative Dir: Mel Abfier
Head Writer & Film/Video Prodr: Shawn McAllister
Internet Mktg Coord: Butch Butler
Mktg, Media & Website Devt: Rusty Durham
Media Specialist: Sam Smyth
Founded: 1983
Create books to be used as marketing & media tools. For over two decades have maintained access to the best researchers, writers, editors, proofreaders, designers & printers in the industry, while offering public relations & marketing services. Specialize in creating books for clients to enhance their credibility & position them as experts in their field.
This publisher has indicated that 75% of their product line is author subsidized.
ISBN Prefix(es): 978-1-884886
Number of titles published annually: 25 Print
Total Titles: 150 Print
Membership(s): Florida Authors & Publishers Association Inc; The Independent Book Publishers Association

State University of New York Press
22 Corporate Woods Blvd, 3rd fl, Albany, NY 12211-2504
SAN: 760-7261
Tel: 518-472-5000 *Toll Free Tel:* 877-204-6073 (orders) *Fax:* 518-472-5038 *Toll Free Fax:* 877-204-6074 (orders)
E-mail: suny@presswarehouse.com (orders); info@sunypress.edu (edit off)
Web Site: www.sunypress.edu
Key Personnel
Co-Dir: Donna Dixon *Tel:* 518-641-0651 *E-mail:* donna.dixon@sunypress.edu; James Peltz *Tel:* 518-641-0668 *E-mail:* james.peltz@sunypress.edu
Assoc Dir & Dir, Sales & Busn Devt: Daniel Flynn *Tel:* 518-641-0676 *E-mail:* daniel.flynn@sunypress.edu
Dir, Mktg & Publicity: Fran Keneston *Tel:* 518-641-0660 *E-mail:* fran.keneston@sunypress.edu
Rts & Perms: Sharla Clute *Tel:* 518-641-0653 *E-mail:* sharla.clute@sunypress.edu
Founded: 1966
Scholarly nonfiction, especially works in philosophy, psychology, African American studies, gender/sexuality studies, American Indian studies, museum/archival science, Asian studies & religious studies.
ISBN Prefix(es): 978-0-87395; 978-0-88706; 978-0-7914; 978-1-4384
Number of titles published annually: 150 Print; 140 Online; 140 E-Book; 2 Audio
Total Titles: 5,525 Print; 3,500 Online; 3,500 E-Book; 2 Audio
Imprints: Excelsior Editions
Distributor for Albany Institute of History & Art; Codhill Press; Samuel Dorsky Museum of Art; Mount Ida Press; Muswell Hill Press; New Netherland Institute; Rockefeller Institute Press; Uncrowned Queens
Foreign Rep(s): Apac Publishers Services Pte Ltd (China, Hong Kong, Indonesia, Malaysia, Singapore, Taiwan, Thailand, Vietnam); Eleanor Brasch Enterprises (Australia, New Zealand); Cassidy & Associates Inc (China, Hong Kong, Taiwan); Lexa Publishers' Representatives (Canada); Mediamatics (India); United Publishers Services Ltd (Japan); University Presses Marketing (Continental Europe, Ireland, Israel, UK); US PubRep (Caribbean, Central America, Mexico, Puerto Rico, South America)
Billing Address: PO Box 960, Herndon, VA 20172-0960, Cust Serv *Tel:* 703-661-1575 *Fax:* 703-996-1010
Orders to: PO Box 960, Herndon, VA 20172-0960, Cust Serv *Tel:* 703-661-1575 *Fax:* 703-996-1010
Returns: 22883 Quicksilver Dr, Dulles, VA 20166, Cust Serv *Tel:* 703-661-1575 *Fax:* 703-996-1010
Shipping Address: 22835 Quicksilver Dr, Dulles, VA 20166 *Tel:* 703-661-1575 *Fax:* 703-996-1010
Warehouse: PO Box 960, Herndon, VA 20172-0960, Cust Serv *Tel:* 703-661-1575 *Fax:* 703-996-1010
Distribution Center: NBN International, Estover Rd, Plymouth PL6 7PY, United Kingdom *Tel:* (01752) 202-301 *Fax:* (01752) 202-233 *E-mail:* orders@nbninternational.com
Membership(s): ABA; Association of American University Presses
See separate listing for:
Excelsior Editions

Steerforth Press
45 Lyme Rd, Suite 208, Hanover, NH 03755-1222
Tel: 603-643-4787 *Fax:* 603-643-4788
E-mail: info@steerforth.com
Web Site: www.steerforth.com
Key Personnel
Publr: Chip Fleischer *E-mail:* chip@steerforth.com
Sr Ed: Alan Lelchuk; Michael Moore; Thomas Powers
Fiction Ed: Roland Pease *E-mail:* roland@steerforth.com
Publg Opers & Foreign Rts: Helga Schmidt *E-mail:* helga@steerforth.com
Founded: 1993
ISBN Prefix(es): 978-1-883642; 978-0-944072; 978-1-58195; 978-1-58642
Number of titles published annually: 18 Print
Total Titles: 250 Print
Imprints: Zoland Books
Foreign Rights: Agence Bookman (Scandinavia); Big Apple Agency Inc (Taiwan); The English

Agency (Japan); Anouk H Foerg; Harris-Elon Agency (Israel); International Editors' Co SA (Argentina, Brazil, Latin America, Portugal, Spain); Katai & Bolza (Hungary); David Marshall; Daniela Micura Literary Services (Italy); Onk Agency (Turkey)
Distribution Center: Random House Distribution Center, 400 Hahn Rd, Westminster, MD 21157 *Toll Free Tel:* 800-733-3000 *Toll Free Fax:* 800-659-2436
Membership(s): ABA; The Independent Book Publishers Association; New England Independent Booksellers Association

§SteinerBooks
610 Main St, Great Barrington, MA 01230
Tel: 413-528-8233 *Fax:* 413-528-8826
E-mail: friends@steinerbooks.org
Web Site: www.steinerbooks.org
Key Personnel
CEO & Pres: Gene Gollogly *Tel:* 212-414-2275 ext 11 *Fax:* 212-414-2412 *E-mail:* gene@steinerbooks.org
Edit & Art Dir: Mary Giddens
Ed-in-Chief: Christopher Bamford
Founded: 1928
American & English editions of works by Rudolf Steiner & related authors.
ISBN Prefix(es): 978-0-910142; 978-0-88010
Number of titles published annually: 29 Print
Total Titles: 451 Print
Imprints: Bell Pond Books; Lindisfarne Books
Distributed by Rudolf Steiner Press UK
Distributor for Chiron Publications; Clairview Books; Floris Books; Hawthorn Press; Lantern Books; Rudolph Steiner Press; Temple Lodge Publishing
Foreign Rep(s): Ceres (New Zealand); Peter Hyde & Associates (South Africa); Rudolf Steiner Press (UK)
Orders to: PO Box 960, Herndon, VA 20172-0960 *Tel:* 703-661-1594 *Fax:* 703-661-1501 *E-mail:* service@steinerbooks.org SAN: 201-1824
See separate listing for:
Lindisfarne Books

Stellar Publishing
2114 S Live Oak Pkwy, Wilmington, NC 28403
SAN: 860-2298
Tel: 910-269-7444
Web Site: www.stellar-publishing.com
Key Personnel
Publr: Winifred Jones *E-mail:* publisher@stellar-publishing.com
Founded: 2000
This publisher has indicated that 50% of their product line is author subsidized.
ISBN Prefix(es): 978-0-970341
Number of titles published annually: 3 Print
Total Titles: 9 Print

Stemmer House Publishers Inc
Division of Pathway Book Service
4 White Brook Rd, Gilsum, NH 03448
SAN: 207-9623
Mailing Address: PO Box 89, Gilsum, NH 03448
Tel: 603-357-0236 *Toll Free Tel:* 800-345-6665 *Fax:* 603-357-2073
E-mail: pbs@pathwaybook.com
Web Site: www.stemmer.com
Key Personnel
Pres & Publr: Judith Peter
Founded: 1975
Books in the arts & crafts, audiocassettes, illustrated books, multicultural studies & children's books on the environment.
ISBN Prefix(es): 978-0-916144; 978-0-88045
Number of titles published annually: 10 Print
Total Titles: 150 Print; 5 Audio
Imprints: Great Architectural Replica Series; International Design Library®; NaturEncyclopedia Series
Foreign Rep(s): Gazelle Ltd (Europe, UK); John Reed Books (Australia, New Zealand)
Returns: Pathway Book Service, 4 White Brook Rd, Gilsum, NH 03448
Shipping Address: Pathway Book Service, 4 White Brook Rd, Gilsum, NH 03448
Warehouse: Pathway Book Service, 4 White Brook Rd, Gilsum, NH 03448
Distribution Center: Pathway Book Service, 4 White Brook Rd, Gilsum, NH 03448

§Stenhouse Publishers
Division of Highlights for Children Education Group
480 Congress St, Portland, ME 04101-3451
Tel: 207-253-1600 *Toll Free Tel:* 888-363-0566 *Fax:* 207-253-5121 *Toll Free Fax:* 800-833-9164
E-mail: customerservice@stenhouse.com
Web Site: www.stenhouse.com
Key Personnel
Mng Ed: William Varner *E-mail:* wvarner@stenhouse.com
Founded: 1993
Professional books for teachers.
ISBN Prefix(es): 978-1-57110
Number of titles published annually: 20 Print; 3 Online; 15 E-Book
Total Titles: 350 Print; 250 E-Book; 3 Audio
Distributor for Pembroke Publishers
Foreign Rep(s): Curriculum Corp (Australia, New Zealand); EUROSPAN (Africa, Central America, China, Europe, Hong Kong, India, Japan, Korea, South America, Taiwan, UK); Pembroke Publishers (Canada); Publishers Marketing Services (Southeast Asia)
Billing Address: PO Box 11020, Portland, ME 04104-7020, Opers Mgr: Elaine Cyr *E-mail:* ecyr@stenhouse.com
Warehouse: 4200 Parkway Ct, Hilliard, OH 43026, Contact: Vicki Woolwhine *Tel:* 614-487-2883 *Fax:* 614-529-0670

Stephens Press™
Subsidiary of Stephens Media LLC
1111 W Bonanza Rd, Las Vegas, NV 89106
Mailing Address: PO Box 70, Las Vegas, NV 89125-0070
Tel: 702-387-5260 *Toll Free Tel:* 888-951-2665 *Fax:* 702-387-2997
E-mail: info@stephenspress.com
Web Site: www.stephenspress.com
Key Personnel
Pres: Carolyn Hayes Uber *Tel:* 702-383-0486 *E-mail:* cuber@stephenspress.com
Publg Coord: Stacey Stonum Fott *E-mail:* sfott@stephenspress.com
Bookkeeper: Serena Smith *Tel:* 702-383-0253 *E-mail:* ssmith@stephenspress.com
Founded: 2003
Book division of Las Vegas Review-Journal & 40 other US newspapers.
ISBN Prefix(es): 978-1-932173; 978-1-935043; 978-1-939330
Number of titles published annually: 15 Print
Total Titles: 140 Print; 4 E-Book
Imprints: CityLife Books
Sales Office(s): Midpoint Trade Books, 27 W 20 St, Suite 1102, New York, NY 10011 *Tel:* 212-727-0190 *Fax:* 212-727-0195 *Web Site:* midpointtradebooks.com
Shipping Address: Midpoint Trade Books, 1263 Southwest Blvd, Kansas City, KS 66103 *Tel:* 913-362-7400 *Fax:* 913-362-7401 *E-mail:* info@midpointtradebooks.com *Web Site:* www.midpointtradebooks.com
Warehouse: Midpoint Trade Books, 1263 Southwest Blvd, Kansas City, KS 66103 *Tel:* 913-362-7400 *Fax:* 913-362-7401 *E-mail:* info@midpointtradebooks.com *Web Site:* www.midpointtradebooks.com
Distribution Center: Midpoint Trade Books, 1263 Southwest Blvd, Kansas City, KS 66103 *Tel:* 913-362-7400 *Fax:* 913-362-7401 *E-mail:* info@midpointtradebooks.com *Web Site:* www.midpointtradebooks.com
Membership(s): The Independent Book Publishers Association

Sterling Publishing Co Inc
Subsidiary of Barnes & Noble Inc
1166 Avenue of the Americas, 17th fl, New York, NY 10036
SAN: 211-6324
Tel: 212-532-7160 *Toll Free Tel:* 800-367-9692 *Fax:* 212-213-2495
Web Site: www.sterlingpublishing.com
Key Personnel
Cont: Tom Allen
EVP: Theresa Thompson
VP, Sales Opers: Adria Dougherty *Tel:* 646-688-2444 *E-mail:* adougherty@sterlingpub.com
Dir, HR: Kerri Cuocci
Dir, Spec Sales: Nicole Vines Verlin
Dir, Subs Rts & Export: Marilyn Kretzer
Sr Mgr, Natl Accts Trade Sales: Josh Mrvos
Founded: 1949
Publisher of quality nonfiction & fiction books for adults & children. Subject categories include art & photography, cookbooks, wine, self-improvement, mind/body/spirit, business, history, reference, science & nature, home reference, gardening, music, sports, lifestyle & design, hobbies, crafts, classics, study guides, puzzles & games, children's nonfiction, picture, board & humor books.
ISBN Prefix(es): 978-0-7607; 978-0-945352; 978-0-304; 978-0-87192; 978-0-937274; 978-1-887374; 978-1-57990; 978-0-8069; 978-1-86351; 978-1-895569; 978-0-233; 978-0-85177; 978-0-297; 978-1-85375; 978-1-85585; 978-1-84188; 978-0-7528; 978-1-85648; 978-1-4027; 978-1-58816; 978-1-84212; 978-1-84340; 978-1-889538; 978-1-931543; 978-1-58663; 978-1-59308; 978-1-84442; 978-1-84486; 978-1-84483; 978-1-60059; 978-0-7134; 978-0-7538; 978-1-4091; 978-1-4114; 978-1-4440; 978-0-9786968; 978-0-9799433; 978-1-84732; 978-1-877080; 978-1-905417; 978-1-905857; 978-1-906250; 978-1-906388; 978-1-931559; 978-1-933027; 978-1-934618; 978-1-906370; 978-1-4351; 978-1-4547; 978-1-4549; 978-1-60736; 978-1-61837; 978-1-78097; 978-1-84994; 978-1-84796; 978-1-86200; 978-1-907152; 978-1-907554; 978-1-907967; 978-1-908449; 978-1-936096; 978-1-78312; 978-1-905638; 978-1-906714; 978-1-907184; 978-1-908177; 978-1-908759; 978-1-908973; 978-1-909397
Number of titles published annually: 1,500 Print
Total Titles: 6,000 Print
Imprints: Ecosystem; Flashkids; Hearst Books; Lark Crafts; Puzzlewright Press; Sterling; Sterling Children's Books; Sterling Epicure; Sterling Ethos
Distributor for Batsford (selected titles); Boxer Books; Brooklyn Botanic Garden (selected titles); Carlton Books; Cassell (selected titles); Collins & Brown (selected titles); Conway; Davis Publications (selected titles); Sally Milner (selected titles); Orion (selected titles); Phoenix Press (selected titles); Salaryia (selected titles); Sixth & Spring (selected titles); Sky Publishing; Weidenfeld & Nicolson (selected titles); White Star Publishers
Foreign Rep(s): Angell Eurosales (Scandinavia); Ariel Balatbat (Guam, Philippines); David Bateman Ltd (New Zealand); Capricorn Link Ltd (Australia); Guild of Master Craftsman (UK); Hardy Bigfoss International Co Ltd (Cambodia, Laos, Thailand, Vietnam); BK Norton (Taiwan); Penguin Books Malaysia (Malaysia); Penguin Books SA (Portugal,

Spain); Penguin Books Singapore (Singapore); Penguin India (Bangladesh, India, Nepal, Sri Lanka); Penguin Italia SRL (Italy); Phambili Agencies (adult titles only) (South Africa); Publishers International Marketing (Malta, Middle East); Grazyna Soszynska (Central Europe, Eastern Europe)
Foreign Rights: Agence Litteraire Lora Fountain (France); Graal Literary Agency (Poland); Katai & Bolza Literary Agents; Ute Korner Literary Agent (Spain); Alexander Korzhenevski (Russia); Kristin Olson Literary Agency (Czech Republic); Literarische Agentur Silke Weniger
Warehouse: Sterling Warehouse, 40 Saw Mill Pond Rd, Edison, NJ 08817 *Tel:* 732-248-6563 *Toll Free Fax:* 800-775-8736
See separate listing for:
Lark Crafts

Stewart, Tabori & Chang
Imprint of Harry N Abrams Inc
115 W 18 St, 6th fl, New York, NY 10011
SAN: 239-0361
Tel: 212-519-1200 *Fax:* 212-519-1210
Web Site: www.abramsbooks.com
Key Personnel
CEO & Pres: Michael Jacobs
Exec Dir, Publicity: Katrina Weidknecht
Sr Ed: Liana Allday; Natalie Kaire
Founded: 1981
Art, illustrated gift books, gardening, cookbooks, African American history, interior design, New Age, photography, popular culture, humor, weddings.
ISBN Prefix(es): 978-1-55670; 978-0-941434; 978-1-58479
Number of titles published annually: 80 Print
Total Titles: 350 Print
Foreign Rep(s): Ralph & Sheila Summers (Southeast Asia); Paul Walton (South Africa); David Williams (South America)
Foreign Rights: General Publishing (Canada); H I Marketing LTD (Europe, UK); Korea Copyright Center (Korea); New Holland (Australia); Onslow Books Ltd (Europe); Sigma Literary Agency (Korea); Southern Publishers Group (New Zealand); Tuttle-Mori Agency Inc (Japan); David Williams (South America)

§Stipes Publishing LLC
204 W University, Champaign, IL 61820
Mailing Address: PO Box 526, Champaign, IL 61824-0526
Tel: 217-356-8391 *Fax:* 217-356-5753
E-mail: stipes01@sbcglobal.net
Web Site: www.stipes.com
Key Personnel
Partner & Electronic Publg: Benjamin Watts
Partner: J L Hecker
Founded: 1927
Primarily educational, some overlap trade publishing in music & horticulture.
ISBN Prefix(es): 978-0-87563; 978-1-58874
Number of titles published annually: 15 Print
Total Titles: 550 Print; 2 CD-ROM; 1 Online; 1 E-Book; 2 Audio

STM Learning Inc
55 Westport Plaza, Suite 455, St Louis, MO 63146
Tel: 314-434-2424 *Toll Free Tel:* 800-600-0330 *Fax:* 314-434-2425
E-mail: info@stmlearning.com; orders@stmlearning.com
Web Site: www.stmlearning.com
Key Personnel
Pres: Marianne Whaley *E-mail:* marianne@stmlearning.com
VP: Glenn Whaley *E-mail:* glenn@stmlearning.com
Founded: 1993
Medical & legal, nursing & allied health texts & references; medical consumer books; child care & development, clinical & forensic medical references.
ISBN Prefix(es): 978-1-878060; 978-1-936590
Number of titles published annually: 4 Print; 3 CD-ROM
Total Titles: 24 Print; 7 CD-ROM
Advertising Agency: GW Graphics & Publishing
Distribution Center: Amazon.com
Barnes & Noble
Rittenhouse Book Distributors Inc, 511 Feheley Dr, King of Prussia, PA 19406 *Toll Free Tel:* 800-345-6425 *Toll Free Fax:* 800-223-7488 *Web Site:* www.rittenhouse.com

STOCKCERO Inc
3785 NW 82 Ave, Suite 302, Doral, FL 33166
Tel: 305-722-7628 *Fax:* 305-477-5794
E-mail: academicservices@stockcero.com; sales@stockcero.com
Web Site: www.stockcero.com
Key Personnel
CEO: Pablo Agrest Berge *E-mail:* pagrest@stockcero.com
Founded: 2000
Committed to building an ever expanding collection of significant books, comprising Spanish literature, both Peninsular & Latin American. Our editions are conceived with modern non-native Spanish speaking readers & students in mind, so they include updated & sharply focused footnotes, prefaces & bibliographies written by scholarly literary editors.
ISBN Prefix(es): 978-1-934768
Number of titles published annually: 14 Print
Total Titles: 114 Print

§Stone Bridge Press Inc
1393 Solano Ave, Suite C, Albany, CA 94706
Mailing Address: PO Box 8208, Berkeley, CA 94706
Tel: 510-524-8732 *Toll Free Tel:* 800-947-7271 (orders) *Fax:* 510-524-8711
E-mail: sbp@stonebridge.com; sbpedit@stonebridge.com
Web Site: www.stonebridge.com
Key Personnel
Founder & Publr: Peter Goodman
Founded: 1989
Books on Japan & Asia.
ISBN Prefix(es): 978-0-89346 (Heian International); 978-1-880656; 978-0-9628137; 978-1-933330; 978-1-61172
Number of titles published annually: 6 Print; 10 Online; 20 E-Book
Total Titles: 100 Print; 15 Online; 15 E-Book
Imprints: Heian International (children's & crafts)
Foreign Rep(s): Perseus International (Australia)
Distribution Center: Consortium Book Sales & Distribution Inc (US & CN) *Toll Free Tel:* 800-283-3572
Membership(s): Bay Area Independent Publishers Association; The Independent Book Publishers Association
See separate listing for:
Heian

Stonewall, see BrickHouse Books Inc

Stoneydale Press Publishing Co
523 Main St, Stevensville, MT 59870-2839
Mailing Address: PO Box 188, Stevensville, MT 59870-0188
Tel: 406-777-2729 *Toll Free Tel:* 800-735-7006 *Fax:* 406-777-2521
Web Site: www.stoneydale.com
Key Personnel
Publr: Dale A Burk
Founded: 1976
Outdoor recreation, regional history & reminisces of Northern Rockies region.
ISBN Prefix(es): 978-0-912299; 978-1-931291
Number of titles published annually: 8 Print
Total Titles: 160 Print
Membership(s): Mountains & Plains Booksellers Association; Pacific Northwest Booksellers Association

Storey Publishing LLC
210 MASS MoCA Way, North Adams, MA 01247
SAN: 203-4158
Tel: 413-346-2100 *Toll Free Tel:* 800-441-5700 (orders); 800-793-9396 (edit) *Fax:* 413-346-2199; 413-346-2196 (edit)
E-mail: sales@storey.com
Web Site: www.storey.com
Key Personnel
CEO & Pres: Dan Reynolds *E-mail:* dan.reynolds@storey.com
Publr: Deborah Balmuth *E-mail:* deborah.balmuth@storey.com
Mng Ed & Dir, Contracts: Jennifer Travis
Dir, Publicity: Amy Greeman *E-mail:* amy.greeman@storey.com
Rts Dir: Maribeth Casey *Tel:* 413-346-2135 *E-mail:* maribeth.casey@storey.com
Design Mgr: Carolyn Eckert
HR & Opers Mgr: Marci Saunders *E-mail:* marci.saunders@storey.com
Trade, Gift & Ebook Sales Mgr: Adrienne Franceschi
Book Designer: Michaela Jebb
Founded: 1983
How-to books on country living, gardening, cooking, natural health, home building, country business, crafts, small-scale livestock, pets, beer & wine, children's nonfiction.
ISBN Prefix(es): 978-0-945352; 978-0-88266; 978-1-58017
Number of titles published annually: 50 Print
Total Titles: 500 Print
Distributed by Workman Publishing Co Inc
Foreign Rep(s): Thomas Allen & Sons Ltd (Canada); Bill Bailey Publishers' Representatives (Europe); Bookreps NZ Ltd (Susan Holmes) (New Zealand); Capricorn Link Australia Pty Ltd (Australia); Michelle Morrow Curreri (Asia, Middle East); IMA/Intermediaamericana Ltd (David Williams) (Caribbean, Latin America); Melia Publishing Services (UK); Trinity Books CC (South Africa)

§The Story Plant
Division of Studio Digital CT LLC
PO Box 4331, Stamford, CT 06907
Tel: 203-722-7920
E-mail: thestoryplant@thestoryplant.com
Web Site: www.thestoryplant.com
Key Personnel
Publr: Lou Aronica *E-mail:* lou.aronica@thestoryplant.com
Assoc Publr: Mitchell Maxwell *E-mail:* mitchell.maxwell@thestoryplant.com
Founded: 2008
Independent publisher of commercial fiction. The focus is on author development & building publishing programs for each author.
ISBN Prefix(es): 978-1-61188
Number of titles published annually: 35 Print; 35 E-Book; 5 Audio
Total Titles: 75 Print; 75 E-Book; 2 Audio
Foreign Rights: Trident Media (all other territories)
Distribution Center: Perseus Distribution, 250 W 57 St, New York, NY 10107, Contact: Jessica Schmidt *Toll Free Tel:* 800-343-4499 *E-mail:* jessica.schmidt@perseusbooks.com
Membership(s): AAP

Strata Publishing Inc
PO Box 1303, State College, PA 16804
SAN: 298-9794

Tel: 814-234-8545 *Fax:* 814-238-7222
E-mail: stratapub@stratapub.com
Web Site: www.stratapub.com
Key Personnel
Publr: Kathleen Domenig
Gen Mgr: Brian Henry
Founded: 1990
Books in communication & journalism for mid-level & advanced college courses, scholars & professionals. Return authorization required.
ISBN Prefix(es): 978-0-9634489; 978-1-891136
Number of titles published annually: 3 Print
Total Titles: 16 Print

Strategic Book Publishing & Rights Agency (SBPRA)
12620 FM 1960, Suite A-4507, Houston, TX 77065
SAN: 853-8492
Toll Free Tel: 888-808-6190
Web Site: www.sbpra.com
Key Personnel
CEO: Robert Fletcher
Founded: 2007
Provides book publishing, marketing & ebook services to writers around the world. Catalog of more than 5000 authors. Books are available through Ingram as well as in bookstores such as Barnes & Noble & all online channels. Attends & exhibits at the major book expositions in London, New York, China & Germany each year.
This publisher has indicated that 50% of their product line is author subsidized.
ISBN Prefix(es): 978-1-61204
Number of titles published annually: 475 Print; 85 E-Book
Total Titles: 2,786 Print; 3,062 Online; 336 E-Book
Imprints: Eloquent/Strategic

§Strategic Media Books LLC
782 Wofford St, Rock Hill, SC 29730
Tel: 803-366-5440
E-mail: contact@strategicmediabooks.com
Web Site: strategicmediabooks.com
Key Personnel
Pres: Ron Chepesiuk
VP: Barbara Casey
Tech Opers: Al Casey
Founded: 2010
Publisher of crime, true crime & southern interest books.
ISBN Prefix(es): 978-0-9852440; 978-1-939521
Number of titles published annually: 8 Print; 8 Online; 8 E-Book; 3 Audio
Total Titles: 28 Print; 25 Online; 25 E-Book; 3 Audio
Foreign Rep(s): Cardinal Publishers Group (UK)
Membership(s): The Independent Book Publishers Association

§Stress Free Kids®
2561 Chimney Springs Dr, Marietta, GA 30062
Toll Free Tel: 800-841-4204 *Toll Free Fax:* 866-302-2759
E-mail: media@stressfreekids.com
Web Site: www.stressfreekids.com
Key Personnel
Founder: Lori Lite; Rick Lite
Founded: 1996
Books, CDs (physical & digital formats), lesson plans to help children & teens manage stress, lower anxiety & decrease anger, while improving self-esteem.
ISBN Prefix(es): 978-0-9708633; 978-0-9787781; 978-0-9800328
Number of titles published annually: 2 Print; 5 Online; 4 E-Book; 4 Audio
Total Titles: 35 Print; 12 Audio

The Jesse Stuart Foundation (JSF)
1645 Winchester Ave, Ashland, KY 41101
SAN: 245-8837
Mailing Address: PO Box 669, Ashland, KY 41105-0669
Tel: 606-326-1667 *Fax:* 606-325-2519
E-mail: jsf@jsfbooks.com
Web Site: www.jsfbooks.com
Key Personnel
CEO & Sr Ed: James M Gifford, PhD
Founded: 1979
Publisher of Appalachia-Kentuckiana. Not accepting unsol mss at this time.
ISBN Prefix(es): 978-0-945084
Number of titles published annually: 4 Print
Total Titles: 75 Print

Studio Fun International Inc
Subsidiary of The Reader's Digest Association Inc
44 S Broadway, White Plains, NY 10601
SAN: 283-2143
Tel: 914-238-1000 *Toll Free Tel:* 800-934-0977
Web Site: www.rdtradepublishing.com
Key Personnel
Pres & Publr: Harold Clarke
E-mail: Harold_Clarke@rd.com
VP, Assoc Publr: Rosanne McManus
E-mail: Rosanne_McManus@rd.com
Creative Dir: Julia Sabbagh
E-mail: Julia_Sabbagh@rd.com
Dir of Publg: Debra Polansky
E-mail: Debra_Polansky@rd.com
Sales Dir: Frank Fochetta *E-mail:* frank.fochetta@studiofun.com
Founded: 1994
Publishers of children's interactive books, including major world class brands.
ISBN Prefix(es): 978-0-7944
Number of titles published annually: 150 Print
Total Titles: 400 Print
Foreign Rep(s): Jennifer Fifield (Worldwide exc USA)

Stylus Publishing LLC
22883 Quicksilver Dr, Sterling, VA 20166-2012
SAN: 299-1853
Mailing Address: PO Box 605, Herndon, VA 20172-0605
Tel: 703-661-1504 (edit & sales)
Toll Free Tel: 800-232-0223 (orders & cust serv) *Fax:* 703-661-1547
E-mail: stylusmail@presswarehouse.com (orders & cust serv); stylusinfo@styluspub.com
Web Site: www.styluspub.com
Key Personnel
Pres & Publr: John von Knorring *E-mail:* jvk@styluspub.com
VP, Mktg & Busn Devt: Andrea Ciecierski
E-mail: andrea@styluspub.com
Mktg & Publicity Mgr: Shaqunia Clark
E-mail: shaqunia@styluspub.com
Opers: Robin von Knorring *E-mail:* robin@styluspub.com
Founded: 1996
Publish books for faculty & administrators in higher education. Distributes books in the areas of art, business, training, psychology & psychotherapy as well as educational & scholarly titles & books on Third World development & the environment.
ISBN Prefix(es): 978-1-57922
Number of titles published annually: 30 Print
Total Titles: 400 Print; 2 CD-ROM
Subsidiaries: The Institution of Engineering & Technology (IET)
Distributor for Aeon Books; American Association for Higher Education; Cabi Books; Commonwealth Scientific & Industrial Research Organization (CSIRO); The Commonwealth Secretariat; Cork University Press; Global Professional Publishing; IDRC; Institute of Education; Karnac Books; LM Publishing; The Institution of Engineering & Technology (IET); Nordic Africa Institute; Oxfam Publishing; Practical Action; Thorogood Publishing; Trentham Books Ltd; Women, Law & Development International (WLDI); World Health Organization (WHO)
Foreign Rep(s): Eurospan (Kumarian Press) (Europe, Middle East, UK)
Distribution Center: Books International Inc, 22883 Quicksilver Dr, Dulles, VA 20166

Success Advertising & Publishing
Division of The Success Group
3419 Dunham Rd, Warsaw, NY 14569
SAN: 678-9501
Tel: 585-786-5663
Key Personnel
Pres & Publr: Allan H Smith
E-mail: allan33001@aol.com
VP: Ginger B Smith
Book Ed: Robin Garretson
Founded: 1978
How-to, self-help, crafts, business, home-based business.
ISBN Prefix(es): 978-0-931113
Number of titles published annually: 7 Print
Total Titles: 58 Print
Divisions: Academy of Continuing Education; National Doll Society of America; Success Advertising

Summa Publications
PO Box 660725, Birmingham, AL 35266-0725
Tel: 205-822-0463 *Fax:* 205-822-0463
Web Site: summapub2.googlepages.com
Key Personnel
Owner & Publr: Thomas M Hines
E-mail: tmhines@samford.edu
Founded: 1983
Critical works, scholarly publications in French & Francophone; no fiction.
ISBN Prefix(es): 978-0-917786; 978-1-883479
Number of titles published annually: 6 Print
Total Titles: 119 Print

Summer Institute of Linguistics Inc, see SIL International

§Summertime Publications Inc
7502 E Berridge Lane, Scottsdale, AZ 85250
Tel: 480-409-1554
E-mail: handell@summertimepublications.com
Web Site: www.summertimepublications.com
Key Personnel
CEO & Dir, Pubns: Laurel Leffmann
Founded: 2009
Small press. Quality books about France; also memoirs, history, sci-fi, short story, literary fiction & nonfiction.
ISBN Prefix(es): 978-0-9823698; 978-1-940333
Number of titles published annually: 3 Print; 4 E-Book
Total Titles: 9 Print; 14 E-Book
Imprints: PWN; Summertime
Distributor for ACHCBYZ (Paris academic press specialized in Byzantine history)
Foreign Rights: IPR License Ltd (Worldwide exc China); Rightol Media (China)
Membership(s): The Independent Book Publishers Association

§Summit University Press
63 Summit Way, Gardiner, MT 59030-9314
Tel: 406-848-9742; 406-848-9500
Toll Free Tel: 800-245-5445 (retail orders)
Fax: 406-848-9650 *Toll Free Fax:* 800-221-8307
E-mail: info@summituniversitypress.com
Web Site: www.summituniversitypress.com
Key Personnel
Dir: Norman N Millman *Tel:* 406-848-9743
E-mail: director@summituniversitypress.com

Prodn Dir: Christopher Allen
E-mail: production@summituniversitypress.com
Founded: 1975
Global publisher of fine books & audiotapes on spirituality. Very active foreign rights sales. Specialize in New Age & mind, body & spirit.
ISBN Prefix(es): 978-0-916766; 978-0-922729
Number of titles published annually: 4 Print; 45 Online; 45 E-Book
Total Titles: 100 Print; 20 CD-ROM; 45 Online; 47 E-Book; 70 Audio
Distribution Center: National Book Network, 4501 Forbes Blvd, Suite 200, Lanham, MD 20706 *Tel:* 301-459-3366 *Fax:* 301-429-5746 *E-mail:* custserv@nbnbooks.com *Web Site:* www.nbnbooks.com
NBN Canada/Rowman & Littlefield Publishing Group, 67 Mowat Ave, Suite 241, Toronto, ON M6K 3E3, Canada *Tel:* 416-534-1660 *Toll Free Tel:* 877-626-2665 *Fax:* 416-534-3699 *Web Site:* www.nbnbooks.com
NBN International, Plymbridge House, Estover Rd, Plymouth, Devon PL6 7PY, United Kingdom *Tel:* (01752) 202300 *Fax:* (01752) 202330 *E-mail:* enquiries@nbninternational.com
Membership(s): The Independent Book Publishers Association

Sun Books, see Sun Publishing Company

Sun Publishing Company
Division of The Sun Companies
PO Box 5588, Santa Fe, NM 87502-5588
SAN: 206-1325
Tel: 505-471-5177; 505-473-4161
Toll Free Tel: 877-849-0051 *Fax:* 505-473-4458
E-mail: info@sunbooks.com
Web Site: www.sunbooks.com
Key Personnel
Pres & Rts & Perms: Skip Whitson
Founded: 1973
Motivational, success, business, recovery, inspirational, history, self-help, new thought, philosophy, western mysticism, scholarly; oriental philosophy & studies. No unsol mss. Query first by e-mail.
ISBN Prefix(es): 978-0-89540
Number of titles published annually: 10 Print
Total Titles: 400 Print
Imprints: Far West Publishing; Sun Books
Advertising Agency: Sun Agency

Sunbelt Publications Inc
1256 Fayette St, El Cajon, CA 92020-1511
SAN: 630-0790
Mailing Address: PO Box 191126, San Diego, CA 92159
Tel: 619-258-4911 *Toll Free Tel:* 800-626-6579 (cust serv) *Fax:* 619-258-4916
E-mail: service@sunbeltpub.com; info@sunbeltpub.com
Web Site: www.sunbeltbooks.com
Key Personnel
CEO: Lowell Lindsay *Tel:* 619-258-4911 ext 111 *E-mail:* llindsay@sunbeltpub.com
Pres: Diana Lindsay *Tel:* 619-258-4911 ext 104 *E-mail:* dlindsay@sunbeltpub.com
Acctg & Opers Mgr: Terry Cochran *Tel:* 619-258-4905 ext 110 *E-mail:* tcochran@sunbeltpub.com
Pubns Mgr: Debi Young *Tel:* 619-258-4905 ext 103 *E-mail:* dyoung@sunbeltpub.com
Founded: 1984
Publisher & distributor of natural history, science, pictorial & travel specializing in Alta & Baja, California.
ISBN Prefix(es): 978-0-932653; 978-0-916251
Number of titles published annually: 10 Print
Total Titles: 75 Print
Imprints: First Choice
Distributor for Abbott Publishing; Alti Corporation; Amaroma Ediciones (architectural & design publisher in Mexico); Anza-Borrego Foundation; W H Berger; Bobolink Media; Joan Brady; California Sea Grant; Paul Douglas Campbell; Dawsons Book Shop; Leland Fetzer; Fun Places Publishing; Jeffrey Garcia; Maureen Gilmer; Glove Pequot; Green Grass Press; Healey Publishing; Huckleberry House LLC; Intellect Publishing; Island Paradise Publishing; Jaguar Tales; Scott G Kyle; Lawtech Publishing; Little Oak Press; Mission San Juan Capistrano Women's Guild; Newtona LLC; Northcross Books; Nelson Papucci; Bette L Pegas; Linda Pequegnat; Picaro Publishing; Planeta Peninsula (Mexican publisher); Phil R Pryde; Quick Reference Publishing; R & B Food & Culture Production; Random House; Renegade Enterprises; San Diego Architecture Foundation; San Diego Association of Geologists; San Diego City Works Press; San Diego Natural History Museum; San Diego Police Historical Association; San Dieguito River Park Joint Powers Authority; Save Our Heritage Organization; Surf Angel Publications; Trail Wisdom; University of California Press; Armand Vallee; Wigton Publishing; Wilderness Press; Wolf Water Press
Membership(s): Association of Earth Science Editors; The Independent Book Publishers Association; Outdoor Writers Association of America; Publishers Association of the West

Sunburst Digital Inc
3150 W Higgins Rd, Suite 140, Hoffman Estates, IL 60169
Toll Free Tel: 800-321-7511 *Toll Free Fax:* 888-800-3028
E-mail: service@sunburst.com; sales@sunburst.com
Web Site: sunburst.com; edresources.com
Key Personnel
Dir, Sales: Dan Sladek
Founded: 1972
Developer & publisher of multimedia educational software, videos & printed supplements for use in schools. Publish school products for grades K-12 under the Sunburst brand & distribute Knowledge Adventure® brand school products.
ISBN Prefix(es): 978-0-395; 978-0-89466
Number of titles published annually: 3 Print

Sundance/Newbridge Publishing
Division of Rowman & Littlefield Publishing Group
33 Boston Post Rd W, Suite 440, Marlborough, MA 01752
Toll Free Tel: 888-200-2720; 800-343-8204 (Sundance cust serv & orders); 800-867-0307 (Newbridge cust serv & orders)
Toll Free Fax: 800-456-2419 (orders)
E-mail: info@sundancepub.com; info@newbridgeonline.com
Web Site: www.sundancepub.com; www.newbridgeonline.com
Key Personnel
Pres: Paul Konowitch *E-mail:* pkonowitch@sundancepub.com
SVP, Sales: John Atkocaitis *E-mail:* jatkocaitis@sundancepub.com
Founded: 1981
Supplemental educational publisher for PreK-8 that creates standards-based classroom materials for reading in the content areas.
ISBN Prefix(es): 978-1-56784; 978-1-58273; 978-1-4007
Number of titles published annually: 150 Print; 36 Audio
Total Titles: 680 Print; 118 Audio
Imprints: Early Math; Early Science; Early Social Studies; GoFacts Guided Writing; Kids Corner; Newbridge Discovery Links; Ranger Rick Science Program; Thinking Like a Scientist
Foreign Rep(s): Schmelzer PSI
Membership(s): AAP; International Literacy Association; National Science Teachers Association

§Sunrise River Press
Affiliate of Cartech Books/Specialty Press
39966 Grand Ave, North Branch, MN 55056
Tel: 651-277-1400 *Toll Free Tel:* 800-895-4585
Fax: 651-277-1203
E-mail: info@sunriseriverpress.com; sales@sunriseriverpress.com
Web Site: www.sunriseriverpress.com
Publisher of consumer books & books for the professional healthcare market with an emphasis on self-help, weight loss, nutrition, diet, food & recipes with additional focus on family health, fitness & specific diseases such as cancer, anorexia, Alzheimer's, autism & depression.
ISBN Prefix(es): 978-0-9624814; 978-1-934716
Number of titles published annually: 10 Print

Sunstone Press
Imprint of The Sunstone Corp
PO Box 2321, Santa Fe, NM 87504-2321
SAN: 214-2090
Tel: 505-988-4418 *Toll Free Tel:* 800-243-5644
Fax: 505-988-1025 (orders only)
Web Site: www.sunstonepress.com
Key Personnel
Pres & Treas: James Clois Smith, Jr
Dir, Opers & Sales: Carl Daniel Condit
Founded: 1971
Mainstream & Southwestern US titles, general nonfiction, fiction & how-to craft books.
ISBN Prefix(es): 978-0-913270; 978-0-86534; 978-1-61139 (ebooks); 978-1-63293
Number of titles published annually: 100 Print; 300 E-Book
Total Titles: 1,600 Print; 1,500 E-Book
Foreign Rights: Daniel Bial Literary Agency
Membership(s): New Mexico Book Association

SUNY Press, see State University of New York Press

Superintendent of Documents, see US Government Publishing Office (GPO)

Surrey Books
Imprint of Agate Publishing
1328 Greenleaf St, Evanston, IL 60202
SAN: 275-8857
Tel: 847-475-4457 *Toll Free Tel:* 800-326-4430
Web Site: agatepublishing.com/surrey
Key Personnel
Pres & Publr: Doug Seibold *E-mail:* seibold@agatepublishing.com
Founded: 1982
Trade books. Specialize in nonfiction: cooking, health & lifestyle.
ISBN Prefix(es): 978-0-940625; 978-1-57284
Number of titles published annually: 20 Print
Total Titles: 120 Print
Distribution Center: Publishers Group West, 1700 Fourth St, Berkeley, CA 94710 *Tel:* 510-809-3700 *Toll Free Tel:* 800-788-3123 (cust serv) *Fax:* 510-809-3777 *E-mail:* info@pgw.com *Web Site:* www.pgw.com
Membership(s): International Association of Culinary Professionals

Susquehanna University Press
Affiliate of Associated University Presses
514 University Ave, Selinsgrove, PA 17870
Tel: 570-372-4175 *Fax:* 570-372-4021
E-mail: supress@susqu.edu
Key Personnel
Dir: Dr Rachana Sachdev *Tel:* 570-372-4200 *E-mail:* rsachdev@susqu.edu

Mng Ed: Sarah Bailey
Founded: 1944
Publish books that participate in recent ongoing conversations about scholarly issues, & that offer new insights on traditional materials.
ISBN Prefix(es): 978-0-941664; 978-0-945636; 978-1-57591
Number of titles published annually: 15 Print
Total Titles: 250 Print
Distributed by Associated University Presses
Foreign Rep(s): The Eurospan Group (Africa, Europe, Middle East, UK); Scholarly Book Services (Canada)
Orders to: Associated University Presses, 10 Schalks Crossing Rd, Suite 501-330, Plainsboro, NJ 08536 *Tel:* 609-269-8094 *Fax:* 609-269-8096 *E-mail:* aup440@aol.com; Scholarly Book Services Inc, 473 Adelaide St W, 4th fl, Toronto, ON M5A 1T1, Canada *Toll Free Tel:* 800-847-9736 *Toll Free Fax:* 800-220-9895 *E-mail:* orders@sbookscan.com; The Eurospan Group (EDS), Covent Garden, 3 Henrietta St, London WC2E 8LU, United Kingdom *Tel:* (020) 7240 0856 *Fax:* (020) 7379 0609 *E-mail:* orders@edspubs.co.uk

Swallow Press
Imprint of Ohio University Press
215 Columbus Rd, Suite 101, Athens, OH 45701-1373
Fax: 740-593-4536
Web Site: www.ohioswallow.com
Key Personnel
Dir: Gillian Berchowitz *Tel:* 740-593-1159 *E-mail:* berchowi@ohio.edu
Acqs Ed: Ricky S Huard *Tel:* 740-593-1157 *E-mail:* huard@ohio.edu
Mng Ed: Nancy Basmajian *Tel:* 740-593-1161 *E-mail:* basmajia@ohio.edu
Busn Mgr: Omar Aziz *Tel:* 740-593-1156 *E-mail:* azizo@ohio.edu
Perms & Serv Specialist: Sally R Welch *Tel:* 740-593-1154 *E-mail:* welchs@ohio.edu
Founded: 1940
Publisher of scholarly & trade books.
ISBN Prefix(es): 978-0-8040
Number of titles published annually: 10 Print
Total Titles: 600 Print
Foreign Rep(s): Combined Academic Publishers (Europe); EWEB (Pacific Rim)
Orders to: Chicago Distribution Center, 11030 S Langley Ave, Chicago, IL 60628 *Toll Free Tel:* 800-621-2736 *Toll Free Fax:* 800-621-8476
Warehouse: Chicago Distribution Center, 11030 S Langley Ave, Chicago, IL 60628 *Toll Free Tel:* 800-621-2736 *Toll Free Fax:* 800-621-8476

Swan Isle Press
11030 S Langley Ave, Chicago, IL 60628
Mailing Address: PO Box 408790, Chicago, IL 60640-8790
Tel: 773-728-3780 (edit); 773-702-7000 (cust serv) *Toll Free Tel:* 800-621-2736 (cust serv) *Fax:* 773-702-7212 (cust serv) *Toll Free Fax:* 800-621-8476 (cust serv)
E-mail: info@swanislepress.com
Web Site: www.swanislepress.com
Key Personnel
Founder, Dir & Ed: David Rade
Founded: 1999
Not-for-profit literary publisher, dedicated to publishing poetry, fiction & nonfiction that inspire & educate while advancing the knowledge & appreciation of literature, art & culture.
ISBN Prefix(es): 978-0-9678808; 978-0-9748881
Number of titles published annually: 4 Print; 2 E-Book
Total Titles: 42 Print; 3 E-Book
Editorial Office(s): PO Box 408790, Chicago, IL 60640-8790
Distributed by University of Chicago Press
Foreign Rep(s): University of Chicago Press (Worldwide)
Orders to: Baker & Taylor, 2550 W Tyvola Rd, Suite 300, Charlotte, NC 28217 *Tel:* 704-998-3100 *Toll Free Tel:* 800-775-1800 *E-mail:* btinfo@baker-taylor.com *Web Site:* www.btol.com; Ingram Book Co, One Ingram Blvd, La Vergne, TN 37086 *Tel:* 615-793-5000 *Toll Free Tel:* 800-937-8200 *E-mail:* customer.service@ingrambook.com *Web Site:* www.ingrambook.com
Membership(s): AAP

Swedenborg Foundation
320 N Church St, West Chester, PA 19380
SAN: 202-5280
Tel: 610-430-3222 *Toll Free Tel:* 800-355-3222 (cust serv) *Fax:* 610-430-7982
E-mail: info@swedenborg.com
Web Site: www.swedenborg.com
Key Personnel
Opers Mgr: Morgan Beard *Tel:* 610-430-3222 ext 12 *E-mail:* mbeard@swedenborg.com
Founded: 1849
Books & DVDs by, or relating to, the theological works & spiritual insights of Emanuel Swedenborg & related literature.
ISBN Prefix(es): 978-0-87785
Number of titles published annually: 10 Print
Total Titles: 200 Print
Orders to: Continental Sales Inc (CSI), 213 W Main St, Barrington, IL 60010 *Tel:* 847-381-6530 *Fax:* 847-382-0419 *E-mail:* bookreps@wybel.com; Wybel Marketing Group Inc, 213 W Main St, Barrington, IL 60010 *Tel:* 847-382-0384 *Fax:* 847-382-0385 *E-mail:* bookreps@wybel.com; Melman-Moster Associates Inc, 43 Yawpo Ave, Suite 6, Oakland, NJ 07436 *Tel:* 201-651-9400 *Fax:* 201-651-9440 *E-mail:* books@melmanmoster.com; Faherty & Associates, 6665 SW Hampton St, Suite 100, Portland, OR 97223 *Tel:* 503-639-3113 *Fax:* 503-598-9850 *E-mail:* faherty@fahertybooks.com; Southern Territory Associates, 4508 64 St, Lubbock, TX 79414 *Tel:* 806-799-9997 *Fax:* 806-799-9777 *E-mail:* sta77@suddenlink.net; Rainbow Book Agencies, 303 Arthur St, Fairfield 3078, Australia *Tel:* (0613) 9481 6611 *Fax:* (0613) 9481 2371 *E-mail:* rba@rainbowbooks.com.au *Web Site:* www.rainbowbooks.com.au
Returns: University of Chicago Press/The Chicago Distribution Center, 11030 S Langley Ave, Chicago, IL 60628
Distribution Center: University of Chicago Press/The Chicago Distribution Center, 11030 S Langley Ave, Chicago, IL 60628

§SYBEX Inc
Division of John Wiley & Sons Inc
111 River St, Hoboken, NJ 07030-5774
SAN: 211-1667
Tel: 201-748-6000 *Fax:* 201-748-6088
E-mail: info@wiley.com
Web Site: www.sybex.com; www.wiley.com
Founded: 1976
For beginning, intermediate & advanced users of all types of software & hardware, including how-to books on various networking, word processing, database, graphics & spreadsheet software, certification, as well as computer games & Internet books, graphics & programming.
ISBN Prefix(es): 978-0-89588; 978-0-7821; 978-0-47028
Number of titles published annually: 150 Print
Total Titles: 601 Print; 2 CD-ROM
Foreign Rep(s): Robert Blake (Central America, Mexico); Phillip Bowie (Caribbean); Cynthia Chiang (China); Rolando De Vera (Philippines); Tadashi Hase (Japan); Hee-Jeong Ihn (South Korea); Steven Loo (Malaysia); Natalie Lord (Europe, UK); Ledy Martinez (Brazil, South America); Roger Ming (Taiwan); Glenn Allen Smith (Hong Kong); Kriangsak Subsinburana (Thailand); Retno Sugiarti (Indonesia); Joyce Yang (China); Angela Yeo (Singapore)

§Synapse Information Resources Inc
1247 Taft Ave, Endicott, NY 13760
Tel: 607-748-4145 *Toll Free Tel:* 888-SYN-CHEM (796-2436) *Fax:* 607-786-3966
E-mail: salesinfo@synapseinfo.com
Web Site: www.synapseinfo.com
Key Personnel
Owner & Pres: Irene Ash *E-mail:* iash@synapseinfo.com
Owner: Michael Ash
Founded: 1981
Chemical database references for industry. Publish both books & CD-ROMs in industrial chemistry. Reference books & software serving the industrial chemical market.
ISBN Prefix(es): 978-1-890595
Number of titles published annually: 3 Print; 3 CD-ROM
Total Titles: 20 Print; 23 CD-ROM

§SynergEbooks
948 New Hwy 7, Columbia, TN 38401
SAN: 254-4962
Tel: 931-548-2494
E-mail: synergebooks@aol.com
Web Site: www.synergebooks.com
Key Personnel
Publr & Exec Ed: Debra Staples
Founded: 1999
Electronic publishing house & bookstore that also include CD-ROMs, audio books & trade paperbacks. Genres include fiction, nonfiction, romance, young adults fantasy, science fiction, poetry, humor, mystery/suspense, inspiration, cookbooks, self-help/reference, business, true crime, New Age, Native American & a children's section.
ISBN Prefix(es): 978-0-9702; 978-0-7443; 978-1-931540
Number of titles published annually: 25 Print; 30 E-Book
Total Titles: 170 Print; 360 Online; 360 E-Book
Imprints: SynErotica (erotic titles); YourSpecs (self-publishing ebook conversion service)
Membership(s): Electronically Published Internet Connection; The Independent Book Publishers Association

Syracuse University Press
621 Skytop Rd, Suite 110, Syracuse, NY 13244-5290
SAN: 206-9776
Tel: 315-443-5534 *Toll Free Tel:* 800-365-8929 (cust serv) *Fax:* 315-443-5545
E-mail: supress@syr.edu
Web Site: syracuseuniversitypress.syr.edu
Key Personnel
Dir: Alice Randal Pfeiffer *Tel:* 315-443-5535 *E-mail:* arpfeiff@syr.edu
Sr Busn Mgr: Karen Lockwood *Tel:* 315-443-5536 *E-mail:* kflockwo@syr.edu
Acqs Ed: Deanna McCay *Tel:* 315-443-5543 *E-mail:* dhmccay@syr.edu
Order Supv: Lori Lazipone *Tel:* 315-443-2597
Design Specialist: Lynn Wilcox *Tel:* 315-443-1975 *E-mail:* lphoppel@syr.edu
Mktg Coord: Lisa Kuerbis *Tel:* 315-443-5546 *E-mail:* lkuerbis@syr.edu
Founded: 1943
Scholarly, general & regional nonfiction; Middle East; Irish studies; medieval; women studies; Iroquois studies; television; religion & politics; geography; sports & leisure; space, place & society; literature; Jewish studies (fiction & nonfiction).
ISBN Prefix(es): 978-0-8156
Number of titles published annually: 60 Print
Total Titles: 1,800 Print

Imprints: Adirondack Museum
Distributed by Alen House; Dedelas Press
Foreign Rep(s): Victoria Davies (Western USA); Eurospan University Press Group Ltd (Africa, Continental Europe, Middle East, UK); EWEB (Royden Muranaka) (Asia, Australia, Far East, Hawaii, India, New Zealand, Pakistan); Miller Trade Book Marketing (Midwestern States); Scholarly Book Services Inc (Canada); Nancy Suib & Associates (Western USA); UMG Publishers Representatives (David K Brown) (Eastern States); UMG Publishers Representatives (Jay Bruff) (Eastern States)
Orders to: Long Leaf Services, 116 S Boundary St, Chapel Hill, NC 27514-3808 *Toll Free Tel:* 800-848-6224 *Toll Free Fax:* 800-272-6817 *E-mail:* customerservice@longleafservices.org *Web Site:* www.longleafservices.org
Returns: Long Leaf Services, 116 S Boundary St, Chapel Hill, NC 27514-3808 *Toll Free Tel:* 800-848-6224 *Toll Free Fax:* 800-272-6817 *E-mail:* customerservice@longleafservices.org *Web Site:* www.longleafservices.org
Distribution Center: Long Leaf Services, 116 S Boundary St, Chapel Hill, NC 27514-3808 *Toll Free Tel:* 800-848-6224 *Toll Free Fax:* 800-272-6817 *E-mail:* customerservice@longleafservices.org *Web Site:* www.longleafservices.org

Tachyon Publications
1459 18 St, No 139, San Francisco, CA 94107
Tel: 415-285-5615
E-mail: tachyon@tachyonpublications.com
Web Site: www.tachyonpublications.com
Key Personnel
Publr & Ed: Jacob Weisman *E-mail:* jw@tachyonpublications.com
Mng Ed: Jill Roberts *E-mail:* jill@tachyonpublications.com
Publicist: James DeMaiolo *E-mail:* jim@tachyonpublications.com
Soc Media: Rick Klaw *Tel:* 512-777-9036 *E-mail:* rick@tachyonpublications.com
Founded: 1995
Science fiction, fantasy & genre publishing.
ISBN Prefix(es): 978-0-9648320; 978-1-892391; 978-1-61696
Number of titles published annually: 10 Print; 6 E-Book
Total Titles: 163 Print; 52 E-Book
Foreign Rights: Joshua Bilmes (Worldwide)
Orders to: Legato/Publishers Group West (PGW), 1700 Fourth St, Berkeley, CA 94710 *Tel:* 510-809-3700 *Toll Free Tel:* 800-343-4499 *Toll Free Fax:* 800-351-5073 *E-mail:* orderentry@perseusbooks.com *Web Site:* www.pgw.com/home/customers.aspx
Shipping Address: Perseus Distribution, 210 American Dr, Jackson, TN 38301, Contact: Jennifer Pascal *Tel:* 510-809-3700 *E-mail:* jennifer.pascal@pgw.com
Warehouse: Perseus Distribution, 210 American Dr, Jackson, TN 38301, Contact: Jennifer Pascal *Tel:* 510-809-3700 *E-mail:* jennifer.pascal@pgw.com
Distribution Center: Legato/Publishers Group West (PGW), 1700 Fourth St, Berkeley, CA 94710, Contact: Laura Wasserman *Tel:* 510-809-3700 *E-mail:* laura.wasserman@pgw.com *Web Site:* www.pgw.com
Membership(s): Science Fiction & Fantasy Writers of America

§Tahrike Tarsile Qur'an Inc
80-08 51 Ave, Elmhurst, NY 11373
Tel: 718-446-6472 *Fax:* 718-446-4370
E-mail: read@koranusa.org
Web Site: www.koranusa.org
Key Personnel
Pres: Aun Ali Khalfan
Publishers & distributors of the Holy Quran & other Islamic books, videos & CDs.
ISBN Prefix(es): 978-0-940368; 978-1-879402
Number of titles published annually: 5 Print
Total Titles: 50 Print

TAN Books
Imprint of Saint Benedict Press LLC
PO Box 410487, Charlotte, NC 28241
Toll Free Tel: 800-437-5876 *Fax:* 815-226-7770
E-mail: customerservice@tanbooks.com
Web Site: tanbooks.benedictpress.com; benedictpress.com
Key Personnel
Publr: Robert Gallagher
Founded: 1967
Publish traditional Catholic books, especially reprint classic works.
ISBN Prefix(es): 978-0-89555
Number of titles published annually: 15 Print
Total Titles: 550 Print

T&T Clark International
Imprint of Bloomsbury Publishing PLC
1385 Broadway, 5th fl, New York, NY 10018
Tel: 212-953-5858 *Toll Free Tel:* 800-561-7704 (orders) *Fax:* 212-953-5944
Web Site: www.continuumbooks.com
Key Personnel
Assoc Publr, Theology: Anna Turton
Sr Ed, Biblical Studies: Dominic Mattos
Mktg Mgr: Kim Petit *E-mail:* kim.petit@bloomsbury.com
Founded: 1821
Biblical studies, theology & church history.
ISBN Prefix(es): 978-0-8264; 978-1-56338; 978-0-334; 978-0-7162; 978-0-567
Number of titles published annually: 100 Print
Total Titles: 2,200 Print
Foreign Rep(s): Codasat (Canada)

Tanglewood Press
PO Box 3009, Terre Haute, IN 47803
Tel: 812-877-9488; 412-741-1579 (orders) *Toll Free Tel:* 800-836-4994 (orders) *Fax:* 412-741-0609 (orders)
Web Site: www.tanglewoodbooks.com
Key Personnel
Publr: Peggy Tierney *E-mail:* ptierney@tanglewoodbooks.com
Acqs Ed: Kairi Hamlin
Founded: 2003
Ms submissions accepted, see web site for guidelines. Send picture book mss or query letter with sample chapters for middle reader or young adult novels to Kairi Hamlin, Acqs Ed with SASE.
ISBN Prefix(es): 978-0-9749303; 978-1-933718
Number of titles published annually: 5 Print; 1 Audio
Total Titles: 35 Print; 2 Audio
Distribution Center: Publishers Group West (PGW), 1700 Fourth St, Berkeley, CA 94710 *Tel:* 510-809-3700 *Toll Free Tel:* 800-788-3123 *Fax:* 510-809-3777 *E-mail:* info@pgw.com *Web Site:* www.pgw.com

§Tantor Media Inc
2 Business Park, Old Saybrook, CT 06475
Toll Free Tel: 877-782-6867 *Toll Free Fax:* 888-782-7821
Web Site: www.tantor.com
Key Personnel
VP, Sales: John Molish *Tel:* 877-782-6867 ext 34 *E-mail:* jmolish@tantor.com
Dir, Acqs: Ron Formica *Tel:* 877-782-6867 ext 31 *E-mail:* ron@tantor.com
Mktg Mgr: Allan Hoving *Tel:* 877-782-6867 ext 76 *E-mail:* ahoving@tantor.com
Founded: 2001
Independent publisher & producer of audiobooks, ebooks, trade & paperback books. Publish fiction & nonfiction titles across all genres & categories.
Number of titles published annually: 12 Print; 750 Online; 15 E-Book; 700 Audio
Total Titles: 10 Print; 3,600 Online; 45 E-Book; 3,500 Audio
Imprints: Tantor Audio; Tantor Media
Foreign Rep(s): IPS (Worldwide)
Membership(s): ALA; Audio Publishers Association; Public Library Association

Tapestry Press Ltd
19 Nashoba Rd, Littleton, MA 01460
Tel: 978-486-0200 *Toll Free Tel:* 800-535-2007 *Fax:* 978-486-0244
E-mail: publish@tapestrypress.com
Web Site: www.tapestrypress.com
Key Personnel
Pres: Michael J Miskin
Publr: Elizabeth A Larsen
VP & Ed-in-Chief: Sara E Hofeldt
Founded: 1988
College textbooks & journals; custom textbooks & anthologies.
ISBN Prefix(es): 978-0-924234; 978-1-56888; 978-1-59830
Number of titles published annually: 100 Print
Total Titles: 175 Print

Taplinger Publishing Co Inc
PO Box 175, Marlboro, NJ 07746-0175
SAN: 213-6821
Tel: 305-256-7880 *Fax:* 305-256-7816
E-mail: taplingerpub@yahoo.com (rts & perms, edit, corp only)
Key Personnel
CEO: Theodore D Rosenfeld
Founded: 1955
General nonfiction, including art, biography, calligraphy, graphic arts, history, music.
ISBN Prefix(es): 978-0-8008
Number of titles published annually: 4 Print
Total Titles: 100 Print
Imprints: Crescendo
Foreign Rep(s): Baker & Taylor International (Africa, Asia, Europe, South Africa, South America)
Orders to: Parkwest Publications LLC, PO Box 310251, Miami, FL 33231-0251, Contact: Brian Squire *Tel:* 305-256-7880 *E-mail:* mail@parkwestpubs.com *Web Site:* www.parkwestpubs.com
Returns: Parkwest Publications LLC, 14332 SW 142 Ave, Miami, FL 33186, Contact: Brian Squire *Tel:* 305-256-7880
Warehouse: Parkwest Publications LLC, 14332 SW 142 Ave, Miami, FL 33186, Contact: Brian Squire *Tel:* 305-256-7880
Distribution Center: Parkwest Publications LLC, PO Box 310251, Miami, FL 33231-0251, Contact: Brian Squire *Tel:* 305-256-7880 *E-mail:* mail@parkwestpubs.com *Web Site:* www.parkwestpubs.com

Jeremy P Tarcher
Imprint of Penguin Group (USA) LLC
375 Hudson St, New York, NY 10014
SAN: 282-5074
Tel: 212-366-2000
E-mail: online@penguinputnam.com
Web Site: www.penguinputnam.com; us.penguingroup.com
Key Personnel
VP & Publr: Joel Fotinos
VP, Ed-in-Chief & Exec Ed: Mitchell Horowitz
Publicity & Mktg Dir: Brianna Yamashita
Publicity & Mktg Coord: Tyler Fields
Exec Ed: Sara Carder
Ed: Andrew Yackira
Assoc Ed: Joanna Ng
Founded: 1965
Nonfiction: cookbooks, crafts, humor, music & dance, health, nutrition, psychology, self-help, social sciences & sociology, biography, child

care & development, behavioral sciences, business, human relations, education.
ISBN Prefix(es): 978-0-87477
Number of titles published annually: 51 Print
Total Titles: 566 Print

Taschen America
6671 Sunset Blvd, Suite 1508, Los Angeles, CA 90028
Tel: 323-463-4441 *Toll Free Tel:* 888-TASCHEN (827-2436) *Fax:* 323-463-4442
E-mail: contact-us@taschen.com
Web Site: www.taschen.com
Key Personnel
Busn Mgr: Meghan Clarke *E-mail:* m.clarke@taschen.com
Founded: 1996
Publishers of high-quality, reasonably priced illustrated books on the subjects of art, architecture, design, photography, erotica, gay interest & popular culture.
ISBN Prefix(es): 978-3-8228; 978-3-8365
Number of titles published annually: 80 Print
Total Titles: 500 Print
Imprints: Taschen GmbH
Distribution Center: Ingram, One Ingram Blvd, La Vergne, TN 37086 *Toll Free Tel:* 888-558-2624

§The Taunton Press Inc
63 S Main St, Newtown, CT 06470
SAN: 210-5144
Mailing Address: PO Box 5506, Newtown, CT 06470-5506
Tel: 203-426-8171 *Toll Free Tel:* 800-477-8727 (cust serv); 800-888-8286 (orders) *Fax:* 203-426-3434
E-mail: booksales@taunton.com
Web Site: www.taunton.com
Key Personnel
CEO: Dan McCarthy
VP, Trade Sales: Jay Annis
Founded: 1975
Woodworking, home building, fiber arts, cooking & gardening books, magazines, DVDs & web sites.
ISBN Prefix(es): 978-0-918804; 978-0-942391; 978-1-56158; 978-1-60085
Number of titles published annually: 50 Print; 10 CD-ROM; 60 E-Book; 1 Audio
Total Titles: 525 Print; 100 CD-ROM; 10 Online; 300 E-Book; 1 Audio
Distributor for Academia Barilla
Foreign Rep(s): Capricorn Books (Australia); Guild of Master Craftsman (Europe); Random House Canada (Canada); Stanson Yeung (Asia); Zimpfer Books (Caribbean, Latin America)
Foreign Rights: Librisource Inc (Worldwide)
Warehouse: 141 Sheridan Dr, Naugatuck, CT 06770
Distribution Center: Ingram Publisher Services, One Ingram Blvd, La Vergne, TN 37086 *Tel:* 615-793-5000

Taylor & Francis Inc
325 Chestnut St, Suite 800, Philadelphia, PA 20036-1802
Tel: 215-625-8900 *Toll Free Tel:* 800-354-1420 *Fax:* 215-625-2940
E-mail: customer.service@taylorandfrancis.com
Web Site: www.taylorandfrancis.com
Key Personnel
Pres: Kevin J Bradley
VP, Prodn: Ed Cilurso *E-mail:* ed.cilurso@taylorandfrancis.com
Global Publg Dir, Journals: Leon Heward-Mills
Journals Mktg Dir: Deborah Lovell *E-mail:* deborah.lovell@taylorandfrancis.com
Journals Sales Dir: Margaret Walker *Tel:* 215-625-8900 ext 14346 *E-mail:* margaret.walker@taylorandfrancis.com
Founded: 1974
Journals in engineering, physical science, psychology, sociology, physics, chemistry, mathematics, environmental science, business, public health, marketing, arts, anthropology, political science, library science & LGBT studies.
ISBN Prefix(es): 978-1-56032; 978-0-87630; 978-0-86377; 978-0-8448; 978-0-85066; 978-0-85109; 978-0-905273; 978-1-85000
Number of titles published annually: 585 Print
Total Titles: 1,500 Print
Imprints: CRC Press; Garland Science; Psychology Press; Routledge; Taylor & Francis Asia Pacific; Taylor & Francis Books
Foreign Office(s): Taylor & Francis Group, Milton Park, 2 & 4 Park Sq, Abingdon, Oxford OX14 4RN, United Kingdom *Tel:* (020) 7017 4258 *Fax:* (020) 7017 6336
Orders to: 7625 Empire Dr, Florence, KY 41042-2929 *Toll Free Tel:* 800-634-7064 *Toll Free Fax:* 800-248-4724 *E-mail:* orders@taylorandfrancis.com; Bookpoint, 130 Milton Park, Abingdon, Oxon OX14 4SB, United Kingdom (Africa, Asia, Australia, Europe) *Tel:* (01235) 400 400 *Fax:* (01235) 400 401 *E-mail:* book.orders@tandf.co.uk
Distribution Center: 7625 Empire Dr, Florence, KY 41042 *Toll Free Tel:* 800-634-7064 *Toll Free Fax:* 800-248-4724 *E-mail:* orders@taylorandfrancis.com

Taylor-Dth Publishing
108 Caribe Isle, Novato, CA 94949
Tel: 415-299-1087
Web Site: www.taylor-dth.com
Key Personnel
Owner: Harold Miller *E-mail:* hmiller@taylor-dth.com
Founded: 2001
Limited book publisher.
ISBN Prefix(es): 978-0-9747532; 978-0-9727583; 978-0-9774431
Number of titles published annually: 4 Print
Total Titles: 40 Print

TCU Press, see Texas Christian University Press

Teach Me Tapes Inc
6016 Blue Circle Dr, Minnetonka, MN 55343
Tel: 952-933-8086 *Toll Free Tel:* 800-456-4656 *Fax:* 952-933-0512
E-mail: marie@teachmetapes.com
Web Site: www.teachmetapes.com
Key Personnel
Owner & Pres: Judy Mahoney *E-mail:* judy@teachmetapes.com
Founded: 1985
ISBN Prefix(es): 978-0-934633; 978-1-59972
Number of titles published annually: 3 Print
Total Titles: 100 Print; 37 Audio
Distribution Center: Amazon.com
Follett School Solutions Inc, 1340 Ridgeview Dr, McHenry, IL 60050 *Tel:* 815-759-1700 *Toll Free Tel:* 888-511-5114 (cust serv) *Fax:* 815-759-9831 *Toll Free Fax:* 800-852-5458 *E-mail:* info@follettlearning.com *Web Site:* www.follettlearning.com SAN: 169-1902

Teacher Created Resources Inc
6421 Industry Way, Westminster, CA 92683
Tel: 714-891-7895 *Toll Free Tel:* 800-662-4321; 888-343-4335 *Fax:* 714-892-0283 *Toll Free Fax:* 800-525-1254
E-mail: custserv@teachercreated.com
Web Site: www.teachercreated.com
Key Personnel
Founder & Pres: Mary Dupuy Smith
Founded: 1982
Publishes PreK-12 curriculum programs, supplemental resource materials & technology products. Also, provides professional staff development for teachers.
ISBN Prefix(es): 978-1-55734
Number of titles published annually: 250 Print
Total Titles: 1,500 Print

§Teachers College Press
Affiliate of Teachers College, Columbia University
1234 Amsterdam Ave, New York, NY 10027
SAN: 213-263X
Mailing Address: PO Box 20, Williston, VT 05495-0020
Tel: 212-678-3929 *Toll Free Tel:* 800-575-6566 *Fax:* 212-678-4149; 802-864-7626
E-mail: tcpress@tc.columbia.edu; tcp.orders@aidcvt.com (orders)
Web Site: www.teacherscollegepress.com
Key Personnel
Dir: Carole Saltz
Exec Acqs Ed: Brian Ellerbeck *E-mail:* ellerbeck@tc.edu
Sr Acqs Ed: Marie Ellen Larcada *E-mail:* larcada@tc.edu
Acqs Ed: Meg Lemke *E-mail:* lemke@tc.edu
Prod Mgr: Peter Sieger
Founded: 1904
Professional books & textbooks in education; tests, classroom materials & reference works.
ISBN Prefix(es): 978-0-8077
Number of titles published annually: 60 Print; 1 CD-ROM
Total Titles: 1,123 Print; 1 CD-ROM
Foreign Rep(s): Baker & Taylor International (Africa, Asia, Australia, Latin America, Middle East, Orient, South America); Eurospan Ltd (Europe, UK); Guidance Center (Canada)
Orders to: Baker & Taylor International, PO Box 6885, Bridgewater, NJ 08807-0885 *Tel:* 908-541-7305 *Fax:* 908-541-7853 *E-mail:* btinfo@btol.com *Web Site:* www.btol.com; University of Toronto Press-Guidance Centre, 5201 Dufferin St, Toronto, ON M3H 5T8, Canada (CN) *Toll Free Tel:* 800-565-9523 *Toll Free Fax:* 800-221-9958 *E-mail:* utpbooks@utpress.utoronto.ca *Web Site:* www.utpress.utoronto.ca; Pademelon Press Pty Ltd, PO Box 6500, Baulkham Hills, NSW 2153, Australia (Australia & New Zealand) *Tel:* (02) 9634 4655 *Fax:* (02) 9680 4634 *E-mail:* enquiry@pademelonpress.com.au; Kinokuniya Co Ltd, Book Import Dept, 3-7-10 Shimo-Meguro, Meguro-Ku, 153-8504 Tokyo, Japan (Japan) *Tel:* (03) 6910-0531 *Fax:* (03) 6420-1362 *E-mail:* info@kinokuniya.co.jp *Web Site:* www.kinokuniya.co.jp/english/index.html; Publishers Marketing Services Pte Ltd, Unit 509, Block E, Phileo Damansara 1, Jalan 16/11, Off Jalan Damansara, 46350 Petaling Jaya, Selangor, Malaysia (Brunei & Malaysia), Contact: Karen Lim *Tel:* (0603) 7955 3588 *Fax:* (0603) 7955 3017 *E-mail:* karenlim@pms.com.sg *Web Site:* www.pms.com.sg; CRW Marketing Services for Publishers Inc, 4 Topaz Rd, Greenheights, Taytay, 1920 Rizal, Philippines (Guam & Philippines), Contact: Tony Sagun *Tel:* (0632) 660 8430 *Fax:* (0632) 660 0342 *E-mail:* lwwagent@pldtdsl.net; Publishers Marketing Services Pte Ltd, 10C Jalan Ampas, No 07-01, Ho Seng Lee Flatted Warehouse, Singapore 329513, Singapore (Singapore), Contact: Raymond Lim *Tel:* (065) 6256 5166 *Fax:* (065) 6253 0008 *E-mail:* raymondlim@pms.com.sg *Web Site:* www.pms.com.sh; Everybody's Books, PO Box 301321, Durban North 4016, South Africa (South Africa) *Tel:* (031) 569 2229 *Fax:* (031) 569 2234 *E-mail:* warren@ebbooks.co.za; Unifacmanu Trading Co Ltd, 4F, 91, Ho-Ping E Rd, Sec 1, Taipei 10609, Taiwan (Taiwan) *Tel:* (02) 2391-4280 *Fax:* (02) 2394-3103 *E-mail:* unifacmu@ms34@hinet.net *Web Site:* www.unifacmanu.com.tw/unifhome3.htm; Eurospan, c/o Turpin Distribution, Stratton Business Park, Pegasus Dr, Biggleswade, Bedfordshire SG18 8TQ, United Kingdom

(Africa, Continental Europe, Middle East & UK) *Tel:* (01767) 604972 *Fax:* (01767) 601640 *E-mail:* eurospan@turpin-distribution.com *Web Site:* www.eurospanbookstore.com/tcp
Returns: Returns Dept, 82 Wintersport Lane, Williston, VT 05495
Membership(s): AAP; American Association of University Presses; BISG

§Teacher's Discovery
Division of American Eagle Co Inc
2741 Paldan Dr, Auburn Hills, MI 48326
Toll Free Tel: 800-832-2437 *Toll Free Fax:* 800-287-4509
E-mail: foreignlanguage@teachersdiscovery.com
Key Personnel
Owner: Skip McWilliams
Mktg Mgr: Steve Giroux
Founded: 1968
Distribute several proprietary items we create; also publish several works written by authors other than those employed by Teachers Discovery; Social Studies, English & teachers of Spanish, French & German.
Number of titles published annually: 200 Print
Branch Office(s)
2676 Paldan Dr, Auburn Hills, MI 48326 *Toll Free Tel:* 800-583-6454 *Toll Free Fax:* 888-395-6686 *E-mail:* english@teachersdiscovery.com

Teachers of English to Speakers of Other Languages Inc (TESOL)
1925 Ballenger Ave, Alexandria, VA 22314-6820
Tel: 703-836-0774 *Toll Free Tel:* 888-547-3369 *Fax:* 703-836-7864
E-mail: info@tesol.org
Web Site: www.tesol.org
Key Personnel
Exec Dir: Rosa Aronson *Tel:* 703-836-0774 ext 505 *E-mail:* raronson@tesol.org
Publg Mgr: Carol Edwards *Tel:* 703-836-0774 ext 525 *E-mail:* cedwards@tesol.org
Founded: 1966
Professional educator association & publisher of professional education related books.
ISBN Prefix(es): 978-0-939791; 978-1-1931
Number of titles published annually: 6 Print
Total Titles: 90 Print; 1 CD-ROM
Distributed by Alta Book Ctr; Delta Systems Inc; New Readers Press; Saddleback Educational
Orders to: PO Box 79283, Baltimore, MD 21279 *Tel:* 240-646-7037 *Toll Free Tel:* 888-891-0041 *Fax:* 301-206-9789 *E-mail:* tesolpubs@brightkey.net
Distribution Center: Tesol Publications at Tasco, PO Box 753, Waldorf, MD 20604 *E-mail:* tesolpubs@brightkey.net

§Teaching & Learning Co
501 E Third St, Dayton, OH 45402
Mailing Address: PO Box 802, Dayton, OH 45401-0802
Tel: 937-228-6118 *Toll Free Tel:* 800-444-1144 *Fax:* 937-223-2042
E-mail: info@lorenz.com
Key Personnel
VP, Mktg: Debra Kaiser *E-mail:* debk@lorenz.com
Founded: 1994
Educational publishing division includes visual resources, instructional guides & reproducibles, elementary supplementals.
ISBN Prefix(es): 978-1-57310
Number of titles published annually: 35 Print
Total Titles: 400 Print; 325 E-Book; 10 Audio
Membership(s): Education Market Association

§Teaching Strategies
7101 Wisconsin Ave, Suite 700, Bethesda, MD 20814
Tel: 301-634-0818 *Toll Free Tel:* 800-637-3652 *Fax:* 301-657-0250
E-mail: customerrelations@teachingstrategies.com
Web Site: www.teachingstrategies.com
Key Personnel
COO: Andrea Valentine *E-mail:* andreav@teachingstrategies.com
Founded: 1988
Curriculum, assessment & training materials for early childhood education (birth-age 8) & parent's guides; web subscription service.
ISBN Prefix(es): 978-1-879537; 978-0-9602892; 978-1-60617
Number of titles published annually: 5 Print
Total Titles: 66 Print
Distributor for Gryphon House
Orders to: PO Box 42243, Washington, DC 20015
Returns: Teaching Strategies Inc, c/o RRD P & F, 1077 Prospect Lane, Kaukauna, WI 54130

§Temple University Press
Division of Temple University of the Commonwealth System of Higher Education
1852 N Tenth St, Philadelphia, PA 19122-6099
SAN: 202-7666
Tel: 215-926-2140 *Toll Free Tel:* 800-621-2736 *Fax:* 215-926-2141
E-mail: tempress@temple.edu
Web Site: www.temple.edu/tempress
Key Personnel
Dir: Alex Holzman *E-mail:* aholzman@temple.edu
Dir, Prodn & Electronic Publg: Charles Ault *E-mail:* charles.ault@temple.edu
Mktg Dir & Asst Dir: Ann-Marie Anderson *E-mail:* anderson@temple.edu
Exec Ed: Micah Kleit *E-mail:* micah.kleit@temple.edu
Ad & Promo Mgr: Irene Imperio Kull *E-mail:* irene.imperio@temple.edu
Busn Mgr: Barry Adams *E-mail:* barry.adams@temple.edu
Cust Serv Mgr: Karen Baker *E-mail:* karen.baker@temple.edu
Publicity Mgr: Gary Kramer *E-mail:* gkramer@temple.edu
Rts & Perms & Intl Rts: Sara Cohen *E-mail:* sara.cohen@temple.edu
Founded: 1969
Scholarly books; all regional interests.
ISBN Prefix(es): 978-0-87722; 978-1-56639; 978-1-59213; 978-1-4399
Number of titles published annually: 45 Print
Total Titles: 1,450 Print
Foreign Rep(s): Baker & Taylor Ltd (Asia, The Pacific, Worldwide exc Canada); Combined Academic Publishing (CAP) (Europe); East-West Export Books (Royden Muranaka) (Asia, The Pacific); Lynn McClory (Canada)
Returns: Temple University Press Chicago Distribution Center, 11030 S Langley, Chicago, IL 60628 *Tel:* 773-702-7000 *Fax:* 773-702-7000 *Toll Free Fax:* 800-621-8476
Warehouse: Temple University Press Chicago Distribution Center, 11030 S Langley, Chicago, IL 60628, Contact: Sue Tranchita *Tel:* 773-702-7000 *Fax:* 773-702-7000 *Toll Free Fax:* 800-621-8476
Membership(s): Association of American University Presses; Society for Scholarly Publishing

Templegate Publishers
302 E Adams St, Springfield, IL 62701
SAN: 123-0115
Mailing Address: PO Box 5152, Springfield, IL 62705-5152
Tel: 217-522-3353 (edit & sales); 217-522-3354 (billing) *Toll Free Tel:* 800-367-4844 (orders only) *Fax:* 217-522-3362
E-mail: wisdom@templegate.com; orders@templegate.com (sales)
Web Site: www.templegate.com
Key Personnel
Dir & Owner: Thomas M Garvey *E-mail:* tmg@templegate.com
Exec Ed, Rts & Perms & Publicity: John Fisher
Sales & Ad Mgr, ISBN & Lib Sales Dir: Elaine Garvey
Founded: 1947
Nonfiction.
ISBN Prefix(es): 978-0-87243
Number of titles published annually: 4 Print
Total Titles: 225 Print
Imprints: Octavo Press
Foreign Rep(s): Gracewing (Europe)

Templeton Press
Subsidiary of John Templeton Foundation
300 Conshohocken State Rd, Suite 550, West Conshohocken, PA 19428
Tel: 484-531-8380 *Fax:* 484-531-8382
E-mail: tpinfo@templetonpress.org
Web Site: www.templetonpress.org
Key Personnel
Ed-in-Chief: Susan Arellano *E-mail:* sarellano@templetonpress.org
Mktg Mgr: Matt Smiley *E-mail:* msmiley@templetonpress.org
Founded: 1987
Focus on science & religion, spirituality & health, character development & business.
ISBN Prefix(es): 978-1-890151; 978-1-932031; 978-1-59947
Number of titles published annually: 20 Print; 20 E-Book
Total Titles: 167 Print; 100 E-Book; 20 Audio
Foreign Rights: Rainbow Book Agencies (Australia)
Billing Address: Chicago Distribution Center, 11030 S Langley Ave, Chicago, IL 60628 *Tel:* 773-702-7000 *Toll Free Tel:* 800-621-2736 *Fax:* 773-702-7212 *Toll Free Fax:* 800-621-8476 *Web Site:* www.chicagodistributioncenter.org
Orders to: Chicago Distribution Center, 11030 S Langley Ave, Chicago, IL 60628 *Tel:* 773-702-7000 *Toll Free Tel:* 800-621-2736 *Fax:* 773-702-7212 *Toll Free Fax:* 800-621-8476 *Web Site:* www.chicagodistributioncenter.org
Returns: Chicago Distribution Center, 11030 S Langley Ave, Chicago, IL 60628 *Tel:* 773-702-7000 *Toll Free Tel:* 800-621-2736 *Fax:* 773-702-7212 *Toll Free Fax:* 800-621-8476 *Web Site:* www.chicagodistributioncenter.org
Shipping Address: Chicago Distribution Center, 11030 S Langley Ave, Chicago, IL 60628 *Tel:* 773-702-7000 *Toll Free Tel:* 800-621-2736 *Fax:* 773-702-7212 *Toll Free Fax:* 800-621-8476 *Web Site:* www.chicagodistributioncenter.org
Warehouse: Chicago Distribution Center, 11030 S Langley Ave, Chicago, IL 60628 *Tel:* 773-702-7000 *Toll Free Tel:* 800-621-2736 *Fax:* 773-702-7212 *Toll Free Fax:* 800-621-8476 *Web Site:* www.chicagodistributioncenter.org
Distribution Center: Chicago Distribution Center, 11030 S Langley Ave, Chicago, IL 60628 *Tel:* 773-702-7000 *Toll Free Tel:* 800-621-2736 *Fax:* 773-702-7212 *Toll Free Fax:* 800-621-8476 *Web Site:* www.chicagodistributioncenter.org
Membership(s): The Independent Book Publishers Association; Network of Alternatives for Publishers, Retailers & Artists Inc

Temporal Mechanical Press
Division of Enos Mills Cabin Museum & Gallery
6760 Hwy 7, Estes Park, CO 80517-6404
Tel: 970-586-4706
E-mail: enosmillscbn@earthlink.net
Web Site: www.enosmills.com
Key Personnel
Owner: Elizabeth M Mills; Eryn Mills
ISBN Prefix(es): 978-1-928878

Number of titles published annually: 3 Print
Total Titles: 32 Print

Ten Speed Press
Imprint of Crown Publishing Group
2625 Alcatraz Ave, Unit 505, Berkeley, CA 94705
SAN: 202-7674
Tel: 510-285-3000 *Toll Free Tel:* 800-841-BOOK (841-2665)
E-mail: csorders@randomhouse.com
Web Site: crownpublishing.com/imprint/ten-speed-press
Key Personnel
SVP & Publr: Aaron Wehner
VP, Assoc Publr & Gen Ed, Food52 Works: Hannah Rahill
VP & Edit Dir: Julie Bennett
Sr Art Dir: Kara Plikaitis; Elizabeth Stromberg; Toni Tajima
Sr Dir, Mktg: Michele Crim
Art Dir: Ashley Lima
Assoc Art Dir: Katy Brown
Creative Dir: Emma Boys Campion
Publicity Dir: Kristin Casemore
Exec Ed: Jenny Wapner
Sr Ed: Emily Timberlake; Lisa Westmoreland
Ed: Patrick Barb; Sara Golski; Kelly Snowden
Assoc Ed: Kaitlin Ketchum
Sr Design Mgr: Chloe Rawlins
Sr Mktg & Publicity Mgr: David Hawk
Mktg & Publicity Mgr, Cookbooks: Lorraine Woodcheke
Assoc Mktg Mgr: Daniel Wikey
Assoc Mgr, Foreign Rts: Nidhi Berry
Assoc Publicity & Mktg Mgr: Erin Welke
Sr Publicist: Kara Van de Water
Designer: Sarah Pulver
Jr Designer: Tatiana Pavola
Prodn Designer: Anitra Alcantara
Mktg Asst: Ashley Matuszak
Founded: 1971
Trade, paperbound, fine editions: Americana & regional, art, book trade, business, history, social sciences, cooking, gardening, hobbies, recreation, health, meditation, philosophy, education, humor, animal/pet, self-help, how-to, travel, reference.
ISBN Prefix(es): 978-1-58761; 978-1-58091; 978-1-58008; 978-1-60774
Number of titles published annually: 100 Print
Total Titles: 587 Print
Imprints: Food52 Works
Foreign Rep(s): Random House (Worldwide)

Teora USA LLC
505 Hampton Park Blvd, Unit G, Capitol Heights, MD 20743
SAN: 256-1220
Tel: 301-986-6990 *Toll Free Tel:* 800-974-2105 *Fax:* 301-350-5480 *Toll Free Fax:* 800-358-3754
E-mail: 2010@teora.com
Web Site: www.teora.com
Key Personnel
Busn Mgr: Teodor Raducanu
Contact: Maria Nedelcu
Founded: 2003
ISBN Prefix(es): 978-1-59496
Number of titles published annually: 6 Print
Total Titles: 60 Print
Imprints: Teora
Distribution Center: Fitzhenry & Whiteside, 195 Allstate Pkwy, Markham, ON L3R 4T8, Canada *Tel:* 904-477-9700 *Toll Free Fax:* 800-260-9777
Membership(s): The Independent Book Publishers Association

TESOL, see Teachers of English to Speakers of Other Languages Inc (TESOL)

Teton NewMedia
90 E Simpson, Suite 110, Jackson, WY 83001
Mailing Address: PO Box 4833, Jackson, WY 83001
Tel: 307-732-0028 *Toll Free Tel:* 877-306-9793 *Fax:* 307-734-0841
E-mail: sales@tetonnm.com
Web Site: www.tetonnm.com
Key Personnel
Mktg Mgr: Sara Scartz-Montesano *Tel:* 307-732-0028 ext 101 *E-mail:* sara@tetonnm.com
Founded: 1999 (By John Sphar & Carroll Cann)
Health science publisher that focuses on producing high quality, affordable veterinary text & reference books.
ISBN Prefix(es): 978-1-893441; 978-1-59161
Number of titles published annually: 6 Print; 2 CD-ROM
Total Titles: 25 Print; 18 CD-ROM
Distributed by Blackwells; LifeLearn; Logan Brothers; Rittenhouse; Yankee
Distributor for LifeLearn

Tetra Press
Division of Pfizer Inc
3001 Commerce St, Blacksburg, VA 24060
Tel: 540-951-5400 *Toll Free Tel:* 800-526-0650 *Fax:* 540-951-5415
E-mail: consumer@tetra-fish.com
Web Site: www.tetra-fish.com
Key Personnel
Prod Mgr: Wayne Marton
Fish, reptiles, amphibians & ponds.
ISBN Prefix(es): 978-1-56465
Number of titles published annually: 3 Print
Total Titles: 114 Print
Branch Office(s)
Speciality Book Marketing Inc, 443 Park Ave S, New York, NY 10016, Contact: William Corsa
Distributed by Voyageur Press

Texas A&M University Press
Division of Texas A&M University
John H Lindsey Bldg, Lewis St, 4354 TAMU, College Station, TX 77843-4354
SAN: 207-5237
Tel: 979-845-1436 *Toll Free Tel:* 800-826-8911 (orders) *Fax:* 979-847-8752 *Toll Free Fax:* 888-617-2421 (orders)
E-mail: tampress@tamu.edu
Web Site: www.tamupress.com
Key Personnel
Dir: Dr Charles Backus *Tel:* 979-458-3980 *E-mail:* charles.backus@tamu.edu
Lib Sales Dir & Mktg Mgr: Gayla Christiansen *Tel:* 979-845-0148 *E-mail:* gayla-c@tamu.edu
Ed-in-Chief & Mng Ed: Shannon Davies *Tel:* 979-845-0759 *E-mail:* sdavies@tamu.edu
Mgr, Cust Rel: Sharon Mills *Tel:* 979-458-3994 *E-mail:* sharon-mills@tamu.edu
Design Mgr: Mary Ann Jacob *Tel:* 979-845-3694 *E-mail:* m-jacob@tamu.edu
Fin Mgr: Dianna Sells *Tel:* 979-845-0146 *E-mail:* d-sells@tamu.edu
Publicity & Ad Mgr: Holli Estridge *Tel:* 979-458-3982 *E-mail:* holli.stridge@tamu.edu
Trade Sales: David Neel *Tel:* 979-458-3981 *E-mail:* d-neel@tamu.edu
Founded: 1974
Scholarly nonfiction, regional studies, economics, history, natural history, presidential studies, anthropology, US-Mexican borderlands studies, women's studies, nautical archaeology, military studies, agriculture, Texas history & archaeology.
ISBN Prefix(es): 978-0-89096; 978-1-58544; 978-1-60344; 978-1-60344
Number of titles published annually: 60 Print; 1 CD-ROM
Total Titles: 1,400 Print; 2 CD-ROM; 900 E-Book; 4 Audio
Distributor for Stephen F Austin State University Press; McWhiney Foundation Press/State House Press; Southern Methodist University Press; Texas Christian University Press; Texas Review Press; Texas State Historical Association; University of North Texas Press
Foreign Rep(s): Eurospan Group (Europe, UK); EWEB (Asia, Australia, Middle East, New Zealand, Pacific Islands); Scholarly Book Services (Laura Rust) (Canada); US PubRep (Craig Falk) (Latin America)
Foreign Rights: Tamu Press
Membership(s): Association of American University Presses

Texas Christian University Press
3000 Sandage Ave, Fort Worth, TX 76109
Mailing Address: PO Box 298300, Fort Worth, TX 76129
Tel: 817-257-7822 *Toll Free Tel:* 800-826-8911 *Fax:* 817-257-5075
Web Site: www.prs.tcu.edu
Key Personnel
Dir: Dan Williams *Tel:* 817-257-5907 *E-mail:* d.e.williams@tcu.edu
Prodn Mgr: Melinda Esco *Tel:* 817-257-6874 *E-mail:* m.esco@tcu.edu
Mktg Coord: Rebecca Allen *Tel:* 817-257-6872 *E-mail:* rebecca.a.allen@tcu.edu
Ed: Kathy S Walton *Tel:* 817-257-5074 *E-mail:* k.s.walton@tcu.edu
Founded: 1966
History & literature of Texas & the American West.
ISBN Prefix(es): 978-0-912646; 978-0-87565
Number of titles published annually: 15 Print; 20 Online
Total Titles: 440 Print; 20 Online; 50 E-Book; 1 Audio
Distributed by Texas A&M University Press
Foreign Rep(s): Texas A&M University Press
Shipping Address: Texas A&M University Press, Tamus 4354, College Station, TX 77843-4354, Contact: Sharon Mills
Warehouse: Texas A&M University Press, Tamus 4354, College Station, TX 77843-4354, Contact: Sharon Mills
Membership(s): Association of American University Presses

Texas State Historical Association
Stovall Hall 175, 1400 W Highland St, Denton, TX 76203
Mailing Address: 1155 Union Circle, Suite 311580, Denton, TX 76203-5017
Tel: 940-369-5200 *Fax:* 940-369-5248
Web Site: www.tshaonline.org
Key Personnel
Dir: Kent Calder
Assoc Ed: Ryan Schumacher *E-mail:* ryanschumacher@tshaonline.org
Founded: 1897
Books & articles related to Texas history.
ISBN Prefix(es): 978-0-87611
Number of titles published annually: 4 Print
Total Titles: 125 Print; 3 Online
Distributed by Texas A&M University Press

Texas Tech University Press
2903 Fourth St, Suite 201, Lubbock, TX 79409
Mailing Address: Box 41037, Lubbock, TX 79409-1037
Tel: 806-742-2982 *Toll Free Tel:* 800-832-4042 *Fax:* 806-742-2979
E-mail: ttup@ttu.edu
Web Site: www.ttupress.org
Key Personnel
Dir: Robert Mandel *E-mail:* robert.mandel@ttu.edu
Exhibits & Publicity Mgr: John Brock *E-mail:* john.brock@ttu.edu
Off Mgr: Isabel Williams *E-mail:* isabel.williams@ttu.edu
Ed-in-Chief: Judith Keeling *E-mail:* judith.keeling@ttu.edu

Mng Ed: Joanna Conrad *E-mail:* joanna.conrad@ttu.edu
Prodn: Kasey McBeath *E-mail:* kasey.mcbeath@ttu.edu
Cust Serv Rep: LaTisha Roberts *E-mail:* latisha.roberts@ttu.edu
Asst to Dir: Jada Rankin *E-mail:* jada.rankin@ttu.edu
Founded: 1971
Scholarly books & journals: biological sciences, literary criticism, museum-related sciences, specialized regional, poetry, history, fiction. Also costume history.
ISBN Prefix(es): 978-0-89672
Number of titles published annually: 25 Print
Total Titles: 364 Print
Distributor for National Ranching Heritage Center
Distribution Center: Chicago Distribution Center, 11030 S Langley Ave, Chicago, IL 60628 SAN: 202-5280
Membership(s): Association of American University Presses; Publishers Association of the West

§University of Texas Press
Division of University of Texas
2100 Comal St, Austin, TX 78722
SAN: 212-9876
Mailing Address: PO Box 7819, Austin, TX 78713-7819
Tel: 512-471-7233 *Fax:* 512-232-7178
E-mail: utpress@uts.cc.utexas.edu
Web Site: www.utexaspress.com
Key Personnel
CFO: Joyce Lewandoski
Dir, Press: Dave Hamrick
Ed-in-Chief: Theresa May
Acq Ed: Jim Burr
Mgr & Intl Rts Contact: Laura Bost
Asst Mktg Mgr: Nancy Bryan
Sales Mgr: Gianna La Norte
Credit Mgr & Cust Serv: Brenda Jo Hoggutt
Prodn Mgr: Ellen McKie
Ad, Exhibits Mgr: Chris Farmer
Founded: 1950
General scholarly nonfiction, Latin America, Middle Eastern studies, Southwest regional, social sciences, humanities & science, linguistics, architecture, classics, natural history, Latin American literature in translation.
ISBN Prefix(es): 978-0-292
Number of titles published annually: 100 Print
Total Titles: 2,200 Print; 1 CD-ROM; 1 Online
Distributor for Bat Conservation International; Institute for Mesoamerican Studies; Menil Foundation; Rothko Chapel; Texas Parks & Wildlife Department
Foreign Rep(s): East-West Export Books (Australia, New Zealand); Nicholas Esson (Europe, UK); Hargraves, Fuller & Paton (Canada); Marketing Dept, University of Texas (Caribbean)
Membership(s): AAP; Association of American University Presses

Texas Western Press
Affiliate of University of Texas at El Paso
c/o University of Texas at El Paso, 500 W University Ave, El Paso, TX 79968-0633
SAN: 202-7712
Tel: 915-747-5688 *Toll Free Tel:* 800-488-3798 (orders only) *Fax:* 915-747-7515
E-mail: twpress@utep.edu
Web Site: twp.utep.edu
Key Personnel
Dir: Robert Stakes
Founded: 1952
Scholarly books on the history, art, photography & culture of the American Southwest.
ISBN Prefix(es): 978-0-87404
Number of titles published annually: 3 Print
Total Titles: 63 Print; 1 Audio
Imprints: Southwestern Studies
Distributed by University of Texas Press
Membership(s): American Association of University Presses

TFH Publications Inc
Subsidiary of Central Garden & Pet Corp
One TFH Plaza, Third & Union Aves, Neptune City, NJ 07753
SAN: 202-7720
Tel: 732-988-8400 *Toll Free Tel:* 800-631-2188 *Fax:* 732-776-8763
E-mail: info@tfh.com
Web Site: www.tfh.com
Key Personnel
CEO & Pres: Glen Axelrod
Publr: Christopher T Reggio *E-mail:* creggio@tfh.com
Founded: 1952
Pet care reference books & specialty magazines.
ISBN Prefix(es): 978-0-87666; 978-0-86622; 978-0-7938; 978-1-890087 (Microcosm Books); 978-0-9820262 (Microcosm Books)
Number of titles published annually: 40 Print; 40 E-Book
Total Titles: 1,200 Print; 200 E-Book
Imprints: Microcosm Books
Divisions: Nylabone Products
Foreign Rep(s): Brooklands Aquarium Ltd (New Zealand); Fitzhenry & Whiteside (Canada); Rolf C Hagen Ltd (Canada); Interpet Publishing (England); TFH Pty Ltd (Australia); Trinity Books (South Africa)
Foreign Rights: Richard Gay (all other territories)
Warehouse: 50 TFH Way, Neptune City, NJ 07753

Thames & Hudson
500 Fifth Ave, New York, NY 10110
SAN: 202-5795
Tel: 212-354-3763 *Toll Free Tel:* 800-233-4830 *Fax:* 212-398-1252
E-mail: bookinfo@thames.wwnorton.com
Web Site: www.thamesandhudsonusa.com
Key Personnel
CEO: Rolf Grisebach
Pres & Publr: Will Balliett
Edit Dir: Christopher Sweet
Assoc Mktg Dir: Lauren Miller
Publicity: Tiffany McKenna
Founded: 1977
Nonfiction trade, quality paperbacks & college texts on art, archaeology, architecture, crafts, history & photography.
ISBN Prefix(es): 978-0-500
Number of titles published annually: 150 Print
Total Titles: 1,000 Print
Distributed by W W Norton & Co Inc
Advertising Agency: Verso
Shipping Address: National Book Co Inc, Keystone Industrial Park, Scranton, PA 18512
Membership(s): AAP

Theatre Communications Group
520 Eighth Ave, 24th fl, New York, NY 10018-4156
Tel: 212-609-5900 *Fax:* 212-609-5901
E-mail: tcg@tcg.org
Web Site: www.tcg.org
Key Personnel
Publr: Terence Nemeth *E-mail:* tnemeth@tcg.org
Edit Dir & Ed: Kathy Sova
Founded: 1961
Performing arts, dramatic literature.
ISBN Prefix(es): 978-0-930452; 978-1-55936
Number of titles published annually: 20 Print
Total Titles: 250 Print
Distributor for Absolute Classics; Aurora Metro Publications; Nick Hern Books; Oberon Books; Padua Playwrights Press; PAJ Publications; Playwrights Canada Press; Martin E Segal Theatre Center Publications; Ubu Repertory Theatre Publications
Foreign Rep(s): Nick Hern Books (UK); Playwrights Canada Press (Canada)
Distribution Center: Consortium Book Sales & Distribution, The Keg House, 34 13 Ave NE, Suite 101, Minneapolis, MN 55413-1007 *Tel:* 612-746-2600 *Toll Free Tel:* 800-283-3572 (cust serv) *Fax:* 612-746-2606 *Web Site:* www.cbsd.com

Theosophical Publishing House/Quest Books
Division of The Theosophical Society in America
306 W Geneva Rd, Wheaton, IL 60187
SAN: 202-5698
Mailing Address: PO Box 270, Wheaton, IL 60189-0270
Tel: 630-665-0130 (ext 347) *Toll Free Tel:* 800-669-9425 (ext 347) *Fax:* 630-665-8791
E-mail: customerservice@questbooks.net
Web Site: www.questbooks.net
Key Personnel
Publg Mgr: Sharron Dorr *E-mail:* sdorr@questbooks.net
Opers Mgr: Pat Griebeler *Tel:* 630-665-0130 ext 354 *E-mail:* operations@questbooks.net
Mktg Mgr: Nicole Smoley *E-mail:* marketing@questbooks.net
Rts & Perms: Laly Diaz *E-mail:* permissions@questbooks.net
Intl Rts: DeLacy Sarantos *E-mail:* foreignrights@questbooks.net
Ed: Richard Smoley *E-mail:* editor@questbooks.net
Founded: 1965
Publish books of intelligence, readability & insight for the contemporary spiritual seeker. Our books explore ancient wisdom, modern science, world religions, philosophy, the arts & the inner meaning of life to provide dynamic tools for spiritual healing & self-transformation.
ISBN Prefix(es): 978-0-8356
Number of titles published annually: 10 Print
Total Titles: 400 Print; 50 Audio
Imprints: Quest Books
Foreign Rep(s): Airlift Book Co (Europe, UK); Alternative Books (South Africa); Aquamarin Verlag (Germany); Brumby Books (Australia); Theosofische Vereniging in Nederland (Netherlands); Theosophical Publishing House (India); Theosophical Publishing House Manila (Philippines); Theosophical Society in New Zealand (New Zealand)
Distribution Center: National Book Network, 15200 NBN Way, Blue Ridge Summit, PA 17214
Membership(s): ABA; ALA; The Independent Book Publishers Association

§Theosophical University Press
Affiliate of Theosophical Society (Pasadena)
PO Box C, Pasadena, CA 91109-7107
SAN: 205-4299
Tel: 626-798-3378
E-mail: tupress@theosociety.org
Web Site: www.theosociety.org
Key Personnel
Dir: Randell C Grubb
Mgr & Intl Rts: Will Thackara
Cust Serv: Ina Belderis
Founded: 1886
Quality theosophical literature.
ISBN Prefix(es): 978-0-911500; 978-1-55700
Number of titles published annually: 3 Print; 5 Online
Total Titles: 86 Print
Imprints: Sunrise Library
Foreign Office(s): Theosophischer Verlag GmbH, Brunnenstr 11, 56414 Hundsangen, Germany, Contact: Jochen Hannappel *Tel:* (06435) 96033 *Fax:* (06435) 96053 *E-mail:* info@theosophischer-verlag.de *Web Site:* www.theosophischer-verlag.de
Theosophical University Press Agency, Daal en Bergselaan 68, 2565 AG The Hague, Nether-

lands, Contact: Coen Vonk *Tel:* (070) 323 1776 *Fax:* (070) 325 7275 *E-mail:* tupa@theosofie.net *Web Site:* www.theosofie.net
Theosophical University Press South African Agency, PO Box 504, Constantia 7848, South Africa, Contact: Dewald Bester *Tel:* (021) 4342281 *E-mail:* besterdewald@gmail.com
Teosofiska Bokforlaget, Barnhusgatan 13, 411 11 Gothenburg, Sweden, Contact: Herbert Edlund *Tel:* (08) 411 6581 *Fax:* (08) 896 8697 *E-mail:* teobok@glocalnet.net *Web Site:* www.theosociety.org/pasadena/sverige/TeosofiskaBokforlaget/index.htm
The Theosophical Society, PO Box 48, Penrhyndeudraeth, Gwynedd LL49 0AQ, United Kingdom, Contact: Patrick Powell *E-mail:* ts-uk@talktalk.net *Web Site:* www.theosophical.org.uk/tup.html
Warehouse: 2416 N Lake Ave, Altadena, CA 91001

§Thieme Medical Publishers Inc
Subsidiary of Georg Thieme Verlag KG
333 Seventh Ave, 18th fl, New York, NY 10001
SAN: 202-7399
Tel: 212-760-0888 *Toll Free Tel:* 800-782-3488 *Fax:* 212-947-1112
E-mail: customerservice@thieme.com
Web Site: www.thieme.com
Key Personnel
Pres: Brian Scanlan *Tel:* 212-584-4707 *E-mail:* bscanlan@thieme.com
Sales Dir: Mike Roseman *Tel:* 631-365-4625 *E-mail:* mike.roseman@thieme.com
Founded: 1979
Electronic products, apps, books, journals, textbooks in clinical medicine, dentistry, speech & hearing, allied health, audiology, organic chemistry plus electronic products, medical education & databases.
ISBN Prefix(es): 978-0-913258; 978-0-86577; 978-1-58890; 978-1-60406
Number of titles published annually: 50 Print; 3 CD-ROM; 50 Online
Total Titles: 605 Print; 50 Online; 605 E-Book
Foreign Office(s): Thieme Publishers Rio, Argentina Bldg, 16th fl, Ala A, 228, Praia do Botafogo, 22250-040 Rio de Janeiro-RJ, Brazil, VP: Daniel Schiff *Tel:* (021) 3736-3631
Thieme Medical & Scientific Publishers Pvt Ltd, A-12, Sector 2, 2nd fl, Noida, Uttar Pradesh 201 301, India *Tel:* (0120) 427 4461 *Fax:* (0120) 427 4465 *E-mail:* customerservice@thieme.in
Georg Thieme Verlag, PO Box 30 11 20, 70451 Stuttgart, Germany *Tel:* (0711) 89310 *Fax:* (0711) 8931410 *E-mail:* customerservice@thieme.de *Web Site:* www.thieme.de
Distributor for AO Foundation
Foreign Rep(s): Login Canada (Canada); Woodslane (Australia)
Foreign Rights: Heike Schwabenthan (Worldwide)
Warehouse: Mount Joy Distribution Center, 1000 Strickler Rd, Mount Joy, PA 17552
Membership(s): AAP; Independent Publishers Association; STM

Thinkers' Press Inc
1524 Le Claire St, Davenport, IA 52803
SAN: 176-4632
Tel: 563-271-6657
E-mail: info@chessbutler.com
Web Site: www.thinkerspressinc.com
Key Personnel
Pres & Busn Mgr: Bob Long
Founded: 1971 (International, wholesale, retail applications)
Books/DVDs, information newsletters. International, wholesale, retail applications.
This publisher has indicated that 50% of their product line is author subsidized.
ISBN Prefix(es): 978-0-938650; 978-1-888710
Number of titles published annually: 6 Print
Total Titles: 175 Print

Third World Press
7822 S Dobson Ave, Chicago, IL 60619
Mailing Address: PO Box 19730, Chicago, IL 60619
Tel: 773-651-0700 *Fax:* 773-651-7286
E-mail: twpress3@aol.com
Web Site: www.thirdworldpressbooks.com
Key Personnel
Publr: Haki R Madhubuti
Ed: Gwendolyn Mitchell
Founded: 1967
Publishers of quality Black fiction, nonfiction, poetry, drama, young adult & children literature; primarily adult literature.
ISBN Prefix(es): 978-0-88378
Number of titles published annually: 10 Print
Total Titles: 100 Print
Distribution Center: Independent Publishers Group (IPG), 814 N Franklin St, Chicago, IL 60610 *Tel:* 312-337-0747
Ingram Publisher Services, One Ingram Blvd, La Vergne, TN 37086 *Toll Free Tel:* 866-400-5351

Charles C Thomas Publisher Ltd
2600 S First St, Springfield, IL 62704
SAN: 201-9485
Tel: 217-789-8980 *Toll Free Tel:* 800-258-8980 *Fax:* 217-789-9130
E-mail: books@ccthomas.com
Web Site: www.ccthomas.com
Key Personnel
Pres: Michael Payne Thomas
Cont: Cheryl Steelman
Founded: 1927
Medicine, allied health sciences, science, technology, education, public administration, law enforcement, behavioral & social sciences, special education.
ISBN Prefix(es): 978-0-398
Number of titles published annually: 60 Print
Total Titles: 905 Print
Advertising Agency: Thomas Advertising Agency
Returns: PO Box 19265, Springfield, IL 62794-6265

Thomas Geale Publications Inc
PO Box 370540, Montara, CA 94037-0540
Tel: 650-728-5219 *Toll Free Tel:* 800-554-5457 *Fax:* 650-728-0918
E-mail: justthink@comcast.net
Key Personnel
Pres: Sydney Tyler-Parker
Secy: Nancy L Geale
Founded: 1982
Curriculum for schools PreK-8; general educational materials, reading & thinking.
Number of titles published annually: 20 Print
Total Titles: 30 Print
Imprints: Just Think®; Stretch Think®; Think Quest®; Young Think®
Foreign Rights: Nederlands Corp (Japan)
Shipping Address: 583 Sixth St, Montara, CA 94037

§Thomas Nelson
Imprint of HarperCollins Christian Publishing
501 Nelson Place, Nashville, TN 37214
SAN: 209-3820
Mailing Address: PO Box 141000, Nashville, TN 37214-1000
Tel: 615-889-9000 *Toll Free Tel:* 800-251-4000 *Fax:* 615-902-1548
E-mail: publicity@thomasnelson.com
Web Site: www.thomasnelson.com
Key Personnel
CEO & Pres, Christian Publg Div: Mark Schoenwald
EVP & Chief Live Events Offr: Carol Nygren
SVP, Book Publg: David Moberg
SVP, Specialty Publg: Laura Minchew
VP & Publr, Fiction Div: Daisy Hutton
VP, Independent Christian Retail Sales: Russ Schwartz
VP, Mktg: Chad Cannon
VP, Mktg, Gift Books: Michael Aulisio
VP, Mktg, Live Events: Patrick Koors
VP, Mktg, Nelson Books: Jeff James
Dir, Corp Communs: Casey Francis
Sr Acqs Ed: Jessica Wong
Founded: 1798
Bibles & Testaments, trade, Christian & inspirational books, gift books, children's books & videos.
ISBN Prefix(es): 978-0-8407; 978-1-4047
Number of titles published annually: 600 Print
Total Titles: 3,500 Print; 6 CD-ROM; 30 Audio
Distributed by Winston-Derek
Shipping Address: 506 Nelson Place, Nashville, TN 37214

Thomas Publications
3245 Fairfield Rd, Gettysburg, PA 17325
Mailing Address: PO Box 3031, Gettysburg, PA 17325
Tel: 717-642-6600 *Toll Free Tel:* 800-840-6782 *Fax:* 717-642-5555
E-mail: info@thomaspublications.com
Web Site: www.thomaspublications.com
Key Personnel
Owner: Dean S Thomas
Founded: 1986
Civil War, U-boats, historical, all nonfiction.
ISBN Prefix(es): 978-0-939631; 978-1-57747
Number of titles published annually: 5 Print
Total Titles: 200 Print

Thomson Reuters Westlaw™
610 Opperman Dr, Eagan, MN 55123
Tel: 651-687-7000 *Toll Free Tel:* 800-328-9352 (sales); 800-328-4880 (cust serv) *Fax:* 651-687-7302
Web Site: www.westlawnext.com; store.westlaw.com
Key Personnel
Sr Dir, Cust Serv Opers: Scott Morgan
Founded: 1804
Publisher of state statutes, attorney general opinions & practice manuals for the US & international.
ISBN Prefix(es): 978-0-8322; 978-0-7620; 978-0-8366; 978-0-87632
Number of titles published annually: 4 Print
Branch Office(s)
Aqueduct Bldg, Rochester, NY 14694 *Tel:* 585-546-5530 *Toll Free Tel:* 800-527-0430 *Fax:* 585-327-6269
Distributor for Law Library Microform Consortium
Returns: 545 Wescott Rd, Eagan, MN 55123

Thorndike Press
Imprint of Gale
10 Water St, Suite 310, Waterville, ME 04901
Toll Free Tel: 800-233-1244 (ext 4, cust serv/orders) *Toll Free Fax:* 800-558-4676 (orders)
E-mail: gale.printorders@cengage.com; international@cengage.com (cust orders outside US & CN)
Web Site: thorndike.gale.com
Key Personnel
Publr: Jamie Knobloch *E-mail:* jamie.knobloch@cengage.com
Edit Dir: Mary P Smith
Promos Assoc: Barb Littlefield
Founded: 1980
Large print titles for the public library market.
ISBN Prefix(es): 978-0-7862; 978-1-4104; 978-1-58724; 978-1-59414; 978-1-59413; 978-1-59415
Number of titles published annually: 1,500 Print

Total Titles: 4,000 Print
Distributor for Grand Central/Hachette Large Print; HarperLuxe; Mills & Boon Large Print; Random House Large Print

Threshold Editions, see Gallery Books

ThunderStone Books
6575 Horse Dr, Las Vegas, NV 89131
E-mail: info@thunderstonebooks.com
Web Site: www.thunderstonebooks.com
Key Personnel
Mng Dir: Robert Noorda *E-mail:* robert.noorda@thunderstonebooks.com
Edit Dir: Rachel Noorda *E-mail:* rachel.noorda@thunderstonebooks.com
Founded: 2014
Specialize in children's books that have an educational aspect. We are not looking for curriculum for learning certain subjects, but rather stories that encourage learning for children, whether that be learning about a new language/culture or learning more about science & math in a fun, fictional format. We want to help children to gain a love for other languages & subjects so that they are curious about the world around them. We are currently accepting fiction & nonfiction submissions. In the area of language, our expertise lies in stories concerning Mandarin Chinese (language, culture, setting +/or mythology), but we are open to other languages as well. For submissions concerning other subjects, we are quite open to anything which creatively teaches & inspires, particularly in areas such as math or science. Fiction submissions that have an educational element are encouraged & welcome.
ISBN Prefix(es): 978-1-63411
Number of titles published annually: 6 Print; 6 E-Book
Total Titles: 5 Print; 5 E-Book
Foreign Office(s): 3B Bow St, Stirling FK8 1BS, United Kingdom *Tel:* (07825) 483348
Orders to: Ingram Content Group, One Ingram Blvd, La Vergne, TN 37086, Contact: Ron Smithson *Toll Free Tel:* 800-937-8222 ext 35176 *E-mail:* ron.smithson@ingramcontent.com
Returns: Ingram Content Group, One Ingram Blvd, La Vergne, TN 37086, Contact: Ron Smithson *Toll Free Tel:* 800-937-8222 ext 35176 *E-mail:* ron.smithson@ingramcontent.com
Shipping Address: Ingram Content Group, One Ingram Blvd, La Vergne, TN 37086, Contact: Ron Smithson *Toll Free Tel:* 800-937-8222 ext 35176 *E-mail:* ron.smithson@ingramcontent.com
Warehouse: Ingram Content Group, One Ingram Blvd, La Vergne, TN 37086, Contact: Ron Smithson *Toll Free Tel:* 800-937-8222 ext 35176 *E-mail:* ron.smithson@ingramcontent.com
Distribution Center: Ingram Content Group, One Ingram Blvd, La Vergne, TN 37086, Contact: Ron Smithson *Toll Free Tel:* 800-937-8222 ext 35176 *E-mail:* ron.smithson@ingramcontent.com

Tide-mark Press
22 Prestige Park Circle, East Hartford, CT 06108-1917
SAN: 222-1802
Tel: 860-310-3370 *Toll Free Tel:* 800-338-2508 *Fax:* 860-310-3654
E-mail: customerservice@tide-mark.com
Web Site: www.tidemarkpress.com
Key Personnel
Publr: Scott Kaeser *Tel:* 860-310-3370 ext 108 *E-mail:* scott@tide-mark.com
ISBN Prefix(es): 978-1-63114
Number of titles published annually: 4 Print
Total Titles: 24 Print
Foreign Rep(s): Gazelle (Europe)

Tiger Tales
5 River Rd, Suite 128, Wilton, CT 06897
SAN: 253-6382
Tel: 920-387-2333 *Fax:* 920-387-9994
Web Site: www.tigertalesbooks.com
Key Personnel
Dir, Sales: Barb Knight *E-mail:* barbknight@netwurx.net
Founded: 2000
Publish imaginative, entertaining hardcover & paperback picture books as well as board & novelty books for children ages 2-7. Committed to publishing children's books that will capture the imagination of children & adults alike.
ISBN Prefix(es): 978-1-58925
Number of titles published annually: 65 Print
Total Titles: 280 Print
Sales Office(s): PO Box 70, Iron Ridge, WI 53035
Orders to: PO Box 411037, Kansas City, MO 64141-1037, Contact: Vanessa Ottens *Tel:* 913-362-7400 *Fax:* 913-362-7401 *E-mail:* vanessa@midpt.com
Returns: 1263 Southwest Blvd, Kansas City, KS 66103 *Tel:* 913-362-7400 *Fax:* 913-362-7401 *E-mail:* warehouse@midpt.com
Shipping Address: 1263 Southwest Blvd, Kansas City, KS 66103, Contact: Linda Reeder *Tel:* 913-362-7400 *Fax:* 913-362-7401 *E-mail:* linda@midpt.com
Warehouse: 1263 Southwest Blvd, Kansas City, KS 66103, Contact: Linda Reeder *Tel:* 913-362-7400 *Fax:* 913-362-7401 *E-mail:* linda@midpt.com

Tilbury House Publishers
Imprint of WordSplice Studio LLC
12 Starr St, Thomaston, ME 04861
Tel: 207-582-1899 *Toll Free Tel:* 800-582-1899 (orders) *Fax:* 207-582-8227
E-mail: tilbury@tilburyhouse.com
Web Site: www.tilburyhouse.com
Key Personnel
Publr: Tristram Coburn; Jonathan Eaton
Children's Book Ed: Audrey Maynard
Founded: 1990
ISBN Prefix(es): 978-0-88448
Number of titles published annually: 10 Print
Total Titles: 100 Print
Membership(s): ABA; The Independent Book Publishers Association

Timber Press Inc
Subsidiary of Workman Publishing Co
133 SW Second Ave, Suite 450, Portland, OR 97204
SAN: 216-082X
Tel: 503-227-2878 *Toll Free Tel:* 800-327-5680 *Fax:* 503-227-3070
E-mail: info@timberpress.com
Web Site: www.timberpress.com
Key Personnel
Publr: Andrew Beckman
Ed-in-Chief: Tom Fischer
Trade, Gift & Ebook Sales Mgr: Adrienne Franceschi
Founded: 1976
Gardening, horticulture, botany, natural history, Pacific Northwest regional.
ISBN Prefix(es): 978-0-88192
Number of titles published annually: 50 Print
Total Titles: 300 Print
Imprints: Timber Press
Foreign Office(s): 6a Lonsdale Rd, London NW6 6RD, United Kingdom, Contact: Anna Mumford *Tel:* (020) 7372 4601 *Fax:* (020) 7372 4601 *E-mail:* info@timberpress.co.uk
Distributed by Thomas Allen & Son

§Time Being Books
Imprint of Time Being Press
10411 Clayton Rd, Suites 201-203, St Louis, MO 63131
Tel: 314-432-1771 *Fax:* 314-432-7939
E-mail: tbbooks@sbcglobal.net
Web Site: www.timebeing.com
Key Personnel
Mng Ed: Jerry Call *E-mail:* tbbookseditor@sbcglobal.net
Off Mgr & Asst Ed: Trilogy Mattson
Founded: 1988
No authorization required for returns - books must be returned within one year of invoice date.
ISBN Prefix(es): 978-1-877770; 978-1-56809
Number of titles published annually: 6 Print; 6 Online; 8 E-Book
Total Titles: 113 Print; 113 Online; 14 E-Book; 11 Audio
Distribution Center: Amazon.com, 440 Terry Ave N, Seattle, WA 98901
BarnesandNoble.com
Follett School Solutions Inc, 1340 Ridgeview Dr, McHenry, IL 60050 *Tel:* 815-759-1700 *Toll Free Tel:* 888-511-5114 (cust serv) *Fax:* 815-759-9831 *Toll Free Fax:* 800-852-5458 *E-mail:* info@follettlearning.com *Web Site:* www.follettlearning.com SAN: 169-1902
Small Press Distribution, 1341 Seventh St, Berkeley, CA 94710-1409

TLC, see THE Learning Connection®

The Toby Press LLC
PO Box 8531, New Milford, CT 06776-8531
SAN: 253-9985
Tel: 203-830-8508 *Fax:* 203-830-8512
E-mail: toby@tobypress.com
Web Site: korenpub.com/toby/intusd/
Key Personnel
Publr: Matthew Miller
Sales Dir: Daniel Mishkin
Founded: 1999
Publish fiction, essays & literature.
ISBN Prefix(es): 978-1-902881; 978-1-59264
Number of titles published annually: 37 Print
Total Titles: 800 Print
Imprints: Koren; Maggid; Steinsaltz
Shipping Address: Focus Mailing, One Prindle Lane, Danbury, CT 06811 *Tel:* 203-830-8500 *Fax:* 203-830-2516 *Web Site:* www.focusmailing.com
Warehouse: Focus Mailing, One Prindle Lane, Danbury, CT 06811 *Tel:* 203-830-8500 *Fax:* 203-830-2516 *Web Site:* www.focusmailing.com
Distribution Center: Focus Mailing, One Prindle Lane, Danbury, CT 06811 *Tel:* 203-830-8500 *Fax:* 203-830-2516 *Web Site:* www.focusmailing.com
Baker & Taylor, 2550 W Tyvola Rd, Suite 300, Charlotte, NC 28217 *Tel:* 714-998-3100 *Toll Free Tel:* 800-775-1800 *Fax:* 704-998-3319
Brodart, 500 Arch St, Williamsport, PA 17701 *Tel:* 570-326-2461 *Toll Free Tel:* 800-999-6799 *Fax:* 570-326-1479
Ingram, One Ingram Blvd, La Vergne, TN 37086 *Toll Free Tel:* 800-400-5351

§Todd Publications
1388 Sabal Palm Dr, Boca Raton, FL 33432
SAN: 207-0804
Tel: 561-910-0440 *Fax:* 561-910-0440
E-mail: toddpub@yahoo.com
Key Personnel
Ed/Publr: Barry Klein
Founded: 1973
Directories & reference books to the trade. Returns accepted within 30 days when in resalable condition.
ISBN Prefix(es): 978-0-87340; 978-0-915344

Number of titles published annually: 10 Print; 2 CD-ROM
Total Titles: 15 Print; 2 CD-ROM

Tommy Nelson
Imprint of HarperCollins Christian Publishing
501 Nelson Place, Nashville, TN 37214
Mailing Address: PO Box 141000, Nashville, TN 37214-1000
Tel: 615-889-9000; 615-902-1485 (cust serv)
Toll Free Tel: 800-251-4000 *Fax:* 615-391-5225
Web Site: www.tommynelson.com
Key Personnel
CEO & Pres: Mark Schoenwald
Sr Dir, Mktg: AnnJanette Toth
Founded: 1984
Inspirational children's books for evangelical & secular marketplace & other products.
ISBN Prefix(es): 978-0-8499; 978-1-4003
Number of titles published annually: 75 Print; 10 Audio
Total Titles: 200 Print; 8 E-Book; 50 Audio

§Top of the Mountain Publishing
Division of Powell Productions
PO Box 2244, Pinellas Park, FL 33780-2244
SAN: 287-590X
Tel: 727-391-3958
E-mail: tag@abcinfo.com; info@abcinfo.com
Web Site: abcinfo.com; www.topofthemountain.com
Key Personnel
Dir: Judith Powell *E-mail:* judi@abcinfo.com; Tag Powell
Intl Rts & Lib Sales Dir: Sharon Boulder
PR: Lance Wilson
Founded: 1979
Exhibits at international, national bookfairs, BFA, Frankfurt Book Fairs; no unsol mss.
ISBN Prefix(es): 978-0-914295; 978-1-56087
Number of titles published annually: 6 Print; 100 Audio
Total Titles: 30 Print; 12 CD-ROM
Advertising Agency: Powell Productions
Shipping Address: 4837 62 St N, Kenneth City, FL 33709
Distribution Center: New Leaf Distributing Co, 401 Thornton Rd, Lithia Springs, GA 30122-1557 *Tel:* 770-948-7845 *Fax:* 770-944-2313 *E-mail:* domestic@newleaf-dist.com *Web Site:* www.newleaf-dist.com

§Top Publications Ltd
12221 Merit Dr, Suite 950, Dallas, TX 75251
Tel: 972-628-6414 *Fax:* 972-233-0713
E-mail: info@toppub.com
Web Site: toppub.com
Key Personnel
Mgr: Bill Manchee
Founded: 1999
Number of titles published annually: 3 Print; 2 CD-ROM; 3 E-Book
Total Titles: 58 Print; 19 CD-ROM; 58 E-Book; 19 Audio
Imprints: TOP
Orders to: Ingram Book Co, One Ingram Blvd, La Vergne, TN 37086-3650 *Web Site:* ipage.ingramcontent.com
Membership(s): The Independent Book Publishers Association

Tor Books, see Tom Doherty Associates, LLC

Torah Aura Productions
4423 Fruitland Ave, Los Angeles, CA 90058
Tel: 323-585-7312 *Toll Free Tel:* 800-238-6724 *Fax:* 323-585-0327
E-mail: misrad@torahaura.com; orders@torahaura.com
Web Site: www.torahaura.com
Key Personnel
Pres: Alan Rowe *E-mail:* alan@torahaura.com
Founded: 1981
Textbooks, Judaica.
ISBN Prefix(es): 978-0-933873; 978-0-943527
Number of titles published annually: 30 Print
Total Titles: 500 Print
Distributor for Free Spirit (selected titles)

Torah Umesorah Publications
Division of Torah Umesorah-National Society for Hebrew Day Schools
620 Foster Ave, Brooklyn, NY 11230
Tel: 718-259-1223 *Fax:* 718-259-1795
E-mail: publications@torah-umesorah.org
Key Personnel
Dir, Pubns: Shmuel Yaakov Klein
Founded: 1946
Text teaching aids & visual aids for Yeshiva-day schools & Hebrew schools, students & teachers; posters & workbooks.
ISBN Prefix(es): 978-0-914131
Number of titles published annually: 5 Print
Total Titles: 82 Print
Foreign Rep(s): Chaim Turkel Volume Distributors (UK)

Tortuga Press
2777 Yulupa Ave, PMB 181, Santa Rosa, CA 95405
SAN: 299-1756
Tel: 707-544-4720 *Toll Free Tel:* 866-4TORTUGA (486-7884) *Fax:* 707-544-5609
E-mail: info@tortugapress.com
Web Site: www.tortugapress.com
Key Personnel
Publr: Matthew Gollub *E-mail:* mg@tortugapress.com
Off Mgr: Simone Peters
Founded: 1997
Creator of award-winning children's literature & multi-media products to delight & open young people's minds.
ISBN Prefix(es): 978-1-889910
Number of titles published annually: 4 Print; 2 Audio
Total Titles: 24 Print; 7 Audio
Warehouse: Anchor Mini Storage, 220 Business Park Dr, Rohnert Park, CA 94928 *Tel:* 707-588-1919 *Fax:* 707-588-9330
Membership(s): California Association of Bilingual Education; California School Library Association; The Independent Book Publishers Association; TLA

§TotalRecall Publications Inc
1103 Middlecreek, Friendswood, TX 77546
Tel: 281-992-3131
E-mail: sales@totalrecallpress.com
Web Site: www.totalrecallpress.com
Key Personnel
Pres: Bruce Moran *E-mail:* bruce@totalrecallpress.com
Gen Mgr: Corby Tate *E-mail:* corby@totalrecallpress.com
Mktg Dir: Terri Mitchem *Tel:* 352-596-1192 *E-mail:* mtmitchem@aol.com
Founded: 1999
Publish nonfiction books in a variety of professional fields, including library science & library assistant/technician education (Learn Library Skills Series) & financial certification exam preparation, with many titles adopted as college texts. The exam preparation study guides offer free downloads of a proprietary interactive test engine that generates randomized mock exams designed to identify a candidate's strengths & weaknesses & determine where to allocate study time. These titles are also distributed electronically to libraries, corporations & government agencies via EBSCOHost, ebrary & Books24x7.com. The company has expanded into fiction, especially mystery/thrillers, along with self-help, travel & religion.
ISBN Prefix(es): 978-1-59095
Number of titles published annually: 50 Print; 10 Online; 50 E-Book
Total Titles: 400 Print; 120 Online; 250 E-Book

Touchstone
Imprint of Scribner Publishing Group
1230 Avenue of the Americas, New York, NY 10020
Key Personnel
Pres & Publr: Susan Moldow
VP, Assoc Publr: David Falk
VP & Dir, Subs Rts: Paul O'Halloran
VP, Dir of Publicity: Brian Belfiglio
Art Dir: Cherlynne Li
Sr Mktg Mgr: Meredith Vilarello
Digital Mktg Mgr: Laura Flavin
Subs Rts Assoc: Elisabeth Watson
Edit Dir: Sally Kim
Sr Ed: Michelle Howry; Matthew Benjamin; Lauren Spiegel
Publr's Asst: Lauren Friedlander
Edit Asst: Elaine Wilson; Miya Kumangai; Etinosa Agbonlahor
Asst Dir, Publicity: Shida Carr
Publicity Mgr: Jessica Roth
Publicist: Amelia Possanza
Publicity Asst: Maria Whelan; Courtney Brach
ISBN Prefix(es): 978-0-684
Number of titles published annually: 60 Print
Imprints: Libros en Espanol
Foreign Rights: Akcali Copyright Agency (Turkey); Antonella Antonelli Agenzia (Italy); Book Publishers Association of Israel (Israel); Japan UNI Agency (Japan); JLM Literary Agency (Greece); KCC (Korea Copyright Center); Mohrbooks Literary Agency (Germany); La Nouvelle Agence; Andrew Nurnberg Associates (Bulgaria, Croatia, Czech Republic, Estonia, Hungary, Latvia, Lithuania, Montenegro, Poland, Romania, Russia, Serbia, Slovakia, Slovenia); Sane Toregard Agency (Denmark, Finland, Iceland, Norway, Sweden); Sebes & Van Gelderen Literary Agency (Netherlands); Tuttle-Mori Agency Inc (Thailand)

§Tower Publishing Co
588 Saco Rd, Standish, ME 04084
Tel: 207-642-5400 *Toll Free Tel:* 800-969-8693 *Fax:* 207-264-3870
E-mail: info@towerpub.com
Web Site: www.towerpub.com
Key Personnel
Publr: Michael Lyons
Mng Ed: Mary Anne Hildreth
Business & manufacturing directories, law publications, business databases.
ISBN Prefix(es): 978-0-89442
Number of titles published annually: 20 Print

Tracks Publishing
140 Brightwood Ave, Chula Vista, CA 91910
Tel: 619-476-7125 *Toll Free Tel:* 800-443-3570 *Fax:* 619-476-8173
E-mail: tracks@cox.net
Web Site: www.startupsports.com
Key Personnel
Owner: Doug Werner
Founded: 1993
ISBN Prefix(es): 978-1-884654; 978-1-935937
Number of titles published annually: 2 Print; 6 E-Book
Total Titles: 35 Print; 105 E-Book
Distribution Center: Independent Publishers Group (IPG), 814 N Franklin St, Chicago, IL 60610 *Tel:* 312-337-0747 *Fax:* 312-337-5985 *E-mail:* frontdesk@ipgbook.com *Web Site:* www.ipgbook.com
Membership(s): The Independent Book Publishers Association

Trafalgar Square Books
388 Howe Hill Rd, North Pomfret, VT 05053
SAN: 213-8859
Mailing Address: PO Box 257, North Pomfret, VT 05053-0257
Tel: 802-457-1911 *Toll Free Tel:* 800-423-4525 *Fax:* 802-457-1913
E-mail: contact@trafalgarbooks.com
Web Site: www.trafalgarbooks.com; www.horseandriderbooks.com
Key Personnel
Pres & Publr: Caroline Robbins
Mng Dir: Martha Cook *E-mail:* mcook@trafalgarbooks.com
Dir, Mktg & Promo: Kim Cook *E-mail:* kcook@trafalgarbooks.com
Sr Ed: Rebecca Didier *E-mail:* rdidier@trafalgarbooks.com
Founded: 1972
ISBN Prefix(es): 978-0-943955; 978-1-57076
Number of titles published annually: 25 Print
Total Titles: 300 Print
Distributed by Legato Publishing Group
Distributor for J A Allen; Kenilworth Press; Pferdia TV

Trafford
Division of Author Solutions Inc
1663 Liberty Dr, Bloomington, IN 47403
Toll Free Tel: 888-232-4444
E-mail: customersupport@trafford.com
Web Site: www.trafford.com
Key Personnel
CEO & Pres: Andrew Phillips
SVP, Mktg: Keith Ogorek
SVP, Prodn Servs & Output Opers: Bill Becher
SVP, Worldwide Sales: Don Seitz
Media Mgr: Kevin Gray *Tel:* 812-339-6000 *E-mail:* kgray@authorsolutions.com
Founded: 1995
The first company in the world to offer an "on-demand publishing service" & led the independent publishing revolution since its establishment. One of the earliest publishers to utilize the Internet for selling books. More than 10,000 authors from over 120 countries have utilized Trafford's experience for self-publishing their books.
This publisher has indicated that 100% of their product line is author subsidized.
ISBN Prefix(es): 978-1-55369; 978-1-55212; 978-1-55395; 978-1-4120; 978-1-4122; 978-1-4251
Number of titles published annually: 800 Print
Total Titles: 2,243 Print
Distribution Center: Baker & Taylor Inc, 2550 W Tyvola Rd, Suite 300, Charlotte, NC 28217 *Tel:* 704-998-3100 *Toll Free Tel:* 800-775-1800 *E-mail:* btinfo@baker-taylor.com *Web Site:* www.btol.com
Ingram Book Group, One Ingram Blvd, La Vergne, TN 37086 *Tel:* 615-793-5000 *Toll Free Tel:* 800-937-8200 *E-mail:* customer.service@ingrambook.com *Web Site:* www.ingrambook.com
Membership(s): ABA; Canadian Booksellers Association

Trails Books
Division of Big Earth Publishing
3005 Center Green Dr, Suite 225, Boulder, CO 80301
Tel: 303-541-1506 *Toll Free Tel:* 800-258-5830
E-mail: books@bigearthpublishing.com
Web Site: www.trailsbooks.com
Key Personnel
Publr: Linda Doyle
Founded: 1970
Regional trade books-Wisconsin & Upper Great Lakes, travel guide books.
ISBN Prefix(es): 978-1-879483; 978-1-931599; 978-0-915024
Number of titles published annually: 20 Print
Total Titles: 120 Print
Imprints: Acorn Guides; Prairie Classics; Prairie Oak Press; Quiz Master Books (pop culture trivia); Trails Books Guide
Membership(s): Midwest Independent Booksellers Association

Training Resource Network Inc (TRN)
PO Box 439, St Augustine, FL 32085-0439
SAN: 299-2647
Tel: 904-823-9800 (cust serv) *Toll Free Tel:* 800-280-7010 (orders) *Fax:* 904-823-3554
E-mail: customerservice@trninc.com
Web Site: www.trn-store.com
Key Personnel
Sr Ed: Dawn Langton *E-mail:* dawnl@trninc.com
Founded: 1990
Publisher & distributor.
ISBN Prefix(es): 978-1-883302
Number of titles published annually: 4 Print
Total Titles: 20 Print
Returns: 316 Saint George St, St Augustine, FL 32084
Membership(s): Public Relations Society of America

Tralco-Lingo Fun
3909 Witmer Rd, Suite 856, Niagara Falls, NY 14305
Tel: 905-575-5717 *Toll Free Tel:* 888-487-2526 *Fax:* 905-575-1783 *Toll Free Fax:* 866-487-2527
E-mail: contact@tralco.com
Web Site: www.tralco.com
Key Personnel
Owner & Pres: Karen Traynor *E-mail:* karen@tralco.com
Founded: 1982
Publisher & distributor of second language educational materials.
ISBN Prefix(es): 978-0-921376
Number of titles published annually: 10 Print; 12 CD-ROM
Total Titles: 300 Print
Branch Office(s)
1030 Upper James St, Suite 101, Hamilton, ON L9C 6X6, Canada
Distributor for Languages for Kids
Membership(s): Education Market Association

Trans-Atlantic Publications Inc
311 Bainbridge St, Philadelphia, PA 19147
SAN: 694-0234
Tel: 215-925-5083 *Fax:* 215-925-1912
Web Site: www.transatlanticpub.com; www.businesstitles.com
Key Personnel
Pres & Intl Rts: Ronald Smolin
Mgr: Jeff Goldstein *E-mail:* jeffgolds@comcast.net
Founded: 1984
Popular culture.
ISBN Prefix(es): 978-1-891696
Number of titles published annually: 200 Print
Total Titles: 2,500 Print
Imprints: BainBridgeBooks
Distributor for Book Guild; Book House; Financial Times Publishing; Hodder Education; Instituto Monsa de Ediciones SA (art books from Spain); Longman; Arnoldo Mondadori Electa; Nexus Special Interests; Pearson Education; Nelson Thornes

Trans Tech Publications
c/o Enfield Distribution Co, 234 May St, Enfield, NH 03748
Mailing Address: PO Box 699, Enfield, NH 03748-0699
Tel: 603-632-7377 *Fax:* 603-632-5611
E-mail: usa-ttp@ttp.net; info@enfieldbooks.com
Web Site: www.ttp.net
Key Personnel
Owner & VP: Thomas Woehlbier *E-mail:* t.woehlbier@ttp.net
Intl Rts: Fred Woehlbier *E-mail:* f.woehlbier@ttp.net
Dir, US Dist: Linda Jones
Founded: 1967
Materials sciences & engineering.
ISBN Prefix(es): 978-0-87849; 978-3-908450
Number of titles published annually: 150 Print
Total Titles: 1,200 Print
Imprints: Scitec Publications
Foreign Office(s): Kreuzstr 10, 8635 Durnten-Zurich, Switzerland *Tel:* (041) 44922 1033 *E-mail:* info@ttp.net
Distributed by Curran Associates Inc; Yankee Book Peddler
Distributor for Enfield Publishers

Transaction Publishers Inc
10 Corporate Place S, 35 Berrue Circle, Piscataway, NJ 08854
Tel: 732-445-2280; 732-445-1245 (orders) *Toll Free Tel:* 888-999-6778 (dist ctr) *Fax:* 732-445-3138
E-mail: trans@transactionpub.com; orders@transactionpub.com
Web Site: www.transactionpub.com
Key Personnel
Pres: Mary E Curtis *E-mail:* mcurtis@transactionpub.com
IT Mgr & Rts & Perms Mgr: Jeffrey Stetz
Mktg Mgr: Mindy Waizer *E-mail:* mwaizer@transactionpub.com
Order Dept Mgr: Nancy Conine
Founded: 1962
Independent publisher of books & serials in all disciplines of the social sciences & related areas.
ISBN Prefix(es): 978-0-202 (Aldine Transaction); 978-1-56000; 978-0-87855; 978-0-88738; 978-0-7658; 978-1-4128
Number of titles published annually: 150 Print; 100 E-Book
Total Titles: 6,200 Print; 1,000 E-Book
Imprints: Aldine Transaction; Center for Urban Policy Research; Transaction Large Print
Distributor for Bridge 21; International Communication Organization (ICO); IWGIA; The Netherlands Institute for Social Research; Editions Scholasticae; Studien Verlag
Foreign Rights: The Asano Agency (Mr Kiyoshi Azano) (Japan); Eliane Benisti Agent Litteraire (Eliane Benisti) (France); Big-Apple Tuttle-Mori Agency (Vinelle Pan) (Taiwan); Big-Apple Tuttle-Mori Agency (Lily Chen) (China); International Editors' Co (Isabel Monteagudo) (Spain); International Editors' Co (Flavia Sala) (Brazil); International Editors' Co (Nicolas Costa) (Argentina, Latin America); Korea Copyright Center Inc (Korea)
Advertising Agency: Paine-Whitman Agency
Warehouse: Raritan Center, 300 McGaw Dr, Edison, NJ 08837
Membership(s): AAP

Transcontinental Music Publications
Division of Union for Reform Judaism
633 Third Ave, New York, NY 10017
Tel: 212-650-4101; 212-650-4120 *Toll Free Tel:* 888-489-8242 (orders) *Fax:* 212-650-4119
E-mail: tmp@urj.org; press@urj.org
Web Site: www.transcontinentalmusic.com
Key Personnel
Music Ed: Jayson Rodovsky
Music Libn/Edit Asst: Rachel Wetstein
Founded: 1938
Publishers of Jewish music.
ISBN Prefix(es): 978-1-8074
Number of titles published annually: 50 Print; 5 Audio
Total Titles: 1,000 Print; 75 Audio

Imprints: Cantors Assembly; Hazamir; Sacred Music Press; Theophilis
Membership(s): MPA - The Association of Magazine Media; National Music Publishers' Association

§Transportation Research Board
Division of The National Academies
500 Fifth St NW, Washington, DC 20001
Mailing Address: Lock Box 289, Washington, DC 20055
Tel: 202-334-2934; 202-334-3213 (orders); 202-334-3072 (subns) *Fax:* 202-334-2519
E-mail: trbsales@nas.edu
Web Site: trb.org
Key Personnel
Mgr, Pubn Sales & Affiliate Servs: Andrea Kisiner *Tel:* 202-334-3214
Founded: 1920
Research results, TRR (online journal), bibliographies & abstracts on books pertaining to civil engineering, public transit, aviation, freight, transportation administration & economics & transportation law.
ISBN Prefix(es): 978-0-309
Number of titles published annually: 150 Print; 5 CD-ROM; 100 Online
Total Titles: 2,600 Print; 40 CD-ROM; 1,000 Online
Imprints: National Cooperative Highway Research Program; Transit Cooperative Research Program

Travel Keys
PO Box 160691, Sacramento, CA 95816-0691
SAN: 682-2452
Mailing Address: PO Box 162266, Sacramento, CA 95816-2266
Tel: 916-452-5200 *Fax:* 916-452-5200
Key Personnel
Publr & Ed: Peter B Manston
Ed: Robert C Bynum
Founded: 1984
How-to travel books & antique guides; travel books worldwide; newsletter about travel books.
ISBN Prefix(es): 978-0-931367
Number of titles published annually: 7 Print
Total Titles: 17 Print
Advertising Agency: Travel Key Media, 2510 "S" St, Sacramento, CA 95816-7307
Shipping Address: Travel Key Media, 2510 "S" St, Sacramento, CA 95816-7307

Travelers' Tales
Subsidiary of Solas House Inc
2320 Bowdoin St, Palo Alto, CA 94306
Tel: 650-462-2110 *Fax:* 650-462-6305
E-mail: ttales@travelerstales.com
Web Site: www.travelerstales.com
Key Personnel
Publr: James O'Reilly
Exec Ed: Larry Habegger
Ed-at-Large: Sean O'Reilly
Founded: 1992
Sponsors annual Solas Awards for Best Travel Writing. For more information see www.besttravelwriting.com.
ISBN Prefix(es): 978-1-885211; 978-1-932361
Number of titles published annually: 8 Print; 10 E-Book
Total Titles: 135 Print
Sales Office(s): Publishers Group West, 1700 Fourth St, Berkeley, CA 94710 *Tel:* 510-528-1444 *Fax:* 510-528-3444
Billing Address: Publishers Group West, 1700 Fourth St, Berkeley, CA 94710 *Tel:* 510-528-1444 *Fax:* 510-528-3444
Orders to: Publishers Group West, 1700 Fourth St, Berkeley, CA 94710 *Tel:* 510-528-1444 *Fax:* 510-528-3444
Shipping Address: Perseus PGW, 193 Edwards Dr, Jackson, TN 38301 *Toll Free Tel:* 800-343-4499
Warehouse: Publishers Group West, 1700 Fourth St, Berkeley, CA 94710 *Tel:* 510-528-1444 *Fax:* 510-528-3444
Distribution Center: Publishers Group West, 1700 Fourth St, Berkeley, CA 94710 *Tel:* 510-528-1444 *Fax:* 510-528-3444

Treasure Bay Inc
PO Box 119, Novato, CA 94948
Tel: 415-884-2888 *Fax:* 415-884-2840
E-mail: webothread@comcast.net
Web Site: www.webothread.com
Key Personnel
Pres: Don Panec
Founded: 1997
Publish educational children's books, that specialize in books for parent involvement in reading.
ISBN Prefix(es): 978-1-891327; 978-1-60115
Number of titles published annually: 12 Print
Total Titles: 100 Print

Treehaus Communications Inc
906 W Loveland Ave, Loveland, OH 45140
Mailing Address: PO Box 249, Loveland, OH 45140-0249
Tel: 513-683-5716 *Toll Free Tel:* 800-638-4287 (orders) *Fax:* 513-683-2882 (orders)
E-mail: treehaus@treehaus1.com
Web Site: www.treehaus1.com
Key Personnel
Pres: Gerard A Pottebaum
Founded: 1973
Children's books, liturgical & catechetical material for children & adults.
ISBN Prefix(es): 978-0-929496; 978-1-886510
Number of titles published annually: 6 Print
Total Titles: 55 Print

Triad Publishing Co
Imprint of Triad Communications Ltd
PO Box 13355, Gainesville, FL 32604
Tel: 352-373-5800 *Fax:* 352-373-1488
Toll Free Fax: 800-854-4947
E-mail: orders@triadpublishing.com
Web Site: www.triadpublishing.com
Key Personnel
Chmn of the Bd & Publr: Lorna Rubin
E-mail: lorna@triadpublishing.com
Treas: Melvin L Rubin
Order Dept & Cust Rel: Donna L Hamon
E-mail: donna@triadpublishing.com
Founded: 1978
Consumer health & medical education for professionals.
ISBN Prefix(es): 978-0-937404
Number of titles published annually: 3 Print; 1 CD-ROM
Total Titles: 25 Print; 2 CD-ROM
Returns: IFM Services, 2302 Kanawha Terr, St Albans, WV 25177-3212
Shipping Address: IFM Services, 2302 Kanawha Terr, St Albans, WV 25177-3212
Membership(s): The Association of Publishers for Special Sales; The Independent Book Publishers Association; National Association of Science Writers

Trident Inc
885 Pierce Butler Rte, St Paul, MN 55104
Tel: 651-638-0077 *Fax:* 651-638-0084
E-mail: info@atlas-games.com
Web Site: www.atlas-games.com
Key Personnel
Pres & Intl Rts: John Nephew
Founded: 1990
Role-playing games, card games.
ISBN Prefix(es): 978-1-887801
Number of titles published annually: 20 Print
Total Titles: 120 Print
Imprints: Atlas Games

Trigram Music Inc, see Wimbledon Music Inc & Trigram Music Inc

The Trinity Foundation
PO Box 68, Unicoi, TN 37692-0068
Tel: 423-743-0199 *Fax:* 423-743-2005
Web Site: www.trinityfoundation.org
Key Personnel
Pres & Dir: Thomas W Juodaitis
E-mail: tjtrinityfound@aol.com
Founded: 1977
Scholarly Christian books.
ISBN Prefix(es): 978-0-940931; 978-1-891777
Number of titles published annually: 5 Print; 5 E-Book; 1 Audio
Total Titles: 75 Print; 1 CD-ROM; 17 E-Book; 2 Audio

Trinity University Press
Unit of Trinity University
One Trinity Place, San Antonio, TX 78212-7200
Tel: 210-999-8884 *Fax:* 210-999-8838
E-mail: books@trinity.edu
Web Site: www.tupress.org
Key Personnel
Dir: Barbara Ras
Mng Ed: Sarah Nawrocki
Assoc Dir, Sales & Mktg: Thomas Payton
Busn Mgr: Lee Ann Sparks
Mktg Mgr: Ms Burgin Streetman
Edit Asst: Steffanie Mortis
Founded: 2002 (after 14 years of inoperation)
Publish titles for the general trade & academic markets.
ISBN Prefix(es): 978-1-59534; 978-0-911536
Number of titles published annually: 12 Print; 12 E-Book
Total Titles: 150 Print; 100 E-Book
Distribution Center: Publishers Group West, 1700 Fourth St, Berkeley, CA 94710 (booksellers & libraries) *Toll Free Tel:* 800-788-3123 *Fax:* 510-528-3614

TripBuilder Media Inc
180 Post Rd E, Suite 200, Westport, CT 06880
SAN: 297-7893
Tel: 203-227-1255 *Toll Free Tel:* 800-525-9745 *Fax:* 203-227-1257
E-mail: info@tripbuildermedia.com
Web Site: www.tripbuildermedia.com
Key Personnel
Pres: Nancy Judson *E-mail:* njudson@tripbuilder.com
EVP: Steven Tanzer
Founded: 1989
Travel guides.
ISBN Prefix(es): 978-1-56621
Number of titles published annually: 20 Print

TriQuarterly Books
Imprint of Northwestern University Press
629 Noyes St, Evanston, IL 60201
Toll Free Tel: 800-621-2736 (orders only)
Fax: 847-467-2096
E-mail: nupress@northwestern.edu
Web Site: www.nupress.northwestern.edu
Key Personnel
Dir: Jane Bunker *Tel:* 847-491-8111 *E-mail:* j-bunker@northwestern.edu
Founded: 1989
Special attention to new writing talent, the non-commercial work of established writers & writing in translation. Special emphasis on poetry.
ISBN Prefix(es): 978-0-8101
Number of titles published annually: 6 Print
Total Titles: 75 Print

TRISTAN Publishing
2355 Louisiana Ave, Minneapolis, MN 55427
Tel: 763-545-1383 *Toll Free Tel:* 866-545-1383
Fax: 763-545-1387
E-mail: info@tristanpublishing.com
Web Site: www.tristanpublishing.com
Key Personnel
Owner & Publr: Brett Waldman
E-mail: bwaldman@tristanpublishing.com
Owner & VP Sales, Mktg & Relationships: Sheila Waldman *E-mail:* swaldman@tristanpublishing.com
Cont: Roger Challman *E-mail:* rchallman@tristanpublishing.com
Founded: 2002
Exquisite gift books that inspire, uplift & touch lives.
ISBN Prefix(es): 978-0-931674
Number of titles published annually: 6 Print
Total Titles: 40 Print; 2 Audio
Imprints: TRISTAN OUTDOORS; Waldman House Press

Triumph Books
814 N Franklin St, Chicago, IL 60610
Toll Free Tel: 800-888-4741 (orders only)
Fax: 312-280-5470
Web Site: www.triumphbooks.com
Key Personnel
Publr: Mitch Rogatz
Edit Dir: Tom Bast
Dir, Sales: Phil Springstead
Mktg Mgr: Tom Galvin
Publicist: Samantha Frontera
Founded: 1989
Leading publisher of sports titles & official rule books of NFL, NHL, MLB, NCAA, among others.
ISBN Prefix(es): 978-0-9624436; 978-1-880141; 978-1-57243; 978-1-892049 (Benchmark Press); 978-1-60078; 978-1-62368; 978-1-61749; 978-1-62937
Number of titles published annually: 95 Print; 75 E-Book
Total Titles: 600 Print; 450 E-Book
Imprints: Benchmark Press; Triumph Entertainment
Foreign Rep(s): Monarch Books of Canada (Canada); Peribo Pty Ltd (Australia, New Zealand)
Foreign Rights: RoundHouse Publishing Ltd (Europe, UK)
Distribution Center: Independent Publishers Group (IPG), 814 N Franklin St, Chicago, IL 60610 *Web Site:* www.ipgbook.com
Membership(s): ABA

§Triumph Learning LLC
Division of Haights Cross Communications®
136 Madison Ave, 7th fl, New York, NY 10016
Mailing Address: PO Box 1270, Littleton, MA 01460-4270
Tel: 212-652-0200 *Toll Free Tel:* 800-338-6519 (cust serv) *Toll Free Fax:* 866-805-5723
E-mail: info@triumphlearning.com; customerservice@triumphlearning.com
Web Site: www.triumphlearning.com
Key Personnel
EVP, Sales & Mktg: Ken Butkus *Tel:* 212-652-0234 *E-mail:* kbutkus@triumphlearning.com
Founded: 1964
Print & digital K-12 Common Core resources, standards-aligned instructional materials & effective literacy programs.
ISBN Prefix(es): 978-0-87694; 978-1-58620; 978-1-59823; 978-1-60471; 978-1-60824; 978-1-61997; 978-1-62362; 978-1-62928
Number of titles published annually: 150 Print; 40 CD-ROM
Total Titles: 1,000 Print; 40 CD-ROM
Imprints: Coach; Jumpstart; Ladders; Workout
Warehouse: One Beeman Rd, Northborough, MA 01532
Membership(s): AAP

Truman State University Press
Unit of Truman State University
100 E Normal Ave, Kirksville, MO 63501-4221
Tel: 660-785-7336 *Toll Free Tel:* 800-916-6802
Fax: 660-785-4480
E-mail: tsup@truman.edu
Web Site: tsup.truman.edu
Key Personnel
Dir & Ed-in-Chief: Barbara Smith-Mandell
E-mail: bsm@truman.edu
Sales & Mktg: Marty Jewett *E-mail:* mjewett@truman.edu
Founded: 1986
University Press, scholarly, early modern studies, American studies, regional & general titles, contemporary nonfiction & poetry.
ISBN Prefix(es): 978-0-940474; 978-0-943549; 978-1-931112; 978-1-935503
Number of titles published annually: 12 Print; 15 E-Book
Total Titles: 180 Print; 50 E-Book
Foreign Rep(s): Gazelle Book Services (Europe); Scholarly Book Services (Canada)
Membership(s): PMA International

TSG Foundation, see TSG Publishing Foundation Inc

§TSG Publishing Foundation Inc
28641 N 63 Place, Cave Creek, AZ 85331
SAN: 250-6726
Mailing Address: PO Box 7068, Cave Creek, AZ 85237-7068
Tel: 480-502-1909 *Fax:* 480-502-0713
E-mail: info@tsgfoundation.org
Web Site: www.tsgfoundation.org
Key Personnel
Pres & Intl Rts: Gita Saraydarian
Founded: 1987
Publish & sell books by Torkom Saraydarian, spiritual training center.
ISBN Prefix(es): 978-0-929874; 978-0-911794; 978-0-9656203
Number of titles published annually: 3 Print
Total Titles: 120 Print; 1 CD-ROM
Foreign Rep(s): TSG (UK) Ltd (Europe, UK)

Tudor Publishers Inc
3109 Shady Lawn Dr, Greensboro, NC 27408
Tel: 336-288-5395
E-mail: tudorpublishers@triad.rr.com
Key Personnel
Pres: Eugene E Pfaff, Jr
Sr Publr: Pamela Cocks
Assoc Ed: Nancy Strange
Founded: 1985
ISBN Prefix(es): 978-0-936389
Number of titles published annually: 12 Print
Total Titles: 80 Print
Imprints: Cornwallis Press; Parker/Thomas Press

Tughra Books
345 Clifton Ave, Clifton, NJ 07011
Tel: 973-777-2704 *Fax:* 973-457-7334
E-mail: info@tughrabooks.com
Web Site: www.tughrabooks.com
Key Personnel
Dir, Pubns: Huseyin Senturk *E-mail:* senturk@tughrabooks.com
Dir, Mktg: Ahmet Idil *E-mail:* agi@tughrabooks.com
Sr Ed: Yusuf Alan *E-mail:* alan@tughrabooks.com
Founded: 2001
Publishing, design & printing.
ISBN Prefix(es): 978-975-7388; 978-0-9704370; 978-1-932099 (Blue Dome); 978-1-59784
Number of titles published annually: 15 Print
Total Titles: 185 Print
Imprints: The Fountain; The Light
Foreign Office(s): Bulgurlu Mahallesi Bagcýlar Caddesi No 1, 34676 Uskudar, Istanbul, Turkey *Tel:* (0216) 5221144 *Fax:* (0216) 6509444
Distributor for Kaynak; Nile Publishing; Zambak
Foreign Rep(s): Gazelle (Europe, UK)
Foreign Rights: Kaynak Licensing (Africa, Asia, Australia, Europe, Middle East)
Distribution Center: National Book Network (NBN), 4501 Forbes Blvd, Suite 200, Lanham, MD 20706 *Tel:* 301-459-3366 *Fax:* 301-429-5746 *Web Site:* www.nbnbooks.com
Membership(s): AAP; ABA; The Independent Book Publishers Association

Tumblehome Learning Inc
PO Box 171386, Boston, MA 02117
E-mail: info@tumblehomelearning.com
Web Site: www.tumblehomelearning.com
Key Personnel
Chair: Penny Noyce *E-mail:* penny@tumblehomelearning.com
Pres: Barnas Monteith *E-mail:* barnas@tumblehomelearning.com
Opers: Yuyi Ling *E-mail:* yuyi@tumblehomelearning.com
Founded: 2010
Helps kids imagine themselves as young scientists & engineers & encourages them to experience science through adventure & discovery. Publish science & adventure mystery stories, picture books & occasional nonfiction.
ISBN Prefix(es): 978-0-9850008
Number of titles published annually: 6 Print; 4 Online; 4 E-Book
Total Titles: 13 Print
Foreign Rights: Letter Soup Agency (Allison Olson) (Worldwide)
Membership(s): The Children's Book Council

Tupelo Press Inc
PO Box 1767, North Adams, MA 01247
SAN: 254-3281
Tel: 413-664-9611 *Fax:* 413-664-9711
E-mail: info@tupelopress.org
Web Site: www.tupelopress.org
Key Personnel
Publr & Ed-in-Chief: Jeffrey Levine
E-mail: publisher@tupelopress.org
Mng Ed: Jim Schley
Founded: 1999
Independent, nonprofit literary press.
ISBN Prefix(es): 978-1-932195
Number of titles published annually: 10 Print
Total Titles: 60 Print
Membership(s): Association of Writers and Writing Programs; Community of Literary Magazines & Presses

Turner Publishing Co
200 Fourth Ave N, Suite 950, Nashville, TN 37219
Tel: 615-255-BOOK (255-2665) *Fax:* 615-255-5081
E-mail: marketing@turnerpublishing.com; submissions@turnerpublishing.com
Web Site: www.turnerpublishing.com
Key Personnel
Pres & Publr: Todd Bottorff
Acctg Mgr: Angie Lithgow
Founded: 1984
Trade publisher.
ISBN Prefix(es): 978-1-56311
Number of titles published annually: 36 Print
Total Titles: 2,100 Print
Imprints: Ancestry; Fieldstone Alliance; Iroquois Press (fiction); Ramsey & Todd; Turner; Wiley
Branch Office(s)
445 Park Ave, 9th fl, New York, NY 10022
Tel: 646-291-8961 *Fax:* 646-291-8962

Warehouse: c/o IPS, 1210 Ingram Dr, Chambersburg, PA 17202
Membership(s): AAP; ABA; The Independent Book Publishers Association

Turtle Point Press
233 Broadway, Rm 946, New York, NY 10279
Tel: 212-945-6622
E-mail: countomega@aol.com
Web Site: www.turtlepointpress.com
Key Personnel
Pres & Intl Rts Contact: Jonathan D Rabinowitz
Founded: 1990
Lost literary fiction, contemporary fiction, art history, art criticism, poetry, biography.
ISBN Prefix(es): 978-0-9627987; 978-1-885983; 978-1-885583; 978-1-933527
Number of titles published annually: 4 Print
Total Titles: 100 Print
Imprints: Books & Co/Turtle Point; Helen Marx/Turtle Point; Turtle Point
Foreign Rep(s): Turnaround (UK)
Distribution Center: Consortium Book Sales & Distribution, 1094 Flex Dr, Jackson, TN 38301-5070 *Tel:* 612-746-2600 *Toll Free Tel:* 800-283-3572 (cust serv) *Toll Free Fax:* 800-351-5073 *E-mail:* info@cbsd.com *Web Site:* www.cbsd.com

Tuttle Publishing
Member of Periplus Publishing Group
Airport Business Park, 364 Innovation Dr, North Clarendon, VT 05759-9436
SAN: 213-2621
Tel: 802-773-8930 *Toll Free Tel:* 800-526-2778 *Fax:* 802-773-6993 *Toll Free Fax:* 800-FAX-TUTL
E-mail: info@tuttlepublishing.com
Web Site: www.tuttlepublishing.com
Key Personnel
CEO & Pres: Eric Oey
Mng Dir: Michael Sargent
Publg Dir: Ed Walters
Sales & Mktg Dir: Christopher Johns *E-mail:* cjohns@tuttlepublishing.com
Founded: 1948
Founded by Charles E Tuttle in Tokyo, Tuttle Publishing publishes books to span the East & West, publisher of high quality books & book kits on a wide range of topics including Asian culture, cooking, martial arts, spirituality, philosophy, travel, language, art, architecture & design.
ISBN Prefix(es): 978-0-8048; 978-4-333 (Kosei Publishing Co); 978-1-85391 (Merehurst Ltd); 978-0-460 (Everyman Paperbacks); 978-4-07 (Shufunotomo Co); 978-4-900737; 978-962-593 (Periplus Editions); 978-0-945971 (Periplus Editions); 978-0-935621 (Healing Tao Books); 978-0-933756 (Paperweight Press); 978-0-7946 (Periplus Editions); 978-0-970171 (Kotan); 978-1-840590 (Milet); 978-4-8053
Number of titles published annually: 200 Print
Total Titles: 2,000 Print; 20 Audio
Imprints: Everyman's Classic Library in Paperback; Kosei Publishing Co; Kotan Publishing Inc; Merehurst Ltd; Milet Publishing Ltd; Periplus Editions
Foreign Office(s): 5-4-12 Osaki Shinagawa-ku, 141-0032 Tokyo, Japan *Tel:* (03) 5437 0171 *Fax:* (03) 5437 0755 *E-mail:* tuttle-sales@gol.com
Periplus Publishing Group, Olivine Bldg No 06-01/03, 130 Joo Seng Rd, Singapore 368357, Singapore *Tel:* 6280 3320 *Fax:* 6280 6290 *E-mail:* inquiries@periplus.com.sg *Web Site:* www.periplus.com
Distributed by Publishers Group West (digital only)
Distributor for Healing Tao Books; Kosei Publishing Co; Kotan Publishing Inc; Milet Publishing Ltd; Paperweight Press; Periplus Editions; Shanghai Press; Shufunotomo Co; Tai Chi Foundation
Foreign Rep(s): Airlift Book Co (UK); Bill Bailey Publishers Representatives (Europe); Berkeley Books Pte Ltd (Southeast Asia); Humphrys Roberts Associates (Caribbean, Central America, Mexico, South America); Nilsson & Lamm (Netherlands); Ray Potts (Middle East); Ten Speed (Canada); Trinity Books (South Africa); Tuttle Publishing (Japan)

Tuxedo Press
546 E Springville Rd, Carlisle, PA 17015
Tel: 717-258-9733 *Fax:* 717-243-0074
E-mail: info@tuxedo-press.com
Web Site: tuxedo-press.com
Key Personnel
Publr: Thomas R Benjey *E-mail:* tom@tuxedo-press.com
Assoc Ed: Ann Fitch *E-mail:* ann@tuxedo-press.com
Founded: 2005
Small press of nonfiction books. Titles released to date have been historical in nature. Future releases may also include political topics. New releases are offset print; reprints are POD. Considering expansion to audiobooks. Titles are of US interest only.
ISBN Prefix(es): 978-0-9774486; 978-1-936161
Number of titles published annually: 5 Print
Total Titles: 15 Print; 3 E-Book
Advertising Agency: Anne Dozier & Associates, 313 E 84 St, Suite 1-B, New York, NY 10028, Contact: Anne Dozier *Tel:* 212-717-0276 *E-mail:* annedozier@aol.com
Orders to: Ingram Book Co, 14 Ingram Blvd, La Vergne, TN 37086 *Tel:* 615-213-5335 *Fax:* 615-213-5430
Distribution Center: Ingram Book Co, 14 Ingram Blvd, La Vergne, TN 37086 *Tel:* 615-213-5335 *Fax:* 615-213-5430
Membership(s): The Independent Book Publishers Association

§Twayne Publishers™
Imprint of Gale
27500 Drake Rd, Farmington Hills, MI 48331-3535
Mailing Address: PO Box 9187, Farmington Hills, MI 48333-9187
Tel: 248-699-4253 *Toll Free Tel:* 800-877-4253; 800-363-4253 *Toll Free Fax:* 800-414-5043
E-mail: gale.galeord@cengage.com
Web Site: www.gale.com
Founded: 1949
Critical biographies & studies on literature authors from around the world.
ISBN Prefix(es): 978-0-8057
Number of titles published annually: 6 E-Book
Returns: Cengage Learning, 10650 Toebben Dr, Independence, KY 41051-5100

Twenty-First Century Books
Division of Lerner Publishing Group Inc
241 First Ave N, Minneapolis, MN 55401
Tel: 612-332-3344 *Toll Free Tel:* 800-328-4929 *Fax:* 612-332-7615 *Toll Free Fax:* 800-332-1132
E-mail: info@lernerbooks.com
Web Site: www.lernerbooks.com
Key Personnel
Chmn: Harry J Lerner
CFO & EVP: Margaret Wunderlich
Pres & Publr: Adam Lerner
EVP, Sales: David Wexler
EVP & Dir, Mktg & Digital Prods: Terri Soutor
VP, Ed-in-Chief: Patricia M Stockland
Edit Dir: Domenica Di Piazza
VP, Prodn: Gary Hansen
VP, Digital Prod Mgmt: Daniel Wallek
Rts Dir: Maria Kjoller
Dir, HR: Cyndi Radant
Art Dir: Zach Marell
Group Mktg Dir: Jill Braithwaite
School & Lib Mktg Dir: Lois Wallentine
Publisher of nonfiction books for the upper grades & young adults.
ISBN Prefix(es): 978-0-8050; 978-1-56294; 978-0-7613; 978-0-941477
Total Titles: 480 Print; 255 E-Book
Foreign Rep(s): INT Press Distribution (Australia); Phambili (Southern Africa); Publishers Marketing Service (Brunei, Malaysia, Singapore); South Pacific Books (New Zealand)
Foreign Rights: Sandra Bruna Agencia Literaria (Spain); Japan Foreign-Rights Centre (Japan); Korea Copyright Center (Korea); Michelle Lapautre Agence Junior (France)
Warehouse: Lerner Publishing Group, 1251 Washington Ave N, Minneapolis, MN 55401

§Twenty-Third Publications
Division of Bayard Inc
One Montauk Ave, Suite 200, New London, CT 06320
Tel: 860-437-3012 *Toll Free Tel:* 800-321-0411 (orders) *Toll Free Fax:* 800-572-0788
E-mail: 23ppweb@bayard-inc.com
Web Site: www.twentythirdpublications.com
Key Personnel
Publr: Therese Ratliff
Edit Dir: Dan Connors
Mktg Dir: Dan Smart
Compt: Leslie Williams
Prodn Mgr: Paul Borque
Rts & Perms: Kerry Moriarty
Founded: 1967
ISBN Prefix(es): 978-0-89622; 978-1-58595
Number of titles published annually: 45 Print; 6 CD-ROM
Total Titles: 450 Print; 24 CD-ROM
Distributed by Columba (UK); John Garrett (Australia); Novalis (Canada)
Distributor for Novalis (Canada)
Foreign Rights: Bayard Presse International (Asia, Central Europe, Eastern Europe)
Membership(s): Association of Catholic Publishers Inc; Catholic Press Association

§Twilight Times Books
PO Box 3340, Kingsport, TN 37664-0340
Tel: 423-323-0183 *Fax:* 423-323-0183
E-mail: publisher@twilighttimes.com
Web Site: www.twilighttimesbooks.com
Key Personnel
Publr: Lida E Quillen
Mng Ed: Ardy M Scott
Ed: Eric Olsen
Tech Support: Michael D Bobbitt
Founded: 1999
Royalty paying small press trade publisher of speculative fiction. Our mission is to promote excellence in writing & great literature. Currently publishing limited edition hardcover, first edition trade paperback books & ebooks as downloads in various formats.
ISBN Prefix(es): 978-1-931201; 978-1-933353; 978-1-60619
Number of titles published annually: 14 Print; 20 E-Book
Total Titles: 105 Print; 130 E-Book
Imprints: Paladin Timeless Books; Twilight Visions
Distributed by Brodart Co; BWI Books
Foreign Rep(s): Editura Eminescu (Romania)
Membership(s): AAP; The Association of Publishers for Special Sales; Electronically Published Internet Connection; The Independent Book Publishers Association; Small Publishers, Artists & Writers Network; Speculative Literature Foundation

Two Thousand Three Associates
4180 Saxon Dr, New Smyrna Beach, FL 32169

Tel: 386-690-2503
E-mail: ttta1@att.net
Web Site: www.twothousandthree.com
Key Personnel
Intl Rts & Lib Sales Dir: Frederick B Smith
Mktg Dir: Hank Hankshaw
Publicity Dir: Barbara Brent
Asst to Pres: Geoffery Crawford Tell
Founded: 1995
Nonfiction including memoirs, humor, sports & travel.
ISBN Prefix(es): 978-0-9639905; 978-1-892285
Number of titles published annually: 4 Print
Total Titles: 16 Print
Membership(s): Independent Publishers Association; Independent Publishers Group

§Tyndale House Publishers Inc
351 Executive Dr, Carol Stream, IL 60188
SAN: 206-7749
Tel: 630-668-8300 *Toll Free Tel:* 800-323-9400
Web Site: www.tyndale.com
Key Personnel
CEO & Pres: Mark Taylor
COO: Jeff Johnson
VP, Group Publr: Ron Beers; Doug Knox; Jim Kraus
VP, Publg Servs: CJ Van Wagner
Sr PR Mgr: Todd Starowitz
Intl Accts Mgr: James Elwell
Natl Accts Mgr: Mark Di Cicco
Foreign & Dom Rts & Perms: Jade Doyel
Spec Sales: Charlie Swaney
E-Books: Alan Huizenga
Cust Serv: Lori Walling
Founded: 1962
Religion: hardcover & paperback originals & reprints, ebooks, Bibles, reference, DVDs, audio CDs & software.
ISBN Prefix(es): 978-0-8423; 978-1-4143
Number of titles published annually: 125 Print; 1 CD-ROM; 73 Online; 75 E-Book; 25 Audio
Total Titles: 1,000 Print; 5 CD-ROM; 300 E-Book; 225 Audio
Imprints: BarnaBooks (George Barna titles); Living Books (mass paperback); Resurgence (Mars Hill Church); SaltRiver (deeper Christian thought); Tyndale Audio (adult audio books); Tyndale Entertainment (kids' audio/video products); Tyndale Kids (children's); Tyndale Momentum; Tyndale Ninos (Spanish children's)
Distributor for Focus on the Family
Advertising Agency: Design Promotion
Membership(s): Evangelical Christian Publishers Association

§Type & Archetype Press
Imprint of Type & Temperament Inc
846 Dupont Rd, Suite-C, Charleston, SC 29407
Mailing Address: PO Box 14285, Charleston, SC 29422-4285
Tel: 843-406-9113 *Toll Free Tel:* 800-447-8973 *Fax:* 843-406-9118
E-mail: info@typetemperament.com
Web Site: www.typetemperament.com; typenewsletter.com
Key Personnel
Pres: William D G Murray *E-mail:* wdgmurray@aol.com
Founded: 1974
Books, materials, seminar kits, audio & video tapes for people interested in personality styles & practical applications of psychological type & archetypes, the Myers Briggs Type Indicator & the Pearson-Marr Archetype Indicator.
ISBN Prefix(es): 978-1-878287
Number of titles published annually: 3 Print
Total Titles: 23 Print; 7 CD-ROM; 24 Audio

UBM Global Trade, see The JOC Group Inc

UCLA Fowler Museum of Cultural History
PO Box 951549, Los Angeles, CA 90095-1549
Tel: 310-825-4361 *Fax:* 310-206-7007
Web Site: www.fmch.ucla.edu
Key Personnel
Mng Ed & Intl Rts Contact: Lynne Kostman *Tel:* 310-794-9582 *E-mail:* lkostman@arts.ucla.edu
Founded: 1963
Active publisher of African, Southeast Asian & Latin American arts publications.
ISBN Prefix(es): 978-0-930741; 978-0-9748729
Number of titles published annually: 5 Print
Total Titles: 71 Print
Distributed by University of Washington Press
Shipping Address: 308 Charles E Young Dr N, Los Angeles, CA 90095

UCLA Latin American Center Publications
UCLA Latin American Institute, 10343 Bunche Hall, Los Angeles, CA 90095
Mailing Address: PO Box 951447, Los Angeles, CA 90095-1447
Tel: 310-825-4571 *Fax:* 310-206-6859
E-mail: latinamctr@international.ucla.edu
Web Site: www.international.ucla.edu/lai
Key Personnel
Dir: Kevin Terraciano *E-mail:* terraciano@international.ucla.edu
Exec Dir: David Arriaza
Dir, Pubns: Orchid Mazurkiewicz
Founded: 1959
Scholarly books & journals in Latin American studies.
ISBN Prefix(es): 978-0-87903
Number of titles published annually: 6 Print; 1 CD-ROM; 1 Online
Total Titles: 124 Print; 1 CD-ROM; 1 Online

Ugly Duckling Presse
The Old American Can Factory, 232 Third St, Suite E002, Brooklyn, NY 11215
Tel: 347-948-5170
E-mail: udp_mailbox@yahoo.com; info@uglyducklingpresse.org
Web Site: www.uglyducklingpresse.org
Key Personnel
Pres: Matvei Yankelevich
Mng Ed: Anna Moschovakis
Ed: Gregory L Ford; Ryan Haley
Artist Book Ed: Ellie Ga
Founded: 1993
A nonprofit arts & publishing collective.
ISBN Prefix(es): 978-0-9727684
Number of titles published annually: 8 Print; 2 Audio
Total Titles: 20 Print
Imprints: Emergency Gazette; Knock-off Books; New York Nights; 6 x 6 Magazine
Distributor for United Artists
Membership(s): Community of Literary Magazines & Presses

ULI-The Urban Land Institute
1025 Thomas Jefferson St NW, Suite 500-W, Washington, DC 20007-5201
Tel: 202-624-7000; 410-626-7505 (cust serv outside US) *Toll Free Tel:* 800-321-5011 (cust serv) *Fax:* 202-624-7140; 410-626-7147 (orders only) *Toll Free Fax:* 800-248-4585
E-mail: bookstore@uli.org; customerservice@uli.org
Web Site: www.uli.org
Key Personnel
SVP & Publr: Gayle Berens *E-mail:* gayle.berens@uli.org
Founded: 1936
Books related to land use & development; real estate.
ISBN Prefix(es): 978-0-87420
Number of titles published annually: 10 Print; 10 E-Book
Total Titles: 100 Print; 26 Online; 10 E-Book
Foreign Rights: Joanne Wang
Orders to: Independent Publishers Group, 814 N Franklin St, Chicago, IL 60610 *Toll Free Tel:* 800-888-4741 *E-mail:* orders@ipgbook.com
Warehouse: 810 Cromwell Park Dr, Suite D, Glen Burnie, MD 21061
Distribution Center: Independent Publishers Group, 814 N Franklin St, Chicago, IL 60610, VP: Paul Murphy *Tel:* 312-337-0747 *Toll Free Tel:* 800-888-4741 *Fax:* 312-337-5985 *E-mail:* frontdesk@ipgbook.com *Web Site:* ipgbook.com

Ultramarine Publishing Co Inc
12 Washington Ave, Hastings-on-Hudson, NY 10706
Tel: 914-478-1339
Key Personnel
Sales Mgr: Christopher P Stephens *E-mail:* csteph01@sprynet.com
Founded: 1970
ISBN Prefix(es): 978-0-89366
Number of titles published annually: 5 Print
Total Titles: 250 Print

Ulysses Press
PO Box 3440, Berkeley, CA 94703-0440
Tel: 510-601-8301 *Toll Free Tel:* 800-377-2542 *Fax:* 510-601-8307
E-mail: ulysses@ulyssespress.com
Web Site: www.ulyssespress.com
Key Personnel
Publr: Ray Riegert *E-mail:* rayriegert@ulyssespress.com
EVP: Bryce Willett *E-mail:* brycewillett@ulyssespress.com
Founded: 1983
Travel guides, health books, mind, body & spirit, lifestyle & sexuality titles.
ISBN Prefix(es): 978-0-915233; 978-1-56975
Number of titles published annually: 50 Print
Total Titles: 150 Print
Imprints: Hidden Travel Series; Seastone
Distributed by Publishers Group West
Foreign Rep(s): Hi Marketing (Central America, Continental Europe, Far East, South Africa, South America, UK); Raincoast Book Distribution Ltd (Canada)
Foreign Rights: InterLicense
Shipping Address: 3286 Adeline St, Suite 1, Berkeley, CA 94703 *Toll Free Tel:* 800-377-2542
Membership(s): The Independent Book Publishers Association; SATW

Unarius Academy of Science Publications
Division of Unarius Educational Foundation
145 S Magnolia Ave, El Cajon, CA 92020-4522
SAN: 168-9614
Tel: 619-444-7062 *Toll Free Tel:* 800-475-7062 *Fax:* 619-444-9637
E-mail: uriel@unarius.org
Web Site: www.unarius.org
Key Personnel
Ed: Celeste Appel
Founded: 1954
Books, CDs & DVDs describing a new science of life, past-life therapy, extraterrestrial civilizations, the prehistory of earth, the psychology of consciousness: a course in self mastery. Unarius provides the foundation for personal growth that will lead to the development of self-mastery & the clairvoyant aptitudes of the mind. Alternate formats offered in addition to DVDs: Mp3, CD & videos in Mp4. Classes in past-life therapy are webcast on Sunday 7pm Pacific time.
ISBN Prefix(es): 978-0-932642; 978-0-935097
Number of titles published annually: 4 Print

Total Titles: 90 Print; 70 Audio
Divisions: Audio Books; Greeting Cards; Inspirational Art; Public Access Broadcasting; Unarius Video Productions

Unicor Medical Inc
4160 Carmichael Rd, Montgomery, AL 36106
Tel: 334-260-8150 *Toll Free Tel:* 800-825-7421
Toll Free Fax: 800-305-8030
E-mail: sales@unicormed.com
Web Site: www.unicormed.com
Key Personnel
CEO: Rex Stanley
CFO: Wanda K Hamm *E-mail:* whamm@unicormed.com
VP, Pubns: Nikki Vrocher
VP, Busn Devt: Stuart Newsome
E-mail: snewsome@unicormed.com
Medical books, medical ICD-9 coding books & coding software.
ISBN Prefix(es): 978-1-56781
Number of titles published annually: 14 Print
Total Titles: 14 Print

Editorial Unilit
Division of Spanish House Inc
8167 NW 84 St, Medley, FL 33166
Tel: 305-592-6136 *Toll Free Tel:* 800-767-7726
Fax: 305-592-0087
E-mail: info@editorialunilit.com; customerservice@editorialunilit.com
Web Site: www.editorialunilit.com
Key Personnel
Pres: David Ecklebarger
Sales Mgr: Mariana Tafura *E-mail:* mariana@editorialunilit.com
Mktg Coord: Hilda Urra *E-mail:* hilda@editorialunilit.com
Founded: 1989
Publishing for the Spanish family.
ISBN Prefix(es): 978-1-56063; 978-0-7899; 978-0-945792
Number of titles published annually: 120 Print
Total Titles: 800 Print
Membership(s): CBA; Evangelical Christian Publishers Association; SEPA

The United Educators Inc
900 N Shore Dr, Suite 279, Lake Bluff, IL 60044-2210
SAN: 204-8795
Tel: 847-234-3700 *Toll Free Tel:* 800-323-5875
Fax: 847-234-8705
E-mail: unitededucators@yahoo.com
Web Site: www.theunitededucatorsinc.com
Key Personnel
Pres: Remo D Piazzi
Secy: Diane W Jones
Treas: Peter Ewing
Founded: 1993
Encyclopedias & subscription books.
ISBN Prefix(es): 978-0-87566
Subsidiaries: Standard Educational Corp

§United Nations Publications
300 E 42 St, 9th fl, New York, NY 10017
SAN: 206-6718
Tel: 703-661-1571 *Fax:* 703-996-1010
E-mail: publications@un.org
Web Site: un.org/publications
Key Personnel
Chief: Sherri Aldis *E-mail:* aldis@un.org
Acqs Offr: Nicolas Bovay *E-mail:* bovay@un.org
Opers & Technol Offr: Steve Slawsky
E-mail: slawsky@un.org
Sales & Mktg Offr: Irina Lumelsky
E-mail: lumelsky@un.org
Founded: 1946
Promotes the knowledge & work of the UN to scholars, information specialists, policy-makers & influencers. We publish approximately 500 new titles per year in economic & social development, international law & justice, peacekeeping & security, human rights & refugees, natural resources & more.
ISBN Prefix(es): 978-92-1 (United Nations Publications); 978-92-807 (UNEP); 978-92-808 (United Nations University); 978-92-806 (UNICEF); 978-88-000 (UNICEF); 978-184-966 (DESA); 978-1-849 (UNEP); 978-1-618 (UNFPA); 978-92-9137 (ITC)
Number of titles published annually: 500 Print; 60 Online
Total Titles: 2,300 Print; 35 CD-ROM; 160 E-Book
Sales Office(s): PO Box 960, Herndon, VA 20172
Distributor for Food & Agriculture Organization of the United Nations (FAO); International Atomic Energy Agency (IAEA); International Criminal Tribunal for Rwanda (UNICTR); International Criminal Tribunal for the former Yugoslavia (ICTY); International Organization for Migration (IOM); International Trade Centre (ITC); Office of the United Nations High Commissioner for Human Rights (OHCHR); United Nations Children's Fund (UNICEF); United Nations Development Programme (UNDP); United Nations Economic & Social Commission for Asia & the Pacific (ESCAP); United Nations Economic & Social Commission for Western Asia (ESCWA); United Nations Economic Commission for Africa (ECA); United Nations Economic Commission for Europe (ECE); United Nations Economic Commission for Latin America & the Caribbean (ECLAC); United Nations High Commissioner for Refugees (UNHCR); United Nations Human Settlements Programme (UN-HABITAT); United Nations Industrial Development Organization (UNIDO); United Nations Institute for Disarmament Research (UNIDIR); United Nations Institute for Training & Research (UNITAR); United Nations International Research & Training Institute for the Advancement of Women (INSTRAW); United Nations Interregional Crime & Justice Research Institute (UNICRI); United Nations Office for Project Services (UNOPS); United Nations Office for the Coordination of Humanitarian Affairs (OCHA); United Nations Office on Drugs & Crime (UNODC); United Nations Population Fund (UNFPA); United Nations Research Institute for Social Development (UNRISD); United Nations University (UNU)
Foreign Rep(s): Eurospan Group (Africa, Asia, China, Europe, Hong Kong, Middle East, Taiwan)
Returns: 22883 Quicksilver Dr, Dulles, VA 20166
Shipping Address: PO Box 960, Herndon, VA 20172
Warehouse: 22883 Quicksilver Dr, Dulles, VA 20166

§United States Holocaust Memorial Museum
100 Raoul Wallenberg Place SW, Washington, DC 20024-2126
Tel: 202-314-7837; 202-488-6144 (orders)
Toll Free Tel: 800-259-9998 (orders) *Fax:* 202-479-9726; 202-488-0438 (orders)
E-mail: cahs_publications@ushmm.org
Web Site: www.ushmm.org
Key Personnel
Dir, Academic Pubns, Jack, Joseph & Morton Mandel Center for Advanced Holocaust Studies: Benton M Arnovitz *Tel:* 202-488-6117
E-mail: barnovitz@ushmm.org
Dir, Museum Bookstore & Holocaust Lib Sales Opers: Jerry Rehm
Emerging Scholars Prog Offr: Steven Feldman
Pubns Offr, Mandel Ctr Staff Applied Res Projs: Mel Hecker
Creative Servs, Prodn: Amy Donovan
Exhibitions Projs: Ted Phillips
Perms: Karen Coe
Founded: 1993
Co-publish original monographs, translations, classic reprints, testimonial materials & a scholarly journal; publish memoirs & related titles of Holocaust Publications' Holocaust Library imprint (assets acquired in 1993) as well as occasional papers, exhibition catalogues & related works.
ISBN Prefix(es): 978-0-89604
Number of titles published annually: 12 Print
Total Titles: 130 Print
Imprints: Holocaust Library
Foreign Rights: Goldfarb & Associates (selected titles)

United States Institute of Peace Press
2301 Constitution Ave NW, Washington, DC 20037
Tel: 202-457-1700 (edit); 703-661-1590 (cust serv) *Toll Free Tel:* 800-868-8064 (cust serv)
Fax: 202-429-6063; 703-661-1501 (cust serv)
Web Site: bookstore.usip.org
Key Personnel
Dir, Pubns: Valerie Norville *Tel:* 202-429-4147
E-mail: vnorville@usip.org
Prodn Mgr: Marie Marr Jackson
Sales, Mktg & Rts Mgr, Pubns Off: Kay Hechler
Tel: 202-429-3816 *E-mail:* khechler@usip.org
Mng Ed: Michelle Slavin
Founded: 1989
Area of international peacebuilding, policy analysis & conflict resolution. Primarily publish research results from grants, fellowship & commissioned research.
ISBN Prefix(es): 978-1-878379; 978-1-929223; 978-1-601270
Number of titles published annually: 10 Print
Total Titles: 160 Print
Foreign Rep(s): University Presses Marketing (Europe, Greece, India, Ireland, Israel, Scandinavia, UK)
Orders to: PO Box 605, Herndon, VA 20172-0605 (sales & returns/bookseller, wholesaler & instl) *E-mail:* usipmail@presswarehouse.com
SAN: 254-6965
Shipping Address: 22883 Quicksilver Dr, Dulles, VA 20166 (indiv returns)

United States Pharmacopeia
12601 Twinbrook Pkwy, Rockville, MD 20852-1790
Tel: 301-881-0666 *Toll Free Tel:* 800-227-8772
Fax: 301-816-8237 (mktg)
E-mail: marketing@usp.org
Web Site: www.usp.org
Key Personnel
CEO: Dr Roger L Williams, MD *Tel:* 301-881-0666 ext 8300
Founded: 1820
Reference books & directories; Databases in print & electronic formats.
ISBN Prefix(es): 978-0-913595
Number of titles published annually: 5 Print
Total Titles: 25 Print; 2 CD-ROM
Distributed by Consumer Reports; Login Brothers Book Co; Login Publishing Consortium
Foreign Rep(s): Deutscher Apotheker Verlag (Austria, Germany, Switzerland); Login Brothers Canada (Canada); Maruzen Co Ltd (Japan); Pharmaceutical Society of Australia (Australia); Pharmasystems (Canada); Ernesto Reichmann Distribuidora de Livros Ltda (Brazil)
Distribution Center: Matthews Book Co, 11559 Rock Island Ct, Maryland Heights, MO 63043
Tel: 314-432-1400 *Toll Free Fax:* 800-421-8816
National Technical Information Service, 5285 Port Royal Rd, Springfield, VA 22161 *Tel:* 703-487-4825 *Fax:* 703-487-4098
Promachem LLC, PO Box 1126, 2931 Soldier Springs Rd, Laramie, WY 82070 *Tel:* 307-742-6343 *Fax:* 307-745-7936
Rittenhouse Book Distributors, Inc, 522 Feheley Dr, King of Prussia, PA 19406 *Toll Free Tel:* 800-345-6425 *Toll Free Fax:* 800-223-7488

United States Tennis Association
70 W Red Oak Lane, White Plains, NY 10604
Tel: 914-696-7000 *Fax:* 914-696-7027
Web Site: www.usta.com
Key Personnel
Dir, Publg: Richard S Rennert *E-mail:* rennert@usta.com
Edit Dir: Mark Preston *E-mail:* preston@usta.com
Founded: 1881
Tennis materials; books, magazines & souvenir programs.
ISBN Prefix(es): 978-0-938822
Number of titles published annually: 5 Print
Total Titles: 25 Print
Distributed by Triumph Books; Universe Publishing; H O Zimman Inc

United Synagogue Book Service
Division of United Synagogue of Conservative Judaism
820 Second Ave, New York, NY 10017
SAN: 203-0551
Tel: 212-533-7800 *Toll Free Tel:* 800-594-5617 (warehouse only) *Fax:* 212-253-5422
E-mail: booksvc@uscj.org
Web Site: secure.uscj.org/bookservice
Key Personnel
Admin Asst: Robert Clurman
Founded: 1913
Religion (Jewish); textbooks, juveniles; history, music, Hebrew language instruction, AV materials, liturgical, adult books & prayer books.
ISBN Prefix(es): 978-0-8381
Number of titles published annually: 5 Print
Total Titles: 230 Print
Imprints: Burning Bush Press; National Academy for Adult Jewish Studies; United Synagogue Commission on Jewish Education; United Synagogue of Conservative Judaism
Distributor for Rabbinical Assembly of America
Shipping Address: Mercedes Book Distributors, Brooklyn Navy Yard, Bldg 3, Brooklyn, NY 11205

Univelt Inc
Affiliate of American Astronautical Society
740 Metcalf St, No 13 & 15, Escondido, CA 92025
Mailing Address: PO Box 28130, San Diego, CA 92198-0130
Tel: 760-746-4005 *Fax:* 760-746-3139
E-mail: sales@univelt.com
Web Site: www.univelt.com; www.astronautical.org
Key Personnel
Pres & Publr: Robert H Jacobs
Founded: 1970
Publisher for American Astronautical Society, International Academy of Astronautics, Lunar & Planetary Society, National Space Society. Specialize in astronautics & aerospace engineering.
ISBN Prefix(es): 978-0-912183; 978-0-87703
Number of titles published annually: 10 Print; 6 CD-ROM
Total Titles: 363 Print
Distributor for Astronautical Society of Western Australia; US Space Foundation

Universal-Publishers Inc
23331 Water Circle, Boca Raton, FL 33486-8540
SAN: 299-3635
Tel: 561-750-4344 *Toll Free Tel:* 800-636-8329 *Fax:* 561-750-6797
Web Site: www.universal-publishers.com
Key Personnel
Publr: Jeffrey R Young
Founded: 1997
Dictionaries, encyclopedias, textbooks-all, university presses. Scholarly books, reprints, professional books, paperbacks, directories & reference books.
ISBN Prefix(es): 978-1-58112; 978-1-59942; 978-1-61233; 978-1-62734
Number of titles published annually: 60 Print; 50 E-Book
Total Titles: 1,500 Print; 1,000 E-Book
Imprints: Brown Walker Press; Dissertation.com
Distribution Center: Ingram Book Group, One Ingram Blvd, La Vergne, TN 37086 *Tel:* 615-793-5000 *Web Site:* www.ingramcontent.com
Bertrams, One Broadland Business Park, Norwich NR7 0WF, United Kingdom *E-mail:* books@bertrams.com *Web Site:* www.bertrams.com
See separate listing for:
Dissertation.com

Universe Publishing
Imprint of Rizzoli International Publications Inc
300 Park Ave S, 4th fl, New York, NY 10010
Tel: 212-387-3400 *Fax:* 212-387-3535
Web Site: www.rizzoliusa.com
Founded: 1956
Architecture, fine art, photography, illustrated gift books, fashion, culinary, popular culture, children's, design, style & calendars.
ISBN Prefix(es): 978-0-87663; 978-1-55550; 978-0-7893
Number of titles published annually: 60 Print
Imprints: Universe; Universe Calendars
Distributed by Random House
Foreign Rep(s): Bill Bailey (Central Europe); Bookport Associates (Southern Europe); Michelle Curreri (Asia); Hi Marketing (UK); IMA (Eastern Europe); IPR (Middle East); Marston Book Services Ltd (Europe, UK); Random House (Canada); Murray Sutton (Scandinavia); Cynthia Zimpfer (Latin America)

University Council for Educational Administration
The University of Texas at Austin, Dept of Educ Admin, Coll of Educ, One University Sta, D-5400, Austin, TX 78712-0374
Tel: 512-475-8592 *Fax:* 512-471-5974
E-mail: ucea.org@gmail.com
Web Site: www.ucea.org
Key Personnel
Exec Dir: Michelle D Young *E-mail:* mdy8n@eservices.virginia.edu
Founded: 1934
Books, journals, monographs, newsletters.
ISBN Prefix(es): 978-1-55996
Number of titles published annually: 5 Print
Total Titles: 23 Print
Shipping Address: The University of Texas at Austin, Dept of Educ Admin, Sanchez Bldg, Rm 310N, 1900 Speedway, Austin, TX 78705

University of Alabama Press
200 Hackberry Lane, 2nd fl, Tuscaloosa, AL 35487
Tel: 205-348-5180 *Fax:* 205-348-9201
Web Site: www.uapress.ua.edu
Key Personnel
Dir: Curtis L Clark *Tel:* 205-348-1560 *E-mail:* cclark@uapress.ua.edu
Dir, Sales & Mktg: J D Wilson
Mng Ed: Crissie Johnson *Tel:* 205-348-9708 *E-mail:* cjohnson@uapress.ua.edu
Busn Mgr: Rosalyn Carr *Tel:* 205-348-1567 *E-mail:* rcarr@uapress.ua.edu
Mktg & Sales Mgr: Shana R Rivers *Tel:* 205-348-9534 *E-mail:* srrivers@uapress.ua.edu
Prodn Mgr: W Richard Cook *Tel:* 205-348-1571 *E-mail:* rcook@uapress.ua.edu
Sales Mgr: Julie Beckwith
Mktg Coord: Courtney Blanchard
Rts & Perms: Claire Lewis Evans *Tel:* 205-348-1561 *E-mail:* levans@uapress.ua.edu
Founded: 1945
American & Latin American history & culture, religious & ethnohistory, rhetoric & communications, African American & Native American studies, Judaic studies, Southern regional studies, theatre & regional trade titles.
ISBN Prefix(es): 978-0-8173; 978-0-914590; 978-0-932511; 978-1-57366
Number of titles published annually: 70 Print; 25 E-Book
Total Titles: 1,200 Print; 100 E-Book
Imprints: Fiction Collective 2 (FC2); Fire Ant Books
Foreign Rep(s): East-West Export Books (Asia); Eurospan (Europe); Scholarly Book Services (Canada)
Distribution Center: Chicago Distribution Center, 11030 S Langley, Chicago, IL 60628 (orders) *Tel:* 773-702-7000 (orders) *Toll Free Tel:* 800-621-2736 (orders) *Fax:* 773-702-7212
SAN: 630-6047
See separate listing for:
Fiction Collective Two Inc (FC2)

§University of Alaska Press
794 University Ave, Suite 220, Fairbanks, AK 99709
SAN: 203-3011
Mailing Address: PO Box 756240, Fairbanks, AK 99775-6240
Tel: 907-474-5831 *Toll Free Tel:* 888-252-6657 (US only) *Fax:* 907-474-5502
E-mail: fypress@uaf.edu
Web Site: www.uaf.edu/uapress
Key Personnel
Dir: Joan Braddock, PhD *E-mail:* jfbraddock@alaska.edu
Acqs Ed & Mng Ed: James Engelhardt *E-mail:* james.engelhardt@alaska.edu
Prodn Mgr: Sue Mitchell *E-mail:* sue.mitchell@alaska.edu
Sales & Dist Coord: Laura Walker *E-mail:* laura.walker@alaska.edu
Asst to Dir: Amy Simpson *E-mail:* amy.simpson@alaska.edu
Founded: 1967
Emphasis on scholarly & nonfiction works related to Alaska, the circumpolar regions & the North Pacific rim.
ISBN Prefix(es): 978-0-912006; 978-1-889963; 978-1-60223
Number of titles published annually: 24 Print
Total Titles: 220 Print
Imprints: Alaska Writer Laureate Series; Classic Reprint Series; Geology and Geography of Alaska Series; Great Explorer Series; Lantern-Light Library; Literary Reprint Series; Oral Biography Series; Rasmuson Library Historical Translation Series; Snowy Owl Books
Distributor for Alaska Native Language Center; Alaska Quarterly Review; Alaska Sea Grant; Alutiiq Museum; Anchorage Museum Association; Anchorage Museum of Art History; Arctic Studies Center of the Smithsonian Museum; Far to the North Press; Geophysical Institute; Limestone Press; Spirit Mountain Press; UA Museum; Vanessapress
Distribution Center: Chicago Distribution Center, 11030 S Langley Ave, Chicago, IL 60628 (for orders outside Alaska) *Toll Free Tel:* 800-621-2736 *Toll Free Fax:* 800-621-8476
Membership(s): Alaska History Association; Alaska Library Association; Association of American University Presses; The Independent Book Publishers Association; Pacific Northwest Booksellers Association

The University of Arizona Press
1510 E University Blvd, Tucson, AZ 85721
SAN: 205-468X
Mailing Address: PO Box 210055, Tucson, AZ 85721-0055
Tel: 520-621-1441 *Toll Free Tel:* 800-426-3797 (orders) *Fax:* 520-621-8899 *Toll Free Fax:* 800-426-3797
E-mail: uap@uapress.arizona.edu

Web Site: www.uapress.arizona.edu
Key Personnel
Interim Dir & Sales & Mktg Mgr: Kathryn Conrad *E-mail:* kconrad@uapress.arizona.edu
Ed-in-Chief: Dr Allyson Carter *E-mail:* allysonc@uapress.arizona.edu
Acquiring Ed: Kristen Buckles *E-mail:* kbuckles@uapress.arizona.edu
Editing & Prodn Mgr: Sylvia Mendoza *E-mail:* smendoza@uapress.arizona.edu
Publicity Mgr: Holly Schaffer *Tel:* 520-621-3920 *E-mail:* hollys@uapress.arizona.edu
Founded: 1959
Scholarly & regional nonfiction about Arizona, the American West & Mexico, Latino Studies, Latin American Studies, Native American studies, anthropology & environmental studies.
ISBN Prefix(es): 978-0-8165
Number of titles published annually: 55 Print
Total Titles: 783 Print
Foreign Rep(s): East-West Export Books (Asia, The Pacific); William Gills (Africa, Europe, Middle East); University of British Columbia Press (Canada)
Membership(s): American Association of University Presses; Arizona Book Publishing Association; Publishers Association of the West

The University of Arkansas Press
Division of The University of Arkansas
McIlroy House, 105 N McIlroy Ave, Fayetteville, AR 72701
Tel: 479-575-3246 *Toll Free Tel:* 800-626-0090 *Fax:* 479-575-6044
E-mail: uapress@uark.edu
Web Site: www.uapress.com
Key Personnel
Dir: Lawrence Malley *Tel:* 479-575-3096 *E-mail:* lmalley@uark.edu
Dir, Editing, Design & Prodn: Brian King *Tel:* 479-575-6780 *E-mail:* brking@uark.edu
Busn Mgr: Mike Bieker *Tel:* 479-575-3859 *E-mail:* mbieker@uark.edu
Founded: 1980
General humanities: popular culture, Middle East studies, Civil War & civil rights studies.
ISBN Prefix(es): 978-0-938626; 978-1-55728; 978-0-912456
Number of titles published annually: 20 Print
Total Titles: 560 Print; 150 E-Book
Distributor for Butler Center for Arkansas Studies; Hearne Fine Art; Moon City Press; Ozark Society; Phoenix International
Foreign Rights: Eurospan (Africa, Europe, Middle East, UK)
Advertising Agency: Ad Lib *Fax:* 479-575-6044
Orders to: 1580 W Mitchell St, Fayetteville, AR 72701
Returns: 1580 W Mitchell St, Fayetteville, AR 72701
Warehouse: 1580 W Mitchell St, Fayetteville, AR 72701
Distribution Center: 1580 W Mitchell St, Fayetteville, AR 72701
Membership(s): American Association of University Presses

University of California, ANR Publications, see ANR Publications University of California

§University of California Institute on Global Conflict & Cooperation
Subsidiary of University of California
9500 Gilman Dr, MC 0518, La Jolla, CA 92093-0518
Tel: 858-534-3352 *Fax:* 858-534-7655
E-mail: igcc-cp@ucsd.edu
Web Site: www-igcc.ucsd.edu
Key Personnel
Sr Ed: Lynne Bush *Tel:* 858-534-1979 *E-mail:* lbush@ucsd.edu
Founded: 1983
IGCC NEWSWired (policy briefs & newsletters), IGCC Review (policy papers) & books authored by members of the University of California faculty & other participants in sponsored research programs.
ISBN Prefix(es): 978-0-934637
Number of titles published annually: 6 Print
Total Titles: 74 Print; 60 E-Book
Distributed by Brookings Institution Press; Columbia International Affairs Online (CIAO); Cornell University Press; Garland Publishers; Lynn-Reinner Publishing; Penn State University Press; Princeton University Press; Transaction Publishers; University of Michigan Press; Westview Press

§University of California Press
2120 Berkeley Way, Berkeley, CA 94704-1012
Tel: 510-642-4247 *Fax:* 510-643-7127
E-mail: askucp@ucpress.edu (books); customerservice@ucpressjournals.com
Web Site: www.ucpress.edu
Key Personnel
CFO & Asst Dir: Anna Weidman
Mng Dir, UK & Europe: Andrew Brewer
Dir: Alison Mudditt
Deputy Dir: Rebekah Darksmith
Dir, Design & Prodn: Anthony Crouch
Dir, Digital Content Devt & Acqs Ed: Laura Cerruti
Dir, Mktg & Sales: Julie Christianson *E-mail:* julie.christianson@ucpress.edu
Dir, Sales & Licensing: Clare Wellnitz
Edit Dir: Kim Robinson
Mktg Dir: Deb Nasitka
Assoc Dir, Sales: Amy-Lynn Fischer
Assoc Dir, UC Press & Dir, Journals & Digital Publg Div: Rebecca Simon
Exec Ed: Chuck Crumly
Mng Ed: Marilyn Schwartz
Poetry Ed: Rachel Berchten
Acqs Ed: Kari Dahlgren; Blake Edgar; Mary C Francis; Niels Hooper; Hannah Love; Reed Malcolm; Kate Marshall; Eric A Schmidt; Naomi Schneider
ISBN Contact: Sierra Filucci
Founded: 1893
Trade nonfiction, scholarly & scientific nonfiction, translations & journals; paperbacks, limited fiction (reprints).
ISBN Prefix(es): 978-0-520
Number of titles published annually: 260 Print; 10 Online; 10 E-Book
Total Titles: 4,200 Print; 60 Online; 60 E-Book
Imprints: The Ahmanson Foundation Humanities Endowment Fund; Ahmanson-Murphy (fine arts); The Atkinson Family Imprint (higher educ); Authors; The Stephen Bechtel Fund (ecology & the environment); The George Gund Foundation (African American studies); The Fletcher Jones Foundation (humanities); Philip E Lilienthal (Asian studies); Joan Palevsky (classical lit); Roth Family Foundation (music in America); A Naomi Schneider Book; Simpson (humanities); The S Mark Taper Foundation (Jewish studies)
Branch Office(s)
Journals & Digital Publishing, 155 Grand Ave, Suite 400, Oakland, CA 94612-3758 *Tel:* 510-643-7154 *Fax:* 510-642-9917
Foreign Office(s): University Presses of California, Columbia & Princeton Ltd, One Oldlands Way, Bognor Regis, West Sussex P022 9SA, United Kingdom *Tel:* (01243) 843291 *Fax:* (01243) 820250 *E-mail:* sales@upccp.demon.co.uk
Distributor for art-SITES; British Film Institute; Sierra Club Books (adult trade)
Foreign Rep(s): Thomas V Cassidy (China); Adrian Greenwood (Europe, UK); Andrew & Atsuko Ishigami (Japan); David Stimpson (Australia, Canada)
Advertising Agency: Fiat Lux
Orders to: Perseus Distribution, Order Dept, 210 American Dr, Jackson, TN 38301 *Toll Free Tel:* 800-343-4499 *Toll Free Fax:* 800-351-5073 *E-mail:* orderentry@perseusbooks.com
Distribution Center: Perseus Distribution, Order Dept, 210 American Dr, Jackson, TN 38301 *Toll Free Tel:* 800-343-4499 *Toll Free Fax:* 800-351-5073 *E-mail:* orderentry@perseusbooks.com
Ampersand Inc, 2440 Viking Way, Richmond, BC V6V 1N2, Canada *Toll Free Tel:* 800-561-8583 *Toll Free Fax:* 888-323-7118
Membership(s): AAP

University of Chicago Press
1427 E 60 St, Chicago, IL 60637-2954
SAN: 202-5280
Tel: 773-702-7700; 773-702-7600 *Toll Free Tel:* 800-621-2736 (orders) *Fax:* 773-702-9756; 773-660-2235 (orders); 773-702-2708
E-mail: custserv@press.uchicago.edu; marketing@press.uchicago.edu
Web Site: www.press.uchicago.edu
Key Personnel
Dir: Garrett P Kiely *Tel:* 773-702-8878 *E-mail:* gkiely@uchicago.edu; Donald Linn *Tel:* 773-702-7020 *E-mail:* linndl@uchicago.edu
Deputy Dir: Christopher Heiser *Tel:* 773-702-2998 *E-mail:* cheiser@uchicago.edu
Exec Dir, IT: Patti O'Shea *Tel:* 773-702-8521 *E-mail:* poshea@uchicago.edu
Journals Dir: Michael Magoulias *Tel:* 773-753-2669 *E-mail:* mmagoulias@uchicago.edu
Exec Ed: Susan Bielstein *Tel:* 773-702-7633 *E-mail:* smb1@uchicago.edu; T David Brent *Tel:* 773-702-7642 *E-mail:* tbrent@uchicago.edu; Douglas C Mitchell *Tel:* 773-702-0427 *E-mail:* dmitchel@uchicago.edu; John Tryneski *Tel:* 773-702-7648 *E-mail:* tryn@uchicago.edu
Edit Dir, Humanities & Sci: Alan G Thomas *Tel:* 773-702-7644 *E-mail:* athomas2@uchicago.edu
Edit Dir, Sci & Soc Sci: Christie Henry *Tel:* 773-702-0468 *E-mail:* chenry@uchicago.edu
Sr Ed: Karen Merikangas Darling *Tel:* 773-702-7641 *E-mail:* darling@uchicago.edu; Timothy Mennel *Tel:* 773-702-0158 *E-mail:* tmennel@uchicago.edu
Sr Proj Ed: Mary Laur *Tel:* 773-702-7326 *E-mail:* mlaur@uchicago.edu
Ed: Joe Jackson *Tel:* 773-702-7769 *E-mail:* joejackson@uchicago.edu; Christopher Rhodes *Tel:* 773-702-4517 *E-mail:* clrhodes@uchicago.edu; Marta Tonegutti *Tel:* 773-702-0427 *E-mail:* mtonegut@uchicago.edu
Pbk Ed: Maggie Hivnor *Tel:* 773-702-7649 *E-mail:* mhivnorl@uchicago.edu
Asst Ed: Christopher Chung *E-mail:* cdchung@uchicago.edu; Randolph Petilos *Tel:* 773-702-7647 *E-mail:* rpetilos@uchicago.edu
UK Ed-at-Large: James Attlee
Asst to Dir: Ellen Zalewski *Tel:* 773-702-8879 *E-mail:* emz1@uchicago.edu
Founded: 1891
Scholarly, nonfiction, advanced texts, monographs, clothbound & paperback, scholarly & professional journals, reference books & atlases.
ISBN Prefix(es): 978-0-226
Number of titles published annually: 250 Print
Total Titles: 5,400 Print; 1 E-Book
Foreign Rep(s): Academic Book Promotions (Benelux, France, Scandinavia); The American University Press Group (Hong Kong, Japan, Korea, Taiwan); Thomas Cassidy (China); Ewa Ledochowicz (Eastern Europe); Uwe Ludemann (Austria, Germany, Italy, Switzerland); Mediamatics (India); Publishers Marketing & Research Associates (Caribbean, Latin America); Arie Ruitenbeek (Portugal, Spain); The University Press Group (Australia, Canada,

New Zealand); University Presses Marketing (Greece, Ireland, Israel, UK)
Distribution Center: Chicago Distribution Center, 11030 S Langley Ave, Chicago, IL 60628 *Toll Free Fax:* 800-621-8476 (US & CN)
Membership(s): AAP; American Association of University Presses

University of Delaware Press
200A Morris Library, 181 S College Ave, Newark, DE 19717-5267
Tel: 302-831-1149 *Fax:* 302-831-6549
E-mail: ud-press@udel.edu
Web Site: library.udel.edu/udpress
Key Personnel
Chair, Bd of Eds: Prof Donald C Mell
E-mail: dmell@udel.edu
Sr: Julia Oestreich *E-mail:* joestrei@udel.edu
Founded: 1922
Literary studies, especially Shakespeare, Renaissance & Early Modern literature; Eighteenth-Century Studies, French literature, art history & history & cultural studies of Delaware & the Eastern Shore.
ISBN Prefix(es): 978-0-87413; 978-1-61149
Number of titles published annually: 37 Print
Total Titles: 1,053 Print
Distributed by Rowman & Littlefield
Distribution Center: Rowman & Littlefield, 15200 NBN Way, Blue Ridge Summit, PA 17214 *Toll Free Tel:* 800-462-6420 *Toll Free Fax:* 800-338-4550 *Web Site:* rowmanlittlefield.com
Quantum Publishing Solutions Ltd, 2 Cheviot Rd, Paisley PA2 8AN, United Kingdom *Tel:* (07702) 831967
Durnell Marketing Ltd, 2 Linden Close, Tunbridge Wells TN4 8HH, United Kingdom (Europe including Ireland) *Tel:* (01892) 544272 *Fax:* (01892) 511152 *E-mail:* orders@durnell.co.uk

University of Georgia Press
Main Library, 3rd fl, 320 S Jackson St, Athens, GA 30602
Tel: 706-369-6130 *Fax:* 706-542-2558; 706-369-6162
E-mail: books@ugapress.uga.edu (orders)
Web Site: www.ugapress.org
Key Personnel
Dir: Lisa Bayer *Tel:* 706-542-0027
E-mail: lbayer@ugapress.uga.edu
Ed-in-Chief: Mick Gusinde-Duffy *Tel:* 706-542-9907 *E-mail:* mgd@ugapress.uga.edu
Sales & Mktg Dir: David Des Jardines *Tel:* 706-542-9758 *E-mail:* ddesjard@ugapress.uga.edu
Asst Dir, Design & Prodn: Kathi Morgan
Tel: 706-542-2491 *E-mail:* kdmorgan@ugapress.uga.edu
Founded: 1938
Publisher of scholarly works, creative & literary works, regional works & digital projects.
ISBN Prefix(es): 978-0-8203
Number of titles published annually: 80 Print; 60 E-Book
Total Titles: 1,800 Print; 450 E-Book
Distributor for Golden Coast Publishing Co; Telfair Museums
Foreign Rep(s): East-West Export Books (Asia, Far East); Eurospan Group (Africa, Europe, Middle East); Scholarly Book Services Inc (Canada)
Orders to: 4435 Atlanta Hwy, West Dock, Athens, GA 30602 *Toll Free Tel:* 800-266-5842 *Fax:* 706-425-3061
Membership(s): Association of American University Presses

University of Hawaii Press
2840 Kolowalu St, Honolulu, HI 96822
SAN: 202-5353
Tel: 808-956-8255 *Toll Free Tel:* 888-UHPRESS (847-7377) *Fax:* 808-988-6052
Toll Free Fax: 800-650-7811
E-mail: uhpbooks@hawaii.edu
Web Site: www.uhpress.hawaii.edu
Key Personnel
CFO: Joel Cosseboom *Tel:* 808-956-6292
E-mail: cosseboo@hawaii.edu
Dir: Michael Duckworth *E-mail:* mpd4@hawaii.edu
Dir, Devt & Outreach: Colins Kawai *Tel:* 808-956-6417 *E-mail:* ckawai@hawaii.edu
Interim Exec Ed: Pamela Kelley *Tel:* 808-956-6207 *E-mail:* pkelley@hawaii.edu
Acq Ed: Stephanie Chun *Tel:* 808-956-8695
E-mail: chuns@hawaii.edu; Masako Ikeda *Tel:* 808-956-8696 *E-mail:* masakoi@hawaii.edu; Nadine Little *Tel:* 808-956-6208
E-mail: nlittle@hawaii.edu
Digital Mgr & Interim Mktg Mgr: Trond Knutsen *Tel:* 808-956-6227 *E-mail:* tknutsen@hawaii.edu
Journals Mgr: Pamela Wilson *Tel:* 808-956-6790
E-mail: pwilson6@hawaii.edu
Prod Mgr: Steve Hirashima *Tel:* 808-956-8698
E-mail: stevehir@hawaii.edu
Prodn Mgr: Santos Barbasa *Tel:* 808-956-8277
E-mail: barbasa@hawaii.edu
Promo Mgr: Carol Abe *Tel:* 808-956-8697
E-mail: abec@hawaii.edu
Sales Mgr: Royden Muranaka *Tel:* 808-956-6214
E-mail: royden@hawaii.edu
IT Specialist: Collin Wong *Tel:* 808-956-6209
E-mail: cwong808@hawaii.edu
Founded: 1947
Scholarly & general books & monographs, particularly those dealing with the Pacific & Asia; regional books; journals.
ISBN Prefix(es): 978-0-8248; 978-0-87022
Number of titles published annually: 70 Print; 100 E-Book
Total Titles: 1,500 Print; 1,500 E-Book
Imprints: Kolowalu Books; Latitude 20
Subsidiaries: East-West Export Books
Distributor for Ateneo De Manila University Press; Cornell University East Asia Program; Huia Publishers; MerwinAsia; NIAS Press; The Numata Center; NUS Press; Renaissance Press; Seoul Selection; Shanghai Press; Three Pines Press; University of the Phillippines Press
Foreign Rep(s): East-West Export Books (Asia, Australia, New Zealand); The Eurospan Group (Africa, Continental Europe, Middle East, UK); Scholarly Book Services (Canada)
Membership(s): American Association of University Presses

University of Illinois Press
Unit of University of Illinois
1325 S Oak St, MC-566, Champaign, IL 61820-6903
SAN: 202-5310
Tel: 217-333-0950 *Fax:* 217-244-8082
E-mail: uipress@uillinois.edu; journals@uillinois.edu
Web Site: www.press.uillinois.edu
Key Personnel
Dir: Willis G Regier *Tel:* 217-244-0728
E-mail: wregier@uillinois.edu
Art Dir: Dustin Hubbart *Tel:* 217-333-9227
E-mail: dhubbert@uillinois.edu
Ed-in-Chief: Laurie Matheson *Tel:* 217-244-4685
E-mail: lmatheso@uillinois.edu
Direct Mktg & Ad Mgr: Denise Peeler *Tel:* 217-244-4690 *E-mail:* dpeeler@uillinois.edu
Edit Design & Prodn Mgr: Jennifer Reichlin *Tel:* 217-244-3279 *E-mail:* reichlin@uillinois.edu
Exhibits Mgr: Margo Chaney *Tel:* 217-244-6491
E-mail: mehaney@uillinois.edu
Journals Mgr: Clydette Wantland *Tel:* 217-244-6496 *E-mail:* cwantland@uillinois.edu
Prodn Mgr: Kristine Ding *Tel:* 217-244-4701
E-mail: kding@uillinois.edu
Publicity Mgr: Michael Roux *Tel:* 217-244-4689
E-mail: mroux@uillinois.edu
Sales Mgr: Lynda Schuh *Tel:* 217-333-9071
E-mail: lschuh@uillinois.edu
Founded: 1918
Working-class & ethnic studies, religion, architecture, film studies, political science, folklore, Chicago, food studies, immigration studies, American history, women's history, music history, regional history.
ISBN Prefix(es): 978-0-252
Number of titles published annually: 100 Print
Total Titles: 1,700 Print; 10 Online
Foreign Rep(s): Combined Academic Publishers Ltd (Africa, Europe, Middle East, UK); B K Norton (China, Hong Kong, Korea, Taiwan); Scholarly Book Services Inc (Canada); United Publishers Services Ltd (Japan)
Orders to: c/o Chicago Distribution Center, 11030 S Langley Ave, Chicago, IL 60628 *Tel:* 773-702-7000 *Toll Free Tel:* 800-621-2736 *Fax:* 773-702-7212 *Toll Free Fax:* 800-621-8476 *E-mail:* orders@press.uchicago.edu
Returns: c/o Chicago Distribution Center, 11030 S Langley Ave, Chicago, IL 60628 *Tel:* 773-702-7000 *Toll Free Tel:* 800-621-2736 *Fax:* 773-702-7212 *Toll Free Fax:* 800-621-8476 *E-mail:* orders@press.uchicago.edu
Warehouse: c/o Chicago Distribution Center, 11030 S Langley Ave, Chicago, IL 60628 *Tel:* 773-702-7000 *Toll Free Tel:* 800-621-2736 *Fax:* 773-702-7212 *Toll Free Fax:* 800-621-8476 *E-mail:* orders@press.uchicago.edu
Membership(s): AAP; Association of American University Presses

University of Iowa Press
119 W Park Rd, 100 Kuhl House, Iowa City, IA 52242-1000
SAN: 282-4868
Tel: 319-335-2000 *Toll Free Tel:* 800-621-2736 (orders only) *Fax:* 319-335-2055
Toll Free Fax: 800-621-8476 (orders only)
E-mail: uipress@uiowa.edu
Web Site: www.uiowapress.org
Key Personnel
Dir: James McCoy *Tel:* 319-335-2013
E-mail: james-mccoy@uiowa.edu
Ed: Holly Carver *E-mail:* holly-carver@uiowa.edu
Assoc Dir & Design & Prodn Mgr: Karen Copp *Tel:* 319-335-2014 *E-mail:* karen-copp@uiowa.edu
Founded: 1969
Creative fiction, nonfiction, poetry, regional studies, theatre history & literary criticism.
ISBN Prefix(es): 978-0-87745; 978-1-58729
Number of titles published annually: 35 Print
Total Titles: 400 Print
Foreign Rep(s): Eurospan (Europe, UK); EWEB (Asia, Australia, New Zealand, The Pacific)
Orders to: Chicago Distribution Center, 11030 S Langley Ave, Chicago, IL 60628 *E-mail:* orders@press.uchicago.edu
Returns: Chicago Distribution Center, 11030 S Langley Ave, Chicago, IL 60628 *E-mail:* orders@press.uchicago.edu
Distribution Center: Chicago Distribution Center, 11030 S Langley Ave, Chicago, IL 60628 *Toll Free Tel:* 800-621-2736 *Toll Free Fax:* 800-621-8476 *E-mail:* orders@press.uchicago.edu
Membership(s): American Association of University Presses

University of Louisiana at Lafayette Press
PO Box 40831, UL, Lafayette, LA 70504-0831
Tel: 337-482-6027 *Fax:* 337-482-6028
E-mail: cls@louisiana.edu
Web Site: www.ulpress.org
Key Personnel
Dir: Michael Martin
Asst Dir: James Wilson

Sales & Mktg Dir: Melissa Teutsch
Founded: 1973
Publish titles on Louisiana culture & history.
ISBN Prefix(es): 978-0-940984; 978-1-887366; 978-1-935754
Number of titles published annually: 10 Print
Total Titles: 150 Print
Shipping Address: 302 E Saint Mary Blvd, Lafayette, LA 70504

University of Massachusetts Press
East Experiment Sta, 671 N Pleasant St, Amherst, MA 01003
Tel: 413-545-2217 *Fax:* 413-545-1226
E-mail: info@umpress.umass.edu
Web Site: www.umass.edu/umpress
Key Personnel
Dir: Bruce Wilcox *Tel:* 413-545-4990 *E-mail:* wilcox@umpress.umass.edu
Busn Mgr: Yvonne Crevier *Tel:* 413-545-4994 *E-mail:* ycrevier@umpress.umass.edu
Design & Prodn Mgr: Jack Harrison *Tel:* 413-545-4998 *E-mail:* harrison@umpress.umass.edu
Promo Mgr: Karen Fisk *Tel:* 413-545-4987 *E-mail:* kfisk@umpress.umass.edu
Assoc Prodn Mgr & Design: Sally Nichols *Tel:* 413-545-4997 *E-mail:* snichols@umpress.umass.edu
Mng Ed: Carol Betsch *Tel:* 413-545-4991 *Fax:* 413-545-2216 *E-mail:* betsch@umpress.umass.edu
Sr Ed: Clark Dougan *Tel:* 413-545-4989 *E-mail:* cdougan@umpress.umass.edu
Ed: Brian Halley *Tel:* 617-287-6510 *Fax:* 617-287-5616 *E-mail:* brian.halley@umb.edu
Founded: 1963
Scholarly works & serious nonfiction, including African American studies, American history, American studies, architecture & landscape design, disability studies, environmental studies, gender studies, history of the book, journalism & media studies, literary & cultural studies, Native American studies, technology studies, urban studies & books of regional interest.
ISBN Prefix(es): 978-0-87023; 978-1-55849; 978-1-62534
Number of titles published annually: 40 Print; 35 E-Book
Total Titles: 1,000 Print; 400 E-Book
Sales Office(s): Columbia Consortium, Sales Consortium Mgr: Catherine Hobbs *Tel:* 804-690-8529 *E-mail:* catherinehobbs@earthlink.net
Foreign Rep(s): East-West Export Books (Asia, Australia); Eurospan (Africa, Europe, Middle East); Scholarly Book Services (Canada)
Orders to: Hopkins Fulfillment Services, PO Box 50370, Baltimore, MD 21211-4370 *Tel:* 410-516-6965 *Toll Free Tel:* 800-537-5487 *Fax:* 410-516-6998 *E-mail:* hfcustserv@mail.press.jhu.edu
Shipping Address: Hopkins Fulfillment Services, PO Box 50370, Baltimore, MD 21211-4370 *Tel:* 410-516-6965 *Toll Free Tel:* 800-537-5487 *Fax:* 410-516-6998 *E-mail:* hfcustserv@mail.press.jhu.edu
Distribution Center: INscribe Digital, 444 Spear St, Suite 213, San Francisco, CA 94105
Membership(s): Association of American University Presses

University of Michigan Center for Japanese Studies
Unit of University of Michigan
1007 E Huron St, Ann Arbor, MI 48104-1690
Tel: 734-647-8885 *Fax:* 734-647-8886
E-mail: ii.cjspubs@umich.edu
Web Site: www.cjspubs.lsa.umich.edu
Key Personnel
Exec Ed: Bruce E Willoughby *E-mail:* bew@umich.edu
Founded: 1947
This publisher has indicated that 50% of their product line is author subsidized.
ISBN Prefix(es): 978-0-939512; 978-1-929280
Number of titles published annually: 4 Print
Total Titles: 130 Print

University of Michigan Press
Unit of University of Michigan
839 Greene St, Ann Arbor, MI 48104-3209
SAN: 202-5329
Tel: 734-764-4388 *Fax:* 734-615-1540
E-mail: esladmin@umich.edu
Web Site: www.press.umich.edu
Key Personnel
Dir: Charles Watkinson
Edit Dir: Aaron McCollough *Tel:* 734-763-4134 *E-mail:* amccollo@umich.edu
Dir, Mktg & Res: Renee Tambeau *Tel:* 734-936-0388 *E-mail:* rtambeau@umich.edu
Founded: 1930
Aims for diversity in its books & in its audiences.
ISBN Prefix(es): 978-0-472
Number of titles published annually: 110 Print; 100 E-Book
Total Titles: 3,000 Print; 700 E-Book; 24 Audio
Imprints: Ann Arbor Paperbacks; digitalculture
Distributed by Eurospan (territory restricted to Europe, Africa & UK)
Distributor for Center for Chinese Studies, University of Michigan; Center for South & Southeast Asian Studies, University of Michigan
Foreign Rep(s): APAC Publishers Services (Asia, The Pacific); EUROSPAN (Europe); United Publishers Services Ltd (Japan)
Foreign Rights: University of Chicago Press
Returns: Chicago Distribution Center (CDC), 11030 S Langley Ave, Chicago, IL 60628 *Toll Free Tel:* 800-343-4499 *Toll Free Fax:* 800-351-5073 *E-mail:* orderentry@perseusbooks.com
Distribution Center: Chicago Distribution Center (CDC), 11030 S Langley Ave, Chicago, IL 60628

University of Minnesota Press
Unit of University of Minnesota
111 Third Ave S, Suite 290, Minneapolis, MN 55401-2520
SAN: 213-2648
Tel: 612-627-1970 *Fax:* 612-627-1980
E-mail: ump@umn.edu
Web Site: www.upress.umn.edu
Key Personnel
Dir: Doug Armato
Edit Dir: Jason Weidemann
Asst Dir, Book Div & Mktg Dir: Emily Hamilton
Assoc Dir, MMPI: Beverly Kaemmer
Copy-Editing Mgr: Laura Westlund
Opers Mgr: Susan Doerr
Prodn Mgr: Daniel Ochsner
Sales Mgr: Matt Smiley
Regl Ed: Erik Anderson
Publicist: Heather Skinner
Intl Rts Contact: Jeff Moen
Direct Mail: Maggie Sattler
Founded: 1925
Recognized internationally for its innovative, boundary-breaking editorial program in the humanities & social sciences & as publisher of the Minnesota Multiphasic Personality Inventory (MMPI), the most widely used objective tests of personality in the world. Minnesota also maintains as part of its mission a strong commitment to publishing books on the people, history & natural environment of Minnesota & the Upper Midwest.
Among the founding members of the Association of American University Presses (AAUP).
ISBN Prefix(es): 978-0-8166; 978-1-4529
Number of titles published annually: 110 Print; 95 E-Book
Total Titles: 3,081 Print; 2,597 E-Book
Foreign Rep(s): Lexa Publishers (Canada); NewSouth Books (Australia, New Zealand); United Publishers Services Ltd (Japan); University Presses Marketing (Continental Europe, Ireland, UK)
Returns: Chicago Distribution Center, 11030 S Langley Ave, Chicago, IL 60628
Shipping Address: Chicago Distribution Center, 11030 S Langley Ave, Chicago, IL 60628 *Tel:* 773-568-1550 *Toll Free Tel:* 800-621-2736 (orders only) *Toll Free Fax:* 800-621-8476 (orders only)
Warehouse: Chicago Distribution Center, 11030 S Langley Ave, Chicago, IL 60628 *Tel:* 773-702-7000 *Toll Free Tel:* 800-621-2736 *Fax:* 773-702-7212 *Toll Free Fax:* 800-621-8476
Membership(s): AAP; Association of American University Presses; CrossRef; Minnesota Book Publishers Roundtable

University of Missouri Press
2910 Le Mone Blvd, Columbia, MO 65201
SAN: 203-3143
Tel: 573-882-7641 *Toll Free Tel:* 800-621-2736 (orders) *Fax:* 573-884-4498
Web Site: press.umsystem.edu
Key Personnel
Interim Dir: Dwight Browne
Interim Mktg Mgr: Beth Chandler
Publicity Mgr: Lyn Smith *E-mail:* smithls@missouri.edu
Ed-in-Chief & Assoc Dir: Clair Willcox
Rts: Steve Hammer
Founded: 1958
Scholarly books, general trade, art, regional, intellectual thought, history, literary criticism, African-American, journalism, political science, sports & women's studies.
ISBN Prefix(es): 978-0-8262
Number of titles published annually: 30 Print
Total Titles: 900 Print
Distributor for Missouri History Museum; St Louis Mercantile Library
Foreign Rep(s): East-West Export Books (Asia, New Zealand, Pacific Islands); Eurospan (Africa, Continental Europe, Middle East, UK); Scholarly Book Services (Canada)

University of Nebraska at Omaha Center for Public Affairs Research
CPACS Bldg, Rm 108, 6001 Dodge St, Omaha, NE 68182
SAN: 665-4339
Tel: 402-554-2134
Web Site: www.unomaha.edu/cpar
Key Personnel
Dir & Sr Res Assoc: Jerry Deichert *E-mail:* jdeicher@unomaha.edu
Professional books.
ISBN Prefix(es): 978-1-55719
Number of titles published annually: 6 Print
Total Titles: 130 Print

University of Nebraska Press
Division of University of Nebraska at Lincoln
1111 Lincoln Mall, Lincoln, NE 68588-0630
Tel: 402-472-3581; 919-966-7449 (cust serv & foreign orders) *Toll Free Tel:* 800-848-6224 (cust serv & US orders) *Fax:* 402-472-6214; 919-962-2704 (cust serv & foreign orders) *Toll Free Fax:* 800-526-2617 (cust serv & US orders)
E-mail: pressmail@unl.edu
Web Site: www.nebraskapress.unl.edu
Key Personnel
Dir: Donna Shear *Tel:* 402-472-2861 *E-mail:* dshear2@unl.edu
Mktg Mgr: Martyn Beeny
Rts & Perms, Intl Rts: Leif Milliken *Tel:* 402-472-7702 *E-mail:* lmilliken2@unl.edu
Publicity Mgr: Cara Pesek *Tel:* 402-472-7710 *E-mail:* cpesek2@unl.edu
Humanities Ed: Kristen Elias-Rowley *Tel:* 402-472-5949 *E-mail:* keliasrowley2@unl.edu
Founded: 1941

General scholarly nonfiction, including agriculture & natural resources, anthropology, history, literature & criticism, musicology, philosophy, psychology, wildlife & reference works; emphasis on literature & the history of the Trans-Mississippi West. Trade paperbacks, including fiction & science fiction.
ISBN Prefix(es): 978-0-8032
Total Titles: 3,200 Print; 2 CD-ROM
Imprints: Bison Books; Potomac Books
Distributor for Buros Institute; Caxton Press; Creighton University Press; Society for American Baseball Research
Foreign Rep(s): Codasat Canada (Canada); Combined Academic Publishers Ltd (Europe); East-West Export Books (EWEB) (Asia, Australia, New Zealand, The Pacific)
Foreign Rights: McIntosh & Otis
Advertising Agency: Scholarly Press Advertising Services
Warehouse: Maple Press Co, Lebanon Distribution Ctr, 704 Legionaire Dr, Fredericksburg, PA 17026
Membership(s): American Association of University Presses
See separate listing for:
Potomac Books Inc

University of Nevada Press
University of Nevada, M/S 0166, Reno, NV 89557-0166
SAN: 203-316X
Tel: 775-784-6573 *Fax:* 775-784-6200
Web Site: www.unpress.nevada.edu
Key Personnel
Dir: Joanne O'Hare *Tel:* 775-682-7389 *E-mail:* johare@unpress.nevada.edu
Busn Mgr: Jo Anne Banducci *Tel:* 775-682-7387 *E-mail:* jbanducci@unpress.nevada.edu
Design & Prodn Mgr: Kathleen Szawiola *Tel:* 775-682-7391 *E-mail:* szawiola@unpress.nevada.edu
Founded: 1961
ISBN Prefix(es): 978-0-87417
Number of titles published annually: 20 Print; 20 E-Book
Total Titles: 400 Print
Foreign Rep(s): East-West Books (Asia-Pacific); Eurospan University Press Group (Africa, Central America, Europe, Middle East, South America, UK); Scholarly Book Service (Canada)
Orders to: Chicago Distribution Center, 11030 S Langley Ave, Chicago, IL 60628 (Pubnet@202.5280) *Toll Free Tel:* 800-621-2736 *Toll Free Fax:* 800-621-8476 *E-mail:* custserv@press.uchicago.edu
Warehouse: Chicago Distribution Center, 11030 S Langley Ave, Chicago, IL 60628 (Pubnet@202.5280) *Toll Free Tel:* 800-621-2736 *Toll Free Fax:* 800-621-8476 *E-mail:* custserv@press.uchicago.edu
Membership(s): American Association of University Presses; Publishers Association of the West

University of New Mexico
One University of New Mexico, Albuquerque, NM 87131-0001
SAN: 213-9588
Mailing Address: MSC05 3185, One Univ of New Mexico, Albuquerque, NM 87131-0001
Tel: 505-277-2346; 505-272-7777 (cust serv) *Toll Free Tel:* 800-249-7737 (orders only) *Fax:* 505-277-3343; 505-272-7778 (cust serv) *Toll Free Fax:* 800-622-8667 (orders only)
E-mail: unmpress@unm.edu; custserv@upress.unm.edu (order dept)
Web Site: unmpress.com
Key Personnel
Dir: John W Byram *Tel:* 505-277-3495 *E-mail:* jbyram@upress.unm.edu
Assoc Dir, Busn Opers: Richard Schuetz *Tel:* 505-277-3284 *E-mail:* rschuetz@upress.unm.edu
Rts & Perms Coord: Briony Jones *E-mail:* briony@unm.edu
Book Designer: Catherine Leonardo *Tel:* 505-277-3299
Founded: 1929
General, young adult, scholarly & regional books.
ISBN Prefix(es): 978-0-8263
Number of titles published annually: 90 Print
Total Titles: 1,750 Print
Distributor for Avanyu Publishing; Fresco Fine Art Publications LLC; La Frontera Publishing; West End Press
Foreign Rep(s): Codasat (Canada); Eurospan Ltd (Africa, Europe, Middle East, UK); EWEB (Asia, Australia); US PubRep (Craig Falk) (Caribbean including Puerto Rico, Central America, Latin America, Mexico)
Shipping Address: 1312 Basehart Rd SE, Albuquerque, NM 87106-4363
Membership(s): Association of American University Presses

§The University of North Carolina Press
116 S Boundary St, Chapel Hill, NC 27514-3808
SAN: 203-3151
Tel: 919-966-3561 *Fax:* 919-966-3829
E-mail: uncpress@unc.edu
Web Site: www.uncpress.unc.edu
Key Personnel
Dir: John Sherer
Sr Dir, Mktg & Digital Busn Devt: Dino Battista *Tel:* 919-962-0579 *E-mail:* dino_battista@unc.edu
Dir, Contracts & Subs Rts: Vicky Wells *Tel:* 919-962-0369 *E-mail:* vicky_wells@unc.edu
Dir, Publicity & ISBN Contact: Gina M Mahalek *Tel:* 919-962-0581 *E-mail:* gina_mahalek@unc.edu
Edit Dir: Mark Simpson-Vos *Tel:* 919-962-0535
Sales Dir: Michael Donatelli *Tel:* 919-962-0475 *E-mail:* michael_donatelli@unc.edu
Asst Dir & Sr Ed: Charles Grench *Tel:* 919-962-0481 *E-mail:* charles_grench@unc.edu
Mng Ed: Paul Betz *Tel:* 919-962-0530 *E-mail:* paul_betz@unc.edu
Acqs Ed: Brandon Proia
Founded: 1922
General, scholarly, regional.
ISBN Prefix(es): 978-0-8078
Number of titles published annually: 100 Print
Total Titles: 776 E-Book
Distributor for Museum of Early Southern Decorative Arts; North Carolina Museum of Art; Southeastern Center for Contemporary Art; Valentine Museum
Foreign Rep(s): East-West Export Books (Asia, Australia, New Zealand, The Pacific); EDIREP (Caribbean, Central America, Mexico, South America); Eurospan University Press Group (Africa, Continental Europe, Middle East, UK); Scholarly Book Services (Canada)
Advertising Agency: Brimley Agency
Orders to: Long Leaf Services Inc, PO Box 8895, Chapel Hill, NC 27515-8895 *Toll Free Tel:* 800-848-6224 *Toll Free Fax:* 800-272-6817 *E-mail:* customerservice@longleafservices.org
Returns: Longleaf Returns, c/o Maple Press Co, Lebanon Distribution Center, 704 Legionaire Dr, Fredericksburg, PA 17026
Membership(s): AAP; BISG

University of North Texas Press
Stovall Hall, Suite 174, 1400 Highland St, Denton, TX 76201
SAN: 249-4280
Mailing Address: 1155 Union Circle, No 311336, Denton, TX 76203-5017
Tel: 940-565-2142 *Fax:* 940-565-4590
Web Site: www.unt.edu/untpress
Key Personnel
Dir: Ronald Chrisman *E-mail:* ronald.chrisman@unt.edu
Asst Dir: Karen De Vinney *E-mail:* karen.devinney@unt.edu
Founded: 1987
ISBN Prefix(es): 978-0-929398; 978-1-57441
Number of titles published annually: 16 Print; 5 Online; 16 E-Book
Total Titles: 300 Print; 75 Online; 100 E-Book
Foreign Rep(s): East-West Export Books (Asia, Australia, Hawaii, New Zealand, Pacific Islands); Eurospan Group (Europe); Scholarly Book Services (Canada); US PubRep (Latin America)
Distribution Center: Texas Book Consortium, John H Lindsey Bldg, Lewis St, 4354 Tamu, College Station, TX 77843-4354 *Toll Free Tel:* 800-826-8911 *Toll Free Fax:* 888-617-2421
Membership(s): American Association of University Presses

University of Notre Dame Press
310 Flanner Hall, Notre Dame, IN 46556
SAN: 203-3178
Tel: 574-631-6346 *Fax:* 574-631-8148
E-mail: undpress@nd.edu
Web Site: www.undpress.nd.edu
Key Personnel
Interim Mng Dir: Harv Humphrey *Tel:* 574-631-3265 *E-mail:* hjhumphrey@nd.edu
Mng Ed: Rebecca De Boer *Tel:* 574-631-4908 *E-mail:* rdeboer@nd.edu
Busn Mgr: Diane Schaut *Tel:* 574-631-4904 *E-mail:* dschaut@nd.edu
Prodn & Design Mgr: Wendy McMillen *Tel:* 574-631-4907 *E-mail:* wmcmill@nd.edu
Coord, Off Servs: Gina Bixler *Tel:* 574-631-4915 *E-mail:* gbixler@nd.edu
Founded: 1949
Academic books, hardcover & paperback; philosophy, Irish studies, literature, theology, international relations, sociology & general interest.
ISBN Prefix(es): 978-0-268
Number of titles published annually: 50 Print
Total Titles: 800 Print
Foreign Rep(s): Eurospan; EWEB
Returns: Chicago Distribution Center, 11030 S Langley, Chicago, IL 60628 *Tel:* 773-702-7000 (rest of world) *Toll Free Tel:* 800-621-2736 (US & CN) *Fax:* 773-702-7212 (rest of world) *Toll Free Fax:* 800-621-8476 (US & CN)
Distribution Center: Chicago Distribution Center, 11030 S Langley Ave, Chicago, IL 60628 *Tel:* 773-702-7000 (rest of world) *Toll Free Tel:* 800-621-2736 (US & CN) *Fax:* 773-702-7212 (rest of world) *Toll Free Fax:* 800-621-8476 (US & CN)
Membership(s): Association of American University Presses

University of Oklahoma Press
2800 Venture Dr, Norman, OK 73069-8216
SAN: 203-3194
Tel: 405-325-2000 *Toll Free Tel:* 800-627-7377 (orders) *Fax:* 405-364-5798 (orders) *Toll Free Fax:* 800-735-0476 (orders)
E-mail: presscs@ou.edu
Web Site: www.oupress.com
Key Personnel
CFO & Rts & Perms: Diane Cotts *Tel:* 405-325-3276 *E-mail:* dcotts@ou.edu
Dir: B Byron Price *Tel:* 405-325-5666 *E-mail:* b_byron_price@ou.edu
Dir, Sales & Mktg: Dale Bennie *Tel:* 405-325-3207 *E-mail:* dbennie@ou.edu
Ed-in-Chief: Charles Rankin *Tel:* 405-325-2873 *E-mail:* cerankin@ou.edu
Mng Ed: Steven Baker *Tel:* 405-325-1325 *E-mail:* steven.b.baker@ou.edu
Fulfillment Mgr: Diane Cotts *Tel:* 405-325-3276 *E-mail:* dcotts@ou.edu

Prodn Mgr: Emmy Ezzell *Tel:* 405-325-3186
E-mail: eezzell@ou.edu
Publicity Mgr: Sandy See *Tel:* 405-325-3200
E-mail: ssee@ou.edu
Founded: 1928
Scholarly & general interest books on Americana, Native American studies, Western history, regional interest, natural history, anthropology, archaeology, military history, literature, classical studies, women's studies & political science.
ISBN Prefix(es): 978-0-8061; 978-0-87062 (Arthur H Clark Co)
Number of titles published annually: 90 Print; 80 E-Book
Total Titles: 1,850 Print; 5 CD-ROM; 1,280 E-Book
Imprints: Arthur H Clark Co
Distributor for Cherokee National Press; Dakota Institute; Denver Art Museum; Gilcrease Museum; Vanderbilt University Press
Membership(s): American Association of University Presses

§University of Pennsylvania Museum of Archaeology & Anthropology
Division of University of Pennsylvania
3260 South St, Philadelphia, PA 19104-6324
Tel: 215-898-5723 *Fax:* 215-573-2497
E-mail: info@pennmuseum.org; publications@pennmuseum.org
Web Site: www.penn.museum
Key Personnel
Dir, Pubns: James R Mathieu
Admin Coord: Maureen Goldsmith
Founded: 1887
ISBN Prefix(es): 978-0-934718; 978-0-924171; 978-1-931707
Number of titles published annually: 14 Print
Total Titles: 210 Print; 6 CD-ROM
Billing Address: Hopkins Fulfillment Service, PO Box 50370, Baltimore, MD 21211-4370 *Toll Free Tel:* 800-537-5487 *Fax:* 410-516-6998 *E-mail:* hfscustserv@press.jhu.edu
Orders to: Hopkins Fulfillment Service, PO Box 50370, Baltimore, MD 21211-4370 *Toll Free Tel:* 800-537-5487 *Fax:* 410-516-6998 *E-mail:* hfscustserv@press.jhu.edu
Returns: Hopkins Fulfillment Service, PO Box 50370, Baltimore, MD 21211-4370 *Toll Free Tel:* 800-537-5487 *Fax:* 410-516-6998 *E-mail:* hfscustserv@press.jhu.edu
Shipping Address: Hopkins Fulfillment Service, PO Box 50370, Baltimore, MD 21211-4370 *Toll Free Tel:* 800-537-5487 *Fax:* 410-516-6998 *E-mail:* hfscustserv@press.jhu.edu

University of Pennsylvania Press
3905 Spruce St, Philadelphia, PA 19104
SAN: 202-5345
Tel: 215-898-6261 *Fax:* 215-898-0404
E-mail: custserv@pobox.upenn.edu
Web Site: www.pennpress.org
Key Personnel
Dir: Eric Halpern *Tel:* 215-898-6263
E-mail: ehalpern@upenn.edu
Mktg Dir: Laura Waldron *Tel:* 215-898-1673
E-mail: lwaldron@upenn.edu
Busn Mgr: Joseph Guttman *Tel:* 215-898-1670
E-mail: josephgg@upenn.edu
Editing & Prodn Mgr: Elizabeth Glover *Tel:* 215-898-1675 *E-mail:* gloverel@upenn.edu
Publicity & PR Mgr: Gigi Lamm *Tel:* 215-898-1674 *E-mail:* glamm@upenn.edu
Ed-in-Chief: Peter A Agree *Tel:* 215-573-3816
E-mail: agree@upenn.edu
Mng Ed: Alison Anderson *Tel:* 215-898-1678
E-mail: anderaa@upenn.edu
History Ed: Robert Lockhart *Tel:* 215-898-1677
E-mail: rlockhar@upenn.edu
Humanities Ed: Jerome E Singerman *Tel:* 215-898-1681 *E-mail:* singerma@upenn.edu
Consulting Editor: Damon Linker
Tel: 610-613-4546 *Fax:* 215-898-0404
E-mail: linkerpennpress@gmail.com
Consulting Editor (UK): Deborah Blake
E-mail: dcblake.pennpress@virginmedia.com
Founded: 1890
Scholarly & semipopular nonfiction, especially in architecture, history, literature & criticism, social sciences, & human rights.
ISBN Prefix(es): 978-0-8122
Number of titles published annually: 120 Print; 120 Online
Total Titles: 1,200 Print; 800 E-Book
Imprints: Pine Street Books
Foreign Rep(s): University Presses Marketing (Europe, UK)
Foreign Rights: Avicenna Partnership (Middle East); Durnell Marketing (Europe exc Ireland & UK); East-West Export Books Inc (Southeast Asia); Scholarly Book Services (Canada); University Presses Marketing (UK)
Orders to: Penn Press, c/o Hopkins Fulfillment Services, Hampden Sta, Box 50370, Baltimore, MD 21211 *Toll Free Tel:* 800-537-5487 *Fax:* 410-516-6998 *E-mail:* hfscustserv@press.jhu.edu
Returns: Penn Press, c/o Maple Press Co, Lebanon Distribution Ctr, 704 Legionaire Dr, Fredericksburg, PA 17026
Warehouse: Maple Press Distribution Ctr, PO Box 1287, 704 Legionaire Dr, Lebanon, PA 17042 *Tel:* 717-865-7600 *Web Site:* www.maple-vail.com
Membership(s): AAP Professional & Scholarly Publishing Division; American Association of University Presses

University of Pittsburgh Press
7500 Thomas Blvd, Pittsburgh, PA 15260
Tel: 412-383-2456 *Fax:* 412-383-2466
E-mail: info@upress.pitt.edu
Web Site: www.upress.pitt.edu
Key Personnel
Dir: Cynthia Miller *E-mail:* cymiller@pitt.edu
Edit Dir & Dir, Electronic Publg: Peter Kracht
E-mail: pek6@pitt.edu
Mktg Dir: Lowell Britson *E-mail:* lbritson@pitt.edu
Mng Ed: Alexander Wolfe *E-mail:* apw20@pitt.edu
Busn Mgr: Cindy Wessels *E-mail:* caw1@pitt.edu
Rts & Perms: Margie K Bachman *Tel:* 412-383-2544 *E-mail:* mkbachma@pitt.edu
Publicist: Maria Sticco *E-mail:* mes5@pitt.edu
Founded: 1936
Scholarly nonfiction; poetry, regional books, short fiction; Russian & East European studies; composition & rhetoric, Latin American studies, environmental history, urban studies, philosophy of science, political science.
ISBN Prefix(es): 978-0-8229
Number of titles published annually: 65 Print
Total Titles: 1,012 Print; 65 E-Book
Imprints: Golden Triangle Books (historical fiction for young readers)
Sales Office(s): Chicago Distribution Center, 11030 S Langley Ave, Chicago, IL 60628
Distributed by University of Chicago Press Distribution Center
Foreign Rep(s): East-West Export Books (Asia, The Pacific); Eurospan (Africa, Europe, Middle East, UK); Scholarly Book Services (Canada)
Billing Address: Chicago Distribution Center, 11030 S Langley Ave, Chicago, IL 60628
Returns: Chicago Distribution Center, 11030 S Langley Ave, Chicago, IL 60628
Warehouse: Chicago Distribution Center, 11030 S Langley Ave, Chicago, IL 60628 *Tel:* 773-702-7000 *Toll Free Tel:* 800-621-2736 *Fax:* 773-702-7212 *Toll Free Fax:* 800-621-8471
Distribution Center: Chicago Distribution Center, 11030 S Langley Ave, Chicago, IL 60628
Membership(s): Association of American University Presses

University of Puerto Rico Press
(Editorial de la Universidad de Puerto Rico)
Subsidiary of University of Puerto Rico
Edificio La Editorial (level 2), Carr No 1, KM 12.0, Jardin Botanico Norte, San Juan, PR 00927
Mailing Address: PO Box 23322, Rio Piedras, PR 00931-3322 SAN: 208-1245
Tel: 787-250-0435; 787-250-0550
Toll Free Tel: 877-338-7788 *Fax:* 787-753-9116
E-mail: info@laeditorialupr.com
Web Site: www.laeditorialupr.com
Founded: 1947
General fiction & nonfiction, reference books, college texts; Latin America.
ISBN Prefix(es): 978-0-8477
Number of titles published annually: 10 Print
Total Titles: 1,047 Print
Imprints: Coleccion Antologia Personal; Coleccion Aqui y Ahora; Coleccion Caribena; Coleccion Ciencias Naturales; Coleccion Clasicos No Tan Clasicos; Coleccion Cuadernos La Torre; Coleccion Cuentos de un Mundo Perdido; Coleccion Cultura Basica; Coleccion Obras Completas Eugenio Maria de Hostos (edicion critica); Coleccion Dos Lenguas; Coleccion Mujeres de Palabra; Coleccion Nueve Pececitos; Coleccion Puertorriquena; Coleccion San Pedrito
Foreign Rep(s): Baker & Taylor/Libros Sin Fronteras (USA); DESA (Latin America); Lectorum Publications (USA); Libreria La Trinitaria (Dominican Republic)
Membership(s): American Association of University Presses

University of Rochester Press
Affiliate of Boydell & Brewer Inc
668 Mount Hope Ave, Rochester, NY 14620-2731
Tel: 585-275-0419 *Fax:* 585-271-8778
E-mail: boydell@boydellusa.net
Web Site: www.urpress.com
Key Personnel
Edit Dir: Suzanne Guiod *E-mail:* suzanne.guiod@rochester.edu
Prodn Dir: Sue Smith *E-mail:* smith@boydellusa.net
Dir, Sales & Mktg: Michael Richards
Accts Mgr: Eloise Puls *Tel:* 585-273-5777
E-mail: puls@boydellusa.net
Founded: 1989
Philosophy, music & African studies titles.
ISBN Prefix(es): 978-1-878822; 978-1-58046
Number of titles published annually: 25 Print
Total Titles: 132 Print
Foreign Office(s): PO Box 9, Woodbridge Suffolk IP12 3DF, United Kingdom
Foreign Rep(s): Boydell & Brewer (Europe, Japan)
Warehouse: Publishers Storage & Shipping Corp, 231 Industrial Park, 46 Development Rd, Fitchburg, MA 01420-6019, Contact: John Salvey *Tel:* 978-345-2121 *Fax:* 978-348-1233

§University of South Carolina Press
Affiliate of University of South Carolina
1600 Hampton St, Suite 544, Columbia, SC 29208
SAN: 203-3224
Tel: 803-777-5245 *Toll Free Tel:* 800-768-2500 (orders) *Fax:* 803-777-0160 *Toll Free Fax:* 800-868-0740 (orders)
Web Site: www.sc.edu/uscpress
Key Personnel
Dir: Jonathan Haupt *Tel:* 800-777-2243
E-mail: jhaupt@mailbox.sc.edu
Asst Dir, Opers: Linda Haines Fogle *Tel:* 803-777-4848 *E-mail:* lfogle@mailbox.sc.edu
Busn Mgr: Vicki Sewell *Tel:* 803-777-7754
E-mail: sewellv@mailbox.sc.edu
Design & Prodn Mgr: Pat Callahan *Tel:* 803-777-2449 *E-mail:* mpcallah@mailbox.sc.edu

Mng Ed: William Adams *Tel:* 803-777-5075
E-mail: adamswb@mailbox.sc.edu
Asst to Dir: Vicki Bates *Tel:* 803-777-5245
E-mail: batesvc@mailbox.sc.edu
Founded: 1944
American history/studies, Southern studies, military history, maritime history, literary studies including contemporary American & British literature & modern world literature, religious studies, speech/communication, social work.
ISBN Prefix(es): 978-0-87249; 978-1-57003
Number of titles published annually: 50 Print
Total Titles: 700 Print; 2 CD-ROM; 2 Audio
Imprints: Story River Books (southern fiction)
Distributor for McKissick Museum; Saraland Press; South Carolina Bar Association; South Carolina Historical Society
Foreign Rep(s): East-West Export Books (Asia, The Pacific); Eurospan University Press Group (Europe, UK); Scholarly Book Services (Canada)
Warehouse: 718 Devine St, Columbia, SC 29208, Orders: Ms Lee Heckle *Tel:* 803-777-1774 *Fax:* 803-777-0026
Membership(s): American Association of University Presses; Southern Independent Booksellers Alliance

University of Tennessee Press
110 Conference Center Bldg, 600 Henley St, Knoxville, TN 37996-4108
SAN: 212-9930
Tel: 865-974-3321 *Toll Free Tel:* 800-621-2736 (orders) *Fax:* 865-974-3724 *Toll Free Fax:* 800-621-8476 (orders)
E-mail: custserv@utpress.org
Web Site: www.utpress.org
Key Personnel
Dir: Scott Danforth *E-mail:* danforth@utk.edu
Acqs Ed: Thomas Wells *E-mail:* twells@utk.edu
Busn Mgr: Lisa Davis *E-mail:* ldavis49@utk.edu
Mktg Mgr: Cheryl Carson *E-mail:* ccarson3@utk.edu
Publicist: Tom Post *Tel:* 865-974-5466
E-mail: tpost@utk.edu
Founded: 1940
Scholarly & regional nonfiction.
ISBN Prefix(es): 978-0-87049; 978-1-57233; 978-1-62190
Number of titles published annually: 40 Print
Total Titles: 900 Print; 1 Online
Foreign Rep(s): East-West Export Books Inc (Asia, The Pacific); Eurospan Group (Africa, Central Asia, Europe, Middle East, UK)
Distribution Center: Chicago Distribution Center, 11030 S Langley, Chicago, IL 60628 *Toll Free Tel:* 800-621-2736 *Fax:* 773-702-7212
Membership(s): AAP; Association of American University Presses

University of Texas at Arlington School of Urban & Public Affairs
511 University Hall, 5th fl, 601 S Nedderman Dr, Arlington, TX 76010
Mailing Address: PO Box 19588, Arlington, TX 76019
Tel: 817-272-3071 *Fax:* 817-272-3415
E-mail: supa@uta.edu
Web Site: www.uta.edu/supa
Key Personnel
Dir, Communs: Joanne Lovito-Nelson
E-mail: nelsonjm@uta.edu
Contact: Prof Richard L Cole *E-mail:* cole@uta.edu
Newsletter, working papers, books, reports on community revitalization, population projection, charter school evaluation, strategic planning, land use planning, transportation planning, social welfare policy, urban politics, social planning, urban public finance, consensus, building & dispute resolution, group facilitation, urban management, environmental planning & analysis.
ISBN Prefix(es): 978-0-936440
Number of titles published annually: 15 Print
Total Titles: 40 Print

§The University of Utah Press
Subsidiary of University of Utah
J Willard Marriott Library, Suite 5400, 295 S 1500 E, Salt Lake City, UT 84112-0860
SAN: 220-0023
Tel: 801-581-6771 *Toll Free Tel:* 800-621-2736 (orders) *Fax:* 801-581-3365 *Toll Free Fax:* 800-621-8471
E-mail: info@upress.utah.edu
Web Site: www.uofupress.com
Key Personnel
Dir & Mng Ed: Glenda Cotter *E-mail:* glenda.cotter@utah.edu
Busn Mgr & Perms: Sharon Day *E-mail:* sharon.day@utah.edu
Prodn Mgr: Jessica Booth *E-mail:* jessica.booth@utah.edu
Founded: 1949
Scholarly books, regional studies, anthropology, archaeology, linguistics, Mesoamerican studies, natural history, western history, outdoor recreation.
ISBN Prefix(es): 978-0-87480; 978-1-60781
Number of titles published annually: 30 Print
Total Titles: 375 Print; 1 CD-ROM
Imprints: Bonneville Books (trade)
Distributor for BYU Museum of Peoples & Cultures; BYU Studies; KUED (Utah PBS affiliate); Canyonlands Natural History Association; Western Epics Publications
Foreign Rep(s): East-West Export Books (Asia, Australia, Hawaii, New Zealand, Oceania); Scholarly Book Services Inc (Canada)
Orders to: The Chicago Distribution Center, 11030 S Langley Ave, Chicago, IL 60628 *Tel:* 773-702-7000 *Toll Free Tel:* 800-621-2736 *Fax:* 773-702-7212 *Toll Free Fax:* 800-621-8741 *Web Site:* www.uofupress.com
Returns: The Chicago Distribution Center, 11030 S Langley Ave, Chicago, IL 60628

The University of Virginia Press
Affiliate of University of Virginia
PO Box 400318, Charlottesville, VA 22904-4318
Tel: 434-924-3468 (cust serv); 434-924-3469 (cust serv) *Toll Free Tel:* 800-831-3406 (orders) *Fax:* 434-982-2655 *Toll Free Fax:* 877-288-6400
E-mail: vapress@virginia.edu
Web Site: www.upress.virginia.edu
Key Personnel
Dir: Mark H Saunders *Tel:* 434-924-6064
E-mail: msaunders@virginia.edu
Asst Dir/Ed-in-Chief & Humanities Ed: Eric Brandt
Dir, Mktg: Jason Coleman *Tel:* 434-924-1450
E-mail: jgc3h@virginia.edu
Sales & Publicity Dir: Emily Grandstaff *Tel:* 434-982-2932 *E-mail:* ekg4a@virginia.edu
Database Mgr: Mary MacNeil *E-mail:* mmm5w@virginia.edu
Mgr, Design & Prodn: Martha Farlow *Tel:* 434-924-3585 *E-mail:* mfarlow@virginia.edu
Acqs Ed, Architecture & Environmental: Boyd Zenner
Acqs Ed, Humanities: Cathie Brettschneider *Tel:* 434-982-3033 *E-mail:* cib8b@virginia.edu
Acqs Ed, Soc Sci & History: Richard Holway *Tel:* 434-924-7301 *E-mail:* rkh2a@virginia.edu
Cust Serv: Brenda Fitzgerald
Founded: 1963
General scholarly nonfiction with emphasis on history, literature & regional books.
ISBN Prefix(es): 978-0-8139; 978-978-0
Number of titles published annually: 65 Print; 60 E-Book
Total Titles: 1,350 Print
Distributor for Colonial Society of Massachusetts; Mount Vernon Ladies Association
Foreign Rep(s): East-West Export Books (The Pacific); Eurospan (Europe); Scholarly Book Services (Canada)
Shipping Address: 500 Edgemont, Charlottesville, VA 22903
Membership(s): American Association of University Presses

§University of Washington Press
433 Brooklyn Ave NE, Seattle, WA 98195-9570
SAN: 212-2502
Mailing Address: PO Box 50096, Seattle, WA 98145-5096
Tel: 206-543-4050 *Toll Free Tel:* 800-537-5487 (orders) *Fax:* 206-543-3932; 410-516-6998 (orders)
E-mail: uwpress@u.washington.edu
Web Site: www.washington.edu/uwpress/
Key Personnel
Dir: Nicole Mitchell
Assoc Dir & Gen Mgr: Mary Anderson
E-mail: maryande@u.washington.edu
Exec Ed: Lorri Hagman *E-mail:* lhagman@u.washington.edu
Mng Ed: Marilyn Trueblood *E-mail:* marilynt@u.washington.edu
Asst Mng Ed: Mary Ribesky *E-mail:* ribesky@u.washington.edu
Mktg Mgr: Alice Herbig *Tel:* 206-221-4994
E-mail: aherbig@u.washington.edu
Prodn Mgr: Pam Canell *Tel:* 206-221-5893
Sales Mgr: Rachael Levay *Tel:* 617-871-0295 *Fax:* 617-945-0137 *E-mail:* remann@u.washington.edu
Subs Rts Mgr & Asst to Dir: Denise Clark *Tel:* 206-543-4057 *E-mail:* ddclark@u.washington.edu
Sr Designer: Tom Eykemans *Tel:* 206-221-7004
Founded: 1920
General scholarly nonfiction, reprints, imports.
ISBN Prefix(es): 978-0-295
Number of titles published annually: 68 Print
Total Titles: 1,500 Print; 1 CD-ROM
Foreign Rep(s): Combined Academic Publisher Ltd (UK); Douglas & McIntyre (Canada); University of British Columbia Press (Canada)

University of Wisconsin Press
1930 Monroe St, 3rd fl, Madison, WI 53711-2059
SAN: 501-0039
Tel: 608-263-0668 *Toll Free Tel:* 800-621-2736 (orders) *Fax:* 608-263-1173 *Toll Free Fax:* 800-621-2736 (orders)
E-mail: uwiscpress@uwpress.wisc.edu (main off)
Web Site: www.wisc.edu/wisconsinpress
Key Personnel
Dir: Dennis Lloyd
Communs Dir: Sheila M Leary *Tel:* 608-263-0734
Journals Mgr: Jason Gray *Tel:* 608-263-0667
E-mail: jmgray5@wisc.edu
Prodn Mgr & ISBN Contact: Terry Emmrich *Tel:* 608-263-0731 *E-mail:* temmrich@wisc.edu
Sales & Mktg Mgr: Andrea Christofferson *Tel:* 608-263-0814 *E-mail:* aschrist@wisc.edu
Sr Acqs Ed: Raphael Kadushin *Tel:* 608-263-1062
E-mail: kadushin@wisc.edu
Founded: 1937
Academic Press, including regional Midwest titles & trade titles.
ISBN Prefix(es): 978-0-87972; 978-0-299; 978-1-928755; 978-0-87020; 978-0-9671787; 978-1-931; 978-8-158; 978-0-9682722; 978-0-924119; 978-0-9655464; 978-0-9718963; 978-0-9624369; 978-0-932900; 978-1-931569
Number of titles published annually: 80 Print; 1 CD-ROM; 1 Audio
Total Titles: 1,385 Print; 8 CD-ROM; 3 Audio
Imprints: Popular Press; Terrace Books
Distributor for The Center for the Study of Upper Midwestern Culture; Dryad Press; Elvehjem Museum of Art; International Brecht Society; Max Kade Institute for German-American Studies; Spring Freshet Press; Wis-

consin Academy of Sciences, Arts & Letters; Wisconsin Historical Society Press; Wisconsin Veterans Museum
Foreign Rights: East-West Export Books Inc (Asia, Australia, New Zealand, The Pacific); Eurospan Ltd (Africa, Continental Europe, Iceland, Ireland, Middle East, UK)
Advertising Agency: Ad Vantage, Anne Herger
Orders to: Chicago Distribution Center, 11030 S Langley Ave, Chicago, IL 60628-3892 SAN: 202-5280
Returns: Chicago Distribution Center, 11030 S Langley Ave, Chicago, IL 60628-3892 SAN: 202-5280
Shipping Address: Chicago Distribution Center, 11030 S Langley Ave, Chicago, IL 60628-3892 SAN: 202-5280
Warehouse: Chicago Distribution Center, 11030 S Langley Ave, Chicago, IL 60628-3892 SAN: 202-5280
Distribution Center: East-West Export Books, c/o University of Hawaii Press, 2840 Kolowalu St, Honolulu, HI 96822 (Asia, the Pacific, Australia & New Zealand) *Tel:* 808-956-8830 *Fax:* 808-988-6052 *E-mail:* eweb@hawaii.edu
Chicago Distribution Center, 11030 S Langley Ave, Chicago, IL 60628-3892 *Tel:* 773-568-1550 *Toll Free Tel:* 800-621-2736 *Fax:* 773-660-2235 *Toll Free Fax:* 800-621-8476 SAN: 202-5280
Eurospan Group, c/o Turpin Distribution, Stratton Business Park, Pegasus Dr, Biggleswade, Beds SG18 8TQ, United Kingdom (Africa, Europe, Middle East, UK & Russia) *Tel:* (01767) 604972 *Fax:* (01767) 601640 *E-mail:* eurospan@turpin-distribution.com
Membership(s): Association of American University Presses; Midwest Independent Booksellers Association; Wisconsin Library Association

University Press of America Inc
Imprint of Rowman & Littlefield Publishing Group
4501 Forbes Blvd, Suite 200, Lanham, MD 20706
SAN: 200-2256
Tel: 301-459-3366 *Toll Free Tel:* 800-462-6420 *Fax:* 301-429-5748 *Toll Free Fax:* 800-338-4550
Web Site: www.univpress.com
Key Personnel
Chmn: Stanley D Plotnick
CEO & Pres: James E Lyons
CFO: George Franzak
VP & Publr: Julie Kirsch *E-mail:* jkirsch@rowman.com
VP, Mfg & Prodn: Stephen Driver
Dir, Mktg: Dave Horvath *E-mail:* dhorvath@rowman.com
Mgr, Rts & Perms & Intl Rts Contact: Clare Cox *E-mail:* ccox@rowman.com
Acqs Ed: Nicolette Amstuta *E-mail:* namstutz@univpress.com; Stella Donovan *E-mail:* sdonovan@univpress.com
Founded: 1975
Scholarly monographs, college texts, conference proceedings, professional books & reprints in the social sciences & the humanities.
ISBN Prefix(es): 978-0-8191; 978-0-7618
Number of titles published annually: 150 Print; 100 E-Book
Total Titles: 10,000 Print
Imprints: Hamilton Books
Branch Office(s)
67 Mowat Ave, Suite 241, Toronto, ON M6K 3E3, Canada, Contact: Les Petriw *Tel:* 416-534-1660 *Toll Free Tel:* 877-626-2665 *Fax:* 416-534-3699 *E-mail:* kstinson@rowmanlittlefield.com
Distributor for Atlantic Council; Center for National Policy Press; Harvard Center for International Affairs; International Law Institute; Joint Center for Political & Economic Studies Press; White Burkett Miller Center; Society of the Cincinnati
Foreign Rep(s): NBN Plymbridge (Europe, UK); United Publishers Services (Japan)
Foreign Rights: United Publishers Service (Japan)
Shipping Address: 15200 NBN Way, Blue Ridge Summit, PA 17214-0191 *Toll Free Tel:* 800-462-6420 *Fax:* 717-794-3812 *Toll Free Fax:* 800-338-4550
Membership(s): AAP
See separate listing for:
Hamilton Books

University Press of Colorado
5589 Arapahoe Ave, Suite 206-C, Boulder, CO 80303
SAN: 202-1749
Tel: 720-406-8849 *Toll Free Tel:* 800-621-2736 (orders) *Fax:* 720-406-3443
Web Site: www.upcolorado.com
Key Personnel
Dir: Darrin Pratt *E-mail:* darrin@upcolorado.com
Acqs Ed: Jessica d'Arbonne *E-mail:* jessica@upcolorardo.com
Founded: 1965
Scholarly & regional nonfiction.
ISBN Prefix(es): 978-0-87081; 978-1-60732
Number of titles published annually: 30 Print; 30 E-Book
Total Titles: 340 Print; 3 CD-ROM; 334 E-Book
Imprints: Utah State University Press
Distributor for Center for Literary Publishing; History Colorado; Western Press Books
Foreign Rep(s): Codasat Canada Ltd (Canada); NBN International (Australia, UK & the continent)
Returns: Chicago Distribution Center, Returns Processing Ctr, 11030 S Langley, Chicago, IL 60628 *Toll Free Tel:* 800-621-2736
Distribution Center: Chicago Distribution Center, 11030 S Langley, Chicago, IL 60628 *Toll Free Tel:* 800-621-2736
Membership(s): Association of American University Presses
See separate listing for:
Utah State University Press

University Press of Florida
Affiliate of State University System of Florida
15 NW 15 St, Gainesville, FL 32603-2079
SAN: 207-9275
Tel: 352-392-1351 *Toll Free Tel:* 800-226-3822 (orders only) *Fax:* 352-392-0590 *Toll Free Fax:* 800-680-1955 (orders only)
E-mail: info@upf.com
Web Site: www.upf.com
Key Personnel
Dir: Meredith Morris-Babb *E-mail:* mb@upf.com
Assoc Dir & Prepress Mgr: Lynn Werts *E-mail:* lw@upf.com
Asst Dir & Mng Ed: Michele Fiyak-Burkley *E-mail:* mf@upf.com
Ed-in-Chief: Amy Gorelick *E-mail:* ag@upf.com
Busn Mgr: Kim Lake *E-mail:* kl@upf.com
Founded: 1945
Scholarly & regional nonfiction.
ISBN Prefix(es): 978-0-8130
Number of titles published annually: 100 Print; 100 E-Book
Total Titles: 2,830 Print; 1,850 E-Book
Imprints: Orange Grove Textbooks
Membership(s): American Association of University Presses

§University Press of Kansas
2502 Westbrooke Circle, Lawrence, KS 66045-4444
SAN: 203-3267
Tel: 785-864-4154; 785-864-4155 (orders) *Fax:* 785-864-4586
E-mail: upress@ku.edu; upkorders@ku.edu (orders)
Web Site: www.kansaspress.ku.edu
Key Personnel
Dir: Charles T Myers *Tel:* 785-864-9160 *E-mail:* ctmyers@ku.edu
Ed-in-Chief: Michael Briggs *Tel:* 785-864-9162 *E-mail:* mbriggs@ku.edu
Acqs Ed: Kim Hogeland *Tel:* 785-864-9161 *E-mail:* khogeland@ku.edu
Art Dir & Ad Mgr: Karl Janssen *Tel:* 785-864-9164 *E-mail:* kjanssen@ku.edu
Busn Mgr: Conrad Roberts *Tel:* 785-864-9158 *E-mail:* ceroberts@ku.edu
Exhibits & Direct Mail Mgr: Debra Diehl *Tel:* 785-864-9166 *E-mail:* ddiehl@ku.edu
Publicity Mgr: Rebecca Murray Schuler *Tel:* 785-864-9170 *E-mail:* rmschuler@ku.edu
Founded: 1946
General scholarly nonfiction: American, environmental & western history, government & political science, military history, legal history, regional, women's studies, cultural studies, presidential studies.
ISBN Prefix(es): 978-978-07006
Number of titles published annually: 50 Print
Total Titles: 1,200 Print; 1 CD-ROM
Foreign Rep(s): East-West Export Books (Asia, The Pacific); Eurospan Ltd (Africa, Europe, Middle East, UK); Scholarly Book Services Inc (Canada)
Returns: University Press of Kansas Warehouse, 2445 Westbrooke Circle, Lawrence, KS 66045-4440
Warehouse: University Press of Kansas Warehouse, 2445 Westbrooke Circle, Lawrence, KS 66045-4440
Membership(s): Association of American University Presses

The University Press of Kentucky
663 S Limestone St, Lexington, KY 40508-4008
SAN: 203-3275
Tel: 859-257-8400 *Fax:* 859-257-8481
Web Site: www.kentuckypress.com
Key Personnel
Dir: Stephen M Wrinn *Tel:* 859-257-8432 *E-mail:* smwrin2@uky.edu
Dir, Fin & Admin: Craig Wilkie *Tel:* 859-257-8436 *E-mail:* crwilk00@uky.edu
Dir, Mktg & Sales: John P Hussey *Tel:* 859-257-4249 *Fax:* 859-323-4981 *E-mail:* jphuss2@uky.edu
Acting Dir, Editing, Design & Prodn: David Cobb *Tel:* 859-257-4252 *Fax:* 859-257-2984 *E-mail:* dlcobb2@uky.edu
Asst Dir, Fin & Admin: Teresa Wells Collins *Tel:* 859-257-8405 *E-mail:* twell1@uky.edu
Acqs Ed: Anne Dean Watkins *Tel:* 859-257-8434 *Fax:* 859-257-2984 *E-mail:* adwatk0@uky.edu
Founded: 1943
ISBN Prefix(es): 978-0-8131
Number of titles published annually: 70 Print; 70 E-Book
Total Titles: 1,200 Print; 550 E-Book
Distributor for Kentucky Historical Society
Foreign Rep(s): Eurospan (UK & the continent); Scholarly Book Services (Canada)
Orders to: Hopkins Fulfillment Services, PO Box 50370, Baltimore, MD 21211-4370 *Tel:* 410-516-6956 *Toll Free Tel:* 800-537-5487 *Fax:* 410-516-6998 *E-mail:* hfscustserv@press.jhu.edu
Returns: Hopkins Fulfillment Services, c/o Maple Press Co, Lebanon Dist Center, 704 Legionaire Dr, Fredericksburg, PA 17026 *Toll Free Tel:* 800-537-5487 *Fax:* 410-516-6998 *E-mail:* hfscustserv@press.jhu.edu
Membership(s): AAP; Association of American University Presses

University Press of Mississippi
3825 Ridgewood Rd, Jackson, MS 39211-6492
SAN: 203-1914

Tel: 601-432-6205 *Toll Free Tel:* 800-737-7788 (orders & cust serv) *Fax:* 601-432-6217
E-mail: press@mississippi.edu
Web Site: www.upress.state.ms.us
Key Personnel
Dir: Leila W Salisbury *E-mail:* lsalisbury@mississippi.edu
Asst Dir/Ed-in-Chief: Craig Gill *E-mail:* cgill@mississippi.edu
Asst Dir/Art Dir: John Langston *E-mail:* jlangston@mississippi.edu
Asst Dir/Mktg Dir: Steve Yates *E-mail:* syates@mississippi.edu
Asst Dir/Busn Mgr: Isabel Metz *E-mail:* imetz@mississippi.edu
Data Servs & Course Adoptions Mgr: Kathy Burgess *E-mail:* kburgess@mississippi.edu
Ad & Publicity Mgr: Clint Kimberling *E-mail:* ckimberling@mississippi.edu
Mng Ed: Anne Stascavage *E-mail:* astascavage@mississippi.edu
Sr Prodn Ed: Mrs Shane Gong Stewart *E-mail:* sgong@mississippi.edu
Acqs Ed: Vijay Shah *E-mail:* vshah@mississippi.edu
Asst Prodn Mgr/Designer/Electronic Projs Mgr: Todd Lape *E-mail:* tlape@mississippi.edu
Cust Serv & Order Supv: Ms Sandy Alexander *Tel:* 601-432-6704 *E-mail:* salexander@mississippi.edu
Admin Asst/Rts & Perms Mgr: Cynthia Foster *E-mail:* cfoster@mississippi.edu
Designer: Pete Halverson *E-mail:* phalverson@mississippi.edu
Edit Assoc: Valerie Jones *E-mail:* vjones@mississippi.edu; Katie Keene *E-mail:* kkeene@mississippi.edu
Electronic & Direct-to-Consumer Mktg Specialist: Kristin Kirkpatrick *E-mail:* kkirkpatrick@mississippi.edu
Mktg Asst: Courtney McCreary *E-mail:* cmccreary@mississippi.edu
Founded: 1970
Publisher of trade & scholarly books, nonfiction, fiction & regional.
ISBN Prefix(es): 978-0-87805; 978-1-57806; 978-1-934110; 978-1-60473; 978-1-61703; 978-1-62103; 978-1-62846; 978-1-62674; 978-1-4968
Number of titles published annually: 80 Print; 80 E-Book
Total Titles: 1,100 Print; 760 E-Book
Foreign Rep(s): Bill Bailey Publishers' Representatives (Europe); East-West Export Books (Asia, Australia, Hawaii, The Pacific); Roundhouse Group (Africa, India, Ireland, Middle East, UK); Scholarly Book Services Inc (Canada)
Advertising Agency: PM Productions, 203 Summer Hill Rd, Madison, MS 39110, Designer: Patti Mitchell *E-mail:* pattipmpro@aol.com
Returns: Maple Logistics Solutions, Lebanon Distribution Ctr, 704 Legionnaire Dr, Fredericksburg, PA 17026 (non-USPS deliveries); Maple Logistics Solutions, Lebanon Distribution Ctr, PO Box 1287, Lebanon, PA 17042 (all USPS deliveries)
Warehouse: Maple Logistics Solutions, Lebanon Distribution Ctr, 704 Legionnaire Dr, Fredericksburg, PA 17026
Membership(s): American Association of University Presses

University Press of New England
One Court St, Suite 250, Lebanon, NH 03766
SAN: 203-3283
Tel: 603-448-1533 *Toll Free Tel:* 800-421-1561 (orders only) *Fax:* 603-448-7006; 603-643-1540
E-mail: university.press@dartmouth.edu
Web Site: www.upne.com
Key Personnel
Dir: Michael Burton
Dir, Mktg & Sales: Richard Henning
Assoc Dir, Opers: Thomas Johnson
Acqs Ed-in-Chief: Phyllis Deutsch
Acqs Ed: Stephen Hull; Richard Pult
Publicity & Rts Mgr: Barbara Briggs
Sales & Trade Exhibits Mgr: Sherri Strickland
Founded: 1970
Scholarly, nonfiction, regional, New England fiction.
ISBN Prefix(es): 978-0-87451; 978-1-58465
Number of titles published annually: 70 Print
Total Titles: 825 Print; 300 E-Book
Imprints: Brandeis University Press; Dartmouth College Press; Hardscrabble Books; Northeastern University Press; Tufts University Press; University of New Hampshire Press; University of Vermont Press
Distributor for Beinecke Rare Book & Manuscript Library; Bibliopola Press; CavanKerry Press; Chipstone Foundation; Fence Books; Four Way Books; Isabella Stewart Gardner Museum; Harvest Hill Press; National Poetry Foundation; New England College; Nicolin Fields Publishing; Peter E Randall Publisher; The Sheep Meadow Press; Vermont Folklife Center; Warring States Project; Wesleyan University Press; Winterthur Museum Garden & Library
Foreign Rep(s): East-West Export Books (Australia, New Zealand, The Pacific); Eurospan University Press Group (Europe, Middle East, UK); University of British Columbia Press (Canada)
Advertising Agency: New England Imprints, One Court St, Lebanon, NH 03766, Contact: Sara J Carpenter *Tel:* 603-448-1533 ext 231 *Fax:* 603-448-7006
Returns: UPNE Fulfillment, c/o Maple Press Co, Lebanon Distribution Ctr, PO Box 1287, Lebanon, PA 17026 *Tel:* 603-448-1533 ext 503 *Fax:* 603-448-9429
Warehouse: UPNE Fulfillment, c/o Maple Press Co, Lebanon Distribution Ctr, PO Box 1287, Lebanon, PA 17026 *Tel:* 603-448-1553 ext 503 *Fax:* 603-448-9429
Distribution Center: Ampersand Inc, 2440 Viking Way, Richmond, BC V6V 1N2, Canada *Tel:* 604-448-7111 *Toll Free Tel:* 800-561-8583 *Fax:* 604-448-7118 *Toll Free Fax:* 888-323-7118 *E-mail:* info@ampersandinc.ca *Web Site:* ampersandinc.ca
Membership(s): Association of American University Presses; NEBA

University Publishing Group
6 Public Sq, Suite 206, Hagerstown, MD 21740
Tel: 240-420-0036 *Toll Free Tel:* 800-654-8188 *Fax:* 240-718-7100
E-mail: editorial@upgbooks.com; orders@upgbooks.com; sales@upgbooks.com
Web Site: www.upgbooks.com
Key Personnel
Owner & Treas: Norman Quist
Pres: Leslie Le Blanc *E-mail:* leblanc@upgbooks.com
Cust Serv Mgr: Mary Gesford
Founded: 1985
Publish books in medicine, social sciences, philosophy & law.
ISBN Prefix(es): 978-1-55572
Number of titles published annually: 6 Print
Total Titles: 35 Print

University Publishing House
PO Box 1664, Mannford, OK 74044
Tel: 918-865-4726
E-mail: upub3@juno.com
Web Site: www.universitypublishinghouse.net
Key Personnel
Owner & Pres: Randell Nyborg
Founded: 1987
Industrial & automotive, classic fiction reprints, mail order books & industrial processes.
ISBN Prefix(es): 978-1-877767; 978-1-57002
Number of titles published annually: 5 Print
Total Titles: 140 Print

University Science Books
20 Edgeshill Rd, Mill Valley, CA 94941
SAN: 213-8085
Tel: 415-332-5390 *Fax:* 415-332-5390
E-mail: univscibks@igc.org
Web Site: www.uscibooks.com
Key Personnel
Pres: Bruce Armbruster
VP & Intl Rts Contact: Kathy Armbruster
Assoc Publr/Edit: Jane Ellis *Tel:* 973-378-3900 *Fax:* 973-378-3925 *E-mail:* bjellis@igc.org
Founded: 1978
Intermediate level college textbooks & monographs in astronomy, chemistry, biochemistry & physics, environmental science, technical writing, biology, reference books, children's books.
ISBN Prefix(es): 978-0-935702; 978-1-891389
Number of titles published annually: 8 Print; 5 E-Book
Total Titles: 200 Print; 150 E-Book
Foreign Rep(s): W H Freeman (Europe)
Foreign Rights: Alfaomega Grupo Editor (Mexico); Eastern Book Service Inc (Japan); Palgrave/Macmillan's Global Academic Publishing (Europe, India)
Orders to: Books International Inc, PO Box 605, Herndon, VA 20172, Contact: Todd Riggleman *Tel:* 703-661-1572 *Fax:* 703-661-1501
Returns: Books International Inc, 22883 Quicksilver Dr, Dulles, VA 20166 (15% restocking fee, damaged books not accepted, books must be in original shrinkwrap for credit) *Tel:* 703-661-1572 *Fax:* 703-661-1501
Distribution Center: Books International Inc, 22883 Quicksilver Dr, Dulles, VA 20166 (15% discount on all web orders) *Tel:* 703-661-1572 *Fax:* 703-661-1501 *E-mail:* usbmail@presswarehouse.com

UnKnownTruths.com Publishing Co
8815 Conroy Windermere Rd, Suite 190, Orlando, FL 32835
SAN: 255-6375
Tel: 407-929-9207 *Fax:* 407-876-3933
E-mail: info@unknowntruths.com
Web Site: unknowntruths.com
Key Personnel
CFO: Lynda Cassidy *Tel:* 407-876-7737
Pres: Walter Parks *E-mail:* wparks@unknowntruths.com
PR: Cherie Carter *E-mail:* cherie@unknowntruths.com
Founded: 2002
Formed to publish true stories of the unusual or of the previously unexplained. Stories typically provide radically different views from those that have shaped the understandings of our natural world, our religions, our science, our history & even the foundations of our civilizations. Also include stories of the very important life-extending medical breakthroughs: stem cell therapies, genetic therapies, cloning & other emerging findings that promise to change the very meaning of life.
ISBN Prefix(es): 978-0-9745393
Number of titles published annually: 12 Print; 4 Online
Advertising Agency: James Brooke & Associates, 2660 Second St, Suite 1, Santa Monica, CA 90405, PR: Cherie Carter *Tel:* 310-396-8070 *Fax:* 310-396-8071 *E-mail:* cherie@unknowntruths.com
Distribution Center: New Leaf Distributing Co, 401 Thornton Rd, Lithia Springs, GA 30122 *Tel:* 770-948-7845 *Fax:* 770-944-2313

Quality Books Inc, 1003 W Pines Rd, Oregon, IL 61061 *Toll Free Tel:* 800-323-4241 *Fax:* 815-732-4499
Membership(s): The Association of Publishers for Special Sales; The Independent Book Publishers Association

§Unlimited Publishing LLC
PO Box 99, Nashville, IN 47448
Tel: 206-666-5484
E-mail: acquisitions@unlimitedpublishing.com
Web Site: www.unlimitedpublishing.com
Founded: 2000
Bringing back out-of-print books & new nonfiction by professional writers. Visit web site for submission guidelines before sending a proposal. No simultaneous submissions; e-mail queries preferred, proposals sent by post will not be returned.
ISBN Prefix(es): 978-1-58832
Number of titles published annually: 25 Print; 25 Online; 25 E-Book
Total Titles: 250 Print
Membership(s): The Independent Book Publishers Association

UNO Press
Division of University of New Orleans
University of New Orleans Metro College, Educ Bldg, Suite 210, 2000 Lakeshore Dr, New Orleans, LA 70148
Tel: 504-280-7457 *Fax:* 504-280-7317
E-mail: unopress@uno.edu
Web Site: unopress.org
Founded: 2000
University Publishing House.
ISBN Prefix(es): 978-0-9728143; 978-0-9706190; 978-1-60801
Number of titles published annually: 9 Print; 3 E-Book
Total Titles: 12 Print; 3 E-Book
Distribution Center: Hopkins Fulfillment Services, PO Box 50370, Baltimore, MD 21211-4370 *Tel:* 410-516-6965 *Toll Free Tel:* 800-537-5487 *Fax:* 410-516-6998 *E-mail:* hfscustserv@press.jhu.edu *Web Site:* hfs.jhu.edu
Membership(s): The Independent Book Publishers Association

Unveiled Media LLC
PO Box 930463, Verona, WI 53593
Tel: 707-986-8345
Web Site: www.unveiledmedia.com
Key Personnel
Publr: Michael Seelen *E-mail:* mseelen@unveiledmedia.com
Founded: 2012
Boutique publisher. Specialize in photography, works of fiction & children's books.
ISBN Prefix(es): 978-0-9776385
Number of titles published annually: 3 Print; 3 E-Book
Total Titles: 3 Print; 3 E-Book
Imprints: Cotton Candy Press; Iron Icon Books
Distribution Center: Create Space
Lightning Source
Membership(s): The Independent Book Publishers Association

W E Upjohn Institute for Employment Research
300 S Westnedge Ave, Kalamazoo, MI 49007-4686
Tel: 269-343-5541; 269-343-4330 (pubns) *Toll Free Tel:* 888-227-8569 *Fax:* 269-343-7310
E-mail: publications@upjohn.org
Web Site: www.upjohn.org
Key Personnel
Mgr, Pubns: Richard Wyrwa *E-mail:* wyrwa@upjohn.org
Founded: 1959
Labor economics & industrial relations.
ISBN Prefix(es): 978-0-88099; 978-0-911558
Number of titles published annually: 12 Print; 8 E-Book
Total Titles: 160 Print; 80 E-Book
Membership(s): Association of American University Presses

§Upper Access Inc
87 Upper Access Rd, Hinesburg, VT 05461
SAN: 667-1195
Tel: 802-482-2988 *Toll Free Tel:* 800-310-8320 (orders) *Fax:* 802-417-3002
E-mail: info@upperaccess.com
Web Site: www.upperaccess.com
Key Personnel
VP & Publr: Stephen T Carlson *E-mail:* steve@upperaccess.com
Assoc Publr: Thomas Gray
Devt Dir: Ron Lawrence *Tel:* 802-899-2276 *Fax:* 802-899-1291 *E-mail:* ron@pubassist.com
Sales Dir: Kristen Lewis
Founded: 1986
Publisher of nonfiction books to improve the quality of life. Also publish business software.
ISBN Prefix(es): 978-0-942679
Number of titles published annually: 3 Print; 2 E-Book
Total Titles: 54 Print; 6 E-Book
Imprints: Upper Access Books; Publishers' Assistant (software & related servs)
Orders to: Midpoint National, 1263 Southwest Blvd, Kansas City, KS 66103 (trade sales & returns) *Tel:* 913-362-7400 *E-mail:* info@midpt.com *Web Site:* www.midpt.com
Returns: Midpoint National, 1263 Southwest Blvd, Kansas City, KS 66103 (trade sales & returns) *Tel:* 913-362-7400 *E-mail:* info@midpt.com *Web Site:* www.midpt.com
Shipping Address: Midpoint Trade Books, 27 W 20 St, Suite 1102, New York, NY 10011 (trade sales & returns) *Tel:* 212-727-0190 *Fax:* 212-727-0195 *E-mail:* nina@midpointtrade.com *Web Site:* www.midpointtrade.com
Warehouse: Midpoint Trade Books, 1550 Heil Quaker Blvd, La Vergne, TN 37086 (trade sales & returns) *Tel:* 212-616-2021 *E-mail:* julie@midpointtrade.com *Web Site:* www.midpointtrade.com
Distribution Center: Midpoint National, 1263 Southwest Blvd, Kansas City, KS 66103 (trade sales & returns) *Tel:* 913-362-7400 *E-mail:* info@midpt.com *Web Site:* www.midpt.com
Membership(s): The Association of Publishers for Special Sales; The Independent Book Publishers Association; Independent Publishers of New England; Publishers North

§Upper Room Books
Division of The Upper Room
1908 Grand Ave, Nashville, TN 37212
SAN: 203-3364
Tel: 615-340-7200 *Toll Free Tel:* 800-972-0433 *Fax:* 615-340-7266
Web Site: books.upperroom.org
Key Personnel
Asst Ed & Admin Coord: Joanna Bradley *E-mail:* jbradley@umcdiscipleship.org
Dir, Prodn & Scheduling: Debbie Gregory *Tel:* 615-340-7224
Founded: 1935
Prayer & devotional life publications. No fiction or poetry accepted.
ISBN Prefix(es): 978-0-8358
Number of titles published annually: 20 Print; 20 E-Book
Imprints: Fresh Air Books
Foreign Rights: Riggins International Rights (Worldwide exc North America)
Warehouse: PBD Inc, 1650 Bluegrass Pkwy, Alpharetta, GA 30201
Membership(s): ABA; CBA: The Association for Christian Retail; Evangelical Christian Publishers Association
See separate listing for:
Fresh Air Books

Upstart Books™
Imprint of Highsmith Inc
4810 Forest Run Rd, Madison, WI 53704
Mailing Address: PO Box 14410, Madison, WI 53708
Tel: 608-241-1201 *Toll Free Tel:* 800-448-4887 (orders) *Toll Free Fax:* 800-448-5828
E-mail: custsvc@upstartpromotions.com
Web Site: www.upstartbooks.com
Key Personnel
Dir, Pubns: Matt Mulder *E-mail:* mmulder@highsmith.com
Mng Ed: Michelle McCardell *E-mail:* mmcardell@highsmith.com
Founded: 1990
Reading activities & library skills for teachers & children's librarians; storytelling activity books & Internet resources.
ISBN Prefix(es): 978-0-917846; 978-0-913853; 978-1-57950; 978-1-932146
Number of titles published annually: 12 Print
Total Titles: 100 Print

§The Urban Institute
2100 "M" St NW, Washington, DC 20037
SAN: 203-3380
Tel: 202-833-7200
Web Site: www.urban.org
Key Personnel
Dir, Edit Servs & Pubns: Scott Forrey
Founded: 1968
Public policy, economics, government, social sciences.
ISBN Prefix(es): 978-0-87766
Number of titles published annually: 10 Print
Membership(s): American Association of University Presses

§Urban Land Institute
1025 Thomas Jefferson St NW, Suite 500-W, Washington, DC 20007
Tel: 202-624-7000 *Toll Free Tel:* 800-321-5011 (cust serv) *Fax:* 410-626-7140
E-mail: bookstore@uli.org; customerservice@uli.org
Web Site: www.uli.org/books
Key Personnel
VP, Mktg: Lori Hatcher *E-mail:* lori.hatcher@uli.org
Sr Accts Payable Coord: Ben Abraham *Tel:* 202-624-7156 *E-mail:* babraham@uli.org
Founded: 1936
International nonprofit research & education institute concentrating on best practices in real estate development & responsible use of land.
ISBN Prefix(es): 978-0-87420
Number of titles published annually: 15 Print; 1 CD-ROM
Total Titles: 78 Print; 4 CD-ROM
Imprints: ULI
Foreign Rep(s): Joanne Wang (China)

Urim Publications
Division of Lambda Publishers Inc
c/o Lambda Publications Inc, 527 Empire Blvd, Brooklyn, NY 11225-3121
Tel: 718-972-5449 *Fax:* 718-972-6307
E-mail: publisher@urimpublications.com
Web Site: urimpublications.com
Key Personnel
Pres & Publr: Tzvi Mauer
Children's Book Ed: Shari Dash Greenspan *E-mail:* children@urimpublications.com
Founded: 1997
Publisher & worldwide distributor of new & classic books with Jewish content.

ISBN Prefix(es): 978-965-7108
Number of titles published annually: 8 Print
Total Titles: 35 Print
Subsidiaries: Flashlight Press
Editorial Office(s): PO Box 52287, Jerusalem 91521, Israel *Tel:* (02) 679-7633 *Fax:* (02) 679-7634 *Web Site:* www.urimpublications.com

§URJ Books & Music
Division of Union for Reform Judaism
633 Third Ave, New York, NY 10017-6778
SAN: 203-3291
Tel: 212-650-4120 *Fax:* 212-650-4119
E-mail: press@urj.org
Web Site: www.urjbooksandmusic.com
Key Personnel
Mktg Dir: Stephen Becker
Ed-in-Chief: Michael H Goldberg
Founded: 1873
Religion (Jewish), Reform Judaism; textbooks, juveniles & adult trade books, audiovisual materials, social action, history, biography, ceremonies.
ISBN Prefix(es): 978-0-8074
Number of titles published annually: 25 Print
Total Titles: 250 Print; 1 CD-ROM; 200 Audio
Distribution Center: Mercedes Distribution Center, Brooklyn Navy Yard, Bldg 3, Brooklyn, NY 11205
Membership(s): AAP

US Conference of Catholic Bishops
USCCB Publishing, 3211 Fourth St NE, Washington, DC 20017
Tel: 202-541-3090 *Toll Free Tel:* 800-235-8722 (orders only) *Fax:* 202-722-8709
E-mail: css@usccb.org; publications@usccb.org
Web Site: www.usccbpublishing.org
Key Personnel
Dir & Publr: Paul Henderson
Founded: 1938
The official publisher for the US Catholic Bishop & Vatican documents; English & Spanish.
ISBN Prefix(es): 978-1-55586; 978-1-57455
Number of titles published annually: 20 Print
Total Titles: 820 Print
Returns: USCCB Returns, 3570 Blatensburg Rd, Brentwood, MD 20722
Membership(s): Association of Catholic Publishers Inc

US Games Systems Inc
179 Ludlow St, Stamford, CT 06902
SAN: 206-1368
Tel: 203-353-8400 *Toll Free Tel:* 800-54-GAMES (544-2637) *Fax:* 203-353-8431
E-mail: info@usgamesinc.com
Web Site: www.usgamesinc.com
Key Personnel
Founder & Chmn: Stuart R Kaplan
VP, Export Sales: Barbara Bensaid
Treas: Ricky Cruz
Art Dir: Paula Palmer
Founded: 1968
Popular & scholarly works in the field of tarot, educational games & the history of symbolism of playing cards; reprints of historical tarot decks & playing cards from the past five centuries.
ISBN Prefix(es): 978-0-913866; 978-0-88079; 978-1-57281
Number of titles published annually: 10 Print
Total Titles: 400 Print
Imprints: Cove Press
Distributor for A G Muller & Cie
Foreign Rep(s): Airlift Book Company (UK); Koppenhol Agenturen (Netherlands); Lion Playing Card Co (Israel); A G Muller & Cie (Switzerland); David Westnedge Ltd (UK)

US Government Printing Office, see US Government Publishing Office (GPO)

§US Government Publishing Office (GPO)
Formerly US Government Printing Office
Division of US Government
Superintendent of Documents, 732 N Capitol St NW, Washington, DC 20401
Tel: 202-512-1800 *Toll Free Tel:* 866-512-1800 (orders) *Fax:* 202-512-2104
E-mail: contactcenter@gpo.gov
Web Site: bookstore.gpo.gov (sales)
Key Personnel
Mng Dir, Lib Servs & Content Mgmt: Laurie Hall
Dir, Sales & Mktg: Jeffrey Turner *Tel:* 202-512-1055
Founded: 1861
Distributor & printer of federal government publications & public documents in various formats including ebooks; military, space exploration, political science.
ISBN Prefix(es): 978-0-16
Number of titles published annually: 250 Print; 15 Online
Total Titles: 2,500 Print; 140 CD-ROM
Imprints: Energy Information Administration (EIA)
Orders to: PO Box 979050, Saint Louis, MO 63197-9000
See separate listing for:
Energy Information Administration (EIA)

Utah Geological Survey
Division of Utah Department of Natural Resources
1594 W North Temple, Suite 3110, Salt Lake City, UT 84116-3154
Mailing Address: PO Box 146100, Salt Lake City, UT 84114-6100
Tel: 801-537-3300 *Toll Free Tel:* 888-UTAH-MAP (882-4627 bookstore) *Fax:* 801-537-3400
E-mail: geostore@utah.gov
Web Site: geology.utah.gov
Key Personnel
Geological Pubns Ed: Vicky Clarke *Tel:* 801-537-3330 *E-mail:* vickyclarke@utah.gov
Founded: 1935
ISBN Prefix(es): 978-1-55791
Number of titles published annually: 30 Print; 15 CD-ROM; 5 Online
Total Titles: 702 Print

Utah State University Press
Imprint of University Press of Colorado
3078 Old Main Hill, Logan, UT 84322-3078
Tel: 435-797-1362 *Fax:* 435-797-0313
Web Site: www.usupress.org
Key Personnel
Dir: Michael Spooner *E-mail:* michael.spooner@usu.edu
Mktg Mgr: Dan Miller *E-mail:* d.miller@usu.edu
Founded: 1969
ISBN Prefix(es): 978-0-87421
Number of titles published annually: 18 Print
Total Titles: 120 Print
Membership(s): Association of American University Presses

VanDam Inc
The VanDam Bldg, 121 W 27 St, New York, NY 10001
Tel: 212-929-0416 *Toll Free Tel:* 800-UNFOLDS (863-6537) *Fax:* 212-929-0426
E-mail: info@vandam.com
Web Site: www.vandam.com
Key Personnel
Pres/Creative Dir: Stephan Van Dam *Tel:* 212-929-0416 ext 10 *E-mail:* stephan@vandam.com
VP, Sales: Bob Troast *Tel:* 212-929-0416 ext 12 *E-mail:* bob@vandam.com
Founded: 1984
Publisher of UNFOLDS® maps; licensor of patented folding technology used to produce UNFOLDS® products.
ISBN Prefix(es): 978-0-931141; 978-1-932527; 978-1-934395
Number of titles published annually: 25 Print
Total Titles: 100 Print
Imprints: Eurostar; Smartmaps®; That VanDam Book; UNFOLDS®; @tlas®
Divisions: VanDam Advertising; VanDam Licensing; VanDam Publishing
Foreign Rep(s): LAC (Italy); RV Verlag (Germany)
Advertising Agency: Streetsmart®; Travelsmart®; VanDam Advertising

Vandamere Press
3580 Morris St N, St Petersburg, FL 33713
SAN: 657-3088
Mailing Address: PO Box 149, St Petersburg, FL 33731
Tel: 727-556-0950 *Toll Free Tel:* 800-551-7776 *Fax:* 727-556-2560
E-mail: orders@vandamere.com
Web Site: www.vandamere.com
Key Personnel
Publr & Ed-in-Chief: Arthur Brown *E-mail:* abrown@vandamere.com
Dir, Spec Sales: Stephanie Brown
Sr Book Ed: Pat Berger
Acq Ed: Jerry Frank
Wholesale Sales: John Cabin
Founded: 1984
Tradebook.
ISBN Prefix(es): 978-0-918339
Number of titles published annually: 8 Print
Total Titles: 70 Print
Distributor for ABI Professional Publications (non-exclusive); JMC Press (exclusive to trade); NRH Press (non-exclusive); Quodlibetal Features

Vanderbilt University Press
Division of Vanderbilt University
2014 Broadway, Suite 320, Nashville, TN 37203
SAN: 202-9308
Mailing Address: VU Sta B, No 351813, Nashville, TN 37235-1813
Tel: 615-322-3585 *Toll Free Tel:* 800-627-7377 (orders only) *Fax:* 615-343-8823 *Toll Free Fax:* 800-735-0476 (orders only)
E-mail: vupress@vanderbilt.edu
Web Site: www.vanderbiltuniversitypress.com
Key Personnel
Dir: Michael Ames
Mng Ed: Joell Smith Borne
Design & Prodn Mgr: Dariel Mayer *E-mail:* dariel.mayer@vanderbilt.edu
Busn Mgr & Rts & Perms: Bethany Graham
Sales & Mktg Mgr: Sue Havlish
Mktg & New Media Assoc: Betsy Phillips *E-mail:* betsy.phillips@vanderbilt.edu
Founded: 1940
Scholarly nonfiction, humanities, social sciences, literary criticism, history, regional studies, applied mathematics, philosophy.
ISBN Prefix(es): 978-0-8265
Number of titles published annually: 25 Print
Total Titles: 250 Print; 2 CD-ROM; 1 E-Book
Imprints: Country Music Foundation Press; Vanderbilt Library of American Philosophy
Distributed by University of Oklahoma Press
Distributor for Country Music Foundation Press
Foreign Rep(s): Royden Muranaka (Australia, China, Hong Kong, India, Japan, Korea, New Zealand, Pacific Islands, Pakistan, Philippines, Southeast Asia, Taiwan)

Vault.com Inc
132 W 31 St, 17th fl, New York, NY 10001
Tel: 212-366-4212 *Toll Free Tel:* 800-535-2074 *Fax:* 212-366-6117 (cust serv)
E-mail: editors@vault.com; customerservice@vault.com
Web Site: www.vault.com

Key Personnel
Sr Fin Ed: Derek Loosvelt
Law Ed: Nicole Weber
Consulting Ed: Phil Stott
Assoc Prodr: Cathy Vandewater
Founded: 1997
"Insider" career development for professionals.
ISBN Prefix(es): 978-1-58131
Number of titles published annually: 4 Print; 10 Online
Total Titles: 61 Print; 124 Online
Distribution Center: Client Distribution Services Inc, 193 Edwards Dr, Jackson, TN 38301, Pres: Gilbert Perlman *Toll Free Tel:* 800-343-4499 *Toll Free Fax:* 800-351-5073 *E-mail:* orderentry@cdsbooks.com SAN: 631-760X

Vedanta Press
Subsidiary of Vedanta Society of Southern California
1946 Vedanta Place, Hollywood, CA 90068
Tel: 323-960-1736 *Toll Free Tel:* 800-816-2242
E-mail: info@vedanta.com
Web Site: www.vedanta.com
Key Personnel
Mgr: Robert Adjemian *E-mail:* bob@vedanta.org
Founded: 1945
ISBN Prefix(es): 978-81-85301 (Advaita Ashrama); 978-0-87481; 978-81-8172 (Ramakrishna Math)
Number of titles published annually: 13 CD-ROM; 13 Online; 14 Audio
Total Titles: 13 CD-ROM; 13 Online; 14 Audio
Distributor for Advaita Ashrama; Ananda Ashrama; Ramakrishna Math
Membership(s): The Independent Book Publishers Association

Velazquez Press
Division of Academic Learning Co LLC
9682 Telstar Ave, Suite 110, El Monte, CA 91731
Tel: 626-448-3448 *Fax:* 626-602-3817
E-mail: info@academiclearningcompany.com
Web Site: www.velazquezpress.com
Key Personnel
Sales Mgr: Jonathan Ruiz *E-mail:* jruiz@academiclearningcompany.com
Founded: 2003
Publisher of bilingual dictionaries.
ISBN Prefix(es): 978-1-59495
Number of titles published annually: 4 Print
Total Titles: 10 Print

The Vendome Press
1334 York Ave, 3rd fl, New York, NY 10021
Tel: 212-737-5297 *Fax:* 212-737-5340
E-mail: info@vendomepress.com
Web Site: www.vendomepress.com
Key Personnel
Founder & Chmn: Alexis Gregory
Pres: Mark Magowan
Prodn Ed: Alecia Reddick
Ed: Jackuelen Decter
Founded: 1981
Illustrated art, architecture & lifestyle books.
ISBN Prefix(es): 978-0-86565
Number of titles published annually: 15 Print
Total Titles: 85 Print
Distributed by Harry N Abrams Inc

Venture Publishing Inc
1999 Cato Ave, State College, PA 16801
SAN: 240-897X
Tel: 814-234-4561 *Fax:* 814-234-1651
E-mail: vpublish@venturepublish.com
Web Site: www.venturepublish.com
Key Personnel
Off Mgr: Kay Whiteside *E-mail:* cawhiteside@venturepublish.com
Prodn: George Lauer *E-mail:* glauer@venturepublish.com; Richard Yocum *E-mail:* vpublish@venturepublish.com
Founded: 1979
Parks & recreation, social sciences & sociology, leisure studies, long-term care, therapeutic recreation.
ISBN Prefix(es): 978-0-910251; 978-1-892132
Number of titles published annually: 8 Print
Total Titles: 86 Print
Foreign Rep(s): Creative & More Inc (Taiwan); HM Leisure Planning Pty Ltd (Australia, Canada, New Zealand)

Vernon Press
Imprint of Vernon Art & Science Inc
1000 N West St, Suite 1200, Wilmington, DE 19801
Tel: 302-250-4440
E-mail: info@vernonpress.com
Web Site: www.vernonpress.com
Key Personnel
Dir: Rosario Batana
ISBN Prefix(es): 978-1-62273
Number of titles published annually: 10 Print

Verso
20 Jay St, Suite 1010, Brooklyn, NY 11201
Tel: 718-246-8160 *Fax:* 718-246-8165
E-mail: verso@versobooks.com
Web Site: www.versobooks.com
Key Personnel
Mng Dir: Jacob Stevens
Creative Dir: Rachel Rosenfelt
Mktg Mgr: Anne Rumberger
Founded: 1970
Nonfiction, progressive studies on politics, history, society & culture.
ISBN Prefix(es): 978-0-86091; 978-0-85984; 978-0-84467
Number of titles published annually: 80 Print
Total Titles: 2,000 Print
Foreign Office(s): 6 Meard St, London W1F OE6, United Kingdom
Distributed by Penguin (Canada); W W Norton (USA)
Foreign Rep(s): Verso (England)
Foreign Rights: Verso (Worldwide)
Shipping Address: Marston Book Services, Kemp Hall Bindery, Osney Mead, Oxford, United Kingdom
Warehouse: National Book Co Inc, 800 Keystone Industrial Park, Scranton, PA 18512

Victory in Grace Press
Division of Victory in Grace Ministries
60 Quentin Rd, Lake Zurich, IL 60047
Tel: 847-438-4494 *Toll Free Tel:* 800-78-GRACE (784-7223) *Fax:* 847-438-4232
Web Site: www.victoryingrace.org
Founded: 2000
Publish conservative evangelical books, audio series, magazines & tracts.
ISBN Prefix(es): 978-0-9679145; 978-0-9719262
Number of titles published annually: 3 Print; 4 E-Book; 3 Audio
Total Titles: 9 Print; 4 E-Book; 15 Audio

Viking
Imprint of Penguin Group (USA) LLC
375 Hudson St, New York, NY 10014
SAN: 282-5074
Tel: 212-366-2000
E-mail: online@penguinputnam.com
Web Site: www.penguinputnam.com; us.penguingroup.com
Key Personnel
Pres & Publr: Brian Tart
VP & Publr, Pamela Dorman Books: Pamela Dorman
VP, Assoc Publr & Dir, Mktg: Kate Stark
VP, Assoc Publr & Edit Dir (Nonfiction): Wendy Wolf
VP & Exec Creative Dir: Paul Buckley
VP & Exec Dir, Copyediting: Tory Klose
VP & Dir, Mktg: Nancy Sheppard
VP & Dir, Publicity: Carolyn Coleburn
VP & Exec Ed: Paul Slovak
VP & Exec Ed, Viking/Penguin: Carole DeSanti
Dir, Ad & Promo: Dennis Swaim
Ed-in-Chief: Andrea Schulz
Exec Mng Ed: Tricia Conley
Exec Ed: Carolyn Carlson; Joy de Menil; Rick Kot
Publicity Mgr: Meredith Burks
Founded: 1925
ISBN Prefix(es): 978-0-670
Number of titles published annually: 80 Print
Total Titles: 250 Print
Imprints: Viking Compass
Advertising Agency: Spier NY

Viking Children's Books
Imprint of Penguin Group (USA) LLC
345 Hudson St, New York, NY 10014
Tel: 212-366-2000
E-mail: online@penguinputnam.com
Web Site: www.penguinputnam.com; us.penguingroup.com
Key Personnel
VP & Publr: Ken Wright
Assoc Publr & Mng Ed: Gerard Mancini
VP & Art Dir: Denise Cronin
Edit Dir, Picture Books: Tracy Gates
Sr Ed: Sharyn November
Editor-at-Large: Regina Hayes
Founded: 1925
ISBN Prefix(es): 978-0-670
Number of titles published annually: 55 Print
Total Titles: 557 Print
Membership(s): The Children's Book Council

Viking Studio
Imprint of Penguin Group (USA) LLC
375 Hudson St, New York, NY 10014
SAN: 282-5074
Tel: 212-366-2000
E-mail: online@penguinputnam.com
Web Site: www.penguinputnam.com; us.penguingroup.com
Key Personnel
Pres & Publr: Brian Tart
Founded: 1988
ISBN Prefix(es): 978-0-14; 978-0-670
Number of titles published annually: 4 Print
Total Titles: 40 Print
Advertising Agency: Spier NY

Carl Vinson Institute of Government
University of Georgia, 201 N Milledge Ave, Athens, GA 30602
Tel: 706-542-2736 *Fax:* 706-542-9301
Web Site: www.cviog.uga.edu
Key Personnel
Dir: Laura Meadows *Tel:* 706-542-6192
Communs Coord: Courtney Yarbrough *Tel:* 706-542-6221
Founded: 1927
Instruction, technical assistance, research & publications for state & local governments & communities.
ISBN Prefix(es): 978-0-89854
Number of titles published annually: 10 Print; 2 CD-ROM
Total Titles: 70 Print; 3 CD-ROM

Vintage & Anchor Books
Imprint of Knopf Doubleday Publishing Group
c/o Random House Inc, 1745 Broadway, New York, NY 10019
Tel: 212-572-2420
E-mail: vintageanchorpublicity@randomhouse.com

Web Site: vintage-anchor.knopfdoubleday.com
Key Personnel
EVP & Publr: Anne Messitte
SVP & Exec Edit Dir: Luann Walther
VP & Assoc Publr: Beth Lamb
VP & Exec Dir, Publicity & Soc Media: Russell Perreault
VP & Exec Ed: Edward Kastenmeier
Design Dir: Claudia Martinez
Dir, Academic Mktg: Keith Goldsmith
Dir, Ad & Promos: Irena Vukov-Kendes
Dir, Digital Devt: Laura Crisp
Dir, Online Mktg: Paige Smith
Dir, Publicity: Kate Runde
Dir, Spanish Lang Publg: Jaime de Pablos
Mng Ed: Stephen McNabb
Mgr, Backlist: Barbara Richard
Sr Ed: Lexy Bloom; Tim O'Connell
Ed: Andrea Robinson
Asst Ed: Mark Chiusano; Emily Giglierano; Jocelyn Miller
Sr Publicist: Angie Venezia
Founded: 1952
Random House Inc & its publishing entities are not accepting unsol submissions, queries via e-mail at this time.
ISBN Prefix(es): 978-0-307; 978-0-679 (Vintage); 978-0-385 (Anchor Books); 978-0-7679 (Anchor Books); 978-0-375 (Vintage); 978-1-4000; 978-0-394 (Vintage)
Number of titles published annually: 350 Print; 380 E-Book
Total Titles: 5,300 Print; 3,500 E-Book
Imprints: Anchor Books; Vintage Shorts (ebooks)
Foreign Rights: Anthea Agency (Katalina Sabeva) (Bulgaria); Bardon-Chinese Media Agency (Xu Weiguang) (China); Bardon-Chinese Media Agency (Yu Shiuan Chen) (Taiwan); Bardon-Chinese Media Agency (David Tsai) (Taiwan); The English Agency (Hamish Macaskill) (Japan); The English Agency (Junzo Sawa) (Japan); Graal Literary Agency (Maria Strarz-Kanska) (Poland); The Deborah Harris Agency (Ilana Kurshan) (Israel); JLM Literary Agency (Nelly Moukakou) (Greece); Katai & Bolza Literary (Peter Bolza) (Croatia, Hungary, Serbia); Simona Kessler Agency (Simona Kessler) (Romania); Korea Copyright Center (MiSook Hong) (Korea); Licht & Burr Literary Agency (Trine Licht) (Scandinavia); La Nouvelle Agence (Vanessa Kling) (France); Kristin Olson Literary Agency (Kristin Olson) (Czech Republic); Agenzia Letteraria Santachiara (Roberto Santachiara) (Italy); Sebes & Van Gelderen Literary Agency (Holland)

Visible Ink Press®
43311 Joy Rd, Suite 414, Canton, MI 48187-2075
Tel: 734-667-3211 *Fax:* 734-667-4311
E-mail: info@visibleink.com
Web Site: www.visibleink.com
Key Personnel
Owner: Roger Janecke
Founded: 1990
Popular reference publisher specializing in handy answer books, spiritual phenomena & encyclopedias.
ISBN Prefix(es): 978-0-8103; 978-0-7876; 978-1-57859
Number of titles published annually: 10 Print; 10 E-Book
Total Titles: 50 Print; 50 E-Book
Distribution Center: Independent Publishers Group, 814 N Franklin St, Chicago, IL 60610 *Tel:* 312-337-0747 *Toll Free Tel:* 800-888-4741 (orders) *Fax:* 312-337-5985

§Visual Profile Books Inc
389 Fifth Ave, Suite 1105, New York, NY 10016
SAN: 213-1552
Tel: 212-279-7000 *Fax:* 212-279-7014
Web Site: www.visualreference.com
Key Personnel
Group Publr: Larry Fuersich *Tel:* 212-279-7000 ext 314 *E-mail:* larry@visualreference.com
Founded: 1931
Architecture, interior & graphic design.
ISBN Prefix(es): 978-0-9825989
Number of titles published annually: 15 Print
Total Titles: 115 Print; 75 Online
Distributed by Innovative Logistics (US & CN)
Foreign Rep(s): HarperCollins International (Worldwide exc Canada & USA)
Foreign Rights: Larry Fuersich

Viva Editions, see Cleis Press

Volcano Press
21496 National St, Volcano, CA 95689
Mailing Address: PO Box 270, Volcano, CA 95689-0270 SAN: 220-0015
Tel: 209-296-7989 *Toll Free Tel:* 800-879-9636 *Fax:* 209-296-4515
E-mail: sales@volcanopress.com
Web Site: www.volcanopress.com
Key Personnel
Publr: Adam Gottstein *E-mail:* adam@volcanopress.com
Publr Emerita & Edit Consultant: Ruth Gottstein
Founded: 1969
General trade, professional books, Spanish language books; medicine, health & nutrition, psychology, social sciences, women's studies, domestic violence.
ISBN Prefix(es): 978-0-912078; 978-1-884244
Number of titles published annually: 3 Print; 3 E-Book
Total Titles: 50 Print; 1 Audio
Imprints: Glide Publications; Kazan Media
Sales Office(s): PO Box 270, Volcano, CA 95689-0270 SAN: 220-0015
Billing Address: PO Box 270, Volcano, CA 95689-0270 SAN: 220-0015

Ludwig von Mises Institute
518 W Magnolia Ave, Auburn, AL 36832
Tel: 334-321-2100 *Fax:* 334-321-2119
E-mail: info@mises.org
Web Site: www.mises.org
Key Personnel
CEO: Lew Rockwell
Bookstore Mgr: Brandon Hill *E-mail:* brandon@mises.org
Founded: 1982
Nonprofit educational organization devoted to the Austrian School of Economics.
ISBN Prefix(es): 978-0-945466; 978-1-933550
Number of titles published annually: 7 Print; 8 Audio
Total Titles: 54 Print

Wadsworth, see Wadsworth Publishing

§Wadsworth Publishing
Division of Cengage Learning™
20 Davis Dr, Belmont, CA 94002
SAN: 200-2213
Tel: 650-595-2350 *Fax:* 650-592-3022 *Toll Free Fax:* 800-522-4923
Web Site: www.cengage.com
Key Personnel
CEO & Pres: Ronald Dunn
CFO: Dean Durbin
Pres, Soc Sci & Humanities Publg: Sean Wakely
Pres, Mathematics & Sci Publg: Michael Johnson
Pres, Busn & Prof Publg: Ed Mousa
SVP, Mktg: Jonathan Hulbert
SVP & CTO: Pat Call
VP, HR: Paula Sari
Dir, Corp Communs: Lindsay Stanley
Founded: 1956
A leading provider of higher education textbooks, software & Internet materials for the humanities, social sciences, behavioral sciences, mathematics, science, statistics, business & professional.
ISBN Prefix(es): 978-0-314; 978-0-312; 978-0-534; 978-0-8222; 978-0-8384; 978-0-89582; 978-0-8304; 978-1-56593; 978-0-8125; 978-1-57259; 978-0-324; 978-0-922914; 978-0-028; 978-0-030; 978-0-126; 978-0-155; 978-0-759; 978-0-766; 978-0-769; 978-0-827; 978-0-829; 978-0-8783; 978-0-882; 978-1-87910; 978-0-9997
Number of titles published annually: 700 Print
Total Titles: 5,000 Print; 125 CD-ROM; 170 E-Book; 325 Audio
Imprints: Brooks/Cole; Course Technology; Delmar; Heinle; Schirmer; South-Western; Wadsworth
Distributed by Cengage Learning™
Foreign Rep(s): Nelson Thomson Learning (Canada); Thomas Nelson Australia-Thomson Learning (Australia, New Zealand); Thomson Learning Editories (Caribbean, Latin America); Thomson Learning International (Asia, Europe, France, Germany, Japan, Middle East, South Africa)
Foreign Rights: Thomson Learning, Foreign Rights Division (Worldwide)
Distribution Center: Cengage Learning Distribution Center, 10650 Toebben Dr, Independence, KY 41051 *Toll Free Tel:* 800-544-0550 *Fax:* 859-647-4599 *E-mail:* claimscs@cengage.com
Membership(s): AAP

Wake Forest University Press
A5 Tribble Hall, Wake Forest University, Winston-Salem, NC 27109
Mailing Address: PO Box 7333, Winston-Salem, NC 27109-7333
Tel: 336-758-5448 *Fax:* 336-758-5636
E-mail: wfupress@wfu.edu
Web Site: www.wfu.edu/wfupress
Key Personnel
Founder & Advising Ed: Dillon Johnston
Dir & Ed: Jefferson Holdridge
Mgr & Asst Dir: Candide Jones *E-mail:* jonescm@wfu.edu
Founded: 1975
Contemporary Irish poetry.
ISBN Prefix(es): 978-0-916390; 978-1-930630
Number of titles published annually: 5 Print
Total Titles: 85 Print

Walch Education
40 Walch Dr, Portland, ME 04103-1286
SAN: 203-0268
Tel: 207-772-2846 *Toll Free Tel:* 800-558-2846 *Fax:* 207-772-3105 *Toll Free Fax:* 888-991-5755
E-mail: customerservice@walch.com
Web Site: www.walch.com
Key Personnel
Chmn of the Bd: Peter S Walch
CFO: James R Walker, Jr *E-mail:* jwalker@walch.com
Pres: Al Noyes *E-mail:* anoyes@walch.com
VP, Educ: Jill Rosenblum *E-mail:* jrosenblum@walch.com
Sales Mgr: Amy Kayne *E-mail:* akayne@walch.com
Founded: 1927
Educational books & supplementary materials for middle school through adult.
ISBN Prefix(es): 978-0-8251
Number of titles published annually: 100 Print; 75 Online
Total Titles: 1,700 Print; 850 Online
Membership(s): ASCD; International Literacy Association; National Council for the Social Studies; National Council of Teachers of English; National Council of Teachers of Mathematics; National Science Teachers Association

Walch Publishing, see Walch Education

Frederick Warne
Imprint of Penguin Group (USA) LLC, a Penguin Random House Company
345 Hudson St, New York, NY 10014
SAN: 282-5074
Tel: 212-366-2000
Web Site: www.penguinrandomhouse.com
Founded: 1865
ISBN Prefix(es): 978-0-7232
Number of titles published annually: 22 Print
Total Titles: 201 Print
Foreign Rep(s): Agenzia Letteraria Internazionale (Italy); Bardon-Chinese (China); DRT International (Korea); ICBS (Netherlands, Scandinavia); International Press Agency (South Africa); Japan UNI (Japan); Literari Agentura (Czech Republic); Mohrbooks (Germany); La Nouvelle Agence (France); I Pikarski Ltd Literary Agency (Israel)

Warner Press
Affiliate of Church of God
1201 E Fifth St, Anderson, IN 46018
Tel: 765-644-7721 *Toll Free Tel:* 800-741-7721 (orders) *Fax:* 765-640-8005 *Toll Free Fax:* 800-347-6411
E-mail: wporders@warnerpress.org
Web Site: www.warnerpress.org
Key Personnel
Pres: Eric King
VP, Sales: Connie Crist
VP, Prod Mktg: Regina Jackson
Founded: 1881
Specialize in religious books, activity books, coloring books & greeting cards.
ISBN Prefix(es): 978-0-87162; 978-1-59317
Number of titles published annually: 6 Print

Warren Communications News Inc
2115 Ward Ct NW, Washington, DC 20037
Tel: 202-872-9200 *Toll Free Tel:* 800-771-9202 *Fax:* 202-293-3435; 202-318-8350
E-mail: info@warren-news.com; newsroom@warren-news.com
Web Site: www.warren-news.com
Key Personnel
Chmn & Publr: Paul Warren
Pres & Ed: Daniel Warren *E-mail:* dwarren@warren-news.com
Exec Ed Emeritus: Dawson B Nail
Exec Ed: R Michael Feazel
Sr Ed: Jeff Berman
Assoc Mng Ed: Gaye Nail
NY Bureau Chief: Paul Gluckman
Founded: 1945
Newsletters & directories.
ISBN Prefix(es): 978-0-911486
Number of titles published annually: 10 Print
Total Titles: 10 Print
Branch Office(s)
276 Fifth Ave, Suite 1111, New York, NY 10001 *Toll Free Tel:* 800-771-5410

Washington State University Press
Division of Washington State University
Cooper Publications Bldg, Grimes Way, Pullman, WA 99164
SAN: 206-6688
Mailing Address: PO Box 645910, Pullman, WA 99164-5910
Tel: 509-335-3518; 509-335-7880 (order fulfillment) *Toll Free Tel:* 800-354-7360 *Fax:* 509-335-8568
E-mail: wsupress@wsu.edu
Web Site: wsupress.wsu.edu
Key Personnel
Dir: Mary Read *E-mail:* read@wsu.edu
Prodn Ed & Fulfillment/Sales Coord: Nancy Grunewald *Tel:* 509-335-5817 *E-mail:* grunewan@wsu.edu
Mktg Mgr & Acqs: Caryn Lawton *Tel:* 509-335-7877 *E-mail:* lawton@wsu.edu
Founded: 1928
Trade & scholarly books focusing on the history, natural history, military history, culture & politics of the greater Pacific Northwest region (Washington, Idaho, Oregon, Western Montana, British Columbia & Alaska). Refer to web site for submission guidelines.
ISBN Prefix(es): 978-0-87422
Number of titles published annually: 4 Print
Total Titles: 182 Print
Sales Office(s): Hand Associates, 408 30 Ave, Seattle, WA 98122, Sales Rep: David Diehl *Tel:* 206-328-0295 *E-mail:* david_diehl@mindspring.com
Wholesale Solutions, 1959 NW Dock Place, Suite 3002, Seattle, WA 98107, Contact: Neal Warnick *Tel:* 206-310-9207 *E-mail:* neal@wholesale-solutions.net
Hand Associates, 16 Nelson Ave, Mill Valley, CA 94941-2120, Sales Rep: Jock Hayward *Tel:* 415-383-3883 *E-mail:* handhayward@earthlink.net
Hand Associates, 3851 Daisy Circle, Seal Beach, CA 90740-2901, Sales Rep: Pam Sheppard *Tel:* 562-431-0771 *E-mail:* hand.pams@gmail.com
Distributor for The Hutton Settlement (single title); Oregon Writers Colony (single title); Pacific Institute (single title); Washington State Historical Society (single title); WSU Museum of Art
Distribution Center: Partners Book Distributing West Inc, 1901 Raymond Ave SW, Suite C, Renton, WA 98055 *Tel:* 425-227-8486 *Fax:* 425-204-1448
Baker & Taylor Books, PO Box 8888, Momence, IL 60954 (US & CN) *Toll Free Tel:* 800-775-1100 *Toll Free Fax:* 800-775-7480
Ingram Book Co, One Ingram Blvd, La Vergne, TN 37086 (US & CN) *Toll Free Tel:* 800-937-8000
Membership(s): Association of American University Presses; Pacific Northwest Booksellers Association

Water Environment Federation
601 Wythe St, Alexandria, VA 22314-1994
Tel: 703-684-2400 *Toll Free Tel:* 800-666-0206 *Fax:* 703-684-2492
E-mail: csc@wef.org (cust serv)
Web Site: www.wef.org
Key Personnel
Association Devt: Jack Benson *Tel:* 703-684-2493 *E-mail:* jbenson@wef.org
Founded: 1928
Scientific publisher of environmental titles. Seeks authors of sound, state-of-the-art environmental material.
ISBN Prefix(es): 978-0-943244; 978-1-881369
Number of titles published annually: 15 Print
Total Titles: 220 Print

§Water Resources Publications LLC
PO Box 630026, Highlands Ranch, CO 80163-0026
SAN: 209-9136
Tel: 720-873-0171 *Toll Free Tel:* 800-736-2405 *Fax:* 720-873-0173 *Toll Free Fax:* 800-616-1971
E-mail: info@wrpllc.com
Web Site: www.wrpllc.com
Key Personnel
Busn Mgr: Jennie Campbell
Founded: 1971
Publish & distribute books & computer programs on water resources & related fields.
ISBN Prefix(es): 978-0-918334; 978-1-887201
Number of titles published annually: 10 Print
Total Titles: 450 Print; 35 CD-ROM
Distributor for ASAE; ASCE
Shipping Address: 10607 Flatiron Rd, Littleton, CO 80124
Warehouse: 10607 Flatiron Rd, Littleton, CO 80124

Water Row Press
Subsidiary of Water Row Books
PO Box 438, Sudbury, MA 01776
Tel: 508-485-8515 *Fax:* 508-229-0885
E-mail: contact@waterrowbooks.com
Web Site: www.waterrowbooks.com
Key Personnel
Publr: Jeffrey H Weinberg
Ed: Cisco Harland
Prodn Mgr: Betsy Kirschbaum
Founded: 1985
Publishers of modern literature, poetry, graphic novels; specialize in books by & about "Beat" writers; comic art.
ISBN Prefix(es): 978-0-934953
Number of titles published annually: 12 Print
Total Titles: 29 Print
Distributed by Water Row Books
Distributor for Water Row Books; Weinberg Books

WaterBrook Multnomah Publishing Group
Imprint of Random House Inc
12265 Oracle Blvd, Suite 200, Colorado Springs, CO 80921
Tel: 719-590-4999 *Toll Free Tel:* 800-603-7051 (orders) *Fax:* 719-590-8977 *Toll Free Fax:* 800-294-5686 (orders)
E-mail: info@waterbrookmultnomah.com
Web Site: waterbrookmultnomah.com
Key Personnel
VP & Publr: Alexander Field
VP & Dir, Opers: Debbie Mitchell
VP & Dir, Mktg: Ginia Hairston
VP & Edit Dir: Laura Barker
Dir, Sales: Lori Addicott
Publicity Dir: Beverly Rykerd
Sr Ed: Ron Lee
Sr Ed, Fiction: Shannon Hill Marchese
Ed: Andrew Stoddard; Susan Tjaden
Asst Ed: Kendall Davis
Sr Mgr, Community Opers: Chris Sigfrids
Sr Mgr, Mktg: Amy Haddock
Mgr, Gen Mkt Sales Support: Sara Selkirk
Exec Marketer: Johanna Inwood
Mktg Assoc: Jessica Gingrich
Founded: 1996
Offer a broad range of Christian nonfiction & fiction titles in hardcover & trade paperback for adult & young readers, as well as children's books.
Random House Inc & its publishing entities are not accepting unsol submissions, proposals, mss, or submission queries via e-mail at this time.
ISBN Prefix(es): 978-0-87788; 978-1-57856; 978-1-4000
Number of titles published annually: 80 Print; 1 CD-ROM; 1 Audio
Total Titles: 1,000 Print; 4 CD-ROM; 6 E-Book; 15 Audio
Imprints: Shaw Books (fisherman)
Membership(s): Evangelical Christian Publishers Association

Watermark Publishing
1088 Bishop St, Suite 310, Honolulu, HI 96813
Tel: 808-587-7766 *Toll Free Tel:* 866-900-BOOK (900-2665) *Fax:* 808-521-3461
E-mail: info@bookshawaii.net
Web Site: www.bookshawaii.net
Key Personnel
Dir, Sales & Mktg: Dawn Sakamoto *Tel:* 808-534-7170 *E-mail:* dawn@bookshawaii.net
ISBN Prefix(es): 978-0-9720932; 978-0-9705787; 978-0-9631154; 978-0-9753740; 978-0-9779143; 978-0-9790647; 978-0-9796769; 978-0-9815086

Number of titles published annually: 15 Print
Total Titles: 55 Print

Watson-Guptill Publications
Imprint of Crown Publishing Group
c/o Random House Inc, 1745 Broadway, New York, NY 10019
Tel: 212-782-9000 *Fax:* 212-940-7381
E-mail: crownbiz@randomhouse.com
Web Site: www.randomhouse.com/crown/watsonguptill
Key Personnel
Art Dir: Jess Morphew *E-mail:* jmorphew@randomhouse.com
Prodn Dir: Alyn Evans *E-mail:* alevans@randomhouse.com
Publicity Dir: Kim Small *E-mail:* ksmall@randomhouse.com
Deputy Mktg Dir: Donna Passannante *E-mail:* dpassannante@randomhouse.com
Mktg & Publicity Mgr: Natalie Mulford
Assoc Mktg Mgr: Daniel Wikey
Exec Ed, Art: Candace Raney
Sr Ed, Potter Craft: Betty Wong *E-mail:* bwong@randomhouse.com
Sr Acqs Ed, Amphoto Books: Julie Mazur *E-mail:* jmazur@randomhouse.com
Founded: 1937
Art instruction, graphic design, fine arts, comics & cartooning, video game art, photography, crafts (jewelry, fiber arts, paper crafts), fashion, film & pop culture.
ISBN Prefix(es): 978-0-8230; 978-0-8174; 978-1-58065
Number of titles published annually: 60 Print
Total Titles: 800 Print
Foreign Rep(s): Bookwise International (Australia, New Zealand); The Guild of Master Craftsmen (UK); Peter Hyde Associates (South Africa)
Orders to: Specialty Retail Div, Random House Inc, 1745 Broadway, MD 6-3, New York, NY 10019 *Toll Free Tel:* 800-729-2960 *Toll Free Fax:* 800-292-9071 *E-mail:* specialmarkets@randomhouse.com

Watson Publishing International LLC
PO Box 1240, Sagamore Beach, MA 02562-1240
Tel: 508-888-9113 *Fax:* 508-888-3733
E-mail: orders@watsonpublishing.com; orders@shpusa.com
Web Site: www.shpusa.com; www.watsonpublishing.com
Key Personnel
CEO & Pres: Neale W Watson, Esq *E-mail:* nww@shpusa.com
Founded: 1971
Scholarly books on the history, philosophy & sociology of science, technology & medicine.
ISBN Prefix(es): 978-0-88135
Number of titles published annually: 5 Print
Total Titles: 120 Print
Imprints: Prodist; Science History Publications USA; Neale Watson Academic Publications
Shipping Address: Publishers Storage & Shipping Corp, 46 Development Rd, Fitchburg, MA 01420-6020, Publr Rep: Donna Machonis *Tel:* 978-345-2121 ext 380

Waveland Press Inc
4180 IL Rte 83, Suite 101, Long Grove, IL 60047-9580
SAN: 209-0961
Tel: 847-634-0081 *Fax:* 847-634-9501
E-mail: info@waveland.com
Web Site: www.waveland.com
Key Personnel
Pres & Publr: Neil Rowe
Ed: Carol Rowe
Ed & Mktg Mgr: Thomas Curtin
Ed, Prodn Mgr, & Intl Rts: Don Rosso
Off Mgr: Jennifer Jackolin
Founded: 1975
College textbooks & supplements.
ISBN Prefix(es): 978-0-88133; 978-0-917974; 978-1-57766; 978-1-4786
Number of titles published annually: 40 Print
Total Titles: 700 Print
Subsidiaries: Sheffield Publishing Co
Warehouse: 9009 Antioch Rd, Salem, WI 53168, Gen Mgr: Steve Nelson
See separate listing for:
Sheffield Publishing Co

Wayne State University Press
Leonard N Simons Bldg, 4809 Woodward Ave, Detroit, MI 48201-1309
SAN: 202-5221
Tel: 313-577-6120 *Toll Free Tel:* 800-978-7323 *Fax:* 313-577-6131
Web Site: www.wsupress.wayne.edu
Key Personnel
Chmn, Edit Bd: Jerry Herron
Dir: Jane Hoehner
Mgr, Sales & Mktg: Emily Nowak
Acqs Mgr: Kathryn Wildfong
Busn Mgr: Andrew Kaufman
Edit Design & Prodn: Kristin Harpster Lawrence
Order Fulfillment: Theresa Martinelli
Founded: 1941
Scholarly & trade books in African American studies, film & television, women's studies, Jewish studies, poetry, speech & language pathology, fairy tales & folklore, regional studies & urban studies.
ISBN Prefix(es): 978-0-8143
Number of titles published annually: 40 Print
Total Titles: 2,500 Print; 2 CD-ROM
Imprints: Great Lakes Books; Painted Turtle Books (general-interest trade imprint)
Distributor for Cranbrook Institute of Science; Detroit Institute of Arts; Hebrew Union College Press; Marick Press
Foreign Rep(s): Eurospan (Africa, Europe, Middle East, UK); EWEB (Far East); Scholarly Book Services (Canada)
Warehouse: 40 W Hancock St, Detroit, MI 48201
Membership(s): Association of American University Presses

Wayside Publishing
11 Jan Sebastian Dr, Suite 5, Sandwich, MA 02563
Tel: 508-833-5096 *Toll Free Tel:* 888-302-2519 *Fax:* 508-833-6284
E-mail: wayside@sprintmail.com
Web Site: www.waysidepublishing.com
Key Personnel
Owner & Publr: Greg Greuel
Assoc: Lee Ann Carstanjen
Founded: 1988
Humanities, English & foreign language textbooks & history.
ISBN Prefix(es): 978-1-877653
Number of titles published annually: 5 Print
Total Titles: 54 Print

Welcome Books®
Imprint of Rizzoli International Publications Inc
300 Park Ave S, New York, NY 10010
Tel: 212-387-3400
Web Site: www.rizzoliusa.com
Founded: 1980
Illustrated books for adult trade & gift market.
ISBN Prefix(es): 978-0-941807
Number of titles published annually: 8 Print
Total Titles: 100 Print
Distributed by Random House
Distributor for AAP; Cerf & Peterson; Music Sales; Zeke Holdings Ltd
Distribution Center: Random House, 400 Hahn Rd, Westminster, MD 21157 *Toll Free Tel:* 800-733-3000 *Toll Free Fax:* 800-659-2436
Membership(s): American Book Producers Association

Welcome Rain Publishers LLC
217 Thompson St, Suite 473, New York, NY 10012
Tel: 212-686-1909
Web Site: welcomerain.com
Key Personnel
Publr: John Weber
Founded: 1997
General trade publisher.
ISBN Prefix(es): 978-1-56649
Number of titles published annually: 21 Print
Total Titles: 95 Print
Distributed by National Book Network

Wellington Press
Division of BooksUPrint.com Inc
9601-30 Miccosukee Rd, Tallahassee, FL 32309
E-mail: peacegames@aol.com
Web Site: www.peacegames.com
Key Personnel
Pres & Intl Rts: David W Felder, PhD
Founded: 1982
Publish philosophy books, including texts, & role play peacegames that examine conflicts of all types.
ISBN Prefix(es): 978-0-910959; 978-1-57501
Number of titles published annually: 10 Print; 10 E-Book
Total Titles: 85 Print; 90 Online; 100 E-Book

Wellness Institute/Self Help Books LLC
515 W North St, Pass Christian, MS 39571-2605
Tel: 228-452-0770 *Fax:* 228-452-0775
Key Personnel
Dir: Harold Dawley, Jr *E-mail:* hdawley@bellsouth.net
Founded: 1974
Exclusively publisher of self-help books.
ISBN Prefix(es): 978-1-58741
Number of titles published annually: 30 Print; 30 E-Book
Total Titles: 100 Print; 70 E-Book

Eliot Werner Publications Inc
31 Willow Lane, Clinton Corners, NY 12514
Mailing Address: PO Box 268, Clinton Corners, NY 12514
Tel: 845-266-4241 *Fax:* 845-266-3317
E-mail: eliotwerner@optonline.net
Web Site: www.eliotwerner.com
Founded: 2001
Academic & scholarly books in anthropology, archaeology, psychology, sociology & related fields; writing, editing & contract publishing.
ISBN Prefix(es): 978-0-9712427; 978-0-9719587; 978-0-9752738; 978-0-9797731; 978-0-9898249
Number of titles published annually: 6 Print
Total Titles: 52 Print
Imprints: Percheron Press
Distribution Center: Ian Stevens Distribution, 70 Enterprise Dr, No 2, Bristol, CT 06010, Fin & Off Mgr: Melanie Palleria *Tel:* 860-584-6546 *Fax:* 860-516-4873 *E-mail:* melanie@isdistribution.com *Web Site:* www.isdistribution.com

Wescott Cove Publishing Co
Imprint of Far Horizons Media Co
1227 S Florida Ave, Rockledge, FL 32955
Mailing Address: PO Box 560989, Rockledge, FL 32956
Tel: 321-690-2224 *Fax:* 321-690-0853
E-mail: customerservice@farhorizonsmedia.com
Web Site: www.farhorizonsmedia.com
Key Personnel
Publr: Will Standley
Books on boating, cruising, yachting & the adventurous life.
ISBN Prefix(es): 978-0-918752

Number of titles published annually: 16 Print; 4 E-Book
Total Titles: 16 Online; 16 E-Book
Distribution Center: Ingram Book Co, One Ingram Blvd, La Vergne, TN 37086 *Tel:* 615-793-5000 *Toll Free Tel:* 800-937-8200 *E-mail:* customer.service@ingrambook.com *Web Site:* www.ingrambook.com
Membership(s): The Association of Publishers for Special Sales

Wesleyan Publishing House
Division of Wesleyan Church Corp
13300 Olio Rd, Fishers, IN 46037
Mailing Address: PO Box 50434, Indianapolis, IN 46250-0434
Tel: 317-774-3853 *Toll Free Tel:* 800-493-7539 *Fax:* 317-774-3865 *Toll Free Fax:* 800-788-3535
E-mail: wph@wesleyan.org
Web Site: www.wesleyan.org/wph
Key Personnel
CEO: Craig A Dunn
Gen Publr: Donald Cady
Founded: 1968
ISBN Prefix(es): 978-0-89827
Number of titles published annually: 11 Print
Total Titles: 60 Print
Returns: Innovative Inc, 4280 Piedmont Pkwy, Suite 105, Greensboro, NC 27410 (Attn: Cust Serv)
Membership(s): CBA: The Association for Christian Retail; Christian Holiness Partnership; Evangelical Christian Publishers Association; Holiness Publisher's Association; Protestant Church-Owned Publishers Association

Wesleyan University Press
215 Long Lane, Middletown, CT 06459-0433
Tel: 860-685-7711 *Fax:* 860-685-7712
Web Site: www.wesleyan.edu/wespress
Key Personnel
Dir & Ed-in-Chief: Suzanna L Tamminen *Tel:* 860-685-7727 *E-mail:* stamminen@wesleyan.edu
Asst Dir & Mktg Mgr: Leslie Starr *Tel:* 860-685-7725 *E-mail:* lstarr@wesleyan.edu
Acqs Ed: Parker Smathers *Tel:* 860-685-7730 *E-mail:* psmathers@wesleyan.edu
Publicist: Stephanie Elliott *Tel:* 860-685-7723 *E-mail:* selliott@wesleyan.edu
Founded: 1957
Editorial program which has been awarded six Pulitzer Prizes; distinguished history of publishing scholarly & trade books that have influenced American poetry & critical thought over the last four decades.
ISBN Prefix(es): 978-0-8195
Number of titles published annually: 25 Print
Total Titles: 425 Print
Imprints: Music/Culture; Early Classics of Science Fiction; Wesleyan Poetry
Foreign Rep(s): East-West Export Books (Asia, Australia, New Zealand, The Pacific); Eurospan University Press Group (Europe, Middle East, UK); University of British Columbia Press (Canada)
Shipping Address: UPNE, One Court St, Suite 250, Lebanon, NH 03766-1358 *Tel:* 603-448-1533 *Toll Free Tel:* 800-421-1561 *Fax:* 603-448-9429 *E-mail:* university.press@dartmouth.edu
Distribution Center: University Press of New England, One Court St, Suite 250, Lebanon, NH 03766 *Tel:* 603-448-1533 *Fax:* 603-643-1540 *E-mail:* university.press@dartmouth.edu
Membership(s): AAP; Association of American University Presses; NEBA

§West Academic Publishing
444 Cedar St, Suite 700, St Paul, MN 55101
Toll Free Tel: 877-888-1330
E-mail: customerservice@westacademic.com; support@westacademic.com
Web Site: www.westacademic.com
Founded: 1953
Law school casebook, statute, study aid & career success publisher.
ISBN Prefix(es): 978-0-1590; 978-0-3141
Number of titles published annually: 50 Print; 2 CD-ROM
Total Titles: 375 Print; 10 CD-ROM; 60 Audio
Imprints: Foundation Press
See separate listing for:
Foundation Press

West Virginia University Press
West Virginia University, PO Box 6295, Morgantown, WV 26506-6295
Tel: 304-293-8400 *Toll Free Tel:* 866-WVU-PRES (988-7737) *Fax:* 304-293-6585
E-mail: press@wvu.edu
Web Site: www.wvupress.com
Key Personnel
Dir: Derek Krissoff
Journals Mgr: Hilary Attfield *Tel:* 304-293-8400 ext 5 *E-mail:* hilary.attfield@mail.wvu.edu
Mktg Mgr: Abby Freeland *Tel:* 304-293-8400 ext 6 *E-mail:* abby.freeland@mail.wvu.edu
Prodn & Design Mgr: Than Saffel *Tel:* 304-293-8400 ext 4 *E-mail:* than.saffel@mail.wvu.edu
Off Mgr: Floann Downey *Tel:* 304-293-8400 ext 1 *E-mail:* fdowney2@mail.wvu.edu
Edit & Prodn Asst: Rachel King *Tel:* 304-293-8400 ext 3 *E-mail:* rachel.king@mail.wvu.edu
Founded: 1965
ISBN Prefix(es): 978-1-933202; 978-0-937058
Number of titles published annually: 12 Print; 1 CD-ROM; 1 Audio
Total Titles: 75 Print; 8 CD-ROM; 2 Audio
Imprints: Vandalia Press
Orders to: Chicago Distribution Center, 11030 S Langley Ave, Chicago, IL 60628 *Toll Free Tel:* 800-621-2736 *Toll Free Fax:* 800-621-8476 *E-mail:* orders@press.chicago.edu
Distribution Center: Chicago Distribution Center, 11030 S Langley Ave, Chicago, IL 60628 *Tel:* 773-702-7000 (Intl) *Toll Free Tel:* 800-621-2736 *Fax:* 773-702-7212 (Intl) *Toll Free Fax:* 800-621-8476
Membership(s): Association of American University Presses

Westcliffe Publishers Inc
Imprint of Big Earth Publishing
3360 Mitchell Lane, Suite E, Boulder, CO 80301
SAN: 239-7528
Toll Free Tel: 800-258-5830 *Fax:* 303-443-9687
E-mail: books@bigearthpublishing.com
Web Site: www.bigearthpublishing.com/westcliffe-publishers
Key Personnel
CEO & Pres: John Fielder
Founded: 1979
Photographic publisher; specialize in landscape, nature & scenic subjects, trail guides.
ISBN Prefix(es): 978-0-942394; 978-0-929969; 978-1-56579
Number of titles published annually: 18 Print; 16 Online
Total Titles: 125 Print; 125 Online

Western Pennsylvania Genealogical Society
4400 Forbes Ave, Pittsburgh, PA 15213-4080
Tel: 412-687-6811 (answering machine)
E-mail: info@wpgs.org
Web Site: www.wpgs.org
Key Personnel
Pubns Chair: Irene Dinning *E-mail:* publications@wpgs.org
Committee Chair: Suzanne M Johnston
Pres: Debbie Kapp *E-mail:* president@wpgs.org
Pres Elect: Marilyn Cocchiola Holt
Founded: 1974
ISBN Prefix(es): 978-0-9745162
Number of titles published annually: 10 Print; 1 CD-ROM; 40 Online
Total Titles: 40 Print; 1 CD-ROM; 1 Online; 1 E-Book
Distributed by Mechling Associates
Membership(s): National Genealogical Society

Western Reflections Publishing Co
951 N Hwy 149, Lake City, CO 81235
Mailing Address: PO Box 1149, Lake City, CO 81235-1149
Tel: 970-944-0110 *Toll Free Tel:* 800-993-4490 *Fax:* 970-944-0273
E-mail: publisher@westernreflectionspublishing.com
Web Site: www.westernreflectionspublishing.com
Key Personnel
Pres: P David Smith
Founded: 1996
History & culture of the western US with an emphasis on Colorado.
ISBN Prefix(es): 978-1-890437; 978-1-932738
Number of titles published annually: 6 Print
Total Titles: 170 Print

Westernlore Press
PO Box 35305, Tucson, AZ 85740-5305
SAN: 202-9650
Tel: 520-297-5491 *Fax:* 520-297-1722
Key Personnel
Pres & Ed: Lynn R Bailey
Treas & ISBN Contact: Anne G Bailey
Founded: 1941
History & biography, anthropology, historic archaeology & historic sites & ethnohistory pertaining to the greater American West.
ISBN Prefix(es): 978-0-87026
Number of titles published annually: 6 Print
Total Titles: 65 Print

§Westminster John Knox Press (WJK)
Imprint of Presbyterian Publishing Corp (PPC)
100 Witherspoon St, Louisville, KY 40202-1396
SAN: 202-9669
Tel: 502-569-5052 *Toll Free Tel:* 800-227-2872 (US only) *Fax:* 502-569-8308 *Toll Free Fax:* 800-541-5113 (US & CN)
E-mail: wjk@wjkbooks.com; customer_service@wjkbooks.com
Web Site: www.wjkbooks.com
Key Personnel
COO: Monty Anderson *E-mail:* manderson@wjkbooks.com
Pres & Publr: Marc Lewis *E-mail:* mlewis@wjkbooks.com
Exec Dir, Publg & Edit Dir: David Dobson *E-mail:* ddobson@wjkbooks.com
Exec Dir, Sales & Mktg: Gavin Stephens *E-mail:* gstephens@presbypub.com
Mktg Mgr: Emily Kiefer *E-mail:* ekiefer@wjkbooks.com
Acqs Ed: Jana Riess *E-mail:* jreiss@wjkbooks.com
Rts & Perms: Michele Blum *E-mail:* mblum@wjkbooks.com
Founded: 1838
With a publishing heritage that dates back more than 160 years, WJK Press publishes religious & theological books & resources for scholars, clergy, laity & general readers. The publisher employs the motto "Challenging the Mind, Nourishing the Soul".
ISBN Prefix(es): 978-0-664; 978-0-8042
Number of titles published annually: 150 Print
Total Titles: 1,100 Print; 2 CD-ROM; 2 Audio
Foreign Office(s): 13 Hellesdon Park Rd, Norwich Norfolk NR6 5DR, United Kingdom *Tel:* (01603) 612 914 *E-mail:* orders@norwichbooksandmusic.co.uk
Distributor for SCM

Foreign Rep(s): Academic Books for Seminaries (Rocky C L Chen) (Taiwan); Africa Christian Textbooks (Nigeria); Canaanland Distributors Sdn Bhd (Malaysia); Christian Book Discounters (South Africa); Claretian Communications Inc (Philippines); Cross Communications Ltd (Alexander Y C Lee) (Hong Kong); Import-Export & Wholesale Center (India); Korea Christian Book Service Inc (South Korea); Methodist Publishing House (South Africa); Omega Distributors Ltd (New Zealand); SKS Books Warehouse (Lek Eng Khiang) (Singapore)

Distribution Center: Presbyterian Publishing Corp (PPC), 341 Great Circle Rd, Nashville, TN 37228 *Toll Free Tel:* 800-227-2872 *Toll Free Fax:* 800-541-5113 *Web Site:* www.ppcpub.com

Westview Press

Member of The Perseus Books Group
2465 Central Ave, Boulder, CO 80301
SAN: 219-970X
Tel: 303-444-3541 *Fax:* 720-406-7336
E-mail: westview.orders@perseusbooks.com
Web Site: www.perseusbooksgroup.com; www.westviewpress.com
Key Personnel
CEO & Pres: David Steinberger
Publr: Cathleen Tetro
Exec Dir & Edit Dir, History & Area Studies: Priscilla McGeehon
Exec Ed: Karl Yambert *E-mail:* karly@perseusbooks.com
Acqs Dir: Grace Fujimoto
Assoc Sales & Mktg Dir: Renee Legatt
Sales & Mktg Mgr: Victoria Henson
Founded: 1975
Quality nonfiction, general audience trade books & college textbooks in the following areas: history, political science, international relations, military history, sociology, current affairs, criminology, women's studies, gender studies, journalism, anthropology, archaeology, art & art history, philosphy, religion, physics, mathematics, earth, planetary & space sciences.
ISBN Prefix(es): 978-0-8133
Number of titles published annually: 100 Print
Total Titles: 2,000 Print
Sales Office(s): The Perseus Books Group, 387 Park Ave S, 12th fl, New York City, NY 10016 *Tel:* 212-340-8100 *Toll Free Tel:* 800-343-4499 *Fax:* 212-340-8125 *Toll Free Fax:* 800-351-5073 *Web Site:* www.perseusbooksgroup.com
Foreign Office(s): Perseus Running Press UK, 69-70 Temple Chambers, 3-7 Temple Ave, London EC4Y 0HP, United Kingdom *Tel:* (020) 7353 7771 *Fax:* (020) 7353 7786 *E-mail:* enquiries@perseusbooks.co.uk
Foreign Rep(s): Sabrina Cote (France); Bernd Feldman (Austria, Germany, Switzerland); Charles Gibbes (Greece); Ben Greig (Scandinavia); Lazlo Horvath (Central Europe, Eastern Europe); Kemper Conseil (Belgium, Luxembourg, Netherlands); Mare Nostrum Publishing Consultants (David Pickering) (Italy); Mare Nostrum Publishing Consultants (Cristina De Lara) (Portugal, Spain); Perseus Running Press UK (Europe, UK); Publishers Scandinavian Consultancy (Ben Greig); Publishers Scandinavian Consultancy (Colin Flint) (Scandinavia); Zytek Publishing (South Africa)
Foreign Rights: Anthea Agency (Katalina Sabeva) (Bulgaria); Bardon-Chinese Media Agency (David Tsai) (China, Taiwan); Raquel de la Concha Agencia Literaria (Raquel de la Concha) (Brazil, Latin America, Portugal, Spain); Paul & Peter Fritz Agency (Peter Fritz, Christian Dittus & Antonia Fritz) (Germany); Deborah Harris Agency (Efrat Lev) (Israel); Anna Jarota Agency (Anna Jarota) (France); Nurcihan Kesim Literary Agency Inc (Filiz Karaman) (Turkey); Duran Kim Agency (Duran Kim & Joe Moon) (Korea); Alexander Korzhenevski Agency (Alexander Korzhenevski & Tania Korzhenevski) (Russia); Maxima Creative Agency (Santo Manurung) (Indonesia); Kristin Olson Literary Agency (Kristin Olson) (Czech Republic, Slovakia); Oxford Literary & Rights Agency (Hana Whitton) (Ukraine); Read n' Right Agency (Nike Davarinou) (Greece); Lennart Sane Agency (Phillip Sane) (Scandinavia); Santachiara Literary Agency (Roberto Santachiara) (Italy); Sebes & Van Gelderen Literary Agency (Paul Sebes) (Netherlands); Livia Stoia Agency (Livia Stoia & Cristiana Lazareanu) (Albania, Bosnia and Herzegovina, Croatia, Macedonia, Montenegro, Romania, Serbia, Slovenia); Torus-Books Literary & Scouting Agency Ltd (Gynn Kalman) (Hungary); Tuttle-Mori Agency Inc (Manami Tamaoki) (Japan); Tuttle-Mori Agency Inc (Mr Thananchai Pandey) (Thailand, Vietnam)
Advertising Agency: Bennett Books
Orders to: The Perseus Books Group, 1094 Flex Dr, Jackson, TN 38301 *Toll Free Tel:* 800-343-4499 *Toll Free Fax:* 800-351-5073
Distribution Center: Consortium Book Sales & Distribution, The Keg House, Suite 101, 34 13 Ave NE, Minneapolis, MN 55413-1007 *Tel:* 612-746-2600 *Toll Free Tel:* 800-283-3572 *Fax:* 612-746-2606 *Web Site:* www.cbsd.com
The Perseus Books Group, 1094 Flex Dr, Jackson, TN 38301 *Toll Free Tel:* 800-343-4499 *Toll Free Fax:* 800-351-5073
Publishers Group West, 1700 Fourth St, Berkeley, CA 97410 *Tel:* 510-809-3700 *Fax:* 510-809-3777 *E-mail:* info@pgw.com *Web Site:* www.publishersgroupwest.com
Membership(s): AAP

Wheatherstone Press

Subsidiary of Dickinson Consulting Group
PO Box 257, Portland, OR 97207-0257
Tel: 503-244-8929 *Fax:* 503-244-9795
E-mail: relocntr@nwlink.com
Web Site: www.wheatherstonepress.com
Key Personnel
CEO & Pres: Jan Dickinson
Founded: 1983
Publishes handbooks & step-by-step guides covering all phases of relocation, including internationally.
ISBN Prefix(es): 978-0-9613011
Number of titles published annually: 3 Print
Total Titles: 49 Print
Foreign Rep(s): 111

§Whiskey Creek Press LLC

541 Long Lane, Casper, WY 82609
Mailing Address: PO Box 51052, Casper, WY 82605-1052
Tel: 307-265-8585 *Fax:* 307-265-4640
E-mail: publisher@whiskeycreekpress.com; whiskeycreekpress@bresnan.net
Web Site: www.whiskeycreekpress.com; www.torridbooks.com; www.weecreekpress.com
Key Personnel
Publr: Debra A Womack, MA
Sr Partner: Steven D Womack, PhD
Founded: 2003 (Torrid Books, 2004 & Wee Creek Press 2013)
Traditional royalty-paying small press, publishing fiction in ebook & print formats. Titles can be purchased through Amazon Kindle, Barnes & Noble Nook & Apple ITunes.
ISBN Prefix(es): 978-1-60313; 978-1-61160
Number of titles published annually: 50 Print; 200 E-Book
Total Titles: 400 Print; 1,350 E-Book
Imprints: Torrid Books (sensual & erotic romances); Wee Creek Press (children's books); Whiskey Creek Press (fiction-all genres)

§Whitaker House

1030 Hunt Valley Circle, New Kensington, PA 15068
Tel: 724-334-7000 *Fax:* 724-334-1200
E-mail: publisher@whitakerhouse.com
Web Site: www.whitakerhouse.com
Key Personnel
Mng Dir: Tom Cox
Founded: 1970
ISBN Prefix(es): 978-0-88368; 978-1-60374; 978-1-62911
Number of titles published annually: 70 Print; 1 CD-ROM; 70 E-Book; 8 Audio
Total Titles: 500 Print; 20 CD-ROM; 400 E-Book; 40 Audio
Imprints: Banner Publishing
Foreign Rep(s): Diane Rogers
Warehouse: Anchor Distributors, 1030 Hunt Valley Circle, New Kensington, PA 15068, Mgr: Dave Brennan
Membership(s): American Christian Fiction Writers; CBA; Evangelical Christian Publishers Association

White Cloud Press

300 E Hersey St, Suite 11, Ashland, OR 97520
Mailing Address: PO Box 3400, Ashland, OR 97520
Tel: 541-488-6415 *Toll Free Tel:* 800-380-8286 *Fax:* 541-482-7708
E-mail: info@whitecloudpress.com
Web Site: www.whitecloudpress.com
Key Personnel
Publr: Steve Scholl *E-mail:* scholl@whitecloudpress.com
Prodn Mgr: Christy Collins *E-mail:* christy@whitecloudpress.com
Admin Asst & Intl Rts & Perms: Ezra Penalba *E-mail:* ezra@whitecloudpress.com
Founded: 1993
General trade, emphasis on religion & fiction.
ISBN Prefix(es): 978-1-883991; 978-0-9745245
Number of titles published annually: 6 Print
Total Titles: 60 Print; 40 E-Book; 4 Audio
Imprints: Caveat Press; Confluence Books; RiverWood Books
Subsidiaries: Confluence Book Services
Foreign Rights: Danny Baror; Nigel Yorwerth
Distribution Center: Publishers Group West, 1700 Fourth St, Berkeley, CA 94710 *Toll Free Tel:* 800-788-3123 *Toll Free Fax:* 800-351-5073 *Web Site:* www.pgw.com
Membership(s): The Independent Book Publishers Association

White Pine Press

PO Box 236, Buffalo, NY 14201
Tel: 716-627-4665 *Fax:* 716-627-4665
E-mail: wpine@whitepine.org
Web Site: www.whitepine.org
Key Personnel
Mng Dir: Elaine La Mattina
Publr & Ed: Dennis Maloney *E-mail:* dennismaloney@yahoo.com
Founded: 1973
Specialize in poetry, essays, fiction, literature in translation.
ISBN Prefix(es): 978-0-934834; 978-1-877727; 978-1-877800; 978-1-893996
Number of titles published annually: 10 Print
Total Titles: 160 Print
Subsidiaries: Springhouse Editions
Distributor for Springhouse Editions
Distribution Center: Consortium Book Sales & Distribution, The Keg House, Suite 101, 34 13 Ave NE, Minneapolis, MN 55413-1007 *Tel:* 612-746-2600 *Toll Free Tel:* 800-283-3572 (cust serv) *Fax:* 612-746-2606 *Web Site:* www.cbsd.com

White Wolf Publishing Inc

Division of CCP North America
250 Ponce de Leon Ave, Suite 700, Decatur, GA 30030
Tel: 404-292-1819 *Toll Free Tel:* 800-454-9653
E-mail: questions@white-wolf.com

Web Site: www.white-wolf.com
Key Personnel
Mktg Dir: Philippe Boulle
Founded: 1991
Fiction & game books.
ISBN Prefix(es): 978-1-56504; 978-1-58846
Number of titles published annually: 60 Print
Total Titles: 280 Print
Imprints: Borealis; Exalted; Sword & Sorcery; Two Wolf Press; World of Darkness

Whitehorse Press
107 E Conway Rd, Center Conway, NH 03813-4012
Tel: 603-356-6556 *Toll Free Tel:* 800-531-1133 *Fax:* 603-356-6590
E-mail: customerservice@whitehorsepress.com
Web Site: www.whitehorsebooks.com
Key Personnel
Owner & Publr: Daniel W Kennedy
Owner & Mktg Mgr: Judith M Kennedy *E-mail:* judy@whitehorsepress.com
Founded: 1989
Travel guides & how-to books: motorcycle touring, care & maintenance, restoration.
ISBN Prefix(es): 978-0-9621834; 978-1-884313
Number of titles published annually: 6 Print
Total Titles: 50 Print
Foreign Rep(s): Gazelle Books Ltd (UK); Woodslane (Australia)
Distribution Center: Quarto Publishing US, 100 Cummings Ctr, Suite 406-L, Beverly, MA 01915 *Tel:* 978-282-3500

Whitman, Albert & Co, see Albert Whitman & Co

§Whittier Publications Inc
3115 Long Beach Rd, Oceanside, NY 11572
Tel: 516-432-8120 *Toll Free Tel:* 800-897-TEXT (897-8398) *Fax:* 516-889-0341
E-mail: info@whitbooks.com
Key Personnel
Pres: Judith Etra
Founded: 1990
Textbooks, trade, self-help, biology, history, mathematics, chemistry, sociology.
ISBN Prefix(es): 978-1-878045; 978-1-57604
Number of titles published annually: 200 Print
Imprints: Obelisk Books
Branch Office(s)
6429 Warren Dr, Norcross, GA 30093

§Whole Person Associates Inc
210 W Michigan St, Duluth, MN 55802-1908
Tel: 218-727-0500 *Toll Free Tel:* 800-247-6789 *Fax:* 218-727-0505
E-mail: books@wholeperson.com
Web Site: www.wholeperson.com
Key Personnel
Owner & Publr: Carlene Sippola
Founded: 1980
Stress management & wellness promotion.
ISBN Prefix(es): 978-0-938586; 978-1-57025
Number of titles published annually: 8 Print; 5 Audio
Total Titles: 160 Print; 29 CD-ROM; 38 Audio
Imprints: Whole Person Associates

§Wide World of Maps Inc
2626 W Indian School Rd, Phoenix, AZ 85017
Tel: 602-279-2324 *Toll Free Tel:* 800-279-7654 *Fax:* 602-279-2350
E-mail: sales@maps4u.com
Web Site: www.maps4u.com
Key Personnel
Pres: James L Willinger *Tel:* 602-433-0616 *Fax:* 602-433-0695 *E-mail:* james@maps4u.com
Founded: 1976
Atlases, charts, guide books, maps, map software, map accessories & more.
ISBN Prefix(es): 978-0-938448; 978-1-887749
Number of titles published annually: 6 Print; 2 CD-ROM
Total Titles: 20 Print; 2 CD-ROM
Imprints: Yellow 1
Divisions: Desert Charts; Metro Maps; Phoenix Mapping Service
Distributed by Rand McNally
Distributor for Benchmark Maps; Big Sky Maps; Franko Maps; MacVan Maps (Colorado Springs); Metro Maps; Rand McNally

Wide World Publishing
PO Box 476, San Carlos, CA 94070-0476
SAN: 211-1462
Tel: 650-593-2839 *Fax:* 650-595-0802
E-mail: wwpbl@aol.com
Web Site: wideworldpublishing.com
Key Personnel
Partner & Intl Rts: Elvira Monroe
Founded: 1976
Trade paperbacks, cookbooks, mathematics books/calendars, travel books & guides.
ISBN Prefix(es): 978-0-933174; 978-1-884550
Number of titles published annually: 6 Print
Total Titles: 35 Print
Imprints: Math Products Plus; Wide World Publishing; Wide World Publishing/Tetra
Distributed by Perseus Books Group
Foreign Rep(s): Publishers Group West (Asia, Canada, Europe)
Distribution Center: Publishers Group West, 1700 Fourth St, Berkeley, CA 94710 SAN: 202-8522

Markus Wiener Publishers Inc
231 Nassau St, Princeton, NJ 08542
SAN: 282-5465
Tel: 609-921-1141 *Fax:* 609-921-1140
E-mail: publisher@markuswiener.com
Web Site: www.markuswiener.com
Key Personnel
Pres: M Markus Wiener
VP & Ed: Shelley Frisch
Ed: Janet Stern
Mktg & Ad: Stacey Garstein *E-mail:* stacey@markuswiener.com
Prodn: Cheryl Mirkin
Founded: 1981
Books & journals in Middle Eastern, Latin American, African & Caribbean studies, world history & religion. Textbooks, artificial intelligence. Returns: write for permission.
ISBN Prefix(es): 978-0-910129; 978-0-945179; 978-1-55876
Number of titles published annually: 25 Print
Total Titles: 300 Print
Imprints: Rutgers Series in Accounting Research; Topics in World History
Foreign Rep(s): Eurospan (Africa, Asia, Asia-Pacific, Australia, Europe)
Foreign Rights: Verlagsburo Wetterstein Munich (Africa, Asia, Europe, Germany, Latin America, Middle East)

Michael Wiese Productions
12400 Ventura Blvd, No 1111, Studio City, CA 91604
Tel: 818-379-8799 *Toll Free Tel:* 800-833-5738 (orders) *Fax:* 818-986-3408
E-mail: mwpsales@mwp.com; fulfillment@portcity.com
Web Site: www.mwp.com
Key Personnel
Founder & Publr: Michael Wiese
VP: Ken Lee *Tel:* 206-283-2948 *E-mail:* kenlee@mwp.com
Spec Sales: Michele Chong *Tel:* 818-841-4123
Founded: 1981
Publisher of books on screenwriting & filmmaking.
ISBN Prefix(es): 978-0-941188
Number of titles published annually: 15 Print
Total Titles: 170 Print
Imprints: Divine Arts
Distribution Center: Ingram Publisher Services, One Ingram Blvd, La Vergne, TN 37086 *Toll Free Tel:* 866-400-5351 *E-mail:* customerservice@ingrampublisherservices.com *Web Site:* www.ingrampublisherservices.com

Wilderness Adventures Press Inc
45 Buckskin Rd, Belgrade, MT 59714
Tel: 406-388-0112 *Toll Free Tel:* 866-400-2012
E-mail: books@wildadvpress.com
Web Site: store.wildadvpress.com
Key Personnel
Pres & Prodn Ed: Chuck Johnson *Tel:* 406-388-0112 ext 12 *Fax:* 406-388-0120 *E-mail:* chuckj@wildadvpress.com
Secy & Treas: Blanche Johnson *Tel:* 406-388-0112 ext 14 *Fax:* 406-388-0120 *E-mail:* blanche@wildadvpress.com
Founded: 1994
Outdoor guidebooks, sporting books & cookbooks, fly fishing, dog training & big game hunting, plus maps.
ISBN Prefix(es): 978-1-885106; 978-1-932098
Number of titles published annually: 6 Print
Total Titles: 82 Print
Distributed by Angler's Book Supply; Books West; Inter Sports; Partners Book Distributor; Partners West; Raymond C Rumpf & Son Inc
Distribution Center: Baker & Taylor, 2550 W Tyvola Rd, Suite 300, Charlotte, NC 28217 *Tel:* 704-998-3100 *Toll Free Tel:* 800-775-1800 *Web Site:* www.btol.com
Ingram Publisher Services, One Ingram Blvd, La Vergne, TN 37086 *Toll Free Tel:* 866-400-5351 *E-mail:* customerservice@ingrampublisherservices.com *Web Site:* www.ingrampublisherservices.com

Wildflower Press
Affiliate of Oakbrook Press
Oakbrook Press, 3301 S Valley Dr, Rapid City, SD 57703
Mailing Address: PO Box 3362, Rapid City, SD 57709
Tel: 605-381-6385 *Fax:* 605-343-8733
E-mail: info@wildflowerpress.org; bookorder@wildflowerpress.org
Web Site: www.wildflowerpress.org
Key Personnel
Pres: L J Bryant *E-mail:* wildflowerpress@live.com
Publicity Dir: Robert E Fuchs *E-mail:* pr@wildflowerpress.org
Literary Agent: Charlene Caulfield
Sales: Jordan Dadah
Edit: Leisette Fox
Publicity Asst: William Everett
Billing: Christina MacLachlan
Founded: 2010
Small press specializing in publishing works of fiction with a significant message. Not a vanity press; no funds required to publish.
ISBN Prefix(es): 978-0-9835332
Number of titles published annually: 5 Print; 5 E-Book
Total Titles: 1 Print
Membership(s): The Independent Book Publishers Association

Wildlife Education Ltd
2418 Noyes St, Evanston, IL 60201
Toll Free Tel: 800-477-5034
E-mail: owls5@zoobooks.com; helpdesk@zoobooks.com
Web Site: www.zoobooks.com; wildlife-ed.com
Key Personnel
CEO & Pres: Robert W Harper

COO & VP: John O Toraason
Publr: Ed Shadek
Edit Dir: Renee C Burch; Marjorie Shaw
Sales Mgr: Kurt Von Hertsenberg *E-mail:* kurt@zoobooks.com
Founded: 1980
Books on wildlife & animals. Also publishes Zoobooks Magazine.
ISBN Prefix(es): 978-0-937934; 978-1-888153
Number of titles published annually: 12 Print
Total Titles: 200 Print
Membership(s): AAP PreK-12 Learning Group

Wildside Press LLC
414 Hungerford Dr, Suite 234, Rockville, MD 20850
Mailing Address: 9710 Traville Gateway Dr, Suite 234, Rockville, MD 20850
Tel: 301-762-1305 *Fax:* 301-762-1306
E-mail: wildside@wildsidepress.com
Web Site: www.wildsidebooks.com; www.wildsidemagazines.com; www.wildsidepress.com
Key Personnel
Publr: John Betancourt
Dir, Publg Opers: Carla Coupe
Founded: 1989
Reprints of classic science fiction, fantasy, mystery, reference & mainstream.
ISBN Prefix(es): 978-1-880448; 978-1-58715; 978-1-59224
Number of titles published annually: 1,500 Print; 400 E-Book; 100 Audio
Total Titles: 16,000 Print; 1,400 E-Book; 800 Audio
Imprints: Borgo Press; Owlswick Press
Foreign Rights: Donald Maass Agency (Worldwide exc USA)

§Wiley-Blackwell
Commerce Place, 350 Main St, Malden, MA 02148
Tel: 781-388-8200 *Fax:* 781-388-8210
E-mail: info@wiley.com
Web Site: www.wiley.com
Key Personnel
Publr: Alison Labbate *E-mail:* alabbate@wiley.com
Founded: 1984
General, scholarly, reference & college texts, with an emphasis on the humanities, social sciences & business. Also medical allied health, veterinary, earth & life sciences, environment & engineering.
ISBN Prefix(es): 978-0-631; 978-0-85520; 978-0-86216; 978-1-55786; 978-1-57718
Number of titles published annually: 500 Print
Total Titles: 4,500 Print

§John Wiley & Sons Inc
111 River St, Hoboken, NJ 07030-5774
SAN: 202-5183
Tel: 201-748-6000 *Toll Free Tel:* 800-225-5945 (cust serv) *Fax:* 201-748-6088
E-mail: info@wiley.com
Web Site: www.wiley.com
Key Personnel
Chmn of the Bd: Peter Booth Wiley
Pres & CEO: Matthew Kissner
Corp Secy: Michael L Preston
CEO: Mark Allin
CFO & EVP: John Kritzmacher
Chief Acctg Offr & VP: Edward J Melando
SVP, HR: William J Arlington
SVP & Gen Coun: Gary M Rinck
SVP & Gen Mgr, Global Educ: Joseph Sheridan Heider
SVP, STMS Div: Steve Miron
VP & Treas: Vincent Marzano
VP & Dir, Open Access: Rachel Burley
Dir, Corp Media Rel: Linda Dunbar
Founded: 1807
Global publisher of print & electronic products specializing in professional & consumer books & subscription services; scientific, technical, medical books & journals; textbooks & educational materials for undergraduate & graduate students as well as lifelong learners. Wiley has publishing, marketing & distribution centers in the US, Canada, Europe, Asia & Australia.
ISBN Prefix(es): 978-0-470; 978-0-471; 978-0-442; 978-0-8436; 978-0-87055
Number of titles published annually: 1,500 Print
Total Titles: 15,000 Print
Imprints: Audel™; Capstone; Ernst & Sohn; For Dummies®; Halsted Press; Howell Book House; Jossey-Bass; Pfeiffer; Scripta-Technica; Valusource; Visual™; Wiley; Wiley-Heyden; Wiley Interscience®; John Wiley & Sons; Wiley-Liss; Wiley-VCH; Wrox™
Orders to: 1045 Crosspoint Blvd, Indianapolis, IN 46256 *Toll Free Tel:* 877-762-2974 *Toll Free Fax:* 800-597-3299
Returns: Heller Park Ctr, 360 Mill Rd, Edison, NJ 08817 *Tel:* 732-650-4600 *Fax:* 732-650-4619
Shipping Address: One Wiley Dr, Somerset, NJ 08875-1272 *Tel:* 732-469-4400 *Toll Free Tel:* 800-225-5945 *Fax:* 732-302-2300
Membership(s): AAP
See separate listing for:
Jossey-Bass
John Wiley & Sons Inc Higher Education
John Wiley & Sons Inc Professional/Trade Group
John Wiley & Sons Inc Scientific, Technical, Medical & Scholarly (STMS)

John Wiley & Sons Inc Higher Education
Division of John Wiley & Sons Inc
111 River St, Hoboken, NJ 07030-5774
Tel: 201-748-6000 *Toll Free Tel:* 800-225-5945 (cust serv) *Fax:* 201-748-6008
E-mail: info@wiley.com
Web Site: www.wiley.com
Key Personnel
Exec Publr: Kaye Pace
VP & Natl Sales Mgr: Patty Stark
VP, Prodn & Mfg, High School: Ann Berlin
VP, Prod & E-Busn Devt: Joe Heider
VP & Dir, Mktg: Susan Elbe
VP, Sales & Mktg: M J O'Leary
VP, Strategic Devt: Bruce Spatz
Mktg & Sales Coord: Kathi Zhang
Total Titles: 615 Print

John Wiley & Sons Inc Professional/Trade Group
Division of John Wiley & Sons Inc
111 River St, Hoboken, NJ 07030
Tel: 201-748-6000 *Toll Free Tel:* 800-225-5945 (cust serv) *Fax:* 201-748-6088
E-mail: info@wiley.com
Web Site: www.wiley.com
Key Personnel
VP, Trade Sales: Dean Karrel
VP, Prodn & Mfg: Elizabeth Doble
VP & Dir, Sales: George Stanley
VP, Mktg & Opers: Margie Schustack
VP, Mktg: Larry Olson
Dir, Digital Publg: David Goehring

John Wiley & Sons Inc Scientific, Technical, Medical & Scholarly (STMS)
Division of John Wiley & Sons Inc
111 River St, Hoboken, NJ 07030
Tel: 201-748-6000 *Toll Free Tel:* 800-225-5945 (cust serv) *Fax:* 201-748-6088
E-mail: info@wiley.com
Web Site: www.wiley.com
Key Personnel
SVP: Steve Miron
VP, Global Content Mgmt: Craig Van Dyck
VP, Global Sales: Reed Elfenbein

William Carey Library Publishers
Division of Frontier Ventures
1605 E Elizabeth St, Pasadena, CA 91104
Tel: 626-720-8210 *Toll Free Tel:* 866-732-6657 (orders & cust serv)
E-mail: assistant@wclbooks.com
Web Site: www.missionbooks.org
Key Personnel
Gen Mgr: Jeff Minard *E-mail:* manager@wclbooks.com
Founded: 1969
Cross-cultural Christian mission work & experiences in frontier countries.
ISBN Prefix(es): 978-0-87808
Number of titles published annually: 15 Print
Total Titles: 250 Print; 3 CD-ROM
Imprints: Mandate Press
Orders to: STL Distribution, 100 Biblica Way, Elizabethton, TN 37643 *Toll Free Tel:* 800-647-7466
Membership(s): Evangelical Christian Publishers Association; The Independent Book Publishers Association

§Williams & Company Book Publishers
1317 Pine Ridge Dr, Savannah, GA 31406
Tel: 912-352-0404
E-mail: bookpub@comcast.net
Web Site: www.pubmart.com
Key Personnel
Publr & Ed-in-Chief: Thomas A Williams, PhD
Founded: 1989
Niche market nonfiction.
ISBN Prefix(es): 978-1-878853
Number of titles published annually: 15 Print
Total Titles: 25 Print
Imprints: Venture Press; Williams & Co Publishers
Warehouse: Juliana Group, 1110 Staley Ave, Savannah, GA 31405
Membership(s): Independent Publishers Association

Willow Creek Press
9931 Hwy 70 W, Minocqua, WI 54548
Mailing Address: PO Box 147, Minocqua, WI 54548
Tel: 715-358-7010 *Toll Free Tel:* 800-850-9453 *Fax:* 715-358-2807
E-mail: info@willowcreekpress.com
Web Site: www.willowcreekpress.com
Key Personnel
Publr: Tom Petrie
VP, Sales: Jeremy Petrie *E-mail:* jpetrie@willowcreekpress.com
Mng Dir: Donny Ruebel
Founded: 1986
Willow Creek Press specializes in publishing high quality books most specifically related to nature, animals, wildlife, hunting, fishing & gardening. The company also offers a unique line of cookbooks & has established a niche in the pet book market. The company also publishes high quality nature, wild life, fishing, pet & sporting calendars.
ISBN Prefix(es): 978-1-57223
Number of titles published annually: 24 Print
Total Titles: 130 Print; 3 Audio
Membership(s): AAM; AAP

Wilshire Book Co
9731 Variel Ave, Chatsworth, CA 91311-4315
SAN: 205-5368
Tel: 818-700-1522 *Fax:* 818-700-1527
E-mail: sales@mpowers.com
Web Site: www.mpowers.com
Key Personnel
Pres & Rts & Perms: Marcia Powers
Founded: 1947 (by Melvin Powers)
Psychological, self-help, motivational & inspirational books, adult fables; mail order, business, advertising & marketing; sports, gam-

bling, horse, game & joke books; originals & reprints.
ISBN Prefix(es): 978-0-87980
Number of titles published annually: 20 Print
Total Titles: 300 Print; 300 Online

H W Wilson
Division of EBSCO Information Services
2 University Plaza, Suite 310, Hackensack, NJ 07601
Tel: 201-968-0500 *Toll Free Tel:* 800-221-1592 *Fax:* 201-968-0511
E-mail: info@hwwilsoninprint.com; csr@hwwilsoninprint.com; information@ebscohost.com
Web Site: www.hwwilsoninprint.com; www.ebscohost.com/wilson
Key Personnel
CEO & Pres: Harold Regan
VP, Sales & Mktg: Deborah V Loeding
VP, Cont: James F Phelan
VP, Info Systems: Lucian A Parziale
VP, Off of Personnel: John O'Connor
VP, Cataloging & Gen Ref Servs: Joseph Miller, MLS, PhD
VP, Indexing & Edit Servs: Mark Gauthier
Dir, Mktg: Frank W Daly
US Sales Mgr: Nancy Kolady
Founded: 1898
An icon in the library community for more than 100 years, H W Wilson is dedicated to providing the highest-quality references in the world. Via the WilsonWeb Internet Service, on WilsonDisc CD-ROM & in print, more than 50 H W Wilson reference databases meet the research needs of customers around the globe. Wilson periodicals databases bring users full-text, page images, abstracts & indexing of thousands of leading magazines & journals. Acclaimed Wilson specialty library catalogs support collection development in children's, school & public libraries & Wilson print references consistently earn reviewers' praise. For more on H W Wilson visit www.hwwilson.com. Types of publications: reference databases (biography databases, periodicals databases: full text articles, abstracts, indexing) & reference books.
ISBN Prefix(es): 978-0-8242
Number of titles published annually: 13 Print
Total Titles: 200 Print; 50 CD-ROM; 80 Online
Returns: Grey House Publishing, 5979 N Elm Ave, Millerton, NY 12546

Wimbledon Music Inc & Trigram Music Inc
1801 Century Park E, Suite 2400, Los Angeles, CA 90067
Tel: 310-556-9683 *Fax:* 310-277-1278
E-mail: irishmex127@gmail.com
Web Site: www.wimbtri.net
Key Personnel
Dir, Pubns: Peter Dorfman
Founded: 1978
ISBN Prefix(es): 978-0-938170
Number of titles published annually: 35 Print

Wimmer Cookbooks
Division of Mercury Printing
4650 Shelby Air Dr, Memphis, TN 38118
Tel: 901-362-8900 *Toll Free Tel:* 800-363-1771
E-mail: wimmer@wimmerco.com
Web Site: www.wimmerco.com
Key Personnel
Pres: Danny Bailey
VP: Doug McNeill *E-mail:* dmcneill@wimmerco.com
Dir, Dist: Robyn Hite *E-mail:* rhite@wimmerco.com
Founded: 1946
Development, publishing, manufacturing, marketing & distribution of community & self-published cookbooks.
ISBN Prefix(es): 978-1-879958
Number of titles published annually: 50 Print
Total Titles: 250 Print
Imprints: Tradery House

§Wind Canyon Books
PO Box 7035, Stockton, CA 95267
Tel: 209-956-1600 *Toll Free Tel:* 800-952-7007 *Fax:* 209-956-9424 *Toll Free Fax:* 888-289-7086
E-mail: books@windcanyonbooks.com
Web Site: www.windcanyonbooks.com
Key Personnel
Owner: George Jaquith
Founded: 1996
ISBN Prefix(es): 978-0-943691; 978-1-891118
Number of titles published annually: 5 Print
Total Titles: 70 Print

Windsor Books
Division of Windsor Marketing Corp
260 Montauk Hwy, Suite 5, Bayshore, NY 11706
SAN: 203-2945
Mailing Address: PO Box 280, Brightwaters, NY 11718
Tel: 631-665-6688 *Toll Free Tel:* 800-321-5934
E-mail: windsor.books@att.net
Web Site: www.windsorpublishing.com
Key Personnel
Founder: Alfred Schmidt
Mng Ed: Jeff Schmidt
Founded: 1968
Business, economics & investment.
ISBN Prefix(es): 978-0-930233
Number of titles published annually: 5 Print
Advertising Agency: A Schmidt Agency

Windward Publishing
Imprint of Finney Company Inc
5995 149 St W, Suite 105, Apple Valley, MN 55124
Tel: 952-469-6699 *Toll Free Tel:* 800-846-7027 *Fax:* 952-469-1968 *Toll Free Fax:* 800-330-6232
E-mail: info@finneyco.com
Web Site: www.finneyco.com
Key Personnel
Pres: Alan E Krysan
Mktg Mgr: Krista Danielson
Founded: 1973
Publishes books with educational value; children's books & trade books. Topics covered are natural history/science, nature & outdoor recreation.
ISBN Prefix(es): 978-0-89317
Number of titles published annually: 5 Print
Total Titles: 42 Print

§The Wine Appreciation Guild Ltd
360 Swift Ave, Suites 30 & 34, South San Francisco, CA 94080
SAN: 201-9515
Tel: 650-866-3020 *Toll Free Tel:* 800-231-9463 *Fax:* 650-866-3513
E-mail: info@wineappreciation.com
Web Site: www.wineappreciation.com
Key Personnel
Pres: Donna Bottrell
Ed: Maurice Sullivan
Intl Rts: Elliott Mackey
Lib Sales Dir: Bryan Imelli *Tel:* 650-866-3020 ext 22 *E-mail:* bryan@wineappreciation.com
Founded: 1974
Publisher of books on the subject of wine.
ISBN Prefix(es): 978-0-932664; 978-1-891267
Number of titles published annually: 7 Print; 1 CD-ROM; 7 E-Book; 4 Audio
Total Titles: 112 Print; 3 CD-ROM; 16 Audio
Imprints: Vintage Image
Foreign Rep(s): Books for Europe (Continental Europe, Middle East); Eos Libros (Latin America); Horizon Books (Malaysia, Singapore); McArthur & Co (Canada); Peribo Books (Australia); Stephen Phillips Pty Ltd (South Africa); Vine House Distribution (UK)
Advertising Agency: Vintage Image, 360 Swift Ave, Suite 34, South San Francisco, CA 94080 *Toll Free Tel:* 800-231-9463 *Fax:* 650-866-3513 *E-mail:* info@wineappreciation.com *Web Site:* www.wineappreciation.com

§Wings Press
627 E Guenther, San Antonio, TX 78210-1134
Tel: 210-271-7805 *Fax:* 210-271-7805
E-mail: press@wingspress.com
Web Site: www.wingspress.com
Key Personnel
Publr & Ed: Bryce Milligan *E-mail:* milligan@wingspress.com
Founded: 1975
Literary book publishing.
ISBN Prefix(es): 978-0-916727; 978-0-930324
Number of titles published annually: 15 Print; 20 Online; 20 E-Book; 1 Audio
Total Titles: 113 Print; 1 CD-ROM; 4 Audio
Foreign Rights: Independent Publisher's Group (Susan M Sewall)
Orders to: Independent Publisher's Group (IPG), 814 N Franklin St, Chicago, IL 60624, Contact: Tito Garcia *Tel:* 312-337-0747 *Fax:* 312-337-5985 *E-mail:* tgarcia@ipgbook.com
Returns: Independent Publisher's Group Distribution Center, 600 N Pulaski Rd, Chicago, IL 60624, Contact: Tito Garcia *Tel:* 312-337-0747 *Fax:* 312-337-5985 *E-mail:* tgarcia@ipgbook.com
Shipping Address: Independent Publisher's Group Distribution Center, 600 N Pulaski Rd, Chicago, IL 60624, Contact: Tito Garcia *Tel:* 312-337-0747 *Fax:* 312-337-5985 *E-mail:* tgarcia@ipgbook.com
Warehouse: Independent Publisher's Group Distribution Center, 600 N Pulaski Rd, Chicago, IL 60624, Contact: Tito Garcia *Tel:* 312-337-0747 *Fax:* 312-337-5985 *E-mail:* tgarcia@ipgbook.com
Distribution Center: Independent Publisher's Group Distribution Center, 600 N Pulaski Rd, Chicago, IL 60624, Contact: Tito Garcia *Tel:* 312-337-0747 *Fax:* 312-337-5985 *E-mail:* tgarcia@ipgbook.com

WingSpread Publishers
Division of Zur Ltd
2020 State Rd, Camp Hill, PA 17011
Tel: 717-761-7044 *Toll Free Tel:* 800-884-4571 *Fax:* 717-761-7273
E-mail: customerservice@echurchdepot.com
Web Site: wingspreadpublishers.com
Key Personnel
Pres: Ken Paton
Publr: Doug Waardenburg *Tel:* 717-761-7044 ext 302
Publicist: Pam Vossman
Trade Sales Dir & Intl Rts: Drew Park *E-mail:* dpark@christianpublications.com
Founded: 1883
ISBN Prefix(es): 978-0-87509; 978-0-88965; 978-1-60066
Number of titles published annually: 10 Print
Total Titles: 80 Print

Winters Publishing
705 E Washington St, Greensburg, IN 47240
SAN: 298-1645
Mailing Address: PO Box 501, Greensburg, IN 47240
Tel: 812-663-4948 *Toll Free Tel:* 800-457-3230 *Fax:* 812-663-4948
E-mail: winterspublishing@gmail.com
Web Site: www.winterspublishing.com
Key Personnel
Owner & Publr: Mr Tracy Winters
Founded: 1988

Produces high-quality, custom books for individuals & groups. We publish community & corporate history books for cities & organizations celebrating centennials, bicentennials & other milestone events. We also work with individual authors & publish children's books, books for the Christian market, cookbooks for the bed & breakfast industry & a variety of other fiction & nonfiction books.
ISBN Prefix(es): 978-0-9625329; 978-1-883651
Number of titles published annually: 15 Print; 2 E-Book
Total Titles: 75 Print; 2 E-Book
Imprints: Faith Press; Winters Publishing
Distribution Center: Partners Book Distributors, 2325 Jarco Dr, Holt, MI 48842 *Tel:* 517-694-3205
STL Distribution, 100 Biblica Way, Elizabethton, TN 37643 *Toll Free Tel:* 800-289-2772
Ingram Book Co, One Ingram Blvd, La Vergne, TN 37086 *Tel:* 615-793-5000
Partners West Book Distributors, 1901 Raymond Ave SW, Renton, WA 98057 *Tel:* 425-227-8486

Winterthur Museum & Country Estate
5105 Kennett Pike, Wilmington, DE 19735
Tel: 302-888-4663 *Toll Free Tel:* 800-448-3883 *Fax:* 302-888-4950
Web Site: www.winterthur.org
ISBN Prefix(es): 978-0-912724
Number of titles published annually: 4 Print
Total Titles: 40 Print
Distributed by Abrams; Acanthus; W W Norton & Company Inc; Schiffer; University Press of New England
Membership(s): ABA; American Alliance of Museums; Art Libraries Society

§Wisconsin Department of Public Instruction
125 S Webster St, Madison, WI 53703
Mailing Address: PO Box 7841, Madison, WI 53707-7841
Tel: 608-266-2188 *Toll Free Tel:* 800-441-4563 *Fax:* 608-267-9110
E-mail: pubsales@dpi.state.wi.us
Web Site: www.dpi.wi.gov/pubsales
Key Personnel
Communs Dir: John Johnson *Tel:* 608-266-1771 *E-mail:* john.johnson@dpi.state.wi.us
State Superintendent of Public Instruction: Tony Evers, PhD
Specialize in English, math, science & social studies, character education, driver education & traffic safety, career & technical education, world languages & teaching strategies.
ISBN Prefix(es): 978-1-57337
Number of titles published annually: 8 Print; 4 CD-ROM
Total Titles: 120 Print; 10 CD-ROM
Sales Office(s): Drawer 179, Milwaukee, WI 53293-0179, Dir: John Johnson *Tel:* 608-266-2188 *Toll Free Tel:* 800-243-8782 *Fax:* 608-267-9110 *E-mail:* john.johnson@dpi.state.wi.us *Web Site:* dpi.wi.gov/pubsales

Wisdom Publications Inc
199 Elm St, Somerville, MA 02144
Tel: 617-776-7416 *Toll Free Tel:* 800-272-4050 (orders) *Fax:* 617-776-7841
E-mail: info@wisdompubs.org
Web Site: www.wisdompubs.org
Key Personnel
Publr: Timothy McNeill *Tel:* 617-776-7416 ext 22
Promo: Lydia Anderson *E-mail:* promo@wisdompubs.org
Acqs Ed: Josh Bartok *Tel:* 617-776-7416 ext 26
Founded: 1976
Books on Buddhism published in various series encompassing theory & practice, biography, history, art & culture.
ISBN Prefix(es): 978-0-86171
Number of titles published annually: 20 Print
Total Titles: 158 Print
Imprints: Pali Text Society
Divisions: Wisdom Archive
Distributed by Simon & Schuster
Foreign Rep(s): Wisdom Books (Europe)
Foreign Rights: ACER (Spain); Eliane Benisti (France); Chinese Connection Agency (China); Fritz Literary Agency (Germany); Eric Yang Agency (Korea)
Orders to: Publishers Group West (PGW), 1700 Fourth St, Berkeley, CA 94710 *Tel:* 510-809-3700 *Fax:* 510-809-3777

Wish Publishing
PO Box 10337, Terre Haute, IN 47801-0337
Web Site: www.wishpublishing.com
Key Personnel
Publr: Holly Kondras *E-mail:* holly@wishpublishing.com
Founded: 1999
Trade publishing focused exclusively on women's sports, health & fitness.
ISBN Prefix(es): 978-1-930546
Number of titles published annually: 3 E-Book
Total Titles: 50 Print; 5 E-Book
Imprints: Equilibrium Books
Distributed by Cardinal Publishers Group
Membership(s): The Independent Book Publishers Association

Wittenborn Art Books
Division of Alan Wofsy Fine Arts
1109 Geary Blvd, San Francisco, CA 94109
Tel: 415-292-6500 *Toll Free Tel:* 800-660-6403 *Fax:* 415-292-6594
E-mail: wittenborn@art-books.com
Web Site: www.art-books.com
Key Personnel
Ed: Alan Hyman *E-mail:* editeur@earthlink.net
Opers Mgr: J Thrombly
Acqs: Lancelot Andrewes *E-mail:* beauxarts@earthlink.net
Rts: Mark Hyman *Tel:* 510-666-1150 *E-mail:* art-books.com@jps.net
Prodn: Duke Mantee *Tel:* 510-482-3677
Founded: 1939
Publish deluxe edition art reference books & artist books. Subject specialties include art, bibliography & decorative arts. Warehouse located in Ashland, OH.
ISBN Prefix(es): 978-0-8150
Number of titles published annually: 9 Print; 4 CD-ROM
Total Titles: 180 Print; 30 CD-ROM
Imprints: Documents of Modern Art; George Wittenborn
Distributor for Ides et Calendes SA; Menil Foundation; UCLA/Hammer Museum
Billing Address: PO Box 2210, San Francisco, CA 94126
Warehouse: Ashland, OH 44805
Membership(s): AAP

Wizards of the Coast LLC
Subsidiary of Hasbro Inc
1600 Lind Ave SW, Renton, WA 98057-3305
Mailing Address: PO Box 707, Renton, WA 98057-0707
Tel: 425-226-6500
Web Site: company.wizards.com
Founded: 1975 (as TSR Inc)
Publisher of fantasy, science fiction & horror novels. Young adult game material; role-playing games, trading card games, board games & books, makers of Dungeons & Dragons. Not seeking proposals for our shared world lines at this time.
ISBN Prefix(es): 978-0-88038; 978-1-56076; 978-0-7869
Number of titles published annually: 50 Print; 60 E-Book
Total Titles: 300 Print
Distributed by Random House

Alan Wofsy Fine Arts
1109 Geary Blvd, San Francisco, CA 94109
SAN: 207-6438
Mailing Address: PO Box 2210, San Francisco, CA 94126-2210
Tel: 415-292-6500 *Toll Free Tel:* 800-660-6403 *Fax:* 415-292-6594 (off & cust serv); 510-251-1840 (acctg)
E-mail: order@art-books.com (orders); editeur@earthlink.net (edit); beauxarts@earthlink.net (cust serv)
Web Site: www.art-books.com
Key Personnel
Chmn of the Bd: Lord Cohen
CEO: Alan Wofsy
Art Dir: Zeke Greenberg
Ed, French Books: Charles DuPont
Ed, German Books: Willi Rahm
PR Mgr: Milton J Goldbaum
Website Mgr: Steven Barich
Website & Imaging: Matt Novack
Mktg: Andy Redkin
Libn: Adios Butler
Coun: Judith Mazia
Rts: Elizabeth Regina Snowden
Founded: 1969
Art reference books, bibliographies, art books, iconographies, prints, posters & notecards. Distribution center & warehouse located in Ashland, OH.
ISBN Prefix(es): 978-0-915346; 978-1-55660
Number of titles published annually: 20 Print; 5 CD-ROM; 60 Online
Total Titles: 350 Print; 10 CD-ROM; 500 Online
Imprints: Beauxarts; Collegium Graphicum; The Picasso Project
Divisions: Wittenborn Art Books
Branch Office(s)
401 China Basin St, Suite 202, San Francisco, CA 94158-2133 (sales & cust serv)
Distributor for Bora; Brusberg (Berlin); Cramer (Geneva); Huber; Ides et Calendes; Kornfeld & Co (Bern); Welz; Wittenborn Art Books
Warehouse: Ashland, OH 44805
Distribution Center: Ashland, OH 44805
Membership(s): AAP
See separate listing for:
Picasso Project
Wittenborn Art Books

Wolters Kluwer US Corp
Subsidiary of Wolters Kluwer NV (The Netherlands)
2700 Lake Cook Rd, Riverwoods, IL 60015
Tel: 847-267-7000 *Fax:* 847-580-5192
Web Site: www.wolterskluwer.com
Key Personnel
Chmn: Nancy McKinstry
Medical books & journals, law books, business & tax publications.
Total Titles: 5,000 Print
Imprints: Adis International; Aspen Publishers Incorporated; CCH INCORPORATED; CT Corporation; Lippincott, Williams & Wilkins
Foreign Office(s): Zuidpoolsingel 2, PO Box 1030, 2400 BA Alphen aan den Rijn, Netherlands (headquarters) *Tel:* (0172) 641 400 *Fax:* (0172) 474 889 *E-mail:* info@wolterskluwer.com

Woodbine House
6510 Bells Mill Rd, Bethesda, MD 20817
SAN: 692-3445
Tel: 301-897-3570 *Toll Free Tel:* 800-843-7323 *Fax:* 301-897-5838
E-mail: info@woodbinehouse.com
Web Site: www.woodbinehouse.com
Key Personnel
Publr: Fran Marinaccio

Mktg Mgr & Intl Rts: Fran M Marinaccio
E-mail: fmarinaccio@woodbinehouse.com
Mktg & Sales Mgr: Beth Binns *E-mail:* bbinns@woodbinehouse.com
Prodn Mgr: Brenda A Ruby *E-mail:* bruby@woodbinehouse.com
Ed & Perms: Susan S Stokes *E-mail:* sstokes@woodbinehouse.com
Acqs Ed: Nancy Gray Paul *E-mail:* ngpaul@woodbinehouse.com
Founded: 1985
Trade nonfiction, hardcover & paperback.
ISBN Prefix(es): 978-0-933149; 978-1-890627; 978-1-60613
Number of titles published annually: 10 Print; 8 E-Book
Total Titles: 90 Print; 35 E-Book
Foreign Rep(s): Gazelle Book Service (Europe); Monarch Books (Canada); Silvereye Education Publications (Australia, Pacific Rim)
Foreign Rights: Writer's House
Returns: IFC, 3570 Bladensburg Rd, Brentwood, MD 20722 *Tel:* 301-779-4660
Warehouse: Woodbine House, c/o IFC, 3570 Bladensburg Rd, Brentwood, MD 20722

Woodland Publishing Inc
515 S 700 E, Suite 2D, Salt Lake City, UT 84102
SAN: 219-3531
Toll Free Tel: 800-277-3243 *Fax:* 801-334-1913
E-mail: info@woodlandpublishing.com
Web Site: www.woodlandpublishing.com
Key Personnel
Mng Ed: Michelle Billeter
Founded: 1975
General trade & paperbacks, professional books; health & nutrition.
ISBN Prefix(es): 978-0-89557; 978-1-58054
Number of titles published annually: 15 Print
Total Titles: 200 Print
Distributed by Summit Beacon
Warehouse: 500 N 1030 W, Lindon, UT 84042 *Toll Free Tel:* 800-777-2665 *Fax:* 801-785-8511
Distribution Center: New Leaf Distributing Co, 401 Thornton Rd, Lithia Springs, GA 30122-1557 *Tel:* 770-948-7845 *Toll Free Tel:* 800-326-2665 *Fax:* 770-944-2313 *Web Site:* www.newleaf-dist.com
Nutri-Books, 790 W Tennessee Ave, Denver, CO 80217 *Toll Free Tel:* 800-279-2048

Woodrow Wilson Center Press
Division of The Woodrow Wilson International Center for Scholars
One Woodrow Wilson Plaza, 1300 Pennsylvania Ave NW, Washington, DC 20004-3027
Tel: 202-691-4000 *Fax:* 202-691-4001
Web Site: wilsoncenter.org
Key Personnel
Dir: Joseph F Brinley, Jr *Tel:* 202-691-4042
E-mail: joe.brinley@wilsoncenter.org
Deputy Dir: Shannon Granville *Tel:* 202-691-4192
E-mail: shannon.granville@wilsoncenter.org
Founded: 1988
Humanities & social sciences; policy studies.
ISBN Prefix(es): 978-0-943875; 978-1-930365
Number of titles published annually: 12 Print
Total Titles: 200 Print
Imprints: Wilson Center Press; Woodrow Wilson Center Press/Johns Hopkins University Press; Woodrow Wilson Center Press/Stanford University Press; Woodrow Wilson Center Press/Columbia University Press
Distributed by Columbia University Press; The Johns Hopkins University Press; Stanford University Press; University of California Press
Membership(s): AAP; Association of American University Presses

WoodstockArts
PO Box 1342, Woodstock, NY 12498
Tel: 845-679-8111
E-mail: info@woodstockarts.com
Web Site: www.woodstockarts.com
Key Personnel
Founder: Julia Blelock; Weston Blelock
Founded: 1999
ISBN Prefix(es): 978-0-9679268
Number of titles published annually: 3 Print
Membership(s): The Independent Book Publishers Association

Workers Compensation Research Institute
955 Massachusetts Ave, Cambridge, MA 02139
Tel: 617-661-9274 *Fax:* 617-661-9284
E-mail: wcri@wcrinet.org
Web Site: www.wcrinet.org
Founded: 1983
Workers compensation public policy research.
ISBN Prefix(es): 978-0-935149
Number of titles published annually: 14 Print
Total Titles: 100 Print

§Workman Publishing Co Inc
225 Varick St, 9th fl, New York, NY 10014-4381
SAN: 203-2821
Tel: 212-254-5900 *Toll Free Tel:* 800-722-7202 *Fax:* 212-254-8098
E-mail: info@workman.com
Web Site: www.workman.com
Key Personnel
Exec Chair of the Bd & Pres: Carolan Workman
CEO: Dan Reynolds
COO: Glenn D'Agnes *Tel:* 212-614-7798
E-mail: glenn@workman.com
Chief Sales Offr: Walter Weintz *Tel:* 212-614-7593 *E-mail:* walter@workman.com
Cont: Bill Jackson *Tel:* 212-614-7552
E-mail: bill@workman.com
Publr & Edit Dir: Susan Bolotin *Tel:* 212-614-7514 *E-mail:* susan@workman.com
Assoc Publr: Page Edmunds *Tel:* 212-614-7528
E-mail: page@workman.com
Group Creative Dir: David Schiller
Exec Dir, Digital Strategy & Opers: Andrea Fleck-Nisbet *Tel:* 212-614-7579
E-mail: andrea@workman.com
Exec Dir, New Busn Devt: Jenny Mandel *Tel:* 212-614-7508 *E-mail:* jenny@workman.com
Exec Dir, Publicity & Mktg: Selina Meere
E-mail: selina@workman.com
Exec Dir, Spec Projs: Ann Bramson
Creative Dir: Vaughn Andrews
Dir, Children's Publg: Daniel Nayeri
Dir, Digital Busn: Kate Travers
Dir, Gift & Mass Merchant Sales: Jodi Weiss *Tel:* 212-614-7529 *E-mail:* jodiw@workman.com
Dir, Gift Field Sales: Marilyn Barnett *Tel:* 212-614-7737 *E-mail:* marilyn@workman.com
Dir, Intl Sales & Licensing: Kristina Peterson *Tel:* 212-614-5617 *E-mail:* kristina@workman.com
Dir, Online Retail Accts: Randall Lotowycz
Dir, Spec Mkts & Custom Publg: Emily Krasner
Licensing Dir: Pat Upton *Tel:* 212-614-7588
E-mail: pat@workman.com
Assoc Art Dir, Children's Dept: Colleen Venable
Assoc Dir, Publicity: Noreen Herits
Gen Mgr: Jill Salayi *Tel:* 212-614-7532
E-mail: jill@workman.com
Sales Mgr, Retail: Steven Pace *Tel:* 212-614-7780
E-mail: steven@workman.com
Exec Ed: Suzanne Rafer *Tel:* 212-614-7516
E-mail: suzanne@workman.com
Mng Ed: Claire McKean
Sr Ed: Mary Ellen O'Neill; Maisie Tivnan; Bruce Tracy
Sr Ed, Children's Group: Nathalie Le Du
Asst Ed: Justin Krasner
Ed-at-Large: Raquel Jaramillo
Prodn Mgr: Doug Wolff *Tel:* 212-614-7595
E-mail: doug@workman.com
Mgr, Cust Serv: Shirley Ortiz *Tel:* 212-614-7583
E-mail: shirley@workman.com
Asst Mgr, Cust Serv: Natalya Pilguy *Tel:* 212-614-7555 *E-mail:* natalya@workman.com
Sr Publicist: John Jenkinson
Founded: 1967
General nonfiction, calendars.
ISBN Prefix(es): 978-0-89480; 978-1-56305; 978-0-7611
Number of titles published annually: 345 Print
Divisions: Algonquin Books; Artisan; Storey Publishing; Timber Press; Workman Speakers Bureau
Distributor for The Experiment; Greenwich Workshop Press
Foreign Rep(s): Thomas Allen & Son Ltd (Canada); Bookreps New Zealand (New Zealand); Hardie Grant Books (Australia); Melia Publishing Services (Ireland, UK)
Foreign Rights: Big Apple Agency Inc (China, Taiwan); Graal Literary Agency (Poland); Japan UNI Agency (Japan); JLM Literary Agency (Greece); Katai & Bolza Literary Agency (Hungary); KCC (Korea); Alexander Korahenevski Agency (Russia); Kristin Olson Literary Agency (Czech Republic); Mickey Pikarski (Israel); Sebes & Van Gelderen Literary Agency (Netherlands); Julio F Yanez Agencia Literaria (Latin America, Portugal, Spain)
Returns: RR Donnelley Fulfillment, 655 Brighton Beach Rd, Menasha, WI 54952
Warehouse: RR Donnelley Fulfillment, N9234 Lake Park Rd, Appleton, WI 54915, Mgr, Cust Serv: Kim Rose *Tel:* 920-969-6411 *Fax:* 920-969-6441 *E-mail:* kim.m.rose@rrd.com
Membership(s): AAP
See separate listing for:
Algonquin Books
Artisan Books
Timber Press Inc

World Almanac®
Imprint of Infobase Learning
132 W 31 St, New York, NY 10001
SAN: 211-6944
Toll Free Tel: 800-322-8755
E-mail: almanac@factsonfile.com
Web Site: www.worldalmanac.com
Key Personnel
Sr Ed: Sarah Janssen *E-mail:* sjanssen@factsonfile.com
Rts & Licensing: Ben Jacobs *E-mail:* bjacobs@factsonfile.com
Founded: 1868
Annual juvenile & adult reference books.
ISBN Prefix(es): 978-1-60057
Number of titles published annually: 3 Print
Total Titles: 3 Print
Foreign Rep(s): Adnkronos Libri SRL (Italy)

§World Bank Publications
Member of The World Bank Group
Office of the Publisher, 1818 "H" St NW, U-11-1104, Washington, DC 20433
Tel: 202-458-4497 *Toll Free Tel:* 800-645-7247 (cust serv) *Fax:* 202-522-2631; 202-614-1237
E-mail: books@worldbank.org; pubrights@worldbank.org (foreign rts)
Web Site: www.worldbank.org/publications; publications.worldbank.org
Key Personnel
Publr: H Dirk Koehler
Sales Mgr: Jose de Buerba *Tel:* 202-473-0393
E-mail: jdebuerba@worldbank.org
Founded: 1944
Publish over 200 new titles annually in support of the World Bank's mission to fight poverty & distributes them globally in both print & electronic formats; electronic online subscription database; international affairs.
ISBN Prefix(es): 978-0-8213
Number of titles published annually: 200 Print; 10 CD-ROM; 3 Online; 30 E-Book

Total Titles: 2,000 Print; 50 CD-ROM; 3 Online; 50 E-Book
Imprints: World Bank
Foreign Rep(s): International Publishing Services (Middle East, North Africa)
Billing Address: Books International Inc, PO Box 959, Herndon, VA 20172-0960
Orders to: Books International Inc, PO Box 959, Herndon, VA 20172-0960
Returns: Books International Inc Returns Dept, 22883 Quicksilver Dr, Dulles, VA 20166
Shipping Address: Books International Inc, 22883 Quicksolver Dr, Dulles, VA 20166
Warehouse: Books International Inc, PO Box 959, Herndon, VA 20172-0960
Distribution Center: Books International Inc, PO Box 959, Herndon, VA 20172-0960
Membership(s): AAP

§World Book Inc
Subsidiary of The Scott Fetzer Co
233 N Michigan, Suite 2000, Chicago, IL 60601
SAN: 201-4815
Tel: 312-729-5800 *Toll Free Tel:* 800-967-5325 (consumer sales, US); 800-463-8845 (consumer sales, CN); 800-975-3250 (school & lib sales, US); 800-837-5365 (school & lib sales, CN); 866-866-5200 (web sales) *Fax:* 312-729-5600; 312-729-5606 *Toll Free Fax:* 800-433-9330 (school & lib sales, US); 888-690-4002 (school lib sales, CN)
Web Site: www.worldbook.com
Key Personnel
Pres: Donald D Keller
VP, Edit & Ed-in-Chief: Paul A Kobasa
VP, Licensing Busn Devt: Richard Flower
Founded: 1917
Publisher of high-quality, award-winning, educational reference & nonfiction publications for the school & library market & home market, in print, CD-ROM & online formats.
ISBN Prefix(es): 978-0-7166
Number of titles published annually: 40 Print; 6 CD-ROM
Total Titles: 320 Print; 91 CD-ROM; 10 Online

World Citizens
Affiliate of Cinema Investments Co Inc
PO Box 131, Mill Valley, CA 94942-0131
Tel: 415-380-8020 *Toll Free Tel:* 800-247-6553 (orders only)
Key Personnel
Ed-in-Chief: Joan Ellen
Ed: John Ballard
Assoc Ed: Jack Henry
Sales Mgr & Intl Rts: Steve Ames
Founded: 1984
Cross cultural & multi-cultural novels & texts. Adult, educational, trade & young adult divisions.
ISBN Prefix(es): 978-0-932279
Number of titles published annually: 6 Print; 4 CD-ROM; 6 E-Book; 4 Audio
Total Titles: 18 Print
Imprints: Classroom Classics; New Horizons Book Publishing Co; Skateman Publications
Distributed by Inland
Distribution Center: Bookmasters, PO Box 388, Ashland, OH 44805-0388 *Fax:* 419-201-6883

§World Resources Institute
10 "G" St NE, Suite 800, Washington, DC 20002
Tel: 202-729-7600 *Fax:* 202-729-7610
Web Site: www.wri.org
Key Personnel
Dir, Pubns: Hyacinth Billings *Tel:* 202-729-7712
Founded: 1982
Professional, scholarly & general interest publications, including energy, the environment, agriculture, forestry, natural resources, economics, geography, climate, biotechnology & development. Some titles co-published with university presses & commercial publishers.
ISBN Prefix(es): 978-0-915825; 978-1-56973
Number of titles published annually: 10 Print
Total Titles: 420 Print; 2 CD-ROM

§World Scientific Publishing Co Inc
27 Warren St, Suite 401-402, Hackensack, NJ 07601
Tel: 201-487-9655 *Toll Free Tel:* 800-227-7562 *Fax:* 201-487-9656 *Toll Free Fax:* 888-977-2665
E-mail: wspc@wspc.com
Web Site: www.wspc.com
Key Personnel
Publr: K K Phuna
Contact: Calandra Braswell *Tel:* 201-487-9655 ext 309
Founded: 1981
Number of titles published annually: 400 Print
Total Titles: 5,000 Print
Subsidiaries: Imperial College Press
Warehouse: 46 Development Rd, Fitchburg, MA 01420

§World Trade Press
800 Lindberg Lane, Suite 190, Petaluma, CA 94952
Tel: 707-778-1124 *Toll Free Tel:* 800-833-8586 *Fax:* 707-778-1329
Web Site: www.worldtradepress.com
Key Personnel
CEO & Publr: Edward G Hinkelman *Tel:* 707-778-1124 ext 204 *E-mail:* egh@worldtradepress.com
Founded: 1990
Professional books for international trade & business travel.
ISBN Prefix(es): 978-0-9631864; 978-1-885073
Number of titles published annually: 8 Print; 240 Online; 26 E-Book
Total Titles: 118 Print; 2,260 Online; 88 E-Book
Distributed by Reference Press

World Vision Resources
Subsidiary of World Vision International
800 W Chestnut Ave, Monrovia, CA 91016-3198
Tel: 626-303-8811; 909-463-2998 (intl orders) *Toll Free Tel:* 800-777-7752 (US only) *Fax:* 909-463-2999
E-mail: wvresources@worldvision.org
Web Site: www.worldvisionresources.com
Key Personnel
Exec Ed: Jojo Palmer *Tel:* 626-303-8811 ext 7720
Founded: 1968
Books & other products promoting strategies for the mission activities of the Christian churches.
ISBN Prefix(es): 978-0-912552; 978-1-887983
Number of titles published annually: 20 Print

WorldTariff
Division of FedEx Corp
220 Montgomery St, Suite 448, San Francisco, CA 94104-3410
Tel: 415-391-7501; 415-591-6666 *Toll Free Tel:* 800-556-9334 *Fax:* 415-391-7537 (Fax/Modem)
Web Site: www.worldtariff.com; ftn.fedex.com/wtonline
Key Personnel
Acct Exec & Contact: Ray Brown
Founded: 1961
Publish customs duty & tax information.
ISBN Prefix(es): 978-1-56745
Number of titles published annually: 100 Print
Total Titles: 22 Online
Foreign Office(s): Eurotariff, National House, 60-66 Wardour St, 6th fl, London W1V 3HP, United Kingdom

§Worth Publishers
Imprint of Macmillan Higher Education
41 Madison Ave, 37th fl, New York, NY 10010
Tel: 212-576-9400 *Fax:* 212-561-8281
Web Site: www.worthpub.com
Key Personnel
Pres: Elizabeth Widdicombe
Founded: 1966
Social science texts for the higher education market & advanced high school courses.
ISBN Prefix(es): 978-1-57259; 978-1-4292; 978-0-7167
Number of titles published annually: 10 E-Book
Total Titles: 300 Print
Foreign Rep(s): Macmillan East Asia (China, Hong Kong, Indonesia, Korea, Philippines, Singapore, Thailand, Vietnam); Macmillan Publishers (Taiwan); Palgrave Macmillan (Australia, New Zealand); Palgrave Macmillan UK (Africa, Caribbean, Europe, India, Japan, Latin America, Middle East, Pakistan, UK); USBD Distribution SDN BHD (Malaysia)
Warehouse: MPS Distribution Center, 16365 James Madison Hwy (US Rte 15), Gordonsville, VA 22942 *Toll Free Tel:* 888-330-8477 *Fax:* 540-672-7540 (cust serv) *Toll Free Fax:* 800-672-2054 (orders)

§Wright Group/McGraw-Hill
Division of McGraw-Hill School Education Group
8787 Orion Place, Columbus, OH 43240
Tel: 614-430-4000 *Toll Free Tel:* 800-537-4740
Founded: 1975
Publish a wide array of instructional materials for PreK-adult education. Specialize in reading, language arts, mathematics, ELL & intervention programs for small group & whole group instruction. Offerings include substantial teacher materials, including detailed lesson plans, teacher guides & professional resources & staff development opportunities.
ISBN Prefix(es): 978-0-02; 978-0-940156; 978-0-07; 978-0-7802; 978-0-7327; 978-1-57039; 978-0-658; 978-0-322; 978-0-7622; 978-0-7699; 978-1-4045; 978-1-58210; 978-1-55624; 978-1-55911; 978-1-57257; 978-0-8092; 978-0-8442; 978-0-88488; 978-1-56107; 978-1-57699; 978-1-876842
Number of titles published annually: 2,000 Print; 100 CD-ROM; 100 Online; 200 Audio
Total Titles: 18,000 Print; 500 CD-ROM; 500 Online; 10,000 Audio
Imprints: Breakthrough to Literacy; Contemporary; Creative Publications; DLM; Everyday Mathematics
Membership(s): AAP; AAP PreK-12 Learning Group; American Educational Publishers

Write Bloody Publishing
2306 E Cesar Chavez, Suite 103, Austin, TX 78706
E-mail: writebloody@gmail.com
Web Site: writebloody.com
Key Personnel
Pres: Derrick Brown
Founded: 2004
Poetry publisher.
ISBN Prefix(es): 978-0-9789989; 978-0-9815213; 978-0-9821488; 978-0-9842515; 978-0-9845031; 978-1-935904
Number of titles published annually: 14 Print; 6 E-Book; 6 Audio
Total Titles: 90 Print; 40 E-Book; 6 Audio
Imprints: Write Fuzzy
Sales Office(s): SCB Distributing, 15608 S New Century Dr, Gardena, CA 90248, Contact: Gabriel Wilmoth *Toll Free Tel:* 800-729-6423 *E-mail:* gabriel@scbdistributors.com
Foreign Rep(s): Gabriel Wilmoth (Canada, Germany, USA)
Advertising Agency: Public Eye, Dir: Kevin Finley
Orders to: SCB Distributing, 15608 S New Century Dr, Gardena, CA 90248, Contact:

Gabriel Wilmoth *Toll Free Tel:* 800-729-6423 *E-mail:* gabriel@scbdistributors.com
Shipping Address: SCB Distributing, 15608 S New Century Dr, Gardena, CA 90248, Contact: Gabriel Wilmoth *Toll Free Tel:* 800-729-6423 *E-mail:* gabriel@scbdistributors.com
Distribution Center: SCB Distributing, 15608 S New Century Dr, Gardena, CA 90248, Contact: Gabriel Wilmoth *Toll Free Tel:* 800-729-6423 *E-mail:* gabriel@scbdistributors.com

Write Stuff Enterprises LLC
1001 S Andrews Ave, Suite 120, Fort Lauderdale, FL 33316
Tel: 954-462-6657 *Toll Free Tel:* 800-900-2665 *Fax:* 954-462-6023
E-mail: legends@writestuffbooks.com
Web Site: www.writestuffbooks.com
Key Personnel
CEO & Pres: Jeffrey L Rodengen
Leading publisher of historical works focusing on industry & technology.
ISBN Prefix(es): 978-0-945903
Number of titles published annually: 4 Print; 4 E-Book
Imprints: Write Stuff®
Membership(s): ABA; The Independent Book Publishers Association

WriteLife LLC
2323 S 171 St, Suite 202, Omaha, NE 68130
Tel: 402-934-1412 *Toll Free Tel:* 877-974-8354
E-mail: info@writelife.com
Web Site: www.writelife.com; www.facebook.com/WriteLife; twitter.com/WriteLifeLLC
Key Personnel
Publr: Cindy Grady
Sr Ed & In-House Agent: Erin Reel
Mktg Dir: Kristl Finnes
Founded: 2008
ISBN Prefix(es): 978-1-60808
Number of titles published annually: 12 Print; 12 E-Book
Total Titles: 81 Print; 11 E-Book
Membership(s): The Independent Book Publishers Association; Midwest Independent Booksellers Association; Mountains & Plains Independent Booksellers Association

Writer's AudioShop
1316 Overland Stage Rd, Dripping Springs, TX 78620
Tel: 512-264-7067 *Fax:* 512-264-7067
E-mail: wrtaudshop@aol.com
Web Site: www.writersaudio.com
Key Personnel
Publr: Elaine Davenport
Founded: 1985
Audio publisher.
ISBN Prefix(es): 978-1-880717
Number of titles published annually: 4 Audio
Total Titles: 35 Audio
Membership(s): Audio Publishers Association

Writer's Digest Books
Imprint of F+W, A Content + eCommerce Company
10151 Carver Rd, Suite 200, Blue Ash, OH 45242
Tel: 513-531-2690 *Toll Free Tel:* 800-289-0963
E-mail: writersdigest@fwmedia.com (edit)
Web Site: www.writersdigest.com
Key Personnel
CEO: David Nuwsbaum
Pres: Sara Domville
Publr & Edit Dir: Phil Sexton *E-mail:* phillip.sexton@fwcommunity.com
Prodn Dir: Phil Graham
Rts & Perms: Stephanie McKenna *E-mail:* stephanie.mckenna@fwcommunity.com
Top-quality instructional & reference books to help creative people find personal satisfaction & professional success. Topics covered include writing, publishing, songwriting & personal growth.
ISBN Prefix(es): 978-0-89879; 978-1-58297
Number of titles published annually: 28 Print
Total Titles: 150 Print
Foreign Rep(s): David Bateman Ltd (New Zealand); BookMovers Group (Canada); Capricorn Link (Australia); David & Charles Ltd (UK); Real Books (South Africa); Marta Schooler (Asia, Central America, Mexico, Middle East, South America)
Returns: Aero Fulfillment Services, 2800 Henkle Dr, Lebanon, OH 45036

Writers of the Round Table Press
990 Bob-O-Link Rd, Highland Park, IL 60035
Mailing Address: PO Box 511, Highland Park, IL 60035
Tel: 949-375-1006 *Fax:* 815-346-2398
Web Site: www.roundtablecompanies.com
Key Personnel
Pres: Corey Michael Blake *Tel:* 847-682-3493 *E-mail:* corey@roundtablecompanies.com
Organizational Off Architect: Mike Winicour *E-mail:* mike@roundtablecompanies.com
Founded: 1996
Produce stories that inform, educate, entertain & inspire with a personalized approach to every project. Bestselling authors as well as first time authors & entrepreneurs, our clients are thought leaders & heart-centered businesses eager to engage in a collaborative creative process to amplify their message & emotionally connect with their audiences. A percentage of business is in repurposing nonfiction content in the illustrated form of graphic novels that we capture & then repurpose across creative mediums.
ISBN Prefix(es): 978-0-61066; 978-0-9814545; 978-0-9822206
Imprints: Round Table Comics
Editorial Office(s): PO Box 511, Highland Park, IL 60035
Sales Office(s): PO Box 511, Highland Park, IL 60035
Foreign Rights: Graal Literary Agency (Albania, Bulgaria, Croatia, Czech Republic, Estonia, Hungary, Latvia, Lithuania, Poland, Romania, Serbia, Slovakia, Slovenia); Grayhawk Agency (China, Indonesia, Taiwan, Thailand, Vietnam); Dany Hong Agency (Korea); International Editors' Co (Argentina, Brazil, Portugal, Spain); Tuttle-Mori Agency Inc (Japan)
Advertising Agency: Alison & Partners, 8880 Rio San Diego Dr, Suite 1090, San Diego, CA 92108, Contact: Amy Toosley *Tel:* 619-533-7976 *Fax:* 619-543-0030 *E-mail:* amy@allisonpr.com
Returns: 15200 NBN Way, Blue Ridge Summit, PA 17214, Contact: Vicki Funk *Tel:* 717-794-3800 ext 3538 *E-mail:* vfunk@nbnbooks.com
Shipping Address: 15200 NBN Way, Blue Ridge Summit, PA 17214, Contact: Karen Mattscheck *Tel:* 717-794-3800 ext 3513 *E-mail:* kmattscheck@nbnbooks.com
Distribution Center: 15200 NBN Way, Blue Ridge Summit, PA 17214, Contact: Karen Mattscheck *Tel:* 717-794-3800 ext 3513 *E-mail:* kmattscheck@nbnbooks.com
Membership(s): The Independent Book Publishers Association

Wyndham Hall Press
5050 Kerr Rd, Lima, OH 45806
SAN: 686-6743
Tel: 419-648-9124 *Toll Free Tel:* 866-895-0977 *Fax:* 419-648-9124; 413-208-2409
E-mail: whpbooks@wyndhamhallbooks.com; orders@wyndhamhallbooks.com
Web Site: www.wyndhamhallpress.com
Key Personnel
Mng Ed: Mark S McCullough *E-mail:* mark@wyndhamhallpress.com
Founded: 1981
Scholarly monographs & textbooks.
ISBN Prefix(es): 978-1-55605; 978-0-932269
Number of titles published annually: 8 Print
Total Titles: 242 Print

XanEdu Publishing Inc, see Copley Custom Textbooks

§Xist Publishing
PO Box 61593, Irvine, CA 92602
Tel: 949-478-2568
E-mail: info@xistpublishing.com
Web Site: www.xistpublishing.com
Key Personnel
COO: Jacob Lee
Pres: Calee Lee
Founded: 2010
Digital-first publisher. Specialize in children's ebooks for every major device.
ISBN Prefix(es): 978-1-62395
Number of titles published annually: 30 Print; 50 E-Book; 30 Audio
Total Titles: 220 Print; 250 E-Book; 60 Audio
Foreign Rep(s): Sylvia Hayse (Worldwide)
Membership(s): Society of Children's Book Writers & Illustrators

Xlibris Corp
Division of Author Solutions Inc
1663 Liberty Dr, Suite 200, Bloomington, IN 47403
Toll Free Tel: 888-795-4274 *Fax:* 610-915-0294
E-mail: info@xlibris.com
Web Site: www.xlibris.com
Key Personnel
CEO: Andrew Phillips
CFO: Kevin G Gregory
CIO: James Stanley
SVP, Prodn Servs: Bill Becher
SVP, Sales: Mr Terry Dwyer
VP, HR: Christopher Schrader
VP, Mktg: Keith Ogorek
VP, Prodn & Edit Servs: Ms Robin Lasek
Founded: 1997
One of the leading publishing services providers for authors, Xlibris provides authors with a broad set of publishing options including hardcover, trade paperback, custom leather bound & full-color formats. In addition, Xlibris offers its authors the widest selection of professional, marketing & bookselling services. Since its founding, Xlibris has published more than 25,000 titles.
This publisher has indicated that 100% of its product line is author subsidized.
ISBN Prefix(es): 978-0-7388; 978-0-9663501; 978-1-4010; 978-1-4134; 978-1-59926; 978-1-4257; 978-1-4363; 978-1-4415
Number of titles published annually: 5,100 Print
Total Titles: 25,000 Print
Distribution Center: Baker & Taylor Inc
Ingram Book Group
Membership(s): ABA; Canadian Booksellers Association

§XML Press
Subsidiary of R L Hamilton & Associates LLC
24310 Moulton Pkwy, Suite O-175, Laguna Hills, CA 92637
Tel: 970-231-3624
E-mail: publisher@xmlpress.net
Web Site: xmlpress.net
Key Personnel
Publr: Richard Hamilton *E-mail:* hamilton@xmlpress.net
CFO: Mei-li Lu *E-mail:* meili@xmlpress.net
Founded: 2008
Specialize in publications for technical communicators, content strategists, managers & marketers, with an emphasis on XML technology, social media & management. Also provides publication services to corporations that want

to make their technical documentation available in print form through retail channels.
ISBN Prefix(es): 978-0-9822191; 978-1-937434
Number of titles published annually: 12 Print; 5 E-Book
Total Titles: 20 Print
Distribution Center: Ingram, One Ingram Blvd, La Vergne, TN 37086
Membership(s): Organization of Advancement of Structured Information Standards; Society for Technical Communication

Yale Center for British Art
1080 Chapel St, New Haven, CT 06510-2302
Mailing Address: PO Box 208280, New Haven, CT 06520-8280
Tel: 203-432-2800 *Toll Free Tel:* 877-274-8278 *Fax:* 203-432-9628
E-mail: ycba.info@yale.edu
Web Site: www.yale.edu/ycba; britishart.yale.edu
Key Personnel
Dir: Amy Meyers
Founded: 1977
Exhibition catalogues.
ISBN Prefix(es): 978-0-930606
Number of titles published annually: 4 Print
Total Titles: 61 Print
Foreign Office(s): Premier Book Marketing, One Gower St, London WC1E 6HA, United Kingdom
Foreign Rep(s): Premier Book Marketing (UK)

§Yale University Press
Division of Yale University
302 Temple St, New Haven, CT 06511-8909
SAN: 203-2740
Mailing Address: PO Box 209040, New Haven, CT 06520-9040
Tel: 203-432-0960; 203-432-0966 (sales); 401-531-2800 (cust serv) *Toll Free Tel:* 800-405-1619 (cust serv) *Fax:* 203-432-0948; 203-432-8485 (sales); 401-531-2801 (cust serv) *Toll Free Fax:* 800-406-9145 (cust serv)
E-mail: sales.press@yale.edu (sales); customer.care@trilateral.org (cust serv)
Web Site: www.yalebooks.com; yalepress.yale.edu/yupbooks
Key Personnel
COO: Kate Brown
Deputy Dir, Fin & Opers: John D Rollins
Publr: John Donatich
Art Dir: Nancy Ovedovitz
Edit Dir: Christopher Rogers
Dir, Mktg & Promo: Heather D'Auria
Dir, Publg Opers: Christina Coffin
Promo Dir: Sarah Clark
Publicity Dir: Brenda King
Sales Dir: Jay Cosgrove
Sr Sales Mgr, Art & Digital Publg: Stephen Cebik
Asst Promo Dir: Debra Bozzi
Publr, Art & Architecture: Patricia Fidler
Online Mktg Mgr: Michael Hoak
Sr Publicist: Jennifer Doerr
Publicist: Alden Ferro
Publicist, Art & Architecture: Joshua Machat
Exec Ed: William Frucht
Exec Ed, Sci & Medicine: Jean E Thomson Black
Exec Ed-at-Large: Steve Wasserman
Sr Ed: Jennifer Banks
Ed, Art & Architecture: Katherine Boller
Ed, Coursebooks: Sarah Miller
Ed, Sci & Technol: Joseph Calamia
Consulting Ed: John Loudon
Assoc Ed, History: Laura Davulis
Asst Ed, Politics & Intl Rel: Jaya Aninda Chatterjee
Asst Ed, History: Erica Hanson
Founded: 1908
Scholarly publications.
ISBN Prefix(es): 978-0-300
Number of titles published annually: 350 Print
Total Titles: 5,000 Print
Foreign Office(s): 47 Bedford Sq, London WC1B 3DP, United Kingdom, Head of Rts: Anne Bihan *Tel:* (020) 7079-4900 *Fax:* (020) 7079-4901 *E-mail:* sales@yaleup.co.uk *Web Site:* www.yalebooks.co.uk
Distributor for Addison Gallery of American Art, Phillips Academy; The Art Institute of Chicago; The Bard Graduate Center; Dallas Museum of Art; Harvard University Art Museums; Japan Society; The Jewish Museum; Kimbell Art Museum; Paul Mellon Centre; The Menil Collection; The Metropolitan Museum of Art; National Gallery, London; National Gallery of Art (Washington, DC); Philadelphia Museum of Art; Princeton University Art Museum; Sterling & Francine Clark Art Institute; Whitney Museum of American Art; Yale Center for British Art; Yale University Art Gallery
Foreign Rep(s): Rockbook (Japan, South Korea, Taiwan); David Stimpson (Australia, Canada, New Zealand)
Foreign Rights: Ann Bihan (England); Craig Falk (Latin America, Mexico, South America)
Shipping Address: TriLiteral, 100 Maple Ridge Dr, Cumberland, RI 02864-1769 *Tel:* 401-658-4226
Membership(s): AAP; Association of American University Presses

Yard Dog Press
710 W Redbud Lane, Alma, AR 72921-7247
Tel: 479-632-4693 *Fax:* 479-632-4693
Web Site: www.yarddogpress.com
Key Personnel
Ed-in-Chief: Selina Rosen *E-mail:* selinarosen@cox.net
Tech Ed & Orders Contact: Lynn Stranathan *E-mail:* lynnstran@cox.net
Founded: 1995
Micro press specializing in science fiction, fantasy & horror.
ISBN Prefix(es): 978-1-893687; 978-0-9824704; 978-1-937105
Number of titles published annually: 5 Print
Total Titles: 120 Print
Imprints: Double Dog (flip books - two short novels); Just Cause (non-genre books)
Membership(s): Science Fiction & Fantasy Writers of America

YBK Publishers Inc
39 Crosby St, New York, NY 10013
Tel: 212-219-0135 *Fax:* 212-219-0136
E-mail: info@ybkpublishers.com
Key Personnel
Pres: Otto Barz *E-mail:* obarz@ybkpublishers.com
Founded: 2001
Print-on-demand; general trade & nonfiction.
ISBN Prefix(es): 978-0-9703923; 978-0-9764359; 978-1-936411
Number of titles published annually: 7 Print
Total Titles: 55 Print
Distribution Center: Lightning Source, 1246 Heil Quaker Blvd, La Vergne, TN 37086 *Tel:* 615-213-5815 *Fax:* 615-213-4426 *E-mail:* inquiry@ybkpublishers.com
Membership(s): The Independent Book Publishers Association

Yeshiva University Press
500 W 185 St, New York, NY 10033-3201
Mailing Address: KTAV Publishing House Inc, 2540 Amerstam Ave, New York, NY 10033
Tel: 212-960-5400 *Fax:* 212-960-0043
Web Site: www.yu.edu
Key Personnel
Pres: Richard Joel *Tel:* 212-960-5300 *E-mail:* president@yu.edu
ISBN Prefix(es): 978-0-87068; 978-0-88125; 978-1-60280
Total Titles: 71 Print
Distributed by KTAV Publishing House Inc

YMAA Publication Center
PO Box 480, Wolfeboro, NH 03894
SAN: 665-2077
Tel: 603-569-7988 *Toll Free Tel:* 800-669-8892 *Fax:* 603-569-1889
E-mail: ymaa@aol.com
Web Site: www.ymaa.com
Key Personnel
Publr: David Ripianzi *E-mail:* davidr@ymaa.com
Prodn Mgr: Tim Comrie *E-mail:* tcomrie@ymaa.com
Sales Rep: David Silver *E-mail:* dsilver@ymaa.com
Founded: 1984
Publisher of in-depth books, videos & DVDs on martial arts, meditation, traditional Chinese medicine & alternative health therapies.
ISBN Prefix(es): 978-0-940871; 978-1-886969; 978-1-59439
Number of titles published annually: 10 Print; 10 E-Book
Total Titles: 80 Print; 50 E-Book; 4 Audio
Distributor for Wind Records (Chinese healing music)
Foreign Rep(s): Agencia Literarie SL (Montse F Yanez) (Mexico, Spain); Big Apple Agency (Maggie Han) (China); Big Apple Agency (China, Taiwan); The Book Publishers Association of Israel (Shoshi Grajower) (Israel); Daniel Doglioli (Italy); Graal Literary Agency (Madga Cabajewska) (Poland); Imprima Korea Agency (Joseph Lee) (Korea); International Copyright Agency (Simona Kessler) (Romania); Christiane Janssen (Germany); Japan Uni Agency (Taeko Nagatsuka) (Japan); JS Literary & Media Agency (Somjai Raksasee) (Thailand); Nurcihan Kesim Literary Agency Inc (Filiz Karaman) (Turkey); Maxima Creative Agency (Santo Manurung) (Indonesia); Nova Littera SL (Konstantin Paltchikov) (Russia); Andrew Nurnberg Associates (Tatjana Zoldnere) (Latvia, Lithuania, Ukraine); Andrew Nurnberg Associates (Petra Tobiskova) (Czech Republic); Andrew Nurberg Associates (Anna Droumeva) (Bulgaria); OA Literary Agency (Michael Avramides) (Greece); Plima Literary Agency (Mila Perisic) (Croatia, Serbia, Slovenia); Karin Schindler Rights Rep (Suely Pedro Dos Santos) (Brazil); Karin Schindler Rights Rep (Karin Schindler) (Brazil); Ralph & Sheila Summers (Hong Kong, Korea, Malaysia, Philippines, Singapore, Taiwan, Thailand); Tuttle Mori Agency Inc (Fumi Nishijima) (Japan)
Foreign Rights: Agencia Literaria (Brazil, Portugal); Big Apple Agency Inc (China, Taiwan); Bookman (Denmark, Finland, Iceland, Norway, Sweden); Imprima Korea Agency (Korea); Jarir Bookstore (Egypt, Middle East, Saudi Arabia); JS Literary & Media Agency (Thailand); Maxima Creative (Indonesia); La Nouvelle Agency (Belgium, Switzerland); Nova Littera Ltd (Russia); Andrew Nurnberg Associates (Baltic States); Andrew Nurnberg Associates Sofia (Bulgaria); OA Literary Agency (Greece); Permissions & Rights (Albania, Croatia, Montenegro, Serbia, Slovenia); Tuttle-Mori Agency Inc (Japan); Julio F Yanez Agencia Leteraria (Mexico, Spain, Spanish languages, Spanish Latin America)
Orders to: Baker & Taylor, 2550 W Tyvola Rd, Charlotte, NC *Toll Free Tel:* 800-775-1800 *Fax:* 704-998-3100 *Web Site:* www.btol.com; Ingram Book Co, One Ingram Blvd, La Vergne, TN *Tel:* (615) 793-5000 *Toll Free Tel:* 800-937-8200 *Web Site:* www.ingrambook.com; National Book Network, 15200 NBN Way, Blue Ridge Summit, PA 17214 *Tel:* 717-794-3800 *Toll Free Tel:* 800-462-6420 *Toll Free Fax:* 800-338-4550 *E-mail:* custserv@nbnbooks.com *Web Site:* www.nbnbooks.com;

New Leaf Distributing Co, 401 Thornton Rd, Lithia Springs, GA 30122-1557 *Tel:* 770-948-7845 *Toll Free Tel:* 800-944-2313 *Fax:* 770-994-2313 *E-mail:* newleaf@newleaf-dist.com *Web Site:* www.newleaf-dist.com
Distribution Center: National Book Network, 15200 NBN Way, Blue Ridge Summit, PA 07214 *Tel:* 717-794-3800 *Toll Free Tel:* 800-338-4550 *Toll Free Fax:* 800-338-4550 *E-mail:* custserv@nbnbooks.com *Web Site:* www.nbnbooks.com
Membership(s): ABA; The Independent Book Publishers Association

§Yotzeret Publishing
PO Box 18662, St Paul, MN 55118-0662
Tel: 651-470-3853 *Fax:* 651-224-7447
E-mail: info@yotzeretpublishing.com; orders@yotzeretpublishing.com
Web Site: yotzeretpublishing.com
Key Personnel
Publr: Sheyna Galyan
Founded: 2002
Adult & children's books & ebooks from a Jewish perspective.
ISBN Prefix(es): 978-1-59287
Number of titles published annually: 2 Print; 2 E-Book; 1 Audio
Total Titles: 10 Print; 7 E-Book
Orders to: Partners Publishers Group (PPG), 2325 Jarco Dr, Holt, MI 48842 (distributes to Ingram, Baker & Taylor & others) *Tel:* 517-694-3205 *Fax:* 517-694-0617 *E-mail:* info@partnerspublishersgroup.com *Web Site:* www.partnerspublishersgroup.com
Distribution Center: Partners Publishers Group (PPG), 2325 Jarco Dr, Holt, MI 48842 *Tel:* 517-694-3205 *Fax:* 517-694-0617 *E-mail:* info@partnerspublishersgroup.com *Web Site:* www.partnerspublishersgroup.com
Membership(s): The Independent Book Publishers Association; Midwest Independent Publishers Association; Minnesota Book Publishers Roundtable

Young People's Press Inc (YPPI)
Affiliate of Kens Math
1527 Reed Ave, San Diego, CA 92109
Tel: 619-992-3258 (orders) *Toll Free Tel:* 800-231-9774
E-mail: admin@youngpeoplespress.com
Web Site: www.youngpeoplespress.com
Key Personnel
Pres: Robert J Saielli *E-mail:* rjs@youngpeoplespress.com
EVP: Patricia Pflum *E-mail:* ppflum@youngpeoplespress.com
Acctg Mgr: Janice Sawyer *E-mail:* janice@youngpeoplespress.com
Head Designer: Lorie Kennedy *Tel:* 619-405-6266 *E-mail:* lorie@kencomgraphics.com
Info Systems: Zach Saielli *Tel:* 619-723-0070 *E-mail:* zsaielli@aol.com
Founded: 1994
Elementary curriculum in math, pre-school, home schooling, social skills & character building, language arts, literature & social sciences.
ISBN Prefix(es): 978-1-885658; 978-1-57279
Number of titles published annually: 10 Print; 5 E-Book
Total Titles: 245 Print; 15 E-Book; 16 Audio
Imprints: Kens Math
Returns: 411 Main St, Mosinee, WI 54455, Contact: Tim Kennedy *Tel:* 715-693-4682 *Fax:* 715-693-4682 *E-mail:* forms@mtc.net
Warehouse: 411 Main St, Mosinee, WI 54455, Contact: Tim Kennedy

Your Culture Gifts
12801 Old Columbia Pike, Apt 218, Silver Spring, MD 20904
SAN: 854-3208
Tel: 410-900-0184 *Fax:* 410-461-2415
E-mail: info@yourculturegifts.com
Web Site: www.yourculturegifts.com
Key Personnel
Pres: Frank Sauri
Mgr: Trudy Sauri
Founded: 2002
Publishes cultural stories presented in a combination of historical fiction & nonfiction genres for the purpose of introducing children to the richness of world cultures, social geography, world history, language, food & tradition.
ISBN Prefix(es): 978-0-9797637
Number of titles published annually: 5 Print
Total Titles: 4 Print
Membership(s): The Independent Book Publishers Association

YPPI, see Young People's Press Inc (YPPI)

YWAM Publishing
Division of Youth with a Mission
PO Box 55787, Seattle, WA 98155-0787
Tel: 425-771-1153 *Toll Free Tel:* 800-922-2143 *Fax:* 425-775-2383
E-mail: books@ywampublishing.com
Web Site: www.ywampublishing.com
Key Personnel
Mktg Dir: Wenche Warren *E-mail:* marketing@ywampublishing.com
Founded: 1960
Books on missions, evangelism & discipleship & also religious classics.
ISBN Prefix(es): 978-0-927545
Number of titles published annually: 10 Print; 2 CD-ROM
Total Titles: 260 Print; 15 CD-ROM; 10 Audio
Distributor for Emerald Books
Shipping Address: 7825 230 St SW, Edmonds, WA 98026
Warehouse: 7825 230 St SW, Edmonds, WA 98026

§Zagat Survey LLC
76 Ninth Ave, 4th fl, New York, NY 10011
SAN: 289-4777
Tel: 212-977-6000 *Toll Free Tel:* 866-817-9947 (orders); 800-540-9609 *Fax:* 212-977-9760; 802-864-9846 (order related)
E-mail: corpsales@zagat.com; shop@zagat.com
Web Site: www.zagat.com
Key Personnel
Founder & Chair: Nina S Zagat *E-mail:* nina@zagat.com; Tim Zagat
Founded: 1979
Provider of consumer survey-based information on where to eat, drink, stay & play worldwide.
ISBN Prefix(es): 978-1-57006
Number of titles published annually: 40 Print
Total Titles: 40 Print
Foreign Rep(s): Prentice-Hall (Canada)

Zaner-Bloser Inc
Subsidiary of Highlights for Children Inc
1201 Dublin Rd, Columbus, OH 43215-1026
Tel: 614-486-0221 *Toll Free Tel:* 800-421-3018 (cust serv) *Toll Free Fax:* 800-992-6087 (orders)
E-mail: zbcsd@zaner-bloser.com; international@zaner-bloser.com
Web Site: www.zaner-bloser.com
Key Personnel
Pres: Robert Page
Founded: 1888
Elementary textbooks for critical thinking, whole language, substance abuse prevention, spelling & handwriting; modality (learning styles) kit, professional education books, storytelling kits & early childhood education.
ISBN Prefix(es): 978-0-88309; 978-0-88085
Number of titles published annually: 200 Print
Foreign Rep(s): Childrens Press
Advertising Agency: EDPUB
Orders to: PO Box 16764, Columbus, OH 43216-6764
Warehouse: 4200 Parkway Ct, Hilliard, OH 43026

Zarahemla Books
869 E 2680 N, Provo, UT 84604
Tel: 801-368-7374 *Fax:* 801-418-2081
E-mail: info@zarahemlabooks.com
Web Site: zarahemlabooks.com
Key Personnel
Publr: Christopher Bigelow *E-mail:* chris@zarahemlabooks.com
Founded: 2006
Alternative Mormon-themed fiction & memoir.
ISBN Prefix(es): 978-0-9787971; 978-0-9843603
Number of titles published annually: 3 Print
Total Titles: 18 Print

Zebra Books, see Kensington Publishing Corp

Zeig, Tucker & Theisen Inc
3614 N 24 St, Phoenix, AZ 85016
Tel: 480-389-4342 *Toll Free Tel:* 800-666-2211 (orders) *Fax:* 602-944-8118
E-mail: marketing@zeigtucker.com
Web Site: www.zeigtucker.com
Key Personnel
Pres: Jeffrey K Zeig *Tel:* 602-944-6529 *Fax:* 602-944-8118 *E-mail:* jeff@zeigtucker.com
Busn Mgr: Stacey Moore *E-mail:* stacey@zeigtucker.com
Mng Ed: Chuck Lakin *E-mail:* chuck@zeigtucker.com
Founded: 1998
ISBN Prefix(es): 978-1-891944; 978-1-932462
Number of titles published annually: 10 Print
Total Titles: 45 Print; 8 Audio
Editorial Office(s): 3606 N 24 St, Phoenix, AZ 86015 *Tel:* 480-389-4342 *Fax:* 602-944-8118
Billing Address: Cornell University Press Services, PO Box 6525, Ithaca, NY 14851-6525
Orders to: Cornell University Press Services, PO Box 6525, Ithaca, NY 14851-6525 *Tel:* 607-277-2211 *Toll Free Tel:* 800-666-2211 *E-mail:* orderbook@cupserv.org
Returns: Cornell University Press Services, PO Box 6525, Ithaca, NY 14851-6525 *Tel:* 607-277-2211 *Toll Free Tel:* 800-666-2211 *E-mail:* orderbook@cupserv.org
Shipping Address: Cornell University Press Services, PO Box 6525, Ithaca, NY 14851-6525
Warehouse: Cornell University Press Services, PO Box 6525, Ithaca, NY 14851-6525 *Toll Free Tel:* 800-666-2211
Distribution Center: Cornell University Press Services, PO Box 6525, Ithaca, NY 14851-6525

Zephyr Press, see Chicago Review Press

Zest Books
35 Stillman St, Suite 121, San Francisco, CA 94107
Tel: 415-777-8654 *Fax:* 415-777-8653
E-mail: info@zestbooks.net; publicity@zestbooks.net
Web Site: zestbooks.net
Key Personnel
Publr: Hallie Warshaw *E-mail:* hallie@zestbooks.net
Edit Dir: Daniel Harmon
Mktg & Publicity Mgr: Jo Beaton
ISBN Prefix(es): 978-0-9772660
Number of titles published annually: 14 Print; 14 E-Book
Total Titles: 60 Print
Distributed by Houghton Mifflin Harcourt
Distribution Center: Houghton Mifflin Harcourt, Trade & Ref Cust Serv, 9205 Southpark Center Loop, 3rd fl, Orlando, FL 32819 *Toll Free Tel:* 800-225-3362 *Toll Free Fax:* 800-634-7568 *E-mail:* customercare@hmhco.com

§Zondervan
Imprint of HarperCollins Christian Publishing
3900 Sparks Dr, Grand Rapids, MI 49546
SAN: 203-2694
Tel: 616-698-6900 *Toll Free Tel:* 800-226-1122; 800-727-1309 (retail orders) *Fax:* 616-698-3350 *Toll Free Fax:* 800-698-3256 (retail orders)
E-mail: zinfo@zondervan.com
Web Site: www.zondervan.com
Key Personnel
CFO & EVP: Gary Wicker *Tel:* 616-698-3269
EVP & Ed-in-Chief: Stan Gundry
EVP, Sales: Verne Kenney *Tel:* 616-698-3548
Pres, Youth Specialties: Mark Oestreicher *Tel:* 619-440-2333 *E-mail:* marko@youthspecialties.com
EVP, Support Opers & HR: Allen R Kerkstra *Tel:* 616-698-3409 *E-mail:* al.kerkstra@zondervan.com
SVP, Busn Technol Servs: Sue J Boylan *Tel:* 616-698-3361 *E-mail:* sue-anne.boylan@zondervan.com
VP, Mktg: Tom Dean
VP, PR & Communs: Jason Vines *E-mail:* jason.vines@zondervan.com
VP & Publr, Fiction Div: Daisy Hutton
VP & Publr, Nonfiction Trade Books: David Morris
Assoc Publr, Bibles: Melinda Bourma
Dir, Intl Sales: Jennifer Dibble *E-mail:* jennifer.dibble@zondervan.com
PR Dir, Nonfiction Trade: Robin Barnett
Sr Acqs Ed, Digital, Ref & Reflective Titles: Madison Trammel
Sr Ed, Biblical Langs, Textbooks & Ref Tools: Christopher Beetham
Founded: 1931
A world leader in Christian communications & the leading Christian publishing brand. For more than 75 years, Zondervan has delivered transformational Christian experiences through general & academic resources authored by influential leaders & emerging voices & been honored with more Christian Book Awards than any other publisher. Headquartered in Grand Rapids, Mich., with offices in San Diego & Miami, Zondervan conducts events & publishes its bestselling Bibles, books, audio, video, curriculum, software & digital products through its Zondervan, eZondervan, Zonderkidz, Youth Specialties, Editorial Vida & National Pastors Convention brands. Zondervan resources are sold worldwide through retail stores, online & by Zondervan ChurchSource & are translated into nearly 200 languages in more than 60 countries.
ISBN Prefix(es): 978-0-310
Number of titles published annually: 200 Print; 4 CD-ROM; 30 Online; 50 E-Book; 50 Audio
Total Titles: 5,000 Print; 30 CD-ROM; 300 Online; 300 E-Book; 400 Audio
Foreign Office(s): Zondervan, Shrewsbury, United Kingdom, Sales & Mktg Mgr: Ian Matthews *E-mail:* ian.matthews@zondervan.com *Web Site:* www.zondervan.com/world
Membership(s): AAP; ABA; Audio Publishers Association; Better Business Bureau; BISG; CBA; Chamber of Commerce; Evangelical Christian Publishers Association; Evangelical Press Association; Society of Bible Literature; Society of Children's Book Writers & Illustrators; Software & Information Industry Association

Zone Books dba Urzone Inc
1226 Prospect Ave, Brooklyn, NY 11218
Tel: 718-686-0048 *Toll Free Tel:* 800-405-1619 (orders & cust serv) *Fax:* 718-686-9045 *Toll Free Fax:* 800-406-9145 (orders)
E-mail: orders@triliteral.org
Web Site: www.zonebooks.org
Key Personnel
Gen Mgr & Intl Rts: Gus Kiley *E-mail:* gkiley@zonebooks.org
Mng Ed: Meighan Gale *E-mail:* mgale@zonebooks.org
Ed: Jonathan Crary; Michel Feher; Hal Foster; Ramona Naddaff
Founded: 1985
Publish books in the arts & humanities & social sciences.
ISBN Prefix(es): 978-0-942299; 978-1-890951
Number of titles published annually: 6 Print
Total Titles: 59 Print
Imprints: Swerve Editions
Distributed by The MIT Press
Foreign Rights: Carmen Balcells (Spain); English Agency (Japan); Paul & Peter Fritz (Germany); Graal Literary Agency (Eastern Block); Agnese Incisa (Italy)
Warehouse: The MIT Press c/o Triliteral LLC, 100 Maple Ridge Dr, Cumberland, RI 02864-1769
Distribution Center: The MIT Press, 55 Hayward St, Cambridge, MA 02142 *E-mail:* mitpress-orders@mit.edu
John Wiley & Sons, Southern Cross Trading Estate, One Oldlands Way, Bognor Regis, West Sussex P022 9SA, United Kingdom (UK & the Continent) *Tel:* (01243) 779777 *Fax:* (01243) 820250 *E-mail:* cs-books@wiley.co.uk

ZOVA Books
PO Box 21833, Long Beach, CA 90801
Tel: 805-426-9682 *Fax:* 562-394-9568
Web Site: www.zovabooks.com
Key Personnel
CEO: Matthew Pizzo
Publr: Molly Lewis *E-mail:* molly@zovabooks.com
Ed-in-Chief: Daniel Silva
Founded: 2010
A boutique publishing company specializing in unique fiction for young & old. Catalog is built on partnerships with local authors & screenwriters, creating a collection of cinematic fiction suitable for multimedia developement.
ISBN Prefix(es): 978-0-9827880; 978-0-9840350
Number of titles published annually: 10 Print; 10 E-Book
Total Titles: 14 Print; 14 E-Book
Distribution Center: Baker & Taylor, 2550 W Tyvola Rd, Suite 300, Charlotte, NC 28217 *Tel:* 704-998-3100 *Fax:* 704-998-3319

Zumaya Publications LLC
3209 S IH 35, Suite 1086, Austin, TX 78741
Tel: 512-402-5298 *Fax:* 253-660-2009
E-mail: acquisitions@zumayapublications.com
Web Site: www.zumayapublications.com
Key Personnel
Exec Ed/Publr: Liz Burton
Partner: Joyanne Moul
CFO: Marianne Moul
Acqs Ed: Rie Sheridan Rose
Founded: 2001
Trade paperback & ebook formats offering full-length works of fiction & nonfiction.
ISBN Prefix(es): 978-1-93413; 978-1-93484
Number of titles published annually: 30 Print; 30 E-Book
Total Titles: 200 Print; 200 E-Book
Imprints: Arcane (mysteries of the spirit); Boundless; Embraces; Enigma; Otherworlds (speculative fiction, science fiction, fantasy & paranormal suspense); Thresholds (imagination); Yesterdays (journeys into the past - both real & imaginary)
Membership(s): The Independent Book Publishers Association

U.S. Publishers — Geographic Index

COLORADO

CONNECTICUT

DELAWARE

DISTRICT OF COLUMBIA

FLORIDA

GEORGIA

HAWAII

IDAHO

ILLINOIS

INDIANA

IOWA

KANSAS

KENTUCKY

LOUISIANA

MAINE

MARYLAND

MASSACHUSETTS

MICHIGAN

MINNESOTA

MISSISSIPPI

MISSOURI

NORTH CAROLINA

NORTH DAKOTA

OHIO

OKLAHOMA

OREGON

PENNSYLVANIA

RHODE ISLAND

SOUTH CAROLINA

SOUTH DAKOTA

TENNESSEE

TEXAS

UTAH

VERMONT

VIRGINIA

WASHINGTON

WEST VIRGINIA

WISCONSIN

WYOMING

PUERTO RICO

U.S. Publishers — Type of Publication Index

ASSOCIATION PRESSES

AUDIOBOOKS

AV MATERIALS

BELLES LETTRES

BIBLES

BIBLIOGRAPHIES

BRAILLE BOOKS

CD-ROM, EBOOKS

CHILDREN'S BOOKS

COMPUTER SOFTWARE

DATABASES

DICTIONARIES, ENCYCLOPEDIAS

DIRECTORIES, REFERENCE BOOKS

FINE EDITIONS, ILLUSTRATED BOOKS

FOREIGN LANGUAGE & BILINGUAL BOOKS

GENERAL TRADE BOOKS - HARDCOVER

JUVENILE & YOUNG ADULT BOOKS

LARGE PRINT BOOKS

MAPS, ATLASES

PAPERBACK BOOKS - MASS MARKET

PAPERBACK BOOKS - TRADE

PERIODICALS, JOURNALS

PROFESSIONAL BOOKS

REPRINTS

SCHOLARLY BOOKS

SIDELINES

SUBSCRIPTION & MAIL ORDER BOOKS

TEXTBOOKS - ELEMENTARY

TEXTBOOKS - SECONDARY

TEXTBOOKS - COLLEGE

TRANSLATIONS

UNIVERSITY PRESSES

VIDEOS, DVDS

U.S. Publishers — Subject Index

ACCOUNTING

ADVERTISING

AERONAUTICS, AVIATION

AFRICAN AMERICAN STUDIES

AGRICULTURE

ALTERNATIVE

AMERICANA, REGIONAL

ANIMALS, PETS

ANTHROPOLOGY

ANTIQUES

ARCHAEOLOGY

ARCHITECTURE & INTERIOR DESIGN

ART

ASIAN STUDIES

ASTROLOGY, OCCULT

ASTRONOMY

AUTOMOTIVE

BEHAVIORAL SCIENCES

BIBLICAL STUDIES

BIOGRAPHY, MEMOIRS

BIOLOGICAL SCIENCES

BUSINESS

CAREER DEVELOPMENT

CHEMISTRY, CHEMICAL ENGINEERING

CHILD CARE & DEVELOPMENT

CIVIL ENGINEERING

COMMUNICATIONS

COMPUTER SCIENCE

COMPUTERS

COOKERY

CRAFTS, GAMES, HOBBIES

CRIMINOLOGY

DEVELOPING COUNTRIES

DISABILITY, SPECIAL NEEDS

DRAMA, THEATER

EARTH SCIENCES

ECONOMICS

EDUCATION

ELECTRONICS, ELECTRICAL ENGINEERING

ENERGY

ENGINEERING (GENERAL)

ENGLISH AS A SECOND LANGUAGE

ENVIRONMENTAL STUDIES

EROTICA

ETHNICITY

FASHION

FICTION

FILM, VIDEO

FINANCE

FOREIGN COUNTRIES

GARDENING, PLANTS

GAY & LESBIAN

GENEALOGY

GEOGRAPHY, GEOLOGY

GOVERNMENT, POLITICAL SCIENCE

HEALTH, NUTRITION

HISTORY

HOUSE & HOME

HOW-TO

HUMAN RELATIONS

HUMOR

INSPIRATIONAL, SPIRITUALITY

JOURNALISM

LABOR, INDUSTRIAL RELATIONS

LANGUAGE ARTS, LINGUISTICS

LAW

LIBRARY & INFORMATION SCIENCES

LITERATURE, LITERARY CRITICISM, ESSAYS

MANAGEMENT

MARITIME

MARKETING

MATHEMATICS

MECHANICAL ENGINEERING

MEDICINE, NURSING, DENTISTRY

MILITARY SCIENCE

MUSIC, DANCE

MYSTERIES, SUSPENSE

NATIVE AMERICAN STUDIES

NATURAL HISTORY

NONFICTION (GENERAL)

OUTDOOR RECREATION

PARAPSYCHOLOGY

PHILOSOPHY

PHOTOGRAPHY

PHYSICAL SCIENCES

PHYSICS

POETRY

POP CULTURE

PSYCHOLOGY, PSYCHIATRY

PUBLIC ADMINISTRATION

PUBLISHING & BOOK TRADE REFERENCE

RADIO, TV

REAL ESTATE

REGIONAL INTERESTS

RELIGION - BUDDHIST

RELIGION - CATHOLIC

RELIGION - HINDU

RELIGION - ISLAMIC

RELIGION - JEWISH

RELIGION - PROTESTANT

RELIGION - OTHER

ROMANCE

SCIENCE (GENERAL)

SCIENCE FICTION, FANTASY

SECURITIES

SELF-HELP

SOCIAL SCIENCES, SOCIOLOGY

SPORTS, ATHLETICS

TECHNOLOGY

THEOLOGY

TRANSPORTATION

TRAVEL & TOURISM

VETERINARY SCIENCE

WESTERN FICTION

WINE & SPIRITS

WOMEN'S STUDIES

Imprints, Subsidiaries & Distributors

A Cappella Books, *imprint of* Chicago Review Press

A G Fiction™, *imprint of* American Girl Publishing

A-R Editions Inc, *distributor for* AIM (American Institute of Musicology)

A U A Language Center, *distributed by* Cornell University Southeast Asia Program Publications

AAAI Press, *imprint of* Association for the Advancement of Artificial Intelligence, *distributed by* The MIT Press

AAH Graphics Inc, *subsidiary of* Loft Press Inc

A&D Xtreme, *imprint of* ABDO Publishing Group

AAP, *distributed by* Welcome Books®

AAPG (American Association of Petroleum Geologists), *distributor for* Geological Society of London, *distributed by* Affiliated East - West Press Private Ltd, Canadian Society of Petroleum Geologists, Geological Society of London

Aardvark, *distributor for* No Frills Buffalo

AATEC Publications, *distributed by* Chelsea Green Publishing Co

Abaris Books, *division of* Opal Publishing Corp

Abbeville Kids, *imprint of* Abbeville Publishing Group

Abbeville Press, *imprint of* Abbeville Publishing Group

Abbey of Saint Peter of Solesmes, *distributed by* Paraclete Press Inc

Abbott Publishing, *distributed by* Sunbelt Publications Inc

ABC-CLIO Online Solutions, *subsidiary of* ABC-CLIO

ABC International Group Inc, *imprint of* Kazi Publications Inc

Abdo & Daughters Publishing, *imprint of* ABDO Publishing Group

Abdo Kids, *imprint of* ABDO Publishing Group

ABDO Publishing Group, *subsidiary of* Abdo Consulting Group Inc (ACGI), Abdo Consulting Group Inc (ACGI), *distributed by* Rockbottom Book Co

The Aberdeen Group, *distributor for* Craftsman Book Co

ABI Professional Publications, *distributed by* Vandamere Press

Abingdon Press, *imprint of* The United Methodist Publishing House, *distributor for* Church Publishing Inc, Judson Press, Morehouse Publishing, Upper Room Books

Abjad Books, *imprint of* Kazi Publications Inc

Abrams, *distributor for* National Gallery of Art, Winterthur Museum & Country Estate, *distributed by* Perfection Learning Corp

Abrams & Chronicle Books, *distributor for* Harry N Abrams Inc

Abrams Appleseed, *imprint of* Harry N Abrams Inc

Abrams Books, *imprint of* Harry N Abrams Inc

Abrams Books for Young Readers, *imprint of* Harry N Abrams Inc

Abrams ComicArts, *imprint of* Harry N Abrams Inc

Harry N Abrams Inc, *distributed by* Hachette Book Group

Harry N Abrams Inc, *subsidiary of* La Martiniere Groupe, *distributor for* American Federation of Arts, Booth-Clibborn Editions, The Colonial Williamsburg Foundation, 5 Continents Editions, Royal Academy Publications, Tate Publishing, V&A Publishing, The Vendome Press, *distributed by* Abrams & Chronicle Books (Great Britain), Editions Alain

Abrams Image, *imprint of* Harry N Abrams Inc

Abrams Learning Trends, *subsidiary of* Learning Trends LLC, *distributor for* General Education Services (New Zealand)

The ABS Group, *distributed by* American Academy of Environmental Engineers & Scientists™

Absolute Classics, *distributed by* Theatre Communications Group

ACA, *imprint of* American Counseling Association

Academia Barilla, *distributed by* The Taunton Press Inc

Academic Book Center, *distributor for* Primary Research Group Inc

Academic Press, *imprint of* Elsevier BV, *distributed by* Marine Techniques Publishing

Academy Chicago, *imprint of* Chicago Review Press

Academy Chicago Publishers, *imprint of* Chicago Review Press

Academy of Continuing Education, *division of* Success Advertising & Publishing

Academy of Natural Sciences, *distributed by* Diane Publishing Co

Academy of Nutrition & Dietetics, *distributed by* Small Press United (Eat Right Press)

Acanthus, *distributor for* Winterthur Museum & Country Estate

Acanthus Publishing, *division of* The Ictus Group LLC

ACC Distribution, *division of* Antique Collectors' Club Ltd

ACC Editions, *imprint of* Antique Collectors' Club Ltd

Access, *imprint of* HarperCollins Publishers Sales

Accord Publishing, *imprint of* Andrews McMeel Publishing LLC

Accuity, *division of* Reed Business Information Ltd

Ace, *imprint of* Penguin Group (USA) LLC, a Penguin Random House company

Ace Books, *imprint of* Berkley Books, Berkley Publishing Group, *distributed by* Perfection Learning Corp

Ace/Putnam, *imprint of* Penguin Group (USA) LLC, a Penguin Random House company, GP Putnam's Sons (Hardcover)

ACER, *distributor for* Psychological Assessment Resources Inc (PAR)

ACHCBYZ, *distributed by* Summertime Publications Inc

Acorn, *imprint of* Oak Tree Press

Acorn Guides, *imprint of* Trails Books

Acres USA, *division of* Acres USA Inc, Acres USA Inc

Acropolis Books, *distributed by* De Vorss & Co

ACS Publications, *imprint of* Starcrafts LLC

ACT Proficiency Examination Program, *imprint of* National Learning Corp

ACTA Publications, *distributor for* Grief Watch, Veritas

Action Language Learning, *distributed by* Cheng & Tsui Co Inc

ACU Press, *affiliate of* Abilene Christian University

Ac-u-Kwik, *imprint of* Penton Media

AcuTab Publications Inc, *distributed by* Mel Bay Publications Inc

Ad Infinitum Books, *distributor for* Cross-Cultural Communications

Ad Infinitum Press, *distributed by* Cross-Cultural Communications

Adams Business, *imprint of* Adams Media

Adams Media, *imprint of* F+W, A Content + eCommerce Company

ADASI Publishing Co, *distributor for* Wall & Thompson

ADC the Map People, *subsidiary of* American Map Corp, *distributed by* Hagstrom Map

Addison Gallery of American Art, Phillips Academy, *distributed by* Yale University Press

Addison Wesley, *distributor for* Public Citizen

Adirondack Museum, *imprint of* Syracuse University Press

Adis International, *imprint of* Wolters Kluwer US Corp

Admission Test Series, *imprint of* National Learning Corp

Advaita Ashrama, *distributed by* Vedanta Press

Adventure Guides, *imprint of* Hunter Publishing Inc

Adventure Publications, *distributor for* Blacklock Nature Photography, Kollath-Stensaas, Nodin Press, Pocket Guides Publishing, Raven Productions Inc

Adventure Roads Travel, *imprint of* Ocean Tree Books

Adventures in Odyssey, *imprint of* Focus on the Family

Adventures Unlimited Press (AUP), *distributor for* Eagle Wing Books, EDFU Books, Yelsraek Publishing

The AEI Press, *division of* American Enterprise Institute, *distributed by* MIT (selected titles)

Aeon Books, *distributed by* Stylus Publishing LLC

Aequitas Books, *imprint of* Pleasure Boat Studio: A Literary Press

Aerie Books, *imprint of* Tom Doherty Associates, LLC

Aeronautical Publishers, *imprint of* Markowski International Publishers

AF Editions, *distributed by* Casemate Publishers & Book Distributors LLC

AFB Press, *imprint of* American Foundation for the Blind, American Foundation for the Blind (AFB)

Affiliated East - West Press Private Ltd, *distributor for* AAPG (American Association of Petroleum Geologists)

African-American Book Distributors Inc, *subsidiary of* Path Press Inc

African American Islamic Institute, *distributed by* Fons Vitae

Editions d'Afrique du Nord, *distributed by* Edgewise Press Inc

Aftershocks Media, *division of* Epicenter Press Inc

Agape, *division of* Hope Publishing Co

Agathon Press, *imprint of* Algora Publishing

Agronomy Publications, *imprint of* Hobar Publications

Aguilar, *imprint of* Santillana USA Publishing Co Inc

AHA (American Hospital Association), *imprint of* Health Forum Inc

aha! Chinese, *distributed by* Cheng & Tsui Co Inc

Aha Communications, *distributed by* Gryphon House Inc

AHA Press, *imprint of* Health Forum Inc

AHLP Books, *imprint of* Africana Homestead Legacy Publishers Inc

AHLP Communications, *imprint of* Africana Homestead Legacy Publishers Inc

The Ahmanson Foundation Humanities Endowment Fund, *imprint of* University of California Press

Ahmanson-Murphy, *imprint of* University of California Press

AICPA Professional Publications, *subsidiary of* American Institute of Certified Public Accountants, *distributor for* Wiley, *distributed by* CCH, Practitioners Publishing Co, Thomson Reuters

AIM (American Institute of Musicology), *distributed by* A-R Editions Inc

Keith Ainsworth Pty Ltd, *distributor for* Interweave Press LLC

Air Conditioning Contractors of America, *distributor for* Cengage Learning, *distributed by* Contractor Resource

Aircraft of the Aces, *imprint of* Osprey Publishing Inc

Airfile Publications, *distributed by* Casemate Publishers & Book Distributors LLC

Airmont, *distributed by* Perfection Learning Corp

Airphoto International Ltd/Odyssey Publications, *distributed by* W W Norton & Company Inc

AK Press, *distributed by* AK Press Distribution

AK Press Distribution, *subsidiary of* AK Press Inc, AK Press Inc, *distributor for* AK Press, Crimethinc, Freedom Press, Payback Press, Phoenix Press, Rebel Inc, Rebel Press

Aladdin Paperbacks, *imprint of* Simon & Schuster Children's Publishing

Editions Alain, *distributor for* Harry N Abrams Inc

Alamos Press, *imprint of* Park Place Publications

Alan Wofsy Fine Arts, *distributor for* Bora, Brusberg (Berlin), Cramer (Geneva), Huber, Ides et Calendes, Kornfeld & Co (Bern), Picasso Project, Welz, Wittenborn Art Books

Alaska Native Language Center, *division of* University of Alaska Fairbanks, *distributed by* University of Alaska Press

Alaska Northwest Books®, *imprint of* Graphic Arts Books

Alaska Quarterly Review, *distributed by* University of Alaska Press

Alaska Sea Grant, *distributed by* University of Alaska Press

Alaska Writer Laureate Series, *imprint of* University of Alaska Press

Albany Institute of History & Art, *distributed by* Excelsior Editions, State University of New York Press

Albatross Publishing House, *distributed by* W W Norton & Company Inc

Albert Whitman & Co, *distributed by* Open Road

Alchemical Press, *imprint of* Holmes Publishing Group LLC

Aldine Transaction, *imprint of* Transaction Publishers Inc

Alen House, *distributor for* Syracuse University Press

Alexandrian Press, *imprint of* Holmes Publishing Group LLC

Alfaguara, *imprint of* Santillana USA Publishing Co Inc

Alfred Music Publishing, *distributor for* Daisy Rock Girl Guitars, Dover Publications, Drum Channel, Faber Music, MakeMusic Inc, Penguin, WEA

Algonquin Books, *division of* Workman Publishing Co Inc, *distributor for* Fearless Critic Media, Greenwich Workshop Press, HighBridge Audio, *distributed by* Workman Publishing Co Inc

Algonquin Young Readers, *imprint of* Algonquin Books

ALI-ABA, *distributor for* The Professional Education Group Inc (PEG), *distributed by* The Professional Education Group Inc (PEG)

Alibi, *imprint of* Penguin Random House Inc, Random House Publishing Group

Alice James Books, *division of* Alice James Poetry Cooperative Inc

Alive Guides, *imprint of* Hunter Publishing Inc

All Rights Reserved, *distributed by* Gingko Press Inc

Allen & Unwin, *distributor for* Quarto Publishing Group USA Inc

J A Allen, *distributed by* Trafalgar Square Books

Thomas Allen & Son, *distributor for* Square One Publishers Inc, Timber Press Inc

Allmaps, *subsidiary of* Rand McNally

Alloy Entertainment LLC, *member of* Warner Bros Entertainment Group, *distributed by* Avon Books, HarperCollins, Hyperion, Little, Brown & Co, Penguin Group (USA) LLC, Random House Inc, Scholastic Books, Simon & Schuster

Allworth Press, *imprint of* Skyhorse Publishing Inc, *distributed by* W W Norton

Allyn & Bacon, *imprint of* Pearson Higher Education, *distributor for* National Association of Broadcasters (NAB)

Alma Edizioni, *distributed by* Delta Publishing Co

Alma Little, *imprint of* Elva Resa Publishing

Almont Books, *imprint of* Ingalls Publishing Group Inc (IPG)

Alpha Books, *imprint of* Penguin Group (USA) LLC, Penguin Group (USA) LLC, a Penguin Random House company

ALPHA Publications of America Inc, *affiliate of* Alpha Legal Forms & More

ALPS Publishing, *distributor for* Pieces of Learning

Alta Book Ctr, *distributor for* Teachers of English to Speakers of Other Languages Inc (TESOL)

AltaMira Press, *imprint of* Rowman & Littlefield Publishing Group, *distributor for* American Association for State & Local History

Alti Corporation, *distributed by* Sunbelt Publications Inc

Alutiiq Museum, *distributed by* University of Alaska Press

AMA, *distributed by* Mel Bay Publications Inc

AMA Research, *distributed by* FurnitureCore

AMACOM Books, *division of* American Management Association (AMA), American Management Association®, *distributor for* J J Keller & Associates, Inc, *distributed by* McGraw-Hill International, SAS Publishing

Amadeus Press, *imprint of* Hal Leonard Books, *distributed by* Hal Leonard Corp

Amadeus Press/Hal Leonard Performing Arts Publishing Group, *imprint of* Hal Leonard Performing Arts Publishing Group

Amaroma Ediciones, *distributed by* Sunbelt Publications Inc

Frank Amato Publications Inc, *distributor for* Haugen Enterprises (cooking & hunting titles)

Amazing People Club, *distributed by* Hachette Book Group

Amazon.com, *distributor for* Ozark Publishing Inc, Paladin Press

Ambassador Books, *distributor for* Primary Research Group Inc

Ambassador International, *division of* Emerald House Inc

Amber-Allen Publishing, *imprint of* New World Library

Amber Allure, *imprint of* Amber Quill Press LLC

Amber Books, *distributed by* Casemate Publishers & Book Distributors LLC

Amber Heat, *imprint of* Amber Quill Press LLC

Amber Quill, *imprint of* Amber Quill Press LLC

Amberley Publishing, *distributed by* Casemate Publishers & Book Distributors LLC

Amble Press, *imprint of* Bywater Books

AMC Discover Series, *imprint of* Appalachian Mountain Club Books

AMC Nature Walks Series, *imprint of* Appalachian Mountain Club Books

AMC Quiet Water Guides, *imprint of* Appalachian Mountain Club Books

AMC River Guides, *imprint of* Appalachian Mountain Club Books

AMC Trail Guides, *imprint of* Appalachian Mountain Club Books

America West Publishers, *subsidiary of* Global Insights Inc

American Academy for Park & Recreation Administration, *distributed by* Sagamore Publishing LLC

American Academy of Environmental Engineers & Scientists™, *distributor for* The ABS Group, CRC Press, McGraw-Hill, Pearson Education, Prentice Hall, John Wiley & Sons Inc

American Academy of Orthopaedic Surgeons (AAOS), *distributed by* Jones & Bartlett Publishers

The American Alpine Club Press, *division of* The American Alpine Club, *distributed by* Mountaineers Books, The Mountaineers Books

American Anthropological Association (AAA), *distributed by* Wiley-Blackwell

American Antiquarian Society, *distributed by* Oak Knoll Press

American Association for Higher Education, *distributed by* Stylus Publishing LLC

American Association for State & Local History, *distributed by* AltaMira Press

American Association for Vocational Instructional Materials, *distributor for* Southeastern Cooperative Wildlife Disease Study

American Association of State Highway & Transportation Officials, *distributed by* Professional Publications Inc (PPI)

American Bar Association, *distributor for* The Professional Education Group Inc (PEG), *distributed by* The Professional Education Group Inc (PEG)

American Carriage House Publishing, *distributed by* Faith Works Books

American Ceramic Society (ACerS), *distributor for* American Society for Nondestructive Testing

American Chamber of Commerce to the European Union, *distributed by* The Brookings Institution Press

The American Chemical Society, *distributor for* Royal Society of Chemistry, *distributed by* Oxford University Press, Oxford University Press USA

American College of Healthcare Executives Management Series, *imprint of* Health Administration Press

American College of Surgeons, *distributed by* Cine-Med Inc, Scientific American Medicine

American Council for an Energy Efficient Economy (ACEEE), *distributed by* Chelsea Green Publishing Co

American Council on Education, *distributed by* Rowman & Littlefield

American Dust Publications, *distributed by* Dustbooks

American Express, *distributed by* Charlesbridge Publishing Inc

American Federation of Arts, *distributed by* Harry N Abrams Inc, Distributed Art Publishers, D Giles Ltd, Hudson Hills Press Inc, Scala Publishers, Skira Rizzoli Publishers, University of Washington Press, Yale University Press

American Food History, *imprint of* R J Berg Publisher

American Geosciences Institute (AGI), *distributed by* W H Freeman, It's About Time Inc, Prentice Hall

American Girl Library®, *imprint of* American Girl Publishing

American Girl Publishing, *subsidiary of* Mattel

The American Girls Collection®, *imprint of* American Girl Publishing

American Guidance Service, *distributed by* Psychological Assessment Resources Inc (PAR)

American Heritage Dictionary, *imprint of* Houghton Mifflin Harcourt Trade & Reference Division

American Institute of Buddhist Studies, *distributed by* Columbia University Press

American Institute of Chemical Engineers (AIChE), *distributor for* ASM International (selected titles), Dechema (selected titles), Engineering Foundation, IchemE (selected titles), *distributed by* Dechema (selected titles)

American Institute of Physics, *distributed by* Springer-Verlag

American Institute of Physics (AIP), *distributor for* The Electrochemical Society (ECS)

American Law Institute Continuing Legal Education (ALI CLE), *affiliate of* American Law Institute

American Map Corp, *member of* Kappa Map Group, Kappa Map Group LLC, *distributor for* De Lorme Atlas, Kappa Map Group, RV Guides, Stubs Magazine, *distributed by* Arrow Maps Inc, Creative Sales Corp, Hagstrom Map

American Maritain Association, *distributed by* The Catholic University of America Press

American Maritime Library, *imprint of* Mystic Seaport Museum Inc

American Mathematical Society, *distributor for* Annales de la faculte des sciences de Toulouse mathematiques, Bar-Ilan University, Brown University, European Mathematical Society, Hindustan Book Agency, Independent University of Moscow, International Press, Mathematica Josephina, Mathematical Society of Japan, Narosa Publishing House, Ramanujan Mathematical Society, Science Press New York & Science Press Beijing, Societe Mathematique de France, Tata Institute of Fundamental Research, Theta Foundation of Bucharest, University Press, Vieweg Verlag Publications

American Medical Association, *distributor for* OptumInsight™, *distributed by* Medical Group Management Association (MGMA), OptumInsight™

American Milestones, *imprint of* Gallopade International Inc

American Parks & Resorts, *imprint of* R J Berg Publisher

American Philosophical Society, *distributed by* Diane Publishing Co

American Poetry Review/Honickman, *distributed by* Copper Canyon Press

American Products Publishing Co, *division of* American Products Corp

American Psychiatric Association (APA), *imprint of* American Psychiatric Publishing (APP), *distributed by* American Psychiatric Publishing (APP)

American Psychiatric Publishing (APP), *division of* American Psychiatric Association (APA), *imprint of* American Psychiatric Publishing (APP), *distributor for* American Psychiatric Association (APA), Group for the Advancement of Psychiatry

American School of Classical Studies at Athens, *imprint of* ASCSA Publications

American Society for Mechanical Engineers (ASME), *distributor for* American Society for Nondestructive Testing

American Society for Metals (ASM), *distributor for* American Society for Nondestructive Testing

American Society for Nondestructive Testing, *distributed by* American Ceramic Society (ACerS), American Society for Mechanical Engineers (ASME), American Society for Metals (ASM), The American Welding Society (AWS), ASTM, Edison Welding Institute, Mean Free Path

American Society for Quality (ASQ), *distributed by* GOAL/QPC, IEEE Computer Society Press, McGraw-Hill Professional Publishing, Productivity Press

American Society of Association Executives, *distributor for* BoardSource

American Sports Publishing, *imprint of* Athletic Guide Publishing

American Swedish Historical Museum, *distributed by* Diane Publishing Co

American Technical Publishers Inc, *distributor for* Craftsman Book Co, Society of Manufacturing Engineers

American University in Cairo, *distributed by* Oxford University Press USA

American Water Works Association (AWWA), *distributor for* CRC Press, McGraw-Hill, John Wiley & Sons

The American Welding Society (AWS), *distributor for* American Society for Nondestructive Testing

American Wood Council (American Forest & Paper Association), *distributed by* Professional Publications Inc (PPI)

The Americas Review, *subsidiary of* Arte Publico Press

Amerotica, *imprint of* NBM Publishing Inc

Amherst Media Inc, *distributor for* Firefly

Amistad, *imprint of* HarperCollins Children's Books, HarperCollins General Books Group, HarperCollins Publishers Sales

Amphoto Books, *imprint of* Crown Publishing Group

AMS, *distributor for* International Press of Boston Inc

Amulet Books, *imprint of* Harry N Abrams Inc

Anacus Press, *imprint of* Finney Company Inc

Ananda Ashrama, *distributed by* Vedanta Press

Ancestry, *imprint of* Turner Publishing Co

Anchor Bible Commentary, *imprint of* Penguin Random House Inc

Anchor Bible Dictionary, *imprint of* Penguin Random House Inc

Anchor Bible Reference Library, *imprint of* Penguin Random House Inc

Anchor Books, *imprint of* Penguin Random House Inc, Vintage & Anchor Books

Anchor Distributors, *distributor for* Pentecostal Publishing House

Anchorage Museum Association, *distributed by* University of Alaska Press

Anchorage Museum of Art History, *distributed by* University of Alaska Press

Ancient City Press, *imprint of* Gibbs Smith Publisher

Ancient Faith Publishing, *division of* Ancient Faith Ministries, *distributor for* Light & Life, *distributed by* Light & Life, St Vladimir's

And/Or Books, *imprint of* Ronin Publishing Inc

Andersen Press USA, *distributed by* Lerner Publishing Group Inc

Anderson Design, *distributed by* Resilient Publishing

Andrews McMeel Publishing LLC, *division of* Andrews McMeel Universal, *distributor for* Gooseberry Patch (North America), Signatures Network, Sporting News, Universe Publishing Calendars, Vegan Heritage Press, *distributed by* Simon & Schuster, Inc, Simon & Schuster Sales Division

Andrews University Press, *division of* Andrews University

Angel Books, *distributed by* Dufour Editions Inc

Angel City Press, *distributor for* Los Angeles Times Books

Angelus Press, *distributed by* Catholic Treasures, Fatima Crusader

Angler's Book Supply, *distributor for* Wilderness Adventures Press Inc

Anglican Book Centre, *distributed by* Forward Movement

Animal Media Group LLC, *subsidiary of* Animal Inc

Ann Arbor Paperbacks, *imprint of* University of Michigan Press

Annales de la faculte des sciences de Toulouse mathematiques, *distributed by* American Mathematical Society

Annick Press, *distributed by* Perfection Learning Corp

Anomaly Press, *distributed by* Chelsea Green Publishing Co

Another Great Achiever Series, *imprint of* Advance Publishing Inc

Anqa Press, *distributed by* Fons Vitae

ANR Publications University of California, *division of* Agriculture & Natural Resources, University of California

Antinous Press, *distributed by* powerHouse Books

Antique Collectors' Club Ltd, *division of* Antique Collectors Club Ltd (England), Antique Collectors Club Ltd (England), *distributor for* George Braziller Inc

Antique Trader, *imprint of* Krause Publications Inc

Antique Trader Books, *imprint of* F+W, A Content + eCommerce Company, Krause Publications Inc

Coleccion Antologia Personal, *imprint of* University of Puerto Rico Press

Anvil Series, *imprint of* Krieger Publishing Co

Anza-Borrego Foundation, *distributed by* Sunbelt Publications Inc

AO Foundation, *distributed by* Thieme Medical Publishers Inc

AOCS Press, *division of* American Oil Chemists' Society

Aonian Press, *imprint of* James A Rock & Co Publishers

APA Books®, *imprint of* American Psychological Association

APA Planners Press, *imprint of* American Planning Association

Aperture, *distributed by* Fons Vitae

Aperture Books, *division of* Aperture Foundation Inc, *distributed by* Farrar, Straus & Giroux Inc

Aperture Monographs, *imprint of* Aperture Books

The Apex Press, *imprint of* Rowman & Littlefield Publishers Inc, Rowman & Littlefield Publishing Group

Aphrodisia, *imprint of* Kensington Publishing Corp

Apollo Managed Care Inc, *distributed by* Health Information Network, MarketResearch.com, Researchandmarkets.com

Apostrofa Publishers, *distributed by* Central European University Press

Appalachian, *distributor for* Faith Library Publications

Appalachian Mountain Club Books, *division of* Appalachian Mountain Club, *distributed by* The Globe Pequot Press

Appell Publishing, *distributed by* Epicenter Press Inc

Applause Theatre & Cinema Books, *imprint of* Hal Leonard Books, Hal Leonard Performing Arts Publishing Group, *distributor for* The Working Arts Library, Glenn Young Books, *distributed by* Hal Leonard Corp, Hal Leonard Corporation

Apple, *distributor for* Ozark Publishing Inc

Applesauce Press, *imprint of* Cider Mill Press Book Publishers LLC, *distributed by* Simon & Schuster Sales Division

Appraisal Institute, *distributed by* Dearborn Trade

Apress, *imprint of* Springer

Apress Media LLC, *subsidiary of* Springer Science+Business Media, Springer Science+Business Media LLC

APS PRESS, *imprint of* The American Phytopathological Society (APS)

AQS, *imprint of* American Quilter's Society

Coleccion Aqui y Ahora, *imprint of* University of Puerto Rico Press

Arba Sicula, *distributed by* Cross-Cultural Communications

ARC (Magazine & Press), *imprint of* Cross-Cultural Communications

Arcade Publishing Inc, *imprint of* Skyhorse Publishing Inc, *distributed by* Perseus Books Group

Arcadia Books (London), *distributed by* Dufour Editions Inc

Arcana Publishing, *imprint of* Lotus Press

Arcane, *imprint of* Zumaya Publications LLC

Archetype, *distributed by* Fons Vitae

Archimap, *distributed by* Gingko Press Inc

Archival, *distributed by* Donald M Grant Publisher Inc

Archway, *distributed by* Perfection Learning Corp

Arctic Studies Center of the Smithsonian Museum, *distributed by* University of Alaska Press

Arcturus Publishing, *imprint of* Black Rabbit Books

Arcturus Publishing Ltd, *distributor for* Big Guy Books Inc

Arcus, *distributed by* Franklin, Beedle & Associates Inc

Ardent Media Inc, *distributor for* Cyrco Press, Irvington Publishers, MSS Information Corp

Ardis Russian Literature, *imprint of* The Overlook Press

ARE Press, *division of* The Association for Research & Enlightenment Inc (ARE), The Association for Research & Enlightenment Inc (ARE)

Ariel Press, *subsidiary of* Light, *distributor for* Enthea Press, Kudzu House

The Arion Press, *division of* Lyra Corp

Arkangel, *distributed by* Penguin Group (USA) LLC, a Penguin Random House company, Putnam Berkley Audio

Arktoi Books, *imprint of* Red Hen Press

Eric Armin Inc Education Ctr, *distributor for* National Council of Teachers of Mathematics (NCTM)

The Army War College Foundation Press, *distributed by* Stackpole Books

Jason Aronson Inc, *imprint of* Rowman & Littlefield Publishing Group

Arrow Maps Inc, *subsidiary of* American Map Corp, *distributor for* American Map Corp, *distributed by* Hagstrom Map

ARSIS Audio, *imprint of* ECS Publishing Corp

Arsis Press, *imprint of* Empire Publishing Service, *distributed by* Empire Publishing Service

Art Books/D A P, *distributor for* MFA Publications

Art Image Publications, *division of* GB Publishing Inc

The Art Institute of Chicago, *distributed by* Yale University Press

Art Media Resources Inc, *distributor for* Serindia Publications

Art Power, *distributed by* Gingko Press Inc

Art Scroll Series, *imprint of* Mesorah Publications Ltd

art-SITES, *distributed by* University of California Press

Art Treasures, *imprint of* Branden Books

Artabras, *imprint of* Abbeville Publishing Group

ArtAge Publications, *distributor for* Heinemann, Hal Leonard

Arte Publico Press, *affiliate of* University of Houston, *distributor for* Bilingual Review Press, Latin American Review Press, *distributed by* Empire Publishing Service

Artech House Inc, *subsidiary of* Horizon House Publications Inc, Horizon House Publications Inc

Artemis Books, *imprint of* Gateways Books & Tapes

Arthritis Research, *imprint of* Progressive Press

Arthur A Levine Books, *imprint of* Scholastic Trade Division

Artisan, *division of* Workman Publishing Co Inc

Artisan Books, *division of* Workman Publishing Co Inc, *imprint of* Algonquin Books, *distributor for* Greenwich Workshop Press

Artistpro, *distributed by* Hal Leonard Corp

ArtWorks, *imprint of* MFA Publications

As Sabr, *imprint of* Imago Press

ASAE, *distributed by* Water Resources Publications LLC

Asante®, *imprint of* Peoples Education Inc

ASCA, *distributor for* MAR*CO Products Inc

ASCE, *distributed by* Water Resources Publications LLC

ASCE Press, *imprint of* American Society of Civil Engineers (ASCE)

Ascension Press, *member of* Catholic Word

ASCP Press, *subsidiary of* American Society for Clinical Pathology

Ash Tree Publishing, *distributor for* Ash Tree Publishing, *distributed by* Ash Tree Publishing, Brumby Sunstate, Dempsey Your Distributor, New Leaf, Nutri-Books, Partners

Ashgate, *imprint of* Ashgate Publishing Co, *distributed by* William S Hein & Co Inc

Ashgate Publishing Co, *subsidiary of* Ashgate Publishing Ltd, *distributor for* Pickering & Chatto

Ashland Creek Press, *imprint of* Ashland Creek Press

Ashland Poetry Press, *affiliate of* Ashland University

Ashley Music, *distributed by* Hal Leonard Corp

ASI Books, *imprint of* Information Today, Inc

Asian Development Bank Institute, *distributed by* The Brookings Institution Press

Asian Humanities Press, *imprint of* Jain Publishing Co

AsiaPac, *distributed by* China Books

ASIS&T Monograph Series, *imprint of* Information Today, Inc

ASL, *distributed by* Copywriter's Council of America (CCA)

Aslan Publishing, *division of* Renaissance Book Services Corp

ASM International, *distributed by* American Institute of Chemical Engineers (AIChE), NACE International

ASM Press, *division of* American Society for Microbiology

ASME Press, *imprint of* American Society of Mechanical Engineers (ASME)

Aspatore Books, *division of* Thomson Reuters

Aspatore Thought Leadership, *imprint of* Aspatore Books

ASPEN, *distributed by* William S Hein & Co Inc, The Professional Education Group Inc (PEG)

Aspen Institute, *distributed by* The Brookings Institution Press

Aspen Publishers, *distributed by* Medical Group Management Association (MGMA)

Aspen Publishers Incorporated, *imprint of* Wolters Kluwer US Corp

Assessment, *division of* Scholastic Education

Associated University Presses, *distributor for* Susquehanna University Press

Association for Information Science & Technology (ASIS&T), *distributed by* Information Today Inc, John Wiley & Sons Inc

Association for Talent Development (ATD), *distributed by* Cengage Learning Asia Pte Ltd (Asia), Eurospan Group (Europe, Middle East & the former Soviet Bloc), Knowledge Resources (South Africa), National Book Network (NBN) (US, CN, Australia & New Zealand)

Association of College & Research Libraries (ACRL), *division of* The American Library Association (ALA)

ASTM, *distributor for* American Society for Nondestructive Testing, *distributed by* NACE International

Astragal Press, *imprint of* Finney Company Inc

Astronautical Society of Western Australia, *distributed by* Univelt Inc

ASVP, *imprint of* Elsevier, Health Sciences Division

Asylum Arts Press, *imprint of* Leaping Dog Press/Asylum Arts Press

At a Glance, *distributor for* The Jim Henson Co

At Home on the Road, *imprint of* Park Place Publications

Ateneo De Manila University Press, *distributed by* University of Hawaii Press

Athenaeum Books, *distributed by* Enfield Publishing & Distribution Co

Atheneum, *distributed by* Perfection Learning Corp

Atheneum Books for Young Readers, *imprint of* Simon & Schuster Children's Publishing

The Atkinson Family Imprint, *imprint of* University of California Press

Atlantic Boating Almanac, *imprint of* ProStar Publications Inc

Atlantic Books Ltd, *imprint of* Grove Atlantic Inc

Atlantic Council, *distributed by* University Press of America Inc

Atlantic Law Book Co, *division of* Peter Kelsey Publishing Inc, Peter Kelsey Publishing Inc

Atlantic Monthly Press, *imprint of* Grove Atlantic Inc

Atlas & Co, *distributed by* W W Norton & Company Inc

Atlas Games, *imprint of* Trident Inc

AtRandom.com, *imprint of* Penguin Random House Inc

Atria Books, *imprint of* Atria Publishing Group

Atria Trade Paperback, *imprint of* Atria Books

Attara, *distributed by* Hachai Publishing

Attic Press, *distributed by* Dufour Editions Inc

@tlas®, *imprint of* VanDam Inc

Audel™, *imprint of* John Wiley & Sons Inc

Audio Books, *division of* Unarius Academy of Science Publications

Audioworks, *imprint of* Simon & Schuster Audio

Augsburg Books, *imprint of* Augsburg Fortress Publishers, Publishing House of the Evangelical Lutheran Church in America

August House Audio, *imprint of* August House Inc

August House Little Folk, *imprint of* August House Inc

August House Story Cove, *imprint of* August House Inc

Augustinian Press, *distributed by* Diane Publishing Co

AUPHA Press/Health Administration Press, *imprint of* Health Administration Press

Aura Imaging, *imprint of* Blue Dolphin Publishing Inc

Aurora Metro Publications, *distributed by* Theatre Communications Group

Stephen F Austin State University Press, *distributed by* Texas A&M University Press

Australasian Corrosion Association, *distributor for* NACE International

Austrian Film Museum Books, *distributed by* Columbia University Press

Auteur Publishing, *distributed by* Columbia University Press

AuthorHouse, *division of* Author Solutions Inc

Authorlink Press, *imprint of* Authorlink®

Authors, *imprint of* University of California Press

AuthorsandExperts.com, *division of* Five Star Publications Inc

Avalon House, *distributed by* Chelsea Green Publishing Co

Avalon Travel, *imprint of* The Perseus Books Group

Avalon Travel Publishing, *member of* The Perseus Books Group, *distributed by* Perseus Books Group-International Sales, Publishers Group Canada, Publishers Group West

Avamra Institute, *distributed by* Moznaim Publishing Corp

Avant-Guide, *imprint of* Empire Press Media/Avant-Guide

Avanyu Publishing, *distributed by* University of New Mexico

Avatar Press, *distributed by* Simon & Schuster Sales Division

Ave Maria Press, *imprint of* Ave Maria Press

Avery, *imprint of* Penguin Group (USA) LLC, Penguin Group (USA) LLC, a Penguin Random House company, The Putnam Publishing Group

Avery Color Studios, *distributed by* Partners Book Distributing

Aviation Elite Units, *imprint of* Osprey Publishing Inc

AVKO Educational Research Foundation Inc, *division of* AVKO Foundation

Avon, *imprint of* HarperCollins General Books Group

Avon Books, *imprint of* HarperCollins Publishers Sales, *distributor for* Alloy Entertainment LLC

Avon Impulse, *imprint of* HarperCollins General Books Group

Avon Inspire, *imprint of* HarperCollins General Books Group

Avon Red, *imprint of* HarperCollins General Books Group

Awe-Struck, *imprint of* Mundania Press LLC

Awe-Struck Publishing, *imprint of* Mundania Press LLC

AWS, *distributed by* NACE International

AWWA, *imprint of* American Water Works Association (AWWA)

Artes Monte Azul, *imprint of* Blue Mountain Arts Inc

Back Bay Books, *imprint of* Little, Brown and Company

Back to Eden Books, *distributed by* Lotus Press

Backbeat Books, *imprint of* Hal Leonard Books, Hal Leonard Performing Arts Publishing Group, *distributed by* Hal Leonard Corp

Backcountry Publications, *imprint of* W W Norton & Company Inc

Backlist LLC, *distributed by* Simon & Schuster, Inc

BADM Books, *distributed by* Father & Son Publishing Inc

Baen Books, *distributed by* Simon & Schuster, Inc, Simon & Schuster Sales Division

Baen Publishing Enterprises, *distributed by* Simon & Schuster

Bagwyn Books, *imprint of* Arizona Center for Medieval & Renaissance Studies (ACMRS)

Baha'i Publishing, *subsidiary of* The National Spiritual Assembly of the Baha'is of the United States, The National Spiritual Assembly of the Baha'is of the United States

BainBridgeBooks, *imprint of* Trans-Atlantic Publications Inc

Baker Books, *division of* Baker Publishing Group, *distributor for* Focus on the Family, *distributed by* Perfection Learning Corp

Baker's Plays, *distributor for* Samuel French Inc, *distributed by* Samuel French Inc

Balboa Press, *division of* Hay House Inc

Balcony Press, *distributed by* Princeton Architectural Press

Baldar, *imprint of* Ross Books

Ball Publishing, *imprint of* Chicago Review Press

Ballantine, *distributed by* Perfection Learning Corp

Ballantine Books, *imprint of* Penguin Random House Inc, Random House Publishing Group

Ballantine Wellspring, *imprint of* Penguin Random House Inc

Baltos Lankos, *distributed by* Central European University Press

Balzer + Bray, *imprint of* HarperCollins Children's Books

Bancroft-Sage Publishing, *imprint of* Finney Company Inc

B&H Publishing Group, *division of* LifeWay Christian Resources

Bandit Books, *distributed by* John F Blair Publisher

Banned Books, *imprint of* Progressive Press

Banner Publishing, *imprint of* Whitaker House

Bantam, *distributor for* Parachute Publishing LLC, *distributed by* Perfection Learning Corp, Specialty Press Inc

Bantam Books, *imprint of* Penguin Random House Inc, Random House Publishing Group

Bantam Hardcover, *imprint of* Penguin Random House Inc

Bantam Mass Market, *imprint of* Penguin Random House Inc

Bantam Skylark, *imprint of* Penguin Random House Inc

Bantam Starfire, *imprint of* Penguin Random House Inc

Bantam Trade Paperback, *imprint of* Penguin Random House Inc

Bar Ilan, *distributed by* Gefen Books

Bar-Ilan University, *distributed by* American Mathematical Society

Barbary Coast Books, *subsidiary of* Berkeley Slavic Specialties

Barbour Books, *imprint of* Barbour Publishing Inc

The Bard Graduate Center, *distributed by* Yale University Press

BarnaBooks, *imprint of* Tyndale House Publishers Inc

Barnes & Noble, *distributor for* Ozark Publishing Inc, Paladin Press

Barnes & Noble Classics, *imprint of* Fine Creative Media, Inc

Barricade Books, *imprint of* Barricade Books Inc

Barringer, *distributor for* Marriage Transformation LLC

Barringer Publishing, *division of* Schlesinger Advertising & Marketing

Barron's, *distributed by* Delta Publishing Co

Barrons, *distributed by* Perfection Learning Corp

Bartleby Press, *subsidiary of* Jackson Westgate Publishing Group

Basch, *distributor for* Business Research Services Inc

Baseball America, *distributed by* Simon & Schuster, Inc, Simon & Schuster Sales Division

Basheer, *distributed by* Gingko Press Inc

Bashu Publishing, *distributed by* CN Times Books

Basic Books, *member of* The Perseus Books Group, *imprint of* The Perseus Books Group, *distributed by* CDS Distributors, HarperCollins Publishers

Basic Civitas, *imprint of* Basic Books

Basic Civitas Books, *imprint of* The Perseus Books Group

Basic Health Guides, *imprint of* Basic Health Publications Inc

Basic Health Publications, *imprint of* Basic Health Publications Inc

Randol Bass Music, *distributed by* ECS Publishing Corp

Bat Conservation International, *distributed by* University of Texas Press

David Bateman Ltd, *distributor for* Interweave Press LLC, Price World Publishing

Batsford, *distributed by* Sterling Publishing Co Inc

Battle Orders, *imprint of* Osprey Publishing Inc

Battlebridge, *distributed by* Franklin, Beedle & Associates Inc

Bayard, *distributed by* Crabtree Publishing Co

Baylor University Press, *distributed by* The Johns Hopkins University Press, Johns Hopkins University Press Fullfillment Service

BBC Audiobooks America, *distributor for* Macmillan Audio

BDD Audio Publishing, *imprint of* Penguin Random House Inc

Beach Lane Books, *imprint of* Simon & Schuster Children's Publishing

Beach Lloyd Publishers LLC, *distributor for* Le Chambon-sur-Lignon, CIDEB (Italy), Fondation pour la Memoire de la Shoah (Paris), Kar-Ben Publishing, Kiron Editions du Felin (Paris), JP Lattes (Paris), Le Manuscrit (Paris), Oxford University Press (NYC), *distributed by* Tralco (CN)

BeachHouse Books, *imprint of* Science & Humanities Press

Beacon Hill Press of Kansas City, *subsidiary of* Nazarene Publishing House

Beacon Music, *distributed by* Hal Leonard Corp

Beacon Press, *distributed by* Random House Publisher Services

Bear & Co Inc, *imprint of* Inner Traditions International Ltd

Bear Cub Books, *imprint of* Inner Traditions International Ltd

Bear Meadows Research Group, *imprint of* Crumb Elbow Publishing

Beauxarts, *imprint of* Alan Wofsy Fine Arts

Mitchell Beazley, *distributed by* Phaidon Press Inc

Bebop Books, *imprint of* Lee & Low Books Inc

The Stephen Bechtel Fund, *imprint of* University of California Press

Bedford/St Martin's, *imprint of* Macmillan Higher Education

Beech River Books, *distributed by* Enfield Publishing & Distribution Co

Beech Tree Books, *imprint of* HarperCollins Publishers

Beekman Books Inc, *distributor for* C W Daniel, Gomer Press, Music Sales Corp, Kogan Page

Begell-Atom LLC, *subsidiary of* Begell House Inc Publishers

Beginner Books, *imprint of* Random House Children's Books

Behrman House Inc, *distributor for* Rossel Books

Beinecke Rare Book & Manuscript Library, *distributed by* University Press of New England

Belknap Press, *imprint of* Harvard University Press

Bell Bridge Books, *imprint of* BelleBooks

Bell Pond Books, *imprint of* SteinerBooks

Bell Tower, *imprint of* Penguin Random House Inc

Bella Books, *distributed by* Turnaround (London)

Bellagio Press, *imprint of* TAJ Books International LLC

Belle Isle Books, *imprint of* Brandylane Publishers Inc

Belwin, *imprint of* Alfred Music Publishing

Benchmark Maps, *distributed by* Wide World of Maps Inc

Benchmark Press, *imprint of* Triumph Books

Bendon, *distributor for* Parachute Publishing LLC

John Benjamins North America Inc, *subsidiary of* John Benjamins Publishing Co

Bentley Publishers, *division of* Robert Bentley Inc, Robert Bentley Inc

BePuzzled, *division of* University Games

Berg Publishers, *distributed by* Palgrave Macmillan, St Martin's Press, LLC

W H Berger, *distributed by* Sunbelt Publications Inc

Berghahn Books, *distributor for* Yad Vashem

Berghahn Books Ltd (UK), *division of* Berghahn Books

Berklee Press, *imprint of* Hal Leonard Corp, *distributed by* Hal Leonard Corp

Berkley, *distributor for* Parachute Publishing LLC, *distributed by* Perfection Learning Corp

Berkley Books, *imprint of* Berkley Publishing Group, Penguin Group (USA) LLC, Penguin Group (USA) LLC, a Penguin Random House company

Berkley Publishing Group, *division of* Penguin Group (USA) LLC, Penguin Group (USA) LLC, a Penguin Random House company

Bernan, *imprint of* Rowman & Littlefield Publishing Group

Bertelsmann Foundation Publishers, *distributed by* The Brookings Institution Press

Bertrams UK, *distributor for* Dissertation.com

Bess Press, *distributed by* The Islander Group (TIG) (Hawaii wholesaler/book dist)

Best Books International, *subsidiary of* Empire Publishing Service

Best Dives Guides, *imprint of* Hunter Publishing Inc

Best Places® Guidebooks Series, *imprint of* Sasquatch Books

Best Publishing Co, *distributed by* Marine Techniques Publishing

Emily Bestler Books, *imprint of* Atria Books

Beta Books, *imprint of* Bandanna Books

Bethany House Publishers, *division of* Baker Publishing Group

Bethlehem Books, *affiliate of* Bethlehem Community, *distributed by* Ignatius Press

Betterway Books, *imprint of* F+W, A Content + eCommerce Company

Betty Crocker®, *imprint of* Houghton Mifflin Harcourt Trade & Reference Division

Between the Lines, *distributed by* Dufour Editions Inc

Beyond Words, *imprint of* Atria Books, Simon & Schuster Audio, *distributed by* Simon & Schuster, Inc

Beyond Words Publishing Inc, *imprint of* Simon & Schuster, *distributed by* Simon & Schuster

Bibli O'Phile, *distributed by* Penguin Group (USA) LLC, a Penguin Random House company

Biblio, *distributed by* Bloch Publishing Co

Bibliographical Society of America, *distributed by* Oak Knoll Press

Bibliographical Society of University of Virginia, *distributed by* Oak Knoll Press

The Bibliographical Society (UK), *distributed by* Oak Knoll Press

Bibliopola Press, *distributed by* University Press of New England

Bider Technology, *distributed by* Cheng & Tsui Co Inc

Big Buddy Books, *imprint of* ABDO Publishing Group

Big Guy Books Inc, *distributed by* Arcturus Publishing Ltd (United Kingdom), Bookwise International (Australia), Independent Publishers Group (handles all Trade Distribution in the US), Scholastic New Zealand (New Zealand), Iwasaki Shoten (Japanese Translation)

Big Meteor, *distributed by* Omnibus Press

Big Meteor Publishing, *distributed by* Schirmer Trade Books

Big Picture Press, *imprint of* Candlewick Press

Big Sky Maps, *distributed by* Wide World of Maps Inc

Big Tree Books, *imprint of* Easy Money Press

Bigwig Briefs, *imprint of* Aspatore Books

Bilingual Review Press, *distributed by* Arte Publico Press

Binational Press, *imprint of* San Diego State University Press

Bindu Books, *imprint of* Inner Traditions International Ltd

Biographical Publishing Co, *distributor for* Eagles Landing Publishing, Spyglass Books LLC

BioMed Central, *imprint of* Springer

BioTechniques Books, *division of* Informa Business Information

Birch Brook Impressions, *subsidiary of* Birch Brook Press

Birch Brook Press, *imprint of* Birch Brook Press, *distributor for* Carpenter Gothic Press, Natural Heritage Press, Persephone Press

Bird Dog Publishing, *imprint of* Bottom Dog Press

Birkhauser Science, *imprint of* Springer

Birlinn Publishing, *distributed by* Casemate Publishers & Book Distributors LLC

Bisk Education, *distributed by* Bisk Publishing Co

Bisk Publishing Co, *distributor for* Bisk Education

Bison Books, *imprint of* University of Nebraska Press

BizBest Media Features, *division of* BizBest Media Corp

BizBestLocal.com, *subsidiary of* BizBest Media Corp

BizBriefing.com, *subsidiary of* BizBest Media Corp

BizLaunchPad.com, *subsidiary of* BizBest Media Corp

BizOwnerOnly.com, *subsidiary of* BizBest Media Corp

BizTaxes.com, *subsidiary of* BizBest Media Corp

BJU Press, *unit of* Bob Jones University

BL Publishing, *distributed by* Simon & Schuster, Inc

Black Amber Press, *distributed by* Dufour Editions Inc

Black & White Publishing (UK), *distributed by* Interlink Publishing Group Inc

Black Cat, *imprint of* Grove Atlantic Inc

Black Classic Press, *distributed by* Publishers Group West (PGW)

Black Coral, *imprint of* Genesis Press Inc

Black Dog & Leventhal, *imprint of* Hachette Books

Black Heritage: Celebrating Culture, *imprint of* Gallopade International Inc

Black Iron Cookin' Co, *imprint of* Quixote Press

Black Iron Cooking Co, *imprint of* Hearts & Tummies Cookbook Co

Black Sparrow, *imprint of* David R Godine Publisher Inc

Black Squirrel Books, *imprint of* Kent State University Press

Blacklock Nature Photography, *distributed by* Adventure Publications

Blackstaff Press Ltd, *distributed by* Dufour Editions Inc

Blackwells, *distributor for* Teton NewMedia

John F Blair Publisher, *distributor for* Bandit Books, Bright Mountain Books, Canterbury House Publishing, The Colonial Williamsburg Foundation, Down Home Press, Eno Publishers, Hub City Press, Looking Glass Books, Lookout Books, NewSouth Books, Niche Publishing, Pennywell Press, Upper Ohio Valley Books, Walkabout Press, Willow Hill Press

Blake Books, *distributed by* Perfection Learning Corp

The Blaxis, *imprint of* Cedar Grove Books

Bliss, *imprint of* Entangled Publishing, *distributed by* Dufour Editions Inc

Bloch Publishing Co, *distributor for* Biblio, Menorah, Scarf Press, Sephardic House, Soncino

Block Board Books, *imprint of* Modern Publishing

Block Museum, *distributed by* Oak Knoll Press

Bloodaxe Books Ltd, *distributed by* Dufour Editions Inc

Bloody Brits Press, *imprint of* Bywater Books

Bloom's Literary Criticism, *imprint of* Infobase Learning

Bloomsbury, *imprint of* Bloomsbury Publishing Inc

Bloomsbury Academic, *distributor for* Paragon House, Spring Publications

Bloomsbury International Publishing USA, *distributor for* Paragon House

Bloomsbury Press, *imprint of* Bloomsbury Publishing Inc

Bloomsbury Publishing Inc, *distributed by* Macmillan

Bloomsbury USA, *imprint of* Bloomsbury Publishing Inc, *distributed by* St Martin's Press, LLC

Blue & Gray, *imprint of* Book Sales Inc

Blue Apple Books, *distributed by* Chronicle Books LLC

Blue Beacon Books, *imprint of* Regal Crest Enterprises LLC

Blue Dolphin Publishing Inc, *distributor for* The Lotus Seed Press (China) (ISBN prefix: 978-962-8602)

Blue Guides Ltd, *distributed by* W W Norton & Company Inc

Blue Mountain Press®, *imprint of* Blue Mountain Arts Inc

Blue Note, *imprint of* Blue Note Publications Inc

Blue Note Books, *imprint of* Blue Note Publications Inc

Blue Poppy Press, *division of* Blue Poppy Enterprises Inc, *distributed by* China Books, New Leaf Books, Partner's Book Distributing Inc, Partner's/West Book Distributing Inc, Redwing Book Co, Satas, Tools4Healing (Scott Mieras)

Blue Rider, *imprint of* Penguin Group (USA) LLC, a Penguin Random House company

Blue Rider Press, *imprint of* Penguin Group (USA) LLC, a Penguin Random House company, Penguin Group (USA) LLC, a Penguin Random House company

Blue Sky Gallery, *distributed by* Franklin, Beedle & Associates Inc

The Blue Sky Press, *imprint of* Scholastic Trade Division

Blue Snake Books, *imprint of* North Atlantic Books

BlueBridge, *imprint of* United Tribes Media Inc

BNA Books, *division of* Bloomberg BNA

BNI Publications, *distributor for* Craftsman Book Co, *distributed by* Craftsman Book Co

BoardSource, *distributed by* American Society of Association Executives

Bobolink Media, *distributed by* Sunbelt Publications Inc

Fred Bock Music Company, *distributed by* Hal Leonard Corp

Bollingen Series, *imprint of* Princeton University Press

Bonneville Books, *imprint of* Cedar Fort Inc, The University of Utah Press

Book Guild, *distributed by* Trans-Atlantic Publications Inc

Book House, *distributor for* Business Research Services Inc, *distributed by* Trans-Atlantic Publications Inc

The Book House, *distributor for* Primary Research Group Inc

Book Marketing Works, *subsidiary of* Book Marketing Works LLC

Book Peddlers, *distributed by* Gryphon House Inc

Book Publishing Co, *distributor for* Cherokee Publications, Crazy Crow, CRCS Publications, Critical Path, Gentle World, Hippocrates Publications, Magni Co, Sproutman Publications

The Book Publishing Co, *distributed by* Orca Book Publishers

Book Sales Inc, *division of* Quarto Publishing Group USA Inc, *distributed by* Heimburger House Publishing Co

Booklines Hawaii, *distributor for* Centerstream Publishing LLC

Books Alive, *imprint of* Book Publishing Co

Books Americana, *imprint of* Krause Publications Inc

Books & Co/Turtle Point, *imprint of* Turtle Point Press

Books for Independent Minds, *imprint of* Ronin Publishing Inc

Books Good For Young Children™, *imprint of* Maren Green Publishing Inc

Books In Motion, *division of* Classic Ventures Ltd, Classic Ventures Ltd

Books on Tape®, *imprint of* Penguin Random House Inc, *distributor for* Listening Library®

Books West, *distributor for* Wilderness Adventures Press Inc

Bookwise International, *distributor for* Big Guy Books Inc

Boom! Studios, *distributed by* Simon & Schuster, Inc, Simon & Schuster Sales & Marketing, Simon & Schuster Sales Division

Boone & Crockett Club, *distributed by* The Globe Pequot Press

Boosey & Hawkes, *distributed by* Hal Leonard Corp

Booth-Clibborn Editions, *distributed by* Harry N Abrams Inc

Bora, *distributed by* Alan Wofsy Fine Arts

Borden Publishing, *distributed by* Gem Guides Book Co

Borders, *distributor for* Paladin Press

Boreal Books, *imprint of* Red Hen Press

Borealis, *imprint of* White Wolf Publishing Inc

Borealis Books, *imprint of* Minnesota Historical Society Press

Borgo Press, *imprint of* Wildside Press LLC

Boson Books, *imprint of* Bitingduck Press LLC

Boston College, *distributed by* Oak Knoll Press

Boston Globe Puzzle Books, *imprint of* Random House Reference/Random House Puzzles & Games/House of Collectibles

Botanica Press, *imprint of* Book Publishing Co

Bottom Dog Press, *imprint of* Bottom Dog Press, *distributor for* The Firelands Writing Center (Heartlands Magazine)

Lee Boudreaux Books, *imprint of* Little, Brown and Company

Boulden, *distributed by* MAR*CO Products Inc

Boulden Publishing, *distributor for* MAR*CO Products Inc

Boundless, *imprint of* Zumaya Publications LLC

Bourbon Street Books, *imprint of* HarperCollins General Books Group

R R Bowker LLC, *subsidiary of* ProQuest LLC

R R Bowker's Books in Print Series, *imprint of* Grey House Publishing Inc™

Boxer Books, *distributed by* Sterling Publishing Co Inc

Boydell & Brewer Inc, *affiliate of* Boydell & Brewer Ltd (UK)

Boyds Mills Press, *division of* Highlights for Children Inc, *subsidiary of* Highlights for Children Inc, *distributed by* Heimburger House Publishing Co

Boye Knives Press, *distributed by* Chelsea Green Publishing Co

Boynton/Cook Publishers, *imprint of* Heinemann, *distributed by* Pearson Australia-Schools Division, Pearson Education Canada, Pearson New Zealand-Schools Division

Boys Town Press, *division of* Boys Town, *distributor for* Specialty Press Inc, *distributed by* Deep Books Ltd (Europe & UK), Footprint Books (Australia & New Zealand), Monarch Books of Canada Ltd (Canada)

BPI Records, *imprint of* Bridge Publications Inc

Bradford Books, *imprint of* The MIT Press

Brady, *distributed by* Fire Engineering Books & Videos

Joan Brady, *distributed by* Sunbelt Publications Inc

BradyGames, *member of* Penguin Group (USA) LLC, Penguin Group (USA) LLC, a Penguin Random House company

Braided River, *imprint of* The Mountaineers Books

Brandeis University Press, *imprint of* University Press of New England

Branden Books, *subsidiary of* Branden Publishing Co, *distributor for* Dante University of America Press Inc

Branden Publishing Co, *distributor for* Dante University of America Press Inc

Brandon Books, *distributed by* Dufour Editions Inc

Brandon Books Cinematic Novels, *imprint of* Branden Books

Brashear Music Co, *imprint of* Branden Books

Deya Brashears, *distributed by* Gryphon House Inc

Brava, *imprint of* Kensington Publishing Corp

Brazen, *imprint of* Entangled Publishing

George Braziller Inc, *distributed by* Antique Collectors' Club Ltd, W W Norton & Company Inc

A Karen & Michael Braziller Book, *imprint of* Persea Books

Breakfast Communications, *distributed by* SAS Publishing

Breakthrough Publications, *imprint of* Breakthrough Publications Inc

Breakthrough to Literacy, *imprint of* Wright Group/McGraw-Hill

Brenner Information Group, *division of* Brenner Microcomputing Inc

Breslov Research Institute, *distributed by* Moznaim Publishing Corp

Brethren Press, *division of* Church of the Brethren

Brewers Publications, *division of* Brewers Association

Brick Tower Press, *imprint of* J T Colby & Co Inc

BrickHouse Books Inc, *distributed by* Itasca

Bridge, *imprint of* Bridge-Logos Inc

Bridge Audio, *imprint of* Bridge Publications Inc

Bridge-Logos Inc, *distributor for* New Wine Press, RoperPenberthy Publishing Ltd, Sovereign World, Warboys LLC

Bridge 21, *distributed by* Transaction Publishers Inc

Brief Books, *imprint of* Birch Brook Press

Bright Mountain Books, *distributed by* John F Blair Publisher

Bright Ring Publishing, *distributed by* Gryphon House Inc

Brigids Books, *subsidiary of* Leilah Publications

Brill Inc, *subsidiary of* Koninklijke Brill NV

Brilliance Audio, *subsidiary of* Amazon.com, Amazon.com Inc

Brio Girls, *imprint of* Focus on the Family

British Film Institute, *distributed by* Palgrave Macmillan, University of California Press

Broadside Books, *imprint of* HarperCollins General Books Group

Broadstone Books, *distributed by* Fons Vitae

Broadway Books, *imprint of* Crown Publishing Group

Brodart Co, *distributor for* Do-It-Yourself Legal Publishers, Twilight Times Books

Brookings Institution Press, *distributor for* Council on Foreign Relations Press, University of California Institute on Global Conflict & Cooperation

The Brookings Institution Press, *division of* Brookings Institution, *distributor for* American Chamber of Commerce to the European Union, Asian Development Bank Institute, Aspen Institute, Bertelsmann Foundation Publishers, Carnegie Endowment for International Peace, Center for Global Development, The Centre for Economic Policy Research, Centre for European Policy Studies, The Century Foundation, Chatham House, Economica, Institute of Latin American Studies, International Labor Offices, Jamestown Foundation, Japan Center for International Exchange, Migration Policy Institute, OECD, Perseus Academic, Shorenstein Asia-Pacific Research Center, The Trilateral Commission, United Nations University Press, World Trade Organization, *distributed by* The Johns Hopkins University Press

Brooklands Books Ltd, *distributed by* CarTech Inc

Brooklyn Botanic Garden, *distributed by* Sterling Publishing Co Inc

Brooks, *distributed by* Council for Exceptional Children (CEC)

Brooks/Cole, *imprint of* Wadsworth Publishing

Brotherhood of Saint Herman of Alaska, *imprint of* Saint Herman Press

Gustav Broukal Press, *imprint of* American Atheist Press

Brown Bear Books, *imprint of* Black Rabbit Books

Brown Books Agency, *division of* Brown Books Publishing Group

Brown Books Kids, *division of* Brown Books Publishing Group

John Carter Brown Library, *distributed by* Oak Knoll Press

Brown Judaic Studies, *distributed by* SBL Press

Brown University, *distributed by* American Mathematical Society

Brown Walker Press, *imprint of* Universal-Publishers Inc

Karen Brown's Guides, *distributed by* Penguin Random House Inc

Brumby Sunstate, *distributor for* Ash Tree Publishing

Brusberg (Berlin), *distributed by* Alan Wofsy Fine Arts

Bryn Mawr College, *distributed by* Oak Knoll Press

Bryn Mawr Commentaries, *distributed by* Hackett Publishing Co Inc

Brynmorgen Press, *distributed by* Gem Guides Book Co

Brynwood Publishing, *distributed by* Resilient Publishing

Bubble Books, *imprint of* Modern Publishing

Bucking Horse Books, *distributed by* Mountain Press Publishing Co

Bucknell University Press, *distributed by* Rowman & Littlefield

Buddy Books, *imprint of* ABDO Publishing Group

Buena Vista DVDs, *distributed by* Recorded Books LLC

Bufflehead Books, *imprint of* Down The Shore Publishing Corp

BuilderBooks.com, *division of* National Association of Home Builders (NAHB), *distributor for* National Association of Home Builders (NAHB)

Builders Book Inc, *distributor for* Craftsman Book Co, *distributed by* Craftsman Book Co

Building Blocks, *distributed by* Gryphon House Inc

Building Excellence, *imprint of* Mel Bay Publications Inc

Building News Inc, *distributed by* Craftsman Book Co

Bulfinch/Little, *distributor for* National Gallery of Art

Bulgarian-American Cultural Society ALEKO, *subsidiary of* Cross-Cultural Communications

Bureau of Economic Geology, University of Texas at Austin, *division of* University of Texas at Austin, *distributor for* Gulf Coast Association of Geological Societies, Gulf Coast Section, Texas Memorial Museum (selected titles)

Burnell Books, *distributor for* MAR*CO Products Inc

Burning Bush Press, *imprint of* United Synagogue Book Service

Burns Archive Press, *imprint of* Burns Archive Photographic Distributors Ltd

Buros Institute, *distributed by* University of Nebraska Press

Business & Research Associates, *distributed by* FurnitureCore

Business Expert Press, *subsidiary of* IGroup

Business Research Services Inc, *distributor for* Riley & Johnson, *distributed by* Basch, Book House, Coutts, Gale Research Inc, Midwest Library Service

Business Success Series, *imprint of* PREP Publishing

Butler Center for Arkansas Studies, *distributed by* The University of Arkansas Press

Butterworth Heinemann, *distributed by* SAMS Technical Publishing LLC

Butterworth-Heinemann, *distributed by* Marine Techniques Publishing, NACE International

Butterworths, *distributed by* William S Hein & Co Inc

BWI Books, *distributor for* Twilight Times Books

By Design Press, *imprint of* Quite Specific Media Group Ltd

Byte Level Books, *imprint of* Ashland Creek Press

BYU Museum of Peoples & Cultures, *distributed by* The University of Utah Press

BYU Studies, *distributed by* The University of Utah Press

C & T Publishing Inc, *distributed by* Watson-Guptill Publications

C E P Inc, *imprint of* Paladin Press

Cabi Books, *distributed by* Stylus Publishing LLC

Cademon, *imprint of* HarperCollins Publishers Sales

Caissa Editions, *affiliate of* Dale A Brandreth Books

CAL Books, *distributed by* Casemate Publishers & Book Distributors LLC

Cal-Earth, *distributed by* Chelsea Green Publishing Co

Caliber, *imprint of* Berkley Books

Calico, *imprint of* ABDO Publishing Group

California Sea Grant, *distributed by* Sunbelt Publications Inc

Calkins Creek, *imprint of* Boyds Mills Press

Calloway House, *distributor for* MAR*CO Products Inc

Cambridge Educational, *imprint of* Infobase Learning

Cambridge Scientific Publishers, *distributed by* Enfield Publishing & Distribution Co

Cambridge University Press, *division of* University of Cambridge, *distributor for* The Mathematical Association of America, National Gallery of Art, *distributed by* Delta Publishing Co, Dominie Press, NACE International

Camden House, *imprint of* Boydell & Brewer Inc

Camel Press, *distributed by* Epicenter Press Inc

Camelion Plays, *distributed by* Players Press Inc

Camerapix Publishers International, *distributed by* Interlink Publishing Group Inc

Campaign, *imprint of* Osprey Publishing Inc

Georgina Campbell Guides (Ireland), *distributed by* Interlink Publishing Group Inc

Paul Douglas Campbell, *distributed by* Sunbelt Publications Inc

Canadian Caboose Press, *distributed by* Heimburger House Publishing Co

Canadian Centre for Architecture, *distributed by* The MIT Press

Canadian Society of Petroleum Geologists, *distributor for* AAPG (American Association of Petroleum Geologists)

Canal Press, *imprint of* Schiffer Publishing Ltd

Candle Books, *distributed by* Kregel Publications

Candlewick Entertainment, *imprint of* Candlewick Press

Candlewick Press, *subsidiary of* Walker Books Ltd (London), *distributed by* Perfection Learning Corp

CandyCane Press, *imprint of* Ideals Publications, a Guideposts Co

Canterbury House Publishing, *distributed by* John F Blair Publisher

Gloriae Dei Cantores, *distributed by* Paraclete Press Inc

Cantors Assembly, *imprint of* Transcontinental Music Publications

Canyonlands Natural History Association, *distributed by* The University of Utah Press

Capall-Bann, *distributed by* Holmes Publishing Group LLC

Capital Enquiry Inc, *distributor for* Center for Investigative Reporting

Capstone, *imprint of* John Wiley & Sons Inc

Capstone Press, *imprint of* Capstone Publishers™

Caravan Books, *subsidiary of* Academic Resources Corp, Academic Resources Corp

Caravel Books, *imprint of* Pleasure Boat Studio: A Literary Press

Cardinal Publishers Group, *distributor for* Price World Publishing, Wish Publishing

Cardoza, *distributed by* Simon & Schuster Sales Division

Cardoza Publishing, *distributor for* Simon & Schuster, *distributed by* Simon & Schuster, Inc

Career Examination Series, *imprint of* National Learning Corp

Career Kids FYI, *distributor for* MAR*CO Products Inc

Caribe Betania Editores, *division of* Grupo Nelson Inc

Coleccion Caribena, *imprint of* University of Puerto Rico Press

Carina Press, *imprint of* Harlequin Enterprises Ltd

Carlton Books, *distributed by* Sterling Publishing Co Inc

Carmania Press London, *distributed by* Purple Mountain Press Ltd

Carnegie Endowment for International Peace, *distributed by* The Brookings Institution Press

Carolrhoda Books, *division of* Lerner Publishing Group Inc

Carolrhoda Books Inc, *imprint of* Lerner Publishing Group Inc

Carolrhoda Lab™, *imprint of* Lerner Publishing Group Inc

Carpe Diem Professional Calendars, *imprint of* Flying Pen Press LLC

Carpenter Gothic Press, *distributed by* Birch Brook Press

Carpet Bombing Culture, *distributed by* Gingko Press Inc

Carson-Dellosa Publishing LLC, *distributor for* Key Education, Mark Twain Media

Carstens, *distributed by* Heimburger House Publishing Co

CarTech Inc, *distributor for* Brooklands Books Ltd, Wolfgang Publications

Carthage Reprints, *imprint of* St Augustine's Press Inc

Cartwheel Books, *imprint of* Scholastic Trade Division

Carysfort Press, *distributed by* Dufour Editions Inc

Casa Bautista, *distributed by* Editorial Bautista Independiente

Casa Bautista de Publicaciones, *affiliate of* Southern Baptist Convention, *distributed by* LifeWay Christian Resources

Casa Creation, *imprint of* Charisma Media

Cascade Expeditions, *imprint of* Crumb Elbow Publishing

Cascade Geographic Society, *imprint of* Crumb Elbow Publishing

Casemate, *distributed by* Casemate Publishers & Book Distributors LLC

Casemate/Flashpoint, *distributed by* Casemate Publishers & Book Distributors LLC

Casemate Publishers & Book Distributors LLC, *distributor for* AF Editions, Airfile Publications, Amber Books (UK), Amberley Publishing (UK), Birlinn Publishing (UK), CAL Books, Casemate (USA), Casemate/Flashpoint, Compendium Films, Compendium Publishing (UK), D-Day Publishing (Belgium), Eagle Editions, Earthbound Publications, Formac Publishing (Canada), Foundry, Front Street Press (USA), Frontline Books, Greenhill Books, Grub Street (UK), Harpia Publishing, Heimdal, Helion & Co Ltd (UK), Editions Charles Herissey (France), Histoire & Collections (France), Historical Archive Press, Historical Indexes (USA), History Facts, Paul Holberton Publishing, Indo Editions (France), Ironclad Publishing (USA), De Krijger (Belgium), Lancer Publishers, Lorimer, Military Illustrated, MMP (UK/ Poland), OREP, Pen & Sword Books Ltd (UK), Pen & Sword Digital, Philedition, Riebel-Roque, RZM Publishing (USA), S I Publicaties BV, Savas Beatie (USA), Scarab Miniatures, Seaforth Publishing, Tattered Flag, 30 Degrees South Publishers, Vanwell-Looking Back Press, Vanwell Publishing (Canada), WAG Books, Warlord Games, Wharncliffe

Cassell, *distributed by* Sterling Publishing Co Inc

Cast Books, *imprint of* Bandanna Books

CASTI Publishing, *distributed by* NACE International

Castle Books, *imprint of* Book Sales Inc

Castle Keep Books, *imprint of* James A Rock & Co Publishers

Catalpa Press, *distributed by* Oak Knoll Press

Catechesis of the Good Shepherd Publications, *imprint of* Liturgy Training Publications

Cathedral Music Press, *division of* Mel Bay Publications Inc, *imprint of* Mel Bay Publications Inc

Catholic Approach Series, *imprint of* Pauline Books & Media

Catholic Treasures, *distributor for* Angelus Press

Catholic University of America Press, *distributed by* The Johns Hopkins University Press

The Catholic University of America Press, *distributor for* American Maritain Association, Institute for the Psychological Sciences Press (IPS), Sapientia Press

CavanKerry Press, *distributed by* University Press of New England

Caveat Press, *imprint of* White Cloud Press

Caxton Club, *distributed by* Oak Knoll Press

Caxton Press, *division of* The Caxton Printers Ltd, The Caxton Printers Ltd, *distributor for* Hambleton Publishing, Historic Idaho Series, Photosmith Books, Snake Country Publishing, University of Idaho Asian American Comparative Collection, University of Idaho Press, *distributed by* University of Nebraska Press

CBP/EMH, *imprint of* Casa Bautista de Publicaciones

CCA, *imprint of* Copywriter's Council of America (CCA), The Linick Group Inc

CCH, *distributor for* AICPA Professional Publications

CCH, a Wolters Kluwer business, *subsidiary of* Wolters Kluwer

CCH INCORPORATED, *imprint of* Wolters Kluwer US Corp

CCH Peterson, *subsidiary of* CCH, a Wolters Kluwer business

CCH Riverwoods, *subsidiary of* CCH, a Wolters Kluwer business

CCH St Petersburg, *subsidiary of* CCH, a Wolters Kluwer business

CCH Tax Compliance, *subsidiary of* CCH, a Wolters Kluwer business

CCH Washington DC, *subsidiary of* CCH, a Wolters Kluwer business

CDS Distributors, *distributor for* Basic Books

Cedar Fort Inc, *distributor for* Horizon Publishers & Distributors Inc

CEF Press, *subsidiary of* Child Evangelism Fellowship Inc, Child Evangelism Fellowship Inc

Celebra, *imprint of* Penguin Group (USA) LLC, Penguin Group (USA) LLC, a Penguin Random House company

Celebrity Profiles Publishing, *division of* Edison & Kellogg

Cengage Learning, *distributed by* Air Conditioning Contractors of America

Cengage Learning™, *distributor for* Wadsworth Publishing

Cengage Learning Asia Pte Ltd, *distributor for* Association for Talent Development (ATD)

Cengage Learning Australia, *distributed by* Cheng & Tsui Co Inc

Centaur Books, *imprint of* Joshua Tree Publishing

Center for Book Arts, *distributed by* Oak Knoll Press

Center for Chinese Studies, University of Michigan, *distributed by* University of Michigan Press

Center for Contemporary Judaica, *imprint of* Prayer Book Press Inc

Center for Creative Leadership LLC, *affiliate of* Smith Richardson Foundation, *distributor for* Free Press, Harvard Business School Press, Jossey-Bass, Lominger Inc, John Wiley & Sons Inc, *distributed by* Jossey-Bass, John Wiley & Sons Inc

Center for East Asian Studies (CEAS), *subsidiary of* Western Washington University

Center for Global Development, *distributed by* The Brookings Institution Press, Peterson Institute for International Economics (PIIE)

Center for Investigative Reporting, *distributed by* Capital Enquiry Inc

The Center for Learning, *division of* Social Studies School Service

Center for Literary Publishing, *distributed by* University Press of Colorado

Center for National Policy Press, *distributed by* University Press of America Inc

Center for South & Southeast Asian Studies, University of Michigan, *distributed by* University of Michigan Press

Center for Talented Youth, *distributed by* The Johns Hopkins University Press

Center for the Child Care Workforce, *distributed by* Gryphon House Inc

The Center for the Study of Upper Midwestern Culture, *distributed by* University of Wisconsin Press

Center for US-Mexican Studies, *distributed by* Lynne Rienner Publishers Inc

Center for Urban Policy Research, *imprint of* Transaction Publishers Inc

Center for Youth Issues/STARS, *distributed by* MAR*CO Products Inc

Center of Emigrants from Serbia, *distributed by* Cross-Cultural Communications

Center Street, *imprint of* Hachette Nashville

Centerbrook Publishing, *subsidiary of* Centerstream Publishing LLC

Centerstream Publications, *imprint of* Hal Leonard Corp, *distributed by* Hal Leonard Corp

Centerstream Publishing LLC, *distributed by* Booklines Hawaii, Hal Leonard Corp

Central European University Press, *distributor for* Apostrofa Publishers, Baltos Lankos, Helena History Press, International Debate Education Association, Open Society Institute, *distributed by* University of Toronto Press (Canada)

Central Recovery Press (CRP), *unit of* Central Recovery Treatment

The Centre for Economic Policy Research, *distributed by* The Brookings Institution Press

Centre for European Policy Studies, *distributed by* The Brookings Institution Press

The Century Foundation, *distributed by* The Brookings Institution Press

The Century Foundation Press, *division of* The Century Foundation

Cerf & Peterson, *distributed by* Welcome Books®

Certification Press, *imprint of* McGraw-Hill Professional

Certified Nurse Series (CN), *imprint of* National Learning Corp

Cervantes & Co, *imprint of* European Masterpieces, *distributed by* European Masterpieces

CFI, *imprint of* Cedar Fort Inc

CFKR Career, *distributor for* MAR*CO Products Inc

CGN, *imprint of* Cedar Grove Books

Chalice Press, *division of* Christian Board of Publications, *distributed by* Cokesbury

Challenges of Aging Instruction Booklets, *imprint of* Letterbox/Papyrus of London Publishers USA

Chambers, *distributed by* Houghton Mifflin Harcourt

Le Chambon-sur-Lignon, *distributed by* Beach Lloyd Publishers LLC

Chandos, *distributed by* Neal-Schuman Publishers Inc

Chanterelle, *distributed by* Mel Bay Publications Inc

Chapin Library, *distributed by* Oak Knoll Press

Chapter Books, *imprint of* ABDO Publishing Group

Character Development, *distributor for* MAR*CO Products Inc

CharismaLife, *distributed by* CharismaLife Publishers

CharismaLife Publishers, *distributor for* CharismaLife

The Charles Press, Publishers, *subsidiary of* Oxbridge Corp, The Oxbridge Corp

Charles River Media, *imprint of* Cengage Learning

Charles Scribner's Sons®, *imprint of* Gale

Charlesbridge Press, *distributed by* Perfection Learning Corp

Charlesbridge Publishing Inc, *distributor for* American Express (travel & leisure, food & wine), EarlyLight Books, *distributed by* Penguin Random House Canada Limited

Chartwell Books, *imprint of* Book Sales Inc

Chatham House, *distributed by* The Brookings Institution Press

Chatterbox Press, *distributed by* Gryphon House Inc

Cheap Bastards, *imprint of* The Globe Pequot Press

Checkerboard Library, *imprint of* ABDO Publishing Group

Chef Express, *imprint of* Standard International Media Holdings

Chef Success, *imprint of* Standard International Media Holdings

Chelsea Clubhouse, *imprint of* Chelsea House Publishers

Chelsea Green Publishing Co, *distributor for* AATEC Publications, American Council for an Energy Efficient Economy (ACEEE), Anomaly Press, Avalon House, Boye Knives Press, Cal-Earth, Earth Pledge, Eco Logic Books, Ecological Design Institute, Ecological Design Press, Empowerment Institute, Filaree Productions, Flower Press, Foundation for Deep Ecology, Fox Maple Press, Green Books, Green Building Press, Green Man Publishing, Groundworks, Hand Print Press, Holmgren Design Services, Jenkins Publishing, Knossus Project, Left To Write Press, Madison Area Community Supported Agriculture Coalition,

Marion Institute, marketumbrella.org, Metamorphic Press, Moneta Publications, Ottographics, Peregrinzilla, Permanent Publications, Daniela Piazza Editore, Polyface, Rainsource Press, Raven Press, Anita Roddick Publications, Rural Science Institute, Seed Savers, Service Employees International Union, Slow Food Editore, Solar Design Association, Stonefield Publishing, Sun Plans Inc, Sustainability Press, Trailblazer Press, Trust for Public Land, Yes Books

Chelsea House, *distributed by* Perfection Learning Corp

Chelsea House Publishers, *imprint of* Infobase Learning

Chelsea Publishing Co Inc, *imprint of* American Mathematical Society

Chemical Heritage Foundation, *distributed by* Diane Publishing Co

Cheng & Tsui Co Inc, *distributor for* Action Language Learning, aha! Chinese, Bider Technology, Cengage Learning Australia, China International Book Trading Co (Beijing, selected titles only), China Soft, China Sprout, Crabtree Publishing, Curriculum Corporation, Facets Video, Ilchokak Publishers, Italian School of East Asian Studies, JPT America Inc, Oxford University Press, Pan Asian Publications, Panmun Academic Services, Panpac Education, Paradigm Busters, Pearson Australia, Royal Asiatic Society (Korea Branch), SMC Publishing, Sogang University Institute, Stone Bridge Press, SUP Publishing Logistics, Tuttle Publishing, US International Publishing, White Rabbit Press, Yale University Press, Zeitgeist Films

Cherokee National Press, *distributed by* University of Oklahoma Press

Cherokee Publications, *distributed by* Book Publishing Co

Cherry Lane Music Co, *imprint of* Hal Leonard Corp, *distributed by* Hal Leonard Corp

Chesapeake Bay Maritime Museum, *distributed by* Cornell Maritime Press Inc

Chess Information & Research Center, *distributed by* W W Norton & Company Inc

Chester Book Co, *division of* Finney Company Inc

Chestnut Hills Press, *imprint of* BrickHouse Books Inc

Chicago Review Press, *distributed by* Gryphon House Inc

Chicago Tribune Crosswords, *imprint of* Random House Reference/Random House Puzzles & Games/House of Collectibles

Chicken House, *imprint of* Scholastic Trade Division

Chicken Soup for the Soul, *distributed by* Simon & Schuster Sales Division

Chicken Soup for the Soul Publishing, *distributed by* Simon & Schuster, Inc

Child Play, *distributor for* Specialty Press Inc

Children's Book Press, *imprint of* Lee & Low Books, Lee & Low Books Inc

Children's Classics, *imprint of* Penguin Random House Inc

Children's Media, *imprint of* Penguin Random House Inc

Children's Plus, *distributor for* Saddleback Educational Publishing

Children's Press, *distributed by* Perfection Learning Corp

Children's Press®, *imprint of* Scholastic Education

Children's Resources International, *distributed by* Gryphon House Inc

Child's Play®, *affiliate of* Child's Play (International) Ltd

Child's Play International, *distributed by* Heimburger House Publishing Co

The Child's World Inc, *distributor for* Tradition Books

Childswork/Childsplay LLC, *subsidiary of* The Guidance Group Inc

Chilton Book Co, *distributed by* J J Keller & Associates, Inc

China Books, *division of* Sinomedia International Group, *distributor for* AsiaPac, Blue Poppy Press, CIBTC, Commercial Press, Foreign Languages Press, Joint Publishers, New World Press, Panda Books, Peace Books, Red Mansions Publishing

China Encyclopedia Publishing House, *distributed by* Homa & Sekey Books

China Institute, *distributed by* EastBridge

China Intercontinental Press, *distributed by* Homa & Sekey Books

China International Book Trading Co, *distributed by* Cheng & Tsui Co Inc

China Soft, *distributed by* Cheng & Tsui Co Inc

China Sprout, *distributed by* Cheng & Tsui Co Inc

China Zhejiang Publishing United Group, *distributed by* Homa & Sekey Books

Chinese University Press, *distributed by* Columbia University Press

Chipstone Foundation, *distributed by* University Press of New England

Chiral House, *imprint of* Joshua Tree Publishing

Chiron Publications, *distributed by* SteinerBooks

Chlen$kiy Publishing, *imprint of* Cross-Cultural Communications

Choi's Gallery, *distributed by* Gingko Press Inc

Chosen Books, *division of* Baker Publishing Group

Chosen People Ministries, *distributed by* Lederer Books, Messianic Jewish Publishers

Christ Church-Philadelphia, *distributed by* Diane Publishing Co

Christian Classics, *imprint of* Ave Maria Press

Christian Fellowship, *distributed by* CLC Ministries

Christian Focus, *distributed by* Pilgrim Publications

Christian Large Print, *imprint of* Gale

Christian Network International, *distributor for* Pentecostal Publishing House

Christian Press, *division of* Brown Books Publishing Group

The Christian Science Publishing Society, *division of* First Church of Christ, Scientist, The First Church of Christ, Scientist

Chronicle, *distributor for* Country Music Foundation Press

Chronicle Books, *distributor for* Handprint Books Inc, Princeton Architectural Press, Sierra Club Books, *distributed by* Hachette Book Group, Perfection Learning Corp

Chronicle Books LLC, *distributor for* Blue Apple Books, Handprint Books, Laurence King Publishing, Moleskine, Princeton Architectural Press, Quadrille Publishing, SmartLab, SmartsCo

Chronology Books, *imprint of* History Publishing Co LLC

Church Publishing Inc, *distributed by* Abingdon Press

CIBTC, *distributed by* China Books

CIDEB, *distributed by* Beach Lloyd Publishers LLC

Cider Mill Press, *imprint of* Cider Mill Press Book Publishers LLC

Cider Mill Press Book Publishers, *distributed by* Simon & Schuster Sales Division

Cider Mill Press Book Publishers LLC, *distributed by* Simon & Schuster, Simon & Schuster, Inc

Coleccion Ciencias Naturales, *imprint of* University of Puerto Rico Press

Cine-Med Inc, *distributor for* American College of Surgeons

Cinema Books, *distributed by* Hal Leonard Corp

Circle Time Publishers, *distributed by* Gryphon House Inc

Circlet Press Inc, *distributed by* SCB Distributors

Circumflex, *imprint of* Circlet Press Inc

Cistercian Publications, *imprint of* Liturgical Press, *distributed by* Liturgical Press

Citadel, *imprint of* Kensington Publishing Corp

CityLife Books, *imprint of* Stephens Press™

Ciudad Nueva (Spain/Argentina), *distributed by* New City Press

Civitas, *distributed by* HarperCollins Publishers

Clairview Books, *distributed by* SteinerBooks

Clara House Books, *imprint of* The Oliver Press Inc

Arnold Clarendon, *distributed by* Oxford University Press USA

Clarendon Press, *imprint of* Oxford University Press USA

Clarion Books, *imprint of* Houghton Mifflin Harcourt, Houghton Mifflin Harcourt Trade & Reference Division, *distributed by* Houghton Mifflin Harcourt

Clarity Sound & Light, *imprint of* Crystal Clarity Publishers

Arthur H Clark Co, *imprint of* University of Oklahoma Press

Clark City Press, *distributed by* Mountain Press Publishing Co

Ayebia Clarke Publishing Ltd, *distributed by* Lynne Rienner Publishers Inc

Clarkson Potter, *imprint of* Crown Publishing Group, Penguin Random House Inc, Clarkson Potter Publishers

Clarkson Potter Publishers, *imprint of* Crown Publishing Group, *distributor for* The Colonial Williamsburg Foundation, *distributed by* Random House

Clarkson Research Services Ltd, *distributed by* Marine Techniques Publishing

Coleccion Clasicos No Tan Clasicos, *imprint of* University of Puerto Rico Press

Classic Library, *imprint of* Recorded Books LLC

Classic Reprint Series, *imprint of* University of Alaska Press

Editions Classicae, *imprint of* Mel Bay Publications Inc

Classics With a Twist, *imprint of* Empire Publishing Service

Classroom Classics, *imprint of* World Citizens

CLC Ministries, *distributor for* Christian Fellowship

Clear Creek Publishing, *distributed by* Gem Guides Book Co

Clear Day Books, *imprint of* Clarity Press Inc

Clearfield, *distributed by* Ericson Books

Clearfield Co Inc, *subsidiary of* Genealogical Publishing Co

Cleartype American Map Corp, *imprint of* American Map Corp

Cleis Press, *imprint of* Start Publishing LLC

Sydney Gurewitz Clemens, *distributed by* Gryphon House Inc

Clerc Books, *imprint of* Gallaudet University Press

Clerisy Press, *imprint of* Keen Communications, Keen Communications LLC

CLIE, *distributed by* Editorial Bautista Independiente

Client Distribution Services, *distributor for* Harvard Business Review Press

CliffNotes™, *imprint of* Houghton Mifflin Harcourt Trade & Reference Division

Clinical Advances, *imprint of* Oakstone Publishing LLC

Clipper Audio (UK), *imprint of* Recorded Books LLC

Clo Iar-Chonnachta, *distributed by* Dufour Editions Inc

Clockroot Books, *imprint of* Interlink Publishing Group Inc

Cloister Recordings, *distributed by* Gateways Books & Tapes

Close Up Publishing, *division of* Close Up Foundation

Closson Press, *distributor for* Hearthside Books, Darvin Martin CDs, Retrospect Publishing, *distributed by* Janaway Publishing, Masthof Press

Clymer ProSeries, *imprint of* Penton Media

Clymer Publications, *imprint of* Penton Media

CMC, *distributor for* dbS Productions

CN Times Books, *imprint of* CN Times Inc, *distributor for* Bashu Publishing, Foreign Language Press, Intercontinental Press, Phoenix Publishing

Coach, *imprint of* Triumph Learning LLC

Coastal Living Books, *imprint of* Oxmoor House

Coastal New England Publications, *imprint of* Harvest Hill Press

Coastal Publishing, *distributed by* Epicenter Press Inc

Codagen Guides USA, *imprint of* Interlink Publishing Group Inc

Codasat Canada Ltd, *distributor for* Silman-James Press

Codhill Press, *distributed by* State University of New York Press, SUNY Press

Coffeetown Press, *distributed by* Epicenter Press Inc

Cokesbury, *distributor for* Chalice Press, Morehouse Publishing

Cold Spring Harbor Laboratory Press, *division of* Cold Spring Harbor Laboratory, *distributed by* Oxford University Press USA

Cold Spring Press, *imprint of* Open Road Publishing

Collections Livrier, *imprint of* Progressive Press

College Board, *distributed by* St Martin's Press, LLC

The College Board, *distributed by* Macmillan

College Days Press, *imprint of* R J Berg Publisher

College Level Examination Series, *imprint of* National Learning Corp

College Proficiency Examination Series, *imprint of* National Learning Corp

Collegium Graphicum, *imprint of* Alan Wofsy Fine Arts

Collins & Brown, *distributed by* Sterling Publishing Co Inc

Collins Press, *distributed by* Dufour Editions Inc

Colonial Society of Massachusetts, *distributed by* The University of Virginia Press

Colonial Williamsburg, *imprint of* The Colonial Williamsburg Foundation

The Colonial Williamsburg Foundation, *distributed by* Harry N Abrams Inc, John F Blair Publisher, Clarkson Potter Publishers, Lexington Books, National Geographic, Ohio University Press, Quite Specific Media Group Ltd, Random House Children's Books, Rodale, Rowman & Littlefield, Scholastic Inc, Stackpole Books, Texas Tech University Press, The University of Virginia Press, University Press of New England, Yale University Press

Colorado Mountain Club Press, *distributed by* The Mountaineers Books

Colorprint American Map Corp, *imprint of* American Map Corp

Columba, *distributor for* Twenty-Third Publications

Columba Books, *distributed by* Dufour Editions Inc

Columbia Business School Publishing, *imprint of* Columbia University Press

Columbia International Affairs Online (CIAO), *distributor for* University of California Institute on Global Conflict & Cooperation

Columbia University Press, *distributor for* American Institute of Buddhist Studies, Austrian Film Museum Books, Auteur Publishing, Chinese University Press, Columbia University Press (Hitchcock Annual), Maria Curie-Sklodowska University Press, Dalkey Archive Press, GSAPP Books, Harrington Park Press (frontlist titles), Hong Kong University Press, ibidem Press (English-lang titles exc China & India), Jagiellonian University Press, Slovenian Cinematheque, Social Science Research Council, Transcript Verlag, University of Tokyo Press, Woodrow Wilson Center Press, *distributed by* Columbia University Press

Columbus Zoo, *distributed by* Lerner Publishing Group Inc

Combat Aircraft, *imprint of* Osprey Publishing Inc

Combined Academic Publishers Ltd, *distributed by* New York University Press

ComicsLit, *imprint of* NBM Publishing Inc

Command, *imprint of* Osprey Publishing Inc

Commercial Press, *distributed by* China Books

Common Courage Press, *distributor for* Odonian Press, Real Story Series

Commonwealth Editions, *imprint of* Applewood Books Inc

Commonwealth Scientific & Industrial Research Organization (CSIRO), *distributed by* Stylus Publishing LLC

The Commonwealth Secretariat, *distributed by* Stylus Publishing LLC

Community Intervention, *distributor for* MAR*CO Products Inc

Community Music Videos, *distributed by* Hal Leonard Corp

Companion Guides, *imprint of* Boydell & Brewer Inc

Compass, *imprint of* Brigantine Media

Compass American Guides, *imprint of* Fodor's Travel Publications

Compass Point Books, *imprint of* Capstone Publishers™

Compass Point Mysteries, *imprint of* Quincannon Publishing Group

Compass Publications, *distributed by* NACE International

Compendium Films, *distributed by* Casemate Publishers & Book Distributors LLC

Compendium Publishing, *distributed by* Casemate Publishers & Book Distributors LLC

Compu-Tek, *distributed by* Copywriter's Council of America (CCA)

CompuMaster, *division of* SkillPath Publications

Computer Connections, *imprint of* THE Learning Connection®

Comstock Publishing Associates, *imprint of* Cornell University Press

Conari Press, *distributed by* Gryphon House Inc

Concord Library, *imprint of* Beacon Press

Concordia Academic Press, *division of* Concordia Publishing House

Concordia Publishing House, *subsidiary of* The Lutheran Church, Missouri Synod, The Luthern Church, Missouri Synod

Confluence Book Services, *subsidiary of* White Cloud Press

Confluence Books, *imprint of* White Cloud Press

Congress Watch, *division of* Public Citizen

The Connecticut Law Tribune, *imprint of* Law Tribune Books

Consciousness Classics, *imprint of* Gateways Books & Tapes

Consortium, *distributor for* Enchanted Lion Books

Consortium Book Sales & Distribution, *distributor for* Ocean Press

Conspire Creative, *division of* Everything Goes Media LLC

Consumer Guide/PIL, *distributed by* Penguin Group (USA) LLC, a Penguin Random House company

Consumer Reports, *distributor for* United States Pharmacopeia

Consumertronics, *affiliate of* Top Secret Consumertronics Global (TSC-Global)

Contemporary, *imprint of* Wright Group/McGraw-Hill

Context Press, *imprint of* New Harbinger Publications Inc

Continental AfrikaPublishers, *division of* Afrikamawu Miracle Mission, AMI Inc

Contra/Thought, *imprint of* Holmes Publishing Group LLC

Contractor Resource, *distributor for* Air Conditioning Contractors of America

Convergence, *imprint of* Six Gallery Press

Convergent Books, *imprint of* Crown Publishing Group

Conway, *distributed by* Sterling Publishing Co Inc

Cook Communications, *distributor for* Focus on the Family

David C Cook Distribution Canada, *division of* David C Cook

Thomas Cook Publishing, *distributed by* The Globe Pequot Press

Cooking Light Books, *imprint of* Oxmoor House

Cool Springs Press, *imprint of* Quarto Publishing Group USA Inc

Coordinating Research Council Inc, *distributed by* SAE (Society of Automotive Engineers International)

Copernicus, *imprint of* Springer

Copley Custom Textbooks, *imprint of* XanEdu Publishing Inc

Copley Editions, *imprint of* Copley Custom Textbooks

Copley Publishing Group, *imprint of* Copley Custom Textbooks

Copper Canyon Press, *distributor for* American Poetry Review/Honickman

Copper Raven Press, *distributed by* Epicenter Press Inc

Coptales, *imprint of* Oak Tree Press

Copywriter's Council of America (CCA), *division of* The Linick Group Inc, *distributor for* ASL, Compu-Tek, National Association of Photo Sellers, PictureProfits® Tool Kit

Corbey Books, *imprint of* ACTA Publications

Core Library, *imprint of* ABDO Publishing Group

Robin Corey Books, *imprint of* Random House Children's Books

Cork University Press, *distributed by* Stylus Publishing LLC

Cormorant Books, *imprint of* Down The Shore Publishing Corp

Cormorant Calendars, *imprint of* Down The Shore Publishing Corp

Cornell Maritime Press, *imprint of* Schiffer Publishing Ltd

Cornell Maritime Press Inc, *imprint of* Schiffer Publishing Ltd, *distributor for* Chesapeake Bay Maritime Museum, Independent Seaport Museum, Literary House Press, Maryland Historical Trust Press, Maryland Sea Grant Program

Cornell Southeast Asia Program (SEAP) Publications, *distributed by* Cornell University Press

Cornell University East Asia Program, *distributed by* University of Hawaii Press

Cornell University Press, *division of* Cornell University, *distributor for* Cornell Southeast Asia Program (SEAP) Publications, Leuven University Press, University of California Institute on Global Conflict & Cooperation

Cornell University Southeast Asia Program Publications, *unit of* Cornell University, *distributor for* A U A Language Center

Cornwallis Press, *imprint of* Tudor Publishers Inc

Cortina Institute of Languages, *division of* Cortina Learning International Inc (CLI)

Corwin, a Sage Co, *distributor for* SAGE UK Resources for Educators

Corwin Press, *imprint of* SAGE Publications

Corwin Press Inc, *subsidiary of* SAGE Publications

Cosimo Books, *imprint of* Cosimo Inc

Cosimo Classics, *imprint of* Cosimo Inc

Cosimo Reports, *imprint of* Cosimo Inc

Cost Annuals, *division of* R S Means from The Gordian Group

Costume & Fashion Press, *imprint of* Quite Specific Media Group Ltd

Coteau Books, *distributed by* Orca Book Publishers

Cotton Candy Press, *imprint of* Unveiled Media LLC

Cottonwood Publishing, *distributed by* Mountain Press Publishing Co

Council for Exceptional Children (CEC), *distributor for* Brooks (selected titles), Longman, Love Publishing, Pearson, Pro Ed, Sopris West, *distributed by* Free Spirit Publishing Inc, LMD Inc (selected titles), Orchard House Inc

The Council for Research in Values & Philosophy, *imprint of* Council for Research in Values & Philosophy (RVP)

Council Oak Books, *distributed by* Gryphon House Inc

Council of Europe, *distributed by* Manhattan Publishing Co

Council on Foreign Relations Press, *division of* Council on Foreign Relations, *distributed by* Brookings Institution Press

Counterpoint, *imprint of* Basic Books, Counterpoint Press LLC, *distributed by* HarperCollins Publishers

Counterpoint Press, *distributed by* Sierra Club Books

Country Bumpkin, *distributed by* Krause Publications Inc

Country Music Foundation Press, *division of* Country Music Hall of Fame® & Museum, *imprint of* Vanderbilt University Press, *distributed by* Chronicle, Oxford University Press Inc, Providence Publishing, Universe, Vanderbilt University Press

Countryman Press, *imprint of* W W Norton & Company Inc

The Countryman Press, *division of* W W Norton & Co Inc, W W Norton & Company Inc, *distributed by* W W Norton & Co Inc, Penguin Books (CN only)

Courage Books, *imprint of* The Perseus Books Group, Running Press Book Publishers

Courage to Change, *distributor for* MAR*CO Products Inc

Course Technology, *imprint of* Wadsworth Publishing

Coutts, *distributor for* Business Research Services Inc

Coutts Library Service, *distributor for* Primary Research Group Inc

Cove Press, *imprint of* US Games Systems Inc

Cover Craft, *imprint of* Perfection Learning Corp

Cover-to-Cover, *imprint of* Perfection Learning Corp

Covet, *imprint of* Entangled Publishing

Franklin Covey, *distributed by* SkillPath Publications

Coyote Press, *affiliate of* Archaeological Consulting

CQ Press, *imprint of* SAGE Publications

Crabtree Publishing, *distributed by* Cheng & Tsui Co Inc, Perfection Learning Corp

Crabtree Publishing Co, *distributor for* Bayard, Maren Green

Crabtree Publishing Co Ltd, *subsidiary of* Crabtree Publishing Co

Crabtree Publishing Inc, *distributor for* Maren Green Publishing Inc

Craftsman Book Co, *distributor for* BNI Publications, Builders Book Inc, Building News Inc, Home Builders Press, *distributed by* The Aberdeen Group, American Technical Publishers Inc, BNI Publications, Builders Book Inc

Robert L Crager & Co, *imprint of* Pelican Publishing Co

Cramer (Geneva), *distributed by* Alan Wofsy Fine Arts

Cramer (Switzerland), *distributed by* Picasso Project

Cranbrook Institute of Science, *distributed by* Wayne State University Press

Craven Street Books, *imprint of* Linden Publishing Co Inc

Crazy Crow, *distributed by* Book Publishing Co

Crazy Games, *imprint of* Price Stern Sloan

CRC Press, *imprint of* Routledge/Taylor & Francis, Taylor & Francis Inc, *distributor for* The Fairmont Press Inc, Science Publishers Inc, *distributed by* American Academy of Environmental Engineers & Scientists™, American Water Works Association (AWWA), NACE International, SAS Publishing

CRC Press LLC, *subsidiary of* Taylor & Francis

CRCS Publications, *distributed by* Book Publishing Co

Creation House, *imprint of* Charisma Media

Creative Book Publishing, *distributed by* Orca Book Publishers

Creative Concepts, *distributed by* Hal Leonard Corp

Creative Editions, *imprint of* The Creative Co

Creative Education, *imprint of* The Creative Co

Creative Homeowner, *imprint of* Fox Chapel Publishing Co Inc

Creative Keyboard, *imprint of* Mel Bay Publications Inc

Creative Keyboard Publications, *division of* Mel Bay Publications Inc

Creative Paperbacks, *imprint of* The Creative Co

Creative Publications, *imprint of* Wright Group/McGraw-Hill

Creative Publishing International, *imprint of* Quarto Publishing Group USA Inc

Creative Sales Corp, *subsidiary of* American Map Corp, *distributor for* American Map Corp, *distributed by* Hagstrom Map

Creighton University Press, *distributed by* Fordham University Press, University of Nebraska Press

Crescendo, *imprint of* Taplinger Publishing Co Inc

Crescent Books, *imprint of* Penguin Random House Inc

Cress Productions Co, *distributor for* MAR*CO Products Inc

Crestline, *imprint of* Book Sales Inc

Crickhollow Books, *imprint of* Great Lakes Literary LLC

Crimeline, *imprint of* Penguin Random House Inc

Crimethinc, *distributed by* AK Press Distribution

Crimson Romance, *imprint of* F+W, A Content + eCommerce Company

Crisp Books, *distributed by* Michigan Municipal League

Critical Mass Energy Project, *division of* Public Citizen

Critical Path, *distributed by* Book Publishing Co

Croatian Musicological Society, *distributed by* Pendragon Press

Crocodile Books, *imprint of* Interlink Publishing Group Inc

Croft House Books, *distributor for* Primary Research Group Inc

Cross-Cultural Communications, *division of* Cross-Cultural Literary Editions Inc, *distributor for* Ad Infinitum Press, Arba Sicula (Magazine, US), Center of Emigrants from Serbia (Serbia), Decalogue Books (US), The Feral Press (US), Greenfield Review Press (US), Hochelaga (Canada), Immagine&Poesia (Italy), Legas Publishers (CN), Lips (Magazine & Press) (US), Pholiota Press Inc (England), The Seventh Quarry Press (Wales), Shabdaguchha (Magazine & Press) (Bangladesh & US), Sicilia Parra (Magazine, US), Word & Quill Press (US), *distributed by* Ad Infinitum Books, Hochelaga (Canada)

Cross-Cultural Prototypes, *imprint of* Cross-Cultural Communications

Crossquarter Breeze, *imprint of* Crossquarter Publishing Group

Crossroad, *imprint of* The Crossroad Publishing Co

CrossTIME, *imprint of* Crossquarter Publishing Group

Crossway, *division of* Good News Publishers

Crown, *distributed by* Perfection Learning Corp

Crown Archetype, *imprint of* Crown Publishing Group

Crown Books for Young Readers, *imprint of* Penguin Random House Inc, Random House Children's Books

Crown Business, *imprint of* Crown Publishing Group

Crown Forum, *imprint of* Crown Publishing Group

Crown House Publishing Co LLC, *division of* Crown House Publishing Ltd, Crown House Publishing Ltd (UK Co), *distributor for* Developing Press Co, Human Alchemy Publications, Institute Press, Transforming Press

Crown Publishers, *imprint of* Crown Publishing Group

Crown Publishers Inc, *imprint of* Penguin Random House Inc

Crown Publishing Group, *division of* Penguin Random House Inc

Cruise Guides, *imprint of* Hunter Publishing Inc

Cruise Memories, *imprint of* R J Berg Publisher

CSI Publications, *imprint of* Christian Schools International

The CSIS Press, *division of* Center for Strategic & International Studies, *distributed by* Rowman & Littlefield

CSLI Publications, *distributed by* University of Chicago Press

CT Corporation, *imprint of* Wolters Kluwer US Corp

CTB/McGraw-Hill, *division of* McGraw-Hill Education, *imprint of* McGraw-Hill Education

CTW Publishing, *imprint of* Penguin Random House Inc

Coleccion Cuadernos La Torre, *imprint of* University of Puerto Rico Press

Coleccion Cuentos de un Mundo Perdido, *imprint of* University of Puerto Rico Press

Juan de la Cuesta Hispanic Monographs, *imprint of* LinguaText Ltd

Juan de la Cuesta—Hispanic Monographs, *distributed by* LinguaText Ltd

Coleccion Cultura Basica, *imprint of* University of Puerto Rico Press

Cumberland House, *imprint of* Sourcebooks Inc

CUNY Journalism Press, *division of* CUNY Graduate School of Journalism, *distributed by* OR Books

Cup of Tea Books, *imprint of* PageSpring Publishing

Curbstone Books, *imprint of* Northwestern University Press

Maria Curie-Sklodowska University Press, *distributed by* Columbia University Press

Curiosities, *imprint of* Norilana Books

Currach Press, *distributed by* Dufour Editions Inc

Curran Associates Inc, *distributor for* Trans Tech Publications

Currency, *imprint of* Penguin Random House Inc

Current, *imprint of* Penguin Group (USA) LLC, a Penguin Random House company

Current Medicine Group, *imprint of* Springer

Curriculum Corporation, *distributed by* Cheng & Tsui Co Inc

Curriculum Solutions, *division of* Scholastic Education

James Curry Ltd, *imprint of* Boydell & Brewer Inc

Fondation Custodia, *distributed by* Oak Knoll Press

CWLA Press, *imprint of* Child Welfare League of America (CWLA)

CyberAge Books, *imprint of* Information Today, Inc

Cycle Publishing, *imprint of* Cycle Publishing LLC

Cynthia Publishing Co, *distributor for* HarperCollins Publishers

CYPI, *distributed by* Gingko Press Inc

Cypress House, *imprint of* Comp-Type Inc

Cyrco Press, *distributed by* Ardent Media Inc

D'Asia Vu Reprint Library, *imprint of* EastBridge

D-Day Publishing, *distributed by* Casemate Publishers & Book Distributors LLC

Da Capo Lifelong Books, *imprint of* The Perseus Books Group

Da Capo Press, *imprint of* The Perseus Books Group

Da Capo Press & Lifelong Books, *member of* The Perseus Books Group, *distributed by* The Perseus Books Group

DA Information Services, *distributor for* Peterson Institute for International Economics (PIIE)

Dafina, *imprint of* Kensington Publishing Corp

Dagger, *imprint of* Riverdale Avenue Books (RAB)

Daisy Rock Girl Guitars, *distributed by* Alfred Music Publishing

Dakota Institute, *distributed by* University of Oklahoma Press

Dalkey Archive Press, *distributed by* Columbia University Press, W W Norton & Company Inc

Dallas Museum of Art, *distributed by* Yale University Press

Dance Books Ltd, *distributor for* Princeton Book Co Publishers, *distributed by* Princeton Book Co Publishers

Dance Horizons, *imprint of* Princeton Book Co Publishers

Dance Horizons Video, *imprint of* Princeton Book Co Publishers

Dance Notation Bureau, *distributed by* Princeton Book Co Publishers

D&B Publishing, *distributed by* The Globe Pequot Press

C W Daniel, *distributed by* Beekman Books Inc

John Daniel & Co, *division of* Daniel & Daniel Publishers Inc, Daniel & Daniel Publishers Inc, *distributor for* Fithian Press, Perseverance Press

Dante Series, *imprint of* National Learning Corp

Dante University of America Press Inc, *distributed by* Branden Books, Branden Publishing Co

DAP Distributed Art Publishers, *distributor for* MIT List Visual Arts Center

Dar Nun, *distributed by* Fons Vitae

Darby Creek Publishing, *imprint of* Lerner Publishing Group Inc

Dark Horse Books, *imprint of* Dark Horse Comics

Dark Horse Comics, *affiliate of* Dark Horse Entertainment, *distributed by* LPC Group Inc

Dark Oak Mysteries, *imprint of* Oak Tree Press

Darling & Co, *imprint of* Laughing Elephant

Dartmouth College Press, *imprint of* University Press of New England

The Dartnell Corporation, *subsidiary of* Eli Research Inc

Darwin® Books, *imprint of* The Darwin Press Inc

The Darwin Press Inc, *imprint of* Darwin® Books

David & Charles, *imprint of* F+W, A Content + eCommerce Company, *distributed by* Krause Publications Inc

David Fickling Books, *imprint of* Penguin Random House Inc, Scholastic Trade Division

David Publishing, *distributor for* Fire Engineering Books & Videos

Davies-Black Publishing, *imprint of* Nicholas Brealey Publishing

Davis Publications, *distributed by* Sterling Publishing Co Inc

DAW, *imprint of* Penguin Group (USA) LLC, a Penguin Random House company

DAW Books Inc, *imprint of* Penguin Group (USA) LLC, Penguin Group (USA) LLC, a Penguin Random House company, *distributed by* Penguin Group (USA) LLC; Penguin Group (USA) LLC, a Penguin Random House company

DAW/Fantasy, *imprint of* DAW Books Inc

DAW/Fiction, *imprint of* DAW Books Inc

DAW/Science Fiction, *imprint of* DAW Books Inc

The Dawn Horse Press, *division of* Avataric Pan-Communion of Adidam

Dawn Sign Press, *distributed by* Gryphon House Inc

DawnSignPress, *distributor for* Gallaudet University Press, MIT Press, Random House Inc, *distributed by* Gryphon House

Kathy Dawson Books, *imprint of* Penguin Young Readers Group

Dawsons Book Shop, *distributed by* Sunbelt Publications Inc

Day Hike Books Inc, *distributed by* The Globe Pequot Press

The Day That Was Different, *imprint of* Gallopade International Inc

DBI Books, *imprint of* Krause Publications Inc

dbS Productions, *distributed by* CMC

DC Comics, *imprint of* DC Entertainment

DC Entertainment, *division of* Warner Bros Entertainment, Warner Bros Entertainment Co, *distributed by* Random House Publisher Services (RHPS)

DC Nation, *imprint of* DC Entertainment

DC Publications, *distributed by* Hal Leonard Corp

Walter De Gruyter Inc, *division of* Walter de Gruyter GmbH & Co KG, Walter de Gruyter GmbH & Co KG, *distributor for* De Gruyter Mouton

Coleccion Obras Completas Eugenio Maria de Hostos, *imprint of* University of Puerto Rico Press

Juan De La Cuesta-Hispanic Monographs, *imprint of* European Masterpieces, *distributed by* European Masterpieces

De Lorme Atlas, *distributed by* American Map Corp, Hagstrom Map

De Vorss & Co, *distributor for* Acropolis Books (Joel S Goldsmith titles), Touch for Health, White Eagle Publishing Trust (England)

Dearborn Trade, *distributor for* Appraisal Institute

Decalogue Books, *distributed by* Cross-Cultural Communications

Decent Hill, *imprint of* Decent Hill Publishers LLC

Dechema, *distributor for* American Institute of Chemical Engineers (AIChE), *distributed by* American Institute of Chemical Engineers (AIChE)

Dechema Series, *distributed by* Scholium International Inc

B C Decker, *imprint of* Elsevier, Health Sciences Division

Dedelas Press, *distributor for* Syracuse University Press

Deep Books Ltd, *distributor for* Boys Town Press

Marcel Dekker Inc, *distributed by* NACE International

Del Rey, *imprint of* Penguin Random House Inc, Random House Publishing Group

Delacorte Books for Young Readers, *imprint of* Penguin Random House Inc, Random House Children's Books

Delacorte Press, *imprint of* Penguin Random House Inc

Delaney, *distributor for* Saddleback Educational Publishing

Delaney Books Inc, *subsidiary of* National Learning Corp

Delano Publishing, *distributed by* Epicenter Press Inc

Dell, *imprint of* Penguin Random House Inc, Random House Publishing Group

Dell Laurel Leaf, *imprint of* Penguin Random House Inc

Dell Yearling, *imprint of* Penguin Random House Inc

Delmar, *imprint of* Wadsworth Publishing

Delmar Publishers Inc, *distributed by* Gryphon House Inc

Delphinium Books, *distributed by* HarperCollins, HarperCollins Publishers

Delta, *imprint of* Penguin Random House Inc

Delta Education, *distributor for* National Council of Teachers of Mathematics (NCTM)

Delta Publishing Co, *division of* Delta Systems Co Inc, *distributor for* Alma Edizioni, Barron's, Cambridge University Press, Edilingual, Oxford University Press

Delta Systems Inc, *distributor for* Teachers of English to Speakers of Other Languages Inc (TESOL)

Demos Health, *imprint of* Demos Medical Publishing

Demos Medical Publishing, *division of* Springer Publishing Co

Dempsey Your Distributor, *distributor for* Ash Tree Publishing

Denver Art Museum, *distributed by* University of Oklahoma Press

Derrydale, *imprint of* Penguin Random House Inc

Deseret Book, *imprint of* Deseret Book Co

Deseret Book Co, *subsidiary of* Deseret Management Corp, Deseret Management Corp

Desert Charts, *division of* Wide World of Maps Inc

Design Originals, *imprint of* Fox Chapel Publishing Co Inc

Destiny Books, *imprint of* Inner Traditions International Ltd

Destiny Image Inc, *subsidiary of* Nori Media Group

Destiny Recordings, *imprint of* Inner Traditions International Ltd

Detect-A-Word, *imprint of* Modern Publishing

Detroit Institute of Arts, *distributed by* Wayne State University Press

Developing Press Co, *distributed by* Crown House Publishing Co LLC

Devine Entertainment Corp, *distributed by* Hal Leonard Corp

Dey Street Books, *imprint of* HarperCollins General Books Group, HarperCollins Publishers

DharmaCafe, *distributed by* North Atlantic Books

Dial Books for Young Readers, *imprint of* Penguin Group (USA) LLC, Penguin Group (USA) LLC, a Penguin Random House company, Penguin Young Readers Group

The Dial Press, *imprint of* Penguin Random House Inc, Random House Publishing Group

Diamond Books, *imprint of* Berkley Publishing Group

Diane Publishing Co, *distributor for* Academy of Natural Sciences, American Philosophical Society, American Swedish Historical Museum, Augustinian Press, Chemical Heritage Foundation, Christ Church-Philadelphia, Friends of University of Princeton, Geneological Society of Pennsylvania, Library Company of Philadelphia, University of Pennsylvania Libraries

Dictionary Series, *imprint of* Bandanna Books

Didax Educational Resources, *distributor for* National Council of Teachers of Mathematics (NCTM)

Die Gestalten Verlag (DGV), *distributed by* Prestel Publishing

Dietz Press, *distributed by* Ericson Books

Difficult Subjects Made Easy Instruction Booklets, *imprint of* Letterbox/Papyrus of London Publishers USA

digitalculture, *imprint of* University of Michigan Press

Dipti, *imprint of* Lotus Press, *distributed by* Lotus Press

Discovery Books, *imprint of* Penguin Random House Inc

Discovery House Publishers, *division of* Our Daily Bread Ministries

Disney Book Group, *distributed by* Hachette Book Group

Disney Books for Young Readers, *imprint of* Penguin Random House Inc

Disney Children's Book Group, *division of* Disney Publishing Worldwide

Disney Editions, *imprint of* Disney Publishing Worldwide

Disney-Hyperion Books, *imprint of* Disney Book Group

Disney Libri, *imprint of* Disney Publishing Worldwide

Disney Press, *division of* The Walt Disney Co, The Walt Disney Co, *imprint of* Disney Publishing Worldwide, *distributed by* Hachette Book Group USA, Perfection Learning Corp

Disney Publishing Worldwide, *subsidiary of* The Walt Disney Co

Dissertation.com, *imprint of* Universal-Publishers Inc, *distributed by* Bertrams UK

Distri Books, *distributed by* Perfection Learning Corp

Distributed Art Publishers, *distributor for* American Federation of Arts

Distributed Art Publishers (DAP), *distributor for* The Museum of Modern Art (MoMA)

Diversion Books, *distributor for* Zubaan Books

Divine Arts, *imprint of* Michael Wiese Productions

Dixie Press, *imprint of* Pelican Publishing Co

DJ Inkers, *imprint of* Carson-Dellosa Publishing LLC

DK, *distributed by* Perfection Learning Corp

DK Publishing, *division of* Penguin Group (USA) LLC, Penguin Group (USA) LLC, a Penguin Random House company

DLM, *imprint of* Wright Group/McGraw-Hill

Do-It-Yourself Legal Publishers, *affiliate of* Selfhelper Law Press of America, *distributed by* Brodart Co, Midwest Library Service, Quality Books, Unique Books

Documentary Media, *distributed by* Epicenter Press Inc

Documentext, *imprint of* McPherson & Co

Documents of Modern Art, *imprint of* Wittenborn Art Books

Dogwise Publishing, *division of* Direct Book Service Inc

Dogwood Ridge Books, *distributed by* Maryland History Press

Tom Doherty Associates, LLC, *subsidiary of* Macmillan, *distributed by* Macmillan

Domain, *imprint of* Penguin Random House Inc

Dominie Press, *imprint of* Pearson Learning Group, *distributor for* Cambridge University Press (limited number of titles, adult GED)

Domus Latina Publishing, *distributed by* Focus

The Donning Co, *distributed by* Schiffer Publishing Ltd

The Donning Company Publishers, *subsidiary of* Walsworth Publishing Co Inc

Doodle Art, *imprint of* Price Stern Sloan

Dordt College Press, *affiliate of* Dordt College

Dorland Health, *division of* DecisionHealth LLC

Dorling Kindersley, *distributor for* Parachute Publishing LLC

Pam Dorman Books, *imprint of* Penguin Group (USA) LLC, a Penguin Random House company

Samuel Dorsky Museum of Art, *distributed by* State University of New York Press

Coleccion Dos Lenguas, *imprint of* University of Puerto Rico Press

Double Dog, *imprint of* Yard Dog Press

Doubleday, *imprint of* Penguin Random House Inc, *distributed by* Perfection Learning Corp

Doubleday Bible Commentary, *imprint of* Penguin Random House Inc

Doubleday Books for Young Readers, *imprint of* Penguin Random House Inc, Random House Children's Books

Doubleday/Galilee, *imprint of* Penguin Random House Inc

Doubleday/Image, *imprint of* Penguin Random House Inc

Doubleday/Nan A Talese, *imprint of* Knopf Doubleday Publishing Group

Doubleday Religion, *imprint of* Crown Publishing Group

Dove Inspirational Press, *imprint of* Pelican Publishing Co

Dover Publications, *distributed by* Alfred Music Publishing

Down East, *imprint of* The Globe Pequot Press

Down East Books, *imprint of* The Globe Pequot Press, Rowman & Littlefield Publishers Inc, *distributor for* Nimbus Publishing Ltd (selected titles, CN sales only)

Down Home Press, *distributed by* John F Blair Publisher

Downtown Bookworks, *distributed by* Simon & Schuster, Inc, Simon & Schuster Sales Division

Downtown Press, *imprint of* Gallery Books

Drache Publications, *distributed by* Finney Company Inc, Hobar Publications

Dragonfairy Press, *imprint of* Dragonfairy Press LLC

DragonFish Comics, *imprint of* Gauthier Publications Inc

Dragonfly, *imprint of* Random House Children's Books

Dragonfly Books, *imprint of* Penguin Random House Inc

Drama Publishers, *imprint of* Quite Specific Media Group Ltd

Drawn & Quarterly, *distributed by* Farrar, Straus & Giroux, LLC

Dream Works, *distributed by* Penguin Group (USA) LLC, a Penguin Random House company

Dreaming Robot Press, *imprint of* Studio Weaver

Dreamscape Media LLC, *division of* Midwest Tapes, *distributor for* HarperCollins, Penguin Random House

Drum Channel, *distributed by* Alfred Music Publishing

Dryad Press, *distributed by* University of Wisconsin Press

DTP, *imprint of* Penguin Random House Inc

Duel, *imprint of* Osprey Publishing Inc

Dufour Editions' Distributed Presses, *imprint of* Dufour Editions Inc

Dufour Editions Inc, *distributor for* Angel Books, Arcadia Books (London) (including Black Amber, Bliss, Eurocrime & Maia), Attic Press (including Atrium), Between the Lines, Black Amber Press, Blackstaff Press Ltd, Bliss, Bloodaxe Books Ltd, Brandon Books, Carysfort Press, Clo Iar-Chonnachta, Collins Press, Columba Books, Currach Press, Eland Books/Sickle Moon Books, Eurocrime, Flyleaf Press, Gill & Macmillan, Goblinshead, Hersilia, The Liffey Press, Lilliput Press Ltd, Little Toller Books, Y Lolfa (including Alcemi), Maia Press, Mercier, Messenger Publications, New Island Books, Norvik Press, O'Brien Press, Orpen Press, Persephone Books, Portnoy Publishing, Route, Salmon Poetry, Sandstone Press, Smokestack Books, Colin Smythe Ltd, Stinging Fly Press, University College Dublin Press, Vagabond Voices, Veritas, The Waywiser Press

Tim Duggan Books, *imprint of* Crown Publishing Group

Duke University Press, *distributor for* Forest History Society

Dumb Ox Books, *distributed by* St Augustine's Press Inc

Dumbarton Oaks, *distributed by* Harvard University Press

Dunhill Publishing, *division of* Warwick Associates

Thomas Dunne Books, *imprint of* St Martin's Press, LLC

Dunstan House, *distributed by* ECS Publishing Corp

Dustbooks, *affiliate of* Associated Writing Programs, *distributor for* American Dust Publications

Dutton, *division of* Penguin Group (USA) LLC, Penguin Group (USA) LLC, a Penguin Random House company, *imprint of* Dutton Children's Books, Penguin Group (USA) LLC, a Penguin Random House company, *distributed by* Perfection Learning Corp

Dutton Children's Books, *imprint of* Penguin Group (USA) LLC, Penguin Group (USA) LLC, a Penguin Random House company, Penguin Young Readers Group

Dutton Interactive, *imprint of* Penguin Young Readers Group

Duxbury, *distributed by* SAS Publishing

Eagan Press, *imprint of* AACC International

Eagle Editions, *imprint of* Heritage Books Inc, *distributed by* Casemate Publishers & Book Distributors LLC

Eagle Wing Books, *distributed by* Adventures Unlimited Press (AUP)

Eagles Landing Publishing, *distributed by* Biographical Publishing Co

Eagle's View Publishing, *subsidiary of* Westwind Inc, Westwind Inc

Eakin Press, *imprint of* Wild Horse Media Group

Eamon Dolan Books, *imprint of* Houghton Mifflin Harcourt Trade & Reference Division

E&FN Spon, *distributed by* NACE International

Early Childhood Education, *division of* Scholastic Education

Early Classics of Science Fiction, *imprint of* Wesleyan University Press

Early Editions Books, *imprint of* Science & Humanities Press

Early Educator's Press, *distributed by* Gryphon House Inc

Early English Text Society, *imprint of* Boydell & Brewer Inc

Early Learners, *imprint of* Modern Publishing

Early Math, *imprint of* Sundance/Newbridge Publishing

Early Science, *imprint of* Sundance/Newbridge Publishing

Early Social Studies, *imprint of* Sundance/Newbridge Publishing

EarlyLight Books, *distributed by* Charlesbridge Publishing Inc

Earth Love Publishing, *distributed by* Gem Guides Book Co

Earth Pledge, *distributed by* Chelsea Green Publishing Co

Earthbound Publications, *distributed by* Casemate Publishers & Book Distributors LLC

Earthling Press, *subsidiary of* Awe-Struck Publishing

East Asian Legal Studies Program (EALSP), *division of* University of Maryland School of Law

East Gate Books, *imprint of* M E Sharpe Inc

East West Cultural Center, *distributed by* Lotus Press

East West Export Books, *distributor for* Peterson Institute for International Economics (PIIE)

East-West Export Books, *subsidiary of* University of Hawaii Press

EastBridge, *distributor for* China Institute, John Helde, International Christian University Foundation, Nippon Foundation, Yosifumi Taguchi

Eastern Book Company, *distributor for* Primary Research Group Inc

Eastland Press, *distributor for* Journal of Chinese Medicine Publications

Easy Money Press, *subsidiary of* Wolford & Associates

EC&M Books, *imprint of* Penton Media

Ecco, *imprint of* HarperCollins General Books Group, HarperCollins Publishers Sales

Eco Logic Books, *distributed by* Chelsea Green Publishing Co

Ecological Design Institute, *distributed by* Chelsea Green Publishing Co

Ecological Design Press, *distributed by* Chelsea Green Publishing Co

Econoclad, *distributor for* Ozark Publishing Inc

Economica, *distributed by* The Brookings Institution Press

Ecopress, *imprint of* Finney Company Inc

Ecosystem, *imprint of* Sterling Publishing Co Inc

Ecosystem Research Group, *imprint of* Crumb Elbow Publishing

ECS Publishing Corp, *distributor for* Randol Bass Music, Dunstan House, Edition Delrieu, Gaudia Music & Arts, Stainer & Bell Ltd, Vireo Press

EDC Publishing, *division of* Educational Development Corp, Educational Development Corp, *distributor for* Usborne Publishing

Edda Publishing, *distributed by* Holmes Publishing Group LLC

Edda USA, *division of* Edda Publishing Ltd, Edda Publishing Ltd (Iceland)

EDFU Books, *distributed by* Adventures Unlimited Press (AUP)

Edgewise Press Inc, *distributor for* Editions d'Afrique du Nord, Libri Canali Bassi, Paolo Torti degli Alberti

ediciones Lerner, *division of* Lerner Publishing Group Inc, *imprint of* Lerner Publishing Group Inc

Edilingual, *distributed by* Delta Publishing Co

Edison Welding Institute, *distributor for* American Society for Nondestructive Testing

Edition Delrieu, *distributed by* ECS Publishing Corp

Editions du Signe, *distributed by* Gem Guides Book Co

Editions Durand, *distributed by* Hal Leonard Corp

Les Editions E T C, *distributed by* Lotus Press

Editions Max Eschig, *distributed by* Hal Leonard Corp

Editions Orphee Inc, *distributed by* Theodore Presser Co

Editions Salabert, *distributed by* Hal Leonard Corp

Editorial Bautista Independiente, *division of* Baptist Mid-Missions, *distributor for* Casa Bautista, CLIE, Portavoz

Editorial Concordia, *division of* Concordia Publishing House

Editorial Portavoz, *division of* Kregel Publications, *imprint of* Kregel Publications

EDU Reference, *distributor for* MAR*CO Products Inc

Educational Impressions Inc, *distributed by* Newbridge Communications Inc, Scholastic Inc, Scholastic-Tab Publications

Educational Insights, *subsidiary of* Learning Resources

Educational Media, *distributed by* MAR*CO Products Inc

Educational Media Corp, *distributor for* MAR*CO Products Inc

Educators for Social Responsibility, *distributed by* Gryphon House Inc

Educators Outlet, *distributor for* National Council of Teachers of Mathematics (NCTM)

Edupress Inc, *division of* Demco

Edward & Dee, *imprint of* Russian Information Service Inc

Eerdmans Books for Young Readers, *imprint of* Wm B Eerdmans Publishing Co

Eland Books/Sickle Moon Books, *distributed by* Dufour Editions Inc

Elbow Books, *imprint of* Crumb Elbow Publishing

Elderberry Press Inc, *distributor for* Poison Vine Books, Red Anvil Press

Electa, *distributed by* Phaidon Press Inc

Electric Strawberry Press, *imprint of* Radix Press

Electrical Wholesaling, *imprint of* Penton Media

The Electrochemical Society (ECS), *distributed by* American Institute of Physics (AIP) (journals), John Wiley & Sons (monographs)

The Electronics Source Book, *imprint of* Penton Media

Elephant's Eye, *imprint of* The Overlook Press

Elite, *imprint of* Osprey Publishing Inc

Elite Books, *division of* Author's Publishing Cooperative (APC)

Elliott & Clark Publishing, *imprint of* River City Publishing LLC

Ellora's Cave, *imprint of* Ellora's Cave Publishing Inc

Eloquent/Strategic, *imprint of* Strategic Book Publishing & Rights Agency (SBPRA)

Elsevier, *distributed by* Gulf Publishing Co

Elsevier Engineering Information (Ei), *subsidiary of* Elsevier Inc

Elsevier, Health Sciences Division, *division of* RELX Group PLC, *distributor for* G W Medical Publisher

Elsevier Inc, *subsidiary of* RELX Group PLC

Elsevier, Science & Technology Books, *distributed by* Marine Techniques Publishing

Elsevier Science Publishers, *distributed by* NACE International

Elsevier Science, Technology & Business Books, *distributor for* Marine Techniques Publishing

Elstreet Educational, *imprint of* Bartleby Press

Elva Resa, *imprint of* Elva Resa Publishing

Elvehjem Museum of Art, *distributed by* University of Wisconsin Press

Elysian Editions, *imprint of* Princeton Book Co Publishers

EM Books, *distributed by* Hal Leonard Corp

Embrace, *imprint of* Entangled Publishing

Embraces, *imprint of* Zumaya Publications LLC

EMC Publishing LLC, *division of* New Mountain Learning LLC, *distributor for* Sybex Inc

Emerald Book Co, *imprint of* Greenleaf Book Group LLC

Emerald Books, *affiliate of* YWAM Publishing, *distributed by* YWAM Publishing

Emergency Gazette, *imprint of* Ugly Duckling Presse

EMI Christian, *distributed by* Hal Leonard Corp

Emmaus Road Publishing Inc, *division of* St Paul Center for Biblical Theology

EMP, *imprint of* Easy Money Press

Empire, *imprint of* Empire Press Media/Avant-Guide

Empire Press Media/Avant-Guide, *unit of* Empire Press Media Inc, *distributed by* Publishers Group West

Empire Publishing Service, *division of* The Empire, The Empire (media group), *distributor for* Arsis Press (world), Arte Publico Press (world), Ian Henry Publications (world), ISH Group (Worldwide exc Australia), Paul Mould Publishing (world)

Empire State Editions, *imprint of* Fordham University Press

Empowerment Institute, *distributed by* Chelsea Green Publishing Co

Empty Bowl Press, *division of* Pleasure Boat Studio: A Literary Press, *distributed by* Pleasure Boat Studio: A Literary Press

Enchanted Lion Books, *distributed by* Consortium, Farrar, Straus & Giroux, LLC

Encore, *imprint of* Simon & Schuster Audio

Encore Editions, *imprint of* Star Publishing Co Inc

Encounter the Saints Series, *imprint of* Pauline Books & Media

Encyclopaedia Africana, *imprint of* Reference Publications Inc

Energy Arts, *distributed by* North Atlantic Books

Energy Information Administration (EIA), *imprint of* US Government Publishing Office, US Government Publishing Office (GPO), *distributed by* EPO, NTIS

Energy Psychology Press, *division of* Soul Medicine Institute

Enfield Publishers, *distributed by* Trans Tech Publications

Enfield Publishing & Distribution Co, *distributor for* Athenaeum Books, Beech River Books, Cambridge Scientific Publishers, Faculty Ridge Books, Heart Path Press, Institution of Chemical Engineers, Isles of Shoals Association (Star Island), Jetty House (imprint of Peter Randall Press), Verlag Valentin Koerner, Kom Forlag, Letterland International Ltd (phonics progs grades K-2), Moose Country Press, Norwegian Petroleum Agency, Picture Book Press, Portsmouth Marine Society, Safe Harbor Books, Sights Unscene Press (photography), Singing Brook Press, Smith-Gordon, Thistle Hill Publications, Trans Tech Publications, Treeline Press, Vett og Viten Forlag (Norwegian petroleum safety titles), Vital Communities (family quests in VT & NH), Wageningen Academic Publishers

Engineering Foundation, *distributed by* American Institute of Chemical Engineers (AIChE)

Engineering Press, *distributed by* Oxford University Press USA

The English Spanish Foundation Series, *imprint of* me+mi publishing inc

Enigma, *imprint of* Zumaya Publications LLC

Enliven, *imprint of* Atria Books

Eno Publishers, *distributed by* John F Blair Publisher

Ensign Peak, *imprint of* Deseret Book Co

Enslow, *imprint of* Enslow Publishing LLC

Enslow Elementary, *imprint of* Enslow Publishing LLC

Entangled Edge, *imprint of* Entangled Publishing

Entangled Publishing, *distributed by* Macmillan

Entangled Select, *imprint of* Entangled Publishing

Entangled Teen, *imprint of* Entangled Publishing

EntertainmentPro, *imprint of* Quite Specific Media Group Ltd

Enthea Press, *imprint of* Ariel Press, *distributed by* Ariel Press

Enthusiast Books, *division of* Iconografix Inc

Entomological Society of America, *distributed by* Oxford University Press

Environmental Law Institute, *distributed by* Island Press

Eos, *imprint of* HarperCollins Publishers Sales

Epicenter Press Inc, *distributor for* Appell Publishing, Camel Press, Coastal Publishing, Coffeetown Press, Copper Raven Press, Delano Publishing, Documentary Media, Far North Press, Five Star Misadventures, Gold Fever Press, Joyful Productions, McRoy & Blackburn, Publishers, Meditation Press, Old Seattle Press, Patos Island Press, Raising Lucy Studios LLC, Raleigh Press, Reach for the Sky Publishing, RLO Media Productions, Saltry Press, Sprucehaven Publishing, Westridge Art, Winternights Publishing, Yamhill Press

Epigraph Publishing Service, *division of* Monkfish Book Publishing Co

EPO, *distributor for* Energy Information Administration (EIA)

EPS/School Specialty Literacy & Intervention, *division of* School Specialty Inc

Epworth, *distributed by* Presbyterian Publishing Corp (PPC)

Equilibrium Books, *imprint of* Wish Publishing

Equipment Watch, *imprint of* Penton Media

Ergos Institute, *distributed by* North Atlantic Books

Ericson Books, *distributor for* Clearfield, Dietz Press, Southern Historical Press, *distributed by* Mountain Press, Byron Sistler

Lawrence Erlbaum Assoc, *distributor for* National Association of Broadcasters (NAB)

Ernst & Sohn, *imprint of* John Wiley & Sons Inc

Eschat Press, *imprint of* Loft Press Inc

Eshel Books, *imprint of* Bartleby Press

Essential Histories, *imprint of* Osprey Publishing Inc

Essential Library, *imprint of* ABDO Publishing Group

ETA Cuisenaire, *distributor for* National Council of Teachers of Mathematics (NCTM)

Eurocrime, *distributed by* Dufour Editions Inc

European Court of Human Rights, *distributed by* Manhattan Publishing Co

European Masterpieces, *imprint of* LinguaText Ltd, *distributor for* Cervantes & Co (Spanish Classics series), Juan De La Cuesta-Hispanic Monographs, Moliere & Co (French Classics series), *distributed by* LinguaText Ltd

European Mathematical Society, *distributed by* American Mathematical Society

Eurospan, *distributor for* University of Michigan Press

Eurospan Group, *distributor for* Association for Talent Development (ATD)

The Eurospan Group, *distributor for* Health Professions Press, Peterson Institute for International Economics (PIIE)

Eurostar, *imprint of* VanDam Inc

Eurotica, *imprint of* NBM Publishing Inc

M Evans & Company, *imprint of* Rowman & Littlefield Publishing Group

Evergreen Pacific Publishing, *imprint of* Evergreen Pacific Publishing Ltd

Evergreen Press, *distributed by* Heimburger House Publishing Co

Everyday Mathematics, *imprint of* Wright Group/McGraw-Hill

Everyman Chess, *distributed by* The Globe Pequot Press

Everyman's Classic Library in Paperback, *imprint of* Tuttle Publishing

Everyman's Library, *imprint of* Penguin Random House Inc

Everything, *imprint of* Adams Media

Everything Goes Media, *imprint of* Everything Goes Media LLC

Evolver Editions, *imprint of* North Atlantic Books

Ex Libris, *imprint of* Rizzoli International Publications Inc

Exalted, *imprint of* White Wolf Publishing Inc

Excelsior Editions, *imprint of* State University of New York Press, *distributor for* Albany Institute of History & Art, Uncrowned Queens

Executive Essentials, *imprint of* Health Administration Press

Executive Reports, *imprint of* Aspatore Books

The Experiment, *imprint of* Algonquin Books, *distributed by* Workman Publishing, Workman Publishing Co Inc

Explorer Publishing, *distributed by* The Globe Pequot Press

Exploring Community History Series, *imprint of* Krieger Publishing Co

Expressive Editions, *imprint of* Cross-Cultural Communications

F+W Media Business Now, *imprint of* Adams Media

Faber Music, *distributed by* Alfred Music Publishing

Faber Music Ltd, *distributed by* Hal Leonard Corp

Facet, *distributed by* Neal-Schuman Publishers Inc

Facets Video, *distributed by* Cheng & Tsui Co Inc

Fact Publishers, *imprint of* Cross-Cultural Communications

Facts On File, *imprint of* Infobase Learning

Faculty Ridge Books, *distributed by* Enfield Publishing & Distribution Co

Fair Winds Press, *imprint of* Quarto Publishing Group USA, Quarto Publishing Group USA Inc

Fairchild Books, *division of* Bloomsbury Publishing PLC

Fairfax Genealogical Society, *distributed by* Heritage Books Inc

Fairfield Press, *distributor for* Maharishi University of Management Press

Fairleigh Dickinson University Press, *affiliate of* Rowman & Littlefield, *distributed by* Rowman & Littlefield

The Fairmont Press Inc, *distributed by* CRC Press, Taylor & Francis

Faith Alive, *imprint of* Faith Alive Christian Resources

Faith Alive Christian Resources, *imprint of* Christian Reformed Church in North America

Faith & Culture, *imprint of* Pauline Books & Media

Faith & Fellowship Publishing, *subsidiary of* Church of the Lutheran Brethren

Faith Library Publications, *subsidiary of* RHEMA Bible Church, *distributed by* Appalachian, Harrison House, Spring Arbor, Whitaker

Faith Press, *imprint of* Winters Publishing

Faith Weaver Bible Curriculum™, *imprint of* Group Publishing Inc

Faith Works Books, *distributor for* American Carriage House Publishing

faithQuest, *imprint of* Brethren Press

FaithWalk Publishing, *imprint of* CSS Publishing Co Inc

FaithWords, *imprint of* Hachette Nashville

Falcon®, *imprint of* The Globe Pequot Press

Falcon Press, *imprint of* The Original Falcon Press

Family Center of Nova University, *distributed by* Gryphon House Inc

Family Films, *division of* Concordia Publishing House

Family Tree Books, *imprint of* Betterway Books

Famous Artists School, *division of* Cortina Learning International Inc (CLI)

Famous Writers School, *division of* Cortina Learning International Inc (CLI)

F+W, A Content + eCommerce Company, *distributed by* Perfection Learning Corp

Fanfare, *imprint of* Penguin Random House Inc

Fantagraphics Books, *distributed by* W W Norton & Company Inc

Far Muse Press, *imprint of* Loft Press Inc

Far North Press, *distributed by* Epicenter Press Inc

Far to the North Press, *distributed by* University of Alaska Press

Far West Publishing, *imprint of* Sun Publishing Company

Farrar, Straus & Giroux Books for Young Readers, *imprint of* Farrar, Straus & Giroux, LLC, Macmillan Children's Publishing Group

Farrar, Straus & Giroux Inc, *distributor for* Aperture Books, *distributed by* Perfection Learning Corp

Farrar, Straus & Giroux, LLC, *subsidiary of* Macmillan, *distributor for* Drawn & Quarterly, Enchanted Lion Books, Gray Wolf Books

Father & Son Publishing Inc, *distributor for* BADM Books

Fatima Crusader, *distributor for* Angelus Press

Favorable Impressions, *affiliate of* The Lincoln Library (now part of the FactCite family of databases)

Fawcett, *imprint of* Penguin Random House Inc, *distributed by* Perfection Learning Corp

Fearless Critic Media, *distributed by* Algonquin Books

Federal Street Press, *division of* Merriam-Webster Inc, *imprint of* Merriam-Webster Inc

Feldheim Publishers (Philipp Feldheim Inc), *distributor for* Hamadia Publishing, Jerusalem Publications

Feldheim Publishers USA, *imprint of* Feldheim Publishers (Philipp Feldheim Inc)

Jean Feldman, *distributed by* Gryphon House Inc

Felsen Press, *imprint of* Decent Hill Publishers LLC

Fence Books, *distributed by* University Press of New England

H B Fenn, *distributor for* Oxmoor House

Fenris Brothers, *imprint of* Crossquarter Publishing Group

The Feral Press, *distributed by* Cross-Cultural Communications

Margaret Ferguson Books, *imprint of* Farrar, Straus & Giroux Books for Young Readers

Ferguson Publishing, *imprint of* Infobase Learning

Leland Fetzer, *distributed by* Sunbelt Publications Inc

Fiction Collective 2 (FC2), *imprint of* University of Alabama Press

Fiction Collective Two Inc (FC2), *imprint of* University of Alabama Press, *distributed by* University of Alabama Press

Field of Glory, *imprint of* Osprey Publishing Inc

Fieldstone Alliance, *imprint of* Turner Publishing Co

Filaree Productions, *distributed by* Chelsea Green Publishing Co

The Film Movement DVDs, *distributed by* Recorded Books LLC

Filmakers Library, *imprint of* Alexander Street Press LLC

The Final Edition, *imprint of* Crumb Elbow Publishing

Financial Executives Research Foundation Inc (FERF), *affiliate of* Financial Executives International (FEI)

Financial Ratings Series, *imprint of* Grey House Publishing Inc™

Financial Times Press, *imprint of* Pearson

Financial Times Publishing, *distributed by* Trans-Atlantic Publications Inc

FineEdge.com LLC, *distributed by* Heritage House, Sunbelt Publications Inc

Finney Company Inc, *distributor for* Drache Publications, Images Unlimited Publishing, Pine Forest Publishing, Joyce Shellhart, Snaptail Press

Fire Ant Books, *imprint of* University of Alabama Press

Fire Engineering Books & Videos, *division of* PennWell Books, *distributor for* Brady, Idea Bank, IFSTA, Mosby, *distributed by* David Publishing, Fire Protection Publications

Fire Protection Publications, *distributor for* Fire Engineering Books & Videos

Firefly, *distributed by* Amherst Media Inc, Perfection Learning Corp

Firefly Books Ltd, *distributed by* Heimburger House Publishing Co

The Firelands Writing Center (Heartlands Magazine), *distributed by* Bottom Dog Press

Fireside Fiction, *imprint of* Heritage Books Inc

First Avenue, *distributed by* Perfection Learning Corp

First Avenue Editions, *imprint of* Lerner Publishing Group Inc

First Choice, *imprint of* Sunbelt Publications Inc

First Choice Chapter Books, *imprint of* Penguin Random House Inc

First Fruits of Zion, *distributed by* Lederer Books, Messianic Jewish Publishers

First Lessons, *imprint of* Mel Bay Publications Inc

First Second Books, *imprint of* Roaring Brook Press

FirstForumPress, *division of* Lynne Rienner Publishers Inc

Fisher Productions, *imprint of* Franciscan Media

Fithian Press, *distributed by* John Daniel & Co

Fitzhenry & Whiteside Ltd, *distributed by* Heimburger House Publishing Co

5 Continents Editions, *distributed by* Harry N Abrams Inc

500/5000 Press Inc, *imprint of* Greenleaf Book Group LLC

Five Rainbows Services for Authors & Publishers, *subsidiary of* Slipdown Mountain Publications LLC

Five Star™, *imprint of* Gale

Five Star Express Press, *imprint of* Five Star Publications Inc

Five Star Legends, *imprint of* Five Star Publications Inc

Five Star Misadventures, *distributed by* Epicenter Press Inc

Five Star Sleuths, *imprint of* Five Star Publications Inc

Flammarion, *imprint of* Rizzoli International Publications Inc

Editions Flammarion, *distributed by* Rizzoli International Publications Inc

Flashkids, *imprint of* Sterling Publishing Co Inc

Flashlight Press, *subsidiary of* Urim Publications

Flip N Fun, *imprint of* Modern Publishing

Flirt, *imprint of* Penguin Random House Inc, Random House Publishing Group

Florida Academic Press, *division of* FAP Books Inc, *distributor for* Publisher's Stone Publications

Florida Literary Foundation (FLF) Press, *imprint of* STARbooks Press

Floris Books, *distributor for* Lindisfarne Books, *distributed by* Gryphon House Inc, Steiner-Books

Flower Press, *distributed by* Chelsea Green Publishing Co

Flux, *imprint of* Llewellyn Publications

Flying Machines Press, *imprint of* Paladin Press

Flying Pen Press Colorado, *imprint of* Flying Pen Press LLC

Flying Pen Press Park Trek, *imprint of* Flying Pen Press LLC

Flying Pen Press Rocky Mountain West, *imprint of* Flying Pen Press LLC

Flying Pen Press Science Fiction, *imprint of* Flying Pen Press LLC

Flying Pen Press Southwest, *imprint of* Flying Pen Press LLC

Flying Pen Press Travel Guides, *imprint of* Flying Pen Press LLC

Flying Piggybank Press, *imprint of* Flying Pen Press LLC

Flyleaf Press, *distributed by* Dufour Editions Inc

FMP, *imprint of* Forward Movement

Focal Press, *distributor for* National Association of Broadcasters (NAB), *distributed by* Marine Techniques Publishing

Focus, *imprint of* Hackett Publishing Co Inc, *distributor for* Domus Latina Publishing

Focus on the Family, *imprint of* Focus on the Family, *distributed by* Baker Books, Cook Communications, Harvest House, Moody Press, Tommy Nelson, Standard Publishing Co, Tyndale House Publishers, Tyndale House Publishers Inc, Zondervan

Fodor's, *imprint of* Fodor's Travel Publications, Penguin Random House Inc

Fodor's Travel Publications, *division of* Penguin Random House Inc

Folgers Shakespeare Library, *imprint of* Simon & Schuster

Fondation pour la Memoire de la Shoah, *distributed by* Beach Lloyd Publishers LLC

Fons Vitae, *distributor for* African American Islamic Institute, Anqa Press (UK), Aperture (NY), Archetype (UK), Broadstone Books,

Dar Nun, Golganooza Press (UK), Islamic Texts Society (UK), Matheson Trust, Parabola, Paragon, Parvardigar Press, Sophia Perennis, Pir Press (NY), Qiblah Books, Quilliam Press (UK), Sandala Productions, Sri Lanka Institute of Traditional Studies, Thesaurus Islamicus Foundation, Tradigital, White Thread Press (US), Wisdom Foundation, World Wisdom (US), Zaytuna Institute Press (US)

Food & Agriculture Organization of the United Nations (FAO), *distributed by* United Nations Publications

Food52 Works, *imprint of* Ten Speed Press

The Food Paper, *division of* Gault Millau Inc/ Gayot Publications

Footprint Books, *distributor for* Boys Town Press, *distributed by* New York University Press

Footprint Books Pty Ltd, *distributor for* Health Professions Press

For Dummies®, *imprint of* John Wiley & Sons Inc

Force on Force, *imprint of* Osprey Publishing Inc

Fordham University Press, *distributor for* Creighton University Press, Institute for Advanced Study in the Theatre Arts (IASTA), Little Room Press, The Reconstructionist Press, Rockhurst University Press, St Bede's Publications, University of San Francisco Press, *distributed by* Heimburger House Publishing Co, Oxford University Press (US & CN), Oxford University Press USA

Foreign Affairs Information Service, *imprint of* George Kurian Reference Books

Foreign Language Press, *distributed by* CN Times Books

Foreign Languages Press, *distributed by* China Books

Forest History Society, *distributed by* Duke University Press

Forest of Peace, *imprint of* Ave Maria Press

Forever, *imprint of* Grand Central Publishing

Forever Nuts, *imprint of* NBM Publishing Inc

Forever Regency, *imprint of* ImaJinn Books Inc

Forever Yours, *imprint of* Grand Central Publishing

Forge Books, *imprint of* Tom Doherty Associates, LLC

Formac Publishing, *distributed by* Casemate Publishers & Book Distributors LLC, Orca Book Publishers

Formatio, *imprint of* InterVarsity Press

Fort Ross Inc Russian-American Publishing Projects, *division of* Fort Ross Inc

Fortress, *imprint of* Osprey Publishing Inc

Fortress Press, *imprint of* Augsburg Fortress Publishers, Publishing House of the Evangelical Lutheran Church in America

Fortytwo Bookz Galaxy, *distributor for* Price World Publishing

Forward Movement, *affiliate of* The Episcopal Church, *distributor for* Anglican Book Centre

Frances Foster Books, *imprint of* Farrar, Straus & Giroux Books for Young Readers

Walter Foster, *distributor for* The Jim Henson Co

Walter Foster Publishing, *imprint of* Quarto Publishing Group USA Inc, *distributed by* Lerner Publishing Group Inc

Walter Foster Publishing Inc, *imprint of* Quarto Publishing Group USA, Quarto Publishing Group USA Inc

G T Foulis, *distributed by* Haynes Manuals Inc

Foundation for Deep Ecology, *distributed by* Chelsea Green Publishing Co

Foundation Press, *imprint of* West Academic Publishing

Foundry, *distributed by* Casemate Publishers & Book Distributors LLC

The Fountain, *imprint of* Tughra Books

Four Rivers Press, *imprint of* McClanahan Publishing House Inc

Four Seas, *imprint of* Branden Books

Four Way Books, *distributed by* University Press of New England

4th Dimension Press, *imprint of* ARE Press

Fourth Estate, *imprint of* HarperCollins Publishers Sales

Fox Chapel Publishing Co Inc, *distributor for* Reader's Digest, Taunton Sterling Dover, *distributed by* Ingram Publisher Services

Fox Maple Press, *distributed by* Chelsea Green Publishing Co

Fox River Press, *distributed by* Pilgrim Publications

Franciscan Communications, *imprint of* Franciscan Media, *distributed by* Franciscan Media

Franciscan Media, *distributor for* Franciscan Communications (books & videos), Ikonographics (videos)

Franklin, Beedle & Associates Inc, *distributor for* Arcus, Battlebridge, Blue Sky Gallery, Photolucida Book, Ringing Bell Press, Tayo Press, Wordstock

Franklin Street Books, *imprint of* Inkwater Press

Franklin Watts®, *imprint of* Scholastic Education

Franko Maps, *distributed by* Wide World of Maps Inc

Frederator Books LLC, *distributed by* Simon & Schuster, Inc, Simon & Schuster Sales Division

Free Press, *imprint of* Simon & Schuster, *distributed by* Center for Creative Leadership LLC

Free Spirit, *distributed by* Perfection Learning Corp, Torah Aura Productions

Free Spirit Publishing Inc, *distributor for* Council for Exceptional Children (CEC)

Freedom Fox Press, *imprint of* Dancing Lemur Press LLC

Freedom Press, *distributed by* AK Press Distribution

W H Freeman, *imprint of* Macmillan Higher Education, *distributor for* American Geosciences Institute (AGI)

Freestone, *imprint of* Peachtree Publishers

Samuel French Inc, *distributor for* Baker's Plays, Samuel French Ltd (UK), *distributed by* Baker's Plays, Samuel French Ltd (UK)

Samuel French Ltd, *distributor for* Samuel French Inc, *distributed by* Samuel French Inc

Fresco Fine Art Publications LLC, *distributed by* University of New Mexico

Fresh Air Books, *imprint of* Upper Room Books

Friends of University of Princeton, *distributed by* Diane Publishing Co

Friends United Press, *subsidiary of* Friends United Meeting

Friendship Bible Studies, *imprint of* Faith Alive Christian Resources

Frog Books, *imprint of* North Atlantic Books, *distributed by* North Atlantic Books, Random House

Frog Legs Ink, *imprint of* Gauthier Publications Inc

Front Street Press, *distributed by* Casemate Publishers & Book Distributors LLC

Front Table Books, *imprint of* Cedar Fort Inc

La Frontera Publishing, *distributed by* University of New Mexico

Frontline Books, *distributed by* Casemate Publishers & Book Distributors LLC

FT Press, *imprint of* Financial Times Press

Fulcrum, *distributed by* Perfection Learning Corp

Fulgur Ltd, *distributed by* Holmes Publishing Group LLC

David Fulton Books, *distributed by* Routledge/Taylor & Francis

Fun Places Publishing, *distributed by* Sunbelt Publications Inc

FurnitureCore, *distributor for* AMA Research, Business & Research Associates

FW Friends™, *imprint of* Group Publishing Inc

G Q Publishing, *imprint of* Great Quotations Inc

G-unit, *imprint of* Gallery Books

G W Medical Publisher, *distributed by* Elsevier, Health Sciences Division

Galaxy Audio, *imprint of* Galaxy Press

Galaxy Music Corp, *imprint of* ECS Publishing Corp

Gale, *division of* Cengage Learning, *unit of* Cengage Learning, *subsidiary of* Cengage Learning

Gale Research Inc, *distributor for* Business Research Services Inc

Gallaudet University Press, *imprint of* Gallaudet University Press, *distributor for* Signum Verlag, *distributed by* DawnSignPress

Gallery Books, *imprint of* Gallery Publishing Group

Gallup, *distributed by* Simon & Schuster, Inc, Simon & Schuster Sales Division

Gambit Books, *imprint of* The Harvard Common Press

Games Workshop, *distributed by* Simon & Schuster, Inc, Simon & Schuster Sales Division

Jeffrey Garcia, *distributed by* Sunbelt Publications Inc

Garden Art Press, *imprint of* Antique Collectors' Club Ltd

Isabella Stewart Gardner Museum, *distributed by* University Press of New England

Gareth Stevens Publishing, *imprint of* The Rosen Publishing Group Inc

Garland-Clark Editors, *distributed by* Players Press Inc

Garland Publishers, *distributor for* University of California Institute on Global Conflict & Cooperation

Garland Science, *imprint of* Routledge/Taylor & Francis, Taylor & Francis Inc

Garland Science Publishing, *member of* Taylor & Francis Group, The Taylor & Francis Group

John Garrett, *distributor for* Twenty-Third Publications

Gaslight Publications, *imprint of* Empire Publishing Service

Gateway, *imprint of* Regnery Publishing Inc

Gateway to Healthcare Management, *imprint of* Health Administration Press

Gateways Books & Tapes, *division of* Institute for the Development of the Harmonious Human Being Inc, Institute for the Development of the Harmonious Human Being Inc, *distributor for* Cloister Recordings (audio & video tapes)

Gateways Fine Art Series, *imprint of* Gateways Books & Tapes

Gaudia Music & Arts, *distributed by* ECS Publishing Corp

Gault Millau, *imprint of* Gault Millau Inc/Gayot Publications

Gault Millau Inc/Gayot Publications, *distributed by* Publishers Group West

GAYOT, *imprint of* Gault Millau Inc/Gayot Publications

Geared Up Publications, *imprint of* Schiffer Publishing Ltd

Gecko Press, *distributed by* Lerner Publishing Group Inc

Gefen Books, *distributor for* Bar Ilan, Magnes Press

Gefen Publishing Ltd, *imprint of* Gefen Books

Gem Guides Book Co, *distributor for* Borden Publishing, Brynmorgen Press, Clear Creek Publishing, Earth Love Publishing, Editions du Signe, Gemstone Press, Golden West Books, Grand Canyon Association, Heaven & Earth Press, Hexagon Press, International Jewelry Publications, George R Jezek Photography, Cy Johnson & Son, KC Publications Inc, Many Moons Press, Naturegraph, Nevada Publications, Out of This World Press, Pinyon Publishing, Primer Publications, Ram Publishing, Recreation Sales, Shortfuse Press, Sierra Press, Delos Toole, Trees Co, Tri-Star Boze Books, Weseanne Publications, *distributed by* Nevada Publications

Gembooks, *imprint of* Gem Guides Book Co

Gemstone Press, *distributed by* Gem Guides Book Co

Gender Genre, *imprint of* Bandanna Books

Genealogical Publishing Co, *subsidiary of* Genealogical.com

Geneological Society of Pennsylvania, *distributed by* Diane Publishing Co

General Aviation, *imprint of* Osprey Publishing Inc

General Education Services (New Zealand), *distributed by* Abrams Learning Trends

General Military, *imprint of* Osprey Publishing Inc

Genesis Press, *distributed by* Kensington Publishing Corp

Genetic Engineering & Biotechnology News, *division of* Mary Ann Liebert Inc

Geneva Press, *imprint of* Presbyterian Publishing Corp (PPC)

Gennadeion Monographs, *imprint of* ASCSA Publications

Gentle World, *distributed by* Book Publishing Co

Geological Society of London, *distributor for* AAPG (American Association of Petroleum Geologists), *distributed by* AAPG (American Association of Petroleum Geologists)

Geology and Geography of Alaska Series, *imprint of* University of Alaska Press

Geology Underfoot Series, *imprint of* Mountain Press Publishing Co

Geophysical Institute, *distributed by* University of Alaska Press

Georgetown University Press, *distributed by* The Johns Hopkins University Press

The Georgia Literary Association, *imprint of* Blood Moon Productions Ltd

GetFitNow.com Books, *imprint of* Hatherleigh Press Ltd

Getting Into, *imprint of* Mel Bay Publications Inc

Getty, *distributed by* Oxford University Press USA

Getty Publications, *distributed by* University of Chicago Press (US only)

Gibbs Smith, *distributor for* Sierra Club Books

Gibbs-Smith, *distributor for* Sourced Media Books

Gifted Psychology Press, *imprint of* Great Potential Press Inc

Gig Savers, *imprint of* Mel Bay Publications Inc

Gilcrease Museum, *distributed by* University of Oklahoma Press

Gildan Media, *distributed by* Hachette Book Group

D Giles Ltd, *distributor for* American Federation of Arts

Gill & Macmillan, *distributed by* Dufour Editions Inc

Maureen Gilmer, *distributed by* Sunbelt Publications Inc

Gingko Press, *distributed by* Gingko Press Inc

Gingko Press Inc, *distributor for* All Rights Reserved, Archimap, Art Power, Basheer, Carpet Bombing Culture, Choi's Gallery, CYPI, Gingko Press, Grand Central Art Center, Rebel Arts, Sandu Publications, Sendpoints Books Co Ltd, Upper Playground, Victionary, Wax Facts Press, Zero+ Publishing

Gival Press, *imprint of* Gival Press LLC

Michael Glazier Books, *imprint of* Liturgical Press

Glencannon, *distributed by* Mystic Seaport Museum Inc

Glencoe, *imprint of* McGraw-Hill School Education Group

Glencoe/McGraw-Hill, *imprint of* McGraw-Hill Education

Peter Glenn Publications, *division of* Blount Communications Corp

Glide Publications, *imprint of* Volcano Press

Glimmer Train Press Inc, *distributor for* Glimmer Train Stories

Glimmer Train Stories, *distributed by* Glimmer Train Press Inc

Global eBook Awards, *division of* Para Publishing LLC

Global Professional Publishing, *distributed by* Stylus Publishing LLC

Global Research, *distributed by* Progressive Press

Global Trade Watch, *division of* Public Citizen

Globe Pequot, *imprint of* The Globe Pequot Press

Globe Pequot Press, *distributor for* Montana Historical Society Press, *distributed by* Heimburger House Publishing Co

The Globe Pequot Press, *division of* Rowman & Littlefield Publishing Group, *distributor for* Appalachian Mountain Club Books, Boone & Crockett Club, Thomas Cook Publishing, D&B Publishing, Day Hike Books Inc, Everyman Chess, Explorer Publishing, Globetrotter, Good Sam's, Jonglez Publishing, Montana Historical Society Press, New Holland Publishers (UK) Ltd, Oval Books (UK), Alastair Sawday Publishing (co-publr), Stoecklein Publishing, 30 Words, Trailblazer Publications, Western Horseman Books

Globetrotter, *distributed by* The Globe Pequot Press

Glove Pequot, *distributed by* Sunbelt Publications Inc

GOAL/QPC, *distributor for* American Society for Quality (ASQ)

Goblinshead, *distributed by* Dufour Editions Inc

GoFacts Guided Writing, *imprint of* Sundance/ Newbridge Publishing

Gold Fever Press, *distributed by* Epicenter Press Inc

Golden Books, *imprint of* Penguin Random House Inc, Random House Children's Books, *distributed by* Perfection Learning Corp

Golden Books Family Entertainment, *distributor for* The Jim Henson Co

Golden Coast Publishing Co, *distributed by* University of Georgia Press

Golden Dawn Publications, *imprint of* The Original Falcon Press

Golden Hill Press, *distributed by* Heimburger House Publishing Co

Golden Triangle Books, *imprint of* University of Pittsburgh Press

Golden West Books, *distributed by* Gem Guides Book Co

Golden West Cookbooks, *division of* American Traveler Press

Golganooza Press, *distributed by* Fons Vitae

Gollehon Books, *imprint of* Gollehon Press Inc

Gomer Press, *distributed by* Beekman Books Inc

Good Sam's, *distributed by* The Globe Pequot Press

Gooseberry Patch, *imprint of* The Globe Pequot Press, *distributed by* Andrews McMeel Publishing LLC

Goosebottom Books, *imprint of* Goosebottom Books LLC

Gorgias Press LLC, *distributor for* Yeshiva University Museum Press

Gospel Publishing House, *imprint of* Gospel Publishing House (GPH)

Gospel Publishing House (GPH), *division of* General Council of the Assemblies of God

Government Jobs Series, *imprint of* PREP Publishing

Gower, *imprint of* Ashgate Publishing Co, Elsevier, Health Sciences Division

Colin Gower, *distributed by* Krause Publications Inc

GPC/Gollehon, *imprint of* Gollehon Press Inc

GPP® Travel, *imprint of* The Globe Pequot Press

Grab a Pencil Press, *imprint of* Applewood Books Inc

Graduate Record Examination Series, *imprint of* National Learning Corp

Gramercy Books, *imprint of* Penguin Random House Inc

Gramophone, *distributed by* Omnibus Press

Grand Canyon Association, *distributed by* Gem Guides Book Co

Grand Central Art Center, *distributed by* Gingko Press Inc

Grand Central/Hachette Large Print, *distributed by* Thorndike Press

Grand Central Life & Style, *imprint of* Grand Central Publishing

Grand Central Publishing, *division of* Hachette Book Group

Grand Harbor Press, *imprint of* Brilliance Audio

Donald M Grant Publisher Inc, *distributor for* Archival, Oswald Train

Granta, *distributed by* Penguin Group (USA) LLC, a Penguin Random House company

Graphia, *imprint of* Houghton Mifflin Harcourt Trade & Reference Division

Graphic Arts Books, *unit of* Ingram Content Group Inc

Graphic Arts Books®, *imprint of* Graphic Arts Books

Graphic History, *imprint of* Osprey Publishing Inc

Graphic Planet, *imprint of* ABDO Publishing Group

Graphic Universe™, *division of* Lerner Publishing Group Inc, *imprint of* Lerner Publishing Group Inc

Graphix, *imprint of* Scholastic Trade Division

Grave Issues, *imprint of* Spinsters Ink

Gray Wolf Books, *distributed by* Farrar, Straus & Giroux, LLC

Great Architectural Replica Series, *imprint of* Stemmer House Publishers Inc

Great Books of the Islamic World, *imprint of* Kazi Publications Inc

Great Explorer Series, *imprint of* University of Alaska Press

Great Lakes Books, *imprint of* Wayne State University Press

Great Outdoors Publishing Co, *imprint of* Finney Company Inc

Great Potential Press Inc, *division of* Anodyne Inc, Anodyne Inc

Great Source, *imprint of* Harcourt Inc

Great Source Education Group, *subsidiary of* Houghton Mifflin Harcourt, Houghton Mifflin Harcourt Publishing Company

The Greeley Co, *subsidiary of* HCPro Inc

Green Books, *distributed by* Chelsea Green Publishing Co

Green Building Press, *distributed by* Chelsea Green Publishing Co

Green Grass Press, *distributed by* Sunbelt Publications Inc

Green Knees, *imprint of* Azro Press

Green Man Publishing, *distributed by* Chelsea Green Publishing Co

Green Tiger Press, *imprint of* Laughing Elephant

Greenberg Books, *imprint of* Kalmbach Publishing Co

Greenbranch, *distributed by* Medical Group Management Association (MGMA)

Alice Greene & Co, *imprint of* T H Peek Publisher

Greenfield Review Press, *distributed by* Cross-Cultural Communications

Greenhaven Imprints, *distributor for* Lucent Books®

Greenhaven Press, *distributed by* Lucent Books®

Greenhaven Press®, *imprint of* Gale

Greenhaven Press Inc, *distributed by* Perfection Learning Corp

Greenhill Books, *distributed by* Casemate Publishers & Book Distributors LLC

Greenleaf Book Group Press, *imprint of* Greenleaf Book Group LLC

Greenwich Medical Media, *distributed by* Oxford University Press USA

Greenwich Workshop Press, *distributed by* Algonquin Books, Artisan Books, Workman Publishing Co Inc

Greenwillow Books, *imprint of* HarperCollins Children's Books, HarperCollins Publishers

Greenwood Press, *imprint of* ABC-CLIO

Greenwood Research Books & Software, *division of* Greenwood Research

Greeting Cards, *division of* Unarius Academy of Science Publications

Grey House, *imprint of* Grey House Publishing Inc™

Grey House Publishing Canada, *division of* Grey House Publishing Inc™

Grief Watch, *distributed by* ACTA Publications

Griffin, *imprint of* St Martin's Press, LLC

Griot Audio, *imprint of* Recorded Books LLC

Griot Enterprises, *imprint of* Cedar Grove Books

Grolier, *distributor for* The Jim Henson Co

The Grolier Club, *distributed by* Oak Knoll Press

Grolier Online®, *imprint of* Scholastic Education

Grosset, *distributor for* Parachute Publishing LLC

Grosset & Dunlap, *subsidiary of* Penguin Group (USA) LLC, a Penguin Random House company, *imprint of* Penguin Group (USA) LLC, a Penguin Random House company, Penguin Group (USA) LLC, a Penguin Random House company, Penguin Young Readers Group

Grosset/Putnam, *imprint of* Penguin Group (USA) LLC, a Penguin Random House company, GP Putnam's Sons (Hardcover)

Stefan Grossman's Guitar Workshop, *distributed by* Mel Bay Publications Inc

Groundworks, *distributed by* Chelsea Green Publishing Co

Group for the Advancement of Psychiatry, *distributed by* American Psychiatric Publishing (APP)

Group Publishing, *distributed by* Saint Mary's Press

Group Workcamps™, *imprint of* Group Publishing Inc

Group's Hands-On Bible Curriculum™, *imprint of* Group Publishing Inc

Grove Dictionaries, *distributed by* Oxford University Press USA

Grove Press, *imprint of* Grove Atlantic Inc

The Grow Network/McGraw-Hill, *imprint of* McGraw-Hill Education

Grub Street, *distributed by* Casemate Publishers & Book Distributors LLC

B R Gruener Publishing Co, *imprint of* John Benjamins Publishing Co

Gryphon House, *distributor for* DawnSignPress, *distributed by* Teaching Strategies

Gryphon House Inc, *subsidiary of* Kaplan Early Learning Co, *distributor for* Aha Communications, Book Peddlers, Deya Brashears, Bright Ring Publishing, Building Blocks, Center for the Child Care Workforce, Chatterbox Press, Chicago Review Press, Children's Resources International, Circle Time Publishers, Sydney Gurewitz Clemens, Conari Press, Council Oak Books, Dawn Sign Press, Delmar Publishers Inc, Early Educator's Press, Educators for Social Responsibility, Family Center of Nova University, Jean Feldman, Floris Books, Hawthorne Press, Hunter House Publishers, Kaplan Press, Miss Jackie Inc, Monjeu Press, National Center Early Childhood Workforce, New England AEYC, New Horizons, Nova Southeastern University, Pademelon Press, Partner Press, Pollyanna Productions, Robins Lane Press, School Renaissance, Southern Early Childhood Association, Steam Press, Syracuse University Press, Teaching Strategies, Telshare Publishing

GSAPP Books, *distributed by* Columbia University Press

GT Publishing, *distributed by* HarperCollins Publishers

Guilford Press, *distributed by* Specialty Press Inc

Guiness World Records, *distributed by* Hachette Book Group

Guitar One, *distributed by* Hal Leonard Corp

Guitar World, *distributed by* Hal Leonard Corp

Gulf Coast Association of Geological Societies, *distributed by* Bureau of Economic Geology, University of Texas at Austin

Gulf Coast Section, *distributed by* Bureau of Economic Geology, University of Texas at Austin

Gulf Professional Publishers, *distributed by* Marine Techniques Publishing

Gulf Publishing, *distributed by* NACE International

Gulf Publishing Co, *distributor for* Elsevier, Pennwell, Simon & Schuster, Editions Technip, Wiley

Gumdrop, *distributor for* Ozark Publishing Inc

Gun Digest® Books, *imprint of* Krause Publications Inc

The George Gund Foundation, *imprint of* University of California Press

Haase House, *imprint of* Easy Money Press

Hachai Publishing, *distributor for* Attara, Kerem

Hachette Audio, *division of* Hachette Book Group

Hachette Book Group, *division of* Hachette Livre, *subsidiary of* Hachette Livre, *distributor for* Harry N Abrams Inc, Amazing People

Club, Chronicle Books, Disney Book Group, Gildan Media, Guiness World Records, Hachette UK, Hearst Books, Houghton Mifflin Harcourt, Houghton Mifflin Harcourt Trade & Reference Division, Kensington Publishing, Kids Can Press, Marvel Worldwide Inc, Octopus Books, Oxmoor House, Phaidon Press, Quarto Publishing, Quercus Books, Time Home Entertainment Inc

Hachette Book Group USA, *distributor for* Disney Press, Kensington Publishing Corp

Hachette Books, *division of* Hachette Book Group

Hachette Nashville, *division of* Hachette Book Group

Hachette UK, *distributed by* Hachette Book Group

Hackett Publishing Co Inc, *distributor for* Bryn Mawr Commentaries

Hagstrom Map, *subsidiary of* American Map Corp, *distributor for* ADC The Map People, American Map Corp, Arrow Maps Inc, Creative Sales Corp, De Lorme Atlas, Hammond World Atlas Corp, RV International Maps & Atlases, Stubs Guides, Trakker Maps Inc

Hagstrom Map Co Inc, *subsidiary of* American Map Corp

Hal Leonard Books, *imprint of* Hal Leonard Performing Arts Publishing Group, Hal Leonard Performing Arts Publishing Group

Hal Leonard Corp, *distributor for* Amadeus Press, Applause Theatre & Cinema Books, Artistpro, Ashley Music, Backbeat Books, Beacon Music, Berklee Press, Fred Bock Music Company, Boosey & Hawkes, Centerstream Publications, Centerstream Publishing LLC, Cherry Lane Music Co, Cinema Books, Community Music Videos, Creative Concepts, DC Publications, Devine Entertainment Corp, Editions Durand, Editions Max Eschig, Editions Salabert, EM Books, EMI Christian, Faber Music Ltd, Guitar One, Guitar World, Home Recording, Homespun Tapes, Houston Publications, Hudson Music, iSong CD-ROMs, Jawbone Press, Kenyon Publications, Limelight Editions, Ashley Mark Publishing Co, Edward B Marks Music, Meredith Music, Modern Drummer Publications, Music Sales America, Musicians Institute Press, Musikverlage Han Sikorski, Christopher Parkening, Reader's Digest, Record Research, Ricordi, Lee Roberts Publications, Rubank Publications, G Schirmer Inc (Associated Music Publishers), Second Floor Music, Sing Out Corp, Star Licks Videos, Bernard Stein Music Co, String Letter Press, Tara Publications, Transcontinental Music, 21st Century Publications, Vintage Guitar, Word Music, Writer's Digest

Hal Leonard Corporation, *distributor for* Applause Theatre & Cinema Books

Hal Leonard Performing Arts Publishing Group, *division of* Hal Leonard Corp

Halcyon House, *imprint of* National Book Co

Halcyon House Publishers, *imprint of* Acres USA

Halsted Press, *imprint of* John Wiley & Sons Inc

Hamadia Publishing, *distributed by* Feldheim Publishers (Philipp Feldheim Inc)

Hambleton Publishing, *distributed by* Caxton Press

Hamewith, *imprint of* Baker Books

Hamilton Books, *imprint of* University Press of America Inc

Hammond Pub, *distributed by* Perfection Learning Corp

Hammond World Atlas Corp, *subsidiary of* American Map Corp, *distributed by* Hagstrom Map

Hampton Roads Publishing, *imprint of* Red Wheel/Weiser/Conari

Hampton Roads Publishing Co, *distributed by* Red Wheel/Weiser Books/Conari Press

Hand Print Press, *distributed by* Chelsea Green Publishing Co

Handprint Books, *distributed by* Chronicle Books LLC

Handprint Books Inc, *imprint of* Chronicle Books LLC, *distributed by* Chronicle Books

Hanser Publications LLC, *subsidiary of* Carl Hanser Verlag GmbH & Co KG, Carl Hanser Verlag GmbH & Co KG, *distributor for* Hanser Publishers (call Hanser Verlag)

Hanser Publishers, *distributed by* Hanser Publications LLC

HAP (Health Adminstration Press), *distributed by* Medical Group Management Association (MGMA)

Happy Day Books, *imprint of* Standard Publishing

Harbor Hill Books, *division of* Purple Mountain Press Ltd

Harbor Lights, *imprint of* LangMarc Publishing

Harbour Publishing, *distributed by* Heimburger House Publishing Co

Harcourt, *distributor for* Parachute Publishing LLC, *distributed by* Learning Links Inc, SAS Publishing

Harcourt Achieve, *division of* Houghton Mifflin Harcourt, *imprint of* Harcourt Inc

Harcourt Children's, *imprint of* Houghton Mifflin Harcourt Trade & Reference Division

Harcourt Inc, *division of* Houghton Mifflin Harcourt, *distributed by* Perfection Learning Corp

Hard Shell, *imprint of* Mundania Press LLC

Hard Shell Word Factory, *imprint of* Mundania Press LLC

Hardie Press, *distributed by* Mel Bay Publications Inc

Hardscrabble Books, *imprint of* University Press of New England

Hardwood Press, *distributed by* St Augustine's Press Inc

Harlequin, *imprint of* Harlequin Enterprises Ltd, *distributed by* Simon & Schuster Sales Division

Harlequin Enterprises Ltd, *division of* HarperCollins, *distributed by* Simon & Schuster, Inc, Simon & Schuster Mass Merchandise Sales Co

Harmony, *imprint of* Crown Publishing Group

Harmony Books, *imprint of* Penguin Random House Inc

Harper, *imprint of* HarperCollins General Books Group

Harper Arrington Publishing, *distributor for* The Little Entrepreneur

Harper Business, *imprint of* HarperCollins General Books Group

Harper Design, *imprint of* HarperCollins General Books Group

Harper Elixir, *imprint of* HarperCollins General Books Group

Harper Paperbacks, *imprint of* HarperCollins General Books Group

Harper Perennial, *imprint of* HarperCollins General Books Group

Harper Voyager, *imprint of* HarperCollins General Books Group

Harper Wave, *imprint of* HarperCollins General Books Group

HarperAudio, *imprint of* HarperCollins Children's Books, HarperCollins General Books Group, HarperCollins Publishers Sales

HarperBibles, *imprint of* HarperCollins General Books Group

HarperBusiness, *imprint of* HarperCollins Publishers Sales

HarperCollins, *imprint of* HarperCollins General Books Group, HarperCollins Publishers, HarperCollins Publishers Sales, *distributor for* Alloy Entertainment LLC, Delphinium Books, Parachute Publishing LLC, *distributed by* Dreamscape Media LLC, Heimburger House Publishing Co, Learning Links Inc, MAR*CO Products Inc

HarperCollins Children's Books, *division of* HarperCollins Publishers, *imprint of* HarperCollins Children's Books

HarperCollins e-books, *imprint of* HarperCollins Children's Books, HarperCollins General Books Group

HarperCollins General Books Group, *division of* HarperCollins Publishers

HarperCollins Publishers, *subsidiary of* News Corporation, *distributor for* Basic Books, Civitas, Counterpoint, Delphinium Books, GT Publishing, Perseus (Addison Wesley Trade), Public Affairs, TV Books, *distributed by* Cynthia Publishing Co, Ingram Publisher Services/Spring Arbor (Christian market)

HarperCollins 360, *imprint of* HarperCollins General Books Group

HarperDesign, *imprint of* HarperCollins Publishers Sales

HarperEntertainment, *imprint of* HarperCollins Publishers Sales, *distributor for* Parachute Publishing LLC

HarperFestival, *imprint of* HarperCollins Children's Books

HarperLarge Print, *imprint of* HarperCollins Publishers Sales

HarperLuxe, *imprint of* HarperCollins General Books Group, *distributed by* Thorndike Press

HarperOne, *imprint of* HarperCollins General Books Group

HarperResource, *imprint of* HarperCollins Publishers Sales

HarperSanFrancisco, *imprint of* HarperCollins Publishers Sales

HarperTeen, *imprint of* HarperCollins Children's Books

HarperTeen Impulse, *imprint of* HarperCollins Children's Books

HarperTorch, *imprint of* HarperCollins Publishers Sales

Harpia Publishing, *distributed by* Casemate Publishers & Book Distributors LLC

Harrap, *distributed by* Houghton Mifflin Harcourt

Harrington Park Press, *distributed by* Columbia University Press

Harrison House, *distributor for* Faith Library Publications

Tom Harrison Cartography, *distributed by* Mountain n' Air Books

Harvard Art Museums, *distributed by* Yale University Press

Harvard Business Reference, *imprint of* Harvard Business Review Press

Harvard Business Review Press, *division of* Harvard Business Publishing, *distributed by* Client Distribution Services

Harvard Business School Press, *distributed by* Center for Creative Leadership LLC, SAS Publishing

Harvard Center for International Affairs, *distributed by* University Press of America Inc

Harvard Center for Middle Eastern Studies, *distributed by* Harvard University Press

Harvard Center for Population Studies, *distributed by* Harvard University Press

Harvard Center for the Study of World Religions, *distributed by* Harvard University Press

Harvard College Library, *distributed by* Harvard University Press

Harvard Common Press, *distributed by* Houghton Mifflin Harcourt Trade & Reference Division

The Harvard Common Press, *distributed by* Houghton Mifflin Harcourt

Harvard Department of Sanskrit & Indian Studies, *distributed by* Harvard University Press

Harvard Department of the Classics, *distributed by* Harvard University Press

Harvard Education Letter, *imprint of* Harvard Education Publishing Group

Harvard Education Press, *imprint of* Harvard Education Publishing Group

Harvard Education Publishing Group, *division of* Harvard Graduate School of Education

Harvard Educational Review Reprint Series, *imprint of* Harvard Education Publishing Group

Harvard Ukrainian Research Institute, *subsidiary of* Business History Review, Harvard University, *distributed by* Harvard University Press

Harvard University Art Museums, *distributed by* Yale University Press

Harvard University Asia Center, *distributed by* Harvard University Press

Harvard University David Rockefeller Center for Latin American Studies, *distributed by* Harvard University Press

Harvard University Press, *distributor for* Dumbarton Oaks, Harvard Center for Middle Eastern Studies, Harvard Center for Population Studies, Harvard Center for the Study of World Religions, Harvard College Library (including Houghton Library Judaica division), Harvard Department of Sanskrit & Indian Studies, Harvard Department of the Classics, Harvard Ukrainian Research Institute, Harvard University Asia Center, Harvard University David Rockefeller Center for Latin American Studies, Harvard-Yenching Institute, Peabody Museum of Archaeology & Ethnology

Harvard-Yenching Institute, *distributed by* Harvard University Press

Harvest Hill Press, *distributed by* University Press of New England

Harvest House, *distributor for* Focus on the Family

Haugen Enterprises, *distributed by* Frank Amato Publications Inc

Haven, *imprint of* Bridge-Logos Inc

Hawthorn Press, *distributed by* SteinerBooks

Hawthorne Press, *distributed by* Gryphon House Inc

Hayes, *distributed by* Perfection Learning Corp

Haynes Manuals Inc, *division of* The Haynes Publishing Group, *distributor for* G T Foulis, Haynes Owners Workshop Manuals, Oxford Illustrated Press, *distributed by* Motorbooks International

Haynes Owners Workshop Manuals, *distributed by* Haynes Manuals Inc

Nicolas Hays Inc, *distributed by* Red Wheel/Weiser/Conari

Hazamir, *imprint of* Transcontinental Music Publications

Hazelden/Johnson Institute, *imprint of* Hazelden Publishing

Hazelden/Keep Coming Back, *imprint of* Hazelden Publishing

Hazelden-Pittman Archives Press, *imprint of* Hazelden Publishing

Hazelden Publishing, *division of* Hazelden Foundation, *distributor for* Obsessive Anonymous, *distributed by* Health Communications Inc (trade)

HCI Books, *imprint of* Health Communications Inc

HCI Printing & Publishing, *division of* Health Communications Inc

HCI Teens, *imprint of* Health Communications Inc

Headwater Books, *distributed by* Stackpole Books

Healey Publishing, *distributed by* Sunbelt Publications Inc

Healing Arts Press, *imprint of* Inner Traditions International Ltd

Healing Tao Books, *distributed by* Tuttle Publishing

Health Administration Press, *division of* Foundation of the American College of Healthcare Executives

Health Books, *imprint of* Oxmoor House

Health Communications Inc, *distributor for* Hazelden Publishing

Health Forum Inc, *subsidiary of* American Hospital Association

Health Information Network, *distributor for* Apollo Managed Care Inc

Health Information Press (HIP), *imprint of* Practice Management Information Corp (PMIC)

Health Professions Press, *division of* Paul H Brookes Publishing Co Inc, Brookes Publishing Co Inc, *subsidiary of* Brookes Publishing Co Inc, *distributed by* The Eurospan Group (Africa, Europe & Middle East), Footprint Books Pty Ltd (Australia, Fiji, New Zealand & Papua New Guinea), Login Brothers (Canada), Unifacmanu Trading Co Ltd (Taiwan)

Health Research GP Buyers UP, *division of* Public Citizen

Healthcare Performance Press, *imprint of* Productivity Press

Healthwatch, *imprint of* Players Press Inc

Healthy Living, *imprint of* Book Publishing Co

Healthy Living Books, *imprint of* Hatherleigh Press Ltd

Hearne Fine Art, *distributed by* The University of Arkansas Press

Hearst Books, *imprint of* HarperCollins Publishers, Sterling Publishing Co Inc, *distributed by* Hachette Book Group

Heart Path Press, *distributed by* Enfield Publishing & Distribution Co

Hearthside Books, *distributed by* Closson Press

Hearts & Tummies Cookbook Co, *division of* Quixote Press, *imprint of* Quixote Press

Hearts 'n Tummies Cookbook Co, *imprint of* Hearts & Tummies Cookbook Co

HeatWave Romance, *subsidiary of* Awe-Struck Publishing

Heaven & Earth Press, *distributed by* Gem Guides Book Co

Heaven & Earth Publications, *distributed by* North Atlantic Books

Hebrew Union College Press, *division of* Hebrew Union College, *distributed by* Wayne State University Press

Heian, *imprint of* Stone Bridge Press Inc

Heian International, *imprint of* Stone Bridge Press Inc

Heimburger House Publishing Co, *distributor for* Book Sales Inc, Boyds Mills Press, Canadian Caboose Press, Carstens, Child's Play International, Evergreen Press, Firefly Books Ltd, Fitzhenry & Whiteside Ltd, Fordham University Press, Globe Pequot Press, Golden Hill Press, Harbour Publishing, HarperCollins, Johns Hopkins University Press, Hot Box Press, Houghton Mifflin Harcourt, Howling at the Moon Press, Iconografix, Indiana University Press, Kalmbach Publishing, Krause Publications, Motorbooks International, National Book Network, New York University Press, W W Norton & Co, Penguin Putnam Inc, Pictorial Histories Publishing Co, Sono Nis Press, Steam Passages Publishing, Sterling Publishing, Sugar Cane Press, Syracuse University Press, Thunder Bay Press, University of Minnesota Press, University of Scranton, Westcliffe Publishing, John Wiley & Sons

Heimdal, *distributed by* Casemate Publishers & Book Distributors LLC

William S Hein & Co Inc, *distributor for* Ashgate, Aspen, Butterworths, Sweet & Maxwell, John Wiley & Sons Inc

Heinemann, *division of* Houghton Mifflin Harcourt, *distributed by* ArtAge Publications, Pearson (Canada, Australia & New Zealand)

Heinemann Raintree, *division of* Capstone Publishers™, *imprint of* Capstone Publishers™

Heinle, *subsidiary of* Cengage Learning, *imprint of* Wadsworth Publishing

Heirloom Children's Book Publishers, *imprint of* Schiel & Denver Book Publishers

John Helde, *distributed by* EastBridge

Helena History Press, *distributed by* Central European University Press

Heliconia Press, *imprint of* Fox Chapel Publishing Co Inc

Helion & Co Ltd, *distributed by* Casemate Publishers & Book Distributors LLC

Hellgate Press, *imprint of* L & R Publishing

Henry Holt, *imprint of* Henry Holt and Company, LLC

Ian Henry Publications, *distributed by* Empire Publishing Service

Joseph Henry Press, *imprint of* National Academies Press (NAP)

Herald Press, *imprint of* MennoMedia

Herald Publishing House, *division of* Community of Christ

Herb & Spice, *imprint of* Crossquarter Publishing Group

Herder & Herder, *imprint of* The Crossroad Publishing Co

Here & Now, *imprint of* Gallopade International Inc

Editions Charles Herissey, *distributed by* Casemate Publishers & Book Distributors LLC

Heritage Books, *imprint of* Heritage Books Inc

Heritage Books Inc, *distributor for* Fairfax Genealogical Society, National Genealogical Society, Virginia Genealogical Society

Heritage Builders, *imprint of* Focus on the Family

Heritage House, *distributor for* FineEdge.com LLC

Nick Hern Books, *distributed by* Theatre Communications Group

Heroes & Helpers, *imprint of* Gallopade International Inc

Heroides Publishing, *imprint of* Joshua Tree Publishing

Hersilia, *distributed by* Dufour Editions Inc

Hes & De Graaf, *distributed by* Oak Knoll Press

Hesperia, *imprint of* ASCSA Publications

Hess Publications, *distributed by* Pilgrim Publications

Heuristic Books, *imprint of* Science & Humanities Press

Hewitt Homeschooling Resources, *division of* Hewitt Research Foundation

Hexagon Press, *distributed by* Gem Guides Book Co

Hidden Travel Series, *imprint of* Ulysses Press

HiddenSpring, *imprint of* Paulist Press

High Tide Monograph Series, *imprint of* High Tide Press

High Tide Press, *subsidiary of* The Trinity Foundation

HighBridge Audio, *imprint of* Algonquin Books, *distributed by* Algonquin Books, Penguin Group (USA) LLC, a Penguin Random House company

Highgate Press, *imprint of* ECS Publishing Corp

Highland/Etling, *imprint of* Alfred Music Publishing

HighRoads Media, *distributed by* Macmillan Audio

Hill & Wang, *division of* Farrar, Straus & Giroux, LLC, *imprint of* Farrar, Straus & Giroux, LLC

Lawrence Hill Books, *imprint of* Chicago Review Press

Hillenbrand Books, *imprint of* Liturgy Training Publications

Hillsdale College Press, *division of* Hillsdale College

Himalayan Institute Press, *division of* Himalayan International Institute of Yoga Science & Philosophy

Hindustan Book Agency, *distributed by* American Mathematical Society

Hinkler Books, *distributed by* Ideals Publications, a Guideposts Co

Hippocrates Publications, *distributed by* Book Publishing Co

Histoire & Collections, *distributed by* Casemate Publishers & Book Distributors LLC

Historic Idaho Series, *distributed by* Caxton Press

Historic New Orleans Collection, *distributed by* Oak Knoll Press

Historical Archive Press, *distributed by* Casemate Publishers & Book Distributors LLC

Historical Indexes, *distributed by* Casemate Publishers & Book Distributors LLC

Historical Society of Western Pennsylvania, *distributed by* Stackpole Books

History Colorado, *distributed by* University Press of Colorado

History Facts, *distributed by* Casemate Publishers & Book Distributors LLC

History Press, *imprint of* Arcadia Publishing Inc

HMH Franchise, *imprint of* Houghton Mifflin Harcourt Trade & Reference Division

Hoard's Dairyman Magazine, *imprint of* W D Hoard & Sons Co

Hobar Publications, *division of* Finney Company Inc, *distributor for* Drache Publications

Hobbes End Publishing LLC, *subsidiary of* Hobbes End Entertainment LLC

Hobble Creek Press, *imprint of* Cedar Fort Inc

Hochelaga, *distributor for* Cross-Cultural Communications, *distributed by* Cross-Cultural Communications

Hodder Education, *distributed by* Trans-Atlantic Publications Inc

Hogarth, *imprint of* Crown Publishing Group

Verlag Hans Huber Hogrefe AG, *distributed by* Hogrefe Publishing

Hogrefe Publishing, *distributor for* Verlag Hans Huber Hogrefe AG (Switzerland), Hogrefe Verlag (Germany)

Hogrefe Verlag, *distributed by* Hogrefe Publishing

Hohm Press, *subsidiary of* HSM LLC

Paul Holberton Publishing, *distributed by* Casemate Publishers & Book Distributors LLC

Holloway House, *imprint of* Kensington Publishing Corp

Holmes Publishing Group, *imprint of* Holmes Publishing Group LLC

Holmes Publishing Group LLC, *distributor for* Capall-Bann (UK), Edda Publishing (Sweden), Fulgur Ltd (UK), Jerusalem Press (UK), Starfire Publishing (UK), Theion Publishing (Germany), Three Hands Press (US), Xoanon Publishing (US)

Holmgren Design Services, *distributed by* Chelsea Green Publishing Co

Holocaust Library, *imprint of* United States Holocaust Memorial Museum

Henry Holt and Company, LLC, *division of* Macmillan, Macmillan

Holt Paperbacks, *imprint of* Henry Holt and Company, LLC

Holy Cross Orthodox Press, *division of* Hellenic College Holy Cross

Homa & Sekey Books, *distributor for* China Encyclopedia Publishing House, China Intercontinental Press, China Zhejiang Publishing United Group

Home Builders Press, *distributed by* Craftsman Book Co

Home Recording, *distributed by* Hal Leonard Corp

Homespun Tapes, *distributed by* Hal Leonard Corp

Homestead Publishing, *affiliate of* Book Design Ltd

Honey Bear Books, *imprint of* Modern Publishing

Hong Kong University Press, *distributed by* Columbia University Press

Alan C Hood & Co Inc, *distributor for* Maryland Historical Society

Hooked on Phonics, *distributed by* Simon & Schuster, Inc

Hoover Institution Press, *subsidiary of* Hoover Institution on War, Revolution & Peace

Hoover's Business Press, *imprint of* Hoover's Inc

Hoover's Handbooks, *imprint of* Hoover's Inc

Hoover's Inc, *subsidiary of* Dun & Bradstreet

Hope Publishing House, *distributed by* Pelican Publishing Co

Johns Hopkins University Press, *distributor for* Inter-American Development Bank, International Food Policy Research Institute, *distributed by* Heimburger House Publishing Co

Hops Press, *distributed by* Mountain Press Publishing Co

Horizon Publishers, *imprint of* Cedar Fort Inc

Horizon Publishers & Distributors Inc, *distributed by* Cedar Fort Inc

Horse Latitudes Press, *imprint of* Crumb Elbow Publishing

Horticulture Books, *imprint of* Betterway Books

Hospital & Healthcare Compensation Service, *subsidiary of* John R Zabka Associates Inc, John R Zabka Associates Inc

Hot Box Press, *distributed by* Heimburger House Publishing Co

Houghton Mifflin Books for Children, *imprint of* Houghton Mifflin Harcourt Trade & Reference Division

Houghton Mifflin Harcourt, *imprint of* Houghton Mifflin Harcourt Trade & Reference Division, *distributor for* Chambers, Clarion Books, Harrap, The Harvard Common Press, Larousse Bilingual, Larousse Mexico, The Old Farmer's Almanac, Zest Books, *distributed by* Hachette Book Group, Heimburger House Publishing Co

Houghton Mifflin Harcourt K-12 Publishers, *division of* Houghton Mifflin Harcourt

Houghton Mifflin Harcourt Publishing Company, *distributed by* Learning Links Inc

Houghton Mifflin Harcourt School Publishers, *division of* Houghton Mifflin Harcourt

Houghton Mifflin Harcourt Trade & Reference Division, *division of* Houghton Mifflin Harcourt, *distributor for* Harvard Common Press, Larausse, Old Farmers Almanac, *distributed by* Hachette Book Group

Hourglass, *imprint of* Baker Books

House of Collectibles, *imprint of* Penguin Random House Inc, Random House Information Group, Random House Reference/Random House Puzzles & Games/House of Collectibles

House to House Publications, *division of* DOVE International

Houston Publications, *distributed by* Hal Leonard Corp

HOW Books, *imprint of* F+W, A Content + eCommerce Company

Howard Books, *imprint of* Atria Publishing Group

Howard University Press, *distributed by* The Johns Hopkins University Press

Howell Book House, *imprint of* John Wiley & Sons Inc

Howling at the Moon Press, *distributed by* Heimburger House Publishing Co

HPBooks, *imprint of* Berkley Publishing Group, Penguin Group (USA) LLC, Penguin Group (USA) LLC, a Penguin Random House company

HQN Books, *imprint of* Harlequin Enterprises Ltd

HRD Press, *distributed by* Training & Development Materials of Canada (Canada)

HSWF, *imprint of* Hard Shell Word Factory

Hub City Press, *distributed by* John F Blair Publisher

Huber, *distributed by* Alan Wofsy Fine Arts

Huckleberry House LLC, *distributed by* Sunbelt Publications Inc

Hudson Hills, *distributor for* National Gallery of Art

Hudson Hills Press Inc, *distributor for* American Federation of Arts

Hudson Hills Press LLC, *distributed by* National Book Network

Hudson Music, *distributed by* Hal Leonard Corp

Huia Publishers, *distributed by* University of Hawaii Press

Human Alchemy Publications, *distributed by* Crown House Publishing Co LLC

Human Rights Watch Books, *imprint of* Human Rights Watch

Humana Press, *imprint of* Springer

Humanity Books, *imprint of* Prometheus Books

Humanix Books LLC, *division of* NewsMaxx

Bruce Humphries, *imprint of* Branden Books

Lund Humphries, *imprint of* Ashgate Publishing Co

Hungry Goat Press, *imprint of* Gauthier Publications Inc

Hunter House Publishers, *distributed by* Gryphon House Inc

Karen Hunter Publishing, *imprint of* Gallery Books

Huntington Library Press, *division of* Huntington Library, Art Collections & Botanical Gardens

Hurst, *distributed by* Oxford University Press USA

The Hutton Settlement, *distributed by* Washington State University Press

Hydra, *imprint of* Penguin Random House Inc, Random House Publishing Group

Hyperbole, *imprint of* San Diego State University Press

Hyperion, *distributor for* Alloy Entertainment LLC

Hyperion Books for Children, *imprint of* Disney Publishing Worldwide

Hypermedia Inc, *imprint of* Frederic C Beil Publisher Inc

Hyphen Press, *distributed by* Princeton Architectural Press

I Love You, *imprint of* Modern Publishing

I&T Shop Service, *imprint of* Penton Media

IBEX Press, *imprint of* Ibex Publishers

Ibex Publishers, *distributor for* Farhang Moaser

IBFD North America Inc (International Bureau of Fiscal Documentation), *division of* IBFD Foundation

ibidem Press, *distributed by* Columbia University Press

IchemE, *distributed by* American Institute of Chemical Engineers (AIChE)

Ichor Business Books, *imprint of* Purdue University Press

ICLE, *imprint of* Institute of Continuing Legal Education

Iconografix, *distributed by* Heimburger House Publishing Co

Idaho Center for the Book, *affiliate of* Library of Congress

Idea Bank, *distributed by* Fire Engineering Books & Videos

Ideals, *imprint of* Ideals Publications, a Guideposts Co

Ideals Children's Books, *imprint of* Ideals Publications, a Guideposts Co

Ideals Publications, a Guideposts Co, *distributor for* Hinkler Books, Rourke Publishing, Smart Ink, Smart Kidz, Someday Baby

Ides et Calendes, *distributed by* Alan Wofsy Fine Arts

Ides et Calendes SA, *distributed by* Wittenborn Art Books

IDRC, *distributed by* Stylus Publishing LLC

IEE, *imprint of* IET USA Inc

IEEE Computer Society Press, *distributor for* American Society for Quality (ASQ)

IEEE Press, *division of* Institute of Electrical & Electronics Engineers Inc (IEEE), *distributed by* John Wiley & Sons Inc

IFSTA, *distributed by* Fire Engineering Books & Videos

Ignatius Press, *division of* Guadalupe Associates Inc, Guadalupe Associates Inc, *distributor for* Bethlehem Books, Veritas

Ignite, *imprint of* Entangled Publishing

IHS Jane's, *subsidiary of* IHS Inc

IIP Consumers Series, *imprint of* Independent Information Publications

Ikonographics, *imprint of* Franciscan Media, *distributed by* Franciscan Media

Ilchokak Publishers, *distributed by* Cheng & Tsui Co Inc

Illinois State Museum Society, *affiliate of* Illinois State Museum

Illuminating Engineering Society of North America (IES), *distributor for* Taylor & Francis, Techstreet

The Illustrated Bartsch, *imprint of* Abaris Books

ILR Press, *imprint of* Cornell University Press

Image Books, *imprint of* Crown Publishing Group

Images Unlimited Publishing, *distributed by* Finney Company Inc

Imagine Publishing, *imprint of* Charlesbridge Publishing Inc

Imago Mundi, *imprint of* David R Godine Publisher Inc

ImaJinn, *imprint of* BelleBooks

ImaJinn Books, *imprint of* ImaJinn Books Inc

ImaJinn Books Inc, *imprint of* BelleBooks

IMM Lifestyle Books, *imprint of* Fox Chapel Publishing Co Inc

Immagine&Poesia, *distributed by* Cross-Cultural Communications

Immedium, *imprint of* Immedium Inc

Impact Publications/Development Concepts Inc, *distributed by* National Book Network

Impact Publishers Inc, *distributor for* STEP Publishers (Systematic Training for Effective Parenting)

Imperial College Press, *subsidiary of* World Scientific Publishing Co Inc

In Extenso Press, *imprint of* ACTA Publications

In the Garden Publishing, *division of* What Would Love Do Intl

Incentive Plus, *distributor for* MAR*CO Products Inc

Independence Press, *imprint of* Herald Publishing House

Independent Information Publications, *division of* Computing!, *distributed by* Pathway Book Service

Independent Music Press, *distributed by* Schirmer Trade Books

Independent Publishers Group, *division of* Chicago Review Press, *distributor for* Big Guy Books Inc

Independent Seaport Museum, *distributed by* Cornell Maritime Press Inc

Independent University of Moscow, *distributed by* American Mathematical Society

Indian Culture Series, *imprint of* The Montana Council for Indian Education

Indiana University Press, *distributed by* Heimburger House Publishing Co

INDIGO, *imprint of* Genesis Press Inc

Indigo Love Spectrum, *imprint of* Genesis Press Inc

Indigo Vibe, *imprint of* Genesis Press Inc

Indo Editions, *distributed by* Casemate Publishers & Book Distributors LLC

Indulgence, *imprint of* Entangled Publishing

Industrial Press, *distributed by* NACE International, Society of Manufacturing Engineers

Indy-Tech Publishing, *imprint of* SAMS Technical Publishing LLC

Infinitum Nihil, *imprint of* HarperCollins General Books Group

Influence Resources, *imprint of* Gospel Publishing House (GPH)

Information & Media Services, *division of* McGraw-Hill Financial

Information Today Books, *imprint of* Information Today, Inc

Information Today Inc, *distributor for* Association for Information Science & Technology (ASIS&T)

Ingalls Publishing, *imprint of* Ingalls Publishing Group Inc (IPG)

Ingalls Publishing Group Inc (IPG), *distributor for* Southlore Press

Ingram Publisher Services, *distributor for* Fox Chapel Publishing Co Inc

Ingram Publisher Services/Spring Arbor, *distributor for* HarperCollins Publishers

Inkwater Press, *imprint of* Firstbooks.com Inc, Firstbooks.com Inc

Inland, *distributor for* World Citizens

Inner Traditions, *imprint of* Inner Traditions International Ltd

Inner Traditions/Bear & Company, *distributed by* Simon & Schuster, Inc

Inner Traditions en espanol, *imprint of* Inner Traditions International Ltd

Inner Traditions India, *imprint of* Inner Traditions International Ltd

Inner Worlds Music, *distributed by* Lotus Press

Innovation & Tourisms (INTO), *imprint of* Cognizant Communication Corp

Innovative Logistics, *distributor for* Visual Profile Books Inc

Innovative Marketing, *distributor for* Pentecostal Publishing House

innovativeKids®, *division of* Innovative USA® Inc, Innovative USA® Inc

InnoVision Health Media, *distributed by* Square One Publishers Inc

Inprint Editions, *imprint of* Black Classic Press

Inservice Reviews, *imprint of* Oakstone Publishing LLC

Inside the Minds, *imprint of* Aspatore Books

Insight Media, *imprint of* Alexander Street Press LLC

Inspec, *imprint of* IET USA Inc

Inspirational Art, *division of* Unarius Academy of Science Publications

Inspire Books, *imprint of* Peter Pauper Press, Inc

Instant Help, *imprint of* New Harbinger Publications Inc

Institute for Advanced Study in the Theatre Arts (IASTA), *distributed by* Fordham University Press

Institute for Mesoamerican Studies, *distributed by* University of Texas Press

Institute for Regional Studies of the Californias, *distributed by* San Diego State University Press

Institute for Research Information, *division of* PJD Publications Ltd

Institute for the Psychological Sciences Press (IPS), *distributed by* The Catholic University of America Press

Institute of Education, *distributed by* Stylus Publishing LLC

Institute of Governmental Studies, *subsidiary of* University of California, Berkeley

Institute of Latin American Studies, *distributed by* The Brookings Institution Press

Institute of Materials, *distributed by* NACE International

Institute of Mathematical Geography, *division of* Arlinghaus Enterprises LLC

Institute of Police Technology & Management, *division of* University of North Florida

Institute Press, *distributed by* Crown House Publishing Co LLC

Institution of Chemical Engineers, *distributed by* Enfield Publishing & Distribution Co

The Institution of Engineering & Technology (IET), *subsidiary of* Stylus Publishing LLC, *distributed by* Stylus Publishing LLC

Instituto Monsa de Ediciones SA, *distributed by* Trans-Atlantic Publications Inc

Integrity Music, *division of* David C Cook

Intellect Publishing, *distributed by* Sunbelt Publications Inc

Inter-American Development Bank, *division of* Multilateral Development Bank, *distributed by* Johns Hopkins University Press

Inter Sports, *distributor for* Wilderness Adventures Press Inc

Inter-University Consortium for Political & Social Research (ICPSR), *affiliate of* University of Michigan Institute for Social Research

Intercontinental Press, *distributed by* CN Times Books

Intercultural Press Inc, *division of* Nicholas Brealey Publishing, *distributed by* NBN

Interlink Books, *imprint of* Interlink Publishing Group Inc

Interlink Publishing Group Inc, *distributor for* Black & White Publishing (UK), Camerapix Publishers International, Georgina Campbell Guides (Ireland), Macmillan Caribbean (UK), Quartet Books (UK), Rucksack Readers (UK), Serif Publishing Ltd (UK), Sheldrake Press (UK), Signal Books (UK), Waverley Books (UK), Neil Wilson Publishing (UK)

InterMix, *imprint of* Penguin Group (USA) LLC, a Penguin Random House company

International Air Transport Association, *distributed by* J J Keller & Associates, Inc

International Atomic Energy Agency (IAEA), *distributed by* United Nations Publications

International Book Centre Inc, *distributor for* Library du Liban (Lebanon), Stacey International Ltd (London), University of Michigan

International Brecht Society, *distributed by* University of Wisconsin Press

International Christian University Foundation, *distributed by* EastBridge

International Code Council, *distributed by* Professional Publications Inc (PPI)

International Communication Organization (ICO), *distributed by* Transaction Publishers Inc

International Country Risk Guide, *imprint of* The PRS Group Inc

International Criminal Tribunal for Rwanda (UNICTR), *distributed by* United Nations Publications

International Criminal Tribunal for the former Yugoslavia (ICTY), *distributed by* United Nations Publications

International Debate Education Association, *distributed by* Central European University Press

International Design Library®, *imprint of* Stemmer House Publishers Inc

International Energy Agency, *distributed by* Organization for Economic Cooperation & Development

International Food Policy Research Institute, *member of* Consultative Group on International Agricultural Research (CGIAR), *distributed by* Johns Hopkins University Press

International Jewelry Publications, *distributed by* Gem Guides Book Co

International Labor Offices, *distributed by* The Brookings Institution Press

International Law Institute, *distributed by* University Press of America Inc

International Marine Publishing, *imprint of* McGraw-Hill Professional

International Organization for Migration (IOM), *distributed by* United Nations Publications

International Pocket Library, *imprint of* Branden Books

International Press, *distributed by* American Mathematical Society

International Press of Boston Inc, *distributed by* AMS

International Trade Centre (ITC), *distributed by* United Nations Publications

International Transportation Forum, *distributed by* Organization for Economic Cooperation & Development

InterVarsity Press, *division of* InterVarsity Christian Fellowship/USA

Interweave, *imprint of* F+W, A Content + eCommerce Company

Interweave Press LLC, *imprint of* F+W, A Content + eCommerce Company, *distributed by* Keith Ainsworth Pty Ltd (Australia), David Bateman Ltd (New Zealand), Search Press (UK)

Ione Press, *imprint of* ECS Publishing Corp

IPG, *distributor for* Manning Publications Co

Iranbooks Press, *imprint of* Ibex Publishers

IRL, *distributed by* Oxford University Press USA

Iron Icon Books, *imprint of* Unveiled Media LLC

Ironclad Publishing, *distributed by* Casemate Publishers & Book Distributors LLC

Iroquois Press, *imprint of* Turner Publishing Co

Irvington Publishers, *distributed by* Ardent Media Inc

Irwin Professional, *imprint of* McGraw-Hill Professional

ISH Group, *distributed by* Empire Publishing Service

ISI Books, *imprint of* Intercollegiate Studies Institute Inc

Islamic Texts Society, *distributed by* Fons Vitae

Island, *imprint of* Penguin Random House Inc

Island Paradise Publishing, *distributed by* Sunbelt Publications Inc

Island Press, *distributor for* Environmental Law Institute, IUCN, Techne Press

Islander Group, *distributor for* Kamehameha Publishing

The Islander Group (TIG), *distributor for* Bess Press

Islander Press, *imprint of* Shepard Publications

Isles of Shoals Association, *distributed by* Enfield Publishing & Distribution Co

ISO, *distributed by* NACE International

iSong CD-ROMs, *distributed by* Hal Leonard Corp

IsraBook, *subsidiary of* Gefen Books

Isshin-Ryu Productions, *imprint of* The Linick Group Inc

Issues Press, *imprint of* Idyll Arbor Inc

Italian School of East Asian Studies, *distributed by* Cheng & Tsui Co Inc

Itasca, *distributor for* BrickHouse Books Inc

It's About Time Inc, *distributor for* American Geosciences Institute (AGI)

IUCN, *distributed by* Island Press

iUniverse, *division of* Author Solutions Inc

IVP Academic, *imprint of* InterVarsity Press

IVP Books, *imprint of* InterVarsity Press

IVP Connect, *imprint of* InterVarsity Press

IVP Crescendo, *imprint of* InterVarsity Press

IVP Praxis, *imprint of* InterVarsity Press

Ivy, *imprint of* Penguin Random House Inc

IWGIA, *distributed by* Transaction Publishers Inc

Jackson Square Press, *imprint of* Pelican Publishing Co

Jacobsville Books, *imprint of* Slipdown Mountain Publications LLC

Jade Rabbit, *imprint of* Quite Specific Media Group Ltd

Jagiellonian University Press, *distributed by* Columbia University Press

Jaguar Tales, *distributed by* Sunbelt Publications Inc

Jam, *imprint of* Berkley Books

Jamestown Foundation, *distributed by* The Brookings Institution Press

Janaway Publishing, *distributor for* Closson Press

Janus Library, *imprint of* Abaris Books

Japan Center for International Exchange, *distributed by* The Brookings Institution Press

Japan Publications Inc, *distributed by* Kodansha USA Inc

Japan Publications Trading Co Inc, *distributed by* Kodansha USA Inc

Japan Society, *distributed by* Yale University Press

Jawbone Press, *distributed by* Hal Leonard Corp

JayJo Books LLC, *subsidiary of* The Guidance Group

Jems, *imprint of* Elsevier, Health Sciences Division

Jenkins Publishing, *distributed by* Chelsea Green Publishing Co

Jericho Books, *imprint of* Hachette Nashville

Jersey Yarns, *imprint of* Quincannon Publishing Group

Jerusalem Press, *distributed by* Holmes Publishing Group LLC

Jerusalem Publications, *distributed by* Feldheim Publishers (Philipp Feldheim Inc)

Jeter Publishing, *imprint of* Gallery Books

Jetty House, *distributed by* Enfield Publishing & Distribution Co

Jewish Lights Publishing, *division of* Longhill Partners Inc, Longhill Partners Inc

The Jewish Museum, *distributed by* Yale University Press

Jewish New Testament Publications, *distributed by* Lederer Books, Messianic Jewish Publishers

Jewish Publication Society, *distributed by* University of Nebraska Press

George R Jezek Photography, *distributed by* Gem Guides Book Co

Jhpiego, *affiliate of* The Johns Hopkins University

The Jim Henson Co, *distributed by* At a Glance, Walter Foster, Golden Books Family Entertainment, Grolier, KidsBooks, Penguin Group (USA) LLC, PK, Random House, Reader's Digest Children's Books, Running Press, Simon & Schuster

Jist, *distributor for* MAR*CO Products Inc

JIST Career Solutions, *imprint of* JIST Publishing

JIST Publishing, *division of* EMC Publishing LLC

JMC Press, *distributed by* Vandamere Press

The JOC Group Inc, *division of* IHS Inc

John Deere Publishing, *division of* Deere & Co

John Macrae Books, *imprint of* Henry Holt and Company, LLC

Johns Hopkins Aids Service, *distributed by* The Johns Hopkins University Press

Johns Hopkins University Press, *distributor for* Inter-American Development Bank, International Food Policy Research Institute, *distributed by* Heimburger House Publishing Co

The Johns Hopkins University Press, *affiliate of* The Johns Hopkins University, *distributor for* Baylor University Press, The Brookings Institution Press, Catholic University of America Press, Center for Talented Youth, Georgetown University Press, Howard University Press, Johns Hopkins Aids Service, Maryland Historical Society, Resources for the Future, University of Massachusetts Press, University of Pennsylvania Museum, University of Pennsylvania Press, University of Washington Press, The University Press of Kentucky, Urban Institute Press, The Woodrow Wilson Center Press, Woodrow Wilson Center Press, World Resources Institute

Johns Hopkins University Press Fullfillment Service, *distributor for* Baylor University Press

Johnson Books, *division of* Big Earth Publishing

Cy Johnson & Son, *distributed by* Gem Guides Book Co

Joint Center for Political & Economic Studies Press, *distributed by* University Press of America Inc

Joint Publishers, *distributed by* China Books

Jones & Bartlett Learning, *distributed by* Medical Group Management Association (MGMA)

Jones & Bartlett Learning LLC, *division of* Ascend Learning

Jones & Bartlett Publishers, *distributor for* American Academy of Orthopaedic Surgeons (AAOS)

The Fletcher Jones Foundation, *imprint of* University of California Press

Jonglez Publishing, *distributed by* The Globe Pequot Press

Joshua Tree Publishing, *imprint of* Joshua Tree Publishing

Jossey-Bass, *imprint of* John Wiley & Sons Inc, John Wiley & Sons Inc, *distributor for* Center for Creative Leadership LLC, *distributed by* Center for Creative Leadership LLC

Journal of Chinese Medicine Publications, *distributed by* Eastland Press

Journal Publishing, *division of* Slack Incorporated

Journalbytes.com, *imprint of* Oakstone Publishing LLC

JourneyForth Books, *division of* BJU Press, *imprint of* BJU Press

Jove, *imprint of* Berkley Books, Berkley Publishing Group, Penguin Group (USA) LLC, a Penguin Random House company

Joy Publishing Co, *division of* California Clock Co, California Clock Co

Joyful Productions, *distributed by* Epicenter Press Inc

JPT America Inc, *distributed by* Cheng & Tsui Co Inc

JR Comics, *distributed by* Lerner Publishing Group Inc

Judeo Christian Ethics Series, *imprint of* PREP Publishing

Judson Press, *division of* American Baptist Churches in the USA, *distributed by* Abingdon Press

Juloya, *imprint of* Elva Resa Publishing

Jump at the Sun, *imprint of* Disney-Hyperion Books, Disney Publishing Worldwide

Jumpstart, *imprint of* Triumph Learning LLC

Junebug Books, *imprint of* NewSouth Books

Juno Books, *distributed by* powerHouse Books

Jury Verdict Research; LRP Magazine Group, *division of* LRP Publications

Just Cause, *imprint of* Yard Dog Press

Just Think®, *imprint of* Thomas Geale Publications Inc

K A Publishing, *imprint of* Hobar Publications

Kabbalah Publishing, *division of* Kabbalah Centre International

Max Kade Institute for German-American Studies, *distributed by* University of Wisconsin Press

Kaeden Books, *imprint of* Kaeden Corp

Kaiser-Barlow, *imprint of* Schiffer Publishing Ltd

Kales Press, *distributed by* W W Norton & Company Inc

Kalindi Press, *imprint of* Hohm Press

Kalmbach Books, *imprint of* Kalmbach Publishing Co

Kalmbach Publishing, *distributed by* Heimburger House Publishing Co

Kalmbach Publishing Co, *distributed by* Publishers Group West (PGW)

Kalmus, *imprint of* Alfred Music Publishing

Kamehameha Publishing, *division of* Kamehameha Schools, *distributed by* Islander Group

Kamehameha Schools Press, *imprint of* Kamehameha Publishing

Kane Miller Books, *division of* Educational Development Corp, Educational Development Corp

The Kane Press, *distributed by* Lerner Publishing Group Inc

Kane Press Inc, *distributed by* Lerner Publishing Group

Kaplan Press, *distributed by* Gryphon House Inc

Kaplan Publishing, *distributed by* Simon & Schuster, Inc, Simon & Schuster Sales Division

Kappa Map Group, *distributed by* American Map Corp

Kar-Ben Partners, *distributed by* Lerner Publishing Group Inc

Kar-Ben Publishing, *division of* Lerner Publishing Group Inc, *distributed by* Beach Lloyd Publishers LLC

Karnac Books, *distributed by* Stylus Publishing LLC

Karnak House, *imprint of* Red Sea Press Inc

Katalitix Media, *distributed by* Simon & Schuster, Inc

KAV Books, *distributed by* Royal Fireworks Press

Kaynak, *distributed by* Tughra Books

Kazan Media, *imprint of* Volcano Press

KC Publications Inc, *distributed by* Gem Guides Book Co

Keen Custom Media, *imprint of* Clerisy Press

J J Keller & Associates, Inc, *distributor for* Chilton Book Co, International Air Transport Association, National Archives & Records Administration, National Institute of Occupational Safety & Health, Office of the Federal Register, Research & Special Programs Administration of the US Department of Transportation, John Wiley & Sons Inc, *distributed by* AMACOM Books

Kendall Green, *imprint of* Gallaudet University Press

Kendall Hunt Publishing, *distributor for* Seedling Publications Inc

Kenilworth Press, *distributed by* Trafalgar Square Books

Kennedy Information Inc, *division of* Bloomberg BNA

Kens Math, *imprint of* Young People's Press Inc (YPPI)

Kensington, *distributor for* Parachute Publishing LLC

Kensington Books, *imprint of* Kensington Publishing Corp

Kensington Publishing, *distributed by* Hachette Book Group

Kensington Publishing Corp, *distributor for* Genesis Press, Marimba Books, New Horizon Press, Urban Books, Vibe Books, *distributed by* Hachette Book Group USA, Penguin Group (USA) LLC, Penguin Group (USA) LLC, a Penguin Random House company

Kentucky Historical Society, *distributed by* The University Press of Kentucky

Kenyon Publications, *distributed by* Hal Leonard Corp

Kerem, *distributed by* Hachai Publishing

Kessinger Publishing®, *imprint of* Kessinger Publishing LLC

Key Education, *distributed by* Carson-Dellosa Publishing LLC

Keynote Speakers Today, *imprint of* Empire Press Media/Avant-Guide

Keystone Books, *imprint of* The Pennsylvania State University Press

Keywords Press, *imprint of* Atria Books

Kid Help Publishing Co, *imprint of* Hearts & Tummies Cookbook Co

Kidhaven Press, *distributed by* Lucent Books®

KidHaven Press™, *imprint of* Gale

Kids Can Press, *distributed by* Hachette Book Group

Kids Corner, *imprint of* Sundance/Newbridge Publishing

Kids Own Worship™, *imprint of* Group Publishing Inc

KidsBooks, *imprint of* Kidsbooks LLC, *distributor for* The Jim Henson Co

Kimani, *imprint of* Harlequin Enterprises Ltd

Kimbell Art Museum, *distributed by* Yale University Press

Kinfolk, *distributed by* Simon & Schuster, Inc

Laurence King Publishing, *distributed by* Chronicle Books LLC

The King Legacy, *imprint of* Beacon Press

Kiron Editions du Felin, *distributed by* Beach Lloyd Publishers LLC

Klutz, *division of* Scholastic Corp, *imprint of* Scholastic Trade Division

Wolters Kluwer Law & Business, *subsidiary of* Wolters Kluwer, Wolters Kluwer

Knickerbocker Press, *imprint of* Book Sales Inc

Knock-off Books, *imprint of* Ugly Duckling Presse

Alfred A Knopf, *imprint of* Penguin Random House Inc

Alfred A Knopf Books for Young Readers, *imprint of* Random House Children's Books

Alfred A Knopf/Everyman's Library, *imprint of* Knopf Doubleday Publishing Group

Knopf Books for Young Readers, *imprint of* Penguin Random House Inc

Knopf Delacorte Dell Young Readers Group, *division of* Random House Children's Books

Knopf Guides, *imprint of* Penguin Random House Inc

Knossus Project, *distributed by* Chelsea Green Publishing Co

Knowledge Resources, *distributor for* Association for Talent Development (ATD)

Kodansha, *distributed by* Oxford University Press USA

Kodansha America, *imprint of* Kodansha USA Inc

Kodansha Globe, *imprint of* Kodansha USA Inc

Kodansha International, *imprint of* Kodansha USA Inc

Kodansha USA Inc, *subsidiary of* Kodansha Ltd (Japan), Kodansha Ltd (Japan), *distributor for* Japan Publications Inc, Japan Publications Trading Co Inc, *distributed by* Oxford University Press

Verlag Valentin Koerner, *distributed by* Enfield Publishing & Distribution Co

Kollath-Stensaas, *distributed by* Adventure Publications

Kolowalu Books, *imprint of* University of Hawaii Press

Kom Forlag, *distributed by* Enfield Publishing & Distribution Co

Konecky & Konecky (K&K), *imprint of* Konecky & Konecky LLC

Konecky & Konecky LLC, *distributor for* Octavo Editions

Koren, *imprint of* The Toby Press LLC

Kornfeld & Co (Bern), *distributed by* Alan Wofsy Fine Arts

Kornfeld (Switzerland), *distributed by* Picasso Project

Kosei Publishing Co, *imprint of* Tuttle Publishing, *distributed by* Tuttle Publishing

Kotan Publishing Inc, *imprint of* Tuttle Publishing, *distributed by* Tuttle Publishing

H J Kramer Inc, *division of* New World Library

HJ Kramer Inc, *division of* New World Library

Krause Publications, *imprint of* F+W, A Content + eCommerce Company, *distributed by* Heimburger House Publishing Co

Krause Publications Inc, *subsidiary of* F+W, A Content + eCommerce Company, *distributor for* Country Bumpkin, David & Charles, Colin Gower, Quarto Books

Pam Krauss Books, *imprint of* Clarkson Potter Publishers

Kregel Academic & Professional, *imprint of* Kregel Publications

Kregel Classics, *imprint of* Kregel Publications

Kregel Kidzone, *imprint of* Kregel Publications

Kregel Publications, *division of* Kregel Inc, Kregel Inc, *imprint of* Kregel Publications, *distributor for* Candle Books, Monarch Books

De Krijger, *distributed by* Casemate Publishers & Book Distributors LLC

KTAV Publishing House Inc, *distributor for* Yeshiva University Press

KTeen, *imprint of* Kensington Publishing Corp

KTeen Dafina, *imprint of* Kensington Publishing Corp

Kudzu House, *imprint of* Ariel Press, *distributed by* Ariel Press

KUED, *distributed by* The University of Utah Press

Kumarian Press, *division of* Lynne Rienner Publishers Inc, *distributor for* Management Sciences for Health

Scott G Kyle, *distributed by* Sunbelt Publications Inc

Ladders, *imprint of* Triumph Learning LLC

Lady Fern Press, *imprint of* Crumb Elbow Publishing

LadybugPress, *division of* NewVoices Inc

Lake Claremont Press, *imprint of* Everything Goes Media LLC

Lake Forrest College Press, *distributed by* Northwestern University Press

Lakeshore Learning Materials, *distributor for* National Council of Teachers of Mathematics (NCTM)

Lancer Publishers, *distributed by* Casemate Publishers & Book Distributors LLC

Peter Lang Publishing Inc, *subsidiary of* Verlag Peter Lang AG (Switzerland), Verlag Peter Lang AG (Switzerland)

Lange Medical Books, *imprint of* McGraw-Hill Professional

Langenscheidt Publishing Group, *distributor for* Michelin Maps & Guides

Languages for Kids, *distributed by* Tralco-Lingo Fun

Lantern Books, *division of* Booklight Inc, *distributed by* SteinerBooks

LanternLight Library, *imprint of* University of Alaska Press

Larausse, *distributed by* Houghton Mifflin Harcourt Trade & Reference Division

Large Print Press™, *imprint of* Gale

Lark Crafts, *imprint of* Sterling Publishing Co Inc

Larousse Bilingual, *distributed by* Houghton Mifflin Harcourt

Larousse Mexico, *distributed by* Houghton Mifflin Harcourt

Latin American Review Press, *distributed by* Arte Publico Press

Latitude 20, *imprint of* University of Hawaii Press

JP Lattes, *distributed by* Beach Lloyd Publishers LLC

Laurel-Leaf, *imprint of* Random House Children's Books

Laurel Leaf Books, *imprint of* Penguin Random House Inc

Law Library Microform Consortium, *distributed by* Thomson Reuters Westlaw™

Law Tribune Books, *division of* American Lawyer Media

Merloyd Lawrence Inc, *distributed by* The Perseus Books Group

Lawtech Publishing, *distributed by* Sunbelt Publications Inc

LBKids, *imprint of* Little, Brown Books for Young Readers

Leafwood Publishers, *imprint of* ACU Press

Learn Roots Music, *distributed by* Mel Bay Publications Inc

Learning & Coloring Books, *imprint of* Quincannon Publishing Group

Learning Challenge, *imprint of* Kidsbooks LLC

The Learning Company, *imprint of* Houghton Mifflin Harcourt

Learning Links Inc, *distributor for* Harcourt, HarperCollins, Houghton Mifflin Harcourt Publishing Company, Little, Brown & Company, Penguin Group (USA) LLC, Random House Inc, Scholastic, Simon & Schuster

Learning Matters, *imprint of* SAGE Publications

LearningExpress, *imprint of* LearningExpress LLC

LearningExpress LLC, *distributed by* National Book Network

Leaves of Healing, *imprint of* Progressive Press

Leda, *imprint of* Norilana Books

Lederer Books, *division of* Messianic Jewish Publishers, *distributor for* Chosen People Ministries, First Fruits of Zion, Jewish New Testament Publications

Left Coast Press Inc, *distributor for* UCL Institute of Archaeology (UK)

Left To Write Press, *distributed by* Chelsea Green Publishing Co

Legacy Press, *imprint of* Rainbow Publishers

Legas Publishers, *distributed by* Cross-Cultural Communications

Legato Publishers Group, *division of* The Perseus Books Group

Legato Publishing Group, *distributor for* Trafalgar Square Books

Legendary Locals, *imprint of* Arcadia Publishing Inc

Dennis Lehane Books, *imprint of* HarperCollins General Books Group

Lehigh University Press, *affiliate of* Rowman & Littlefield Publishing Group (RLPG), *distributed by* Rowman & Littlefield

Leisure Arts Inc, *division of* Liberty Media, *distributor for* Oxmoor House

The Lentz Leadership Institute, *imprint of* The Refractive Thinker Press

Hal Leonard, *distributed by* ArtAge Publications

Hal Leonard Corp, *distributor for* Amadeus Press, Applause Theatre & Cinema Books, Artistpro, Ashley Music, Backbeat Books, Beacon Music, Berklee Press, Fred Bock Music Company, Boosey & Hawkes, Centerstream Publications, Centerstream Publishing LLC, Cherry Lane Music Co, Cinema Books, Community Music Videos, Creative Concepts, DC Publications, Devine Entertainment Corp, Editions Durand, Editions Max Eschig, Editions Salabert, EM Books, EMI Christian, Faber Music Ltd, Guitar One, Guitar World, Home Recording, Homespun Tapes, Houston Publications, Hudson Music, iSong CD-ROMs, Jawbone

Press, Kenyon Publications, Limelight Editions, Ashley Mark Publishing Co, Edward B Marks Music, Meredith Music, Modern Drummer Publications, Music Sales America, Musicians Institute Press, Musikverlage Han Sikorski, Christopher Parkening, Reader's Digest, Record Research, Ricordi, Lee Roberts Publications, Rubank Publications, G Schirmer Inc (Associated Music Publishers), Second Floor Music, Sing Out Corp, Star Licks Videos, Bernard Stein Music Co, String Letter Press, Tara Publications, Transcontinental Music, 21st Century Publications, Vintage Guitar, Word Music, Writer's Digest

Lerner Books UK, *division of* Lerner Publishing Group Inc

Lerner Publications, *division of* Lerner Publishing Group Inc, *imprint of* Lerner Publishing Group Inc

Lerner Publisher Services, *division of* Lerner Publishing Group Inc

Lerner Publishing, *distributor for* Red Chair Press

Lerner Publishing Group, *distributor for* Kane Press Inc

Lerner Publishing Group Inc, *distributor for* Andersen Press USA, Columbus Zoo, Walter Foster Publishing, Gecko Press, JR Comics, The Kane Press, Kar-Ben Partners, MVP Books, Red Chair Press, Sandy Creek, Scobre Educational, Stoke Books, We Do Listen

LernerClassroom, *division of* Lerner Publishing Group Inc, *imprint of* Lerner Publishing Group Inc

The Letter People®, *imprint of* Abrams Learning Trends

Letterland International Ltd, *distributed by* Enfield Publishing & Distribution Co

Leuven University Press, *distributed by* Cornell University Press

Lexington Books, *imprint of* Rowman & Littlefield Publishing Group, *distributor for* The Colonial Williamsburg Foundation

LexisNexis®, *distributor for* Standard Publishing Corp

LexisNexis®, *division of* RELX Group PLC

LexisNexis® Matthew Bender®, *member of* The LexisNexis® Group

Libraries Unlimited, *imprint of* ABC-CLIO

Libraries Unlimited/Linworth Publishing, *imprint of* ABC-CLIO

Library Company of Philadelphia, *distributed by* Diane Publishing Co

Library du Liban (Lebanon), *distributed by* International Book Centre Inc

The Library of America, *distributed by* Penguin Group (USA) LLC, Penguin Group (USA) LLC, a Penguin Random House company

Library of Congress-Center for the Book, *distributed by* Oak Knoll Press

Library of Contemporary Thought, *imprint of* Penguin Random House Inc

Library of Islam, *imprint of* Kazi Publications Inc

Libri Canali Bassi, *distributed by* Edgewise Press Inc

Libros Desafio, *imprint of* Faith Alive Christian Resources

Libros en Espanol, *imprint of* Touchstone

Libros Liguori, *imprint of* Liguori Publications

Life Cycle Books, *division of* Life Cycle Books Ltd (Canada)

Life on the Edge, *imprint of* Focus on the Family

Life Wisdom, *imprint of* Paragon House

LifeGuide Bible Studies, *imprint of* InterVarsity Press

LifeLearn, *distributor for* Teton NewMedia, *distributed by* Teton NewMedia

Lifestream, *imprint of* Beacon Hill Press of Kansas City

LifeTimes, *imprint of* Rayve Productions Inc

LifeWay Christian Resources, *distributor for* Casa Bautista de Publicaciones

The Liffey Press, *distributed by* Dufour Editions Inc

Lift Every Voice, *imprint of* Moody Publishers

The Light, *imprint of* Tughra Books

Light & Life, *distributor for* Ancient Faith Publishing, *distributed by* Ancient Faith Publishing

Light & Life Publishing Co, *distributor for* Saint Herman Press

Lighthouse Press, *imprint of* ProStar Publications Inc

Lightning Rod Press, *imprint of* American Philosophical Society

Liguori Publications, *distributor for* Redemptorist Publications

Liguori/Triumph, *imprint of* Liguori Publications

L'il Acorns, *imprint of* Cedar Grove Books

Philip E Lilienthal, *imprint of* University of California Press

Lillenas Publishing Co, *imprint of* Beacon Hill Press of Kansas City

Lilliput Press Ltd, *distributed by* Dufour Editions Inc

LIM Editrice SRL (Italy), *distributor for* Pendragon Press

Limelight Editions, *imprint of* Hal Leonard Books, Hal Leonard Performing Arts Publishing Group, *distributed by* Hal Leonard Corp

Limestone Press, *distributed by* University of Alaska Press

Lindisfarne Books, *imprint of* SteinerBooks, SteinerBooks, *distributed by* Floris Books

Line by Line, *imprint of* Aspatore Books

John Liner Organization, *subsidiary of* Standard Publishing Corp

LinguaText, *imprint of* LinguaText Ltd

LinguaText Ltd, *distributor for* Juan de la Cuesta—Hispanic Monographs, European Masterpieces

The Linick Group Inc, *distributor for* Linick International, LKA Inc, National Association of Photo Sellers™, *distributed by* New World Press Books, Okinawan Kobujutsu Kyokai Association (OKKA)

Linick International, *distributed by* The Linick Group Inc

Linux Journal Press, *imprint of* Belltown Media, No Starch Press Inc

Linworth Learning, *imprint of* Linworth Publishing

Linworth Publishing, *imprint of* Libraries Unlimited

Lippincott Williams & Wilkins, *unit of* Wolters Kluwer Health

Lippincott, Williams & Wilkins, *imprint of* Wolters Kluwer US Corp

Lips (Magazine & Press), *distributed by* Cross-Cultural Communications

LIS (Legal Information Services), *subsidiary of* CCH, a Wolters Kluwer business

Listening Library®, *division of* Books on Tape®, *imprint of* Books on Tape®, *distributed by* Books on Tape®

Literary House Press, *distributed by* Cornell Maritime Press Inc

Literary Reprint Series, *imprint of* University of Alaska Press

Literature & Thought, *imprint of* Perfection Learning Corp

Litigation GP, *division of* Public Citizen

Little Bee Books, *imprint of* Bonnier Publishing, *distributed by* Simon & Schuster, Inc

Little, Brown, *distributor for* Parachute Publishing LLC

Little, Brown & Co, *distributor for* Alloy Entertainment LLC

Little, Brown & Company, *distributed by* Learning Links Inc

Little, Brown and Company, *division of* Hachette Book Group

Little, Brown Books for Young Readers, *division of* Hachette Book Group

The Little Entrepreneur, *imprint of* Harper Arrington Publishing & Media, *distributed by* Harper Arrington Publishing

Little Five Star, *imprint of* Five Star Publications Inc

Little Imp Books, *imprint of* Impact Publishers Inc

Little Lucy & Friends™, *imprint of* Playhouse Publishing

Little Oak Press, *distributed by* Sunbelt Publications Inc

Little Patriot Press, *imprint of* Regnery Publishing Inc

Little Room Press, *distributed by* Fordham University Press

Little Shepherd, *imprint of* Scholastic Trade Division

Little Simon, *imprint of* Simon & Schuster Children's Publishing

Little Toller Books, *distributed by* Dufour Editions Inc

Liturgical Press, *division of* The Order of St Benedict Inc, *distributor for* Cistercian Publications

Liturgical Press Books, *imprint of* Liturgical Press

Liturgy Training Publications, *subsidiary of* Archdiocese of Chicago, *distributor for* United States Catholic Conference Publications

Liveright & Co, *imprint of* W W Norton & Company Inc

Living Books, *imprint of* Tyndale House Publishers Inc

Living Language, *imprint of* Penguin Random House Audio, Penguin Random House Inc

Livingston Press, *division of* University of West Alabama, *distributor for* Swallow's Tale Press

LKA Inc, *imprint of* The Linick Group Inc, *distributed by* The Linick Group Inc

Llewellyn Publications, *division of* Llewellyn Worldwide Ltd, *distributor for* Lo Scarabeo

LM Publishing, *distributed by* Stylus Publishing LLC

LMD Inc, *distributor for* Council for Exceptional Children (CEC)

Lobster Press, *distributed by* Orca Book Publishers

Locks Art Publications/Locks Gallery, *division of* Locks Gallery

Loft, *distributed by* Prestel Publishing

Logan Brothers, *distributor for* Teton NewMedia

Login Brothers, *distributor for* Health Professions Press

Login Brothers Book Co, *distributor for* United States Pharmacopeia

Login Publishing Consortium, *distributor for* United States Pharmacopeia

Logion Press, *imprint of* Gospel Publishing House (GPH)

Logos, *imprint of* Bridge-Logos Inc

Logos Press, *imprint of* thinkBiotech LLC

Y Lolfa, *distributed by* Dufour Editions Inc

Lominger Inc, *distributed by* Center for Creative Leadership LLC

Lone Oak Press, *imprint of* Finney Company Inc

Lone Star Audio, *imprint of* Recorded Books LLC

Long River Press, *imprint of* Sinomedia International Group

Longman, *distributor for* Marriage Transformation LLC, *distributed by* Council for Exceptional Children (CEC), Trans-Atlantic Publications Inc

Look & Learn™, *imprint of* Playhouse Publishing

Look at Me, *imprint of* Modern Publishing

Looking Glass Books, *distributed by* John F Blair Publisher

Looking Glass Library, *imprint of* ABDO Publishing Group

Lookout Books, *distributed by* John F Blair Publisher

Looseleaf Law Publications Inc, *division of* Warodean Corp

The Lord's Press, *imprint of* Decent Hill Publishers LLC

Lorenz Educational Press, *division of* The Lorenz Corp

Lorimer, *distributed by* Casemate Publishers & Book Distributors LLC

James Lorimer & Co, *distributed by* Orca Book Publishers

Los Angeles Times Books, *distributed by* Angel City Press

Los Angeles Times Crosswords, *imprint of* Random House Reference/Random House Puzzles & Games/House of Collectibles

Lost Horse Press, *distributed by* University of Washington Press

Lothrop, Lee & Shepard Books, *imprint of* HarperCollins Publishers

Lotus Press, *division of* Lotus Brands Inc, Lotus Brands Inc, *distributor for* Back to Eden Books, Dipti, East West Cultural Center, Les Editions E T C, Inner Worlds Music, November Moon, S A B D A, Sadhana Publications, Samata Books, Sri Aurobindo Ashram, Star Sounds

The Lotus Seed Press (China), *distributed by* Blue Dolphin Publishing Inc

Louisiana Book Distributors, *imprint of* Pelican Publishing Co

Love Inspired, *imprint of* Love Inspired Books

Love Inspired Books, *imprint of* Harlequin Enterprises Ltd

Love Inspired Historical, *imprint of* Love Inspired Books

Love Inspired Suspense, *imprint of* Love Inspired Books

Love Publishing, *distributed by* Council for Exceptional Children (CEC)

Lovestruck, *imprint of* Entangled Publishing

Loveswept, *imprint of* Penguin Random House Inc, Random House Publishing Group

LPC Group Inc, *distributor for* Dark Horse Comics

LRP Magazine Group, *subsidiary of* LRP Publications

LRS, *division of* Library Reproduction Service

Lucent Books®, *imprint of* Gale, *distributor for* Greenhaven Press, Kidhaven Press, *distributed by* Greenhaven Imprints

Lucky Marble Books, *imprint of* PageSpring Publishing

Luna Books, *imprint of* Harlequin Enterprises Ltd

Lund Humphries/Ashgate, *distributor for* National Gallery of Art

Luster Editions, *imprint of* Circlet Press Inc

Luxury Destinations & Resorts, *imprint of* R J Berg Publisher

Luxury Destinations & Resorts Press, *imprint of* R J Berg Publisher

Luxury Destinations Press, *imprint of* R J Berg Publisher

LW Books, *imprint of* Schiffer Publishing Ltd

Lynn-Reinner Publishing, *distributor for* University of California Institute on Global Conflict & Cooperation

Lynx House Press, *distributed by* University of Washington Press

The Lyons Press, *imprint of* The Globe Pequot Press

Lyrical Press, *imprint of* Kensington Publishing Corp

Lyrical Shine, *imprint of* Kensington Publishing Corp

Lyrical Underground, *imprint of* Kensington Publishing Corp

M & H Type, *division of* The Arion Press

Pat MacKay Projects, *imprint of* Quite Specific Media Group Ltd

Mackinac Historic Parks, *distributed by* Michigan State University Press (MSU Press)

Macmillan, *subsidiary of* Verlagsgruppe Georg von Holtzbrinck GmbH, Verlagsgruppe Georg von Holtzbrinck GmbH, *imprint of* McGraw-Hill School Education Group, *distributor for* Bloomsbury Publishing Inc, The College Board, Tom Doherty Associates, LLC, Entangled Publishing, Papercutz, Rodale Inc

Macmillan Audio, *division of* Macmillan, Macmillan Holdings, LLC, *distributor for* HighRoads Media, *distributed by* BBC Audiobooks America (library editions)

Macmillan Caribbean (UK), *distributed by* Interlink Publishing Group Inc

Macmillan Education (UK), *distributed by* Players Press Inc

Macmillan Higher Education, *subsidiary of* Macmillan

Macmillan/McGraw-Hill, *imprint of* McGraw-Hill Education

Macmillan Publishing Co, *distributor for* National Association of Broadcasters (NAB)

Macmillan Reference USA™, *imprint of* Gale

Macmillan (UK), *distributed by* Scholium International Inc

MacroPrintBooks, *imprint of* Science & Humanities Press

MacVan Maps, *distributed by* Wide World of Maps Inc

MAD Books, *imprint of* DC Entertainment

Madison Area Community Supported Agriculture Coalition, *distributed by* Chelsea Green Publishing Co

Mage Persian Editions, *imprint of* Mage Publishers Inc

Mage Publishers Inc, *distributed by* University of Toronto Press (Canada)

Maggid, *imprint of* The Toby Press LLC

Maggies Music, *distributed by* Mel Bay Publications Inc

Magic Readers, *imprint of* ABDO Publishing Group

Magill's Choice, *imprint of* Salem Press Inc

Magnes Press, *distributed by* Gefen Books

MAGNI, *imprint of* The Magni Co

Magni Co, *distributed by* Book Publishing Co

The Magni Co, *subsidiary of* The Magni Group Inc

Maharishi University of Management Press, *subsidiary of* Maharishi University of Management, *distributed by* Fairfield Press, Penguin Group (USA) LLC

Maia Press, *distributed by* Dufour Editions Inc

Main Street Books, *imprint of* Penguin Random House Inc

Maisonneuve Press, *division of* Institute for Advanced Cultural Studies, *distributed by* Merlin Press (London, England)

JA Majors, *distributor for* MedBooks

Make Prophetz, *imprint of* Cedar Grove Books

MakeMusic Inc, *distributed by* Alfred Music Publishing

Malley's, *distributed by* Mel Bay Publications Inc

Management Sciences for Health, *distributed by* Kumarian Press

ManagingSmart.com, *subsidiary of* BizBest Media Corp

Manchester University Press, *distributed by* Palgrave Macmillan, St Martin's Press, LLC

Mandala Earth, *imprint of* Insight Editions

Mandate Press, *imprint of* William Carey Library Publishers

Manhattan Prep, *distributed by* Simon & Schuster Sales Division

Manhattan Publishing Co, *division of* US & Europe Books Inc, *distributor for* Council of Europe, European Court of Human Rights

Manning Publications Co, *distributed by* IPG, Pearson Education, Prentice Hall, TransQuest Publishers Pte Ltd

The Manuscript Society, *distributed by* Oak Knoll Press

Le Manuscrit, *distributed by* Beach Lloyd Publishers LLC

Many Hats Media, *distributor for* Sourced Media Books

Many Moons Press, *distributed by* Gem Guides Book Co

MAPART Publishing, *distributor for* Michelin Maps & Guides

MAR*CO Products Inc, *distributor for* Boulden, Center for Youth Issues/STARS, Educational Media, HarperCollins, *distributed by* ASCA, Boulden Publishing, Burnell Books, Calloway House, Career Kids FYI, CFKR Career, Character Development, Community Intervention, Courage to Change, Cress Productions Co, EDU Reference, Educational Media Corp, Incentive Plus, Jist, Mental Health Resources, National Professional Resources, National Resource Center Youth Services, NIMCO Bookstore, Paperbacks for Educators, School Speciality, SourceResource, STARS-National Center for Youths, WRS Group, YouthLight Inc

Marble Arch, *imprint of* Atria Books

Maren Green, *distributed by* Crabtree Publishing Co

Maren Green Publishing Inc, *distributed by* Crabtree Publishing Inc

Marick Press, *distributed by* Wayne State University Press

Marimba Books, *distributed by* Kensington Publishing Corp

Marine Survey Press, *imprint of* Marine Education Textbooks

Marine Techniques Publishing, *distributor for* Academic Press, Best Publishing Co, Butterworth-Heinemann, Clarkson Research Services Ltd, Elsevier, Science & Technology Books, Focal Press, Gulf Professional Publishers, PennWell Business & Industrial Division, W B Saunders Co, Waterfront Soundings Productions, Witherby Seamanship International Ltd, *distributed by* Elsevier Science, Technology & Business Books, PennWell Business & Industrial Division

Mariner Books, *imprint of* Houghton Mifflin Harcourt Trade & Reference Division

Marion Institute, *distributed by* Chelsea Green Publishing Co

Ashley Mark Publishing Co, *imprint of* Hal Leonard Corp, *distributed by* Hal Leonard Corp

marketumbrella.org, *distributed by* Chelsea Green Publishing Co

MarketResearch.com, *distributor for* Apollo Managed Care Inc, Primary Research Group Inc

Edward B Marks Music, *distributed by* Hal Leonard Corp

The Marlboro Press, *imprint of* Northwestern University Press

Marmac Publishing Co, *distributed by* Pelican Publishing Co

Marriage Transformation LLC, *distributed by* Barringer, Longman

Carole Marsh Books, *imprint of* Gallopade International Inc

Carole Marsh Mysteries, *imprint of* Gallopade International Inc

Marshall & Swift, *distributed by* McGraw-Hill Book Co

Marshall Cavendish Adult Trade, *imprint of* Marshall Cavendish Corp

Marshall Cavendish Benchmark, *imprint of* Marshall Cavendish Corp

Marshall Cavendish Corp, *member of* Times International Publishing Group, *distributed by* Marshall Cavendish Ltd (UK)

Marshall Cavendish Digital, *imprint of* Marshall Cavendish Corp

Marshall Cavendish Education, *imprint of* Marshall Cavendish Corp

Marshall Cavendish Ltd, *distributor for* Marshall Cavendish Corp

Marshall Cavendish Reference, *imprint of* Marshall Cavendish Corp

Marsilio, *imprint of* Rizzoli International Publications Inc

Darvin Martin CDs, *distributed by* Closson Press

Rux Martin Books, *imprint of* Houghton Mifflin Harcourt Trade & Reference Division

Marvel Worldwide Inc, *distributed by* Hachette Book Group

Helen Marx/Turtle Point, *imprint of* Turtle Point Press

Maryland Historical Society, *distributed by* Alan C Hood & Co Inc, The Johns Hopkins University Press

Maryland Historical Trust Press, *distributed by* Cornell Maritime Press Inc

Maryland History Press, *distributor for* Dogwood Ridge Books, Tapestry Press Ltd

Maryland Sea Grant Program, *distributed by* Cornell Maritime Press Inc

Mason Crest Publishers, *imprint of* National Highlights

The Massachusetts Historical Society, *distributed by* University of Virginia Press

Master Books, *subsidiary of* New Leaf Publishing Group

Masters of Photography, *imprint of* Aperture Books

Masterwork Books, *imprint of* Kidsbooks LLC

Masthof Press, *distributor for* Closson Press

Math Products Plus, *imprint of* Wide World Publishing

Math Solutions®, *unit of* Houghton Mifflin Harcourt

Mathematica Josephina, *distributed by* American Mathematical Society

The Mathematical Association of America, *distributed by* Cambridge University Press

Mathematical Society of Japan, *distributed by* American Mathematical Society

Matheson Trust, *distributed by* Fons Vitae

Adam Matthew, *imprint of* SAGE Publications

Maunsel & Co Publishers, *imprint of* Academica Press LLC

Max Books, *imprint of* The RoadRunner Press

Margaret K McElderry Books, *imprint of* Simon & Schuster Children's Publishing

McFarland & Co Ltd Publishers, *subsidiary of* McFarland

McGraw-Hill, *imprint of* McGraw-Hill Science, Engineering, Mathematics, *distributor for* Society of Manufacturing Engineers, *distributed by* American Academy of Environmental Engineers & Scientists™, American Water Works Association (AWWA), NACE International, SAMS Technical Publishing LLC, SAS Publishing, Society of Manufacturing Engineers

McGraw-Hill Book Co, *distributor for* Marshall & Swift

McGraw-Hill Career Education, *division of* McGraw-Hill Higher Education

McGraw-Hill Contemporary, *imprint of* McGraw-Hill Education

McGraw-Hill Contemporary Learning Series, *division of* McGraw-Hill Higher Education

McGraw-Hill Create, *division of* McGraw-Hill Higher Education, *imprint of* McGraw-Hill Education, McGraw-Hill Higher Education

McGraw-Hill Education, *division of* McGraw-Hill Financial

McGraw-Hill Education Australia, New Zealand & South Africa, *imprint of* McGraw-Hill Education

McGraw-Hill Education Europe, Middle East and Africa, *imprint of* McGraw-Hill Education

McGraw-Hill Education Latin America, *imprint of* McGraw-Hill Education

McGraw-Hill Education - Mexico, *imprint of* McGraw-Hill Education

McGraw-Hill Education - Spain, *imprint of* McGraw-Hill Education

McGraw-Hill Higher Education, *division of* McGraw-Hill Education

McGraw-Hill Humanities, Social Sciences, Languages, *division of* McGraw-Hill Higher Education, *imprint of* McGraw-Hill Education

McGraw-Hill International, *distributor for* AMACOM Books

McGraw-Hill International Publishing Group, *division of* McGraw-Hill Education

McGraw-Hill/Irwin, *division of* McGraw-Hill Higher Education, *imprint of* McGraw-Hill Education, McGraw-Hill Higher Education

McGraw-Hill Learning Solutions, *imprint of* McGraw-Hill Higher Education

McGraw-Hill Professional, *division of* McGraw-Hill Education, McGraw-Hill Education, *imprint of* McGraw-Hill Education, *distributed by* Professional Publications Inc (PPI)

McGraw-Hill Professional Publishing, *distributor for* American Society for Quality (ASQ)

McGraw-Hill Ryerson, *imprint of* McGraw-Hill Education

McGraw-Hill School Education Group, *division of* McGraw-Hill Education

McGraw-Hill Science, Engineering, Mathematics, *division of* McGraw-Hill Higher Education, *imprint of* McGraw-Hill Education, McGraw-Hill Higher Education

McGraw-Hill Professional Development, *imprint of* McGraw-Hill Education

McKay Chess Library, *imprint of* Random House Reference/Random House Puzzles & Games/House of Collectibles

Anne McKinney Career Series, *imprint of* PREP Publishing

McKissick Museum, *distributed by* University of South Carolina Press

McRoy & Blackburn, Publishers, *distributed by* Epicenter Press Inc

McWhiney Foundation Press/State House Press, *distributed by* Texas A&M University Press

Md Books, *imprint of* May Davenport Publishers

MDR, A D&B Co, *division of* Dun & Bradstreet Corp

Meadow Creek Press, *imprint of* Crumb Elbow Publishing

Meadowbrook Press, *distributed by* Simon & Schuster, Simon & Schuster, Inc, Simon & Schuster Sales Division

Mean Free Path, *distributor for* American Society for Nondestructive Testing

R S Means from The Gordian Group, *distributed by* John Wiley & Sons Inc

Measuring Up®, *imprint of* Peoples Education Inc

Mechling Associates, *distributor for* Western Pennsylvania Genealogical Society

MedBooks, *division of* Professional Education Workshops & Seminars, *distributed by* JA Majors

Medford Press, *imprint of* Plexus Publishing, Inc

Medical Economics, *distributed by* OptumInsight™

Medical Group Management Association (MGMA), *distributor for* American Medical Association, Aspen Publishers, Greenbranch, HAP (Health Adminstration Press), Jones & Bartlett Learning, J Wiley & Sons

Medical Publishing (Gefen), *division of* Gefen Books

Medieval Institute Publications, *division of* Medieval Institute of Western Michigan University

Meditation Press, *distributed by* Epicenter Press Inc

Mel Bay Publications Inc, *distributor for* AcuTab Publications Inc, AMA, Chanterelle, Stefan Grossman's Guitar Workshop, Hardie Press, Learn Roots Music, Maggies Music, Malley's, Registry of Guitar Tutors (RGT), RGB Arte Visual, Scott's Highland Services, Voggenreiter Publishers, Walton's, SR Wheat

Paul Mellon Centre, *distributed by* Yale University Press

Memoirs, *imprint of* American Philosophical Society

Memorable Meetings Press, *imprint of* R J Berg Publisher

Men at Arms, *imprint of* Osprey Publishing Inc

Menasha Ridge Press Inc, *imprint of* Keen Communications

C E Mendez Foundation Inc, *distributor for* Rocky River Publishers LLC

The Menil Collection, *distributed by* Yale University Press

Menil Foundation, *distributed by* University of Texas Press, Wittenborn Art Books

Menorah, *distributed by* Bloch Publishing Co

Mental Health Resources, *distributor for* MAR*CO Products Inc

Mercier, *distributed by* Dufour Editions Inc

Merck, *distributed by* Simon & Schuster Sales Division

Merck Publishing, *distributed by* Simon & Schuster, Inc

Meredith Music, *distributed by* Hal Leonard Corp

Merehurst Ltd, *imprint of* Tuttle Publishing

Merit Press Books, *imprint of* F+W, A Content + eCommerce Company

Meriwether Publishing, *division of* Pioneer Drama Service Inc

Merlin Press (London, England), *distributor for* Maisonneuve Press

Merriam-Webster Inc, *subsidiary of* Encyclopaedia Britannica Inc

Frank Merriwell Inc, *subsidiary of* National Learning Corp

Merry Muse Press, *imprint of* Loft Press Inc

MerwinAsia, *distributed by* Saint Johann Press, University of Hawaii Press

Mesorah Publications Ltd, *distributor for* NCSY Publications

Messenger Publications, *distributed by* Dufour Editions Inc

Messianic Jewish Publishers, *division of* Messianic Jewish Communications, *distributor for* Chosen People Ministries, First Fruits of Zion, Jewish New Testament Publications

Metamorphic Press, *distributed by* Chelsea Green Publishing Co

Metro Maps, *division of* Wide World of Maps Inc, *distributed by* Wide World of Maps Inc

Metropolitan Books, *imprint of* Henry Holt and Company, LLC

The Metropolitan Museum of Art, *distributed by* Yale University Press

MFA Publications, *imprint of* Museum of Fine Arts Boston, *distributed by* Art Books/D A P

MGI Management Institute Inc, *subsidiary of* SmartPros Ltd

MHS, *distributor for* Specialty Press Inc

Micelle Press, *distributed by* Scholium International Inc

Michael di Capua Books, *imprint of* Disney-Hyperion Books

Michelin Maps & Guides, *division of* Michelin North America Inc, *distributed by* Langenscheidt Publishing Group, MAPART Publishing (CN only), NBN (guides for North America), Editions du Renouveau Pedagogique (French titles in Canada), Penguin Canada (English titles in Canada)

Michie, *imprint of* LexisNexis®

Michigan Municipal League, *affiliate of* National League of Cities, *distributor for* Crisp Books

Michigan State University Press (MSU Press), *division of* Michigan State University, *distributor for* Mackinac Historic Parks, MSU Museum, University of Alberta Press, University of Calgary Press, University of Manitoba Press, *distributed by* UBC Press, Canada

Microcosm Books, *imprint of* TFH Publications Inc

Microsoft Press, *division of* Microsoft Corp, *distributed by* O'Reilly Media (Asia, Australia, Europe, New Zealand, North America, UK), O'Reilly Media Inc, Shroff Publishers & Distributors (India)

Microsoft Press France, *subsidiary of* Microsoft Press

Microsoft Press Germany, *subsidiary of* Microsoft Press

Microtraining Associates, *imprint of* Alexander Street Press LLC

Midewin Series, *imprint of* High Tide Press

Midnight Editions, *imprint of* Cleis Press

Midnight Ink, *imprint of* Llewellyn Publications

Midnight Marquee Press Inc, *affiliate of* Luminary Press

Midrashic Editions, *imprint of* Cross-Cultural Communications

Midwest Library Service, *distributor for* Business Research Services Inc, Do-It-Yourself Legal Publishers, Primary Research Group Inc

MidWest Plan Service (MWPS), *affiliate of* Iowa State University-Information Technology Services, *distributor for* Natural Resource Agriculture & Engineering Service, *distributed by* Natural Resource Agriculture & Engineering Service

Mighty Media Junior Readers, *imprint of* Mighty Media Press

Mighty Media Kids, *imprint of* Mighty Media Press

Migration Policy Institute, *distributed by* The Brookings Institution Press

Mike Murach & Associates Inc, *distributed by* Shroff Publishers (reprints)

Milady, *division of* Cengage Learning

Milestone Documents, *division of* Schlager Group Inc

Milet Publishing Ltd, *imprint of* Tuttle Publishing, *distributed by* Tuttle Publishing

Military Illustrated, *distributed by* Casemate Publishers & Book Distributors LLC

Military Living Publications, *division of* Military Marketing Services Inc, Military Marketing Services Inc

Millbrook Press, *division of* Lerner Publishing Group Inc, *imprint of* Lerner Publishing Group Inc

White Burkett Miller Center, *distributed by* University Press of America Inc

Milliken Publishing Co, *division of* The Lorenz Corp, The Lorenz Corp

Mills & Boon Large Print, *distributed by* Thorndike Press

Sally Milner, *distributed by* Sterling Publishing Co Inc

Minedition, *imprint of* Penguin Group (USA) LLC, a Penguin Random House company

The Minerals, Metals & Materials Society (TMS), *affiliate of* AIME

Minnesota Historical Society Press, *division of* Minnesota Historical Society

Minotaur, *imprint of* St Martin's Press, LLC

MIRA Books, *imprint of* Harlequin Enterprises Ltd

Miranda Press Trade Division, *imprint of* Cognizant Communication Corp

Miss Jackie Inc, *distributed by* Gryphon House Inc

Miss Rosen Edition, *imprint of* powerHouse Books

Mission San Juan Capistrano Women's Guild, *distributed by* Sunbelt Publications Inc

The Missionary Enterprise in Asia, *imprint of* EastBridge

Missouri History Museum, *distributed by* University of Missouri Press

MIT, *distributor for* The AEI Press

MIT List Visual Arts Center, *distributed by* DAP Distributed Art Publishers

MIT Press, *distributed by* DawnSignPress

The MIT Press, *distributor for* AAAI Press, Canadian Centre for Architecture, Zone Books, Zone Books dba Urzone Inc

Mitten Press, *imprint of* Spry Publishing

MJF Books, *imprint of* Fine Creative Media, Inc

MKSAP® Audio Companion, *imprint of* Oakstone Publishing LLC

MMP, *distributed by* Casemate Publishers & Book Distributors LLC

Farhang Moaser, *distributed by* Ibex Publishers

Modelling Manuals, *imprint of* Osprey Publishing Inc

Modelling Masterclass, *imprint of* Osprey Publishing Inc

Modern Drummer Publications, *distributed by* Hal Leonard Corp

Modern History Press, *imprint of* Loving Healing Press Inc

Modern Learning Press, *imprint of* EPS/School Specialty Literacy & Intervention

Modern Library, *imprint of* Penguin Random House Inc, Random House Publishing Group

Modern Masters, *imprint of* Abbeville Publishing Group

Modern Publishing, *division of* Kappa Books Publishers LLC, Unisystems Inc

Moleskine, *distributed by* Chronicle Books LLC

Moliere & Co, *imprint of* European Masterpieces, *distributed by* European Masterpieces

The Monacelli Press, *imprint of* Penguin Random House Inc, *distributed by* Penguin Group (USA) LLC, a Penguin Random House company

Monacelli Studio, *imprint of* The Monacelli Press

Monarch Books, *distributed by* Kregel Publications

Monarch Books of Canada Ltd, *distributor for* Boys Town Press

Arnoldo Mondadori Electa, *distributed by* Trans-Atlantic Publications Inc

Mondadori Spanish Language, *distributed by* Penguin Random House Inc

Mondo, *imprint of* Mondo Publishing

Moneta Publications, *distributed by* Chelsea Green Publishing Co

Money Market Directories, *unit of* Standard & Poor's

Monjeu Press, *distributed by* Gryphon House Inc

Monostereo, *distributed by* Simon & Schuster Audio

Montana Historical Society Press, *distributed by* Globe Pequot Press, The Globe Pequot Press

Monthly Review Press, *division of* Monthly Review Foundation Inc, Monthly Review Foundation Inc, *distributed by* New York University Press

Moody Press, *distributor for* Focus on the Family

Moody Publishers, *affiliate of* Ministry of Moody Bible Institute

Moon City Press, *distributed by* The University of Arkansas Press

Moondance Press, *imprint of* Quarto Publishing Group USA Inc

Moose Country Press, *distributed by* Enfield Publishing & Distribution Co

Morehouse Publishing, *imprint of* Church Publishing Inc, *distributed by* Abingdon Press (wholesale orders only), Cokesbury (retail orders only)

Morgan Kaufmann, *imprint of* Elsevier Inc

Morrow Junior Books, *imprint of* HarperCollins Publishers

William Morrow, *imprint of* HarperCollins General Books Group, HarperCollins Publishers Sales, *distributor for* Nightingale-Conant

William Morrow Cookbooks, *imprint of* HarperCollins General Books Group, HarperCollins Publishers Sales

William Morrow Paperbacks, *imprint of* HarperCollins General Books Group

Mosby, *imprint of* Elsevier, Health Sciences Division, *distributor for* OptumInsight™, *distributed by* Fire Engineering Books & Videos, OptumInsight™

Motorbooks, *imprint of* Quarto Publishing Group USA Inc

Motorbooks International, *distributor for* Haynes Manuals Inc, *distributed by* Heimburger House Publishing Co

Paul Mould Publishing, *imprint of* Empire Publishing Service, *distributed by* Empire Publishing Service

Mt Blue, *imprint of* Genesis Press Inc

Mount Ida Press, *distributed by* State University of New York Press

Mount Olive College Press, *affiliate of* Mount Olive College

Mount Vernon Ladies Association, *distributed by* The University of Virginia Press

Mountain Air Books, *imprint of* Mountain n' Air Books

Mountain Biking Press, *imprint of* FineEdge.com LLC

Mountain n' Air Books, *distributor for* Tom Harrison Cartography

Mountain Press, *distributor for* Ericson Books

Mountain Press Publishing Co, *distributor for* Bucking Horse Books, Clark City Press, Cottonwood Publishing, Hops Press, Npustin Publishing, Western Edge Press

Mountain Sports Press Series, *imprint of* Mountain Press Publishing Co

Mountaineers Books, *distributor for* The American Alpine Club Press

The Mountaineers Books, *division of* The Mountaineers Club, *distributor for* The American Alpine Club Press, Colorado Mountain Club Press

De Gruyter Mouton, *imprint of* Walter de Gruyter GmbH & Co KG, Walter de Gruyter GmbH & Co KG, *distributed by* Walter de Gruyter Inc

Moyer Bell, *imprint of* Beaufort Books

Moznaim Publishing Corp, *distributor for* Avamra Institute, Breslov Research Institute, Red Wheel-Weiser Inc

MRTS, *imprint of* Arizona Center for Medieval & Renaissance Studies (ACMRS)

MSS Information Corp, *distributed by* Ardent Media Inc

MSU Museum, *distributed by* Michigan State University Press (MSU Press)

MTI, *distributed by* NACE International

MTV Books, *imprint of* Gallery Books

MTV Press, *distributed by* powerHouse Books

Mudborn Press, *imprint of* Bandanna Books

Coleccion Mujeres de Palabra, *imprint of* University of Puerto Rico Press

Mulberry Books, *imprint of* HarperCollins Publishers

Mulholland Books, *imprint of* Little, Brown and Company

A G Muller & Cie, *distributed by* US Games Systems Inc

Lars Muller, *distributed by* Prestel Publishing

Multicultural Publications Inc, *subsidiary of* Making Education Reform Imperative Today Inc (MERIT)

MultiMedia Reviews®, *imprint of* Oakstone Publishing LLC

Museum of Early Southern Decorative Arts, *distributed by* The University of North Carolina Press

The Museum of Modern Art (MoMA), *affiliate of* Circulating Film & Video Library, *distributed by* Distributed Art Publishers (DAP) (US & Canada only)

Museum of New Mexico Press, *unit of* New Mexico State Department of Cultural Affairs, *distributed by* University of New Mexico Press

Music/Culture, *imprint of* Wesleyan University Press

Music Inc, *imprint of* Alfred Music Publishing

Music Sales, *distributed by* Welcome Books®

Music Sales America, *distributed by* Hal Leonard Corp

Music Sales Corp, *distributed by* Beekman Books Inc

Musicians Institute Press, *imprint of* Hal Leonard Corp, *distributed by* Hal Leonard Corp

Musikverlage Han Sikorski, *distributed by* Hal Leonard Corp

Muswell Hill Press, *distributed by* State University of New York Press

MVP Books, *distributed by* Lerner Publishing Group Inc

My Healthy Church, *imprint of* Gospel Publishing House (GPH)

MyBizDaily.com, *subsidiary of* BizBest Media Corp

Mycroft & Moran, *imprint of* Arkham House Publishers Inc

MyReportLinks.com Books, *imprint of* Enslow Publishing LLC

The Mysterious Press, *imprint of* Grove Atlantic Inc

Mystic Books, *imprint of* Regal Crest Enterprises LLC

Mystic Oaks, *imprint of* Oak Tree Press

Mystic Seaport Museum Inc, *distributor for* Glencannon, Ten Pound Island Books

N & A, *imprint of* The Nautical & Aviation Publishing Co of America Inc

NACE International, *distributor for* ASM International, ASTM, AWS, Butterworth-Heinemann, Cambridge University Press, CASTI Publishing, Compass Publications, CRC Press, Marcel Dekker Inc, E&FN Spon, Elsevier Science Publishers, Gulf Publishing, Industrial Press, Institute of Materials, ISO, McGraw-Hill, MTI, Prentice Hall, Professional Publications, SSPC, Swedish Corrosion Institute, John Wiley & Sons Inc, *distributed by* Australasian Corrosion Association

NAL, *division of* Penguin Group (USA) LLC, Penguin Group (USA) LLC, a Penguin Random House company

Narosa Publishing House, *distributed by* American Mathematical Society

NASCO, *distributor for* National Council of Teachers of Mathematics (NCTM)

NASSP, *imprint of* National Association of Secondary School Principals (NASSP)

NASW Press, *division of* National Association of Social Workers (NASW)

Nataraj, *imprint of* New World Library

Nation Books, *imprint of* The Nation Institute, The Perseus Books Group

National Academies Press (NAP), *division of* National Academies

National Academy for Adult Jewish Studies, *imprint of* United Synagogue Book Service

The National Alliance Research Academy, *division of* The National Alliance for Insurance Education & Research

National Archives & Records Administration, *distributed by* J J Keller & Associates, Inc

National Association for Music Education (NAfME), *distributed by* Rowman & Littlefield Education

National Association of Broadcasters (NAB), *distributed by* Allyn & Bacon, Lawrence Erlbaum Assoc, Focal Press, Macmillan Publishing Co, Tab Books, Wadsworth Inc

National Association of Home Builders (NAHB), *distributed by* BuilderBooks.com

National Association of Photo Sellers, *imprint of* Copywriter's Council of America (CCA), *distributed by* Copywriter's Council of America (CCA)

National Association of Photo Sellers™, *imprint of* The Linick Group Inc, *distributed by* The Linick Group Inc

National Book Co, *division of* Educational Research Associates

National Book Network, *distributor for* Hudson Hills Press LLC, Impact Publications/Development Concepts Inc, LearningExpress LLC, Open Horizons Publishing Co, Welcome Rain Publishers LLC, *distributed by* Heimburger House Publishing Co

National Book Network (NBN), *distributor for* Association for Talent Development (ATD)

National Center Early Childhood Workforce, *distributed by* Gryphon House Inc

National Center for Children in Poverty, *division of* Mailman School of Public Health at Columbia University

National Cooperative Highway Research Program, *imprint of* Transportation Research Board

National Council of Examiners for Engineering & Surveying, *distributed by* Professional Publications Inc (PPI)

National Council of Teachers of Mathematics (NCTM), *distributed by* Eric Armin Inc Education Ctr, Delta Education, Didax Educational Resources, Educators Outlet, ETA Cuisenaire, Lakeshore Learning Materials, NASCO, Spectrum

National Doll Society of America, *division of* Success Advertising & Publishing

National Farm Book Co, *division of* Hobar Publications

National Gallery, London, *distributed by* Yale University Press

National Gallery of Art, *distributed by* Abrams, Bulfinch/Little, Cambridge University Press, Hudson Hills, Lund Humphries/Ashgate, OAP, Princeton University Press, Thames & Hudson, Yale University Press

National Genealogical Society, *distributed by* Heritage Books Inc

National Geographic, *distributor for* The Colonial Williamsburg Foundation, *distributed by* Penguin Random House Inc

National Geographic Adventure Classics, *imprint of* National Geographic Books

National Geographic Adventure Press, *imprint of* National Geographic Books

National Geographic Books, *division of* National Geographic Society, *distributed by* PGUK / Hi Marketing (United Kingdom), Random House (Worldwide exc UK)

National Geographic Children's Books, *imprint of* National Geographic Books

National Geographic Directions, *imprint of* National Geographic Books

National Geographic Learning, *unit of* Cengage Learning

National Geographic Society, *distributed by* Random House

National Information Standards Organization, *distributor for* Niso Press

National Institute of Occupational Safety & Health, *distributed by* J J Keller & Associates, Inc

National Park Service Media Services, *subsidiary of* US Department of the Interior

National Poetry Foundation, *distributed by* University Press of New England

National Professional Resources, *distributor for* MAR*CO Products Inc

National Ranching Heritage Center, *distributed by* Texas Tech University Press

National Register Publishing, *division of* Marquis Who's Who LLC

National Resource Center for Youth Services (NRCYS), *division of* University of Oklahoma-Outreach

National Resource Center Youth Services, *distributor for* MAR*CO Products Inc

National Teacher Examination Series, *imprint of* National Learning Corp

The National Underwriter Co, *division of* Summit Business Media

Native Ink Press, *imprint of* Ink Smith Publishing

Native Voices, *imprint of* Book Publishing Co

Natural Heritage Press, *distributed by* Birch Brook Press

Natural Resource Agriculture & Engineering Service, *distributor for* MidWest Plan Service (MWPS), *distributed by* MidWest Plan Service (MWPS)

Naturegraph, *distributed by* Gem Guides Book Co

NaturEncyclopedia Series, *imprint of* Stemmer House Publishers Inc

Naval Institute Press, *division of* US Naval Institute, *distributed by* Publishers Group West (digital only)

NavPress, *imprint of* NavPress Publishing Group

NavPress Publishing Group, *division of* The Navigators

Nazarene Publishing House, *imprint of* Beacon Hill Press of Kansas City

NBN, *distributor for* Intercultural Press Inc, Michelin Maps & Guides, Para Publishing LLC

NCP, *imprint of* New City Press

NCSY Publications, *distributed by* Mesorah Publications Ltd

NEA Professional Library, *imprint of* National Education Association (NEA)

Neal-Schuman Publishers Inc, *distributor for* Chandos, Facet

Near Eastern Press, *imprint of* Holmes Publishing Group LLC

E T Nedder Publishing, *imprint of* Paulist Press

Nefu Books, *imprint of* Africana Homestead Legacy Publishers Inc

Neibauer Press & ChurchSupplier.com, *division of* Louis Neibauer Co Inc, Louis Neibauer Co Inc

Tommy Nelson, *imprint of* HarperCollins Christian Publishing, *distributor for* Focus on the Family

The Netherlands Institute for Social Research, *distributed by* Transaction Publishers Inc

Nevada Publications, *distributor for* Gem Guides Book Co, *distributed by* Gem Guides Book Co

New American Fiction Series, *imprint of* Green Integer

New American Library, *imprint of* NAL

New American Poetry Series, *imprint of* Green Integer

New Beginnings Press, *imprint of* Hay House Inc

The New Careers Center, *division of* Finney Company Inc

New City (Great Britain), *distributed by* New City Press

New City Press, *division of* Focolare Movement, *distributor for* Ciudad Nueva (Spain/Argentina), New City (Great Britain)

New Criterion Books, *distributed by* St Augustine's Press Inc

New Directions Publishing Corp, *distributed by* W W Norton & Company Inc, W W Norton Co

New England AEYC, *distributed by* Gryphon House Inc

New England Bibliographies, *distributed by* Oak Knoll Press

New England College, *distributed by* University Press of New England

New England History Press, *imprint of* Picton Press

New Falcon Publications, *imprint of* The Original Falcon Press

New Forest Press, *imprint of* Black Rabbit Books

New Harvest, *imprint of* Houghton Mifflin Harcourt Trade & Reference Division

New Holland Publishers (UK) Ltd, *distributed by* The Globe Pequot Press

New Horizon Press, *distributed by* Kensington Publishing Corp

New Horizons, *distributed by* Gryphon House Inc

New Horizons Book Publishing Co, *imprint of* World Citizens

New Island Books, *distributed by* Dufour Editions Inc

New Issues Poetry & Prose, *affiliate of* Western Michigan University

The New Jerusalem Bible, *imprint of* Penguin Random House Inc

New Leaf, *distributor for* Ash Tree Publishing

New Leaf Books, *distributor for* Blue Poppy Press

New Leaf Press Inc, *division of* New Leaf Publishing Group

New Marketplace, *imprint of* Oaklea Press

New Netherland Institute, *distributed by* State University of New York Press

New Pacific Press, *distributed by* North Atlantic Books

New Page Books, *imprint of* The Career Press Inc

New Path Learning, *distributed by* Peoples Education Inc

New Poets Series, *imprint of* BrickHouse Books Inc

New Readers Press, *division of* ProLiteracy, ProLiteracy, *distributor for* Teachers of English to Speakers of Other Languages Inc (TESOL)

New Traditions, *imprint of* Gallopade International Inc

New Vanguard, *imprint of* Osprey Publishing Inc

New Voices, *imprint of* Florida Academic Press

New Win Publishing, *division of* Academic Learning Co LLC

New Wine Press, *distributed by* Bridge-Logos Inc

New World Library, *division of* Whatever Publishing Inc, Whatever Publishing Inc

New World Paperbacks, *imprint of* International Publishers Co Inc

New World Press, *imprint of* Copywriter's Council of America (CCA), The Linick Group Inc, *distributed by* China Books

New World Press Books, *distributor for* The Linick Group Inc

New York Academy of Sciences, *distributed by* Wiley Blackwell Publishers

The New York Botanical Garden Press, *division of* New York Botanical Garden, The New York Botanical Garden

New York Nights, *imprint of* Ugly Duckling Presse

New York University Press, *distributor for* Combined Academic Publishers Ltd, Footprint Books, Monthly Review Press, *distributed by* Heimburger House Publishing Co

New Yorker Desk Diary, *distributed by* Per Annum Inc

Newbridge Communications Inc, *distributor for* Educational Impressions Inc

Newbridge Discovery Links, *imprint of* Sundance/Newbridge Publishing

Newbury Street Press, *imprint of* New England Historic Genealogical Society

The Newman Press, *imprint of* Paulist Press

Newmarket Press for It Books, *imprint of* HarperCollins General Books Group

NewSouth Books, *imprint of* NewSouth Books, NewSouth Inc, *distributed by* John F Blair Publisher

NewSouth Classics, *imprint of* NewSouth Books

Newtona LLC, *distributed by* Sunbelt Publications Inc

Nexus Special Interests, *distributed by* Trans-Atlantic Publications Inc

NIAS Press, *distributed by* University of Hawaii Press

Nibble Me Books™, *imprint of* Playhouse Publishing

Niche Publishing, *distributed by* John F Blair Publisher

Nicolin Fields Publishing, *distributed by* University Press of New England

Nightingale-Conant, *distributed by* William Morrow, Simon & Schuster

Nightingale-Conant (UK), *subsidiary of* Nightingale-Conant

Nightingale Editions, *imprint of* Cross-Cultural Communications

Nile Publishing, *distributed by* Tughra Books

Nilgiri Press, *division of* Blue Mountain Center of Meditation

Nimbus Publishing, *distributed by* Orca Book Publishers

Nimbus Publishing Ltd, *distributed by* Down East Books

NIMCO Bookstore, *distributor for* MAR*CO Products Inc

Nippon Foundation, *distributed by* EastBridge

Niso Press, *distributed by* National Information Standards Organization

NK Publications Inc, *affiliate of* Loukoumi Books

No Frills Buffalo, *distributed by* Aardvark

No Starch Press Inc, *distributed by* O'Reilly Media

Nodin Press, *distributed by* Adventure Publications

Noel Press, *imprint of* Nova Science Publishers Inc

Noesis Press, *imprint of* The Davies Group Publishers

Noetic Books, *imprint of* New Harbinger Publications Inc

NOLO, *subsidiary of* Internet Brands Inc

Nonpareil Books, *imprint of* David R Godine Publisher Inc

The Noontide Press, *imprint of* Legion for the Survival of Freedom

Nordic Africa Institute, *distributed by* Stylus Publishing LLC

North Atlantic Books, *division of* Society for the Study of Native Arts & Sciences, *distributor for* DharmaCafe, Energy Arts, Ergos Institute, Frog Books, Heaven & Earth Publications, New Pacific Press, Rangjung Yeshe Publications, Sunfood Living

North Carolina Museum of Art, *distributed by* The University of North Carolina Press

North Castle Books, *imprint of* M E Sharpe Inc

North Country Books, *imprint of* North Country Books Inc

North Country Classics, *imprint of* North Country Books Inc

North Light Books, *imprint of* F+W, A Content + eCommerce Company

North Point Press, *imprint of* Farrar, Straus & Giroux, LLC

North Star Way, *imprint of* Gallery Books

Northcross Books, *distributed by* Sunbelt Publications Inc

Northeastern University Press, *imprint of* University Press of New England

Northfield Publishing, *imprint of* Moody Publishers

Northwestern University Press, *distributor for* Lake Forrest College Press, Third World Press, Tia Chucha Press

W W Norton, *distributor for* Allworth Press, Verso

W W Norton & Co, *distributor for* Peace Hill Press, Persea Books, *distributed by* Heimburger House Publishing Co

W W Norton & Co Inc, *distributor for* The Countryman Press, The Overlook Press, Pushcart Press, Thames & Hudson

W W Norton & Company Inc, *distributor for* Airphoto International Ltd/Odyssey Publications, Albatross Publishing House, Atlas & Co, Blue Guides Ltd, George Braziller Inc, Chess Information & Research Center, Dalkey Archive Press, Fantagraphics Books, Kales Press, New Directions Publishing Corp, Ontario Review Press, The Overlook Press, Peace Hill Press, Pegasus Books, Persea Books Inc, Pushcart Press, Quantuck Lane Press, Skyhorse Publishing, Thames & Hudson, Tin House Books, Winterthur Museum & Country Estate

W W Norton Co, *distributor for* New Directions Publishing Corp

Norvik Press, *distributed by* Dufour Editions Inc

Norwalk Press, *imprint of* Book Publishing Co

Norwegian Petroleum Agency, *distributed by* Enfield Publishing & Distribution Co

Nosy Crow, *imprint of* Candlewick Press

Nota Bell Books, *imprint of* Purdue University Press

Nova Biomedical Press, *imprint of* Nova Science Publishers Inc

Nova Global Affairs Press, *imprint of* Nova Science Publishers Inc

Nova History Press, *imprint of* Nova Science Publishers Inc

Nova Music, *imprint of* Nova Science Publishers Inc

Nova Science Books, *imprint of* Nova Science Publishers Inc

Nova Southeastern University, *distributed by* Gryphon House Inc

Novalis, *distributor for* Twenty-Third Publications, *distributed by* Twenty-Third Publications

Novel-Ties Study Guides, *imprint of* Learning Links Inc

November Moon, *distributed by* Lotus Press

Novinka Books, *imprint of* Nova Science Publishers Inc

NOW, *distributor for* The Perseus Books Group

Npustin Publishing, *distributed by* Mountain Press Publishing Co

NRH Press, *distributed by* Vandamere Press

NSTA Ebooks+, *imprint of* National Science Teachers Association (NSTA)

NSTA Kids, *imprint of* National Science Teachers Association (NSTA)

NSTA Press, *imprint of* National Science Teachers Association (NSTA)

NTC Contemporary Books, *imprint of* McGraw-Hill Professional

NTIS, *distributor for* Energy Information Administration (EIA)

Nuclear Energy Agency, *distributed by* Organization for Economic Cooperation & Development

Coleccion Nueve Pececitos, *imprint of* University of Puerto Rico Press

The Numata Center, *distributed by* University of Hawaii Press

Number Success, *imprint of* Advance Publishing Inc

Numismatics Books, *imprint of* Betterway Books

nursesbooks.org, The Publishing Program of ANA, *division of* American Nurses Association

NUS Press, *distributed by* University of Hawaii Press

Nutri-Books, *distributor for* Ash Tree Publishing

Nylabone Products, *division of* TFH Publications Inc

Oak Knoll Press, *distributor for* American Antiquarian Society, Bibliographical Society of America, Bibliographical Society of University of Virginia, The Bibliographical Society (UK), Block Museum, Boston College, John Carter Brown Library, Bryn Mawr College, Catalpa Press, Caxton Club, Center for Book Arts, Chapin Library, Fondation Custodia, The Grolier Club, Hes & De Graaf, Historic New Orleans Collection, Library of Congress-Center for the Book, The Manuscript Society, New England Bibliographies, Providence Athenaeum, Rivendale Press, Tate Galleries, Texas State Historical Association, Typophiles, Winterthur Museum, Yushodo Press

Oaklea Press, *unit of* Oaklea Press Inc

Oakstone Publishing LLC, *division of* Boston Ventures

Oak Tree Books, *imprint of* Oak Tree Press

OAP, *distributor for* National Gallery of Art

Obelisk Books, *imprint of* Whittier Publications Inc

Oberlin College Press, *subsidiary of* Oberlin College, *distributed by* University Press of New England (UPNE)

Oberon Books, *distributed by* Theatre Communications Group

O'Brien Press, *distributed by* Dufour Editions Inc

Obsessive Anonymous, *distributed by* Hazelden Publishing

Obsidian, *imprint of* Genesis Press Inc

Occupational Competency Examination Series, *imprint of* National Learning Corp

Ocean Press, *distributed by* Consortium Book Sales & Distribution

Ocean Publishing, *division of* The Gromling Group Inc

Ocean Tree Books, *distributed by* Treasure Chest Books

Octavo Editions, *distributed by* Konecky & Konecky LLC

Octavo Press, *imprint of* Templegate Publishers

Octopus Books, *distributed by* Hachette Book Group

Odonian Press, *distributed by* Common Courage Press

Odyssey Books, *division of* The Ciletti Publishing Group Inc

OECD, *distributed by* The Brookings Institution Press

Office & Print Technologies, *division of* PJD Publications Ltd

Office of External Affairs, *division of* RAND Corp

Office of the Federal Register, *distributed by* J J Keller & Associates, Inc

Office of the United Nations High Commissioner for Human Rights (OHCHR), *distributed by* United Nations Publications

Ohio State University Foreign Language Publications, *division of* Foreign Language Center

Ohio University Press, *distributor for* The Colonial Williamsburg Foundation

Okinawan Kobujutsu Kyokai Association (OKKA), *distributor for* The Linick Group Inc

Old Barn Publishing, *imprint of* Old Barn Enterprises Inc

Old Farmers Almanac, *distributed by* Houghton Mifflin Harcourt Trade & Reference Division

The Old Farmer's Almanac, *distributed by* Houghton Mifflin Harcourt

Old House, *imprint of* Osprey Publishing Inc

Old Kings Road Press, *imprint of* Athletic Guide Publishing

Old Seattle Press, *distributed by* Epicenter Press Inc

Olive Branch Press, *imprint of* Interlink Publishing Group Inc

Olive Tree Book Co, *imprint of* Greenleaf Book Group LLC

Omnibus Press, *division of* Music Sales Ltd, *distributor for* Big Meteor, Gramophone

Omnific Publishing, *distributed by* Simon & Schuster, Inc

Omohundro Institute of Early American History & Culture (OIEAHC), *distributed by* The University of North Carolina Press

On My Own, *imprint of* Appletree Press Inc

140Main.com, *subsidiary of* BizBest Media Corp

1000 Readers, *imprint of* Gallopade International Inc

One World, *imprint of* Penguin Random House Inc, Random House Publishing Group

Ontario Review Press, *distributed by* W W Norton & Company Inc, Persea Books

Onyx, *imprint of* NAL, Penguin Group (USA) LLC, a Penguin Random House company

OPAMP Technical Books, *distributor for* Primary Research Group Inc

Open Court, *division of* Carus Publishing Co

Open Horizons Publishing Co, *distributed by* National Book Network

Open Road, *distributor for* Albert Whitman & Co, *distributed by* Simon & Schuster Sales Division

Open Road Integrated Media, *distributor for* Philosophical Library Inc

Open Road Publishing, *distributed by* Simon & Schuster, Simon & Schuster, Inc

Open Scroll, *imprint of* Bridge-Logos Inc

Open Society Institute, *distributed by* Central European University Press

OPIS/STALSBY Directories & Databases, *division of* United Communications Group

OptumInsight™, *distributor for* American Medical Association, Medical Economics, Mosby, *distributed by* American Medical Association, Mosby

Opus Communications, *imprint of* HCPro Inc

OR Books, *distributor for* CUNY Journalism Press

Oracle Press, *imprint of* McGraw-Hill Professional

Oral Biography Series, *imprint of* University of Alaska Press

Orange Grove Textbooks, *imprint of* University Press of Florida

Orb Books, *imprint of* Tom Doherty Associates, LLC

Orbis Books, *division of* Maryknoll Fathers & Brothers

Orbit, *division of* Hachette Book Group

Orbit Series, *imprint of* Krieger Publishing Co

Orca Book Publishers, *distributor for* The Book Publishing Co, Coteau Books, Creative Book Publishing, Formac Publishing, Lobster Press, James Lorimer & Co, Nimbus Publishing, Polestar Calendars, Second Story Press, 7th Generation, Sono Nis Press, Sumach Press, Tradewind Books, Tuckamore Books, Tudor House

Orchard Books, *imprint of* Scholastic Trade Division

Orchard House Inc, *distributor for* Council for Exceptional Children (CEC)

Oregon Fever Books, *imprint of* Crumb Elbow Publishing

Oregon River Watch, *imprint of* Crumb Elbow Publishing

Oregon Writers Colony, *distributed by* Washington State University Press

O'Reilly Media, *distributor for* Microsoft Press, No Starch Press Inc

O'Reilly Media Inc, *distributor for* Microsoft Press (North America), Packt Publishing (technol ebook prog)

OREP, *distributed by* Casemate Publishers & Book Distributors LLC

Organization for Economic Cooperation & Development, *division of* Organization for Economic Cooperation & Development (France), *distributor for* International Energy Agency (Imprint), International Transportation Forum, Nuclear Energy Agency (Imprint)

Oriental Institute Publications, *division of* University of Chicago

Orion, *distributed by* Sterling Publishing Co Inc

Orpen Press, *distributed by* Dufour Editions Inc

Osprey, *imprint of* Osprey Publishing Inc

Osprey Modelling, *imprint of* Osprey Publishing Inc

Osprey Publishing Inc, *distributed by* Random House (US & CN)

Ostrich Editions, *imprint of* Cross-Cultural Communications

OTB Legacy Editions, *imprint of* Ocean Tree Books

Other Press LLC, *distributed by* Random House Inc

Otherworlds, *imprint of* Zumaya Publications LLC

Ottographics, *distributed by* Chelsea Green Publishing Co

Our Sunday Visitor Publishing, *division of* Our Sunday Visitor Inc

Out of This World Press, *distributed by* Gem Guides Book Co

Outdoor Books & Maps, *imprint of* Adler Publishing Inc

Oval Books, *distributed by* The Globe Pequot Press

The Overlook Press, *subsidiary of* Peter Mayer Publishers Inc, Peter Mayer Publishers Inc, *distributed by* W W Norton & Company Inc, W W Norton & Co Inc

The Overmountain Press, *division of* Sabre Industries Inc, Sabre Industries Inc

Owlswick Press, *imprint of* Wildside Press LLC

Oxfam Publishing, *distributed by* Stylus Publishing LLC

Oxford, *distributed by* SAS Publishing

Oxford Illustrated Press, *distributed by* Haynes Manuals Inc

Oxford University Press, *distributor for* The American Chemical Society, Entomological Society of America, Fordham University Press, Kodansha USA Inc, *distributed by* Beach Lloyd Publishers LLC, Cheng & Tsui Co Inc, Delta Publishing Co

Oxford University Press Inc, *distributor for* Country Music Foundation Press

Oxford University Press USA, *division of* University of Oxford, *distributor for* The American Chemical Society, American University in Cairo, Arnold Clarendon, Cold Spring Harbor Laboratory Press, Engineering Press, Fordham University Press, Getty, Greenwich Medical Media, Grove Dictionaries, Hurst, IRL, Kodansha, Roxbury Publishing, Saunders, Thomson Publishing

Oxmoor House, *imprint of* Time Inc Books, *distributed by* H B Fenn (Canada), Hachette Book Group, Leisure Arts Inc

Oyinde Publishing, *imprint of* Africana Homestead Legacy Publishers Inc

Ozark Publishing Inc, *distributed by* Amazon.com, Apple, Barnes & Noble, Econoclad, Gumdrop, Perma-Bound, Stay Bound

Ozark Society, *distributed by* The University of Arkansas Press

Pace University Press, *unit of* Pace University

Pacific Boating Almanac, *imprint of* ProStar Publications Inc

Pacific Institute, *distributed by* Washington State University Press

Pacific Press Publishing Association, *division of* Seventh-Day Adventist Church

Packt Publishing, *distributed by* O'Reilly Media Inc

Pademelon Press, *distributed by* Gryphon House Inc

Pademelon Press Pty Ltd, *distributor for* Redleaf Press

Padua Playwrights Press, *distributed by* Theatre Communications Group

Kogan Page, *distributed by* Beekman Books Inc

Painted Pony Inc, *subsidiary of* Wind River Development Fund

Painted Turtle Books, *imprint of* Wayne State University Press

PAJ Publications, *distributed by* Theatre Communications Group

PAKS-Parents & Kids, *imprint of* THE Learning Connection®

Paladin Press, *division of* Paladin Enterprises Inc, *distributed by* Amazon.com, Barnes & Noble, Borders

Paladin Timeless Books, *imprint of* Twilight Times Books

Joan Palevsky, *imprint of* University of California Press

Palgrave Macmillan, *imprint of* Macmillan Higher Education, *distributor for* Berg Publishers, British Film Institute, Manchester University Press, Pluto Press, I B Tauris & Co Ltd, Zed Books, *distributed by* St Martin's Press, LLC

Pali Text Society, *imprint of* Wisdom Publications Inc

Pan Asian Publications, *distributed by* Cheng & Tsui Co Inc

Panda Books, *distributed by* China Books

Panmun Academic Services, *distributed by* Cheng & Tsui Co Inc

Panpac Education, *distributed by* Cheng & Tsui Co Inc

Pantheon Books, *imprint of* Penguin Random House Inc

Pantheon Books/Schocken Books, *imprint of* Knopf Doubleday Publishing Group

Paolo Torti degli Alberti, *distributed by* Edgewise Press Inc

Paperbacks for Educators, *distributor for* MAR*CO Products Inc

Papercutz, *distributed by* Macmillan, St Martin's Press, LLC

PaperStar, *imprint of* Penguin Group (USA) LLC, a Penguin Random House company, Penguin Young Readers Group, GP Putnam's Sons (Children's)

Paperweight Press, *distributed by* Tuttle Publishing

Papier-Mache Press, *imprint of* Beaufort Books

Papillion Publishing, *imprint of* Blue Dolphin Publishing Inc

Nelson Papucci, *distributed by* Sunbelt Publications Inc

Para Publishing LLC, *distributed by* NBN

Para Publishing Seminars, *division of* Para Publishing LLC

Para Research, *imprint of* Schiffer Publishing Ltd

Parabola, *distributed by* Fons Vitae

Parabola Books, *subsidiary of* Society for the Study of Myth & Tradition

Parachute Publishing LLC, *division of* Parachute Properties LLC, *distributed by* Bantam, Bendon, Berkley, Dorling Kindersley, Grosset, Harcourt, HarperCollins, HarperEntertainment, Kensington, Little, Brown, Pocket, Random House, Running Press, Scholastic, Simon & Schuster

Parachuting Publications, *imprint of* Para Publishing LLC

Paraclete Press Inc, *division of* Creative Joys Inc, *distributor for* Abbey of Saint Peter of Solesmes, Gloriae Dei Cantores

Paradigm Busters, *distributed by* Cheng & Tsui Co Inc

Paradigm Publications, *division of* Redwing Book Co

Paradigm Publishing Inc, *division of* EMC Publishing LLC

Paragon, *distributed by* Fons Vitae

Paragon House, *distributor for* Professors World Peace Academy, *distributed by* Bloomsbury Academic, Bloomsbury International Publishing USA (fulfillment by Macmillan)

Paralists, *division of* Para Publishing LLC

Parallax Press, *division of* Unified Buddhist Church

Paraview Pocket Books, *imprint of* Cosimo Inc

Paraview Press, *division of* Cosimo Inc

Paraview Special Editions, *imprint of* Cosimo Inc

Pardey Publications, *imprint of* Paradise Cay Publications Inc

Parenting Press Inc, *distributor for* Raefield-Roberts, Publishers

Park Street Press, *imprint of* Inner Traditions International Ltd

Christopher Parkening, *distributed by* Hal Leonard Corp

Parker/Thomas Press, *imprint of* Tudor Publishers Inc

ParmenidesAudio™, *division of* Parmenides Publishing

ParmenidesFiction™, *division of* Parmenides Publishing

Partner Press, *distributed by* Gryphon House Inc

Partners, *distributor for* Ash Tree Publishing

Partners Book Distributing, *distributor for* Avery Color Studios

Partner's Book Distributing Inc, *distributor for* Blue Poppy Press

Partners Book Distributor, *distributor for* Wilderness Adventures Press Inc

Partners West, *distributor for* Wilderness Adventures Press Inc

Partner's/West Book Distributing Inc, *distributor for* Blue Poppy Press

Partnership Publications, *imprint of* House to House Publications

Parvardigar Press, *distributed by* Fons Vitae

Passages, *imprint of* Perfection Learning Corp

Passbooks, *imprint of* National Learning Corp

Pastoral Press, *imprint of* OCP, OCP Publications Inc, OCP Publications Inc

Pathway Book Service, *distributor for* Independent Information Publications

Patos Island Press, *distributed by* Epicenter Press Inc

Jimmy Patterson, *imprint of* Little, Brown and Company

Pauline Books & Media, *division of* Daughters of St Paul

Pauline Comics & Graphic Novels, *imprint of* Pauline Books & Media

Pauline Teen, *imprint of* Pauline Books & Media

Nancy Paulsen Books, *imprint of* Penguin Young Readers Group

Paws IV, *imprint of* Sasquatch Books

Payback Press, *distributed by* AK Press Distribution

Peabody Museum of Archaeology & Ethnology, *distributed by* Harvard University Press

Peabody Museum Press, *unit of* Peabody Museum of Archaeology & Ethnology, Peabody Museum of Archaeology & Ethnology, Harvard University

Peace Books, *distributed by* China Books

Peace Hill Press, *distributed by* W W Norton & Co, W W Norton & Company Inc

Peacewatch Editions, *imprint of* Ocean Tree Books

Peachpit Press, *division of* Pearson Education, Pearson Education Ltd (International)

Peachtree Jr, *imprint of* Peachtree Publishers

Pearson, *distributor for* Heinemann, *distributed by* Council for Exceptional Children (CEC)

Pearson Addison Wesley, *imprint of* Pearson Higher Education

Pearson Allyn & Bacon, *imprint of* Pearson Higher Education

Pearson Arts & Sciences, *division of* Pearson Education

Pearson Australia, *distributed by* Cheng & Tsui Co Inc

Pearson Australia-Schools Division, *distributor for* Boynton/Cook Publishers

Pearson Benjamin Cummings, *imprint of* Pearson Higher Education

Pearson Business Publishing, *unit of* Pearson Higher Education, Pearson Higher Education Division

Pearson Career, Health, Education & Technology, *division of* Pearson Education

Pearson Education, *distributor for* Manning Publications Co, *distributed by* American Academy of Environmental Engineers & Scientists™, Trans-Atlantic Publications Inc

Pearson Education Canada, *distributor for* Boynton/Cook Publishers

Pearson ELT, *division of* Pearson Education

Pearson Higher Education, *division of* Pearson Education

Pearson Humanities & Social Sciences, *unit of* Pearson Higher Education, Pearson Higher Education Division

Pearson Learning Solutions, *unit of* Pearson Higher Education

Pearson Longman, *imprint of* Pearson Higher Education

Pearson New Zealand-Schools Division, *distributor for* Boynton/Cook Publishers

Pearson Prentice Hall, *imprint of* Pearson Higher Education

Pearson School, *unit of* Pearson Education

Pearson Technology, *distributed by* SkillPath Publications

Pearson Technology Group Canada, *distributed by* Penguin Books

Editions du Renouveau Pedagogique, *distributor for* Michelin Maps & Guides

T H Peek Publisher, *division of* Clearweave Corp

Bette L Pegas, *distributed by* Sunbelt Publications Inc

Pegasus Books, *distributed by* W W Norton & Company Inc

Pelican International Corp, *subsidiary of* Pelican Publishing Co

Pelican Pond Publishing, *imprint of* Blue Dolphin Publishing Inc

Pelican Publishing Co, *distributor for* Hope Publishing House, Marmac Publishing Co, Self-Help Success Books

A W Peller & Associates, *distributor for* Pieces of Learning

Pembroke Publishers, *distributed by* Stenhouse Publishers

Pen & Sword Books Ltd, *distributed by* Casemate Publishers & Book Distributors LLC

Pen & Sword Digital, *distributed by* Casemate Publishers & Book Distributors LLC

Pendragon Press, *subsidiary of* Camelot Publishing Co Inc, Camelot Publishing Co Inc, *distributor for* Croatian Musicological Society, *distributed by* LIM Editrice SRL (Italy), G Ricordi (Italy)

Penguin, *imprint of* Penguin Books, Penguin Group (USA) LLC, a Penguin Random House company, *distributor for* Verso, *distributed by* Alfred Music Publishing

Penguin Books, *imprint of* Penguin Group (USA) LLC, Penguin Group (USA) LLC, a Penguin Random House company, *distributor for* The Countryman Press, Pearson Technology Group Canada, Persea Books

Penguin Canada, *distributor for* Michelin Maps & Guides

Penguin Classics, *imprint of* Penguin Books, Penguin Group (USA) LLC, a Penguin Random House company

Penguin Compass, *imprint of* Penguin Books

Penguin Group (USA) LLC, *distributor for* Alloy Entertainment LLC, DAW Books Inc, The Jim Henson Co, Kensington Publishing Corp, The Library of America, Maharishi University of Management Press, Rough Guides, *distributed by* Learning Links Inc

Penguin Group (USA) LLC, a Penguin Random House company, *distributor for* Arkangel, Bibli O'Phile, Consumer Guide/PIL, DAW Books Inc, Dream Works, Granta, HighBridge Audio, Kensington Publishing Corp, The Library of America, The Monacelli Press

The Penguin Press, *imprint of* Penguin Group (USA) LLC, Penguin Group (USA) LLC, a Penguin Random House company

Penguin Putnam Inc, *distributed by* Heimburger House Publishing Co

Penguin Random House, *distributed by* Dreamscape Media LLC

Penguin Random House Audio, *subsidiary of* Penguin Random House, Penguin Random House LLC

Penguin Random House Canada Limited, *distributor for* Charlesbridge Publishing Inc

Penguin Random House Inc, *distributor for* Karen Brown's Guides, Mondadori Spanish Language, National Geographic, Princeton Review, Rizzoli, Rugged Land, Shambhala, Smithsonian Books, Soho Press, Steerforth Press, The Taunton Press, Ten Speed Press, Wizards of the Coast

Penguin 20th Century Classics, *imprint of* Penguin Books

Penguin Young Readers Group, *division of* Penguin Group (USA) LLC, Penguin Group (USA) LLC, a Penguin Random House company

Peninsula Publishing, *distributed by* Scitech Publishing Inc

PenMark Press, *imprint of* The Davies Group Publishers

Penn State University Press, *distributor for* University of California Institute on Global Conflict & Cooperation

Pennsylvania Historical & Museum Commission, *subsidiary of* The Commonwealth of Pennsylvania

Pennsylvania State Data Center, *subsidiary of* Institute of State & Regional Affairs

The Pennsylvania State University Press, *division of* The Pennsylvania State University

Pennwell, *distributed by* Gulf Publishing Co

PennWell Books, *division of* PennWell

PennWell Business & Industrial Division, *distributor for* Marine Techniques Publishing, *distributed by* Marine Techniques Publishing

Pennywell Press, *distributed by* John F Blair Publisher

Pennywyse Press, *imprint of* Imago Press

Penobscot Press, *imprint of* Picton Press

Pensiero Press, *imprint of* The Lentz Leadership Institute

Pentecostal Publishing House, *subsidiary of* United Pentecostal Church International, *distributed by* Anchor Distributors, Christian Network International, Innovative Marketing, Spring Arbor

Penton Price Digests, *imprint of* Penton Media

Peoples Education Inc, *subsidiary of* Peoples Educational Holdings Inc, *distributor for* New Path Learning

Linda Pequegnat, *distributed by* Sunbelt Publications Inc

Per Annum Inc, *distributor for* New Yorker Desk Diary

Peradam Press, *subsidiary of* The Center for Cultural & Naturalist Studies

Percheron Press, *imprint of* Eliot Werner Publications Inc

Peter Peregrinus Ltd, *imprint of* IET USA Inc

Peregrinzilla, *distributed by* Chelsea Green Publishing Co

Perennial, *imprint of* HarperCollins Publishers Sales

Perennial Currents, *imprint of* HarperCollins Publishers Sales

Perennial Dark Alley, *imprint of* HarperCollins Publishers Sales

Sophia Perennis, *distributed by* Fons Vitae

PerfectBound, *imprint of* HarperCollins Publishers Sales

Perfection Learning Corp, *distributor for* Abrams, Ace Books, Airmont, Annick Press, Archway, Atheneum, Baker Books, Ballantine, Bantam, Barrons, Berkley, Blake Books, Candlewick Press, Charlesbridge Press, Chelsea House, Children's Press, Chronicle Books, Crabtree Publishing, Crown, Disney Press, Distri Books, DK, Doubleday, Dutton, F+W, A Content + eCommerce Company, Farrar, Straus & Giroux Inc, Fawcett, Firefly, First Avenue, Free Spirit, Fulcrum, Golden Books, Greenhaven Press Inc, Hammond Pub, Harcourt Inc, Hayes, Gareth Stevens, Frederick Warne

Perigee, *imprint of* Berkley Publishing Group, Penguin Group (USA) LLC, a Penguin Random House company

Perigee Books, *imprint of* Penguin Group (USA) LLC, Penguin Group (USA) LLC, a Penguin Random House company

Periplus Editions, *imprint of* Tuttle Publishing, *distributed by* Tuttle Publishing

Periscope, *distributed by* Prestel Publishing

Perma-Bound, *distributor for* Ozark Publishing Inc

Permanent Publications, *distributed by* Chelsea Green Publishing Co

Permuted Press LLC, *distributed by* Simon & Schuster, Inc, Simon & Schuster Sales Division

Persea Books, *distributor for* Ontario Review Press, *distributed by* W W Norton & Co (worldwide exc Canada), Penguin Books (Canada only)

Persea Books Inc, *distributed by* W W Norton & Company Inc

Persephone Books, *distributed by* Dufour Editions Inc

Persephone Press, *imprint of* Birch Brook Press, *distributed by* Birch Brook Press

Perseus Academic, *distributed by* The Brookings Institution Press

Perseus (Addison Wesley Trade), *distributed by* HarperCollins Publishers

Perseus Books Group, *distributor for* Arcade Publishing Inc, Wide World Publishing

The Perseus Books Group, *distributor for* Da Capo Press & Lifelong Books, Merloyd Lawrence Inc, *distributed by* NOW, Perseus Distribution Services

Perseus Books Group-International Sales, *distributor for* Avalon Travel Publishing

Perseus Distribution Services, *distributor for* The Perseus Books Group

Perseverance Press, *distributed by* John Daniel & Co

Personal Profiles, *division of* Brown Books Publishing Group

Peterson Institute for International Economics (PIIE), *distributor for* Center for Global Development, *distributed by* DA Information Services (Australia, New Zealand & Papua New Guinea), East West Export Books (Cambodia, China, Indonesia, Japan, Philippines, Singapore, Taiwan, Thailand & Vietnam), The Eurospan Group (Africa, Eastern & Western Europe, Iran, Israel, Russia & Turkey), Renouf Bookstore (Canada), United Publishers Services Ltd (Japan & Republic of Korea), Viva Books PVT (Bangladesh, India, Nepal & Sri Lanka)

Peterson's/Pacesetter Books, *imprint of* Peterson's, a Nelnet Company

Petroleum Extension Service (PETEX), *division of* University of Texas

Pfeiffer, *imprint of* Jossey-Bass, John Wiley & Sons Inc

Pferdia TV, *distributed by* Trafalgar Square Books

Pflaum Publishing Group, *division of* Peter Li Inc

PGUK / Hi Marketing, *distributor for* National Geographic Books

Phaidon Press, *distributed by* Hachette Book Group

Phaidon Press Inc, *subsidiary of* Phaidon Press Ltd, *distributor for* Mitchell Beazley, Electa

Phantom Books & Music, *imprint of* Empire Publishing Service

Phaze Books, *imprint of* Mundania Press LLC

Philadelphia Museum of Art, *distributed by* Yale University Press

Philedition, *distributed by* Casemate Publishers & Book Distributors LLC

Philomel, *imprint of* Penguin Group (USA) LLC, Penguin Group (USA) LLC, a Penguin Random House company, Penguin Young Readers Group

Philomel Books, *imprint of* Penguin Group (USA) LLC, a Penguin Random House company

Philosophical Library Inc, *distributed by* Open Road Integrated Media

Philosophy Documentation Center, *distributor for* Zeta Books (online access)

Phoenix International, *distributed by* The University of Arkansas Press

Phoenix Mapping Service, *division of* Wide World of Maps Inc

Phoenix Press, *distributed by* AK Press Distribution, Sterling Publishing Co Inc

Phoenix Publishing, *distributed by* CN Times Books

Pholiota Press Inc, *distributed by* Cross-Cultural Communications

Phonics Adventure, *imprint of* Advance Publishing Inc

Photofact®, *imprint of* SAMS Technical Publishing LLC

Photolucida Book, *distributed by* Franklin, Beedle & Associates Inc

Photosmith Books, *distributed by* Caxton Press

Daniela Piazza Editore, *distributed by* Chelsea Green Publishing Co

Picador, *subsidiary of* Macmillan

Picaro Publishing, *distributed by* Sunbelt Publications Inc

Picasso Project, *division of* Alan Wofsy Fine Arts, Alan Wofsy Fine Arts, *distributor for* Cramer (Switzerland), Kornfeld (Switzerland), Ramie (France), *distributed by* Alan Wofsy Fine Arts

The Picasso Project, *imprint of* Alan Wofsy Fine Arts

Pickering & Chatto, *distributed by* Ashgate Publishing Co

Picton Press, *subsidiary of* Picton Corp

Pictorial Histories Publishing Co, *distributed by* Heimburger House Publishing Co

Picture Book Press, *distributed by* Enfield Publishing & Distribution Co

Picture Me Books™, *imprint of* Playhouse Publishing

Picture, Play & Tote™, *imprint of* Playhouse Publishing

PictureProfits® Tool Kit, *distributed by* Copywriter's Council of America (CCA)

Picture Window Books, *imprint of* Capstone Publishers™

Picture Yearling, *imprint of* Penguin Random House Inc

Pie Books, *imprint of* Rizzoli International Publications Inc

Pieces of Learning, *division of* Creative Learning Consultants Inc, Creative Learning Consultants Inc, *distributed by* ALPS Publishing, A W Peller & Associates, Professional Associate Publishing, Prufrock Press Inc

Piggyback Interactive, *distributed by* Simon & Schuster, Inc, Simon & Schuster Sales Division

Pikachu Press, *distributed by* Simon & Schuster, Inc

Pilgrim Publications, *distributor for* Christian Focus, Fox River Press, Hess Publications

Pimlseur Language Programs, *imprint of* Recorded Books LLC

Pimsleur, *imprint of* Simon & Schuster Audio

Pinata Books, *imprint of* Arte Publico Press

Pine Forest Publishing, *distributed by* Finney Company Inc

Pine Forge Press, *subsidiary of* SAGE Publications Inc, *imprint of* SAGE Publications

Pine Street Books, *imprint of* University of Pennsylvania Press

Pine Winds Press, *imprint of* Idyll Arbor Inc

Pinnacle Books, *imprint of* Kensington Publishing Corp

Pinyon Publishing, *distributed by* Gem Guides Book Co

Pioneer Press, *imprint of* Cedar Fort Inc

Pir Press, *distributed by* Fons Vitae

PJD Electronic Publishing, *division of* PJD Publications Ltd

PK, *distributor for* The Jim Henson Co

Plain Sight Publishing, *imprint of* Cedar Fort Inc

Planeta Peninsula, *distributed by* Sunbelt Publications Inc

Platinum Press, *imprint of* Adams Media

Platypus Media LLC, *affiliate of* Science, Naturally!™

Player Press A/Z Ltd, *division of* Players Press Inc

Player Press Ltd (UK), *division of* Players Press Inc

Players Press, *imprint of* Players Press Inc

Players Press (Canada), *division of* Players Press Inc

Players Press Inc, *distributor for* Camelion Plays, Garland-Clark Editors, Macmillan Education (UK), Preston Editions

Playwrights Canada Press, *distributed by* Theatre Communications Group

Pleasure Boat Studio: A Literary Press, *distributor for* Empty Bowl Press

Plenum, *distributed by* Specialty Press Inc

Plexus Books, *imprint of* Plexus Publishing, Inc

Plexus Publishing, Inc, *affiliate of* Information Today, Inc

PLI, *imprint of* Practising Law Institute, *distributor for* Practising Law Institute

Ploughshares, *subsidiary of* Ploughshares Inc

Plum Blossom Books, *imprint of* Parallax Press

Plum Tree Books, *imprint of* Classical Academic Press, Classical Academic Press LLC

Plumbago Books, *imprint of* Boydell & Brewer Inc

Plume, *division of* Penguin Group (USA) LLC, Penguin Group (USA) LLC, a Penguin Random House company, *imprint of* Penguin Group (USA) LLC, a Penguin Random House company

Pluto Press, *distributed by* Palgrave Macmillan

PMP, *imprint of* Paramount Market Publishing Inc

Pocket, *distributor for* Parachute Publishing LLC

Pocket Books Trade Paperback, *imprint of* Gallery Books

Pocket Guides Publishing, *distributed by* Adventure Publications

Pocket Star, *imprint of* Gallery Books

Pogo Press, *imprint of* Finney Company Inc

Pogo Press Inc, *imprint of* Finney Company Inc

Point, *imprint of* Scholastic Trade Division

Poison Vine Books, *imprint of* Elderberry Press Inc, *distributed by* Elderberry Press Inc

Poisoned Pen Press, *imprint of* Poisoned Pen Press

The Poisoned Pencil, *imprint of* Poisoned Pen Press

Polebridge Press, *division of* Westar Institute

Polestar Calendars, *distributed by* Orca Book Publishers

Political Risk Services, *imprint of* The PRS Group Inc

Polka Dot Press, *imprint of* Adams Media

Pollyanna Productions, *distributed by* Gryphon House Inc

Polyface, *distributed by* Chelsea Green Publishing Co

PomegranateKids, *imprint of* Pomegranate Communications Inc

Pond Frog Editions, *imprint of* Red Moon Press

Poplar Books, *imprint of* Book Sales Inc

Poppy, *imprint of* Little, Brown Books for Young Readers

Popular Press, *imprint of* University of Wisconsin Press

Popular Technology, *imprint of* Branden Books

Popular Woodworking Books, *imprint of* Betterway Books

Portavoz, *distributed by* Editorial Bautista Independiente

Neal Porter Books, *imprint of* Roaring Brook Press

Portfolio, *subsidiary of* Penguin Group (USA) LLC, Penguin Group (USA) LLC, a Penguin Random House company, *imprint of* Penguin Group (USA) LLC, a Penguin Random House company

Portnoy Publishing, *distributed by* Dufour Editions Inc

Portraits of America, *imprint of* The Donning Company Publishers

Portsmouth Marine Society, *distributed by* Enfield Publishing & Distribution Co

Possibility Press, *imprint of* Markowski International Publishers

Post Hill Press LLC, *distributed by* Simon & Schuster, Inc, Simon & Schuster Sales Division

Potomac Books, *imprint of* University of Nebraska Press

Potomac Books Inc, *imprint of* University of Nebraska Press

Clarkson Potter Publishers, *imprint of* Crown Publishing Group, *distributor for* The Colonial Williamsburg Foundation, *distributed by* Random House

Potter Craft, *imprint of* Crown Publishing Group, Clarkson Potter Publishers

Potter Style, *imprint of* Crown Publishing Group, Clarkson Potter Publishers

Power Kids Press, *imprint of* The Rosen Publishing Group Inc

powerHouse Books, *division of* powerHouse Cultural Entertainment Inc, *distributor for* Antinous Press, Juno Books, MTV Press, Throckmorton Press, VH1 Press, Vice Books, *distributed by* Random House Publisher Services

Poynter Consulting, *division of* Para Publishing LLC

Practical Action, *distributed by* Stylus Publishing LLC

Practical Reviews®, *imprint of* Oakstone Publishing LLC

The Practical Therapist Series, *imprint of* Impact Publishers Inc

Practising Law Institute, *distributed by* PLI

Practitioners Publishing Co, *distributor for* AICPA Professional Publications

Praeger, *imprint of* ABC-CLIO

Prairie Classics, *imprint of* Trails Books

Prairie Oak Press, *imprint of* Trails Books

Emory Pratt, *distributor for* Primary Research Group Inc

Prayer Book Press Inc, *subsidiary of* Media Judaica Inc, Media Judaica Inc

Prensa Pensar, *imprint of* Progressive Press

Prentice Hall, *distributor for* American Geosciences Institute (AGI), Manning Publications Co, *distributed by* American Academy of Environmental Engineers & Scientists™, NACE International, Society of Manufacturing Engineers

Prentice-Hall, *distributed by* SAS Publishing

Prentice Hall Press, *division of* Penguin Group (USA) LLC, Penguin Group (USA) LLC, a Penguin Random House company, *imprint of* Berkley Publishing Group

PREP Publishing, *subsidiary of* PREP Inc, PREP Inc

Presbyterian Publishing Corp (PPC), *distributor for* Epworth, SCM, *distributed by* Spring Arbor Distributors

Presidio Press, *imprint of* Random House Publishing Group

The Press at California State University, Fresno, *unit of* California State University, Fresno

The Press for Humanitarian Causes, *imprint of* Flying Pen Press LLC

Theodore Presser Co, *distributor for* Editions Orphee Inc

Prestel Publishing, *distributor for* Die Gestalten Verlag (DGV), Loft, Lars Muller, Periscope, Schirmer/Mosel

Preston Editions, *distributed by* Players Press Inc

Pretend & Play™, *imprint of* Playhouse Publishing

Price Stern Sloan, *imprint of* Penguin Group (USA) LLC, Penguin Group (USA) LLC, a Penguin Random House company, Penguin Young Readers Group

Price Stern Sloan Inc, *imprint of* Penguin Group (USA) LLC, a Penguin Random House company

Price World Publishing, *distributed by* David Bateman Ltd (New Zealand), Cardinal Publishers Group (US), Fortytwo Bookz Galaxy (India)

Prima Games, *imprint of* Random House Information Group

Primary Research Group Inc, *distributed by* Academic Book Center, Ambassador Books, The Book House, Coutts Library Service, Croft House Books, Eastern Book Company, MarketResearch.com, Midwest Library Service, OPAMP Technical Books, Emory Pratt, Research & Markets, Rittenhouse Book Distributors, Total Information, Yankee Book Peddler

Primary Source Media™, *imprint of* Gale

Prime Crime, *imprint of* Berkley Books, Berkley Publishing Group

Primer Publications, *distributed by* Gem Guides Book Co

Princeton Architectural Press, *distributor for* Balcony Press, Hyphen Press, *distributed by* Chronicle Books, Chronicle Books LLC

Princeton Book Co Publishers, *distributor for* Dance Books Ltd, Dance Notation Bureau, *distributed by* Dance Books Ltd

Princeton Review, *distributed by* Penguin Random House Inc

The Princeton Review, *imprint of* Penguin Random House Inc, Random House Information Group

Princeton University Art Museum, *distributed by* Yale University Press

Princeton University Press, *distributor for* National Gallery of Art, University of California Institute on Global Conflict & Cooperation

Principles in Practice, *imprint of* National Council of Teachers of English (NCTE)

Pro Ed, *distributed by* Council for Exceptional Children (CEC)

Pro-Ed, *distributor for* Psychological Assessment Resources Inc (PAR), *distributed by* Psychological Assessment Resources Inc (PAR)

Proceedings, *imprint of* American Philosophical Society

Process Media, *imprint of* Feral House

Prodist, *imprint of* Watson Publishing International LLC

Productivity Press, *division of* Taylor & Francis Group, *distributor for* American Society for Quality (ASQ), Society of Manufacturing Engineers

Productivity Press Spanish Imprint, *imprint of* Productivity Press

Professional Associate Publishing, *distributor for* Pieces of Learning

Professional Book Publishing, *division of* Slack Incorporated

Professional Development, *division of* Scholastic Education

The Professional Education Group Inc (PEG), *subsidiary of* CredibleLaw, *distributor for* ALI-ABA, American Bar Association, ASPEN, *distributed by* ALI-ABA, American Bar Association

Professional Practices, *imprint of* Krieger Publishing Co

Professional Publications, *distributed by* NACE International

Professional Publications Inc (PPI), *distributor for* American Association of State Highway & Transportation Officials, American Wood Council (American Forest & Paper Association) (National Design Specification for Wood Construction (NDS) & others), International Code Council, McGraw-Hill Professional (green building, design & construction titles, LEED titles), National Council of Examiners for Engineering & Surveying, SmartPros, Transportation Research Board Code, US Green Building Council (LEED reference guides)

Professional Resource Press, *imprint of* Professional Resource Exchange Inc

Professors World Peace Academy, *distributed by* Paragon House

Progressive Press, *imprint of* Progressive Press, *distributor for* Global Research

Prologue Books, *imprint of* F+W, A Content + eCommerce Company

Prompt Publications, *distributed by* SAMS Technical Publishing LLC

Proper Romance, *imprint of* Shadow Mountain

ProQuest LLC, *subsidiary of* Cambridge Information Group Inc

Provenance Press, *imprint of* Adams Media

Providence Athenaeum, *distributed by* Oak Knoll Press

Providence Press, *division of* Hope Publishing Co

Providence Publishing, *distributor for* Country Music Foundation Press

Prufrock Press, *distributed by* Sourcebooks Inc

Prufrock Press Inc, *distributor for* Pieces of Learning

Phil R Pryde, *distributed by* Sunbelt Publications Inc

PS&E Publications, *imprint of* Bartleby Press

PSG, *imprint of* Elsevier, Health Sciences Division

PSS, *imprint of* Grosset & Dunlap, Penguin Young Readers Group

Psychological Assessment Resources Inc (PAR), *distributor for* American Guidance Service, Pro-Ed, The Psychological Corp, Riverside Publishing, Rorschach Workshops, *distributed by* ACER, Pro-Ed, The Psychological Corp, Riverside Publishing, Western Psychological Service

The Psychological Corp, *distributor for* Psychological Assessment Resources Inc (PAR), *distributed by* Psychological Assessment Resources Inc (PAR)

Psychology Press, *imprint of* Routledge/Taylor & Francis, Taylor & Francis Group, Taylor & Francis Inc

Public Access Broadcasting, *division of* Unarius Academy of Science Publications

Public Affairs, *distributed by* HarperCollins Publishers

Public Citizen, *distributed by* Addison Wesley, Simon & Schuster Pocket Books

Public History, *imprint of* Krieger Publishing Co

PublicAffairs, *member of* The Perseus Books Group, *imprint of* The Perseus Books Group

Publishers' Assistant, *imprint of* Upper Access Inc

Publishers Group Canada, *distributor for* Avalon Travel Publishing

Publishers Group West, *distributor for* Avalon Travel Publishing, Empire Press Media/Avant-Guide, Gault Millau Inc/Gayot Publications, Naval Institute Press, Tuttle Publishing, Ulysses Press

Publishers Group West (PGW), *distributor for* Black Classic Press, Kalmbach Publishing Co

Publisher's Stone Publications, *distributed by* Florida Academic Press

Publishers Support Services, *division of* Five Star Publications Inc

Publishers Trade Secrets Library, *imprint of* Copywriter's Council of America (CCA)

Publishing Poynters Newsletter, *division of* Para Publishing LLC

Publishing Services, *division of* Scholastic Education

Pueblo Books, *imprint of* Liturgical Press

Coleccion Puertorriquena, *imprint of* University of Puerto Rico Press

Puffin, *imprint of* Penguin Group (USA) LLC, a Penguin Random House company

Puffin Books, *imprint of* Penguin Group (USA) LLC, Penguin Group (USA) LLC, a Penguin Random House company, Penguin Young Readers Group

Punch Press, *imprint of* Loft Press Inc

PUP Books, *imprint of* Purdue University Press

Purple House Press, *imprint of* Purple House Inc

Purple Mountain Press Ltd, *distributor for* Carmania Press London (North America only)

Purple Pomegranate Productions, *division of* Jews for Jesus

PUSH, *imprint of* Scholastic Trade Division

Pushcart Press, *distributed by* W W Norton & Co Inc, W W Norton & Company Inc

Putnam, *imprint of* Penguin Group (USA) LLC, a Penguin Random House company, GP Putnam's Sons (Hardcover)

Putnam Adult, *imprint of* The Putnam Publishing Group

Putnam Berkley Audio, *imprint of* Penguin Group (USA) LLC, Penguin Group (USA) LLC, a Penguin Random House company, The Putnam Publishing Group, GP Putnam's Sons (Hardcover), *distributor for* Arkangel

Putnam Juvenile, *imprint of* The Putnam Publishing Group

The Putnam Publishing Group, *division of* Penguin Group (USA) LLC, Penguin Group (USA) LLC, a Penguin Random House company

G P Putnam's Sons, *imprint of* Penguin Young Readers Group

GP Putnam's Sons (Children's), *member of* Penguin Young Readers Group

GP Putnam's Sons (Hardcover), *imprint of* Penguin Group (USA) LLC, Penguin Group (USA) LLC, a Penguin Random House company

Puzzlewright Press, *imprint of* Sterling Publishing Co Inc

PWN, *imprint of* Summertime Publications Inc

PWPA Books, *imprint of* Paragon House

PYO (Publish Your Own Co), *imprint of* Hearts & Tummies Cookbook Co

Pyr, *imprint of* Prometheus Books

QDS, *imprint of* Quarto Publishing Group USA Inc

QED Press, *imprint of* Cypress House

Qiblah Books, *distributed by* Fons Vitae

QMP, *imprint of* Quality Medical Publishing Inc

Quadrille Publishing, *distributed by* Chronicle Books LLC

Quality Books, *distributor for* Do-It-Yourself Legal Publishers

Quantuck Lane Press, *distributed by* W W Norton & Company Inc

Quarry Books, *imprint of* Indiana University Press, Quarto Publishing Group USA Inc

Quartet Books (UK), *distributed by* Interlink Publishing Group Inc

Quarto Books, *distributed by* Krause Publications Inc

Quarto Publishing, *distributed by* Hachette Book Group

Quarto Publishing Group USA Inc, *subsidiary of* Quarto Group Inc, Quarto Group Inc (London, UK), *distributed by* Allen & Unwin (Australia & New Zealand)

Quayside Distribution Services, *division of* Quarto Publishing Group USA Inc

Quercus Books, *distributed by* Hachette Book Group

Quest Books, *imprint of* Regal Crest Enterprises LLC, Theosophical Publishing House/Quest Books

Quest for Success, *imprint of* Advance Publishing Inc

Quick Reference Publishing, *distributed by* Sunbelt Publications Inc

QuickScan Reviews®, *imprint of* Oakstone Publishing LLC

Quill Driver Books, *imprint of* Linden Publishing Co Inc

Quill House Publishers, *imprint of* Kirk House Publishers

Quill Trade Paperbacks, *imprint of* HarperCollins Publishers

Quiller, *distributed by* Safari Press

Quiller Press Ltd, *distributed by* Stackpole Books

Quilliam Press, *distributed by* Fons Vitae

Quintessence Books, *imprint of* Quintessence Publishing Co Inc

Quintessence of Dental Technology, *imprint of* Quintessence Publishing Co Inc

Quintessence Pockets, *imprint of* Quintessence Publishing Co Inc

Quintessence Publishing Co Inc, *distributor for* Quintessence Publishing Co Ltd (Japan), Quintessence Publishing Ltd (London), Quintessence Verlags GmbH

Quintessence Publishing Co Ltd (Japan), *distributed by* Quintessence Publishing Co Inc

Quintessence Publishing Ltd (London), *distributed by* Quintessence Publishing Co Inc

Quintessence Verlags GmbH, *distributed by* Quintessence Publishing Co Inc

Quirk Books, *distributed by* Random House Publisher Services

Quite Specific Media Group Ltd, *distributor for* The Colonial Williamsburg Foundation

Quixote Press, *imprint of* Hearts & Tummies Cookbook Co

Quiz Master Books, *imprint of* Trails Books

Quodlibetal Features, *distributed by* Vandamere Press

Qwikguide, *imprint of* Mel Bay Publications Inc

R & B Food & Culture Production, *distributed by* Sunbelt Publications Inc

RAB Desire, *imprint of* Riverdale Avenue Books (RAB)

RAB HSF, *imprint of* Riverdale Avenue Books (RAB)

RAB Pop, *imprint of* Riverdale Avenue Books (RAB)

RAB Truth, *imprint of* Riverdale Avenue Books (RAB)

Rabbinical Assembly of America, *distributed by* United Synagogue Book Service

Rabbit's Foot Press™, *imprint of* Blue Mountain Arts Inc

Race Point Publishing, *imprint of* Quarto Publishing Group USA Inc

Radiant Life Curriculum, *imprint of* Gospel Publishing House (GPH)

Radio Theatre, *imprint of* Focus on the Family

Radix Press, *subsidiary of* UGF/OR

Raefield-Roberts, Publishers, *distributed by* Parenting Press Inc

Ragged Mountain Press, *imprint of* McGraw-Hill Professional

Raid, *imprint of* Osprey Publishing Inc

Rainbow Bridge Publishing, *imprint of* Carson-Dellosa Publishing LLC

Rainbow Ridge Books, *distributed by* Square One Publishers Inc

Raincoast Books, *distributor for* Sourcebooks Inc

Rainsource Press, *distributed by* Chelsea Green Publishing Co

Raise the Dough in 30 Days Co, *imprint of* Quixote Press

Raising Lucy Studios LLC, *distributed by* Epicenter Press Inc

Raleigh Press, *distributed by* Epicenter Press Inc

Ram Publishing, *distributed by* Gem Guides Book Co

Ram Publishing Co, *subsidiary of* Garrett Electronics

Ramakrishna Math, *distributed by* Vedanta Press

Ramanujan Mathematical Society, *distributed by* American Mathematical Society

Ramie (France), *distributed by* Picasso Project

Ramsey & Todd, *imprint of* Turner Publishing Co

Rand McNally, *distributor for* Wide World of Maps Inc, *distributed by* Wide World of Maps Inc

Rand McNally for Kids, *imprint of* Rand McNally

Peter E Randall Publisher, *distributed by* University Press of New England

Random House, *imprint of* Penguin Random House Inc, Random House Publishing Group, *distributor for* Frog Books, The Jim Henson Co, National Geographic Books, National Geographic Society, Osprey Publishing Inc, Parachute Publishing LLC, Clarkson Potter Publishers, Rizzoli International Publications Inc, Smithsonian Scholarly Press, Soho Press Inc, Universe Publishing, Welcome Books®, Wizards of the Coast LLC, *distributed by* Sunbelt Publications Inc

Random House Books for Young Readers, *imprint of* Penguin Random House Inc, Random House Children's Books

Random House Children's Books, *division of* Penguin Random House Inc, Random House Inc, *distributor for* The Colonial Williamsburg Foundation

Random House Children's Publishing, *imprint of* Penguin Random House Inc

Random House Digital, *imprint of* Penguin Random House Inc

Random House/Golden Books Young Readers Group, *division of* Random House Children's Books

Random House Inc, *distributor for* Alloy Entertainment LLC, Other Press LLC, Shambhala Publications Inc, *distributed by* DawnSignPress, Learning Links Inc

Random House Large Print, *division of* Penguin Random House Inc, Random House Inc, *distributed by* Thorndike Press

Random House Large Print Publishing, *imprint of* Penguin Random House Inc

Random House Publisher Services, *distributor for* Beacon Press, powerHouse Books, Quirk Books

Random House Publisher Services (RHPS), *distributor for* DC Entertainment

Random House Publishing Group, *division of* Penguin Random House Inc, Random House Inc

Random House Reference & Information Publishing, *imprint of* Penguin Random House Inc

Random House Reference/Random House Puzzles & Games/House of Collectibles, *imprint of* Penguin Random House Inc, Random House Audio Publishing Group

Random House Websters, *imprint of* Random House Reference/Random House Puzzles & Games/House of Collectibles

Ranger Rick Science Program, *imprint of* Sundance/Newbridge Publishing

Rangjung Yeshe Publications, *distributed by* North Atlantic Books

Rasmuson Library Historical Translation Series, *imprint of* University of Alaska Press

Raven Press, *distributed by* Chelsea Green Publishing Co

Raven Productions Inc, *distributed by* Adventure Publications

Raven Tree Press, *division of* Delta Publishing Co

Shannon Ravenel Books, *imprint of* Algonquin Books

Ravenhawk™ Books, *division of* The 6DOF Group, The 6DOF Group

Rayo, *imprint of* HarperCollins Children's Books, HarperCollins Publishers Sales

Razorbill, *imprint of* Penguin Group (USA) LLC, Penguin Group (USA) LLC, a Penguin Random House company

RCS Libri, *imprint of* Rizzoli International Publications Inc

RDV Books, *imprint of* Akashic Books

Reach for the Sky Publishing, *distributed by* Epicenter Press Inc

Reader's Digest, *distributed by* Fox Chapel Publishing Co Inc, Hal Leonard Corp

Reader's Digest Books, *distributed by* Simon & Schuster, Inc

Reader's Digest Children's Books, *distributor for* The Jim Henson Co, *distributed by* Simon & Schuster Sales Division

Reader's Digest General Books, *division of* The Reader's Digest Association Inc, The Reader's Digest Association Inc, *distributed by* Simon & Schuster

Reader's Digest Trade Books, *division of* Reader's Digest Association Inc, The Reader's Digest Association Inc, *distributed by* Simon & Schuster

Reader's Digest USA Select Editions, *division of* The Reader's Digest Association Inc

Reading Success, *imprint of* Advance Publishing Inc

Read'n Run Books, *imprint of* Crumb Elbow Publishing

Ready Reader Storybooks, *imprint of* Modern Publishing

REAL Phonics™, *imprint of* Broden Books LLC

Real Story Series, *distributed by* Common Courage Press

Rebel Arts, *imprint of* Gingko Press Inc, *distributed by* Gingko Press Inc

Rebel Base Books, *imprint of* Kensington Publishing Corp

Rebel Inc, *distributed by* AK Press Distribution

Rebel Press, *distributed by* AK Press Distribution

Rebellion, *distributed by* Simon & Schuster Sales Division

Rebellion Publishing, *distributed by* Simon & Schuster, Inc

Rebuilding Books, *imprint of* Impact Publishers Inc

The Reconstructionist Press, *distributed by* Fordham University Press

Record Research, *distributed by* Hal Leonard Corp

Recorded Books Audiolibros, *imprint of* Recorded Books LLC

Recorded Books Evergreen, *imprint of* Recorded Books LLC

Recorded Books Inspirational, *imprint of* Recorded Books LLC

Recorded Books LLC, *distributor for* Buena Vista DVDs, The Film Movement DVDs

Recovered Classics, *imprint of* McPherson & Co

Recreation Sales, *distributed by* Gem Guides Book Co

Red Anvil Press, *imprint of* Elderberry Press Inc, *distributed by* Elderberry Press Inc

Red Chair Press, *distributed by* Lerner Publishing, Lerner Publishing Group Inc

Red Dress Ink, *imprint of* Harlequin Enterprises Ltd

Red Lead Press, *imprint of* Dorrance Publishing Co Inc

Red Mansions Publishing, *distributed by* China Books

Red Portal Press, *imprint of* Mighty Media Press

Red River Books, *imprint of* The RoadRunner Press

Red Wheel/Weiser Books/Conari Press, *distributor for* Hampton Roads Publishing Co

Red Wheel/Weiser/Conari, *distributor for* Nicolas Hays Inc

Red Wheel-Weiser Inc, *distributed by* Moznaim Publishing Corp

Redemptorist Publications, *distributed by* Liguori Publications

Redhook, *imprint of* Orbit

Redleaf Press, *division of* Think Small, *distributed by* Pademelon Press Pty Ltd (Australia)

Redwing Book Co, *distributor for* Blue Poppy Press

Redwood Press, *imprint of* Stanford University Press

Referee Books, *imprint of* Referee Enterprises Inc

Reference Press, *distributor for* World Trade Press

Regal Books, *division of* Gospel Light

Regal Crest, *imprint of* Regal Crest Enterprises LLC

Regan Arts, *distributed by* Simon & Schuster, Inc, Simon & Schuster Sales Division

Regan Books, *imprint of* HarperCollins Publishers Sales

Regents External Degree Series, *imprint of* National Learning Corp

Registry of Guitar Tutors (RGT), *distributed by* Mel Bay Publications Inc

Regnery, *imprint of* Regnery Publishing Inc

Regnery History, *imprint of* Regnery Publishing Inc

Regnery Publishing Inc, *subsidiary of* Eagle Publishing Inc

Regular Baptist Press, *division of* General Association of Regular Baptist Churches

RELS Press, *imprint of* Plowshare Media

Renaissance House, *imprint of* Laredo Publishing Co Inc, *distributed by* SRA/McGraw-Hill

Renaissance Press, *distributed by* University of Hawaii Press

Renegade Enterprises, *distributed by* Sunbelt Publications Inc

Renewing the Heart, *imprint of* Focus on the Family

Renouf Bookstore, *distributor for* Peterson Institute for International Economics (PIIE)

Research, *division of* Scholastic Education

Research & Markets, *distributor for* Primary Research Group Inc

Research & Special Programs Administration of the US Department of Transportation, *distributed by* J J Keller & Associates, Inc

Research Centrex, *imprint of* Crumb Elbow Publishing

Researchandmarkets.com, *distributor for* Apollo Managed Care Inc

Resilient Publishing, *distributor for* Anderson Design, Brynwood Publishing

Resources for the Future, *distributed by* The Johns Hopkins University Press

Resurgence, *imprint of* Tyndale House Publishers Inc

Resurrection Press, *imprint of* Catholic Book Publishing Corp

Retold Classics, *imprint of* Perfection Learning Corp

Retro Science Fiction, *imprint of* Gateways Books & Tapes

RetroRomance™, *imprint of* Samhain Publishing Ltd

Retrospect Publishing, *distributed by* Closson Press

Revell, *division of* Baker Publishing Group

RGB Arte Visual, *distributed by* Mel Bay Publications Inc

Ribbits, *imprint of* Focus on the Family

Ricordi, *distributed by* Hal Leonard Corp

G Ricordi (Italy), *distributor for* Pendragon Press

Riebel-Roque, *distributed by* Casemate Publishers & Book Distributors LLC

Lynne Rienner Publishers Inc, *distributor for* Center for US-Mexican Studies, Ayebia Clarke Publishing Ltd (African lit), St Andrews Center for Syrian Studies

Rigby, *imprint of* Harcourt Inc, Houghton Mifflin Harcourt K-12 Publishers

Riley & Johnson, *distributed by* Business Research Services Inc

Ringing Bell Press, *distributed by* Franklin, Beedle & Associates Inc

Rio Chico, *imprint of* Rio Nuevo Publishers

Rio Grande Books, *imprint of* LPD Press

Ripley Entertainment, *distributed by* Simon & Schuster Sales Division

Ripley Entertainment Inc, *distributed by* Simon & Schuster, Inc

Rittenhouse, *distributor for* Teton NewMedia

Rittenhouse Book Distributors, *distributor for* Primary Research Group Inc

Rivendale Press, *distributed by* Oak Knoll Press

River City Kids, *imprint of* River City Publishing LLC

River Grove Books, *imprint of* Greenleaf Book Group LLC

River North, *imprint of* Moody Publishers

Riverdale Ave Books/Magnus Books, *imprint of* Riverdale Avenue Books (RAB)

Riverhead Books, *imprint of* Penguin Group (USA) LLC, a Penguin Random House company, The Putnam Publishing Group

Riverhead Books (Hardcover), *imprint of* Penguin Group (USA) LLC, Penguin Group (USA) LLC, a Penguin Random House company

Riverhead Books (Paperback), *imprint of* Berkley Publishing Group

Riverhead Books (Trade Paperback), *imprint of* Penguin Group (USA) LLC, Penguin Group (USA) LLC, a Penguin Random House company

Riverside Publishing, *subsidiary of* Houghton Mifflin Harcourt, Houghton Mifflin Harcourt Publishing Co, *distributor for* Psychological Assessment Resources Inc (PAR), *distributed by* Psychological Assessment Resources Inc (PAR)

RiverWood Books, *imprint of* White Cloud Press

Rizzoli, *distributed by* Penguin Random House Inc

Rizzoli First, *imprint of* Rizzoli International Publications Inc

Rizzoli International Publications Inc, *subsidiary of* RCS Rizzoli Corp New York, RCS Rizzoli Corp New York, *distributor for* Editions Flammarion, Skira Editore, *distributed by* Random House

Rizzoli, New York, *imprint of* Rizzoli International Publications Inc

RLO Media Productions, *distributed by* Epicenter Press Inc

Road Dog Publications, *imprint of* Lost Classics Book Company LLC

The RoadRunner Press, *imprint of* The RoadRunner Press

Roadside Geology Series, *imprint of* Mountain Press Publishing Co

Roadside History Series, *imprint of* Mountain Press Publishing Co

Roaring Brook Press, *member of* Macmillan Children's Publishing Group

Lee Roberts Publications, *distributed by* Hal Leonard Corp

Robins Lane Press, *distributed by* Gryphon House Inc

Roc, *imprint of* NAL, Penguin Group (USA) LLC, a Penguin Random House company

Rock Point Gift & Stationery, *imprint of* Quarto Publishing Group USA Inc

Rockbottom Book Co, *distributor for* ABDO Publishing Group

Rockefeller Institute Press, *distributed by* State University of New York Press

The Rockefeller University Press, *unit of* Rockefeller University

Rockhurst University Press, *distributed by* Fordham University Press

Rockport Publishers, *imprint of* Quarto Publishing Group USA Inc

Rocky River Publishers LLC, *distributed by* C E Mendez Foundation Inc

Rodale, *distributor for* The Colonial Williamsburg Foundation, *distributed by* St Martin's Press, LLC

Rodale Inc, *distributed by* Macmillan

Anita Roddick Publications, *distributed by* Chelsea Green Publishing Co

Roman Catholic Books, *division of* Catholic Media Apostolate Inc

Romantic Sounds Audio, *imprint of* Recorded Books LLC

Romantic Weekends, *imprint of* Hunter Publishing Inc

Roncorp Music, *division of* Northeastern Music Publications

Roost Books, *imprint of* Shambhala Publications Inc

RoperPenberthy Publishing Ltd, *distributed by* Bridge-Logos Inc

Rorschach Workshops, *distributed by* Psychological Assessment Resources Inc (PAR)

Rose Dog Books, *imprint of* Dorrance Publishing Co Inc

Fr Seraphim Rose Foundation, *imprint of* Saint Herman Press

Rosebud Books, *imprint of* Raven Productions Inc

Rosen Classroom Books & Materials, *division of* The Rosen Publishing Group Inc

Rossel Books, *distributed by* Behrman House Inc

Roth Family Foundation, *imprint of* University of California Press

Rothko Chapel, *distributed by* University of Texas Press

Rothstein Publishing, *division of* Rothstein Associates Inc

Rough Guides, *subsidiary of* Pearson PLC, *distributed by* Penguin Group (USA) LLC

The Rough Notes Co Inc, *subsidiary of* Insurance Publishing Plus Corp, Insurance Publishing Plus Corp

Round Table Comics, *imprint of* Writers of the Round Table Press

Rourke Publishing, *distributed by* Ideals Publications, a Guideposts Co

Route, *distributed by* Dufour Editions Inc

Routledge, *imprint of* Routledge/Taylor & Francis, Taylor & Francis Inc

Routledge/Taylor & Francis, *member of* Taylor & Francis Group, *distributor for* David Fulton Books

Rowman & Littlefield, *distributor for* American Council on Education, Bucknell University Press, The Colonial Williamsburg Foundation, The CSIS Press, Fairleigh Dickinson University Press, Lehigh University Press, University of Delaware Press

Rowman & Littlefield Education, *distributor for* National Association for Music Education (NAfME)

Rowman & Littlefield Publishers Inc, *imprint of* Rowman & Littlefield Publishing Group

Roxbury Publishing, *distributed by* Oxford University Press USA

Royal Academy Publications, *distributed by* Harry N Abrams Inc

Royal Asiatic Society (Korea Branch), *distributed by* Cheng & Tsui Co Inc

Royal Fireworks Press, *distributor for* KAV Books, Silk Label Books, Trillium Press

Royal Historical Society, *imprint of* Boydell & Brewer Inc

Royal Society of Chemistry, *distributed by* The American Chemical Society

Royal Society of London, *distributed by* Scholium International Inc

Rubank Publications, *distributed by* Hal Leonard Corp

Rucksack Readers (UK), *distributed by* Interlink Publishing Group Inc

Rugged Land, *distributed by* Penguin Random House Inc

Raymond C Rumpf & Son Inc, *distributor for* Wilderness Adventures Press Inc

Rune-Tales, *imprint of* Quincannon Publishing Group

Running Press, *imprint of* The Perseus Books Group, Running Press Book Publishers, *distributor for* The Jim Henson Co, Parachute Publishing LLC

Running Press Book Publishers, *member of* The Perseus Books Group, *distributor for* Wine Enthusiast

Running Press Kids, *imprint of* The Perseus Books Group, Running Press Book Publishers

Running Press Miniature Editions, *imprint of* The Perseus Books Group, Running Press Book Publishers

Rural Science Institute, *distributed by* Chelsea Green Publishing Co

Rutgers Series in Accounting Research, *imprint of* Markus Wiener Publishers Inc

Rutgers University Press, *division of* Rutgers, The State University of New Jersey

RV Guides, *distributed by* American Map Corp

RV International Maps & Atlases, *distributed by* Hagstrom Map

Ryton Publications, *distributed by* Stackpole Books

RZM Publishing, *distributed by* Casemate Publishers & Book Distributors LLC

S A B D A, *distributed by* Lotus Press

S-A Design Books, *imprint of* CarTech Inc

S I Publicaties BV, *distributed by* Casemate Publishers & Book Distributors LLC

Sacred Music Press, *imprint of* Transcontinental Music Publications

Saddleback Educational, *distributor for* Teachers of English to Speakers of Other Languages Inc (TESOL)

Saddleback Educational Publishing, *distributed by* Children's Plus, Delaney

Sadhana Publications, *distributed by* Lotus Press

Sadlier, *division of* William H Sadlier Inc

Sadlier-Oxford, *division of* William H Sadlier Inc

SAE (Society of Automotive Engineers International), *distributor for* Coordinating Research Council Inc

Safari Press, *distributor for* Quiller

Safe Harbor Books, *distributed by* Enfield Publishing & Distribution Co

Safer Society Press, *imprint of* Safer Society Foundation Inc

Saga Press, *imprint of* Simon & Schuster Children's Publishing

Sagamore Publishing LLC, *distributor for* American Academy for Park & Recreation Administration

Sage Books, *imprint of* Genesis Press Inc

SAGE UK Resources for Educators, *distributed by* Corwin, a Sage Co

St Andrews Center for Syrian Studies, *distributed by* Lynne Rienner Publishers Inc

St Andrews College Press, *subsidiary of* St Andrews University

St Augustine's Press Inc, *distributor for* Dumb Ox Books (publishes the Aristotelian Commentaries of Thomas Aquinas & like works), Hardwood Press (trade books, mostly in sports & regional works), New Criterion Books (poetry prize), *distributed by* University of Chicago Press

St Bede's Publications, *distributed by* Fordham University Press

Saint Herman Press, *subsidiary of* Brotherhood of Saint Herman of Alaska, *distributed by* Light & Life Publishing Co

St Herman Press, *imprint of* Saint Herman Press

St James Press®, *imprint of* Gale

Saint Johann Press, *distributor for* MerwinAsia

St Louis Mercantile Library, *distributed by* University of Missouri Press

St Martin's Press, LLC, *subsidiary of* Macmillan, *distributor for* Berg Publishers, Bloomsbury USA, College Board, Manchester University Press, Palgrave Macmillan, Papercutz, Rodale, I B Tauris, Walker and Company, Zed Books

Saint Mary's Press, *subsidiary of* Christian Brothers Publications, *distributor for* Group Publishing

St Paisius Abbey, *imprint of* Saint Herman Press

St Paisius Missionary School, *imprint of* Saint Herman Press

St Pauls, *division of* The Society of Saint Paul

St Vladimir's, *distributor for* Ancient Faith Publishing

St Xenia Skete, *imprint of* Saint Herman Press

The Saints Series, *imprint of* Pauline Books & Media

Salaryia, *distributed by* Sterling Publishing Co Inc

Salem Press, *imprint of* Grey House Publishing Inc™, *distributor for* Schlager Group Inc

Salem Press Inc, *division of* EBSCO Information Services

Sales & Marketing, *division of* Scholastic Education

SalesSavvy.com, *subsidiary of* BizBest Media Corp

Salmon Poetry, *distributed by* Dufour Editions Inc

SaltRiver, *imprint of* Tyndale House Publishers Inc

Saltry Press, *distributed by* Epicenter Press Inc

Salubris Resources, *imprint of* Gospel Publishing House (GPH)

Samata Books, *distributed by* Lotus Press

Samhain Horror, *imprint of* Samhain Publishing Ltd

Samhain Romance, *imprint of* Samhain Publishing Ltd

SAMS Technical Publishing LLC, *division of* AGS Capital LLC, *distributor for* Butterworth Heinemann, McGraw-Hill, Prompt Publications

San Diego Architecture Foundation, *distributed by* Sunbelt Publications Inc

San Diego Association of Geologists, *distributed by* Sunbelt Publications Inc

San Diego City Works Press, *distributed by* Sunbelt Publications Inc

San Diego Natural History Museum, *distributed by* Sunbelt Publications Inc

San Diego Police Historical Association, *distributed by* Sunbelt Publications Inc

San Diego State University Press, *division of* San Diego State University Foundation, *distributor for* Institute for Regional Studies of the Californias

San Dieguito River Park Joint Powers Authority, *distributed by* Sunbelt Publications Inc

Coleccion San Pedrito, *imprint of* University of Puerto Rico Press

Sandala Productions, *distributed by* Fons Vitae

Sandcastle, *imprint of* ABDO Publishing Group

Sandpiper, *imprint of* Houghton Mifflin Harcourt Trade & Reference Division

Sandstone Press, *distributed by* Dufour Editions Inc

The Sandstone Press, *imprint of* Frederic C Beil Publisher Inc

Sandu Publications, *distributed by* Gingko Press Inc

Sandy Creek, *distributed by* Lerner Publishing Group Inc

Santillana, *imprint of* Santillana USA Publishing Co Inc

Santillana USA Publishing Co Inc, *division of* The Richmond Publishing Co Inc

Sapientia Press, *distributed by* The Catholic University of America Press

Sapling, *imprint of* Cedar Grove Books

Saraland Press, *distributed by* University of South Carolina Press

Saroff Editions, *imprint of* McPherson & Co

SAS Publishing, *imprint of* SAS Institute Inc, *distributor for* AMACOM Books, Breakfast Communications, CRC Press, Duxbury, Harcourt, Harvard Business School Press, McGraw-Hill, Oxford, Prentice-Hall, Springer, John Wiley & Sons Inc, *distributed by* John Wiley & Sons Inc

Satas, *distributor for* Blue Poppy Press

Saunders, *imprint of* Elsevier, Health Sciences Division, *distributed by* Oxford University Press USA

W B Saunders Co, *distributed by* Marine Techniques Publishing

The Sausage Maker, *distributed by* Stackpole Books

Savas Beatie, *distributed by* Casemate Publishers & Book Distributors LLC

Save Our Heritage Organization, *distributed by* Sunbelt Publications Inc

Alastair Sawday Publishing, *distributed by* The Globe Pequot Press

Saxon, *imprint of* Harcourt Inc, Houghton Mifflin Harcourt K-12 Publishers

SBL Press, *unit of* Society of Biblical Literature, *distributor for* Brown Judaic Studies, Sheffield Phoenix Press

Scala Publishers, *distributor for* American Federation of Arts

Scandalous, *imprint of* Entangled Publishing

Scarab Miniatures, *distributed by* Casemate Publishers & Book Distributors LLC

Lo Scarabeo, *distributed by* Llewellyn Publications

Scarecrow Press Inc, *imprint of* Rowman & Littlefield Publishing Group

Scarf Press, *distributed by* Bloch Publishing Co

SCB Distributors, *distributor for* Circlet Press Inc

Schaum, *imprint of* McGraw-Hill Professional

Schiffer, *imprint of* Schiffer Publishing Ltd, *distributor for* Winterthur Museum & Country Estate

Schiffer Fashion Press, *imprint of* Schiffer Publishing Ltd

Schiffer LTD, *imprint of* Schiffer Publishing Ltd

Schiffer Military History, *imprint of* Schiffer Publishing Ltd

Schiffer Publishing Ltd, *distributor for* The Donning Co

Schirmer, *imprint of* Wadsworth Publishing

E C Schirmer Music Co, *imprint of* ECS Publishing Corp

G Schirmer Inc (Associated Music Publishers), *distributed by* Hal Leonard Corp

Schirmer/Mosel, *distributed by* Prestel Publishing

Schirmer Reference™, *imprint of* Gale

Schirmer Trade Books, *imprint of* Music Sales Corp, *distributor for* Big Meteor Publishing, Independent Music Press

Schlager Group Inc, *distributed by* Salem Press (ref books only)

A Naomi Schneider Book, *imprint of* University of California Press

Schocken Books, *imprint of* Pantheon Books/ Schocken Books, Penguin Random House Inc

Scholarly Digital Editions, *imprint of* Boydell & Brewer Inc

Scholarly Resources Inc, *imprint of* Gale

Scholars' Facsimiles & Reprints, *subsidiary of* Academic Resources Corp, Academic Resources Corp

Scholastic, *distributor for* Parachute Publishing LLC, *distributed by* Learning Links Inc

Scholastic Asia, *subsidiary of* Scholastic International

Scholastic Australia Pty Ltd, *subsidiary of* Scholastic International

Scholastic Books, *distributor for* Alloy Entertainment LLC

Scholastic Canada Ltd, *subsidiary of* Scholastic International

Scholastic Education, *division of* Scholastic Inc

Scholastic en Espanol, *imprint of* Scholastic Trade Division

Scholastic Inc, *distributor for* The Colonial Williamsburg Foundation, Educational Impressions Inc

Scholastic International, *division of* Scholastic Inc

Scholastic Ltd UK, *subsidiary of* Scholastic International

Scholastic New Zealand, *distributor for* Big Guy Books Inc

Scholastic New Zealand Ltd, *subsidiary of* Scholastic International

Scholastic Nonfiction, *imprint of* Scholastic Trade Division

Scholastic Paperbacks, *imprint of* Scholastic Trade Division

Scholastic Press, *imprint of* Scholastic Trade Division

Scholastic Reference, *imprint of* Scholastic Trade Division

Scholastic-Tab Publications, *distributor for* Educational Impressions Inc

Scholastic Trade Division, *division of* Scholastic Inc

Editions Scholasticae, *distributed by* Transaction Publishers Inc

Scholium International Inc, *distributor for* Dechema Series, Macmillan (UK), Micelle Press, Royal Society of London, Zuckschwerdt Verlag (Munich, Germany)

School Express Press, *imprint of* Five Star Publications Inc

School of the Blues, *imprint of* Mel Bay Publications Inc

School of Government, *division of* The University of NC Chapel Hill

School Renaissance, *distributed by* Gryphon House Inc

School Speciality, *distributor for* MAR*CO Products Inc

SchoolBookings.com, *division of* Five Star Publications Inc

Schwartz & Wade Books, *imprint of* Penguin Random House Inc, Random House Children's Books

Sci-Fi Audio, *imprint of* Recorded Books LLC

Science & Humanities Press, *subsidiary of* Banis & Associates

Science History Publications USA, *imprint of* Watson Publishing International LLC

Science, Naturally!™, *affiliate of* Platypus Media

Science Press New York & Science Press Beijing, *distributed by* American Mathematical Society

Science Publishers Inc, *imprint of* Edenbridge Ltd, *distributed by* CRC Press

Scientific American, *imprint of* Farrar, Straus & Giroux, LLC

Scientific American Medicine, *distributor for* American College of Surgeons

Scitec Publications, *imprint of* Trans Tech Publications

Scitech Publishing Inc, *distributor for* Peninsula Publishing

SCM, *distributed by* Presbyterian Publishing Corp (PPC), Westminster John Knox Press (WJK)

Scobre Educational, *distributed by* Lerner Publishing Group Inc

Scolari, *division of* SAGE Publications

Scots Plaid Press, *imprint of* Old Barn Enterprises Inc

Scott Publishing Co, *division of* AMOS Publishing Co

Scottish Text Society, *imprint of* Boydell & Brewer Inc

Scott's Highland Services, *distributed by* Mel Bay Publications Inc

Scout Press, *imprint of* Gallery Books

Scribner, *imprint of* Scribner Publishing Group

Scribner Classics, *imprint of* Scribner

Scribner Poetry, *imprint of* Scribner

Scripta Humanistica Publishing International, *subsidiary of* Brumar Communications

Scripta-Technica, *imprint of* John Wiley & Sons Inc

Scythian Books, *imprint of* Berkeley Slavic Specialties

Sea-to-Sea Publishing, *imprint of* Black Rabbit Books

Seaboard Press, *imprint of* James A Rock & Co Publishers

Seaforth Publishing, *distributed by* Casemate Publishers & Book Distributors LLC

Seagrass Press, *imprint of* Quarto Publishing Group USA Inc

Seal Press, *imprint of* The Perseus Books Group

Sealife Research Alliance, *imprint of* Crumb Elbow Publishing

Search Institute Press®, *division of* Search Institute

Search Press, *distributor for* Interweave Press LLC

Seastone, *imprint of* Ulysses Press

Second Chance Press, *imprint of* The Permanent Press

Second Floor Music, *distributed by* Hal Leonard Corp

Second Story Press, *distributed by* Orca Book Publishers

Seed Savers, *distributed by* Chelsea Green Publishing Co

Seedling Publications Inc, *imprint of* Continental Press, Continental Press Inc, *distributed by* Kendall Hunt Publishing

Martin E Segal Theatre Center Publications, *distributed by* Theatre Communications Group

Select, *imprint of* Oakstone Publishing LLC

SelfHelp Success Books, *distributed by* Pelican Publishing Co

The Selfhelper Law Press of America, *imprint of* Do-It-Yourself Legal Publishers

SelfMadeHero, *imprint of* Harry N Abrams Inc

Sendpoints Books Co Ltd, *distributed by* Gingko Press Inc

Sensation, *imprint of* Berkley Books, Berkley Publishing Group

Sense of Wonder Press, *imprint of* James A Rock & Co Publishers

Sentinel, *imprint of* Penguin Group (USA) LLC, a Penguin Random House company

Seoul Selection, *distributed by* University of Hawaii Press

Sephardic House, *distributed by* Bloch Publishing Co

Serendipity, *imprint of* Price Stern Sloan

Serif Publishing Ltd (UK), *distributed by* Interlink Publishing Group Inc

Serindia Publications, *distributed by* Art Media Resources Inc (US & CN)

Servant Books, *imprint of* Franciscan Media

Service Employees International Union, *distributed by* Chelsea Green Publishing Co

SESAP Audio Companion, *imprint of* Oakstone Publishing LLC

SETAC Press, *imprint of* Society of Environmental Toxicology & Chemistry

Seven Footer Kids, *imprint of* Seven Footer Press

Seven Footer Press, *subsidiary of* Seven Footer Entertainment LLC

7th Generation, *imprint of* Book Publishing Co, *distributed by* Orca Book Publishers

The Seventh Quarry, *imprint of* Cross-Cultural Communications

The Seventh Quarry Press, *imprint of* Cross-Cultural Communications, *distributed by* Cross-Cultural Communications

Shaar Press, *imprint of* Mesorah Publications Ltd

Shabdaguchha (Magazine & Press), *distributed by* Cross-Cultural Communications

Shadow Mountain, *imprint of* Deseret Book Co

Shakespeare Playbooks, *imprint of* Bandanna Books

Shambhala, *distributed by* Penguin Random House Inc

Shambhala Publications Inc, *distributed by* Random House Inc

Shanghai Press, *distributed by* Tuttle Publishing, University of Hawaii Press

Shangri-La, *imprint of* Lotus Press

Sharpe Focus, *imprint of* M E Sharpe Inc

Sharpe Online Reference, *imprint of* M E Sharpe Inc

Sharpe Reference, *imprint of* M E Sharpe Inc

Shaw Books, *imprint of* WaterBrook Multnomah Publishing Group

Shaye Areheart Books, *imprint of* Penguin Random House Inc

Shearwater Books, *imprint of* Island Press

The Sheep Meadow Press, *distributed by* University Press of New England

Sheffield Phoenix Press, *distributed by* SBL Press

Sheffield Publishing Co, *subsidiary of* Waveland Press Inc

Sheldrake Press (UK), *distributed by* Interlink Publishing Group Inc

Joyce Shellhart, *distributed by* Finney Company Inc

Shengold Books, *imprint of* Schreiber Publishing Inc

Shen's Books, *imprint of* Lee & Low Books, Lee & Low Books Inc

Shepard & Piper, *imprint of* Shepard Publications

Shepard Publications, *imprint of* Shepard Publications

W B Sheridan, *imprint of* Academica Press LLC

Shire, *imprint of* Osprey Publishing Inc

G Shirmer, *imprint of* Hal Leonard Corp

Shorenstein Asia-Pacific Research Center, *distributed by* The Brookings Institution Press

Short Tales, *imprint of* ABDO Publishing Group

Shortfuse Press, *distributed by* Gem Guides Book Co

Iwasaki Shoten, *distributor for* Big Guy Books Inc

Showcase, *imprint of* Players Press Inc

ShowForth Videos, *division of* BJU Press, *imprint of* BJU Press

Shroff Publishers, *distributor for* Mike Murach & Associates Inc

Shroff Publishers & Distributors, *distributor for* Microsoft Press

Shufunotomo Co, *distributed by* Tuttle Publishing

Sicilia Parra, *distributed by* Cross-Cultural Communications

Side Street, *imprint of* BrickHouse Books Inc

Sierra Club Adult Books, *imprint of* Penguin Random House Inc

Sierra Club Books, *imprint of* Counterpoint Press LLC, *distributor for* Counterpoint Press, *distributed by* Chronicle Books (Sierra Club Calendars), Gibbs Smith (Sierra Club Books for Children), University of California Press

Sierra Club Books for Children, *division of* Sierra Club Books

Sierra Club Calendars, *division of* Sierra Club Books

Sierra College Press, *imprint of* Heyday Books

Sierra Press, *distributed by* Gem Guides Book Co

Sights Unscene Press, *distributed by* Enfield Publishing & Distribution Co

Signal Books (UK), *distributed by* Interlink Publishing Group Inc

Signature Books, *imprint of* EastBridge

Signatures Network, *distributed by* Andrews McMeel Publishing LLC

Signet, *imprint of* NAL, Penguin Group (USA) LLC, a Penguin Random House company

Signet Classics, *imprint of* NAL, Penguin Group (USA) LLC, a Penguin Random House company

Signum Verlag, *distributed by* Gallaudet University Press

Siles Press, *division of* Silman-James Press

Silhouette, *imprint of* Harlequin Enterprises Ltd

Silhouette Imprints, *imprint of* Crumb Elbow Publishing

Silk & Magic, *imprint of* ImaJinn Books Inc

Silk Label Books, *distributed by* Royal Fireworks Press

Silman-James Press, *distributed by* Codasat Canada Ltd

Siloam Press, *imprint of* Charisma Media

Silver Dagger Mysteries, *imprint of* The Overmountain Press

Silver Dragon Books, *imprint of* Regal Crest Enterprises LLC

Silverplume, a Vertafore Co, *distributor for* Standard Publishing Corp

Simba Information, *division of* Market Research.com

Simcha Press, *imprint of* Health Communications Inc

Simon & Schuster, *imprint of* Simon & Schuster Publishing Group, *distributor for* Alloy Entertainment LLC, Baen Publishing Enterprises, Beyond Words Publishing Inc, Cider Mill Press Book Publishers LLC, The Jim Henson Co, Meadowbrook Press, Nightingale-Conant, Open Road Publishing, Parachute Publishing LLC, Reader's Digest General Books, Reader's Digest Trade Books, Wisdom Publications Inc, *distributed by* Cardoza Publishing, Gulf Publishing Co, Learning Links Inc, Specialty Press Inc

Simon & Schuster Audio, *division of* Simon & Schuster, Inc, *distributor for* Monostereo

Simon & Schuster Books for Young Readers, *imprint of* Simon & Schuster Children's Publishing

Simon & Schuster Children's Publishing, *division of* Simon & Schuster, Inc

Simon & Schuster Digital, *division of* Simon & Schuster, Inc

Simon & Schuster, Inc, *division of* CBS Corporation, *distributor for* Andrews McMeel Publishing LLC, Backlist LLC (div of Chicken Soup for the Soul Publishing), Baen Books, Baseball America, Beyond Words, BL Publishing (div of Games Workshop), Boom! Studios, Cardoza Publishing, Chicken Soup for the Soul Publishing, Cider Mill Press Book Publishers LLC (including Applesauce Press & Appleseed imprint), Downtown Bookworks, Frederator Books LLC, Gallup (worldwide), Games Workshop, Harlequin Enterprises Ltd (billing only), Hooked on Phonics (Sandviks HOP Inc/Sandvik Publishing), Inner Traditions/Bear & Company, Kaplan Publishing (including Manhattan Prep), Katalitix Media, Kinfolk, Little Bee Books, Meadowbrook Press, Merck Publishing, Omnific Publishing, Open Road Publishing, Permuted Press LLC, Piggyback Interactive, Pikachu Press (Pokemon Company International), Post Hill Press LLC, Reader's Digest Books, Rebellion Publishing, Regan Arts, Ripley Entertainment Inc (Ripley's Believe it or Not), Studio Fun International (formerly Reader's Digest Children's Publishing), TC Media Books, To The Stars Inc, Tuttle Publishing, Uncrate LLC, Victory Belt Publishing, VIZ Media, Weldon Owen, Wisdom Publications, World Almanac (div of Facts on File), Yilin Press (Mandarin ebooks)

Simon & Schuster Mass Merchandise Sales Co, *distributor for* Harlequin Enterprises Ltd

Simon & Schuster Pocket Books, *distributor for* Public Citizen

Simon & Schuster Sales & Marketing, *distributor for* Boom! Studios

Simon & Schuster Sales Division, *division of* Simon & Schuster, Inc, *distributor for* Andrews McMeel Publishing LLC, Applesauce Press (children's), Avatar Press, Baen Books, Baseball America, Boom! Studios, Cardoza, Chicken Soup for the Soul, Cider Mill Press Book Publishers, Downtown Bookworks, Frederator Books LLC, Gallup (worldwide), Games Workshop, Harlequin (billing only), Kaplan Publishing, Manhattan Prep, Meadowbrook Press, Merck, Open Road, Permuted Press LLC, Piggyback Interactive, Post Hill Press LLC, Reader's Digest Children's Books, Rebellion, Regan Arts, Ripley Entertainment, To the Stars Inc, Uncrate LLC, VIZ Media, Weldon Owen, World Almanac (div of Facts on File)

Simon Pulse, *imprint of* Simon & Schuster Children's Publishing

Simon Spotlight, *imprint of* Simon & Schuster Children's Publishing

Simple Productions, *imprint of* Shepard Publications

Simpson, *imprint of* University of California Press

Sing Out Corp, *distributed by* Hal Leonard Corp

Singing Brook Press, *distributed by* Enfield Publishing & Distribution Co

Singing Dragon, *imprint of* Jessica Kingsley Publishers Inc

Sisra Music Publishing, *imprint of* Empire Publishing Service

Byron Sistler, *distributor for* Ericson Books

6 x 6 Magazine, *imprint of* Ugly Duckling Presse

Six House, *subsidiary of* Gallopade International Inc

Six Points Press, *imprint of* Five Star Publications Inc

Sixth & Spring, *distributed by* Sterling Publishing Co Inc

Skateman Publications, *imprint of* World Citizens

SkillPath Publications, *division of* The Graceland University Center for Professional Development & Lifelong Learning Inc, *distributor for* Franklin Covey, Pearson Technology, Thomson Publishing, John Wiley

SkillsTutor, *imprint of* Houghton Mifflin Harcourt

Skinner House Books, *imprint of* Unitarian Universalist Assn, Unitarian Universalist Association

SkipJack Press, *imprint of* Finney Company Inc

Skipstone, *imprint of* The Mountaineers Books

Skira Editore, *distributed by* Rizzoli International Publications Inc

Skira Rizzoli Publishers, *distributor for* American Federation of Arts

SkiraRizzoli Publishing, *imprint of* Rizzoli International Publications Inc

Sky Pony Press, *imprint of* Skyhorse Publishing Inc

Sky Publishing, *distributed by* Sterling Publishing Co Inc

Skyhook Press, *imprint of* Shepard Publications

Skyhorse Publishing, *distributed by* W W Norton & Company Inc

Skylark, *imprint of* Penguin Random House Inc

SkyLight Paths Publishing, *division of* Longhill Partners Inc, LongHill Partners Inc

Slossen, *distributed by* Specialty Press Inc

Slovenian Cinematheque, *distributed by* Columbia University Press

Slow Food Editore, *distributed by* Chelsea Green Publishing Co

Small Horizons, *imprint of* New Horizon Press

Small Press United, *distributor for* Academy of Nutrition & Dietetics

SmallBusiness.tv, *subsidiary of* BizBest Media Corp

Smart Apple Media, *imprint of* Black Rabbit Books

Smart Ink, *distributed by* Ideals Publications, a Guideposts Co

Smart Kidz, *distributed by* Ideals Publications, a Guideposts Co

Smart Pop, *imprint of* BenBella Books Inc

Smart Sex Stuff for Kids, *imprint of* Gallopade International Inc

SmartLab, *distributed by* Chronicle Books LLC

Smartmaps®, *imprint of* VanDam Inc

SmartPros, *distributed by* Professional Publications Inc (PPI)

SmartsCo, *distributed by* Chronicle Books LLC

SMC Publishing, *distributed by* Cheng & Tsui Co Inc

Smiley Books, *imprint of* Hay House Inc

Smith & Kraus Books For Kids, *imprint of* Smith & Kraus Publishers Inc

Smith & Kraus Global, *subsidiary of* Smith & Kraus Publishers Inc

Smith-Gordon, *distributed by* Enfield Publishing & Distribution Co

Smithsonian Books, *distributed by* Penguin Random House Inc

Smithsonian Scholarly Press, *division of* Smithsonian Institution, *distributed by* Random House

Smokestack Books, *distributed by* Dufour Editions Inc

SMP Swerve, *imprint of* St Martin's Press, LLC

Colin Smythe Ltd, *distributed by* Dufour Editions Inc

Snake Country Publishing, *distributed by* Caxton Press

Snaptail Press, *distributed by* Finney Company Inc

Snova Books, *imprint of* Nova Science Publishers Inc

Snow Lion, *imprint of* Shambhala Publications Inc

Snow Lion Publications Inc, *imprint of* Shambhala Publications, Shambhala Publications Inc

Snowy Owl Books, *imprint of* University of Alaska Press

Social Science Research Council, *distributed by* Columbia University Press

SocialMyBusiness.com, *subsidiary of* BizBest Media Corp

Societe Mathematique de France, *distributed by* American Mathematical Society

Society for American Baseball Research, *distributed by* University of Nebraska Press

Society of Manufacturing Engineers, *distributor for* Industrial Press, McGraw-Hill, Prentice Hall, John Wiley & Sons Inc, *distributed by* American Technical Publishers Inc, McGraw-Hill, Productivity Press

Society of the Cincinnati, *distributed by* University Press of America Inc

Soffietto Editions, *imprint of* Red Moon Press

Soft Skull Press, *imprint of* Counterpoint Press LLC

Sogang University Institute, *distributed by* Cheng & Tsui Co Inc

Soho Constable, *imprint of* Soho Press Inc

Soho Crime, *imprint of* Soho Press Inc

Soho Press, *distributed by* Penguin Random House Inc

Soho Press Inc, *distributed by* Random House

Soho Teen, *imprint of* Soho Press Inc

Solar Design Association, *distributed by* Chelsea Green Publishing Co

SOM Publishing, *subsidiary of* School of Metaphysics

Someday Baby, *distributed by* Ideals Publications, a Guideposts Co

Somerset Press, *division of* Hope Publishing Co

Somerville House USA, *imprint of* Grosset & Dunlap

Sommer-Time Story Classics Series, *imprint of* Advance Publishing Inc

Sommer-Time Story Series, *imprint of* Advance Publishing Inc

Soncino, *distributed by* Bloch Publishing Co

Sono Nis Press, *distributed by* Heimburger House Publishing Co, Orca Book Publishers

Sopris West, *distributed by* Council for Exceptional Children (CEC)

Sopris West Educational Services, *imprint of* Cambium Learning Inc

Sorin Books, *imprint of* Ave Maria Press

Sound Ideas, *imprint of* Simon & Schuster Audio

SoundForth Music, *division of* BJU Press, *imprint of* BJU Press

Sourcebooks Casablanca, *imprint of* Sourcebooks Inc

Sourcebooks Fire, *imprint of* Sourcebooks Inc

Sourcebooks Inc, *distributor for* Prufrock Press, *distributed by* Raincoast Books (Canada)

Sourcebooks Jabberwocky, *imprint of* Sourcebooks Inc

Sourcebooks Landmark, *imprint of* Sourcebooks Inc

Sourcebooks MediaFusion, *imprint of* Sourcebooks Inc

Sourced Media Books, *distributed by* Gibbs-Smith, Many Hats Media

SourceResource, *distributor for* MAR*CO Products Inc

South Carolina Bar Association, *distributed by* University of South Carolina Press

South Carolina Historical Society, *distributed by* University of South Carolina Press

South End Press, *affiliate of* Institute for Social & Cultural Change

South-Western, *imprint of* Wadsworth Publishing

Southeastern Center for Contemporary Art, *distributed by* The University of North Carolina Press

Southeastern Cooperative Wildlife Disease Study, *distributed by* American Association for Vocational Instructional Materials

Southern Early Childhood Association, *distributed by* Gryphon House Inc

Southern Historical Press, *distributed by* Ericson Books

Southern Illinois University Press, *division of* Southern Illinois University

Southern Living Books, *imprint of* Oxmoor House

Southern Methodist University Press, *distributed by* Texas A&M University Press

Southern Voices Audio, *imprint of* Recorded Books LLC

Southlore Press, *distributed by* Ingalls Publishing Group Inc (IPG)

Southwestern Studies, *imprint of* Texas Western Press

Sovereign World, *distributed by* Bridge-Logos Inc

Sparkhouse, *imprint of* Augsburg Fortress Publishers, Publishing House of the Evangelical Lutheran Church in America

Sparkle Shapes, *imprint of* Playhouse Publishing

Speaker's Corner, *imprint of* Fulcrum Publishing Inc

Specialized Software, *imprint of* Lotus Press

Specialty Press Inc, *distributor for* Bantam, Guilford Press, Plenum, Simon & Schuster, Slossen, Woodbine House, *distributed by* Boys Town Press, Child Play, MHS

Spectra, *imprint of* Penguin Random House Inc

Spectrum, *distributor for* National Council of Teachers of Mathematics (NCTM)

Sphinx Publishing, *imprint of* Sourcebooks Inc

SPIE Press, *imprint of* SPIE

Spiegel & Grau, *imprint of* Random House Publishing Group

Spinsters Ink, *division of* Spinsters Ink Publishing Co

Spire Books, *imprint of* Revell

Spirit, *imprint of* Norilana Books

Spirit Mountain Press, *distributed by* University of Alaska Press

Sporting News, *distributed by* Andrews McMeel Publishing LLC

Sports Collectors Digest, *imprint of* Betterway Books

SportsZone, *imprint of* ABDO Publishing Group

Spotlight, *imprint of* ABDO Publishing Group

Spotlight Books, *imprint of* Empire Publishing Service

Jack Spratt Choral Music, *imprint of* Empire Publishing Service

Spring Arbor, *distributor for* Faith Library Publications, Pentecostal Publishing House

Spring Arbor Distributors, *distributor for* Presbyterian Publishing Corp (PPC)

Spring Freshet Press, *distributed by* University of Wisconsin Press

Spring Publications, *distributed by* Bloomsbury Academic

Springer, *subsidiary of* Springer Science+Business Media, *imprint of* Springer, *distributed by* SAS Publishing

Springer Healthcare, *imprint of* Springer

Springer-Verlag, *distributor for* American Institute of Physics

Springhouse Editions, *subsidiary of* White Pine Press, *distributed by* White Pine Press

Sproutman Publications, *distributed by* Book Publishing Co

Sprucehaven Publishing, *distributed by* Epicenter Press Inc

Spyglass Books LLC, *distributed by* Biographical Publishing Co

Square One Publishers Inc, *distributor for* InnoVision Health Media, Rainbow Ridge Books, *distributed by* Thomas Allen & Son

SRA/McGraw-Hill, *division of* McGraw-Hill School Education Group, *imprint of* McGraw-Hill Education, *distributor for* Renaissance House

Sri Aurobindo Ashram, *distributed by* Lotus Press

Sri Lanka Institute of Traditional Studies, *distributed by* Fons Vitae

SSPC, *distributed by* NACE International

SSPC: The Society for Protective Coatings, *distributed by* Technology Publishing Co

ST Media Group Book Division, *division of* ST Media Group Intl

Stacey International Ltd (London), *distributed by* International Book Centre Inc

Stackpole Books, *distributor for* The Army War College Foundation Press, The Colonial Williamsburg Foundation, Headwater Books, Historical Society of Western Pennsylvania, Quiller Press Ltd, Ryton Publications, The Sausage Maker, Stackpole Magazines, Swan Hill

Stackpole Magazines, *distributed by* Stackpole Books

Stainer & Bell Ltd, *distributed by* ECS Publishing Corp

Standard & Poor's, *division of* McGraw-Hill Financial

Standard Educational Corp, *subsidiary of* The United Educators Inc

Standard Publishing Co, *distributor for* Focus on the Family

Standard Publishing Corp, *distributed by* LexisNexis, Silverplume, a Vertafore Co

Stanford Business Books, *imprint of* Stanford University Press

Stanford Security Studies, *imprint of* Stanford University Press

Stanford Law Books, *imprint of* Stanford University Press

Stanford General Books, *imprint of* Stanford University Press

Stanford University Press, *imprint of* Stanford University Press, *distributor for* Woodrow Wilson Center Press

Star Licks Videos, *distributed by* Hal Leonard Corp

Star Sounds, *distributed by* Lotus Press

Star Trek®, *imprint of* Gallery Books

Starbooks, *imprint of* STARbooks Press

STARbooks Press, *affiliate of* Florida Literary Foundation (FLF)

Starcrafts LLC, *imprint of* Starcrafts LLC

Starfire Publishing, *distributed by* Holmes Publishing Group LLC

Stargazer Books, *imprint of* Black Rabbit Books

Starrhill Press, *imprint of* River City Publishing LLC

STARS-National Center for Youths, *distributor for* MAR*CO Products Inc

Starscape, *imprint of* Tom Doherty Associates, LLC

StartupSmarts.com, *subsidiary of* BizBest Media Corp

State & National Parks Guides, *imprint of* Hunter Publishing Inc

State Experience, *imprint of* Gallopade International Inc

State Stuff, *imprint of* Gallopade International Inc

State University of New York Press, *distributor for* Albany Institute of History & Art, Codhill Press, Samuel Dorsky Museum of Art, Mount Ida Press, Muswell Hill Press, New Netherland Institute, Rockefeller Institute Press, Uncrowned Queens

Stay Bound, *distributor for* Ozark Publishing Inc

STC Craft, *imprint of* Harry N Abrams Inc

Steam Passages Publishing, *distributed by* Heimburger House Publishing Co

Steam Press, *distributed by* Gryphon House Inc

Steck Vaughn, *imprint of* Harcourt Inc

Steeple Hill, *imprint of* Harlequin Enterprises Ltd

Steerforth Press, *distributed by* Penguin Random House Inc

Bernard Stein Music Co, *distributed by* Hal Leonard Corp

Rudolf Steiner Press UK, *distributor for* SteinerBooks

Rudolph Steiner Press, *distributed by* SteinerBooks

SteinerBooks, *distributor for* Chiron Publications, Clairview Books, Floris Books, Hawthorn Press, Lantern Books, Rudolph Steiner Press, Temple Lodge Publishing, *distributed by* Rudolf Steiner Press UK

Steinsaltz, *imprint of* The Toby Press LLC

Stemmer House Publishers Inc, *division of* Pathway Book Service

Stenhouse Publishers, *division of* Highlights for Children Education Group, *distributor for* Pembroke Publishers

STEP Publishers (Systematic Training for Effective Parenting), *distributed by* Impact Publishers Inc

Stephens Press™, *subsidiary of* Stephens Media LLC

Sterling, *imprint of* Sterling Publishing Co Inc

Sterling & Francine Clark Art Institute, *distributed by* Yale University Press

Sterling Children's Books, *imprint of* Sterling Publishing Co Inc

Sterling Epicure, *imprint of* Sterling Publishing Co Inc

Sterling Ethos, *imprint of* Sterling Publishing Co Inc

Sterling Publishing, *distributed by* Heimburger House Publishing Co

Sterling Publishing Co Inc, *subsidiary of* Barnes & Noble Inc, *distributor for* Batsford (selected titles), Boxer Books, Brooklyn Botanic Garden (selected titles), Carlton Books, Cassell (selected titles), Collins & Brown (selected titles), Conway, Davis Publications (selected titles), Sally Milner (selected titles), Orion (selected titles), Phoenix Press (selected titles), Salaryia (selected titles), Sixth & Spring (selected titles), Sky Publishing, Weidenfeld & Nicolson (selected titles), White Star Publishers

Gareth Stevens, *distributed by* Perfection Learning Corp

Stewart, Tabori & Chang, *imprint of* Harry N Abrams Inc

Stimulus Books, *imprint of* Paulist Press

Stinging Fly Press, *distributed by* Dufour Editions Inc

Stoecklein Publishing, *distributed by* The Globe Pequot Press

Stoke Books, *distributed by* Lerner Publishing Group Inc

Stone Arch Books, *imprint of* Capstone Publishers™

Stone Bridge Press, *distributed by* Cheng & Tsui Co Inc

Stonefield Publishing, *distributed by* Chelsea Green Publishing Co

Stonewall, *imprint of* BrickHouse Books Inc

Storey Publishing, *division of* Workman Publishing Co Inc, *imprint of* Algonquin Books

Storey Publishing LLC, *distributed by* Workman Publishing Co Inc

The Story Plant, *division of* Studio Digital CT LLC

Story River Books, *imprint of* University of South Carolina Press

StoryMonsters Ink, *imprint of* Five Star Publications Inc

Strebor Books, *imprint of* Atria Books

Stretch Think®, *imprint of* Thomas Geale Publications Inc

String Letter Press, *distributed by* Hal Leonard Corp

Strong Books, *imprint of* Book Marketing Works LLC

Lyle Stuart Books, *imprint of* Kensington Publishing Corp

Stubs Guides, *distributed by* Hagstrom Map

Stubs Magazine, *distributed by* American Map Corp

Studien Verlag, *distributed by* Transaction Publishers Inc

Studio, *imprint of* Penguin Group (USA) LLC, a Penguin Random House company

Studio Fun International, *distributed by* Simon & Schuster, Inc

Studio Fun International Inc, *subsidiary of* The Reader's Digest Association Inc

Stylus Publishing LLC, *distributor for* Aeon Books, American Association for Higher Education, Cabi Books, Commonwealth Scientific & Industrial Research Organization (CSIRO), The Commonwealth Secretariat, Cork University Press, Global Professional Publishing, IDRC, Institute of Education, The Institution of Engineering & Technology (IET), Karnac Books, LM Publishing, Nordic Africa Institute, Oxfam Publishing, Practical Action, Thorogood Publishing, Trentham Books Ltd, Women, Law & Development International (WLDI), World Health Organization (WHO)

Success Advertising, *division of* Success Advertising & Publishing

Success Advertising & Publishing, *division of* The Success Group

Suffolk Records Society, *imprint of* Boydell & Brewer Inc

Sugar Cane Press, *distributed by* Heimburger House Publishing Co

Sumach Press, *distributed by* Orca Book Publishers

Summertime, *imprint of* Summertime Publications Inc

Summertime Publications Inc, *distributor for* ACHCBYZ (Paris academic press specialized in Byzantine history)

Summit Beacon, *distributor for* Woodland Publishing Inc

Summit Books, *imprint of* Perfection Learning Corp

Sun & Moon Classics, *imprint of* Green Integer

Sun Books, *imprint of* Sun Publishing Company

Sun Plans Inc, *distributed by* Chelsea Green Publishing Co

Sun Publishing Company, *division of* The Sun Companies

Sunbelt Publications Inc, *distributor for* Abbott Publishing, Alti Corporation, Amaroma Ediciones (architectural & design publisher in Mexico), Anza-Borrego Foundation, W H Berger, Bobolink Media, Joan Brady, California Sea Grant, Paul Douglas Campbell, Dawsons Book Shop, Leland Fetzer, FineEdge.com LLC, Fun Places Publishing, Jeffrey Garcia, Maureen Gilmer, Glove Pequot, Green Grass Press, Healey Publishing, Huckleberry House LLC, Intellect Publishing, Island Paradise Publishing, Jaguar Tales, Scott G Kyle, Lawtech Publishing, Little Oak Press, Mission San Juan Capistrano Women's Guild, Newtona LLC, Northcross Books, Nelson Papucci, Bette L Pegas, Linda Pequegnat, Picaro Publishing, Planeta Peninsula (Mexican publisher), Phil R Pryde, Quick Reference Publishing, R & B Food & Culture Production, Random House, Renegade Enterprises, San Diego Architecture Foundation, San Diego Association of Geologists, San Diego City Works Press, San Diego Natural History Museum, San Diego Police Historical Association, San Dieguito River Park Joint Powers Authority, Save Our Heritage Organization, Surf Angel Publications, Trail Wisdom, University of California Press, Armand Vallee, Wigton Publishing, Wilderness Press, Wolf Water Press

Sundance/Newbridge Publishing, *division of* Rowman & Littlefield Publishing Group

Sunfood Living, *distributed by* North Atlantic Books

Sunrise Library, *imprint of* Theosophical University Press

Sunrise River Press, *affiliate of* Cartech Books/ Specialty Press

Sunset Books, *imprint of* Oxmoor House

Sunstone Press, *imprint of* The Sunstone Corp

SUNY Press, *distributor for* Codhill Press

SUP Publishing Logistics, *distributed by* Cheng & Tsui Co Inc

Super Sandcastle, *imprint of* ABDO Publishing Group

SuperGenius, *imprint of* Papercutz

Supplement Editions, *imprint of* Bandanna Books

Sure Fire Press, *imprint of* Holmes Publishing Group LLC

Surf Angel Publications, *distributed by* Sunbelt Publications Inc

Surrey Books, *imprint of* Agate Publishing

Susquehanna University Press, *affiliate of* Associated University Presses, *distributed by* Associated University Presses

Sustainability Press, *distributed by* Chelsea Green Publishing Co

Swallow Press, *imprint of* Ohio University Press

Swallow's Tale Press, *imprint of* Livingston Press, *distributed by* Livingston Press

Swan Books, *division of* Learning Links Inc

Swan Hill, *distributed by* Stackpole Books

Swan Isle Press, *distributed by* University of Chicago Press

Swedish Corrosion Institute, *distributed by* NACE International

Sweet & Maxwell, *distributed by* William S Hein & Co Inc

Sweetwater Books, *imprint of* Cedar Fort Inc

Swerve Editions, *imprint of* Zone Books dba Urzone Inc

Switchgrass Books, *imprint of* Northern Illinois University Press

Sword & Sorcery, *imprint of* White Wolf Publishing Inc

The Sword of Norilana, *imprint of* Norilana Books

Sybex Inc, *division of* John Wiley & Sons Inc, John Wiley & Sons Inc, *distributed by* EMC Publishing LLC

Sycamore Island Books, *imprint of* Paladin Press

Symposium Publishing, *imprint of* Blue Dolphin Publishing Inc

Synergy, *imprint of* Bridge-Logos Inc

SynErotica, *imprint of* SynergEbooks

Syracuse University Press, *distributed by* Alen House, Dedelas Press, Gryphon House Inc, Heimburger House Publishing Co

Tab Books, *distributor for* National Association of Broadcasters (NAB)

Tabard Press, *imprint of* Konecky & Konecky LLC

Tabernacle Publishing, *division of* Hope Publishing Co

The TAFT Group®, *imprint of* Gale

Yosifumi Taguchi, *distributed by* EastBridge

Tai Chi Foundation, *distributed by* Tuttle Publishing

Tale Blazers, *imprint of* Perfection Learning Corp

Taleka, *imprint of* Norilana Books

Nan A Talese, *imprint of* Penguin Random House Inc

Tamar Books, *imprint of* Mesorah Publications Ltd

Tamesis Books, *imprint of* Boydell & Brewer Inc

TAN Books, *imprint of* Saint Benedict Press LLC

T&T Clark International, *imprint of* Bloomsbury Publishing PLC

Tantor Audio, *imprint of* Tantor Media Inc

Tantor Media, *imprint of* Tantor Media Inc

The S Mark Taper Foundation, *imprint of* University of California Press

Tapestry Press Ltd, *distributed by* Maryland History Press

Tara Publications, *distributed by* Hal Leonard Corp

Jeremy P Tarcher, *imprint of* Penguin Group (USA) LLC, Penguin Group (USA) LLC, a Penguin Random House company, The Putnam Publishing Group

Tarcher/Penguin, *imprint of* The Putnam Publishing Group

Taschen GmbH, *imprint of* Taschen America

Tastes Newsletter, *subsidiary of* Gault Millau Inc/ Gayot Publications

Tata Institute of Fundamental Research, *distributed by* American Mathematical Society

Tata/McGraw-Hill, *imprint of* McGraw-Hill Education

Tate Galleries, *distributed by* Oak Knoll Press

Tate Publishing, *distributed by* Harry N Abrams Inc

Tattered Flag, *distributed by* Casemate Publishers & Book Distributors LLC

The Taunton Press, *distributed by* Penguin Random House Inc

The Taunton Press Inc, *distributor for* Academia Barilla

Taunton Sterling Dover, *distributed by* Fox Chapel Publishing Co Inc

I B Tauris, *distributed by* St Martin's Press, LLC

I B Tauris & Co Ltd, *distributed by* Palgrave Macmillan

Taurus, *imprint of* Santillana USA Publishing Co Inc

Taylor & Francis, *distributor for* The Fairmont Press Inc, *distributed by* Illuminating Engineering Society of North America (IES)

Taylor & Francis Asia Pacific, *imprint of* Taylor & Francis Inc

Taylor & Francis Books, *imprint of* Taylor & Francis Inc

Taylor Trade, *imprint of* The Globe Pequot Press

Tayo Press, *distributed by* Franklin, Beedle & Associates Inc

TC Media Books, *distributed by* Simon & Schuster, Inc

Teachers College Press, *affiliate of* Teachers College, Columbia University

Teacher's Discovery, *division of* American Eagle Co Inc

Teachers License Examination Series, *imprint of* National Learning Corp

Teachers of English to Speakers of Other Languages Inc (TESOL), *distributed by* Alta Book Ctr, Delta Systems Inc, New Readers Press, Saddleback Educational

Teaching Strategies, *distributor for* Gryphon House, *distributed by* Gryphon House Inc

Techne Press, *distributed by* Island Press

Editions Technip, *distributed by* Gulf Publishing Co

Technology, *division of* Scholastic Education

Technology Publishing Co, *distributor for* SSPC: The Society for Protective Coatings

Techstreet, *distributed by* Illuminating Engineering Society of North America (IES)

Katherine Tegen Books, *imprint of* HarperCollins Children's Books

Telfair Museums, *distributed by* University of Georgia Press

Telshare Publishing, *distributed by* Gryphon House Inc

Templar Books, *imprint of* Candlewick Press

Temple Lodge Publishing, *distributed by* SteinerBooks

Temple University Press, *division of* Temple University of the Commonwealth System of Higher Education

Templeton Press, *subsidiary of* John Templeton Foundation

Temporal Mechanical Press, *division of* Enos Mills Cabin Museum & Gallery

Ten Pound Island Books, *distributed by* Mystic Seaport Museum Inc

Ten Speed Press, *imprint of* Crown Publishing Group, *distributed by* Penguin Random House Inc

Teora, *imprint of* Teora USA LLC

Terrace Books, *imprint of* University of Wisconsin Press

Terrapin Greetings, *imprint of* Down The Shore Publishing Corp

Test Your Knowledge Books, *imprint of* National Learning Corp

Testament Books, *imprint of* Penguin Random House Inc

Teton NewMedia, *distributor for* LifeLearn, *distributed by* Blackwells, LifeLearn, Logan Brothers, Rittenhouse, Yankee

Tetra Press, *division of* Pfizer Inc, *distributed by* Voyageur Press

Texas A&M University Press, *division of* Texas A&M University, *distributor for* Stephen F Austin State University Press, McWhiney Foundation Press/State House Press, Southern Methodist University Press, Texas Christian University Press, Texas Review Press, Texas State Historical Association, University of North Texas Press

Texas Christian University Press, *distributed by* Texas A&M University Press

Texas Memorial Museum, *distributed by* Bureau of Economic Geology, University of Texas at Austin

Texas Parks & Wildlife Department, *distributed by* University of Texas Press

Texas Review Press, *distributed by* Texas A&M University Press

Texas State Historical Association, *distributed by* Oak Knoll Press, Texas A&M University Press

Texas Tech University Press, *distributor for* The Colonial Williamsburg Foundation, National Ranching Heritage Center

University of Texas Press, *division of* University of Texas, *distributor for* Bat Conservation International, Institute for Mesoamerican Studies, Menil Foundation, Rothko Chapel, Texas Parks & Wildlife Department, Texas Western Press

Texas Western Press, *affiliate of* University of Texas at El Paso, *distributed by* University of Texas Press

TFH Publications Inc, *subsidiary of* Central Garden & Pet Corp

Thames & Hudson, *distributor for* National Gallery of Art, *distributed by* W W Norton & Co Inc, W W Norton & Company Inc

That Patchwork Place, *imprint of* Martingale®

That the World May Know, *imprint of* Focus on the Family

That VanDam Book, *imprint of* VanDam Inc

Theatre Communications Group, *distributor for* Absolute Classics, Aurora Metro Publications, Nick Hern Books, Oberon Books, Padua Playwrights Press, PAJ Publications, Playwrights Canada Press, Martin E Segal Theatre Center Publications, Ubu Repertory Theatre Publications

Theion Publishing, *distributed by* Holmes Publishing Group LLC

Theology of the Body Series, *imprint of* Pauline Books & Media

Theophilis, *imprint of* Transcontinental Music Publications

Theosophical Publishing House/Quest Books, *division of* The Theosophical Society in America

Theosophical University Press, *affiliate of* Theosophical Society (Pasadena)

Thesaurus Islamicus Foundation, *distributed by* Fons Vitae

Theta Books, *imprint of* Bridge Publications Inc

Theta Foundation of Bucharest, *distributed by* American Mathematical Society

Thieme Medical Publishers Inc, *subsidiary of* Georg Thieme Verlag KG, *distributor for* AO Foundation

Think, *imprint of* NavPress Publishing Group

Think Quest®, *imprint of* Thomas Geale Publications Inc

Thinking Like a Scientist, *imprint of* Sundance/Newbridge Publishing

Third World Press, *distributed by* Northwestern University Press

30 Degrees South Publishers, *distributed by* Casemate Publishers & Book Distributors LLC

37 Ink, *imprint of* Atria Books

30 Words, *distributed by* The Globe Pequot Press

Thistle Hill Publications, *distributed by* Enfield Publishing & Distribution Co

Thomas Nelson, *imprint of* HarperCollins Christian Publishing, *distributed by* Winston-Derek

Thomson Publishing, *distributed by* Oxford University Press USA, SkillPath Publications

Thomson Reuters, *distributor for* AICPA Professional Publications

Thomson Reuters Westlaw™, *distributor for* Law Library Microform Consortium

Thorndike Press, *subsidiary of* Cengage Learning, *imprint of* Gale, *distributor for* Grand Central/Hachette Large Print, HarperLuxe, Mills & Boon Large Print, Random House Large Print

Thorndike Press®, *imprint of* Gale

Nelson Thornes, *distributed by* Trans-Atlantic Publications Inc

Thorogood Publishing, *distributed by* Stylus Publishing LLC

Three Hands Press, *distributed by* Holmes Publishing Group LLC

Three Pines Press, *distributed by* University of Hawaii Press

Three Rivers Press, *imprint of* Crown Publishing Group, Penguin Random House Inc

Threshold Editions, *imprint of* Gallery Books

Thresholds, *imprint of* Zumaya Publications LLC

Throckmorton Press, *distributed by* powerHouse Books

Thunder Bay Press, *distributed by* Heimburger House Publishing Co

Tia Chucha Press, *distributed by* Northwestern University Press

Tidewater Publishers, *imprint of* Cornell Maritime Press Inc, Schiffer Publishing Ltd

Tilbury House Publishers, *imprint of* WordSplice Studio LLC

Timber Press, *division of* Workman Publishing Co Inc, *imprint of* Algonquin Books, Timber Press Inc

Timber Press Inc, *subsidiary of* Workman Publishing Co, Workman Publishing Co Inc, *distributed by* Thomas Allen & Son

Timerberline Productions, *imprint of* Crumb Elbow Publishing

Time Being Books, *imprint of* Time Being Press

Time Home Entertainment Inc, *distributed by* Hachette Book Group

Timeless Love, *imprint of* Oak Tree Press

Times Books, *imprint of* Henry Holt and Company, LLC, Penguin Random House Inc

Tin House Books, *distributed by* W W Norton & Company Inc

To the Stars Inc, *distributed by* Simon & Schuster, Inc, Simon & Schuster Sales Division

Toccata Press, *imprint of* Boydell & Brewer Inc

Today's Books, *imprint of* History Publishing Co LLC

TOKYOPOP, *imprint of* HarperCollins Children's Books

Tommy Nelson, *imprint of* HarperCollins Christian Publishing, *distributor for* Focus on the Family

Tonga Books, *imprint of* Europa Editions

Delos Toole, *distributed by* Gem Guides Book Co

Tools4Healing (Scott Mieras), *distributor for* Blue Poppy Press

TOP, *imprint of* Top Publications Ltd

Top of the Mountain Publishing, *division of* Powell Productions

Topaz, *imprint of* NAL, Penguin Group (USA) LLC, a Penguin Random House company

Topic Series, *imprint of* Oakstone Publishing LLC

Topics in World History, *imprint of* Markus Wiener Publishers Inc

Tor, *imprint of* Tom Doherty Associates, LLC

Tor Teen, *imprint of* Tom Doherty Associates, LLC

Torah Aura Productions, *distributor for* Free Spirit (selected titles)

Torah Umesorah Publications, *division of* Torah Umesorah-National Society for Hebrew Day Schools

Torrid Books, *imprint of* Whiskey Creek Press LLC

Tory Corner Editions, *imprint of* Quincannon Publishing Group

Total Information, *distributor for* Primary Research Group Inc

Toucan Tales, *imprint of* Rayve Productions Inc

Touch for Health, *distributed by* De Vorss & Co

Touchstone, *imprint of* Scribner Publishing Group

Tourism Dynamic, *imprint of* Cognizant Communication Corp

Towers Maguire Publishing, *imprint of* The Local History Co

Trade Book Publishing, *division of* Slack Incorporated

Tradery House, *imprint of* Wimmer Cookbooks

Tradewind Books, *distributed by* Orca Book Publishers

Tradigital, *distributed by* Fons Vitae

Tradition Books, *imprint of* The Child's World Inc, *distributed by* The Child's World Inc

Trafalgar Square Books, *distributor for* J A Allen, Kenilworth Press, Pferdia TV, *distributed by* Legato Publishing Group

Trafford, *division of* Author Solutions Inc

Trail Wisdom, *distributed by* Sunbelt Publications Inc

Trailblazer Press, *distributed by* Chelsea Green Publishing Co

Trailblazer Publications, *distributed by* The Globe Pequot Press

Trails Books, *division of* Big Earth Publishing

Trails Books Guide, *imprint of* Trails Books

Oswald Train, *distributed by* Donald M Grant Publisher Inc

Training & Development Materials of Canada, *distributor for* HRD Press

Trakker Maps Inc, *subsidiary of* American Map Corp, *distributed by* Hagstrom Map

Tralco, *distributor for* Beach Lloyd Publishers LLC

Tralco-Lingo Fun, *distributor for* Languages for Kids

Trans-Atlantic Publications Inc, *distributor for* Book Guild, Book House, Financial Times Publishing, Hodder Education, Instituto Monsa de Ediciones SA (art books from Spain), Longman, Arnoldo Mondadori Electa, Nexus Special Interests, Pearson Education, Nelson Thornes

Trans Tech Publications, *distributor for* Enfield Publishers, *distributed by* Curran Associates Inc, Enfield Publishing & Distribution Co, Yankee Book Peddler

Transaction Large Print, *imprint of* Transaction Publishers Inc

Transaction Publishers, *distributor for* University of California Institute on Global Conflict & Cooperation

Transaction Publishers Inc, *distributor for* Bridge 21, International Communication Organization (ICO), IWGIA, The Netherlands Institute for Social Research, Editions Scholasticae, Studien Verlag

Transactions, *imprint of* American Philosophical Society

Transcontinental Music, *distributed by* Hal Leonard Corp

Transcontinental Music Publications, *division of* Union for Reform Judaism

Transcript Verlag, *distributed by* Columbia University Press

Transforming Press, *distributed by* Crown House Publishing Co LLC

Transit Cooperative Research Program, *imprint of* Transportation Research Board

Transportation Research Board, *division of* National Academies, The National Academies

Transportation Research Board Code, *distributed by* Professional Publications Inc (PPI)

TransQuest Publishers Pte Ltd, *distributor for* Manning Publications Co

Travel Memories Press, *imprint of* R J Berg Publisher

Travelers' Tales, *subsidiary of* Solas House Inc

Traveling Pen Press, *imprint of* Flying Pen Press LLC

Treacle Press, *imprint of* McPherson & Co

Treasure Chest Books, *distributor for* Ocean Tree Books

Tree Frog Publications, *imprint of* Rada Press Inc

Tree of Life Books, *imprint of* Progressive Press

Treeline Press, *distributed by* Enfield Publishing & Distribution Co

Trees Co, *distributed by* Gem Guides Book Co

Trentham Books Ltd, *distributed by* Stylus Publishing LLC

Tri-Star Boze Books, *distributed by* Gem Guides Book Co

Triad Publishing Co, *imprint of* Triad Communications Ltd

Triangle Square Books for Young Readers, *imprint of* Seven Stories Press

Trident Reference, *imprint of* Standard International Media Holdings

The Trilateral Commission, *distributed by* The Brookings Institution Press

Trillium Mountain Productions, *imprint of* Crumb Elbow Publishing

Trillium Press, *distributed by* Royal Fireworks Press

Trinity Grace Press, *imprint of* Signalman Publishing

Trinity University Press, *unit of* Trinity University

TriQuarterly Books, *imprint of* Northwestern University Press

TRISTAN OUTDOORS, *imprint of* TRISTAN Publishing

Triumph Books, *imprint of* Random House Publishing Group, *distributor for* United States Tennis Association

Triumph Entertainment, *imprint of* Triumph Books

Triumph Learning, *division of* Haights Cross Communications®

Triumph Learning LLC, *division of* Haights Cross Communications®

Troitsa Books, *imprint of* Nova Science Publishers Inc

Troubador Press, *imprint of* Price Stern Sloan

Troubadour Books, *imprint of* Regal Crest Enterprises LLC

Truman State University Press, *unit of* Truman State University

Trust for Public Land, *distributed by* Chelsea Green Publishing Co

Tu Books, *imprint of* Lee & Low Books Inc

Tuckamore Books, *distributed by* Orca Book Publishers

Tudor House, *distributed by* Orca Book Publishers

Tufts University Press, *imprint of* University Press of New England

Tughra Books, *distributor for* Kaynak, Nile Publishing, Zambak

Tumbleweed Series, *imprint of* Mountain Press Publishing Co

Turnaround (London), *distributor for* Bella Books

Turner, *imprint of* Turner Publishing Co

Turtle Point, *imprint of* Turtle Point Press

Tusk Ivory, *imprint of* The Overlook Press

Tusk Paperbacks, *imprint of* The Overlook Press

Tuttle Publishing, *member of* Periplus Publishing Group, *distributor for* Healing Tao Books, Kosei Publishing Co, Kotan Publishing Inc, Milet Publishing Ltd, Paperweight Press, Periplus Editions, Shanghai Press, Shufunotomo Co, Tai Chi Foundation, *distributed by* Cheng & Tsui Co Inc, Publishers Group West (digital only), Simon & Schuster, Inc

TV Books, *distributed by* HarperCollins Publishers

Mark Twain Media, *distributed by* Carson-Dellosa Publishing LLC

Twayne Publishers™, *imprint of* Gale

Twelve, *imprint of* Grand Central Publishing

Twenty-First Century Books, *division of* Lerner Publishing Group Inc, *imprint of* Lerner Publishing Group Inc

21st Century Publications, *distributed by* Hal Leonard Corp

Twenty-Third Publications, *division of* Bayard Inc, *distributor for* Novalis (Canada), *distributed by* Columba (UK), John Garrett (Australia), Novalis (Canada)

Twilight Times Books, *distributed by* Brodart Co, BWI Books

Twilight Visions, *imprint of* Twilight Times Books

Two Wolf Press, *imprint of* White Wolf Publishing Inc

TwoDot®, *imprint of* The Globe Pequot Press

Tyee Press, *imprint of* Crumb Elbow Publishing

Tyndale Audio, *imprint of* Tyndale House Publishers Inc

Tyndale Entertainment, *imprint of* Tyndale House Publishers Inc

Tyndale House Publishers, *distributor for* Focus on the Family

Tyndale House Publishers Inc, *distributor for* Focus on the Family

Tyndale Kids, *imprint of* Tyndale House Publishers Inc

Tyndale Momentum, *imprint of* Tyndale House Publishers Inc

Tyndale Ninos, *imprint of* Tyndale House Publishers Inc

Type & Archetype Press, *imprint of* Type & Temperament Inc

Typophiles, *distributed by* Oak Knoll Press

Tyrus Books, *imprint of* F+W, A Content + eCommerce Company

U X L™, *imprint of* Gale

UA Museum, *distributed by* University of Alaska Press

UBC Press, Canada, *distributor for* Michigan State University Press (MSU Press)

Ubu Repertory Theatre Publications, *distributed by* Theatre Communications Group

UCL Institute of Archaeology, *distributed by* Left Coast Press Inc

UCLA Fowler Museum of Cultural History, *distributed by* University of Washington Press

UCLA/Hammer Museum, *distributed by* Wittenborn Art Books

Udig, *imprint of* Andrews McMeel Publishing LLC

Ugly Duckling Presse, *distributor for* United Artists

ULI, *imprint of* Urban Land Institute

The Ultra Violet Library, *imprint of* Circlet Press Inc

Ulysses Press, *distributed by* Publishers Group West

Unarius Academy of Science Publications, *division of* Unarius Educational Foundation

Unarius Video Productions, *division of* Unarius Academy of Science Publications

Uncrate LLC, *distributed by* Simon & Schuster, Inc, Simon & Schuster Sales Division

Uncrowned Queens, *distributed by* Excelsior Editions, State University of New York Press

Undergraduate Program Field Test Series, *imprint of* National Learning Corp

UNFOLDS®, *imprint of* VanDam Inc

Unifacmanu Trading Co Ltd, *distributor for* Health Professions Press

Editorial Unilit, *division of* Spanish House Inc

Unique Books, *distributor for* Do-It-Yourself Legal Publishers

United Artists, *distributed by* Ugly Duckling Presse

The United Educators Inc, *subsidiary of* Standard Educational Corp

United Nations Children's Fund (UNICEF), *distributed by* United Nations Publications

United Nations Development Programme (UNDP), *distributed by* United Nations Publications

United Nations Economic & Social Commission for Asia & the Pacific (ESCAP), *distributed by* United Nations Publications

United Nations Economic & Social Commission for Western Asia (ESCWA), *distributed by* United Nations Publications

United Nations Economic Commission for Africa (ECA), *distributed by* United Nations Publications

United Nations Economic Commission for Europe (ECE), *distributed by* United Nations Publications

United Nations Economic Commission for Latin America & the Caribbean (ECLAC), *distributed by* United Nations Publications

United Nations High Commissioner for Refugees (UNHCR), *distributed by* United Nations Publications

United Nations Human Settlements Programme (UN-HABITAT), *distributed by* United Nations Publications

United Nations Industrial Development Organization (UNIDO), *distributed by* United Nations Publications

United Nations Institute for Disarmament Research (UNIDIR), *distributed by* United Nations Publications

United Nations Institute for Training & Research (UNITAR), *distributed by* United Nations Publications

United Nations International Research & Training Institute for the Advancement of Women (INSTRAW), *distributed by* United Nations Publications

United Nations Interregional Crime & Justice Research Institute (UNICRI), *distributed by* United Nations Publications

United Nations Office for Project Services (UNOPS), *distributed by* United Nations Publications

United Nations Office for the Coordination of Humanitarian Affairs (OCHA), *distributed by* United Nations Publications

United Nations Office on Drugs & Crime (UNODC), *distributed by* United Nations Publications

United Nations Population Fund (UNFPA), *distributed by* United Nations Publications

United Nations Publications, *distributor for* Food & Agriculture Organization of the United Nations (FAO), International Atomic Energy Agency (IAEA), International Criminal Tribunal for Rwanda (UNICTR), International Criminal Tribunal for the former Yugoslavia (ICTY), International Organization for Migration (IOM), International Trade Centre (ITC), Office of the United Nations High Commissioner for Human Rights (OHCHR), United Nations Children's Fund (UNICEF), United Nations Development Programme (UNDP), United Nations Economic & Social Commission for Asia & the Pacific (ESCAP), United Nations Economic & Social Commission for Western Asia (ESCWA), United Nations Economic Commission for Africa (ECA), United Nations Economic Commission for Europe (ECE), United Nations Economic Commission for Latin America & the Caribbean (ECLAC), United Nations High Commissioner for Refugees (UNHCR), United Nations Human Settlements Programme (UN-HABITAT), United Nations Industrial Development Organization (UNIDO), United Nations Institute for Disarmament Research (UNIDIR), United Nations Institute for Training & Research (UNITAR), United Nations International Research & Training Institute for the Advancement of Women (INSTRAW), United Nations Interregional Crime & Justice Research Institute (UNICRI), United Nations Office for Project Services (UNOPS), United Nations Office for the Coordination of Humanitarian Affairs (OCHA), United Nations Office on Drugs & Crime (UNODC), United Nations Population Fund (UNFPA), United Nations Research Institute for Social Development (UNRISD), United Nations University (UNU)

United Nations Research Institute for Social Development (UNRISD), *distributed by* United Nations Publications

United Nations University (UNU), *distributed by* United Nations Publications

United Nations University Press, *distributed by* The Brookings Institution Press

United Publishers Services Ltd, *distributor for* Peterson Institute for International Economics (PIIE)

United States Catholic Conference Publications, *distributed by* Liturgy Training Publications

United States Pharmacopeia, *distributed by* Consumer Reports, Login Brothers Book Co, Login Publishing Consortium

United States Tennis Association, *distributed by* Triumph Books, Universe Publishing, H O Zimman Inc

United Synagogue Book Service, *division of* United Synagogue of Conservative Judaism, *distributor for* Rabbinical Assembly of America

United Synagogue Commission on Jewish Education, *imprint of* United Synagogue Book Service

United Synagogue of Conservative Judaism, *imprint of* United Synagogue Book Service

Univelt Inc, *affiliate of* American Astronautical Society, *distributor for* Astronautical Society of Western Australia, US Space Foundation

Universe, *imprint of* Rizzoli International Publications Inc, Universe Publishing, *distributor for* Country Music Foundation Press

Universe Calendars, *imprint of* Universe Publishing

Universe Publishing, *imprint of* Rizzoli International Publications Inc, *distributor for* United States Tennis Association, *distributed by* Random House

Universe Publishing Calendars, *distributed by* Andrews McMeel Publishing LLC

University College Dublin Press, *distributed by* Dufour Editions Inc

University of Alabama Press, *distributor for* Fiction Collective Two Inc (FC2)

University of Alaska Press, *distributor for* Alaska Native Language Center, Alaska Quarterly Review, Alaska Sea Grant, Alutiiq Museum, Anchorage Museum Association, Anchorage Museum of Art History, Arctic Studies Center of the Smithsonian Museum, Far to the North Press, Geophysical Institute, Limestone Press, Spirit Mountain Press, UA Museum, Vanessapress

University of Alberta Press, *distributed by* Michigan State University Press (MSU Press)

The University of Arkansas Press, *division of* The University of Arkansas, *distributor for* Butler Center for Arkansas Studies, Hearne Fine Art, Moon City Press, Ozark Society, Phoenix International

University of Calgary Press, *distributed by* Michigan State University Press (MSU Press)

University of California Institute on Global Conflict & Cooperation, *subsidiary of* University of California, *distributed by* Brookings Institution Press, Columbia International Affairs Online (CIAO), Cornell University Press, Garland Publishers, Lynn-Reinner Publishing, Penn State University Press, Princeton University Press, Transaction Publishers, University of Michigan Press, Westview Press

University of California Press, *distributor for* artSITES, British Film Institute, Sierra Club Books (adult trade), Woodrow Wilson Center Press, *distributed by* Sunbelt Publications Inc

University of Chicago Press, *distributor for* CSLI Publications, Getty Publications, St Augustine's Press Inc, Swan Isle Press

University of Chicago Press Distribution Center, *distributor for* University of Pittsburgh Press

University of Delaware Press, *distributed by* Rowman & Littlefield

University of Georgia Press, *distributor for* Golden Coast Publishing Co, Telfair Museums

University of Hawaii Press, *distributor for* Ateneo De Manila University Press, Cornell University East Asia Program, Huia Publishers, MerwinAsia, NIAS Press, The Numata Center, NUS Press, Renaissance Press, Seoul Selection, Shanghai Press, Three Pines Press, University of the Phillippines Press

University of Idaho Asian American Comparative Collection, *distributed by* Caxton Press

University of Idaho Press, *distributed by* Caxton Press

University of Illinois Press, *unit of* University of Illinois

University of Manitoba Press, *distributed by* Michigan State University Press (MSU Press)

University of Massachusetts Press, *distributed by* The Johns Hopkins University Press

University of Michigan, *distributed by* International Book Centre Inc

University of Michigan Center for Japanese Studies, *unit of* University of Michigan

University of Michigan Press, *unit of* University of Michigan, *distributor for* Center for Chinese Studies, University of Michigan, Center for South & Southeast Asian Studies, University of Michigan, University of California Institute on Global Conflict & Cooperation, *distributed by* Eurospan (territory restricted to Europe, Africa & UK)

University of Minnesota Press, *unit of* University of Minnesota, *distributed by* Heimburger House Publishing Co

University of Missouri Press, *distributor for* Missouri History Museum, St Louis Mercantile Library

University of Nebraska Press, *division of* University of Nebraska at Lincoln, *distributor for* Buros Institute, Caxton Press, Creighton University Press, Jewish Publication Society, Society for American Baseball Research

University of New Hampshire Press, *imprint of* University Press of New England

University of New Mexico, *distributor for* Avanyu Publishing, Fresco Fine Art Publications LLC, La Frontera Publishing, West End Press

University of New Mexico Press, *distributor for* Museum of New Mexico Press

The University of North Carolina Press, *distributor for* Museum of Early Southern Decorative Arts, North Carolina Museum of Art, Omohundro Institute of Early American History & Culture (OIEAHC), Southeastern Center for Contemporary Art, Valentine Museum

University of North Texas Press, *distributed by* Texas A&M University Press

University of Oklahoma Press, *distributor for* Cherokee National Press, Dakota Institute, Denver Art Museum, Gilcrease Museum, Vanderbilt University Press

University of Pennsylvania Libraries, *distributed by* Diane Publishing Co

University of Pennsylvania Museum, *distributed by* The Johns Hopkins University Press

University of Pennsylvania Museum of Archaeology & Anthropology, *division of* University of Pennsylvania

University of Pennsylvania Press, *distributed by* The Johns Hopkins University Press

University of Pittsburgh Press, *distributed by* University of Chicago Press Distribution Center

University of Puerto Rico Press, *subsidiary of* University of Puerto Rico

University of Rochester Press, *imprint of* Boydell & Brewer Inc, *affiliate of* Boydell & Brewer Inc

University of San Francisco Press, *distributed by* Fordham University Press

University of Scranton, *distributed by* Heimburger House Publishing Co

University of South Carolina Press, *affiliate of* University of South Carolina, *distributor for* McKissick Museum, Saraland Press, South Carolina Bar Association, South Carolina Historical Society

University of Texas Press, *division of* University of Texas, *distributor for* Bat Conservation International, Institute for Mesoamerican Studies, Menil Foundation, Rothko Chapel, Texas Parks & Wildlife Department, Texas Western Press

University of the Phillippines Press, *distributed by* University of Hawaii Press

University of Tokyo Press, *distributed by* Columbia University Press

University of Toronto Press, *distributor for* Central European University Press, Mage Publishers Inc

The University of Utah Press, *subsidiary of* University of Utah, *distributor for* BYU Museum of Peoples & Cultures, BYU Studies, Canyonlands Natural History Association, KUED (Utah PBS affiliate), Western Epics Publications

University of Vermont Press, *imprint of* University Press of New England

The University of Virginia Press, *affiliate of* University of Virginia, *distributor for* Colonial Society of Massachusetts, The Colonial Williamsburg Foundation, Mount Vernon Ladies Association

University of Virginia Press, *distributor for* The Massachusetts Historical Society

University of Washington Press, *imprint of* Combined Academic Publishers, *distributor for* American Federation of Arts, Lost Horse Press, Lynx House Press, UCLA Fowler Museum of Cultural History, *distributed by* The Johns Hopkins University Press

University of Wisconsin Press, *distributor for* The Center for the Study of Upper Midwestern Culture, Dryad Press, Elvehjem Museum of Art, International Brecht Society, Max Kade Institute for German-American Studies, Spring Freshet Press, Wisconsin Academy of Sciences, Arts & Letters, Wisconsin Historical Society Press, Wisconsin Veterans Museum

University Press, *distributed by* American Mathematical Society

University Press of America Inc, *imprint of* Rowman & Littlefield Publishing Group, *distributor for* Atlantic Council, Center for National Policy Press, Harvard Center for International Affairs, International Law Institute, Joint Center for Political & Economic Studies Press, White Burkett Miller Center, Society of the Cincinnati

University Press of Colorado, *distributor for* Center for Literary Publishing, History Colorado, Western Press Books

University Press of Florida, *affiliate of* State University System of Florida

The University Press of Kentucky, *distributor for* Kentucky Historical Society, *distributed by* The Johns Hopkins University Press

University Press of Maryland, *imprint of* CDL Press

University Press of New England, *distributor for* Beinecke Rare Book & Manuscript Library, Bibliopola Press, CavanKerry Press, Chipstone Foundation, The Colonial Williamsburg Foundation, Fence Books, Four Way Books, Isabella Stewart Gardner Museum, Harvest Hill Press, National Poetry Foundation, New England College, Nicolin Fields Publishing, Peter E Randall Publisher, The Sheep Meadow Press, Vermont Folklife Center, Warring States Project, Wesleyan University Press, Winterthur Museum & Country Estate, Winterthur Museum Garden & Library

University Press of New England (UPNE), *distributor for* Oberlin College Press

UNO Press, *division of* University of New Orleans

Upper Access Books, *imprint of* Upper Access Inc

Upper Ohio Valley Books, *distributed by* John F Blair Publisher

Upper Playground, *distributed by* Gingko Press Inc

Upper Room Books, *division of* The Upper Room, *imprint of* Abingdon Press, *distributed by* Abingdon Press

Upstart Books™, *imprint of* Highsmith Inc, Upstart Books

Urban Books, *distributed by* Kensington Publishing Corp

Urban Institute Press, *distributed by* The Johns Hopkins University Press

Urim Publications, *division of* Lambda Publishers Inc

URJ Books & Music, *division of* Union for Reform Judaism

US Coast Pilot, *imprint of* ProStar Publications Inc

US Games Systems Inc, *distributor for* A G Muller & Cie

US Government Publishing Office (GPO), *division of* US Government

US Green Building Council, *distributed by* Professional Publications Inc (PPI)

US International Publishing, *distributed by* Cheng & Tsui Co Inc

US Space Foundation, *distributed by* Univelt Inc

Usborne Books, *imprint of* EDC Publishing

Usborne Publishing, *distributed by* EDC Publishing

User's Guides, *imprint of* Basic Health Publications Inc

Utah Geological Survey, *division of* Utah Department of Natural Resources

Utah State University Press, *imprint of* University Press of Colorado

Vagabond Voices, *distributed by* Dufour Editions Inc

Valaam Society of America, *imprint of* Saint Herman Press

Valentine Museum, *distributed by* The University of North Carolina Press

Armand Vallee, *distributed by* Sunbelt Publications Inc

Valuation Press, *imprint of* Marshall & Swift

Valusource, *imprint of* John Wiley & Sons Inc

Van der Plas Publications, *imprint of* Cycle Publishing LLC

V&A Publishing, *distributed by* Harry N Abrams Inc

Vandalia Press, *imprint of* West Virginia University Press

VanDam Advertising, *division of* VanDam Inc

VanDam Licensing, *division of* VanDam Inc

VanDam Publishing, *division of* VanDam Inc

Vandamere Press, *distributor for* ABI Professional Publications (non-exclusive), JMC Press (exclusive to trade), NRH Press (non-exclusive), Quodlibetal Features

Vanderbilt Library of American Philosophy, *imprint of* Vanderbilt University Press

Vanderbilt University Press, *division of* Vanderbilt University, *distributor for* Country Music Foundation Press, *distributed by* University of Oklahoma Press

Vanessapress, *distributed by* University of Alaska Press

Vanwell-Looking Back Press, *distributed by* Casemate Publishers & Book Distributors LLC

Vanwell Publishing, *distributed by* Casemate Publishers & Book Distributors LLC

Varlik, *subsidiary of* Cross-Cultural Communications

Yad Vashem, *distributed by* Berghahn Books

Vedanta Press, *subsidiary of* Vedanta Society of Southern California, *distributor for* Advaita Ashrama, Ananda Ashrama, Ramakrishna Math

Vegan Heritage Press, *distributed by* Andrews McMeel Publishing LLC

Vegas Lit, *imprint of* Huntington Press Publishing

Velazquez Press, *division of* Academic Learning Co LLC

The Vendome Press, *distributed by* Harry N Abrams Inc

Venture Press, *imprint of* Williams & Company Book Publishers

Verba Mundi, *imprint of* David R Godine Publisher Inc

Veritas, *distributed by* ACTA Publications, Dufour Editions Inc, Ignatius Press

Vermont Folklife Center, *distributed by* University Press of New England

Vernon Press, *imprint of* Vernon Art & Science Inc

Verso, *distributed by* W W Norton (USA), Penguin (Canada)

Vertigo, *imprint of* DC Entertainment

Vett og Viten Forlag, *distributed by* Enfield Publishing & Distribution Co

VH-1, *imprint of* Gallery Books

VH1 Press, *distributed by* powerHouse Books

Vibe Books, *distributed by* Kensington Publishing Corp

Vice Books, *distributed by* powerHouse Books

Victionary, *distributed by* Gingko Press Inc

Victorian Heritage Press, *imprint of* Loving Healing Press Inc

Victory Belt Publishing, *distributed by* Simon & Schuster, Inc

Victory History of the Counties of England, *imprint of* Boydell & Brewer Inc

Victory in Grace Press, *division of* Victory in Grace Ministries

Vieweg Verlag Publications, *distributed by* American Mathematical Society

Viking, *imprint of* Penguin Group (USA) LLC, Penguin Group (USA) LLC, a Penguin Random House company

Viking Children's Books, *imprint of* Penguin Group (USA) LLC, Penguin Group (USA) LLC, a Penguin Random House company, Penguin Young Readers Group

Viking Compass, *imprint of* Penguin Group (USA) LLC, a Penguin Random House company, Viking

Viking Studio, *imprint of* Penguin Group (USA) LLC, Penguin Group (USA) LLC, a Penguin Random House company

Villard, *imprint of* Random House Publishing Group

Villard Books, *imprint of* Penguin Random House Inc

Vintage & Anchor Books, *imprint of* Knopf Doubleday Publishing Group

Vintage Books, *imprint of* Penguin Random House Inc

Vintage Guitar, *imprint of* Hal Leonard Corp, *distributed by* Hal Leonard Corp

Vintage Image, *imprint of* The Wine Appreciation Guild Ltd

Vintage Shorts, *imprint of* Vintage & Anchor Books

Vireo Press, *distributed by* ECS Publishing Corp

Virginia Genealogical Society, *distributed by* Heritage Books Inc

Vision, *imprint of* Grand Central Publishing

Visual™, *imprint of* John Wiley & Sons Inc

Visual Profile Books Inc, *distributed by* Innovative Logistics (US & CN)

Vital Communities, *distributed by* Enfield Publishing & Distribution Co

Vital Resources, *imprint of* Gospel Publishing House (GPH)

Viva Books PVT, *distributor for* Peterson Institute for International Economics (PIIE)

Viva Editions, *imprint of* Cleis Press

VIZ Media, *distributed by* Simon & Schuster, Inc, Simon & Schuster Sales Division

Voggenreiter Publishers, *distributed by* Mel Bay Publications Inc

Voices of Asia, *imprint of* EastBridge

Volo, *imprint of* Disney-Hyperion Books

Voyage, *imprint of* Brigantine Media

Voyageur Press, *imprint of* Quarto Publishing Group USA Inc, *distributor for* Tetra Press

W W Norton, *distributor for* Allworth Press, Verso

W W Norton & Co Inc, *distributor for* The Countryman Press, The Overlook Press, Pushcart Press, Thames & Hudson

Wadsworth, *subsidiary of* Cengage Learning, *imprint of* Wadsworth Publishing

Wadsworth Inc, *distributor for* National Association of Broadcasters (NAB)

Wadsworth Publishing, *division of* Cengage Learning, Cengage Learning™, *distributed by* Cengage Learning™

WAG Books, *distributed by* Casemate Publishers & Book Distributors LLC

Wageningen Academic Publishers, *distributed by* Enfield Publishing & Distribution Co

Walden Pond Press, *imprint of* HarperCollins Children's Books

Waldman House Press, *imprint of* TRISTAN Publishing

Walkabout Press, *distributed by* John F Blair Publisher

Walker and Company, *distributed by* St Martin's Press, LLC

Wall & Thompson, *distributed by* ADASI Publishing Co

Wallflower Press, *imprint of* Columbia University Press

Walton's, *distributed by* Mel Bay Publications Inc

Warboys LLC, *distributed by* Bridge-Logos Inc

Wargaming, *imprint of* Osprey Publishing Inc

Warlord Games, *distributed by* Casemate Publishers & Book Distributors LLC

Warman's, *imprint of* F+W, A Content + eCommerce Company, Krause Publications Inc

Frederick Warne, *subsidiary of* Penguin Group (USA) LLC, a Penguin Random House company, *imprint of* Penguin Group (USA) LLC, a Penguin Random House company, Penguin Group (USA) LLC, a Penguin Random House Company, Penguin Young Readers Group, *distributed by* Perfection Learning Corp

Warner/Chappell Music Inc, *imprint of* Alfred Music Publishing

Warner Press, *affiliate of* Church of God

Warring States Project, *distributed by* University Press of New England

Warrior, *imprint of* Osprey Publishing Inc

Washington Post Crosswords, *imprint of* Random House Reference/Random House Puzzles & Games/House of Collectibles

Washington Service Bureau, *subsidiary of* CCH, a Wolters Kluwer business

Washington Square Press, *imprint of* Atria Books

Washington State Historical Society, *distributed by* Washington State University Press

Washington State University Press, *division of* Washington State University, *distributor for* The Hutton Settlement (single title), Oregon Writers Colony (single title), Pacific Institute (single title), Washington State Historical Society (single title), WSU Museum of Art

Water Resources Publications LLC, *distributor for* ASAE, ASCE

Water Row Books, *distributor for* Water Row Press, *distributed by* Water Row Press

Water Row Press, *subsidiary of* Water Row Books, *distributor for* Water Row Books, Weinberg Books, *distributed by* Water Row Books

WaterBrook Multnomah, *imprint of* Crown Publishing Group

WaterBrook Multnomah Publishing Group, *imprint of* Penguin Random House Inc, Random House Inc

Waterfall Press, *imprint of* Brilliance Audio

Waterfront Soundings Productions, *distributed by* Marine Techniques Publishing

Watersport Books, *imprint of* Aqua Quest Publications Inc

Watson-Guptill, *imprint of* Crown Publishing Group

Watson-Guptill Publications, *imprint of* Crown Publishing Group, *distributor for* C & T Publishing Inc

Neale Watson Academic Publications, *imprint of* Watson Publishing International LLC

Waverley Books (UK), *distributed by* Interlink Publishing Group Inc

Wax Facts Press, *distributed by* Gingko Press Inc

Wayne State University Press, *distributor for* Cranbrook Institute of Science, Detroit Institute of Arts, Hebrew Union College Press, Marick Press

The Waywiser Press, *distributed by* Dufour Editions Inc

WBusiness Books, *imprint of* New Win Publishing

We Do Listen, *distributed by* Lerner Publishing Group Inc

WEA, *distributed by* Alfred Music Publishing

Weapon, *imprint of* Osprey Publishing Inc

Web Offset Association (WOA), *division of* Printing Industries of America

Wee Creek Press, *imprint of* Whiskey Creek Press LLC

Wee Sing, *imprint of* Penguin Group (USA) LLC, a Penguin Random House company, Price Stern Sloan

Weidenfeld & Nicolson, *distributed by* Sterling Publishing Co Inc

Weight Watchers, *imprint of* St Martin's Press, LLC

Weinberg Books, *distributed by* Water Row Press

Irene Weinberger Books, *imprint of* Hamilton Stone Editions

Weinstein Books, *imprint of* The Perseus Books Group

Welcome Books, *imprint of* Rizzoli International Publications Inc

Welcome Books®, *imprint of* Rizzoli International Publications Inc, *distributor for* AAP, Cerf & Peterson, Music Sales, Zeke Holdings Ltd, *distributed by* Random House

Welcome Rain Publishers LLC, *distributed by* National Book Network

Weldon Owen, *distributed by* Simon & Schuster, Inc, Simon & Schuster Sales Division

Wellfleet Press, *imprint of* Book Sales Inc, Quarto Publishing Group USA Inc

Wellington Press, *division of* BooksUPrint.com Inc

Welz, *distributed by* Alan Wofsy Fine Arts

Wendy Lamb Books, *imprint of* Penguin Random House Inc, Random House Children's Books

Wescott Cove Publishing Co, *imprint of* Far Horizons Media Co

Weseanne Publications, *distributed by* Gem Guides Book Co

Wesleyan Poetry, *imprint of* Wesleyan University Press

Wesleyan Publishing House, *division of* Wesleyan Church Corp, Wesleyan Church Corporation

Wesleyan University Press, *distributed by* University Press of New England

West End Press, *distributed by* University of New Mexico

Westcliffe Publishers Inc, *imprint of* Big Earth Publishing

Westcliffe Publishing, *distributed by* Heimburger House Publishing Co

Western Edge Press, *imprint of* Sherman Asher Publishing, *distributed by* Mountain Press Publishing Co

Western Epics Publications, *distributed by* The University of Utah Press

Western Horseman, *imprint of* The Globe Pequot Press

Western Horseman Books, *distributed by* The Globe Pequot Press

Western Pennsylvania Genealogical Society, *distributed by* Mechling Associates

Western Press Books, *distributed by* University Press of Colorado

Western Psychological Service, *distributor for* Psychological Assessment Resources Inc (PAR)

Westminster John Knox Press (WJK), *imprint of* Presbyterian Publishing Corp (PPC), *distributor for* SCM

Westridge Art, *distributed by* Epicenter Press Inc

Westview Press, *member of* The Perseus Books Group, *imprint of* The Perseus Books Group, *distributor for* University of California Institute on Global Conflict & Cooperation

WestWinds Press®, *imprint of* Graphic Arts Books

Wharncliffe, *distributed by* Casemate Publishers & Book Distributors LLC

What Do You Know About Books, *imprint of* National Learning Corp

SR Wheat, *distributed by* Mel Bay Publications Inc

Wheatherstone Press, *subsidiary of* Dickinson Consulting Group

Wheeler Publishing™, *imprint of* Gale

Whiskey Creek Press, *imprint of* Whiskey Creek Press LLC

Whitaker, *distributor for* Faith Library Publications

White Eagle Publishing Trust (England), *distributed by* De Vorss & Co

White Pine Press, *distributor for* Springhouse Editions

White Poppy Press, *imprint of* Modern Memoirs

White Rabbit Press, *distributed by* Cheng & Tsui Co Inc

White Star Publishers, *distributed by* Sterling Publishing Co Inc

White Thread Press, *distributed by* Fons Vitae

White Wolf Publishing Inc, *division of* CCP North America

Whitford Press, *imprint of* Schiffer Publishing Ltd

Whitney Museum of American Art, *distributed by* Yale University Press

Whole Person Associates, *imprint of* Whole Person Associates Inc

Wide World of Maps Inc, *distributor for* Benchmark Maps, Big Sky Maps, Franko Maps, MacVan Maps (Colorado Springs), Metro Maps, Rand McNally, *distributed by* Rand McNally

Wide World Publishing, *imprint of* Wide World Publishing, *distributed by* Perseus Books Group

Wide World Publishing/Tetra, *imprint of* Wide World Publishing

Wigton Publishing, *distributed by* Sunbelt Publications Inc

Wildcat Canyon Press, *imprint of* Council Oak Books LLC

Wild Mountain Press, *imprint of* Crumb Elbow Publishing

Wild Oak, *imprint of* Oak Tree Press

Wilderness Adventures Press Inc, *distributed by* Angler's Book Supply, Books West, Inter Sports, Partners Book Distributor, Partners West, Raymond C Rumpf & Son Inc

Wilderness Press, *distributed by* Sunbelt Publications Inc

Wildflower Press, *affiliate of* Oakbrook Press

Wildlife Research Group, *imprint of* Crumb Elbow Publishing

Wiley, *imprint of* Turner Publishing Co, John Wiley & Sons Inc, *distributed by* AICPA Professional Publications, Gulf Publishing Co

Wiley-IEEE Press, *imprint of* IEEE Press

Wiley-Blackwell, *distributor for* American Anthropological Association (AAA)

Wiley Blackwell Publishers, *distributor for* New York Academy of Sciences

Wiley-Heyden, *imprint of* John Wiley & Sons Inc

Wiley Interscience®, *imprint of* John Wiley & Sons Inc

J Wiley & Sons, *distributed by* Medical Group Management Association (MGMA)

John Wiley, *distributed by* SkillPath Publications

John Wiley & Sons, *imprint of* John Wiley & Sons Inc, *distributor for* The Electrochemical Society (ECS), *distributed by* American Water Works Association (AWWA), Heimburger House Publishing Co

John Wiley & Sons Inc, *distributor for* Association for Information Science & Technology (ASIS&T), Center for Creative Leadership LLC, IEEE Press, R S Means from The Gordian Group, SAS Publishing, *distributed by* American Academy of Environmental Engineers & Scientists™, Center for Creative Leadership LLC, William S Hein & Co Inc, J J Keller & Associates, Inc, NACE International, SAS Publishing, Society of Manufacturing Engineers

John Wiley & Sons Inc Higher Education, *division of* John Wiley & Sons Inc, John Wiley & Sons Inc

John Wiley & Sons Inc Professional/Trade Group, *division of* John Wiley & Sons Inc

John Wiley & Sons Inc Scientific, Technical, Medical & Scholarly (STMS), *division of* John Wiley & Sons Inc

Wiley-Liss, *imprint of* John Wiley & Sons Inc

Wiley-VCH, *imprint of* John Wiley & Sons Inc

William Carey Library Publishers, *division of* Frontier Ventures

William, James & Co, *imprint of* Franklin, Beedle & Associates Inc

William of Moerbeke Translation, *imprint of* St Augustine's Press Inc

Williams & Co Publishers, *imprint of* Williams & Company Book Publishers

Williamson Books, *imprint of* Ideals Publications, a Guideposts Co

Willow Bend Books, *imprint of* Heritage Books Inc

Willow Hill Press, *distributed by* John F Blair Publisher

Wilson Center Press, *imprint of* Woodrow Wilson Center Press

H W Wilson, *division of* EBSCO Information Services, *imprint of* Grey House Publishing Inc™

Neil Wilson Publishing (UK), *distributed by* Interlink Publishing Group Inc

Wimmer Cookbooks, *division of* Mercury Printing

Winchester Press, *imprint of* New Win Publishing

Wind Records, *distributed by* YMAA Publication Center

Windflower Press, *imprint of* Crumb Elbow Publishing

Windsor Books, *division of* Windsor Marketing Corp, Windsor Marketing Corp

Windward Publishing, *imprint of* Finney Company Inc

Wine Enthusiast, *distributed by* Running Press Book Publishers

Kelley Wingate Publications, *imprint of* Carson-Dellosa Publishing LLC

Wings Books, *imprint of* Penguin Random House Inc

WingSpread Publishers, *division of* Zur Ltd

Winston-Derek, *distributor for* Thomas Nelson

Wintergreen/Orchard House Inc, *imprint of* Riverside Publishing

Winternights Publishing, *distributed by* Epicenter Press Inc

Winters Publishing, *imprint of* Winters Publishing

Winterthur Museum, *distributed by* Oak Knoll Press

Winterthur Museum & Country Estate, *distributed by* Abrams, Acanthus, W W Norton & Company Inc, Schiffer, University Press of New England

Winterthur Museum Garden & Library, *distributed by* University Press of New England

Wisconsin Academy of Sciences, Arts & Letters, *distributed by* University of Wisconsin Press

Wisconsin Historical Society Press, *distributed by* University of Wisconsin Press

Wisconsin Veterans Museum, *distributed by* University of Wisconsin Press

Wisdom Archive, *division of* Wisdom Publications Inc

Wisdom Foundation, *distributed by* Fons Vitae

Wisdom Publications, *distributed by* Simon & Schuster, Inc

Wisdom Publications Inc, *distributed by* Simon & Schuster

Paula Wiseman Books, *imprint of* Simon & Schuster Children's Publishing

Wish Publishing, *distributed by* Cardinal Publishers Group

Witherby Seamanship International Ltd, *distributed by* Marine Techniques Publishing

Witness Impulse, *imprint of* HarperCollins General Books Group

Wittenborn Art Books, *division of* Alan Wofsy Fine Arts, *distributor for* Ides et Calendes SA, Menil Foundation, UCLA/Hammer Museum, *distributed by* Alan Wofsy Fine Arts

George Wittenborn, *imprint of* Wittenborn Art Books

Wizards of the Coast, *distributed by* Penguin Random House Inc

Wizards of the Coast LLC, *subsidiary of* Hasbro Inc, *distributed by* Random House

Alan Wofsy Fine Arts, *distributor for* Bora, Brusberg (Berlin), Cramer (Geneva), Huber, Ides et Calendes, Kornfeld & Co (Bern), Picasso Project, Welz, Wittenborn Art Books

Wolf Water Press, *distributed by* Sunbelt Publications Inc

Wolfe, *imprint of* Elsevier, Health Sciences Division

Wolfgang Publications, *distributed by* CarTech Inc

Wolters Kluwer US Corp, *subsidiary of* Wolters Kluwer NV (The Netherlands)

Women In Nontraditional Careers, *imprint of* Her Own Words LLC

Women, Law & Development International (WLDI), *distributed by* Stylus Publishing LLC

Women's Publications, *imprint of* Consumer Press

Marian Wood Books, *imprint of* GP Putnam's Sons (Hardcover)

Woodbine House, *distributed by* Specialty Press Inc

S Woodhouse Books, *imprint of* Everything Goes Media LLC

Woodland Publishing Inc, *distributed by* Summit Beacon

The Woodrow Wilson Center Press, *distributed by* The Johns Hopkins University Press

Woodrow Wilson Center Press, *division of* The Woodrow Wilson International Center for Scholars, Woodrow Wilson International Center for Scholars, *distributed by* Columbia University Press, The Johns Hopkins University Press, Stanford University Press, University of California Press

Woodrow Wilson Center Press/Columbia University Press, *imprint of* Woodrow Wilson Center Press

Woodrow Wilson Center Press/Johns Hopkins University Press, *imprint of* Woodrow Wilson Center Press

Woodrow Wilson Center Press/Stanford University Press, *imprint of* Woodrow Wilson Center Press

Word Aflame Press, *subsidiary of* Pentecostal Publishing House, *imprint of* Pentecostal Publishing House

Word & Quill Press, *distributed by* Cross-Cultural Communications

Word Dancer Press, *imprint of* Linden Publishing Co Inc

Word Music, *distributed by* Hal Leonard Corp

Wordsong, *imprint of* Boyds Mills Press

Wordstock, *distributed by* Franklin, Beedle & Associates Inc

The Working Arts Library, *distributed by* Applause Theatre & Cinema Books

Workman Publishing, *distributor for* The Experiment

Workman Publishing Co Inc, *distributor for* Algonquin Books, The Experiment, Greenwich Workshop Press, Storey Publishing LLC

Workman Speakers Bureau, *division of* Workman Publishing Co Inc

Workout, *imprint of* Triumph Learning LLC

World Almanac, *distributed by* Simon & Schuster, Inc, Simon & Schuster Sales Division

World Almanac®, *imprint of* Infobase Learning

World Bank, *imprint of* World Bank Publications

World Bank Publications, *member of* The World Bank Group

World Book Inc, *subsidiary of* The Scott Fetzer Co

World Catholic Press, *imprint of* Catholic Book Publishing Corp

World Citizens, *affiliate of* Cinema Investments Co Inc, *distributed by* Inland

World Health Organization (WHO), *distributed by* Stylus Publishing LLC

World Literature Ministries, *imprint of* Faith Alive Christian Resources

World of Darkness, *imprint of* White Wolf Publishing Inc

World Resources Institute, *distributed by* The Johns Hopkins University Press

World Trade Organization, *distributed by* The Brookings Institution Press

World Trade Press, *distributed by* Reference Press

World Vision Resources, *subsidiary of* World Vision International

World Wisdom, *distributed by* Fons Vitae

World Wrestling Entertainment, *imprint of* Gallery Books

The World's Largest Publishing Co, *subsidiary of* Gallopade International Inc

WorldTariff, *division of* FedEx Corp

Worth Publishers, *imprint of* Macmillan Higher Education

The Wright Group/McGraw-Hill, *imprint of* McGraw-Hill Education

Wright Group/McGraw-Hill, *division of* McGraw-Hill School Education Group

Write Fuzzy, *imprint of* Write Bloody Publishing

Write Stuff®, *imprint of* Write Stuff Enterprises LLC

Writers & Artists on Photography Series, *imprint of* Aperture Books

Writer's Digest, *distributed by* Hal Leonard Corp

Writer's Digest Books, *imprint of* F+W, A Content + eCommerce Company

Wrox™, *imprint of* John Wiley & Sons Inc

WRS Group, *distributor for* MAR*CO Products Inc

WSU Museum of Art, *distributed by* Washington State University Press

www.simonandschuster.com, *imprint of* Simon & Schuster Digital

Wyrick & Co, *imprint of* Gibbs Smith Publisher

Xemplar, *imprint of* Crossquarter Publishing Group

Xeno Books, *imprint of* Red Hen Press

Xlibris Corp, *division of* Author Solutions Inc

XML Press, *subsidiary of* R L Hamilton & Associates LLC

Xoanon Publishing, *distributed by* Holmes Publishing Group LLC

Xpat Fiction, *imprint of* Franklin, Beedle & Associates Inc

YA Angst, *imprint of* Norilana Books

YA Books, *imprint of* Regal Crest Enterprises LLC

Yale Center for British Art, *distributed by* Yale University Press

Yale University Art Gallery, *distributed by* Yale University Press

Yale University Press, *division of* Yale University, *distributor for* Addison Gallery of American Art, Phillips Academy, American Federation of Arts, The Art Institute of Chicago, The Bard Graduate Center, The Colonial Williamsburg Foundation, Dallas Museum of Art, Harvard Art Museums, Harvard University Art Museums, Japan Society, The Jewish Museum, Kimbell Art Museum, Paul Mellon Centre, The Menil Collection, The Metropolitan Museum of Art, National Gallery, London, National Gallery of Art, National Gallery of Art (Washington, DC), Philadelphia Museum of Art, Princeton University Art Museum, Sterling & Francine Clark Art Institute, Whitney Museum of American Art, Yale Center for British Art, Yale University Art Gallery, *distributed by* Cheng & Tsui Co Inc

Yamhill Press, *distributed by* Epicenter Press Inc

Yankee, *distributor for* Teton NewMedia

Yankee Book Peddler, *distributor for* Primary Research Group Inc, Trans Tech Publications

Year Book, *imprint of* Elsevier, Health Sciences Division

Yearling, *imprint of* Penguin Random House Inc, Random House Children's Books

Yellow Books, *imprint of* Leadership Directories

Yellow 1, *imprint of* Wide World of Maps Inc

Yellow Rose Books, *imprint of* Regal Crest Enterprises LLC

Yellowback Mysteries, *imprint of* James A Rock & Co Publishers

Yelsraek Publishing, *distributed by* Adventures Unlimited Press (AUP)

Yen Press, *imprint of* Orbit

Yes Books, *distributed by* Chelsea Green Publishing Co

Yeshiva University Museum Press, *distributed by* Gorgias Press LLC

Yeshiva University Press, *distributed by* KTAV Publishing House Inc

Yesterdays, *imprint of* Zumaya Publications LLC

Yilin Press, *distributed by* Simon & Schuster, Inc

YMAA Publication Center, *distributor for* Wind Records (Chinese healing music)

York Medieval Press, *imprint of* Boydell & Brewer Inc

You Can Teach Yourself, *imprint of* Mel Bay Publications Inc

Glenn Young Books, *distributed by* Applause Theatre & Cinema Books

Young Patriots Series, *imprint of* Patria Press Inc

Young People's Press Inc (YPPI), *affiliate of* Kens Math

Young Think®, *imprint of* Thomas Geale Publications Inc

Your Coach in a Box, *imprint of* Recorded Books LLC

YourBusinessMinute.com, *subsidiary of* BizBest Media Corp

YourSpecs, *imprint of* SynergEbooks

YouthLight Inc, *distributor for* MAR*CO Products Inc

Yushodo Press, *distributed by* Oak Knoll Press

YWAM Publishing, *division of* Youth with a Mission, *distributor for* Emerald Books

Z140.com, *subsidiary of* BizBest Media Corp

Zahava Publications, *imprint of* Judaica Press Inc

Zak Books, *imprint of* Black Rabbit Books

Zambak, *distributed by* Tughra Books

Zaner-Bloser Inc, *subsidiary of* Highlights for Children Inc

Zaytuna Institute Press, *distributed by* Fons Vitae

Zebra Books, *imprint of* Kensington Publishing Corp

Zed Books, *distributed by* Palgrave Macmillan, St Martin's Press, LLC

Zeitgeist Films, *distributed by* Cheng & Tsui Co Inc

Zeke Holdings Ltd, *distributed by* Welcome Books®

Zenith Press, *imprint of* Quarto Publishing Group USA Inc

Zephyr Press, *imprint of* Chicago Review Press

Zero+ Publishing, *distributed by* Gingko Press Inc

Zest Books, *distributed by* Houghton Mifflin Harcourt

Zeta Books, *distributed by* Philosophy Documentation Center

ZHealth Books, *imprint of* New Win Publishing

H O Zimman Inc, *distributor for* United States Tennis Association

Zinc Ink, *imprint of* Random House Publishing Group

Zoland Books, *imprint of* Steerforth Press

Zondervan, *imprint of* HarperCollins Christian Publishing, *distributor for* Focus on the Family

Zone Books, *distributed by* The MIT Press

Zone Books dba Urzone Inc, *distributed by* The MIT Press

Zubaan Books, *distributed by* Diversion Books

Zuckschwerdt Verlag (Munich, Germany), *distributed by* Scholium International Inc

Zumaya Publications LLC, *imprint of* eXtasy Books

Canadian Publishers

Listed in alphabetical order are those Canadian publishers that have reported to *LMP* that they produce an average of three or more books annually. Publishers that have appeared in a previous edition of *LMP*, but whose output currently does not meet our defined rate of activity, will be reinstated when their annual production reaches the required level. It should be noted that this rule of publishing activity does not apply to publishers of dictionaries, encyclopedias, atlases and braille books or to university presses.

The definition of a book is that used for *Books in Print* (Grey House Publishing, PO Box 56, Amenia, NY 12501-0056, USA) and excludes charts, pamphlets, folding maps, sheet music and material with stapled bindings. Publishers that make their titles available only in electronic or audio format are included if they meet the stated criteria. In the case of packages, the book must be of equal or greater importance than the accompanying piece. With few exceptions, new publishers are not listed prior to having published at least three titles within a year.

§ before the company name indicates those publishers involved in electronic publishing.

ACTA Press
2509 Dieppe Ave SW, Bldg B6, Suite 101, Calgary, AB T3E 7J9
Tel: 403-288-1195 *Fax:* 403-247-6851
E-mail: journals@actapress.com; publish@actapress.com; sales@actapress.com
Web Site: www.actapress.com
Key Personnel
Owner & Mng Dir: Dr Mohamed H Hamza
Sr Publr & Graphic Designer: Debbie Quinton
Conference & Pubns Mgr: Aaron Swanbergson
Founded: 1972
Scientific & technical conference proceedings & journals; Computers, control & power systems, information technology, robotics, signal & image processing.
Publishes in English.
ISBN Prefix(es): 978-0-88986
Number of titles published annually: 50 Print; 50 CD-ROM
Total Titles: 900 Print; 50 CD-ROM
Branch Office(s)
1811 W Katella Ave, No 101, Anaheim, CA 92804, United States, US Rep: Sunny Yacenda *Tel:* 714-778-3230 *Fax:* 714-778-5463 *E-mail:* usa@iasted.org

The Althouse Press
Unit of University of Western Ontario
John George Althouse Bldg, 1137 Western Rd, London, ON N6G 1G7
SAN: 115-1142
Tel: 519-661-2096 *Fax:* 519-661-3714
E-mail: press@uwo.ca
Web Site: www.edu.uwo.ca/althousepress
Key Personnel
Dir: Dr Greg Dickinson *E-mail:* gdickins@uwo.ca
Edit Asst & Busn Mgr: Katherine Butson
Founded: 1977
Scholarly books & research monographs in education; professional books & materials for educators in elementary & secondary schools & faculties of education; AV & other materials in related fields.
Publishes in English.
ISBN Prefix(es): 978-0-920354
Number of titles published annually: 5 Print
Total Titles: 54 Print
Distributed by SUNY Press; Teachers College Press; University of Chicago Press
Distributor for Lorimer; SUNY Press; Teachers College Press; University of Chicago Press

Annick Press Ltd
15 Patricia Ave, Toronto, ON M2M 1H9
SAN: 115-0065
Tel: 416-221-4802 *Fax:* 416-221-8400
E-mail: annickpress@annickpress.com
Web Site: www.annickpress.com
Key Personnel
Assoc Publr & Ed: Colleen MacMillan *E-mail:* colleenm@annickpress.com
Dir: Rick Wilks
Mktg Mgr: Brigitte Waisberg *E-mail:* brigittew@annickpress.com
Sales & Rts Mgr: Gayna Theophilus *E-mail:* gaynat@annickpress.com
Founded: 1975
Fiction & nonfiction for children & young adults.
Publishes in English, French.
ISBN Prefix(es): 978-0-920236; 978-0-920303; 978-1-55037; 978-1-55451
Number of titles published annually: 30 Print
Total Titles: 425 Print
Branch Office(s)
119 W Pender St, Suite 108, Vancouver, BC V6B 1S5 *Tel:* 604-718-1888
Distributed by Firefly Books Ltd; Open Road
U.S. Rep(s): Ian Booth; Nicholas Booth; Bob Ditter; Rachel Ginsburg; Tom Hamburg; Larry Hollern; David Lewis; Ted Lucia; Thomas Martin; Thomas J McFadden Associates; McLemore/Hollern & Associates Inc; Parisa Michailidis (spec sales); Kevin T Monahan; Frank Porter; Ann Quinn; Sirak & Sirak; Jennifer Sorensen (spec sales); Michael R Watson; Karen Winters; Debra Woodward; Karen Woodward
Foreign Rep(s): CSH Educational Resources Pte Ltd (Singapore); Jay Books (New Zealand); Lexsys Ltd (Caribbean); John Reed Book Distribution (Australia); Ediciones Samara (Mexico)
Foreign Rights: Agency Lapautre (Catherine Lapautre) (France); Bardon Chinese Media Agency (Jian-Mei Wang) (China); Bardon Chinese Media Agency (Cynthia Chang) (Hong Kong, Taiwan); The Deborah Harris Agency (Efrat Lev) (Israel); International Editors' Co (Flavia Sala) (Brazil); International Editors' Co (Liliana Costa) (Latin America); International Editors' Co (Jennifer Hoge) (Portugal, Spain); Japan UNI Agency Inc (May Fujinaga) (Japan); Simona Kessler Agency (Romania); Literarische Agentur & Medienservice (Barbara Kuper) (Germany); Servizi Editoriali Guido Lagomarsino (Anna Spadolini) (Italy)
Membership(s): Association of Canadian Publishers; Canadian Booksellers Association; Ontario Arts Council; Organization of Book Publishers of Ontario

Anvil Press Publishers
278 E First Ave, Vancouver, BC V5T 1A6
Mailing Address: PO Box 3008, MPO, Vancouver, BC V6B 3X5
Tel: 604-876-8710 *Fax:* 604-879-2667
E-mail: info@anvilpress.com
Web Site: www.anvilpress.com
Key Personnel
Publr: Brian Kaufman
Asst Publr & Mktg Coord: Karen Green
Publg Asst: Shazia Hafiz Ramji
Founded: 1988
Literary, all genres; theatre & modern contemporary literature. Canadian authored titles only.
Publishes in English.
ISBN Prefix(es): 978-1-895636; 978-1-897535; 978-1-927380
Number of titles published annually: 12 Print
Total Titles: 90 Print
Distribution Center: Raincoast Books, 2440 Viking Way, Richmond, BC V6V 1N3 *Toll Free Tel:* 800-663-5714 *Fax:* 604-270-7161 *Toll Free Fax:* 800-565-3770 *E-mail:* orders@raincoast.com
Small Press Distribution, 1341 Seventh St, Berkeley, CA 94710-1409, United States *Tel:* 510-524-1668 *Toll Free Tel:* 800-869-7553 (US) *Fax:* 510-524-0852 *E-mail:* spd@spdbooks.org
Membership(s): Association of Book Publishers of British Columbia; Association of Canadian Publishers; Literary Press Group

Aquila Communications Inc
2642 Diab St, Montreal, QC H4S 1E8
Tel: 514-338-1065 *Toll Free Tel:* 800-667-7071 *Fax:* 514-338-1948 *Toll Free Fax:* 866-338-1948
E-mail: orders@aquilacommunications.com
Web Site: www.aquilacommunications.com; aquilacommunications.net
Key Personnel
Founder & Pres: Sami Kelada
Contact: Mike Kelada *E-mail:* mike@aquilacommunications.com
Founded: 1970
High-interest/low-vocabulary readers for learners of French as a second language, grades 4 through college. Also, short humorous situational dialogues in comic book format for kids & teens. Funny episodes of daily life of North American kids & teens (home & school).
Publishes in English, French.
ISBN Prefix(es): 978-0-88510; 978-2-89054
Number of titles published annually: 15 Print
Total Titles: 500 Print; 40 Audio
Imprints: Scaramouche
Distributed by Aquila Communications Ltd

Arsenal Pulp Press
211 E Georgia St, No 202, Vancouver, BC V6A 1Z6
Tel: 604-687-4233 *Toll Free Tel:* 888-600-PULP (600-7857) *Fax:* 604-687-4283
E-mail: info@arsenalpulp.com
Web Site: www.arsenalpulp.com
Key Personnel
Publr: Brian Lam
Assoc Publr: Robert Ballantyne *E-mail:* robert@arsenalpulp.com
Mktg Mgr: Cynara Geissler
Prodn Mgr: Gerilee McBride
Assoc Ed: Susan Safyan
Founded: 1982 (as Pulp Press Book Publishers)
Literary.

Publishes in English.
ISBN Prefix(es): 978-0-88978; 978-1-55152
Number of titles published annually: 20 Print
Total Titles: 260 Print
Imprints: Advance Editions; Little Sister's Classics; Pulp Press; Tillacum Library
U.S. Rep(s): Consortium Book Sales & Distribution
Foreign Rep(s): NewSouth Books (Australia, New Zealand); Turnaround Publisher Services (Europe, UK)
Distribution Center: University of Toronto Press Distribution, 5201 Dufferin St, Toronto, ON M3H 5T8 *Toll Free Tel:* 800-565-9523 *Toll Free Fax:* 800-221-9985 *E-mail:* utpbooks@utpress.utoronto.ca *Web Site:* www.utpress.utoronto.ca
Consortium Book Sales & Distribution, c/o Perseus Distribution, 1094 Flex Dr, Jackson, TN 38301-5070, United States *Toll Free Tel:* 800-283-3572 *Toll Free Fax:* 800-351-5073 *E-mail:* orderentry@perseusbooks.com *Web Site:* www.cbsd.com

Association pour l'Avancement des Sciences et des Techniques de la Documentation
2065 rue Parthenais, Bureau 387, Montreal, QC H2K 3T1
Tel: 514-281-5012 *Fax:* 514-281-8219
E-mail: info@asted.org
Web Site: www.asted.org
Key Personnel
Exec Dir: Suzanne Morin *Tel:* 514-281-5012 ext 234 *E-mail:* smorin@asted.org
Founded: 1973
Association of specialists in information science.
Publishes in French.
ISBN Prefix(es): 978-2-921548; 978-2-89055; 978-2-923563
Number of titles published annually: 3 Print

ASTED, see Association pour l'Avancement des Sciences et des Techniques de la Documentation

Athabasca University Press
Edmonton Learning Ctr, Peace Hills Trust Tower, 1200, 10011-109 St, Edmonton, AB T5J 3S8
Tel: 780-497-3412 *Fax:* 780-421-3298
E-mail: aupress@athabascau.ca
Web Site: www.aupress.ca
Key Personnel
Acting Dir: Kathy Killoh *E-mail:* director.aupress@athabascau.ca
Sr Ed: Pamela Holway *E-mail:* editor.aupress@athabascau.ca
Mktg & Prodn Coord: Megan Hall *E-mail:* marketing.aupress@athabascau.ca
Founded: 2008
This publisher has indicated that 25% of their product line is author subsidized.
Publishes in English, French.
ISBN Prefix(es): 978-0-919737; 978-0-920982; 978-1-897425; 978-1-926836; 978-1-927356
Number of titles published annually: 20 Print
Distribution Center: UBC Press, c/o UTP Distribution, 5201 Dufferin St, Toronto, ON M3H 5T8 *Tel:* 416-667-7791 *Toll Free Tel:* 800-565-9523 *Fax:* 416-667-7832 *Toll Free Fax:* 800-221-9985 *E-mail:* utpbooks@utpress.utoronto.ca
University of Washington Press, c/o Hopkins Fulfillment Service, PO Box 50370, Baltimore, MD 21211-4370, United States *Tel:* 410-516-6956 *Toll Free Tel:* 800-537-5487 *E-mail:* hfscustserv@press.jhu.edu
Eurospan Group, c/o Turpin Distribution, Pegasus Dr, Stratton Business Park, Biggleswade, Beds SG18 8TQ, United Kingdom (Africa, Europe, Middle East, UK) *Tel:* (01767) 604972 *Fax:* (01767) 601640 *E-mail:* eurospan@turpin-distribution.com

B & B Publishing
4823 Sherbrooke St W, Off 275, Westmount, QC H3Z 1G7
Tel: 514-932-9466 *Fax:* 514-932-5929
E-mail: editions@ebbp.ca
Key Personnel
Publr: Paul Beullac
Founded: 1996
Publisher of educational materials; books & wall maps for schools across Canada.
Publishes in English, French.
ISBN Prefix(es): 978-0-88537; 978-2-7615
Number of titles published annually: 10 Print
Total Titles: 400 Print
Distributed by Brault & Bouthillier Ltee; Brault & Bouthillier School Supplies
Foreign Rep(s): Bricolux (Belgium); Canada Ortho (France); Intelligence Insight LLP (Singapore); Wesco (France)
Distribution Center: 700, ave Beaumont, Montreal, QC H3N 1V5 *Tel:* 514-273-9186 *Fax:* 514-273-8627

Banff Centre Press
107 Tunnel Mountain Dr, Banff, AB T1L 1H5
Mailing Address: Box 1020, Banff, AB T1L 1H5
Tel: 403-762-6408
E-mail: press@banffcentre.ca
Web Site: www.banffcentre.ca/press
Founded: 1995
Publisher of books on contemporary art & culture.
Publishes in English, French.
ISBN Prefix(es): 978-0-920159; 978-1-894773
Number of titles published annually: 4 Print
Total Titles: 41 Print; 2 CD-ROM; 4 E-Book
Orders to: LitDistCo, 100 Armstrong Ave, Georgetown, ON L7G 5S4 *Tel:* 905-877-4411 *Toll Free Tel:* 800-591-6250 *Fax:* 905-877-4410 *Toll Free Fax:* 800-591-6251 *E-mail:* orders@litdistco.ca
Returns: LitDistCo, 100 Armstrong Ave, Georgetown, ON L7G 5S4 *Tel:* 905-877-4411 *Toll Free Tel:* 800-591-6250 *Fax:* 905-877-4410 *Toll Free Fax:* 800-591-6251
Warehouse: LitDistCo, 100 Armstrong Ave, Georgetown, ON L7G 5S4 *Tel:* 905-877-4411 *Toll Free Tel:* 800-591-6250 *Fax:* 905-877-4410 *Toll Free Fax:* 800-591-6251
Distribution Center: LitDistCo, 100 Armstrong Ave, Georgetown, ON L7G 5S4 *Tel:* 905-877-4411 *Toll Free Tel:* 800-591-6250 *Fax:* 905-877-4410 *Toll Free Fax:* 800-591-6251 *E-mail:* orders@litdistco.ca
Membership(s): Book Publishers Association of Alberta; Literary Press Group

§Bayeux Arts Inc
119 Stratton Crescent SW, Calgary, AB T3H 1T7
Tel: 403-249-2477
E-mail: mail@bayeux.com
Web Site: bayeux.com
Key Personnel
Co-Publr & Dir: Swapna Gupta
Co-Publr: Ashis Gupta *E-mail:* agupta@bayeux.com
Ed, Children's Lit: Judd Palmer *E-mail:* jpalmer@bayeux.com
Ed, Fiction/Nonfiction/Poetry: Mercedes Batiz-Benet *E-mail:* mercedes@bayeux.com
Founded: 1994
Committed to producing books of beauty that build bridges across cultures.
Publishes in English.
ISBN Prefix(es): 978-1-896209; 978-1-897411
Number of titles published annually: 10 Print
Imprints: Alebrije; Gondolier; Odd Little Books; Rosencrantz Comics
Distribution Center: LitDistCo, 100 Armstrong Ave, Georgetown, ON L7G 5S4 *Toll Free Tel:* 800-591-6250 *Toll Free Fax:* 800-591-6251 *E-mail:* ordering@litdistco.ca
Chicago Distribution Center, 11030 S Langley Ave, Chicago, IL 60628, United States *Tel:* 773-702-7010 *Toll Free Fax:* 800-621-8476

Beliveau Editeur
920, rue Jean-Neveu, Longueuil, QC J4G 2M1
Tel: 450-679-1933; 514-253-0403 *Fax:* 450-679-6648
E-mail: info@beliveauediteur.com
Web Site: www.beliveauediteur.com
Key Personnel
CEO & Pres: Mathieu Beliveau *E-mail:* mbeliveau@beliveauediteur.com
VP, Fin: Sylvain Pichette *E-mail:* spichette@beliveauediteur.com
Asst Ed: Diane Perreault *E-mail:* dperreault@beliveauediteur.com
Press: Marthe Saint-Laurent *E-mail:* mstlaurent@beliveauediteur.com
Founded: 1975
Specialize in recovery, geopolitics & self-help, medicine, taxation & motivation.
Publishes in French.
ISBN Prefix(es): 978-2-89092
Number of titles published annually: 15 Print
Total Titles: 250 Print
Foreign Rep(s): DG Diffusion (France); Servidis (Switzerland)
Distribution Center: Prologue Inc, 1650, Lionel-Bertrand, Boisbriand, QC J7H 1N7 *Toll Free Tel:* 800-363-2864

Between the Lines (BTL)
401 Richmond St W, No 277, Toronto, ON M5V 3A8
SAN: 115-0189
Tel: 416-535-9914 *Toll Free Tel:* 800-718-7201 *Fax:* 416-535-1484
E-mail: info@btlbooks.com
Web Site: btlbooks.com
Key Personnel
Art Dir & Prodn Mgr: Jennifer Tiberio
Accts Mgr: Paula Brill
Mktg & Sales Mgr: Renee Knapp
Mng Ed: Amanda Crocker
Publicist: Matthew Adams *E-mail:* publicity@btlbooks.com
Founded: 1977
Nonfiction, social, economic & political works dealing with international development issues & Canadian social issues.
Publishes in English.
ISBN Prefix(es): 978-0-919946; 978-0-921284; 978-1-896357; 978-1-897071; 978-1-926662; 978-1-77113
Number of titles published annually: 16 Print
Total Titles: 153 Print
U.S. Rep(s): SCB Distributors
Foreign Rep(s): Fernwood Books (Canada)
Orders to: University of Toronto Press, 5201 Dufferin St, North York, ON M3H 5T8 (CN & US) *Toll Free Tel:* 800-565-9523 *Toll Free Fax:* 800-221-9985; Central Books Ltd, 99 Wallis Rd, London E9 5LN, United Kingdom *Tel:* (020) 8986 4854 *E-mail:* orders@centralbooks.com
Membership(s): Canada Council for the Arts; Ontario Arts Council

Black Rose Books Ltd
CP 35788 Succ Leo Pariseau, Montreal, QC H2X 0A4
SAN: 115-2653
Tel: 514-844-4076 *Toll Free Tel:* 800-565-9523 (orders) *Fax:* 514-849-1956 *Toll Free Fax:* 800-221-9985 (orders)
E-mail: info@blackrosebooks.net
Web Site: www.blackrosebooks.net
Key Personnel
Mktg Promo: Lucia Kowaluk

Edit Administrator: Robert Dollins
Founded: 1970
Politics, book & journal publishing in the social sciences & humanities.
Publishes in English.
ISBN Prefix(es): 978-0-919618; 978-0-919619; 978-0-920057; 978-0-921689; 978-1-55164; 978-1-895431
Number of titles published annually: 15 Print; 20 Online; 30 E-Book
Total Titles: 585 Print; 300 E-Book
Branch Office(s)
c/o University of Toronto Press, 2250 Military Rd, Tonawanda, NY 14150, United States *Tel:* 716-683-4547 *Fax:* 716-685-6895
Foreign Office(s): Book & Volume, PO Box 35, 3242 Birregurra, Victoria, Australia *Tel:* (03) 5236 2593 *Fax:* (03) 5236 2030 *E-mail:* info@bookandvolume.com.au *Web Site:* www.bookandvolume.com.au
c/o Central Books, 99 Wallis Rd, London E9 5LN, United Kingdom *Tel:* (020) 8986 4854 *Fax:* (020) 8533 5821 *E-mail:* orders@centralbooks.com *Web Site:* www.centralbooks.com
Distributed by University of Toronto Press
Advertising Agency: Central Books, 99 Wallis Rd, London E9 5LN, United Kingdom *Tel:* (020) 8986 4854 *Fax:* (020) 8533 5821 *E-mail:* orders@centralbooks.com
Orders to: Consortium Book Sales & Distribution, The Keg House, Suite 101, 34 13 Ave NE, Minneapolis, MN 55413-1007, United States, Sales Mgr: Julie Schaper *Tel:* 612-746-2600 *Toll Free Tel:* 800-283-3572 (cust serv) *Fax:* 612-746-2606 *E-mail:* consortium@cbsd.com *Web Site:* www.cbsd.com
Returns: Consortium Book Sales & Distribution, The Keg House, Suite 101, 34 13 Ave NE, Minneapolis, MN 55413-1007, United States, Sales Mgr: Julie Schaper *Tel:* 612-746-2600 *Toll Free Tel:* 800-283-3572 (cust serv) *Fax:* 612-746-2606 *E-mail:* consortium@cbsd.com *Web Site:* www.cbsd.com
Shipping Address: Consortium Book Sales & Distribution, The Keg House, Suite 101, 34 13 Ave NE, Minneapolis, MN 55413-1007, United States, Sales Mgr: Julie Schaper *Tel:* 612-746-2600 *Toll Free Tel:* 800-283-3572 (cust serv) *Fax:* 612-746-2606 *E-mail:* consortium@cbsd.com *Web Site:* www.cbsd.com
Distribution Center: Consortium Book Sales & Distribution, The Keg House, Suite 101, 34 13 Ave NE, Minneapolis, MN 55413-1007, United States, Sales Mgr: Julie Schaper *Tel:* 612-746-2600 *Toll Free Tel:* 800-283-3572 (cust serv) *Fax:* 612-746-2606 *E-mail:* consortium@cbsd.com *Web Site:* www.cbsd.com

Blue Bike Books
11919 125 St, Edmonton, AB T5L 0S3
Tel: 780-951-0032
E-mail: info@bluebikebooks.com
Web Site: www.bluebikebooks.com
Key Personnel
Publr: Nicholle Carriere
Founded: 2005
Publish humor & trivia books. Large number of regional trivia titles as well as national ones.
Publishes in English.
ISBN Prefix(es): 978-1-897278; 978-0-9739116
Number of titles published annually: 5 Print
Total Titles: 80 Print
Distributed by Lone Pine Publishing
Orders to: Lone Pine Publishing, 2311 96 St, Edmonton, AB T6N 1G3, Contact: Jon Murphy *Toll Free Tel:* 800-875-7108 (CN); 800-518-3541 (US) *E-mail:* accounts@lonepinepublishing.com
Shipping Address: Lone Pine Publishing, 2311 96 St, Edmonton, AB T6N 1G3
Membership(s): Book Publishers Association of Alberta

Editions du Bois-de-Coulonge
1140 Ave de Montigny, Sillery, QC G1S 3T7
Tel: 418-683-6332
Web Site: www.ebc.qc.ca
Key Personnel
Owner & Pres: Dr Richard Leclerc, PhD
Founded: 1995
Publish & distribute books about music, multimedia, television & movies.
Publishes in French.
ISBN Prefix(es): 978-2-9801397
Number of titles published annually: 1 Print
Total Titles: 7 Print
Membership(s): Association for the Export of Canadian Books

§Books We Love Ltd
192 Lakeside Greens Dr, Chestermere, AB T1X 1C2
Tel: 403-710-4869
E-mail: bookswelove@shaw.ca
Key Personnel
Pres: Judith Pittman *E-mail:* judecalgary@shaw.ca
VP: Jamie Hill
Founded: 2010
Full service fiction publisher featuring romance, mystery, suspense, young adult, fantasy & science fiction. Royalty paying, non-subsidy publisher who specializes in works by established authors who have had their rights returned from major publishers & are interested in a publisher with a primarily online focus, but with the ability to bring their book out in print & electronic if desired. Provides extensive marketing & promotion assistance to its authors. Offers one of the most generous contracts in the industry & promotes its authors extensively.
Publishes in English.
ISBN Prefix(es): 978-1-927476
Number of titles published annually: 300 Print; 600 E-Book
Total Titles: 300 Print; 500 E-Book
Membership(s): Romance Writers of America

§Borealis Press Ltd
8 Mohawk Crescent, Nepean, ON K2H 7G6
Tel: 613-829-0150 *Toll Free Tel:* 877-696-2585 *Fax:* 613-829-7783
E-mail: drt@borealispress.com
Web Site: www.borealispress.com
Founded: 1972
Canadian-oriented general titles of most types. No unsol mss, query first. Include synopsis +/or outline & sample chapter with SASE.
Publishes in English, French.
ISBN Prefix(es): 978-0-88887; 978-1-896133; 978-0-919594; 978-0-919662
Number of titles published annually: 24 Print
Subsidiaries: Tecumseh Press
Distributed by Blackwell; Dawson; EBSCO; Ex Libris; Hein

The Boston Mills Press
Division of Firefly Books Ltd
50 Staples Ave, Unit 1, Richmond Hill, ON L4B 0A7
Tel: 416-499-8412 *Toll Free Tel:* 800-387-6192 *Fax:* 416-499-8313 *Toll Free Fax:* 800-450-0391
E-mail: service@fireflybooks.com
Web Site: www.fireflybooks.com
Key Personnel
Dir, Prodn & Co-Editions: Jacqueline Hope Raynor
Founded: 1974
Canadian & American history, guide books, large format colour photograph books.
Publishes in English.
ISBN Prefix(es): 978-0-919822; 978-0-919783; 978-1-55046
Number of titles published annually: 20 Print
Total Titles: 200 Print
Distributed by Firefly Books Ltd

BPS Books
Division of Bastian Publishing Services Ltd
42 Donalda Crescent, Toronto, ON M1S 1N7
Tel: 416-609-2004 *Fax:* 416-609-2936
Web Site: www.bpsbooks.com
Key Personnel
Publr & Ed-in-Chief: Donald G Bastian
Founded: 2007
Print-on-demand publisher of original & reprint trade paperbacks for the US, Canadian & UK markets via bookstore web sites such as the Amazon sites in all three countries. No unsol mss, query first using online form.
This publisher has indicated that 90% of their product is author subsidized.
Publishes in English, French.
ISBN Prefix(es): 978-1-926645; 978-0-9784402; 978-0-9809231; 978-1-927483; 978-0-9783286
Number of titles published annually: 15 Print; 10 E-Book
Total Titles: 75 Print; 26 E-Book
Membership(s): Word Guild

Brault & Bouthillier
Division of B & B School Supplies
700 ave Beaumont, Montreal, QC H3N 1V5
Tel: 514-273-9186 *Toll Free Tel:* 800-361-0378 *Fax:* 514-273-8627 *Toll Free Fax:* 800-361-0378
E-mail: ventes@bb.ca
Web Site: bb.ca
Key Personnel
Pres: Paul LeBrun *E-mail:* paullebrun@bb.ca
VP, Busn Devt: Yves Brault *Tel:* 514-273-9186 ext 219 *E-mail:* yvesbrault@bb.ca
VP, Mktg: Ms Josee Legault *E-mail:* jlegault@bb.ca
Sales Dir: Claude Vaillancourt *Tel:* 514-273-9186 ext 227 *E-mail:* cvaillancourt@bb.ca
Founded: 1944
Pedagogical & scientific.
Publishes in English, French.
ISBN Prefix(es): 978-0-88537; 978-2-7615
Number of titles published annually: 100 Print
Branch Office(s)
150 Brittania Rd E, Unit 7, Mississauga, ON L4Z 2A4 *Tel:* 905-890-0404 *Toll Free Tel:* 800-668-1108 *Fax:* 905-890-7999 *Toll Free Fax:* 800-839-7718
Distributed by DPLU Inc (Montreal); B B Jocus (Toronto)

Breakwater Books Ltd
One Stamp's Lane, St John's, NL A1C 6E6
Mailing Address: PO Box 2188, St John's, NL A1C 6E6
Tel: 709-722-6680 *Toll Free Tel:* 800-563-3333 (orders) *Fax:* 709-753-0708
E-mail: info@breakwaterbooks.com; orders@breakwaterbooks.com
Web Site: www.breakwaterbooks.com
Key Personnel
Owner & Pres: Rebecca Rose
Founded: 1973
Books primarily about education & trade books.
Publishes in English, French.
ISBN Prefix(es): 978-0-919519; 978-0-919948; 978-0-920911; 978-1-55081
Number of titles published annually: 16 Print
Total Titles: 600 Print

Brick Books
Box 20081, 431 Boler Rd, London, ON N6K 4G6
Tel: 519-657-8579
E-mail: brick.books@sympatico.ca
Web Site: www.brickbooks.ca
Key Personnel
Gen Mgr: Kitty Lewis
Prodn Mgr: Alayna Munce

Founded: 1975
Publish poetry collections by Canadian authors.
Publishes in English.
ISBN Prefix(es): 978-0-919626; 978-1-894078
Number of titles published annually: 7 Print
Total Titles: 200 Print; 150 E-Book
Distribution Center: LitDistCo, 100 Armstrong Ave, Georgetown, ON L7G 5S4 *Toll Free Tel:* 800-591-6250 *Toll Free Fax:* 800-591-6251 *E-mail:* orders@litdistco.ca *Web Site:* www.litdistco.ca
Membership(s): Association of Canadian Publishers; Literary Press Group of Canada

Brindle & Glass Publishing Ltd
Imprint of TouchWood Editions
1075 Pendergast St, Suite 103, Victoria, BC V8V 0A1
Tel: 250-360-0829 *Fax:* 250-386-0829
E-mail: info@brindleandglass.com
Web Site: www.brindleandglass.com
Key Personnel
Publr: Ruth Linka
Assoc Publr: Taryn Boyd
Founded: 2001
Literary press.
Publishes in English.
ISBN Prefix(es): 978-1-897142; 978-0-9732481; 978-1-926972; 978-1-927366
Number of titles published annually: 8 Print
Total Titles: 85 Print
Foreign Rep(s): Ingram Book Co (USA); Literary Press Group of Canada (Canada)
Foreign Rights: Acacia House
Distribution Center: Heritage Group Distribution, 19272 96 Ave, Suite 8, Surrey, BC V4N 4C1 *Tel:* 604-881-7067 *Toll Free Tel:* 800-665-3302 *Fax:* 604-881-7068 *Toll Free Fax:* 800-566-3336 *E-mail:* orders@hgdistribution.com *Web Site:* www.hgdistribution.com
Ingram Book Group, One Ingram Blvd, La Vergne, TN 37086, United States *Toll Free Tel:* 800-947-8000 *Toll Free Fax:* 800-876-0186 *E-mail:* orders@ingramcontent.com *Web Site:* www.ingramcontent.com
Membership(s): Canada Council for the Arts

Broadview Press
280 Perry St, Unit 5, Peterborough, ON K9J 2J4
SAN: 115-6772
Mailing Address: PO Box 1243, Peterborough, ON K9J 7H5
Tel: 705-743-8990 *Fax:* 705-743-8353
E-mail: customerservice@broadviewpress.com
Web Site: www.broadviewpress.com
Key Personnel
Founder & CEO: Don Le Pan *Tel:* 250-824-5015 *Fax:* 250-824-5001 *E-mail:* don.lepan@broadviewpress.com
Pres: Leslie Dema *Tel:* 519-821-0706 *Fax:* 519-265-6544 *E-mail:* dema@broadviewpress.com
Mng Ed: Tara Lowes *E-mail:* taralowes@broadviewpress.com
Accts Mgr: LeeAnna Dykstra *E-mail:* ldykstra@broadviewpress.com
Exam Copies Coord: Lisa Reid *E-mail:* examcopies@broadviewpress.com
Founded: 1985
The word "broadview" expresses a great deal about the approach that guides our publishing program. Our focus is very much on English studies & philosophy, but within those two core subject areas we are open to a broad range of academic approaches & political viewpoints. We are proud to publish pedagogically valuable books that make a real contribution to scholarship. We welcome feminist perspectives & we have a strong commitment to the environment. Our publishing program is internationally oriented & our individual titles often appeal to a broad readership; we publish many titles that are of as much interest to the general reader as they are to academics & students.
Publishes in English.
ISBN Prefix(es): 978-0-921149; 978-1-55111; 978-1-55481
Number of titles published annually: 45 Print; 40 E-Book
Total Titles: 600 Print; 425 E-Book
Branch Office(s)
10 Douglas St, Suite B, Guelph, ON N1H 2S9 *Tel:* 519-821-2171 *Fax:* 519-265-6544
515-815 First St SW, Calgary, AB T2P 1N3 *Tel:* 403-232-1443 *Fax:* 403-233-0001 *E-mail:* broadview@broadviewpress.com
2215 Kenmore Ave, Buffalo, NY 14207, United States
U.S. Rep(s): Brad DeVetten
Returns: 2215 Kenmore Ave, Buffalo, NY 14207, United States

Broken Jaw Press Inc
Box 596, Sta A, Fredericton, NB E3B 5A6
Tel: 506-454-5127 *Fax:* 506-454-5134
E-mail: editors@brokenjaw.com
Web Site: www.brokenjaw.com
Key Personnel
Pres & Publr: Joe Blades
Founded: 1984 (incorporated 2003)
Publish mostly Canadian-authored literary books: poetry, fiction & creative nonfiction.
Publishes in English, French.
ISBN Prefix(es): 978-0-921411; 978-1-896647; 978-1-55391
Number of titles published annually: 4 Print
Total Titles: 120 Print; 1 CD-ROM; 50 E-Book; 2 Audio
Imprints: Book Rat; Broken Jaw Press; Broken Jaw Press eBooks; Dead Sea Physh Products; SpareTime Editions
Distributor for White Dwarf Editions (Montreal)
Membership(s): Atlantic Publishers Marketing Association

Broquet Inc
97-B, Montee des Bouleaux, St-Constant, QC J5A 1A9
Tel: 450-638-3338 *Fax:* 450-638-4338
E-mail: info@broquet.qc.ca
Web Site: www.broquet.qc.ca
Key Personnel
Pres & Ed: Antoine Broquet
Artistic Dir: Brigit Levesque
Prodn Dir: Ms Josee Fortin
Founded: 1979
Nature books & astronomy.
Publishes in English, French.
ISBN Prefix(es): 978-2-89000; 978-2-89654
Number of titles published annually: 80 Print; 1 CD-ROM
Total Titles: 800 Print; 1 CD-ROM
Foreign Rep(s): Dilisco (Benelux, France); Servidis (Switzerland)
Distribution Center: Prologue Inc, 1650, blvd Lionel-Bertrand, Boisbriand, QC J7H 1N7 *Tel:* 450-434-0306 *Toll Free Tel:* 800-363-2864 *Fax:* 450-434-2627 *Toll Free Fax:* 800-361-8088

Brush Education Inc
6531 111 St, Edmonton, AB T6H 4R5
SAN: 115-0324
Tel: 780-989-0910 *Toll Free Tel:* 855-283-0900 *Fax:* 780-989-0930 *Toll Free Fax:* 855-283-6947
E-mail: contact@brusheducation.ca
Web Site: www.brusheducation.ca
Key Personnel
Partner: Glenn Rollans *E-mail:* glen.rollans@brusheducation.ca
Mng Ed: Lauri Seidlitz *E-mail:* lauri.seidlitz@brusheducation.ca
Founded: 1975
Independent publisher of books for college, university & professional audiences. Our publishing program includes medial & health sciences, education & K9 training.
Publishes in English.
ISBN Prefix(es): 978-0-920490; 978-1-55059
Number of titles published annually: 17 Print; 15 E-Book
Total Titles: 200 Print; 22 E-Book
Distributed by University of Toronto Press
Orders to: University of Toronto Press, 5201 Dufferin St, Toronto, ON M3H 5T8 (CN & US) *Tel:* 416-667-7791 *Toll Free Tel:* 800-565-9523 *Fax:* 416-667-7832 *Toll Free Fax:* 800-221-9985 *E-mail:* utpbooks@utpress.utoronto.ca
Membership(s): Association of Canadian Publishers; Book Publishers Association of Alberta

Callawind Publications Inc
3551 St Charles Blvd, Suite 179, Kirkland, QC H9H 3C4
Tel: 514-685-9109
E-mail: info@callawind.com
Web Site: www.callawind.com
Key Personnel
Mktg: Pamela Carmen *E-mail:* pamela@callawind.com
Founded: 1995
Custom book publisher. Specialize in cookbooks & children's books.
This publisher has indicated that 100% of their product line is author subsidized.
Publishes in English.
ISBN Prefix(es): 978-1-896511
Number of titles published annually: 15 Print
Total Titles: 75 Print
Membership(s): The Association of Publishers for Special Sales; The Independent Book Publishers Association

§Canada Law Book®
Division of Thomson Reuters Canada Ltd
One Corporate Plaza, 2075 Kennedy Rd, Toronto, ON M1T 3V4
Tel: 416-609-3800 (cust rel & orders) *Toll Free Tel:* 800-387-5351 (cust rel, CN & US only); 800-347-5164 (cust rel & orders, CN & US) *Fax:* 416-298-5082 (cust rel & orders, Toronto) *Toll Free Fax:* 877-750-9041 (cust rel & orders, CN only)
E-mail: carswell.customerrelations@thomsonreuters.com; carswell.orders@thomsonreuters.com
Web Site: www.canadalawbook.ca; www.carswell.com
Founded: 1855 (as Upper Canada Law Journal)
Law books.
Publishes in English.
ISBN Prefix(es): 978-0-88804
Number of titles published annually: 50 Print; 3 CD-ROM; 3 E-Book
Total Titles: 480 Print; 25 CD-ROM; 40 Online; 9 E-Book
Subsidiaries: Canadian Lawyer/Law Times Media, A Thomson Reuters business
Returns: 245 Bartley Dr, Toronto, ON M4A 2V8
Distribution Center: 245 Bartley Dr, Toronto, ON M4A 2V8

Canadian Bible Society
10 Carnforth Rd, Toronto, ON M4A 2S4
SAN: 112-5559
Tel: 416-757-4171 *Toll Free Tel:* 866-946-1711 *Fax:* 416-757-3376
E-mail: custserv@biblesociety.ca
Web Site: www.biblescanada.com; www.biblesociety.ca
Key Personnel
Dir, Prod Devt Acq & Dist: Joel Coppieters
Founded: 1904
Bibles, new testaments, scripture portions, selections; scriptures in foreign languages.
Publishes in English, French.
ISBN Prefix(es): 978-0-88834

Number of titles published annually: 20 Print; 3 CD-ROM; 3 Online; 5 Audio
Total Titles: 2,500 Print; 10 CD-ROM; 50 Audio
U.S. Publishers Represented: American Bible Society
Foreign Rep(s): United Bible Societies (Worldwide)
Membership(s): United Bible Societies

Canadian Circumpolar Institute (CCI) Press
Imprint of University of Alberta Press
University of Alberta, Ring House 2, Edmonton, AB T6G 2E1
Tel: 780-492-3662 *Fax:* 780-492-0719
Web Site: www.uap.ualberta.ca
Founded: 1960 (as Boreal Institute for Northern Studies; reconfigured & renamed 1990 as CCI; acquired 2013 by University of Alberta Press)
Publishes in English.
ISBN Prefix(es): 978-1-896445; 978-0-919058
Number of titles published annually: 2 Print; 2 E-Book
Total Titles: 140 Print
Sales Office(s): Ampersand Canada's Book & Gift Agency Inc, 321 Carlaw Ave, Suite 213, Toronto, ON M4M 2S1, Contact: Saffron Beckwith *Tel:* 416-703-0666 ext 124 *Fax:* 416-703-4745 *E-mail:* saffronb@ampersandinc.ca *Web Site:* www.ampersandinc.ca
U.S. Rep(s): Wayne State University Press
Billing Address: University of Alberta Press, c/o 34 Armstrong Ave, Georgetown, ON L7G 4R9 *Tel:* 905-873-2750 *Toll Free Tel:* 877-864-8477 *Fax:* 905-873-6170 *Toll Free Fax:* 877-864-4272 *Web Site:* www.gtwcanada.com
Orders to: Georgetown Terminal Warehouses (GTW), 34 Armstrong Ave, Georgetown, ON L7G 4R9 *Tel:* 905-873-2750 *Toll Free Tel:* 877-864-8477 *Fax:* 905-873-6170 *Toll Free Fax:* 877-864-4272 *E-mail:* orders@gtwcanada.com *Web Site:* www.gtwcanada.com
Returns: Georgetown Terminal Warehouses (GTW), 34 Armstrong Ave, Georgetown, ON L7G 4R9 *Tel:* 905-873-2750 *Toll Free Tel:* 877-864-8477 *Fax:* 905-873-6170 *Toll Free Fax:* 877-864-4272 *E-mail:* orders@gtwcanada.com *Web Site:* www.gtwcanada.com
Shipping Address: Georgetown Terminal Warehouses (GTW), 34 Armstrong Ave, Georgetown, ON L7G 4R9 *Tel:* 905-873-2750 *Toll Free Tel:* 877-864-8477 *Fax:* 905-873-6170 *Toll Free Fax:* 877-864-4272 *E-mail:* orders@gtwcanada.com *Web Site:* www.gtwcanada.com
Distribution Center: Georgetown Terminal Warehouses (GTW), 34 Armstrong Ave, Georgetown, ON L7G 4R9, Contact: Lesley Reynolds *Tel:* 905-873-2750 ext 7082 *Fax:* 905-873-6170 *E-mail:* lreynolds@gtwcanada.com
Wayne State University Press (WSUP), Shipping & Receiving, 40 W Hancock, Detroit, MI 48201-1309, United States (does not carry all CCI Press titles) *Tel:* 313-577-6120 *Fax:* 313-577-6131 *E-mail:* bookorders@wayne.edu *Web Site:* wsupress.wayne.edu
Gazelle Book Services Ltd, White Cross Mills, Hightown, Lancs LA1 4XS, United Kingdom *Tel:* (01524) 68765 *Fax:* (01524) 63232 *E-mail:* sales@gazellebooks.co.uk *Web Site:* www.gazellebooks.co.uk

Canadian Council on Social Development (Conseil canadien de developpement social)
190 O'Connor St, Suite 100, Ottawa, ON K2P 2R3
Mailing Address: PO Box 13713, Kanata, ON K2K 1X6
Tel: 613-236-8977 *Fax:* 613-236-2750
E-mail: info@ccsd.ca
Web Site: www.ccsd.ca
Key Personnel
CEO & Pres: Peggy Taillon *Tel:* 613-236-8977 ext 1 *E-mail:* taillon@ccsd.ca
VP, Res & Policy: Katherine Scott *Tel:* 613-236-8977 ext 2 *E-mail:* scott@ccsd.ca
Founded: 1920
Social policy, poverty, retirement, income security, economics, sustainable development self-help & aboriginal peoples.
Publishes in English, French.
ISBN Prefix(es): 978-0-88810
Number of titles published annually: 12 Print
Total Titles: 100 Print
Distributed by Renouf Publishing Ltd

Canadian Energy Research Institute
3512 33 St NW, Suite 150, Calgary, AB T2L 2A6
Tel: 403-282-1231 *Fax:* 403-284-4181
E-mail: info@ceri.ca
Web Site: www.ceri.ca
Key Personnel
CEO & Pres: Peter Howard
Exec Asst: Megan Murphy *Tel:* 403-220-2370 *Fax:* 403-220-9579 *E-mail:* mmurphy@ceri.ca
Founded: 1975
Energy research, conferences.
Publishes in English.
ISBN Prefix(es): 978-0-920522; 978-1-896091
Number of titles published annually: 5 Print
Total Titles: 150 Print

Canadian Government Publishing, see Government of Canada Publications

Canadian Institute of Chartered Accountants-CICA (L'Institut Canadien des Comptables Agrees)
277 Wellington St W, Toronto, ON M5V 3H2
Tel: 416-977-3222 *Toll Free Tel:* 800-268-3793 (CN orders) *Fax:* 416-977-8585
E-mail: orders@cica.ca
Web Site: www.cpacanada.ca
Key Personnel
Dir, Publg: Brian Loney *Tel:* 416-204-3235 *E-mail:* bloney@cpacanada.ca
Founded: 1917
Taxation, accounting, auditing, financial.
Publishes in English, French.
ISBN Prefix(es): 978-0-88800; 978-1-55385
Number of titles published annually: 15 Print
Total Titles: 200 Print; 40 CD-ROM

Canadian Institute of Resources Law (L'Institut canadien du droit des ressources)
Faculty of Law, University of Calgary, 2500 University Dr NW, MFH 3353, Calgary, AB T2N 1N4
Tel: 403-220-3200 *Fax:* 403-282-6182
E-mail: cirl@ucalgary.ca
Web Site: www.cirl.ca
Key Personnel
Info Resources Offr: Sue Parsons *E-mail:* sparsons@ucalgary.ca
Founded: 1979
Leading national centre of expertise on legal & policy issues relating to Canada's natural resources.
Publishes in English.
ISBN Prefix(es): 978-0-919269
Number of titles published annually: 3 Print; 3 Online
Total Titles: 96 Print; 64 Online

Canadian Institute of Ukrainian Studies Press
Division of Canadian Institute of Ukrainian Studies
University of Toronto, 256 McCaul St, Rm 308, Toronto, ON M5T 1W5
Tel: 416-978-6934 *Fax:* 416-978-2672
E-mail: cius@ualberta.ca
Web Site: www.ciuspress.com
Key Personnel
Exec Dir: Marko R Stech *E-mail:* m.stech@utoronto.ca
Sr Ed: Myroslav Yurkevich *Tel:* 780-492-2058 *E-mail:* myroslav.yurkevich@ualberta.ca
Founded: 1976
Publisher of scholarly works in Ukranian studies & Ukranian Canadian studies.
Publishes in English, French.
ISBN Prefix(es): 978-0-920862; 978-1-895571; 978-1-894865; 978-1-894301
Number of titles published annually: 6 Print
Total Titles: 180 Print
U.S. Rep(s): Baker & Taylor Books
Orders to: University of Alberta, 4-30 Pembina Hall, Edmonton, AB T6G 2H8 *Tel:* 780-492-2973 *Fax:* 780-492-4967 *E-mail:* cius@ualberta.ca
Returns: University of Alberta, 4-30 Pembina Hall, Edmonton, AB T6G 2H8 *Tel:* 780-492-2973 *Fax:* 780-492-4967 *E-mail:* cius@ualberta.ca

Canadian Museum of History (Musee Canadien de l'Histoire)
100 Laurier St, Gatineau, QC K1A 0M8
Tel: 819-776-7000 *Toll Free Tel:* 800-555-5621 (North American orders only) *Fax:* 819-776-7187
Web Site: www.historymuseum.ca
Key Personnel
VP, Pub Aff & Publg: Chantal Schryer *Tel:* 819-776-8499 *E-mail:* chantal.schryer@historymuseum.ca
Mgr, Corp Communs & Publg: Bill Carman *Tel:* 819-776-8386 *E-mail:* bill.carman@historymuseum.ca
Founded: 1968 (as the National Museum of Man)
Publications in the subject areas of museology, anthropology, archaeology, ethnology, folk culture, history, contemporary Native & Inuit art, native studies.
Publishes in English, French.
ISBN Prefix(es): 978-0-660
Number of titles published annually: 15 Print
Total Titles: 400 Print; 8 CD-ROM
U.S. Rep(s): University of Washington Press
Membership(s): Association for the Export of Canadian Books; Association of Canadian Publishers; Canadian Booksellers Association

Canadian Poetry Press
Dept of English, University of Western Ontario, London, ON N6A 3K7
Tel: 519-661-2111 (ext 85813); 519-661-2111 (ext 85834) *Fax:* 519-661-3776
E-mail: canadianpoetry@uwo.ca
Web Site: canadianpoetry.org
Key Personnel
Gen Ed: D M R Bentley *E-mail:* dbentley@uwo.ca
Gen Mgr: Susan Bentley
Founded: 1986
Publish scholarly editions of early Canadian long poems, editions of the work of the Confederation poets & critical studies of Canadian poetry.
Publishes in English.
ISBN Prefix(es): 978-0-921243
Number of titles published annually: 3 Print; 4 Online
Total Titles: 30 Print; 40 Online

§Canadian Scholars' Press Inc
425 Adelaide St W, Suite 200, Toronto, ON M5V 3C1
SAN: 118-9484
Tel: 416-929-2774 *Toll Free Tel:* 800-463-1998 *Fax:* 416-929-1926
E-mail: info@cspi.org; editorial@cspi.org; orders@cspi.org
Web Site: www.cspi.org; womenspress.cspi.org
Key Personnel
Pres: Andrew Wayne *Tel:* 416-929-2774 ext 220 *E-mail:* awayne@cspi.org

VP: Drew Hawkins *Tel:* 416-929-2774 ext 225 *E-mail:* dhawkins@coursepack.ca
Dir, Publg: Lily Bergh *Tel:* 416-929-2774 ext 218 *E-mail:* lily.bergh@cspi.org
Prodn Mgr: Caley Clements *Tel:* 416-929-2774 ext 222 *E-mail:* caley.clements@cspi.org
Mgr, Sales & Mktg: David Glover *Tel:* 416-929-2774 ext 231 *E-mail:* david.glover@cspi.org
Founded: 1986
Scholarly books & texts for post-secondary education. Trade books-feminist orientation.
Publishes in English, French.
ISBN Prefix(es): 978-0-921627; 978-1-55130; 978-0-921881; 978-0-88961 (Women's Press); 978-1-89418
Number of titles published annually: 24 Print; 10 E-Book
Total Titles: 400 Print; 6 CD-ROM; 80 E-Book
Divisions: Women's Press
Orders to: Gazelle Book Services Ltd, White Cross Mills, Hightown, Lancaster, Lancs LA1 4XS, United Kingdom, Cust Serv Mgr: Ian Waterhouse *Tel:* (01524) 68765 *Fax:* (01524) 63232 *E-mail:* sales@gazellebooks.co.uk *Web Site:* www.gazellebooks.co.uk
Returns: Gazelle Book Services Ltd, White Cross Mills, Hightown, Lancaster, Lancs LA1 4XS, United Kingdom, Cust Serv Mgr: Ian Waterhouse *Tel:* (01524) 68765 *Fax:* (01524) 63232 *E-mail:* sales@gazellebooks.co.uk *Web Site:* www.gazellebooks.co.uk
Distribution Center: Gazelle Book Services Ltd, White Cross Mills, Hightown, Lancaster, Lancs LA1 4XS, United Kingdom, Cust Serv Mgr: Ian Waterhouse *Tel:* (01524) 68765 *Fax:* (01524) 63232 *E-mail:* sales@gazellebooks.co.uk *Web Site:* www.gazellebooks.co.uk
Membership(s): Association of Canadian Publishers; Canada Council for the Arts; Ontario Arts Council; Organization of Book Publishers of Ontario

Cape Breton University Press Inc (CBU Press)
1250 Grand Lake Rd, Sydney, NS B1M 1A2
Mailing Address: PO Box 5300, Sydney, NS B1P 6L2
Tel: 902-563-1604 (orders & cust serv) *Fax:* 902-563-1177
E-mail: cbu_press@cbu.ca
Web Site: cbup.ca
Key Personnel
Ed-in-Chief: Mike R Hunter *Tel:* 902-563-1955 *E-mail:* mike_hunter@cbu.ca
Asst Ed: Laura Bast *Tel:* 902-563-1990 *E-mail:* laura_bast@cbu.ca
Secy: Anne Marie MacKenzie *Tel:* 902-563-1421 *E-mail:* anne_mackenzie@cbu.ca
Founded: 1974
Nonfiction regional books; fiction, short stories, poetry, community economic development.
Publishes in English.
ISBN Prefix(es): 978-0-920336; 978-1-897009; 978-1-927492
Number of titles published annually: 6 Print
Total Titles: 84 Print
Distributed by Nimbus Publishing
Orders to: Nimbus Publishing, PO Box 9166, Halifax, NS B3K 5M8 (trade sales & fulfillment), Sales Mgr: Terrilee Bulger *Toll Free Tel:* 800-646-2879 *Toll Free Fax:* 888-253-3133 *E-mail:* customerservice@nimbus.ns.ca *Web Site:* www.nimbus.ca
Distribution Center: Nimbus Publishing, PO Box 9166, Halifax, NS B3K 5M8 (trade sales & fulfillment), Sales Mgr: Terrilee Bulger *Toll Free Tel:* 800-646-2879 *Toll Free Fax:* 888-253-3133 *E-mail:* customerservice@nimbus.ns.ca *Web Site:* www.nimbus.ca
Brunswick Books, 20 Maud St, Suite 303, Toronto, ON M5V 2M5 (academic sales) *Tel:* 416-703-3598 *Fax:* 416-703-6561 *E-mail:* info@brunswickbooks.ca *Web Site:* www.brunswickbooks.ca
Comhairle nan Leabhraichean Gaelic Books Council, 32 Mansfield St, Glasgow G11 5QP, United Kingdom *Tel:* (0141) 337 6211 *E-mail:* shelagh@gaelicbooks.net *Web Site:* www.gaelicbooks.org
Membership(s): APMA; Association of Canadian Publishers

Captus Press Inc
1600 Steeles Ave W, Units 14 & 15, Concord, ON L4K 4M2
Tel: 416-736-5537 *Fax:* 416-736-5793
E-mail: info@captus.com
Web Site: www.captus.com
Key Personnel
Pres: Randy Hoffman *E-mail:* randy@captus.com
Mgr: Pauline Lai *E-mail:* pauline@captus.com
Accts Admin & Intl Rts: Lily Chu *E-mail:* lily@captus.com
Founded: 1987
Publication of textbooks, scholarly books, professional books, nonfiction trade books & multimedia Internet courses. Publishes in Spanish also.
Publishes in English, French.
ISBN Prefix(es): 978-0-921801; 978-1-896691; 978-1-895712; 978-1-55322
Number of titles published annually: 46 Print; 2 Online; 5 E-Book
Total Titles: 157 Print; 2 Online; 5 E-Book
Imprints: Captus Press; Captus University Publications; University Press of Canada

Carswell
Division of Thomson Reuters Canada Ltd
One Corporate Plaza, 2075 Kennedy Rd, Toronto, ON M1T 3V4
Tel: 416-298-5141; 416-609-3800 *Toll Free Tel:* 800-387-5164 (CN & US) *Fax:* 416-298-5094; 416-298-5082 *Toll Free Fax:* 877-750-9041 (CN only)
E-mail: carswell.customerrelations@thomsonreuters.com; carswell.orders@thomsonreuters.com
Web Site: www.carswell.com
Founded: 1864
Canada's leading provider of specialized information & electronic research solutions to the legal, tax, accounting & human resources markets. Headquartered in Toronto, ON, Carswell provides integrated information in a range of formats, including books, looseleaf services, journals, newsletters, CD-ROMs & online. Carswell is a business within The Thomson Corporation.
Publishes in English, French.
ISBN Prefix(es): 978-0-459; 978-0-88820; 978-0-7798
Number of titles published annually: 100 Print
Total Titles: 1,113 Print; 10 Online
Imprints: Richard De Boo
Branch Office(s)
430 rue St Pierre, Montreal, QC H2Y 2M5 *Tel:* 514-842-3937 *Toll Free Tel:* 800-363-3047 *Fax:* 514-842-7144
Distributor for Australian Tax Practice (ATP); Editions Yvon Blais; Brookers; Compu-Mark; Editorial Aranrzadi; ELLIS Publications; Fakta Info Direkt; Federal & State Government Printers; Forlaget Thomson; Foundation Press; GEE Publishing; W Green; Incorporated Council (London); IOB; La Ley; Lawbook Co; Legal Solutions USA; McGill University Air & Space Institute (Montreal); Native Law Center University of Saskatchewan; Professional Publishing (London); Provincial Government Printers; Research Institute of America; Round Hall Ltd; The Stationary Office (London); Sweet & Maxwell Asia; Sweet & Maxwell Group; Sweet & Maxwell UK; Thomson Legal & Regulatory; Thomson Tax Ltd (London); Transactive SARL; West Group
U.S. Publishers Represented: Research Institute of America; West
Foreign Rep(s): Brookers (New Zealand, Pacific Islands, Solomon Islands); Legal & Regulatory Australia (Australia); Sweet & Maxwell (Africa, Europe, Middle East); Sweet & Maxwell Hong Kong (China, Hong Kong, Japan, Korea, Macau, Taiwan); Sweet & Maxwell Malaysia (Brunei, Indonesia, Malaysia, Singapore)
Returns: 245 Bartley Dr, Toronto, ON M4A 2V8
Distribution Center: 245 Bartley Dr, Toronto, ON M4A 2V8

CCI Press, see Canadian Circumpolar Institute (CCI) Press

Centre for Reformation & Renaissance Studies (CRRS)
71 Queen's Park Crescent E, Toronto, ON M5S 1K7
Tel: 416-585-4465 *Fax:* 416-585-4430 (attn: CRRS)
E-mail: crrs.publications@utoronto.ca
Web Site: crrs.ca
Key Personnel
Interim Dir: Ethan Matt Kavaler *E-mail:* crrs.director@utoronto.ca
Graduate Fellow, Pubns & Promos: Vanessa McCarthy
Founded: 1965
Specialty library & academic publisher.
Publishes in English, French.
ISBN Prefix(es): 978-0-7727; 978-0-9697512
Number of titles published annually: 10 Print
Total Titles: 102 Print
Imprints: Dovehouse Press

Centre Franco-Ontarien de Ressources en Alphabetisation (Centre FORA)
450 Notre Dame Ave, Suite 0103, Sudbury, ON P3C 5K8
Tel: 705-524-3672 *Toll Free Tel:* 888-814-4422 (orders, CN only) *Fax:* 705-524-8535
E-mail: info@centrefora.on.ca
Web Site: www.centrefora.on.ca
Founded: 1989
Nonprofit organization that publishes learning materials for adult literacy & distribute education materials for all ages.
Publishes in French.
ISBN Prefix(es): 978-2-921706; 978-1-895336; 978-2-89567
Number of titles published annually: 20 Print
Total Titles: 150 Print

The Charlton Press
Division of Charlton International Inc
5845 Yonge St, PO Box 69509, North York, ON M2M 4K3
Tel: 416-488-1418 *Toll Free Tel:* 800-442-6042 (North America) *Fax:* 416-488-4656 *Toll Free Fax:* 800-442-1542 (North America)
E-mail: chpress@charltonpress.com
Web Site: www.charltonpress.com
Key Personnel
CEO: William K Cross
Founded: 1952
Specialize in Royal Doulton, Royal Worcester etc. Collectibles & antiques, 20th century numismatics, sports cards, ceramics.
Publishes in English.
ISBN Prefix(es): 978-0-88968; 978-2-9800475
Number of titles published annually: 20 Print
Total Titles: 35 Print
Orders to: Book Systems Plus Ltd, 8 Hill St, 1st fl, Saffron Walden, Essex CB10 1JD, United Kingdom (UK & Europe) *Tel:* (01799) 524458 *Fax:* (01799) 524459 *E-mail:* bsp2b@aol.com
Membership(s): The Independent Book Publishers Association

ChemTec Publishing
38 Earswick Dr, Toronto, ON M1E 1C6
Tel: 416-265-2603 *Fax:* 416-265-1399
E-mail: orderdesk@chemtec.org
Web Site: www.chemtec.org
Key Personnel
CEO: Anna Wypych
Circ Mgr: Anna Fox
Founded: 1988
Additives, blends, polymers, recycling & rheology.
Publishes in English.
ISBN Prefix(es): 978-1-895198
Number of titles published annually: 5 Print
Total Titles: 80 Print; 5 CD-ROM
Subsidiaries: ChemTec Laboratories Inc

Cheneliere Education Inc
Division of TC Media
5800, rue St Denis, bureau 900, Montreal, QC H2S 3L5
Tel: 514-273-1066 *Toll Free Tel:* 800-565-5531 *Fax:* 514-276-0324 *Toll Free Fax:* 800-814-0324
E-mail: info@cheneliere.ca
Web Site: www.cheneliere.ca
Key Personnel
Pres: Jacques Rochefort *E-mail:* jacques.rochefort@tc.tc
Founded: 1971
School, college & university textbooks; vocational; French Immersion; teaching skills & book packaging (French & English languages).
Publishes in French.
ISBN Prefix(es): 978-2-89310; 978-2-89461; 978-2-7650
Number of titles published annually: 200 Print
Imprints: Beauchemin; Gaetan Morin Editeur; Graficor
U.S. Publishers Represented: McGraw-Hill Inc
Warehouse: McGraw-Hill Ryerson Limited, 300 Water St, Whitby, ON L1N 9B6
See separate listing for:
Gaetan Morin Editeur

Chestnut Publishing Group Inc
44 Stubbs Dr, Suite 207, Toronto, ON M2L 2R3
Tel: 416-224-5824 *Fax:* 416-224-0595
Web Site: www.chestnutpublishing.com
Key Personnel
Pres: Stanley Starkman *E-mail:* sharkstark@sympatico.ca
VP, Publg: Grace Yang
VP, Fin: Allan Goldbach *Tel:* 416-499-1253 *Fax:* 416-499-1652 *E-mail:* agoldbach@on.aibn.com
Founded: 2001
Publish education, school & college, trade, adult, children, juvenile, young adult & English as a second language titles.
Publishes in English, French.
ISBN Prefix(es): 978-1-894601; 978-1-894929; 978-0-9689522; 978-0-9688946
Number of titles published annually: 20 Print; 4 CD-ROM; 3 Audio
Total Titles: 220 Print; 20 CD-ROM; 20 Audio
Imprints: Chestnut Publishing; Doyen Publishing (el-hi books; mathematics); Lynx Publishing (ESL); Patnor Publishing (books for reluctant readers & ESL)
Foreign Rights: INT Press (Australia, New Zealand)
Warehouse: TTS Distributing Inc, 155 Edward St, Aurora, ON L4G 1W3, Contact: Duncan Stewart *Tel:* 905-841-3898 *Fax:* 905-841-3026 *E-mail:* dstewart@ttsdistributing.com *Web Site:* www.ttsdistributing.com
Membership(s): Organization of Book Publishers of Ontario

Chouette Publishing
1001 Lenoir St, Suite B-238, Montreal, QC H4C 2Z6
Tel: 514-925-3325 *Fax:* 514-925-3323
E-mail: info@editions-chouette.com
Web Site: www.chouette-publishing.com
Key Personnel
Publr & Ed: Anne Paradis
Founded: 1987
Produce children's books adapted to each age group from birth to age six, with the well-known Caillou character.
Publishes in English, French.
ISBN Prefix(es): 978-2-9800909; 978-2-921198; 978-2-89450; 978-2-89718
Number of titles published annually: 20 Print
Distributed by PGW/Legato Publishers Group
U.S. Rep(s): Client Distribution Services
Foreign Rep(s): Simon Payette
Warehouse: PGW/Legato Publishers Group, 210 American Dr, Jackson, TN 38301, United States *Toll Free Tel:* 800-343-4499 (Perseus) *Toll Free Fax:* 800-351-5073 *E-mail:* orderentry@perseusbooks.com
Distribution Center: Canadian Manda Group, 165 Dufferin St, Toronto, ON M6K 3H6 *Tel:* 416-516-0911 *Fax:* 416-516-0917 *E-mail:* info@mandagroup.com *Web Site:* www.canadianmandagroup.ca
PGW/Legato Publishers Group, 210 American Dr, Jackson, TN 38301, United States *Toll Free Tel:* 800-343-4499 (Perseus) *Toll Free Fax:* 800-351-5073 *E-mail:* orderentry@perseusbooks.com

CIUS Press, see Canadian Institute of Ukrainian Studies Press

Clements Publishing
6021 Yonge St, Suite 213, Toronto, ON M2M 3W2
Tel: 647-477-2509 *Fax:* 647-477-2058
E-mail: info@clementspublishing.com
Web Site: www.clementspublishing.com
Key Personnel
Dir: Rob Clements
Founded: 2000
Seeks to educate, nurture & equip men & women to live & work as mature Christians through the publication & distribution of academic books, audio materials & online resources. Also provides editorial consulting & design services to other Christian publishers.
Publishes in English, French.
ISBN Prefix(es): 978-1-894667; 978-1-897260; 978-1-926798
Number of titles published annually: 10 Print
Total Titles: 30 Print; 7 Audio
Orders to: Ingram Book Group/Spring Arbor, One Ingram Blvd, La Vergne, TN 37086, United States *Tel:* 615-793-5000 *Toll Free Tel:* 800-937-8200 *E-mail:* customerservice@ingramcontent.com *Web Site:* www.ingramcontent.com
Distribution Center: Ingram Book Group/Spring Arbor, One Ingram Blvd, La Vergne, TN 37086, United States *Tel:* 615-793-5000 *Toll Free Tel:* 800-937-8200 *E-mail:* customerservice@ingramcontent.com *Web Site:* www.ingramcontent.com

Coach House Books
80 bpNichol Lane, Toronto, ON M5S 3J4
Tel: 416-979-2217 *Toll Free Tel:* 800-367-6360 (outside Toronto) *Fax:* 416-977-1158
E-mail: mail@chbooks.com
Web Site: www.chbooks.com
Key Personnel
Founder & Publr: Stan Bevington *E-mail:* stan@chbooks.com
Edit Dir: Alana Wilcox *E-mail:* alana@chbooks.com
Publicist: Sarah Smith-Eivemark *E-mail:* sarah@chbooks.com
Publg Asst: Leigh Nash *E-mail:* leigh@chbooks.com
Founded: 1965
Literary small press specializing in experimental fiction & poetry.
Publishes in English.
ISBN Prefix(es): 978-1-55245
Number of titles published annually: 16 Print; 5 Online
Total Titles: 140 Print; 60 Online
Foreign Rights: Amo Agency (Amo Noh) (South Korea); AnatoliaLit Copyright & Translation Agency (Amy Spangler) (Turkey); Sandra Bruna Agencia Literaria SL (Natalia Berenguer) (Portugal, Spain); English Agency Japan (Hamish Macaskill) (Japan); The Grayhawk Agency (Lora Fountain) (China, Taiwan); Mohr Books Literary Agency (Annelie Geissler) (Germany); Piergiorgio Nicolazzini Literary Agency (Maura Solinas) (Italy); Sandrine Paccher (France)
Distribution Center: LitDistCo, 100 Armstrong Ave, Georgetown, ON L7G 5S4 (CN orders) *Toll Free Tel:* 800-591-6250 *Toll Free Fax:* 800-591-6251 *E-mail:* orders@litdistco.ca *Web Site:* www.litdistco.ca
Small Press Distribution, 1341 Seventh St, Berkeley, CA 94710-1409, United States (US orders) *Toll Free Tel:* 800-869-7553 *Fax:* 510-524-0852 *E-mail:* spd@spdbooks.org *Web Site:* www.spdbooks.org
Consortium Book Sales & Distribution, The Keg House, 34 13 Ave NE, Suite 101, Minneapolis, MN 55413-1007, United States (US orders) *Tel:* 612-746-2600 *Fax:* 612-746-2606 *E-mail:* orderentry@perseusbooks.com *Web Site:* www.cbsd.com
Membership(s): Association of Canadian Publishers; Community of Literary Magazines & Presses; Literary Press Group

Collector Grade Publications Inc
PO Box 1046, Cobourg, ON K9A 4W5
Tel: 905-342-3434 *Fax:* 905-342-3688
E-mail: info@collectorgrade.com
Web Site: www.collectorgrade.com
Key Personnel
Pres: R Blake Stevens
Founded: 1979
Accurate, in-depth studies of modern small arms. Technical reference books.
Publishes in English.
ISBN Prefix(es): 978-0-88935
Number of titles published annually: 3 Print
Total Titles: 38 Print

Company's Coming Publishing Ltd
87 E Pender St, Vancouver, BC V6A 1S9
Tel: 780-450-6223 (orders & inquiries) *Toll Free Tel:* 800-661-9017 (CN); 800-518-3541 (US) *Fax:* 780-450-1857
E-mail: info@companyscoming.com
Web Site: www.companyscoming.com
Key Personnel
Pres: Grant Lovig
Founded: 1981
Publish cookbooks, craft books & stationery products.
Publishes in English.
ISBN Prefix(es): 978-0-9690695; 978-0-9693322; 978-1-895455; 978-1-896891; 978-1-897069; 978-1-897477; 978-1-927126
Number of titles published annually: 25 Print
Total Titles: 200 Print
Distribution Center: Booklogic, 2311 96 St, Edmonton, AB T6N 1G3

Conseil canadien de developpement social, see Canadian Council on Social Development (Conseil canadien de developpement social)

The Continuing Legal Education Society of British Columbia (CLEBC)
500-1155 W Pender St, Vancouver, BC V6E 2P4
Tel: 604-669-3544; 604-893-2121 (cust serv) *Toll Free Tel:* 800-663-0437 (CN) *Fax:* 604-669-9260
E-mail: custserv@cle.bc.ca
Web Site: www.cle.bc.ca
Key Personnel
CEO: Ron Friesen *Tel:* 604-893-2114 *E-mail:* rfriesen@cle.bc.ca
Dir, Pubns: Susan Munro *Tel:* 604-893-2106 *E-mail:* smunro@cle.bc.ca
Sales & Mktg Liaison: Karen Kerfoot *Tel:* 604-893-2110 *E-mail:* kkerfoot@cle.bc.ca
Founded: 1976
Publish course materials, practice manuals & case digests.
Publishes in English.
ISBN Prefix(es): 978-0-86504; 978-1-55258
Number of titles published annually: 11 Print
Total Titles: 50 Print; 1 CD-ROM; 48 Online
Imprints: CLEBC

Cormorant Books Inc
10 St Mary St, Suite 615, Toronto, ON M4Y-1P6
Tel: 416-925-8887
E-mail: info@cormorantbooks.com
Web Site: www.cormorantbooks.com
Key Personnel
Pres & Publr, Cormorant Books: Marc Cote *E-mail:* m.cote@cormorantbooks.com
Assoc Publr, Cormorant Books & Publr, DCB/Dancing Cat Books: Barry Jowett *E-mail:* b.jowett@cormorantbooks.com
Founded: 1986
Independent literary publisher of Canadian authors.
Publishes in English.
ISBN Prefix(es): 978-0-920953; 978-1-896951; 978-1-896332; 978-1-897151
Number of titles published annually: 26 Print; 26 Online; 26 E-Book
Total Titles: 150 Print; 150 Online; 82 E-Book
Imprints: The Riverbank Press
Sales Office(s): Ampersand Inc, 2440 Viking Way, Richmond, BC V6V 1N2, Contact: Saffron Beckwith *Tel:* 416-703-0666 *Toll Free Tel:* 866-736-5620 *Fax:* 416-703-4745 *Toll Free Fax:* 866-849-3819 *E-mail:* saffronb@ampersand.ca
Distribution Center: University of Toronto Press, 5201 Dufferin St, Toronto, ON M3H 5T8 *Tel:* 416-667-7791 *Toll Free Tel:* 800-565-9523 *Fax:* 416-667-7832 *Toll Free Fax:* 800-221-9985 *E-mail:* utpbooks@utpress.utoronto.ca *Web Site:* www.utpress.utoronto.ca
Membership(s): Association of Canadian Publishers; Canadian Booksellers Association; Organization of Book Publishers of Ontario

Coteau Books
Division of Thunder Creek Publishing Co-operative
2517 Victoria Ave, Regina, SK S4P 0T2
SAN: 115-1037
Tel: 306-777-0170 *Toll Free Tel:* 800-440-4471 (CN only) *Fax:* 306-522-5152
E-mail: coteau@coteaubooks.com
Web Site: www.coteaubooks.com
Key Personnel
Mng Ed: Nik L Burton
Design & Prodn: Susan Buck *E-mail:* production@coteaubooks.com
Mktg: Amber Goldie *E-mail:* marketing@coteaubooks.com
Off/Fin Mgr: Dwayne Dreher *E-mail:* administration@coteaubooks.com
Founded: 1975
Publish & promote examples of the best fiction, poetry, drama & young readers' fiction written in Canada.
Publishes in English.
ISBN Prefix(es): 978-0-919926; 978-0-55050; 978-0-9780316
Number of titles published annually: 12 Print; 8 E-Book
Total Titles: 130 Print; 15 E-Book
Orders to: Publishers Group Canada, Raincoast Books, 2440 Viking Way, Richmond, BC V6V 1N2 *Toll Free Tel:* 800-663-5714 *Toll Free Fax:* 800-565-3770 *E-mail:* customerservice@raincoast.com
Distribution Center: Publishers Group Canada, Raincoast Books, 2440 Viking Way, Richmond, BC V6V 1N2 *Toll Free Tel:* 800-663-5714 *Toll Free Fax:* 800-565-3770 *E-mail:* customerservice@raincoast.com

La Courte Echelle
160, rue St-Viateur E, bureau 404, Montreal, QC H2T 1A8
Tel: 514-274-2004 *Fax:* 514-270-4160
E-mail: info@courteechelle.com
Web Site: www.courteechelle.com
Key Personnel
Pres: Helene Derome
Dir, Communs & Promo: Mia Caron *Tel:* 514-274-2004 ext 236 *E-mail:* mcaron@courteechelle.com
Ed-in-Chief: Lise Duquette
Prodn Coord: Nicolas Rouleau
Sales Coord: Veronique Bedard
Founded: 1978
Children's, young adult & adult fiction. No unsol mss accepted.
Publishes in French.
ISBN Prefix(es): 978-2-89021; 978-1-894731; 978-2-89651; 978-2-89695
Number of titles published annually: 50 Print
Total Titles: 545 Print
Distribution Center: Hachette Canada, 9001 de l'Acadie, bureau 1002, Montreal, QC H4N 3H5 *Tel:* 514-382-3034 *Fax:* 514-381-5088 *E-mail:* info@hachette.qc.ca *Web Site:* www.hachette.qc.ca
Librairie du Quebec a Paris, Diffusion du Nouveau Monde (DNM), 30, rue Gay-Lussac, 75005 Paris, France (France & Europe) *Tel:* 01 43 54 49 02 *Fax:* 01 43 54 39 15 *E-mail:* dnm@librairieduquebec.fr *Web Site:* www.librairieduquebec.fr

§Crabtree Publishing Co Ltd
Subsidiary of Crabtree Publishing Co (USA)
616 Welland Ave, St Catharines, ON L2M-5V6
SAN: 115-1436
Tel: 905-682-5221 *Toll Free Tel:* 800-387-7650 *Fax:* 905-682-7166 *Toll Free Fax:* 800-355-7166
E-mail: custserv@crabtreebooks.com; sales@crabtreebooks.com; orders@crabtreebooks.com
Web Site: www.crabtreebooks.com
Key Personnel
Pres: Peter A Crabtree *E-mail:* peter_c@crabtreebooks.com
Publr: Bobbie Kalman *E-mail:* bobbiek@crabtreebooks.com
Cont & Gen Mgr: John Siemens *E-mail:* john_s@crabtreebooks.com
VP, Opers: Craig Culliford *E-mail:* craig_c@crabtreebooks.com
Dir, Edit: Kathy Middleton *E-mail:* kathy_m@crabtreebooks.com
Mktg Mgr: Julie Alguire *E-mail:* julie_a@crabtreebooks.com
Dir, Sales: Andrea Crabtree *E-mail:* andrea_c@crabtreebooks.com
Dir, New Media: Rob MacGregor *E-mail:* rob_m@crabtreebooks.com
Cust Serv Mgr: Linda Wade *E-mail:* linda_w@crabtreebooks.com
Warehouse Mgr: Karl Kasper *E-mail:* warehouse@crabtreebooks.com
Founded: 1978
Children's nonfiction & fiction, library binding & paperback for school & trade.
Publishes in English, French.
ISBN Prefix(es): 978-0-86505; 978-0-7787; 978-1-4271
Number of titles published annually: 300 Print; 150 E-Book
Total Titles: 4,375 Print; 1,400 E-Book; 105 Audio
Imprints: Look, Listen & Learn Audio Books
Distributor for Bayard; Maren Green
Foreign Rep(s): INT Press (Australia, New Zealand); Roundhouse Group (European Union, UK); Titles (South Africa)
Membership(s): ABA; ALA; American Alliance of Museums; American Marketing Association; Association of Canadian Publishers; Canadian Booksellers Association; Educational Book & Media Association; National Science Teachers Association; Ontario Library Association

CRRS, see Centre for Reformation & Renaissance Studies (CRRS)

§Database Directories
588 Dufferin Ave, London, ON N6B 2A4
Tel: 519-433-1666 *Fax:* 519-430-1131
E-mail: mail@databasedirectory.com
Web Site: www.databasedirectory.com
Key Personnel
CEO: Lesley Classic *E-mail:* lclassic@databasedirectory.com
Pres: Robert Kasher
Founded: 1995
Directories & e-files on libraries, schools, colleges, universities, academic retailers & municipalities.
Publishes in English.
ISBN Prefix(es): 978-1-896537
Number of titles published annually: 3 Print; 4 CD-ROM; 4 Online
Total Titles: 10 Print; 10 CD-ROM; 4 Online
Branch Office(s)
1234-A Ninth Ave, Honolulu, HI 96816, United States

§DC Canada Education Publishing (DCCED)
180 Metcalfe St, Suite 204, Ottawa, ON K2P 1P5
Tel: 613-565-8885 *Toll Free Tel:* 888-565-0262 *Fax:* 613-565-8881
E-mail: info@dc-canada.ca
Web Site: www.dc-canada.ca
Key Personnel
Publg Dir: Mei Dang
Mng Ed: Debbie Gervais
Ed: Anja Pujic
Mktg Mgr: George Liu
Proj Mgr: Scott Paterson
Founded: 1995
Publishes in English.
ISBN Prefix(es): 978-0-9738439; 978-0-9738440; 978-0-9808816; 978-0-9810549; 978-1-926776
Number of titles published annually: 6 Print

Decker Intellectual Properties Publisher
69 John St S, Suite 310, Hamilton, ON L8N 2B9
Tel: 905-522-8526 *Toll Free Tel:* 855-647-6511 (CN & US) *Fax:* 905-522-9273
E-mail: customercare@deckerip.com
Web Site: www.deckerpublishing.com
Key Personnel
Dir & Content Mgr: Ryan Decker
Mgr, Cust Care & Dist: Marie Moore *Tel:* 905-522-8526 ext 2233
Founded: 1982
Publishes textbooks & journals in all areas of medical & dental.
Publishes in English.
ISBN Prefix(es): 978-1-55009; 978-0-941158; 978-1-55664
Number of titles published annually: 2 Print; 3 CD-ROM; 15 Online
Total Titles: 3 Print; 25 Online

Divisions: Decker Electronic Publishing Inc
Distributed by Ebsco

§Double Dragon Publishing Inc
1-5762 Hwy 7 E, Markham, ON L3P 7Y4
Mailing Address: PO Box 54016, Markham, ON L3P 7Y4
Tel: 603-778-7191
E-mail: info@double-dragon-ebooks.com; sales@double-dragon-ebooks.com
Web Site: www.double-dragon-ebooks.com
Key Personnel
CEO & Publr: Deron Douglas
Founded: 2001
Publishes ebooks & trade paperbacks in the fantasy, science fiction, speculative fiction, horror & suspense genres. Established with the goal of building a Canadian-based publishing venue for the growing number of good but unpublished fiction writers around the world. Dedicated to publishing quality works of fiction & nonfiction & will continue to publish works in various genres in both the ebook & traditional paper book formats. Make special efforts to publish a specific number of works written by North American Aboriginal authors each year.
Publishes in English.
ISBN Prefix(es): 978-1-894841; 978-1-55404
Number of titles published annually: 40 Print; 100 E-Book
Total Titles: 40 Print; 125 E-Book
Imprints: Blood Moon Publishing; Carnal Desires Publishing; DDP Literary Press; Double Dragon eBooks; Double Dragon Media Group; Dragon Dance; Dragon Tooth Fantasy; Dragon's Heart Romance

Doubleday Canada
Imprint of Penguin Random House Canada Limited
One Toronto St, Suite 300, Toronto, ON M5C 2V6
SAN: 115-0340
Tel: 416-364-4449 *Fax:* 416-364-6863
Web Site: www.randomhouse.ca
Key Personnel
CEO & Pres: Brad Martin
CFO & EVP: Douglas Foot
Pres & Publr, RHC: Kristin Cochrane
EVP & Dir, Sales: Duncan Shields
SVP & Dir, Busn Devt Online Digital Sales Strategy: Robert Wheaton
SVP & Dir, Mktg & Corp Communs: Tracey Turriff
VP & Dir, Prodn: Janine Laporte
Assoc Publr: Amy Black
Ed-in-Chief: Martha Kanya-Forstner
Founded: 1937
General trade nonfiction (current affairs, politics, business, sports); fiction, children's illustrated.
Penguin Random House Canada Limited & its publishing entities are not accepting unsol submissions, proposals, mss, or submission queries via e-mail at this time.
Publishes in English.
ISBN Prefix(es): 978-0-385; 978-0-7704
Number of titles published annually: 60 Print; 5 E-Book
Total Titles: 1,172 Print; 41 E-Book
Imprints: Anchor Canada; Bond Street Books; Seal Books
Membership(s): Canadian Booksellers Association; Canadian Library Association; Canadian Publishers' Council

Douglas & McIntyre (2013) Ltd
4437 Rondeview Rd, Madeira Park, BC V0N 2H1
Mailing Address: PO Box 219, Madeira Park, BC V0N 2H0
Toll Free Tel: 800-667-2988
E-mail: info@douglas-mcintyre.com
Web Site: www.douglas-mcintyre.com
Key Personnel
Interim Publr: Howard White
Founded: 1970
Focus on biographies, native art & history, architecture, literary fiction & cookbooks.
Publishes in English.
ISBN Prefix(es): 978-0-88894; 978-1-55054; 978-1-55365; 978-1-77100; 978-0-920841; 978-1-55051; 978-1-926812; 978-1-926685; 978-1-926706
Number of titles published annually: 90 Print
Total Titles: 1,500 Print
Distributed by University of Toronto Press
Membership(s): AAP; Association for the Export of Canadian Books; Association of Book Publishers of British Columbia; Association of Canadian Publishers; Canadian Booksellers Association

Dundurn Press Ltd
3 Church St, Suite 500, Toronto, ON M5E 1M2
SAN: 115-0359
Tel: 416-214-5544 *Fax:* 416-214-5556
E-mail: info@dundurn.com
Web Site: www.dundurn.com
Key Personnel
Pres & Publr: Kirk Howard *E-mail:* khoward@dundurn.com
Founded: 1972
Specialize in Canadian history, social sciences, some biography & art, fiction & mysteries.
Publishes in English.
ISBN Prefix(es): 978-0-919670; 978-0-9690454; 978-0-88924; 978-0-88882; 978-1-55488; 978-1-4597
Number of titles published annually: 100 Print
Foreign Rep(s): Gazelle Book Services (Europe)
Distribution Center: University of Toronto Press Distribution, 5201 Dufferin St, Toronto, ON M3H 5T8 *Tel:* 416-978-2239 *Fax:* 416-978-4738 *Web Site:* www.utpress.utoronto.ca
Ingram Publisher Services, One Ingram Blvd, La Vergne, TN 37086-1986, United States *Toll Free Tel:* 866-400-5351
Membership(s): Association of Canadian Publishers

Ecrits des Forges
992-A rue Royale, Trois-Rivieres, QC G9A 4H9
Tel: 819-840-8492
E-mail: ecritsdesforges@gmail.com
Web Site: www.ecritsdesforges.com
Key Personnel
Literary Dir: Bernard Pozier
Admin Dir: Delphine Lefevre
Cont: Jamie Lee Vosburg
Founded: 1971
Publish poetry.
Publishes in French.
ISBN Prefix(es): 978-2-89046
Number of titles published annually: 50 Print
Total Titles: 1,050 Print
Distributed by DCR; Prologue
Membership(s): Association Nationale des Editeurs de Livres

ECW Press
665 Gerrard St E, Toronto, ON M4M 1Y2
SAN: 115-1274
Tel: 416-694-3348 *Fax:* 416-698-9906
E-mail: info@ecwpress.com
Web Site: www.ecwpress.com
Key Personnel
Co-Publr: Jack David *E-mail:* jack@ecwpress.com
Founded: 1974
Publishes in English.
ISBN Prefix(es): 978-0-920763; 978-1-55022; 978-0-920802; 978-1-77041
Number of titles published annually: 50 Print
Total Titles: 800 Print; 205 E-Book
Imprints: misFit
Foreign Rights: Bill Hanna (Worldwide exc Canada & USA)
Membership(s): Association of Canadian Publishers; Literary Press Group

EDGE Science Fiction & Fantasy Publishing
Imprint of Hades Publications Inc
PO Box 1714, Sta M, Calgary, AB T2P 2L7
Tel: 403-254-0160
Web Site: www.edgewebsite.com
Key Personnel
Pres & Publr: Brian Hades *E-mail:* publisher@hadespublications.com
Mktg Mgr: Janice Shoults
Founded: 1996
Encourage, produce & promote thought-provoking science fiction & fantasy & horror literature by "bringing the magic alive-one world at a time" with each new book released. Independent publisher of science fiction & fantasy novels in hardcover or trade paperback format. Produce high-quality books with lots of attention to detail & lots of marketing effort.
Publishes in English.
ISBN Prefix(es): 978-1-894063; 978-1-896944; 978-1-77053
Number of titles published annually: 8 Print
Total Titles: 87 Print; 1 Audio
Imprints: Absolute XPress; EDGE Science Fiction & Fantasy Publishing; Tesseract Books
U.S. Rep(s): Baker & Taylor; Fitzhenry & Whiteside; Ingram Book Co
Distribution Center: Fitzhenry & Whiteside, 195 Allstate Pkwy, Markham, ON L3R 4T8 *Toll Free Tel:* 800-387-9776 *Toll Free Fax:* 800-260-9777 *E-mail:* bookinfo@fitzhenry.ca
Membership(s): Book Publishers Association of Alberta; The Independent Book Publishers Association; IPAC; PMA International

Les Editions Alire
CP 67, Succursale B, Quebec, QC G1K 7A1
Tel: 418-835-4441 *Fax:* 418-838-4443
E-mail: info@alire.com
Web Site: www.alire.com
Key Personnel
Admin Dir: Melanie Bissonnette *E-mail:* melanie.bissonnette@alire.com
Edit Dir: Jean Pettigrew *E-mail:* jean.pettigrew@alire.com
Dir, Sales: Louise Alain *E-mail:* louise.alain@alire.com
Founded: 1996
Publish French Canadian popular genre fiction.
Publishes in French.
ISBN Prefix(es): 978-2-922145; 978-2-89615; 978-2-9801068
Number of titles published annually: 10 Print
Total Titles: 131 Print
Distribution Center: Messageries ADP, 2315, rue de la Province, Longueuil, QC J4G 1G4 (CN & US) *Tel:* 450-640-1237 *Fax:* 450-674-6237
Interforum Editis SA, Fond Jean-Pauqes, 6, 1348 Louvain-la-Neuve, Belgium (Belgium & Luxembourg) *Tel:* (010) 42 03 20 *Fax:* (010) 41 20 24 *E-mail:* info@interforum.be
Interforum Editis, Immeuble Paryseine, 3, allee de la Seine, 94854 Ivry Cedex, France (France & other countries exc Belgium, Canada, Luxembourg, Switzerland & US) *Tel:* 01 49 59 11 56 *Fax:* 01 49 59 11 33 *E-mail:* cdes-export@interforum.fr *Web Site:* www.interforum.fr
OLF, ZI3 Corminboef, PO Box 1152, 1701 Fribourg, Switzerland *Tel:* (026) 467 51 11 *Fax:* (026) 467 54 66 *E-mail:* information@olf.ch
Membership(s): Association Nationale des Editeurs de Livres

Les Editions Caractere
Division of TC Media

5800, rue St-Denis, bureau 900, Montreal, QC H2S 3L5
Tel: 514-273-1066 *Fax:* 514-276-0324
E-mail: caractere@tc.tc
Web Site: www.editionscaractere.com
Founded: 2004
Publishes in French.
ISBN Prefix(es): 978-2-923351; 978-2-89642; 978-2-89643
Number of titles published annually: 130 Print
Distribution Center: Prologue Inc, 1650, Lionel Bertrand, Boisbriand, QC J7H 1N7 *Tel:* 450-434-0306 *Toll Free Tel:* 800-363-2864 *Fax:* 450-434-4135 *Toll Free Fax:* 800-361-8088

editions CERES Ltd/Le Moyen Francais
CP 1089, Succursale B, Maison de la Poste, Montreal, QC H3B 3K9
Tel: 514-937-7138 *Fax:* 514-937-9875
E-mail: editionsceres@gmail.com
Web Site: www.editionsceres.ca
Key Personnel
Pres & Ed: G Di Stefano
Secy & Ed: R M Bidler
Founded: 1979
Dictionaries & erudite volumes on 14th, 15th & 16th centuries French language, literature & philology. Our authors are international. It is open to everyone who specializes in this discipline. University specialists & research libraries.
Publishes in English, French.
ISBN Prefix(es): 978-0-919089
Number of titles published annually: 2 Print
Total Titles: 86 Print

Editions de la Pleine Lune
223 34 Ave, Lachine, QC H8T 1Z4
Tel: 514-634-7954 *Fax:* 514-637-6366
E-mail: editpllune@videotron.ca
Web Site: www.pleinelune.qc.ca
Key Personnel
Literary Dir: Marie-Madeleine Raoult
Media Rel: Patricia Lamy *Tel:* 514-912-7443 *E-mail:* lamypat@videotron.ca
Founded: 1975
Publishes in French.
ISBN Prefix(es): 978-2-89024
Number of titles published annually: 8 Print
Total Titles: 185 Print
Distribution Center: Diffusion Dimedia, 539, Lebau Blvd, St-Laurent, QC H4N 1S2 *Tel:* 514-336-3941 *Fax:* 514-331-3916 *E-mail:* general@dimedia.qc.ca *Web Site:* www.dimedia.com
La Librairie du Quebec a Paris et DNM, 30, rue Gay Lussac, 75005 Paris, France *Tel:* 01 43 54 49 02 *Fax:* 01 43 54 39 15 *Web Site:* www.librairieduquebec.fr
Membership(s): Association Nationale des Editeurs de Livres

Les Editions de l'Hexagone
Division of Le Groupe Ville Marie Litterature
1010 rue de la Gauchetiere E, Montreal, QC H2L 2N5
Tel: 514-523-7993 *Fax:* 514-282-7530
Web Site: www.edhexagone.com
Key Personnel
VP: Martin Balthazar
Literary Dir: Danielle Fournier *E-mail:* danielle.fournier@groupevml.com; Annie Goulet *E-mail:* annie.goulet@groupevml.com
Literary Dir, Essays: Alain-Nicolas Renaud *E-mail:* alain.nicolas.renaud@groupevml.com
Prodn: Lucie Delemer *E-mail:* lucie.delemer@groupevml.com
Exec Asst: Sylvie Briere *Tel:* 514-523-1182 ext 4213 *E-mail:* sylvie.briere@groupevml.com
Founded: 1953
Publishes in French.
ISBN Prefix(es): 978-2-89006; 978-2-89295; 978-2-89648; 978-0-88508
Number of titles published annually: 30 Print
Total Titles: 35 Print
Foreign Office(s): Immeuble Paryseine, 3, allee de la Seine, 94854 Ivry Cedex, France *Tel:* 01 49 59 12 40 *Fax:* 06 16 94 14 38
Orders to: Messageries ADP, 2315 rue de la Province, Longueuil, QC J4G 1G4 *Tel:* 450-640-1234 *Toll Free Tel:* 800-771-3022 *Fax:* 450-640-1251 *Toll Free Fax:* 800-603-0433 *E-mail:* adpcommandes@messageries-adp.com *Web Site:* www.messageries-adp.com
Warehouse: Messageries ADP, 2315 rue de la Province, Longueuil, QC J4G 1G4 *Tel:* 450-640-1234 *Toll Free Tel:* 800-771-3022 *Fax:* 450-640-1251 *Toll Free Fax:* 800-603-0433 *Web Site:* www.messageries-adp.com

Les Editions de Mortagne
CP 116, Boucherville, QC J4B 5E6
Tel: 450-641-2387 *Fax:* 450-655-6092
E-mail: info@editionsdemortagne.com
Web Site: www.editionsdemortagne.com
Key Personnel
Founder & Pres: Max Permingeat
VP, Admin & Prodn: Alexandra Pellerin
VP, Editions & Promo: Sandy Pellerin
Founded: 1978
Novels.
Publishes in French.
ISBN Prefix(es): 978-2-89074
Number of titles published annually: 15 Print
Total Titles: 15 Print
Foreign Office(s): BP 13, 16700 Ruffec, France *Tel:* 05 45 85 79 00
Distribution Center: Prologue, 1650 blvd Lionel-Bertrand, Broisbriand, QC J7N 1N7 *Tel:* 450-434-0306 *Toll Free Tel:* 800-363-2864 *Fax:* 450-434-2627 *Toll Free Fax:* 800-361-8088 *E-mail:* prologue@prologue.ca *Web Site:* www.prologue.ca
SDL La Caravelle, 303 rue du pre aux oies, 1130 Brussels, Belgium *Tel:* (02) 240 93 00 *Fax:* (02) 216 35 98 *Web Site:* www.sdlcaravelle.com
Dilisco Distribution, Rue du Limousin, BP 25, 23220 Cheniers, France *Tel:* 05 55 51 80 00 *Fax:* 05 55 62 17 39 *E-mail:* relation.client@dilisco.fr *Web Site:* www.dilisco-diffusion-distribution.fr
Dilisco Diffusion, Parc Mure 2-Bat 4-4, 128 Bis ave Jean-Jaures, BP 102, 94208 Ivry-sur-Seine, France *Tel:* 01 49 59 50 50 *Fax:* 01 46 71 05 06 *E-mail:* relation.client@dilisco.fr *Web Site:* www.dilisco-diffusion-distribution.fr
Distribution Servidis, Chemin des Chalets 7, 1279 Chavannes-de-Bogis, Switzerland *Tel:* (022) 960-95-23 *Fax:* (022) 960-95-77 *Web Site:* www.servidis.ch
Membership(s): Association Nationale des Editeurs de Livres

Editions Marcel Didier Inc
1815, ave De Lorimier, Montreal, QC H2K 3W6
Tel: 514-523-1523 *Toll Free Tel:* 800-361-1664 (Ontario to Maritimes) *Fax:* 514-523-5955
E-mail: marceldidier@hurtubisehmh.com
Web Site: www.marceldidier.com
Key Personnel
Edit Dir: Loic Hervouet *E-mail:* loic.hervouet@marceldidier.com
Ed: Isabelle Laberge *E-mail:* isabelle.laberge@marceldidier.com
Founded: 1964
Literary essays, novels.
Publishes in English, French.
ISBN Prefix(es): 978-2-89144
Number of titles published annually: 60 Print
Distributed by Editions Hurtubise
U.S. Rep(s): Sosnowski Associates

Les Editions du Ble
340 Provencher Blvd, St Boniface, MB R2H 0G7
Tel: 204-237-8200 *Fax:* 204-233-8182
E-mail: direction@editionsduble.ca
Web Site: ble.avoslivres.ca
Key Personnel
Admin Dir: Anne Molgat
Founded: 1974
Publish books in French (novels, essays, poetry) pertaining mainly to the Canadian West (but not exclusively).
Publishes in French.
ISBN Prefix(es): 978-2-921347; 978-2-923673
Number of titles published annually: 6 Print
Total Titles: 100 Print
Distribution Center: Diffusion Prologue, 1650 boul Lionel-Bertrand, Boisbriand, QC J7E 4H4 *Tel:* 450-434-0306 *Fax:* 450-434-2627

Les Editions du Boreal
4447, rue St-Denis, Montreal, QC H2J 2L2
Tel: 514-287-7401 *Fax:* 514-287-7664
E-mail: boreal@editionsboreal.qc.ca
Web Site: www.editionsboreal.qc.ca
Key Personnel
Dir Gen: Pascal Assathiany
Dir: Jean Bernier
Founded: 1963
General literature, essays, history, translations, children's & philosophy.
Publishes in French.
ISBN Prefix(es): 978-2-89052; 978-2-7646; 978-0-88503
Number of titles published annually: 70 Print
Total Titles: 1,700 Print
Distributed by Editions Du Seuil (Europe)
Foreign Rights: AMV Agencia Literaria (Eduardo Melon Vallat) (Portugal, Spain); Anatolialit Literary & Copyright Agency (Amy Spangler) (Turkey); Balla & Co Literary Agents (Catherine Balla) (Hungary); Bureau des Copyrights Francais (Corinne Quentin) (Japan); Agence Litteraire Wandel Cruse (Arabella Cruse) (Iceland, Netherlands, Scandinavia); Niki Douge (Greece); Agence de l'Est (Patricia Morinet-Pasqualini) (Bosnia and Herzegovina, Bulgaria, Croatia, Czech Republic, Estonia, Kosovo, Latvia, Lithuania, Macedonia, Montenegro, Poland, Serbia, Slovakia, Slovenia); The Grayhawk Agency (Nicholas Wu) (China, Taiwan); Agnese Incisa Agenzia Letteraria (Italy); Simona Kessler Agency (Marina Adriana) (Romania); Anastasia Lester (Belarus, Russia, Ukraine); Liepman AG Literary Agency (Eva Koralnik) (Germany); I Pikarski Ltd Literary Agency (Gabi Hertzman) (Israel)
Distribution Center: Exportlivre Inc, 289, blvd Desaulniers, St-Lambert, QC J4P 1M8 (US) *Tel:* 450-671-3888 *Fax:* 450-671-2121 *E-mail:* order@exportlivre.com *Web Site:* www.exportlivre.com
Diffusion Dimedia, 539, blvd Lebeau, Ville St-Laurent, QC H4N 1S2 *Tel:* 514-336-3941 *Fax:* 514-331-3916 *E-mail:* info@dimedia.qc.ca *Web Site:* www.dimedia.com
Volumen, 25, blvd Romain Rolland, CS 21418, 75993 Paris Cedex 14, France (Europe) *Tel:* 01 41 48 84 60 *Fax:* 01 64 48 49 63 *E-mail:* volumen@volumen.fr

Editions du CHU Sainte-Justine
Unit of Direction de l'enseignement
3175, chemin de la Cote-Sainte-Catherine, Montreal, QC H3T 1C5
Tel: 514-345-4671 *Fax:* 514-345-4631
E-mail: edition.hsj@ssss.gouv.qc.ca
Web Site: www.editions-chu-sainte-justine.org
Key Personnel
Publg Dir: Marise Labrecque *Tel:* 514-345-7743 *E-mail:* marise.labrecque.hsj@ssss.gouv.qc.ca
Publr: Marie-Eve Lefebvre *Tel:* 514-345-2350 *E-mail:* marie-eve.lefebvre.hsj@ssss.gouv.qc.ca

Sales Dir: Jean-Francois Hebert *Tel:* 514-345-4931 ext 5541 *E-mail:* jean-francois.hebert.hsj@ssss.gouv.qc.ca
Sales Mgr: Susy Coutu *E-mail:* susy.coutu.hsj@ssss.gouv.qc.ca
ISBN Prefix(es): 978-2-921215; 978-2-921858; 978-2-922770; 978-2-89619
Number of titles published annually: 20 Print
Distribution Center: Prologue, 1650 blvd Lionel-Bertrand, Boisbriand, QC J7H 1N7 *Tel:* 450-434-0306 *Toll Free Tel:* 800-363-2864 *Fax:* 450-434-2627 *Toll Free Fax:* 800-361-8088 *E-mail:* prologue@prologue.ca *Web Site:* www.prologue.ca
SDL La Caravelle, Rue du Pre-aux-oies, 303, 1130 Brussels, Belgium (Belgium & Luxembourg) *Tel:* (02) 240 93 08 *Fax:* (02) 216 35 98 *E-mail:* info@sdlcaravelle.com
Daudin Distribution, One, rue Guynemer, 78114 Magny-les Hameaux, France *Tel:* 01 30 48 74 74 *Fax:* 01 34 98 02 44 *E-mail:* commandes@daudin.fr
Servidis, Chemin des chalets, 1279 Chavannes-de-Bogis, Switzerland *Tel:* (022) 960 95 32 *Fax:* (022) 960 95 77 *E-mail:* commande@servidis.ch

§Les Editions du CRAM Inc
1030, Cherrier, bureau 205, Montreal, QC H2L 1H9
Tel: 514-598-8547 *Fax:* 514-598-8788
E-mail: service@editionscram.com
Web Site: www.editionscram.com
Key Personnel
Edit Dir: Pierre Lavigne *Tel:* 514-598-8547 ext 229 *E-mail:* plavigne@groupecram.com
Mktg Dir: Guillaume Lavigne *Tel:* 514-598-8547 ext 224 *E-mail:* glavigne@groupecram.com
Founded: 1988
ISBN Prefix(es): 978-2-89721; 978-2-922050; 978-2-9801489
Number of titles published annually: 20 Print
Foreign Rights: Agence Ambre Communication (Pascale Patte-Wilbert)
Distribution Center: Prologue, 1650 Lionel Bertrand, Boisbriand, QC J7H 1N7 *Tel:* 450-434-0306 *Fax:* 450-434-2627
SDL Caravelle, Rue du Pre-aux-oies, 303, 1130 Brussels, Belgium *Tel:* (02) 240 93 00 *Fax:* (02) 216 35 98
DG Diffusion, Zl de Bogues, 31750 Escalquens, France *Tel:* 05 61 00 09 99 *Fax:* 05 61 00 23 12
Transat Distribution SA, Chemin des Chalets, 1279 Chavannes de Bogis, Switzerland *Tel:* (022) 342 77 40 *Fax:* (022) 343 46 46 *E-mail:* transat@transatdiffusion.ch

Les Editions du Noroit
4609 rue D'Iberville, espace 202, Montreal, QC H2H 2L9
Tel: 514-727-0005
E-mail: lenoroit@lenoroit.com
Web Site: www.lenoroit.com
Key Personnel
Literary Dir: Paul Belanger
Founded: 1971
Poetry.
Publishes in French.
ISBN Prefix(es): 978-2-89018; 978-0-88524
Number of titles published annually: 25 Print
Total Titles: 730 Print; 1 CD-ROM; 10 Audio
Distribution Center: Diffusion Dimedia Inc, 539 blvd Lebeau, Montreal, QC H4N 1S2 *Tel:* 514-336-3941 *Fax:* 514-331-3916 *E-mail:* general@dimedia.qc.ca *Web Site:* www.dimedia.com

Les Editions du Remue-Menage
La Maison Parent-Roback, 110 rue Ste-Therese, bureau 501, Montreal, QC H2Y 1E6
Tel: 514-876-0097 *Fax:* 514-876-7951
E-mail: info@editions-rm.ca
Web Site: www.editions-rm.ca
Key Personnel
Publr: Rachel Bedard
Ed: Elise Bergeron
Founded: 1976
Specialize in feminist books.
Publishes in English, French.
ISBN Prefix(es): 978-2-89091
Number of titles published annually: 15 Print
Total Titles: 170 Print
Distributed by Export Livre (Europe, US); Hushion House Publishing Ltd (CN, US); Librarie du Quebec (France)
Foreign Rep(s): Library Plaisir (Egypt); S A Vander (Belgium)
Distribution Center: Diffusion Dimedia, 539 blvd Lebeau, St-Laurent, QC H4N 1S2 *Tel:* 514-336-3941 *Fax:* 514-331-3916 *Toll Free Fax:* 800-667-3941 *E-mail:* commandes@dimedia.qc.ca
Membership(s): Association Nationale des Editeurs de Livres

Les Editions du Septentrion
1300 Maguire Ave, Sillery, QC G1T 1Z3
Tel: 418-688-3556 *Fax:* 418-527-4978
E-mail: info@septentrion.qc.ca
Web Site: www.septentrion.qc.ca
Key Personnel
Pres & Publr: Denis Vaugeois
Dir Gen & Ed: Gilles Herman
Ed: Sophie Imbeault
Founded: 1988
Full service publisher.
Publishes in English, French.
ISBN Prefix(es): 978-2-89448; 978-0-89664; 978-0-88514; 978-0-921114; 978-0-89011
Number of titles published annually: 30 Print
Total Titles: 700 Print
Divisions: Hamac
Distribution Center: Dimedia, 539 blvd Lebeau, St-Laurent, QC H4N 1S2

Les Editions du Vermillon
305, rue St-Patrick, Ottawa, ON K1N 5K4
Tel: 613-241-4032 *Fax:* 613-241-3109
E-mail: leseditionsduvermillon@rogers.com
Web Site: www.leseditionsduvermillon.ca
Key Personnel
Founder & Edit Dir: Jacques Flamand
CEO: Monique Bertoli
Founded: 1982
Poetry, novels, children's books, textbooks, essays.
Publishes in English, French.
ISBN Prefix(es): 978-0-919925; 978-1-895873; 978-1-894547; 978-1-897058; 978-1-926628; 978-2-89040; 978-1-77120
Number of titles published annually: 12 Print
Total Titles: 400 Print
Foreign Rep(s): Diffusion Albert-le-Grand (Switzerland); Librairie du Quebec (France)
Foreign Rights: Montreal-Contacts (Worldwide)
Distribution Center: Prologue Inc, 1650, boul Lionel-Bertrand, Boisbriand, AB J7H 1N7 *Tel:* 450-434-0306 *Toll Free Tel:* 800-363-2864 *Fax:* 450-434-2627 *Toll Free Fax:* 800-361-8088
Librairie du Quebec, 300, rue Gay Lussac, 75005 Paris, France *Tel:* 01 43 54 49 02 *Fax:* 01 43 54 39 15 *E-mail:* liquebec@noos.fr
Diffusion Albert le Grand SA, 20, rue de Beaumont, 1701 Fribourg, Switzerland *Tel:* (026) 425 85 95 *Fax:* (026) 425 85 90 *E-mail:* diffusion@albert-le-grand.ch
Membership(s): Canada Council for the Arts; Ontario Arts Council

Les Editions Fides
Subsidiary of Coopsco
7333 place des Roseraies, bureau 100, Anjou, QC H1M 2X6
Tel: 514-745-4290 *Fax:* 514-745-4299
E-mail: editions@groupefides.com
Web Site: www.editionsfides.com
Key Personnel
CEO: Claude Rheaume
Edit Dir: Guylaine Girard *Tel:* 514-745-4290 ext 355
Dir, Fin & Admin: Michel Perreault
Mktg: David Senechal
Founded: 1937
Publishes in French.
ISBN Prefix(es): 978-0-7755; 978-2-7621; 978-2-87374; 978-2-89007
Number of titles published annually: 60 Print
Total Titles: 2,000 Print
Distribution Center: Socadis, 420 rue Stinson, Ville St-Laurent, QC H4N 3L7 *Tel:* 514-331-3300 *Toll Free Tel:* 800-361-2847 *Fax:* 514-745-3282 *Toll Free Fax:* 866-803-5422 *E-mail:* socinfo@socadis.com
Sofedis, 11, rue Soufflot, 75005 Paris, France (Europe) *Tel:* 01 53 10 25 25 *Fax:* 01 53 10 25 26 *E-mail:* info@sofedis.fr

Editions FouLire
4339, rue des Becassines, Quebec, QC G1G 1V5
Tel: 418-628-4029 *Toll Free Tel:* 877-628-4029 (CN & US) *Fax:* 418-628-4801
E-mail: info@foulire.com; edition@foulire.com
Web Site: www.foulire.com
Key Personnel
Ed: Yvon Brochu
Head, Communs & Social Media: Marc Proulx
Prodn & Mktg: Danielle Lajeunesse
Founded: 2002
Publishers of books for children.
Publishes in French.
ISBN Prefix(es): 978-2-89591
Number of titles published annually: 10 Print
Total Titles: 39 Print
Foreign Rights: Ambre Communication (Pascale Patte-Wilbert) (France)
Distribution Center: Prologue Inc, 1650, blvd Lionel-Bertrand, Boisbriand, QC J7H 1N7 *Tel:* 450-434-0306 *Toll Free Tel:* 800-363-2864 *Fax:* 450-434-2627 *Toll Free Fax:* 800-361-8088 *E-mail:* prologue@prologue.ca
Librairie du Quebec, 30, rue Gay-Lussac, 75005 Paris, France *Tel:* 01 43 54 49 02 *Fax:* 01 43 54 39 15 *E-mail:* liquebec@noos.fr

Les Editions Ganesha Inc
CP 484, succursale d'Youville, Montreal, QC H2P 2W1
Tel: 450-641-2395
E-mail: courriel@editions-ganesha.qc.ca
Web Site: www.editions-ganesha.qc.ca
Key Personnel
Publr: Andre Beaudoin
Founded: 1978
Publishes in French.
ISBN Prefix(es): 978-2-89145
Number of titles published annually: 4 Print
Total Titles: 56 Print

Les Editions Goelette Inc
1350 Marie-Victorin, St-Bruno-de-Montarville, Quebec, QC J3V 6B9
Tel: 450-653-1337 *Toll Free Tel:* 800-463-4961 *Fax:* 450-653-9924
E-mail: info@boutiquegoelette.com
Web Site: www.editionsgoelette.com
Key Personnel
Pres: Alain Delorme
Publr: Ingrid Remazeilles
Dir, Prodn: Caroline Coutu
Founded: 1997
Publishes in English, French.
ISBN Prefix(es): 978-2-9804941; 978-2-9806291; 978-2-922983; 978-2-89638; 978-2-89690
Number of titles published annually: 60 Print

Distribution Center: Les Messageries ADP, 2315, rue de la Province, Longueuil, QC J4G 1G4 *Tel:* 450-640-1234 *Toll Free Tel:* 800-771-3022 *Fax:* 450-640-1251 *Toll Free Fax:* 800-603-0433
Interforum, Immeuble Paryseine, 3, allee de la Seine, 94854 Ivry Cedex, France (France) *Tel:* 01 49 59 11 56

Les Editions Heritage Inc
1101, ave Victoria, St-Lambert, QC J4R 1P8
Tel: 514-875-0327 *Toll Free Tel:* 800-561-3737 *Fax:* 450-672-5448
Key Personnel
CEO & Pres of the Council: Jacques Payette
Pres: Sylvie Payette
Founded: 1968
Juvenile, adult & French language.
Publishes in French.
ISBN Prefix(es): 978-0-7773; 978-2-7625
Number of titles published annually: 250 Print
Total Titles: 2,000 Print
Foreign Rights: Barbara Creary
Membership(s): Association for Canadian Publishers in the US

Editions Hurtubise
1815, ave De Lorimier, Montreal, QC H2K 3W6
Tel: 514-523-1523 *Toll Free Tel:* 800-361-1664 *Fax:* 514-523-9969
Web Site: www.editionshurtubise.com
Key Personnel
Pres: Herve Foulon
VP, Editions & Opers: Arnaud Foulon *E-mail:* arnaud.foulon@groupehmh.com
VP, Sales & Mktg: Alexandrine Foulon *E-mail:* alexandrine.foulon@grouphmh.com
Dir, Prodn: Dominique Lemay *E-mail:* dominique.lemay@editionshurtubise.com
Ed: Annie Filion *E-mail:* annie.filion@editionshurtubise.com
Founded: 1960
French Canadian publishing house. Fiction, nonfiction & textbooks.
Publishes in French.
ISBN Prefix(es): 978-2-89045; 978-2-89428; 978-2-89647; 978-0-7758
Number of titles published annually: 110 Print
Total Titles: 1,200 Print
Imprints: Bibliotheque Quebecoise (BQ)
Distributor for Marcel Didier Inc; Hurtubise HMH Ltee

Les Editions JCL
930, rue Jacques-Cartier E, Chicoutimi, QC G7H 7K9
Tel: 418-696-0536 *Fax:* 418-696-3132
E-mail: jcl@jcl.qc.ca
Web Site: www.jcl.qc.ca
Key Personnel
Pres & Intl Rts: Jean-Claude Larouche *E-mail:* jclarouche@jcl.qc.ca
Dir Gen: Judith Bouchard *E-mail:* judith@jcl.qc.ca
Founded: 1977
Novels & nonfiction.
Publishes in French.
ISBN Prefix(es): 978-2-920176; 978-2-89431; 978-2-89432
Number of titles published annually: 26 Print
Total Titles: 475 Print
Foreign Rights: Michael Wenzel (European Union)
Distribution Center: Messageries ADP, 2315, rue de la Province, Longueuil, QC J4G 1G4 *Tel:* 450-640-1234 *Toll Free Tel:* 800-771-3022 *Fax:* 450-640-1251 *Toll Free Fax:* 800-603-0433
Librairie du Quebec, 30, rue Gay Lussac, 75005 Paris, France (France & Europe) *Tel:* 01 45 54 49 02 *Fax:* 01 43 54 39 15 *E-mail:* libraires@librairiequebec.fr *Web Site:* www.librairieduquebec.fr
Servidis/Transat, Chemin des Chalets 7, 1279 Chavannes-de-Bogis, Switzerland *Tel:* (022) 960 95 10 *Fax:* (022) 776 63 64 *E-mail:* admin@servidis.ch *Web Site:* www.servidis.ch
Membership(s): Association Nationale des Editeurs de Livres

Editions Le Dauphin Blanc Inc
825, boul Lebourgneuf, Suite 125, Quebec, QC G2J 0B9
Tel: 418-845-4045 *Fax:* 418-845-1933
E-mail: info@dauphinblanc.com
Web Site: www.dauphinblanc.com
Key Personnel
CEO: Alain Williamson *E-mail:* alainwilliamson@dauphinblanc.com
Asst Dir & Prodn Mgr: Sonia Marois *E-mail:* soniamarois@dauphinblanc.com
Founded: 1991
Publishes in French.
ISBN Prefix(es): 978-2-89436
Number of titles published annually: 60 Print
Distribution Center: Prologue Inc, 1650, Lionel-Bertrand, Boisbriand, QC J7H 1N7 *Tel:* 450-434-0306 *Toll Free Tel:* 800-363-2864 *Fax:* 450-434-2627 *Web Site:* www.prologue.ca
DG Diffusion, Zl de Bogues, 31750 Escalquens, France (Belgium & France) *Tel:* 05 61 00 09 99 *Fax:* 05 61 00 23 12 *E-mail:* adv@dgdiffusion.com *Web Site:* www.dgdiffusion.com
Diffusion Transat/Servidis, Chemin des Chalets 7, 1279 Chavannes-de-Bogis, Switzerland *Tel:* (022) 42 77 40 *Fax:* (022) 43 46 46 *E-mail:* transat@transatdiffusion.ch

Editions Marie-France
9900 Ave des Laurentides, Montreal, QC H1H 4V1
Tel: 514-329-3700 *Toll Free Tel:* 800-563-6644 (CN) *Fax:* 514-329-0630
E-mail: editions@marie-france.qc.ca
Web Site: www.marie-france.qc.ca
Key Personnel
Pres: Jean Lachapelle
VP: Joanne Lacombe
Founded: 1977
School, kindergarten, elementary & secondary adult & university in French, natural sciences, human sciences, music, economic education & physics. Some titles in both French & English.
Publishes in English, French.
ISBN Prefix(es): 978-2-89168
Number of titles published annually: 25 Print
Total Titles: 1,001 Print
Membership(s): Association Nationale des Editeurs de Livres

Editions Mediaspaul
3965, blvd Henri-Bourassa E, Montreal, QC H1H 1L1
Tel: 514-322-7341 *Fax:* 514-322-4281
E-mail: editeur@mediaspaul.ca
Web Site: mediaspaul.ca
Key Personnel
Exec Dir: Joseph Sciortino *E-mail:* jsciortino@mediaspaul.ca
Publr: Gilles Collicelli
Founded: 1975
Religious & photographic books.
This publisher has indicated that 20% of their product line is author subsidized.
Publishes in French.
ISBN Prefix(es): 978-2-7122; 978-0-88840; 978-2-89039; 978-2-89420
Number of titles published annually: 20 Print
Total Titles: 300 Print
Foreign Rep(s): Paul Johnston

Editions Michel Quintin
4770 rue Foster, Waterloo, QC J0E 2N0
SAN: 116-5356
Tel: 450-539-3774 *Fax:* 450-539-4905
E-mail: info@editionsmichelquintin.ca
Web Site: www.editionsmichelquintin.ca
Key Personnel
Pres: Michel Quintin
VP: Collette Dufresne
Founded: 1982
Nonfiction on fauna, nature, environment.
Publishes in French.
ISBN Prefix(es): 978-2-920438; 978-2-89435
Number of titles published annually: 30 Print
Total Titles: 200 Print
Editorial Office(s): PO Box 340, Waterloo, QC J0E 2N0
Foreign Rep(s): Bacon & Hughes (Canada); Interforum; Servidis SA (Belgium)
Distribution Center: Les Messageries ADP, 1261-A rue Shearer, Montreal, QC H3K 3G4 *Tel:* 514-523-1182 *Fax:* 514-939-0705

Editions MultiMondes
930 rue Pouliot, Quebec, QC G1V 3N9
Tel: 418-651-3885 *Toll Free Tel:* 800-840-3029 *Fax:* 418-651-6822 *Toll Free Fax:* 888-303-5931
E-mail: multimondes@multim.com
Web Site: www.multim.com
Key Personnel
Pres: Jean-Marc Gagnon *E-mail:* jmgagnon@multim.com
VP: Lise Morin *E-mail:* lmorin@multim.com
Edit Asst: Melanie Beaulieu *E-mail:* mbeaulieu@multim.com
Founded: 1988
Books on science & the environment.
Publishes in English, French.
ISBN Prefix(es): 978-2-921146; 978-2-89544
Number of titles published annually: 20 Print
Total Titles: 200 Print
Distribution Center: Prologue, 1650, blvd Lionel-Bertrand, Boisbriand, QC J7H 1N7 *Tel:* 450-434-0306 *Fax:* 450-434-2627 *E-mail:* prologue@prologue.ca
The SDL Caravelle, Rue du Pre aux Geese, 303, Brussels, Belgium *Tel:* (02) 240 93 00 *Fax:* (02) 216 35 98
Librairie du Quebec in Paris, 30, rue Gay Lussac, 75005 Paris, France *Tel:* 01 43 54 49 02 *Fax:* 01 43 54 39 15 *E-mail:* direction@librairieduquebec.fr
Servidis SA, Chemin des Chalets 7, 1279 Chavannes-de-Bogis, Switzerland *Tel:* (022) 960 95 32 *Fax:* (022) 960 95 77 *E-mail:* pgavillet@servidis.ch

Les Editions Phidal Inc
5740 Ferrier, Montreal, QC H4P 1M7
Tel: 514-738-0202 *Toll Free Tel:* 800-738-7349 *Fax:* 514-738-5102
E-mail: info@phidal.com; customer@phidal.com (sales & export)
Key Personnel
Publr: Lionel Soussan
Founded: 1979
Full service publisher.
Publishes in English, French.
ISBN Prefix(es): 978-2-89393; 978-2-7643; 978-2-920129
Number of titles published annually: 35 Print
Divisions: Edilivre Inc

Les Editions Pierre Tisseyre
155, rue Maurice, Rosemere, QC J7A 2S8
Tel: 514-335-0777 *Fax:* 514-335-6723
E-mail: info@edtisseyre.ca
Web Site: www.tisseyre.ca
Key Personnel
Pres: Charles Tisseyre
Dir: Sylvia De Angelis

Literary Dir: Marie-Andree Clermont; Melanie Perreault
Founded: 1947
Primarily publish books for children & young adults ages 5-17.
Publishes in French.
ISBN Prefix(es): 978-2-89051; 978-2-89633; 978-0-7753
Number of titles published annually: 55 Print
Total Titles: 350 Print
Distribution Center: Prologue, 1650, Lionel-Bertrand, Boisbriand, QC J7H 1N7 *Tel:* 450-434-0306 *Toll Free Tel:* 800-363-2864 *E-mail:* prologue@prologue.ca

Editions Trecarre
Subsidiary of Quebecor Media
La Tourelle, Bureau 800, 1055, Blvd Rene-Levesque E, Montreal, QC H2L 4S5
Tel: 514-849-5259 *Fax:* 514-849-1388
Web Site: www.edtrecarre.com
Key Personnel
Rts Mgr: Carole Boutin *Tel:* 514-373-2743 *E-mail:* carol.boutin@groupelibrex.com
Founded: 1982
Coffee-table books, nature books, cookbooks, practical books.
Publishes in French.
ISBN Prefix(es): 978-2-89249; 978-2-89568
Number of titles published annually: 30 Print
Total Titles: 700 Print
Warehouse: 2185 Autoroute des Laurentides, Laval, QC H7S 1Z6

Les Editions Un Monde Different
3905 Isabelle, bureau 101, Brossard, QC J4Y 2R2
Mailing Address: CP 51546, Greenfield Park, QC J4V 3N8
Tel: 450-656-2660 *Toll Free Tel:* 800-443-2582 *Fax:* 450-659-9328
E-mail: info@umd.ca
Web Site: www.umd.ca
Key Personnel
Owner & Ed: Michel Ferron
Asst Ed: Manon Martel
Cust Serv/Promo & Mktg: Monique Duchesneau *E-mail:* mduchesneau@umd.ca
Founded: 1977
Motivational & inspirational books.
Publishes in French.
ISBN Prefix(es): 978-2-89225; 978-2-920000
Number of titles published annually: 25 Print
Total Titles: 750 Print
Distribution Center: Messageries ADP, 2315, rue de la Province, Longueuil, QC J4G 1G4 *Tel:* 450-640-1234 *Fax:* 450-640-1251
Interforum Editis, Immeuble Paryseine, 3, alle de la Seine, 94854 Ivry, Cedex, France (Europe) *Tel:* 01 49 59 11 56 *Fax:* 01 49 59 11 91

Les Editions Vents d'Ouest
109, rue Wright, bureau 202, Gatineau, QC J8X 2G7
Tel: 819-770-6377 *Fax:* 819-770-0559
E-mail: info@ventsdouest.ca
Web Site: www.ventsdouest.ca
Key Personnel
Pres: Benoit Tolszczuk
VP: Gilles Parent
Dir, Gen Lit: Jeanne Duhaime; Pierre Gregoire; Jacques Michaud
Coord & Dir, Young Adult Lit: Michel Lavoie
Founded: 1993
Novels, short stories, history.
Publishes in French.
ISBN Prefix(es): 978-2-921603; 978-2-89537
Number of titles published annually: 18 Print
Total Titles: 220 Print
Distribution Center: Prologue Inc, 1650 Blvd Lionel-Bertrand, Boisbriand, QC J7H 1N7 *Tel:* 450-434-0306 *Toll Free Tel:* 800-363-2864 *Fax:* 450-434-2627 *Toll Free Fax:* 800-361-8088
Librairie du Quebec a Paris, 30, rue Gay-Lussac, 750005 Paris, France *Tel:* 01 43 54 49 02 *Fax:* 01 43 54 39 15

Les Editions XYZ inc
1815, ave De Lorimier, Montreal, QC H2K 3W6
Tel: 514-525-2170 *Fax:* 514-525-7537
E-mail: info@editionsxyz.com
Web Site: www.editionsxyz.com
Key Personnel
Head, Communs: Alexandrine Foulon *E-mail:* alexandrine.foulon@groupehmh.com
Prodn Mgr: Nathalie Tasse *Tel:* 514-525-2170 ext 255 *E-mail:* nathalie.tasse@editionsxyz.com
Ed: Marie-Pierre Barathon *Tel:* 514-525-2170 ext 270 *E-mail:* marie-pierre.barathon@editionsxyz.com; Pascal Genet *Tel:* 514-525-2170 ext 260 *E-mail:* pascal.genet@editionsxyz.com
Founded: 1985
Novels, short stories & essays on literature.
Publishes in French.
ISBN Prefix(es): 978-2-89261
Number of titles published annually: 20 Print
Total Titles: 457 Print
Distribution Center: HMH *Tel:* 514-523-1523 *Toll Free Tel:* 800-361-1664 *Fax:* 514-523-9969 *Web Site:* www.distributionhmh.com
Membership(s): Association of Canadian Publishers; Literary Press Group

Editions Yvon Blais
137 John, CP 180, Cowansville, QC J2K 3H6
Mailing Address: PO Box 180, Cowansville, QC J2K 3H6
Tel: 450-266-1086 *Toll Free Tel:* 800-363-3047 *Fax:* 450-263-9256
E-mail: editionsyvonblais.commentaires@thomsonreuters.com; editionsyvonblais.commandes@thomsonreuters.com (cust serv)
Web Site: www.editionsyvonblais.qc.ca
Key Personnel
Dir, Pubns: Louis Busse; Marie-Noelle Guay
Founded: 1978
Law books.
Publishes in French.
ISBN Prefix(es): 978-2-89073; 978-2-89451; 978-2-89635
Number of titles published annually: 30 Print
Total Titles: 500 Print
Returns: 245 Bartley Dr, Toronto, ON M4A 2V8

ELS Editions
University of Victoria, Dept of English, PO Box 1700, Sta CSC, Victoria, BC V8W 2Y2
Tel: 250-721-7236 *Fax:* 250-721-6498
E-mail: els@uvic.ca
Web Site: english.uvic.ca/els
Key Personnel
Ed: Dr Luke Carson
Founded: 1975
Scholarly monographs related to literature.
Publishes in English.
ISBN Prefix(es): 978-0-9691436; 978-0-920604
Number of titles published annually: 1 Print
Total Titles: 107 Print

Emond Montgomery Publications Ltd
60 Shaftesbury Ave, Toronto, ON M4T 1A3
Tel: 416-975-3925 *Toll Free Tel:* 888-837-0815 *Fax:* 416-975-3924
E-mail: orders@emp.ca
Web Site: www.emp.ca
Key Personnel
Pres: D Paul Emond *Tel:* 416-975-3925 ext 233 *E-mail:* pemond@emp.ca
VP, Educ Div: Anthony Rezek *Tel:* 416-975-3925 ext 229 *E-mail:* arezek@emp.ca
VP, Prodn & Admin: Paula Pike *Tel:* 416-975-3925 ext 223 *E-mail:* ppike@emp.ca
Mktg Mgr: Christine Davidson *Tel:* 416-975-3925 ext 246 *E-mail:* cdavidson@emp.ca
Founded: 1978
Academic publisher.
Publishes in English.
ISBN Prefix(es): 978-0-920722; 978-1-55239
Number of titles published annually: 30 Print; 40 E-Book
Total Titles: 200 Print; 40 E-Book
Returns: 240 Industrial Pkwy S, Unit 4, Door 1, Aurora, ON L4G 3V6, Contact: Judith Lynn *E-mail:* jlynn@emp.ca
Warehouse: 240 Industrial Pkwy S, Unit 4, Door 1, Aurora, ON L4G 3V6, Contact: Judith Lynn *E-mail:* jlynn@emp.ca

ERPI, see Pearson ERPI

Fairwinds Press
PO Box 668, Lions Bay, BC V0N 2E0
Tel: 604-913-0649
E-mail: orders@fairwinds-press.com
Web Site: www.fairwinds-press.com
Key Personnel
Publr & Intl Rts: Leslie Nolin *E-mail:* leslie@fairwinds-press.com
Founded: 1997
Publishes in English.
ISBN Prefix(es): 978-0-9682149; 978-0-9780974; 978-0-9881081
Number of titles published annually: 3 Print; 2 E-Book
Total Titles: 17 Print; 6 E-Book
Membership(s): Independent Publishers Association

Fernwood Publishing
32 Oceanvista Lane, Black Point, NS B0J 1B0
Tel: 902-857-1388 *Fax:* 902-857-1328
E-mail: info@fernpub.ca; roseway@fernpub.ca
Web Site: fernwoodpublishing.ca
Key Personnel
Co-Publr: Wayne Antony *E-mail:* wayne@fernpub.ca; Errol Sharpe *E-mail:* errol@fernpub.ca
Prodn Coord & Publr/Mng Ed, Roseway: Beverly Rach *E-mail:* bev@fernpub.ca
Mng Ed: Jessica Antony *E-mail:* jessica@fernpub.ca; Candida Hadley *E-mail:* candida@fernpub.ca
Promos Coord: Curran Faris; Nancy Malek
Founded: 1991
Social sciences & humanities, emphasizing labour studies, women's studies, gender studies, critical theory & research, political economy, cultural studies & social work for use in undergraduate courses in colleges & universities.
Publishes in English.
ISBN Prefix(es): 978-1-895686; 978-1-55266
Number of titles published annually: 29 Print
Total Titles: 450 Print
Imprints: Roseway Publishing
Branch Office(s)
748 Broadway Ave, Winnipeg, MB R3G 0X3 *Tel:* 204-474-2958 *Fax:* 204-475-2813
U.S. Rep(s): Independent Publishers Group
Foreign Rep(s): Merlin Press (Europe, Ireland, UK)
Orders to: Brunswick Books, 20 Maud St, Suite 303, Toronto, ON M5V 2M5 (North America & Australia) *Tel:* 416-703-3598 *Fax:* 416-703-6561 *E-mail:* orders@brunswickbooks.ca *Web Site:* www.brunswickbooks.ca; The Merlin Press/Central Books Ltd, 99 Wallis Rd, London E9 5LN, United Kingdom (UK & Europe) *Tel:* (020) 8986 4854 *Fax:* (020) 8533 5821 *E-mail:* orders@centralbooks.com *Web Site:* www.centralbooks.co.uk
Returns: Brunswick Books, c/o TTS Distributing, 155 Edward St, Aurora, ON L4G IW3

Fifth House Publishers
Division of Fitzhenry & Whiteside Limited
195 Allstate Pkwy, Markham, ON L3R 4T8
Tel: 905-477-9700 *Toll Free Tel:* 800-387-9776 *Toll Free Fax:* 800-260-9777
E-mail: godwit@fitzhenry.ca; bookinfo@fitzhenry.ca (cust serv)
Web Site: www.fitzhenry.ca/fifthhouse.aspx
Key Personnel
Publr: Tracey Dettman *E-mail:* tdettman@fitzhenry.ca
Founded: 1982
Trade publisher focusing on Western Canadian interest books; aviation, gardening.
Publishes in English, French.
ISBN Prefix(es): 978-0-920079; 978-1-895618; 978-1-894004; 978-1-894856; 978-1-897252; 978-1-927083
Number of titles published annually: 18 Print
Total Titles: 211 Print; 1 CD-ROM; 5 E-Book; 1 Audio
Distributed by Fitzhenry & Whiteside Limited
Orders to: Ingram Publisher Services, 1210 Ingram Dr, Chambersburg, PA 17202, United States
Returns: Ingram Publisher Services, 1210 Ingram Dr, Chambersburg, PA 17202, United States
Membership(s): Book Publishers Association of Alberta

Firefly Books Ltd
50 Staples Ave, Unit 1, Richmond Hill, ON L4B 0A7
Tel: 416-499-8412 *Toll Free Tel:* 800-387-6192 (CN); 800-387-5085 (US) *Fax:* 416-499-8313 *Toll Free Fax:* 800-450-0391 (CN); 800-565-6034 (US)
E-mail: service@fireflybooks.com
Web Site: www.fireflybooks.com
Key Personnel
Pres: Lionel Koffler
EVP: Leon Gouzoules
Lib Sales Dir: Ann Quinn *Tel:* 416-499-8412 ext 134 *E-mail:* annq@fireflybooks.com
Publicity Dir: Valerie Hatton *Tel:* 416-499-8412 ext 128 *E-mail:* valerie@fireflybooks.com
Rts & Contracts Mgr: Diane Vanderkooy *Tel:* 416-499-8412 ext 153 *E-mail:* dianevan@fireflybooks.com
Founded: 1977
Books & calendars.
Publishes in English.
ISBN Prefix(es): 978-0-920668; 978-1-895565; 978-1-896284; 978-1-55209; 978-1-55297; 978-1-55407; 978-1-77085
Number of titles published annually: 220 Print
Total Titles: 2,000 Print; 25 Online
Divisions: The Boston Mills Press
Branch Office(s)
8514 Long Canyon Dr, Austin, TX 78730-2183, United States, Contact: Thomas C Martin *Tel:* 512-372-8500 *Fax:* 512-372-2499 *E-mail:* fireflytom@mindspring.com
Distributor for Annick Press; Boston Mills Press; Camden House; Cottage Life; Firefly Books; The Genealogical Research Library Inc; Great North Books; Kiddy Chronicles Publishing; Mikaya Press; Robert Rose Inc; Sound & Vision
Foreign Rep(s): Angell Eurosales (Gill Angell & Stewart Siddall) (Denmark, Finland, Iceland, Norway, Scandinavia, Sweden); Ashton International Marketing Services (Julian Ashton) (Asia); Baccus Books (Owen Early) (South Africa, Sub-Saharan Africa); Bookport Associates (Joe Portelli) (Greece, Italy, Malta, Portugal, Southern Europe, Spain); Cranbury International LLC (Ethan Atkin) (Caribbean, Latin America); European Marketing Services (Anselm Robinson) (Austria, Belgium, France, Germany, Switzerland, Western Europe); IMA (Anthony Moggach) (East Africa, Eastern Europe, West Africa); Chris Lloyd Sales & Marketing Services (Northern Europe, UK); Peribo Pty Ltd (Australia); Butler Sims Ltd (Ireland)
Returns: c/o Frontier Distributing, 145 Gruner Rd, Cheektowaga, NY 14227, United States
Membership(s): ABA; Association of Canadian Publishers; Canadian Booksellers Association
See separate listing for:
The Boston Mills Press

Fitzhenry & Whiteside Limited
195 Allstate Pkwy, Markham, ON L3R 4T8
SAN: 115-1444
Tel: 905-477-9700 *Toll Free Tel:* 800-387-9776 *Fax:* 905-477-2834 *Toll Free Fax:* 800-260-9777
E-mail: bookinfo@fitzhenry.ca; godwit@fitzhenry.ca
Web Site: www.fitzhenry.ca
Key Personnel
Pres: Sharon Fitzhenry *Tel:* 905-477-9700 ext 228 *E-mail:* sfitz@fitzhenry.ca
COO: Holly Doll *E-mail:* hdoll@fitzhenry.ca
CFO: Peter Stubbs
Compt: Earl Leibovitch *E-mail:* earll@fitzhenry.ca
Mktg Dir: Winston Stilwell *E-mail:* winston@fitzhenry.ca
Mgr, Cust Serv: Judy Ghoura *E-mail:* jghoura@fitzhenry.ca
Mgr, Prodn: Uma Subramanian
Publr Rel: Sonya Gilliss *E-mail:* sonya.gilliss@fitzhenry.ca
Founded: 1966
Trade, reference & children's books, educational material for elementary, high school & college.
Publishes in English.
ISBN Prefix(es): 978-0-88902; 978-1-55005; 978-1-55041; 978-1-894004 (Fifth House); 978-1-894856 (Fifth House); 978-0-88995; 978-1-55455
Number of titles published annually: 70 Print
Total Titles: 1,100 Print
Divisions: Fifth House Publishers; Red Deer Press Inc
Distributor for Black Moss Press; Boulder Publications; Capstone Press; Compass Point Books; Coughlan Publishing; DC Books; EDGE Science Fiction & Fantasy Publishing; The Glenbow Museum; Grub Street; Heinemann Raintree; Icon Empire Press; Inhabit Media Inc; Japan Publishing Trading Co; Kodansha; Veronica Lane Books; Lee & Low Books; Mel Bay; Meriwether Publishing Ltd; Annika Parance Publishing; Peachtree Publishers; Picture Window Books; Pokeweed Press; Preferred Nutrition; Railfare DC Books; Red Brick Learning; Stone Arch Books; TFH Publications Inc; Thirty Six Peonies Publishing; Tilbury House Publishers; Tradewind Books; Tree House Press Inc; Wine Appreciation Guild
U.S. Publishers Represented: The Beacon Press; Coteau Books; Kodansha International; Hal Leonard; Peachtree Publishers; Stackpole Books; Thistledown Press; Albert Whitman
U.S. Rep(s): Booklink; Eichkorn & Associates; Nor'East Sales; R&R Book Co
Returns: Ingram Publisher Services, 1210 Ingram Dr, Chambersburg, PA 17202, United States
See separate listing for:
Fifth House Publishers
Red Deer Press Inc
Whitecap Books Ltd

Flammarion Quebec
375 Ave Laurier W, Montreal, QC H2V 2K3
Tel: 514-277-8807 *Fax:* 514-278-2085
E-mail: info@flammarion.qc.ca
Web Site: www.flammarion.qc.ca
Key Personnel
Publr: Louise Loiselle *E-mail:* lloiselle@flammarion.qc.ca
Gen Dir, Dist: Guy Gougeon
Founded: 1974
Best sellers, translations, Quebec literature, novels.
Publishes in French.
ISBN Prefix(es): 978-2-89077
Number of titles published annually: 20 Print
Total Titles: 286 Print
Imprints: Advenir; Bis (Pocket Book)
Distributor for AB Ludis; Alibi; Ambre SA; Amethis-Grenouille; Ariane; Arola; Art Global; Art Lys; Art Lys Jeunesse; Atelier 10; Artemis; Aubier; Auzou; Autrement; Beaux-Arts mag; Belize; Des Bulles dans l'Ocean; Casterman; Centre Georges Pompidou; Centre Pompidou Jeunesse; Champs; Chariot d'or; Climats; Contre-dires; De Courberon; Courrier du Livre; Dangles; Dervy; DG Duffuseur; Le Dilettante; Documents; Ego Comme X; Ensba; Esprit du livre; Exergue; Eveil et Decouvertes; Eyrolles; Fablus; Flammarion; Fluide Glacial; Genex Editions; GF; Grancher; Viviane Hamy; Harlequin; Hoebeke; Horay; J'ai lu; Jouvence Bussiere; Jungle; Lacroix; Nicole Lambert; Lerelie; De L'Herne; Librio; Lux; Josette Lyon; McGray; Medicis; Mic Mac; MK2 Editions; Musee du quai Branly; Neige-Galerie; Neopol; Nouveau Projet; Nova; Organisation-Management; Paquet; La Pasteque; Le Petit Fute; Pierre de soleil; Piktos; La Presse; Profil Sante; Pygmalion; Editions Retrouvees; Rizzoli International Publications; RMN Adulte; RMN Jeunesse; Rogers; Rue de Sevre; Sarbacane; Sarbacane BD; Sassi; Leo Scheer; Septembre Inc; Septembre Jeunesse; Skira Editore; Editions Societe du Figaro; Somogy; Sophia Publications; Spice Box; Steinkis; La Tengo; 13e Note Editions; Tom'poche; Trajectoire; Guy Tredaniel; Ullman; VDB; Vega; Vox Populi; Warum-Vraoum; Zeste
Warehouse: 420 Stinson, St-Laurent, QC H4N 2E9

Flanker Press Ltd
1243 Kenmount Rd, Unit A, Paradise, NL A1L 0V8
Mailing Address: PO Box 2522, Sta C, St John's, NL A1C 6K1
Tel: 709-739-4477 *Toll Free Tel:* 866-739-4420 *Fax:* 709-739-4420
E-mail: info@flankerpress.com
Web Site: www.flankerpress.com
Key Personnel
Pres: Garry Cranford *Tel:* 709-739-4477 ext 23
Mgr: Robert Woodworth *Tel:* 709-739-4477 ext 21
Prodn Mgr: Jerry Cranford *Tel:* 709-739-4477 ext 30
Digital Coord: Peter Hanes *Tel:* 709-739-4477 ext 29
Mktg & Publicity: Laura Cameron *Tel:* 709-739-4477 ext 24
Sales: Randy Drover *Tel:* 709-739-4477 ext 22
Founded: 1994
Wholly Canadian-owned trade book publisher.
Publishes in English.
ISBN Prefix(es): 978-0-9698767; 978-1-894463; 978-1-897317; 978-1-926881; 978-1-771170
Number of titles published annually: 20 Print; 20 E-Book
Imprints: Brazen Books; Flanker Press; Pennywell Books
Membership(s): Association of Canadian Publishers; Atlantic Publishers Marketing Association

Folklore Publishing
11717-9B Ave NW, Unit 2, Edmonton, AB T6J 7B7
Tel: 780-435-2376 *Fax:* 780-435-0674
E-mail: submissions@folklorepublishing.com (ms submissions)
Web Site: www.folklorepublishing.com
Key Personnel
Pres & Publr: Faye Boer *E-mail:* fboer@folklorepublishing.com

Founded: 2001
Publisher of popular history of North America & celebrity biographies.
Publishes in English.
ISBN Prefix(es): 978-1-894864; 978-1-897206
Number of titles published annually: 5 Print
Total Titles: 87 Print
Imprints: Full Court Press (sports history); ICON Press (celebrity bios)
Sales Office(s): Lone Pine Publishing/BookLogic, 2311 96 St, Edmonton, AB T6N 1G3 *Tel:* 780-433-9333 *Toll Free Tel:* 800-661-9017 *Fax:* 780-433-9646 *Toll Free Fax:* 800-424-7173 *E-mail:* info@lonepinepublishing.com *Web Site:* www.lonepinepublishing.com
Distributed by Lone Pine Publishing/BookLogic
U.S. Rep(s): Lone Pine Publishing
Foreign Rep(s): Gazelle Book Services (UK & the continent); Lone Pine Publishing (USA)
Billing Address: Lone Pine Publishing/BookLogic, 2311 96 St, Edmonton, AB T6N 1G3 *Tel:* 780-433-9333 *Toll Free Tel:* 800-661-9017 *Toll Free Fax:* 800-424-7173 *E-mail:* accounts@lonepinepublishing.com *Web Site:* www.lonepinepublishing.com
Orders to: Lone Pine Publishing/BookLogic, 2311 96 St, Edmonton, AB T6N 1G3 *Tel:* 780-433-9333 *Toll Free Tel:* 800-661-9017 *Toll Free Fax:* 800-424-7173 *E-mail:* accounts@lonepinepublishing.com *Web Site:* www.lonepinepublishing.com
Returns: Lone Pine Publishing/BookLogic, 2311 96 St, Edmonton, AB T6N 1G3 *Tel:* 780-433-9333 *Toll Free Tel:* 800-661-9017 *Toll Free Fax:* 800-424-7173 *E-mail:* info@lonepinepublishing.com *Web Site:* www.lonepinepublishing.com
Distribution Center: Lone Pine Publishing/BookLogic, 2311 96 St, Edmonton, AB T6N 1G3 *Tel:* 780-433-9333 *Toll Free Tel:* 800-661-9017 *Fax:* 780-433-9646 *Toll Free Fax:* 800-424-7173 *E-mail:* accounts@lonepinepublishing.com *Web Site:* www.lonepinepublishing.com
Membership(s): Book Publishers Association of Alberta

The Fraser Institute
1770 Burrard St, 4th fl, Vancouver, BC V6J 3G7
Tel: 604-688-0221 *Toll Free Tel:* 800-665-3558 *Fax:* 604-688-8539
E-mail: info@fraserinstitute.org; sales@fraserinstitute.org
Web Site: www.fraserinstitute.org
Key Personnel
Dir, Communs: Dean Pelkey *Tel:* 604-714-4582 *E-mail:* dean.pelkey@fraserinstitute.org
Dir, Pubn Prodn: Kristin McCahon *Tel:* 604-688-0221 ext 583 *E-mail:* kristin.mccahon@fraserinstitute.org
Sr Advisor, Devt: Sherry Stein *E-mail:* sherry.stein@fraserinstitute.org
Founded: 1974
Publish regulatory studies, health policy, social affairs, taxation, environmental studies, energy policy, immigration, welfare/poverty. Publish magazine *Fraser Forum* 6 times a year (in English) & *Perspectives*, quarterly (in French). Also publish current research in the form of books, monographs & Fraser Alerts.
Publishes in English, French.
ISBN Prefix(es): 978-0-88975
Number of titles published annually: 3 Print; 50 Online; 1 E-Book
Total Titles: 500 Print; 350 Online; 2 E-Book
Branch Office(s)
403-525 11 Ave SW, Calgary, AB T2R 0C9 *Tel:* 403-216-7175 *Fax:* 403-234-9010
401-1491 Yonge St, Toronto, ON M4T 1Z4 *Tel:* 416-363-6575 *Fax:* 416-934-1639
Hermes Bldg, Tower B, Suite 252, 1470 Peel St, Montreal, QC H3A 1T1 *Tel:* 514-281-9550 *Fax:* 514-281-9464

Gaetan Morin Editeur
Imprint of Cheneliere Education Inc
5800, rue St-Denis, bureau 900, Montreal, QC H2S 3L5
Tel: 514-273-1066 *Toll Free Tel:* 800-565-5531 *Fax:* 514-276-0324 *Toll Free Fax:* 800-814-0324
E-mail: info@cheneliere.ca
Web Site: www.cheneliere.ca
Key Personnel
Pres & Mng Dir: Jacques Rochefort *E-mail:* jrochefort@tc.tc
Founded: 1977
Textbooks, college, university & professional books.
Publishes in French.
ISBN Prefix(es): 978-2-89105; 978-0-88612; 978-2-910749; 978-2-89632
Number of titles published annually: 20 Print; 1 CD-ROM
Total Titles: 300 Print; 2 CD-ROM

General Store Publishing House (GSPH)
Division of IDP Group (Image Digital Printing)
499 O'Brien Rd, Renfrew, ON K7V 3Z3
Tel: 613-599-2064 *Toll Free Tel:* 800-465-6072
E-mail: orders@gsph.com; submissions@gsph.com
Web Site: www.gsph.com
Key Personnel
Founder & Publr: Tim Gordon *E-mail:* timgordon@gsph.com
Founded: 1981
Local history, sport books, senior fitness, military, history, poetry, cookbooks, self-help.
This publisher has indicated that 50% of their product line is author subsidized.
Publishes in English.
ISBN Prefix(es): 978-0-919431; 978-1-896182; 978-1-894263; 978-1-897113; 978-1-897508; 978-1-926962; 978-1-77123
Number of titles published annually: 25 Print; 15 E-Book
Total Titles: 900 Print; 15 E-Book
Membership(s): Association of Canadian Publishers; Organization of Book Publishers of Ontario

Gilpin Publishing
PO Box 597, Alliston, ON L9R 1V7
Tel: 705-424-6507 *Toll Free Tel:* 800-867-3281 *Fax:* 705-424-6507
E-mail: mail@gilpin.ca
Web Site: www.gilpin.ca
Key Personnel
Pres: Wayne Gilpin *E-mail:* wayne@gilpin.ca
Founded: 1987
Music publisher.
ISBN Prefix(es): 978-0-921046
Number of titles published annually: 4 Print; 1 CD-ROM
Total Titles: 35 Print; 1 CD-ROM

Gold Eagle
Imprint of Harlequin Enterprises Ltd
225 Duncan Mill Rd, 4th fl, Don Mills, ON M3B 3K9
Tel: 416-445-5860 *Toll Free Tel:* 888-432-4879 *Fax:* 416-445-8655; 416-445-8736
E-mail: readgoldeagle@hotmail.com; customerservice@harlequin.com
Web Site: www.harlequin.com
Founded: 1982
Mass market fiction, science fiction, action & adventure.
Publishes in English.
ISBN Prefix(es): 978-0-373
Number of titles published annually: 36 Print
Warehouse: 3010 Walden Ave, Depew, NY 14043, United States

Golden Meteorite Press
Subsidiary of Golden Meteorite Press Ltd
11919 82 St NW, Suite 103, Edmonton, AB T5B 2W4
Tel: 780-378-0063 *Fax:* 780-378-0063
Key Personnel
Ed & Lib Sales Dir: Austin Mardon *E-mail:* aamardon@yahoo.ca
Intl Rts: C Curry
Founded: 1989
Preferred submission is outline. Canadian SASE or IRC is required or else material is recycled. Accept fiction & nonfiction mss in all categories & genres. Submit to editor. Response in 12 weeks on all complete ms submissions. No phone calls please.
Publishes in English.
ISBN Prefix(es): 978-1-895385; 978-1-897; 978-1-894573; 978-0-929024; 978-1-897480
Number of titles published annually: 4 Print
Total Titles: 59 Print
Imprints: Golden Meteorite Press; RTAJ Fry Press; Shoestring Press

Goose Lane Editions
500 Beaverbrook Ct, Suite 330, Fredericton, NB E3B 5X4
SAN: 115-3420
Tel: 506-450-4251 *Toll Free Tel:* 888-926-8377 *Fax:* 506-459-4991
E-mail: info@gooselane.com; customerservice@gooselane.com
Web Site: www.gooselane.com
Key Personnel
Publr: Susanne Alexander *Tel:* 506-450-4251 ext 1 *E-mail:* s.alexander@gooselane.com
Creative Dir: Julie Scriver *Tel:* 506-450-4251 ext 2 *E-mail:* jscriver@gooselane.com
Fiction Ed: Bethany Gibson *E-mail:* bgibson@gooselane.com
Poetry Ed: Ross Leckie *E-mail:* rleckie@gooselane.com
Founded: 1954
Primarily deal with Canadian authors. Submissions not accepted from outside of Canada.
Publishes in English.
ISBN Prefix(es): 978-0-920110; 978-0-919197; 978-0-86492
Number of titles published annually: 20 Print; 20 E-Book
Total Titles: 310 Print; 20 E-Book
Distributed by University of Toronto Press
Distribution Center: University of Toronto Press Distribution, 5201 Dufferin St, Toronto, ON M3H 5T8 *Tel:* 416-667-7791 *Fax:* 416-667-7832 *E-mail:* utpbooks@utpress.utoronto.ca
University of Toronto Press Distribution, 2250 Military Rd, Tonawanda, NY 14150, United States *Toll Free Tel:* 800-221-9523 *Toll Free Fax:* 800-221-9985
Membership(s): American Audiobook Publishers Association; Association of Canadian Publishers; Atlantic Publishers Marketing Association; Literary Press Group of Canada

Government of Canada Publications
Publishing & Depository Services, Public Works & Government Services Canada, Ottawa, ON K1A 0S5
Tel: 613-941-5995 *Toll Free Tel:* 800-635-7943 *Fax:* 613-954-5779 *Toll Free Fax:* 800-565-7757
E-mail: publications@tpsgc-pwgsc.gc.ca
Web Site: publications.gc.ca
Key Personnel
Dir: Joanne Joanisse *E-mail:* joanne.joanisse@tpsgc-pwgsc.gc.ca
Official publisher for the government of Canada. Active inventory of 22,000 titles in a wide variety of scientific, health, public policy, public administration, etc.
Publishes in English, French.

ISBN Prefix(es): 978-0-660; 978-0-662; 978-0-315
Number of titles published annually: 11 CD-ROM

Greystone Books Ltd
Affiliate of The Heritage Group
343 Railway St, Suite 201, Vancouver, BC V6A 1A4
SAN: 115-1886
Tel: 604-875-1550 *Fax:* 604-875-1556
E-mail: info@greystonebooks.com
Web Site: www.greystonebooks.com
Key Personnel
Publr: Rob Sanders *Tel:* 604-875-1550 ext 205
Assoc Publr: Nancy Flight *Tel:* 604-875-1550 ext 210
Sales & Mktg Dir: Jen Gauthier
Founded: 1993
Publishes in English.
ISBN Prefix(es): 978-0-88894; 978-1-55054; 978-1-55365; 978-0-88833; 978-1-77100; 978-1-927435; 978-1-77164
Number of titles published annually: 30 Print
Total Titles: 400 Print
Distributed by University of Toronto Press
U.S. Rep(s): Publishers Group West
Orders to: HarperCollins Canada Ltd, 1995 Markham Rd, Scarborough, ON M1B 5M8 (CN orders) *Tel:* 416-321-2241 *Toll Free Tel:* 800-387-0117 *Fax:* 416-321-3033 *Toll Free Fax:* 800-668-5788 *E-mail:* hcorder@harpercollins.com SAN: 115-026X; Publishers Group West/Perseus Books Group, 1700 Fourth St, Berkeley, CA 94710, United States (US orders) *Toll Free Tel:* 800-343-4499 *Toll Free Fax:* 800-351-5073 *E-mail:* orderentry@perseusbooks.com SAN: 202-8522; Publishers Group West/Perseus International, 250 W 57 St, 15th fl, New York, NY 10107, United States (intl orders) *Tel:* 212-581-7839 *E-mail:* intlorders@perseusbooks.com
Membership(s): AAP; Association for the Export of Canadian Books; Association of Book Publishers of British Columbia; Association of Canadian Publishers

Groundwood Books
Affiliate of House of Anansi Press Inc
110 Spadina Ave, Suite 801, Toronto, ON M5V 2K4
Tel: 416-363-4343 *Fax:* 416-363-1017
E-mail: genmail@groundwoodbooks.com
Web Site: www.houseofanansi.com
Key Personnel
Pres & Publr, House of Anansi Press Inc: Sarah MacLachlan
VP, Publg Opers & Royalties & Contracts: Matt Williams
VP, Sales & Licensing: Barbara Howson
Publr: Sheila Barry
Mktg Dir, House of Anansi Press Inc: Laura Repas
Mktg Mgr: Fred Horler
Founded: 1978
Publish children's books, picture books, novels, nonfiction & folktales; publishes in Spanish also.
Publishes in English.
ISBN Prefix(es): 978-0-88899; 978-1-55498
Number of titles published annually: 25 Print
Total Titles: 500 Print
Sales Office(s): Martin & Associates Sales Agency, 594 Windermere Ave, Toronto, ON M6S 3L8 (Atlantic, ON & QC), Contact: Michael Martin *Tel:* 416-769-3947 *Toll Free Tel:* 866-225-3439 *Fax:* 416-769-5967 *E-mail:* memartin@interlog.com
Michael Reynolds & Associates, 339 Tenth Ave SE, Calgary, AB T2G 0W2 (AB, BC, MB & SK), Sales Rep: Heather Parsons *Tel:* 403-233-8771 *Fax:* 403-233-8772 *E-mail:* heather.parsons@shaw.ca
Michael Reynolds & Associates, 210-30 E Sixth Ave, Vancouver, BC V5T 1J4 (AB, BC, MB & SK), Sales Rep: Michael Reynolds *Tel:* 604-688-6918 *Fax:* 604-687-4624 *E-mail:* pubrep@telus.net
Michael Reynolds & Associates, 566 Montrose St, Winnipeg, MB R3M 2M1 (AB, BC, MB & SK), Sales Rep: Lisa Pearce *Tel:* 204-489-4409 *Fax:* 204-487-7314 *E-mail:* lpearce@mts.net
Foreign Rights: Bardon Media Agency (Jianmei Wang & Cynthia Chang) (China); Japan Uni Agency Inc (Maiko Fujinaga) (Japan)
Returns: HarperCollins Canada, 1995 Markham Rd, Scarborough, ON M1B 5M8 *Tel:* 416-321-2241 *Toll Free Tel:* 800-387-0117 *Fax:* 416-321-3033 *Toll Free Fax:* 800-668-5788
Distribution Center: HarperCollins Distribution & Fulfillment, 1995 Markham Rd, Scarborough, ON M1B 5M8 *Tel:* 416-321-2241 *Toll Free Tel:* 800-387-0117 *Fax:* 416-321-3033 *Toll Free Fax:* 800-668-5788 *E-mail:* hcorder@harpercollins.com
Publishers Group West/Perseus Books Group, 1700 Fourth St, Berkeley, CA 94710, United States *Toll Free Tel:* 800-343-4499 *Toll Free Fax:* 800-351-5073 *E-mail:* orderentry@perseusbooks.com
Membership(s): Association of Canadian Publishers; International Board on Books for Young People; Organization of Book Publishers of Ontario

Groupe Educalivres Inc
955, rue Bergar, Laval, QC H7L 4Z6
Tel: 514-334-8466 *Toll Free Tel:* 800-567-3671 (info serv) *Fax:* 514-334-8387
E-mail: infoservice@grandduc.com
Web Site: www.educalivres.com
Key Personnel
Owner & Pres: Jean-Guy Blanchette
VP, Fin & Admin: Joe Cristofaro
Founded: 1992
School & professional textbooks.
Publishes in English, French.
ISBN Prefix(es): 978-2-7607; 978-0-03
Number of titles published annually: 3 Print

Groupe Modulo
Imprint of TC Media Books Inc
c/o TC Media Books Inc, 5800 St Denis St, Suite 900, Montreal, QC H2S 3L5
Tel: 514-273-1066 *Toll Free Tel:* 800-565-5531 *Fax:* 514-276-0234 *Toll Free Fax:* 800-814-0324
Web Site: www.groupemodulo.com
Founded: 1975
School books, dictionaries, children's books, professional & technical textbooks.
Publishes in English, French.
ISBN Prefix(es): 978-2-920922; 978-2-89443; 978-2-89113; 978-2-920210; 978-2-89593; 978-0-88560
Number of titles published annually: 100 Print
Total Titles: 2,000 Print

Groupe Sogides Inc
Division of Groupe Livre Quebecor Media Inc
955 rue Amherst, Montreal, QC H2L 3K4
Tel: 514-523-1182 *Fax:* 514-597-0370
Web Site: www.sogides.com
Key Personnel
Pres, Sogides: Celine Massicotte
VP, Publg, Grouphomme: Pierre Bourdon
Rts & Perms, Grouphomme: Florence Bisch
Founded: 1967
Practical books, cookbooks, biographies, general interest books, popular psychology, art books, poetry, diaries, art calendars & stationery, novels, drama.
Publishes in French.
ISBN Prefix(es): 978-2-7619; 978-0-7760; 978-2-89026; 978-2-89194; 978-2-89044; 978-2-89043; 978-2-89347
Number of titles published annually: 150 Print
Total Titles: 2,000 Print
Imprints: Les Editions de l'Homme; Le Jour Editeur; Utilis
Subsidiaries: Le Groupe Ville-Marie Litterature; Quinze
Branch Office(s)
Les Editions de l'Homme, c/o Messageries ADP, Immeuble Paryseine, 3 Allee de la Seine, 94854 Ivry Cedex, France, Contact: Anne Da Cunha-Guillegault *Tel:* 01 49 59 11 56 *Fax:* 01 49 59 11 33
Distributed by Vivendi Universal Publishing
Distributor for Actif; Atlas; Berlitz Fixot; Chouette; Le Cri; Edimag; Fleuve Noir; Gault & Millau; Heritage; De L'Homme; Hors Collection; JCL; Albin Michel Jeunesse; Julliard; Robert Laffont; Langues pour tous; Albin Michel; Albin Michel Education; Editions Modus Vivendi; Nathan; Nathan Education; Option Sante; Olivier Orban; Perrin; Plon; Pocket; La Presse; Presses de la Cite (Poche); Presses de la Cite Litterature; Presses Libres; Michel Quintin; Quinze; Du Rocher; Rouge & Or; Seghers; Selection du Reader's Digest; Solar; Time-Life; Trapeze; Usborne; Claire Vigne; VLB; XYZ (Typo Seulement)
U.S. Publishers Represented: Reader's Digest

Guerin Editeur Ltee
4501 rue Drolet, Montreal, QC H2T 2G2
Tel: 514-842-3481 *Fax:* 514-842-4923
Web Site: www.guerin-editeur.qc.ca
Key Personnel
Pres: France Larochelle *E-mail:* france.larochelle@guerin-editeur.qc.ca
VP: Claude Legault
Secy: Ginette Laperriere
Founded: 1970
Publisher of books for schools from kindergarten to university.
Publishes in English, French.
ISBN Prefix(es): 978-2-7601
Number of titles published annually: 80 Print; 2 Audio
Total Titles: 2,300 Print; 43 Audio
Foreign Rep(s): Librairie du Quebec (France); Librairie Pelagie (Eastern Canada); Patrimoine SPRL (Belgium); Servidis SA (Switzerland); Sopodriff Sarl (Africa); Pierre Carme Yves Levy (Haiti)

§Guernica Editions Inc
1569 Heritage Way, Oakville, ON L6M 2Z7
Fax: 416-576-9403
E-mail: info@guernicaeditions.com
Web Site: guernicaeditions.com
Key Personnel
Publr & Chief Admin Offr: Connie McParland *Tel:* 514-893-9211 *E-mail:* conniemcparland@guernicaeditions.com
Publr & Ed-in-Chief: Michael Mirolla *Tel:* 514-712-5304 *E-mail:* michaelmirolla@guernicaeditions.com
Asst Publicist: Sam Brown *E-mail:* sam.brown@guernicaeditions.com
Founded: 1978
Literary press specializing in Canadian writing (prose, poetry, literary criticism, drama & social studies), translation into English, some foreign publications in the English language.
Publishes in English.
ISBN Prefix(es): 978-0-919349; 978-0-920717; 978-2-89135; 978-1-55071; 978-1-77183
Number of titles published annually: 25 Print
Total Titles: 450 Print
Sales Office(s): Literary Press Group, 425 Adelaide St W, Suite 700, Toronto, ON M5V 3C1, Sales Mgr & US Rep: Tan Light *Tel:* 416-483-

1321 *Fax:* 416-483-2510 *E-mail:* sales@lpg.ca
Web Site: www.lpg.ca
Shipping Address: University of Toronto Press, 5201 Dufferin St, Toronto, ON M3H 5T8 *Tel:* 416-667-7846 *Toll Free Tel:* 800-565-9523 *Fax:* 416-667-7832 *Toll Free Fax:* 800-221-9985
Distribution Center: University of Toronto Press, 5201 Dufferin St, Toronto, ON M3H 5T8 *Tel:* 416-667-7846 *Toll Free Tel:* 800-565-9523 *Fax:* 416-667-7832 *Toll Free Fax:* 800-221-9985
Gazelle Book Services, White Cross Mills, High Town, Lancaster, Lancs LA1 1XS, United Kingdom *Tel:* (0152) 46-87-65 *Fax:* (0152) 46-32-32

Hancock House Publishers Ltd
19313 Zero Ave, Surrey, BC V3S 9R9
Mailing Address: 1431 Harrison Ave, Blaine, WA 98230-5005, United States
Tel: 604-538-1114 *Toll Free Tel:* 800-938-1114 *Fax:* 604-538-2262 *Toll Free Fax:* 800-983-2262
E-mail: sales@hancockhouse.com
Web Site: www.hancockhouse.com
Key Personnel
Pres: David Hancock
Founded: 1975
Biographical nature guide books.
Publishes in English.
ISBN Prefix(es): 978-0-88839; 978-0-919654; 978-1-55205
Number of titles published annually: 20 Print
Total Titles: 450 Print
Foreign Rep(s): Gazelle Book Services (UK)

Harbour Publishing Co Ltd
4437 Rondeview Rd, Madeira Park, BC V0N 2H0
Mailing Address: PO Box 219, Madeira Park, BC V0N 2H0
Tel: 604-883-2730 *Toll Free Tel:* 800-667-2988 *Fax:* 604-883-9451
E-mail: info@harbourpublishing.com
Web Site: www.harbourpublishing.com
Key Personnel
Publr: Howard White
Mktg Mgr: Marisa Alps
Prodn Coord: Anna Comfort
Founded: 1972
History & culture of British Columbia & West Coast, including fiction & poetry by Canadian authors.
Publishes in English.
ISBN Prefix(es): 978-0-920080; 978-1-55017
Number of titles published annually: 20 Print; 1 CD-ROM; 1 Audio
Total Titles: 600 Print; 1 CD-ROM; 5 Audio
Imprints: Lost Moose
Distributor for Nightwood Editions
U.S. Rep(s): Partners Group West
Foreign Rep(s): Gazelle Book Services Ltd (Eastern Europe, Ireland, UK, Western Europe)
Orders to: 12672 Lagoon Rd, Madeira Park, BC V0N 2H0 *E-mail:* orders@harbourpublishing.com
Warehouse: 12672 Lagoon Rd, Madeira Park, BC V0N 2H0 *Tel:* 604-883-2460
Distribution Center: 12672 Lagoon Rd, Madeira Park, BC V0N 2H0

Harlequin Enterprises Ltd
Division of HarperCollins
225 Duncan Mill Rd, Don Mills, ON M3B 3K9
SAN: 115-3749
Mailing Address: PO Box 615, Fort Erie, ON L2A 5X3
Tel: 416-445-5860 *Toll Free Tel:* 888-432-4879; 800-370-5838 (ebook inquiries)
E-mail: customerservice@harlequin.com
Web Site: www.harlequin.com
Key Personnel
CEO & Publr: Craig Swinwood
COO, Intl: Steve Miles
CFO: Andrew Wright
EVP, Direct to Consumer: Christina Clifford
EVP, Global Publg & Strategy: Loriana Sacilotto
EVP, Mktg & Digital: Brent Lewis
VP, Opers & Admin: Jim Robinson
VP, Retail Sales: Alex Osuszek
VP & CIO Info Systems: Margaret Morrison
VP, Series Edit & Subs Rts: Dianne Moggy
VP, Gen Coun & Secy: Karen Louie
Dir, Digital Prods: Farah Mullick
Dir, Overseas Publg Strategy: Emily Martin
Dir, Young Adult Prod: Amy Jones
Edit Dir, Carina Press: Angela James
Exec Ed: Susan Swinwood
Global Mng Ed: Roxanne Finkelstein
Asst Mng Ed: Punam Patel
Mng Edit Coord, NY/Toronto: Beth Attwood
Sr Ed, HQN, LUNA & Teen: Margo Lipschultz
Sr Ed, MIRA: Nicole Brebner
Ed: Adrienne Macintosh
Assoc Ed, Harlequin Superromance: Karen Reid
Assoc Ed, Kimani: Rachel Burkot
Asst Ed, Harlequin American, Blaze, Worldwide Library, BAC: Dana Hopkins
Asst Ed, Harlequin Romantic Suspense: Dana Hamilton
Asst Ed, Heartwarming & Gold Eagle: Dana Grimaldi
Asst Ed, HQN: Brittany Lavery; Kate Studer
Asst Ed, MIRA: Michelle Venditti
Asst Ed, Superromance & DTC: Piya Campana
Sr Mgr, PR: Michelle Renaud *E-mail:* publicrelations@harlequin.ca
Mgr, Author Engagement: Miranda Indrigo
Founded: 1949 (in Winnipeg, MB, CN)
Publishes in 34 languages in 110 international markets on 6 continents.
Publishes in English, French.
ISBN Prefix(es): 978-0-373; 978-1-55166; 978-0-7783; 978-1-58314; 978-1-55254; 978-1-4268; 978-1-4603; 978-1-4592
Number of titles published annually: 1,320 Print; 30 Online; 1,530 E-Book; 75 Audio
Total Titles: 30 Online; 1,850 E-Book; 95 Audio
Imprints: Carina Press (digital-first); Gold Eagle (action-adventure); Harlequin Books (series romance); Harlequin HQN (romance fiction); Harlequin Kimani Arabesque; Harlequin Kimani Press (African-American); Harlequin Kimani TRU; Harlequin LUNA (fantasy/paranormal); Harlequin MIRA (mainstream women's fiction); Harlequin Teen (young adult fiction); Love Inspired Books (inspirational romance); Rogue Angel; Silhouette Books (series romance); Spice (erotic fiction); Worldwide Library (mystery fiction); Worldwide Mystery
Branch Office(s)
233 Broadway, Suite 1001, New York, NY 10279, United States *Tel:* 212-553-4200 *Fax:* 212-227-8969 SAN: 200-2450
Foreign Office(s): Harlequin Mills & Boon, 18-24 Paradise Rd, Richmond, Surrey TW9 1SR, United Kingdom *Tel:* (020) 8288 2800 *Fax:* (020) 8288 2899 *Web Site:* www.millsandboon.co.uk
Advertising Agency: Vickers & Benson-Direct
Distribution Center: 3010 Walden Ave, Depew, NY 14043, United States
Membership(s): AAP; Association of Canadian Publishers; BISG
See separate listing for:
Gold Eagle
Worldwide Library

HarperCollins Canada Ltd
Division of HarperCollins Publishers
2 Bloor St E, 20th fl, Toronto, ON M4W 1A8
Tel: 416-975-9334 *Fax:* 416-975-9884
E-mail: hcorder@harpercollins.com
Web Site: www.harpercollins.ca
Key Personnel
SVP & Exec Publr: Iris Tupholme *Tel:* 416-975-9334 ext 123 *E-mail:* Iris.Tupholme@HarperCollins.com
SVP, Mktg & Sales: Leo MacDonald *Tel:* 416-975-9334 ext 122 *E-mail:* Leo.MacDonald@HarperCollins.com
VP, HR & Admin: Dianne Aquilina *Tel:* 416-321-2241 ext 216 *E-mail:* Dianne.Aquilina@HarperCollins.com
Publr, Patrick Crean Editions: Patrick Crean
Sr Dir, Publicity & Communs: Rob Firing *Tel:* 416-975-9334 ext 141 *E-mail:* Rob.Firing@HarperCollins.com
Sr Coun & Dir, Legal Aff: Jeremy Rawlings *Tel:* 416-975-9334 ext 117 *E-mail:* Jeremy.Rawlings@HarperCollins.com
Dir, Subs Rts & List Mgmt: Lisa Rundle *Tel:* 416-975-9334 ext 113 *E-mail:* Lisa.Rundle@HarperCollins.com
Founded: 1989
Literary & commercial fiction, nonfiction, children's books, cookbooks, reference & spiritual books. Distribute for all HarperCollins companies in the US, UK & Australia.
Publishes in English.
ISBN Prefix(es): 978-1-4434
Number of titles published annually: 100 Print
Total Titles: 1,500 Print
Imprints: Collins Canada; Patrick Crean Editions; HarperAvenue; HarperCollins Canada; HarperPerennial Canada; HarperTrophy Canada; HarperWeekend Canada

Herald Press
Imprint of MennoMedia
50 Kent Ave, Suite 204, Kitchener, ON N2G 3R1
Tel: 519-747-5722 (US) *Toll Free Tel:* 800-631-6535 (CN) *Fax:* 519-747-5721
E-mail: hpcan@mpn.net
Web Site: www.heraldpress.com
Key Personnel
Edit Dir: Amy Gingerich *E-mail:* amyg@mennomedia.org
Mktg & Sales Mgr: Craig Anderson *E-mail:* craiga@mennomedia.org
Acqs & Perms: Dorothy Hartman *E-mail:* dorothyh@mennomedia.org
Founded: 1908
Christian books.
Publishes in English.
ISBN Prefix(es): 978-0-8361
Number of titles published annually: 20 Print
Total Titles: 450 Print
Branch Office(s)
718 N Main St, Newton, KS 67114, United States *Tel:* 316-281-4412 *Toll Free Tel:* 800-245-7894 ext 220 *Fax:* 316-283-0454
1251 Virginia Ave, Harrisonburg, VA 22802-2434, United States *Toll Free Tel:* 800-245-7894 *Toll Free Fax:* 877-271-0760
Membership(s): Canadian Booksellers Association

Heritage House Publishing Co Ltd
Member of The Heritage Group
1075 Pendergast St, No 103, Victoria, BC V8V 0A1
Tel: 250-360-0829 *Fax:* 250-386-0829
E-mail: heritage@heritagehouse.ca
Web Site: www.heritagehouse.ca
Key Personnel
Publr: Rodger Touchie
Sr Ed: Lara Kordic
Publicity: Leslie Kenny
Founded: 1969
Publishes in English.
ISBN Prefix(es): 978-1-895811; 978-1-894384; 978-1-894974; 978-0-919214; 978-0-9690546; 978-1-926613; 978-1-926936; 978-1-927051; 978-1-927527
Number of titles published annually: 30 Print
Total Titles: 175 Print

Distributor for Frank Amato; Bellerophon; Fine Edge Productions; Horsdal & Schubart; Sunfire; Whitecap
Orders to: Heritage Group Distribution, 19272 96 Ave, Suite 8, Surrey, BC V4N 4C1 *Tel:* 604-881-7067 *Toll Free Tel:* 800-665-3302 *Fax:* 604-881-7068 *Toll Free Fax:* 800-566-3336 *E-mail:* orders@hgdistribution.com
Distribution Center: Heritage Group Distribution, 19272 96 Ave, Suite 8, Surrey, BC V4N 4C1 *Tel:* 604-881-7067 *Toll Free Tel:* 800-665-3302 *Fax:* 604-881-7068 *Toll Free Fax:* 800-566-3336 *E-mail:* orders@hgdistribution.com
Membership(s): Association of Book Publishers of British Columbia; Association of Canadian Publishers

Les Heures bleues
560 Mercier, St-Lambert, QC J4P 1Z5
Tel: 450-671-7718 *Fax:* 450-671-7718
E-mail: info@heuresbleues.com
Web Site: www.heuresbleues.com
Key Personnel
Pres: Rene Bonenfant
Founded: 1996
Publishes in French.
ISBN Prefix(es): 978-2-922265
Number of titles published annually: 8 Print
Total Titles: 90 Print; 40 E-Book
Distribution Center: Dimedia, 539 boul Lebeau, St-Laurent, QC H4N 1S2
Membership(s): Association Nationale des Editeurs de Livres

House of Anansi Press Inc
110 Spadina Ave, Suite 801, Toronto, ON M5V 2K4
Tel: 416-363-4343 *Fax:* 416-363-1017
E-mail: customerservice@houseofanansi.com
Web Site: www.houseofanansi.com
Key Personnel
VP, Publg Opers: Matt Williams
Pres & Publr: Sarah MacLachlan
VP, Sales & Licensing: Barbara Howson
Edit Dir: Janie Yoon
Publicity Dir: Laura Meyer
Mng Ed: Kelly Joseph
Ed: Meredith Dees
Digital Mktg Mgr: Carolyn McNeillie
Natl Accts Mgr: Jenna Simpson
Sr Publicist: Emily Mockler
Publicist: Cindy Ma
Founded: 1967
Literary publishing; fiction, poetry, criticism & belles lettres.
Publishes in English.
ISBN Prefix(es): 978-0-88784; 978-1-77089
Number of titles published annually: 30 Print
Total Titles: 200 Print
Imprints: Anansi International; Arachnide Editions; Astoria; Spiderline (crime fiction)
Subsidiaries: Groundwood Books
Foreign Rights: Akcali Copyright Agency (Atilla Turgut) (Turkey); Anthea Agency (Zlatka Paskaleva) (Bulgaria); Bestun Agency (Yumi Chun) (Korea); Big Apple Agency (Amanda Chen) (Mainland China); Big Apple Agency (Chris Lin) (Taiwan); Paul & Peter Fritz Agency (Antonia Fritz) (Germany); Japan Uni Agency Inc (Yukiko Kurioka) (Japan); Antonia Kerrigan Agency (Antonia Kerrigan) (Latin America, Spain); Simona Kessler Agency (Simona Kessler) (Romania)
Distribution Center: Publishers Group West/ Perseus Books Group, 1700 Fourth St, Berkeley, CA 94710, United States (US orders) *Tel:* 510-809-3700 *Toll Free Tel:* 800-343-4499 *Fax:* 510-809-3777 *Toll Free Fax:* 800-351-5073 *E-mail:* orderentry@perseusbooks.com *Web Site:* www.pgw.com
See separate listing for:
Groundwood Books

C D Howe Institute
67 Yonge St, Suite 300, Toronto, ON M5E 1J8
Tel: 416-865-1904 *Fax:* 416-865-1866
E-mail: cdhowe@cdhowe.org
Web Site: www.cdhowe.org
Key Personnel
CEO & Pres: William B P Robson *E-mail:* bill_robson@cdhowe.org
COO & SVP: Duncan Munn *E-mail:* dmunn@cdhowe.org
VP, Media & Ed: James Fleming *Tel:* 416-865-1904 ext 9216 *E-mail:* jfleming@cdhowe.org
Dir, Communs: Hal Koblin *E-mail:* hkoblin@cdhowe.org
Founded: 1958
Economics & social policy studies.
Publishes in English, French.
ISBN Prefix(es): 978-0-88806
Number of titles published annually: 48 Print
Total Titles: 150 Print
Distributed by Renouf Publishing Co (Ottawa)

Inclusion Press International
47 Indian Trail, Toronto, ON M6R 1Z8
Tel: 416-658-5363 *Fax:* 416-658-5067
E-mail: inclusionpress@inclusion.com
Web Site: www.inclusion.com
Key Personnel
Founding Publr: Marsha Forest; Jack Pearpoint *E-mail:* jack@inclusion.com
Founded: 1989
Inclusion, change, diversity & community.
Publishes in English.
ISBN Prefix(es): 978-1-895418
Number of titles published annually: 5 Print; 2 CD-ROM; 2 E-Book
Total Titles: 100 Print; 10 CD-ROM; 4 E-Book
Distribution Center: Inclusion Distribution, United Kingdom

Insomniac Press
520 Princess Ave, London, ON N6B 2B8
Tel: 416-504-6270
Web Site: www.insomniacpress.com
Key Personnel
Publr: Mike O'Connor *E-mail:* mike@insomniacpress.com
Sales & Mktg Mgr: Linda Palmer *E-mail:* linda@insomniacpress.com
Mng Ed: Dan Varrette *E-mail:* dan@insomniacpress.com
Founded: 1992
General trade publisher of fiction, nonfiction & poetry.
Publishes in English.
ISBN Prefix(es): 978-1-895837; 978-1-894663; 978-1-897178; 978-1-897414; 978-1-897415; 978-1-926582; 978-1-55483
Number of titles published annually: 16 Print
Total Titles: 235 Print
Orders to: LitDistCo, 100 Armstrong Ave, Georgetown, ON L7G 5S4 (CN & US) *Toll Free Tel:* 800-591-6250 *Toll Free Fax:* 800-591-6251 *E-mail:* orders@litdistco.ca *Web Site:* www.litdistco.ca; The Literary Press Group of Canada, 425 Adelaide St W, Suite 700, Toronto, ON M5V 3C1 (CN & US) *Tel:* 416-483-1321 *Fax:* 416-483-2510 *Web Site:* www.lpg.ca; Wakefield Press, One The Parade West, Kent Town, SA 5067, Australia (Australia) *Tel:* (08) 8362 8800 *Fax:* (08) 8362 7592 *Web Site:* www.wakefieldpress.com.au; BookWise Asia Pte Ltd, D'Centennial, Suite 03-02, 100 Lorong 23 Geylang, Singapore 388398, Singapore (Southeast Asia) *Tel:* 6743 2815 *Fax:* 6743 2817 *Web Site:* www.bookwise.com.au/publishers; Gazelle Books, Falcon House, Queen Sq, Lancaster LA1 1RN, United Kingdom (UK & Europe) *Tel:* (01524) 68765 *Fax:* (01524) 63232 *E-mail:* sales@gazellebooks.co.uk *Web Site:* www.gazellebooks.co.uk

L'Institut Canadien des Comptables Agrees, see Canadian Institute of Chartered Accountants-CICA (L'Institut Canadien des Comptables Agrees)

L'Institut canadien du droit des ressources, see Canadian Institute of Resources Law (L'Institut canadien du droit des ressources)

Institut Nord-Sud, see The North-South Institute (Institut Nord-Sud)

Institute for Research on Public Policy (IRPP)
1470 Peel St, No 200, Montreal, QC H3A 1T1
Tel: 514-985-2461 *Fax:* 514-985-2559
E-mail: irpp@irpp.org
Web Site: www.irpp.org
Key Personnel
Pres: Graham Fox *E-mail:* gfox@irpp.org
VP, Opers: Suzanne Ostiguy McIntyre *Tel:* 514-787-0740 *E-mail:* smcintyre@irpp.org
Edit Coord: Francesca Worrall *E-mail:* fworrall@irpp.org
Founded: 1972
Research on public policy.
Publishes in English, French.
ISBN Prefix(es): 978-0-88645; 978-0-920380
Number of titles published annually: 200 Online
Total Titles: 500 Print

Institute of Intergovernmental Relations
Queen's University, Robert Sutherland Hall, Rm 301, Kingston, ON K7L 3N6
Tel: 613-533-2080 *Fax:* 613-533-6868
E-mail: iigr@queensu.ca
Web Site: www.queensu.ca/iigr
Key Personnel
Dir: Dr John R Allan
Pubns Coord & Admin Secy: Mary Kennedy
Founded: 1965
Publish research & other scholarly work on Canadian federalism & intergovernmental relations; ethnicity, government & political science.
Publishes in English, French.
ISBN Prefix(es): 978-1-55339
Number of titles published annually: 4 Print
Total Titles: 96 Print
Distribution Center: McGill-Queen's University Press, Georgetown Terminal Warehouses, 34 Armstrong Ave, Georgetown, ON L7G 4R9 *Tel:* 905-873-2750 *Fax:* 905-873-6170

Institute of Psychological Research, Inc.
76 Ave, Mozart W, Montreal, QC H2S 1C4
Tel: 514-382-3000 *Toll Free Tel:* 800-363-7800 *Fax:* 514-382-3007 *Toll Free Fax:* 888-382-3007
E-mail: info@irpcanada.com
Web Site: www.irpcanada.com
Founded: 1958 (incorporated in 1964)
Psychological tests & materials.
Publishes in English, French.
ISBN Prefix(es): 978-0-88509; 978-2-89109
Number of titles published annually: 10 Print
Imprints: IPR; IRP
Distributed by Editions Editest (Belgium); Librairie du Quebec a Paris (France)
Distributor for Aseba (CN); Hogrefe France (CN); Hans Huber (Rorschach only)
U.S. Publishers Represented: Academic Therapy Publications; American Orthopsychiatric; Behavior Sciences Systems; Editions Behaviora; Martin M Bruce; Cardall Associates; Center for Psychological Services; Clinical Psychology Publishing; Nigel Cox; Educational & Clinical Publications; Educational Industrial Testing Service; Educational Performance Associate; Educators Publishing Services; Granada Learning; Guidance Associates of Delaware; Harvard University Press; Hogrefe UK; Industrial Psychology; Institute for Personality &

Ability Testing; International Tests; Lafayette Instrument; Language Research Associates; Multi Health Systems; National Foundation for Educational Research; Pacific Book; Pro Ed; Psychological Assessment Resources; Psychological Test Specialists; Psychologists & Educators; Research Psychologist Press; Sheridan Psychological Services; Stoelting; Western Psychological Services

Institute of Public Administration of Canada
1075 Bay St, Suite 401, Toronto, ON M5S 2B1
Tel: 416-924-8787 *Fax:* 416-924-4992
E-mail: ntl@ipac.ca
Web Site: www.ipac.ca; www.iapc.ca
Key Personnel
CEO: Robert Taylor, PhD *Tel:* 416-924-8787 ext 230 *E-mail:* rtaylor@ipac.ca
Mng Ed: Christy Paddick *Tel:* 905-447-6351 (cell) *E-mail:* cpaddick@ipac.ca
Ed: Evert A Lindquist
Founded: 1947
National bilingual English/French nonprofit organization, concerned with the theory & practice of public management, with 20 regional groups across Canada. Provide networks & forums regionally, nationally & internationally. Specialize in political science, Canadian history & Canadian law.
Publishes in English, French.
ISBN Prefix(es): 978-0-919400; 978-0-920715; 978-0-919696; 978-1-55061
Number of titles published annually: 10 Print; 5 E-Book
Total Titles: 600 Print; 50 Online; 10 E-Book; 5 Audio

International Development Research Centre (IDRC)
150 Kent St, Ottawa, ON K1P 0B2
Mailing Address: PO Box 8500, Ottawa, ON K1G 3H9
Tel: 613-236-6163 *Fax:* 613-238-7230
E-mail: info@idrc.ca
Web Site: www.idrc.ca
Key Personnel
Publr: Nola Haddadian *Tel:* 613-696-2163
Founded: 1970
Publishes research results & scholarly studies on global & regional issues related to sustainable & equitable development.
Publishes in English, French.
ISBN Prefix(es): 978-0-88936; 978-1-55250
Number of titles published annually: 30 Print; 20 Online
Total Titles: 500 Print
Foreign Office(s): 8 Ahmed Nessim St, 8th fl, Giza, Cairo, Egypt *Tel:* (02) 3336-7051 *Fax:* (02) 3336-7056 *E-mail:* mero@idrc.ca *Web Site:* www.idrc.ca/mero
208 Jor Bagh, New Delhi 110 003, India *Tel:* (011) 2461-9411 *Fax:* (011) 2462-2707 *E-mail:* aro@idrc.ca *Web Site:* www.idrc.ca/aro
PO Box 62084, Nairobi 00200, Kenya *Tel:* (020) 2713-160 *Fax:* (020) 2711-063 *E-mail:* rossa@idrc.ca *Web Site:* www.idrc.ca/rossa
Ave Brasil 2655, 11300 Montevideo, Uruguay *Tel:* (02) 709-0042 *Fax:* (02) 708-6776 *E-mail:* lacro@idrc.ca *Web Site:* www.idrc.ca/lacro
Distributed by ITDG Publishing (Europe); Renouf Publishing Co Ltd (worldwide); Stylus Publishing Inc (Latin America & US)

International Travel Maps & Books, see ITMB Publishing Ltd

Irwin Law Inc
14 Duncan St, Suite 206, Toronto, ON M5H 3G8
Tel: 416-862-7690 *Toll Free Tel:* 888-314-9014 *Fax:* 416-862-9236
Web Site: www.irwinlaw.com
Key Personnel
Pres & Publr: Jeffrey Miller *Tel:* 416-862-7690 ext 23 *E-mail:* jmiller@irwinlaw.com
VP: Alisa Posesorski *E-mail:* aposes@irwinlaw.com
Founded: 1996
Publisher of books & other material for lawyers & law students.
Publishes in English.
ISBN Prefix(es): 978-1-55221
Number of titles published annually: 20 Print; 20 E-Book
Total Titles: 200 Print; 100 E-Book
Distributor for The Federation Press (North America only)
Foreign Rep(s): The Federation Press (Australia, New Zealand)
Distribution Center: Gaunt Inc, Gaunt Bldg, 3011 Gulf Dr, Holmes Beach, FL 34217, United States *Tel:* 941-778-5211 *Toll Free Tel:* 800-942-8683 *Fax:* 941-778-5252 SAN: 202-9413
Membership(s): Association of Canadian Publishers; Organization of Book Publishers of Ontario

ITMB Publishing Ltd
12300 Bridgeport Rd, Richmond, BC V6V 1J5
Tel: 604-273-1400 *Fax:* 604-273-1488
E-mail: itmb@itmb.com
Web Site: www.itmb.com
Key Personnel
Pres: Jack Joyce
Founded: 1983
Publisher/distributor of international travel maps & atlases.
Publishes in English.
ISBN Prefix(es): 978-1-55341; 978-0-921463; 978-1-895907
Number of titles published annually: 30 Print
Total Titles: 425 Print
Distributor for Borch; Freytag & Bernot; Gizi; National Geographic; Nelles; Rand McNally
Membership(s): International Map Industry Association

Ivey Publishing, see Richard Ivey School of Business

Richard Ivey School of Business
Division of Ivey Management Services
Ivey Business School at Western University, 1255 Western Rd, London, ON N6G 0N1
Tel: 519-661-3206; 519-661-3208 *Toll Free Tel:* 800-649-6355 *Fax:* 519-661-3485; 519-661-3882
E-mail: cases@ivey.uwo.ca
Web Site: www.iveycases.com; www.ivey.uwo.ca
Key Personnel
Busn Devt Coord: Shelli Hunter *Tel:* 519-661-4258 *E-mail:* shunter@ivey.ca
Founded: 1923
Publish business case studies for university business courses.
Publishes in English, French.
ISBN Prefix(es): 978-0-919534
Number of titles published annually: 200 Print
Total Titles: 3,500 Print
Distributed by Caseplace (The Aspen Institute's Centre for Business Education); Cengage Learning (USA); Centrale de Cas et de Medias Pedagogiques (CCMP) (Paris, France); College of Commerce (National Chengchi University, Taiwan); European Case Clearing House (ECCH) (UK); IESE Publishing (Spain); Institute for International Studies and Training (IIST) (Japan); LAD Publishing (USA); McGraw-Hill (USA); National Archive Publishing (USA); Pearson Custom Publishing (USA); Study.Net (USA); University Readers Inc (USA)
Distributor for Asian Business Case Center/Nanyang Business School at Nanyang Technological University; China-Europe International Business School (CEIBS); China Management Case Sharing Centre; China University of Hong Kong; College of Commerce (National Chengchi University, Taiwan); Darden Business School; Gordon Institute of Business Science (University of Pretoria, South Africa); Harvard Business Review; Harvard Business School Publishing; Indian Institute of Management Bangalore; Indian School of Business (India); Ivey Business Journal (reprints); National University of Singapore; Northeastern University; Peking University (China); Thunderbird School of Global Management; Tsinghua University (China); University of Regina-Paul J Hill School of Business; University of West Indies; Yonsei University (Korea; Harvard Business School cases & Harvard Business Review reprints)
U.S. Rep(s): Harvard Business School Publishing (case studies & HBR reprints)
Foreign Rep(s): European Case Clearing House (Europe)

Kids Can Press Ltd
Division of Corus Entertainment Inc
25 Dockside Dr, Toronto, ON M5A 0B5
Tel: 416-479-7000 *Toll Free Tel:* 800-265-0884 *Fax:* 416-960-5437
E-mail: info@kidscan.com; customerservice@kidscan.com
Web Site: www.kidscanpress.com; www.kidscanpress.ca
Key Personnel
Pres: Lisa Lyons Johnston
Cont, Corus Entertainment: June Samms
Art Dir: Marie Bartholomew
Edit Dir: Yvette Ghione *Tel:* 416-479-7000 ext 36551
Mng Ed: Ms Semareh Al-Hillal
Sr Ed: Stacey Roderick; Yasemin Ucar
Sr Digital Innovator in Mktg, Cust Engagement & Publg: Lisa Charters
Rts Mgr: Adrienne Tang
Prodn Ed: Jennifer Grimbleby; DoEun Kwon
Cross Media Specialist: Danielle Mulhall
Graphic Designer: Mike Reis
Founded: 1973
Books for children exclusively.
Publishes in English.
ISBN Prefix(es): 978-0-919964; 978-1-55074; 978-1-55337; 978-0-921103; 978-1-55453; 978-1-77138
Number of titles published annually: 75 Print
Total Titles: 500 Print
Imprints: CitizenKid™; Franklin the Turtle; Kids Can Do It; Scaredy Squirrel
Distributed by Open Road
Orders to: University of Toronto Press, 10 Sainte Mary St, Suite 700, Toronto, ON M4Y 2W8 *Tel:* 416-978-2239 *Fax:* 416-978-4738 *Web Site:* www.utpress.utoronto.ca
Returns: University of Toronto Press, 10 Sainte Mary St, Suite 700, Toronto, ON M4Y 2W8 *Tel:* 416-978-2239 *Fax:* 416-978-4738 *Web Site:* www.utpress.utoronto.ca; 2250 Military Rd, Tonawanda, NY 14150, United States
Shipping Address: University of Toronto Press, 10 Sainte Mary St, Suite 700, Toronto, ON M4Y 2W8 *Tel:* 416-978-2239 *Fax:* 416-978-4738 *Web Site:* www.utpress.utoronto.ca
Distribution Center: University of Toronto Press, 10 Sainte Mary St, Suite 700, Toronto, ON M4Y 2W8 *Tel:* 416-978-2239 *Fax:* 416-978-4738 *Web Site:* www.utpress.utoronto.ca
Membership(s): The Children's Book Council

Kindred Productions
Division of Mennonite Brethren Church
1310 Taylor Ave, Winnipeg, MB R3M 3Z6
Tel: 204-669-6575 *Toll Free Tel:* 800-545-7322 *Fax:* 204-654-1865

E-mail: custserv@kindredproductions.com; kindred@mbchurches.ca
Web Site: www.kindredproductions.com
Key Personnel
Cust Serv Rep: Kate Woltman
Founded: 1982
Denominational material, Low German Bible, trade books & church resources.
Publishes in English, French.
ISBN Prefix(es): 978-0-919797; 978-0-921788; 978-1-894791
Number of titles published annually: 15 Print
Total Titles: 250 Print
Branch Office(s)
PO Box 421, Goessel, KS 67053, United States
U.S. Publishers Represented: Kindred Productions USA

Knopf Canada
Imprint of Penguin Random House Canada Limited
One Toronto St, Suite 300, Toronto, ON M5C 2V6
SAN: 201-3975
Tel: 416-364-4449 *Toll Free Tel:* 888-523-9292 *Fax:* 416-364-6863
Web Site: www.randomhouse.ca
Key Personnel
CEO & Pres: Brad Martin
CFO & EVP: Doug Foot
Pres & Publr, RHC: Kristin Cochrane
Exec Publr, RHC: Louise Dennys
EVP & Dir, Sales: Duncan Shields
SVP & Dir, Busn Devt Online Digital Sales Strategy: Robert Wheaton
SVP & Dir, Mktg & Corp Communs: Tracey Turriff
VP & Dir, Prodn: Janine Laporte
VP & Deputy Publr, RHC: Marion Garner
Publr, KRC: Anne Collins
Publg Dir: Lynn Henry
Founded: 1991
Penguin Random House Canada Limited & its publishing entities are not accepting unsol submissions, proposals, mss, or submission queries via e-mail at this time.
Publishes in English.
ISBN Prefix(es): 978-0-307; 978-0-676
Number of titles published annually: 40 Print
Imprints: Vintage Canada
Distributed by Penguin Random House Canada Limited
Shipping Address: Penguin Random House Canada Limited, 6971 Columbus Rd, Mississauga, ON L5T 1K1
Membership(s): Canadian Booksellers Association; Canadian Publishers' Council

Laurier Books Ltd
PO Box 8493, Ottawa, ON K1G 3H9
SAN: 168-2806
Tel: 613-738-2163 *Toll Free Fax:* 855-736-9160
E-mail: laurierbooks@yahoo.com
Key Personnel
Pres: L Marthe
Lib Sales Dir: R Lalwani
Founded: 1975
All foreign language dictionaries, Native American publications, annuals, bibliographic products, business directories, distribution, publishing, mail orders.
Publishes in English.
ISBN Prefix(es): 978-1-895959; 978-1-55394
Number of titles published annually: 15 Print
Total Titles: 3,000 Print
U.S. Rep(s): IBD Ltd

§LexisNexis® Canada Inc
Member of The LexisNexis® Group
123 Commerce Valley Dr E, Suite 700, Markham, ON L3T 7W8
Tel: 905-479-2665 *Toll Free Tel:* 800-668-6481; 800-387-0899 (cust care) *Fax:* 905-479-2826 *Toll Free Fax:* 800-461-3275
E-mail: orders@lexisnexis.ca; service@lexisnexis.ca (cust serv)
Web Site: www.lexisnexis.ca
Key Personnel
Academic Solutions Specialist: Luc Meloche *E-mail:* luc.meloche@lexisnexis.ca
Mgr, Mktg Servs: Yolanda Majury *E-mail:* yolanda.majury@lexisnexis.ca
Dir, Training & Cust Care: Jeff Morrison *E-mail:* jeff.morrison@lexisnexis.ca
Cust Serv Mgr, Print & CD-ROM Div: Barbara Brumwell *Tel:* 905-415-5816 *E-mail:* barbara.brumwell@lexisnexis.ca
Founded: 1912
Books, looseleaf services, newsletters, journals, legal publishing & online services.
Publishes in English, French.
ISBN Prefix(es): 978-0-409; 978-0-433
Number of titles published annually: 80 Print; 20 CD-ROM
Imprints: Butterworths
Branch Office(s)
355 Burrard St, Suite 920, Vancouver, BC V6C 2G8 *Tel:* 604-684-1462 *Fax:* 604-684-5581
112 Kent St, Suite 700, Ottawa, ON K1P 5P2 *Tel:* 613-238-3499 *Fax:* 613-238-7597
215 St-Jacques St, Suite 1111, Montreal, QC H2Y 1M6 *Tel:* 514-287-0339 *Toll Free Tel:* 800-227-9597 *Fax:* 514-287-0350

Lidec Inc
4501, rue Drolet, Montreal, QC H2T 2G2
Tel: 514-843-5991 *Toll Free Tel:* 800-350-5991 (CN only) *Fax:* 514-843-5252
E-mail: lidec@lidec.qc.ca
Web Site: www.lidec.qc.ca
Key Personnel
Gen Mgr & ISBN Contact: Claude Legault
Founded: 1965
Publisher of school books.
Publishes in English, French.
ISBN Prefix(es): 978-2-7608
Number of titles published annually: 30 Print
Total Titles: 1,500 Print

Life Cycle Books Ltd
1085 Bellamy Rd N, Suite 20, Toronto, ON M1H 3C7
SAN: 110-8417
Tel: 416-690-5860 *Toll Free Tel:* 866-880-5860 *Toll Free Fax:* 866-260-8172
E-mail: orders@lifecyclebooks.com; billing@lifecyclebooks.com; support@lifecyclebooks.com
Web Site: www.lifecyclebooks.com
Key Personnel
Founder & Pres: Paul Broughton *E-mail:* paulb@lifecyclebooks.com
Founded: 1973
Human life issues.
Publishes in English, French.
ISBN Prefix(es): 978-0-919225
Number of titles published annually: 3 Print
Total Titles: 41 Print
Branch Office(s)
PO Box 799, Fort Collins, CO 80522, United States *Toll Free Tel:* 800-214-5849

Lone Pine Publishing
2311 96 St, Edmonton, AB T6N 1G3
SAN: 115-4125
Tel: 780-433-9333 *Toll Free Tel:* 800-661-9017 *Fax:* 780-433-9646 *Toll Free Fax:* 800-424-7173
E-mail: info@lonepinepublishing.com
Web Site: www.lonepinepublishing.com
Key Personnel
Pres: Shane Kennedy
Dir, Mktg: Ken Davis
US Sales Mgr: Michael O Campbell
Sr Ed: Nancy Foulds
Founded: 1980
Natural history, travel, recreation, popular history, bird guides & gardening.
Publishes in English.
ISBN Prefix(es): 978-1-55105; 978-1-894877 (Ghost House Books); 978-0-919433
Number of titles published annually: 30 Print
Total Titles: 800 Print
Imprints: Ghost House Books
Branch Office(s)
87 E Pender St, Vancouver, BC V5A 1S9
1808 "B" St NW, Suite 140, Auburn, WA 98001, United States, Sales Mgr: Helen Ibach *Tel:* 253-394-0400 *Toll Free Tel:* 800-518-3541 *Fax:* 253-394-0405 *Toll Free Fax:* 800-548-1169 *E-mail:* hibach@lonepinepublishing.com
Distributor for Coteau Books; Folklore Publishing; InForum; Johnson & Gorman; Red Deer College Press
U.S. Rep(s): Baker & Taylor; Benjamin News; Book People; Ingram Book Co; Partners; Partners/West; Sunbelt

James Lorimer & Co Ltd, Publishers
317 Adelaide St W, Suite 1002, Toronto, ON M5V 1P9
SAN: 115-1134
Tel: 416-362-4762 *Fax:* 416-362-3939
Web Site: www.lorimer.ca
Key Personnel
Pres & Publr: James Lorimer
Promos: Morgan Tunzelmann
Founded: 1970
Hardcover & paperback trade; business, economics, finance, history, politics; children's books; social sciences & sociology; cookbooks; illustrated history.
Publishes in English.
ISBN Prefix(es): 978-1-55028; 978-0-88862; 978-1-55277; 978-1-4594
Number of titles published annually: 12 Print
Total Titles: 600 Print
Orders to: Formac Distributing, 5502 Atlantic St, Halifax, NS B3H 1G4 *Toll Free Tel:* 800-565-1975 *Fax:* 902-425-0166 *E-mail:* orderdesk@formac.ca
Warehouse: Formac Distributing, 5502 Atlantic St, Halifax, NS B3H 1G4 *Tel:* 902-421-7022 *Toll Free Tel:* 800-565-1975 *Fax:* 902-425-0166 *E-mail:* orderdesk@formac.ca *Web Site:* www.formac.ca

Lugus Publications
Division of Lugus Productions Ltd
28 Industrial St, Studio 203, Toronto, ON M4G 1Y9
Tel: 416-467-0924
Web Site: www.thestudio203.com
Key Personnel
Pres: Gethin James *E-mail:* james.gethin@gmail.com
Secy: Jacqueline James
Founded: 1981
Educational & trade publishing.
Publishes in English, French.
ISBN Prefix(es): 978-0-921633
Number of titles published annually: 5 Print
Total Titles: 120 Print
U.S. Publishers Represented: Blackwells North America

Madison Press Books
155 Edward St, Suite 1, Aurora, ON L4G 1W3
Mailing Address: PO Box 239, Cannington, ON L0E 1E0
Tel: 905-841-9300
E-mail: info@madisonpressbooks.com
Web Site: www.madisonpressbooks.com

Key Personnel
Pres & Publr: Oliver Salzmann
E-mail: osalzmann@madisonpressbooks.com
Founded: 1979
Book producer for the international publishing community; illustrated nonfiction co-editions, narrative nonfiction, books for young readers, history, culinary, humour, reference, contemporary culture, fine art.
Publishes in English.
ISBN Prefix(es): 978-1-895892; 978-1-897330
Number of titles published annually: 20 Print
Total Titles: 250 Print

Madison Press Ltd, see Madison Press Books

Madonna House Publications
RR 2, 2888 Dafoe Rd, Combermere, ON K0J 1L0
Tel: 613-756-3728 *Toll Free Tel:* 888-703-7110 *Fax:* 613-756-0103 *Toll Free Fax:* 877-717-2888
E-mail: publications@madonnahouse.org
Web Site: www.madonnahouse.org/publications
Founded: 1988
Publishes in English, French.
ISBN Prefix(es): 978-0-921440; 978-1-897145
Number of titles published annually: 4 Print; 2 Audio
Total Titles: 68 Print; 68 Online; 15 Audio
Branch Office(s)
879-431 State St, Ogdensburg, NY 13669, United States
Membership(s): Catholic Publishers Association; CMN

§Master Point Press
331 Douglas Ave, Toronto, ON M5M 1H2
Tel: 416-781-0351 *Fax:* 416-781-1831
E-mail: info@masterpointpress.com
Web Site: www.masterpointpress.com; www.ebooksbridge.com (ebook sales)
Key Personnel
Founder & Co-Owner: Ray Lee
Co-Owner: Linda Lee
Founded: 1994
Books on contract bridge.
Publishes in English.
ISBN Prefix(es): 978-0-9698461; 978-1-894154; 978-1-897106; 978-1-55494
Number of titles published annually: 20 Print; 20 E-Book
Total Titles: 200 Print; 8 CD-ROM; 300 E-Book
Distributor for Better Bridge Now
U.S. Rep(s): Strauss Consultants, 45 Main St, Brooklyn, NY 11201, United States
Foreign Rep(s): The Bridge Shop (Australia); Orca Book Services (UK)
Orders to: Georgetown Terminal Warehouses Ltd, 34 Armstrong Ave, Georgetown, ON L7G 4R9 *Tel:* 905-873-2750 *Fax:* 905-873-6170 *E-mail:* orders@gtwcanada.com *Web Site:* www.gtwcanada.com; Baker & Taylor, 2550 W Tyvola Rd, Suite 300, Charlotte, NC 28217, United States *Tel:* 704-998-3100 *Toll Free Tel:* 800-775-1800 *E-mail:* btinfo@btol.com *Web Site:* www.btol.com; Ingram Book Group, One Ingram Blvd, La Vergne, TN 37086, United States *Tel:* 615-793-5000 *Toll Free Tel:* 800-937-8200 *E-mail:* customer.service@ingramcontent.com; Orca Book Services, 160 Eastern Ave, Milton Park, Abingdon, Oxon OX14 4SB, United Kingdom *Tel:* (01235) 465500 *E-mail:* tradeorders@orcabookservices.co.uk *Web Site:* www.orcabookservices.co.uk
Shipping Address: Georgetown Terminal Warehouses Ltd, 34 Armstrong Ave, Georgetown, ON L7G 4R9

McClelland & Stewart Ltd
Imprint of Penguin Random House Canada Limited
One Toronto St, Toronto, ON M5C 2V6
SAN: 115-4192
Tel: 416-364-4449 *Fax:* 416-957-1587
E-mail: editorial@mcclelland.com
Web Site: www.mcclelland.com
Key Personnel
Pres & Publr: Douglas Pepper
SVP & Publr: Ellen Seligman
Publr, Fenn/McClelland & Stewart Ltd: Jordan Fenn
Exec Ed: Lara Hinchberger
Sr Ed & Assoc Publr, Emblem Editions: Anita Chong
Founded: 1906
Publishes in English.
ISBN Prefix(es): 978-0-7710
Number of titles published annually: 70 Print
Total Titles: 2,000 Print
Divisions: Tundra Books
See separate listing for:
Tundra Books

McGill-Queen's University Press
Imprint of Combined Academic Publishers
1010 Sherbrooke W, Suite 1720, Montreal, QC H3A 2R7
Tel: 514-398-3750 *Fax:* 514-398-4333
E-mail: mqup@mqup.ca
Web Site: www.mqup.ca
Key Personnel
Exec Dir: Philip Cercone *Tel:* 514-398-2910 *E-mail:* philip.cercone@mcgill.ca
Assoc Dir & Mktg Dir: Susan McIntosh *Tel:* 514-398-6306 *E-mail:* susan.mcintosh@mcgill.ca
Ed-in-Chief: Jonathan Crago *Tel:* 514-398-7480 *E-mail:* jonathan.crago@mcgill.ca
Sr Ed: Kyla Madden *Tel:* 514-398-2056 *E-mail:* kyla.madden@mcgill.ca
Acqs Ed: James MacNevin *Tel:* 613-533-2155 *E-mail:* james.macnevin@queensu.ca
Mng Ed: Ryan Van Huijstee *Tel:* 514-398-3922 *E-mail:* ryan.vanhuijstee@mcgill.ca
Asst Mng Ed: Jessica Howarth *Tel:* 514-398-2068 *E-mail:* jessica.howarth@mcgill.ca
Prodn Mgr: Elena Goranescu McAdam *Tel:* 514-398-7395 *E-mail:* elena.goranescu@mcgill.ca
Rts & Projs Mgr: Julia Monks *Tel:* 514-398-2121 *E-mail:* julia.monks@mcgill.ca
Sales Mgr: Jack Hannan *Tel:* 514-398-5165 *E-mail:* jack.hannan@mcgill.ca
Founded: 1970
Original peer-reviewed, high-quality books in all areas of social sciences & humanities. Our emphasis is on providing an outlet for Canadian authors & scholarship. Publish authors from around the world.
Publishes in English, French.
ISBN Prefix(es): 978-0-88629; 978-0-88911; 978-0-7735; 978-0-7709; 978-1-55240; 978-0-9690334
Number of titles published annually: 120 Print
Total Titles: 3,000 Print; 5 CD-ROM
Branch Office(s)
Douglas Library Bldg, 93 University Ave, Kingston, ON K7L 5C4, Roger Martin *Tel:* 613-533-2155 *Fax:* 613-533-6822 *E-mail:* mqup@queensu.ca
Distributor for John Deutsch Institute for the Study of Economic Policy; Equinox Publishing; Fontanus Monograph Series; Institute for Research on Public Policy; McCord Museum; Queen's Policy Studies Series; Les Editions du Septentrion (English titles)
Foreign Rep(s): The African Moon Press (Chris Reinders) (South Africa); CAP Ltd (David Pickering) (Belgium, Luxembourg, Netherlands); Colin Flint Ltd (Ben Greig, Steven Haslemere & Wilf Jones) (Denmark, Finland, Iceland, Norway, Sweden); Combined Academic (Emma Hester) (UK); Claire De Gruchy (Middle East); Charles Gibbes (Greece); Bill Kennedy (Middle East); Mare Nostrum (Frauke Feldmann) (Austria, Germany, Switzerland); Mare Nostrum (David Pickering) (France, Italy, Southern Europe); Mare Nostrum (Cristina De Lara Ruiz) (Portugal, Spain); Tony Moggach (Africa exc South Africa, Eastern Europe); Gabrielle Redmond (Ireland, Northern Ireland)
Distribution Center: c/o Georgetown Terminal Warehouses, 34 Armstrong Ave, Georgetown, ON L7G 4R9 *Tel:* 905-873-9781 *Toll Free Tel:* 877-864-8477 *Fax:* 905-873-6170 *Toll Free Fax:* 877-864-4272 *E-mail:* orders@gtwcanada.com
Chicago Distribution Center, 11030 S Langley Ave, Chicago, IL 60628, United States *Tel:* 773-702-7000 *Toll Free Tel:* 800-621-2736 *Fax:* 773-702-7212 *Toll Free Fax:* 800-621-8476 *E-mail:* orders@press.uchicago.edu SAN: 202-5280
Research Press, 302-A ABW Tower, M G Rd, IFFCO Crossing, Gurgaon 122 011, India *Tel:* (0124) 4040017 *Fax:* (011) 23281819 *E-mail:* marketing@researchpress.co.in
Marston Book Services Ltd, 160 Milton Park, PO Box 269, Abingdon, Oxon OX14 4YN, United Kingdom *Tel:* (01235) 465500 *Fax:* (01235) 465555 *E-mail:* trade.orders@marston.co.uk *Web Site:* www.pubeasy.com
Membership(s): American Association of University Presses; Association of Canadian Publishers; Association of Canadian University Presses

McGraw-Hill Ryerson Limited
Division of McGraw-Hill Education
300 Water St, Whitby, ON L1N 9B6
SAN: 115-060X
Tel: 905-430-5000 *Toll Free Tel:* 800-565-5758 (cust serv) *Fax:* 905-430-5020 *Toll Free Fax:* 800-463-5885
Web Site: www.mheducation.ca
Key Personnel
CEO & Pres: David Swail *E-mail:* davids@mcgrawhill.ca
CFO & Secy-Treas: Brenda Arseneault *E-mail:* brendaa@mcgrawhill.ca
Pres, Higher Educ Div: Patrick Ferrier *E-mail:* patf@mcgrawhill.ca
Pres, School Div: Nancy Gerrish *E-mail:* nancyg@mcgrawhill.ca
EVP, Cust Satisfaction: Marshall I Morris
Founded: 1971 (as McGraw-Hill Book Co)
Publishes & distributes educational & professional products in both print & non-print media.
Publishes in English.
ISBN Prefix(es): 978-0-07; 978-0-7700
Number of titles published annually: 70 Print; 40 CD-ROM; 30 Online
Total Titles: 1,300 Print; 150 CD-ROM; 200 Online; 50 E-Book
Imprints: McGraw-Hill Ryerson
Distributed by McGraw-Hill Publishing Cos
Distributor for Glencoe/McGraw-Hill; Jamestown Education; McGraw-Hill; McGraw-Hill/Irwin; MedMaster Inc; Open Court; Osborne; Schaum's; SRA; Wright Group
U.S. Publishers Represented: The McGraw-Hill Companies
Membership(s): Canadian Educational Resources Council; Canadian Publishers' Council

Modus Vivendi Publishing Inc
55, rue Jean-Talon Ouest, 2e etage, Montreal, QC H2R 2W8
Tel: 514-272-0433 *Fax:* 514-272-7234
E-mail: info@groupemodus.com
Web Site: www.groupemodus.com
Key Personnel
Founder & CEO: Marc Alain
Dir, Sales & Ed: Isabelle Jodoin
Founded: 1992
General trade publishing.

Publishes in French.
ISBN Prefix(es): 978-2-921556; 978-2-89523; 978-2-89543 (Presses Aventure); 978-2-923720 (Editions Bravo!); 978-2-89670 (Editions Bravo!)
Number of titles published annually: 200 Print
Divisions: Editions Bravo!; Editions Rouge; Presses Aventure
Distribution Center: Les Messageries ADP, 2315, rue de la Province, Longueuil, QC J4G 1G4 *Tel:* 450-640-1237 *Toll Free Tel:* 866-874-1237 *Fax:* 450-674-6237 *Toll Free Fax:* 866-874-6237 *E-mail:* adpcommandes@sogides.com

Moose Hide Books
Imprint of Moose Enterprise Book & Theatre Play Publishing
684 Walls Rd, Prince Township, ON P6A 6K4
Tel: 705-779-3331 *Fax:* 705-779-3331
E-mail: mooseenterprises@on.aibn.com
Web Site: www.moosehidebooks.com
Key Personnel
Owner & Publr: Richard Mousseau
E-mail: rmousseau@moosehidebooks.com
Ed: Edmond Alcid *E-mail:* ealcid@moosehidebooks.com
Book & theatre play publishing. Full author royalties paid. 90% of authors are new. House assists new first time authors.
This publisher has indicated that 50% of their product line is author subsidized.
Publishes in English.
ISBN Prefix(es): 978-1-894650
Number of titles published annually: 7 Print; 7 E-Book; 1 Audio
Total Titles: 200 Print; 100 Online; 25 E-Book; 1 Audio

Musee Canadien de l'Histoire, see Canadian Museum of History (Musee Canadien de l'Histoire)

Narada Press
3165-133 Weber St N, Waterloo, ON N2J 3G9
Tel: 519-886-1969
Founded: 1993
General books on economics, development studies, Asian studies, Vietnamese studies. Directories, reference books, foreign language, scholarly books, college textbooks.
Publishes in English.
ISBN Prefix(es): 978-1-895938
Number of titles published annually: 5 Print

National Gallery of Canada, The Bookstore
380 Sussex Dr, Ottawa, ON K1N 9N4
Mailing Address: PO Box 427, Sta A, Ottawa, ON K1N 9N4
Tel: 613-990-0962 (mail order sales) *Fax:* 613-990-1972
E-mail: ngcbook@gallery.ca
Web Site: www.national.gallery.ca
Founded: 1980
Exhibition catalogues, monographs, permanent collection series, books on photography, exhibition handouts, videos & posters.
Publishes in English, French.
ISBN Prefix(es): 978-0-88884
Number of titles published annually: 4 Print
Total Titles: 38 Print
U.S. Rep(s): ABC Art Books
Membership(s): Canadian Booksellers Association; Canadian Museums Association; Museum Store Association

Nelson Education Ltd
Affiliate of Cengage Learning
1120 Birchmount Rd, Scarborough, ON M1K 5G4
Tel: 416-752-9100 *Toll Free Tel:* 800-268-2222 (cust serv) *Fax:* 416-752-8101 *Toll Free Fax:* 800-430-4445
E-mail: peopleandengagement@nelson.com
Web Site: www.nelson.com
Key Personnel
CEO & Pres: Greg Nordal
CFO: Michael Andrews
SVP, Media & Prodn Servs: Susan Cline
SVP & Mng Dir, School Div: Chris Besse
VP, People & Engagement & Chief Privacy Offr: Jessica Phinn
Founded: 1914
School, college, test, professional & reference.
Publishes in English.
ISBN Prefix(es): 978-0-919913; 978-1-896081; 978-0-7705; 978-0-17; 978-0-7725; 978-1-85032
Number of titles published annually: 700 Print
Total Titles: 11,864 Print; 30 CD-ROM; 30 E-Book; 100 Audio
U.S. Publishers Represented: American Technical Publishers Inc (ATP); Aseba; Brooks-Cole Publishing; Canada Housing & Mortgage Corp (CMHC); Centennial Press; Course Technology Inc; Craftsman; DC Heath Canada Ltd (school & college); Delmar Publishers Inc; Douglas & McIntyre; Duxbury Press; Exclusive; Goodheart Willcox; Great Source Educational; Groupe Beauchemin; HarperCollins; Heinemann; Heinle & Heinle Publishers Inc; Houghton Mifflin Harcourt Publishing Company (school, college & trade); Indigo Instrument; Industrial Press; International Thomson Publishing Services; Irwin Publishing; Learning Media Co; McDougall Littell & Co; Mondo; Nelson Thomson Learning; Nelson Thomson Learning Australia; Norbry; Peterson's; Phoenix Learning Resources; PWS Publishing; Reidmore Publishing; The Riverside Publishing Co; William H Sadlier; Scott Jones; South Western Education & College Publishing; Texere; Thomas Learning Asia; VideoActive Production; Wadsworth Publishers; West Publishing (educational product only); West Virginia University (FIT)
Membership(s): Canadian Educational Resources Council; Canadian Publishers' Council

§New Author Publishing
4 E Fulford Place, Brockville, ON K6V 2Z8
Tel: 613-865-7471
Web Site: www.newauthorpublishing.com
Key Personnel
Owner: Gary Wolfe *E-mail:* gary@newauthorpublishing.com
Founded: 2013
Print on demand & ebook publishing.
Publishes in English.
ISBN Prefix(es): 978-1-928045
Number of titles published annually: 8 Print; 8 Online; 8 E-Book
Total Titles: 14 Print; 14 Online; 14 E-Book

New Star Books Ltd
107-3477 Commercial St, Vancouver, BC V5N 4E8
SAN: 115-1908
Tel: 604-738-9429 *Fax:* 604-738-9332
E-mail: info@newstarbooks.com
Web Site: www.newstarbooks.com
Key Personnel
Pres & Publr: Rolf Maurer
Founded: 1970
Social issues & current affairs, fiction, literary, history, international politics, labor, feminist, gay/lesbian studies & poetry. Emphasis on British Columbia & Western Canada.
Publishes in English.
ISBN Prefix(es): 978-0-919888; 978-0-919573; 978-0-921586; 978-1-55420; 978-0-96860
Number of titles published annually: 10 Print
Total Titles: 76 Print
Branch Office(s)
1574 Gulf Rd, No 1517, Point Roberts, WA 98281, United States
Orders to: LitDistCo, 100 Armstrong Ave, Georgetown, ON L7G 5S4 *Toll Free Tel:* 800-591-6250 *Toll Free Fax:* 800-591-6251 *E-mail:* orders@litdistco.ca *Web Site:* www.litdistco.ca
Distribution Center: LitDistCo, 100 Armstrong Ave, Georgetown, ON L7G 5S4 *Toll Free Tel:* 800-591-6250 *Toll Free Fax:* 800-591-6251 *E-mail:* orders@litdistco.ca *Web Site:* www.litdistco.ca
Membership(s): Literary Press Group

§New World Publishing (Canada)
PO Box 36075, Halifax, NS B3J 3S9
Tel: 902-576-2055 (inquiries) *Toll Free Tel:* 877-211-3334 (orders) *Fax:* 902-576-2095
Web Site: www.newworldpublishing.com
Key Personnel
Owner & Mng Ed: Dr Francis Mitchell
E-mail: francis@newworldpublishing.com
Founded: 1995
Publishes in English.
ISBN Prefix(es): 978-1-895814
Number of titles published annually: 4 Print; 1 Online; 1 E-Book
Total Titles: 44 Print; 7 CD-ROM; 3 Online; 3 E-Book; 3 Audio
Distributed by Glen Margaret Publishing (most independent & gift stores in Maritimes)
Returns: 19 Frenchman's Rd, Oakfield, NS B2T 1A9 *E-mail:* nwp1@eastlink.ca
Membership(s): Atlantic Publishers Marketing Association; Canadian Booksellers Association

NeWest Press
8540 109 St, No 201, Edmonton, AB T6G 1E6
Tel: 780-432-9427 *Toll Free Tel:* 866-796-5473 *Fax:* 780-433-3179
E-mail: info@newestpress.com; orders@newestpress.com
Web Site: www.newestpress.com
Key Personnel
Gen Mgr: Paul Matwychuk
Mktg & Prodn Coord: Matt Bowes
Founded: 1977
Committed to developing & publishing first-time writers, as well as ensuring the availability of Canadian classics.
Publishes in English.
ISBN Prefix(es): 978-0-920316; 978-0-920897; 978-1-896300; 978-1-897126; 978-1-927063
Number of titles published annually: 12 Print
Total Titles: 140 Print
Imprints: Nunatak
Sales Office(s): Literary Press Group, 425 Adelaide St W, Suite 700, Toronto, ON M5V 3C1, Sales Mgr: Tan Light *Tel:* 416-483-1321 *Fax:* 416-483-2510 *E-mail:* sales@lpg.ca
Foreign Rep(s): Gazelle Books (Europe, UK)
Distribution Center: LitDistCo, c/o 100 Armstrong Ave, Georgetown, ON L7G 5S4 *Toll Free Tel:* 800-591-6250 *Toll Free Fax:* 800-591-6251 *E-mail:* ordering@litdistco.ca
Membership(s): Association of Canadian Publishers; Book Publishers Association of Alberta; Canadian Booksellers Association; Crime Writers of Canada; Literary Press Group

Nimbus Publishing Ltd
3731 Mackintosh St, Halifax, NS B3K 5A5
SAN: 115-0685
Mailing Address: PO Box 9166, Halifax, NS B3K 5M8
Tel: 902-455-4286; 902-454-7404
Toll Free Tel: 800-NIMBUS9 (646-2879)
Fax: 902-455-5440 *Toll Free Fax:* 888-253-3133
E-mail: customerservice@nimbus.ca
Web Site: www.nimbus.ca
Key Personnel
Mng Ed: Patrick Murphy *E-mail:* editorial@nimbus.ca

Prodn Mgr: Heather Bryan *E-mail:* hbryan@nimbus.ca
Sales Mgr & Foreign Rts: Terrilee Bulger *Tel:* 902-455-4286 ext 223 *E-mail:* tbulger@nimbus.ca
Mktg Coord: Emily Mackinnon *Tel:* 902-455-4286 ext 230 *E-mail:* emackinnon@nimbus.ca
Billing: Phyllis Murray
Founded: 1978
Regional nonfiction books, relevant to the Atlantic-Canadian experience, social & natural history, children's books, cookbooks, travel, biography, photography & nautical.
Publishes in English.
ISBN Prefix(es): 978-0-920852; 978-0-919380; 978-0-921054; 978-0-921128; 978-1-55109; 978-1-77108
Number of titles published annually: 40 Print
Total Titles: 500 Print
Imprints: Nimbus; Vagrant Press (fiction)
Distributor for Acadiensis Press; Acorn Press; Bouton D'or Acadie; Breton Books; Bunim & Bannigan; Cape Breton University Press; Down East; Heritage House; Maritime Lines; Pottersfield Press
U.S. Publishers Represented: Down East; Flat Hammock Press; Mystic Seaport Museum Inc; Sheridan House; Wooden Boat
U.S. Rep(s): Downeast Books
Membership(s): Association for the Export of Canadian Books; Association of Canadian Publishers; Atlantic Publishers Marketing Association; Canadian Booksellers Association; NEBA

§The North-South Institute (Institut Nord-Sud)
100 Argyle Ave, Suite 200, Ottawa, ON K2P 1B6
Tel: 613-241-3535 *Fax:* 613-241-7435
E-mail: nsi@nsi-ins.ca
Web Site: www.nsi-ins.ca
Key Personnel
Dir, Fin & Admin: Diane Guevremont *E-mail:* dguevremont@nsi-ins.ca
Founded: 1976
North-South relations & foreign aid, economics & trade, with emphasis on Canada & developing countries, foreign policy & multilateral cooperation, gender & development, human rights, civil society, conflict & human security, markets & social responsibility. Also publishes newsletters & Canadian Development Report (annual).
Publishes in English, French.
ISBN Prefix(es): 978-1-896770; 978-1-897358; 978-2-9802095
Number of titles published annually: 8 Print; 15 Online
Total Titles: 60 Print; 450 Online

Northern Canada Evangelical Mission (NCEM)
PO Box 3030, Prince Albert, SK S6V 7V4
Tel: 306-764-3388 *Fax:* 306-764-3390
E-mail: ncem@ncem.ca
Web Site: www.ncem.ca
Founded: 1946
Publish books, pamphlets, tracts, Bibles, audio CDs. Subject specialty is native North American literature.
Publishes in English, French.
ISBN Prefix(es): 978-0-920731
Number of titles published annually: 3 Print
Total Titles: 111 Print
Branch Office(s)
PO Box 50806, Billings, MT 59105-0806, United States *Tel:* 406-259-2061 *Fax:* 406-259-2061 *E-mail:* ncemus@ncem.ca
Membership(s): CBA: The Association for Christian Retail

Northstone Publishing
Imprint of Wood Lake Publishing Inc
485 Beaver Lake Rd, Kelowna, BC V4V 1S5
SAN: 117-7346
Tel: 250-766-2778 *Toll Free Tel:* 800-299-2926; 800-663-2775 (orders) *Fax:* 250-766-2736 *Toll Free Fax:* 888-841-9991
E-mail: info@woodlakebooks.com
Web Site: www.woodlakebooks.com
Key Personnel
Pres & Mktg Dir: Patty Berube
Founded: 1996
Books essential spirituality for our day.
Publishes in English.
ISBN Prefix(es): 978-1-55145; 978-1-896836; 978-1-77064
Number of titles published annually: 8 Print
Total Titles: 150 Print

Novalis Publishing
Division of Bayard Canada
10 Lower Spadina Ave, Suite 400, Toronto, ON M5V 2Z2
Tel: 416-363-3303 *Toll Free Tel:* 877-702-7773 *Fax:* 416-363-9409 *Toll Free Fax:* 877-702-7775
E-mail: books@novalis.ca
Web Site: www.novalis.ca
Key Personnel
Publg Dir: Joseph Sinasac *E-mail:* joseph.sinasac@novalis.ca
Assoc Publr: Glenn Byer *E-mail:* glenn.byer@novalis.ca
Mktg Mgr: Don Beyers
Sales Mgr: Maria Medeiros
Mng Ed: Anne Louise Mahoney
Prodn Ed: Karen Stevens
Founded: 1936
Religious children's & adult books, periodicals & religious books (Catholic/Christian).
Publishes in English, French.
ISBN Prefix(es): 978-2-89088; 978-2-89507; 978-2-89646; 978-0-88587; 978-1-895195
Number of titles published annually: 30 Print
Total Titles: 360 Print
Distributor for Canterbury Press; Catholic Health Alliance of Canada (CHAC); Church House Publishing; Columba Press; Creative Communications for the Parish; Crossroad Publishing; Darton Longman & Todd; Editions du Signe; Flowerpot Press; Gemstone Press; Jewish Lights Publishing/Skylight Paths; Liguori Publications; Loyola Press; Morehouse Publishing/Church Publishing/Seabury; Orbis Books; Paulist Press; Penguin Random House; Pflaum Publishing Group; Printery House; Saint Mary's Press; St Vladimir Seminary Press; SCM Press; Twenty Third Publications; Wild Goose Publications
U.S. Publishers Represented: Creative Communications for the Parish; Jewish Lights Publishing; Orbis Books; Paulist Press; Pflaum Gospel Weeklies; Saint Mary's Press; Twenty-Third Publications
Billing Address: BND Distribution, 4475 Frontenac St, Montreal, QC H2H 2S2 *Tel:* 514-278-3020 *Toll Free Tel:* 800-387-7164 *Fax:* 514-278-3030 *Toll Free Fax:* 800-204-4140 *Web Site:* www.novalis.com
Orders to: BND Distribution, 4475 Frontenac St, Montreal, QC H2H 2S2 *Tel:* 514-278-3020 *Toll Free Tel:* 800-387-7164 *Fax:* 514-278-3030 *Toll Free Fax:* 800-204-4140 *Web Site:* www.novalis.com
Returns: BND Distribution, 4475 Frontenac St, Montreal, QC H2H 2S2 *Tel:* 514-278-3020 *Toll Free Tel:* 800-387-7164 *Fax:* 514-278-3030 *Toll Free Fax:* 800-204-4140 *Web Site:* www.novalis.com
Shipping Address: BND Distribution, 4475 Frontenac St, Montreal, QC H2H 2S2 *Tel:* 514-278-3020 *Toll Free Tel:* 800-387-7164 *Fax:* 514-278-3030 *Toll Free Fax:* 800-204-4140 *Web Site:* www.novalis.com
Warehouse: BND Distribution, 4475 Frontenac St, Montreal, QC H2H 2S2 *Tel:* 514-278-3020 *Toll Free Tel:* 800-387-7164 *Fax:* 514-278-3030 *Toll Free Fax:* 800-204-4140 *Web Site:* www.novalis.com

Oberon Press
145 Spruce St, Suite 205, Ottawa, ON K1R 6P1
SAN: 115-0723
Tel: 613-238-3275 *Fax:* 613-238-3275
E-mail: oberon@sympatico.ca
Web Site: www.oberonpress.ca
Key Personnel
Pres: Michael Macklem
VP & Gen Mgr: Nicholas Macklem
Founded: 1966
Canadiana, fiction, history, biography, poetry & travel.
Publishes in English.
ISBN Prefix(es): 978-0-88750; 978-0-7780
Number of titles published annually: 8 Print
Total Titles: 664 Print

One Act Play Depot
618 Memorial Dr, PO Box 335, Spiritwood, SK S0J 2M0
E-mail: plays@oneactplays.net; orders@oneactplays.net
Web Site: oneactplays.net
Key Personnel
Mng Ed: Fraser MacFarlane
Ed: K Balvenie
Founded: 2002
Publication, sale & distribution of one-act plays. Orders ship within 24 hours. Accept submissions only in Feb of each year.
Publishes in English.
ISBN Prefix(es): 978-1-894910; 978-1-926849
Number of titles published annually: 10 Print; 5 E-Book
Total Titles: 137 Print; 11 E-Book

Oolichan Books
PO Box 2278, Fernie, BC V0B 1M0
SAN: 115-4680
Tel: 250-423-6113
E-mail: info@oolichan.com
Web Site: www.oolichan.com
Key Personnel
Founder & Ed: Ronald Smith
Publr: Randal Macnair
Consulting Ed: Pat Smith
Asst to the Publr: Carolyn Nikodym
Founded: 1974
Publishers of literary fiction, poetry & literary nonfiction. Publish only Canadian authors.
Publishes in English.
ISBN Prefix(es): 978-0-88982
Number of titles published annually: 10 Print
Total Titles: 140 Print
Shipping Address: 542 B Second Ave, Fernie, BC V0B 1M0
Distribution Center: University of Toronto Press, 5201 Dufferin St, Toronto, ON M3H 5T8 *Toll Free Tel:* 800-565-9523 *E-mail:* utpbooks@utpress.utoronto.ca
Membership(s): Association of Book Publishers of British Columbia; Association of Canadian Publishers; Literary Press Group

Owlkids Books Inc
Division of Bayard Canada
10 Lower Spadina Ave, Suite 400, Toronto, ON M5V 2Z2
Tel: 416-340-2700 *Fax:* 416-340-9769
E-mail: owlkids@owlkids.com
Web Site: www.owlkidsbooks.com
Key Personnel
Publr: Karen Boersma *E-mail:* karen.boersma@owlkids.com
Edit Dir: Karen Li
Dir, Sales & Mktg: Judy Brunsek
Founded: 1976

Award winning publisher of books for children ages 3-13.
Publishes in English.
ISBN Prefix(es): 978-0-920775; 978-1-895688; 978-1-894379; 978-1-897066; 978-1-897349; 978-1-926973; 978-0-919872; 978-1-926818
Number of titles published annually: 25 Print
Total Titles: 150 Print; 50 E-Book
Orders to: University of Toronto Press, 5201 Dufferin St, Toronto, ON M3H 5T8 *Tel:* 416-667-7791 *Toll Free Tel:* 800-565-9523 *Fax:* 416-667-7832 *Toll Free Fax:* 800-221-9985 *E-mail:* utpbooks@utpress.utoronto.ca *Web Site:* www.utpress.utoronto.ca; Publishers Group West/Perseus, 1700 Fourth St, Berkeley, CA 94710, United States *Toll Free Tel:* 800-788-3123 *Toll Free Fax:* 800-351-5073 *E-mail:* orderentry@perseusbooks.com *Web Site:* www.pgw.com

Pacific Educational Press
Unit of University of British Columbia
c/o University of British Columbia, Faculty of Education, 411-2389 Health Sciences Mall, Vancouver, BC V6T 1Z4
SAN: 115-1266
Tel: 604-822-5385 *Fax:* 604-822-6603
E-mail: pep.admin@ubc.ca; pep.sales@ubc.ca
Web Site: www.pacificedpress.educ.ubc.ca
Key Personnel
Dir: Susan Howell *E-mail:* susan.howell@ubc.ca
Mgr, Edit & Prodn Servs: Elizabeth Salomons *E-mail:* elizabeth.salomons@ubc.ca
Devt Art Dir: Barbara Kuhne *E-mail:* barbara.kuhne@ubc.ca
Founded: 1971
Textbooks for teacher education programs, education materials, materials which are generally used in classrooms or educational institutes, books on education topics & issues for a general readership.
Publishes in English.
ISBN Prefix(es): 978-0-88865; 978-1-895766
Number of titles published annually: 6 Print
Total Titles: 104 Print; 16 E-Book
Distributor for Critical Thinking Consortium (TC 2)
Distribution Center: Georgetown Terminal Warehouse, 34 Armstrong Ave, Georgetown, ON L7G 4R9 *Tel:* 905-873-9781 *Toll Free Tel:* 877-864-8477 (CN only) *Fax:* 905-873-6170 *Toll Free Fax:* 877-864-4272 (CN only) *E-mail:* orders@gtwcanada.com
Membership(s): Association of Book Publishers of British Columbia; Association of Canadian Publishers

Palimpsest Press
1171 Eastlawn Ave, Windsor, ON N8S 3J1
Tel: 519-563-9981
E-mail: info@palimpsestpress.ca
Web Site: www.palimpsestpress.ca
Key Personnel
Publr/Ed: Aimee Parent Dunn *E-mail:* aimee@palimpsestpress.ca
Poetry Ed & Graphic Designer: Dawn Kresan *E-mail:* dawnkresan@palimpsestpress.ca
Founded: 2000
Publish poetry collections, nonfiction, essays, limited editions chapbooks & children's picture books.
Publishes in English.
ISBN Prefix(es): 978-0-9733952; 978-1-926794; 978-0-9784917
Number of titles published annually: 6 Print
Total Titles: 30 Print
Sales Office(s): Literary Press Group, 425 Adelaide St W, Suite 700, Toronto, ON M5V 3C1 *Tel:* 416-483-1321 *Fax:* 416-483-2510 *E-mail:* sales@lpg.ca *Web Site:* www.lpg.ca
Orders to: LitDistCo, 100 Armstrong Ave, Georgetown, ON L7G 5S4 *Toll Free Tel:* 800-591-6250 *Toll Free Fax:* 800-591-6251 *E-mail:* orders@litdistco.ca *Web Site:* www.litdistco.ca
Shipping Address: LitDistCo, 100 Armstrong Ave, Georgetown, ON L7G 5S4
Warehouse: LitDistCo, 100 Armstrong Ave, Georgetown, ON L7G 5S4
United States
Distribution Center: LitDistCo, 100 Armstrong Ave, Georgetown, ON L7G 5S4 *Toll Free Tel:* 800-591-6250 *Toll Free Fax:* 800-591-6251 *E-mail:* orders@litdistco.ca *Web Site:* www.litdistco.ca
Membership(s): Association of Canadian Publishers; Literary Press Group of Canada

Paulines Editions
5610 rue Beaubien est, Montreal, QC H1T 1X5
Tel: 514-253-5610 *Fax:* 514-253-1907
E-mail: fsp-paulines@videotron.ca
Web Site: www.editions.paulines.qc.ca
Key Personnel
Dir & Intl Rts Contact: Vanda Salvador
Lib Sales Dir: Lucille Paradis
Founded: 1955
Religious books.
Publishes in English, French.
ISBN Prefix(es): 978-2-920912
Number of titles published annually: 4 Print
Total Titles: 60 Print
Distributed by Mediaspaul (Montreal)

Pearson Education Canada
Division of Pearson Canada Inc
26 Prince Andrew Place, Don Mills, ON M3C 2T8
SAN: 115-0022
Tel: 416-447-5101 *Toll Free Tel:* 800-263-9965 *Fax:* 416-443-0948 *Toll Free Fax:* 800-263-7733; 888-465-0536
Web Site: www.pearsoned.ca
Key Personnel
Higher Educ Div: Jessica Mosher *E-mail:* jessica.mosher@pearsoned.com
Founded: 1966
Educational textbooks, trade, reference.
Publishes in English, French.
ISBN Prefix(es): 978-0-201
Total Titles: 5,700 Print
Imprints: Addison Wesley; Allyn & Bacon; Copp Clark; Benjamin Cummings; Ginn; Longman; Prentice Hall
Orders to: Pearson Education Operations Centre, PO Box 335, Newmarket, ON L3Y 4X7 *Toll Free Tel:* 800-567-3800 (cust serv); 800-361-6128 (school) *Toll Free Fax:* 800-236-7733 (cust serv); 800-563-9196 (school)
Returns: Pearson Education Operations Centre, PO Box 335, Newmarket, ON L3Y 4X7 *Toll Free Tel:* 800-567-3800 (cust serv); 800-361-6128 (school) *Toll Free Fax:* 800-236-7733 (cust serv); 800-563-9196 (school)
Distribution Center: 195 Harry Walker Pkwy, Newmarket, ON L3Y 7B3 *Tel:* 905-853-7888 *Fax:* 905-853-7865

Pearson ERPI
Division of Pearson PLC
5757 rue Cypihot, St-Laurent, QC H4S 1R3
Tel: 514-334-2690 *Toll Free Tel:* 800-263-3678 *Fax:* 514-334-4720 *Toll Free Fax:* 800-643-4720
E-mail: erpidlm@erpi.com
Web Site: www.erpi.com; pearsonplc.ca
Key Personnel
Artistic Dir: Helene Cousineau *E-mail:* helene.cousineau@erpi.com
Intl Rts: Lise Barras *Tel:* 514-334-2690 ext 2445 *E-mail:* lise.barras@erpi.com
Founded: 1965
Textbooks.
Publishes in English, French.
ISBN Prefix(es): 978-2-7613; 978-0-7767
Number of titles published annually: 15 Print; 12 CD-ROM; 10 Online
Total Titles: 850 Print; 15 CD-ROM; 10 Online
Imprints: ERPI
Divisions: Diffusion du Livre Mirabel
Distributed by De Boeck; Pearson Education France; Penguin Readers; Village Mondial
Distributor for Addison-Wesley, Pearson Education (English as a second language series); Campus Press France; Duculot; Michelin North America (Canada) (French titles in Canada); Prentice-Hall
Membership(s): Association Nationale des Editeurs de Livres

Pembroke Publishers Ltd
538 Hood Rd, Markham, ON L3R 3K9
Tel: 905-477-0650 *Toll Free Tel:* 800-997-9807 *Fax:* 905-477-3691 *Toll Free Fax:* 800-339-5568
Web Site: www.pembrokepublishers.com
Key Personnel
Pres & Intl Rts: Mary Macchiusi *E-mail:* mary@pembrokepublishers.com
Mng Dir: Claudia Connolly
Founded: 1985
Educational books.
Publishes in English.
ISBN Prefix(es): 978-0-921217; 978-1-55138
Number of titles published annually: 15 Print
Total Titles: 230 Print
Distributor for Stenhouse Publishers
U.S. Publishers Represented: Stenhouse Publishers, 477 Congress St, Suite 4B, Portland, ME 04101-3417, United States
U.S. Rep(s): Stenhouse Publishers, 477 Congress St, Suite 4B, Portland, ME 04101-3417, United States
Foreign Rep(s): Curriculum Corp (Australia); Eurospan (UK); PMS (Singapore); Stenhouse Publishers (USA)
Distribution Center: Eurospan, 3 Henrietta St, Covent Garden, London WC2E 8LU, United Kingdom (UK)
Membership(s): Organization of Book Publishers of Ontario

Pemmican Publications Inc
150 Henry Ave, Winnipeg, MB R3B 0J7
SAN: 115-1657
Tel: 204-589-6346 *Fax:* 204-589-2063
E-mail: pemmican@pemmican.mb.ca
Web Site: www.pemmican.mb.ca
Key Personnel
Mng Ed: Randal McIlroy
Founded: 1980
Books of Metis & native concern, juvenile & young adult books, trade paperbacks, scholarly books. Submissions outside Canada must include international reply coupons.
Publishes in English, French.
ISBN Prefix(es): 978-0-919143; 978-0-921827; 978-1-894717
Number of titles published annually: 5 Print
Total Titles: 120 Print

Penguin Books Canada Limited, see Penguin Group (Canada)

Penguin Group (Canada)
Division of Penguin Random House Canada
90 Eglinton Ave E, Suite 700, Toronto, ON M4P 2Y3
SAN: 115-074X
Tel: 416-925-2249 *Fax:* 416-925-0068
E-mail: customerservicescanada@penguinrandomhouse.com
Web Site: penguinrandomhouse.ca
Key Personnel
Chmn: Rob Prichard
COO: Barry Gallant
Pres & Publr: Nicole Winstanley
VP, Fin: Helena Hung

VP, HR: Ann Wood
Dir, Prodn: Janette Lush
Rts & Contracts Mgr: David Whiteside
Founded: 1974
General trade & paperback books, hardcover & classics, audio cassettes.
Publishes in English.
ISBN Prefix(es): 978-0-14; 978-0-452; 978-0-451; 978-0-453; 978-0-7214; 978-0-216
Number of titles published annually: 3,280 Print
Total Titles: 76,500 Print
Imprints: A&C Black UK; Ace; Albatross; Alpha Books; Arden; Arkana; Atlantic Books; Avery; BBC Children's Books; Berkley; Berkshire House; Bibli O'Phile; Bloomberg Press; Bloomsbury UK; Bloomsbury USA; Blue Hen; Boulevard; Callaway; Canongate; Celebra; Chamberlain Brothers; Children's High Level Group; Corinthian Books; The Countryman Press; Current; Dalkey Archive Press; DAW; Dial Books for Young Readers; Dutton; Dutton Children's Books; Europa Editions; Faber & Faber Ltd; Fig Tree; Firebird; Foul Play Press; Gotham Books; GP Putnam & Sons; Grosset & Dunlap; Hamish Hamilton; Hamish Hamilton Canada; Hamish Hamilton Juvenile; Heat; Hippocrene Books; Home; HP Books; Hudson Street Press; Humanity Books; Icon Books; Michael Joseph; Michael Joseph Juvenile; Jove; Kales Press; Ladybird; Allen Lane; Library of America; Liveright; Meridian; Methuen Canadian List; Minedition; Modern Gems; New Directions; Noah Publications; W W Norton; Onyx; Overlook Press; Peace Hill Press; Pegasus Books; Penguin Audio UK; Penguin Audio USA; Penguin Australia; Penguin Canada; Penguin Classics; Penguin Compass; Penguin 007; Penguin India; Penguin Ireland; Penguin New Zealand; Penguin Paperbacks; Penguin Press; Penguin South Africa; Penguin UK; Perigee; Persea Books; Philomel Books; Pi Press; Planet Dexter; Plume; Portfolio; Prentice Hall Cda; Prentice Hall Press; Price Stern Sloan; Price Stern Sloan Merchandise; Prime Crime; Profile Books; Prometheus Books; Puffin Canada; Puffin UK; Puffin USA; Pushcart Press; Putnam Audio; PYR Books; Quantuck Lane; Razorbill; Rose Reisman; Riverhead; Roadside Amusements; Roc; Screen Press Books; Sentinel; Short Books; Signet; Smithsonian; Speak; Tarcher; Thames & Hudson; Time Out Guides Ltd; Tusk/Ivories; Verso Press Canada; Verso Press UK; Verso Press USA; Viking Canada; Viking Children's Books; Viking Penguin Audio; Viking Studio; Viking UK; Viking UK Juvenile; Viking USA; Walting Street; Frederick Warne; Wee Sing; Which Books; Wizard Books
Distributor for Alpha Books; Arkangel; Atlantic Books; Avery; BBC Children's Books; Berkley Publishing; Bibli O'Phile; Bloomsbury Press; Callaway; Canongate; DAW; Dutton; Europa Editions; Faber & Faber Ltd; Fig Tree; Gotham Books; Hamish Hamilton; Hamish Hamilton Canada; Hippocrene Books; Hudson Street Press; Icon Books; Michael Joseph; Ladybird; Allen Lane; Library of America; Michelin North America (Canada) (English titles in Canada); New American Library; W W Norton; Overlook Press; Penguin Audio UK; Penguin Audio USA; Penguin Australia; Penguin Books USA; Penguin Canada; Penguin India; Penguin New Zealand; Penguin Press; Penguin South Africa; Penguin UK; Penguin Young Readers; Plume; Portfolio; Prometheus Books; Puffin Canada; Putnam; Rose Reisman; Verso Press USA; Viking Canada; Viking Penguin Audio; Viking USA; Frederick Warne; Which Book
Distribution Center: Pearson Canada Distribution Centre, 195 Harry Walker Pkwy, Newmarket, ON L3Y 7B4 *Tel:* 905-713-3852 *Toll Free Tel:* 800-399-6858 *Toll Free Fax:* 800-363-2665 *Web Site:* www.pearsoned.ca

Penguin Random House Canada Limited
320 Front St W, Suite 1400, Toronto, ON M5V 3B6
SAN: 201-3975
Tel: 416-364-4449 *Toll Free Tel:* 888-523-9292 (cust serv) *Fax:* 416-364-6863; 416-364-6653 (subs rts)
Web Site: penguinrandomhouse.ca
Key Personnel
CEO & Pres: Brad Martin
CFO & EVP: Douglas Foot
COO: Barry Gallant
Pres & Publr, RHC: Kristin Cochrane
Pres & Publr: Nicole Winstanley
EVP & Dir, Sales: Duncan Shields
Exec Publr, RHC: Louise Dennys
SVP & Dir, Busn Devt, Online Digital Sales Strategy: Robert Wheaton
SVP & Dir, Mktg & Communs: Tracey Turriff
VP & Publr, Appetite by Random House: Robert McCullough
VP, Publicity & Mktg: Beth Lockley
Dir, Prodn: Janine Laporte
Founded: 1944
Penguin Random House Canada Limited & its publishing entities are not accepting unsol submissions, proposals, mss, or submission queries via e-mail at this time.
Publishes in English.
ISBN Prefix(es): 978-0-307; 978-0-679; 978-0-553; 978-0-385; 978-0-7704; 978-0-345; 978-0-449; 978-0-676
Imprints: Anchor Canada; Appetite by Random House; Bond Street Books; Doubleday Canada; Emblem Editions; Fenn; Douglas Gibson Books; Hamish Hamilton Canada; Knopf Canada; Allen Lane Canada; McClelland & Stewart; Penguin Canada; Portfolio Penguin Canada; Puffin Canada; Random House Canada; Razorbill Canada; Seal Books; Signal; Tundra Books; Viking Canada; Vintage Canada
Warehouse: 6971 Columbus Rd, Mississauga, ON L5T 1K1
Membership(s): Canadian Booksellers Association; Canadian Library Association; Canadian Publishers' Council
See separate listing for:
Doubleday Canada
Knopf Canada
McClelland & Stewart Ltd
Penguin Group (Canada)
Seal Books

Pippin Publishing
Division of University of Toronto Press
5201 Dufferin St, Toronto, ON M3H 5T8
Tel: 416-667-8731; 426-667-7791 (CN warehouse) *Toll Free Tel:* 800-565-9523 (CN warehouse) *Fax:* 416-667-7832 *Toll Free Fax:* 800-221-9985 (CN warehouse)
E-mail: utpbooks@utpress.utoronto.ca (CN warehouse)
Web Site: www.utpguidancecentre.com
Key Personnel
Mgr: Cindy Hall *E-mail:* chall@utpress.utoronto.ca
Founded: 1995
Educational books: English as a foreign language; English language teaching, books for teachers & students. Also trade military memoirs.
Publishes in English.
ISBN Prefix(es): 978-0-88751
Number of titles published annually: 6 Print
Total Titles: 85 Print
Imprints: Dominie Press (CN)
Distributed by University of Toronto Press (Worldwide)
Foreign Rep(s): NBN International (Africa, Europe, UK)
Warehouse: University of Toronto Press, 2250 Military Rd, Tonawanda, NY 14150, United States

Pontifical Institute of Mediaeval Studies, Department of Publications
59 Queen's Park Crescent E, Toronto, ON M5S 2C4
SAN: 115-0804
Tel: 416-926-7142 *Fax:* 416-926-7292
Web Site: www.pims.ca
Key Personnel
Ed-in-Chief: Fred R Unwalla *E-mail:* unwalla@chass.utoronto.ca
Founded: 1936
Scholarly material on the Middle Ages.
Publishes in English, French.
ISBN Prefix(es): 978-0-88844
Number of titles published annually: 10 Print; 10 Online
Total Titles: 340 Print; 340 Online
Orders to: University of Toronto Press, 5201 Dufferin St, Toronto, ON M3H 5T8 *Tel:* 416-667-7791 *Toll Free Tel:* 800-565-9523 *Fax:* 416-667-7832 *Toll Free Fax:* 800-221-9985 *E-mail:* orders@utpress.utoronto.ca *Web Site:* www.utpress.utoronto.ca
Distribution Center: University of Toronto Press, 5201 Dufferin St, Toronto, ON M3H 5T8 *Tel:* 416-667-7791 *Toll Free Tel:* 800-565-9523 *Fax:* 416-667-7832 *Toll Free Fax:* 800-221-9985 *E-mail:* orders@utpress.utoronto.ca *Web Site:* www.utpress.utoronto.ca

Porcupine's Quill Inc
68 Main St, Erin, ON N0B 1T0
Mailing Address: PO Box 160, Erin, ON N0B 1T0
Tel: 519-833-9158 *Fax:* 519-833-9845
E-mail: pql@sentex.net
Web Site: porcupinesquill.ca
Key Personnel
Publr: Tim Inkster
Founded: 1974
Modern Canadian literature, poetry & art.
Publishes in English.
ISBN Prefix(es): 978-0-88984
Number of titles published annually: 10 Print
Total Titles: 100 Print
U.S. Rep(s): University of Toronto Press
Membership(s): Association of Canadian Publishers; Canada Council for the Arts; Literary Press Group; Ontario Arts Council

Portage & Main Press
318 McDermot, Suite 100, Winnipeg, MB R3A 0A2
Tel: 204-987-3500 *Toll Free Tel:* 800-667-9673 *Fax:* 204-947-0080 *Toll Free Fax:* 866-734-8477
E-mail: books@portageandmainpress.com
Web Site: www.portageandmainpress.com
Key Personnel
Owner, Publr & Rts & Perms: Catherine Gerbasi
Edit Dir: Annalee Greenberg
Dir, Mktg: Kirsten Phillips
Founded: 1967 (as Peguis Publishers)
Educational resource (K-8), interior design.
Publishes in English.
ISBN Prefix(es): 978-0-919566; 978-0-920541; 978-1-895411; 978-1-894110; 978-1-55379; 978-0-9699032; 978-0-9694264
Number of titles published annually: 14 Print
Total Titles: 200 Print
Imprints: HighWater Press

Pottersfield Press
83 Leslie Rd, East Lawrencetown, NS B2Z 1P8
SAN: 115-0790
Toll Free Fax: 888-253-3133
Web Site: www.pottersfieldpress.com
Key Personnel
Pres & Publr: Lesley Choyce *E-mail:* lchoyce@ns.sympatico.ca
Founded: 1979

Fiction, books about the sea, books of Atlantic & Canada; nonfiction, books of literary travel.
Publishes in English.
ISBN Prefix(es): 978-0-919001; 978-1-895900; 978-1-897426
Number of titles published annually: 6 Print
Total Titles: 104 Print; 2 CD-ROM; 4 Audio
Imprints: Atlantic Classics Series
Distributed by Nimbus Publishing
U.S. Rep(s): Nimbus Publishing
Orders to: c/o Nimbus Publishing, Box 9166, Halifax, NS B3K 5M8 *Toll Free Tel:* 800-646-2879 *Toll Free Fax:* 888-253-3133 *E-mail:* customerservice@nimbus.ca
Shipping Address: c/o Nimbus Publishing, Box 9166, Halifax, NS B3K 5M8 *Tel:* 904-454-7404 *Toll Free Tel:* 800-646-2879 *Toll Free Fax:* 888-253-3133 *E-mail:* customerservice@nimbus.ca *Web Site:* www.nimbus.ca
Membership(s): Association of Canadian Publishers

PrairieView Press
PO Box 460, Rosenort, MB R0G-1W0
Tel: 204-327-6543 *Toll Free Tel:* 800-477-7377 *Fax:* 204-327-6544
Web Site: www.prairieviewpress.com
Key Personnel
Owner & Pres: Chester Goossen
Secy: Darleen Loewen
Contact: Chad Goossen
Founded: 1968
Quality reading material for children & adults; songbooks. Over 1300 titles in distribution, listed in catalog.
Publishes in English.
ISBN Prefix(es): 978-0-920035; 978-1-896199; 978-1-897080
Number of titles published annually: 36 Print
Total Titles: 1,450 Print
Branch Office(s)
PO Box 88, Neche, ND 58265-0088, United States

Les Presses de l'Université d'Ottawa, see University of Ottawa Press (Les Presses de l'Université d'Ottawa)

Les Presses de l'Universite du Quebec
Division of Universite du Quebec
2875 blvd Laurier, Suite 450, Quebec, QC G1V 2M2
Tel: 418-657-4399 *Fax:* 418-657-2096
E-mail: puq@puq.ca
Web Site: www.puq.ca
Founded: 1969
University press.
Publishes in English, French.
ISBN Prefix(es): 978-2-7605; 978-0-7770; 978-2-920073
Number of titles published annually: 80 Print
Total Titles: 1,300 Print
Distributor for Figura; Imaginaire du Nord; Tele-Universite
Distribution Center: Prologue Inc, 1650, blvd Lionel-Bertrand, Boisbriand, QC J7H 1N7
Exportlivre, 289 Desaulniers Blvd, St-Lambert, QC J4P 1M8 *Tel:* 450-671-3888 *Fax:* 450-671-2121 *E-mail:* order@exportlivre.com *Web Site:* www.exportlivre.com
Patrimoine SPRL, Milcamps Ave 119 B, 1030 Brussels, Belgium *Tel:* (02) 7366847 *Fax:* (02) 7366847 *E-mail:* patrimoine@telenet.be
Sodis, 128 Ave du Marechal de Lattre de Tassigny, 77400 Lagny-sur-Marne, France *Tel:* 01 60 07 82 00 *Fax:* 01 64 30 92 22 *E-mail:* portail@sodis.fr *Web Site:* www.sodis.fr
Servidis SA, Chemin des Chalets 7, 1279 Chavannes-de-Bogis, Switzerland *Tel:* (022) 940 95 32 *Fax:* (022) 960 95 77 *E-mail:* pgavillet@servidis.ch *Web Site:* www.servidis.ch

Les Presses De L'Universite Laval
Division of Universite Du Quebec
2180, Chemin Ste-Foy, 1st fl, Quebec, QC G1V 0A6
Tel: 418-656-2803 *Fax:* 418-656-3305
E-mail: presses@pul.ulaval.ca
Web Site: www.pulaval.com
Key Personnel
Gen Dir: Denis Dion *E-mail:* denis.dion@pul.ulaval.ca
Gen Ed: Andre Baril *E-mail:* andr.baril@sympatico.ca; Dominique Gingras *E-mail:* dominique.gingras@pul.ulaval.ca
Founded: 1950
Books in the humanities & social sciences with an emphasis on subjects of interest in Quebec & Canada, administration, economy.
Publishes in French.
ISBN Prefix(es): 978-2-7637; 978-0-7746
Number of titles published annually: 120 Print
Foreign Rights: Librairie du Quebec (France); Patrimoine SPRL (Belgium); Servidis (Switzerland)
Distribution Center: Prologue Inc, 1650, blvd Lionel-Bertrand, Boisbriand, QC J7H 1N7 (CN & US) *Tel:* 450-434-0306 *Toll Free Tel:* 800-363-2864 *Fax:* 450-434-2627 *E-mail:* prologue@prologue.ca *Web Site:* www.prologue.ca

Prise de Parole Inc
109 Elm St, Suite 205, Sudbury, ON P3C 1T4
Mailing Address: CP 550, Sudbury, ON P3E 4R2
Tel: 705-675-6491 *Fax:* 705-673-1817
E-mail: info@prisedeparole.ca
Web Site: www.prisedeparole.ca
Key Personnel
Exec Dir: Denise Truax *E-mail:* dtruax@prisedeparole.ca
Administrator: Alain Mayotte *E-mail:* amayotte@prisedeparole.ca
Dir of Mktg & Digital Publg: Stephane Cormier *E-mail:* scormier@prisedeparole.ca
Prodn Asst: Cynthia Inabashitsi *E-mail:* manuscrits@prisedeparole.ca
Mktg Asst: Mireille Charlebois
Founded: 1973
Poetry, novels, drama, textbooks, essays.
Publishes in French.
ISBN Prefix(es): 978-0-920814; 978-0-921573; 978-2-89423
Number of titles published annually: 18 Print
Total Titles: 325 Print; 277 Online; 110 E-Book
Distribution Center: Diffusion Dimedia, 1650 boul Lionel-Bertrand, Boisbriand, QC J7H 1N7 *Tel:* 450-434-0306
Membership(s): Association Nationale des Editeurs de Livres; Regroupement des Editeurs Canadiens-Francais

Productive Publications
7-B Pleasant Blvd, Unit 1210, Toronto, ON M4T 1K2
SAN: 117-1712
Mailing Address: PO Box 7200, Sta A, Toronto, ON M5W 1X8
Tel: 416-483-0634 *Toll Free Tel:* 877-879-2669 (orders) *Fax:* 416-322-7434
E-mail: productivepublications@rogers.com
Web Site: www.productivepublications.ca
Key Personnel
Owner & Pres: Iain Williamson
Founded: 1985
Trade paperback books; business, finance, communications, computers, management, marketing, taxation, personal finance, entrepreneurship, self-help.
Publishes in English.
ISBN Prefix(es): 978-0-920847; 978-1-896210; 978-1-55270
Number of titles published annually: 28 Print
Total Titles: 180 Print

Les Publications du Quebec
1000, rte de l'Eqalise, Bureau 500, Quebec, QC G1V 3V9
Tel: 418-643-5150 *Toll Free Tel:* 800-463-2100 (Quebec province only) *Fax:* 418-643-6177 *Toll Free Fax:* 800-561-3479
E-mail: publicationsduquebec@cspq.gouv.qc.ca
Web Site: www.publicationsduquebec.gouv.qc.ca
Key Personnel
Dir: Sylvie Ferland
Founded: 1982
Government publications.
Publishes in English, French.
ISBN Prefix(es): 978-2-550; 978-2-551; 978-0-7754
Number of titles published annually: 200 Print; 20 Online
Total Titles: 4,000 Print; 100 Online

Purich Publishing Ltd
PO Box 23032, Market Mall Postal Outlet, Saskatoon, SK S7J 5H3
Tel: 306-373-5311 *Fax:* 306-373-5315
E-mail: purich@sasktel.net
Web Site: www.purichpublishing.com
Key Personnel
Founding Publr: Donald Purich
Publr: Karen Bolstad
Founded: 1992
Books specializing in Aboriginal & social justice issues, law & Canadian history.
Publishes in English.
ISBN Prefix(es): 978-1-895830
Number of titles published annually: 4 Print
Total Titles: 50 Print
Orders to: Brunswick Books, 20 Maud St, Suite 303, Toronto, ON M5V 2M5 *Tel:* 416-703-3598 *Fax:* 416-703-6561 *E-mail:* orders@brunswickbooks.ca
Returns: Brunswick Books, c/o TTS Distributing, 155 Edward St, Aurora, ON L4G 1W3
Distribution Center: Brunswick Books, 20 Maud St, Suite 303, Toronto, ON M5V 2M5 *Tel:* 416-703-3598 *Fax:* 416-703-6561 *E-mail:* orders@brunswickbooks.ca
Membership(s): Association of Canadian Publishers; Saskatchewan Publishers Group

§QA International (QAI)
Division of Groupe Quebec Amerique
329 De la Commune W, 3rd fl, Montreal, QC H2Y 2E1
Tel: 514-499-3000 *Fax:* 514-499-3010
Web Site: www.qa-international.com
Key Personnel
Founder & CEO: Jacques Fortin
Rts Dir, Editions Quebec Amerique: Rita Biscotti
Dir, Busn Devt: Rossana Sommaruga
Founded: 1989
Create, develop & produce editorial content built around state-of-the-art computer images for publication in print & electronic media throughout the world.
Publishes in French.
Number of titles published annually: 60 Print
Total Titles: 770 Print

Quattro Books Inc
Centre for Social Innovation, 2nd fl, 720 Bathurst St, Toronto, ON M5S 2R4
Mailing Address: Royal Orchard Postal Sta, 10 Royal Orchard Blvd, PO Box 53031, Thornhill, ON L3T 3C0
Tel: 647-748-7484
E-mail: info@quattrobooks.ca
Web Site: www.quattrobooks.ca

Key Personnel
VP & Publr: Allan Briesmaster *E-mail:* allan@quattrobooks.ca; Luciano Iacobelli *E-mail:* liacobelli1@yahoo.com
Asst Publr & Off Mgr: Kristen Blank
Publishes in English.
ISBN Prefix(es): 978-0-9782806; 978-0-9810186; 978-1-926802
Number of titles published annually: 16 Print; 16 E-Book
Imprints: Fourfront Editions

Quebec Dans Le Monde
335, rue Saint-Joseph E, bureau 600, Quebec, QC G1K 3B4
SAN: 116-8657
Tel: 418-659-5540 *Fax:* 418-659-4143
E-mail: info@quebecmonde.com
Web Site: www.quebecmonde.com
Key Personnel
Exec Dir: Helene Thibault
Founded: 1983
Databases, guides & reference books on Quebec at large.
Publishes in French.
ISBN Prefix(es): 978-2-9801130; 978-2-921309
Number of titles published annually: 7 Print
Total Titles: 21 Print; 15 E-Book
Distribution Center: Librairie du Quebec a Paris, 30 rue Gay Lussac, 75005 Paris, France *Tel:* 01 43 54 49 02

Reader's Digest Association Canada ULC (Selection du Reader's Digest Canada SRL)
1100 Rene Levesque Blvd W, Montreal, QC H3B 5H5
Tel: 514-940-0751 *Toll Free Tel:* 866-236-7789 (cust serv) *Fax:* 514-940-3637
E-mail: erdcustserv@cdsfulfillment.com
Web Site: www.readersdigest.ca
Founded: 1943
Mail order & retail books on cookery, crafts, games & hobbies, money management, gardening, geography & geology, health & nutrition, history, house & home, how-to, law, general medicine, nature & science, travel; dictionaries, atlases, encyclopedias; fiction & general nonfiction in condensed form.
Publishes in English, French.
ISBN Prefix(es): 978-0-89577; 978-0-88850; 978-0-276; 978-2-7098; 978-0-7621; 978-1-55475
Number of titles published annually: 100 Print
Total Titles: 450 Print
Warehouse: 300 Orenda Rd, Brampton, ON L6T 1G2

Red Deer Press Inc
Division of Fitzhenry & Whiteside Limited
195 Allstate Pkwy, Markham, ON L3R 4T8
Tel: 905-477-9700 *Toll Free Tel:* 800-387-9776 (orders) *Fax:* 905-477-2834 *Toll Free Fax:* 800-260-9777 (orders)
E-mail: rdp@reddeerpress.com; bookinfo@fitzhenry.ca
Web Site: www.reddeerpress.com
Key Personnel
Publr: Richard Dionne *Tel:* 800-387-9776 ext 248 *E-mail:* dionne@reddeerpress.com
Dir, Sales: Sonya Gilliss *Tel:* 800-387-9776 ext 250 *E-mail:* sonya.gilliss@fitzhenry.ca
Children's Ed: Peter Carver
Promos: Cheryl Chen *Tel:* 800-387-9776 ext 258 *E-mail:* cheryl.chen@fitzhenry.ca
Cust Serv: Judy Ghoura *Tel:* 800-387-9776 ext 225
Founded: 1975
Publishes in English, French.
ISBN Prefix(es): 978-0-88995
Number of titles published annually: 18 Print
Imprints: Northern Lights Books for Children; Robert J Sawyer Books

Orders to: Ingram Publisher Services, 1210 Ingram Dr, Chambersburg, PA 17202, United States *Toll Free Tel:* 866-400-5351 *Toll Free Fax:* 800-838-1149 *E-mail:* customerservice@ingrampublisherservices.com *Web Site:* www.ingrampublisherservices.com
Returns: Ingram Publisher Services, 1210 Ingram Dr, Chambersburg, PA 17202, United States *Toll Free Tel:* 866-400-5351 *Toll Free Fax:* 800-838-1149 *E-mail:* customerservice@ingrampublisherservices.com *Web Site:* www.ingrampublisherservices.com
Distribution Center: Ingram Publisher Services, 1210 Ingram Dr, Chambersburg, PA 17202, United States *Toll Free Tel:* 866-400-5351 *Toll Free Fax:* 800-838-1149 *E-mail:* customerservice@ingrampublisherservices.com *Web Site:* www.ingrampublisherservices.com
Membership(s): Book Publishers Association of Alberta; Literary Press Group of Canada

Rocky Mountain Books Ltd (RMB)
Member of The Heritage Group
103-1075 Pendergast St, Victoria, BC V8V 0A1
Tel: 250-360-0829 *Fax:* 250-386-0829
Web Site: www.rmbooks.com
Key Personnel
Publr, Publicity, Sales & Mktg: Don Gorman *E-mail:* don@rmbooks.com
Art Dir: Chyla Cardinal *E-mail:* chyla@rmbooks.com
Sr Ed: Joe Wilderson *E-mail:* joe@rmbooks.com
Founded: 1979
Regional publisher of books on outdoor activities, mountain literature & mountain biographies.
Publishes in English.
ISBN Prefix(es): 978-0-9690038; 978-0-921102; 978-1-894765; 978-1-897522; 978-1-926855; 978-1-927330; 978-1-77160
Number of titles published annually: 20 Print
Total Titles: 188 Print
Branch Office(s)
414 13 Ave, NE, Calgary, AB T2E 1C2 (design & edit) *Tel:* 403-271-3145 *Fax:* 403-249-2968
Sales Office(s): Heritage Group Distribution, 19272 96 Ave, Suite 8, Surrey, BC V4N 4C1 *Tel:* 604-881-7067 *Toll Free Tel:* 800-665-3302 *Fax:* 604-881-7068 *Toll Free Fax:* 800-566-3336 *Web Site:* www.hgdistribution.com
Billing Address: Heritage Group Distribution, 19272 96 Ave, Suite 8, Surrey, BC V4N 4C1 *Tel:* 604-881-7067 *Toll Free Tel:* 800-665-3302 *Fax:* 604-881-7068 *Toll Free Fax:* 800-566-3336 *Web Site:* www.hgdistribution.com
Orders to: Heritage Group Distribution, 19272 96 Ave, Suite 8, Surrey, BC V4N 4C1 *Tel:* 604-881-7067 *Toll Free Tel:* 800-665-3302 *Fax:* 604-881-7068 *Toll Free Fax:* 800-566-3336 *E-mail:* orders@hgdistribution.com *Web Site:* www.hgdistribution.com
Returns: Heritage Group Distribution, 19272 96 Ave, Suite 8, Surrey, BC V4N 4C1 *Tel:* 604-881-7067 *Toll Free Tel:* 800-665-3302 *Fax:* 604-881-7068 *Toll Free Fax:* 800-566-3336 *Web Site:* www.hgdistribution.com
Shipping Address: Heritage Group Distribution, 19272 96 Ave, Suite 8, Surrey, BC V4N 4C1 *Tel:* 604-881-7067 *Toll Free Tel:* 800-665-3302 *Fax:* 604-881-7068 *Toll Free Fax:* 800-566-3336 *Web Site:* www.hgdistribution.com
Warehouse: Heritage Group Distribution, 19272 96 Ave, Suite 8, Surrey, BC V4N 4C1 *Tel:* 604-881-7067 *Toll Free Tel:* 800-665-3302 *Fax:* 604-881-7068 *Toll Free Fax:* 800-566-3336 *Web Site:* www.hgdistribution.com
Distribution Center: Heritage Group Distribution, 19272 96 Ave, Suite 8, Surrey, BC V4N 4C1 *Tel:* 604-881-7067 *Toll Free Tel:* 800-665-3302 *Fax:* 604-881-7068 *Toll Free Fax:* 800-566-3336 *E-mail:* orders@hgdistribution.com *Web Site:* www.hgdistribution.com
Membership(s): Book Publishers Association of Alberta

Ronsdale Press Ltd
3350 W 21 Ave, Vancouver, BC V6S 1G7
SAN: 116-2454
Tel: 604-738-4688 *Fax:* 604-731-4548
E-mail: ronsdale@shaw.ca
Web Site: ronsdalepress.com
Key Personnel
Dir & Intl Rts: Ronald Hatch
Lib Sales Dir: Veronica Hatch
Founded: 1988
Literary press, children's, history, literary & regional. Specialize in Canadian authors.
Publishes in English.
ISBN Prefix(es): 978-0-921870; 978-1-55380
Number of titles published annually: 12 Print; 12 E-Book
Total Titles: 230 Print
Distribution Center: LitDistCo, 100 Armstrong Ave, Georgetown, ON L7G 5S4 *Toll Free Tel:* 800-591-6250 *Toll Free Fax:* 800-591-6251 *Web Site:* www.litdistco.ca
Raincoast Books, 2440 Viking Way, Richmond, BC V6V 1N2 *Toll Free Tel:* 800-663-5714 *Toll Free Fax:* 800-565-3770 *E-mail:* customerservice@raincoast.com *Web Site:* www.raincoast.com
Small Press Distribution, 1341 Seventh St, Berkeley, CA 94710-1409, United States *Tel:* 510-524-1668 *Toll Free Tel:* 800-869-7553 *Fax:* 510-524-0852 *E-mail:* spd@spdbooks.org *Web Site:* www.spdbooks.org
Baker & Taylor, 2550 W Tyvola Rd, Suite 300, Charlotte, NC 28217, United States *Tel:* 704-998-3100 *Toll Free Tel:* 800-775-1800 *E-mail:* btinfo@baker-taylor.com *Web Site:* www.btol.com
Ingram Content Group, One Ingram Blvd, La Vergne, TN 37086, United States *Tel:* 615-793-5000 *E-mail:* inquiry@ingramcontent.com *Web Site:* www.ingramcontent.com
Gazelle Book Services, White Cross Mills, Hightown, Lancaster, Lancs LA1 4XS, United Kingdom (UK & Europe) *Tel:* (01524) 68765 *Web Site:* www.gazellebookservices.co.uk
Membership(s): Association of Book Publishers of British Columbia; Association of Canadian Publishers; Literary Press Group

Robert Rose Inc
120 Eglinton Ave E, Suite 800, Toronto, ON M4P 1E2
Tel: 416-322-6552 *Fax:* 416-322-6936
Web Site: www.robertrose.ca
Founded: 1995
Publishes in English.
ISBN Prefix(es): 978-1-896503; 978-0-7788
Number of titles published annually: 25 Print
Total Titles: 250 Print
Distributed by Firefly Books Ltd

Royal Ontario Museum Press
100 Queen's Park, Toronto, ON M5S 2C6
Tel: 416-586-8000 *Fax:* 416-586-5642
E-mail: info@rom.on.ca
Web Site: www.rom.on.ca
Key Personnel
Lead Concierge: Corey Dahl
Founded: 1912
Scholarly & general books on art, archaeology & sciences.
Publishes in English, French.
ISBN Prefix(es): 978-0-88854
Number of titles published annually: 8 Print
Total Titles: 100 Print
U.S. Rep(s): University of Toronto Press (NY)
Warehouse: University of Toronto Press, 5201 Dufferin St, Toronto, ON M3H 5T8, Contact: Carol Trainor *Tel:* 416-667-7791 *Toll Free Tel:* 800-565-9523 *Fax:* 416-667-7832 *E-mail:* utpbooks@utpress.utoronto.ca *Web Site:* www.utpress.utoronto.ca
Distribution Center: University of Toronto Press, 5201 Dufferin St, Toronto, ON M3H 5T8, Con-

tact: Carol Trainor *Tel:* 416-667-7791 *Toll Free Tel:* 800-565-9523 *Fax:* 416-667-7832 *E-mail:* utpbooks@utpress.utoronto.ca *Web Site:* www.utpress.utoronto.ca

Guy Saint-Jean Editeur Inc
3440 Blvd Industriel, Laval, QC H7L 4R9
Tel: 450-663-1777 *Fax:* 450-663-6666
E-mail: info@saint-jeanediteur.com
Web Site: www.saint-jeanediteur.com
Key Personnel
Owner: Nicole Saint-Jean
VP, Publg: Marie-Claire Saint-Jean
VP, Opers: Jacques Frechette
Founded: 1981
Publishes in English, French.
ISBN Prefix(es): 978-2-920340; 978-2-89455
Number of titles published annually: 30 Print; 10 E-Book
Total Titles: 550 Print
Imprints: Green Frog Publishing
Foreign Office(s): Saint-Jean Editeur (France), 30-32 rue de Lappe, 75011 Paris, France, Contact: Christian Richard *Tel:* 01 39 76 99 43 *Fax:* 01 39 76 21 78 *E-mail:* gsj.editeur@free.fr
U.S. Publishers Represented: CDS
Foreign Rep(s): Int Press (Australia, New Zealand); Christian Richard (Europe)
Foreign Rights: Elizabeth Brayne (Europe)
Membership(s): Association Nationale des Editeurs de Livres

Sara Jordan Publishing
Division of Jordan Music Productions Inc
RPO Lakeport Box 28105, St Catharines, ON L2N 7P8
Tel: 905-938-5050 *Toll Free Tel:* 800-567-7733 *Fax:* 905-938-9970 *Toll Free Fax:* 800-229-3855
Web Site: www.sara-jordan.com
Key Personnel
Pres: Sara Jordan
Founded: 1990
Publish educational resources.
Publishes in English, French.
ISBN Prefix(es): 978-1-895523; 978-1-894262; 978-1-55386
Number of titles published annually: 6 Print; 2 Audio
Total Titles: 100 Print; 60 Audio
Distribution Center: Gazelle Book Services Ltd, White Cross Mills, Lancaster, Lancs LA1 4XS, United Kingdom *Tel:* (01524) 68765 *Fax:* (01524) 63232 *E-mail:* sales@gazellebooks.co.uk *Web Site:* www.gazellebookservices.co.uk
Membership(s): Association of Canadian Publishers

Scholastic Canada Ltd
Subsidiary of Scholastic Inc
604 King St W, Toronto, ON M5V 1E1
SAN: 115-5164
Tel: 905-887-7323 *Toll Free Tel:* 800-268-3860 (CN) *Toll Free Fax:* 866-387-4944
E-mail: custserve@scholastic.ca
Web Site: www.scholastic.ca
Key Personnel
Pres: Linda Gosnell; Iole Lucchese
VP, Publg: Diane Kerner
VP, Mktg: Nancy Pearson *Tel:* 905-887-7323 ext 3515
VP, French Mktg & Publg: Chantale LaLonde
VP, Educ: Wendy Graham
VP, Book Fairs: Brigitte Birtch
Sr Dir, Trade: Kathy Goncharenko
Rts/Perms Mgr: Maral Maclagan *E-mail:* mmaclagan@scholastic.ca
Founded: 1957
Publish & distribute children's books & educational materials in both official languages.
Publishes in English, French.
ISBN Prefix(es): 978-0-590; 978-0-439; 978-0-7791; 978-1-55268; 978-0-545; 978-1-4431
Imprints: Les Editions Scholastic; North Winds Press; Scholastic Canada
Divisions: Scholastic Book Fairs Canada Inc
Branch Office(s)
175 Hillmount Rd, Markham, ON L6C 1Z7
Distributor for Blue Sky Press (exclusive in CN); Cartwheel Books (exclusive in CN); Chicken House (exclusive in CN); Children's Press (exclusive in CN); Franklin Watts (US) (exclusive in CN); Grolier (exclusive in CN); Klutz (exclusive in CN); Arthur A Levine Books (exclusive in CN); Orchard Books (exclusive in CN); Scholastic en Espanol (exclusive in CN); Scholastic Graphix (exclusive in CN); Scholastic Nonfiction (exclusive in CN); Scholastic Paperbacks (exclusive in CN); Scholastic Press (exclusive in CN); Scholastic Reference (exclusive in CN)
U.S. Publishers Represented: Scholastic Inc
U.S. Rep(s): Scholastic Inc
Foreign Rights: Akcali Copyright Agency (Bengu Ayfer) (Turkey); Bardon Chinese Media Agency (Electra Chang & Shirley Viva Chang) (Mainland China); Bardon Chinese Media Agency (Cynthia Chang) (Taiwan); Marcin Biegaj (Poland); Sandra Bruna Agencia Literaria (Sandra Bruna) (Spain); JLM Literary Agency (Nelly, Tatiana & John Moukakos) (Greece); Simona Kessler Agency (Adriana Marina) (Romania); Maxima Creative Agency (Santo Manurung) (Indonesia); Nika Literary Agency (Vania Kadiyska) (Bulgaria); Karin Schindler Literary Agency (Brazil); Seibel Publishing Services Ltd (Patricia Seibel) (Brazil); Shinwon Agency Co (Yona Kang) (Korea); Tuttle-Mori Agency Inc (Solan Natsume) (Japan); Tuttle-Mori Agency Inc (Pimolporn Yutisri) (Thailand)

Seal Books
Imprint of Penguin Random House Canada Limited
One Toronto St, Suite 300, Toronto, ON M5C 2V6
SAN: 201-3975
Tel: 416-364-4449 *Toll Free Tel:* 888-523-9292 (order desk) *Fax:* 416-364-6863
Web Site: www.randomhouse.ca
Key Personnel
CEO & Pres: Brad Martin
CFO & EVP: Doug Foot
Pres & Publr, RHC: Kristin Cochrane
EVP & Dir, Sales: Duncan Shields
SVP & Dir, Mktg & Corp Communs: Tracey Turriff
VP & Dir, Mktg Strategy & Assoc Publr, RHC: Scott Sellers
VP & Dir, Prodn: Janine Laporte
Assoc Dir, Prodn: Carla Kean
Founded: 1977
No unsol mss; prefer queries in advance from potential authors.
Publishes in English.
ISBN Prefix(es): 978-0-7704
Number of titles published annually: 18 Print
Membership(s): Canadian Booksellers Association; Canadian Library Association; Canadian Publishers' Council

Second Story Press
20 Maud St, Suite 401, Toronto, ON M5V 2M5
Tel: 416-537-7850 *Fax:* 416-537-0588
E-mail: info@secondstorypress.ca
Web Site: secondstorypress.ca
Key Personnel
Publr, Owner & Pres: Margie Wolfe
Gen Mgr: Phuong Truong
Prodn Mgr: Melissa Kaita
Mng Ed: Carolyn Jackson; Katherine Cole
Mktg & Promos Mgr: Emma Rodgers
Mktg & Promos Coord: Allie Chenoweth
Publicity & Mktg Coord: Michelle Melski
Founded: 1988
Feminist-inspired books for adults & young readers.
Publishes in English.
ISBN Prefix(es): 978-0-929005; 978-1-896764; 978-1-897187; 978-0-921299
Number of titles published annually: 14 Print
Total Titles: 108 Print
Distributor for The Azrieli Foundation; The Book Publishing Co; Desputeaux & Aubin (aka The Caillou Books) (English-speaking CN)
U.S. Rep(s): Orca Books (children's books)
Orders to: University of Toronto Press, 5201 Dufferin St, North York, ON M3H 5T8 *Tel:* 416-667-7791 *Toll Free Tel:* 800-565-9523 *Fax:* 416-667-7832 *Toll Free Fax:* 800-221-9985; Orca Book Publishers, PO Box 468, Custer, WA 98240-0468, United States (US-children's books) *Toll Free Tel:* 800-210-5277 *Fax:* 250-380-1892 *Web Site:* www.us.orcabook.com; CSH Educational Resources, 10 Ubi Crescent, Ubi Techpark Lobby B, No 03-21, Singapore 408564, Singapore *Web Site:* www.csh.com.sg; Everybody's Books, PO Box 201321, Durban N 4016, South Africa *Tel:* (031) 569 2229; (031) 569 2249 *Fax:* (031) 569 2234 *Web Site:* www.ebbooks.co.za; Gazelle, White Cross Mills, Lancaster, Lancs LA1 4XS, United Kingdom *Tel:* (01524) 68765 *Fax:* (01524) 63232 *E-mail:* sales@gazellebooks.co.uk *Web Site:* www.gazellebooks.co.uk
Shipping Address: University of Toronto Press, 5201 Dufferin St, North York, ON M3H 5T8 *Tel:* 416-667-7791 *Toll Free Tel:* 800-565-9523 *Fax:* 416-667-7832 *Toll Free Fax:* 800-221-9985
Distribution Center: University of Toronto Press, 5201 Dufferin St, North York, ON M3H 5T8 *Tel:* 416-667-7791 *Toll Free Tel:* 800-565-9523 *Fax:* 416-667-7832 *Toll Free Fax:* 800-221-9985

Selection du Reader's Digest Canada SRL, see Reader's Digest Association Canada ULC (Selection du Reader's Digest Canada SRL)

J Gordon Shillingford Publishing Inc
PO Box 86, RPO Corydon Ave, Winnipeg, MB R3M 3S3
Tel: 204-779-6967
Web Site: www.jgshillingford.com
Key Personnel
Pres & Publr: Gordon Shillingford
Founded: 1992
Primarily a literary publisher (drama & poetry), but also 3-4 nonfiction titles per year. Publish works of Canadian citizens only.
Publishes in English.
ISBN Prefix(es): 978-0-9689709; 978-0-920486; 978-1-896239; 978-0-9697261; 978-1-897289; 978-1-927922
Number of titles published annually: 12 Print
Total Titles: 272 Print
Sales Office(s): Canadian Manda Group, 165 Dufferin St, Toronto, ON M6K 3H6 *Tel:* 416-516-0911 *Fax:* 416-516-0917 *E-mail:* info@mandagroup.com *Web Site:* www.mandagroup.com
The Literary Press Group of Canada, 425 Adelaide St W, Suite 700, Toronto, ON M5V 2C1 (US Rep), Contact: Tan Light *Tel:* 416-483-1321 ext 3 *Fax:* 416-483-2510 *E-mail:* sales@lpg.ca
Distribution Center: University of Toronto Press, 5210 Dufferin St, Toronto, ON M3H 5T8 (CN) *Tel:* 416-667-7791 *Toll Free Tel:* 800-565-9523 *Toll Free Fax:* 800-221-9985 *E-mail:* utpbooks@utpres.utoronto.ca
University of Toronto Press, 2250 Military Rd, Tonowanda, NY 14150, United States (US) *Tel:* 416-667-7791 *Toll Free Tel:* 800-565-9523

Fax: 416-667-7832 *Toll Free Fax:* 800-221-9985 *E-mail:* utpbooks@utoronto.ca
Membership(s): Association of Canadian Publishers; Association of Manitoba Book Publishers; Literary Press Group

Shoreline Press
23 Ste-Anne, Ste-Anne-de-Bellevue, QC H9X 1L1
SAN: 116-9564
Tel: 514-457-5733
E-mail: info@shorelinepress.ca
Web Site: shorelinepress.ca
Key Personnel
Sr Ed: Judith Isherwood
Founded: 1991
Publishes in English, French.
ISBN Prefix(es): 978-0-9695180; 978-0-9698752; 978-1-896754
Number of titles published annually: 5 Print; 4 E-Book
Total Titles: 125 Print; 4 E-Book
Orders to: Coutts Information Services Ltd, 6900 Kinsman Ct, Niagara Falls, ON L2E 7E7 *Tel:* 905-356-6382; Baker & Taylor, 2550 W Tyvola Rd, Suite 300, Charlotte, NC 28217, United States *Tel:* 704-998-3100 *Toll Free Tel:* 800-775-1800 *Web Site:* www.btol.com
Distribution Center: Coutts Information Services Ltd, 6900 Kinsman Ct, Niagara Falls, ON L2E 7E7 *Tel:* 905-356-6382
Baker & Taylor, 2550 W Tyvola Rd, Suite 300, Charlotte, NC 28217, United States *Tel:* 704-998-3100 *Toll Free Tel:* 800-775-1800 *Web Site:* www.btol.com
Membership(s): Association of English-language Publishers of Quebec; Quebec Library Association

Signature Editions
RPO Corydon, PO Box 206, Winnipeg, MB R3M 3S7
Tel: 204-779-7803 *Fax:* 204-779-6970
E-mail: signature@allstream.net; orders@signature-editions.com
Web Site: www.signature-editions.com
Key Personnel
Publr: Karen Haughian
Drama Ed: Kit Brennan
Mystery Ed: Doug Whiteway
Founded: 1986 (as Nuage Editions)
Literary publisher which publishes Canadian authors in the genres of fiction, nonfiction, poetry & drama.
Publishes in English.
ISBN Prefix(es): 978-0-921833; 978-1-897109; 978-1-927426
Number of titles published annually: 9 Print
Total Titles: 116 Print; 10 Audio
Distributor for Cyclops Press
Foreign Rep(s): The Literary Press Group of Canada (Tan Light) (USA)
Orders to: University of Toronto Press (UTP), 5201 Dufferin St, North York, ON M3H 5T8 *Tel:* 416-667-7791 *Toll Free Tel:* 800-565-9523 *Fax:* 416-667-7832 *Toll Free Fax:* 800-221-9985 *E-mail:* utpbooks@utpress.utoronto.ca; University of Toronto Press (UTP), 2250 Military Rd, Tonawanda, NY 14150, United States *Tel:* 416-667-7791 *Toll Free Tel:* 800-565-9523 *Fax:* 416-667-7832 *Toll Free Fax:* 800-221-9985 *E-mail:* utpbooks@utpress.utoronto.ca
Returns: University of Toronto Press (UTP), 5201 Dufferin St, North York, ON M3H 5T8 *Tel:* 416-667-7791 *Toll Free Tel:* 800-565-9523 *Fax:* 416-667-7832 *Toll Free Fax:* 800-221-9985 *E-mail:* utpbooks@utpress.utoronto.ca
Shipping Address: University of Toronto Press (UTP), 5201 Dufferin St, North York, ON M3H 5T8 *Tel:* 416-667-7791 *Toll Free Tel:* 800-565-9523 *Fax:* 416-667-7832 *Toll Free Fax:* 800-221-9985 *E-mail:* utpbooks@utpress.utoronto.ca
Distribution Center: University of Toronto Press (UTP), 5201 Dufferin St, North York, ON M3H 5T8 *Tel:* 416-667-7791 *Toll Free Tel:* 800-565-9523 *Fax:* 416-667-7832 *Toll Free Fax:* 800-221-9985 *E-mail:* utpbooks@utpress.utoronto.ca
University of Toronto Press (UTP), 2250 Military Rd, Tonawanda, NY 14150, United States *Tel:* 416-667-7791 *Toll Free Tel:* 800-565-9523 *Fax:* 416-667-7832 *Toll Free Fax:* 800-221-9985 *E-mail:* utpbooks@utpress.utoronto.ca
Membership(s): Association of Canadian Publishers; Association of Manitoba Book Publishers; Literary Press Group of Canada

Simon & Pierre Publishing Co Ltd
Imprint of The Dundurn Group
3 Church St, Suite 500, Toronto, ON M5E 1M2
Tel: 416-214-5544 *Fax:* 416-214-5556
E-mail: info@dundurn.com
Web Site: www.dundurn.com
Key Personnel
Pres & Publr: J Kirk Howard *E-mail:* khoward@dundurn.com
Founded: 1991
Fiction.
Publishes in English.
ISBN Prefix(es): 978-0-9690454; 978-0-88924
Number of titles published annually: 80 Print
Total Titles: 133 Print
Distributed by Dundurn Press
Distribution Center: University of Toronto Press, 5201 Dufferin St, Toronto, ON M3H 5T8 *Tel:* 416-667-7791 *Toll Free Tel:* 800-565-9523 *Toll Free Fax:* 800-221-9985 *E-mail:* utpbooks@utpress.utoronto.ca *Web Site:* www.utpress.utoronto.ca
Ingram Content Group, One Ingram Blvd, La Vergne, TN 37086, United States *Tel:* 615-793-5000 *Toll Free Tel:* 866-400-5351 *E-mail:* customerservice@ingrampublisherservices.com *Web Site:* www.ingramcontent.com
Gazelle Book Services, White Cross Mills, High Town, Lancaster, Lancs LA1 4XS, United Kingdom (UK & Europe) *Tel:* (01524) 68765 *Fax:* (01524) 63232 *E-mail:* sales@gazellebooks.co.uk

§Simon & Schuster Canada
Subsidiary of Simon & Schuster, Inc
166 King St E, Suite 300, Toronto, ON M5A 1J3
Tel: 647-427-8882 *Toll Free Tel:* 800-387-0446; 800-268-3216 (orders) *Fax:* 647-430-9446 *Toll Free Fax:* 888-849-8151 (orders)
E-mail: info@simonandschuster.ca
Web Site: www.simonandschuster.ca
Key Personnel
Pres & Publr: Kevin Hanson *E-mail:* kevin.hanson@simonandschuster.ca
VP, Sales & Mktg: David Millar *E-mail:* david.millar@simonandschuster.ca
VP, Sales: Nancy Purcell *E-mail:* nancy.purcell@simonandschuster.ca
VP, Mktg & Publicity: Felicia Quon *E-mail:* felicia.quon@simonandschuster.ca
Dir, Busn Aff: Kien Vuong *E-mail:* kien.vuong@simonandschuster.ca
Dir, Publicity: Amy Cormier *E-mail:* amy.cormier@simonandschuster.ca
Edit Dir: Nita Pronovost *E-mail:* nita.pronovost@simonandschuster.ca
Mng Ed: Patricia Ocampo *E-mail:* patricia.ocampo@simonandschuster.ca
Assoc Ed: Brendan May *E-mail:* brendan.may@simonandschuster.ca
Publishes in English.
Distributor for Andrews McMeel Publishing LLC; Baen Books; Baseball America; Black Library; Blue Heeler Books; Cardoza; Chicken Soup for the Soul; Cider Mill Press Book Publishers LLC; Downtown Books; Games Workshop; Good Books; Hooked on Phonics; Kaplan Publishing; KinFolk; John Locke Publishing; Merck; Open Road Press; Rebellion; Ripley's Publishing; Simon & Schuster; Viz; Weldon Owen Inc; World Almanac

Simply Read Books
501-5525 West Blvd, Vancouver, BC V6M 3W6
Tel: 604-727-2960
E-mail: go@simplyreadbooks.com
Web Site: www.simplyreadbooks.com
Founded: 2001
Our approach to illustrated children's books follows the finest publishing tradition & spirit with inspired content, extraordinary artwork, outstanding graphic design form & quality production. We introduce contemporary books with a modern appeal & fresh outlook & offer a careful selection of timeless stories that link the past with the present. We specialize in high-quality, unique picture books & fiction. Before submitting, please browse our web site, bookstores & libraries to look at & read what we publish. This will give you an idea of whether or not your story or illustrations would fit with our list.
Publishes in English, French.
ISBN Prefix(es): 978-1-894965; 978-0-9688768; 978-1-897476; 978-1-927018
Number of titles published annually: 25 Print
Total Titles: 150 Print
Sales Office(s): Ingram Content Group, One Ingram Blvd, La Vergne, TN 37086, United States *Tel:* 615-793-5000 *E-mail:* inquiry@ingramcontent.com *Web Site:* www.ingramcontent.com
Orders to: Ingram Content Group, One Ingram Blvd, La Vergne, TN 37086, United States *Tel:* 615-793-5000 *E-mail:* inquiry@ingramcontent.com *Web Site:* www.ingramcontent.com
Returns: Publisher Services, 1210 Ingram Dr, Chambersburg, PA 17202, United States *Tel:* 717-262-4860 *E-mail:* customerservice@ingrampublisherservices.com
Warehouse: Ingram Content Group, One Ingram Blvd, La Vergne, TN 37086, United States *Tel:* 615-793-5000 *E-mail:* inquiry@ingramcontent.com *Web Site:* www.ingramcontent.com
Distribution Center: Ingram Content Group, One Ingram Blvd, La Vergne, TN 37086, United States *Tel:* 615-793-5000 *E-mail:* inquiry@ingramcontent.com *Web Site:* www.ingramcontent.com
Membership(s): Association for Canadian Publishers in the US; The Independent Book Publishers Association

Gordon Soules Book Publishers Ltd
1359 Amble Side Lane, West Vancouver, BC V7T 2Y9
SAN: 115-0987
Tel: 604-922-6588 *Fax:* 604-922-6574
E-mail: books@gordonsoules.com
Web Site: www.gordonsoules.com
Key Personnel
Pres: Gordon Soules
Founded: 1965
Publishers & distributors of high quality trade books.
Publishes in English.
ISBN Prefix(es): 978-0-919574; 978-1-894661; 978-0-920045
Number of titles published annually: 4 Print
Total Titles: 65 Print

Sport Books Publisher
212 Robert St (side basement door), Toronto, ON M5S 2K7
Tel: 416-323-9438 *Fax:* 416-966-9022
E-mail: sbp@sportbookspub.com; kbp@sportbookspub.com
Web Site: www.sportbookspub.com

Key Personnel
Pres: Dr Peter Klavora *E-mail:* peter.klavora@utoronto.ca
Exec Dir: Tania Klavora
Founded: 1983
Activity books, sports books & DVDs; subjects include physical education, exercise science textbooks & kinesiology. Orders accepted by mail, fax or online. Returns accepted if in mint condition.
Publishes in English, French.
ISBN Prefix(es): 978-0-920905
Number of titles published annually: 5 Print; 1 CD-ROM
Total Titles: 48 Print; 3 CD-ROM
Branch Office(s)
PO Box 2583, Niagara Falls, NY 14302, United States

Statistics Canada
Subsidiary of Canadian Government
150 Tunney's Pasture Driveway, Ottawa, ON K1A 0T6
Tel: 514-283-8300 *Toll Free Tel:* 800-263-1136 (CN & US, gen inquiries); 800-267-6677 (prods & servs) *Toll Free Fax:* 877-287-4369 (orders)
E-mail: infostats@statcan.gc.ca
Web Site: statcan.gc.ca
Key Personnel
Dir Gen: Claude Graziadie *Tel:* 613-951-6128 *Fax:* 613-951-0411
Founded: 1919
Federal government's principal data collection agency in Canada. Collects, analyzes & publishes statistical information on Canada's population, labor force, economy, education, housing, transportation & social cultural life.
Publishes in English, French.
ISBN Prefix(es): 978-0-660
Number of titles published annually: 60 Print
Total Titles: 300 Print; 1,013 CD-ROM; 1,764 Online
Returns: Distribution Ctr, Main Bldg, Rm 0505, Ottawa, ON K1A 0T6

Sumach Press
Imprint of Three O'Clock Press
425 Adelaide St W, Suite 200, Toronto, ON M5V 3C1
Tel: 416-929-2964 *Fax:* 416-929-1926
E-mail: info@threeoclockpress.com
Web Site: www.threeoclockpress.com
Key Personnel
Publr: Sarah Wayne
Founded: 2000
Presents writings by & about women.
Publishes in English.
ISBN Prefix(es): 978-1-894549; 978-1-927513
Number of titles published annually: 4 Print
Total Titles: 95 Print
Sales Office(s): LitDistCo, 100 Armstrong Ave, Georgetown, ON L7G 5S4 *Toll Free Tel:* 800-591-6250 *Toll Free Fax:* 800-591-6251 *E-mail:* ordering@litdistco.ca
Orca Book Publishers, PO Box 468, Custer, WA 98240-0468, United States *Toll Free Tel:* 800-210-5277 *Toll Free Fax:* 877-408-1551 *E-mail:* orca@orcabook.com *Web Site:* www.orcabook.com
Distributed by Orca Book Publishers (young adult titles in US)
Billing Address: LitDistCo, 100 Armstrong Ave, Georgetown, ON L7G 5S4 *Toll Free Tel:* 800-591-6250 *Toll Free Fax:* 800-591-6251; Orca Book Publishers, PO Box 468, Custer, WA 98240-0468, United States *Toll Free Tel:* 800-210-5277 *Toll Free Fax:* 877-408-1551 *E-mail:* orca@orcabook.com *Web Site:* www.orcabook.com
Orders to: LitDistCo, 100 Armstrong Ave, Georgetown, ON L7G 5S4 *Toll Free Tel:* 800-591-6250 *Toll Free Fax:* 800-591-6251 *E-mail:* ordering@litdistco.ca; Orca Book Publishers, PO Box 468, Custer, WA 98240-0468, United States *Toll Free Tel:* 800-210-5277 *Toll Free Fax:* 877-408-1551 *E-mail:* orca@orcabook.com *Web Site:* www.orcabook.com; Gazelle Book Services Ltd, White Cross Mills, Hightown, Lancaster LA1 4XS, United Kingdom *Tel:* (01524) 68765 *Fax:* (01524) 63232 *E-mail:* sales@gazellebooks.co.uk
Returns: LitDistCo, 100 Armstrong Ave, Georgetown, ON L7G 5S4 *Toll Free Tel:* 800-591-6250 *Toll Free Fax:* 800-591-6251; Orca Book Publishers, PO Box 468, Custer, WA 98240-0468, United States *Toll Free Tel:* 800-210-5277 *Toll Free Fax:* 877-408-1551 *E-mail:* orca@orcabook.com *Web Site:* www.orcabook.com
Shipping Address: LitDistCo, 100 Armstrong Ave, Georgetown, ON L7G 5S4 *Toll Free Tel:* 800-591-6250 *Toll Free Fax:* 800-591-6251 *E-mail:* ordering@litdistco.ca; Orca Book Publishers, PO Box 468, Custer, WA 98240-0468, United States *Toll Free Tel:* 800-210-5277 *Toll Free Fax:* 877-408-1551 *E-mail:* orca@orcabook.com *Web Site:* www.orcabook.com
Warehouse: LitDistCo, 100 Armstrong Ave, Georgetown, ON L7G 5S4 *Toll Free Tel:* 800-591-6250 *Toll Free Fax:* 800-591-6251 *E-mail:* ordering@litdistco.ca
Orca Book Publishers, PO Box 468, Custer, WA 98240-0468, United States *Toll Free Tel:* 800-210-5277 *Toll Free Fax:* 877-408-1551 *E-mail:* orca@orcabook.com *Web Site:* www.orcabook.com
Distribution Center: LitDistCo, 100 Armstrong Ave, Georgetown, ON L7G 5S4 *Toll Free Tel:* 800-591-6250 *Toll Free Fax:* 800-591-6251 *E-mail:* ordering@litdistco.ca
Orca Book Publishers, PO Box 468, Custer, WA 98240-0468, United States *Toll Free Tel:* 800-210-5277 *Toll Free Fax:* 877-408-1551 *E-mail:* orca@orcabook.com *Web Site:* www.orcabook.com
Membership(s): Association of Canadian Publishers; Organization of Book Publishers of Ontario

Summerthought Publishing
PO Box 2309, Banff, AB T1L 1C1
Tel: 403-762-0535 *Fax:* 403-762-3095 *Toll Free Fax:* 800-762-3095 (orders)
E-mail: info@summerthought.com; sales@summerthought.com
Web Site: summerthought.com
Key Personnel
Co-Owner & Publr: Andrew Hempstead
Sales, Mktg & Opers: Dianne Melton *E-mail:* dianne@summerthought.com
Founded: 1971
Publisher of Canadian Rockies nonfiction books.
Publishes in English.
ISBN Prefix(es): 978-0-9782375; 978-0-9699732; 978-0-9811491; 978-0-919934; 978-1-926983
Number of titles published annually: 3 Print
Total Titles: 20 Print
Imprints: EJH Literary Enterprises
Foreign Rep(s): Cordee (UK); Freytag & Berndt (Europe); Partners West (USA)
Warehouse: 536 Deer St, Banff, AB T1L 1C1

Synaxis Press
37323 Hawkins Rd, Dewdney, BC V0M 1H0
Tel: 604-826-9336
E-mail: synaxis@new-ostrog.org
Web Site: synaxispress.ca
Key Personnel
Illus: Vasili Novakshonoff
Ed: Archbishop Lazar Puhalo
Founded: 1972
Theology for the Orthodox church & children's books.
Publishes in English, French.
ISBN Prefix(es): 978-0-919672
Number of titles published annually: 6 Print
Total Titles: 90 Print
Distributed by Light & Life Publishing Co

TCP Press
Imprint of The Communication Project
Legacy Ctr, 9 Lobraico Lane, Whitchurch-Stouffville, ON L4A 7X5
Tel: 905-640-8914 *Toll Free Tel:* 800-772-7765
E-mail: tcp@tcpnow.com
Web Site: www.tcppress.com
Key Personnel
Dir, Publg: Brian Puppa
Founded: 1984
Trade & educational books for both children & adults.
Publishes in English, French.
ISBN Prefix(es): 978-1-896232
Number of titles published annually: 4 Print; 1 CD-ROM; 5 E-Book; 1 Audio
Total Titles: 26 Print; 3 CD-ROM; 6 E-Book; 3 Audio
Membership(s): Independent Publishers Association

Tecumseh Press, see Borealis Press Ltd

Theytus Books Ltd
Subsidiary of Okanagan Indian Educational Resources Society
RR 2, Green Mountain Rd, Site 50, Comp 8, Lot 45, Penticton, BC V2A 6J7
SAN: 115-1517
Tel: 250-493-7181 *Fax:* 250-493-5302
E-mail: order@theytus.com
Web Site: www.theytus.com
Key Personnel
Publr: Paul Seesequasis *Tel:* 250-493-7181 ext 2233
Founded: 1980
Native history, culture, politics, education & literature.
Publishes in English, French.
ISBN Prefix(es): 978-0-919441; 978-1-894778
Number of titles published annually: 8 Print; 2 CD-ROM
Total Titles: 76 Print; 3 CD-ROM
Distribution Center: Sandhill Book Marketing, Mill Crook Industrial Park, Unit 4, 3308 Appaloosa Rd, Kelowna, BC V1V 2G9 (AB & BC), Contact: Nancy Wise *Tel:* 250-491-1446 *Toll Free Tel:* 800-667-3848 *Fax:* 250-491-4066 *E-mail:* info@sandhillbooks.com
University of Toronto Press, 5201 Dufferin St, North York, ON M3H 5T8 (CN exc AB & BC) *Tel:* 416-667-7791 *Toll Free Tel:* 800-565-9523 *Fax:* 416-667-7832 *Web Site:* www.utpress.utoronto.ca
University of Toronto Press, 2250 Military Rd, Tonawanda, NY 14150, United States *Tel:* 416-667-7791 *Toll Free Tel:* 800-565-9523 *Fax:* 416-667-7832 *Toll Free Fax:* 800-221-9985 *E-mail:* utpbooks@utpress.utoronto.ca *Web Site:* www.utpress.utoronto.ca
Membership(s): Association of Canadian Publishers

Thistledown Press
410 Second Ave, Saskatoon, SK S7N 2C3
SAN: 115-1061
Tel: 306-244-1722 *Fax:* 306-244-1762
E-mail: tdpress@thistledownpress.com; editorial@thistledownpress.com; marketing@thistledownpress.com
Web Site: www.thistledownpress.com
Key Personnel
Owner & Publr: Allan Forrie
Publg & Prodn Mgr: Jackie Forrie
In-House Sales & Fulfillment, Awards & Inventory Control: Michelle Daly
Founded: 1975
Poetry, fiction & nonfiction by Canadian authors; Irish poetry; fiction for young adults.

Publishes in English.
ISBN Prefix(es): 978-0-920066; 978-0-920633; 978-1-895449; 978-1-894345; 978-1-897235
Number of titles published annually: 14 Print
Total Titles: 250 Print
U.S. Rep(s): Amazon.com; University of Toronto Press
Distribution Center: University of Toronto Press Distribution, 5201 Dufferin St, Toronto, ON M3H 5T8 *Tel:* 416-667-7791 *Toll Free Tel:* 800-565-9523 (CN & US) *Fax:* 416-667-7832 *Toll Free Fax:* 800-221-9985 (CN & US) *E-mail:* utpbooks@utpress.utoronto.ca *Web Site:* www.utpress.utoronto.ca

Thompson Educational Publishing Inc
20 Ripley Ave, Toronto, ON M6S 3N9
Tel: 416-766-2763 (admin & orders) *Toll Free Tel:* 877-366-2763 *Fax:* 416-766-0398 (admin & orders)
E-mail: info@thompsonbooks.com
Web Site: www.thompsonbooks.com
Key Personnel
Pres: Keith Thompson
VP: Faye Thompson
Busn Dir: Peter Thompson; Rowan Thompson
Edit & Prodn Mgr: Katy Bartlett
Educ Consultant, Health & Physical Educ: Ted Temertzoglou
Cust Serv: Janet Yap
Founded: 1987
High school, college & university textbooks.
Publishes in English.
ISBN Prefix(es): 978-1-55077; 978-0-921332
Number of titles published annually: 6 Print
Total Titles: 90 Print
Distribution Center: University of Toronto Press Distribution, 5201 Dufferin St, Toronto, ON M3H 5T8 (CN orders-higher educ) *Toll Free Tel:* 800-565-9523 *Toll Free Fax:* 800-221-9985 *E-mail:* utpbooks@utpress.utoronto.ca
University of Toronto Press Distribution, 2250 Military Rd, Tonawanda, NY 14150, United States (US orders-higher educ) *Toll Free Tel:* 800-565-9523 *Toll Free Fax:* 800-221-9985 *E-mail:* utpbooks@utpress.utoronto.ca
Membership(s): Association of Canadian Publishers; Ontario Business Educator's Association; Organization of Book Publishers of Ontario

TouchWood Editions
Member of The Heritage Group
103-1075 Pendergast St, Victoria, BC V8V 0A1
Tel: 250-360-0829 *Fax:* 250-386-0829
E-mail: info@touchwoodeditions.com
Web Site: www.touchwoodeditions.com
Key Personnel
Assoc Publr: Taryn Boyd *E-mail:* taryn@touchwoodeditions.com
Founded: 1985
Publishes in English.
ISBN Prefix(es): 978-1-894898; 978-1-926741; 978-1-926971; 978-0-920663; 978-1-927129; 978-1-77151
Number of titles published annually: 12 Print; 18 E-Book
Total Titles: 224 Print; 170 E-Book
Imprints: Brindle & Glass Publishing Ltd
Orders to: Heritage Group Distribution, 19272-96 Ave, Suite 8, Surrey, BC V4N 4C1 *Tel:* 604-881-7067 *Toll Free Tel:* 800-665-3302 *Fax:* 604-881-7068 *Toll Free Fax:* 800-566-3336 *E-mail:* orders@hgdistribution.com *Web Site:* www.hgdistribution.com
Returns: Heritage Group Distribution, 19272-96 Ave, Suite 8, Surrey, BC V4N 4C1 *Tel:* 604-881-7067 *Toll Free Tel:* 800-665-3302 *Fax:* 604-881-7068 *Toll Free Fax:* 800-566-3336 *E-mail:* orders@hgdistribution.com *Web Site:* www.hgdistribution.com
Shipping Address: Heritage Group Distribution, 19272-96 Ave, Suite 8, Surrey, BC V4N 4C1 *Tel:* 604-881-7067 *Toll Free Tel:* 800-665-3302 *Fax:* 604-881-7068 *Toll Free Fax:* 800-566-3336 *E-mail:* orders@hgdistribution.com *Web Site:* www.hgdistribution.com
Warehouse: Heritage Group Distribution, 19272-96 Ave, Suite 8, Surrey, BC V4N 4C1 *Tel:* 604-881-7067 *Toll Free Tel:* 800-665-3302 *Fax:* 604-881-7068 *Toll Free Fax:* 800-566-3336 *E-mail:* orders@hgdistribution.com *Web Site:* www.hgdistribution.com
Distribution Center: Heritage Group Distribution, 19272-96 Ave, Suite 8, Surrey, BC V4N 4C1 *Tel:* 604-881-7067 *Toll Free Tel:* 800-665-3302 *Fax:* 604-881-7068 *Toll Free Fax:* 800-566-3336 *E-mail:* orders@hgdistribution.com *Web Site:* www.hgdistribution.com
Membership(s): Association of Book Publishers of British Columbia; Association of Canadian Publishers
See separate listing for:
Brindle & Glass Publishing Ltd

Townson Publishing Co Ltd
Affiliate of General Publishing Inc
PO Box 1404, Sta A, Vancouver, BC V6C 2P7
Tel: 604-886-0594 (CN)
E-mail: townsonpublishing@gmail.com
Web Site: generalpublishing.co.uk
Key Personnel
Chmn: Donald Townson
Ed & Rts: Jackson House
Founded: 1977
General trade books, literature in translation.
Publishes in English, French.
Number of titles published annually: 6 Print; 6 E-Book
Total Titles: 16 Print; 16 E-Book
Imprints: General Publishing; Townson Publishing; translatedbooks.com
Subsidiaries: Associated Merchandisers Inc (USA)
Foreign Rep(s): Associated Merchandisers Inc (UK, USA)

Tradewind Books
202-1807 Maritime Mews, Vancouver, BC V6H 3W7
Tel: 604-662-4405
E-mail: tradewindbooks@yahoo.com
Web Site: www.tradewindbooks.com
Key Personnel
Owner & Publr: Michael Katz
Ed: Alison Acheson; Cynthia Nugent; R David Stephens; MaryAnn Thompson
Founded: 1996
Children's picture books, chapter books & young adults novels.
Publishes in English.
ISBN Prefix(es): 978-1-896580
Number of titles published annually: 8 Print
Total Titles: 95 Print
Distributed by Fitzhenry & Whiteside (CN)
U.S. Rep(s): Orca Books
Foreign Rep(s): John Reed Book Distribution (Australia, New Zealand); Turnaround Publisher Services Ltd (UK)
Distribution Center: Fitzhenry & Whiteside, 195 Allstate Pkwy, Markham, ON L3R 4T8 *Tel:* 905-477-9700 *Toll Free Tel:* 800-387-9776 *Toll Free Fax:* 800-260-9777 *E-mail:* godwit@fitzhenry.ca *Web Site:* www.fitzhenry.ca
Orca Book Publishers, PO Box 468, Custer, WA 98240-0468, United States *Toll Free Tel:* 800-210-5277 *Toll Free Fax:* 877-408-1551 *E-mail:* orca@orcabook.com
John Reed Book Distribution, 11 Yandala St, PO Box 257, Tea Gardens, NSW 2324, Australia (Australia & New Zealand) *Tel:* (02) 4997 2936 *Fax:* (02) 4997 2937 *E-mail:* johnmreed@johnreedbooks.com.au
Turnaround Publisher Services Ltd, Olympia Trading Estate, Unit 3, Coburg Rd, Wood Green, London N22 6TZ, United Kingdom *Tel:* (020) 8829 3000 *Fax:* (020) 8881 5088 *E-mail:* enquirie@turnaround-uk.com
Membership(s): Association of Book Publishers of British Columbia; Association of Canadian Publishers

TSAR Publications
PO Box 6996, Sta A, Toronto, ON M5W 1X7
Tel: 416-483-7191 *Fax:* 416-486-0706
E-mail: inquiries@tsarbooks.com
Web Site: www.tsarbooks.com
Key Personnel
Publr: Ms Nurjehan Aziz *E-mail:* naziz@tsarbooks.com
Founded: 1985
Canadian literature, multicultural & international literature.
Publishes in English.
ISBN Prefix(es): 978-0-920661; 978-1-894770
Number of titles published annually: 8 Print
Total Titles: 101 Print
Imprints: TSAR
U.S. Rep(s): Small Press Distribution Inc, 1341 Seventh St, Berkeley, CA 94710, United States
Distribution Center: University of Toronto Press Inc, 5201 Dufferin St, Toronto, ON M3H 5T8 *Tel:* 416-667-7791 *Toll Free Tel:* 800-565-9523 *Fax:* 416-667-7832 *Toll Free Fax:* 800-221-9985
Small Press Distribution Inc, 1341 Seventh St, Berkeley, CA 94710, United States *Tel:* 510-524-1668 *Toll Free Tel:* 800-869-7553 *Fax:* 510-524-0852
Membership(s): Literary Press Group

Tundra Books
Division of McClelland & Stewart Ltd
One Toronto St, Suite 300, Toronto, ON M5C 2V6
SAN: 115-5415
Tel: 416-364-4449 *Toll Free Tel:* 888-523-9292 (orders); 800-588-1074 *Fax:* 416-598-0247 *Toll Free Fax:* 888-562-9924 (orders)
E-mail: tundra@mcclelland.com
Web Site: www.tundrabooks.com
Key Personnel
Edit Dir: Tara Walker *Tel:* 416-364-4449 ext 813951
Founded: 1967
Children's books.
Publishes in English, French.
ISBN Prefix(es): 978-0-88776
Number of titles published annually: 50 Print
Total Titles: 350 Print
Branch Office(s)
Tundra Books of Northern New York, PO Box 1030, Plattsburgh, NY 12901, United States
Distributed by Everybody's Books CC (South Africa); Forrester Books NZ Ltd (New Zealand); El Hombre de la Mancha (Costa Rica & Panama); El Hormiguero (Guatemala)
U.S. Publishers Represented: Tundra Books of Northern New York
U.S. Rep(s): Jack Eichkorn & Associates Inc; R&R Book Co; Southern Territory Associates Inc; Nancy Suib & Associates
Foreign Rights: Cooke Agency International
Orders to: Random House of Canada Limited, 2775 Matheson Blvd E, Mississauga, ON L4W 4P7; Random House Inc - Distribution Center, 400 Hahn Rd, Westminster, MD 21157, United States *Toll Free Tel:* 800-726-0600; 800-733-3000 *Toll Free Fax:* 800-659-2436
Returns: Random House Inc, 1019 N State Rd 47, Crawfordsville, IN 47933, United States
Warehouse: Random House Inc - Distribution Center, 400 Hahn Rd, Westminster, MD 21157, United States *Toll Free Tel:* 800-726-0600 *Toll Free Fax:* 800-659-2436
Membership(s): ABA; ALA; Association of Booksellers for Children; International Board on Books for Young People

Turnstone Press
Artspace Bldg, 206-100 Arthur St, Winnipeg, MB R3B 1H3
SAN: 115-1096
Tel: 204-947-1555 *Toll Free Tel:* 888-363-7718 *Fax:* 204-942-1556
E-mail: info@turnstonepress.com
Web Site: www.turnstonepress.com
Key Personnel
Assoc Publr & Intl Rts: Jamis Paulson
Founded: 1976
Literary press including fiction, nonfiction, poetry, literary criticism, biography, travel fiction & adventure all with a strong Canadian focus.
Publishes in English.
ISBN Prefix(es): 978-0-88801
Number of titles published annually: 10 Print
Total Titles: 300 Print
Imprints: Ravenstone Books
Returns: LitDistCo, c/o 100 Armstrong Ave, Georgetown, ON L7G 5S4 *Tel:* 905-877-4411 *Toll Free Tel:* 800-591-6250 (CN) *Fax:* 905-877-4410 *Toll Free Fax:* 800-591-6251 (CN) *E-mail:* orders@litdistco.ca
Distribution Center: LitDistCo, c/o 100 Armstrong Ave, Georgetown, ON L7G 5S4 *Tel:* 905-877-4411 *Toll Free Tel:* 800-591-6250 (CN) *Fax:* 905-877-4410 *Toll Free Fax:* 800-591-6251 (CN) *E-mail:* orders@litdistco.ca

UBC Press, see University of British Columbia Press

UCCB Press, see Cape Breton University Press Inc (CBU Press)

Ulysses Travel Guides
4176 Rue St-Denis, Montreal, QC H2W 2M5
Tel: 514-843-9447 (bookstore); 514-843-9882 (ext 2232) *Toll Free Tel:* 800-748-9171 *Fax:* 514-843-9448
E-mail: info@ulysses.ca; st-denis@ulysses.ca
Web Site: www.ulyssesguides.com
Key Personnel
Pres: Daniel Desjardins *Tel:* 514-843-9447 ext 2224 *E-mail:* daniel@ulysses.ca
VP, Sales & Mktg: Claude Morneau *E-mail:* claude@ulysses.ca
Founded: 1980
Travel books.
Publishes in English, French.
ISBN Prefix(es): 978-2-921444; 978-2-89464; 978-2-9801872; 978-1-894676
Number of titles published annually: 25 Print; 25 E-Book; 2 Audio
Total Titles: 175 Print; 175 E-Book; 2 Audio
Imprints: Guides de Voyage Ulysses; Ulysses Travel Guides
Distributor for A A Publications; Dakota; Footprint Handbooks; Editions Syvain Harvey; Hunter Publishing; ITMB Publishing Ltd; Odyssey Publications; PassPorter Travel Press; Rother Walking Guides; Trans Canada Trail Foundation; Vacation Works Publications

University of Alberta Press
Ring House 2, Edmonton, AB T6G 2E1
SAN: 118-9794
Tel: 780-492-3662 *Fax:* 780-492-0719
Web Site: www.uap.ualberta.ca
Key Personnel
Dir: Linda Cameron *Tel:* 780-492-0717 *E-mail:* linda.cameron@ualberta.ca
Mng Ed: Mary Lou Roy *Tel:* 780-492-9488 *E-mail:* marylou.roy@ualberta.ca
Acq Ed: Peter Midgley *Tel:* 780-492-7714 *E-mail:* pmidgley@ualberta.ca
Sales & Mktg Mgr: Cathie Crooks *Tel:* 780-492-5820 *E-mail:* ccrooks@ualberta.ca
Prodn & Designer: Alan Brownoff *Tel:* 780-492-8285 *E-mail:* abrownof@ualberta.ca
Off Mgr: Sharon Wilson *E-mail:* sharon.wilson@ualberta.ca
Founded: 1969
The UAP publishes in the areas of biography, history, language, literature, natural history, regional interest, native studies, travel narratives & reference books. UAP contributes to the intellectual & cultural life of Alberta & Canada by publishing well-edited, research-based knowledge & creative thought.
Publishes in English.
ISBN Prefix(es): 978-0-88864; 978-1-77212
Number of titles published annually: 22 Print; 15 E-Book
Total Titles: 718 Print; 110 E-Book; 1 Audio
Imprints: CCI Press; Gutteridge Books; Pica Pica Books
Sales Office(s): Ampersand Canada's Book & Gift Agency Inc, 321 Carlaw Ave, Suite 213, Toronto, ON M4M 2S1, Contact: Saffron Beckwith *Tel:* 416-703-0666 ext 124 *Fax:* 416-703-4745 *E-mail:* saffronb@ampersandinc.ca *Web Site:* www.ampersand.ca
U.S. Rep(s): Wayne State University Press
Foreign Rep(s): Gazelle Academic (Albania, Andorra, Armenia, Austria, Bahrain, Belarus, Belgium, Bosnia and Herzegovina, Botswana, Bulgaria, Cambodia, China, Continental Europe, Croatia, Cyprus, Czech Republic, Denmark, Egypt, Ethiopia, Europe, Finland, France, Georgia, Germany, Gibraltar, Greece, Hungary, Iceland, India, Indonesia, Iran, Iraq, Ireland, Israel, Italy, Japan, Jordan, Kenya, Laos, Latvia, Liechtenstein, Lithuania, Luxembourg, Macedonia, Malaysia, Malta, Moldova, Monaco, Montenegro, Mozambique, Myanmar, Namibia, Netherlands, Norway, Oman, Poland, Portugal, Qatar, Romania, Russia, Serbia, Slovakia, Slovenia, South Africa, Spain, Sweden, Switzerland, Taiwan, Turkey, Uganda, Ukraine, United Arab Emirates, UK, UK & the continent, UK Commonwealth)
Orders to: Georgetown Terminal Warehouses, 34 Armstrong Ave, Georgetown, ON L7G 4R9 *Tel:* 905-873-9781 *Toll Free Tel:* 877-864-8477 *Fax:* 905-873-6170 *Toll Free Fax:* 877-864-4272 *E-mail:* orders@gtwcanada.com *Web Site:* gtwcanada.com
Returns: Georgetown Terminal Warehouses, 34 Armstrong Ave, Georgetown, ON L7G 4R9 *Tel:* 905-873-9781 *Toll Free Tel:* 877-864-8477 *Fax:* 905-873-6170 *Toll Free Fax:* 877-864-4272 *E-mail:* orders@gtwcanada.com *Web Site:* gtwcanada.com
Shipping Address: Georgetown Terminal Warehouses, 34 Armstrong Ave, Georgetown, ON L7G 4R9 *Tel:* 905-873-9781 *Toll Free Tel:* 877-864-8477 *Fax:* 905-873-6170 *Toll Free Fax:* 877-864-4272 *E-mail:* orders@gtwcanada.com *Web Site:* gtwcanada.com
Warehouse: Georgetown Terminal Warehouses, 34 Armstrong Ave, Georgetown, ON L7G 4R9 *Tel:* 905-873-9781 *Toll Free Tel:* 877-864-8477 *Fax:* 905-873-6170 *Toll Free Fax:* 877-864-4272 *E-mail:* orders@gtwcanada.com *Web Site:* gtwcanada.com
Distribution Center: Georgetown Terminal Warehouses, 34 Armstrong Ave, Georgetown, ON L7G 4R9 *Tel:* 905-873-9781 *Toll Free Tel:* 877-864-8477 *Fax:* 905-873-6170 *Toll Free Fax:* 877-864-4272 *E-mail:* orders@gtwcanada.com *Web Site:* gtwcanada.com
Wayne State University Press (WSUP), Shipping & Receiving, 40 W Hancock, Detroit, MI 48201-1309, United States *Tel:* 313-577-6120 *Fax:* 313-577-6131 *E-mail:* bookorders@wayne.edu *Web Site:* wsupress.wayne.edu
Gazelle Book Services Ltd, White Cross Mills, Hightown, Lancaster LA1 4XS, United Kingdom *Tel:* (01524) 68765 *Fax:* (01524) 63232 *E-mail:* sales@gazellebooks.co.uk *Web Site:* www.gazellebooks.co.uk
Membership(s): Association of American University Presses; Association of Canadian Publishers; Association of Canadian University Presses; Book Publishers Association of Alberta
See separate listing for:
Canadian Circumpolar Institute (CCI) Press

University of British Columbia Press
2029 West Mall, Vancouver, BC V6T 1Z2
SAN: 115-1118
Tel: 604-822-5959 *Toll Free Tel:* 877-377-9378 *Fax:* 604-822-6083 *Toll Free Fax:* 800-668-0821
E-mail: frontdesk@ubcpress.ca
Web Site: www.ubcpress.ca
Key Personnel
Dir: Melissa Pitts *Tel:* 604-822-6376 *E-mail:* pitts@ubcpress.ca
Asst Dir, Fin & Opers: Devni De Silva *Tel:* 604-822-8938 *E-mail:* desilva@ubcpress.ca
Asst Dir, Prodn & Edit Servs: Holly Keller *Tel:* 604-822-4545 *E-mail:* keller@ubcpress.ca
Sr Ed (Kelowna): Randy Schmidt *Tel:* 250-764-4761 *Fax:* 250-764-4709 *E-mail:* schmidt@ubcpress.ca
Sr Ed (Toronto): Emily Andrew *Tel:* 416-429-0322 *E-mail:* andrew@ubcpress.ca
Acqs Ed (Vancouver): Darcy Cullen *Tel:* 604-822-5744 *E-mail:* cullen@ubcpress.ca
Mgr, Inventory Data & Dist: Shari Martin *Tel:* 604-822-1221 *E-mail:* martin@ubcpress.ca
Mktg Mgr: Laraine Coates *Tel:* 604-822-6486 *E-mail:* coates@ubcpress.ca
Publicity & Events Mgr: Kerry Kilmartin *Tel:* 604-822-8244 *E-mail:* kilmartin@ubcpress.ca
Agency Mktg Coord: Emily Rielly *Tel:* 604-822-8226 *E-mail:* rielly@ubcpress.ca
Ed: Megan Brand *Tel:* 604-822-5885 *E-mail:* brand@ubcpress.ca; Leslie Erickson *Tel:* 604-822-4548 *E-mail:* lerickson@ubcpress.ca; Ann Macklem *Tel:* 604-822-0093 *E-mail:* macklem@ubcpress.ca
Academic Sales & Mktg Mgr: Harmony Johnson *Tel:* 604-822-1978 *E-mail:* johnson@ubcpress.ca
Founded: 1971
Academic & scholarly publications; native studies, law & society, military history, northern studies, sexuality, political science & forestry.
Publishes in English.
ISBN Prefix(es): 978-0-88865; 978-0-7748
Number of titles published annually: 70 Print
Total Titles: 700 Print; 2 CD-ROM; 1 E-Book
Imprints: UBC Press
Branch Office(s)
587 Markham St, 2nd fl, Toronto, ON M6G 2L7 *Fax:* 416-535-9677
Distributed by University of Washington Press (US)
Distributor for AU Press; Berghahn Books; Brookings Institution Press; Canadian Forest Service (worldwide); Canadian Wildlife Service-Pacific Region (worldwide); Environmental Training Centre; Hong Kong University Press; Island Press; Jessica Kingsley Publishers; Laval University Press (English-lang books); Manchester University Press; Oregon State University Press; Paradigm Publishers; Transaction Publishers; Tufts University Press; University of Arizona Press; University of Washington Press (includes Hong Kong UP, KITLV Press, National Gallery of Australia Press, Silkworm Books, UCLA Fowler Museum of Cultural History & Waanders Publishers); Wesleyan University Press; Western Geographical Press (worldwide); University Press of New England (includes Brandels University Press, Dartmouth College Press, Northeastern University Press, University of New Hampshire Press & University of Vermont Press)
U.S. Publishers Represented: Berghahn Books; Brookings Institution Press; Island Press; Oregon State University Press; Paradigm Publish-

ers; Transaction Publishers; Tufts University Press; University of Arizona Press; University of Washington Press (includes Hong Kong UP, KITLV Press, National Gallery of Australia Press, Silkworm Books, UCLA Fowler Museum of Cultural History & Waanders Publishers); University Press of New England (includes Brandeis University Press, Dartmouth College Press, Northeastern University Press, University of New Hampshire Press & University of Vermont Press); Wesleyan University Press
U.S. Rep(s): University of Washington Press
Foreign Rep(s): Asia Publishers Services Ltd (China, Hong Kong, Korea, Taiwan); East-West Export Books (Royden Muranaka) (Asia exc China, Australia, Hong Kong, Korea, New Zealand, The Pacific, Taiwan); Eurospan Group (Africa, Europe, Middle East, UK)
Orders to: University of Toronto Press Distribution, 5201 Dufferin St, Toronto, ON M3H 5T8 *Tel:* 416-667-7791 *Toll Free Tel:* 800-565-9523 *Fax:* 416-667-7832 *Toll Free Fax:* 800-221-9985 *E-mail:* utpbooks@utpress.utoronto.ca; University of Washington Press, c/o Hopkins Fulfillment Services, PO Box 50370, Baltimore, MD 21211-4370, United States *Tel:* 410-516-6956 *Toll Free Tel:* 800-537-5487 (US) *Fax:* 410-516-6998 *E-mail:* hfscustserv@press.jhu.edu
Shipping Address: UNI Press, 34 Armstrong Ave, Georgetown, ON L7G 4R9, Contact: Cust Serv *Tel:* 905-873-9781 *Toll Free Tel:* 877-864-8477 *Fax:* 905-873-6170 *Toll Free Fax:* 877-864-4272 *E-mail:* orders@gtwcanada.com
Distribution Center: University of Toronto Press Distribution, 5201 Dufferin St, Toronto, ON M3H 5T8 *Tel:* 416-667-7791 *Toll Free Tel:* 800-565-9523 *Fax:* 416-667-7832 *Toll Free Fax:* 800-221-9985 *E-mail:* utpbooks@utpress.utoronto.ca
Membership(s): Association of American University Presses; Association of Book Publishers of British Columbia; Association of Canadian Publishers; Association of Canadian University Presses; International Association of Scholarly Publishers

University of Calgary Press
2500 University Dr NW, Calgary, AB T2N 1N4
Tel: 403-220-7578 *Fax:* 403-282-0085
E-mail: ucpress@ucalgary.ca
Web Site: uofcpress.com
Key Personnel
Interim Dir: John Wright *Tel:* 403-220-3511 *E-mail:* jpwright@ucalgary.ca
Opers Mgr: Michelle Lipp *E-mail:* mlipp@ucalgary.ca
Edit Secy & Mktg Assoc: Karen Buttner *Tel:* 403-220-3979 *E-mail:* kbuttner@ucalgary.ca
Founded: 1981
Specialize in scholarly books that make a difference. Series subjects include history, parks & protected areas, regional history, Northern studies, Africa, cinema studies, cultural studies, Canadian military & military history & communications studies.
Publishes in English, French.
ISBN Prefix(es): 978-0-919813; 978-1-895176; 978-1-55238
Number of titles published annually: 20 Print; 2 CD-ROM; 10 Online; 20 E-Book
Total Titles: 400 Print; 5 CD-ROM; 25 Online; 150 E-Book
Distributor for Michigan State University Press
U.S. Rep(s): Michigan State University Press
Foreign Rep(s): Gazelle Book Services (Europe, UK)
Foreign Rights: Roli Books (New Delhi)
Distribution Center: Georgetown Terminal Warehouses, 34 Armstrong Ave, Georgetown, ON L7G 4R9 *Toll Free Tel:* 877-864-8477 *Toll Free Fax:* 877-864-4272 *E-mail:* orders@gtwcanada.com
Michigan State University Press, c/o Chicago Distribution Center, 11030 S Langley Ave, Chicago, IL 60628, United States *Toll Free Tel:* 800-621-2736 *Toll Free Fax:* 800-621-8476 *E-mail:* orders@press.chicago.edu
Gazelle Book Services, White Cross Mills, High Town, Lancaster, Lancs LA1 4XS, United Kingdom (UK, Europe, Asia, Middle East & South Africa) *Tel:* (01524) 68765 *Fax:* (01524) 63232 *E-mail:* sales@gazellebooks.co.uk
Membership(s): Association for Canadian Publishers in the US; Association of Canadian Publishers; Book Publishers Association of Alberta

University of Manitoba Press
University of Manitoba, 301 St Johns College, 92 Dysart Rd, Winnipeg, MB R3T 2M5
SAN: 115-5474
Tel: 204-474-9495 *Fax:* 204-474-7566
E-mail: uofmpress@umanitoba.ca
Web Site: uofmpress.ca
Key Personnel
Dir: David Carr *Tel:* 204-474-9242 *E-mail:* carr@cc.umanitoba.ca
Mng Ed: Glenn Bergen *Tel:* 204-474-7338 *E-mail:* glenn_bergen@umanitoba.ca
Acqs Ed: Jill McConkey *Tel:* 204-474-8804 *E-mail:* jill.mcconkey@umanitoba.ca
Sales & Mktg Supv: David Larsen *Tel:* 204-474-9998 *E-mail:* david.larsen@umanitoba.ca
Founded: 1967
Scholarly & general titles in humanities & social sciences; western Canadian history & native studies.
Publishes in English.
ISBN Prefix(es): 978-0-88755
Number of titles published annually: 14 Print
Total Titles: 120 Print
Distributed by University of Toronto Press (Canadian sales); Michigan State University Press (US sales)
Distribution Center: University of Toronto Press Distribution, 5201 Dufferin St, Toronto, ON M3H 5T8 *Tel:* 416-667-7791 *Toll Free Tel:* 800-565-9523 *Fax:* 416-667-7832 *Toll Free Fax:* 800-221-9985 *E-mail:* utpbooks@utpress.utoronto.ca
Michigan State University Press, c/o Chicago Distribution Center, 11030 S Langley Ave, Chicago, IL 60628, United States *Toll Free Tel:* 800-621-2736 *Toll Free Fax:* 800-621-8476 *E-mail:* orders@press.chicago.edu *Web Site:* www.msupress.org

University of Ottawa Press (Les Presses de l'Université d'Ottawa)
Affiliate of University of Ottawa
542 King Edward Ave, Ottawa, ON K1N 6N5
Tel: 613-562-5246 *Fax:* 613-562-5247
E-mail: puo-oup@uottawa.ca
Web Site: www.press.uottawa.ca
Key Personnel
Dir: Lara Mainville *Tel:* 613-562-5663 *E-mail:* lara.mainville@uottawa.ca
Digital Content Mgr: Lisa Marie Smith *Tel:* 613-562-5800 ext 2854 *E-mail:* lisa.smith@uottawa.ca
Prodn Mgr: Suzanne Cloutier *Tel:* 613-562-5800 ext 2853 *E-mail:* scloutier@uottawa.ca; Didier Pilon *Tel:* 613-562-5800 ext 3064 *E-mail:* dpilon@uottawa.ca
Acqs Ed: Dominike Thomas *Tel:* 613-562-5800 ext 3065 *E-mail:* dthomas@uottawa.ca
Founded: 1936
Scholarly & trade books. University of Ottawa Press is the oldest French-language university press & only fully bilingual university press in North America.
Publishes in English, French.
ISBN Prefix(es): 978-0-7766; 978-2-7603
Number of titles published annually: 15 Print; 15 E-Book
Total Titles: 400 Print; 200 E-Book
Foreign Rep(s): Ampersand Inc (Canada (English-speaking)); CEDIF (France); Durnell Marketing (Europe exc UK); Oxford Publicity Partnership Ltd (UK); Patrimoine Diffusion SPRL (Belgium); Prologue Inc (Canada (French-speaking)); Servidis SA (Switzerland)
Distribution Center: University of Toronto Press (UTP), 5201 Dufferin St, North York, ON M3H 5T8 (English titles-CN) *Toll Free Tel:* 800-565-9523 *Toll Free Fax:* 800-221-9985 *E-mail:* utpbooks@utpress.utoronto.ca *Web Site:* www.utpress.utoronto.ca
Prologue Inc, 1650 Lionel-Bertrand Blvd, Boisbriand, QC J7H 1N7 (French titles-CN) *Tel:* 450-434-0306 *Toll Free Tel:* 800-363-2864 *Toll Free Fax:* 800-361-8088 *E-mail:* prologue@prologue.ca *Web Site:* www.prologue.ca
Exportlivre, 505 Belanger St, Montreal, QC H2S 1G5 (French & English titles-other regions) *Tel:* 450-671-3888 *Fax:* 450-671-2121 *E-mail:* order@exportlivre.com *Web Site:* www.exportlivre.com
University of Toronto Press (UTP), 2250 Military Rd, Tonawanda, NY 14150, United States (English titles-US) *Toll Free Tel:* 800-565-9523 *Toll Free Fax:* 800-221-9985 *E-mail:* uptbooks@utpress.utoronto.ca *Web Site:* www.uptress.utoronto.ca
Patrimoine SPRL, Ave Milcamps 119, 1030 Brussels, Belgium (French titles-Belgium, Luxembourg & Netherlands) *Tel:* (02) 7366847 *Fax:* (02) 7366847 *E-mail:* patrimoie@telenet.be
Distribution du Nouveau Monde, 30 rue Guy Lussac, 75005 Paris, France (French titles-France) *Tel:* (01) 43 54 49 02 *Fax:* (01) 43 54 39 15 *E-mail:* dnm@librairieduquebec.fr *Web Site:* www.librairieduquebec.fr
Servidis SA, Chemin des Chalets 7, 1279 Chavannes-de-Bogis, Switzerland (French titles-Switzerland) *Tel:* (022) 960 95 25 *Fax:* (022) 776 63 64 *E-mail:* commande@servidis.ch *Web Site:* www.servidis.ch
Marston Book Services Ltd, 160 Milton Park, PO Box 269, Abingdon, Oxon OX14 4YN, United Kingdom (English titles-Europe & UK) *Tel:* (01235) 465521 *Fax:* (01235) 465555 *E-mail:* direct.orders@marston.co.uk *Web Site:* www.marston.co.uk
Membership(s): American Association of University Presses; Association Nationale des Editeurs de Livres; Association of Canadian Publishers; Association of Canadian University Presses

University of Regina Press
2 Research Dr, Suite 246, Regina, SK S4S 7H9
SAN: 115-0278
Mailing Address: University of Regina, 3737 Wascana Pkwy, Regina, SK S4S 0A2
Tel: 306-585-4758 *Toll Free Tel:* 866-874-2257 *Fax:* 306-585-4699
E-mail: uofrpress@uregina.ca
Web Site: uofrpress.ca
Key Personnel
Publr & Dir: Bruce Walsh *Tel:* 306-585-4795 *E-mail:* bruce.walsh@uregina.ca
Sr Ed: Donna Grant *Tel:* 306-585-4787 *E-mail:* donna.grant@uregina.ca
Ed: David McLennan *Tel:* 306-585-4789 *E-mail:* david.mclennan@uregina.ca
Mktg Coord: Jackie Lay *Tel:* 306-337-3325 *E-mail:* jackie.lay@uregina.ca
Founded: 1973
Scholarly paperbacks & hardcovers on cultural & economic development & history of Canadian Plains & western Canada.
Publishes in English, French.
ISBN Prefix(es): 978-0-88977
Number of titles published annually: 15 Print
Total Titles: 90 Print; 1 CD-ROM

Distribution Center: University of Toronto Press Distribution, 5201 Dufferin St, Toronto, ON M3H 5T8 *Tel:* 416-667-7791 *Toll Free Tel:* 800-565-9523 (CN & US) *Fax:* 416-667-7832 *Toll Free Fax:* 800-221-9985 (CN & US) *E-mail:* utpbooks@utpress.utoronto.ca *Web Site:* www.utpress.utoronto.ca
Membership(s): Association of Canadian Publishers; Association of Canadian University Presses; Saskatchewan Publishers Group

§University of Toronto Press
Division of Multicultural History Society of Canada
10 St Mary St, Suite 700, Toronto, ON M4Y 2W8
Tel: 416-978-2239 *Fax:* 416-978-4738
E-mail: info@utpress.utoronto.ca
Web Site: www.utpress.utoronto.ca; www.utppublishing.com
Key Personnel
CEO, Publr & Pres: John Yates *Tel:* 416-978-2239 ext 222 *E-mail:* jyates@utpress.utoronto.ca
VP, Dist & MIS: Hamish Cameron *Tel:* 416-667-7773 *E-mail:* hcameron@utpress.utoronto.ca
VP, Higher Educ: Michael Harrison *Tel:* 519-837-1403 ext 222 *Fax:* 519-767-1643 *E-mail:* mharrison@utphighereducation.com
VP, Journals: Anne Marie Corrigan *Tel:* 416-667-7777 ext 7838 *E-mail:* acorrigan@utpress.utoronto.ca
VP, Scholarly Publg: Lynn Fisher *Tel:* 416-978-2239 ext 243 *E-mail:* lfisher@utpress.utoronto.ca
Sales & Mktg Mgr: Brian MacDonald *Tel:* 416-978-2239 ext 253 *E-mail:* brianm@utpress.utoronto.ca
Founded: 1901
Publisher, distributor & university bookstore.
Publishes in English.
ISBN Prefix(es): 978-0-8020; 978-0-7727; 978-1-4426
Number of titles published annually: 200 Print; 100 E-Book
Total Titles: 3,500 Print; 500 E-Book
Imprints: Rotman-UTP Publishing; University of Toronto
Divisions: Pippin Publishing; University of Toronto Press Guidance Centre; University of Toronto Press Journals Division
Branch Office(s)
2250 Military Rd, Tonawanda, NY 14150, United States *Tel:* 716-693-2768 *Fax:* 716-693-2167
Distributor for Anvil Press; Ashlar House; Aspasia Books; Baltray Books; Between the Lines; Black Rose Books; Book Publishing Co; The British Library (CN only); Canadian Museum of Nature; Caslon Publishing; CAW/TCA Canada; Central European University Press; Centre for Urban & Community Studies, University of Toronto; Codasat Canada Ltd; Cormorant Books; Diamond Mind Enterprises; Douglas & McIntyre; DreamCatcher Publishing Co; The Dundurn Group; Faculty of Applied Science & Engineering; G7 Funds; Goose Lane Editions; Great Plains Publishing Ltd; Greystone Books; Guernica Editions; Guidance Centre; Help...We've Got Kids; Integrative Leadership International Ltd; ISSI; Journals-Canadian Theatre Review; Jump Math; KapableKidz Inc; Edgar Kent; Kids Can Press; Knowledge Bureau; Wilfrid Laurier University Press; Legas Publishing; Lobster Press Ltd; Mage Publishers; Mayant Press; McDonald & Woodward Publishing Co; McGilligan Books; La Montage Secrete; Multicultural History Society of Ontario; Multilingual Matters (North America only); National Museum of Science & Technology; New Society Publishers; OISE Press; Oolichan Books; Penn State University Press; Pippin Publishing; Porcupine's Quill; Princess Margaret Hospital Foundation; Quill Driver Books/Word Dancer Press Inc; RDR Books; Royal Ontario Museum; RREES Inc; Elysa Schwartzman; Second Story Press; Secret Mountain; Seraphim Editions; J Gordon Shillingford Publishing Inc; Signature Editions; Sister Vision Press; Square One Publishing Inc; Subway Books Ltd; Sumach Press; Teachers College Press; Theytus Books Ltd; Thompson Educational Publishing; Toronto Heschel School; TSAR Publications; Twin Guinep Ltd; University of British Columbia Press; University of Manitoba Press; University of Ottawa Press; University of Toronto Center for Public Management; University of Toronto Press-Higher Education; Wall & Emerson Inc; Wolsak & Wynn Publishers; Word of Mouth Production
U.S. Rep(s): Book Traveler (Roger Sauls) (southeast); Terry & Read LLC (southwest coast); Ben Schrager (northeast); Trim Associates (Gary Trim) (midwest)
Foreign Rep(s): APAC Publishers Services (China, Hong Kong, Indonesia, Malaysia, Philippines, Singapore, Taiwan, Thailand, Vietnam); Cranbury International LLC (Ethan Atkin) (Caribbean, Central America, South America); Durnell Marketing Ltd (Andrew Durnell) (Europe, Iceland, Ireland, Israel, Northern Ireland, Russia); East-West Export Books (Royden Muranaka) (Australia, New Zealand, Pacific Islands); Everest International Publishing Services (Wei Zhao) (China); Oxford Publicity Partnership Ltd (Gary Hall) (UK); United Publishers Services (Japan); Viva Books Pvt Ltd (India)
Orders to: 2250 Military Rd, Tonawanda, NY 14150, United States *Tel:* 716-693-2768 *Fax:* 716-692-7479; 5201 Dufferin St, North York, ON M3H 5T8 *Tel:* 416-667-7791 *Toll Free Tel:* 800-565-9523 *Fax:* 416-667-7832 *Toll Free Fax:* 800-221-9985 *E-mail:* utpbooks@utpress.utoronto.ca; NBN International, Airport Business Ctr, 10 Thornbury Rd, Plymouth, Devon PL6 7PP, United Kingdom (UK & Europe) *Tel:* (01752) 202301 *Fax:* (01752) 202333 *E-mail:* orders@nbninternational.com
Returns: 5201 Dufferin St, North York, ON M3H 5T8
Warehouse: 2250 Military Rd, Tonawanda, NY 14150, United States
5201 Dufferin St, North York, ON M3H 5T8
Distribution Center: 5201 Dufferin St, North York, ON M3H 5T8 *Tel:* 416-667-7791 *Toll Free Tel:* 800-565-9523 *Fax:* 416-667-7832 *Toll Free Fax:* 800-221-9985 *E-mail:* utpbooks@utpress.utoronto.ca
Membership(s): American Association of University Presses; Association of Canadian Publishers; Association of Canadian University Presses; Organization of Book Publishers of Ontario
See separate listing for:
Pippin Publishing

Vehicule Press
PO Box 42094, CP Roy, Montreal, QC H2W-2T3
Tel: 514-844-6073 *Fax:* 514-844-7543
E-mail: vp@vehiculepress.com; admin@vehiculepress.com
Web Site: www.vehiculepress.com
Key Personnel
Publr & Gen Ed: Simon Dardick; Nancy Marrelli
Mng Ed: Vicki Marcok
Ed, Esplanade Books: Dimitri Nasrallah
Ed, Signal Editions: Carmine Starnino
Mktg & Promos Mgr: Maya Assouad
Founded: 1973
Paperback trade; fiction, jazz, biography, literature, poetry, translation.
Publishes in English.
ISBN Prefix(es): 978-0-919890; 978-1-55065
Number of titles published annually: 14 Print
Total Titles: 480 Print
Imprints: Esplanade Books (fiction); Signal Editions (poetry)
U.S. Rep(s): IPG (Independent Publishers Group)
Returns: LitDistCo, 100 Armstrong Ave, Georgetown, ON L7G 5S4 *Tel:* 905-877-4411 *Toll Free Tel:* 800-591-6250 *Fax:* 905-877-4410 *Toll Free Fax:* 800-591-6251
Shipping Address: LitDistCo, 100 Armstrong Ave, Georgetown, ON L7G 5S4 *Tel:* 905-877-4411 *Toll Free Tel:* 800-591-6250 *Fax:* 905-877-4410 *Toll Free Fax:* 800-591-6251
Distribution Center: LitDistCo, 100 Armstrong Ave, Georgetown, ON L7G 5S4 *Tel:* 905-877-4411 *Toll Free Tel:* 800-591-6250 *Fax:* 905-877-4410 *Toll Free Fax:* 800-591-6251
Membership(s): Association of Canadian Publishers; Literary Press Group

VLB Editeur Inc
Division of Le Groupe Ville-Marie Litterature
1010, Rue de la Gauchetiere Est, Montreal, QC H2L 2N5
Tel: 514-523-7993 *Fax:* 514-282-7530
Web Site: www.edvlb.com
Key Personnel
Pres: Donald Lizotte
VP, Publg & Ed: Martin Balthazar
Literary Dir for Essays: Alain-Nicolas Renaud
Literary Dir for Fiction: Annie Goulet
Asst Ed: Sylvie Briere *Tel:* 514-523-7993 ext 223 *E-mail:* sylvie.briere@sogides.com
Founded: 1976
Publishes in French.
ISBN Prefix(es): 978-2-89005
Number of titles published annually: 90 Print
Total Titles: 900 Print
Distribution Center: Messageries ADP, 2315 Rue de la Province, Longueuil, QC J4G 1G4

Weigl Educational Publishers Ltd
6325 Tenth St SE, Calgary, AB T2H 2Z9
SAN: 115-1312
Tel: 403-233-7747 *Toll Free Tel:* 800-668-0766 *Fax:* 403-233-7769 *Toll Free Fax:* 866-449-3445
E-mail: info@weigl.com; orders@weigl.com
Web Site: www.weigl.ca; av2books.com
Key Personnel
Pres & Publr: Linda Weigl *E-mail:* linda@weigl.com
Founded: 1979
School library resources & textbooks for grades K-12 in English & French. Emphasis on: Canadian history, social studies & public affairs; science; multiculturalism; career/vocational/life management; distance education; books & guides for teachers.
Publishes in English.
ISBN Prefix(es): 978-0-919879; 978-1-896990; 978-1-55388
Number of titles published annually: 40 Print
Total Titles: 200 Print
Branch Office(s)
350 Fifth Ave, 59th fl, New York, NY 10118, United States *Toll Free Tel:* 866-649-3445 *E-mail:* av2books@weigl.com
Distributed by The Creative Co (United States); Rourke Publishing; Saunders Book Co (Canada); Smart Apple Media (United States)

Whitecap Books Ltd
Imprint of Fitzhenry & Whiteside Limited
314 W Cordova St, Suite 210, Vancouver, BC V6B 1E8
Tel: 604-681-6181 *Toll Free Tel:* 800-387-9776 *Toll Free Fax:* 800-260-9777
Web Site: www.whitecap.ca
Key Personnel
Publr: Nick Rundall *Tel:* 905-477-9700 ext 244 *E-mail:* nickr@whitecap.ca
Assoc Publr: Jesse Marchand *E-mail:* jessem@whitecap.ca

Ed: Jordie Yow *Tel:* 604-681-6181 ext 204 *E-mail:* jordiey@whitecap.ca
Art Dir: Michelle Furbacher *Tel:* 604-681-6181 ext 203 *E-mail:* michellef@whitecap.ca
Publicist: Stephanie Hill *Tel:* 604-681-6181 ext 201 *E-mail:* steph@whitecap.ca
Founded: 1977
Trade books, photography, cookery, regional, gardening, outdoor guide books, natural history, juvenile nonfiction & illustrated children's books, juvenile fiction.
Publishes in English.
ISBN Prefix(es): 978-1-55110; 978-1-55285; 978-1-77050
Number of titles published annually: 85 Print
Total Titles: 480 Print
Imprints: Walrus Books
Branch Office(s)
195 Allstate Pkwy, Markham, ON L3R 4T8 *Tel:* 905-477-6666 *E-mail:* bookinfo@fitzhenry.ca *Web Site:* fitzhenry.ca
U.S. Rep(s): Midpoint Trade

John Wiley & Sons Canada Ltd
Subsidiary of John Wiley & Sons Inc
5353 Dundas St W, Suite 400, Toronto, ON M9B 6H8
Tel: 416-236-4433 *Toll Free Tel:* 800-467-4797 (orders only) *Fax:* 416-236-8743 (cust serv); 416-236-4447 *Toll Free Fax:* 800-565-6802 (orders)
E-mail: canada@wiley.com
Web Site: www.wiley.ca
Key Personnel
COO: Bill Zerter
Founded: 1968
Textbooks for colleges & universities; trade, professional & reference.
Publishes in English, French.
ISBN Prefix(es): 978-0-470; 978-0-471
Number of titles published annually: 50 Print
Total Titles: 600 Print
Distributor for John Wiley & Sons Inc
Distribution Center: 6045 Freemont Blvd, Mississauga, ON L5R 4J3 *Tel:* 416-236-4433 *Fax:* 416-236-8743

Wilfrid Laurier University Press
255 King St N, Suite 401, Waterloo, ON N2J 4V2
Mailing Address: 75 University Ave W, Waterloo, ON N2L 3C5
Tel: 519-884-0710 (ext 6124) *Toll Free Tel:* 866-836-5551 (CN & US) *Fax:* 519-725-1399
E-mail: press@wlu.ca
Web Site: www.wlupress.wlu.ca
Key Personnel
Dir: Brian Henderson *Tel:* 519-884-0710 ext 6123 *E-mail:* brian@press.wlu.ca
Mng Ed: Rob Kohlmeier *Tel:* 519-884-0710 ext 6119 *E-mail:* rob@press.wlu.ca
Acqs Ed: Lisa Quinn *Tel:* 519-884-0710 ext 2843 *E-mail:* quinn@press.wlu.ca
Developmental Ed: Blaire Comacchio *Tel:* 519-884-0710 ext 2034 *E-mail:* bcomacchio@wlu.ca
Sales, Mktg & Foreign Rts Mgr: Penelope Grows *Tel:* 519-884-0710 ext 6605 *E-mail:* pgrows@press.wlu.ca
Prodn Coord: Mike Bechthold *Tel:* 519-884-0710 ext 6122 *E-mail:* mbechthold@wlu.ca
Sales & Subn Servs Coord: Cheryl Beaupre *Tel:* 519-884-0710 ext 6124 *E-mail:* cheryl@press.wlu.ca
Founded: 1974
Publish scholarly & general interest books in the social sciences & humanities.
Publishes in English.
ISBN Prefix(es): 978-0-88920; 978-1-55458; 978-0-921821
Number of titles published annually: 30 Print; 30 Online
Total Titles: 416 Print; 400 Online
Imprints: Laurier Digital
Distributor for Laurier Centre for Military Strategic & Disarmament Studies; Toronto International Film Festival
Foreign Rep(s): Blue4Books Inc (Midwest USA, Southeast USA, Southwest USA); CRW Marketing Services for Publishers (Tony Sagun) (Philippines, Thailand); Terry Fernihough (Ontario, CN); Gazelle Book Services Ltd (Caribbean, Continental Europe, India, Ireland, Israel, Japan, Latin America, Middle East, South Africa, Southeast Asia, Sub-Saharan Africa, UK); Hargreaves, Fuller & Paton (Terry Fernihough) (Ontario, CN); Hargreaves, Fuller & Paton (Karen Stacey) (Quebec, CN); Hargreaves, Fuller & Paton (Alberta, BC, CN, British Columbia, CN, Manitoba, CN, Northwest Territories, CN, Saskatchewan, CN, West Toronto, ON, CN, Yukon, CN); Bob Rosenberg Group (Western USA); Ben Schrager (Northeast USA); Karen Stacey (Quebec, CN); Leona & Jerry Trainer (Eastern Canada)
Orders to: University of Toronto Press Distribution, 5201 Dufferin Street, Toronto, ON M3H 5T8 (CN orders) *Toll Free Tel:* 800-565-9523 *Toll Free Fax:* 800-221-9985 *E-mail:* utpbooks@utpress.utoronto.ca; Gazelle Book Services Ltd, White Cross Mills, High Town, Lancaster, Lancs LA1 4XS, United Kingdom (Continental Europe, India, Ireland, Israel, Japan, Latin America & the Caribbean, Middle East, South Africa, Southeast Asia, Sub-Saharan Africa & UK) *Tel:* (01524) 68765 *Fax:* (01524) 63232 *E-mail:* sales@gazellebooks.co.uk *Web Site:* www.gazellebookservices.co.uk; University of Toronto Press Distribution, 2250 Military Rd, Tonawanda, NY 14150, United States (US orders) *Toll Free Tel:* 800-565-9523 *Toll Free Fax:* 800-221-9985 *E-mail:* utpbooks@utpress.utoronto.ca
Membership(s): Association of American University Presses; Association of Canadian Publishers; Association of Canadian University Presses; Canadian Booksellers Association; Organization of Book Publishers of Ontario

WLU Press, see Wilfrid Laurier University Press

Wolters Kluwer CCH Canada, see Wolters Kluwer Ltd

§Wolters Kluwer Ltd
Subsidiary of Wolters Kluwer NV (The Netherlands)
90 Sheppard Ave E, Suite 300, Toronto, ON M2N 6X1
Tel: 416-224-2224 *Toll Free Tel:* 800-268-4522 (CN & US cust serv) *Fax:* 416-224-2243 *Toll Free Fax:* 800-461-4131
E-mail: cservice@cch.ca (cust serv)
Web Site: www.cch.ca
Key Personnel
CFO & VP, Fin & Opers: Allan Orr *E-mail:* allan.orr@wolterskluwer.com
Pres: Doug Finley
VP, Devt: Marie Croteau
VP, Law & Busn: Steve Monk
Founded: 1946
Produce information products that help its customers take command of complex regulatory issues in tax, financial planning, business & law. One of Canada's largest & most respected professional information providers, producing leading-edge research materials & application software in both English & French. Products are available via the Internet as well as in CD-ROM & print formats. The company's long-standing success is based on technological innovation, information management expertise & a commitment to industry leadership. Works closely with experts from a variety of disciplines to provide insight & professional commentary that advances our customers' knowledge & productivity.
Publishes in English, French.
ISBN Prefix(es): 978-1-55141; 978-0-88796; 978-1-55367
Number of titles published annually: 50 Print
Total Titles: 800 Print
Branch Office(s)
Publications CCH Ltee, 7005 boul Taschereau bur 190, Brossard, QC J4Z 1A7 *Tel:* 450-678-4443
CCH Canadienne Limitee, 1120 rue Cherbourg, CP 2300, Sherbrooke, QC J1H 5N7 *Tel:* 819-566-2000
U.S. Publishers Represented: Aspen Publishers; CCH US

Wood Lake Publishing Inc
485 Beaver Lake Rd, Kelowna, BC V4V 1S5
Tel: 250-766-2778 *Toll Free Tel:* 800-663-2775 (orders & cust serv) *Fax:* 250-766-2736 *Toll Free Fax:* 888-841-9991 (orders & cust serv)
E-mail: info@woodlake.com; customerservice@woodlake.com
Web Site: www.woodlakebooks.com
Key Personnel
Pres & Publr: Patty Berube
Mktg Promos & Sales: Lynette Nicholas *E-mail:* lynetten@woodlake.com
Founded: 1980
Books, church curriculum & periodicals.
Publishes in English.
ISBN Prefix(es): 978-1-55145; 978-0-919599; 978-0-929032
Number of titles published annually: 4 Print
Total Titles: 135 Print
Imprints: The Best of Whole People of God Online; CopperHouse; Northstone; Seasons of the Spirit; Wood Lake
Distributed by Augsburg Canada; Presbyterian Church of Canada; United Church of Canada
Distributor for Northstone

Worldwide Library
Imprint of Harlequin Enterprises Ltd
225 Duncan Mill Rd, Don Mills, ON M3B 3K9
Mailing Address: PO Box 615, Fort Erie, ON L2A 5X3
Tel: 416-445-5860 *Toll Free Tel:* 888-432-4879 *Fax:* 416-445-8655; 416-445-8736
E-mail: customerservice@harlequin.com
Web Site: www.harlequin.com
Key Personnel
Exec Ed: Kathleen Scheibling
Intl Rts: Sandra Caunter
Founded: 1982
Mass market fiction.
Publishes in English.
ISBN Prefix(es): 978-0-373
Number of titles published annually: 78 Print
Imprints: Gold Eagle Books; Worldwide Mystery
Branch Office(s)
PO Box 5190, Buffalo, NY 14240-5190, United States
Foreign Rights: Booklink (Europe)
Warehouse: 3010 Walden Ave, Depew, NY 14043, United States

Small Presses

Listed here, in alphabetical order, are U.S. & Canadian publishers who were not eligible to be listed in the sections covering U.S. Publishers or Canadian Publishers. Many of these publishers are new or offer distinctive titles they wish to make known to the users of *Literary Market Place*. Entries in this section are paid listings.

Publishers interested in participating in this section in future editions of LMP are invited to contact **Lauri Rimler, Advertising Sales** by e-mail at lwrimler@infotoday.com, by phone at 800-409-4929 (press 1) or 908-219-0088, or by mail at Information Today, Inc., 121 Chanlon Rd, Suite G-20, New Providence, NJ 07974-2195.

Adams-Pomeroy Press
103 N Jackson St, Albany, WI 53502
Mailing Address: PO Box 189, Albany, WI 53502
Tel: 608-862-3645 *Toll Free Tel:* 877-862-3645 *Fax:* 608-862-3647
E-mail: adamspomeroy@tds.net
Founded: 1996
Adams-Pomeroy Press publishes books in the areas of education, multicultural nonfiction, juvenile fiction & fiction.
Titles include *Haunted Hill (A Sam & Stephanie Mystery)*; *How Big Is Your Class? Practical Tips for Teaching Small and Large Primary Grade Classes*; *Missing What's-Her-Name*; *Mixed Heritage: Your Source for Books for Children and Teens about Persons and Families of Mixed Racial, Ethnic, and/or Religious Heritage*; *My Reading Buddy Is a Dog!: Your Resource for Creating and Running a Canine Reading Buddy Program*
ISBN Prefix(es): 978-0-9661009
Membership(s): The Association of Publishers for Special Sales; Colorado Independent Publishers Association; The Independent Book Publishers Association

AIC Publications
PO Box 181467, Arlington, TX 76002-1467
E-mail: submissions@aicpublications.com
Web Site: aicpublications.com
Key Personnel
Pres: M Hamzah
Our literature focuses on adult nonfiction, young adult fiction & children's picture book stories highlighting the unique & diverse experiences of Blacks in America & Africa designed to promote positive advancement, socioeconomic empowerment & literacy rates. We take real community issues presented in fiction, offer solutions for them while providing the positive end result of success. Our nonfiction provides a historical understanding & analysis for community growth in a fast changing world. We want our readers to Attain the knowledge, Innovate for success & take Command of their future!
Titles include *A Worthy Muslim: Quranic Tools Needed to Overcome Oppression and Imperialism in Order to Institute Justice*
ISBN Prefix(es): 978-0-9799464
Membership(s): The Independent Book Publishers Association

Alazar Press
Imprint of Royal Swan Enterprises Inc
201 Orchard Lane, Carrboro, NC 27510
SAN: 853-0521
Tel: 919-274-0653
E-mail: alazar.press@gmail.com
Web Site: www.alazar-press.com
Key Personnel
Publr: Rosemarie Gulla *E-mail:* rgulla@nc.rr.com
Mgr: Joseph Gulla
Founded: 2007
Focused on engaging young people with ideas, Alazar press is dedicated to producing quality books for children of all ages & is aligned with the mission of Royal Swan Enterprises.
Royal Swan offers high quality literature & accompanying ideas in a vital & relevant manner in order to best serve the developing minds of young people. Royal Swan acknowledges the inherent worth & dignity of all children & works to equip them with the tools of a literate & reflective society. Asserting the primacy of building true emotional engagement to learning, Royal Swan develops books, story frameworks, methods, products & services for young learners & their families.
Titles include *I'm Going to Sing, Black American Spirituals Volume Two*; *Walk Together Children, Black American Spirituals Volume One*
ISBN Prefix(es): 978-0-9793000
Distributed by Independent Publishers Group (IPG)
Membership(s): International Literacy Association; North Carolina Reading Association; Triangle Reading Council

BCFL
4806 Martinique Way, Naples, FL 34119
Tel: 908-447-3553 *Fax:* 239-596-8611
E-mail: BCFLGroup@gmail.com
Web Site: judgingfloraldesign.com
Key Personnel
Opers: Bill Whalen
Founded: 2012
Nonfiction publisher specializing in books on floral design for students, teachers, competitors, garden club arrangers, professional designers & judges.
Titles include *A Fresh Look at Judging Floral Design*
ISBN Prefix(es): 978-0-9854476
Distributed by BCFLGroup.com; Publishers Storage & Shipping Corp (PSSC) (fulfillment)
Membership(s): The Independent Book Publishers Association

Class Action Ink
1300 NE 16 Ave, Suite 712, Portland, OR 97232-1483
Tel: 503-280-2448
E-mail: pam@classactionink.com
Web Site: www.classactionink.com
Key Personnel
Owner/Publr: Pam Glenn
Founded: 2009
Publishes literary fiction & poetry for mature, culturally savvy readers. Some projects may be partially author subsidized.
Titles include *All the Wrong Places: Mrs. Frog's Improbable Search for Love*; *Barter World*; *Even As We Speak: Selected Poems*; *What you least expect: selected poems 1980-2011*
ISBN Prefix(es): 978-0-9841530
Distributed by Partners/West
Membership(s): The Independent Book Publishers Association

Dreaming Publications LLC
1938 Old Balsam Rd, Waynesville, NC 28786
SAN: 859-4333
Tel: 828-423-0226
E-mail: dreamingpublications@gmail.com
Web Site: dreamingpublications.com
Key Personnel
Pres: Lyn Marsh, PhD *E-mail:* lynmarshphd@gmail.com
Mktg Promos Dir: Ines Sinon
Founded: 2010
Dreaming Publications LLC publishes juvenile & adult fiction & nonfiction. Our focus is to publish work that inspires new dreams & future visions, innovative thinking & imagination. We are currently focusing on ebook & paperback/softcover publishing.
Titles include *Conversations with Einstein at the Edge of the Cosmos*; *The Grand Tree (2nd ed) (book 1 of 3 in the Rainbow Crystal series)*
ISBN Prefix(es): 978-0-9844495
Membership(s): The Independent Book Publishers Association

Filsinger & Company Ltd
288 W 12 St, Suite 2R, New York, NY 10014
Tel: 212-243-7421
E-mail: filsingercompany@gmail.com
Web Site: www.filsingerco.com
Key Personnel
Pres: Cheryl Filsinger
Founded: 1974
Publisher of museum-quality children's books including the NEIGHBORS series. *Philippe the Black Sheep* & the sequel to *BUMMER* will be published in 2016.
Titles available at Teich Toys + Books (NYC); Book Hampton, Canio's Books, Harbor Books & the South Fork Natural History Museum (The Hamptons, Long Island, NY), Sustenance Books (Murphys, CA) & others.
Titles include *BUMMER (print & ebook)*; *The Children's Pack of Frames*; *NEIGHBORS The Water Critters*; *NEIGHBORS The Yard Critters Book 1*; *NEIGHBORS The Yard Critters TOO*
ISBN Prefix(es): 978-0-916754
Distributed by Amazon.com; Baker & Taylor; Brodart; Follett School Solutions; Charles Marangio Distribution

Heart and Mind Press LLC
3135 E Palo Verde Dr, Phoenix, AZ 85016
Tel: 602-790-4009
E-mail: info@heartandmindpress.com
Web Site: heartandmindpress.com
Key Personnel
Publr: Teresa Villegas
Founded: 2013
Heart and Mind Press is dedicated to helping parents & educators to inspire & cultivate conscious, empathetic, responsible children with an understanding of the natural world & how it impacts us on a deeper personal level. Exploring the interconnectedness of heart & mind is where we thrive.
Titles include *How to Celebrate Winter Solstice*; *How We Became a Family (series)*
ISBN Prefix(es): 978-0-9884501
Distributed by Amazon.com; Brodart Co; Ingram

Infusionmedia
140 N Eighth St, Suite 214, The Apothecary, Lincoln, NE 68508-1353
SAN: 253-9136
Tel: 402-477-2065
E-mail: info@infusionmediadesign.com
Web Site: www.infusionmediadesign.com
Key Personnel
Pres: Cris Trautner *E-mail:* cris@infusionmediadesign.com
VP: Aaron Vacin *E-mail:* aaron@infusionmediadesign.com
Founded: 1994
In this rapidly changing publishing industry, you need to have a partner who still steer you in the right direction for your book or periodical & provide good counsel on the best way to publish based on your goals & definition of success. Infusionmedia has the experience (over 20 years & counting) to develop & execute a publishing solution that meets your needs & budget. We are a graphic design shop specializing in custom book design & publishing, ebook development, & web site design. Our expertise, resources & deep commitment to our craft make us an excellent choice to meet your custom publishing needs.
Titles include *A History of the World*; *The Loren Eiseley Reader*; *Put Your Mouth Where the Money Is: How to Refocus Your Marketing Communications for the Greatest Impact on Sales*; *Shafer's Nebraska Pheasant Hunting Almanac*; *Shortcuts to Gourmet Cooking & Family Favorites*
ISBN Prefix(es): 978-0-9704852; 978-0-9718677; 978-0-9796586; 978-0-9888122; 978-0-9916455
Imprints: Abbatia Press; Amanuent Press; Asteria Press; Infusionmedia Publishing; Plains Chronicles Press
Distributed by Baker & Taylor; Ingram
Membership(s): Better Business Bureau; The Independent Book Publishers Association

Lemon Grove Press
1158 26 St, Suite 502, Santa Monica, CA 90403
Tel: 310-471-1740 *Fax:* 310-476-7627
E-mail: info@lemongrovepress.com
Web Site: www.thetakechargepatient.com
Key Personnel
Publr: Martine Ehrenclou
Asst: Christine Buffaloe
Founded: 2007
Boutique imprint specializing in adult self-help, health & nonfiction. No children's or young adult books.
Titles include *Critical Conditions: The Essential Hospital Guide to Get Your Loved One Out Alive*; *The Take-Charge Patient: How You Can Get the Best Medical Care*
ISBN Prefix(es): 978-0-9815240
Distributed by Baker & Taylor Inc; The Book House Inc; Bookmasters; Brodart Co Books & Automation; Emery-Pratt Co; Follett School Solutions Inc; Ingram Book Group; Midwest Library Service; Quality Books Inc; Unique Books Inc
Membership(s): The Independent Book Publishers Association

Magic Hill Press LLC
144 Magic Hill Rd, Hinesburg, VT 05461
Tel: 802-482-3287
E-mail: MagicHillPress@gmail.com
Web Site: www.MagicHillPress.com
Key Personnel
Principal: William H Schubart *E-mail:* Bill@Schubart.com
Founded: 2010
Magic Hill Publishing LLC is the imprint of novelist, short story & op-ed writer Bill Schubart. Titles available in print & electronically.
Titles include *Fat People (ISBN: 978-0-615-39751-1)*; *I Am Baybie (ISBN: 978-0-9834852-9-2)*; *The Lamoille Stories (ISBN: 978-0-9897121-0-1)*; *The Lamoille Stories II (ISBN: 978-9897121-3-2)*; *Panhead (ISBN: 978-0-9834852-6-1)*; *Photographic Memory (ISBN: 978-0-9834852-8-5)*
ISBN Prefix(es): 978-0-9834852; 978-0-9897121
Distributed by Ingram Book Group (full trade discount)
Membership(s): The Independent Book Publishers Association; Independent Publishers of New England

Moonstone Press LLC
4816 Carrington Circle, Sarasota, FL 34243
SAN: 852-5625
Tel: 301-765-1081 *Fax:* 301-765-0510
E-mail: mazeprod@erols.com
Web Site: www.moonstonepress.net
Key Personnel
Publr: Stephanie Maze
Founded: 2001
Publishes quality photography-based books in English & Spanish for ages 3 & up. Award-winning book titles include: *Healthy Foods from A to Z/Comida sana de la A a la Z*; *Keeping Fit from A to Z/Mantente en forma de la A a la Z*; *Breastfeeding Around the World/Amamantar alrededor del mundo*; *Moments in the Wild/Momentos en el reino animal* (4 title series).
ISBN Prefix(es): 978-0-9707768; 978-0-9769542; 978-0-9834983
Distributed by IPG/Small Press United
Membership(s): The Independent Book Publishers Association; White House Press Photogaphers Association

Move Books
PO Box 183, Beacon Falls, CT 06403
Web Site: www.move-books.com
Key Personnel
Publr: Eileen Robinson *E-mail:* eileen.robinson@move-books.com
Design Dir: Virginia Pope
Mfg Dir: Joe Sita
Edit Asst: Krista Ehrentraut *E-mail:* kehrentraut@move-books.com
Edit: Harold Underdown
Founded: 2012
Move Books is a children's publisher dedicated to getting more boys to read. We want to inspire them to read on their own, not just for educational purposes but to become emotionally invested in characters & stories that resonate with them, thereby creating a lifelong love of reading. We have published adventure, fantasy & realistic fiction. Humor, historical fiction & graphic novels are on our agenda too. Publicity trailers & social media for Move Books handled by OTB Film Reel.
Titles include *The Lost Tribes*; *Surviving Bear Island*
ISBN Prefix(es): 978-0-9854810
Distributed by Independent Publishers Group (IPG)
Membership(s): The Independent Book Publishers Association

New York Media Works
Imprint of New York Media Works LLC
112 Franklin St, New York, NY 10013
SAN: 920-5187
Tel: 646-369-5681 *Fax:* 646-810-4033
E-mail: info@nymediaworks.com
Web Site: www.nymediaworks.com
Key Personnel
Owner: Julie Gribble *E-mail:* JGribble@nymediaworks.com
PR/Media: Kassia Graham *E-mail:* pr@nymediaworks.com
Media Strategy: Rachel Kent *E-mail:* pr@nymediaworks.com
Founded: 2012
New York Media Works is a publisher & content provider for new media & film located in the heart of Tribeca, NYC. We collaborate with artists & filmmakers from around the world to create inspiring & compelling stories to entertain audiences of all ages. Four new titles coming soon.
Titles include *Bubblegum Princess*
ISBN Prefix(es): 978-0-9890914
Distributed by Amazon.com; Brodart; Quality Books Inc
Membership(s): AAP; Children's Literature Association; The Independent Book Publishers Association

Painted Hills Publishing
16500 Dakota Ridge Rd, Longmont, CO 80503
Tel: 303-823-6642 *Fax:* 303-825-5119
E-mail: cw@livingimagescjw.com
Web Site: www.wildhoofbeats.com; www.horsephotographyworkshops.com
Key Personnel
Owner: Carol Walker
Founded: 2008
Publishes photography books on wild horses with the purpose of educating the public about the wild horse situation in the US. Also publishes books on the techniques of photographing domestic & wild horses.
Titles include *Galloping to Freedom: Saving the Adobe Town Appaloosas*; *Horse Photography: The Dynamic Guide for Horse Lovers*; *Wild Hoofbeats: America's Vanishing Wild Horses*
ISBN Prefix(es): 978-0-9817936
Distributed by Baker & Taylor; Books West; Gazelle International; Greenleaf Book Group; Quality Books
Membership(s): The Independent Book Publishers Association; PPA

ProChain Press
Imprint of ProChain Solutions Inc
3460 Commission Ct, No 301, Lake Ridge, VA 22192
Tel: 703-490-8821 *Fax:* 703-494-1414
E-mail: publishing@prochain.com
Web Site: prochain.com
Key Personnel
CEO: Robert Newbold *E-mail:* rnewbold@prochain.com
COO: William Lynch *E-mail:* blynch@prochain.com
Founded: 2008
Publish & manage books related primarily to project management & critical chain scheduling.
Titles include *Be Fast or Be Gone*; *The Billion Dollar Solution*
ISBN Prefix(es): 978-1-934979
Distributed by Amazon.com; Baker & Taylor; Barnes & Noble; Ingram
Membership(s): The Independent Book Publishers Association

Ransom Note Press
143 E Ridgewood Ave, Box 419, Ridgewood, NJ 07451
Tel: 201-835-2790
E-mail: editorial@ransomnotepress.com
Web Site: www.ransomnotepress.com

Key Personnel
Publr: Christian Alighieri
Sr Ed: Emily Marlowe
Publicist: Max St John
Founded: 2005
Ransom Note Press publishes modern & traditional mysteries & novels of suspense. Query via e-mail with descriptive letter & first 25 pages. No pet mysteries, serial killers or short story collections. We are interested only in novels that offer gripping story lines & well-executed plots. In general, we prefer novels in which the author has attempted to do something different to break from tradition & explore new ground.
Titles include *Never Kill a Friend*; *Nine Man's Murder*; *The Outsmarting of Criminals: A Mystery Introducing Miss Felicity Prim*
ISBN Prefix(es): 978-0-9773787
Distributed by Baker & Taylor; Brodart Books; Partners Publishing Group
Membership(s): The Independent Book Publishers Association

Rivendell Books
PO Box 29348, St Louis, MO 63126-0348
SAN: 854-1531
Tel: 314-609-6534
E-mail: butch@rivendellbooks.com
Web Site: www.rivendellbooks.com
Key Personnel
Publr: Butch Drury
Founded: 2008
Rivendell Books is a very narrowly focused, niche publisher for a select group of authors who write nonfiction books that explore the collaboration of the conscious & the unconscious using the Transcendent Function, the process at the heart of Carl Jung's theory of psychological growth, by which one is guided, through active imagination or dialogue with the unconscious, toward the person one is meant to become.
Titles include *A Different Kind of Sentinel*
ISBN Prefix(es): 978-0-9797023
Distributed by Amazon.com; Barnes & Noble (online); Ingram; Lightning Source
Membership(s): The C G Jung Society of Saint Louis; The Independent Book Publishers Association; The International Hearing Voices Network; Missouri Writers' Guild; St Louis Publishers Association; St Louis Writers Guild

Thompson Mill Press LLC
2865 S Eagle Rd, No 368, Newtown, PA 18940
Tel: 215-431-1424
E-mail: bob.regan@thompsonmillpress.com
Web Site: www.thompsonmillpress.com; www.KobeeManatee.com
Key Personnel
Principal: Bob Regan
Founded: 2012
Located in the northern suburbs of Philadelphia, Thompson Mill Press LLC focuses on the development, publishing & distribution of children's educational picture books containing anthropomorphic characters. Our initial plans for distribution include all of North America. Future distribution plans include Asia, Australia, Central & South America, Europe & Mexico.
Titles include *Kobee Manatee: A Wild Weather Adventure*; *Kobee Manatee: Heading Home to Florida*
ISBN Prefix(es): 978-0-9883269
Distributed by Small Press United (through Independent Publishers Group)
Membership(s): ABA; The Children's Book Council; The Independent Book Publishers Association

Three Wishes Publishing Company
26500 W Agoura Rd, Suite 102-754, Calabasas, CA 91302
Tel: 818-878-0902 *Fax:* 818-878-1805
E-mail: Alva710@aol.com
Web Site: www.threewishespublishing.com
Founded: 2007
Children's book publisher.
Titles include *Circus Fever*; *Dear Master Dragon*; *I'm 5*; *On Your Mark, Get Set, Go!*
ISBN Prefix(es): 978-0-9796380
Distributed by Amazon.com; Baker & Taylor; Barnes & Noble; Follett School Solutions Inc
Membership(s): ALA; Angels of the Alliance; Association of Jewish Libraries of Southern California; California Literary Arts Society; California School Library Association; Children's Literature Council; The Independent Book Publishers Association; Reading Is Fundamental of Southern California; Society of Children's Book Writers & Illustrators

TJ Publishers Inc
PO Box 702701, Dallas, TX 75370
Toll Free Tel: 800-999-1168 *Fax:* 972-416-0944
E-mail: TJPubinc@aol.com
Key Personnel
Pres: T Patrick O'Rourke
Founded: 1978
Publisher & distributor of quality books, DVDs & other materials related to sign language & deafness including several best sellers.
Titles include *A Basic Course in American Sign Language (2nd ed)*; *From Mime to Sign*; *Student Study Guide to A Basic Course in American Sign Language*
ISBN Prefix(es): 978-0-932666

Worthy & James Publishing
PO Box 362015, Milpitas, CA 95036
SAN: 852-5765
Tel: 408-945-3963
E-mail: worthy1234@sbcglobal.net; mail@worthyjames.com
Web Site: www.worthyjames.com
Key Personnel
Mgr: Diane James
Mgr/Author: Greg Mostyn
Founded: 2006
Publications in basic accounting, basic finance & basic math.
Titles include *Basic Accounting Concepts, Principles, and Procedures (vols 1 & 2)*
ISBN Prefix(es): 978-0-9791494
Membership(s): The Independent Book Publishers Association

Editorial Services & Agents

Editorial Services — Activity Index

ABSTRACTING

ADAPTATIONS, NOVELIZATIONS

ADVERTISING & PROMOTION COPYWRITING

BIBLIOGRAPHIES

BROKER FOR MANUFACTURING

CONDENSATIONS

COPY-EDITING

FACT CHECKING

GHOSTWRITING

INDEXING

INTERVIEWING

LINE EDITING

MANUSCRIPT ANALYSIS

PERMISSIONS

PHOTO RESEARCH

PROOFREADING

RESEARCH

REWRITING

SPECIAL ASSIGNMENT WRITING

STATISTICS

TECHNICAL WRITING

TRANSCRIPTION EDITING

TYPEMARKING

Editorial Services

For information on other companies who provide services to the book industry, see **Consultants, Book Producers, Typing & Word Processing Services** and **Artists & Art Services**.

A+ English LLC/Book-Editing.com/Book Editing Associates
PO Box 1369, Mansfield, TX 76063
Tel: 469-789-3030
E-mail: editingnetwork@gmail.com
Web Site: www.editing-writing.com; www.book-editing.com; www.HelpWithStatistics; www.apawriting.com; childrensbookeditors.com; dissertationeditor.com
Key Personnel
Freelance Network Coord: Lynda Lotman
Founded: 1976
Serving writers (unpublished, published), publishers (mainstream, genre, trade, academic), agents, researchers & businesses. Ms evaluations, copy-editing, developmental editing, submission materials (query letters, book proposals), mentoring & ghostwriting. We work with fiction, nonfiction, medical/scientific/technical material, business documents & textbooks.
Membership(s): Science Fiction & Fantasy Writers of America

A Westport Wordsmith
101 Winfield St, Norwalk, CT 06855
Tel: 203-939-9484
E-mail: pj104daily@aol.com
Key Personnel
Prop: Peggy Daily
Founded: 1999
Proofreading (nonfiction & fiction) & indexing of trade books. Americanization.
Membership(s): American Society for Indexing; Editorial Freelancers Association

AAA Photos
401 Ocean Dr, Unit 804, Miami Beach, FL 33139
Tel: 305-534-0804
Web Site: www.photosphotos.net
Key Personnel
Pres: Jeff Greenberg *E-mail:* jeffreygreenberg@aol.com
Provides photos to tourism bureau, book publishers, magazine publishers, newspapers, travel publications, web sites & by assignment & stock.

AAH Graphics Inc
Subsidiary of Loft Press Inc
9293 Fort Valley Rd, Fort Valley, VA 22652-2020
Tel: 540-933-6211 *Fax:* 540-933-6523
E-mail: srhunter@aahgraphics.com
Web Site: www.aahgraphics.com
Key Personnel
Pres: Ann A Hunter
Founded: 1973
Complete editorial through production serving publishers & individuals. Design of text, jackets & covers, composition & production management through manufacturing.

Aaron-Spear
PO Box 42, Brooksville, ME 04617
Tel: 207-326-8764
Key Personnel
Prop: Jody Spear
Developmental editing & copy-editing of scholarly mss in the humanities. Rewriting for style & sensibility as well as clarity, consistency & accuracy. Specialize in art history & environmental studies.

About Books Inc
1001 Taurus Dr, Colorado Springs, CO 80906
Tel: 719-632-8226 *Fax:* 719-213-2602
Web Site: www.about-books.com
Key Personnel
Owner & Pres: Debi Flora *E-mail:* debiflora@about-books.com
Owner & VP: Scott Flora *E-mail:* scott@about-books.com
Founded: 1977
Complete writing, editorial & book development services: editing; cover & interior design; ebooks & print books; specialize in nonfiction books on all subjects.
Membership(s): The Association of Publishers for Special Sales

Access Editorial Services
1133 Broadway, Suite 528, New York, NY 10010
Tel: 212-255-7306
E-mail: wiseword@juno.com
Key Personnel
Dir: Louise Weiss
Founded: 1990
Services include travel writing.
Membership(s): The Authors Guild; New York Travel Writers Association; SATW; Toastmasters International

Accurate Writing & More
Affiliate of Business For a Better World
16 Barstow Lane, Hadley, MA 01035
Tel: 413-586-2388
Web Site: www.accuratewriting.com; www.business-for-a-better-world.com; www.greenandprofitable.com; www.makinggreensexy.com; frugalmarketing.com; www.frugalfun.com; www.twitter.com/shelhorowitz
Key Personnel
Owner & Dir: Shel Horowitz *E-mail:* shel@principledprofit.com
Dir: Dina Friedman
Founded: 1981
Advertising & promotion copywriting, ghostwriting, editing, publishing consulting, interviewing, ms analysis, research, rewriting, special assignment writing & publishing consulting for authors, publishers & green businesses.
Membership(s): Connecticut Authors & Publishers Association; The Independent Book Publishers Association; Independent Publishers of New England; National Writers Union; Western New England Editorial Freelancers Network

J Adel Art & Design
586 Ramapo Rd, Teaneck, NJ 07666
Tel: 201-836-2606
E-mail: jadelnj@aol.com
Key Personnel
Creative Dir: Judith Adel
Founded: 1985
Freelance copy, illustration & design services for publishers.

AEIOU Inc
894 Piermont Ave, Piermont, NY 10968
Tel: 845-680-5380
Key Personnel
Pres: Cynthia Crippen *E-mail:* ccrippen@verizon.net
Founded: 1976

AFS Wordstead
1062 Vallee-a-Josaphat, Lac-des-Iles, QC J0W 1J0, Canada
Tel: 819-597-4072 *Fax:* 819-597-4547
Web Site: www.wordstead.com
Key Personnel
Owner & Sr Writer: Anthony F Shaker, PhD *E-mail:* afshaker@aol.com
Founded: 2001 (in the writing business since 1988)
Ghosting, rewriting, editing. Works in fiction & nonfiction (memoirs, autobiographies, biographies, business & self-improvement books, articles, scripts, book-to-screen adaptations). Works regularly with publishers on client projects & his own scholarly books.
For online query, please include full name, phone number, short description of project & nature of request (ghostwriting, editing, copywriting, etc).

Rodelinde Albrecht
PO Box 444, Lenox Dale, MA 01242-0444
Tel: 413-243-4350
E-mail: rodelinde@gmail.com
Founded: 1979
Full editorial services; scanning; copy/line editing (hardcopy/electronic); rewriting; castoff, typemarking; proofreading; proof-checking & consulting.

AllWrite Advertising & Publishing
241 Peachtree St NE, Suite 400, Atlanta, GA 30303
Mailing Address: PO Box 1071, Atlanta, GA 30301
Tel: 404-221-0703 *Fax:* 770-284-8986
E-mail: questions@allwritepublishing.com
Web Site: www.e-allwrite.com
Key Personnel
Pres & Publr: Annette R Johnson *Tel:* 770-284-8956 *E-mail:* annette@allwritepublishing.com
Founded: 1996
A conventional publisher that also offers editorial services for self-publishers & those who need promotional documents or materials, including booklets & brochures. Provides comprehensive editing & proofreading services: checking syntax, grammar, punctuation & style; & offering substantive/line editing, developmental editing & production editing. Get a free online quote at www.e-allwrite.com.
Membership(s): Writers Guild of America East

Jeanette Almada
452 W Aldine, Unit 215, Chicago, IL 60657
Tel: 773-404-9350
E-mail: jmalmada@sbcglobal.net
Writer, reporter, editor. Rewrite, co-author or author any story for publication as a book, article, newsletter or brochure. Areas of research & writing interest include urban affairs & lifestyle; organic standards & organic consumer topics; slow & local food; corporate cultural issues & corporate profiles, land use & conservation; neighborhood or community development & other nonfiction topics.

Ampersand Group
12 Morenz Terr, Kanata, ON K2K 3G9, Canada
Tel: 613-435-5066

Key Personnel
Pres: Ed Matheson *E-mail:* ematheson@bell.net
Book publishing consultants for publishers, business, government & individuals with publishing problems. Specialize in project management, general book design & production.

Joyce L Ananian
25 Forest Circle, Waltham, MA 02452-4719
Tel: 781-894-4330
E-mail: jlananian@hotmail.com
Founded: 1981
Copy-editing, fact checking, indexing, proofreading & line editing.

Barbara S Anderson
706 W Davis Ave, Ann Arbor, MI 48103-4855
Tel: 734-995-0125
E-mail: bsa328@earthlink.net
Key Personnel
Owner: Barbara S Anderson
Admin Asst: Martin B Tittle *Tel:* 734-846-3864 *E-mail:* mtittle@umich.edu
Rewriting, proofreading, ms analysis & line editing. For related services see listing in Artists & Art Services.

Denice A Anderson
210 E Church St, Clinton, MI 49236
Tel: 517-456-4990 *Fax:* 517-456-4990
E-mail: deniceanderson@frontier.com
Founded: 1984
Copy-editing, line editing & proofreading; fiction & nonfiction; art, history, medical, legal, business, newspapers, journals & directories.
Membership(s): Editorial Freelancers Association

Jim Anderson
77 S Second St, Brooklyn, NY 11249
Tel: 718-388-1083
E-mail: jim.and@att.net

Patricia Anderson PhD, Literary Consultant
1489 Marine Dr, Suite 515, West Vancouver, BC V7T 1B8, Canada
Tel: 604-740-0805
E-mail: query@helpingyougetpublished.com; patriciaanderson@helpingyougetpublished.com
Web Site: www.helpingyougetpublished.com
Key Personnel
Literary Consultant: Dr Patricia Anderson, PhD
Founded: 1998 (online since 1999)
Offering ms assessment, book editing, proofreading, book proposals, market research, book trailers & press releases. Specialist in personalized writing & publishing strategies for emerging novelists & authors of book-length nonfiction.
Membership(s): The Authors Guild; Editors' Association of Canada/Association canadienne des reviseurs; The Writers' Union of Canada

Angel Editing Services
PO Box 752, Mountain Ranch, CA 95246
Tel: 209-728-8364
E-mail: info@stephaniemarohn.com
Web Site: www.stephaniemarohn.com
Key Personnel
Owner & Ed: Stephanie Marohn
Founded: 1993
Full range of editorial services, from developmental editing through copy-editing. Specialize in nonfiction trade books, particularly psychospiritual topics, metaphysics, natural medicine & other alternative thought.
Membership(s): Bay Area Editors' Forum

Angels Editorial Services
1630 Main St, Suite 41, Coventry, CT 06238
Tel: 860-742-5279
E-mail: angelsus@aol.com
Key Personnel
Pres: Prof Claire Connelly, PhD
Founded: 1969
MS or disk: Counseling & psychotherapy, science & computers, textbooks, GLBT, fiction & nonfiction, animals.
Membership(s): American Copy Editors Society; Society for Technical Communication

Aptara Inc
3110 Fairview Park Dr, Suite 900, Falls Church, VA 22042
Tel: 703-352-0001
E-mail: info@aptaracorp.com
Web Site: www.aptaracorp.com
Key Personnel
COO: Scott Weeren
CFO: Neil Campling
Pres: Bill Penders
VP, Accts & Fin: Prashant Kapoor
VP, Mktg: Megan Prosser
Busn Devt: Michael Scott *E-mail:* michael.scott@aptaracorp.com
Liaison for complete or any combination of production services, ranging from simple 1-color to complex 4-color projects & copy-editing. Offer ebook conversions & end-to-end solutions publishing services in print & digital.

Archon Editorial LLC
815 King St, Suite 204, Alexandria, VA 22314
Tel: 703-838-1650
Key Personnel
Owner: Brooke C Stoddard *E-mail:* stoddardbc@gmail.com
Founded: 1983
Magazine & book writing & editing. Can handle design & production.
Membership(s): American Society of Journalists & Authors; The Authors Guild; Editorial Freelancers Association; National Press Club

ASJA Freelance Writer Search
Affiliate of American Society of Journalists & Authors Inc
355 Lexington Ave, 15th fl, New York, NY 10017
Tel: 212-997-0947
E-mail: asjaoffice@asja.org
Web Site: www.freelancewritersearch.com
Key Personnel
Exec Dir: Alexandra Owens
Founded: 1948
Vital resource for anyone seeking the services of professsional writers for articles, books, book proposals, brochures, annual reports, speeches, TV & film scripts, advertising copy, publicity campaigns, corporate communications & more. Free, private listing service goes only to the 1,300 professional members of ASJA.

Associated Editors
27 W 96 St, New York, NY 10025
Tel: 212-662-9703
Key Personnel
Contact: Lynne Glasner *E-mail:* lyngla1@gmail.com; Maury Siegel
Copy-editing, rewriting, proofreading, indexing, research, developmental editing. Specialize in elementary & secondary textbooks; nonfiction trade books.

Astor Indexers
256 Blue Ridge Dr, Canadensis, PA 18325
Tel: 570-595-2336; 570-534-8951 (cell)
Key Personnel
Owner: Jane Farnol *E-mail:* bjfarnol@snet.net
Founded: 1970
Indexing is our only business. Staff handles all subjects; hard copy, e-mail or disk. Quality, speed & accuracy are our trademarks.

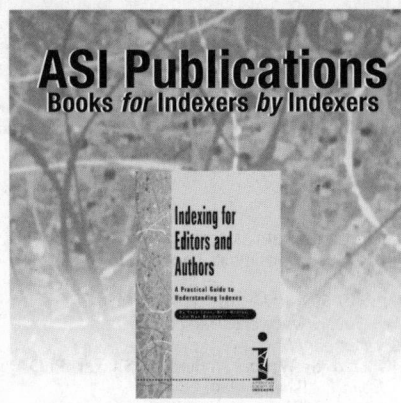

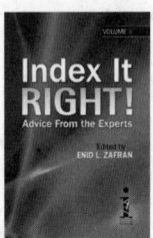

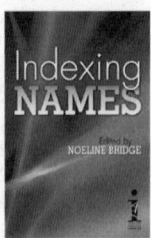

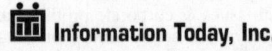

Audrey Owen
494 Eaglecrest Dr, Gibsons, BC V0N 1V8, Canada
E-mail: editor@writershelper.com
Web Site: www.writershelper.com
Founded: 2002
Besides the editing services offered by other agencies, I also specialize in educative editing that becomes a mini tutorial designed for, but is not restricted to, self-publishing writers. Also offer substantive editing.
Membership(s): Editors' Association of Canada/ Association canadienne des reviseurs; Federation of British Columbia Writers; Society of Children's Book Writers & Illustrators

The Author's Friend
548 Ocean Blvd, No 12, Long Branch, NJ 07740
Tel: 732-571-8051
Key Personnel
Prop: Judith Stein *E-mail:* jstein@panix.com
Founded: 1976
Copy & line editing, proofreading & transcription editing. Specialize in religion & spirituality, psychology, medicine, self-help, bibliographies & esoterica.

Backman Writing & Communications
32 Hillview Ave, Rensselaer, NY 12144
Tel: 518-449-4985
Web Site: www.backwrite.com
Key Personnel
Principal: John Backman *E-mail:* johnb@backwrite.com
Founded: 1986
Articles, blogs, advertising & marketing copy. Areas of focus: spirituality, higher education, engineering, financial services & generally making the complex simple.

Baldwin Literary Services
935 Hayes St, Baldwin, NY 11510-4834
Tel: 516-546-8338 *Fax:* 516-546-8338
Key Personnel
Pres: Marjorie Gillette Jones
Founded: 1982
Creative writing courses. Specialize in novels, historical novels, autobiographies, medical, gardening & nature, spiritual.
Membership(s): International Women's Writing Guild

Kathleen Barnes
238 W Fourth St, Suite 3-C, New York, NY 10014
Tel: 212-924-8084
E-mail: kbarnes@compasscommunications.org
Writing, rewriting, line editing, copy-editing & proofreading.

Melinda Barrett
37915 Sundance Dr, Coarsegold, CA 93614
Tel: 559-641-0944
E-mail: mbarrett_3@netzero.net
Founded: 1989
Copy-editing, proofreading, rewriting & special assignment writing.

Diana Barth
535 W 51 St, Suite 3-A, New York, NY 10019
Tel: 212-307-5465
E-mail: diabarth@juno.com
Founded: 1970
All subjects; specialize in performing arts, health, psychology, education & travel. Feature & ghostwriter.

Anita Bartholomew
8535 SE 92 Ave, Portland, OR 97266
Tel: 941-358-0495
E-mail: anita@anitabartholomew.com
Web Site: www.anitabartholomew.com
Founded: 1993
Developmental editor. Specialize in fiction & narrative nonfiction. Have ghosted fiction & nonfiction. Co-authored a leading OB-GYN's award-winning memoir. Clients include authors (typically referred by their literary agents), publishers & nonprofits. Endorsements/testimonials available on web site & LinkedIn profile.
Membership(s): Investigative Reporters & Editors

Mark E Battersby
PO Box 527, Ardmore, PA 19003
Tel: 610-924-9157 *Fax:* 610-924-9159
E-mail: mebatt12@earthlink.net
Founded: 1971
Freelance writer. Specialize in tax & financial features, columns, Web content & White Papers.

Beaver Wood Associates
655 Alstead Center Rd, Alstead, NH 03602
Mailing Address: PO Box 717, Alstead, NH 03602
Tel: 603-835-7900
Web Site: www.beaverwood.com
Key Personnel
Owner: Jeanne C Moody *E-mail:* jcmoody@beaverwood.com
Founded: 1985
Indexing, copy-editing & proofreading.
Membership(s): American Society for Indexing

Barbara Bergstrom MA LLC
13 Stockton Way, Howell, NJ 07731
Tel: 732-363-8372
Offers complete editorial services: copy-editing, ms analysis, critique, development of mss, proofreading, research, revision, rewriting, condensations, copy fitting, writing, ghostwriting, transcription editing, project development & management, production services & editing for publishers, authors, academics, medical professionals, psychologists, businesses, public figures, associations & organizations. Act as publisher-author liaison, or as author's agent, full project management for publishers with mss needing copy-editing, revision +/or editor to work with author, or for self-publishing authors. Will travel to meet with authors to develop & edit mss. Meticulous editor (former university faculty) will copyedit Masters Thesis & Doctoral Dissertation, or we can help you to prepare your ms for publication. Business, medical, psychological & technical writing, editing of user manuals into clearly understood English, project management & editing of inhouse publications. Transcribe & edit books to tape. Special expertise in psychology, comparative literature, fiction, nonfiction, autobiography & memoirs, biography, art, art history, history, East Asian culture (China, Korea, Japan), Eastern philosophy & religions (Buddhism, Taoism, Confucianism, Shinto), T'ai Ch'i, martial arts, women's studies, natural healing, New Age, Native American, alternative healing sciences, meditation, "how-to", health & fitness, self-help, English, English as a Second Language (ESL) & more. ESL authors welcome. We are the editing/contracting agency for Dr Fred Penzel whose books include the award-winning *Obsessive-Compulsive Disorders: A Complete Guide to Getting Well and Staying Well* & *The Hair-Pulling Problem: A Complete Guide to Trichotillomania.* We also edited Jae Woong Kim's *Polishing the Diamond Enlightening the Mind.* Call before submitting mss. Leave your name, number & brief message about your project. Ask about our specials. Also see listing under Consultants.

Berlow Technical Communications Inc
9 Prairie Ave, Suffern, NY 10901
E-mail: bteccinc@yahoo.com
Key Personnel
Pres: Lawrence H Berlow
Medical writing & editing, special assignment writing & secondary research.

Jean Brodsky Bernard
4609 Chevy Chase Blvd, Chevy Chase, MD 20815-5343
Tel: 301-654-8914
E-mail: dranreb@starpower.net
Founded: 1982

Daniel Bial & Associates
41 W 83 St, Suite 5-C, New York, NY 10024
Tel: 212-721-1786
E-mail: dbialagency@msn.com
Web Site: www.danielbialagency.com
Key Personnel
Founder & Prop: Daniel Bial
Founded: 1991
Creating, designing & producing illustrated el-hi & adult books; emphasis on reference sports.

Bibliogenesis
152 Coddington Rd, Ithaca, NY 14850
Tel: 607-277-9660
Web Site: www.bibliogenesis.com
Key Personnel
Owner: Marian Hartman Rogers *E-mail:* mrogers@lightlink.com
Founded: 1987
Full editorial services encompassing all aspects of ms development: analysis, writing, rewriting, content editing, copy-editing, line editing, proofreading, fact checking, research & special assignment writing. Specialize in scholarly works (classical & medieval studies, European history & literature, anthropology & gender studies, Middle Eastern studies, geography & travel); languages (French, German, Greek, Latin).

Christopher Blackburn
16 Purple Sageway, Toronto, ON M2H 2Z5, Canada
Tel: 416-491-4857
E-mail: cblackburn@rogers.com
Indexing of books, using appropriate software. Other skills include copy-editing & proofreading.
Membership(s): Indexing Society of Canada/Societe canadienne d'indexation

Bloom Ink
3497 Bennington Ct, Bloomfield Hills, MI 48301
Tel: 248-291-0370
E-mail: info@bloomwriting.com
Web Site: www.bloomwriting.com
Key Personnel
Founder & Principal: Barbara Bloom
Founded: 2008
Provides a range of editing & publishing services including copy-editing, developmental editing, audio abridgements (fiction, nonfiction), book proposals, query letters, ghostwriting, book layout & design as well as assistance with self-publishing.
Membership(s): Editorial Freelancers Association

Heidi Blough, Book Indexer
502 Tanager Rd, St Augustine, FL 32086
Tel: 904-797-6572
E-mail: indexing@heidiblough.com
Web Site: www.heidiblough.com
Key Personnel
Owner: Heidi Blough
Founded: 2001

Indexing diverse topics that include: aerospace; biography; business, cooking, food & nutrition; engineering; general trade subjects; health & hospital administration; history, government & politics; how-to; maritime & transportation subjects.
Membership(s): American Society for Indexing

Blue & Ude Writers' Services
4249 Nuthatch Way, Clinton, WA 98236
Mailing Address: PO Box 145, Clinton, WA 98236-0145
Tel: 360-341-1630
E-mail: blueyude@whidbey.com
Web Site: www.blueudewritersservices.com
Key Personnel
Partner: Marian Blue; Wayne Ude
Founded: 1991
Provides all aspects of creative & technical writing & editing, including critiques, revisions & promotional copy.

Book Editing Associates, see A+ English LLC/Book-Editing.com/Book Editing Associates

Book-Editing.com, see A+ English LLC/Book-Editing.com/Book Editing Associates

BookCrafters LLC
Box C, Convent Station, NJ 07961
Tel: 973-984-7880
Web Site: bookcraftersllc.com
Key Personnel
Founder, Pres & Ed: Elizabeth Zack
E-mail: ezack@bookcraftersllc.com
Founded: 2003
Specialize in ms development & editing. Offers services for published authors, literary agents & first-time writers from creating a marketable book proposal to fine-tuning a ms. The editor has over 23 years of experience in book publishing.

The Bookmill
501 Palisades Dr, No 315, Pacific Palisades, CA 90272-2848
Tel: 310-459-0190
E-mail: thebookmill1@verizon.net
Web Site: www.thebookmill.us
Key Personnel
Dir & Ed: Barbara Marinacci
Founded: 1982
MS critiques; developmental editing for books, articles; preparing queries & proposals; word processing; contacts with agents, editors & publishers; blurb writing, book "doctoring", proposals, restructuring & revising, transcribing.

Boston Informatics
35 Byard Lane, Westborough, MA 01581
Tel: 508-366-8176
Web Site: www.bostoninformatics.com
Key Personnel
Principal: M (May) H Hasso *E-mail:* mhsh2009@verizon.net
Founded: 2002
Provides indexing services for ebooks, databases, web & back of the book. Subjects covered include: business, finance & management, nutrition, health & allied sciences, social sciences, technology & engineering. Other services include taxonomy development, fact checking, information searching & word processing.
Membership(s): American Society for Indexing

Boston Road Communications
227 Boston Rd, Groton, MA 01450-1959
Tel: 978-448-8133
Web Site: www.bostonrdcom.com
Key Personnel
Owner: Christine R Lindemer
E-mail: crlindemer@gmail.com
Founded: 2002
Indexing business, computer technology, quality management, project management, health care, history, agriculture, cookbooks, how-to, literary criticism & other subjects. Over 400 books indexed.
Membership(s): American Society for Indexing

The Boston Word Works
PO Box 56419, Sherman Oaks, CA 91413-1419
Tel: 818-904-9088 *Fax:* 818-787-1431
Key Personnel
Owner: Leslie Paul Boston
Founded: 1985
General fiction & nonfiction. Writing & editing. Evaluation, preparation of book proposals & sample chapters. Consultation on ideas, approaches & development.
Membership(s): Independent Writers of Southern California; National Writers Union

bradylit
81 Town Farm Hill, Hartland Four Corners, VT 05049
Mailing Address: PO Box 64, Hartland Four Corners, VT 05049
Tel: 802-436-2455
Key Personnel
Owner: Sally R Brady *E-mail:* bradylit@vermontel.net
Founded: 1988
Ms analysis, conceptual, developmental & line editing, book doctoring, rewriting; trade fiction & nonfiction; contacts with agents, editors & publishers. Work on a fee +/or percentage basis.

Hilary R Burke
59 Sparks St, Ottawa, ON K1P 6C3, Canada
Mailing Address: Box 133, Sta B, Ottawa, ON K1P 6C3, Canada
Tel: 613-237-4658
E-mail: hburke99@yahoo.com
Promotional writing of fiction & nonfiction.

BZ/Rights & Permissions Inc
145 W 86 St, New York, NY 10024
Tel: 212-924-3000 *Fax:* 212-924-2525
E-mail: info@bzrights.com
Web Site: www.bzrights.com
Key Personnel
Pres: Barbara Zimmerman *E-mail:* bz@bzrights.com
Founded: 1980
Clears rights for literary materials, music, film & TV clips, photos, art, celebrities for educational projects - printed textbooks, spoken word recordings, new electronic media, DVDs/videocassettes. Work with film & TV producers & ad agencies. Publisher of *The Mini-Encyclopedia of Public Domain Songs & They Never Renewed: Songs You Never Dreamed Were in the Public Domain.*
Membership(s): Association of Independent Music Publishers; Copyright Society of the USA; The Independent Book Publishers Association; Media Communications Association

Carpe Indexum
364 Woodbine Ave, Syracuse, NY 13206-3324
Tel: 315-431-4949
E-mail: info@carpeindexum.com
Web Site: www.carpeindexum.com
Key Personnel
Owner: Michele Combs *E-mail:* mrothen2@twcny.rr.com
Founded: 2004
Services include back-of-book & XML indexing services; research & fact-checking; editing at various levels; copywriting & work-for-hire; XML/XSLT consulting.
Membership(s): American Society for Indexing; Editorial Freelancers Association; Society of American Archivists

R E Carsch, MS-Consultant
1453 Rhode Island St, San Francisco, CA 94107-3248
Tel: 415-641-1095
E-mail: recarsch@mzinfo.com
Web Site: www.mzinfo.com
Founded: 1973
Full range custom information/editorial services including, fact checking, interviewing, ms analysis, proofreading, research & industry overviews.
Membership(s): Art Libraries Society

Anne Carson Associates
3323 Nebraska Ave NW, Washington, DC 20016
Tel: 202-244-6679
Key Personnel
Ed-in-Chief: Anne Conover Carson
Founded: 1976
Proofreading, research, rewriting, special assignment writing, ms analysis. Specialize in Latin American culture & history, biographies of women & 20th century expats in Paris.
Membership(s): Academy of American Poets; The Authors Guild; MLA; National Coalition of Independent Scholars; National Press Club

Carol Cartaino
2000 Flat Run Rd, Seaman, OH 45679
Tel: 937-764-1303 *Fax:* 937-764-1303
E-mail: cartaino@aol.com
Founded: 1986
Content, developmental & line editing; ms analysis; rewriting & collaboration; development & packaging of book ideas & book programs. Nonfiction & selected fiction including how-to, self-help, reference, humorous & highly illustrated books. Also expert assistance of all kinds for self-publishers & solutions for problem mss.

Claudia Caruana
PO Box 654, Murray Hill Sta, New York, NY 10016
Tel: 516-488-5815
E-mail: ccaruana29@hotmail.com
Copy-editing, ms analysis, rights & permissions, picture search, proofreading, research, rewriting, special assignment writing, magazine photography.

Angela M Casey
42 Nathaniel Blvd, Delmar, NY 12054
Tel: 518-729-2693
E-mail: casey.angela.m@gmail.com
Founded: 2000
Book editing & ghostwriting for established authors. Categories include psychology, health, diet, exercise & relationships. Advertising & promotion copy written for print & for web according to search engine optimization (SEO) standards.

Catalyst Communication Arts
94 Chuparrosa Dr, San Luis Obispo, CA 93401
Tel: 805-235-2351 *Fax:* 805-543-7140
Web Site: www.sonsieconroy.com
Key Personnel
Owner: Sonsie Carbonara Conroy
E-mail: sconroy@slonet.org
Founded: 1980
Editorial services, specializing in indexing college textbooks, cookbooks, self-help, trade nonfiction.

Catalyst Creative Services
619 Marion Plaza, Palo Alto, CA 94301-4251
Tel: 650-325-1500
E-mail: afriendlyghostwriter@gmail.com
Web Site: www.catalystcreative.us
Key Personnel
Owner & Chief Catalyst: Dennis Alan Briskin
E-mail: chief@catalystcreative.us
Founded: 1975
Our clients get published. We offer complete editorial services, from intelligent strategy (you must aim at the right target) to the structure, composition, revisions & final polish. We help non-professional writers clarify, craft & publish their work for educated adult readers. We also ghostwrite for well-funded individuals with a story to tell or a cause to promote. (We respect academic integrity.) Writing contains both art & technique. We can show you the art & teach you the technique. We accept debit/credit cards.
Membership(s): Association of Ghostwriters; National Writers Union

Jeanne Cavelos Editorial Services
PO Box 75, Mont Vernon, NH 03057
Tel: 603-673-6234
Web Site: jeannecavelos.com
Key Personnel
Owner: Jeanne Cavelos *E-mail:* jcavelos@sff.net
Founded: 1994
Published, best-selling writer & former senior editor at major publishing house. Full editorial services for publishers, book packagers, businesses, agents & authors. From line edit to thorough edit, to heavy edit. Detailed reader's reports. Book proposal doctoring. Editorial consulting, creative development. Newsletters, magazine articles, novelizations. Handle the full range of fiction & nonfiction. Specialize in thrillers, literary fiction, fantasy, science fiction, horror, popular culture, self-help, health & science.
Membership(s): Horror Writers Association; Science Fiction & Fantasy Writers of America

CeciBooks Editorial & Publishing Consultation
7057 26 Ave NW, Seattle, WA 98117
Mailing Address: PO Box 17229, Seattle, WA 98127
Tel: 206-706-9565
E-mail: cecibooks@gmail.com
Web Site: www.cecibooks.com
Key Personnel
Owner: Ceci Miller
Founded: 1988
Provide complete book development & production from concept & content to finished book. Innovative in assembling teams of experts to develop, write, edit, design & produce superior products. Specialty is kids nonfiction (both trade & curriculum), but we also do adult books on topics such as history, biography, science, how-to & business. We do education (textbooks, teacher resources, reference), focusing on social sciences, literacy & soft science. Produce publisher-initiated titles as well as original books. Will work with other packagers to co-produce books.
Membership(s): Book Publishers of the Northwest; Pacific Northwest Writers Association; Society of Children's Book Writers & Illustrators; Women's Business Exchange

Margaret Cheasebro
246 Rd 2900, Aztec, NM 87410
Tel: 505-334-2869
E-mail: margaretcheasebro@yahoo.com
Web Site: www.wordsandwellness.com
Founded: 1986
Freelance writer. Specialize in articles about people, places & issues of the Four Corners area, nonfiction books about alternative healing & related subjects.
Membership(s): The Authors Guild; National Federation of Press Women; New Mexico Press Women

Ruth Chernia
198 Victor Ave, Toronto, ON M4K 1B2, Canada
Tel: 416-466-0164
E-mail: rchernia@editors.ca; rchernia@sympatico.ca
Founded: 1983
Provides professional editorial & publishing consultation to companies & individuals. Branch office in Toronto.
Membership(s): Editors' Association of Canada/Association canadienne des reviseurs

Clear Concepts
1329 Federal Ave, Suite 6, Los Angeles, CA 90025
Tel: 310-473-5453
Key Personnel
Owner: Karen Kleiner
Founded: 1986
Provides writing, substantive editing & research. Specializes in holistic health, fiction, children's books, technology & business. Owner holds BA from UCLA in Communication Studies.
Membership(s): Society for Technical Communication

Clerical Plus
97 Blueberry Lane, Shelton, CT 06484
Tel: 203-225-0879 *Fax:* 203-225-0879
E-mail: clericalplus@aol.com
Web Site: www.clericalplus.net
Key Personnel
Pres: Rose E Brown
Founded: 1990
Transcription/office support service company.

Clotilde's Secretarial & Management Services
PO Box 871926, New Orleans, LA 70187
Tel: 504-242-2912; 504-800-4853 (cell)
E-mail: elcsy58@aol.com; elcsy58@att.net
Key Personnel
Pres & Admin Mgr: Elvira C Sylve
Asst: Lillian Gail Tillman
Founded: 1989
Proofread & edit journals, newsletters, mss, research papers & medical documents. Specialize in preparing & typing research papers, grant proposals, medical & legal documents. Legal course work—Louisiana laws: briefs, business law, computer research & software, family law, interviewing, legal writing, litigation & researching in West Law.
Membership(s): American Health Information Management Association; National Association of Legal Assistants

Dwight Clough
1223 W Main St, No 228, Sun Prairie, WI 53590
Tel: 608-834-8291
E-mail: lmp@dwightclough.com
Web Site: dwightclough.com
Founded: 1983
Serving authors & publishers.

Coastside Editorial
PO Box 181, Moss Beach, CA 94038
E-mail: bevjoe@pacific.net
Key Personnel
Contact: Beverly McGuire
Membership(s): Editcetera

Robert L Cohen
182-12 Horace Harding Expwy, Suite 2M, Fresh Meadows, NY 11365
Tel: 718-762-1195 *Toll Free Tel:* 866-EDITING (334-8464)
E-mail: wordsmith@sterlingmp.com
Web Site: www.rlcwordsandmusic.com; www.linkedin.com/in/robertcohen17
Copy, line (substantive) & developmental editing of academic, trade & reference books; editing & rewriting of public policy books/reports/policy briefs/newsletters/monographs; lexicography; radio & AV scriptwriting; speechwriting & other contract writing. Specialize in urban affairs & public policy, international relations (especially Middle East & related countries & regions), history (including military history) & social sciences, politics & government, psychology & education, media & communications, Judaica & religion, music. Also writing coach & teacher for businesses/nonprofits/individuals.
Membership(s): American Society for Jewish Music; Cambridge Academic Editors Network; Editorial Freelancers Association

Copywriter's Council of America (CCA)
Division of The Linick Group Inc
CCA Bldg, 7 Putter Lane, Middle Island, NY 11953-1920
Mailing Address: PO Box 102, Middle Island, NY 11953-0102
Tel: 631-924-8555 *Fax:* 631-924-8555
E-mail: cca4dmcopy@gmail.com
Web Site: www.AndrewLinickDirectMarketing.com/Copywriters-Council.html; www.NewWorldPressBooks.com
Key Personnel
Chmn, Consulting Group: Andrew S Linick, PhD
E-mail: andrew@asklinick.com
VP: Roger Dextor
Dir, Spec Projs: Barbara Deal
Over 25,000 freelance advertising copywriters, editors, communication specialists & journalists; covering publishing, Internet direct response/direct mail field for health, physical fitness, gourmet, how-to, martial arts, self improvement, travel & tourism, photography, sports & recreation, business communications & high tech for books, magazines, manuals, newsletters, in-house organs & courses. Marketing, research, rewriting, special assignment writing, copy-editing, indexing, proofreading, ms analysis; video production, audio-video news releases; interviews & profiles; rights & permissions. Also offer annual seminars, workshops & trade show to writers/editors who would like to increase their income. Phone consultation available. Provide comprehensive graphic redesign/new web site content development, interactive services with web site marketing makeover advice for first-time authors, self-publishers, professionals & entrepreneurs. Specializes in flash, animation, merchant accounts, online advertising/PR, links to top search engines, consulting on a 100% satisfaction guarantee. Free site evaluation for LMP readers.

Corbett Gordon Co
6 Fort Rachel Place, Mystic, CT 06355
Tel: 860-536-4108 *Fax:* 860-536-3732
E-mail: corbettgordon@comcast.net
Key Personnel
Owner: Rose Corbett Gordon
Fine art & historical research for books, book covers & exhibits. Art copyright expertise.

Course Crafters Inc
116 Pleasant Valley Rd, Amesbury, MA 01913
Mailing Address: PO Box 100, Amesbury, MA 01913
Tel: 978-372-3446
E-mail: info@coursecrafters.com
Web Site: www.coursecrafters.com

Key Personnel
CEO & Publr: Lise B Ragan *E-mail:* lragan@coursecrafters.com
Consultant: Melissa Ragan
Founded: 1993
Full service development house & packager of educational materials, K-adult, with a unique focus in the growing English Language Learner Market (ELL). Specialize in English as a second language (ESL), bilingual education & literacy material for English language learners, their teachers & parents. Provide services to publishers in market research, consulting, conceptualizing, writing/editing, production, translation & developing marketing/sales plans. Also can develop customized materials for schools. Print, audio, video & multimedia in ESL & Spanish; professional development, instructional materials & assessment.

Creative Freelancers Inc
PO Box 366, Tallevast, FL 34270
Toll Free Tel: 800-398-9544
Web Site: www.freelancers1.com
Key Personnel
Pres: Marilyn Howard
Freelance copy & art services for publishing & advertising. Designers, artists, copy-editors, all creative areas, translations.

Creative Inspirations Inc
6203 Old Springville Rd, Pinson, AL 35126
Mailing Address: PO Box 362, Clay, AL 35048
Web Site: www.manuscriptcritique.com
Key Personnel
Pres: Michael Garrett *E-mail:* mike@manuscriptcritique.com
Founded: 1995
Editorial services for aspiring authors, including line edit & content evaluation.

Ruth C Cross
196 Melrose St, Unit 52, Brattleboro, VT 05301
Tel: 802-579-1368

CS International Literary Agency
43 W 39 St, New York, NY 10018
Tel: 212-921-1610; 212-391-9208
E-mail: query@csliterary.com; csliterary08@gmail.com
Web Site: www.csliterary.com
Key Personnel
Literary Agent: Cynthia Neesemann
Ms analysis, evaluation & agent representation available for nonfiction, fiction & screenplays. We assist writers in developing strategies to achieve ms publication or film production & to find the writing niche that suits their talents & personality in general or specialized markets. We are particularly responsive to helping beginning writers to improve their writing skills & style with suggestions for better plotting, characterization, dialogue & structure. Fees are very reasonable. Interests extend to full range of topics whether fact or fantasy, including international, occult, ethnic, political, historical & religious subjects, mysteries & comedies. Query with short synopsis of project.

Cultural Studies & Analysis
1123 Montrose St, Philadelphia, PA 19147-3721
Tel: 215-592-8544 *Fax:* 215-413-9041
E-mail: info@culturalanalysis.com
Web Site: www.culturalanalysis.com
Key Personnel
Dir: Margaret J King, PhD *E-mail:* mjking9@comcast.net
Sr Analyst: Jamie O'Boyle
Founded: 1994
Specialize in cultural analysis; identify consumer values & decision making. We do not provide novel writing.

Cypress House
155 Cypress St, Fort Bragg, CA 95437
Tel: 707-964-9520 *Toll Free Tel:* 800-773-7782 *Fax:* 707-964-7531
E-mail: cypresshouse@cypresshouse.com
Web Site: www.cypresshouse.com
Key Personnel
Pres: Cynthia Frank *E-mail:* cynthia@cypresshouse.com
Prodn Mgr: Michael Brechner *E-mail:* unclemike@cypresshouse.com
Mng Ed: Joe Shaw *E-mail:* joeshaw@cypresshouse.com
Complete editorial, design, production, marketing & promotion services to independent publishers. Editorial services include ms evaluation, editing, rewriting, copymarking & proofing. Production services include book, cover & page design & make-up to camera-ready. Marketing & promotion services for selected titles.
Membership(s): ABA; Bay Area Independent Publishers Association; The Independent Book Publishers Association; Northern California Independent Booksellers Association; Pacific Northwest Booksellers Association

John M Daniel Literary Services
PO Box 2790, McKinleyville, CA 95519
Tel: 707-839-3495 *Fax:* 707-839-3242
E-mail: jmd@danielpublishing.com
Web Site: www.danielpublishing.com/litserv.htm
Key Personnel
Ed: John M Daniel
Specialize in fiction & memoir.

Darla Bruno Writer & Editor
PO Box 243, Madison, NJ 07940
E-mail: editor@darlabruno.com
Web Site: www.darlabruno.com
Developmental editing, rewriting, critiques, marketing. Specialize in memoir & literary fiction, as well as self-help, personal development, spiritual, health & wellness.

Suzanne B Davidson
8084 N 44 St, Brown Deer, WI 53223
Tel: 414-355-6640
E-mail: davidson@milwpc.com
Founded: 1984
College texts, scholarly works; law & criminal justice, business & finance, politics, public policy, history, social sciences, genealogy.

Mari Lynch Dehmler, see Fine Wordworking

Christina Di Martino Literary Services
139 Sandpiper Ave, Royal Palm Beach, FL 33411
Tel: 212-996-9086
E-mail: writealotmail@gmail.com
Key Personnel
Owner: Christina Di Martino
Full book line services, collaboration of book projects, freelance writing for national magazines & teaching of writing.

diacriTech Inc
667 Boylston St, 5th fl, Boston, MA 02116
Tel: 617-236-7500 *Fax:* 617-848-2938
Web Site: www.diacritech.com
Key Personnel
EVP: Madhu Rajamani *Tel:* 617-600-3366 *E-mail:* madhu@diacritech.com
Client Relationship Mgr: Maureen Ross *E-mail:* m.ross@diacritech.com
Founded: 1997
Specialize in meeting educational publishing needs. Full service development & project management experience includes editorial, production, art & prepress services for textbooks & ancillaries. From developing, writing & editing mss to state-of-the-art page production, art rendering & prepress capabilities. In-house staff is experienced with all phases & disciplines of K-17.

DK Research Inc
14 Mohegan Lane, Commack, NY 11725
Tel: 631-543-5537 *Fax:* 631-543-5549
Web Site: www.dkresearchinc.com
Key Personnel
Owner & Pres: Diane Kraut *E-mail:* dianekraut@att.net
Founded: 1993
Handle all phases of text permission clearance. Also available for ms assessments & review for permission items. Photo research services also available.
Membership(s): Editorial Freelancers Association

Double Play
303 Hillcrest Rd, Belton, MO 64012-1852
Tel: 816-651-7118
Key Personnel
Pres: Lloyd Johnson
VP: Connie Johnson
Writing & research about baseball; sports, baseball museum consultant, exhibits; working on database of professional baseball.
Membership(s): Pro Football Researchers Association; Society for American Baseball Research

Drennan Communications
6 Robin Lane, East Kingston, NH 03827
Tel: 603-642-8002 *Fax:* 603-642-8002
Key Personnel
Pres & Edit Dir: William D Drennan
VP & Sr Ed: Christina L Drennan
Founded: 1980
Line editing, copy-editing, ms analysis, proofreading, rewriting, ghostwriting, special assignment writing, condensations, typemarking, abstracting, fact checking, interviewing, research, advertising & promotion copywriting.

Drummond Books
2111 Cleveland St, Evanston, IL 60202
Tel: 847-302-2534
E-mail: drummondbooks@gmail.com
Key Personnel
Owner: Siobhan Drummond
Editorial & production services for web, print & ebooks, editorial management, project management from raw ms to finished book, copy editing, substantive editing, proofreading & indexing.

DWJ BOOKS LLC
46 Cliff Dr, Sag Harbor, NY 11963
Mailing Address: PO Box 996, Sag Harbor, NY 11963
Tel: 631-899-4500
E-mail: info@dwjbooks.com
Web Site: www.dwjbooks.com
Key Personnel
EVP: Lauren Fedorko
Edit Dir: Darrell Kozlowski
Founded: 2005 (developing & packaging original content since 1988)
Full service book & electronic development of large scale nonfiction projects & single titles for library & general reference publishing, test prep publishing, & curriculum-aligned publishing. Editorial services include: proposals, consulting, hiring of freelance staffs, writing, research, line & content editing, copy-editing, proofreading, indexing, fact checking, translating, special assignment writing, preparing files for print & online products.
Membership(s): ALA; American Book Producers Association

Earth Edit
PO Box 114, Maiden Rock, WI 54750
Tel: 715-448-3009
Key Personnel
Contact: George Dyke *E-mail:* gmdyke@gmail.com
Copy-editing & proofreading of earth science & geography texts.

East Mountain Editing Services
PO Box 1895, Tijeras, NM 87059-1895
Tel: 505-281-8422
Web Site: www.spanishindexing.com
Key Personnel
Mgr: Francine Cronshaw *E-mail:* cronshaw@nmia.com
Founded: 1992
Indexing (back-of-the-book) in Spanish or English. Also French, Italian & Portuguese. Expert witness on Spanish surnames. Special attention to Canadian editions. Consulting on bilingual or Spanish-language editions; copy-editing translations. For experience, see web site.
Membership(s): American Society for Indexing

EditAndPublishYourBook.com
PO Box 2965, Nantucket, MA 02584-2965
E-mail: michaeltheauthor@yahoo.com
Web Site: www.editandpublishyourbook.com
Key Personnel
Principal: Michael Wells Glueck
Founded: 2002
Services offered include abstracting, condensations, copy-editing, interviewing, line editing, ms analysis, proofreading, rewriting, special assignment writing & transcription editing. Can also submit work to a reasonably priced subsidy publisher, shepherd it through the publication process & monitor online booksellers' web sites to make sure that it remains available for purchase, that they list it correctly & that the listing includes a front-cover photograph & other features. Can also suggest unorthodox but effective marketing techniques & write & submit reviews to online booksellers' web sites.
Recent projects include arranging online distribution for Donald E DeMarco's Nantucket Taste Memories: The DeMarco Restaurant Cookbook (self-published Oct 2007); as well as both writing & editing reviews for the Fictional Rome web site linked to the Richard Stockton College of New Jersey.

Edit Etc
20 Rock Harbor Rd, Orleans, MA 02653
Tel: 914-715-5849
E-mail: atkedit@cs.com
Web Site: www.anntkeene.com
Key Personnel
Pres: Ann T Keene
Founded: 1985
Editing, writing, copywriting, research, photo research.
Membership(s): The Authors Guild

Edit Resource LLC
Division of Stanford Creative Services LLC
3578-E Hartsel Dr, Suite 387, Colorado Springs, CO 80920
Tel: 719-290-0757
E-mail: info@editresource.com (main)
Web Site: www.editresource.com (main); www.inspirationalghostwriting.com
Key Personnel
Owner: Elisa Stanford *E-mail:* elisa@editresource.com; Eric Stanford *E-mail:* eric@editresource.com
Founded: 1998
A writing & editing services provider.

EditAmerica
115 Jacobs Creek Rd, Ewing, NJ 08628
Tel: 609-882-5852
Web Site: www.editamerica.com; www.linkedin.com/in/PaulaPlantier
Key Personnel
Owner/Founder: Paula Plantier *E-mail:* paula@editamerica.com
Founded: 1979
Expert copy-editing, line editing, ms editing, rewriting/revising/repurposing, fact checking & proofreading of written communications in the areas of accounting, advertising, bibliography, biography, brochures, business, college application essays, company annual reports, cover letters, curricula vitae, dissertations, education, finance, Form 10-Ks, Form 10-Qs, marketing, medicine, newsletters, news releases, peer-reviewed & refereed medical/scientific journal articles, pharmaceutics, pharmacology, press releases, religious treatises, resumes, theses, user's manuals & web site content. Strict adherence to client-set deadlines. Satisfaction guaranteed for editorial services performed.
Membership(s): International Society for Peritoneal Dialysis.

Editcetera
2034 Blake St, Suite 5, Berkeley, CA 94704
Tel: 510-849-1110 *Fax:* 510-900-6141
E-mail: info@editcetera.com
Web Site: www.editcetera.com
Key Personnel
Dir: Barbara Fuller
Founded: 1971
Association of freelance publishing professionals. Clients include authors, packagers, trade publishers, el-hi & college textbook publishers, self-publishers, computer companies (software & hardware) & corporations. Services available include production management from mss through bound books as well as writing, rewriting, developmental editing, copy-editing, coaching of writers, proofreading, indexing & web editing. Rigorous testing & review of all members.

EditCraft Editorial Services
422 Pine St, Grass Valley, CA 95945
Tel: 530-263-3688
Web Site: www.editcraft.com
Key Personnel
Prop: Eric W Engles, PhD *E-mail:* eric@editcraft.com
Founded: 1986
Editorial services for publishers, independent authors, scholars & technology companies.
Membership(s): Bay Area Editors' Forum; National Association of Science Writers

The Editorial Dept LLC
7650 E Broadway, Suite 308, Tucson, AZ 85710
Tel: 520-546-9992 *Fax:* 520-979-3408
E-mail: admin@editorialdepartment.com
Web Site: www.editorialdepartment.com
Key Personnel
Founder: Renni Browne
Pres & Dir, Edit Servs: Ross Browne *E-mail:* rsb@editorialdepartment.com
Lead Ed, Romance & Women's Fiction: Lindsay Guzzardo
Founded: 1980
Ms critique & evaluation, line & copy-editing, novelizations & adaptations, book proposals, agent referral service, book cover design, book illustration, interior layout, ebook formatting, book/author marketing, publishing consultation, screenplay critique & consultation.

The Editors Circle
462 Grove St, Montclair, NJ 07043
Tel: 973-783-5082
E-mail: query@theeditorscircle.com
Web Site: www.theeditorscircle.com
Key Personnel
Ed: Bonny Fetterman *Tel:* 718-739-1057 *E-mail:* bvfetterman@aol.com; Rob Kaplan *Tel:* 914-736-7182 *E-mail:* robkaplan@optonline.net; Beth Lieberman *Tel:* 310-403-1602 *E-mail:* liebermanedit@socal.rr.com; John Paine *E-mail:* jpaine@johnpaine.com; Susan Schwartz *Tel:* 212-877-3211 *E-mail:* susan.sas22@gmail.com
Founded: 2005
A group of five independent book editors with more than 100 years of collective experience on-staff with major New York book publishers offering the following editorial services: editing & writing book proposals, query letters & complete mss; providing referrals to agents & publishers; consulting on self-publishing & digital publishing opportunities. Specialize in popular & scholarly nonfiction, memoirs & commercial & literary fiction.

EEI Communications
6301 Ivy Lane, Suite 250, Greenbelt, MD 20770
Tel: 410-309-8200 *Fax:* 410-630-3980
E-mail: info@eeicom.com
Web Site: www.eeicom.com
Key Personnel
CEO & Pres: Gregory K McDonough
Dir, Edit Servs: Sheila Gagen
Substantive editing, copy-editing, writing, transcription, design, graphics, keyboarding, publications management, training in software & editorial skills. Specialize in books & reports, government, technical/defense, management, communications & public health.

Diane Eickhoff
3808 Genessee St, Kansas City, MO 64111
Tel: 816-561-6693
E-mail: diane.eickhoff@gmail.com
Founded: 2000

Irene Elmer
2806 Cherry St, Berkeley, CA 94705-2310
Tel: 510-841-0466
E-mail: ielmer@earthlink.net
Founded: 1969
Rewriting, line editing & copy-editing of trade fiction & nonfiction, textbooks & scholarly works. Specialize in difficult rewrites, dialogue & lively presentation of difficult material. Special assignment writing of adult texts; trade nonfiction; high-interest, low-readability el-hi texts (fiction, drama, nonfiction).
Membership(s): Editcetera

Catherine C Elverston ELS
9 Red Bay Lane, Kitty Hawk, NC 27949-3307
Tel: 352-222-0625 (cell)
E-mail: celverston@gmail.com
All aspects of editing, preparing mss for publication, information research & retrieval. Also an agent.
Membership(s): American Medical Writers Association; Board of Editors in the Life Sciences

R Elwell Indexing
193 Main St, Cold Spring, NY 10516
Tel: 845-667-1036
E-mail: ruth.elwell@yahoo.com
Founded: 1975
Indexing.

Enough Said
3959 NW 29 Lane, Gainesville, FL 32606
Tel: 352-262-2971 *Fax:* 352-372-5747 (call first)
E-mail: enoughsaid@cox.net
Web Site: users.navi.net/~heathlynn
Key Personnel
Ed: Ms Heath Lynn Silberfeld

Founded: 1984
Full range of hard-copy & electronic editorial services for nonfiction trade, mass market, textbook & self-publishing projects.

Farrar Writing & Editing
4638 Manchester Rd, Mound, MN 55364
Tel: 952-472-6874 *Fax:* 952-472-6874 (call first)
Web Site: www.writeandedit.net
Key Personnel
Freelance Writer & Ed: Amy E Farrar
E-mail: amyfarrar@mchsi.com
Founded: 1999
Published book author (educational books for K-12 readers & general nonfiction); journalistic writing; book editor (copy-editing to substantive editing & rewriting); web site writing & editing. Clients include book publishers, nonprofits, magazines, newspapers & general businesses. Subjects include environmental, social, travel & health/medical.
Interested parties with book project in need of editing, send e-mail with synopsis of book, type of editorial service being sought, budget & deadline.
Membership(s): Professional Editors Network

Betsy Feist Resources
140 E 81 St, Unit 8-G, New York, NY 10028-1875
Tel: 212-861-2014
E-mail: bfresources@rcn.com
Key Personnel
Pres: Betsy Feist
Complete editorial services, including development, writing, project management & editorial/production coordination. Specialize in instructional & informational materials.

Jerry Felsen
3960 NW 196 St, Miami Gardens, FL 33055-1869
Tel: 305-625-5012
E-mail: jfelsen0@att.net
Web Site: beatthemarket.org
Computer science, artificial intelligence, information systems & computer applications in business & investing; professional papers & business reports.

Fine Wordworking
PO Box 3041, Monterey, CA 93942-3041
Tel: 831-375-6278
E-mail: info@finewordworking.com
Web Site: marilynch.com
Key Personnel
Owner: Mari Lynch Dehmler
Founded: 1981
Writing, editing & proofreading of literary, business, personal & other material. Ghostwriting, collaborative writing & editing of adult, young adult & children's nonfiction books. Editing & proofreading of fiction. Well versed in Chicago style. Web content development & design collaboration. Interviewing, research & other support. Phone calls welcome.

Richard A Flom, see Lynn C Kronzek & Richard A Flom

Focus Strategic Communications Inc
2474 Waterford St, Oakville, ON L6L 5E6, Canada
Tel: 905-825-8757 *Toll Free Tel:* 866-263-6287 *Fax:* 905-825-5724 *Toll Free Fax:* 866-613-6287
E-mail: info@focussc.com
Web Site: www.focussc.com
Key Personnel
Dir: Adrianna Edwards *E-mail:* aedwards@focussc.com; Ron Edwards *E-mail:* redwards@focussc.com
Founded: 1988
Provide complete book development & production from concept & content to finished book. Innovative in assembling teams of experts to develop, write, edit, design & produce superior products. Specialty is children's nonfiction (both trade & curriculum) but also do adult books on topics such as history, biography, science, how-to & business. Also education (textbooks, teacher resources, reference), focusing on social sciences, literacy & soft science. Produce publisher-initiated titles as well as original books. Will work with other packagers to co-produce books.
Membership(s): AAP; AAP PreK-12 Learning Group; American Book Producers Association; Association of Canadian Publishers; International Literacy Association; International Society for Technology in Education; National Association for the Education of Young Children; National Council for the Social Studies; National Council of Teachers of English; National Science Teachers Association; Teachers of English to Speakers of Other Languages

Foster Travel Publishing
PO Box 5715, Berkeley, CA 94705
Tel: 510-549-2202
Web Site: www.fostertravel.com
Key Personnel
Owner & Pres: Lee Foster *E-mail:* lee@fostertravel.com
Founded: 1970
Picture search, research, writing; travel (emphasizing locations, history, wine, nature). Specialize in Northern California, the West, Mexico-Baja, Europe, the Orient. Writing & photography available on web site. Provides travel writing/photography services for print & web editorial markets.
Membership(s): Bay Area Travel Writers; SATW

Sandi Frank
8 Fieldcrest Ct, Cortlandt Manor, NY 10567
Tel: 914-739-7088
E-mail: sfrankmail@aol.com
Specialize in nonfiction in many disciplines, including textbooks, bibliographies, medical texts & journals, social sciences, scholarly material & cookbooks.
Membership(s): American Society for Indexing

Fromer Editorial Services
1606 Noyes Dr, Silver Spring, MD 20910-2224
Tel: 301-585-8827
Key Personnel
Pres: Margot J Fromer *E-mail:* margotfromer@erols.com
Founded: 1980
Writing, rewriting & consultation in all aspects of health care & medicine; ms analysis, special assignment writing.
Membership(s): American Medical Writers Association; Science Writers' Association

Diane Gallo
49 Hilton St, Gilbertsville, NY 13776
Mailing Address: PO Box 106, Gilbertsville, NY 13776
Tel: 607-783-2386 *Fax:* 607-783-2386
E-mail: dgallo@stny.rr.com
Web Site: www.dianegallo.com
Interviewing & video scripts.

Michael Garrett, see Creative Inspirations Inc

The Gary-Paul Agency
1549 Main St, Stratford, CT 06615
Tel: 203-345-6167
Web Site: www.thegarypaulagency.com; www.nutmegpictures.com
Key Personnel
Owner: Gary Maynard *E-mail:* garret@thegarypaulagency.com
Founded: 1994
Literary agency that represents & promotes screenplays. Specialize in script development. WGAE Signatory.
Branch Office(s)
127 Horseshoe Dr, Fayston, VT 05660 *Tel:* 203-556-8671
Membership(s): Writers Guild of America East

Fred Gebhart
PO Box 111, Gold Hill, OR 97525
Tel: 541-855-8975
E-mail: fgebhart@pobox.com
Web Site: www.fredgebhart.com
Founded: 1981
Editorial & advertorial writing. Specialize in business, consumer education, travel, healthcare, foreign countries, medicine, science, transportation, wine & spirits.
Membership(s): American Medical Writers Association; American Society of Journalists & Authors; International Society of Travel Medicine; National Association of Science Writers

Gelles-Cole Literary Enterprises
135 John Joy Rd, Woodstock, NY 12498-0341
Tel: 845-679-2452
Web Site: www.literaryenterprises.com
Key Personnel
Founder & Pres: Sandi Gelles-Cole
E-mail: sandigc@aol.com
Founded: 1983
Editorial consultant ("Book Doctor") specializing in commercial fiction & nonfiction serving authors, publishers & literary agents; writing coach; consultant for self publishing authors, collaboration. Editorial specialty is development of concept & character development. Provide an intense word by word tutorial focusing on concept, style, voice, pace & characterization & for nonfiction, structure. Also offer help to experts & other authors developing their material for the general public. Also have small publishing arm. Soft spot - first novels.
Membership(s): Consulting Editors Alliance

Nancy C Gerth PhD
1431 Harlan's Trail, Sagle, ID 83860
Tel: 208-304-9066
E-mail: docnangee@nancygerth.com
Web Site: www.nancygerth.com
Founded: 2005
Freelance indexing & related services. Index focus: scholarly specializing in American History, Indigenous Studies, Post Modernism. PhD in philosophy (Cornell University). Providing information services since 1988.
Membership(s): American Society for Indexing; Pacific Northwest Chapter of American Society for Indexing

GGP Publishing Inc
105 Calvert St, Suite 201, Harrison, NY 10528-3138
Tel: 914-834-8896 *Fax:* 914-834-7566
Web Site: www.GGPPublishing.com
Key Personnel
Pres & Publg Dir: Generosa Gina Protano
E-mail: GGProtano@GGPPublishing.com
Founded: 1991
Packager for trade & educational publishers. All editorial, art & design, production & printing services—from concept to bound books or any segment(s) of this publishing process. Trade (fiction & nonfiction) & children's books, textbooks (el-hi, college & adult education), professional, reference & how-to books, cook-

books, audiotapes & videotapes, CDs & CD-ROMs. Specialize in the development of materials for the study of foreign languages (such as French, German, Italian, Japanese, Latin, Portuguese, Russian & Spanish) & English as a Second Language, as well as in the development of materials for bilingual education & language arts. In addition, we translate complete or partial programs from & into the various languages & act as literary agents & foreign publisher representatives.
Membership(s): American Book Producers Association

Cathe Giffuni, see Research Research

Sheri Gilbert
123 Van Voorhis Ave, Rochester, NY 14617
Tel: 585-342-0331
E-mail: gilbert@permissionseditor.com
Web Site: permissionseditor.com
Reviews mss for permissions identification; preparing permissions reports; obtaining permissions for text, art, photographs & song lyrics. Creating credit lines & source notes.

Michael Wells Glueck, see EditAndPublishYourBook.com

Gold Leaf Press
3670 Morrissey Ave, Warren, MI 48091
Tel: 313-331-3571
Web Site: www.goldleafpress.com
Key Personnel
Publr & Publg Consultant: Rebecca J Ensign *E-mail:* rensign2014@gmail.com
Founded: 1994
Independent publisher & publishing services provider to the trade, corporate & academic markets. Our proprietary publishing program, for qualifying works & authors, emphasizes editorial development for market worthiness. Through our services, Gold Leaf Press has edited, published & represented fiction & nonfiction titles & authors in a variety of genres, from scholarly works, autobiographies & company training manuals to corporate identity publications, self-help books & novels.

Donald Goldstein
1500 E 17 St, Brooklyn, NY 11230
Tel: 718-375-9346
E-mail: dgoldsbkyn@aol.com
Founded: 1988
Sports, sociology, American politics, the labor movement, Israel, Jewish related subjects; research, interviewing, copy-editing, rewriting, special assignment writing & proofreading.

Robert M Goodman
140 West End Ave, Unit 11-J, New York, NY 10023
Tel: 917-439-1097
E-mail: bobbybgood@gmail.com
Membership(s): Editorial Freelancers Association

P M Gordon Associates Inc
2115 Wallace St, Philadelphia, PA 19130
Tel: 215-769-2525
E-mail: pmga@pond1.net
Web Site: www.pmgordon.com
Key Personnel
Pres: Peggy M Gordon
VP: Douglas C Gordon
Founded: 1982
Developmental editing, rewriting & copy-editing for trade, text & corporate books; indexing. Complete design & production services.

C+S Gottfried
619 Cricklewood Dr, State College, PA 16803
Tel: 814-237-2580
Web Site: www.lookoutnow.com/index2.html
Key Personnel
Owner & Mktg Dir: Chet Gottfried *E-mail:* me@lookoutnow.com
Mgr: Susan Gottfried
Founded: 1988
From electronic or paper ms to camera copy, as well as printing-binding supervision.

Sherry Gottlieb
Unit of wordservices.com
4900 Dunes St, Oxnard, CA 93035
Tel: 805-382-3425
E-mail: writer@wordservices.com
Web Site: www.wordservices.com
Founded: 1991
Private editorial service that specialize in fiction & screenplays. Edited over 350 book mss, mostly fiction. Several clients have sold their books to major publishers.

Graphic World Publishing Services
Division of Graphic World Inc
11687 Adie Rd, St Louis, MO 63043
Tel: 314-567-9854 *Fax:* 314-567-7178
E-mail: quote@gwinc.com
Web Site: www.gwinc.com
Key Personnel
CEO & Pres: Kevin P Arrow
EVP, Opers: Michael J Loomis *E-mail:* mike.loomis@gwps.com
EVP, Technol: Andrew R Vosburgh *E-mail:* a.vosburgh@gwinc.com
VP, Sales: Dean Grantham *Tel:* 610-918-9820 *E-mail:* directorsales@gwinc.com
Dir, Publg & Media Servs: Suzanne Kastner
Complete editorial & project management services from ms through final files, including interior & cover design, composition services, electronic publishing services & art rendering.

Paul Greenland Editorial Services
9184 Longfellow Lane, Machesney Park, IL 61115
Tel: 815-540-0911
Web Site: www.paulgreenland.com
Key Personnel
Owner: Paul R Greenland
Services include writing, ghostwriting & collaboration, research, editing & proofreading. Published nonfiction author, marketing/communications professional & former senior editor of national business magazine. Contributor to many leading reference books (Gale Group, University of Chicago Press, St. James Press). Interview subjects include celebrities, athletes & leading business executives. Specialize in reference, business, biography & history. References available upon request.

Rosemary F Gretton
1029 El Capitan Dr, Danville, CA 94526
Tel: 925-336-0003 *Fax:* 925-336-0003
E-mail: rgretton@lyricism.ca
Web Site: www.lyricism.ca
Founded: 2003
Writing, editing & research services for publishers, government, business, nonprofit organizations & individuals. Specializes in copy writing, copy-editing, fact checking, line editing, proofreading, research & rewriting.
Membership(s): American Copy Editors Society; Editorial Freelancers Association; Editors' Association of Canada/Association canadienne des reviseurs

Joan K Griffitts Indexing
3909 W 71 St, Indianapolis, IN 46268-2257
Tel: 317-297-7312
E-mail: jkgriffitts@gmail.com
Web Site: www.joankgriffittsindexing.com
Founded: 1989
Indexing & proofreading of textbooks, trade books, reference books, technical documentation, catalogs & newspapers by former librarian. Most subjects; specialize in business, science, sports, gardening, computer science, library science, education, taxation & social science. Various computer formats & e-mail delivery. Technical editing of various types of books & magazines including crochet, knit, weaving, etc.
Membership(s): American Society for Indexing

Judith S Grossman
715 Cherry Circle, Wynnewood, PA 19096
Tel: 610-642-0906
E-mail: stogiz@aol.com
Founded: 1973
Editing, ms evaluation & analysis, proofreading, rewriting; fiction, humanities, social sciences.

Anne Hebenstreit
20 Tip Top Way, Berkeley Heights, NJ 07922
Tel: 908-665-0536
Copy-editing & proofreading of el-hi & college texts & trade books.

Helm Editorial Services
707 SW Eighth Way, Fort Lauderdale, FL 33315
Tel: 954-525-5626
E-mail: lynnehelm12@aol.com
Freelance writing, line editing & publishing for executives & authors.

Herr's Indexing Service
76-340 Kealoha St, Kailua Kona, HI 96740
Tel: 808-365-4348
E-mail: lindahallinger@gmail.com
Web Site: www.herrsindexing.com
Key Personnel
Owner: Linda Herr Hallinger *E-mail:* linda@herrsindexing.com
Founded: 1944
Provide quality & affordable indexes for a variety of topics. Specialize in medical books.
Membership(s): American Medical Writers Association; American Society for Indexing; Editorial Freelancers Association

L Anne Hirschel DDS
5990 Highgate Ave, East Lansing, MI 48823
Tel: 517-333-1748
E-mail: alicerichard@comcast.net
Medicine & dentistry, consumer/patient information, continuing education & editing for foreign speaking scientists.
Membership(s): American Dental Association; Medical Writers Association

Burnham Holmes
182 Lakeview Hill Rd, Poultney, VT 05764-9179
Tel: 802-287-9707 *Fax:* 802-287-9707 (computer fax/modem)
E-mail: burnham.holmes@castleton.edu
Founded: 1990
Write textbooks, fiction & general nonfiction, juvenile, young adult, plays & children's books.
Membership(s): The Authors Guild; League of Vermont Writers

Henry Holmes Literary Agent/Book Publicist/Marketing Consultant
PO Box 433, Swansea, MA 02777
Tel: 508-672-2258
E-mail: henryholmesandassociates@yahoo.com
Key Personnel
Pres & Literary Agent: Henry Holmes
Founded: 1997

Nonfiction: biography, business, education, law, health, history, sports, etc. Exclusive literary agent/book publicist for authors. Authors must present complete book proposal with SASE when submitting. Impeccable presentation is a must. Prefer books targeted at general audiences rather than an exclusive or limited market. Send letter with a good hook & a list of publishers you have contacted in the past. Do not send any spiral bound proposals; word count must be stated. Include past publicity & endorsement(s). Commission 15%. Contract must be signed. Upon receipt of signed contract, author will be sent a media portfolio with marketing data, tip sheet & full compliment of media contact listings. Professional consultation related to all media, freelance assignments, interviewing celebrities, professional athletes, musicians, political figures & other famous people.

Imagefinders Inc
6101 Utah Ave NW, Washington, DC 20015
Tel: 202-244-4456 *Fax:* 202-244-3237
Key Personnel
Pres: Elisabeth M Hartjens *E-mail:* hartjens@erols.com
Founded: 1985
Photo & illustration research & editing; fact checking, information research. Specialize in Washington public domain sources.

IndexEmpire Indexing Services
16740 Orville Wright Dr, Riverside, CA 92518
Tel: 951-697-2819
E-mail: indexempire@gmail.com
Key Personnel
Indexer: Jean F Middleton
Founded: 1999
Provides back-of-the-book indexes for nonfiction books of all types.
Membership(s): American Society for Indexing

Indexing by the Book
PO Box 12513, Tucson, AZ 85732-2513
Tel: 520-750-8439
E-mail: indextran@cox.net
Web Site: www.indexingbythebook.com
Key Personnel
Indexer: Cynthia J Coan
Founded: 2003
Index books & serials. Subject specialties include health/medicine, history (especially Arizona/Southwest), education, language studies, library science, social sciences & psychology. Index adult, children's & Spanish language titles. Also translate print materials from Spanish & Swedish into English.
Membership(s): American Society for Indexing; ATA; National Council on Interpreting in Health Care

Integra Software Services Inc
Division of Integra Software Services Pvt Ltd
1110 Jorie Blvd, Suite 200, Oak Brook, IL 60523
Tel: 630-586-2579 *Fax:* 630-586-2599
E-mail: marketing@integra.co.in
Web Site: www.integra.co.in
Key Personnel
Dir, Edit Devt: Ingrid Benson *E-mail:* ingrid.benson@integra.co.in
Mng Ed: Michelle Dellinger *E-mail:* michelle.dellinger@integra.co.in
Design Mgr: Emily Friel *E-mail:* emily.friel@integra.co.in
Founded: 1991
Project management, development & production support for book publishers. Full range of publishing services, including development editing, design, rights & permissions, photo research, copyediting & indexing, proofreading, project management, language polishing, typesetting, XML & conversion, illustrations & artwork, ebooks & digital services. Specialty areas are business & economics, computer science, mathematics, science, history, English, medical & education texts.

Iridescent Orange Press, see Wambtac Communications

Jan Williams Indexing Services
300 Dartmouth College Hwy, Lyme, NH 03768-3207
Tel: 603-795-4924
Web Site: www.janwilliamsindexing.com
Key Personnel
Prop: Jan Williams
Founded: 1998
Back-of-book indexes for trade, scholarly, reference & textbooks; database/online indexes for journals.
Membership(s): American Society for Indexing

Jenkins Group Inc
1129 Woodmere Ave, Suite B, Traverse City, MI 49686
Tel: 231-933-0445 *Toll Free Tel:* 800-706-4636 *Fax:* 231-933-0448
E-mail: info@bookpublishing.com
Web Site: www.bookpublishing.com
Key Personnel
CEO: Jerrold R Jenkins *Tel:* 231-933-0445 ext 1008 *E-mail:* jrj@bookpublishing.com
COO & Pres: James Kalajian *Tel:* 231-933-0445 ext 1006 *E-mail:* jjk@bookpublishing.com
Dir, Consulting & Mktg Servs: Kim Hornyak *Tel:* 231-933-0445 ext 1013 *E-mail:* khornyak@bookpublishing.com
Mng Ed, Independent Publisher Online: Jim Barnes *E-mail:* jimb@bookpublishing.com
Book Prodn Mgr: Leah Nicholson *Tel:* 231-933-0445 ext 1015 *E-mail:* lnicholson@bookpublishing.com
Founded: 1990
Full service custom book publishing services for corporations, independent authors, organizations & small press publishers. Services include registrations, typesetting, cover design, color separations, ghostwriting, illustration & photo placement, galley preparation & print management.

JFE Editorial
8425 Doreen Ave, Fort Worth, TX 76116-4922
Tel: 817-560-7018
Key Personnel
Owner & Pres: June Ford *E-mail:* jford@jfe-editorial.com
Founded: 1987
Founded by Ms Ford, a nationally published author, ghostwriter, project manager, editor & proofreader. Focus includes: writing, ghostwriting, rewriting, special assignment writing; developmental, copy, line, style & content editing; proofreading; ms analysis; permissions, interviewing; fact checking; database research, coding, editing. Published in genres ranging from children's, trade & true crime to scholastic, self-help & sports books; also a variety of magazine articles. Coordinator of many high-dollar projects & extremely successful at transforming complex material into easily understood information. Ms Ford is a speaker for grades 3-12, universities & conferences. Fax number provided upon request.

JL Communications
10205 Green Holly Terr, Silver Spring, MD 20902
Tel: 301-593-0640
Key Personnel
Writer, Ed & Poet: Joyce Eileen Latham
Founded: 1996

Cliff Johnson & Associates
10867 Fruitland Dr, Studio City, CA 91604
Tel: 818-761-5665 *Fax:* 818-761-9501
E-mail: quest543@yahoo.com
Key Personnel
Pres: Cliff Johnson
Founded: 1976
Nonfiction specialists (primarily medical, psychology, religious, self-help & philosophical books).

Jouve North America Inc
Division of Jouve Group (France)
70 Landmark Hill Dr, Brattleboro, VT 05301
Mailing Address: PO Box 1338, Brattleboro, VT 05302
Tel: 802-254-6073 *Toll Free Tel:* 800-451-4328 *Fax:* 802-257-1511
Web Site: www.jouve.com
Key Personnel
CEO & Pres: Emmanuel Benoit
Founded: 1997

Just Creative Writing & Indexing Services (JCR)
301 Wood Duck Dr, Greensboro, MD 21639
Tel: 410-482-6337
E-mail: jreveal@verizon.net; support@justcreativewriting.com
Web Site: www.justcreativewriting.com
Key Personnel
Sole Prop: Judith Reveal
Founded: 2005
Provides editorial services for fiction & nonfiction; professional back-of-the-book indexing.
Membership(s): Eastern Shore Writers' Association; Editorial Freelancers Association; Greensboro Business & Civic Association

Sharon Kapnick
185 West End Ave, New York, NY 10023-5547
Tel: 212-787-7231
Web Site: sharonswineline.wordpress.com
Food & wine articles for magazines, web sites, newspapers & books.

Ann T Keene, see Edit Etc

Keim Publishing
66 Main St, Suite 807, Yonkers, NY 10701
Tel: 917-655-7190
Key Personnel
Owner & Pres: Betty Keim *E-mail:* blkeim@earthlink.net
Founded: 1985
Books & art catalogs, corporate reports, newsletters, brochures, pamphlets, electronic materials (e.g., web sites, advertisements, etc), promotional items, reference books, production & design, line editing, copy-editing, indexing, permissions, photo research, proofreading, reference assignments, research, rewriting, typemarking, special assignment writing. All subjects; specialize in art, broadcasting, history, literature, science, mathematics & music.

Jascha Kessler
218 16 St, Santa Monica, CA 90402-2216
Tel: 310-393-7968 *Fax:* 310-393-7968 (by request only)
E-mail: urim.urim@gmail.com
Web Site: www.jfkessler.com; www.xlibris.com
Freelance reviews of poetry, fiction, history, philosophy, current affairs. Criticism as well as "cultural commentary" on the arts, theater & dance.
Membership(s): The American Society of Composers, Authors and Publishers

Theodore Knight PhD
RockCliff Farm, 40 Old Louisquisset Pike, Unit 101A, North Smithfield, RI 02896
Tel: 401-597-6982
E-mail: tedknight1@cox.net
Founded: 1989
Editorial & project management for trade, textbook, university press & reference.

Bill Koehnlein
236 E Fifth St, New York, NY 10003-8545
Tel: 212-674-9145
E-mail: koehnlein.bill@gmail.com
Founded: 1982
Indexing & editing: all subjects, especially current affairs, social science, American labor & radical history, radical political movements & theory: socialism, Marxism, anarchism. Also food & nutrition issues, especially vegetarianism & veganism.

Barry R Koffler
Featherside, 14 Ginger Rd, High Falls, NY 12440
Tel: 845-687-9851
E-mail: barkof@feathersite.com
Founded: 1979
Indexing, proofreading, editing. Writing most subjects (including encyclopedic). Specialize in popular & scientific works on animals & natural history.

KOK Edit
15 Hare Lane, East Setauket, NY 11733-3606
Tel: 631-997-8191 *Fax:* 631-474-9849
E-mail: editor@kokedit.com
Web Site: www.kokedit.com; twitter.com/kokedit; www.facebook.com/k.omooreklopf; www.linkedin.com/in/kokedit; www.editor-mom.blogspot.com
Key Personnel
Owner: Katharine O'Moore-Klopf
Founded: 1995
Provides copyediting & substantive editing to authors & publishers of textbooks, professional books & journal articles (medicine, psychology, psychiatry, allied health) & nonfiction trade books (mainstream health care, alternative health care, child care, human sexuality, psychology, women's issues). Certified by the Board of Editors in the Life Sciences.
Membership(s): American Medical Writers Association; Board of Editors in the Life Sciences; Council of Science Editors; Editorial Freelancers Association; World Association of Medical Editors

Kraft & Kraft
40 Memorial Hwy, Apt 23-C, New Rochelle, NY 10801
Tel: 914-319-3320
Web Site: www.erickraft.com
Key Personnel
Owner & Edit Dir: Eric Kraft *E-mail:* eric-kraft@post.harvard.edu
Contact: Madeline Kraft
Founded: 1975
Design & development of educational materials.

Eileen Kramer
336 Great Rd, Stow, MA 01775
Tel: 978-897-4121
E-mail: kramer@tiac.net
Web Site: www.ekramer.com
Copyeditor/proofreader/ESL teacher/curriculum developer. Specialties include ESL textbooks & courseware; web, science, math, statistics, technical books, academic journals & textbooks.

Lynn C Kronzek & Richard A Flom
Affiliate of Lynn C Kronzek & Associates
145 S Glenoaks Blvd, Suite 240, Burbank, CA 91502
Tel: 818-768-7688 *Fax:* 818-768-7648
Key Personnel
Principal: Lynn C Kronzek *E-mail:* lckronzek@sbcglobal.net
Founded: 1989
Nonfiction writing & editorial services, with particular expertise in history, multicultural & Judaic studies, government/public affairs & religion. Affiliated with the National Council on Public History, American Association for State & Local History & the Rabbinical Assembly.

Polly Kummel
624 Boardman Rd, Aiken, SC 29803
Tel: 803-641-6831
E-mail: editor@amazinphrasin.com; pollyk1@msn.com
Web Site: www.amazinphrasin.com
Founded: 1990
Nonfiction (all subjects; trade & academic): copyediting; substantive/developmental editing; coaching. Specialties: journalism, history, political science, memoir, equestrian subjects. Dissertation/thesis help for humanities grad students; electronic editing. More than 35 years of experience.

Lachina Publishing Services Inc
3793 S Green Rd, Cleveland, OH 44122
Tel: 216-292-7959
E-mail: info@lachina.com
Web Site: www.lachina.com
Key Personnel
Founder & Pres: Jeffrey A Lachina
Founded: 1989
Project management, editorial development, copy editing, biomedical illustration, indexing, page composition, book & jacket design, proofreading, technical illustration.

Lynne Lackenbach Editorial Services
31 Pillsbury Rd, East Hampstead, NH 03826
Tel: 603-329-8133
E-mail: lynnelack@gmail.com
Full line of editorial services to college & professional publishers. Specialize in scientific & technical material.

Bob Land, see Land on Demand

Land on Demand
20 Long Crescent Dr, Bristol, VA 24201
Tel: 423-366-0513
E-mail: landondemand@gmail.com
Web Site: boblandedits.blogspot.com
Key Personnel
Prop & Ed: Bob Land
Founded: 1994 (Full-time freelancer since 1994; freelancer since 1986; full-time editor, writer, proofreader 1981-1994)
Editing, indexing, proofreading.

The Learning Source Ltd
644 Tenth St, Brooklyn, NY 11215
Tel: 718-768-0231 (ext 10) *Fax:* 718-369-3467
E-mail: info@learningsourceltd.com
Web Site: www.learningsourceltd.com
Key Personnel
Dir: Gary Davis; Wendy Davis
Mng Ed: Brian Ableman
Provides a full range of editorial & book-producing services from concept through ms & design to film & bound book. Specialty areas include children's fiction & nonfiction, adult reference & nonfiction series & classroom materials. Sister company to Ivy Gate Books.
Membership(s): American Book Producers Association; International Literacy Association; National Council of Teachers of Mathematics

Debra Lemonds
PO Box 5516, Pasadena, CA 91117-0516
Tel: 626-844-9363
E-mail: dlemonds@earthlink.net
Founded: 1984
Photo editor. Layout & a bit of graphic design.
Membership(s): ASPP

Elizabeth J Leppman
631 Worcester Dr, Lexington, KY 40503
Tel: 859-245-4325 *Fax:* 859-245-4325
E-mail: ejleppman@windstream.net
Founded: 1974
Published author & experienced book/journal editor will perform developmental, content & copy editing, ms reviewing, writing. Specialize in geography & map editing.

Andrew S Linick PhD, The Copyologist®
Subsidiary of The Linick Group Inc
Linick Bldg, 7 Putter Lane, Middle Island, NY 11953
Mailing Address: PO Box 102, Middle Island, NY 11953-0102
Tel: 631-924-3888 *Fax:* 631-924-8555
E-mail: linickgroup@gmail.com
Web Site: www.AndrewLinickDirectMarketing.com/The-Copyologist.html; www.NewWorldPressBooks.com
Key Personnel
CEO & Creative Dir: Andrew S Linick, PhD *E-mail:* andrew@asklinick.com
VP: Roger Dextor
Founded: 1968
Complete editorial & copywriting services: copy analysis & line editing, research, rewriting for direct response, direct mail, mail order, sales promotions; specialize in newsletters, newspapers, magazines, house organs & seminars; catalog writing, business & consumer launch packages & in-house seminars on how to sell what you write; articles, nonfiction books & manuals. Phone consultation available; consumer, trade, business to business, all markets, media & subjects; ms analysis & development, proofreading, special assignment writing, ghostwriting, e-mail marketing campaigns for publishers. Provide comprehensive graphic redesign/new web site content development, interactive services with web site marketing makeover advice for first-time authors, self-publishers, professionals & entrepreneurs. Specializes in flash, animation, merchant accounts, online advertising/PR, links to top search engines, consulting on a 100% satisfaction guarantee. Free site evaluation for LMP readers. For over 43 years we have helped first-time authors & best-selling authors/publishers/entrepreneurs successfully promote books. Call for help today.
Membership(s): The Independent Book Publishers Association

Elliot Linzer
126-10 Powells Cove Blvd, College Point, NY 11356
Tel: 718-353-1261 *Fax:* 814-253-1261
E-mail: elinzer@juno.com
Founded: 1971
Indexing of trade books, textbooks, reference books & scholarly books. Fifty years experience.
Membership(s): American Society for Indexing; Editorial Freelancers Association

E Trina Lipton
60 E Eighth St, Suite 15-F, New York, NY 10003
Tel: 212-674-5558 (call first, messages); 917-327-6886 (cell) *Fax:* 212-674-3523
E-mail: trinalipton@hotmail.com
Thirty-seven years experience of picture research & picture editing: historical & contemporary

still photos & film footage, art illustrations. Photography: stock photos (B&W & color, all subjects). Also editorial research, fact checking & permissions interviewing.
Membership(s): National Press Photographers Association; New York Museum of Education Roundtable; UFT

Little Chicago Editorial Services
154 Natural Tpke, Ripton, VT 05766
Mailing Address: PO Box 185, Ripton, VT 05766
Tel: 802-388-9782
Web Site: andreachesman.com
Key Personnel
Writer & Ed: Andrea Chesman
E-mail: andreachesman@gmail.com
Membership(s): International Association of Culinary Professionals

Lumina Datamatics
4 Collins Ave, Plymouth, MA 02360
Tel: 508-746-0300 *Fax:* 508-746-3233
E-mail: info@luminadatamatics.com
Web Site: luminadatamatics.com
Key Personnel
SVP, Busn Devt: Jack Mitchell *Tel:* 508-415-6158 (cell) *E-mail:* jmitchell@luminadatamatics.com
SVP, Busn Solutions: Shivaji Sengupta
E-mail: shiveaji.senguptu@luminadatamatics.com
SVP, Content Technol: John Wheeler
E-mail: john.wheeler@luminadatamatics.com
SVP, Prod Devt: Gordon Laws *Tel:* 508-746-0300 ext 212 *E-mail:* gordon.laws@luminadatamatics.com
VP, Fin & Acctg: John Chappell *Tel:* 508-746-0300 ext 304 *E-mail:* john.chappell@luminadatamatics.com
Founded: 2005
Providing full service content creation, design/packaging & media delivery systems to publishers. Services include authoring/writing, editorial research & development, media development & production, editing, photo & text research/permissions, photography/photo shoot direction, indexing, proofreading, fact checking, design/design direction, art direction/editing, technical/illustrative art packages, photo manipulation & page make-up/composition services. Employs over 1,200 US & offshore resources specializing in content/media creation & make-up including file conversions/repurposing & content management & delivery services. All services are offered both in the US & at offshore facilities. Areas of specialization include school, higher education & professional publishing: mathematics (grade school/algebra/calculus/physics), foreign language (French/Spanish/German/Italian), English & English composition, history, political science, science (chemistry/biology/astronomy), social studies, computer science, business (economics/finance/marketing), engineering & technical trades as well as professional/reference material. Products range from simple one-color ancillaries components to highly complex design & art intensive core content.
Branch Office(s)
345 Seventh Ave, 22nd fl, New York, NY 10001 *Tel:* 646-453-1000
1797 Seddon Ct, Ashland, OH 44805 *Tel:* 419-289-0558
3265 Farmtrail Rd, York, PA 17406 *Tel:* 717-764-4000

Mari Lynch, see Fine Wordworking

Elizabeth Lyon
3530 E Game Farm Rd, No 39, Springfield, OR 97477
Tel: 541-357-4181
E-mail: elyon123@comcast.net
Web Site: www.elizabethlyon.com
Founded: 1988
Full-time freelance book editor. Specialize in novels, memoirs, nonfiction books & proposals. Advises writers about how to write, connect with literary agents &, should 'Plan A' not succeed, how to successfully self-publish an ebook +/or print-on-demand. Over 60 writers have found publication with large publishers & small presses, while dozens have "gone indie," some to great success & acclaim. Edits query letters & synopses for clients. Has written 6 books on writing, including the bestsellers *Nonfiction Book Proposals Anybody Can Write & Manuscript Makeover. Writing Subtext* is the first in a booklet series, sold as an ebook & in paperback.
Membership(s): Oregon Writers Colony; Williamette Writers Association

Phyllis Manner
17 Springdale Rd, New Rochelle, NY 10804
Tel: 914-834-4707 *Fax:* 914-834-4707
E-mail: pmanner@aol.com
Specialize in medicine, biochemistry & archeology.
Membership(s): American Society for Indexing; Archeological Institute of America

Danny Marcus Word Worker
Division of D M Enterprises
62 Washington St, Suite 2, Marblehead, MA 01945-3553
Tel: 781-631-3886; 781-290-9174 (cell) *Fax:* 781-631-3886
E-mail: emildanelle@yahoo.com
Founded: 1984
Proofreading, line editing & copy-editing. Specialize in politics, income taxes, government, history, current events, all kinds of fiction & general nonfiction.
Membership(s): Cambridge Academic Editors Network

Joy Matkowski
212 Ridge Hill Rd, Mechanicsburg, PA 17050
Tel: 717-620-8881
E-mail: jmatkowski1@comcast.net
Copy-editing & proofreading.

Peter Mayeux
8148 Regent Dr, Lincoln, NE 68507-3366
Tel: 402-466-8547
E-mail: pm41923@windstream.net
Resumes, original research, writing papers & projects, Power Point presentations, broadcast commercial writing, textbooks & media scripts.

Anita D McClellan Associates
464 Common St, Suite 142, Belmont, MA 02478-2704
Tel: 617-575-9203 *Fax:* 617-315-8983
E-mail: adm@anitamcclellan.com
Web Site: www.anitamcclellan.com
Key Personnel
Mng Dir: Anita D McClellan
Founded: 1988
Developmental editing, nonfiction proposal development, revising, restructuring, book doctoring, fiction & nonfiction.
Membership(s): The Authors Guild; Bay Area Editors' Forum; Bookbuilders of Boston; Cape Cod Writers Center; Editorial Freelancers Association; Independent Publishers of New England; International Women's Writing Guild; Sisters in Crime; Society of Children's Book Writers & Illustrators; Women's National Book Association

Pamela Dittmer McKuen
87 Tanglewood Dr, Glen Ellyn, IL 60137
Tel: 630-545-0867 *Fax:* 630-545-0868
E-mail: pmckuen@gmail.com
Web Site: www.allthewritethings.com; www.pamelamckuen.com
Special assignment writing, editorial & corporate projects, periodicals, copy-editing, interviewing & research.
Membership(s): Association of Women in Journalism; National Association of Real Estate Editors

Pat McNees
10643 Weymouth St, Suite 204, Bethesda, MD 20814
Tel: 301-897-8557
E-mail: patmcnees@gmail.com
Web Site: www.patmcnees.com; www.writersandeditors.com
Founded: 1971
Articles, books, photohistories. Specialize in memoirs, personal histories, biographies & organizational histories, especially in fields of medicine & psychiatry. Teach life story & legacy writing; do substantial editing, rewriting & book doctoring. Theme anthologies & stories about food, dancing & travel.
Membership(s): American Society of Journalists & Authors; Association of Health Care Journalists; Association of Personal Historians; The Authors Guild; Biographers International Organization; The Independent Book Publishers Association; National Association of Science Writers; PEN International; Society for Technical Communication

MC2 Solutions LLC
5101 Violet Lane, Madison, WI 53714
Tel: 608-240-4959
Key Personnel
Writer/Ed: Mark Crawford *E-mail:* mark.crawford@charter.net
Founded: 1995
Servicing all audiences including academic, technical, science, corporate & public relations. Additional services include: substantive editing, promotional writing & writing of corporate histories, business writing, marketing & communications, feature writing, editing & proofreading.

Barbara A Mele
2525 Holland Ave, New York, NY 10467-8703
Tel: 718-654-8047 *Fax:* 718-654-8047
E-mail: bannmele@aol.com
Freelance permissions.

Tom Mellers Publishing Services (TMPS)
60 Second Ave, New York, NY 10003
Tel: 212-254-4958
E-mail: tmps71@yahoo.com
Comprehensive rights & permissions administration, acquiring & granting rights for text of all kinds, photos, art, video, film, music, spoken word. Acquiring services range from consulting with rightseekers, to evaluating permissionable material, setting up projects, sending & tracking requests, negotiating fees, preparing acknowledgments, administering payment & righting contracts. Granting services include drafting contracts, negotiating & collecting fees & preparing records (edit-in). Copyright registration. Specialize in literary estates. All subjects & media. Extensive editing & editorial services, from author consultation to ms analysis, fact checking & rewriting to project supervision (including typemarking, book design, line editing, copy-editing, proofreading). Ghostwriting & special assignment writing, author representation & photo research, drafting contracts, image research & international work with museums.
Branch Office(s)
4629 Vestal Pkwy E, Vestal, NY 13850 *Tel:* 607-798-7994

Fred C Mench Professor of Classics Emeritus
207 Saint Martins Lane, Smyrna, TN 37167
Tel: 615-459-0765
E-mail: fmench@earthlink.net
Text editing, especially classical antiquity or English literature. Past projects included reading drafts of Roman historical novels for content & form, writing reviews of scholarly & fictional works (especially on ancient Rome). Book Review Editor of the journal *Classical World* for 15 years, involving extensive condensing of submitted texts. Special areas: Julius Caesar, Roman republic, Latin texts, the Bible, Greek mythology & G B Shaw. Also available for general editing.
Membership(s): American Philological Association

Metropolitan Editorial & Writing Service
Subsidiary of Metropolitan Research Co
4455 Douglas Ave, Riverdale, NY 10471
Tel: 718-549-5518
Key Personnel
Pres: Chauncey G Olinger, Jr
Founded: 1982
Editing, ms analysis, rewriting & restyling of general, professional & scholarly writing, especially in economics, business, social sciences, humanities, medicine & pharmacy. Specialize in editorial collaboration with authors; oral history interviewing.

Susan T Middleton
366-A Norton Hill Rd, Ashfield, MA 01330-9601
Tel: 413-628-4039
E-mail: smiddle@crocker.com
Founded: 1985
Book revision, collaboration, developmental & copy-editing for individuals & for trade & college markets primarily in the sciences.
Membership(s): Western New England Editorial Freelancers Network

Robert J Milch
9 Millbrook Dr, Stony Brook, NY 11790-2914
Tel: 631-689-8546 *Fax:* 631-689-8546
E-mail: milchedit@aol.com

Stephen M Miller Inc
15727 S Madison Dr, Olathe, KS 66062
Tel: 913-768-7997
Web Site: www.stephenmillerbooks.com
Key Personnel
Pres: Stephen M Miller *E-mail:* steve@stephenmillerbooks.com
Founded: 1994
Writing, editing; bible specialty & health subspecialty. Fulltime freelance writer & former editor, books, magazines & newspaper. Seminary & journalism school graduate, Kansas City area. Clientele of top national book publishers & magazines.
Membership(s): CBA: The Association for Christian Retail; Evangelical Christian Publishers Association; Society of Bible Literature; Wesleyan Theological Society

Kathleen Mills Editorial Services
PO Box 214, Chardon, OH 44024
Tel: 440-285-4347
E-mail: mills_edit@yahoo.com
Key Personnel
Edit Dir: Kathleen Mills
Founded: 1990
More than 30 years of publishing experience. Editing, indexing, writing, author liaison & project management. Arts & humanities, social sciences, technical, reference, medical, college, business, general nonfiction & web sites. Clients include the Cleveland Museum of Art, Western Reserve Historical Society, Case Western Reserve University, ASM International, UCLA & many others.

Sondra Mochson
18 Overlook Dr, Port Washington, NY 11050
Tel: 516-883-0961
All subjects, text & trade.

Mary Mueller
516 Bartram Rd, Moorestown, NJ 08057
Tel: 856-778-4769
E-mail: mamam49@aol.com
Abstracting, copy-editing, ghostwriting, indexing, proofreading, rewriting & book reviewing-publicity. Specialize in consumer education, gardening, health, nutrition, house & home organizing, science & technology, hobby art & craft books & how-to-books.

Nina Neimark Editorial Services
543 Third St, Brooklyn, NY 11215
Tel: 718-499-6804
E-mail: pneimark@hotmail.com
Key Personnel
Pres: Nina Neimark
Founded: 1965
Specialize in scholarly books & college texts on environmental issues, history, art, music, social sciences; also general nonfiction. Mss analysis & development, content & photo research, rewriting, copy-editing, proofreading, production editing & complete book packaging services.

Nesbitt Graphics Inc
Division of Cenveo Publisher Services
555 Virginia Dr, Fort Washington, PA 19034
Tel: 215-591-9125 *Fax:* 215-591-9093
Web Site: cenveopublisherservices.com
Key Personnel
VP: Harry J Nesbitt, III *E-mail:* harry.nesbitt@cenveo.com
Dir, Technol: Bruce Nesbitt *E-mail:* bruce.nesbitt@cenveo.com
Sr Prodn Coord: Harry F Druding *E-mail:* harry.druding@cenveo.com
Founded: 1998
Our school division offers complete PreK-12 educational publishing services including conceptual development, prototype development, research, writing, content editing, copy-editing, fact checking & production editing. Editorial expertise includes mathematics, science/health & reading/language arts. Extensive experience creating student & teacher's editions, alternative programs, supplemental materials, assessment, curriculum alignment, state customizations, correlations & professional developmental materials. Our higher education division provides expert full service management for college, medical, nursing, allied health & scholarly publications. Production services for both school & higher education include instructional design, page layouts, art creation & art services, photo research/shoots, electronic composition & prepress services.
Membership(s): Book Industry Guild of New York; Bookbuilders of Boston; Midwest Publishing Association; National Association for the Education of Young Children; National Council of Supervisors of Mathematics; National Council of Teachers of Mathematics; National Science Teachers Association; Publishing Professionals Network

Newgen North America Inc
Subsidiary of Newgen KnowledgeWorks
2714 Bee Cave Rd, Suite 201, Austin, TX 78746
Tel: 512-478-5341 *Fax:* 512-476-4756
Web Site: www.newgen.co
Key Personnel
Pres: Maran Elancheran *Tel:* 512-870-7106 (cell)
E-mail: maran@newgen.co
VP, Cust Support: Bill M Grosskopf
E-mail: bill@newgen.co
Sales Dir, USA: Linda Thomas *Tel:* 703-297-1473 *E-mail:* lindat@newgen.co
Founded: 1955
Prepares project material for copy-editor, supervises the copy-editing, serves as liaison with the author, reviews the final ms & makes sure that all elements of the project are complete & ready to be turned over to a designer. Ensures that file conversions, coding & cleanup properly prepare book material for each stage in the process. Convert files to ebook formats. Scan printed books to prepare new print file & ebook files.

Sue Newton
1385 Cypress Point Lane, Suite 202, Ventura, CA 93003
Tel: 805-553-8087
E-mail: sue.edit@gmail.com
Ms & line editing services including the correction of spelling errors, grammar, punctuation, syntax & consistency. Minor rewrites. 20 years experience in the publishing industry including fiction, nonfiction, autobiographies & advertising.
Membership(s): Small Publishers, Artists & Writers Network; Ventura County Writers Club

Donald Nicholson-Smith
50 Plaza St E, Brooklyn, NY 11238
Tel: 718-636-4732
E-mail: mnr.dns@verizon.net
French-English literary translation.

Northeastern Graphic Inc
33 Crystal Bay Ct, Palm Coast, FL 32137
Tel: 386-246-9942
E-mail: contact@northeasterngraphic.com
Web Site: www.northeasterngraphic.com
Key Personnel
CFO: Kathryn Sussman
Pres: Kate Scully *E-mail:* kscully@northeasterngraphic.com
Founded: 1987
Copy-editing, fact checking, indexing, line editing, ms analysis, permissions, photo research, proofreading, rewriting & typemarking.

nSight Inc
One Van de Graaff Dr, Suite 202, Burlington, MA 01803
Tel: 781-273-6300 *Fax:* 781-273-6301
Web Site: www.nsightworks.com
Key Personnel
Pres & Gen Mgr: Tess Kastning
E-mail: tkastning@nsightworks.com
Founded: 1982
Complete book & journal content development & production services: writing, copy-editing, developmental editing, indexing, proofreading; project management; abstracting, advertising & promotion copywriting, bibliographies, fact checking, interviewing, developmental editing, ms analysis, rewriting, special assignment writing, transcription editing; design, art rendering, photo research, covers & jackets; permissions; in-house composition as well as development of electronic publishing products, including HTML & XML coding & supervising printing. Online editing experts (visit EditExpress.com). Specialize in technical subject areas: college, medical & allied health, computer science, law, physical & life sciences & engineering.
Membership(s): AAP PreK-12 Learning Group; Bookbuilders of Boston

Veronica Oliva
304 Lily St, San Francisco, CA 94102-5608
Tel: 415-337-7707
E-mail: veronicaoliva@sbcglobal.net
Founded: 1994
Permissions editor: Trade & educational publishers. Specialty: French, Spanish & Italian college-level textbooks.
Membership(s): Bay Area Editors' Forum

Oyster River Press
36 Oyster River Rd, Durham, NH 03824-3029
Tel: 603-868-5006
E-mail: oysterriverpress@comcast.net
Web Site: www.oysterriverpress.com
Key Personnel
Publr & Ed: Cicely Buckley
Interviewing, special assignment writing, translating services to/from French, Spanish, Russian, Polish.
Membership(s): New Hampshire Writers Project

Pacific Publishing Services
PO Box 1150, Capitola, CA 95010-1150
Tel: 831-476-8284 *Fax:* 831-476-8294
E-mail: pacpubs@attglobal.net
Key Personnel
Pres: Albert Lee Strickland
Assoc: Lynne Ann De Spelder
Research, editorial & writing services for trade, text & corporate publications.

Karen L Pangallo
27 Buffum St, Salem, MA 01970
Tel: 978-744-8796
E-mail: pangallo@noblenet.org

Diane Patrick
140 Carver Loop, No 21A, Bronx, NY 10475-2954
E-mail: dpatrickediting@aol.com
Web Site: www.dianepatrick.net
Professional editor who polishes words for publishers, editors, agents, academics, legal professionals, entertainers & business owners. Especially enjoy working with biography.
Membership(s): International Women's Writing Guild; New York Association of Black Journalists

PeopleSpeak
25260-I La Paz Rd, Suite 1, Laguna Hills, CA 92653
Mailing Address: 25602 Alicia Pkwy, Suite 512, Laguna Hills, CA 92653
Tel: 949-581-6190 *Fax:* 949-581-4958
E-mail: pplspeak@att.net
Web Site: www.detailsplease.com/peoplespeak
Key Personnel
Sr Ed: Sharon Goldinger
Founded: 1985
An eye for details. Copyediting; specialize in nonfiction mss, marketing materials, newsletters, directories.
Membership(s): The Independent Book Publishers Association; Publishers Association of Los Angeles; San Diego Professional Editors Network

Rebecca Pepper
434 NE Floral Place, Portland, OR 97232
Tel: 503-236-5802
E-mail: rpepper@rpepper.net
Founded: 1986
Membership(s): Editcetera; Editorial Freelancers Association; Northwest Independent Editors Guild

The Permissions Group Inc
1247 Milwaukee Ave, Suite 303, Glenview, IL 60025
Tel: 847-635-6550 *Toll Free Tel:* 800-374-7985 *Fax:* 847-635-6968
E-mail: info@permissionsgroup.com
Web Site: www.permissionsgroup.com
Key Personnel
Dir: Sherry Hoesly *E-mail:* sherry_hoesly@permissionsgroup.com
Founded: 1990
Full service copyright & permissions consulting company. Specialize in ms review & analysis, rights negotiation, individualized consulting.

Elsa Peterson Ltd
41 East Ave, Norwalk, CT 06851-3919
Tel: 203-846-8331
E-mail: epltd@earthlink.net
Founded: 1984
Offer a full range of editorial services personalized to your project: developmental editing, substantive editing, writing, rights clearance, picture research, translation (Spanish to English).
Membership(s): Association for Psychological Science; Editorial Freelancers Association; Text & Academic Authors

Evelyn Walters Pettit
114 S Park Ave, Suite E, Winter Park, FL 32789-7012
Tel: 407-620-0131 (cell); 407-644-1711 *Fax:* 407-644-1711
E-mail: bookseller@brandywinebooks.com
Copy & line editing, rewriting & proofreading. Specialize in professional & reference books & journal articles & in general magazines & books. Experience in subjects ranging from social & biological sciences to engineering & mathematics to business.

Meredith Phillips
Subsidiary of Perseverance Editorial Services
4127 Old Adobe Rd, Palo Alto, CA 94306
Tel: 650-857-9555
E-mail: mphillips0743@comcast.net
Former author & award-nominated mystery publisher (Perseverance Press). Editing (developmental, line, copy), researching, fact checking, proofreading of trade books (fiction or nonfiction).

PhotoEdit Inc
3505 Cadillac Ave, Suite P-101, Costa Mesa, CA 92626
Toll Free Tel: 800-860-2098 *Fax:* 714-434-5937 *Toll Free Fax:* 800-804-3707
E-mail: sales@photoeditinc.com
Web Site: www.photoeditinc.com
Key Personnel
Photo Edit Dir: Tashauna Johnson *Tel:* 714-434-5935 *E-mail:* tashauna.johnson@photoeditinc.com
Founded: 1987
Photographers; large stock on hand.

Pictures & Words Editorial Services
3100 "B" Ave, Anacortes, WA 98221
Tel: 360-293-8476
E-mail: editor@picturesandwords.com
Web Site: www.picturesandwords.com/words
Key Personnel
Owner: Kristi Hein
Founded: 1995
Versatile generalist with decades of experience serving trade publishers & authors. Expertise in cookbooks, health & well-being, gardening (ornamental & food), nature & environment, education, consumer interest & activism, business & fiction.
Membership(s): Bay Area Editors' Forum; Northwest Independent Editors Guild

Caroline Pincus Book Midwife
101 Wool St, San Francisco, CA 94110
Tel: 415-516-6206
E-mail: cpincus100@sbcglobal.net
Key Personnel
Book Midwife: Caroline Pincus
Founded: 1998
Ms development & book doctoring for the general trade. Specialize in health, personal growth, women's issues & narrative nonfiction.

Marilyn Pincus
1320 W Bloomington Place, Tucson, AZ 85755
Tel: 520-742-6699
E-mail: MPscribe@aol.com
Web Site: www.marilynpincus.info
Author, ghostwriter & consultant-to-management. Books published in many languages. Works with clients on book development from A-Z. Ghostwrites some or all of clients' books. Highly skilled interviewer & researcher. Also originates or updates policies, procedures, job descriptions & related documents. Accepts some speaking invitations. See web site for short bio & some book titles.
Membership(s): Association of Ghostwriters; The Authors Guild

J P Pochron Writer for Hire
830 Lake Orchid Circle, No 203, Vero Beach, FL 32962
Tel: 772-569-2967
E-mail: hotwriter15@hotmail.com
Key Personnel
Owner & Writer: J P Pochron
Former editor, reporter & freelance writer, with marketing, advertising & public relations experience. Press releases, promotional copy, commercials, personal & business letter writing are services offered. Eight years library reference experience to assist with research.

Wendy Polhemus-Annibell
PO Box 464, Peconic, NY 11958
Tel: 631-276-0684
E-mail: wannibell@gmail.com; wannibel@suffolk.lib.ny.us
Founded: 1987
Freelance copy-editing, line editing, development editing, proofreading, project management (ms to prepress). Specialize in college textbooks (particularly English/grammar/writing/rhetoric texts) & fiction/nonfiction trade books, with an emphasis on editorial excellence.

The Professional Writer
175 W 12 St, Suite 6D, New York, NY 10011
Tel: 212-414-0188; 917-658-1946 (cell)
E-mail: paul@theprofessionalwriter.com
Web Site: www.theprofessionalwriter.com
Key Personnel
Owner: Paul Wisenthal *E-mail:* paulwisenthal@gmail.com
Founded: 1989
Book networking to the industry, book development-includes creative writing/editing, writer's block, project preparation. Copywriting for brochures, media kits, newsletters, business & investment proposals, writers coach & grants. Script writing, script doctor for TV/film/radio. Speechwriting. Youth market specialists.
Membership(s): The Authors Guild; National Writers Union

Pronk Media Inc
PO Box 340, Beaverton, ON L0K 1A0, Canada
Tel: 416-441-3760
E-mail: info@pronk.com
Web Site: www.pronk.com
Key Personnel
Pres: Gord Pronk *Tel:* 416-441-3760 ext 203 *E-mail:* gord@pronk.com

Founded: 1981 (as Pronk & Associates Inc)
Offers complete PreK-12 educational publishing services including project management, writing, content editing, developmental editing, concept development, cover design, art direction, photo research, technical art, page composition, typography, page layout, Photoshop work, typesetting, complete prepress services, permissions, developmental editing, copy-editing, proofreading, indexing, fact checking & production editing for student resources, teacher editions & ancillaries. Expertise in mathematics, science, social studies & language arts/reading materials for print, on CD-ROM, the Internet & design & production.

Proofed to Perfection Editing Services
4018 Summer Lane, Hillsborough, NC 27278
Tel: 919-732-8565
E-mail: inquiries@proofedtoperfection.com
Web Site: www.proofedtoperfection.com
Key Personnel
Sr Ed & Proj Coord: Pamela Guerrieri *E-mail:* pamg@proofedtoperfection.com
Founded: 2006
Full service editing company specializing in comprehensive, professional book editing. We offer proofreading, copy-editing, developmental editing, book critiques & book proposals at competitive rates. We hire editors with experience in the industry & guarantee personal, quality service. All new clients are offered a free sample edit & book critique.
Membership(s): American Christian Fiction Writers; Editorial Freelancers Association; Evangelical Christian Publishers Association

Generosa Gina Protano Publishing, see GGP Publishing Inc

Publishing Resources Inc
425 Carr 693, PMB 160, Dorado, PR 00646
Tel: 787-626-0607 *Toll Free Fax:* 866-547-3005
E-mail: pri@chevako.net
Web Site: www.publishingresources.net
Key Personnel
Pres: Ronald J Chevako
EVP & Ed: Anne W Chevako
Prodn: Jay A Chevako
Founded: 1982
Complete services including ms development, research, writing, translation (Spanish-English; English-Spanish), indexing, content editing & line editing by US trained professionals & full production services.

Publishing Services
525 E 86 St, Suite 8-E, New York, NY 10028
Tel: 212-535-6248 *Fax:* 212-988-1999
E-mail: publishingservices@mac.com
Key Personnel
Pres: Amy S Goldberger
Copy-editing, fact checking, line editing, photo research, ms analysis, permissions, research & rewriting.
Membership(s): Editorial Freelancers Association; Women's National Book Association

Publishing Synthesis Ltd
39 Crosby St, New York, NY 10013
Tel: 212-219-0135 *Fax:* 212-219-0136
E-mail: mainmail@pubsyn.com
Web Site: www.pubsyn.com
Key Personnel
Pres: Otto H Barz *E-mail:* obarz@pubsyn.com
VP & Spec Projs Coord: Ellen Small *E-mail:* esmall@pubsyn.com
Founded: 1975
Editing, design, typesetting & prepress production of college text & highly technical trade books.
Membership(s): Book Industry Guild of New York; The Independent Book Publishers Association

The Quarasan Group Inc
405 W Superior St, Chicago, IL 60654
Tel: 312-981-2500
E-mail: info@quarasan.com
Web Site: www.quarasan.com
Key Personnel
Founder & Pres: Randi S Brill *E-mail:* randi@quarasan.com
SVP, Fin & Delivery: Bob Taylor
VP, Conceptualization & Customization: Ellen Standafer *E-mail:* ellen_standafer@quarasan.com
Founded: 1982
From concept to completion, Quarasan provides planning, product conceptualization, complete customized publishing systems, editorial, design, marketing & product development services including original writing, substantive & content editing, correlations, focus/field testing, visual design, image procurement & all online & print delivery services for educational & edutainment products. Top caliber project management. Specialize in PreK-16 products in reading, literature, language arts, integrated curriculum programs, intervention, science, math, social studies, music, art, test prep & assessment/standardized tests.
Membership(s): AAP PreK-12 Learning Group; ASCD; International Literacy Association; National Council for the Social Studies; National Council of Teachers of English; National Council of Teachers of Mathematics; National Middle School Association; National Science Teachers Association; Teachers of English to Speakers of Other Languages

Jane Rafal Editing Associates
325 Forest Ridge Dr, Scottsville, VA 24590
Tel: 434-286-6949
Key Personnel
Owner: Jane Rafal *E-mail:* janerafal@ntelos.net
Founded: 1993
Developmental editing, cutting & book proposal development. Specialize in general trade fiction & nonfiction.

Jerry Ralya
7909 Vt Rte 14, Craftsbury Common, VT 05827
Tel: 802-586-7514
E-mail: jerryralya@gmail.com
Editing, development & indexing of trade, technical, medical & reference books. Specialties include computers, behavioral sciences & the humanities. Twenty-five years of experience.
Membership(s): Editorial Freelancers Association

The Reading Component
3900 Parkview Lane, 3B, Irvine, CA 92612-2003
Tel: 949-387-6330
Key Personnel
Owner: Helen M Winton *E-mail:* hmwinton@outlook.com
Founded: 1994

Research Research
240 E 27 St, Suite 20-K, New York, NY 10016-9238
Tel: 212-779-9540 *Fax:* 212-779-9540
E-mail: ehtac@msn.com
Key Personnel
Pres: Cathe Giffuni
Founded: 1987

Judith Riven Literary Agent LLC
250 W 16 St, Suite 4F, New York, NY 10011
Tel: 212-255-1009 *Fax:* 212-255-8547
E-mail: rivenlitqueries@gmail.com
Web Site: rivenlit.com
Key Personnel
Owner & Pres: Judith Riven
Founded: 1993
Editorial consultation, developmental & structural editing, line editing, ms analysis.

The Roberts Group
12803 Eastview Curve, Apple Valley, MN 55124
Tel: 952-322-4005
E-mail: info@editorialservice.com
Web Site: www.editorialservice.com
Key Personnel
Owner: Sherry Roberts; Tony Roberts
Founded: 1990
Book design, production, editorial services & web development. A one-stop creative resource for quality interior book design, typesetting, editing, proofreading, indexing, Kindle & e-pub formatting. Serving established presses & self-publishers. Competitive prices. We pay attention to details & will work to meet your deadlines. See web site for more info & samples.
Membership(s): The Independent Book Publishers Association; Midwest Independent Publishers Association; Professional Editors Network

Peter Rooney
332 Bleecker St, PMB X-6, New York, NY 10014-2980
Tel: 917-376-1792 *Fax:* 212-226-8047
E-mail: magnetix@ix.netcom.com
Web Site: www.magneticreports.com
Indexer, programmer/consultant for indexes, databases, directories, catalogues raisonnes. Large & small projects.
Membership(s): American Society for Indexing

Dick Rowson
4701 Connecticut Ave NW, Suite 503, Washington, DC 20008
Tel: 202-244-8104
E-mail: rcrowson2@aol.com
Helps authors find good publishers & appraise mss.

Sachem Publishing Associates Inc
402 W Lyon Farm Dr, Greenwich, CT 06831
Mailing Address: PO Box 4040, Greenwich, CT 06831
Tel: 203-813-3077 *Fax:* 203-531-2879
E-mail: sachempub@optonline.net
Key Personnel
Pres & Ed: Stephen P Elliott
Founded: 1974
Complete trade & mail order book preparation & packaging; editorial services, from concept to finished books. Specialize in consumer & educational reference books, including encyclopedias & dictionaries.

Barbara S Salz LLC Photo Research
127 Prospect Place, South Orange, NJ 07079
Tel: 973-762-6486
E-mail: bsalz.photo@gmail.com
Image research & permissions for books, magazines, exhibitions & advertising.
Membership(s): ASPP

Paul Samuelson
117 Oak Dr, San Rafael, CA 94901
Tel: 415-459-5352; 415-517-0700 (cell) *Fax:* 415-459-5352
E-mail: paul@storywrangler.com
Web Site: www.storywrangler.com
Also consults on narrative material & screenplays.

C J Scheiner Books
275 Linden Blvd, Suite B-2, Brooklyn, NY 11226

Tel: 718-469-1089 *Fax:* 718-469-1089
Key Personnel
Owner: C J Scheiner
Literature searches, special assignment writing, fact checking, research, photo research illustrations provided, bibliographies & source lists, text & introduction writing. Specialize in erotica, curiosa & sexology.

Schoolhouse Indexing
10-B Parade Ground Rd, Etna, NH 03750
Tel: 603-643-1617
Web Site: schoolhouseindexing.com
Key Personnel
Owner & Indexer: Christine Hoskin
E-mail: christine@schoolhousefarm.net
Schoolhouse Indexing is a freelance indexing business. Professional indexing services offered include the fields of law & legal issues, education (in both English & French), business & economics, children's elementary education/nonfiction, travel, hospitality & tourism, social sciences & culture, health & psychology, history & biography, environmental sciences, geology, engineering, construction & architecture. Indexing queries regarding general indexing information, rates & availability are welcome.
Membership(s): American Society for Indexing

Schoolhouse Network Inc
PO Box 17676, Fountain Hills, AZ 85269
Tel: 973-206-1389
E-mail: info@schoolhousenetwork.com
Web Site: www.schoolhousenetwork.com
Key Personnel
Pres: Marilyn Greco *E-mail:* mgreco@schoolhousenetwork.com
Dir, Curriculum: Mary K Messick
E-mail: mmessick@schoolhousenetwork.com
Founded: 1998
Provides a comprehensive range of editorial services to educational publishers, development groups, schools & other educational institutions for PreK, K-12 & college in both print & electronic media in the content areas of reading/language arts, ESL, literature, social studies, health & science. Develop student & teacher editions, leveled readers, fiction & nonfiction, graphic novels, literature searches, readability analyses, video scripts, animations, interactive web-based content, software, educational games, workbooks, assessment components & state customizations with more than three decades of experience in the field of educational publishing.
Membership(s): Editorial Freelancers Association; International Literacy Association; National Association for the Education of Young Children; Teachers of English to Speakers of Other Languages

Schroeder Indexing Services
23 Camilla Pink Ct, Bluffton, SC 29909
Tel: 843-705-9779
E-mail: sanindex@schroederindexing.com
Web Site: www.schroederindexing.com
Key Personnel
Owner & CEO: Sandi Schroeder
Produce custom indexes using dedicated indexing software. Company web site includes current information on clients & titles indexed, information on planning an index, downloadable Project Information Sheet & request for an estimate.
Membership(s): American Society for Indexing

Franklin L Schulaner
PO Box 507, Kealakekua, HI 96750-0507
Tel: 808-322-3785
E-mail: fschulaner@hawaii.rr.com

Sherri Schultz/Words with Grace
1916 Pike Place, Suite 12, No 118, Seattle, WA 98101
Tel: 415-297-5708
E-mail: WordsWithGraceEditorial@gmail.com
Web Site: www.wordswithgrace.com
Founded: 1992
Experienced copy-editor & proofreader, primarily for nonfiction books, nonprofits & consultants. Works with clients around the country. Special expertise in travel, environment, politics, literary nonfiction & art. Refers fiction writers to other editors.
Membership(s): Bay Area Editors' Forum; Northwest Independent Editors Guild

Scribendi Inc
405 Riverview Dr, Chatham, ON N7M 0N3, Canada
Tel: 519-351-1626 (cust serv) *Fax:* 519-354-0192
E-mail: customerservice@scribendi.com
Web Site: www.scribendi.com
Key Personnel
Pres: Chandra Clarke *Tel:* 519-351-1626 ext 706
E-mail: chandra.clarke@scribendi.com
VP: Terence Johnson, MA *Tel:* 519-351-1626 ext 707 *E-mail:* terry@scribendi.com
Founded: 1997
On demand proofreading & editing services available 24/7. Web site offers instant quotes on all standard services; call or e-mail for special project quotes or long term arrangements.

SDP Publishing Solutions LLC
36 Captain's Way, East Bridgewater, MA 02333
Tel: 617-775-0656
Web Site: www.sdppublishingsolutions.com
Key Personnel
Publr & Agent: Lisa Akoury-Ross *E-mail:* lross@sdppublishing.com
Developmental Ed, Copyeditor & Proofreader: Shayla Perry
Developmental Ed & Copyeditor: Neysa Jensen; Shannon Miller; Lisa Schleifer
Ghost Writer: Aileen McDonough
Professional Proofreader/Proofchecker: Karen Grennan; Kim Sexton
Asst & Proj Mgr: Emily Kent *E-mail:* ekent@sdppublishing.com
Founded: 2009
Specialize in editorial services for all genres including fiction, nonfiction, memoirs, business books, children's books & more. Our business is designed to review mss & determine the best editorial approach for each author. From ghostwriting, developmental editing, copy-editing & proofreading, we help our authors become better writers! We also write effective marketing kits, query letters, analysis of the competitive marketplace, along with the marketing & media landscape for those who wish to pitch to literary agents & traditional publishers. We offer optimal publishing solutions for authors worldwide from literary agency representation, to worldwide marketing, including international rights & independent publishing.

Hank Searls
Box 1877, 4435 Holly Lane NW, Gig Harbor, WA 98335
Tel: 253-851-9896 *Fax:* 253-851-9897
E-mail: hanksearls@comcast.net
Founded: 1986
Ms consultation & analysis. Screenplays, marketing counsel for authors. Previous publications includes Jaws 2, Jaws: The Revenge (Universal Pictures), The New Breed (Creator), Overboard (Norton), Kataki (McGraw-Hill), Sounding (Random House), Blood Song (Villard Books), The Hero Ship (NAC World), Firewind (Doubleday), The Crowded Sky (Harper), The Fugitive: Never Wave Goodbye (ABC).
Membership(s): The Authors Guild; National Writers Union; Writers Guild of America

Richard Selman
14 Washington Place, New York, NY 10003
Tel: 212-473-1874 *Fax:* 212-473-1875
Multimedia & electronic desktop publishing, advertising & promotional copywriting; fact checking, line editing, permissions, research, photo research, proofreading, ms analysis, bibliographies, copy-editing, interviewing, rewriting, special assignment writing, transcript editing, indexing, audio/video text.

Alexa Selph
4300 McClatchey Circle, Atlanta, GA 30342
Tel: 404-256-3717
E-mail: lexa101@aol.com

Barry Sheinkopf
c/o The Writing Ctr, 601 Palisade Ave, Englewood Cliffs, NJ 07632
Tel: 201-567-4017 *Fax:* 201-567-7202
E-mail: bsheinkopf@optonline.net
Founded: 1977
Trade, scholarly & professional publications, book design & self-publishing.
Membership(s): The Authors Guild; Mystery Writers of America

Monika Shoffman-Graves
70 Transylvania Ave, Key Largo, FL 33037
Tel: 305-451-1462 *Fax:* 305-451-1462
E-mail: keysmobill@earthlink.net; mograv@gmail.com
Indexing, ms analysis, proofreading & research.

Roger W Smith
59-67 58 Rd, Maspeth, NY 11378-3211
Tel: 718-416-1334
E-mail: roger.smith106@verizon.net
Founded: 1982
Membership(s): Editorial Freelancers Association

Stackler Editorial Agency
555 Lincoln Ave, Alameda, CA 94501
Tel: 510-814-9694 *Fax:* 510-814-9694
E-mail: stackler@aol.com
Web Site: www.fictioneditor.com
Key Personnel
Owner: Ed Stackler
Founded: 1996
Editorial services for novelists of crime, thriller & suspense fiction.

Nancy Steele
2210 Pine St, Philadelphia, PA 19103-6516
Tel: 215-732-5175
E-mail: Nancy.Steele.Edits@gmail.com
Founded: 1999
Versatile, intuitive editor with 20 years of experience in editing nonfiction. Expertise in American art & antiques, anthologies, biographies & memoirs, business & technology, psychology, reference & illustrated books. Special interest in the arts of Japan.
Membership(s): National Association of Science Writers

Sterling Media Productions LLC, see Robert L Cohen

Jean Stoess
1600 Royal Dr, Reno, NV 89503
Tel: 775-322-5326
E-mail: jstoess@aol.com
Founded: 1977
Oral history transcription in all styles, cassette & CDs. Word processing for publishers & authors; oral history transcription rewriting. Type

& revise mss from first through final draft. Editing when needed. Micro & regular tape cassettes. WordPerfect 11.0 & Microsoft Word 2007. APA style is a specialty.

Jeri L Stolk
8 Rush Vine Ct, Owings Mills, MD 21117
Tel: 410-864-8109
E-mail: jeristolk@gmail.com
Edit journals & books, especially academic.

Vivian Sudhalter
1202 Loma Dr, No 117, Ojai, CA 93023
Tel: 805-640-9737
E-mail: vivians09@att.net
Freelance editor specializing in fiction & nonfiction books on women's studies, holistic health, memoirs & other genres. I improve finished mss by copy-editing for good grammar, flow, punctuation, usage & consistency. I also help shape books from their inception by working with authors to create the structure that will best serve their vision. Having been in the book publishing industry for more than four decades, I provide insights into the publication process, whether conventional or POD. Contact by e-mail preferred.

Fraser Sutherland
39 Helena Ave, Toronto, ON M6G 2H3, Canada
Tel: 416-652-5735
E-mail: rodfrasers@gmail.com
Founded: 1970
General editorial services. Specialize in dictionaries & reference books (lexicography), ms analysis & rewriting.
Membership(s): Dictionary Society of North America; Editors' Association of Canada/Association canadienne des reviseurs; PEN Canada

Textbook Writers Associates Inc
25 Crescent St, Suite 733, Waltham, MA 02453
Tel: 781-209-0051 *Fax:* 781-899-2084
Web Site: www.textbookwriters.com
Key Personnel
Pres: Rose Sklare *E-mail:* rsklare@montefiorepress.com
Founded: 1993
Full service editorial/production company offering comprehensive scientific & professional book development & production. Provide extensive editorial work on pharmaceutical writing of monographs, peer-reviewed articles & clinical trials. Services include project management, research, writing, online editing, design, art rendering, photo research, composition, proofreading, permissions, indexing. Specialize in basic sciences, math, engineering, bibliographies & memoirs.
Membership(s): American Medical Writers Association; Bookbuilders of Boston; Drug Information Association

Thodestool Fiction Editing
40 McDougall Rd, Waterloo, ON N2L 2W5, Canada
Web Site: www.thodestool.com
Key Personnel
Owner: Vanessa Ricci-Thode
E-mail: vanessariccithode@gmail.com
Founded: 2010
Thodestool Fiction Editing focuses on providing editing services for fiction of varying lengths, with a specialty in speculative fiction (science fiction, fantasy, horror) & a focus on structural/developmental editing & ms evaluations.
Membership(s): Canadian Author's Association; Editors' Association of Canada/Association canadienne des reviseurs

Susan Thornton
6090 Liberty Ave, Vermilion, OH 44089
Tel: 440-967-1757
E-mail: allenthornton@earthlink.net
Key Personnel
Freelance Copy Ed: Allen Thornton; Susan Thornton
Medical, technical, mathematics, university press, college text, reference, trade nonfiction & journals on hard copy & on disk.

Twin Oaks Indexing
Division of Twin Oaks Community
138 Twin Oaks Rd, Suite W, Louisa, VA 23093
Tel: 540-894-5126
Web Site: www.twinoakscommunity.org
Key Personnel
Mgr: Rachel Nishan
Founded: 1981
Subsidiaries: Twin Oaks Industries Inc

Arlene S Uslander, see Writeway Editing

Visuals Unlimited
27 Meadow Dr, Hollis, NH 03049
Tel: 603-465-3340 *Fax:* 603-465-3360
E-mail: staff@visualsunlimited.com
Web Site: visualsunlimited.com
Key Personnel
VP & Busn Devt Mgr, Ad: Robert Folz
E-mail: rfolz@visualsunlimited.com
Dir: Shelly Folz *E-mail:* sfolz@visualsunlimited.com
Photo agent, photo research & stock agency.

Vocabula Communications Co
5-A Holbrook Ct, Rockport, MA 01966
Tel: 978-309-8730
E-mail: info@vocabula.com
Web Site: www.vocabula.com; www.vocabula.com/dailyvocabula.asp (Daily Vocabula)
Key Personnel
Pres: Robert Hartwell Fiske
Founded: 1986
Copy-editing, developmental editing, technical editing & writing, copywriting, special assignment writing, abstracting, interviewing, research, transcription editing, on-screen editing, html coding & editing, web site editing, proofreading & typemarking. Publisher of *The Vocabula Review* & *The Daily Vocabula*.

Wambtac Communications
1512 E Santa Clara Ave, Santa Ana, CA 92705
Tel: 714-954-0580 *Toll Free Tel:* 800-641-3936
E-mail: wambtac@wambtac.com
Web Site: www.wambtac.com; claudiasuzanne.com (prof servs)
Key Personnel
Owner, Founder & Creative Partner: Claudia Suzanne *E-mail:* claudiasuzanne@gmail.com
Founded: 1995
Book writing & publishing.
Membership(s): The Independent Book Publishers Association

WC Publishing, see Wambtac Communications

Anne Jones Weitzer
Subsidiary of Weitzer & Associates
60 Sutton Place South, Suite 9-B South, New York, NY 10022-4168
Tel: 212-758-8149
E-mail: 47dehaven@msn.com; enamel@yahoo.com
Founded: 1989
Freelance writer & editor.
Membership(s): National Writers Union

Toby Wertheim
240 E 76 St, New York, NY 10021
Tel: 212-472-8587
E-mail: tobywertheim@yahoo.com
Research/editor.

Rosemary Wetherold
4507 Cliffstone Cove, Austin, TX 78735
Tel: 512-892-1606
E-mail: roses@ix.netcom.com
Founded: 1985
Copy-editing, substantive editing, desktop publishing. Varied subjects, including biological sciences & natural history.

Helen Rippier Wheeler
1909 Cedar St, Suite 212, Berkeley, CA 94709-2037
Tel: 510-549-2970
E-mail: pen136@dslextreme.com
Consulting & professional development training. Sole proprietor of Womanhood Media.
Membership(s): Writers Guild of America

Barbara Mlotek Whelehan
7064 SE Cricket Ct, Stuart, FL 34997
Tel: 954-554-0765 (cell); 772-463-0818 (home)
E-mail: barbarawhelehan@bellsouth.net
More than 20 years of publishing experience. All subjects; specialize in personal finance, investments, mutual funds, business & consumer topics. Also copy-edit fiction.

Martin L White
10511 Preston St, Westchester, IL 60154-5311
Tel: 708-492-1253 *Fax:* 708-492-1253
E-mail: mlw@mlwindexing.com
Web Site: www.mlwindexing.com
Founded: 1990
Book & journal indexing.
Membership(s): American Society for Indexing; Society for Scholarly Publishing; Society for Technical Communication

White Oak Editions, see Carol Cartaino

Eleanor B Widdoes
417 W 120 St, New York, NY 10027
Tel: 212-870-3051; 917-886-6401 (cell)
E-mail: widdoese@aa.org
Indexing, proofreading, research, bibliographies & newsletters.

Windhaven®
466 Rte 10, Orford, NH 03777
Tel: 603-483-0929
E-mail: info@windhaven.com
Web Site: www.windhaven.com
Key Personnel
Dir & Ed: Nancy C Hanger *Tel:* 603-512-9251 (cell) *E-mail:* nhanger@windhaven.com
Ed & Consultant: Andrew V Phillips
E-mail: andrew@windhaven.com
Founded: 1985
Consulting & developmental editing, line editing, copy-editing, proofreading.
Membership(s): Editorial Freelancers Association; National Writers Union

Wolf Pirate Project Inc
337 Lost Lake Dr, Divide, CO 80814
Tel: 305-333-3186
E-mail: contact@wolfpiratebooks.com; workshop@wolfpiratebooks.com
Web Site: www.wolf-pirate.com
Key Personnel
Founder & Pres: Catherine Rudy
E-mail: catherinerudy@wolfpiratebooks.com
VP: Bryan Rudy
Volunteer Ed: May Bestall *E-mail:* maybestall@wolfpiratebooks.com
Founded: 2010

Nonprofit company established to mentor, educate, develop & promote new writers & artists & focus on the general public to instill a desire to read for leisure. Fiction/nonfiction literary; content & development blue line edit. Service offered only through acceptance into the workshop. Otherwise online class is open to all at no cost & editors are available to answer questions.

Nancy Wolff
125 Gates Ave, No 14, Montclair, NJ 07042
Tel: 973-746-7415
E-mail: wolffindex@aol.com
Founded: 1991
Indexing, generalist; professional; prompt. Most fields: art (Italian Renaissance); cookbooks (Mrs Wheelbarrow's Pantry); biography (Ty Cobb); biography/history (Thirteen Soldiers), literature (Oscar Wilde's Chatterton), memoir (The Porcelain Thief), media (News Sorority), young readers (Sitting Bull).

WordCo Indexing Services Inc
49 Church St, Norwich, CT 06360
Tel: 860-886-2532 *Toll Free Tel:* 877-WORDCO-3 (967-3263) *Fax:* 860-886-1155
E-mail: office@wordco.com
Web Site: www.wordco.com
Key Personnel
Founder & Pres: Stephen Ingle *E-mail:* sringle@wordco.com
Proj Coord: Amy Moriarty *E-mail:* amoriarty@wordco.com
Founded: 1988
Since 1988, WordCo has completed thousands of thorough & accurate indexes in hundreds of subject areas for many major publishers. WordCo's in-house team of professionally trained indexers has the experience & capability to complete your indexing projects professionally & on time. Rush service & ebook indexing available.
Membership(s): American Society for Indexing; Bookbuilders of Boston

WordForce Communications
35 Ormskirk Ave, Suite 805, Toronto, ON M6S 1A8, Canada
Tel: 416-534-9881
E-mail: info@wordforce.ca
Web Site: www.wordforce.ca
Key Personnel
CEO & Pres: Maja Rehou *E-mail:* mrehou@wordforce.ca
Founded: 2003
Provide editing, writing & consulting services to help engineers, scientists, lawyers, web developers & business professionals improve the effectiveness & profitability of their technical documents & marketing materials.

Words into Print
57 Prince St, Suite 4R, New York, NY 10012
Tel: 212-741-1393 *Fax:* 419-441-1393
E-mail: query@wordsintoprint.org
Web Site: www.wordsintoprint.org
Key Personnel
Ed: Martin Beiser *Tel:* 973-202-9694 *E-mail:* martin.beiser@gmail.com; Linda Carbone *Tel:* 914-374-8790 *E-mail:* lindacarbone@optonline.net; Ruth Greenstein *E-mail:* rg@greenlinepublishing.com; Emily Loose *E-mail:* emilylooselit@gmail.com; Anne Cole Norman *E-mail:* acole157@gmail.com; Alice Rosengard *Tel:* 212-662-4323 *E-mail:* arosengard1@yahoo.com; Katharine Turok *E-mail:* kturok@gmail.com; Michael Wilde *Tel:* 518-672-7172 *E-mail:* michaelwildeeditorial@earthlink.net
Founded: 1998
An alliance of top New York publishing professionals who offer a broad range of editorial services to authors, publishers, literary agents, book packagers & content providers from around the world.

Words with Grace, see Sherri Schultz/Words with Grace

WordWitlox
70 Grainger Crescent, Ajax, ON L1T 4Y6, Canada
Tel: 647-505-9673
Web Site: www.wordwitlox.com
Key Personnel
Copy Ed: Cathy Witlox *E-mail:* cathy@wordwitlox.com
Founded: 2004
Editing professionally since 1998, including 6-1/2 years full-time in-house experience copy-editing for a large North American fiction publisher. WordWitlox is based near Toronto.
Membership(s): Editors' Association of Canada/Association canadienne des reviseurs

Working With Words
9720 SW Eagle Ct, Beaverton, OR 97008
Tel: 503-644-4317
E-mail: editor@zzz.com
Key Personnel
Owner: Sue Mann
Founded: 1985
Freelance editorial services. General trade, nonfiction. Subjects include children's, cookbooks, creativity, historical, inspirational, memoirs, self-help, spiritual, training. Substantive editing. Online & hard copy.
Membership(s): Northwest Independent Editors Guild; Northwest Writers & Publishers Association

Wright Information Indexing Services
PO Box 658, Sandia Park, NM 87047
Tel: 505-281-2600
Web Site: www.wrightinformation.com
Key Personnel
Owner & Pres: Jan C Wright *E-mail:* jancw@wrightinformation.com
Founded: 1991
Book, ebook & online indexing services, specializing in single-source publications; 2009 winner of H W Wilson Award for Excellence in Indexing.
Membership(s): American Society for Indexing

Write for Success (WFS)
PO Box 292153, Los Angeles, CA 90029-8653
Tel: 323-356-8833
E-mail: writeforsuccess@yahoo.com
Web Site: www.write-for-success.com
Key Personnel
Owner/Ed: Christine Van Zandt
Ed: Michael Biehl; Patricia Fox; Megan Katz
Founded: 2009
Full service professional editing, from creation to publication. A collective of professional editors with advanced degrees who are also published writers. Detail oriented & committed to providing quality editing services. Based in Hollywood, with editors in San Francisco & Minneapolis. Self-publishing, freelance & agented authors welcome. Assistance at any stage & all genres accepted. Quick turnaround with competitive pricing. Additional services include developmental editing, co-writing & query letters.
Membership(s): Bay Area Editors' Forum; Editorial Freelancers Association; The Greater Los Angeles Writers Society; The Independent Book Publishers Association; Society of Children's Book Writers & Illustrators

The Write Way
3048 Horizon Lane, Suite 1102, Naples, FL 34109
Tel: 239-273-9145
E-mail: darekane@gmail.com
Key Personnel
Pres: Roberta Kane
Also handle advertising & marketing.

Writers Anonymous Inc
1302 E Coronado Rd, Phoenix, AZ 85006
Tel: 602-256-2830 *Fax:* 602-256-2830
Web Site: writersanonymousinc.blogspot.com
Key Personnel
Pres: Jordan Richman *E-mail:* jordanp.richman@gmail.com
Edit Dir: Vita Richman
Substantive editing, scholarly, education, humanities, social science, environment, philosophy, music, art, literature, health, general science, medical, legal.
Membership(s): Editorial Freelancers Association

The Writer's Lifeline Inc
400 S Burnside Ave, Suite 11B, Los Angeles, CA 90036
Tel: 323-932-1685 *Fax:* 323-932-1220
Web Site: www.thewriterslifeline.com
Key Personnel
CEO: Kenneth Atchity, PhD *E-mail:* kja@thewriterslifeline.com
EVP: Lisa Cerasoli
Founded: 1996
A full service editorial company, providing nonfiction book writers, novelists, business, professional, technical & screenwriters with assistance in storytelling, mentoring, perfecting their style & craft, style-structure-concept-line editing, ghostwriting, publishing consulting, development, translation, advertising & promotion, printing & self-publishing, distribution & research.
Sister companies: Atchity Entertainment International Inc; Atchity Productions; Story Merchant; Story Merchant Books.
Membership(s): American Comparative Literature Association; The Authors Guild; National Academy of Television Arts & Sciences; PEN American Center; Women in Film; Writers Guild of America

Writer's Relief, Inc
207 Hackensack St, Wood-Ridge, NJ 07075
Tel: 201-641-3003 *Toll Free Tel:* 866-405-3003 *Fax:* 201-641-1253
E-mail: info@wrelief.com
Web Site: www.WritersRelief.com
Key Personnel
Pres: Ronnie L Smith *E-mail:* ronnie@wrelief.com
Founded: 1994
Don't have time to submit your writing? We can help. Submission leads & cover/query letter guidelines. Join the 50,000+ writers who subscribe to *Submit Write Now*, our free e-publication.

Writeway Editing
11256 Vista Sorrento Pkwy, Apt 102, San Diego, CA 92130
Tel: 858-925-7042 *Fax:* 209-532-2661
Web Site: www.uslander.net
Key Personnel
Owner & Freelance Book Ed: Arlene S Uslander *E-mail:* uslander.arlene@gmail.com
Founded: 1980
Editing services: whatever is necessary to prepare a ms to send to an agent or publisher, but no typing or ghost writing.
Membership(s): National Federation of Press Women; Publishers & Writers of San Diego; Small Publishers, Artists & Writers Network

Wyman Indexing
1311 Delaware Ave SW, No S332, Washington, DC 20024
Tel: 443-336-5497
Web Site: www.wymanindexing.com
Key Personnel
Owner & Chief Indexer: Pilar Wyman *E-mail:* pilarw@wymanindexing.com
Founded: 1990
Freelance indexing & consulting (specialties include medicine, technology & current events). Also provide Spanish-to-English translation services.
Membership(s): American Medical Writers Association; American Society for Indexing

Zebra Communications
230 Deerchase Dr, Woodstock, GA 30188-4438
Tel: 770-924-0528
Web Site: www.zebraeditor.com
Key Personnel
Owner: Bobbie Christmas *E-mail:* bobbie@zebraeditor.com
Founded: 1992
Editorial services that specialize in fiction & nonfiction books.
Membership(s): Atlanta Writers Club; Better Business Bureau; Florida Writers Association; Georgia Writers Association; International Guild of Professional Business Consultants; Society for the Preservation of English Language Literature; South Carolina Writers Workshop; Southeastern Writers Association; The Writers' Network

Robert Zolnerzak
101 Clark St, Unit 20-K, Brooklyn, NY 11201
Tel: 718-522-0591
E-mail: bobzolnerzak@verizon.net
Computer-assisted indexing for medical, scientific & computer science textbooks & journals since 1973.
Membership(s): American Society for Indexing; Editorial Freelancers Association

Literary Agents

The agents listed here are among the most active in the field. Prior to obtaining a listing in *LMP*, potential entrants are required to submit verifiable references from publishers with whom they have placed titles. Letters in parentheses following the agency name indicate fields of activity:

(L)–Literary Agent (D)–Dramatic Agent (L-D)–Literary & Dramatic Agent

Those individuals who are members of the Association of Authors' Representatives are identified by the presence of (AAR) after their name.

Authors seeking literary representation are advised that some agents request a nominal reading fee that may be applied to the agent's commission upon representation. Other agencies may charge substantially higher fees which may not be applicable to a future commission and which are not refundable. The recommended course is to first send a query letter with an outline, sample chapter, and a self-addressed stamped envelope (SASE). Should an agent express interest in handling the manuscript, full details of fees and commissions should be obtained in writing before the complete manuscript is sent. Should an agency require significant advance payment from an author, the author is cautioned to make a careful investigation to determine the agency's standing in the industry before entering an agreement. The author should always retain a copy of the manuscript in his or her possession.

AAA Books Unlimited (L)
88 Greenbriar E Dr, Deerfield, IL 60015
Tel: 847-444-1220 *Fax:* 847-607-8335
Web Site: www.aaabooksunlimited.com
Key Personnel
Principal: Nancy Rosenfeld *E-mail:* nancy@aaabooksunlimited.com
Founded: 1993
Full service literary agency to provide clients with first class service "over & above" what normally is handled by a literary agency. We offer content-copy-line editing services. No unsol mss, query first.
Titles recently placed: *A Couple's Guide to Sexual Addiction: A Step-by-Step Plan to Rebuild Trust and Restore Intimacy*, Paldrom Catharine Collins, George N Collins, MA; *A Woman's Framework for a Successful Career and Life*, James Hamerstone, Lindsay Musser Hough; *AD/HD Success! Solutions for Boosting Self-Esteem (The Diary Method)*, Kerin B Adams, ACC; *An Introduction to Mozart: "The Music, The Man, The Myths"*, Roye E Wates, PhD; *Attached at the Heart: 8 Proven Parenting Principles for Raising Connected and Compassionate Children*, Barbara Nicholson, Lysa Parker; *Breaking the Cycle: Free Yourself From Sex Addiction, Porn Obsession, and Shame*, George N Collins, MA, Andrew Adleman, MA; *Celebrity Obsession*, Michael S Levy, PhD; *Children of Separation and Loss: Picking Up the Pieces After Hitler*, Dr Gertrude Pollitt; *Do You Mind if I Order the Cheeseburger?*, Sherry F Colb, PhD; *Freedom of Assembly and Petition: The First Amendment: Its Constitutional History and the Contemporary Debate (Bill of Rights series)*, Margaret M Russell; *Hurakan*, Mike Stewart; *I'm Not a Mind Reader: Using Three-Dimensional Communication to Make Your Relationship Better*, Marty Babits, LCSW, BCD; *It Came from the '70s: from the Godfather to Apocalypse Now*, Connie Corcoran Wilson; *Jacob's Courage: A Holocaust Love Story (reprint)*, Charles S Weinblatt; *Justice Indicted*, Michael Shahnasarian; *Leviathan's Scales*, Jim Slusher; *Many Seconds Into the Future*, John J Clayton; *Milk and Oranges*, Charlene Wexler; *Mindfulness for Borderline Personality Disorder*, Blaise Aguirre, MD, Dr Gillian Galen; *Mitzvah Man (Modern Jewish Literature and Culture)*, John J Clayton; *Mood: The Key to Understanding Ourselves and Others*, Patrick M Burke, PhD; *My Neck Hurts! Nonsurgical Treatments for Neck and Upper Back Pain*, Martin Taylor, DO, PhD; *Negroes with Guns: The Black Tradition of Arms*, Nicholas Johnson; *Outsmarting Mother Nature: A Woman's Complete Guide to Plastic Surgery*, Iliana E Sweis, MD, FACS; *Parenting Your Child with Autism: Practical Solutions, Strategies, and Advice for Helping Your Family*, M Anjali Sastry, PhD, Blaise Aguirre, MD; *Pryme Knumber*, Matthew J Flynn; *Searches and Seizures: The Fourth Amendment: Its Constitutional History and Contemporary Debate (Bill of Rights series)*, Cynthia Lee; *Sunder Breach*, Richard Fountain; *Survival to Growth*, Sam A Hout, PhD; *The Gift of Mortality*, Steve Gordon, Irene Kacandes; *The Nature of Nature: 200,000 Years of History of Science*, Demetris Nicolaides, PhD; *The Nun's Rabbi: The Rabbi-Psychiatrist and the Sisters of St Francis*, Abraham J Twerski, MD; *The Pathway to Healthy Anger*, Bernard Golden, PhD; *The Politics of Joint University-Community Housing Development in Cambridge, Boston and Beyond*, Richard Sobel; *The Problem Was Me: How to End Negative Self-Talk and Take Your Life to a New Level*, Thomas Gagliano, Abraham J Twerski, MD; *The Prospective Spouse Checklist: Evaluating Your Potential Partner*, Isabelle Fox, PhD, Robert M Fox, JD; *The Unlikeliest of Places: How Nachman Libeskind Survived the Nazis, the Gulags and Soviet Communism*, Annette Libeskind Berkovits; *Transparency in Government: What it Means and How You Can Make it Happen*, Donald Gordon; *Unfinished Business*, Lee Woodward; *Walls, a Metaphor*, Will Lonardo; *War and Sex: A Brief History of Men's Urge for Battle*, John V H Dippel; *Wayang*, Robert Harding; *Wrestling with Angels: New & Collected Stories*, John J Clayton

The Aaland Agency (L)
PO Box 849, Inyokern, CA 93527-0849
Tel: 760-384-3910
Web Site: www.the-aaland-agency.com
Key Personnel
Dir & Fiction/Nonfiction: Jo Ann Krueger *E-mail:* anniejo41@gmail.com
Foreign Rep, CN & Europe: Richard Allan
Nonfiction: Mitzi Rhone
Romance/Adventure: Susan Russell
Founded: 1991
Adult fiction & nonfiction. One-inch margins & space and a half. Any format, e-mail file attachment, hardcopy or CD is acceptable (e-mail file attachment preferred). Crime drama, romance/adventure, children's stories, biographies & textbooks gladly accepted. No fees for ms review or evaluation. Complete ms or first three chapters. No unsol mss, query first.
Titles recently placed: *F/A-18E/F Hornet: America's Frontline Fighter*, W W Harrold; *The Hydra Brief*, William Davison; *USS Kitty Hawk: The Last Warrior*, Marty S Bourdon

Dominick Abel Literary Agency Inc (L)
146 W 82 St, Suite 1-A, New York, NY 10024
Tel: 212-877-0710 *Fax:* 212-595-3133
E-mail: agency@dalainc.com
Web Site: www.dalainc.com
Key Personnel
Pres: Dominick Abel (AAR) *E-mail:* dominick@dalainc.com
Founded: 1975
Adult fiction & nonfiction. Handle film & TV rights. No unsol mss, query first by e-mail; no reading fee. Representatives in Hollywood & all major foreign countries.
Foreign Rep(s): Akcali Agency (Turkey); Luigi Bernabo & Associates (Italy); Big Apple Agency Inc (China, Indonesia, Malaysia, Taiwan, Vietnam); The Buckman Agency (Israel, Scandinavia); The English Agency (Japan); David Grossman Agency (UK Commonwealth); Korean Copyright Center (Korea); Lex Copyright Agency (Hungary); La Nouvelle Agence (France); Prava I Prevodi Agency (Eastern Europe, Greece, Russia, Ukraine); Lennart Sane Agency (Brazil, Central America, Netherlands, Portugal, South America, Spain); Thomas Schlueck Agency (Germany); Tuttle-Mori Agency Inc (Thailand)
Membership(s): The Authors Guild; Authors Registry; Copyright Clearance Center; Mystery Writers of America

Abrams Artists Agency (L-D)
275 Seventh Ave, 26th fl, New York, NY 10001
Tel: 646-486-4600 *Fax:* 646-486-2358
E-mail: literary@abramsartny.com
Web Site: www.abramsartists.com
Key Personnel
Dir, Book Div: Steve Ross
Dir, Foreign Rts: David Doerrer
Literary Agent: Beth Blickers (AAR); Sarah L Douglas (AAR); Peter Hagan (AAR); Morgan Jenness; Charles Kopelman (AAR); Maura Teitelbaum (AAR)
Founded: 1977
Plays, screenplays, film & TV rights. No unsol mss, query first. Submit synopsis. No reading fee.
Branch Office(s)
9200 Sunset Blvd, 11th fl, Los Angeles, CA 90069, Contact: Norma Robbins *Tel:* 310-859-0625 *E-mail:* contactla@abramsartists.com

Acacia House Publishing Services Ltd (L)
51 Chestnut Ave, Brantford, ON N3T 4C3, Canada
Tel: 519-752-0978 *Fax:* 519-752-8349
Key Personnel
Mng Dir: Bill Hanna *E-mail:* bhanna.acacia@rogers.com
Founded: 1985
Adult fiction; no science fiction, occult, horror; most nonfiction. Handle film & TV rights for authors. Handle foreign rights for nine client publishers. Territories handled directly by Aca-

cia include Czech Republic, Estonia, Latvia, Lithuania, Slovak Republic, Canada (English), USA, UK & Australia. No unsol mss, query first; submit outline & first 50 pages. Only typed, double-spaced mss may be submitted with return postage. No reading fee. Fee charged for photocopying & postage or courier.
Foreign Rights: Akcali (Turkey); Argosy Agency (Italy); Carmen Balcells Agencia Literaria SA (Portugal, Spain); Big Apple Agency Inc (China, Hong Kong, Malaysia, Taiwan, Vietnam); Paul & Peter Fritz A G (Austria, Germany); Graal Literary Agency (Poland); Harris-Elon Agency (Ilana Kurshan) (Israel); International Literatuur Bureau BV (Netherlands); International Press Agency (South Africa); Japan UNI Agency Inc; Anna Jarota Agency (France); Katai & Bolza (Bosnia and Herzegovina, Croatia, Hungary, Montenegro, Serbia, Slovenia); Simona Kessler (Romania); Duran Kim Agency (Korea); Alexander Korzhenevski (Russia); Maxima Creative Agency (Santo Manarung) (Indonesia); Daniela Micura Literary Services (Italy); Montreal Contact (Canada (French-speaking)); A Nicolaissen Agency (Scandinavia); Read n' Right (Greece); Silk Road Agency (Thailand)

AEI (Atchity Entertainment International Inc) (L-D)
9601 Wilshire Blvd, Unit 1202, Beverly Hills, CA 90210
Tel: 323-932-0407 *Fax:* 323-932-0321
E-mail: submissions@aeionline.com
Web Site: www.aeionline.com
Key Personnel
CEO: Dr Kenneth Atchity
Pres & COO: Ms Chi-Li Wong
Submissions Coord: Jennifer Pope *E-mail:* jp@aeionline.com
Founded: 1996
E-mail & snail mail queries for novels, nonfiction book proposals, screenplays & treatments should consist of a compelling & businesslike letter giving us a brief overview of your story, the audience for which it is intended & a one sentence pitch. Screenplays submitted without SASE will not be returned.
Sister companies: Atchity Productions; Story Merchant; Story Merchant Books; The Writer's Lifeline Inc.
Titles recently placed: *Dead Peasants*, Larry D Thompson; *Realms of Gold: Ritual to Romance*, Terry Stanfill; *The Messiah Matrix*, Kenneth John Atchity
Subsidiaries: The Writer's Lifeline Inc
Foreign Rights: Baror International (Worldwide exc Canada & USA)
Membership(s): The Authors Guild; Writers Guild of America

Agency Chicago (L-D)
332 S Michigan Ave, Suite 1032, No A600, Chicago, IL 60604
E-mail: ernsant@aol.com
Key Personnel
Owner: Ernest Santucci
Assoc: Shelly Chou
Founded: 1988
Professional & cross-over writers. No unsol mss, query letter first; handle film, stage & TV rights; no reading fee. True crime & investigations, historical fiction, humor, politics & general wellness.

Agency for the Performing Arts Inc, see APA Talent & Literary Agency

Agent's Ink (L)
PO Box 4956, Fresno, CA 93744-4956
Tel: 559-438-1883 *Fax:* 559-438-8289
Web Site: agents-ink.com
Key Personnel
Owner/Dir: Sydney H Harriet, PhD
E-mail: sydharriet@yahoo.com
Founded: 1988
Health related nonfiction, business, cookbooks, sports, fiction, mystery, psychology, how-to & literary for medical & mental health professionals; no unsol mss-query first; send outline or sample chapters with a SASE; no phone or e-mail queries, query by mail only. No reading fee or monthly fee for representation. Marketing fee of $300 covers mailing, production, postage, phone calls, etc. Commission of 15%.
Titles recently placed: *I Got Caught Cheating! How Can I Save My Marriage?*, Dr Othniel Seiden, Jane L Bilett PhD; *I'm "Heeling" One Day at a Time*, Carole Brody Fleet
Branch Office(s)
9400 E Iliff Ave, Suite 361, Denver, CO 80231
Tel: 720-369-1851

The Ahearn Agency Inc (L)
2021 Pine St, New Orleans, LA 70118
Tel: 504-861-8395 *Fax:* 504-866-6434
Web Site: www.ahearnagency.com
Key Personnel
Pres: Pamela G Ahearn *E-mail:* pahearn@aol.com
Founded: 1992
General fiction, adult; no poetry, plays, young adult, articles or autobiographies. Specialize in women's fiction & suspense. No unsol mss, query first with SASE. No reading fee. Do not send attachments with e-mail queries unless requested.
Titles recently placed: *Black-Eyed Susans*, Julia Haeberlin; *Can't Find My Way Home*, Carlene Thompson; *Flirting With Felicity*, Gerri Russell; *The Art of Sinning*, Sabrina Jeffries; *The Comfort of Black*, Carter Wilson; *The Iris Fan*, Laura Joh Rowland; *The Washington Lawyer*, Allan Topol
Foreign Rights: Agence Benisti (Eliane Benisti) (France); Lorella Belli Agency (Lorella Belli) (UK); Prava i Prevodi (Eastern Europe); Thomas Schluek (Germany)
Membership(s): International Thriller Writers Inc; Mystery Writers of America; Romance Writers of America

Aitken Alexander Associates LLC (L)
30 Vandam St, Suite 5A, New York, NY 10013
Tel: 212-929-4100
Web Site: www.aitkenalexander.co.uk
Key Personnel
Sr Agent: Anna Stein (AAR) *E-mail:* anna@aitkenalexander.com
Founded: 2009
Independent New York branch of the establish London-based Aitken Alexander Associates Ltd specializing in literary fiction & narrative nonfiction. No unsol mss, query first. No fees charged.
Titles recently placed: *Asunder*, Chloe Aridjis; *Goliath*, Max Blumenthal; *I Want to Show You More*, Jamie Quatro; *Kill Chain*, Andrew Cockburn; *Leaving the Atocha Station*, Ben Lerner; *Longbourn*, Jo Baker; *Love Me Back*, Merritt Tierce; *Panorama City*, Antoine Wilson; *Revenge*, Yoko Ogawa; *Salvation for a Saint*, Keigo Higashino; *Suddenly a Knock on the Door*, Etgar Keret; *The Butterfly Cabinet*, Bernie McGill; *The Free*, Willy Vlautin; *The Lady's Handbook for Her Mysterious Illness*, Sarah Ramsey; *The People in the Trees*, Hanya Yanagihara; *The Story of My Purity*, Francesco Pacifico; *The Unknowns*, Gabriel Roth; *The Virgins*, Pamela Erens; *Under the Sun: The Letters of Bruce Chatwin*, Bruce Chatwin; *Unremarried Widow*, Artis Henderson; *Where'd You Go Bernadette*, Maria Semple; *Winter King*, Tom Penn

Akin & Randolph Agency (L-D)
Literary Div, One Gateway Ctr, Suite 2600, Newark, NJ 07102
Tel: 973-353-8409; 973-623-6834 *Fax:* 973-353-8417
E-mail: info@akinandrandolph.com
Web Site: www.akinandrandolph.com
Key Personnel
Founding Agent: Wanda M Akin *E-mail:* wakin@akinandrandolph.com
Agent: Carol Randolph; Eric Easter; Angeli Rasbury
Founded: 1996 (by Wanda M Akin & Carol Randolph)
Specialize in nonfiction & fiction. Public affairs & African American interest; query first with SASE; handle film & TV rights; submit fiction-synopsis & sample chapters; nonfiction send proposal & sample chapters; no reading fee. Subs rights agent for Random House in some foreign countries, Genesis Press & Africa World Press. Mail or fax queries, submissions, etc to NJ mailing address.

Linda Allen Literary Agency (L)
1949 Green St, Suite 5, San Francisco, CA 94123
Tel: 415-921-6437
Key Personnel
Owner & Dir: Linda Allen (AAR)
E-mail: linda@lallenlitagency.com
Not taking new clients at this time. Projects by referral only.

Miriam Altshuler Literary Agency (L)
53 Old Post Rd N, Red Hook, NY 12571
Tel: 845-758-9408
Web Site: www.miriamaltshulerliteraryagency.com
Key Personnel
Pres: Miriam Altshuler (AAR)
Founded: 1994
Quality commercial & literary fiction & nonfiction, including children's books (young adult & middle grade). No unsol mss, query first. No fax; send queries by e-mail or regular mail. Submit synopsis & first chapter of book, pasted in body of e-mail. Handle film & TV rights. Representatives in all major countries. No reading fee.
Foreign Rights: AM Heath & Co (England, Europe); Tuttle-Mori Agency (China, Japan, Korea)

Betsy Amster Literary Enterprises (L)
6312 SW Capitol Hwy, No 503, Portland, OR 97239
Tel: 503-496-4007
E-mail: rights@amsterlit.com (rts inquiries); b.amster.assistant@gmail.com (adult book queries); b.amster.kidsbooks@gmail.com (children & young adult book queries)
Web Site: www.amsterlit.com
Key Personnel
Pres: Betsy Amster (AAR)
Agent, Children's & Young Adult: Mary Cummings
Founded: 1992
Literary fiction, upscale commercial fiction (specifically mysteries/thrillers & women's fiction) & adult nonfiction. Subject areas of interest: narrative nonfiction (especially by journalists), travelogues, psychology, self-help, social issues, popular culture, cultural criticism, history, art & design, health, parenting, careers, lifestyle, cookbooks, gardening, gift books; no unsol mss. Handle film & TV rights for client book properties via co-agents; no reading fee. Address queries for adult books to b.amster.assistant@gmail.com & for children's & young adult titles to b.amster.kidsbooks@gmail.com. For fiction or memoirs, embed the first three pages in the body of your e-mail; for nonfiction, embed

your proposal. Do not represent screenplays, poetry, western, fantasy, science fiction, action adventure, techno thrillers, spy capers, apocalyptic scenarios or political or religious arguments. We do not open attachments unless we have requested them; no phone, fax or snail mail queries.
Foreign Rights: Big Apple Agency Inc (China); Donatella d'Ormesson (France); The English Agency (Japan) Ltd (Japan); Japan Uni (Japan); Asli Karasuil Literary Agency (Asli Ermis) (Turkey); Korea Copyright Center (KCC) (MiSook Hong) (Korea); Mohrbooks (Germany); Prava I Prevodi (Bulgaria, Croatia, Czech Republic, Estonia, Greece, Hungary, Latvia, Lithuania, Macedonia, Poland, Romania, Russia, Serbia, Slovakia, Slovenia); Lennart Sane Agency AB (Philip Sane) (Brazil, Holland, Portugal, Scandinavia, Spain, Spanish Latin America); Vicki Satlow (Italy); Abner Stein Agency (Arabella Stein) (UK)
Membership(s): PEN Center USA

Marcia Amsterdam Agency (L)
41 W 82 St, Suite 9A, New York, NY 10024-5613
Tel: 212-873-4945
Founded: 1970
Adult & young adult fiction; horror, science fiction, suspense, mainstream, historical romance & contemporary women's etc. Handle film & TV rights. No unsol mss, query with SASE. Submit outline & first three chapters. No reading fee. Other fees: standard agency fees.
Foreign Rights: Daniel Bial Agency
Membership(s): Writers Guild of America

Anderson Literary Management LLC (L)
244 Fifth Ave, 11th fl, New York, NY 10001
Tel: 212-645-6045 *Fax:* 212-741-1936
E-mail: info@andersonliterary.com
Web Site: www.andersonliterary.com
Key Personnel
Pres: Kathleen Anderson (AAR)
E-mail: kathleen@andersonliterary.com
Represents quality fiction & nonfiction (adult, young adult & middle-grade) for print, electronic, film & television.
Membership(s): PEN American Center

Andy Ross Literary Agency (L)
767 Santa Ray Ave, Oakland, CA 94610
Tel: 510-238-8965
E-mail: andyrossagency@hotmail.com
Web Site: www.andyrossagency.com
Key Personnel
Agent: Andy Ross (AAR)
Founded: 2008
Specialize in narrative nonfiction, journalism, history, current events, literary, commercial & young adult fiction.
Queries: send by e-mail only including "query" in the title header. Letters should be kept to 1/2 page. State the project category in the first sentence & provide a very brief description. Proposals: submit by e-mail only. See web site for additional query & proposal guidelines. No fees.
Titles recently placed: *A Country, Not a Bomb: North Korea Behind the Facade*, Andrew Lankov; *A Quantum Guide to Life*, Kunal Das; *Apex Predator: Orcas, Humans, and the Origins of Good and Evil*, Jeffrey Moussaleff Masson; *Broken Promises: How the AIDS Establishment Has Betrayed the Developing World*, Dr Edward Green; *Dead Love*, Lynda Watanabe McFerrin; *Dogs Make Us Human: A Global Family Album*, Jeffrey Moussaleff Masson (text), Art Wolfe (photography); *Drinking Water: The Past, Present and Future of Our Essential Ingredient*, David Sedlak; *Make Your Story a Movie*, John Marlow; *Maya Roads: One Woman's Journey Among the People of the Rainforest*, Mary Jo McConahay; *Mornings at the Stanton Street Shul: A Summer on the Lower East Side*, Dr Jonathan Boyarin; *No Simple Highway: The Life and Times of the Grateful Dead*, Peter Richardson; *Phoebe and the Ghost of Chagall*, Jill Koenigsdorf; *Salad Dressing: 50 Recipes*, Michele Anna Jordan; *The American Doomsday Machine*, Daniel Ellsberg; *The Dog Who Couldn't Stop Loving: How Dogs Have Captured Our Hearts for Thousands of Years*, Jeffrey Moussaleff Masson; *The Jersey Sting: Chris Christie & the Most Brazen Case of Jersey-Style Corruption—Ever*, Josh Margolin, Ted Sherman; *The Jewish Gospels*, Daniel Boyarin

APA Talent & Literary Agency (L-D)
405 S Beverly Dr, Beverly Hills, CA 90212
Tel: 310-888-4200 *Fax:* 310-888-4242
Web Site: www.apa-agency.com
Key Personnel
Owner: Lee Dinstman
SVP (Nashville): Steve Lassiter
Agent: David Saunders
Agent (Nashville): Frank Wing
Handle film & TV rights. No unsol mss; query first. Submit outline & sample chapters & SASE. No reading fee; 10% commission. Represent writers & producers.
Branch Office(s)
45 W 45 St, 4th fl, New York, NY 10036
Tel: 212-687-0092 *Fax:* 212-245-5062
3010 Poston Ave, Nashville, TN 37203 *Tel:* 615-297-0100 *Fax:* 615-297-5434

Arcadia (L)
31 Lake Place N, Danbury, CT 06810
Tel: 203-797-0993
E-mail: arcadialit@sbcglobal.net
Key Personnel
Pres: Victoria Gould Pryor (AAR)
Founded: 1986
Not seeking new clients.
Foreign Rights: Japan UNI Agency Inc (Japan); Barbara Levy Agency (UK); The Marsh Agency (translation)
Membership(s): The Authors Guild

Arthur Pine Associates Inc, see InkWell Management

Atchity Entertainment International Inc, see AEI (Atchity Entertainment International Inc)

Aurous Inc, see Pimlico/Aurous Inc

Author Author Literary Agency Ltd (L)
130-1005 Columbia St, PO Box 42522, Columbia Sq, New Westminster, BC V3M 6H5, Canada
Tel: 604-415-0056 *Fax:* 604-415-0076
Key Personnel
Pres & CEO: Joan Rickard *E-mail:* joan@authorauthor.ca
Founded: 1991
Multi-service literary agency. Represents fiction & nonfiction for adults, young adults & children. No poetry, screenplays, magazine stories or articles. Visit web site for submission guidelines. Unpublished authors welcome. We also provide editing, ghostwriting & consulting services. An entry evaluation fee of $125 CDN charged per proposal. Editorial & ghostwriting service fee schedule available on web site. Currently accepting few new properties for marketing to publishers & focus on mentoring authors with evaluative feedback & literary guidance toward their writing endeavors.

The Axelrod Agency (L)
55 Main St, Chatham, NY 12037
Mailing Address: PO Box 357, Chatham, NY 12037
Tel: 518-392-2100
Key Personnel
Pres: Steven Axelrod (AAR) *E-mail:* steve@axelrodagency.com
Foreign Rts Dir: Lori Antonson *E-mail:* lori@axelrodagency.com
Founded: 1983
Fiction & nonfiction, film & TV rights. No unsol mss, query first. No reading fee. E-mail queries receive attention first.

Elizabeth H Backman (L)
86 Johnnycake Hollow Rd, Pine Plains, NY 12567
Mailing Address: PO Box 762, Pine Plains, NY 12567-0762
Tel: 518-398-9344 *Fax:* 518-398-6368
E-mail: bethcountry@fairpoint.net
Key Personnel
Owner: Elizabeth H Backman
Ad Serv: Donn King Potter
Founded: 1981
Literary & commercial fiction; nonfiction; current events, politics, business, biography, the arts, cooking, diet, health, sports, gardening, history, science, self-help & psychology; audio & video cassettes. Author representatives, consulting editors, advertising & promotion copywriters. No unsol mss, query first with SASE; submit introduction, cover letter, chapter by chapter outline or table of contents, three sample chapters & authors bio or complete ms with cover letter & author's bio. Reading fees: $100 for proposals, $500 for complete mss; 15% agency fee plus expenses (phone, mail, photocopying, etc). Handle film & TV rights.
Foreign Rights: Lennart Sane (Netherlands, Portugal, Scandinavia, Spain); Thomas Schlueck (Germany); Tuttle-Mori Agency Inc (Japan)

Malaga Baldi Literary Agency (L-D)
233 W 99, Suite 19C, New York, NY 10025
Tel: 212-222-3213
E-mail: baldibooks@gmail.com; info@baldibooks.com
Web Site: www.baldibooks.com
Key Personnel
Pres: Malaga Baldi
Founded: 1986
Cultural history, nonfiction & literary-edgy fiction. No unsol mss, query first with SASE; no reading fee.
Titles recently placed: *A Lexicon of Terror: Argentina & The Legacies of Torture, Rev*, Marguerite Feitlowitz; *A Queer & Pleasant Danger: The True Story of a Nice Jewish Boy Who Joins the Church of Scientology & Leaves Twelve Years Later to Become the Lovely Lady She is Today, A Memoir*, Kate Bornstein; *All or Nothing: The Life & Times of Romaine Brooks*, Cassandra Langer; *Body Geographic*, Barrie Jean Borich; *Erotic Awakening*, Barbara Carellas; *Fishing Dogs (revised)*, Ray Coppinger, Peter Pinardi; *Great Sex Made Simple: Tantric Tips to Deepen Intimacy & Heighten Pleasure*, Mark Michaels, Patricia Johnson; *Hello Georgeous: Becoming Barbra Streisand*, William J Mann; *Machiavelli: A Renaissance Life*, Joseph Markulin; *Mermaids (E-book ed)*, Patty Dann; *My New Gender Workbook: Now with More High Theory, Quizzes & Sex*, Kate Bornstein; *Promising Young Women*, Suzanne Scanlon; *PYG*, Russell Potter; *Robots & Pirates!*, Kate Bornstein; *Smart Casual: The Transformation of Gourmet Restaurant Style in America*, Alison Pearlman; *Starfish*, Patty Dann; *Three Minutes in Poland*, Glenn Kurtz; *Tinseltown: Murder Mayhem & Morphine in Hollywood*, William J Mann
Foreign Rights: Eliane Benisti Literary Agency (France); The Grayhawk Agency (Michelle

Lin) (China, Taiwan); The Marsh Agency; Owls Agency (Japan); Abner Stein Agency (UK)

The Balkin Agency Inc, see Ward & Balkin Agency, Inc

A Richard Barber/Peter Berinstein & Associates (L)
60 E Eighth St, Suite 21-N, New York, NY 10003
Tel: 212-737-7266 *Fax:* 860-927-3942
E-mail: barberrich@aol.com
Key Personnel
Pres: A Richard Barber
Sr Assoc: Peter Berinstein
Handle software, film & TV rights. Specialize in fiction & nonfiction. No fees. No unsol mss, query first by mail (include SASE). No fax or e-mail submissions.
Branch Office(s)
80 N Main St, Kent, CT 06757-0887 *Tel:* 860-927-4911

Baror International Inc (L)
PO Box 868, Armonk, NY 10504-0868
Tel: 914-273-9199 *Fax:* 914-273-5058
Web Site: www.barorint.com
Key Personnel
Pres: Danny Baror *E-mail:* danny@barorint.com
Literary Agent: Heather Baror-Shapiro *E-mail:* heather@barorint.com
Specialize in international & domestic representation of literary works in both fiction & nonfiction ranging in genre including commercial fiction, literary titles, science fiction, fantasy, young adult & more. No unsol mss.

Loretta Barrett Books Inc (L)
220 E 23 St, 11th fl, New York, NY 10010
Tel: 212-242-3420
E-mail: query@lorettabarrettbooks.com
Web Site: www.lorettabarrettbooks.com
Key Personnel
VP & Dir, Foreign Rts: Nick Mullendore (AAR)
Jr Agent: Nicole Lowary
Founded: 1990
Fiction & nonfiction. Handle film, TV & multimedia rights. No poetry or children's literature, no screenplays; no unsol mss, query first with SASE. Submit outlines, sample chapters, bio (nonfiction); synopsis, bio (fiction). Representatives on the West Coast & in all major foreign countries. No reading fee.

Meredith Bernstein Literary Agency Inc (L)
2095 Broadway, Suite 505, New York, NY 10023
Tel: 212-799-1007 *Fax:* 212-799-1145
E-mail: MGoodBern@aol.com
Web Site: www.meredithbernsteinliteraryagency.com
Key Personnel
Agent: Meredith Bernstein (AAR)
Adult fiction (commercial & literary) & nonfiction; memoirs, current events, biography, health & fitness, women's issues, mysteries & special projects; crafts & creative endeavors. No poetry or screenplays. No unsol mss, query first online (no attachments) or by mail (include SASE). For fiction submit a 1 page query letter; nonfiction send 1 page query letter, table of contents & information on why you are an expert in this field. Handle film & TV rights only for books represented. Representatives in foreign countries & on the west coast. No reading fee.
Membership(s): The Authors Guild; Sisters in Crime; Women's Media Group

Bethel Agency (L-D)
PO Box 21043, Park West Sta, New York, NY 10025
Tel: 212-864-4510
E-mail: bethelagcy@aol.com
Key Personnel
Pres: Lewis R Chambers
Founded: 1967
Books & articles, fiction & nonfiction; stage plays, motion picture & TV properties; foreign & domestic. Represents photojournalists. Handles film & TV rights. No unsol mss, query first. No initial reading fee. Submissions of proposals are accepted via "snail mail" ONLY.

Daniel Bial Agency (L-D)
41 W 83 St, Suite 5-C, New York, NY 10024
Tel: 212-721-1786
E-mail: dbialagency@msn.com
Web Site: www.danielbialagency.com
Key Personnel
Founder & Prop: Daniel Bial
Founded: 1991
Nonfiction: business, cookbooks, history, humor, languages, popular culture, psychology, reference, science, sports, travel; fiction: quality fiction. No juvenile, poetry, genre fiction, screenplays, textbooks. No unsol mss, query letter first with SASE or short e-mail (e-mail queries without attachments are fine). No reading fee.

Vicky Bijur Literary Agency (L-D)
333 West End Ave, Suite 5-B, New York, NY 10023
Tel: 212-580-4108
E-mail: queries@vickybijuragency.com
Web Site: www.vickybijuragency.com
Key Personnel
Agent: Vicky Bijur (AAR)
Founded: 1988
Adult fiction & nonfiction. No children's books, poetry, science fiction, fantasy or horror. No unsol mss, query first with SASE. Fiction: query, synopsis & first chapter. Nonfiction: query & proposal. If e-mailed, paste proposal into body of e-mail, no attachments. No phone or fax queries. If query by hard copy, include SASE for response. If material to be returned, include SASE large enough to contain pages. No reading fee. Agents in all principal foreign countries. Handle film & TV rights.
Titles recently placed: *A Fatal Winter*, G M Malliet; *And When She Was Good*, Laura Lippman; *Drive*, James Sallis; *Driven*, James Sallis; *Love Anthony*, Lisa Genova; *Others of My Kind*, James Sallis; *Pagan Spring*, G M Malliet; *Serious Eats*, Ed Levine; *The Buzzard Table*, Margaret Maron; *The Killer is Dying*, James Sallis; *Three-Day Town*, Margaret Maron
Foreign Rights: Agenzia Letteraria Internazionale (Italy); AnatoliaLit Agency (Turkey); The English Agency Japan (Japan); The Grayhawk Agency (China, Taiwan); The Deborah Harris Agency (Israel); Agence Michelle Lapautre (France); Lennart Sane Agency (Argentina, Brazil, Denmark, Finland, Holland, Norway, Portugal, Spain, Sweden); Liepman Agency AG (Germany); Maxima Creative Agency (Indonesia); Prava I Prevodi (Bulgaria, Czech Republic, Estonia, Greece, Hungary, Poland, Russia, Serbia, Slovakia); Abner Stein Agency (England); Tuttle Mori Agency Inc (Thailand); Eric Yang Agency (Korea)

David Black Agency (L-D)
Subsidiary of Black Inc
335 Adams St, 27th fl, Suite 2707, Brooklyn, NY 11201
Tel: 718-852-5500 *Fax:* 718-852-5539
Web Site: www.davidblackagency.com
Key Personnel
Pres: David Black (AAR) *E-mail:* dblack@dblackagency.com
Agent: Linda Loewenthal *Tel:* 718-852-5523 *E-mail:* lloewenthal@dblackagency.com; Gary Morris *Tel:* 718-852-5518 *E-mail:* gmorris@dblackagency.com; Susan Raihofer *Tel:* 718-852-5542 *E-mail:* sraihofer@dblackagency.com; Sarah Smith *E-mail:* ssmith@dblackagency.com; Luke Thomas *Tel:* 718-852-5544 *E-mail:* lthomas@dblackagency.com; Joy Tutela *Tel:* 718-852-5533 *E-mail:* jtutela@dblackagency.com
Founded: 1990
Literary & commercial fiction & nonfiction, especially sports, politics, business, health, fitness, romance, parenting, psychology & social issues. No poetry. No unsol mss, query first with SASE. No reading fee. Agents in all principal foreign countries. Handle film & TV rights. No mysteries or thrillers.
Foreign Rights: Bardon-Chinese Media Agency (Ming-Ming Liu) (China); Eliane Benisti Agent Litteraire (Eliane Benisti & Noemi Rollet) (France); Luigi Bernabo Associates (Luigi Bernabo) (Italy); The Deborah Harris Agency (Efrat Lev) (Israel); International Editors' Co (Spanish) (Latin America, Spain); Katai & Bolza Literary Agents (Peter Bolza) (Hungary); Maxima Creative Agency (Santo Manurung) (Indonesia); Mohrbooks (Sabine Ibach, Bettina Kaufmann, Sebastian Ritscher & Cristina Uytiepo) (Germany); Prava I Prevodi Literary Agency (Milena Lukic, Ana Milenkovic & Jelena Todosijevic) (Bulgaria, Croatia, Czech Republic, Estonia, Greece, Latvia, Lithuania, Poland, Russia, Serbia, Slovenia); Riff Agency (Portuguese) (JP, Laura & Lucia Riff) (Brazil, Portugal); Sebes & van Gelderen Literary Agency (Paul Sebes) (Netherlands); Abner Stein (Abner & Arabella Stein, Caspian Dennis) (Australia, UK); Tuttle-Mori Agency Inc (Japan, Thailand); Eric Yang Agency (Sue Yang) (Korea)

Bleecker Street Associates Inc (L)
217 Thompson St, Suite 519, New York, NY 10012
Tel: 212-677-4492 *Fax:* 212-388-0001
Key Personnel
Pres: Agnes Birnbaum (AAR)
Founded: 1984
No unsol mss, query first about book project & author with SASE (cannot respond nor return materials without SASE). Do not query via e-mail, phone or fax. Handle film & TV rights for clients' own work only. Fiction & nonfiction; no poetry, plays or screenplays; handle magazine articles by book clients only. No reading fee.
Titles recently placed: *Everybody Goes to Jimmy's*, Michael W Mayo; *Heist!*, Jeff Diamant; *St Catherine of Sienna*, Shelley Emling; *The Cat That Came in from the Wild*, Forrest Bryant Johnson; *The Magnificent Medills*, Megan McKinney; *UFO's Today*, Brad Steiger, Sherry Steiger; *Why Do Women Crave More Sex in the Summer*, Patricia Barnes-Svarney
Foreign Rights: Agenzia Letteraria Internazionale (Italy); Bookman (Netherlands, Scandinavia); The English Agency (Japan) Ltd (Japan); International Editors' Co (Portugal, South America, Spain); Thomas Schlueck (Germany); Abner Stein Agency (Arabella Stein) (British Commonwealth)

Reid Boates Literary Agency (L-D)
69 Cooks Crossroad, Pittstown, NJ 08867-0328
Mailing Address: PO Box 328, Pittstown, NJ 08867-0328
Tel: 908-797-8087
E-mail: reid.boates@gmail.com
Key Personnel
Sole Prop: Reid Boates
Founded: 1985
Narrative +/or how-to nonfiction, health, spirituality, wellness, business & sports. Handle film & TV rights. No fiction. Most new clients by

referral. No reading fee. Agents in all major foreign markets. No unsol mss, submit written query with SASE.
Titles recently placed: *Most Intimate*, Roshi Pat Enkyo O'Hara; *Soul Fury and Kindness*, Coleman Barks; *The Shambhala Principle*, Sakyong Mipham Rinpoche
Foreign Rep(s): Eliane Benisti (France); Raquel de la Concha (Spain); Michael Meller (Eastern Europe, Germany, UK); Owl's Agency (Japan) Ltd (Japan)

Alison Bond Literary Agency (L)
171 W 79 St, No 143, New York, NY 10024
Key Personnel
Principal: Alison M Bond *E-mail:* alison@bondlit.com
Founded: 1982
Literary fiction, memoir/biography, women's issues, foodie & narrative nonfiction. Not accepting new writers at present. Agents in most European countries. No science fiction or genre categories. No fees charged.
Membership(s): Women's Media Group

Bond Literary Agency (L)
4340 E Kentucky Ave, Suite 471, Denver, CO 80246
Tel: 303-781-9305
E-mail: queries@bondliteraryagency.com
Web Site: bondliteraryagency.com
Key Personnel
Owner & Agent: Sandra Bond *E-mail:* sandra@bondliteraryagency.com
Founded: 1998
Specialize in adult commercial & literary fiction including mysteries & women's fiction (no romance, children's picture books, health, science fiction, adult fantasy or poetry); juvenile fiction; narrative nonfiction, science, memoir, biography & business. Talented, previously unpublished writers will be considered. Nonfiction authors must have excellent credentials & a strong platform. No unsol mss, query by e-mail first (letter in the body of the e-mail, no attachments). No phone calls please. Ms submissions by request only. Sell foreign & film/TV rights through subagents. No fees charged.
Titles recently placed: *Butch Cassidy: Beyond the Grave*, W C Jameson; *Claws of the Cat: A Shinobi Mystery*, Susan Spann; *Death in the 12th House: Where Neptune Rules*, Mitchell Scott Lewis; *Fatal Descent*, Beth Groundwater; *Her Story: A Timelin of the Women Who Changed America*, Charlotte S Waisman, Jill S Tietjen; *To Hell in a Handbasket*, Beth Groundwater; *Wicked Eddies*, Beth Groundwater

BookEnds LLC (L)
136 Long Hill Rd, Gillette, NJ 07933
Web Site: www.bookends-inc.com
Key Personnel
Owner & Literary Agent: Jessica H Faust (AAR) *E-mail:* jfsubmissions@bookends-inc.com
Agent: Jessica Alvarez (AAR) *E-mail:* jasubmissions@bookends-inc.com; Kim Lionetti (AAR) *E-mail:* klsubmissions@bookends-inc.com
Agent & Subs Rts Dir: Moe Ferrara
Dir, Digital Content: Bill Harris
Literary Asst & Rights Coord: Beth Campbell *E-mail:* bcsubmissions@bookends-inc.com
Founded: 1999
Founded by former editors from Berkley Publishing, BookEnds is a literary agency that represents fiction & nonfiction for adult audiences. No unsol mss, query first. Review web site for submission instructions & get tips on queries & proposals. No fees.
Titles recently placed: *A Witch Before Dying*, Heather Blake; *Bared*, Stacey Kennedy; *Bedding Lord Ned*, Sally Mackenzie; *Buried in a Bog*, Sheila Connolly; *Chapter & Hearse: A Booktown Mystery*, Lorna Barrett; *Due or Die: A Library Mystery*, Jenn McKinlay; *Every Trick in the Book*, Lucy Arlington; *Final Catcall*, Sofie Kelly; *Fire Kissed*, Erin Kellison; *Hope at Dawn*, Stacy Henrie; *Immortally Yours*, Angie Fox; *Never Entice an Earl*, Lily Dalton; *Nine Days*, Minerva Koenig; *One Hot Murder*, Lorraine Bartlett; *Reborn (Shadow Falls: After Dark)*, C C Hunter; *Risky Business*, Melissa Cutler; *Some Enchanted Éclair*, Bailey Cates; *The Farm*, Emily McKay; *The Reason is You*, Sharla Scroggs; *The Retail Doctor's Guide to Growing Your Business*, Bob Phibbs; *Viral Nation*, Shaunta Grimes; *What's Left Behind*, Lorrie Thomson
Membership(s): Mystery Writers of America; Romance Writers of America

Books & Such (L)
52 Mission Circle, Suite 122, PMB 170, Santa Rosa, CA 95409-5370
Tel: 707-538-4184
Web Site: booksandsuch.com
Key Personnel
Founder & Pres: Janet Kobobel Grant (AAR) *E-mail:* janet@booksandsuch.com
VP: Wendy Lawton *E-mail:* wendy@booksandsuch.com
Literary Agent, Adult Fiction, Nonfiction & Teen: Rachelle Gardner *E-mail:* rachelle@booksandsuch.com
Literary Agent, Adult Fiction & Nonfiction: Mary Keeley *E-mail:* mary@booksandsuch.com
Literary Agent, Teens, Twenties & Thirties: Rachel Kent *E-mail:* rachel@booksandsuch.com
Founded: 1997
Handles fiction & nonfiction. Submission by e-mail (no attachments). No phone calls. No unsol mss, query first. No fees.
Titles recently placed: *101 Ways to Affirm Your Husband*, Kathi Lipp; *Finding Church*, Rachel Held Evans; *Grace Intervention*, Bill Giovannetti; *Hope of Heaven*, Al Halleen, Erin Keeley Marshall; *How to Talk Evangelical*, Addie Zierman; *Silenced*, Dani Pettrey; *Someday Home*, Lauraine Snelling; *Spoken For: Embracing Who You Are and Whose You Are*, Robin Jones Gunn, Alyssa Joy Bethke
Branch Office(s)
PO Box 1227, Hilmar, CA 95324-1227 *Tel:* 209-634-1913
Membership(s): Advanced Writers & Speakers Association; American Christian Fiction Writers; CBA; Romance Writers of America

BookStop Literary Agency LLC (L-D)
67 Meadow View Rd, Orinda, CA 94563
E-mail: info@bookstopliterary.com
Web Site: www.bookstopliterary.com
Key Personnel
CEO & Pres: Kendra Marcus
Literary Agent: Ms Minju Chang
Foreign Rts Coord: Isle Craane
Founded: 1984
Juvenile & young adult mss only (fiction & nonfiction) & illustration for children's books, especially humorous voices, intense young adult fiction, clever middle-grade & topics & mss for the Hispanic market in the U.S. Accept unsol mss. Submit full mss for picture books; first 10 pages for fiction; sample chapters & outline for nonfiction. See web site for additional submission information. No reading fee.
Titles recently placed: *Press Here*, Herve Tullet; *Scarlet*, A C Gaughen; *The Three Ninja Pigs*, Corey Schwartz

Georges Borchardt Inc (L-D)
136 E 57 St, New York, NY 10022
Tel: 212-753-5785
E-mail: georges@gbagency.com
Web Site: www.gbagency.com
Key Personnel
Founder & Pres: Georges Borchardt (AAR)
Founder: Anne Borchardt (AAR)
VP & Foreign Rts Dir: Valerie Borchardt (AAR) *E-mail:* valerie@gbagency.com
Agent: Samantha Shea *E-mail:* samantha@gbagency.com
Foreign Rts Asst: Rachel Brooke *E-mail:* rachel@gbagency.com
Asst: Will Vunderink *E-mail:* will@gbagency.com
Founded: 1967
Fiction & nonfiction. No unsol mss; handle film & TV rights & software. No fees charged.
Titles recently placed: *COME VA, AMERICA?*, Beppe Severgnini; *Five on Scully*, Arthur Danto; *Killer Come Hither*, Louis Begley; *Lorraine*, Ketch Secor; *Salka Viertel*, Donna Rifkind; *Short Stories*, Susan Minot; *State of Play*, Suzanne Gordon; *The Children Act*, Ian McEwan; *The Double Life of Liliane*, Lily Tuck; *The Harder they Come*, TC Boyle; *The Joys of Being Buddhist*, Charles Johnson; *Two Book Contract*, John Lahr; *Up From Sanctity*, Susan Jacoby; *Visiting Hours: A Memoir of Friendship and Murder*, Amy Butcher
Foreign Rights: The Asano Agency (Kiyoshi Asano) (Japanese); Bardon Chinese Media Agency (Ming-Ming Lui) (Chinese); Luigi Bernabo Associates SRL (Luigi Branabo) (Italian); English Agency (Junzo Sawa) (Japanese); Graal Literary Agency (Marcin Biegaj) (Polish); Deborah Harris Agency (Efrat Lev) (Israel); International Editors (Maribel Luque) (Spanish); Japan UNI Agency (Miko Yamanouchi) (Japanese); JLM Agency (Nelly & John Moukakou) (Greek); Asli Karasuil Literary Agency (Turkish); Katai & Bolza (Peter Bolza) (Hungarian); Korean Copyright Center (Misook Hong) (Korean); Agence Michelle Lapautre (Michelle Lapautre) (French); Mohrbooks (Sabine Ibach & Sebastian Ritscher) (German); Andrew Nurnberg Associates (Kristine Shatrovska) (Baltic States); Andrew Nurnburg Associates (Anna Droumeva) (Bulgarian & Romanian); Andrew Nurnberg Associates (Ludmilla Sushkova) (Russian); Kristin Olson Literary Agency SRO (Kristin Olson) (Czech); RDC Agencia Literaria (Raquel de la Concha) (Portuguese) (Portugal); Karin Schindler (Portuguese) (Brazil); Marianne Schoenbach Literary Agency BV (Marianne Schonbach) (Dutch); Sheil Land Associates (Vivien Green) (British); Sane Toregard Agency (Ulf Toregard) (Scandinavia); Tuttle-Mori Agency Inc (Asako Kawachi) (Japanese)

Bradford Literary Agency (L)
5694 Mission Center Rd, Suite 347, San Diego, CA 92108
Tel: 619-521-1201
E-mail: queries@bradfordlit.com
Web Site: www.bradfordlit.com
Key Personnel
Agent: Laura Bradford (AAR) *E-mail:* laura@bradfordlit.com; Natalie Lakosil *E-mail:* natalie@bradfordlit.com; Sarah LaPolla (AAR) *E-mail:* sarah@bradfordlit.com; Monica Odom *E-mail:* monica@bradfordlit.com
Founded: 2001
A boutique agency offering a full range of representation services to authors, both published & pre-published. We are an editorial-focused agency & prefer to work closely with our authors in helping to build strong, sustainable careers. We believe the best author-agent relationships extend beyond making sales; in order to best serve our client's needs, we must also be a partner, advisor, a careful listener, a troubleshooter & an advocate.

We are currently acquiring fiction: romance (historical, romantic suspense, paranormal, category, contemporary, erotic), urban fantasy, women's fiction, mystery, thrillers, young adult, middle grade (Natalie & Sarah only) & picture books (Natalie only). Also nonfiction: business, relationships, biography/memoir, self-help, parenting, narrative humor, pop culture, illustrated/graphic design, food & cooking, history & social issues. We are not currently acquiring: poetry, screenplays, short stories, westerns, horror, new age, religion, crafts.

We accept unsol mss. Queries are accepted by e-mail only to queries@bradfordlit.com. We do not open e-mail attachments, unless specifically requested by an agent. Your entire submission must appear in the body of the e-mail & not as an attachment. The subject line should begin as follows: QUERY: (The title of the ms or any short message you would like us to see should follow). For fiction: Please e-mail a query letter along with the first chapter of your ms & a synopsis. Please be sure to include the genre & word count in your cover letter. For nonfiction: submit a book proposal including an outline, sample material, author bio & competitive survey. No fees.

Titles recently placed: *Back to You*, Lauren Dane; *Beyond the Cut*, Sarah Castille; *Bliss & the Art of Forever*, Alison Kent; *Breakout*, Ann Aguirre; *Burn It Up*, Cara McKenna; *Cornered*, HelenKay Dimon; *Dia de los Muertos*, Roseanne Greenfield Thong; *Dinosaur Boy*, Cory Putman Oakes; *Falling Under*, Lauren Dane; *Gerald the Giant Giant*, Geoff Stevenson; *Grave Phantoms*, Jenn Bennett; *Hold Me Close*, Megan Hart; *I Want It That Way*, Ann Aguirre; *Magnate*, Joanna Shupe; *Make Me*, Tessa Bailey; *Mine*, HelenKay Dimon; *Most Likely to Succeed*, Jennifer Echols; *Noodle Magic*, Roseanne Thong; *Not After Everything*, Michelle Levy; *Piper Morgan Joins the Circus*, Stephanie Faris; *Public Enemies*, Ann Aguirre; *Run to You*, Clara Kensie; *Shadow of the War Machine*, Kristin Bailey; *Skinny Dipping with Murder*, Auralee Wallace; *Taking the Boss to Bed*, Joss Wood; *Taming the Legend*, Kat Latham; *The Anatomical Shape of a Heart*, Jenn Bennett; *The Devil Wears Spurs*, Soraya Lane; *The Heart of the Duke*, Victoria Morgan; *The Marriage Contract*, Katee Robert; *The Unsuitable Secretary*, Maggie Robinson; *Time's Up*, Janey Mack; *Trains Don't Sleep*, Andria Rosenbaum; *Trust Me, I'm Trouble*, Mary Elizabeth Summer; *Under the Surface*, Anne Calhoun; *Unwrapped*, Katie Lane; *Weave of Absence*, Carol Ann Martin; *When Joss Met Matt*, Ellie Cahill

Foreign Rights: Taryn Fagerness Agency (Taryn Fagerness) (Albania, Argentina, Australia, Brazil, Bulgaria, Canada, China, Croatia, Czech Republic, Denmark, Estonia, Finland, France, Germany, Greece, Hungary, Iceland, India, Indonesia, Israel, Italy, Japan, Korea, Latvia, Lithuania, Mexico, Netherlands, Norway, Poland, Portugal, Romania, Russia, Serbia, Slovakia, Spain, Sweden, Taiwan, Thailand, Turkey, Ukraine, UK, Vietnam)

Membership(s): ALA; Romance Writers of America; Society of Children's Book Writers & Illustrators

Brandt & Hochman Literary Agents Inc (L)
1501 Broadway, Suite 2310, New York, NY 10036
Tel: 212-840-5760 *Fax:* 212-840-5776
Web Site: brandthochman.com
Key Personnel
Pres: Gail Hochman (AAR) *E-mail:* ghochman@bromasite.com
Agent & Foreign Rts: Marianne Merola (AAR) *E-mail:* mmerola@bromasite.com
Agent: Bill Contardi (AAR) *E-mail:* bill@billcontardi.com; Emily Forland (AAR) *E-mail:* eforland@bromasite.com; Jody Kahn (AAR) *E-mail:* jkahn@bromasite.com; Emma Patterson (AAR) *E-mail:* epatterson@bromasite.com; Charles Schlessiger (AAR) *E-mail:* cschlessiger@bromasite.com; Henry Thayer (AAR) *E-mail:* hthayer@bromasite.com
Audio Rts & Perms Contact: Lina Granada *E-mail:* reply@bromasite.com

Represents fiction & nonfiction, including mystery/thriller, memoir, narrative nonfiction, journalism, history, current affairs, health, science, pop culture, lifestyle, art history & children's books. No screenplays or textbooks. No unsol mss, query first by e-mail or regular mail. Responses to e-mailed queries not guaranteed. Queries limited to 2 pages. Include SASE if sending by regular mail. See web site for specific submission preferences for each agent. No reading fee. Fee charged for making copies & book/galley purchases. Co-agents in most foreign countries.

The Joan Brandt Agency (L)
788 Wesley Dr NW, Atlanta, GA 30305
Tel: 404-351-8877 *Fax:* 404-351-0068
Key Personnel
Pres: Joan Brandt
Founded: 1990

Fiction & nonfiction (no science fiction, horror, fantasy, historical or romance). No unsol mss, query first with SASE; submit letter plus brief synopsis. Agents present in all principal countries.

Barbara Braun Associates Inc (L)
7 E 14 St, Suite 19F, New York, NY 10003
Tel: 212-604-9023
Web Site: www.barbarabraunagency.com
Key Personnel
Pres: Barbara Braun (AAR) *E-mail:* barbara@barbarabraunagency.com
Assoc: John F Baker
Founded: 1994

Represents both literary & commercial fiction as well as serious nonfiction, including memoir, biography, cultural history, women's issues, pop culture, art & architecture. Fiction is strong on stories for women, art-related fiction, historical & multicultural stories & mysteries & thrillers. Interested in narrative nonfiction & current affairs. No unsol mss, query first by e-mail to bbasubmissions@gmail.com. Include brief summary of book, word count, genre, any relevant publishing experience & first 5 pages of ms pasted into the body of the e-mail. No reading or other fees.

Foreign Rights: Jean V Naggar Literary Agency (Jennifer Weltz) (Worldwide)

Membership(s): The Authors Guild; PEN American Center

M Courtney Briggs Esq, Authors Representative (L)
Chase Tower, 28th fl, 100 N Broadway Ave, Oklahoma City, OK 73102
Key Personnel
Author's Rep: M Courtney Briggs
Founded: 1994

Fiction & nonfiction, adult & juvenile with emphasis on children's books, including picture books, middle-grade & young adult books. Represent authors & illustrators of trade books of all types. Handle film & TV rights. No unsol mss, query first by regular mail with SASE, include publishing history; published authors only; no reading fees.

Membership(s): Society of Children's Book Writers & Illustrators

Brockman Inc (L)
260 Fifth Ave, 10th fl, New York, NY 10001
Tel: 212-935-8900 *Fax:* 212-935-5535
E-mail: rights@brockman.com
Web Site: www.brockman.com
Key Personnel
Chmn & CEO: John Brockman
Pres: Katinka Matson
VP: Max Brockman
Rts Dir: Russell Weinberger

Literary & software agency. No unsol mss. Deal direct in all foreign markets. No fees charged.

Curtis Brown Ltd (L-D)
10 Astor Place, New York, NY 10003
Tel: 212-473-5400
Web Site: www.curtisbrown.com
Key Personnel
CEO: Timothy F Knowlton (AAR)
Pres: Peter L Ginsberg (AAR)
EVP & Book Agent: Ginger Knowlton (AAR)
SVP & Book Agent: Maureen Walters (AAR)
VP & Book Agent: Elizabeth Harding (AAR); Laura Blake Peterson (AAR)
Dir, Digital Strategy & Book Agent: Steve Kasdin (AAR)
Dir, Foreign Rts & Book Agent: Jonathan Lyons (AAR)
Book Agent: Ginger Clark (AAR); Katherine Fausset (AAR); Mitchell Waters (AAR)
Film & TV Rts: Holly Frederick (AAR)
Founded: 1914

Handle general trade fiction & nonfiction, juvenile. No unsol mss, query first with SASE. Submit outline or sample chapters. No reading fee. Other fees charged (for photocopies, express mail, etc). Handle film & TV rights & merchandising & multimedia. No playwrights. Representatives in all major foreign countries.

Branch Office(s)
1750 Montgomery St, San Francisco, CA 94111 *Tel:* 415-954-8566

Marie Brown Associates (L)
412 W 154 St, New York, NY 10032
Tel: 212-939-9725 *Fax:* 212-939-9728
E-mail: mbrownlit@aol.com
Key Personnel
Owner & Pres: Marie D Brown
Founded: 1984

Adult & juvenile fiction & nonfiction. Handle film & TV rights through representatives in Hollywood. No unsol mss, query first; submit outline & sample chapters or full ms on request, 12-point, double-spaced, one-sided only, typed, white paper & unbound. Include SASE. No e-mail queries. No reading fee.

Browne & Miller Literary Associates (L)
410 S Michigan Ave, Suite 460, Chicago, IL 60605
Tel: 312-922-3063
E-mail: mail@browneandmiller.com
Web Site: www.browneandmiller.com
Key Personnel
Pres & Owner: Danielle Egan-Miller (AAR) *E-mail:* danielle@browneandmiller.com
Agent & Internship Coord: Joanna MacKenzie (AAR) *E-mail:* joanna@browneandmiller.com
Assoc Agent: Abby Saul *E-mail:* abby@browneandmiller.com
Founded: 1971

General adult trade fiction, nonfiction & young adult. No horror, sci-fi, or children's books. No unsol mss, query first by e-mail; no reading fee.

Foreign Rep(s): Agence Eliane Benisti (Eliane Benisti) (France); Big Apple Agency Inc (China, Taiwan); Book Publishers Association of Israel (Israel); The English Agency (Japan) Ltd (Japan); International Copyright Agency Ltd (Simona Kessler) (Romania); Japan UNI

Agency Inc (Japan); KCBS Literary Agency (Hosung Maeng) (Korea); The Marsh Agency UK (Netherlands, Poland, Scandinavia); Natoli, Stefan & Oliva (Roberta Oliva) (Italy); Andrew Nurnberg Associates Baltic (Tatjana Zoldnere) (Baltic States); Andrew Nurnberg Associates (Hungary); O A Literary Agency (Greece); Prava i Prevodi (Croatia, Montenegro, Serbia, Slovenia); Riff Agency (Brazil); Thomas Schluck Agency (Germany); Tuttle-Mori Agency Inc (Japan); Julio F Yanez Agencia Literaria (Montse F Yanez) (Mexico, South America, Spain); Eric Yang Agency (Korea)
Foreign Rights: Andrew Nurnberg Literary Agency (Liudmilla Sushkova) (Russia)
Membership(s): The Authors Guild; Mystery Writers of America; Romance Writers of America

Don Buchwald & Associates Inc (L)
10 E 44 St, New York, NY 10017
Tel: 212-867-1200 *Fax:* 212-867-2434
E-mail: info@buchwald.com
Web Site: www.buchwald.com
Key Personnel
CEO & Pres (NY): Don Buchwald *E-mail:* don@buchwald.com
CFO & VP: Stephen Fisher *E-mail:* steve@buchwald.com
EVP, Legal & Admin Aff: Richard Basch *E-mail:* richard@buchwald.com
Agent (NY): David Lewis *E-mail:* davidl@buchwald.com; Jonathan Mason *E-mail:* jmason@buchwald.com; Joanne Nici *E-mail:* jonici@buchwald.com; Rachel Sheedy *E-mail:* rachel@buchwald.com; Alan Willig *E-mail:* alanw@buchwald.com
Talent representatives & literary agency: TV, film, commercial, theatre & broadcasting. No unsol mss, query first. No reading fee.
Branch Office(s)
6500 Wilshire Blvd, Suite 2200, Los Angeles, CA 90048 *Tel:* 323-665-7400 *Fax:* 323-665-7470

Howard Buck Agency (L-D)
80 Eighth Ave, Suite 1107, New York, NY 10011
Tel: 212-924-9093
Key Personnel
Pres: Howard Buck
Founded: 1978
Fiction (no science fiction, fantasy, horror or screenplays) & nonfiction, adult; no juvenile or children's. No unsol mss, query first by letter with SASE. No original screenplays, teleplays or TV episodes. No reading fees; handle film rights.
Foreign Rep(s): A M Heath & Co Ltd (UK)

Judith Buckner Literary Agency (L-D)
12721 Hart St, North Hollywood, CA 91605
Tel: 818-982-8202 *Fax:* 818-764-6844
Key Personnel
Pres: Judith Buckner *E-mail:* jbuckner@pacbell.net
Founded: 1970
Handle commercial & literary fiction & nonfiction, some film & TV scripts. No children's, young adult, romance, science fiction or horror. No unsol mss; query first by letter or e-mail. No reading fee. Commission 15% domestic, 20% foreign. Handle film & TV rights. If invited to submit, for fiction send first fifty pages & brief synopsis of remainder. For nonfiction, send proposal including overview, target market, outline or table of contents, sample chapter, author's bio, survey of competition & reasons why your book is superior & marketing plan.

The Bukowski Agency Ltd (L)
14 Prince Arthur Ave, Suite 202, Toronto, ON M5R 1A9, Canada
Tel: 416-928-6728 *Fax:* 416-963-9978
E-mail: info@bukowskiagency.com
Web Site: www.bukowskiagency.com
Key Personnel
Pres & Primary Agent: Denise Bukowski
Founded: 1986
Adult trade except genre fiction by Canadian authors. No unsol mss, query first by regular mail. Submit proposal & sample for nonfiction; query & sample for fiction. No reading fees. Commission plus disbursements.
Foreign Rights: AJA Literary Agency (Anna Jarota) (France); Akcali Copyright Agency (Atilla Izgi Turgut) (Istanbul); Big Apple Agency (Vincent Lin) (China, Taiwan); The Foreign Office (Teresa Vilarrubla) (Latin America, Portugal, Spain); Graal Liteary Agency (Filip Wojciechowski) (Eastern Europe, Poland); Grandi & Associati (Alessandra Mele) (Italy); The Deborah Harris Agency (Ilana Kurshan) (Israel); A M Heath & Co Ltd (Bill Hamilton) (UK); Japan UNI Agency Inc (Cecilia Kashiwamura) (Japan); JLM Literary Agency (John Moukakou) (Greece); Katai & Bolza Literary Agents (Peter Bolza) (Hungary); Duran Kim Agency (Duran Kim) (Korea); Licht & Burr (Trine Licht) (Scandinavia); Mohrbooks AG (Annelie Geissler) (Germany); Marianne Schoenbach Literary Agency (Marianne Schoenbach) (Holland); The Van Lear Agency (Elizabeth Van Lear) (Russia)

Sheree Bykofsky Associates Inc (L)
PO Box 706, Brigantine, NJ 08203
E-mail: submitbee@aol.com
Web Site: www.shereebee.com
Key Personnel
Pres & Agent: Sheree Bykofsky (AAR)
Founded: 1991
Adult trade & mass market nonfiction & fiction. No unsol mss, send e-query in body of e-mail to submitbee@aol.com. Handle film & TV rights through subagents. No fees.
Foreign Rep(s): Betty Anne Crawford
Foreign Rights: Big Apple Agency Inc (China); International Editors' Co (Spain); Alexander Korzhenevski (Russia); Piergiorgio Nicolazzini (Italy); Radoslav Trenev (Eastern Europe, Greece, Turkey); Tuttle-Mori Agency Inc (Japan); Diana Voigt (Germany); Eric Yang (Korea)
Membership(s): The Authors Guild; North American Travel Journalists Association

Cambridge Literary Associates (L-D)
Division of Valentino Enterprises Inc
135 Beach Rd, Unit C-3, Salisbury, MA 01952
Tel: 978-499-0374 *Fax:* 978-499-9774
Web Site: www.cambridgeliterary.com
Key Personnel
Pres: Michael Valentino
VP: Ralph Valentino
Full literary agency. Fiction & nonfiction: action, mystery, romance, science fiction, screenplays. No unsol mss, query first with letter. No reading fee. Fee of $3 per page for editing.

Carlisle & Co LLC, see InkWell Management

Maria Carvainis Agency Inc (L)
Rockefeller Center, 1270 Avenue of the Americas, Suite 2320, New York, NY 10020
Tel: 212-245-6365 *Fax:* 212-245-7196
E-mail: mca@mariacarvainisagency.com
Web Site: mariacarvainisagency.com
Key Personnel
Pres: Maria Carvainis (AAR)
Assoc: Elizabeth Copps (AAR)
Contract & Subs Rts Mgr: Martha Guzman
Asst: Bryce Gold
Founded: 1977
Literary & mainstream fiction: suspense/mystery, thriller, historical, contemporary women's fiction/romance, middle grade/young adult. Nonfiction: business, biography, memoir, psychology, women's issues, popular science, history, pop culture. No screenplays, children's picture books, science fiction or poetry. Magazine rights handled for clients who are book authors. No unsol mss, query first with SASE, do not accept e-mailed or faxed submissions. Submit outline & sample chapters or full ms only on request. Handle film & TV rights. No reading fee. Signatory to Writers Guild of America (WGA). Representatives in Hollywood & all major foreign markets.
Titles recently placed: *A Winter Scandal*, Candace Camp; *Eternal Captive*, Laura Wright; *Last Man Standing*, Cindy Gerard; *Lethal*, Sandra Brown; *The Killing Song*, PJ Parrish; *The Secret Mistress*, Mary Balogh; *Until There Was You*, Kristan Higgins
Membership(s): ABA; The Authors Guild; International Thriller Writers Inc; Mystery Writers of America; Romance Writers of America

Castiglia Literary Agency (L)
1155 Camino Del Mar, Suite 510, Del Mar, CA 92014
Tel: 858-755-8761 *Fax:* 858-755-7063
Web Site: www.castiglialiteraryagency.com
Key Personnel
Pres & Agent: Julie Castiglia
Assoc Agent: Winifred Golden *E-mail:* win@castigliaagency.com
Founded: 1993
Ethnic, commercial & literary fiction, science, biography, psychology, women's issues, popular culture, health & niche books. No unsol mss; submit query letter with bio & one page writing sample of project, fiction or nonfiction, including SASE. No phone queries, only by e-mail. Represent books to TV & film rights. Specialize in science, health, biography, narrative nonfiction & literary fiction. No fees charged. Representives in all major foreign countries.
Titles recently placed: *Airbrushed Nation: The Lure and Loathing of Women's Magazines*, Jennifer Nelson; *Angels of Paris: An Architectural Tour Through the History of Paris*, Rosemary Flannery; *Barry Dixon Inspirations*, Brian Coleman; *Critical Companion to Jack London*, Jeanne Reesman; *Cuisine Nicoise*, Hillary Davis; *Fortuny Interiors*, Brian Coleman; *From Splendor to Revolution*, Julia P Gelardi; *Gloria Swanson: The Ultimate Star*, Stephen Michael Shearer; *Meringue*, Linda Jackson, Jennifer Evans Gardner; *Orphan's Journey*, Robert Buettner; *Overkill*, Robert Buettner; *Paris Wedding*, Kimberley Petyt; *Rocket Girl: The Story of America's First Female Rocket Scientist*, George P Morgan; *Salad for Dinner: Complete Meals for all Seasons*, Jeanne Kelley; *Stories in Stone New York*, Doug Keister; *The Art of the Visit*, Kathy Bertone; *The Two Krishnas*, Ghalib Shiraz Dhalla; *Undercurrents*, Robert Buettner
Foreign Rights: ACER Literary Agency (Spain); Asano Agency Inc (Japan); Lora Fountain Agence Litteraire (France); Grandi & Assoc (Italy); Imprima Korea Agency (Korea); MBA Literary Agents Ltd (UK); Michael Meller Agency (Germany); Svetlana Pironko (Russia); Vantage Copyright Agency (China)

Jane Chelius Literary Agency Inc (L)
548 Second St, Brooklyn, NY 11215
Tel: 718-499-0236; 718-499-0714 *Fax:* 718-832-7335
E-mail: queries@janechelius.com; rights@janechelius.com
Web Site: www.janechelius.com

Key Personnel
Pres: Jane Chelius (AAR) *E-mail:* jane@janechelius.com
Founded: 1995
Adult fiction & nonfiction including mystery, women's literature, humor, women's issues, medicine & science for a general audience, nature & natural world, biography. No children's books, poetry, stage plays or screenplays, science fiction, fantasy or category romance. No unsol mss. Query first with SASE; no e-mail queries with attachments. Paste one page synopsis, first 10 pages & short biography in body of e-mail. No reading fee; handle film & TV rights. Representation in all foreign markets.
Membership(s): International Association of Crime Writers; Mystery Writers of America; Women's Media Group

Linda Chester Literary Agency (L-D)
630 Fifth Ave, Suite 2000, New York, NY 10111
Tel: 212-218-3350 *Fax:* 212-218-3343
E-mail: submissions@lindachester.com
Web Site: www.lindachester.com
Key Personnel
Principal: Linda Chester (AAR)
Exec Mgr: Gary Jaffe *E-mail:* gjaffe@lindachester.com
Quality adult fiction & nonfiction. Handle film & TV rights. No reading fes; no unsol mss, query first.
Branch Office(s)
2342 Shattuck Ave, No 506, Berkeley, CA 94704, Contact: Laurie Fox *Tel:* 510-704-0971 *E-mail:* laurie@lindachester.com
Foreign Rights: The Fielding Agency LLC (Whitney Lee)

Faith Childs Literary Agency Inc (L)
111 John St, Suite 1620, New York, NY 10038
Tel: 212-995-9600
Web Site: faithchildsliteraryagency.com
Key Personnel
Pres: Faith Hampton Childs (AAR) *E-mail:* faith@faithchildsliteraryagency.com
Founded: 1990
Specialize in fiction & nonfiction film & TV rights. No unsol mss, queries or unreferred clients accepted. Agents in all principal countries.
Foreign Rep(s): The English Agency (Japan) Ltd (Japan)

Chinese Connection Agency (L-D)
Division of The Yao Enterprises LLC
67 Banksville Rd, Armonk, NY 10504
Tel: 914-765-0296 *Fax:* 914-765-0297
E-mail: info@yaollc.com
Web Site: www.yaollc.com
Key Personnel
Pres: Mei C Yao
Founded: 1995
Translation rights sales of adult fiction & nonfiction, professional/business management books, college books, personal development, leisure books, etc. No unsol mss, query first (e-mail queries welcome). No reading fee. Handle software & film & TV rights.

William F Christopher Publication Services (L)
Unit of The Management Innovations Group
Kensington No 237, 1580 Geary Rd, Walnut Creek, CA 94597-2744
Tel: 925-943-5584 *Fax:* 925-943-5594
E-mail: wfcmgmt.innovations@yahoo.com
Key Personnel
Pres: William F (Bill) Christopher
Founded: 2000
Represent authors to place their books with publishers. Specialize only in business books & books on science & technology. No unsol mss, query first.
Membership(s): American Society for Quality; National Association of Business Economists; Society of Manufacturing Engineers; Society of Plastics Engineers; World Academy of Productivity Science

Cine/Lit Representation (L-D)
PO Box 802918, Santa Clarita, CA 91380-2918
Tel: 661-513-0268
E-mail: cinelit@att.net
Key Personnel
Partner: Anna Cottle; Mary Alice Kier (AAR)
Founded: 1991
Commercial & literary fiction & nonfiction. Emphasis in mainstream thrillers, suspense/mysteries, supernatural, horror & speculative. Nonfiction interest in narrative environmental, travel & pop culture. Not accepting submissions at this time. No reading fee. Representatives in all major foreign markets. Handle film & TV rights.
Membership(s): British Academy of Film & Television Arts/Los Angeles; Independent Film Project/West

Wm Clark Associates (L)
186 Fifth Ave, 2nd fl, New York, NY 10010
Tel: 212-675-2784 *Fax:* 347-649-9262
E-mail: general@wmclark.com
Web Site: www.wmclark.com
Key Personnel
Principal: William Clark (AAR) *E-mail:* wmclark@wmclark.com
Founded: 1999
Represents mainstream & literary fiction & quality nonfiction to the book publishing, motion picture, television & new media fields; e-mail queries only & should include a general description of the work, a synopsis/outline, biographical information & publishing history, if any. E-mails must be text only & e-mails with attachments will not be accepted. Unsol queries sent by any method other than through web site query page or e-mail to query@wmclark.com in the form described will be discarded unread. No reading fees; handle film & TV rights for books written by clients only; does not represent screenplays. In addition to selling directly in the global English language markets, translation rights are sold directly in the German, Italian, Spanish, Portuguese, Latin American, French, Dutch, & Scandinavian territories; in association with Andrew Nurnberg Associates Ltd (UK) through offices in China, Bulgaria, Czech Republic, Latvia, Poland & Hungary; & through corresponding agents in Russia, Ukraine, Japan, Greece, Israel, Turkey, Korea, Taiwan & Thailand. Other network partners provide services including editorial consultation, media training, lecture booking, marketing support & public relations.
Titles recently placed: *How Could This Happen? The Causes of the Holocaust*, Dan McMillan; *Marilyn: The Passion and the Paradox*, Lois Banner; *Paris Reborn: Napoleon III, Baron Haussmann and the Quest to Build a Modern City*, Stephane Kirkland; *Strange Stones: Dispatches from East to West*, Peter Hessler; *The Afterlife of Emerson Tang*, Paula Champa
Foreign Rights: Andrew Nurnberg Associates Ltd (China, Eastern Europe, Taiwan)
Membership(s): The Authors Guild; PEN International

Collier Associates (L)
37 Marina Gardens Dr, Palm Beach Gardens, FL 33410
Mailing Address: PO Box 20149, West Palm Beach, FL 33416
Tel: 561-514-6548 *Fax:* 561-799-4067
E-mail: dmccabooks@gmail.com
Key Personnel
Owner & Agent: Dianna Collier
Founded: 1976
Fiction & nonfiction adult books. Fiction: war novels, mysteries, true crime, romance, contemporary & historical. Nonfiction: biographies & autobiographies of well-known people, popular works of political subjects & history, exposes, popular works on medical & scientific subjects, finance, popular reference & how-to books, health, beauty & motherhood. Also handle film & TV rights for adult books only with co-agents. No unsol mss, query first with SASE; submit outline, sample chapters & bio; no reading fee for published authors of trade books, may charge fee for full length book mss for unpublished authors; charge cost of copying ms; submission postage; books ordered for subsidiary rights. Co-agents on West Coast & in many foreign countries.
Foreign Rep(s): Big Apple Agency Inc (Taiwan); International Literature Bureau BV (Netherlands); Johnson & Alcock Ltd (British Commonwealth); Mohrbooks AG (Austria, Germany, Switzerland); Tuttle-Mori Agency Inc (Japan); Julio F Yanez Agencia Literaria (Portugal, South America, Spain)
Foreign Rights: Agence Michelle Lapautre (France); Light & Burr (Denmark, Finland, Iceland, Norway, Sweden)
Membership(s): Mystery Writers of America

Frances Collin Literary Agent (L)
PO Box 33, Wayne, PA 19087
E-mail: queries@francescollin.com
Web Site: www.francescollin.com
Key Personnel
Owner: Frances Collin (AAR)
Literary Agent: Sarah Yake *E-mail:* sarah@francescollin.com
Founded: 1948
Successor to Marie Rodell-Frances Collin Literary Agency (1975).
Trade fiction & nonfiction; no original screenplays. Special interest in the following areas: literary fiction, biography, history, travel, environmental, nature, memoir, fantasy/science fiction. No unsol mss, query via e-mail to queries@francescollin.com. Send query letter describing your project (text in the body of the e-mail only, e-mails with unsol attachments will be deleted unread). Handle film & TV rights through sub-agents; representatives in all foreign markets. No fees.

Don Congdon Associates Inc (L)
110 William St, Suite 2202, New York, NY 10038-3914
Tel: 212-645-1229 *Fax:* 212-727-2688
E-mail: dca@doncongdon.com
Web Site: www.doncongdon.com
Key Personnel
Agent: Cristina Concepcion (AAR); Michael Congdon (AAR); Katie Grimm; Katie Kotchman (AAR); Maura Kye-Casella (AAR); Susan Ramer (AAR)
Founded: 1983
Handle any & all trade books. Handle film & TV rights for regular clients. No unsol mss, query first with a one page synopsis of your work & relevant background & SASE or e-mail without attachments. In heading include "Query" & agent's full name. Include a sample chapter in body of e-mail. Now accepting new & professional authors. No reading fee.
Foreign Rep(s): AnatoliaLit Agency; Big Apple Agency Inc (China, Taiwan); Nurichan Kesim Literary Agency Inc; Agence Michelle Lapautre (France); Maxima Creative Agency (Indonesia); Andrew Nurnberg Associates (Eastern Europe, Germany, Russia); Owls Agency Inc (Japan); Read n' Right Agency (Greece); Lennart Sane Agency (Netherlands, Scandi-

navia); Vicki Satlow Literary Agency (Italy); Abner Stein Agency (UK); Tuttle-Mori Agency Inc (Japan); Julio F Yanez (Portugal, Spain); Eric Yang Agency (Korea)

The Doe Coover Agency (L)
PO Box 668, Winchester, MA 01890
Tel: 781-721-6000 *Fax:* 781-721-6727
E-mail: info@doecooveragency.com
Web Site: www.doecooveragency.com
Key Personnel
Pres: Doe Coover
Agent: Colleen Mohyde (AAR)
Assoc: Frances Kennedy
Founded: 1986
Nonfiction & fiction. Specialize in literary fiction, business, history & biography, psychology, science & health, cooking & food writing, gardening, humor, sports & music. No poetry, fantasy, science fiction or screenplays. E-mail queries only; see web site for submission guidelines.
Handle film & TV rights on agency projects only. 15% commission.
Titles recently placed: *Biography of Garry Trudeau*, Steve Weinberg; *Darjeeling: The Colorful History and Precarious Fate of the World's Greatest Tea*, Jeff Koehler; *Jacques Pepin Heart & Soul in the Kitchen*, Jacques Pepin; *Kitchen Gypsy*, Joanne Weir; *Priest of Nature: The Religious Lives of Isaac Newton*, Robert Iliffe; *PTL: The Rise and Fall of Jim and Tammy Faye Bakker's Evangelical Empire*, John Wigger; *Restaurant Martin: Exquisite Cuisine from Santa Fe's Famed Chef*, Martin Rios, Cheryl Jamison, Bill Jamison; *The Bearing Tree*, Karen Fisher; *The Photographer and the President*, Richard Lowry; *The Vermont Country Store Cookbook*, Ellen Ecker Ogden, Andrea Diehl, The Orton Family
Foreign Rights: The English Agency (Japan) Ltd (Japan); The Marsh Agency (Europe); Abner Stein Agency (UK)

CreativeWell Inc (L)
PO Box 3130, Memorial Sta, Upper Montclair, NJ 07043
Tel: 973-783-7575 *Toll Free Tel:* 800-743-9182 *Fax:* 973-783-7530
E-mail: info@creativewell.com
Web Site: www.creativewell.com
Key Personnel
Pres: George M Greenfield *E-mail:* george@creativewell.com
Founded: 2003
Fiction & nonfiction, film & TV rights. No unsol mss. No reading fee; other fees charged (for photocopies, express mail, etc). Representatives in principal foreign countries. Full service lecture representation is also available.

Crichton & Associates Inc (L)
6940 Carroll Ave, Takoma Park, MD 20912
Tel: 301-495-9663
E-mail: cricht1@aol.com
Web Site: www.crichton-associates.com
Key Personnel
Pres: Sha-Shana Crichton
Founded: 2002
For fiction, submit first three chapters with synopsis & bio. For nonfiction, submit proposal with bio. No fees charged. Send queries to query@crichton-associates.com.
Membership(s): Romance Writers of America

Richard Curtis Associates Inc (L)
171 E 74 St, 2nd fl, New York, NY 10021
Tel: 212-772-7363 *Fax:* 212-772-7393
Web Site: www.curtisagency.com
Key Personnel
Pres: Richard Curtis (AAR) *E-mail:* rcurtis@curtisagency.com
Founded: 1979
Commercial fiction/nonfiction. No stage plays or screenplays, short fiction, nonfiction or poetry. Handle film & TV rights. No unsol mss, query first via US mail with SASE. No e-mail or fax queries. No reading fee.
Foreign Rights: Baror International Inc (Worldwide exc USA)
Membership(s): Mystery Writers of America; Romance Writers of America; Science Fiction & Fantasy Writers of America

Darhansoff & Verrill (L)
236 W 26 St, Suite 802, New York, NY 10001-6736
Tel: 917-305-1300 *Fax:* 917-305-1400
E-mail: info@dvagency.com
Web Site: www.dvagency.com
Key Personnel
Agent: Liz Darhansoff; Catherine Luttinger
Agent & Rights Dir: Michele Mortimer
Agent: Chuck Verrill
Off Mgr: Eric Amling
Founded: 1975
Fiction & nonfiction, literary fiction, young adult, memoirs, sophisticated suspense, history, science, biography, pop culture & current affairs. No theatrical plays or film scripts. No unsol mss, query first with SASE or by e-mail via submissions@dvagency.com. Film & TV rights handled by Los Angeles associates, Lynn Pleshette, Richard Green & UTA. Agents in many foreign countries. No fees charged.
Foreign Rights: Alkcali Copyright Agency (Ozgur Emir) (Turkey); Bardon-Chinese Media (Joanne Yang) (China); Eliane Benisti Agency (France); Luigi Bernabo Associates (Italy); The Book Publishers Association of Israel (Dalia Ever Hadani) (Israel); The English Agency (Hamish Macaskill) (Japan); Graal Literary Agency (Maria Strarz-Kanska) (Poland); International Copyrights Agency (Simona Kessler) (Romania); Interrights (Svetlana Stefanova) (Bulgaria); JLM Literarary Angency (John Moukakis) (Greece); Katai & Bolza (Peter Bolza) (Hungary); Licht & Burr (Trine Licht) (Scandinavia); Zvonimir Majdak (Croatia); Mohrbooks (Sebastian Ritscher) (Germany); Andrew Nurnberg Agency (Lumilla Shushkova) (Russia); Andrew Nurnberg Association Baltic (Tatjana Zoldnere) (Latvia); Kristin Olson Literary Agency (Kristin Olson) (Czech Republic); Agencia Riff (Laura Riff & Joao Paulo Riff) (Brazil, Portugal); The Sayle Agency (Rachel Calder) (UK); Sebes & Van Gelderen Agency (Paul Sebes) (Holland); Shin Won Agency (Tae Kim) (Korea); Yanez Agencia Literaria (Montse F Yanez) (Spain)

Liza Dawson Associates (L)
350 Seventh Ave, Suite 2003, New York, NY 10001
Tel: 212-465-9071 *Fax:* 212-947-0460
Web Site: www.lizadawsonassociates.com
Key Personnel
CFO & Agent: Havis Dawson *E-mail:* queryhavis@lizadawsonassociates.com
Pres: Liza Dawson (AAR) *E-mail:* queryliza@lizadawsonassociates.com
Literary Agent: Caitlin Blasdell *E-mail:* querycaitlin@lizadawsonassociates.com; Hannah Bowman *E-mail:* queryhannah@lizadawsonassociates.com
Literary Asst: Judith Engracia *E-mail:* queryjudith@lizadawsonassociates.com
Asst Agent: Caitie Flum
Founded: 1996
Liza Dawson: Fiction, both literary & commercial. Nonfiction: strong narratives, history, psychology, memoirs, parenting & business books. No poetry, westerns or children's books.
Caitlin Blasdell: science fiction, fantasy, romance, women's fiction & young adult.
Havis Dawson: practical nonfiction, business, spiritual, thrillers & southern fiction.
No unsol mss. Send query letter first with SASE. No reading fee. Agents in Hollywood & all foreign countries.
Foreign Rights: Akcali Copyright Agency (Atilla Izgi Turgut) (Turkey); Eliane Benisti Agency (Leon de la Menadiere, sci-fi/fantasy only) (France); Graal Literary Agency (Marcin Biegaj) (Albania, Baltic States, Bulgaria, Greece, Hungary, Iceland, Macedonia, Poland, Romania, Serbia, Slovenia); The Grayhawk Agency (Gray Tan) (China, Taiwan, Thailand, Vietnam); Danny Hong Agency (Danny Hong) (Korea); Alexander Korzhenevski Agency (Alexander Korzhenevski) (Russia); Piergiorgio Nicollazzini Agency (Maura Solinas, sci-fi/fantasy only) (Italy); Kristin Olson Literary Agency (Kristin Olson) (Czech Republic); Thomas Schlueck GmbH (Bastian Schlueck, sci-fi/fantasy only) (Germany); Tuttle-Mori Agency Inc (Misa Morikawa, fiction; Manami Tamaoki, nonfiction) (Japan)
Membership(s): Women's Media Group

J de S Associates Inc (L)
9 Shagbark Rd, South Norwalk, CT 06854
Tel: 203-838-7571 *Fax:* 203-866-2713
Web Site: www.jdesassociates.com
Key Personnel
Pres: Jacques de Spoelberch *E-mail:* jdespoel@aol.com
Founded: 1975
Fiction & nonfiction. No unsol mss, query first. Send outline & two sample chapters; no reading fee. Agents & film representatives in major foreign countries.

The Jennifer DeChiara Literary Agency (L)
31 E 32 St, Suite 300, New York, NY 10016
Tel: 212-481-8484 (ext 362) *Fax:* 212-481-9582
Web Site: www.jdlit.com
Key Personnel
Owner, Pres & Agent: Jennifer DeChiara *E-mail:* jenndec@aol.com
Agent: Stephen Fraser *E-mail:* fraserstephena@gmail.com
Assoc Agent: Linda Epstein *E-mail:* linda.p.epstein@gmail.com; Marie Lamba *E-mail:* marie.jdlit@gmail.com; Victoria Selvaggio *E-mail:* vselvaggio@windstream.nt; Roseanne Wells *E-mail:* roseannelitagent@gmail.com
Film/TV Agent: Kimberly Guidone
Foreign Rts Agent: Betty Anne Crawford
Founded: 2001
Accepting queries in the following areas: children's books for every age (picture books, middle-grade & young adult), adult fiction & nonfiction in a wide range of genres. Accept e-mail queries only, with "Query" in the subject line; no attachments. Co-agents in every country. No fees.
Titles recently placed: *A Memoir*, Danny Aiello; *Annika Riz, Math Whiz*, Claudia Mills; *Bees In The Trees*, Ruth Horowitz; *Bizz and Buzz Make Honeybuns*, Dee Leone; *Eliza Bing Is (Not) A Big, Fat Quitter*, Carmella Van Vleet; *Fannie Never Flinches*, Mary Cronk Farrell; *Guts For Glory*, JoAnna Lapati; *Izzy Barr, Running Star*, Claudia Mills; *Luke Veracruz Saves The Day*, Jeff Anderson; *Not Young, Still Restless: My Life So Far*, Jeanne Cooper; *Omega Days*, John L Campbell; *Openly Straight*, Bill Konigsberg; *Peanut Butter and Brains*, Joe McGee; *Quack*, Jennifer Hamburg; *Sitting Next to Jesus*, Carol Lynch Williams; *Stuck In My Sister's Fat*, Carol Lynch Williams; *The Ed Lucas Story*, Ed Lucas, Christopher Lucas; *The Hole Story of the Doughnut*, Pat Miller; *The Jumbie Seed*, Tracey Baptiste; *The Nora Notebooks*, Claudia Mills; *The One-Way Bridge*, Cathie Pelletier; *The Porcupine of Truth*, Bill

Konigsberg; *The Quantum League*, Matthew Kirby; *The Summer Experiment*, Cathie Pelletier; *The Write-Brain Workbook (10th anniversary ed)*, Bonnie Neubauer; *The Year After Henry*, Cathie Pelletier; *To The Stars! The Story of Kathy Sullivan, First American Woman to Walk in Space*, Carmella Van Vleet, Kathy Sullivan; *Waggers*, Stacy A Nyikos; *Whistle Root*, Christopher Pennell

DeFiore and Company, LLC (L)
47 E 19 St, 3rd fl, New York, NY 10003
Tel: 212-925-7744 *Fax:* 212-925-9803
E-mail: submissions@defioreandco.com; info@defioreandco.com
Web Site: www.defioreandco.com
Key Personnel
Founder & Pres: Brian DeFiore (AAR) *E-mail:* querybrian@defioreandco.com
Dir, Busn Aff: Adam Schear *E-mail:* ajs@defioreandco.com
Dir, Foreign Rts: Linda Kaplan
Literary Agent: Laurie Abkemeier (AAR) *E-mail:* LMA@defioreandco.com; Debra Goldstein
Literary Agent & UK Rts Dir: Meredith Kaffel (AAR) *E-mail:* meredith@defioreandco.com
Literary Agent: Matthew Elblonk *E-mail:* matthew@defioreandco.com; Lisa Gallagher; Caryn Karmatz Rudy (AAR) *E-mail:* ckr@defioreandco.com; Rebecca Strauss *E-mail:* Rebecca@defioreandco.com
Founded: 1999
Handles mainstream fiction, suspense fiction, business, self-help, narrative nonfiction, cook books & memoirs.
Titles recently placed: *If You Were Here*, Jen Lancaster; *So Good They Can't Ignore You*, Cal Newport; *The 21-Day Weight Loss Kick Start*, Neal Barnard; *The Evolution of Bruno Littlemore*, Benjamin Hale; *The Fame Game*, Lauren Conrad; *When Parents Text*, Lauren Kaelin, Sophia Fraioli; *Wine to Water*, Doc Hendley
Foreign Rep(s): Gillon Aitken Associates (UK); Andrew Nurnberg Associates
Foreign Rights: The Book Publishers Association of Israel (Delia Ever Hadani) (Israel); JLM Literary Agency (John Moukakos) (Greece); Kayi Agency (Dilek Kayi) (Turkey); Andrew Nurnberg Associates (Sabine Pfannenstiel, London) (Germany); Andrew Nurnberg Associates (Claire Anouchian, London) (France, Quebec, CN); Andrew Nurnberg Associates (Lucy Flynn) (Latin America exc Brazil, Portugal, Spain); Andrew Nurnberg Associates (Barbara Barbieri) (Brazil, Italy); Andrew Nurnberg Associates (Marei Pittner, London) (Netherlands, Scandinavia); Andrew Nurnberg Associates (Anna & Mira Droumeva, Sofia) (Bulgaria, Romania, Serbia); Andrew Nurnberg Associates (Petra Tobiskova & Jana Borovanova, Prague) (Czech Republic, Slovakia, Slovenia); Andrew Nurnberg Associates (Aleksandra Lapinska & Renata Paczewska, Warsaw) (Poland); Andrew Nurnberg Associates (Judit Hermann, Budapest) (Croatia, Hungary); Andrew Nurnberg Associates (Ludmilla Sushkova, Moscow) (Russia); Andrew Nurnberg Associates (Tatjana Zoldnere, Latvia) (Estonia, Latvia, Lithuania, Ukraine); Andrew Nurnberg Associates (Jackie Huang, Beijing) (China); Andrew Nurnberg Associates (Whitney Hsu, Taipei) (Taiwan); Tuttle-Mori Agency Inc (Ken Mori & Manami Tamaoki) (Japan); Tuttle-Mori Agency Inc (Thananchai Pandey, Bangkok) (Thailand); Eric Yang Agency (Henry Shin) (Korea)

Joelle Delbourgo Associates Inc (L)
101 Park St, Montclair, NJ 07042
Tel: 973-773-0836 (call only during standard business hours)
Web Site: www.delbourgo.com
Key Personnel
Founder & Pres, Agent & Consultant: Joelle Delbourgo (AAR) *E-mail:* joelle@delbourgo.com
Assoc Agent & Ed: Carrie Cantor *Tel:* 973-783-1005 *E-mail:* cantor.carrie@gmail.com
Ed: John Paine *E-mail:* jpaine@johnpaine.com; Fran Schumer *E-mail:* frannyrs2@gmail.com
Publicity Consultant: Jennifer Prost *E-mail:* jennifer@delbourgo.com
Agent: Jacquie Flynn *Tel:* 973-783-6800 ext 3 *E-mail:* jacquie@delbourgo.com
Founded: 2000
Boutique firm handling a wide range of adult fiction (literary & commercial) & nonfiction (narrative, prescriptive, reference). YA & middle grade fiction. E-mail queries only accepted, but check submission guidelines on web site. Materials will not be returned.
Titles recently placed: *A World of Trouble*, Ben H Winters; *American Pain*, John Temple; *Asking for It: The Culture of Rape*, Kate Harding; *Be Nobody*, Lama Marut; *College Revalued*, Kristin White; *Fighting for Love*, Judith Wright, PhD, Bob Wright, PhD; *Game On (Bod Squad Series)*, Gabra Zackman; *Pretty in Ink*, Lindsey J Palmer; *Promise Bound*, Anne Greenwood Brown; *Searching for Sappho*, Philip Freeman; *St Brigid's Bones*, Philip Freeman; *Stress-Free Parenting*, Sara Au, Peter Stavinoha; *Teach a Woman to Fish*, Ritu Sharma; *The French Cook: Soups and Stews*, Holly Herrick; *The Friendship Lab*, Rob Garfield; *The Innovator's Path*, Madge M Meyer; *The Lost Gospel*, Simcha Jacobovici, Barrie Wilson; *The Unofficial Guide to "Girls"*, Judy Gelman, Peter Zheutlin; *The Winged Herds of Anok*, Jennifer Alvarez; *Then Came Life*, Geralyn Lucas
Foreign Rights: Duran Kim Agency (Korea); Maxima Agency (Indonesia); Jenny Meyer Literary Agency (Worldwide exc Asia); Andrew Nurnberg Associates Inc (China); Owls Agency Inc (Japan)
Membership(s): Women's Media Group

D4EO Literary Agency (L-D)
7 Indian Valley Rd, Weston, CT 06883
Tel: 203-544-7180 *Fax:* 203-544-7160
Web Site: www.d4eoliteraryagency.com
Key Personnel
Principal: Robert (Bob) G Diforio *E-mail:* bob@d4eo.com
Agent (literary fiction, historical fiction, mystery, select YA): Samantha Dighton *E-mail:* samantha@d4eo.com
Agent (mysteries, thrillers, romance & nonfiction): Joyce Holland *E-mail:* joyce@d4eo.com
Agent (YA & middle grade): Mandy Hubbard *E-mail:* mandy@d4eo.com
Agent (picture books, middle grade & YA): Kristin Miller-Vincent *E-mail:* kristin@d4eo.com
Agent (genre fiction, middle grade, YA & new adult fiction): Pam van Hylckama Vlieg
Founded: 1989
Represent trade books of all types, fiction, nonfiction, business. Visit www.d4eoliteraryagency.com to see each agent's preferred method of submission. Only Bob Diforio is at the Weston, CT address. All agents prefer e-mail submissions.
Titles recently placed: *Echoes of My Soul*, Robert K Tanenbaum; *If You find Me*, Emily Murdoch; *Linked*, Imogene Howson; *Mirage*, Jack DuBrul, Clive Cussler; *Targets of Revenge*, Jeffrey S Stephens; *The Pandora Society*, Joy Hensley
Foreign Rep(s): Eliane Benisti (France)

Sandra Dijkstra Literary Agency (L)
1155 Camino del Mar, PMB 515, Del Mar, CA 92014-2605
E-mail: queries@dijkstraagency.com
Web Site: dijkstraagency.com
Key Personnel
Pres & Agent: Sandra Dijkstra (AAR)
Agency Mgr & Agent: Elise Capron (AAR) *Tel:* 858-755-3115 ext 100 *E-mail:* elise@dijkstraagency.com
Fin & Agent: Thao Le (AAR) *Tel:* 858-755-3115 ext 106 *E-mail:* thao@dijkstraagency.com
Agent: Roz Foster (AAR) *E-mail:* roz@dijkstraagency.com; Jill Marr (AAR) *Tel:* 858-755-3115 ext 108 *E-mail:* jmsubmissions@dijkstraagency.com
Asst & Agent: Jessica Watterson (AAR) *Tel:* 858-755-3115 ext 101 *E-mail:* jessica@dijkstraagency.com
Founded: 1981
Fiction: contemporary, women's, literary, suspense, thrillers, science-fiction & fantasy. Nonfiction: narrative, history, business, psychology, self-help, science & memoir/biography. Works in conjunction with foreign & film agents. E-mail submissions only. See web site for most up-to-date guidelines. No reading fee.
Foreign Rights: Bardon-Chinese Media Agency (China, Taiwan); Bernabo Associates (Italy); Sandra Bruna Agencia Literaria (Portugal, Spain); The English Agency (Japan) Ltd (Japan); Graal Literary Agency (Poland); Agence Hoffman (Germany); Katai & Bolza (Hungary); Licht & Burr (Scandinavia); Maxima Creative Agency (Indonesia); La Nouvelle Agence (France); Onk Agency (Turkey); Prava I Prevodi (Eastern Europe); Sebes & Van Gelderen Literary Agency (Netherlands); Abner Stein Agency (UK); Synopsis Agency (Baltic States, Russia); TBPAI (Israel); Tuttle-Mori Agency Inc (Thailand); Eric Yang Agency (Korea)
Membership(s): The Authors Guild

Donadio & Olson Inc (L-D)
121 W 27 St, Suite 704, New York, NY 10001
Tel: 212-691-8077 *Fax:* 212-633-2837
E-mail: mail@donadio.com
Web Site: donadio.com
Key Personnel
Agent: Edward Hibbert; E Carrie Howland *E-mail:* carrie@donadio.com; Neil Olson (AAR)
Founded: 1969
Fiction, nonfiction & young adult. Handle film & TV rights for clients. No fees.
Foreign Rights: AnatoliaLit Agency (Amy Spangler) (Turkey); Agence Eliane Benisti (Noemie Rollet) (France); Luigi Bernabo Associates SRL (Luigi Bernabo) (Italy); Big Apple Agency Inc (Luc Kwanten) (China, Thailand); Paul & Peter Fritz AG (Christian Dittus) (Germany); The Deborah Harris Agency (Efrat Lev) (Israel); Japan Uni Agency (Miko Yamanouchi) (Japan); JLM Literary Agency (John Moukakos) (Greece); Korea Copyright Center (KCC) (Misun Kwon) (Korea); Licht & Burr (Trine Licht) (Denmark, Finland, Iceland, Norway, Sweden); MB Agencia Literaria (Monica Martin) (Catalonia, Portugal, Spain); Andrew Nurnberg Associates (Mira Droumeva, Sofia) (Albania, Macedonia, Romania, Serbia); Andrew Nurnberg Associates (Judit Hermann) (Croatia, Hungary); Andrew Nurnberg Associates (Aleksandra Matuszak, Warsaw) (Poland); Andrew Nurnberg Associates (Ludmilla Sushkova) (Russia); Andrew Nurnberg Associates (Tatjana Zoldnere, Baltic) (Estonia, Latvia, Lithuania, Ukraine); Andrew Nurnberg Associates (Petra Tobiskova, Prague) (Czech Republic); The Riff Agency (Laura Riff) (Brazil); Marianne Schoenbach Literary Agency (Marianne Schoenbach) (Netherlands)

Janis A Donnaud & Associates Inc (L-D)
525 Broadway, 2nd fl, New York, NY 10012
Tel: 212-431-2663 *Fax:* 212-431-2667

E-mail: jdonnaud@aol.com
Key Personnel
Pres: Janis A Donnaud (AAR)
Founded: 1993
Nonfiction by experts in their fields: narrative nonfiction; healthcare & medicine; humor; cookbooks; women's issues; pop psychology, memoir; pop culture; Belle lettres & etymology. No unsol mss, query first; if requested, submit outline & sample chapters & curriculum vitae, with SASE with return postage or by e-mail, if return requested. No fiction. Handle film & TV rights. No phone calls. No reading fee.
Titles recently placed: *Jamie Deen at the Family Table*, Jamie Deen; *One Doctor*, Brendan Reilly, MD; *Oxford Companion to Spirits and Cocktails*, David Wondrich; *Real Korean Cooking*, Maangchi; *Yo Cuz!*, Steve Martorano
Foreign Rep(s): Abner Stein Agency (Worldwide)
Membership(s): The Authors Guild

Jim Donovan Literary (L)
5635 SMU Blvd, Suite 201, Dallas, TX 75206
Tel: 214-696-9411
E-mail: jdlqueries@sbcglobal.net
Key Personnel
Owner & Pres: Jim Donovan
Agent: Melissa Shultz
Founded: 1993
Literary & commercial fiction & nonfiction, especially biography, health, history, popular culture & sports. No poetry, short stories or children's. Accept unsol mss only with SASE. For nonfiction, query first with letter & SASE. For fiction, submit first 30-40 pages & synopsis with SASE. May query with e-mail, no attachments, response only if interested. No online submissions accepted. Handle film & TV rights for clients only. Agents in Hollywood & major foreign countries. No fees, 15% commission on monies earned.
Titles recently placed: *Below*, Ryan Lockwood; *Give Me a Fast Ship*, Tim Mc Grath; *Honor in the Dust*, Gregg Jones; *Manson*, Jeff Guinn; *The Lords of Apacheria*, Paul Andrew Hutton

Doyen Literary Services Inc (L)
1931 660 St, Newell, IA 50568
Web Site: www.barbaradoyen.com
Key Personnel
Pres: Barb J Doyen
Founded: 1988
Handles all types of trade nonfiction for adults; authors available to fill editorial needs in most topics. Specialize in business, health, fitness, how-to, psychology, self-improvement, cookbooks, narrative nonfiction, biography & memoir & many more. No fees charged. Query via e-mail only, submit through web site. No snail mail.
Titles recently placed: *Eating Clean for Dummies*, Jonathan Wright MD, Linda Larsen; *The Beginner's Guide to Growing Heirloom Vegetables*, Marie Iannotti

Drennan Literary Agency (L)
6 Robin Lane, East Kingston, NH 03827
Tel: 603-642-8002 *Fax:* 603-642-8002
Key Personnel
Pres: William D Drennan
Contact: Christina L Drennan
Founded: 1980
Scholarly only. No unsol mss, query first with outline & SASE. No reading fee.

Dunham Literary Inc (L)
110 William St, Suite 2202, New York, NY 10038
Tel: 212-929-0994
Web Site: dunhamlit.com
Key Personnel
Agent: Bridget Smith (AAR)
Founded: 2000
Literary fiction & nonfiction, children's book writers & illustrators. No plays or screenplays. Handle film & TV rights for books represented. No unsol mss, query letter first with SASE. No fax or e-mail queries. No reading fee.
Foreign Rights: Big Apple Agency Inc (China); A M Heath (Europe, UK); Shin-Won (Korea); Tuttle-Mori Agency Inc (Japan)
Membership(s): Society of Children's Book Writers & Illustrators

Dunow, Carlson & Lerner Literary Agency Inc (L)
27 W 20 St, Suite 1107, New York, NY 10011
Tel: 212-645-7606
E-mail: mail@dclagency.com
Web Site: www.dclagency.com
Key Personnel
Literary Agent: Jennifer Carlson (AAR); Henry Dunow (AAR); Erin Hosier; Amy Hughes; Eleanor Jackson; Julia Kenny; Betsy Lerner; Edward Necarsulmer, IV; Yishai Seidman
Founded: 2005
Query first, fiction & nonfiction. Handle film & TV rights. Agents in all foreign territories. Submit outlines & sample chapters with SASE. No reading fee.
Foreign Rights: Akcali Copyright Agency (Turkey); Big Apple Agency Inc (China, Taiwan); The English Agency (Japan); Grayhawk Agency (China, Taiwan); The Deborah Harris Agency (Israel); David Higham Associates (UK); JLM Literary Agency (Greece); Andrew Nurnberg Associates (Eastern Europe, Europe, Russia, South America); Owl Agency (Japan); Abner Stein Agency (UK); Tuttle-Mori Agency Inc (Japan); Eric Yang (Korea)

Dupree, Miller & Associates Inc (L)
100 Highland Park Village, Suite 350, Dallas, TX 75205
Tel: 214-559-2665 *Fax:* 214-559-7243
E-mail: editorial@dupreemiller.com
Web Site: www.dupreemiller.com
Key Personnel
Pres: Jan Miller *E-mail:* jmr@dupreemiller.com
EVP: Shannon Marven
Agent: Nena Madonia
Fiction & nonfiction. No children's, science fiction, fantasy, horror, short stories, poetry or screenplays. No unsol mss; accept query letter only, with SASE enclosed for reply. No fees. Market & promote own books both regionally & nationally.

Dystel & Goderich Literary Management (L-D)
One Union Sq W, Suite 904, New York, NY 10003
Tel: 212-627-9100 *Fax:* 212-627-9313
Web Site: www.dystel.com
Key Personnel
Pres & Partner: Jane Dystel (AAR)
Agent & Partner: Miriam Goderich *E-mail:* miriam@dystel.com
VP & Agent: Stacey Kendall Glick (AAR) *E-mail:* sglick@dystel.com
Subs Rts Dir & Agent: Lauren E Abramo *E-mail:* labramo@dystel.com
Proj Mgr, Ebook Prog & Agent: Sharon Pelletier *E-mail:* spelletier@dystel.com
Royalties Mgr & Agent: Michael Hoogland *E-mail:* mhoogland@dystel.com
Sr Agent: Jim McCarthy (AAR) *E-mail:* jmccarthy@dystel.com
Agent: Michael Bourret (AAR) *E-mail:* mbourret@dystel.com; Eric Myers; Jessica Papin *E-mail:* jpapin@dystel.com; John Rudolph *E-mail:* jrudolph@dystel.com; Rachel Stout *E-mail:* rstout@dystel.com
Asst: Erin Young
Founded: 1994 (as Jane Dystel Literary Management)
General fiction & nonfiction, also cookbooks & children's books. No unsol mss, query letter or e-mail query with outline & first 50 pages. No reading fee. Handle film & TV rights. Firm also has a west coast office staffed by Michael Bourret (e-mail queries only).
Titles recently placed: *A Serving of Scandal*, Prue Leith; *All In*, Raine Miller; *An American Bride in Kabul*, Phyllis Chesler; *Autumn Bones*, Jacqueline Carey; *Because of Low*, Abbi Glines; *Bootstrapper*, Mardi Jo Link; *Brianna on the Brink*, Nicole McInnes; *Country Roads*, Nancy Herkness; *Covet*, Tracey Garvis Graves; *Crush*, Nicole Williams; *Dandelion Hunter*, Rebecca Lerner; *Darwen Arkwright and the Insidious Bleck*, A J Hartley; *Darwen Arkwright and the Peregrine Pact*, A J Hartley; *Doctor Who*, Richelle Mead; *Fall for Me*, Sydney Landon; *Fiance by Friday*, Catherine Bybee; *First Class*, Allison Stewart; *Flour, Too*, Joanne Chang; *Gameboard of the Gods*, Richelle Mead; *Hothouse*, Boris Kachka; *How to Write Short*, Roy Peter Clark; *If I Should Die*, Amy Plum; *Indian Cooking Unfolded*, Raghavan Iyer; *Just For Now*, Abbi Glines; *Just Like Fate*, Suzanne Young, Cat Patrick; *Keep Your Eye on the Marshmallow*, Joachim de Posada, Bob Andelman; *Long Journey with Mr Jefferson*, William G Hyland, Jr; *Losing Hope*, Colleen Hoover; *Married by Monday*, Catherine Bybee; *Murder as a Fine Art*, David Morrell; *Naked*, Raine Miller; *Never Kiss a Rake*, Anne Stuart; *Not Planning On You*, Sydney Landon; *Not Quite Mine*, Catherine Bybee; *Small Changes, Big Results*, Ellie Krieger; *Tainted Angel*, Anne Cleeland; *Tap the Magic Tree*, Christie Matheson; *That's That*, Colin Broderick; *The Courage to Hope*, Shirley Sherrod; *The Dinnertime Survival Cookbook*, Debra Ponzek; *The Edge of Never*, J A Redmerski; *The Game Changer*, J Sterling; *The Prince of Paradise*, John Glatt; *The Program*, Suzanne Young; *The Real Skinny*, Katherine Brooking, Julie Upton; *The Sisterhood*, Helen Bryan; *Toms River*, Dan Fagin; *Weekends Required*, Sydney Landon; *What Would Brian Boitano Make?*, Brian Boitano; *While It Lasts*, Abbi Glines; *Wife by Wednesday*, Catherine Bybee; *Work Happy: What Great Bosses Know*, Jill Geisler; *Writers Rehab*, D B Gilles; *Yogalosophy*, Mandy Ingber
Foreign Rep(s): Ali (Italy); ANAW (Poland); Eliane Benisti (France); Big Apple Agency Inc (China); EAJ (Japan); International Editors' Co (Latin America, Spain); Kayi Literary (Turkey); Mohrbooks (Germany); Andrew Nurnberg (Eastern Europe); Read 'n' Right (Greece); Agencia Riff (Brazil); Sebes & Van Gelderen (Netherlands); Abner Stein Agency (UK); TBPAI (Israel); Ulf Toregard Agency (Scandinavia); Tuttle-Mori Agency Inc (Thailand); Eric Yang Agency (Korea)

Anne Edelstein Literary Agency LLC (L)
404 Riverside Dr, New York, NY 10025
Tel: 212-414-4923
E-mail: info@aeliterary.com; rights@aeliterary.com
Web Site: www.aeliterary.com
Key Personnel
Pres: Anne Edelstein (AAR)
Literary Agent & Rts Contact: Krista Ingebretson
Founded: 1990
Literary fiction & narrative nonfiction (including memoir, history, psychology, religion & culinary); handle film & TV rights; agents in all principal foreign countries.

No unsol mss, e-mail query first with outline & sample chapters. Include 25 pages (fiction) or proposal (nonfiction) in body of e-mail. If we are interested in seeing more, we will respond within 4 weeks. Because of the high number of submissions we receive, we cannot guarantee a response to those queries in which we are not interested. No phone queries or hard copies accepted. See web site for guideline details. No reading fee.
Foreign Rights: Akcali Copyright Agency (Turkey); AM Heath (Victoria Hobbs) (UK); L'Autre Agence (Corinne Marotte) (France); Silvia Bastos Agencia Literaria SL (Pau Centellas) (Spain); Luigi Bernabo Associates (Italy); Petra Eggers Agency (Petra Eggers) (Germany); The English Agency (Japan); The Grayhawk Agency (China, Taiwan); The Harris Agency (Efrat Lev) (Israel); Danny Hong Agency (Danny Hong) (Korea); Prava I Prevodi (Eastern Europe); The Riff Agency (Brazil); Marianne Schoenbach Literary Agency (Marianne Schoenbach) (Holland); Ulf Toregard Agency (Ulf Toregard) (Scandinavia); The Van Lear Agency (Russia)
Membership(s): The Authors Guild

Educational Design Services LLC (L)
5750 Bou Ave, Suite 1508, North Bethesda, MD 20852
Tel: 301-881-8611
Web Site: www.educationaldesignservices.com
Key Personnel
Pres: Bertram L Linder *E-mail:* blinder@educationaldesignservices.com
Founded: 1981
Materials for the el-hi & professional education market. Accept unsol mss with SASE, prefer query by e-submission first. Submit outline & sample chapter. No reading fee.
Titles recently placed: *Better Writing*, Travis Koll; *Bully Nation*, Susan Eva Porter; *Fire Up Your Life in Retirement*, Catherine DePino; *Individualized Learning With Technology*, Chris Bernat, Richard J Mueller; *Making a Difference in the Classroom*, Charlese E Brown; *Standardized Testing Skills*, Guinevere Durham; *Success in Schools*, Susan Andres, Felicity Pines; *The Teachers' Lounge (Uncensored)*, Kelly Flynn

The Lisa Ekus Group LLC (L)
57 North St, Hatfield, MA 01038
Tel: 413-247-9325 *Fax:* 413-247-9873
E-mail: lisaekus@lisaekus.com
Web Site: lisaekus.com
Key Personnel
Principal & Pres: Lisa Ekus (AAR)
E-mail: lisaekus@lisaekus.com
Mgr: Sally Ekus
Founded: 1982
Since our inception in 1982, we have been helping both new & established authors & chefs make their mark on the culinary landscape. All of our nationally recognized culinary promotions are built on the same foundation: to create innovative strategies, pay meticulous attention to client needs & effectively & productively network across the culinary, media & publishing industries.
In 2000 we expanded our award-winning expertise to include author representation & literary agent services. Within 8 years, our literary agency has facilitated more than 150 book deals, representing over 90 authors & numerous leading publishers internationally.
We also offer comprehensive media training programs designed for authors, chefs, spokespeople, show hosts & food professionals & orchestrate creative partnerships between individuals & corporations in the culinary industry. Specialty areas include: food, nutrition, health & wine & spirit.
Accept unsol mss. Submissions should be in the form of a complete proposal & we provide detailed guidelines on our web site. No fees, clients are billed for expenses.
Titles recently placed: *125 Gluten-Free Vegetarian Recipes*, Carol Fenster PhD; *150 Best Donut Recipes*, George Geary; *150 Best Grilled Cheese Sandwiches*, Alison Lewis; *175 Best Babycakes*, Kathy Moore, Roxanne Wyss; *175 Best Babycakes Cupcake Maker Recipes*, Kathy Moore, Roxanne Wyss; *200 Mexican Recipes*, Kelley Cleary Coffeen; *300 Best Rice Cooker Recipes*, Katie Chin; *300 Sensational Soups*, Carla Snyder, Meredith Deeds; *A Spoonful of Promises*, T Susan Chang; *As American as Shoofly Pie*, William Woys Weaver; *Bake and Destroy: Good Food for Bad Vegans*, Natalie Slater; *Basic to Brillant, Y'all*, Virginia Willis; *Big Ranch, Big City*, Lou Lambert, June Naylor; *Bountiful Baby Purees*, Anni Daulter; *Championship BBQ Secrets for Real Smoked Food*, Karen Putnam, Judith Fertig; *Clean Eating for Busy Families*, Michelle Dudash, R.D.; *Come In, We're Closed*, Christine Carroll, Jody Eddy; *Cooking For Your Gluten-Free Teen*, Carlyn Berghoff, Sarah Berghoff McClure, Dr. Susanne P Nelson, Nancy Ross Ryan; *Easy Indian Cooking (second edition)*, Suneeta Vaswani; *Edible Brooklyn: The Cookbook*, Rachel Wharton; *Edible Dallas & Fort Worth*, Terri Taylor; *Farm Fresh Tennessee*, Paul Knipple, Angela Knipple; *Fire in My Belly*, Kevin Gillespie, David Joachim; *Gluten-Free Baking for the Holidays*, Jeanne Sauvage; *Gluten-Free Makeovers*, Beth Hillson; *Great Gluten-Free Vegan Eats from Around the World: Fantastic, Allergy-Free Ethnic Recipes*, Allyson Kramer; *Homemade Soda*, Andrew Schloss; *I Love Cinnamon Rolls!*, Judith Fertig; *Man Bites Dog*, Bruce Kraig, Patty Carroll; *My Kitchen Cure: How I Cooked My Way Out of Chronic Autoimmune Disease and Prevented Cancer with Whole Foods and Healing Recipes*, Mee Tracy McCormick; *Piece of Cake!*, Camilla V Saulsbury; *Pink Princess Party Cookbook*, Barbara Beery; *Pop-Out-and-Paint Horse Breeds*, Cindy A Littlefield; *Pretzel Making at Home*, Andrea Slonecker; *Put 'em Up! Fruit: A Preserving Guide & Cookbook*, Sherri Brooks Vinton; *Raising the Bar: The Future of Fine Chocolate*, Pam Williams, Jim Eber; *Roots The Definitive Compendium with More Than 225 Recipes*, Diane Morgan; *Rustic Italian Food*, Marc Vetri, Dave Joachim; *Salt Block Cooking: 70 Recipes for Grilling, Chilling, Searing, and Serving on Himalyan Salt Blocks*, Mark Bitterman; *Sunday Roasts*, Betty Rosbottom; *The Art of Beef Cutting*, Kari Underly; *The Back in the Swing Cookbook*, Barbara C Unell, Judith Fertig; *The Big Book of Babycakes Cake Pop Maker Recipes*, Kathy Moore, Roxanne Wyss; *The Big Book of Babycakes Cupcake Maker Recipes*, Kathy Moore, Roxanne Wyss; *The Complete Baking Cookbook*, George Geary; *The Dead Celebrity Cookbook Presents Christmas in Tinseltown: Celebrity Recipes and Hollywood Memories from Six Feet Under the Mistletoe*, Frank DeCaro; *The Dead Celebrity Cookbook: A Resurrection of Recipes from More Than 145 Stars of Stage and Screen*, Frank DeCaro; *The Fresh Honey Cookbook: 84 Recipes from a Beekeeper's Kitchen*, Laurey Masterton; *The Great Vegan Bean Book: More than 100 Delicious Plant-Based Dishes Packed with the Kindest Protein in Town! – Includes Soy-Free and Gluten-Free Recipes!*, Kathy Hester; *The Grown-Up Lunch Box*, Joy Manning; *The I Love Trader Joe's Around the World Cookbook*, Cherie Mercer Twohy; *The Karma Chow Ultimate Cookbook*, Melissa Costello; *The Meat Lover's Meatless Celebrations*, Kim O'Donnel; *The New Southern-Latino Table*, Sandra A Gutierrez; *The Paleo Summer Survival Guide: 12 Must-Have Recipes Plus Insider Tips for a Healthy, Happy Summer*, Charles Mayfield, Julie Mayfield; *The Tailgater's Cookbook*, David Joachim; *The Vetri Cookbook*, Marc Vetri, Dave Joachim, Jeff Benjamin; *Top 100 Step-by-Step Napkin Folds*, Denise Vivaldo; *Triple Slow Cooker Entertaining*, Kathy Moore, Roxanne Wyss; *Vegan Diner*, Julie Hasson; *Vegan Holiday Kitchen*, Nava Atlas; *Wicked Good Burgers*, Andy Husbands, Andrea Pyenson, Chris Hart; *Wild About Greens*, Nava Atlas; *Williams-Sonoma Rustic Italian*, Domenica Marchetti
Foreign Rights: The Jean V Naggar Literary Agency
Membership(s): International Association of Culinary Professionals; Women Presidents' Organization

Ethan Ellenberg Literary Agency (L)
548 Broadway, Suite 5-E, New York, NY 10012
Tel: 212-431-4554
E-mail: agent@ethanellenberg.com
Web Site: www.ethanellenberg.com
Key Personnel
Pres & Agent: Ethan Ellenberg (AAR)
Agent: Evan Gregory (AAR)
Off Mgr & Subs Rts Assoc: BiBi Lewis
Founded: 1984
Commercial & literary fiction & nonfiction. Fiction: specialize in science fiction, fantasy, romance & all women's fiction, suspense, thriller, mystery, first novels, all children's books including new adult & middle grade. Nonfiction: narrative nonfiction, history, adventure, science. Acceping new clients, both published & unpublished. No reading fees; accept unsol submissions with SASE. E-mail submissions without attachments accepted, but prefer submissions by mail. For fiction: first 3 chapters, synopsis & SASE. For nonfiction: proposal, including outline & author bio, sample chapters, if available. Co-agents in Hollywood & all principal foreign countries.
Titles recently placed: *Bite Me*, Shelly Laurenston; *Bulldozer's Birthday*, Candace Fleming, Erich Rohmann (illus); *Corsair*, James Cambias; *Dark Digital Sky*, Carac Allison; *Dark Matter*, Ian Douglas; *Frozen Solid*, James M Tabor; *Lock In*, John Scalzi; *Love in the Age of Mechanical Production*, Judd Trichter; *Luciana*, Bertrice Small; *Master Sargeant of Macaum*, Mel Odom; *Never Surrender*, Lindsay McKenna; *Night's Surrender*, Amanda Ashley; *Queen of the Deep*, Kay Kenyon; *Reign of Ashes*, Gail Martin; *Stone Cold Lover*, Christine Warren; *Terms of Enlistment*, Marko Kloos; *The Falcon Throne*, Karen Miller; *The Northern Fire Series, Book 1: Wild Heat*, Lucy Monroe; *The Northern Fire Series, Book 2: Hot Night*, Lucy Monroe; *The Northern Fire Series, Book 3: Flash Point*, Lucy Monroe; *The Turning Circle*, Sharon Shinn; *To Tame a Wilde*, Kim Terry; *Undead and Unwary*, MaryJanice Davidson; *What We Hide*, Marthe Jocelyn
Foreign Rights: The Agency (Thomas Schlueck) (Germany); Eliane Benisti (France); Berla & Griffini (Italy); Big Apple Agency (China); Book Publishers Association of Israel (Israel); BookCosmos Agency (Korea); The English Agency (Japan); Alexander Korzhenevski Agency (Russia); Mo Literary Agency (Holland); Prava I Prevodi (Eastern Europe); RDC Agencia Literaria SL (Spain)
Membership(s): The Authors Guild; Authors Registry; Mystery Writers of America; Romance Writers of America; Science Fiction & Fantasy Writers of America; Society of Children's Book Writers & Illustrators

Nicholas Ellison Agency (L)
Division of Sanford J Greenburger Associates Inc
55 Fifth Ave, 15th fl, New York, NY 10003
Tel: 212-206-5600 *Fax:* 212-463-8718

Web Site: greenburger.com/agent/nick-ellison
Key Personnel
Pres: Nicholas Ellison *E-mail:* nellison@sjga.com
Foreign Rts: Chloe Walker *E-mail:* cwalker@sjga.com
Founded: 1932
Fiction & narrative nonfiction (all subjects). No children's or science fiction. No unsol mss, query first. Submit sample chapters. Include a cover letter & brief synopsis of first 20 pgs of mss. Handle film & TV rights. Fees charged for photocopying & books ordered. Agents in principal foreign countries.

Elaine P English PLLC (L)
4710 41 St NW, Suite D, Washington, DC 20016
Tel: 202-362-5190 *Fax:* 202-362-5192
E-mail: foreignrights@elaineenglish.com
Web Site: www.elaineenglish.com
Key Personnel
Attorney & Literary Agent: Elaine English (AAR) *E-mail:* elaine@elaineenglish.com
Founded: 2006
Law firm & literary agency. Romance, women's fiction & cozy mystery stories only. No other genres accepted. No unsol mss, query first via e-mail. Electronic submissions strongly preferred. Detailed submission guidelines on web site. Charge no fees, standard commission & reimbursement of some expenses only. Not accepting submissions at this time.
Titles recently placed: *Art of Seduction*, Stephanie Julian; *Download Drama*, Celeste O Norfleet; *Last Chance Beauty Queen*, Hope Ramsey; *Sex, Lies & Valentines*, Tawny Weber; *Tall, Dark & Cowboy*, Joanne Kennedy; *The Preacher's Bride*, Laurie Kingery
Membership(s): Mystery Writers of America; Romance Writers of America; Sisters in Crime

Felicia Eth Literary Representation (L)
555 Bryant St, Suite 350, Palo Alto, CA 94301
Tel: 415-970-9717
E-mail: feliciaeth.literary@gmail.com
Web Site: www.ethliterary.com
Key Personnel
Pres: Felicia Eth (AAR)
Founded: 1989
Diverse nonfiction including narrative, psychology, health & popular science; including women's issues, investigative journalism & biography. Selective mainstream literary fiction. No unsol mss, query first for fiction, proposal for nonfiction. No discs, no files by e-mail. Handle film & TV rights for clients, books only through sub-agents in LA. No reading fee. Xeroxing costs & overseas mail, FedEx charged to client, $75 for full-length ms to cover mailing. Commission is 15% domestic & 20% foreign. Foreign rights agents in all major territories.
Titles recently placed: *Fastest Things on Wings*, Terry Masear; *Letting Kids Decide*, Leonard Sax; *Tales of Alpine Obsession*, Daniel Arnold; *The Memory Thief*, Emily Coin; *Walking with Abel*, Anna Badkhen

Mary Evans Inc (L)
242 E Fifth St, New York, NY 10003-8501
Tel: 212-979-0880 *Fax:* 212-979-5344
E-mail: info@maryevansinc.com
Web Site: www.maryevansinc.com
Key Personnel
Pres: Mary Evans (AAR)
Agent & Foreign Rts Dir: Julia Kardon
Agent: Kaela Noel; Rosie Peele
Literary fiction, narrative nonfiction, commercial fiction, self-help, science & history, graphic novels & memoirs. Nonfiction should be submitted in proposal form & fiction with a query letter, a synopsis & three sample chapters, SASE required. Accept unsol mss. Handle film & TV rights, no reading fee.
Foreign Rights: Akcali Copyright Agency (Ozgur Emir) (Turkey); Berla and Griffini Rights Agency (Erica Berla) (Italy); The Book Publishers Association of Israel (Dalia Ever-Hadani) (Israel); Chandler Crawford Agency (Holland); The Grayhawk Agency (Gray Tan) (China, Taiwan); International Editors (Maru de Montserrat) (Portugal, Spain); LEX Copyright Office (Norbert Uzseka) (Hungary); Licht & Burr (Trine Licht) (Scandinavia); Liepman Agency (Mark Koralnik) (Germany); La Nouvelle Agence (Michele Kanonidis) (France); Andrew Nurnberg Associates (Ludmilla Sushkova) (Russia); Owls Agency Inc (Mario Tauchi) (Japan); Prava I Prevodi (Ana Milenkovic) (Eastern Europe, Greece); Riff Agency (Lauri Riff) (Brazil); Eric Yang Agency (Henry Shin) (Korea)

Farber Literary Agency Inc (L-D)
14 E 75 St, New York, NY 10021
Tel: 212-861-7075 *Fax:* 212-861-7076
E-mail: farberlit@gmail.com
Key Personnel
Pres: Ann Farber
Attorney: Donald C Farber *Tel:* 212-861-2325 *E-mail:* donaldc142@gmail.com
Contact: Dr Seth Farber
Founded: 1990
Fiction, nonfiction, plays. Do not accept unsol mss. Handle film & TV rights. No reading fee.

Farris Literary Agency Inc (L)
PO Box 570069, Dallas, TX 75357-0069
Tel: 972-203-8804
E-mail: farris1@airmail.net
Web Site: www.farrisliterary.com
Key Personnel
Pres: Michael D Farris
Agent: Susan Morgan Farris
Founded: 2002
Handles fiction & nonfiction books, also occasional screenplay. Query first by e-mail or regular mail. If interested, we will request further submission. No fees charged.
Titles recently placed: *To Sketch a Thief*, Sharon Pape

Feigenbaum Publishing Consultants Inc (L)
61 Bounty Lane, Jericho, NY 11753
Tel: 516-647-8314 (cell) *Fax:* 516-935-0507
E-mail: readrover5@aol.com
Key Personnel
Pres: Laurie Feigenbaum
Founded: 1991
Contract negotiations & review, agenting, trademark & copyright registration, permissions clearance & general publishing advice. Expertise in book publishing & electronic publishing. No unsol mss, query first. Hourly fee or commission. Contracts negotiation, $95 per hour for contracts review, negotiation, trademark & copyright registration & permissions.

Robert L Fenton PC; Entertainment Attorney & Literary Agent (L)
Affiliate of Fenton Entertainment Group Inc
31800 Northwestern Hwy, Suite 204, Farmington Hills, MI 48334
Tel: 248-855-8780 *Fax:* 248-855-3302
Web Site: www.robertlfenton.com
Key Personnel
Literary Agent: Robert L Fenton
Founded: 1984
Specialize in nonfiction, fiction, women's fiction, historical romances, action & suspense; limited poetry, children's photographic books. Handle film & TV scripts. No unsol mss, preliminary letter or telephone call first. Submit outline & sample chapters. Reading fee: $350. Frequently charge an additional retainer along with a percentage if there is an agreement of representation. Extensive experience in all areas of publishing, film & TV. Producer at Universal Studios & 20th Century Fox; produced several feature films & Movies of the Week; published three best selling novels; Literary Guild, Doubleday Book-of-the-Month. Founded 1960. Writer's Workshop on Holland America Cruise Lines, Adjunct Professor, Creative Writing at Marygrove College, Detroit, MI; Writer's Digest Presents; The RLF Writer's Workshop on cruise lines, 2000; 1999 Guest Lecturer, Entertainment Law Seminar, University of MI Law School, April 1998. Mr Fenton prefers English but has limited working knowledge of French, Spanish, German & Russian. Will only represent seven or eight new writers each year. There is a waiting list.

FinePrint Literary Management (L)
115 W 29 St, 3rd fl, New York, NY 10001
Tel: 212-279-1282
Web Site: www.fineprintlit.com
Key Personnel
CEO: Peter Rubie (AAR) *E-mail:* peter@fineprintlit.com
Pres: Stephany Evans (AAR) *E-mail:* stephany@fineprintlit.com
In-House Subs Rts Dir: Jacqueline Murphy *E-mail:* jacqueline@fineprintlit.com
Agent: June Clark *E-mail:* june@fineprintlit.com; Rachel Coyne *E-mail:* rachel@fineprintlit.com; Janet Reid *E-mail:* janet@fineprintlit.com; Becky Vinter *E-mail:* becky@fineprintlit.com; Laura Wood *E-mail:* laura@fineprintlit.com
Founded: 2000 (formed by the merger of the Peter Rubie Agency & the Imprint Agency)
High quality fiction & nonfiction. Handle film, TV & foreign rights through sub-agents. No unsol mss, query first. Submit outline & first two chapters with one page query letter & proposal. No reading fees. Photocopying fees. Some foreign mailing charges. Please send queries to the appropriate e-mail for the agent you wish to query.
Titles recently placed: *Better Homes and Hauntings*, Molly Harper; *Breathing Room*, Dr Melva Green, Lauren Rosenfeld; *California Quakes*, John Dvorak; *Chorus*, Emma Trevayne; *Combat-Ready Kitchen*, Anastacia Marx de Salcedo; *Dark Wolf*, Dani Harper; *Doped Up*, Sam Quinones; *Double Whammy*, Gretchen Archer; *Emergence*, Derek Rydall; *Gaining Ground*, Forrest Pritchard; *Gearwing*, Emma Trevayne; *Getting Back Out There*, Susan J Elliot; *How to Raise a Billionaire Genius*, Sean Campbell, D Horby; *I Am Otter*, Sam Garton; *I Don't Like Koala*, Sean Ferrell; *I Was M/ad Man*, Richard Gilbert; *Ice Cold Kill*, Dana Haynes; *Indefensible*, Lee Goodman; *It's In His Kiss*, Aimee Thurlo; *Lowcountry Bombshell*, Susan Boyer; *My Best Race*, Chris Cooper; *My Bluegrass Baby*, Molly Harper; *My First Kafka*, Matthue Roth; *Sacred Games*, Gary Corby; *Storm Warrior*, Dani Harper; *Tequila!*, Chantal Martineau; *The Beautiful Thing That Awaits Us All*, Laird Barron; *The Break-Up Artist*, Philip Siegel; *The Good Luck Cat*, Lissa Warren; *The Pawn Broker*, David Thurlo, Aimee Thurlo; *The Repeat Year*, Andrea Lochen; *The Tao and The Bard*, Phillip DePoy; *The Temporary Wife*, Jeannie Moon; *Thornbrook Park*, Sherri Erwin; *Trickster*, Jeff Somers; *Up Mud Creek*, Molly Harper
Foreign Rep(s): Lorella Belli (UK); Donatella d'Ormesson (France); Greyhawk Agency (China, Taiwan); International Editors (Latin America, Spain); Nurcihan Kesim (Turkey); Lennart Sane (Scandinavia, Spain); Piergiorgio Nicolazzini (Italy); Owl's Agency (Japan); Prava I Prevodi (Eastern Europe); Thomas Schlueck (Germany); Eric Yang Agency (Korea)

The Fischer-Harbage Agency Inc (L)
540 President St, 3rd fl, Brooklyn, NY 11215
Tel: 212-695-7105
E-mail: info@fischerharbage.com
Web Site: www.fischerharbage.com
Key Personnel
Pres: Ryan Fischer-Harbage
Assoc Agent: Christopher Hermelin
Founded: 2007
Full service boutique literary agency specializing in fiction, memoir, narrative nonfiction & current events. No unsol mss, query first with a short description, bio & first chapter of your book in the body of an e-mail to submissions@fischerharbage.com. No fees, standard commission paid.
Titles recently placed: *An American Caddie in St Andrews: Growing Up, Girls, and Looping on the Old Course*, Oliver Horovitz; *Angels Gate: A Shortcut Man Novel*, P G Sturges; *Domestic Affairs: A Novel*, Bridget Siegel; *Gray: A Novel*, Pete Wentz, James Montgomery; *Open Wound: The Tragic Obsession of Dr William Beaumont*, Jason Karlawish; *The Great Dissent: How Oliver Wendell Holmes Changed His Mind–and Changed the History of Free Speech in America*, Thomas Healy; *The Zombie Chasers 1*, John Kloepfer; *The Zombie Chasers 2: Undead Ahead*, John Kloepfer; *The Zombie Chasers 3: Sludgement Day*, John Kloepfer; *Tribulations of the Shortcut Man*, P G Sturges; *When We Wuz Famous*, Greg Takoudes
Foreign Rights: Linda Biagi Rights Management (Worldwide)

Flannery Literary (L)
1140 Wickfield Ct, Naperville, IL 60563
Tel: 630-428-2682
Web Site: flanneryliterary.com
Key Personnel
Owner: Jennifer Flannery
Founded: 1992
Represents authors of books written for children & young adults. No unsol mss, query first with SASE or via e-mail (preferred). No fees.
Membership(s): ABA; ALA; Chicago Women in Publishing; International Literacy Association; National Council of Teachers of English; Society of Children's Book Writers & Illustrators

Peter Fleming Agency (L)
PO Box 458, Pacific Palisades, CA 90272
Tel: 310-454-1373
E-mail: peterfleming@earthlink.net
Key Personnel
Pres: Peter Fleming
Nonfiction: that rare expertise so vital in America that non-book readers will buy it, read it! Includes populist, contrarian, dissent, suppressed information overlooked or avoided by mainstream media (ex: corporate/political crimes). Interested in authors with strong platforms, web sites, blogs & seminar experience. No unsol mss, query first with SASE. Submit outline. No reading fee. Clients billed for major postage, FedEx, foreign communication & other pre-approved expenses.

Sheldon Fogelman Agency Inc (L)
10 E 40 St, Suite 3205, New York, NY 10016
Tel: 212-532-7250 *Fax:* 212-685-8939
E-mail: info@sheldonfogelmanagency.com
Web Site: sheldonfogelmanagency.com
Key Personnel
Pres & Literary Agent: Sheldon Fogelman
Asst Agent/Foreign Rts Mgr: Janine Hauber
Asst Agent: Amy Stern
Trade books of all types, fiction & nonfiction, adult & juvenile, including all rights. Handle film, TV, film & software rights. No unsol mss, query first, include publishing history. No reading fee.

The Foley Literary Agency (L)
34 E 38 St, Suite 1B, New York, NY 10016
Tel: 212-686-6930
Key Personnel
Partner: Joan Foley
Founded: 1961
Fiction & nonfiction books. No unsol mss, query first with SASE & brief outline. No reading fee. 10% sales commission, 15% foreign rights fees. Rare but occasional fees for phone, mail or copying. ICM handles film & TV rights. Agents in all major European countries.

Folio Jr, see Folio Literary Management LLC

Folio Literary Management LLC (L)
The Film Center Bldg, 630 Ninth Ave, Suite 1101, New York, NY 10036
Tel: 212-400-1494 *Fax:* 212-967-0977
Web Site: www.foliolit.com
Key Personnel
Founding Partner & Agent: Scott Hoffman; Jeff Kleinman (AAR) *E-mail:* jkleinman@foliolit.com
SVP: Michelle Brower (AAR)
SVP, Dir of Opers & Agent: Frank Weimann *E-mail:* frank@foliolit.com
SVP & Agent: Erin Niumata; Steve Troha (AAR) *E-mail:* steve@foliolitmanagement.com; Emily van Beek
Co-Dir of Intl Rts & Agent: Molly Jaffa (AAR) *E-mail:* molly@foliolit.com; Melissa Sarver *E-mail:* melissa@foliolit.com
Agent: Claudia Cross (AAR) *E-mail:* claudia@foliolitmanagement.com; Jita Fumich *E-mail:* jita@foliolit.com; Michael Harriot *E-mail:* michael@foliolit.com; Erin Harris; Katherine Latshaw *E-mail:* klatshaw@foliolitmanagement.com; Marcy Posner
Literary & Dramatic Rts Agent: Ruth Pomerance
Founded: 1997
Places both fiction & nonfiction. Seeking adult fiction appropriate for book club discussion, literary & commercial fiction. Also specializes in narrative nonfiction including memoirs. No poetry, stage plays or screen plays. Represents many first time authors as well as established authors. No unsol mss. E-mail queries only. For each agent's specialties, contact information & submission preference go to foliolit.com/folio-staff. No fees.
Folio Jr is a division devoted to representing outstanding children's book authors & artists.
Titles recently placed: *America's Most Haunted*, Eric Olsen, Theresa Argie; *Because Your Grandparents Love You*, Andrew Clement; *Bourbon Empire: Whiskey and the Story of America*, Reid Mitenbuler; *Broken Hearts, Fences, & Other Things to Mend*, Katie Finn; *Catch A Falling Star*, Kim Culbertson; *City Love*, Susan Colasanti; *Dumplin'*, Julie Murphy; *Firebird*, Misty Copeland, Christopher Myer; *Glimpses of Life: The Story of Mary Cassatt*, Barbara Herkert; *Henry Holton Takes the Ice*, Sandra Bradley; *Little Green*, Roni Schotter; *Sadie Mac*, Sara O'Leary; *Sebastian and the Balloon*, Philip C Stead; *Soy Sauce For Beginners*, Kirstin Chen; *Tabula Rasa*, Kristen Lippert-Martin; *The Amazing Harvey*, Don Passman; *The Bollywood Bride*, Sonali Dev; *The Cheesy Vegan*, John Schlimm; *The Echoes of an Angel: A Mother's Journey Through Faith, Love, and Seeing the Unseen*, Aquanetta Gordon; *The Girls of Summer*, Morgan Matson; *The Maiden Tower*, Ella Leya; *The Reset Juice Cleanse Diet*, Lori Kenyon, Marra St Clair; *The United Hate of America*, Brooks Gibbs; *What Really Happened: John Edwards, Our Daughter, and Me*, Rielle Hunter; *When Santa Was a Baby*, Linda Bailey; *Wish*, Jake Smith
Foreign Rights: Asli Karasuil Telif Haklari (Turkey); Berla & Griffini (children's & women's fiction) (Italy); The Book Publishers Association of Israel (Israel); Graal Literary Agency (Poland); The Grayhawk Agency (China, Taiwan); Danny Hong Agency (Korea); IECO (Portugal, Spain); Iris Literary Agency (Catherine Fragou) (Greece); Japan Uni Agency (Japan); Michelle Lapautre Agency (France); Maxima Creative Agency (Indonesia); Prava I Prevodi Literary Agency (Czech Republic, Russia, Serbia); Riff Agency (Brazil); Schlueck Literary Agency (Germany); Marianne Schoenbach Literary Agency (Netherlands); Livia Stoia Literary Agency (Romania); Ulf Toregard Agency (Scandinavia); Tuttle-Mori Agency Inc (Thailand, Vietnam); Susanna Zevi Angezia Letteraria (Italy)

Fort Ross Inc - International Representation for Artists (L)
Division of Fort Ross Inc
26 Arthur Place, Yonkers, NY 10701
Tel: 914-375-6448
Web Site: www.fortrossinc.com
Key Personnel
Pres & Exec Dir: Dr Vladimir P Kartsev *E-mail:* vkartsev2000@gmail.com
Founded: 1992
Fiction: romance, mysteries, science fiction, fantasy, adventure. Provide American publishers with illustrations from Russia. Find European publishers for American book authors & illustrators. No unsol mss, query first.
Foreign Rep(s): Nova Littera (Baltic States, Belarus, Russia, Ukraine)

Lynn C Franklin Associates Ltd (L)
1350 Broadway, Suite 2015, New York, NY 10018
Tel: 212-868-6311 *Fax:* 212-868-6312
E-mail: agency@franklinandsiegal.com
Key Personnel
Pres & Agent: Lynn C Franklin (AAR)
Rts Mgr: Claudia Nys
Adult commercial & literary fiction; middle-grade & young adult fiction; & general nonfiction with special interest in self-help, health, psychology, personal growth & biographies, as well as current international affairs. No unsol mss, query e-mail (no attachments). No reading fee. Representatives in Hollywood & in all major foreign countries. Handle film & TV rights.
Titles recently placed: *The Book of Forgiving: The Four-Fold Path of Healing for Ourselves and Our World*, Desmond M Tutu, Mpho A Tutu; *The Customer Rules: The 39 Essential Rules for Delivering Sensational Service*, Lee Cockerell; *The Wahls Protocol*, Terry Wahls, MD, Eve Adamson
Foreign Rights: ACER Agencia Literaria (Elizabeth Atkins) (Portugal, Spain, Spanish Latin America); Eliane Benisti Literary Agency (France); Book Publishers Association of Israel (Israel); Chinese Connection Agency (China, Taiwan); Mary Clemmey Literary Agency (Mary Clemmey) (Australia, New Zealand, UK); The English Agency (Japan) Ltd (Japan); Fritz Agency (Germany); Graal Literary Agency (Poland); Berla e Griffini (Erica Berla) (Italy); Katai & Bolza (Hungary); Simona Kessler International Copyright Agency (Romania); Maxima Creative (Indonesia); Andrew Nurnberg Associates (Russia); Kristin Olson (Czech Republic); Prava & Prevodi Literary Agency (Bulgaria, Croatia, Montenegro, Serbia, Slovenia); Read n' Right Agency (Greece); Agencia Riff (Brazil); Lennart Sane Agency (Netherlands, Scandinavia); Eric Yang Agency (Korea)

Jeanne Fredericks Literary Agency Inc (L)
221 Benedict Hill Rd, New Canaan, CT 06840
Tel: 203-972-3011 *Fax:* 203-972-3011

E-mail: jeanne.fredericks@gmail.com (no unsol attachments)
Web Site: jeannefredericks.com
Key Personnel
Pres: Jeanne Fredericks (AAR)
Founded: 1997 (purchased assets of Susan P Urstadt Inc in May 1997)
Adult nonfiction only, especially practical popular reference, health & medical, gardening, business, travel, practical how-to, biography, antiques & decorative arts, sports, natural history, cookbooks, women's issues, history. No unsol mss, query first by e-mail or by mail with SASE. If requested, submit proposal, author biography (including previous publishing history), detailed outline & sample chapters by e-mail or by mail with SASE. Do not require signature for delivery. Handle film & TV rights with co-agent. No reading fee.
Titles recently placed: *American Quilts*, Robert Shaw; *Barleywine Farm Herb Gardening Guide*, Melissa Snyder; *For Sale - American Paradise*, Willie Drye; *Growing Vegetables in Drought, Desert & Dry Times*, Maureen Gilmer; *MD's Guide to Alternative Health*, Lloyd May, MD; *My Scarlett: Margaret Mitchell and the Motion Picture Gone with the Wind*, John Wiley Jr; *The Best There Ever Was: The Story of Dan Patch*, Sharon Smith; *The Greenhouse Gardener's Manual*, Roger Marshall; *Yoga Nidra for Stress Relief*, Julie Lusk; *Yoga Therapy*, Eden Goldman, DC, Terra Gold, DOM, Larry Payne, PhD
Foreign Rep(s): Books Crossing Borders (Worldwide)
Membership(s): The Authors Guild

Robert A Freedman Dramatic Agency Inc (D)
1501 Broadway, Suite 2310, New York, NY 10036
Tel: 212-840-5760 *Fax:* 212-840-5776
Key Personnel
Pres: Robert A Freedman (AAR)
E-mail: rfreedmanagent@aol.com
SVP: Selma Luttinger (AAR)
VP & Agent: Marta Praeger (AAR)
Founded: 1928 (as Harold Freedman Brandt & Brandt Dramatic Department Inc, until 1981)
Dramatic scripts for stage, motion picture & TV. No unsol mss, query first. No reading fee. Material placed for production/publication is subject to 10% commission. Agents in all European countries. Will co-agent with literary agents to handle film rights & books.

Samuel French Inc (D)
235 Park Ave S, 5th fl, New York, NY 10003
Tel: 212-206-8990 *Toll Free Tel:* 866-598-8449 *Fax:* 212-206-1429
E-mail: info@samuelfrench.com
Web Site: www.samuelfrench.com
Key Personnel
Pres: Nate Collins *E-mail:* ncollins@samuelfrench.com
VP & Dir, Opers: Kenneth Dingledine *E-mail:* kdingledine@samuelfrench.com
Literary Dir: Amy Rose Marsh *E-mail:* amarsh@samuelfrench.com
Founded: 1830
Plays for publication & agency representation. Accept unsol mss, standard US play form. No reading fee. Handle film & TV rights for published works only. Send $4 for guidelines (recommended mss format).
Branch Office(s)
Samuel French Bookshop, 7623 Sunset Blvd, Hollywood, CA 90046
Foreign Office(s): Samuel French Ltd, 52 Fitzroy St, London W1T 5JR, United Kingdom, Opers Dir: David Webster *Tel:* (020) 7387 9373 *Fax:* (020) 7387 2161 *E-mail:* theatre@samuelfrench-london.co.uk *Web Site:* www.samuelfrench-london.co.uk

Sarah Jane Freymann Literary Agency LLC (L)
59 W 71 St, Suite 9-B, New York, NY 10023
Tel: 212-362-9277
E-mail: submissions@sarahjanefreymann.com
Web Site: www.sarahjanefreymann.com
Key Personnel
Owner & Agent: Sarah Jane Freymann *E-mail:* sarah@sarahjanefreymann.com
Assoc: Katharine Sands *Tel:* 212-751-8892 *E-mail:* katharinesands@nyc.rr.com; Steven Schwartz *Tel:* 212-362-1998 *E-mail:* steve@sarahjanefreymann.com; Jessica Sinsheimer *E-mail:* jessica@sarahjanefreymann.com
Founded: 1974
Represents book-length fiction & general nonfiction. Fiction: popular fiction plus quality mainstream, literary fiction & young adult. Nonfiction: spiritual/inspirational, psychology, self-help; women's/men's issues; health (conventional & alternative); cookbooks; narrative nonfiction, natural science, nature, memoirs, biography; current events, multicultural issues, popular culture; illustrated books, lifestyle, garden, design, architecture, humor, sports, travel & business. No unsol mss, query first with SASE. Handle film & TV rights with subagents. Representation in all foreign markets. No reading fee.
Titles recently placed: *Falling Under*, Gwen Hayes

Fredrica S Friedman & Co Inc (L)
136 E 57 St, 14th fl, New York, NY 10022
Tel: 212-829-9600 *Fax:* 212-829-9669
E-mail: info@fredricafriedman.com; submissions@fredricafriedman.com
Web Site: www.fredricafriedman.com
Key Personnel
Pres: Fredrica S Friedman (AAR)
Founded: 2000
Literary management firm that represents best selling & award winning authors. General nonfiction & fiction. No poetry, plays, screenplays, children's picture books, science fiction/fantasy or horror. No unsol mss-query first. Send all queries by e-mail, no attachments. See web site for detailed submission information. Hardcopy materials will not be returned; no fees.
Foreign Rep(s): Georges Borchardt Agency
Foreign Rights: Georges Borchardt Agency

Candice Fuhrman Literary Agency (L)
10 Cypress Hollow Dr, Tiburon, CA 94920
Tel: 415-383-1014
E-mail: candicef@pacbell.net
Key Personnel
Pres & Owner: Candice Fuhrman (AAR)
Nonfiction: health, memoir, psychology, women's issues, how-to & self-help; literary & commercial fiction. No unsol mss.
Currently not accepting new clients.
Foreign Rights: Jenny Meyer Literary Agency

The Garamond Agency Inc (L)
12 Horton St, Newburyport, MA 01950
E-mail: query@garamondagency.com
Web Site: www.garamondagency.com
Key Personnel
Dir: Lisa Adams; David Miller
Adult nonfiction, all subjects. No unsol mss, query by e-mail first. Submit cover letter, outline, synopsis, author bio & SASE. No reading fees. Handle TV & movie rights.
Foreign Rights: AnatoliaLit Agency (Turkey); Bardon-Chinese Media Agency (China, Taiwan); Berla & Griffini Rights Agency (Italy); Raquel de la Concha Agencia Literaria (Portugal, Spain); Graal Literary Agency (Poland); Anna Jarota Agency (France); Katai & Bolza Literary Agents (Hungary); Duran Kim Agency (Korea); Mo Literary Services (Netherlands); Mohrbooks (Germany); Andrew Nurnberg Association Sofia (Bulgaria); Andrew Nurnberg Literary Agency (Russia & former USSR); The Riff Agency (Brazil); Agentia Literara Sun (Romania); Tuttle-Mori Agency Inc (Japan)
Membership(s): The Authors Guild

Max Gartenberg Literary Agency (L)
912 N Pennsylvania Ave, Yardley, PA 19067
Tel: 215-295-9230
Web Site: www.maxgartenberg.com
Key Personnel
Agent: Anne G Devlin *E-mail:* agdevlin@aol.com
Founded: 1954
Adult nonfiction books & fiction. No unsol mss, query first. Submit formal book proposal, outline & sample as requested. No reading fee. Handle film & TV rights. Agents in all principal foreign markets.
Titles recently placed: *Everything A New Elementary School Teacher REALLY Needs to Know*, Otis Kreigel; *Killers in the Family*, Robert L Snow; *Land Your Dream Career: 11 Steps To Take In College*, Tori Randolph Terhune, Betsy A Hays; *Running With Cosmos Flowers*, Shizume Minale, Richard Marshall; *Surviving Your Bar/Bat Mitzvah: The Ultimate Insider's Guide*, Matt Axelrod; *The New Senior Women*, Thelma Reese, Barbara Fleisher; *Understanding Lung Cancer*, Naheed Ali MD; *Verdi for Kids: His Life & Music*, Helen Bauer
Foreign Rights: International Editors' Co (Argentina); Mohrbooks AG, Literary Agency (Switzerland); La Nouvelle Agence (France); Pollinger Ltd (UK); Lennart Sane (Sweden); Tuttle-Mori Agency Inc (Japan)

Gelfman/Schneider/ICM (L)
Affiliate of John Farquharson Ltd
850 Seventh Ave, Suite 903, New York, NY 10019
Tel: 212-245-1993 *Fax:* 212-245-8678
E-mail: mail@gelfmanschneider.com
Web Site: gelfmanschneider.com
Key Personnel
Contact: Jane Gelfman (AAR); Deborah Schneider (AAR)
General trade fiction & nonfiction. Queries by mail only, no e-mail queries will be considered. No unsol mss, query first with SASE. Submit sample chapters & outline. Handle film & TV rights. No reading fee.
Foreign Rights: Curtis Brown Ltd (translation, UK)
Membership(s): The Authors Guild

The Gersh Agency (TGA) (L-D)
41 Madison Ave, 33rd fl, New York, NY 10010
Tel: 212-997-1818
E-mail: info@gershla.com
Web Site: www.gershagency.com
Key Personnel
Head of Books Dept: J Joseph Veltre, III (AAR)
Literary Agent: Phyllis Wender (AAR) *E-mail:* pwender@gershny.com; Susan Perlman Cohen *E-mail:* njcohen@aol.com
Founded: 2007 (1949 as talent agency)
Fiction, nonfiction, adult & juvenile, film & TV rights & plays. No unsol mss. Unsol materials will not be accepted or considered. No online submission unless requested. No reading fee.
Branch Office(s)
9465 Wilshire Blvd, 6th fl, Beverly Hills, CA 90212 (talent div) *Tel:* 310-274-6611
Foreign Rights: The English Agency (Japan) Ltd (Japan); Licht & Burr (Scandinavia); Mohrbooks (Germany); La Nouvelle Agence (France)

GGP Publishing Inc (L)
105 Calvert St, Suite 201, Harrison, NY 10528-3138

Tel: 914-834-8896 *Fax:* 914-834-7566
Web Site: www.GGPPublishing.com
Key Personnel
Pres & Publg Dir: Generosa Gina Protano
E-mail: GGProtano@GGPPublishing.com
Founded: 1991
Fiction & nonfiction; educational materials, English & foreign languages. Handle film & TV rights. No unsol mss, query first. Reading fees on all submissions, refundable from commission; fee charged for photocopying & postage or courier. Editorial & translation services also available.
Membership(s): American Book Producers Association

Susan Gleason (L)
325 Riverside Dr, Suite 41, New York, NY 10025
Tel: 212-662-3876 *Fax:* 212-864-3298
E-mail: sgleasonliteraryagent@gmail.com
Founded: 1992
Adult trade & mass market, fiction & nonfiction. No unsol mss, query first with SASE.
Handle film & TV rights, foreign rights. No reading fees.
Membership(s): International Women's Writing Guild

Global Lion Intellectual Property Management Inc (L-D)
Affiliate of Millennium Lion Inc
PO Box 669238, Pompano Beach, FL 33066
Tel: 754-222-6948 *Fax:* 754-222-6948
E-mail: queriesgloballionmgt@gmail.com
Web Site: www.globallionmanagement.com
Key Personnel
Pres: Peter Miller
Assoc: Hugh Walter; Zachary Yerian
Represents transformational & spiritual nonfiction, young adult, commercial fiction, nonfiction, true crime & celebrity books. Handles film & TV rights. Represent literary & film properties internationally. No unsol mss, query first. Submit one page synopsis or finished treatment & author bio. See web site for additional submission guidelines. Co-agents in select foreign territories & deal directly with foreign publishers. Affiliate packages & produces feature films & TV. No fees charged.
Titles recently placed: *Class Act*, Sir Ken Robinson; *Dying Light*, Raymond Benson; *Finding Your Element*, Sir Ken Robinson, Lou Aronica; *King Rules*, Alveda King; *Organic Innovation*, Sir Ken Robinson; *The Encyclopedia of American Food & Drink*, John Mariani; *The Story of Christianity*, Jean-Pierre Isbouts; *Wines of California*, Mike DeSimone, Jeff Jensen, et al; *Your Next Big Thing*, Dr Ben Michaelis
Foreign Rep(s): Big Apple Agency Inc (China); Peter Bolza (Hungary); Tuttle-Mori Agency Inc (Japan)

Globo Libros Literary Agency (L)
402 E 64 St, Suite 6-C, New York, NY 10065
Tel: 212-888-4655
Web Site: www.globo-libros.com; publishersmarketplace.com/members/dstockwell
Key Personnel
Founder: Diane Stockwell *E-mail:* dstockwell@nyc.rr.com
Founded: 2006
Specializes in Hispanic nonfiction authors from the US & abroad. Also represents works in English. Looking for compelling narrative nonfiction, cookbooks, memoir, biography, parenting & self-help by authors of any background. We also offer book length & short translations from Spanish into English. Query by e-mail only with a detailed summary of the project & author bio in the body of the message. No attachments. No fees charged.
Titles recently placed: *Buried Alive: The True Story of the Chilean Mining Disaster & the Extraordinary Rescue at Camp Hope*, Manuel Pino; *Cartel: The Coming Invasion of Mexico's Drug Wars*, Sylvia Longmire; *Cocino Latin*, Raquel Roque; *El Poder de Tu Cumpleanos*, Andrea Valeria; *El Salto: Aprovecha de las Nuevas Tecnologias y Alcance tu potencial*, Ariel Coro; *Killing the American Dream: How Anti-Immigrant Extremists are Destroying the Nation*, Pilar Marrero; *Los 10 Errores que las Mujeres Hacen en el Amor*, Maria Marin; *Volver a Morir*, Rosana Ubanell
Membership(s): The Authors Guild

Krista Goering Literary Agency LLC (L)
3514 Clinton Pkwy, Suite A-404, Lawrence, KS 66047
Tel: 785-841-0634 *Fax:* 785-841-8500
E-mail: query@kristagoering.com
Web Site: www.kristagoering.com
Key Personnel
Agent: Krista Goering
Founded: 2007
Specialize in nonfiction projects by authors with a platform who wish to build a brand with multiple projects. Nonfiction: send query by e-mail; no fees. No unsol mss, query first. While we are not accepting new clients, we are continuing to work with existing clients.
Titles recently placed: *101 Signs of Psychic Ability*, Melissa Alvarez; *101 Success Secrets for Gifted Kids*, Christine N Fonseca Ms Pps; *108 Spiritual Practices*, Debra Moffitt; *365 Ways to Raise Your Frequency*, Melissa Alvarez; *A Cure for Emma*, Julie Colvin; *Becoming Your Best Self: The Guide to Clarity, Inspiration & Healing*, Sara Wiseman; *Chemo: Secrets to Thriving*, Roxanne Brown, Barbara Mastej; *Community College Success: Networking Secrets for Winning Friends, Scholarships, Internships & Jobs*, Isa Adney; *Confessions of a Scroundel! From the Secret Memoirs of General James Wilkinson (1757-1825)*, Keith Thompson; *Full Cup, Thirsty Spirit: 6 Shifts to Nourish the Soul When Life's Too Busy & Too Much*, Karen Horneffer-Ginter PhD; *Homework Helpers: Essays & Term Papers*, Michelle Mclean; *Idol Hands*, Ted Scofield; *Say This Not That to Your Professor: 42 Talking Tips for College Success*, Ellen Bremen MA; *Slow Parenting Teens*, Molly Wingate, Marti Woodward; *That Should Still Be Us: The Flat World Myths That Are Keeping Us Flat on Our Backs*, Martin Sieff; *The Healthy Habit Plan*, Wes Cole; *The Little Book of Light: 100 Ways to Bring Light Into Your Life*, Mikaela Jones; *The Ultimate Guide for Creating Quick & Healthy Meals*, Franceen Friefeld Rd PH Ec; *Unchain the Pain*, Bob Livingstone Lcsw

Goldfarb & Associates (L-D)
721 Gibbon St, Alexandria, VA 22314
Tel: 202-466-3030 *Fax:* 703-836-5644
E-mail: rglawlit@gmail.com
Web Site: www.ronaldgoldfarb.com
Key Personnel
Founder & Owner: Ronald L Goldfarb
Literary Agent: Robbie Anna Hare
Founded: 1966
Only select new clients accepted. Fiction & serious nonfiction; no romance or sci-fi. No unsol mss, query first with letter, outline or synopsis, sample of best chapter, bio & SASE. Handle film & TV rights. No reading fee.
Branch Office(s)
177 Ocean Lane Dr, Suite 1101, Key Biscayne, FL 33149

Frances Goldin Literary Agency, Inc (L-D)
57 E 11 St, Suite 5-B, New York, NY 10003
Tel: 212-777-0047 *Fax:* 212-228-1660
E-mail: agency@goldinlit.com
Web Site: www.goldinlit.com
Key Personnel
Principal & Agent: Frances Goldin (AAR)
VP & Sr Agent: Ellen Geiger (AAR); Sam Stoloff (AAR)
Rts Dir & Agent: Matt McGowan (AAR)
E-mail: mm@goldinlit.com
Assoc Agent & Off Mgr: Sarah Bridgins
Coun: Ria Julien
Founded: 1977
No unsol mss or work previously submitted to publishers, query first with letter & SASE. No racist, sexist, agist, homophobic or pornographic material considered. Adult literary fiction & serious progressive nonfiction. Agents in Hollywood & all major foreign countries. No software. Handle film & TV rights. No reading fee.
Foreign Rep(s): Eliane Benisti (France); The English Agency (Japan) Ltd (Hamish Macaskill) (Japan); Graal Literary Agency (Maria Starz-Kanska) (Poland); David Grossman Literary Agency Ltd (David Grossman) (England, UK); International Editors' Co (Isabel Monteagudo) (Spain); International Editors' Co (Nicholas Costa) (Argentina); International Editors' Co (Flavia Sala) (Brazil); Jia-Xi Books (Gray Tan) (China, Taiwan); JLM Literary Agency (John L Moukakos) (Greece); Nurcihan Kesim Literary Agency Inc (Asli Karasuil) (Istanbul, Turkey); Ruth Liepman Agency (Ruth Weibel) (Germany); Living Literary Agency (Elfriede Pexa) (Italy); Jovan Milenkovic (Vuk Perisic) (Montenegro, Serbia); Kristin Olson Literary Agency (Kristin Olson) (Czech Republic); Pikarski Literary Agency Ltd (Gal Pikarski) (Israel); Lennart Sane Agency (Lennart Sane) (Iceland, Netherlands, Scandinavia, Sweden); Synopsis Literary Agency (Natalia Sanina) (Russia); Tuttle-Mori Agency Inc (Supanya Pratum) (Indonesia, Thailand, Vietnam); The Eric Yang Agency (Sue Yang) (Korea)

Goodman Associates (L)
500 West End Ave, New York, NY 10024
Tel: 212-873-4806
Key Personnel
Pres: Arnold P Goodman (AAR)
VP: Elise Simon Goodman
Founded: 1976
Adult book-length fiction & nonfiction. No plays, screenplays, poetry, textbooks, science fiction, children's books. No unsol mss, query first with SASE. No fees. Handle film & TV rights for clients' published materials. Representatives in Hollywood & major foreign markets. Accepting new clients by recommendation only.

Irene Goodman Literary Agency (L)
27 W 24 St, Suite 700B, New York, NY 10010
Tel: 212-604-0330
E-mail: queries@irenegoodman.com
Web Site: www.irenegoodman.com
Key Personnel
Pres: Irene Goodman (AAR) *E-mail:* irene.queries@irenegoodman.com
SVP: Beth Vesel *E-mail:* beth.queries@irenegoodman.com
VP: Miriam Kriss *E-mail:* miriam.queries@irenegoodman.com
Agent: Barbara Poelle *E-mail:* barbara.queries@irenegoodman.com; Rachel Ekstrom
E-mail: rachel.queries@irenegoodman.com
Mgr, Audio Rts: Sara Grubb
Founded: 1978
Commercial & literary fiction & nonfiction including mysteries, romance, women's fiction, thrillers & suspense. No poetry, inspirational fiction, screenplays or children's picture books. Handle film & TV rights through Steven Fisher in Los Angeles. No unsol mss, query first with first 10 pages & synopsis via e-mail. No snail

mail. See web site under submission guidelines for each agent's preferences. No reading fee.
Foreign Rep(s): Danny Baror
Foreign Rights: Baror International Agency

Sasha Goodman Agency Inc (L)
6680 Colgate Ave, Los Angeles, CA 90048
Tel: 310-387-0242 *Fax:* 323-653-3457
E-mail: ukseg@sbcglobal.net
Key Personnel
Owner: Sasha Goodman
Founded: 2012
Fiction (commercial & literary) & nonfiction, all areas. No unsol mss, query first. Submit outline & 2 sample chapters. No telephone queries; no reading fees. 15% agency commission.
Foreign Rights: Linda Michaels Agency (Worldwide)

Gotham Literary Agency (L)
170 E 83 St, New York, NY 10028
Tel: 212-249-2615
Key Personnel
Mng Ed: Nathalie Scott *E-mail:* nathalie@gothamliteraryagency.com
Founded: 2004
Specialize in mystery/thriller, romance, memoir, bio, celebrity, new thoughts, psychological suspense, women's fiction & chic-lit. No sci-fi, fantasy, gay/lesbian, short stories, poetry or children's books. We are actively seeking action thrillers, suspense, historical & contemporary paranormal. Submit a synopsis & author bio, each no more than 1 page, 1 side, double-spaced. Do not staple pages. Include first 3 chapters for fiction or a proposal for nonfiction. Include a large SASE if you want your materials returned. No reading fee. If accepted for representation, there is a charge for agency costs to submit your ms: copies, priority mail & a one half hour agency fee per submission. We also offer editing services, proposal development, critique & Spanish translation.
Titles recently placed: *Eagle's Gold*, Vince De Paul Lupiano

Doug Grad Literary Agency Inc (L)
68 Jay St, Suite W11, Brooklyn, NY 11201-1189
Tel: 718-788-6067
E-mail: query@dgliterary.com
Web Site: www.dgliterary.com
Key Personnel
Pres: Doug Grad *E-mail:* doug.grad@dgliterary.com
Assoc Agent: George Bick *Tel:* (917) 561-2038 *E-mail:* george.bick@dgliterary.com
Founded: 2008
Commercial fiction & nonfiction in a wide variety of genres & subjects. See web site for additional information. Send cover letter only with brief description of book. Will ask to see more material if interested, via e-mail only to query@dgliterary.com. Do not send hard copies of proposals or mss. No fees.
Titles recently placed: *A Vision of Fire: Book One of the EarthEnd Saga*, Gillian Anderson, Jeff Rovin; *Abandoned in Hell: The Fight for Vietnam's Fire Base Kate*, William Albracht, Marvin J Wolf; *Bounty*, Michael Byrnes; *Cobra King: How the 4th Armored Division Raced to Bastogne and Turned the Tide of the Battle of the Bulge*, Leo Barron; *Duke City Split*, Max Austin; *Gordie Howe's Son: A Hall of Fame Life in the Shadow of Mr Hockey*, Mark Howe, Jay Greenberg; *Growth*, Jeff Jacobson; *Here By the Bloods*, Brandon Boyce; *Lords of an Empty Land*, Randy Denmon; *Never Alone*, C J Carpenter; *The Field Guide to Sports Metaphors*, Josh Chetwynd
Foreign Rep(s): Baror International Inc (Worldwide)
Foreign Rights: Baror International Inc (Worldwide)

Graham Agency (D)
250 W 57 St, Suite 2430, New York, NY 10107
Tel: 212-489-7730
Key Personnel
Prop: Earl Graham
Founded: 1971
Full-length stage plays & musicals only. No unsol mss, query by mail first. Submit brief description. No reading fee, 10% commission.

Ashley Grayson Literary Agency (L)
1342 W 18 St, San Pedro, CA 90732
Tel: 310-548-4672
E-mail: graysonagent@earthlink.net; rights@graysonagency.com
Web Site: graysonagency.com/blog/
Key Personnel
Dir & Agent: Ashley Grayson (AAR); Carolyn Grayson (AAR) *E-mail:* carolyngraysonagent@earthlink.net
Agent: Lois Winston *E-mail:* lois.graysonagent@earthlink.net
Founded: 1976
Literary & commercial fiction, nonfiction & young adult; no poetry or short stories. No reading fee. No unsol mss, query first with e-mail. Include letter, first 3 pages of ms or outline of proposal. If querying about children's picture book, submit entire ms. We prefer to receive queries from previously published authors. Handle film & TV rights for books already represented; no original screenplays. Represent literary rights in all principal countries, also represent international publishers in US & UK.
Foreign Rights: Bestun Korea Literary Agency (Yumi Chun) (Korea); Lora Fountain & Associates (France); Graal Literary Agency (Poland)
Membership(s): Romance Writers of America; Science Fiction & Fantasy Writers of America; Society of Children's Book Writers & Illustrators

Sanford J Greenburger Associates Inc (L)
55 Fifth Ave, New York, NY 10003
Tel: 212-206-5600 *Fax:* 212-463-8718
Web Site: greenburger.com; www.sjga.com/
Key Personnel
VP: Heide Lange (AAR) *E-mail:* queryhl@sjga.com
Dir, Intl Rts: Stefanie Diaz *Tel:* 221-206-5628 *E-mail:* sdiaz@greenburger.com
Dir, Intl Scouting Dept: Agnes Krup *E-mail:* akrup@sjga.com
Agent: Matt Bialer *E-mail:* lribar@sjga.com; Brenda Bowen (AAR) *E-mail:* querybb@sjga.com; Faith Hamlin (AAR) *E-mail:* fhamlin@sjga.com; Daniel Mandel *E-mail:* querydm@sjga.com; Courtney Miller-Callihan *E-mail:* cmiller@sjga.com; Nicholas Ellison *E-mail:* nellison@sjga.com; Chelsea Lindman *E-mail:* clindman@sjga.com; Tom Miller
Children's & Young Adult Scout: Hanna Masaryk
Founded: 1932
Fiction, nonfiction, handle film & TV rights. No unsol mss. Query first. Submit outline or synopsis & sample chapter. No reading fee. Copying fee. Agents in all principal foreign countries.
Foreign Rights: Luigi Bernabo & Associates (Italy); Graal Agency (Poland); Deborah Harris Agency (Israel); Licht & Burr (Scandinavia); MB Agencia Literaria (Brazil, Catalonia, Galicia, Portugal, Spain); Mohrbooks (Germany); La Nouvelle Agence (France, Quebec, CN); Andrew Nurnberg Associates (Netherlands); Andrew Nurnberg Associates (Baltic) (Estonia, Latvia, Lithuania, Ukraine); Andrew Nurnberg Associates (Bucharest) (Romania); Andrew Nurnberg Associates (Budapest) (Croatia, Hungary); Andrew Nurnberg Associates International Ltd (China, Taiwan); Andrew Nurnberg Associates (Prague) (Czech Republic, Slovakia, Slovenia); Andrew Nurnberg Associates (Sofia) (Albania, Bulgaria, Macedonia, Serbia); Andrew Nurnberg Literary Agency (Russia); Read n Right Agency (Greece); Abner Stein Agency (UK); Tuttle-Mori Agency Inc (Indonesia, Japan, Thailand, Vietnam); Eric Yang Agency (Korea)

Jill Grinberg Literary Management LLC (L)
392 Vanderbilt Ave, Brooklyn, NY 11238
Tel: 212-620-5883
E-mail: info@jillgrinbergliterary.com
Web Site: www.jillgrinbergliterary.com
Key Personnel
Pres: Jill Grinberg (AAR) *E-mail:* jill@jillgrinbergliterary.com
Agent: Katelyn Detweiler (AAR) *E-mail:* katelyn@jillgrinbergliterary.com
Agent & Dir of Foreign & Subs Rts: Cheryl Pientka (AAR) *E-mail:* cherly@jillgrinbergliterary.com
Founded: 1999
Send query letter to info@jillgrinbergliterary.com. For fiction attach first 50 pages; for nonfiction send proposal (word document). Regular mail accepted but e-mail preferred.

Jill Grosjean Literary Agency (L)
1390 Millstone Rd, Sag Harbor, NY 11963
Tel: 631-725-7419 *Fax:* 631-725-8632
E-mail: JillLit310@aol.com
Key Personnel
Owner & Literary Agent: Jill Grosjean
Founded: 1999
Literary fiction, mystery/suspense, women's fiction. No unsol mss, query first; e-mail queries preferred, no downloads or attachments. No fees charged. Foreign rights in UK, France, Italy, Spain, Netherlands, South America.
Titles recently placed: *A Capacity for Murder*, Bernadette Pajer; *A Spark of Death*, Bernadette Pajer; *A Thread So Thin*, Marie Bostwick; *Beating the Babushka*, Tim Maleeny; *Comfort and Joy*, Marie Bostwick; *Emma and the Vampires*, Wayne Josephson; *Fatal Induction*, Bernadette Pajer; *I Love You Like a Tomato*, Marie Giordano; *Jump*, Tim Maleeny; *Murder in Time*, Julie McElwain; *Nectar*, David Fickett; *Shame*, Greg Garrett; *Snow Angels*, Marie Bostwick; *Spectres in the Smoke*, Tony Broadbent; *Spun Tales*, Felicia Donovan; *Stealing the Dragon*, Tim Maleeny; *The Black Widow Agency*, Felicia Donovan; *The Edison Effect*, Bernadette Pajer; *The Reluctant Journey of David Connors*, Don Locke; *The Smoke*, Tony Broadbent; *Thread of Truth*, Marie Bostwick; *Threading the Needle*, Marie Bostwick; *Tim Cratchit's Christmas Carol*, Jim Piecuch

Laura Gross Literary Agency Ltd (L)
PO Box 610326, Newton Highlands, MA 02461
Tel: 617-964-2977 *Fax:* 617-964-3023
E-mail: query@lg-la.com
Web Site: www.lg-la.com
Key Personnel
Pres: Laura Gross (AAR)
Founded: 1988
No unsol mss, query or e-mail first. On web site, submit query using form: lg-la.com/contact. Fiction, commercial & literary; nonfiction, serious topics, social, political, cultural issues & psychology. Include list of previous publications & bio. No reading fee.
Foreign Rights: Teri Tobias Agency LLC (Worldwide exc UK)

The Charlotte Gusay Literary Agency (L-D)
10532 Blythe Ave, Los Angeles, CA 90064
Tel: 310-559-0831 *Fax:* 310-559-2639
E-mail: gusay1@ca.rr.com (queries only)
Web Site: www.gusay.com

Founded: 1988

Fiction & nonfiction, screenplay, children & adult, humor, parenting; crossover literary/commercial fiction; gardening, women's & men's issues, feminism, psychology, memoir, biography, travel. Handle film & TV rights. Represent selected illustrators, especially children's. No unsol mss, query first with SASE; ONLY when agency requests, submit one page synopsis & first three chapters or first 50 pages (for fiction); proposal (for nonfiction). Include SASE. No reading fee. For borderline queries we sometimes give prospective clients the benefit of the doubt & impose a nominal processing fee allowing the prospective clients to decide whether to submit their material or not. Once client is signed, client is responsible for providing agency hard copies of mss (as necessary) & shipping expenses (as necessary).

Titles recently placed: *Bar Flaubert*, Alexis Stamatis; *Chorus: A Literary Mixtape*, Saul Williams; *Forty-One Seconds to Freedom: An Insider's Account of the Lima Hostage Crisis, 1996-97*, Admiral Luis Giampietrei, Bill Salisbury, Lorena Ausejo; *Light a Penny Candle (film rts)*, Maeve Binchy; *Mother Ash*, Alexis Stamatis; *Outrageous Fortune: Growing Up at Leeds Castle*, Anthony Russell; *Richard Landry Estates*, Lynn Morgan; *What Angels Know: The Story of Elizabeth Barrett & Robert Browning*, Phil Davis (screenplay); *Wild West 2.0: How to Protect & Restore Your Reputation on the Untamed Social Frontier*, Michael Fertik, David Thompson

Foreign Rep(s): The Fielding Agency (Whitney Lee) (Worldwide)

Membership(s): The Authors Guild; PEN Center USA West; Writers Guild of America West

Lisa Hagan Literary (L)
110 Martin Dr, Bracey, VA 23919
Tel: 434-636-4138
E-mail: LisaHaganLiterary@yahoo.com
Web Site: www.publishersmarketplace.com/members/LisaHagan/
Key Personnel
Owner, Pres & Agent: Lisa Hagan
Founded: 1985

Business/investing/finance, health, memoir, mind/body/spirit, science, self-help, travel, political. No unsol mss, query first with letter & proposal. Submit outline & sample chapters. Handles film & TV rights. No fee charged.

Titles recently placed: *101 Ways to Enhance Your Bliss*, Amy Leigh Mercree; *501 Ways to Roll Out the Red Carpet for Your Customers*, Donna Cutting; *A Little Book of Buddha*, Chad Mercree; *Connecting with Coincidence*, Dr Bernard Beitman; *From Worry to Wealthy: A Woman's Guide to Financial Success Without the Stress*, Chellie Campbell; *Mind Wars: The History of Mind Control and Electronic Surveillance*, Marie D Jones, Larry Flaxman; *Nessie: Tales of the Loch Ness Monster*, Nick Redfern; *The Alchemy of Self Healing: A Revolutionary 30-Day Plan to Change How You Relate to Your Body and Health*, Jeannine Wiest; *The E-Word: Ego, Enlightenment & Other Essentials*, Cate Montana; *The Gift of Cancer: A Miraculous Journey to Healing*, Brenda Michaels, Marsha Mercant; *The Holistic Heart Book: A Preventive Cardiologist's Guide to Halt Heart Disease Now*, Joel K Kahn, MD; *Trust, Inc.: How to Create a Business Culture That Will Ignite Passion, Engagement, and Innovation*, Nan Russell; *Use the Force: The Jedi Science Behind the Law of Attraction*, Joshua Warren

The Mitchell J Hamilburg Agency (L-D)
149 S Barrington Ave, Suite 732, Los Angeles, CA 90049
Tel: 310-471-4024 *Fax:* 310-471-9588
Key Personnel
Owner & Literary Agent: Michael Hamilburg

Fiction & nonfiction. No unsol mss, query first. Submit outline & two sample chapters, include SASE. Handle film & TV rights. No reading fee. No software.

Founded in the 1930s, literary agency since 1967.

The Joy Harris Literary Agency Inc (L)
381 Park Ave S, Suite 428, New York, NY 10016
Tel: 212-924-6269 *Fax:* 212-725-5275
E-mail: contact@jhlitagent.com
Web Site: www.joyharrisliterary.com
Key Personnel
Pres: Joy Harris (AAR) *E-mail:* joyharris@jhlitagent.com
Agent & Subs Rts: Adam Reed *E-mail:* adamreed@jhlitagent.com

No unsol mss, query first. No poetry, screenplays or self-help.

Foreign Rights: Andrew Nurnberg Associates (Europe exc Greece, Italy, Turkey & UK); Roberto Santachiara Agency (Italy)

Hartline Literary Agency LLC (L)
123 Queenston Dr, Pittsburgh, PA 15235
Web Site: www.hartlineliterary.com
Key Personnel
Owner & CEO: Joyce Hart *E-mail:* joyce@hartlineliterary.com
VP & Agent: Jim Hart *E-mail:* jim@hartlineliterary.com
Agent: Terry Burns *E-mail:* terry@hartlineliterary.com; Diana Flegal *E-mail:* diana@hartlineliterary.com; Linda Glaz *E-mail:* linda@hartlineliterary.com; Andy Scheer *Tel:* 719-282-3729 *E-mail:* andy@hartlineliterary.com
Founded: 1992

Advise clients on how to prepare proposals & advise them concerning what various publishers are looking for. Also help clients plan their literary careers. Our expertise is in the Christian market & we also work in the general market. Looking for clean, wholesome fiction for adults & inspiring nonfiction. Mss reflecting a Christian worldview preferred, even for the general market. Fiction: romance, romantic suspense, women's fiction, mystery/suspense, humor, chick/mom lit & general fiction. Nonfiction: self-help, Christian living, prayer, health, humor & business.

Accepts unsol mss. Submit cover letter, author bio, marketing analysis, summary & 3 sample chapters. If submitting via e-mail, send as an attachment & send the entire submission in one file. We do not accept submissions in multiple files. We accept e-mail, US mail, UPS & FedEx submissions. See web site for complete submission details. No fees.

Titles recently placed: *A Light in the Wilderness*, Jane Kirkpatrick; *A Search for Purple Cows*, Susan Call; *Bash and the Pirate Pig*, Burton Cole; *Charming Nancy*, Suzanne Woods Fisher; *Deadliest in Show*, Christy Barritt; *Deadly Safari*, Lisa Harris; *Dynamo*, Ellie Gustafson; *Following Rain*, Darrel Nelson; *For Such a Time as This*, Kate Breslin; *Friend Me*, Jay Fabion; *Let's Talk Dementia*, Carol Howell; *Love Finds You in Lake Geneva, WI*, Pamela S Meyers; *Man's Best Hero*, Ace Collins; *Missing Person Task Forces Series*, Lisa Harris; *Music for Your Heart*, Ace Collins; *Of Vines and Roses*, Linda Rondeau; *One Glorious Ambition*, Jane Kirkpatrick; *Petticoat Row*, Suzanne Woods Fisher; *Protecting the Widow's Heart*, Lorraine Beatty; *Remants of Love*, Lorraine Beatty; *Ruth, Mother of Kings*, Diana Wallis Taylor; *Small Town Mom*, Jean Gordon; *Smuggler's Cove*, Christy Barritt; *Stolen Identity*, Lisa Harris; *The Bishop's Family (series)*, Suzanne Woods Fisher; *The Butterfly and the Violin*, Kristy Cambron; *The Color of Justice*, Ace Collins; *The Fruitcake Murders*, Ace Collins; *The Maze*, Jason Brannon; *The Preacher's Wife Wears Biker Boots*, Karla Akins; *The Quakers of New Gardon*, Jennifer Hudson Taylor, Claire Sanders, Ann Schrock, Susette Williams; *The Top Ten Most Outrageous Couples in the Bible*, David Clarke; *Wedding on the Rocks*, Rose Zediker

Membership(s): American Christian Fiction Writers

John Hawkins and Associates Inc (L)
71 W 23 St, Suite 1600, New York, NY 10010
Tel: 212-807-7040
E-mail: jha@jhalit.com
Web Site: jhalit.com
Key Personnel
Pres & Foreign Rts Dir: Moses Cardona *E-mail:* moses@jhalit.com
Agent: William Reiss (AAR) *E-mail:* reiss@jhalit.com; Warren Frazier *E-mail:* frazier@jhalit.com; Anne Hawkins (AAR) *E-mail:* ahawkins@jhalit.com
Perms & Rts: Liz Free *E-mail:* free@jhalit.com
Founded: 1893 (by Paul R Reynolds)

No unsol mss, query first. Submit one-page bio & 1- to 3-page outline with SASE. No reading fee. Photocopy charges & fees for other services. Handle film & TV rights, software.

Titles recently placed: *Beautiful Ruins*, Jess Walter; *Behind the Shattered Glass*, Tasha Alexander; *Black Dahlia White Rose*, Joyce Carol Oates; *Daddy Love*, Joyce Carol Oates; *Flora*, Gail Godwin; *High Treason*, John Gilstrap; *Now I'll Tell You Everything*, Phyllis Reynolds Naylor; *The Accused*, Joyce Carol Oates; *The Affairs of Others*, Amy Grace Loyd; *The Doll*, Taylor Stevens; *The Orphan Master's Son*, Adam Johnson; *The Right Side of Wrong: A Red River Mystery*, Reavis S Wortham; *The Star of Istanbul*, Robert Olen Butler

Foreign Rep(s): Sara Menguc Inc (UK)

The Jeff Herman Agency LLC (L)
29 Park St, Stockbridge, MA 01262
Mailing Address: PO Box 1522, Stockbridge, MA 01262
Tel: 413-298-0077 *Fax:* 413-298-8188
E-mail: submissions@jeffherman.com
Web Site: www.jeffherman.com
Key Personnel
Pres: Jeffrey H Herman *E-mail:* jeff@jeffherman.com
VP: Deborah Levine
Founded: 1985

Nonfiction, reference, health, self-help, how-to business, technology, spirituality & textbooks. No unsol mss, query first with letter & SASE. No reading fee. Handle software, film & TV rights. Agents in all principal foreign countries.

Foreign Rep(s): Asano (Japan); De la Concha (Portugal, Spain)

Susan Herner Rights Agency Inc (L)
10 Upper Shad Rd, Pound Ridge, NY 10576
Tel: 914-234-2864 *Fax:* 914-234-2866
E-mail: sherneragency@optonline.net
Key Personnel
Pres: Susan N Herner
Founded: 1987

A full service literary agency representing a broad range of fiction & nonfiction authors. Not looking for new clients at the present time.

Hill Nadell Literary Agency (L)
8899 Beverly Blvd, Suite 805, Los Angeles, CA 90048
Tel: 310-860-9605 *Fax:* 310-860-9672
E-mail: queries@hillnadell.com; rights@hillnadell.com (rts & perms)
Web Site: www.hillnadell.com
Key Personnel
Pres: Bonnie Nadell

Agent: Dara Hyde
Founded: 1979
Literary & commercial fiction, narrative nonfiction, current affairs, memoirs & pop culture; film & TV rights only if handling the book. No unsol mss, query first with SASE. No reading fee. Co-agents in various foreign countries.
Titles recently placed: *Bellweather Rhapsody*, Kate Racculia; *Fridays at Enrico's*, Don Carpenter, Jonathan Lethem (Afterword); *Living with Shakespeare: Essays by Writers, Actors, and Directors*, Susannah Carson; *My Paris Kitchen*, David Lebovitz; *Night in Shanghai*, Nicole Mones; *O, Africa!*, Andrew Lewis Conn; *S Street Rising*, Ruben Castaneda; *Signifying Rappers*, David Foster Wallace, Mark Costello; *The Beatles Are Here!: 50 Years after the Band Arrived in America, Writers, Musicians & Other Fans Remember*, Penelope Rowlands; *The Faraway Nearby*, Rebecca Solnit; *The Pale King*, David Foster Wallace; *Virgin Soul*, Judy Juanita
Foreign Rights: ILA (Western Europe)

The Barbara Hogenson Agency Inc (L-D)
165 West End Ave, Suite 19-C, New York, NY 10023
Tel: 212-874-8084 *Fax:* 212-595-6748
E-mail: bhogenson@aol.com
Key Personnel
Pres: Barbara Hogenson (AAR)
Contract Mgr: Lori Styler
Founded: 1994
Recommendation by clients only. Literary fiction, nonfiction, full length plays, consider some illustrated books. No screenplays or teleplays. No fees.
Membership(s): The Authors Guild; Authors Registry; The Dramatists Guild of America; Society of Stage Directors & Choreographers; Writers Guild of America

Henry Holmes Literary Agent/Book Publicist/Marketing Consultant (L)
PO Box 433, Swansea, MA 02777
Tel: 508-672-2258
E-mail: henryholmesandassociates@yahoo.com
Key Personnel
Pres & Literary Agent: Henry Holmes
Founded: 1997
Nonfiction, no unsol mss, query first. Send query letter with chapters 1 & 2. If published, include past publicity, endorsement(s) etc. SASE. Ten mailings sent to preferred publishers via mss/CDs (this includes publisher research, query letter, packing, mailing, etc, at competitive rates. Independent of my representation, professional consultation via freelance assignments/project work would be based on involvement & duration of project based on competitive fees. Specialize in consulting, marketing, media publicity, talk show placement, etc. 15% standard commission. No reading fee. Retainer fee charged if ms is acceptable.

Hornfischer Literary Management LP (L)
PO Box 50544, Austin, TX 78763
Tel: 512-472-0011
E-mail: queries@hornfischerlit.com
Web Site: www.hornfischerlit.com
Key Personnel
Pres: Jim Hornfischer *E-mail:* jim@hornfischerlit.com
Founded: 2001
Quality narrative nonfiction, biography & autobiography, current events, US history, military history & world history, political & cultural subjects science, medicine/health, business/management/finance, academic writing & research that has a general-interest audience. No unsol mss; query first through e-mail, no longer accept queries through mail. No fees.
Titles recently placed: *A Curious Madness: An American Combat Psychiatrist, a Japanese War Crimes Suspect, and an Unsolved Mystery from World War II*, Eric Jaffe; *Area 51*, Annie Jacobsen; *Brothers, Rivals, Victors*, Jonathan Jordan; *Operation Paperclip: The Secret Intelligence Program that Brought Nazi Scientists to America*, Annie Jacobsen; *Outlaw Platoon*, Sean Parnell, John Bruning; *Running the Maze (Sniper)*, Jack Coughlin, Donald A Davis; *The Guerrilla Factory: The Making of Special Forces Officers, the Green Berets*, Tony Schwalm; *The Liberator*, Alex Kershaw; *The Possibility Dogs: What a Handful of "Unadoptables" Taught Me About Service, Hope, and Healing*, Susannah Charleston; *The Second Nuclear Age: Strategy, Danger, and the New Power Politics*, Paul Bracken; *The Trident: The Forging and Reforging of a Navy SEAL Leader*, Jason Redman, John Bruning; *Under Fire: The Untold Story of the Attack in Benghazi*, Fred Burton, Samuel M Katz; *Verdun: The Lost History of the Most Important Battle of World War I, 1914-1918*, John Mosier

ICM Partners (L-D)
730 Fifth Ave, New York, NY 10019
Tel: 212-556-5600
Web Site: www.icmtalent.com
Key Personnel
Partner: Kristine Dahl; Sloan Harris; Jennifer Joel; Esther Newberg; Amanda Urban
Head, Book-to-Film Dept, Los Angeles: Josie Freedman
Literary Agent: Lisa Bankoff (AAR); Helen Brann; Kristyn Keene; Dan Kirschen; Alexandra Machinist; Kari Stuart
Founded: 1975
Handle film & TV rights. No unsol mss, query first. No reading fee. Offices in New York, Los Angeles & London.
Branch Office(s)
10250 Constellation Blvd, Los Angeles, CA 90067 *Tel:* 310-550-4000
Foreign Office(s): Marlborough House, 3rd fl, 10 Earlham St, London WC2H 9LN, United Kingdom *Tel:* (020) 7836 8564

ICM/Sagalyn (L)
1250 Connecticut Ave, 7th fl, Washington, DC 20036
Tel: 202-419-1525
E-mail: query@sagalyn.com
Web Site: www.sagalyn.com
Key Personnel
Owner: Raphael Sagalyn (AAR)
Quality nonfiction & mainstream fiction. No romance, westerns, science fiction, poetry, children's books or screenplays. No unsol mss, query first with e-mail. Handle film & TV rights. No reading fee.
Foreign Rights: Akcali Agency (Turkey); Carmen Balcells Agency (Spain); Bardon-Chinese Media (China); Graal Literary Agency (Poland); Greene & Heaton (UK); The Deborah Harris Agency (Israel); Japan Uni Agency (Japan); JLM Literary Agency (Greece); Korea Copyright Center (Korea); Michelle Lapautre (France); Licht & Burr (Scandinavia); Mohrbooks (Germany); Prava i Prevodi (Eastern Europe); Riff Agency (Lucia Riff) (Brazil); Synopsis Agency (Russia); Caroline Van Gelderen Agency (Holland); Suzanne Zevi Agency (Italy)

InkWell Management (L)
521 Fifth Ave, 26th fl, New York, NY 10175
Tel: 212-922-3500 *Fax:* 212-922-0535
E-mail: info@inkwellmanagement.com; submissions@inkwellmanagement.com
Web Site: inkwellmanagement.com
Key Personnel
Founder & Pres: Michael Carlisle; Richard S Pine; Kim Witherspoon *E-mail:* kim@inkwellmanagement.com
Dir, Subs Rts: Lyndsey Blessing; Alexis Hurley *E-mail:* alexis@inkwellmanagement.com
Agent: Stephen Barbara; William Callahan; David Forrer; George Lucas; Jacqueline Murphy; Charlie Olsen; David Hale Smith; Lauren Smythe
Busn Mgr: Jennifer Witherell *E-mail:* jwitherell@inkwellmanagement.com
PR & Soc Media Strategist: Lisa Vanterpool
Founded: 2004 (created through the merger of Arthur Pine Associates Inc, Carlisle & Co LLC & Witherspoon Associates Inc)
General nonfiction & fiction books. No screenplays, plays, poetry. Motion picture, TV & foreign rights. No unsol mss, query first with SASE; submissions must be on an exclusive basis. No fees.
Foreign Rights: Anthea (Bulgaria); Graal Literary Agency (Poland); JLM (Greece); Katia & Bolza (Hungary); Simona Kessler (Romania); Korea Copyright Center (Korea); Michelle Lapautre (France); Maxima (Indonesia); MB Agency (Latin America, Portugal, Spain); Mohrbooks (Germany); Andrew Nurnberg Associates (China, Estonia, Latvia, Lithuania, Taiwan); Kristin Olson (Czech Republic, Slovakia); ONK Agency (Turkey); Pikarski (Israel); Prava I Prevodi (Albania, Croatia, Serbia, Slovenia); Riff (Brazil); Sane Toregard (Scandinavia); Roberto Santachiara (Italy); Serbes & van Golderen Literary Agency (Netherlands); Synopsis (Russia); Tuttle-Mori Agency Inc (Japan, Thailand, Vietnam); Eric Yang (Korea)

InterLicense Ltd (L)
110 Country Club Dr, Suite A, Mill Valley, CA 94941
Tel: 415-381-9780 *Fax:* 415-381-6485
E-mail: interlicense@sbcglobal.net; ilicense@aol.com
Key Personnel
Exec Dir: Manfred Mroczkowski
Subsidiary rights with focus on foreign rights agency & management, sales, administrations & on domestic subsidiary rights such as film, reprint, TV & merchandising rights. No unsol mss, query first. Handle software. Submit synopsis & sample chapters. Nonfiction. No reading fee. Charge for consultations.

International Titles (L)
931 E 56 St, Austin, TX 78751-1724
Tel: 512-909-2447
Web Site: www.internationaltitles.com
Key Personnel
Dir: Loris Essary *E-mail:* loris@internationaltitles.com
Represent all genres; primary emphasis on sales of foreign rights. No fees charged, no submission policy.

International Transactions Inc (L)
28 Alope Way, Gila, NM 88038
Mailing Address: PO Box 97, Gila, NM 88038
Tel: 845-373-9696 *Fax:* 480-393-5162
E-mail: info@intltrans.com
Web Site: www.intltrans.com
Key Personnel
Pres: Peter Riva *E-mail:* priva@intltrans.com
VP & Dir: Sandra Anne Riva *E-mail:* sriva@intltrans.com
Assoc Ed: JoAnn Collins *E-mail:* jcollins@intltrans.com
Founded: 1975
International literary & licensing agency. Specialize in nonfiction (including large projects), fiction, illustrated & children's. We cannot help every prospective author nor can we review

every ms. Send a fiction submission query (only) to Submission-Fiction@IntlTrans.com. If, within three weeks, we are interested, we will call for more material. In the case of nonfiction authors, each query for submission must include a one-page summary of the book proposed as well as a brief description of the author's bona fides or expertise as author, including links to any media platform he or she may be able to employ. Send the nonfiction submission query to Submission-NonFiction@IntlTrans.com. Also handles film & TV rights. No fees.

Titles recently placed: *Aung Sung Suu Kyi*, Jesper Bengtsson; *Bell of the Desert*, Alan Gold; *Bringing Up Oscar*, Debra Ann Pawlak; *Drive on Moscow*, Niklas Zetterling; *Evil of the Age*, Allan Levine; *Fire Knife Dancing*, John Enright; *Flame Angels*, Robert Wintner; *Flypaper*, Chris Angus; *Neptune Speaks*, Robert Wintner; *One More River*, Mary Glickman; *Pago Pago Tango*, John Enright; *Painting the Corners*, Bob Weintraub; *Sail of Stone*, Ake Edwardson; *Secret Heart: The Lives of Robert Ryan*, J R Jones; *The Black Hills*, Rod Thompson; *The Last Titanic Story*, Chris Angus; *The Sleeping & the Dead*, Jeff Crook; *The Square of Revenge*, Pieter Aspe; *The Tao of Joy Every Day: 365 Days of Tao Living*, Derek Lin

Foreign Office(s): Rechtsanwalt Roth, Gewurzmuhlstr 5, 80538 Munich, Germany *Tel:* (089) 55 26 26 55

JABberwocky Literary Agency Inc (L)
49 W 45 St, 12th fl, New York, NY 10036
Tel: 917-388-3010 *Fax:* 917-388-2998
Web Site: www.awfulagent.com
Founded: 1994
Full line of fiction & nonfiction trade books, particularly genre fiction (science fiction, fantasy, mystery, horror), literary fiction, young adult & middle grade & serious nonfiction (biography, science, history). No unsol mss, query first with biographical information & SASE. Will request mss after reviewing query if interested. Handle film & TV rights for regular clients. No reading fee. No fax or e-mail queries & always check web site to see which agents are currently accepting queries.
Titles recently placed: *Alcatraz (5th in series)*, Brandon Sanderson; *All Rights Reserved*, Gret Katsoulis; *America Rising*, William C Dietz; *Duskfall*, Christopher Husberg; *Mystic*, Jason Denzel; *Secret Histories (10th in series)*, Simon R Green; *Slotter Key*, Elizabeth Moon; *The Unnoticeables*, Robert Brockway
Foreign Rep(s): AnatoliaLit Agency (Turkey); ANAW (Poland); Tassy Barham Associates (Brazil); Book Publishers Association (Israel); Bookman (Scandinavia); The English Agency (Japan) Ltd (Japan); Paul & Peter Fritz AG (Germany); The Grayhawk Agency (China, Indonesia, Taiwan, Thailand, Vietnam); Danny Hong Agency (Korea); Katai & Bolza (Hungary); Simona Kessler (Romania); Alexander Korzhenevski (Russia); Agence Litteraire Lenclud (France); Piergiorgio Nicolazzini (Italy); Andrew Nurnberg (Baltic States); Kristin Olson (Czech Republic); Prava I Prevodi (Albania, Bulgaria, Croatia, Serbia, Slovenia); Read N Right (Greece); Julio F Yanez (Portugal, Spain); Zeno Agency Ltd (UK)
Membership(s): Science Fiction & Fantasy Writers of America

Melanie Jackson Agency LLC (L)
41 W 72 St, Suite 3F, New York, NY 10023
Tel: 212-873-3373
Key Personnel
Owner & Agent: Melanie Jackson
Perms: Julia Lee McGill
No unsol mss, query first.
Foreign Rep(s): Liepman Agency (Germany); Rogers, Coleridge & White (UK); Roberto Santachiara (Italy)

James Peter Associates Inc (L)
PO Box 358, New Canaan, CT 06840
Tel: 203-972-1070
Web Site: www.jamespeterassociates.com
Key Personnel
Pres: Gene Brissie *E-mail:* gene_brissie@msn.com
Founded: 1971
Nonfiction only, all subject areas. Handle software, film & TV rights through sub-agents in many foreign countries. No unsol mss, query first with SASE. Submit brief description of book, potential market, chapter outline, one sample chapter, competitive titles & author's credentials. No reading fee.

Janklow & Nesbit Associates (L)
445 Park Ave, New York, NY 10022
Tel: 212-421-1700 *Fax:* 212-980-3671
E-mail: info@janklow.com
Web Site: www.janklowandnesbit.com
Key Personnel
Sr Partner: Morton L Janklow
Partner: Lynn Nesbit
SVP: Anne Sibbald
VP & Dir, Foreign Rts: Cullen Stanley
Agent: Lucas W Janklow; Kirby Kim; P J Mark; Richard Morris; Emma Parry
Founded: 1989 (successor to Morton L Janklow Assoc Inc founded in 1975)
General fiction & nonfiction. Handle film & TV rights for book represented; no reading fee.
Foreign Office(s): Janklow & Nesbit (UK) Ltd, 13-A Hillgate St, London W87SP, United Kingdom, Contact: Tim Glister *Tel:* (020) 7243 2975 *Fax:* (020) 7243 4339 *E-mail:* queries@janklow.co.uk *Web Site:* www.janklowandnesbit.co.uk

Janus Literary Agency (L)
PO Box 837, Methuen, MA 01844
Tel: 978-273-4227
E-mail: janusliteraryagency@gmail.com
Web Site: janusliteraryagency.com
Key Personnel
Owner: Lenny Cavallaro
Founded: 1980
No new clients at this time. No reading fee. Possible handling fees if agency represents author & deals with editors via hard copy; none for electronic submissions. Provide editing, ghostwriting services +/or rewrites for a fee; also consultation on digital publication & POD/self-publication. No unsol mss, query first by e-mail only without attachments unless requested. Nonfiction: prospectus, outline, sample chapter. No longer handling fiction. Will reply only if interested.

Jellinek & Murray Literary Agency (L-D)
47-231 Kamakoi Rd, Kaneohe, HI 96744
Tel: 808-239-8451
Key Personnel
Pres: Roger Jellinek *E-mail:* rgr.jellinek@gmail.com
Founded: 1995
General adult fiction & nonfiction. No genre fiction. No unsol mss, query first with an e-mail. Submit proposal, outline, 2 sample chapters, author bio & credentials & platform, by e-mail. No reading fees. Handle film & TV rights.

Carolyn Jenks Agency (L-D)
30 Cambridge Park Dr, Suite 3140, Cambridge, MA 02140
Tel: 617-354-5099 *Fax:* 617-354-5099
E-mail: queries@carolynjenksagency.com (submissions)
Web Site: www.carolynjenksagency.com
Key Personnel
Owner & Dir: Carolyn Jenks
E-mail: carolynjenks@comcast.net
Agent-at-Large: Tildy Banker Johnson
Sr Agent: Eric Wing
Founded: 1979
Literary & commercial fiction & nonfiction. All genres. Theatre, film & screenwriters represented. Signatory to Writers Guild of America. Contact by e-mail or via web site. Electronic submissions only; prefer query via web site. No fees charged.
Titles recently placed: *Magnolia City*, Duncan Alderson; *Sinners & the Sea*, Rebecca Kanner; *Tale of Two Maidens*, Anne Echols; *The Coal Elf*, Maria de Vivo; *The Dagger Quick*, Brian Eames; *The Dagger X*, Brian Eames; *Tragedy and Trust*, Thom Vines
Membership(s): Writers Guild of America

JET Literary Associates Inc (L)
941 Calle Mejia, Suite 507, Santa Fe, NM 87501
Tel: 212-971-2494 (NY voice mail); 505-780-0721
E-mail: query@jetliterary.com
Web Site: www.jetliterary.wordpress.com
Key Personnel
Pres (Austria off): Jim Trupin *E-mail:* jetlit@hotmail.com
VP: Elizabeth Trupin-Pulli *E-mail:* etp@jetliterary.com
Founded: 1975
General book-length fiction & nonfiction. Specialize in adult fiction & commercial nonfiction; no plays, poetry, science fiction/fantasy, young adult or books for young children. No unsol mss, query first, preferably via e-mail. No reading fees. Mail & copying charges to be reimbursed. Full representation in all foreign markets.
Foreign Office(s): Esterhazygasse 9A/26, 1060 Vienna, Austria *Tel:* (01) 587 0077 *Fax:* (01) 587 0077
Foreign Rep(s): Eliane Benisti (France); Big Apple Agency Inc (China); Educational Materials Enterprises (Greece); Fritz Agency (Germany); Nurcihan Kesim Literary Agency Inc (Turkey); Kohn (Netherlands); Lennart Sane (Sweden); Living Literary Agency (Italy); Tuttle-Mori Agency Inc (Japan); Julio F Yanez (Brazil, Spain)
Foreign Rights: Abner Stein Agency (UK)

JMW Group Inc (L)
One West Ave, Suite 219, Larchmont, NY 10538
Tel: 914-834-7800 *Fax:* 914-834-7824
E-mail: info@jmwgroup.net
Web Site: jmwgroup.net
Key Personnel
Pres: William Diedrick
VP, Rts: Brice Diedrick *E-mail:* bdiedrick@att.net
Founded: 1949
Rights agency; no fees charged.

Jody Rein Books Inc (L)
7741 S Ash Ct, Centennial, CO 80122
Tel: 303-694-9386
Web Site: www.jodyreinbooks.com
Key Personnel
Pres: Jody Rein (AAR) *E-mail:* jodyrein@jodyreinbooks.com
Literary Assoc & Off Mgr: Johnna Hietala
E-mail: jhietala@jodyreinbooks.com
Founded: 1994
Author representation for existing clients only, no new agented clients. Specialize in adult narrative & commercial nonfiction. Some literary fiction. Handle film & TV rights through

agents. See also Author Planet Publishing Services listing.
Titles recently placed: *In the Cradle of Storms*, Mark Obmascik; *Sensational Kids Revised Edition*, Lucy Jane Miller; *Teaching Savages to Fly*, Logan Ward
Foreign Rep(s): The English Agency (Japan); Grayhawk Agency (China, Taiwan); Japan UNI (Japan); Eric Yang Agency (Korea)
Foreign Rights: Judy Klein (Worldwide exc China, Japan, Korea, Thailand & USA)
Membership(s): The Authors Guild

Jones Hutton Literary Associates (L)
140D Heritage Way, Southbury, CT 06488
Tel: 203-558-4478
E-mail: huttonbooks@hotmail.com
Key Personnel
Mng Ed: Caroline DuBois Hutton
Founded: 1994
Welcomes new & established writers. Will work closely with clients to get material into the best possible shape for presentation to editors at various publishing houses. Works with publishers both in the US & abroad. Handles mainly nonfiction in many categories, but always on the lookout for good new novels. Handles only a few authors at a time & gives to each the utmost personal attention. Turnaround time is short, usually less than two weeks. Earns fees from advances & royalties (15% domestic & 20% foreign sales). No reading or submission fees. For nonfiction, form for proposal may be e-mailed upon request. For fiction, a one- to two-page synopsis is required, as well as a short author's biography & two to three chapters of the novel. Please send all submissions by hard copy after first querying via e-mail. Affiliates in both editing & PR fields are available for referral.

The Karpfinger Agency (L)
357 W 20 St, New York, NY 10011-3379
Tel: 212-691-2690 *Fax:* 212-691-7129
E-mail: info@karpfinger.com (no queries or submissions)
Web Site: karpfinger.com
Key Personnel
Owner: Barney M Karpfinger
Foreign Rts Mgr: Cathy Jaque
Agent: Kate Garrick
Contact: Matt Spindler
Founded: 1985
Quality fiction & nonfiction. No unsol mss. Query first by mail only. See web site for specific instructions. No reading fee. Direct representation in all foreign markets.

Keller Media Inc (L)
578 Washington Blvd, No 745, Marina del Rey, CA 90292
Toll Free Tel: 800-278-8706
E-mail: query@kellermedia.com
Web Site: kellermedia.com/query
Key Personnel
CEO & Sr Agent: Wendy Keller
Assoc Agent: Megan Close
Edit Dir: Alex Schnitzler
Founded: 1989
Represent only nonfiction in these categories: business (sales, management, marketing); finance; self-help (parenting, women's issues, relationships, pop psychology, etc.); health (alternative & allopathic); metaphysical/spiritual/inspirational (never religious); nature, science, archaeology, reference, how-to (do anything). Do not send poetry, scripts, your memoir unless you are a celebrity, fiction, religious or juvenile books, or first person accounts of overcoming some medical or mental condition. Most of agency's authors are either experts in their field, successful professional speakers, have their own radio, infomercial or television program, or are a household name. For best results, fill in the simple form on the web site. Please do not mail your self-published book unless we request it. No reading fee.
Titles recently placed: *Disruptive Marketing*, Geoffrey Colon; *Entrepreneurial Thinking*, Jeffrey Hayzlett; *In the Garden of Happiness*, Dodinsky; *The History of Television*, Seth Shapiro; *The Millionaire Master Plan*, Roger James Hamilton; *The People Equation: Innovation Implementation*, Deborah Perry Piscione
Membership(s): National Association for Female Executives; National Speakers Association; United States Women's Chamber of Commerce

Natasha Kern Literary Agency Inc (L)
PO Box 1069, White Salmon, WA 98672
Tel: 509-493-3803
E-mail: agent@natashakern.com
Web Site: www.natashakern.com
Key Personnel
Pres: Natasha Kern *E-mail:* natasha@natashakern.com
Busn & Translation Rts Mgr: Jack Lauer
Sr Agent: Susan Bower *E-mail:* susan@natashakern.com
Agent: Athena Kern *E-mail:* athena@natashakern.com
Founded: 1986
Represent commercial adult fiction, inspirational fiction & young adult fiction. Actively represent all women's fiction; multicultural fiction; mainstream fiction; inspirational, historical & contemporary romance; romantic suspense, thrillers, and all subgenres of mysteries from cozies to PIs. DO NOT represent children's, horror, science fiction, short stories, poetry, sports, scholarly or coffee-table books. Handle film & TV rights only on represented books. Represented in all principal foreign countries as well as in Hollywood. No unsol mss, query first via e-mail (queries@natashakern.com). Please look at web site for submission info. Queries by mail are not accepted. Will respond only if interested. Include a 2-3 page synopsis & the first chapter of the novel.
Titles recently placed: *By Your Side*, Candace Calvert; *Gunpowder Tea*, Margaret Brownley; *Indulgences: The Marriage of Martin Luther and Katharina Von Bora*, Jody Hedlund; *Once Upon A Plaid*, Mia Marlowe; *Saving Amelie*, Cathy Gohlke; *Soul of Fire*, Eliott Pattison; *Striking Distance*, Pamela Clare; *The Bracelet*, Dorothy Love; *The Miracle Thief*, Iris Anthony; *The Perfect Affair*, Lutishia Lovely; *The Sharp Hook of Love*, Sherry Jones; *The Summer of Me*, Angela Benson; *To Win Her Favor*, Tamera Alexander
Foreign Rep(s): Carmen Balcells (Spain); Agence Eliane Benisti (France); Luigi Bernabo (Italy); Phillip Chen (China, Taiwan); Prava i Prevodi (Eastern Europe); Lucia Riff (Brazil); Lennart Sane (Scandinavia); Junzo Sawa (Japan); Tom Schlueck (Germany); Lorna Soifer (Israel)

Louise B Ketz Agency (L)
414 E 78 St, Suite 1-B, New York, NY 10075
Tel: 212-249-0668
E-mail: ketzagency@aol.com
Key Personnel
Pres: Louise B Ketz
Founded: 1986
Nonfiction only: science, business, sports, reference, history. No unsol mss, query letter, chapter outline, table of contents, sample chapter, author biography. No reading fee.
Titles recently placed: *The Traveler's Guide to Space: For One-Way Settlers and Round-Trip Tourists*, Neil F Comins
Membership(s): Editorial Freelancers Association; National Association of Professional & Executive Women; United States Commission on Military History

Virginia Kidd Agency Inc (L)
538 E Harford St, PO Box 278, Milford, PA 18337
Tel: 570-296-6205
Web Site: vk-agency.com
Key Personnel
Literary Agent, Foreign & Translation Rts, Film Queries: Christine M Cohen *E-mail:* christine@vk-agency.com
Literary Agent, Ebooks, Contracts & Royalties: Vaughne L Hansen *E-mail:* vaughne@vk-agency.com
Literary Agent, Submissions & Perms: William D Reeve *E-mail:* wmreeve@ptd.net
Founded: 1965
Specialize in fiction; special interest in science fiction, fantasy, speculative fiction. Query us first via USPS (no phone queries); submit one to three page synopsis, with cover letter & SASE or e-mail address for reply; no reading fee. Representative for dramatic rights: Bill Contardi, New York contact. 15% commission; 15% higher commission on dramatic & foreign sales.
Titles recently placed: *A Borrowed Man*, Gene Wolfe; *Allegiance*, Beth Bernobich; *Star Trek: Into Darkness*, Alan Dean Foster; *The Continuous Katherine Mortenhoe*, D G Compton; *The Deavys*, Alan Dean Foster; *The Land Across*, Gene Wolfe; *The Time Roads*, Beth Bernobich; *The Year's Best Science Fiction 32*, Gardner Dozois
Foreign Rep(s): Bardon Chinese Media Agency (China); The Book Publishers Association of Israel (Israel); Bridge Communications Co (Thailand); Paul & Peter Fritz AG (Germany); International Editors' Co (Portugal, South America, Spain); Alexander Korzhenevski (Estonia, Latvia, Lithuania, Russia); Agence Litteraire Lenclud (France); Agenzia Letteraria Internazionale (Italy); Prava I Prevodi (Central Europe, Eastern Europe, Greece, Turkey); Lennart Sane (Netherlands, Scandinavia); Tuttle-Mori Agency Inc (Japan); Eric Yang Agency Inc (Korea)
Foreign Rights: LEX Copyright Office (Hungary)

Kimberley Cameron & Associates (L)
1550 Tiburon Blvd, Suite 704, Tiburon, CA 94920
Tel: 415-789-9191 *Fax:* 415-789-9177
E-mail: info@kimberleycameron.com
Web Site: www.kimberleycameron.com
Key Personnel
Pres & Literary Agent: Kimberley Cameron (AAR) *E-mail:* kimberley@kimberleycameron.com
Literary Agent: Elizabeth Krach *E-mail:* elizabeth@kimberleycameron.com; Pooja Menon; Ethan Vaughn
Founded: 1957
Represent quality writing in book length fiction & nonfiction, including memoirs, biographies, literary fiction, mainstream fiction, science fiction, mysteries & thrillers. Do not handle screenplays, poetry or children's literature. Handle film & TV rights. E-mail all queries. For fiction, include one-page synopsis & first 50 pages as separate attachments. For nonfiction, send complete proposal including sample chapters. No fees charged. Additional office located in Paris.
Foreign Rights: The Fielding Agency (Whitney Lee) (Worldwide)
Membership(s): Sisters in Crime

Kirchoff/Wohlberg Inc (L)
897 Boston Post Rd, Madison, CT 06443

Tel: 203-245-7308 *Fax:* 203-245-3218
Web Site: www.kirchoffwohlberg.com
Key Personnel
Pres: Morris A Kirchoff
VP: Ronald P Zollshan *E-mail:* rzollshan@kirchoffwohlberg.com
Founded: 1974
Children & young adult fiction & nonfiction trade books only. Agency does not handle adult titles. No fees. Handle film & TV rights.
Membership(s): AIGA, the professional association for design; ALA; Book Industry Guild of New York; Bookbuilders of Boston; International Literacy Association; Society of Children's Book Writers & Illustrators; Society of Illustrators

Harvey Klinger Inc (L-D)
300 W 55 St, Suite 11V, New York, NY 10019
Tel: 212-581-7068 *Fax:* 212-315-3823
E-mail: queries@harveyklinger.com
Web Site: www.harveyklinger.com
Key Personnel
Pres: Harvey Klinger (AAR) *E-mail:* harvey@harveyklinger.com
Agent: David Dunton *E-mail:* david@harveyklinger.com; Sara Crowe *E-mail:* sara@harveyklinger.com; Andrea Somberg *E-mail:* andrea@harveyklinger.com
Founded: 1977
Mainstream adult & children's fiction & nonfiction. Handle film & TV rights. No unsol mss, faxes or e-mails; do not phone or fax; no reading fee. Representatives in Hollywood & all principal foreign countries. New clients obtained by referrals.
Foreign Rights: Eliane Benisti (France); David Grossman Literary Agency Ltd (David Grossman) (UK); Daniela Micura Literary Services (Daniela Micura) (Italy); Prava I Prevodi (Ana Milenkovic) (Eastern Europe, Russia); Lennart Sane (Philip Sane) (Brazil, Holland, Latin America, Portugal, Scandinavia, Spain); Thomas Schlueck GmbH (Thomas Schlueck) (Germany); Tuttle-Mori Agency Inc (Ken Mori) (Japan); Eric Yang Agency (Sue Yang) (Korea)
Membership(s): PEN Center USA

Kneerim & Williams Agency (L-D)
90 Canal St, Boston, MA 02114
Tel: 617-303-1650
Web Site: www.kwblit.com
Key Personnel
Agency Administrator: Hope Denekamp *Tel:* 617-303-1651 *E-mail:* hope@kwblit.com
Partner: John Taylor "Ike" Williams *E-mail:* ike@kwblit.com
Mng Partner: Jill Kneerim *E-mail:* jill@kwblit.com
Agent: Katherine Flynn *Tel:* 617-303-1659 *E-mail:* kflynn@kwblit.com
Agency Asst: Lucy Cleland *Tel:* 617-303-1654 *E-mail:* lucy@kwblit.com
Founded: 1990
Handles books, film & television rights. Does not handle poetry, children's picture books & genre fiction; no romance, western or science fiction & fantasy. Does not charge fees. For dramatic rights inquries, contact Ike Williams or Katherine Flynn.
Titles recently placed: *A Border Passage*, Leila Ahmed; *A Garden in Africa*, Nina Sovich; *A Thousand Years With You*, Elizabeth Marshall Thomas; *Almost Normal*, Katherine Preston; *Arguably*, Christopher Hitchens; *Attuned to Customers*, Forrester Research; *Culture Map*, Erin Meyer; *Debtor's Prison*, Robert Kuttner; *Decoded*, Brad Meltzer; *Eleanor & Hick*, Sue Quinn; *FDR at War*, Nigel Hamilton; *Fire and Light: How the Enlightenment Transformed Our World*, James MacGregor Burns; *Focus*, Ned Hallowell; *Homesick Texan's Family Table*, Lisa Fain; *Jimmy Carter*, Randall Balmer; *Letter to a Young Scientist*, E O Wilson; *Mindful Love*, Polly Young-Eisendrath; *More Than Just Sex*, Jim Downs; *Ninth Street Women*, Mary Gabriel; *No One Ever Told Me That*, John Spooner; *Smile at Strangers*, Susan Schorn; *Some Nerve*, Patty Chang Acker; *Taormina*, Patrick Somerville; *The Dark of Morning*, Sarah Willis; *The Engagements*, J Courtney Sullivan; *The Good Job Strategy*, Zeynep Ton; *The Life of Bobby Kennedy*, Larry Tye; *The Making of an Historian*, Joe Ellis; *The New Arabs*, Juan Cole; *The Oldest Living Things in the World*, Rachel Sussman; *The Singles*, Meredith Goldstein; *The Tower of Babel*, Ouroussoff; *To Be a Friend Is Fatal*, Kirk W Johnson; *X vs Y*, Eve & Leonora Epstein
Foreign Rep(s): Baror International Inc
Foreign Rights: Baror International Inc

The Knight Agency Inc (L)
570 East Ave, Madison, GA 30650
E-mail: submissions@knightagency.net
Web Site: www.knightagency.net
Key Personnel
Owner & Pres: Deidre Knight (AAR)
VP: Judson Knight
VP, Sales & Agent: Pamela Harty (AAR)
VP, Opers & Agent: Elaine Spencer (AAR)
Mktg Dir: Jia Gayles
Agent: Melissa Jeglinski
Agent, CA Office: Nephele Tempest (AAR)
Agent, FL Office: Lucienne Diver (AAR)
Submissions Coord: Kristy Hunter
Founded: 1996
Fiction: romance, women's fiction, commercial fiction, literary & multicultural fiction, young adult, science fiction & fantasy, middle-grade fiction. In nonfiction: business, self-help, finance, music/entertainment, media-related, pop culture, how-to, psychology, travel, health, inspirational/religious, reference & holiday books. No anthology collections, short stories or poetry. No unsol mss, query first by sending a brief summary or proposal, author info & first five pages by e-mail (no attachments). Allow a two to four week response time for queries. Upon request only submit the following: for fiction: first three chapters, synopsis or outline & copy of original query; nonfiction: proposal or outline, first one to three chapters, summary of author's qualifications, unique marketing opportunities & copy of original query. Allow 8-12 weeks for ms review. No reading fee. 15% commission on domestic sales, 15-25% on foreign. May use sub-agent for sale or film & foreign rights. Screenplays not accepted.
Titles recently placed: *A Man to Hold on To*, Marilyn Pappano; *Archangel's Legion*, Nalini Singh; *Burning Dawn*, Gena Showalter; *Cal Leandros (series)*, Rob Thurman; *Chicagoland Vampire*, Chloe Neill; *Eversea*, Natasha Boyd; *Ghost Seer*, Robin Owens; *Ink*, Amanda Sun; *Linger*, Lauren Hawkeye; *Nexus*, Ramez Naam; *Risky Game*, Tracy Solheim; *Sanctuary Island*, Lily Everett; *Stupid Girl*, Cindy Miles; *Talk Dirty to Me*, Dakota Cassidy; *Teach Me a Lesson*, Jasmine Haynes; *The Deamon Prism*, Carol Berg; *The Duke Can Go to the Devil*, Erin Knightley; *The Golden City*, J Kathleen Cheney; *The Great Library*, Rachel Caine; *The Last Monster*, Ginger Garrett; *The Memory Child*, Steena Holmes; *Wickedly Powerful*, Deborah Blake
Branch Office(s)
14622 Ventura Blvd, No 785, Sherman Oaks, CA 91403
PO Box 2659, Land O Lakes, FL 34639
Foreign Rights: ANA Sofia Ltd (Bulgaria); The Fielding Agency (Whitney Lee) (Brazil, Bulgaria, China, Croatia, Czech Republic, Estonia, Greece, Hungary, Israel, Korea, Latvia, Lithuania, Poland, Portugal, Romania, Russia, Serbia, Slovakia, Slovenia, Taiwan, UK); Graal Literary Agency (Poland); Katai & Bolza Literary Agents (Hungary); Kayi Literary Agency Ltd (Turkey); The Lenclud Agency (France); Nova Littera (Russia); Kristin Olson Literary Agency (Czech Republic); PNLA / Piergiorgio Nicolazzini Literary Agency (Maura Solinas) (Italy); Read N Right Agency (Greece); Lennart Sane Agency (Scandinavia); Thomas Schlueck GmbH (Germany); Julio F Yanez Agency (Montse F Yanez) (Brazil, Portugal, Spain)
Membership(s): The Authors Guild; Mystery Writers of America; Romance Writers of America; Science Fiction & Fantasy Writers of America; Society of Children's Book Writers & Illustrators

Paul Kohner Agency (L-D)
9300 Wilshire Blvd, Suite 555, Beverly Hills, CA 90212
Tel: 310-550-1060 *Fax:* 310-276-1083
Key Personnel
Pres & Owner: Pearl Wexler
Literary Agent: Stephen Moore
Founded: 1938
Film & TV rights. No unsol mss, query first. No reading fee; fees for extensive copying or binding charges.

Linda Konner Literary Agency (L)
10 W 15 St, Suite 1918, New York, NY 10011
Tel: 212-691-3419 *Fax:* 212-691-0935
Web Site: www.lindakonnerliteraryagency.com
Key Personnel
Pres: Linda Konner (AAR) *E-mail:* ldkonner@cs.com
Founded: 1996
Health, nutrition, diet, relationships, sex, pop psychology, self-help, parenting, cookbooks, business & career/personal finance, celebrity/pop culture. No fiction, children's or memoir. No unsol mss, query first with one-page query & SASE or via e-mail. Submit outline & one to two sample chapters. No reading fee. 15% fee on US sales & up to 25% on foreign sales. One-time expense fee of $65, deducted from publisher's advance payment.
Titles recently placed: *Body Intelligence*, Joseph Cardillo, PhD; *How to Fake Real Beauty*, Ramy Gafni; *Thin from Within*, Joseph J Luciani, PhD; *Tiny Buddha's 365 Tiny Love Challenges*, Lori Deschene
Branch Office(s)
Books Crossing Borders, 110 W 40 St, Suite 2305, New York, NY 10018 *E-mail:* bc@bookscrossingborders.com
Foreign Rights: Books Crossing Borders (Betty Anne Crawford) (Worldwide exc USA)
Membership(s): American Society of Journalists & Authors; The Authors Guild

Elaine Koster Literary Agency LLC (L)
55 Central Park West, Suite 6, New York, NY 10023
Tel: 212-362-9488 *Fax:* 212-712-0164
Key Personnel
Assoc Agent: Stephanie Lehmann (AAR)
Founded: 1998
Literary & quality commercial fiction, including medical, legal & young adult fiction, international thrillers, suspense, psychological suspense, contemporary fiction & women's fiction. Diverse nonfiction: psychology, science, self-help, cookbooks, popular culture, business, spirituality & inspiration, women's issues & health. No unsol mss, query first. Submit first 50 pages for fiction or a proposal for nonfiction. Queries & submissions must include SASE. No reading fee. Handle film & TV rights. Representatives on the West Coast &

in major foreign countries. No longer taking on new clients.
Titles recently placed: *Those Across the River*, Christopher Buehlman
Foreign Rep(s): David Grossman Literary Agency (UK)
Foreign Rights: Chandler Crawford Agency (translations)
Membership(s): The Authors Guild; Mystery Writers of America; Women's Media Group

Barbara S Kouts Literary Agency LLC (L)
PO Box 560, Bellport, NY 11713
Tel: 631-286-1278 *Fax:* 631-286-1538
E-mail: bkouts@aol.com
Key Personnel
Owner: Barbara S Kouts (AAR)
Founded: 1980
Specialize in children's fiction & nonfiction. No unsol mss, query first. Submit synopsis or outline & sample chapters. No reading fee, but copy fees would apply, no software. Handle film & TV rights from sale of books. Agents in all principal foreign countries.
Membership(s): Society of Children's Book Writers & Illustrators

Stuart Krichevsky Literary Agency Inc (L)
381 Park Ave South, Suite 428, New York, NY 10016
Tel: 212-725-5288 *Fax:* 212-725-5275
E-mail: query@skagency.com
Web Site: skagency.com
Key Personnel
Pres: Stuart Krichevsky (AAR)
Literary Agent & Rts Dir: Shana Cohen (AAR) *E-mail:* sc@skagency.com
Literary Agent: Ross Harris; Allison Hunter; David Patterson
Founded: 1995
Fiction & nonfiction. No reading fee. No unsol mss, query first; prefer e-mail queries (no attachments) to query@skagency.com. Include query letter & synopsis. To submit to Shana Cohen include letter, synopsis & first 2 pgs to SCquery@skagency.com.
Foreign Rights: Akcali Copyright Trade & Tourism Co Ltd (Turkey); The Deborah Harris Agency (Israel); Andrew Nurnberg Associates (China, Europe, South Africa); Tuttle-Mori Agency Inc (Japan); Eric Yang (Korea)

Edite Kroll Literary Agency Inc (L)
20 Cross St, Saco, ME 04072
Tel: 207-283-8797 *Fax:* 207-283-8799
Key Personnel
Pres: Edite Kroll *E-mail:* ekroll@maine.rr.com
Founded: 1981
Adult general & feminist nonfiction & humor; children's fiction, young adult & picture books. No unsol mss, query first by e-mail.
Titles recently placed: *Eqbal Achmed Biography*, Stuart Schaar; *Kate the Great (three titles in series)*, Suzy Becker; *Pig in the Wig (four titles in series)*, Emma Virjan
Foreign Rights: ACER (Brazil, Portugal); ACER (children's) (Spain, Spanish Latin America); Agencia Litteraria Internazionale (Italy); Akcali (Turkey); IA Atterholm Agency (Scandinavia); Author Rights Agency (Estonia, Latvia, Russia); L'Autre Agence (France); Bardon Chinese Media (China); Big Apple (China); Book Publishers Association of Israel (Israel); Bookbank (adult) (Spain, Spanish Latin America); English Agency (Japan); David Grossman (adult) (UK); International Literatuur Bureau (Netherlands); JLM (Greece); Simona Kessler (Romania); Prava I Prevodi (Bulgaria, Czech Republic, Estonia, Hungary, Montenegro, Poland, Serbia, Slovakia, Slovenia); Rights People (children's) (UK); Schlueck Agency (Germany); Eric Yang Agency (Korea)

The LA Literary Agency (L)
PO Box 46370, Los Angeles, CA 90046
Tel: 323-654-5288
E-mail: laliteraryagency@mac.com; mail@laliteraryagency.com
Web Site: www.laliteraryagency.com
Key Personnel
Literary Agent: Ann Cashman *E-mail:* ann@laliteraryagency.com; Eric Lasher *E-mail:* eric.laliterary@mac.com; Maureen Lasher *E-mail:* maureen.laliterary@mac.com
Founded: 1980
Specialize in narrative nonfiction, commercial & literary fiction. Accept unsol mss. Nonfiction: query, qualifications & proposal; Fiction: query & 50 pages. See web site for books, clients & submission information.

Peter Lampack Agency Inc (L)
350 Fifth Ave, Suite 5300, New York, NY 10118
Tel: 212-687-9106 *Fax:* 212-687-9109
Web Site: www.peterlampackagency.com
Key Personnel
Pres: Peter A Lampack
Agent & Foreign Rts: Rema Dilanyan *E-mail:* rema@peterlampackagency.com
Agent: Andrew Lampack *E-mail:* andrew@peterlampackagency.com
Off Mgr: Christie Russell *E-mail:* christie@peterlampackagency.com
Founded: 1977
Commercial & literary fiction; nonfiction by recognized experts in a given field (especially autobiography, biography, law, finance, politics, history). Handle motion picture & TV rights from book properties only. No stageplays, teleplays or screenplays. No unsol mss. Query with letter which describes the nature of the ms plus author's credentials if any, sample chapter & synopsis by e-mail only.
Titles recently placed: *Ghost Ship*, Clive Cussler, Graham Brown; *Havana Storm*, Clive Cussler, Dirk Cussler; *Oregon Files (11th in series)*, Clive Cussler, Boyd Morrison; *Patriot*, Ted Bell; *The Assassin*, Clive Cussler, Justin Scott; *The Good Story*, J M Coetzee, Arabella Kurtz; *The Solomon Curse*, Clive Cussler, Russell Blake
Foreign Rep(s): Big Apple Agency Inc (China, Taiwan); Prava I Prevodi Literary Agency (Eastern Europe, Greece); Tuttle-Mori Agency Inc (Japan, Thailand); Eric Yang Agency (Korea)

Michael Larsen/Elizabeth Pomada Literary Agents (L)
1029 Jones St, San Francisco, CA 94109
Tel: 415-673-0939
E-mail: larsenpoma@aol.com
Web Site: www.larsenpomada.com
Key Personnel
Partner: Michael Larsen (AAR); Elizabeth Pomada (AAR)
Founded: 1972
General adult, book-length nonfiction. No unsol mss, query first. Nonfiction: after reading Michael's "How to Write a Book Proposal," see web site for submission guidelines. No reading fee. Representatives in major foreign countries & in Hollywood. Handle film & TV rights for clients. Nonfiction: books with enduring social, practical, or literary value that will excite big & midsize houses because of the idea, the writing & the writer's platform & promotion plan. Subjects include business, psychology, spirituality, biography, history, science, how-to, music, spirituality, futurism, technology, architecture, social issues, biographies, the arts, health, France, new ideas, narrative nonfiction.
Elizabeth Pomada is not accepting queries at this time.

Titles recently placed: *Lady Phoebe*, Ella Quinn; *The Forgotten Queen*, D L Bogdan; *Zen Mind, Zen Horse*, Alan Hamilton
Foreign Rep(s): David Grossman (England)
Foreign Rights: Chandler Crawford (Worldwide)
Membership(s): American Society of Journalists & Authors; The Authors Guild; National Speakers Association; Women's National Book Association

Sarah Lazin Books (L)
121 W 27 St, Suite 704, New York, NY 10001
Tel: 212-989-5757 *Fax:* 212-989-1393
Web Site: lazinbooks.com
Key Personnel
Pres: Sarah Lazin (AAR)
Founded: 1983
General nonfiction, fiction & illustrated books. Handle film, TV & theater rights. Domestic & foreign rights in all principal countries. No unsol mss, referral only. No fees.
Foreign Rights: Julio F-Yanez Agencia Literaria (Montse F-Yanez) (Brazil, Latin America, Portugal, Spain); Graal Literary Agency (Marcin Biegaj) (Poland); Katai & Bolza Literary Agents (Peter Bolza) (Hungary); Simona Kessler International Copyright Agency (Simona Kessler) (Romania); La Nouvelle Agence (Vanessa Kling) (France); Andrew Nurnberg Associates (Tatjana Zoldnere) (Estonia, Latvia, Lithuania); Kristin Olson Literary Agency (Thereza Dubova) (Czech Republic); Prava I Prevadi (Milena Kaplarevic) (Bulgaria, Croatia, Slovenia); Vicki Satlow Agency (Italy); Thomas Schlueck GmbH (Joachim Jessen) (Germany); Sebes & Van Gelderen Literary Agnecy (Paul Sebes & Mariska Kleinhoonte van Os) (Netherlands); Ulf Toregard Agency AB (Lina Hammerling) (Iceland, Scandinavia)

The Ned Leavitt Agency (L)
70 Wooster St, Suite 4-F, New York, NY 10012
Tel: 212-334-0999
Web Site: www.nedleavittagency.com
Key Personnel
Pres: Ned Leavitt (AAR)
Agent: Britta Alexander; Jillian Sweeney
Literary & commercial fiction & nonfiction, books on spirituality & psychology. No unsol mss. Submissions by recommendation only. Rejections not returned, no reading fee.

Levine|Greenberg|Rostan Literary Agency Inc (L)
307 Seventh Ave, Suite 2407, New York, NY 10001
Tel: 212-337-0934 *Fax:* 212-337-0948
Web Site: lgrliterary.com
Key Personnel
Principal: Daniel Greenberg (AAR) *E-mail:* dgreenberg@lgrliterary.com; James Levine (AAR) *E-mail:* jlevine@lgrliterary.com; Stephanie Rostan (AAR) *E-mail:* srostan@lgrliterary.com
Busn Mgr: Melissa Rowland *E-mail:* mrowland@lgrliterary.com
Rts Mgr: Elizabeth Fisher *E-mail:* efisher@lgrliterary.com
Agent: Lindsay Edgecombe (AAR) *E-mail:* ledgecombe@lgrliterary.com; Victoria Skurnick (AAR) *E-mail:* vskurnick@lgrliterary.com; Danielle Svetcov *E-mail:* dsvetcov@lgrliterary.com; Monika Verma *E-mail:* mverma@lgrliterary.com
Assoc Agent: Kerry Sparks *E-mail:* ksparks@lgrliterary.com
Agent-at-Large: Arielle Eckstut *E-mail:* aeckstut@lgrliterary.com
Edit & Rts Asst: Tim Wojcik *E-mail:* ksparks@lgrliterary.com
Founded: 1989

Narrative nonfiction, business, technology, psychology, parenting, health, humor, women's, men's, sexuality, education & social issues, popular culture, narrative nonfiction, fiction, cookbooks, sports. Online queries via the How To Submit page on web site or e-mail queries to submit@levinegreenberg.com. Attachments limited to 50 pages. Handle software, film & TV rights. No reading fee.

Foreign Rights: AnatoliaLit Copyright & Translation Agency (Turkey); Bardon-Chinese Media Agency (China, Taiwan); Eliane Benisti Agence Litteraire (France); The Book Publishers Association of Israel (Israel); Bridge Communications (Thailand); The English Agency (Japan); Ersilia Literary Agency (Greece); The Foreign Office (Latin America, Portugal, Spain); Graal Literary Agency (Czech Republic, Eastern Europe, Poland); Agence Hoffman (Germany); Internationaal Literatuur Bureau (Netherlands); Korea Copyright Center (KCC) (Korea); Maxima Creative Agency (Indonesia, Malaysia); Agencia Riff (Brazil); Vicki Satlow Agency (Italy); Abner Stein Literary Agency (UK); Synopsis Literary Agency (Baltic States, Estonia, Russia); Ulf Toregard Agency (Scandinavia)

Robert Lieberman Agency (L)
Subsidiary of Ithaca Film Works
475 Nelson Rd, Ithaca, NY 14850
Tel: 607-273-8801
Web Site: www.kewgardensmovie.com/CUPeople/users/rhl10
Key Personnel
Pres: Robert H Lieberman *E-mail:* RHL10@cornell.edu
Founded: 1994
ABSOLUTELY NONFICTION ONLY! Specialize in college level textbooks by established & recognized academics in all fields, as well as trade books in science, math, economics, engineering, medicine, psychology, computers & other academic areas that would be of general or popular interest. Represent producers of CD-ROM/multimedia/software, film & videos that fall into these categories. Submissions can be proposals +/or sample chapters, resume & table of contents. No unsol mss, query first (prefer e-mail query); will give quick response by e-mail but will accept mail query with SASE; handle software; no reading fee.

Literary & Creative Artists Inc (L)
3543 Albemarle St NW, Washington, DC 20008-4213
Tel: 202-362-4688 *Fax:* 202-362-8875
E-mail: lca9643@lcadc.com (queries, no attachments)
Web Site: www.lcadc.com
Key Personnel
Founder & Pres: Muriel G Nellis (AAR)
VP: Jane F Roberts
Founded: 1981
Specialize in adult trade fiction & nonfiction credentialed authors only. No poetry or academic/technical work. No unsol mss, query first by mail addressed to Muriel Nellis with SASE or by e-mail (no attachments). Require exclusive review period of two to three weeks. No reading fee. Visit the submission page on our web site for more information.
Membership(s): ABA; American Bar Association; The Authors Guild

Literary Artists Representatives (L)
575 West End Ave, Suite GRC, New York, NY 10024-2711
Tel: 212-679-7788 *Fax:* 212-595-2098
E-mail: litartists@aol.com
Key Personnel
Pres: Madeline Perrone
VP: Samuel Fleishman
Founded: 1993
Emphasizes adult trade, nonfiction, (narrative, biography, memoir, current affairs, business, culture, history, how-to, film/TV, personal finance, sciences, sports, motivational). Handle film, TV electronic rights. Co-agents in Hollywood & other selected cities. No unsol mss, query first via e-mail, No fees.
Titles recently placed: *Disney U: How Disney University Develops the World's Most Engaged, Loyal, and Customer-Centric Employees*, Doug Lipp; *Financial Fitness Forever: 5 Steps to More Money, Less Risk, and More Peace of Mind*, Paul Merriman, Richard Buck; *First Over There: America's First Battle Of World War I: The Attack At Cantigny May 28-31, 1918*, Matthew James Davenport; *Golf's Holy War: The Battle for the Soul of a Game in an Age of Science*, Brett Cyrgalis; *Investment Mistakes Even Smart Investors Make and How to Avoid Them*, Larry E Swedroe, RC Balaban; *JFK in the Senate: Pathway to the Presidency*, John T Shaw; *Kaiten: Japan's Secret Manned Suicide Submarine And the First American Ship It Sank in WWI: The Untold Story*, Michael Mair, Joy Waldron; *Lady in the Dark: Iris Barry and the Art of Film*, Robert Sitton; *Political Mercenaries: How Fundraisers Allowed Billionaires to Take Over Politics*, Lindsay Mark Lewis, Jim Arkedis; *The $1,000 Challenge: How One Family Slashed Its Budget Without Moving Under a Bridge or Living on Government Cheese*, Brian J O'Connor; *The Intelligent Option Investor: Applying Value Investing to the World of Options*, Erik Kobayashi-Solomon; *The Women's Guide to Successful Investing: Achieving Financial Security and Realizing Your Goals*, Nancy Tengler; *Think, Act, and Invest Like Warren Buffett: The Winning Strategy to Help You Achieve Your Financial and Life Goals*, Larry Swedroe

Literary Management Group LLC (L)
16970 San Carlos Blvd, Suite 160-100, Fort Myers, FL 33908
Tel: 615-812-4445
Web Site: www.literarymanagementgroup.com
Key Personnel
CEO & Pres: Bruce R Barbour *E-mail:* brucebarbour@literarymanagementgroup.com
VP, Prod Devt: Karen Moore *Tel:* 614-266-2876 *E-mail:* karen@karenmoore.net
Founded: 1997
Nonfiction: Christian, motivational & inspirational. No unsol mss, query first with letter prior to submission of ms for review. Submit proposal, outline, sample chapters including return postage. E-mail queries preferred. We do not represent fiction, screenplays, children's, poetry, text or reference.
Membership(s): CBA: The Association for Christian Retail; Evangelical Christian Publishers Association

Lowenstein Associates Inc (L-D)
115 E 23 St, 4th fl, New York, NY 10010
Tel: 212-206-1630 *Fax:* 212-727-0280
E-mail: assistant@bookhaven.com (queries, no attachments)
Web Site: www.lowensteinassociates.com
Key Personnel
Pres: Barbara Lowenstein (AAR)
Agent, Contracts & Foreign Rts Mgr: Emily Gref *E-mail:* emily@bookhaven.com
Assoc Agent & Digital Strategist: Connor Goldsmith
Founded: 1976
Electronic queries (no attachments). No westerns, textbooks, children's picture books or books needing translation. Fiction: send a one page query with first 10 pages in the body of the e-mail; nonfiction: submit one page query, table of contents & a proposal (if available) in the body of the e-mail to assistant@bookhaven.com. Include the word QUERY & the project name in the subject line. Address the e-mail to the agent you want to consider your work. Visit our web site to find more information about each agent's interests. We will respond in 4-6 weeks. No reading fee.
Membership(s): Romance Writers of America

Donald Maass Literary Agency (L)
121 W 27 St, Suite 801, New York, NY 10001
Tel: 212-727-8383 *Fax:* 212-727-3271
E-mail: info@maassagency.com
Web Site: www.maassagency.com
Key Personnel
Pres: Donald Maass (AAR) *E-mail:* dmaass@maassagency.com
VP & Agent: Jennifer Jackson (AAR) *E-mail:* jjackson@maassagency.com
Agent & Rts Dir: Katie Shea Boutillier *E-mail:* ksboutillier@maassagency.com
Agent: Amy Boggs; Stacia Decker *E-mail:* sdecker@maassagency.com; Cameron McClure *E-mail:* cmcclure@maassagency.com
Asst to VP: Michael Curry *E-mail:* mcurry@maassagency.com
Founded: 1980
Literary agency for professional novelists, representing more than 100 authors & selling more than 150 novels every year to major publishers in the US & overseas. Also handles book-to-film & TV rights. Leading clients include Anne Bishop, Jim Butcher, Joelle Charbonneau, Diane Duane, Todd McCaffrey, Anne Perry & Brent Weeks. See web site for submission guidelines. Query via e-mail with one-page letter, first five pages of novel & one- to two-page synopsis, pasted into e-mail; no attachments.
Titles recently placed: *Chapelwood*, Cherie Priest; *Cinder Spires: The Aeronaut's Windlass*, Jim Butcher; *How To Win at High School*, Owen Matthews; *Karen Memory*, Elizabeth Bear; *Kris Longknife: Unrelenting*, Mike Shepherd; *N.E.E.D.*, Joelle Charbonneau; *Of Noble Family*, Mary Robinette Kowal; *The Angel Court Affair*, Anne Perry; *The Border*, Robert McCammon; *The Broken Eye*, Brent Weeks; *The Far End of Happy*, Kathryn Craft; *The Traitor Baru Cormorant*, Seth Dickinson; *Vision in Silver*, Anne Bishop; *What Kind of A Man*, Fiona Maazel
Foreign Rights: Agenzia Letteraria Internazionale (Italy); Book Publishers Association of Israel (Israel); The English Agency (Japan) (Japan); Grayhawk Agency (China, Taiwan); International Editors Co (Brazil, South America, Spain); Anna Jarota Agency (France); A Korzhenevski Agency (Russia); MBA Literary Agents Ltd (UK); ONK Agency Ltd (Turkey); Prava I Prevodi (Bulgaria, Czech Republic, Montenegro, Poland, Romania, Serbia); Lennart Sane Agency AB (Denmark, Finland, Netherlands, Norway, Sweden); Thomas Schluck (Germany); Eric Yang Agency (Korea)
Membership(s): The Authors Guild; Mystery Writers of America; Romance Writers of America; Science Fiction & Fantasy Writers of America

Gina Maccoby Literary Agency (L)
PO Box 60, Chappaqua, NY 10514-0060
Tel: 914-238-5630
E-mail: query@maccobylit.com
Web Site: www.publishersmarketplace.com/members/GinaMaccoby
Key Personnel
Principal: Gina Maccoby (AAR)
Founded: 1986
High quality fiction & nonficton for adults & children. Handle film & TV rights for clients' work only. No screenplays. No unsol mss;

query first. E-mail queries preferred. Include SASE if querying by regular mail. Owing to the volume of queries received, we will only respond if interested. No reading fee. May recover the cost of books purchased for submissions; airmail shipping of books overseas; overnight shipping domestically if requested by client; bank fees incurred related to transfers of payments; legal fees incurred with prior client approval. Co-agents in Hollywood & overseas.
Foreign Rep(s): Luigi Bernabo Associates (Italy); Big Apple Agency Inc (China); Mohrbooks (Germany); Andrew Nurnberg Associates (Bulgaria, Estonia, Latvia, Lithuania, Russia, Ukraine); Lennart Sane Agency (Brazil, Portugal, Scandinavia, Spain, Spanish Latin America)
Membership(s): The Authors Guild

Carol Mann Agency (L)
55 Fifth Ave, New York, NY 10003
Tel: 212-206-5635 *Fax:* 212-675-4809
E-mail: submissions@carolmannagency.com
Web Site: www.carolmannagency.com
Key Personnel
Pres: Carol Mann (AAR)
Agent: Eliza Dreier; Gareth Esersky; Myrsini Stephanides; Joanne Wyckoff; Laura Yorke
Founded: 1977
Literary & commercial fiction, no genre fiction, general nonfiction & memoir. Subs-agents in Los Angeles & for all foreign languages. No unsol mss, query first. E-mail queries only (no attachments). Mailed queries no longer accepted. For fiction & memoir, send a synopsis, brief bio & first 25 pages of ms. All other nonfiction, submit synopsis & brief bio. No reading fee. Handle film & TV rights for book clients only.
Foreign Rights: Ackali Copyright Agency (Atilla Izgi Turgut) (Turkey); Anthea Agency (Zlatka Paskaleva) (Bulgaria); Eliane Benisti Agency (France); Luigi Bernabo Associates (Italy); Big Apple Agency Inc (Vicky Chen) (Taiwan); Big Apple Agency Inc (Lily Chen) (China, Indonesia); Graal Literary Agency (Magdalena Cabajewska) (Poland); JLM Literary Agency (John Moukakos) (Greece); Katai & Bolza Literary Agents (Peter Bolza) (Hungary); Simona Kessler Intl Copyright Agency (Romania); Licht & Burr Literary Agency (Trine Licht) (Denmark, Iceland, Norway, Sweden); Meigas Agencia Literaria (Ruth Garcia-Lago) (Mexico); Mohrbooks (Sabine Ibach) (Germany); Andrew Nurnberg Associates Baltic (Kristine Supe) (Latvia); Andrew Nurnberg Literary Agency (Ludmilla Sushkova) (Russia); Kristin Olson Literary Agency (Czech Republic); I Pikarski Literary Agency (Gal Pikarski) (Israel); Prava I Prevodi Literary Agency (Ana Milenkovic) (Serbia); Guillermo Schavelzon & Associados (Jacoba Casier) (Spain); Karin Schindler (Brazil); Sebes & Van Gelderen Literary Agency (Paul Sebes) (Netherlands); Abner Stein Associates (Arabella Stein) (England); Tuttle-Mori Agency Inc (Manami Tamaoki) (Japan); Tuttle-Mori Agency Inc (Pimolporn Yutisri) (Thailand); Shin Won Agency (Tae Eun Kim) (Korea)

Freya Manston Associates Inc (L)
145 W 58 St, New York, NY 10019
Tel: 212-247-3075
Key Personnel
Pres: Freya Manston
Fiction & nonfiction. No unsol mss; not accepting new queries at this time. Agents in all principal countries. No fees charged.

Manus & Associates Literary Agency Inc (L)
425 Sherman Ave, Suite 200, Palo Alto, CA 94306
Tel: 650-470-5151 *Fax:* 650-470-5159
E-mail: manuslit@manuslit.com
Web Site: www.manuslit.com
Key Personnel
Pres: Jillian W Manus (AAR) *E-mail:* jillian@manuslit.com
Assoc: Jandy Nelson (AAR) *E-mail:* jandy@manuslit.com
General fiction & dramatic nonfiction books, TV & motion picture rights. No unsol mss. Fiction: query first with synopsis & first 30 pages. Nonfiction: query letter & proposal. No reading fee. Offices in NY & CA; representatives in all major foreign countries. The New York office does NOT accept any unsol mss.
Foreign Rep(s): Danny Baror (Worldwide)
Foreign Rights: Baror International Inc

March Tenth Inc (L)
24 Hillside Terr, Montvale, NJ 07645
Tel: 201-387-6551 *Fax:* 201-387-6552
Web Site: www.marchtenthinc.com
Key Personnel
Pres: Sandra Choron *E-mail:* schoron@aol.com
VP: Harry Choron *E-mail:* hchoron@aol.com
Founded: 1980
General nonfiction & fiction; specialize in popular culture. No children's or young adult novels, plays, screenplays or poetry. No unsol mss, query first. E-mail queries accepted. If mailing hard copy, include a SASE for materials you want returned. See web site for additional information. No reading fee. Book production services available. Handle film & TV rights. 15% commission.
Titles recently placed: *How Shakespeare Saved My Life*, Laura Bates; *Streets of Fire*, Eric Meola

Denise Marcil Literary Agency LLC (L)
483 Westover Rd, Stamford, CT 06902
Tel: 203-327-9970 *Fax:* 203-327-9970
E-mail: dmla@denisemarcilagency.com
Web Site: www.denisemarcilagency.com
Key Personnel
Mgr & Agent: Denise Marcil (AAR) *E-mail:* dmla@denisemarcilagency.com
Agent: Anne Marie O'Farrell (AAR) *Tel:* 516-365-6029 *E-mail:* annemarie@denisemarcilagency.com
Founded: 1977
Nonfiction: Personal growth, intelligent self-help & how-to's including mind-body-spirit, sports, business, careers, psychology & cookbooks. Send nonfiction e-mail queries to annemarie@denisemarcilagency.com. Represents contemporary women's fiction & thrillers. Not accepting any new fiction queries or novelists. No unsol mss, query first, via e-mail. Subagents in all major countries.
Titles recently placed: *Discovering Vintage New York*, Mitch Broder; *Gratitude Prayers*, June Cotner; *Home to Seaview Key*, Sherryl Woods; *Idea Stormers, How To Lead and Inspire Creative Breakthroughs*, Bryan W Mattimore; *Sand Castle Bay*, Sherryl Woods; *Something About Sophie*, Mary Kay McComas; *Swinging '73, Baseball's Wildest Season*, Matthew Silverman; *The College Bound Organizer*, Anna Costaras, Gail Liss; *The Healthy Pregnancy Book*, William Sears, MD, Martha Sears, RN
Membership(s): The Authors Guild; Women's Media Group

Markson Thoma Literary Agency Inc (L)
44 Greenwich Ave, New York, NY 10011
Tel: 212-243-8480 *Fax:* 212-691-9014
E-mail: info@marksonthoma.com
Web Site: www.marksonthoma.com
Key Personnel
Partner & Agent: Elaine Markson (AAR)
Dir, Subs Rts: Gary Johnson
Founded: 1972
Literary fiction & nonfiction. No unsol mss. No fees charged.
Foreign Rights: Liepman (Germany); MB Agencia Literaria (Latin America, Portugal, Spain); La Nouvelle Agence (France); Elizabeth Sheinkman (UK); Marco Vigevani (Italy)

Mildred Marmur Associates Ltd (L)
2005 Palmer Ave, PMB 127, Larchmont, NY 10538
Tel: 914-834-1170 *Fax:* 914-833-1175
E-mail: marmur@westnet.com
Key Personnel
Pres: Mildred Marmur (AAR)
Founded: 1987
Nonfiction only. No unsol mss; referrals only. Represented in Hollywood & foreign markets. Does not charge fees.
Membership(s): The Authors Guild

Marsal Lyon Literary Agency LLC (L)
665 San Rodolfo Dr, Suite 124, PMB 121, Solana Beach, CA 92075
Tel: 760-814-8507
Web Site: www.marsallyonliteraryagency.com
Key Personnel
Owner & Literary Agent: Kevan Lyon *E-mail:* kevan@marsalyonliteraryagency.com; Jill Marsal *E-mail:* jill@marsallyonliteraryagency.com
Literary Agent: Shannon Hassan; Patricia Nelson; Deborah Ritchken *E-mail:* deborah@marsallyonliteraryagency.com; Kathleen Rushall *E-mail:* kathleen@marsallyonliteraryagency.com
Founded: 2009
Dedicated to helping authors successfully place their work. Members have many years of experience in the publishing industry & possess a diverse & unique skill set. Have worked with many bestselling & award-winning authors, as well as first-time authors.
Fiction genres & categories represented: commercial, mainstream, multicultural, mystery, suspense, thriller, women's fiction, romance (all genres), young adult & middle grade. Nonfiction represented: biography, business/economics/investing/finance, diet, fitness & health, history/politics/current events, investigative journalism, lifestyle, memoirs, narrative nonfiction, parenting, pets/animals, pop culture & music, psychology, relationships/advice, science & nature, self-help, sports, women's issues. No unsol ms, query first. Writers are encouraged to visit the web site to determine who might be the best fit for your work. For electronic submissions (preferred), send query letter & write QUERY in the subject line of the e-mail. Hard copy submissions: for fiction, send cover letter, one-page synopsis of work & first 10 pages of ms; for nonfiction, include either cover letter or cover letter & complete proposal. No fees.
The Taryn Fagerness Agency represents foreign, audio & film subsidiary rights.
Titles recently placed: *A Convenient Bride*, Cheryl Ann Smith; *A Hometown Boy*, Janice Kay Johnson; *A Man of Privilege*, Sarah M Anderson; *A Rustic Chic Wedding*, Morgann Hill; *A Socialite Scorned*, Kerrie Droban; *An Affair of Vengeance*, Jamie Michele; *And Hell Followed with Her*, David Neiwert; *Back to You*, Robin Kaye; *Backhoe Joe*, Lori Alexander; *Beach Town Baking: An Endless Summer of Delicious Desserts*, Lee Shishak; *Behind the Lies*, Robin Perini; *Bleeding Talent: How the US Military Mismanages Great Leaders and Why it's Time for a Revolution*, Time Kane; *Bloodhound in Blue*, Adam Russ; *Buried Memories*, Katie Beers, Carolyn Gusoff; *Caged Warrior*, Lindsey Piper; *Call Me Zelda*, Ericka Robuck; *Dangerous Memories*, Angi Morgan; *Dangerous Waters*, Toni Ander-

son; *Dare You to*, Katie McGarry; *Dark Awakening*, Kendra Leigh Castle; *Dollface*, Renee Rosen; *Don't Look Back*, Jennifer Armentrout; *Essential Car Care for Women*, Jamie Little, Danielle McCormick; *Ex on the Beach*, Kim Law; *Exposed*, Laura Griffin; *Far Time Incident*, Neve Maslakovic; *Forest Fairy Crafts*, Lenka Vodicka, Asia Curry; *Freedom to Learn*, Peter Gray; *Gold Fire*, Starr Ambrose; *Hemingway's Girl*, Erika Robuck; *How to Deceive a Duke*, Lecia Cornwall; *Insomnia*, Jenn Johansson; *It Takes More than Talent*, Kristen Fischer; *It's Raining Bats and Frogs*, Rebecca Colby; *Life's a Witch*, Brittany Geragotelis; *Lone Wolf Terrorism*, Jeffrey Simon; *Mating Instinct*, Katie Reus; *Midnight Sacrifice*, Melinda Leigh; *My Migraine Miracle*, Joshua Turknett; *Out of All Knowing*, Jennifer Robson; *Profit from the Positive*, Margaret Greenberg, Senia Maymin; *Pushing the Limits*, Katie McGarry; *Rock Your Business*, David Fishof, Michael Levin; *Sacrifice*, Cayla Kluver; *Secrets of a Virgin*, Anna Randol; *Secrets of a Wedding Night*, Valerie Bowman; *She Can Scream*, Melinda Leigh; *She Can Tell*, Melinda Leigh; *Sinfully Yours*, Kendra Leigh Castle; *Sins of a Ruthless Rogue*, Anna Randol; *Starlight*, Carrie Lofty; *Sugar Springs*, Kim Law; *Summer in Napa*, Marina Adair; *Sweet Revenge*, Zoe Archer; *Targeted*, Katie Reus; *Temptation in a Kilt*, Victoria Roberts; *The Anatomist's Wife*, Anna Lee Huber; *The Baby Deal*, Kat Cantrell; *The Candidate*, Samuel Popkin; *The Challenger Sale*, Matthew Dixon, Brent Adamson; *The Chiefton*, Margaret Mallory; *The Claimed*, Caridad Pineiro; *The Darling Strumpet*, Gillian Bagwell; *The Delight Paradox*, Matthew Dixon, Nicholas Toman, Richard Delisi; *The Highlander's Prize*, Mary Wine; *The Joy Brigade*, Martin Limon; *The Last Time I Saw Paris*, Lynn Sheene; *The Love Dog*, Elsa Watson; *The Mango Bride*, Marivi Soliven; *The Price of Temptation*, Lecia Cornwall; *The Sinner*, Margaret Mallory; *The Valentine's Arrangement*, Kelsie Leverich; *The Van Winkle Project*, Karri Thompson; *The Vanishing Thief*, Kate Parker; *The Wisdom of Hair*, Kim Boykin; *Touch*, Jus Accardo; *Twisted*, Laura Griffin; *Unstoppable*, Laura Griffin; *Vagos, Mongols & Outlaws*, Charles Falco, Kerrie Droban; *Venus in Winter*, Gillian Bagwell; *Victorian Secret: What a Corset Taught Me about the Past, the Present, and Myself*, Sarah Chrisman; *Vinnie Gorgeous*, Anthony DeStefano; *Wait for You*, J Lynn; *Welcome Home Mama and Boris*, Carey Neesley, Michael Levin; *What Happens in Scotland*, Jennifer McQuiston; *What Makes Your Brain Happy & Why You Should Do the Opposite*, David DiSalvo; *What the Spell*, Brittany Geragotellis; *What's Wrong with Fat?*, Abigail Saguy; *Wild Princess*, Mary Hart Perry; *Witchy Crafts*, Lexa Olick; *Writing from the Senses*, Laura Deutsch; *X Marks the Scot*, Victoria Roberts

Foreign Rights: Taryn Fagerness Agency LLC (Albania, Argentina, Australia, Brazil, Bulgaria, Canada, China, Croatia, Czech Republic, Denmark, Estonia, Finland, France, Germany, Greece, Hungary, Iceland, India, Indonesia, Israel, Italy, Japan, Korea, Latvia, Lithuania, Mexico, Netherlands, Norway, Poland, Portugal, Romania, Russia, Serbia, Slovakia, Slovenia, Spain, Sweden, Taiwan, Thailand, Turkey, Ukraine, UK, Vietnam)

Membership(s): Romance Writers of America

The Evan Marshall Agency (L)
One Pacio Ct, Roseland, NJ 07068-1121
Tel: 973-287-6216 *Fax:* 973-488-7910
Key Personnel
Pres: Evan Marshall (AAR) *E-mail:* evan@evanmarshallagency.com
Founded: 1987
Representatives in Hollywood & foreign countries. No unsol mss; do not query or send submissions. Clients considered by professional referral only.
Membership(s): Mystery Writers of America; Sisters in Crime

The Martell Agency (L)
1350 Avenue of the Americas, Suite 1205, New York, NY 10019
Tel: 212-317-2672
Web Site: www.themartellagency.com
Key Personnel
Owner: Alice Fried Martell
Contact: Stephanie Finman
Founded: 1985
Fiction & nonfiction. Handle film & TV rights. No unsol mss, query first. Submit query letters by e-mail, sample material only on request. Include market analysis for nonfiction & author biography. No reading fee. Represented in foreign markets.
Foreign Rep(s): Eliane Benisti (France); Jill Hughes Agent (Eastern Europe, Greece, Middle East); Nurchian Kesim (Filiz Karaman) (Turkey); Liepman Agency (Germany); Sara Menguc (Australia, UK); Natoli Stefan & Oliva SA (Italy); Andrew Nurnberg Associates International (Whitney Hsu) (Taiwan); Andrew Nurnberg Associates International (Jackie Huang) (China); Lennart Sane Agency (Netherlands, Scandinavia); Tuttle-Mori Agency Inc (Japan); Tuttle-Mori Agency Inc (Thananchai Pandey) (Indonesia, Thailand); Julio F Yanez Agencia Literaria (Montse Yanez) (Brazil, Portugal, Spain, Spanish Latin America); Eric Yang Agency (Henry Shin) (Korea)

Martin Literary Management (L)
7683 SE 27 St, No 307, Mercer Island, WA 98040
Tel: 206-466-1773 (no queries) *Fax:* 206-466-1774
Web Site: www.martinliterarymanagement.com
Key Personnel
Literary Mgr & Agent: Sharlene Martin *E-mail:* sharlene@martinliterarymanagement.com
Agent: Clelia Gore *E-mail:* clelia@martinliterarymanagement.com
Founded: 2003
Nonfiction only. No unsol mss, query first. Now a "green agency", only e-mail queries (no attachments) will be accepted. No fees charged.
Titles recently placed: *100 Words*, William Murtha; *A Craving for Crab*, Christine Quinn; *A Craving for Noodles*, Christine Quinn; *A Season of Darkness*, Doug Jones, Phyllis Gobbell; *Bad Girls*, Carole Lieberman MD; *Blindsided*, Jim Cole, Tim Vandehey; *Changing the Odds*, Susan Neuman; *Evil Next Door*, Amanda Lamb; *Fringe Dweller*, Monica Holy; *Front of the Class*, Brad Cohen, Lisa Wysocky; *Frozen*, Scott Baldyga, Larry Johnson; *Getting It Through My Thick Skull*, MaryJo Buttafuoco; *Happily Ever After Divorce*, Jessica Bram; *It's a Break-Up Not a Breakdown Workbook*, Lisa Steadman; *iWant*, Jane Velez-Mitchell; *Lady Killer*, Shanna Hogan; *Literary Fails: Totally (sic)!*, Sharlene Martin, Anthony Flacco; *Live Your Bliss*, Terry Cole-Whittaker; *Love Lies*, Amanda Lamb; *My Stolen Son*, Susan Markowitz, Jenna Glatzer; *No One's the Bitch*, Jennifer Marine, Carol Marine; *Notes Left Behind*, Keith Desserich; *Our Little Secret*, Kevin Flynn, Rebecca La Voie; *Publish Your Nonfiction Book*, Sharlene Martin, Anthony Flacco; *Sign of Life*, Hilary Williams, M B Roberts; *Special Agent Man*, Steve Moore; *Taking Aim at the President*, Geri Spieler; *The Bridge*, Michael Glasgow; *The No Gossip Zone*, Sam Chapman; *The Pregnancy Project*, Gaby Rodriguez, Jenna Glatzer; *The Road Out of Hell*, Anthony Flacco; *Wicked Intentions*, Kevin Flynn
Foreign Rights: Taryn Fagerness Agency (Worldwide exc Canada & US Territories)

Martin-McLean Literary Associates LLC (L)
5023 W 120 Ave, Suite 228, Broomfield, CO 80020
Tel: 303-465-2056 *Fax:* 303-465-2057
E-mail: martinmcleanlit@aol.com
Web Site: www.martinmcleanlit.com; www.mcleanlit.com
Key Personnel
CEO & Agent: Lisa Ann Martin, PhD
Founded: 1986
Literary fiction, nonfiction, health issues, psychology, how-to, self-help, sports, new thought, critical thinking, scholarly, biographies, memoirs, autobiographies & murder mystery. No unsol mss. Query first with letter, synopsis, total word count of ms & e-mail address to the agency's street address or by e-mail. Requirements: send proposal with SASE, follow submission directions on web site, or call for agency brochure. No evaluation or reading fee; work at $60/hour. New writers welcome.
Services: editing, proposal development & critique. Book development available. Ghostwriters can be matched to author. Agents worldwide with Internet access.
Titles recently placed: *A Bird in the Hand*, Jerry Banks; *Angel Kisses: Kildare Beginnings*, Karen K Hoiland; *Angel Kisses: The Gift of Infirmity*, Karen K Hoiland; *Diary of a Mad Seducer*, Paul de Vito; *How to Avoid the Overdiagnosis and Over-treatment of Prostate Cancer*, Anthony H Horan, MD; *Indian Zero to American Hero: An Incredible Story of a Slumdog Scientist*, Dr B Vithal Shetty; *Mandy and Thelma*, Billie Thomas; *Mountains of Poetry: Colorado Poems by Colorado Kids*, Coyote Authors Club; *Pact of the Seven Stones: The Mist of Maletoc*, Kevin Cooke; *The Elements of Selling: Everyone Has Something to Sell*, Alan Zell; *The End of Days*, J R Bacon; *The Feral Pistillate*, Warner Bair II; *The Fifth Estate*, Steven Berger; *The Magic Law of Increase: Tithing Your Way to Prosperity*, Lisa Ann Martin, PhD; *The Second District*, Jerry Banks; *The Three R's Make the World Go Around!*, Jade Martin, Dylan George, Kyra Mowry, Valerie Ulsh; *The Uncertain Believer*, Edward Correia; *Vulture Culture*, Eric Gerst; *Who Killed Public TV?*, Smith; *Winter is Upon Us*, Kevin Cooke

Harold Matson Co Inc (L)
276 Fifth Ave, New York, NY 10001
Tel: 212-679-4490 *Fax:* 212-545-1224
Key Personnel
Agent: Ben Camardi (AAR); Jonathan Matson (AAR)
Founded: 1937
No unsol mss, query first with SASE. No reading fee. Handle film & TV rights. No screenplays.
Foreign Rep(s): Intercontinental Literary Agency (Europe); Abner Stein Agency (UK)
Membership(s): The Authors Guild

Margret McBride Literary Agency (L)
PO Box 9128, La Jolla, CA 92038
Tel: 858-454-1550
E-mail: staff@mcbridelit.com
Web Site: www.mcbrideliterary.com
Key Personnel
Owner & Pres: Margret McBride (AAR)
Founded: 1981
Specialize in fiction, nonfiction & business. No unsol mss, query first with synopsis or outline. E-mail submissions preferred. If submitting via regular mail, include SASE. No poetry, romance, children's or screenplays. Foreign rights sub-agents in all major countries.

Titles recently placed: *Adversaries into Allies*, Bob Burg; *Among Heroes: A US Navy SEAL's True Story of Friendship, Heroism, and the Ultimate Sacrifice*, Brandon Webb, John D Mann; *Red Flags: How to Spot Frenemies, Underminers, and Toxic People in Your Life*, Dr Wendy Patrick; *The Making of a Navy SEAL*, Brandon Webb; *Think to Win: Unleashing the Power of Strategic Thinking*, Paul Butler, John Manfredi, Peter Klein; *Under the Hood: Fire up and Fine Tune Your Employee Culture*, Stan Slap; *What Works: Common Sense Solutions for a Stronger America*, Cal Thomas
Foreign Rights: Akcali Copyright (Turkey); The Asano Agency (Kiyoshi Asano) (Japan); Bardon Chinese Media Agency (David Tsai) (China); Eliane Benisti Agency (France); Raquel De La Concha Agencia Literaria (Portugal, Spain, Spanish & Portuguese, Spanish languages, Spanish Latin America); Caroline van Gelderen Literary Agency (Netherlands); Agence Hoffman (Claudia Lichte) (Germany); KCC (Korea Copyright Center) (Korea); Licht & Burr (Scandinavia); Maxima Creative Agency (Santo Manarung) (Indonesia); I Pikarski (Israel); Pravi i Prevodi (Eastern Europe)
Membership(s): Writers Guild of America

E J McCarthy Agency (L)
405 Maple St, Suite A, Mill Valley, CA 94941
Tel: 415-383-6639 *Fax:* 415-383-6639
E-mail: ejmagency@gmail.com
Web Site: www.publishersmarketplace.com/members/ejmccarthy
Key Personnel
Owner: E J McCarthy
Founded: 2003
Independent literary agency. Subject specialties: history, military history, politics, sports, biography, media, memoir, thrillers & other nonfiction. No reading fee. Query first by e-mail.
Titles recently placed: *American General*, John S D Eisenhower; *An Angel from Hell*, Ryan A Conklin; *Forty-Seven Days*, Mitchell Yockelson; *Guerilla Leader*, James Schneider; *Hell's Angels*, Jay A Stout; *Lincoln's Counsel*, Arthur Rizer; *One Bullet Away*, Nathaniel Fick; *Resilience*, Eric Greitens; *The Heart & the Fist*, Eric Greitens; *The Sling & the Stone*, Thomas X Hammes; *The Unforgiving Minute*, Craig M Mullaney; *Wanted Dead or Alive*, Benjamin Runkle; *War Play*, Corey Mead; *Why We Lost*, Daniel P Bolger

Gerard McCauley Agency Inc (L)
PO Box 844, Katonah, NY 10536-0844
Tel: 914-232-5700
Key Personnel
Pres: Gerard McCauley (AAR)
E-mail: gerrymccauley44@gmail.com
Founded: 1970
Nonfiction; educational materials. No unsol mss. Representatives in all major foreign countries. Not currently considering new mss. Does not charge fees.

Anita D McClellan Associates (L)
464 Common St, Suite 142, Belmont, MA 02478-2704
Tel: 617-575-9203 *Fax:* 617-315-8983
E-mail: adm@anitamcclellan.com
Web Site: www.anitamcclellan.com
Key Personnel
Agent: Anita McClellan (AAR)
Founded: 1988
General fiction & nonfiction, including feminism. No unsol mss, query first by e-mail without attachments, no work previously submitted to publishers. Submit outline or synopsis & first 2,500 words. No software. No reading fees charged.
Membership(s): The Authors Guild; Bay Area Editors' Forum; Bookbuilders of Boston; Cape Cod Writers Center; Editorial Freelancers Association; Grub Street; International Women's Writing Guild; Sisters in Crime; Society of Children's Book Writers & Illustrators; Women's National Book Association

McIntosh & Otis Inc (L)
353 Lexington Ave, New York, NY 10016-0900
Tel: 212-687-7400 *Fax:* 212-687-6894
E-mail: info@mcintoshandotis.com
Web Site: www.mcintoshandotis.com
Key Personnel
Owner & CEO: Eugene H Winick (AAR)
Pres & Sr Adult Agent: Elizabeth Winick Rubinstein (AAR)
Agent & Dir, Subs Rts: Shira Hoffman (AAR)
Agent, Children's Dept: Christa Heschke (AAR)
Agent: Adam Muhlig
Royalty Admin: Alecia Douglas
Founded: 1928
Represent adult & juvenile fiction & nonfiction books. No unsol mss, query first via e-mail. See web site for instructions. No reading fees. Handle film & TV rights for represented clients only. Agents in most major foreign countries.
Foreign Rep(s): Anatolia Literary Agency (Adult) (Turkey); Bardon-Chinese Media (Mainland China, Taiwan); Luigi Bernabo (Italy); The Deborah Harris Agency (Israel); Japan Uni Agency Inc (Japan); Simona Kessler International Copyright Agency Ltd (Romania); Mohrbooks (Germany); La Nouvelle Agence (Adult) (France); Andrew Nurenburg (Eastern Europe); Prava I Prevodi Agency (Croatia, Serbia); Read n 'Right Agency (Greece); Abner Stein Agency (UK); Julio F Yanez (Latin America, Portugal, Spain)

McLean Literary Associates, see
Martin-McLean Literary Associates LLC

Sally Hill McMillan LLC (L)
429 E Kingston Ave, Charlotte, NC 28203
Tel: 704-334-0897
E-mail: mcmagency@aol.com
Key Personnel
Pres: Sally Hill McMillan (AAR)
Founded: 1990 (converted to a LLC in 2011)
Southern fiction & adult trade nonfiction; no unsol mss, query first & await further instructions. No sci-fi, military, horror, fantasy/adventure children's books or cookbooks. No reading fee. Handle film, TV, foreign & electronic rights through sub-agents.
Titles recently placed: *Pie Town*, Lynne Hinton; *The Armchair Birder: Discovering the Secret Lives of Familiar Birds*, John Yow
Foreign Rights: The Fielding Agency (all other territories); Thomas Schlueck GmbH (Germany)
Membership(s): Women's National Book Association

Mendel Media Group LLC (L)
115 W 30 St, Suite 800, New York, NY 10001
Tel: 646-239-9896 *Fax:* 212-685-4717
Web Site: www.mendelmedia.com
Key Personnel
Mng Partner: Scott Mendel (AAR)
E-mail: scott@mendelmedia.com
Founded: 2002
Represent nonfiction writers in most subject areas, from biography & serious history to health & relationships. Nonfiction clientele includes individual authors & institutions whose works, collections, archives, researchers +/or policy experts contribute to important public discussions & debates. Also represent more lighthearted nonfiction projects, when they suit the market particularly well. The agency's fiction writers principally write historical & contemporary multicultural fiction, contemporary thrillers & mainstream women's fiction. Do not accept fax or e-mail submissions. Submission guidelines are available on the web site. No fees.
Titles recently placed: *Agorafabulous!: Dispatches from My Bedroom*, Sara Benincasa; *Allah: The Biography*, Abbas Milani; *Aretha Franklin: The Queen of Soul*, Mark Bego; *Art Girls Are Easy*, Julie Klausner; *Great*, Sara Benincasa; *How to Exercise When You're Expecting*, Lindsay Brin; *How to Win at Everything*, Daniel Kibblesmith, Sam Weiner; *I Could Pee on This: And Other Poems by Cats*, Francesco Marciuliano; *I, Steve: Steve Jobs in His Own Words*, George Beahm; *Impatient Optimist: Bill Gates in His Own Words*, Lisa Rogak; *Off the Menu*, Stacey Ballis; *Our Man in the Dark*, Rashad Harrison; *Patient One*, Leonard Goldberg; *Slow Fire: The Beginner's Guide to Barbecue*, Ray "Dr BBQ" Lampe; *Super Boys: The Amazing Adventures of Jerry Siegel and Joe Shuster-the Creators of Superman*, Brad Ricca; *The Dogs of War: The Courage, Love, and Loyalty of Military Working Dogs*, Lisa Rogak; *The First Lady of Fleet Street: The Life, Fortune and Tragedy of Rachel Beer*, Yehuda Koren, Eilat Negev; *The King Whisperers: Power Behind the Throne, from Rasputin to Rove*, Kerwin Swint; *The March of the Bohemian Irregulars*, Peter Carlson; *The Raft*, S A Bodeen; *United Nations: A History*, Stanley Meisler; *Whitney Houston!: The Spectacular Rise and Tragic Fall of the Woman Whose Voice Inspired a Generation*, Mark Bego
Membership(s): American Association of University Professors; The Authors Guild; MLA; Mystery Writers of America; Romance Writers of America; Society of Children's Book Writers & Illustrators

Scott Meredith Literary Agency LP (L)
200 W 57 St, Suite 904, New York, NY 10019-3211
Tel: 646-274-1970 *Fax:* 212-977-5997
E-mail: info@scottmeredith.com
Web Site: www.scottmeredith.com
Key Personnel
Pres: Arthur M Klebanoff *Tel:* 646-274-1970 ext 102 *E-mail:* aklebanoff@rosettabooks.com
Dir, Subs Rts: Mary Jo Anne Valko-Warner
Founded: 1946
More than 1,500 titles in print. No unsol mss, query first. No fees charged.

Mews Books Ltd (L)
20 Bluewater Hill, Westport, CT 06880
Tel: 203-227-1836 *Fax:* 203-227-1144
E-mail: mewsbooks@aol.com
Key Personnel
Pres: Sidney B Kramer
Assoc: Valerie Seiling Jacobs *E-mail:* valerie@mewsbooks.com
Asst: Fran Pollak
Founded: 1975
Seeking professional quality edited works in all categories. In business for nearly 40 years, we offer full literary services. Mr. Kramer is an attorney & former publisher (Bantam Books co-founder & SVP & former president of New American Library) & offers legal consultation for authors with contractual issues.
Please send a one paragraph summary of your work, a second paragraph of your publishing history including full details of whether this submission was previously offered elsewhere & if needed, a third paragraph with other pertinent information. All queries should be submitted to mewsbooks@aol.com. We require an exclusive while reading. If we are interested,

we will ask for a chapter by chapter overview, two sample chapters & a promotion plan. No fees.

The Miller Agency Inc (L)
630 Ninth Ave, Suite 1102, New York, NY 10036
Tel: 212-206-0913 *Fax:* 212-206-1473
Key Personnel
Contact: Sharon Bowers *E-mail:* sharon@mbgliterary.com; Jennifer Griffin *E-mail:* jennifer@mbgliterary.com; Angela Miller *E-mail:* angela@mbgliterary.com
Fiction & nonfiction. No unsol mss. Handle software, film & TV rights. No reading fee. Subagents in all principal foreign countries.

Montreal-Contacts/The Rights Agency (L)
1350 Sherbrooke St E, Suite 1, Montreal, QC H2L 1M4, Canada
Tel: 514-400-7075 *Fax:* 514-400-1045
Web Site: www.montreal-contacts.com/?lang=en
Key Personnel
Owner: Jean-Sebastien Dufresne *E-mail:* jsdufresne@montreal-contacts.com
Founded: 1981
Represents publishers +/or literary agents exclusively for foreign rights. No author representation. Does not handle original mss. Representation in all principal countries through 20 corresponding agents covering 50 languages. Representing full catalogues or selected titles with new online promotional platform eMediaRights.

Moore Literary Agency (L)
10 State St, Suite 210, Newburyport, MA 01950
Tel: 978-465-9015 *Fax:* 978-465-6653
Key Personnel
Owner & Pres: Claudette Moore *E-mail:* cmoore@moorelit.com
Founded: 1989
High tech books & select nonfiction. No unsol mss, query first. Submit proposal or outline & sample chapter. No reading fee, commission only.
Titles recently placed: *Windows® 7 Inside Out, Deluxe Edition*, Ed Bott, Carl Siechert, Craig Stinson

Howard Morhaim Literary Agency Inc (L)
30 Pierrepont St, Brooklyn, NY 11201-3371
Tel: 718-222-8400 *Fax:* 718-222-5056
E-mail: info@morhaimliterary.com
Web Site: www.morhaimliterary.com
Key Personnel
Pres: Howard Morhaim (AAR) *E-mail:* howard@morhaimliterary.com
Agent: Paul Lamb; Kate McKean (AAR) *E-mail:* kate@morhaimliterary.com; DongWon Song
General adult & young adult fiction & nonfiction. Howard Morhaim is not accepting unsol mss. Kate McKean is open to submissions. E-mail your query letter along with three sample chapters (for fiction) or full proposal (for nonfiction). No reading fee. Handle film & TV rights. Representatives in all principal foreign markets.
Foreign Rep(s): Baror International (Worldwide exc Portugal, Spain & UK); The Gotham Group (Michael Prevett, film & TV); RDC Agencia Literaria (Portugal, Spain); Abner Stein Agency (UK)

Henry Morrison Inc (L)
PO Box 235, Bedford Hills, NY 10507-0235
Tel: 914-666-3500 *Fax:* 914-241-7846
E-mail: hmorrison1@aol.com
Key Personnel
Pres: Henry Morrison
Founded: 1965
Fiction & nonfiction. Handle film & TV rights. Accept unsol mss but must send query & outline first with SASE; no reading fee. Fee for ms copies, galleys, bound books for foreign & movie sales & ordering books for subs rights.
Titles recently placed: *Lost City of the Templars*, Paul Christopher; *The Bootlegger*, Clive Cussler, Justin Scott; *The Bourne Retribution*, Eric Van Lustbader

Movable Type Management (L)
244 Madison Ave, Suite 334, New York, NY 10016
Tel: 646-431-6134 *Fax:* 646-810-5757
Web Site: www.mtmgmt.net
Key Personnel
Owner: Adam Chromy *E-mail:* achromy@movabletm.com
Sr Literary Mgr: Mary Kole *Tel:* 650-520-5287 *E-mail:* mkole@movabletm.com
Founded: 2002
Provides inventive & expansive management services, working with authors in a wide variety of categories & genres to develop properties for distribution across platforms, devices & territories. A bicoastal management company, MTM performs in-house film. television & digital development, leveraging our relationships with digital start-ups & veteran producers to add value to an author's work at every opportunity. Dramatic rights only to books sold.

Bonnie Nadell Literary Agency, see Hill Nadell Literary Agency

Jean V Naggar Literary Agency Inc (JVNLA) (L)
216 E 75 St, Suite 1-E, New York, NY 10021
Tel: 212-794-1082
E-mail: jvnla@jvnla.com
Web Site: www.jvnla.com
Key Personnel
Pres: Jennifer Weltz (AAR) *E-mail:* jweltz@jvnla.com
Agent: Laura Biagi (AAR) *E-mail:* lbiagi@jvnla.com; Elizabeth Evans (AAR) *E-mail:* eevans@jvnla.com; Alice Tasman (AAR) *E-mail:* atasman@jvnla.com
Founded: 1978
Trade & mass market fiction & nonfiction. Motion picture, TV & foreign representation, film & TV rights for the books represented. No unsol mss, query first (see web site for complete, up-to-date submission guidelines). No reading fee. Commissions: 15% domestic, 20% UK & foreign translation.
Please be advised that Jean Naggar is no longer accepting new clients.
Titles recently placed: *An Unseemly Wife*, E B Moore; *Behind the Canvas*, Alexander Vance; *Blue Stars*, Emily Gray Tedrowe; *Hanukkah is Coming*, Tracy Newman; *Jonathan Franzen: The Comedy of Rage*, Philip Weinstein; *Lost in Translation*, Ella Frances Sanders; *Mademoiselle Chanel*, C W Gortner; *Meet Me in Venice*, Suzanne Ma; *Mort(e)*, Robert Repino; *Not If I See You First*, Eric Lindstrom; *Piper Green and the Fairy Tree*, Ellen Potter; *The Appetite Solution*, Dr Joseph Colella; *The Empire of the Senses*, Alexis Landau; *The Man Who Walked Away*, Maud Casey; *This is a Moose*, Richard T Morris; *Who Knows Tomorrow*, Lisa Lovatt-Smith; *Woman With a Gun*, Phillip Margolin
Foreign Rep(s): Akcali Copyright Agency (Turkey); Luigi Bernabo Associates (Italy); Big Apple Agency (Mainland China, Taiwan); Graal Literary Agency (Poland); Greene & Heaton (UK); Deborah Harris Agency (Israel); Danny Hong Agency (Korea); International Editors Co (Brazil, Latin America, Portugal, Spain); JLM Agency (Greece); Katai & Bolza Literary Agency (Hungary); Simona Kessler International Copyright Agency (Romania); Michelle Lapautre Agency (France); Licht & Burr Literary Agency (Scandinavia); Liepman Agency (Germany); Maxima Creative Agency (Indonesia); Mo Literary Services (Netherlands); Andrew Nurnberg Literary Agency (Baltic States, Bulgaria, Czech Republic, Russia); PLIMA (Montenegro, Serbia); Silkroad Publishers Agency (Thailand); Tuttle-Mori Agency Inc (Japan)

BK Nelson Inc Literary Agency (L-D)
Division of BK Nelson Inc
1565 Paseo Vida, Palm Springs, CA 92264
Tel: 760-778-8800 *Fax:* 760-778-6242
E-mail: bknelson4@cs.com
Web Site: www.bknelson.com; www.bknelsonlecturebureau.com; www.nelsonbookmovielecture.com; www.bknelsonmovieproduction.com
Key Personnel
Pres & CEO: Bonita K Nelson
CFO: Corp Reed
VP: John W Benson
Edit Dir: Tony Pastor
Acctg Dept: Erv Rosenfeld
Founded: 1998
All subjects; handle books, films, TV rights & careers of authors for books, movies & lectures. Edit ms to prepare for publishing & negotiate movie rights for major film companies as well as television. Office at the American Film Market, BEA & Frankfurt Book Fair. Represent major film distributor. If we sell the movie for a book you have written, we will help put you on the lecture circuit.
Titles recently placed: *A Play on Words*, John Starcevich; *Creating Wealth Without Risk*, Marc Garrison; *Death Waltz*, Marc Garrison, Brenda Garrison; *Mansions of the Leopard Mistress*, Dr Ted Austin Telford; *People of the Bear Mother: Periphus of the Sea of Souls (book 1)*, Dr Ted Austin Telford; *Platypuss Trilogy*, Jovanka Bach; *The Adventures of Sebastian the Angel Kitty (vol 2)*, S J Knight
Foreign Rep(s): David Bolt Associates (England); Ulla Lohren Literary Agency (Scandinavia); McKee & Mouche (France, Germany); Tuttle-Mori Agency Inc (Japan)
Foreign Rights: Alexandra Chapman
Membership(s): American Association of University Women; The Authors Guild; The Dramatists Guild of America; Motion Picture Alliance; NACA

Nelson Literary Agency LLC (L)
1732 Wazee St, Suite 207, Denver, CO 80202-1284
Tel: 303-292-2805
E-mail: query@nelsonagency.com
Web Site: www.nelsonagency.com
Key Personnel
Pres & Sr Literary Agent: Kristin Nelson (AAR)
Digital Liaison: Lori Bennett
Contracts & Royalties Mgr: Angie Hodapp
Submissions & Asian Territory Rts Coord: Anita Mumm
Founded: 2002
Accepts queries by e-mail only to query@nelsonagency.com. Represents fiction (literary, mainstream, women's, chick lit, romance, science fiction, fantasy, young adult, middle grade). No nonfiction, screenplays, short story collections, poetry, children's picture books, chapter books or Christian/inspirational. See web site for additional submission guidelines; no attachments, phone calls, postal mail or office visits. Some query letters & FAQs posted on web site. No fees charged.
Titles recently placed: *After*, Rhiannon Thomas; *Bird Box*, Josh Malerman; *Cold Stone Desire*, Eleri Stone; *Eddie Red Undercover: Mystery*

On Museum Mile, Marcia Wells; *Embassy Row (series)*, Ally Carter; *Evernight*, Kristen Callihan; *Exposure Therapy*, Roni Loren; *Golden Boys*, Stacey Lee; *Hester*, Paula Reed; *Proof By Seduction*, Courtney Milan; *Rebel Mechanics*, Shanna Swendson; *Score*, Miranda Kenneally; *Shooting Stars*, Allison Rushby; *Soulless*, Gail Carriger; *The Bane Chronicles*, Cassandra Clare, Maureen Johnson, Sarah Rees Brennan; *The Cabinet of Curiosities*, Stefan Bachmann, Katherine Catmull, Claire Legrand, et al; *The Prize*, Jamie Ford; *The Siren*, Tiffany Reisz; *Tigerseye*, Jennifer Shaw Wolf; *Wool*, Hugh Howey; *Young Elites*, Marie Lu; *Younger Gods*, Michael Underwood
Foreign Rights: Jenny Meyer Literary Agency (Jenny Meyer) (Worldwide exc Asia)
Membership(s): Romance Writers of America; Science Fiction & Fantasy Writers of America; Society of Children's Book Writers & Illustrators

New England Publishing Associates Inc (L-D)
One Carver Place, Lawrenceville, NJ 08648
Mailing Address: PO Box 66066, Lawrenceville, NJ 08648-6066
Tel: 860-973-2439
Web Site: www.nepagency.com
Key Personnel
Agent & Mng Dir: Roger S Williams (AAR) *E-mail:* roger@nepagency.com
Founded: 1983
No unsol mss, query first. See web site for submission details.
Foreign Rights: Books Crossing Borders (Worldwide)
Membership(s): ABA; The Authors Guild; Organization of American Historians

Regula Noetzli Literary Agent (L)
Affiliate of Charlotte Sheedy Literary Agency Inc
2344 County Rte 83, Pine Plains, NY 12567
Tel: 518-398-6260
E-mail: regula@taconic.net; regula@sheedylit.com
Adult fiction & nonfiction only with special interest in mysteries, biographies, psychology, popular science, sociology & environmental issues. Query first with outline & sample chapter. Representatives in Hollywood & most major foreign countries. No reading fees, no software.

The Betsy Nolan Literary Agency (L)
Division of The Nolan/Lehr Group Inc
214 W 29 St, Suite 1002, New York, NY 10001
Tel: 212-967-8200 *Fax:* 212-967-7292
E-mail: dblehr@cs.com
Key Personnel
Founding Partner: Betsy Nolan
Pres: Donald Lehr
Agent: Carla Glasser
Off Mgr: Jennifer Alperen
Nonfiction, popular culture, child care, psychology, cookbooks, how-to, biography, African-American & Judaica. No poetry. No unsol mss, query first; submit outline, no more than three sample chapters & author background; no reading fee; SASE.
Titles recently placed: *66 Square Feet*, Marie Viljoen; *Complete Herb Book*, Steven Orr; *Mad Hungry*, Lucinda Scala Quinn; *The Casserole Queens Cookbook: Put Some Lovin' in Your Oven with 100 Easy One-Dish Recipes*, Crystal Cook, Sandy Pollock

Harold Ober Associates Inc (L)
425 Madison Ave, New York, NY 10017
Tel: 212-759-8600 *Fax:* 212-759-9428
Web Site: www.haroldober.com
Key Personnel
Pres: Phyllis Westberg (AAR)
Agent: Jake Elwell (AAR)
Agent, Film Rts: Don Laventhall
Agent, Foreign Rts: Pamela Malpas (AAR)
Agent (backlist), Perms: Craig Tenney (AAR) *Tel:* 212-759-8600 ext 216
Founded: 1929
General fiction & nonfiction. No screenplays or plays. No e-mail queries. No unsol mss, query first with letter & SASE. Queries are accepted by postal mail & must be addressed to a specific agent for consideration. Enclose concise cover letter, the first five pages of the ms or proposal & SASE for reply. No reading fee.
Foreign Rep(s): David Higham Associates Ltd (UK)

Objective Entertainment (L-D)
609 Greenwich St, 6th fl, New York, NY 10014
Tel: 212-431-5454 *Fax:* 917-464-6394
Web Site: www.objectiveent.com
Key Personnel
COO: Jarred Weisfeld *E-mail:* Jarred@objectiveent.com
Pres: Ian Kleinert *E-mail:* IK@objectiveent.com
Head, Busn Aff: Mark S Frey *E-mail:* mfrey@marksfrey.com
Agent: Leora Rosenberg *E-mail:* Leora@objectiveent.com
Founded: 2007
Full service management company specializing in book publishing, dramatic writing, talent & television packaging. Handles literary, dramatic & film rights, all commerical & adult trade publishing. No unsol mss. Submit query letter. No fees charged.

Fifi Oscard Agency Inc (L-D)
110 W 40 St, 16th fl, New York, NY 10018
Tel: 212-764-1100 *Fax:* 212-840-5019
E-mail: agency@fifioscard.com
Web Site: fifioscard.com
Key Personnel
Pres & Lit Agent: Peter Sawyer
VP & Lit Agent: Carmen La Via
Founded: 1955
General fiction & nonfiction, all areas; film & TV rights; scripts for stage, motion picture & TV. Have always represented talent as well. No fees charged. No unsol mss, query first; submit outline & sample chapter if requested. See web site for more instruction.
Foreign Rep(s): Agenzia Letteraria Internazionale (Italy); Bardon-Chinese Media (China); Caroline Van Gelderan (Netherlands); Imprima Korea (Korea); Agence Michelle Lapautre (France); Thomas Schlueck (Germany); Abner Stein Agency (England); Julio F Yanez Agencia Literaria (Spain)

The Richard Parks Agency (L)
PO Box 693, Salem, NY 12865
Tel: 518-854-9466 *Fax:* 518-854-9466
E-mail: rp@richardparksagency.com
Web Site: www.richardparksagency.com
Key Personnel
Sole Prop: Richard Parks (AAR)
Founded: 1989
Fiction & nonfiction. No unsol mss, query first with SASE only. Cannot respond to phone, fax or e-mail queries. No reading fee.
Foreign Rep(s): Barbara Levy Literary Agency (UK)
Foreign Rights: The Marsh Agency

Kathi J Paton Literary Agency (L)
Box 2236, Radio City Sta, New York, NY 10101-2236
Tel: 212-265-6586 *Fax:* 908-647-2117
E-mail: kjplitbiz@optonline.net
Web Site: www.patonliterary.com
Key Personnel
Owner: Kathi J Paton
Founded: 1987
Interested in biography, computers/technology, business/investing/finance, history, health, sports, science, literary fiction, parenting, Christian life & issues, popular culture, humor, investigative journalism & progressive politics/current affairs. No unsol mss; e-mail queries only with a brief description. If requested, e-mail proposal (nonfiction) or synopsis (fiction) & sample chapter. Sorry, no science fiction, horror, poetry, juvenile or self-published books. No reading fee. Subs-agents in all major foreign markets & Hollywood.
Titles recently placed: *Wild New Jersey: Nature Adventures in the Garden State*, David Wheeler, Margaret O'Gorman
Membership(s): The Authors Guild

Pema Browne Ltd (L)
71 Pine Rd, Woodbourne, NY 12788
E-mail: ppbltd@optonline.net
Web Site: www.pemabrowneltd.com
Key Personnel
Pres: Pema Browne
VP: Perry Browne
Founded: 1966
All subjects including genre romance, mass market & trade; fiction, nonfiction, business, how-to, cookbooks, health, reference, inspirational. Children's picture books, novelty, middle-grade, young adult, illustration. No unsol mss, query first (no fax, e-mail or phone queries). Submit cover letter, one page query with bio & SASE. Neat, wide margins, dark type, double-spaced, only one side of paper printed. We do NOT review mss that have previously been sent out to publishers. No reading fee. Work with foreign agents in major countries. Signatory to Writers Guild, Society of Children's Book Writers & Illustrators, Romance Writers of America.
Titles recently placed: *Fire and Smoke*, Susan Scott; *Never Kiss A Stranger*, Heather Grothaus; *Never Seduce A Scoundrel*, Heather Grothaus; *Salvation*, Susan Scott; *To Fight With Intrepidity*, JD Lock
Membership(s): Romance Writers of America; Society of Children's Book Writers & Illustrators; Writers Guild of America

Dan Peragine Literary Agency (L)
227 Beechwood Ave, Bogota, NJ 07603
Tel: 201-390-0468
E-mail: dpliterary@aol.com
Key Personnel
Owner & Pres: Dan Peragine
EVP: Karen A Peragine
Founded: 1991
Specialize in behavioral sciences, biography, environment, history, Christian, inspirational, nonfiction, self-help, computers, sports, photography, all high school & college textbooks, Advanced placement & testing. Musical Groups, World War I, World War II, Handle software, film & TV rights. Represent photographic archives & books of all types. No unsol mss, query first with a complete proposal; if sending fiction, include any type of readers report or outside review with the submission; submit sample chapters single page, double-spaced, or on disk (do not send by e-mail if it needs to be downloaded). No reading fees, fees charged for editorial development, re-writes, ghostwriters, publishing consulting, full book packaging & book marketing.
Membership(s): ABA; ASPP; National Press Photographers Association; PPA

Stephen Pevner Inc (L-D)
382 Lafayette St, Suite 8, New York, NY 10003
Tel: 212-674-8403 *Fax:* 212-529-3692
E-mail: spidevelopment@gmail.com
Key Personnel
Pres: Stephen Pevner *E-mail:* spevner@aol.com
Founded: 1991

New fiction & general nonfiction, pop culture, humor, international film, TV & audio & electronic rights, plays, screenplays, independent producers & directors. No unsol mss or scripts, query first with SASE; submit outline & sample chapters or synopsis. No reading fees.

Alison Picard Literary Agent (L-D)
PO Box 2000, Cotuit, MA 02635
Tel: 508-477-7192 *Fax:* 508-477-7192 (call first)
E-mail: ajpicard@aol.com
Founded: 1985
Representing adult & juvenile/young adult fiction & nonfiction. Beginners welcome. No unsol mss, query first with letter & SASE; no phone or fax queries. Upon positive response, submit double-spaced complete ms. No fees charged.
Titles recently placed: *365 Days of Slow Cooker Recipes*, Stephanie O'Dea; *Curse of the Jade Lily*, David Housewright; *Decided on the Battlefield*, David Johnson; *Fear of Beauty*, Susan Froetschel; *Not Your Mother's Freezer Cookbook*, Jessica Fisher; *Seconds (new ed)*, David Ely; *The Efficiency Trap: Finding a Better Way to Achieve a Sustainable Energy Future*, Steve Hallett; *The Finest Hours (middle grade ed)*, Michael Tougias, Casey Sherman; *Three Cheers for Girls*, Sara Hunt; *Torn*, Stephanie Guerra; *Totally Together: Shortcuts to an Organized Life*, Stephanie O'Dea
Foreign Rights: John Pawsey (Europe)

Pimlico/Aurous Inc (L)
Subsidiary of Aurous Inc
PO Box 20490, New York, NY 10017
Tel: 212-628-9729 *Fax:* 212-535-7861
Key Personnel
Pres: Kay McCauley *E-mail:* kaymcc25@aol.com
Busn Mgr: Christopher Shepard
Agent: Kirby McCauley
Founded: 1974
Adult fiction & nonfiction. Motion picture & TV rights from book properties only. No unsol mss. Projects by referral only. No reading fee. Agents in all principal foreign countries.

Pinder Lane & Garon-Brooke Associates Ltd (L-D)
159 W 53 St, New York, NY 10019
Tel: 212-489-0880 *Fax:* 212-489-7104
E-mail: pinderlanegaronbrooke@gmail.com
Web Site: www.pinderlaneandgaronbrooke.com
Key Personnel
Owner & Agent: Dick Duane (AAR); Robert Thixton (AAR)
Founded: 1996
Fiction & nonfiction, film & TV rights. No unsol mss, query first. No reading fee. Submit short synopsis, double-spaced & unbound. Representatives in Hollywood & all foreign markets.
Foreign Rep(s): Abner Stein Agency (UK)
Foreign Rights: Rights Unlimited

Pippin Properties Inc (L)
110 W 40 St, Suite 1704, New York, NY 10018
Tel: 212-338-9310 *Fax:* 212-338-9579
E-mail: info@pippinproperties.com
Web Site: www.pippinproperties.com; www.facebook.com/pippinproperties
Key Personnel
Pres & Creative Dir: Holly M McGhee
E-mail: hmcghee@pippinproperties.com
Agent & Mgr, Foreign Rts: Elena Giovinazzo
E-mail: egiovinazzo@pippinproperties.com
Agent, Audio Rts: Heather Alexander
Asst, Dramatic Rts & Perms: Courtney Stevenson
Founded: 1998
Represent authors & artists for children's picture books, middle-grade novels, chapter books & young adult novels. To submit, e-mail query & first chapter. Handle film, TV & foreign rights.

Poirot & Co Literary Agency (L)
3887 Nimbus Rd, Longmont, CO 80503
Tel: 303-494-0668 *Fax:* 303-494-9396
E-mail: poirotco@comcast.net
Key Personnel
Pres: Henry M Poirot
Founded: 1976
Nonfiction, no poetry. Handle film & TV rights. No unsol mss, query first. No reading fee.

Pom Inc (L-D)
18-15 215 St, Bayside, NY 11360
Tel: 516-487-3441
Key Personnel
Pres: Dan Green *E-mail:* dangreen@pomlit.com
Founded: 1990
Fiction & general nonfiction. No unsol mss. Please do not fax or e-mail. Handle electronic, film & TV rights. No reading fee.
Titles recently placed: *American Apostles*, Christine Heyrman; *Crucible of the West*, Brian Catlos; *Thaddeus Stevens*, Bruce Levine; *The Bill of Rights*, Carol Berkin; *The Scarlet Sisters: Sex, Scandal and Suffrage in the Gilded Age*, Myra MacPherson

The Poynor Group (L)
13454 Yorktown Dr, Bowie, MD 20715
Tel: 301-805-6788
Key Personnel
Pres: Jay Poynor *E-mail:* jpoynor@aol.com
Founded: 1985
Literary representation service & sales. Submit e-mail query first (mandatory). If agreeable, then send a synopsis & first three chapters. Commission: 15% of advance & royalties. No other fees.

Linn Prentis Literary (L)
6830 NE Bothell Way, PMB 496, Kenmore, WA 98028
Tel: 212-876-8557 *Fax:* 206-984-0837
E-mail: linn@linnprentis.com
Web Site: www.linnprentis.com
Key Personnel
Literary Agent: Linn Prentis
Fine fiction, limited nonfiction: special interest in speculative fiction, science fiction & fantasy. Special interest in family saga. Also mainstream, women's, literary, young adult & middle-reader, men's, mystery, suspense, historical, non-category romance. Literary nonfiction. Film rights only as outgrowth of book sales through Bill Contardi, New York. No phone, fax or e-mail queries; no unsol mss; query by mail with SASE; cover letter (credits, bio facts, word count, title & genre/target audience) 2 page synopsis, first 10 pages. Mss: double-spaced, unbound, one side of page, boxed with cover. No reading fee; 15% commission, 20% on dramatic & foreign sales. Founded as an affiliate of the Virginia Kidd Agency, now independent.
Foreign Rep(s): ALI (Italy); P & P Fritz (Germany); International Editors' Co (Portugal, South America, Spain); Korshenevski (Russia & former USSR); Lenclud (France); LEX (Hungary); MBA (Meg Davis) (UK); PIP (Eastern Europe); Lennart Sane (Scandinavia); Tuttle-Mori Agency Inc (Japan)
Membership(s): Science Fiction & Fantasy Writers of America

The Aaron M Priest Literary Agency Inc (L)
708 Third Ave, 23rd fl, New York, NY 10017-4201
Tel: 212-818-0344 *Fax:* 212-573-9417
E-mail: info@aaronpriest.com
Web Site: www.aaronpriest.com
Key Personnel
Pres & Agent: Aaron M Priest (AAR)
E-mail: querypriest@aaronpriest.com
Agent: Lucy Childs Baker (AAR)
E-mail: querychilds@aaronpriest.com; Melissa Edwards (AAR) *E-mail:* queryedwards@aaronpriest.com; Lisa Erbach Vance (AAR)
E-mail: queryvance@aaronpriest.com
Founded: 1974
Our agents are interested in the following. Aaron Priest: thrillers, general fiction. Lisa Erbach Vance: general fiction, mystery, thrillers, up market women's fiction, historical fiction, narrative nonfiction, memoir. Lucy Childs: literary & commercial fiction, historical fiction, memoir, edgy women's fiction. Melissa Edwards: mystery/suspense, cozy mysteries, young adult, women's fiction, commercial fiction. For all agents: no poetry, no screenplays. The best way to query all agents is to submit a query letter via e-mail. The query should be about one page long describing your work as well as your background. No attachments, however a first chapter pasted into the body of an e-mail query is acceptable. Do not submit to more than one agent at a time at this agency (we urge you to consider each agent's emphasis before submitting). We will get back to you within four weeks, but only if interested. No fees are charged.

Prospect Agency (L)
285 Fifth Ave, PMB 445, Brooklyn, NY 11215
Tel: 718-788-3217 *Fax:* 718-360-9582
Web Site: www.prospectagency.com
Key Personnel
Founder, Pres & Literary Agent (NJ office): Emily Sylvan Kim *E-mail:* esk@prospectagency.com
Literary Agent: Linda Camacho; Carrie Pestritto
E-mail: carrie@prospectagency.com; Becca Stumpf *E-mail:* becca@prospectagency.com
Literary Agent (NJ Office): Rachel Orr
E-mail: rko@prospectagency.com; Teresa Kietlinski *E-mail:* tk@prospectagency.com
Founded: 2005
Full service literary agency representing a range of fiction, nonfiction, illustrators, romance, literary fiction, middle grade fiction & picture books, adult commercial fiction, women's fiction & young adult titles. No unsol mss, query first via web. Only queries submitted through our web site are accepted. Queries sent by e-mail or regular mail not accepted. Send query letter, three chapters & a brief synopsis on web site. No fees charged. See web site for detailed submission guidelines.
Titles recently placed: *A Friend for Bo*, Elisabeth Zuniga; *A Weird and Wild Beauty*, Erin Peabody; *Ghost Hunters*, Jeff Cole, Johnathan Robson; *Have Mercy*, Shelley Ann Clark; *Play Me*, Tracy Wolff; *Pug & Pig*, Joyce Wan; *Ruined*, Tracy Wolff; *Shattered*, Tracy Wolff; *Shredded*, Tracy Wolff; *Sinful Rewards*, Cynthia Sax; *Snail and Worm*, Tina Kugler; *Swallow the Leader*, Kevin Sherry; *The Change Your Name Store*, Tina Kugler; *The Critter Club (books 10-12)*, Marsha Riti; *The Yeti Files (1 & 2)*, Kevin Sherry; *Unnatural Selection*, Sara Joiner; *Worth the Fall*, Claudia Connor; *Worth the Risk*, Claudia Connor
Branch Office(s)
551 Valley Rd, PMB 377, Upper Montclair, NJ 07043
Foreign Rights: The Fielding Agency (Whitney Lee) (Worldwide)

Generosa Gina Protano Publishing, see GGP Publishing Inc

Publishing Services (L)
525 E 86 St, Suite 8-E, New York, NY 10028
Tel: 212-535-6248 *Fax:* 212-988-1999
E-mail: publishingservices@mac.com
Key Personnel
Pres: Amy S Goldberger

Upscale women's fiction & nonfiction. No unsol mss, query first with SASE. No phone calls. For fiction, send first 50 pages. For nonfiction, send outline & first three chapters. Handle film & TV rights. No reading fee.

Puddingstone Literary, Authors' Agents (L-D)
Subsidiary of Cohen Group LLC
11 Mabro Dr, Denville, NJ 07834-9607
Tel: 973-366-3622
Key Personnel
Dir: Alec Bernard
Sr Memb: Saul Cohen
Memb: Michael R Cohen
Contact: Eugenia Kielbicki
Founded: 1972
General trade & mass market fiction & nonfiction; motion picture scripts & teleplays. Handle film & TV rights. No unsol mss, query first with SASE. Submit outline & sample chapters. No reading fee. Representatives in Hollywood & foreign countries. Fee for ms copies, galleys & bound books for foreign & domestic submissions.

Susan Rabiner Literary Agency Inc (L)
315 W 39 St, Suite 1501, New York, NY 10018-3907
Web Site: RabinerLit.com
Key Personnel
Founder & Pres: Susan Rabiner *E-mail:* susan@rabiner.net
Agent: Holly Bemiss *E-mail:* hollyb@rabiner.net; Sydelle Kramer *E-mail:* sydellek@rabiner.net; Helena Schwarz *E-mail:* helens@rabiner.net
Founded: 1997
Serious nonfiction, narrative nonfiction, business, memoirs, sports, college texts; history, politics, economics, psychology, science, gender studies, popular culture, education, anthropology, archeology, law & biography. Represent trade authors trying to place their mss with the major commercial publishing houses. Also represent a limited number of college text authors. Primarily academics, journalists, scientists & independent scholars; query first by e-mail as an attachment, no faxes; no reading fees. No screenplays, poetry or fiction.
Titles recently placed: *A Fleece of Celestial Importance*, Greg Grandin; *Lady Bird & Lyndon*, Betty Caroli; *Paleocapitalism*, Jacob Hacker, Paul Pierson; *That Infamous Woman Polly Adler*, Debby Applegate; *The Age of Eisenhower*, William Hitchcock; *The Everyday Parenting Toolkit: The Kazdin Method for Easy, Step-by-Step, Lasting Change for You and Your Child*, Alan Kazdin, Carlo Rotella; *The Grid*, Gretchen Bakke; *The Indispensable Nation*, Vali Nasr; *The Signal & the Noise*, Nate Silver
Foreign Rights: The English Agency (Japan); Agence Hoffmann (Germany); Agnese Incisa (Italy)

Raines & Raines (L-D)
103 Kenyon Rd, Medusa, NY 12120
Tel: 518-239-8311 *Fax:* 518-239-6029
Key Personnel
Partner: Joan Raines (AAR); Keith Korman
Founded: 1961
Handle film & TV rights. No unsol mss, query first; submit one page; no reading fee. Agents in all principal countries.
Foreign Rep(s): Agenzia Letteraria Internazionale; Balcells; Big Apple Agency Inc; Bookman; Campbell Thomson & McLaughlin; Fritz; Lapautre; Nurnberg; Tuttle-Mori Agency Inc

Charlotte Cecil Raymond, Literary Agent (L)
32 Bradlee Rd, Marblehead, MA 01945
Tel: 781-631-6722 *Fax:* 781-631-6722
E-mail: raymondliterary@gmail.com
Adult nonfiction & literary fiction; no juvenile, young adult, poetry, short stories, fantasy, science fiction or screenplays. No unsol mss, query first with SASE; submit outline & sample chapters. No reading fee.

Rees Literary Agency (L)
14 Beacon St, Suite 710, Boston, MA 02108
Tel: 617-227-9014 *Fax:* 617-227-8762
E-mail: reesagency@reesagency.com
Web Site: reesagency.com
Key Personnel
Agent: Ann Collette *E-mail:* agent10702@aol.com; Nicole LaBombard (AAR) *E-mail:* nicole@reesagency.com; Mr Lorin Rees (AAR) *E-mail:* lorin@reesagency.com
Founded: 1982
Literary fiction, nonfiction, business, biography, health, history, self-help, psychology, current affairs, humor, mystery, thrillers, etc. For fiction, include query letter +/or synopsis & the first three chapters. For nonfiction, enclose a complete book proposal or substantial treatment.
Titles recently placed: *A Hatred of Tulips*, Richard Lourie; *Andy Grove*, Richard Tedlow; *Art's Blood*, Vicki Lane; *Blood Makes the Grass Grow Green*, Johnny Rico; *Bone Factory*, Steve Sidor; *Busy Monsters*, William Giraldi; *Clair Fontaine, Crime Fighter*, Tracey Enright; *Driving Excellence: Management Principles From the Little Bus Company That Could*, Mark Aesch; *Girl Most Likely To*, Poonam Sharma; *Hot Spots*, Martin Fletcher; *Innovation Nation*, John Kao; *Leadership Therapy: Inside the Mind of Microsoft*, Anna Rowley; *Letter from Kabul*, Hamid Karzi; *Out Of Thin Air: The Book On Entrepreneurship*, Gregg Fairbrothers, Tessa Winter; *Primal Health*, William Meller; *Selling B2B Made Simple*, Geoffrey James; *Stirring it Up: How Business Can & Must Save the World*, Gary Hirshberg; *The Border Crosser*, Johnny Rico; *The Satisfied Customer*, Claes Fornell; *The Ultimate Sales Machine*, Chet Holmes; *Travel Writing*, Peter Ferry; *What Americans Really Want...Really*, Frank Luntz; *What Israel Means to Me*, Alan Dershowitz; *Who: Solve Your #1 Problem*, Geoff Smart, Randy Street; *Why Terrorism Works*, Alan Dershowitz; *Winning*, Jack Welch; *Words that Work*, Frank Luntz; *You Know When The Men Are Gone*, Siobhan Fallon
Foreign Rights: Taryn Fagerness (Albania, Argentina, Australia, Brazil, Bulgaria, Canada, China, Croatia, Czech Republic, Denmark, Estonia, Finland, France, Germany, Greece, Hungary, Iceland, India, Indonesia, Israel, Italy, Japan, Korea, Latvia, Lithuania, Mexico, Netherlands, Norway, Poland, Portugal, Romania, Russia, Serbia, Slovakia, Slovenia, Spain, Sweden, Taiwan, Thailand, Turkey, UK, Vietnam)
Membership(s): PEN American Center

Marian Reiner (L)
71 Disbrow Lane, New Rochelle, NY 10804
Tel: 914-235-7808 *Fax:* 914-576-1432
E-mail: mreinerlit@aol.com
Founded: 1963
Handle only work for children; fiction, nonfiction. No unsol mss. No online submissions. No new clients. No reading fee. Charge for photocopying & overseas phone & mail. Handle film & TV rights only for books agency sold.
Membership(s): The Authors Guild; Society of Authors & Illustrators; Society of Children's Book Writers & Illustrators

Renaissance Literary & Talent (L-D)
PO Box 17379, Beverly Hills, CA 90209
Tel: 323-848-8305 *Fax:* 424-298-2588
E-mail: query@renaissancemgmt.net
Web Site: www.facebook.com/RenaissanceLiteraryTalent
Key Personnel
Pres: Alan Nevins *E-mail:* alan@renaissancemgmt.net
Founded: 1993
Commercial fiction & nonfiction. Handle film & TV rights; novels. No unsol mss. Query first. Handle highly recommended mss. Submit outlines & sample chapters. No reading fee, 15% commission.

The Amy Rennert Agency Inc (L)
1550 Tiburon Blvd, Suite 302, Tiburon, CA 94920
Tel: 415-789-8955
E-mail: queries@amyrennert.com
Web Site: amyrennert.com
Key Personnel
Pres: Amy Rennert
Busn Mgr: Laura Velkei *E-mail:* lvelkei@frfllp.com
Assoc: Louise Kollenbaum *E-mail:* louise@amyrennert.com
Founded: 1999
The agency specializes in books that matter. Amy has spent more than 20 years in the publishing business, pursuing her passion for the written word. The agency represents a select group of quality fiction & nonfiction writers - many of them award-winners & dozens of agency books have been New York Times & national bestsellers. We provide career management for established & first time authors & our breadth of experience in many genres enables us to meet the needs of a diverse clientele. The agency has developed a reputation since its inception for a passionate commitment to agency writers. We are purposely a small organization to facilitate hands-on personalized service & attention to our authors & their books. We are not currently accepting unsol submissions.
Foreign Rights: Taryn Fagerness (Worldwide)
Membership(s): The Authors Guild

Jodie Rhodes Literary Agency (L)
8840 Villa La Jolla Dr, Suite 315, La Jolla, CA 92037
E-mail: jrhodesl@san.rr.com
Key Personnel
Pres: Jodie Rhodes
Fiction Agent at Large: Clark McCutcheon
Nonfiction Agent at Large: Robert McCarter
Founded: 1998
Established to bring talented new writers to the attention of publishers & establish a successful long term career for all writers. Interested in literary fiction, memoirs, intelligent, sophisticated mysteries, suspense & thrillers with fresh original plots, women's books with a unique story, quirky coming-of-age books, African American & multicultural literature, both fiction & nonfiction, politics, history, military, international affairs, science, medicine, health, fitness, women's issues, parenting. Have no interest in science fiction, fantasy, horror, erotica, religion, spiritual or inspiration books. Also do not handle children's books, only a few literary young adult/teen novels. Send query, brief synopsis, first 30 to 50 pages, SASE with stamps—not metered slip. No fees charged; handles film & TV rights. Do not call or e-mail us. We will contact you if your query +/or sample pages interest us. You do not have to enclose a SASE but we will not reply without a SASE unless your query has generated great interest - in case that occurs, always include your e-mail address with your query letter. Important: We cannot return any material that weights 13 ounces or more, even if you enclose a SASE – so if you send material that weights

that much, keep in mind the material will not be returned to you.
Titles recently placed: *A Year of Cats & Dogs*, Margaret Hawkins; *Aging: Modern Theories & Therapies*, Joseph Panno; *Black Boy - White School*, Brian Walker; *Black Sea Twilight*, Domnica Radulescu; *Bombay Girl*, Kavita Daswani; *Broken Blue Line*, Connie Dial; *Combat Trama*, James D Johnson; *Computers and Creativity*, Robert Plotkin; *Computers, Internet & Society*, Robert Plotkin; *Confessions: A Memoir*, Jodie Rhodes; *Cosmic Numbers*, James D Stein, PhD; *Critical Components of J R R Tolkien*, Jay Ruud; *Dead Wrong*, Connie Dial; *Do You Really Need Back Surgery*, Aaron G Filler; *Encyclopedia of Enviromental Studies*, Marc Menetrez; *Encyclopedia of Science and Technology*, William Gough; *Fallen Angels*, Connie Dial; *Fighting for Dontae*, Mike Castan; *First Six Minutes of Life on Earth*, Christine Reed; *Forensic Science at Work*, Jay Siegal; *How to Survive a Natural Disaster*, Margaret Hawkins; *How We Got Barb Back*, Margaret Hawkins; *Impossible Problems, Ingenious Solutions: What Math and Science Do When They Hit the Wall*, James D Stein, PhD; *Internal Affairs*, Connie Dial; *Iran's Revolutionary Guard*, Stephen O'Hern; *Life of Earth*, Stanley A Rice; *Lovetorn*, Kavita Daswani; *My Beautiful Hippie*, Janet Nichols Lynch; *Nuclear Accidents and Disasters (Nuclear Power)*, James A Mahaffey; *Racing California*, Janet Nichols Lynch; *Straightening the Bell Curve: How Stereotypes about Black Masculinity Drive Research on Race and Intelligence*, Constance Hilliard; *Stranded*, J T Dutton; *The Alzheimer's Answer*, Marwan Sabbagh; *The Genie in the Machine*, Robert Plotkin; *The History of Nuclear Power*, James A Mahaffey; *The Night Battles*, M F Bloxam; *The Paranormal Equation: A New Scientific Perspective on Remote Viewing, Clairvoyance, and Other Inexplicable Phenomena*, James D Stein, PhD; *The Price of Loyalty*, Mike Castan; *The Red Flag in American Bathrooms*, Dr Wesley Jones; *Understanding Biodiversity*, Julie Casper
Foreign Rep(s): The English Agency (Japan); KCC Agency (Korea)
Foreign Rights: Jill Hughes Literary Agency (Worldwide)

John R Riina Literary Agency (L)
1055 W Joppa Rd, Unit 651, Towson, MD 21204-3777
Tel: 410-296-1499
Founded: 1972
Nonfiction books: science, health, medicine, textbooks & how-to. No unsol mss, query first with author's bio, one paragraph synopsis & outline. No return of material without SASE. No reading fee. No phone queries.
Titles recently placed: *The Critical Role of Parenting in Human Development*, Marianna S Klebanov, Adam D Travis

The Angela Rinaldi Literary Agency (L)
PO Box 7877, Beverly Hills, CA 90212-7877
Tel: 310-842-7665 *Fax:* 310-837-8143
E-mail: info@rinaldiliterary.com (submissions)
Web Site: www.rinaldiliterary.com
Key Personnel
Pres: Angela Rinaldi (AAR) *E-mail:* amr@rinaldiliterary.com
Founded: 1994
Commercial & literary fiction, nonfiction, lifestyle/travel/food. Accept unsol mss. Do not query by phone or fax. E-mail queries only, no attachments unless requested. Advise if sending out multiple submissions. Fiction submissions: Paste the first ten pages in the e-mail query. Nonfiction submissions: query with detailed covering letter. No reading fee. Representation in film & foreign markets for clients only.

Titles recently placed: *A Deadly Legacy*, Julie Vail; *Entwined Lives: Twins and What They Tell Us About Human Behavior*, Nancy L Segal, PhD; *Hand-Crafted Candy Bars: From-Scratch, All-Natural, Gloriously Grown-Up Confections*, Susan Heeger, Susie Norris; *Hitchhiking with Larry David: An Accidental Tourist's Summer of Self-Discovery in Martha's Vineyard*, Paul Samuel Dolman; *How to Make Every Putt: The Secret to Winning Golf's Game Within the Game*, Dr Joseph Parent; *The Night Gardener*, Drusilla Campbell; *When She Came Home*, Drusilla Campbell
Foreign Rights: The Taryn Fagerness Agency (Worldwide)
Membership(s): PEN Center USA West

Ann Rittenberg Literary Agency Inc (L)
15 Maiden Lane, Suite 206, New York, NY 10038
Tel: 212-684-6936 *Fax:* 212-684-6929
E-mail: info@rittlit.com
Web Site: www.rittlit.com
Key Personnel
Pres: Ann Rittenberg (AAR)
Assoc: Camille Goldin *E-mail:* camille@rittlit.com
Contact: Rosie Jonker *E-mail:* rosie@rittlit.com
Founded: 1992
Literary fiction & nonfiction; no genre fiction, no screenplays. Co-agents in all principal foreign countries as well as Hollywood. Query letter & first three chapters of double-spaced ms with SASE; no queries by fax.
Membership(s): The Authors Guild

Judith Riven Literary Agent LLC (L)
250 W 16 St, Suite 4F, New York, NY 10011
Tel: 212-255-1009 *Fax:* 212-255-8547
E-mail: rivenlitqueries@gmail.com
Web Site: rivenlit.com
Key Personnel
Owner & Pres: Judith Riven
Founded: 1993
Fiction & nonfiction. Handle film & TV rights for book clients only. One page query letter describing material with SASE. Unless requested, no mss accepted. E-mail queries are accepted but no attachments. We are not currently accepting science fiction, fantasy, or horror submissions.
Titles recently placed: *Over There: America in The Great War, 1917-1918*, Lisa Davis; *The Divorce Diet (novel)*, Ellen Hawley; *The Reason for Flowers: How Flowers Changed Our World*, Stephen Buchmann

Riverside Literary Agency (L)
41 Simon Keets Rd, Leyden, MA 01337
Tel: 413-772-0067 *Fax:* 413-772-0969
E-mail: rivlit@sover.net
Web Site: www.riversideliteraryagency.com
Key Personnel
Pres: Susan Lee Cohen
Founded: 1990
Adult fiction & nonfiction. No unsol mss, query first with SASE. No reading fees. Handle film & TV rights & foreign rights with co-agents.

RLR Associates Ltd (L-D)
7 W 51 St, New York, NY 10019
Tel: 212-541-8641 *Fax:* 212-262-7084
Web Site: www.rlrassociates.net
Key Personnel
VP & Literary Agent: Scott Gould *E-mail:* sgould@rlrassociates.net
Founded: 1980
A boutique literary agency in Manhattan, representing fiction of all types (from genre to literary) & narrative nonfiction. No unsol mss; e-mail or regular mail query letters.

RMA (L)
85 Lincoln St, 1st fl, Meriden, CT 06451
Tel: 718-434-1893
Web Site: www.ricia.com
Key Personnel
Owner: Ricia Mainhardt *E-mail:* ricia@ricia.com
VP, West Coast Opers: Charla Mustard-Foote
Founded: 1987
Popular fiction, especially science fiction, fantasy, mystery, thriller, romance; nonfiction, especially pop culture, history & science. Does not accept poetry. Online submissions preferred. Submit query letter, 1 brief paragraph pitch, 1-2 page synopsis & ms by attachment. Handle software & drama for client's books only. Affiliates handle film & TV rights for client's books. No reading fee. Branch offices in Seattle & Hollywood.
Membership(s): Horror Writers Association; Mystery Writers of America; Romance Writers of America; Science Fiction & Fantasy Writers of America

B J Robbins Literary Agency (L)
5130 Bellaire Ave, North Hollywood, CA 91607
E-mail: robbinsliterary@gmail.com
Key Personnel
Owner & Pres: B J Robbins (AAR)
Asst: Peter DiGiovanni
Founded: 1992
Literary & commercial fiction, general nonfiction. Handle film & TV rights for agency clients only. E-mail queries accepted. No unsol attachments. Mailed submissions must include SASE.
Titles recently placed: *A Pinch of Ooh La La*, Renee Swindle; *Blood Brothers*, Deanne Stillman; *Blood of the Tiger*, J A Mills; *Headhunters on My Doorstep*, J Maarten Troost; *Little Bighorn*, John Hough, Jr; *Mongrels*, Stephen Graham Jones; *Reliance*, Mary Volmer; *Shoot for the Moon*, James Donovan; *The Fiction Writer's Guide to Dialogue*, John Hough, Jr; *The Paris Deadline*, Max Byrd
Foreign Rights: The Marsh Agency (all other territories); Abner Stein Agency (UK)
Membership(s): PEN Center USA

Rockmill & Company (L)
647 Warren St, Brooklyn, NY 11217
E-mail: agentrockmill@yahoo.com
Key Personnel
Pres & Agent: Jayne Rockmill
Founded: 1989
Represents artists, photographers & writers, specializing in illustrated books & licensing. Initial submission is preferred by e-mail. For illustrated titles, submit a 1 page book summary, with sample text & illustrations along with author bio. For fiction & nonfiction book projects, submit a query letter with 3 sample chapters. Send SASE if anything needs to be returned. No fee charged to review project.
Titles recently placed: *Makeup for Ageless Beauty: More than 40 Colorful, Creative Looks for Women 40 and Over*, Linda Mason

Linda Roghaar Literary Agency LLC (L)
133 High Point Dr, Amherst, MA 01002
Tel: 413-256-1921
E-mail: contact@lindaroghaar.com
Web Site: www.lindaroghaar.com
Key Personnel
Owner & Pres: Linda L Roghaar (AAR) *E-mail:* linda@lindaroghaar.com
Founded: 1996
Full service agency handling mainly nonfiction; women's issues, religion & spirituality, history, self-help, memoir. No romance, horror or science fiction. Manage comprehensive rights. Query with SASE first. No reading fee. Domestic sales commission: 15%. No unsol mss.

The Roistacher Literary Agency (L)
545 W 111 St, Suite 7-J, New York, NY 10025
Tel: 212-222-1405
Key Personnel
Pres: Robert E Roistacher *E-mail:* rer41@columbia.edu
Founded: 1978
General nonfiction, especially journalism, social science & public policy. Literary fiction only from published writers. No unsol mss, query first. For nonfiction, submit prospectus, curriculum vitae, two sample chapters, chapter outline & table of contents. No reading fee.

The Rosenberg Group (L)
23 Lincoln Ave, Marblehead, MA 01945
Tel: 781-990-1341 *Fax:* 781-990-1344
Web Site: www.rosenberggroup.com
Key Personnel
Agent: Barbara Collins Rosenberg (AAR)
Founded: 1998
Representing romance & women's fiction, trade nonfiction & college level textbooks for the first & second year courses. Check web site for areas of nonfiction interest. No unsol mss, query first. No reading fee. No e-mail queries. Representatives in all foreign markets.
Membership(s): Romance Writers of America

Rita Rosenkranz Literary Agency (L)
440 West End Ave, Suite 15D, New York, NY 10024-5358
Tel: 212-873-6333 *Fax:* 212-873-5225
Web Site: www.ritarosenkranzliteraryagency.com
Key Personnel
Agent: Rita Rosenkranz (AAR)
E-mail: rrosenkranz@mindspring.com
Founded: 1990
Nonfiction, adult; no unsol mss, query first with SASE or via e-mail; no fees.
Membership(s): The Authors Guild; International Women's Writing Guild; Women's Media Group

Jane Rotrosen Agency LLC (L)
318 E 51 St, New York, NY 10022
Tel: 212-593-4330 *Fax:* 212-935-6985
Web Site: janerotrosen.com
Key Personnel
Founder: Jane Rotrosen Berkey (AAR)
Agent: Andrea Cirillo *E-mail:* acirillo@janerotrosen.com; Meg Ruley *E-mail:* mruley@janerotrosen.com; Annelise Robey *E-mail:* arobey@janerotrosen.com; Christina Hogrebe *E-mail:* chogrebe@janerotrosen.com; Amy Tannenbaum *E-mail:* atannenbaum@janerotrosen.com
Edit Asst: Rebecca Scherer *E-mail:* rscherer@janerotrosen.com
Asst Off Mgr: Kristina Frey *E-mail:* kfrey@janerotrosen.com
Exec Dir, Busn Aff: Christina Prestia *E-mail:* cprestia@janerotrosen.com
Global Rts Dir: Peggy Boulos Smith *E-mail:* pboulossmith@janerotrosen.com
Global Rts Mgr: Danielle Sickles *E-mail:* dsickles@janerotrosen.com
Asst Contracts Mgr: Julianne Tinari
Royalty Mgr: Donald W Cleary
Data Mgr: Michael Conroy *E-mail:* mconroy@janerotrosen.com
Founded: 1974
Fiction & nonfiction. No unsol mss or queries. Query by referral only. Handle film & TV rights. No reading fee. 15% commission in USA & Canada. Co-represented abroad & on the west coast.
Membership(s): The Authors Guild

Damaris Rowland (L)
115 Elm St, Unit 7b, Hatfield, MA 01038-3808
Tel: 413-247-6011
E-mail: nicholerowland5@mac.com
Key Personnel
Agent: Damaris Rowland
Founded: 1994
Fiction & nonfiction. Handle film & TV rights. No unsol mss, query first with SASE. Submit outline & sample chapters.
Membership(s): The Authors Guild; Mystery Writers of America; Romance Writers of America

Regina Ryan Books (L)
251 Central Park W, Suite 7-D, New York, NY 10024
Tel: 212-787-5589
E-mail: queries@reginaryanbooks.com
Web Site: www.reginaryanbooks.com
Key Personnel
Pres: Regina Ryan (AAR) *E-mail:* reginaryan@reginaryanbooks.com
Founded: 1976
Book length works of nonfiction for the adult market. Specialize in narrative nonfiction, psychology, popular culture, cooking & food, health, diet & fitness, self-help, parenting, nature, gardening, pets, art, architecture, design, memoirs, general history & biography, science - especially natural history & cognitive neuroscience, women's issues. No poetry, screenplays or software. Query first, using the guidelines on our web site. No queries or follow-up by fax or phone. No reading fee; handle film, TV & foreign rights. Representation in all foreign countries.
Titles recently placed: *Amazing Wildlife Spectacles of the US*, Vladimir Dinets; *Bountiful Bonsai*, Richard Bender; *Charles Dickens and the Street Children of London*, Andrea Warren; *Cookies for Grown-Ups*, Kelly Cooper; *Hair: A Human History*, Kurt Stenn; *I Hear America Singing*, Donald W Kroodsma; *Jewish Wisdom for Daily Life*, Gabriel Lisowski, Miriam Chaikin; *Mingus Speaks*, John F Goodman; *So You Think You Know Football?*, Ben Austro; *The Death Penalty: What's Keeping it Alive?*, Andrea D Lyon; *The Peterson Guide to Bird Sounds*, Nathan Pieplow; *The Peterson Guide to Finding Mammals*, Vladimir Dinets; *The Sugar Season*, Douglas Whynott; *What's Wrong With My House Plant?*, David Deardorff, Kathryn Wadsworth
Foreign Rights: Books Crossing Borders (Worldwide exc UK); Abner Stein Agency (UK & Commonwealth)
Membership(s): The Authors Guild; The Linnaean Society of New York; PEN American Center; Women's Media Group

Victoria Sanders & Associates LLC (L)
241 Avenue of the Americas, Suite 11-H, New York, NY 10014
Tel: 212-633-8811 *Fax:* 212-633-0525
E-mail: queriesvsa@gmail.com
Web Site: www.victoriasanders.com
Key Personnel
Pres: Victoria Sanders (AAR)
Agent: Bernadette Baker-Baughman; Mr Chris Kepner
Founded: 1992
Always interested in new material & welcome all genres: literary & commercial fiction, nonfiction, memoir, women's fiction, thrillers, humor, science fiction/fantasy, graphic novels & self-help/motivational, just to name a few. No unsol mss, query first. E-mail queries only. Please include first 3 chapters (or about 25 pages) pasted into the body of the e-mail. Consult web site for further information. Handle film & TV rights & translation rights. No reading fees.
Titles recently placed: *50 Mice*, Dan Pyne; *All the Happiness You Deserve*, Michael Piafsky; *Animus*, Kim Green; *Catching Air*, Sarah Pekkanen; *Children of the Jacaranda Tree*, Sahar Delijani; *Cop Town*, Karin Slaughter; *Delilah Dirk and the Blades of England*, Tony Cliff; *Descending Son*, Scott Shepherd; *Five Days Left*, Julie Lawson Timmer; *Safe With Me*, Sarah Pekkanen; *The Adventures of Super Hero Girl*, Faith Erin Hicks; *The Black Cabinet*, Jill Watts; *The Death Trail*, Sara Blaedel; *The Forgotten Girls*, Sara Blaedel; *The Gods of Tango*, Carolina De Robertis; *The Human Body Theatre*, Maris Wicks; *The Prey*, Tom Isbell; *The Seventh Day*, Scott Shepherd; *The Strange and Beautiful Sorrows of Ava Lavender*, Leslye Walton; *The Wedding Gift*, Marlen Suyapa Bodden; *The Wind is Not a River*, Brian Payton; *Those Above*, Daniel Polansky; *Three Years in Wonderland*, Todd James Pierce; *Til the Well Runs Dry*, Lauren Francis-Sharma; *Unseen*, Karin Slaughter; *Wanderers*, Susan Kim, Laurence Klavan; *Who We Be: The Colorization of America*, Jeff Chang
Branch Office(s)
440 Buck Rd, Stone Ridge, NY 12484 *Tel:* 845-687-6140
Foreign Rights: Chandler Crawford (Worldwide)

Jack Scagnetti Talent & Literary Agency (L-D)
5136 Vineland Ave, North Hollywood, CA 91601
Tel: 818-762-3871
Key Personnel
Owner: Jack Scagnetti
Agent: David Goldman
Founded: 1974
Screenplays, TV & film treatments. No unsol mss, query first. Submit synopsis, first chapter for books; paragraph or one-page synopsis for scripts. No reading fee, charge one-way postage for multiple submissions, 10% commission. Detailed critique & consultation services available for books on hourly basis. Signatory to Writer's Guild of America-West. Represented self in sale of 15 books which led to representing writer friends & others.
Membership(s): Television Academy; Writers Guild of America West

Schiavone Literary Agency Inc (L-D)
236 Trails End, West Palm Beach, FL 33413-2135
Tel: 561-966-9294 *Fax:* 561-966-9294
E-mail: profschia@aol.com
Web Site: www.publishersmarketplace.com/members/profschia
Key Personnel
CEO: Dr James Schiavone
Pres (Bronx, NY off): Jennifer DuVall *E-mail:* jendu77@aol.com
EVP (NY off): Kevin McAdams *E-mail:* kvn.mcadams@yahoo.com
Founded: 1996
Fiction & nonfiction, all genres: young adult, scholarly books, textbooks, business, motivational, advertising, marketing. Specialize in celebrity biography & autobiography & memoirs. No poetry or children's picture books. No unsol mss. No queries via phone, fax or post. Accept only e-mail queries consisting of one page (no attachments). No previously published work in any format. Query only one agent at the company. No fees. Commission: 15% domestic, 20% foreign. Representation in foreign markets. Send e-mail queries to individual personnel at their e-mail address noted. Also have offices in New York, NY.
Titles recently placed: *Accused*, Brittany Ducker; *Beautiful Old Dogs*, David Tabatsky; *Blending Families Successfully*, George Glass, MD; *Edwardian Cooking: 80 Recipes Inspired by Downton Abbey's Elegant Meals*, Larry Edwards; *Finding Jack: A Novel*, Gareth Crocker; *Get a Clue: Mystery Devotions for Kids*, Mark Littleton; *Hungry Love: Classy Eating, Trashy Reading*, Cindy Silvert; *The Last Meal: Defending an Accused Mass Murderer*, Dennis

Shere; *The Overparenting Epidemic*, George Glass, MD, David Tabatsky; *Through the New Testament: Devotions for Kids*, Mark Littleton; *Trust Me: A Memoir*, George Kennedy; *Unlikely Liberal: Sarah Palin's Curious Record as Alaska's Governor*, Matthew Zencey
Branch Office(s)
Bronx, NY 10463-1139 (Jennifer DuVall only considers books on real estate. Kevin McAdams only considers work on contemporary music)
New York, NY (contact Kevin McAdams for musical entertainment titles, Francine Edelman for all other genres - special interest in business, marketing, advertising & self-help)
Foreign Rights: Chloe Ataroff (Central Europe, France); Asli Ermis (Turkey); Feliz Karaman (Turkey); Hamish Mackaskill (Japan); Radoslav Trenev (Bulgaria, Eastern Europe); Annisa Waharyudisti (Indonesia, Vietnam); Yang Young-Chul (Korea)
Membership(s): National Education Association

Wendy Schmalz Agency (L)
402 Union St, Unit 831, Hudson, NY 12534
Tel: 518-672-7697
E-mail: wendy@schmalzagency.com
Web Site: www.schmalzagency.com
Key Personnel
Owner: Wendy Schmalz (AAR)
Founded: 2002
Adult & children's fiction & nonfiction. No unsol mss, e-mail queries only. See web site for submission details.
Titles recently placed: *1918 Flu Pandemic*, Albert Marrin; *Boy Stolen*, April Henry; *Lilli's Quest*, Lila Perl; *Lost and Found*, Katrina Leno; *The Birth of American Propaganda*, John Maxwell Hamilton; *The Borden Murders*, Sarah Miller; *The Girl I Used to Be*, April Henry; *The Stellow Project*, Shari Becker; *The Thunder of Giants*, Joel Fishbane; *The Truth*, Jeffry W Johnston; *Threads*, Ami Polonsky; *Uprooted*, Albert Marrin
Foreign Rights: Rights People (Worldwide)

Harold Schmidt Literary Agency (L-D)
415 W 23 St, Suite 6-F, New York, NY 10011
Tel: 212-727-7473
Key Personnel
Pres: Harold D Schmidt (AAR) *E-mail:* hslanyc@aol.com
Specialize in book-length fiction & nonfiction. No unsol mss, query first by e-mail & include up to the first 5 pages of your book embedded in the e-mail; do not send as an attachment. Telephone queries not accepted. Do not send material through the mail unless requested. Representatives in Hollywood & in all principal foreign countries.

Susan Schulman Literary Agency LLC (L-D)
454 W 44 St, New York, NY 10036
Tel: 212-713-1633 *Fax:* 212-581-8830
Key Personnel
Owner: Susan Schulman (AAR)
Founded: 1980
Adult book-length genre & literary fiction & nonfiction especially women's studies, biography, psychology & the social sciences. No unsol mss. Query first with SASE or by e-mail. Submit outline & three sample chapters. No reading fee. Co-agent in all principal foreign countries. Handles film & TV rights for other agencies & individual titles.
Foreign Rep(s): ACER Agencia Literaria (Spain); Agenzia Letteraria Internazionale (Italy); Big Apple Agency Inc (China); Lora Fountain & Associates (France); Nurcihan Kesim Literary Agency Inc (Turkey); Korea Copyright Center (Korea); Leipman AG (Germany); Lennart Sane Agency (Sweden); Owl's Agency Inc (Japan); I Pikarski Literary Agency (Israel); Prava I Prevodi (Eastern Europe); The Rights Agency (Canada (French-speaking)); Susanna Zevi Agenzia Letteraria (Italy)
Membership(s): The Authors Guild; The Dramatists Guild of America; Society of Children's Book Writers & Illustrators; Women in Film; Women's Media Group; Writers Guild of America East

A E Schwartz & Associates (L-D)
13 Conversation Way, Stoughton, MA 02072
Tel: 781-436-5033
E-mail: info@aeschwartz.com
Web Site: aeschwartz.com
Key Personnel
CEO: Andrew E Schwartz
Founded: 1985
Comprehensive organization, business, rights & permissions, publishing; specialize in human resource development, organizational development & related training topics, management, training & business how-to's. No unsol mss; query first. Submit outline & sample chapters. Handle software. Assist authors on all facets of contracting with publishers. Evaluation fee: $125 (report). Satellite office in New York, NY.

Laurens R Schwartz, Esquire (L-D)
5 E 22 St, Suite 15-D, New York, NY 10010-5325
Tel: 212-228-2614
Founded: 1981
Full service agency handling all media for all ages worldwide. No fees; standard commissions; WGA Signatory. No unsol mss, CD-ROMs, etc. Query first with synopsis of one project & resume. Also provide information relating to the project having been with other agents or shopped around. Enclose return mailer with postage. Require 4-week right-of-first refusal if request submission of entire project. Handle film, TV & L&M rights.
Membership(s): Writers Guild of America

S©ott Treimel NY (L)
434 Lafayette St, New York, NY 10003-6943
Tel: 212-505-8353
E-mail: general@scotttreimelny.com
Web Site: scotttreimelny.com; scotttreimelny.blogspot.com
Key Personnel
Owner & Pres: Scott Treimel (AAR)
Asst: Jon Courtier *E-mail:* jon.courtier.stny@gmail.com
Founded: 1995
Sells & administers intellectual property rights - foreign, dramatic, electronic, broadcast, merchandise, promotion - for children's book creators. No unsol submissions.
Titles recently placed: *A Mad Wicked Folly*, Sharon Biggs-Waller; *Bad Balloon*, Julie Phillipps; *Fire in the Sky*, David Ward; *Flickers*, Arthur Slade; *Girl + Gorilla*, Rick Walton; *Girls Like Us*, Gail Giles; *Horrible Bear!*, Ame Dyckman; *Jump!*, J C Phillipps; *Lucky Me*, Richard Scrimger; *Other Wordly*, Yee-Lum Mak; *Pupunzel*, Maribeth Boelts; *The Fairy Dogmother*, Maribeth Boelts; *The Girls' Bible*, Barbara Diamond Goldin, Jane Yolen; *There Will Be Bears*, Ryan Gephart; *What's Mine*, Maribeth Boelts; *Wolfie the Bunny*, Ame Dyckman; *Zomboy*, Richard Scrimger
Foreign Rep(s): Akcali Copyright (Turkey); Donatalla d'Ormesson Agent Litteraire (France); Japan Uni (Japan); Barbara Kuper Literarische Agentur + Medienservice (Germany)
Membership(s): The Authors Guild

Scovil Galen Ghosh Literary Agency Inc (L)
276 Fifth Ave, Suite 708, New York, NY 10001
Tel: 212-679-8686 *Fax:* 212-679-6710
E-mail: info@sgglit.com
Web Site: www.sgglit.com
Key Personnel
Pres: Russell Galen (AAR) *Fax:* 646-349-1868 *E-mail:* russellgalen@sgglit.com
Agent: Ann Behar *E-mail:* annbehar@sgglit.com
Founded: 1993
All types fiction & nonfiction, adult & juvenile. Handle film & TV rights. No unsol mss, query first. Submit outline & sample chapters. E-mailed queries preferred but without attachments. Does not charge fees.
Titles recently placed: *An Echo in the Bone*, Diana Gabaldon
Foreign Rep(s): Baror International Inc (Worldwide exc USA)

Lynn Seligman (L)
400 Highland Ave, Upper Montclair, NJ 07043
Tel: 973-783-3631 *Fax:* 973-783-3691
E-mail: seliglit@aol.com
Founded: 1986
Adult & young adult fiction; adult nonfiction. Handle film & TV rights through agents in Hollywood. Submit letter describing project with short sample. No unsol mss; query first with SASE. No e-mail submissions. No reading fee.
Titles recently placed: *All Afternoon with a Scandalous Marquess (Lords of Vice series)*, Alexandra Hawkins; *Better Off Without Him*, Dee Ernst; *Dark World (series)*, Cara Lynn Shultz; *Dusk with a Dangerous Duke (Lords of Vice series)*, Alexandra Hawkins; *Not Quite What I Expected*, Dee Ernst; *Sunrise with a Notorious Lord (Lords of Vice series)*, Alexandra Hawkins; *Twilight with an Infamous Earl (Lords of Vice series)*, Alexandra Hawkins
Foreign Rights: Books Crossing Borders (Betty Anne Crawford) (Worldwide)
Membership(s): Women's Media Group

Edythea Ginis Selman Literary Agency Inc (L-D)
14 Washington Place, New York, NY 10003
Tel: 212-473-1874 *Fax:* 212-473-1875
Key Personnel
Pres & Agent: Edythea Ginis Selman (AAR)
VP & Electronic Rights: Richard Selman (AAR)
Literary commercial fiction & serious issue-oriented narrative nonfiction. Selected children's fiction & young adult picture books, handles film & TV rights from adult novels & young adult (by referral only). No unsol mss, query first, only upon request (with SASE). Submit author bio, two sample chapters or 50 pages (nonfiction) or complete ms (fiction).
Foreign Rights: Eliane Benisti (France); David Grossman (England); Japan UNI Agency Inc (Japan); Ruth Liepman (Germany); Isabel Monteagudo (Spain); Andrew Nurnburg (Eastern Europe)
Membership(s): The Authors Guild; CSA; National Writers Union; PEN American Center; Society of Children's Book Writers & Illustrators; Women's National Book Association

Seventh Avenue Literary Agency (L)
2052 124 St, South Surrey, BC V4A 9K3, Canada
Tel: 604-538-7252 *Fax:* 604-538-7252
E-mail: info@seventhavenuelit.com
Web Site: www.seventhavenuelit.com
Key Personnel
Pres & Dir: Robert Mackwood *E-mail:* rmackwood@seventhavenuelit.com
Founded: 1974
Nonfiction agency representing international authors from a wide range of subjects & interests. No unsol mss, query first by e-mail; no fees charged.

Titles recently placed: *Great Companies Deserve Great Boards: A CEO's Guide to the Boardroom*, Beverly Behan; *Happy Healthy Gut: The Natural Diet Solution to Curing IBS and Other Chronic Digestive Disorders*, Jennifer Browne; *Route 66 Still Kicks: Driving America's Main Street*, Rick Antonson; *The Mom Shift: Women Share Their Thoughts of Career Success After Having Children*, Reva Seth; *Things That Must Not Be Forgotten: A Childhood in Wartime China (updated)*, Michael David Kwan; *Thrive Energy Cookbook: 150 Plant-Based Whole Food Recipes*, Brendan Brazier
Foreign Rights: Big Apple Agency Inc (Luc Kwantlen) (China, Indonesia, Taiwan); Fritz Agency (Christan Dittus) (Germany); Deborah Harris Agency (Ilana Kurshan) (Israel); Nurcihan Kesim Literary Agency (Dilek Kaya) (Turkey); Simona Kessler Agency (Adriana Marinara) (Romania); Korea Copyright Agency (Ms MiSook Hong) (Korea); Nova Littera Ltd (Daria Pridatkina) (Russia); Kristin Olson Agency (Czech Republic); The Riff Agency (Lucia Riff) (Brazil, Portugal); Sebes & Van Gelderen Literary Agency (Netherlands)

Mary Sue Seymour (L-D)
475 Miner Street Rd, Canton, NY 13617
Tel: 315-386-1831
Web Site: www.theseymouragency.com
Key Personnel
Founder & Agent: Mary Sue Seymour (AAR) *E-mail:* marysue@twcny.rr.com
Sr Agent: Nicole Resciniti
Assoc Agent: Marisa Cleveland
Founded: 1992
Christian romance & women's fiction, nonfiction & secular romance.
Membership(s): The Authors Guild; Romance Writers of America; Writers Guild of America; Writers Guild of America East

Charlotte Sheedy Literary Agency Inc (L)
928 Broadway, Suite 901, New York, NY 10010
Tel: 212-780-9800
Web Site: www.sheedylit.com
Key Personnel
Owner: Charlotte Sheedy *E-mail:* charlotte@sheedylit.com
Agent: Mackenzie Brady *E-mail:* mackenzie@sheedylit.com
Agent/Rts & Perms: Joan Rosen *E-mail:* joan@sheedylit.com
Fiction & nonfiction film & TV rights. No unsol mss, query first (no screenplays); submit outline & sample chapters; no reading fee. Agents in all principal countries.
Titles recently placed: *29 Myths on the Swinster Pharmacy*, Lemony Snicket; *File Under: 13 Suspicious Incidents*, Lemony Snicket; *Girls Standing on Lawns*, Daniel Handler; *Meanwhile, in San Francisco: The City in its Own Words*, Wendy MacNaughton; *Monday, Wednesday and Every Other Weekend*, Karen Stanton; *One Hour in Paris*, Karyn L Freedman; *Red Now and Laters*, Marcus J Guillory; *The Winner's Curse*, Marie Rutkoski; *Thomas Jefferson: Life, Liberty and the Pursuit of Everything*, Maira Kalman; *Tyler Makes a Cake!*, Tyler Florence
Foreign Rep(s): The English Agency (Japan); Agnes Krup (Australia, Germany, Italy, Portugal, Switzerland); Lennart Sane (Netherlands, Scandinavia, Spain); Abner Stein Agency (England)

The Shepard Agency (L)
73 Kingswood Dr, Bethel, CT 06801
Tel: 203-790-4230; 203-790-1780 *Fax:* 203-798-2924
E-mail: shepardagcy@mindspring.com
Key Personnel
Pres & Dir: Jean H Shepard
VP & Treas: Lance Hastings Shepard
Founded: 1986
Specialize in adult, children, general trade fiction & nonfiction, professional, reference & business. Handle film & TV rights. Not accepting mss at this time.

The Robert E Shepard Agency (L)
4804 Laurel Canyon Blvd, Box 592, Valley Village, CA 91607-3717
Web Site: www.shepardagency.com
Founded: 1994
No longer accepting submissions.

Ken Sherman & Associates (L-D)
1275 N Hayworth, Suite 103, Los Angeles, CA 90046
Tel: 310-273-8840
E-mail: kenshermanassociates@gmail.com
Web Site: www.kenshermanassociates.com
Key Personnel
Owner & Pres: Ken Sherman
Founded: 1989
Fiction & nonfiction books plus screenplays, teleplays, film & TV rights to books & life rights. No unsol mss or screenplays. Accept by referral only. Submit outline & minimum three sample chapters. No reading fee. International Advisory Board Member, The Christopher Isherwood Foundation.
Titles recently placed: *Good Manners For Nice People Who Sometimes Say F*ck*, Amy Alkon
Membership(s): American Film Institute Third Decade Council; British Academy of Film & Television Arts/Los Angeles; PEN International

Wendy Sherman Associates Inc (L)
27 W 24 St, Suite 700-B, New York, NY 10010
Tel: 212-279-9027
E-mail: submissions@wsherman.com
Web Site: www.wsherman.com
Key Personnel
Founder, Owner & Pres: Wendy Sherman (AAR) *E-mail:* wendy@wsherman.com
Agent: Kimberly Perel (AAR) *E-mail:* kim@wsherman.com
Founded: 1999
Represents a wide range of fiction & nonfiction. Literary & commercial fiction, including upmarket women's fiction; Nonfiction includes, memoir, narrative nonfiction, health & wellness, gender issues, practical, self-help, popular psychology, lifestyle, home & design, fashion. No unsol mss, query first with SASE. For fiction, a letter & synopsis. Paste first 10 pages, No attachments. For nonfiction, send proposal & two sample chapters. See web site for submission guidelines: No paper submissions. No poetry, screenplays, mysteries, romance, westerns, science fiction, fantasy or children's books.
Titles recently placed: *After This*, Claire Bidwell Smith; *Ann Sage*, Sage Living; *Bright Lights Paris*, Angie Niles; *Change Your lIfe in 4 Four Minutes*, Bex Borucki; *Crush*, Cathy Alter, Dave Singleton; *Eight Flavors*, Sarah Lohman; *How to Live a Good Life*, Jonathan Fields; *Liveable Patterns*, Rebecca Atwood; *Meet Your Soul*, Elisa Romeo; *Oh! You Pretty Things*, Shanna Mahin; *Picnic in Provence*, Elizabeth Bard; *So Much a Part of You*, Polly Dugan; *The Book of Wanderings*, Kimberly Meyer; *The Fatherless Daughter Project*, Denna Babul, Dr Karin Smithson; *The Gluten Free Revolution*, Jax Lowell; *The Power Greens Cookbook*, Dana Jacobi; *The Silence of Bonaventure Arrow: A Novel*, Rita Leganski; *The Street of Eternal Happiness*, Rob Schmitz; *The Stress Bump*, Dr Ali Domar; *The Sun and Other Stars*, Brigid Pasulka; *The Sweetheart Deal*, Polly Dugan; *Together Tea*, Marjan Kamali; *Women, Food, and Desire*, Alexandra Jamieson; *Z: A Novel of Zelda Fitzgerald*, Therese Anne Fowler
Foreign Rights: Duran Kim Agency (Duran Kim) (Korea); Jenny Meyer Literary Agency (Jenny Meyer) (Worldwide exc Asia); Andrew Nurnberg Associates Inc (Whitney Hsu) (Taiwan); Andrew Nurnberg Associates Inc (Jackie Huang) (China); Owls Agency (Japan)
Membership(s): Women's Media Group

Side by Side Literary Productions Inc (L)
145 E 35 St, Suite 7FE, New York, NY 10016
Tel: 646-442-2905 *Fax:* 212-888-3650
Web Site: sidebysidelit.com
Key Personnel
Founder & Pres: Laurie Bernstein *Fax:* 212-481-6037 *E-mail:* laurie@sidebysidelit.com
Founded: 2004
Literary agency handling general trade fiction & nonfiction as well as select juvenile titles. Specialize in popular health, medicine, self-help, parenting, popular culture, diet & narrative nonfiction. No unsol mss, query first. Will review hard copy & digital submissions. Handles film & TV rights.

Rosalie Siegel, International Literary Agent Inc (L)
One Abey Dr, Pennington, NJ 08534
Tel: 609-737-1007 *Fax:* 609-737-3708
Web Site: www.rosaliesiegel.com
Key Personnel
Pres: Rosalie Siegel *E-mail:* rosalie@rosaliesiegel.com
Founded: 1977
Adult fiction, nonfiction & foreign books, film & TV rights. No unsol mss; query first; no reading fee. Representatives in all major European countries & Asian countries. Not actively seeking new clients.

Irene Skolnick Literary Agency (L)
27 W 20 St, Suite 305, New York, NY 10011
Tel: 212-727-3648 *Fax:* 212-352-2059
E-mail: office@skolnickliterary.com (queries)
Web Site: www.skolnickagency.com
Key Personnel
CEO: Irene Skolnick (AAR) *E-mail:* irene@skolnickliterary.com
Asst: Sally Chabert
Founded: 1994
Literary & historical fiction, thrillers; narrative nonfiction: memoir, biography, history, travel, humor; YA, middle grade. Handle film & TV rights. Representation in all major countries & Hollywood through co-agents. No unsol mss, query first. Send queries via e-mail or mail with SASE. Include/attach outline & sample chapter.
Titles recently placed: *Give Me Everything You Have: On Being Stalked*, James Lasdun; *Love, Dishonor, Marry, Die, Cherish, Perish*, David Rakoff; *Middle School Cool*, Maiya Williams; *The Chalk Artist*, Allegra Goodman; *The Ice Cream Queen of Orchard Street*, Susan Jane Gilman; *The Long Shadow: The Great War and the Twentieth Century*, David Reynolds; *The Poe Annex*, Polly Shulman; *Where the Dead Pause and the Japanese Say Goodbye*, Marie Mutsuki Mockett
Foreign Rights: Lippincott Massie McQuilkin (Maria Massie)
Membership(s): PEN American Center; Women's Media Group

SLC Enterprises Inc (L-D)
332 S Michigan Ave, No 1032-C216, Chicago, IL 60604
Tel: 616-942-2665 (answering serv & voice mail)
E-mail: scasari1@hotmail.com

Key Personnel
Pres: Stephen Cogil Casari *E-mail:* scasari1@hotmail.com
Founded: 1985
Fiction & nonfiction; specialize in first novelists. Children's books, sports, baseball. No unsol mss, query first. Submit proposal, outline +/or sample chapters. Evaluation & discussion of publishability. Handle film & TV rights. $150 reading fee.
Titles recently placed: *Paige Goes to Philadelphia*, Diann Boehm

Beverley Slopen Literary Agency (L)
131 Bloor St W, Suite 711, Toronto, ON M5S 1S3, Canada
Tel: 416-964-9598 *Fax:* 416-921-7726
Web Site: www.slopenagency.com
Key Personnel
Owner: Beverley Slopen *E-mail:* beverley@slopenagency.ca
Founded: 1973
Serious fiction & nonfiction. No children's books, illustrated books, science fiction or fantasy. No software, no film or TV rights handled. Query letter & brief proposal sent by mail with Canadian postage if you want it returned, but e-mail queries preferred. Not taking on many new clients.
Titles recently placed: *20b*, Martyn Burke; *50 Canadians Who Changed the World*, Ken McGoogan; *Al Qaeda Declares War: The African Embassy Bombings and America's Search for Justice*, Tod Hoffman; *Believing: The Neuroscience of Fantasies, Fears, and Convictions*, Michael McGuire; *Beyond Intelligence: Secrets for Raising Happily Productive Kids*, Dona Matthews, Joanne Foster; *Butterfly of Venus*, Susan Ferrier MacKay; *City of Fallen Angels*, Howard Engel; *Is Work Killing You?: A Doctor's Prescription for Treating Workplace Stress*, David Posen MD; *Life Class*, Ann Charney; *Mr Selden's Map of China: Decoding the Secrets of a Vanished Cartographer*, Tim Brook; *Music for Love or War*, Martyn Burke; *No Relation*, Terry Falles; *Perdita*, Hilary Scharper; *The Harem Midwife*, Roberta Rich; *The Hole in the Middle*, Kate Hilton; *The Memory Clinic*, Tiffany Chow
Foreign Rep(s): Agenzia Letteraria Internazionale (ALI) (Italy); Akcali Copyright Agency (Turkey); Paul & Peter Fritz AG (Germany); The Grayhawk Agency (Gray Tan) (China); David Grossman Literary Agency Ltd (David Grossman) (UK); The Deborah Harris Agency (Israel); International Literatuur Bureau (Netherlands); JLM Literary Agency (Greece); Katai & Bolza Literary Agency (Hungary); Alexander Korzhenevski (Russia); Agence Michelle Lapautre (Michelle Lapautre) (France); Licht & Burr Literary Agency (Scandinavia); Agencia Riff (Lucia Riff) (Brazil); Tuttle-Mori Agency Inc (Japan); Julio F Yanez Agencia Literaria SL (Julio F Yanez) (Spain); Eric Yang Agency (Korea)

Valerie Smith, Literary Agent (L)
1746 Rte 44-55, Modena, NY 12548
Tel: 845-883-5848
Key Personnel
Contact: Valerie Smith
Founded: 1978
Fiction & nonfiction; special interest in fantasy & science fiction. No unsol mss, query first; no reading fee. Outline & 3 sample chapters. Representatives in Hollywood & all principal foreign countries.

Michael Snell Literary Agency (L)
PO Box 1206, Truro, MA 02666-1206
Tel: 508-349-3718
Web Site: www.michaelsnellagency.com
Key Personnel
Pres & Edit Dir: Michael Snell
EVP: Patricia Snell *E-mail:* patricia@michaelsnellagency.com
Founded: 1978
Adult nonfiction; all levels of business & management from popular trade to professional reference; legal, medical, health, psychology, self-help & how-to books; animals & pets; women's issues in business, family & society; popular science & business; technical & scientific; professional & general computer books; parenting & relationships; project development & rewrite services. Welcome new authors. No unsol mss, query first. Submit outline, synopsis & up to 50 sample pages with SASE. Publication *How to Write a Book Proposal* available upon request with SASE, or consult Michael Snell's book *From Book Idea to Bestseller* (Prima Publishing). Write for information on purchasing a model book proposal. Consider new clients on an exclusive basis. No reading fee, but do arrange for developmental editors & ghostwriters who do charge a fee.
Titles recently placed: *Finding Peace in Your Heart When Your Heart is in Pieces*, Paul Coleman; *Glorybound*, Jessie van Eerden; *Now I Get It*, Donny Ebenstein; *Primal Teams: Harnessing the Incredible Power of Group Energy*, Jacqueline A Barretta; *Springboard: Launching Your Personal Search for Success*, G Richard Shell; *Sun House*, David James Duncan; *The Gentle Art of Horseback Riding*, Gincy Self Bucklin; *Tipping Sacred Cows: Kick the Bad Work Habits that Masquerade as Virtues*, Jake Breeden; *What Keeps Leaders Up at Night: Recognizing and Resolving Your Most Troubling Management Issues*, Nicole Lipkin

Sobel Weber Associates Inc (L)
146 E 19 St, New York, NY 10003-2404
Tel: 212-420-8585 *Fax:* 212-505-1017
E-mail: info@sobelweber.com
Web Site: www.sobelweber.com
Key Personnel
Principal: Nat Sobel; Judith Weber
Founded: 1970
General fiction & nonfiction. No unsol mss, query first with SASE, no electronic submissions. No reading fee. Handle film, TV & foreign rights; serialization & audio rights. Representatives on the West Coast & in all major foreign countries. Consult web site for submission guidelines & client list.
Titles recently placed: *Heart of Palm*, Laura Lee Smith; *My Son*, Robert McClure; *Perfidia*, James Ellroy; *Ratlines*, Stuart Neville; *Starting at Zero*, Jimi Hendrix; *The Black Dahlia Graphic Novel*, James Ellroy, Myles Hyman, et al; *The Bloomed Life of Harriet Wolf*, Julianna Baggott; *The Darkest Hour*, Tony Schumacher; *The Future for Curious People*, Gregory Sherl; *The Ghostman*, Roger Hobbs; *The Girl With a Clock for a Heart*, Peter Swanson; *The Rules of Wolfe*, James Carlos Blake; *The Tilted World*, Tom Franklin, Beth Ann Fennelly; *This Dark Road to Mercy*, Wiley Cash; *Wynne's War*, Aaron Gwyn
Foreign Rights: Akcali Copyright Agency (Turkey); Agencia Carmen Balcells (Portugal, Spain); Tassy Barham Associates (Brazil); Paul & Peter Fritz Agency (Germany); The Deborah Harris Agency (Israel); Katai & Bolza (Hungary); Agence Michelle Lapautre (France); Andrew Nurnberg Associates International Ltd (China, Taiwan); Kristin Olson Agency (Czech Republic, Slovakia); Prava I Prevodi (Eastern Europe exc Czech Republic, Hungary & Slovenia, Greece, Russia); Santachiara Literary Agency (Italy); The Abner Stein Agency (UK); Tuttle-Mori Agency Inc (Indonesia, Japan, Thailand, Vietnam); Eric Yang Agency (Korea)

Spectrum Literary Agency (L)
320 Central Park W, Suite 1-D, New York, NY 10025
Tel: 212-362-4323 *Fax:* 212-362-4562
Web Site: www.spectrumliteraryagency.com
Key Personnel
Pres & Agent: Eleanor Wood
Agent: Justin Bell
Founded: 1976
Science fiction, mysteries, thrillers, horror & fantasy. No unsol mss, query first with letter, synopsis, first ten pages & SASE. No reading fee. Agents in all principal foreign countries.
Titles recently placed: *1920: America's Great War*, Robert Conroy; *Pillar to the Sky*, William R Forstcher; *The Diamond Deep (Ruby's Song)*, Brenda Cooper
Foreign Rights: Big Apple Agency Inc (Mr Luc Kwanten) (China); Book Cosmos Agency (Elva Seo) (Korea); The Book Publishers Association of Israel (Dalia Ever-Hadani) (Israel); Graal Ltd (Lukasz Wrobel) (Poland); Japan Uni Agency Inc (Cecilia Akiko Kashiwamura & Kenny Okuyama) (Japan); Katai & Bolza Literary Agents (Peter Bolza) (Hungary); Katai & Bolza Literary Agents (Reka Bartha) (Croatia, Serbia, Slovenia); Nurcihan Kesim Literary Agency Ltd (Dilek Kayi) (Turkey); Agence Litteraire Lenclud (Anne Lenclud & Pierre Lenclud) (France); Piergiorgio Nicolazzini Literary Agency (Maura Solinas) (Italy); Nova Littera Ltd (Konstantin Palchikov & Sergei Cheredov) (Russia); Andrew Nurnberg Associates Sofia (Mira Droumeva) (Bulgaria); Andrew Nurnberg Associates Sofia (Anna Droumeva & Mira Droumeva) (Romania); Kristin Olson Literary Agency SRO (Kristin Olson & Tereza Dubova) (Czech Republic); Prava I Prevodi (Russia); Read n Right Agency (Nike Davarinou) (Greece); Thomas Schlueck GmbH (Thomas Schlueck & Franka Zastrow) (Germany); Sebes & Van Gelderen Literary Agency (Lester Hekking & Jeanine Langenberg) (Netherlands); Silkroad Agency (Jane Vejjajiva) (Thailand); Julio F Yanez Agencia Literaria SL (Montse F Yanez & Sandra Biel) (Portugal, Spain)
Membership(s): Mystery Writers of America; Science Fiction & Fantasy Writers of America

The Spieler Agency (L)
27 W 20 St, Suite 305, New York, NY 10011
Tel: 212-757-4439 *Fax:* 212-333-2019
E-mail: spieleragency@spieleragency.com
Key Personnel
Agent: Joseph Spieler
Nonfiction & literary fiction; thrillers, children's books including middle grade, young adult & new adult. Areas of interest include: environmental issues, business; women's issues; natural history & science for religious studies, psychology; health; history; biography. No unsol mss, query first with letter (prefer e-mail), first chapter/contents or detailed proposal. No phone queries. Submit author background, description of work & sample chapter with SASE. Handle film & TV rights only for book clients. No reading fee, only commissions.
Titles recently placed: *Escape From Mr Lemoncello's Library*, Chris Grabenstein; *Pity the Billionaire: The Hard-Times Swindle and the Unlikely Comeback of the Right*, Thomas Frank; *The $14 Billion Year*, Anne Thompson; *The Financial Crisis Inquiry Report*; *The Lost Mona Lisa: The Extraordinary True Story of the Greatest Art Theft in History*, R A Scotti
Foreign Rights: The Marsh Agency (Continental Europe); Abner Stein Literary Agency (England)

Philip G Spitzer Literary Agency Inc (L)
50 Talmage Farm Lane, East Hampton, NY 11937

Tel: 631-329-3650 *Fax:* 631-329-3651
Web Site: www.spitzeragency.com
Key Personnel
Pres: Philip Spitzer (AAR) *E-mail:* spitzer516@aol.com
Mng Agent: Lukas Ortiz (AAR) *E-mail:* lukas.ortiz@spitzeragency.com
Founded: 1969
Literary fiction, suspense/thriller, general nonfiction, sports, politics, social issues, biography, film & TV rights. No unsol mss, query first with SASE, submit outline & sample chapters. No reading fee, photocopying fee. Foreign rights agents in all major markets.
Foreign Rights: Luigi Bernabo & Associates (Italy); Big Apple Agency Inc (Luc Kwanten & Lily Chen) (China, Malaysia, Taiwan, Vietnam); Big Apple Agency Inc (Erica Zhou) (Indonesia); ELST Literary Agency (Kalina Stefanova) (Bulgaria); Enters Korea Co Ltd (Chrysan You) (Korea); The Deborah Harris Agency (Efrat Lev) (Israel); Kayi Literary Agency Ltd (Dilek Kayi) (Turkey); Agence Michelle Lapautre (Catherine Lapautre) (France); Mohrbooks Literary Agency (Sebastian Ritcsher & Annelie Geissler) (Austria, Germany, Switzerland); Prava I Prevodi (Milena Kaplarevic) (Eastern Europe exc Russia); Prava I Prevodi (Anna Milenkovic) (Russia); Agencia Literaria Riff (Laura Riff & Joao Paulo Riff) (Brazil); Lennart Sane Agency AB (Philip Sane) (Holland, Latin America, Portugal, Scandinavia, Spain); The Abner Stein Agency (Arabella Stein & Caspian Dennis) (UK); Tuttle-Mori Agency Inc (Pimolporn Yutisri) (India, Sri Lanka, Thailand); Tuttle-Mori Agency Inc (Mira Morikawa) (Japan); Eric Yang Agency (Sue Yang) (Korea)

Nancy Stauffer Associates (L)
30 Corbin Dr, Suite 1203, Darien, CT 06820
Mailing Address: PO Box 1203, Darien, CT 06820
Tel: 203-202-2500
Web Site: publishersmarketplace.com/members/nstauffer; staufferliterary.com
Key Personnel
Owner: Nancy Stauffer Cahoon *E-mail:* nancy@staufferliterary.com
Founded: 1989
Literary fiction, narrative nonfiction & young adult fiction. No mysteries, science fiction, fantasy, romance novels, screenplays or children's picture books. Query by e-mail only, with first 10 pages of your work. No attachments. Agents in all foreign markets.
Titles recently placed: *Benediction*, Kent Haruf; *Blasphemy, New & Selected Stories*, Sherman Alexie
Membership(s): The Authors Guild

Michael Steinberg Literary Agent (L)
PO Box 274, Glencoe, IL 60022-0274
Tel: 847-626-1000 *Fax:* 847-626-1002
E-mail: michael14steinberg@comcast.net
Key Personnel
Principal: Michael Steinberg
Founded: 1980
Book-length fiction (mystery, science fiction) & nonfiction (business topics). No unsol mss, query first. Submit outline & first three chapters (hardcopy). Will read only by personal reference from represented author or editor.
Titles recently placed: *All About Day Trading*, Jake Bernstein

Sterling Lord Literistic Inc (L)
65 Bleecker St, New York, NY 10012
Tel: 212-780-6050 *Fax:* 212-780-6095
E-mail: info@sll.com
Web Site: www.sll.com
Key Personnel
Co-Chmn: Sterling Lord; Peter Matson
Pres: Philippa Brophy (AAR)
VP: Laurie Liss (AAR)
Mng Dir: Nadyne Pike
Agent: Celeste Fine; Robert Guinsler; Judy Heiblum; Alison Mackeen; Neeti Madan; Martha Millard; Jim Rutman (AAR); Erica Rand Silverman; Douglas Stewart
Assoc Agent: Mary Krienke; John Maas; Caitlin McDonald; Sarah Passick
Foreign Rts Mgr: Szilvia Molnar
Fiction & nonfiction; film & TV rights. No unsol mss, query first; submit outline & sample chapters with SASE; no reading fee. Affiliated agency: Charlotte Sheedy Agency.
Foreign Rep(s): Anatolialit Agency (Amy Spangler) (Turkey); Agence Eliane Benisti (Eliane Benisti) (France); Luigi Bernabo Associates (Luigi Bernabo) (Italy); Paul & Peter Fritz Literary Agency (Antonia Fritz) (Austria, Germany); The Grayhawk Agency (Gray Tan) (China, Taiwan); The Deborah Harris Agency (Efrat Lev) (Israel); Danny Hong Agency (Danny Hong) (Korea); JLM Literary (John Moukakos) (Greece); Licht & Burr Literary Agency (Trine Licht) (Denmark, Finland, Iceland, Norway, Sweden); MB Agencia Literaria (Monica Martin) (Andorra, Catalonia, Portugal, Spain); Andrew Nurnberg Associates Baltic (Tatjana Zoldnere) (Estonia, Latvia, Lithuania, Ukraine); Andrew Nurnberg Associates Budapest (Judit Hermann) (Croatia, Hungary); Andrew Nurnberg Associates Prague (Petra Tobiskova) (Czech Republic, Slovakia, Slovenia); Andrew Nurnberg Associates Sofia (Mira Droumeva) (Albania, Bulgaria, Macedonia, Romania, Serbia); Andrew Nurnberg Associates Warsaw (Agata Zabowska) (Poland); Andrew Nurnberg Literary Agency Russia (Ludmilla Sushkova) (Russia); Riff Agency (Laura Riff) (Brazil); Marianne Schoenbach Literary Agency (Marianne Schoenbach) (Netherlands); Tuttle-Mori Agency Inc (Ken Mori) (Japan); Tuttle-Mori Agency Thailand (Pimolporn Yutisri) (Indonesia, Thailand, Vietnam)

Miriam Stern, Entertainment Attorney/Literary Agent (L-D)
303 E 83 St, 20th fl, New York, NY 10028
Tel: 212-794-1289
Fiction & nonfiction. No unsol mss, call or letter query first. Submit finished mss, outlines with sample chapters when applicable. Negotiate for license or sale of motion picture rights for film & TV projects.

The Joan Stewart Agency (L)
One Dag Hammarskjold Plaza, 35th fl, 885 Second Ave, New York, NY 10017
Tel: 212-418-7255 *Fax:* 212-832-3809
Key Personnel
Pres: Joan Stewart
Founded: 1983
Handle film & TV rights. No reading fee.

Stimola Literary Studio Inc (L)
308 Livingston Ct, Edgewater, NJ 07020
Tel: 201-945-9353 *Fax:* 201-945-9353; 201-490-5920
E-mail: info@stimolaliterarystudio.com
Web Site: www.stimolaliterarystudio.com
Key Personnel
Pres: Rosemary B Stimola (AAR)
Founded: 1997
Specialize in fiction & nonfiction, preschool through young adult. Queries via e-mail preferred. Respond only to those queries we wish to pursue further. No unsol attachments. See web site for submission guidelines. No fees.
Titles recently placed: *A Tale of Highly Unusual Magic*, Lisa Papademetriou; *Duncan the Story Dragon*, Amanda Driscoll; *How To Hang A Witch*, Adriana Mather; *I Text Dead People*, Rose Cooper; *Listen, Slowly*, Thanhha Lai; *My Diary from the Edge of the World*, Jodi Lynn Anderson; *Rude Cakes*, Rowboat Watkins; *Simon Thorn (series)*, Aimee Carter; *The Noisy Paint Box*, Barb Rosenstock, Mary Grand Pre; *The Remnant Chronicles*, Mary Pearson; *The Secret Hum of a Daisy*, Tracy Holczer; *Wish*, Matthew Cordell
Foreign Rep(s): Intercontinental Literary Agency (translation); Schleuck Agency (Germany)
Foreign Rights: Rights People (UK)
Membership(s): ALA; National Council of Teachers of English; Society of Children's Book Writers & Illustrators

The Stonesong Press LLC (L)
270 W 39 St, No 201, New York, NY 10018
Tel: 212-929-4600
E-mail: editors@stonesong.com
Web Site: www.stonesong.com
Key Personnel
Partner & Literary Agent: Alison Fargis
Partner & Prodn Servs: Ellen Scordato
EVP & Literary Agent: Judy Linden
Literary Agent: Emmanuelle Morgen; Leila Campoli; Maria Ribas
Founded: 1979
Complete trade hardcover, paperback & ebook development, from concept to delivery. Represents commercial nonfiction & popular reference books on many subjects: cooking, business, how-to, self-help, memoir, beauty & fashion; also represents fiction, including middle-grade, young adult, & adult titles. Consultants on backlist exploitation, acquisitions, publicity planning & editorial systems. Custom publishing for professional associations & magazines. No unsol mss, query first by e-mail. Include a brief synopsis & the first 10 pages of your work in the e-mail body. Complete submission guidelines are on our web site. No fees charged.
Titles recently placed: *Below the Belt*, Jeanette Murray; *Cook for Your Life*, Ann Ogden; *Love & Lemons*, Jeanine Donofrio; *Ruined*, Amy Tintera; *The Forest Feast*, Erin Gleeson; *The Forest Feast Gatherings*, Erin Gleeson; *The Forst Feast Children's Cookbook*, Erin Gleeson; *The Unquiet*, Ruth Dada writing as Mikaela Everett
Foreign Rep(s): Allen & Unwin (Australia, New Zealand); Commonwealth (China); Editora Record (Brazil); Maxim Konyvkiado (Hungary); Oceana (Spain); Piemme (Italy); Random House Canada (Canada); Jacqui Small (England)
Foreign Rights: The Fielding Agency (Whitney Lee) (Worldwide)
Membership(s): American Book Producers Association

Straus Literary (L)
319 Lafayette St, Suite 220, New York, NY 10012
Tel: 646-843-9950 *Fax:* 646-390-3320
Web Site: www.strausliterary.com
Key Personnel
Agent: Jonah Straus *E-mail:* jonah@strausliterary.com
Founded: 2003
Focus on literary fiction, historical fiction, works in translation (especially Spanish & Portuguese), literary mystery & thriller, cookbooks, food & travel narratives, photography, politics, history, international affairs, biography, memoir.
Straus Literary acts as English sub-agent for: Editorial Everest, Spain; Mertin Agency (Nicole Witt), Germany; Riff Agency, Brazil.
Branch office in San Francisco, CA.

Titles recently placed: *1808: The Flight of the Emperor*, Laurentino Gomes, Andrew Nevins; *Crow-Blue*, Adriana Lisboa, Alison Entrekin; *Death & Co (Cocktail Book)*, David Kaplan, Nick Fauchald; *Di Palo's Essential Guide to the Foods of Italy*, Lou Di Palo, Rachel Wharton; *Jeni's Spendid Ice Cream Desserts*, Jeni Britton Bauer; *Lockdown (Carandiru Station)*, Drauzio Varella; *P's Three Women*, Paulo Emilio Salles Gomes; *Poison Spring: The Secret History of the EPA*, Evaggelos Vallianatos; *Several Ways to Die in Mexico City*, Kurt Hollander; *Smuggler's Cove: Cocktails, Rum and the Cult of Tiki*, Martin Cate; *The Cage: The Fight for Sri Lanka and the Last Days of the Tamil Tigers*, Gordon Weiss; *The Collected Poems of Carlos Drummond de Andrade*, Carlos Drummond de Andrade, Richard Zenith; *The Cruelest Gift: Inherited Disease in the Age of DNA*, Clark Blaise; *The Descartes Highlands*, Eric Gamalinda; *The Essential Book of Fermentation (Fermentation Nation)*, Jeff Cox; *The House in Smyrna*, Tatiana Salem Levy; *Weaponized (Exile)*, Nicholas Mennuti, David Guggenheim

Foreign Rights: AK Agency (Alex Korzhenevski) (Baltic States, Russia, Ukraine); Amo Agency (Amo Noh) (Korea); Silvia Bastos Agency (Pau Centellas) (Latin America exc Brazil, Portugal, Spain); Big Apple Agency (Luc Kwanten) (China, Southeast Asia, Thailand); DS Budapest (Szabolcs Torok) (Hungary); ELST Literary Agency (Kalina Stefanova) (Bulgaria); The English Agency (Tsutomu Yawata) (Japan); Graal Literary Agency (Filip Wojiechowski) (Poland); Deborah Harris Agency (Rena Rossner) (Israel); Iris Literary (Catherine Fragou) (Greece); Kalem Agency (Sedef Ligic) (Turkey); Simona Kessler International Copyright Agency (Adriana Marina) (Romania); Michelle Lapautre Agency (Catherine Lapautre) (France, Quebec, CN, Switzerland (French-speaking)); Michael Meller Agency (Regina Seitz) (Austria, Germany, Switzerland (German-speaking)); Andrew Nurnberg, Prague (Petra Tobiskova) (Czech Republic, Slovakia); Plima Literary (Vuk Perisic) (Albania, Bosnia and Herzegovina, Croatia, Macedonia, Montenegro, Serbia); Riff Agency (Joao Paulo Riff) (Brazil); Lennart Sane Agency (Philip Sane) (Netherlands, Scandinavia); Susanna Zevi Agency (Susanna Zevi) (Italy)

Robin Straus Agency Inc (L)
229 E 79 St, Suite 5A, New York, NY 10075
Tel: 212-472-3282
E-mail: info@robinstrausagency.com
Web Site: www.robinstrausagency.com
Key Personnel
Pres: Robin Straus (AAR) *E-mail:* robin@robinstrausagency.com
Asst: Logan Herries
Founded: 1983
High quality fiction & nonfiction. Handle film & TV rights for represented clients' books. Foreign agents in all major foreign countries. No unsol mss, query first. No screenplays, plays, romance, westerns, science fiction, fantasy, horror, children's or poetry. Mail query with outline or synopsis, short author biography & sample chapters; SASE for response & return of mateiral must be included, or send brief e-mail letter describing book project (no downloads). No reading fees.
Foreign Rights: Deborah Harris (Israel); JLM Literary Agency (Greece); Andrew Nurnberg Associates (Worldwide exc Japan & Thailand); ONK Agency (Turkey); Tuttle-Mori Agency Inc (Japan, Thailand); Eric Yang Agency (Korea)

Marianne Strong Literary Agency (L)
65 E 96 St, New York, NY 10128
Tel: 212-249-1000 *Fax:* 212-831-3241
Web Site: stronglit.com
Key Personnel
Owner & Pres: Marianne Strong
E-mail: mariannestrong@stronglit.com
Agent: Nicole Lowary
Founded: 1978
In addition to select fiction, we handle general nonfiction, how-to books, biographies, gossip, society & entertainment, celebrity books, social history, lifestyle, cookbooks, investigative biographies, mysteries, adventure, true crime fictionalized (or actual true crime), politics, self-help, inspirational, historic & memoirs. A separate service is provided that obtains assignments for professional writers. No fees charged; no unsol mss, query first with one page (no attachments) to mariannestrong@stronglit.com.
Titles recently placed: *Affirmed: The Last Triple Crown Winner*, Lou Sahadi; *Capital of the World: A Portrait of New York City in the Roaring Twenties*, David Wallace; *Night Harvest*, Michael Alexiades
Membership(s): The Authors Guild

Strothman Agency LLC (L)
63 E Ninth St, 10X, New York, NY 10003
E-mail: info@strothmanagency.com
Web Site: www.strothmanagency.com
Key Personnel
Principal & Agent: Wendy Strothman (AAR)
Agent: Lauren E MacLeod (AAR)
Founded: 2003
Dedicated to promoting authors of significant books through the entire publishing cycle. No unsol mss, query first by e-mail only. Submit query letter, synopsis & SASE to strothmanagency@gmail.com, no attachments. Submissions will be acknowledged by an autoresponder. No fees charged.
Titles recently placed: *Frenzy & Untitled Book Two*, Robert Lettrick; *Lillian & Dash*, Sam Toperoff; *Mourning Lincoln*, Martha Hodes; *Of Horses & Humans*, Wendy Williams; *On the Edge: A Tiny Bird, An Ancient Crab, and An Epic Journey*, Deborah Cramer; *Origins of the British Empire*, Steve Pincus; *Real Mermaids Don't Sell Seashells (Real Mermaids Book 4)*, Helene Boudreau; *Serenading Earthworms: How Darwin Proved Darwin*, James Cost; *The Incarnate Trilogy*, Jodi Meadows; *The Pope & Mussolini*, David Kertzer; *Unequal Protections: The Last Legacy of Warren Burger's Court*, Linda Greenhouse, Michael Graetz
Membership(s): The Authors Guild

Swagger Literary Agency (L)
601 Shenandoah Valley Dr, Front Royal, VA 22630
Tel: 540-636-7076
E-mail: swaggerlit@gmail.com
Web Site: www.swaggerliterary.com
Key Personnel
Owner & Literary Agent: Joseph Brendan Vallely
Founded: 2014
Represents upmarket nonfiction: current events, history, biography, sports & outdoors, word books & the occasional upscale project that doesn't easily fit into these categories. Submit query letter & book proposal by e-mail only. Representation on the West Coast & in foreign countries.
Titles recently placed: *Johnny Football*, Mike Shropshire; *Law & Disorder*, Charles Sevilla; *What So Proudly We Hailed: Francis Scott Key, A Life*, Marc Leepson
Foreign Rep(s): Anthea Literary Agency (Katalina Sabeva) (Bulgaria); Eliane Benisti Agent Litteraire (France); Luigi Bernabo Associates (Luigi Bernabo) (Italy); Big Apple Agency Inc (Grace Yang, Dr Luk Kwanten & Lily Chen) (China, Taiwan); GRAAL Ltd (Maria Strarz-Kanska) (Poland); International Copyright Agency Ltd (Simona Kessler) (Romania); International Editors' Co (Isabel Monteagudo) (Portugal, Spain); International Editors' Co (Nicolas Costa) (Argentina); International Editors' Co (Ms Flavia Sala) (Brazil, Portugal); Japan UNI (Miko Yamanouchi) (Japan); JLM Literary Agency (Nelly Moukakou) (Greece); Katai & Bolza (Peter Bolza) (Hungary); Linda Kohn International Literatuur (Netherlands); Nurcihan Kesim® Literary Agency (Filiz Karaman) (Turkey); Kristin Olson Literary Agency sro (Czech Republic); I Pikarski Literary Agency (Ms Gal Pikarski) (Israel); Lennart Sane Agency SB (Lina Hammarling) (Scandinavia); Thomas Schlueck Literary & Art Agency (Tom Schlueck) (Bulgaria); Thomas Schlueck Literary & Art Agency (Joachim Jessen) (Germany); Shin Won Agency (Eunja Beck, Mr Sang Hyung & Steve Yang) (Korea); Tuttle-Mori Agency Inc (Anongnard Podchanajun & Pimolporn Yutisri) (Thailand); Eric Yang Agency (Vince Baek) (Korea)

Carolyn Swayze Literary Agency Ltd (L)
7360 137 St, Suite 319, Surrey, BC V3W 1A3, Canada
Tel: 604-503-3895
E-mail: reception@swayzeagency.com
Web Site: www.swayzeagency.com
Key Personnel
Pres: Carolyn Swayze *E-mail:* carolyn@swayzeagency.com
Founded: 1994
Representing emerging & established authors of literary fiction, some commercial fiction, nonfiction, middle grade & YA books. No science fiction, no self-help, no picture books. An inquiry must include an author bio, a short description of the available project & short sample. No fees charged. Authors may consult web site for current submission guidelines. Mostly Canadian authors & US Pacific Northwest.
Titles recently placed: *A Sweet Montana Christmas*, Roxanne Snopek; *Assault on Juno*, Mark Zuehlke; *Fallen*, Kara Stanley; *Once They Were Hats*, Frances Backhouse; *Ortona Street Fight*, Mark Zuehlke; *Pandas on the Eastside*, Gabrielle Prendergast; *Prisoner of Snowflake Falls*, John Lekich; *Resisting the Rancher*, Roxanne Snopek; *Tangled in Tennessee*, Alexandra Holden; *The Bastard of Fort Stikine*, Debra Komar; *The Bride Stripped Bare by her Bachelors, Even*, Chris F Westbury; *The Conjoined*, Jen Sookfong Lee; *The Cowboy Next Door*, Roxanne Snopek; *The Essential WP Kinsella*, W P Kinsella; *The Frail Days*, Gabrielle Prendergast; *The Stonehenge Letters*, Harry Karlinsky
Foreign Rep(s): L'Autre Agence (Corinne Marotte) (France)
Foreign Rights: ALI (Stefania Fietta) (Italy); AM Heath & Co Ltd, Authors' Agents (UK); AMV Agencia Literaria (Spain); AnatoliaLit Copyright & Translation Agency (Turkey); L'Autre Agence (France); The Book Publishers Association of Israel (Dalia Ever Hadani) (Israel); Chinese Connection Agency (China, Taiwan); Paul Christoph Literary Agency (Brazil, Portugal); ELST Literary Agency (Kalina Stefanova) (Bulgaria); International Copyright Agency (Simona Kessler) (Moldova, Romania); Lex Copyright (Hungary); Mo Literary Services (Netherlands); Mohr Books (Germany); Andrew Nurnberg Associates (Baltic States); O A Literary Agency (Greece); Maria Starz-Kanska (Poland); Tuttle-Mori Agency Inc (Japan)

Robert E Tabian/Literary Agent (L)
229 Paterson Ave, Suite 2, East Rutherford, NJ 07073
Tel: 631-987-2293 *Fax:* 201-438-1327
E-mail: retlit@mindspring.com

Key Personnel
Owner & Sole Prop: Bob E Tabian
Founded: 1992
Adult & young adult fiction, adult nonfiction; thrillers, mysteries, women's fiction, self-help, psychology, cookbooks, health & medicine, history, biography & popular culture & spirituality. No unsol mss, query first with SASE. Submit 100 pages (fiction) or outline & two sample chapters (nonfiction). Handle film & TV rights. Representatives in many foreign countries & Hollywood. No reading fee. Clients are charged ms copying & submission mailing charges.
Foreign Rights: Chandler Crawford Agency (Worldwide)

Tessler Literary Agency LLC (L)
27 W 20 St, Suite 1003, New York, NY 10011
Tel: 212-242-0466 *Fax:* 212-242-2366
Web Site: www.tessleragency.com
Key Personnel
Pres: Michelle Tessler (AAR)
Founded: 2004
Full service boutique agency dedicated to writers of high quality fiction & nonfiction. Nonfiction list includes narrative, popular science, memoir, history, psychology, business, biography, food & travel. In fiction, represents literary, women's & commercial. No unsol mss, query first via web form. No fees charged.
Titles recently placed: *Are We Smart Enough to Know How Smart Animals Are?*, Frans de Waal; *Blood & Ivy: The True Story of Money, Murder & the Trial that Shocked Harvard*, Paul Collins; *Breaking the Standard: The Upstarts and Underdogs Who Toppled Rockefeller*, Peter Doran; *Emotional First Aid: Practical Strategies for Treating Failure, Rejection, Guilt, and Other Everyday Psychological Injuries*, Guy Winch, PhD; *Girl Waits With Gun*, Amy Stewart; *Heir to the Empire City: New York and the Making of Theodore Roosevelt*, Edward Kohn; *Homecoming*, Amanda Eyre Ward; *Part Time Paleo*, Leanne Ely; *Saving Baby: How One Woman's Love for a Racehorse Led Her to Redemption*, Jo Anne Normile, Lawrence Lindner; *Shanghai Grand: A True Tale of Forbidden Love, International Intrigue, and Doomed Glamour in Old Cathay*, Taras Grescoe; *The Alchemy of Algae: How Commonplace Creatures Created Us, Sustain Us, and Just Might Save Us*, Ruth Kassinger; *The Drunken Botanist*, Amy Stewart; *The Sleepwalker's Guide to Dancing*, Mira Jacob; *Thirsty Dragon: China's Lust for Bordeaux, A Story of Conquest, Crime, and Wine*, Suzanne Mustacich; *Underwater Puppies*, Seth Casteel
Foreign Rights: The Deborah Harris Agency (Israel); Andrew Nurnberg & Associates (China, Europe, Latin America); Tuttle-Mori Agency Inc (Japan); Eric Yang Agency (Korea)

3 Seas Literary Agency (L)
PO Box 8571, Madison, WI 53708
Tel: 608-834-9317
Key Personnel
Literary Agent: Michelle Grajkowski (AAR) *E-mail:* threeseaslit@aol.com; Cori Deyoe *E-mail:* cori@threeseaslit.com; Linda Scalissi
Founded: 2000
E-mail queries only. For fiction titles, query with first chapter & synopsis embedded in the e-mail. For nonfiction, query with complete proposal attached. For picture books, query with complete text. Illustrations are not necessary. Considers simultaneous submissions. Responds within one month to e-mail submissions. No snail mail queries. 3 Seas will not respond to queries that are sent to e-mail addresses other than queries@threeseaslit.com. Obtains most new clients through recommendations from others & conferences. No fees charged.

Titles recently placed: *A Navy SEAL'S Surprise Baby*, Laura Marie Altom; *A Time For Home*, Alexis Morgan; *Captive*, KM Fawcett; *Changed By His Son*, Robin Gianakopoulus; *Do or Diner*, Christine Wenger; *Every Breath She Takes*, Norah Wilson; *Forever Friday*, Timothy Lewis; *Haley's Mountain Man*, Tracy Madison; *Her Perfect Cowboy*, Trish Milburn; *His Uptown Girl*, Liz Talley; *How to Write a Book in 30 Days*, Karen Wiesner; *Jimmie Joe Johnson: Manwhore*, Lindsey Brookes; *Just Perfect*, JoMarie DeGioia; *Must Love Dukes*, Elizabeth Michaels; *One Night with the Sheikh*, Kristi Gold; *Passion and Pretense*, Susan Gee Heino; *Queen of Song and Souls*, C L Wilson; *Queen of the Sylphs*, LJ McDonald; *Say It With Roses*, Devon Vaughn Archer; *Six Months Later*, Natalie D. Richards; *The Art of Stealing Time*, Katie MacAlister; *The Bride Next Door*, Winnie Griggs; *The Casanova Code*, Donna MacMeans; *The Champion*, Carla Capshaw; *The Rancher's Homecoming*, Cathy McDavid; *The Sister Season*, Jennifer Brown; *The Vampire With a Dragon Tattoo*, Kerrelyn Sparks; *The Winter King*, C L Wilson; *Thousand Words*, Jennifer Brown; *Three Days on Mimosa Lane*, Anna DeStefano
Foreign Rights: Marleen Seegers (China, France, Holland, Scandinavia); Ingo Stein (Germany)
Membership(s): Romance Writers of America

The Tomasino Agency Inc (L)
70 Chestnut St, Dobbs Ferry, NY 10522
Tel: 914-674-9659 *Fax:* 914-693-0381
E-mail: info@tomasinoagency.com
Web Site: www.tomasinoagency.com
Key Personnel
Pres: Christine K Tomasino
Founded: 1998
Commercial & literary fiction & nonfiction. Represent all subrights for book clients only. Specialize in conventional & mind/body health, women's issues, self-improvement, spirituality/esoterica, narrative nonfiction, lifestyle, adult illustrated & packaged books, sports. Translation of non-book content into book-related formats for corporate & nonprofit organizational clients such as major web businesses & museums. No poetry, genre fiction, plays, science fiction or purely scholarly work. Foreign agents in all major markets. No unsol mss, query first.

Transatlantic Agency (L)
2 Bloor St E, Suite 3500, Toronto, ON M4W 1A8, Canada
Tel: 416-488-9214
E-mail: info@transatlanticagency.com
Web Site: www.transatlanticagency.com
Key Personnel
Pres: David Bennett *E-mail:* david@transatlanticagency.com
VP: Lynn Bennett *E-mail:* lynn@transatlanticagency.com
Partner & Agent: Shaun Bradley (AAR) *E-mail:* shaun@transatlanticagency.com; Marie Campbell *E-mail:* marie@transatlanticagency.com; Samantha Haywood *E-mail:* samantha@transatlanticagency.com
Assoc Agent: Stephanie Sinclair; Amy Tompkins *E-mail:* amy@transatlanticagency.com
Agent: Sandra Bishop (AAR); Fiona Kenshole (AAR) *E-mail:* fiona@transatlanticagency.com
Founded: 1993
Children's, adult literary fiction & literary nonfiction. Markets Canadian & American literary properties to English language publishers in the UK, USA & Canada & through sub-agents to publishers around the world. Handles film & TV rights for literary properties only: no film scripts or tele-plays. No unsol mss; initial letter of inquiry essential. No reading fees. See web site for individual agents' submission details.

Titles recently placed: *Boundless*, Kathleen Winter; *McKenna - American Girl*, Mary Casanova; *Punishment*, Linden MacIntyre; *Tell It to the World*, Eliott Behar; *The Circus Dogs of Prague*, Rachelle Delaney; *The Devil You Know*, Elizabeth de Mariaffi; *The Gospel Truth*, Carolyn Pignat; *The Gypsy King*, Maureen Fergus; *The Silent Wife*, A S A Harrison; *The Unlikely Hero of 13B*, Teresa Toten; *They Left Us Everything*, Plum Johnson; *Walking Home*, Eric Walters; *Will Starling*, Ian Weir
Foreign Rights: The agency (Korea); Akcali Copyright (Turkey); ANAW Literary Agency (Poland); Berla & Griffini Rights Agency (Italy); The Book Publishers Association of Israel (Israel); ELST Literary Agency (Bulgaria); The English Agency (Japan) Ltd (Japan); Agence Litteraire Lora Fountain (France, Portugal, Spain); International Editors' Co (Spanish & Portuguese); Japan Uni Agency Inc (Japan); The Anna Jarota Agency (France); JLM Literary Agency (Greece); Katai & Bolza Literary Agents (Hungary); Liepman AG (Germany); Literarische Agentur+Medienservice (Germany); Mo Literary Services (Netherlands, Scandinavia); Andrew Nurnberg Associates International Ltd (China, Hong Kong, Taiwan); Kristin Olson Literary Agency sro (Czech Republic); Orange Agency (Korea); Agencia Literaria RIFF (Brazil); Shinwon Agency Co (Korea); Tuttle-Mori Agency Inc (Indonesia, Japan, Malaysia, Thailand, Vietnam); Young Agency (Korea)

Treimel, S©ott, NY, see S©ott Treimel NY

TriadaUS Literary Agency (L)
PO Box 561, Sewickley, PA 15143
Tel: 412-401-3376 *Fax:* 412-749-0842
Web Site: www.triadaus.com
Key Personnel
Agent: Dr Uwe Stender (AAR) *E-mail:* uwe@triadaus.com
Founded: 2004
Full service literary agency including fiction, nonfiction. Also international sales, film & TV options. No unsol mss, query first.
Titles recently placed: *Flight 93: The Story and the Legacy*, Tom McMillan; *Garden Therapy*, Stephanie Rose; *Hotter Than a Match Head*, Steve Boone, Tony Moss; *How to Barter for Your Dream Home-A Journey Around the World*, Michael Wigge; *In Faith and In Doubt*, Dale McGowan; *My Seventh Grade Life in Tights*, Brooks Benjamin; *Summer Bucket List*, Deanna Romito; *The Kids' Outdoor Myth Book*, Stacy Tornio, Ken Keffer; *The Land of 10,000 Madonnas*, Kate Hattemer; *The Reappearing Act*, Kate Fagan; *The Restaurant Critic's Wife*, Elizabeth LaBan; *The Secret Lives of Animals*, Stacy Tornio, Ken Keffer; *The Vigilante Poets of Selwyn Academy*, Kate Hattemer; *Thieving Weasels*, Billy Taylor; *Think Like a Baby*, Dr Amber Ankowski, Andy Ankowski; *Wild Connection*, Dr Jennifer Verdolin

Trident Media Group LLC (L)
41 Madison Ave, 36th fl, New York, NY 10010
Tel: 212-333-1511
E-mail: info@tridentmediagroup.com; press@tridentmediagroup.com
Web Site: www.tridentmediagroup.com
Key Personnel
Chmn: Robert Gottlieb
CEO: Daniel Strone
EVP: Ellen Levine (AAR); Scott Miller; John Silbersack; Kimberly Whalen
Literary & Audio Rts Agent: Mark Gottlieb (AAR)
Literary Agent: Don Fehr; Melissa Flashman; MacKenzie Fraser-Bub; Alyssa Eisner Henkin; Amanda O'Connor; Erica Spellman-Silverman

Assoc Agent: Tara Carberry
Dir, Foreign Rts: Claire Roberts
Assoc Dir, Foreign Rts: Sylvie Rosokoff
Dom Agent: Alex Slater
Audio Rts Agent: Sarah Bush
Foreign Rts Agent: Meredith Miller; Lauren Paverman
Founded: 2000
General fiction & nonfiction. No unsol mss, query first by e-mail. Submit outline & sample chapters if requested. No reading fee. Handle film & TV rights for clients only. Representation in Hollywood.
Titles recently placed: *365 Days of Wonder: Mr Browne's Book of Precepts*, R J Palacio; *A Fall From Grace*, Adam Mitzner; *Alluring Indulgence*, Nicole Edwards; *Angel Killer*, Andrew Mayne; *Avenged*, Daniel Judson; *Bad Blood*, Mark Sennen; *Blacklist*, Sylvia Day; *Bound by Night*, Larissa Ione; *Breaking Nova*, Jessica Sorensen; *Call Me*, Kristina Knight; *Chained by Night*, Larissa Ione; *Cloud City: An Anna Strong Novella*, Jeanne Stein; *Collateral Damage*, Kyra Davis; *Cut Dead*, Mark Sennen; *Dangerous Alliance*, Kyra Davis; *Deceptive Innocence*, Kyra Davis; *Family by Design*, Kristina Knight; *Future Humans: The Ongoing Evolution of Homo Sapiens*, Prof Scott Solomon; *Green Girl*, Kate Zambreno; *Hemingway's War*, Terry Mort; *In Pursuit: The Saga of the Nazi Hunters*, Andrew Nagorski; *In the Skin of a Lion*, Michael Ondaatje; *Light My Fire*, Kristina Knight; *Music Class Today!*, David Weinstone; *Mystique*, Julie Berry; *No Time to Die*, Kira Peikoff; *Pics*, Nathan Jurgenson; *President Me: The America That's in My Head*, Adam Carolla; *Rebel Democracy: Digital Warriors and Islamic World*, Haroon Ullah; *Resistance*, Ryk Brown; *Ruin*, Rachel Van Dyken; *Running in the Family*, Michael Ondaatje; *Sistering*, Hannah Roberts-McKinnon; *Slow Burn (series)*, Maya Banks; *Starfire*, Dale Brown; *Start Me Up*, Kristina Knight; *The Birth of Capitalism in Islam*, Benedikt Koehler; *The Confessors' Club*, Jack Fredrickson; *The Distance Between Lost and Found*, Kathryn Holmes; *The Ever After of Ella and Micha*, Jessica Sorensen; *The Great Surge*, Steven Radelet; *The Julian Chapter: A Wonder Story*, R J Palacio; *The Last Days*, Joel Rosenberg; *The Last Jihad*, Joel Rosenberg; *The Last Rescue*, Howard Wasdin, Debbie Wasdin; *The Monet Murders*, Terry Mort; *The Mountain*, T Jefferson Parker; *The New Abolition*, Gary Dorrien; *The Other Side of Impossible: How to Let Go of the Life You Planned and Find a Happy Ending*, Tracey Cleantis; *The Rose Hotel*, Rahimeh Andalibian; *The Scandalous Sisterhood of Prickwillow Place*, Julie Berry; *The Struggle for Liberation*, Gary Dorrien; *The Winter Place*, Alexander Yates; *The Youngs: The Brothers Who Built AC/DC*, Jesse Fink; *Thieves Road: General George Custer and the Invasion of the Black Hills*, Terry Mort; *To Silence the Screaming Dead*, Jack Fredrickson; *Touch*, Mark Sennen; *Tower of Winds*, Ilana Myer; *Toxic*, Rachel Van Dyken; *Transit Girl*, Jamie Shupak; *Treading on Thin Air*, Dr Elizabeth Austin; *True Lies*, Monica Murphy; *Unspeakable Things*, Kathleen Spivack; *Welcome to Dog Beach*, Lisa Greenwald; *Werewolf Cop*, Andrew Klavan

2M Communications Ltd (L)
19 W 21 St, Suite 501, New York, NY 10010
Tel: 212-741-1509 *Fax:* 212-691-4460
Web Site: www.2mcommunications.com
Key Personnel
Pres: Madeleine Morel (AAR) *E-mail:* morel@2mcommunications.com
Founded: 1982
Only represent previously published ghostwriters & collaborators who work with platformed authors already represented by recognized literary agents or acquired by publishing houses. Numerous New York Times bestsellers but all confidential. No unsol mss, query first. Submit CV or resume.
Membership(s): PEN American Center; Women's Media Group

United Talent Agency (L-D)
9336 Civic Center Dr, Beverly Hills, CA 90210
Tel: 310-273-6700 *Fax:* 310-247-1111
Web Site: www.unitedtalent.com
Key Personnel
CEO: Jeremy Zimmer
Mng Dir: David Kramer
Founded: 1991
Fiction, nonfiction. Handle film & TV rights. No unsol mss, query first; reading fee.
Branch Office(s)
888 Seventh Ave, 9th fl, New York, NY 10106
Tel: 212-659-2600

Janis Vallely Literary Agency (L)
111 Raup Rd, Chatham, NY 12037
Tel: 518-392-0897
E-mail: janisvallely@gmail.com
Web Site: www.janisvallely.com
Key Personnel
Owner & Literary Agent: Janis Vallely
Founded: 2014
Represents upscale commercial nonfiction: memoir, self-help, diet, narrative nonfiction, popular psychology & health. No unsol mss; no phone calls, no reading fee. Submit query letter & book proposal by e-mail only. Representation on the West Coast & in foreign countries.
Titles recently placed: *Eat Right 4 Your Type Cookbooks*, Dr Peter J Dadamo; *The Chemistry of Youth*, Henrry Emmons, MD, David Alter, PhD; *The Microbiome Diet*, Raphael Kellman, MD
Foreign Rep(s): Anthea Literary Agency (Katalina Sabeva) (Bulgaria); Eliane Benisti Agent Litteraire (France); Luigi Bernabo Associates (Luigi Bernabo) (Italy); Big Apple Agency Inc (Grace Yang, Dr Luk Kwanten & Lily Chen) (China, Taiwan); Graal Literary Agency (Maria Strarz-Kanska) (Poland); International Copyright Agency Ltd (Simona Kessler) (Romania); International Editors' Co (Isabel Monteagudo) (Portugal, Spain); International Editors' Co (Nicolas Costa) (Argentina); International Editors' Co (Ms Flavia Sala) (Brazil, Portugal); Japan UNI Agency Inc (Miko Yamanouchi) (Japan); JLM Literary Agency (Nelly Moukakou) (Greece); Katai & Bolza (Peter Bolza) (Hungary); Linda Kohn International Literatuur (Netherlands); Nurcihan Kesim® Literary Agency (Filiz Karaman) (Turkey); Kristin Olson Literary Agency sro (Czech Republic); I Pikarski Literary Agency (Ms Gal Pikarski) (Israel); Lennart Sane Agency SB (Lina Hammarling) (Scandinavia); Thomas Schlueck Literary & Art Agency (Tom Schlueck) (Bulgaria); Thomas Schlueck Literary & Art Agency (Joachim Jessen) (Germany); Shin Won Agency (Eunja Beck, Mr Sang Hyung & Steve Yang) (Korea); Tuttle-Mori Agency Inc (Anongnard Podchanajun & Pimolporn Yutisri) (Thailand); Eric Yang Agency (Vince Baek) (Korea)

Wales Literary Agency Inc (L)
1508 Tenth Ave E, No 401, Seattle, WA 98102
Tel: 206-284-7114
E-mail: waleslit@waleslit.com
Web Site: www.waleslit.com
Key Personnel
Owner & Literary Agent: Elizabeth Wales (AAR)
Asst Agent & Foreign Rts: Neal Swain
Founded: 1990
Specialize in quality fiction & nonfiction. Does not handle screenplays, children's books, genre fiction or most category nonfiction. No unsol mss, query first by e-mail only (no attachments). No phone queries. Accept electronic submissions only. Simultaneous submissions accepted. Response provided within 3 weeks to queries, 3 months to mss.
Titles recently placed: *Badluck Way: A Year on the Ragged Edge of the West*, Bryce Andrews; *Find the Good*, Heather Lende; *Still Time*, Jean Hegland; *The Hidden Half of Nature: Uncovering the Microbial Roots of Life and Health*, David Montgomery, Anne Bikle; *Witness Tree*, Lynda Mapes
Foreign Rights: Big Apple Agency Inc (China, Taiwan); Nurcihan Kesim Literary & Licensing Agency (Turkey); Agence Lapautre (France); Mohrbooks Literary Agency (Austria, Germany, Switzerland); Andrew Nurnberg Associates (Croatia, Hungary); Sebes & van Gelderen Literary Agency (Netherlands, Scandinavia); Shinwon Agency (Korea); Silk Road Agency (Thailand); Abner Stein Agency (UK); Tuttle-Mori Agency Inc (Japan)

Wallace Literary Agency Inc (L)
229 E 79 St, No 5A, New York, NY 10075
Tel: 212-472-3282 *Fax:* 212-472-3833
E-mail: info@wallaceliteraryagency.com
Key Personnel
Pres: Robin Straus *E-mail:* robin@wallaceliteraryagency.com
Founded: 1988
Handle film & TV rights for agency clients only. No unsol mss, query first with SASE. No reading fee.
Foreign Rights: Andrew Nurnberg Associates (Europe, UK); Tuttle-Mori Agency Inc (Japan)

Ward & Balkin Agency, Inc (L)
30 Brock Way, South Hadley, MA 01075
Tel: 413-322-8697
Web Site: www.wardbalkin.com
Key Personnel
Pres: Richard A Balkin *E-mail:* rick62838@crocker.com
Founded: 1972
Adult nonfiction only. No unsol mss, or queries. No reading fee, 15% agency commission; 25% foreign rights. Currently not accepting new clients.
Clients of the late Christina (Kit) Ward are now handled by Colleen Mohyde at The Doe Coover Agency. Colleen can be reached at 718-721-6000 or colleen@doecooveragency.com.
Titles recently placed: *American Isis: A Biography of Sylvia Plath*, Carl Rollyson; *Apocalypse Forever*, Betsy Hartmann; *Changing Lives: Gustavo Dudamel, El Sistema, and the Transformative Power of Music*, Tricia Tunstall; *Newton Fever*, Sarah Dry; *The Approaching Great Transformation: Toward a Livable Post Carbon Economy*, Joel Magnuson; *The Wizard and the Prophet*, Charles Mann; *Why Geology Matters: Decoding the Past, Anticipating the Future*, Doug Macdougall
Foreign Rights: Taryn Fagerness Agency (Worldwide exc USA)

Warwick Associates (L)
18340 Sonoma Hwy, Sonoma, CA 95476
Tel: 707-939-9212 *Fax:* 707-938-3515
E-mail: warwick@vom.com
Web Site: www.warwickassociates.com
Key Personnel
Pres: Simon Warwick-Smith
Founded: 1985
A "one-stop" agency handling any or all parts of literary agenting through publicity & sales, etc. Specialize in spirituality, metaphysics, religion & psychology, celebrity memoirs, business & self-help, pop culture. Literary agent for a

number of celebrity spiritual authors. No reading fee. Accept unsol mss. Query first with 2 chapters & SASE. No fiction or poetry.

Waterside Productions Inc (L)
2055 Oxford Ave, Cardiff, CA 92007
Tel: 760-632-9190 *Fax:* 760-632-9295
E-mail: admin@waterside.com
Web Site: www.waterside.com
Key Personnel
Founder & Literary Agent: Bill Gladstone *E-mail:* bgladstone@waterside.com
VP & Agent: Carole Jelen *Tel:* 925-968-9066 *E-mail:* carole@jelenpub.com
Sr Agent: Margot Maley Hutchison *Tel:* 858-483-0426 *E-mail:* mmaley@waterside.com
Foreign Rts Dir & Agent: Neil Gudovitz *E-mail:* neilg@earthlink.net
Agent: Kimberly Brabec; David Nelson; Jill Kramer *Tel:* 760-201-5737 *E-mail:* WatersideAgentJK@aol.com; Brad Schepp; Lawrence Jackel *Tel:* 941-364-3601 *E-mail:* jackelpub1@verizon.net
Founded: 1982
Specialize in nonfiction. Professional how-to: technology, business, software, test-prep, etc. General: self-help, spiritual, health, human interest, etc. No phone calls. No unsol mss. Submit a full book proposal per guidelines found at, or query through, the web site form. No reading fee. Handles software, film & TV rights with co-agents. In-house international division. Affiliations with PR agencies. Waterside now has its own print on demand & ebook publishing division.
Titles recently placed: *Conscious Money: Living, Creating & Investing with Your Values for a Sustainable New Prosperity*, Patricia Aburdene; *I Got a Name: The Jim Croce Story*, Ingrid Croce, Jimmy Rock; *The Crash of 2015*, Thom Hartmann; *The Golden Motorcycle Gang: A Story of Transformation*, Jack Canfield, William Gladstone; *The Steve Jobs Way: iLeadership for a New Generation*, Jay Elliot, William L Simon; *The Storm Before the Calm*, Neale Donald Walsch

Watkins/Loomis Agency Inc (L)
PO Box 20925, New York, NY 10025
Tel: 212-532-0080 *Fax:* 646-383-2449
E-mail: assistant@watkinsloomis.com
Web Site: www.watkinsloomis.com
Key Personnel
Pres: Gloria Loomis
Agent: Julia Masnik
Founded: 1908
Literary fiction, political nonfiction. No unsol material.
Foreign Rights: The Marsh Agency; Abner Stein Agency (UK)

Waverly Place Literary Agency (L)
189 Waverly Place, Unit 4, New York, NY 10014-3135
Tel: 212-925-3721
E-mail: waverlyplaceliterary@aol.com
Web Site: www.waverlyplaceliterary.com; twitter.com/waverlyplacelit
Key Personnel
Literary Agent: Deborah Carter
Founded: 1998
Representing writing with charisma for adults, teens & children. No reading or editorial fees. Expenses for photocopying & postage, if any, pre-approved by client. Interests include multicultural & international fiction relatable to American readers; narrative nonfiction in memoir/biography about extraordinary people & experiences; mysteries, thrillers & suspense novels; mainstream fiction (no romance, sci-fi, fantasy, horror, religious/spiritual); historical fiction; literary novels; short story & poetry collections with popular appeal; children's & teen fiction. Send 1- to 2-paragraph synopsis & description of your background. E-mail queries only. In the subject line write Q: followed by a description of your book. Unsol mss sent by post will be discarded. Multiple submissions ok. If no response within two weeks, try again.
Titles recently placed: *Adventures of Molly Whuppie & Other Appalachian Folktales (Taiwan)*, Anne Shelby; *Homeplace (McGraw-Hill Spanish Kindergarten kit)*, Anne Shelby; *What to Do About Pollution/South Korea*, Anne Shelby
Foreign Rights: Akacali Copyright Agency (Bengu Ayfer) (Turkey); Book Publishers of Israel (Beverley Levit) (Israel); EntersKorea Agency (Lauren Kim) (Korea); Jiaxi Books (China, Taiwan); Tuttle-Mori Agency Inc (Worapong Wilai) (Indonesia, Malaysia, Thailand, Vietnam); Jack Zhou (China, Taiwan)
Membership(s): The Authors Guild; Historical Novel Society; International Thriller Writers Inc

Waxman Leavell Literary Agency (L)
Affiliate of Diversion Publishing Corp
443 Park Ave S, No 1004, New York, NY 10016
Tel: 212-675-5556 *Fax:* 212-675-1381
Web Site: www.waxmanleavell.com
Key Personnel
Founder & Agent: Scott Waxman; Byrd Leavell
Sr Agent: Larry Kirshbaum
Agent: Kirsten Carlton; Cassie Hanjian; Fleetwood Robbins; Holly Root; Julie Stevenson; Rachel Vogel
Founded: 1997
Fiction & nonfiction. No unsol mss, query first via e-mail. No reading fee, charge for reproductions.

Cherry Weiner Literary Agency (L)
925 Oak Bluff Ct, Dacula, GA 30019-6660
Tel: 732-446-2096 *Fax:* 732-792-0506
E-mail: cherry8486@aol.com
Key Personnel
Owner: Cherry Weiner
Founded: 1977
Science fiction, general fiction & nonfiction. No unsol mss. Referred authors submit letter saying who referred. Submissions or recommendations only. Query letter where applicable, no downloads. No reading fee. Handle film & TV rights. Foreign representatives in England, Germany, Italy, Japan, Netherlands, Scandinavia, Russia, Spain, Eastern Europe & France.
Titles recently placed: *Alien Nation*, Gini Koch; *Aliens Abroad*, Gini Koch; *Death in Cantera*, John Nesbitt; *Kutter*, Tim Waggoner; *See Also Murder II & III*, Larry D Sweazy; *The Box Jumper*, Lisa Mannetti; *The Dark Days*, P M Griffin; *The Outfit*, Matthew P Mayo

The Weingel-Fidel Agency (L)
310 E 46 St, Suite 21-E, New York, NY 10017
Tel: 212-599-2959 *Fax:* 212-286-1986
E-mail: queries@theweingel-fidelagency.com
Key Personnel
Owner: Loretta Weingel-Fidel *E-mail:* lwf@theweingel-fidelagency.com
Founded: 1989
General fiction & nonfiction. Provide services to book authors/writers. No unsol mss, query first, by referral only; no reading fee.
Foreign Rep(s): Mary Clemmey (UK); Fritz Agency (Germany); Japan UNI (Japan); Michelle Lapautre (France); Lennart Sane (Netherlands, Scandinavia, Spain)
Foreign Rights: Jill Hughes (Albania, Bulgaria, Croatia, Estonia, Hungary, Latvia, Lithuania, Macedonia, Montenegro, Romania, Serbia, Slovakia, Slovenia)

Westwood Creative Artists Ltd (L)
94 Harbord St, Toronto, ON M5S 1G6, Canada
Tel: 416-964-3302 *Fax:* 416-975-9209
E-mail: wca_office@wcaltd.com
Web Site: www.wcaltd.com
Key Personnel
Chmn: Michael Levine
Pres & COO: Jackie Kaiser
Founder & CEO: Bruce Westwood
EVP: Hilary McMahon
Exec Asst & Perms Mgr: Chris Cassuccio
Exec Asst: Jake Babad
Agent & Intl Rts Mgr: Carolyn Forde
Agent: Linda McKnight; John Pearce
Founded: 1995
General trade fiction & nonfiction for international marketplace. Canadian authors only. No unsol mss, query first. Handle film & TV rights. No screenwriters. No reading fee.
Foreign Rep(s): Akcali Copyright (Kezban Akcali) (Turkey); Akcali Copyright (Atilla Izgi Turgut) (Turkey); Sandra Bruna Literary Agency (Natalia Berenguer) (Brazil, Latin America, Portugal, Spain); Sandra Bruna Literary Agency (Sandra Bruna) (Brazil, Latin America, Portugal, Spain); The English Agency (Hamish Macaskill) (Japan); Graal Literary Agency (Maria Starz-Kanska) (Poland); Graal Literary Agency (Marcin Biegaj) (Poland); The Deborah Harris Agency (Efrat Lev) (Israel); International Copyright Agency (Simona Kessler) (Romania); Japan Uni Agency (Miko Suga Yamanouchi) (Japan); Anna Jarota (Anna Jarota) (France); Anna Jarota (Sandrine Bilan) (France); JLM Literary Agency (John Moukakos) (Greece); Katai & Bolza (Peter Bolza) (Hungary); Liepman Agency (Ruth Weibel) (Germany); Liepman Agency (Suzanne de Roche) (Germany); Maxima Creative Agency (Santo Manurung) (Indonesia); NiKa (Vania Kadiyska) (Bulgaria); Andrew Nurnberg & Associates (Lisa Brannstrom) (Netherlands, Scandinavia); Andrew Nurnberg & Associates (Eleonoora Kirk) (Netherlands, Scandinavia); Andrew Nurnberg Associates International (Whitney Hsu) (China); Kristin Olson (Czech Republic); PLIMA (Vuk Perisic) (Croatia, Serbia, Slovenia); Shin Won Agency (Tae Eun Kim) (Korea); Synopsis (Natalia Sanina) (Russia); Tuttle-Mori Agency Co Ltd (Thananchai Pandey) (Thailand); Tuttle-Mori Agency Inc (Ken Mori) (Japan); Marco Vigevani Agency (Italy)

Rhoda Weyr Agency, see Dunham Literary Inc

Witherspoon Associates Inc, see InkWell Management

WME (L-D)
1325 Avenue of the Americas, New York, NY 10019
Tel: 212-586-5100 *Fax:* 212-246-3583
E-mail: wma@interport.net
Web Site: www.wma.com
Key Personnel
Partner: Tina Bennett; Dorian Karchmar (AAR)
CFO: Peter Klein
Head, NY Lit Dept: Suzanne Gluck
EVP, Co-Head: Jennifer Rudolph Walsh
Dept Head: Eric Simonoff
Agent: Mel Berger; Tracy Fisher
Contact: Jay Mandel
All subjects; handle software, film & TV rights. No unsol mss, query first; no reading fee.
Branch Office(s)
9601 Wilshire Blvd, Beverly Hills, CA 90210 *Tel:* 310-285-9000 *Fax:* 310-285-9010
119 Washington Ave, Suite 400, Miami Beach, FL 33139 *Tel:* 305-938-2000 *Fax:* 305-938-2002

1600 Division St, Suite 300, Nashville, TN 37203
Tel: 615-963-3000 *Fax:* 615-963-3090
Foreign Office(s): Center Point, 103 New Oxford St, London WC1A 1DD, United Kingdom *Tel:* (020) 7534 6800 *Fax:* (020) 7534 6900

Writers House (L)
21 W 26 St, New York, NY 10010
Tel: 212-685-2400 *Fax:* 212-685-1781
Web Site: www.writershouse.com
Key Personnel
Founder: Albert Zuckerman
Chmn & CEO: Amy Berkower
Pres: Simon Lipskar (AAR)
EVP, Fiction & Nonfiction: Merrilee Heifetz (AAR)
VP & Dir, Juv & Young Adult: Susan Cohen (AAR)
Children's Subs Rts Dir: Cecelia de la Campa
Subs Rts Dir: Maja Nikolic
Subs Rts Assoc: Kathryn Stuart
Dir, Digital Rts: Julie Trelstad
Sr Agent: Stephen Barr; Dan Conaway (AAR); Susan Ginsburg; Dan Lazar (AAR) *E-mail:* dlazar@writershouse.com
Sr Agent, Juv & Young Adult: Jodi Reamer, Esq (AAR); Rebecca Sherman *E-mail:* rsherman@writershouse.com
Sr Agent, Mainstream Fiction & Nonfiction: Robin Rue (AAR)
Agent: Soumeya Bendimerad; Lisa DiMona; Susan Golomb; Brianne Johnson; Geri Thoma
Founded: 1973
Represent trade books of all types, fiction & nonfiction, including all rights. Handle film & TV rights. No screenplays, teleplays or software. No unsol mss, query first with an intelligent one page letter stating what's wonderful about the book, what it's about & what background & experience you, as an author, bring to it. Queries generally responded to within 2 weeks & mss within 4 weeks. No reading fee.
Branch Office(s)
3368 Governor Dr, San Diego, CA 92122, Dir, Juv, Young Adult & Illus: Steven Malk *Tel:* 858-678-8767 *Fax:* 858-678-8530
Foreign Office(s): Writers House UK, c/o Good Business, 25 Gerrard St, London W1D 6JL, United Kingdom, Contact: Angharad Kowal *E-mail:* akowal@writershouse.com
Foreign Rep(s): Angharad Kowal (UK)
Foreign Rights: Ia Atterholm (Scandinavia); Bardon Agency (Taiwan); Eliane Benisti (France); Luigi Bernabo (Italy); Claude Choquette (Canada (French-speaking)); Raquel de la Concha (Portugal, Spain); DRT (Korea); Japan Uni (juv & young adult) (Japan); JLM Literary Agency (Greece); Simona Kessler (Romania); Ulla Lohren (Scandinavia); Aleksandra Matuszak (Poland); Jovan Milenkovic (Croatia, Montenegro, Serbia); Andrew Nurnberg Associates (Baltic States); The Owl's Agency (Japan); I Pikarski Literary Agency (Israel); Katalina Sabeva (Bulgaria); Karin Schindler (Brazil); Thomas Schlueck (Germany); Sebes & Van Gelderen Literary Agency (Netherlands); Synopsis Literary Agency (Russia); Petra Tobiskova (Czech Republic)

Writers' Productions (L-D)
PO Box 630, Westport, CT 06881-0630
Tel: 203-227-8199
Key Personnel
Owner & Pres: David L Meth *E-mail:* dlm67@mac.com
Founded: 1977
Literary quality fiction & nonfiction. Handle film, TV & licensing rights. Foreign Reps available as & where needed. No fees. No unsol mss; not accepting new clients. No mss or samples by e-mail. No phone calls.
Membership(s): Academy of American Poets; The Dramatists Guild of America; PEN American Center

Writers' Representatives LLC (L)
116 W 14 St, 11th fl, New York, NY 10011-7305
Tel: 212-620-9009 *Fax:* 212-620-0023
E-mail: transom@writersreps.com
Web Site: www.writersreps.com
Key Personnel
Principal: Lynn Chu; Glen Hartley *E-mail:* glen@writersreps.com
Founded: 1985
Represents authors of book-length works of nonfiction & literary fiction for adults. Once WR agrees to represent an author, we give advice on how best to structure or edit a book proposal, discuss ideas for book pojects & comment on finished ms material, with the goal of placing a book with the right publisher on the best possible terms for our author. We also discuss our authors' backgrounds & interests with publishers to promote upcoming projects or to find new ones. We sell to major publishers in the US & abroad.
Prefer to see ms material rather than synopses. Background about the author's professional experience, particularly that which is relevant to the book, as well as a list of previously published works. We respond within 4 to 6 weeks on average. We require that all authors fully advise us as to whether any project has been previously submitted to a publisher & what the response was & if the project has been submitted to another agent. Submissions should be accompanied by SASE; no reading fees.
Titles recently placed: *Duke: A Life of Duke Ellington*, Terry Teachout; *On Paper: The Everything of Its Two-Thousand-Year History*, Nicholas A. Basbanes
Foreign Rights: Agence Hoffman (Boris Hoffman) (France); Agencia Literaria Carmen Balcells (Anna Bofill) (Portugal); Agencia Literaria Carmen Balcells (Maribel Luque) (Spain); Tassy Barham Associates (Tassy Barham) (Brazil); Eggers & Landwehr KG (Petra Eggers) (Germany); Japan Uni Agency (Miko Yamanouchi) (Japan); Susanna Zevi Agencia Letteraria (Susanna Zevi) (Italy)

The Wylie Agency Inc (L)
250 W 57 St, Suite 2114, New York, NY 10107
Tel: 212-246-0069 *Fax:* 212-586-8953
E-mail: mail@wylieagency.com
Web Site: www.wylieagency.com
Key Personnel
Founder & Pres: Andrew Wylie
Literary Agent: Jin Auh; Sarah Chalfant; Jeffrey Posternak
Founded: 1980
Literary fiction & nonfiction; no unsol mss; query first with SASE. Handle film & TV rights. Contact for fee information.
Foreign Office(s): The Wylie Agency (UK) Ltd, 17 Bedford Sq, London WC1B 3JA, United Kingdom *Tel:* (020) 7908-5900 *Fax:* (020) 7908-5901 *E-mail:* mail@wylieagency.co.uk
Foreign Rights: The Wylie Agency (UK) Ltd (UK)

Mary Yost Books (L)
135 W 95 St, New York, NY 10025
Tel: 212-980-4988
E-mail: yostbooks59@aol.com
Founded: 1958
Psychology, women's topics. No unsol mss, query first. Submit outline & sample chapters. Representatives in many countries. Does not charge fees.
Foreign Rep(s): Abner Stein Agency (UK)
Foreign Rights: Ruth Liepman (Germany); Lennart Sane (Scandinavia)

The Young Agency (L)
115 W 29 St, 3rd fl, New York, NY 10001
Tel: 212-695-2431
Key Personnel
Prop: Marian Young
Founded: 1986
Fiction & nonfiction. No unsol mss; no reading fees. Handle film & TV rights after book is sold.

Zachary Shuster Harmsworth Agency (L-D)
1776 Broadway, Suite 1405, New York, NY 10019
Tel: 212-765-6900 *Fax:* 212-765-6490
Web Site: www.zshliterary.com
Key Personnel
Partner: Jennifer Gates *E-mail:* jgates@zshliterary.com; Esmond Harmsworth *E-mail:* eharmsworth@zshliterary.com; Todd Shuster *E-mail:* tshuster@zshliterary.com; Lane Zachary *E-mail:* lzachary@zshliterary.com
Literary Dir: Janet Silver *E-mail:* jsilver@zshliterary.com
Subs Rts Dir: Chelsey Heller
Agent: Elias Altman; Sarah Levitt; Nan Vermylen Thornton
At-Large Agent: Eve Bridburg
Affiliate Agent: Jane von Mehren; Bridget Wagner
Literary, commercial & genre fiction & nonfiction (except no science fiction or fantasy), mystery, thriller, non-category romance, biography, current affairs, business, psychology, memoir, science & history. Some young adult; no children's. No unsol mss, e-mail only query letters, full plot; synopsis or detailed chapters summary plus three sample chapters up to 50 pages. No mss returned without SASE. No reading fee.
Branch Office(s)
535 Boylston St, 11th fl, Boston, MA 02116, Contact: MaryBeth Chappell *Tel:* 617-262-2400 *Fax:* 617-262-2468
Foreign Rep(s): Esmond Harmsworth (UK)
Foreign Rights: Big Apple Agency Inc (China); Agencia Literaria BMSR (Brazil); Sandra Bruna Agency (Spain); Ann-Christine Danielson Agency (Scandinavia); The English Agency (Japan); Agence Hoffman (Germany); Japan UNI (Japan); Asli Karasuil Telif Haklari Ajansi ve Tic AS (Ms Asli Karasuil) (Turkey); Alexander Korzhenevski Agency (Alexander Korzhenevski) (Russia); Michelle Lapautre (France); Owl's (Japan); I Pikarski Ltd (Israel); Prava I Prevodi (Eastern Europe, Greece); Tuttle-Mori Agency Inc (Japan); Eric Yang Agency (Korea)

Barbara J Zitwer Agency (L-D)
525 West End Ave, Unit 11-H, New York, NY 10024
Tel: 212-501-8423 *Fax:* 646-514-0497
E-mail: zitwer@gmail.com
Key Personnel
Pres: Barbara J Zitwer *E-mail:* bjzitwerag@aol.com
Founded: 1991
Fiction & popular nonfiction; memoir, pop culture, pop psychology. Look for international authors.
No unsol mss. Electronic queries only. Will look at ms on exclusive basis only. No reading fee. Handle software only in conjunction with ancillary rights of a book. Handle film & TV rights with co-agents in Hollywood.
Titles recently placed: *The Savior (The Sudarium Trilogy)*, Leonard Foglia, David Richards; *The Son (The Sudarium Trilogy)*, Leonard Foglia,

David Richards; *The Surrogate (The Sudarium Trilogy)*, Leonard Foglia, David Richards

Foreign Rights: Gabriella Ambrosioni (Italy); Donatalla D'Ormesson (France); Anoukh Foerg Litteraire Agent (Germany); Grayhawk Agency (China, Taiwan); Imprima (Korea); International Editors' Co (Portugal, Spanish languages); I Pikarski Agency (Israel); Prava i Prevodi (Eastern Europe, Russia); Lenart Sane Agency (Scandinavia); Marianne Schoenbach Literary Agency; Tuttle-Mori Agency Inc (Japan)

Illustration Agents

Artists Associates
4416 La Jolla Dr, Bradenton, FL 34210-3927
Tel: 941-756-8445
Key Personnel
Dir: Bill Erlacher
Represents 9 artists.

Artworks Illustration
PO Box 453, New York, NY 10156
Tel: 212-239-4946
E-mail: artworksillustration@earthlink.net
Web Site: www.artworksillustration.com
Founded: 1990
Represents 30 artists.
Membership(s): Society of Illustrators

Carol Bancroft & Friends
PO Box 2030, Danbury, CT 06813
Tel: 203-730-8270 *Fax:* 203-730-8275
E-mail: cb_friends8270@sbcglobal.net
Web Site: www.carolbancroft.com
Key Personnel
Owner: Joy Elton Tricarico
Founded: 1972
Represents many fine illustrators specializing in art for children of all ages. Servicing the publishing industry including, but not limited to: picture/mass market books & educational materials. We work with packagers, studios, toy companies & corporations in addition to licensing art to related products. Promotional packets sent upon request. Unsol artwork not accepted.
Membership(s): Graphic Artists Guild; Society of Children's Book Writers & Illustrators; Society of Illustrators

Benoit & Associates
279 S Schuyler Ave, Kankakee, IL 60901
Tel: 815-932-2582 *Fax:* 815-932-2594
Web Site: www.benoit-associates.com
Key Personnel
Pres: Michael J Benoit *E-mail:* mbenoit@benoit-associates.com
Full service design & advertising studio. Specialize in technical & color airbrush illustration & computer generated art (Mac & IBM) design, art direction, in-house photography, elementary through college textbook cover & newsletters, brochures, letterheads & annual reports. High volume, high quality, quick turnaround & satisfaction guaranteed.

Bernstein & Andriulli Inc
58 W 40 St, 6th fl, New York, NY 10018
Tel: 212-682-1490 *Fax:* 212-286-1890
E-mail: info@ba-reps.com
Web Site: www.ba-reps.com
Key Personnel
Illustration: Louisa St Pierre
Commercial illustration & photography.
Represents 70 artists.

Bookmakers Ltd
32 Parkview Ave, Wolfville, NS B4P 2K8, Canada
Tel: 902-697-2569
Web Site: bookmakersltd.com
Key Personnel
Owner & Pres: Reg Ogilvie *E-mail:* reg@bookmakersltd.com
Owner & Contact: June Ogilvie *E-mail:* june@bookmakersltd.com
Founded: 1975
Represents a group of the best children's book illustrators in the business & continues to also provide a full range of book design & production services.
Represents 25 artists.
Membership(s): Society of Children's Book Writers & Illustrators

Byer-Sprinzeles Agency
5800 Arlington Ave, Suite 16-C, Riverdale, NY 10471
Tel: 718-543-9399
Web Site: www.maggiebyersprinzeles.com
Key Personnel
Agent: Maggie Byer-Sprinzeles *E-mail:* maggie@maggiebyersprinzeles.com
Founded: 1991
Represents children's book illustrators.
Represents 27 artists.
Membership(s): Society of Children's Book Writers & Illustrators

Cornell & McCarthy LLC
2-D Cross Hwy, Westport, CT 06880
Tel: 203-454-4210
E-mail: contact@cmartreps.com
Web Site: www.cmartreps.com
Key Personnel
Partner: Merial Cornell; Pat McCarthy
Founded: 1989
Professional illustrators, specializing in the children's book markets; educational, trade & mass market. Representing over 35 artists with a variety of styles & techniques.
Membership(s): Graphic Artists Guild; Society of Children's Book Writers & Illustrators

Craven Design Inc
1202 Lexington Ave, Box 242, New York, NY 10028
Tel: 212-288-1022 *Fax:* 212-249-9910
E-mail: cravendesign@mac.com
Web Site: www.cravendesignstudios.com
Key Personnel
Artist Rep: Meryl Jones
Founded: 1981
Artist's representative: book illustration (text & trade), juvenile through adult; humorous, realistic, decorative & technical; maps, charts, graphs.
Represents 30 artists.

Creative Arts of Ventura
PO Box 684, Ventura, CA 93002-0684
Tel: 805-643-4160; 805-654-1927
Web Site: www.sculpture-museum.com
Key Personnel
Owner & Artist: Don Ulrich *E-mail:* ulrichxcal@aol.com; Lamia Ulrich
Founded: 1973 (gallery/studio)
Specialize in fine art, mixed media (from 2002-2005) wall sculptures curated by US State Department for the US Embassy in Riga Latvia. Painting & sculpture-abstract, public art sculpture design, lyric poetry, exhibitions & logos.
Represents 4 artists.

Deborah Wolfe Ltd
731 N 24 St, Philadelphia, PA 19130
Tel: 215-232-6666 *Fax:* 215-232-6585
E-mail: info@illustrationonline.com
Web Site: www.illustrationonline.com
Founded: 1978
Commercial illustrators & animators representative.
Represents 30 artists.

Fort Ross Inc - International Representation for Artists
Division of Fort Ross Inc
26 Arthur Place, Yonkers, NY 10701
Tel: 914-375-6448; 718-775-8340
Web Site: www.fortrossinc.com
Key Personnel
Pres & Exec Dir: Dr Vladimir P Kartsev *E-mail:* vkartsev2000@gmail.com
Founded: 1992
Foreign sales of secondary rights for illustrations, photographs & covers made by American & Canadian artists. Representation of Russian & East European artists & photographers in the USA & Canada.
Represents 50 artists.

Foto Expression International (Toronto)
266 Charlotte St, Suite 297, Peterborough, ON K9J 2V4, Canada
Tel: 705-745-5770
E-mail: operations@fotopressnews.org
Web Site: www.fotopressnews.org
Key Personnel
Owner & Opers Dir: John Milan Kubik
Founded: 1983

Carol Guenzi Agents Inc
Subsidiary of Artagent.com
865 Delaware St, Denver, CO 80204
Tel: 303-820-2599 *Toll Free Tel:* 800-417-5120 *Fax:* 303-820-2598
E-mail: info@artagent.com; art@artagent.com
Web Site: www.artagent.com
Key Personnel
Pres: Carol Guenzi
Founded: 1984
A wide selection of talent in all areas of visual communications.
Represents 30 artists.
Membership(s): AIGA, the professional association for design; Art Directors Club of Denver

The Charlotte Gusay Literary Agency
10532 Blythe Ave, Los Angeles, CA 90064
Tel: 310-559-0831 *Fax:* 310-559-2639
E-mail: gusay1@ca.rr.com (queries only)
Web Site: www.gusay.com
Founded: 1988
Selectively represent children's book artists & illustrators.

Herman Agency
350 Central Park W, Apt 4I, New York, NY 10025
Tel: 212-749-4907
Web Site: www.hermanagencyinc.com
Key Personnel
Owner & Pres: Ronnie Ann Herman *E-mail:* ronnie@hermanagencyinc.com
Founded: 1999
Represent illustrators, authors & author/illustrators of children's books, trade & educational.
Represents 23 artists.
Membership(s): The Authors Guild; Society of Children's Book Writers & Illustrators

The Ivy League of Artists Inc
7 Coventry Rd, Livingston, NJ 07039-5105
Tel: 973-992-4048 *Fax:* 973-992-4049
E-mail: ilartists@comcast.net
Key Personnel
Owner & Pres: Ivy Mindlin
Illustration, spot drawings, comps, storyboards, design, infographics, PowerPoint & mechanical art.

Levy Creative Management LLC
425 E 58 St, Suite 37F, New York, NY 10022
Tel: 212-687-6463 *Fax:* 212-661-4839
E-mail: info@levycreative.com
Web Site: www.levycreative.com
Key Personnel
Pres & Founder: Sari Schorr *E-mail:* sari@levycreative.com
Founded: 1996
Boutique agency representing only award-winning international artists.

Lindgren & Smith
888C Eighth Ave, No 329, New York, NY 10019
Tel: 212-397-7330
E-mail: info@lindgrensmith.com
Web Site: lindgrensmith.com
Key Personnel
Owner: Pat Lindgren *E-mail:* pat@lindgrensmith.com; Piper Smith *E-mail:* piper@lindgrensmith.com
Founded: 1987
Do not accept mss; examples of illustrator's work can be requested via e-mail. The best way to contact us is by e-mail.
Represents 25 artists.

Lott Representatives
PO Box 3607, New York, NY 10163
Tel: 212-755-5737
Web Site: www.lottreps.com
Key Personnel
Pres: Peter Lott *E-mail:* peter@lottreps.com
Represent commercial illustrators.

MB Artists
775 Sixth Ave, Suite 6, New York, NY 10001
Tel: 212-689-7830 *Fax:* 212-689-7829
Web Site: www.mbartists.com
Key Personnel
Pres & Agent: Mela Bolinao *E-mail:* mela@mbartists.com
Founded: 1986
Represents illustrators whose work is intended for juvenile market.
Represents 64 artists.
Membership(s): The Children's Book Council; Graphic Artists Guild; Society of Children's Book Writers & Illustrators; Society of Illustrators

Melissa Turk & the Artist Network
9 Babbling Brook Lane, Suffern, NY 10901
Tel: 845-368-8606 *Fax:* 845-368-8608
E-mail: melissa@melissaturk.com
Web Site: www.melissaturk.com
Key Personnel
Contact: Dorothy Ziff
Founded: 1986
Represents professional artists supplying quality illustration, calligraphy & cartography. Specialize in children's trade & educational illustration as well as natural science illustration (wildlife, botanical, medical, etc), publishing & interpretive signage.
Represents 12 artists.
Membership(s): Graphic Artists Guild; Society of Children's Book Writers & Illustrators

Morgan Gaynin Inc
149 Madison Ave, Suite 1140, New York, NY 10016
Tel: 212-475-0440
E-mail: info@morgangaynin.com
Web Site: www.morgangaynin.com
Key Personnel
Owner, Principal & Rep: Gail Gaynin
Rep: Kate Kelly
Founded: 1974
Illustrator's representative.
Represents 40 artists.
Membership(s): Graphic Artists Guild; Society of Children's Book Writers & Illustrators; Society of Illustrators

Wanda Nowak Creative Illustrators Agency
231 E 76 St, Suite 5-D, New York, NY 10021
Tel: 212-535-0438
E-mail: wanda@wandanow.com
Web Site: www.wandanow.com
Key Personnel
Pres: Wanda Nowak
Founded: 1995
Children's trade books, elementary & secondary textbook illustration & book cover illustration.
Represents 16 artists.

Painted-Words Inc
310 W 97 St, Suite 24, New York, NY 10025
Tel: 212-663-2311 *Fax:* 212-663-2891
E-mail: info@painted-words.com
Web Site: www.painted-words.com
Key Personnel
Agent: Lori Nowicki *E-mail:* lori@painted-words.com
Founded: 1992 (as Lori Nowicki & Associates)
Artist & literary agent.
Represents 41 artists.
Membership(s): Society of Children's Book Writers & Illustrators

Portfolio Solutions LLC
136 Jameson Hill Rd, Clinton Corners, NY 12514
Tel: 845-266-1001
Web Site: www.portfoliosolutionsllc.com
Key Personnel
Owner & Agent: Bernadette Szost *E-mail:* b.szost@portfoliosolutionsllc.com
Founded: 1999
Agency representing illustrators of children's books & related materials.
Represents 35 artists.
Membership(s): The Authors Guild; Society of Children's Book Writers & Illustrators

Publishers' Graphics Inc
231 Judd Rd, Easton, CT 06612-1025
Tel: 203-445-1511 *Fax:* 203-445-1411
E-mail: sales@publishersgraphics.com
Web Site: www.publishersgraphics.com
Key Personnel
Pres: Paige Gillies *E-mail:* paigeg@publishersgraphics.com
Founded: 1970
Represents 3 artists.

Gerald & Cullen Rapp
420 Lexington Ave, New York, NY 10170
Tel: 212-889-3337 *Fax:* 212-889-3341
E-mail: info@rappart.com
Web Site: www.rappart.com
Key Personnel
Rep: Nancy Moore *Tel:* 212-889-3337 ext 103 *E-mail:* nancy@rappart.com
Founded: 1944
Represent leading commercial illustrators on an exclusive basis. Sell to magazine & book publishers, ad agencies, design firms & major corporations.
Represents 60 artists.
Membership(s): Graphic Artists Guild; Society of Illustrators

Kerry Reilly: Representatives
1826 Asheville Place, Charlotte, NC 28203
Tel: 704-372-6007
E-mail: kerry@reillyreps.com
Web Site: www.reillyreps.com
Illustration & photography.
Represents 25 artists.

Renaissance House
Imprint of Laredo Publishing Co Inc
465 Westview Ave, Englewood, NJ 07631
Tel: 201-408-4048 *Fax:* 201-408-5011
E-mail: laredo@renaissancehouse.net; info@renaissancehouse.net
Web Site: www.renaissancehouse.net
Founded: 1991
Book developer that specializes in children's books, educational materials & bilingual market (English/Spanish). Represents illustrators who specialize in art for children that provide a wide variety of styles & techniques. Services the advertising & publishing industries, including children's books & educational materials. Multicultural artists are available. Promotional booklet sent upon request.
Represents 90 artists.

Rosenthal Represents
3850 Eddingham Ave, Calabasas, CA 91302
Tel: 818-222-5445 *Fax:* 818-222-5650
E-mail: eliselicenses@earthlink.net
Web Site: www.rosenthalrepresents.com
Key Personnel
Pres: Elise Rosenthal
Sales & Mktg & Artists Rep: Neil Sandler
Founded: 1979
Illustrate book covers, children's & adult books. Licensing agents.
Represents 35 artists.
Membership(s): LIMA; Society of Illustrators

Salzman International
1751 Charles Ave, Arcata, CA 95521
Tel: 415-285-8267; 212-997-0115 (NY) *Fax:* 707-822-5500
Web Site: www.salzint.com
Key Personnel
Owner: Richard Salzman *E-mail:* rs@salzint.com
Founded: 1982
Agents for visual artists for educational & trade books specializing in art illustrators. Feature art for magazines & periodicals. Editorial services available.
Represents 25 artists.

Richard W Salzman Artists' Representative, see Salzman International

The Schuna Group Inc
1503 Briarknoll Dr, Arden Hills, MN 55112
Tel: 651-631-8480
Web Site: www.schunagroup.com
Key Personnel
Pres: Jo Anne Schuna *E-mail:* joanne@schunagroup.com
Represents 12 artists.

Storybook Arts Inc
414 Poplar Hill Rd, Dover Plains, NY 12522
Mailing Address: PO Box 672, Dover Plains, NY 12522
Tel: 845-877-3305
Web Site: www.storybookartsinc.com
Key Personnel
Owner & Pres: Janet De Carlo *E-mail:* janet@storybookartsinc.com
Founded: 2005

Artist representative agency.
Represents 23 artists.
Membership(s): Society of Children's Book Writers & Illustrators

Christina A Tugeau Artist Agency LLC
3009 Margaret Jones Lane, Williamsburg, VA 23185
Tel: 757-221-0666; 917-434-3141
E-mail: chris@catugeau.com
Web Site: www.catugeau.com
Key Personnel
Owner & Rep: Christina Tugeau
Partner: Christy Ewers *E-mail:* christy@catugeau.com
Founded: 1994
Represents North American illustrators for children's publishing: mass market & trade books, educational (preschool through young adult). Agency effectively closed to new artists but will view e-mail samples.
Represents 30 artists.
Membership(s): Society of Children's Book Writers & Illustrators

Tugeau 2 Inc
2231 Grandview Ave, Cleveland Heights, OH 44106
Tel: 216-707-0854 *Fax:* 216-795-8404
Web Site: www.tugeau2.com
Key Personnel
Owner: Nicole Tugeau *E-mail:* nicole@tugeau2.com
Founded: 2003
Agency for artist representation in the children's publishing industry.
Represents 35 artists.
Membership(s): Society of Children's Book Writers & Illustrators

WendyLynn & Co
504 Wilson Rd, Annapolis, MD 21401
Tel: 410-224-2729; 410-507-1059
Web Site: wendylynn.com
Key Personnel
Pres & Illustration Agent: Wendy Mays *E-mail:* wendy@wendylynn.com
Busn Mgr & Illustration Agent: Janice Onken *E-mail:* janice@wendylynn.com
Founded: 2002
Specialize in the children's publishing market. Represent & promote our illustrators to publishing companies which produce work for children & young adults.
Represents 35 artists.
Membership(s): Society of Children's Book Writers & Illustrators

Wilkinson Studios Inc
1121 E Main St, Suite 310, St Charles, IL 60174
Tel: 630-549-0504
Web Site: www.wilkinsonstudios.com
Key Personnel
Founder & Pres: Christine Wilkinson *E-mail:* chris@wilkinsonstudios.com
VP: Lisa O'Hara *E-mail:* lisa@wilkinsonstudios.com
Founded: 1999
Specializing in representing illustrators & managing art programs for educational, trade book & mass market publishing, children's magazines, games & related fields. Over 100 illustrators offering age appropriate artwork for pre-K through college in a wide range of styles, techniques & media, both conventional & electronic. Project management of large volume blackline or color illustration programs by dedicated staff with art & design backgrounds, working directly with the publisher or interfacing with design & development house vendors.
Represents 100 artists.
Membership(s): Graphic Artists Guild; Society of Children's Book Writers & Illustrators

Lecture Agents

Listed below are some of the most active lecture agents who handle tours and single engagements for writers.

American Program Bureau Inc
313 Washington St, Suite 225, Newton, MA 02458
Tel: 617-965-6600 *Toll Free Tel:* 800-225-4575 *Fax:* 617-965-6610
E-mail: apb@apbspeakers.com
Web Site: www.apbspeakers.com
Key Personnel
VP, Speaker Rel & New Busn: Ken Eisenstein *Tel:* 617-614-1612 *E-mail:* keisenstein@apbspeakers.com
Founded: 1965
Lecture representation/speakers bureau. Branches located in Princeton, NJ & San Diego, CA.
Membership(s): International Association of Speakers Bureaus; NACA

Authors Unlimited Inc
31 E 32 St, Suite 300, New York, NY 10016
Tel: 212-481-8484 (ext 336) *Fax:* 212-481-9582
Web Site: www.authorsunlimited.com
Key Personnel
Pres: Arlynn Greenbaum *E-mail:* arlynnj@cs.com
Founded: 1991
Speakers bureau representing over 400 authors of adult trade books. Arrange speaking engagements with colleges, libraries, corporations, trade associations & the like.
Membership(s): International Association of Speakers Bureaus; Women's Media Group

The Barnabas Agency
Division of The B&B Media Group Inc
PO Box 3113, Corsicana, TX 75110-3113
Toll Free Tel: 800-927-0517
E-mail: info@barnabasagency.com
Web Site: www.barnabasagency.com
Key Personnel
Pres/CEO: Tina Jacobson *Tel:* 800-927-0517 ext 101 *E-mail:* tina@barnabasagency.com
VP/COO: Rick Roberson *Tel:* 800-927-0517 ext 100 *E-mail:* rick@barnabasagency.com
VP of PR: Diane Morrow *Tel:* 800-927-1517 *E-mail:* diane@barnabasagency.com
Founded: 2002
Objectives: To increase recognition of the client, his/her ministry, products & service; to establish client's credibility, help achieve long-term & short-term goals & help client develop a vision. Services range from consulting to full-scale personal management of the client & implementation of the various components of the campaign.

Burns Entertainment & Sports Marketing
820 Davis St, Suite 222, Evanston, IL 60201
Tel: 847-866-9400 *Fax:* 847-491-9778
E-mail: burnsl@burnsent.com
Web Site: burnsent.com
Key Personnel
CEO & COO: Bob Williams
Pres & Gen Coun: Marc Ippolito
Pres: Doug Shabelman
Founded: 1970
Sports & entertainment marketing, match corporations with talent celebrities for appearances, speeches & endorsements.

CreativeWell Inc
PO Box 3130, Memorial Sta, Upper Montclair, NJ 07043
Tel: 973-783-7575 *Toll Free Tel:* 800-743-9182 *Fax:* 973-783-7530
E-mail: info@creativewell.com
Web Site: www.creativewell.com
Key Personnel
Pres: George M Greenfield *E-mail:* george@creativewell.com
Founded: 2003
Literary, lecture & arts management.

The Fischer Ross Group Inc
75 Holly Hill Lane, Suite 100, Greenwich, CT 06830
Tel: 203-622-4950 *Fax:* 203-531-4132
E-mail: frgstaff@frg-speakers.com
Web Site: www.frg-speakers.com
Key Personnel
Pres: Grada Fischer
Exclusive lecture agents for authors (fiction, nonfiction, trade) & journalists (print & broadcast), as well as nationally known celebrities & personalities. Arrange lecture tours, individual speaking engagements, product endorsements, public openings & appearances for the university, association & corporate markets.

Greater Talent Network Inc
437 Fifth Ave, New York, NY 10016
Tel: 212-645-4200 *Toll Free Tel:* 800-326-4211 *Fax:* 212-627-1471
E-mail: info@greatertalent.com
Web Site: www.greatertalent.com
Key Personnel
CEO: Don R Epstein
Founded: 1981
Exclusive lecture & entertainment management. Represent authors, journalists & nationally & internationally known individuals. Arrange speaking engagements & tours for corporations, associations, colleges & universities, town halls, hospitals & other organizations, as well as literary, motion picture, television & radio representation.
Membership(s): International Association of Speakers Bureaus

ICM Lecture Division
Division of International Creative Management
730 Fifth Ave, New York, NY 10019
Tel: 212-556-5600 *Fax:* 212-556-5665
Web Site: www.icmtalent.com
Key Personnel
Dir: Betsy Berg *Tel:* 212-556-5676
Exclusively represents a long list of authors, entertainers & distinguished clients & celebrities from all fields for lectures & personal appearances.
Branch Office(s)
10250 Constellation Blvd, Los Angeles, CA 90067 *Tel:* 310-550-4000
Marlborough House, 3rd fl, 10 Earlham St, London WC2H 9LN, United Kingdom *Tel:* (020) 7836 8564

International Entertainment Bureau
3612 N Washington Blvd, Indianapolis, IN 46205-3592
Tel: 317-926-7566
E-mail: ieb@prodigy.net
Key Personnel
Founder: David Leonards
Founded: 1972
Database, resource center & clearing house. Information on speakers, celebrities & entertainers available in the marketplace. Planning, consulting, booking & producing.
Membership(s): Indiana Association of Fairs, Festivals & Events; Indiana Society of Association Executives; Meeting Professionals International

Eddie Kritzer Productions
Subsidiary of The Kritzer Entertainment Group
1112 Montana Ave, Suite 449, Santa Monica, CA 90403
Tel: 310-702-5356 *Fax:* 310-394-5770
E-mail: producedby@aol.com
Web Site: eddiekritzer.com
Key Personnel
CEO & Pres: Eddie Kritzer
Founded: 1983
Produce corporate shows for conventions & meetings. "A Night At The Improv" will write, create & produce comedy shows & corporate videos. Created Rockline Live National Radio Show. Produce shows worldwide, TV movies & movie specials. Accept submissions for mss, prefer nonfiction. Also produces movies. See web site for details.

BK Nelson Inc Lecture Bureau
Division of BK Nelson Inc
1565 Paseo Vida, Palm Springs, CA 92264
Tel: 760-778-8800 *Fax:* 760-778-6242
E-mail: bknelson4@cs.com
Web Site: www.bknelson.com; www.bknelsonlecturebureau.com; www.nelsonbookmovielecture.com; www.bknelsonmovieproduction.com
Key Personnel
Pres & CEO: Bonita K Nelson
CFO: Corp Reed
VP: John W Benson
Edit Dir: Tony Pastor
Acctg Dept: Erv Rosenfeld
Founded: 1998
Book authors & personalities, experts in diverse fields. Arrange seminars & keynote speaking engagements. Speechwriting/coaching. Publish BK Nelson's Speaker's Directory with photos each year. Online booking. Certification status granted by New York State Department of Economic Development.
Membership(s): American Association of University Women; The Authors Guild; The Dramatists Guild of America; Motion Picture Alliance; NACA

Penguin Random House Speakers Bureau
1745 Broadway, Mail Drop 13-1, New York, NY 10019
Tel: 212-572-2013
E-mail: speakers@penguinrandomhouse.com
Web Site: www.prhspeakers.com
Key Personnel
Exec Dir: Tiffany Tomlin
Agent Dir: Jayme Boucher *Tel:* 212-572-7309 *E-mail:* jboucher@randomhouse.com; Mary Coyne *Tel:* 212-572-2247 *E-mail:* mcoyne@randomhouse.com; Kathy Dunn *Tel:* 631-283-5923 *E-mail:* kdunn@randomhouse.com; Kim Thornton Ingenito *Tel:* 212-572-2299 *E-mail:* kthornton@randomhouse.com; Wade Lucas *Tel:* 212-572-6113 *E-mail:* walucas@randomhouse.com; Caitlin McCaskey *Tel:* 212-

572-8661 *E-mail:* cmccaskey@randomhouse.com
Agent Dir, Random House Children's: Christine Labov
Asst Agent Dir: Lisa Barnes
Assoc: Stasia Whalen
Mgr: Erin Simpson; Elaine Trevorrow *Tel:* 212-572-2175 *E-mail:* etrevorrow@randomhouse.com
Mktg Mgr: Stefanie Von Beoczy *Tel:* 212-572-2398 *E-mail:* svonbeoczy@randomhouse.com
Coord: Jessie Garretson *Tel:* 212-572-2396 *E-mail:* jgarretson@randomhouse.com
Founded: 2006
Full service lecture agency that represents best-selling authors, literary legends, cutting-edge thinkers & current tastemakers.
Membership(s): International Association of Speakers Bureaus

Random House Speakers Bureau, see Penguin Random House Speakers Bureau

Royce Carlton Inc
866 United Nations Plaza, Suite 587, New York, NY 10017-1880
Tel: 212-355-7700 *Toll Free Tel:* 800-LECTURE (532-8873) *Fax:* 212-888-8659
E-mail: info@roycecarlton.com
Web Site: www.roycecarlton.com
Key Personnel
Pres: Carlton Sedgeley *Tel:* 212-822-0999 *E-mail:* carlton@roycecarlton.com
EVP: Lucy Lepage *Tel:* 212-822-0979 *E-mail:* lucy@roycecarlton.com
VP: Helen Churko *Tel:* 212-822-0981 *E-mail:* helen@roycecarlton.com
Founded: 1968
Agents, managers & brokers for speakers.

Jodi Solomon Speakers Bureau
295 Huntington Ave, Suite 211, Boston, MA 02115
Tel: 617-266-3450 *Fax:* 617-266-5660
E-mail: jodi@jodisolomon.biz
Web Site: www.jodisolomonspeakers.com

The Tuesday Agency
132 1/2 E Washington St, Iowa City, IA 52240
Tel: 319-338-7080
E-mail: trinity@tuesdayagency.com
Web Site: tuesdayagency.com
Key Personnel
Pres: Trinity Ray
VP: Kevin Mills
Founded: 2011
Exclusive speaker representation.

World Class Speakers & Entertainers
5200 Kanan Rd, Suite 210, Agoura Hills, CA 91301
Tel: 818-991-5400
E-mail: wcse@wcspeakers.com
Web Site: www.wcspeakers.com
Key Personnel
Pres: Joseph I Kessler *E-mail:* jkessler@wcspeakers.com
Founded: 1970
Represents world class speakers & entertainers. Database of 25,000 speakers & entertainers; directory/guide available.

Writers' League of Texas (WLT)
611 S Congress Ave, Suite 200 A-3, Austin, TX 78704
Tel: 512-499-8914
E-mail: wlt@writersleague.org
Web Site: www.writersleague.org
Key Personnel
Prog Dir: Jennifer Ziegler *E-mail:* jennifer@writersleague.org
Founded: 1981

Associations, Events, Courses & Awards

Book Trade & Allied Associations — Index

LITERARY

MAGAZINE & PRESS

MEDIA - COMMUNICATIONS

PUBLISHING

PUBLISHING SERVICES

WRITERS

Book Trade & Allied Associations

Listed here are associations and organizations that are concerned with books, literacy, language and speech, media and communications as well as groups who provide services to the publishing community.

AAP PreK-12 Learning Group
Division of Association of American Publishers (AAP)
325 Chestnut St, Suite 1110, Philadelphia, PA 19106
Tel: 267-351-4310 *Fax:* 267-351-4317
E-mail: prek12learning@publishers.org
Web Site: www.aepweb.org
Key Personnel
Exec Dir: Jay Diskey *Tel:* 202-220-4549 *E-mail:* jdiskey@publishers.org
Sr Dir: Susan Fletcher *Tel:* 267-351-4314 *E-mail:* sfletcher@publishers.org
Strategic Partnerships Exec: Jo-Ann McDevitt *Tel:* 267-351-4327 *E-mail:* jmcdevitt@publishers.org
Dir, Policy & Res: Julie Copty *Tel:* 202-220-4548 *E-mail:* jcopty@publishers.org
Edit Dir: Stacey Pusey *Tel:* 267-351-4331 *E-mail:* spusey@publishers.org
Dir of Digital Initiatives: Dave Gladney *Tel:* 267-351-4329 *E-mail:* dgladney@publishers.org
Awards Prog Mgr: Linda Swank *Tel:* 267-351-4322 *E-mail:* lswank@publishers.org
Membership Servs Mgr: Brittany Lawrence *Tel:* 267-351-4316 *E-mail:* blawrence@publishers.org
Admin/Mktg Assoc: Rachel Burgos *Tel:* 267-351-4320 *E-mail:* rburgos@publishers.org
Founded: 2013 (merger of AAP School Division & Association of Educational Publishers (AEP))
Supports educational publishing through its programs & member services.
Number of Members: 350
2016 Meeting(s): Content in Context (CIC), Loews Philadelphia Hotel, Philadelphia, PA, June 6-8, 2016
Branch Office(s)
455 Massachusetts Ave, Suite 700, Washington, DC 20001 *Tel:* 202-347-3375 *Fax:* 202-347-3690

AAR, see Association of Authors' Representatives Inc

ABAC/ALAC
368 Dalhousie St, Suite 301, Ottawa, ON K1N 7G3, Canada
Tel: 416-364-2376
E-mail: info@abac.org
Web Site: www.abac.org
Key Personnel
Pres: Liam McGahern
Treas: Michael Park
Founded: 1966
The association's aim is to foster an interest in rare books & mss & to maintain high standards in the antiquarian book trades.
Number of Members: 70
Publication(s): *ABAC/ALAC Membership Directory* (free by request)
Membership(s): International League of Antiquarian Booksellers

The Academy of American Poets Inc
75 Maiden Lane, Suite 901, New York, NY 10038
Tel: 212-274-0343 *Fax:* 212-274-9427
E-mail: academy@poets.org
Web Site: www.poets.org
Key Personnel
Exec Dir: Jennifer Benka
Awards Coord & Exec Asst: Alex Dimitrov *Tel:* 212-274-0343 ext 15 *E-mail:* adimitrov@poets.org
Founded: 1934
The country's largest nonprofit association devoted to poetry. Sponsors the James Laughlin Poetry Award, Walt Whitman Award, Harold Morton Landon Translation Award, Wallace Stevens Award, Lenore Marshall Poetry Prize & annual college poetry prizes; workshops for high school students; award fellowship to American poets for distinguished poetic achievement; presents an annual national series of poetry readings & symposia. Publishes biannual journal. Also administers the National Poetry Month.
Number of Members: 6,000
Publication(s): *American Poet* (biannual, newsletter)

Academy of Motion Picture Arts & Sciences (AMPAS)
8949 Wilshire Blvd, Beverly Hills, CA 90211
Tel: 310-247-3000 *Fax:* 310-859-9619
E-mail: ampas@oscars.org
Web Site: www.oscars.org
Key Personnel
CEO: Dawn Hudson
To advance the arts & sciences of motion pictures & to foster cooperation among the creative leadership of the motion picture industry for cultural, educational & technological progress. Confer annual awards of merit, serving as a constant incentive within the industry & focusing public attention upon the best in motion pictures.
Number of Members: 5,024
Publication(s): *Academy Players Directory, Annual Index to Motion Picture Credits, Nominations & Winners, List of Eligible Releases* (bulletin)

Academy of Television Arts & Sciences (ATAS), see Television Academy

Access Copyright, The Canadian Copyright Licensing Agency
56 Wellesley St W, Suite 401A, Toronto, ON M5S 2S3, Canada
Tel: 416-868-1620 *Toll Free Tel:* 800-893-5777 *Fax:* 416-868-1621
E-mail: info@accesscopyright.ca
Web Site: www.accesscopyright.ca
Key Personnel
Exec Dir: Roanie Levy
Founded: 1988
Number of Members: 36
Publication(s): *Online Access* (quarterly, newsletter, free, electronic)
Membership(s): Book & Periodical Council; International Federation of Reproduction Rights Organizations

Advertising Research Foundation (ARF)
432 Park Ave S, 6th fl, New York, NY 10016-8013
Tel: 212-751-5656 *Fax:* 212-319-5265
E-mail: info@thearf.org; jar@thearf.org (edit)
Web Site: www.thearf.org
Key Personnel
CEO & Pres: Gayle Fuguitt
EVP, Digital: Ted McConnell
EVP, Res & Innovation: Don Gloeckler *Tel:* 646-465-5725
Ed-in-Chief: Geoffrey Precourt
Mng Ed: Nanette Burns *Tel:* 646-465-5728 *E-mail:* nanette@thearf.org
Leadership Progs Mgr: Zena Pagan *Tel:* 646-465-5721 *E-mail:* zena@thearf.org
Founded: 1936
Advertising research service trade association.
2016 Meeting(s): The ARF Annual Convention & Insights Zone (also known as Re:think), New York Hilton, New York, NY, March 13-16, 2016
Publication(s): *Journal of Advertising Research (JAR)* (quarterly, $365 standard subn; includes 4 print issues & a 2 yr online archive)

AIGA, the professional association for design
233 Broadway, 17th fl, New York, NY 10279
Tel: 212-807-1990 *Fax:* 212-807-1799
E-mail: general@aiga.org
Web Site: www.aiga.org
Key Personnel
COO: Denise Wood *Tel:* 212-710-3135 *E-mail:* denise_wood@aiga.org
CEO & Exec Dir: Richard Grefe *Tel:* 212-710-3100 *E-mail:* grefe@aiga.org
Mng Ed: Rebecca Sears *Tel:* 212-710-3123
Founded: 1914
National nonprofit organization for graphic design profession. Organizes competitions, exhibitions, publications, educational activities & projects in the public interest to promote excellence in the graphic design industry.
Number of Members: 25,000
New Election: Annually in June
2016 Meeting(s): AIGA Design Conference, Las Vegas, NV, Oct 17-19, 2016

ALA Editions, see The American Library Association (ALA)

Alcuin Society
PO Box 3216, Vancouver, BC V6B 3X8, Canada
Tel: 604-733-1204; 604-732-5403
E-mail: info@alcuinsociety.com
Web Site: www.alcuinsociety.com
Judges book design; publishes articles on book arts, collecting, typography, private presses, book collections, book binding.
Number of Members: 321
Publication(s): *Amphora* (3 issues/yr, journal, $50/yr membs, $75 instns)
Membership(s): Fellowship of American Bibliophilic Societies

Alliance for Audited Media (AAM)
48 W Seegers Rd, Arlington Heights, IL 60005
Tel: 224-366-6939 *Fax:* 224-366-6949
Web Site: www.auditedmedia.com
Key Personnel
CEO, Pres & Mng Dir: Tom Drouillard *Tel:* 224-366-6500 *E-mail:* tom.drouillard@auditedmedia.com
Cooperative association of advertisers, advertising agencies & publishers of newspapers, magazines, farm & business publications. Audit & report circulation, web site & additional digital

edition analytics, including mobile application activity for publisher brands in North America.
Number of Members: 4,500
Branch Office(s)
The Chanin Bldg, 122 E 42 St, Suite 807, New York, NY 10168-0899 *Tel:* 212-867-8992 *Fax:* 212-867-8947
151 Bloor St W, Suite 850, Toronto, ON M5S 1S4, Canada, VP & Gen Mgr: Joan Brehl *Tel:* 416-962-5840 *Fax:* 416-962-5844 *E-mail:* joan.brehl@auditedmedia.com *Web Site:* www.auditedmedia.com

Alliance for Audited Media (AAM), Canadian Office
151 Bloor St W, Suite 850, Toronto, ON M5S 1S4, Canada
Tel: 416-962-5840 *Fax:* 416-962-5844
Web Site: www.auditmedia.com
Key Personnel
VP & Gen Mgr: Joan Brehl *Tel:* 416-962-5840 ext 224 *E-mail:* joan.brehl@auditmedia.com
Number of Members: 4,500

Alliance for Women in Media (AWM)
1250 24 St NW, Suite 300, Washington, DC 20037
Tel: 202-750-3664 *Fax:* 202-750-3664
E-mail: info@allwomeninmedia.org
Web Site: allwomeninmedia.org
Key Personnel
Exec Dir: Becky Brooks
Founded: 1951
For members of the electronic & media industries.
Number of Members: 3,000
Publication(s): *FastForward* (enewsletter)

American Academy of Arts & Sciences (AAAS)
Norton's Woods, 136 Irving St, Cambridge, MA 02138
Tel: 617-576-5000 *Fax:* 617-576-5050
E-mail: aaas@amacad.org
Web Site: www.amacad.org
Key Personnel
Pres: Jonathan Fanton
Promote interchange of ideas through seminars & publications.
Number of Members: 6,000
Publication(s): *Daedalus*

American Academy of Political & Social Science
202 S 36 St, Philadelphia, PA 19104-3806
Tel: 215-746-6500 *Fax:* 215-573-2667
Web Site: www.aapss.org
Key Personnel
Exec Dir: Tom Kecskemethy *Tel:* 215-746-7321 *E-mail:* thomask@asc.upenn.edu
Assoc Dir & Mng Ed: Emily Wood *Tel:* 215-898-5081 *E-mail:* ewood@asc.upenn.edu
Founded: 1889
Publication(s): *The Annals of American Academy of Political & Social Science* (6 issues/yr, $112/yr indivs, $898/yr instns, $824/yr instns (e-access), $916/yr (print & e-access))

American Antiquarian Society (AAS)
185 Salisbury St, Worcester, MA 01609-1634
Tel: 508-755-5221 *Fax:* 508-753-3311
E-mail: library@americanantiquarian.org
Web Site: www.americanantiquarian.org
Key Personnel
Pres: Ellen S Dunlap *Tel:* 508-471-2161 *E-mail:* edunlap@mwa.org
Founded: 1812
Maintain research library in American history & culture through 1876.
Number of Members: 1,028

American Association for the Advancement of Science (AAAS)
1200 New York Ave NW, Washington, DC 20005
Tel: 202-326-6400
Web Site: www.aaas.org
Key Personnel
CEO: Alan I Leschner
Dir, Exec Off Aff: Gretchen Seiler
Founded: 1848
Mission is to further the work of scientists, to facilitate cooperation among them, foster scientific freedom & responsibility, improve effectiveness of science in the promotion of human welfare & to increase public understanding & appreciation of the importance & promise of the methods of science in human progress. There are many membership organizations & professional societies which have similar aims or have interest in supporting these objectives. For further information, contact the AAAS Office of News & Information at the above address. US regional divisions: Arctic; Caribbean; Pacific; Southwest & Rocky Mountains.
2016 Meeting(s): Annual Meeting (Global Science Engagement), Washington, DC, Feb 11-15, 2016
Publication(s): *Science* (weekly, journal, $10/issue, $135/yr prof rate); *Science Signaling* (journal); *Science Translational Medicine* (journal)

American Auto Racing Writers & Broadcasters
922 N Pass Ave, Burbank, CA 91505
Tel: 818-842-7005 *Fax:* 818-842-7020
Key Personnel
Pres: Ms Dusty Brandel
Media people who cover auto racing.
Number of Members: 300

American Book Producers Association (ABPA)
31 W Eighth St, 2nd fl, New York, NY 10011
Tel: 212-675-1363 *Fax:* 212-675-1364
E-mail: office@abpaonline.org
Web Site: www.abpaonline.org
Key Personnel
Pres: Richard Rothschild
VP: Nancy Hall
Treas: Valerie Tomaselli
Bd of Dirs: Leslie Carola; Karen Matsu Greenberg; Susan Knopf
Founded: 1980
An organization of independent book producing companies in the US & CN.
Number of Members: 60
Publication(s): *Booknews* (membs only)

American Booksellers Association
333 Westchester Ave, Suite S202, White Plains, NY 10604
Tel: 914-406-7500 *Toll Free Tel:* 800-637-0037 *Fax:* 914-410-6297
E-mail: info@bookweb.org
Web Site: www.bookweb.org
Key Personnel
CEO: Oren Teicher *Tel:* 800-637-0037 ext 6611 *E-mail:* oren@bookweb.org
CFO: Robyn DesHotel
Content Offr: Dan Cullen *Tel:* 800-637-0037 ext 6660 *E-mail:* dan@bookweb.org
Devt Offr: Mark Nichols *Tel:* 800-637-0037 ext 6640 *E-mail:* mark@bookweb.org
Meetings & Planning Offr: Jill Perlstein *Tel:* 800-637-0037 ext 6642 *E-mail:* jill@bookweb.org
Membership & Mktg Offr: Meg Z Smith *Tel:* 800-637-0037 ext 6641 *E-mail:* meg@bookweb.org
Sr Prog Offr: Joy Dallanegra-Sanger *Tel:* 800-637-0037 ext 6618 *E-mail:* joy@bookweb.org
Technol Dir: Greg Galloway *Tel:* 800-637-0037 ext 6668 *E-mail:* greg@bookweb.org
Mgr, ABC Children's Group: Matthew Zoni *Tel:* 800-637-0037 ext 6651 *E-mail:* matthew@bookweb.org
Mgr, IndieCommerce: Geeta Nathan
Founded: 1900
Trade organization representing independent booksellers.
Number of Members: 3,500
2016 Meeting(s): BookExpo America (BEA), McCormick Place, West Bldg, Chicago, IL, May 11-13, 2016
Publication(s): *Book Buyers Handbook* (electronic); *Bookselling This Week* (electronic)
Membership(s): BISG

American Business Media
Division of Software & Information Industry Association (SIIA)
675 Third Ave, 22nd fl, New York, NY 10017-5704
Tel: 212-661-6360 *Fax:* 212-370-0736
E-mail: info@abmmail.com
Web Site: www.americanbusinessmedia.com
Key Personnel
Mng Dir: Michael Marchesano *Tel:* 212-784-6398 *E-mail:* m.marchesano@abmmail.com
Founded: 1906
Nonprofit, global association for business-to-business information providers, including producers of magazines, web site content/service providers, trade shows, newsletters, databases, custom publishers, as well as conventions, conferences, seminars & other ancillary media that build on the print medium. Call association for listing of events scheduled.
Number of Members: 173

American Christian Writers
PO Box 110390, Nashville, TN 37222-0390
Tel: 615-331-8668 *Toll Free Tel:* 800-21-WRITE (219-7483)
E-mail: acwriters@aol.com
Web Site: regaforder.wordpress.com
Key Personnel
Founder & Publr: Reg A Forder
2015 Meeting(s): Mentoring Retreat, Western Caribbean Cruise, Tampa, FL, Nov 29-Dec 6, 2015
2016 Meeting(s): Mentoring Retreat, Nashville, TN, April 22-23, 2016; Mentoring Retreat, Grand Rapids, MI, June 10-11, 2016; Mentoring Retreat, Atlanta, GA, July 8-9, 2016; Mentoring Retreat, Minneapolis, MN, Aug 5-6, 2016; Mentoring Retreat, Phoenix, AZ, Sept 9-10, 2016; Mentoring Retreat, Orlando, FL, Nov 18-19, 2016
Membership(s): Evangelical Christian Publishers Association; Evangelical Press Association; Global Network of Christian Ministries

American Civil Liberties Union
125 Broad St, 18th fl, New York, NY 10004
Tel: 212-549-2500
E-mail: media@aclu.org
Web Site: www.aclu.org
Key Personnel
Pres: Susan N Herman
Exec Dir: Anthony D Romero
Communs Dir: Emily Tynes
Protection of constitutional rights & civil liberties through litigation, legislative lobbying & public education; 250 branch offices.
Number of Members: 500,000

American Council on Education
One Dupont Circle NW, Washington, DC 20036
Tel: 202-939-9300 *Fax:* 202-939-9302
Web Site: www.acenet.edu
Key Personnel
Pres: Molly Corbett Broad
Founded: 1918

The nation's major coordinating body for postsecondary education. Professional books & guides in higher education (special studies & reports on higher education).
Number of Members: 1,850
2016 Meeting(s): Annual Meeting, San Francisco Marriott Marquis, San Francisco, CA, March 12-15, 2016
2017 Meeting(s): Annual Meeting, Marriott Marquis, Washington, DC, March 11-14, 2017
Publication(s): *The Presidency* (3 issues/yr, $30/yr membs, $40/yr nonmembs)

American Forest Paper Association (AF&PA)
1101 "K" St NW, Suite 700, Washington, DC 20005
Tel: 202-463-2700
E-mail: info@afandpa.org
Web Site: www.afandpa.org
Key Personnel
CEO & Pres: Donna A Harman
CFO & VP, Admin: Samuel Kerns
VP, Gen Coun & Corp Secy: Jan A Poling
Founded: 1993
National trade association of the forest products industry.
Number of Members: 120
2016 Meeting(s): Paper2016, New York, NY, March 6-8, 2016

American Institute of Graphic Arts, see AIGA, the professional association for design

American Jewish Committee (AJC)
Affiliate of Institute of Human Relations
Jacob Blaustein Bldg, 165 E 56 St, New York, NY 10022
Tel: 212-751-4000; 212-891-1456 (membership) *Fax:* 212-891-1450
Web Site: www.ajc.org
Key Personnel
Exec Dir: David A Harris *E-mail:* harrisd@ajc.org
Dir, Pubns: Lawrence Grossman *Tel:* 212-751-4000 ext 308 *E-mail:* grossmanl@ajc.org
Founded: 1906
Civic & religious rights of Jews in the USA & abroad; intergroup relations & human rights.
Number of Members: 43,000
Publication(s): *AJC Journal* (6 issues/yr, free to membs); *American Jewish Year Book* ($30); *Commentary* (magazine, $19.95/yr)
Branch Office(s)
2027 Massachusetts Ave NW, Washington, DC 20036

The American Library Association (ALA)
50 E Huron St, Chicago, IL 60611
Tel: 312-944-6780; 312-280-4299 (memb & cust serv) *Toll Free Tel:* 800-545-2433 *Fax:* 312-440-9374
E-mail: ala@ala.org; customerservice@ala.org
Web Site: www.ala.org
Key Personnel
Exec Dir: Keith Michael Fiels *Tel:* 800-545-2433 ext 1392 *E-mail:* kfiels@ala.org
Lib Ref Specialist: Valerie Hawkins *Tel:* 312-280-2154 *E-mail:* vhawkins@ala.org
Founded: 1876
ALA is the oldest & largest library association in the world. ALA promotes the highest quality library & information services & public access to information. Offers professional services & publications to members & nonmembers.
Number of Members: 60,000
2016 Meeting(s): Midwinter Meeting, Boston, MA, Jan 8-12, 2016; National Library Week, Nationwide throughout the USA, April 10-16, 2016; Annual Conference, Orlando, FL, June 23-28, 2016
2017 Meeting(s): Midwinter Meeting, Atlanta, GA, Jan 20-24, 2017; National Library Week, Nationwide throughout the USA, April 9-15, 2017; Annual Conference, Chicago, IL, June 22-27, 2017
2018 Meeting(s): Midwinter Meeting, Denver, CO, Feb 9-13, 2018; Annual Conference, New Orleans, LA, June 21-26, 2018
2019 Meeting(s): Midwinter Meeting, Seattle, WA, Jan 25-29, 2019; Annual Conference, Washington, DC, June 20-25, 2019
2020 Meeting(s): Midwinter Meeting, Philadelphia, PA, Jan 17-21, 2020; Annual Conference, Chicago, IL, June 23-28, 2020
Publication(s): *American Libraries* (6 issues/yr, magazine, free to membs, $70/yr instns US & CN, $80/yr instns foreign)
Branch Office(s)
1615 New Hampshire Ave NW, 1st fl, Washington, DC 20009-2520 *Tel:* 202-628-8410 *Toll Free Tel:* 800-941-8478 *Fax:* 202-628-8419

American Literacy Council
1441 Mariposa Ave, Boulder, CO 80302
Tel: 303-440-7385
Web Site: www.americanliteracy.com
Key Personnel
Pres: Alan Mole *E-mail:* president@americanliteracy.com
Dir & Opers Mgr: Joseph R Little *Tel:* 212-663-4200 *E-mail:* spellingprogress@americanliteracy.com
Founded: 1876
To convey information on new solutions, innovative technologies & tools for engaging more boldly in the battle for literacy.
Number of Members: 12
Publication(s): *Sound-Write®* (free)

American Literary Translators Association (ALTA)
900 E Seventh St, PMB 266, Bloomington, IN 47405-3201
Tel: 972-883-2093 *Fax:* 972-883-6303
Web Site: www.literarytranslators.org
Key Personnel
Pres: Russell Valentino *E-mail:* russell.v@indiana.edu
Literary translation & translators.
Number of Members: 800
Publication(s): *Translation Review* (3 issues/yr, $100/yr indivs, $30/students)

American Management Association (AMA)
1601 Broadway, New York, NY 10019
Tel: 212-586-8100 *Toll Free Tel:* 877-566-9441 *Fax:* 212-903-8168; 518-891-0368
E-mail: customerservice@amanet.org
Web Site: www.amanet.org
Key Personnel
CEO & Pres: Edward T Reilly
SVP: Diane Laurenzo
PR Mgr: Roger Kelleher *Tel:* 212-903-7976 *E-mail:* rkelleher@amanet.org
Over 140 seminars in 20 areas including management, project management, time management, leadership, finance, interpersonal skills, communication, supervisory skills & human resources.
Number of Members: 700,000
New Election: Annually in March

American Marketing Association
311 S Wacker Dr, Suite 5800, Chicago, IL 60606
Tel: 312-542-9000 *Toll Free Tel:* 800-AMA-1150 (262-1150) *Fax:* 312-542-9001
E-mail: info@ama.org
Web Site: www.ama.org
Key Personnel
CEO: Dennis Dunlap *E-mail:* ceo@ama.org
CFO: Beth Taylor *E-mail:* btaylor@ama.org
CTO: Bob Panger *E-mail:* bpanger@ama.org
Chief Mktg Offr: Nancy Costopulos *E-mail:* ncostopulos@ama.org
Chief Prof Devt Offr: Carol Arnold *E-mail:* carnold@ama.org
Dir of Publg, Journals: Christopher Bartone *Tel:* 312-542-9029 *E-mail:* cbartone@ama.org
Founded: 1937
A nonprofit, educational institution. Offers online marketing info. Sponsors seminars, conferences & student marketing clubs & doctoral consortium. Publish books, journals, magazines & proceedings of conferences.
Number of Members: 30,000
Publication(s): *Journal of International Marketing*; *Journal of Marketing*; *Journal of Marketing Research* (6 issues/yr); *Journal of Public Policy & Marketing* (semiannual); *Marketing Health Services* (quarterly); *Marketing Insights*; *Marketing News* (biweekly)

American Medical Association
AMA Plaza, 330 N Wabash, Suite 39300, Chicago, IL 60611-5885
Tel: 312-464-5000 *Toll Free Tel:* 800-621-8335 *Fax:* 312-464-4184
Web Site: www.ama-assn.org
Key Personnel
CEO & EVP: James L Madara, MD
SVP & Publr, Periodic Pubns: Thomas J Easley *Tel:* 312-464-5000 ext 5740
Promotes the science & art of medicine & betterment of public health. Association of physicians.
Publication(s): *JAMA: Dermatology* (monthly); *JAMA: Facial Plastic Surgery* (6 issues/yr); *JAMA: Internal Medicine* (monthly); *JAMA: Neurology* (monthly); *JAMA: Ophthalmology* (monthly); *JAMA: Otolaryngology* (monthly); *JAMA: Pediatrics* (monthly); *JAMA: Psychiatry* (monthly); *JAMA: Surgery* (monthly); *JAMA: The Journal of the American Medical Association* (weekly)
Branch Office(s)
119 Cherry Hill Rd, Parsippany, NJ 07054

American Medical Writers Association (AMWA)
30 W Gude Dr, Suite 525, Rockville, MD 20850-4357
Tel: 240-238-0940 *Fax:* 301-294-9006
E-mail: amwa@amwa.org
Web Site: www.amwa.org
Key Personnel
Exec Dir: Susan Krug *Tel:* 240-238-0940 ext 109 *E-mail:* skrug@amwa.org
Deputy Dir: Shari Rager *Tel:* 240-238-0940 ext 107 *E-mail:* srager@amwa.org
Founded: 1940
Professional organization for writers, editors & other communicators of medical information.
Number of Members: 5,300
2016 Meeting(s): Annual Conference, Denver, CO, Oct 5-8, 2016
2017 Meeting(s): Annual Conference, Orlando, FL, Nov 1-4, 2017
Publication(s): *AMWA Journal* (quarterly, journal, free to membs, $75/yr nonmembs); *AMWA Membership Directory* (annual, directory); *Freelance Directory* (online, directory, free); *Jobs Online* (monthly, classified listing)

American Political Science Association
1527 New Hampshire Ave NW, Washington, DC 20036-1203
Tel: 202-483-2512 *Fax:* 202-483-2657
E-mail: apsa@apsanet.org
Web Site: www.apsanet.org
Key Personnel
Exec Dir: Steven Rathgeb Smith *E-mail:* smithsr@apsanet.org
Founded: 1903
Provide services to facilitate research, teaching & professional development in political science, including publications & services to assist college faculty, graduate students & researchers.

Number of Members: 15,000
2016 Meeting(s): Teaching & Learning Conference, Marriott Portland Downtown Waterfront, Portland, OR, Feb 12-14, 2016; Annual Meeting & Exhibition, Philadelphia, PA, Sept 1-4, 2016
2017 Meeting(s): Annual Meeting & Exhibition, San Francisco, CA, Aug 31-Sept 3, 2017
2018 Meeting(s): Annual Meeting & Exhibition, Boston, MA, Aug 31-Sept 2, 2018
2019 Meeting(s): Annual Meeting & Exhibition, Washington, DC, Aug 29-Sept 1, 2019
2020 Meeting(s): Annual Meeting & Exhibition, San Francisco, CA, Sept 3-6, 2020
Publication(s): *American Political Science Review* (quarterly); *Perspectives on Politics* (quarterly); *PS: Political Science & Politics* (quarterly)

American Printing History Association
PO Box 4519, Grand Central Sta, New York, NY 10163
Tel: 202-544-2422
E-mail: secretary@printinghistory.org
Web Site: printinghistory.org
Key Personnel
Pres: Robert McCamant
VP, Membership: Casey Smith
VP, Progs: Sara T Sauers
VP, Pubns: James P Ascher
Treas: David Goodrich
Secy: Charles Cuykendall Carter
Local chapters in New York City, New England, Inland, Chesapeake, Southern & Northern California.
Number of Members: 700
New Election: Annually in Jan

American Psychological Association
750 First St NE, Washington, DC 20002-4242
Tel: 202-336-5500 *Toll Free Tel:* 800-374-2721
E-mail: order@apa.org
Web Site: www.apa.org
Key Personnel
Publr: Jasper Simons
Exec Dir, Sci Directorate: Steven J Breckler, PhD *Tel:* 202-336-5938 *E-mail:* sbreckler@apa.org
Exec Dir, Public & Memb Communs: Rhea K Farberman *Tel:* 202-336-5709 *E-mail:* rfarberman@apa.org
Founded: 1892
Publish numerous periodicals & books in the field of psychology.
Number of Members: 130,000
Publication(s): *American Psychologist* (9 times/yr beginning in Jan); *APA Membership Register* (annual); *APA Monitor* (monthly); *Directory of the APA* (1 issue/4 yrs, directory)

American Public Human Services Association
1133 19 St NW, Suite 400, Washington, DC 20036
Tel: 202-682-0100 *Fax:* 202-289-6555
Web Site: www.aphsa.org
Key Personnel
Exec Dir: Tracy Wareing *Tel:* 202-682-0100 ext 231 *E-mail:* tracy.wareing@aphsa.org
Mgr, Membership & Mktg: Brittany Donald *Tel:* 202-682-0100 ext 276 *E-mail:* brittany.donald@aphsa.org
Founded: 1930
Membership organization of public human services professionals.
Number of Members: 5,000
New Election: Annually in Dec
Publication(s): *Policy & Practice* (6 issues/yr, directory, $65 single copy, $75 single copy intl, $400/yr, $475/yr intl); *This Week In Washington* (weekly when Congress is in session, newsletter, free, electronic)

American Society for Indexing Inc (ASI)
1628 E Southern Ave, Suite 9-223, Tempe, AZ 85282
Tel: 480-245-6750
E-mail: info@asindexing.org
Web Site: www.asindexing.org
Key Personnel
Exec Dir: Gwen Henson *E-mail:* gwen@asindexing.org
Founded: 1968
Educational programs for indexing field.
Number of Members: 550
New Election: Annually in May
Publication(s): *KeyWords* (monthly, magazine, free to membs, $40 nonmembs)

American Society of Composers, Authors & Publishers (ASCAP)
1900 Broadway, New York City, NY 10023
Tel: 212-621-6000 *Toll Free Tel:* 800-952-7227 *Fax:* 212-612-8453
E-mail: info@ascap.com
Web Site: www.ascap.com
Key Personnel
Chmn of the Bd & Pres: Paul Williams *E-mail:* pwilliams@ascap.com
CEO: John Lo Frumento
Founded: 1914
License nondramatic right of public performance of members' copyrighted musical compositions & distribute royalties to members on basis of performances. Members are composers, songwriters, lyricists & music publishers.
Number of Members: 500,000
Branch Office(s)
7920 W Sunset Blvd, 3rd fl, Los Angeles, CA 90046 *Tel:* 323-883-1000 *Fax:* 323-883-1049
420 Lincoln Rd, Suite 385, Miami Beach, FL 33139 *Tel:* 305-673-3446 *Fax:* 305-673-2446
950 Joseph E Lowery Blvd NW, Suite 23, Atlanta, GA 30318 *Tel:* 404-685-8699 *Fax:* 404-685-8701
Two Music Sq W, Nashville, TN 37203 *Tel:* 615-742-5000 *Fax:* 615-742-5020
Ave Martinez Nadal, c/ Hill Side 623, San Juan 00920, Puerto Rico *Tel:* 787-707-0782 *Fax:* 787-707-0783
8 Cork St, London W1S 3LJ, United Kingdom *Tel:* (020) 7439 0909 *Fax:* (020) 7434 0073

American Society of Journalists and Authors (ASJA)
1501 Broadway, Suite 403, New York, NY 10036
Tel: 212-997-0947 *Fax:* 212-937-2315
Web Site: asja.org
Key Personnel
Exec Dir: Alexandra Owens *E-mail:* director@asja.org
Founded: 1948
Service organization providing exchange of ideas & market information. Regular meetings with speakers from the industry, annual writers conference; medical plans available. Professional referral service, annual membership directory; first amendment advocacy group.
Number of Members: 1,400
Publication(s): *ASJA Monthly* (11 times/yr online, printed quarterly, newsletter, membs only)

American Society of Magazine Editors (ASME)
757 Third Ave, 11th fl, New York, NY 10017
Tel: 212-872-3700 *Fax:* 212-906-0128
E-mail: asme@magazine.org
Web Site: www.magazine.org/asme
Key Personnel
Chief Exec: Sid Holt
Dir: Nina Fortuna *Tel:* 212-872-3737
Founded: 1963
Professional society for senior magazine editors. Sponsor the National Magazine Awards in association with the Columbia Journalism School; hold monthly luncheons for members & conduct periodic seminars.
Number of Members: 700
New Election: Annually in April

American Society of Media Photographers (ASMP)
150 N Second St, Philadelphia, PA 19106
Tel: 215-451-2767 *Fax:* 215-451-0880
E-mail: info@asmp.org
Web Site: asmp.org
Key Personnel
Exec Dir: Eugene Mopsik *Tel:* 215-451-2767 ext 201 *E-mail:* mopsik@asmp.org
Dir, Communs: Peter Dyson *Tel:* 215-451-2767 ext 205 *E-mail:* dyson@asmp.org
Gen Coun: Victor Perlman *Tel:* 215-451-2767 ext 207 *E-mail:* perlman@asmp.org
Gen Mgr: Elena Goertz *Tel:* 215-451-2767 ext 203 *E-mail:* goertz@asmp.org
Bookkeeper: Chris Chandler *Tel:* 215-451-2767 ext 209 *E-mail:* chandler@asmp.org
Founded: 1944
Maintain & promote high professional standards & ethics in photography; cultivate mutual understanding among professional photographers; protect & promote interests of photographers whose work is for publication.
Number of Members: 7,000
Publication(s): *The ASMP Guide to New Markets in Photography* (free to membs); *ASMP Professional Business Practices in Photography, 7th Ed* (free to membs); *Digital Photography Best Practices & Workflow & Handbook* ($22 membs)

American Sociological Association (ASA)
1430 "K" St NW, Suite 600, Washington, DC 20005-4701
Tel: 202-383-9005 *Fax:* 202-638-0882
E-mail: customer@asanet.org
Web Site: www.asanet.org
Key Personnel
Exec Offr: Sally Hillsman *Tel:* 202-383-9005 ext 316 *E-mail:* executive.office@asanet.org
Pubns Dir: Karen Gray Edwards *Tel:* 202-383-9005 ext 319 *E-mail:* publications@asanet.org
Founded: 1905
Nonprofit membership association dedicated to advancing sociology as a scientific discipline & profession serving the public good. Encompass sociologists who are faculty members at colleges & universities, researchers, practitioners & students.
Number of Members: 13,000
New Election: Annually in Aug
2016 Meeting(s): Annual Meeting, Washington State Convention Center & Sheraton Seattle Hotel, Seattle, WA, Aug 20-23, 2016
2017 Meeting(s): Annual Meeting, Palais des Congres de Montreal, Montreal, QB, CN, Aug 12-15, 2017
2018 Meeting(s): Annual Meeting, Pennsylvania Convention Center & Philadelphia Marriott, Philadelphia, PA, Aug 11-14, 2018
2019 Meeting(s): Annual Meeting, Hilton New York Midtown & Sheraton New York Times Square Hotel, New York City, NY, Aug 10-13, 2019
Publication(s): *American Sociological Review* (6 issues/yr, $45 membs, $30 student membs, $400 instns (print/online), $360 instns (online only)); *Contemporary Sociology* (6 issues/yr, $45 membs, $30 student membs, $382 instns (print/online), $344 instns (online only)); *Contexts* (quarterly, magazine, $45 membs, $30 student membs, $225 instns (print/online), $247 instns (online only)); *Footnotes* (monthly exc July/Aug, Sept/Oct, May/June, newsletter, free online); *Journal of Health & Social Behavior* (quarterly, $45 membs, $30 student membs, $340 instns (print/online), $305 instns (online only)); *Social Psychology Quarterly* (quarterly,

$45 membs, $30 student membs, $340 instns (print/online), $305 instns (online only)); *Sociological Methodology* (annual, $45 membs, $30 student membs, $365 instns (print/online), $330 instns (online only)); *Sociological Theory* (quarterly, $45 membs, $30 student membs, $370 instns (print/online), $334 instns (online only)); *Sociology of Education* (quarterly, $45 membs, $30 student membs, $340 instns (print/online), $305 instns (online only)); *Teaching Sociology* (quarterly, $45 membs, $30 student membs, $340 instns (print/online), $305 instns (online only))

American Speech-Language-Hearing Association (ASHA)
2200 Research Blvd, Rockville, MD 20850-3289
Tel: 301-296-5700 *Toll Free Tel:* 800-638-8255 (nonmembs); 800-498-2071 (membs) *Fax:* 301-296-5777; 301-296-8580
E-mail: actioncenter@asha.org
Web Site: www.asha.org
Founded: 1925
Membership organization for 182,000 speech-language pathologists & audiologists. Provide consumers with information & referral on speech, language & hearing. Publish information brochures & packets.
Number of Members: 182,000
New Election: Annually in Sept
Publication(s): *American Journal of Audiology* (quarterly, journal, $15/single article for 24 hours, $30 for entire site for 24 hours, $97/yr electronic nonmembs, $238/yr electronic instns, $151/yr online archive nonmembs & instns); *American Journal of Speech-Language Pathology* (quarterly, journal, $15/single article for 24 hours, $30 for entire site for 24 hours, $97/yr electronic nonmembs, $238/yr electronic instns, $151/yr online archives nonmembs & instns); *The ASHA Leader* (monthly, newspaper, $113/yr nonmembs, $151/yr foreign nonmembs, $170/instns, $214 foreign instns); *Journal of Speech, Language & Hearing Research* (6 issues/yr, journal, $15/single article for 24 hours, $30 for entire site for 24 hours, $204/yr electronic nonmembs, $576/yr electronic instns, $435/yr online archives nonmembs & instns); *Language, Speech & Hearing Services In Schools* (quarterly, journal, $15/single article for 24 hours, $30 for entire site for 24 hours, $97/yr electronic nonmembs, $238/yr electronic instns, $186/yr online archives nonmembs & instns)
Branch Office(s)
444 N Capitol St NW, Suite 715, Washington, DC 20001 *Tel:* 202-624-5884

American Translators Association (ATA)
225 Reinekers Lane, Suite 590, Alexandria, VA 22314
Tel: 703-683-6100 *Fax:* 703-683-6122
E-mail: ata@atanet.org
Web Site: www.atanet.org
Key Personnel
Exec Dir: Walter W Bacak, Jr *Tel:* 703-683-6100 ext 3006 *E-mail:* walter@atanet.org
Founded: 1959
Membership consists of those professionally engaged in translating, interpreting or closely allied work, as well as those who are interested in these fields. Membership: $190/yr indivs, $350/yr corps, $235/yr instl, $80/yr student.
Number of Members: 11,000
2016 Meeting(s): Annual Conference, San Francisco, CA, Nov 2-5, 2016
2017 Meeting(s): Annual Conference, Washington, DC, Oct 25-28, 2017
2018 Meeting(s): Annual Conference, New Orleans, LA, Oct 24-27, 2018
Publication(s): *The ATA Chronicle* (11 issues/yr, $65, $90 CN & Mexico, $110 all other countries)
Membership(s): Federation of International Translators

AMSP/NAPL/NAQP, see Epicomm

Antiquarian Booksellers' Association of America
20 W 44 St, Suite 507, New York, NY 10036
Tel: 212-944-8291 *Fax:* 212-944-8293
E-mail: hq@abaa.org
Web Site: www.abaa.org
Key Personnel
Exec Dir: Susan Benne *E-mail:* sbenne@abaa.org
Founded: 1949
Chapters: Northern California, Southern California, Midwest, Middle Atlantic, New England, Southeast, Southwest & Pacific Northwest. Membership open to antiquarian booksellers only. ABAA sponsors three or four international book fairs per year in Los Angeles & San Francisco (alternately) in mid-winter; in New York in the spring; in Boston in late autumn.
Number of Members: 450
2016 Meeting(s): California International Antiquarian Book Fair, Pasadena Convention Center, 300 E Green St, Pasadena, CA, Feb 12-14, 2016; New York Antiquarian Book Fair, Park Avenue Armory, 643 Park Ave at 67 St, New York, NY, April 7-10, 2016
2017 Meeting(s): California International Antiquarian Book Fair, Oakland Marriott City Center, Oakland, CA, Feb 10-12, 2017
Publication(s): *Newsletter* (quarterly, free, electronic)

Antiquarian Booksellers' Association of Canada/Association de la Librairie Ancienne du Canada, see ABAC/ALAC

ASHA, see American Speech-Language-Hearing Association (ASHA)

Asian American Writers' Workshop
110-112 W 27 St, Suite 600, New York, NY 10001
Tel: 212-494-0061
E-mail: desk@aaww.org
Web Site: aaww.org
Key Personnel
Exec Dir: Ken Chen
Not-for-profit arts organization devoted to the creating, publishing, developing & disseminating of creative writing by Asian Americans.

Aspen Writers' Foundation
110 E Hallam St, Suite 116, Aspen, CO 81611
Tel: 970-925-3122 *Fax:* 970-920-5700
E-mail: awfinfo@aspenwriters.org
Web Site: www.aspenwriters.org
Key Personnel
Dir: Maurice LaMee *Tel:* 970-925-3122 ext 1 *E-mail:* maurice.lamee@aspeninstitute.org
Creative Dir: Adrienne Brodeur *Tel:* 970-925-3122 ext 1 *E-mail:* adrienne.brodeur@aspeninstitute.org
Prog Mgr: Jamie Kravitz *Tel:* 970-925-3122 ext 2 *E-mail:* jamie.kravitz@aspeninstitute.org
Progs Coord: Caroline Tory *Tel:* 970-925-3122 ext 3 *E-mail:* caroline.tory@aspeninstitute.org
Founded: 1976
Program of the Aspen Institute. Encourages writers, inspires readers & connects people through the exchange of words, stories & ideas.
Meeting(s): Aspen Summer Words Writing Retreat & Literary Festival, Aspen, CO, June

Associated Business Writers of America Inc
Division of National Writers Association
10940 S Parker Rd, Suite 508, Parker, CO 80134
Tel: 303-841-0246
E-mail: natlwritersassn@hotmail.com
Web Site: www.nationalwriters.com
Key Personnel
Exec Dir: Sandy Whelchel *E-mail:* authorsandy@hotmail.com
To help business writers & those seeking their services.
Number of Members: 100

Associated Press Broadcast
1100 13 St NW, Suite 700, Washington, DC 20005
Tel: 202-641-9000 *Toll Free Tel:* 800-821-4747 *Fax:* 202-370-2710
E-mail: info@ap.org
Web Site: www.ap.org
Number of Members: 5,800
Publication(s): *AP Stylebook* (annual, $20.95)

Association canadienne d'education, see Canadian Education Association (Association canadienne d'education)

Association Canadienne des bibliotheques (ACB), see Canadian Library Association-CLA (Association Canadienne des bibliotheques)

Association canadienne des reviseurs, see Editors' Association of Canada (Association canadienne des reviseurs)

Association des Editeurs de Langue Anglaise du Quebec, see The Association of English-Language Publishers of Quebec-AELAQ (Association des Editeurs de Langue Anglaise du Quebec)

Association des Libraires du Quebec (ALQ)
407 St-Laurent, bureau 801, Montreal, QC H2Y 2Y5, Canada
Tel: 514-526-3349 *Fax:* 514-526-3340
E-mail: info@alq.qc.ca
Web Site: www.alq.qc.ca
Key Personnel
CEO: Katherine Fafard *E-mail:* kfafard@alq.qc.ca
Founded: 1969
Quebec association of booksellers.
Number of Members: 95

Association for Information & Image Management International (AIIM)
1100 Wayne Ave, Suite 1100, Silver Spring, MD 20910
Tel: 301-587-8202 *Toll Free Tel:* 800-477-2446 *Fax:* 301-587-2711
E-mail: aiim@aiim.org; info@aiim.org
Web Site: www.aiim.org
Key Personnel
Ed & Community Mgr: Bryant Duhon *Tel:* 301-916-7182 *E-mail:* bduhon@aiim.org
Global association bringing together the users of document technologies with the providers of that technology.
Number of Members: 9,197
Branch Office(s)
8, Canalside, Lowesmoor Wharf, Worcester WR1 2RR, United Kingdom *Tel:* (01905) 727600 *Fax:* (01905) 727609

Association for Information Science & Technology (ASIS&T)
8555 16 St, Suite 850, Silver Spring, MD 20910
Tel: 301-495-0900 *Fax:* 301-495-0810
E-mail: asis@asis.org
Web Site: www.asis.org

Key Personnel
Exec Dir: Richard Hill *E-mail:* rhill@asis.org
Founded: 1937
To foster & lead the advancement of information science & technology.
Number of Members: 4,000
2016 Meeting(s): The IA Summit, Omni Atlanta Hotel at CNN Center, 100 CNN Center, Atlanta, GA, May 4-8, 2016; ASIS&T Annual Meeting, Copenhagen, Denmark, Oct 14-18, 2016
Publication(s): *Bulletin of the Association for Information Science & Technology* (6 issues/yr); *Journal of the Association for Information Science & Technology (JASIST)*

Association Media & Publishing (AM&P)
12100 Sunset Hills Rd, Suite 130, Reston, VA 20190
Tel: 703-234-4063 *Fax:* 703-435-4390
E-mail: info@associationmediaandpublishing.org
Web Site: associationmediaandpublishing.org
Key Personnel
Exec Dir: John T Adams, III *Tel:* 703-234-4107 *E-mail:* jadams@associationmediaandpublishing.org
Edit Dir: Carla Kalogeridis *Tel:* 313-884-0988 *E-mail:* ckalogeridis@associationmediaandpublishing.org
Sales Dir: Joseph Cavarretta *Tel:* 703-234-4095 *E-mail:* joe@associationmediaandpublishing.org
Mktg Mgr: Heather Konya *Tel:* 703-234-4112 *E-mail:* heather@associationmediaandpublishing.org
Administrator: Lauren Norkin *Tel:* 703-234-4121 *E-mail:* lnorkin@associationmediaandpublishing.org
Founded: 1963 (as Society of National Association Publications)
A nonprofit professional society that serves the needs of association & society publications & their staff to represent, promote & advance the common interest of periodicals of voluntary associations & societies.
Number of Members: 1,400
2016 Meeting(s): AMP 16, Ronald Reagan Bldg, Washington, DC, June 27-29, 2016
Publication(s): *Signature* (6 issues/yr, magazine)

Association Nationale des Editeurs de Livres
2514 boul Rosemont, Montreal, QC H1Y 1K4, Canada
Tel: 514-273-8130 *Toll Free Tel:* 866-900-ANEL (900-2635)
E-mail: info@anel.qc.ca
Web Site: www.anel.qc.ca
Key Personnel
Dir Gen: Richard Prieur *E-mail:* prieur@anel.qc.ca
Deputy Dir Gen: Karine Vachone *E-mail:* vachon@anel.qc.ca
Mgr, Memb Servs: Helene Letourneau *E-mail:* letourneau@anel.qc.ca
Founded: 1992
Professional association of French publishers in Canada.
Number of Members: 100

Association of American Editorial Cartoonists
3899 N Front St, Harrisburg, PA 17110
Tel: 717-703-3003 *Fax:* 717-703-3008
E-mail: aaec@pa-news.org
Web Site: www.editorialcartoonists.com
Key Personnel
Pres: Jack Ohman
Gen Mgr: Teresa Shaak
Founded: 1957
Professional association.
Number of Members: 260
Publication(s): *Notebook* (quarterly, free to membs, $40/yr nonmembs)

Association of American Publishers (AAP)
71 Fifth Ave, 2nd fl, New York, NY 10003-3004
Tel: 212-255-0200 *Fax:* 212-255-7007
E-mail: info@publishers.org
Web Site: publishers.org
Key Personnel
Pres & CEO: Tom Allen *E-mail:* tallen@publishers.org
VP: Tina Jordan *Tel:* 212-255-0275 *E-mail:* tjordan@publishers.org
VP & Exec Dir, Prof & Scholarly Publg: John Tagler *Tel:* 212-255-1407 *E-mail:* jtagler@publishers.org
Gen Coun & VP, Govt Aff: Allan R Adler *Tel:* 202-220-4544 *E-mail:* adler@publishers.org
Exec Dir, PreK-12 Learning Group: Jay Diskey *Tel:* 202-220-4549 *E-mail:* jdiskey@publishers.org
Founded: 1970
Monitor & promote the USA publishing industry. Members: those actively engaged in the creation, publication & production of books, journals, electronic media, testing materials & a range of educational materials.
Number of Members: 450
2016 Meeting(s): Annual Meeting, March 2016
Publication(s): *AAP Export Sales Report* (annual); *AAP StatShot* (monthly)
Branch Office(s)
455 Massachusetts Ave NW, Suite 700, Washington, DC 20001-2777, Dir, Communs: Marisa Bluestone *Tel:* 202-347-3375 *Fax:* 202-347-3690 *E-mail:* mbluestone@publishers.org
325 Chestnut St, Suite 1110, Philadelphia, PA 19106-7761 *Tel:* 267-351-4310 *Fax:* 267-351-4317
Membership(s): BISG

Association of American University Presses (AAUP)
28 W 36 St, Suite 602, New York, NY 10018
Tel: 212-989-1010 *Fax:* 212-989-0275
E-mail: info@aaupnet.org
Web Site: www.aaupnet.org
Key Personnel
Exec Dir: Peter Berkery *Tel:* 212-989-1010 ext 29 *E-mail:* pberkery@aaupnet.org
Dir of Mktg & Communs: Brenna McLaughlin *Tel:* 518-436-3586 *E-mail:* bmclaughlin@aaupnet.org
Off Mgr & Program Administrator: Kim Miller *Tel:* 212-989-1010 ext 26 *E-mail:* kmiller@aaupnet.org
Membership & affiliation consists of university presses in North America & abroad that function as the publishing arms of their respective universities, issuing some 11,000 titles & more than 600 journals annually. AAUP helps these presses do their work more economically, creatively & effectively through its own activities in professional development; fund raising; statistical research & analysis; promoting the value of university presses; community & institutional relations & through its marketing programs.
Number of Members: 128
2016 Meeting(s): Annual Meeting, Loews Philadelphia, Philadelphia, PA, June 16-19, 2016
Publication(s): *AAUP Book, Jacket & Journal Show* (catalog, $20 current yr, $15 past yrs); *Annual Directory* ($30); *The Exchange* (quarterly, newsletter, free); *University Press Books for Public & Secondary School Libraries* (annual, free)
Membership(s): BISG

Association of Authors' Representatives Inc
302A W 12 St, No 122, New York, NY 10014
Tel: 212-840-5770
E-mail: administrator@aaronline.org
Web Site: www.aaronline.org
Founded: 1991
Voluntary & elective professional association of literary & play agents whose individual members subscribe to certain ethical practices. Members meet to discuss industry developments & problems of mutual interest.
Number of Members: 386
New Election: Annually in June

Association of Book Publishers of British Columbia
Affiliate of Association of Canadian Publishers
600-402 W Pender St, Vancouver, BC V6B 1T6, Canada
Tel: 604-684-0228 *Fax:* 604-684-5788
E-mail: admin@books.bc.ca
Web Site: www.books.bc.ca
Key Personnel
Exec Dir: Margaret Reynolds *E-mail:* margaret@books.bc.ca
Founded: 1974
Trade association representing the interests of Canadian-owned & operated book publishing companies based in BC.
Number of Members: 31
New Election: Annually in April

Association of Canadian Publishers (ACP)
174 Spadina Ave, Suite 306, Toronto, ON M5T 2C2, Canada
Tel: 416-487-6116 *Fax:* 416-487-8815
E-mail: admin@canbook.org
Web Site: publishers.ca
Key Personnel
Exec Dir: Kate Edwards *Tel:* 416-487-6116 ext 234 *E-mail:* kate_edwards@canbook.org
Founded: 1976
Association of English-language Canadian-owned book publishing companies in Canada. Sponsor professional development seminars for book publishers. Publish membership directories, studies & reports.
Number of Members: 135
Publication(s): *Membership Directory* (annual)

Association of Canadian University Presses
10 St Mary St, Suite 700, Toronto, ON M4Y 2W8, Canada
Tel: 416-978-2239 ext 237 *Fax:* 416-978-4738
Web Site: www.acup.ca
Key Personnel
Administrator: Charley La Rose *E-mail:* clarose@utpress.utoronto.ca
Founded: 1972
Number of Members: 16
New Election: Annually in Autumn

Association of Catholic Publishers Inc
4725 Dorsey Hall Dr, Suite A, PMB 709, Elliott City, MD 21042
Tel: 410-988-2926 *Fax:* 410-571-4946
Web Site: www.catholicsread.org; www.catholicpublishers.org; www.midatlanticcongress.org
Key Personnel
Pres: Bret Thomas
VP: Mary Beth Oria
Secy: Mary Beth Kunde-Anderson
Treas: Tom Shumate
Exec Dir: Therese Brown
Facilitate the sharing of professional information, networking, cooperation & friendship among those involved in Catholic book publishing in the US & abroad. Offers trade co-op catalog, mailing list, Catholic bestsellers, advertising insert program & professional skills workshops.
Number of Members: 100
2016 Meeting(s): Mid-Atlantic Congress, Baltimore Hilton Hotel, Baltimore, MD, Feb 4-6, 2016
Publication(s): *Promotional Brochure* (annually)

Association of College & University Printers (ACUP)
PO Box 285, Carrabelle, FL 32322
Tel: 850-570-5241
Web Site: www.acup-edu.org
Key Personnel
Admin Dir: Jennifer Bowers *E-mail:* jennifer.bowers@acup-edu.org
Number of Members: 300
2016 Meeting(s): Annual Conference, Embassy Suites Albuquerque Hotel & Spa, Albuquerque, NM, April 10-14, 2016

The Association of English-Language Publishers of Quebec-AELAQ (Association des Editeurs de Langue Anglaise du Quebec)
Atwater Library, 1200 Atwater Ave, Suite 3, Westmount, QC H3Z 1X4, Canada
Tel: 514-932-5633
E-mail: admin@aelaq.org
Web Site: aelaq.org
Key Personnel
Pres: Keith Henderson
Exec Dir: Julia Kater
Advance the publication, distribution & promotion of English-language books from Quebec.
Number of Members: 18
Publication(s): *Montreal Review of Books* (3 times/yr, report, free)

Association of Free Community Papers (AFCP)
7445 Morgan Rd, Suite 103, Liverpool, NY 13090
Toll Free Tel: 877-203-2327 *Fax:* 781-459-7770
E-mail: afcp@afcp.org
Web Site: www.afcp.org
Key Personnel
Exec Dir: Loren Colburn *E-mail:* loren@afcp.org
Founded: 1950
Organization of publishers serving the free-circulation community publication industry.
Number of Members: 250
2016 Meeting(s): Annual Conference & Trade Show, Sheraton San Diego Hotel & Marina, San Diego, CA, April 28-30, 2016
Publication(s): *Freepaper Ink* (monthly, newsletter, free)

Association of Jewish Libraries (AJL) Inc
PO Box 1118, Teaneck, NJ 07666
Tel: 201-371-3255
E-mail: info@jewishlibraries.org
Web Site: www.jewishlibraries.org
Key Personnel
Pres: Heidi Estrin *E-mail:* president@jewishlibraries.org
Member libraries in two divisions: RAS (Research Libraries, Archives & Special Collections) & SCC (Schools, Synagogues & Centers). Promote librarianship, services & standards in the field of Judaica. Affiliate of the American Library Association & the American Theological Library Association.
Number of Members: 1,000
2016 Meeting(s): Annual Conference, Charleston, SC, June 19-22, 2016
Publication(s): *AJL Conference Proceedings* (annual); *AJL News* (quarterly); *AJL Reviews* (quarterly); *Judaica Librarianship* (annual, journal)

Association of Manitoba Book Publishers
100 Arthur St, Suite 404, Winnipeg, MB R3B 1H3, Canada
Tel: 204-947-3335 *Fax:* 204-956-4689
E-mail: ambp@mts.net
Web Site: ambp.ca
Key Personnel
Exec Dir: Michelle Peters
Projs Coord: Karen San Filippo
Founded: 1979
Publishing industry association.
Number of Members: 13
Publication(s): *Prairie Books Now* (3 issues/yr, magazine)
Membership(s): Association of Canadian Publishers

Association of Marketing Service Providers (AMSP), see Epicomm

The Association of Medical Illustrators (AMI)
201 E Main St, Suite 1405, Lexington, KY 40507
Toll Free Tel: 866-393-4264 *Fax:* 859-514-9166
E-mail: hq@ami.org
Web Site: www.ami.org
Key Personnel
Exec Dir, Ex-Officio: Melanie Bowzer *E-mail:* mbowzer@amrms.com
Founded: 1945
Promote the use of high-quality artwork in medical publications to advance medical education.
Number of Members: 850

Association of Opinion Journalists (AOJ)
2301 Vanderbilt Place, VU Sta B 351669, Nashville, TN 37235-1669
E-mail: opinionjounalists@gmail.com
Web Site: www.opinionjournalists.org
Key Personnel
Pres: Miriam Pepper *Tel:* 816-234-4421 *E-mail:* mpepper@kcstar.com
VP: Kate Riley *Tel:* 206-464-2260 *E-mail:* kriley@seattletimes.com
Secy-Treas: Carolyn Lumsden *Tel:* 860-241-3698 *E-mail:* clumsden@courant.com
Founded: 1947 (as The National Conference of Editorial Writers)
Nonprofit professional organization that exists to improve the quality of opinion writing in newspapers, for broadcast editorials & online & to promote high standards among opinion writers & editors.
Number of Members: 275
New Election: Annually in Sept
Publication(s): *The Masthead* (magazine, free online)

Association of Publishers for Special Sales (APSS)
PO Box 715, Avon, CT 06001-0715
Tel: 860-675-1344
Web Site: www.spannet.org
Key Personnel
Exec Dir: Brian Jud *E-mail:* brianjud@bookapss.org
Busn Mgr: Kaye Krassner
A trade association for independent presses, self-publishers & pro-active authors who want to sell more books.
Publication(s): *The Sales Informer* (monthly)

Association of Writers & Writing Programs (AWP)
George Mason University, 4400 University Dr, MSN 1E3, Fairfax, VA 22030
Tel: 703-993-4301 *Fax:* 703-993-4302
E-mail: awp@awpwriter.org
Web Site: www.awpwriter.org
Key Personnel
Exec Dir: David W Fenza
Dir, Conferences: Christian Teresi
Dir, Devt: Pamela Mills
Dir, Membership Servs: Diane Zinna
Dir, Pubns: Supriya Bhatnagar
Assoc Ed: Jason Gray
Conference Events Coord: Abigail Campbell
Founded: 1967
Magazine, publications, directory, competitions for awards (including publication), advocacy for literature & education, annual meeting, job placement.
Number of Members: 34,000
2016 Meeting(s): Annual Conference & Bookfair, JW Marriott Los Angeles & Los Angeles Convention Center, Los Angeles, CA, March 30-April 2, 2016
2017 Meeting(s): Annual Conference & Bookfair, Washington Marriott Marquis & Washington Convention Center, Washington, DC, Feb 8-11, 2017
2018 Meeting(s): Annual Conference & Bookfair, Tampa Convention Center & Marriott Tampa Waterside, Tampa, FL, March 7-10, 2018
Publication(s): *The Writer's Chronicle* (6 issues/yr, free to membs)

Association pour l'Avancement des Sciences et des Techniques de la Documentation
2065 rue Parthenais, Bureau 387, Montreal, QC H2K 3T1, Canada
Tel: 514-281-5012 *Fax:* 514-281-8219
E-mail: info@asted.org
Web Site: www.asted.org
Key Personnel
Exec Dir: Suzanne Morin *Tel:* 514-281-5012 ext 234 *E-mail:* smorin@asted.org
Objective is the promotion of standards of excellence in the services & personnel of libraries, documentation & information centers.
Number of Members: 550
New Election: Annually during congress
Publication(s): *Documentation et Bibliotheques* (quarterly, $65/yr CN, $85/yr elsewhere)

ASTED, see Association pour l'Avancement des Sciences et des Techniques de la Documentation

The Authors Guild
31 E 32 St, 7th fl, New York, NY 10016
Tel: 212-563-5904 *Fax:* 212-564-5363
E-mail: staff@authorsguild.org
Web Site: www.authorsguild.org
Key Personnel
Pres: Roxana Robinson
VP: Judy Blume; Richard Russo; James Shapiro
Exec Dir: Mary Rasenberger
Founded: 1912
National membership organization for nonfiction & fiction book authors & freelance journalists. Deals with the business & professional interests of authors in such fields as book contracts, copyright, subsidiary rights, free expression, taxes & others. Offer free contract reviews, web site development & hosting & health insurance.
Number of Members: 9,000
Publication(s): *The Bulletin* (quarterly, free to membs)

The Authors League Fund
31 E 32 St, 7th fl, New York, NY 10016
Tel: 212-268-1208 *Fax:* 212-564-5363
E-mail: staff@authorsleaguefund.org
Web Site: www.authorsleaguefund.org
Key Personnel
Pres: Pat Cummings
VP: Sidney Offit
Exec Dir: Isabel Howe
Secy: Peter Straub
Treas: James B Stewart
Founded: 1917
Provides emergency assistance to professional writers facing financial hardship.
Number of Members: 900

The Authors League of America Inc, see The Authors Guild

The Authors Registry Inc
31 E 32 St, 7th fl, New York, NY 10016
Tel: 212-563-6920 *Fax:* 212-564-5363
E-mail: staff@authorsregistry.org

Web Site: www.authorsregistry.org
Key Personnel
Opers Dir: Terry King *E-mail:* tking@authorsregistry.org
A nonprofit corporation that provides a royalty collection & distribution service.
Number of Members: 40,000

The Baker Street Irregulars (BSI)
7938 Mill Stream Circle, Indianapolis, IN 46278
Tel: 317-293-2212; 317-956-6666 (cell)
Web Site: bakerstreetjournal.com
Key Personnel
Wiggins, Chmn: Michael F Whelan
Literary society with a small press operation including a quarterly journal with a Christmas annual & 3-4 published books annually.
Number of Members: 300
Publication(s): *The Baker Street Journal* (quarterly & Christmas annual, $38.50/yr, $49/yr foreign)

Before Columbus Foundation
The Raymond House, 655 13 St, Suite 302, Oakland, CA 94612
SAN: 159-2955
Tel: 510-268-9775
E-mail: info@beforecolumbusfoundation.com
Web Site: www.beforecolumbusfoundation.com
Key Personnel
Founder: Ishmael Reed
Founded: 1976
Provide information, research, consultation & promotional services for contemporary American multicultural writers & publishers. A nonprofit service organization that also sponsors classes, workshops, readings, public events & the annual American Book Awards.

Bibliographical Society of America
PO Box 1537, Lenox Hill Sta, New York, NY 10021-0043
Tel: 212-452-2710 *Fax:* 212-452-2710
E-mail: bsa@bibsocamer.org
Web Site: www.bibsocamer.org
Key Personnel
Pres: Martin Antonetti
Treas: G Scott Clemons
VP: John Chrichton
Exec Dir: Michele E Randall
Secy: Barbara Heritage
Sponsor short-term fellowships for bibliographic projects. Membership open to anyone interested in bibliographic projects & process.
Number of Members: 1,100
New Election: Annually in Jan
Meeting(s): Annual Meeting, New York, NY, Jan (Friday following the 4th Thursday)
Publication(s): *The Papers of the Bibliographical Society of America* (quarterly, free for membs)

Bibliographical Society of the University of Virginia
c/o Alderman Library, University of Virginia, McCormick Rd, Charlottesville, VA 22904
Mailing Address: PO Box 400152, Charlottesville, VA 22904-4152
Tel: 434-924-7013 *Fax:* 434-924-1431
E-mail: bibsoc@virginia.edu
Web Site: bsuva.org
Key Personnel
Pres: G Thomas Tanselle
Exec Secy & Treas: Anne G Ribble
E-mail: ar3g@virginia.edu
Founded: 1947
Scholarly society promoting the study of books as physical objects, the history of the book & of printing & publishing.
Number of Members: 550
Publication(s): *Studies in Bibliography* (annual, $55)

Binding Industries Association (BIA)
Affiliate of Printing Industries of America
200 Deer Run Rd, Sewickley, PA 15143
Web Site: www.printing.org/bia
Key Personnel
VP, Mktg: Lisa Rawa *Tel:* 412-259-1810
E-mail: lrawa@printing.org
Dir: Michael Packard *Tel:* 412-259-1704
E-mail: mpackard@printing.org
Founded: 1955
Trade finishers & loose-leaf manufacturers united to conduct seminars, hold conventions, formulate & maintain industry standards. Bestow annual product of excellence awards.
Number of Members: 100
Publication(s): *The Binding Edge* (quarterly, magazine); *Bound for Excellence* (monthly, newsletter, membs only); *Membership Directory* (in print biennially & online, book)

BISG, see Book Industry Study Group Inc (BISG)

BlackPressUSA, see National Newspaper Publishers Association (NNPA)

BMI®
7 World Trade Ctr, 250 Greenwich St, New York, NY 10007-0030
Tel: 212-586-2000; 212-220-3000
Toll Free Tel: 888-689-5264 (sales); 800-925-8451 (cust rel) *Fax:* 212-246-2163
E-mail: foundation@bmi.com
Web Site: www.bmi.com
Key Personnel
CEO: Michael O'Neill
Pres: Del R Bryant
Sr Dir, Corp Mktg: Darlene Rosado
Founded: 1939
Secure & license the performing rights of music on behalf of its creators.
Number of Members: 600,000
Publication(s): *BMI MusicWorld Online* (monthly)
Branch Office(s)
8730 Sunset Blvd, 3rd fl W, West Hollywood, CA 90069-2211 *Tel:* 310-659-9109
E-mail: losangeles@bmi.com
1691 Michigan Ave, Suite 350, Miami Beach, FL 33139 *Tel:* 305-673-5148 *E-mail:* miami@bmi.com
3340 Peachtree Rd NE, Suite 570, Atlanta, GA 30326 *Tel:* 404-261-5151 *E-mail:* atlanta@bmi.com
10 Music Sq E, Nashville, TN 37203-4399
Tel: 615-401-2000 *E-mail:* nashville@bmi.com
San Jose Bldg, Suite 1008, 1250 Ave Ponce de Leon, Santurce 00907, Puerto Rico *Tel:* 787-754-6490
84 Harley House, Marylebone Rd, London NW1 5HN, United Kingdom *Tel:* (020) 7846 2036
E-mail: london@bmi.com

Book & Periodical Council (BPC)
192 Spadina Ave, Suite 107, Toronto, ON M5T 2C2, Canada
Tel: 416-975-9366 *Fax:* 416-975-1839
E-mail: info@thebpc.ca
Web Site: www.thebpc.ca
Key Personnel
Exec Dir: Anne McClelland
Founded: 1975
Umbrella organization for Canadian associations that are or whose members are primarily involved with the writing, editing, translating, publishing, producing, distributing, lending, marketing, reading & selling of written words.
Number of Members: 32
Publication(s): *Dividends: The Value of Public Libraries in Canada* (free); *Freedom to Read Kit* (annual); *When the Censor Comes* (free online)

Book Industry Guild of New York
PO Box 2001, New York, NY 10113-2001
E-mail: admin@bookindustryguildofny.org
Web Site: www.bookindustryguildofny.org
Key Personnel
Pres: Michael Weinstein
VP: Steve Bedney
Fin Secy & Book Show Comm Co-Chair: Emily Larsen *Tel:* 413-210-1275 *E-mail:* emily.larsen@gmail.com
Founded: 1926
For book publishing production, editorial, design & manufacturing people from the book community. Monthly dinner meetings, book show & educational seminars.
Number of Members: 800

Book Industry Study Group Inc (BISG)
145 W 45 St, Suite 601, New York, NY 10036
Tel: 646-336-7141 *Fax:* 646-336-6214
E-mail: info@bisg.org
Web Site: www.bisg.org
Key Personnel
Exec Dir: Mark Kuyper
Mktg Strategist: Jeanette Zwart *Tel:* 646-336-7141 ext 11 *E-mail:* jeanette@bisg.org
Proj Mgr, Res & Info: Nadine Vassallo *Tel:* 646-336-7141 ext 13 *E-mail:* nadine@bisg.org
Proj Mgr, Standards & Best Practices: Julie Morris *Tel:* 646-336-7141 ext 14 *E-mail:* julie@bisg.org
Coord, Educ & Events: Thomson Guster *Tel:* 646-336-7141 ext 15 *E-mail:* thomson@bisg.org
Founded: 1975
Trade association for policy, standards & research. The member-driven organization uniquely represents all segments of our industry from publishers & e-publishers to paper manufacturers, libraries, authors, printers, wholesalers, retailers & e-tailers, as well as organizations concerned with the book industry as a whole. For over 35 years, BISG has provided a forum for all industry professionals to come together & efficiently address issues & concerns to advance the book community.
Number of Members: 220
New Election: Annually in Sept
Publication(s): *BookStats* (annual)

Book Manufacturers' Institute Inc (BMI)
2 Armand Beach Dr, Suite 1B, Palm Coast, FL 32137-2612
Tel: 386-986-4552 *Fax:* 386-986-4553
E-mail: info@bmibook.com
Web Site: www.bmibook.org
Key Personnel
EVP: Daniel N Bach *E-mail:* dbach@bmibook.com
Founded: 1933
BMI is the leading nationally recognized trade association of the book manufacturing industry.
Number of Members: 80
2016 Meeting(s): Management Conference, Wild Dunes Resort, Isle of Palms, SC, April 24-26, 2016; Annual Conference, Marco Island Marriott Beach Resort, Marco Island, FL, Oct 23-25, 2016
Membership(s): Book Industry Guild of New York; National Association of Manufacturers

Book Publicists of Southern California
714 Crescent Dr, Beverly Hills, CA 90210
Tel: 323-461-3921 *Fax:* 323-461-0917
Web Site: www.bookpublicists.org
Key Personnel
Founder & Pres, Emeritus: Irwin Zucker
Tel: 310-497-4001 (cell) *E-mail:* irwin@promotioninmotion.net
Pres: Patty Weckbaugh
VP: Donna Larsen
Treas: Bruce Braunstein
Publicity: Melinda Sue Worin

Founded: 1976
Literary club. Bimonthly meetings, varied, anything pertinent to promotion of books & authors.
Number of Members: 1,200
New Election: Annually in Nov
Publication(s): *Know Thy Shelf* (6 issues/yr, newsletter, free to membs)

The Book Publishers Association of Alberta (BPAA)
Affiliate of Association of Canadian Publishers (ACP)
10523 100 Ave, Edmonton, AB T5J 0A8, Canada
Tel: 780-424-5060 *Fax:* 780-424-7943
E-mail: info@bookpublishers.ab.ca
Web Site: www.bookpublishers.ab.ca
Key Personnel
Exec Dir: Kieran Leblanc *E-mail:* kleblanc@bookpublishers.ab.ca
Sponsor professional development seminars, workshops & Alberta Book Industry Awards.
Number of Members: 32
Publication(s): *Membership Directory* (free)

Bookbuilders of Boston
115 Webster Woods Lane, North Andover, MA 01845
Tel: 781-378-1361 *Fax:* 419-821-2171
E-mail: office@bbboston.org
Web Site: www.bbboston.org
Key Personnel
Pres: Jamie Carter
Meetings, New England Book Show, seminars & scholarships; nonprofit organization.
New Election: Annually in April
Publication(s): *Directory* (annually, free)

Books for Everybody
111 Queen St E, Suite 320, Toronto, ON M5C 1S2, Canada
Tel: 416-364-3333 *Toll Free Tel:* 888-360-6658 *Fax:* 416-595-5415
Key Personnel
Assoc Publr: Attila Berki *Tel:* 416-364-3333 ext 3160 *E-mail:* aberki@booksforeverybody.com
Founded: 1937
Publish consumer catalogues for independent book stores.
Publication(s): *Books for Everybody* (annual); *Books for Everybody British Columbia Edition*; *Books for Everybody Young Readers Edition*
Membership(s): Canadian Booksellers Association

Boston Authors Club Inc
33 Brayton Rd, Brighton, MA 02135
Tel: 617-783-1357
E-mail: bostonauthors@aol.com
Web Site: www.bostonauthorsclub.org
Key Personnel
Pres: Alan Lawson *E-mail:* lawson@bc.edu
VP: Shirley Moskow *Tel:* 781-862-7697 *E-mail:* shirley.moskow@rtr.com
Founded: 1899
Nonprofit organization promoting discourse & community among authors with various programs & gives annual awards.
Number of Members: 140
New Election: Annually in May
Branch Office(s)
79 Moore Rd, Wayland, MA 01778 *Tel:* 508-358-4098

BPA Worldwide
100 Beard Sawmill Rd, 6th fl, Shelton, CT 06484
Tel: 203-447-2800 *Fax:* 203-447-2900
E-mail: info@bpaww.com
Web Site: www.bpaww.com
Key Personnel
CEO & Pres: Glenn J Hansen *E-mail:* ghansen@bpaww.com
SVP & Chief Quality Offr: Russell Haderer *E-mail:* rhaderer@bpaww.com
SVP, Auditing: Richard J Murphy *E-mail:* rmurphy@bpaww.com
SVP, Busn Devt: Peter D Black *E-mail:* pblack@bpaww.com
SVP, Fin & Admin: Doreen Castignoli *E-mail:* dcastignoli@bpaww.com
Founded: 1931
International, independent, not-for-profit organization whose membership consists of advertiser companies, advertising agencies & publications. Audit all-paid, all-controlled or any combination of paid & controlled circulation for more than 2,600 media properties including business, technical, professional publications, consumer magazines, newspapers, web sites, e-mail, newsletters & face-to-face events-expos & shows as well as more than 2,700 advertising & agency members.
Number of Members: 5,300
Foreign Office(s): PO Box 502458, Dubai Media City, Dubai, United Arab Emirates *Tel:* (04) 3692468 *Fax:* (04) 3697073 *E-mail:* gshashati@bpaww.com
2 John St, London WC1N 2ES, United Kingdom *Tel:* (020) 3405 4255 *E-mail:* fstones@bpaww.com
Branch Office(s)
10119 Maronda Dr, Riverview, FL 33578 *Tel:* 813-741-3142 *Fax:* 813-741-3162
One Concorde Gate, Suite 800, Toronto, ON M3C 3N6, Canada, Contact: Tim Peel *Tel:* 416-487-2418 *Fax:* 416-487-6405 *E-mail:* mpeel@bpaww.com
1010 Rue Sherbrooke Ouest, Bureau 1800, Montreal, QC H2A 2R7, Canada *Tel:* 514-845-0003 *Fax:* 514-845-0905 *E-mail:* mpasquale@bpaww.com
Suite 505, Bldg 4, China Central Palace, 89 Jianguo Rd, Chaoyang District, Beijing 100025, China *Tel:* (010) 8591 0691 *Fax:* (010) 8591 0589 *E-mail:* dchan@bpaww.com
Suite 2640, 26th fl, Anlian Bldg, 4018 Jintian Rd, Futian District, Shenzhen 518026, China *Tel:* (0755) 3395 5735 *Fax:* (0755) 3395 5999

Broadcast Music Inc, see BMI®

Business Forms Management Association (BFMA)
1147 Fleetwood Ave, Madison, WI 53716
Toll Free Tel: 888-367-3078
E-mail: bfma@bfma.org
Web Site: www.bfma.org
Key Personnel
CFO: Ray Killam
Pres: Kelly Halseth
VP, Membership: Mike Mulcahy
VP, Opers: Robin Miller
VP, Progs: Shantelle Boatright
Dir, Educ: J P Terry
Dir, Membership: Shannon Lerner
Founded: 1958
Sponsor professional training in all aspects of information resource management; classes are conducted in major cities in the US & CN. Bestow the association's highest award, the Jo Warner Award, to professionals in the information resources industry. Recipients do not have to be BFMA members.
Number of Members: 600

Business Marketing Association (BMA)
Division of Association of National Advertisers (ANA)
708 Third Ave, New York, NY 10017
Tel: 212-697-5950 *Fax:* 212-687-7310
E-mail: info@marketing.org
Web Site: www.marketing.org
Key Personnel
Exec Dir: Michael Palmer *Tel:* 646-369-4898 *E-mail:* mpalmer@marketing.org
Sr Dir: Arthur Tharpe *Tel:* 212-455-8004 *E-mail:* atharpe@marketing.org
Fin Dir: Lana Mavreshko *Tel:* 212-340-0087 *E-mail:* lmavreshko@marketing.org
Founded: 1922 (as National Industrial Advertising Association)
Provides information & resources to business-to-business marketers & marketing communicators.
Number of Members: 2,200
Publication(s): *BMA Buzz* (monthly, newsletter)

Canada Council for the Arts (Conseil des arts du Canada)
150 Elgin St, Ottawa, ON K1P 1L4, Canada
Mailing Address: PO Box 1047, Ottawa, ON K1P 5V8, Canada
Tel: 613-566-4414 *Toll Free Tel:* 800-263-5588 (CN only) *Fax:* 613-566-4390
E-mail: info@canadacouncil.ca
Web Site: www.canadacouncil.ca
Key Personnel
Admin Coord, Writing & Publg Section: Brigitte Fontille *Tel:* 613-566-4414 ext 4571 *E-mail:* brigitte.fontille@canadacouncil.ca
Federal cultural granting agency for Canadian literature. See web site for various awards, prize contests, fellowships & grants.

Canadian Authors Association (CAA)
6 West St N, Suite 203, Orillia, ON L3V 5B8, Canada
Tel: 705-325-3926 *Toll Free Tel:* 866-216-6222
E-mail: admin@canadianauthors.org
Web Site: www.canadianauthors.org
Key Personnel
Exec Dir: Anita Purcell
Founded: 1921
Encourage & develop a climate favorable to the literary arts in Canada. Assistance to professional & emerging writers. Represent the concerns & interests of members.
Number of Members: 600
Publication(s): *The Bookshelf* (annual, complementary); *Canadian Writers Guide* (biennial, $36)

Canadian Bookbinders and Book Artists Guild (CBBAG)
80 Ward St, Suite 207, Toronto, ON M6H 4A6, Canada
Tel: 416-581-1071
E-mail: cbbag@cbbag.ca
Web Site: www.cbbag.ca
Key Personnel
Pres: Mary MacIntyre
Founded: 1983
Presents workshops & courses on a wide variety of topics, including bookbinding, box making, paper making & decorating, letterpress printing, paper conservation & more. Also maintains a reference library & an audio-visual catalogue.
Number of Members: 600
Publication(s): *Book Arts arts due livre* Canada (semiannual, May & Nov, magazine)

Canadian Booksellers Association (CBA)
Division of Retail Council of Canada (RCC)
1881 Yonge St, Suite 800, Toronto, ON M4S 3C4, Canada
Tel: 416-922-6678 *Toll Free Tel:* 888-373-8245 *Toll Free Fax:* 877-790-4271
E-mail: info@retailcouncil.org
Web Site: www.retailcouncil.org
Key Personnel
CEO & Pres, Retail Council of Canada: Diane J Briseboas
Founded: 1952
For firms or persons actively engaged in the retail sale of books & supplies.

Canadian Cataloguing in Publication Program
Library & Archives Canada, 395 Wellington St, Ottawa, ON K1A 0N4, Canada
Tel: 819-994-6881 *Toll Free Tel:* 866-578-7777 (CN) *Fax:* 819-934-6777
E-mail: cip@lac-bac.gc.ca
Web Site: www.collectionscanada.gc.ca/cip/index-e.html
Voluntary program of cooperation between publishers & libraries.
Publication(s): *Livres a Paraitre/Forthcoming Books* (monthly, free)

Canadian Children's Book Centre
40 Orchard View Blvd, Suite 217, Toronto, ON M4R 1B9, Canada
Tel: 416-975-0010 *Fax:* 416-975-8970
E-mail: info@bookcentre.ca
Web Site: www.bookcentre.ca
Key Personnel
Exec Dir: Charlotte Teeple *E-mail:* charlotte@bookcentre.ca
Lib Coord: Meghan Howe *E-mail:* meghan@bookcentre.ca
Outreach Educ Coord: Sandra O'Brien *E-mail:* sandra@bookcentre.ca
Mktg & Website Coord: Camilia Kahrizi *E-mail:* camilia@bookcentre.ca
Prog Coord: Shannon Howe Barnes *E-mail:* shannon@bookcentre.ca
Founded: 1976
National not-for-profit organization to promote the reading, writing & illustrating of Canadian books for young readers. We provide programs, publications & resources for teachers, librarians, authors, illustrators, publishers, booksellers & parents.
Number of Members: 748
Publication(s): *Best Books for Kids & Teens* (semiannual, catalog, $5.95/issue); *Canadian Children's Book News* (4 times/yr, magazine, $4.95/issue, $24.95/single subn includes copies of Best Books for Kids & Teens)

Canadian Circulations Audit Board, see CCAB Inc

Canadian Education Association (Association canadienne d'education)
119 Spadina Ave, Suite 705, Toronto, ON M5V 2L1, Canada
Tel: 416-591-6300 *Toll Free Tel:* 866-803-9549 *Fax:* 416-591-5345
E-mail: info@cea-ace.ca
Web Site: www.cea-ace.ca
Key Personnel
CEO: Ron Canuel *Tel:* 416-591-6300 ext 227 *E-mail:* rcanuel@cea-ace.ca
COO: Gilles Latour *Tel:* 416-591-6300 ext 237 *E-mail:* glatour@cea-ace.ca
Dir, Communs: Max Cooke *Tel:* 416-591-6300 ext 225 *E-mail:* mcooke@cea-ace.ca
Founded: 1891
A national bilingual, charitable organization that promotes transformation in education.
Number of Members: 304
New Election: Annually in Sept or Oct
2016 Meeting(s): Dropping Out-What Neuroscience Can Teach Us, Quebec City, Quebec, Nov 4-5, 2016
Publication(s): *Education Canada* (4 issues/yr, magazine, $53/yr US, $37.29/yr CN, $67.74/yr elsewhere; all prices CAD, price includes shipping & applicable taxes (CN only))

Canadian Institute for Studies in Publishing
Simon Fraser University at Harbour Centre, 515 W Hastings St, Suite 3576, Vancouver, BC V6B 5K3, Canada
Tel: 778-782-5242 *Fax:* 778-782-5239
E-mail: ccsp-info@sfu.ca
Web Site: publishing.sfu.ca
Key Personnel
Prog Mgr: Jo-Anne Ray *Tel:* 778-782-5242
Founded: 1987
Undergraduate, graduate & noncredit courses; research on print & digital publishing.

Canadian ISBN Agency
Unit of Library & Archives Canada
Library & Archives Canada, 395 Wellington St, Ottawa, ON K1A 0N4, Canada
Tel: 613-996-5115 *Toll Free Tel:* 866-578-7777 (CN & US) *Fax:* 613-995-6274
E-mail: isbn@lac-bac.gc.ca
Web Site: www.collectionscanada.gc.ca/ciss-ssci/index-e.html

Canadian Library Association-CLA (Association Canadienne des bibliotheques)
1150 Morrison Dr, Suite 400, Ottawa, ON K2H 8S9, Canada
Tel: 613-232-9625 *Fax:* 613-563-9895
E-mail: info@cla.ca
Web Site: www.cla.ca
Key Personnel
Exec Dir: Valoree McKay *Tel:* 613-232-9625 ext 306 *E-mail:* vmckay@cla.ca
Founded: 1946
National organization of personal & institutional members devoted to improving the quality of library & information service in Canada & developing higher standards of librarianship.
Number of Members: 1,500
2016 Meeting(s): National Conference & Trade Show, Halifax, NS, CN, June 1-4, 2016
Publication(s): *Feliciter* (6 issues/yr, free to membs, $95/yr to nonmembs)

Canadian Newspaper Association
890 Yonge St, Suite 200, Toronto, ON M4W 3P4, Canada
Tel: 416-923-3567; 416-482-1090 *Toll Free Tel:* 877-305-2262 *Fax:* 416-923-7206; 416-482-1908
E-mail: info@newspaperscanada.ca
Web Site: www.newspaperscanada.ca
Key Personnel
CEO & Pres: John Hinds *Tel:* 416-923-3567 ext 244 *E-mail:* jhinds@newspaperscanada.ca
Dir, Pub Aff: Adele Ritchie *E-mail:* aritchie@newspaperscanada.ca
Founded: 1996
An organization providing service to its members in the area of marketing, member services & contesting legislation that is potentially harmful to newspapers & freedom of the press in general. The association brings the wisdom & dedication of all its members to foster & nurture a free press committed to providing the best possible service to its readers.
Number of Members: 99

Canadian Publishers' Council (CPC)
250 Merton St, Suite 203, Toronto, ON M4S 1B1, Canada
Tel: 416-322-7011 *Fax:* 416-322-6999
Web Site: www.pubcouncil.ca
Key Personnel
Exec Dir, External Rel & Copyright: Jacqueline Hushion *Tel:* 416-322-7011 ext 222 *E-mail:* jhushion@pubcouncil.ca
Exec Dir, Trade & Higher Educ Publishers Groups: Colleen O'Neill *Tel:* 416-322-7011 ext 226 *E-mail:* coneill@pubcouncil.ca
Acctg Offr: Joanna Ames *Tel:* 416-322-7011 ext 228 *E-mail:* james@pubcouncil.ca
Founded: 1910
Represents the interests of Canadian publishing companies that publish books & other media for elementary & secondary schools, colleges & universities, professional & reference markets, the retail & library markets.
Number of Members: 20
New Election: Annually in Feb
Publication(s): *Publishing: A View from the Inside* ($2 plus GST); *Who Buys Books?* ($50 plus GST)
Membership(s): International Federation of Reproduction Rights Organizations; International Publishers Association

Canadian Society of Children's Authors Illustrators & Performers (CANSCAIP)
720 Bathurst St, Suite 503, Toronto, ON M5S 2R4, Canada
Tel: 416-515-1559
E-mail: office@canscaip.org
Web Site: www.canscaip.org
Key Personnel
Pres: Sharon Jennings
VP: Lena Coakley
Admin Dir: Helena Aalto
Founded: 1977
Dedicated to the celebration & promotion of Canadian children's authors, illustrators & performers & their work. Provide promotional & networking opportunities.
Number of Members: 1,000
New Election: April even yrs
Meeting(s): Packaging Your Imagination, Toronto, Ontario, CN, annually in Nov
Publication(s): *Canscaip News* (quarterly, $45/yr nonmembs, free to membs, electronic)

CASW, see Council for the Advancement of Science Writing (CASW)

Catholic Book Publishers Association Inc, see Association of Catholic Publishers Inc

Catholic Library Association
8550 United Plaza Blvd, Suite 1001, Baton Rouge, LA 70809-2256
Tel: 225-408-4417
E-mail: cla2@cathla.org
Web Site: www.cathla.org
Key Personnel
Pres: Mary Kelleher *Tel:* 225-408-4417 *E-mail:* kellehm@stthom.edu
Exec Dir: Bland O'Connor *E-mail:* cla2@cathla.org
Founded: 1921
Initiate, foster & encourage activities & library programs that promote literature & libraries of a Catholic nature & of an ecumenical spirit.
Number of Members: 1,000
Publication(s): *Catholic Library World* (4 issues/yr, $100 nonmembs US; $140/yr foreign & $25 S&H)

Catholic Press Association of the United States & Canada
205 W Monroe St, Suite 470, Chicago, IL 60606
Tel: 312-380-6789 *Fax:* 312-361-0256
E-mail: cathjourn@catholicpress.org
Web Site: www.catholicpress.org
Key Personnel
Exec Dir: Timothy M Walter *E-mail:* twalter@catholicpress.org
Founded: 1911
Writing, publishing, advertising; all facets of publishing.
Number of Members: 800
2016 Meeting(s): Catholic Media Conference, St Louis, MO, June 1-3, 2016
Publication(s): *The Catholic Journalist* (monthly (exc Aug), $18/yr US, $24/yr CN & elsewhere); *Catholic Press Directory* (annual)

CBA: The Association for Christian Retail
1365 Garden of the Gods Rd, Suite 105, Colorado Springs, CO 80907
Tel: 719-265-9895 *Toll Free Tel:* 800-252-1950 *Fax:* 719-272-3508
E-mail: info@cbaonline.org

Web Site: cbaonline.org
Key Personnel
Chmn of the Bd: Sue Smith *E-mail:* sue.smith@bakerbookhouse.com
Vice Chair: Andrew Criswell, Sr *E-mail:* andrew@pdbcs.com
Pres: Curtis Riskey *E-mail:* criskey@cbaonline.org
Treas: Bill Covey *E-mail:* billc@dayspring.com
Secy: Robin Hogan *E-mail:* rhogan@cccinfo.org
Founded: 1950
Association members are Christian publishers, music publishers & gift houses.
Number of Members: 3,200
New Election: Annually in July
2016 Meeting(s): International Christian Retail Show (ICRS), Duke Energy Convention Center, 525 Elm St, Cincinnati, OH, June 26-29, 2016
Publication(s): *CBA Retailers+Resources* (monthly, magazine, $49.95/yr membs, $59.95/yr nonmembs)

CCAB Inc
Division of BPA Worldwide
One Concorde Gate, Suite 800, Toronto, ON M3C 3N6, Canada
Tel: 416-487-2418 *Fax:* 416-487-6405
E-mail: info@bpaww.com
Web Site: www.bpaww.com
Key Personnel
VP: Tim Peel *E-mail:* mpeel@bpaww.com
Founded: 1931
Number of Members: 550

The Center for Book Arts
28 W 27 St, 3rd fl, New York, NY 10001
Tel: 212-481-0295
E-mail: info@centerforbookarts.org
Web Site: www.centerforbookarts.org
Key Personnel
Exec Dir & Curator: Alexander Campos
Founded: 1974
Nonprofit, provides workspace, education, exhibitions & slide registry for book artists, hand papermakers & letter press printers; publication of fine art editions, lectures, outreach program.
Number of Members: 6,500
Publication(s): *Exhibition Catalogs* (4 issues/yr, $15 membs, $20 nonmembs)

The Center for Exhibition Industry Research (CEIR)
12700 Park Central Dr, Suite 308, Dallas, TX 75251
Tel: 972-687-9242 *Fax:* 972-692-6020
E-mail: info@ceir.org
Web Site: www.ceir.org
Key Personnel
CEO & Pres: Brian D Casey *Tel:* 972-687-9219 *E-mail:* bcasey@ceir.org
Exec Dir: Cathy Breden *Tel:* 972-687-9201 *E-mail:* cbreden@ceir.org
Promote the exhibition industry by promoting the value & benefits of exhibitions in an integrated marketing program through research, information & communications.
Number of Members: 600

The Center for Fiction
17 E 47 St, New York, NY 10017
Tel: 212-755-6710 *Fax:* 212-826-0831
E-mail: info@centerforfiction.org
Web Site: centerforfiction.org/awards
Key Personnel
Chmn & Pres: Peter Ginna
Exec Dir: Noreen Tomassi *E-mail:* noreen@centerforfiction.org
Founded: 1820 (as the Mercantile Library)
Devoted to the vital art of fiction & to encourage people to read & value fiction. Circulating library of mainly fiction titles. Monthly programs, literary lectures & readings. Writers' studio. Inquiries invited.
Number of Members: 500
Publication(s): *The Literarian* (quarterly, newsletter, $5.95/issue (print), online free)

The Center for the Book in the Library of Congress
The Library of Congress, 101 Independence Ave SE, Washington, DC 20540-4920
Tel: 202-707-5221 *Fax:* 202-707-0269
E-mail: cfbook@loc.gov
Web Site: www.read.gov; www.read.gov/cfb
Key Personnel
Dir: John Y Cole *E-mail:* jcole@loc.gov
Communs Offr: Guy Lamolinara
Prog Offr: Anne Boni
Founded: 1977 (est by law)
Uses the influence & resources of the Library of Congress to stimulate public interest in books & reading & to encourage the study of books. Its program of symposia, projects, lectures, exhibitions & publications is supported by tax-deductible contributions from corporations & individuals. National reading promotion network includes more than 50 affiliated state centers & more than 80 educational & civic organizations.

Chicago Women in Publishing
PO Box 268107, Chicago, IL 60626
Tel: 773-508-0351 *Fax:* 435-604-6049
E-mail: info@cwip.org
Web Site: www.cwip.org
Key Personnel
VP, Busn Opers: Alexandra Uth *E-mail:* vp_bus_op@cwip.org
Secy: Jill Welsh *E-mail:* secretary@cwip.org
Founded: 1972
Jobline employment listing service, monthly newsletter, monthly program meetings, free-lance directory, annual conference, membership directory.
Number of Members: 500
Publication(s): *CWIP Clips* (6 issues/yr, newsletter, free to membs)

The Children's Book Council (CBC)
54 W 39 St, 14th fl, New York, NY 10018
Tel: 212-966-1990 *Toll Free Fax:* 888-807-9355 (orders only)
E-mail: cbc.info@cbcbooks.org
Web Site: www.cbcbooks.org
Key Personnel
Exec Dir: Jon Colman *E-mail:* jon.colman@cbcbooks.org
Communs Dir: Nicole Deming *E-mail:* nicole.deming@cbcbooks.org
Mgr, Events & Progs/Libn: Ayanna Coleman *E-mail:* ayanna.coleman@cbcbooks.org
Founded: 1945
Nonprofit trade association of children's book publishers & related companies. Publish reading promotion display & informational materials. New electronic edition of Children's Books: Awards & Prizes; provides professional education & online member services.
Number of Members: 80
New Election: Annually in Sept
2016 Meeting(s): Children's Book Week, Nationwide across the USA, May 2-8, 2016
2017 Meeting(s): Children's Book Week, Nationwide across the USA, May 1-7, 2017
2018 Meeting(s): Children's Book Week, Nationwide across the USA, May 7-13, 2018
2019 Meeting(s): Children's Book Week, Nationwide across the USA, May 6-12, 2019
2020 Meeting(s): Children's Book Week, Nationwide across the USA, May 4-10, 2020
Publication(s): *Awards & Prizes Online* (online database, annual, $150); *CBC Features* (semi-annual, $60 one-time charge)

Christian Booksellers Association, see CBA: The Association for Christian Retail

CIP Program, see Canadian Cataloguing in Publication Program

City & Regional Magazine Association
1970 E Grand Ave, Suite 330, El Segundo, CA 90245
Tel: 310-364-0193 *Fax:* 310-364-0196
E-mail: admin@citymag.org
Web Site: www.citymag.org
Key Personnel
Pres: Todd Matherne
VP: Christine Allison
Secy-Treas: Rich Gamble
Exec Dir: C James Dowden *Tel:* 310-364-0193 ext 11
PR Coord: Barton Ortberg *Tel:* 310-364-0193 ext 16 *E-mail:* barton.ortberg@dowdenmanagement.com
The purpose of the association is to facilitate professional development & training opportunities for member magazines & provide opportunities to exchange information & ideas. Also the sponsor of CRMA Awards Competition, The City & Regional Magazine Award Program at the University of Missouri School of Journalism; city & regional magazine competition as well as an annual conference.
Number of Members: 89
Publication(s): *CRMA Newsletter* (free to membs, electronic)

Colorado Authors' League
PO Box 24905, Denver, CO 80224
Web Site: coloradoauthors.org
Key Personnel
Pres: Michael Madigan *E-mail:* madideasllc@gmail.com
Founded: 1931
Organization of independent, professional writers united to further members' success.
Number of Members: 250

Committee On Scholarly Editions
Subsidiary of Modern Language Association of America (MLA)
c/o Modern Language Association of America, 26 Broadway, 3rd fl, New York, NY 10004-1789
Tel: 646-576-5044 *Fax:* 646-458-0030
Web Site: www.mla.org
Key Personnel
Sr Acqs Ed: James C Hatch
Founded: 1979
Assists editors & publishers in preparing reliable scholarly editions.
Number of Members: 9

Community of Literary Magazines & Presses (CLMP)
Formerly Council of Literary Magazines & Presses (CLMP)
154 Christopher St, Suite 3C, New York, NY 10014-9110
Tel: 212-741-9110 *Fax:* 212-741-9112
E-mail: info@clmp.org
Web Site: www.clmp.org
Key Personnel
Exec Dir: Jeffrey Lependorf *Tel:* 212-741-9110 ext 14 *E-mail:* jlependorf@clmp.org
Dir, Membership: Ted Dodson
Progs Dir: Kathy Daneman *E-mail:* kdaneman@clmp.org
Founded: 1967
A national nonprofit organization that provides services to small independent literary magazine & book publishers, including technical assistance, various publications, marketing workshops, an online directory of literary magazines

& granting programs for literary magazines & presses.
Number of Members: 500

Connecticut Authors & Publishers Association (CAPA)
PO Box 715, Avon, CT 06001-0715
Tel: 203-729-5335 *Fax:* 203-729-5335
Web Site: www.aboutcapa.com
Key Personnel
Founder: Brian Jud *E-mail:* brianjud@bookmarketing.com
Founded: 1994
Number of Members: 150
Meeting(s): Monthly Meeting, Avon Community Center, Avon, CT, 3rd Saturday of the month
Publication(s): *The Authority* (monthly, newsletter, free with membership)

Conseil des arts du Canada, see Canada Council for the Arts (Conseil des arts du Canada)

Copywriter's Council of America (CCA)
Division of The Linick Group Inc
CCA Bldg, 7 Putter Lane, Middle Island, NY 11953-1920
Mailing Address: PO Box 102, Middle Island, NY 11953-0102
Tel: 631-924-8555 *Fax:* 631-924-8555
E-mail: cca4dmcopy@gmail.com
Web Site: www.AndrewLinickDirectMarketing.com/Copywriters-Council.html; www.NewWorldPressBooks.com
Key Personnel
Chmn, Consulting Group: Andrew S Linick, PhD *E-mail:* andrew@asklinick.com
Pres: Gaylen Andrews
VP: Roger Dextor
Dir, Spec Projs: Barbara Deal
Freelance direct response advertising copywriters, direct marketing consultants, PR & communication specialists & marketing researchers. Cover business-to-business, consumer & industrial markets. Creative services covering all media, all products & services A-Z, e-commerce, e-marketing, e-targeted public relations. Provide comprehensive graphic redesign/new web site content development, interactive services with marketing web site makeover advice for first-time authors, self-publishers, professionals & entrepreneurs. Specialize in flash, animation, merchant accounts, online advertising/PR, links to top search engines, consulting on a 100% satisfaction guarantee. Free site evaluation for LMP readers.
Number of Members: 25,000
Publication(s): *The Digest* (quarterly, for membs only, ezine, $40)

Corporation for Public Broadcasting (CPB)
401 Ninth St NW, Washington, DC 20004-2129
Tel: 202-879-9600
Web Site: www.cpb.org
Key Personnel
CEO & Pres: Patricia de Stacy Harrison
COO & EVP: Vincent Curren
CFO & Treas: William P Tayman, Jr
EVP, Corp & Pub Aff: Michael Levy
SVP & Gen Coun: Westwood Smithers, Jr
SVP & Corp Secy: Teresa Safon
Support the nation's public TV & public radio industry through federally appropriated funds. Conduct support services & to stimulate the creation of programming on TV, radio & online.

Corporation of Professional Librarians of Quebec
1453, rue Beaubien Est, Bureau 215, Montreal, QC H2G 3C6, Canada
Tel: 514-845-3327 *Fax:* 514-845-1618
E-mail: info@cbpq.qc.ca
Web Site: www.cbpq.qc.ca
Key Personnel
Exec Dir: Regine Horinstein
Founded: 1969
Publications, continuing education for information professionals.
Number of Members: 700
Publication(s): *Argus* (3 issues/yr, $48 CN, $50 foreign)

Council for Advancement & Support of Education (CASE)
1307 New York Ave NW, Suite 1000, Washington, DC 20005-4701
Tel: 202-328-CASE (328-2273) *Fax:* 202-387-4973
E-mail: membersupportcenter@case.org
Web Site: www.case.org
Key Personnel
Pres: John Lippincott *Tel:* 202-478-5655 *E-mail:* lippincott@case.org
VP, Busn & Fin: Donald Falkenstein *Tel:* 202-478-5637 *E-mail:* falkenstein@case.org
Dir, Communs: Pam Russell *Tel:* 202-478-5680 *E-mail:* russell@case.org
Founded: 1974
International association of educational institutions. Helps its members build stronger relationships with their alumni & donors, raise funds for campus projects, produce recruitment materials, market their institutions to prospective students, diversity the profession & foster public support of education.
Number of Members: 23,500
Publication(s): *Currents* (9 issues/yr (3 double issues), $150/yr, $220/2 yrs, $180/yr intl, $280/2 yrs intl)

Council for the Advancement of Science Writing (CASW)
PO Box 910, Hedgesville, WV 25427
Tel: 304-754-6786
Web Site: www.casw.org
Key Personnel
Exec Dir: Rosalind Reid *E-mail:* rosreid@gmail.com
Administrator: Diane McGurgan *E-mail:* diane@casw.org
Founded: 1959
To advance science writing.
2016 Meeting(s): New Horizons in Science, Texas Biomedical Research Institute, San Antonio, TX, Oct 20-Nov 2, 2106

Council of Literary Magazines & Presses (CLMP), see Community of Literary Magazines & Presses (CLMP)

CWA/SCA Canada
Affiliate of Canadian Labour Congress
2200 Prince of Wales Dr, Suite 301, Ottawa, ON K2E 6Z9, Canada
Tel: 613-820-9777 *Toll Free Tel:* 877-486-4292 *Fax:* 613-820-8188
E-mail: info@cwa-scacanada.ca
Web Site: www.cwa-scacanada.ca
Key Personnel
Pres: Martin O'Hanlon *Tel:* 613-820-8460 *E-mail:* mohanlon@cwa-scacanada.ca
Contracts Coord: Marj Botsford *E-mail:* mbotsford@cwa-scacanada.ca
Fin Coord: Joanne Scheel *E-mail:* jscheel@cwa-scacanada.ca
Founded: 1995 (as TNG Canada)
Media union representing members in Canada.
Affiliate of: The Newspaper Guild, Communication Workers of America (CWA) & Canadian Labour Congress.
Number of Members: 7,000

Deadline Club
Division of Society of Professional Journalists
c/o Salmagundi Club, 47 Fifth Ave, New York, NY 10003
Tel: 646-481-7584
E-mail: info@deadlineclub.org
Web Site: www.deadlineclub.org
Key Personnel
Chairwoman: J Alex Tarquinio
Pres: Peter Szekely
Secy: Melissa Heule
VP, Awards Contest: Michael Arena
VP, Awards Dinner: Jacqueline Leo
VP, Membership: Polly Whittell
Founded: 1925
Monthly meetings. Membership includes professionals working in print, broadcast, online & journalism education. Professional membership $30, student membership $20. Must be SPJ member.
Number of Members: 300
Meeting(s): Annual Awards Dinner, Waldorf Astoria, New York, NY
Publication(s): *Deadliner Express* (newsletter); *Quill* (6 issues/yr, magazine, free to membs, $75/yr nonmembs); *SPJ Leads* (weekly, newsletter, free to membs)

Direct Marketing Association (DMA)
1120 Avenue of the Americas, New York, NY 10036-6700
SAN: 692-6487
Tel: 212-768-7277 *Fax:* 212-302-6714
E-mail: memberservices@the-dma.org
Web Site: thedma.org
Key Personnel
CEO: Thomas J Benton
VP, Conferences & Events: Paul A McDonnough
Sr Dir, Memb Communs & Sr Ed: Susan Taplinger *Tel:* 212-790-1589
Dir, Educ & Prof Devt: Michelle Tiletnick
Founded: 1917
A member organization representing the direct marketing business to legislators, regulators & the media, also offering educational & networking experiences for members.
2016 Meeting(s): DMA2016, Los Angeles Convention Center, Los Angeles, CA, Oct 16-19, 2016
2017 Meeting(s): DMA2017, New Orleans Convention Center, New Orleans, LA, Oct 8-10, 2017
Publication(s): *3D-DMA Daily Digest* (3 times/wk)
Branch Office(s)
1615 "L" St NW, Suite 1100, Washington, DC 20036 *Tel:* 202-955-5030 *Fax:* 202-955-0085

Dog Writers' Association of America Inc (DWAA)
66 Adams St, Jamestown, NY 14701
Tel: 716-484-6155
E-mail: dogwriter@windstream.net
Web Site: www.dwaa.org
Key Personnel
Pres: Ida Estep, Esq *Tel:* 252-478-6088 *Fax:* 252-478-6089 *E-mail:* ida@dogwriters.org
VP & Contest Chair: Elaine Gerwitz *Tel:* 805-418-7899 *Fax:* 821-374-9231 *E-mail:* elaine@dogwriters.org
Treas: Marsha Pugh *E-mail:* marsha@dogwriters.org
Secy: Susan M Ewing *E-mail:* su@dogwriters.org
Founded: 1935
Provide information about dogs (sport, breeding & ownership) & assist writers in gaining access to exhibitions. Annual writing competition.
Number of Members: 545
Meeting(s): Annual Meeting, Hotel Pennsylvania, 401 Seventh Ave, New York, NY, Feb
Publication(s): *Ruff Drafts* (quarterly, newsletter, free to membs)

Editorial Freelancers Association (EFA)
71 W 23 St, 4th fl, New York, NY 10010-4102
Tel: 212-929-5400 *Toll Free Tel:* 866-929-5425 *Fax:* 212-929-5439 *Toll Free Fax:* 866-929-5439
E-mail: office@the-efa.org
Web Site: www.the-efa.org
Key Personnel
Exec: William P Keenan, Jr; J P Partland
Founded: 1970
A nonprofit, volunteer-based professional association of freelance editors, writers, copy editors, proofreaders, indexers, production specialists, researchers & translators. Provides job listing service, courses, member directory & related professional services. More than 20 chapters nationwide.
Number of Members: 2,300
Publication(s): *EFA Directory* (online, free); *EFA Newsletter* (6 issues/yr, newsletter, free to membs)

Editors' Association of Canada (Association canadienne des reviseurs)
27 Carlton St, Suite 502, Toronto, ON M5B 1L2, Canada
Tel: 416-975-1379 *Toll Free Tel:* 866-CAN-EDIT (226-3348) *Fax:* 416-975-1637
E-mail: info@editors.ca; info@reviseurs.ca
Web Site: www.editors.ca; www.reviseurs.ca
Key Personnel
Exec Dir: Carolyn L Burke
E-mail: executivedirector@editors.ca
Communs Mgr: Michelle Ou
E-mail: communications@editors.ca
Founded: 1979
Promotes professional editing as key in producing effective communication. Our members work with individuals in the corporate, technical, government, not-for-profit & publishing sectors. Sponsor professional development seminars, promotes & maintains high standards of editing & publishing in Canada, establishes guidelines to help editors secure fair pay & good working conditions, helps both in-house & freelance editors to network & cooperates with other publishing associations in areas of common concern. The association is incorporated federally as a not-for-profit organization & is governed at the national level by an executive council.
Number of Members: 1,500
New Election: Annually in June
Publication(s): *Active Voice (La Voix Active)* (semiannual, newsletter, free to membs)
Membership(s): Book & Periodical Council; Cultural Human Resources Council

Education Writers Association (EWA)
3516 Connecticut Ave NW, Washington, DC 20008-2401
Tel: 202-452-9830 *Fax:* 202-452-9837
E-mail: ewa@ewa.org
Web Site: www.ewa.org
Key Personnel
COO: George Dieter *E-mail:* gdieter@ewa.org
Exec Dir: Caroline W Hendrie *E-mail:* chendrie@ewa.org
Asst Dir: Lori Crouch *E-mail:* lcrouch@ewa.org
Multimedia Mgr: Glen Baity *E-mail:* gbaity@ewa.org
Founded: 1947
Professional organization of members of the media who cover education at all levels with a mission to increase the quality & quantity of education coverage to create a better informed society. Conferences, seminars, newsletters, publications, employment services, freelance referral, workshops & national awards.
Number of Members: 3,000
Publication(s): *Standards for Education Reporters* (free)

Educational Book & Media Association (EBMA)
37 Main St, Suite 203, Warrenton, VA 20186
Mailing Address: PO Box 3363, Warrenton, VA 20188
Tel: 540-318-7770 *Fax:* 202-962-3939
E-mail: info@edupaperback.org
Web Site: www.edupaperback.org
Key Personnel
Pres: Jennifer Allen
VP: Jill Faherty
Treas: Joyce Skokut
Exec Dir: Brian Gorg
Meeting Mgr: Maureen Gelwicks
Founded: 1975
To develop better techniques & procedures for the sales, marketing & distribution of paperback books, prebound books & related media in the school & library markets. Regular membership consists of educational paperback & prebound book wholesalers; associate members are paperback publishers.
Number of Members: 125
Meeting(s): Annual Meeting, Jan

Epicomm
Formerly AMSP/NAPL/NAQP
1800 Diagonal Rd, Suite 320, Alexandria, VA 22314-2862
Tel: 703-836-9200
E-mail: webmaster@epicomm.org
Web Site: epicomm.org
Key Personnel
Pres & CEO: Ken Garner *Tel:* 703-972-2730
E-mail: kgarner@epicomm.org
EVP: Dean D'Ambrosi *Tel:* 201-523-6314
E-mail: ddambrosi@epicomm.org
SVP & Chief Economist: Andrew D Paparozzi *Tel:* 201-523-6353 *E-mail:* apaparozzi@epicomm.org
Founded: 2014 (through merger of AMSP, NAPL & NAQP)
Association for leaders in print, mail, fulfillment & marketing services. Epicomm provides management tools & learning & professional development opportunities to help make informed business decisions in an ever-changing market environment.
Number of Members: 3,600
Publication(s): *Bottom Line* (6 issues/yr, magazine); *Management Bulletin* (quarterly, newsletter); *Owner Operator* (quarterly, newsletter); *REVIEW* (monthly, newsletter, electronic); *State of the Industry Update* (quarterly, newsletter)
Branch Office(s)
One Meadowlands Plaza, Suite 1511, East Rutherford, NJ 07073 *Tel:* 201-634-9600

Evangelical Christian Publishers Association (ECPA)
9633 S 48 St, Suite 195, Phoenix, AZ 85044-5697
Tel: 480-966-3998 *Fax:* 480-966-1944
E-mail: info@ecpa.org
Web Site: www.ecpa.org
Founded: 1974
Trade association supporting Christian publishers worldwide. Provides professional seminars, compiles statistical studies & presents religious book awards.
Number of Members: 280
2016 Meeting(s): Leadership Summit & Annual Meeting, Nashville, TN, May 3-4, 2016
Membership(s): BISG

Evangelical Press Association (EPA)
PO Box 20198, El Cajon, CA 92021
Toll Free Tel: 888-311-1731
E-mail: info@evangelicalpress.com
Web Site: www.evangelicalpress.com
Key Personnel
Exec Dir: Lamar Keener
CFO: Lamar Keener
Founded: 1948
Professional association of Christian freelancers, associates, magazines, newsletters, newspapers & content-rich web sites.
Number of Members: 300
2016 Meeting(s): Annual Convention, Lancaster Marriott at Penn Sq, 25 S Queen St, Lancaster, PA, April 6-8, 2016
Publication(s): *Liaison* (3 times/yr, newsletter)

FAPA, see Florida Authors & Publishers Association Inc (FAPA)

Federation of BC Writers
PO Box 16028, 617 Belmont St, New Westminster, BC V3M 6W6, Canada
E-mail: info@bcwriters.ca
Web Site: bcwriters.ca
Key Personnel
Pres: Coco Aders-Weremczuk
Exec Dir: Craig Spence
Founded: 1976
Not-for-profit organization established to contribute to a supportive environment for writing in the province. Writers of all levels working in all genres & specialties welcome. We publish a magazine & hold readings, workshops & literary competitions.
Number of Members: 400
New Election: Annually in May
Publication(s): *WordWorks*

Florida Authors & Publishers Association Inc (FAPA)
PO Box 915822, Longwood, FL 32791
E-mail: member.services@floridapublishersassociation.com
Web Site: www.floridapublishersassociation.com
Key Personnel
Pres: Mark Wayne Adams *E-mail:* president@floridapublishersassociation.com
Founded: 1983
Networking seminars, newsletter, publishing, book shows, workshops, small presses, independents & self-publishers; annual President's Book Award competition. Affiliate of IBPA (Independent Book Publishers Association), AAP (Association of American Publishers) & APSS (Association of Publishers for Small Sales).
Number of Members: 144
Publication(s): *FAPA REaD* (monthly, newsletter, free to membs, media, booksellers, libraries & reviewers, electronic)

Florida Freelance Writers Association
Affiliate of Cassell Network of Writers
45 Main St, North Stratford, NH 03590
Mailing Address: PO Box A, North Stratford, NH 03590
Tel: 603-922-8338 *Fax:* 603-922-8339
E-mail: ffwa@writers-editors.com; info@writers-editors.com
Web Site: www.writers-editors.com; www.ffwamembers.com
Key Personnel
Exec Dir: Dana K Cassell *E-mail:* dana@writers-editors.com
Founded: 1982
Network of freelance writers & editors, offering a job bank, Florida Markets directory, newsletter, etc.
Number of Members: 200
Publication(s): *Directory of Florida Markets for Writers* (newsletter & electronic formats, $35 or free with membership); *Freelance Writer's Report* (monthly, free with FFWA membership); *Guide to CNW/FFWA Writers* (continuously updated, free to qualified publishing companies & businesses)

Florida Outdoor Writers Association Inc
24 NW 33 Ct, Suite A, Gainesville, FL 32607

Tel: 352-284-1763
E-mail: info@fowa.org
Web Site: www.fowa.org
Key Personnel
Chmn of the Bd: Ron Presley
Pres: Bob Wattendorf
1st VP: Jill Zima Borski
2nd VP: Rob Modys
Secy: Susan Young
Treas: Frank Morello
Exec Dir: Tommy Thompson
Founded: 1946
Not-for-profit 501(c)(3) statewide paid professional communicators organization made up of outdoor communicators who report & reflect upon Florida's diverse interests in the outdoors to educate & encourage the public in ways to protect & conserve our natural heritage.
Number of Members: 300
New Election: Annually in Sept
Publication(s): *The Market Edge* (6 issues/yr, newsletter, free to membs, electronic)

Florida Writers Association Inc
PO Box 66069, St Pete Beach, FL 33736-6069
Web Site: www.floridawriters.net
Key Personnel
Pres: Chrissy Jackson *E-mail:* chrissyj@floridawriters.net
EVP: Jade Kerrion
VP, Admin & Fin: Larry Kokko
VP, Fin: Robyn Weinbaum
Founded: 2001
Association of "writers helping writers" to improve writing skills, produce good work in all genres & successfully publish.
Number of Members: 1,200
Publication(s): *The Florida Writer* (quarterly, $4.95, free to membs)

Foil & Specialty Effects Association (FSEA)
2150 SW Westport Dr, Suite 101, Topeka, KS 66614
Tel: 785-271-5816 *Fax:* 785-271-6404
E-mail: info@fsea.com; fseamail@fsea.com
Web Site: www.fsea.com
Key Personnel
Exec Dir: Jeff Peterson *E-mail:* jeff@fsea.com
Asst Dir: Kym Conis *E-mail:* kym@fsea.com
Sales Dir: Gayla Peterson *E-mail:* gayla@petersonpublications.com
Founded: 1992
Trade association for graphics finishing industry.
Number of Members: 325
Publication(s): *Inside Finishing Magazine* (3 issues/yr)

La Fondation Emile Nelligan
100, rue Sherbrooke, Montreal, QC H2X 1C3, Canada
Tel: 514-278-4657 *Fax:* 514-278-1943
E-mail: info@fondation-nelligan.org
Web Site: www.fondation-nelligan.org
Key Personnel
CEO: Manon Gagnon
Pres: Michel Dallaire
VP: Marie-Andree Beaudet
Treas/Secy: Michel Gonneville
Founded: 1979
Sponsoring organization.
Number of Members: 1,000

4A's (American Association of Advertising Agencies)
1065 Avenue of the Americas, 16th fl, New York, NY 10018
Tel: 212-682-2500
Web Site: www.aaaa.org
Key Personnel
CEO & Pres: Nancy Hill *E-mail:* nhill@aaaa.org
COO & CFO: Laura J Bartlett *E-mail:* lbartlett@aaaa.org
EVP, Strategic Partnerships: Michael D Donahue *E-mail:* donahue@aaaa.org
Bd Secy: Michele Adams *E-mail:* adams@aaaa.org
Founded: 1917
National trade association for the advertising agency business.
Number of Members: 430
2016 Meeting(s): Transformation, Miami, FL, March 20-23, 2016
Branch Office(s)
9595 Wilshire Blvd, Suite 900, Beverly Hills, CA 90212, EVP, Western Reg: Jerry McGee *Tel:* 310-300-3422 *Fax:* 310-300-3421 *E-mail:* jmcgee@aaaa.org
1707 "L" St NW, Suite 600, Washington, DC 20036, EVP: Dick O'Brien *Tel:* 202-331-7345 *Fax:* 202-857-3675 *E-mail:* dobrien@aaaa.org
3050 Bellingrath Blvd, Roswell, GA 30076, VP, Agency Rel & Membership: Greg Walker *Tel:* 770-639-6720 (cell) *Fax:* 770-587-1217 *E-mail:* gwalker@aaaa.org
747 N Wabash Ave, Suite 902, Chicago, IL 60611, VP, Agency Rel & Membership: Laura Stern *Tel:* 312-388-7470 *E-mail:* lstearn@aaaa.org

Garden Writers Association
7809 FM 179, Shallowater, TX 79363-3637
Tel: 806-832-1870 *Fax:* 806-832-5244
E-mail: info@gardenwriters.org
Web Site: www.gardenwriters.org
Key Personnel
Exec Dir: Robert LaGasse *E-mail:* execdir@gardenwriters.org
Founded: 1948
Professional association garden communicators working as staff or freelance as newspaper columnists, magazine columnists, photographers & radio/TV hosts. Sponsor annual writer's contest & annual Garden Media award program for published articles or books, as well as an annual symposium.
Number of Members: 1,800
2016 Meeting(s): Annual Symposium, Sheraton Downtown, Atlanta, GA, Sept 16-19, 2016
Publication(s): *Quill & Trowel* (6 issues/yr, newsletter)

The Graphic Artists Guild Inc
32 Broadway, Suite 1114, New York, NY 10004
Tel: 212-791-3400 *Fax:* 212-791-0333
Web Site: www.graphicartistsguild.org
Key Personnel
Pres: Haydn Adams *E-mail:* president@gag.org
Exec Dir: Patricia McKiernan *Tel:* 212-791-3400 ext 15 *E-mail:* admin@gag.org
Founded: 1967
Labor organization which advocates the advancement of artists' rights. Members are illustrators, graphic designers, surface & textile designers, computer graphics artists, cartoonists & others.
Number of Members: 1,100
Publication(s): *Pricing & Ethical Guidelines, 14th ed* ($39.99)

Graphic Arts Show Company (GASC)
1899 Preston White Dr, Reston, VA 20191
Tel: 703-264-7200 *Fax:* 703-620-9187
E-mail: info@gasc.org
Web Site: www.gasc.org
Key Personnel
Pres: Ralph Nappi *Tel:* 703-264-7200 ext 227
VP: Chris Price *Tel:* 703-264-7200 ext 221 *E-mail:* cprice@gasc.org
Founded: 1982
Tradeshow management for printing, publishing & graphic communications events.
2016 Meeting(s): Graph Expo®, Orange County Convention Center, North Hall, Orlando, FL, Sept 25-28, 2016
2017 Meeting(s): PRINT 17, McCormick Place, 2301 S Lake Shore Dr, Chicago, IL, Sept 10-14, 2017

Gravure Association of the Americas Inc
8281 Pine Lake Rd, Denver, NC 28037
Tel: 201-523-6042 *Fax:* 201-523-6048
E-mail: gaa@gaa.org
Web Site: www.gaa.org
Key Personnel
Exec Dir: Philip Pimlott *Tel:* 812-406-5434 *E-mail:* ppimlott@gaa.org
Dir, Planning & Admin: Pamela W Schenk *Tel:* 585-288-2297 *E-mail:* pwschenk@gaa.org
Foster the advancement of gravure printing industry. Sponsor of the Golden Cylinder Awards.
Number of Members: 250
Publication(s): *Gravure Magazine* (quarterly, free to qualified companies)

Great Lakes Graphics Association
Affiliate of Printing Industries of America
W232 N2950 Roundy Circle E, Pewaukee, WI 53072
Tel: 262-522-2210 *Toll Free Tel:* 855-522-2210 *Fax:* 262-522-2211
E-mail: admin@piw.org
Web Site: www.piw.org
Key Personnel
Pres: Joe Lyman *Tel:* 262-522-2212
Founded: 1886
Number of Members: 175
Publication(s): *NewScan* (electronic, newsletter, free to membs)

Guild of Book Workers
521 Fifth Ave, 17th fl, New York, NY 10175
Tel: 212-292-4444
E-mail: communications@guildofbookworkers.org
Web Site: www.guildofbookworkers.org
Key Personnel
Pres: Mark Andersson *Tel:* 520-682-7241 *E-mail:* president@guildofbookworkers.org
VP: Bexx Caswell *E-mail:* vicepresident@guildofbookworkers.org
Secy: Catherine Burkhard *Tel:* 214-363-7946 *E-mail:* secretary@guildofbookworkers.org
Treas: Alicia Bailey *E-mail:* treasurer@guildofbookworkers.org
Founded: 1906
A national nonprofit educational organization which fosters the hand book arts: binding, calligraphy, illumination, paper decorating. Sponsor exhibits, lectures, workshops. See web site for membership fee information.
Number of Members: 850
Publication(s): *Journal* (annual, free to membs); *Newsletter* (6 issues/yr, free to membs)

Horror Writers Association (HWA)
244 Fifth Ave, Suite 2767, New York, NY 10001
E-mail: hwa@horror.org
Web Site: horror.org
Key Personnel
Pres: Rocky Wood *E-mail:* president@horror.org
VP: Lisa Morton *E-mail:* vp@horror.org
Treas: Leslie Klinger *E-mail:* treasurer@horror.org
Secy: Joe McKinney *E-mail:* secretary@horror.org
Administrator: Brad Hodson *E-mail:* admin@horror.org
Founded: 1985
To encourage public interest in & foster an appreciation of good horror & dark fantasy literature. Publishes monthly newsletter, provides online information & resources, Hardship Fund, Grievance Committee, scholarships. Sponsors

Bram Stoker Awards & presents an annual Lifetime Achievement Award.
Membership fees: $69 indiv, $48 supporting, $115 corp, $89 family.
Number of Members: 600
Publication(s): *Horror Writers Association Newsletter* (monthly, electronic, free)

The Ibsen Society of America
University of California, Dept of Scandinavian, 6303 Dwinelle Hall, No 2690, Berkeley, CA 94720-2690
Tel: 510-642-4484 *Fax:* 510-642-6220
Web Site: www.ibsensociety.liu.edu
Founded: 1978
Nonprofit corporation which fosters an understanding of Ibsen's works through lectures, readings, performances, conferences & publications.
Number of Members: 250
Publication(s): *Ibsen News & Comment* (annual, newsletter, $15 libs & nonmembs, free to membs)

ICEA, see The Institute for Cooperation on Adult Education (Institut de Cooperation pour l'Education des Adultes-ICEA)

IDEAlliance®
1600 Duke St, Suite 420, Alexandria, VA 22314
Tel: 703-837-1070 *Fax:* 703-837-1072
E-mail: registrar@idealliance.org
Web Site: www.idealliance.org
Key Personnel
Pres & CEO: David J Steinhardt *Tel:* 703-837-1066 *E-mail:* dsteinhardt@idealliance.org
EVP: Steve Bonoff *Tel:* 952-896-1908 *E-mail:* sbonoff@idealliance.org
VP, Opers & Mng Dir: Frank Balser *Tel:* 703-837-1089 *E-mail:* fbalser@idealliance.org
Founded: 1966
Represent printing, publishing, newspapers, suppliers, government organizations & advertising agencies. Seek productivity & technical improvement in creation & distribution of printed & digital materials.
Number of Members: 200
2016 Meeting(s): PRIMEX East, New York, NY, March 15, 2016

In-Plant Printing & Mailing Association (IPMA)
455 S Sam Barr Dr, Suite 203, Kearney, MO 64060
Tel: 816-919-1691
E-mail: ipmainfo@ipma.org
Web Site: www.ipma.org
Key Personnel
Exec Dir: Carma Goin *E-mail:* cgoin@ipma.org
Fin Coord & Off Asst: Jennifer Chambers *E-mail:* jchambers@ipma.org
Founded: 1964
Professional association dedicatd to the specific needs of all industry sgements of in-house professionals who provide graphic design, copy, print, mail & distribution services to their organizations. Annual Educational Conference & Vendor Fair.
Number of Members: 500
Publication(s): *Inside Edge* (monthly, newsletter)

The Independent Book Publishers Association (IBPA)
1020 Manhattan Beach Blvd, Suite 204, Manhattan Beach, CA 90266
Tel: 310-546-1818 *Fax:* 310-546-3939
E-mail: info@ibpa-online.org
Web Site: www.ibpa-online.org
Key Personnel
COO: Terry Nathan *E-mail:* terry@ibpa-online.org
Exec Dir: Angela Bole *E-mail:* angela@ibpa-online.org
Asst Dir: Lisa Krebs Magno *E-mail:* lisa@ibpa-online.org
Vendor Rel, Mktg & Ad: Chris Kahn *E-mail:* chris@ibpa-online.org
Founded: 1983 (as Publishers Association of Southern California)
A national nonprofit publishers' co-operative which coordinates discounted participation in major book & library exhibits & trade shows throughout the country, as well as ad placement in major publications & direct mail programs. Sponsor workshops, awards & prizes.
Number of Members: 3,000
Publication(s): *IBPA Independent* (monthly, newsletter, free to membs, $60/yr nonmembs); *Membership & Service Directory* (free to membs)

Independent Writers of Chicago (IWOC)
332 S Michigan Ave, Suite 1032, Chicago, IL 60604
Toll Free Tel: 800-804-IWOC (804-4962)
E-mail: info@iwoc.org
Web Site: www.iwoc.org
Key Personnel
Pres: James Kepler *E-mail:* jkepler@adamspress.com
Monthly meetings, workshops & seminars dealing with the business aspects of independent writing. Writers' line job referral. Speakers' bureau.
Number of Members: 125
Publication(s): *Membership Directory* (annual, $10); *STET* (11 issues/yr, newsletter, $20/yr)

InScribe Christian Writers' Fellowship (ICWF)
PO Box 6201, Wetaskiwin, AB T9A 2E9, Canada
E-mail: inscribe.mail@gmail.com
Web Site: inscribe.org
Key Personnel
Pres: Ruth L Snyder *E-mail:* sun.beam3@yahoo.ca
Treas: Bobbi Junior *E-mail:* bobbi.junior@gmail.com
Secy: Sandi Somers *E-mail:* sksomers@shaw.ca
Founded: 1980 (as Alberta Christian Writers' Fellowship)
Stimulate, encourage & support Christians who write anywhere across Canada, to advance effective Christian writing & to promote the influence of all Christians who write.
Number of Members: 150
Meeting(s): Fall Conference, Annually last weekend in Sept
Publication(s): *FellowScript* (quarterly, newsletter, included with membership)

Institut de Cooperation pour l'Education des Adultes, see The Institute for Cooperation on Adult Education (Institut de Cooperation pour l'Education des Adultes-ICEA)

The Institute for Cooperation on Adult Education (Institut de Cooperation pour l'Education des Adultes-ICEA)
55, ave du Mont-Royal Ouest, Bureau 303, Montreal, QC H2T 2S6, Canada
Tel: 514-948-2044 *Fax:* 514-948-2046
E-mail: icae@icea.qc.ca
Web Site: www.icea.qc.ca
Key Personnel
Pres: Lea Cousineau
Dir Gen: Ronald Cameron *Tel:* 514-948-2044 ext 238 *E-mail:* rcameron@icea.qc.ca
Founded: 1946
Adult education lifelong learning.
Number of Members: 107
Publication(s): *ICAE News* (newsletter, free to membs)

Inter American Press Association (IAPA)
Jules Dubois Bldg, 1801 SW Third Ave, Miami, FL 33129
Tel: 305-634-2465 *Fax:* 305-635-2272
E-mail: info@sipiapa.org
Web Site: www.sipiapa.org
Key Personnel
Exec Dir: Ricardo Trotti *E-mail:* rtrotti@sipiapa.org
Founded: 1942
To guard freedom of speech & freedom of the press; to foster & protect the general & specific interests of the daily & periodical press of the Americas; to promote & maintain the dignity, rights & responsibilities of journalism; to encourage uniform standards of professional & business conduct; to exchange ideas & information which contribute to the cultural, material & technical development of the press; to foster a wider knowledge & greater interchange in support of the basic principles of a free society & individual liberty.
Number of Members: 1,300
Publication(s): *Hora de Cierre* (quarterly); *IAPA Annual Report* (annual); *IAPA News* (6 issues/yr); *Notisip* (quarterly)

International Association of Business Communicators (IABC)
601 Montgomery St, Suite 1900, San Francisco, CA 94111
Tel: 415-544-4700 *Toll Free Tel:* 800-776-4222 (US & CN) *Fax:* 415-544-4747
E-mail: leader_centre@iabc.com
Web Site: www.iabc.com
Key Personnel
Exec Dir: Carlos Fulcher *Tel:* 415-544-4706 *E-mail:* cfulcher@iabc.com
Mgr, Ad Sales: Mary Coppola *Tel:* 415-544-4720 *E-mail:* mcoppola@iabc.com
Founded: 1970
Communication association.
Number of Members: 14,000
2016 Meeting(s): World Conference, Hilton New Orleans Riverside, 2 Poydras, New Orleans, LA, June 5-8, 2016
Publication(s): *Communication World* (monthly)

International Association of Crime Writers Inc, North American Branch
243 Fifth Ave, Suite 537, New York, NY 10016
Tel: 212-243-8966 *Fax:* 815-361-1477
E-mail: info@crimewritersna.org
Web Site: www.crimewritersna.org
Key Personnel
Exec Dir: Mary A Frisque *E-mail:* mfrisque@igc.org
Pres: J Madison Davis
Secy-Treas: Jim Weikart
Secy: Steven Steinbock
Founded: 1987
Promote communication among crime writers worldwide & enhance awareness & encourage translations of the genre in the US & abroad.
Number of Members: 285
Publication(s): *Border Patrol* (quarterly, free to membs)

International Digital Enterprise Alliance, see IDEAlliance®

International Encyclopedia Society
3689 Campbell Ct, Yorktown Heights, NY 10598
Tel: 914-962-3287 *Fax:* 914-962-3287
Key Personnel
Pres & Ed: George Thomas Kurian *E-mail:* gtkurian@aol.com
Publication of books & journals; conferences; award of prizes.
Number of Members: 210

International Literacy Association (ILA)
Formerly International Reading Association (IRA)
800 Barksdale Rd, Newark, DE 19711-3204
Mailing Address: PO Box 8139, Newark, DE 19714-8139
Tel: 302-731-1600 *Toll Free Tel:* 800-336-7323 (US & CN) *Fax:* 302-731-1057
E-mail: customerservice@reading.org
Web Site: www.literacyworldwide.org; www.reading.org
Key Personnel
Exec Dir: Marcie Craig Post *E-mail:* mpost@reading.org
Exec Asst: Kathy Baughman *Tel:* 302-731-3761 *E-mail:* kbaughman@reading.org
Founded: 1956
Conferences; publications, research, membership services; publications on reading & related topics; professional journals.
Number of Members: 60,000
2016 Meeting(s): Annual Conference, Boston, MA, July 9-11, 2016

International Reading Association (IRA), see International Literacy Association (ILA)

International Society of Weekly Newspaper Editors
Missouri Southern State University, 3950 E Newman Rd, Joplin, MO 64801-1595
Tel: 417-625-9736 *Fax:* 417-659-4445
Web Site: www.iswne.org
Key Personnel
Exec Dir: Dr Chad Stebbins *E-mail:* stebbins-c@mssu.edu
Founded: 1955
Help those in weekly press to improve standards of editorial writing & news reporting. Encourages strong independent editorial voices.
Number of Members: 300
2017 Meeting(s): ISWNE Conference, College Park, MD, June 28-July 2, 2017
Publication(s): *Grassroots Editor* (quarterly, $25/yr US & CN, $28 elsewhere)

International Standard Book Numbering (ISBN) US Agency, A Cambridge Information Group Co
Affiliate of R R Bowker LLC
630 Central Ave, New Providence, NJ 07974
Toll Free Tel: 877-310-7333 *Fax:* 908-219-0188
E-mail: isbn-san@bowker.com
Web Site: www.isbn.org
Coordinate implementation of the ISBN, SAN & ISNI standards.
Number of Members: 120,000

The International Women's Writing Guild (IWWG)
274 Madison Ave, Suite 1202, New York, NY 10016
Tel: 917-720-6959
E-mail: iwwgquestions@gmail.com
Web Site: www.iwwg.org
Key Personnel
Dir of Opers: Kristin Rath
Founded: 1976
Network for the empowerment of women through writing. Services include updated list of close to 35 literary agents, independent small presses & other writing services. Writing conferences & events annually, subn to the newsletter *Network*, regional clusters & opportunities for publications. IWWG is a supportive network open to any woman regardless of portfolio. As such, it has established a remarkable record of achievement in the publishing world as well as in circles where lifelong learning & personal information are valued for their own sake.
Number of Members: 5,000
Publication(s): *Network* (quarterly, free)

Internet Alliance (IA)
1615 "L" St NW, Suite 1100, Washington, DC 20036-5624
Tel: 202-861-2407
Web Site: www.internetalliance.org
Key Personnel
Exec Dir: Tammy Cota *Tel:* 802-279-3534 (cell) *E-mail:* tammy@internetalliance.org
State relations on Internet issues. Lobbyists.

Investigative Reporters & Editors
Missouri School of Journalism, 141 Neff Annex, Columbia, MO 65211
Tel: 573-882-2042 *Fax:* 573-882-5431
E-mail: info@ire.org
Web Site: www.ire.org
Key Personnel
Exec Dir: Mark Horvit *Tel:* 573-882-1984 *E-mail:* mhorvit@ire.org
Founded: 1975
Nonprofit organization to improve the quality of investigative journalism.
Number of Members: 5,000
Publication(s): *The IRE Journal* (quarterly, free with membership, $70/yr nonmembs, $125/yr instns, $85/yr libs, $90/yr foreign nonmembs, $150/yr foreign instns)

Jewish Book Council
520 Eighth Ave, 4th fl, New York, NY 10018
Tel: 212-201-2920 *Fax:* 212-532-4952
E-mail: jbc@jewishbooks.org
Web Site: www.jewishbookcouncil.org
Key Personnel
Dir: Naomi Firestone-Teeter
Prog Dir: Mira Pomerantz Dauber
Founded: 1925
Sponsors programs based on its conviction that books of Jewish interest are an invaluable contribution to the welfare of the Jewish people. Works to promote the reading, writing, publishing & distribution of worthy books of Jewish content. Honors excellence in all fields of Jewish literary endeavor with awards to writers & citations to publishers. Serves as a resource providing guidance, program tools & publications; acts as a clearinghouse for information on all aspects of Jewish literature & publishing in North America.
Publication(s): *Jewish Book Month Poster*; *Jewish Book World* (quarterly, $36/yr)

The League of Canadian Poets
192 Spadina Ave, Suite 312, Toronto, ON M5T 2C2, Canada
Tel: 416-504-1657 *Fax:* 416-504-0096
Web Site: poets.ca
Key Personnel
Exec Dir: Joanna Poblocka *E-mail:* joanna@poets.ca
Asst Dir: Ingel Madrus *E-mail:* readings@poets.ca
Admin & Communs Coord: Barbara Erochina *E-mail:* admin@poets.ca
Founded: 1966
Promote Canadian poetry & poets.
Number of Members: 700
New Election: Annually in June
Publication(s): *Poetry Markets for Canadians* (online only, $20/yr public, $100/yr schools or libraries)

League of Vermont Writers
PO Box 172, Underhill Center, VT 05490
Tel: 802-349-7475
E-mail: lvw@leaguevtwriters.org
Web Site: www.leagueofvermontwriters.org
Founded: 1929
Four meetings per year (Jan, April, July, Sept), reader & promotional services; occasional instructional seminars & workshops, publication of anthologies of members' work, writer's service.
Number of Members: 275
New Election: Annually in Jan
Publication(s): *League Lines* (quarterly, newsletter); *Vermont Voices Jubilee, 75th Anniversary Edition*; *Vermont Voices III, An Anthology*

League of Women Voters of the United States
1730 "M" St NW, Suite 1000, Washington, DC 20036-4508
Tel: 202-429-1965 *Fax:* 202-429-0854; 202-429-4343
E-mail: lwv@lwv.org
Web Site: www.lwv.org
Key Personnel
Pres: Elisabeth MacNamara
Exec Dir: Nancy E Tate
Sr Dir, Communs: Kelly Ceballos
Founded: 1920
Nonpartisan, grass roots political organization. Publish information on public policy issues in fields of natural resources, social policy, government, voter service & international relations.
Number of Members: 150,000
Publication(s): *The National Voter* (3 issues/yr, magazine); *Thinking Globally, Acting Locally: A Citizen's Guide to Community Education on Global Issues*; *Women in Action: Rebels and Reformers 1920-1980*

Library Association of Alberta (LAA)
80 Baker Crescent NW, Calgary, AB T2L 1R4, Canada
Tel: 403-284-5818 *Toll Free Tel:* 877-522-5550 *Fax:* 403-282-6646
E-mail: info@laa.ca
Web Site: www.laa.ca
Key Personnel
Exec Dir/Conference Coord: Christine Sheppard
Founded: 1930
Nonprofit organization.
Number of Members: 625
2016 Meeting(s): Alberta Library Conference, Fairmont Jasper Park Lodge, Jasper, AB, CN, April 28-May 1, 2016
2017 Meeting(s): Alberta Library Conference, Fairmont Jasper Park Lodge, Jasper, AB, CN, April 27-30, 2017
2018 Meeting(s): Alberta Library Conference, Fairmont Jasper Park Lodge, Jasper, AB, CN, April 26-29, 2018
2019 Meeting(s): Alberta Library Conference, Fairmont Jasper Park Lodge, Jasper, AB, CN, April 25-28, 2019
2020 Meeting(s): Alberta Library Conference, Fairmont Jasper Park Lodge, Jasper, AB, CN, April 30-May 3, 2020

Library Binding Council
4440 PGA Blvd, Suite 600, Palm Beach Gardens, FL 33410
Tel: 561-745-6821 *Toll Free Fax:* 800-837-7321
E-mail: info@lbibinders.org
Web Site: www.lbibinders.org
Key Personnel
Exec Dir: Debra S Nolan *E-mail:* dnolan@lbibinders.org
Founded: 1935
Trade association for bookbinders. Hold annual meetings & workshops; provide information services, certification & technical review.
Number of Members: 80
Publication(s): *ShelfLife* (quarterly, $29 dom; $31 CN; $36 intl)

Library of American Broadcasting (LAB)
Unit of University of Maryland Libraries
University of Maryland, Hornbake Library, College Park, MD 20742
Tel: 301-405-9212
Web Site: www.lib.umd.edu/special/collections/massmedia/about-us

Key Personnel
Dir & Donor Rel: Chuck Howell *Tel:* 301-314-0401 *E-mail:* chuckh@umd.edu
Founded: 1972
Library devoted to history of public & commercial broadcasting including collections of audio & video recordings, books, pamphlets, periodicals, personal collections, oral histories, photographs, scripts & vertical files. Referral center to other sources of broadcast history.
Number of Members: 21
New Election: Annually in Nov
Publication(s): *Airwaves*

Linguistic Society of America
1325 18 St NW, Suite 211, Washington, DC 20036-6501
Tel: 202-835-1714 *Fax:* 202-835-1717
E-mail: lsa@lsadc.org
Web Site: www.linguisticsociety.org
Key Personnel
Exec Dir: Alyson Reed *E-mail:* areed@lsadc.org
Dir, Communs: Brice Russ *E-mail:* bruss@lsadc.org
Dir, Membership & Meetings: David Robinson *E-mail:* drobinson@lsadc.org
Founded: 1924
Advancing the scientific study of language.
Number of Members: 5,000
New Election: Annually in Sept
Publication(s): *Language* (quarterly, free to membs, $140-190/yr organizations); *LSA Meeting Handbook* (annual, free, electronic)

The Literary Press Group of Canada
425 Adelaide St W, Suite 700, Toronto, ON M5V 3C1, Canada
Tel: 416-483-1321 *Fax:* 416-483-2510
Web Site: www.lpg.ca
Key Personnel
Exec Dir: Christen Thomas *Tel:* 416-483-1321 ext 1 *E-mail:* christen@lpg.ca
Busn Mgr: Barb Phillips *Tel:* 416-483-1321 ext 2 *E-mail:* barb@lpg.ca
Mktg Mgr: Tanya Snyder *Tel:* 416-483-1321 ext 3 *E-mail:* tsnyder@lpg.ca
Sales Mgr: Tan Light *Tel:* 416-483-1321 ext 4 *E-mail:* sales@lpg.ca
National trade association providing cooperative sales, marketing, advertising & publicity services to members.
Number of Members: 52
New Election: Annually in May

Literary Translators' Association of Canada
Concordia University, LB 601, 1455 De Maisonneuve West, Montreal, QC H3G 1M8, Canada
Tel: 514-848-2424 (ext 8702)
E-mail: info@attlc-ltac.org
Web Site: www.attlc-ltac.org
Key Personnel
Pres: Jo-Anne Elder
Dir: Yves Dion
Founded: 1975
Promote & protect interests of literary translators in Canada; occasional meetings with local universities & occasional workshops, lobby for funding, organize readings & other events.
Number of Members: 150
New Election: Annually in June

Livestock Publications Council
910 Currie St, Fort Worth, TX 76107
Tel: 817-336-1130 *Fax:* 817-232-4820
Web Site: www.livestockpublications.com
Key Personnel
Exec Dir: Diane E Johnson *E-mail:* diane@livestockpublications.com
Founded: 1974
A nonprofit organization designed to serve the livestock communications industry.
Number of Members: 195
New Election: Annually in July
Publication(s): *Actiongram* (monthly, newsletter)

Livres Canada Books
One Nicholas, Suite 504, Ottawa, ON K1N 7B7, Canada
Tel: 613-562-2324 *Fax:* 613-562-2329
E-mail: info@livrescanadabooks.com
Web Site: www.livrescanadabooks.com
Key Personnel
Exec Dir: Francois Charette *Tel:* 613-562-2324 ext 223 *E-mail:* fcharette@livrescanadabooks.com
Mgr, Digital Publg & Intl Mkts: Rebecca Ross *Tel:* 613-562-2324 ext 229 *E-mail:* rross@livrescanadabooks.com
As the only national trade association that connects English & French language publishers across Canada, Livres Canada Books has a mandate to foster Canadian publishers' export sales. Coordinates Canadian publishers' presence at international book fairs, promotes Canadian titles abroad through its catalogues, exhibits & web site, provides market intelligence & acts as a liaison between Canadian publishers & foreign buyers. Also assists the industry by providing funding assistance for Canadian publishers' international marketing strategies & activities.
Publication(s): *Canadian Studies Flyer* (annual, free); *Rights Canada Catalogue* (semiannual, free)

Magazine Publishers of America, see MPA - The Association of Magazine Media

Magazines Canada (MC)
425 Adelaide St W, Suite 700, Toronto, ON M5V 3C1, Canada
Tel: 416-504-0274 *Fax:* 416-504-0437
E-mail: info@magazinescanada.ca
Web Site: www.magazinescanada.ca/development/magnet
Key Personnel
CEO: Mark Jamison *Tel:* 416-504-0274 ext 223 *E-mail:* mjamison@magazinescanada.ca
Gen Mgr & Publr: Barbara Zatyko *Tel:* 416-504-0274 ext 222 *E-mail:* bzatyko@magazinescanada.ca
Mgr, Communs: Brianne DiAngelo *Tel:* 416-504-0274 ext 227 *E-mail:* bdiangelo@magazinescanada.ca
Founded: 1973
Distribution, promotion, professional development & lobbying for Canadian magazines.
Number of Members: 350
2016 Meeting(s): MagNet, The Courtyard Downtown Toronto, 475 Yonge St, Toronto, ON, CN, June 7-10, 2016
Publication(s): *Small Magazine Advertising* ($25 membs); *Small Magazine Business* ($25 membs); *Small Magazine Circulation* ($25 membs); *Small Magazine Editorial* ($25 membs); *Small Magazine Human Resources* ($35 membs)

Maine Writers & Publishers Alliance
314 Forest Ave, Rm 318, Portland, ME 04101
Tel: 207-228-8263 *Fax:* 207-228-8150
E-mail: info@mainewriters.org
Web Site: mainewriters.org
Key Personnel
Exec Dir: Joshua Bodwell *E-mail:* director@mainewriters.org
Asst Dir: Stephen E Abbott *E-mail:* abbot@mainewriters.org
Founded: 1975
Writing retreats, writing workshops, information services.
Number of Members: 1,600
Publication(s): *Ex Libris Maine* (monthly, newsletter, membs, supporters & parenting organizations); *The Peavey* (weekly, newsletter, membs only)

Manitoba Arts Council
525-93 Lombard Ave, Winnipeg, MB R3B 3B1, Canada
Tel: 204-945-2237 *Toll Free Tel:* 866-994-2787 *Fax:* 204-945-5925
E-mail: info@artscouncil.mb.ca
Web Site: artscouncil.mb.ca
Key Personnel
Exec Dir: Douglas Riske *Tel:* 204-945-2239 *E-mail:* driske@artscouncil.mb.ca
Assoc Dir, Policy, Planning & Partnerships: Patricia Sanders *Tel:* 204-945-0422 *E-mail:* psanders@artscouncil.mb.ca
Communs Mgr: Leanne Foley *Tel:* 204-945-0646 *E-mail:* lfoley@artscouncil.mb.ca
Founded: 1965
Provincial arts council that funds professional Manitoban artists & arts organizations.

The Manitoba Writers' Guild Inc
218-100 Arthur St, Winnipeg, MB R3B 1H3, Canada
Tel: 204-944-8013
E-mail: info@mbwriter.mb.ca
Web Site: www.mbwriter.mb.ca
Key Personnel
Exec Dir: Carolyn Gray
Founded: 1981
Provides professional & personal support to Manitoba writers throughout their writing lives. Membership $60/yr regular, $30/yr students & low income.
Number of Members: 550

Media Alliance
2830 20 St, Suite 102, San Francisco, CA 94110
Tel: 415-746-9475
E-mail: information@media-alliance.org
Web Site: www.media-alliance.org
Key Personnel
Exec Dir: Tracy Rosenberg *Tel:* 510-684-6853 (cell) *E-mail:* tracy@media-alliance.org
Info Coord: Phavia Kujichagulia *E-mail:* jobfile@media-alliance.org
Educational programs in editing, writing & journalism skills. Media relations & advocacy & hands-on computer skills. Job listings & resources, media watchdog activities.
Number of Members: 3,200
Publication(s): *Media How-to Guide* (book, $15 membs, $20 nonmembs)

Media Coalition Inc
19 Fulton St, Suite 407, New York, NY 10038
Tel: 212-587-4025 *Fax:* 212-587-2436
E-mail: info@mediacoalition.org
Web Site: mediacoalition.org
Key Personnel
Exec Dir: David Horowitz *Tel:* 212-587-4025 ext 3 *E-mail:* horowitz@mediacoalition.org
Communs Coord: Kris Anne Bonifacio
Founded: 1973
Trade association, defends first amendment rights to produce & distribute constitutionally-protected books, magazines, recordings, home video & video games.
Number of Members: 12
Publication(s): *Shooting the Messenger, Why Censorship Won't Stop Violence* ($1); *The Vanity of Bonfires*

The Melville Society
Johns Hopkins University Press, PO Box 19966, Baltimore, MD 21211-0966
Web Site: melvillesociety.org

Key Personnel
Pres: Geoffrey Sanborn
Treas: Steven Olsen-Smith
Ed, Leviathan: Samuel Otter
Exec Secy: Tony McGowan
Annual & special meetings & publications. Conferences in association with the Modern Language Association annual convention & American Literature Association annual convention.
Number of Members: 760
New Election: Annually in Spring
Publication(s): *Leviathan: A Journal of Melville Studies* (3 issues/yr, free with membership)

Metropolitan Lithographers Association Inc
c/o Pictorial Offset, 111 Amor Ave, Carlstadt, NJ 07072
Tel: 201-935-7100
Key Personnel
Pres: Gary Samuels
Multi-employer lithographic trade association active in collective bargaining, labor relations, management educational programs & public relations.
Number of Members: 7
New Election: Annually in Jan

Midwest Independent Booksellers Association (MIBA)
2355 Louisiana Ave N, Suite A, Golden Valley, MN 55427-3646
Tel: 763-544-2993 *Toll Free Tel:* 800-784-7522 *Fax:* 612-354-5728
E-mail: info@midwestbooksellers.org
Web Site: midwestbooksellers.org
Key Personnel
Exec Dir: Carrie Obry *E-mail:* carrie@midwestbooksellers.org
Founded: 1981
Association of independent bookstores in Midwest: Illinois, Iowa, Kansas, Minnesota, Missouri, Nebraska, North Dakota, South Dakota & Wisconsin. Annual trade show & meeting. Book catalog for member stores to use with consumers. Sponsors educational programs for booksellers, Spring meeting, Midwest Booksellers' Choice Awards & "Midwest Connections" regional marketing program.
Number of Members: 500
Publication(s): *Membership Directory* (online); *MIBA Trade Show Program* (annual); *Midwest Booksellers Association Winter Catalog* (annual)

Midwest Publishing Association (MPA)
275 N York St, Suite 401, Elmhurst, IL 60126
Tel: 630-833-4220 *Fax:* 630-563-9181
E-mail: info@midwestpublish.org
Web Site: www.midwestpublish.org
Founded: 1936
Encourages excellence in publishing by providing a platform for educational, social & professional interaction. Members are professionals in book & media publishing, printing, editorial, design & all business aspects of our industry. Accomplishes mission through a variety of educational programs, publications & special events designed to promote the publishing media industry & its members.
Number of Members: 300
Publication(s): *MPA E-news* (weekly, free to membs)

Midwest Travel Writers Association
902 S Randall Rd, Suite C311, St Charles, IL 60174
Toll Free Tel: 888-551-8184
E-mail: admin@mtwa.org
Web Site: www.mtwa.org
Key Personnel
Admin Asst: Patti Ciccone
Founded: 1951
To promote & practice travel writing as a profession. Subjects addressed include: food, wine, music, dance, theater, photography, sports, recreation, travel & resorts.
Number of Members: 100
Publication(s): *MTWA Directory* (annual, $100 print, $150 print & electronic)

Miniature Book Society Inc
702 Rosecrans St, San Diego, CA 92106-3013
Tel: 619-226-4441 *Fax:* 619-226-4441
E-mail: minibook@cox.net
Web Site: www.mbs.org
Key Personnel
Pres: Mark Palkovic
Secy: Edward Hoyenski
Founded: 1983
Number of Members: 302
Publication(s): *Miniature Book Society Newsletter* (3 issues/yr, newsletter, $40/yr)
Membership(s): Fellowship of American Bibliophilic Societies

Modern Language Association of America (MLA)
26 Broadway, 3rd fl, New York, NY 10004-1789
SAN: 202-6422
Tel: 646-576-5000 *Fax:* 646-458-0030
E-mail: convention@mla.org
Web Site: www.mla.org
Key Personnel
Exec Dir: Rosemary G Feal *E-mail:* rfeal@mla.org
Founded: 1883
Convention; employment information, professional organization, scholarly publications.
Number of Members: 30,000
2016 Meeting(s): Annual Convention, Austin, TX, Jan 7-10, 2016
2017 Meeting(s): Annual Convention, Philadelphia, PA, Jan 5-8, 2017
2018 Meeting(s): Annual Convention, New York, NY, Jan 4-7, 2018
Publication(s): *MLA International Bibliography* (annual, inquire); *MLA Newsletter* (quarterly, free to membs); *PMLA* (5 issues/yr, $12/issue); *Profession* (annual, journal, free to membs, $7.50 nonmembs, online)

Motion Picture Association of America Inc (MPAA)
1600 "I" St NW, Washington, DC 20006
Tel: 202-293-1966 *Fax:* 202-296-7410
E-mail: contactus@mpaa.org
Web Site: www.mpaa.org
Key Personnel
Chmn & CEO: Christopher Dodd
VP: Patrick Kilcur
VP, Corp Communs: Kate Bedingfield *E-mail:* kate_bedingfield@mpaa.org
Founded: 1922
Trade association for the major motion picture producers & distributors. Administer motion picture industry's system of self-regulation & are spokespeople for production & distribution of motion pictures for theatrical, home video & TV use in the USA.
Number of Members: 60
Branch Office(s)
15301 Ventura Blvd, Bldg E, Sherman Oaks, CA 91403 *Tel:* 818-995-6600 *Fax:* 818-285-4403
500 Mamaroneck Ave, Suite 403, Harrison, NY 10528 *Tel:* 914-333-8892 *Fax:* 914-333-7541
1425 Greenway Dr, Suite 270, Irving, TX 75038 *Tel:* 972-756-9078 *Fax:* 972-756-9402
55 St Clair Ave W, Suite 210, Toronto, ON M4V 2Y7, Canada *Tel:* 416-961-1888 *Fax:* 416-968-1016 *E-mail:* info@mpa-canada.org *Web Site:* www.mpa-canada.org
FSA 74, Driver Ave, Moore Park, NSW 2021, Australia
Avenue des Arts 46, 8th fl, 1000 Brussels, Belgium *Tel:* (02) 778 27 11 *Fax:* (02) 778 27 00
Rua Jeronimo da Veiga, 45, Conj 121/122, 12th fl, Jardim Europa, 04536-000 Sao Paulo-SP, Brazil *Tel:* (011) 3667-2080 *Web Site:* www.mpaal.org.br
Rm 508, No 16 Bldg, Jianwai SOHO, 39 Dongsanhuan Zhonglu Rd, Beijing 100022, China
215 Atrium, A 206, Chakala, Andheri-Kurla Rd, Andheri (East), Mumbai 400 059, India
Nihon Seimei Ichibancho Bldg, 6F 23-3, Inchiben-Cho, Chiyoda-ku, Tokyo 102-0082, Japan
Lafontaine No 42, Chapultepec Polanco, 11560 Mexico, DF, Mexico *Tel:* (0155) 5280-6878; (0155) 5281-6090 (main)
No 04-07 Central Mall, No 1 Magazine Rd, Singapore 059567, Singapore *Tel:* 6253 1033 *Fax:* 6255 1838 *Web Site:* www.mpa-i.org
1007, 10th fl, Monaco Bldg, 1316-5 Seocho-dong, Seocho-gu, Seoul 137-856, South Korea

MPA - The Association of Magazine Media
757 Third Ave, 11th fl, New York, NY 10012
Tel: 212-872-3700 *Fax:* 212-888-4217
Web Site: www.magazine.org
Key Personnel
CEO & Pres: Mary Berner *Tel:* 212-872-3710 *E-mail:* president@magazine.org
EVP, Mktg: Linda Mason *Tel:* 212-872-3734 *E-mail:* lmason@magazine.org
VP, Creative Servs: Patty Bogie *Tel:* 212-872-3729 *E-mail:* pbogie@magazine.org
Founded: 1919
Promote the value of magazines.
Number of Members: 305
Branch Office(s)
1211 Connecticut Ave NW, Washington, DC 20036, EVP, Govt Aff: James Cregan *Tel:* 202-296-7277 *Fax:* 202-296-0343 *E-mail:* jcregan@magazine.org

Music Publishers Association (MPA)
243 Fifth Ave, Suite 236, New York, NY 10016
Tel: 212-327-4044
E-mail: admin@mpa.org
Web Site: www.mpa.org
Founded: 1895
Foster trade & commerce in the interest of those in the music publishing business & encourage understanding of & compliance with the copyright law to protect musical works against piracies & infringements.
Number of Members: 300
New Election: Annually, first week of June

Mystery Writers of America (MWA)
1140 Broadway, Suite 1507, New York, NY 10001
Tel: 212-888-8171
E-mail: mwa@mysterywriters.org
Web Site: www.mysterywriters.org
Key Personnel
Admin Dir: Margery Flax
Founded: 1945
The premier organization for mystery writers & other professionals in the mystery field. MWA watches developments in legislation & tax laws, sponsors symposia & mystery conferences, presents the Edgar Awards® & provides information for mystery writers. Membership open to published authors, editors, screenwriters & other professionals in the field.
Number of Members: 3,000
Publication(s): *Mystery Writers of American Anthology*; *The Third Degree* (10 issues/yr, free to membs)

NAB, see National Association of Broadcasters (NAB)

NASW, see National Association of Science Writers (NASW)

National Association for Printing Leadership (NAPL), see Epicomm

National Association of Black Journalists (NABJ)
1100 Knight Hall, Suite 3100, College Park, MD 20742
Tel: 301-405-0248 *Fax:* 301-314-1714
E-mail: nabj@nabj.org
Web Site: www.nabj.org
Key Personnel
Exec Dir: Darryl R Matthews, Sr *E-mail:* drmatthews@nabj.org
Devt Dir: Denise Brooking *Tel:* 301-405-6986 *E-mail:* dbrooking@nabj.org
Fin Mgr: Nathaniel Chambers *Tel:* 301-405-0532 *E-mail:* nchambers@nabj.org
Membership Mgr: Veronique Dodson *Tel:* 301-405-0554 *E-mail:* vdodson@nabj.org
Prog Coord: Lisa Waldschmitt *Tel:* 301-405-2592 *E-mail:* lwaldschmitt@nabj.org
Founded: 1975
Organization of journalists, students & media-related professionals that provides quality programs & services to & advocates on behalf of black journalists worldwide.
Number of Members: 3,300
New Election: Biennially, odd yrs
2016 Meeting(s): NABJ & NAHJ Joint Convention & Career Fair, Washington Marriott Wardman Park Hotel, 2660 Woodley Rd NW, Washington, DC, Aug 3-7, 2016
Publication(s): *NABJ Journal* (quarterly, journal)

National Association of Broadcasters (NAB)
1771 "N" St NW, Washington, DC 20036
Tel: 202-429-5300 *Fax:* 202-429-4199
E-mail: nab@nab.org
Web Site: www.nab.org
Key Personnel
CEO & Pres: Gordon H Smith
EVP, Conventions & Busn Opers: Mr Chris Brown
EVP, Mktg & Communs: Michelle Lehman *Tel:* 202-429-5444 *E-mail:* mlehman@nab.org
Trade association for radio & television stations. Provide products, publications (over 130) & other services related to broadcasting.
Number of Members: 9,000
2016 Meeting(s): NAB Show®, Las Vegas, NV, April 16-21, 2016; Radio Show, Omni Nashville Hotel, Nashville, TN, Sept 21-23, 2016

National Association of College Stores (NACS)
500 E Lorain St, Oberlin, OH 44074
Tel: 440-775-7777 *Toll Free Tel:* 800-622-7498 *Fax:* 440-775-4769
Web Site: www.nacs.org
Key Personnel
Dir of Expositions: Mary Adler-Kozak *Tel:* 800-622-7498 ext 2265 *E-mail:* madler-kozak@nacs.org
Dir, Meetings: Jodie Wilmot *Tel:* 800-622-7498 ext 2272 *E-mail:* jwilmot@nacs.org
Exhibit Sales & Serv Rep: Linda Vargo *Tel:* 800-622-7498 ext 2302 *E-mail:* lvargo@nacs.org
Trade association for college store industry.
Number of Members: 4,000
2016 Meeting(s): CAMEX (Campus Market Expo), George R Brown Convention Center, Houston, TX, March 4-8, 2016
Publication(s): *Campus Marketplace* (weekly, newsletter, online); *The College Store* (6 issues/yr, magazine); *Directory of Colleges & College Stores* (annual); *The Torchlight* (semiannual, newsletter)
Membership(s): BISG

National Association of Hispanic Publications Inc (NAHP)
529 14 St NW, Suite 1126, Washington, DC 20045
Tel: 202-662-7250
Web Site: www.nahp.org
Key Personnel
Pres: Eddie Escobedo, Jr *Tel:* 702-649-8553 *E-mail:* eddiejr.escobedo@yahoo.com
VP, Membership: Martha Montoya *Tel:* 714-366-3225 (cell) *E-mail:* martha@elmundous.com
Founded: 1982
Promote Hispanic media.
Number of Members: 100
Publication(s): *NAHP Newsletter* (quarterly)
Membership(s): Hispanic Association on Corporate Responsibility; National Hispanic Leadership Agenda; United States Hispanic Chamber of Commerce

National Association of Independent Publishers Representatives
111 E 14 St, PMB 157, New York, NY 10003
Tel: 267-546-6561 *Toll Free Tel:* 888-624-7779
Web Site: naipr.org
Key Personnel
Exec Dir: Robert Rooney *E-mail:* robert.rooney@naipr.org
Founded: 1990
Information & promotion of commission selling for book publishers.
Seasonal offering of Publishers Frontlist trade catalogs.
Number of Members: 850
Publication(s): *The Call Report*™ (monthly, newsletter, free); *Marketing Advice for the Very Small or Self-Publishers* (newsletter, free); *NAIPR News Online* (monthly, newsletter, free); *Selling on Commission* (free)

National Association of Printing Ink Manufacturers (NAPIM)
15 Technology Pkwy S, Peachtree Corners, GA 30092
Tel: 770-209-7289 *Fax:* 678-680-4920; 770-209-7217
E-mail: napim@napim.org
Web Site: www.napim.org
Key Personnel
Exec Dir: Brad Bergey *Tel:* 770-209-7290 *E-mail:* bbergey@napim.org
Dir, Regulatory Aff & Technol: George Fuchs *Tel:* 770-209-7291 *E-mail:* gfuchs@napim.org
Memb Rel Mgr: Ben Hopper *E-mail:* bhopper@napim.org
Assn Coord: Elise Hitchcock *Tel:* 770-209-7214
Founded: 1916
Trade association representing the printing ink industry & providing information & assistance to members to better manage their business.
Number of Members: 82
2016 Meeting(s): Annual Convention, Red Rock Resort, Las Vegas, NV, March 31-April 4, 2016
Publication(s): *Introduction to Printing Ink* ($6 membs, $10 nonmembs); *Printing Ink Handbook, 6th ed* ($90 membs, $150 nonmembs); *Raw Materials Data Handbook, 2nd ed* ($200 membs, $400 nonmembs)

National Association of Quick Printers (NAQP), see Epicomm

National Association of Real Estate Editors (NAREE)
1003 NW Sixth Terr, Boca Raton, FL 33486-3455
Tel: 561-391-3599 *Fax:* 561-391-0099
Web Site: www.naree.org
Key Personnel
Pres: Daniel Taub
Exec Dir: Mary Doyle-Kimball *E-mail:* madkimba@aol.com
Contact: David Kimball *E-mail:* dakimball@aol.com
Founded: 1929
Nonprofit professional association of writers Journalism Contest & seminars in winter, spring & fall; memberships active for journalists & associate for communications professionals. Bruss Real Estate Book Awards annual competition.
Number of Members: 650
2016 Meeting(s): NAREE Winter Meeting, Las Vegas Convention Center, Las Vegas, NV, Jan 19-21, 2016; Spring Real Estate Journalism Conference, Spring 2016
Publication(s): *NAREE Directory* (annual, directory, free to membs); *NAREE News* (quarterly, free to membs); *Spring Conference Book* (free to membs)

National Association of Science Writers (NASW)
PO Box 7905, Berkeley, CA 94707
Tel: 510-647-9500
Web Site: www.nasw.org
Key Personnel
Exec Dir: Tinsley Davis *E-mail:* director@nasw.org
Founded: 1934
Number of Members: 2,200
New Election: Biennially, even yrs
2016 Meeting(s): Annual Meeting (ScienceWriters2016), San Antonio, TX, Oct 28-Nov 1, 2016
Publication(s): *ScienceWriters* (quarterly, magazine, free for membs)
Membership(s): World Federation of Science Journalists

National Cartoonists Society (NCS)
341 N Maitland Ave, Suite 260, Maitland, FL 32751
Tel: 407-647-8839 *Fax:* 407-629-2502
E-mail: info@reuben.org
Web Site: www.reuben.org
Key Personnel
Pres: Tom Richmond
Exec Dir: Phil Pyster *E-mail:* phil@crowsegal.com
Founded: 1946
Fraternal Organization of Cartoonists.
Number of Members: 500
Publication(s): *The Cartoonist*

National Coalition Against Censorship (NCAC)
19 Fulton St, Suite 407, New York, NY 10038
Tel: 212-807-6222 *Fax:* 212-807-6245
E-mail: ncac@ncac.org
Web Site: www.ncac.org
Key Personnel
Exec Dir: Joan E Bertin
Communs Dir: Michael O'Neil
Dir, Progs: Svetlana Mintcheva
Founded: 1974
Promote & defend free speech, inquiry & expression; monitor & publicize censorship incidents; sponsor public programs; assist in censorship controversies through advice, materials, contacts with local organizations & individuals. Membership is comprised of 50 national participating organizations. Reprints & informational materials available upon request.
Publication(s): *Censorship News* (semiannual, $30/yr)

National Coalition for Literacy (NCL)
PO Box 2932, Washington, DC 20013-2932
E-mail: ncl@ncladvocacy.org
Web Site: www.national-coalition-literacy.org
Key Personnel
Pres: Marty Finsterbusch *Tel:* 484-443-8457
Founded: 1981
A member organization made up of major service, research & policy organizations in adult education, family literacy & English language

acquisition. NCL's mission is to advance adult education, family literacy & English language acquisition in the US - from the most basic skills proficiency level across a continuum of services including the transition into postsecondary education & job training.
Number of Members: 30
Publication(s): *NCL Update* (monthly, newsletter, Free)

National Communication Association
1765 "N" St NW, Washington, DC 20036
Tel: 202-464-4622 *Fax:* 202-464-4600
E-mail: inbox@natcom.org
Web Site: www.natcom.org
Key Personnel
Chief of Staff: Mark Fernando *Tel:* 202-534-1105 *E-mail:* mfernando@natcom.org
Exec Dir: Nancy Kidd, PhD *Tel:* 202-534-1120 *E-mail:* nkidd@natcom.org
Founded: 1914
To promote effective & ethical communication.
Number of Members: 7,500
2016 Meeting(s): Annual Convention, Philadelphia Marriott Downtown/Courtyard, Philadelphia, PA, Nov 10-13, 2016
2017 Meeting(s): Annual Convention, Sheraton Dallas Hotel, Dallas, TX, Nov 16-19, 2017
2018 Meeting(s): Annual Convention, Salt Lake City, UT, Nov 8-11, 2018
2019 Meeting(s): Annual Convention, Baltimore, MD, Nov 14-17, 2019
Publication(s): *Communication and Critical/Cultural Studies*; *Communication Education* (quarterly); *Communication Monographs* (quarterly, journal); *Communication Teacher* (quarterly); *Critical Studies in Media Communication* (journal); *First Amendment Studies*; *Journal of Applied Communication Research*; *Journal of International & Intercultural Communication*; *The Quarterly Journal of Speech*; *Review of Communication*; *Text & Performance Quarterly* (journal)

National Conference for Community & Justice
820A Prospect Hill Rd, Windsor, CT 06095
Tel: 860-683-1039 *Fax:* 860-683-1409
E-mail: info@nccj.org
Web Site: www.nccj.org
Key Personnel
Assoc Dir: Amanda Gumbs *Tel:* 860-298-5313 *E-mail:* agumbs@nccj.org
A human relations organization dedicated to fighting bias, bigotry & racism in America by promoting respect & understanding among all races, religions & cultures through advocacy, conflict resolution & education.
Number of Members: 5,000
Publication(s): *Bulletin* (monthly)

National Council of Teachers of English (NCTE)
1111 W Kenyon Rd, Urbana, IL 61801-1096
Tel: 217-328-3870 *Toll Free Tel:* 877-369-6283 (cust serv) *Fax:* 217-328-9645
E-mail: public_info@ncte.org
Web Site: www.ncte.org
Key Personnel
Interim Exec Dir: Barbara Cambridge *Tel:* 217-278-3601
Deputy Exec Dir: Mila Fuller *Tel:* 217-278-3628 *E-mail:* mfuller@ncte.org
Communs Specialist: Lori Bianchini *Tel:* 217-278-3644 *Fax:* 217-278-3761 *E-mail:* lbianchini@ncte.org
Perms Coord: Shellie Elson *Tel:* 217-278-3638 *Fax:* 217-328-0977 *E-mail:* permissions@ncte.org
Founded: 1911
Focus on the major concerns of teachers of English & the language arts; offer teaching aids, advice, direction & guidance for members. Publish educational books, journals, pamphlets, research reports & position papers for all levels of the English teaching profession. Hold annual convention for members in November; sponsor conferences & workshops.
Number of Members: 30,000
2016 Meeting(s): NCTE Annual Convention, Atlanta, GA, Nov 17-20, 2016
2017 Meeting(s): NCTE Annual Convention, St Louis, MO, Nov 16-19, 2017
2018 Meeting(s): NCTE Annual Convention, Houston, TX, Nov 15-18, 2018
Publication(s): *College Composition & Communication* (quarterly, journal, $75/yr, includes NCTE & CCCC membership); *College English* (6 times/yr, journal, $75/yr, includes NCTE membership); *English Education* (quarterly, journal, $75/yr, includes NCTE & CEE membership); *English Journal* (6 times/yr, $75/yr, includes NCTE membership); *English Leadership Quarterly* (journal, $75/yr, includes NCTE & CEL membership); *Language Arts* (6 times/yr, journal, $75/yr, includes NCTE membership); *Research in the Teaching of English* (quarterly, journal, $75/yr, includes NCTE membership); *Talking Points* (semiannual, journal, $75/yr, includes NCTE & WLU membership); *Teaching English in the Two-Year College* (quarterly, journal, $75/yr, includes NCTE & TYCA membership); *Voices from the Middle* (quarterly, journal, $75/yr, includes NCTE membership)

National Education Association (NEA)
1201 16 St NW, Washington, DC 20036-3290
Tel: 202-833-4000 *Fax:* 202-822-7974
Web Site: www.nea.org
Key Personnel
Pres: Dennis Van Roekel
VP: Lily Eskelsen
Secy/Treas: Rebecca "Becky" Pringle
Exec Dir: John C Stocks
Founded: 1857
Professional employee organization for over 3 million educators, with affiliates in every state & in more than 14,000 communities committed to advancing the cause of public education.
Number of Members: 3,200,000
Publication(s): *Higher Education Advocate* (6 issues/yr, newsletter); *The NEA Almanac of Higher Education* (annual); *NEA Today* (quarterly, magazine); *NEA Today for NEA-Retired Members* (quarterly, magazine); *This Active Life* (6 issues/yr, magazine); *Thought & Action* (annual, journal); *Tomorrow's Teachers* (annual, magazine)

National Federation of Advanced Information Services (NFAIS)
801 Compass Way, Suite 201, Annapolis, MD 21401
Tel: 443-221-2980 *Fax:* 443-221-2981
E-mail: nfais@nfais.org
Web Site: www.nfais.org
Key Personnel
Exec Dir: Marcie Granahan *Tel:* 443-221-2980 ext 101 *E-mail:* mgranahan@nfais.org
Dir, Prof Devt: Jill O'Neill *Tel:* 443-221-2980 ext 102 *E-mail:* jilloneill@nfais.org
Dir, Mktg & Communs: Ken Berlack *Tel:* 443-221-2980 ext 103 *E-mail:* kberlack@nfais.org
Sponsors research; carries out a comprehensive program of continuing education; issues pertinent publications in all areas of documentation & information dissemination.
Number of Members: 60
Publication(s): *Membership Directory* (directory, online only); *NFAIS E Notes* (online only)
Membership(s): CENDI; ICSTI; National Information Standards Organization

National Federation of Press Women Inc (NFPW)
PO Box 5556, Arlington, VA 22205-0798
Tel: 703-237-9804 *Fax:* 703-237-9808
E-mail: presswomen@aol.com
Web Site: www.nfpw.org
Key Personnel
Off Mgr: Carol Pierce
Founded: 1936
Organization of professional women & men pursuing careers across the communications spectrum.
Number of Members: 2,000
New Election: Annually in Sept
2016 Meeting(s): Communications Conference, DoubleTree by Hilton Hotel Wichita Airport, 2098 Airport Rd, Wichita, KS, Sept 8-10, 2016
Publication(s): *Agenda* (quarterly)

National Freedom of Information Coalition (NFOIC)
Affiliate of Missouri School of Journalism
101C Reynolds Journalism Institute, Columbia, MO 65211
Tel: 573-882-4856
Web Site: nfoic.org
Key Personnel
Prog Coord: Melissa MacGowan *Tel:* 573-882-3229 *E-mail:* macgowanm@missouri.edu
Founded: 1989 (as National Freedom of Information Assembly)
Nonpartisan alliance of state & regional affiliates promoting collaboration, education & advocacy for open government; transparency & freedom of information.
Number of Members: 62
Publication(s): *The FOI Advocate: The NFOIC News Blog*; *FOI InSight* (newsletter)

National Information Standards Organization
3600 Clipper Mill Rd, Suite 302, Baltimore, MD 21211
Tel: 301-654-2512 *Fax:* 410-685-5278
E-mail: nisohq@niso.org
Web Site: www.niso.org
Key Personnel
Exec Dir: Todd Carpenter *E-mail:* tcarpenter@niso.org
Assoc Dir: Nettie Lagace *E-mail:* nlagace@niso.org
Memb Servs & Engagement Mgr: DeVonne Parks *E-mail:* dparks@niso.org
Educational Prog Mgr: Juliana Wood *E-mail:* jwood@niso.org
Founded: 1939
Developing, maintaining & publishing technical standards used by libraries, information services & publishers. Accredited by the American National Standards Institute.
Number of Members: 90
Publication(s): *Information Standards Quarterly (ISQ)* (4 issues/yr, $130/yr US, $165/yr CN & foreign, free to voting membs)

National League of American Pen Women
c/o National Pen Women-Scholarship, Pen Arts Bldg, 1300 17 St NW, Washington, DC 20036-1973
Tel: 202-785-1997 *Fax:* 202-452-8868
E-mail: contact@nlapw.org
Web Site: www.nlapw.org
Key Personnel
Pres: Candace Long
Founded: 1897
Scholarships, letters, art & music workshops, awards & prizes. Must send SASE for information.
Number of Members: 3,500
Publication(s): *The Pen Woman* (quarterly, magazine, $25/yr; free to membs)

National Music Publishers' Association (NMPA)
975 "F" St NW, Suite 315, Washington, DC 20004
Tel: 202-393-6672 *Fax:* 202-393-6673
E-mail: pr@nmpa.org
Web Site: www.nmpa.org
Key Personnel
CEO & Pres: David M Israelite
Founded: 1917
Trade association of American Music Publishers.
Number of Members: 3,000
Branch Office(s)
The Harry Fox Agency (HFA), 40 Wall St, 6th fl, New York, NY 10005-1344 *Tel:* 212-834-0100 *Fax:* 646-487-6779 *Web Site:* www.harryfox.com

National Newspaper Association
309 S Providence Rd, Columbia, MO 65203-4267
Mailing Address: PO Box 7540, Columbia, MO 65205-7540
Tel: 573-777-4980 *Fax:* 573-777-4985
E-mail: nna@nna.org
Web Site: nnaweb.org
Key Personnel
Assoc Dir: Lynn Edinger *Tel:* 573-777-4982 *E-mail:* lynn@nna.org
Founded: 1885
Trade association with a mission to protect, promote & enhance America's community newspapers.
Number of Members: 2,500
2016 Meeting(s): Annual Convention & Trade Show, Franklin Marriott, 700 Cool Springs Blvd, Franklin, TN, Sept 22-25, 2016
Publication(s): *Publishers Auxiliary* (monthly, online)

National Newspaper Publishers Association (NNPA)
1816 12 St NW, Washington, DC 20009
Tel: 202-588-8764 *Fax:* 202-588-8960
E-mail: info@nnpa.org
Web Site: www.nnpa.org; www.blackpressusa.com
Key Personnel
Chmn: Cloves C Cambell, Jr
CEO & Pres: Bill Tompkins
Founded: 1941 (as the National Negro Publishers Association)
Federation of more than 200 black community newspapers from across the US.
Number of Members: 200

National Press Club (NPC)
529 14 St NW, 13th fl, Washington, DC 20045
Tel: 202-662-7500 *Fax:* 202-662-7569
E-mail: infocenter@npcpress.org
Web Site: www.press.org
Key Personnel
Club Pres: Myron Belkind
Lib Dir: Julie Schoo *E-mail:* jschoo@press.org
Gen Mgr: William McCarren
Founded: 1908
Private professional organization for journalists. Sponsors workshops, rap sessions with authors, press forums, morning newsmakers, famous speaker luncheons; awards prizes for consumer journalism, environmental reporting; freedom of the press; diplomatic writing, Washington coverage & newsletters; book & art exhibits; computerized reference library; annual Book Fair & Authors' Night.
Number of Members: 4,000
Publication(s): *The Record* (weekly)

National Press Club of Canada Foundation Inc
17 York St, Suite 201, Ottawa, ON K1N 9J6, Canada
E-mail: info@pressclubcanada.ca
Web Site: pressclubcanada.ca
Key Personnel
Pres: James Baxter
Dir: Phil Gibson; Lois Siegel; Hugh Winsor
Founded: 1928
Not-for-profit association for reporters, journalists & media-related people; organizes small & large events of interest to the media community in & around Ottawa's political circles; awards annual scholarships for journalism students.
Number of Members: 50

National Press Foundation
1211 Connecticut Ave NW, Suite 310, Washington, DC 20036
Tel: 202-663-7280
Web Site: nationalpress.org
Key Personnel
COO & Pres: Bob Meyers *E-mail:* bob@nationalpress.org
Dir, Opers: Jessica Jean-Francois *E-mail:* jessica@nationalpress.org
Dir, Progs: Linda Topping Streitfeld *E-mail:* linda@nationalpress.org
Digital Media Mgr: Reyna Abigale Levine *E-mail:* reyna@nationalpress.org
Founded: 1976
Provide all expenses paid educational programs to help journalists understand & report on complex topics in Washington, DC & around the world.

National Press Photographers Association Inc (NPPA)
3200 Croasdaile Dr, Suite 306, Durham, NC 27705
Tel: 919-383-7246 *Fax:* 919-383-7261
E-mail: info@nppa.org
Web Site: www.nppa.org
Key Personnel
Exec Dir: Chip Deale *E-mail:* cdeale@nppa.org
Prof Servs Dir: Thomas Kenniff *Tel:* 919-383-7246 ext 10 *E-mail:* tkenniff@nppa.org
Founded: 1946
To promote & protect integrity & excellence in visual journalism.
Number of Members: 5,500
Publication(s): *News Photographer Magazine* (monthly, free with membership)

National Society of Newspaper Columnists (NSNC)
PO Box 411532, San Francisco, CA 94141
Tel: 415-488-NCNC (488-6762) *Fax:* 484-297-0336
Web Site: www.columnists.com
Key Personnel
Exec Dir: Luenna H Kim *E-mail:* director@columnists.com
Founded: 1977
Promotes professionalism & camaraderie among columnists & other writers of the serial essay, including bloggers. Advocates for columnists & free-press issues.
Number of Members: 500
Publication(s): *Newsletter* (monthly, free)

National Writers Association
10940 S Parker Rd, Suite 508, Parker, CO 80134
Tel: 303-841-0246
E-mail: natlwritersassn@hotmail.com
Web Site: www.nationalwriters.com
Key Personnel
Exec Dir & Ed: Sandy Whelchel *E-mail:* authorsandy@hotmail.com
Founded: 1937
Nonprofit representative organization of new & established writers, serving freelance writers throughout the world.
Number of Members: 2,000
Publication(s): *Authorship* (quarterly, $20/yr); *NWA Newsletter* (monthly by e-mail only, newsletter)

National Writers Union/UAW Local 1981
Affiliate of UAW International of the United Automobile Aerospace & Agricultural Implement Workers of America
256 W 38 St, Suite 703, New York, NY 10018
Tel: 212-254-0279 *Fax:* 212-254-0673
E-mail: nwu@nwu.org
Web Site: www.nwu.org/
Key Personnel
Pres: Larry Goldbetter
Founded: 1981
Organizing for better treatment of freelance writers by publishers; grievance procedures; negotiate union contracts with publishers; health insurance; conferences. Direct services include the Technical Writers Job Hotline & the Publication Rights Clearinghouse, a groundbreaking license fee collection system. National health insurance programs around the country; national grievance officers & contract advisors; agents database online for members; Authors Network, a Bed & Breakfast program for touring authors at over 160 sites throughout the country, including local reviewer's database, local press contacts & local bookstores/vendors.
Number of Members: 1,200
Publication(s): *local chapter newsletters* (quarterly, free to membs); *National Membership News* (monthly, newsletter, free to membs)

NCTA, see Northern California Translators Association

New England Independent Booksellers Association Inc (NEIBA)
1955 Massachusetts Ave, Cambridge, MA 02140
Web Site: www.newenglandbooks.org
Key Personnel
Exec Dir: Steven Fischer *E-mail:* steve@neba.org
Admin Coord: Nan Sorensen *E-mail:* nan@neba.org
Trade association. Fall trade show annually in September or October; educational workshops, holiday gift catalog, book awards.
Number of Members: 500
Publication(s): *NEIBA News* (weekly, membs only)

New England Poetry Club
2 Farrar St, Cambridge, MA 02138
Mailing Address: 376 School St, Watertown, MA 02472
Tel: 617-744-6034
E-mail: info@nepoetryclub.org
Web Site: www.nepoetryclub.org
Key Personnel
Pres: Diana Der-Hovanessian
VP: Sally Cragin; Daniel Tobin
Contest Coord: Audrey Kalajin
Founded: 1915
Society for professional published poets. Sponsor various poetry contests & workshops. Workshops meet at the Yen Ching Institute (2 Divinity Ave Harvard Campus). Readings on first Monday, 7 pm at a location to be announced; workshops third Mondays 7:30 pm; monthly from Sept-May. Special programs at Longfellow House Sunday pm out of doors, $3,000 in prizes annually.
Number of Members: 500
Publication(s): *Writ* (semiannual, newsletter, free with annual dues)
Branch Office(s)
137 W Newton St, Boston, MA 02118 (inquiries on membership), Membership Chmn: Victor Howes

New Hampshire Writers' Project
2500 N River Rd, Manchester, NH 03106
Tel: 603-314-7980 *Fax:* 603-314-7981
E-mail: info@nhwritersproject.org
Web Site: www.nhwritersproject.org

Founded: 1988
Supports the development of individual writers & encourages an audience for literature in the state.
Number of Members: 780
Publication(s): *NH Writer* (6 issues/yr, newsletter)

New Mexico Book Association (NMBA)
1219 Luisa St, Suite 1, Santa Fe, NM 87505
Mailing Address: PO Box 1285, Santa Fe, NM 87504
Tel: 505-660-6357
E-mail: admin@nmbook.org
Web Site: www.nmbook.org
Key Personnel
Pres: Paula Lozar *Tel:* 505-473-3479 *E-mail:* lozarpaula@cs.com
Off Administrator: Susan Waterman
Archivist & Sr Advisor: Richard Polese *Tel:* 505-983-1412 *E-mail:* richard@oceantree.com
Founded: 1994
Nonprofit association serving the interests of publishing, writing, designing, editing, selling & marketing for book professionals throughout New Mexico. Open to all involved in books or publishing. Need not be a resident of New Mexico.
Number of Members: 180
Publication(s): *LIBRO Book News* (6 issues/yr, newsletter, $50/yr membs)
Membership(s): The Association of Publishers for Special Sales; The Independent Book Publishers Association; New Mexico Library Association; Publishers Association of the West

Newspaper Association of America (NAA)
4401 Wilson Blvd, Suite 900, Arlington, VA 22203
Tel: 571-366-1000
Web Site: www.naa.org
Key Personnel
CEO & Pres: Caroline H Little *E-mail:* caroline.little@naa.org
CFO & EVP: Margaret Vassilikos *Tel:* 571-366-1010 *E-mail:* margaret.vassilikos@naa.org
SVP, Busn Devt: Rich Schiekofer *Tel:* 571-366-1184 *E-mail:* rich.schiekofer@naa.org
VP, HR & Opers: Sarah Burkman *Tel:* 571-366-1012 *E-mail:* sarah.burkman@naa.org
Dir, Communs: Sean O'Leary *Tel:* 571-366-1009 *E-mail:* sean.oleary@naa.org
Serves newspapers & newspaper executives by working to advance the cause of a free press; to encourage the efficiency & economy of the newspaper publishing business in all departments & aspects; to engage in & promote research of use to newspapers; to gather & distribute among its member newspapers accurate, reliable & useful information about newspapers & their environment & to promote the highest standard of journalism.
Number of Members: 2,000
2016 Meeting(s): mediaXchange, Marriott Marquis, Washington, DC, April 17-20, 2016
Publication(s): *Presstime* (weekly, membs only)

The Newspaper Guild
501 Third St NW, 6th fl, Washington, DC 20001-2797
Tel: 202-434-7177; 202-434-7162 (The Guild Reporter) *Fax:* 202-434-1472
E-mail: guild@cwa-union.org
Web Site: www.newsguild.org
Key Personnel
Pres: Bernard Lunzer
Ed, The Guild Reporter: Janell Hartman *E-mail:* jhartman@cwa-union.org
Founded: 1934
Labor union; AFL-CIO, CLC.
Number of Members: 26,000
Publication(s): *The Guild Reporter* (quarterly, free to membs, $20 subn rate nonmembs)

North American Agricultural Journalists (NAAJ)
6434 Hurta Lane, Bryan, TX 77808
Tel: 979-845-2872
Web Site: www.naaj.net
Key Personnel
Exec Secy & Treas: Kathleen Phillips *E-mail:* ka-phillips@tamu.edu
Founded: 1952
Self-improvement seminars; annual writing contest for members & nonmembers.
Number of Members: 120
2016 Meeting(s): Annual Meeting, Washington, DC, April 2016
2017 Meeting(s): Annual Meeting, Washington, DC, April 2017
2018 Meeting(s): Annual Meeting, Washington, DC, April 2018
2019 Meeting(s): Annual Meeting, Washington, DC, April 2019
2020 Meeting(s): Annual Meeting, Washington, DC, April 2020
Publication(s): *NAAJ Newsletter* (varies/online to membs as needed)

North American Bookdealers Exchange (NABE)
PO Box 606, Cottage Grove, OR 97424-0026
Tel: 541-942-7455
E-mail: nabe@bookmarketingprofits.com
Web Site: www.bookmarketingprofits.com
Key Personnel
Exec Dir: Al Galasso
Promo Dir: Russ Von Hoelscher
Assoc Dir: Ingrid Crawford
Founded: 1980
International book marketing organization of independent publishers & mail order entrepreneurs. Activities include NABE Combined Book Exhibits at national & regional conventions serving the book, educational, gift & business trade. Publishers Preview Mail Order Program, National Press Release, Electronic Marketing plus complete publisher consultation services for printing, promoting & marketing books.
Number of Members: 1,000
Publication(s): *Book Dealers World* (quarterly, circ 10,000, $5/sample, $50/yr & $90/semiannual membership)

North American Snowsports Journalists Association
11728 SE Madison St, Portland, OR 97216-3849
Tel: 503-255-3771 *Fax:* 503-255-3771
Web Site: www.nasja.org
Key Personnel
VP, Communs: Kristen Lummis *E-mail:* jjklummis@bresnan.net
Exec Secy-Treas: Vicki Andersen *E-mail:* execsec@nasja.org
Founded: 1963 (first founded as the US Ski Writers Association)
Professional group of writers, photographers, broadcasters, filmmakers, authors & editors who report ski & snowboard related news, info & features throughout the US & Canada.
Number of Members: 340
New Election: Annually in March
2016 Meeting(s): Annual Meeting, Big Sky, MT, April 10-14, 2016

North Carolina Writers' Network
PO Box 21591, Winston-Salem, NC 27120-1591
Tel: 336-293-8844
Web Site: www.ncwriters.org
Key Personnel
Exec Dir: Ed Southern
Founded: 1985
Nonprofit, statewide.
Number of Members: 1,500
Publication(s): *Writers' Network News* (semiannual, newspaper, free to membs)

Northern California Independent Booksellers Association (NCIBA)
The Presidio, 1007 General Kennedy Ave, San Francisco, CA 94129
Mailing Address: PO Box 29169, San Francisco, CA 94129-0169
Tel: 415-561-7686 *Fax:* 415-561-7685
E-mail: office@nciba.com
Web Site: www.nciba.com
Key Personnel
Exec Dir: Calvin Crosby
Administrator: Ann Seaton
Trade Show Mgr & Administrator: Elsa Eder *E-mail:* elsa@nciba.com
Tradeshow, education seminars, collaborative advertising, regional holiday catalog. Special memberships for authors include mailing list on labels & e-blast discounts.
Number of Members: 500
Publication(s): *Holiday Catalog*; *Membership Directory* (free); *NCIBA News* (6 issues/yr, newsletter, free to membs); *Northern California Rep Directory* (annual, free)
Membership(s): ABA

Northern California Translators Association
Affiliate of Chapter of the American Translators Association
2261 Market St, Suite 160, San Francisco, CA 94114-1600
Tel: 510-845-8712
E-mail: administrator@ncta.org
Web Site: www.ncta.org
Key Personnel
Pres: Sonia Wichmann
Administrator: Juliet Viola Kniffen
Founded: 1978
Professional translators & interpreters association publishing Translorial; online referral service.
Number of Members: 600
New Election: Annually in Feb
Publication(s): *Translorial* (2 issues/yr, print & online, journal, free to membs at www.translorial.com; free PDF access for *Translorial Reader* registrants at www.ncta.org)

Northwest Independent Editors Guild
PO Box 1630, Snoqualmie, WA 98065
E-mail: info@edsguild.org
Web Site: www.edsguild.org
Key Personnel
Administrator: Toddie Downs
Founded: 1997
Professional association of more than 300 editors in the Pacific Northwest. Members work on all types of communication projects, from brochures & newsletters to books & web sites. The Editors Guild connects clients with professional editors, fosters community among its members & provides resources for their career development.
Number of Members: 300

Northwest Territories Public Library Services
Unit of Department of Education, Culture & Employment
75 Woodland Dr, Hay River, NT X0E 1G1, Canada
Tel: 867-874-6531 *Toll Free Tel:* 866-297-0232 (CN) *Fax:* 867-874-3321
Web Site: www.nwtpls.gov.nt.ca
Key Personnel
Territorial Libn: Alison Hopkins *E-mail:* alison_hopkins@gov.nt.ca
Provide leadership in coordinating public library services throughout the Northwest Territories.

Northwest Writers & Publishers Association (NWPA)
Division of Papyrus Press LLC
21860 Willamette Dr, West Linn, OR 97068
Web Site: northwestwriterspublishers.weebly.com
Key Personnel
Pres: Dr Veronica Esagui *Tel:* 503-913-6006 *Fax:* 503-212-3275
Founded: 2012
Medium for networking between authors & publishers. Membership fees: $50/yr (includes 12 lectures), nonmemb attending meeting $10, member's guest $5, no fee for students under 18. Guest speakers at monthly meetings.
Number of Members: 80
Meeting(s): NWPA Monthly Meeting, Tualatin Public Lib, Tualatin, OR, 2nd Tues of each month; NW Annual Book Festival, Pioneer Courthouse Sq, Portland, OR, Annually last Sat in July

NPES The Association for Suppliers of Printing, Publishing & Converting Technologies
1899 Preston White Dr, Reston, VA 20191
Tel: 703-264-7200 *Fax:* 703-620-0994
E-mail: npes@npes.org
Web Site: www.npes.org
Key Personnel
Pres: Ralph J Nappi *E-mail:* rnappi@npes.org
Dir, Communs & Mktg: Deborah Vieder *E-mail:* dvieder@npes.org
Founded: 1933 (as the National Printing Equipment Association)
Represent manufacturers & distributors of equipment, supplies, systems & software for printing, publishing & converting.
Number of Members: 600
2016 Meeting(s): Graph Expo®, Orange County Convention Center, North Hall, Orlando, FL, Sept 25-28, 2016
Publication(s): *NPES Pressroom Safety Manual*; *Safe Cleaning of Offset Sheetfed Presses*; *Safe Cleaning of Offset Webfed Presses*

NPTA Alliance
330 N Wabash Ave, Suite 2000, Chicago, IL 60611
Tel: 312-321-4092 *Toll Free Tel:* 800-355-NPTA (355-6782) *Fax:* 312-673-6736
Web Site: www.gonpta.com
Key Personnel
CEO & Pres: Kevin Gammonley
Mgr, Membership Opers: Gretchen Fox
Founded: 1903
Trade association serving the printing, publishing, catalog, direct mail, imaging, retail & corporate markets.
Number of Members: 2,600
New Election: Annually in Autumn
Publication(s): *Paper Merchant Weekly* (newsletter, free to membs, electronic)
Membership(s): National Association of Wholesaler-Distributors

NWT Public Library Services, see Northwest Territories Public Library Services

Ontario Book Publishers Organization (OBPO)
20 Maud St, No 401, Toronto, ON M5V 2M5, Canada
Tel: 416-536-7584 *Fax:* 416-536-7692
Web Site: obpo.ca
Key Personnel
Exec Dir: Marg Anne Morrison
Founded: 1990
Represent the needs, interests, concerns & issues of Ontario book publishers; facilitate information sharing & educational opportunities; facilitate group marketing projects.
Number of Members: 35

Ontario Library Association
2 Toronto St, 3rd fl, Toronto, ON M5C 2B6, Canada
Tel: 416-363-3388 *Toll Free Tel:* 866-873-9867 *Fax:* 416-941-9581
E-mail: info@accessola.com
Web Site: www.accessola.com
Key Personnel
Exec Dir: Shelagh Paterson *Tel:* 416-363-3388 ext 224 *E-mail:* spaterson@accessola.com
Founded: 1900
Memberships available: Personal membership (for one individual, based on salary earned in library work, whether full-time or part-time) $40-$100, Institutional Membership (for one or two-persons, transferable within an institution) $140-$190, Associate Membership (for businesses/corporations to provide support) $195.
Number of Members: 5,300
New Election: Annually in Dec
Publication(s): *The Teaching Librarian* (3 issues/yr, magazine, $36/yr CN)

Ordre des traducteurs, terminologues et interpretes agrees du quebec
Affiliate of Federation Internationale de Traducteurs
2021 Union Ave, Suite 1108, Montreal, QC H3A 2S9, Canada
Tel: 514-845-4411 *Toll Free Tel:* 800-265-4815 *Fax:* 514-845-9903
E-mail: info@ottiaq.org
Web Site: www.ottiaq.org
Key Personnel
Exec Dir: Johanne Boucher *Tel:* 514-845-4411 ext 227 *E-mail:* direction@ottiaq.org
Communs Coord: Catherine Guillemette-Bedard *Tel:* 514-845-4411 ext 225 *E-mail:* cgbedard@ottiaq.org
Bring translators together to exchange information, send out offers of employment to members. Promote profession & protect public interest. Conferences, annual meeting, social activities, seminars, continuing education. Newsletter for membs only.
Number of Members: 2,073
Publication(s): *Circuit* (quarterly, ezine, $42 CN, $50 elsewhere); *L'antenne Express* (newsletter)

Oregon Christian Writers (OCW)
1075 Willow Lake Rd N, Keizer, OR 97303
Tel: 503-393-3356
E-mail: contact@oregonchristianwriters.org
Web Site: www.oregonchristianwriters.org
Key Personnel
Pres: Maxine Marsolini
Prog Chmn: Marilyn Rhoads
Summer Conference Dir: Lindy Jacobs *E-mail:* summerconf@oregonchristianwriters.org
Registrar & Busn Mgr: Sue Miholer
Founded: 1963
Workshops & seminars for beginning & advanced writers; guest speakers & critiques by professional writers.
Number of Members: 350
New Election: Annually in Oct
2016 Meeting(s): Oregon Christian Writers Seminar, Salem, OR, Feb 27, 2016; Oregon Christian Writers Seminar, Eugene, OR, May 14, 2016; Summer Coaching Conference, Jantzen Beach Red Lion Hotel, Portland, OR, Aug 15-18, 2016; Oregon Christian Writers Seminar, Portland, OR, Oct 15, 2016
Publication(s): *Oregon Christian Writers Newsletter* (3 issues/yr, newsletter)

Overseas Press Club of America (OPC)
40 W 45 St, New York, NY 10036
Tel: 212-626-9220 *Fax:* 212-626-9210
Web Site: www.opcofamerica.org
Key Personnel
Exec Dir: Patricia Kranz *E-mail:* patricia@opcofamerica.org
Founded: 1939
Maintain an international association of journalists, encourage professional skill & integrity of reportage, contribute to the freedom & independence of journalism & the press worldwide.
Number of Members: 440
New Election: Annually in Aug
Publication(s): *Bulletin* (monthly, newsletter, free to membs); *Dateline* (annual, magazine, free to membs)

Pacific Northwest Booksellers Association
338 W 11 Ave, Unit 108, Eugene, OR 97401
Tel: 541-683-4363 *Toll Free Tel:* 800-353-6764 *Fax:* 541-683-3910
E-mail: info@pnba.org
Web Site: www.pnba.org
Key Personnel
Exec Dir: Thom Chambliss *E-mail:* thom@pnba.org
Mktg Dir: Brian Juenemann *E-mail:* brian@pnba.org
Founded: 1965
Annual trade lists of publishing companies' sales reps; educational seminars; work with local literacy groups & anticensorship organizations; sponsor annual booksellers awards presented for books of exceptional quality by Northwest writers or publishers; sponsor workshops & prizes.
Number of Members: 300
Publication(s): *Footnotes* (monthly e-mail, newsletter, free to membs); *PNBA Member Handbook* (annual, handbook, free to membs, electronic)

Pacific Northwest Writers Association, see PNWA - a writer's resource

Pacific Printing Industries Association
Affiliate of Printing Industries of America
6825 SW Sandburg St, Portland, OR 97223
Mailing Address: PO Box 23575, Portland, OR 97281-3575
Tel: 503-221-3944 *Toll Free Tel:* 877-762-7742 *Fax:* 503-221-5691
E-mail: info@ppiassociation.org
Web Site: www.ppiassociation.org
Key Personnel
Exec Dir: Jules Van Sant *E-mail:* jules@ppiassociation.org
Membership Sales & Support: Chris Ryce
Trade association.
Number of Members: 230

Palm Springs Writers Guild
PO Box 947, Rancho Mirage, CA 92270-0947
Web Site: www.palmspringswritersguild.org
Key Personnel
Pres: Diana Miller-Castells *E-mail:* president.pswg@gmail.com
VP, Membership: Hillary Christiansen *E-mail:* vpmembership.pswg@gmail.com
Founded: 1977
Number of Members: 280

PEN American Center
Affiliate of PEN International
588 Broadway, Suite 303, New York, NY 10012
Tel: 212-334-1660 *Fax:* 212-334-2181
E-mail: info@pen.org
Web Site: www.pen.org
Key Personnel
Exec Dir: Suzanne Nossel
Pres: Andrew Solomon
Intl Pres: John Ralston Saul
Dir, Literary Progs: Paul Morris *Tel:* 212-334-1660 ext 4824 *E-mail:* paul@pen.org
Membership Coord: Daniel Guzman *Tel:* 212-334-1660 ext 4819 *E-mail:* daniel@pen.org

Asst Ed & Soc Media Assoc: Wei-Ling Woo *Tel:* 212-334-1660 ext 4832 *E-mail:* weiling@pen.org
An association of writers working to advance literature, defend free expression & foster international literary fellowship.
Number of Members: 4,000
Publication(s): *Grants & Awards Available to American Writers* (online directory, $12)

PEN Canada
24 Ryerson Ave, Suite 301, Toronto, ON M5T 2P3, Canada
Tel: 416-703-8448 *Fax:* 416-703-3870
E-mail: queries@pencanada.ca
Web Site: www.pencanada.ca
Key Personnel
Pres: Phillip Slayton
Exec Dir: Tasleem Thawar *Tel:* 416-703-8448 ext 24
Administrator: Pari Rajagopalan *Tel:* 416-703-8448 ext 25
Progs & Communs Coord: Brendan De Cairns *Tel:* 416-703-8448 ext 21
Founded: 1926
Promotes freedom of expression through writing.
Number of Members: 500

PEN Center USA
Affiliate of PEN International
PO Box 6037, Beverly Hills, CA 90212
Tel: 323-424-4939 *Fax:* 323-424-4944
E-mail: pen@penusa.org
Web Site: www.penusa.org
Key Personnel
Exec Dir: Michelle Meyering
Founded: 1943
National association of poets, playwrights, screenwriters, essayists, editors, novelists, historians, critics, journalists & translators whose purpose is to foster a sense of community among writers in the Western US & to advance the freedom to write throughout the world.
Number of Members: 800
Publication(s): *Electric PEN* (biweekly, free); *Membership Directory* (annual, free)

PEN New England
Unit of PEN American Center
MIT, 14N-221A, 77 Massachusetts Ave, Cambridge, MA 02139
Tel: 617-324-1729
E-mail: pen-newengland@mit.edu
Web Site: www.pen-ne.org
Key Personnel
Exec Dir: Karen Wulf *E-mail:* kwulf@mit.edu
Advance the cause of literature & reading in New England & defending free expression everywhere.

Periodical & Book Association of America Inc (PBAA)
481 Eighth Ave, Suite 526, New York, NY 10001
Tel: 212-563-6502 *Fax:* 212-563-4098
Web Site: www.pbaa.net
Key Personnel
Exec Dir: Lisa W Scott *E-mail:* lisawscott@hotmail.com
Assoc Dir: Jose Cancio *E-mail:* jcancio@pbaa.net
Founded: 1965
Nonprofit organization for publishers, distributors, wholesalers, retailers, consultants & industry service providers.
Number of Members: 102

Photographic Society of America® (PSA®)
8241 S Walker Ave, Suite 104, Oklahoma City, OK 73139
Tel: 405-843-1437 *Toll Free Tel:* 855-PSA-INFO (855-772-4636) *Fax:* 405-843-1438
E-mail: hq@psa-photo.org
Web Site: www.psa-photo.org
Key Personnel
Opers Mgr: Kara Goodson
Founded: 1934
Sponsor workshops & awards for members.
Number of Members: 6,500
2016 Meeting(s): PSA® International Conference of Photography, Wyndham San Antonio Riverwalk, 111 E Pecan St, San Antonio, TX, Sept 10-17, 2016
Publication(s): *PSA Journal* (monthly, journal, free to membs)

Playwrights Guild of Canada
401 Richmond St W, Suite 350, Toronto, ON M5V 3A8, Canada
Tel: 416-703-0201 *Fax:* 416-703-0059
E-mail: info@playwrightsguild.ca
Web Site: www.playwrightsguild.ca
Key Personnel
Exec Dir: Robin Sokoloski *E-mail:* robin@playwrightsguild.ca
Membership & Prof Contracts Mgr: Rebecca Burton *E-mail:* membership@playwrightsguild.ca
Off & Progs Mgr: Tina Salek *E-mail:* tina@playwrightsguild.ca
Founded: 1982
Professional association. Contracts, amateur agent productions, script service, readings.
Number of Members: 735
Membership(s): Professional Association of Canadian Playwrights

PNWA - a writer's resource
1420 NW Gilman Blvd, Suite 2, PMB 2717, Issaquah, WA 98027
Tel: 425-673-2665 *Fax:* 425-961-0768
E-mail: pnwa@pnwa.org
Web Site: www.pnwa.org
Key Personnel
Pres: Pam Binder
Founded: 1955
Nonprofit association. Develops writing talent through education, accessibility to publishing industry & participation in a vital writer community.
Number of Members: 1,400

Poetry Society of America (PSA)
15 Gramercy Park, New York, NY 10003
Tel: 212-254-9628 *Fax:* 212-673-2352
Web Site: www.poetrysociety.org
Key Personnel
Pres: Ruth Kaplan
Exec Dir: Alice Quinn
Deputy Dir: Brett Fletcher Lauer *E-mail:* brett@poetrysociety.org
Membership & Devt Dir: Elsbeth Pancrazi *E-mail:* elsbeth@poetrysociety.org
Progs Dir: Charif Shanahan *E-mail:* charif@poetrysociety.org
Founded: 1910
Contests, readings, lectures, symposia, seminars, weekly workshops for members.
Number of Members: 2,900

Poets & Writers Inc
90 Broad St, Suite 2100, New York, NY 10004
Tel: 212-226-3586 *Fax:* 212-226-3963
E-mail: admin@pw.org
Web Site: www.pw.org
Key Personnel
Exec Dir: Elliot Figman
Dir, Fin & Acctg: William F Hayes
Mng Dir: Melissa Ford Gradel
Founded: 1970
A nonprofit organization which offers information, support & exposure to writers at all stages in their careers. Founded to foster the development of poets & fiction writers & to promote communication throughout the literary community. It publishes the bimonthly *Poets & Writers Magazine*, which delivers to its readers profiles of noted authors & publishing professionals, practical how-to articles, a comprehensive listing of grants & awards for writers & special sections on subjects ranging from small presses to writers conferences. The Readings/Workshops Program supports public literary events through matching grants to community organizations.
Publication(s): *Poets & Writers Magazine* (6 issues/yr, $15.95/yr, $25.95/2 yrs, $4.95 single copy 1999 forward; prior to 1999 $3.95)
Branch Office(s)
2035 Westwood Blvd, Suite 211, Los Angeles, CA 90025, Dir: Jamie Fitzgerald *Tel:* 310-481-7195 *Fax:* 310-481-7193 *E-mail:* calif@pw.org

PRIMIR, see Print Industries Market Information & Research Organization

Print Industries Market Information & Research Organization
Affiliate of NPES The Association for Suppliers of Printing, Publishing & Converting Technologies
1899 Preston White Dr, Reston, VA 20191
Tel: 703-264-7200 *Fax:* 703-620-0994
E-mail: npes@npes.org
Web Site: www.primir.org; www.npes.org/primirresearch/primir.aspx
Key Personnel
Mng Dir: Jacqueline M Bland *E-mail:* jbland@primir.org
Founded: 2005
Research association of the graphic arts industry; provide data & research to printers, publishers & manufacturers of equipment & supplies for the printing/publishing industry & converting industries.
Number of Members: 60
New Election: Annually in Dec

Printing & Graphics Association MidAtlantic (PGAMA)
9685 Gerwig Lane, Suite A, Columbia, MD 21046-1520
Tel: 410-319-0900 *Toll Free Tel:* 877-319-0906 *Fax:* 410-319-0905
E-mail: info@pgama.com
Web Site: www.pgama.com
Key Personnel
Pres: Kerry C Stackpole *E-mail:* kerry@pgama.com
Founded: 1894
Number of Members: 360

Printing Association of Florida Inc (PAF)
Affiliate of Printing Industries of America (PIA)
6250 Hazeltine National Dr, Suite 114, Orlando, FL 32822
Tel: 407-240-8009 *Toll Free Tel:* 800-331-0461 *Fax:* 407-240-8333
Web Site: www.flprint.org
Key Personnel
Dir, Communs: Monica Turner *E-mail:* monica@flprint.org
Dir, Membership & Pub Aff: Harold Yankelevitz *E-mail:* harold@flprint.org
Opers Mgr: Rich Bider *E-mail:* rich@flprint.org
Founded: 1937
Trade association for the graphic arts industry.
Number of Members: 380
2016 Meeting(s): Graphics of the Americas, Miami Beach Convention Center, 1901 Convention Center Dr, Miami Beach, FL, Feb 18-20, 2016
Publication(s): *Graphics Update* (monthly, free to membs)

Printing Brokerage/Buyers Association International (PBBA)
1530 Locust St, Mezzanine 124, Philadelphia, PA 19102

Tel: 215-821-6581
E-mail: contactus@pbba.org
Web Site: pbba.org
Key Personnel
Chmn: Vincent Mallardi *E-mail:* vince@pbba.org
Founded: 1985
Trade association for printing, sales brokerage & purchasing.
Number of Members: 830
Publication(s): *Brokerage* (monthly, newsletter, free to membs); *Hot Markets for Print Demand Annual Rankings of Buyers, Print Products & Geographies* (annual, $995); *Hot Markets for Print Supply Annual Rankings of Providers, Intermediaries & Geographies* (annual, $995); *Law v. Print: Avoid Problems & Protect Opportunities Buying & Selling Prints* ($395); *Printing Brokerage in North America: The Survey* ($195); *Why Use a Printing Independent? Outsourcing is In* ($95)

Printing Industries of America
200 Deer Run Rd, Sewickley, PA 15143-2324
Tel: 412-741-6860 *Toll Free Tel:* 800-910-4283 *Fax:* 412-741-2311
E-mail: printing@printing.org
Web Site: www.printing.org
Key Personnel
CEO & Pres: Michael F Makin *E-mail:* mmakin@printing.org
Dir, Mktg: Lisa Rawa *E-mail:* lrawa@printing.org
Mgr, Mktg: Chrystal Kapanyko *E-mail:* ckapanyko@printing.org
Founded: 1887
Member organization providing research, educational & technical services to printing industry worldwide.
Number of Members: 14,000
Publication(s): *The Magazine* (10 issues/yr, free to membs); *Publications Catalog* (annual, free); *QC Catalog* (annual, free)
Branch Office(s)
601 13 St NW, Suite 350S, Washington, DC 20005-3807 *Tel:* 202-730-7970

Printing Industries Press, see Printing Industries of America

Printing Industry Association of the South (PIAS)
305 Plus Park Blvd, Nashville, TN 37217
Tel: 615-366-1094 *Fax:* 615-366-4192
E-mail: info@pias.org
Web Site: www.pias.org
Key Personnel
Pres: Ed Chalifoux
Provide services & support to the printing industry.
Number of Members: 400
Publication(s): *Print South* (monthly, magazine, free with membership)

Professional Writers Association of Canada (PWAC)
215 Spadina Ave, Suite 130, Toronto, ON M5T 2C7, Canada
Tel: 416-504-1645
E-mail: info@pwac.ca
Web Site: pwac.ca; www.writers.ca
Key Personnel
Exec Dir: Sandy Crawley
Assoc Dir: Margaret DeRosia *Tel:* 416-504-1645 ext 1
Protect & promote the interests of freelance writers in Canada, develop & maintain professional standards in editor-writer relationships, lobby for higher standard fees for freelancers, sponsor professional development workshops & offset freelancers' isolation by circulating news, information & market data on the industry.
Number of Members: 625
2016 Meeting(s): PWAC@MagNet National Conference & Annual General Meeting, The Courtyard Toronto Downtown, 475 Yonge St, Toronto, ON, CN, June 7-10, 2016
Publication(s): *PWAC Guide to Editing as a Sideline* (book); *PWAC Guide to Roughing in the Market* (book)

Protestant Church-Owned Publishers Association
6631 Westbury Oaks Ct, Springfield, VA 22152
Tel: 703-220-5989
Web Site: www.pcpaonline.org
Key Personnel
Dir: Gary Mulder *E-mail:* mulder@pcpaonline.org
Founded: 1951
Number of Members: 40

Public Relations Society of America
33 Maiden Lane, 11th fl, New York, NY 10038-5150
Tel: 212-460-1400 *Fax:* 212-995-0757
Web Site: www.prsa.org
Key Personnel
CFO: Philip Bonaventura *Tel:* 212-460-1440 *E-mail:* philip.bonaventura@prsa.org
VP, Mktg: Nicole Zerillo *Tel:* 212-460-1417 *E-mail:* nicole.zerillo@prsa.org
VP, PR: Stephanie Cegielski *Tel:* 212-460-1495 *E-mail:* stephanie.cegielski@prsa.org
Dir, Memb Servs: Eileen Lintao *Tel:* 212-460-1490 *E-mail:* eileen.lintao@prsa.org
Founded: 1947
Association of public relations professionals dedicated to development & ethical practice of public relations.
Publication(s): *The Public Relations Strategist* (quarterly, $150/yr); *Public Relations Tactics* (monthly, $100/yr)

Publishers Association of the West (PubWest)
17501 Hill Way, Lake Oswego, OR 97035
Tel: 503-901-9865
Web Site: pubwest.org
Key Personnel
Exec Dir: Kent Watson *E-mail:* executivedirector@pubwest.org
Founded: 1977
Members are small & medium-sized book publishers located throughout North America. Supply marketing & technical information to members; conduct annual educational seminars; promote sales in the region. Trade show, including BEA, MPBA & PNBA. Publisher of the Huenefeld-PubWest Survey of Financial Operations.
Number of Members: 360
Publication(s): *The Endsheet* (quarterly, journal, free); *PubWest Membership Directory* (annual, directory, free to membs, $25 for nonmembs)

Publishers Information Bureau (PIB)®
Division of MPA - The Association of Magazine Media
757 Third Ave, 11th fl, New York, NY 10017
Tel: 212-872-3745; 212-872-3700 (MPA)
E-mail: infocenter@magazine.org
Web Site: www.magazine.org
Key Personnel
CEO & Pres: Mary Berner *Tel:* 212-872-3710 *E-mail:* president@magazine.org
CFO & SVP: William Wood *Tel:* 212-872-3722 *E-mail:* wwood@magazine.org
EVP, Communs: Meredith Wagner *Tel:* 212-872-3732 *E-mail:* mwagner@magazine.org
EVP, Mktg: Linda Mason *Tel:* 212-872-3734 *E-mail:* lmason@magazine.org
Dir, Info Servs: Sandy Jimenez *Tel:* 212-872-3795 *E-mail:* sjimenez@magazine.org
Measure advertising pages & rate card revenues in consumer magazines & newspaper supplements.
Number of Members: 250

Publishing Professionals Network
9328 Elk Grove, Suite 105-250, Elk Grove, CA 95624
Tel: 415-279-2334
E-mail: operations@pubpronetwork.org
Web Site: www.pubpronetwork.org
Key Personnel
Pres: Tona Pearce Myers
Founded: 1969
Specialize in supporting the book publishing industry. Offers educational programs, seminars & scholarships. Produces an annual book show & has monthly dinner meetings.
Number of Members: 400
New Election: Annually in Jan
Publication(s): *Bookbuilders West Newsletter* (5 times/yr, newsletter)

PubWest, see Publishers Association of the West (PubWest)

Quebec Writers' Federation (QWF)
1200 Atwater Ave, Suite 3, Westmount, QC H3Z 1X4, Canada
Tel: 514-933-0878
E-mail: info@qwf.org
Web Site: www.qwf.org
Key Personnel
Exec Dir: Lori Schubert *E-mail:* admin@qwf.org
Coord, Membership Servs & Communs: Deanna Radford *E-mail:* deanna@qwf.org
Association of Quebec writers to promote English language writing in Quebec through literary awards, writing workshops & literary events.
Number of Members: 545

Reporters Committee for Freedom of the Press
1101 Wilson Blvd, Suite 1100, Arlington, VA 22209-1817
Tel: 703-807-2100 *Toll Free Tel:* 800-336-4243 *Fax:* 703-807-2109
E-mail: info@rcfp.org
Web Site: www.rcfp.org
Key Personnel
Exec Dir: Bruce Brown *Tel:* 703-807-2101
Communs Dir: Debra Gersh Hernandez *Tel:* 703-807-2104
Busn Mgr: Lois Loyd *Tel:* 571-481-9321
Founded: 1970
Legal defense & research services for journalists & media lawyers.
Publication(s): *Access to Electronic Communications* (handbook); *Access to Juror Questionnaires* (handbook); *Access to Juvenile Justice* (handbook); *Access to Police Records* (handbook); *Access to Terrorism Proceedings* (handbook); *Agents of Discovery* (report); *Alternative Dispute Resolution* (handbook); *Anonymous Juries* (report); *Federal FOIA Appeals Guide* (handbook); *Federal Open Government Guide* (handbook); *FERPA, HIPAA & DPPA* (handbook); *The First Amendment Handbook* (booklet); *Gag Orders* (handbook); *Grand Juries* (handbook); *Homefront Confidential* (report); *Judicial Speech* (handbook); *Jury Proceedings and Records* (handbook); *The Lost Stories* (handbook); *The News Media & the Law* (quarterly, magazine, $20/yr, free online a few weeks after released to subscribers); *Off Base: Military Court Dockets* (handbook); *Online Access to Plea Agreements* (handbook); *Open Courts Compendium* (handbook); *Open Government Guide, 6th ed*; *Photographers' Guide to Privacy* (handbook); *Police, Protesters and the Press*; *Private Eyes* (handbook); *Privatization v the Public's Right to Know* (handbook); *Privilege Compendium*; *A Reporter's*

Field Guide (handbook); *A Reporter's Guide to American Indian Law* (handbook); *A Reporter's Guide to Medical Privacy Law* (handbook); *A Reporter's Guide to Military Justice* (handbook); *Reporter's Recording Guide* (handbook); *Secret Dockets* (handbook); *Secret Juries* (handbook); *SLAPP Stick* (handbook); *Sunshine Inc* (handbook); *Warrants & Wiretaps* (handbook); *White Paper: Military Dockets* (handbook)

Romance Writers of America®
14615 Benfer Rd, Houston, TX 77069
Tel: 832-717-5200 *Fax:* 832-717-5201
E-mail: info@rwa.org
Web Site: www.rwa.org
Key Personnel
Exec Dir: Allison Kelley *Tel:* 832-717-5200 ext 124 *E-mail:* allison.kelley@rwa.org
Deputy Exec Dir: Carol Ritter *Tel:* 832-717-5200 ext 127 *E-mail:* carol.ritter@rwa.org
Ed & Pubns Mgr: Erin Fry *Tel:* 832-717-5200 ext 122 *E-mail:* erin.fry@rwa.org
Educ & Progs Mgr: Stephani Fry *Tel:* 832-717-5200 ext 126 *E-mail:* steph.fry@rwa.org
Membership Servs Rep: Donna Mathoslah *Tel:* 832-717-5200 ext 121 *E-mail:* donna.mathoslah@rwa.org
Founded: 1980
Romance Writers of America is dedicated to advancing the professional interests of career-focused romance writers through networking & advocacy.
Membership: $95/yr; $25 processing fee (new & reinstating).
Number of Members: 10,000
2016 Meeting(s): Annual Conference, San Diego Marriott Hotel & Marina, San Diego, CA, July 13-16, 2016
2017 Meeting(s): Annual Conference, Walt Disney World Swan & Dolphin, 1500 Epcot Resorts Blvd, Lake Buena Vista, FL, July 26-29, 2017
2018 Meeting(s): Annual Conference, Sheraton Denver Downtown Hotel, Denver, CO, July 25-28, 2018
2019 Meeting(s): Annual Conference, New York Marriott® Marquis, New York, NY, July 24-27, 2019
Publication(s): *Romance Writers Report* (monthly, magazine, free to membs)

SABEW, see Society of American Business Editors & Writers Inc (SABEW)

Saskatchewan Arts Board
1355 Broad St, Regina, SK S4R 7V1, Canada
Tel: 306-787-4056 *Toll Free Tel:* 800-667-7526 (Saskatchewan only) *Fax:* 306-787-4199
E-mail: info@artsboard.sk.ca
Web Site: www.artsboard.sk.ca
Key Personnel
Exec Dir: David Kyle *Tel:* 306-787-4019 *E-mail:* dkyle@artsboard.sk.ca
Assoc Exec Dir: Peter Sametz *Tel:* 306-787-4194 *E-mail:* sametz@artsboard.sk.ca
Dir, Opers: Sandi Desjarlais *Tel:* 306-787-4069 *E-mail:* sandi@artsboard.sk.ca
Founded: 1948
Provide consultation, advice, grants, programs +/or services to individual artists, arts groups & organizations & members of the public. Programs support & encourage the development of artists, arts groups & organizations in the literary, performing, visual, media & multidisciplinary arts. Also develop & maintain a permanent collection of original works by Saskatchewan artists.
Branch Office(s)
417 24 St E, Saskatoon, SK S7K 0K7, Canada *Tel:* 306-964-1155 *Fax:* 306-964-1167

Science Fiction & Fantasy Writers of America Inc (SFWA)
PO Box 3238, Enfield, CT 06083-3238
E-mail: office@sfwa.org
Web Site: www.sfwa.org
Key Personnel
Pres: Steven Gould *E-mail:* president@sfwa.org
VP: Cat Rambo *E-mail:* vp@sfwa.org
Treas & CFO: Bud Sparhawk *E-mail:* cfo@sfwa.org
Secy: Susan Forest *E-mail:* secretary@sfwa.org
Dir, Communs: Jaym Gates *E-mail:* communications@sfwa.org
Opers Mgr: Kate Baker
Founded: 1965
An organization of professional writers, editors, artists, agents & others in the science fiction & fantasy field.
Number of Members: 1,800
New Election: Annually in May
Publication(s): *Annual Membership Directory*; *SFWA Bulletin* (quarterly, $32/yr nonmembs, $48/yr foreign nonmembs, $38 CN/Mexico)

SF Canada
7433 E River Rd, Washago, ON L0K 2B0, Canada
Web Site: www.sfcanada.org
Key Personnel
Pres: Peter Halasz
VP: Colleen Anderson
Secy-Treas: Diane Walton *E-mail:* waltondi@gmail.com
Founded: 1989
Exists to foster a sense of community among Canadian writers of speculative fiction, to improve communication between Canadian writers of speculative fiction, to foster the growth of quality writing in Canadian speculative fiction, to lobby on behalf of Canadian writers of speculative fiction & to encourage the translation of Canadian speculative fiction. Supports positive social action.
Number of Members: 130

SHARP, see Society for the History of Authorship, Reading & Publishing Inc (SHARP)

SIBA, see Southern Independent Booksellers Alliance

Small Publishers, Artists & Writers Network (SPAWN)
323 E Matilija St, Suite 110, PMB 123, Ojai, CA 93023
Tel: 805-646-3045 *Fax:* 805-640-8213
E-mail: execdir@spawn.org
Web Site: www.spawn.org
Key Personnel
Exec Dir: Kathleen Sexton Kaiser
Secy-Treas: Mindy Reed
Membership Dir: Helen Gallagher
Founded: 1996
Number of Members: 200

Social Sciences & Humanities Research Council of Canada (SSHRC)
350 Albert St, Ottawa, ON K1P 6G4, Canada
Mailing Address: PO Box 1610, Ottawa, ON K1P 6G4, Canada
Tel: 613-992-0691
E-mail: research@sshrc-crsh.gc.ca
Web Site: www.sshrc.ca
Key Personnel
EVP: Ted Hewitt
VP, Future Challenges: Ursula Gobel
VP, Res Progs: Brent Herbert-Copley
Offers two programs of support for scholarly publishing: aid to scholarly publication program, aid to research & transfer journal program. Only Canadian citizens or permanent residents of Canada are eligible to apply under either program. SSHRC is a Federal Crown Corporation.
Number of Members: 22

Sociedad Interamericana de Prensa (SIP), see Inter American Press Association (IAPA)

Society for Features Journalism (SFJ)
University of Maryland, Philip Merrill College of Journalism, 1100 Knight Hall, College Park, MD 20742
Tel: 301-314-2631 *Fax:* 301-314-9166
Web Site: featuresjournalism.org
Key Personnel
Exec Dir: Merrilee Cox *E-mail:* merrileesfj@gmail.com
Founded: 1947 (as AASFE (American Association of Sunday & Feature Editors))
Nonprofit trade association of Sunday & feature editors.
Number of Members: 250
Publication(s): *Style Magazine* (annual)

Society for Scholarly Publishing (SSP)
10200 W 44 Ave, Suite 304, Wheat Ridge, CO 80033-2840
Tel: 303-422-3914 *Fax:* 720-881-6101
E-mail: info@sspnet.org
Web Site: www.sspnet.org
Key Personnel
Exec Dir: Ann Mehan Crosse *Tel:* 720-881-6114 *E-mail:* amcrosse@kellencompany.com
Dir, Info Servs: Ruth Gleason Roth
Dir, Memb Servs: Kristi Klinke
Founded: 1978
Professional association for people in scholarly publishing industry; 12-16 seminars/workshops sponsored each year.
Number of Members: 1,000
2016 Meeting(s): Annual Meeting, The Westin Bayshore, 1601 Bayshore Dr, Vancouver, BC, CN, May 31-June 3, 2016
Publication(s): *Directory* (annual, membs only)

Society for Technical Communication
9401 Lee Hwy, Suite 300, Fairfax, VA 22031
Tel: 703-522-4114 *Fax:* 703-522-2075
E-mail: stc@stc.org
Web Site: www.stc.org
Key Personnel
CEO: Chris Lyons *Tel:* 571-366-1901 *E-mail:* chris.lyons@stc.org
Dir, Communs & Intercom Ed: Liz Pohland *Tel:* 571-366-1910 *E-mail:* liz.pohland@stc.org
Dir, Meetings & Educ: Lloyd Tucker *Tel:* 571-366-1904 *E-mail:* lloyd.tucker@stc.org
Founded: 1960 (as Society of Technical Writers & Publishers)
Professional society dedicated to the advancement of the theory & practice of technical communication in all media.
Number of Members: 15,000
Publication(s): *Intercom* (monthly, magazine, electronic version free to membs; print version $60/yr membs, $160/yr nonmembs, $185/yr nonmembs CN, $215/yr nonmembs elsewhere); *Technical Communication* (quarterly, journal, free to membs, $275/yr nonmembs, electronic)

Society for the History of Authorship, Reading & Publishing Inc (SHARP)
c/o The Johns Hopkins University Press, Journals Publishing Div, PO Box 19966, Baltimore, MD 21211-0966
Tel: 410-516-6987 *Toll Free Tel:* 800-548-1784 *Fax:* 410-516-3866
E-mail: members@sharpweb.org
Web Site: www.sharpweb.org
Key Personnel
Ed: Sydney Sharp *E-mail:* editor@sharpweb.org
Founded: 1993

Promotes the study of book history among academics & non-academics. Publishing & scholarly attention to its history.
Number of Members: 1,175
Publication(s): *Book History* (annual, journal, included with individual membership, $73/yr instns); *SHARP News* (quarterly, included with membership); *SHARP Online Membership & Periodicals Directory* (annual, access to online included with membership)

Society of American Business Editors & Writers Inc (SABEW)
Walter Cronkite School of Journalism & Mass Communication, Arizona State University, 555 N Central Ave, Suite 406 E, Phoenix, AZ 85004-1248
Tel: 602-496-7862 *Fax:* 602-496-7041
E-mail: sabew@sabew.org
Web Site: sabew.org
Key Personnel
Pres: Kevin Hall
Exec Dir: Warren Watson *Tel:* 602-496-5041 *E-mail:* watson@sabew.org
Dir, Web/Membership: Spring Eselgroth *Tel:* 602-261-7655 ext 105 *E-mail:* eselgroth@sabew.org
Founded: 1964
Professional development. Sponsor regional workshops. Specialize in business journalism.
Number of Members: 3,500
2016 Meeting(s): Spring Conference, Washington, DC, May 2016

Society of American Travel Writers (SATW)
11950 W Lake Park Dr, Suite 320, Milwaukee, WI 53224-3049
Tel: 414-359-1625 *Fax:* 414-359-1671
E-mail: info@satw.org
Web Site: www.satw.org
Key Personnel
Pres: Steve Giordano
Exec Dir: Mike Mathy *Tel:* 414-359-1625 ext 1108 *E-mail:* mmathy@satw.org
Membership Coord: Haley Montsma *Tel:* 414-359-1625 ext 1105 *E-mail:* hmontsma@satw.org
Founded: 1955
Promote responsible journalism, provide professional support & development for our members, encourage the conservation & preservation of travel resources worldwide.
Number of Members: 1,100
Publication(s): *Directory of Members* (annual, $250 print + $7.50 S&H)

Society of Children's Book Writers and Illustrators (SCBWI)
4727 Wilshire Blvd, Suite 301, Los Angeles, CA 90010
Tel: 323-782-1010 *Fax:* 323-782-1892
E-mail: membership@scbwi.org; scbwi@scbwi.org
Web Site: www.scbwi.org
Key Personnel
Pres: Stephen Mooser *E-mail:* stephenmooser@scbwi.org
Exec Dir: Lin Oliver *E-mail:* linoliver@scbwi.org
Dir, Opers & Membership Coord: Gee Cee Addison Bahador *E-mail:* gcaddison@scbwi.org
Founded: 1971
An organization of children's writers & illustrators & others devoted to the interests of children's literature; annual workshops & conferences throughout the world.
Number of Members: 22,000
2016 Meeting(s): Winter Conference, Grand Hyatt New York, 109 E 42 St at Grand Central Terminal, New York, NY, Feb 12-14, 2016; Summer Conference, Hyatt Regency Century Plaza, 2025 Avenue of the Stars, Los Angeles, CA, Aug 5-7, 2016
Publication(s): *SCBWI Bulletin* (6 issues/yr, newsletter, with membership)

Society of Illustrators (SI)
128 E 63 St, New York, NY 10065
Tel: 212-838-2560 *Fax:* 212-838-2561
E-mail: info@societyillustrators.org
Web Site: www.societyillustrators.org
Key Personnel
Exec Dir: Anelle Miller *E-mail:* anelle@societyillustrators.org
Dir, Opers: John Capobiano *E-mail:* john@societyillustrators.org
Founded: 1901
Museum of American Illustration.
Number of Members: 950
New Election: Annually in June
Publication(s): *American Illustration* (annual, $45)

The Society of Midland Authors (SMA)
PO Box 10419, Chicago, IL 60610
E-mail: info@midlandauthors.com
Web Site: www.midlandauthors.com
Key Personnel
Pres: Meg Tebo *E-mail:* megteboesq@gmail.com
VP: Robert Loerzel *E-mail:* loerzel@comcast.net
Treas: Richard Bales
Corresponding Secy: Charles J Masters
Recording Secy: Richard Frisbie
Newsletter Ed: Thomas Frisbie *E-mail:* tomfrisbie@aol.com
Webmaster: Mary Claire Hersh *E-mail:* maryclaire@prodigy.net
Founded: 1915
Nonprofit writer's association that seeks to stimulate creative efforts & closer association among Midwest writers; maintain collections of writer's works & encourage interest in reading, literature & writing in cooperation with other educational & cultural institutions. Members are qualified authors & co-authors of works from recognized publishers or associates (nonvoting) who live in Illinois, Indiana, Kansas, Michigan, Minnesota, Missouri & Nebraska. Monthly literary & professional programs, annual awards dinner, $500 & recognition plaque, for best books of previous year in six categories: adult fiction, adult nonfiction, poetry, biography & memoirs (adult), children's fiction, children's nonfiction.
Number of Members: 400
Publication(s): *Literary License* (8 issues/yr, newsletter)

Society of Motion Picture & Television Engineers® (SMPTE®)
3 Barker Ave, 5th fl, White Plains, NY 10601
Tel: 914-761-1100 *Fax:* 914-761-3115
Web Site: www.smpte.org
Key Personnel
Exec Dir: Barbara Lange *Tel:* 914-205-2370
Dir, Opers: Sally-Ann D'Amato *Tel:* 914-205-2375
Dir, Standards & Engg: Peter D Symes *Tel:* 914-205-2371
Mgr, Memb Rel: Roberta Gorman *Tel:* 914-205-2376
Mktg & Communs: Aimee Ricca *Tel:* 914-205-2381
Founded: 1916
To advance theory & practice of engineering in film, TV, motion imaging & allied arts & sciences; establishment of standards & practices. Annual membership dues are $145.
Number of Members: 6,000
Publication(s): *SMPTE Motion Imaging Journal* (8 issues/yr, journal, free with membership, $180/yr US & CN, $195/yr elsewhere)

The Society of Southwestern Authors (SSA)
PO Box 30355, Tucson, AZ 85751-0355
Tel: 520-546-9382
Web Site: www.ssa-az.org
Key Personnel
Pres: Chris Stern *E-mail:* azwritten@gmail.com
VP: Donna Young *E-mail:* karmaniranda@aol.com
Treas: Jay McCall *E-mail:* jmcca11415@msn.com
Recording Secy: Jean Young *E-mail:* migralaws@aol.com
Founded: 1972
Nonprofit association of writers & other publishing professionals. Sponsors a writing contest which includes three categories: short story, personal essay/memoirs & poetry.
Number of Members: 400
Publication(s): *The Write Word* (6 issues/yr, newsletter, free to membs)

Software & Information Industry Association (SIIA)
1090 Vermont Ave NW, 6th fl, Washington, DC 20005-4095
Tel: 202-289-7442 *Fax:* 202-289-7097
Web Site: www.siia.net
Key Personnel
Pres: Kenneth Wasch *Tel:* 202-789-4440
VP, Membership: Eric Fredell *Tel:* 202-789-4464
Principal trade association of the software & information industry.
Number of Members: 850
Publication(s): *Upgrade* (6 issues/yr, magazine, free to membs, $79 nonmembs)

Southern Independent Booksellers Alliance
3806 Yale Ave, Columbia, SC 29205
Tel: 803-994-9530 *Fax:* 309-410-0211
E-mail: info@sibaweb.com
Web Site: www.sibaweb.com
Key Personnel
Exec Dir: Wanda Jewell *E-mail:* wanda@sibaweb.com
Number of Members: 500
2016 Meeting(s): SIBA Fall Discovery Show, Hilton Savannah Desoto, Savannah, GA, Sept 16-18, 2016
2017 Meeting(s): SIBA Fall Discovery Show, Sheraton New Orleans, New Orleans, LA, Sept 15-17, 2017
Publication(s): *SEBA Holiday Catalog*

Special Libraries Association (SLA)
331 S Patrick St, Alexandria, VA 22314-3501
Tel: 703-647-4900 *Fax:* 703-647-4901
Web Site: www.sla.org
Key Personnel
Deputy CEO: Doug Newcomb *Tel:* 703-647-4923 *E-mail:* dnewcomb1@sla.org
CFO: Linda N Broussard *Tel:* 703-647-4938 *E-mail:* lbroussard@sla.org
Dir, Membership: Paula Diaz *Tel:* 703-647-4926 *E-mail:* pdiaz@sla.org
Founded: 1909
Serial & nonserial publications; public relations; professional development; employment clearinghouse; resume referral service; computer-assisted, self-study programs; chapters, divisions, student groups & caucuses; government relations; fund development; scholarships; grants; honors & awards; annual conference & exhibit; winter meeting; information resources center.
Number of Members: 8,000
2016 Meeting(s): Annual Conference & INFO-EXPO, Philadelphia Convention Center, Philadelphia, PA, June 12-14, 2016
2017 Meeting(s): Annual Conference & INFO-EXPO, Phoenix, AZ, June 18-20, 2017
Publication(s): *Information Outlook* (6 issues/yr, ezine, $240)

Specialized Information Publishers Association (SIPA)
Division of Software & Information Industry Association (SIIA)

1090 Vermont Ave NW, 6th fl, Washington, DC 20005-4095
Web Site: www.sipaonline.com
Key Personnel
VP: Luis Hernandez *Tel:* 202-789-4469 *E-mail:* lhernandez@siia.net
Edit Dir: Ronn Levine *Tel:* 202-789-4491 *E-mail:* rlevine@siia.net
Members are subscription-based publishers representing small & large companies. Activities include e-mail, marketing, technical developments, copyright, business practices & editorial development.
Number of Members: 250
Publication(s): *SIPAlert Daily*

Specialty Graphic Imaging Association
10015 Main St, Fairfax, VA 22031-3489
Tel: 703-385-1335 *Toll Free Tel:* 888-385-3588 *Fax:* 703-273-0456
E-mail: sgia@sgia.org
Web Site: www.sgia.org
Key Personnel
CEO & Pres: Michael Robertson
Founded: 1992
Members are digital imaging producers, suppliers who sell to digital imagers & schools which teach digital imaging.
Number of Members: 900
2016 Meeting(s): SGIA Expo, Las Vegas, NV, Sept 14-16, 2016
2017 Meeting(s): SGIA Expo, Ernest N Morial Convention Center, New Orleans, LA, Oct 10-12, 2017
2018 Meeting(s): SGIA Expo, Las Vegas Convention Center, Las Vegas, NV, Oct 18-20, 2018
Publication(s): *SGIA Journal Graphic Edition* (6 issues/yr, free to membs); *SGIA Journal Garment Edition* (quarterly, free to membs)

Tag & Label Manufacturers Institute Inc (TLMI)
One Blackburn Ctr, Gloucester, MA 01930
Tel: 978-282-1400 *Fax:* 978-282-3238
E-mail: office@tlmi.com
Web Site: tlmi.com
Key Personnel
Pres: Frank Sablone *E-mail:* fas@tlmi.com
Membership Coord & Off Adminstrator: Beth Morris *E-mail:* beth@tlmi.com
Proj Coord: Julie Sablone *E-mail:* julie@tlmi.com
Founded: 1933
Number of Members: 300
2016 Meeting(s): Converter Meeting, Grand Hyatt Kauai Resort & Spa, Koloa, HI, March 6-8, 2016; Annual Meeting, The Breakers, Palm Beach, FL, Oct 16-19, 2016
Publication(s): *Hot Off The Press* (monthly, newsletter, free to membs, electronic); *Illuminator Newsletter* (quarterly, newsletter, membs only, electronic)

Teachers & Writers Collaborative
520 Eighth Ave, Suite 2020, New York, NY 10018-4165
Tel: 212-691-6590 *Toll Free Tel:* 888-BOOKS-TW (266-5789) *Fax:* 212-675-0171
E-mail: info@twc.org
Web Site: www.twc.org
Key Personnel
Dir: Amy Swauger *E-mail:* aswauger@twc.org
Dir, Opers: Jade Triton *E-mail:* jtriton@twc.org
Educ Dir: Jordan Dann *E-mail:* jdann@twc.org
Founded: 1967
Information source for those interested in teaching writing & literary arts; publish books & magazines about creative writing; sponsor workshops. Basic annual membership: $35.
Publication(s): *Teachers & Writers* (quarterly, magazine, $20/yr or $35/2 yrs indiv, $45/yr instns & organizations)

Technical Association of the Pulp & Paper Industry (TAPPI)
15 Technology Pkwy S, Suite 115, Peachtree Corners, GA 30092
Tel: 770-446-1400 *Toll Free Tel:* 800-332-8686 (US); 800-446-9431 (CN) *Fax:* 770-446-6947
E-mail: memberconnection@tappi.org
Web Site: www.tappi.org
Key Personnel
CEO & Pres: Larry N Montague
VP, Opers: Eric Fletty *Tel:* 770-209-7535 *E-mail:* efletty@tappi.org
Press Mgr: Jeff Wells *Tel:* 770-209-7228 *E-mail:* jwells@tappi.org
Founded: 1915
Professional society of executives, operating managers, engineers, scientists & technologists serving the pulp, paper & allied industries.
Number of Members: 7,000
2016 Meeting(s): PaperCon 2016, Duke Energy Convention Center, Cincinnati, OH, May 15-18, 2016; TAPPI PEERS Conference, Hyatt Regency Jacksonville Riverfront, 225 E Coastline Dr, Jacksonville, FL, Sept 28-30, 2016; TAPPI/AICC SuperCorrExpo®, Orange County Convention Center, Orlando, FL, Oct 17-20, 2016
Publication(s): *TAPPI JOURNAL* (monthly, free to membs, electronic)

Television Academy
5220 Lankershim Blvd, North Hollywood, CA 91601-3109
Tel: 818-754-2800 *Fax:* 818-761-2827
Web Site: www.emmys.com
Key Personnel
CEO & Chmn of the Bd: Bruce Rosenblum
CFO: Heather Cochran
Pres: Maury McIntyre
SVP, Awards: John Leverence
Founded: 1977
Organization for those involved in national television; bestows Emmy awards for excellence in television; college television awards & college internship program; inducts deserving individuals in "Television Academy Hall of Fame".
Number of Members: 20,000
Publication(s): *EMMY Magazine*

Texas Institute of Letters (TIL)
c/o 7748 Hwy 290 W, Austin, TX 78736-3202
E-mail: president@texasinstituteofletters.org; secretary@texasinstituteofletters.org
Web Site: www.texasinstituteofletters.org
Key Personnel
Pres: Andres Tijerina
VP: Steve Davis
Treas: James Hoggard
Secy: Darwin Payne
Recording Secy: Betty Wiesepape
Founded: 1936
Awards over $20,000 annually to recognize outstanding literary works in several categories. Cooperate in sponsorship of various writing fellowships.
Number of Members: 250
Publication(s): *Newsletter* (quarterly, membs only)

The Society of Professional Journalists (SPJ)
Eugene S Pulliam National Journalism Ctr, 3909 N Meridian St, Indianapolis, IN 46208
Tel: 317-927-8000 *Fax:* 317-920-4789
E-mail: spj@spj.org
Web Site: www.spj.org
Key Personnel
Exec Dir: Joe Skeel *Tel:* 317-927-8000 ext 216 *E-mail:* jskeel@spj.org
Assoc Exec Dir: Chris Vachon *Tel:* 317-927-8000 ext 207 *E-mail:* cvachon@spj.org
Creative Dir: Tony Peterson *Tel:* 317-927-8000 ext 214 *E-mail:* tpeterson@spj.org
Dir, Educ: Scott Leadingham *Tel:* 317-927-8000 ext 211 *E-mail:* sleadingham@spj.org
Dir, Events: Heather Dunn *Tel:* 317-927-8000 ext 204 *E-mail:* hdunn@spj.org
Dir, Membership: Linda Hall *Tel:* 317-927-8000 ext 203 *E-mail:* lindah@spj.org
Awards Coord: Chad Hosier *Tel:* 317-927-8000 ext 210 *E-mail:* chosier@spj.org
Communs Coord: Ellen Kobe *Tel:* 317-927-8000 ext 205 *E-mail:* ekobe@spj.org
Founded: 1909 (as Sigma Delta Chi fraternity)
Professional organization that includes broadcast, print & online journalists, journalism educators & students interested in journalism as a career.
Number of Members: 9,000
2016 Meeting(s): Excellence in Journalism, Sheraton New Orleans, 500 Canal St, New Orleans, LA, Sept 18-20, 2016
Publication(s): *Quill* (6 times/yr, magazine, $75/yr, free for membs)

United for Libraries
Division of The American Library Association (ALA)
109 S 13 St, Suite 117B, Philadelphia, PA 19107
Tel: 312-280-2161 *Toll Free Tel:* 800-545-2433 (ext 2161) *Fax:* 215-545-3821
E-mail: united@ala.org
Web Site: www.ala.org/united
Key Personnel
Exec Dir: Sally Gardner Reed *E-mail:* sreed@ala.org
Dir, Mktg & Communs: Beth Nawalinski *E-mail:* bnawalinski@ala.org
Mktg/PR Specialist: Jillian Kalonick *E-mail:* jkalonick@ala.org
Founded: 2009
Support citizens who govern, advocate & fundraise for all type of libraries.
Number of Members: 5,000

United Nations Association of the United States of America
1750 Pennsylvania Ave NW, Suite 300, Washington, DC 20006
Tel: 202-887-9040 *Fax:* 202-887-9021
Web Site: www.unausa.org
Key Personnel
Exec Dir: Chris Whatley *E-mail:* cwhatley@unausa.org
Deputy Exec Dir: Mary-Frances Wain *E-mail:* mwain@unausa.org
Membership Dir: Laura Giroux *E-mail:* lgiroux@unausa.org
Founded: 1946
Publications, nonprofit information & educational services about international affairs & organizations.
Number of Members: 25,000
Branch Office(s)
801 Second Ave, 9th fl, New York, NY 10017 *Tel:* 212-697-3315 *Fax:* 212-697-3316

US Board on Books For Young People (USBBY)
Division of International Board on Books for Young People (IBBY)
c/o V Ellis Vance, 5503 N El Adobe Dr, Fresno, CA 93711-2363
Tel: 559-351-6119
Web Site: www.usbby.org
Key Personnel
Exec Dir: V Ellis Vance *E-mail:* executive.director@usbby.org
Founded: 1953
To promote international understanding & goodwill through books for children & adolescents.
Number of Members: 500
Publication(s): *Bridges: A Publication of USBBY* (semiannual, newsletter)
Membership(s): ALA; The Children's Book Council; International Literacy Association; National Council of Teachers of English

USBE: United States Book Exchange
2969 W 25 St, Cleveland, OH 44113
Tel: 216-241-6960 *Fax:* 216-241-6966
E-mail: usbe@usbe.com
Web Site: www.usbe.com
Key Personnel
Mng Dir: John T Zubal; Marilyn Zubal
Redistribution of library materials to & from libraries.
Number of Members: 15,888

Visual Artists & Galleries Association Inc (VAGA)
111 Broadway, Suite 1006, New York, NY 10006
Tel: 212-736-6666 *Fax:* 212-736-6767
E-mail: info@vagarights.com
Web Site: vagarights.com
Key Personnel
Exec Dir: Robert Panzer *E-mail:* rpanzer@vagarights.com
Rts Specialist: Lucie Amour *E-mail:* lamour@vagarights.com
Protects artists copyrights; provides art licensing & reproduction rights clearances & royalties collection for artists. Have archive of color transparencies & B&W images.
Number of Members: 18,000

Visual Media Alliance (VMA)
665 Third St, Suite 500, San Francisco, CA 94107-1956
Tel: 415-489-7601 *Toll Free Tel:* 800-659-3363 *Toll Free Fax:* 800-824-1911
E-mail: info@vma.bz
Web Site: main.vma.bz
Key Personnel
Pres: Dan Nelson *Tel:* 415-489-7617 *E-mail:* dan@vma.bz
Trade association.
Number of Members: 950

Web Offset Association (WOA)
Division of Printing Industries of America
200 Deer Run Rd, Sewickley, PA 15143
Tel: 412-741-6860 *Toll Free Tel:* 800-910-4283 *Fax:* 412-741-2311
E-mail: printing@printing.org
Web Site: www.printing.org/page/3419
Key Personnel
EVP: Mary Garnett *E-mail:* mgarnett@printing.org
Dir, Special Interest Groups: Laurie Reynolds *Tel:* 412-259-1802 *Fax:* 412-259-1800 *E-mail:* lreynolds@printing.org
Printing Trade Association members work in web offset printing. Meetings, publications & awards competition.
Number of Members: 8,000
New Election: Annually in Nov

Western Writers of America Inc (WWA)
271 CR 219, Encampment, WY 82325
Tel: 307-329-8942 *Fax:* 307-327-5465
Web Site: westernwriters.org
Key Personnel
Pres: Sherry Monahan *E-mail:* president@westernwriters.org
VP: Kirk Ellis *E-mail:* vice-president@westernwriters.org
Exec Dir & Secy-Treas: Candy Moulton *E-mail:* wwa.moulton@gmail.com
Founded: 1953
Nonprofit confederation of professional writers of fiction & nonfiction pertaining to, or inspired by tradition, legends, development & history of the American West.
Number of Members: 650
2016 Meeting(s): Annual Convention, Holiday Inn, Cheyenne, WY, June 21-25, 2016
Publication(s): *Roundup Magazine* (6 times/yr, $40/yr)

Willamette Writers
2108 Buck St, West Linn, OR 97068
Tel: 503-305-6729 *Fax:* 503-344-6174
E-mail: wilwrite@willamettewriters.com
Web Site: www.willamettewriters.com
Key Personnel
Pres: Jenny Schrader
Off Mgr: Bill Johnson
Monthly meeting (open to public); critique groups; writer referrals; monthly newsletter; annual literary contest, annual conference.
Number of Members: 1,550
Publication(s): *The Willamette Writer* (monthly, free to membs)

Women Who Write Inc
PO Box 652, Madison, NJ 07940-0652
E-mail: info@womenwhowrite.org
Web Site: womenwhowrite.org
Key Personnel
Pres: Ginger Pate
VP, Membership: Amy Reade
VP, Progs: Debbie Gerrish
Ed, Writers' Notes: Michelle Hollander
Founded: 1988
Writing groups, Writer's Conference, workshops, readings, literary events, newsletter & literary magazine.
Number of Members: 130
Publication(s): *Goldfinch* (annual, magazine, $10); *Writers' Notes* (quarterly, newsletter)

Women's National Book Association Inc
PO Box 237, FDR Sta, New York, NY 10150-0231
Tel: 212-208-4629 *Fax:* 212-208-4629
E-mail: publicity@bookbuzz.com; info@wnba-books.org
Web Site: www.wnba-books.org; www.NationalReadingGroupMonth.org
Key Personnel
PR: Susannah Greenberg
Founded: 1917
Increase opportunities for women & recognition of women in the world of books. Sponsor WNBA Award (formerly Constance Lindsay Skinner Award), WNBA Pannell Award & WNBA Eastman Grant. Ten chapters: Boston, Charlotte, Detroit, Los Angeles, Nashville, New Orleans, New York, San Francisco, Seattle & Washington, DC.
Number of Members: 1,000
New Election: Biennially in May
Publication(s): *The Bookwoman* (3 issues/yr, free to membs)

Writers' Alliance of Newfoundland & Labrador
Haymarket Sq, 223 Duckworth St, Suite 208, St John's, NL A1C 6N1, Canada
Tel: 709-739-5215 *Toll Free Tel:* 866-739-5215
E-mail: wanl@nf.aibn.com
Web Site: wanl.ca
Key Personnel
Exec Dir: Alison Dyer
Founded: 1987
Not-for-profit, member-based organization established to contribute to a supportive environment for writing & serve the needs & protect the rights of writers in the province.
Number of Members: 350
New Election: Annually in Oct

Writers' Federation of Nova Scotia
1113 Marginal Rd, Halifax, NS B3H 4P7, Canada
Tel: 902-423-8116 *Fax:* 902-422-0881
E-mail: contact@writers.ns.ca
Web Site: writers.ns.ca
Key Personnel
Exec Dir: Jonathan Meakin *E-mail:* director@writers.ns.ca
Arts Educ & Admin Offr: Heidi Hallett *E-mail:* wits@writers.ns.ca
Communs & Devt Offr: Robin Spittal *E-mail:* programs@writers.ns.ca
Mentorship & Outreach Offr: Sue Goyette *E-mail:* events@writers.ns.ca
Founded: 1976
Foster creative writing & the profession of writing in the province of Nova Scotia; provide advice & assistance to writers at all stages of their careers; encourage greater public recognition of Nova Scotian writers & their achievements; enhance the literary arts in our regional & national culture.
Number of Members: 800
New Election: Annually in June
Publication(s): *Eastword* (6 issues/yr, newsletter, electronic version free to membs, hard copy $45/yr)

Writers' Guild of Alberta
11759 Groat Rd, Edmonton, AB T5M 3K6, Canada
Tel: 780-422-8174 *Toll Free Tel:* 800-665-5354 (AB only) *Fax:* 780-422-2663 (attn WGA)
E-mail: mail@writersguild.ab.ca
Web Site: www.writersguild.ab.ca
Key Personnel
Exec Dir: Carol Holmes *E-mail:* carol.holmes@writersguild.ab.ca
Communs & Partnerships Coord: Nicholas Mather *E-mail:* nicholas.mather@writersguild.ab.ca
Memb Servs Coord: Giorgia Severini
Progs Coord: Natalie Cook *E-mail:* natalie.cook@writersguild.ab.ca; Nichole Quiring *E-mail:* nichole.quiring@writersguild.ab.ca
Founded: 1980
Our mission is to support, encourage & promote writers & writing, to safeguard the freedom to write & to read & to advocate for the well-being of writers.
Number of Members: 1,000
Publication(s): *WestWord* (6 issues/yr, magazine)
Branch Office(s)
505 21 Ave SW, Calgary, AB T2S 0G9, Canada, Prog Coord: Samantha Warwick *Tel:* 403-265-2226 *E-mail:* samathawarwick@writersguild.ab.ca

Writers Guild of America, East (WGAE)
250 Hudson St, Suite 700, New York, NY 10013
Tel: 212-767-7800 *Fax:* 212-582-1909
Web Site: www.wgaeast.org
Key Personnel
Exec Dir: Lowell Peterson *Tel:* 212-767-7828 *E-mail:* lpeterson@wgaeast.org
Dir, Communs: Jason Gordon *Tel:* 212-767-7809 *E-mail:* jgordon@wgaeast.org
Dir, Progs: Dana Weissman *Tel:* 212-767-7835 *E-mail:* dweissman@wgaeast.org
Labor union representing professional writers in motion pictures, TV, radio, as well as digital media content. Membership available only through the sale of literary material or employment for writing services in one of these areas.
Number of Members: 4,200
New Election: Annually in Sept
Publication(s): *On Writing* (online web series)

Writers Guild of America, West (WGAW)
7000 W Third St, Los Angeles, CA 90048
Tel: 323-951-4000 *Toll Free Tel:* 800-548-4532 *Fax:* 323-782-4800
Web Site: www.wga.org
Key Personnel
Pres: Christopher Keyser
VP: Howard Rodman
Secy & Treas: Carl Gottlieb
Labor union: collective bargaining representation for film, TV broadcast, interactive & new media writers. Awards dinner & seminars (sometimes for public).

Number of Members: 12,000
Publication(s): *Written By Magazine* (6 issues/yr, $50/yr)

Writers' League of Texas (WLT)
611 S Congress Ave, Suite 200 A-3, Austin, TX 78704
Tel: 512-499-8914
E-mail: wlt@writersleague.org
Web Site: www.writersleague.org
Key Personnel
Exec Dir: Becka Oliver *E-mail:* becka@writersleague.org
Prog Dir: Jennifer Ziegler *E-mail:* jennifer@writersleague.org
Mktg/Memb Servs Mgr: Noelle O'Donnell
Founded: 1981
Workshops, seminars, classes, library resource center, technical assistance, newsletter, monthly programs, educational programs for young people. Memberships: $50 (indiv/family), $100 & up (premium), $250 & up (businesses & organizations).
Number of Members: 1,200
Publication(s): *Footnotes* (26 issues/yr, newsletter, free, electronic); *Scribe* (blog)

The Writers' Union of Canada (TWUC)
600-460 Richmond St W, Toronto, ON M5V 1Y1, Canada
Tel: 416-703-8982 *Fax:* 416-504-9090
E-mail: info@writersunion.ca
Web Site: www.writersunion.ca
Key Personnel
Exec Dir: John Degen *Tel:* 416-703-8982 ext 221
Assoc Dir: Siobhan O'Connor *Tel:* 416-703-8982 ext 222 *E-mail:* soconnor@writersunion.ca
Off Administrator: Valerie Laws *Tel:* 416-703-8982 ext 224
Specialize in service for members & non-members including publications, newsletter, contract advice, competitions, ms evaluation & advocacy.
Number of Members: 2,000

Foundations

Listed below are foundations that are closely affiliated with the book trade.

Books for Asia
Division of The Asia Foundation
2490 Verna Ct, San Leandro, CA 94577
Mailing Address: PO Box 193223, San Francisco, CA 94119-3223
E-mail: booksforasia@asiafound.org
Web Site: booksforasia.org
Key Personnel
Dir: Melody Zavala *Tel:* 510-667-6475 *Fax:* 510-351-2602 *E-mail:* mzavala@asiafound.org
Founded: 1954
A program of the Asia Foundation that has distributed well over 46 million books, journals & non-print educational resources to libraries, schools, universities & research centers in over 40 nations throughout Asia since 1954. Averages one million books per year in all educational fields at all educational levels sent to Asia Foundation field offices located throughout the region. Books are distributed by Foundation staff to recipient institutions based on requests received by our staff from representatives of those needy organizations. The overwhelming majority of books distributed are donated new books to the Asia Foundation by American publishers. Publishers may receive a tax deduction of up to twice the manufacturing cost for each book donated to qualified 501(c)(3) nonprofit organizations, such as the Asia Foundation. Monetary donations welcome.

Bridge to Asia
1505 Juanita Way, Berkeley, CA 94702-1103
Tel: 510-665-3998
E-mail: asianet@bridge.org
Web Site: www.bridge.org
Key Personnel
Pres: Jeffrey Smith
VP: Newton Liu
Founded: 1987
A nonprofit book-donation program, which provides donated books, journals & Internet based research services to developing countries in Asia. Primary book-donors include members of the American Council of Learned Societies, the Nebraska Book Company, Follett Higher Education Group & several thousand individual book donors.

The Canadian Writers' Foundation Inc (La Fondation des Ecrivains Canadiens)
PO Box 13281, Kanata Sta, Ottawa, ON K2K 1X4, Canada
Tel: 613-256-6937 *Fax:* 613-256-5457
E-mail: info@canadianwritersfoundation.org
Web Site: www.canadianwritersfoundation.org
Key Personnel
Pres: Marianne Scott *Tel:* 613-733-4223 *Fax:* 613-733-8752
Exec Secy: Suzanne Williams *E-mail:* smw.enterprises@sympatico.ca
Founded: 1931
Benevolent trust. Provides financial assistance to distinguished senior Canadian writers in need.

The Century Foundation
One Whitehall St, 15 fl, New York, NY 10004
Tel: 212-452-7700 *Fax:* 212-535-7534
E-mail: info@tcf.org
Web Site: www.tcf.org
Key Personnel
Pres: Mark Zuckerman
Edit Dir: Jason Renker *Tel:* 212-452-7715 *E-mail:* renker@tcf.org
Chief Admin Offr: Philip Li *E-mail:* li@tcf.org
Founded: 1919
Engaged in research & public education on significant contemporary policy issues. Emphasis on international political affairs, national, economic & social questions, government & media issues. No grants to institutions or individuals, but foundation will review independent project proposals within program guidelines as well as soliciting its own.
Branch Office(s)
1333 "H" St NW, 10th fl, Washington, DC 20005 *Tel:* 202-387-0400

La Foundation des Ecrivains Canadiens, see The Canadian Writers' Foundation Inc (La Fondation des Ecrivains Canadiens)

Graphic Arts Education & Research Foundation (GAERF)
1899 Preston White Dr, Reston, VA 20191
Tel: 703-264-7200 *Toll Free Tel:* 866-381-9839 *Fax:* 703-620-3165
E-mail: gaerf@npes.org
Web Site: www.gaerf.org
Key Personnel
Pres: Ralph J Nappi
Dir: Eileen D Cassidy *E-mail:* ecassidy@npes.org
Founded: 1983
A major source of financial support for projects & programs designed to provide a graphic communications work force for the future.

John Simon Guggenheim Memorial Foundation
90 Park Ave, New York, NY 10016
Tel: 212-687-4470 *Fax:* 212-697-3248
E-mail: fellowships@gf.org
Web Site: www.gf.org
Key Personnel
CFO & VP: Coleen Higgins-Jacob
Pres: Edward Hirsch
SVP & Secy: Andre Bernard
Dir, Devt & PR: Richard W Hatter
Founded: 1925
Provide fellowships to further the development of scholars & artists by assisting them to engage in research in any field of knowledge & creation in any of the arts; awarded to persons who have already demonstrated exceptional capacity for productive scholarship or exceptional creative ability in the arts.

The Heritage Foundation
214 Massachusetts Ave NE, Washington, DC 20002-4999
Tel: 202-546-4400 *Toll Free Tel:* 800-544-4843 *Fax:* 202-546-8328
E-mail: info@heritage.org
Web Site: www.heritage.org
Key Personnel
Pres: Jim DeMint
Creative Dir: Melissa Bluey
Founded: 1973
A tax exempt public policy research institute; complete publications list on request.

The National Endowment for the Arts
Nancy Hanks Ctr, Rm 703, 1100 Pennsylvania Ave NW, Washington, DC 20506-0001
Tel: 202-682-5400
Web Site: www.arts.gov; www.nea.gov
Key Personnel
Acting Chmn: Joan Shigekawa
Div Specialist: A Phil McNeal, II *Tel:* 202-682-5099 *E-mail:* mcnealp@arts.gov
Dir, Lit: Amy Stolls
Grant-giving agency. Give grants to nonprofit literary organizations. Guidelines available on web site.

Western States Arts Federation
1743 Wazee St, Suite 300, Denver, CO 80202
Tel: 303-629-1166 *Toll Free Tel:* 888-562-7232 *Fax:* 303-629-9717
E-mail: staff@westaf.org
Web Site: www.westaf.org
Key Personnel
Exec Dir: Anthony Radich *E-mail:* anthony.radich@westaf.org
Dir, Mktg & Communs: Leah Horn *E-mail:* leah.horn@westaf.org
Sr Fin Assoc: Adrianne Devereux *E-mail:* adrianne.devereux@westaf.org
Assoc Dir: Seyan Lucero *E-mail:* seyan.lucero@westaf.org
Performing, visual & folk arts programs.

H W Wilson Foundation
10 Estes St, Ipswich, MA 01938
Tel: 978-356-6500 *Toll Free Tel:* 800-653-2726 (US & CN) *Fax:* 978-356-6565
E-mail: information@ebscohost.com
Web Site: www.ebscohost.com
Key Personnel
CEO & Pres: Harold Regan
Scholarship program for American Library Association accredited library schools & grants for library-related research.

Calendar of Book Trade & Promotional Events—Alphabetical Index of Sponsors

Calendar of Book Trade & Promotional Events—Alphabetical Index of Events

Calendar of Book Trade & Promotional Events

Arranged chronologically by year and month, this section lists book trade events worldwide. Preceding this section are two indexes: the Sponsor Index is an alphabetical list of event sponsors and includes the names and dates of the events they sponsor; the Event Index is an alphabetical list of events along with the dates on which they are held.

2015

NOVEMBER

Feria Internacional del Libro de Guadalajara
Av Alemania 1370, Colonia Moderna, 44190 Guadalajara, Jalisco, Mexico
Tel: (033) 3810 0331; (033) 3268 0900 *Fax:* (033) 3268 0921
E-mail: fil@fil.com.mx
Web Site: www.fil.com.mx
Key Personnel
Chmn: Raul Padilla Lopez
Gen Dir: Marisol Schulz Manaut *E-mail:* marisol.schulz@fil.com.mx
Contents Mgmt: Laura Niembro Diaz *E-mail:* laura.niembro@fil.com.mx
Exhibitors Coord: Armando Montes de Santiago *E-mail:* armando.desantiago@fil.com.mx
Location: Centro de Exposiciones, Expo Guadalajara, Av Mariano Otero, 1499, Col Verde Valle, Guadalajara, Jalisco, Mexico
Nov 28-Dec 6, 2015

Jewish Book Month
Sponsored by Jewish Book Council
520 Eighth Ave, 4th fl, New York, NY 10018
Tel: 212-201-2920 *Fax:* 212-532-4952
E-mail: jbc@jewishbooks.org
Web Site: www.jewishbookcouncil.org; www.facebook.com/JewishBookCouncil; twitter.com/jewishbook
Key Personnel
Dir: Carolyn Starman Hessel
Assoc Dir: Naomi Firestone-Teeter
Dedicated to the celebration of Jewish books held annually during the month leading up to Hanukkah.
Location: Nationwide throughout the USA
Nov 5-Dec 5, 2015

Karlsruher Buecherschau (Karlsruhe Book Fair)
Sponsored by Boersenverein des Deutschen Buchhandels, Landesverband Baden-Wuerttemberg eV (Association of Publishers & Booksellers in Baden-Wuerttemberg eV)
Paulinenstr 53, 70178 Stuttgart, Germany
Tel: (0711) 61941-0 *Fax:* (0711) 61941-44
E-mail: post@buchhandelsverband.de
Web Site: www.karlsruher-buecherschau.de; www.buchhandelsverband.de
Key Personnel
Contact: Carolin Schneider *Tel:* (0711) 61941-26 *E-mail:* schneider@buchhandelsverband.de
Location: Karlsruhe, Germany
Nov 13-Dec 6, 2015

Stuttgarter Buchwochen (Stuttgart Book Weeks)
Sponsored by Boersenverein des Deutschen Buchhandels, Landesverband Baden-Wuerttemberg eV (Association of Publishers & Booksellers in Baden-Wuerttemberg eV)
Paulinenstr 53, 70178 Stuttgart, Germany
Tel: (0711) 61941-0 *Fax:* (0711) 61941-44
E-mail: post@buchhandelsverband.de
Web Site: www.stuttgarter-buchwochen.de; www.buchwochen.de; www.buchhandelsverband.de
Key Personnel
Contact: Andrea Baumann *Tel:* (0711) 61941-28 *E-mail:* baumann@buchhandelsverband.de
Location: Haus de Wirtschaft, Willi-Bleicher-Str 19, Stuttgart, Germany
Nov 12-Dec 6, 2015

DECEMBER

Salon du Livre et de la Presse Jeunesse (SLPJ)
Sponsored by Centre de Promotion du Livre de Jeunesse (CPLJ)
3, rue Francois Debergue, 93100 Montreuil, France
Tel: 01 55 86 86 55 *Fax:* 01 48 57 04 62
E-mail: contact@slpj.fr
Web Site: www.salon-livre-presse-jeunesse.net
Key Personnel
Dir: Sylvie Vassallo
Leading publishing event dedicated to children's books.
Location: l'Espace Paris-Est-Montreuil, 128 rue de Montreuil, Paris, France
Dec 2-7, 2015

Sofia International Book Fair
Sponsored by Bulgarian Book Association (BBA)
blvd Vitosha 64, 2nd fl, ap 4, 1463 Sofia, Bulgaria
Tel: (02) 958 15 25; (02) 958 92 11
E-mail: office@abk.bg
Web Site: www.abk.bg
Key Personnel
Event Mgr: Mariya Marinova *E-mail:* m.popstefanova@abk.bg
The first Sofia International Book fair was organized in 1968. Since then it brings together over 40,000 visitors yearly to meet with exhibiting companies from Bulgaria & abroad & offers unrivalled access to the national & international book publishing & bookseller communities.
Location: National Palace of Culture, One Bulgaria Blvd, Sofia, Bulgaria
Dec 8-13, 2015

2016

JANUARY

American Library Association Midwinter Meeting
Sponsored by The American Library Association (ALA)
50 E Huron St, Chicago, IL 60611
Tel: 312-944-6780 *Toll Free Tel:* 800-545-2433 (ext 3223) *Fax:* 312-440-9374
E-mail: ala@ala.org
Web Site: www.ala.org/midwinter
Key Personnel
Registration & Housing Specialist: Alicia Babcock *Tel:* 800-545-2433 ext 3229 *E-mail:* ababcock@ala.org
Conference Dir: Paul Graller *Tel:* 800-545-2433 ext 3219 *E-mail:* pgraller@ala.org
Conference Mgr: Amy McGuigan *Tel:* 800-545-2433 ext 3226 *E-mail:* amcguigan@ala.org
Meetings, AV & Catering Coord: Yvonne McLean *Tel:* 800-545-2433 ext 3222 *E-mail:* ymclean@ala.org
Conference Coord: Lindsay Rosales *Tel:* 800-545-2433 ext 3227 *E-mail:* lrosales@ala.org
Meeting Coord: Alicia (Alee) Navarro *Tel:* 800-545-2433 ext 3216 *E-mail:* anavarro@ala.org
Location: Boston, MA, USA
Jan 8-12, 2016

APE 2016
Sponsored by digiprimo GmbH & Co KG
Lutherstr 18, 12167 Berlin, Germany
Mailing Address: PO Box 41 07 05, 12117 Berlin, Germany
Tel: (030) 79 74 05 55 *Fax:* (030) 81 82 73 03
E-mail: info@digiprimo.com
Web Site: www.digiprimo.com
Location: Berlin, Germany
Jan 19-20, 2016

Football Writers Association of America Annual Meeting
Sponsored by Football Writers Association of America (FWAA)
18652 Vista del Sol, Dallas, TX 75287
Tel: 214-870-6516
Web Site: www.sportswriters.net/fwaa; twitter.com/thefwaa
Key Personnel
Exec Dir: Steve Richardson *E-mail:* tiger@fwaa.com
Location: Marriott Camelback Inn, Scottsdale, AZ, USA
Jan 8-11, 2016

MLA Annual Convention
Sponsored by Modern Language Association of America (MLA)
26 Broadway, 3rd fl, New York, NY 10004-1789
SAN: 202-6422
Tel: 646-576-5266; 646-576-5000 *Fax:* 646-458-0030
E-mail: convention@mla.org
Web Site: www.mla.org/convention
Key Personnel
Assoc Dir of Convention Progs: Karin L Bagnall *E-mail:* kbagnall@mla.org
Location: Austin, TX, USA
Jan 7-10, 2016

Remainder & Promotional Book Fair
Sponsored by Ciana Ltd
Rockholt, Ellimore Rd, Lustleigh, Newton Abbot TQ13 9TF, United Kingdom
Tel: (01626) 897 106 *Fax:* (01626) 897 107
E-mail: enquiries@ciana.co.uk
Web Site: www.ciana.co.uk
Key Personnel
Contact: Sarah Weedon; Robert Collie
Location: ILEC Conference Centre, 47 Lillie Rd, London, UK
Jan 17-18, 2016

FEBRUARY

Adelaide Festival
Sponsored by Adelaide Festival Corp
Level 9, 33 King William St, Adelaide, SA 5000, Australia
Mailing Address: PO Box 8221, Station Arcade, Adelaide, SA 5000, Australia
Tel: (08) 8216 4444 *Fax:* (08) 8216 4455
E-mail: info@adelaidefestival.com.au
Web Site: www.adelaidefestival.com.au
Key Personnel
Artistic Dir: David Sefton
Assoc Prodr: Jude Gun
Prog Dir: Lesley Newton
Spec Events Prodn Mgr: Adam Hornhardt
Annual event highlighting the arts, including literature. Adelaide Writers' Week is one of the high-profile events held during the festival.
Location: Adelaide's Central Business District, Adelaide, SA, Australia
Feb 26-March 14, 2016

California International Antiquarian Book Fair
Sponsored by Antiquarian Booksellers' Association of America
20 W 44 St, Suite 507, New York, NY 10036
Tel: 212-944-8291 *Fax:* 212-944-8293
E-mail: cafair@whiterainproductions.com; info@whiterainproductions.com
Web Site: www.cabookfair.com; www.sfbookfair.com; www.abaa.org
Key Personnel
Exec Dir: Susan Benne *E-mail:* sbenne@abaa.org
Annual event co-sponsored by International League of Antiquarian Booksellers & managed by White Rain Productions.
Location: Pasadena Convention Center, 300 E Green St, Pasadena, CA, USA
Feb 12-14, 2016

Graphics of the Americas Expo & Conference (GOA)
Sponsored by Printing Association of Florida Inc (PAF)
Affiliate of Printing Industries of America (PIA)
6250 Hazeltine National Dr, Suite 114, Orlando, FL 32822
Tel: 407-240-8009 *Toll Free Tel:* 800-331-0461 *Fax:* 407-240-6942
E-mail: info@goaexpo.com
Web Site: www.goaexpo.com; www.flprint.org
Key Personnel
Pres/CEO: George Ryan *Tel:* 407-243-8009 ext 3 *E-mail:* georger@flprint.org
Dir, Trade Show Opers: Adham Faltas *Tel:* 407-240-8009 ext 5 *E-mail:* adham@flprint.org
Location: Miami Beach Convention Center, 1901 Convention Center Dr, Miami Beach, FL, USA
Feb 18-20, 2016

IS&T Electronic Imaging Conference
Sponsored by Society for Imaging Science & Technology (IS&T)
7003 Kilworth Lane, Springfield, VA 22151
Tel: 703-642-9090 *Fax:* 703-642-9094
E-mail: info@imaging.org
Web Site: www.imaging.org
Key Personnel
Exec Dir: Suzanne E Grinnan *E-mail:* sgrinnan@imaging.org
Conference Prog Mgr: Diana Gonzalez *Tel:* 703-642-9090 ext 106 *E-mail:* dgonzalez@imaging.org
Exec Asst: Donna Smith *E-mail:* dsmith@imaging.org
Location: San Francisco, CA, USA
Feb 14-18, 2016

PSP Annual Conference
Sponsored by Association of American Publishers (AAP)
71 Fifth Ave, 2nd fl, New York, NY 10003-3004
Tel: 212-255-0200 *Fax:* 212-255-7007
Web Site: www.publishers.org/psp
Key Personnel
VP & Exec Dir, Prof & Scholarly Publg: John Tagler *Tel:* 212-255-1407 *E-mail:* jtagler@publishers.org
Dir: Sara Pinto *Tel:* 212-255-1716 *E-mail:* spinto@publishers.org
Location: Fairmont Hotel, Washington, DC, USA
Feb 3-5, 2016

SCBWI Winter Conference
Sponsored by Society of Children's Book Writers and Illustrators (SCBWI)
4727 Wilshire Blvd, Suite 301, Los Angeles, CA 90010
Tel: 323-782-1010 *Fax:* 323-782-1892
E-mail: scbwi@scbwi.org
Web Site: www.scbwi.org
Key Personnel
Pres: Stephen Mooser *E-mail:* stephenmooser@scbwi.org
Exec Dir: Lin Oliver *E-mail:* linoliver@scbwi.org
Location: Grand Hyatt New York, 109 E 42 St at Grand Central Terminal, New York, NY, USA
Feb 12-14, 2016

Texas Outdoor Writers Association Annual Conference
Sponsored by Texas Outdoor Writers Association (TOWA)
PO Box 151293, Austin, TX 78715-1293
Tel: 512-358-8000 *Fax:* 512-358-8010
E-mail: towa@towa.org
Web Site: www.towa.org
Key Personnel
Exec Dir: Burney Brown
Location: Y O Ranch Hotel & Conference Center, 2033 Sidney Baker St, Kerrville, TX, USA
Feb 25-28, 2016

WestPack®
Sponsored by UBM Canon
2901 28 St, Suite 100, Santa Monica, CA 90405
Tel: 310-445-4200
E-mail: packaginginfo@ubm.com
Web Site: www.canontradeshows.com; ubmcanon.com
Location: Anaheim Convention Center, 800 W Katella Ave, Anaheim, CA, USA
Feb 9-11, 2016

SPRING

Xploration® 16
Sponsored by Xplor International
24156 State Rd 54, Suite 4, Lutz, FL 33559
Tel: 813-949-6170 *Fax:* 813-949-9977
E-mail: info@xplor.org
Web Site: www.xplor.org
Key Personnel
Mktg Coord: Chad Henk *Tel:* 813-949-6171
Prog Coord: Missy Henk
Spring 2016

MARCH

The ARF Annual Convention & Insights Zone
Sponsored by Advertising Research Foundation (ARF)
432 Park Ave S, 6th fl, New York, NY 10016-8013
Tel: 212-751-5656
Web Site: www.thearf.org
Key Personnel
SVP, Events Prog Prodr: Rachael Feigenbaum
Mgr of Events: Christina Marks *E-mail:* christina@thearf.org
Also known as Re:think.
Location: New York Hilton, New York, NY, USA
March 13-16, 2016

Association of American Publishers Annual Meeting
Sponsored by Association of American Publishers (AAP)
71 Fifth Ave, 2nd fl, New York, NY 10003-3004
Tel: 212-255-0200 *Fax:* 212-255-7007
E-mail: info@publishers.org
Web Site: publishers.org
Key Personnel
VP: Tina Jordan *Tel:* 212-255-0275 *E-mail:* tjordan@publishers.org
March 2016

AWP Annual Conference & Bookfair
Sponsored by Association of Writers & Writing Programs (AWP)
George Mason University, 4400 University Dr, MSN 1E3, Fairfax, VA 22030
Tel: 703-993-4301 *Fax:* 703-993-4302
E-mail: awp@awpwriter.org; events@awpwriter.org
Web Site: www.awpwriter.org/awp_conference/; www.awpwriter.org
Key Personnel
Exec Dir: David W Fenza
Dir, Conferences: Christian Teresi
Assoc Dir of Conferences: Cynthia Sherman
Location: Los Angeles Convention Center & JW Marriott Los Angeles, Los Angeles, CA, USA
March 30-April 2, 2016

CAMEX
Sponsored by National Association of College Stores (NACS)
500 E Lorain St, Oberlin, OH 44074
Tel: 440-775-7777 *Toll Free Tel:* 800-622-7498 *Fax:* 440-775-4769
Web Site: www.camex.org; 2016.camex.org; www.nacs.org
Key Personnel
CEO: Brian Cartier *Tel:* 800-622-7498 ext 2201 *E-mail:* bcartier@nacs.org
VP, Meetings & Expositions: Hugh Easley *Tel:* 800-622-7498 ext 2269 *E-mail:* heasley@nacs.org
Dir of Expositions: Mary Adler-Kozak *Tel:* 800-622-7498 ext 2265 *E-mail:* madler-kozak@nacs.org
Conference & tradeshow dedicated exclusively to the more than $10 billion collegiate retailing industry.
Location: George R Brown Convention Center, Houston, TX, USA
March 4-8, 2016

Leipzig Book Fair (Leipziger Buchmesse)
Sponsored by Leipziger Messe GmbH
Messe-Allee 1, 04356 Leipzig, Germany
Mailing Address: Postfach 10 07 20, 04007 Leipzig, Germany
Tel: (0341) 678-0 *Fax:* (0341) 678-8762
E-mail: info@leipziger-buchmesse.de
Web Site: www.leipziger-buchmesse.de
Key Personnel
Dir: Oliver Zille *Tel:* (0341) 678-8240
Held annually in conjunction with The Leipzig Antiquarian Book Fair.
Location: Leipzig Exhibition Centre, Messe-Allee 1, Leipzig, Germany
March 17-20, 2016

NAPIM Annual Convention
Sponsored by National Association of Printing Ink Manufacturers (NAPIM)
15 Technology Pkwy S, Peachtree Corners, GA 30092
Tel: 770-209-7289 *Fax:* 678-680-4920; 770-209-7217
Web Site: www.napim.org
Key Personnel
Exec Dir: Brad Bergey *Tel:* 770-209-7290 *E-mail:* bbergey@napim.org
Memb Rel Mgr: Ben Hopper *E-mail:* bhopper@napim.org
Location: Red Rock Resort, Las Vegas, NV, USA
March 31-April 4, 2016

Paper2016
Sponsored by American Forest Paper Association (AF&PA)
1101 "K" St NW, Suite 700, Washington, DC 20005
Tel: 202-463-2700 *Fax:* 202-463-2708
E-mail: info@afandpa.org
Web Site: www.afandpa.org
Key Personnel
Dir of Meetings: Susan Van Eaton
Sr Mgr, Meetings & Member Servs: Kathy Smith
Co-hosted with the National Paper Trade Association (NPTA), this annual paper industry event offers participants access to decision makers from an impressive array of manufacturers, merchants, publishers, distributors of printing paper, packaging material & industrial material & supplies.
Location: New York Palace Hotel, New York, NY, USA
March 6-8, 2016

PRIMEX East
Sponsored by IDEAlliance®
1600 Duke St, Suite 420, Alexandria, VA 22314
Tel: 703-837-1070 *Fax:* 703-837-1072
E-mail: registrar@idealliance.org
Web Site: www.idealliance.org
Meeting of publishing, print & integrated media executives.
Location: New York, NY, USA
March 15, 2016

Salon du Livre de Paris
(Paris Book Fair)
Sponsored by Reed Expositions France
Subsidiary of Reed Exhibition Companies
52-54 quai de Dion-Bouton, CS 80001, 92806 Puteaux Cedex, France
Tel: 01 47 56 64 31 *Fax:* 01 47 56 64 44
E-mail: livre@reedexpo.fr
Web Site: www.salondulivreparis.com
Key Personnel
Fair Mgr: Bertrand Morisset
Commun Coord: Carole Godefroy *E-mail:* carole.godefroy@reedexpo.fr
Annual international publishing event for publishers, booksellers, teachers & librarians. Open to the trade & the public.
Location: Paris Expo, Porte de Versailles, Paris, France
March 18-21, 2016

SouthPack®
Sponsored by UBM Canon
2901 28 St, Suite 100, Santa Monica, CA 90405
Tel: 310-445-4200
E-mail: packaginginfo@ubm.com
Web Site: www.canontradeshows.com; ubmcanon.com
Location: Charlotte Convention Center, 501 S College St, Charlotte, NC, USA
March 16-17, 2016

Transformation
Sponsored by 4A's (American Association of Advertising Agencies)
1065 Avenue of the Americas, 16th fl, New York, NY 10018
Tel: 212-682-2500
E-mail: eventhelp@aaaa.org
Web Site: transformation.aaaa.org; www.aaaa.org
Key Personnel
CEO & Pres: Nancy Hill *E-mail:* nhill@aaaa.org
VP, Events & Conferences: Brenda Major *Tel:* 212-850-0730 *E-mail:* bmajor@aaaa.org
Events Mgr: Troy Starwalt *Tel:* 212-850-0733 *E-mail:* tstarwalt@aaaa.org
The annual gathering of C-level executives from various disciplines within the marketing, media & agency businesses.
Location: Miami, FL, USA
March 21-23, 2016

Virginia Festival of the Book
Sponsored by Virginia Foundation for the Humanities
145 Ednam Dr, Charlottesville, VA 22903
Tel: 434-924-3296 *Fax:* 434-296-4714
E-mail: vabook@virginia.edu
Web Site: www.vabook.org
Key Personnel
Prog Dir: Jane Kulow *Tel:* 434-924-7548
Annual public festival for children & adults featuring authors, illustrators, publishers, publicists, agents & other book professionals in panel discussions & readings. Most events are free. Almost 400 authors invited annually.
Location: Charlottesville, VA, USA
March 16-20, 2016

APRIL

Alberta Library Conference
Sponsored by Library Association of Alberta (LAA)
80 Baker Crescent NW, Calgary, AB T2L 1R4, Canada
Tel: 403-284-5818 *Toll Free Tel:* 877-522-5550
E-mail: info@laa.ca
Web Site: www.albertalibraryconference.com; www.laa.ca
Key Personnel
Exec Dir/Conference Coord: Christine Sheppard
Co-hosted by Alberta Library Trustees Association (ALTA).
Location: Fairmont Jasper Park Lodge, Jasper, AB, CN
April 28-May 1, 2016

BMI Management Conference
Sponsored by Book Manufacturers' Institute Inc (BMI)
2 Armand Beach Dr, Suite 1B, Palm Coast, FL 32137-2612
Tel: 386-986-4552 *Fax:* 386-986-4553
E-mail: info@bmibook.com
Web Site: www.bmibook.org
Key Personnel
EVP: Daniel N Bach *E-mail:* dbach@bmibook.com
Conference Coord: Jackie Murray
Off Mgr: Dianne Morris
Location: Wild Dunes Resort, Isle of Palms, SC, USA
April 24-26, 2016

Bologna Children's Book Fair
Sponsored by BolognaFiere SpA
Piazza Costituzione, 6, 40128 Bologna, Italy
Tel: (051) 282 111 *Fax:* (051) 637 4011
E-mail: bookfair@bolognafiere.it
Web Site: www.bolognachildrensbookfair.com
Key Personnel
Exhibition Mgr: Roberta Chinni *Tel:* (051) 282 269 *E-mail:* roberta.chinni@bolognafiere.it
Location: Bologna Fair Centre, Piazza Costituzione, 6, Bologna, Italy
April 4-7, 2016

EPA Annual Convention
Sponsored by Evangelical Press Association (EPA)
PO Box 20198, El Cajon, CA 92021
Toll Free Tel: 888-311-1731
Web Site: www.evangelicalpress.com
Key Personnel
Exec Dir: Lamar Keener
Annual convention for editors, publishers, writers & other staff (print & online publications). Workshop tracks & plenary sessions, opportunities for networking & fellowship.
Location: Lancaster Marriott at Penn Sq, 25 S Queen St, Lancaster, PA, USA
April 6-8, 2016

The Federation of Children's Book Groups Annual Conference
Sponsored by The Federation of Children's Book Groups (FCBG)
10 St Laurence Rd, Bradford on Avon BA15 1JG, United Kingdom
Tel: (0300) 102 1559
E-mail: info@fcbg.org.uk
Web Site: www.fcbg.org.uk
Organized by one of our local children's book groups in collaboration with the national executive, this conference is an opportunity for authors, illustrators, parents, teachers, librarians & all interested children's book lovers to come together to promote their mission of bringing children & books together.
Location: UK
April 2016

Inter American Press Association Midyear Meeting
Sponsored by Inter American Press Association (IAPA)
Jules Dubois Bldg, 1801 SW Third Ave, Miami, FL 33129
Tel: 305-634-2465 *Fax:* 305-635-2272
E-mail: info@sipiapa.org
Web Site: www.sipiapa.org
Key Personnel
Exec Dir: Ricardo Trotti *E-mail:* rtrotti@sipiapa.org
Location: Punta Cana, Dominican Republic
April 8-11, 2016

International Children's Book Day
Sponsored by International Board on Books for Young People (IBBY)
Nonnenweg 12, Postfach, 4009 Basel, Switzerland
Tel: (061) 272 29 17 *Fax:* (061) 272 27 57
E-mail: ibby@ibby.org
Web Site: www.ibby.org
Key Personnel
Exec Dir: Liz Page *E-mail:* liz.page@ibby.org
Admin Asst: Luzmaria Stauffenegger *E-mail:* luzmaria.stauffenegger@ibby.org
On Hans Christian Andersen's birthday, April 2nd, International Children's Book Day (ICBD) is celebrated to inspire a love of reading & to call attention to children's books. Each year a different national section has the opportunity to be the international sponsor. It decides upon a theme & invites a prominent author to write a message to the children of the world & a well-known illustrator to design a poster. These materials are used in different ways to promote books & reading around the world.
April 2, 2016

IPA Congress
Sponsored by International Publishers Association (IPA)
23, ave de France, 1202 Geneva, Switzerland
Tel: (022) 704 18 20 *Fax:* (022) 704 18 21
E-mail: secretariat@internationalpublishers.org
Web Site: www.ipacongress.com
Key Personnel
Secy Gen: Mr Jens Bammel *E-mail:* bammel@internationalpublishers.org
Held every 2 years. Co-sponsored by the Publishers Association (UK) & London Book Fair.
Location: Hammersmith Rd; Kensington, London, UK
April 10-12, 2016

IS&T Archiving Conference
Sponsored by Society for Imaging Science & Technology (IS&T)
7003 Kilworth Lane, Springfield, VA 22151
Tel: 703-642-9090 *Fax:* 703-642-9094
E-mail: info@imaging.org
Web Site: www.imaging.org
Key Personnel
Exec Dir: Suzanne E Grinnan *E-mail:* sgrinnan@imaging.org
Conference Prog Mgr: Diana Gonzalez *Tel:* 703-642-9090 ext 106 *E-mail:* dgonzalez@imaging.org
Location: National Archives and Records Administration (NARA), 700 Pennsylvania Ave NW, Washington, DC, USA
April 19-22, 2016

The London Book Fair
Sponsored by Reed Exhibitions UK
Division of RELX Group PLC
Gateway House, 28 The Quadrant, Richmond, Surrey TW9 1DN, United Kingdom
Tel: (020) 8271 2124
E-mail: lbf.helpline@reedexpo.co.uk; lbfteam@reedexpo.co.uk
Web Site: www.londonbookfair.co.uk
Key Personnel
Bus Devt Exec: Sam D'Elia *Tel:* (020) 8910 7149 *E-mail:* sam.delia@reedexpo.co.uk
Event Coord: Rachael Seaton *Tel:* (020) 8439 5445 *E-mail:* rachael.seaton@reedexpo.co.uk
The London Book Fair is the global marketplace for rights negotiation & the sale & distribution of content across print, audio, TV, film & digital channels. Taking place every spring in the world's premier publishing & cultural capital, it is a unique opportunity to hear from authors, enjoy the vibrant atmosphere & explore innovations shaping the publishing world of the future. The London Book Fair brings you 3 days of focused access to customers, content & emerging markets.
Location: Olympia London, Hammersmith Rd, Kensington, London, UK
April 12-14, 2016

Los Angeles Times Festival of Books
Sponsored by Los Angeles Times
Subsidiary of Tribune Publishing Co
202 W First St, Los Angeles, CA 90012
Tel: 213-237-5000 *Toll Free Tel:* 800-528-4637 *Fax:* 213-237-2335
E-mail: fobinfo@latimes.com; eventinfo@latimes.com
Web Site: events.latimes.com/festivalofbooks
Location: The University of Southern California (USC), Los Angeles, CA, USA
April 9-10, 2016

mediaXchange
Sponsored by Newspaper Association of America (NAA)
4401 Wilson Blvd, Suite 900, Arlington, VA 22203
Tel: 571-366-1000 *Fax:* 571-366-1219
Web Site: www.naa.org/mediaXchange.aspx; www.naa.org
Annual technical exposition & conference for newspaper media executives.
Location: Marriott Marquis, Washington, DC, USA
April 17-20, 2016

NAAJ Annual Meeting
Sponsored by North American Agricultural Journalists (NAAJ)
6434 Hurta Lane, Bryan, TX 77808
Tel: 979-845-2872 *Fax:* 979-862-1202
Web Site: www.naaj.net
Key Personnel
Exec Secy & Treas: Kathleen Phillips *E-mail:* ka-phillips@tamu.edu
Annual meeting.
Location: Washington, DC, USA
April 2016

National Library Week
Sponsored by The American Library Association (ALA)
50 E Huron St, Chicago, IL 60611
Tel: 312-944-6780 *Toll Free Tel:* 800-545-2433 (ext 3223) *Fax:* 312-440-9374
E-mail: ala@ala.org
Web Site: www.ala.org/nlw
Key Personnel
Campaign Coord: Megan McFarlane *Tel:* 800-545-2433 ext 2148 *E-mail:* mmcfarlane@ala.org
Location: Nationwide throughout the USA
April 10-16, 2016

New York Antiquarian Book Fair
Sponsored by Antiquarian Booksellers' Association of America
20 W 44 St, Suite 507, New York, NY 10036
Tel: 212-944-8291 *Fax:* 212-944-8293
E-mail: hq@abaa.org
Web Site: www.nybookfair.com; www.abaa.org
Key Personnel
Exec Dir: Susan Benne Dixon *E-mail:* sbenne@abaa.org
Co-sponsored by International League of Antiquarian Booksellers (ILAB) & managed by Sanford L Smith & Associates.
Location: Park Avenue Armory, 643 Park Ave at 67 St, New York, NY, USA
April 7-10, 2016

The Quest for Excellence® Conference
Sponsored by National Institute of Standards and Technology (NIST)
100 Bureau Dr, Stop 1020, Gaithersburg, MD 20899-1020
Tel: 301-975-2036 *Fax:* 301-948-3716
E-mail: baldrige@nist.gov
Web Site: www.nist.gov/baldrige/qe/index.cfm
Key Personnel
Conference Chair: Barbara Fischer *Tel:* 301-975-8942 *E-mail:* barbara.fischer@nist.gov
Official conference of the Malcolm Baldrige National Quality Award, held in partnership with American Society for Quality (ASQ) & Association for Talent Development (ATD).
Location: Baltimore Marriott Waterfront, 700 Aliceanna St, Baltimore, MD, USA
April 3-6, 2016

Southern Kentucky Book Fest
WKU Libraries, Cravens 106, 1906 College Heights Blvd, Bowling Green, KY 42101-1067
Tel: 270-745-4502 *Fax:* 270-745-6422
Web Site: www.sokybookfest.org
Key Personnel
Mtkg Coord: Jennifer Wilson *E-mail:* jennifer.wilson@wku.edu
The Southern Kentucky Book Fest is one of the state's largest literary events & is presented by WKU Libraries, Warren County Public Library & Barnes & Noble Booksellers. Book Fest is a fundraiser for the promotion of literacy in our community.
Location: Knicely Conference Center, 645 Campbell Lane, Bowling Green, KY, USA
April 22-23, 2016

UKSG Annual Conference & Exhibition
Sponsored by UKSG (United Kingdom Serials Group)
Bowman & Hillier Bldg, The Old Brewery, Priory Lane, Burford, Oxon OX18 4SG, United Kingdom
Mailing Address: PO Box 5594, Newbury RG20 0YD, United Kingdom
Web Site: www.uksg.org
Key Personnel
Busn Mgr: Alison Whitehorn *Tel:* (01635) 254292 *Fax:* (01635) 253826 *E-mail:* alison@uksg.org
Administrator: Karen Sadler *Tel:* (01865) 310834 *Fax:* (01865) 310834 *E-mail:* karen@uksg.org
Annual 3 day event open to everyone.
Location: Bournemouth, UK
April 11-13, 2016

MAY

ASQ World Conference on Quality & Improvement
Sponsored by American Society for Quality (ASQ)
600 N Plankinton Ave, Milwaukee, WI 53203
Mailing Address: PO Box 3005, Milwaukee, WI 53201-3005
Tel: 414-272-8575 *Toll Free Tel:* 800-248-1946 (US & CN) *Fax:* 414-272-1734
E-mail: help@asq.org
Web Site: www.asq.org
Key Personnel
Conference Mgr: Michael Dzick *E-mail:* mdzick@asq.org
Location: 400 W Wisconsin Ave (corner 4th St & Wisconsin Ave), Milwaukee, WI, USA
May 16-18, 2016

BookCon
Sponsored by ReedPOP
Division of Reed Exhibitions USA
383 Main Ave, Norwalk, CT 06851
Tel: 203-840-5632; 203-840-4800 *Toll Free Tel:* 800-777-8774
E-mail: inquiry@TheBookCon.com; info@reedpop.com; sales@reedpop.com
Web Site: www.thebookcon.com; www.reedpop.com
Key Personnel
Global SVP: Lance Fensterman *E-mail:* Lance@ReedPOP.com
Show Mgr: Brien McDonald *E-mail:* bmcdonald@reedexpo.com
Sales Exec: Doug Scully *Tel:* 203-840-5364 *E-mail:* dscully@reedexpo.com
Consumer event following BookExpo America.
Location: McCormick Place, West Bldg, Chicago, IL, USA
May 14, 2016

BookExpo America (BEA)
Sponsored by Reed Exhibitions USA
Division of RELX Group PLC
383 Main Ave, Norwalk, CT 06851
Tel: 203-840-4800 *Toll Free Tel:* 800-840-5614 *Fax:* 203-840-5805
E-mail: inquiry@bookexpoamerica.com

Web Site: bookexpoamerica.com
Key Personnel
Event Dir: Steve Rosato *Tel:* 203-840-5463 *Fax:* 203-840-9463 *E-mail:* srosato@reedexpo.com
Produced & managed by Reed Exhibitions USA, BEA is sponsored by the American Booksellers Association (ABA), the Association of American Publishers Inc (AAP) & the Association of Authors' Representatives Inc (AAR).
Location: McCormick Place, West Bldg, Chicago, IL, USA
May 11-13, 2016

Children's Book Week
Sponsored by The Children's Book Council (CBC)
54 W 39 St, 14th fl, New York, NY 10018
Tel: 212-966-1990
E-mail: cbc.info@cbcbooks.org
Web Site: www.bookweekonline.com; www.cbcbooks.org
Key Personnel
Exec Dir: Jon Colman *E-mail:* jon.colman@cbcbooks.org
Communs Dir: Nicole Deming *E-mail:* nicole.deming@cbcbooks.org
Programming Dir: Shaina Birkhead *E-mail:* shaina.birkhead@cbcbooks.org
Mgr, Events & Progs/Libn: Ayanna Coleman *E-mail:* ayanna.coleman@cbcbooks.org
Events & Progs Asst/Membership Coord: Matthew Poulter *E-mail:* matthew.poulter@cbcbooks.org
Location: Nationwide across the USA
May 2-8, 2016

The IA Summit
Sponsored by Association for Information Science & Technology (ASIS&T)
8555 16 St, Suite 850, Silver Spring, MD 20910
Tel: 301-495-0900 *Fax:* 301-495-0810
E-mail: meetings@asis.org; asis@asis.org
Web Site: www.asis.org
Key Personnel
Exec Dir: Richard Hill *E-mail:* rhill@asis.org
Dir of Meetings & Membership: Vanessa Foss *E-mail:* vfoss@asis.org
Location: Omni Atlanta Hotel at CNN Center, 100 CNN Center, Atlanta, GA, USA
May 4-8, 2016

PaperCon
Sponsored by Technical Association of the Pulp & Paper Industry (TAPPI)
15 Technology Pkwy S, Suite 115, Peachtree Corners, GA 30092
Tel: 770-446-1400 *Toll Free Tel:* 800-332-8686 (US); 800-446-9431 (CN) *Fax:* 770-446-6947; 770-209-7206
E-mail: memberconnection@tappi.org
Web Site: www.papercon.org; www.tappi.org
Key Personnel
Meeting Mgr: Libby Settle *Tel:* 770-209-7345 *E-mail:* lsettle@tappi.org
Dir of Mktg: Simona Marcellus *Tel:* 770-209-7293 *E-mail:* smarcellus@tappi.org
Location: Duke Energy Convention Center, Cincinnati, OH, USA
May 15-18, 2016

Society of American Business Editors & Writers Spring Conference
Sponsored by Society of American Business Editors & Writers Inc (SABEW)
Walter Cronkite School of Journalism & Mass Communication, Arizona State University, 555 N Central Ave, Suite 406 E, Phoenix, AZ 85004-1248
Tel: 602-496-7862 *Fax:* 602-496-7041
E-mail: sabew@sabew.org
Web Site: sabew.org
Key Personnel
Exec Dir: Kathleen Graham *Tel:* 602-496-5186 *E-mail:* kgraham@sabew.org
Location: Washington, DC, USA
May 2016

SSP Annual Meeting
Sponsored by Society for Scholarly Publishing (SSP)
10200 W 44 Ave, Suite 304, Wheat Ridge, CO 80033-2840
Tel: 303-422-3914 *Fax:* 720-881-6101
E-mail: info@sspnet.org
Web Site: www.sspnet.org
Key Personnel
Exec Dir: Ann Mehan Crosse *Tel:* 720-881-6114 *E-mail:* amcrosse@kellencompany.com
Exec/Meetings Asst: Jennifer Lanphere *Tel:* 720-881-6130 *E-mail:* jlanphere@kellencompany.com
Location: The Westin Bayshore, 1601 Bayshore Dr, Vancouver, BC, CN
May 31-June 3, 2016

JUNE

AAUP Annual Meeting
Sponsored by Association of American University Presses (AAUP)
28 W 36 St, Suite 602, New York, NY 10018
Tel: 212-989-1010 *Fax:* 212-989-0275
E-mail: annualmeeting@aaup.org; info@aaupnet.org
Web Site: www.aaupnet.org
Key Personnel
Exec Dir: Peter Berkery *Tel:* 212-989-1010 ext 29 *E-mail:* pberkery@aaupnet.org
Asst Dir & Cont: Tim Muench *Tel:* 212-989-1010 ext 28 *E-mail:* tmuench@aaupnet.org
Dir of Mktg & Communs: Brenna McLaughlin *Tel:* 518-436-3586 *E-mail:* bmclaughlin@aaupnet.org
Off Mgr & Program Administrator: Kim Miller *Tel:* 212-989-1010 ext 26 *E-mail:* kmiller@aaupnet.org
Location: Loews Philadelphia, Philadelphia, PA, USA
June 16-19, 2016

American Library Association Annual Conference
Sponsored by The American Library Association (ALA)
50 E Huron St, Chicago, IL 60611
Tel: 312-944-6780 *Toll Free Tel:* 800-545-2433 (ext 3223) *Fax:* 312-440-9374
E-mail: ala@ala.org
Web Site: www.ala.org
Key Personnel
Registration & Housing Specialist: Alicia Babcock *Tel:* 800-545-2433 ext 3229 *E-mail:* ababcock@ala.org
Conference Dir: Paul Graller *Tel:* 800-545-2433 ext 3219 *E-mail:* pgraller@ala.org
Conference Mgr: Amy McGuigan *Tel:* 800-545-2433 ext 3226 *E-mail:* amcguigan@ala.org
Meetings, AV & Catering Coord: Yvonne McLean *Tel:* 800-545-2433 ext 3222 *E-mail:* ymclean@ala.org
Conference Coord: Lindsay Rosales *Tel:* 800-545-2433 ext 3227 *E-mail:* lrosales@ala.org
Meeting Coord: Alicia (Alee) Navarro *Tel:* 800-545-2433 ext 3216 *E-mail:* anavarro@ala.org
Location: Orlando, FL, USA
June 23-28, 2016

Canadian Library Association National Conference & Trade Show
Sponsored by Canadian Library Association-CLA (Association Canadienne des bibliotheques)
1150 Morrison Dr, Suite 400, Ottawa, ON K2H 8S9, Canada
Tel: 613-232-9625 *Fax:* 613-563-9895
E-mail: info@cla.ca
Web Site: www.cla.ca
Key Personnel
Exec Dir: Valoree McKay *Tel:* 613-232-9625 ext 306 *E-mail:* vmckay@cla.ca
Location: Halifax, NS, CN
June 1-4, 2016

Catholic Media Conference
Sponsored by Catholic Press Association of the United States & Canada
205 W Monroe St, Suite 470, Chicago, IL 60606
Tel: 312-380-6789 *Fax:* 312-361-0256
Web Site: www.catholicpress.org
Key Personnel
Exec Dir: Timothy M Walter *E-mail:* twalter@catholicpress.org
Location: St Louis, MO, USA
June 1-3, 2016

Content in Context (CIC)
Sponsored by AAP PreK-12 Learning Group Division of Association of American Publishers (AAP)
325 Chestnut St, Suite 1110, Philadelphia, PA 19106
Tel: 267-351-4310 *Fax:* 267-351-4317
E-mail: prek12learning@publishers.org
Web Site: www.aepweb.org
Key Personnel
Exec Dir: Jay Diskey *Tel:* 202-220-4549 *E-mail:* jdiskey@publishers.org
Sr Dir: Susan Fletcher *Tel:* 267-351-4314 *E-mail:* sfletcher@publishers.org
Membership Servs Mgr: Brittany Lawrence *Tel:* 267-351-4316 *E-mail:* blawrence@publishers.org
Admin/Mktg Assoc: Rachel Burgos *Tel:* 267-351-4320 *E-mail:* rburgos@publishers.org
Annual conference for those involved in the creation, marketing, or sales of educational content.
Location: Loews Philadelphia Hotel, Philadelphia, PA, USA
June 6-8, 2016

EastPack®
Sponsored by UBM Canon
2901 28 St, Suite 100, Santa Monica, CA 90405
Tel: 310-445-4200
E-mail: packaginginfo@ubm.com
Web Site: www.canontradeshows.com; ubmcanon.com
Location: Jacob K Javits Convention Center, 655 W 43 St, New York, NY, USA
June 14-16, 2016

IABC World Conference
Sponsored by International Association of Business Communicators (IABC)
601 Montgomery St, Suite 1900, San Francisco, CA 94111
Tel: 415-544-4700 *Toll Free Tel:* 800-776-4222 (US & CN) *Fax:* 415-544-4747
E-mail: conference@iabc.com
Web Site: wc.iabc.com; www.iabc.com
Key Personnel
Coord, Events & Registration: Tammi Lightle *Tel:* 415-544-4714 *E-mail:* tlightle@iabc.com
Location: Hilton New Orleans Riverside, 2 Poydras, New Orleans, LA, USA
June 5-8, 2016

International Christian Retail Show (ICRS)
Sponsored by CBA: The Association for Christian Retail
1365 Garden of the Gods Rd, Suite 105, Colorado Springs, CO 80907
Tel: 719-265-9895 *Toll Free Tel:* 800-252-1950 *Fax:* 719-272-3508
E-mail: info@cbaonline.org
Web Site: christianretailshow.com; cbaonline.org
Key Personnel
Pres: Curtis Riskey *E-mail:* criskey@cbaonline.org
For over 50 years, the annual International Christian Retail Show has been our industry's single-most impacting week. During this week, people of the industry from all over the world meet face-to-face for buying & selling, education, inspiration, fellowship & future planning. Here individuals unite to further the mission of seeing Christian products impact lives for God's Kingdom the world over. At this unique gathering, our industry's strength is most evident & our goals are most clearly in focus. It is, in short, the most important week in the ministry of your business & of the industry as a whole.
Location: Duke Energy Convention Center, 525 Elm St, Cincinnati, OH, USA
June 26-29, 2016

MagNet
Sponsored by Magazines Canada (MC)
425 Adelaide St W, Suite 700, Toronto, ON M5V 3C1, Canada
Tel: 416-504-0274 *Fax:* 416-504-0437
E-mail: info@magazinescanada.ca
Web Site: www.magazinescanada.ca/development/magnet; twitter.com/magnetcanada
Key Personnel
Mgr, Events: Edra Sefton *Tel:* 416-504-0274 ext 224 *E-mail:* esefton@magazinescanada.ca
Canada's magazine conference, MagNet is a jointly sponsored by Magazines Canada (MC), Canadian Society of Magazine Editors (CSME), Circulation Management Association of Canada (CMC) & Professional Writers Association of Canada (PWAC).
Location: The Courtyard Downtown Toronto, 475 Yonge St, Toronto, ON, CN
June 7-10, 2016

PWAC@MagNet National Conference & Annual General Meeting
Sponsored by Professional Writers Association of Canada (PWAC)
215 Spadina Ave, Suite 130, Toronto, ON M5T 2C7, Canada
Tel: 416-504-1645
E-mail: info@pwac.ca
Web Site: pwac.ca
Key Personnel
Assoc Dir: Margaret DeRosia *Tel:* 416-504-1645 ext 1
Held during Magazines Canada Annual Conference (MagNet).
Location: The Courtyard Downtown Toronto, 475 Yonge St, Toronto, ON, CN
June 7-10, 2016

SLA Annual Conference & INFO-EXPO
Sponsored by Special Libraries Association (SLA)
331 S Patrick St, Alexandria, VA 22314-3501
Tel: 703-647-4900 *Fax:* 703-647-4901
Web Site: www.sla.org
Key Personnel
Deputy CEO: Doug Newcomb *Tel:* 703-647-4923 *E-mail:* dnewcomb1@sla.org
Dir, Events: Caroline Hamilton *Tel:* 703-647-4949 *E-mail:* chamilton@sla.org
Dir, Mktg & Exhibits: Jeff Leach *Tel:* 703-647-4922 *E-mail:* jleach@sla.org
Location: Philadelphia Convention Center, Philadelphia, PA, USA
June 12-14, 2016

JULY

Church & Synagogue Library Association Conference
Sponsored by Church & Synagogue Library Association (CSLA)
10157 SW Barbur Blvd, No 102C, Portland, OR 97219
Tel: 503-244-6919 *Toll Free Tel:* 800-542-2752 (LIB-CSLA) *Fax:* 503-977-3734
E-mail: csla@worldaccessnet.com
Web Site: cslainfo.org
Key Personnel
Administrator: Judith Janzen
July 2016

Hong Kong Book Fair
Sponsored by Hong Kong Trade Development Council
c/o Exhibition Dept, Unit 13, Expo Galleria, Hong Kong Convention & Exhibition Centre, Wan Chai, Hong Kong
Tel: 1830 670; 1830 668 (cust serv) *Fax:* 2824 0026; 2824 0249
E-mail: exhibitions@hktdc.org
Web Site: hkbookfair.hktdc.com; hkbookfair.hktdc.com/en (English)
Location: Hong Kong Convention & Exhibition Center, One Expo Dr, Wan Chai, Hong Kong
July 2016

IAML Annual Conference
Sponsored by International Association of Music Libraries, Archives & Documentation Centres Inc (IAML)
c/o Gothenburg University Library, Music & Drama Library, Box 210, 405 30 Gothenburg, Sweden
Tel: (031) 786 40 57 *Fax:* (031) 786 40 59
E-mail: contact@iaml.info
Web Site: www.iaml.info
Key Personnel
Secy Gen: Pia Shekhter *E-mail:* secretary@iaml.info
Location: Rome, Italy
July 3-8, 2016

ILA Annual Conference
Sponsored by International Literacy Association (ILA)
800 Barksdale Rd, Newark, DE 19711-3204
Mailing Address: PO Box 8139, Newark, DE 19714-8139
Tel: 302-731-1600 *Toll Free Tel:* 800-336-7323 (US & CN) *Fax:* 302-731-1057
E-mail: customerservice@reading.org
Web Site: www.literacyworldwide.org; www.reading.org
Key Personnel
Exec Dir: Marcie Craig Post *E-mail:* mpost@reading.org
Location: Boston, MA, USA
July 9-11, 2016

Outdoor Writers Association of America Annual Conference
Sponsored by Outdoor Writers Association of America (OWAA)
615 Oak St, Suite 201, Missoula, MT 59801
Tel: 406-728-7434 *Fax:* 406-728-7445
E-mail: info@owaa.org
Web Site: owaa.org
Key Personnel
Membership & Conference Servs: Jessica (Pollett) Seitz *E-mail:* jseitz@owaa.org
Location: Holiday Inn Grand Montana, Billings, MT, USA
July 16-18, 2016

Payson Book Festival
Sponsored by Arizona Professional Writers (APW)
PO Box 1495, Payson, AZ 85547
E-mail: info@paysonbookfestival.org
Web Site: www.paysonbookfestival.org; www.facebook.com/PaysonBookFestival
Key Personnel
Chair: Connie Cockrell
Co-hosted by Gila Community College, the Payson Book Festival is held to promote literacy & showcase Arizona authors. Our mission is to enhance the love of reading by providing a friendly environment that encourages personal interaction between Arizona authors & readers of all ages. A portion of the proceeds will benefit the scholarship funds of both non-profit organizations. Sixty Arizona authors participate by signing books & visiting with readers of all ages. Some will speak about their books & the craft of writing. There will be a full schedule of speakers & several workshops throughout the day.
Location: Gila Community College, 201 North Mud Springs Rd, Payson, AZ, USA
July 23, 2016

Romance Writers of America Annual Conference
Sponsored by Romance Writers of America®
14615 Benfer Rd, Houston, TX 77069
Tel: 832-717-5200 *Fax:* 832-717-5201
E-mail: conference@rwa.org; info@rwa.org
Web Site: www.rwa.org
Key Personnel
Exec Dir: Allison Kelley *Tel:* 832-717-5200 ext 124 *E-mail:* allison.kelley@rwa.org
Location: San Diego Marriott Hotel and Marina, San Diego, CA, USA
July 13-16, 2016

TIBF: Tokyo International Book Fair
Sponsored by Reed Exhibitions Japan Ltd
18F Shinjuku-Nomura Bldg, 1-26-2 Nishishinjuku, Shinjuku-ku, Tokyo 163-0570, Japan
Tel: (03) 3349 8519 *Fax:* (03) 3349 8530
E-mail: tibf-eng@reedexpo.co.jp; tibf@reedexpo.co.jp
Web Site: www.bookfair.jp; www.bookfair.jp/en (English)
Organized by Reed Exhibitions Japan Ltd, TIBF executive committee. Held concurrently with e-Book Expo Tokyo.
Location: Tokyo International Exhibition Center (Tokyo Big Sight), Tokyo, Japan
July 2016

AUGUST

The Dorothy L Sayers Society Annual Convention
Sponsored by The Dorothy L Sayers Society
Witham Library, 18 Newland St, Witham CM8 2AQ, United Kingdom
Tel: (01376) 519625
E-mail: info@sayers.org.uk
Web Site: www.sayers.org.uk
Key Personnel
Convention Admin: Simon Medd
Membership Secy: Lenelle Davis *E-mail:* membership@sayers.org.uk

Members only event.
Location: UK
Aug 2016

Edinburgh International Book Festival
5 Charlotte Sq, Edinburgh EH2 4DR, United Kingdom
Tel: (0131) 718 5666
Web Site: www.edbookfest.co.uk
The festival takes place in Charlotte Square Gardens (just off the west end of Princes St) over 17 days each August. Over 750 world-class authors & thinkers gather to take part in events for people of all ages.
Location: Charlotte Square Gardens, Edinburgh, UK
Aug 14-30, 2016

IFLA World Library & Information Congress
Sponsored by International Federation of Library Associations & Institutions (IFLA) (Federation internationale des associations de bibliothecaires et des bibliotheques)
Prins Willem-Alexanderhof 5, 2595 BE The Hague, Netherlands
Mailing Address: Postbus 95312, 2509 CH The Hague, Netherlands
Tel: (070) 3140884 *Fax:* (070) 3834827
E-mail: ifla@ifla.org
Web Site: conference.ifla.org; www.ifla.org
Key Personnel
Secy Gen: Jennefer Nicholson
Mgr, Conferences & Busn Rel: Josche Ouwerkerk *E-mail:* josche.ouwerkerk@ifla.org
Held simultaneously with IFLA General Conference & Assembly.
Location: Columbus, OH, USA
Aug 13-19, 2016

International Board on Books for Young People Biennial Congress
Sponsored by International Board on Books for Young People (IBBY)
Nonnenweg 12, Postfach, 4009 Basel, Switzerland
Tel: (061) 272 29 17 *Fax:* (061) 272 27 57
E-mail: ibby@ibby.org
Web Site: www.ibby.org
Key Personnel
Admin Asst: Luzmaria Stauffenegger *E-mail:* luzmaria.stauffenegger@ibby.org
IBBY's biennial congresses, hosted by different countries, are the most important meeting points for IBBY members & other people involved in children's books & reading development. They are wonderful opportunities to make contacts, exchange ideas & open horizons.
Location: Auckland, New Zealand
Aug 18-21, 2016

SCBWI Summer Conference
Sponsored by Society of Children's Book Writers and Illustrators (SCBWI)
4727 Wilshire Blvd, Suite 301, Los Angeles, CA 90010
Tel: 323-782-1010 *Fax:* 323-782-1892
E-mail: scbwi@scbwi.org
Web Site: www.scbwi.org
Key Personnel
Pres: Stephen Mooser *E-mail:* stephenmooser@scbwi.org
Exec Dir: Lin Oliver *E-mail:* linoliver@scbwi.org
Location: Hyatt Regency Century Plaza, 2025 Avenue of the Stars, Los Angeles, CA, USA
Aug 5-7, 2016

South African Booksellers Association Annual Conference
Sponsored by South African Booksellers Association (SABA)
WJ Louw Bldg, 7 Old Paarl Rd, Bellville, South Africa
Mailing Address: PO Box 870, Bellville 7535, South Africa
Tel: (021) 945 1572 *Fax:* (021) 945 2169
E-mail: saba@sabooksellers.com
Web Site: www.sabooksellers.com
Aug 2016

Swanwick: The Writers' Summer School
Sponsored by Writers' Summer School
130 Wood Lane, Hucknall, Notts NG15 6PN, United Kingdom
Tel: (07765) 890 733 (enquiries)
Web Site: www.swanwickwritersschool.org.uk
Key Personnel
Secy: Pauline Hallam Mason *E-mail:* secretary@swanwickwritersschool.org.uk
A week-long residential writing school with top name speakers & tutors, plus informative panels, talks & discussion groups. Comfortable rooms with all meals & tuition included in the price. Open to everyone, from absolute beginners to published authors. Beautiful setting, licensed bar & evening entertainment. Believed to be the longest established residential writers' school in the world, Swanwick, held annually in August, is a must attend event in every writer's diary.
Location: The Hayes Conference Centre, Swanwick, Derbyshire, UK
Aug 2016

AUTUMN

Louisiana Book Festival
Sponsored by Louisiana Center for the Book
Subsidiary of State Library of Louisiana
701 N Fourth St, Baton Rouge, LA 70802
Tel: 225-219-9503 *Fax:* 225-219-9840
Web Site: louisianabookfestival.org
Key Personnel
Dir: Jim Davis *Tel:* 225-342-9714 *E-mail:* jdavis@slol.lib.la.us
Asst Dir: Robert Wilson *E-mail:* rwilson@slol.lib.la.us
A free festival celebrating readers, writers & books with events for all ages & genres, food, music.
Location: State Library of Louisiana, Louisiana State Capitol, Capitol Park Museum & nearby locations, Baton Rouge, LA, USA
Autumn 2016

SEPTEMBER

Christian Resources Retailers & Suppliers Retreat
Sponsored by Christian Resources Together
Cedar Tree, 4 Ditchingham Close, Aylesbury, Bucks HP19 7SA, United Kingdom
Tel: (01296) 489860
Web Site: www.christianresourcestogether.co.uk
Key Personnel
Event Organizer: Steve Briars *E-mail:* steve@christianresourcestogether.co.uk
Location: Hayes Conference Centre, Swanwick, Alfreton, Derbyshire, UK
Sept 14-15, 2016

Excellence in Journalism
Sponsored by The Society of Professional Journalists (SPJ)
Eugene S Pulliam National Journalism Ctr, 3909 N Meridian St, Indianapolis, IN 46208
Tel: 317-927-8000 *Fax:* 317-920-4789
E-mail: convention@spj.org
Web Site: excellenceinjournalism.org; www.spj.org
Key Personnel
Assoc Exec Dir: Chris Vachon *Tel:* 317-927-8000 ext 207 *E-mail:* cvachon@spj.org
Dir, Events: Heather Dunn *Tel:* 317-927-8000 ext 204 *E-mail:* hdunn@spj.org
Annual conference co-organized by Radio Television Digital News Association (RTDNA).
Location: Sheraton New Orleans, 500 Canal St, New Orleans, LA, USA
Sept 18-20, 2016

EXPOLIT (Exposicion de Literatura Cristiana Book Fair)
Sponsored by Spanish Evangelical Publishers Association (SEPA)/Asociacion Evangelica espanola de Editores
8167 NW 84 St, Medley, FL 33166
Tel: 305-503-1191 *Toll Free Tel:* 866-782-3976 *Fax:* 305-717-6886
Web Site: www.expolit.com
Key Personnel
Enrollment Coord: Jessica Hernandez *E-mail:* registration@exploit.com
Media & Ad Coord: Maria Pastor *E-mail:* medios@expolit.com
Exhibit Coord: Mayra De Moya-Garcia *Tel:* 305-503-1191 ext 146 *E-mail:* mayra@expolit.com
Spanish Christian literature convention. Also sponsored by Editorial Unilit.
Location: DoubleTree Hotel and Miami Airport Convention Center, Miami, FL, USA
Sept 15-18, 2016

Garden Writers Association Annual Symposium
Sponsored by Garden Writers Association
7809 FM 179, Shallowater, TX 79363-3637
Tel: 806-832-1870 *Fax:* 806-832-5244
E-mail: info@gardenwriters.org
Web Site: www.gardenwriters.org; www.gwaa.org
Key Personnel
Exec Dir: Robert LaGasse *E-mail:* execdir@gardenwriters.org
Location: Sheraton Downtown, Atlanta, GA, USA
Sept 16-19, 2016

Goteborg Book Fair
Sponsored by Bok & Bibliotek i Norden AB
Maessans Gata 20, 412 94 Gothenburg, Sweden
Tel: (031) 708 84 00 *Fax:* (031) 20 91 03
E-mail: info@goteborg-bookfair.com; info@bokmassan.se
Web Site: www.bokmassan.se
Key Personnel
CEO: Anna Falck *E-mail:* af@goteborg-bookfair.com
Book Fair Dir: Maria Kaellsson *E-mail:* maka@goteborg-bookfair.com
Head of Prog: Gunilla Sandin *E-mail:* gs@goteborg-bookfair.com
Prog Coord: Anneli Jonasson *Tel:* (031) 708 84 03 *E-mail:* aj@goteborg-bookfair.com
Location: Gothenburg, Sweden
Sept 29-Oct 2, 2016

Graph Expo®
Sponsored by Graphic Arts Show Company (GASC)
1899 Preston White Dr, Reston, VA 20191
Tel: 703-264-7200 *Fax:* 703-620-9187
E-mail: info@gasc.org
Web Site: www.graphexpo.com; www.gasc.org
Key Personnel
VP: Chris Price *Tel:* 703-264-7200 ext 221 *E-mail:* cprice@gasc.org
Dir of Opers: Kelly Kilga *Tel:* 703-264-7200 ext 213 *E-mail:* kkilga@gasc.org
Conference Mgr: Lilly Kinney *Tel:* 703-264-7200 ext 255 *E-mail:* lkinney@gasc.org

Produced for NPES The Association for Suppliers of Printing, Publishing & Converting Technologies.
Location: Orange County Convention Center, North Hall, Orlando, FL, USA
Sept 25-28, 2016

National Federation of Press Women Communications Conference
Sponsored by National Federation of Press Women Inc (NFPW)
PO Box 5556, Arlington, VA 22205-0798
Tel: 703-237-9804 *Fax:* 703-237-9808
E-mail: presswomen@aol.com
Web Site: www.nfpw.org
Location: DoubleTree by Hilton Hotel Wichita Airport, 2098 Airport Rd, Wichita, KS, USA
Sept 8-10, 2016

National Newspaper Association Annual Convention & Trade Show
Sponsored by National Newspaper Association
200 Little Falls St, Suite 405, Falls Church, VA 22046
Mailing Address: PO Box 50301, Arlington, VA 22205
Tel: 703-237-9802 *Toll Free Tel:* 800-829-4NNA (829-4662) *Fax:* 703-237-9808
Web Site: nnaweb.org
Key Personnel
Mng Dir: Carol Pierce *E-mail:* carol@nna.org
Location: Franklin Marriott, 700 Cool Springs Blvd, Franklin, TN, USA
Sept 22-25, 2016

PSA® International Conference of Photography
Sponsored by Photographic Society of America® (PSA®)
8241 S Walker Ave, Suite 104, Oklahoma City, OK 73139
Tel: 405-843-1437 *Toll Free Tel:* 855-PSA-INFO (855-772-4636) *Fax:* 405-843-1438
E-mail: hq@psa-photo.org
Web Site: www.psa-photo.org
Key Personnel
Conference VP: Stan Bormann *E-mail:* conferencevp@psa-photo.org
Location: Wyndham San Antonio Riverwalk, 111 E Pecan St, San Antonio, TX, USA
Sept 10-17, 2016

SIBA Fall Discovery Show
Sponsored by Southern Independent Booksellers Alliance
3806 Yale Ave, Columbia, SC 29205
Tel: 803-994-9530 *Fax:* 309-410-0211
E-mail: info@sibaweb.com
Web Site: www.sibaweb.com/trade-show; www.sibaweb.com
Key Personnel
Exec Dir: Wanda Jewell *E-mail:* wanda@sibaweb.com
Members only event.
Location: Hilton Savannah Desoto, Savannah, GA, USA
Sept 16-18, 2016

TAPPI PEERS Conference
Sponsored by Technical Association of the Pulp & Paper Industry (TAPPI)
15 Technology Pkwy S, Suite 115, Peachtree Corners, GA 30092
Tel: 770-446-1400 *Toll Free Tel:* 800-332-8686 (US); 800-446-9431 (CN) *Fax:* 770-446-6947
E-mail: memberconnection@tappi.org
Web Site: www.tappi.org
Key Personnel
Meeting Mgr: Libby Settle *Tel:* 770-209-7345 *E-mail:* lsettle@tappi.org
Dir of Mktg: Simona Marcellus *Tel:* 770-209-7293 *E-mail:* smarcellus@tappi.org
Location: Hyatt Regency Jacksonville Riverfront, 225 E Coastline Dr, Jacksonville, FL, USA
Sept 28-30, 2016

Worlddidac India
Sponsored by Worlddidac Association
Bollwerk 21, 3011 Bern, Switzerland
Tel: (031) 311 76 82 *Fax:* (031) 312 17 44
E-mail: info@worlddidac.org
Web Site: worlddidacindia.com; www.worlddidac.org
Key Personnel
Dir Gen: Beat Jost *E-mail:* jost@worlddidac.org
Proj & Communs Mgr: Kateryna Schuetz *E-mail:* schuetz@worlddidac.org
International exhibition for education, training, technology & supply. Organized by Arclights Eventz Network Pvt Ltd.
Location: New Delhi, India
Sept 2016

OCTOBER

ACP/CMA National College Media Convention
Sponsored by Associated Collegiate Press (ACP) Division of National Scholastic Press Association
2221 University Ave SE, Suite 121, Minneapolis, MN 55414
Tel: 612-625-8335 *Fax:* 612-605-0072
E-mail: info@studentpress.org
Web Site: www.studentpress.org; facebook.com/acpress; twitter.com/acpress
Key Personnel
Exec Dir, National Scholastic Press Association: Diana Mitsu Klos *Tel:* 612-625-7359 *E-mail:* diana@studentpress.org
Co-sponsored by College Media Association.
Location: Grand Hyatt, Washington, DC, USA
Oct 20-23, 2016

AMWA Annual Conference
Sponsored by American Medical Writers Association (AMWA)
30 W Gude Dr, Suite 525, Rockville, MD 20850-4357
Tel: 240-238-0940 *Fax:* 301-294-9006
E-mail: amwa@amwa.org
Web Site: www.amwa.org
Key Personnel
Conference Prog Mgr & Workshop Coord: Becky Phillips *Tel:* 240-238-0940 ext 103 *E-mail:* becky@amwa.org
Location: Denver, CO, USA
Oct 5-8, 2016

ASIS&T Annual Meeting
Sponsored by Association for Information Science & Technology (ASIS&T)
8555 16 St, Suite 850, Silver Spring, MD 20910
Tel: 301-495-0900 *Fax:* 301-495-0810
E-mail: meetings@asis.org; asis@asis.org
Web Site: www.asis.org
Key Personnel
Exec Dir: Richard Hill *E-mail:* rhill@asis.org
Dir of Meetings & Membership: Vanessa Foss *E-mail:* vfoss@asis.org
Location: Copenhagen, Denmark
Oct 14-18, 2016

BMI Annual Conference
Sponsored by Book Manufacturers' Institute Inc (BMI)
2 Armand Beach Dr, Suite 1B, Palm Coast, FL 32137-2612
Tel: 386-986-4552 *Fax:* 386-986-4553
E-mail: info@bmibook.com
Web Site: www.bmibook.org
Key Personnel
EVP: Daniel N Bach *E-mail:* dbach@bmibook.com
Conference Coord: Jackie Murray
Off Mgr: Dianne Morris
Location: Marco Island Marriott Beach Resort, Marco Island, FL, USA
Oct 23-25, 2016

Distripress Annual Congress
Sponsored by Distripress
Seefeldstr 35, CH-8008 Zurich, Switzerland
Tel: (044) 202 41 21 *Fax:* (044) 202 10 25
E-mail: info@distripress.net
Web Site: www.distripress.net
Key Personnel
Mng Dir: David Owen *E-mail:* david.owen@distripress.net
Congress Coord: Susanne Koebe *E-mail:* susanne.koebe@distripress.net
Commun & Governing Bodies: Gabriela Rietmann *E-mail:* gabriela.rietmann@distripress.net
Annual event sponsored by Distripress, a nonprofit association for the promotion of international press distribution.
Location: Dubai, United Arab Emirates
Oct 3-6, 2016

DMA2016
Sponsored by Direct Marketing Association (DMA)
1120 Avenue of the Americas, New York, NY 10036-6700
SAN: 692-6487
Tel: 212-768-7277 *Fax:* 212-302-6714
Web Site: thedma.org
Key Personnel
VP, Conferences & Events: Paul A McDonnough
Location: Los Angeles Convention Center, Los Angeles, CA, USA
Oct 16-19, 2016

Frankfurt Book Fair
Sponsored by Ausstellungs-und Messe-GmbH des Boersenvereins des Deutschen Buchhandels
Braubachstr 16, 60311 Frankfurt am Main, Germany
Mailing Address: Postfach 100116, 60001 Frankfurt am Main, Germany
Tel: (069) 21020 *Fax:* (069) 2102 277
E-mail: info@book-fair.com
Web Site: www.frankfurt-book-fair.com; www.book-fair.com
Key Personnel
CEO & Dir: Juergen Boos
Largest international book & media fair attracting 7,100 exhibitors from over 100 countries & 270,000 visitors.
Location: Frankfurt Fairgrounds, Frankfurt, Germany
Oct 19-23, 2016

AIGA Design Conference
Sponsored by AIGA, the professional association for design
233 Broadway, 17th fl, New York, NY 10279
Tel: 212-807-1990
Web Site: www.aiga.org
Key Personnel
Dir of Events: Jonathan Feinberg *Tel:* 212-710-3142
Prog Dir: Kathleen Budny *Tel:* 212-710-3144
Annual conference.
Location: Las Vegas, NV, USA
Oct 17–19, 2016

Inter American Press Association General Assembly
Sponsored by Inter American Press Association (IAPA)

Jules Dubois Bldg, 1801 SW Third Ave, Miami, FL 33129
Tel: 305-634-2465 *Fax:* 305-635-2272
E-mail: info@sipiapa.org
Web Site: www.sipiapa.org
Key Personnel
Exec Dir: Ricardo Trotti *E-mail:* rtrotti@sipiapa.org
Gathering of important international figures for workshops, seminars & other related activities, while offering networking opportunities for those interested on press/media freedom & freedom of expression issues.
Location: Mexico City, Mexico
Oct 2016

LIBER Feria Internacional del Libro
Sponsored by Federacion de Gremios de Editores de Espana (FGEE) (Spanish Association of Publishers Guilds)
Cea Bermudez, 44-2º Dcha, 28003 Madrid, Spain
Tel: 91 534 51 95 *Fax:* 91 535 26 25
E-mail: fgee@fge.es
Web Site: www.federacioneditores.org
Key Personnel
Exec Dir: Antonio M Avila
Location: Barcelona, Spain
Oct 12-14, 2016

NAIBA Fall Conference
Sponsored by New Atlantic Independent Booksellers Association (NAIBA)
2667 Hyacinth St, Westbury, NY 11590
Tel: 516-333-0681 *Fax:* 516-333-0689
E-mail: naibabooksellers@gmail.com
Web Site: www.naiba.com
Key Personnel
Exec Dir: Eileen Dengler *E-mail:* NAIBAeileen@gmail.com
Location: DoubleTree by Hilton Somerset Hotel & Conference Center, 200 Atrium Dr, Somerset, NJ, USA
Oct 16-18, 2016

National Association of Science Writers Annual Meeting
Sponsored by National Association of Science Writers (NASW)
PO Box 7905, Berkeley, CA 94707
Tel: 510-647-9500
Web Site: www.nasw.org
Key Personnel
Exec Dir: Tinsley Davis *E-mail:* director@nasw.org
Location: San Antonio, TX, USA
Oct 28-Nov 1, 2016

TAPPI/AICC SuperCorrExpo® 2016
Sponsored by Technical Association of the Pulp & Paper Industry (TAPPI)
15 Technology Pkwy S, Suite 115, Peachtree Corners, GA 30092
Tel: 770-446-1400 *Toll Free Tel:* 800-332-8686 (US); 800-446-9431 (CN) *Fax:* 770-446-6947
E-mail: memberconnection@tappi.org
Web Site: www.tappi.org
Key Personnel
Meeting Mgr: Libby Settle *Tel:* 770-209-7345 *E-mail:* lsettle@tappi.org
Dir of Mktg: Simona Marcellus *Tel:* 770-209-7293 *E-mail:* smarcellus@tappi.org
Location: Orange County Convention Center, Orlando, FL, USA
Oct 17-20, 2016

Texas Book Festival
610 Brazos, Suite 200, Austin, TX 78701
Tel: 512-477-4055 *Fax:* 512-322-0722
E-mail: bookfest@texasbookfestival.org
Web Site: www.texasbookfestival.org
Key Personnel
Exec Dir: Lois Kim *E-mail:* loiskim@texasbookfestival.org
Logistics & Outreach Coord: Kendall Miller *E-mail:* kendall@texasbookfestival.org
Opers Coord: Claire Burrows *E-mail:* claire@texasbookfestival.com
The festival is a statewide program that promotes reading & literacy highlighted by a two-day festival, held annually in October, featuring authors from Texas & across the USA. Money raised from the festival is distributed as grants to public libraries throughout the state.
Location: State Capitol Bldg, Austin, TX, USA
Oct 2016

Twin Cities Book Festival
Sponsored by Rain Taxi
PO Box 3840, Minneapolis, MN 55403
Tel: 612-825-1528 *Fax:* 612-825-1528
E-mail: bookfest@raintaxi.com
Web Site: www.raintaxi.com/twin-cities-book-festival
Key Personnel
Dir: Eric Lorberer
Gala celebration of books, featuring large exhibition, author readings & signings, book art activities, panel discussions, used book sale & children's events.
Location: Minneapolis, MN, USA
Oct 2016

Utah Humanities Book Festival
Sponsored by Utah Humanities Council
Affiliate of Utah Center for the Book
202 W 300 N, Salt Lake City, UT 84103
Tel: 801-359-9670 *Fax:* 801-531-7869
Web Site: www.utahhumanities.org/BookFestival.htm
Key Personnel
Exec Dir: Cynthia Buckingham *Tel:* 801-359-9670 ext 101 *E-mail:* buckingham@utahhumanities.org
Devt Dir: Kathleen Harmon Gardner *Tel:* 801-359-9670 ext 108 *E-mail:* gardner@utahhumanities.org
Lit Prog Offr: Michael McLane *Tel:* 801-359-9670 ext 104 *E-mail:* mclane@utahhumanities.org
Communs Dir: Deena Pyle *Tel:* 801-359-9670 ext 111 *E-mail:* pyle@utahhumanities.org
Free literary event featuring national, regional & local authors held Oct 1-31 annually (National Book Month).
Location: Statewide, UT, USA
Oct 1-31, 2016

WORLDDIDAC Basel
Sponsored by Worlddidac Association
Bollwerk 21, 3011 Bern, Switzerland
Tel: (031) 311 76 82; (058) 200 20 20 *Fax:* (031) 312 17 44; (058) 206 21 89
E-mail: info@worlddidac.org
Web Site: www.worlddidacbasel.com; www.worlddidac.org
Key Personnel
Exhibition Dir: Philipp Schmid *E-mail:* philipp.schmid@worlddidacbasel.com
International exhibition for education, training, technology & supply. Organized by MCH Swiss Exhibition (Basel) Ltd & held in conjunction with Didacta Schweiz Basel. Held biennially in even-numbered years.
Location: Basel Exhibition Center, Hall 1.1, Basel, Switzerland
Oct 26-28, 2016

NOVEMBER

American Translators Association Annual Conference
Sponsored by American Translators Association (ATA)
225 Reinekers Lane, Suite 590, Alexandria, VA 22314
Tel: 703-683-6100 *Fax:* 703-683-6122
E-mail: ata@atanet.org
Web Site: www.atanet.org
Key Personnel
Exec Dir: Walter W Bacak, Jr *Tel:* 703-683-6100 ext 3006 *E-mail:* walter@atanet.org
Meetings Mgr: Teresa C Kelly *Tel:* 703-683-6100 ext 3014 *E-mail:* teresak@atanet.org
Location: San Francisco, CA, USA
Nov 2-5, 2016

Istanbul Book Fair
Sponsored by Tuyap Fairs & Exhibitions Organization Inc (Tuyap Fuar ve Sergiler A S)
E-5 Karayolu Uezeri, Guerpinar Kavsagi, Bueyuekcekmece, 34500 Istanbul, Turkey
Tel: (0212) 867 11 00 *Fax:* (0212) 886 66 98
E-mail: fairarea@tuyap.com.tr
Web Site: www.istanbulbookfair.com; www.istanbulkitapfuari.com; www.tuyap.com.tr
Annual event organized in cooperation with the Turkish Publishers Association.
Location: International Hall, Tuyap Fair, Convention & Congress Center, Buyukcekmece/Istanbul, Turkey
Nov 8-11, 2016

Jewish Book Month
Sponsored by Jewish Book Council
520 Eighth Ave, 4th fl, New York, NY 10018
Tel: 212-201-2920 *Fax:* 212-532-4952
E-mail: jbc@jewishbooks.org
Web Site: www.jewishbookcouncil.org; www.facebook.com/JewishBookCouncil; twitter.com/jewishbook
Key Personnel
Dir: Carolyn Starman Hessel
Assoc Dir: Naomi Firestone-Teeter
Dedicated to the celebration of Jewish books held annually during the month leading up to Hanukkah.
Location: Nationwide throughout the USA
Nov 23-Dec 23, 2016

Miami Book Fair International
Sponsored by Florida Center for the Literary Arts
c/o Miami Dade College, 401 NE Second Ave, Suite 4102, Miami, FL 33132
Tel: 305-237-3258 *Fax:* 305-237-3978
E-mail: wbookfair@mdc.edu
Web Site: www.miamibookfair.com
Key Personnel
Dir of Opers: Delia Lopez *Tel:* 305-237-3066 *E-mail:* delia.lopez@mdc.edu
Admin Asst: Giselle Hernandez *E-mail:* giselle.hernandez@mdc.edu
Miami Book Fair International is the largest event of its kind in the USA. For more than 30 years, the fair has been held over 8 days each November. In addition to readings by more than 400 authors from all over the world & the sale of thousands of books in many languages, the fair offers book-centered fun for children, panel discussions & writing classes in English & Spanish. For up to date information, call or visit the book fair web site at www.miamibookfair.com.
Location: Miami Dade College, Wolfson Campus, Miami, FL, USA
Nov 13-20, 2016

PACK EXPO International
Sponsored by PMMI: The Association for Packaging and Processing Technologies
11911 Freedom Dr, Suite 600, Reston, VA 20190
Tel: 703-243-8555; 571-612-3200
Toll Free Tel: 888-ASK-PMMI (275-7664)
Fax: 703-243-8556
E-mail: expo@pmmi.org
Web Site: www.packexpointernational.com; www.packexpo.com; www.pmmi.org
Key Personnel
VP, Meetings & Events: Patti Fee *Tel:* 571-612-3193 *E-mail:* pfee@pmmi.org
Dir, Expositions: Ray Luca *Tel:* 571-266-4404 *E-mail:* rluca@pmmi.org
Dir, Tradeshow Opers: Laura B Thompson *Tel:* 571-612-3217 *E-mail:* laura@pmmi.org
Dir, Tradeshow Mktg: Jeannine Gibson *Tel:* 571-612-3203 *E-mail:* jeannine@pmmi.org
Events Mgr: Anna Hudson *Tel:* 571-612-3198 *E-mail:* anna@pmmi.org
Exhibitor Servs Mgr: Merideth Newman *Tel:* 571-612-3208 *E-mail:* merideth@pmmi.org
Exhibitor Servs Coord: Deanna Hoffman *Tel:* 571-266-4409 *E-mail:* deanna@pmmi.org
Exhibitor Servs & Sales Assoc: Beth Murray *Tel:* 571-612-3186 *E-mail:* bmurray@pmmi.org
Tradeshow Asst: Krista Debrosse *Tel:* 571-612-3215 *E-mail:* krista@pmmi.org
Biennial event held in even-numbered years.
Location: McCormick Place, 2301 S Lake Shore Dr, Chicago, IL, USA
Nov 6-9, 2016

Salon du Livre de Montreal
(Montreal Book Show)
300, rue du St-Secrement, Suite 430, Montreal, QC H2Y 1X4, Canada
Tel: 514-845-2365 *Fax:* 514-845-7119
E-mail: slm.info@videotron.ca
Web Site: www.salondulivredemontreal.com
Key Personnel
Gen Mgr: Francine Bois
Location: Place Bonaventure, Montreal, QC, CN
Nov 16-21, 2016

2017

JANUARY

American Library Association Midwinter Meeting
Sponsored by The American Library Association (ALA)
50 E Huron St, Chicago, IL 60611
Tel: 312-944-6780 *Toll Free Tel:* 800-545-2433 (ext 3223) *Fax:* 312-440-9374
E-mail: ala@ala.org
Web Site: www.ala.org/midwinter
Key Personnel
Registration & Housing Specialist: Alicia Babcock *Tel:* 800-545-2433 ext 3229 *E-mail:* ababcock@ala.org
Conference Dir: Paul Graller *Tel:* 800-545-2433 ext 3219 *E-mail:* pgraller@ala.org
Conference Mgr: Amy McGuigan *Tel:* 800-545-2433 ext 3226 *E-mail:* amcguigan@ala.org
Meetings, AV & Catering Coord: Yvonne McLean *Tel:* 800-545-2433 ext 3222 *E-mail:* ymclean@ala.org
Conference Coord: Lindsay Rosales *Tel:* 800-545-2433 ext 3227 *E-mail:* lrosales@ala.org
Meeting Coord: Alicia (Alee) Navarro *Tel:* 800-545-2433 ext 3216 *E-mail:* anavarro@ala.org
Location: Atlanta, GA, USA
Jan 20-24, 2017

MLA Annual Convention
Sponsored by Modern Language Association of America (MLA)
26 Broadway, 3rd fl, New York, NY 10004-1789
SAN: 202-6422
Tel: 646-576-5266; 646-576-5000 *Fax:* 646-458-0030
E-mail: convention@mla.org
Web Site: www.mla.org/convention
Key Personnel
Assoc Dir of Convention Progs: Karin L Bagnall *E-mail:* kbagnall@mla.org
Location: Philadelphia, PA, USA
Jan 5-8, 2017

FEBRUARY

AWP Annual Conference & Bookfair
Sponsored by Association of Writers & Writing Programs (AWP)
George Mason University, 4400 University Dr, MSN 1E3, Fairfax, VA 22030
Tel: 703-993-4301 *Fax:* 703-993-4302
E-mail: awp@awpwriter.org; events@awpwriter.org
Web Site: www.awpwriter.org/awp_conference/; www.awpwriter.org
Key Personnel
Exec Dir: David W Fenza
Dir, Conferences: Christian Teresi
Assoc Dir of Conferences: Cynthia Sherman
Location: Washington Convention Center & Washington Marriott Marquis, Washington, DC, USA
Feb 8-11, 2017

California International Antiquarian Book Fair
Sponsored by Antiquarian Booksellers' Association of America
20 W 44 St, Suite 507, New York, NY 10036
Tel: 212-944-8291 *Fax:* 212-944-8293
E-mail: cafair@whiterainproductions.com; info@whiterainproductions.com
Web Site: www.cabookfair.com; www.sfbookfair.com; www.abaa.org
Key Personnel
Exec Dir: Susan Benne *E-mail:* sbenne@abaa.org
Annual event co-sponsored by International League of Antiquarian Booksellers & managed by White Rain Productions.
Location: Oakland Marriott City Center, 1001 Broadway, Oakland, CA, USA
Feb 10-12, 2017

Jerusalem International Book Fair
Sponsored by Ariel Municipal Co Ltd
PO Box 775, Jerusalem 91007, Israel
Tel: (02) 629 6415 *Fax:* (02) 624 0663
E-mail: jerfair@jerusalem.muni.il
Web Site: https://www.jerusalem.muni.il/en/Messages/SpecialEvents/Pages/BookFair.aspx
Biennial event.
Location: Jerusalem International Convention Center, Jerusalem, Israel
Feb 2017

SPRING

Bologna Children's Book Fair
Sponsored by BolognaFiere SpA
Piazza Costituzione, 6, 40128 Bologna, Italy
Tel: (051) 282 111 *Fax:* (051) 637 4011
E-mail: bookfair@bolognafiere.it
Web Site: www.bolognachildrensbookfair.com
Key Personnel
Exhibition Mgr: Roberta Chinni *Tel:* (051) 282 269 *E-mail:* roberta.chinni@bolognafiere.it
Location: Bologna Fair Centre, Piazza Costituzione, 6, Bologna, Italy
Spring 2017

Poligrafia
Sponsored by Poznan International Fair Ltd
ul Glogowska 14, 60-734 Poznan, Poland
Tel: (61) 869 20 00 *Fax:* (61) 869 29 99
E-mail: poligrafia@mtp.pl; info@mtp.pl
Web Site: www.poligrafiaexpo.pl/en (English); www.poligrafiaexpo.pl/pl (Polish); www.mtp.pl/en/ (English); www.mtp.pl/pl/ (Polish)
Key Personnel
Proj Mgr: Piotr Kaminski *Tel:* (0603) 410 225 *E-mail:* piotr.kaminski@mtp.pl
International fair of printing machines, materials & services held biennially.
Location: Poznan International Fair Grounds, Poznan, Poland
Spring 2017

MARCH

Leipzig Book Fair (Leipziger Buchmesse)
Sponsored by Leipziger Messe GmbH
Messe-Allee 1, 04356 Leipzig, Germany
Mailing Address: Postfach 10 07 20, 04007 Leipzig, Germany
Tel: (0341) 678-0 *Fax:* (0341) 678-8762
E-mail: info@leipziger-buchmesse.de
Web Site: www.leipziger-buchmesse.de
Key Personnel
Dir: Oliver Zille *Tel:* (0341) 678-8240
Held annually in conjunction with The Leipzig Antiquarian Book Fair.
Location: Leipzig Exhibition Centre, Messe-Allee 1, Leipzig, Germany
March 23-26, 2017

Virginia Festival of the Book
Sponsored by Virginia Foundation for the Humanities
145 Ednam Dr, Charlottesville, VA 22903
Tel: 434-924-3296 *Fax:* 434-296-4714
E-mail: vabook@virginia.edu
Web Site: www.vabook.org
Key Personnel
Prog Dir: Jane Kulow *Tel:* 434-924-7548
Annual public festival for children & adults featuring authors, illustrators, publishers, publicists, agents & other book professionals in panel discussions & readings. Most events are free. Almost 400 authors invited annually.
Location: Charlottesville, VA, USA
March 22-26, 2017

APRIL

Alberta Library Conference
Sponsored by Library Association of Alberta (LAA)
80 Baker Crescent NW, Calgary, AB T2L 1R4, Canada
Tel: 403-284-5818 *Toll Free Tel:* 877-522-5550
E-mail: info@laa.ca
Web Site: www.albertalibraryconference.com; www.laa.ca
Key Personnel
Exec Dir/Conference Coord: Christine Sheppard
Co-hosted by Alberta Library Trustees Association (ALTA).

Location: Fairmont Jasper Park Lodge, Jasper, AB, CN
April 27-30, 2017

International Children's Book Day
Sponsored by International Board on Books for Young People (IBBY)
Nonnenweg 12, Postfach, 4009 Basel, Switzerland
Tel: (061) 272 29 17 *Fax:* (061) 272 27 57
E-mail: ibby@ibby.org
Web Site: www.ibby.org
Key Personnel
Exec Dir: Liz Page *E-mail:* liz.page@ibby.org
Admin Asst: Luzmaria Stauffenegger *E-mail:* luzmaria.stauffenegger@ibby.org
On Hans Christian Andersen's birthday, April 2nd, International Children's Book Day (ICBD) is celebrated to inspire a love of reading & to call attention to children's books. Each year a different national section has the opportunity to be the international sponsor. It decides upon a theme & invites a prominent author to write a message to the children of the world & a well-known illustrator to design a poster. These materials are used in different ways to promote books & reading around the world.
April 2, 2017

NAAJ Annual Meeting
Sponsored by North American Agricultural Journalists (NAAJ)
6434 Hurta Lane, Bryan, TX 77808
Tel: 979-845-2872 *Fax:* 979-862-1202
Web Site: www.naaj.net
Key Personnel
Exec Secy & Treas: Kathleen Phillips *E-mail:* kaphillips@tamu.edu
Annual meeting.
Location: Washington, DC, USA
April 2017

National Library Week
Sponsored by The American Library Association (ALA)
50 E Huron St, Chicago, IL 60611
Tel: 312-944-6780 *Toll Free Tel:* 800-545-2433 (ext 3223) *Fax:* 312-440-9374
E-mail: ala@ala.org
Web Site: www.ala.org/nlw
Key Personnel
Campaign Coord: Megan McFarlane *Tel:* 800-545-2433 ext 2148 *E-mail:* mmcfarlane@ala.org
Location: Nationwide throughout the USA
April 9-15, 2017

The Quest for Excellence® Conference
Sponsored by National Institute of Standards and Technology (NIST)
100 Bureau Dr, Stop 1020, Gaithersburg, MD 20899-1020
Tel: 301-975-2036 *Fax:* 301-948-3716
E-mail: baldrige@nist.gov
Web Site: www.nist.gov/baldrige/qe/index.cfm
Key Personnel
Conference Chair: Barbara Fischer *Tel:* 301-975-8942 *E-mail:* barbara.fischer@nist.gov
Official conference of the Malcolm Baldrige National Quality Award, held in partnership with American Society for Quality (ASQ) & Association for Talent Development (ATD).
Location: Baltimore Marriott Waterfront, 700 Aliceanna St, Baltimore, MD, USA
April 2-5, 2017

MAY

Children's Book Week
Sponsored by The Children's Book Council (CBC)
54 W 39 St, 14th fl, New York, NY 10018
Tel: 212-966-1990
E-mail: cbc.info@cbcbooks.org
Web Site: www.bookweekonline.com; www.cbcbooks.org
Key Personnel
Exec Dir: Jon Colman *E-mail:* jon.colman@cbcbooks.org
Communs Dir: Nicole Deming *E-mail:* nicole.deming@cbcbooks.org
Programming Dir: Shaina Birkhead *E-mail:* shaina.birkhead@cbcbooks.org
Mgr, Events & Progs/Libn: Ayanna Coleman *E-mail:* ayanna.coleman@cbcbooks.org
Events & Progs Asst/Membership Coord: Matthew Poulter *E-mail:* matthew.poulter@cbcbooks.org
Location: Nationwide across the USA
May 1-7, 2017

PacPrint 2017
Sponsored by Reed Exhibitions Australia Pty Ltd
Tower 2, 475 Victoria Ave, Chatswood, NSW 2067, Australia
Mailing Address: Locked Bag 4500, Chatswood, NSW 2067, Australia
Tel: (02) 9422 2500
E-mail: inquiry@reedexhibitions.com.au
Web Site: www.pacprint.com.au
Sponsored by Graphic Arts Merchants Association of Australia Inc (GAMAA) & the Printing Industries Association of Australia (PIAA), this event is held every 4 years.
Location: Melbourne Convention & Exhibition Centre (MCEC), South Wharf, Victoria, Australia
May 23-27, 2017

JUNE

American Library Association Annual Conference
Sponsored by The American Library Association (ALA)
50 E Huron St, Chicago, IL 60611
Tel: 312-944-6780 *Toll Free Tel:* 800-545-2433 (ext 3223) *Fax:* 312-440-9374
E-mail: ala@ala.org
Web Site: www.ala.org
Key Personnel
Registration & Housing Specialist: Alicia Babcock *Tel:* 800-545-2433 ext 3229 *E-mail:* ababcock@ala.org
Conference Dir: Paul Graller *Tel:* 800-545-2433 ext 3219 *E-mail:* pgraller@ala.org
Conference Mgr: Amy McGuigan *Tel:* 800-545-2433 ext 3226 *E-mail:* amcguigan@ala.org
Meetings, AV & Catering Coord: Yvonne McLean *Tel:* 800-545-2433 ext 3222 *E-mail:* ymclean@ala.org
Conference Coord: Lindsay Rosales *Tel:* 800-545-2433 ext 3227 *E-mail:* lrosales@ala.org
Meeting Coord: Alicia (Alee) Navarro *Tel:* 800-545-2433 ext 3216 *E-mail:* anavarro@ala.org
Location: Chicago, IL, USA
June 22-27, 2017

Outdoor Writers Association of America Annual Conference
Sponsored by Outdoor Writers Association of America (OWAA)
615 Oak St, Suite 201, Missoula, MT 59801
Tel: 406-728-7434 *Fax:* 406-728-7445
E-mail: info@owaa.org
Web Site: owaa.org
Key Personnel
Membership & Conference Servs: Jessica (Pollett) Seitz *E-mail:* jseitz@owaa.org
Location: Duluth Entertainment & Convention Center, Duluth, MN, USA
June 24-26, 2017

SLA Annual Conference & INFO-EXPO
Sponsored by Special Libraries Association (SLA)
331 S Patrick St, Alexandria, VA 22314-3501
Tel: 703-647-4900 *Fax:* 703-647-4901
Web Site: www.sla.org
Key Personnel
Deputy CEO: Doug Newcomb *Tel:* 703-647-4923 *E-mail:* dnewcomb1@sla.org
Dir, Events: Caroline Hamilton *Tel:* 703-647-4949 *E-mail:* chamilton@sla.org
Dir, Mktg & Exhibits: Jeff Leach *Tel:* 703-647-4922 *E-mail:* jleach@sla.org
Location: Phoenix, AZ, USA
June 18-20, 2017

JULY

Romance Writers of America Annual Conference
Sponsored by Romance Writers of America®
14615 Benfer Rd, Houston, TX 77069
Tel: 832-717-5200 *Fax:* 832-717-5201
E-mail: conference@rwa.org; info@rwa.org
Web Site: www.rwa.org
Key Personnel
Exec Dir: Allison Kelley *Tel:* 832-717-5200 ext 124 *E-mail:* allison.kelley@rwa.org
Location: Walt Disney World Swan and Dolphin, 1500 Epcot Resorts Blvd, Lake Buena Vista, FL, USA
July 26-29, 2017

SEPTEMBER

Christian Resources Retailers & Suppliers Retreat
Sponsored by Christian Resources Together
Cedar Tree, 4 Ditchingham Close, Aylesbury, Bucks HP19 7SA, United Kingdom
Tel: (01296) 489860
Web Site: www.christianresourcestogether.co.uk
Key Personnel
Event Organizer: Steve Briars *E-mail:* steve@christianresourcestogether.co.uk
Location: Hayes Conference Centre, Swanwick, Alfreton, Derbyshire, UK
Sept 13-14, 2017

Distripress Annual Congress
Sponsored by Distripress
Seefeldstr 35, CH-8008 Zurich, Switzerland
Tel: (044) 202 41 21 *Fax:* (044) 202 10 25
E-mail: info@distripress.net
Web Site: www.distripress.net
Key Personnel
Mng Dir: David Owen *E-mail:* david.owen@distripress.net
Congress Coord: Susanne Koebe *E-mail:* susanne.koebe@distripress.net
Commun & Governing Bodies: Gabriela Rietmann *E-mail:* gabriela.rietmann@distripress.net
Annual event sponsored by Distripress, a non-profit association for the promotion of international press distribution.
Location: Lisbon, Portugal
Sept 25-28, 2017

PACK EXPO Las Vegas
Sponsored by PMMI: The Association for Packaging and Processing Technologies
11911 Freedom Dr, Suite 600, Reston, VA 20190
Tel: 703-243-8555; 571-612-3200
Toll Free Tel: 888-ASK-PMMI (275-7664)
Fax: 703-243-8556
E-mail: expo@pmmi.org
Web Site: www.packexpolasvegas.com; www.packexpo.com; www.pmmi.org
Key Personnel
VP, Meetings & Events: Patti Fee *Tel:* 571-612-3193 *E-mail:* pfee@pmmi.org
Dir, Expositions: Ray Luca *Tel:* 571-266-4404 *E-mail:* rluca@pmmi.org
Dir, Tradeshow Opers: Laura B Thompson *Tel:* 571-612-3217 *E-mail:* laura@pmmi.org
Dir, Tradeshow Mktg: Jeannine Gibson *Tel:* 571-612-3203 *E-mail:* jeannine@pmmi.org
Events Mgr: Anna Hudson *Tel:* 571-612-3198 *E-mail:* anna@pmmi.org
Exhibitor Servs Mgr: Merideth Newman *Tel:* 571-612-3208 *E-mail:* merideth@pmmi.org
Exhibitor Servs Coord: Deanna Hoffman *Tel:* 571-266-4409 *E-mail:* deanna@pmmi.org
Exhibitor Servs & Sales Assoc: Beth Murray *Tel:* 571-612-3186 *E-mail:* bmurray@pmmi.org
Tradeshow Asst: Krista Debrosse *Tel:* 571-612-3215 *E-mail:* krista@pmmi.org
Biennial event held in odd-numbered years.
Location: Las Vegas Convention Center, 3150 Paradise Rd, Las Vegas, NV, USA
Sept 25-27, 2017

PRINT®
Sponsored by Graphic Arts Show Company (GASC)
1899 Preston White Dr, Reston, VA 20191
Tel: 703-264-7200 *Fax:* 703-620-9187
E-mail: info@gasc.org
Web Site: www.gasc.org
Key Personnel
VP: Chris Price *Tel:* 703-264-7200 ext 221 *E-mail:* cprice@gasc.org
Dir of Opers: Kelly Kilga *Tel:* 703-264-7200 ext 213 *E-mail:* kkilga@gasc.org
Conference Mgr: Lilly Kinney *Tel:* 703-264-7200 ext 255 *E-mail:* lkinney@gasc.org
Quadrennial event produced for NPES The Association for Suppliers of Printing, Publishing & Converting Technologies.
Location: McCormick Place, South Hall, 2301 S Lake Shore Dr, Chicago, IL, USA
Sept 10-14, 2017

SIBA Fall Discovery Show
Sponsored by Southern Independent Booksellers Alliance
3806 Yale Ave, Columbia, SC 29205
Tel: 803-994-9530 *Fax:* 309-410-0211
E-mail: info@sibaweb.com
Web Site: www.sibaweb.com/trade-show; www.sibaweb.com
Key Personnel
Exec Dir: Wanda Jewell *E-mail:* wanda@sibaweb.com
Members only event.
Location: Sheraton New Orleans, New Orleans, LA, USA
Sept 15-17, 2017

OCTOBER

American Translators Association Annual Conference
Sponsored by American Translators Association (ATA)
225 Reinekers Lane, Suite 590, Alexandria, VA 22314
Tel: 703-683-6100 *Fax:* 703-683-6122
E-mail: ata@atanet.org
Web Site: www.atanet.org
Key Personnel
Exec Dir: Walter W Bacak, Jr *Tel:* 703-683-6100 ext 3006 *E-mail:* walter@atanet.org
Meetings Mgr: Teresa C Kelly *Tel:* 703-683-6100 ext 3014 *E-mail:* teresak@atanet.org
Location: Washington, DC, USA
Oct 25-28, 2017

DMA2017
Sponsored by Direct Marketing Association (DMA)
1120 Avenue of the Americas, New York, NY 10036-6700
SAN: 692-6487
Tel: 212-768-7277 *Fax:* 212-302-6714
Web Site: thedma.org
Key Personnel
VP, Conferences & Events: Paul A McDonnough
Location: New Orleans Convention Center, New Orleans, LA, USA
Oct 8-10, 2017

Frankfurt Book Fair
Sponsored by Ausstellungs-und Messe-GmbH des Boersenvereins des Deutschen Buchhandels
Braubachstr 16, 60311 Frankfurt am Main, Germany
Mailing Address: Postfach 100116, 60001 Frankfurt am Main, Germany
Tel: (069) 21020 *Fax:* (069) 2102 277
E-mail: info@book-fair.com
Web Site: www.frankfurt-book-fair.com; www.book-fair.com
Key Personnel
CEO & Dir: Juergen Boos
Largest international book & media fair attracting 7,100 exhibitors from over 100 countries & 270,000 visitors.
Location: Frankfurt Fairgrounds, Frankfurt, Germany
Oct 11-15, 2017

Inter American Press Association General Assembly
Sponsored by Inter American Press Association (IAPA)
Jules Dubois Bldg, 1801 SW Third Ave, Miami, FL 33129
Tel: 305-634-2465 *Fax:* 305-635-2272
E-mail: info@sipiapa.org
Web Site: www.sipiapa.org
Key Personnel
Exec Dir: Ricardo Trotti *E-mail:* rtrotti@sipiapa.org
Gathering of important international figures for workshops, seminars & other related activities, while offering networking opportunities for those interested on press/media freedom & freedom of expression issues.
Location: Salt Lake City, UT, USA
Oct 2017

Utah Humanities Book Festival
Sponsored by Utah Humanities Council
Affiliate of Utah Center for the Book
202 W 300 N, Salt Lake City, UT 84103
Tel: 801-359-9670 *Fax:* 801-531-7869
Web Site: www.utahhumanities.org/BookFestival.htm
Key Personnel
Exec Dir: Cynthia Buckingham *Tel:* 801-359-9670 ext 101 *E-mail:* buckingham@utahhumanities.org
Devt Dir: Kathleen Harmon Gardner *Tel:* 801-359-9670 ext 108 *E-mail:* gardner@utahhumanities.org
Lit Prog Offr: Michael McLane *Tel:* 801-359-9670 ext 104 *E-mail:* mclane@utahhumanities.org
Communs Dir: Deena Pyle *Tel:* 801-359-9670 ext 111 *E-mail:* pyle@utahhumanities.org
Free literary event featuring national, regional & local authors held Oct 1-31 annually (National Book Month).
Location: Statewide, UT, USA
Oct 1-31, 2017

NOVEMBER

AMWA Annual Conference
Sponsored by American Medical Writers Association (AMWA)
30 W Gude Dr, Suite 525, Rockville, MD 20850-4357
Tel: 240-238-0940 *Fax:* 301-294-9006
E-mail: amwa@amwa.org
Web Site: www.amwa.org
Key Personnel
Conference Prog Mgr & Workshop Coord: Becky Phillips *Tel:* 240-238-0940 ext 103 *E-mail:* becky@amwa.org
Location: Orlando, FL, USA
Nov 1-4, 2017

Jewish Book Month
Sponsored by Jewish Book Council
520 Eighth Ave, 4th fl, New York, NY 10018
Tel: 212-201-2920 *Fax:* 212-532-4952
E-mail: jbc@jewishbooks.org
Web Site: www.jewishbookcouncil.org; www.facebook.com/JewishBookCouncil; twitter.com/jewishbook
Key Personnel
Dir: Carolyn Starman Hessel
Assoc Dir: Naomi Firestone-Teeter
Dedicated to the celebration of Jewish books held annually during the month leading up to Hanukkah.
Location: Nationwide throughout the USA
Nov 11-Dec 11, 2017

Salon du Livre de Montreal
(Montreal Book Show)
300, rue du St-Secrement, Suite 430, Montreal, QC H2Y 1X4, Canada
Tel: 514-845-2365 *Fax:* 514-845-7119
E-mail: slm.info@videotron.ca
Web Site: www.salondulivredemontreal.com
Key Personnel
Gen Mgr: Francine Bois
Location: Place Bonaventure, Montreal, QC, CN
Nov 15-20, 2017

2018

JANUARY

MLA Annual Convention
Sponsored by Modern Language Association of America (MLA)
26 Broadway, 3rd fl, New York, NY 10004-1789
SAN: 202-6422
Tel: 646-576-5266; 646-576-5000 *Fax:* 646-458-0030
E-mail: convention@mla.org
Web Site: www.mla.org/convention
Key Personnel
Assoc Dir of Convention Progs: Karin L Bagnall *E-mail:* kbagnall@mla.org
Location: New York, NY, USA
Jan 4-7, 2018

FEBRUARY

American Library Association Midwinter Meeting
Sponsored by The American Library Association (ALA)
50 E Huron St, Chicago, IL 60611
Tel: 312-944-6780 *Toll Free Tel:* 800-545-2433 (ext 3223) *Fax:* 312-440-9374
E-mail: ala@ala.org
Web Site: www.ala.org/midwinter
Key Personnel
Registration & Housing Specialist: Alicia Babcock *Tel:* 800-545-2433 ext 3229 *E-mail:* ababcock@ala.org
Conference Dir: Paul Graller *Tel:* 800-545-2433 ext 3219 *E-mail:* pgraller@ala.org
Conference Mgr: Amy McGuigan *Tel:* 800-545-2433 ext 3226 *E-mail:* amcguigan@ala.org
Meetings, AV & Catering Coord: Yvonne McLean *Tel:* 800-545-2433 ext 3222 *E-mail:* ymclean@ala.org
Conference Coord: Lindsay Rosales *Tel:* 800-545-2433 ext 3227 *E-mail:* lrosales@ala.org
Meeting Coord: Alicia (Alee) Navarro *Tel:* 800-545-2433 ext 3216 *E-mail:* anavarro@ala.org
Location: Denver, CO, USA
Feb 9-13, 2018

MARCH

AWP Annual Conference & Bookfair
Sponsored by Association of Writers & Writing Programs (AWP)
George Mason University, 4400 University Dr, MSN 1E3, Fairfax, VA 22030
Tel: 703-993-4301 *Fax:* 703-993-4302
E-mail: awp@awpwriter.org; events@awpwriter.org
Web Site: www.awpwriter.org/awp_conference/; www.awpwriter.org
Key Personnel
Exec Dir: David W Fenza
Dir, Conferences: Christian Teresi
Assoc Dir of Conferences: Cynthia Sherman
Location: Tampa Convention Center & Marriott Tampa Waterside, Tampa, FL, USA
March 7-10, 2018

Leipzig Book Fair (Leipziger Buchmesse)
Sponsored by Leipziger Messe GmbH
Messe-Allee 1, 04356 Leipzig, Germany
Mailing Address: Postfach 10 07 20, 04007 Leipzig, Germany
Tel: (0341) 678-0 *Fax:* (0341) 678-8762
E-mail: info@leipziger-buchmesse.de
Web Site: www.leipziger-buchmesse.de
Key Personnel
Dir: Oliver Zille *Tel:* (0341) 678-8240
Held annually in conjunction with The Leipzig Antiquarian Book Fair.
Location: Leipzig Exhibition Centre, Messe-Allee 1, Leipzig, Germany
March 15-18, 2018

Virginia Festival of the Book
Sponsored by Virginia Foundation for the Humanities
145 Ednam Dr, Charlottesville, VA 22903
Tel: 434-924-3296 *Fax:* 434-296-4714
E-mail: vabook@virginia.edu
Web Site: www.vabook.org
Key Personnel
Prog Dir: Jane Kulow *Tel:* 434-924-7548
Annual public festival for children & adults featuring authors, illustrators, publishers, publicists, agents & other book professionals in panel discussions & readings. Most events are free. Almost 400 authors invited annually.
Location: Charlottesville, VA, USA
March 21-25, 2018

APRIL

Alberta Library Conference
Sponsored by Library Association of Alberta (LAA)
80 Baker Crescent NW, Calgary, AB T2L 1R4, Canada
Tel: 403-284-5818 *Toll Free Tel:* 877-522-5550
E-mail: info@laa.ca
Web Site: www.albertalibraryconference.com; www.laa.ca
Key Personnel
Exec Dir/Conference Coord: Christine Sheppard
Co-hosted by Alberta Library Trustees Association (ALTA).
Location: Fairmont Jasper Park Lodge, Jasper, AB, CN
April 26-29, 2018

International Children's Book Day
Sponsored by International Board on Books for Young People (IBBY)
Nonnenweg 12, Postfach, 4009 Basel, Switzerland
Tel: (061) 272 29 17 *Fax:* (061) 272 27 57
E-mail: ibby@ibby.org
Web Site: www.ibby.org
Key Personnel
Exec Dir: Liz Page *E-mail:* liz.page@ibby.org
Admin Asst: Luzmaria Stauffenegger *E-mail:* luzmaria.stauffenegger@ibby.org
On Hans Christian Andersen's birthday, April 2nd, International Children's Book Day (ICBD) is celebrated to inspire a love of reading & to call attention to children's books. Each year a different national section has the opportunity to be the international sponsor. It decides upon a theme & invites a prominent author to write a message to the children of the world & a well-known illustrator to design a poster. These materials are used in different ways to promote books & reading around the world.
April 2, 2018

NAAJ Annual Meeting
Sponsored by North American Agricultural Journalists (NAAJ)
6434 Hurta Lane, Bryan, TX 77808
Tel: 979-845-2872 *Fax:* 979-862-1202
Web Site: www.naaj.net
Key Personnel
Exec Secy & Treas: Kathleen Phillips *E-mail:* ka-phillips@tamu.edu
Annual meeting.
Location: Washington, DC, USA
April 2018

The Quest for Excellence® Conference
Sponsored by National Institute of Standards and Technology (NIST)
100 Bureau Dr, Stop 1020, Gaithersburg, MD 20899-1020
Tel: 301-975-2036 *Fax:* 301-948-3716
E-mail: baldrige@nist.gov
Web Site: www.nist.gov/baldrige/qe/index.cfm
Key Personnel
Conference Chair: Barbara Fischer *Tel:* 301-975-8942 *E-mail:* barbara.fischer@nist.gov
Official conference of the Malcolm Baldrige National Quality Award, held in partnership with American Society for Quality (ASQ) & Association for Talent Development (ATD).
Location: Baltimore Marriott Waterfront, 700 Aliceanna St, Baltimore, MD, USA
April 8-11, 2018

MAY

Children's Book Week
Sponsored by The Children's Book Council (CBC)
54 W 39 St, 14th fl, New York, NY 10018
Tel: 212-966-1990
E-mail: cbc.info@cbcbooks.org
Web Site: www.bookweekonline.com; www.cbcbooks.org
Key Personnel
Exec Dir: Jon Colman *E-mail:* jon.colman@cbcbooks.org
Communs Dir: Nicole Deming *E-mail:* nicole.deming@cbcbooks.org
Programming Dir: Shaina Birkhead *E-mail:* shaina.birkhead@cbcbooks.org
Mgr, Events & Progs/Libn: Ayanna Coleman *E-mail:* ayanna.coleman@cbcbooks.org
Events & Progs Asst/Membership Coord: Matthew Poulter *E-mail:* matthew.poulter@cbcbooks.org
Location: Nationwide across the USA
May 7-13, 2018

JUNE

American Library Association Annual Conference
Sponsored by The American Library Association (ALA)
50 E Huron St, Chicago, IL 60611
Tel: 312-944-6780 *Toll Free Tel:* 800-545-2433 (ext 3223) *Fax:* 312-440-9374
E-mail: ala@ala.org
Web Site: www.ala.org
Key Personnel
Registration & Housing Specialist: Alicia Babcock *Tel:* 800-545-2433 ext 3229 *E-mail:* ababcock@ala.org
Conference Dir: Paul Graller *Tel:* 800-545-2433 ext 3219 *E-mail:* pgraller@ala.org
Conference Mgr: Amy McGuigan *Tel:* 800-545-2433 ext 3226 *E-mail:* amcguigan@ala.org
Meetings, AV & Catering Coord: Yvonne McLean *Tel:* 800-545-2433 ext 3222 *E-mail:* ymclean@ala.org
Conference Coord: Lindsay Rosales *Tel:* 800-545-2433 ext 3227 *E-mail:* lrosales@ala.org
Meeting Coord: Alicia (Alee) Navarro *Tel:* 800-545-2433 ext 3216 *E-mail:* anavarro@ala.org
Location: New Orleans, LA, USA
June 21-26, 2018

JULY

Romance Writers of America Annual Conference
Sponsored by Romance Writers of America®
14615 Benfer Rd, Houston, TX 77069
Tel: 832-717-5200 *Fax:* 832-717-5201
E-mail: conference@rwa.org; info@rwa.org
Web Site: www.rwa.org
Key Personnel
Exec Dir: Allison Kelley *Tel:* 832-717-5200 ext 124 *E-mail:* allison.kelley@rwa.org

Location: Sheraton Denver Downtown Hotel, Denver, CO, USA
July 25-28, 2018

SEPTEMBER

International Board on Books for Young People Biennial Congress
Sponsored by International Board on Books for Young People (IBBY)
Nonnenweg 12, Postfach, 4009 Basel, Switzerland
Tel: (061) 272 29 17 *Fax:* (061) 272 27 57
E-mail: ibby@ibby.org
Web Site: www.ibby.org
Key Personnel
Admin Asst: Luzmaria Stauffenegger *E-mail:* luzmaria.stauffenegger@ibby.org
IBBY's biennial congresses, hosted by different countries, are the most important meeting points for IBBY members & other people involved in children's books & reading development. They are wonderful opportunities to make contacts, exchange ideas & open horizons.
Location: Istanbul, Turkey
Sept 1-4, 2018

OCTOBER

American Translators Association Annual Conference
Sponsored by American Translators Association (ATA)
225 Reinekers Lane, Suite 590, Alexandria, VA 22314
Tel: 703-683-6100 *Fax:* 703-683-6122
E-mail: ata@atanet.org
Web Site: www.atanet.org
Key Personnel
Exec Dir: Walter W Bacak, Jr *Tel:* 703-683-6100 ext 3006 *E-mail:* walter@atanet.org
Meetings Mgr: Teresa C Kelly *Tel:* 703-683-6100 ext 3014 *E-mail:* teresak@atanet.org
Location: New Orleans, LA, USA
Oct 24-27, 2018

Frankfurt Book Fair
Sponsored by Ausstellungs-und Messe-GmbH des Boersenvereins des Deutschen Buchhandels
Braubachstr 16, 60311 Frankfurt am Main, Germany
Mailing Address: Postfach 100116, 60001 Frankfurt am Main, Germany
Tel: (069) 21020 *Fax:* (069) 2102 277
E-mail: info@book-fair.com
Web Site: www.frankfurt-book-fair.com; www.book-fair.com
Key Personnel
CEO & Dir: Juergen Boos
Largest international book & media fair attracting 7,100 exhibitors from over 100 countries & 270,000 visitors.
Location: Frankfurt Fairgrounds, Frankfurt, Germany
Oct 10-14, 2018

Inter American Press Association General Assembly
Sponsored by Inter American Press Association (IAPA)
Jules Dubois Bldg, 1801 SW Third Ave, Miami, FL 33129
Tel: 305-634-2465 *Fax:* 305-635-2272
E-mail: info@sipiapa.org
Web Site: www.sipiapa.org
Key Personnel
Exec Dir: Ricardo Trotti *E-mail:* rtrotti@sipiapa.org
Gathering of important international figures for workshops, seminars & other related activities, while offering networking opportunities for those interested on press/media freedom & freedom of expression issues.
Location: Medellin, Colombia
Oct 2018

Utah Humanities Book Festival
Sponsored by Utah Humanities Council
Affiliate of Utah Center for the Book
202 W 300 N, Salt Lake City, UT 84103
Tel: 801-359-9670 *Fax:* 801-531-7869
Web Site: www.utahhumanities.org/BookFestival.htm
Key Personnel
Exec Dir: Cynthia Buckingham *Tel:* 801-359-9670 ext 101 *E-mail:* buckingham@utahhumanities.org
Devt Dir: Kathleen Harmon Gardner *Tel:* 801-359-9670 ext 108 *E-mail:* gardner@utahhumanities.org
Lit Prog Offr: Michael McLane *Tel:* 801-359-9670 ext 104 *E-mail:* mclane@utahhumanities.org
Communs Dir: Deena Pyle *Tel:* 801-359-9670 ext 111 *E-mail:* pyle@utahhumanities.org
Free literary event featuring national, regional & local authors held Oct 1-31 annually (National Book Month).
Location: Statewide, UT, USA
Oct 1-31, 2018

NOVEMBER

Jewish Book Month
Sponsored by Jewish Book Council
520 Eighth Ave, 4th fl, New York, NY 10018
Tel: 212-201-2920 *Fax:* 212-532-4952
E-mail: jbc@jewishbooks.org
Web Site: www.jewishbookcouncil.org; www.facebook.com/JewishBookCouncil; twitter.com/jewishbook
Key Personnel
Dir: Carolyn Starman Hessel
Assoc Dir: Naomi Firestone-Teeter
Dedicated to the celebration of Jewish books held annually during the month leading up to Hanukkah.
Location: Nationwide throughout the USA
Nov 1-Dec 1, 2018

Salon du Livre de Montreal
(Montreal Book Show)
300, rue du St-Secrement, Suite 430, Montreal, QC H2Y 1X4, Canada
Tel: 514-845-2365 *Fax:* 514-845-7119
E-mail: slm.info@videotron.ca
Web Site: www.salondulivredemontreal.com
Key Personnel
Gen Mgr: Francine Bois
Location: Place Bonaventure, Montreal, QC, CN
Nov 14-19, 2018

2019

JANUARY

American Library Association Midwinter Meeting
Sponsored by The American Library Association (ALA)
50 E Huron St, Chicago, IL 60611
Tel: 312-944-6780 *Toll Free Tel:* 800-545-2433 (ext 3223) *Fax:* 312-440-9374
E-mail: ala@ala.org
Web Site: www.ala.org/midwinter
Key Personnel
Registration & Housing Specialist: Alicia Babcock *Tel:* 800-545-2433 ext 3229 *E-mail:* ababcock@ala.org
Conference Dir: Paul Graller *Tel:* 800-545-2433 ext 3219 *E-mail:* pgraller@ala.org
Conference Mgr: Amy McGuigan *Tel:* 800-545-2433 ext 3226 *E-mail:* amcguigan@ala.org
Meetings, AV & Catering Coord: Yvonne McLean *Tel:* 800-545-2433 ext 3222 *E-mail:* ymclean@ala.org
Conference Coord: Lindsay Rosales *Tel:* 800-545-2433 ext 3227 *E-mail:* lrosales@ala.org
Meeting Coord: Alicia (Alee) Navarro *Tel:* 800-545-2433 ext 3216 *E-mail:* anavarro@ala.org
Location: Seattle, WA, USA
Jan 25-29, 2019

MARCH

Virginia Festival of the Book
Sponsored by Virginia Foundation for the Humanities
145 Ednam Dr, Charlottesville, VA 22903
Tel: 434-924-3296 *Fax:* 434-296-4714
E-mail: vabook@virginia.edu
Web Site: www.vabook.org
Key Personnel
Prog Dir: Jane Kulow *Tel:* 434-924-7548
Annual public festival for children & adults featuring authors, illustrators, publishers, publicists, agents & other book professionals in panel discussions & readings. Most events are free. Almost 400 authors invited annually.
Location: Charlottesville, VA, USA
March 20-24, 2019

APRIL

Alberta Library Conference
Sponsored by Library Association of Alberta (LAA)
80 Baker Crescent NW, Calgary, AB T2L 1R4, Canada
Tel: 403-284-5818 *Toll Free Tel:* 877-522-5550
E-mail: info@laa.ca
Web Site: www.albertalibraryconference.com; www.laa.ca
Key Personnel
Exec Dir/Conference Coord: Christine Sheppard
Co-hosted by Alberta Library Trustees Association (ALTA).
Location: Fairmont Jasper Park Lodge, Jasper, AB, CN
April 25-28, 2019

International Children's Book Day
Sponsored by International Board on Books for Young People (IBBY)
Nonnenweg 12, Postfach, 4009 Basel, Switzerland
Tel: (061) 272 29 17 *Fax:* (061) 272 27 57
E-mail: ibby@ibby.org
Web Site: www.ibby.org
Key Personnel
Exec Dir: Liz Page *E-mail:* liz.page@ibby.org
Admin Asst: Luzmaria Stauffenegger *E-mail:* luzmaria.stauffenegger@ibby.org
On Hans Christian Andersen's birthday, April 2nd, International Children's Book Day (ICBD) is celebrated to inspire a love of reading & to

call attention to children's books. Each year a different national section has the opportunity to be the international sponsor. It decides upon a theme & invites a prominent author to write a message to the children of the world & a well-known illustrator to design a poster. These materials are used in different ways to promote books & reading around the world.
April 2, 2019

NAAJ Annual Meeting
Sponsored by North American Agricultural Journalists (NAAJ)
6434 Hurta Lane, Bryan, TX 77808
Tel: 979-845-2872 *Fax:* 979-862-1202
Web Site: www.naaj.net
Key Personnel
Exec Secy & Treas: Kathleen Phillips *E-mail:* kaphillips@tamu.edu
Annual meeting.
Location: Washington, DC, USA
April 2019

MAY

Children's Book Week
Sponsored by The Children's Book Council (CBC)
54 W 39 St, 14th fl, New York, NY 10018
Tel: 212-966-1990
E-mail: cbc.info@cbcbooks.org
Web Site: www.bookweekonline.com; www.cbcbooks.org
Key Personnel
Exec Dir: Jon Colman *E-mail:* jon.colman@cbcbooks.org
Communs Dir: Nicole Deming *E-mail:* nicole.deming@cbcbooks.org
Programming Dir: Shaina Birkhead *E-mail:* shaina.birkhead@cbcbooks.org
Mgr, Events & Progs/Libn: Ayanna Coleman *E-mail:* ayanna.coleman@cbcbooks.org
Events & Progs Asst/Membership Coord: Matthew Poulter *E-mail:* matthew.poulter@cbcbooks.org
Location: Nationwide across the USA
May 6-12, 2019

PrintEx 2019
Sponsored by Reed Exhibitions Australia Pty Ltd
Tower 2, 475 Victoria Ave, Chatswood, NSW 2067, Australia
Mailing Address: Locked Bag 4500, Chatswood, NSW 2067, Australia
Tel: (02) 9422 2500
E-mail: inquiry@reedexhibitions.com.au
Web Site: www.printex.net.au
PrintEx brings the latest printing & graphic communications technologies to the industry. Sponsored by Graphic Arts Merchants Association of Australia Inc (GAMAA) & the Printing Industries Association of Australia (PIAA), this event is held every 4 years.
Location: Sydney Showground, Sydney Olympic Park, Sydney, NSW, Australia
May 2019

JUNE

American Library Association Annual Conference
Sponsored by The American Library Association (ALA)
50 E Huron St, Chicago, IL 60611
Tel: 312-944-6780 *Toll Free Tel:* 800-545-2433 (ext 3223) *Fax:* 312-440-9374
E-mail: ala@ala.org
Web Site: www.ala.org
Key Personnel
Registration & Housing Specialist: Alicia Babcock *Tel:* 800-545-2433 ext 3229 *E-mail:* ababcock@ala.org
Conference Dir: Paul Graller *Tel:* 800-545-2433 ext 3219 *E-mail:* pgraller@ala.org
Conference Mgr: Amy McGuigan *Tel:* 800-545-2433 ext 3226 *E-mail:* amcguigan@ala.org
Meetings, AV & Catering Coord: Yvonne McLean *Tel:* 800-545-2433 ext 3222 *E-mail:* ymclean@ala.org
Conference Coord: Lindsay Rosales *Tel:* 800-545-2433 ext 3227 *E-mail:* lrosales@ala.org
Meeting Coord: Alicia (Alee) Navarro *Tel:* 800-545-2433 ext 3216 *E-mail:* anavarro@ala.org
Location: Washington, DC, USA
June 20-25, 2019

JULY

Romance Writers of America Annual Conference
Sponsored by Romance Writers of America®
14615 Benfer Rd, Houston, TX 77069
Tel: 832-717-5200 *Fax:* 832-717-5201
E-mail: conference@rwa.org; info@rwa.org
Web Site: www.rwa.org
Key Personnel
Exec Dir: Allison Kelley *Tel:* 832-717-5200 ext 124 *E-mail:* allison.kelley@rwa.org
Location: New York Marriott® Marquis, New York, NY, USA
July 24-27, 2019

OCTOBER

Utah Humanities Book Festival
Sponsored by Utah Humanities Council
Affiliate of Utah Center for the Book
202 W 300 N, Salt Lake City, UT 84103
Tel: 801-359-9670 *Fax:* 801-531-7869
Web Site: www.utahhumanities.org/BookFestival.htm
Key Personnel
Exec Dir: Cynthia Buckingham *Tel:* 801-359-9670 ext 101 *E-mail:* buckingham@utahhumanities.org
Devt Dir: Kathleen Harmon Gardner *Tel:* 801-359-9670 ext 108 *E-mail:* gardner@utahhumanities.org
Lit Prog Offr: Michael McLane *Tel:* 801-359-9670 ext 104 *E-mail:* mclane@utahhumanities.org
Communs Dir: Deena Pyle *Tel:* 801-359-9670 ext 111 *E-mail:* pyle@utahhumanities.org
Free literary event featuring national, regional & local authors held Oct 1-31 annually (National Book Month).
Location: Statewide, UT, USA
Oct 1-31, 2019

NOVEMBER

Jewish Book Month
Sponsored by Jewish Book Council
520 Eighth Ave, 4th fl, New York, NY 10018
Tel: 212-201-2920 *Fax:* 212-532-4952
E-mail: jbc@jewishbooks.org
Web Site: www.jewishbookcouncil.org; www.facebook.com/JewishBookCouncil; twitter.com/jewishbook
Key Personnel
Dir: Carolyn Starman Hessel
Assoc Dir: Naomi Firestone-Teeter
Dedicated to the celebration of Jewish books held annually during the month leading up to Hanukkah.
Location: Nationwide throughout the USA
Nov 21-Dec 21, 2019

2020

JANUARY

American Library Association Midwinter Meeting
Sponsored by The American Library Association (ALA)
50 E Huron St, Chicago, IL 60611
Tel: 312-944-6780 *Toll Free Tel:* 800-545-2433 (ext 3223) *Fax:* 312-440-9374
E-mail: ala@ala.org
Web Site: www.ala.org/midwinter
Key Personnel
Registration & Housing Specialist: Alicia Babcock *Tel:* 800-545-2433 ext 3229 *E-mail:* ababcock@ala.org
Conference Dir: Paul Graller *Tel:* 800-545-2433 ext 3219 *E-mail:* pgraller@ala.org
Conference Mgr: Amy McGuigan *Tel:* 800-545-2433 ext 3226 *E-mail:* amcguigan@ala.org
Meetings, AV & Catering Coord: Yvonne McLean *Tel:* 800-545-2433 ext 3222 *E-mail:* ymclean@ala.org
Conference Coord: Lindsay Rosales *Tel:* 800-545-2433 ext 3227 *E-mail:* lrosales@ala.org
Meeting Coord: Alicia (Alee) Navarro *Tel:* 800-545-2433 ext 3216 *E-mail:* anavarro@ala.org
Location: Philadelphia, PA, USA
Jan 17-21, 2020

MARCH

Virginia Festival of the Book
Sponsored by Virginia Foundation for the Humanities
145 Ednam Dr, Charlottesville, VA 22903
Tel: 434-924-3296 *Fax:* 434-296-4714
E-mail: vabook@virginia.edu
Web Site: www.vabook.org
Key Personnel
Prog Dir: Jane Kulow *Tel:* 434-924-7548
Annual public festival for children & adults featuring authors, illustrators, publishers, publicists, agents & other book professionals in panel discussions & readings. Most events are free. Almost 400 authors invited annually.
Location: Charlottesville, VA, USA
March 18-22, 2020

APRIL

Alberta Library Conference
Sponsored by Library Association of Alberta (LAA)
80 Baker Crescent NW, Calgary, AB T2L 1R4, Canada
Tel: 403-284-5818 *Toll Free Tel:* 877-522-5550
E-mail: info@laa.ca

Web Site: www.albertalibraryconference.com; www.laa.ca
Key Personnel
Exec Dir/Conference Coord: Christine Sheppard
Co-hosted by Alberta Library Trustees Association (ALTA).
Location: Fairmont Jasper Park Lodge, Jasper, AB, CN
April 30-May 3, 2020

International Children's Book Day
Sponsored by International Board on Books for Young People (IBBY)
Nonnenweg 12, Postfach, 4009 Basel, Switzerland
Tel: (061) 272 29 17 *Fax:* (061) 272 27 57
E-mail: ibby@ibby.org
Web Site: www.ibby.org
Key Personnel
Exec Dir: Liz Page *E-mail:* liz.page@ibby.org
Admin Asst: Luzmaria Stauffenegger *E-mail:* luzmaria.stauffenegger@ibby.org
On Hans Christian Andersen's birthday, April 2nd, International Children's Book Day (ICBD) is celebrated to inspire a love of reading & to call attention to children's books. Each year a different national section has the opportunity to be the international sponsor. It decides upon a theme & invites a prominent author to write a message to the children of the world & a well-known illustrator to design a poster. These materials are used in different ways to promote books & reading around the world.
April 2, 2020

NAAJ Annual Meeting
Sponsored by North American Agricultural Journalists (NAAJ)
6434 Hurta Lane, Bryan, TX 77808
Tel: 979-845-2872 *Fax:* 979-862-1202
Web Site: www.naaj.net
Key Personnel
Exec Secy & Treas: Kathleen Phillips *E-mail:* ka-phillips@tamu.edu
Annual meeting.
Location: Washington, DC, USA
April 2020

MAY

Children's Book Week
Sponsored by The Children's Book Council (CBC)
54 W 39 St, 14th fl, New York, NY 10018
Tel: 212-966-1990
E-mail: cbc.info@cbcbooks.org
Web Site: www.bookweekonline.com; www.cbcbooks.org
Key Personnel
Exec Dir: Jon Colman *E-mail:* jon.colman@cbcbooks.org
Communs Dir: Nicole Deming *E-mail:* nicole.deming@cbcbooks.org
Programming Dir: Shaina Birkhead *E-mail:* shaina.birkhead@cbcbooks.org
Mgr, Events & Progs/Libn: Ayanna Coleman *E-mail:* ayanna.coleman@cbcbooks.org
Events & Progs Asst/Membership Coord: Matthew Poulter *E-mail:* matthew.poulter@cbcbooks.org
Location: Nationwide across the USA
May 4-10, 2020

JUNE

American Library Association Annual Conference
Sponsored by The American Library Association (ALA)
50 E Huron St, Chicago, IL 60611
Tel: 312-944-6780 *Toll Free Tel:* 800-545-2433 (ext 3223) *Fax:* 312-440-9374
E-mail: ala@ala.org
Web Site: www.ala.org
Key Personnel
Registration & Housing Specialist: Alicia Babcock *Tel:* 800-545-2433 ext 3229 *E-mail:* ababcock@ala.org
Conference Dir: Paul Graller *Tel:* 800-545-2433 ext 3219 *E-mail:* pgraller@ala.org
Conference Mgr: Amy McGuigan *Tel:* 800-545-2433 ext 3226 *E-mail:* amcguigan@ala.org
Meetings, AV & Catering Coord: Yvonne McLean *Tel:* 800-545-2433 ext 3222 *E-mail:* ymclean@ala.org
Conference Coord: Lindsay Rosales *Tel:* 800-545-2433 ext 3227 *E-mail:* lrosales@ala.org
Meeting Coord: Alicia (Alee) Navarro *Tel:* 800-545-2433 ext 3216 *E-mail:* anavarro@ala.org
Location: Chicago, IL, USA
June 23-28, 2020

OCTOBER

Utah Humanities Book Festival
Sponsored by Utah Humanities Council
Affiliate of Utah Center for the Book
202 W 300 N, Salt Lake City, UT 84103
Tel: 801-359-9670 *Fax:* 801-531-7869
Web Site: www.utahhumanities.org/BookFestival.htm
Key Personnel
Exec Dir: Cynthia Buckingham *Tel:* 801-359-9670 ext 101 *E-mail:* buckingham@utahhumanities.org
Devt Dir: Kathleen Harmon Gardner *Tel:* 801-359-9670 ext 108 *E-mail:* gardner@utahhumanities.org
Lit Prog Offr: Michael McLane *Tel:* 801-359-9670 ext 104 *E-mail:* mclane@utahhumanities.org
Communs Dir: Deena Pyle *Tel:* 801-359-9670 ext 111 *E-mail:* pyle@utahhumanities.org
Free literary event featuring national, regional & local authors held Oct 1-31 annually (National Book Month).
Location: Statewide, UT, USA
Oct 1-31, 2020

NOVEMBER

Jewish Book Month
Sponsored by Jewish Book Council
520 Eighth Ave, 4th fl, New York, NY 10018
Tel: 212-201-2920 *Fax:* 212-532-4952
E-mail: jbc@jewishbooks.org
Web Site: www.jewishbookcouncil.org; www.facebook.com/JewishBookCouncil; twitter.com/jewishbook
Key Personnel
Dir: Carolyn Starman Hessel
Assoc Dir: Naomi Firestone-Teeter
Dedicated to the celebration of Jewish books held annually during the month leading up to Hanukkah.
Location: Nationwide throughout the USA
Nov 9-Dec 9, 2020

Writers' Conferences & Workshops

The following lists workshops and seminars dealing with various aspects of the book trade. See **Courses for the Book Trade** for a list of college level programs and courses.

Alice B Acheson's Workshops for Writers, Illustrators & Photographers
Alice B Acheson
Unit of Acheson-Greub Inc
PO Box 735, Friday Harbor, WA 98250
Tel: 360-378-2815
E-mail: aliceba7@gmail.com
Key Personnel
Pres: Alice B Acheson
One- or two-day workshops on making a ms succeed in the market place. Writers utilize a pre-class assignment to determine techniques for finding & impressing an agent +/or publisher while class discussion includes discovering what's to come once the ms is under contract. Extensive written materials provided. Instructor shares 30 years of book publishing expertise in negotiating contracts, editing books & achieving award-winning book publicity.
The Greatest Marketing Tool of All, on verbal pitch (Spring & Fall)
Publishing Choices: Print-on-Demand, Self-Publishing, Traditional Publisher, pros/cons of each (Spring & Fall)
Your Book: What's Next?, how to find an agent & publisher, how to influence the publisher's marketing of your book (Spring & Fall)
Bound-for-Success Book Proposals (Spring & Fall).
Location: Richard Hugo House, Seattle, WA
Date: Spring (see hugohouse.org for exact dates)
Location: Book Passage, Corte Madera, CA
Date: March 4-6, 2016
Location: Richard Hugo House, Seattle, WA
Date: Fall 2016 (see hugohouse.org for exact dates)
Location: Book Passage, Corte Madera, CA
Date: Sept 23-25, 2016

American Society of Journalists and Authors Annual Writers Conference
American Society of Journalists and Authors (ASJA)
1501 Broadway, Suite 403, New York, NY 10036
Tel: 212-997-0947 *Fax:* 212-937-2315
Web Site: asja.org
Key Personnel
Exec Dir: Alexandra Owens *E-mail:* director@asja.org
Inside information from editors, agents & publishers, find inspiration & gain income-boosting ideas. Open to all, the conference features topics for newer & more experienced pros. New panels & workshops will enrich you no matter where you are in your writing career.

AMWA Annual Conference
American Medical Writers Association (AMWA)
30 W Gude Dr, Suite 525, Rockville, MD 20850-4357
Tel: 240-238-0940 *Fax:* 301-294-9006
E-mail: amwa@amwa.org
Web Site: www.amwa.org
Key Personnel
Educ Mgr: Lauren Ero
Annual conference includes workshops, open sessions & networking opportunities.
Location: Denver, CO
Date: Oct 5-8, 2016
Location: Orlando, FL
Date: Nov 1-4, 2017

Antioch Writers' Workshop
Antioch University Midwest
900 Dayton St, Yellow Springs, OH 45387
Tel: 937-769-1803
E-mail: info@antiochwritersworkshop.com
Web Site: www.antiochwritersworkshop.com
Key Personnel
Pres: Rebecca Morean
Exec Dir: Sharon Short
A week-long summer workshop featuring morning classes, midday presentations on writing profession, afternoon intensive seminars in a genre or type, evening faculty talks & readings. Non-refundable registration fee $125.

Appalachian Writers' Workshop
Hindman Settlement School
71 Center St, Hindman, KY 41822
Mailing Address: PO Box 844, Hindman, KY 41822-0844
Tel: 606-785-5475 *Fax:* 606-785-3499
E-mail: info@hindmansettlement.org
Web Site: www.hindmansettlement.org
Key Personnel
Exec Dir, Hindman Settlement School: Brent D Hutchinson *E-mail:* bdhutchinson@hindmansettlement.org
Poetry, nonfiction, short story, novel, dramatic writing & children's writing.

Arkansas Writers' Conference
Pioneer Branch of National League of American Pen Women/Arkansas Branch
Division of National League of American Pen Women
13005 Misty Creek Dr, Little Rock, AR 72211
Tel: 501-224-5823 *Fax:* 501-224-5823
Web Site: www.arkansaswritersconference.org
Key Personnel
Poet Laureate of AR & Contact: Peggy Vining
E-mail: pvining@aristotle.net
Two-day annual conference; conference information available Feb 1. Thirty plus competitions are available. Write for brochure at above address & enclose SASE. Check web site for conference details.
Location: Presidential Holiday Inn, Little Rock, AR
Date: Annually first full weekend in June, Fri & Sat

Artists & Writers Summer Fellowships
The Constance Saltonstall Foundation for the Arts
435 Ellis Hollow Creek Rd, Ithaca, NY 14850
Tel: 607-539-3146
E-mail: artscolony@saltonstall.org
Web Site: www.saltonstall.org
Key Personnel
Dir: Lesley Williamson
Provide month long summer fellowships for New York state artists & writers May-Sept.

Aspen Summer Words Writing Retreat & Literary Festival
Aspen Writers' Foundation
110 E Hallam St, Suite 116, Aspen, CO 81611
Tel: 970-925-3122 *Fax:* 970-920-5700
E-mail: awfinfo@aspenwriters.org
Web Site: www.aspenwriters.org
Key Personnel
Exec Dir: Lisa Consiglio *Tel:* 970-925-3122 ext 1
E-mail: lisa@aspenwriters.org
Prog Mgr: Natalie Lacy *Tel:* 970-925-3122 ext 3
E-mail: natalie@aspenwriters.org
A 5-day writing retreat with morning workshops in fiction, poetry, memoir & essay complimented by a 5-day literary festival in the afternoons & evenings, featuring 20 events for readers & writers.

The Association for Women In Communications
The Association for Women in Communications
3337 Duke St, Alexandria, VA 22314
Tel: 703-370-7436 *Fax:* 703-342-4311
E-mail: info@womcom.org
Web Site: www.womcom.org
Key Personnel
Exec Dir: Pamela Valenzuela
Communs Mgr: Beth Veney
E-mail: awcconnect@womcom.org
Professional development workshops & exposition in various areas of the communications field.

Association pour l'Avancement des Sciences et des Techniques de la Documentation
2065 rue Parthenais, Bureau 387, Montreal, QC H2K 3T1, Canada
Tel: 514-281-5012 *Fax:* 514-281-8219
E-mail: info@asted.org
Web Site: www.asted.org
Key Personnel
Exec Dir: Suzanne Morin *Tel:* 514-281-5012 ext 234 *E-mail:* smorin@asted.org

Atlantic Center for the Arts Artists-in-Residence Program
Atlantic Center for the Arts (ACA)
1414 Art Center Ave, New Smyrna Beach, FL 32168
Tel: 386-427-6975 *Toll Free Tel:* 800-393-6975
Fax: 386-427-5669
E-mail: program@atlanticcenterforthearts.org
Web Site: www.atlanticcenterforthearts.org
Key Personnel
Co-Dir/Community: Nancy Lowden Norman
Co-Dir/Residency: Jim Frost
Residency Dir: Nick Conroy
Dir of Fin & Acctg: Kevin Miller
Opers Mgr: Jim Zock
Mktg Mgr: Kathryn Peterson
Since 1982, Atlantic Center's residency program has provided artists from all artistic disciplines with spaces to live, work & collaborate during three-week residencies. Each residency session includes three master artists of different disciplines. The master artists each personally select a group of associates - talented, emerging artists - through an application process administered by ACA. During the residency, artists participate in informal sessions with their group, collaborate on projects & work independently on their own projects. The relaxed atmosphere & unstructured program provide considerable time for artistic regeneration & creation.

Bard Society Fiction Writing Workshop
Bard Society
3113 Crosby Lane, Jacksonville, FL 32216

Key Personnel
Dir: Frank Green
Fiction writing workshop in existence for more than 35 years. Schedule: one workshop a week, Wednesday evening, three hours; more than 40 books published by members. No fee but contributions welcome. All lovers of the written word welcome.

Beyond the Book
Copyright Clearance Center (CCC)
222 Rosewood Dr, Danvers, MA 01923
Tel: 978-750-8400 *Fax:* 978-646-8600
E-mail: beyondthebook@copyright.com
Web Site: www.copyright.com; beyondthebookcast.com
Key Personnel
HR: Meredith McCully
Programs also include online seminars & telephone conference calls with distinguished experts. Created with authors in mind, Beyond the Book seeks to provide information on the latest business issues facing the creative professions - from initial research to final publication & beyond. Your connection to leading editors, publishing analysts & information technology experts, as well as innovative authors.

Big Apple Conference
The International Women's Writing Guild (IWWG)
274 Madison Ave, Suite 1202, New York, NY 10016
Tel: 917-720-6959
E-mail: iwwgquestions@gmail.com
Web Site: www.iwwg.org
Key Personnel
Dir of Opers: Kristin Rath
Held twice annually in April & Oct in New York, NY.

Blockbuster Plots for Writers Retreat
Martha Alderson
PO Box 1402, Capitola, CA 95010
Tel: 408-482-4678
E-mail: contact@blockbusterplots.com
Web Site: www.blockbusterplots.com
Key Personnel
Owner & Author: Martha Alderson
Four day writers retreat in the Santa Cruz mountains which provides simple techniques to help you grasp plot with ease & increase your chances of getting published. Whether you write screenplays, novels, short stories or memoirs, now is the time to learn what separates a blockbuster hit from a book that falls flat.

Bread Loaf Writers' Conference
Middlebury College
5525 Middlebury College, 14 Old Chapel Rd, Middlebury, VT 05753
Tel: 802-443-5286 *Fax:* 802-443-2087
E-mail: blwc@middlebury.edu
Web Site: www.middlebury.edu/blwc
Key Personnel
Dir: Michael Collier
Asst Dir: Jennifer Grotz
Admin Mgr: Noreen Cargill
Admin Assoc: Megan Fitzgerald
Ten-day conference for writers of poetry, fiction & nonfiction. Fellowship covers tuition, room & board. Work-study scholarship covers tuition, with pay to offset room & board. Tuition scholarship covers tuition.

Bucknell Seminar for Younger Poets
Stadler Center for Poetry
Bucknell University, Bucknell Hall, Moore Ave, Lewisburg, PA 17837
Tel: 570-577-1853 *Fax:* 570-577-1885
E-mail: stadlercenter@bucknell.edu
Web Site: www.bucknell.edu/stadlercenter
Key Personnel
Dir: G C Waldrep
Mng Ed & Book Review Ed: Andrew Ciotola
Ten applicants are accepted to participate in a three-week residence in writing for undergraduate poets. Applications should include an academic transcript, two supporting recommendations (at least one from a poetry-writing instructor) & a 10-12 page portfolio. A letter of self-presentation (letter of intro stressing commitment to poetry writing, experience & any publications) should accompany the application. Applications must be submitted online (deadline Jan 31). See web site for details.
Location: Stadler Center for Poetry, Bucknell University, Lewisburg, PA
Date: June 12-July 3, 2016

Annual Cape Cod Writers' Center Conference
Cape Cod Writers' Center
919 Main St, Osterville, MA 02655
Mailing Address: PO Box 408, Osterville, MA 02655
Tel: 508-420-0200
E-mail: writers@capecodwriterscenter.org
Web Site: www.capecodwriterscenter.org
Key Personnel
Pres: Jennie Wiley
Exec Dir: Nancy Rubin Stuart
Busn Mgr: Janet Gardner
Hone skills as you learn from top professionals about your craft & the business of writing. In addition to classes in fiction, nonfiction, mystery, poetry, children's & other genres, the conference offers opportunities to meet with agents-in-residence. Personal conferences & ms evaluations are available as well as a Young Writers Workshop. A banquet & other special events.

Chautauqua Writers' Workshop
The Writers' Center at Chautauqua
PO Box 28, Chautauqua, NY 14722-0408
Tel: 716-357-6316; 716-357-6250
Toll Free Tel: 800-836-ARTS (836-2787)
Fax: 716-269-7444
Web Site: writers.ciweb.org
Key Personnel
Prog Dir, Writer's Ctr: Clara Silverstein
E-mail: clrsilver@gmail.com
Writing workshop in poetry & prose at 137 year-old Chautauqua Institution, international center for the arts, education, religion & recreation.
Location: Chautauqua Institution, Chautauqua, NY
Date: Last week in June-end of August

Christian Writers' Conference, see Writers Mentoring Retreat

The Clarion Science Fiction & Fantasy Writers' Workshop
The Clarion Foundation
Dept of Literature, Mail Code 0410, UC San Diego, 9500 Gilman Dr, La Jolla, CA 92093-0410
Tel: 858-534-2115
E-mail: clarion@ucsd.edu
Web Site: clarion.ucsd.edu
Key Personnel
Pres: Karen Joy Fowler
Prog Coord: Tania Mayer
Science fiction & fantasy writing workshop held for 6 weeks each summer.

Conference on Poetry
The Frost Place
158 Ridge Rd, Franconia, NH 03580
Mailing Address: PO Box 74, Franconia, NH 03580-0074
Tel: 603-823-5510
E-mail: frost@frostplace.org
Web Site: www.frostplace.org
Key Personnel
Exec Dir: Maudelle Driskell
Offers lectures, talks & craft panels by faculty in a seven-day program. See web site for details.

Creative Writing Day & Workshops
Virginia Highlands Festival
335 Cummings St, Abingdon, VA 24210
Mailing Address: PO Box 801, Abingdon, VA 24212-0801
Tel: 276-623-5266 *Fax:* 276-676-3076
E-mail: vhf@eva.org
Web Site: www.vahighlandsfestival.org
Key Personnel
Chair: Tommy Bryant *E-mail:* tbryant@vhcc.edu
Lectures, readings & workshops in creative writing with noteworthy authors held each summer.

Djerassi Resident Artists Program
2325 Bear Gulch Rd, Woodside, CA 94062
Tel: 650-747-1250 *Fax:* 650-747-0105
E-mail: drap@djerassi.org
Web Site: www.djerassi.org
Key Personnel
Exec Dir: Margot Knight *Tel:* 650-747-1250 ext 14 *E-mail:* margot@djerassi.org
One-month residencies for writers & other artists.

Education Writers Association Workshops
Education Writers Association (EWA)
3516 Connecticut Ave NW, Washington, DC 20008-2401
Tel: 202-452-9830 *Fax:* 202-452-9837
E-mail: ewa@ewa.org
Web Site: www.ewa.org
Key Personnel
Exec Dir: Caroline W Hendrie *E-mail:* chendrie@ewa.org
Multimedia Mgr: Glen Baity *E-mail:* gbaity@ewa.org
National seminar, regional meetings.

Emerson College Literary Publishing Certificate Program
Emerson College Professional Studies
Dept of Professional Studies, 120 Boylston St, Boston, MA 02116-8750
Tel: 617-824-8280 *Fax:* 617-824-8158
E-mail: continuing@emerson.edu
Web Site: www.emerson.edu/ce
Key Personnel
Exec Dir, Prof Studies: Hank Zappala

Five Star Publishing & Marketing Secrets
Five Star Publications Inc
4696 W Tyson St, Chandler, AZ 85226-2903
Tel: 480-940-8182 *Fax:* 480-940-8787
E-mail: info@fivestarpublications.com
Web Site: www.FiveStarPublications.com
Key Personnel
Pres: Linda F Radke
A six-hour publishing & marketing intensive workshop that teaches participants how to set up their own publishing company, produce well-designed printed books from a written ms, outsource ebook conversions, secure distribution for printed & ebooks, create a press kit & pitch it to the media & create & implement a marketing plan. The seminar is taught by Linda F Radke, President of Five Star Publications Inc. At times, Radke will be joined by other industry experts or executives of Five Star. The full-day workshop is divided into two three-hour segments with lunch in between. The first half focuses on publishing & the second half is dedicated to public relations & marketing. Participants may attend the first or second segment only at a reduced price. Groups are limited to 15 & one-on-one sessions are also available. Lunch is included. Participants receive two free

hours of follow-up consultation with Radke & a free copy each of *Promote Like a Pro & The Economical Guide to Self-Publishing* when taking the full workshop. Call for location & date.

Florida Writers Association Conference
Florida Writers Association Inc
PO Box 66069, St Pete Beach, FL 33736-6069
Web Site: www.floridawriters.net
Key Personnel
Pres: Chrissy Jackson *E-mail:* chrissyj@floridawriters.net
EVP: Jade Kerrion
VP, Admin & Fin: Larry Kokko
VP, Fin: Robyn Weinbaum
Assortment of workshops, networking, interviews with agents & editors, literary contest & banquet.
Date: Annually in Oct

Fun in the Sun Conference
Florida Romance Writers Inc (FRW)
Affiliate of Romance Writers of America®
PO Box 480211, Fort Lauderdale, FL 33348
E-mail: frwfuninthesun@yahoo.com
Web Site: www.frwriters.org/fun-in-the-sun-conference/; frwfuninthesunmain.blogspot.com/; www.frwriters.org
Key Personnel
Pres: Kristin Wallace
VP, Progs: Victoria Pinder
VP, Communs: Kimberly Gonzales
Secy: Aleka Nakis
Treas: Tina Stitzer
Highlights include a full series of workshops on the art, craft & business of writing that will appeal to writers in all genres. Exclusive Q&A with our keynote speaker, live & silent auction & raffle, on-site bookstore, author book signing event, editor/agent appointments & more. Registration fees from $170-$200. Workshop speakers entitled to discounted registration fee. Group rates available for groups of 5 or more; special hotel rates for conference attendees also available. Use the mailing address for all conference correspondence.
Date: Jan 2016; Jan 2017

The Gell Center of the Finger Lakes
Writers & Books
740 University Ave, Rochester, NY 14607-1259
Tel: 585-473-2590 *Fax:* 585-442-9333
Web Site: www.wab.org
Key Personnel
Dir, Opers & Programming: Kathy Pottetti *Tel:* 585-473-2590 ext 103 *E-mail:* kathyp@wab.org
Meeting center that hosts classes, workshops, conferences, etc for groups of up to 50 people.

The Glen Workshop
Image Journal
3307 Third Ave W, Seattle, WA 98119
Tel: 206-281-2988 *Fax:* 206-281-2979
E-mail: glenworkshop@imagejournal.org
Web Site: www.imagejournal.org/page/events/the-glen-workshop
Key Personnel
Prog Dir: Anna Johnson *E-mail:* ajohnson@imagejournal.org
A week long arts workshop for writers & visual artists that combines an intensive learning experience with a lively festival of the arts.

Gotham Writers' Workshop
555 Eighth Ave, Suite 1402, New York, NY 10018-4358
Tel: 212-974-8377 *Toll Free Tel:* 877-974-8377
E-mail: office@write.org
Web Site: www.writingclasses.com
Key Personnel
Pres: Alex Steele *E-mail:* alex@write.org
Professional writers teach acclaimed creative writing workshops online & in New York City throughout the year. NYC classes begin in Jan, April, July & Sept.

Harvard Summer Writing Program
Harvard University, Div of Continuing Education
51 Brattle St, Dept S760, Cambridge, MA 02138-3722
Tel: 617-495-4024 *Fax:* 617-495-9176
E-mail: summer@hudce.harvard.edu
Web Site: www.summer.harvard.edu
Key Personnel
Dir & Prog Contact: Dr Patricia Bellanca
Eight-week program starting at the end of June; full-semester college-credit workshop courses in creative, professional & expository writing. These include: beginning fiction, poetry, journalism & screenwriting; advanced creative nonfiction; writing grant proposals, effective business communication, legal writing & principles of editing; cross-cultural expository writing, writing about social & ethical issues & writing about literature.

Hedgebrook Master Class Retreat Series
Hedgebrook
PO Box 1231, Freeland, WA 98249
Tel: 360-321-4786 *Fax:* 360-321-2171
E-mail: hedgebrook@hedgebrook.org
Web Site: www.hedgebrook.org; www.facebook.com/hedgebrook
Key Personnel
Prog Dir: Vito Zingarelli *E-mail:* vitoz@hedgebrook.org
Prog Assoc: Julie O'Brien *E-mail:* julieo@hedgebrook.org
Craft-focused writing workshops, where participants have the unique opportunity to be in residence & study with a celebrated teacher. Weeklong Master Classes include 6-7 participants, each housed in her own cottage. Participants receive 5 days of writing workshops, instructor-led constructive group feedback sessions, one-on-one sessions with the instructor & an additional day of retreat time. Meals featuring produce harvested from our organic garden are prepared by Hedgebrook's chefs, Writers at all levels of experience, published or not, are accepted into Hedgebrook's Master Classes. Cost is $2,500 - $3,500, which covers lodging, meals & workshops; all taxes included. A portion is tax-deductible.

Hedgebrook VORTEXT
Hedgebrook
PO Box 1231, Freeland, WA 98249
Tel: 360-321-4786 *Fax:* 360-321-2171
E-mail: hedgebrook@hedgebrook.org
Web Site: www.hedgebrook.org; www.facebook.com/hedgebrook
Key Personnel
Prog Dir: Vito Zingarelli *E-mail:* vitoz@hedgebrook.org
Prog Assoc: Julie O'Brien *E-mail:* julieo@hedgebrook.org
Weekend salon led by 6 established women writers. Connect & hone your craft in diverse & powerful small-group workshops. Enjoy dynamic keynotes & discussions about opportunities & challenges for women who write. Engage in dynamic discussions on hot topics specific to women who write. Share meals, open mics, conversation & community in a stunningly beautiful setting. Held at the Whidbey Institute at Chinook on Whidbey Island, WA in late May, a registration fee of $950 includes all keynotes & 3 workshops of your choice, group sessions & free time to write as well as breakfast, lunch & daily reception.

Hedgebrook Winter Salon
Hedgebrook
PO Box 1231, Freeland, WA 98249
Tel: 360-321-4786 *Fax:* 360-321-2171
E-mail: hedgebrook@hedgebrook.org
Web Site: www.hedgebrook.org; www.facebook.com/hedgebrook
Key Personnel
Prog Dir: Vito Zingarelli *E-mail:* vitoz@hedgebrook.org
Prog Assoc: Julie O'Brien *E-mail:* julieo@hedgebrook.org
Creative workshops, held early December, are led by & for women writers. Enjoy a day filled with lively conversation & delicious food, culminating in a party with an open mic. Write, learn, share stories & leave freshly inspired.

Hedgebrook Writers in Residence Program
Hedgebrook
PO Box 1231, Freeland, WA 98249
Tel: 360-321-4786 *Fax:* 360-321-2171
E-mail: hedgebrook@hedgebrook.org
Web Site: www.hedgebrook.org; www.facebook.com/hedgebrook
Key Personnel
Prog Dir: Vito Zingarelli *E-mail:* vitoz@hedgebrook.org
Prog Assoc: Julie O'Brien *E-mail:* julieo@hedgebrook.org
Program supporting fully-funded residencies of approximately 40 women writers (6 or 7 at a time) at a retreat each year on Whidbey Island, WA. Hedgebrook is one of the few writer's colonies in the world exclusively dedicated to supporting women writers & bringing their work to the world through innovative public programs. Emerging & established writers (all genres) worldwide attend. Each writer is housed in her own cottage. Residents share a home-cooked evening meal prepared by Hedgebrook's chefs. The community formed around the kitchen table is growing as Hedgebrook hosts alumnae gatherings, events & professional development workshops around the country. Applications for the upcoming residency season are available via our web site by mid-June, with a deadline in late July.

Highland Summer Writers' Conference
The Appalachian Regional Studies Center (ARSC)
Division of Radford University
PO Box 7014, Radford University, Radford, VA 24142
Tel: 540-831-5366; 540-831-6152 *Fax:* 540-831-5951
Web Site: www.radford.edu/~arsc
Key Personnel
Dir: Dr Theresa Burriss *Tel:* 540-831-6857 *E-mail:* tburriss@radford.edu
Instructor & ARSC Assoc: Ruth Derrick *E-mail:* rbderrick@radford.edu
Annual program based on Appalachian culture & writing; directed for two weeks by a fiction writer/poet/dramatist. Elective seminar-workshop combination offers the opportunity to study & practice creative & expository writing & earn 3 hours graduate/undergraduate credit.
Location: Radford University, Radford, VA

Historical Novel Society North American Conference
Historical Novel Society
400 Dark Star Ct, Fairbanks, AK 99709
Tel: 217-581-7538 *Fax:* 217-581-7534
Web Site: www.historicalnovelsociety.org
Key Personnel
US Membership Secy: Georgine Olson *E-mail:* georgine@mosquitonet.com
Date: June 2017

How to be Published Workshops
Michael Garrett
c/o Creative Inspirations Inc, PO Box 362, Clay, AL 35048
E-mail: mgteach352@gmail.com
Web Site: www.writing2sell.com
Key Personnel
Pres: Michael Garrett *E-mail:* mike@writing2sell.com
Workshops teaching all aspects of how to be successfully published. See web site for dates & locations.

Hurston/Wright Writer's Week
The Zora Neale Hurston/Richard Wright Foundation
12138 Central Ave, Suite 209, Bowie, MD 20721
Tel: 301-459-2108 *Fax:* 301-277-1262
E-mail: info@hurstonwright.org
Web Site: www.hurstonwright.org
Key Personnel
Founder & Pres Emeritus: Marita Golden
Exec Dir: Clyde McElvene
Multi-genre Summer writer's workshop for writers of African descent. $20 submission fee.

Idyllwild Arts Summer Workshops
Idyllwild Arts Summer Program
52500 Temecula Dr, Idyllwild, CA 92549-0038
Mailing Address: PO Box 38, Idyllwild, CA 92549-0038
Tel: 951-659-2171 *Fax:* 951-659-4552
E-mail: summer@idyllwildarts.org
Web Site: www.idyllwildarts.org/writersweek
Key Personnel
Summer Prog Registrar: Diane Dennis *Tel:* 951-659-2171 ext 2365 *E-mail:* dianed@idyllwildarts.org
Five day writing workshops for adults in creative nonfiction, fiction, chapbooks, poetry, screenwriting & more. Two-week writing workshops for high school students in fiction, poetry & much more.

Indiana University Writers' Conference
Indiana University
464 Ballantine Hall, Dept of English, 1020 E Kirkwood Ave, Bloomington, IN 47405
Tel: 812-855-1877 *Fax:* 812-855-9535
E-mail: writecon@indiana.edu
Web Site: www.indiana.edu/~writecon/
Key Personnel
Dir: Bob Bledsoe *E-mail:* rbledso@indiana.edu
Asst Dir: Caroline Diggins
Week-long, annual conference in June for writers of poetry, fiction, nonfiction & script writing. Second oldest such conference in the US. Past staff includes Raymond Carver, Allen Tate & Katherine Anne Porter.

Iowa Summer Writing Festival
Division of University of Iowa Continuing Education
250 Continuing Educ Facility, University of Iowa, Iowa City, IA 52242
Tel: 319-335-4160
E-mail: iswfestival@uiowa.edu
Web Site: iowasummerwritingfestival.org
Key Personnel
Dir: Amy Margolis *E-mail:* amy-margolis@uiowa.edu
Annual week-long & weekend non-credit, intensive writing workshops in all genres, all levels (for adults).

Jentel Artist Residency Program
Jentel Foundation
130 Lower Piney Rd, Banner, WY 82832
Tel: 307-737-2311 *Fax:* 307-737-2305
E-mail: jentel@jentelarts.org
Web Site: www.jentelarts.org
Key Personnel
Exec Dir: Mary Jane Edwards
Offers one month residencies throughout the year to visual artists in all media & writers in fiction, creative nonfiction & poetry. Located on a working cattle ranch in the foothills of the Big Horn Moutains, 20 miles from Sheridan, WY. The award includes comfortable accommodations, a separate private studio & a stipend. Residents are invited to share their work through various outreach opportunities in the community. For more info or an application, see web site. Deadline is Sept 15 & Jan 15 each year.

Juniper Summer Writing Institute
Juniper Institute
c/o University Conference Services, 810 Campus Ctr, One Campus Ctr Way, Amherst, MA 01003
Tel: 413-545-5510
E-mail: juniperinstitute@hfa.umass.edu
Web Site: www.umass.edu/juniperinstitute
Key Personnel
Dir: Betsy Wheeler
Seven days of intensive writing workshops, craft sessions, readings & ms consultation in the beautiful Pioneer Valley. Scholarships available.

Kentucky Women Writers Conference
University of Kentucky
232 E Maxwell St, Lexington, KY 40506-0344
Tel: 859-257-2874
E-mail: kentuckywomenwriters@gmail.com
Web Site: www.kentuckywomenwriters.org
Key Personnel
Dir: Julie Kuzneski Wrinn
Founded in 1979, this is the oldest conference of its kind in the country featuring invited women writers offering workshops, reading & panel discussions.
Location: Lexington, KY
Date: Annually in Sept

Kentucky Writers Conference
Southern Kentucky Book Fest
1906 College Heights Blvd, Suite 11067, Bowling Green, KY 42101-1067
Tel: 270-745-4502
Web Site: www.sokybookfest.org
Key Personnel
Mktg Coord: Jennifer Wilson *Tel:* 270-745-6977 *E-mail:* jennifer.wilson@wku.edu
Location: Knicely Conference Center, 645 Campbell Lane, Bowling Green, KY
Date: April 22, 2016

Key West Literary Seminar
718 Love Lane, Key West, FL 33040
Toll Free Tel: 888-293-9291
E-mail: mail@kwls.org
Web Site: www.kwls.org
Key Personnel
Exec Dir: Miles Frieden
Media Dir: Arlo Haskell *Tel:* 305-293-9291
Annual literary seminar held in two parts with workshops taking place between the two sessions. The 2016 theme is "SHORTS: Stories, Essays & Other Briefs". Writers' workshops take place Jan 11-15. See web site for details.
Location: Key West, FL
Date: Jan 7-10, 2016

Ligonier Valley Writers Conference
Ligonier Valley Writers
PO Box B, Ligonier, PA 15658-1602
Tel: 724-238-3692
Key Personnel
Conference Dir: Judith Gallagher *E-mail:* jgallagher@lhtot.com
Contact: Mary Ann Mogus
Writers' Conference.

Maine Writers Conference at Ocean Park
Affiliate of Ocean Park Association
14 Temple Ave, Ocean Park, ME 04063
Tel: 401-598-1424
E-mail: www.opa@oceanpark.org
Web Site: www.oceanpark.org
Key Personnel
Dir: Dr Jim Brosnan
An eclectic, economical & intensive annual conference for writers of both poetry & prose of varying abilities & accomplishments.

Maritime Writers' Workshops
College of Extended Learning, University of New Brunswick, Fredericton
Affiliate of University of New Brunswick (Canada)
PO Box 4400, Fredericton, NB E3B 5A3, Canada
Tel: 506-458-7106 *Toll Free Tel:* 866-599-4646 *Fax:* 506-458-5012
E-mail: extend@unb.ca
Web Site: www.unb.ca/cel
Key Personnel
Prog Asst: Laurie Glenn Norris *E-mail:* laurie.norris@unb.ca
Maritime Writers' Workshops (MWW) will get you started or help you take your writing to the next level. Over its long history, hundreds of MWW participants have learned critical skills, found their voice & benefited from its comfortable & inviting atmosphere. You'll be actively involved & will receive helpful feedback in a supportive environment from instructors who are themselves successful writers. We offer workshops, retreats & rentings. Choose from a series of workshops suited to your particular interest or needs.
Also offer retreats & readings.

McHugh's Rights/Permissions Workshop™
John B McHugh Publishing Consultant
PO Box 170665, Milwaukee, WI 53217-8056
Tel: 414-351-3056
E-mail: jack@johnbmchugh.com
Web Site: www.johnbmchugh.com
Key Personnel
Principal & Consultant: John B McHugh
Provide on-site customized workshops in all aspects of publishing management.

Mississippi River Creative Writing Workshop
St Cloud State University, English Dept
720 Fourth Ave S, B-151, Rm 100, St Cloud, MN 56301-4498
Tel: 320-308-4947 *Fax:* 320-308-5524
Web Site: www.stcloudstate.edu
Key Personnel
Dir, Poet, Fiction Writer & Novelist & Instructor: Bill Meissner *E-mail:* wjmeissner@stcloudstate.edu
Four-day workshop in poetry & fiction. Participants will develop creative writing skills & learn writing techniques & ideas. Includes presentation by professional published authors.

Mt Chocorua Writing Workshop
World Fellowship Center
PO Box 2280, Conway, NH 03818-2280
Tel: 603-447-2280
E-mail: reservations@worldfellowship.org
Web Site: www.worldfellowship.org
Key Personnel
Dir: Ellen Meeropol; Ekere Tallie
An opportunity to create new poems & prose & apply what we know about craft to writing. Writers of all levels encouraged to come.
Location: Conway (White Mountains), NH
Date: Annually in July

Mount Hermon Christian Writers Conference
Mount Hermon Christian Camps & Conference Center
c/o Mount Hermon Association Inc, 37 Conference Dr, Felton, CA 95018
Mailing Address: c/o Mount Hermon Association Inc, PO Box 413, Mount Hermon, CA 95041
Tel: 831-335-4466 *Toll Free Tel:* 888-MH-CAMPS (642-2677 - registration) *Fax:* 831-335-9218
E-mail: info@mounthermon.org
Web Site: www.mounthermon.org/writers
Key Personnel
Adult Prog Specialist: Rachel Williams *Tel:* 831-430-1238 *E-mail:* rachel.williams@mounthermon.org
Two day Head Start Mentoring Clinic for beginning writers; 5 day Writers Conference for all abilities, including beginning to professional.
Location: Mount Hermon Conference Center, Felton, CA
Date: March 16-22, 2016

Mountain Writers Series
2804 SE 27 Ave, Suite 2, Portland, OR 97202
Tel: 503-232-4517 *Fax:* 503-232-4517
E-mail: pdxmws@mountainwriters.org
Web Site: www.mountainwriters.org
Key Personnel
Artistic Dir: Sandra Williams
Work with nationally recognized poets, fiction writers, nonfiction writers, screenwriters & agents.

MWG Writer Workshops
Mississippi Writers Guild (MWG)
PO Box 3845, Meridian, MS 39303-3845
Tel: 601-880-1089
Web Site: www.mississippiwritersguild.com
Key Personnel
Pres: Robert Ray *E-mail:* robertray601@bellsouth.net
Events Coord: Richelle Putnam *E-mail:* richput@mywebemail.net
For information about this workshop, e-mail Richelle Putnam.

Mystery Writers of America Workshops
Mystery Writers of America (MWA)
1140 Broadway, Suite 1507, New York, NY 10001
Tel: 212-888-8171
E-mail: mwa@mysterywriters.org
Web Site: www.mysterywriters.org
Key Personnel
Admin Dir: Margery Flax
Mystery writing workshops given at various times throughout the year by regional chapters.

Napa Valley Writers' Conference
Napa Valley Community College
Upper Valley Campus, 1088 College Ave, St Helena, CA 94574
Tel: 707-967-2900 (ext 1611) *Fax:* 707-967-2909
E-mail: writecon@napavalley.edu
Web Site: www.napawritersconf.org
Key Personnel
Mng Dir: Andrea Bewick
Prog Dir: Anne Matlack Evans *Tel:* 707-253-3168 *E-mail:* abewick@napavalley.edu; John Leggett *Tel:* 707-253-3168
Poetry Prog Dir: Nan Cohen
Fiction Dir: Ms Lakin Khan
Admin Asst: Charlotte Morgan
Poetry & fiction sessions each year, offering small workshops, lectures & readings. Begins last Sunday in July & runs for one week.

National Society of Newspaper Columnists Annual Conference
National Society of Newspaper Columnists (NSNC)
1345 Fillmore St, Suite 507, San Francisco, CA 94115
Mailing Address: PO Box 411532, San Francisco, CA 94141
Tel: 415-488-NCNC (488-6762)
Toll Free Tel: 866-440-NSNC (440-6762)
Fax: 484-297-0336 *Toll Free Fax:* 866-635-5759
Web Site: www.columnists.com
Key Personnel
Pres: Ben Pollock
VP: Larry Cohen
Exec Dir: Luenna H Kim *E-mail:* director@columnists.com
Secy: Wayne Chan
Treas: James A Casto
Conference Chair: Brian O'Connor
Contest Chair: Mike Deupree
Membership Chair: Rose A Valenta
Newsletter Ed: Robert Haught
Archivist: Dave Astor
Annual conference & contest, occasional newsletter & networking with staff & syndicated columnists & regular freelance columnists.

New York State Writers Institute
State University of New York
Division of University at Albany/SUNY
University at Albany, Science Library 320, Albany, NY 12222
Tel: 518-442-5620 *Fax:* 518-442-5621
E-mail: writers@uamail.albany.edu
Web Site: www.albany.edu/writers-inst
Key Personnel
Exec Dir: William Kennedy
Dir: Donald Faulkner
Asst Dir: Suzanne Lance
Literary program organization featuring year-round visiting writers, classic film, special literary events & conferences, writing courses & workshops. Write or see web site for dates & locations.

North Carolina Writers' Network Annual Fall Conference
North Carolina Writers' Network
PO Box 21591, Winston-Salem, NC 27120-1591
Tel: 336-293-8844
E-mail: mail@ncwriters.org
Web Site: www.ncwriters.org
Key Personnel
Exec Dir: Ed Southern
Workshops, readings, conferences, critiquing service & round table discussions, panels & meetings with agents, publishing workshops.

Northeast Texas Community College Annual Writers Conference
Northeast Texas Community College
Continuing Education, PO Box 1307, Mount Pleasant, TX 75456-1307
Tel: 903-434-8134 *Toll Free Tel:* 800-870-0142 *Fax:* 903-572-6712
Web Site: www.ntcc.edu
Key Personnel
Pres: Dr Brad Johnson *E-mail:* bjohnson@ntcc.edu
Dir, Continuing Educ: Judy Jackson *E-mail:* jjackson@ntcc.edu

Odyssey: The Summer Fantasy Writing Workshop
PO Box 75, Mont Vernon, NH 03057
Tel: 603-673-6234 *Fax:* 603-673-6234
Web Site: www.odysseyworkshop.org
Key Personnel
Dir: Jeanne Cavelos *E-mail:* jcavelos@comcast.net
Intensive 6-week workshop for writers of fantasy, science fiction & horror. Dir Jeanne Cavelos is a former Sr Ed at Bantam Doubleday Dell Publishing & winner of the World Fantasy Award. Guest lecturers include some of the top writers in the field. College credit available. Application deadline: April 7.
Location: Saint Anselm College, Manchester, NH
Date: June 6-July 15, 2016

Oregon Christian Writers Coaching Conference
Oregon Christian Writers (OCW)
1075 Willow Lake Rd N, Keizer, OR 97303
Tel: 503-393-3356
E-mail: contact@oregonchristianwriters.org
Web Site: www.oregonchristianwriters.org
Key Personnel
Summer Conference Dir: Lindy Jacobs *E-mail:* summerconf@oregonchristianwriters.org
Registrar & Busn Mgr: Sue Miholer
Seven hours of hands-on help from well-published professionals, many specialized workshops, consultations with editors & networking with successful writers.
Location: Jantzen Beach Red Lion Hotel, Portland, OR
Date: Aug 15-18, 2016

Oregon Christian Writers Seminar
Oregon Christian Writers (OCW)
1075 Willow Lake Rd N, Keizer, OR 97303
Tel: 503-393-3356
E-mail: contact@oregonchristianwriters.org
Web Site: www.oregonchristianwriters.org
Key Personnel
Pres: Maxine Marsolini
Prog Chmn: Marilyn Rhoads
Registrar & Busn Mgr: Sue Miholer
Writers' workshops.
Location: Winter Conference, Salem, OR
Date: Feb 27, 2016
Location: Spring Conference, Eugene, OR
Date: May 14, 2016
Location: Fall Conference, Portland, OR
Date: Oct 15, 2016

Orientation to the Graphic Arts
Printing Industries of America
200 Deer Run Rd, Sewickley, PA 15143-2324
Tel: 412-259-1711 *Toll Free Tel:* 800-910-4283 *Fax:* 412-741-2311
E-mail: printing@printing.org
Web Site: www.printing.org
Key Personnel
CEO & Pres: Michael F Makin *E-mail:* mmakin@printing.org
VP, Training: Jim Workman *E-mail:* jworkman@printing.org
Sr Custom Training & Consulting Specialist: Karen Keller *E-mail:* kkeller@printing.org

Outdoor Writers Association of America Annual Conference
Outdoor Writers Association of America (OWAA)
615 Oak St, Suite 201, Missoula, MT 59801
Tel: 406-728-7434 *Fax:* 406-728-7445
E-mail: info@owaa.org
Web Site: www.owaa.org
Key Personnel
Exec Dir: Tom Sadler *E-mail:* tsadler@owaa.org
Seminars & writing workshops; photography & outdoor news & conversation.
Location: Holiday Inn Grand Montana, Billings, MT
Date: July 16-18, 2016
Location: Duluth Entertainment & Convention Center, Duluth, MN
Date: June 24-26, 2017

Ozark Creative Writers Inc Annual Conference
Ozark Creative Writers Inc
PO Box 9076, Fayetteville, AR 72703
Tel: 479-751-7246

E-mail: ozarkcreativewriters1@gmail.com
Web Site: www.ozarkcreativewriters.org
Key Personnel
Mgr: Delois McGraw
Writers' conference for beginners & professionals. Contest information in brochures available after May 1. Send No 10 SASE.
Location: Ozarks Convention Ctr, Eureka Springs, AR
Date: 2nd full weekend in Oct

Pacific Northwest Children's Book Conference
Portland State University Graduate School of Education
615 SW Harrison St, Portland, OR 97201
Mailing Address: PO Box 751, Portland, OR 97207
Tel: 503-725-9786 *Toll Free Tel:* 800-547-8887 (ext 9786) *Fax:* 503-725-5599
Web Site: www.pdx.edu/ceed/childrens-book-conference
Key Personnel
Contact: Elizabeth Snyder *E-mail:* snydere@pdx.edu
Focus on the craft of writing & illustrating for children & young people while working with an outstanding faculty of acclaimed editors, authors & illustrators. Housing & meals will be available on campus to allow more opportunities for networking & ongoing discussion with faculty & fellow students. Afternoon small-group, faculty-led workshops for writers & illustrators. Individual mss & portfolio reviews available. Undergraduate & graduate credit available through Portland State University.

Pennwriters Conference
Pennwriters Inc
5706 Sonoma Ridge, Missouri City, TX 77459
Web Site: www.pennwriters.org
Key Personnel
Pres & Conference Chair: Carol Silvis *E-mail:* president@pennwriters.org
Workshops, seminars with authors, agents & editors in romance, mystery, short story, nonfiction, poetry, read & critique sessions, hands-on workshops & contests, agent/editor appointments.
Location: Eden Resort, Lancaster, PA
Date: May 20-22, 2016

Philadelphia Writers' Conference
PO Box 7171, Elkins Park, PA 19027-0171
Tel: 215-782-3288 *Fax:* 215-782-3288
E-mail: info@pwcwriters.org
Web Site: pwcwriters.org
Key Personnel
Trustee & Contact: Gloria T Delamar *E-mail:* delamarg@juno.com
Educational conferences for writers, workshops, critiques, contests, featured speakers, agents, editors.
Location: Philadelphia, PA
Date: random free forums
Location: Philadelphia, PA
Date: annual 3-day event; 2nd full weekend of June

Pima Writers' Workshop
Pima Community College
Pima College West Campus, 2202 W Anklam Rd, Tucson, AZ 85709-0170
Tel: 520-206-6084 *Fax:* 520-206-6020
Web Site: www.pima.edu
Key Personnel
Dir: Meg Files *E-mail:* mfiles@pima.edu
The three-day conference in May offers opportunities to meet with authors, editors & agents & to have mss critiqued.
Location: Pima Community College, West Campus, Tucson, AZ
Date: May 28-31, 2015

Poetry Flash Reading Series
Poetry Flash
1450 Fourth St, Suite 4, Berkeley, CA 94710
Tel: 510-525-5476 *Fax:* 510-525-6752
E-mail: editor@poetryflash.org
Web Site: www.poetryflash.org
Key Personnel
Publr & Ed: Joyce Jenkins
Publication; conducts a reading & poetry series in conjunction with Moe's Books in Berkeley, CA & Diesel, A Bookstore in Oakland, CA. Host poets from all around the US.

Port Townsend Writers' Conference
Centrum Foundation
223 Battery Way, Port Townsend, WA 98368
Mailing Address: PO Box 1158, Port Townsend, WA 98368-0958
Tel: 360-385-3102 *Toll Free Tel:* 800-733-3608 (ticket off) *Fax:* 360-385-2470
E-mail: info@centrum.org
Web Site: www.centrum.org
Key Personnel
Artistic Dir: Erin Belieu
Workshops, lectures & readings.

The Publishing Game
Peanut Butter & Jelly Press LLC
PO Box 590239, Newton, MA 02459-0002
SAN: 299-7444
Tel: 617-630-0945 *Fax:* 617-630-0945 (call first)
E-mail: info@publishinggame.com; workshops@publishinggame.com
Web Site: www.publishinggame.com
Key Personnel
Off Mgr: Alyza Harris *E-mail:* alyza@publishinggame.com
All-day workshop covers how to find a literary agent, how to self-publish & how to successfully promote your book. Offered in 12 cities: New York, Boston, Philadelphia, DC, Boca Raton, Chicago, San Francisco, Los Angeles, Seattle, Phoenix, Dallas & several "floating cities" each year. $195 includes workshop course binder. See www.publishinggame.com for latest locations, dates & details.

PNWA Writers Conference
PNWA - a writer's resource
1420 NW Gilman Blvd, Suite 2, PMB 2717, Issaquah, WA 98027
Tel: 425-673-2665
E-mail: pnwa@pnwa.org
Web Site: www.pnwa.org
Key Personnel
Pres: Pam Binder

Robert Quackenbush's Children's Book Writing & Illustration Workshops
Robert Quackenbush Studios
223 E 78 St, New York, NY 10075
Mailing Address: 460 E 79 St, New York, NY 10075
Tel: 212-744-3822
E-mail: rqstudios@aol.com
Web Site: www.rquackenbush.com
Workshops at author/artists' studio; focus on planning children's books from concept to completion.
Location: New York, NY
Date: Second week in July annually (4 day intensive workshop)

ReIMAGINE the MAGIC Annual Summer Conference
The International Women's Writing Guild (IWWG)
274 Madison Ave, Suite 1202, New York, NY 10016
Tel: 917-720-6959
E-mail: iwwgquestions@gmail.com
Web Site: www.iwwg.org
Key Personnel
Dir of Opers: Kristin Rath
Each summer, the Guild brings together women for three full days of writing, crafting & connecting. Offer over 15 workshops to explore the spiritual, emotional, creative & technical side of writing.

Romance Writers of America Annual Conference
Romance Writers of America®
14615 Benfer Rd, Houston, TX 77069
Tel: 832-717-5200 *Fax:* 832-717-5201
E-mail: info@rwa.org
Web Site: www.rwa.org
Key Personnel
Exec Dir: Allison Kelley *Tel:* 832-717-5200 ext 124 *E-mail:* allison.kelley@rwa.org
Promote recognition of the genre of romance writing as a serious book form. Conduct workshops, sponsor national & regional conferences & awards for members.
Location: San Diego Marriott Hotel and Marina, San Diego, CA
Date: July 13-16, 2016
Location: Walt Disney World Swan and Dolphin, 1500 Epcot Resorts Blvd, Lake Buena Vista, FL
Date: July 26-29, 2017
Location: Sheraton Denver Downtown Hotel, Denver, CO
Date: July 25-28, 2018
Location: New York Marriott® Marquis, New York, NY
Date: July 24-27, 2019

San Diego Christian Writers' Guild Conference
San Diego Christian Writers' Guild
PO Box 270403, San Diego, CA 92198
Tel: 760-294-3269 *Fax:* 760-294-3269
E-mail: info@sandiegocwg.org
Web Site: www.sandiegocwg.org
Key Personnel
Pres: Jennie Gillespie; Robert Gillespie
One day seminar & workshops; personal consultations with editors. Journalism, magazine writing, fiction. Seminar is always the fourth Saturday in Sept.

San Francisco Writers Conference
1029 Jones St, San Francisco, CA 94109
Tel: 415-673-0939
E-mail: sfwriterscon@aol.com
Web Site: www.sfwriters.org
Key Personnel
Founder: Michael Larsen
Founder & Dir: Elizabeth Pomada
Craft & market oriented writers' conference covering fiction, nonfiction, children's books, film & poetry with name authors.
Location: Mark Hopkins Hotel, San Francisco, CA
Date: Feb 11-14, 2016

Sandhills Writers' Series
Augusta State University
Dept of Communications & Professional Writing, 2500 Walton Way, Augusta, GA 30904
Tel: 706-667-4437 *Fax:* 706-667-4770
Web Site: www.sandhills.aug.edu
Key Personnel
Dir & Professor of Creative Writing: Anthony Kellman *E-mail:* akellman@aol.com
Fiction, nonfiction, creative nonfiction & poetry craft-directed readings; participants meet in consultations with literary agents that represent commercial & literary fiction, nonfiction & children's books. Enrollment limited. Ms deadline Feb.

Santa Barbara Book Promotion Workshop
Para Publishing LLC
PO Box 8206-240, Santa Barbara, CA 93118-8206
SAN: 215-8981
Tel: 805-968-7277 *Toll Free Tel:* 800-727-2782 *Fax:* 805-968-1379
E-mail: info@parapublishing.com
Web Site: www.parapublishing.com
Key Personnel
Owner & Publr: Dan Poynter *E-mail:* danpoynter@parapublishing.com
Book marketing, promoting & distributing; four workshops per year.
Location: Santa Barbara, CA
Date: Jan, April, July, Oct; reservations required, attendance limited to 23

Science Fiction Writers Workshop
Center for the Study of Science Fiction
Division of University of Kansas
University of Kansas, Wescoe Hall, Rm 3001, Dept of English, 1445 Jayhawk Blvd, Lawrence, KS 66045-7590
Tel: 785-864-3380 *Fax:* 785-864-1159
Web Site: www.ku.edu/~sfcenter
Key Personnel
Founding Dir: James Gunn *E-mail:* jgunn@ku.edu
Dir: Chris McKitterick *E-mail:* cmckit@ku.edu
A noncredit, two-week intensive workshop offered in association with the Campbell Conference on science fiction by the Center for the Study of Science Fiction.
Location: University of Kansas, Lawrence, KS
Date: Summer

Scribes & Scribblers Writing Camps for Kids
Aspen Writers' Foundation
110 E Hallam St, Suite 116, Aspen, CO 81611
Tel: 970-925-3122 *Fax:* 970-920-5700
E-mail: awfinfo@aspenwriters.org
Web Site: www.aspenwriters.org
Key Personnel
Exec Dir: Lisa Consiglio *Tel:* 970-925-3122 ext 1 *E-mail:* lisa@aspenwriters.org
Helps kids discover writing is fun.
Location: Aspen, CO
Date: Annually July-Aug

SDSU Writers' Conference
San Diego State University College of Extended Studies
5250 Campanile Dr, Rm 2503, San Diego, CA 92182-1920
Tel: 619-594-5821 *Fax:* 619-594-8566
E-mail: sdsuwritersconference@mail.sdsu.edu
Web Site: www.neverstoplearning.net/writers
Key Personnel
Prog Dir: Christine Timbol *E-mail:* ctimbol@mail.sdsu.edu
Annual weekend writers' conference. Topics include fiction, nonfiction, genre novels & children's writing. Personal editor & agent appointments available.
Location: San Diego Marriott, Mission Valley, San Diego, CA
Date: Jan 22-24, 2016

Hank Searls Authors Workshop
4435 Holly Lane NW, Gig Harbor, WA 98335
Mailing Address: Box 1877, Suite 1-C, Gig Harbor, WA 98335
Tel: 253-851-9896 *Fax:* 253-851-9897
E-mail: hanksearls@comcast.net
Key Personnel
CEO & Pres: Hank Searls
Novel & full-length fiction writing, teaching & critiquing full-length fiction & nonfiction. Hank Searls is a member of the Writers Guild of America, West & Authors Guild & the author of *Jaws II*, *Jaws: The Revenge* & *The Lost Prince: Young Joe, the Forgotten Kennedy*.
Location: Gig Harbor, WA

See-More's Workshop Arts & Education Workshops
The Shadow Box Theatre
325 West End Ave, Suite 12-B, New York, NY 10023
Tel: 212-724-0677 *Fax:* 212-724-0767
E-mail: sbt@shadowboxtheatre.org
Web Site: www.shadowboxtheatre.org
Key Personnel
Administrator: Elaine Brand *E-mail:* ebrand@shadowboxtheatre.org
Arts & Educ Dir: Carol Prud'homme Davis
Resident Workshops: Early learning through elementary grades, SBT's teaching artists guide students in the art of storytelling & curriculum exploration through puppetry, dramatics, dance & music. Professional Development Workshops: Hands-on staff development workshops provide classroom teachers with theatre & storytelling techniques. Author Workshops: Includes a trip or in-school SBT musical puppet show, our own storybooks with accompanying audio tapes/CDs & a meeting with playwright & author, Sandra Robbins. For more information contact us, as dates, times & locations change often.

Sewanee Writers' Conference
Stamler Ctr, 119 Gailor Hall, 735 University Ave, Sewanee, TN 37383-1000
Tel: 931-598-1141
E-mail: swc@sewanee.edu
Web Site: www.sewaneewriters.org
Key Personnel
Dir: Wyatt Prunty
Admissions & Creative Writing Administrator: Adam Latham *E-mail:* allatham@sewanee.edu
Administrator: Megan Roberts *E-mail:* mgroberts@sewanee.edu
Workshops in poetry, fiction & playwriting.
Location: The University of the South, Sewanee, TN
Date: Annually the last two weeks in July

Society for Technical Communication's Annual Conference
Society for Technical Communication
9401 Lee Hwy, Suite 300, Fairfax, VA 22031
Tel: 703-522-4114 *Fax:* 703-522-2075
E-mail: stc@stc.org
Web Site: www.stc.org
Key Personnel
CEO: Chris Lyons *Tel:* 571-366-1901 *E-mail:* chris.lyons@stc.org
Dir, Meetings & Educ: Lloyd Tucker *Tel:* 571-366-1904 *E-mail:* lloyd.tucker@stc.org
Educational conference for technical communicators.

Solid Gold Marketing Design Workshops
Sparkle Presentations Inc
PO Box 2373, La Mesa, CA 91943-2373
Tel: 858-569-6555 *Toll Free Tel:* 800-932-0973
Web Site: www.sparklepresentations.com
Key Personnel
CEO & Pres: Sheryl Roush *E-mail:* sheryl@sparklepresentations.com
Design sessions teach creativity, design tactics, feedback & fun. Specializing in newsletters, brochures, flyers & presentation materials. Keynote addresses on attitude, creating a positive workplace. See web site for scheduled events.
Membership(s): IBPA, National Speakers Association & Toastmasters International.

Southampton Writers' Conference
Stony Brook Southampton
239 Montauk Hwy, Southampton, NY 11968
Tel: 631-632-5007
E-mail: southamptonwriters@notes.cc.sunysb.edu
Web Site: www.stonybrook.edu/writers
Key Personnel
Conference Coord: Christian McLean *E-mail:* christian.mclean@stonybrook.edu
Five & twelve day workshops including novel, short story, poetry, memoir & creative nonfiction, playwriting & screenwriting; also evening readings, performances & panels.

Southern California Writers' Conference
Southern California Writers' Conference (SCWC)
Division of Random Cove, ie
18160 Cottonwood Rd, Suite 260, Sunriver, OR 97707
Tel: 619-303-8185 *Fax:* 619-906-7462
E-mail: msg@writersconference.com
Web Site: www.writersconference.com
Key Personnel
Exec Dir: Michael Steven Gregory *Tel:* 619-906-7462 *Fax:* 253-390-8577
Dir: Wes Albers *E-mail:* wes@writersconference.com
Asst Dir: Chrissie A Barnett *E-mail:* chrissie@writersconference.com
Annual writers' conferences. Fiction, nonfiction & scriptwriting mss eligible for advance critique submission before the conference, followed by one-on-one consultation; awards given. Major speakers; banquet; workshops in fiction, nonfiction, legacy & indie publishing; conference emphasis on fiction & nonfiction; one agent panel, multiple read & critique, craft, & troubleshooting workshops.
Location: San Diego, CA
Date: Feb 12-15, 2016

SouthWest Writers Conference Series
SouthWest Writers
3200 Carlisle Blvd NE, Suite 114, Albuquerque, NM 87110-1663
Tel: 505-830-6034
E-mail: swwriters@juno.com
Web Site: www.southwestwriters.com
Key Personnel
Pres: Lee Higbie
Series of one-day conferences, annual writing contest (May 1 deadline), twice-monthly programs, bimonthly writing contest, workshops & writing classes.

Spring Time Writers Creative Writing & Journaling Workshop
Spring Time Writers
PO Box 512, Lyons, CO 80540-0512
Tel: 303-823-0997
E-mail: writers@springtimewriters.com
Web Site: www.springtimewriters.com
Key Personnel
Dir: Kathleen Spring
Creative writing & self discovery journaling workshops. Four days, including lodging, small classes, professional warm instruction in the Rocky Mountains in Colorado. Conferences held 2nd & 4th weekends June-Sept.

Springfed Writers' Retreat
Springfed Arts
PO Box 304, Royal Oak, MI 48068-0304
Tel: 248-589-3913
Web Site: www.springfed.org
Key Personnel
Dir: John D Lamb *E-mail:* johndlamb@ameritech.net
Poets & writers conference, good writers, food & accomodations.

Squaw Valley Community of Writers Summer Workshops
Community of Writers at Squaw Valley
PO Box 1416, Nevada City, CA 95959

Tel: 530-470-8440
E-mail: info@squawvalleywriters.org
Web Site: www.squawvalleywriters.org
Key Personnel
Exec Dir: Ms Brett Hall Jones
Dir, Fiction: Lisa Alvarez; Louis B Jones
Dir, Poetry Workshop: Robert Hass
Dir, Screenwriting: Diana Fuller
Summer writing workshops; each workshop is one week long.
Membership(s): Association of Writers & Writing Programs.

The Summer Experience
Sage Hill Writing Experience Inc
601 Spadina Crescent E, Suite 718, Saskatoon, SK S7K 3G8, Canada
Mailing Address: Box 1731, Saskatoon, SK S7K 3S1, Canada
Tel: 306-652-7395 *Fax:* 306-244-0255
E-mail: sage.hill@sasktel.net
Web Site: www.sagehillwriting.ca
Key Personnel
Exec Dir: Phillip Adams
Offers a special working & learning opportunity to writers at different stages of development. Top quality instruction, a low instructor-writer ratio & the rural Saskatchewan setting offer conditions ideal for the pursuit of excellence in the arts of fiction & poetry. Application to The Summer Experience is open to writers 19 years of age & older, regardless of city, province or country of residence.

Summer Writers Program
Hofstra University
CE, 250 Hofstra University, Hempstead, NY 11549-2500
Tel: 516-463-7200 *Fax:* 516-463-4833
E-mail: ce@hofstra.edu
Web Site: ce.hofstra.edu
Key Personnel
Dir: Richard Pioreck *Tel:* 516-463-0258
E-mail: richard.j.pioreck@hofstra.edu
Two week programs featuring writing classes, readings, special guest speakers & luncheon. Dorm rooms available.

Summer Writing Seminar
Martha's Vineyard Institute of Creative Writing
7 E Pasture Rd, Aquinnah, MA 02535
Tel: 954-242-2903
Web Site: mvicw.com
Key Personnel
Dir/Prog Coord: Alexander Weinstein
E-mail: mvicwdirector@gmail.com
Annual comprehensive week-long writing program, providing writers with the necessary time to devote to their art, on the island of Martha's Vineyard. Program fee is $975, which covers participation in all workshops, evening readings, editing/ms consultation with one of the visiting poets or authors & Friday night dinner with visiting writers. Fee does not include travel or accommodations.
Location: MVICW Seminar House, 324 Main St, Vineyard Haven, MA
Date: Annually in July

Taos Summer Writers' Conference
University of New Mexico
One University of New Mexico, Albuquerque, NM 87131-0001
SAN: 213-9588
Mailing Address: Dept of English Language & Literature, One University of New Mexico, MSC03 2170, Albuquerque, NM 81313-0001
Tel: 505-277-5572
E-mail: taosconf@unm.edu
Web Site: taosconf.unm.edu
Key Personnel
Founding Dir: Sharon Oard Warner
Writing workshops & special events. All events associated with the conference - panels, presentations & readings are free & open to the public.
Location: Sagebrush Inn & Conference Center, Taos, NM

Tony Hillerman Writers Conference
WORDHARVEST LLC
1063 Willow Way, Santa Fe, NM 87507
Tel: 505-471-1565
E-mail: wordharvest@wordharvest.com
Web Site: www.wordharvest.com
Key Personnel
Founder: Anne Hillerman; Jean Schaumberg

UCI Extension Writers' Program
University of California, Irvine Extension
PO Box 6050, Irvine, CA 92616-6050
Tel: 949-824-5990 *Fax:* 949-824-3651
Web Site: www.unex.uci.edu
Key Personnel
Dir, Certificate Prog in Sustainability Leadership: Kirwan Rockefeller, PhD *Tel:* 949-824-6335
E-mail: kirwan.rockefeller@unx.uci.edu
Fiction, nonfiction & screen writing. Check catalogue for dates.
Location: University of California, Irvine Extension, Irvine, CA
Date: Check catalogue

Unicorn Writers' Conference
Unicorn Writers' Conference Inc
17 Church Hill Rd, Redding, CT 06896
Tel: 203-938-7405 *Fax:* 203-938-7405
E-mail: unicornwritersconference@gmail.com
Web Site: unicornwritersconference.com
Key Personnel
Chmn: Jan L Kardys *E-mail:* jan.kardys@gmail.com
Mktg Dir: Annie Sadlon
Sessions Dir: Emily Prescott
Following the keynote address, delivered by a best-selling author or celebrity. Offers 24 different sessions including fiction, nonfiction, memoir, mystery, poetry, screenwriting, writing for the childern's market & other major genres. How-to tutorials from publishing professionals educating writers on all aspects of publishing including contracts, copyrights, permissions, special sales, subsidiary rights, media training, promotion & platform, social media, self-publishing, book distribution & more. Features 3 agent panels & 1 editorial panel. One-to-one ms reviews available with editors, agents & faculty for an additional fee. Price $300, breakfast, lunch & dinner included. Welcome gift for all attendees. One-to-one sessions: $55 for a 30 minute session in-person private ms consultation with the faculty member, agent, editor of your choice. Query letter & book synopses reviews available also; 7:30am-8pm.
Location: Reid Castle, Purchase, NY
Date: March 2017

Visiting Writers Series
University of Alaska Fairbanks
English Dept, PO Box 755720, Fairbanks, AK 99775-5720
Tel: 907-474-7193 *Fax:* 907-474-5247
E-mail: faengl@uaf.edu
Web Site: www.alaska.edu/english
Key Personnel
Asst Professor: Daryl Farmer *E-mail:* dlfarmer@alaska.edu
Readings from & discussion of own writings; poetry, fiction, nonfiction. Other sponsors include: University of Alaska Foundation, Alaska State Council on the Arts, The National Endowment for the Arts, UAF College of Liberal Arts & UA President's Special Project Fund.
Location: Fairbanks, AK
Date: Contact for schedule

The Voices Summer Writing Workshops
Voices of Our Nations Art Foundation
Affiliate of University of San Francisco
c/o Community Initiatives Inc, 354 Pine St, Suite 700, San Francisco, CA 94104
Toll Free Tel: 866-202-6152
E-mail: info@voicesatvona.org
Web Site: www.voicesatvona.org
Key Personnel
Exec Dir: Diem Jones

Wesleyan Writers Conference
Wesleyan University
c/o Wesleyan University, 294 High St, Middletown, CT 06459
Tel: 860-685-3604 *Fax:* 860-685-2441
Web Site: www.wesleyan.edu/writing/conference
Key Personnel
Dir, Wesleyan Writers Conference: Anne Greene
E-mail: agreene@wesleyan.edu
Seminars, readings, ms consultations & talks focused on novels, short stories, film, poetry, nonfiction, journalism, multi-media work, publishing; scholarships & fellowships. Participants are welcome to attend seminars in all genres; visits from editors & agents. Award-winning writers as faculty & guest speakers.
Location: Wesleyan University, Middletown, CT
Date: Annually during the third week in June

Whidbey Island Writers Conference
Northwest Institute of Literary Arts
Old Bayview School, 5611 Bayview Rd, Langley, WA 98260
Mailing Address: PO Box 639, Freeland, WA 98249
Tel: 360-331-0307
E-mail: info@nila.edu
Web Site: www.nila.edu
Key Personnel
Conference Dir: Terry Persun *E-mail:* terry@nila.edu
Meet & learn from authors, editors & agents.

Willamette Writers' Conference
Willamette Writers
2108 Buck St, West Linn, OR 97068
Tel: 503-305-6729 *Fax:* 503-344-6174
E-mail: wilwrite@willamettewriters.com
Web Site: www.willamettewriters.com
Key Personnel
Pres: Jenny Schrader
Off Mgr: Bill Johnson
Annual summer three-day conference: consultations with over 50 national agents, editors, film agents & producers; workshops (fiction, nonfiction, children's, screen/TV, genres, craft of writing); editing room available. Year-round: monthly meetings, writing contest, workshops, newsletter.

Windbreak House Writing Retreat
Windbreak House
PO Box 169, Hermosa, SD 57744-0169
Tel: 605-255-4064
E-mail: info@windbreakhouse.com
Web Site: www.windbreakhouse.com
Key Personnel
Owner & Writer in Residence: Linda M Hasselstrom
Asst: Tamara Rogers
Retreats scheduled to suit applicants.

Winter Words Apres Ski for the Mind
Aspen Writers' Foundation
110 E Hallam St, Suite 116, Aspen, CO 81611
Tel: 970-925-3122 *Fax:* 970-920-5700
E-mail: awfinfo@aspenwriters.org
Web Site: www.aspenwriters.org

Key Personnel
Exec Dir: Lisa Consiglio *Tel:* 970-925-3122 ext 1 *E-mail:* lisa@aspenwriters.org
Prog Mgr: Natalie Lacy *Tel:* 970-925-3122 ext 3 *E-mail:* natalie@aspenwriters.org
Series of readings with remarkable writers. Also includes book signings.

Wisconsin Annual Fall Conferencee
Society of Children's Book Writers & Illustrators, Wisconsin Chapter
PO Box 259303, Madison, WI 53725
Tel: 608-278-0692
Web Site: www.scbwi.org; www.scbwi-wi.com
Key Personnel
Co-Regl Advisor: Michael Kress-Russick; Jamie Swenson
Workshop on writing & illustrating for children. Includes ms or portfolio critique. Guest faculty includes award-winning writers & illustrators.

Write on the Sound Writers' Conference
City of Edmonds Art Commission
700 Main St, Edmonds, WA 98020
Tel: 425-771-0228 *Fax:* 425-771-0253
E-mail: wots@edmondswa.gov
Web Site: www.writeonthesound.com
Key Personnel
City of Edmonds Arts & Culture Mgr: Frances Chapin
Annual event, presented the first weekend in October, with over 30 workshops by noted authors, educators & trade professionals. Features a keynote address, on-site book shop, ms critique appointments & a themed writing contest.

The Writers' Colony at Dairy Hollow
515 Spring St, Eureka Springs, AR 72632
Tel: 479-253-7444
E-mail: director@writerscolony.org
Web Site: www.writerscolony.org
Key Personnel
Dir: Linda Caldwell
See web site for upcoming events & fellowships.

Writers' League of Texas (WLT)
611 S Congress Ave, Suite 200 A-3, Austin, TX 78704
Tel: 512-499-8914
E-mail: wlt@writersleague.org
Web Site: www.writersleague.org
Key Personnel
Prog Dir: Jennifer Ziegler *E-mail:* jennifer@writersleague.org
Conferences, workshops, seminars, classes, e-mail classes.
Location: Writer's League of Texas Resource Center/Library & other locations, ongoing programs throughout Texas
Date: Ongoing throughout year

Writers Mentoring Retreat
Formerly Christian Writers' Conference
American Christian Writers
PO Box 110390, Nashville, TN 37222-0390
Tel: 615-331-8668 *Toll Free Tel:* 800-21-WRITE (219-7483)
E-mail: acwriters@aol.com
Web Site: regaforder.wordpress.com/mentoring; regaforder.wordpress.com
Key Personnel
Founder & Publr: Reg A Forder
Correspondence courses; 36 conferences annually, approximately three per month in major cities throughout the USA. Monthly magazine by subscription.
Location: Nashville, TN Mentoring Retreat
Date: April 22-23, 2016
Location: Grands Rapids, MI Mentoring Retreat
Date: June 10-11, 2016
Location: Atlanta, GA Mentoring Retreat
Date: July 8-9, 2016
Location: Minneapolis, MN Mentoring Retreat
Date: Aug 5-6, 2016
Location: Phoenix, AZ Mentoring Retreat
Date: Sept 9-10, 2016
Location: Orlando, FL Mentoring Retreat
Date: Nov 18-19, 2016

Writers Retreat Workshop (WRW)
PO Box 4236, Louisville, KY 40204
E-mail: wrw04@netscape.net
Web Site: www.writersretreatworkshop.com
Key Personnel
Founder & Creative Dir: Gail Provost Stockwell *E-mail:* gail@writeit-sellit.com
Dir: Jason S Sitzes *E-mail:* jssitzes@aol.com
WRW Ed-in-Residence: Lorin Oberweger *E-mail:* loberweger@aol.com
Ten-day intensive workshop for writers of novels-in-progress, including private writing time & space, guest speakers & consultation with New York agent or editor, author instructor, as well as diagnostic sessions of participants' mss & daily assignments. Other retreats available, see web site for details.

The Writers Workshop
The Kenyon Review
Finn House, 102 W Wiggin St, Gambier, OH 43022
Tel: 740-427-5207 *Fax:* 740-427-5417
E-mail: kenyonreview@kenyon.edu
Web Site: www.kenyonreview.org
Key Personnel
Progs Dir, The Kenyon Review: Anna Duke Reach
Intensive writing workshops for adults & teens, June & July annually.

Writers Workshop in Children's Literature
Society of Children's Book Writers & Illustrators, Florida Region
125 E Merritt Island Causeway, Suite 209, Merritt Island, FL 32952
Tel: 321-338-7208
Web Site: florida.scbwi.org
Key Personnel
Regl Advisor: Linda Rodriguez Bernfeld *E-mail:* lindabernfeld@gmail.com
Workshops in writing & illustrating picture books, juvenile & young adult fiction & nonfiction, children's magazines & marketing, given by published authors, illustrators, editors & agents.
Location: Orlando, FL
Date: June 2016

The Writing Center
601 Palisade Ave, Englewood Cliffs, NJ 07632
Tel: 201-567-4017 *Fax:* 201-567-7202
E-mail: writingcenter@optonline.net
Web Site: www.thewritingcenternj.com
Key Personnel
Dir: Barry Sheinkopf *E-mail:* bsheinkopf@optonline.net
Writing seminars, editorial services, book design & publishing services.
Location: 601 Palisade Ave, Englewood Cliffs, NJ
Date: Year-round, 12-week writing seminars; Fall seminars begin Sept; Winter seminars begin Jan; Spring seminars begin April. Five week Summer session

The Writing for Children Founders Workshops
Highlights Foundation
814 Court St, Honesdale, PA 18431
Tel: 570-253-1192 *Fax:* 570-253-0179
E-mail: jolloyd@highlightsfoundation.org
Web Site: www.highlightsfoundation.org
Key Personnel
Exec Dir: Kent L Brown, Jr *E-mail:* klbrown@highlightsfoundation.org
For children's writers & illustrators seeking to sharpen their focus. Helps to improve your craft with the help of a master, finding the time & space in which to work & marketing yourself & your books. Cost of workshops range from $495 & up which includes tuition, meals, conference supplies & housing.

Writing Workshops
UC Davis Extension
Affiliate of University of California, Davis
1333 Research Park Dr, Davis, CA 95618
Tel: 510-642-6362
E-mail: extension@ucdavis.edu
Web Site: www.extension.ucdavis.edu; writing.ucdavis.edu
Key Personnel
Dir, Univ Writing Prog: Chris Thaiss *Tel:* 530-754-9197 *E-mail:* cjthaiss@ucdavis.edu
Workshops, courses & writing institutes.
Location: University of California, Davis & Sacramento, CA
Date: Year-round, call for dates

Yaddo Artists Residency
Yaddo
312 Union Ave, Saratoga Springs, NY 12866
Mailing Address: PO Box 395, Saratoga Springs, NY 12866-0395
Tel: 518-584-0746 *Fax:* 518-584-1312
E-mail: yaddo@yaddo.org
Web Site: www.yaddo.org
Key Personnel
Pres: Elaina Richardson *E-mail:* erichardson@yaddo.org
Prog Dir: Candace Wait *E-mail:* chwait@yaddo.org
An artists' community established in Saratoga Springs, New York in 1900 by the financier Spencer Trask & his poet wife, Katrina, to offer creative artists the rare gift of a supportive environment with uninterrupted time to think, experiment & create. Over the years, Yaddo has welcomed more than 6,000 artists working in one or more of the following media: choreography, film, literature, musical composition, painting, performance art, photography, printmaking, sculpture & video. About 220 artists are invited each year for residencies lasting up to 2 months. Application deadlines are Jan 1 & Aug 1.

Young Writers' Workshop
Cape Cod Writers' Center
919 Main St, Osterville, MA 02655
Mailing Address: PO Box 408, Osterville, MA 02655
Tel: 508-420-0200
E-mail: writers@capecodwriterscenter.org
Web Site: www.capecodwriterscenter.org
Key Personnel
Pres: Jennie Wiley
Exec Dir: Nancy Rubin Stuart
Busn Mgr: Janet Gardner
Held concurrently with the annual Cape Cod Writers Conference in Aug, this program offers unique learning opportunities to young writers ages 12-18.

Courses for the Book Trade

Various courses covering different phases of the book trade are given each year. Detailed information on any of these courses can be obtained by writing directly to the sponsoring organization. For up-to-date information on book trade courses, workshops and seminars, consult the calendar section of *Publishers Weekly* (PWxyz LLC, 71 W 23 Street, Suite 1608, New York, NY 10010). For related information see **Writers' Conferences & Workshops**.

Arizona State University, Creative Writing Program
851 S Cady Mall, Rm 542, Tempe, AZ 85287-0302
Mailing Address: Dept of English, Box 870302, Tempe, AZ 85287-0302
Tel: 480-965-3528 *Fax:* 480-965-3451
Web Site: www.asu.edu/clas/english/creativewriting
Key Personnel
Prog Dir: Tara Ison *E-mail:* tara.ison@asu.edu
Prog Mgr, Creative Writing: Corey Campbell *E-mail:* corey.campbell@asu.edu
Undergraduate & graduate courses in creative writing: workshops, theory & special topics.

Arkansas State University Graphic Communications Program
PO Box 1930, Dept of Journalism & Graphic Communications, State University, AR 72467-1930
Tel: 870-972-3114 *Fax:* 870-972-3321
Web Site: www.astate.edu
Key Personnel
Dept Chair: Dr Gilbert Fowler *E-mail:* gfowler@astate.edu
Instructor, Graphic Commun: Pradeep C Mishra *Tel:* 870-972-3075 *E-mail:* pmishra@astate.edu
Courses include Digital Pre-Press Workflow & File Creation
Electronic Innovations in Graphic Communications
Graphic Communications - Estimating & Schedules
Graphic Production Systems
Internet Communications
Internship
Intro to Digital Publishing
Intro to Visual Communication
Mass Communication in Modern Society
Multi-Media Production Techniques
News Design Publication
Photography

Baylor University, Writing Program
One Bear Place, Unit 97404, Waco, TX 76798-7404
Tel: 254-710-1768 *Fax:* 254-710-3894
Web Site: www.baylor.edu
Key Personnel
Chmn: Dianna Vitanza
Comprehensive writing program.
Courses include Advanced Argumentative & Persuasive Writing
Advanced Creative Writing: Poetry
Advanced Creative Writing: Prose
Advanced Expository Writing
Advanced Writing for the Popular Market
Creative Writing: Poetry
Creative Writing: Prose
Internship in Professional Writing
Professional & Technical Writing
Screenplay & Scriptwriting
Special Topics in Writing
Thinking & Writing, Freshman Course
Thinking, Writing & Research, Freshman Course
Writing for the Popular Market
Writing for the Workplace

Binghamton University Creative Writing Program
Division of State University of New York at Binghamton
c/o Dept of English, PO Box 6000, Binghamton, NY 13902-6000
Tel: 607-777-2168 *Fax:* 607-777-2408
E-mail: cwpro@binghamton.edu
Web Site: english.binghamton.edu/cwpro
Key Personnel
Dir, Prog: Maria Gillan
Assoc Dir, Creative Writing: Christine Gelineau
Distinguished Professor: John Vernon
Professor: Jaimee Wriston Colbert; Thomas Glave; Leslie Heywood; Liz Rosenberg
Asst Professor: Joe Weil; Alexi Zentner
Asst to Chmn, Eng: Colleen Burke
Undergraduate & graduate courses.
Courses include Advanced Workshops in Creative Writing
Fiction Workshop
Fundamentals of Creative Writing
Independent Study in Creative Writing
Intermediate Creative Writing
Poetry Workshop
Studies for Writers

Boston University
236 Bay State Rd, Boston, MA 02215
Tel: 617-353-2510 *Fax:* 617-353-3653
E-mail: crwr@bu.edu
Web Site: www.bu.edu/writing
Key Personnel
Prog Dir: Leslie Epstein *E-mail:* leslieep@bu.edu
Admin Coord: Caroline Woods
Contact: Prof Ha Jin *E-mail:* xjin@bu.edu; Prof Robert Pinsky *E-mail:* rpinsky@bu.edu; Prof Richard Schotter; Prof Kate Snodgrass; Prof Rosanna Warren *E-mail:* rosanna@bu.edu
Workshops. Offer a one-year Master's degree MSA in creative writing.
Courses include Fiction
Poetry

Bowling Green State University, Creative Writing Program
Dept of English, 211 East Hall, Bowling Green, OH 43403
Tel: 419-372-2576 *Fax:* 419-372-0333
Web Site: www.bgsu.edu/departments/creative-writing
Key Personnel
Dir & Advisor: Sharona Muir *E-mail:* smuir@bgsu.edu
Providers of comprehensive & rigorous education in professional writing, editing & marketing of poetry & fiction, since 1967.
Courses include Advanced Fiction Writing Workshop
Advanced Poetry Writing Workshop
Assistant Editing, Mid-American Review
Graduate Writers' Workshop in Poetry, Fiction
Studies in Contemporary Poetry, Fiction
Techniques of Fiction
Techniques of Poetry

The Center for Book Arts
28 W 27 St, 3rd fl, New York, NY 10001
Tel: 212-481-0295 *Toll Free Fax:* 866-708-8994
E-mail: info@centerforbookarts.org
Web Site: www.centerforbookarts.org
Key Personnel
Exec Dir: Alexander Campos *E-mail:* acampos@centerforbookarts.org
Offers classes & workshops during three semesters each year.
Courses include Hand Bookbinding
Hand Papermaking
Letterpress Printing

College of Liberal & Professional Studies, University of Pennsylvania
3440 Market St, Suite 100, Philadelphia, PA 19104-3335
Tel: 215-898-7326 *Fax:* 215-573-2053
E-mail: lps@sas.upenn.edu
Web Site: www.sas.upenn.edu; www.sas.upenn.edu/lps
Key Personnel
Vice Dean & Assoc Dir: Nora Lewis *E-mail:* nlewis@sas.upenn.edu
Dir, Progs: Kristine Rabberman, PhD
Writing courses, beginning through advanced, taught by published authors; non-residential; fees vary; program catalog available for writing courses Sept-July.

Columbia Publishing Course at Columbia University
2950 Broadway, MC 3801, New York, NY 10027
Tel: 212-854-1898 *Fax:* 212-854-7618
E-mail: publishing@jrn.columbia.edu
Web Site: www.journalism.columbia.edu/publishing
Key Personnel
Dir: Shaye Areheart *E-mail:* sea2148@columbia.edu
Asst Dir: Stephanie Chan *Tel:* 212-854-9775 *E-mail:* swc37@columbia.edu
Provides an intensive introduction to book, magazine & digital publishing. Students learn the entire publishing process from established publishing professionals & gain hands-on experience from evaluations of original mss to the sales & marketing of finished products.
Courses include Book, Magazine & Digital Publishing

Columbia University School of the Arts, Creative Writing Program
Division of Columbia University
617 Kent Hall, New York, NY 10027
Tel: 212-854-3774 *Fax:* 212-854-7704
E-mail: writingprogram@columbia.edu
Web Site: www.columbia.edu/cu/writing
Key Personnel
Chair, Creative Writing: Binnie Kirshenbaum
Dir, Undergraduate Creative Writing: Stacey D'Erasmo
Prog Asst, Creative Writing: Dorla McIntosh
Courses include Fiction
Nonfiction
Poetry

EEI Communications
6301 Ivy Lane, Suite 250, Greenbelt, MD 20770
Tel: 410-309-8200 *Fax:* 410-630-3980
E-mail: info@eeicom.com
Web Site: www.eeicom.com

Key Personnel
CEO & Pres: Gregory K McDonough
Dir, Edit Servs: Sheila Gagen
Dir, Training: Joe Robinson *E-mail:* jrobinson@eeicom.com
Publishing courses, basic through advanced level. Classes held in Alexandria, VA, Silver Spring, MD & Washington, DC & at client facilities. Visit our web site for schedule & fees.
Courses include Design
Desktop Publishing
Editing
Grammar
Graphics
Mac & PC Training
New Media
Photo Manipulation
Production
Proofreading
Publications Management & Newsletters
Web Site Development
Word Processing
Writing

The Lisa Ekus Group LLC
57 North St, Hatfield, MA 01038
Tel: 413-247-9325 *Fax:* 413-247-9873
Web Site: lisaekus.com
Key Personnel
Principal & Pres: Lisa Ekus *E-mail:* lisaekus@lisaekus.com
Assoc Dir, Media Training: Carl Raymond
Literary Assoc: Sally Ekus *E-mail:* sally@lisaekus.com
Comprehensive 1 or 2 day media training programs designed for cookbook authors, chefs, product spokespeople, show hosts & food professionals. Participants will spend their day(s) under the lights & in front of the camera, taping & critiquing actual television demonstrations of varying lengths. Courses are typically held in the professional kitchen of our Hatfield, MA, offices but off-site training is available. Visit culinarymediatraining.com to learn more.
Courses include Cookbook Publishing 101
Honing Your Edge: Media Training for Culinary Professionals
One-On-One Media Training

Emerson College Department of Writing, Literature & Publishing
180 Tremont St, 10th fl, Boston, MA 02116
Mailing Address: 120 Boylston St, Boston, MA 02116-4624
Tel: 617-824-8750 *Fax:* 617-824-7856
Web Site: www.emerson.edu
Key Personnel
Chair: Jerald Walker
Graduate Prog Dir, MA in Publg & Writing: Lisa Diercks *E-mail:* lisa_diercks@emerson.edu
Offers BA, MA, BFA & MFA degrees in publishing & writing.
Courses include Applications for Publishing
Book Design & Production
Book Editing
Book Marketing & Sales
Book Publicity
Book Publishing Overview
Column Writing
Copyediting
Creating Electronic Publications
Digital Publishing for Tablets & Handheld Devices
Editor-Writer Relationship
Electronic Publishing Overview
Magazine Design & Production
Magazine Editing
Magazine Publishing Overview
Magazine Writing
Principles of Management for Publishing
Web Development for Electronic Publishing

Fordham University, Graduate School of Business Administration
Gabelli School of Business, 441 E Fordham Rd, Hughes Hall, Rm 516, Bronx, NY 10458
Tel: 718-817-1894
Web Site: www.bnet.fordham.edu
Key Personnel
Chair/Mktg: Dawn Lerman
Professor: Albert N Greco *E-mail:* agreco@fordham.edu
Offers MBA degree with a major in Communications & Media Management. MBA Graduate courses & additional MBA course work.
Courses include Accounting
Marketing with Public Relations
The Book Publishing Industry
Broadcast & Cable Marketing & Advertising Sales Business & Legal Aspects of Cable TV
Broadcast Management
Business & the Mass Media
Consumer Behavior
Coping with Global Corporate Crisis
Corporate Power & the Public
Direct Marketing
Economics
Executive Communications
Finance
Information & Communications Systems
International Marketing
Legal & Ethical Studies
Magazine Management
Managing Newspapers & Their Electronic Ventures
Marketing Management, Advertising & Media Planning
Mass Media in America
New Media & Mass Communications
Persuasion in Public Relations
Public Relations & Broadcasting
Public Relations as a Management Tool
Sales Management
Special Topics in Communications & Media Management: Book Publishing
The Press, the Law & the Corporation

Gaylord College of Journalism & Mass Communication, Professional Writing Program
Division of University of Oklahoma
c/o University of Oklahoma, 395 W Lindsey St, Rm 3534, Norman, OK 73019-0270
Tel: 405-325-2721 *Fax:* 405-325-7565
Web Site: www.ou.edu/gaylord
Key Personnel
Professor, Prof Writing: J Madison Davis *Tel:* 405-325-4171 *E-mail:* jmadisondavis@ou.edu
Coursework on writing for commercial publication.
Courses include Analyzing Category Fiction
Film Script Writing
Magazine Article Writing
Short Story Writing
Writing The Novel

The Graphic Artists Guild Inc
32 Broadway, Suite 1114, New York, NY 10004
Tel: 212-791-3400 *Fax:* 212-791-0333
Web Site: www.graphicartistsguild.org
Key Personnel
Pres: Haydn Adams *E-mail:* president@gag.org
Exec Dir: Patricia McKiernan *Tel:* 212-791-3400 ext 15 *E-mail:* admin@gag.org
Business workshops & seminars for professional graphic artists.
Eastern, Midwestern, New England, Southern & Western regional chapters.

Graphic Arts Association
1210 Northbrook Dr, Suite 200, Trevose, PA 19053
Tel: 215-396-2300 *Fax:* 215-396-9890
E-mail: gaa@gaaonline.org
Web Site: www.gaa1900.com
Key Personnel
Pres & Dir, Membership: Melissa Jones *E-mail:* mjones@gaaonline.org
Regional trade association for the printing industry serving Pennsylvania, southern New Jersey & Delaware.
Courses include Computer Laptop Training
Estimating
Graphic Arts Fundamentals
Industrial Relations Training
Production
Sales & Management

Hamilton College, English/Creative Writing
English/Creative Writing Dept, 198 College Hill Rd, Clinton, NY 13323
Tel: 315-859-4370 *Fax:* 315-859-4390
E-mail: english@hamilton.edu
Web Site: www.hamilton.edu
Key Personnel
Chair, Dept of Eng: Onno Oerlemans *E-mail:* ooerlema@hamilton.edu
Professor, Eng: Catherine Kodat *E-mail:* ckodat@hamilton.edu; Doran Larson *E-mail:* dlarson@hamilton.edu
Assoc Professor, Eng: Tina Hall *E-mail:* thall@hamilton.edu
Academic program; students may concentrate on creative writing. Three faculty members who specialize in creative writing courses.

Hofstra University, English Dept
204 Mason Hall, Hempstead, NY 11549
Tel: 516-463-5454
Web Site: www.hofstra.edu
Key Personnel
Professor, Eng: Joseph Fichtelberg, PhD *E-mail:* joseph.fichtelberg@hofstra.edu
Dir, Creative Writing Progs: Erik A Brogger *E-mail:* erik.a.brogger@hofstra.edu
Undergraduate courses in all phases of publishing & creative writing, leading to a BA in English. MA in English Literature & an MFA in creative writing.

Hollins University-Jackson Center for Creative Writing
PO Box 9677, Roanoke, VA 24020
Tel: 540-362-6317 *Fax:* 540-362-6097
E-mail: creative.writing@hollins.edu
Web Site: www.hollins.edu
Key Personnel
Dir: Prof Thorpe Moeckel
BA degree in English with concentration in creative writing - 4 academic years; MFA in creative writing - 2-year program in residency.

Louisiana State University Creative Writing Program MFA
English Dept, 260 Allen Hall, Baton Rouge, LA 70803
Tel: 225-578-5922 *Fax:* 225-578-4129
Web Site: www.lsu.edu; www.english.lsu.edu/dept/programs/grad/creative_writing
Key Personnel
Dir, Creative Writing: Laura Mullen *Tel:* 225-578-3049 *E-mail:* lmullen@lsu.edu
Asst Dir: Randolph Thomas *Tel:* 225-578-2830 *E-mail:* rndlpht@aol.com
A graduate program leading to the degree of Master of Fine Arts in creative writing.
Courses include Drama Workship, ENGL 7008
Fiction Workshop, ENGL 7006
Poetry Workshop, ENGL 7007
Screenwriting Workshop, ENGL 7009

Manhattanville College Master of Arts in Writing Program
2900 Purchase St, Purchase, NY 10577
Tel: 914-323-5239 *Fax:* 914-323-3122
Web Site: www.mville.edu/writing

Key Personnel
Dir, MAW Prog: Karen Sirabian
E-mail: sirabiank@mville.edu
Offers courses with faculty who are well-known published writers & poets, all of whom are dedicated to helping writers explore their craft, sharpen their skills & take their writing to the next level - all within a thriving literary community. In addition, students can build on the skills gained in the editing & production course through work on our award-winning journal "Inkwell", which gives them the editorial & production experience to succeed in publishing.
Courses include Editing & Production Workshop
Fiction Workshop
Nonfiction Workshop
Poetry Workshop
Writing for Children & Young Adults
Writing the Contemporary Novel

Massachusetts College of Art & Design Writing Children's Literature
Affiliate of Massachusetts College of Art and Design Continuing Education Dept
621 Huntington Ave, Boston, MA 02115
Tel: 617-879-7200 *Fax:* 617-879-7171
E-mail: ce@massart.edu
Web Site: www.massart.edu/ce
Key Personnel
Dean, Prof & Continuing Educ: Anne Marie Stein
College.
Courses include Book Design
Computer Graphics
Design
Fine Arts
Illustrating Children's Books
Typography

McNeese State University, Writing Program
PO Box 92655, Lake Charles, LA 70609-0001
Tel: 337-475-5325; 337-475-5327
Web Site: www.mcneese.edu.com; www.mfa.mcneese.edu
Key Personnel
Dir, MFA Prog & Coord, Poetry Series: Amy Fleury *E-mail:* afleury@mcneese.edu
Asst Professor, Eng & Fiction: Alex Taylor
E-mail: alextaylor1@mcneese.edu
MFA program in creative writing - 60 hour program.
Courses include Contemporary Novel
Contemporary Poetry
Creative Writing Workshop-Fiction
Creative Writing Workshop-Poetry
Form & Theory of Fiction I
Form & Theory of Fiction II
Form & Theory of Poetry I
Form & Theory of Poetry II

Midwest Publishing Association Webinars
310 W Lake St, Suite 111, Elmhurst, IL 60126
Tel: 630-833-4220 *Fax:* 630-563-9181
E-mail: info@midwestpublish.org
Web Site: www.midwestpublish.org
Key Personnel
Exec Dir: Kimberly LaBounty
Various webinars for publishers, manufacturers, freelancers & printers involved in all publishing markets.

Mississippi Review/University of Southern Mississippi, Center for Writers
Affiliate of University of Southern Mississippi, Dept of English
118 College Dr 5144, Hattiesburg, MS 39406-0001
Tel: 601-266-5600 *Fax:* 601-266-5757
Web Site: www.usm.edu/english/c4w.html; www.usm.edu/english/mississippireview.html
Key Personnel
Ed-in-Chief: Andrew Milward
Graduate & undergraduate courses in fiction & poetry writing.
Mississippi Review.

New York City College of Technology
Division of City University of New York
300 Jay St, Brooklyn, NY 11201
Tel: 718-260-5500 *Fax:* 718-260-5198
E-mail: connect@citytech.cuny.edu
Web Site: www.citytech.cuny.edu
Key Personnel
Pres: Russell K Hotzler, PhD *Tel:* 718-260-5400
E-mail: rhotzler@citytech.cuny.edu
Dir, Graphic Arts Dept: Lloyd Carr *Tel:* 718-260-5822 *E-mail:* lcarr@citytech.cuny.edu
Two year or four year degree in graphic arts, certificates, associates or baccalaureate.
Courses include Advertising
Printing & Publishing

New York University, Center for Publishing
Affiliate of School of Continuing Education
Midtown Ctr, Rm 429, 11 W 42 St, New York, NY 10036
Tel: 212-992-3232 *Fax:* 212-992-3233
E-mail: pub.center@nyu.edu
Web Site: www.scps.nyu.edu/publishing
Key Personnel
Academic Prog Dir & Clinical Asst Professor: Andrea L Chambers
Asst Dir: Sarah McCarthy *E-mail:* sarah.mccarthy@nyu.edu
Offers a certificate in publishing, consisting of five courses. Individual courses may be taken. A total of 13 book, 14 magazine & 7 online publishing. Also offers a certificate in editing with 10 courses each year. The Summer Publishing Institute is an intensive residential program for recent college graduates, planning to enter the publishing industry. Consists of three week module in book publishing & three week module in magazine publishing, each including an overview of the industry, lectures, workshops, field trips & professional simulations, job fair & placement assistance. Application deadline; April 1 MS in publishing; contact Assoc Dir Alyssa Leal. Program consists of 42 graduate credits chosen from a required core of courses in the functional areas of publishing & a concentration in either book or magazine publishing. Courses are all offered in the evening.
Courses include Advanced Copyediting
Advanced Magazine Editing
Advanced Special Project in Publishing
Advertising in Magazines
Advertising Sales & Integrated Marketing for Business-to-Business Publishers
The Basics of the Book Publishing Industry: Today & Tomorrow
Book Design Strategies
Book Editing
Book Marketing
Book Packaging
Book Production & Manufacturing
Book Publicity, Promotion
Books from Writer to Reader: An Overview of the Publishing Process
Bookselling: From Publisher to Reader
The Business of Book Publishing: Financial Management in a Creative Environment
The Business of Business-to-Business Publishing
The Business of Online Publishing
The Business of Publishing for US Hispanic Markets
Children's Book Publishing
The Circulation Challenge: Newsstand, Retail & Speciality Outlets
Controlled Circulation
Cookbook Copyediting
Copyediting & Proofreading Fundamentals
Cross-Media Programs: The Future of Magazine Advertising Sales
Developmental Editing
Disk & Online Editing
The Economics of Magazine Publishing
Economics of Publishing
Editing Periodicals
Effective Marketing in Publishing Via the Digital Channels
Electronic Content Development
Electronic Publishing for Print & Online Part 1: Survey
Electronic Publishing for Print & Online Part II: Portfolio
E-mail Newsletters
The Evolving Business of Custom Publishing
Fact Checking
Financial Analysis I: Introduction to Financial Statement Analysis in Publishing
Financial Copyediting
Freelance Book Indexing
Fundamentals of Copyediting
Fundamentals of Proofreading
Globalization & the Web
Grammar for Publishing Professionals
How to Develop Your Career in Publishing
How to Market Your Freelance Editorial Services
How to Self-Publish Successfully & Profitably in Today's Market–An Intensive Two-Day Seminar
The Independent Publisher: How to Start, Sustain & Build a Small Press
Information Technology Management in Publishing
International Magazine Publishing
International Publishing
Internship
Journal Copyediting & Production
The Laws of Book Publishing: A Practical Guide to Contracts, Copyright & More
Legal Proofreading
Magazine Advertising Sales & Marketing
Magazine Branding & Franchise Development
Magazine Circulation
Magazine Copyediting
Magazine Editorial Planning & Management
Magazine Financial Management
Magazine Production & Manufacturing
Magazine Promotion, Events & Public Relations
Magazine Research: New Techniques to Accelerate Recovery Growth
Magazines from Mission to Magic & More: An Overview
Managing the Publishing Enterprise
Manuscript Editing
Marketing for Publishing
Media Ethics for Publishing Professionals
Mentored Academic Study
Multi-Channel Sales Promotion for Books
Multimedia Marketing & Product Development
ONIX: How Good Product Information Improves Sales
Online Publishing: Business, Technology & Strategy
Principles & Applications of Publishing on the Internet
Principles of Profitability in Book Publishing
Print Technology for Publishing
Production Editing
Professional Book & Information Publishing
Publishing: Books, Magazines & Multimedia
Publishing in Cyberspace: Legal & Practical Problems of Internet & Electronic Publishing
Publishing Law: Issues in Intellectual Property
Publishing On-Line
The Role of the Literary Agent in Book Publishing
Scientific, Technical & Medical Journal Copyediting
Scientific, Technical & Medical Journal Copyediting & Production
Scientific, Technical, Professional Publishing on the Internet
Secrets to Success in Magazine Freelance Writing & Editing

Special Sales, Licensing & Merchandising for Books
Starting a Small Book Publishing Co
Summer Institute in Book & Magazine Publishing
Trade & General Book Publishing
Usability: Information Architecture & the User Experience in Publishing
Web Marketing & E-Commerce
Web Page Development With HTML

Ohio University, English Dept, Creative Writing Program
Ohio University, English Dept, Ellis Hall, Athens, OH 45701
Tel: 740-593-2838 (English Dept) *Fax:* 740-593-2832
E-mail: english.department@ohio.edu
Web Site: english.ohiou.edu
Key Personnel
Dir: Dinty W Moore *E-mail:* moored4@ohio.edu
Offer PhD degree with creative writing emphasis.
Courses include Fiction
Form & Theory
Nonfiction
Novels
Poetry
Short Stories

Pace University, Master of Science in Publishing
Dept of Publishing, Rm 805-E, 551 Fifth Ave, New York, NY 10176
Tel: 212-346-1431 *Toll Free Tel:* 877-284-7670 *Fax:* 212-346-1165
Web Site: www.pace.edu/dyson/mspub
Key Personnel
Chmn & Dir, Publg Progs: Sherman Raskin *E-mail:* sraskin@pace.edu
Program educates its students in all pertinent aspects of the publishing business: books, magazines & digital publishing. Our graduates are equipped for the challenges facing the industry today.
Courses include Book Production & Design, PUB 606
Children's Book Publishing, PUB 634
Digital Issues in Publishing
Ebooks: Technology, Workflow & Business Model, PUB 621
Editorial Principles & Practices, PUB 634
Electronic Publishing for Publishers, PUB 636
Financial Aspects of Publishing, PUB 608
General Interest Books, PUB 610
Information Systems in Publishing, PUB 612
Legal Aspects of Publishing, PUB 618
Magazine Production & Design, PUB 607
Marketing Principles & Practices in Publishing, PUB 628
Modern Technology in Publishing, PUB 620
Publishing Comics & Graphic Novels, PUB 610
Subsidiary Rights, Acquisitions & the Function of the Literary Agent, PUB 610
The Future of Publishing: Transmedia, PUB 613

Parsons School of Design, Continuing Education
Division of New School University
66 Fifth Ave, New York, NY 10011
Tel: 212-229-8933 *Fax:* 212-229-5970
E-mail: ceinformation@newschool.edu; academy@newschool.edu
Web Site: www.parsons.edu/ce
Comprehensive courses & advanced courses appropriate for book, magazine & advertising design.
Courses include Graphic & Advertising Design

Publishing Certificate Program at City College
Division of Humanities NAC 5225, City College of New York, New York, NY 10031
Tel: 212-650-7925 *Fax:* 212-650-7912
E-mail: ccnypub@aol.com
Web Site: www.ccny.cuny.edu/publishing_certificate/index.html
Key Personnel
Dir: David Unger
Asst Dir: Retha Powers
Program for undergraduates. Take four of 20 courses offered & then qualify for a paid internship in a publishing house of your interest.
Courses include Books for Young Readers
Copyediting & Proofreading, etc
Ebooks & Digital Publishing
The Editorial Process
Introduction to Publishing I & II
Legal Issues in Publishing

Rochester Institute of Technology, School of Print Media
69 Lomb Memorial Dr, Rochester, NY 14623-5603
Tel: 585-475-2728; 585-475-5336 *Fax:* 585-475-5336
E-mail: spmofc@rit.edu
Web Site: cias.rit.edu/printmedia
Key Personnel
Chmn, School of Printing: Pat Sorce, PhD *Tel:* 585-475-2313 *E-mail:* psorce@mail.rit.edu
Classes in books & magazine production, typography, printing design, computer use, desktop prepress production, management, sales, finishing & bindery, quality control, marketing, finance & legal problems of publishing.
Courses include Computer Use
Desktop Prepress Production
Finance & Legal Problems of Publishing
Finishing & Bindery
Management
Marketing
Printing Design
Quality Control
Sales
Typography

Rosemont College
Graduate Publg Prog, 1400 Montgomery Ave, Rosemont, PA 19010
Tel: 610-527-0200 (ext 2336) *Fax:* 610-526-2964
Web Site: www.rosemont.edu
Key Personnel
Dir, Graduate Publg Progs: Anne Converse-Willkomm
Offers MA degree in publishing.
Courses include Business of Publishing
Children's & Young Adult
Design
Editorial

School of Visual Arts
209 E 23 St, New York, NY 10010-3994
Tel: 212-592-2100 *Fax:* 212-592-2116
Web Site: www.sva.edu
Key Personnel
Exec Dir, Admissions & Student Aff: Javier Vega
Non-degree programs beginning in Sept, Jan & June, including intensive two-week workshops.
Courses include Advertising & Graphic Design
Artists' Books'
BFA Programs in Advertising & Graphic Design
Book Cover Design & Illustration Book Design
Book Illustration & Children's Book Writing & Illustration
Cartooning
Computer Art & Photography
Computer Graphics
Copywriting
Editorial Design
Fine Arts
Illustration & Cartooning
Interior Design & Photography
MAT in Art Education
MFA Programs in Fine Arts Illustration
Photographic Printing Processes
Type & Design Agency Skills
Video Recording & Editing

Susquehanna University, Department of English
514 University Ave, Selinsgrove, PA 17870
Tel: 570-372-0101
Key Personnel
Professor, Eng: Laurence Roth
Assoc Professor, Communs: Katherine Hastings
Assoc Professor, Creative Writing: Karla Kelsey
Assoc Professor, Eng: Randy Robertson
Asst Professor, Creating Writing: Catherine Dent-Zobal
Courses include Editing, COMM:331 Intermediate focused subject course that focuses on the challenges & issues confronted in editing for journalism & teaches the process of editing a newspaper
Internship, ENGL:540 Working with internships available in publishing or editing either on- or off-campus
Introduction to Modern Publishing, ENGL:190 Introduces students to the history of modern publishing, to the process, art & business of producing books
Publishing: Entertainment, Art, Politics, Ethics, ENGL:388 Analyzes changes & continuities in the cultural role of publishing from the beginning of mass printing to the current day
Small Press Editing & Publishing, WRIT:270 Intermediate focused subject course that focuses on the challenges & issues faced by small literary presses. Students learn to edit fiction, poetry, nonfiction & memoirs

Syracuse University Creative Writing Program
401 Hall of Languages, Syracuse, NY 13244-1170
Tel: 315-443-2173 *Fax:* 315-443-3660
Web Site: english.syr.edu/creative_writing; www.syr.edu
Key Personnel
Dir: Christopher Kennedy *E-mail:* ckennedy@syr.edu
Assoc Dir: Sarah C Harwell *E-mail:* scharwel@syr.edu
Courses include Eastern European Poetry/Translation
The Essay
Fiction Workshop
The Forms of Fiction
The Forms of Poetry
Open Workshop - Fiction
Open Workshop - Poetry
Poetry Workshop
Prose Writing
Writing of Fiction
Writing of Poetry
Writing the Novella

Syracuse University, SI Newhouse School of Public Communications
215 University Place, Syracuse, NY 13244-2100
Tel: 315-443-3627 *Fax:* 315-443-3946
E-mail: newhouse@syr.edu
Web Site: newhouse.syr.edu
Key Personnel
Dean: Lorraine Branham
Undergraduate degrees in advertising; broadcast & arts journalism, magazine, newspaper & online journalism; public relations; television, radio, film; visual & interactive communications; photography & graphics; Master's degrees in advertising; magazine; newspaper; media administration; visual & interactive communications; public relations; television-radio & film. PhD degrees in mass communications.
Courses include Advertising
Broadcast, Magazine & Newspaper Journalism
Film
Media Administration

Photography
Public Relations
Radio
Television

University of Alabama Program in Creative Writing
Affiliate of University of Alabama, Dept of English
PO Box 870244, Tuscaloosa, AL 35487-0244
Tel: 205-348-5065 *Fax:* 205-348-1388
E-mail: english@ua.edu
Web Site: www.as.ua.edu/english
Key Personnel
Poet & Professor: Robin Behn *Tel:* 205-348-8488 *E-mail:* rbehn@english.as.ua.edu
Poet & Assoc Professor: Joel Brouwer *Tel:* 205-348-9524 *E-mail:* joel.brouwer@ua.edu
Poet & Asst Professor: Peter Streckfus *Tel:* 205-348-6265 *E-mail:* plstreckfus@bama.ua.edu
Fiction Writer & Professor: Michael Martone *Tel:* 205-348-5526 *E-mail:* mmartone@english.as.ua.edu
Fiction Writer & Assoc Professor: Wendy Rawlings *Tel:* 205-348-4507 *E-mail:* wendy.rawlings@ua.edu
Graduate Coord: Carol Appling *Tel:* 205-348-9493 *E-mail:* cappling@ua.edu
Three-year MFA degree program & creative writing course for undergraduates, minor in creative writing. See web site for details.

University of Baltimore - Yale Gordon College of Arts & Sciences, Ampersand Institute for Words & Images
Division of Klein Family School of Communications Design
1420 N Charles St, Baltimore, MD 21201-5779
Tel: 410-837-6022 *Fax:* 410-837-6029
E-mail: scd@ubalt.edu
Web Site: www.ubalt.edu
Key Personnel
Dir: Edwin Gold *E-mail:* egold@ubalt.edu
Academic Prog Specialist: Jaye Crooks
Sponsors Fall & Spring lecture series, conducts advanced seminars, workshops, mini-courses & conferences on publishing topics including writing, design; also supports through the School of Communications Design, a Masters of Arts program in Publications Design, an MFA in Integrated Design & an MFA in Creative Writing & Publishing Arts.

University of California Extension Professional Sequence in Copyediting & Courses in Publishing
1995 University Ave, Suite 110, Berkeley, CA 94720-7000
Tel: 510-642-6362 *Fax:* 510-643-0216
E-mail: letters@unex.berkeley.edu
Web Site: www.unex.berkeley.edu
Key Personnel
Prog Dir: Liz McDonough *Tel:* 510-643-1637
Certificate program in editing; evening/weekend courses & one-day seminars.
Courses include Editing
Management
Screenwriting
Writing (fiction, poetry, nonfiction)

University of Chicago, Graham School of General Studies
Division of Professional Programs
1427 E 60 St, Chicago, IL 60637
Tel: 773-702-1722 *Fax:* 773-702-6814
Web Site: www.grahamschool.uchicago.edu
Key Personnel
Prog Dir: Amber Neff *Tel:* 773-702-1682 *E-mail:* aneff@uchicago.edu
Noncredit courses.
Courses include Basic Creative Writing
Elements of Novel Writing
Getting the Story: Freelance Journalism Workshop
Intensive Short Story Workshop
Introduction to Freelance Journalism
Memoir Writing
Poetry Workshop: Outside the Self
Screenwriting Workshop
Writing Novels for Children & Young Adults
Writing the Novel 1
Writing the Novel 2
Writing the Personal Essay

The University of Connecticut, The Realities of Publishing
CLAS, 215 Glenbrook Rd, Unit 4025, Storrs, CT 06269-4025
Tel: 860-486-2141
Web Site: web.uconn.edu/english291
Key Personnel
Dept Head: Wayne Franklin *E-mail:* wayne.franklin@uconn.edu
This course provides a background for undergraduate students interested in professional careers in writing & publishing. Lectures by practitioners describe varied careers. Topics include: Professional Writing Format, Desktop Publishing, Journalism & Freelance Writing, Magazine & Book Publishing. Also offer Introduction to HTML, Ndesign & Dreamweaver.

University of Denver Publishing Institute
2000 E Asbury Ave, Denver, CO 80208
Tel: 303-871-2570 *Fax:* 303-871-2501
Web Site: www.du.edu/publishinginstitute
Key Personnel
Dir: Jill Smith *E-mail:* jill.smith@du.edu
Four-week graduate program in book publishing held July-Aug each year. Provides hands on workshops, lecture-teaching sessions on every phase of book publishing. Faculty consists of leading executives from publishing houses across the country. Emphasis on career counseling & job placement. Offers six quarter hours of graduate credit.
Courses include Children's Books
College Textbooks
E-Books
Economics of Publishing
Editing Workshop
Foreign Rights
Independent Presses
International Publishing
Marketing on the Internet
Marketing Workshop
Production & Design
Publicity & Promotion
Publishing & the Law
Reference Publishing in an Electronic World
Scholarly Books
Special Session on Magazine Publishing
Trade & Scholarly Books
University Presses

University of Houston Creative Writing Program
Affiliate of Hollins University Dept of English
229 Roy Cullen Bldg, Houston, TX 77204-5008
Tel: 713-743-2255 *Fax:* 713-743-3697
E-mail: cwp@uh.edu
Web Site: www.uh.edu/cwp
Key Personnel
Dir: Jay Kastely
Prog Coord: Shatera Anderson
Offers MA, MFA & PhD in creative writing.

University of Illinois at Chicago, Program for Writers
Affiliate of University of Illinois, Dept of English
College of Liberal Arts & Sciences, 2027 University Hall, 601 S Morgan St, Chicago, IL 60607-7120
Tel: 312-413-2200 (Eng Dept) *Fax:* 312-413-1005
Web Site: www.uic.edu
Key Personnel
Dir, Prog for Writers: Cris Mazza *Tel:* 312-413-2795 *E-mail:* cmazza@uic.edu
Graduate program for writers. Students in this program take literature classes as well as writing workshops. Offers MA & PhD in writing. Undergraduates seeking a BA in English may also specialize in writing.
Courses include Experimental Writing Workshop
Fiction Workshop
Nonfiction Workshop
Novel Workshop
Poetry Workshop
Publication Workshop
Translation Practicum

University of Illinois, Department of Journalism
Unit of College of Communications, University of Illinois
Gregory Hall, Rm 120-A, 810 S Wright St, Urbana, IL 61801
Tel: 217-333-0709 *Fax:* 217-333-7931
E-mail: journ@uiuc.edu
Web Site: www.comm.uiuc.edu
Key Personnel
Dept Head: Prof Brian Johnson *Tel:* 217-333-2103 *E-mail:* bjk@illinois.edu
Master's degree program.
Courses include Graphics
Magazine Article Writing
News Editing
Photojournalism
Reporting I & II

University of Iowa, Writers' Workshop, Graduate Creative Writing Program
102 Dey House, 507 N Clinton St, Iowa City, IA 52242-1000
Tel: 319-335-0416 *Fax:* 319-335-0420
Web Site: writersworkshop.uiowa.edu
Key Personnel
Dir: Lan Samantha Chang
Graduate: fiction & poetry workshops & seminars. Undergraduate: creative, fiction & poetry writing.

University of Missouri-Kansas City, New Letters Weekend Writers Conference
College of Arts & Sciences, Continuing Education Div, 5300 Rockhill Rd, Kansas City, MO 64110
Tel: 816-235-2736 *Fax:* 816-235-5279
Web Site: www.umkc.edu
Key Personnel
Contact: Sharon Seaton *Tel:* 816-235-2736 *E-mail:* seatons@umkc.edu
State University: a variety of credit & noncredit courses on creative writing including fiction, poetry, essays & short stories.
Courses include Essay
Fiction
Poetry
Short Story

University of Montana, Environmental Writing Institute
Subsidiary of Environmental Studies Program
Environmental Studies, University of Montana, Missoula, MT 59812
Tel: 406-243-2904 *Fax:* 406-243-6090
Web Site: www.umt.edu/ewi
Key Personnel
Prog Mgr & Dir: Phil Condon *E-mail:* phil.condon@mso.umt.edu
Writing workshop for environmental & nature subjects.

University of Southern California, Master of Professional Writing Program
Mark Taper Hall, THH 355, 3501 Trousedale Pkwy, Los Angeles, CA 90089-0355
Tel: 213-740-3252 *Fax:* 213-740-5002
E-mail: mpw@college.usc.edu
Web Site: college.usc.edu/mpw
Key Personnel
Dir: Brighde Mullins
Prog Specialist: Howard Ho
Student Servs Advisor: Natalie Inouye
Multi-disciplinary Creative Writing Master's program & Master's of Arts degree in Professional Writing.
Courses include Creative Nonfiction
Fiction
New Media
Poetry
Writing for Stage & Screen

University of Texas at Austin, Creative Writing Program
Dept of English, PAR 108, One University Sta, Mailcode B5000, Austin, TX 78712-1164
Tel: 512-471-5132; 512-471-4991 *Fax:* 512-471-4909
Web Site: www.utexas.edu/cola/depts/english/creative-writing
Key Personnel
Chair, Poetry: Dean Young *E-mail:* deanyoung@mail.utexas.edu
Professor Emeritus: Zulfikar A Ghose *E-mail:* zulfj@mail.utexas.edu
Professor: Laura Furman *E-mail:* ljfurman@mail.utexas.edu; Kurt Heinzelman *E-mail:* kheinz@mail.utexas.edu; Rolando Hinojosa-Smith *E-mail:* rorro@mail.utexas.edu
Professor, Creative Writing: Peter N La Salle
Professor, Fiction: James Magnuson *E-mail:* magnuson@mail.utexas.edu
Professor: Thomas Whitbread *E-mail:* whitbread@mail.utexas.edu
Assoc Professor: Michael W Adams *E-mail:* adameve@austin.utexas.edu
Asst Professor: Oscar H Casares *E-mail:* ocasares@yahoo.com
Graduate Prog Coord I: Amy Stewart *Tel:* 512-471-5132 *E-mail:* amy.d.stewart@austin.utexas.edu
Graduate Prog Coord II: Patricia Schaub *E-mail:* gradeng@uts.cc.utexas.edu
A full range of poetry & fiction writing courses is offered, leading to the MA degree in English with concentration in creative writing.

University of Texas at El Paso, Department of Creative Writing, MFA/Department of Creative Writing
Liberal Arts 415 UTEP, 500 W University Ave, El Paso, TX 79968-9991
Tel: 915-747-5713 *Fax:* 915-747-5523
Web Site: www.utep.edu/cw
Key Personnel
Chair, Bilingual MFA: Prof Johnny Payne *Tel:* 915-747-5758 *E-mail:* jpayne@utep.edu
Dept Chair & Professor: Benjamin Alire Saenz *Tel:* 915-747-5721 *E-mail:* bsaenz@utep.edu
Professor: Luis Arturo Ramos *Tel:* 915-747-6511 *E-mail:* laramos@utep.edu
Assoc Professor: Rosa Alcala *Tel:* 915-747-7020 *E-mail:* ralcala1@utep.edu; Daniel Chacon *Tel:* 915-747-6255 *E-mail:* danchacon@utep.edu; Lex Williford *Tel:* 915-747-8806 *E-mail:* lex@utep.edu
Monolingual & bilingual workshops in fiction, poetry, playwriting, screenwriting, nonfiction & literary translation.

University of Wisconsin-Madison Continuing Studies
21 N Park St, 7th fl, Madison, WI 53715
Tel: 608-262-1156
E-mail: info@dsc.wisc.edu
Web Site: continuingstudies.wisc.edu
Key Personnel
Faculty Assoc: Christine DeSmet *Tel:* 608-262-3447 *E-mail:* cdesmet@dcs.wisc.edu
Writing book trade & online writing courses offered, in-person retreats & conferences.
Courses include Critique Services
Weekend With Your Novel Retreat
Write-by-the Lake Writer's Retreat
Writers' Institute Conference

Vermont College of Fine Arts MFA in Writing for Children & Young Adults Program
36 College St, Montpelier, VT 05602
Tel: 802-828-8637; 802-828-8696
Toll Free Tel: 866-934-VCFA (934-8232)
Fax: 802-828-8649
Web Site: www.vcfa.edu
Key Personnel
Prog Dir: Melissa Fisher *E-mail:* melissa.fisher@vcfa.edu
Asst Prog Dir: Shannon Dixon *E-mail:* shannon.dixon@vcfa.edu
Writing for children & young adults. Intensive 10-day residencies & nonresident 6-month writing projects.

Vermont College of Fine Arts, MFA in Writing Program
36 College St, Montpelier, VT 05602
Tel: 802-828-8840; 802-828-8839
Toll Free Tel: 866-934-VCFA (934-8232)
Fax: 802-828-8649
Web Site: www.vcfa.edu
Key Personnel
Prog Dir: Louise Crowley *E-mail:* louise.crowley@vcfa.edu
Asst Prog Dir: Rachel Muehlmann *Tel:* 802-828-8839 *E-mail:* rachel.muehlmann@vcfa.edu
Degree work in poetry, fiction, creative nonfiction.

Warren Wilson College, MFA Program for Writers
701 Warren Wilson Rd, Swannanoa, NC 28778
Mailing Address: PO Box 9000, Asheville, NC 28815-9000
Tel: 828-771-3717 *Fax:* 828-771-7005
E-mail: mfa@warren-wilson.edu
Web Site: www.warren-wilson.edu/~mfa
Key Personnel
Dir, MFA Prog: Debra Allberry
Full-time 2-year program with winter & summer semesters. Ten-day residency of classes, workshops & lectures on campus. The six-month project that follows is supervised through correspondence, with detailed ms criticism by faculty who are both accomplished writers & committed teachers.
Courses include Fiction
Poetry

Writer's Digest University
Division of F+W, A Content + eCommerce Company
10151 Carver Rd, Suite 200, Blue Ash, OH 45242-4760
Tel: 513-531-2690 *Toll Free Tel:* 800-759-0963
Fax: 513-531-0798
E-mail: contact_us@fwmedia.com
Web Site: www.writersonlineworkshops.com
Key Personnel
Online Prodn Mgr: Kevin Quinn
Course workshops are taught by active, published writers in the appropriate area, such as fiction & nonfiction. Students participate online, via the Internet. Workshops range in length from 4 to 28 weeks. Correspondence; student has up to 2 years to complete; tuition installment plans available for most courses.
Courses include 28 Days to Your First WordPress Site, Nonfiction Writing
Advanced Poetry Writing, Specialty Workshops
Blogging 101, Marking and Building a Platform
Breaking into Copywriting, Freelance/Copywriting
Business Writing, Specialty Workshops
Character Development, Fiction Writing Workshops
Conflict and Suspense, Fiction Writing Workshops
Creativity & Expression, Getting Started
Description and Setting, Fiction Writing Workshops
Dialogue, Fiction Writing Workshops
Fiction Writing 101: Fundamentals, Fiction Writing Workshops
Fiction Writing 102: Building Your Novel, Fiction Writing Workshops
Fiction Writing 103: 12 Weeks to Your First Draft, Fiction Writing Workshops
Fiction Writing 104: Advanced Novel Writing, Fiction Writing Workshops
Fitting Writing Into Your Life, Getting Started
Focus on the Short Story, Short Story/Memoir
Form and Composition, Getting Started
Freelance Writing for Stay at Home Moms, Freelance/Copywriting
Fundamentals of Poetry Writing, Specialty Workshops
Getting Started in Writing, Getting Started
Ghostwriting, Freelance/Copywriting
Grammar and Mechanics, Getting Started
Magazine Article Writing, Freelance/Copywriting
Marketing Your Magazine Articles, Nonfiction Writing
Master in Fine Arts Application Preparation Workshop, Graduate Preparation Workshops
Outlining Your Novel, Getting Started
Plot and Structure, Fiction Writing Workshops
Revision & Self Editing, Preparing for Publication
Social Media 101, Nonfiction Writing
Successful Self-Publishing, Preparing for Publication
Technical Writing, Specialty Workshops
The Art of Storytelling 101: Storymapping and Pacing, Fiction Writing Workshops
Travel Writing, Specialty Workshops
Turning Your Personal Essays into a Memoir, Short Story/Memoir
Voice and Viewpoint, Fiction Writing Workshops
Writing a Memoir 101, Short Story/Memoir
Writing a Memoir 102, Short Story/Memoir
Writing a Religious Book, Specialty Workshops
Writing Nonfiction 101: Fundamentals, Nonfiction Writing
Writing Nonfiction 102: Advanced, Nonfiction Writing
Writing Nonfiction for Children, Graduate Preparation Workshops
Writing the Middle Grade Book, Specialty Workshops
Writing the Mystery Novel, Specialty Workshops
Writing the Nonfiction Book Proposal, Preparing for Publication
Writing the Novel Proposal, Preparing for Publication
Writing the Paranormal Novel, Specialty Workshops
Writing the Personal Essay 101: Fundamentals, Short Story/Memoir
Writing the Picture Book, Specialty Workshops
Writing the Query Letter, Preparing for Publication
Writing the Romance Novel, Specialty Workshops
Writing the Science Fiction & Fantasy Novel, Specialty Workshops
Writing the Young Adult Novel, Specialty Workshops

Awards, Prize Contests, Fellowships & Grants

Major awards given to books, authors and publishers by various organizations are, for the most part, not open for application. However, many prize contests may be applied for by writing to the sponsor (for prompt response, always include a self-addressed, stamped envelope). Also included in this section is information relating to fellowships and grants that are primarily available to authors and students who are pursuing publishing related studies.

For more complete information about scholarships, fellowships and grants-in-aid, see *The Annual Register of Grant Support* (Information Today, Inc., 121 Chanlon Rd, Suite G-20, New Providence, NJ 07974-2195).

AAUP Book, Jacket & Journal Design Show
Association of American University Presses (AAUP)
28 W 36 St, Suite 602, New York, NY 10018
Tel: 212-989-1010 *Fax:* 212-989-0275
E-mail: info@aaupnet.org
Web Site: www.aaupnet.org
Key Personnel
Exec Dir: Peter Berkery *Tel:* 212-989-1010 ext 29 *E-mail:* pberkery@aaupnet.org
Dir of Mktg & Communs: Brenna McLaughlin *Tel:* 518-436-3586 *E-mail:* bmclaughlin@aaupnet.org
Off Mgr & Program Administrator: Kim Miller *Tel:* 212-989-1010 ext 26 *E-mail:* kmiller@aaupnet.org
Established: 1965
Excellence in design; competition limited to member presses in AAUP.
Award: Certificate, winning entries are displayed in a traveling exhibit
Presented: AAUP Annual Meeting, Annually in June

ABZ First Book Poetry Prize
ABZ Press
PO Box 2746, Huntington, WV 25727-2746
Tel: 304-638-5701
E-mail: abzpoetry@gmail.com
Web Site: abzpress.sharepoint.com
Key Personnel
Publr & Ed: John McKernan
Established: 2006
Biennial contest for the first full-length book of poems. Reading fee is $30 which entitles the entrant to one copy of the winning book.
Closing Date: May 1-June 30, 2016

Acclaim Film Script Competition
Acclaim Film
300 Central Ave, Suite 501, St Petersburg, FL 33701
Web Site: acclaimscripts.com
Key Personnel
Contest Coord: Frank Drouzas
Open to all writers 18 & over.
Award: $1,000 (1st place)
Closing Date: Ongoing

Acclaim TV Script Competition
Acclaim Film
300 Central Ave, Suite 501, St Petersburg, FL 33701
Web Site: acclaimscripts.com
Key Personnel
Contest Coord: Frank Drouzas
Open to all writers 18 & over. Must be original material of the author. Categories are Spec Scripts (for an existing show), Pilots & Movie of the Week.
Award: $500 for each category
Closing Date: Ongoing

Milton Acorn Poetry Award
Prince Edward Island Writers' Guild
115 Richmond St, Charlottetown, PE C1A 1H7, Canada
Tel: 902-368-4410 *Toll Free Tel:* 888-734-2784 *Fax:* 902-368-4418
E-mail: peiwritersguild@gmail.com
Web Site: www.peiwritersguild.com
Key Personnel
Exec Dir: Darrin White *Tel:* 902-368-6176 *E-mail:* dwhite@peica.ca
Maximum of 8-10 pages of poetry. May submit as many entries as they wish. The work must be original & unpublished. Typewritten & double-spaced on one side of the page only. Entry fee: $20. Contest is for Prince Edward Island residents only. Must be resident for six of the 12 months prior to the contest deadline. For further information call or e-mail.
Award: $400 (1st prize), $200 (2nd prize), $100 (3rd prize)

Herbert Baxter Adams Prize
American Historical Association (AHA)
400 "A" St SE, Washington, DC 20003
Tel: 202-544-2422 *Fax:* 202-544-8307
E-mail: awards@historians.org
Web Site: www.historians.org
Established: 1905
For a distinguished book by an American author in the field of European history, from ancient times through 1815. Entry must be the author's first substantial book; must have been published in 2014 or 2015; must be citizen or permanent resident of the US or Canada. Submission of an entry may be made by an author or by a third party as well as by a publisher. Publishers may submit as many entries as they wish. Along with an application form, applicants must mail a copy of their book to each of the prize committee members who will be posted on our web site as the prize deadline approaches. All updated info on web site.
Award: Cash prize
Closing Date: May 15, 2016 (postmark)
Presented: AHA Annual Meeting, Denver, CO, Jan 5-8, 2017

Jane Addams Children's Book Award
Jane Addams Peace Association
777 United Nations Plaza, 6th fl, New York, NY 10017
Tel: 212-682-8830
E-mail: japa@igc.org
Web Site: www.janeaddamspeace.org
Key Personnel
Award Comm Co-Chair: Ann Carpenter; Heather Palmer
Exec Dir: Linda Belle
Established: 1953
Awarded to children's books published in the U.S. the previous year with themes stressing peace, social justice, world community & the equality of the sexes & all races. Those applying must submit one copy to either current committee chair: Ann Carpenter, Brooks Free Library, 739 Main St, Harwich, IA 02645 or Heather Palmer, Valley View Middle School, 6750 Valley View Rd, Edina, MN 55439.
Award: Certificate; Cash
Closing Date: Annually, Dec 31
Presented: Winners announced April 28; ceremony held third Friday in Oct annually

AFCP's Annual Awards
Association of Free Community Papers (AFCP)
7445 Morgan Rd, Suite 103, Liverpool, NY 13090
Toll Free Tel: 877-203-2327 *Fax:* 781-459-7770
E-mail: afcp@afcp.org
Web Site: www.afcp.org
Key Personnel
Exec Dir: Loren Colburn *E-mail:* loren@afcp.org
Established: 1970
Awards for excellence in 40 categories, revolving around the theme of free community papers.
Award: 1st, 2nd & 3rd place plaques, honorable mention certificates
Closing Date: Annually, Jan 31
Presented: AFCP's Annual Conference

Agatha Awards
Malice Domestic Ltd
PO Box 8007, Gaithersburg, MD 20898-8007
E-mail: malicedomesticpr@gmail.com
Web Site: www.malicedomestic.org
Key Personnel
Malice Dom Chair: Verena Rose *E-mail:* malicebodchair@malicedomestic.org
Agatha Awards Comm Memb: Marian Lesko *Tel:* 301-730-1675 *E-mail:* malice23agathas@aol.com
Established: 1989
Awards for best traditional mysteries of the calendar year. Awards given for best novel, best first novel, best nonfiction work, best short story, best children's/young adult novel.
Closing Date: Annually, Dec 31
Presented: Malice Domestic Conference, Agatha Awards Banquet, Annually in May

Aggiornamento Award
Catholic Library Association
8550 United Plaza Blvd, Suite 1001, Baton Rouge, LA 70809-2256
Tel: 225-408-4417
E-mail: cla2@cathla.org
Web Site: www.cathla.org
Key Personnel
Pres: Mary Kelleher *Tel:* 225-408-4417 *E-mail:* kellehm@stthom.edu
Established: 1980
To recognize contributions made by an individual or an organization for the renewal of parish & community life in the spirit of Pope John XXIII.
Award: Plaque
Closing Date: None; in-house votes
Presented: CLA Annual Convention

AIGA 50 Books/50 Covers
AIGA, the professional association for design
233 Broadway, 17th fl, New York, NY 10279
Tel: 212-807-1990 *Fax:* 212-807-1799
E-mail: competitions@aiga.org
Web Site: www.aiga.org

Key Personnel
Dir, Competitions & Exhibitions:
Gabriela Mirensky *Tel:* 212-710-3143
E-mail: gabriela_mirensky@aiga.org
Established: 1924
Annual award for excellence of design in books & book covers (complete sets of all books selected since 1924 at Columbia University Library - Rare Book Dept).
Award: Certificate of excellence, publication in AIGA annual, exhibition in 5th Avenue Gallery
Closing Date: Annually in March
Presented: Annually in Sept

AJL Judaica Bibliography Award
Association of Jewish Libraries (AJL) Inc
Affiliate of American Library Association (ALA)
PO Box 1118, Teaneck, NJ 07666
Tel: 201-371-3255
E-mail: ajlibs@osu.edu
Web Site: www.jewishlibraries.org
Key Personnel
Pres: Heidi Estrin *E-mail:* president@jewishlibraries.org
Ref & Bibliography Awards Comm Chair: Sharon Benamou *E-mail:* benamou@library.ucla.edu
Established: 1984
For best Judaica bibliography book published in previous calendar year.
Award: The seal of the Association
Closing Date: Annually in March
Presented: AJL Annual Convention, Annually in June

AJL Judaica Reference Award
Association of Jewish Libraries (AJL) Inc
Affiliate of American Library Association (ALA)
PO Box 1118, Teaneck, NJ 07666
Tel: 201-371-3255
E-mail: ajlibs@osu.edu
Web Site: www.jewishlibraries.org
Key Personnel
Pres: Heidi Estrin *E-mail:* president@jewishlibraries.org
Ref & Bibliography Awards Comm Chair: Sharon Benamou *E-mail:* benamou@library.ucla.edu
Established: 1984
Annual award for outstanding Judaica reference book published during previous calendar year.
Award: The seal of the Association
Closing Date: Annually in March
Presented: AJL Annual Convention, Annually in June

AJL Scholarship
Association of Jewish Libraries (AJL) Inc
Affiliate of American Library Association (ALA)
PO Box 1118, Teaneck, NJ 07666
Web Site: www.jewishlibraries.org
Key Personnel
Curator, Spec Collections: Shulamith Berger
In order to encourage students to train for & enter the field of Judaica librarianship, the Association of Jewish Libraries awards a scholarship to a student attending or planning to attend a graduate school of library & information science. Prospective candidates should have an interest in & demonstrate a potential for pursuing a career in Judaica librarianship. In addition, applicants must provide documentation showing participation in Judaica studies at an academic or less formal level +/or experience working in Judaica libraries.
Award: $1,000 per academic year
Closing Date: March 15-April 15 (varies by year)
Presented: AJL Annual Convention, June

AKC Publications Fiction Contest
American Kennel Club Publications
260 Madison Ave, New York, NY 10016
Web Site: www.akc.org/pubs/fictioncontest
Open to anyone. Entries must be original, unpublished stories that have not been offered to or accepted by any other publisher. Only one entry per author. The publisher retains the right to publish the 3 prize-winning entries in an AKC publication. Entries may feature either a purebred or mixed breed dog. Maximum length is 2,000 words. Winners based on the style, content, originality & appeal of the story.
Award: $500 (1st place), $250 (2nd place), $100 (3rd place)

Akron Poetry Prize
The University of Akron Press
The University of Akron Press, 120 E Mill St, Suite 415, Akron, OH 44308
Tel: 330-972-6953 *Fax:* 330-972-8364
E-mail: uapress@uakron.edu
Web Site: www.uakron.edu/uapress/akron-poetry-prize
Key Personnel
Poetry Ed: Mary Biddinger
Established: 1995
Open to all poets writing in English. Mss must be at least 48 pages. Entry fee: $25.
Award: $1,500 & publication
Closing Date: Annually April 15-June 15 (postmarked)
Presented: Winner announced online Sept 30

Alabama Artists Fellowship Awards
Alabama State Council on the Arts
201 Monroe St, Suite 110, Montgomery, AL 36130-1800
Tel: 334-242-4076 *Fax:* 334-240-3269
Key Personnel
Exec Dir: Albert B Head
Lit Prog Mgr: Anne Kimzey *Tel:* 334-242-4076 ext 236 *E-mail:* anne.kimzey@arts.alabama.gov
Awarded based on quality of work +/or career status, achievement & potential; two-year residency required.
Award: Cash; Two $5,000 fellowships
Closing Date: March 1
Presented: Annually, Oct 1

Alberta Book Awards
The Book Publishers Association of Alberta (BPAA)
10523 100 Ave, Edmonton, AB T5J 0A8, Canada
Tel: 780-424-5060 *Fax:* 780-424-7943
E-mail: info@bookpublishers.ab.ca
Web Site: www.bookpublishers.ab.ca
Key Personnel
Exec Dir: Kieran Leblanc *E-mail:* kleblanc@bookpublishers.ab.ca
Established: 1989
Excellence in writing & publishing within the province of Alberta.
Award: Sculpture, certificate
Closing Date: Annually in Jan
Presented: Annually in May

Alcuin Society Awards for Excellence in Book Design in Canada
Alcuin Society
PO Box 3216, Vancouver, BC V6B 3X8, Canada
Tel: 604-733-1204; 604-732-5403
E-mail: awards@alcuinsociety.com
Web Site: www.alcuinsociety.com
Key Personnel
Dir & Chair, Book Design Competition Comm: Leah Gordon
Established: 1981
Recognizes the work of Canadian book designers & publishers through the Alcuin Citations awarded for excellence in book design & production. Must fulfill the following criteria: titles published exclusively in Canada or titles co-published with a publisher in another country but representing a book by a Canadian book designer. Categories are: children, limited editions, pictorial, poetry, prose fiction, prose nonfiction, prose nonfiction illustrated, reference.
Award: Certificate
Closing Date: Annually in March
Presented: Awards ceremonies in Toronto & Vancouver, Annually in Oct

Nelson Algren Awards
Chicago Tribune
Subsidiary of Tribune Co
Chicago Tribune, TT200, 435 N Michigan Ave, Chicago, IL 60611
Toll Free Tel: 800-874-2863 *Fax:* 312-222-5816
E-mail: nelsonalgren@tribune.com
Web Site: www.chicagotribune.com/about
Key Personnel
Book Ed: Elizabeth Taylor *E-mail:* etaylor@tribune.com
Established: 1982
Given for an outstanding unpublished short fiction, double-spaced & less than 10,000 words in length, by an American writer. No entry form or fee required. Entries will not be returned. Entries by mail only to Nelson Algren Awards at the above address: include cover letter with address, phone & e-mail, do not put name on the ms; no telephone or e-mail inquiries.
Award: $5,000 & three runners-up awards of $1,500 each
Closing Date: Annually in Feb
Presented: Chicago, IL, Annually in Autumn

The Aliant Creative Writing Award for Young People
Prince Edward Island Writers' Guild
115 Richmond St, Charlottetown, PE C1A 1H7, Canada
Tel: 902-368-4410 *Toll Free Tel:* 888-734-2784 *Fax:* 902-368-4418
E-mail: peiwritersguild@gmail.com
Web Site: www.peiwritersguild.com
Key Personnel
Exec Dir: Darrin White *Tel:* 902-368-6176 *E-mail:* dwhite@peica.ca
Elementary, junior & high school students may write on the topic of their choice & submit in 1 of 4 categories: Early Elementary (grades 1-3), Late Elementary (grades 4-6), Junior High (grades 7-9) & Senior High (grades 10-12). A maximum of 5 pages of poetry or 10 page short story will constitute an entry. No entry fee. Residents only. For more information contact PEI Council of the Arts at address above.
Award: $100 (1st prize), $75 (2nd prize), $50 (3rd prize)

Alligator Juniper's National Writing Contest
Prescott College, Alligator Juniper
220 Grove Ave, Prescott, AZ 86301
Tel: 928-350-2012
E-mail: alligatorjuniper@prescott.edu
Web Site: www.alligatorjuniper.org
Established: 1995
Stories have a 30 page limit per entry or up to five poems. Entry fee $15; no e-mail submissions.
Award: $1,000 plus publication in fiction, creative nonfiction & poetry
Closing Date: Annually, Aug 15-Oct 1 (postmark)
Presented: Annually, Oct 1

ALSC BWI/Summer Reading Program Grant
Association for Library Service to Children (ALSC)
Division of The American Library Association (ALA)
50 E Huron St, Chicago, IL 60611-2795
Tel: 312-280-2163 *Toll Free Tel:* 800-545-2433 *Fax:* 312-440-9374
E-mail: alsc@ala.org
Web Site: www.ala.org/alsc

Key Personnel
Exec Dir: Aimee Strittmatter *Tel:* 312-280-2162 *E-mail:* astrittmatter@ala.org
Awards Coord: Caroline Jewell *E-mail:* alscawards@ala.org
Prog Coord: Marsha P Burgess *E-mail:* mburgess@ala.org
Encourages reading programs for children in a public library. Applicant must plan & present an outline for a theme-based summer reading program in a public library.
Award: $3,000
Closing Date: Annually, Dec 1
Presented: ALA Midwinter Meeting, Annually in Jan

Amazon Breakthrough Novel Award
Amazon Publishing
c/o Amazon Services LLC, 8329 W Sunset Rd, Suite 200, Las Vegas, NV 89113
Web Site: www.amazon.com
Award for an English language fiction ms. Only one digital entry permitted. Categories: General Fiction, Romance, Mystery/Thriller, Science Fiction/Fantasy/Horror, Young Adult Fiction.
Entrant must first register at createaspace.com/abna & submit full ms (50,000-125,000 words), excerpt from beginning of novel (3,000-5,000 words), novel pitch (up to 300 words) & accompanying contest & biographical information.
Other Sponsor(s): Amazon Content Services LLC; Amazon Services LLC; Audible Inc; On-Demand Publishing LLC (dba CreateSpace)
Award: Publishing contracts to 5 winners; 50,000 grand prize & four 15,000 first prize awards

American Association of University Women Award for Juvenile Literature
AAUW, North Carolina Division
Affiliate of North Carolina Literary & Historical Association
4610 Mail Service Ctr, Raleigh, NC 27699-4610
Tel: 919-807-7290 *Fax:* 919-733-8807
Key Personnel
Awards Coord: Michael Hill *E-mail:* michael.hill@ncdcr.gov
Established: 1953
For a published work of juvenile fiction or nonfiction by a legal or actual resident of North Carolina for at least three years prior to the end of the contest period.
Other Sponsor(s): AAUW
Award: Cup
Closing Date: Annually, July 15
Presented: Raleigh, NC, Annually in Nov

American Book Award
Before Columbus Foundation
The Raymond House, 655 13 St, Suite 302, Oakland, CA 94612
SAN: 159-2955
Tel: 510-268-9775
E-mail: info@beforecolumbusfoundation.com
Web Site: www.beforecolumbusfoundation.com
Key Personnel
Founder: Ishmael Reed
Established: 1978
To recognize outstanding literary achievement by contemporary American authors without restriction for race, sex, ethnic background or genre. The purpose is to acknowledge the excellence & multicultural diversity of American writing. The awards are nonprofit. There are no categories & all winners are accorded equal status. Award is given for books published within the current year. No application forms or fees. Must submit two copies of each entry.
Award: Plaque
Closing Date: Annually, Dec 31
Presented: Berkeley, CA, Annually in Oct

American Illustration/American Photography
Amilus Inc
Subsidiary of Fadner Media
15 E 32 St, 7th fl, New York, NY 10016
Tel: 212-470-0302 *Fax:* 212-532-2064
E-mail: info@ai-ap.com
Web Site: www.ai-ap.com
Key Personnel
Dir: Mark Heflin *E-mail:* mark@ai-ap.com
Established: 1985
For the finest illustrative work by students & professionals. Categories include: editorial, advertising & books, as well as unpublished work. Work will be published in the American Illustration annual & will include the artist's name, address & telephone. Also, similar competition & annual for photography called American Photography. Both books are published in Nov.
Closing Date: Annually, Jan 23 (photography), Feb 20 (illustration)
Presented: The Party, New York City, Nov, Annually in Nov

American Printing History Association Award
American Printing History Association
PO Box 4519, Grand Central Sta, New York, NY 10163
Tel: 202-544-2422
Web Site: printinghistory.org
Key Personnel
Pres: Robert McCamant
VP, Pubns: James P Ascher
VP, Membership: Casey Smith
Established: 1976
For achievement in the printing world or in closely related fields.
Award: Two framed award certificates, one for an individual & one for an institution
Presented: APHA meeting, New York, NY, Annually in Jan

AMWA Medical Book Awards
American Medical Writers Association (AMWA)
30 W Gude Dr, Suite 525, Rockville, MD 20850-4357
Tel: 240-238-0940 *Fax:* 301-294-9006
E-mail: amwa@amwa.org
Web Site: www.amwa.org
Key Personnel
Awards Liaison: Rachel Spassiani
All medical books published in previous year are eligible for the current year's competition.
Award: Trophy

The Amy Award
Poets & Writers Inc
90 Broad St, Suite 2100, New York, NY 10004
Tel: 212-226-3586 *Fax:* 212-226-3963
E-mail: admin@pw.org
Web Site: www.pw.org
Presented to women poets age 30 and under living in the New York metropolitan area or on Long Island.
Award: Honorarium & reading in New York City

Amy Writing Awards
The Amy Foundation & World News Group
PO Box 16091, Lansing, MI 48901-6091
Tel: 517-323-6233 *Toll Free Tel:* 877-727-4262 *Fax:* 517-321-2572
E-mail: amyawards@worldmag.com
Web Site: www.worldmag.com/amyawards
Key Personnel
Pres: Jim Russell
Exec Dir: Mary Spagnuolo
Established: 1985
For writing that presents the Biblical position on issues affecting the world today. To be eligible, submitted articles must be published in a secular, non-religious journalistic outlet & contain a scriptural quote. Must have been published during current calendar year. See web site for submission form.
Award: $10,000 (1st prize), $5,000 (2nd prize), $4,000 (3rd prize), $3,000 (4th prize), $2,000 (5th prize), $1,000 (outstanding merit, 10 prizes)
Closing Date: Jan 31
Presented: The Amy Foundation, Lansing, MI

Hans Christian Andersen Award
US Board on Books For Young People (USBBY)
c/o V Ellis Vance, 5503 N El Adobe Dr, Fresno, CA 93711-2363
Tel: 559-351-6119
E-mail: executive.director@usbby.org
Web Site: www.usbby.org
Key Personnel
Exec Dir: V Ellis Vance *E-mail:* executive.director@usbby.org
Established: 1956
Two medals are awarded biennially, one to an author & one to an illustrator, for their complete oeuvre. An Honor List is established with the books chosen by the National Sections of the International Board on Books for Young People (IBBY). Each section chooses three books from among those published in the country during the preceding biennium: for writing, illustrating & translating.
Award: Medals & honor list
Presented: IBBY Congress, Biennially in even-numbered years

The Anisfield-Wolf Book Awards
The Cleveland Foundation
1422 Euclid Ave, Suite 1300, Cleveland, OH 44115
Tel: 216-861-3810 *Fax:* 216-861-1729
E-mail: awinfo@clevefdn.org
Web Site: www.anisfield-wolf.org; www.clevelandfoundation.org
Key Personnel
CEO & Pres, Cleveland Foundation: Ronald B Richard
Jury Chmn: Henry Louis Gates, Jr
Mgr: Karen R Long
Established: 1935
Recognizes books that have made important contributions to our understanding of racism or our appreciation of the diversity of human cultures.
Award: $10,000 fiction prize (divided equally among fiction winners); $10,000 nonfiction prize (divided equally among nonfiction winners); $5,000 honorarium given to Lifetime Achievement winner
Closing Date: Dec 31

R Ross Annett Award for Children's Literature
Writers' Guild of Alberta
11759 Groat Rd, Edmonton, AB T5M 3K6, Canada
Tel: 780-422-8174 *Toll Free Tel:* 800-665-5354 (AB only) *Fax:* 780-422-2663 (attn WGA)
E-mail: mail@writersguild.ab.ca
Web Site: www.writersguild.ab.ca
Key Personnel
Exec Dir: Carol Holmes *E-mail:* carol.holmes@writersguild.ab.ca
Communs & Partnerships Coord: Nicholas Mather *E-mail:* nicholas.mather@writersguild.ab.ca
Memb Servs Coord: Giorgia Severini
Progs Coord: Natalie Cook *E-mail:* natalie.cook@writersguild.ab.ca; Nichole Quiring *E-mail:* nichole.quiring@writersguild.ab.ca
Established: 1982
Alternates yearly between picture & chapter books.
Award: $1,500
Closing Date: Annually, Dec 31
Presented: Alberta Book Awards Gala

Branch Office(s)
505 21 Ave SW, Calgary, AB T2S 0G9, Canada, Prog Coord: Samantha Warwick *Tel:* 403-265-2226 *E-mail:* samantha.warwick@writersguild.ab.ca

Annual Off Off Broadway Short Play Festival
Samuel French Inc
235 Park Ave S, 5th fl, New York, NY 10003
Tel: 212-206-8990 *Toll Free Tel:* 866-598-8449 *Fax:* 212-206-1429
E-mail: oobfestival@samuelfrench.com
Web Site: oob.samuelfrench.com; www.samuelfrench.com
Key Personnel
Festival Coord: Casey McLain *E-mail:* cmclain@samuelfrench.com
Artistic Coord: Amy Rose Marsh *E-mail:* amarsh@samuelfrench.com
Festival Mktg & Outreach: Ryan Pointer *E-mail:* rpointer@samuelfrench.com
Established: 1975
Selected plays are presented on the final day of the festival.
Award: Publication of top 6 plays
Closing Date: Jan-late Feb
Presented: Annually in July or Aug

Anthony Awards
Bouchercon World Mystery Convention
605 Third Ave, 16th fl, New York, NY 10158
Tel: 917-670-9645
Web Site: www.bouchercon.info
Literary awards for mystery writers. Nominations accepted from full-time registrants of the event & those of the immediately preceding event. Categories: Best Novel, Best First Novel, Best Paperback Original, Best Short Story, Best Critical Nonfiction Work. Three possible wildcard categories.
Presented: Bouchercon World Mystery Convention, New Orleans, LA, Sept 15-18, 2016

The Applegate/Jackson/Parks Future Teacher Scholarship
National Institute for Labor Relations Research
5211 Port Royal Rd, Suite 510, Springfield, VA 22151
Tel: 703-321-9606 *Fax:* 703-321-7143
E-mail: research@nilrr.org
Web Site: www.nilrr.org
Key Personnel
Scholarship Administrator: Cathy Jones
Based solely on scholastic ability demonstrating an understanding of compulsory unionism in education.
Award: $1,000
Closing Date: Annually, Dec 31 (postmark or electronic submission)
Presented: Annually in April

The May Hill Arbuthnot Honor Lecture Award
Association for Library Service to Children (ALSC)
Division of The American Library Association (ALA)
50 E Huron St, Chicago, IL 60611-2795
Tel: 312-280-2163 *Toll Free Tel:* 800-545-2433 *Fax:* 312-440-9374
E-mail: alsc@ala.org
Web Site: www.ala.org/alsc
Key Personnel
Exec Dir: Aimee Strittmatter *Tel:* 312-280-2162 *E-mail:* astrittmatter@ala.org
Awards Coord: Caroline Jewell *E-mail:* alscawards@ala.org
Prog Coord: Marsha P Burgess *E-mail:* mburgess@ala.org
Person appointed prepares a paper of significant contribution to the field of children's literature & delivers a lecture based on the paper in April. Libraries & other institutions apply to host the lecture. The paper is also published in the ALSC journal "Children & Libraries".
Award: $1000
Closing Date: Annually, May 1
Presented: The ALA Midwinter Meeting, Annually in Jan

Arkansas Diamond Primary Book Award
Arkansas State Library
Arkansas State Library, Suite 100, 900 W Capitol Ave, Little Rock, AR 72201-3108
Tel: 501-682-2860 *Fax:* 501-682-1693
Web Site: www.library.arkansas.gov; www.library.arkansas.gov
Key Personnel
Coord, Children's Progs: Cathy Howser *E-mail:* cathy@library.arkansas.gov
Established: 1999
To encourage reading for students in grades K-3. The Arkansas Department of Education & the Arkansas State Library support selected books that students all over Arkansas read or have read to them. The students vote for the one book they most enjoyed & the winning title recieves the award.
Other Sponsor(s): Arkansas Reading Association
Award: Medallion for first place, plaque for Honor Book
Closing Date: Annual vote in April
Presented: Little Rock, AR, Annually in Nov

Artist Grants
South Dakota Arts Council
Affiliate of Department of Tourism
711 E Wells Ave, Pierre, SD 57501-3369
Tel: 605-773-3301 *Fax:* 605-773-5977
E-mail: sdac@state.sd.us
Web Site: www.artscouncil.sd.gov/grants
Key Personnel
Dir: Michael Pangburn
Awards made to residents of South Dakota, based on the quality of art work.
Award: $1,000-$5,000
Closing Date: Annually, March 1

Artist-in-Residence Program
New Brunswick Arts Board (Conseil des arts du Nouveau-Brunswick)
649 rue Queen, 2nd fl, Fredericton, NB E3B 1C3, Canada
Tel: 506-444-4444 *Toll Free Tel:* 866-460-ARTS (460-2787) *Fax:* 506-444-5543
E-mail: nbabcanb@artsnb.ca
Web Site: www.artsnb.ca
Key Personnel
Exec Dir: Akoulina Connell *Tel:* 506-444-4343 *E-mail:* execdirgen@artsnb.ca
Deputy Dir: Vanessa Moeller *Tel:* 506-292-4696 *E-mail:* vmoeller@artsnb.ca
Prog Offr: Joss Richer *Tel:* 506-478-4610 *E-mail:* jricher@artsnb.ca
Intended for New Brunswick public or private institutions & organizations that wish to host professional artists in order to enable them to pursue specific projects relating to their creative work. This program is also open to individual professionals who seek to advance their creative work through participation in residency opportunities at home or outside the province. The artists in residence are to contribute to the promotion & understanding of the arts by means of the artists' contact with the clientele of the establishments.
Closing Date: Feb 1

Artist Projects Grants
Arizona Commission on the Arts
417 W Roosevelt St, Phoenix, AZ 85003-1326
Tel: 602-771-6501 *Fax:* 602-256-0282
E-mail: info@azarts.gov
Web Site: www.azarts.gov
Key Personnel
Grants & IT Mgr: Ginny Berryhill *E-mail:* gberryhill@azarts.gov
Arizona poets, fiction & nonfiction writers only.
Award: Cash up to $5,500
Closing Date: Sept

Artists' Fellowships
New York Foundation for the Arts
20 Jay St, 7th fl, Brooklyn, NY 11201
Tel: 212-366-6900 *Fax:* 212-366-1778
E-mail: info@nyfa.org
Web Site: www.nyfa.org
Key Personnel
Exec Dir: Michael Royce *E-mail:* mroyce@nfya.org
Interim Dir, Progs: Susan Ball *E-mail:* sball@nyfa.org
Fellowship, application limited to New York State residents. Applications in nonfiction literature & poetry; applications will be available online in mid-July. Grants awarded in 16 artistic disciplines.
Award: $7,000
Closing Date: Annually in Dec
Presented: New York, NY

Arts & Letters Awards
American Academy of Arts & Letters
633 W 155 St, New York, NY 10032
Tel: 212-368-5900 *Fax:* 212-491-4615
E-mail: academy@artsandletters.org
Web Site: www.artsandletters.org
Key Personnel
Exec Dir: Virginia Dajani
Given annually to artists, writers, composers & architects to encourage creative work in the arts.
Award: $7,500 each (8 awards to writers)

Arts Scholarships
New Brunswick Arts Board (Conseil des arts du Nouveau-Brunswick)
649 rue Queen, 2nd fl, Fredericton, NB E3B 1C3, Canada
Tel: 506-444-4444 *Toll Free Tel:* 866-460-ARTS (460-2787) *Fax:* 506-444-5543
E-mail: nbabcanb@artsnb.ca
Web Site: www.artsnb.ca
Key Personnel
Exec Dir: Akoulina Connell *Tel:* 506-444-4343 *E-mail:* execdirgen@artsnb.ca
Deputy Dir: Vanessa Moeller *Tel:* 506-292-4696 *E-mail:* vmoeller@artsnb.ca
Prog Offr: Joss Richer *Tel:* 506-478-4610 *E-mail:* jricher@artsnb.ca
Designed to recognize & encourage New Brunswick students who have demonstrated exceptional artistic talent & potential & who are pursuing a career in the arts. This program awards scholarships for full-time, part-time or short-term studies.
Closing Date: Feb 1

ASF Translation Awards
American-Scandinavian Foundation (ASF)
Scandinavia House, 58 Park Ave, New York, NY 10016
Tel: 212-879-9779 *Fax:* 212-686-2115
E-mail: grants@amscan.org
Web Site: www.amscan.org
Key Personnel
Dir, Fellowships: Valerie Hymas *E-mail:* vhymas@amscan.org
Established: 1980
For translations of contemporary poetry or fiction by Danish, Finnish, Icelandic, Norwegian or Swedish authors born after 1800. Write to ASF or visit the ASF web site for full copy of rules.
Award: $2,000 (either poetry or fiction) & publication of excerpt in an issue of Scandinavian Review & commemorative bronze medallion. $1,000 Inger Sjoberg Prize for runner-up

Closing Date: Annually in June
Presented: Varies

Asian American Literary Awards
Asian American Writers' Workshop
110-112 W 27 St, Suite 600, New York, NY 10001
Tel: 212-494-0061
E-mail: desk@aaww.org
Web Site: aaww.org/curation/asian-american-literary-awards
Honors Asian American writers for excellence in three categories: fiction, poetry & nonfiction. Entry fee: $100.
Closing Date: Annually in Spring
Presented: AAWW Food & Books Festival

Athenaeum of Philadelphia Literary Award
Athenaeum of Philadelphia
219 S Sixth St, Philadelphia, PA 19106
Tel: 215-925-2688 *Fax:* 215-925-3755
Web Site: www.philaathenaeum.org
Key Personnel
Circ Libn: Jill LeMin Lee *E-mail:* jilly@philaathenaeum.org
Established: 1950
In recognition & encouragement of outstanding literary achievement in Philadelphia & the vicinity.
Award: Citation
Closing Date: Annually, Dec 31
Presented: Annually in Spring

Atlantic Poetry Prize
Writers' Federation of Nova Scotia
1113 Marginal Rd, Halifax, NS B3H 4P7, Canada
Tel: 902-423-8116 *Fax:* 902-422-0881
E-mail: contact@writers.ns.ca
Web Site: writers.ns.ca
Key Personnel
Exec Dir: Jonathan Meakin *E-mail:* director@writers.ns.ca
Established: 1998
Presented to the best full-length book of poetry by an Atlantic Canadian in the previous calendar year.
Award: $2,000
Closing Date: Annually, 1st Friday in Dec
Presented: Halifax, NS, Canada, Annually in Oct

Atlantic Public Art Funders (APAF) Creative Residency
New Brunswick Arts Board (Conseil des arts du Nouveau-Brunswick)
649 rue Queen, 2nd fl, Fredericton, NB E3B 1C3, Canada
Tel: 506-444-4444 *Toll Free Tel:* 866-460-ARTS (460-2787) *Fax:* 506-444-5543
E-mail: nbabcanb@artsnb.ca
Web Site: www.artsnb.ca
Key Personnel
Exec Dir: Akoulina Connell *Tel:* 506-444-4343 *E-mail:* execdirgen@artsnb.ca
Deputy Dir: Vanessa Moeller *Tel:* 506-292-4696 *E-mail:* vmoeller@artsnb.ca
Prog Offr: Joss Richer *Tel:* 506-478-4610 *E-mail:* jricher@artsnb.ca
Artists from New Brunswick, Nova Scotia, PEI or Newfoundland & Labrador can apply. Covers a 1 to 3 month residency for a creation-based or professional development project in the province that isn't their own. The agreement establishes an annual exchange program that provides professional artists with opportunities for creation & professional development residencies in the participating provinces. Artists participating in this program enjoy complete autonomy & define the objectives of their period of residence & elaborate the parameters & conditions governing its realization in collaboration with an arts community organization in the territory where the period of residence is to take place.
Other Sponsor(s): Arts Nova Scotia; Newfoundland & Labrador Arts Council; Prince Edward Island Council of the Arts
Award: Up to $10,000
Closing Date: Feb 1

Abrendal Austin National Writing Contest
Black Penny Press
5198 Arlington Ave, Unit 923, Riverside, CA 92504
Tel: 951-214-5712; 951-741-7651
E-mail: shortstory@blackpennypresscontest.com; info@blackpennypress.com
Web Site: www.blackpennypresscontest.com
Maximum 2,500 words for short story or essay & up to 5 poems for each entrant. Stories or poems must belong to the original submitter. Original unpublished stories only. Entry fee $20.
Award: $500 (1st place), $250 (2nd place), 2 honorable mentions
Closing Date: Annually in May
Presented: Annually in Aug

Autumn House Poetry, Fiction & Nonfiction Contests
Autumn House Press
87 1/2 Westwood St, Pittsburgh, PA 15211
Mailing Address: PO Box 60100, Pittsburgh, PA 15211
Web Site: www.autumnhouse.org
Poetry Prize: All full-length collections of poetry 50-80 pages in length are eligible.
Fiction Contest: Submissions should be approximately 200-300 pages. All fiction sub-genres or any combination of sub-genres are eligible.
Nonfiction Contest: Submissions should be approximately 200-300 pages. All nonfiction subjects are eligible.
Enclose $30 handling fee for each prize. See web site for complete guidelines.
Award: $1,000, book publication, advance against royalties & $1,500 travel grant to participate in the Master Authors Series in Pittsburgh
Closing Date: Annually, June 30

Award of Merit
American Academy of Arts & Letters
633 W 155 St, New York, NY 10032
Tel: 212-368-5900 *Fax:* 212-491-4615
E-mail: academy@artsandletters.org
Web Site: www.artsandletters.org
Key Personnel
Exec Dir: Virginia Dajani
Established: 1942
Given annually, in rotation, to an outstanding person in America representing one of the following arts: Painting, the Short Story, Sculpture, the Novel, Poetry & Drama.
Award: $25,000 & medal

AWP Award Series
Association of Writers & Writing Programs (AWP)
George Mason University, 4400 University Dr, MSN 1E3, Fairfax, VA 22030
Tel: 703-993-4301 *Fax:* 703-993-4302
E-mail: awp@awpwriter.org
Web Site: www.awpwriter.org
Key Personnel
Exec Dir: David W Fenza
Dir, Conferences: Christian Teresi
Dir, Devt: Pamela Mills
Dir, Membership Servs: Diane Zinna
Dir, Pubns: Supriya Bhatnagar
Assoc Ed: Jason Gray
Established: 1967
An open competition for book-length mss in four categories: poetry, short fiction, novel & creative (nonfiction). Send business-size SASE after Nov 1 for submission guidelines.
Award: Publication by a major university press & an honorarium of $2,500 for nonfiction & novel. Donald Hall Prize in poetry-honorarium $5,500. Grace Paley Prize for short fiction-honorarium $5,500. One winner in each category
Closing Date: Annually, Feb 28 (postmark)

Axiom Business Book Awards
Independent Publisher Online
Division of Jenkins Group Inc
1129 Woodmere Ave, Suite B, Traverse City, MI 49686
Tel: 231-933-0445 *Toll Free Tel:* 800-706-4636 *Fax:* 231-933-0448
E-mail: info@axiomawards.com
Web Site: www.axiomawards.com
Key Personnel
CEO: Jerrold R Jenkins *E-mail:* jrj@bookpublishing.com
Pres: James Kalajian *Tel:* 800-706-4636 ext 1006 *E-mail:* jjk@bookpublishing.com
Mng Ed & Awards Dir: Jim Barnes *Tel:* 800-706-4636 ext 1011 *E-mail:* jimb@bookpublishing.com
Awards Coord: Amy Shamroe
Established: 2006
US-based award contest focused solely on business books. The goal of the awards is to celebrate the innovative, intelligent & creative aspects of the books that make us think, see & work differently every day. The awards offer no global boundaries, giving participants from every continent the opportunity to earn further recognition for their English-language titles. All publishers are eligible, ranging from large multi-title publishing houses to small one-title publishers. Publishers can be throughout North America & overseas publishers who publish English-language books intended for the American market. Print-on-demand & other independent authors are welcome to enter their books themselves.
Other Sponsor(s): Books Are Marketing Tools; Independent Publisher; Jenkins Group
Award: Gold medal (1st place), silver medal (2nd place) & bronze medal (3rd place)
Closing Date: Annually in Jan
Presented: Book Expo America, Annually in May

Marilyn Baillie Picture Book Award
Canadian Children's Book Centre
40 Orchard View Blvd, Suite 217, Toronto, ON M4R 1B9, Canada
Tel: 416-975-0010 *Fax:* 416-975-8970
E-mail: info@bookcentre.ca
Web Site: www.bookcentre.ca
Key Personnel
Exec Dir: Charlotte Teeple *E-mail:* charlotte@bookcentre.ca
Lib Coord: Meghan Howe *E-mail:* meghan@bookcentre.ca
Outreach Educ Coord: Sandra O'Brien *E-mail:* sandra@bookcentre.ca
Mktg & Website Coord: Camilia Kahrizi *E-mail:* camilia@bookcentre.ca
Prog Coord: Shannon Howe Barnes *E-mail:* shannon@bookcentre.ca
Established: 2006
Awarded to a Canadian author & illustrator for excellence in the illustrated picture book format for children ages 3-8.
Other Sponsor(s): Charles Baillie
Award: $20,000 cash
Closing Date: Annually in mid-Dec

Baker & Taylor/YALSA Conference Grants
Young Adult Library Services Association (YALSA)

Division of The American Library Association (ALA)
50 E Huron St, Chicago, IL 60611
Tel: 312-280-4390 *Toll Free Tel:* 800-545-2433 *Fax:* 312-280-5276; 312-664-7459
E-mail: yalsa@ala.org
Web Site: www.ala.org/yalsa
Key Personnel
Exec Dir: Beth Yoke *Tel:* 800-545-2433 ext 4391 *E-mail:* byoke@ala.org
Prog Offr, Events & Conferences: Nichole O'Connor *Tel:* 800-545-2433 ext 4387 *E-mail:* noconnor@ala.org
Communs Specialist: Anna Lam *Tel:* 800-545-2433 ext 5849 *E-mail:* alam@ala.org
Established: 1983
This award is given to young adult librarians in public or school libraries to attend an ALA Annual Conference for the first time. Candidates must be members of YALSA & have one to ten years of library experience.
Award: $1,000 (2 given yearly)
Closing Date: Annually, Dec 1
Presented: ALA's midwinter meeting

Nona Balakian Citation for Excellence in Reviewing
National Book Critics Circle
160 Varick St, 11th fl, New York, NY 10013
E-mail: info@bookcritics.org
Web Site: bookcritics.org
Key Personnel
Committee Chair: Gregg Barrios *E-mail:* greggbarr@outlook.com
Awarded annually to recognize outstanding work by a member of NBCC. Send up to five book reviews (all published during the year of the award) of no more than 5,000 words collectively. For e-mail submissions, include a note listing the venue along with title & word count of each piece submitted. Send links to your reviews as published online. For submissions in hardcopy via mail, include brief cover letter listing the title & word count of each piece submitted.
Award: $1,000

The Balcones Poetry Prize
The Balcones Center for Creative Writing
Subsidiary of Austin Community College
1212 Rio Grande St, Austin, TX 78701
Tel: 512-828-9368
Web Site: www.austincc.edu/crw/html/balconescenter.html
Key Personnel
Assoc Dir: John Herndon *E-mail:* jherndon@austincc.edu
Established: 1994
Recognizes an outstanding book of poetry published during the year. Books of poetry of 42 pgs or more may be submitted by author or publisher. Send 3 copies. Must bear a 2015 publication date. $25 reading fee.
Award: $1,500
Closing Date: Jan 31, 2016

Bancroft Prizes
Columbia University
517 Butler Library, Mail Code 1101, 535 W 114 St, New York, NY 10027
Tel: 212-854-4746 *Fax:* 212-854-9099
Web Site: www.columbia.edu/cu/lweb/eguides/amerihist/bancroft.html
Key Personnel
Devt Offr: Matt Hampel
Established: 1948
Two awards presented annually for distinguished books in the fields of American history (including biography) & diplomacy. Award confined to books originally published in English or those with a published English translation. Books published in year preceding that in which award is made are eligible. Submit four copies & nominating letter.
Award: $10,000 each
Closing Date: Nov 1, page-proof copy may be submitted after Nov 1, provided the work will be published after that date & before Dec 31
Presented: Columbia University

Barnes & Noble Writers for Writers Award
Poets & Writers Inc
90 Broad St, Suite 2100, New York, NY 10004
Tel: 212-226-3586 *Fax:* 212-226-3963
E-mail: admin@pw.org
Web Site: www.pw.org
Established: 1996
Celebrates authors who have given generously to other writers or to the broader literary community.

James P Barry Ohioana Award for Editorial Excellence
Ohioana Library Association
274 E First Ave, Suite 300, Columbus, OH 43201
Tel: 614-466-3831 *Fax:* 614-728-6974
E-mail: ohioana@ohioana.org
Web Site: www.ohioana.org
Key Personnel
Exec Dir, Ohioana Library Association: Linda R Hengst *E-mail:* lhengst@ohioana.org
Established: 1979
Only Ohio-based serial (magazine, journal, newspaper, etc) that covers subjects of interest to the Ohioana Library, namely literature, history, culture, the arts or the general humanities. The award is given at the discretion of the Board of Trustees.
Closing Date: Annually, Dec 31
Presented: Ohioana Day Luncheon, Annually in Autumn

Baskerville Publishers Poetry Award
Texas Christian University
Texas Christian University, Dept of English, TCU Box 297270, Fort Worth, TX 76129
Tel: 817-257-5907 *Fax:* 817-257-7709
E-mail: descant@tcu.edu
Web Site: www.descant.tcu.edu
Key Personnel
Mng Ed: Dan Williams *E-mail:* d.e.williams@tcu.edu
Established: 2003
Annual award for an outstanding poem or poems by a single author in an issue. All published submissions are eligible for prize consideration. There is no application process.
Other Sponsor(s): descant (publication), Dept of English, TCU
Award: $250
Closing Date: Sept 1-April 1
Presented: Winner announced in journal in Summer

The Mildred L Batchelder Award
Association for Library Service to Children (ALSC)
Division of The American Library Association (ALA)
50 E Huron St, Chicago, IL 60611-2795
Tel: 312-280-2163 *Toll Free Tel:* 800-545-2433 *Fax:* 312-440-9374
E-mail: alsc@ala.org
Web Site: www.ala.org/alsc
Key Personnel
Exec Dir: Aimee Strittmatter *Tel:* 312-280-2162 *E-mail:* astrittmatter@ala.org
Awards Coord: Caroline Jewell *E-mail:* alscawards@ala.org
Prog Coord: Marsha P Burgess *E-mail:* mburgess@ala.org
Established: 1966
Awarded to an American publisher for an outstanding book originally published in a foreign language in a foreign country & subsequently translated to English & published in the US during the previous year.
Award: Citation
Closing Date: Annually, Dec 31
Presented: ALSC Awards Program at the ALA Annual Conference, Annually in June

The BC Book Prizes
West Coast Book Prize Society
207 W Hastings St, Suite 901, Vancouver, BC V6B 1H7, Canada
Tel: 604-687-2405 *Fax:* 604-687-2435
E-mail: info@bcbookprizes.ca
Web Site: www.bcbookprizes.ca
Key Personnel
Exec Dir: Bryan Pike *E-mail:* bryan@rebuscreative.com
Gen Mgr: Val Mason *E-mail:* val@rebuscreative.com
Creative Publicity: Karen Green *E-mail:* karen@rebuscreative.com
Proj Coord: Kristie Poole *E-mail:* kristie@rebuscreative.com
Established: 1985
The following BC Book Prizes are awarded to a resident of BC or one who has lived in BC for 3 of the past 5 years: to the author of the best work of fiction; best book written for children 16 years & younger; best original nonfiction literary work; author of the best work of poetry. The following BC Book Prizes are also offered: originating publisher of the best book judged in terms of public appeal, initiative, design, production & content (publisher must have their head office in BC); author of the book which contributes most to the appreciation & understanding of BC (published anywhere & the author may reside outside BC); author & illustrator of the best picture book written for children (author/illustrator must be a BC/Yukon resident or have lived in BC or the Yukon for 3 of the past 5 years).
Other Sponsor(s): AbeBooks; Ampersand Inc; BC Teachers' Federation; British Columbia Booksellers Association; British Columbia Library Association; Friesens; Transcontinental Publishing; Webcom
Award: $2,000 & certificate
Closing Date: Annually, Dec 1, with exceptions made for books published in Dec
Presented: The British Columbia Book Prizes Banquet, Spring

BCHF Historial Writing Competition
British Columbia Historical Federation
PO Box 5254, Sta B, Victoria, BC V8R 6N4, Canada
E-mail: writing@bchistory.ca
Web Site: www.bchistory.ca
Key Personnel
Dir: Maurice Guibord
Top prize is presented annually to the author whose book makes the most significant contribution to the historical literature of British Columbia. The book must be published within the competition year. Additional prizes also given.
Award: $2,500 & The BC Lieutenant-Governor's Medal for Historical Writing (1st place), $1,500 (2nd place), $500 (3rd place), Certificates of Honourable Mention, $500 Community History Award
Closing Date: Dec 31
Presented: BCHF Annual Awards Banquet, May/June

James Beard Foundation Book Awards
James Beard Foundation
Office of Awards, 6 W 18 St, 10th fl, New York, NY 10011
Tel: 212-627-1111 (ext 563)

Web Site: www.jamesbeard.org/awards
Established: 1991
Book, broadcast & journalism awards in the food & beverage industry.
Award: Certificate, bronze medallion & complimentary one-year foundation membership
Presented: Annually in Spring

George Louis Beer Prize
American Historical Association (AHA)
400 "A" St SE, Washington, DC 20003
Tel: 202-544-2422 *Fax:* 202-544-8307
E-mail: awards@historians.org
Web Site: www.historians.org
Established: 1923
Recognition of outstanding historical writing in European international history since 1895 that is submitted by a scholar who is a US citizen or permanent resident. Books published in 2015 are eligible. Only books of a high scholarly historical nature should be submitted. Along with an application form, applicants must mail a copy of their book to each of the prize committee members who will be posted on our web site as the prize deadline approaches. All updated info on web site.
Award: Cash prize
Closing Date: May 15, 2016 (postmark)
Presented: AHA Annual Meeting, Denver, CO, Jan 5-8, 2017

The Pura Belpre Award
Association for Library Service to Children (ALSC)
Division of The American Library Association (ALA)
50 E Huron St, Chicago, IL 60611-2795
Tel: 312-280-2163 *Toll Free Tel:* 800-545-2433 *Fax:* 312-440-9374
E-mail: alsc@ala.org
Web Site: www.ala.org/alsc
Key Personnel
Exec Dir: Aimee Strittmatter *Tel:* 312-280-2162 *E-mail:* astrittmatter@ala.org
Awards Coord: Caroline Jewell *E-mail:* alscawards@ala.org
Prog Coord: Marsha P Burgess *E-mail:* mburgess@ala.org
Established: 1996
Annual award presented to a Latino/Latina writer & illustrator whose children's work best celebrates the Latino cultural experience.
Other Sponsor(s): National Association to Promote Library & Information Services to Latinos & the Spanish Speaking (REFORMA)
Award: Medal
Closing Date: Annually, Dec 31
Presented: ALSC Awards Program at the ALA Annual Conference

Benjamin Franklin Awards™
The Independent Book Publishers Association (IBPA)
1020 Manhattan Beach Blvd, Suite 204, Manhattan Beach, CA 90266
Tel: 310-546-1818 *Fax:* 310-546-3939
E-mail: info@ibpa-online.org
Web Site: www.ibpa-online.org; ibpabenjaminfranklinawards.com
Key Personnel
COO: Terry Nathan *E-mail:* terry@ibpa-online.org
Asst Dir: Lisa Krebs Magno *E-mail:* lisa@ibpa-online.org
Vendor Rel, Mktg & Ad: Chris Kahn *E-mail:* chris@ibpa-online.org
Established: 1987
Excellence in independent publishing in specific genre & design (books, audio & video). Trophies are presented to the publishers during a gala awards ceremony on the last evening of the Publishing University prior to the opening of Book Expo America. Entry fee: membs $95/title/category; nonmembs $225/first title (includes 1yr membership); $95/additional titles.
Award: Gold winners: Engraved crystal trophy & award certificates with gold stickers. Silver winners: Award certificates with silver stickers
Closing Date: Sept 30 (1st call) & Dec 31 (2nd call)
Presented: May

George Bennett Fellowship
Phillips Exeter Academy
Phillips Exeter Academy, Off of the Dean of Faculty, 20 Main St, Exeter, NH 03833-2460
Tel: 603-772-4311 *Fax:* 603-777-4384
E-mail: teaching_opportunities@exeter.edu
Web Site: www.exeter.edu
Key Personnel
Coord, Selection Comm: Todd Hearon
Established: 1968
Established to provide support for one academic year for an individual contemplating or pursuing a career as a professional writer. Selection is based on the literary promise of the ms submitted. The committee favors applicants who have not yet published a book-length work with a major publisher. Send SASE for application or obtain from the Academy web site. Telephone inquiries strongly discouraged.
Award: $13,650, housing & board at the Academy for the academic year & health insurance
Closing Date: Annually, Dec 1
Presented: Annually in April

Naomi Berber Memorial Award
Printing Industries of America
200 Deer Run Rd, Sewickley, PA 15143-2324
Tel: 412-259-1705 *Toll Free Tel:* 800-910-4283 (ext 705) *Fax:* 412-749-9890
E-mail: printing@printing.org
Web Site: www.printing.org/berberaward
Key Personnel
CEO & Pres: Michael F Makin *E-mail:* mmakin@printing.org
Asst to VP, Mktg: Sara Welsh *E-mail:* swelsh@printing.org
Established: 1976
Honors a woman who has made a major contribution to the development of the printing industry. A nominee must have worked in the printing industry for ten years or more. See web site for more information.
Other Sponsor(s): Printing Industries of America's Ben Franklin Society
Award: Engraved plaque
Presented: Printing Industries of America Fall Administrative Meetings

Jessie Bernard Award
American Sociological Association (ASA)
c/o Governance Off, 1430 "K" St NW, Suite 600, Washington, DC 20005
Tel: 202-383-9005 *Fax:* 202-638-0882
E-mail: governance@asanet.org
Web Site: www.asanet.org
Key Personnel
Dir, Governance: Michael Murphy *Tel:* 202-383-9005 ext 327
For scholarly contributions that enlarge the horizons of sociology to encompass fully the role of women in society. Winner announced through newsletter "Footnotes" an ASA publication. See web site for future awards.
Award: Certificate
Closing Date: Jan 31
Presented: ASA Annual Meeting, Montreal, QC, CN, Aug

The Charles Bernheimer Prize
American Comparative Literature Association (ACLA)
University of South Carolina, Dept of Languages, Literature & Cultures, Rm 813-A, 1620 College St, Columbia, SC 29208
Tel: 803-777-3021 *Fax:* 803-777-3041
E-mail: info@acla.org
Web Site: www.acla.org
Key Personnel
Secy & Treas: Alexander Beecroft
An outstanding dissertation in comparative literature completed by July 1. See web site for application details.
Award: $1,000 & a certificate, complimentary registration, a ticket to the banquet & a travel agent of $300 to facilitate the recipient attending the conference
Closing Date: Nov
Presented: Annual meeting, Spring following completed dissertation

Doris Betts Fiction Prize
North Carolina Writers' Network
c/o NC Literary Review, East Carolina University, Dept of English, Greenville, NC 27858-4353
Tel: 336-293-8844
E-mail: mail@ncwriters.org
Web Site: www.ncwriters.org
Key Personnel
Fiction Ed: Liza Wieland *E-mail:* wielandl@ecu.edu
The competition is open to any writer who is a legal resident of North Carolina or a member of NCWN. Entrants should submit two copies of a typed, original & unpublished story, not to exceed 6,000 words. Entrant fee for members of NCWN is $10, nonmembers $20. See www.ncwriters.org/programs-and-services/competitions/25-doris-betts-fiction-prize for full information.
Award: $250 1st prize, ten finalists considered for publication in the "North Carolina Literary Review"
Closing Date: Annually, Feb 15

Beullah Rose Poetry Prize
Smartish Pace
PO Box 22161, Baltimore, MD 21203
Web Site: www.smartishpace.com
Key Personnel
Assoc Ed: Clare Banks *E-mail:* cbsmartishpace@gmail.com
Established: 2005
Prize for exceptional poetry by women. All poems submitted for the prize will be considered for publication in *Smartish Pace*. Online submissions at www.smartishpace.com. Postal submissions: submit 3 poems along with a $5 entry fee. Additional poems may be submitted for $1 per poem. No more than 20 poems may be submitted. All entries must include a bio. Include SASE with entry, include name, address, e-mail & telephone number on each page of poetry submitted. Write or print "Beullah Rose Poetry Prize" on top of each poem submitted.
Award: $200 & publication of winning poem in *Smartish Pace* (1st prize). All finalists will be published in *Smartish Pace*
Closing Date: Annually, Oct 1
Presented: Baltimore, MD

Albert J Beveridge Award in American History
American Historical Association (AHA)
400 "A" St SE, Washington, DC 20003
Tel: 202-544-2422 *Fax:* 202-544-8307
E-mail: awards@historians.org
Web Site: www.historians.org
Established: 1939
To promote & honor outstanding historical writing. The award is given for a distinguished book in English on the history of the US, Latin

America, or Canada, from 1492 to the present. Books that employ new methodological or conceptual tools or that constitute significant re-examinations of important interpretive problems will be given preference. Literary merit is also an important criterion. Biographies, monographs & works of synthesis & interpretation are eligible; translations, anthologies & collections of documents are not. Books published in 2015 are eligible for the award; limited to five titles from any one publisher & must be submitted by sending a copy to each member of the committee. Along with an application form. All updated info on web site.
Award: Cash prize
Closing Date: May 15, 2016 (postmark)
Presented: AHA Annual Meeting, Denver, CO, Jan 5-8, 2017

Albert J Beveridge Grant for Research in the History of the Western Hemisphere
American Historical Association (AHA)
400 "A" St SE, Washington, DC 20003
Tel: 202-544-2422 *Fax:* 202-544-8307
E-mail: awards@historians.org
Web Site: www.historians.org
To support research in the history of the Western hemisphere (US, CN & Latin America). Only members of the Association are eligible. The grants are intended to further research in progress & may be used for travel to a library or archive, for microfilms, photographs or photocopying - a list of purposes that is meant to be merely illustrative not exhaustive. Preference will be given to those with specific research needs, such as the completion of a project or completion of a discrete segment thereof; preference will be given to PhD candidates & junior scholars. Application forms available on web site. Applications must include application form with estimated budget, curriculum vita & statement of no more than 750 words. A one page bibliography of the most recent relevant, secondary works on the topic. Mailed & faxed submissions are not accepted.
Award: Individual grants will not exceed $1,000; preference to PhD candidates & junior scholars
Closing Date: Annually, Feb 15

BHTG - Competition for Youth Theatre Marilyn Hall Awards
The Beverly Hills Theatre Guild
PO Box 148, Beverly Hills, CA 90213
Tel: 310-273-3390
Web Site: www.beverlyhillstheatreguild.com
Key Personnel
Pres: Carolyn Fried
Competition Coord: Candace Coster
Established: 1999
Playwright, children's theatre grade 6th-8th, 9th-12th grade.
Award: $1,200, $600
Closing Date: Annually, Jan 15 through last day of Feb (postmarked)
Presented: Los Angeles, CA, Annually, June 30

BHTG - Julie Harris Playwright Award Competition
The Beverly Hills Theatre Guild
PO Box 148, Beverly Hills, CA 90213
Tel: 310-273-3390
Web Site: www.beverlyhillstheatreguild.com
Key Personnel
Pres: Carolyn Fried
Competition Coord: Candace Coster
Established: 1978
For playwrights. Application & guidelines available upon request with SASE.
Award: $3,500, $2,500 & $1,500
Closing Date: Annually, Aug 1-Nov 1
Presented: Los Angeles, CA, Annually, June 30 (announcement)

The Geoffrey Bilson Award for Historical Fiction for Young People
Canadian Children's Book Centre
40 Orchard View Blvd, Suite 217, Toronto, ON M4R 1B9, Canada
Tel: 416-975-0010 *Fax:* 416-975-8970
E-mail: info@bookcentre.ca
Web Site: www.bookcentre.ca
Key Personnel
Exec Dir: Charlotte Teeple *E-mail:* charlotte@bookcentre.ca
Lib Coord: Meghan Howe *E-mail:* meghan@bookcentre.ca
Outreach Educ Coord: Sandra O'Brien *E-mail:* sandra@bookcentre.ca
Mktg & Website Coord: Camilia Kahrizi *E-mail:* camilia@bookcentre.ca
Prog Coord: Shannon Howe Barnes *E-mail:* shannon@bookcentre.ca
Established: 1988
Awarded to a Canadian author for an outstanding work of historical fiction for young people.
Award: $5,000
Closing Date: Annually in mid-Dec

Robert Bingham Prize for Debut Fiction, see PEN/Robert Bingham Prize for Debut Fiction

Binghamton University John Gardner Fiction Book Award
The Binghamton Center for Writers-State University of New York
Dept of English, General Literature & Rhetoric, Library N, Rm 1149, Vestal Pkwy E, Binghamton, NY 13902
Mailing Address: PO Box 6000, Binghamton, NY 13902-6000
Tel: 607-777-2713
Web Site: www2.binghamton.edu/english/creative-writing
Key Personnel
Dir: Maria Mazziotti Gillan *Tel:* 973-684-5904 *E-mail:* mgillan@binghamton.edu
Established: 2002
Selected by judges as the strongest novel or collection of fiction published in the previous year. Minimum press run of 500 copies. Each book submitted must be accompanied by an application form; publishers may submit more than one book for prize consideration. Submit only two copies of a submitted title. Winners will be announced in "Poets & Writers".
Award: $1,000
Closing Date: March 1

Binghamton University Milt Kessler Poetry Book Award
The Binghamton Center for Writers-State University of New York
Dept of English, General Literature & Rhetoric, Library N, Rm 1149, Vestal Pkwy E, Binghamton, NY 13902
Mailing Address: PO Box 6000, Binghamton, NY 13902-6000
Tel: 607-777-2713
Web Site: www2.binghamton.edu/english/creative-writing
Key Personnel
Dir: Maria Mazziotti Gillan *Tel:* 973-684-5904 *E-mail:* mgillan@binghamton.edu
Established: 2002
For a book of poems, 48 pages or more in length, selected by our judges as the strongest collection of poems by a poet over 40 published in the previous year. Must be accompanied by an application; publishers may submit more than one book for prize consideration; minimum press run of 500 copies; submit only two copies of a title. Winner announced in "Poets & Writers".
Award: $1,000
Closing Date: March 1

Irma S & James H Black Award
Bank Street College of Education
610 W 112 St, New York, NY 10025
Tel: 212-875-4458 *Fax:* 212-875-4558
E-mail: ccl@bankstreet.edu
Web Site: www.bankstreet.edu/center-childrens-literature
Key Personnel
Dir, Lib Servs: Kristin Freda *E-mail:* kfreda@bankstreet.edu
Established: 1972
For unified excellence of story line, language & illustration in a work for young children published during the previous year.
Award: Scroll & Gold Seals
Closing Date: Annually in Dec
Presented: Bank Street College of Education, Annually in May

Black Warrior Review Fiction, Nonfiction & Poetry Contest
Black Warrior Review
Office of Student Media, University of Alabama, Tuscaloosa, AL 35486-0027
Mailing Address: PO Box 870170, Tuscaloosa, AL 35487-0170
Tel: 205-348-4518
Web Site: www.bwr.ua.edu
Key Personnel
Mng Ed: Bronwyn Valentine *E-mail:* managingeditor.bwr@gmail.com
Fiction Ed: Joe Lucido
Nonfiction Ed: Shaelyn Smith
Poetry Ed: Ryan Bollenbach
Established: 2005
Awards given to best nonfiction piece, short story & best poem entered. Submit one story (up to 7,500 words) or 3 poems. Entry fee $20 includes one-year subscription.
Award: $1,000 & publication (one for each category - poetry, nonfiction & fiction). Finalists noted & considered for publication
Closing Date: Annually, Sept 1 (submit online at bwrsubmissions.ua.edu)

Neltje Blanchan Memorial Award
Wyoming Arts Council
Division of Wyoming Department of Parks & Cultural Resources
2320 Capitol Ave, Cheyenne, WY 82002
Tel: 307-777-5234 *Fax:* 307-777-5499
Web Site: wyoarts.state.wy.us
Key Personnel
Literary, Visual & Performing Arts Specialist: Michael Shay *Tel:* 307-777-5234 *E-mail:* mshay@state.wy.us
Arts Council Mgr: Rita Basom *Tel:* 307-777-7473 *E-mail:* rbasom@state.wy.us
Established: 1988
Best writing in any genre inspired by a relationship with nature. Open to Wyoming residents only. Blind judges, single juror.
Other Sponsor(s): Neltje
Award: $1,000
Closing Date: Annually, Oct 31
Presented: ARTSPEAK Conference, Winner announced Nov 1

Theodore C Blegen Award
The Forest History Society Inc
701 William Vickers Ave, Durham, NC 27701-3162
Tel: 919-682-9319 *Fax:* 919-682-2349
Web Site: www.foresthistory.org
Key Personnel
Admin Asst: Andrea Anderson *E-mail:* andrea.anderson@foresthistory.org
Established: 1972
Recognizes the best scholarship in forest & conservation history published in a journal other than Environmental History.

Award: $500 & plaque
Closing Date: Early Spring (specific date varies)

Susan P Bloom Children's Book Discovery Award
PEN New England
Unit of PEN American Center
MIT, 14N-221A, 77 Massachusetts Ave, Cambridge, MA 02139
Tel: 617-324-1729
E-mail: pen-newengland@mit.edu
Web Site: www.pen-ne.org/susan-p-bloom-award
Annual awards to honor emerging writers & writers/illustrators.

The James Boatwright III Prize for Poetry
Shenandoah: The Washington & Lee University Review
Washington & Lee University, Mattingly House, 204 W Washington St, Lexington, VA 24450-2116
Tel: 540-458-8765
E-mail: shenandoah@wlu.edu
Web Site: shenandoahliterary.org; shenandoah.wlu.edu
Key Personnel
Ed: R T Smith *E-mail:* rodsmith@wlu.edu
Annual award for the best poem published in Shenandoah during a volume year.
Award: $1,000

Frederick Bock Prize
Poetry Magazine
444 N Michigan Ave, Suite 1850, Chicago, IL 60611-4034
Tel: 312-787-7070 *Fax:* 312-787-6650
E-mail: editors@poetrymagazine.org
Web Site: www.poetryfoundation.org
Key Personnel
Mng Ed: Valerie Johnson *E-mail:* vjohnson@poetrymagazine.org
Established: 1981
For poetry published during the preceding two volumes of poetry. No application necessary.
Award: $500
Presented: Annually in Dec

George Bogin Memorial Award
Poetry Society of America (PSA)
15 Gramercy Park, New York, NY 10003
Tel: 212-254-9628 *Fax:* 212-673-2352
Web Site: www.poetrysociety.org
Key Personnel
Pres: Ruth Kaplan
Exec Dir: Alice Quinn
Deputy Dir: Brett Fletcher Lauer *E-mail:* brett@poetrysociety.org
Progs Dir: Charif Shanahan *E-mail:* charif@poetrysociety.org
Established by the family & friends of George Bogin, for a selection of four or five poems that reflects the encounter of the ordinary & the extraordinary, uses language in an original way & takes a stand against oppression in any of its forms. No line limit; send No 10 SASE or see web site for more information.
Award: $500
Closing Date: Annually, Oct-Dec
Presented: Annual Awards Ceremony, New York, NY, Annually in Spring

Bogle International Library Travel Fund
International Relations Committee
Unit of The American Library Association (ALA)
50 E Huron St, Chicago, IL 60611-2795
Tel: 312-280-3201 *Toll Free Tel:* 800-545-2433 (ext 3201) *Fax:* 312-280-4392
E-mail: intl@ala.org
Web Site: www.ala.org
Key Personnel
Dir, Off of Chapter & Intl Rel: Michael Dowling
Prog Offr: Delin Guerra *E-mail:* dguerra@ala.org
To enable librarians to travel abroad to study +/or attend first international conferences.
Award: $1,000
Closing Date: Annually in Dec
Presented: ALA Conference, Annually, Jan 1

Laura Day Boggs Bolling Memorial
The Poetry Society of Virginia
1194 Hume Rd, Hume, VA 22639-1806
E-mail: poetryinva@aol.com
Web Site: www.poetrysocietyofvirginia.org
Key Personnel
Pres: Judith K Bragg *E-mail:* musicsavy45@yahoo.com
Adult Contest Chair: Patsy Anne Bickerstaff *E-mail:* granypatsy@yahoo.com; Guy Terrell *E-mail:* ggterr@infionline.net
All entries must be in English, original & unpublished. Submit 2 copies, both copies must have the category name & number on top left of page. Entries will not be returned. Poem written by an adult for school-age children (10-12 yrs); any rhymed form; 20 line limit. Entry fee: $4 nonmembs.
Other Sponsor(s): Children of Laura Day Boggs Bolling: Alma, Flora & Glade
Award: $50 (1st prize), $30 (2nd prize), $20 (3rd prize)
Closing Date: Jan 19
Presented: Annual PSV Awards Luncheon, Richmond, VA, April

Books for a Better Life Awards
National Multiple Sclerosis Society, New York City-Southern New York Chapter
733 Third Ave, 3rd fl, New York, NY 10017
Tel: 212-463-7787 *Toll Free Tel:* 800-344-4867 *Fax:* 212-986-7981
Web Site: www.nationalmssociety.org
Established: 1996
Recognizes self-improvement authors whose messages are aligned with the chapter's mission of inspiring people to live their best lives.

Boston Globe-Horn Book Award
The Boston Globe & The Horn Book Inc
300 The Fenway, Boston, MA 02115-5820
Tel: 617-628-0225 *Toll Free Tel:* 800-325-1170; 888-628-0225 *Fax:* 617-278-6062
E-mail: info@hbook.com
Web Site: www.hbook.com
Key Personnel
Ed-in-Chief, Horn Book Pubns: Roger Sutton *E-mail:* rsutton@hbook.com
Asst Ed: Katrina Hedeen *Tel:* 617-628-0225 ext 222 *E-mail:* khedeen@hbook.com
Established: 1967
Honors excellence in children's & young adult literature in three categories: fiction & poetry, nonfiction & picture books. Published books only, mss not accepted.
Award: $500 each
Closing Date: Annually in May
Presented: Annually in Fall

Boulevard Magazine Short Fiction Contest for Emerging Writers
Boulevard Magazine
6614 Clayton Rd, PMB 325, Richmond Heights, MO 63117
Tel: 314-862-2643
Web Site: www.boulevardmagazine.org
Key Personnel
Founding Ed: Richard Burgin *E-mail:* richardburgin@att.net
Mng Ed: Jessica Rogen *E-mail:* jessicarogen@boulevardmagazine.org
Open to writers who have not yet published a book of fiction, poetry or creative nonfiction with a nationally distributed press. Simultaneous submissions are allowed but previously accepted or published work is ineligible. Send typed, double-spaced mss & SAS postcard for acknowledgment of receipt. No mss will be returned. 8,000 word maximum length; cover sheets not necessary. Entry fee is $15 per story with no limit per author, includes one year subn.
Award: $1,500 & publication in the Spring or the Fall issue of *Boulevard*
Closing Date: Annually, Dec 31

Bound to Stay Bound Books Scholarship
Association for Library Service to Children (ALSC)
Division of The American Library Association (ALA)
50 E Huron St, Chicago, IL 60611-2795
Tel: 312-280-2163 *Toll Free Tel:* 800-545-2433 *Fax:* 312-440-9374
E-mail: alsc@ala.org
Web Site: www.ala.org/alsc
Key Personnel
Exec Dir: Aimee Strittmatter *Tel:* 312-280-2162 *E-mail:* astrittmatter@ala.org
Awards Coord: Caroline Jewell *E-mail:* alscawards@ala.org
Prog Coord: Marsha P Burgess *E-mail:* mburgess@ala.org
For study in field of library service to children toward the MLS or beyond in an ALA-accredited program.
Award: $7,000 - 4 scholarships per yr
Closing Date: Annually, March 1
Presented: ALA Annual Conference, Annually in June

Amber Bowerman Memorial Travel Writing Award
Writers' Guild of Alberta
11759 Groat Rd, Edmonton, AB T5M 3K6, Canada
Tel: 780-422-8174 *Toll Free Tel:* 800-665-5354 (AB only) *Fax:* 780-422-2663 (attn WGA)
E-mail: mail@writersguild.ab.ca
Web Site: www.writersguild.ab.ca
Key Personnel
Exec Dir: Carol Holmes *E-mail:* carol.holmes@writersguild.ab.ca
Communs & Partnerships Coord: Nicholas Mather *E-mail:* nicholas.mather@writersguild.ab.ca
Memb Servs Coord: Giorgia Severini
Progs Coord: Natalie Cook *E-mail:* natalie.cook@writersguild.ab.ca; Nichole Quiring *E-mail:* nichole.quiring@writersguild.ab.ca
Established: 2008
Open to unpublished travel essays by authors under 30; no longer than 3,000 words.
Award: $700
Closing Date: Annually, Dec 31
Presented: Alberta Book Awards Gala
Branch Office(s)
505 21 Ave SW, Calgary, AB T2S 0G9, Canada, Prog Coord: Samantha Warwick *Tel:* 403-265-2226 *E-mail:* samantha.warwick@writersguild.ab.ca

Barbara Bradley Prize
New England Poetry Club
2 Farrar St, Cambridge, MA 02138
Mailing Address: 376 School St, Watertown, MA 02472
Tel: 617-744-6034
E-mail: contests@nepoetryclub.org
Web Site: www.nepoetryclub.org
Key Personnel
Pres: Diana Der-Hovanessian
VP: Sally Cragin; Daniel Tobin
Contest Chair: Nazaleem Smith
Established: 1988
Prize for a poem in lyric form, under 21 lines, written by a woman. Mark name of contest on

envelope, send to address above. Send poem in duplicate with name of writer on one only.
Award: $200
Closing Date: must be postmarked in April & May only
Presented: Public Library, Cambridge, MA, Annually in Autumn

BrainStorm Poetry Contest for Mental Health Consumers
Northern Initiative for Social Action (NISA)
36 Elgin St, 2nd fl, Sudbury, ON P3C 5B4, Canada
Tel: 705-222-6472 (ext 303)
E-mail: openminds@nisa.on.ca
Web Site: www.openmindsquarterly.com
Key Personnel
Publr & Ed: Dinah Laprairie
Established: 2003
Contest open only to people with lived experience of mental illness internationally. It aims to eliminate the stigma associated with mental illness by showcasing the talents & creativity of individuals living with mental illness. Contest details available after Dec 15 online. Contest runs Jan to end of March each year. Call or e-mail to be added to mailing list.
Award: $250 (1st prize), $150 (2nd prize), $75 (3rd prize), plus publication in *Open Minds Quarterly*
Closing Date: Annually Jan-March

Michael Braude Award
American Academy of Arts & Letters
633 W 155 St, New York, NY 10032
Tel: 212-368-5900 *Fax:* 212-491-4615
E-mail: academy@artsandletters.org
Web Site: www.artsandletters.org
Key Personnel
Exec Dir: Virginia Dajani
Triennial award given for light verse written in English regardless of the writer's country of origin.
Award: $5,000

James Henry Breasted Prize
American Historical Association (AHA)
400 "A" St SE, Washington, DC 20003
Tel: 202-544-2422 *Fax:* 202-544-8307
E-mail: awards@historians.org
Web Site: www.historians.org
Established: 1985
Best book in English in any field of history prior to 1000 AD. Different geographic area will be eligible each year. Entries must be published in 2015. Along with an application form, applicants must mail a copy of their book to each of the prize committee members who will be posted on our web site as the prize deadline approaches. All updated info on web site.
Award: Cash prize
Closing Date: May 15, 2016 (postmark)
Presented: AHA Annual Meeting, Denver, CO, Jan 5-8, 2017

The Briar Cliff Review Fiction, Poetry & Creative Nonfiction Contest
The Briar Cliff Review-Briar Cliff University
3303 Rebecca St, Sioux City, IA 51104-2100
Tel: 712-279-1651 *Fax:* 712-279-5486
Web Site: www.briarcliff.edu/bcreview
Key Personnel
Mktg Dir: Judy Thompson
Ed: Tricia Currans-Sheehan
Poetry, creative nonfiction & fiction contest. Submit unpublished story, essay or 3 poems with $20. Entrants receive issue. No name on mss. Include cover page with title(s), name, address, e-mail, phone. Send SASE for results only.
Award: $1,000 each category & publication in Spring
Closing Date: Annually Nov 1

Brick Road Poetry Book Contest
Brick Road Poetry Press
513 Broadway, Columbus, GA 31901
Mailing Address: PO Box 751, Columbus, GA 31902-0751
Tel: 706-649-3080
Web Site: brickroadpoetrypress.com
Key Personnel
Ed: Keith Badowski; Ron Self
Book-length poetry mss only, original collection of 50-80 pages of poetry, excluding cover page. Entry fee $25.
Award: $1,000, publication contract with Brick Road Poetry Press in both print & ebook formats & 25 copies of the printed book
Closing Date: Annually, Aug 1-Nov 1

Brittingham & Pollak Prizes in Poetry
University of Wisconsin Press
Dept of English, 600 N Park St, Madison, WI 53706
Web Site: www.wisc.edu/wisconsinpress
Key Personnel
Ed: Ronald Wallace
Established: 1985
Pollak & Brittingham are two prizes from one competition. For book-length mss of poetry. Mss not accepted before Aug 15 or after Sept 15; $25 reading fee required, check made payable to: University of Wisconsin Press. Mss not returned; send required business-size SASE for contest results. For guidelines check web site. Electronic submissions encouraged.
Other Sponsor(s): University of Wisconsin Creative Writing Program
Award: $1,000 & publication in University of Wisconsin Press Poetry Series for each book
Closing Date: Sept 15

The Heywood Broun Award
The Newspaper Guild
501 Third St NW, 6th fl, Washington, DC 20001-2797
Tel: 202-434-7177; 202-434-7162 (The Guild Reporter) *Fax:* 202-434-1472
Web Site: www.newsguild.org
Key Personnel
Ed: Janelle Hertman
Established: 1941
Journalism.
Award: $5,000
Closing Date: Last Friday in Jan
Presented: Washington, DC, Annually in May

John Nicholas Brown Prize
Medieval Academy of America
104 Mount Auburn St, 5th fl, Cambridge, MA 02138
Tel: 617-491-1622 *Fax:* 617-492-3303
E-mail: speculum@medievalacademy.org
Web Site: www.medievalacademy.org
Key Personnel
Exec Dir & Ed, Speculum: Eileen Gardiner *E-mail:* egardiner@themedievalacademy.org
Established: 1978
For a first book published four years prior to award date, in the field of medieval studies.
Award: $1,000
Closing Date: Annually, Oct 15
Presented: Annually in April

Georges Bugnet Award for Fiction
Writers' Guild of Alberta
11759 Groat Rd, Edmonton, AB T5M 3K6, Canada
Tel: 780-422-8174 *Toll Free Tel:* 800-665-5354 (AB only) *Fax:* 780-422-2663 (attn WGA)
E-mail: mail@writersguild.ab.ca
Web Site: www.writersguild.ab.ca
Key Personnel
Exec Dir: Carol Holmes *E-mail:* carol.holmes@writersguild.ab.ca
Communs & Partnerships Coord: Nicholas Mather *E-mail:* nicholas.mather@writersguild.ab.ca
Memb Servs Coord: Giorgia Severini
Progs Coord: Natalie Cook *E-mail:* natalie.cook@writersguild.ab.ca; Nichole Quiring *E-mail:* nichole.quiring@writersguild.ab.ca
Established: 1982
Alberta Literary Award, author must be resident of Alberta.
Award: $1,500
Closing Date: Annually, Dec 31
Presented: Alberta Book Awards Gala
Branch Office(s)
505 21 Ave SW, Calgary, AB T2S 0G9, Canada, Prog Coord: Samantha Warwick *Tel:* 403-265-2226 *E-mail:* samantha.warwick@writersguild.ab.ca

Burnside Review Fiction Chapbook Competition
Burnside Review
PO Box 1782, Portland, OR 97207
Web Site: burnsidereview.org
Key Personnel
Ed: Sid Miller *E-mail:* sid@burnsidereview.org
Established: 2006
Submit up to 10,000 words in the form of one long story or multiple shorter pieces. Outside judge is brought in. Contest results are announced via telephone, mail & on web site. Entry fee $15.
Award: $200 & 25 copies of the press run of at least 100
Closing Date: Annually, Dec 31
Presented: April 1

The John Burroughs List of Nature Books for Young Readers
John Burroughs Association Inc
15 W 77 St, New York, NY 10024
Tel: 212-769-5169 *Fax:* 212-313-7182
Web Site: research.amnh.org/burroughs
Key Personnel
Secy: Lisa Breslof *E-mail:* lbreslof@amnh.org
To recognize writers, artists & publishers who produce outstanding nature literature for children. Nonfiction subjects of natural history, ecology & environmental studies. Works may include poetry, travel, art, adventure, biography. No guide books to identification, science texts, or reference works. Submit five copies of each entry, addressed to: Secretary, The John Burroughs Association.
Award: John Burroughs Certificate of Recognition to authors, illustrators & publishers of each selected book
Closing Date: Annually, Nov 30
Presented: American Museum of Natural History, 1st Monday in April

John Burroughs Medal
John Burroughs Association Inc
15 W 77 St, New York, NY 10024
Tel: 212-769-5169 *Fax:* 212-313-7182
Web Site: research.amnh.org/burroughs
Key Personnel
Secy: Lisa Breslof *E-mail:* lbreslof@amnh.org
Established: 1926
Annual award for the year's best book in the field of natural history. The work of John Burroughs, a literary naturalist, is the standard for the general character of the books eligible. They should combine literary quality with accuracy & should be based on originality of observation & conclusion. Award is not given for compilations of others' findings. Submit six copies of each entry addressed to Secretary, The John Burroughs Association.
Award: Bronze medal

Closing Date: Annually, Oct 15
Presented: Luncheon at American Museum of Natural History, New York, NY, 1st Monday in April

John Burroughs Outstanding Published Nature Essay Award
John Burroughs Association Inc
15 W 77 St, New York, NY 10024
Tel: 212-769-5169 *Fax:* 212-313-7182
Web Site: research.amnh.org/burroughs
Key Personnel
Secy: Lisa Breslof *E-mail:* lbreslof@amnh.org
To recognize current authors of outstanding essays published in magazines & journals emphasizing John Burroughs Literary works, contributions & skill as an outstanding nature essayist. Submit seven copies of each entry addressed to "Secretary, The John Burroughs Association".
Award: Certificate of Recognition
Closing Date: Annually, Dec 31
Presented: Annual Meeting, 1st Monday in April

CAA Award for Fiction
Canadian Authors Association (CAA)
6 West St N, Suite 203, Orillia, ON L3V 5B8, Canada
Tel: 705-325-3926 *Toll Free Tel:* 866-216-6222
E-mail: admin@canadianauthors.org
Web Site: www.canadianauthors.org
Key Personnel
Exec Dir: Anita Purcell
Entries must be full-length English-language literature for adults by Canadian authors. Reprints are not eligible, nor is self-published work. Fee at $40 per entry to offset a portion of administrative costs.
Award: $2,000 & silver medal
Closing Date: Annually, Dec 15
Presented: CAA's Annual Conference, Awards Gala & Banquet, Annually in June

CAA Emerging Writer Award
Canadian Authors Association (CAA)
6 West St N, Suite 203, Orillia, ON L3V 5B8, Canada
Tel: 705-325-3926 *Toll Free Tel:* 866-216-6222
E-mail: admin@canadianauthors.org
Web Site: www.canadianauthors.org
Key Personnel
Exec Dir: Anita Purcell
Awarded to the Canadian writer under 30 yrs old deemed to show the most promise in the field of literary creation.
Award: $500 & 1 yr membership in Canadian Authors Association
Closing Date: Annually, March 31
Presented: CAA's Annual Conference, Awards Gala & Banquet, Annually in June

CAA Lela Common Award for Canadian History
Canadian Authors Association (CAA)
6 West St N, Suite 203, Orillia, ON L3V 5B8, Canada
Tel: 705-325-3926 *Toll Free Tel:* 866-216-6222
E-mail: admin@canadianauthors.org
Web Site: www.canadianauthors.org
Key Personnel
Exec Dir: Anita Purcell
Established: 1997
All entries must be historical nonfiction, on Canadian topics by Canadian authors. The books must be English language literature for adults (not "young adults"). Translations are not eligible. Fee of $40 per entry to offset a portion of administrative costs.
Award: $2,000 & silver medal
Closing Date: Annually, Dec 15
Presented: CAA's Annual Conference, Awards Gala & Banquet, Annually in June

CAA Poetry Award
Canadian Authors Association (CAA)
6 West St N, Suite 203, Orillia, ON L3V 5B8, Canada
Tel: 705-325-3926 *Toll Free Tel:* 866-216-6222
E-mail: admin@canadianauthors.org
Web Site: www.canadianauthors.org
Key Personnel
Exec Dir: Anita Purcell
For a volume of poetry by one poet. Entry fee $40 per title.
Award: $2000 & silver medal
Closing Date: Annually, Dec 15
Presented: CAA Annual Conference, Awards Gala & Banquet, Annually in June

Gerald Cable Book Award
Silverfish Review Press
PO Box 3541, Eugene, OR 97403
Tel: 541-344-5060
E-mail: sfrpress@earthlink.net
Web Site: www.silverfishreviewpress.com
Key Personnel
Ed & Publr: Rodger Moody
Established: 1995
Poetry Book; for author who has not yet published a collection; selection by May. $25 reading fee.
Award: $1,000 & publication by Silverfish Review Press & 25 copies of the book
Closing Date: Oct 15

The Randolph Caldecott Medal
Association for Library Service to Children (ALSC)
Division of The American Library Association (ALA)
50 E Huron St, Chicago, IL 60611-2795
Tel: 312-280-2163 *Toll Free Tel:* 800-545-2433 *Fax:* 312-440-9374
E-mail: alsc@ala.org
Web Site: www.ala.org/alsc
Key Personnel
Exec Dir: Aimee Strittmatter *Tel:* 312-280-2162 *E-mail:* astrittmatter@ala.org
Prog Coord: Marsha P Burgess *E-mail:* mburgess@ala.org
Awards Coord: Caroline Jewell *E-mail:* alscawards@ala.org
Established: 1937
Given to the artist who created the most distinguished American picture book for children published in the US during the previous year. The artist must be a citizen or resident of the US.
Award: Medal
Closing Date: Annually, Dec 31
Presented: ALA Annual Conference, Annually in June

California Book Awards
Commonwealth Club of California
595 Market St, San Francisco, CA 94105
Tel: 415-597-6700 *Fax:* 415-597-6729
E-mail: bookawards@commonwealthclub.org
Web Site: www.commonwealthclub.org/bookawards
Established: 1931
Honors the exceptional literary merit of California writers & publishers. Awards are presented in the categories of fiction, nonfiction, poetry, first work of fiction, juvenile literature (up to age 10), adult literature (ages 11-16), Californiana, works in translation & notable contribution to publishing. To be eligible, author must be resident in California at the time of publication & books must be published under the year in consideration.
Award: Plaques with medallions for gold & silver awardees
Closing Date: Dec
Presented: Annually 1st Thursday in June

California Writers Exchange Award
Poets & Writers Inc
90 Broad St, Suite 2100, New York, NY 10004
Tel: 212-226-3586 *Fax:* 212-226-3963
E-mail: admin@pw.org
Web Site: www.pw.org
Offered triennially to writers from California.
Other Sponsor(s): James Irvine Foundation
Award: All expenses-paid trip to New York City to meet with top literary professionals & give a public reading

Joe Pendleton Campbell Narrative Contest
The Poetry Society of Virginia
1194 Hume Rd, Hume, VA 22639-1806
E-mail: poetryinva@aol.com
Web Site: www.poetrysocietyofvirginia.org
Key Personnel
Pres: Judith K Bragg *E-mail:* musicsavy45@yahoo.com
Adult Contest Chair: Patsy Anne Bickerstaff *E-mail:* granypatsy@yahoo.com; Guy Terrell *E-mail:* ggterr@infionline.net
All entries must be in English, original & unpublished. Submit 2 copies, each having the category name & number on top left of page. Any form; any subject; narrative poem; 64 line limit. Entry fee: $4 nonmembs.
Other Sponsor(s): Paula Savoy
Award: $50 (1st prize), $30 (2nd prize), $20 (3rd prize)
Closing Date: Jan 19
Presented: Annual PSV Awards Luncheon, Richmond, VA, April

John W Campbell Memorial Award
Center for the Study of Science Fiction
University of Kansas, Wescoe Hall, Rm 3001, Dept of English, 1445 Jayhawk Blvd, Lawrence, KS 66045-7590
Tel: 785-864-3380 *Fax:* 785-864-1159
Web Site: www.ku.edu/~sfcenter; ku.edu/campbell.htm
Key Personnel
Founding Dir: James Gunn *E-mail:* jgunn@ku.edu
Dir: Chris McKitterick *E-mail:* cmckit@ku.edu
Established: 1973
Selected by jury who produces a short list & votes on that list to select a winner. Science fiction novels published in English anywhere in the world in the year of eligibility. Publishers are encouraged to submit works for consideration by the jury.
Award: Trophy & expense paid trip to the conference to receive the award
Presented: Campbell Conference Awards Banquet, University of Kansas, Lawrence, KS

Alexander Patterson Cappon Prize for Fiction
New Letters
UMKC, University House, 5101 Rockhill Rd, Kansas City, MO 64110-2499
Tel: 816-235-1169 *Fax:* 816-235-2611
E-mail: newletters@umkc.edu
Web Site: www.newletters.org
Established: 1986
Literary contest. All entries considered for publication.
Award: $1,500 & publication
Closing Date: Annually, May 18

Dorothy Churchill Cappon Prize for the Essay
New Letters
UMKC, University House, 5101 Rockhill Rd, Kansas City, MO 64110-2499
Tel: 816-235-1169 *Fax:* 816-235-2611
E-mail: newletters@umkc.edu
Web Site: www.newletters.org
Established: 1986

Literary contest. All entries considered for publication.
Award: $1,500 & publication
Closing Date: Annually, May 18

Andrew Carnegie Medals for Excellence in Fiction & Nonfiction
The American Library Association (ALA)
50 E Huron St, Chicago, IL 60611
Tel: 312-944-6780 *Toll Free Tel:* 800-545-2433 *Fax:* 312-440-9374
E-mail: ala@ala.org
Web Site: www.ala.org/awardsgrants/carnegieadult
Key Personnel
Exec Dir: Susan Hornung *E-mail:* shornung@ala.org
Mgr, Mktg & Progs: Marianne Braverman *E-mail:* mbraverman@ala.org
Membership & Awards Coord: Leighann Wood *E-mail:* lwood@ala.org
Established: 2012
To recognize the best fiction & nonfiction books for adult readers published in the US the previous year, chosen by selection committee.
Other Sponsor(s): Booklist; Carnegie Corporation of New York Grant; Reference & User Services Association (RUSA)
Award: $5,000 (winning authors, 1 in each category), $1,500 (2 finalists in each category)
Presented: ALA Annual Conference

Carnegie-Whitney Award
ALA Publishing Committee
Unit of The American Library Association (ALA)
50 E Huron St, Chicago, IL 60611
Tel: 312-280-5416 *Toll Free Tel:* 800-545-2433 *Fax:* 312-280-5275; 312-440-9379
Web Site: www.ala.org
Key Personnel
Grant Administrator: Mary Jo Bolduc *E-mail:* mbolduc@ala.org
For the preparation of bibliographic aids for research with scholarly intent & general applicability. Decisions made at Publishing Committee Meeting, each January. Completed proposals should be sent to Chair, ALA Publishing Committee at the above address.
Other Sponsor(s): James Gyman Whitney Fund, Andrew Carnegie Fund
Award: Up to $5,000 annually
Closing Date: Annually in Nov

The Carter Prize For The Essay
Shenandoah: The Washington & Lee University Review
Washington & Lee University, Mattingly House, 204 W Washington St, Lexington, VA 24450-2116
Tel: 540-458-8765
E-mail: shenandoah@wlu.edu
Web Site: shenandoahliterary.org; shenandoah.wlu.edu
Key Personnel
Ed: R T Smith *E-mail:* rodsmith@wlu.edu
Annual award for the best essay published in Shenandoah during a volume year.
Award: $1000

Catholic Book Awards
Catholic Press Association of the United States & Canada
205 W Monroe St, Suite 470, Chicago, IL 60606
Tel: 312-380-6789 *Fax:* 312-361-0256
E-mail: cathjourn@catholicpress.org
Web Site: www.catholicpress.org
Key Personnel
Exec Dir: Timothy M Walter *E-mail:* twalter@catholicpress.org
Opers Analyst: Barbara Mastrolia
Several awards for best Catholic books in different categories.
Award: Certificate
Closing Date: Feb
Presented: Annual Convention, June

Catholic Press Association of the US & Canada Journalism Awards, see Catholic Press Awards

Catholic Press Awards
Catholic Press Association of the United States & Canada
205 W Monroe St, Suite 470, Chicago, IL 60606
Tel: 312-380-6789 *Fax:* 312-361-0256
E-mail: cathjourn@catholicpress.org
Web Site: www.catholicpress.org
Key Personnel
Exec Dir: Timothy M Walter *E-mail:* twalter@catholicpress.org
Opers Analyst: Barbara Mastrolia
Journalism entries from member publications.
Award: Certificate
Closing Date: Annually in Feb
Presented: Annual Convention, June

Center for Publishing Departmental Scholarships
New York University, School of Continuing & Professional Studies
Midtown Ctr, Rm 429, 11 W 42 St, New York, NY 10036
Tel: 212-992-3232 *Fax:* 212-992-3233
E-mail: pub.center@nyu.edu; ms.publishing@nyu.edu
Web Site: www.scps.nyu.edu
Key Personnel
Assoc Dir: Sarah McCarthy *E-mail:* sarah.mccarthy@nyu.edu
Awarded to students enrolled in at least 6 credits in Master of Science in publishing program (not available to students in first semester). Need excellent academic record. Based on financial need & merit.
Award: $500 & up
Presented: Annually in Fall & Spring

Jane Chambers Playwriting Award
Women in Theatre Program, Association for Theatre in Higher Education
Georgetown University, 108 David Performing Arts Ctr, Box 571063, 37 & "O" St, NW, Washington, DC 20057-1063
Tel: 202-687-1327
Web Site: www.athe.org/?page=Jane_Chambers
Key Personnel
Contact: Maya E Roth *E-mail:* mer46@georgetown.edu
Established: 1984
Award for play or performance text by a woman which reflects a feminist perspective & contains a majority of opportunities for women performers. Scripts may be produced or unproduced; encourage experimentation with dramatic form; send SASE for application & full information or see web site; two bound copies of script required & not returned.
Award: $1,000 for reading of the winning piece at the award conference & free registration to the conference; student winner is also recognized
Closing Date: Feb 15
Presented: Annual ATHE National Conference

The Alfred & Fay Chandler Book Award
Business History Review
c/o Harvard Business School, Connell House 301A, Boston, MA 02163
Tel: 617-495-1003 *Fax:* 617-495-2705
E-mail: bhr@hbs.edu
Web Site: www.hbs.edu/businesshistory/fellowships
Key Personnel
Ed: Walter Friedman *E-mail:* wfriedman@hbs.edu
Established: 1964
Award given every three years for best book published in the US on the history of business. Selection by the editorial board of the Business History Review.
Award: A scroll

G S Sharat Chandra Prize for Short Fiction
BkMk Press - University of Missouri-Kansas City
University House, 5101 Rockhill Rd, Kansas City, MO 64110-2499
Tel: 816-235-2558 *Fax:* 816-235-2611
E-mail: bkmk@umkc.edu
Web Site: www.umkc.edu/bkmk
Key Personnel
Exec Ed: Robert Stewart *Tel:* 816-235-2610 *E-mail:* stewartr@umkc.edu
Mng Ed: Ben Furnish *E-mail:* furnishb@umkc.edu
Assoc Ed: Michelle Boisseau *Tel:* 816-235-2561 *E-mail:* boisseau@umkc.edu
Established: 2001
The best book-length ms of short fiction in English by a living author. Ms must be typed on standard-sized paper in English & should be 125-300 pages double-spaced. Entries must include two title pages: one with author name, address & phone number & one with no author information. Any acknowledgments should appear on a separate piece of paper. Entries must include a table of contents. Author's name must not appear anywhere on the ms. Do not submit your ms by fax or e-mail. A SASE should be included, for notification only. Note: No mss will be returned. A reading fee of $25 in US funds (check payable to BkMk Press) must accompany each ms. Entrants will receive a copy of the winning book when published. Entrants may also now submit online at www.umkc.edu/bkmk.
Award: $1,000 plus book publication of winning ms by BkMk Press
Closing Date: Annually, Jan 15
Presented: Annually in Summer

Chapter One Fiction Competition
Bronx Council On the Arts
1738 Hone Ave, Bronx, NY 10461-1486
Tel: 718-931-9500 *Fax:* 718-409-6445
E-mail: info@bronxarts.org
Web Site: www.bronxarts.org
Key Personnel
Writers Ctr Dir: Maria Romano *Tel:* 718-931-9500 ext 21
Established: 1997
Awarded to five novelists from New York City for the first chapter of an unpublished novel & works in progress.
Award: $1,000 honorarium & a reading in the Bronx
Closing Date: Annually in Sept

Chariton Review Short Fiction Prize
Truman State University Press
100 E Normal Ave, Kirksville, MO 63501-4221
Tel: 660-785-7336 *Toll Free Tel:* 800-916-6802 *Fax:* 660-785-4480
E-mail: tsup@truman.edu
Web Site: tsup.truman.edu
Key Personnel
Dir & Ed-in-Chief: Barbara Smith-Mandell *E-mail:* bsm@truman.edu
Submit a story of up to 5,000 words with a $20 entry fee, which includes a copy of the prize issue. Refer to guidelines on web site.
Award: $500 for winner & $200 each for finalists, plus publication in Chariton Review
Closing Date: Annually, Sept 30

Children's & Teen Choice Book Awards
The Children's Book Council (CBC)
54 W 39 St, 14th fl, New York, NY 10018
Tel: 212-966-1990
E-mail: cbc.info@cbcbooks.org

Web Site: ccbookawards.com; www.cbcbooks.org
Key Personnel
Exec Dir: Jon Colman *E-mail:* jon.colman@cbcbooks.org
Communs Dir: Nicole Deming *E-mail:* nicole.deming@cbcbooks.org
Mgr, Events & Progs/Libn: Ayanna Coleman *E-mail:* ayanna.coleman@cbcbooks.org
Established: 2008
Provides young readers with an opportunity to voice their opinions about the books being written for them.
Other Sponsor(s): DOGObooks; Every Child a Reader

Children's Literature Association Article Award
Children's Literature Association (ChLA)
1301 W 22 St, Suite 202, Oak Brook, IL 60523
Tel: 630-571-4520 *Fax:* 708-876-5598
E-mail: info@childlitassn.org
Web Site: www.childlitassn.org
Award for best literary criticism article published within a given year on the topic of children's literature. See web site for application requirements.
Award: $400 plus award certificate
Presented: ChLA Annual Conference, Annually in June

Children's Literature Association Beiter Graduate Student Research Grants
Children's Literature Association (ChLA)
1301 W 22 St, Suite 202, Oak Brook, IL 60523
Tel: 630-571-4520 *Fax:* 708-876-5598
E-mail: info@childlitassn.org
Web Site: www.childlitassn.org
Key Personnel
Grants Chair: Kenneth Kidd
Awarded for proposals of original scholarship with the expectation that the undertaking will lead to publication or a conference presentation & contribute to the field of children's literature criticism. Winners must either be members of the Children's Literature Association or join the association before they receive any funds. Applications & supporting materials should be written in or translated into English. Encouraging new scholars to enter the field, the scholarship is intended to enable "entry-level" scholars (graduate students, instructors or assistant professors) to bring to a publishable level dissertations, theses or papers that they have written.
Award: $500-$1,500 (based on the number & needs of the winning applicants)
Closing Date: Annually, Feb 1
Presented: ChLA Annual Conference, Annually in June

Children's Literature Association Book Award
Children's Literature Association (ChLA)
1301 W 22 St, Suite 202, Oak Brook, IL 60523
Tel: 630-571-4520 *Fax:* 708-876-5598
E-mail: info@childlitassn.org
Web Site: www.childlitassn.org
Book awards given for best book on children's literature history, scholarship & criticism published as a book in a given year. See web site for application requirements.
Award: $800 plus award certificate
Presented: ChLA Annual Conference, Annually in June

Children's Sequoyah Book Award
Oklahoma Library Association
300 Hardy Dr, Edmond, OK 73013
Tel: 405-525-5100 *Fax:* 405-525-5103
Web Site: www.oklibs.org
Key Personnel
Exec Dir: Kay Boies *E-mail:* kboies@sbcglobal.net
Contact: Tracy Keeley
Established: 1959
School children's choice of a book published by a living US author from a selected list. Students grades 3-5 who have read/listened to at least 3 books from the Children's Masterlist are eligible to vote.
Award: Plaque/medal
Closing Date: Annually, March 1
Presented: OLA Annual Conference, Annually in April

The Christopher Awards
The Christophers
5 Hanover Sq, 22nd fl, New York, NY 10004-2751
Tel: 212-759-4050 *Toll Free Tel:* 888-298-4050 (orders) *Fax:* 212-838-5073
E-mail: mail@christophers.org
Web Site: www.christophers.org
Key Personnel
Prog Mgr & Event Prodr: Tony Rossi *E-mail:* t.rossi@christophers.org
Established: 1949
For adult (nonfiction only) & juvenile fiction & nonfiction published during the current calendar year. Themes must reflect "highest values of the human spirit" criteria.
Award: Bronze medallion
Closing Date: June 1 & Nov 1; books evaluated throughout the calendar year
Presented: New York, NY, Annually in May

John Ciardi Prize for Poetry
BkMk Press - University of Missouri-Kansas City
University House, 5101 Rockhill Rd, Kansas City, MO 64110-2499
Tel: 816-235-2558 *Fax:* 816-235-2611
E-mail: bkmk@umkc.edu
Web Site: www.umkc.edu/bkmk
Key Personnel
Exec Ed: Robert Stewart *Tel:* 816-235-2610 *E-mail:* stewartr@umkc.edu
Mng Ed: Ben Furnish *E-mail:* furnishb@umkc.edu
Assoc Ed: Michelle Boisseau *Tel:* 816-235-2561 *E-mail:* boisseau@umkc.edu
Established: 1998
Presented for the best full-length ms of poetry in English by a living author. Ms must be typed on standard-sized paper & should be approximately 50 pages minimum, 110 pages maximum, single-spaced. Entries must include two title pages: one with author name, address & phone & one with no author information. Any acknowledgements should appear on a separate piece of paper. Entries must include a table of contents. Author's name must not appear anywhere on the ms. Do not submit your ms by fax or e-mail. A SASE should be included, for notification only. Note: No mss will be returned. A reading fee of $25 in US funds (check made payable to BkMk Press) must accompany each ms. Entrants will receive a copy of the winning book when it is published. Entrants may also now submit online at www.umkc.edu/bkmk.
Award: $1,000 plus publication by BkMk Press
Closing Date: Annually, Jan 15
Presented: Annually in Summer

The City of Calgary W O Mitchell Book Prize
Writers' Guild of Alberta
11759 Groat Rd, Edmonton, AB T5M 3K6, Canada
Tel: 780-422-8174 *Toll Free Tel:* 800-665-5354 (AB only) *Fax:* 780-422-2663 (attn WGA)
E-mail: mail@writersguild.ab.ca
Web Site: www.writersguild.ab.ca
Key Personnel
Exec Dir: Carol Holmes *E-mail:* carol.holmes@writersguild.ab.ca
Communs & Partnerships Coord: Nicholas Mather *E-mail:* nicholas.mather@writersguild.ab.ca
Memb Servs Coord: Giorgia Severini
Progs Coord: Natalie Cook *E-mail:* natalie.cook@writersguild.ab.ca; Nichole Quiring *E-mail:* nichole.quiring@writersguild.ab.ca
Recognizes literary achievement by Calgary authors. Types may be fiction, poetry, nonfiction, children's literature & drama.
Award: $5,000
Closing Date: Annually, Dec 31
Presented: Calgary Awards, Spring
Branch Office(s)
505 21 Ave SW, Calgary, AB T2S 0G9, Canada, Prog Coord: Samantha Warwick *Tel:* 403-265-2226 *E-mail:* samantha.warwick@writersguild.ab.ca

City of Vancouver Book Award
City of Vancouver, Cultural Services Dept
Woodward's Heritage Bldg, Suite 501, 111 W Hastings St, Vancouver, BC V6B 1H4, Canada
Tel: 604-871-6634 *Fax:* 604-871-6005
E-mail: culture@vancouver.ca
Web Site: vancouver.ca/bookaward
Key Personnel
Cultural Planner: Marnie Rice *E-mail:* marnie.rice@vancouver.ca
Established: 1989
Annual award for authors of books - any genre - that contribute to the appreciation & understanding of Vancouver's history, unique character or achievements of its residents.
Award: $3,000
Closing Date: Annually in May
Presented: The Mayor's Arts Awards, Annually in Sept/Oct

CLA Book of the Year for Children Award
Canadian Association of Children's Librarians, Canadian Library Association (Association Canadienne des Bibliotheques)
Subsidiary of Canadian Association of Public Libraries
1150 Morrison Dr, Suite 1100, Ottawa, ON K2H 8S9, Canada
Tel: 613-232-9625 *Fax:* 613-563-9895
E-mail: info@cla.ca
Web Site: www.cla.ca
Established: 1947
Awarded to the author of an outstanding Canadian children's book in English. Author must be a citizen or a resident of Canada.
Award: Leather-bound copy of winning book with award seal gold embossed on cover
Closing Date: Annually, Dec 31
Presented: CLA Annual Conference

The Clarion Awards
The Association for Women in Communications
3337 Duke St, Alexandria, VA 22314
Tel: 703-370-7436 *Fax:* 703-342-4311
E-mail: clarion@womcom.org
Web Site: www.womcom.org
Key Personnel
Exec Dir: Pamela Valenzuela
Communs Mgr: Beth Veney *E-mail:* awcconnect@womcom.org
Established: 1972
Honors excellence in more than 100 categories across all communications disciplines.
Award: Engraved crystal plaque, press releases, recognition at national conference
Closing Date: March (early bird), April (general entry)
Presented: National Conference Clarion Awards Banquet, Autumn

Page Davidson Clayton Prize for Emerging Poets
Michigan Quarterly Review

University of Michigan, 0576 Rackham Bldg, 915 E Washington St, Ann Arbor, MI 48109-1070
Tel: 734-764-9265
E-mail: mqr@umich.edu
Web Site: www.umich.edu/~mqr
Key Personnel
Mng Ed: Vicki Lawrence
Ed: Keith Taylor
Awarded annually to the best poet appearing in MQR who has not yet published a book.
Award: $500

Cleveland State University Poetry Center Prizes
Cleveland State University Poetry Center
2121 Euclid Ave, Cleveland, OH 44115-2214
Tel: 216-687-3986 *Fax:* 216-687-6943
E-mail: poetrycenter@csuohio.edu
Web Site: www.csuohio.edu/poetrycenter
Key Personnel
Dir: Michael Dumanis *E-mail:* csupc.mgr@gmail.com
Asst: Christopher Smith
Established: 1986
Poetry book mss, in two categories, First Book or Open Competition. Minimum 48 pages of poetry (one poem per page), SASE guidelines; readers fee required; simultaneous submissions permitted; mss not returned. Open competition is limited to poets who have published a full length collection, 48+ pp, 500+ copies.
Award: $1,000 & publication in the Cleveland State University Poetry Center series
Closing Date: Feb 15 postmark
Presented: July

David H Clift Scholarship
ALA Scholarship Clearinghouse
Unit of The American Library Association (ALA)
50 E Huron St, Chicago, IL 60611
Toll Free Tel: 800-545-2433 (ext 4279) *Fax:* 312-280-3256
E-mail: scholarships@ala.org
Web Site: www.ala.org/scholarships
Key Personnel
Prog Off: Kimberly L Redd *E-mail:* klredd@ala.org
Established: 1969
Awarded annually to worthy US or Canadian citizen or permanent resident to begin an MLS degree in an ALA-accredited program.
Award: $3,000
Closing Date: Annually, March 1; applications available beginning in Sept

Coal Hill Review Poetry Chapbook Contest
Coal Hill Review
c/o Autumn House Press, PO Box 60100, Pittsburgh, PA 15211
E-mail: reviewcoalhill@gmail.com
Web Site: www.coalhillreview.com
Key Personnel
Ed: Christine Stroud
Open to all poets writing in English. Ms may be submitted by attachment to our e-mail address. Submit a ms of 12-20 pages with a $20 entry fee.
Award: $1,000 & publication by Autumn House Press & Coal Hill Review
Closing Date: Nov 1

CODiE Awards
Software & Information Industry Association (SIIA)
1090 Vermont Ave NW, 6th fl, Washington, DC 20005-4095
Tel: 202-289-7442 *Fax:* 202-289-7097
E-mail: info@siia.net
Web Site: www.siia.net
Key Personnel
Pres: Kenneth Wasch *Tel:* 202-789-4440
Coord: Angel Scott *Tel:* 202-789-4458
Established: 1986
Honors excellence in the software & information industries.
Award: Trophy
Closing Date: Annually in Oct
Presented: SIIA CODiE Awards Gala, Annually in May

Coe College Playwriting Festival
Coe College
1220 First Ave NE, Cedar Rapids, IA 52402
Tel: 319-399-8624 *Fax:* 319-399-8557
Web Site: www.theatre.coe.edu; www.coe.edu/academics/theatrearts/theatrearts_playwritingfestival
Key Personnel
Chair, Dept of Theatre Arts: Susan Wolverton *E-mail:* swolvert@coe.edu
Established: 1992
Biennial playwriting award for new, full-length, original, unproduced & unpublished play. No musicals, adaptations, translations or collaborations. Only 1 entry/indiv.
Award: Publicly staged reading by students, faculty +/or individuals from the community, $500 & room, board, travel for one week residency
Closing Date: Nov 1, even-numbered years
Presented: Coe College, Cedar Rapids, IA, April

Carla Furstenberg Cohen Literary Prize
Carla Furstenberg Cohen Literary Prize Inc
1322 Holly St NW, Washington, DC 20012
Established: 2013
Awarded annually to authors of first or second books, in both fiction & nonfiction.
Award: $5,000 to each author

Morton N Cohen Award for a Distinguished Edition of Letters
Modern Language Association of America (MLA)
26 Broadway, 3rd fl, New York, NY 10004-1789
SAN: 202-6422
Tel: 646-576-5141 *Fax:* 646-458-0030
E-mail: awards@mla.org
Web Site: www.mla.org
Key Personnel
Coord, Book Prizes: Annie M Reiser *E-mail:* areiser@mla.org
Established: 1989
Award for an outstanding edition of letters published in 2015 or 2016. Editions may be in single or multiple volumes. For consideration, submit 4 copies. Editors need not be members of the MLA. Presented biennially.
Award: Cash award & certificate
Closing Date: May 1, 2017
Presented: MLA Convention, Jan 2018

The Victor Cohn Prize for Excellence in Medical Science Reporting
Council for the Advancement of Science Writing (CASW)
PO Box 910, Hedgesville, WV 25427
Tel: 304-754-6786
Web Site: www.casw.org
Established: 2000
Medical science writing for the mass media within the last five years. Online submissions.
Award: $3,000
Closing Date: Annually, July 31
Presented: Annually in Oct/Nov

John M Collier Award for Forest History Journalism
The Forest History Society Inc
701 William Vickers Ave, Durham, NC 27701-3162
Tel: 919-682-9319 *Fax:* 919-682-2349
Web Site: www.foresthistory.org
Key Personnel
Pres: Steven Anderson *E-mail:* steven.anderson@foresthistory.org
Admin Asst: Andrea Anderson *E-mail:* andrea.anderson@foresthistory.org
Established: 1987
Recognizes contributions to forest history that are published in newspapers, trade journals & other journalistic media. Open to any newspaper, or general circulation magazine, professional or freelance journalist in North America.
Award: $1,000 & expenses for a visit to The Forest History Society Library & Archives in Durham, NC & participation in an Institutes for Journalism in Natural Resources expedition
Closing Date: Annually, March 15

Carr P Collins Award
Texas Institute of Letters (TIL)
c/o 7748 Hwy 290 W, Austin, TX 78736-3202
Tel: 512-683-5640
E-mail: president@texasinstituteofletters.org
Web Site: www.texasinstituteofletters.org
Key Personnel
Pres: Andres Tijerina
VP: Steve Davis
Treas: James Hoggard
Secy: Darwin Payne
Recording Secy: Betty Wiesepape
Annual award for the best nonfiction book by a Texan or about Texas. Guidelines on the web site.
Other Sponsor(s): Carr P Collins Foundation
Award: $5,000
Closing Date: Annually in Jan
Presented: TIL Awards Banquet, Annually in Spring

The Winston Collins/Descant Prize for Best Canadian Poem
descant
50 Baldwin St, Toronto, ON M5T 1L4, Canada
Mailing Address: PO Box 314, Sta P, Toronto, ON M5S 2S8, Canada
Tel: 416-593-2557 *Fax:* 416-593-9362
E-mail: info@descant.ca
Web Site: www.descant.ca
Key Personnel
Ed-in-Chief: Karen Mulhallen *E-mail:* karenmulhallen@rogers.com
Established: 2006
Entry fee $30 (includes GST & 1 yr subn).
Award: $1,000 (1st prize) plus payment for publication in descant
Closing Date: Oct
Presented: Spring

Colorado Book Awards
Colorado Humanities & Center for the Book
Division of Colorado Humanities
7935 E Prentice Ave, Suite 450, Greenwood Village, CO 80111
Tel: 303-894-7951 (ext 21) *Fax:* 303-864-9361
E-mail: info@coloradohumanities.org
Web Site: www.coloradohumanities.org
Key Personnel
Prog Coord: Stephanie March
Established: 1991
Cash prize to Colorado authors in fiction, nonfiction, young adult, children's, poetry, romance & additional categories vary from year to year.
Award: $250 (cash)
Closing Date: Annually in Nov
Presented: Colorado Book Awards Event, Annually in Summer

Betsy Colquitt Award for Poetry
Texas Christian University
Texas Christian University, Dept of English, TCU Box 297270, Fort Worth, TX 76129
Tel: 817-257-5907 *Fax:* 817-257-7709
E-mail: descant@tcu.edu
Web Site: www.descant.tcu.edu

Key Personnel
Mng Ed: Dan Williams *E-mail:* d.e.williams@tcu.edu
Established: 1996
Annual award for best poem or series of poems by a single author in a volume. No entry fee.
Other Sponsor(s): descant (publication), Dept of English, TCU
Award: $500
Closing Date: Sept 1-April 1
Presented: Winner announced in journa in Summer

Miles Conrad Memorial Lecture
National Federation of Advanced Information Services (NFAIS)
801 Compass Way, Suite 201, Annapolis, MD 21401
Tel: 443-221-2980 *Fax:* 443-221-2981
E-mail: nfais@nfais.org
Web Site: www.nfais.org
Key Personnel
Exec Dir: Marcie Granahan *Tel:* 443-221-2980 ext 101 *E-mail:* mgranahan@nfais.org
Dir, Prof Devt: Jill O'Neill *Tel:* 443-221-2980 ext 102 *E-mail:* jilloneill@nfais.org
Dir, Mktg & Communs: Ken Berlack *Tel:* 443-221-2980 ext 103 *E-mail:* kberlack@nfais.org
Established: 1968
Annually given to an outstanding member of the information community who then delivers the "Miles Conrad Memorial Lecture" at the annual NFAIS Conference.
Award: Plaque & honorarium
Presented: Philadelphia, PA, Annually in Feb

Constance Rooke Creative Non-Fiction Prize
The Malahat Review
University of Victoria, Box 1700, Sta CSC, Victoria, BC V8W 2Y2, Canada
Tel: 250-721-8524 *Fax:* 250-472-5051
E-mail: malahat@uvic.ca
Web Site: malahatreview.ca
Key Personnel
Ed: John Barton
Established: 2007
Invite entries from Canadian, American & overseas authors. Must be between 2,000-3,000 words. No restrictions as to subject matter. Entry fees: $35 Canadian entries, $40 US entries & $45 (US) for entries from Mexico & outside North America. See web site for additional details.
Award: One award of $1,000 CAD
Closing Date: Annually, Aug 1

James Fenimore Cooper Prize
Society of American Historians (SAH)
Affiliate of American Historical Association
603 Fayerweather, MC 2538, New York, NY 10027
Tel: 212-854-6495
E-mail: amhistsociety@columbia.edu
Web Site: sah.columbia.edu
Key Personnel
Pres: David W Blight
VP: David Nasaw
Exec Secy: Andie Tucher
Established: 1993
For a book of historical fiction on an American subject which makes a significant contribution to historical understanding, portrays authentically the people & events of the historical past & displays skills in narrative construction & prose style. Must be published & have a copyright within two years prior to prize year. Awarded biennially in odd-numbered years.
Award: $2,000 & a certificate
Closing Date: Jan 31, 2017
Presented: New York, NY, May 2017

Cordon d' Or - Gold Ribbon International Annual Cook Book & Culinary Arts Culinary Academy Awards
Cordon d' Or - Gold Ribbon Inc
7312 Sixth Ave N, St Petersburg, FL 33710
Tel: 727-347-2437
E-mail: cordondor@aol.com; culinaryparadise@aol.com
Web Site: www.cordondorcuisine.com; www.florida-americasculinaryparadise.com
Key Personnel
CEO & Pres: Noreen Kinney
Established: 2003
Literary Cook Book, Illustrated Cook Book & 'Potluck' Book (any genre) & 'Culinary Arts' Awards. Categories include cookbooks, photographers, food stylists, magazines, articles, web sites, recipes & menus. Full details available on the web site. Entry forms can be downloaded.
Award: $1,000 (overall winner), Crystal Globe Trophies (presented to winners in all categories)
Closing Date: Annually, Dec 31
Presented: St Petersburg, FL, Annually in May

Albert B Corey Prize
Canadian Historical Association (CHA) & American Historical Association (AHA)
c/o American Historical Association, 400 "A" St SE, Washington, DC 20003-3889
Tel: 202-544-2422 *Fax:* 202-544-8307
E-mail: cha-shc@cha-shc.ca
Web Site: www.historians.org/prizes; www.cha-shc.ca
Key Personnel
Admin Asst: Jesse Pierce *Tel:* 202-544-2422 ext 106
Awarded biennially for the best book dealing with Canadian/American relations; awarded jointly with the American Historical Association. Books bearing an imprint of 2014 or 2015 are eligible for the 2016 prize. No application form, applicants must simply mail a copy of their book to each of the prize committee members who will be posted on our web site as the prize deadline approaches. All updated info on web site.
Award: $1,000 CAD
Closing Date: Dec 31, 2015
Presented: CHA Annual Meeting, University of Calgary, Calgary, AB, CN, May 30-June 1, 2016

CPSA Prize in Comparative Politics
Canadian Political Science Association
260 rue Dalhousie St, Suite 204, Ottawa, ON K1N 7E4, Canada
Tel: 613-562-1202 *Fax:* 613-241-0019
E-mail: cpsa-acsp@cpsa-acsp.ca
Web Site: www.cpsa-acsp.ca
Key Personnel
Administrator: Michelle Hopkins
Biennial prize awarded to the best book published in English or in French in the field of comparative politics. To be eligible, a book may be single or multi-authored. Single authored: author must be a Canadian citizen or a permanent resident of Canada or a member of the CPSA in the year the book was published. Multi-authored: at least one of the authors must be a Canadian citizen or a permanent resident of Canada or a member of the CPSA in the year the book was published. For the 2016 award, a book must have a copyright date of 2014 or 2015.
Award: Commemorative plaque & receive/share the set of books submitted to the CPSA office
Presented: Annual Conference, University of Calgary, Calgary, AB, CN, May 31-June 2, 2016

CPSA Prize in International Relations
Canadian Political Science Association
260 rue Dalhousie St, Suite 204, Ottawa, ON K1N 7E4, Canada
Tel: 613-562-1202 *Fax:* 613-241-0019
E-mail: cpsa-acsp@cpsa-acsp.ca
Web Site: www.cpsa-acsp.ca
Key Personnel
Administrator: Michelle Hopkins
This is a biennial competition. The prize was established to recognize the contribution of Canadian political scientists to the study of international relations & to encourage the best Canadian scholarship in this field. Awarded to the best book published in English or in French in the field of international relations. Book may be single-authored or multi-authored. Single-authored: must be a Canadian citizen or a permanent resident of Canada or a member of the CPSA in the year the book was published. Multi-authored: at least one of the authors must be a Canadian citizen or a permanent resident of Canada or a member of the CPSA in the year the book was published. For the 2017 award the book must have a copyright date of 2015 or 2016.
Award: Commerative plaque & receive/share the set of books submitted to the CPSA for the 2015 prize
Presented: Annual Conference, Ryerson University, Toronto, ON, CN, May 30-June 1, 2017

The Crazyhorse Fiction Prize
Crazyhorse
College of Charleston, Dept of English, 66 George St, Charleston, SC 29424
Tel: 843-953-7740 *Fax:* 843-953-7740
E-mail: crazyhorse@cofc.edu
Web Site: crazyhorse.cofc.edu/prizes
Award for best short story. Enter up to 25 pages fiction with $20 entry fee, which includes one-year subscription. Nationally prominent writer judges. See web site for complete instructions.
Award: $2,000 & publication in "Crazyhorse"
Closing Date: Annually, Jan 31

Creation Grant Program
New Brunswick Arts Board (Conseil des arts du Nouveau-Brunswick)
649 rue Queen, 2nd fl, Fredericton, NB E3B 1C3, Canada
Tel: 506-444-4444 *Toll Free Tel:* 866-460-ARTS (460-2787) *Fax:* 506-444-5543
E-mail: nbabcanb@artsnb.ca
Web Site: www.artsnb.ca
Key Personnel
Exec Dir: Akoulina Connell *Tel:* 506-444-4343 *E-mail:* execdirgen@artsnb.ca
Deputy Dir: Vanessa Moeller *Tel:* 506-292-4696 *E-mail:* vmoeller@artsnb.ca
Prog Offr: Joss Richer *Tel:* 506-478-4610 *E-mail:* jricher@artsnb.ca
Designed to provide assistance to professional New Brunswick artists for the research, development & execution of original projects in the arts. Creation Grants are intended to allow artists to devote some or most of their time to research & creative production.
Closing Date: April 1, Oct 1

Cunningham Commission for Youth Theatre
The Theatre School, DePaul University
2135 N Kenmore Ave, Chicago, IL 60614-4100
Tel: 773-325-7932 *Fax:* 773-325-7920
Web Site: theatreschool.depaul.edu
Key Personnel
Assoc Dean & Chair, Theatre Studies: Dean Corrin *E-mail:* dcorrin@depaul.edu
Established: 1991
Playwriting commission, limited to writers whose primary residence is within 100 miles of Chicago's Loop.
Award: Up to $5,000 ($2,000 paid when the commission is contracted, $1,000 paid if the script

moves to a workshop, $2,000 paid as royalty if the script is produced by The Theatre School)
Closing Date: Annually Dec 1
Presented: Presentation TBA, Winner notified by May 1

Karen & Philip Cushman Late Bloomer Award
Society of Children's Book Writers and Illustrators (SCBWI)
4727 Wilshire Blvd, Suite 301, Los Angeles, CA 90010
Tel: 323-782-1010 *Fax:* 323-782-1892
E-mail: grants@scbwi.org
Web Site: www.scbwi.org
Honors authors over the age of 50 who have not been traditionally published in the children's literature field.
Award: $500 and free tuition to any SCBWI conference anywhere in the world
Closing Date: Submitted through the Work-In-Progress application from March 1-31

Dana Awards
Literary Competition, 200 Fosseway Dr, Greensboro, NC 27455
Tel: 336-644-8028
E-mail: danaawards@gmail.com
Web Site: www.danaawards.com
Key Personnel
Chair: Mary Elizabeth Parker
Established: 1996
Three awards: for unpublished group of poems, short story, novel, (or novel-in-progress). Poetry: submit 5 poems of no more than 100 lines each with a $15 entry fee. Short story: submit up to 10,000 words with a $15 entry fee. Novel: the first 40 pages & a $25 entry fee. All types of novels accepted.
Award: $1,000 each category; $3,000 total
Closing Date: Annually, Oct 31
Presented: All awards, checks & notification are presented by mail or e-mail

Robert Dana-Anhinga Prize for Poetry
Anhinga Press
PO Box 3665, Tallahassee, FL 32315
Tel: 850-577-0745
E-mail: info@anhinga.org
Web Site: www.anhinga.org
Key Personnel
Dir: Kristine Snodgrass *E-mail:* kristine.snodgrass@gmail.com
Established: 1983
Poetry book.
Award: $2,000 & publication
Closing Date: Annually, Feb 15-May 15
Presented: Tallahassee, FL

The Danahy Fiction Prize
Tampa Review
University of Tampa Press, 401 W Kennedy Blvd, Tampa, FL 33606
Tel: 813-253-6266
E-mail: utpress@ut.edu
Web Site: tampareview.ut.edu
Key Personnel
Ed: Richard Mathews
Edit Asst: Sean Donnelly
Established: 2006
Award: $1,000 & publication in "Tampa Review"
Closing Date: Annually, Dec 31

Benjamin H Danks Award
American Academy of Arts & Letters
633 W 155 St, New York, NY 10032
Tel: 212-368-5900 *Fax:* 212-491-4615
E-mail: academy@artsandletters.org
Web Site: www.artsandletters.org
Key Personnel
Exec Dir: Virginia Dajani
Established: 2003
Annual prize, in rotation, awarded to a composer of ensemble works, a playwright & a writer.
Award: $20,000

Watson Davis & Helen Miles Davis Prize
History of Science Society
Affiliate of American Council of Learned Societies
440 Geddes Hall, Notre Dame, IN 46556
Tel: 574-631-1194 *Fax:* 574-631-1533
E-mail: info@hssonline.org
Web Site: www.hssonline.org
Key Personnel
Exec Dir: Robert Jay Malone
Established: 1985
For the best book on the history of science directed to a broad public published during the preceding three years.
Award: $1,000 & certificate
Closing Date: April 1
Presented: Awards Banquet, Nov

Dayton Literary Peace Prize
Dayton Literary Peace Prize Foundation
25 Harman Terr, Dayton, OH 45419
Mailing Address: PO Box 461, Wright Brothers Branch, Dayton, OH 45409-0461
Tel: 937-298-5072
Web Site: daytonliterarypeaceprize.org
Key Personnel
DLPP Chair: Sharon Rab *E-mail:* sharon.rab@daytonliterarypeaceprize.org
Established: 2006
First & only annual US literary award recognizing the power of the written word to promote peace. This project is the recognition of adult fiction & nonfiction books that have led readers to a better understanding of other cultures, peoples, religions & political points of view.
Award: $10,000 each genre (fiction & nonfiction)
Closing Date: Annually in March
Presented: Benjamin & Marian Schuster Performing Arts Center, Dayton, OH, Annually in Nov

Dayton Playhouse FutureFest
The Dayton Playhouse
1301 E Siebenthaler Ave, Dayton, OH 45414
Mailing Address: PO Box 3017, Dayton, OH 45401-3017
Tel: 937-424-8477 *Fax:* 937-424-0062
E-mail: dp_futurefest@yahoo.com
Web Site: www.daytonplayhouse.com
Key Personnel
Exec Dir: Wade Hamilton
FutureFest Prog Dir: Fran Pesch
Established: 1991
National Playwriting Competition; send SASE or see web site for submission guidelines.
Award: $1,000 (1st place), $100 (5 runners up) - all 6 finalists are provided travel to & housing for the FutureFest weekend
Closing Date: Annually, Oct 31
Presented: The Dayton Playhouse, Annually in May

Delaware Division of the Arts
Delaware Division of the Arts Individual Artist Fellowships
Carvel State Off Bldg, 4th fl, 820 N French St, Wilmington, DE 19801
Tel: 302-577-8278 *Fax:* 302-577-6561
E-mail: delarts@state.de.us
Web Site: www.artsdel.org
Key Personnel
Art & Artist Servs Coord: Roxanne Stanulis
Individual Artist Fellowships will be awarded to beginning or established poets & other creative writers. Applicants must be Delaware residents.
Award: A Masters Fellowship of $10,000 & established Professional Fellowships of $6,000 each & Emerging Professional Fellowships of $3,000
Closing Date: Annually, Aug 1
Presented: Annually (Master's awarded every three years in literature); winners notified in Dec

Rick DeMarinis Short Story Award
CUTTHROAT, A Journal of the Arts
PO Box 2414, Durango, CO 81302
Tel: 970-903-7914
E-mail: cutthroatmag@gmail.com
Web Site: www.cutthroatmag.com
Key Personnel
Ed-in-Chief: Pamela Uschuk
Mng Ed: Susan Foster
Fiction Ed: Beth Alvarado
Submit one unpublished short story (5000 word limit), any subject, any style. Mss must be 12 point font & double-spaced. Reading fee $17.
Award: $1,250 (1st place), $250 (2nd place), both include publication in *CUTTHROAT*
Closing Date: Annually in Oct
Presented: Annually in Dec

Der-Hovanessian Translation Prize
New England Poetry Club
2 Farrar St, Cambridge, MA 02138
Mailing Address: 376 School St, Watertown, MA 02472
Tel: 617-744-6034
E-mail: contests@nepoetryclub.org
Web Site: www.nepoetryclub.org
Key Personnel
Pres: Diana Der-Hovanessian
VP: Sally Cragin; Daniel Tobin
Contest Chair: Nazaleem Smith
For translation from any language. Send a copy of original with the poem.
Award: $200
Closing Date: Annually, May 31
Presented: Public Library, Cambridge, MA, Annually in Autumn

Alice Fay Di Castagnola Award
Poetry Society of America (PSA)
15 Gramercy Park, New York, NY 10003
Tel: 212-254-9628 *Fax:* 212-673-2352
Web Site: www.poetrysociety.org
Key Personnel
Pres: Ruth Kaplan
Exec Dir: Alice Quinn
Deputy Dir: Brett Fletcher Lauer *E-mail:* brett@poetrysociety.org
Progs Dir: Charif Shanahan *E-mail:* charif@poetrysociety.org
Established: 1965
In honor of a friend & benefactor of the society. For a ms in progress (poetry, prose or verse drama). Preliminary submission not to exceed 300 lines of sample verse if poetry or a sample chapter if prose; a sample scene if verse drama. Open to society members only. Send No 10 SASE or see web site for complete information.
Award: $1,000
Closing Date: Annually, Oct-Dec
Presented: Annual Awards Ceremony, New York, NY, Annually in Spring

Diagram Essay Contest
DIAGRAM
University of Arizona, ML-445, PO Box 210067, Tucson, AZ 85721
E-mail: editor@thediagram.com
Web Site: www.thediagram.com/contest.html
Key Personnel
Ed: Ander Monson
Established: 2008
For an unpublished essay, particularly one that incorporates writing in other genres or unique textual or visual elements. Submit an essay of up to 10,000 words. Entry fee $17.

Award: $1,000 & publication in *DIAGRAM*
Closing Date: Annually in Nov

Diamonstein-Spielvogel Award for the Art of the Essay, see PEN/Diamonstein-Spielvogel Award for the Art of the Essay

Philip K Dick Award
Philadelphia Science Fiction Society
PO Box 3447, Hoboken, NJ 07030
Tel: 201-876-2551
Web Site: www.philipkdickaward.org
Key Personnel
Administrator: Patrick Lo Brutto; John Silbersack; Gordon Van Gelder
Established: 1983
Presented annually for distinguished science fiction in paperback original form in the US.
Other Sponsor(s): Philip K Dick Trust; NorthWest Science Fiction Society
Closing Date: Annually, Dec 1
Presented: Norwescon, SeaTac, WA, Easter Weekend

Dickinson, Emily Award, see The Writer Magazine/Emily Dickinson Award

Annie Dillard Award for Creative Nonfiction
The Bellingham Review
Mail Stop 9053, Western Washington University, Bellingham, WA 98225
Tel: 360-650-4863
E-mail: bhreview@wwu.edu
Web Site: www.bhreview.org
Key Personnel
Ed-in-Chief: Brenda Miller
Mng Ed: Kaitlyn Teer
Established: 1983
Maximum length for prose is 6,000 words. Poems within a series of poems will each be treated as a separate entry. No previously published works, or works accepted for publication, are eligible. Work may be under consideration elsewhere, but must be withdrawn from the competition if accepted for publication. Make checks payable to: The Bellingham Review. All entries will receive a complimentary one-issue subscription. Entry fee for the first entry (one nonfiction work, one short story, or up to three poems) $20. Each additional entry, including each additional poem $10.
Only accept submissions through Submittable. Mailed submissions are no longer accepted.
Award: $1,000 & publication in the Bellingham Review (1st prize), considered for publication (2nd, 3rd & finalists)
Closing Date: Annually, between Dec 1 & March 15
Presented: Annually in July

Gordon W Dillon/Richard C Peterson Memorial Essay Prize
American Orchid Society Inc
Fairfield Tropical Botanic Gardens, 10901 Old Cutler Rd, Coral Gables, FL 33156
Tel: 305-740-2010 *Fax:* 305-740-2011
E-mail: theaos@aos.org
Web Site: www.aos.org
Key Personnel
Dir, Pubns: James Watson *E-mail:* jwatson@aos.org
Established: 1985
Essay contest (orchid topics only; new theme announced each year).
Award: Cash award & a certificate of recognition. Winning essay published in the June issue of *Orchids* magazine the following year
Closing Date: Annually, Nov 30

Discover Great New Writers Award
Barnes & Noble Inc
122 Fifth Ave, New York, NY 10011
Web Site: www.barnesandnoble.com
Key Personnel
Dir: Miwa Messer *Tel:* 212-633-4067
E-mail: mmesser@bn.com
Established: 1990
Authors cannot submit their own work to the program; self-published writers & titles published via print-on-demand or available only as NOOK books are also ineligible for submission. Literary fiction, short story collections & literary nonfiction, such as travel essays, memoirs, or other nonfiction with a strong narrative will be considered. Books should be intended for an adult or a young adult audience. Debuting authors & writers with fewer than 3 previously published books who have yet to received a major literary award are eligible for consideration. Submissions must be original publications, penned by one author.
Award: $35,000 to six young writers

"Discovery"/Boston Review Poetry Contest
Unterberg Poetry Center
Subsidiary of 92nd Street Y/Tisch Center for the Arts
1395 Lexington Ave, New York, NY 10128
Tel: 212-415-5760
E-mail: unterberg@92y.org
Web Site: www.92y.org/discovery
Key Personnel
Mng Dir: Ricardo Maldonado
E-mail: rickymaldonado@92y.org
For poets who have not published a full-length poetry collection; for guidelines visit web site. $12 entry fee must accompany the submission.
Other Sponsor(s): *Boston Review*
Award: Publication in *Boston Review*, reading at The Poetry Center & $500 each to the 4 winning authors
Closing Date: Jan 25, 2016
Presented: Winners will be contacted by phone in April 2016

Distinguished Book Award
American Sociological Association (ASA)
c/o Governance Off, 1430 "K" St NW, Suite 600, Washington, DC 20005
Tel: 202-383-9005 *Fax:* 202-638-0882
E-mail: governance@asanet.org
Web Site: www.asanet.org
Key Personnel
Dir, Governance: Michael Murphy *Tel:* 202-383-9005 ext 327
This award is given for a single book published in the two calendar years preceding the award year. The winner of this award will be offered a lectureship known as the Sorokin Lecture. Regional & state sociological associations/societies may apply to ASA to receive this lecture at ASA's expense after the award recipient is announced. One member of the association must submit letters in support of each nomination for the award. Nominations should include name of author, title of book, date of publication, publisher & brief statements from two (differently located) sources as to why the book should be considered. Send nominations to: ASA office at above address.
Award: Certificate
Closing Date: Jan 31
Presented: ASA Annual Meeting, Montreal, QC, CN, Annually in Aug

Documentation Grant Program
New Brunswick Arts Board (Conseil des arts du Nouveau-Brunswick)
649 rue Queen, 2nd fl, Fredericton, NB E3B 1C3, Canada
Tel: 506-444-4444 *Toll Free Tel:* 866-460-ARTS (460-2787) *Fax:* 506-444-5543
E-mail: nbabcanb@artsnb.ca
Web Site: www.artsnb.ca
Key Personnel
Exec Dir: Akoulina Connell *Tel:* 506-444-4343
E-mail: execdirgen@artsnb.ca
Deputy Dir: Vanessa Moeller *Tel:* 506-292-4696
E-mail: vmoeller@artsnb.ca
Prog Offr: Joss Richer *Tel:* 506-478-4610
E-mail: jricher@artsnb.ca
Designed to provide assistance to New Brunswick arts professionals & professional artists for the research, development & execution of original documentation & contextualization (written, film, video, multimedia) of arts activities, arts products or art history. Documentation grants are intended to foster theoretical & critical discourse in the arts. Preference will be given to proposals concerning New Brunswick art or artists.
Closing Date: April 1, Oct 1

Blake Dodd Prize
American Academy of Arts & Letters
633 W 155 St, New York, NY 10032
Tel: 212-368-5900 *Fax:* 212-491-4615
E-mail: academy@artsandletters.org
Web Site: www.artsandletters.org
Key Personnel
Exec Dir: Virginia Dajani
Established: 2014
Triennial award for a nonfiction writer.
Award: $25,000

Dog Writers' Association of America Inc (DWAA) Annual Writing Competition
Dog Writers' Association of America Inc (DWAA)
2243 Kelmscott Ct, Westlake Village, CA 91361
Tel: 805-418-7899 *Fax:* 831-374-9231
E-mail: dogwriter@windstream.net
Web Site: www.dwaa.org
Key Personnel
Pres: Ida Estep, Esq *Tel:* 252-478-6088 *Fax:* 252-478-6089 *E-mail:* ida@dogwriters.org
VP & Contest Chair: Elaine Gerwitz *Tel:* 805-418-7899 *Fax:* 821-374-9231 *E-mail:* elaine@dogwriters.org
Treas: Marsha Pugh *E-mail:* marsha@dogwriters.org
Secy: Susan M Ewing *E-mail:* su@dogwriters.org
Established: 1935
To give recognition to an individual, club or group which has done an outstanding job in the dog writing field in numerous categories. Only original work published between Sept 1 & Aug 31 of the competition year.
Award: Over several thousand dollars in cash prizes; plaques & certificates
Closing Date: Sept 9 (postmarked or submitted online)
Presented: Annual Awards Banquet, Feb, Sunday before Westminster Dog Show

The Christopher Doheny Award
The Center for Fiction
17 E 47 St, New York, NY 10017
Tel: 212-755-6710 *Fax:* 212-826-0831
E-mail: doheny@centerforfiction.org; info@centerforfiction.org
Web Site: www.centerforfiction.org/awards/the-christopher-doheny-award
Key Personnel
Awards & Progs Mgr: Sara Batkie *E-mail:* sara@centerforfiction.org
Annual award to recognize excellence in fiction or nonfiction on the topic of serious physical illness by a writer who has personally dealt with or is dealing with life-threatening illness, either his or her own or that of a close relative or friend.
Other Sponsor(s): Audible Inc
Award: $10,000, publication & promotion of book in print & audio

Dorothy Canfield Fisher Children's Book Award
Vermont Department of Libraries
109 State St, Montpelier, VT 05609-0601
Tel: 802-828-6954 *Fax:* 802-828-1481
E-mail: cbec@state.vt.us
Web Site: www.dcfaward.org; libraries.vermont.gov/libraries
Key Personnel
Chpn: Mary Linney
Youth Servs Consultant: Grace Worcester Greene *E-mail:* grace.greene@state.vt.us
Established: 1956
For a book by a living American or Canadian author published one year previous, chosen by the children of Vermont, grades 4-8, from a master list of 30 titles.
Other Sponsor(s): Vermont PTA
Award: Illuminated scroll
Closing Date: Annually, Dec 1
Presented: Annually in May

Dorset Prize
Tupelo Press Inc
PO Box 1767, North Adams, MA 01247
SAN: 254-3281
Tel: 413-664-9611 *Fax:* 413-664-9711
E-mail: info@tupelopress.org
Web Site: www.tupelopress.org
Key Personnel
Mng Ed: Jim Schley
Established: 2003
An open book competition for poetry. Full guidelines on the web site.
Award: $3,000, publication & national distribution
Closing Date: Sept 1-Dec 31
Presented: Spring

John Dos Passos Prize for Literature
Longwood University
Dept of English & Modern Languages, 201 High St, Farmville, VA 23909
Tel: 434-395-2155 *Fax:* 434-395-2145
Key Personnel
Chpn, Dos Passos Comm & Assoc Professor: Mary Carroll-Hackett
Dept Chpn: Rhonda Brock-Servais
Established: 1980
To honor an imaginative prose writer. Preference given to those not previously honored. Winners are nominated & selected by a jury. Applications not accepted.
Award: $2,000 & a medallion
Presented: Longwood University, Farmville, VA, During Fall semester

Frank Nelson Doubleday Memorial Award
Wyoming Arts Council
Division of Wyoming Department of Parks & Cultural Resources
2320 Capitol Ave, Cheyenne, WY 82002
Tel: 307-777-5234 *Fax:* 307-777-5499
Web Site: wyoarts.state.wy.us
Key Personnel
Literary, Visual & Performing Arts Specialist: Michael Shay *Tel:* 307-777-5234 *E-mail:* mshay@state.wy.us
Arts Council Mgr: Rita Basom *Tel:* 307-777-7473 *E-mail:* rbasom@state.wy.us
Established: 1988
Best poetry, fiction, nonfiction or drama written by a woman author. Wyoming residents only. Blind judges & single juror.
Other Sponsor(s): Neltje
Award: $1,000
Closing Date: Annually, Oct 31
Presented: Winner announced Jan 1

Carleton Drewry Memorial
The Poetry Society of Virginia
1194 Hume Rd, Hume, VA 22639-1806
E-mail: poetryinva@aol.com
Web Site: www.poetrysocietyofvirginia.org
Key Personnel
Pres: Judith K Bragg *E-mail:* musicsavy45@yahoo.com
Adult Contest Chair: Patsy Anne Bickerstaff *E-mail:* granypatsy@yahoo.com; Guy Terrell *E-mail:* ggterr@infionline.net
Lyric or sonnet. Must be in English, original & unpublished. Submit 2 copies, each having the category name & number on top left of page. Entries will not be returned. Subject: mountains; 48 line limit. Entry fee: $4 nonmembs.
Award: $50 (1st prize), $30 (2nd prize), $20 (3rd prize)
Closing Date: Jan 19
Presented: Annual PSV Awards Luncheon, Richmond, VA, April

Saint Katharine Drexel Award
Catholic Library Association
8550 United Plaza Blvd, Suite 1001, Baton Rouge, LA 70809-2256
Tel: 225-408-4417
E-mail: cla2@cathla.org
Web Site: www.cathla.org
Key Personnel
Pres: Mary Kelleher *Tel:* 225-408-4417 *E-mail:* kellehm@stthom.edu
Established: 1966
Recognizes an outstanding contribution to the growth of high school librarianship.
Award: Plaque
Closing Date: None; in-house votes
Presented: CLA Annual Convention

Drury University One-Act Play Competition
Drury University
900 N Benton Ave, Springfield, MO 65802-3344
Tel: 417-873-6821
Web Site: www.drury.edu
Key Personnel
Professor, Theatre: Dr Mick Sokol *E-mail:* msokol@drury.edu
Established: 1986
Biennial award for one-act plays. Open to all playwrights. Scripts are to be original, unpublished & unproduced; staged readings or workshop productions will not disqualify a script; musicals, monologues, children's plays & adaptations will not be considered; only stage plays will be judged; preference will be given to small cast, one-set shows with running times of no less than 20 & no more than 45 minutes; no more than one script per author; all scripts are to be typewritten & firmly bound; scripts cannot be acknowledged or returned unless accompanied by a SASE.
Award: $300 plus consideration for production by Drury University (1st prize); two honorable mentions $150 each
Closing Date: Dec 1 (even-numbered years)
Presented: By mail no later than April 1 (odd-numbered years)

Dubuque Fine Arts Players Annual One Act Play Festival
Dubuque Fine Arts Players
PO Box 1160, Dubuque, IA 52004-1160
Tel: 563-588-3438
E-mail: contact@dbqoneacts.org
Web Site: www.dbqoneacts.org
Key Personnel
Pres: Art Roche
Established: 1977
Annual national one-act playwriting contest. Entry form & guidelines are available at the web site. Submit the entry form, two copies of the script, a synopsis of the play & entry fee. Plays may be submitted by US mail with a $15 entry fee. SASE should be enclosed if return of the reader evaluation forms +/or the scripts is desired. Plays may be submitted online for an entry fee of $20. The higher fee pays cost of printing & binding the play. Previously published or produced works, musicals & children's plays are not accepted.
Membership(s): Dubuque County Fine Arts Society.
Award: $600 (1st prize), $300 (2nd prize), $200 (3rd prize), production of first 3 winning plays unless production is beyond our capacity
Closing Date: Annually, Jan 31
Presented: Mindframe Theater, Annually late Aug

John H Dunning Prize in United States History
American Historical Association (AHA)
400 "A" St SE, Washington, DC 20003
Tel: 202-544-2422 *Fax:* 202-544-8307
E-mail: awards@historians.org
Web Site: www.historians.org
Established: 1927
Biennial award in recognition of outstanding historical writing in US history. To be awarded to a young scholar for an outstanding monograph in ms or in print on any subject relating to US history. To be eligible for consideration, an entry must be of a scholarly historical nature. It must be the author's first or second book, published in 2015 or 2016. Research accuracy, originality & literary merit are important factors. Along with an application form, applicants must mail a copy of their book to each of the prize committee members who will be posted on our web site as the prize deadline approaches. All updated info on web site.
Award: Cash prize
Closing Date: May 15, 2017 (postmark)
Presented: AHA Annual Meeting, Washington, DC, Jan 4-7, 2018

Eaton Literary Associates Literary Awards
Eaton Literary Agency Inc
PO Box 49795, Sarasota, FL 34230-6795
Tel: 941-366-6589 *Fax:* 941-365-4679
E-mail: eatonlit@aol.com
Web Site: www.eatonliterary.com
Key Personnel
Pres: Ralph A Eaton
VP: Richard Lawrence
Established: 1984
Two awards are given, one for a book-length ms & one for a short story or article. These entries should not have been previously published.
Award: $2,500 (book-length program), $500 (short story or article program)
Closing Date: Annually, March 31 (short story or article program), Aug 31 (book-length program)
Presented: Annually in April (short story or article program), Sept (book-length program)

Edelstein Prize
Society for the History of Technology
Univ of Virginia, Dept of Science, Tech & Society, PO Box 400744, Charlottesville, VA 22904-4744
Tel: 434-987-6230 *Fax:* 434-975-2190 (attention: SHOT)
E-mail: shot@virginia.edu
Web Site: www.shot.jhu.edu
Key Personnel
Secy: Bernie Carlson
Established: 1958
For the best book published on the history of technology for a scholarly audience in the past three years.
Other Sponsor(s): Ruth Edelstein Barrish & Family in memory of Sidney Edelstein
Award: $3,500 & plaque
Closing Date: Annually, April 15
Presented: SHOT annual meeting, Cleveland, OH, Annually in Oct

Education Awards of Excellence
Printing Industries of America

200 Deer Run Rd, Sewickley, PA 15143-2324
Tel: 412-259-1705 *Toll Free Tel:* 800-910-4283 (ext 705) *Fax:* 412-749-9890
E-mail: printing@printing.org
Web Site: www.printing.org/educationaward
Key Personnel
CEO & Pres: Michael F Makin *E-mail:* mmakin@printing.org
Asst to VP, Mktg: Sara Welsh *E-mail:* swelsh@printing.org
Established: 1984
Honors one industry representative & one graphic arts educator who have each made outstanding contributions to graphic arts education +/or training. Entry is free. See web site for more information.
Award: Engraved plaque
Presented: GASC/Printing Industries of America's Teacher's Conference

Educators Award
The Delta Kappa Gamma Society International
PO Box 1589, Austin, TX 78767-1589
Tel: 512-478-5748 *Toll Free Tel:* 888-762-4685 *Fax:* 512-478-3961
E-mail: societyexec@dkg.org
Web Site: www.dkg.org
Key Personnel
Info Servs Administrator: Linda Eller *Tel:* 512-478-5748 ext 120 *E-mail:* lindae@dkg.org
Annual award to the woman author(s) of a book whose work may influence the direction of thought & action necessary to meet the needs of today's complex society. The content must be of more than local interest with relationship, direct or implied, to education everywhere. The author must be a woman from Canada, Costa Rica, Denmark, El Salvador, Estonia, Finland, Germany, Great Britain, Guatemala, Iceland, Mexico, Netherlands, Norway, Puerto Rico, Sweden or the US; call, e-mail or download regulations. All nominations are made by publishers.
Award: $2,500
Closing Date: Feb 1 (postmark)
Presented: One of Five Regional Conferences or Society's International Convention, Summer

Margaret A Edwards Award
Young Adult Library Services Association (YALSA)
Division of The American Library Association (ALA)
50 E Huron St, Chicago, IL 60611
Tel: 312-280-4390 *Toll Free Tel:* 800-545-2433 *Fax:* 312-280-5276
E-mail: yalsa@ala.org
Web Site: www.ala.org/yalsa/edwards
Key Personnel
Exec Dir: Beth Yoke *Tel:* 800-545-2433 ext 4391 *E-mail:* byoke@ala.org
Prog Offr, Events & Conferences: Nichole O'Connor *Tel:* 800-545-2433 ext 4387 *E-mail:* noconnor@ala.org
Communs Specialist: Anna Lam *Tel:* 800-545-2433 ext 5849 *E-mail:* alam@ala.org
Established: 1988
Given to an author for lifetime achievement in writing for teenagers.
Other Sponsor(s): School Library Journal
Award: $2,000 & citation
Closing Date: Annually in Dec
Presented: Announced at ALA's Midwinter Meeting. Winner honored & speaks during a luncheon at ALA's Annual Conference

Edwin Markham Prize for Poetry
Reed Magazine
San Jose State University, English Dept, One Washington Sq, San Jose, CA 95192-0090
Tel: 408-924-4441
Web Site: www.reedmag.org
All submissions must be through the online system with a common file format. Writers may submit multiple entries but each must be submitted separately & accompanied by a separate entry fee of $15.
Award: $1,000 & publication in *Reed Magazine*
Closing Date: Annually, Nov 1 (submissions accepted beginning June 1)

The Maureen Egen Writers Exchange Award
Poets & Writers Inc
90 Broad St, Suite 2100, New York, NY 10004
Tel: 212-226-3586 *Fax:* 212-226-3963
E-mail: admin@pw.org
Web Site: www.pw.org
Established: 1984
Introduces emerging writers to the New York literary community & provides them with a network for professional advancement.
Other Sponsor(s): Hachette Book Group USA
Award: All expenses-paid trip to New York City to meet with top literary professionals & give a public reading

Wilfrid Eggleston Award for Nonfiction
Writers' Guild of Alberta
11759 Groat Rd, Edmonton, AB T5M 3K6, Canada
Tel: 780-422-8174 *Toll Free Tel:* 800-665-5354 (AB only) *Fax:* 780-422-2663 (attn WGA)
E-mail: mail@writersguild.ab.ca
Web Site: www.writersguild.ab.ca
Key Personnel
Exec Dir: Carol Holmes *E-mail:* carol.holmes@writersguild.ab.ca
Communs & Partnerships Coord: Nicholas Mather *E-mail:* nicholas.mather@writersguild.ab.ca
Memb Servs Coord: Giorgia Severini
Progs Coord: Natalie Cook *E-mail:* natalie.cook@writersguild.ab.ca; Nichole Quiring *E-mail:* nichole.quiring@writersguild.ab.ca
Established: 1982
Alberta Literary Award, author must be resident of Alberta.
Award: $1,500 plus leather-bound copy of book
Closing Date: Annually, Dec 31
Presented: Alberta Book Awards Gala
Branch Office(s)
505 21 Ave SW, Calgary, AB T2S 0G9, Canada, Prog Coord: Samantha Warwick *Tel:* 403-265-2226 *E-mail:* samantha.warwick@writersguild.ab.ca

T S Eliot Prize for Poetry
Truman State University Press
100 E Normal Ave, Kirksville, MO 63501-4221
Tel: 660-785-7336 *Toll Free Tel:* 800-916-6802 *Fax:* 660-785-4480
E-mail: tsup@truman.edu
Web Site: tsup.truman.edu
Key Personnel
Dir & Ed-in-Chief: Barbara Smith-Mandell *E-mail:* bsm@truman.edu
Established: 1997
Annual award for the best unpublished book-length collection of poetry in English. Include a non-refundable reading fee of $25 for each ms submitted.
Award: $2,000 & publication
Closing Date: Oct 31
Presented: Jan

eLit Awards
Independent Publisher Online
1129 Woodmere Ave, Suite B, Traverse City, MI 49686
Tel: 231-933-0445 *Toll Free Tel:* 800-706-4636 *Fax:* 231-933-0448
E-mail: info@elitawards.com
Web Site: www.elitawards.com
Key Personnel
CEO: Jerrold R Jenkins *E-mail:* jrj@bookpublishing.com
Pres: James Kalajian *Tel:* 800-706-4636 ext 1006 *E-mail:* jjk@bookpublishing.com
Dir: Andrew Parvel *Tel:* 800-706-4636 ext 1004 *E-mail:* aparvel@bookpublishing.com
Established: 2009
To celebrate the ever growing market of electronic publishing in the wide variety of reader formats. Publishers & authors worldwide creating electronic books written in English & created for the global marketplace are eligible for entry in 65 different categories.
Other Sponsor(s): Jenkins Group
Award: Digital seal, certificate, winners featured online
Closing Date: Annually in Jan
Presented: Online, Annually in April

Ellery Queen Award
Mystery Writers of America (MWA)
1140 Broadway, Suite 1507, New York, NY 10001
Tel: 212-888-8171 *Fax:* 212-888-8107
E-mail: mwa@mysterywriters.org
Web Site: www.mysterywriters.org
Established: 1983
To honor outstanding writing teams & outstanding people in the mystery publishing industry.
Presented: The Edgars Banquet, Annually in Spring

Elliott Prize
Medieval Academy of America
104 Mount Auburn St, 5th fl, Cambridge, MA 02138
Tel: 617-491-1622 *Fax:* 617-492-3303
E-mail: speculum@medievalacademy.org
Web Site: www.medievalacademy.org
Key Personnel
Exec Dir & Ed, Speculum: Eileen Gardiner *E-mail:* egardiner@themedievalacademy.org
Established: 1971
For a first article published two years prior to award date, in the field of medieval studies.
Award: $500
Closing Date: Annually, Oct 15
Presented: Annually in April

Emerging Playwright Award
Urban Stages
555 Eighth Ave, Suite 1800, New York, NY 10018
Tel: 212-421-1380 *Fax:* 212-421-1387
E-mail: urbanstage@aol.com
Key Personnel
Artistic Dir & Founder: Frances Hill
Literary Dir: Antoinette Mullins
Scripts not previously produced; scripts should have no more than 7 characters; well-written, imaginative situations & dialog; multicultural scripts are given special attention. Playwrights in & around NYC are given special attention. No processing fee & SASE with all submissions. Selected scripts are first given a staged reading. A select number of staged readings are given intensive workshops. A select number of workshopped plays are given full off-Broadway productions. Award given to playwrights of full productions at Urban Stages.
Award: $500
Closing Date: Year-round
Presented: New York

The Ralph Waldo Emerson Award
The Phi Beta Kappa Society
1606 New Hampshire Ave NW, Washington, DC 20009
Tel: 202-265-3808 *Fax:* 202-986-1601
E-mail: awards@pbk.org
Web Site: www.pbk.org/bookawards

Key Personnel
Coord, Admin: Laura Hartnett *Tel:* 202-745-3287 *E-mail:* lhartnett@pbk.org
Established: 1960
For scholarly studies that contribute to interpretations of the intellectual & cultural condition of humanity. To be eligible, must have been published in USA by American author. Works in history, philosophy, religion & related fields such as social sciences & anthropology are eligible. Nomination must come from publisher & be submitted online.
Award: $10,000
Closing Date: Annually in Jan
Presented: Washington, DC, Annually in Dec

Empire State Award for Excellence in Literature for Young People
New York Library Association
6021 State Farm Rd, Guilderland, NY 12084
Tel: 518-432-6952 *Toll Free Tel:* 800-252-6952 *Fax:* 518-427-1697
E-mail: info@nyla.org
Web Site: www.nyla.org
Key Personnel
Exec Dir: Michael Borges *Tel:* 518-432-6952 ext 101 *E-mail:* director@nyla.org
Deputy Dir: Jeremy Johannesen *E-mail:* events@nyla.org
Mktg & Communs Mgr: Cara Longobardi *E-mail:* marketing@nyla.org
Established: 1990
One-time award presented to a living author or illustrator currently residing in New York State. The award honors excellence in children's or young adult literature & a body of work that has made a significant contribution to literature for young people.
Award: Engraved medallion
Presented: Annual Conference, Annually in Oct

Norma Epstein Foundation
University of Toronto - University College
15 King's College Circle, UC 173, Toronto, ON M5S 3H7, Canada
Tel: 416-978-8083 *Fax:* 416-971-2027
Web Site: www.utoronto.ca
Key Personnel
Registrar: Shelley Cornack
Academic Servs Asst: Khamla Sengthavy *E-mail:* khamla.sengthavy@utoronto.ca
Literary competition held every odd-numbered year. Three categories: fiction, drama & verse.
Award: $1,000 for each category
Closing Date: May 1, odd-numbered years
Presented: Toronto, Annually in Nov

The Ernest Sandeen & Richard Sullivan Prizes in Fiction & Poetry
University of Notre Dame Press/ND Creative Writing Program, Department of English
356 O'Shaughnessy Hall, Notre Dame, IN 46556
Tel: 574-631-7526 *Fax:* 574-631-4795
E-mail: creativewriting@nd.edu
Web Site: creativewriting.nd.edu
Key Personnel
Dir: Prof Joyelle McSweeney
Awarded to authors who have published at least one volume of short fiction or one volume of poetry. Include a photocopy of the copyright & the title page of your previous volume. Vanity press publications do not fulfill this requirement. Please include a vita +/or a biographical statement which includes your publishing history. We will be glad to see a selection of reviews of the earlier collection. Submit two copies of your ms & inform us if the ms is available on computer disk. Include a SASE for acknowledgment of receipt of your submission. If you would like your ms returned, send a SASE. A $15 administrative fee should accompany submissions.
Both prizes are awarded biannually, Ernest Sandeen Prize in even-numbered years & Richard Sullivan Prize in odd-numbered years.
Award: $1,000 prize, $500 award & $500 advance against royalties from the Notre Dame Press
Closing Date: May 1-Sept 1, 2016 (Richard Sullivan Prize), May 1-Sept 1, 2017 (Ernest Sandeen Prize)
Presented: Spring following submission period

Erskine J Poetry Prize
Smartish Pace
PO Box 22161, Baltimore, MD 21203
Web Site: www.smartishpace.com
Key Personnel
Founder & Ed: Stephen Reichert *E-mail:* sreichert@smartishpace.com
Established: 2001
All poems submitted for the prize will be considered for publication in *Smartish Pace*. Online submissions at www.smartishpace.com. Postal submissions: submit 3 poems along with a $5 entry fee. Additional poems may be submitted for $1 per poem. No more than 20 poems may be submitted. All entries must include bio. Include a SASE with entry & include name, address, e-mail & telephone number on each page of poetry submitted. Write or print "Erskine J" on the top of each poem submitted.
Award: $200 & publication of winning poem in *Smartish Pace* (1st prize). All finalists will be published in *Smartish Pace*
Closing Date: Annually, Sept 1
Presented: Baltimore, MD

ESPN Award for Literary Sports Writing, see PEN/ESPN Award for Literary Sports Writing

ESPN Lifetime Achievement Award for Literary Sports Writing, see PEN/ESPN Lifetime Achievement Award for Literary Sports Writing

David W & Beatrice C Evans Biography & Handcart Awards
Mountain West Center for Regional Studies
Division of College of Humanities & Social Sciences-Utah State University
0735 Old Main Hill, Logan, UT 84322-0735
Tel: 435-797-0299 *Fax:* 435-797-1092
E-mail: mwc@usu.edu
Web Site: mountainwest.usu.edu
Key Personnel
Prog Dir: Patricia Lambert
Established: 1983
For the best published biography or history with a significant biographical content of an individual associated with "Mormon Country" (a geographical, not religious, concept) published in 2015.
Award: $10,000 (The Evans Biography Award); $2,500 (The Evans Handcart Award)
Closing Date: Feb 22, 2016
Presented: Utah State University, Annually in the Fall

EXCEL Awards
Association Media & Publishing (AM&P)
12100 Sunset Hills Rd, Suite 130, Reston, VA 20190
Tel: 703-234-4063 *Fax:* 703-435-4390
E-mail: info@associationmediaandpublishing.org
Web Site: associationmediaandpublishing.org
Key Personnel
Exec Dir: John T Adams, III *Tel:* 703-234-4107 *E-mail:* jadams@associationmediaandpublishing.org
Mktg Mgr: Heather Konya *Tel:* 703-234-4112 *E-mail:* heather@associationmediaandpublishing.org
Service excellence awards program for association publishers. The EXCEL program judges over 1,200 magazines, newsletters, scholarly journals, electronic publications & web sites in the areas of editorial quality, design, general excellence, most improved & more.
Award: Gold Award (1st prize) brass statues; Silver & Bronze (2nd & 3rd prizes) framed certificates; EXTRA! Award, best of the gold, silver & bronze winners
Closing Date: Annually in Jan
Presented: Excel Awards Gala, Annual Meeting, Ronald Reagan Bldg, Washington, DC, June 2016

John K Fairbank Prize in East Asian History
American Historical Association (AHA)
400 "A" St SE, Washington, DC 20003
Tel: 202-544-2422 *Fax:* 202-544-8307
E-mail: awards@historians.org
Web Site: www.historians.org
Established: 1968
Outstanding book on the history of China proper, Vietnam, Chinese Central Asia, Mongolia, Manchuria, Korea or Japan substantially after 1800; books published in 2015 will be eligible; anthologies, edited works & pamphlets are ineligible for the competition. Along with an application form, applicants must mail a copy of their book to each of the prize committee members who will be posted on our web site as the prize deadline approaches. All updated info on web site.
Award: Cash prize
Closing Date: May 15, 2016 (postmark)
Presented: AHA Annual Meeting, Denver, CO, Jan 5-8, 2017

Tom Fairley Award for Editorial Excellence
Editors' Association of Canada (Association canadienne des reviseurs)
27 Carlton St, Suite 502, Toronto, ON M5B 1L2, Canada
Tel: 416-975-1379 *Toll Free Tel:* 866-CAN-EDIT (226-3348) *Fax:* 416-975-1637
E-mail: fairley_award@editors.ca
Web Site: www.editors.ca; www.reviseurs.ca
Key Personnel
Exec Dir: Carolyn L Burke *E-mail:* executivedirector@editors.ca
Communs Mgr: Michelle Ou *E-mail:* communications@editors.ca
Prof Devt Mgr: Helena Aalto *E-mail:* helena.aalto@editors.ca
Membership Coord: Lianne Zwarenstein
Established: 1983
Recognizes the editor's often invisible contribution to written communication.
Other Sponsor(s): Breakwater Books; HarperCollins; The C D Howe Institute; New Society Publishers; Orca Book Publishers; Random House of Canada; UBC Press, Madison; University of Calgary Press
Award: $2,000 cash
Closing Date: Jan of the year after the work took place
Presented: National Annual Conference, June of the year after the work took place

Family Matters
Glimmer Train Press Inc
PO Box 80430, Portland, OR 97280-1430
Tel: 503-221-0836 *Fax:* 503-221-0837
E-mail: editors@glimmertrain.org
Web Site: www.glimmertrain.org
Key Personnel
Co-Ed: Susan Burmeister-Brown *E-mail:* susan@glimmertrain.org
Established: 2007
Open to all writers, family theme, 500-12,000 word count range. Winner notification takes place 2 months after the close of each competition.

Award: $1,500, publication & 20 copies of that issue (1st place), $500 (2nd place), $300 (3rd place)
Closing Date: Annually in March & Sept

Far Horizons Award for Poetry
The Malahat Review
University of Victoria, Box 1700, Sta CSC, Victoria, BC V8W 2Y2, Canada
Tel: 250-721-8524 *Fax:* 250-472-5051
E-mail: malahat@uvic.ca
Web Site: www.malahatreview.ca
Key Personnel
Ed: John Barton
Established: 2006
Open to writers whose poetry has yet to be published in book form. Awarded in alternate years. See web site for details.
Award: $1,000 CAD
Closing Date: May 1, even-numbered yrs

Far Horizons Award for Short Fiction
The Malahat Review
University of Victoria, Box 1700, Sta CSC, Victoria, BC V8W 2Y2, Canada
Tel: 250-721-8524 *Fax:* 250-472-5051
E-mail: malahat@uvic.ca
Web Site: www.malahatreview.ca
Key Personnel
Ed: John Barton
Established: 2005
Open to writers whose fiction has yet to be published in a book of their own. Limited to 3,500 words. Awarded in alternate years. See web site for details.
Award: $1,000 CAD
Closing Date: May 1, odd-numbered yrs

Norma Farber First Book Award
Poetry Society of America (PSA)
15 Gramercy Park, New York, NY 10003
Tel: 212-254-9628 *Fax:* 212-673-2352
Web Site: www.poetrysociety.org
Key Personnel
Pres: Ruth Kaplan
Exec Dir: Alice Quinn
Deputy Dir: Brett Fletcher Lauer *E-mail:* brett@poetrysociety.org
Progs Dir: Charif Shanahan *E-mail:* charif@poetrysociety.org
For a first book of original poetry written by an American poet; publishers only may submit with entry form.
Award: $500
Closing Date: Annually, Oct-Dec
Presented: Annual Awards Ceremony, New York, NY, Annually in Spring

The FC2 Catherine Doctorow Innovative Fiction Prize
Fiction Collective Two Inc (FC2)
c/o Dept of English, Langs & Commun Bldg, 255 S Central Campus Dr, Rm 3500, Salt Lake City, UT 84112-0494
Tel: 773-702-7000
Web Site: www.fc2.org/prizes.html
Key Personnel
Chair, Bd of Dirs: Lance Olsen
Open to any US writer in English with at least 3 books of fiction published. Submissions may include a collection of short stories, one or more novellas or a novel of any length. Works that have previously appeared in magazines or in anthologies may be included.
Award: $15,000 & publication by FC2
Closing Date: Annually, Nov 1
Presented: Annually in May

Fellowship & Scholarship Program for Writers
Bread Loaf Writers' Conference
Middlebury College, Middlebury, VT 05753
Tel: 802-443-5286 *Fax:* 802-443-2087
E-mail: blwc@middlebury.edu
Web Site: www.middlebury.edu/blwc
Key Personnel
Dir: Michael Collier
Asst Dir: Jennifer Grotz
Admin Mgr: Noreen Cargill *E-mail:* ncargill@middlebury.edu
Work study scholarship to be used during conference in August.
Award: Fellowship provides tuition, room & board during 10-day conference; Scholarship provides tuition during conference
Closing Date: Annually, March 1
Presented: Ripton, VT, May

Fellowship Program
Rhode Island State Council on the Arts
Affiliate of Dept of Rhode Island State Government
One Capital Hill, 3rd fl, Providence, RI 02908
Tel: 401-222-3880 *Fax:* 401-222-3018
Web Site: www.arts.ri.gov
Key Personnel
Dir, Indiv Artists Progs: Cristina DiChiera *E-mail:* cristina.dichiera@arts.ri.gov
Established: 1967
Applicants must be Rhode Island residents who are over 18 & not students in an arts discipline. Fellowship recipients are selected by a regional panel of writers. Categories include fiction, poetry, playwriting/screenwriting. Guidelines & applications on web site.
Award: $5,000 recipient; $1,000 merit award
Closing Date: Annually, April 1
Presented: Annually

Fellowships for Creative & Performing Artists & Writers
American Antiquarian Society (AAS)
185 Salisbury St, Worcester, MA 01609-1634
Tel: 508-755-5221 *Fax:* 508-753-3311
Web Site: www.americanantiquarian.org
Key Personnel
Dir, Outreach: James David Moran *Tel:* 508-471-2131 *E-mail:* jmoran@mwa.org
Established: 1994
Award: $1,350 stipend for fellows residing on campus (rent-free) in the Society's Scholars' housing, $1,850 stipend for fellows residing off campus (no travel allowance)
Closing Date: Annually in Oct

Fellowships for Historical Research
American Antiquarian Society (AAS)
185 Salisbury St, Worcester, MA 01609-1634
Tel: 508-471-2131 *Fax:* 508-754-9069
Web Site: www.americanantiquarian.org
Key Personnel
Dir, Outreach: James David Moran *Tel:* 508-471-2131 *E-mail:* jmoran@mwa.org
Given to poets, fiction writers & creative nonfiction writers for month long residencies at the American Antiquarian Society in Worchester, MA, to research pre-twentieth century American history & culture. Submit 10 copies of up to 25 pages of poetry, fiction or creative nonfiction, a resume, 2 letters of recommendation & a 5 page project proposal.
Award: $1,350 stipend & on-campus housing provided; fellows residing off-campus receive $1,850
Closing Date: Annually, Oct 5

Fence Modern Poets Series
Fence Books
University at Albany, Science Library 320, 1400 Washington Ave, Albany, NY 12222
Tel: 518-591-8162
E-mail: fence.fencebooks@gmail.com
Web Site: www.fenceportal.org
Key Personnel
Publr & Ed: Rebecca Wolff *E-mail:* rebeccafence@gmail.com
Mng Ed: Jess Puglisi *E-mail:* jessp.fence@gmail.com
Established: 2001
For a poet writing in English at any stage of his or her publishing career.
Award: $1,000 & publication
Closing Date: Annually, Feb 28

Shubert Fendrich Memorial Playwriting Contest
Pioneer Drama Service Inc
PO Box 4267, Englewood, CO 80155-4267
Tel: 303-779-4035 *Toll Free Tel:* 800-333-7262 *Fax:* 303-779-4315
E-mail: playwrights@pioneerdrama.com
Web Site: www.pioneerdrama.com
Key Personnel
Submissions Ed: Lori Conary
Established: 1990
Presented for plays suitable for publication by Pioneer Drama Service Inc. Submission must include a full copy of your ms, a completed application, a recording of music (if applicable), proof of production & a SASE if you wish your material returned.
Award: $1,000 advance on royalties
Closing Date: Annually, Dec 31
Presented: Annually, June 1

Fiction Open
Glimmer Train Press Inc
PO Box 80430, Portland, OR 97280-1430
Tel: 503-221-0836 *Fax:* 503-221-0837
E-mail: editors@glimmertrain.org
Web Site: www.glimmertrain.org
Key Personnel
Co-Ed: Susan Burmeister-Brown *E-mail:* susan@glimmertrain.org
Established: 1999
Open to all themes & all writers, 2,000 to 20,000 word count range. Winner notification takes place 2 months after the close of each competition.
Award: $2,500, publication & 20 copies of that issue (1st place), $1,000 (2nd place), $600 (3rd place)
Closing Date: Annually in June & Dec

The Field Poetry Prize
Oberlin College Press
Subsidiary of Oberlin College
50 N Professor St, Oberlin, OH 44074-1091
SAN: 212-1883
Tel: 440-775-8408 *Fax:* 440-775-8124
E-mail: oc.press@oberlin.edu
Web Site: www.oberlin.edu/ocpress; www.oberlin.edu/ocpress/prize.htm (guidelines)
Key Personnel
Mng Ed: Marco Wilkinson
Ed: David Walker; David Young
Established: 1996
Original poetry ms of 50 to 80 pages. Open to all poets whether or not they have previously published in book form. Reading fee $28 & includes one year subn to *Field*.
Award: $1,000 & publication in the Field Poetry Series
Closing Date: Annually, May 31
Presented: Annouced in Aug (on web site)

Findley Prize, see Writers' Trust Engel/Findley Prize

Fine Arts Work Center in Provincetown
24 Pearl St, Provincetown, MA 02657
Tel: 508-487-9960 *Fax:* 508-487-8873
E-mail: general@fawc.org
Web Site: www.fawc.org

Key Personnel
Exec Dir: Michael Roberts *Tel:* 508-487-9960 ext 102 *E-mail:* mroberts@fawc.org
Established: 1968
Offer seven-month fellowships to ten artists & ten writers, Oct 1-May 1. The Center aims to aid emerging artists & writers at a critical stage of their careers. For application & brochure, see web site above or send SASE.
Award: Monthly stipends of up to $650 plus free rent for writers living at the Center; same for artists. Families welcome; no pets
Closing Date: Feb 1, visual arts; Dec 1, writers

Doug Fir Fiction Award
Bear Deluxe Magazine
240 N Broadway, Suite 112, Portland, OR 97227
E-mail: bear@orlo.org
Web Site: www.orlo.org
Key Personnel
Ed: Tom Webb
A short story relating to a sense of place or the natural world, interpreted as broadly or narrowly as you wish. Multiple submissions are allowed but must be mailed separately with separate entry fees. Submit a story of up to 5,000 words. Ms must be typed & double-spaced. Author's name must not appear anywhere on the ms. Entry fee: $15.
Award: $1,000 & publication in the magazine & writer's residency
Closing Date: Annually in Sept (postmarked 1st Tues after Labor Day)

Firecracker Awards
Community of Literary Magazines & Presses (CLMP)
154 Christopher St, Suite 3C, New York, NY 10014-9110
Tel: 212-741-9110 *Fax:* 212-741-9112
E-mail: info@clmp.org
Web Site: www.clmp.org/firecracker
Key Personnel
Progs Dir: Kathy Daneman *E-mail:* kdaneman@clmp.org
Celebrate & promote great literary works from independent literary publishers & self-published authors. Categories: Fiction, Creative Nonfiction, Poetry, Graphic Novel & Young Adult. Awards also in three magazine/periodical categories: Poetry, Best Debut & General Excellence.
Other Sponsor(s): American Booksellers Association
Presented: May at public event held in conjunction with Book Expo America

Five Star Dragonfly Book Awards
Five Star Publications Inc
4696 W Tyson St, Chandler, AZ 85226-2903
Tel: 480-940-8182 *Fax:* 480-940-8787
E-mail: info@fivestarpublications.com
Web Site: www.FiveStarBookAwards.com; www.FiveStarPublications.com
Key Personnel
Pres: Linda F Radke
Established: 2009
Three contests to choose from.
The Purple Dragonfly Book Awards honor published authors of children's literature - fiction & nonfiction - with 48 distinct subject categories, ranging from books on the environment & cooking to books on sports & family. Looking for stories that inspire, inform, teach or entertain. The judging panel includes experts from the fields of editing, reviewing, bookselling & publishing, as well as industry experts in specific fields. Books entered in this contest can appeal to children of any age. No restriction on publication date as long as the book is still in print. Authors can enter both ebooks & printed books.
The Royal Dragonfly Book Awards honor published authors of all types of literature - fiction & nonfiction - in a wide variety of genres, including inspirrational, how-to, environmental, travel, fantasy & science fiction, romance, children's books & more. The judging panel includes experts from the fields of editing, reviewing, bookselling & publishing, as well as industry experts in specific fields. Books in this category can appeal to readers of all ages. No restriction on publication date as long as the book is still in print. Authors can enter both ebooks & printed books.
The eBook Dragonfly Book Awards honor literature fiction & nonfiction that is digitally published. Categories include everything from aging to young adult fiction. An eBook Dragonfly seal tells readers they are not only in possession of a book that appeals to their specific taste in reading, but one that is also worthy of praise in the literary circle.
Entry fees: $65 for one title in one category, $60 per title when multiple books are entered, or $60 per category when one book in entered in multiple categories.
Award: Grand prize winner $300; drawing from first place winners $100 (1 winner)
Closing Date: Purple Dragonfly: Annually, March 1 (early), May 1 (final); Royal Dragonfly & eBook Dragonfly: Annually, Aug 1 (early), Oct 1 (final)
Presented: Award is mailed

The Flaherty-Dunnan First Novel Prize
The Center for Fiction
17 E 47 St, New York, NY 10017
Tel: 212-755-6710 *Fax:* 212-826-0831
E-mail: info@centerforfiction.org
Web Site: centerforfiction.org/awards
Key Personnel
Exec Dir: Noreen Tomassi *E-mail:* noreen@centerforfiction.org
Awards & Progs Mgr: Sara Batkie *E-mail:* sara@centerforfiction.org
Established: 2006
Awarded to the best debut novel published between Jan 1 & Dec 31 of the award year.
Award: $10,000 (1st prize), $1,000 (shortlist award)
Presented: The Center for Fiction's Annual Benefit & Awards Dinner, Annually in Dec

Norma Fleck Award for Canadian Children's Non-Fiction
Canadian Children's Book Centre
40 Orchard View Blvd, Suite 217, Toronto, ON M4R 1B9, Canada
Tel: 416-975-0010 *Fax:* 416-975-8970
E-mail: info@bookcentre.ca
Web Site: www.bookcentre.ca
Key Personnel
Exec Dir: Charlotte Teeple *E-mail:* charlotte@bookcentre.ca
Lib Coord: Meghan Howe *E-mail:* meghan@bookcentre.ca
Outreach Educ Coord: Sandra O'Brien *E-mail:* sandra@bookcentre.ca
Mktg & Website Coord: Camilia Kahrizi *E-mail:* camilia@bookcentre.ca
Prog Coord: Shannon Howe Barnes *E-mail:* shannon@bookcentre.ca
Established: 1999
Awarded to a Canadian author/illustrator for an outstanding work of nonfiction for young people.
Other Sponsor(s): Fleck Family Foundation
Award: $10,000
Closing Date: Annually in mid-Dec

Florida Individual Artist Fellowships
Florida Department of State, Division of Cultural Affairs
500 S Bronough St, Tallahassee, FL 32399-0250
Tel: 850-245-6470 *Fax:* 850-245-6497
E-mail: info@florida-arts.org
Web Site: www.florida-arts.org
Key Personnel
Dir: Sandy Shaughnessy *E-mail:* sshaughnessy@dos.state.fl.us
Arts Administrator: Mrs Morgan Lewis *E-mail:* mblewis@dos.state.fl.us
Arts Consultant: Tim Storhoff *E-mail:* timothy.storhoff@dos.state.fl.us
Established: 1976
Awarded biennially (even years), this fellowship program supports the general artistic & career advancement of individual artists & recognizes the creation of new artworks by these artists.

Fordham University, Graduate School of Business Administration
113 W 60 St, New York, NY 10023
Fax: 212-636-7076
Web Site: www.bnet.fordham.edu
Key Personnel
Professor, Communs & Media Mgmt: Philip M Napoli *Tel:* 212-636-6196 *E-mail:* pnapoli@fordham.edu
Established: 1969
Offers MBA degree with a major in Communications & Media Management & Master of Science (MS) in Communications & Media Management for media & entertainment industries. Its mission is to educate business professionals who can manage effectively in a range of leadership roles & who are equipped for continuous growth in a changing global environment. A variety of assistantships, fellowships & scholarships are available to highly qualified MBA candidates, such as Graduate Assistantships; New York Times Foundation Scholarship; Hitachi Fellowship; Xerox Fellowship; National Black MBA Association Scholarships; Minority Business Students Alliance Scholarship & Alexis Welsh Memorial Scholarship.
Closing Date: Ongoing
Presented: Each trimester

ForeWord Reviews Book of the Year Awards
ForeWord Reviews
425 Boardman Ave, Suite B, Traverse City, MI 49684
Tel: 231-933-3699 *Fax:* 231-933-3899
Web Site: www.bookoftheyearawards.com
Key Personnel
Publr: Victoria Sutherland *E-mail:* victoria@forewordreviews.com
Any independently published titles in any format with a copyright date of the previous calendar year. Publishers should submit their entries as soon as possible. Winners named in 60 categories.
Award: $1,500 each given to best book in fiction, nonfiction & independent publisher of the year
Closing Date: Annually, Jan 15 for books published in previous calendar year
Presented: ALA Annual Conference

Morris D Forkosch Prize
American Historical Association (AHA)
400 "A" St SE, Washington, DC 20003
Tel: 202-544-2422 *Fax:* 202-544-8307
E-mail: awards@historians.org
Web Site: www.historians.org
In recognition of the best in English in the field of British, British Imperial or British Commonwealth history since 1485. Submissions of books relating to the shared common law heritage of the English-speaking world are particularly encouraged. Books on British, British Imperial or British Commonwealth history published in 2015 are eligible. Along with an application form, applicants must mail a copy of their book to each of the prize committee members who will be posted on our web site

as the prize deadline approaches. All updated info on web site.
Closing Date: May 15, 2016 (postmark)
Presented: AHA Annual Meeting, Denver, CO, Jan 5-8, 2017

E M Forster Award
American Academy of Arts & Letters
633 W 155 St, New York, NY 10032
Tel: 212-368-5900 *Fax:* 212-491-4615
E-mail: academy@artsandletters.org
Web Site: www.artsandletters.org
Key Personnel
Exec Dir: Virginia Dajani
Given to a young English writer toward a stay in the US.
Award: $20,000

49th Parallel Poetry Award
The Bellingham Review
Mail Stop 9053, Western Washington University, Bellingham, WA 98225
Tel: 360-650-4863
E-mail: bhreview@wwu.edu
Web Site: www.bhreview.org
Key Personnel
Ed-in-Chief: Brenda Miller
Mng Ed: Kaitlyn Teer
Established: 1983
Maximum length for prose is 6,000 words. Poems within a series of poems will each be treated as a separate entry. No previously published works, or works accepted for publication, are eligible. Work may be under consideration elsewhere, but must be withdrawn from the competition if accepted for publication. Make checks payable to: The Bellingham Review. All entries will receive a complimentary one-issue subscription. Entry fee for the first entry $20, additional entries $10.
Only accept submissions through Submittable. Mailed submissions are no longer accepted.
Award: $1,000 & publication in the Bellingham Review (1st prize), considered for publication (2nd, 3rd & finalists)
Closing Date: Annually, between Dec 1 & March 15
Presented: Annually in July

Foster City International Writers Contest
Foster City Parks & Recreation Dept
650 Shell Blvd, Foster City, CA 94404
Tel: 650-286-3386
E-mail: fostercity_writers@yahoo.com
Web Site: www.fostercity.org
Key Personnel
Comm Chair: Ilene Shaine
Contact: Manny Hernandez
Established: 1974
For fiction, humor, children's story & poetry & personal essay, rhymed verse, blank verse. Entries must be original, previously unpublished & in English. Fiction must be no more than 3,000 words; children's story no more than 3,000 words; poetry not to exceed two double-spaced typed pages in length. Open to all writers, no age or geographic limit. Send SASE for contest flyer. Non-refundable entry fee: $20.
Award: $250 in each category (1st prize); $100 (2nd prize): children's, nonfiction, fiction, humor, poetry

Dixon Ryan Fox Manuscript Prize
New York State Historical Association
5798 State Hwy 80, Cooperstown, NY 13326
Mailing Address: PO Box 800, Cooperstown, NY 13326-0800
Tel: 607-547-1480 *Fax:* 607-547-1405
Established: 1974
Encourage original scholarship in the history of New York State. Award granted to the best unpublished ms on the history of New York State. Electronic submissions only.
Award: $3,000
Closing Date: Annually, Jan 2
Presented: New York State Historical Association Board of Trustees Annual Meeting, Cooperstown, NY, Annually in July

Frances Henne YALSA/VOYA Research Grant
Young Adult Library Services Association (YALSA)
Division of The American Library Association (ALA)
50 E Huron St, Chicago, IL 60611
Tel: 312-280-4390 *Toll Free Tel:* 800-545-2433 *Fax:* 312-280-5276
E-mail: yalsa@ala.org
Web Site: www.ala.org/yalsa
Key Personnel
Exec Dir: Beth Yoke *Tel:* 800-545-2433 ext 4391 *E-mail:* byoke@ala.org
Prog Offr, Events & Conferences: Nichole O'Connor *Tel:* 800-545-2433 ext 4387 *E-mail:* noconnor@ala.org
Communs Specialist: Anna Lam *Tel:* 800-545-2433 ext 5849 *E-mail:* alam@ala.org
Established: 1986
To provide seed money to an individual, institution or group for a project to encourage research in library service to young adults.
Other Sponsor(s): Scarecrow Press; Voice of Advocates
Award: $1,000
Closing Date: Annually, Dec 1
Presented: ALA Midwinter Meeting, Annually in Jan

H E Francis Award Short Story Competition
University of Alabama Department of English
UAH Huntsville Dept of English, Morton Hall 222, Huntsville, AL 35899
Web Site: www.uah.edu/la/departments/english/h-e-francis-contest
Key Personnel
Registrar: Patricia Sammon
Established: 1990
Mss must be unpublished & may not exceed 5,000 words in length. Multiple submissions are acceptable so long as we are notified immediately in the event that a ms is selected by another competition or publication. Submission must include $15 entry fee, cover sheet & three copies of ms. May submit story line & pay fee with Pay Pal.
Other Sponsor(s): Ruth Hindman Foundation
Award: $2,000
Closing Date: Jan 15 (postmark)
Presented: Annually in April

Soeurette Diehl Fraser Translation Award
Texas Institute of Letters (TIL)
c/o 7748 Hwy 290 W, Austin, TX 78736-3202
Tel: 512-683-5640
E-mail: president@texasinstituteofletters.org
Web Site: www.texasinstituteofletters.org
Key Personnel
Pres: Andres Tijerina
VP: Steve Davis
Treas: James Hoggard
Secy: Darwin Payne
Recording Secy: Betty Wiesepape
Established: 1990
Biennial award given for the best book of translation by a Texan. Guidelines available on the web site.
Other Sponsor(s): Babette Fraser
Award: $1,000
Closing Date: Jan, odd-numbered years
Presented: TIL Awards Banquet, Spring, odd-numbered years

George Freedley Memorial Award
Theatre Library Association
Roundabout Theatre Co, 231 W 39 St, Suite 1200, New York, NY 10018
Tel: 212-719-9393 (ext 351)
E-mail: info@tla-online.org; tlabookawards@gmail.com
Web Site: www.tla-online.org
Key Personnel
Co-Chair: Linda Miles; Tiffany Nixon
Established: 1968
To the author of a book in the field of theater, published in the US, on the basis of scholarship, readability & general contribution to knowledge. Only books related to live performance (including vaudeville, puppetry, pantomime & circus) will be considered.
Award: $500 (1st prize), $200 (Special Jury Prize); certificate
Closing Date: Feb 28
Presented: New York City, NY, Oct

The Don Freeman Memorial Grant-In-Aid
Society of Children's Book Writers and Illustrators (SCBWI)
4727 Wilshire Blvd, Suite 301, Los Angeles, CA 90010
Tel: 323-782-1010; 310-403-0675 (cell) *Fax:* 323-782-1892
E-mail: membership@scbwi.org; scbwi@scbwi.org
Web Site: www.scbwi.org
Key Personnel
Pres: Stephen Mooser *E-mail:* stephenmooser@scbwi.org
Exec Dir: Lin Oliver *E-mail:* linoliver@scbwi.org
Established: 1977
To enable picture-book artists to further their understanding, training +/or work in any aspect of the picture-book genre. Grant may be used for the purchase of necessary materials, enrollment in illustrators' or writers' workshops or conferences, courses in advanced illustrating or writing techniques & travel for research or to expose work to publishers/art directors. Open to Society members only.
Award: $2,000 & $500 for runner-up
Closing Date: Annually in March
Presented: Annually in Aug

The French-American Foundation & Florence Gould Foundation Annual Translation Prize
The French-American Foundation
28 W 44 St, Suite 1420, New York, NY 10036
Tel: 212-829-8800 *Fax:* 212-829-8810
E-mail: translation@frenchamerican.org
Web Site: www.frenchamerican.org
Key Personnel
Pres: Charles Kopb *Tel:* 212-829-8801 *E-mail:* ckopb@frenchamerican.org
Prog Offr: Eugenie Briet *Tel:* 646-588-6791 *E-mail:* ebriet@frenchamerican.org
Established: 1986
Annual award for distinguished translations of fiction & nonfiction from French into English which have been published in the US. Translations must be submitted by the US publisher. Technical, poetry, scientific, reference works & children's literature are not accepted. Works must have been published in 2015.
Other Sponsor(s): Florence Gould Foundation
Award: 2 awards of $10,000, 1 for fiction; 1 for nonfiction
Closing Date: Dec 31
Presented: New York, NY, Spring

Fresh Fish Award for Emerging Writers
Writers' Alliance of Newfoundland and Labrador (WANL)/Literary Arts Foundation of Newfoundland and Labrador
Haymarket Sq, 208-223 Duckworth St, St John's, NL A1C 6N1, Canada

Tel: 709-739-5215
E-mail: wanl@nf.aibn.com
Web Site: wanl.ca
Key Personnel
Exec Dir: Alison Dyer
Exec Asst: Sheri Coombs *E-mail:* wanlassist@nf.aibn.com
Established: 2006
Intended to serve as an incentive for emerging writers in Newfoundland & Labrador by providing them with financial support, recognition & professional editing services for a book length ms in any genre. Must be registered members of WANL; writers may join WANL at the time of submission.
Award: $5,000, editing services of a professional editor valued at up to $1,000 & miniature sculpture
Closing Date: June, odd-numbered years

Friends of American Writers Awards
Friends of American Writers
506 Rose Ave, Des Plaines, IL 60016
Tel: 847-827-8339
Web Site: www.fawchicago.org
Key Personnel
Pres: Roberta Gates *E-mail:* robmicgates73@gmail.com
Adult Lit Awards: Tammie Bob
E-mail: bobtam410@gmail.com
Established: 1922
For literary fiction & nonfiction books published in the current year. Book must be author's first, second or third work. Author must have lived for 5 years in the Midwest, currently living in the Midwest, or book's setting must be Midwestern. No poetry or mss.
Award: Two cash prizes totaling $4,000
Closing Date: Annually, Dec 20
Presented: The Fortnightly, Chicago, IL, Annually in May

Fulbright Scholar Program
Council for International Exchange of Scholars
Division of The Institute of International Education
1400 "K" St NW, Washington, DC 20005
Tel: 202-686-4000 *Fax:* 202-362-3442
E-mail: scholars@iie.org
Web Site: www.iie.org/cies
Key Personnel
Dir, Scholar Progs: Debra Egan
Dir, Outreach & Pub Aff: Peter Van Derwater
Established: 1946
CIES cooperates with the US Dept of State, Bureau of Educational & Cultural Affairs, in the administration of the Fulbright scholar program, which offers approximately 800 grants annually to US faculty & professionals for university teaching +/or advanced research in more than 125 countries.
Award: Grant benefits, which vary by country, generally include a stipend & round-trip travel for the grantee
Closing Date: Aug 1

Gabriele Rico Creative Nonfiction Challenge
Reed Magazine
San Jose State University, English Dept, One Washington Sq, San Jose, CA 95192-0090
Tel: 408-924-4441
Web Site: www.reedmag.org
All submissions must be through the online system with a common file format. Writers may submit multiple entries but each must be submitted separately & accompanied by a separate entry fee of $15.
Award: $1,333 & publication in *Reed Magazine*
Closing Date: Annually, Nov 1 (submissions accepted beginning June 1)

Lewis Galantiere Translation Award
American Translators Association (ATA)
225 Reinekers Lane, Suite 590, Alexandria, VA 22314
Tel: 703-683-6100 *Fax:* 703-683-6122
E-mail: ata@atanet.org
Web Site: www.atanet.org
Key Personnel
Exec Dir: Walter W Bacak, Jr *Tel:* 703-683-6100 ext 3006 *E-mail:* walter@atanet.org
Established: 1984
Awarded in even years for a distinguished book-length literary translation from any language, except German into English, published in the US.
Award: $1,000, a certificate of recognition & up to $500 toward expenses to attend the ATA Annual Conference
Closing Date: June 1 (even years)
Presented: ATA Annual Conference

Gannon University's High School Poetry Contest
Gannon University English Department
Gannon University, Dept of English, 109 University Sq, Erie, PA 16541
Tel: 814-871-7504
Web Site: www.gannon.edu/departmental/english/poetry.asp
Key Personnel
Professor, Eng: Berwyn Moore
E-mail: moore001@gannon.edu
Established: 1985
HS students in grades 9-12 are invited to participate; must be original poetry.
Award: $100 (1st place), $75 (2nd place), $50 (3rd place), certificate (honorable mention)
Closing Date: Annually, Feb 1
Presented: Gannon University, Waldron Campus Center, Yehl Rm, Erie, PA, April

Francois-Xavier Garneau Medal
Canadian Historical Association
130 Albert St, Suite 501, Ottawa, ON K1P 5G4, Canada
Tel: 613-233-7885 *Fax:* 613-565-5445
E-mail: cha-shc@cha-shc.ca
Web Site: www.cha-shc.ca
Key Personnel
Exec Coord: Michel Duquet *E-mail:* mduquet@cha-shc.ca
Established: 1980
Awarded every 5 years; commemorates the first Canadian Historian. Applicant should be a Canadian citizen or a legal immigrant. Given for the most outstanding scholarly book in the field of Canadian history within the previous five years.
Award: Minted medal & $2,000
Presented: 2020

Alfred C Gary Memorial
The Poetry Society of Virginia
1194 Hume Rd, Hume, VA 22639-1806
E-mail: poetryinva@aol.com
Web Site: www.poetrysocietyofvirginia.org
Key Personnel
Pres: Judith K Bragg *E-mail:* musicsavy45@yahoo.com
Adult Contest Chair: Patsy Anne Bickerstaff
E-mail: granypatsy@yahoo.com; Guy Terrell
E-mail: ggterr@infionline.net
All entries must be in English, original & unpublished. Submit 2 copies, each having the category name & number on top left of page. Entries will not be returned. Subject: a historic event that occurred between 1925 & 1992; iambic pentameter; 48 line limit. Entry fee: $4 nonmembs.
Other Sponsor(s): Claudia Gary
Award: $50 (1st prize), $30 (2nd prize), $20 (3rd prize)

Closing Date: Jan 19
Presented: Annual PSV Awards Luncheon, Richmond, VA, April

John Gassner Memorial Playwriting Award
The New England Theatre Conference Inc
215 Knob Hill Dr, Hamden, CT 06518
Tel: 617-851-8535 *Fax:* 203-288-5938
E-mail: mail@netconline.org
Web Site: www.netconline.org
Established: 1967
Playwriting contest for new full-length plays.
Award: $1,000 (1st prize), $500 (2nd prize)
Closing Date: Annually, April 15
Presented: NETC Annual Convention, Annually in Nov

The Christian Gauss Award
The Phi Beta Kappa Society
1606 New Hampshire Ave NW, Washington, DC 20009
Tel: 202-265-3808 *Fax:* 202-986-1601
E-mail: awards@pbk.org
Web Site: www.pbk.org/bookawards
Key Personnel
Coord, Admin: Laura Hartnett *Tel:* 202-745-3287
E-mail: lhartnett@pbk.org
Established: 1950
For outstanding books in the field of literary scholarship or criticism published in the USA. Nominations must come from publisher & be submitted online.
Award: $10,000
Closing Date: Annually in Jan
Presented: Washington, DC, Annually in Dec

The Gaylactic Spectrum Awards
Gaylactic Spectrum Awards Foundation
PO Box 73602, Washington, DC 20056-3602
Tel: 202-483-6369
Web Site: www.spectrumawards.org
Key Personnel
Exec Dir: Rob Gates
Established: 1998
Presented to outstanding works of science fiction, fantasy or horror with significant gay, lesbian, bisexual or transgender content.
Award: Statuette & cash prize for Best Novel & Best Short Fiction categories
Closing Date: Open between March 15 & April 30 for works released during the previous year
Presented: Varies - World Science Fiction Convention, Gaylaxicon or other, Fall

Lionel Gelber Prize
Lionel Gelber Foundation
University of Toronto, Munk School of Global Affairs, One Devonshire Place, Toronto, ON M5S 3K7, Canada
Tel: 416-946-8901 *Fax:* 416-946-8915
E-mail: events.munk@utoronto.ca
Web Site: munkschool.utoronto.ca/gelber/; www.facebook.com/GelberPrize
Established: 1989
Given to the author of the year's most outstanding work of nonfiction in the field of international relations. Designed to encourage authors who write about international relations & to stimulate the audience for these books to grow. Open to authors of all nationalities. Six copies of each title must be submitted by the publisher. Books must be published between Jan 1 & Dec 31 in English or English translation.
Other Sponsor(s): Munk School of Global Affairs
Award: $15,000
Closing Date: Oct
Presented: Short list announced Jan; prize award in Spring

Georgetown Review Literary Prize
Georgetown Review

Box 227, 400 E College St, Georgetown, KY 40324
Tel: 502-863-8079
E-mail: gtownreview@georgetowncollege.edu
Web Site: georgetownreview.georgetowncollege.edu
Established: 1993
For a single poem, a short story or an essay of any length. All entries are considered for publication. $10 entry fee, $5 for each additional entry.
Award: $1,000 & publication in Georgetown Review
Closing Date: Annually, Oct 15

Leo Gershoy Award
American Historical Association (AHA)
400 "A" St SE, Washington, DC 20003
Tel: 202-544-2422 *Fax:* 202-544-8307
E-mail: awards@historians.org
Web Site: www.historians.org
Established: 1975
In recognition of outstanding historical writing in 17th & 18th century Western European history. Books published in 2015 will be eligible. Along with an application form, applicants must mail a copy of their book (limited to three titles from any one publisher) to each of the prize committee members who will be posted on our web site as the prize deadline approaches. All updated info on web site.
Award: Cash prize
Closing Date: May 15, 2016 (postmark)
Presented: AHA Annual Meeting, Denver, CO, Jan 5-8, 2017

Charles M Getchell Award, see Southeastern Theatre Conference New Play Project

Giller Prize
Scotiabank
543 Logan Ave, Toronto, ON M4K 3B6, Canada
Web Site: www.scotiabankgillerprize.ca
Key Personnel
Exec Dir: Elana Rabinovitch
Annual literary prize for fiction.
Award: $140,000 CAD
Closing Date: Aug 15

Allen Ginsberg Poetry Award
The Poetry Center at Passaic County Community College
One College Blvd, Paterson, NJ 07505-1179
Tel: 973-684-6555 *Fax:* 973-523-6085
Web Site: www.pccc.edu/poetry
Key Personnel
Exec Dir: Maria Mazziotti Gillan
E-mail: mgillan@pccc.edu
Asst Dir: Susan Balik *E-mail:* sbalik@pccc.edu
Poem should not be more than 2 ms pages. Sheets which contain the poems should not contain the poet's name. Do not submit poems that imitate Allen Ginsberg's work. Entry fee $18.
Award: $1,000 (1st prize), $200 (2nd prize), $100 (3rd prize)
Closing Date: Annually, April 1

Gival Press Novel Award
Gival Press
PO Box 3812, Arlington, VA 22203
SAN: 852-9787
Tel: 703-351-0079 *Fax:* 703-351-0079 (call first)
E-mail: givalpress@yahoo.com
Web Site: www.givalpress.com
Key Personnel
Publr & Ed: Robert L Giron
Established: 2005
For best literary novel.
Award: $3,000 & publication
Closing Date: Annually, May 30
Presented: Annually, Oct 1

Gival Press Oscar Wilde Award
Gival Press
PO Box 3812, Arlington, VA 22203
SAN: 852-9787
Tel: 703-351-0079 *Fax:* 703-351-0079 (call first)
E-mail: givalpress@yahoo.com
Web Site: www.givalpress.com
Key Personnel
Publr & Ed: Robert L Giron
Established: 2002
For best GLBT poem.
Award: $100 & online publication
Closing Date: Annually, June 27
Presented: Annually, Sept 1

Gival Press Poetry Award
Gival Press
PO Box 3812, Arlington, VA 22203
SAN: 852-9787
Tel: 703-351-0079 *Fax:* 703-351-0079 (call first)
E-mail: givalpress@yahoo.com
Web Site: www.givalpress.com
Key Personnel
Publr & Ed: Robert L Giron
Established: 1999
For the best collection of poetry.
Award: $1,000 & book publication
Closing Date: Annually, Dec 15
Presented: Annually, May 1

Gival Press Short Story Award
Gival Press
PO Box 3812, Arlington, VA 22203
SAN: 852-9787
Tel: 703-351-0079 *Fax:* 703-351-0079 (call first)
E-mail: givalpress@yahoo.com
Web Site: www.givalpress.com
Key Personnel
Publr & Ed: Robert L Giron
Established: 2004
For best literary short story.
Award: $1,000 & online publication
Closing Date: Annually, Aug 8
Presented: Annually, Dec 1

John Glassco Translation Prize
Literary Translators' Association of Canada
Concordia University, LB 601, 1455 De Maisonneuve West, Montreal, QC H3G 1M8, Canada
Tel: 514-848-2424 (ext 8702)
E-mail: info@attlc-ltac.org
Web Site: www.attlc-ltac.org
Key Personnel
Pres: Jo-Anne Elder
Dir: Yves Dion
Established: 1982
For a first book-length literary translation into French or English published in Canada during the previous year. Must be Canadian citizen or permanent resident.
Award: $1,000
Closing Date: Annually, July 31
Presented: Annually, Sept 30

GLCA New Writers Awards
Great Lakes Colleges Association (GLCA)
535 W William St, Suite 301, Ann Arbor, MI 48103
Tel: 734-661-2350 *Fax:* 734-661-2349
Web Site: www.glca.org
Key Personnel
Dir, Prog Devt: Gregory R Wegner
Established: 1969
For a first published work of fiction or creative nonfiction or a first book of poetry. Submissions may be made only by publishers; one entry each, poetry, fiction or creative nonfiction. Submit 4 copies of the work & an author's statement agreeing to the terms. See web site for details.
Award: Reading engagements at up to 13 colleges & universities of the GLCA; each engagement includes $500 honorarium; all travel expenses are paid
Closing Date: July 25

The Danuta Gleed Literary Award
The Writers' Union of Canada (TWUC)
600-460 Richmond St W, Toronto, ON M5V 1Y1, Canada
Tel: 416-703-8982 *Fax:* 416-504-9090
E-mail: info@writersunion.ca
Web Site: www.writersunion.ca
Key Personnel
Off Administrator: Valerie Laws *Tel:* 416-703-8982 ext 224
Established: 1997
Annual award for best first collection of short fiction by a Canadian published in 2015 & available through bookstores & libraries.
Award: $10,000 (1st prize); $500 (2nd & 3rd prizes)
Closing Date: Jan 31, 2016

Global Ebook Awards
Para Publishing LLC
PO Box 8206-240, Santa Barbara, CA 93118-8206
SAN: 215-8981
Tel: 805-968-7277 *Fax:* 805-968-1379
Web Site: globalebookawards.com
Key Personnel
Owner & Publr: Dan Poynter
E-mail: danpoynter@parapublishing.com
Dir: Becky Carbone *E-mail:* becky@parapublishing.com
Open to authors, publishers, illustrators & photographers. Entry fee: $79.

Gold Medal
American Academy of Arts & Letters
633 W 155 St, New York, NY 10032
Tel: 212-368-5900 *Fax:* 212-491-4615
E-mail: academy@artsandletters.org
Web Site: www.artsandletters.org
Key Personnel
Exec Dir: Virginia Dajani
Rotating Categories of Belles Lettres & Criticism & Painting; Biography & Music; Fiction & Sculpture; History & Architecture, including Landscape Architecture; Poetry & Music; Drama & Graphic Art.
Award: 2 medals annually

Golden Cylinder Awards
Gravure Association of the Americas Inc
8281 Pine Lake Rd, Denver, NC 28037
Tel: 201-523-6042 *Fax:* 201-523-6048
E-mail: gaa@gaa.org
Web Site: www.gaa.org
Key Personnel
Dir, Planning & Admin: Pamela W Schenk
Tel: 585-288-2297 *E-mail:* pwschenk@gaa.org
Encourage highest quality gravure printing from design through production.
Award: Golden Cylinders on pedestals
Closing Date: Annually in April
Presented: Leadership Summit

Golden Kite Awards
Society of Children's Book Writers and Illustrators (SCBWI)
4727 Wilshire Blvd, Suite 301, Los Angeles, CA 90010
Tel: 323-782-1010; 310-403-0675 (cell) *Fax:* 323-782-1892
E-mail: scbwi@scbwi.org; membership@scbwi.org
Web Site: www.scbwi.org

Key Personnel
Pres: Stephen Mooser *E-mail:* stephenmooser@scbwi.org
Exec Dir: Lin Oliver *E-mail:* linoliver@scbwi.org
Established: 1973
Four awards, one each for fiction, nonfiction, picture book text & picture book illustration, awarded each year to the most outstanding children's books published during that year & written or illustrated by members of the Society of Children's Book Writers & Illustrators. An honor book plaque is awarded in each category.
Award: Free transportation & accomodations to summer conference
Closing Date: Annually in Dec
Presented: Annually in Aug

Golden Rose Award
New England Poetry Club
2 Farrar St, Cambridge, MA 02138
Mailing Address: 376 School St, Watertown, MA 02472
Tel: 617-744-6034
E-mail: contests@nepoetryclub.org
Web Site: www.nepoetryclub.org
Key Personnel
Pres: Diana Der-Hovanessian
VP: Sally Cragin; Daniel Tobin
Contest Coord: Audrey Kalajin
Established: 1920
The oldest literary award given annually to poet who has done the most for poetry during previous year or in a lifetime. Chosen by board members.
Award: Rose sculpture
Closing Date: Annually, May 31
Presented: Longfellow Garden, Cambridge, MA, Annually in July

Laurence Goldstein Poetry Prize
Michigan Quarterly Review
University of Michigan, 0576 Rackham Bldg, 915 E Washington St, Ann Arbor, MI 48109-1070
Tel: 734-764-9265
E-mail: mqr@umich.edu
Web Site: www.umich.edu/~mqr
Key Personnel
Mng Ed: Vicki Lawrence
Ed: Keith Taylor
Awarded to the best poem published in MQR each year. No deadline or special application process.
Award: $500

Governor General's Literary Awards
Canada Council for the Arts (Conseil des arts du Canada)
150 Elgin St, Ottawa, ON K1P 1L4, Canada
Mailing Address: PO Box 1047, Ottawa, ON K1P 5V8, Canada
Tel: 613-566-4414 *Toll Free Tel:* 800-263-5588 (CN only) *Fax:* 613-566-4390
E-mail: info@canadacouncil.ca
Web Site: canadacouncil.ca/en/council/prizes
Key Personnel
Prog Offr: Lori Knoll *Tel:* 613-566-4414 ext 5573 *E-mail:* lori.knoll@canadacouncil.ca
Established: 1936
Annual awards to the best English-language & French-language book in each of seven categories: fiction, poetry, drama, nonfiction, children's literature-text, children's literature-illustration & translation (from French to English & English to French).
Award: $25,000 each; non-winning finalists receive $1,000; publisher of each winning book receives $3,000 to promote the book

The Gracies®
Alliance for Women in Media (AWM)
1250 24 St NW, Suite 300, Washington, DC 20037
Tel: 202-750-3664 *Fax:* 202-750-3664
E-mail: info@allwomeninmedia.org
Web Site: allwomeninmedia.org
Key Personnel
Exec Dir: Becky Brooks
Awarded for programming in all mediums which contributes to positive & realistic portrayals of women, addresses interests of concern to women, enhances women's image, position & welfare.
Award: Statue
Presented: Annually in May

Grand Master Award
Mystery Writers of America (MWA)
1140 Broadway, Suite 1507, New York, NY 10001
Tel: 212-888-8171 *Fax:* 212-888-8107
E-mail: mwa@mysterywriters.org
Web Site: www.mysterywriters.org
To acknowledge important contributions to the genre & for a body of work that is both significant & of consistent high quality.
Presented: The Edgars Banquet, Annually in Spring

Grants for Literary Artists
New Brunswick Arts Board (Conseil des arts du Nouveau-Brunswick)
649 rue Queen, 2nd fl, Fredericton, NB E3B 1C3, Canada
Tel: 506-444-4444 *Toll Free Tel:* 866-460-ARTS (460-2787) *Fax:* 506-444-5543
E-mail: nbabcanb@artsnb.ca
Web Site: www.artsnb.ca
Key Personnel
Exec Dir: Akoulina Connell *Tel:* 506-444-4343 *E-mail:* execdirgen@artsnb.ca
Deputy Dir: Vanessa Moeller *Tel:* 506-292-4696 *E-mail:* vmoeller@artsnb.ca
Prog Offr: Joss Richer *Tel:* 506-478-4610 *E-mail:* jricher@artsnb.ca
Program is designed to recognize & encourage arts professionals who have demonstrated exceptional artistic talent & potential & who are pursuing a career in the arts. The program is divided in three components:
Arts by Innovation is for assistance to present work by invitation in established arts events.
Artist in Residence is for assistance for participation in residency opportunities of three months & less. The artists in residence are to contribute to the promotion & understanding of the arts by means of the artists' contact with the clientele of the establishments.
Professional Development is for assistance for professional development scholarships for studies & mentorships.
Closing Date: Jan 15, March 1, April 15, June 1, July 15, Sept 1, Oct 15, Dec 1

James H Gray Award for Short Nonfiction
Writers' Guild of Alberta
11759 Groat Rd, Edmonton, AB T5M 3K6, Canada
Tel: 780-422-8174 *Toll Free Tel:* 800-665-5354 (AB only) *Fax:* 780-422-2663 (attn WGA)
E-mail: mail@writersguild.ab.ca
Web Site: www.writersguild.ab.ca
Key Personnel
Exec Dir: Carol Holmes *E-mail:* carol.holmes@writersguild.ab.ca
Communs & Partnerships Coord: Nicholas Mather *E-mail:* nicholas.mather@writersguild.ab.ca
Memb Servs Coord: Giorgia Severini
Progs Coord: Natalie Cook *E-mail:* natalie.cook@writersguild.ab.ca; Nichole Quiring *E-mail:* nichole.quiring@writersguild.ab.ca
Established: 2009
Open to published pieces on any topic by an Alberta author; no longer than 5,000 words.
Award: $700
Closing Date: Annually, Dec 31
Presented: Alberta Book Awards Gala
Branch Office(s)
505 21 Ave SW, Calgary, AB T2S 0G9, Canada, Prog Coord: Samantha Warwick *Tel:* 403-265-2226 *E-mail:* samantha.warwick@writersguild.ab.ca

The Green Rose Prize in Poetry
New Issues Poetry & Prose
c/o Western Michigan University, 1903 W Michigan Ave, Kalamazoo, MI 49008-5463
Tel: 269-387-8185 *Fax:* 269-387-2562
E-mail: new-issues@wmich.edu
Web Site: www.wmich.edu/newissues/sub-guide.html
Key Personnel
Mng Ed: Kimberly Kolbe
Ed: William Olsen
Poets writing in English who have published one or more full-length collections of poetry. A $25 reading fee must accompany each ms; do not bind ms. Include a brief bio & relevant publication information, cover page with name, address, phone number, e-mail address & title of ms; include table of contents; enclose SASE. The winning ms will be named in Jan & published in the spring of the following year.
Other Sponsor(s): Western Michigan University
Award: $2,000 & book publication
Closing Date: Sept 30

Bess Gresham Memorial
The Poetry Society of Virginia
1194 Hume Rd, Hume, VA 22639-1806
E-mail: poetryinva@aol.com
Web Site: www.poetrysocietyofvirginia.org
Key Personnel
Pres: Judith K Bragg *E-mail:* musicsavy45@yahoo.com
Adult Contest Chair: Patsy Anne Bickerstaff *E-mail:* granypatsy@yahoo.com; Guy Terrell *E-mail:* ggterr@infionline.net
All entries must be in English, original & unpublished. Submit 2 copies of each poem, each having the category name & number on top left of page. Only 1 poem per category; entries will not be returned. Subject: gardens; 48 line limit. Entry fee: $4 nonmembs.
Award: $50 (1st place), $30 (2nd place), $20 (3rd place)
Closing Date: Jan 19
Presented: Annual PSV Awards Luncheon, Richmond, VA, April

Guggenheim-Lehrman Prize in Military History
The Harry Frank Guggenheim Foundation
25 W 53 St, New York, NY 10019
Tel: 646-428-0971 *Fax:* 646-428-0981
E-mail: info@hfg.org
Web Site: www.hfg.org/prize/main.htm
Established: 2013
To recognize the most outstanding book in the field of military history published in English in the previous calendar year. Publishers must submit 8 copies of each book for consideration along with a completed submission form & entry fee of $50 or 30 GBP. Authors may not directly submit their books for consideration. Books can be written by no more than two authors. Self-published & children's books are not eligible.
Award: $50,000
Closing Date: Nov 1
Presented: March

Hackmatack Children's Choice Book Award
Nova Scotia Department of Education & Early Childhood Development

PO Box 34055, Scotia Square RPO, Halifax, NS B3J 3S1, Canada
Tel: 902-424-3774 *Fax:* 902-424-0613
E-mail: hackmatack@hackmatack.ca
Web Site: www.hackmatack.ca
Key Personnel
Prog Coord: Kate Watson
Established: 1999
Atlantic Canadian Children's Choice Award for grades 4-6. Four categories: English fiction, English nonfiction, French fiction & French nonfiction.
Other Sponsor(s): Canada Council for the Arts; New Brunswick Public Library Service
Award: Plaques
Closing Date: Annually, Oct 15
Presented: Award ceremony, Annually in Spring

Hackney Literary Awards
1305 Second Ave N, Suite 103, Birmingham, AL 35203
E-mail: info@hackneyliteraryawards.org
Web Site: www.hackneyliteraryawards.org
Established: 1969
Short story, poetry & novel awards. Check web site or send SASE for contest guidelines. Entry fee: novels $30, short stories $20, poetry $15. Presented in Birmingham Arts Journal.
Award: $600 (1st place), $400 (2nd place), $250 (3rd place), plus a $5,000 prize sponsored by Morris Hackney for an unpublished novel
Closing Date: Annually, Sept 30 for novel entries, Nov 30 for short story & poetry entries
Presented: March 30

Sarah Josepha Hale Award
Trustees of the Richards Library
58 N Main, Newport, NH 03773
Tel: 603-863-3430
E-mail: rfl@newport.lib.nh.us
Web Site: www.newport.lib.nh.us
Key Personnel
Lib Dir & Award Administrator: Andrea Thorpe *E-mail:* athorpe@newport.lib.nh.us
Established: 1956
A distinguished literary figure in some way associated with New England. Nominations or applications are not accepted.
Award: Bronze medal & $1,000
Presented: Newport, NH

Loretta Dunn Hall Memorial
The Poetry Society of Virginia
1194 Hume Rd, Hume, VA 22639-1806
E-mail: poetryinva@aol.com
Web Site: www.poetrysocietyofvirginia.org
Key Personnel
Pres: Judith K Bragg *E-mail:* musicsavy45@yahoo.com
Adult Contest Chair: Patsy Anne Bickerstaff *E-mail:* granypatsy@yahoo.com; Guy Terrell *E-mail:* ggterr@infionline.net
All entries must be in English, original & unpublished. Submit 2 copies, each having the category name & number on top left of page. Subject: family; any form; 24 line limit. VA residents only. Entry fee: $4 nonmembs.
Other Sponsor(s): Phyllis Hall Haislip
Award: $50 (1st prize), $30 (2nd prize), $20 (3rd prize)
Closing Date: Jan 19
Presented: Annual PSV Awards Luncheon, Richmond, VA, April

Marilyn Hall Awards, see BHTG - Competition for Youth Theatre Marilyn Hall Awards

Handy Andy Prize
The Poetry Society of Virginia
1194 Hume Rd, Hume, VA 22639-1806
E-mail: poetryinva@aol.com
Web Site: www.poetrysocietyofvirginia.org
Key Personnel
Pres: Judith K Bragg *E-mail:* musicsavy45@yahoo.com
Adult Contest Chair: Patsy Anne Bickerstaff *E-mail:* granypatsy@yahoo.com; Guy Terrell *E-mail:* ggterr@infionline.net
For a limerick. Must be in English, original & unpublished. Submit 2 copies, each having the category name & number on top left of page. Entry fee: $4 nonmembs.
Award: $25 (1st prize), $15 (2nd prize), $10 (3rd prize)
Closing Date: Jan 19
Presented: Annual PSV Awards Luncheon, Richmond, VA, April

Clarence H Haring Prize
American Historical Association (AHA)
400 "A" St SE, Washington, DC 20003
Tel: 202-544-2422 *Fax:* 202-544-8307
E-mail: awards@historians.org
Web Site: www.historians.org
For work by a Latin American in Latin American history during the preceding five years. Offered quinquennially. There is no language limitation on works submitted. Along with an application form, applicants must mail a copy of their book to each of the prize committee members who will be posted on our web site as the prize deadline approaches. Books published 2011 through 2015 will be considered. All updated info on web site.
Award: Cash prize
Closing Date: May 15, 2016 (postmark)
Presented: AHA Annual Meeting, Denver, CO, Jan 5-8, 2017

Joy Harjo Poetry Award
CUTTHROAT, A Journal of the Arts
PO Box 2414, Durango, CO 81302
Tel: 970-903-7914
E-mail: cutthroatmag@gmail.com
Web Site: www.cutthroatmag.com
Key Personnel
Ed-in-Chief: Pamela Uschuk
Mng Ed: Susan Foster
Fiction Ed: Beth Alvarado; William Luvaas
Poetry Ed: William Pitt Root
Established: 2005
Submit online up to 3 unpublished poems (100 line limit for each). Writers may submit as often as they wish. No poems that have been previously published or have won contests are eligible; $17 reading fee.
Award: $1,250 (1st place), $250 (2nd place), both include publication in *CUTTHROAT*
Closing Date: Annually in Oct
Presented: Annually in Dec

Aurand Harris Memorial Playwriting Award
The New England Theatre Conference Inc
215 Knob Hill Dr, Hamden, CT 06518
Tel: 617-851-8535 *Fax:* 203-288-5938
E-mail: mail@netconline.org
Web Site: www.netconline.org
Established: 1997
Competition for new plays for young audiences. Scripts must be unpublished & unproduced. For guidelines, go to web site.
Award: $1,000 (1st prize), $500 (2nd prize)
Closing Date: Annually, May 1
Presented: NETC Annual Convention, Annually in Nov

Julie Harris Playwright Award Competition, see BHTG - Julie Harris Playwright Award Competition

Haskins Medal Award
Medieval Academy of America
104 Mount Auburn St, 5th fl, Cambridge, MA 02138
Tel: 617-491-1622 *Fax:* 617-492-3303
E-mail: speculum@medievalacademy.org
Web Site: www.medievalacademy.org
Key Personnel
Exec Dir & Ed, Speculum: Eileen Gardiner *E-mail:* egardiner@themedievalacademy.org
Established: 1940
For a book of outstanding importance in the medieval field published no earlier than six years prior to award date.
Award: Gold medal
Closing Date: Annually, Oct 15
Presented: Annually in Spring

Friedrich Hayek Lecture & Book Prize
Manhattan Institute for Policy Research
52 Vanderbilt Ave, New York, NY 10017
Tel: 212-599-7000 *Fax:* 212-599-3494
Web Site: www.manhattan-institute.org
Key Personnel
Contact: Dean Ball *E-mail:* dball@manhattan-institute.org
Honors the book published within the past two years that best reflects political philosopher & Nobel laureate F A Hayek's vision of economic & individual liberty. The winner of the prize will deliver the annual Hayek Lecture in New York in early June.
Award: $50,000
Presented: Late Feb

Headlands Center for the Arts Residency for Writers
944 Fort Barry, Sausalito, CA 94965
Tel: 415-331-2787 *Fax:* 415-331-3857
Web Site: www.headlands.org
Key Personnel
Residency Mgr: Holly Blake *Tel:* 415-331-2787 ext 24 *E-mail:* hblake@headlands.org
Established: 1987
A four to ten week residency at Headlands is granted each year to writers of the Artist in Residency Program. Call or write the HCA for deadline & other information. See web site for application & more information.
Award: Four to ten week stay, with optional stipend of $500
Closing Date: June 4

Heartland Prize
Chicago Tribune
435 N Michigan Ave, Suite 1100, Chicago, IL 60611
Established: 1988
Awarded annually in two categories: fiction & nonfiction.

Drue Heinz Literature Prize
University of Pittsburgh Press
7500 Thomas Blvd, Pittsburgh, PA 15260
Tel: 412-383-2456 *Fax:* 412-383-2466
E-mail: info@upress.pitt.edu
Web Site: www.upress.pitt.edu
Key Personnel
Asst to Dir: Kelley H Johovic *E-mail:* kjohovic@upress.pitt.edu
Established: 1980
For a collection of short fiction 150-300 pages in length. Open to all writers who have published a book-length collection of short fiction or who have had three short stories or novellas published in commercial magazines or literary journals of national distribution. See web site for complete rules.
Other Sponsor(s): Drue Heinz & The Drue Heinz Trust
Award: $15,000 & publication by the University of Pittsburgh Press
Closing Date: Postmarked between May 1 & June 30
Presented: Pittsburgh, PA, Nov

The Hemingway Foundation/PEN Award
PEN New England
Unit of PEN American Center
MIT, 14N-221A, 77 Massachusetts Ave, Cambridge, MA 02139
Tel: 617-324-1729
E-mail: pen-newengland@mit.edu
Web Site: www.pen-ne.org
Key Personnel
Exec Dir: Karen Wulf *E-mail:* kwulf@mit.edu
Award Administrator: Helene Atwan
Established: 1976
Given to a novel or book of short stories by an American writer who has not previously published a book of fiction. Entry fee: $35.
Award: $8,000 & one week residency in the Distinguished Visitors Series (Univ of Idaho)
Closing Date: Annually in Dec
Presented: JFK Library, Boston, MA, Annually in March

Cecil Hemley Memorial Award
Poetry Society of America (PSA)
15 Gramercy Park, New York, NY 10003
Tel: 212-254-9628 *Fax:* 212-673-2352
Web Site: www.poetrysociety.org
Key Personnel
Pres: Ruth Kaplan
Exec Dir: Alice Quinn
Deputy Dir: Brett Fletcher Lauer *E-mail:* brett@poetrysociety.org
Progs Dir: Charif Shanahan *E-mail:* charif@poetrysociety.org
Established: 1969
For an unpublished lyric poem on a philosophical theme, not to exceed 100 lines. Open to society members only. Send No 10 SASE or see web site for more information.
Award: $500
Closing Date: Annually, Oct-Dec
Presented: Annual Awards Ceremony, New York, NY, Annually in Spring

Henrico Theatre Company One-Act Playwriting Competition
Henrico Recreation & Parks
PO Box 90775, Richmond, VA 23273-0775
Tel: 804-501-5138 *Fax:* 804-501-5284
Key Personnel
Theatre Arts Specialist: Amy Perdue
E-mail: per22@henrico.us
Established: 1985
One-act playwriting.
Award: $300 & possible production (1st prize), $200 & possible production (2nd & 3rd prize)
Closing Date: Annually, July 1
Presented: Annually in Feb

Brodie Herndon Memorial
The Poetry Society of Virginia
1194 Hume Rd, Hume, VA 22639-1806
E-mail: poetryinva@aol.com
Web Site: www.poetrysocietyofvirginia.org
Key Personnel
Pres: Judith K Bragg *E-mail:* musicsavy45@yahoo.com
Adult Contest Chair: Patsy Anne Bickerstaff
E-mail: granypatsy@yahoo.com; Guy Terrell
E-mail: ggterr@infionline.net
Poems in any form about the sea; 48 line limit. Must be original, unpublished & in English. Submit 2 copies, each having the category name & number on top left of page. Entry fee: $4 nonmembs.
Award: $50 (1st prize), $30 (2nd prize)
Closing Date: Jan 19
Presented: Annual PSV Awards Luncheon, Richmond, VA, April

Carl Hertzog Award for Excellence in Book Design
Friends of the University Library
Subsidiary of University of Texas at El Paso
c/o Dir of the Library, University of Texas at El Paso, University Library, El Paso, TX 79968-0582
Tel: 915-747-5683 *Fax:* 915-747-5345
Web Site: libraryweb.utep.edu/about/hertzog_call.php
Key Personnel
Assoc VP: Robert L Stakes *Tel:* 915-747-6710
E-mail: rlstakes@utep.edu
Biennial award for excellence in book design. There is a maximum number of 5 entries allowed & must have been printed in 2014 or 2015. While a printer, publisher or designer may submit an entry, only the designer is eligible to receive the award.
Award: $1,000, bronze medal & certificate
Closing Date: Nov 1, odd-numbered years
Presented: University of Texas, El Paso, Biennially in Feb/March

Hidden River Arts Playwriting Award
Hidden River™ Arts
PO Box 63927, Philadelphia, PA 19147
Tel: 610-764-0813
E-mail: hiddenriverarts@gmail.com
Web Site: www.hiddenriverarts.org
Key Personnel
Founding Dir: Debra Leigh Scott
Established: 2002
Annual award for an unpublished, unproduced full-length play. Entry fee: $17.
Award: $1,000 (awarded by mail) & anthology publication
Closing Date: Annually, June 30
Presented: Annually in Dec

Highlights for Children Fiction Contest
Highlights for Children Inc
803 Church St, Honesdale, PA 18431
Tel: 570-253-1080 *Fax:* 570-251-7847
E-mail: eds@highlights.com
Web Site: www.highlights.com
Key Personnel
Sr Ed: Joelle Dujardin
Established: 1980
Fiction for children, subject varies annually. Guidelines & contest topic available on web site under "About Us" area. Indicate word count in upper right-hand corner on the first page of ms. No crime, violence, or derogatory humor. Stories may be any length up to 750 words. Stories for beginning readers should not exceed 475 words.
Award: 3 prizes of $1,000 or tuition for any Highlights Foundation Workshop
Closing Date: Annually, Jan 1-Jan 31 (postmark)
Presented: Annually in June

The Tony Hillerman Prize
Wordharvest LLC
1063 Willow Way, Santa Fe, NM 87507
Tel: 505-471-1565
E-mail: wordharvest@wordharvest.com
Web Site: www.wordharvest.com
Key Personnel
Founder: Anne Hillerman; Jean Schaumberg
Established: 2007
Prize for best first mystery set in the Southwest.
Award: $10,000 & publication by St Martin's Press
Closing Date: Annually, June 1
Presented: Tony Hillerman Writers Conference, Annually

Hillman Prizes in Journalism
The Sidney Hillman Foundation
12 W 31 St, 12th fl, New York, NY 10001
Tel: 646-448-6413
Web Site: www.hillmanfoundation.org
Key Personnel
Pres: Bruce Raynor
Exec Dir: Alexandra Lescaze *Tel:* 917-696-2494
E-mail: alex@hillmanfoundation.org
Established: 1950
For journalism that fosters social & economic justice & for investigative journalism. See web site for categories.
Award: $5,000 & certificate designed by New York cartoonist Edward Sorel
Closing Date: Jan 31
Presented: Award ceremony & cocktail party, New York, NY, Annually in Mid-May

Eric Hoffer Award for Independent Books
www.HofferAward.com
Subsidiary of The Eric Hoffer Project
PO Box 11, Titusville, NJ 08560
Fax: 609-964-1718
E-mail: info@hofferaward.com
Web Site: www.hofferaward.com
Key Personnel
Chmn & Exec Ed: Christopher Klim
Publr & Coord: Dawn Shows
Established: 2002
Open to academic, small & self-published press books in the last two years. Books older than two years must enter the "Legacy" category. Results published in The US Review of Books (www.theusreview.com).
In addition to the two grand prizes, various other honors & distinctions are given for both prose & books, including the Montaigne Medal, the da Vinci Eye & the First Horizon Award.
Award: $2,000 (grand prize independent books); $250 (grand prize short prose)
Closing Date: Nominations Jan 21 (books), March 31 (prose)
Presented: Annually in May

Eric Hoffer Award for Short Prose
www.HofferAward.com
Subsidiary of The Eric Hoffer Project
PO Box 11, Titusville, NJ 08560
Fax: 609-964-1718
E-mail: info@hofferaward.com
Web Site: www.hofferaward.com
Key Personnel
Mng Ed: Brittany Fonte
Ed: Danielle Evennou; Christopher Helvey; Matt Ryan; Jamey Temple
Established: 2002
New fiction & creative nonfiction less than 10,000 words.
Award: $250 (Grand Prize); publication in Best New Writing (20-25 finalists)
Closing Date: Annually, March 31
Presented: Annually in Oct

Bess Hokin Prize
Poetry Magazine
444 N Michigan Ave, Suite 1850, Chicago, IL 60611-4034
Tel: 312-787-7070 *Fax:* 312-787-6650
E-mail: editors@poetrymagazine.org
Web Site: www.poetryfoundation.org
Key Personnel
Mng Ed: Valerie Johnson *E-mail:* vjohnson@poetrymagazine.org
Established: 1948
For poetry published in the preceding two volumes of Poetry. No application necessary.
Award: $1,000
Presented: Annually in Dec

Honickman First Book Prize
American Poetry Review
University of the Arts (UARTS), Hamilton Hall, 320 S Broad St, Rm 313, Philadelphia, PA 19102-4901
Tel: 215-717-6801 *Fax:* 215-717-6805
Web Site: www.aprweb.org
Key Personnel
Ed: Elizabeth Scanlon *E-mail:* escanlon@aprweb.org

Established: 1997
Awarded to any US citizen, writing in English & who has not published a book-length collection of poems with an ISBN. Poems previously published in periodicals or limited-edition chapbooks may be included in the ms, but the ms itself must not have been published as a book-length work exceeding 25 pages. No translations or multiple author entries accepted. Entry fee $25. Now accepting online submissions.
Award: $3,000
Closing Date: Oct 31 (postmark)
Presented: Winner announced in March/April issue of the American Poetry Review

Firman Houghton Prize
New England Poetry Club
2 Farrar St, Cambridge, MA 02138
Mailing Address: 376 School St, Watertown, MA 02472
Tel: 617-744-6034
E-mail: contests@nepoetryclub.org
Web Site: www.nepoetryclub.org
Key Personnel
Pres: Diana Der-Hovanessian
VP: Sally Cragin; Daniel Tobin
Contest Chair: Nazaleem Smith
Established: 1987
Award for a lyric poem in honor of the former president of the NEPC. $10 for 3 contest entries per poem entry & $3 for additional entries, free for members & students.
Award: $250
Closing Date: Annually, May 31
Presented: Public Library, Cambridge, MA, Annually in Autumn

Amelia Frances Howard-Gibbon Illustrator's Award
Canadian Library Association-CLA (Association Canadienne des bibliotheques)
1150 Morrison Dr, Suite 400, Ottawa, ON K2H 8S9, Canada
Tel: 613-232-9625 *Fax:* 613-563-9895
E-mail: info@cla.ca
Web Site: www.cla.ca
Established: 1971
For outstanding work of illustration in current children's literature of Canada. Illustrator must be a Canadian citizen or resident of Canada. Nominations should be sent to Delilah Deane Cummings at the London Public Library, 251 Dundas St, London, ON N6A 6H9.
Award: $1,000 plus plaque
Closing Date: Annually, Dec 31
Presented: CLA Annual Conference

Tom Howard/John H Reid Fiction & Essay Contest
Winning Writers
351 Pleasant St, PMB 222, Northampton, MA 01060-3961
Tel: 413-320-1847 *Toll Free Tel:* 866-WINWRIT (946-9748) *Fax:* 413-280-0539
Web Site: www.winningwriters.com
Key Personnel
Pres: Adam Cohen *E-mail:* adam@winningwriters.com
VP: Jendi Reiter
Established: 1990
Submit short stories, essays or other works of prose, up to 6000 words each. Must be your own original work. Reading fee $16 per entry. Writers of all nations may enter, however, the works you submit should be in English. Both published & unpublished work accepted. Applications accepted Sept 15-April 30.
Award: $1,000 (each 1st prize, fiction & essay), $100 (honorable mention awards, 5 each fiction & essay) & publication on web site for all winners
Closing Date: Annually, April 30 (postmark)
Presented: Winner announced Sept 15 on web site

Tom Howard/Margaret Reid Poetry Contest
Winning Writers
351 Pleasant St, PMB 222, Northampton, MA 01060-3961
Tel: 413-320-1847 *Toll Free Tel:* 866-WINWRIT (946-9748) *Fax:* 413-280-0539
Web Site: www.winningwriters.com
Key Personnel
Pres: Adam Cohen *E-mail:* adam@winningwriters.com
VP: Jendi Reiter
Established: 2002
The Tom Howard Prize is awarded for a poem in any style or genre. The Margaret Reid Prize is awarded for a poem that rhymes or has a traditional style. Entry fee $16 for every 1-2 poems submitted (any length). See web site for complete submission details & contest results. Both published & unpublished work accepted. Poets of all nations may enter, however, the works you submit should be in English.
Award: $1,000 each (1st prize, Tom Howard & Margaret Reid), $100 each (10 honorable mention awards) & publication on web site for all winners
Closing Date: Annually, Sept 30
Presented: Winner announced April 15 on web site

Julia Ward Howe Book Awards
Boston Authors Club Inc
33 Brayton Rd, Brighton, MA 02135
Tel: 617-783-1357
E-mail: bostonauthors@aol.com
Web Site: www.bostonauthorsclub.org
Key Personnel
Pres: Alan Lawson *E-mail:* lawson@bc.edu
1st VP: Betty Lowry *Tel:* 508-358-4098 *E-mail:* bettylowry@aol.com
2nd VP: Sarah Lamstein *Tel:* 617-244-0646 *E-mail:* sml@sarahlamstein.com
Established: 1997
Awards for a trade book, a book for young readers, special award (varies) for book published previous year. Authors must live or have lived, worked or attended college within 100 miles of Boston. No submission fee.
Other Sponsor(s): Boston Public Library (Rare Books Div)
Award: $1,000 each for 2 books; certificates to finalists & authors of recommended books (number varies). All receive 1 year complimentary membership in the Club
Closing Date: Annually, Jan 15
Presented: Boston Public Library, 3rd Thursday in May

The William Dean Howells Medal
American Academy of Arts & Letters
633 W 155 St, New York, NY 10032
Tel: 212-368-5900 *Fax:* 212-491-4615
E-mail: academy@artsandletters.org
Web Site: www.artsandletters.org
Key Personnel
Exec Dir: Virginia Dajani
Established: 1925
Given once every five years in recognition of the most distinguished American novel published during that period.

L Ron Hubbard's Writers of the Future Contest
Author Services Inc
PO Box 1630, Los Angeles, CA 90078
Tel: 323-466-3310 *Fax:* 323-466-6474
E-mail: contests@authorservicesinc.com
Web Site: www.writersofthefuture.com
Key Personnel
Coordinating Judge: K D Wentworth
Contest Dir: Joni Labaqui
Established: 1983
Short stories & novelettes (under 17,000 words) of science fiction & fantasy for new & amateur writers. No entry fee required, entrants retain all publication rights.
Award: Annually: Trophy & $5,000 (Grand prize); Quarterly: $1,000 (1st place), $750 (2nd place), $500 (3rd place)
Closing Date: Quarterly: March 31, June 30, Sept 30, Dec 31

Monica Hughes Award for Science Fiction & Fantasy
Canadian Children's Book Centre
40 Orchard View Blvd, Suite 217, Toronto, ON M4R 1B9, Canada
Tel: 416-975-0010 *Fax:* 416-975-8970
E-mail: info@bookcentre.ca
Web Site: www.bookcentre.ca
Key Personnel
Exec Dir: Charlotte Teeple *E-mail:* charlotte@bookcentre.ca
Lib Coord: Meghan Howe *E-mail:* meghan@bookcentre.ca
Outreach Educ Coord: Sandra O'Brien *E-mail:* sandra@bookcentre.ca
Mktg & Website Coord: Camilia Kahrizi *E-mail:* camilia@bookcentre.ca
Prog Coord: Shannon Howe Barnes *E-mail:* shannon@bookcentre.ca
Established: 2011
Awarded annually to a Canadian author for excellence in science fiction & fantasy writing for children & adolescents.
Other Sponsor(s): HarperCollins Canada
Award: $5,000
Closing Date: Annually in mid-Dec

Lynda Hull Memorial Poetry Prize
Crazyhorse
College of Charleston, Dept of English, 66 George St, Charleston, SC 29424
Tel: 843-953-7740 *Fax:* 843-953-7740
E-mail: crazyhorse@cofc.edu
Web Site: crazyhorse.cofc.edu/prizes
Awarded annually for best single poem. Enter 3 poems with $20 entry fee, which includes one year subscription. Nationally prominent poet judges. See web site for complete instructions.
Award: $2,000 & publication in "Crazyhorse"
Closing Date: Jan 31

Hurston/Wright Award for College Writers
The Zora Neale Hurston/Richard Wright Foundation
12138 Central Ave, Suite 209, Bowie, MD 20721
Tel: 301-459-2108 *Fax:* 301-277-1262
E-mail: info@hurstonwright.org
Web Site: www.hurstonwright.org
Key Personnel
Founder & Pres Emeritus: Marita Golden
Exec Dir: Clyde McElvene
Established: 1990
Literary award presented to honor excellence in fiction writing by African American students enrolled as an undergraduate or graduate student in any college or university. Nonrefundable application fee of $10.
Award: $1,000 & story published in literary journal (1st prize), $500 (awarded to 2 runners-up)
Closing Date: Annually, Jan 31
Presented: Annually in April

Hurston/Wright Legacy Awards
The Zora Neale Hurston/Richard Wright Foundation
12138 Central Ave, Suite 209, Bowie, MD 20721
Tel: 301-459-2108 *Fax:* 301-277-1262
E-mail: info@hurstonwright.org
Web Site: www.hurstonwright.org
Key Personnel
Founder & Pres Emeritus: Marita Golden

Exec Dir: Clyde McElvene
Established: 2000
Annual national literary award for debut fiction, fiction, nonfiction & poetry for published black writers. Application fee: $30.
Other Sponsor(s): Borders Books
Award: $10,000 for winners in 3 categories; $5,000 for 6 runners-up (2 in each category)

IACP Cookbook Awards
International Association of Culinary Professionals (IACP)
1221 Avenue of the Americas, 42nd fl, New York, NY 10020
Tel: 646-358-4957 *Toll Free Tel:* 866-358-4951 *Toll Free Fax:* 866-358-2524
E-mail: info@iacp.com
Web Site: www.iacp.com
Key Personnel
Exec Dir: Meredith Deeds
Dir, Communs & Content: Martha Holmberg
Memb Progs & Opers Mgr: Shani Phelan
Established: 1985
Open to any food or beverage book published in the English language. Allows publishers to enter books in the category of their choice. Through a strict, two-tier system of judging & balloting, the entries are narrowed to three nominees in each category.
Closing Date: Nov 15
Presented: Annual Conference, location varies, Date varies every year, usually held in April

The Idaho Prize for Poetry
Lost Horse Press
105 Lost Horse Lane, Sandpoint, ID 83864
Tel: 208-255-4410 *Fax:* 208-255-1560
E-mail: losthorsepress@mindspring.com
Web Site: www.losthorsepress.org
Key Personnel
Publr: Christine Holbert
Established: 2003
A national competition for a book-length poetry ms written by an American poet. Accompany ms with $25 reading fee (check or money order only). Books distributed by the University of Washington Press. May also submit online using submittable.com.
Award: $1,000 & publication
Closing Date: Annually, May 15
Presented: Annually, Aug 15

ILA Children's & Young Adults' Book Awards
International Literacy Association (ILA)
800 Barksdale Rd, Newark, DE 19711-3204
Mailing Address: PO Box 8139, Newark, DE 19714-8139
Tel: 302-731-1600 *Toll Free Tel:* 800-336-7323 (US & CN) *Fax:* 302-731-1057
E-mail: committees@reading.org
Web Site: www.literacyworldwide.org; www.reading.org
Key Personnel
Exec Dir: Marcie Craig Post *E-mail:* mpost@reading.org
Assoc Exec Dir: Stephen Sye *E-mail:* ssye@reading.org
Exec Asst: Kathy Baughman *Tel:* 302-731-3761 *E-mail:* kbaughman@reading.org
Established: 1975
Awards for newly published authors who show unusual promise in the children's or young adult book field. Awards will be given for fiction & nonfiction in 3 categories: Primary (ages preschool-8), Intermediate (ages 9-13) & Young Adult (ages 14-17). Books from any country & published in English for the first time during the previous calendar year will be considered.
Award: $800 per book
Closing Date: Jan 15, 2016
Presented: Annual Conference, Boston, MA, July 9-11, 2016

Illumination Book Awards
Independent Publisher Online
Division of Jenkins Group Inc
1129 Woodmere Ave, Suite B, Traverse City, MI 49686
Tel: 231-933-0445 *Toll Free Tel:* 800-706-4636 *Fax:* 231-933-0448
E-mail: awards@bookpublishing.com
Web Site: www.illuminationawards.com
Key Personnel
CEO: Jerrold R Jenkins *E-mail:* jrj@bookpublishing.com
Pres: James Kalajian *Tel:* 800-706-4636 ext 1006 *E-mail:* jjk@bookpublishing.com
Mng Ed & Awards Dir: Jim Barnes *Tel:* 800-706-4636 ext 1011 *E-mail:* jimb@bookpublishing.com
Awards Coord: Amy Shamroe
Established: 2013
With the motto "Shining a Light on Exemplary Christian Books," the Illumination Awards are designed to honor the year's best new titles written & published with a Christian worldview. The contest is for published books only, as our judging criteria include cover design, layout, etc. Books from all methods of publishing are welcome & authors of royalty-published books are welcome to enter their books themselves.
Other Sponsor(s): Jenkins Group
Award: Gold medal (1st place), silver medal (2nd place), bronze medal (3rd place), foil seals available, winners featured in *Independent Publisher Online*
Closing Date: Annually in Nov
Presented: Online, Annually in Jan

John Phillip Immroth Memorial Award
Intellectual Freedom Round Table (IFRT)
Unit of The American Library Association (ALA)
50 E Huron St, Chicago, IL 60611
Tel: 312-280-4223 *Toll Free Tel:* 800-545-2433 *Fax:* 312-280-4227
E-mail: oif@ala.org
Web Site: www.ala.org/ifrt
Key Personnel
Prog Offr: Nanette Perez *Tel:* 312-280-4225 *E-mail:* nperez@ala.org
Admin Asst & Award Contact: Shumeca Pickett *Tel:* 312-280-4220 *E-mail:* spickett@ala.org
Established: 1979
Annual award for notable contribution to intellectual freedom & demonstrations of personal courage in defense of freedom of expression.
Award: $500 & citation
Closing Date: Annually, Dec 1
Presented: ALA Annual Conference, Annually in June

The Independent Publisher Book Awards
Independent Publisher Online
Division of Jenkins Group Inc
1129 Woodmere Ave, Suite B, Traverse City, MI 49686
Tel: 231-933-0445 *Toll Free Tel:* 800-706-4636 *Fax:* 231-933-0448
E-mail: awards@bookpublishing.com
Web Site: www.independentpublisher.com/ipland/ipawards.php
Key Personnel
CEO: Jerrold R Jenkins *E-mail:* jrj@bookpublishing.com
Pres: James Kalajian *Tel:* 800-706-4636 ext 1006 *E-mail:* jjk@bookpublishing.com
Mng Ed & Awards Dir: Jim Barnes *Tel:* 800-706-4636 ext 1011 *E-mail:* jimb@bookpublishing.com
Awards Coord: Amy Shamroe
Established: 1996
Recognizes the works of independent publishers in 76 national & 22 regional categories, for excellence in literary merit, design & production, published during previous calendar year. E-books & audio books are welcome.
Other Sponsor(s): Jenkins Group
Award: Gold medal (1st place), silver medal (2nd place) & bronze medal (3rd place); foil seals available; winners featured in *Independent Publisher Magazine Online*
Closing Date: Annually in March
Presented: Book Expo America, Annually in May

Indiana Review Fiction Prize
Indiana Review
Ballantine Hall 465, 1020 E Kirkwood Ave, Bloomington, IN 47405
Tel: 812-855-3439
E-mail: inreview@indiana.edu
Web Site: indianareview.org
Key Personnel
Ed: Katie Moulton
Assoc Ed: Britt Ashley
Submit a short story of up to 8,000 words; only one story per entry, maximum 12 point font. Previously published works & works forthcoming elsewhere cannot be considered; $20 entry fee (which includes a subscription to Indiana Review).
Award: $1,000 & publication in Indiana Review
Closing Date: Annually in Oct

IndieReader Discovery Awards
IndieReader
PO Box 43121, Montclair, NJ 07043
Web Site: indiereader.com/irda
Annual awards open to indie authors who have self-published books. Entry fee: $150 per title per category plus additional $50 for each additional category entered.
Presented: BookExpo America

Indies Choice Book Awards
American Booksellers Association
333 Westchester Ave, Suite S202, White Plains, NY 10604
Tel: 914-406-7500 *Toll Free Tel:* 800-637-0037 *Fax:* 914-410-6297
Web Site: www.bookweb.org
Key Personnel
CEO: Oren Teicher *Tel:* 800-637-0037 ext 6611 *E-mail:* oren@bookweb.org
Devt Offr: Mark Nichols *Tel:* 800-637-0037 ext 6640 *E-mail:* mark@bookweb.org
Established: 1991
Book finalists will be picked by a bookseller jury, but the pool is limited to monthly Indie Next list selections. Categories have been revamped & expanded, now honoring the book of the year in the following categories: adult fiction, adult nonfiction, adult debut, young adults, middle reader, new picture book & most engaging author.
Presented: BookExpo America & ABA Convention

Individual Artist Awards
Maryland State Arts Council
Affiliate of Department of Business & Economic Development
175 W Ostend St, Suite E, Baltimore, MD 21230
Tel: 410-767-6555 *Fax:* 410-333-1062
E-mail: msac@msac.org
Web Site: www.msac.org
Key Personnel
Exec Dir: Theresa Colvin
Solely based on excellence of previous work. Must be a Maryland resident. Applications available. Award categories changed annually. Check with council for individual availability.

Award: $6,000 (1st prize), $3,000 (2nd prize) & $1,000 (3rd prize)
Closing Date: July (see web site for exact date)
Presented: Awards Reception, Early June

Individual Artist Fellowships
Maine Arts Commission
Division of State of Maine
25 State House Sta, 193 State St, Augusta, ME 04333-0025
Tel: 207-287-2726 *Fax:* 207-287-2725
Web Site: mainearts.maine.gov
Key Personnel
Sr Grants Dir: Kathy Ann Shaw *E-mail:* kathy.shaw@maine.gov
Established: 1987
Three prizes awarded annually to visual, performing & literary artists, craft, media/film, traditional arts.
Other Sponsor(s): Maine Community Foundation
Award: $5,000
Closing Date: May
Presented: Fall

Individual Artist Fellowships
Nebraska Arts Council
Division of State of Nebraska
1004 Farnam, Plaza Level, Omaha, NE 68102
Tel: 402-595-2122 *Toll Free Tel:* 800-341-4067 *Fax:* 402-595-2334
Web Site: www.nebraskaartscouncil.org
Key Personnel
Artist Servs & Communs Mgr: Jayne Hutton *E-mail:* jayne.hutton@nebraska.gov
Established: 1991
Fellowship for Nebraska residents only; operates on a 3-yr cycle rotating with visual & performing arts & literature.
Award: $1,000-$5,000
Closing Date: Annually, Nov 15

Individual Artist's Fellowships in Literature
South Carolina Arts Commission (SCAC)
Division of State of South Carolina
1800 Gervais St, Columbia, SC 29201
Tel: 803-734-8696 *Fax:* 803-734-8526
E-mail: info@arts.sc.gov
Web Site: www.southcarolinaarts.com
Key Personnel
Communs Dir: Millie Hough *Tel:* 803-734-8698 *E-mail:* mhough@arts.sc.gov
Established: 2007
Non-matching funds for South Carolina residents only. Four fellowships, two in poetry & two in prose. Offered every other year.
Award: $5,000
Closing Date: Annually, Nov 1

Individual Excellence Awards
Ohio Arts Council
30 E Broad St, 33rd fl, Columbus, OH 43215
Tel: 614-466-2613 *Fax:* 614-466-4494
Web Site: www.oac.state.oh.us
Key Personnel
Exec Dir: Julie Henahan *E-mail:* julie.henahan@oac.state.oh.us
Prog Coord: Kathy Signorino *E-mail:* kathy.signorino@oac.state.oh.us
Indiv Prog: Ken Emerick *E-mail:* ken.emerick@oac.state.oh.us
Established: 1978
Available to creative artists who are residents of Ohio. Applicants must have lived in Ohio for 1 year prior to the Sept 1 deadline & must remain in the state during the grant period. Applications must be submitted online.
Odd-numbered calendar years, applications accepted in the following disciplines: choreography, criticism, fiction/nonfiction, music composition, playwriting/screenplays & poetry.
Even-numbered calendar years, applications accepted in these disciplines: crafts, design arts/illustration, interdisciplinary/performance art, media arts, photography & visual arts.
Award: $5,000 (determined by panel)
Closing Date: Sept 1

Innis-Gerin Medal
Royal Society of Canada
Walter House, 282 Somerset W, Ottawa, ON K2P 0J6, Canada
Tel: 613-991-6990 (ext 106) *Fax:* 613-991-6996
E-mail: nominations@rsc-src.ca
Web Site: www.rsc-src.ca
Key Personnel
Mgr, Fellowship & Awards: Marie-Lyne Renaud *E-mail:* mlrenaud@rsc-src.ca
Established: 1966
Biennial award given in even-numbered years for a distinguished & sustained contribution to literature in social science, human geography & social psychology.
Award: Bronze medal
Closing Date: March 1
Presented: RSC business meeting, Nov

Institute of Puerto Rican Culture National Literary Awards
Institute of Puerto Rican Culture
PO Box 9024184, San Juan, PR 00902-4184
Tel: 787-724-0700 *Fax:* 787-724-8393
Web Site: www.icp.gobierno.pr
Key Personnel
Exec Dir: Jorge Irizarry Vizcarrondo *Tel:* 784-424-0700 ext 1002
Annual awards in the categories of poetry, short story, children's literature, novel & essay. An award in every category each year is not guaranteed.
Award: $5,000 & publication for each winner
Presented: June

Intermediate Sequoyah Book Award
Oklahoma Library Association
300 Hardy Dr, Edmond, OK 73013
Tel: 405-525-5100 *Fax:* 405-525-5103
Web Site: www.oklibs.org
Key Personnel
Exec Dir: Kay Boies *E-mail:* kboies@sbcglobal.net
Contact: Tracy Keeley
Established: 2010
Student choice award; students in grades 6-8 who have read/listened to at least 3 titles from the Intermediate Masterlist are eligible to vote.
Award: Plaque/medal
Closing Date: Annually, March 1
Presented: OLA Annual Conference, Annually in April

International Latino Book Awards
Latino Literacy Now
3445 Catalina Dr, Carlsbad, CA 92010
Tel: 760-434-1223 *Fax:* 760-434-7476
E-mail: kirk@whisler.com
Web Site: www.lbff.us
Established: 1998
Annual book awards celebrating books by & about Latinos. In 2015 there were 246 honorees.
Other Sponsor(s): Libros Publishing; Scholastic; VISA
Presented: American Library Association Conference, Late June

International Poetry Competition
Atlanta Review
PO Box 8248, Atlanta, GA 31106
E-mail: atlanta.review@yahoo.com
Web Site: www.atlantareview.com
Key Personnel
Publr & Ed: Dan Veach
Sr Ed: Lee Passarella; Memye Curtis Tucker
Literary Ed: A E Stallings
Established: 1996
Online entry at www.atlantareview.com.
Award: $1,000 (grand prize), publication in *Atlanta Review* (20 publication prizes)
Closing Date: Annually, March 1

InterTech™ Technology Awards
Printing Industries of America
200 Deer Run Rd, Sewickley, PA 15143-2324
Tel: 412-259-1782 *Toll Free Tel:* 800-910-4283 (ext 782) *Fax:* 412-741-2311
E-mail: intertechaward@printing.org
Web Site: www.printing.org/intertechawards
Key Personnel
CEO & Pres: Michael F Makin *E-mail:* mmakin@printing.org
VP, Technol & Res: Dr Mark Bohan *Tel:* 412-259-1782 *E-mail:* mbohan@printing.org
Established: 1978
Honors innovative technology excellence for the graphic communications industry. The criteria for nomination stresses that the technology be recently developed, proved in industrial application, but not yet in widespread use. See web site for more information.
Award: Lucite Star
Closing Date: Annually, May 31
Presented: Printing Industries of America's Premier Print Awards Gala, Annually in the Fall

IODE Jean Throop Book Award
IODE Ontario
9-45 Frid St, Hamilton, ON L8P 4M3, Canada
Tel: 905-522-9537 *Fax:* 905-522-3637
E-mail: iodeontario@bellnet.ca
Web Site: www.iodeontario.ca
Key Personnel
Convenor: Mary K Anderson
Area VP: Margo Mackinnon
Established: 1974
Children's book (Toronto area author +/or illustrator).
Award: $1,000 & certificate
Closing Date: Annually, Feb 1
Presented: Annually in April

IODE Violet Downey Book Award
The National Chapter of Canada IODE
40 Orchard View Blvd, Suite 219, Toronto, ON M4R 1B9, Canada
Tel: 416-487-4416 *Toll Free Tel:* 866-827-7428 *Fax:* 416-487-4417
E-mail: iodecanada@bellnet.ca
Web Site: www.iode.ca
Key Personnel
Natl Pres: Ann Dyer
Established: 1984
Children's book award. Must be a Canadian author with text in English. At least 500 words & printed in Canada during previous calendar year. Suitable for children 13 years & under.
Award: $5,000
Closing Date: Annually, Dec 31
Presented: The National Annual Meeting, Annually, late May

Iowa Poetry Prize
University of Iowa Press
119 W Park Rd, 100 Kuhl House, Iowa City, IA 52242-1000
SAN: 282-4868
Tel: 319-335-2000 *Fax:* 319-335-2055
E-mail: uipress@uiowa.edu
Web Site: www.uiowapress.org
Key Personnel
Dir: James McCoy
Open to new as well as established poets for a book-length collection of poems written originally in English. Previous winners, current University of Iowa students & current & former University of Iowa Press employees are not eligible. Reading fee $20.

Award: Publication by the University of Iowa Press under a standard royalty agreement
Closing Date: Postmarked during April

The Iowa Review Award
University of Iowa-The Iowa Review
308 EPB, Iowa City, IA 52242-1408
E-mail: iowa-review@uiowa.edu
Web Site: www.iowareview.org
Key Personnel
Mng Ed: Lynne Nugent
Ed: Harilaos Stecopoulos
Established: 2003
Fiction, poetry & nonfiction categories. Submit up to 25 pages of prose (double-spaced) or 10 pgs of poetry (1 poem or several, but no more than 1 poem per page). Work must be previously unpublished. There is a $20 entry fee; enclose an additional $10 for a yearlong subscription to the magazine (optional). Submissions between Jan 1-Jan 31.
Award: $1,500 & publication in Dec issue of Iowa Review (1st place), $750 & pubn in the Dec issue of Iowa Review (1st runners-up)
Closing Date: Annually, Jan 31

The Iowa Short Fiction Award
Writers' Workshop, The University of Iowa
102 Dey House, 507 N Clinton St, Iowa City, IA 52242-1000
Tel: 319-335-0416 *Fax:* 319-335-0420
Web Site: www.uiowapress.org/authors/iowa-short-fiction.htm
Key Personnel
Prog Assoc: Connie Brothers
Dir, Writers' Workshop: Lan Samantha Chang
Established: 1970
For a previously unpublished collection of short stories of at least 150 typewritten pages by a writer who has not previously published a volume of prose fiction. Stories previously published in periodicals are eligible for inclusion. Include SASE. Write for further information.
Other Sponsor(s): University of Iowa Press
Award: Publication by University of Iowa Press
Closing Date: Aug 1-Sept 30

Iowa Short Fiction Awards
University of Iowa Press
119 W Park Rd, 100 Kuhl House, Iowa City, IA 52242-1000
SAN: 282-4868
Tel: 319-335-2000 *Fax:* 319-335-2055
E-mail: uipress@uiowa.edu
Web Site: www.uiowapress.org
Key Personnel
Dir: James McCoy
Any writer who has not previously published a volume of prose fiction is eligible to enter the competition. Previously entered mss that have been revised may be resubmitted. Writers are still eligible if they have published a volume of poetry or any work in a language other than English or if they have self-published any work in a small print run. Writers are still eligible if they are living abroad or are non-US citizens writing in English. Current University of Iowa students are not eligible.
Award: Publication by the University of Iowa Press under the Press's standard contract
Closing Date: Annually, Aug 1-Sept 30 (postmark)

Jackie White Memorial National Children's Playwriting Contest
Columbia Entertainment Co
1400 Forum Blvd, 1C No 214, Columbia, MO 65203
E-mail: jwmcontest@cectheatre.org
Web Site: www.cectheatre.org
Key Personnel
Pres, Community Theatre: Marissa Todd
Contest Co-Dir: Chris Hays; Tom Phillips
Established: 1988
The entry should be a full length play with speaking roles for at least seven characters. The entry may be an unpublished original work or an adaptation; $25 entry fee, send SASE for complete rules & entry form. Each author who enters the contest will receive a letter from the contest director discussing the strengths & weaknesses of his or her play if a SASE is enclosed.
Other Sponsor(s): City of Columbia, Office of Cultural Affairs
Award: $500, for 1st place
Closing Date: Annually, July 1
Presented: Annually, Sept 31

Joseph Henry Jackson Literary Award
The San Francisco Foundation
One Embarcadero Ctr, Suite 1400, San Francisco, CA 94111
Tel: 415-733-8500 *Fax:* 415-477-2783
E-mail: info@sff.org
Web Site: www.sff.org
Key Personnel
Arts & Culture Prog Offr: Terezita Romo
Established: 1957
Award for the author of fiction (novel or short stories), nonfictional prose, poetry. Awards are intended to encourage emerging artists not yet established in the genre who are currently residing in Alameda, Contra Costa, Marin, San Francisco or San Mateo County, for an unpublished ms-in-progress. By nomination only.
Award: $2,000
Presented: Annually in Autumn

The Jackson Poetry Prize
Poets & Writers Inc
90 Broad St, Suite 2100, New York, NY 10004
Tel: 212-226-3586 *Fax:* 212-226-3963
E-mail: admin@pw.org
Web Site: www.pw.org
Established: 2006
Honors an American poet of exceptional talent who deserves wider recognition. Eligible poets must have published at least two books of acknowledged literary merit.
Other Sponsor(s): Liana Foundation
Award: $50,000

The Joan Leiman Jacobson Poetry Prizes, see "Discovery"/Boston Review Poetry Contest

J Franklin Jameson Fellowship in American History
American Historical Association (AHA)
400 "A" St SE, Washington, DC 20003
Tel: 202-544-2422 *Fax:* 202-544-8307
E-mail: awards@historians.org
Web Site: www.historians.org
Established: 1980
To support significant scholarly research for one semester in the collections of the Library of Congress by new historians. At the time of application, applicants must hold the PhD degree or equivalent; must have received this degree within the last 5 years & must not have published or had accepted for publication a book-length historical work. The fellowship will not be awarded to permit completion of a doctoral dissertation. The applicant's project in American history must be one for which the general & special collections of the Library of Congress offer unique research support. Applicants should include a statement substantiating this relationship. Residency for at least three months at Library of Congress is required. Application instructions & all updated info available on web site.
Other Sponsor(s): Library of Congress
Award: Certificate
Closing Date: March 15 (postmark)

Jamestown Prize
Omohundro Institute of Early American History & Culture (OIEAHC)
Swem Library, Ground fl, 400 Landrum Dr, Williamsburg, VA 23185
Mailing Address: PO Box 8781, Williamsburg, VA 23187-8781 SAN: 201-5161
Tel: 757-221-1114 *Fax:* 757-221-1047
E-mail: ieahc1@wm.edu
Web Site: oieahc.wm.edu
Key Personnel
Dir: Karin A Wulf *Tel:* 757-221-1133 *E-mail:* kawulf@wm.edu
Ed, Pubns: Fredrika J Teute *Tel:* 757-221-1118 *E-mail:* fjteut@wm.edu
Biennial prize for an exceptional book length scholarly ms pertaining to the early history & culture of Anglo-America or to related developments in the British Isles, other North American colonial empires & their home countries, West Africa or the Caribbean. In short, any subject encompassing the Atlantic World circa 1450-1815 that bears upon the history & culture of what would & did become the US.
Award: $3,000 & publication
Closing Date: April 30 (odd-numbered years)

Japan-US Friendship Commission Translation Prize
Japan-US Friendship Commission
Affiliate of The Donald Keene Center of Japanese Culture
Columbia University, 507 Kent Hall, MC3920, New York, NY 10027
Tel: 212-854-5036 *Fax:* 212-854-4019
Web Site: www.keenecenter.org
Key Personnel
Faculty Dir: David B Lurie
Established: 1979
Prize is given for the best translation of a modern work of literature or for the best classical literary translation, or the prize is divided between a classical & a modern work. Translators of any nationality are welcome to apply. To qualify, works must be book-length translations of Japanese literary works: novels, collections of short stories, literary essays, memoirs, drama, or poetry. Submissions will be judged on the literary merit of the translation & the accuracy with which it reflects the spirit of the Japanese original. Applications are accepted from translators or their publishers. Previous winners are ineligible.
Award: $6,000 (either to one translator or divided between classical & modern)
Closing Date: Annually, Oct 31
Presented: Columbia University, Annually in April

Jefferson Cup Award
Youth Services Forum
Unit of Virginia Library Association (VLA)
c/o Virginia Library Association (VLA), PO Box 56312, Virginia Beach, VA 23456
Tel: 757-689-0594 *Fax:* 757-447-3478
Web Site: www.vla.org
Key Personnel
VLA Exec Dir: Lisa R Varga *E-mail:* vla.lisav@cox.net
Established: 1983
Honors a distinguished biography, historical fiction or American history book written especially for young people. Two awards given, one for books published for children & one for books published for young adults.
Award: $500 & engraved silver Jefferson Cup for each
Closing Date: Jan 31
Presented: Virginia Library Association (VLA) Annual Conference, Fall

Jerome Award
Catholic Library Association
8550 United Plaza Blvd, Suite 1001, Baton Rouge, LA 70809-2256
Tel: 225-408-4417
E-mail: cla2@cathla.org
Web Site: www.cathla.org
Key Personnel
Pres: Mary Kelleher *Tel:* 225-408-4417 *E-mail:* kellehm@stthom.edu
Established: 1992
For outstanding work in Catholic scholarship; no unsol mss.
Award: Plaque
Closing Date: None; in-house votes
Presented: CLA Annual Convention

Jerome Fellowship
The Playwrights' Center
2301 Franklin Ave E, Minneapolis, MN 55406-1099
Tel: 612-332-7481 *Fax:* 612-332-6037
E-mail: info@pwcenter.org
Web Site: www.pwcenter.org
Key Personnel
Producing Artistic Dir: Jeremy Cohen *Tel:* 612-332-7481 ext 113 *E-mail:* jeremyc@pwcenter.org
Artistic Administrator: Amanda Robbins-Butcher *Tel:* 612-332-7481 ext 115 *E-mail:* amandar@pwcenter.org
Established: 1976
Fellowships awarded annually to emerging playwrights. Provides playwrights with funds & services to aid them in the development of their craft. One year in residence required, July 1 - June 30. Contact above for application & guidelines, or download from www.pwcenter.org.
Award: $16,000
Closing Date: See web site for details

Jewel Box Theatre Playwriting Competition
3700 N Walker, Oklahoma City, OK 73118-7031
Tel: 405-521-1786
Web Site: jewelboxtheatre.org
Key Personnel
Prodn Dir: Charles Tweed
Established: 1986
Original playwriting competition.
Award: $750
Closing Date: Jan 15
Presented: Banquet in Oklahoma City, May

John Steinbeck Short Story Award
Reed Magazine
San Jose State University, English Dept, One Washington Sq, San Jose, CA 95192-0090
Tel: 408-924-4441
Web Site: www.reedmag.org
All submissions must be through the online system with a common file format. Writers may submit multiple entries but each must be submitted separately & accompanied by a separate entry fee of $15.
Award: $1,000 & publication in *Reed Magazine*
Closing Date: Annually, Nov 1 (submissions accepted beginning June 1)

Anson Jones MD Award
Texas Medical Association
401 W 15 St, Austin, TX 78701
Tel: 512-370-1300 *Fax:* 512-370-1630
Web Site: www.texmed.org
Key Personnel
Outreach Coord: Tammy Wishard
Established: 1957
Annual award in recognition of outstanding coverage of health & medical issues to the public by Texas Media.
Award: $500 cash award & plaque for winners
Closing Date: Jan 15

Jesse H Jones Award
Texas Institute of Letters (TIL)
c/o 7748 Hwy 290 W, Austin, TX 78736-3202
Tel: 512-683-5640
E-mail: president@texasinstituteofletters.org
Web Site: www.texasinstituteofletters.org
Key Personnel
Pres: Andres Tijerina
VP: Steve Davis
Treas: James Hoggard
Secy: Darwin Payne
Recording Secy: Betty Wiesepape
Annual award for the best book of fiction by a Texan or about Texas. Guidelines on the web site.
Other Sponsor(s): Houston Endowment Inc
Award: $6,000
Closing Date: Annually in Jan
Presented: TIL Awards Banquet, Annually in Spring

Judah, Sarah, Grace & Tom Memorial
The Poetry Society of Virginia
1194 Hume Rd, Hume, VA 22639-1806
E-mail: poetryinva@aol.com
Web Site: www.poetrysocietyofvirginia.org
Key Personnel
Pres: Judith K Bragg *E-mail:* musicsavy45@yahoo.com
Adult Contest Chair: Patsy Anne Bickerstaff *E-mail:* granypatsy@yahoo.com; Guy Terrell *E-mail:* ggterr@infionline.net
All entries must be in English, original & unpublished. Submit 2 copies of each poem, both copies must have the category name & number on top left of page. Only one poem per category; entries will not be returned. Subject: encouraging reflection on inter-ethnic relations; any form; 48 line limit. Entry fee: $4 nonmembs.
Other Sponsor(s): Stuart & Linda Nottingham
Award: $50 (1st place), $30 (2nd place), $20 (3rd place)
Closing Date: Jan
Presented: Annual PSV Awards Luncheon, Richmond, VA, April

Juniper Prize for Fiction
University of Massachusetts Press
East Experiment Sta, 671 N Pleasant St, Amherst, MA 01003
Tel: 413-545-2217 *Fax:* 413-545-1226
E-mail: info@umpress.umass.edu
Web Site: www.umass.edu/umpress; www.umass.edu/umpress/content/juniper-literary-prize-series
Key Personnel
Promos Mgr: Karen Fisk *E-mail:* kfisk@umpress.umass.edu
Established: 2004
Annual prize to honor & publish outstanding works of literary fiction. Open to all writers in English, whether or not they are US Citizens. Entry fee is $25 (must be drawn on US bank).
Award: $1,500 upon publication
Closing Date: Aug 1-Sept 30 (postmark)
Presented: Winner announced on web site n April

Juniper Prize for Poetry
University of Massachusetts Press
East Experiment Sta, 671 N Pleasant St, Amherst, MA 01003
Tel: 413-545-2217 *Fax:* 413-545-1226
E-mail: info@umpress.umass.edu
Web Site: www.umass.edu/umpress; www.umass.edu/umpress/content/juniper-literary-prize-series
Key Personnel
Promos Mgr: Karen Fisk *E-mail:* kfisk@umpress.umass.edu
Established: 1976
Awarded annually for an original ms of poems. In alternating years, the program is open to poets either with or without previously published books. Entry fee: $25.
Award: $1,500 & publication
Presented: Annually in April; publication by the following spring

Juvenile Literary Awards/Young People's Literature Awards
Friends of American Writers
506 Rose Ave, Des Plaines, IL 60016
Tel: 847-827-8339
Web Site: www.fawchicago.org
Key Personnel
Pres: Roberta Gates *E-mail:* robmicgates73@gmail.com
Juv Lit Awards Chair: Martha Daniel *E-mail:* mcmdaniel@mac.com
Established: 1960
For books written for young people from toddler through high school age & published in the current year, can only be author's 1st, 2nd or 3rd book & the author must be from the Midwest +/or the book must be about the Midwest.
Award: Two $2,000 prizes
Closing Date: Annually, Dec 20
Presented: The Fortnightly, Chicago, IL, Annually in May

Frederick D Kagy Education Award of Excellence
Printing Industries of America
200 Deer Run Rd, Sewickley, PA 15143-2324
Tel: 412-259-1705 *Toll Free Tel:* 800-910-4283 (ext 705) *Fax:* 412-749-9890
E-mail: printing@printing.org
Web Site: www.printing.org/page/3630
Key Personnel
CEO & Pres: Michael F Makin *E-mail:* mmakin@printing.org
Asst to VP, Mktg: Sara Welsh *E-mail:* swelsh@printing.org
Established: 1993
Honors a superior graphic communications program at the junior high, high school or community college level. School must be staffed by Printing Industries of America's teacher member (membership cost $49). Entry is free. See web site for more information.
Other Sponsor(s): Printing Industries of America's Ben Franklin Society
Award: Engraved lithographic stone
Presented: Printing Industries of America Fall Administrative Meetings

Sue Kaufman Prize for First Fiction
American Academy of Arts & Letters
633 W 155 St, New York, NY 10032
Tel: 212-368-5900 *Fax:* 212-491-4615
E-mail: academy@artsandletters.org
Web Site: www.artsandletters.org
Key Personnel
Exec Dir: Virginia Dajani
Established: 1979
For the best published first novel or collection of short stories of the preceding year.
Award: $5,000

Ezra Jack Keats/Kerlan Memorial Fellowship
Ezra Jack Keats Foundation
University of Minnesota, 113 Andersen Library, 222 21 Ave S, Minneapolis, MN 55455
Tel: 612-624-4576 *Fax:* 612-626-0377
E-mail: clrc@umn.edu
Web Site: www.ezra-jack-keats.org; special.lib.umn.edu/clrc
Key Personnel
Curator Kerlan Collection: Karen Hoyle
Awarded to a talented writer +/or illustrator of children's books who wish to use the Kerlan Collection to further his or her artistic development.

Award: $1,500
Closing Date: Jan 30

Joan Kelly Memorial Prize in Women's History
American Historical Association (AHA)
400 "A" St SE, Washington, DC 20003
Tel: 202-544-2422 *Fax:* 202-544-8307
E-mail: awards@historians.org
Web Site: www.historians.org
Established: 1984
For the book in women's history +/or feminist theory that best reflects the high intellectual & scholarly ideals exemplified by the life & work of Joan Kelly. Submissions shall be books in any chronological period, any geographical location, or in any area of feminist theory that incorporates an historical perspective. Books should demonstrate originality of research, creativity of insight, graceful stylistic presentation, analytical skills & a recognition of the important role of sex & gender in the historical process. The inter-relationship between women & the historical process should be addressed. Books published in 2015 are eligible. Along with an application form, one copy of each entry must be received by each of the five committee members. The Association will announce the recipients of prizes & awards at its annual meeting during the first week in Jan. All updated info on web site.
Award: Cash prize
Closing Date: May 15, 2016 (postmark)
Presented: AHA Annual Meeting, Denver, CO, Jan 5-8, 2017

Robert F Kennedy Book Awards
Subsidiary of Robert F Kennedy Memorial
1300 19 St NW, Suite 750, Washington, DC 20036
Tel: 202-463-7575 *Fax:* 202-463-6606
E-mail: info@rfkcenter.org
Web Site: www.rfkcenter.org
Key Personnel
Contact: Christina Taylor *E-mail:* ctaylor@rfkcenter.org
Established: 1980
For a book of fiction or nonfiction that most faithfully & forcefully reflects Robert Kennedy's interests & concerns. Publishers or authors should send four copies of books published in the previous year along with a press release. See web site for further details.
Award: $2,500 & bust of Robert Kennedy
Closing Date: Feb 1
Presented: May

Coretta Scott King Book Awards
The American Library Association (ALA)
50 E Huron St, Chicago, IL 60611
Toll Free Tel: 800-545-2433
E-mail: olos@ala.org
Web Site: www.ala.org/emiert/cskbookawards
Key Personnel
Interim Dir, OLOS: Gwendolyn Prellwitz
E-mail: gprellwitz@ala.org
Literacy Offr: Kristin Lahurd *E-mail:* klahurd@ala.org
Prog Offr: John Amundsen *E-mail:* jamundsen@ala.org
Prog Coord: Zina Clark *E-mail:* zclark@ala.org
Established: 1970
Awarded annually to outstanding African American authors & illustrators of books for children & young adults that demonstrate an appreciation of African American culture & universal human values. Administered by the Ethnic Multicultural Information Exchange Round Table (EMIERT).
Other Sponsor(s): Book Wholesalers Inc; Encyclopedia Britannica; Johnson Publications; World Book
Award: Bronze award seal & $1,000 to both author & illustrator
Closing Date: Annually, Dec 1
Presented: Coretta Scott King Awards Breakfast, ALA Annual Conference, June

Kirkus Prize
Kirkus Media LLC
65 W 36 St, Suite 700, New York, NY 10018
Web Site: www.kirkusreviews.com/prize
Awarded annually to authors of fiction, nonfiction & young readers' literature. Both traditionally published & self-published books reviewed by Kirkus that earn the Kirkus Star are eligible.
Award: $50,000 each category

The Knight-Risser Prize for Western Environmental Journalism
John S Knight Journalism Fellowships
Stanford University, 450 Serra Mall, Bldg 120, Rm 424, Stanford, CA 94305
Tel: 650-721-5955 *Fax:* 650-725-6154
E-mail: knightrisserprize@lists.stanford.edu
Web Site: knightrisser.stanford.edu
Key Personnel
Dir, Knight Fellowships: James R Bettinger
E-mail: jimb@stanford.edu
Established: 2006
Recognizes excellence in reporting on such environmental issues as water, resource, land use & wild life, unique to the North American West, by print, broadcast & online journalists. Work must have been published in 2015. For more information, see web site.
Other Sponsor(s): Bill Lane Center for the American West at Stanford University
Award: $5000 cash
Closing Date: March 15, 2016
Presented: Annual Knight-Risser Prize Symposium, Stanford University, Stanford, CA, Summer

Knightville Poetry Contest
The New Guard
PO Box 5101, Hanover, NH 03755
E-mail: info@newguardreview.com
Web Site: www.newguardreview.com
Key Personnel
Founding Ed & Publr: Shanna McNair
Established: 2009
Submit up to 3 poems of up to 150 lines. Submit all 3 poems in a single document. Online submissions only.
Award: $1,500 & publication in The New Guard
Closing Date: Aug

E M Koeppel Short Fiction Award
Writecorner Press
PO Box 140310, Gainesville, FL 32614
Tel: 352-338-7778
E-mail: contact@writecorner.com
Web Site: www.writecorner.com
Key Personnel
Ed: Robert B Gentry; Mary Sue Koeppel
Established: 2003
For poetry, any theme or style, with no more than 24 lines. Only unpublished work is eligible. Winner published on www.writecorner.com literary web site. Guidelines on web site.
Other Sponsor(s): P L Titus Scholarship
Award: $400 (Writecorner Poetry Award), $50 (Editor's Choice)
Closing Date: Annually, Oct 1-April 30
Presented: Annually in Summer

Katherine Singer Kovacs Prize
Modern Language Association of America (MLA)
26 Broadway, 3rd fl, New York, NY 10004-1789
SAN: 202-6422
Tel: 646-576-5141 *Fax:* 646-458-0030
E-mail: awards@mla.org
Web Site: www.mla.org
Key Personnel
Coord, Book Prizes: Annie M Reiser
E-mail: areiser@mla.org
Established: 1990
Prize for an outstanding book published in 2015 in English or Spanish in the field of Latin American & Spanish literatures & cultures. Authors need not be members of MLA. For consideration, submit 6 copies. Presented annually.
Award: Cash award & certificate
Closing Date: May 1, 2016
Presented: MLA Convention, Jan 2017

Michael Kraus Research Grant in History
American Historical Association (AHA)
400 "A" St SE, Washington, DC 20003
Tel: 202-544-2422 *Fax:* 202-544-8307
E-mail: awards@historians.org
Web Site: www.historians.org
Grant given to a member of the association to recognize the most deserving proposal relating to works in progress on a research project in American colonial history, with particular reference to the intercultural aspects of American & European relations. The grants are intended to further research in progress & may be used for travel to a library or archive, for microfilms, photographs, or xeroxing. Preference will be given to those with specific research needs, such as the completion of a project or completion of a discrete segment thereof. Preference will be given to PhD candidates & junior scholars. Application forms & all updated info on web site. Applications must include application form with estimated budget, curriculum vitae, statement of no more than 750 words & a one-page bibliography of the most recent relevant, secondary works on the topic. Mailed & faxed submissions are not accepted. Only members of the association are eligible to apply.
Award: Individual grants will not exceed $800
Closing Date: Annually, Feb 15

The Robert Kroetsch City of Edmonton Book Prize
Writers' Guild of Alberta
11759 Groat Rd, Edmonton, AB T5M 3K6, Canada
Tel: 780-422-8174 *Toll Free Tel:* 800-665-5354 (AB only) *Fax:* 780-422-2663 (attn WGA)
E-mail: mail@writersguild.ab.ca
Web Site: www.writersguild.ab.ca
Key Personnel
Exec Dir: Carol Holmes *E-mail:* carol.holmes@writersguild.ab.ca
Communs & Partnerships Coord: Nicholas Mather *E-mail:* nicholas.mather@writersguild.ab.ca
Memb Servs Coord: Giorgia Severini
Progs Coord: Natalie Cook *E-mail:* natalie.cook@writersguild.ab.ca; Nichole Quiring *E-mail:* nichole.quiring@writersguild.ab.ca
Entries must deal with some aspect of the City of Edmonton: history, geography, current affairs, its arts or its people or be written by an Edmonton author.
Award: $10,000 & leather-bound copy of book
Closing Date: Annually, Dec 31
Presented: Mayor's Evening for the Arts, Annually in Spring
Branch Office(s)
505 21 Ave SW, Calgary, AB T2S 0G9, Canada, Prog Coord: Samantha Warwick *Tel:* 403-265-2226 *E-mail:* samantha.warwick@writersguild.ab.ca

Steven Kroll Award for Picture Book Writing, see PEN/Steven Kroll Award for Picture Book Writing

Kumu Kahua/UHM Theatre & Dance Department Playwriting Contest
Kumu Kahua/UHM Theatre & Dance Dept
46 Merchant St, Honolulu, HI 96813
Tel: 808-536-4441 (box off); 808-536-4222
Fax: 808-536-4226
E-mail: kumukahuatheatre@hawaiiantel.net
Web Site: www.kumukahua.org
Key Personnel
Artistic Dir: Harry L Wong, III
Hawaii Prize: open to residents of Hawaii & non-residents; full length (50 pages or more); play must be set in Hawaii +/or deal with the Hawaii experience.
Pacific Rim Prize: open to residents of Hawaii & non-residents; full length (50 pages or more); play must be set in +/or dealing with the Pacific Islands, Pacific Rim, or the Pacific/Asian-American experience.
Resident Prize: only open to residents of Hawaii; full length (50 pages or more) or one-acts; play can be on any topic.
Award: $600 (Hawaii Prize), $450 (Pacific Rim Prize), $250 (Resident Prize)
Closing Date: Jan 2
Presented: May

W Kaye Lamb Award
British Columbia Historical Federation
PO Box 5254, Sta B, Victoria, BC V8R 6N4, Canada
E-mail: essays@bchistory.ca
Web Site: www.bchistory.ca
Key Personnel
Contact: Marie Elliot
Scholarship offered for essays written by students in British Columbia colleges or universities on a topic relating to British Columbia history.
Award: $750 (1st or 2nd yr student), $1,000 (3rd or 4th yr student)
Closing Date: Annually, May 15
Presented: BCHF Annual Awards Banquet, Annually in May/June

Lambda Literary Awards (Lammys)
Lambda Literary Foundation
5482 Wilshire Blvd, No 1595, Los Angeles, CA 90036
Tel: 323-643-4281 *Fax:* 323-643-4281
E-mail: info@lambdaliterary.org
Web Site: www.lambdaliterary.org
Key Personnel
Administrator: Kathleen DeBold
Exec Dir: Tony Valenzuela
Established: 1989
Annual award recognizing excellence in gay & lesbian literature. Entry fee required. Guidelines on the web site.
Award: Trophy & 2 $1,000 debut fiction awards
Closing Date: Annually, Dec 1
Presented: Various cities, Annually in May

Gerald Lampert Memorial Award
The League of Canadian Poets
192 Spadina Ave, Suite 312, Toronto, ON M5T 2C2, Canada
Tel: 416-504-1657 *Fax:* 416-504-0096
E-mail: readings@poets.ca
Web Site: poets.ca
Key Personnel
Exec Dir: Joanna Poblocka *E-mail:* joanna@poets.ca
Asst Dir: Ingel Madrus *E-mail:* readings@poets.ca
Admin & Communs Coord: Barbara Erochina *E-mail:* admin@poets.ca
Annual award intended to recognize the work of a Canadian writer early in his or her career. Awarded for a first book of poetry published in the preceding year.
Award: $1,000
Closing Date: Annually, Nov 1
Presented: Annually in May or June

Langum Prize in American Historical Fiction
The Langum Charitable Trust
2809 Berkeley Dr, Birmingham, AL 35242
Tel: 205-726-2424 *Fax:* 205-726-4216
Web Site: www.langumtrust.org
Key Personnel
Dir: David J Langum, Sr *E-mail:* djlangum@samford.edu
Established: 2001
Awarded to a book published by any non-subsidy press for American historical fiction set in the colonial or national periods that is both excellent fiction & excellent history.
Award: $1,000
Closing Date: Annually in Dec; also rolling submissions at our request
Presented: Annually in March

Langum Prize in American Legal History or Biography
The Langum Charitable Trust
2809 Berkeley Dr, Birmingham, AL 35242
Tel: 205-726-2424 *Fax:* 205-726-4216
E-mail: langumtrust@gmail.com
Web Site: www.langumtrust.org
Key Personnel
Dir: David J Langum, Sr *E-mail:* djlangum@samford.edu
Established: 2001
Awarded to a book published by a university press in the area of American legal history or American legal biography that is accessible to the educated general public, rooted in sound scholarship & with themes that touch upon matters of general concern to the American public, past or present.
Award: $1,000
Closing Date: Annually in Dec
Presented: Annually in March

Lannan Literary Awards & Fellowships
Lannan Foundation
313 Read St, Santa Fe, NM 87501-2628
Tel: 505-986-8160 *Fax:* 505-986-8195
E-mail: info@lannan.org
Web Site: www.lannan.org
Established: 1989
The awards recognize writers who have made significant contributions to English-language literature. The fellowships recognize writers of distinctive literary merit who demonstrate potential for continued outstanding work.

Larew, Christian, Memorial Scholarship in Library & Information Technology, see LITA/Christian Larew Memorial Scholarship in Library & Information Technology

Lawrence Foundation Prize
Michigan Quarterly Review
University of Michigan, 0576 Rackham Bldg, 915 E Washington St, Ann Arbor, MI 48109-1070
Tel: 734-764-9265
E-mail: mqr@umich.edu
Web Site: www.umich.edu/~mqr
Key Personnel
Mng Ed: Vicki Lawrence
Ed: Keith Taylor
Awarded to the best work of fiction published in MQR each year. No deadline or special application process.
Award: $1,000

Stephen Leacock Memorial Medal for Humour
Stephen Leacock Association
RR2, 4223 Line 12 N, Coldwater, ON L0K 1E0, Canada
Tel: 705-835-3218 *Fax:* 705-835-5171
Web Site: www.leacock.ca
Key Personnel
Chair, Award Comm: Judith Rapson
E-mail: judith.rapson@gmail.com
Pres: Michael Hill
Contact: Don Reid *E-mail:* don_reid@sympatico.ca
Established: 1946
Humorous writing by Canadian authors. All entries must have been published in the year prior to the year the award is given. Ten copies of each book to be submitted should be sent along with $150 fee, authors bio & a 5x7 or larger B&W photograph. No ebooks accepted. Winner announced late April. Books are non-returnable.
Other Sponsor(s): Lakehead University; Sun Media
Award: $15,000 Canadian TD Bank Financial Group cash award & silver medal, each of 4 finalists receive $1,500 Canadian
Closing Date: Annually, Nov 30
Presented: Gala Award Dinner, Geneva Park, Orillia, ON, Annually, early June

The Ledge Press Fiction Awards Competition
The Ledge Press
40 Maple Ave, Bellport, NY 11713
E-mail: info@theledgemagazine.com
Web Site: theledgemagazine.com
Key Personnel
Publr & Ed-in-Chief: Timothy Monaghan
All stories must be previously unpublished & not exceed 7,500 words. Entry fee is $12 for the first story, $6 each additional story. $20 subscription (2 issues) to The Ledge gains free entry for the first story.
Award: $1,000 & publication in *The Ledge Magazine* (1st), $250 & publication (2nd), $100 & publication (3rd)
Closing Date: Annually, Feb 28

The Ledge Press Poetry Awards Competition
The Ledge Press
40 Maple Ave, Bellport, NY 11713
E-mail: info@theledgemagazine.com
Web Site: theledgemagazine.com
Key Personnel
Publr & Ed-in-Chief: Timothy Monaghan
Established: 1995
All poems must be previously unpublished. Entry fee is $12 for first three poems; $3 each additional poem. $20 subscription (2 issues) to The Ledge gains free entry for the first three poems.
Award: $1,000 & publication in *The Ledge Magazine* (1st), $250 & publication (2nd), $100 & publication (3rd)
Closing Date: Annually, April 30

The Ledge Press Poetry Chapbook Competition
The Ledge Press
40 Maple Ave, Bellport, NY 11713
E-mail: info@theledgemagazine.com
Web Site: theledgemagazine.com
Key Personnel
Publr & Ed-in-Chief: Timothy Monaghan
Established: 1994
Submit 16-28 pages of original poetry with title page, biographic note & acknowledgements, if any; open to all styles & forms of poetry. Entry fee: $18.
Award: $1,000 & 25 author copies of the published chapbook
Closing Date: Annually, Oct 31

Harper Lee Prize for Legal Fiction
The University of Alabama School of Law
101 Paul Bryant Dr, Tuscaloosa, AL 35487
Tel: 205-348-5195
Web Site: www.law.ua.edu/programs/harper-lee-prize-for-legal-fiction

Key Personnel
Contact: Monique Fields *E-mail:* mfields@law.ua.edu
Established: 2011
Awarded annually to a published work of fiction that best illuminates the role of lawyers in society & their power to effect change.
Other Sponsor(s): ABA Journal
Closing Date: Annually, March 31
Presented: Prize ceremony, Sept in conjunction with National Book Festival, Washington, DC

Waldo G Leland Prize
American Historical Association (AHA)
400 "A" St SE, Washington, DC 20003
Tel: 202-544-2422 *Fax:* 202-544-8307
E-mail: awards@historians.org
Web Site: www.historians.org
Established: 1981
Offered every five years for the most outstanding reference tool in the field of history. Reference tool encompasses bibliographies, indexes, encyclopedias & other scholarly apparatus. The award is honorific. Books published between 2011 & 2015, will be eligible for consideration. No application form, applicant must simply mail a copy of their book to each of the prize committee members who will be posted on our web site as the prize deadline approaches. All updated info on web site.
Award: Cash prize
Closing Date: May 15, 2016 (postmark)
Presented: AHA Annual Meeting, Denver, CO, Jan 5-8, 2017

Vincent Lemieux Prize
Canadian Political Science Association
260 rue Dalhousie St, Suite 204, Ottawa, ON K1N 7E4, Canada
Tel: 613-562-1202 *Fax:* 613-241-0019
E-mail: cpsa-acsp@cpsa-acsp.ca
Web Site: www.cpsa-acsp.ca
Key Personnel
Administrator: Michelle Hopkins
Established: 1997
This is a biennial competition awarded to the best thesis in any sub-field of political science submitted at a Canadian University, written in English or French, judged eminently worthy of publication in the form of a book or articles. A thesis is eligible only after nomination by the department of political science in which it was defended. For the 2017 award, a thesis must have been defended in 2015 or 2016.
Award: $1,000 & commemorative certificate
Presented: Annual Conference, Ryerson University, Toronto, ON, CN, May 30-June 1, 2017

John Leonard Award
National Book Critics Circle
160 Varick St, 11th fl, New York, NY 10013
E-mail: info@bookcritics.org
Web Site: bookcritics.org
Key Personnel
Contact: Sarah Russo *Tel:* 917-627-5993
E-mail: sarahlrusso@gmail.com
Established: 2013
Prize honoring an author's first book.
Presented: NBCC Annual Awards Ceremony

Leopold-Hidy Award
The Forest History Society Inc
701 William Vickers Ave, Durham, NC 27701-3162
Tel: 919-682-9319 *Fax:* 919-682-2349
Web Site: www.foresthistory.org
Key Personnel
Admin Asst: Andrea Anderson *E-mail:* andrea.anderson@foresthistory.org
Established: 1996
To honor the best article in the journal they copublish, "Environmental History".
Other Sponsor(s): American Society for Environmental History

Fenia & Yaakov Leviant Memorial Prize in Yiddish Studies
Modern Language Association of America (MLA)
26 Broadway, 3rd fl, New York, NY 10004-1789
SAN: 202-6422
Tel: 646-576-5141 *Fax:* 646-458-0030
E-mail: awards@mla.org
Web Site: www.mla.org
Key Personnel
Coord, Book Prizes: Annie M Reiser
E-mail: areiser@mla.org
Established: 2000
Awarded alternately to an outstanding scholarly or translation work in the field of Yiddish. In 2016, the prize will be awarded to an outstanding scholarly work in the field of Yiddish published between 2012 & 2015. In 2018, the prize will be awarded to an English translation of a Yiddish literary work published between 2014 & 2017. Authors need not be members of the MLA. For consideration, submit 4 copies.
Award: Cash award & certificate
Closing Date: May 1, 2016
Presented: MLA Convention, Jan 2017

Harry Levin Prize
American Comparative Literature Association (ACLA)
University of South Carolina, Dept of Languages, Literature & Cultures, Rm 813-A, 1620 College St, Columbia, SC 29208
Tel: 803-777-3021 *Fax:* 803-777-3041
E-mail: info@acla.org
Web Site: www.acla.org/awards/harry-levin-prize; www.acla.org
Key Personnel
Secy & Treas: Alexander Beecroft
Established: 1968
Prize recognizing an outstanding first book in the discipline of comparative literature published in 2015 or 2016. Awarded annually. See web site for nomination process.
Award: Complimentary conference registration, a banquet ticket & a travel grant to cover the cost of attending the annual meeting to receive the award in person
Closing Date: Oct 2016
Presented: ACLA Annual Meeting, June 2017

Levinson Prize
Poetry Magazine
444 N Michigan Ave, Suite 1850, Chicago, IL 60611-4034
Tel: 312-787-7070 *Fax:* 312-787-6650
E-mail: editors@poetrymagazine.org
Web Site: www.poetryfoundation.org
Key Personnel
Mng Ed: Valerie Johnson *E-mail:* vjohnson@poetrymagazine.org
Established: 1914
For poetry published in the preceding 2 volumes of Poetry. No application necessary.
Award: $500
Presented: Annually in Dec

Levis Reading Prize
Virginia Commonwealth University, Department of English
PO Box 842005, Richmond, VA 23284-2005
Tel: 804-828-1331 *Fax:* 804-828-8684
Web Site: english.vcu.edu/mfa/levis/
Established: 1997
In memory of Larry Levis, awarded for best first or second book of poetry (not for self-published or chapbooks).
Award: $5,000
Closing Date: Annually, Feb 1

Library of Congress Literacy Awards
Library of Congress
101 Independence Ave SE, Washington, DC 20540-1400
Tel: 202-707-5221 (Center for the Book)
Fax: 202-707-0269
Web Site: www.read.gov/literacyawards
Awards to three organizations that have made outstanding contributions to increasing literacy in the US or abroad.
Award: Rubenstein Prize $150,000, American Prize $50,000, International Prize $50,000

Library of Congress Prize for American Fiction
Library of Congress
101 Independence Ave SE, Washington, DC 20540-1400
Tel: 202-707-5221 (Center for the Book)
Web Site: www.loc.gov
Key Personnel
Communs Offr: Guy Lamolinara
Prog Offr: Anne Boni
Established: 2013
Annual award to honor an American literary writer whose body of work is distinguished not only for its mastery of the art but for its originality of thought & imagination. The award seeks to commend strong, unique, enduring voices that, throughout long, consistently accomplished careers, have told us something about the American experience.
Presented: Library of Congress National Book Festival

Libris Award for Author of the Year
Canadian Booksellers Association (CBA)
1881 Yonge St, Suite 800, Toronto, ON M4S 3C4, Canada
Tel: 416-922-6678 *Toll Free Tel:* 888-373-8245
Fax: 416-467-7886
E-mail: info@retailcouncil.org
Web Site: www.retailcouncil.org
Key Personnel
CEO & Pres, Retail Council of Canada: Diane J Briseboas
Sr Mgr: Jodi White *Tel:* 416-467-7883 ext 227
E-mail: jwhite@cbabook.org
Mktg & Communs Mgr: Stephanie Quinlan
Tel: 416-467-7883 ext 230 *E-mail:* squinlan@cbabook.org
Awarded to the Canadian author of an outstanding literary work in the previous year that is a contribution to Canadian culture & that combines readability with strong sales. An author who has offered strong support to the bookselling industry.
Closing Date: Annually in Feb
Presented: Libris Awards Presentation: National Conference, Annually in June

Libris Children's Picture Book of the Year
Canadian Booksellers Association (CBA)
1881 Yonge St, Suite 800, Toronto, ON M4S 3C4, Canada
Tel: 416-922-6678 *Toll Free Tel:* 888-373-8245
Fax: 416-467-7886
E-mail: info@retailcouncil.org
Web Site: www.retailcouncil.org
Key Personnel
CEO & Pres, Retail Council of Canada: Diane J Briseboas
Sr Mgr: Jodi White *Tel:* 416-467-7883 ext 227
E-mail: jwhite@cbabook.org
Mktg & Communs Mgr: Stephanie Quinlan
Tel: 416-467-7883 ext 230 *E-mail:* squinlan@cbabook.org
For a Canadian picture book from the previous year whose imaginative storyline & creative visuals engaged, entertained & delighted young children while generating customer attention & strong sales.

Closing Date: Annually in Feb
Presented: Libris Awards Presentation: National Conference, Annually in June

Libris Distributor of the Year
Canadian Booksellers Association (CBA)
1881 Yonge St, Suite 800, Toronto, ON M4S 3C4, Canada
Tel: 416-922-6678 *Toll Free Tel:* 888-373-8245 *Fax:* 416-467-7886
E-mail: info@retailcouncil.org
Web Site: www.retailcouncil.org
Key Personnel
CEO & Pres, Retail Council of Canada: Diane J Briseboas
Sr Mgr: Jodi White *Tel:* 416-467-7883 ext 227 *E-mail:* jwhite@cbabook.org
Mktg & Communs Mgr: Stephanie Quinlan *Tel:* 416-467-7883 ext 230 *E-mail:* squinlan@cbabook.org
To a Canadian distributor in recognition of an outstanding support of the bookselling industry. Based on customer service, accuracy & speed of order fulfillment, correct invoicing, efficient handling of returns & credits.
Closing Date: Annually in Feb
Presented: Libris Awards Presentation: National Conference, Annually in June

Libris Editor of the Year
Canadian Booksellers Association (CBA)
1881 Yonge St, Suite 800, Toronto, ON M4S 3C4, Canada
Tel: 416-922-6678 *Toll Free Tel:* 888-373-8245 *Fax:* 416-467-7886
E-mail: info@retailcouncil.org
Web Site: www.retailcouncil.org
Key Personnel
CEO & Pres, Retail Council of Canada: Diane J Briseboas
Sr Mgr: Jodi White *Tel:* 416-467-7883 ext 227 *E-mail:* jwhite@cbabook.org
Mktg & Communs Mgr: Stephanie Quinlan *Tel:* 416-467-7883 ext 230 *E-mail:* squinlan@cbabook.org
Awarded to an in-house editor in recognition of excellence in the field. Based on all-around skills, development of new authors, commitment to quality, commercial awareness & originality.
Closing Date: Annually in Feb
Presented: Libris Awards Presentation: National Conference, Annually in June

Libris Fiction Book of the Year
Canadian Booksellers Association (CBA)
1881 Yonge St, Suite 800, Toronto, ON M4S 3C4, Canada
Tel: 416-922-6678 *Toll Free Tel:* 888-373-8245 *Fax:* 416-467-7886
E-mail: info@retailcouncil.org
Web Site: www.retailcouncil.org
Key Personnel
CEO & Pres, Retail Council of Canada: Diane J Briseboas
Sr Mgr: Jodi White *Tel:* 416-467-7883 ext 227 *E-mail:* jwhite@cbabook.org
Mktg & Communs Mgr: Stephanie Quinlan *Tel:* 416-467-7883 ext 230 *E-mail:* squinlan@cbabook.org
For a Canadian work of fiction published in the previous year that had an outstanding impact on the Canadian bookselling industry, created wide media attention, brought people into bookstores & had strong sales.
Closing Date: Annually in Feb
Presented: Libris Awards Presentation: National Conference, Annually in June

Libris Publisher of the Year
Canadian Booksellers Association (CBA)
1881 Yonge St, Suite 800, Toronto, ON M4S 3C4, Canada
Tel: 416-922-6678 *Toll Free Tel:* 888-373-8245 *Fax:* 416-467-7886
E-mail: info@retailcouncil.org
Web Site: www.retailcouncil.org
Key Personnel
CEO & Pres, Retail Council of Canada: Diane J Briseboas
Sr Mgr: Jodi White *Tel:* 416-467-7883 ext 227 *E-mail:* jwhite@cbabook.org
Mktg & Communs Mgr: Stephanie Quinlan *Tel:* 416-467-7883 ext 230 *E-mail:* squinlan@cbabook.org
To a Canadian publisher in recognition of an outstanding contribution to the Canadian bookselling industry. Based on consistent high quality in author relations; editorial, production & marketing skills, retail support & commercial success.
Closing Date: Annually in Feb
Presented: Libris Awards Presentation: National Conference, Annually in June

Libris Sales Rep of the Year
Canadian Booksellers Association (CBA)
1881 Yonge St, Suite 800, Toronto, ON M4S 3C4, Canada
Tel: 416-922-6678 *Toll Free Tel:* 888-373-8245 *Fax:* 416-467-7886
E-mail: info@retailcouncil.org
Web Site: www.retailcouncil.org
Key Personnel
CEO & Pres, Retail Council of Canada: Diane J Briseboas
Sr Mgr: Jodi White *Tel:* 416-467-7883 ext 227 *E-mail:* jwhite@cbabook.org
Mktg & Communs Mgr: Stephanie Quinlan *Tel:* 416-467-7883 ext 230 *E-mail:* squinlan@cbabook.org
Presented in memory of Gordon S Garner in recognition of excellence in the field. Based on all-around skills, development of new authors, commitment to quality, commercial awareness & originality.
Closing Date: Annually in Feb
Presented: Libris Awards Presentation: National Conference, Annually in June

Libris Small Press Publisher of the Year
Canadian Booksellers Association (CBA)
1881 Yonge St, Suite 800, Toronto, ON M4S 3C4, Canada
Tel: 416-922-6678 *Toll Free Tel:* 888-373-8245 *Fax:* 416-467-7886
E-mail: info@retailcouncil.org
Web Site: www.retailcouncil.org
Key Personnel
CEO & Pres, Retail Council of Canada: Diane J Briseboas
Sr Mgr: Jodi White *Tel:* 416-467-7883 ext 227 *E-mail:* jwhite@cbabook.org
Mktg & Communs Mgr: Stephanie Quinlan *Tel:* 416-467-7883 ext 230 *E-mail:* squinlan@cbabook.org
Awarded to a Canadian publisher in recognition of an outstanding contribution to the Canadian bookselling industry. Based on consistent high quality in author relations, editorial production & marketing skills, retail support & commercial success. Nominees must have published 25 or fewer new books the previous year.
Closing Date: Annually in Feb
Presented: Libris Awards Presentation: National Conference, Annually in June

The Lieutenant-Governor's Awards for High Achievement in the Arts
New Brunswick Arts Board (Conseil des arts du Nouveau-Brunswick)
649 rue Queen, 2nd fl, Fredericton, NB E3B 1C3, Canada
Tel: 506-444-4444 *Toll Free Tel:* 866-460-ARTS (460-2787) *Fax:* 506-444-5543
E-mail: nbabcanb@artsnb.ca
Web Site: www.artsnb.ca
Key Personnel
Exec Dir: Akoulina Connell *Tel:* 506-444-4343 *E-mail:* execdirgen@artsnb.ca
Deputy Dir: Vanessa Moeller *Tel:* 506-292-4696 *E-mail:* vmoeller@artsnb.ca
Prog Offr: Joss Richer *Tel:* 506-478-4610 *E-mail:* jricher@artsnb.ca
Established: 1989
To recognize the outstanding contribution of artists to the arts in New Brunswick.
Award: $20,000/year
Closing Date: June 15
Presented: Fredericton, NB

The Lieutenant-Governor's Medal for Historical Writing, see BCHF Historical Writing Competition

Ruth Lilly Poetry Prize
Poetry Foundation
61 W Superior St, Chicago, IL 60654
Tel: 312-787-7070 *Fax:* 312-787-6650
E-mail: editors@poetrymagazine.org
Web Site: poetrymagazine.org
Key Personnel
Mng Ed: Sarah Dodson
Ed: Don Share
Established: 1986
Awarded to a living US poet, to recognize extraordinary artistic accomplishment.
Award: $100,000
Presented: Annually in May

Lindquist & Vennum Prize for Poetry
Milkweed Editions
1011 Washington Ave S, Suite 300, Minneapolis, MN 55415-1246
Tel: 612-332-3192 *Toll Free Tel:* 800-520-6455 *Fax:* 612-215-2550
Web Site: www.milkweed.org
Key Personnel
Contact: Connor Lane *E-mail:* connor_lane@milkweed.org
Established: 2011
Annual regional prize to support outstanding poets & bring their work to a national stage. Submissions accepted in hard copy only from poets currently residing in North Dakota, South Dakota, Minnesota, Iowa, or Wisconsin. No entry fee.
Other Sponsor(s): Lindquist & Vennum Foundation
Award: $10,000 & publication contract
Presented: Annually in April

Joseph W Lippincott Award
The American Library Association (ALA)
50 E Huron St, Chicago, IL 60611
Tel: 312-280-3247 *Toll Free Tel:* 800-545-2433 (ext 3247) *Fax:* 312-944-3897
E-mail: awards@ala.org
Web Site: www.ala.org
Key Personnel
Prog Offr: Cheryl M Malden *E-mail:* cmalden@ala.org
Established: 1938
Annual award presented to a librarian for distinguished service to the profession of librarianship, such service to include outstanding participation in the activities of professional library association, notable published professional writing or other significant activity on behalf of the profession & its aims.
Other Sponsor(s): Joseph W Lippincott III
Award: $1,000 & Citation
Closing Date: Annually, Dec 1
Presented: ALA Annual Conference, Annually in June

LITA/Christian Larew Memorial Scholarship in Library & Information Technology
Library & Information Technology Association (LITA)
Division of American Library Association (ALA)
c/o American Library Association, 50 E Huron St, Chicago, IL 60611-2795
Toll Free Tel: 800-545-2433 (ext 4270) *Fax:* 312-280-3257
E-mail: lita@ala.org
Web Site: www.ala.org/lita
Key Personnel
Prog Coord: Valerie A Edmonds-Merritt *Tel:* 312-280-4269 *E-mail:* vedmonds@ala.org
Established: 1999
Awarded jointly on an annual basis. The scholarship is designed to encourage the entry of qualified persons into the library & information technology field, who plan to follow a career in that field & who demonstrate academic excellence, leadership & a vision in pursuit of library & information technology. This scholarship is for study in an ALA Accredited Master of Library Science (MLS) program.
Other Sponsor(s): Baker & Taylor
Award: $3,000
Closing Date: Annually, March 1
Presented: LITA President's program held at the American Library Association Annual Conference, Annually in June

LITA/LSSI Minority Scholarship in Library & Information Technology
Library & Information Technology Association (LITA)
Division of American Library Association (ALA)
c/o American Library Association, 50 E Huron St, Chicago, IL 60611-2795
Toll Free Tel: 800-545-2433 (ext 4270) *Fax:* 312-280-3257
E-mail: lita@ala.org
Web Site: www.ala.org/lita
Key Personnel
Prog Coord: Valerie A Edmonds-Merritt *Tel:* 312-280-4269 *E-mail:* vedmonds@ala.org
Established: 1994
Scholarship is designed to encourage the entry of qualified minorities into the library & automation field who plan to follow a career in that field & who demonstrate potential in & have a strong commitment to the use of automated systems in libraries. Applicants must be qualified members of a principal minority group (American Indian or Alaskan native, Asian or Pacific Islander, African-American or Hispanic). The recipient must be a US or Canadian citizen. The scholarship is for study in an ALA Accredited Master of Library Science (MLS) program.
Other Sponsor(s): LSSI
Award: $2,500
Closing Date: Annually, March 1
Presented: LITA President's Program held at the American Library Association Annual Conference, Annually in June

LITA/OCLC Minority Scholarship in Library & Information Technology
Library & Information Technology Association (LITA)
Division of American Library Association (ALA)
c/o American Library Association, 50 E Huron St, Chicago, IL 60611-2795
Toll Free Tel: 800-545-2433 (ext 4270) *Fax:* 312-280-3257
E-mail: lita@ala.org
Web Site: www.ala.org/lita
Key Personnel
Prog Coord: Valerie A Edmonds-Merritt *Tel:* 312-280-4269 *E-mail:* vedmonds@ala.org
Established: 1991
For qualified members of a minority group. Must be US or Canadian citizen. For applicants who plan to enter a career in the library & automation field.
Other Sponsor(s): OCLC Inc
Award: $3,000
Closing Date: Annually, March 1
Presented: LITA President's Program at the American Library Association Annual Conference, Annually in June

Literary Translation Projects
National Endowment for the Arts
400 Seventh St SW, Washington, DC 20506-0001
Tel: 202-682-5400; 202-682-5496 (Voice/TTY); 202-682-5034 (lit fellowships hotline)
Fax: 202-682-5609; 202-682-5610
E-mail: litfellowships@arts.gov
Web Site: www.arts.gov; www.nea.gov
Key Personnel
Grants Dir & Contracts Offr: Nicki Jacobs
Tel: 202-682-5546 *E-mail:* jacobsn@arts.gov
Fellowships for published translators: for translations of published literary material into English. Applications accepted by genre. Guidelines available on web site.
Award: $12,500 or $25,000, depending on the artistic excellence & merit of the project
Closing Date: Annually in Jan
Presented: Notification by mail, Annually in Aug

Literature Fellowship
Idaho Commission on the Arts
2410 N Old Penitentiary Rd, Boise, ID 83712
Mailing Address: PO Box 83720, Boise, ID 83720-0008
Tel: 208-334-2119 *Toll Free Tel:* 800-ART-FUND (278-3863 within Idaho) *Fax:* 208-334-2488
E-mail: info@arts.idaho.gov
Web Site: www.arts.idaho.gov
Key Personnel
Lit Dir: Cort Conley *Tel:* 208-334-2119 ext 108
E-mail: cort.conley@arts.idaho.gov
Five fellowships awarded triennially for literary excellence. For Idaho residents only.
Award: $5,000
Closing Date: Jan
Presented: Triennially in July

Littleton-Griswold Prize in American Law & Society
American Historical Association (AHA)
400 "A" St SE, Washington, DC 20003
Tel: 202-544-2422 *Fax:* 202-544-8307
E-mail: awards@historians.org
Web Site: www.historians.org
Established: 1985
Best book in any subject on the history of American law & society. Books published in 2015 will be eligible for consideration. Along with an application form, applicants must mail a copy of their book to each of the prize committee members who will be posted on our web site as the prize deadline approaches. All updated info on web site.
Award: Cash prize
Closing Date: May 15, 2016 (postmark)
Presented: AHA Annual Meeting, Denver, CO, Jan 5-8, 2017

Littleton-Griswold Research Grants
American Historical Association (AHA)
400 "A" St SE, Washington, DC 20003
Tel: 202-544-2422 *Fax:* 202-544-8307
E-mail: awards@historians.org
Web Site: www.historians.org
For research in American legal history & the field of law & society. Only members of the Association are eligible. Applications must include application form with estimated budget, curriculum vitae & statement of no more than 750 words & a one-page bibliography of the most recent, relevant, secondary works on the topic. Application form & all updated info on web site. Preference will be given to junior scholars, PhD candidates & those without access to institutional funds.
Award: Individual grants will not exceed $1,000
Closing Date: Feb 15

Living Now Book Awards
Independent Publisher Online
Division of Jenkins Group Inc
1129 Woodmere Ave, Suite B, Traverse City, MI 49686
Tel: 231-933-0445 *Toll Free Tel:* 800-706-4636
Fax: 231-933-0448
E-mail: awards@bookpublishing.com
Web Site: www.livingnowawards.com
Key Personnel
CEO: Jerrold R Jenkins *E-mail:* jrj@bookpublishing.com
Pres: James Kalajian *Tel:* 800-706-4636 ext 1006
E-mail: jjk@bookpublishing.com
Mng Ed & Awards Dir: Jim Barnes *Tel:* 800-706-4636 ext 1011 *E-mail:* jimb@bookpublishing.com
Awards Coord: Amy Shamroe
Established: 2008
Annual award to celebrate the innovation & creativity of newly published books that can help us improve the quality of our lives, from cooking & entertaining to fitness & travel. The awards are open to all books written in English & intended for the North American market.
Other Sponsor(s): Jenkins Group
Award: Gold medal (1st place), silver medal (2nd place), bronze medal (3rd place), foil seals available, winners featured in *Independent Publisher Online*
Closing Date: July
Presented: Winner announced online in Sept

Locus Awards
Locus Science Fiction Foundation Inc
Division of Locus Publications
PO Box 13305, Oakland, CA 94661-0305
Tel: 510-339-9196 *Fax:* 510-339-9198
E-mail: locus@locusmag.com
Web Site: www.locusmag.com
Key Personnel
Ed-in-Chief: Liza Groen Trombi
Mng Ed: Kirsten Gong-Wong
Established: 1971
Presented for the best science fiction novel, best fantasy novel, best first novel, best young-adult novel, best novella, best novelette, best short fiction, science fiction anthology, best nonfiction, art & artist, editor, magazine, best publisher & collection of the year.
Other Sponsor(s): EMP/SFM; Northwest Media Group; 1-2-3 Awards
Award: Trophy & free subscription
Presented: Science Fiction Museum

The Gerald Loeb Awards
Anderson School of Management at UCLA
Gold Hall, Suite B-305, 110 Westwood Plaza, Los Angeles, CA 90095-1481
Tel: 310-825-4478 *Fax:* 310-825-4479
E-mail: loeb@anderson.ucla.edu
Web Site: www.loeb.anderson.ucla.edu
Key Personnel
Prog Mgr: Jonathan Daillak
Established: 1957
Distinguished business & finance journalism in print & broadcast media.
Award: $2,000 winners; $500 honorable mention
Closing Date: Last Mon in Jan
Presented: Last week in June

Loft-Mentor Series in Poetry & Creative Prose
The Loft Literary Center
Open Book, Suite 200, 1011 Washington Ave S, Minneapolis, MN 55415
Tel: 612-215-2575 *Fax:* 612-215-2576
E-mail: loft@loft.org

Web Site: www.loft.org
Key Personnel
Prog Mgr: Sherrie Fernandez-Williams *Tel:* 612-215-2586 *E-mail:* sfernandezwilliams@loft.org
Established: 1980
Annual award for poetry, nonfiction & fiction mss. Must be Minnesota State resident. Six different residencies scheduled throughout the year. Winners announced on web site. Open to poets, fiction writers & nonfiction writers.
Award: Stipend to defray costs of participating in the program & opportunity to study with six nationally known writer-mentors in brief residence during the course of the year
Closing Date: Mid-Spring
Presented: The Loft

The Jack London Award
Titan Press
Box 17897, Encino, CA 91416-7897
E-mail: cwcsfv@gmail.com
Key Personnel
Mng Ed: Stefanya Wilson
Three quarterly competitions: fiction, poetry & nonfiction. Monthly nominations are made for publication & honorable mention. Of those, one is chosen for the annual Grand Prize. Published & unpublished mss are eligible. $65 annual dues are allowed; one free submission per quarter; nonmembers; $15 reading fee per entry, up to 4 entries per quarter.
Award: Invitation to attend the biannual Writer's Conference, plaque commemorating winner as guest of honor (give a public reading of his work) & publication
Closing Date: Submissions accepted throughout the year
Presented: Biannual Writer's Conference

Judy Lopez Memorial Award For Children's Literature
Women's National Book Association/Los Angeles Chapter
1225 Selby Ave, Los Angeles, CA 90024
Tel: 310-474-9917 *Fax:* 310-474-6436
Web Site: www.wnba-books.org/la; www.judylopezbookaward.org
Key Personnel
Chair, Lopez Comm: Margaret Flanders
Pres: Rachelle Yousef
Chair, Selection Comm: Gail Kim
Established: 1986
For best books for young readers 9-12 years of age, submitted by publishers, written by US citizen/US resident in year that precedes the award.
Award: Bronze medal & cash honorarium
Closing Date: Annually, Feb 1
Presented: Dinner, UCLA Faculty Center, Los Angeles, CA, 3rd Fri in Sept

Los Angeles Times Book Prizes
Los Angeles Times
Subsidiary of Tribune Publishing Co
202 W First St, Los Angeles, CA 90012
Tel: 213-237-5775 *Toll Free Tel:* 800-528-4637 *Fax:* 213-237-7679
Web Site: www.latimesbookprizes.com
Key Personnel
CEO & Publr: Eddy Hartenstein
Administrator: Ann Binney *E-mail:* ann.binney@latimes.com
Established: 1980
Annual prizes to authors in the categories of fiction, first fiction, young adult literature, graphic novels, comics, mystery/thriller, biography, current interest, history, poetry, science & technology. No submissions accepted; nominations are done by committees of appointed judges.
Award: $500 & citation (in 10 different categories). Robert Kirsch Award & Innovator's Award at $1,000 each
Presented: Annually in April

Louise Louis/Emily F Bourne Student Poetry Award
Poetry Society of America (PSA)
15 Gramercy Park, New York, NY 10003
Tel: 212-254-9628 *Fax:* 212-673-2352
Web Site: www.poetrysociety.org
Key Personnel
Pres: Ruth Kaplan
Exec Dir: Alice Quinn
Deputy Dir: Brett Fletcher Lauer *E-mail:* brett@poetrysociety.org
Progs Dir: Charif Shanahan *E-mail:* charif@poetrysociety.org
Established: 1971
For an unpublished poem by an American high school or preparatory school student. Send No 10 SASE or visit web site for further guidelines.
Award: $250
Closing Date: Annually, Oct-Dec
Presented: Annual Awards Ceremony, New York, NY, Annually in Spring

Louisville Grawemeyer Award in Religion
Louisville Presbyterian Theological Seminary & University of Louisville
1044 Alta Vista Rd, Louisville, KY 40205-1798
Tel: 502-895-3411 *Toll Free Tel:* 800-264-1839 *Fax:* 502-894-2286
E-mail: grawemeyer@lpts.edu
Web Site: www.grawemeyer.org
Key Personnel
Dir: Shannon Craigo-Snell
Established: 1990
Given for a work presented or published in the eight years preceding the year of the award. Nominations are invited from religious organizations, appropriate academic associations, religious leaders & scholars, presidents of universities or schools of religion & publishers & editors of scholarly journals. Personal nominations accepted, self-nominations not accepted.
Award: $20,000 per year for 5 years
Closing Date: Nominations by Dec 1
Presented: Annually in Spring

Love Creek Annual Short Play Festival
Love Creek Productions
2144 45 Ave, Long Island City, NY 11101
Tel: 718-786-9397
E-mail: lovecreekle@aol.com; squaank@yahoo.com (submissions)
Key Personnel
Mng & Artistic Dir: Le Wilhelm
Lit Mgr: Becky Copley
Established: 1988
Annual one-act play festival for unpublished scripts unproduced in New York City in previous year. Send SASE for information/guidelines which must be followed exactly.
Award: Cash (1st prize), mini-showcase production (finalists)
Closing Date: Revolving
Presented: New York, NY, various midtown venues, Ongoing

James Russell Lowell Prize
Modern Language Association of America (MLA)
26 Broadway, 3rd fl, New York, NY 10004-1789
SAN: 202-6422
Tel: 646-576-5141 *Fax:* 646-458-0030
E-mail: awards@mla.org
Web Site: www.mla.org
Key Personnel
Coord, Book Prizes: Annie M Reiser *E-mail:* areiser@mla.org
Established: 1969
Annual prize for an outstanding literary or linguistic study, a critical edition of an important work, or critical biography by a current MLA member published in 2015. Authors or publishers should submit 6 copies & confirmation of the author's membership in the MLA.
Award: Cash award & certificate
Closing Date: March 1, 2016
Presented: MLA Convention, Jan 2017

Pat Lowther Memorial Award
The League of Canadian Poets
192 Spadina Ave, Suite 312, Toronto, ON M5T 2C2, Canada
Tel: 416-504-1657 *Fax:* 416-504-0096
E-mail: readings@poets.ca
Web Site: poets.ca
Key Personnel
Exec Dir: Joanna Poblocka *E-mail:* joanna@poets.ca
Asst Dir: Ingel Madrus *E-mail:* readings@poets.ca
Admin & Communs Coord: Barbara Erochina *E-mail:* admin@poets.ca
Annual award for the best book of poetry written by a Canadian woman & published in the preceding year.
Award: $1,000
Closing Date: Annually, Nov 1
Presented: Annually in May or June

Jeremiah Ludington Award
Educational Book & Media Association (EBMA)
37 Main St, Suite 203, Warrenton, VA 20186
Mailing Address: PO Box 3363, Warrenton, VA 20188
Tel: 540-318-7770 *Fax:* 202-962-3939
E-mail: info@edupaperback.org
Web Site: www.edupaperback.org
Key Personnel
Exec Dir: Brian Gorg
Meeting Mgr: Maureen Gelwicks
Established: 1979
Presented to a person for distinguished work with young people & books; selected by EBMA committee & board; no application required.
Award: Citation & contribution to a cause chosen by recipient
Presented: Annually at EBMA meeting, Annually in Jan

Lush Triumphant Literary Awards
subTerrain Magazine
PO Box 3008, MPO, Vancouver, BC V6B 3X5, Canada
Tel: 604-876-8710 *Fax:* 604-879-2667
E-mail: subter@portal.ca
Web Site: www.subterrain.ca
Established: 2003
Annual literary award in 3 categories: fiction, poetry & nonfiction. Entry fee: $27.50.
Award: $1,000 (1st place in each category), 1st runner-up $250 & publication in Spring issue of following year
Closing Date: May 15
Presented: Vancouver, BC, Aug 15

Thomas J Lyon Book Award in Western American Literary and Cultural Studies
Western Literature Association
PO Box 6815, Logan, UT 84341
Web Site: www.westernlit.org/thomas-j-lyon-book-award-in-western-american-literary-and-cultural-studies/; www.westernlit.org
Key Personnel
Dir of Opers: Sabine Barcatta *E-mail:* WLAoperations@gmail.com
Established: 1997
Honors outstanding single-author scholarly book on the literature & culture of the American West published in the previous year. Must submit a statement of support & three copies of the book.
Award: Certificate
Closing Date: June 15
Presented: Annual Conference

Lyric Poetry Award
Poetry Society of America (PSA)
15 Gramercy Park, New York, NY 10003
Tel: 212-254-9628 *Fax:* 212-673-2352
Web Site: www.poetrysociety.org
Key Personnel
Pres: Ruth Kaplan
Exec Dir: Alice Quinn
Deputy Dir: Brett Fletcher Lauer *E-mail:* brett@poetrysociety.org
Progs Dir: Charif Shanahan *E-mail:* charif@poetrysociety.org
Established: 1972
For a lyric poem on any subject, not to exceed 50 lines. Open to society members only. Send No 10 SASE or visit web site for further information.
Award: $500
Closing Date: Annually, Oct-Dec
Presented: Annual Awards Ceremony, New York, NY, Annually in Spring

Lyric Poetry Prizes
The Lyric
PO Box 110, Jericho, VT 05465
Tel: 802-899-3993 *Fax:* 802-899-3993
E-mail: themuse@thelyricmagazine.com
Web Site: thelyricmagazine.com
Key Personnel
Ed: Jean Mellichamp Milliken
Established: 1921
Awarded to undergraduates enrolled full-time in an American or Canadian College. Awarded for poems published in "The Lyric" magazine. Winners of annual awards announced in the winter issue each year. Send SASE for guidelines. Sample copy of "The Lyric" $4; subn price $15/yr, $28/2 yrs, $38/3 yr, $2 extra per year for foreign & Canadian.
Award: Quarterly prize: $50. Annual awards: Lyric Memorial Prize $100, Lyric College Poetry Contest/Scholarship $500, Leslie Mellichamp Prize $100, Roberts Memorial Prize $100, Margaret Hailey Carpenter Prize $50, New England Prize $50, Fluvanna Prize $50. Honorable mentions, 1 yr subn to "The Lyric" magazine. Checks mailed to recipients
Closing Date: Dec 1 (postmark)
Presented: Quarterly prizes awarded in the following issue, annual prizes in the winter issue

Macavity Award
Mystery Readers International
7155 Marlborough Terr, Berkeley, CA 94705
Mailing Address: PO Box 8116, Berkeley, CA 94707
Tel: 510-845-3600
Web Site: www.mysteryreaders.org
Key Personnel
Dir: Janet Rudolph *E-mail:* janet@mysteryreaders.org
Established: 1986
Annually awarded for works nominated by & voted on by members of Mystery Readers International in categories: Best Novel, Best First Novel, Best Short Story, Best Nonfiction/Critical; Sue Feder Award for the Historical Mystery (all published in the US the previous year).
Award: Statue
Closing Date: No application necessary
Presented: Bouchercon, the World Mystery Convention, Oct

Sir John A Macdonald Prize
Canadian Historical Association
130 Albert St, Suite 501, Ottawa, ON K1P 5G4, Canada
Tel: 613-233-7885 *Fax:* 613-565-5445
E-mail: cha-shc@cha-shc.ca
Web Site: www.cha-shc.ca
Key Personnel
Exec Coord: Michel Duquet *E-mail:* mduquet@cha-shc.ca
Established: 1976
Awarded for the best book on Canadian history. See web site for application details.
Award: $5,000
Closing Date: Annually, Dec 1
Presented: Annual meeting, Canadian Historical Association, Annually in May

MacDowell Fellowships
The MacDowell Colony
100 High St, Peterborough, NH 03458
Tel: 603-924-3886 *Fax:* 603-924-9142
E-mail: info@macdowellcolony.org; admissions@macdowellcolony.org
Web Site: www.macdowellcolony.org
Key Personnel
Exec Dir: Cheryl Young
Admissions Dir: Courtney Bethel
Communs Mgr: Jonathan Gourlay
Established: 1907
Fellowships of up to eight weeks are available for writers, composers, film/video artists, visual artists, architects & interdisciplinary artists. Artists-in-residence receive room, board & exclusive use of a studio. The average length of stay is six weeks. Talent is the sole criterion for acceptance to the Colony. Established artists as well as emerging artists are encouraged to apply. Committees of distinguished professionals donate their time to judge applications, which include work samples, references & a brief project description. There are no residency fees. Grants for travel to & from the Colony are available based on need. Financial aid for writers is available through a special grant from a foundation. An aid application will be mailed following acceptance. The Edward MacDowell medal is awarded for a career of outstanding contributions to the arts, including musical composition, visual arts or literature, architecture, film & video & interdisciplinary arts.
Closing Date: For fellowships: Jan 15, April 15 & Sept 15, see application form & guidelines online for details
Presented: Peterborough, NH
Branch Office(s)
163 E 81 St, New York, NY 10028 *Tel:* 212-535-9690 *Fax:* 212-737-3803

Machigonne Fiction Contest
The New Guard
PO Box 5101, Hanover, NH 03755
E-mail: info@newguardreview.com
Web Site: www.newguardreview.com
Key Personnel
Founding Ed & Publr: Shanna McNair
Established: 2009
Submit a short story or novel excerpt up to 5,000 words. Online submissions only.
Award: $1,500 & publication in the New Guard
Closing Date: Aug

C B MacPherson Prize
Canadian Political Science Association
260 rue Dalhousie St, Suite 204, Ottawa, ON K1N 7E4, Canada
Tel: 613-562-1202 *Fax:* 613-241-0019
E-mail: cpsa-acsp@cpsa-acsp.ca
Web Site: www.cpsa-acsp.ca
Key Personnel
Administrator: Michelle Hopkins
Established: 1992
This is a biennial competition. Awarded to the best book published in English or in French in a field relating to the study of political theory. A book may be single-authored or multi-authored. Single-authored book: must be a Canadian citizen or a permanent resident of Canada or a member of the CPSA in the year the book was published. Multi-authored book: at least one of the authors must be a Canadian citizen or a permanent resident of Canada or a member of the CPSA in the year the book was published. For the 2016 award, a book must have a copyright date of 2014 or 2015.
Award: Commemorative plaque & also receive/share the set of books submitted to the CPSA office for the 2016 prize
Presented: Annual Conference, University of Calgary, Calgary, AB, CN, May 31-June 2, 2016

Magazine Merit Awards
Society of Children's Book Writers and Illustrators (SCBWI)
4727 Wilshire Blvd, Suite 301, Los Angeles, CA 90010
Tel: 323-782-1010; 310-403-0675 (cell) *Fax:* 323-782-1892
E-mail: membership@scbwi.org; scbwi@scbwi.org
Web Site: www.scbwi.org
Key Personnel
Pres: Stephen Mooser *E-mail:* stephenmooser@scbwi.org
Exec Dir: Lin Oliver *E-mail:* linoliver@scbwi.org
Established: 1988
For outstanding original magazine work for young people published during the calendar year & having been written or illustrated by SCBWI members.
Award: Four plaques (fiction, nonfiction, illustration, poetry), four honor certificates
Closing Date: Annually in Dec
Presented: Annually in April

The Magazine of the Year Award
Society of Publication Designers Inc
27 Union Sq W, Suite 207, New York, NY 10003
Tel: 212-223-3332 *Fax:* 212-223-5880
E-mail: mail@spd.org
Web Site: www.spd.org
Key Personnel
Exec Dir: Keisha Dean
Established: 1996
For continuing excellence in the field of publication design.
Closing Date: Jan
Presented: Annual Awards Gala, May

J Russell Major Prize
American Historical Association (AHA)
400 "A" St SE, Washington, DC 20003
Tel: 202-544-2422 *Fax:* 202-544-8307
E-mail: awards@historians.org
Web Site: www.historians.org
Established: 2001
Awarded for the best work in English on any aspect of French history. Books published in 2015 are eligible. Along with an application form, applicants must mail a copy of their book to each of the prize committee members who will be posted on our web site as the prize deadline approaches. All updated info on web site.
Award: Cash prize
Closing Date: May 15, 2016 (postmark)
Presented: AHA Annual Meeting, Denver, CO, Jan 5-8, 2017

Malahat Review Long Poem Prize
The Malahat Review
University of Victoria, Box 1700, Sta CSC, Victoria, BC V8W 2Y2, Canada
Tel: 250-721-8524 *Fax:* 250-472-5051
E-mail: malahat@uvic.ca
Web Site: www.malahatreview.ca
Key Personnel
Ed: John Barton
Established: 1988

Two awards for best long poem(s). See web site for details & entry fee. Contest runs every other year (odd-numbered years). Alternates with Novella Prize (even-numbered years).
Award: $1000 CAD (2 prizes)
Closing Date: Feb 1, odd-numbered yrs

Gene E & Adele R Malott Prize for Recording Community Activism
The Langum Charitable Trust
2809 Berkeley Dr, Birmingham, AL 35242
Tel: 205-726-2424 *Fax:* 205-726-4216
E-mail: langumtrust@gmail.com
Web Site: www.langumtrust.org
Key Personnel
Dir: David J Langum, Sr *E-mail:* djlangum@samford.edu
Established: 2007
Biannual prize that recognizes the best literary depiction of an individual or small group of individuals whose efforts resulted in a significant improvement of their local community. Although the work of community improvement must be significant, the basis of the prize will be the skill & power of the literary or film depiction. Must have been published or released within the past 2 years of a prize cycle.
Award: $1,500 for the writer. If film, divided between the director & screenwriter; $1,000 if ongoing, the underlying project of community activism
Closing Date: Jan 1 for materials published or released the previous 2 calendar years

Ralph Manheim Medal for Translation, see PEN/Ralph Manheim Medal for Translation

Margaret Mann Citation
Association for Library Collections & Technical Services (ALCTS)
Division of The American Library Association (ALA)
50 E Huron St, Chicago, IL 60611
SAN: 201-0062
Tel: 312-280-5037 *Toll Free Tel:* 800-545-2433 *Fax:* 312-280-5033
E-mail: alcts@ala.org
Web Site: www.ala.org/alcts
Key Personnel
Exec Dir: Keri Cascio *Tel:* 312-280-5030 *E-mail:* kcascio@ala.org
Pubns & Membership: Christine McConnell *Tel:* 312-280-5037 *E-mail:* cmcconnell@ala.org
Established: 1951
Award for outstanding professional achievement in cataloging or classification in a significant publication or by participation in a professional organization. Candidates are nominated. Citation recipient selected by jury.
Other Sponsor(s): OCLC
Award: Citation & $2,000 scholarship to the US or Canadian library school of winner's choice
Closing Date: Annually, Dec 1
Presented: ALA Annual Conference, Annually in June

Many Voices Fellowships
The Playwrights' Center
2301 Franklin Ave E, Minneapolis, MN 55406-1099
Tel: 612-332-7481 *Fax:* 612-332-6037
E-mail: info@pwcenter.org
Web Site: www.pwcenter.org
Key Personnel
Producing Artistic Dir: Jeremy Cohen *Tel:* 612-332-7481 ext 113 *E-mail:* jeremyc@pwcenter.org
Artistic Administrator: Amanda Robbins-Butcher *Tel:* 612-332-7481 ext 115 *E-mail:* amandar@pwcenter.org
For writers of color. Two distinct programs to serve writers of varying skill/experience levels both locally & nationally.
Award: Many Voices Mentorship: 2 Minnesota playwrights with little or no playwriting experience, $1,000 stipend; Many Voices Fellowship: 2 emerging playwrights receive a $5,650 stipend, $1,250 in play development funds & dramaturgical support. One must reside in Minnesota, the other may be a resident of any US state
Closing Date: See web site for details

Marfield Prize
Arts Club of Washington
2017 "I" St NW, Washington, DC 20006-1804
E-mail: award@artsclubofwashington.org
Web Site: artsclubofwashington.org
Key Personnel
Award Administrator: Blake Stenning
Established: 2006
Given annually to nonfiction books about the visual, literary or performing arts written for a broad audience. Works published in the US during the previous calendar year are eligible for consideration. Publishers, agents, or authors may submit books. No entry fee. Submit three copies of the book with prize submission form.
Award: $10,000
Closing Date: Oct 31

Marian Library Medal
University of Dayton, Marian Library
300 College Park, Dayton, OH 45469-1390
Tel: 937-229-4214 *Fax:* 937-229-4258
Web Site: campus.udayton.edu/mary/mlmedal.html
Key Personnel
Lib Dir: Thomas A Thompson
Established: 1953
To scholars in any country for outstanding achievement in Marian research.
Award: Medal

Marick Press Poetry Prize Competition
Marick Press
PO Box 36253, Grosse Pointe Farms, MI 48236
Tel: 313-407-9236
Web Site: www.marickpress.com
Established: 2010
Submit a ms of 48-80 pages, 2 separate title pages, one with just the title & the other with full author info. Open competition for a poetry ms; submissions are accepted from anyone writing in the English language, whether living in the US or abroad (translations are not eligible). Entry fee: $15.
Award: $1,000 & publication by Marick Press
Closing Date: Annually in Oct
Presented: Annually in March

Morton Marr Poetry Prize
Southwest Review
PO Box 750374, Dallas, TX 75275-0374
Fax: 214-768-1408
E-mail: swr@mail.smu.edu
Web Site: www.smu.edu/southwestreview
Key Personnel
Ed-in-Chief: Willard Spiegelman
Sr Ed: Jennifer Cranfill *Tel:* 214-768-1036
Open to writers who have not yet published a first book of poetry. Contestants may submit no more than 6 previously unpublished poems in a "traditional" form (e.g. sonnet, sestina, villanelle, rhymed stanzas, blank verse, etc). There is a $5 per poem entry/handling fee.
Award: $1,000 (1st prize), $500 (2nd prize) & publication in *Southwest Review*
Closing Date: Annually, Sept 30
Presented: Annually in Dec

Helen & Howard R Marraro Prize in Italian History
American Historical Association (AHA)
400 "A" St SE, Washington, DC 20003
Tel: 202-544-2422 *Fax:* 202-544-8307
E-mail: awards@historians.org
Web Site: www.historians.org
Established: 1973
Each award will be given for the book or article deemed best by the committee which treats Italian history in any epoch, Italian cultural history, or Italian-American relations. Each book must be published in 2015. Entries must first have been published in English by a historian whose usual residence is North America. Along with an application form, applicants must mail a copy of their book together with a curriculum vitae & bibliography of the author to each of the prize committee members who will be posted on our web site as the prize deadline approaches. All updated info on web site.
Other Sponsor(s): American Catholic Historical Association; Society for Italian Historical Studies
Award: Cash prize
Closing Date: May 15, 2016 (postmark)
Presented: AHA Annual Meeting, Denver, CO, Jan 5-8, 2017

Howard R Marraro Prize
Modern Language Association of America (MLA)
26 Broadway, 3rd fl, New York, NY 10004-1789
SAN: 202-6422
Tel: 646-576-5141 *Fax:* 646-458-0030
E-mail: awards@mla.org
Web Site: www.mla.org
Key Personnel
Coord, Book Prizes: Annie M Reiser *E-mail:* areiser@mla.org
Established: 1973
Presented for an outstanding scholarly work on any phase of Italian literature or comparative literature involving Italian by an MLA member. The prize is awarded each even-numbered year. The committee solicits submissions of works published in 2015 by current members. Submit 4 copies of the work & confirm author's membership in the MLA.
Award: Cash award & certificate
Closing Date: May 1, 2016
Presented: MLA Convention, Jan 2017

Massachusetts Book Awards
Massachusetts Center for the Book
Simons College - GSLIS, 300 The Fenway, Boston, MA 02115
Tel: 617-521-2719 *Fax:* 617-521-3035
E-mail: bookawards@massbook.org
Web Site: www.massbook.org
Key Personnel
Exec Dir: Sharon Shaloo *E-mail:* massbook@simmons.edu
Established: 2000
The MassBooks recognize significant achievements by Massachusetts writers in fiction, nonfiction, poetry & children's literature for the previous publishing year. Also awarded, the MA Book medal for creative publishing, programming or lifetime achievement in the Massachusetts book community. Visit web site for details.
Other Sponsor(s): Massachusetts Board of Library Commissioners; Massachusetts Cultural Council; Massachusetts Library Association; Massachusetts Library System; Simmons College Graduate School of Library & Information Science

Masters Literary Awards
Titan Press
PO Box 17897, Encino, CA 91416-7897
Tel: 818-377-4006

E-mail: titan91416@yahoo.com
Key Personnel
Mng Ed: Stefanya Wilson
Established: 1981
Annual awards (including 4 quarterly prizes) for fiction, poetry & song lyrics & nonfiction. All quality published & unpublished mss are eligible, submitted from double-spaced photocopies or tearsheets. Guidelines available with No 10 SASE.
Award: $1,000 Grand Prize, 4 quarterly prizes of Honorable Mention
Closing Date: Submissions received prior to any award date are eligible for the subsequent award
Presented: Titan Press, March 15, June 15, Aug 15, Dec 15

Amy Mathers Teen Book Award
Canadian Children's Book Centre
40 Orchard View Blvd, Suite 217, Toronto, ON M4R 1B9, Canada
Tel: 416-975-0010 *Fax:* 416-975-8970
E-mail: info@bookcentre.ca
Web Site: www.bookcentre.ca
Key Personnel
Exec Dir: Charlotte Teeple *E-mail:* charlotte@bookcentre.ca
Lib Coord: Meghan Howe *E-mail:* meghan@bookcentre.ca
Mktg & Website Coord: Camilia Kahrizi *E-mail:* camilia@bookcentre.ca
Outreach Educ Coord: Sandra O'Brien *E-mail:* sandra@bookcentre.ca
Prog Coord: Shannon Howe Barnes *E-mail:* shannon@bookcentre.ca
Established: 2014
Awarded to a Canadian author for excellence in teen/young adult fiction.
Award: $5,000
Closing Date: Annually in mid-Dec

Matt Cohen Prize: In Celebration of a Writing Life
The Writers' Trust of Canada
460 Richmond St W, Suite 600, Toronto, ON M5V 1Y1, Canada
Tel: 416-504-8222 *Toll Free Tel:* 877-906-6548 *Fax:* 416-504-9090
E-mail: info@writerstrust.com
Web Site: www.writerstrust.com
Key Personnel
Exec Dir: Mary Osborne *Tel:* 416-504-8222 ext 244
Established: 2001
Recognizes a lifetime of distinguished work by a Canadian writer, working in either poetry or prose, in either French or English. Generously sponsored by anonymous donors.
Award: $20,000
Presented: The Writers' Trust Awards, Toronto, ON, CN, Annually in Nov

Mature Women Scholarship Grant - Art/Letters/Music
National League of American Pen Women
c/o National Pen Women-Scholarship, Pen Arts Bldg, 1300 17 St NW, Washington, DC 20036-1973
Tel: 202-785-1997 *Fax:* 202-452-8868
E-mail: contact@nlapw.org
Web Site: www.nlapw.org
Key Personnel
Pres: Candace Long
Established: 1976
Awarded biennially (even-numbered years). Judges in each category (art, letters, music) change for each award every award year. Must send SASE with inquiry for requirements. Include an $8 fee payable to NLAPW with entry.
Award: $1,000 (1st place), $750 (2nd place), $500 (3rd Place); $150 (Photography Award), $150 (Water Media Award), $100 (Jean Baber Memorial Art Fund)
Closing Date: Oct 1 (odd-numbered years)
Presented: NLAPW Convention, Biennially in April (even-numbered years); mail notification March 15

Maxim Mazumdar New Play Competition
Alleyway Theatre
One Curtain Up Alley, Buffalo, NY 14202-1911
Tel: 716-852-2600
E-mail: publicrelations@alleyway.com
Web Site: alleyway.com
Key Personnel
Founder, Alleyway Theatre: Neal Radice
Literary Mgr: Joyce Stilson *Tel:* 716-852-2600 ext 202 *E-mail:* jstilson@rocketmail.com
Contest limited to one submission per author, per year, per category. Entry must be a previously unproduced full-length (not less than 90 minutes) play or musical of any style, requiring no more than 8 performers & able to be presented on a unit or simple set, musicals must include CD, sheet music not necessary. One acts must be less than 20 minutes & no more than five actors. Entries will not be returned without SASE. Entry fee: $25.
Award: Cash & premiere production of entry at Alleyway Theatre
Closing Date: Annually, July 1

Janet B McCabe Poetry Prize
Ruminate Magazine
1041 N Taft Hill Rd, Fort Collins, CO 80521
Tel: 970-449-2726
E-mail: editor@ruminatemagazine.org
Web Site: www.ruminatemagazine.com
Key Personnel
Ed-in-Chief: Brianna Van Dyke
Sr Ed: Amy Lowe
Assoc Ed: Stephanie Lovegrove; Stefani Rossi
All submissions must be previously unpublished & submitted via online submission form. Up to 2 poems per entry, no longer than 40 lines each. Entry fee $18.
Award: $1,500 & publication in Fall issue (1st place), $500 & publication (2nd place)
Closing Date: Annually, May 1

John H McGinnis Memorial Award
Southwest Review
PO Box 750374, Dallas, TX 75275-0374
Fax: 214-768-1408
E-mail: swr@mail.smu.edu
Web Site: www.smu.edu/southwestreview
Key Personnel
Ed-in-Chief: Willard Spiegelman
Sr Ed: Jennifer Cranfill *Tel:* 214-768-1036
Established: 1960
For the best essay & story appearing in the Southwest Review during the preceding year.
Award: $500 (2-4 awards)
Presented: Annually in Jan

Harold W McGraw Jr - Prize in Education
McGraw-Hill Financial
1221 Avenue of the Americas, 47th fl, New York, NY 10020-1095
Tel: 212-904-2000; 212-512-2000 *Fax:* 212-512-3611
Web Site: www.mhfi.com
Key Personnel
Communs Assoc: Jo Ann Craig
Established: 1988
Honors three individuals whose accomplishments, programs & ideas can serve as effective models for the education of future generations.
Award: $50,000 & bronze sculpture award
Closing Date: Feb
Presented: Usually at New York Public Library, End of Sept

McKnight Advancement Grants, see McKnight Fellowships for Playwrights

McKnight Artist Fellowship for Writers
The Loft Literary Center
Open Book, Suite 200, 1011 Washington Ave S, Minneapolis, MN 55415
Tel: 612-215-2575 *Fax:* 612-215-2576
E-mail: loft@loft.org
Web Site: www.loft.org
Key Personnel
Prog Dir: Bao Phi *Tel:* 612-215-2585 *E-mail:* bphi@loft.org
Established: 1982
Contest for Minnesota residents only.
Award: Four $25,000 awards which alternate annually between poetry & creative prose; one $25,000 award in children's literature which alternates annually between writing for children 8 & under & older children
Closing Date: Annually in late Fall
Presented: The Loft, Annually in Spring

McKnight Fellowships for Playwrights
Formerly McKnight Advancement Grants
The Playwrights' Center
2301 Franklin Ave E, Minneapolis, MN 55406-1099
Tel: 612-332-7481 *Fax:* 612-332-6037
E-mail: info@pwcenter.org
Web Site: www.pwcenter.org
Key Personnel
Producing Artistic Dir: Jeremy Cohen *Tel:* 612-332-7481 ext 113 *E-mail:* jeremyc@pwcenter.org
Artistic Administrator: Amanda Robbins-Butcher *Tel:* 612-332-7481 ext 115 *E-mail:* amandar@pwcenter.org
Established: 1990
Grants to recognize mid-career playwrights whose work demonstrates exceptional artistic merit & potential. Playwright's primary residence must be in the state of Minnesota. Applicant must have had a minimum of one work fully produced by a professional theater at the time of application.
Award: Grants of $25,000 each
Presented: Annually in May

McKnight National Residency & Commission
The Playwrights' Center
2301 Franklin Ave E, Minneapolis, MN 55406-1099
Tel: 612-332-7481 *Fax:* 612-332-6037
E-mail: info@pwcenter.org
Web Site: www.pwcenter.org
Key Personnel
Producing Artistic Dir: Jeremy Cohen *Tel:* 612-332-7481 ext 113 *E-mail:* jeremyc@pwcenter.org
Artistic Administrator: Amanda Robbins-Butcher *Tel:* 612-332-7481 ext 115 *E-mail:* amandar@pwcenter.org
Established: 1982
Playwrights whose work has made a significant impact on the contemporary theater. Applicant must be a US citizen or permanent resident & must have had a minimum of two different works fully produced by professional theaters. Call or check web site for application information & deadline guidelines. Minnesota-based playwrights are not eligible for the award. Proposals for the Residency & Commission must be agent/professional only. Send writers resume, a 2- or 3-page proposal & a full-length play script.
Award: $12,500
Closing Date: See web site for details

McLaren Memorial Comedy Play Writing Competition
Midland Community Theatre
2000 W Wadley Ave, Midland, TX 79705

Tel: 432-682-2544
E-mail: tracy@mctmidland.org
Web Site: www.mctmidland.org
Key Personnel
Prodn Mgr: Tracy Alexander *E-mail:* tracy@mctmidland.org
Established: 1990
All entries must be comedies for adults, teens, or children; musical comedies no longer accepted. Requirements: full-length play (70-90 minutes); one-act plays no longer accepted. See web site for competition guidelines & required brochure with entry form. Submissions accepted beginning Jan 1. Attn: McLaren Competition Chairman.
Closing Date: Annually, Feb 28
Presented: McLaren Festival, Annually in early Fall

McLemore Prize
Mississippi Historical Society
Affiliate of Mississippi Department of Archives & History
PO Box 571, Jackson, MS 39205-0571
Tel: 601-576-6850 *Fax:* 601-576-6975
E-mail: mhs@mdah.state.ms.us
Web Site: www.mdah.state.ms.us
Key Personnel
Pres: Charles Sullivan
VP: Ann Simmons
Secy & Treas, Historical Society: Elbert Hilliard
Public Info: Stephenie Morrisey
E-mail: morrisey@mdah.state.ms.us
Established: 1980
For distinguished scholarly book on a topic in Mississippi history or biography.
Award: $700
Closing Date: Annually, Nov 1
Presented: Annual meeting, Annually, 1st weekend in March

John McMenemy Prize
Canadian Political Science Association
260 rue Dalhousie St, Suite 204, Ottawa, ON K1N 7E4, Canada
Tel: 613-562-1202 *Fax:* 613-241-0019
E-mail: cpsa-acsp@cpsa-acsp.ca
Web Site: www.cpsa-acsp.ca
Key Personnel
Administrator: Michelle Hopkins
Established: 2000
To the author or authors of the best article in English or French, published in volume 47 of the "Canadian Journal of Political Science".
Other Sponsor(s): Societe Quebecoise de Science Politique
Award: Certificate of Award & memberships in the Canadian Political Science Association & the Societe Quebecoise de Science Politique
Presented: Annual Conference, May or June

Medal of Honor for Literature
National Arts Club
15 Gramercy Park S, New York, NY 10003
E-mail: literary@thenationalartsclub.org
Web Site: www.nationalartsclub.org
Key Personnel
Chair, Literary Comm: Cherry Provost
Established: 1967
Presented for a body of work of literary excellence; nominations within the committee only & awarded by the Board of Governors.
Award: Gold medal
Presented: Gala Black Tie Dinner, at discretion of recipient

Lucille Medwick Memorial Award
Poetry Society of America (PSA)
15 Gramercy Park, New York, NY 10003
Tel: 212-254-9628 *Fax:* 212-673-2352
Web Site: www.poetrysociety.org
Key Personnel
Pres: Ruth Kaplan
Exec Dir: Alice Quinn
Deputy Dir: Brett Fletcher Lauer *E-mail:* brett@poetrysociety.org
Progs Dir: Charif Shanahan *E-mail:* charif@poetrysociety.org
Established: 1974
For an original poem in any form on a humanitarian theme, not to exceed 100 lines. Translations are ineligible. Open to society members only. Send No 10 SASE for more information, or visit web site.
Award: $500
Closing Date: Annually, Oct-Dec
Presented: Annual Awards Ceremony, New York, NY, Annually in Spring

Melcher Book Award
Unitarian Universalist Association
25 Beacon St, Boston, MA 02108-2800
Tel: 617-948-4303 *Fax:* 617-367-3237
E-mail: info@uua.org
Web Site: www.uua.org
Key Personnel
Asst to EVP: Nancy Lawrence
E-mail: nlawrence@uua.org
Established: 1964
Given to a book making significant contribution to liberal religious thought.
Award: $1,000 & certificate
Closing Date: Dec 31
Presented: Boston, MA, Oct

Frederic G Melcher Scholarship
Association for Library Service to Children (ALSC)
Division of The American Library Association (ALA)
50 E Huron St, Chicago, IL 60611-2795
Tel: 312-280-2163 *Toll Free Tel:* 800-545-2433
Fax: 312-440-9374
E-mail: alsc@ala.org
Web Site: www.ala.org/alsc
Key Personnel
Exec Dir: Aimee Strittmatter *Tel:* 312-280-2162
E-mail: astrittmatter@ala.org
Awards Coord: Caroline Jewell
E-mail: alscawards@ala.org
Prog Coord: Marsha P Burgess
E-mail: mburgess@ala.org
Established: 1956
To students entering the field of library service for graduate work in an ALA-accredited program & majoring in library service to children.
Award: $6,000 - 2 scholarships per yr
Closing Date: Annually, March 1
Presented: ALA Annual Conference, Annually in June

Addison M Metcalf Award in Literature
American Academy of Arts & Letters
633 W 155 St, New York, NY 10032
Tel: 212-368-5900 *Fax:* 212-491-4615
E-mail: academy@artsandletters.org
Web Site: www.artsandletters.org
Key Personnel
Exec Dir: Virginia Dajani
Established: 1986
Biennial award to honor young writers.
Award: $10,000

The David Nathan Meyerson Prize for Fiction
Southwest Review
PO Box 750374, Dallas, TX 75275-0374
Fax: 214-768-1408
E-mail: swr@mail.smu.edu
Web Site: www.smu.edu/southwestreview
Key Personnel
Ed-in-Chief: Willard Spiegelman
Sr Ed: Jennifer Cranfill *Tel:* 214-768-1036
Open to writers who have not yet published a book of fiction, either a novel or collection of stories. Submissions must be no longer than 8,000 words. A $25 reading fee must accompany each submission.
Award: $1,000 & publication in *Southwest Review*
Closing Date: Annually, May 1
Presented: Annually in Fall

Kenneth W Mildenberger Prize
Modern Language Association of America (MLA)
26 Broadway, 3rd fl, New York, NY 10004-1789
SAN: 202-6422
Tel: 646-576-5141 *Fax:* 646-458-0030
E-mail: awards@mla.org
Web Site: www.mla.org
Key Personnel
Coord, Book Prizes: Annie M Reiser
E-mail: areiser@mla.org
Established: 1980
Award for a work in the field of language, culture, literacy or literature with strong application to the teaching of languages other than English. Authors need not be members of the MLA. Awarded for a book published in 2015 or 2016. For consideration, submit 4 copies. Presented biennially.
Award: Cash award & certificate
Closing Date: May 1, 2017
Presented: MLA Convention, Jan 2018

Milkweed National Fiction Prize
Milkweed Editions
1011 Washington Ave S, Suite 300, Minneapolis, MN 55415-1246
Tel: 612-332-3192 *Toll Free Tel:* 800-520-6455
Fax: 612-215-2550
E-mail: submissions@milkweed.org
Web Site: www.milkweed.org
Key Personnel
CEO & Publr: Daniel Slager
Mng Dir: Patrick Thomas
E-mail: patrick_thomas@milkweed.org
Devt Mgr: Kate Strickland
Mktg Assoc: Casey O'Neil
Established: 1988
Annual award for an unpublished novel or collection of short stories +/or one or more novellas. Awarded to the best work of fiction Milkweed accepts for publication during each calendar year by a writer not previously published by Milkweed Editions. Writers must request complete guidelines before submitting ms (send SASE or visit www.milkweed.org). Open year-round.
Award: $5,000 advance against royalties
Closing Date: Annually, Jan-March, July & Sept

Mill Mountain Theatre
Center in the Square, 2nd fl, One Market Sq SE, Roanoke, VA 24011-1437
Tel: 540-224-1250 (ext 7307)
Web Site: www.millmountain.org
Key Personnel
Dir, Devt: Paul M Mylott
Mng Dir & Dir Educ: Ginger Poole *Tel:* 540-224-1250 ext 7308
Prodn Mgr: Shelby Love
Established: 1964
Closing Date: Year-round
Presented: CenterPieces, Mill Mountain Theatre, Monthly exc Sept

Milner Award
Friends of the Atlanta-Fulton Public Library
One Margaret Mitchell Sq NW, Atlanta, GA 30303
Tel: 404-730-1865
E-mail: info@themilneraward.org
Web Site: www.themilneraward.org
Key Personnel
Exec Dir: Kelly Robinson
Established: 1983

For living American authors of children's books voted on by the children of Atlanta. No application process.
Other Sponsor(s): Milner Award Committee
Award: An honorarium & a glass sculpture (inkwell & pen) by Hans Frabel
Closing Date: Second week of Nov
Presented: Atlanta, GA

Milton Dorfman Poetry Prize
Rome Art & Community Center
308 W Bloomfield St, Rome, NY 13440
Tel: 315-336-1040 *Fax:* 315-336-1090
E-mail: racc2@cnymail.com
Web Site: www.romeart.org
Key Personnel
Exec Dir: Lauren Marie Getek
NY state residents only. Application fee per poem: $10.
Award: $150 (1st prize), $75 (2nd prize), $50 (3rd prize)
Closing Date: Aug 31
Presented: Rome Art & Community Center, Rome, NY

Minnesota Book Awards
The Friends of the Saint Paul Public Library
Degree of Honor Bldg, 325 Cedar St, Suite 555, St Paul, MN 55101-1055
Tel: 651-222-3242 *Fax:* 651-222-1988
E-mail: friends@thefriends.org
Web Site: thefriends.org/events/mnba
Key Personnel
Dir: Alayne Hopkins *Tel:* 651-366-6488
E-mail: alayne@thefriends.org
Books created by writers, illustrators, or book artists who are Minnesotans are eligible for the awards through nominations. Awards are given each year for books published in the previous year.
Presented: Minnesota Book Awards Gala, annually in April

Mississippi Review Prize
University of Southern Mississippi Department of English
118 College Dr, Box 5144, Hattiesburg, MS 39406-0001
E-mail: msreview@usm.edu
Web Site: www.usm.edu/mississippi-review/contest.html
Key Personnel
Ed-in-Chief: Andrew Milward
Fiction & poetry prize open to all writers in English except current or former students or employees of the University of Southern Mississippi. Entry fee $15.
Award: Fiction & Poetry: $1,000 each & publication in the print issue of *Mississippi Review* next Spring
Closing Date: Annually, Dec 1
Presented: Annually in May

W O Mitchell Book Prize, see The City of Calgary W O Mitchell Book Prize

MLA Prize for a Bibliography, Archive or Digital Project
Modern Language Association of America (MLA)
26 Broadway, 3rd fl, New York, NY 10004-1789
SAN: 202-6422
Tel: 646-576-5141 *Fax:* 646-458-0030
E-mail: awards@mla.org
Web Site: www.mla.org
Key Personnel
Coord, Book Prizes: Annie M Reiser
E-mail: areiser@mla.org
Established: 1998
Awarded biennually for enumerative & descriptive bibliography, archive or digital project. A multivolume bibliography is eligible if at least one volume was published in 2014 or 2015. Criteria for determining excellence include evidence of analytical rigor, meticulous scholarship, intellectual creativity & subject range & depth. Editors need not be members of MLA. For consideration, submit 4 copies.
Award: Cash award & certificate
Closing Date: May 1, 2016
Presented: MLA Convention, Jan 2017

MLA Prize for a First Book
Modern Language Association of America (MLA)
26 Broadway, 3rd fl, New York, NY 10004-1789
SAN: 202-6422
Tel: 646-576-5141 *Fax:* 646-458-0030
E-mail: awards@mla.org
Web Site: www.mla.org
Key Personnel
Coord, Book Prizes: Annie M Reiser
E-mail: areiser@mla.org
Established: 1993
Awarded annually for an outstanding scholarly work published in year prior to competition as the first book-length publication by a current member of the MLA. For consideration, submit 6 copies & confirmation of author's MLA membership.
Award: Cash award & certificate
Closing Date: April 1, 2016
Presented: MLA Convention, Jan 2017

MLA Prize for a Scholarly Edition
Modern Language Association of America (MLA)
26 Broadway, 3rd fl, New York, NY 10004-1789
SAN: 202-6422
Tel: 646-576-5141 *Fax:* 646-458-0030
E-mail: awards@mla.org
Web Site: www.mla.org
Key Personnel
Coord, Book Prizes: Annie M Reiser
E-mail: areiser@mla.org
Established: 1995
Biennial prize offered in odd-numbered years. Committee solicits submissions of editions published in 2015 or 2016. A multivolume edition is eligible if at least one volume has been published during that period. The editor need not be a member of the MLA. Edition should be based on an examination of all available relevant textual sources. The source texts & the edited text's deviation from them should be fully described. The edition should exhibit the highest standards of accuracy in the presentation of its text & apparatus, which should be presented as accessibly & elegantly as possible. For consideration, submit 4 copies with letter.
Award: Cash award & certificate
Closing Date: May 1, 2017
Presented: MLA Convention, Jan 2018

MLA Prize for Independent Scholars
Modern Language Association of America (MLA)
26 Broadway, 3rd fl, New York, NY 10004-1789
SAN: 202-6422
Tel: 646-576-5141 *Fax:* 646-458-0030
E-mail: awards@mla.org
Web Site: www.mla.org
Key Personnel
Coord, Book Prizes: Annie M Reiser
E-mail: areiser@mla.org
Established: 1983
Offered as a biennial prize with competitions in even-numbered years for a distinguished scholarly book published in 2014 or 2015 in the field of English or another modern language or literature. Author enrolled in a program leading to an academic degree & did not hold a tenured, tenure-accruing, or tenure-track position in post-secondary education at the time of publication is eligible. For consideration, submit 6 copies & a completed entry form.
Award: Cash award & certificate
Closing Date: May 1, 2016
Presented: MLA Convention, Jan 2017

MLA Prize for Studies in Native American Literatures, Cultures & Languages
Modern Language Association of America (MLA)
26 Broadway, 3rd fl, New York, NY 10004-1789
SAN: 202-6422
Tel: 646-576-5141 *Fax:* 646-458-0030
E-mail: awards@mla.org
Web Site: www.mla.org
Key Personnel
Coord, Book Prizes: Annie M Reiser
E-mail: areiser@mla.org
Established: 2012
Awarded to a current MLA member for an outstanding scholarly work in the field of Native American literatures, cultures & languages published in 2014 or 2015. Selection committee is seeking works that examine & broaden understanding of the cultural expressions of first peoples or nations in the US, CN & Mexico. For consideration, submit 4 copies & a letter identifying the work.
Closing Date: May 1, 2016
Presented: MLA Convention, Jan 2017

MLA Prize in United States Latina & Latino & Chicano & Chicano Literary & Cultural Studies
Modern Language Association of America (MLA)
26 Broadway, 3rd fl, New York, NY 10004-1789
SAN: 202-6422
Tel: 646-576-5141 *Fax:* 646-458-0030
E-mail: awards@mla.org
Web Site: www.mla.org
Key Personnel
Coord, Book Prizes: Annie M Reiser
E-mail: areiser@mla.org
Established: 2002
Biennial prize offered in odd-numbered years to a current member of the association for an outstanding scholarly study in any language of United States Latina & Latino or Chicana & Chicano literature or culture published in 2015 or 2016. Books that are primarily translations will not be considered. For consideration the author or publisher should send 4 copies & a letter identifying the work.
Award: Cash award, certificate & 1 year association membership
Closing Date: May 1, 2017
Presented: MLA Convention, Jan 2018

Lucy Maud Montgomery Literature for Children Prize
Prince Edward Island Writers' Guild
115 Richmond St, Charlottetown, PE C1A 1H7, Canada
Tel: 902-368-4410 *Toll Free Tel:* 888-734-2784
Fax: 902-368-4418
E-mail: peiwritersguild@gmail.com
Web Site: www.peiwritersguild.com
Key Personnel
Exec Dir: Darrin White *Tel:* 902-368-6176
E-mail: dwhite@peica.ca
The ms must be a story written for children 5 to 12 yrs of age. Maximum length 60 pages. May submit as many entries as they wish. Entry fee for each submission is $20. The work must be original & unpublished. Entry shall be typewritten & double-spaced on one side of page only. Illustration may be submitted with the story. Contest for Prince Edward Island residents only. Call or e-mail for further information.
Award: $400 (1st prize), $200 (2nd prize), $100 (3rd prize)

Cenie H Moon Prize
The Poetry Society of Virginia
1194 Hume Rd, Hume, VA 22639-1806

E-mail: poetryinva@aol.com
Web Site: www.poetrysocietyofvirginia.org
Key Personnel
Pres: Judith K Bragg *E-mail:* musicsavy45@yahoo.com
Adult Contest Chair: Patsy Anne Bickerstaff *E-mail:* granypatsy@yahoo.com; Guy Terrell *E-mail:* ggterr@infionline.net
All entries must be in English, original & unpublished. Submit 2 copies of each poem, each having the category name & number on top left of page. Only one poem per category; entries will not be returned. Subject: woman or women; 48 line limit; any form. Entry fee: $4 nonmembs.
Award: $50 (1st prize), $30 (2nd prize), $20 (3rd prize)
Closing Date: Jan 19
Presented: Annual PSV Awards Luncheon, Richmond, VA, April

Moonbeam Children's Book Awards
Independent Publisher Online
Division of Jenkins Group Inc
1129 Woodmere Ave, Suite B, Traverse City, MI 49686
Tel: 231-933-0445 *Toll Free Tel:* 800-706-4636 *Fax:* 231-933-0448
E-mail: info@moonbeamawards.com
Web Site: www.moonbeamawards.com
Key Personnel
CEO: Jerrold R Jenkins *E-mail:* jrj@bookpublishing.com
Pres: James Kalajian *Tel:* 800-706-4636 ext 1006 *E-mail:* jjk@bookpublishing.com
Mng Ed & Awards Dir: Jim Barnes *Tel:* 800-706-4636 ext 1011 *E-mail:* jimb@bookpublishing.com
Awards Coord: Amy Shamroe
Established: 2007
Annual award celebrating youthful curiosity, discovery & learning through books & reading. Recognizes the best children's books published each year for the North American market. Authors, illustrators, publishers & self-publishers of children's books intended for the North American market may enter.
Other Sponsor(s): Jenkins Group Inc
Award: Gold medal (1st place), silver medal (2nd place) & bronze medal (3rd place)
Closing Date: Annually in Aug
Presented: Traverse City Children's Book Festival, Annually in Nov

Jenny McKean Moore Writer-in-Washington
George Washington University
English Dept, Rome Hall, 801 22 St NW, Suite 760, Washington, DC 20052
Tel: 202-994-6180 *Fax:* 202-994-7915
E-mail: engldept@gwu.edu
Web Site: www.gwu.edu/~english; departments.columbian.gwu.edu/english/openings (position details)
Key Personnel
Dir, Creative Writing: Lisa Page *E-mail:* lpageinc@aol.com
Established: 1976
To be considered, applications must be made by letter indicating publications, teaching experience & a selection of published work. Genre alternates from year to year. Applications accepted between Oct 1 & Nov 1. Consult AWP job list for advertisement specifying genre.
Award: One year teaching position for approximately $58,000 plus benefits
Closing Date: Annually, Nov 1

Ottoline Morrell Prize
Fence Books
University at Albany, Science Library 320, 1400 Washington Ave, Albany, NY 12222
Tel: 518-591-8162
E-mail: fence.fencebooks@gmail.com
Web Site: www.fenceportal.org
Key Personnel
Publr & Ed: Rebecca Wolff *E-mail:* rebeccafence@gmail.com
Mng Ed: Jess Puglisi *E-mail:* jessp.fence@gmail.com
Established: 2013
For a book of poems by a woman writing in English who has previously published one or more books of poetry.
Award: Cash prize & publication

The William C Morris YA Debut Award
The American Library Association (ALA)
50 E Huron St, Chicago, IL 60611
Tel: 312-280-4390 *Toll Free Tel:* 800-545-2433 (ext 4390) *Fax:* 312-280-5276
E-mail: yalsa@ala.org
Web Site: www.ala.org/yalsa/morris
Established: 2009
Honors a debut book published by a first-time author writing for teens & celebrating impressive new voices in young adult literature. Books must have been published Nov 1-Oct 31 of the year preceding the award. Nominations by committee.
Presented: ALA Midwinter Youth Media Awards, Annually in Winter

William Morris Society in the United States Fellowships
William Morris Society in the United States
PO Box 53263, Washington, DC 20009
E-mail: us@morrissociety.org
Web Site: www.morrissociety.org
Key Personnel
Pres: Margaretta S Frederick
Secy & Treas: Mark Samuels Lasner
Established: 1996
For scholarly or creative projects related to William Morris (1834-96); given to US citizens or permanent residents.
Award: Up to $1,000
Closing Date: Annually, Dec 1

George L Mosse Prize
American Historical Association (AHA)
400 "A" St SE, Washington, DC 20003
Tel: 202-544-2422 *Fax:* 202-544-8307
E-mail: awards@historians.org
Web Site: www.historians.org
Established: 2001
For an outstanding major work of extraordinary scholarly distinction, creativity & originality in the intellectual & cultural history of Europe since the Renaissance. Only books of a high scholarly distinction should be submitted. Research accuracy, originality & literary merit are important selection factors. Books published in 2015 are eligible. Along with an application form, applicants must mail a copy of their book to each of the prize committee members who will be posted on our web site as the prize deadline approaches. All updated info on web site.
Award: Cash prize
Closing Date: May 15, 2016 (postmark)
Presented: AHA Annual Meeting, Denver, CO, Jan 5-8, 2017

Most Significant Scholarly Book Award
Texas Institute of Letters (TIL)
c/o 7748 Hwy 290 W, Austin, TX 78736-3202
Tel: 512-683-5640
E-mail: president@texasinstituteofletters.org
Web Site: www.texasinstituteofletters.org
Key Personnel
Pres: Andres Tijerina
VP: Steve Davis
Treas: James Hoggard
Secy: Darwin Payne
Recording Secy: Betty Wiesepape
Annual award for the most useful & informative scholarly book contributing to general knowledge, by a Texan or about Texas. See web site for guidelines.
Other Sponsor(s): Friends of the Dallas Public Library
Award: $2,500
Closing Date: Annually in Jan
Presented: TIL Awards Banquet, Annually in Spring

Frank Luther Mott-Kappa Tau Alpha Research Award
Kappa Tau Alpha
University of Missouri, School of Journalism, 76 Gannett Hall, Columbia, MO 65211-1200
Tel: 573-882-7685 *Fax:* 573-884-1720
E-mail: umcjourkta@missouri.edu
Web Site: www.kappataualpha.org
Key Personnel
Exec Dir: Keith P Sanders, PhD
Established: 1944
For the best research for books in journalism & mass communication, exclusive of textbooks, published in the previous year.
Award: $1,000 & plaque (1st prize)
Closing Date: Dec (see web site)
Presented: Annually in Aug

Sheila Margaret Motton Prize
New England Poetry Club
2 Farrar St, Cambridge, MA 02138
Mailing Address: 376 School St, Watertown, MA 02472
Tel: 617-744-6034
E-mail: contests@nepoetryclub.org
Web Site: www.nepoetryclub.org
Key Personnel
Pres: Diana Der-Hovanessian
VP: Sally Cragin; Daniel Tobin
Contest Chair: Nazaleem Smith
Prize presented annually for a book of poems published in the last 2 years. Send 2 copies of the book with $5 handling fee for nonmembs. Winner announced online in Sept/Oct.
Award: $500
Closing Date: May 31
Presented: Public Library, Cambridge, MA, Autumn

MPA Midwest Publishing Award Show
Midwest Publishing Association (MPA)
275 N York St, Suite 401, Elmhurst, IL 60126
Tel: 630-833-4220 *Fax:* 630-563-9181
E-mail: info@midwestpublish.org
Web Site: www.midwestpublish.org
Key Personnel
Pres: Del Bishop *E-mail:* bishopgroup@comcast.net
Established: 1949
Juried Show; 100 plus books, journals, magazines & ebooks selected each year. The goal is to demonstrate the outstanding quality of publishing in the midwest & recognize the importance of books or book design & multimedia in our society.
Award: Certificates of Award, photo & listing in show catalog & plaques
Closing Date: Varies
Presented: Downtown Chicago, 2nd Thursday in Oct

Erika Mumford Prize
New England Poetry Club
2 Farrar St, Cambridge, MA 02138
Mailing Address: 376 School St, Watertown, MA 02472
Tel: 617-744-6034
E-mail: contests@nepoetryclub.org
Web Site: www.nepoetryclub.org
Key Personnel
Pres: Diana Der-Hovanessian

VP: Sally Cragin; Daniel Tobin
Contest Chair: Nazaleem Smith
Established: 1988
Annual contest for a poem about foreign culture or travel. Mark name of contest on envelope. Send poem in duplicate, name of writer on one only. Winners announced online Sept/Oct.
Award: $250
Closing Date: May 31
Presented: Public Library, Cambridge, MA, Autumn

Mythopoeic Awards
Mythopoeic Society
Oklahoma State University, 306 Edmon Low Library, Stillwater, OK 74078
Tel: 405-744-9773
E-mail: awards@mythsoc.org
Web Site: www.mythsoc.org
Key Personnel
Awards Administrator: David Oberhelman
Established: 1967
Awards (two) honor scholarship in the Inklings (JRR Tolkien, CS Lewis, Charles Williams) & the general fields of myth & fantasy studies; each is given to the author of a book published in the previous three years. The Fantasy Awards (two) for adult & children's literature honor novels or single-author collections in the spirit of the Inklings; each is given to the author of a book published the previous year.
Award: Statuette
Closing Date: Members make nominations Jan-Feb, winners picked by late July
Presented: Mythcon 43, University of Berkeley, Berkeley, CA, Annually in Aug

National Award for Arts Writing, see Marfield Prize

National Awards for Education Reporting
Education Writers Association (EWA)
3516 Connecticut Ave NW, Washington, DC 20008-2401
Tel: 202-452-9830 *Fax:* 202-452-9837
E-mail: ewa@ewa.org
Web Site: www.ewa.org
Key Personnel
Exec Dir: Caroline W Hendrie *E-mail:* chendrie@ewa.org
Multimedia Mgr: Glen Baity *E-mail:* gbaity@ewa.org
Established: 1960
Best education reporting in print & broadcast media.
Award: Grand prize, 1st prize, 2nd prize, special citation, in 19 categories; plaques & certificates
Closing Date: Annually in Jan
Presented: EWA National Seminar, Annually in Spring

National Book Awards
National Book Foundation
90 Broad St, Suite 604, New York, NY 10004
Tel: 212-685-0261 *Fax:* 212-213-6570
E-mail: nationalbook@nationalbook.org
Web Site: www.nationalbook.org
Key Personnel
Exec Dir: Harold Augerbraun
Asst Dir: Leslie Shipman
Dir, Mktg & Spec Projs: Sherrie Young
Dir, Technol: Meredith Andrews
Mktg Media Mgr: Katie McDonough
Prog Mgr: Rebecca Keith
Established: 1950
Living American authors for books in USA, for fiction, nonfiction, poetry; young people's literature.
Award: $10,000 cash & bronze sculpture for winner in each genre
Closing Date: Annually in June
Presented: New York City, NY, Annually in Nov

The National Business Book Award
PwC
c/o Freedman & Associates Inc, 121 Richmond St W, Suite 605, Toronto, ON M5H 2K1, Canada
Tel: 416-868-4739
Web Site: www.nbbaward.com
Established: 1985
Excellence in business writing.
Other Sponsor(s): BMO Financial Group; Globe & Mail
Award: $20,000
Closing Date: Annually in Dec
Presented: Spring/early Summer

National Endowment for the Humanities, Mellon Foundation & Folger Long-term Fellowships
Folger Shakespeare Library
c/o Fellowship Committee, 201 E Capitol St SE, Washington, DC 20003
Tel: 202-544-4600 *Fax:* 202-544-4623
E-mail: institute@folger.edu
Web Site: www.folger.edu
Key Personnel
Dir: Dr Michael Witmore *Tel:* 202-675-0301 *E-mail:* mwitmore@folger.edu
Fellowship Admin: Carol Brobeck *E-mail:* cbrobeck@folger.edu
Residential fellowships awarded to advanced scholars who have made substantial contributions in their fields of research & who are pursuing research projects appropriate to the collections of the Folger. Application form supported by 4 copies (short-term fellowship) or 8 copies (long-term fellowship) of the applicant's curriculum vitae, 4 copies (short-term fellowship) or 8 copies (long-term fellowship) of a 1,000-word description of the research project & 3 letters of recommendation.
Other Sponsor(s): National Endowment for the Humanities
Award: $2,500 per month (short-term fellowship), Mellon Foundations fellowships $50,000 for 9 months, prorated for fewer than 9 months. Stipend for NEH fellowships are $50,400
Closing Date: Nov 1, long-term fellowship; March 1, short-term fellowship

National Federation of State Poetry Societies Annual Poetry Contest
National Federation of State Poetry Societies (NFSPS)
1375 Green Meadows Way, Ashland, OR 97520
E-mail: contestchair@nfsps.com
Web Site: www.nfsps.com
Key Personnel
Pres: Eleanor Berry *E-mail:* eberry@wvi.com
Contest Chair: Charlotte Abernathy
Established: 1959
Fifty poetry contests, one for students only; rules & categories change, must have current rules provided on web site.
Other Sponsor(s): Individual states' poetry society as host society
Award: $10-$1,500
Closing Date: Annually March 15 (must not be postmarked before Jan 1)

National Jewish Book Award-Children's & Young Adult Literature
Jewish Book Council
520 Eighth Ave, 4th fl, New York, NY 10018
Tel: 212-201-2920 *Fax:* 212-532-4952
E-mail: jbc@jewishbooks.org
Web Site: www.jewishbookcouncil.org
Key Personnel
Dir: Naomi Firestone-Teeter
Award: Citation & publicity
Closing Date: Annually in Sept
Presented: Center for Jewish History, Annually in March

National Jewish Book Award-Contemporary Jewish Life & Practice
Jewish Book Council
520 Eighth Ave, 4th fl, New York, NY 10018
Tel: 212-201-2920 *Fax:* 212-532-4952
E-mail: jbc@jewishbooks.org
Web Site: www.jewishbookcouncil.org
Key Personnel
Dir: Naomi Firestone-Teeter
Award: Citation & publicity
Closing Date: Annually in Sept
Presented: Center for Jewish History, Annually in March

National Jewish Book Award-History
Jewish Book Council
520 Eighth Ave, 4th fl, New York, NY 10018
Tel: 212-201-2920 *Fax:* 212-532-4952
E-mail: jbc@jewishbooks.org
Web Site: www.jewishbookcouncil.org
Key Personnel
Dir: Naomi Firestone-Teeter
Award: Citation & publicity
Closing Date: Annually in Sept
Presented: Center for Jewish History, Annually in March

National Jewish Book Award-Illustrated Children's Book
Jewish Book Council
520 Eighth Ave, 4th fl, New York, NY 10018
Tel: 212-201-2920 *Fax:* 212-532-4952
E-mail: jbc@jewishbooks.org
Web Site: www.jewishbookcouncil.org
Key Personnel
Dir: Naomi Firestone-Teeter
Award: Citation & publicity
Closing Date: Annually in Sept
Presented: Center for Jewish History, Annually in March

National Jewish Book Award-Modern Jewish Thought & Experience
Jewish Book Council
520 Eighth Ave, 4th fl, New York, NY 10018
Tel: 212-201-2920 *Fax:* 212-532-4952
E-mail: jbc@jewishbooks.org
Web Site: www.jewishbookcouncil.org
Key Personnel
Dir: Naomi Firestone-Teeter
Established: 1950
Award: Citation & publicity
Closing Date: Annually in Sept
Presented: Center for Jewish History, Annually in March

National Jewish Book Award-Scholarship
Jewish Book Council
520 Eighth Ave, 4th fl, New York, NY 10018
Tel: 212-201-2920 *Fax:* 212-532-4952
E-mail: jbc@jewishbooks.org
Web Site: www.jewishbookcouncil.org
Key Personnel
Dir: Naomi Firestone-Teeter
Established: 1950
Closing Date: Annually in Sept
Presented: Center for Jewish History, Annually in March

National Jewish Book Awards
Jewish Book Council
520 Eighth Ave, 4th fl, New York, NY 10018
Tel: 212-201-2920 *Fax:* 212-532-4952
E-mail: jbc@jewishbooks.org
Web Site: www.jewishbookcouncil.org
Key Personnel
Dir: Naomi Firestone-Teeter
Established: 1950
Twenty awards to authors & translators of books of outstanding scholarship & literary merit on Jewish themes for the general, no specialist

reader. Writing based on archival material, visual arts, poetry, Jewish family via illustrated children's. Categories: Autobiography, Memoire, Children's Literature, Holocaust, Jewish History, (Gerrard & Ella Berman Award), Jewish Thought (Dorot Foundation Donor), Scholarship, Sephardic Culture (Mimi Frank Award), Jewish Education (Anonymous Donor), General Nonfiction, Fiction & Children's Awards, Eastern European Studies (Ronald Lauder Award), Children's & Young Adult's Books, American Jewish Studies, Women's Studies (Barbara Dobkin Award).
Award: Citation & publicity
Closing Date: Annually in Sept
Presented: Center for Jewish History, Annually in March

National Magazine Awards
National Magazine Awards Foundation
2300 Yonge St, Suite 1600, Toronto, ON M4P 1E4, Canada
Tel: 416-939-6200
E-mail: staff@magazine-awards.com
Web Site: www.magazine-awards.com; https://twitter.com/magawards
Key Personnel
Mng Dir: Barbara Gould *E-mail:* staff@magazine-awards.com
Established: 1977
Annual award honoring excellence in Canadian magazine journalism with awards in 45 categories.
Award: $1000 Gold Award (1st place), $500 Silver Award (2nd place) in each category
Closing Date: Mid-Jan
Presented: Early June

National One-Act Playwriting Competition
Little Theatre of Alexandria
600 Wolfe St, Alexandria, VA 22314
Tel: 703-683-5778 *Fax:* 703-683-1378
E-mail: asklta@thelittletheatre.com
Web Site: www.thelittletheatre.com
Key Personnel
Chmn, One-Act: Nancy L Owens *Tel:* 703-313-0614 *E-mail:* nancy.owens@gsa.gov
Established: 1978
One-Act Playwriting Competition. No more than two plays. Entries must be unpublished & unproduced as of date of entry. Entry fee: $20 per play.
Award: $350 (1st prize), $250 (2nd prize), $150 (3rd prize), usually stage readings of top plays
Closing Date: Annually, Oct 31

National Outdoor Book Awards
National Outdoor Book Awards Foundation Inc
921 S Eighth Ave, Stop 8128, Pocatello, ID 83209-8128
Tel: 208-282-3912 *Fax:* 208-282-2127
Web Site: www.noba-web.org
Key Personnel
Chair: Ron Watters *E-mail:* wattron@isu.edu
Established: 1995
Award recognizing the work of outstanding writers & publishers of outdoor books. Categories include history/biography, outdoor literature, instructional texts, outdoor adventure guides, nature guides, children's books, design/artistic merit & nature & environment. Guidelines on the web site.
Other Sponsor(s): Association of Outdoor Recreation & Education; National Outdoor Book Awards Foundation
Closing Date: Annually in Aug
Presented: International Conference on Outdoor Recreation & Education (depending on the year, held in different locations in the US & CN), Annually in early Nov

National Poetry Series Open Competition
National Poetry Series
57 Mountain Ave, Princeton, NJ 08540
Tel: 609-430-0999 *Fax:* 609-430-9933
Web Site: www.pw.org/content/open_competition
Key Personnel
Coord: Stephanie Stio
Established: 1978
For book-length typed ms of poetry, previously unpublished in book form; $30 entrance fee, payable to National Poetry Series; see web site for guidelines.
Award: Five books to be published by trade publishers, small presses & university publishers. $10,000 cash award for each winner
Closing Date: Annually, Jan 1-Feb 15 (postmark)
Presented: Annually in the Summer

National Ten-Minute Play Contest
Actors Theatre of Louisville
316 W Main St, Louisville, KY 40202-4218
Tel: 502-584-1265
Web Site: actorstheatre.org/national-ten-minute-play-contest/
Key Personnel
Literary Mgr: Sarah Lunnie
National ten-minute play contest. Submssion date begins Sept 1. Accept the first 500 plays submitted.
Award: $1,000 & possible production at Actors Theatre of Louisville
Closing Date: Annually, Nov 1

National Translation Award
American Literary Translators Association (ALTA)
900 E Seventh St, PMB 266, Bloomington, IN 47405-3201
Web Site: www.literarytranslators.org
Key Personnel
Pres: Russell Valentino *E-mail:* russell.v@indiana.edu
Established: 1991
Publishers are invited to nominate one book in each category of contemporary fiction, contemporary poetry, contemporary nonfiction & literature of the past. Must be a full-length book or anthology translated from another language into English & must have been published in the previous year. Send four copies of each book; $25 per entry.
Other Sponsor(s): University of Texas at Dallas
Award: $5,000
Closing Date: Annually, March 31
Presented: ALTA Conference, Philadelphia, PA, Annually in Nov

National Writers Association Novel Contest
National Writers Association
10940 S Parker Rd, Suite 508, Parker, CO 80134
Tel: 303-841-0246
E-mail: natlwritersassn@hotmail.com
Web Site: www.nationalwriters.com
Key Personnel
Exec Dir & Ed: Sandy Whelchel
E-mail: authorsandy@hotmail.com
Established: 1937
Novel contest for unpublished works. Entry fee $35.
Award: $500 (1st prize), $250 (2nd prize), $150 (3rd prize)
Closing Date: Annually, April 1

Nautilus Awards
Marilyn McGuire & Associates Inc
378 Bromley Dr, Eastsound, WA 98245
Mailing Address: PO Box 1359, Eastsound, WA 98245
Tel: 360-376-2001
Web Site: www.nautilusbookawards.com
Key Personnel
Founder, Owner & Pres: Marilyn McGuire
E-mail: marilyn@nautilusbookawards.com
Established: 2001
To recognize authors & titles that make a distinguished literary contribution to spiritual growth, conscious living & positive social change.
Mail book entries to PO Box 1359, Eastsound, WA 98245.
Closing Date: Jan 31

Phyllis Naylor Working Writer Fellowship, see PEN/Phyllis Naylor Working Writer Fellowship

NEA Literature Fellowships
National Endowment for the Arts
400 Seventh St SW, Washington, DC 20506-0001
Tel: 202-682-5400; 202-682-5496 (Voice/TTY); 202-682-5034 (lit fellowships hotline)
Fax: 202-682-5609; 202-682-5610
E-mail: litfellowships@arts.gov
Web Site: www.arts.gov; www.nea.gov
Key Personnel
Grants Dir & Contracts Offr: Nicki Jacobs
Tel: 202-682-5546 *E-mail:* jacobsn@arts.gov
Established: 1967
Given to published writers of poetry, fiction & creative nonfiction; variable number of fellowships, based on available program funds. Applications accepted by genre (prose-odd years & poetry-even years). Applicants are restricted to applying in one fellowship category only in the same year. Must submit 9 copies as part of the application package. Guidelines available on web site.
Award: $25,000
Closing Date: Annually, March 1
Presented: Notifications to be sent by mail late Dec

Nelligan Prize for Short Fiction
Colorado Review
Unit of Colorado State University
Colorado State Univ, Dept of English, Ctr for Literary Publg, 9105 Campus Delivery, Fort Collins, CO 80523-9105
Tel: 970-491-5449
E-mail: creview@colostate.edu
Web Site: nelliganprize.colostate.edu
Key Personnel
Dir: Stephanie G'Schwind
Established: 2004
Awarded annually to the author of an outstanding short story, previously unpublished. Entry fee $15 per story with no limit on number of entries. Stories must be at least 10, but under 50 pages. Online entry fee $17.
Award: $2,000 & publication in Fall/Winter issue of *Colorado Review*
Closing Date: Annually, March 10

Howard Nemerov Sonnet Award
The Formalist
21 Osborne Terr, Wayne, NJ 07470
Web Site: theformalist.evansville.edu/home.htm
Key Personnel
Dir: William Baer
Annual award given for the best unpublished sonnet (no translations).
Award: $1,000 & publication in *Measure: A Review of Formal Poetry*
Closing Date: Annually, Nov 15

The Pablo Neruda Prize for Poetry
Nimrod, The University of Tulsa
Subsidiary of The Nimrod Literary Awards
Nimrod International Journal, 800 S Tucker Dr, Tulsa, OK 74104
Tel: 918-631-3080 *Fax:* 918-631-3033
E-mail: nimrod@utulsa.edu
Web Site: www.utulsa.edu/nimrod

Key Personnel
Ed: Eilis O'Neal
Assoc Ed: Diane Burton
Established: 1978
No previously published works. Omit author's name on mss. Must have a US address by Oct to enter. Works must be in English or translated by the original author. Include a cover sheet containing major title & subtitles of the work, author's name, address & phone along with 3-10 pages of poetry: 1 long poem or several short poems. Mss will not be returned. Retain the rights to publish any contest submission. Works not accepted will be released. Winners & selected finalists will be published. Include SASE & a check for $20 (includes a one-year subscription & processing).
Award: $2,000 (1st prize), $1,000 (2nd prize); published writers receive two copies of the journal; winners will be flown to Tulsa for a conference & banquet
Closing Date: Annually April 30
Presented: Univ of Tulsa, Annually in Oct

Neustadt International Prize for Literature
World Literature Today
Affiliate of University of Oklahoma
c/o University of Oklahoma, 630 Parrington Oval, Suite 110, Norman, OK 73019-4033
Tel: 405-325-4531 *Fax:* 405-325-7495
Web Site: www.worldliteraturetoday.org
Key Personnel
Exec Dir: Robert Con Davis-Undiano *E-mail:* rcdavis@ou.edu
Asst Dir & Ed-in-Chief: Daniel Simon *E-mail:* dsimon@ou.edu
Art Dir: Merleyn Bell *E-mail:* merleyn@ou.edu
Mng Ed: Michelle Johnson *E-mail:* lmjohnson@ou.edu
Book Reviews Ed: Marla Johnson *E-mail:* mfjohnson@ou.edu
Mktg Dir, Progs & Devt: Terri Stubblefield *E-mail:* tdstubb@ou.edu
Circ & Accts Specialist: Kay Blunck *E-mail:* kblunck@ou.edu
Established: 1969
To a living writer for outstanding literary achievement; prize may honor a single major work or an entire oeuvre; writer's work must be available in a representative sample in English, Spanish or French; writer must accept the award in person in ceremonies at the University of Oklahoma; a special issue of *World Literature Today* is devoted to the laureate; Candidates must be nominated by a jury member.
Award: $50,000 & an eagle feather cast in silver
Presented: University of Oklahoma, Biennially (even-numbered years)

Allan Nevins Prize
Society of American Historians (SAH)
Affiliate of American Historical Association
603 Fayerweather, MC 2538, New York, NY 10027
Tel: 212-854-6495
E-mail: amhistsociety@columbia.edu
Web Site: sah.columbia.edu
Key Personnel
Pres: David W Blight
VP: David Nasaw
Exec Secy: Andie Tucher
Established: 1961
For the best written doctoral dissertation on an American subject. The dissertation must have been defended or the PhD degree received in the calendar year preceding the award presentation & must not have already been submitted for publication.
Award: $2,000, a certificate & publication by an award sponsoring publication house
Closing Date: Annually, Jan 31
Presented: New York, NY, Annually in May

New England Book Awards
New England Independent Booksellers Association Inc (NEIBA)
1955 Massachusetts Ave, Cambridge, MA 02140
Tel: 617-547-3642 *Fax:* 617-547-3759
Web Site: www.newenglandbooks.org/bookawards
Key Personnel
Exec Dir: Steven Fischer *E-mail:* steve@neba.org
Admin Coord: Nan Sorensen *E-mail:* nan@neba.org
Established: 1990
Annual awards for fiction, nonfiction, children's & publishing are chosen by booksellers. Fiction, nonfiction & children's awards are awarded to specific titles either about New England, set in New England or by an author residing in New England, published between Sept 1 & Aug 31.
Award: $250 donation to charity or literary group chosen by each author
Closing Date: Annually in July
Presented: Fall trade show & conference, Annually in Sept/Oct

New Hampshire Literary Awards
New Hampshire Writers' Project
2500 N River Rd, Manchester, NH 03106
Tel: 603-314-7980 *Fax:* 603-314-7981
E-mail: info@nhwritersproject.org
Web Site: www.nhwritersproject.org
Key Personnel
Pres: John Herman
Prog Dir: Carla Gericke *E-mail:* nhwp.carla@gmail.com
Off Mgr: Nicole Escobar
Pubns Asst: Dawn Coutu *E-mail:* dcoutu@nhwritersproject.com
Established: 1992
Biennial award. Nominees must live in New Hampshire, be a native or deal with subject matter that is deemed by judges to be inherently connected with New Hampshire.
Closing Date: June 15
Presented: Nov

New Issues Poetry Prize
New Issues Poetry & Prose
c/o Western Michigan University, 1903 W Michigan Ave, Kalamazoo, MI 49008-5463
Tel: 269-387-8185 *Fax:* 269-387-2562
E-mail: new-issues@wmich.edu
Web Site: www.wmich.edu/newissues
Key Personnel
Mng Ed: Kimberly Kolbe
Poets writing in English who have not previously published a full-length collection of poems. Submit ms minimum 40 pages, typed on one side, single-spaced; do not bind ms. Include brief bio & relevant publication information; cover page with name, address, phone & title of ms; include table of contents. A $20 reading fee for each ms; enclose SASE.
Other Sponsor(s): Western Michigan University
Award: $2,000 & book publication
Closing Date: Nov 30

New Jersey Council for the Humanities Book Award
New Jersey Council for the Humanities
28 W State St, 6th fl, Trenton, NJ 08608
Tel: 609-695-4838 *Toll Free Tel:* 888-FYI-NJCH (394-6524) *Fax:* 609-695-4929
E-mail: njch@njch.org
Web Site: www.njch.org
Key Personnel
Exec Dir: Sharon Ann Holt *E-mail:* director@njch.org
Assoc Dir: Mary Rizzo *E-mail:* mrizzo@njch.org
Prog Offr: Robert Apgar *E-mail:* rapgar@njch.org
Established: 1988
Honors a nonfiction humanities book that balances scholarship with general public appeal. The book establishes a connection to NJ either through its subject or the author's birth, residence, or occupation. Nominations must be submitted by the publisher accompanied by six reading copies & a nomination form, which is available from the NJCH.
Award: $1,000 (Author); A gold seal imprinted with the award logo is available
Closing Date: See web site
Presented: Humanities Festival Week, Annual Awards Event, Oct

New Letters Literary Awards
New Letters
UMKC, University House, 5101 Rockhill Rd, Kansas City, MO 64110-2499
Tel: 816-235-1169 *Fax:* 816-235-2611
E-mail: newletters@umkc.edu
Web Site: www.newletters.org
Established: 1986
Annual literary contest.
Award: $1,500 & publication for each category - fiction, poetry & essay (1st prize). All entries considered for publication
Closing Date: Annually, May 18

New Letters Prize for Poetry
New Letters
UMKC, University House, 5101 Rockhill Rd, Kansas City, MO 64110-2499
Tel: 816-235-1169 *Fax:* 816-235-2611
E-mail: newletters@umkc.edu
Web Site: www.newletters.org
Established: 1986
Annual literary contest. All entries considered for publication.
Award: $1,500 & publication
Closing Date: Annually, May 18

New Millennium Awards for Fiction, Poetry & Nonfiction
New Millennium Writings
4021 Garden Dr, Knoxville, TN 37918
Tel: 865-254-4880
Web Site: www.newmillenniumwritings.com
Key Personnel
Publr & Ed: Alexis Williams Carr *E-mail:* alexis.williams@hotmail.com
Each fiction or nonfiction prize should total no more than 6,000 words (short-short fiction no more than 1,000 words). Each poetry entry may include up to 3 poems. A $17 reading fee is required for each entry. See web site for further information.
Award: $1,000 each for Poem, Fiction, Nonfiction & Short-Short Fiction plus publication
Closing Date: Annually in Jan

New Women's Voices Chapbook Competition
Finishing Line Press
PO Box 1626, Georgetown, KY 40324
Tel: 859-514-8966
E-mail: finishingbooks@aol.com; flpbookstore@aol.com
Web Site: www.finishinglinepress.com
Key Personnel
Publr: Leah Maines
Sr Ed: Christen Kincaid
Mng Ed: Kevin Murphy Maines
Established: 1998
Cash & publication of a chapbook of poems for women who have not yet published a full-length collection.
Award: $1,000 & publication
Closing Date: Annually, Feb 15

New York City Book Awards
The New York Society Library
53 E 79 St, New York, NY 10075
Tel: 212-288-6900 *Fax:* 212-744-5832
E-mail: events@nysoclib.org

Web Site: www.nysoclib.org
Key Personnel
Events Coord: Sara Holliday *Tel:* 212-288-6900 ext 222
Established: 1996
Given annually to the authors of the best books about New York City. Must submit copy of nominated book the same year of publication. $20 per book fee. Make check out to The New York Society Library.
Award: Plaque & varied monetary amount
Closing Date: Annually in Dec
Presented: The New York Society Library, Early May

The New York Public Library Helen Bernstein Book Award for Excellence in Journalism
The New York Public Library
Stephen A Schwarzman Bldg, Fifth Ave at 42 St, South Court Bldg, 3rd fl, New York, NY 10018-2788
Tel: 212-930-0876
Web Site: www.nypl.org
Key Personnel
Helen Bernstein Libn, Periodicals: Karen Gisonny *E-mail:* kgisonny@nypl.org
Established: 1988
Requires overall journalistic excellence & a published book that stems from the author's reportage & exemplifies outstanding work. Note: nominations are for books published during the calendar year & are solicited only from publishers & editors-in-chief of major newspapers, news magazines & book publishers nationwide.
Award: $15,000
Closing Date: Oct 1 for books published in calendar year
Presented: The New York Public Library, Annually in April/May

New York State Edith Wharton Citation of Merit for Fiction Writers
New York State Writers Institute
Subsidiary of University at Albany
University at Albany, SL 320, Albany, NY 12222
Tel: 518-442-5620 *Fax:* 518-442-5621
E-mail: writers@uamail.albany.edu
Web Site: www.albany.edu/writers-inst
Key Personnel
Exec Dir: William Kennedy
Dir: Donald Faulkner
Established: 1985
State author designation for a New York state fiction writer. Applications not accepted. Nominations by advisory panel only.
Award: $10,000
Presented: Albany, NY, Biennially

New York State Walt Whitman Citation of Merit for Poets
New York State Writers Institute
Subsidiary of University at Albany
University at Albany, SL 320, Albany, NY 12222
Tel: 518-442-5620 *Fax:* 518-442-5621
E-mail: writers@uamail.albany.edu
Web Site: www.albany.edu/writers-inst
Key Personnel
Exec Dir: William Kennedy
Dir: Donald Faulkner
Asst Dir: Suzanne Lance *Tel:* 518-442-5624 *E-mail:* slance@uamail.albany.edu
Established: 1985
State author designation for New York state poet. Applications not accepted. Nominations by advisory panel only.
Award: $10,000
Presented: Albany, NY, Biennially

John Newbery Medal
Association for Library Service to Children (ALSC)
Division of The American Library Association (ALA)
50 E Huron St, Chicago, IL 60611-2795
Tel: 312-280-2163 *Toll Free Tel:* 800-545-2433 *Fax:* 312-440-9374
E-mail: alsc@ala.org
Web Site: www.ala.org/alsc
Key Personnel
Exec Dir: Aimee Strittmatter *Tel:* 312-280-2162 *E-mail:* astrittmatter@ala.org
Awards Coord: Caroline Jewell *E-mail:* alscawards@ala.org
Prog Coord: Marsha P Burgess *E-mail:* mburgess@ala.org
Established: 1922
Awarded annually to the author of the most distinguished writing in a children's book published during the preceding year. Restricted to authors who are citizens or residents of the US.
Award: Medal
Closing Date: Annually, Dec 31
Presented: ALA Annual Conference, Annually in June

Newfoundland and Labrador Book Awards
Writers' Alliance of Newfoundland and Labrador (WANL)/Literary Arts Foundation of Newfoundland and Labrador
Haymarket Sq, 208-223 Duckworth St, St John's, NL A1C 6N1, Canada
Tel: 709-739-5215
E-mail: wanl@nf.aibn.com
Web Site: wanl.ca
Key Personnel
Exec Dir: Alison Dyer
Exec Asst: Sheri Coombs *E-mail:* wanlassist@nf.aibn.com
Established: 1997
Honor excellence in Newfoundland & Labrador writing in 4 categories: fiction, nonfiction, poetry & children's/young adult literature.
Other Sponsor(s): The Bruneau Family (children's/young adult literature); Downhome Inc (fiction); Historic Sites Association (Heritage & History Book Award); Le Grow's Travel (poetry); Rogers Cable (nonfiction)
Award: $1,500 (1st prize), $500 (2 runners-up)
Closing Date: Jan
Presented: May

Don & Gee Nicholl Fellowships in Screenwriting
Academy of Motion Picture Arts & Sciences (AMPAS)
1313 Vine St, Hollywood, CA 90028
Tel: 310-247-3010 *Fax:* 310-247-3794
E-mail: nicholl@oscars.org
Web Site: www.oscars.org/nicholl
Key Personnel
Dir: Greg Beal
Established: 1986
Screenwriting; for information visit web site.
Award: Up to five awards of $35,000 each
Closing Date: Annually, May 1
Presented: Beverly Hills, CA, Annually in Nov

John Frederick Nims Memorial Prize
Poetry Magazine
444 N Michigan Ave, Suite 1850, Chicago, IL 60611-4034
Tel: 312-787-7070 *Fax:* 312-787-6650
E-mail: editors@poetrymagazine.org
Web Site: www.poetryfoundation.org
Key Personnel
Mng Ed: Valerie Johnson *E-mail:* vjohnson@poetrymagazine.org
Established: 1999
For poetry published in the preceding 2 volumes of Poetry Magazine. No application necessary.
Award: $500
Presented: Annually in Dec

North Carolina Arts Council Writers Fellowships
North Carolina Arts Council
Division of North Carolina State Government
109 E Jones St, Raleigh, NC 27601
Mailing Address: Dept of Cultural Resources, Mail Service Ctr 4632, Raleigh, NC 27699-4632
Tel: 919-807-6500 *Fax:* 919-807-6532
E-mail: ncarts@ncdcr.gov
Web Site: www.ncarts.org
Key Personnel
Exec Dir: Wayne Martin *Tel:* 919-807-6525 *E-mail:* wayne.martin@ncdcr.gov
Prog Dir, Lit: David Potorti *Tel:* 919-807-6512 *E-mail:* david.potorti@ncdcr.gov
Established: 1980
Fellowships are given every 2 years to poets & writers of fiction, literary nonfiction, literary translation playwrights & screenwriters. Writers who have lived in the state for at least 1 year as of application deadline & who intend to remain instate during the fellowship year are eligible.
Award: $10,000
Closing Date: Nov 1st of even-numbered years
Presented: Summer of odd-numbered years

Northern California Book Awards
Northern California Book Reviewers (NCBR)
c/o Poetry Flash, 1450 Fourth St, Suite 4, Berkeley, CA 94710
Tel: 510-525-5476 *Fax:* 510-525-6752
E-mail: editor@poetryflash.org
Web Site: www.poetryflash.org/ncba.html
Key Personnel
Chmn: Joyce Jenkins
Established: 1981
Awarded annually by category (fiction, poetry, nonfiction, children's literature & translation) for best book in category by a Northern California writer. Publishers Award given occasionally for special achievement by a Northern California publisher or a literary organization. Send 3 copies of book; no application or fee necessary.
Other Sponsor(s): The Center for the Art of Translation; Northern California Independent Booksellers Association; PEN West; Poetry Flash; San Francisco Public Library
Award: Cash & certificate
Closing Date: Dec 1
Presented: Koret Auditorium, San Francisco Main Public Library, April

Notable Wisconsin Authors
Wisconsin Library Association Inc
4610 S Biltmore Lane, Madison, WI 53718
Tel: 608-245-3640 *Fax:* 608-245-3646
Web Site: www.wla.lib.wi.us
Key Personnel
Exec Dir: Lisa K Strand *E-mail:* strand@scls.lib.wi.us
Memb Servs Coord: Brigitte Rupp Vacha *E-mail:* ruppvacha@scls.lib.wi.us
Established: 1973
Annual award Honoring Wisconsin authors, past & present, for their literary contributions.
Award: Printed brochure with biographical information on the notable author, including a list of authors' works
Presented: WLA Annual Conference, Annually Oct-Nov

Novella Prize
The Malahat Review
University of Victoria, Box 1700, Sta CSC, Victoria, BC V8W 2Y2, Canada
Tel: 250-721-8524 *Fax:* 250-472-5051
E-mail: malahat@uvic.ca
Web Site: www.malahatreview.ca

Key Personnel
Ed: John Barton
Established: 1995
Awarded every other year (even-numbered years) alternating with Long Poem Prize (odd-numbered years). See web site for details & entry fee.
Award: $1,500 CAD
Closing Date: Feb 1, even-numbered years

NSK Neustadt Prize for Children's Literature
World Literature Today
c/o University of Oklahoma, 630 Parrington Oval, Suite 110, Norman, OK 73019-4033
Tel: 405-325-4531 *Fax:* 405-325-7495
Web Site: www.worldliteraturetoday.org
Key Personnel
Exec Dir: Robert Con Davis-Undiano *E-mail:* rcdavis@ou.edu
Asst Dir & Ed-in-Chief: Daniel Simon *E-mail:* dsimon@ou.edu
Art Dir: Merleyn Bell *E-mail:* merleyn@ou.edu
Mng Ed: Michelle Johnson *E-mail:* lmjohnson@ou.edu
Book Reviews Ed: Marla Johnson *E-mail:* mfjohnson@ou.edu
Mktg Dir, Progs & Devt: Terri Stubblefield *E-mail:* tdstubb@ou.edu
Circ & Accts Specialist: Kay Blunck *E-mail:* kblunck@ou.edu
Established: 2003
An award intended to enhance the quality of children's literature by promoting writing that contributes to the quality of their lives. Awarded to a living writer with significant achievement, either over a lifetime or in a particular publication. The essential criterion for awarding this prize is that the writer's work is having a positive impact on the quality of children's literature.
Other Sponsor(s): Nancy Barcelo; Kathy Neustadt; Susan Neustadt Schwartz; The University of Oklahoma
Award: $25,000, medal & certificate
Closing Date: No outside nominations accepted, nominations by jury member only
Presented: The University of Oklahoma, Norman, OK, Biennially in Oct (odd-numbered years)

Nuestras Voces National Playwriting Competition
MetLife Foundation
138 E 27 St, New York, NY 10016
Tel: 212-225-9950 *Fax:* 212-225-9085
Web Site: www.repertorio.org
Key Personnel
Spec Projs Mgr: Allison Astor Vargas *E-mail:* aav@repertorio.org
Established: 2000
Award: $3,000 & full production (winner), cash awards of $500-$3,000 (top 5), stage reading (top 10)
Closing Date: Annually in June

Eli M Oboler Memorial Award
Intellectual Freedom Round Table (IFRT)
Unit of The American Library Association (ALA)
50 E Huron St, Chicago, IL 60611
Tel: 312-280-4223 *Toll Free Tel:* 800-545-2433 *Fax:* 312-280-4227
E-mail: oif@ala.org
Web Site: www.ala.org/ifrt
Key Personnel
Prog Offr: Nanette Perez *Tel:* 312-280-4225 *E-mail:* nperez@ala.org
Admin Asst & Award Contact: Shumeca Pickett *Tel:* 312-280-4220 *E-mail:* spickett@ala.org
Established: 1986
Biennial award given to an author of a published work in English, or an English translation dealing with issues, events, questions or controversies in the area of intellectual freedom. Must have been published within previous 2 calendar years prior to the ALA annual conference at which it is granted.
Award: $500 & certificate
Closing Date: Dec 1 (odd-numbered years)
Presented: ALA Annual Conference, June (even-numbered years)

The Flannery O'Connor Award for Short Fiction
University of Georgia Press
Main Library, 3rd fl, 320 S Jackson St, Athens, GA 30602
Fax: 706-542-2558
Web Site: www.ugapress.org
Key Personnel
Series Ed: Nancy Zafris
Asst Acqs Ed: Beth Snead *Tel:* 706-542-7613 *E-mail:* bsnead@uga.edu
Established: 1981
Collections of original short fiction. Ms should be 40,000-75,000 words & should be accompanied by a $30 submission fee; ms will not be returned. Submissions accepted between April 1 & May 31. Open to both published & unpublished writers. Applicants should visit The Press web site for guidelines. No phone calls regarding the award will be accepted. Accepting electronic submissions at georgiapress.submishmash.com.
Award: $1,000 & publication by the University of Georgia Press under a standard publishing contract
Closing Date: Annually, May 31

Frank O'Connor Prize for Fiction
Texas Christian University
Texas Christian University, Dept of English, TCU Box 297270, Fort Worth, TX 76129
Tel: 817-257-5907 *Fax:* 817-257-7709
E-mail: descant@tcu.edu
Web Site: www.descant.tcu.edu
Key Personnel
Mng Ed: Dan Williams *E-mail:* d.e.williams@tcu.edu
Established: 1957
Best published fiction in each volume of descant. No entry fee. Winners announced in journal.
Other Sponsor(s): descant (publication), Dept of English, TCU
Award: $500
Closing Date: Annually, Sept 1-April 1
Presented: Annually in Summer

Scott O'Dell Award for Historical Fiction
c/o Horn Book Inc, 56 Roland St, Suite 200, Boston, MA 02129
Tel: 617-628-8471 *Toll Free Tel:* 800-325-1170
Web Site: www.scottodell.com/odellaward.html
Key Personnel
Chair & Ed-in-Chief: Roger Sutton
Judge: Deborah Stevenson
Libn: Ann Carlson
Established: 1982
Presented for a work of historical fiction published in the previous year for children or young adults, by a US publisher & set in the New World. Winner is selected by O'Dell Award Committee.
Award: $5,000
Closing Date: Annually, Dec 31

Dayne Ogilvie Prize
The Writers' Trust of Canada
460 Richmond St W, Suite 600, Toronto, ON M5V 1Y1, Canada
Tel: 416-504-8222 *Toll Free Tel:* 877-906-6548 *Fax:* 416-504-9090
E-mail: info@writerstrust.com
Web Site: www.writerstrust.com
Key Personnel
Exec Dir: Mary Osborne *Tel:* 416-504-8222 ext 244
Established: 2007
Awarded to an emerging LGBT writer.
Other Sponsor(s): Robin Pacific
Award: $4,000
Presented: Pride Week, Toronto, ON, CN, Annually, early Summer

Howard O'Hagan Award for Short Story
Writers' Guild of Alberta
11759 Groat Rd, Edmonton, AB T5M 3K6, Canada
Tel: 780-422-8174 *Toll Free Tel:* 800-665-5354 (AB only) *Fax:* 780-422-2663 (attn WGA)
E-mail: mail@writersguild.ab.ca
Web Site: www.writersguild.ab.ca
Key Personnel
Exec Dir: Carol Holmes *E-mail:* carol.holmes@writersguild.ab.ca
Communs & Partnerships Coord: Nicholas Mather *E-mail:* nicholas.mather@writersguild.ab.ca
Memb Servs Coord: Giorgia Severini
Progs Coord: Natalie Cook *E-mail:* natalie.cook@writersguild.ab.ca; Nichole Quiring *E-mail:* nichole.quiring@writersguild.ab.ca
Established: 1982
Alberta Literary Award for published short stories only, author must be resident of Alberta; no longer than 5,000 words.
Award: $700
Closing Date: Annually, Dec 31
Presented: Alberta Book Awards Gala
Branch Office(s)
505 21 Ave SW, Calgary, AB T2S 0G9, Canada, Prog Coord: Samantha Warwick *Tel:* 403-265-2226 *E-mail:* samantha.warwick@writersguild.ab.ca

Ohioana Award for Children's Literature-Alice Louise Wood Memorial
Ohioana Library Association
274 E First Ave, Suite 300, Columbus, OH 43201
Tel: 614-466-3831 *Fax:* 614-728-6974
E-mail: ohioana@ohioana.org
Web Site: www.ohioana.org
Key Personnel
Exec Dir, Ohioana Library Association: Linda R Hengst *E-mail:* lhengst@ohioana.org
Established: 1990
To an Ohio author of children's literature for a body of work or for a lifetime of contributions to children's literature. The award is given at the discretion of the Board of Trustees.
Award: $1,000
Closing Date: Annually, Dec 31
Presented: Ohioana Day Luncheon, Annually in Autumn

Ohioana Book Awards
Ohioana Library Association
274 E First Ave, Suite 300, Columbus, OH 43201
Tel: 614-466-3831 *Fax:* 614-728-6974
E-mail: ohioana@ohioana.org
Web Site: www.ohioana.org
Key Personnel
Exec Dir, Ohioana Library Association: Linda R Hengst *E-mail:* lhengst@ohioana.org
Established: 1942
For the best books by Ohio authors in various fields of writing or books about Ohio or Ohioans. Submit two copies of a nominated book on or before its publication date.
Award: Citations & medals
Closing Date: Dec 31
Presented: Ohioana Day Luncheon, Oct

Ohioana Career Award
Ohioana Library Association
274 E First Ave, Suite 300, Columbus, OH 43201

Tel: 614-466-3831 *Fax:* 614-728-6974
E-mail: ohioana@ohioana.org
Web Site: www.ohioana.org
Key Personnel
Exec Dir, Ohioana Library Association: Linda R Hengst *E-mail:* lhengst@ohioana.org
Established: 1942
Awarded each year to a native-born Ohioan who has had an outstanding career in the arts & humanities. The recipient is an honored guest at Ohioana Day & must be present to receive the award. The award is given at the discretion of the Board of Trustees.
Closing Date: Annually, Dec 31
Presented: Ohioana Day Luncheon, Annually in Autumn

Ohioana Citations
Ohioana Library Association
274 E First Ave, Suite 300, Columbus, OH 43201
Tel: 614-466-3831 *Fax:* 614-728-6974
E-mail: ohioana@ohioana.org
Web Site: www.ohioana.org
Key Personnel
Exec Dir, Ohioana Library Association: Linda R Hengst *E-mail:* lhengst@ohioana.org
Established: 1945
For outstanding contributions & accomplishments in a specific field or area of the arts & humanities. Four Ohioana Citations, generally given in four different fields, including the Ohioana Music Citation, may be given each year. The recipient must have been born in Ohio or lived in Ohio for a minimum of 5 years. Citations are given at the discretion of the Board of Trustees.
Closing Date: Annually, Dec 31
Presented: Ohioana Day Luncheon, Annually in Autumn

Ohioana Pegasus Award
Ohioana Library Association
274 E First Ave, Suite 300, Columbus, OH 43201
Tel: 614-466-3831 *Fax:* 614-728-6974
E-mail: ohioana@ohioana.org
Web Site: www.ohioana.org
Key Personnel
Exec Dir, Ohioana Library Association: Linda R Hengst *E-mail:* lhengst@ohioana.org
Established: 1964
Given to recognize unique or outstanding contributions or achievements in the arts & humanities. Given at the discretion of the trustees of the association. Must have been born in Ohio or resided in Ohio for a minimum of 5 years.
Closing Date: Dec 31
Presented: Ohioana Day Luncheon, Oct

Ohioana Poetry Award-Memorial to Helen & Laura Krout
Ohioana Library Association
274 E First Ave, Suite 300, Columbus, OH 43201
Tel: 614-466-3831 *Fax:* 614-728-6974
E-mail: ohioana@ohioana.org
Web Site: www.ohioana.org
Key Personnel
Exec Dir, Ohioana Library Association: Linda R Hengst *E-mail:* lhengst@ohioana.org
Established: 1984
Award to an Ohio poet for a body of published work that has made & continues to make a significant contribution to poetry & through whose work as a writer, teacher, administrator or in community service, interest in poetry has been developed. The award is given at the descretion of the Board of Trustees.
Award: $1,000
Closing Date: Annually, Dec 31
Presented: Ohioana Day Luncheon, Annually in Autumn

Ohioana Walter Rumsey Marvin Grant
Ohioana Library Association
274 E First Ave, Suite 300, Columbus, OH 43201
Tel: 614-466-3831 *Fax:* 614-728-6974
E-mail: ohioana@ohioana.org
Web Site: www.ohioana.org
Key Personnel
Exec Dir, Ohioana Library Association: Linda R Hengst *E-mail:* lhengst@ohioana.org
Established: 1982
Writing competition; awarded to young, (30 yrs of age or younger) unpublished Ohio authors who were born or have lived in Ohio 5 years or more.
Award: $1,000
Closing Date: Jan 31
Presented: Ohioana Day Luncheon, Oct

Chris O'Malley Fiction Prize
The Madison Review
University of Wisconsin, 6193 Helen C White Hall, English Dept, 600 N Park St, Madison, WI 53706
Tel: 608-263-0566
E-mail: madisonrevw@gmail.com
Web Site: www.english.wisc.edu/madisonreview
Key Personnel
Chmn Dept: Prof Thomas Schaub *E-mail:* thschaub@wisc.edu
Faculty Advisor & Prog Coord: Ronald Kuka *E-mail:* rfkuka@wisc.edu
Size limit 30 pg maximum. Only one submission is allowed per person per contest. Ms must be previously unpublished & should be double-spaced with stardard 1 inch margins & 12-pt font. Entry fee $10.
Award: $1,000 & publication in the fall issue of The Madison Review
Closing Date: Annually, Feb 1

Open Chapbook Competition
Finishing Line Press
PO Box 1626, Georgetown, KY 40324
Tel: 859-514-8966
E-mail: finishingbooks@aol.com; flpbookstore@aol.com
Web Site: www.finishinglinepress.com
Key Personnel
Publr: Leah Maines
Sr Ed: Christen Kincaid
Mng Ed: Kevin Murphy Maines
Established: 2002
Award for an unpublished chapbook of poems. Winner announced on web site & in *Poets & Writers Magazine*.
Award: $1,000 & publication
Closing Date: June 30

Open Season Awards
The Malahat Review
University of Victoria, Box 1700, Sta CSC, Victoria, BC V8W 2Y2, Canada
Tel: 250-721-8524 *Fax:* 250-472-5051
E-mail: malahat@uvic.ca
Web Site: malahatreview.ca
Key Personnel
Ed: John Barton
Established: 2009
Awards in 3 categories: poetry, short fiction & creative nonfiction. See web site for additional details.
Award: $1,500 CAD in each of three categories
Closing Date: Annually, Nov 1

Opie Prize
American Folklore Society/Children's Folklore Section
Ohio State Univ, Mershon Ctr, 1501 Neil Ave, Columbus, OH 43201-2602
Tel: 614-292-3375 *Fax:* 614-292-2407
Web Site: www.afsnet.org/aboutAFS/AFSprizes.cfm
Key Personnel
Exec Dir: Timothy Lloyd *E-mail:* lloyd.100@osu.edu
Section Convenor: Spencer Green
Annual award for the best book length treatment of children's folklore. Edited volumes, collections of folklore & authored studies published in English during previous 2 years are eligible. Authors or publishers should submit 2 copies of the book.
Award: $200
Closing Date: Varies
Presented: Oct

Oregon Book Awards
Literary Arts
925 SW Washington St, Portland, OR 97205
Tel: 503-227-2583 *Fax:* 503-241-4256
E-mail: la@literary-arts.org
Web Site: www.literary-arts.org
Key Personnel
Dir, Progs & Events: Susan Denning *Tel:* 503-227-2583 ext 107 *E-mail:* susan@literary-arts.org
Available for original work published or produced in the following categories: Poetry, Novel, General Nonfiction, Creative Nonfiction, Children's Literature, Young Adult Literature, Drama & Graphic Literature.
Presented: Jan

George Orwell Award
National Council of Teachers of English (NCTE)
1111 W Kenyon Rd, Urbana, IL 61801-1096
Tel: 217-328-3870 *Toll Free Tel:* 877-369-6283 (cust serv) *Fax:* 217-328-0977
E-mail: publiclangawards@ncte.org
Web Site: www.ncte.org
Key Personnel
Admin Liaison & Awards Contact: Linda Walters
Established: 1975
Recognizes individuals for distinguished contributions to honesty & clarity in public language.
Other Sponsor(s): NCTE Committee on Public Doublespeak
Award: Certificate
Closing Date: Annually, Sept 15
Presented: NCTE Annual Convention, Late Nov

Joyce Osterweil Award for Poetry, see PEN/Joyce Osterweil Award for Poetry

Frank L & Harriet C Owsley Award
Southern Historical Association
University of Georgia, Dept of History, Athens, GA 30602-1602
Tel: 706-542-8848 *Fax:* 706-542-2455
Web Site: sha.uga.edu
Key Personnel
Admin Asst: Shere Dendy *E-mail:* sdendy@uga.edu
Established: 1985
Awarded for most distinguished book in Southern history published in even-numbered years. Awarded in odd-numbered years.
Award: Cash
Closing Date: March 1
Presented: Annual meeting (odd-numbered years), Fall

Pacific Northwest Book Awards
Pacific Northwest Booksellers Association
338 W 11 Ave, Unit 108, Eugene, OR 97401
Tel: 541-683-4363 *Fax:* 541-683-3910
E-mail: info@pnba.org
Web Site: www.pnba.org
Key Personnel
Exec Dir: Thom Chambliss *E-mail:* thom@pnba.org
Mktg Dir: Brian Juenemann *E-mail:* brian@pnba.org
Established: 1965

Annual awards for authors who live in Washington, Oregon, Idaho, Alaska & Montana who have published exceptional books during the calendar year.
Award: Plaque & marketing to independent bookstores of the Pacific Northwest
Closing Date: Annually, Aug 30
Presented: Early Jan

Pacific Northwest Young Reader's Choice Award
Pacific Northwest Library Association (PNLA)
Vancouver Mall Community Library, 8700 NE Vancouver Mall Dr, Suite 285, Vancouver, WA 98662
Tel: 360-892-8256
Web Site: www.pnla.org/yrca
Key Personnel
Chair YRCA: Barbara Meisenheimer
E-mail: bmeisenheimer@fvrl.org
Established: 1940
Nominations taken only from children, teachers, parents & librarians of the Pacific Northwest (WA, OR, AK, ID, MT, BC & AB). Nominated titles were published 3 years previously in the US or CN. Only 4th to 12th graders in the Pacific Northwest vote on a selected list of titles. The categories are Junior grades 4-6, Intermediate grades 7-9 & senior grades 10-12. Awarded to the author of a book most popular with children. Send SASE for information or contact through e-mail address.
Award: Silver Medal
Closing Date: Annually, Feb 1
Presented: Pacific Northwest Library Association's Annual Conference, Annually in Aug

PAGE International Screenwriting Awards
Production Arts Group
7510 Sunset Blvd, Suite 610, Hollywood, CA 90046
E-mail: info@pageawards.com
Web Site: www.pageawards.com
Key Personnel
Admin Dir: Jennifer Berg
Contest Coord: Zoe Simmons
Established: 2003
Each year the judges present a total of 31 awards in 10 different categories.
Award: $25,000 (Grand Prize) plus Gold, Silver & Bronze Prizes in all 10 categories
Closing Date: Annually in May
Presented: Hollywood, CA, Annually in Oct

Dobie Paisano Fellowship Program
University of Texas at Austin, Texas Institute of Letters
Graduate School, 110 Inner Campus Dr, Stop G0400, Austin, TX 78712-0710
Fax: 512-471-7620
Web Site: www.utexas.edu/ogs/Paisano
Key Personnel
Dir: Dr Michael Adams *E-mail:* adameve@mail.utexas.edu
Established: 1967
Provides an opportunity for creative or nonfiction writers to live & write for an extended period in an environment that offers isolation & tranquility. At the time of application, the applicant must: be a native Texan; have lived in Texas at some time for at least 3 years; or have published significant work with a Texas subject. Criteria for making the awards include quality of work, character of the proposed project & suitability of the applicant for life at Paisano, the late J Frank Dobie's ranch near Austin, TX. Applications are available at the above web site or write for more information. Application fee: $20/1 fellowship, $30/both fellowships.
Award: Ralph A Johnston Memorial Fellowship: $25,000 over four months; Jesse H Jones Writing Fellowship: $18,000 over 6 months.
Closing Date: Annually, Dec 15
Presented: Annually in May

Mildred & Albert Panowski Playwriting Award
Northern Michigan University
Forest Roberts Theatre, 1401 Presque Isle Ave, Marquette, MI 49855-5364
Tel: 906-227-2553 *Fax:* 906-227-2567
E-mail: theatre@nmu.edu
Web Site: www.nmu.edu/theatre
Key Personnel
Dir: Ansley Valentine *Tel:* 906-227-1645
E-mail: avalenti@nmu.edu
Established: 1977
Provides students & faculty the unique opportunity to mount & produce an original work on the university stage. The playwright will benefit from seeing the work on its feet in front of an audience & from professional adjudication by guest critics. Please check the web site for theme or genre. Play must be unproduced. Only one play per playwright may be entered. Electronic submission only.
Award: $2,000 cash, airline fare, room & board for the week of production
Closing Date: Sept 1 of odd-numbered years (receipt not postmark)
Presented: Forest Roberts Theatre, Northern Michigan Univ, In upcoming season

Francis Parkman Prize
Society of American Historians (SAH)
Affiliate of American Historical Association
603 Fayerweather, MC 2538, New York, NY 10027
Tel: 212-854-6495
E-mail: amhistsociety@columbia.edu
Web Site: sah.columbia.edu
Key Personnel
Pres: David W Blight
VP: David Nasaw
Exec Secy: Andie Tucher
Established: 1957
For a nonfiction book, including biography, that is distinguished by its literary merit & makes an important contribution to the history of what is now the US. The author need not be a citizen or resident of the US & the book need not be published in the US although must be published & copyrighted in the year preceding the award.
Award: $2,000, certificate & consideration of adoption by the History Book Club
Closing Date: Annually, Jan 31
Presented: New York, NY, Annually in May

The Paterson Fiction Prize
The Poetry Center at Passaic County Community College
One College Blvd, Paterson, NJ 07505-1179
Tel: 973-684-6555 *Fax:* 973-523-6085
Web Site: www.pccc.edu/poetry
Key Personnel
Exec Dir: Maria Mazziotti Gillan
E-mail: mgillan@pccc.edu
Asst Dir: Susan Balik *E-mail:* sbalik@pccc.edu
For a novel or collection of short fiction which, in the opinion of our judges, is the strongest work of fiction published in the previous year. The author will be asked to participate in an awards ceremony & to give a reading at the Poetry Center. Each book submitted must be accompanied by an application form. Publisher may submit more than one book for prize consideration.
Award: $1,000
Closing Date: Annually, April 1

The Paterson Poetry Prize
The Poetry Center at Passaic County Community College
One College Blvd, Paterson, NJ 07505-1179
Tel: 973-684-6555 *Fax:* 973-523-6085
Web Site: www.pccc.edu/poetry
Key Personnel
Exec Dir: Maria Mazziotti Gillan
E-mail: mgillan@pccc.edu
Asst Dir: Susan Balik *E-mail:* sbalik@pccc.edu
For a book of poems, 48 pages or more in length, selected by our judges as the strongest collection of poems published in the previous year. The poet will be asked to participate in an awards ceremony & to give a reading at the Poetry Center. Publisher may submit more than one book for prize consideration.
Award: $1,000
Closing Date: Annually, Feb 1

The Paterson Prize for Books for Young People
The Poetry Center at Passaic County Community College
One College Blvd, Paterson, NJ 07505-1179
Tel: 973-684-6555 *Fax:* 973-523-6085
Web Site: www.pccc.edu/poetry
Key Personnel
Exec Dir: Maria Mazziotti Gillan
E-mail: mgillan@pccc.edu
Asst Dir: Susan Balik *E-mail:* sbalik@pccc.edu
One book in each category will be selected for the most outstanding book for young people published in the previous year.
Award: $500 in each category: PreK-Grade 3, Grades 4-6, Grades 7-12
Closing Date: Annually, March 15

The Alicia Patterson Foundation Fellowship Program
The Alicia Patterson Foundation
1100 Vermont Ave, Suite 900, Washington, DC 20005
Tel: 202-393-5995 *Fax:* 301-951-8512
E-mail: info@aliciapatterson.org
Web Site: www.aliciapatterson.org
Key Personnel
Exec Dir: Margaret Engel
Established: 1963
Yearly or 6 month stipend, not for academic study, for professional print journalist with 5 years experience & must write/photograph for English-language medium.
Award: $40,000 over 12 months, $20,000 over 6 months. Applicants choose whether they want 6 or 12 month grants
Closing Date: Annually, Oct 1
Presented: 2nd week of Dec

William Peden Prize in Fiction
The Missouri Review
357 McReynolds Hall, Columbia, MO 65211
Tel: 573-882-4474 *Toll Free Tel:* 800-949-2505
Fax: 573-884-4671
E-mail: question@moreview.com
Web Site: www.missourireview.com
Key Personnel
Assoc Ed: Evelyn Somers *Tel:* 573-884-7839
E-mail: rogerses@missouri.edu
Awarded annually to the best story to appear in the magazine the previous volume year. Winner is selected by an outside judge. It is not a contest that writers can enter, since the winner is selected from stories already published in the magazine.
Award: $1,000
Presented: Columbia, MO

The PEN Award for Poetry in Translation
PEN American Center
Affiliate of PEN International
588 Broadway, Suite 303, New York, NY 10012
Tel: 212-334-1660 *Fax:* 212-334-2181
E-mail: awards@pen.org
Web Site: www.pen.org
Key Personnel
Exec Dir: Suzanne Nossel

Pres: Andrew Solomon
Dir, Literary Progs: Paul Morris *Tel:* 212-334-1660 ext 4824 *E-mail:* paul@pen.org
Membership Coord: Daniel Guzman *Tel:* 212-334-1660 ext 4819 *E-mail:* daniel@pen.org
Recognizes book-length translations of poetry from any language into English, published during the current calendar year & is judged by a single translator of poetry appointed by the PEN Translation Committee. All books must have been published in the US, although translators may be of any nationality (US residency or citizenship is not required). No application form. May be submitted by publishers, agents or the translators themselves. Entry fee: $50.
Award: $3,000
Closing Date: Annually in Fall
Presented: PEN Literary Awards Ceremony, New York, NY, Annually in Summer

PEN/Bellwether Prize for Socially Engaged Fiction
PEN American Center
588 Broadway, Suite 303, New York, NY 10012
Tel: 212-334-1660
E-mail: awards@pen.org
Web Site: www.pen.org
Key Personnel
Dir, Literary Progs: Paul Morris *Tel:* 212-334-1660 ext 4824 *E-mail:* paul@pen.org
Membership Coord: Daniel Guzman *Tel:* 212-334-1660 ext 4819 *E-mail:* daniel@pen.org
Awarded biennially to the author of a previously unpublished novel of high literary caliber that promotes fiction that addresses issues of social justice & the impact of culture & politics on human relationships. Entry fee: $25.
Award: $25,000 & publishing contract with Algonquin Books

PEN Center USA Literary Awards
PEN Center USA
Affiliate of PEN International
269 S Beverly Dr, Suite 1163, Beverly Hills, CA 90212
Mailing Address: PO Box 6037, Beverly Hills, CA 90212
Tel: 323-424-4939 *Fax:* 323-424-4944
E-mail: awards@penusa.org
Web Site: www.penusa.org
Established: 1982
Literary awards for: fiction, creative nonfiction, nonfiction, poetry, translation, children's literature, drama, research nonfiction, screenplay, teleplay, journalism. Author must live west of Mississippi River. Work must have been published/produced in 2015.
Award: Cash awards $1,000
Closing Date: Book categories Dec 31, 2015, non-book categories Feb 28, 2016
Presented: Dinner & Awards Ceremony, Literary Awards Festival, Beverly Wilshire Hotel, Beverly Hills, CA, Autumn 2016

PEN/Diamonstein-Spielvogel Award for the Art of the Essay
PEN American Center
588 Broadway, Suite 303, New York, NY 10012
Tel: 212-334-1660
E-mail: awards@pen.org
Web Site: www.pen.org/literary-awards
Key Personnel
Dir, Literary Progs: Paul Morris *Tel:* 212-334-1660 ext 4824 *E-mail:* paul@pen.org
Membership Coord: Daniel Guzman *Tel:* 212-334-1660 ext 4819 *E-mail:* daniel@pen.org
Nonfiction award which aims to preserve the dignity & esteem that the essay form imparts to literature. Submissions accepted only from publishers or literary agents.
Award: $10,000

PEN/E O Wilson Literary Science Writing Award
PEN American Center
588 Broadway, Suite 303, New York, NY 10012
Tel: 212-334-1660
E-mail: awards@pen.org
Web Site: www.pen.org/literary-awards
Key Personnel
Dir, Literary Progs: Paul Morris *Tel:* 212-334-1660 ext 4824 *E-mail:* paul@pen.org
Membership Coord: Daniel Guzman *Tel:* 212-334-1660 ext 4819 *E-mail:* daniel@pen.org
Nonfiction award which celebrates writing that exemplifies literary excellence on the subject of physical & biological sciences.
Award: $10,000

PEN/ESPN Award for Literary Sports Writing
PEN American Center
588 Broadway, Suite 303, New York, NY 10012
Tel: 212-334-1660
E-mail: awards@pen.org
Web Site: www.pen.org/literary-awards
Key Personnel
Dir, Literary Progs: Paul Morris *Tel:* 212-334-1660 ext 4824 *E-mail:* paul@pen.org
Membership Coord: Daniel Guzman *Tel:* 212-334-1660 ext 4819 *E-mail:* daniel@pen.org
Award to an author of a nonfiction book about sports.
Award: $5,000

PEN/ESPN Lifetime Achievement Award for Literary Sports Writing
PEN American Center
588 Broadway, Suite 303, New York, NY 10012
Tel: 212-334-1660
E-mail: awards@pen.org
Web Site: www.pen.org/literary-awards
Key Personnel
Dir, Literary Progs: Paul Morris *Tel:* 212-334-1660 ext 4824 *E-mail:* paul@pen.org
Membership Coord: Daniel Guzman *Tel:* 212-334-1660 ext 4819 *E-mail:* daniel@pen.org
Nonfiction award to a writer for their long-time contributions to the field of literary sports writing.
Award: $5,000

PEN/Faulkner Award for Fiction
PEN/Faulkner Foundation
Folger Shakespeare Library, 201 E Capitol St SE, Washington, DC 20003
Tel: 202-898-9063 *Fax:* 202-675-0360
Web Site: www.penfaulkner.org
Key Personnel
Exec Dir: Emma Snyder
Established: 1980
Annual award for a distinguished work of fiction published by an American citizen writer (for published work only). Send 4 copies of each book or 4 bound gallies for those being published in Nov & Dec.
Award: $15,000 (1st prize), $5,000 to each of four finalists
Closing Date: Annually, Oct 31
Presented: Awards Ceremony, Washington, DC, Annually in May

PEN/Fusion Emerging Writers Prize
PEN American Center
588 Broadway, Suite 303, New York, NY 10012
Tel: 212-334-1660
E-mail: awards@pen.org
Web Site: www.pen.org/literary-awards
Key Personnel
Dir, Literary Progs: Paul Morris *Tel:* 212-334-1660 ext 4824 *E-mail:* paul@pen.org
Membership Coord: Daniel Guzman *Tel:* 212-334-1660 ext 4819 *E-mail:* daniel@pen.org
Annual award that recognizes a promising young writer (35 & under) of an unpublished work of nonfiction that addresses a global +/or multicultural issue. Ms submission must be an original, previously unpublished work of nonfiction written by one person, in English, 8,000-80,000 words in length. Entry fee: $35.
Award: $10,000

PEN/Jacqueline Bograd Weld Award for Biography
PEN American Center
588 Broadway, Suite 303, New York, NY 10012
Tel: 212-334-1660
E-mail: awards@pen.org
Web Site: www.pen.org/literary-awards
Key Personnel
Dir, Literary Progs: Paul Morris *Tel:* 212-334-1660 ext 4824 *E-mail:* paul@pen.org
Membership Coord: Daniel Guzman *Tel:* 212-334-1660 ext 4819 *E-mail:* daniel@pen.org
Nonfiction award for excellence in the art of biography.
Award: $5,000

PEN/Joyce Osterweil Award for Poetry
PEN American Center
588 Broadway, Suite 303, New York, NY 10012
Tel: 212-334-1660
E-mail: awards@pen.org
Web Site: www.pen.org
Key Personnel
Dir, Literary Progs: Paul Morris *Tel:* 212-334-1660 ext 4824 *E-mail:* paul@pen.org
Membership Coord: Daniel Guzman *Tel:* 212-334-1660 ext 4819 *E-mail:* daniel@pen.org
Awarded in odd-numbered years (alternates with PEN/Voelcker Award for Poetry). Recognizes the high literary character of the published work to date of a new & emerging American poet of any age & the promise of further literary achievement.
Award: $5,000

PEN/O. Henry Prize Stories
Anchor Books
Division of Random House Inc
University of Texas at Austin, One University Sta B5000, Austin, TX 78712
Tel: 512-572-2428
Web Site: www.ohenryprizestories.com
Key Personnel
Series Ed: Laura Furman
Established: 1918
Annual collection of the best English language short stories published in American & Canadian magazines & written in the English language during the calendar year 2 years prior to the year presented. No submissions; selections made by the series editor from those published in the approximately 260 magazines with print editions submitted to the series.
Closing Date: May 1

PEN Open Book Award
PEN American Center
588 Broadway, Suite 303, New York, NY 10012
Tel: 212-334-1660
E-mail: awards@pen.org
Web Site: www.pen.org/literary-awards
Key Personnel
Dir, Literary Progs: Paul Morris *Tel:* 212-334-1660 ext 4824 *E-mail:* paul@pen.org
Membership Coord: Daniel Guzman *Tel:* 212-334-1660 ext 4819 *E-mail:* daniel@pen.org
For a book-length work by an author of color.
Award: $5,000

PEN/Phyllis Naylor Working Writer Fellowship
PEN American Center
Affiliate of PEN International
588 Broadway, Suite 303, New York, NY 10012
Tel: 212-334-1660 *Fax:* 212-334-2181

E-mail: awards@pen.org
Web Site: www.pen.org
Key Personnel
Exec Dir: Suzanne Nossel
Pres: Andrew Solomon
Dir, Literary Progs: Paul Morris *Tel:* 212-334-1660 ext 4824 *E-mail:* paul@pen.org
Membership Coord: Daniel Guzman *Tel:* 212-334-1660 ext 4819 *E-mail:* daniel@pen.org
Established: 2001
Annual award presented to an author of children's or young adult fiction. Provides a writer with a measure of financial sustenance in order to make possible an extended period of time to complete a book-length work-in-progress & to assist a writer at a crucial moment in his or her career when monetary support is particularly needed.
Award: $5,000
Closing Date: Fall
Presented: PEN Literary Awards Ceremony, New York, NY, Summer

PEN/Ralph Manheim Medal for Translation
PEN American Center
Affiliate of PEN International
588 Broadway, Suite 303, New York, NY 10012
Tel: 212-334-1660 *Fax:* 212-334-2181
E-mail: awards@pen.org
Web Site: www.pen.org
Key Personnel
Exec Dir: Suzanne Nossel
Pres: Andrew Solomon
Dir, Literary Progs: Paul Morris *Tel:* 212-334-1660 ext 4824 *E-mail:* paul@pen.org
Membership Coord: Daniel Guzman *Tel:* 212-334-1660 ext 4819 *E-mail:* daniel@pen.org
Established: 1982
Given every 3 years to a translator who has demonstrated exceptional commitment to excellence throughout the body of his work. Candidates nominated by the PEN Translation Committee; internal nomination only. See web site for more information.
Award: Medal
Closing Date: None
Presented: PEN Literary Awards Ceremony, New York, NY, Every 3 years in Summer

PEN/Robert Bingham Prize for Debut Fiction
PEN American Center
Affiliate of PEN International
588 Broadway, Suite 303, New York, NY 10012
Tel: 212-334-1660 *Fax:* 212-334-2181
E-mail: awards@pen.org
Web Site: www.pen.org
Key Personnel
Exec Dir: Suzanne Nossel
Pres: Andrew Solomon
Dir, Literary Progs: Paul Morris *Tel:* 212-334-1660 ext 4824 *E-mail:* paul@pen.org
Membership Coord: Daniel Guzman *Tel:* 212-334-1660 ext 4819 *E-mail:* daniel@pen.org
Honor an exceptionally talented fiction writer whose debut work–a first fiction novel or collection of short stories – represents distinguished literary achievement & suggests great promise. Nominations are welcome from any source. Candidates must be US residents but American citizenship is not required. Self-published authors are not eligible. Entry fee: $50.
Award: $25,000
Closing Date: Annually in Fall
Presented: PEN Literary Awards Ceremony, New York, NY, Annually in Summer

PEN/Steven Kroll Award for Picture Book Writing
PEN American Center
588 Broadway, Suite 303, New York, NY 10012
Tel: 212-334-1660
E-mail: awards@pen.org
Web Site: www.pen.org/literary-awards
Key Personnel
Dir, Literary Progs: Paul Morris *Tel:* 212-334-1660 ext 4824 *E-mail:* paul@pen.org
Membership Coord: Daniel Guzman *Tel:* 212-334-1660 ext 4819 *E-mail:* daniel@pen.org
Acknowledges the distinct literary merit contributions of picture book writers.
Award: $5,000

PEN Translation Prize
PEN American Center
Affiliate of PEN International
588 Broadway, Suite 303, New York, NY 10012
Tel: 212-334-1660 *Fax:* 212-334-2181
E-mail: awards@pen.org
Web Site: www.pen.org
Key Personnel
Exec Dir: Suzanne Nossel
Pres: Andrew Solomon
Dir, Literary Progs: Paul Morris *Tel:* 212-334-1660 ext 4824 *E-mail:* paul@pen.org
Membership Coord: Daniel Guzman *Tel:* 212-334-1660 ext 4819 *E-mail:* daniel@pen.org
Established: 1963
For the best book-length translation into English from any language published in the US during the previous year. Technical, scientific or reference works are not eligible. See web site for more information. Entry fee: $50.
Award: $3,000
Closing Date: Annually in Fall
Presented: PEN Literary Awards Ceremony, New York, NY, Annually in Summer

PEN/Voelcker Award
PEN American Center
588 Broadway, Suite 303, New York, NY 10012
Tel: 212-334-1660
E-mail: awards@pen.org
Web Site: www.pen.org/literary-awards
Key Personnel
Dir, Literary Progs: Paul Morris *Tel:* 212-334-1660 ext 4824 *E-mail:* paul@pen.org
Membership Coord: Daniel Guzman *Tel:* 212-334-1660 ext 4819 *E-mail:* daniel@pen.org
Awarded to a poet whose distinguished & growing body of work to date represents a notable & accomplished presence in American literature.
Award: $5,000

PEN Writers' Emergency Fund
PEN American Center
Affiliate of PEN International
588 Broadway, Suite 303, New York, NY 10012
Tel: 212-334-1660 *Fax:* 212-334-2181
Web Site: www.pen.org
Key Personnel
Exec Dir: Suzanne Nossel
Pres: Andrew Solomon
Intl Pres: Jiri Grusa
Dir, Literary Progs: Paul Morris *Tel:* 212-334-1660 ext 4824 *E-mail:* paul@pen.org
Membership Coord: Daniel Guzman *Tel:* 212-334-1660 ext 4819 *E-mail:* daniel@pen.org
Established: 1921
Grants for professional published writers & produced playwrights in financial emergencies due to personal circumstances. These are not literary awards. Application form available online.
Award: Up to $2,000
Closing Date: Annually, Jan 15, March 15, June 15, Sept 15

Maxwell E Perkins Award
The Center for Fiction
17 E 47 St, New York, NY 10017
Tel: 212-755-6710 *Fax:* 212-826-0831
E-mail: info@centerforfiction.org
Web Site: www.centerforfiction.org/awards/perkins
Key Personnel
Awards & Progs Mgr: Sara Batkie *E-mail:* sara@centerforfiction.org
Established: 2005
To honor the work of an editor, publisher, or agent who over the course of his or her career has discovered, nurtured and championed writers of fiction in the US.

Perugia Press Prize for a First or Second Book by a Woman
Perugia Press
PO Box 60364, Florence, MA 01062
Web Site: www.perugiapress.com
Key Personnel
Dir: Susan Kan
Established: 1997
For a first or second book of poetry by a woman.
Award: $1,000 & publication
Closing Date: Annually Nov 15
Presented: Winner announced annually by April 15

Pfizer Award
History of Science Society
Affiliate of American Council of Learned Societies
440 Geddes Hall, Notre Dame, IN 46556
Tel: 574-631-1194 *Fax:* 574-631-1533
E-mail: info@hssonline.org
Web Site: www.hssonline.org
Key Personnel
Exec Dir: Robert Jay Malone
Established: 1958
Award given annually for an outstanding book in English, published during the preceding 3 years, on a topic related to the history of science.
Award: $2,500 & a medal
Closing Date: April 1
Presented: Oct or Nov

James D Phelan Literary Award
The San Francisco Foundation
One Embarcadero Ctr, Suite 1400, San Francisco, CA 94111
Tel: 415-733-8500 *Fax:* 415-477-2783
E-mail: info@sff.org
Web Site: www.sff.org
Key Personnel
Arts & Culture Prog Offr: Terezita Romo
Established: 1935
Award for the author of fiction (novel or short stories), nonfictional prose, poetry, spoken word. Awards are intended to encourage emerging artists not yet established in the genre who are California-born & currently residing in Alaneda, Contra Costa, Marin, San Francisco or San Mateo County, for an unpublished ms-in-progress. By nomination only.
Award: $2,000
Presented: Annually in Autumn

Phi Beta Kappa Award in Science
The Phi Beta Kappa Society
1606 New Hampshire Ave NW, Washington, DC 20009
Tel: 202-265-3808 *Fax:* 202-986-1601
E-mail: awards@pbk.org
Web Site: www.pbk.org/bookawards
Key Personnel
Coord, Admin: Laura Hartnett *Tel:* 202-745-3287 *E-mail:* lhartnett@pbk.org
Established: 1959
For an outstanding interpretation of science written by a scientist & published in the US during the previous year. Works in the physical & biological sciences & mathematics are eligible for the award. Highly technical works, monographs & reports on research are not eligible. Nominations must come from publisher & be submitted online.
Award: $10,000

Closing Date: Annually in Jan
Presented: Washington, DC, Annually in Dec

Robert J Pickering Award for Playwriting Excellence
Branch County Community Theatre
89 Division, Coldwater, MI 49036
E-mail: j7eden@aol.com
Web Site: www.branchcct.org
Key Personnel
Comm Chmn: J Richard Colbeck
Contact: Jennifer Colbeck
Established: 1984
Playwriting, must be unproduced full length plays +/or musicals.
Award: $200 & production (1st prize), $50 (2nd prize), $25 (3rd prize)
Closing Date: Annually, Dec 31 (entries ongoing)
Presented: Tibbits Opera House, Coldwater, MI, Annually, Feb or March

Lorne Pierce Medal
Royal Society of Canada
Walter House, 282 Somerset W, Ottawa, ON K2P 0J6, Canada
Tel: 613-991-6990 (ext 106) *Fax:* 613-991-6996
E-mail: nominations@rsc-src.ca
Web Site: www.rsc-src.ca
Key Personnel
Mgr, Fellowship & Awards: Marie-Lyne Renaud
E-mail: mlrenaud@rsc-src.ca
Established: 1926
Biennial award given in even-numbered years for an achievement of significance & conspicuous merit in imaginative or critical literature.
Award: Medal
Closing Date: March 1
Presented: RSC business meeting, Nov

The Pinch Writing Awards in Fiction
Hohenburg Foundation
University of Memphis, English Dept, 435 Patterson Hall, Memphis, TN 38152
Tel: 901-678-4190 *Fax:* 901-678-2226
E-mail: editor@thepinchjournal.com
Web Site: www.thepinchjournal.com
Key Personnel
Ed-in-Chief: Dr Kristen Iversen
E-mail: kiversen@memphis.edu
Mng Ed: Christopher Moyer
Established: 1987
Submit one previously unpublished story not to exceed 5,000 words accompanied by a $20 entrance fee, which includes a one-year subscription to "The Pinch." Additional entries are $10. Stories should be typed, double-spaced & include a cover sheet. The cover sheet must contain the author's name & full communication information. The author's name should not appear anywhere on the ms itself. Indicate contest entry & category on envelope. No mss will be returned.
Award: $1,000 & publication in the following Spring issue of *The Pinch* (1st prize), 2nd & 3rd place winners may also be published. All entrants receive one free copy of the journal
Closing Date: Annually, Dec 15-April 15
Presented: Annually, mid-Sept

The Pinch Writing Awards in Poetry
Hohenburg Foundation
University of Memphis, English Dept, 435 Patterson Hall, Memphis, TN 38152
Tel: 901-678-4190 *Fax:* 901-678-2226
E-mail: editor@thepinchjournal.com
Web Site: www.thepinchjournal.com
Key Personnel
Ed-in-Chief: Dr Kristen Iversen
E-mail: kiversen@memphis.edu
Mng Ed: Christopher Moyer
Established: 1987
Submit up to 3 unpublished poems accompanied by a $20 entrance fee. Additional groups of three poems may be submitted at $10 per group. Mss must be typed & accompanied by a cover letter. Mss themselves should not include the author's name. Indicate contest entry & category on envelope. No mss will be returned.
Award: $1,000 & publication in the subsequent issue of *The Pinch* will be awarded to the 1st place winner, 2nd & 3rd place winners may also be published. All entrants receive 1 free copy of the journal
Closing Date: Annually, Dec 15-April 15
Presented: Annually, Mid-Sept

Playboy College Fiction Contest
Playboy Enterprises Inc
9346 Civic Center Dr, Suite 300, Beverly Hills, CA 90210-3604
Web Site: playboymagazine.submittable.com/submit
Established: 1985
Short story contest for accredited college/university students.
Award: $3,000 & publication in an upcoming issue (1st prize), $500 & an annual subscription (2nd prize), $200 & an annual subscription (3rd prize); open to all college students
Closing Date: Feb 15
Presented: Spring

Playwright Discovery Award
VSA
Affiliate of The John F Kennedy Center for the Performing Arts
818 Connecticut Ave NW, Suite 600, Washington, DC 20006
Tel: 202-628-2800 *Toll Free Tel:* 800-933-8721
Fax: 202-429-0868
Web Site: www.vsarts.org/playwrightdiscovery
Key Personnel
Dir, Performing Arts: Elena Widder
Established: 1984
Playwriting program for students with & without disabilities, grades 6-12. Script must somehow address the subject of disability.
Award: Attend performance of their script at JFK Center, scholarship funds
Closing Date: Annually, April 15
Presented: The John F Kennedy Center for Performing Arts, Washington, DC

Playwrights Project
3675 Ruffin Rd, Suite 330, San Diego, CA 92123
Tel: 858-384-2970 *Fax:* 858-384-2974
E-mail: write@playwrightsproject.org
Web Site: www.playwrightsproject.org
Key Personnel
Exec Dir: Cecelia Kouma
Devt Mgr: Laurel Withers
Established: 1985
Annual playwriting contest for Californians under 19 years of age.
Award: Professional production (location to be announced), royalty
Closing Date: June 1
Presented: Jan-Feb following application

The Plimpton Prize
The Paris Review Foundation
544 W 27 St, New York, NY 10001
Tel: 212-343-1333 *Fax:* 212-343-1988
E-mail: queries@theparisreview.org
Web Site: www.theparisreview.org
Key Personnel
Publr: Antonio Weiss
Mng Ed: Nicole Rudick
Sr Ed: Dierdre Foley-Mendelssohn
Awarded annually to the best work of fiction publishing in The Paris Review that year by an emerging or previously unpublished writer.
Award: $10,000
Presented: April

Plutarch Award
Biographers International Organization
PO Box 33020, Santa Fe, NM 87594
Tel: 505-983-4671
Web Site: biographersinternational.org
Awarded by a committee of biographers for the best biography of the year.

PNWA Literary Contest
PNWA - a writer's resource
1420 NW Gilman Blvd, Suite 2, PMB 2717, Issaquah, WA 98027
Tel: 425-673-2665
E-mail: pnwa@pnwa.org
Web Site: www.pnwa.org
Key Personnel
Pres: Pam Binder
Multiple categories by genre.
Closing Date: Annually in Feb
Presented: Annual Summer Conference

Edgar Allan Poe Awards®
Mystery Writers of America (MWA)
1140 Broadway, Suite 1507, New York, NY 10001
Tel: 212-888-8171
E-mail: mwa@mysterywriters.org
Web Site: www.mysterywriters.org
Key Personnel
Admin Dir: Margery Flax
Established: 1945
For the best mystery novel & best first novel by an American author. Also awards for best juvenile novel & young adult, fact-crime writing, TV episode, short story, paperback original, critical/biographical work. The work must be published for the first time in the US in the calendar year prior to the award.
Award: Ceramic bust of Poe
Closing Date: Annually, Nov 30
Presented: New York, NY, Annually in late Spring

Edgar Allan Poe Memorial
The Poetry Society of Virginia
1194 Hume Rd, Hume, VA 22639-1806
E-mail: poetryinva@aol.com
Web Site: www.poetrysocietyofvirginia.org
Key Personnel
Pres: Judith K Bragg *E-mail:* musicsavy45@yahoo.com
Adult Contest Chair: Patsy Anne Bickerstaff
E-mail: granypatsy@yahoo.com; Guy Terrell
E-mail: ggterr@infionline.net
All entries must be in English, original & unpublished. Submit 2 copies of each poem, each having the category name & number on top left of page. Only one poem per category; entries will not be returned; any form; any subject; 48 line limit. Entry fee: $4 nonmembs.
Award: $100
Closing Date: Jan 19
Presented: Annual PSV Awards Luncheon, Richmond, VA, April

A Poem With a Point of View
The Poetry Society of Virginia
1194 Hume Rd, Hume, VA 22639-1806
E-mail: poetryinva@aol.com
Web Site: www.poetrysocietyofvirginia.org
Key Personnel
Pres: Judith K Bragg *E-mail:* musicsavy45@yahoo.com
Adult Contest Chair: Patsy Anne Bickerstaff
E-mail: granypatsy@yahoo.com; Guy Terrell
E-mail: ggterr@infionline.net
All entries must be in English, original & unpublished. Submit 2 copies, each having the category name & number on top left of page. Any form, any subject that express his or her strong

or particular feelings; 48 line limit. Entry fee: $4 nonmembs.
Other Sponsor(s): Angela Anselmo
Award: $50
Closing Date: Jan 19
Presented: Annual PSV Awards Luncheon, Richmond, VA, April

Poetry Book Contest
Accents Publishing
PO Box 910456, Lexington, KY 40591-0456
Web Site: www.accents-publishing.com/contest.html
Key Personnel
Founder & Sr Ed: Katerina Stoykova-Klemer
Established: 2010
Include submission form, ms, biography or CV & check or confirmation of payment. Ms should be 20-30 pgs of poetry & single spaced. Entry fee $10.
Award: $250 cash, publication & 25 perfect-bound copies
Closing Date: Annually, Feb 1-June 30
Presented: Annually in July

Poetry Center Book Award
Poetry Center & American Poetry Archives at San Francisco State University
1600 Holloway Ave, San Francisco, CA 94132
Tel: 415-338-2227 *Fax:* 415-338-0966
E-mail: poetry@sfsu.edu
Web Site: www.sfsu.edu/~poetry
Key Personnel
Assoc Dir: Elise Ficarra
Established: 1980
For an outstanding book of poetry published in the year of the award. Volumes by individual authors; anthologies & translations not accepted. Poets or publishers should send one copy of each book & a $10 fee. Include a cover letter noting author name, book title(s), name of person issuing check & check number.
Award: $500 & an invitation to read in the Poetry Center's series
Closing Date: Jan 31
Presented: Fall

Poetry Chapbook Contest
Palettes & Quills
1935 Penfield Rd, Penfield, NY 14526
Tel: 585-383-0812
E-mail: palettesnquills@gmail.com
Web Site: www.palettesnquills.com
Key Personnel
Ed & Publr: Donna M Marbach
E-mail: dmmarbach@gmail.com
You must include a statement that all poems are your original work. Poems included in your ms may be previously published, but include an acknowledgement page listing specific publications. Entry fee per $20 per submission. Translations not accepted. Poems longer than two pages are discouraged. See web site for complete submission guidelines.
Award: Cash ($200) plus 50 copies of the published book
Closing Date: Biennially in Sept (even-numbered years)
Presented: Winners announced online in Dec

The George Polk Awards
Long Island University
The Brooklyn Campus, One University Plaza, Brooklyn, NY 11201-5372
Tel: 718-488-1009; 718-488-1115
Web Site: www.liu.edu/polk
Key Personnel
Curator: John Darnton
Coord: Ralph Engelman *E-mail:* ralph.engelman@liu.edu
Established: 1949
For outstanding discernment & reporting of a news or feature story on the Internet, in newspapers, radio or television. Entries originating from publication offices, newsrooms or individual reporters are considered. Submit 2 copies of stories or tapes. No entry fees or application forms; entries will not be returned.
Award: Plaque
Closing Date: Jan 5
Presented: Spring

Katherine Anne Porter Award
American Academy of Arts & Letters
633 W 155 St, New York, NY 10032
Tel: 212-368-5900 *Fax:* 212-491-4615
E-mail: academy@artsandletters.org
Web Site: www.artsandletters.org
Key Personnel
Exec Dir: Virginia Dajani
Established: 2001
Biennial award to honor a prose writer whose achievements & dedication to the literary profession have been demonstrated.
Award: $20,000

Katherine Anne Porter Prize for Fiction
Nimrod, The University of Tulsa
Subsidiary of The Nimrod Literary Awards
Nimrod International Journal, 800 S Tucker Dr, Tulsa, OK 74104
Tel: 918-631-3080 *Fax:* 918-631-3033
E-mail: nimrod@utulsa.edu
Web Site: www.utulsa.edu/nimrod
Key Personnel
Ed: Eilis O'Neal
Assoc Ed: Diane Burton
Established: 1978
Annual prize. 7500 words maximum. No previously published works or works accepted for publication elsewhere. Must have a US address by Oct to enter. Works must be in English or translated by original author. Author's name must not appear on ms. Include a cover sheet containing major title & subtitles, author's name, address, phone number & e-mail address. "Contest Entry" must be on envelope. Mss will not be returned. Nimrod retains the right to publish any submission. Works not accepted will be released; SASE for results only. $20 entry fee includes processing & one year subscription.
Award: $2,000 (1st prize), $1,000 (2nd prize); plus each published writer receives two copies of the journal; winners are flown to Tulsa for a conference & banquet
Closing Date: April 30
Presented: Tulsa, OK, Oct

Prairie Schooner Annual Strousse Award
Prairie Schooner
University of Nebraska, 123 Andrews Hall, 625 N 14 St, Lincoln, NE 68508
Mailing Address: PO Box 880334, Lincoln, NE 68588-0334
Tel: 402-472-0911 *Fax:* 402-472-9771
E-mail: prairieschooner@unl.edu
Web Site: prairieschooner.unl.edu
Key Personnel
Mng Ed: Ashley Strosnider
Ed: Kwame Dawes
Established: 1975
For best poetry published in the magazine each year.
Other Sponsor(s): Friends & famliy of Fora Strousse
Award: $500
Presented: Prairie Schooner, Annually in March

Prairie Schooner Bernice Slote Award
Prairie Schooner
University of Nebraska, 123 Andrews Hall, 625 N 14 St, Lincoln, NE 68508
Mailing Address: PO Box 880334, Lincoln, NE 68588-0334
Tel: 402-472-0911
E-mail: prairieschooner@unl.edu
Web Site: prairieschooner.unl.edu
Key Personnel
Mng Ed: Ashley Strosnider
Ed: Kwame Dawes
Established: 1985
Annual writing prize for best work by a beginning writer published in *Prairie Schooner* in the previous year.
Award: $500
Presented: Winners announced in Spring issue of *Prairie Schooner* magazine

Prairie Schooner Book Prize Contest in Fiction
Prairie Schooner
University of Nebraska, 123 Andrews Hall, 625 N 14 St, Lincoln, NE 68508
Mailing Address: PO Box 880334, Lincoln, NE 68588-0334
Tel: 402-472-0911 *Fax:* 402-472-9771
E-mail: psbookprize@unl.edu
Web Site: prairieschooner.unl.edu
Key Personnel
Mng Ed: Ashley Strosnider
Ed: Kwame Dawes
Welcomes mss from all living writers, including non-US citizens, writing in English. Mss previously published will not be considered. Writers may enter both fiction & poetry contests. For fiction mss, at least 150 pages in length is preferred. Entry fee: $25 per submission. Mss accepted by electronic or hard copy submission beginning Jan 15.
Award: $3,000 & publication through the University of Nebraska Press
Closing Date: March 15, annually

Prairie Schooner Book Prize Contest in Poetry
Prairie Schooner
University of Nebraska, 123 Andrews Hall, 625 N 14 St, Lincoln, NE 68508
Mailing Address: PO Box 880334, Lincoln, NE 68588-0334
Tel: 402-472-0911 *Fax:* 402-472-9771
E-mail: psbookprize@unl.edu
Web Site: prairieschooner.unl.edu
Key Personnel
Mng Ed: Ashley Strosnider
Ed: Kwame Dawes
Welcomes mss from all living writers, including non-US citizens, writing in English. Mss previously published will not be considered. Writers may enter both fiction & poetry contests. For poetry mss, at least 50 pages in length is preferred. Entry fee: $25 per submission. Mss accepted by electronic or hard copy submission beginning Jan 15.
Award: $3,000 & publication through the University of Nebraska Press
Closing Date: March 15, annually

Prairie Schooner Edward Stanley Award
Prairie Schooner
University of Nebraska, 123 Andrews Hall, 625 N 14 St, Lincoln, NE 68508
Mailing Address: PO Box 880334, Lincoln, NE 68588-0334
Tel: 402-472-0911 *Fax:* 402-472-9771
E-mail: prairieschooner@unl.edu
Web Site: prairieschooner.unl.edu
Key Personnel
Mng Ed: Ashley Strosnider
Ed: Kwame Dawes
Established: 1992
Annual writing prize for best poem or group of poems in the volume. Only contributors to the magazine are eligible.
Other Sponsor(s): Friends & family of Marion Edward Stanley (in memorium)

Award: $1,000
Presented: Winners announced in Spring issue of *Prairie Schooner* magazine

Prairie Schooner Glenna Luschei Award
Prairie Schooner
University of Nebraska, 123 Andrews Hall, 625 N 14 St, Lincoln, NE 68508
Mailing Address: PO Box 880334, Lincoln, NE 68588-0334
Tel: 402-472-0911 *Fax:* 402-472-9771
E-mail: prairieschooner@unl.edu
Web Site: prairieschooner.unl.edu
Key Personnel
Mng Ed: Ashley Strosnider
Ed: Kwame Dawes
Established: 1989
Annual writing prizes for best work published in the magazine. Only work published in *Prairie Schooner* in the previous year is considered.
Other Sponsor(s): Glenna Luschei
Award: $1,500 (first place), $250 (10 runners up)
Presented: Winners announced in Spring issue of *Prairie Schooner* magazine

Prairie Schooner Hugh J Luke Award
Prairie Schooner
University of Nebraska, 123 Andrews Hall, 625 N 14 St, Lincoln, NE 68508
Mailing Address: PO Box 880334, Lincoln, NE 68588-0334
Tel: 402-472-0911 *Fax:* 402-472-9771
E-mail: prairieschooner@unl.edu
Web Site: prairieschooner.unl.edu
Key Personnel
Mng Ed: Ashley Strosnider
Ed: Kwame Dawes
Established: 1989
Annual writing prize for best work published in the *Prairie Schooner* magazine in the previous year.
Other Sponsor(s): Friends & family of Hugh J Luke (in memoriam)
Award: $250
Presented: Winners announced in Spring issue of *Prairie Schooner* magazine

Prairie Schooner Jane Geske Award
Prairie Schooner
University of Nebraska, 123 Andrews Hall, 625 N 14 St, Lincoln, NE 68508
Mailing Address: PO Box 880334, Lincoln, NE 68588-0334
Tel: 402-472-0911 *Fax:* 402-472-9771
E-mail: prairieschooner@unl.edu
Web Site: prairieschooner.unl.edu
Key Personnel
Mng Ed: Ashley Strosnider
Established: 2000
Annual award for work in any genre published in *Prairie Schooner* in the previous year.
Other Sponsor(s): Family of Jane Geske
Award: $250
Presented: Winners announced in Spring issue of *Prairie Schooner* magazine

Prairie Schooner Lawrence Foundation Award
Prairie Schooner
University of Nebraska, 123 Andrews Hall, 625 N 14 St, Lincoln, NE 68508
Mailing Address: PO Box 880334, Lincoln, NE 68588-0334
Tel: 402-472-0911 *Fax:* 402-472-9771
E-mail: prairieschooner@unl.edu
Web Site: prairieschooner.unl.edu
Key Personnel
Mng Ed: Ashley Strosnider
Ed: Kwame Dawes
Established: 1978
Annual writing prize for the best short story published in *Prairie Schooner* magazine; only work published in the previous year will be considered.
Other Sponsor(s): The Lawrence Foundation of New York City
Award: $1,000
Presented: Winners announced in Spring issue of *Prairie Schooner* magazine

Prairie Schooner Virginia Faulkner Award for Excellence in Writing
Prairie Schooner
University of Nebraska, 123 Andrews Hall, 625 N 14 St, Lincoln, NE 68508
Mailing Address: PO Box 880334, Lincoln, NE 68588-0334
Tel: 402-472-0911 *Fax:* 402-472-9771
E-mail: prairieschooner@unl.edu
Web Site: prairieschooner.unl.edu
Key Personnel
Mng Ed: Ashley Strosnider
Ed: Kwame Dawes
Established: 1987
Annual writing prize for work published in *Prairie Schooner* magazine. Only work published in the previous year is considered.
Other Sponsor(s): Friends & family of Virginia Faulkner
Award: $1,000
Presented: Winners announced in Spring issue of *Prairie Schooner* magazine

Premier Print Awards
Printing Industries of America
200 Deer Run Rd, Sewickley, PA 15143-2324
Tel: 412-741-6860 *Toll Free Tel:* 800-910-4283 *Fax:* 412-741-2311
E-mail: printing@printing.org
Web Site: www.printing.org/premierprint
Key Personnel
Chmn of the Bd: William Gibson
CEO & Pres: Michael F Makin *E-mail:* mmakin@printing.org
Dir, Mktg: Lisa Rawa *E-mail:* lrawa@printing.org
Established: 1950
Awards competition for printed material. See web site for more information.
Award: Plaques & certificates
Closing Date: Annually in May
Presented: Graph Expo, Annually in Sept or Oct

Derek Price/Rod Webster Prize Award
History of Science Society
Affiliate of American Council of Learned Societies
440 Geddes Hall, Notre Dame, IN 46556
Tel: 574-631-1194 *Fax:* 574-631-1533
E-mail: info@hssonline.org
Web Site: www.hssonline.org
Key Personnel
Exec Dir: Robert Jay Malone
Established: 1978
For article appearing in Isis during the preceding 3 years.
Award: $1,000
Closing Date: Annually, April 1
Presented: Annual meeting, Late Oct or early Nov

Michael L Printz Award
Young Adult Library Services Association (YALSA)
Division of The American Library Association (ALA)
50 E Huron St, Chicago, IL 60611
Tel: 312-280-4390 *Toll Free Tel:* 800-545-2433 *Fax:* 312-280-5276
E-mail: yalsa@ala.org
Web Site: www.ala.org/yalsa/printz
Key Personnel
Exec Dir: Beth Yoke *Tel:* 800-545-2433 ext 4391 *E-mail:* byoke@ala.org
Prog Offr, Events & Conferences: Nichole O'Connor *Tel:* 800-545-2433 ext 4387 *E-mail:* noconnor@ala.org
Communs Specialist: Anna Lam *Tel:* 800-545-2433 ext 5849 *E-mail:* alam@ala.org
Established: 1999
Honors excellence in literature written for young adults. May be fiction, nonfiction, poetry or an anthology & must have been published during the preceding year & designated as young adult book or ages 12-18.
Other Sponsor(s): Booklist
Closing Date: Annually, Dec 1
Presented: YALSA Printz Reception during ALA Annual Conference

PRISM international Literary Non-Fiction Contest
PRISM international
University of British Columbia, Buch E462, 1866 Main Mall, Vancouver, BC V6T 1Z1, Canada
Tel: 778-822-2514 *Fax:* 778-822-3616
E-mail: prismwritingcontest@gmail.com
Web Site: www.prismmagazine.ca
Key Personnel
Exec Ed: Jennifer Lori; Claire Matthews
Poetry Ed: Dominique Bernier Cormier
Prose Ed: Christopher Evans
Entry fee: $35 (includes a 1 yr subn); additional entries: $5.
Other Sponsor(s): University of British Columbia Bookstore
Award: $1,500 (grand prize), $600 (1st runner up), $400 (2nd runner up)
Closing Date: Annually in Nov (check web site for exact date)

PRISM international Poetry Contest
PRISM international
University of British Columbia, Buch E462, 1866 Main Mall, Vancouver, BC V6T 1Z1, Canada
Tel: 778-822-2514 *Fax:* 778-822-3616
E-mail: prismwritingcontest@gmail.com
Web Site: www.prismmagazine.ca
Key Personnel
Exec Ed: Jennifer Lori; Claire Matthews
Poetry Ed: Dominique Bernier Cormier
Prose Ed: Christopher Evans
Established: 1986
Awarded for the best original, unpublished poem (3 poems, up to 25 pages). Works of translation are eligible. Entry fee $35 for 3 poems plus $5 for each additional entry.
Award: $1,500 grand prize, $600 (1st runner up), $400 (2nd runner up); all entries receive a 1 yr subn to *PRISM international*
Closing Date: Annually in Jan

PRISM international Short Fiction Contest
PRISM international
University of British Columbia, Buch E462, 1866 Main Mall, Vancouver, BC V6T 1Z1, Canada
Tel: 778-822-2514 *Fax:* 778-822-3616
E-mail: prismwritingcontest@gmail.com
Web Site: www.prismmagazine.ca
Key Personnel
Exec Ed: Jennifer Lori; Claire Matthews
Poetry Ed: Dominique Bernier Cormier
Prose Ed: Christopher Evans
Established: 1986
Short fiction. Entry fee: $35 (CN), $40 (US), $45 (Intl).
Award: $1,500 (grand prize), $600 (1st runner up), $400 (2nd runner up)
Closing Date: Annually in Jan (check web site for exact date)

Pritzker Literature Award for Lifetime Achievement in Military Writing
Tawani Foundation
Pritzker Military Museum & Library, 104 S Michigan Ave, Suite 525, Chicago, IL 60603

Tel: 312-374-9390 *Fax:* 312-374-9394
E-mail: info@pritzkermilitary.org
Web Site: www.pritzkermilitary.org
Established: 2007
To recognize a living author who has made a significant contribution to the understanding of American military history, including military affairs.
Award: $100,000, citation & medallion

Prix Alvine-Belisle
Association pour l'Avancement des Sciences et des Techniques de la Documentation
2065 rue Parthenais, Bureau 387, Montreal, QC H2K 3T1, Canada
Tel: 514-281-5012 *Fax:* 514-281-8219
E-mail: info@asted.org
Web Site: www.asted.org
Key Personnel
Dir Gen: Francis Farley-Chevrier *E-mail:* ffc@asted.org
To the best books for young people published in French in Canada during the previous year.
Closing Date: Annually, end of June
Presented: Salon Du Livre, Montreal, QC, CN, Annually in Nov

Prix Emile-Nelligan
La Fondation Emile Nelligan
100, rue Sherbrooke, Montreal, QC H2X 1C3, Canada
Tel: 514-278-4657 *Toll Free Tel:* 888-849-8540 *Fax:* 514-278-1943
E-mail: info@fondation-nelligan.org
Web Site: www.fondation-nelligan.org
Key Personnel
CEO: Manon Gagnon
Pres: Michel Dallaire
VP: Marie-Andree Beaudet
Treas/Secy: Michel Gonneville
Established: 1979
Collection must be published between Jan 1-Dec 31 of the preceding year.
Award: $7,500 & a bronze medal
Presented: Annually in May

Prize for the Translation of Japanese Literature, see Japan-US Friendship Commission Translation Prize

Prometheus Awards
Libertarian Futurist Society
650 Castro St, Suite 120-433, Mountain View, CA 94041
Tel: 650-968-6319
E-mail: info@lfs.org
Web Site: www.lfs.org
Key Personnel
Bd Pres: Bill Stoddard
VP: Rick Triplett
Dir: Charles Morrison
Asst Dir: Steve Burgauer
Established: 1979
Awarded to the best published novel of previous year that dramatizes the value of freedom. Hall of Fame—classic libertarian fiction.
Award: Prometheus one ounce gold coin mounted on an engraved plaque; Hall of Fame one-eighth ounce coin mounted on an engraved plaque
Closing Date: Annually, Feb 1 (Special Awards), March 1st (Best Novel), Oct 1 (Best Classic Fiction)
Presented: World Science Fiction Convention or NASFIC, Labor Day weekend

PROSE Awards
Association of American Publishers (AAP)
71 Fifth Ave, 2nd fl, New York, NY 10003-3004
Tel: 212-255-0200 *Fax:* 212-255-7007
Web Site: www.proseawards.com; publishers.org
Key Personnel
Proj Mgr, Prof & Scholarly Publg: Kate Kolendo *Tel:* 212-255-0326 *E-mail:* kkolendo@publishers.org
Established: 1976
The PROSE Awards honor the very best in professional & scholarly publishing. With awards in over 45 catergories, PROSE is unique in its breath & depth. AAP, PSP & AAUP members are eligible.
Award: Plaque & glass cubes
Closing Date: Annually, Oct 31
Presented: Annually in Feb

Public Scholar Program
National Endowment for the Humanities, Division of Research Programs
400 Seventh St SW, Washington, DC 20506
Tel: 202-606-8200
E-mail: publicscholar@neh.gov
Web Site: www.neh.gov/grants/research
Key Personnel
NEH Chmn: William Adams
Supports well-researched books in the humanities intended to reach a broad readership. Fellowship periods last from 6-12 months & must be full-time & continuous. Open to both individuals affiliated with scholarly institutions & independent scholars. All applications to this program must be submitted via Grants.gov. Applications receive peer review & NEH Chairman makes all funding decisions.
Award: $4,200 monthly stipend (maximum $50,400 for 12-month period)
Closing Date: Feb 2, 2016 for projects beginning Oct 2016
Presented: Aug 2016

The Publishing Triangle Literary Awards
The Publishing Triangle
332 Bleecker St, Suite D-36, New York, NY 10014
E-mail: publishingtriangle@gmail.com
Web Site: www.publishingtriangle.org
Established: 1997
Contests for poetry, debut fiction & nonfiction. Books must be published in the US or CN between Jan 1 & Dec 31. Entrants are accepted only between Oct 1 & Dec 1. General instructions, specific guidelines, for each award & submission form are available on web site starting Oct 1. For hard copy, send your mailing address to publishingtriangle@gmail.com. Entry fee is $35.
Award: $1,000 for debut fiction & nonfiction, $500 for poetry
Closing Date: Dec 1
Presented: Ceremony in New York City, Late April/early May

PubWest Book Design Awards
Publishers Association of the West (PubWest)
17501 Hill Way, Lake Oswego, OR 97035
Tel: 503-901-9865 *Fax:* 602-234-3062
Web Site: pubwest.org
Key Personnel
Pres: Derek Lawrence
Exec Dir: Kent Watson *E-mail:* executivedirector@pubwest.org
Asst Dir: Amanda Fessler *E-mail:* amanda@pubwest.org
Established: 1977
Gold, silver & bronze awards are given in 20 categories. Trade book (illustrated), trade book (non-illustrated), children's/young adult (illustrated), artist's book, academic book/non-trade, guide/travel book, how-to book/crafts, cook book, art/photography book, sports/fitness/recreation book, reference book, short stories/poetry/anthologies, gift/holiday/specialty book, historical/biographical book, graphic novel/drawn book, jacket/cover design, digitally produced book (1- color), digitally produced book (4-color), best use of environmental materials & best of show.
Award: Medallions & glass award for best of show

Pulitzer Prizes
709 Journalism Bldg, Columbia University, 2950 Broadway, New York, NY 10027
Tel: 212-854-3841 *Fax:* 212-854-3342
E-mail: pulitzer@pulitzer.org
Web Site: www.pulitzer.org
Key Personnel
Admin: Sig Gissler
Established: 1917
Given to American authors for a distinguished book of fiction, performed play, history of the US, biography or autobiography, verse or general nonfiction, as well as journalism prizes for newspaper work in US dailies or weeklies, books must be first published in the calendar year.
Award: Gold medal for public service journalism category; $10,000 & certificate in all other categories
Closing Date: June 15 for bks published Jan 1-June 14, Oct 15 for bks published June 15-Dec 31; literary prizes, Jan 15 (music), Feb 1 (journalism), Dec 31 (drama)
Presented: Annually in Spring

Pushcart Prize: Best of the Small Presses
Pushcart Press
PO Box 380, Wainscott, NY 11975-0380
SAN: 202-9871
Tel: 631-324-9300
Key Personnel
Pres: Bill Henderson
Established: 1976
Awarded for works previously published by a small press or literary journal.
Award: Copies of the book *The Pushcart Prize: Best of the Small Presses*
Closing Date: Annually, Dec 1
Presented: Annually in Spring

QWF Literary Awards
Quebec Writers' Federation (QWF)
1200 Atwater Ave, Suite 3, Westmount, QC H3Z 1X4, Canada
Tel: 514-933-0878
E-mail: info@qwf.org
Web Site: www.qwf.org
Key Personnel
Exec Dir: Lori Schubert *E-mail:* admin@qwf.org
Coord, Membership Servs & Communs: Deanna Radford *E-mail:* deanna@qwf.org
Established: 1988
Literary for Quebec, English language authors. Request submission details.
Award: A M Klein Prize for Poetry: $2,000; Paragraphe Hugh MacLennan Prize for Fiction: $2,000; Mavis Gallant Prize for Nonfiction: $2,000; Concordia University First Book Prize: $2,000; Cole Foundation Prize for Translation: $2,000; QWF Prize for Children's & Young Adult Literature: $2,000
Closing Date: Annually, May 31
Presented: Annually in Nov

Miriam Rachimi Memorial
The Poetry Society of Virginia
1194 Hume Rd, Hume, VA 22639-1806
E-mail: poetryinva@aol.com
Web Site: www.poetrysocietyofvirginia.org
Key Personnel
Pres: Judith K Bragg *E-mail:* musicsavy45@yahoo.com
Adult Contest Chair: Patsy Anne Bickerstaff *E-mail:* granypatsy@yahoo.com; Guy Terrell *E-mail:* ggterr@infionline.net

All entries must be in English, original & unpublished. Submit 2 copies, each having the category name & number on top left of page. Subject: the spiritual impact of losing (or almost losing) a loved one; any form; 48 line limit. Entry fee: $4 nonmembs.
Other Sponsor(s): Ben Mahgerefteh; Michal Mahgerefteh
Award: $50 (1st prize), $30 (2nd prize), $20 (3rd prize)
Closing Date: Jan 19
Presented: Annual PSV Awards Luncheon, Richmond, VA, April

Radcliffe Fellowship
The Radcliffe Institute for Advanced Study
8 Garden St, Cambridge, MA 02138
Tel: 617-496-1324 (application office) *Fax:* 617-495-8136
Web Site: www.radcliffe.harvard.edu
Key Personnel
Administrator, Fellowships: Alison Ney
Radcliffe Institute fellowships are designed to support scholars, scientists, artists & writers of exceptional promise & demonstrated accomplishments who wish to pursue work in academic & professional fields & in the creative arts.
Award: Stipend & office space
Closing Date: Sept 23 for Creative Arts & Humanities & Social Sciences; Oct 15 for Natural Sciences & Mathematics

Thomas Head Raddall Atlantic Fiction Award
Writers' Federation of Nova Scotia
1113 Marginal Rd, Halifax, NS B3H 4P7, Canada
Tel: 902-423-8116 *Fax:* 902-422-0881
E-mail: contact@writers.ns.ca
Web Site: www.writers.ns.ca
Key Personnel
Exec Dir: Jonathan Meakin *E-mail:* director@writers.ns.ca
Established: 1990
Presented to best fiction book, published by an Atlantic Canadian writer in previous calendar year.
Award: $20,000
Closing Date: Annually, 1st Friday in Dec
Presented: Halifax, NS, CN, Annually in Oct

The Ragan Old North State Award Cup for Nonfiction
North Carolina Literary & Historical Association
Affiliate of Historical Book Club of North Carolina
4610 Mail Service Ctr, Raleigh, NC 27699-4610
Tel: 919-807-7290 *Fax:* 919-733-8807
Web Site: www.history.ncdcr.gov/affiliates/lit-hist/awards/awards.htm
Key Personnel
Awards Coord: Michael Hill *E-mail:* michael.hill@ncdcr.gov
Established: 2003
For published book of nonfiction, not technical or scientific, by a legal or actual resident of North Carolina for at least 3 years prior to end of contest.
Award: Cup
Closing Date: Annually, July 15
Presented: Raleigh, NC, Annually in Nov

Raiziss/de Palchi Fellowship
The Academy of American Poets Inc
75 Maiden Lane, Suite 901, New York, NY 10038
Tel: 212-274-0343 *Fax:* 212-274-9427
E-mail: academy@poets.org
Web Site: www.poets.org
Key Personnel
Pres & Exec Dir: Tree Swenson
Exec Dir: Jennifer Benka
Multimedia Prodr: Paul Legault
E-mail: plegault@poets.org
Awards Coord & Exec Asst: Alex Dimitrov *Tel:* 212-274-0343 ext 15 *E-mail:* adimitrov@poets.org
Established: 1995
Biennial award to recognize outstanding translations into English of modern Italian poetry. Given to enable an American translator of 20th century Italian poetry to travel, study, or otherwise advance a significant work-in-progress. For guidelines & entry form, send SASE in August of even-numbered years.
Award: $10,000 book prize & a $25,000 fellowship
Closing Date: Sept 1-Dec 31 (even-numbered years)
Presented: Jan (odd-numbered years)

Sir Walter Raleigh Award for Fiction
Historical Book Club of North Carolina
Affiliate of North Carolina Literary & Historical Association
4610 Mail Service Ctr, Raleigh, NC 27699-4610
Tel: 919-807-7290 *Fax:* 919-733-8807
Key Personnel
Awards Coord: Michael Hill *E-mail:* michael.hill@ncdcr.gov
Award for the best book of fiction by an author who has been a legal or actual resident of North Carolina for at least 3 years prior to the end of the contest.

Raven Award
Mystery Writers of America (MWA)
1140 Broadway, Suite 1507, New York, NY 10001
Tel: 212-888-8171 *Fax:* 212-888-8107
E-mail: mwa@mysterywriters.org
Web Site: www.mysterywriters.org
Recognizes outstanding achievement in the mystery field outside the realm of creative writing.
Presented: The Edgars Banquet, Annually in Spring

RBC Bronwen Wallace Award for Emerging Writers
The Writers' Trust of Canada
460 Richmond St W, Suite 600, Toronto, ON M5V 1Y1, Canada
Tel: 416-504-8222 *Toll Free Tel:* 877-906-6548 *Fax:* 416-504-9090
E-mail: info@writerstrust.com
Web Site: www.writerstrust.com
Key Personnel
Exec Dir: Mary Osborne *Tel:* 416-504-8222 ext 244
Established: 1994
Awarded to a young author, 35 years of age & under, who has not been previously published in book form. The award alternates each year between short fiction & poetry.
Other Sponsor(s): RBC Foundation
Award: $5,000 (winner), $1,000 (finalists)
Presented: Annually in Spring

The Rea Award for the Short Story
Dungannon Foundation
53 W Church Hill Rd, Washington, CT 06794
Web Site: reaaward.org
Key Personnel
Pres: Elizabeth R Rea
Established: 1986
Established by Michael M Rea to honor a living US or Canadian writer who has made a significant contribution to the short story form. No submissions accepted. The recipient is nominated & selected by a jury.
Award: $30,000

Robert F Reed Technology Medal
Printing Industries of America
200 Deer Run Rd, Sewickley, PA 15143-2324
Tel: 412-259-1705 *Toll Free Tel:* 800-910-4283 (ext 705) *Fax:* 412-749-9890
E-mail: printing@printing.org
Web Site: www.printing.org/reedaward
Key Personnel
CEO & Pres: Michael F Makin
E-mail: mmakin@printing.org
Asst to VP, Mktg: Sara Welsh *E-mail:* swelsh@printing.org
Established: 1974
Acknowledges an individual who has made a major career contribution to the technical & scientific development of the graphic communications industry. See web site for more information.
Other Sponsor(s): Printing Industries of America's Ben Franklin Society
Award: Engraved medal
Presented: TAGA Annual Technical Conference

Regina Medal Award
Catholic Library Association
8550 United Plaza Blvd, Suite 1001, Baton Rouge, LA 70809-2256
Tel: 225-408-4417
E-mail: cla2@cathla.org
Web Site: www.cathla.org
Key Personnel
Pres: Mary Kelleher *Tel:* 225-408-4417
E-mail: kellehm@stthom.edu
Established: 1959
For continued distinguished lifetime contribution to children's literature; no unsol mss.
Award: Sterling silver medal
Closing Date: None; in-house votes
Presented: CLA Annual Convention

Nathan Reingold Prize
History of Science Society
Affiliate of American Council of Learned Societies
440 Geddes Hall, Notre Dame, IN 46556
Tel: 574-631-1194 *Fax:* 574-631-1533
E-mail: info@hssonline.org
Web Site: www.hssonline.org
Key Personnel
Exec Dir: Robert Jay Malone
Established: 1955
For an original essay, not to exceed 8,000 words, in history of science & its cultural influences. Open to graduate students only. Must send in 3 copies of essay with a detachable author/title page.
Award: $500 (& up to $500 travel reimbursement)
Closing Date: Annually, June 1
Presented: Annually in Oct or Nov

Arthur Rense Prize
American Academy of Arts & Letters
633 W 155 St, New York, NY 10032
Tel: 212-368-5900 *Fax:* 212-491-4615
E-mail: academy@artsandletters.org
Web Site: www.artsandletters.org
Key Personnel
Exec Dir: Virginia Dajani
Established: 1998
Given triennially to an exceptional poet.
Award: $20,000

Residency
Millay Colony for the Arts
454 E Hill Rd, Austerlitz, NY 12017
Mailing Address: PO Box 3, Austerlitz, NY 12017-0003
Tel: 518-392-3103; 518-392-4144
E-mail: apply@millaycolony.org
Web Site: www.millaycolony.org
Key Personnel
Exec Dir: Caroline Crumpacker
E-mail: director@millaycolony.org

Residency Dir: Calliope Nicholas
E-mail: residency@millaycolony.org
Residencies for writers, composers & visual artists; send SASE to receive application & information; applications available by e-mail or on web site.
Award: One-month residencies offered including room, studio & meals; no cash award
Closing Date: Oct 1

The Harold U Ribalow Prize
Hadassah Magazine
40 Wall St, New York, NY 10005-1387
Tel: 212-451-6286 *Fax:* 212-451-6257
E-mail: magtemp3@hadassah.org
Web Site: www.hadassah.org/magazine
Key Personnel
Exec Ed: Alan M Tigay
Established: 1983
Annual award for an outstanding English-language work of fiction on a Jewish theme by an author deserving of recognition.
Other Sponsor(s): Harold U Ribalow family
Award: $3,000
Closing Date: April of the year following publication
Presented: Autumn

Evelyn Richardson Memorial Literary Trust Award
Writers' Federation of Nova Scotia
1113 Marginal Rd, Halifax, NS B3H 4P7, Canada
Tel: 902-423-8116 *Fax:* 902-422-0881
E-mail: contact@writers.ns.ca
Web Site: writers.ns.ca
Key Personnel
Exec Dir: Jonathan Meakin *E-mail:* director@writers.ns.ca
Established: 1978
Presented to the best nonfiction book, published by a native or resident Nova Scotian in the previous calendar year.
Award: $2,000
Closing Date: Annually, 1st Friday in Dec
Presented: Halifax, NS, Canada, Annually in Oct

The Ridenhour Book Prize
The Nation Institute
116 E 16 St, 8th fl, New York, NY 10003
Tel: 212-822-0250 *Fax:* 212-253-5356
E-mail: ridenhour@nationinstitute.org
Web Site: www.ridenhour.org
Key Personnel
CEO & Exec Dir: Taya Kitman *Tel:* 212-822-0252 *E-mail:* taya@nationinstitute.org
Honors an outstanding work of social significance from the prior publishing year. The prize also recognizes investigative & reportorial distinction.
Other Sponsor(s): The Fertel Foundation
Award: $10,000 stipend

The Ridenhour Courage Prize
The Nation Institute
116 E 16 St, 8th fl, New York, NY 10003
Tel: 212-822-0250 *Fax:* 212-253-5356
E-mail: ridenhour@nationinstitute.org
Web Site: www.ridenhour.org
Key Personnel
CEO & Exec Dir: Taya Kitman *Tel:* 212-822-0252 *E-mail:* taya@nationinstitute.org
Presented to an individual in recognition of his or her courageous & life-long defense of the public interest & passionate commitment to social justice.
Other Sponsor(s): The Fertel Foundation
Award: $10,000 stipend

The Ridenhour Prize for Truth-Telling
The Nation Institute
116 E 16 St, 8th fl, New York, NY 10003
Tel: 212-822-0250 *Fax:* 212-253-5356
E-mail: ridenhour@nationinstitute.org
Web Site: www.ridenhour.org
Key Personnel
CEO & Exec Dir: Taya Kitman *Tel:* 212-822-0252 *E-mail:* taya@nationinstitute.org
Presented to a citizen, corporate or government whistleblower, investigative journalist, or organization for bringing a specific issue of social importance to the public's attention.
Other Sponsor(s): The Fertel Foundation
Award: $10,000 stipend

Gwen Pharis Ringwood Award for Drama
Writers' Guild of Alberta
11759 Groat Rd, Edmonton, AB T5M 3K6, Canada
Tel: 780-422-8174 *Toll Free Tel:* 800-665-5354 (AB only) *Fax:* 780-422-2663 (attn WGA)
E-mail: mail@writersguild.ab.ca
Web Site: www.writersguild.ab.ca
Key Personnel
Exec Dir: Carol Holmes *E-mail:* carol.holmes@writersguild.ab.ca
Communs & Partnerships Coord: Nicholas Mather *E-mail:* nicholas.mather@writersguild.ab.ca
Memb Servs Coord: Giorgia Severini
Progs Coord: Natalie Cook *E-mail:* natalie.cook@writersguild.ab.ca; Nichole Quiring *E-mail:* nichole.quiring@writersguild.ab.ca
Established: 1982
Alberta Literary Award, author must be resident of Alberta.
Award: $1,500 plus leather-bound copy of book
Closing Date: Annually, Dec 31
Presented: Alberta Book Awards Gala
Branch Office(s)
505 21 Ave SW, Calgary, AB T2S 0G9, Canada, Prog Coord: Samantha Warwick *Tel:* 403-265-2226 *E-mail:* samantha.warwick@writersguild.ab.ca

Jack D Rittenhouse Award
Publishers Association of the West (PubWest)
17501 Hill Way, Lake Oswego, OR 97035
Tel: 503-901-9865
Web Site: pubwest.org
Key Personnel
Exec Dir: Kent Watson
E-mail: executivedirector@pubwest.org
Honors individuals who have made outstanding contributions to the book community in the West.
Presented: PubWest Annual Conference

Roanoke-Chowan Award for Poetry
North Carolina Literary & Historical Association
Affiliate of Historical Book Club of North Carolina
4610 Mail Service Ctr, Raleigh, NC 27699-4610
Tel: 919-807-7290 *Fax:* 919-733-8807
Web Site: www.history.ncdcr.gov/affiliates/lit-hist/awards/awards.htm
Key Personnel
Awards Coord: Michael Hill *E-mail:* michael.hill@ncdcr.gov
Established: 1953
Award for the best published book of poetry by a legal or actual resident of North Carolina for at least 3 years prior to the end of the contest period.
Award: Cup
Closing Date: Annually, July 15
Presented: Raleigh, NC, Annually in Nov

The Roanoke Review Fiction Contest
Roanoke College
221 College Lane, Salem, VA 24153
E-mail: review@roanoke.edu
Web Site: roanokereview.wordpress.com
Key Personnel
Ed: Paul Hanstedt *Tel:* 540-375-2380
Established: 2001
Award: $1,000, (1st prize), $500 (2nd prize)
Closing Date: Annually in Nov

Rocky Mountain Book Award
PO Box 42, Lethbridge, AB T1J 3Y3, Canada
Tel: 403-381-7164
E-mail: rockymountainbookaward@shaw.ca
Web Site: rmba.lethsd.ab.ca
Key Personnel
Contact: Michelle Dimnik
Established: 2001
Grade 4-7. An Alberta Children's Choice Book Award.
Closing Date: Jan 15
Presented: Winner announced electronically on Canada Book Day on April 23

Rogers Writers' Trust Fiction Prize
The Writers' Trust of Canada
460 Richmond St W, Suite 600, Toronto, ON M5V 1Y1, Canada
Tel: 416-504-8222 *Toll Free Tel:* 877-906-6548 *Fax:* 416-504-9090
E-mail: info@writerstrust.com
Web Site: www.writerstrust.com
Key Personnel
Exec Dir: Mary Osborne *Tel:* 416-504-8222 ext 244
Established: 1997
Awarded to the year's best novel or collection of short stories.
Other Sponsor(s): Rogers Communications
Award: $25,000 (winner), $2,500 (finalists)
Presented: The Writers' Trust Awards, Toronto, ON, CN, Annually in Nov

Sami Rohr Prize for Jewish Literature
Jewish Book Council
520 Eighth Ave, 4th fl, New York, NY 10018
Tel: 212-201-2920 *Fax:* 212-532-4952
E-mail: jbc@jewishbooks.org
Web Site: www.jewishbookcouncil.org
Key Personnel
Dir: Naomi Firestone-Teeter
Established: 2006
Annual award which recognizes the unique role of contemporary writers in the transmission & examination of Jewish values & is intended to encourage & promote outstanding writing of Jewish interest. Rewards an emerging writer whose work has demonstrated a fresh vision & evidence of future potential. Recipients must have written a book of exceptional literary merit that stimulates an interest in themes of Jewish concern. Fiction & nonfiction books will be considered in alternate years.
Award: $100,000
Presented: Annually in Spring

Romance Writers of America Awards
Romance Writers of America®
14615 Benfer Rd, Houston, TX 77069
Tel: 832-717-5200 *Fax:* 832-717-5201
E-mail: info@rwa.org
Web Site: www.rwa.org
Key Personnel
Exec Dir: Allison Kelley *Tel:* 832-717-5200 ext 124 *E-mail:* allison.kelley@rwa.org
Deputy Exec Dir: Carol Ritter *Tel:* 832-717-5200 ext 127 *E-mail:* carol.ritter@rwa.org
Established: 1981
Golden Heart: for unpublished romance fiction mss; RITA Award: best published romance fiction mss for preceding year.
Award: Heart necklace for Golden Heart, Statue for RITA Award
Closing Date: Nov
Presented: Annual National Conference, Atlanta, GA, July

Dorothy Sargent Rosenberg Poetry Prizes
Dorothy Sargent Rosenberg Memorial Fund
PO Box 2306, Orinda, CA 94563
Web Site: www.dorothyprizes.org
Key Personnel
Trustee: Barr Rosenberg; Mary Rosenberg
Established: 2004
Awarded for the best lyric poems celebrating the human spirit. Up to 3 entries permitted per person. Entrants to be under the age of 40. Submitted poems to be previously unpublished, original & in English (no translations). Only one poem may be more than 30 lines. Prizes awarded as recommended by the judges. $10 entry fee. See web site for further details.
Award: Up to $25,000
Closing Date: Oct 5
Presented: Winners announce on web site in Feb

Rosenthal Family Foundation Awards
American Academy of Arts & Letters
633 W 155 St, New York, NY 10032
Tel: 212-368-5900 *Fax:* 212-491-4615
E-mail: academy@artsandletters.org
Web Site: www.artsandletters.org
Key Personnel
Exec Dir: Virginia Dajani
Award for a work of fiction published during the preceding year that is a considerable literary achievement. Second award is given for a young painter of distinction.
Other Sponsor(s): The Rosenthal Foundation
Award: $10,000 each

Margaret W Rossiter History of Women in Science Prize
History of Science Society
Affiliate of American Council of Learned Societies
440 Geddes Hall, Notre Dame, IN 46556
Tel: 574-631-1194 *Fax:* 574-631-1533
E-mail: info@hssonline.org
Web Site: www.hssonline.org
Key Personnel
Exec Dir: Robert Jay Malone
Recognition of an outstanding book (or, in even-numbered years, article) on the history of women in science. Books & articles published in the preceding four years are eligible.
Award: $1,000
Closing Date: April 1

Lois Roth Award
Modern Language Association of America (MLA)
26 Broadway, 3rd fl, New York, NY 10004-1789
SAN: 202-6422
Tel: 646-576-5141 *Fax:* 646-458-0030
E-mail: awards@mla.org
Web Site: www.mla.org
Key Personnel
Coord, Book Prizes: Annie M Reiser *E-mail:* areiser@mla.org
Established: 1999
Committee solicits submissions of outstanding translations into English of a book-length literary work. Translations published in 2016 are eligible. For consideration submit 6 copies & 12-15 pages of original text in its original language taken from the beginning, middle & end of the work & a letter identifying the translator & the date of publication. Translators need not be members of the association. Biennial award offered in odd-numbered years.
Award: Cash award & certificate
Closing Date: April 1, 2017
Presented: MLA Convention, Jan 2018

Lexi Rudnitsky Poetry Prize
Persea Books
277 Broadway, Suite 708, New York, NY 10007
SAN: 212-8233
Tel: 212-260-9256 *Fax:* 212-267-3165
E-mail: info@perseabooks.com
Web Site: www.perseabooks.com
Key Personnel
Pres & Publr: Michael Braziller
VP & Edit Dir: Karen Braziller
Established: 2006
First book by an American woman poet.
Award: $1,000 plus publication
Closing Date: Oct 31

William B Ruggles Journalism Scholarship
National Institute for Labor Relations Research
5211 Port Royal Rd, Suite 510, Springfield, VA 22151
Tel: 703-321-9606 *Fax:* 703-321-7143
E-mail: research@nilrr.org
Web Site: www.nilrr.org
Key Personnel
Scholarship Administrator: Cathy Jones
Established: 1974
Scholarship grant for students majoring in journalism or related majors. Based on scholastic ability demonstrating an understanding of the economic, political & social implications of compulsory unionism.
Award: $2,000
Closing Date: Annually, Dec 31
Presented: Annually in April

The Cornelius Ryan Award
Overseas Press Club of America (OPC)
40 W 45 St, New York, NY 10036
Tel: 212-626-9220 *Fax:* 212-626-9210
Web Site: www.opcofamerica.org
Key Personnel
Exec Dir: Patricia Kranz
Awarded for best nonfiction book on international affairs.
Award: Certificate & cash award
Closing Date: Annually, last week of Jan
Presented: New York City, Annually in late April

Saint Louis Literary Award
Saint Louis University Library Associates
Pius XII Memorial Library, 3650 Lindell Blvd, St Louis, MO 63108
Tel: 314-977-3100 *Fax:* 314-977-3587
E-mail: slula@slu.edu
Web Site: www.slu.edu/libraries/associates
Key Personnel
Asst VP, Univ Libs: Gail M Staines, PhD *E-mail:* gstaines@slu.edu
Established: 1967
For body of author's work. No applications; awardee chosen by committee.
Award: Honorarium, Citation
Presented: Award Ceremony, Autumn

San Francisco Writers Contest (SFWC)
San Francisco Writers Conference
1029 Jones St, San Francisco, CA 94109
Tel: 415-673-0939
E-mail: sfwriterscon@aol.com
Web Site: www.sfwriters.org
Key Personnel
Founder: Michael Larsen
Founder & Dir: Elizabeth Pomada
Contest Dir: Laurie McLean
All entries must be original, unpublished work not submitted to this contest in previous years & be in English. Complete an official entry form & attach to the entry. Entry fee: $40. Four catagories: adult fiction, nonfiction/memoir, poety & childrens/young adult. Register online.
Other Sponsor(s): San Francisco Center for the Literary Arts
Award: $500 (grand prize), $100 (first prize in each category)
Closing Date: Annually in Dec
Presented: Annual Conference, InterContinental Mark Hopkins Hotel, San Francisco, CA

The Carl Sandburg Literary Awards
The Chicago Public Library Foundation & Chicago Public Library
20 N Michigan Ave, Suite 520, Chicago, IL 60602
Tel: 312-201-9830 *Fax:* 312-201-9833
Web Site: www.cplfoundation.org
Key Personnel
CEO & Pres: Rhona Frazin *E-mail:* rfrazin@cplfoundation.org
Established: 2000
Honors a significant work or a body of work that has enhanced the public's awareness of the written word & reflects the Library's commitment to the freedom of all people reading, discovery & creativity.
Award: $10,000
Presented: The Forum, University of Illinois at Chicago, Annually in Oct

Ada Sanderson Memorial
The Poetry Society of Virginia
1194 Hume Rd, Hume, VA 22639-1806
E-mail: poetryinva@aol.com
Web Site: www.poetrysocietyofvirginia.org
Key Personnel
Pres: Judith K Bragg *E-mail:* musicsavy45@yahoo.com
Adult Contest Chair: Patsy Anne Bickerstaff *E-mail:* granypatsy@yahoo.com; Guy Terrell *E-mail:* ggterr@infionline.net
All entries must be in English, orginal & unpublished. Submit 2 copies, each having the category name & number on top left of page. Only one poem per category; entries will not be returned. Subject: nature; any form; 48 line limit. Entry fee: $4 nonmembs.
Award: $100
Closing Date: Jan 19
Presented: Annual PSV Awards Luncheon, Richmond, VA, April

Mari Sandoz Award
Nebraska Library Association
PO Box 21756, Lincoln, NE 68542-1756
E-mail: nebraskalibraries@gmail.com
Web Site: www.nebraskalibraries.org
Key Personnel
Exec Dir: Michael Straatmann *E-mail:* nlaexecutivedirector@gmail.com
Established: 1971
Given to a distinguished Nebraska author.
Award: Plaque
Closing Date: Annually, May 30
Presented: NLA/NSLA Fall Convention, Annually in late Oct

Ivan Sandrof Lifetime Achievement Award
National Book Critics Circle
160 Varick St, 11th fl, New York, NY 10013
E-mail: info@bookcritics.org; membership@bookcritics.org (nominations from membs)
Web Site: bookcritics.org
Key Personnel
Contact: Steven Kellman
Awarded annually to a person or institution who has, over time, made significant contributions to book culture.

William Saroyan International Prize for Writing
William Saroyan Foundation
Administrator, Saroyan Prize Committee, Stanford University Libraries, 557 Escondido Mall, Stanford, CA 94305-6004
Tel: 650-736-9538
Web Site: library.stanford.edu
Key Personnel
Contact: Sonia Lee *E-mail:* sonialee@stanford.edu

Biennial competition for newly published books. Entry form & three copies of publication required. Entry fee: $50.
Other Sponsor(s): The Stanford University Libraries
Award: $5,000 each in fiction & nonfiction

May Sarton Award
New England Poetry Club
2 Farrar St, Cambridge, MA 02138
Mailing Address: 376 School St, Watertown, MA 02472
Tel: 617-744-6034
E-mail: contests@nepoetryclub.org
Web Site: www.nepoetryclub.org
Key Personnel
Pres: Diana Der-Hovanessian
VP: Sally Cragin; Daniel Tobin
Contest Chair: Nazaleem Smith
Honorary awards for work that inspires other poets. Chosen by board of directors.
Award: $250
Closing Date: Annually, May 31
Presented: Cambridge Library, Cambridge, MA, Annually in Spring

Saturnalia Books Poetry Prize
Saturnalia Books
105 Woodside Rd, Ardmore, PA 19003
Tel: 267-278-9541
E-mail: info@saturnaliabooks.com
Web Site: www.saturnaliabooks.com
Key Personnel
Publr: Henry Israeli
Established: 2003
Recognizes a poetry ms of high merit.
Award: $2,000 & publication
Closing Date: Annually, April 1

SATW Foundation Lowell Thomas Travel Journalism Competition
Society of American Travel Writers Foundation
306 Summer Hill Dr, Fredericksburg, TX 78654
Tel: 713-973-9985
E-mail: awards@satwf.com
Web Site: www.satwfoundation.org
Key Personnel
Pres: David G Molyneaux
Established: 1985
Premier awards for the best work in travel journalism. Competition is open to all North American journalists & is judged by leading schools of journalism. There are 20-plus categories, including individual & publication awards. Among them: Grand Award for Travel Journalist of the Year for a portfolio of work, Best Newspaper Travel sections (divided by circulation), Best Travel Magazine, Best Travel Coverage in Other Magazines, Best Guidebook, Best Travel Book, Best Online Travel Journalism Site & categories for writing, photography, audio broadcast, video broadcast, multimedia work & apps. For entry details & forms, see web site. New materials usually updated early Feb annually.
Award: Nearly $20,000 total in prize money: $1,500 (top prize), $500 (1st place)
Closing Date: April 1 (subject to change)
Presented: Location varies

Aldo & Jeanne Scaglione Prize for a Translation of a Literary Work
Modern Language Association of America (MLA)
26 Broadway, 3rd fl, New York, NY 10004-1789
SAN: 202-6422
Tel: 646-576-5141 *Fax:* 646-458-0030
E-mail: awards@mla.org
Web Site: www.mla.org
Key Personnel
Coord, Book Prizes: Annie M Reiser
E-mail: areiser@mla.org
Awarded each even-numbered year for an outstanding translation into English of a book-length literary work; books must have been published in 2015. Translators need not be members of the MLA. For consideration, submit 6 copies & 12-15 pages of the text in its original language taken from the beginning, middle & end of the work.
Award: Cash award & certificate
Closing Date: April 1, 2016
Presented: MLA Convention, Jan 2017

Aldo & Jeanne Scaglione Prize for a Translation of a Scholarly Study of Literature
Modern Language Association of America (MLA)
26 Broadway, 3rd fl, New York, NY 10004-1789
SAN: 202-6422
Tel: 646-576-5141 *Fax:* 646-458-0030
E-mail: awards@mla.org
Web Site: www.mla.org
Key Personnel
Coord, Book Prizes: Annie M Reiser
E-mail: areiser@mla.org
Established: 1993
Awarded biennially for an outstanding translation into English of a book-length work of literary history, literary criticism, philology or literary theory published in 2015 or 2016. For consideration, submit 4 copies.
Award: Cash award & certificate
Closing Date: May 1, 2017
Presented: MLA Convention, Jan 2018

Aldo & Jeanne Scaglione Prize for Comparative Literary Studies
Modern Language Association of America (MLA)
26 Broadway, 3rd fl, New York, NY 10004-1789
SAN: 202-6422
Tel: 646-576-5141 *Fax:* 646-458-0030
E-mail: awards@mla.org
Web Site: www.mla.org
Key Personnel
Coord, Book Prizes: Annie M Reiser
E-mail: areiser@mla.org
Established: 1992
Prize awarded annually for an outstanding scholarly work by a current member of the MLA in the field of comparative literary studies involving at least 2 literatures, published in 2015. For consideration, submit 4 copies.
Award: Cash award & certificate
Closing Date: May 1, 2016
Presented: MLA Convention, Jan 2017

Aldo & Jeanne Scaglione Prize for French & Francophone Studies
Modern Language Association of America (MLA)
26 Broadway, 3rd fl, New York, NY 10004-1789
SAN: 202-6422
Tel: 646-576-5141 *Fax:* 646-458-0030
E-mail: awards@mla.org
Web Site: www.mla.org
Key Personnel
Coord, Book Prizes: Annie M Reiser
E-mail: areiser@mla.org
Established: 1992
Awarded annually for an outstanding scholarly work by a current member of the MLA in the field of French or Francophone linguistic or literary studies published in 2015. Books that are primarily translations will not be considered. For consideration, submit 4 copies.
Award: Cash award & certificate
Closing Date: May 1, 2016
Presented: MLA Convention, Jan 2017

Aldo & Jeanne Scaglione Prize for Italian Studies
Modern Language Association of America (MLA)
26 Broadway, 3rd fl, New York, NY 10004-1789
SAN: 202-6422
Tel: 646-576-5141 *Fax:* 646-458-0030
E-mail: awards@mla.org
Web Site: www.mla.org
Key Personnel
Coord, Book Prizes: Annie M Reiser
E-mail: areiser@mla.org
Established: 2000
Awarded each odd-numbered year to the author of an outstanding scholarly book on any phase of Italian literature or culture or comparative literature involving Italian by a current MLA member for books published in 2016. For consideration, submit 4 copies.
Award: Cash award & certificate
Closing Date: May 1, 2017
Presented: MLA Convention, Jan 2018

Aldo & Jeanne Scaglione Prize for Studies in Germanic Languages & Literatures
Modern Language Association of America (MLA)
26 Broadway, 3rd fl, New York, NY 10004-1789
SAN: 202-6422
Tel: 646-576-5141 *Fax:* 646-458-0030
E-mail: awards@mla.org
Web Site: www.mla.org
Key Personnel
Coord, Book Prizes: Annie M Reiser
E-mail: areiser@mla.org
Established: 1992
Awarded biennially in even-numbered years to a current MLA member for an outstanding scholarly work on the linguistics or literatures of the Germanic languages including Danish, Dutch, German, Icelandic, Norwegian, Swedish & Yiddish & published 2014 or 2015. For consideration, submit 4 copies, a letter identifying the work & confirming the author's membership.
Award: Cash award & certificate
Closing Date: May 1, 2016
Presented: MLA Convention, Jan 2017

Aldo & Jeanne Scaglione Prize for Studies in Slavic Languages & Literatures
Modern Language Association of America (MLA)
26 Broadway, 3rd fl, New York, NY 10004-1789
SAN: 202-6422
Tel: 646-576-5141
E-mail: awards@mla.org
Web Site: www.mla.org
Key Personnel
Coord, Book Prizes: Annie M Reiser
E-mail: areiser@mla.org
Established: 1993
Awarded biennially in odd-numbered years for an outstanding scholarly work on the linguistics or literatures of the Slavic languages published in 2015 or 2016. Works of literary history, literary criticism, philology & literary theory are eligible. Books that are primarily translations will not be considered. Authors need not be members of the MLA. For consideration, submit 4 copies.
Award: Cash award & certificate
Closing Date: May 1, 2017
Presented: MLA Convention, Jan 2018

Aldo & Jeanne Scaglione Publication Award for a Manuscript in Italian Literary Studies
Modern Language Association of America (MLA)
26 Broadway, 3rd fl, New York, NY 10004-1789
SAN: 202-6422
Tel: 646-576-5141 *Fax:* 646-458-0030
E-mail: awards@mla.org
Web Site: www.mla.org
Key Personnel
Coord, Book Prizes: Annie M Reiser
E-mail: areiser@mla.org
Established: 1998
Awarded annually to the author of an outstanding ms dealing with any aspect of the languages & literatures of Italy, including medieval Latin &

comparative studies or intellectual history of the work's main point is related to the humanities. Ms ready or accepted for publication by a member of the AAUP before the award deadline; authors must be current members of the MLA residing in the US or CN. For consideration, submit 4 copies.
Award: Cash award & certificate
Closing Date: Aug 1, 2016
Presented: MLA Convention, Jan 2017

William Sanders Scarborough Prize
Modern Language Association of America (MLA)
26 Broadway, 3rd fl, New York, NY 10004-1789
SAN: 202-6422
Tel: 646-576-5141 *Fax:* 646-458-0030
E-mail: awards@mla.org
Web Site: www.mla.org
Key Personnel
Coord, Book Prizes: Annie M Reiser
E-mail: areiser@mla.org
Established: 2001
Annual prize for an outstanding scholarly study of black American literature or culture published the previous calendar year. Author need not be a member of the MLA. For consideration, submit 4 copies.
Award: Cash award & certificate
Closing Date: May 1, 2016
Presented: MLA Convention, Jan 2017

SCBWI Work-In-Progress Grants
Society of Children's Book Writers and Illustrators (SCBWI)
4727 Wilshire Blvd, Suite 301, Los Angeles, CA 90010
Tel: 323-782-1010; 310-403-0675 (cell) *Fax:* 323-782-1892
E-mail: membership@scbwi.org; scbwi@scbwi.org
Web Site: www.scbwi.org
Key Personnel
Pres: Stephen Mooser *E-mail:* stephenmooser@scbwi.org
Exec Dir: Lin Oliver *E-mail:* linoliver@scbwi.org
Established: 1978
The General Work-In-Progress Grant, the Work-In-Progress Grant for Nonfiction Research, the Work-In-Progress Grant for a Contemporary Novel for Young People & the Grant for a Work by an Author Who Has Never Been Published have been established to assist children's book writers in the completion of a specific project. Must be SCBWI member to qualify.
Award: $2,000 each & $500 for one runner-up in each category
Closing Date: Annually in March
Presented: Annually in Aug

William D Schaeffer Environmental Award
Printing Industries of America
200 Deer Run Rd, Sewickley, PA 15143-2324
Tel: 412-259-1705 *Toll Free Tel:* 800-910-4283 (ext 705) *Fax:* 412-749-9890
E-mail: printing@printing.org
Web Site: www.printing.org/page/3783
Key Personnel
CEO & Pres: Michael F Makin
E-mail: mmakin@printing.org
PPA Coord: Sara Welsh *E-mail:* swelsh@printing.org
Honors significant contributions to environmental awareness by an individual in the printing industry. Entry is free. See web site for more information.
Award: Engraved Plaque
Presented: National Environmental Health & Safety (NEHS) Conference

Bernadotte E Schmitt Grants
American Historical Association (AHA)
400 "A" St SE, Washington, DC 20003
Tel: 202-544-2422 *Fax:* 202-544-8307
E-mail: awards@historians.org
Web Site: www.historians.org
Awarded to support research in the history of Europe, Africa & Asia. Only members of the Association are eligible. The grants are intended to further research in progress & may be used for travel to a library or archive, for microfilms, photographs, or xeroxing, for coding & key punching. Preference will be given to those with specific research needs, such as the completion of a project or completion of a discrete segment thereof. Preference will be given to junior scholars, PhD candidates & those without access to institutional funds. Application form (online), CV & one page bibliography must be submitted by deadline. All updated info on web site. Winners notified by e-mail mid-May.
Award: Individual grants will not exceed $1,000; Preference to PhD candidates & scholars
Closing Date: Annually, Feb 15
Presented: June

Scholastic Library/National Library Week Grant
The American Library Association (ALA)
50 E Huron St, Chicago, IL 60611
Tel: 312-280-2148 *Toll Free Tel:* 800-545-2433 (ext 2148) *Fax:* 312-280-5274
Web Site: www.ala.org/nlwgrant
Key Personnel
Coord, The Campaign for America's Libs: Megan McFarlane *E-mail:* mmcfarlane@ala.org
All types of libraries are encouraged to apply. Presented annually to a single library to support its National Library Week communications initiatives that use the National Library Week theme. See web site for more information & for electronic application submission.
Award: $3,000
Closing Date: Annually, Oct 1
Presented: Annually in Jan

Ruth & Sylvia Schwartz Children's Book Award
Ruth Schwartz Foundation
c/o Ontario Arts Council, 151 Bloor St W, 5th fl, Toronto, ON M5S 1T6, Canada
Tel: 416-961-1660 *Toll Free Tel:* 800-387-0058 (ON) *Fax:* 416-961-7447
E-mail: info@arts.on.ca
Web Site: www.arts.on.ca
Key Personnel
Exec Dir: Alan Walker *Tel:* 416-969-7413
E-mail: awalker@arts.on.ca
Assoc Dir: Ann Boyd *Tel:* 416-969-7411
E-mail: aboyd@arts.on.ca
Assoc Awards Offr: Carolyn Gloude *Tel:* 416-969-7423 *E-mail:* cgloude@arts.on.ca
Established: 1975
Annual awards to recognize artistic excellence in writing & illustration in Canadian children's literature.
Other Sponsor(s): Ontario Arts Council; Ontario Arts Foundation
Award: $6,000 (CN) picture book, $6,000 (CN) young adult/middle reader
Presented: An Ontario public school, Annually in May

Science in Society Journalism Awards
National Association of Science Writers (NASW)
PO Box 7905, Berkeley, CA 94707
Tel: 510-647-9500
Web Site: www.nasw.org
Key Personnel
Exec Dir: Tinsley Davis *E-mail:* director@nasw.org
Established: 1972
Awarded annually to provide recognition for investigative reporting about the sciences & their impact for good & bad, for material published or broadcast between the period of Jan 1-Dec 31. Publishers & broadcasters will also receive certificates of recognition.
Award: $2,500, Certificate of Recognition in each category, travel to awards presentation for 1 author or representative
Closing Date: Feb 1 (postmark)
Presented: Annual Meeting, Oct

The Robert S Sergeant Memorial
The Poetry Society of Virginia
1194 Hume Rd, Hume, VA 22639-1806
E-mail: poetryinva@aol.com
Web Site: www.poetrysocietyofvirginia.org
Key Personnel
Pres: Judith K Bragg *E-mail:* musicsavy45@yahoo.com
Adult Contest Chair: Patsy Anne Bickerstaff *E-mail:* granypatsy@yahoo.com; Guy Terrell *E-mail:* ggterr@infionline.net
All entries must be in English, original & unpublished. Submit 2 copies, each having the category name & number on top left of page. Subject: birds; any form; 48 line limit. Entry fee: $4 nonmembs.
Other Sponsor(s): Alyssa Jenkins; Amber Jenkins; Annika Jenkins
Award: $50
Closing Date: Jan 19
Presented: Annual PSV Awards Luncheon, Richmond, VA, April

SFWA Nebula Awards
Science Fiction & Fantasy Writers of America Inc (SFWA)
PO Box 3238, Enfield, CT 06083-3238
E-mail: office@sfwa.org
Web Site: www.sfwa.org
Key Personnel
Pres: Steven Gould *E-mail:* president@sfwa.org
VP: Cat Rambo *E-mail:* vp@sfwa.org
Treas & CFO: Bud Sparhawk *E-mail:* cfo@sfwa.org
Secy: Susan Forest *E-mail:* secretary@sfwa.org
Established: 1965
Winners are selected by the members of the SFWA in the categories of novel, novella, novelette & short story. Andre Norton award for Outstanding Young Adult Fantasy or Science Fiction first presented in 2006. Also Grand Master for lifetime achievement in science fiction & fantasy, not necessarily awarded annually. Ray Bradbury Award for outstanding dramatic presentation first presented in April 2009.
Award: Lucite trophy for Grand Master & Norton; bronze sculpture for Ray Bradbury Award

Shaughnessy Cohen Prize for Political Writing
The Writers' Trust of Canada
460 Richmond St W, Suite 600, Toronto, ON M5V 1Y1, Canada
Tel: 416-504-8222 *Toll Free Tel:* 877-906-6548 *Fax:* 416-504-9090
E-mail: info@writerstrust.com
Web Site: www.writerstrust.com
Key Personnel
Exec Dir: Mary Osborne *Tel:* 416-504-8222 ext 244
Established: 2000
Awarded for a nonfiction book that captures a political subject of relevance to the Canadian reader & enhances understanding of the issue. The winning work combines compelling new insights with depth of research & is of significant literary merit.
Other Sponsor(s): CTV
Award: $25,000 (winner), $2,500 (finalists)
Presented: Politics & the Pen, Ottawa, ON, CN, Annually in Spring

Mina P Shaughnessy Prize
Modern Language Association of America (MLA)

26 Broadway, 3rd fl, New York, NY 10004-1789
SAN: 202-6422
Tel: 646-576-5141 *Fax:* 646-458-0030
E-mail: awards@mla.org
Web Site: www.mla.org
Key Personnel
Coord, Book Prizes: Annie M Reiser
E-mail: areiser@mla.org
Established: 1980
Biennial prize awarded in even-numbered years for an outstanding scholarly book in the fields of language, culture, literacy & literature with strong application to the teaching of English, published in 2014 or 2015. Authors need not be a member of the MLA. For consideration, submit 4 copies & a letter identifying each work submitted.
Award: Cash award & certificate
Closing Date: May 1, 2016
Presented: MLA Convention, Jan 2017

Short Prose Competition for Developing Writers
The Writers' Union of Canada (TWUC)
600-460 Richmond St W, Toronto, ON M5V 1Y1, Canada
Tel: 416-703-8982 *Fax:* 416-504-9090
E-mail: info@writersunion.ca
Web Site: www.writersunion.ca
Key Personnel
Competitions Coord: Nancy MacLeod *Tel:* 416-703-8982 ext 226 *E-mail:* nmacleod@writersunion.ca
Off Administrator: Valerie Laws *Tel:* 416-703-8982 ext 224
Short prose up to 2,500 words by an unpublished Canadian writer.
Award: $2,500
Closing Date: Annually, March 1

Short Story Award
Prince Edward Island Writers' Guild
115 Richmond St, Charlottetown, PE C1A 1H7, Canada
Tel: 902-368-4410 *Toll Free Tel:* 888-734-2784 *Fax:* 902-368-4418
E-mail: peiwritersguild@gmail.com
Web Site: www.peiwritersguild.com
Key Personnel
Exec Dir: Darrin White *Tel:* 902-368-6176
E-mail: dwhite@peica.ca
One short story, maximum 2500 words, constitutes an entry. May submit as many entries as they wish. Work must be original & unpublished. Contest for Prince Edward Island residents only. Call for further information or e-mail. Entry fee for each submission $20.
Award: $400 (1st prize), $200 (2nd prize), $100 (3rd prize)

Short Story Award for New Writers
Glimmer Train Press Inc
PO Box 80430, Portland, OR 97280-1430
Tel: 503-221-0836 *Fax:* 503-221-0837
E-mail: editors@glimmertrain.org
Web Site: www.glimmertrain.org
Key Personnel
Co-Ed: Susan Burmeister-Brown *E-mail:* susan@glimmertrain.org
Established: 1993
Open to writers whose fiction has not appeared in a print publication with a circulation over 5,000, with a 500-12,000 word count range. Winner notification takes place 2 months after the close of each competition.
Award: $1,500, publication & 20 copies of that issue (1st place), $500 (2nd place), $300 (3rd place)
Closing Date: Annually in Feb, May, Aug & Nov

Edwin "Bud" Shrake Award for Best Short Nonfiction
Texas Institute of Letters (TIL)
c/o 7748 Hwy 290 W, Austin, TX 78736-3202
Tel: 512-683-5640
E-mail: president@texasinstituteofletters.org
Web Site: www.texasinstituteofletters.org
Key Personnel
Pres: Andres Tijerina
VP: Steve Davis
Treas: James Hoggard
Secy: Darwin Payne
Recording Secy: Betty Wiesepape
Annual award for best nonfiction writing appearing in a magazine, journal or other periodical or in a newspaper Sunday supplement. Only one story per entrant. Guidelines on the web site.
Award: $1,000
Closing Date: Annually in Jan
Presented: TIL Awards Banquet, Annually in Spring

Robert F Sibert Informational Book Award
Association for Library Service to Children (ALSC)
Division of The American Library Association (ALA)
50 E Huron St, Chicago, IL 60611-2795
Tel: 312-280-2163 *Toll Free Tel:* 800-545-2433 *Fax:* 312-440-9374
E-mail: alsc@ala.org
Web Site: www.ala.org/alsc
Key Personnel
Exec Dir: Aimee Strittmatter *Tel:* 312-280-2162
E-mail: astrittmatter@ala.org
Awards Coord: Caroline Jewell
E-mail: alscawards@ala.org
Prog Coord: Marsha P Burgess
E-mail: mburgess@ala.org
Presented annually to the author of the most distinguished informational book published in English during the previous year for its significant contribution to children's literature.
Award: Medal
Closing Date: Annually, Dec 31
Presented: ALSC Membership Meeting held during ALA

Silver Gavel Awards
American Bar Association
321 N Clark St, Chicago, IL 60654
Tel: 312-988-5733 *Toll Free Tel:* 800-285-2221 (orders) *Fax:* 312-988-5494
Web Site: www.abanow.org; www.americanbar.org
Key Personnel
Staff Liaison: Howard Kaplan
E-mail: howardkaplan@staff.abanet.org
Div Coord & Contact: Pamela Hollins
E-mail: hollinsp@staff.abanet.org
Established: 1958
Media & arts awards competition to recognize communications media that have been exemplary in fostering public understanding of the law & the legal system during the previous calendar year.
Award: Silver Gavel, Honorable Mentions
Closing Date: Jan
Presented: July

Francis B Simkins Award
Southern Historical Association
University of Georgia, Dept of History, Athens, GA 30602-1602
Tel: 706-542-8848 *Fax:* 706-542-2455
Web Site: sha.uga.edu
Key Personnel
Admin Asst: Shere Dendy *E-mail:* sdendy@uga.edu
Established: 1977
Awarded for the most distinguished first book by an author in Southern history over a 2 year period. Awarded in odd-numbered years for book published in 2 previous calendar years.
Award: Cash
Closing Date: March 1
Presented: Annual meeting (odd-numbered years), Fall

The John Simmons Short Fiction Award
Writers' Workshop, The University of Iowa
102 Dey House, 507 N Clinton St, Iowa City, IA 52242-1000
Tel: 319-335-0416 *Fax:* 319-335-0420
Open to any writer who has not previously published a volume of prose fiction. Revised mss which have been previously entered may be resubmitted as well as writers who have published a volume of poetry are eligible. Mss must be a collection of short stories of at least 150 typewritten pages. Photo copies are acceptable; SASE return packaging must accompany the mss or these will not be returned. No cash, checks, or money orders accepted.
Award: Publication by University of Iowa Press
Closing Date: Annually, Aug 1-Sept 30
Presented: Annually in Autumn

Charlie May Simon Children's Book Award
Arkansas State Library
Arkansas State Library, Suite 100, 900 W Capitol Ave, Little Rock, AR 72201-3108
Tel: 501-682-2860 *Fax:* 501-682-1693
Web Site: www.library.arkansas.gov
Key Personnel
Coord, Children's Progs: Cathy Howser
E-mail: cathy@library.arkansas.gov
Established: 1970
State of Arkansas upper elementary students read books selected by the award committee throughout the year & vote on favorite choice. Most popular book wins award (medallion) & second place award rewarded as Honor Book (plaque).
Other Sponsor(s): Arkansas Department of Education; Arkansas Reading Association
Award: CMS Medallion for 1st place, plaque for Honor Book
Closing Date: Annual vote in April
Presented: Little Rock, AR, Nov

Skipping Stones Honor Awards
Skipping Stones Inc
166 W 12 Ave, Eugene, OR 97401
Mailing Address: PO Box 3939, Eugene, OR 97403
Tel: 541-342-4956
E-mail: info@skippingstones.org
Web Site: www.skippingstones.org
Key Personnel
Exec Ed: Arun N Toke *E-mail:* editor@skippingstones.org
Established: 1993
Honors exceptional multicultural & international awareness books, nature/ecology books, bilingual books, teaching resources & educational videos/DVDs. A panel of parents, teachers, librarians, students & editors of Skipping Stones select the honors list in three categories. Entry fee is $50. Winners announced in the Summer issue of *Skipping Stones* & on our web site.
Award: Honor award certificates, award seals, reviews, press releases, e-releases, web site hyperlinks. Also displayed at NAME (National Association for Multicultural Education) Conference in Nov annually. Publicity in many educational journals
Closing Date: Annually, Feb 1
Presented: May

Slipstream Annual Poetry Chapbook Contest
Slipstream Press
PO Box 2071, Dept W-1, Niagara Falls, NY 14301

Web Site: www.slipstreampress.org
Key Personnel
Co-Ed: Dan Sicoli
Established: 1986
Prize awarded to best 40-page ms of poetry. $20 entry fee.
Award: $1,000 & 50 copies of book
Closing Date: Annually Dec 1

Donald Smiley Prize
Canadian Political Science Association
260 rue Dalhousie St, Suite 204, Ottawa, ON K1N 7E4, Canada
Tel: 613-562-1202 *Fax:* 613-241-0019
E-mail: cpsa-acsp@cpsa-acsp.ca
Web Site: www.cpsa-acsp.ca
Key Personnel
Administrator: Michelle Hopkins
Established: 1995
Awarded to the best book published in French & the best book published in English in a field relating to the study of government & politics in Canada. To be eligible, a book may be single-authored or multi-authored. Single-authored book: author must be a Canadian citizen or a permanent resident of Canada or a member of the CPSA in the year the book was published. Multi-authored book: at least one of the authors must be a Canadian citizen or a permanent resident of Canada or a member of the CPSA in the year the book was published.
Award: Commemorative plaque & also receive/share the set of books submitted in the language of their own book
Presented: Annual Conference, University of Calgary, Calgary, AB, CN, May 31-June 2, 2016

Helen C Smith Memorial Award
Texas Institute of Letters (TIL)
c/o 7748 Hwy 290 W, Austin, TX 78736-3202
Tel: 512-683-5640
E-mail: president@texasinstituteofletters.org
Web Site: www.texasinstituteofletters.org
Key Personnel
Pres: Andres Tijerina
VP: Steve Davis
Treas: James Hoggard
Secy: Darwin Payne
Recording Secy: Betty Wiesepape
Annual award for the first best book of poetry by a poet with a Texas association. Guidelines on the web site.
Other Sponsor(s): William Smith
Award: $1,200
Closing Date: Annually in Jan
Presented: TIL Awards Banquet, Annually in Spring

The Jeffrey E Smith Editors' Prize
The Missouri Review
357 McReynolds Hall, Columbia, MO 65211
Tel: 573-882-4474 *Toll Free Tel:* 800-949-2505 *Fax:* 573-884-4671
Web Site: www.missourireview.com
Key Personnel
Assoc Ed: Evelyn Somers *Tel:* 573-884-7839 *E-mail:* rogerses@missouri.edu
Established: 1991
Awarded annually in fiction, essay & poetry. Entry fee entitles entrant to one-year subscription. Writers should consult web site or send a SASE for guidelines.
Award: $5,000 each (short fiction, essay & poetry) & publication in the Spring issue
Closing Date: Annually, Oct 1
Presented: Spring

Kay Snow Literary Contest
Willamette Writers
2108 Buck St, West Linn, OR 97068
Tel: 503-305-6729 *Fax:* 503-344-6174
E-mail: wilwrite@willamettewriters.com
Web Site: www.willamettewriters.com
Key Personnel
Pres: Jenny Schrader
Off Mgr: Bill Johnson
Contest Coord: Blythe Ayne
Established: 1971
Literary competition in six categories: fiction, nonfiction, juvenile, poetry, scriptwriting, student writer. Entry fee: $10-$15, free for students.
Award: $300 (1st prize), $150 (2nd prize), $50 (3rd prize)
Closing Date: Annually, April 23
Presented: Annual Conference, Aug

The Society of Midland Authors Awards
The Society of Midland Authors (SMA)
530 Michigan Ave, Evanston, IL 60202
Mailing Address: PO Box 10419, Chicago, IL 60610
E-mail: info@midlandauthors.com
Web Site: www.midlandauthors.com
Key Personnel
Pres: Meg Tebo *E-mail:* megteboesq@gmail.com
VP: Robert Loerzel *E-mail:* loerzel@comcast.net
Treas: Richard Bales
Corresponding Secy: Charles J Masters
Recording Secy: Richard Frisbie
Webmaster: Mary Claire Hersh *E-mail:* maryclaire@prodigy.net
Established: 1915
Juried award offers prizes in each of 6 literary categories: children's fiction, children's nonfiction, adult fiction & nonfiction, biography & poetry. Awarded to authors in any of the Midland states: Illinois, Indiana, Iowa, Kansas, Michigan, Minnesota, Missouri, Nebraska, North Dakota, South Dakota, Ohio & Wisconsin.
Award: Monetary award (varies, $500 minimum) & plaque
Closing Date: Annually, Feb 1
Presented: Chicago, IL, Annually, second Tuesday in May

The Society of Southwestern Authors Writing Contest
The Society of Southwestern Authors (SSA)
PO Box 30355, Tucson, AZ 85751-0355
Tel: 520-546-9382 *Fax:* 520-751-7877
E-mail: info@ssa-az.org
Web Site: www.ssa-az.org
Key Personnel
Contest Coord: Ashleen O'Gaea
Established: 1972
Annual awards for short fiction, 2,500 words max; personal essays & memoirs, 2,500 words; poetry, 40 lines; short stories for children ages 6-12, 1,500 words max.
Award: $250 (1st prize), $125 (2nd prize), $75 (3rd prize), $25 (honorable mention)
Closing Date: Oct 31
Presented: Sheraton Fourpoints, Tucson, AZ, Dec 18

Sophie Kerr Prize
Washington College
c/o College Relations Off, 300 Washington Ave, Chestertown, MD 21620
Tel: 410-778-2800 *Toll Free Tel:* 800-422-1782 *Fax:* 410-810-7150
Web Site: www.washcoll.edu
Key Personnel
Dir, Communs: Marcia Landskroener *Tel:* 410-778-7797 *E-mail:* mlandskroener2@washcoll.edu
Established: 1968
Literary award to graduating senior. Only open to undergraduates of Washington College.
Award: $61,000
Closing Date: Annually in April
Presented: Washington College Commencement, Chestertown, MD, Annually in May

Southeast Review Narrative Nonfiction Contest
The Southeast Review
Florida State University, Dept of English, Tallahassee, FL 32306
E-mail: southeastreview@gmail.com
Web Site: www.southeastreview.org
Key Personnel
Ed: Erin Hoover
Established: 1986
Best previously unpublished 6,000 word (max) nonfiction story. Include a brief (100 word) bio. All entries will be considered for publication. $16 entry fee per nonfiction entry.
Other Sponsor(s): FSU English Dept's Creative Writing Program
Award: $500
Closing Date: March

Southeast Review's Gearhart Poetry Contest
The Southeast Review
Florida State University, Dept of English, Tallahassee, FL 32306
E-mail: southeastreview@gmail.com
Web Site: www.southeastreview.org
Key Personnel
Ed: Erin Hoover
Established: 1996
Award for best poem. All entries will be considered for publication. $16 entry fee for up to 3 poems, no more than 10 pages total.
Other Sponsor(s): FSU English Dept's Creative Writing Program
Award: $500
Closing Date: Annually in March

Southeastern Theatre Conference New Play Project
Southeastern Theatre Conference (SETC)
1175 Revolution Mill Dr, Suite 14, Greensboro, NC 27405
Tel: 336-272-3645 *Fax:* 336-272-8810
E-mail: info@setc.org
Web Site: www.setc.org
Key Personnel
Chair, New Play Proj: Todd Ristau
New play contest.
Award: $1,000, travel & expenses publication in *Southern Threatre Magazine*
Closing Date: March-June
Presented: Southeastern Theatre Conference Convention, March of the following yr

Southern Books Competition
Southeastern Library Association
PO Box 950, Rex, GA 30273
Tel: 678-466-4334 *Fax:* 678-466-4349
Web Site: selaonline.org
Key Personnel
Chmn: Lorene Flanders
Admin Servs: Dr Gordon N Baker *E-mail:* gordonbaker@clayton.edu
Established: 1952
Recognition for excellence in bookmaking awarded biennially in even-numbered years for a title published during the previous 2 years. Trade publishers, university presses, specialty publishers & private presses located in Alabama, Arkansas, Florida, Georgia, Kentucky, Louisiana, Mississippi, North Carolina, South Carolina, Tennessee, Virginia, West Virginia or Puerto Rico are eligible to enter the competition. Awards are given based on design, typography & quality of production. Winners are displayed at SELA Conference & in a traveling exhibit available to institutions & organizations. It has been borrowed throughout the South, Canada, Scandinavia, Russia & South Africa.
Award: Published recognition list. Rotating & permanent display of winning books

Closing Date: date fluctuates
Presented: SELA Conference (even-numbered years), Oct

Southern Playwrights Competition
Jacksonville State University, Department of English
700 Pelham Rd N, Jacksonville, AL 36265-1602
Tel: 256-782-5498 *Fax:* 256-782-5441
Web Site: www.jsu.edu/english/southpla.html
Key Personnel
Coord: Sarah Moersch *E-mail:* smoersch@jsu.edu
Established: 1988
Drama.
Award: $1,000 honorarium & possible production of winning entry
Closing Date: Annually, Jan 15

Terry Southern Prize
The Paris Review Foundation
544 W 27 St, New York, NY 10001
Tel: 212-343-1333 *Fax:* 212-343-1988
E-mail: queries@theparisreview.org
Web Site: www.theparisreview.org
Honors "humor, wit & sprezzatura" in work from either *The Paris Review* or the *Daily*.
Award: $5,000

Sovereign Award for Writing
The Jockey Club of Canada
Woodbine Sales Pavilion, 555 Rexdale Blvd, Rexdale, ON M9W 5L2, Canada
Mailing Address: PO Box 66, Sta B, Etobicoke, ON M9W 5K9, Canada
Tel: 416-675-7756 *Fax:* 416-675-6378
E-mail: jockeyclub@bellnet.ca
Web Site: www.jockeyclubcanada.com
Key Personnel
Exec Dir: Stacie Roberts
Established: 1975
Submissions must be of Canadian Thoroughbred Racing content. See guidelines on web site.
Award: Bronze statue of Saint Simon
Closing Date: Annually, Dec 31
Presented: Ontario, CN, Annually, the following April

The Sow's Ear Poetry Prize & The Sow's Ear Chapbook Prize
The Sow's Ear Poetry Review
Division of The Word Process Inc
1748 Cave Ridge Rd, Mount Jackson, VA 22842
E-mail: sepoetryreview@gmail.com
Web Site: sows-ear.kitenet.net
Key Personnel
Mng Ed: Sarah Kohrs
Ed: Kristin Zimet
Established: 1988
Single poem & chapbook.
Award: $1,000 each (poem & chapbook), plus 25 copies
Closing Date: Annually, May 1 (chapbook) , Nov 1 (poem)

Spark Award
Society of Children's Book Writers and Illustrators (SCBWI)
4727 Wilshire Blvd, Suite 301, Los Angeles, CA 90010
Tel: 323-782-1010 *Fax:* 323-782-1892
E-mail: grants@scbwi.org
Web Site: www.scbwi.org
Key Personnel
COO: Sara Rutenberg *E-mail:* sararutenberg@scbwi.org
Established: 2013
Annual award that recognizes excellence in a children's book published through a non-traditional publishing route.
Closing Date: Annually, Dec 15
Presented: March 31

John Spray Mystery Award
Canadian Children's Book Centre
40 Orchard View Blvd, Suite 217, Toronto, ON M4R 1B9, Canada
Tel: 416-975-0010 *Fax:* 416-975-8970
E-mail: info@bookcentre.ca
Web Site: www.bookcentre.ca
Key Personnel
Exec Dir: Charlotte Teeple *E-mail:* charlotte@bookcentre.ca
Lib Coord: Meghan Howe *E-mail:* meghan@bookcentre.ca
Outreach Educ Coord: Sandra O'Brien *E-mail:* sandra@bookcentre.ca
Mktg & Website Coord: Camilia Kahrizi *E-mail:* camilia@bookcentre.ca
Prog Coord: Shannon Howe Barnes *E-mail:* shannon@bookcentre.ca
Established: 2011
Awarded to a Canadian author for excellence in mystery writing for children & adolescents.
Other Sponsor(s): John Spray
Award: $5,000
Closing Date: Annually in mid-Dec

Spur Awards
Western Writers of America Inc (WWA)
271 CR 219, Encampment, WY 82325
Tel: 307-329-8942 *Fax:* 307-327-5465
E-mail: wwa.moulton@gmail.com
Web Site: westernwriters.org
Key Personnel
Pres: Sherry Monahan *E-mail:* president@westernwriters.org
VP: Kirk Ellis *E-mail:* vice-president@westernwriters.org
Exec Dir & Secy-Treas: Candy Moulton *E-mail:* wwa.moulton@gmail.com
Established: 1953
Western fiction/nonfiction (various categories).
Award: Plaques & recognition
Closing Date: Jan 4 of year following publication
Presented: Annual Convention, June

The Edna Staebler Award for Creative Non-Fiction
Wilfrid Laurier University
Office of the Dean, Faculty of Arts, 75 University Ave W, Waterloo, ON N2L 3C5, Canada
Tel: 519-884-1970 (ext 3891) *Fax:* 519-884-8854
Key Personnel
Dean: Michael Carroll *Tel:* 519-884-1970 ext 3891
Established: 1991
Annual literary award for a first or second published book of creative nonfiction published in the previous calendar year. Open to Canadian residents only to encourage new Canadian writers.
Award: $10,000
Closing Date: Annually, April 30 (received by)
Presented: Wilfrid Laurier University, Annually in Autumn

Stanley Drama Award
Wagner College
One Campus Rd, Staten Island, NY 10301
Tel: 718-390-3223 *Fax:* 718-390-3323
Key Personnel
Assoc Professor: Todd Alan Price *E-mail:* todd.price@wagner.edu
Established: 1957
Award given for original full-length play or musical which has not been professionally produced or received tradebook publication. Writers of musicals are urged to submit music on cassette tapes as well as books & lyrics. Consideration will also be given to a series of two or three thematically related one-act plays. Scripts must be accompanied by a SASE. Former winners are not eligible to compete. Applications are obtained by sending SASE, application fee of $30.00 must accompany submission.
Award: $2,000
Closing Date: Oct 31
Presented: Annually in April

Agnes Lynch Starrett Poetry Prize
University of Pittsburgh Press
7500 Thomas Blvd, Pittsburgh, PA 15260
Tel: 412-383-2456 *Fax:* 412-383-2466
E-mail: info@upress.pitt.edu
Web Site: www.upress.pitt.edu
Key Personnel
Asst to Dir: Kelley H Johovic *E-mail:* kjohovic@upress.pitt.edu
Established: 1981
Open to any poet who has not had a full-length book previously published. Submit typed 48-100 page poetry mss on white paper with SASE & check or money order of $25 for each ms submitted. See web site for complete rules.
Award: $5,000 & publication
Closing Date: March 1-April 30 (postmark)
Presented: Pittsburgh, PA, Autumn

Stegner Fellowship
Stanford University Creative Writing Program
Stanford Creative Writing Program, Dept of English, Stanford, CA 94305-2087
Tel: 650-723-0011 *Fax:* 650-723-3679
Web Site: creativewriting.stanford.edu
Key Personnel
Prog Asst: Christina Ablaza *E-mail:* stegnerfellowship@stanford.edu
Fellowship; residence required for 2 years at Stanford beginning autumn quarter each year.
Award: $26,000, required tuition & health insurance
Closing Date: Sept 1-Dec 1

Stephan G Stephansson Award for Poetry
Writers' Guild of Alberta
11759 Groat Rd, Edmonton, AB T5M 3K6, Canada
Tel: 780-422-8174 *Toll Free Tel:* 800-665-5354 (AB only) *Fax:* 780-422-2663 (attn WGA)
E-mail: mail@writersguild.ab.ca
Web Site: www.writersguild.ab.ca
Key Personnel
Exec Dir: Carol Holmes *E-mail:* carol.holmes@writersguild.ab.ca
Communs & Partnerships Coord: Nicholas Mather *E-mail:* nicholas.mather@writersguild.ab.ca
Memb Servs Coord: Giorgia Severini
Progs Coord: Natalie Cook *E-mail:* natalie.cook@writersguild.ab.ca; Nichole Quiring *E-mail:* nichole.quiring@writersguild.ab.ca
Established: 1982
Alberta Literary Award, author must be resident of Alberta.
Award: $1,500 plus leather-bound copy of book
Closing Date: Annually, Dec 31
Presented: Alberta Book Awards Gala
Branch Office(s)
505 21 Ave SW, Calgary, AB T2S 0G9, Canada, Prog Coord: Samantha Warwick *Tel:* 403-265-2226 *Fax:* 403-234-9532 (attn: WGA) *E-mail:* samantha.warwick@writersguild.ab.ca

Bram Stoker Awards®
Horror Writers Association (HWA)
244 Fifth Ave, Suite 2767, New York, NY 10001
E-mail: hwa@horror.org
Web Site: www.horror.org/awards/stokers.htm
Key Personnel
Co-Chmn: Ron Breznay; Norm Rubenstein
11 award categories: Novel, First Novel, Short Fiction, Long Fiction, Young Adult, Fiction Collection, Poetry Collection, Anthology, Screenplay, Graphic Novel & Nonfiction.

The Story Prize
41 Watchung Plaza, No 384, Montclair, NJ 07042
Tel: 973-932-0324
E-mail: info@thestoryprize.org
Web Site: www.thestoryprize.org
Key Personnel
Dir: Larry Dark *E-mail:* ldark@thestoryprize.org
Established: 2004
Annual book award honoring the author of an outstanding collection of short fiction.
Award: $20,000, $5,000 (runners up)
Closing Date: July 15 (books published Jan-June), Nov 15 (books published July-Dec)
Presented: The New School, 66 W 12 St, New York, NY, Annually in March

Elizabeth Matchett Stover Memorial Award
Southwest Review
PO Box 750374, Dallas, TX 75275-0374
Fax: 214-768-1408
E-mail: swr@mail.smu.edu
Web Site: www.smu.edu/southwestreview
Key Personnel
Ed-in-Chief: Willard Spiegelman
Sr Ed: Jennifer Cranfill *Tel:* 214-768-1036
Established: 1978
Awarded annually to the author of the best poem or group of poems published in the Southwest Review during the preceding year.
Award: $300

Jessamy Stursberg Poetry Contest for Youth
The League of Canadian Poets
192 Spadina Ave, Suite 312, Toronto, ON M5T 2C2, Canada
Tel: 416-504-1657 *Fax:* 416-504-0096
E-mail: readings@poets.ca
Web Site: www.youngpoets.ca; poets.ca
Key Personnel
Exec Dir: Joanna Poblocka *E-mail:* joanna@poets.ca
Asst Dir: Ingel Madrus *E-mail:* readings@poets.ca
Admin & Communs Coord: Barbara Erochina *E-mail:* admin@poets.ca
Established: 1995
Seeking poems by young poets across the country. Two age categories: Jr (grades 7-9) & Sr (grades 10-12). All winning poems will be published in the e-zine.
Award: $350 cash (1st place), $300 cash (2nd place), $250 cash (3rd place); all winners will receive certificates & student membership in the League for one yr
Closing Date: Annually, Jan 15
Presented: Young Poets Week each year (2nd week in April)

Sudden Fiction Contest
Berkeley Fiction Review
c/o ASUC Publications, Univ of California, 10-B Eshleman Hall, Berkeley, CA 94720-4500
E-mail: bfictionreview@yahoo.com
Web Site: www.ocf.berkeley.edu/~bfr/
Key Personnel
Mng Ed: Jennifer Brown; Brighton Early
All entries must be 1,000 words or less; typed, double-spaced, with a 12 pt font; include cover letter & e-mail only. Entry fee $6 ($4 each additional story).
Award: $200 1st place; 1st, 2nd & 3rd place are published in upcoming newsletter

The Sugarman Family Award for Jewish Children's Literature
Washington DC Jewish Community Center
Irwin P Edlavitch Bldg, 1529 16 St NW, Washington, DC 20036
Tel: 202-518-9400 *Fax:* 202-518-9420
Web Site: www.washingtondcjcc.org
Key Personnel
Festival Coord: Alena Kranzberg *Tel:* 202-777-3254 *E-mail:* alenak@washingtondcjcc.org
Established: 1994
Award for the best Jewish children's book published between Oct 1, 2013 & Oct 1, 2014. Submissions accepted starting Aug 1. Presented biennially; contact office for dates.
Presented: Hyman S & Freda Bernstein Jewish Literary Festival, Fall

Ronald Sukenick American Book Review Innovative Fiction Prize
Fiction Collective Two Inc (FC2)
c/o Dept of English, Langs & Commun Bldg, 255 S Central Campus Dr, Rm 3500, Salt Lake City, UT 84112-0494
Tel: 773-702-7000
Web Site: www.fc2.org/prizes.html
Key Personnel
Chair, Bd of Dirs: Lance Olsen
Open to any US writer in English who has not previously published with Fiction Collective Two. Submissions may include a collection of short stories, one or more novellas or a novel of any length. Works that have previously appeared in magazines or in anthologies may be included.
Award: $1,500 & publication by FC2
Closing Date: Annually, Nov 1
Presented: Annually in May

Hollis Summers Poetry Prize
Ohio University Press
215 Columbus Rd, Suite 101, Athens, OH 45701-1373
Web Site: www.ohioswallow.com/poetry_prize
Key Personnel
Dir: Gillian Berchowitz *Tel:* 740-593-1159 *E-mail:* berchowi@ohio.edu
This competition invites writers to submit unpublished collections of original poems. Individual collections must be the work of a single author. Translations are not accepted. Submit a ms of 60-95 pages of a poetry collection & a $25 entry fee.
Award: $1,000 & publication
Closing Date: Annually in Oct

May Swenson Poetry Award
Utah State University Press
Division of Utah State University
3078 Old Main Hill, Logan, UT 84322-3078
Tel: 435-797-1362 *Fax:* 435-797-0313
Web Site: www.usupress.org
Key Personnel
Dir: Michael Spooner *E-mail:* michael.spooner@usu.edu
Established: 1996
Submitted collections must be original poetry in English, 50 to 100 pages. No restrictions on form or subject. Submit one copy of the ms. Name/address on cover sheet only. Reading fee of $25 (includes copy of winning book). SASE for announcement of winner. Ms will not be returned. Judge reserves the right to declare no winner in any given year.
Award: $1,000, publication & royalties
Closing Date: Annually, Sept 30 (postmark)

Sydney Taylor Book Awards
Association of Jewish Libraries (AJL) Inc
PO Box 1118, Teaneck, NJ 07666
Tel: 973-744-3836
E-mail: chair@sydneytaylorbookaward.org
Web Site: www.sydneytaylorbookaward.org
Key Personnel
Pres: Heidi Estrin *E-mail:* president@jewishlibraries.org
Contact: Aimee Lurie
Established: 1968
Literary content for outstanding children's books in field of Jewish literature. Three categories of prizes: Younger Readers, Older Readers, Teen Readers.
Award: $500 prize for each category; $500 award to illustrator of Young Readers Award book
Closing Date: Dec 1
Presented: AJL Annual Convention, June

Sydney Taylor Manuscript Award
Association of Jewish Libraries (AJL) Inc
Affiliate of American Library Association (ALA)
204 Park St, Montclair, NJ 07042
E-mail: stmacajl@aol.com
Web Site: www.jewishlibraries.org
Key Personnel
Chpn: Aileen Grossberg
To encourage outstanding Jewish themed fiction written by an unpublished author. Story will appeal to all children ages 8-13 & to help launch new children's writers in their careers.
Award: $1,000
Closing Date: Annually, Sept 30
Presented: AJL Annual Convention, June

Charles S Sydnor Award
Southern Historical Association
University of Georgia, Dept of History, Athens, GA 30602-1602
Tel: 706-542-8848 *Fax:* 706-542-2455
Web Site: sha.uga.edu
Key Personnel
Admin Asst: Shere Dendy *E-mail:* sdendy@uga.edu
Established: 1956
Awarded for the most distinguished book in Southern history published in odd-numbered years. Awarded in even-numbered years.
Award: Cash
Closing Date: March 1
Presented: Annual meeting (even-numbered years), Fall

The Tampa Review Prize for Poetry
Tampa Review
University of Tampa Press, 401 W Kennedy Blvd, Tampa, FL 33606
Tel: 813-253-6266
E-mail: utpress@ut.edu
Web Site: tampareview.ut.edu
Key Personnel
Ed: Richard Mathews
Edit Asst: Sean Donnelly
Established: 2001
Award: $2,000 & book publication in hardcover & paperback
Closing Date: Dec 31

The Charles Taylor Prize
Charles Taylor Foundation
26 Berkeley St, Toronto, ON M5A 2W3, Canada
Tel: 416-901-9314
E-mail: rbctaylorprize@gmail.com
Web Site: thecharlestaylorprize.ca
Key Personnel
Administrator: Su Hutchinson
To enhance public appreciation for literary nonfiction.
Award: $25,000 for winner, $2,000 for each runners up

Rennie Taylor & Alton Blakeslee Fellowships in Science Writing
Council for the Advancement of Science Writing (CASW)
PO Box 910, Hedgesville, WV 25427
Tel: 304-754-6786
Web Site: www.casw.org
Key Personnel
Exec Dir: Rosalind Reid *E-mail:* rosreid@gmail.com

Established: 1975
For tuition & books for graduate study only. Online submissions.
Award: $5,000
Closing Date: March 20, 2016

TD Canadian Children's Literature Award
Canadian Children's Book Centre
40 Orchard View Blvd, Suite 217, Toronto, ON M4R 1B9, Canada
Tel: 416-975-0010 *Fax:* 416-975-8970
E-mail: info@bookcentre.ca
Web Site: www.bookcentre.ca
Key Personnel
Exec Dir: Charlotte Teeple *E-mail:* charlotte@bookcentre.ca
Lib Coord: Meghan Howe *E-mail:* meghan@bookcentre.ca
Outreach Educ Coord: Sandra O'Brien *E-mail:* sandra@bookcentre.ca
Mktg & Website Coord: Camilia Kahrizi *E-mail:* camilia@bookcentre.ca
Prog Coord: Shannon Howe Barnes *E-mail:* shannon@bookcentre.ca
Established: 2004
Awarded to a Canadian author/illustrator for the most distinguished book of the year.
Other Sponsor(s): TD Bank Group
Award: $25,000 cash, 1 to an English language book & 1 to a French language book, $10,000 to an English language honour book (maximum of 4), $10,000 to a French language honour book (maximum of 4), $2,500 to the publishers of the grand prize winning books for promotion & publicity purposes
Closing Date: Annually in mid-Dec

Tennessee Arts Commission Fellowships
Tennessee Arts Commission
401 Charlotte Ave, Nashville, TN 37243-0780
Tel: 615-741-1701 *Toll Free Tel:* 800-848-0299 *Fax:* 615-741-8559
Web Site: www.tn.gov/arts
Key Personnel
Dir, Literary Arts & Grants Analyst: Lee Baird *Tel:* 615-532-0493 *E-mail:* lee.baird@tn.gov
Annual literary fellowships given to Tennessee writers of every genre.
Award: $5,000
Closing Date: Annually, Jan 24

The Texas Bluebonnet Award
Texas Library Association
3355 Bee Cave Rd, Suite 401, Austin, TX 78746
Tel: 512-328-1518 *Toll Free Tel:* 800-580-2852 *Fax:* 512-328-8852
Web Site: www.txla.org
Key Personnel
Progs & Events Asst: Julie Serafini *E-mail:* julies@txla.org
Established: 1979
Awarded to favorite title on annual list, voted on by 200,000 children, grades 3-6.
Other Sponsor(s): Children's Round Table; Texas Association of School Librarians
Award: Medallion in desk mount
Closing Date: Aug 1
Presented: April

Texas Institute of Letters Awards
Texas Institute of Letters (TIL)
c/o 7748 Hwy 290 W, Austin, TX 78736-3202
Tel: 512-683-5640
E-mail: president@texasinstituteofletters.org
Web Site: www.texasinstituteofletters.org
Key Personnel
Pres: Andres Tijerina
VP: Steve Davis
Treas: James Hoggard
Secy: Darwin Payne
Recording Secy: Betty Wiesepape
Established: 1936
Annual award for books published by Texas residents or on Texas-related subjects. Guidelines on the web site.
Award: Eleven cash awards, totalling $21,700
Closing Date: Annually in Jan
Presented: TIL Awards Banquet, Annually in Spring

3-Day Novel Contest
The Geist Foundation
201-111 W Hastings St, Vancouver, BC V6B 1H4, Canada
E-mail: info@3daynovel.com
Web Site: www.3daynovel.com
Established: 1977
Annual international novel writing competition. Entry fee of $50 ($35 early bird) for US & CN entries; may be postmarked up until one day before contest.
Award: Publication (1st prize), $500 (2nd prize), $100 (3rd prize)
Closing Date: Fri before Labor Day (postmark)
Presented: Labor Day weekend

Thurber Prize for American Humor
Thurber House
77 Jefferson Ave, Columbus, OH 43215
Tel: 614-464-1032 *Fax:* 614-280-3645
E-mail: thurberhouse@thurberhouse.org
Web Site: www.thurberhouse.org
Key Personnel
Creative Dir: Susanne Jaffe
Mgr: Anne Touvell *Tel:* 614-464-1032 ext 10
Annual award for the most outstanding book of humor writing published in the US. The award is presented by Thurber House, a nonprofit literary center in Columbus, OH & the former home of American humorist, author & New Yorker cartoonist James Thurber.
Award: $5,000, commemorative plaque & a nationwide media campaign
Closing Date: Annually, April 1
Presented: Caroline's Comedy Club on Broadway, New York City, Fall

James Tiptree Jr Award
James Tiptree Jr Literary Award Council
680 66 St, Oakland, CA 94609
Tel: 510-658-7176
E-mail: info@tiptree.org
Web Site: tiptree.org
Key Personnel
Founder: Karen Joy Fowler; Pat Murphy
Established: 1991
Annual literary prize for science fiction or fantasy that expands or explores our understanding of gender.
Presented: WisCon

Toronto Book Awards
Toronto Cultural Partnerships
Division of City of Toronto
c/o Toronto Arts & Culture, City Hall, 9E, 100 Queen St W, Toronto, ON M5H 2N2, Canada
Web Site: www.toronto.ca/book_awards
Key Personnel
Cultural Devt Offr: Christopher Jones *Tel:* 416-392-6832 *E-mail:* cjones2@toronto.ca
Established: 1974
To honor authors of books of literary or artistic merit that are evocative of Toronto published between January 1 & May 31 the preceding year.
Other Sponsor(s): Toronto Public Library (in partnership)
Award: $15,000 annually, $1,000 to each short listed book, usually 4 books, remainder to winner
Closing Date: Last weekday in April
Presented: Toronto, ON, CN, Shortlist announced in Sept & winner in Oct

Towson University Prize for Literature
Towson University
English Dept, 8000 York Rd, Towson, MD 21252
Tel: 410-704-2000 *Fax:* 410-704-3999
Web Site: www.towson.edu/english
Key Personnel
Chair: Dr H George Hahn
Established: 1979
Annual award for a single book or book-length ms of fiction, poetry, drama or imaginative nonfiction by a Maryland writer. Applicant must have resided in Maryland at least 3 years prior to applying & must be a Maryland resident when the prize is awarded.
Award: $1,000
Closing Date: June 15
Presented: Spring

Trillium Book Award/Prix Trillium
Ontario Media Development Corp (OMDC)
Division of Ministry of Culture, Ontario Government
South Tower, Suite 501, 175 Bloor St E, Toronto, ON M4W 3R8, Canada
Tel: 416-314-6858 (ext 698) *Fax:* 416-314-6876
E-mail: trillium23@omdc.on.ca
Web Site: www.omdc.on.ca
Key Personnel
Consultant, Industry Initiaves: Janet Hawkins *Tel:* 416-642-6698 *E-mail:* jhawkins@omdc.on.ca
Established: 1987
Open to books in any genre; fiction, nonfiction, drama & children's books. There are no restrictions regarding the previous works of the author.
Award: $20,000 to winning authors in English & French; $2,500 to publishers of winning book in English & French
Closing Date: Jan
Presented: Award ceremony, Late Spring

Harry S Truman Book Award
Truman Library Institute
500 W US Hwy 24, Independence, MO 64050
Tel: 816-268-8200 *Toll Free Tel:* 800-833-1225
Web Site: trumanlibraryinstitute.org
Key Personnel
Book Award Administrator: Lisa Sullivan *Tel:* 816-268-8248 *E-mail:* sullivan.hstli@gmail.com
Established: 1963
Presented biennially in even-numbered years for the best book published on the presidency of Harry S Truman. The book must deal with some aspect of the political, economic or social development of the US, principally between April 12, 1945 & Jan 20, 1953 or with the life or career of Truman. Submit 6 copies of the nominated book to Lisa Sullivan, Book Award Administrator. Book must have been published between Jan 1, 2014 & Dec 31, 2015.
Award: $2,500
Closing Date: Before Jan 20, 2016
Presented: No later than May 8 (Truman's birthday), 2016

Trustus Playwrights' Festival
Trustus Theatre
520 Lady St, Columbia, SC 29201
Mailing Address: PO Box 11721, Columbia, SC 29211-1721
Tel: 803-254-9732 *Fax:* 803-771-9153
E-mail: trustus@trustus.org
Web Site: www.trustus.org
Key Personnel
Artistic Dir: Dewey Scott-Wiley
Mng Dir: Larry Hembree
Literary Mgr: Sarah Hammond *E-mail:* shammond@trustus.org
Established: 1988
Experimental, hard-hitting, off-the-wall comedies or dramas suitable for open-minded audiences.

No topic taboo, no musicals or plays for young audiences. Two copies of synopsis, resume & completed application. Send SASE for application & guidelines. Applications available on our web site.
Award: Selected play receives public staged reading & $250, followed by a one-year development period, full production, additional $500, plus travel/accommodations for Festival opening
Closing Date: Dec 1-Feb 1
Presented: Trustus, Aug, full production

Kate Tufts Discovery Award
Claremont Graduate University
Harper East, Unit B-7, 160 E Tenth St, Claremont, CA 91711-6165
Tel: 909-621-8974
E-mail: tufts@cgu.edu
Web Site: www.cgu.edu/tufts
Key Personnel
Poetry Awards Coord: Genevieve Kaplan
Established: 1993
Most worthy first book of poetry published between July 1 & June 30. Award presented for a first book by a poet of genuine promise.
Award: $10,000 cash
Closing Date: Annually, July 1
Presented: Claremont Graduate University, Annually in April

Kingsley Tufts Poetry Award
Claremont Graduate University
Harper East, Unit B-7, 160 E Tenth St, Claremont, CA 91711-6165
Tel: 909-621-8974
E-mail: tufts@cgu.edu
Web Site: www.cgu.edu/tufts
Key Personnel
Poetry Awards Coord: Genevieve Kaplan
Established: 1992
Most worthy book of poetry published between July 1 & June 30. Mss, CDs & chapbooks not accepted. This award honors a poet who is past the very beginning, but has not yet reached the acknowledged pinnacle of his or her career.
Award: $100,000 cash
Closing Date: Annually, July 1
Presented: Claremont Graduate University, Claremont, CA, April

Tupelo Press Poetry Contest for First or Second Books of Poetry
Tupelo Press Inc
PO Box 1767, North Adams, MA 01247
SAN: 254-3281
Tel: 413-664-9611 *Fax:* 413-664-9711
E-mail: info@tupelopress.org
Web Site: www.tupelopress.org
Key Personnel
Mng Ed: Jim Schley
Established: 2000
An annual competition for first or second books of poetry. Full guidelines on the web site.
Award: $3,000 & publication & distribution
Closing Date: Jan 1-April 30
Presented: Summer

Tupelo Press Snowbound Series Chapbook Award
Tupelo Press Inc
PO Box 1767, North Adams, MA 01247
SAN: 254-3281
Tel: 413-664-9611 *Fax:* 413-664-9711
E-mail: info@tupelopress.org
Web Site: www.tupelopress.org
Key Personnel
Mng Ed: Jim Schley
Established: 2004
An annual open poetry chapbook competition. Full guidelines on the web site.
Award: $1,000 & publication
Closing Date: Dec 1-Feb 28
Presented: Spring

The Tusculum Review Prize for Fiction
The Tusculum Review
60 Shiloh Rd, PO Box 5113, Greeneville, TN 37743
Web Site: www.tusculum.edu/tusculumreview
Key Personnel
Ed: Wayne Thomas *Tel:* 423-636-7300 ext 5285 *E-mail:* wthomas@tusculum.edu
Established: 2005
Award: $1,000 & publication in *The Tusculum Review*
Closing Date: March 15

The 25 Most "Censored" Stories Annual
Project Censored - Media Freedom Foundation
PO Box 571, Cotati, CA 94931
Tel: 707-874-2695
Web Site: www.projectcensored.org
Key Personnel
Pres, Media Freedom Foundation: Peter Phillips *E-mail:* peter@projectcensored.org
Dir, Project Censored: Mickey Huff *E-mail:* mickey@projectcensored.org
Established: 1976
Investigative journalism.
Award: Certificate
Presented: Annually, Oct 1

Ucross Foundation Residency Program
Ucross Foundation
30 Big Red Lane, Clearmont, WY 82835
Tel: 307-737-2291 *Fax:* 307-737-2322
E-mail: info@ucross.org
Web Site: www.ucrossfoundation.org
Key Personnel
Pres, Ucross Foundation: Sharon Dynak *E-mail:* sdynak@ucross.org
Residency Mgr: Ruth Salvatore *E-mail:* rsalvatore@ucross.org
Established: 1983
Artist & writer residency program. Approximately 85 individuals per year for 2-6 week lengths of time. Application fee: $40.
Award: Room, studio & board
Closing Date: Annually, March 1 (Fall session) & Oct 1 (Spring session)

University of Iowa, Writer's Workshop
University of Iowa, Writers' Workshop, Graduate Creative Writing Program
102 Dey House, 507 N Clinton St, Iowa City, IA 52242-1000
Tel: 319-335-0416 *Fax:* 319-335-0420
Key Personnel
Dir: Lan Samantha Chang
The Iowa Short Fiction Award; The John Simmons Short Fiction Award. For guidelines & further information send SASE.
Other Sponsor(s): The Iowa Arts Council; University of Iowa Press
Award: Publication
Closing Date: Sept 30
Presented: First quarter

John Updike Award
American Academy of Arts & Letters
633 W 155 St, New York, NY 10032
Tel: 212-368-5900 *Fax:* 212-491-4615
E-mail: academy@artsandletters.org
Web Site: www.artsandletters.org
Key Personnel
Exec Dir: Virginia Dajani
Biennial award to recognize a writer in mid-career who has demonstrated consistent excellence.
Award: $20,000

Utah Original Writing Competition
Utah Division of Arts & Museums
Subsidiary of Utah State Department of Heritage & Arts
617 E South Temple, Salt Lake City, UT 84102
Tel: 801-236-7555 *Fax:* 801-236-7556
Web Site: arts.utah.gov
Key Personnel
Literary Arts Specialist: Alyssa Hickman Grove *Tel:* 801-236-7548 *E-mail:* agrove@utah.gov
Established: 1958
Applicants must be Utah residents. Guidelines & forms posted on web site by April 1.
Award: $8,450 in prizes in 7 categories
Closing Date: Last Friday in June
Presented: Salt Lake City, UT, Annually in Oct

William Van Dyke Short Story Prize
Ruminate Magazine
1041 N Taft Hill Rd, Fort Collins, CO 80521
Tel: 970-449-2726
E-mail: editor@ruminatemagazine.org
Web Site: www.ruminatemagazine.com
Key Personnel
Ed-in-Chief: Brianna Van Dyke
Sr Ed: Amy Lowe
Assoc Ed: Stephanie Lovegrove; Stefani Rossi
All submissions must be previously unpublished & submitted via online submission form. One short story per contest entry, 5,500 words or less. No limit on number of entries per person. Entry fee $15.
Award: $1,000 & publication in Spring issue (1st place), publication only (2nd place)
Closing Date: Annually in Oct

The William Van Wert Memorial Fiction Award
Hidden River™ Arts
PO Box 63927, Philadelphia, PA 19147
Tel: 610-764-0813
E-mail: hiddenriverarts@gmail.com
Web Site: www.hiddenriverarts.org
Key Personnel
Founding Dir: Debra Leigh Scott
Established: 2002
Annual award for a work of unpublished short story or novel excerpt of 25 pages or less. Entry fee: $17.
Award: $1,000 (awarded by mail) & anthology publication
Closing Date: Annually, June 30
Presented: Annually in Dec

VanderMey Nonfiction Prize
Ruminate Magazine
1041 N Taft Hill Rd, Fort Collins, CO 80521
Tel: 970-449-2726
E-mail: editor@ruminatemagazine.org
Web Site: www.ruminatemagazine.com
Key Personnel
Ed-in-Chief: Brianna Van Dyke
Sr Ed: Amy Lowe
Assoc Ed: Stephanie Lovegrove; Stefani Rossi
One nonfiction piece per entry, 5,500 words or less & must be previously unpublished. No limit on number of entries per person. Entry fee $15.
Award: $1,000 & publication in Spring issue
Closing Date: Annually in Feb

Daniel Varoujan Award
New England Poetry Club
2 Farrar St, Cambridge, MA 02138
Mailing Address: 376 School St, Watertown, MA 02472
Tel: 617-744-6034
E-mail: contests@nepoetryclub.org
Web Site: www.nepoetryclub.org
Key Personnel
Pres: Diana Der-Hovanessian
VP: Sally Cragin; Daniel Tobin

Contest Chair: Nazaleem Smith
Established: 1979
Award for an unpublished poem (not a translation) in English worthy of the Armenian poet executed by the Turks in 1915 at the onset of the genocide of the Armenian population; $10 for up to 3 entries & $3 for each additional poem for nonmembs. Send poem in duplicate, name of writer on one only. Previous winners may not enter again.
Other Sponsor(s): Anthology of Armenian Poetry royalties from Diana Der Hovanessian
Award: $1,000
Closing Date: Annually, May 31
Presented: Harvard University, Cambridge, MA, Annually in Autumn

Vermont Arts Council Grants
Vermont Arts Council
136 State St, Montpelier, VT 05602
Tel: 802-828-5425 *Fax:* 802-828-3363
E-mail: info@vermontartscouncil.org
Web Site: www.vermontartscouncil.org
Key Personnel
Dir, Artist & Community Progs: Sonia Rae *Tel:* 802-828-5425 *E-mail:* srae@vermontartscouncil.org
Established: 1965
Individual grants are given to Vermont residents annually.
Award: $250-$1000 Artist Development Grant; $3000 Creation Grants
Closing Date: 1 deadline per year for Creation Grants; rolling deadline for Artist Development Grant

Vermont Studio Center Writer's Program Fellowships
Vermont Studio Center
80 Pearl St, Johnson, VT 05656
Mailing Address: PO Box 613, Johnson, VT 05656
Tel: 802-635-2727 *Fax:* 802-635-2730
E-mail: writing@vermontstudiocenter.org; info@vermontstudiocenter.org
Web Site: www.vermontstudiocenter.org
Key Personnel
Writing Prog Dir: Ryan Walsh *E-mail:* ryan@vermontstudiocenter.org
Prog Dir: Kathy Black *E-mail:* kblack@vermontstudiocenter.org
Accepts 16 writers per month year-round. Fellowship awards are given as funds are available through VSC Fellowships.
Award: 4-week residency
Closing Date: Feb 15, June 15, Oct 1, apply 6 months prior to residency date

Very Short Fiction Award
Glimmer Train Press Inc
PO Box 80430, Portland, OR 97280-1430
Tel: 503-221-0836 *Fax:* 503-221-0837
E-mail: editors@glimmertrain.org
Web Site: www.glimmertrain.org
Key Personnel
Co-Ed: Susan Burmeister-Brown *E-mail:* susan@glimmertrain.org
Established: 1997
Open to short stories under 3,000 words. Winner notification takes place 2 months after the close of each competition.
Award: $1,500, publication & 20 copies of that issue (1st place), $500 (2nd place), $300 (3rd place)
Closing Date: Annually in Jan, April, July & Oct

Jill Vickers Prize
Canadian Political Science Association
260 rue Dalhousie St, Suite 204, Ottawa, ON K1N 7E4, Canada
Tel: 613-562-1202 *Fax:* 613-241-0019
E-mail: cpsa-acsp@cpsa-acsp.ca
Web Site: www.cpsa-acsp.ca
Key Personnel
Administrator: Michelle Hopkins
Awarded to the author or authors of the best paper presented in English or French on the topic of gender & politics.
Award: Commemorative certificate
Presented: Annual Conference, University of Calgary, Calgary, AB, CN, May 31-June 2, 2016

Vicky Metcalf Award for Literature for Young People
The Writers' Trust of Canada
460 Richmond St W, Suite 600, Toronto, ON M5V 1Y1, Canada
Tel: 416-504-8222 *Toll Free Tel:* 877-906-6548 *Fax:* 416-504-9090
E-mail: info@writerstrust.com
Web Site: www.writerstrust.com
Key Personnel
Exec Dir: Mary Osborne *Tel:* 416-504-8222 ext 244
Awarded to a Canadian writer of young people's literature for a body of work.
Other Sponsor(s): George Cedric Metcalf Foundation
Award: $20,000
Presented: The Writers' Trust Awards, Toronto, ON, CN, Annually in Nov

Voelcker Award, see PEN/Voelcker Award

Harold D Vursell Memorial Award
American Academy of Arts & Letters
633 W 155 St, New York, NY 10032
Tel: 212-368-5900 *Fax:* 212-491-4615
E-mail: academy@artsandletters.org
Web Site: www.artsandletters.org
Key Personnel
Exec Dir: Virginia Dajani
Given annually to single out recent prose that merits recognition for the quality of its style.
Award: $20,000

Wag's Revue Writers' Contest
Wag's Revue
2865 W Lyndale St, Suite 1, Chicago, IL 60647
E-mail: editors@wagsrevue.com
Web Site: www.wagsrevue.com
Key Personnel
Mng & Essays Ed: Sandra Allen *Tel:* 415-806-2698 *E-mail:* sandra@wagsrevue.com
Fiction Ed: William Litton *Tel:* 919-475-2497 *E-mail:* willylitt@wagsrevue.com
Poetry Ed: William Guzzardi *Tel:* 919-619-0673 *E-mail:* willguzzo@wagsrevue.com
Interface Developer: John Herr *E-mail:* john@wagsrevue.com
Established: 2009
Online only, twice-annual writers' contest (winter & summer).
Award: $1,000 & guaranteed publication in the forthcoming issue (1st prize), $500 (2nd prize), $100 (third prize); all submissions are considered for publication, unless otherwise announced on our web site
Presented: Feb 28 (Winter), Aug 31 (Summer)

Richard Wall Memorial Award
Theatre Library Association
Roundabout Theatre Co, 231 W 39 St, Suite 1200, New York, NY 10018
Tel: 212-719-9393 (ext 351)
E-mail: info@tla-online.org; tlabookawards@gmail.com
Web Site: www.tla-online.org
Key Personnel
Co-Chair: Linda Miles; Tiffany Nixon
Established: 1973
Honors books published in US in the field of recorded performance including motion picture, TV & radio. Ineligible books are: directories, collections from previously published sources & reprints.
Award: $500 (1st prize), $200 (Special Jury prize); certificate
Closing Date: Feb 28
Presented: New York, NY, Oct

Edward Lewis Wallant Book Award
Dr & Mrs Irving Waltman
3 Brighton Rd, West Hartford, CT 06117
Tel: 860-232-1421
Key Personnel
Sponsor of Award: Fran Waltman; Irving Waltman
Established: 1963
Awarded annually for a creative work of fiction (novel or collection of short stories) significant to American Jews. The author must be American & the book must have been published during the current year.
Award: $500 & scroll
Closing Date: Dec 31

George Washington Book Prize
Washington College, CV Starr Center for the Study of the American Experience
101 S Water St, Chestertown, MD 21620
Tel: 410-810-7165 *Fax:* 410-810-7175
Web Site: starrcenter.washcoll.edu/gw_book_prize
Key Personnel
Book Prize Coord: Lois Kitz *E-mail:* lkitz2@washcoll.edu
Established: 2005
Created to recognize outstanding published works that contribute to a greater understanding of America's Founding era. Books must be published in the year prior to the year prize is awarded. Announcement of finalists on George Washington's Birthday, Feb 22. Announcement of winner at Mount Vernon in May.
Other Sponsor(s): George Washington's Mount Vernon; Gilder Lehrman Institute of American History
Award: $50,000
Closing Date: Dec 1
Presented: Mount Vernon Estate & Gardens, Spring

The Robert Watson Literary Prizes in Fiction & Poetry
The Greensboro Review
MFA Writing Program, The Greensboro Review, UNC-Greensboro, 3302 MHRA Bldg, Greensboro, NC 27402-6170
Tel: 336-334-5459 *Fax:* 336-256-1470
Web Site: www.greensbororeview.org
Key Personnel
Ed: Jim Clark *E-mail:* jlclark@uncg.edu
Assoc Ed: Terry Kennedy *E-mail:* tlkenned@uncg.edu
Established: 1984
Short story - poetry.
Other Sponsor(s): MFA Writing Program at UNC Greensboro
Award: $1,000 (each category)
Closing Date: Annually, Sept 15

Jacqueline Bograd Weld Award for Biography, see PEN/Jacqueline Bograd Weld Award for Biography

Rene Wellek Prize
American Comparative Literature Association (ACLA)
University of South Carolina, Dept of Languages, Literature & Cultures, Rm 813-A, 1620 College St, Columbia, SC 29208
Tel: 803-777-3021 *Fax:* 803-777-3041
E-mail: info@acla.org
Web Site: www.acla.org/awards/rene-wellek-prize; www.acla.org

Key Personnel
Secy & Treas: Alexander Beecroft
Established: 1968
To recognize an outstanding work in the field of comparative literature published in the 2 calendar years prior to presentation. See web site for nomination process.
Award: Complimentary conference registration & banquet ticket as well as travel grant to cover the cost of attending the annual meeting to receive the award in person
Closing Date: Oct 1, 2016
Presented: ACLA Annual Meeting, June 2017

Wergle Flomp Humor Poetry Contest
Winning Writers
351 Pleasant St, PMB 222, Northampton, MA 01060-3961
Tel: 413-320-1847 *Toll Free Tel:* 866-WINWRIT (946-9748) *Fax:* 413-280-0539
Web Site: www.winningwriters.com
Key Personnel
Pres: Adam Cohen *E-mail:* adam@winningwriters.com
VP: Jendi Reiter
Established: 2001
Seeks best humor poems. Both published & unpublished works are welcome. Submit poems in English or inspired gibberish. No entry fee. Contestants may enter one poem per year. Poets from all nations welcome.
Award: $1,000 (1st prize), $100 (10 honorable mentions), plus publication on web site for all winners
Closing Date: Annually, April 1
Presented: Winners announced Aug 15 on web site

Wesley-Logan Prize
American Historical Association (AHA)
400 "A" St SE, Washington, DC 20003
Tel: 202-544-2422 *Fax:* 202-544-8307
E-mail: awards@historians.org
Web Site: www.historians.org
Established: 1992
For an outstanding book in African diaspora history. The prize is offered on some aspect of the history of the dispersion, settlement & adjustment +/or return of peoples originally from Africa. Eligible for consideration are books in any chronological period & any geological location. Only books of high scholarly & literary merit will be considered. Along with an application form, applicants must mail a copy of their book to each of the prize committee members who will be posted on our web site as the prize deadline approaches. All updated info on web site. Books published in 2015 will be considered.
Other Sponsor(s): Association for the Study of Afro-American Life & History
Award: Cash
Closing Date: May 15, 2016 (postmark)
Presented: AHA Annual Meeting, Denver, CO, Jan 5-8, 2017

Western Heritage Awards (Wrangler Award)
National Cowboy & Western Heritage Museum®
1700 NE 63 St, Oklahoma City, OK 73111
Tel: 405-478-2250 *Fax:* 405-478-4714
E-mail: info@nationalcowboymuseum.org
Web Site: www.nationalcowboymuseum.org
Key Personnel
Dir, PR & Museum Events: Shayla Simpson *E-mail:* ssimpson@nationalcowboymuseum.org
Established: 1961
Awarded annually honoring works in TV, film, literary & music which preserve the spirit of the American West.
Award: Bronze sculpture of a cowboy on horseback
Closing Date: Annually, Dec 31 (TV, Film & Literary)
Presented: Banquet & Awards Ceremonies, National Cowboy & Western Heritage Museum, Annually in April (must be in attendance to receive bronze sculpture)

Western Magazine Awards Foundation
875 Prairie Ave, Port Coquitlam, BC V3B 1R9, Canada
Tel: 604-945-3711
E-mail: wma@direct.ca
Web Site: www.westernmagazineawards.ca
Key Personnel
Pres: Rebecca Philps
Exec Dir: Corey Van't Haaf *E-mail:* corey@westernmagazineawards.ca
Established: 1983
Magazine awards honors editorial & artistic excellence in 26 categories; restricted to Western Canadian Publications.
Other Sponsor(s): CSME; Manitoba; Readers Digest; Saskatchewan Ministry of Tourism, Parks, Culture & Support; Amber Webb-Bowerman Memorial Foundation
Award: $1,000 in gold categories & $750 in written & visual categories
Closing Date: Annually in Jan
Presented: Vancouver, BC, CN, June

Hilary Weston Writers' Trust Prize for Nonfiction
The Writers' Trust of Canada
460 Richmond St W, Suite 600, Toronto, ON M5V 1Y1, Canada
Tel: 416-504-8222 *Toll Free Tel:* 877-906-6548 *Fax:* 416-504-9090
E-mail: info@writerstrust.com
Web Site: www.writerstrust.com
Key Personnel
Exec Dir: Mary Osborne *Tel:* 416-504-8222 ext 244
Established: 1997
Awarded for literary exellence in nonfiction, which includes personal or journalistic essays, history, biography, memoirs, commentary & criticism, both social & political.
Award: $60,000 (1st prize), $5,000 (finalists)
Presented: Annually in Nov

Charles A Weyerhauser Book Award
The Forest History Society Inc
701 William Vickers Ave, Durham, NC 27701-3162
Tel: 919-682-9319 *Fax:* 919-682-2349
Web Site: www.foresthistory.org
Key Personnel
Admin Asst: Andrea Anderson *E-mail:* andrea.anderson@foresthistory.org
Established: 1977
Rewards superior scholarship in forest & conservation history. Annual award goes to an author who has exhibited fresh insight into a topic & whose narrative analysis is clear, inventive & thought-provoking. Books are selected by award giver to avoid receipt of too many ineligible books.

E B White Award
American Academy of Arts & Letters
633 W 155 St, New York, NY 10032
Tel: 212-368-5900 *Fax:* 212-491-4615
E-mail: academy@artsandletters.org
Web Site: www.artsandletters.org
Key Personnel
Exec Dir: Virginia Dajani
Established: 2013
Given to a writer for achievement in children's literature.
Award: $10,000

White, Jackie, Memorial National Children's Playwriting Contest, see Jackie White Memorial National Children's Playwriting Contest

William Allen White Children's Book Awards
Emporia State University, William Allen White Library
1200 Commercial St, Emporia, KS 66801-5092
Mailing Address: Emporia State University, Campus Box 4051, Emporia, KS 66801-5092
Tel: 620-341-5208 *Toll Free Tel:* 877-613-7323 *Fax:* 620-341-6208
E-mail: wawbookaward@emporia.edu
Web Site: waw.emporia.edu
Key Personnel
Dean: John Sheridan *E-mail:* jsherida@emporia.edu
Established: 1952
Two children's books are selected by the children of Kansas, grades 3-5 & 6-8, from two master lists of books chosen by a selection committee. When a student has read two books from either of the Master Lists, he or she is eligible to vote at their school (homeschooled vote at their local public library) for the annual White Award winners. Votes are recorded by each school, district or public library & submitted to the William Allen White Children Book Awards Program.
Other Sponsor(s): Trusler Foundation
Award: Two bronze medals, one for each grade level & a $2,500 check for each winner
Closing Date: Votes must be received by April 15
Presented: Emporia State University, Albert Taylor Hall, Winners announced late April & awards presented in Autumn

Whiting Writers' Awards
Mrs Giles Whiting Foundation
1133 Avenue of the Americas, 22nd fl, New York, NY 10036-6710
Tel: 212-336-2138
E-mail: info@whitingfoundation.org
Web Site: www.whitingfoundation.org
Key Personnel
Foundation Exec Dir: Daniel Reid
Foundation Pres: Antonia Grumbach
Awards Dir: Courtney Hodell
Established: 1985
For creative writing in fiction, nonfiction, poetry & plays. Applications not accepted by the foundation; confidential nominators propose candidates for selection committee consideration.
Award: Ten awards of $50,000 each
Presented: Annually, late Oct

Walt Whitman Award
The Academy of American Poets Inc
75 Maiden Lane, Suite 901, New York, NY 10038
Tel: 212-274-0343 *Fax:* 212-274-9427
E-mail: academy@poets.org
Web Site: www.poets.org
Key Personnel
Pres & Exec Dir: Tree Swenson
Exec Dir: Jennifer Benka
Multimedia Prodr: Paul Legault *E-mail:* plegault@poets.org
Awards Coord & Exec Asst: Alex Dimitrov *Tel:* 212-274-0343 ext 15 *E-mail:* adimitrov@poets.org
Established: 1975
Annual award for a book-length ms of poetry by a living American poet who has not published a book of poetry. Visit academy web site for entry form & guidelines.
Award: First book publication $5,000 & a one-month residency at the Vermont Studio Center
Closing Date: Sept 15-Nov 15
Presented: Summer

Jon Whyte Memorial Essay Prize
Writers' Guild of Alberta
11759 Groat Rd, Edmonton, AB T5M 3K6, Canada
Tel: 780-422-8174 *Toll Free Tel:* 800-665-5354 (AB only) *Fax:* 780-422-2663 (attn WGA)
E-mail: mail@writersguild.ab.ca
Web Site: www.writersguild.ab.ca
Key Personnel
Exec Dir: Carol Holmes *E-mail:* carol.holmes@writersguild.ab.ca
Communs & Partnerships Coord: Nicholas Mather *E-mail:* nicholas.mather@writersguild.ab.ca
Memb Servs Coord: Giorgia Severini
Progs Coord: Natalie Cook *E-mail:* natalie.cook@writersguild.ab.ca; Nichole Quiring *E-mail:* nichole.quiring@writersguild.ab.ca
Established: 1992
Awarded to an outstanding essay by an Alberta author; no longer than 3,000 words.
Award: $700
Closing Date: Annually, Dec 31
Presented: Alberta Book Awards Gala
Branch Office(s)
505 21 Ave SW, Calgary, AB T2S 0G9, Canada, Prog Coord: Samantha Warwick *Tel:* 403-265-2226 *E-mail:* samantha.warwick@writersguild.ab.ca

Wichita State University Playwriting Contest
School of Performing Arts
Division of Wichita State University
1845 Fairmount St, Wichita, KS 67260-0153
Tel: 316-978-3360 *Fax:* 316-978-3202
Web Site: www.wichita.edu
Key Personnel
Admin Specialist: Renea Goforth *Tel:* 316-978-6634
For college students only (graduate or undergraduate).
Award: Production of play, transportation & housing for playwright to attend performance
Closing Date: Annually, Jan 15
Presented: Welsbacher Theatre, Wichita State University, Wichita, KS, Annually in Autumn

The Laura Ingalls Wilder Medal
Association for Library Service to Children (ALSC)
Division of The American Library Association (ALA)
50 E Huron St, Chicago, IL 60611-2795
Tel: 312-280-2163 *Toll Free Tel:* 800-545-2433 *Fax:* 312-440-9374
E-mail: alsc@ala.org
Web Site: www.ala.org/alsc
Key Personnel
Exec Dir: Aimee Strittmatter *Tel:* 312-280-2162 *E-mail:* astrittmatter@ala.org
Awards Coord: Caroline Jewell *E-mail:* alscawards@ala.org
Prog Coord: Marsha P Burgess *E-mail:* mburgess@ala.org
Established: 1954
Biennial award presented to an author or illustrator whose books have made a substantial & lasting contribution to children's literature. The books must have been published in the US.
Award: Medal
Presented: ALA Conference

Thornton Wilder Prize for Translation
American Academy of Arts & Letters
633 W 155 St, New York, NY 10032
Tel: 212-368-5900 *Fax:* 212-491-4615
E-mail: academy@artsandletters.org
Web Site: www.artsandletters.org
Key Personnel
Exec Dir: Virginia Dajani
Established: 2009
Recognizes a practitioner, scholar, or patron who has made a significant contribution to the art of literary translation.
Award: $20,000

William Flanagan Memorial Creative Persons Center
Edward F Albee Foundation
14 Harrison St, New York, NY 10013
Tel: 212-226-2020 *Fax:* 212-226-5551
E-mail: info@albeefoundation.org
Web Site: www.albeefoundation.org
Key Personnel
Founder & Pres: Edward Albee
Exec Dir: Jakob Holder
Residency program for writers & visual artists. The only requirements are talent & need.
Award: Room (Writers)/Room & Studio (Visual Artists)
Closing Date: Annually, Jan 1-March 1 for Summer season
Presented: The Barn, Montauk, Long Island, NY, Annually mid-May-mid-Oct, every writer or artist can choose 4 or 6 weeks, depending on availability

Oscar Williams/Gene Derwood Award
NY Community Trust
909 Third Ave, New York, NY 10022
Tel: 212-686-0010 *Fax:* 212-532-8528
E-mail: info@nycommunitytrust.org
Web Site: www.nycommunitytrust.org
Key Personnel
Pres: Lorie Slutsky *Tel:* 212-686-0010 ext 257
SVP: Joyce M Bove *Tel:* 212-686-0010 ext 552
VP, Communs: Ani F Hurwitz *Tel:* 212-686-0010 ext 224 *E-mail:* afh@nyct-cfi.org
Dir, Grants Budgeting: Liza Lagunoff *Tel:* 212-686-0010 ext 559 *E-mail:* ll@nyct-cfi.org
Exec Asst: Barbara Wybraniec *Tel:* 212-686-0010 ext 229
Established: 1971
Intended to help needy or worthy poets & artists who have had long & distinguished careers. Nominations or applications are not accepted in any form.
Award: Cash varies in amount
Presented: Annually

William Carlos Williams Award
Poetry Society of America (PSA)
15 Gramercy Park, New York, NY 10003
Tel: 212-254-9628 *Fax:* 212-673-2352
Web Site: www.poetrysociety.org
Key Personnel
Pres: Ruth Kaplan
Exec Dir: Alice Quinn
Deputy Dir: Brett Fletcher Lauer *E-mail:* brett@poetrysociety.org
Progs Dir: Charif Shanahan *E-mail:* charif@poetrysociety.org
For a book of poetry published by a small press or a nonprofit or university press. Submissions, accompanied by an entry form, from publishers only. Send SASE for complete guidelines.
Award: Purchase prize between $500 & $1,000
Closing Date: Annually, Oct-Dec
Presented: Annually in April

E O Wilson Literary Science Writing Award, see PEN/E O Wilson Literary Science Writing Award

Gary Wilson Award for Short Fiction
Texas Christian University
Texas Christian University, Dept of English, TCU Box 297270, Fort Worth, TX 76129
Tel: 817-257-5907 *Fax:* 817-257-7709
E-mail: descant@tcu.edu
Web Site: www.descant.tcu.edu
Key Personnel
Mng Ed: Dan Williams *E-mail:* d.e.williams@tcu.edu
Established: 2005
For an outstanding story in an issue. No application process, no entry fee; all published submissions are eligible for prize consideration. Submit work with a SASE.
Other Sponsor(s): descant (publication), Dept of English, TCU
Award: $250 cash
Closing Date: Annually, Sept 1-April 1
Presented: Winners announced in journal in the Summer

H W Wilson Co Indexing Award
American Society for Indexing Inc (ASI)
1628 E Southern Ave, Suite 9-223, Tempe, AZ 85282
Tel: 480-245-6750
E-mail: info@asindexing.org
Web Site: www.asindexing.org
Key Personnel
Exec Dir: Gwen Henson *E-mail:* gwen@asindexing.org
Established: 1978
Awarded to the indexer & the publisher of year's best monograph index.
Award: $1,000 & citation (indexer), citation (publisher)
Closing Date: Annually in Feb
Presented: Annual Conference

The H W Wilson Library Staff Development Grant
ALA Awards Program
Affiliate of The American Library Association (ALA)
50 E Huron St, Chicago, IL 60611
Tel: 312-280-3247 *Toll Free Tel:* 800-545-2433 (ext 3247) *Fax:* 312-944-3897; 312-440-9379
E-mail: awards@ala.org
Web Site: www.ala.org
Key Personnel
Prog Off: Cheryl Malden *E-mail:* cmalden@ala.org
To a library organization for a program to further its staff development goals & objectives.
Award: $3,500 & 24k gold-framed citation
Closing Date: Annually, Dec 1
Presented: ALA Annual Conference

Herbert Warren Wind Book Award
USGA Museum & Archives
77 Liberty Corner Rd, Far Hills, NJ 07931-0708
Tel: 908-234-2300 *Fax:* 908-470-5013
Web Site: www.usga.org
Key Personnel
Libn: Nancy Stulack *Tel:* 908-781-1107 *E-mail:* nstulack@usga.org
Established: 1987
Recognizes & honors outstanding contributions to golf literature. Named in honor of the famed golf writer, the award acknowledges & encourages outstanding research, writing & publishing about golf. The award attempts to broaden the public's interest & knowledge in the game of golf. Presented by the USGA Museum & Archives, the Book Award is the top literary prize awarded by the USGA.
Award: Silver inkwell with feather
Closing Date: Annually, Dec 31
Presented: Golf Writer's Association of America Annual Meeting, April

Windham-Campbell Prizes
Yale University, Windham-Campbell Prizes Endowment
Beinecke Library, 121 Whitney Ave, Suite 102, New Haven, CT 06510-1242
Fax: 203-432-9033
Web Site: windhamcampbell.org

Key Personnel
Prog Dir: Michael Kelleher *Tel:* 203-432-2956
Prog Asst: Jennifer Castellon *Tel:* 203-432-7325
Global English-language awards that call attention to literary achievement & provide writers with the opportunity to focus on their work independent of financial concerns. Nomination only. Nine prizes available each year. Categories: Fiction, Nonfiction, Drama.
Award: $150,000 unrestricted grant
Presented: Annually in Spring

The Laurence L & Thomas Winship/PEN New England Award
Boston Globe & PEN New England
MIT, 14N-221A, 77 Massachusetts Ave, Cambridge, MA 02139
Tel: 617-324-1729
E-mail: pen-ne@lesley.edu
Web Site: www.pen-ne.org
Key Personnel
Exec Dir: Karen Wulf
Established: 1975
For a US author who is of New England origin or whose work provides a New England theme or atmosphere. Submit 3 copies. Entry fee is $35.
Award: 3 $1,000 awards
Closing Date: Annually in Dec
Presented: Kennedy Presidential Library, Boston, MA, Annually, April 1

Justin Winsor Prize for Library History Essay
The Library History Round Table of the American Library Association
50 E Huron St, Chicago, IL 60611
Tel: 312-280-4283 *Toll Free Tel:* 800-545-2433 (ext 4283) *Fax:* 312-280-4392
Web Site: www.ala.org
Key Personnel
Prog Offr & LHRT Liaison: R Norman Rose *Tel:* 312-280-4283 ext 4283 *E-mail:* nrose@ala.org
To author of an outstanding essay embodying original historical research on a significant subject of library history.
Award: $100 & invitation to have paper considered for publication in Libraries & the Cultural Record
Closing Date: Jan

WLA Literary Award
Wisconsin Library Association Inc
4610 S Biltmore Lane, Madison, WI 53718
Tel: 608-245-3640 *Fax:* 608-245-3646
Web Site: www.wla.lib.wi.us
Key Personnel
Exec Dir: Lisa K Strand *E-mail:* strand@scls.lib.wi.us
Memb Servs Coord: Brigitte Rupp Vacha *E-mail:* ruppvacha@scls.lib.wi.us
Established: 1974
To honor a work by a Wisconsin author for a book published in the preceding year that contributes to the world of literature & ideas.
Award: Monetary award
Closing Date: End of March
Presented: WLA Annual Conference, Annually Oct-Nov

WNBA Pannell Award for Excellence in Children's Bookselling
Women's National Book Association Inc
435 W 23 St, Suite 8-C, New York, NY 10011
Mailing Address: PO Box 237, FDR Sta, New York, NY 10150-0231
Tel: 212-242-6930
E-mail: pannellaward@gmail.com
Web Site: www.wnba-books.org; www.NationalReadingGroupMonth.org; www.wnba-books.org/awards
Key Personnel
Chair: Susan Knopf *E-mail:* susanknopf04@yahoo.com; Quinlan Lee *E-mail:* quinlan@adamsliterary.com
Established: 1981
Recognizes retail bookstores that excel at creatively bringing books & children together & inspiring children's interest in books & reading. One general book store with a children's section & one children's speciality store are selected each year by a jury of 5 book industry professionals based on creativity, responsiveness to community needs, passion & understanding of children's books & young readers. Supported by Penguin Books for Young Readers.
Award: $2,000 (2 at $1,000 each) plus 1 piece of original art for each recipient
Closing Date: Jan
Presented: BookExpo America

Thomas Wolfe Fiction Prize
North Carolina Writers' Network
PO Box 21591, Winston-Salem, NC 27120-1591
E-mail: mail@ncwriters.org
Web Site: www.ncwriters.org
Key Personnel
Exec Dir: Ed Southern
Competition is open to all writers regardless of geographical location or prior publication. Submit 2 copies of an unpublished fiction ms not to exceed 12 double-spaced pages. Entry fee $15 membs, $25 nonmembs. Submissions accepted Dec 1-Jan 30. Send submissions to Thomas Wolfe Fiction Prize, Great Smokies Writing Program, UNCA, One University Heights, Asheville, NC 28804.
Award: $1,000 & possible publication in *The Thomas Wolfe Review*
Closing Date: Annually, Jan 30

Tobias Wolff Award for Fiction
The Bellingham Review
Mail Stop 9053, Western Washington University, Bellingham, WA 98225
Tel: 360-650-4863
E-mail: bhreview@wwu.edu
Web Site: www.bhreview.org
Key Personnel
Ed-in-Chief: Brenda Miller
Mng Ed: Kaitlyn Teer
Novel excerpts up to 6,000 words are accepted. Poems within a series of poems will each be treated as a separate entry. No previously published works, or works accepted for publication, are eligible. Work may be under consideration elsewhere, but must be withdrawn from the competition if accepted for publication. Make checks payable to: The Bellingham Review. All entries will receive a complimentary one-issue subscription. Entry fee for the first entry (one nonfiction work, one short story, or up to three poems) $20. Each additional entry including each additional poem $10
Only accept submissions through Submittable. Mailed submissions are no longer accepted.
Award: $1,000 & publication in the Bellingham Review (1st prize); considered for publication (2nd, 3rd & finalists)
Closing Date: Annually, between Dec 1 & March 15
Presented: Annually in July

Women's National Book Association Award
Women's National Book Association Inc
PO Box 237, FDR Sta, New York, NY 10150-0231
Tel: 212-208-4629 *Fax:* 212-208-4629
E-mail: publicity@bookbuzz.com
Web Site: www.wnba-books.org; www.NationalReadingGroupMonth.org
Key Personnel
Pres: Valerie Tomaselli
Natl Treas: Gloria Toler
Secy: Annette Marie Haley
PR: Susannah Greenberg
Established: 1940
Presented to a living American woman for her outstanding contribution to the world of books as well as society (through books). Offered biennially in even-numbered years.
Award: Citation
Presented: Varies

The J Howard & Barbara M J Wood Prize
Poetry Magazine
444 N Michigan Ave, Suite 1850, Chicago, IL 60611-4034
Tel: 312-787-7070 *Fax:* 312-787-6650
E-mail: editors@poetrymagazine.org
Web Site: www.poetryfoundation.org
Key Personnel
Mng Ed: Valerie Johnson *E-mail:* vjohnson@poetrymagazine.org
Established: 1994
For poetry published in the preceding two volumes of *Poetry*. No application necessary.
Award: $5,000
Presented: Annually in Dec

Carter G Woodson Book Awards
National Council for the Social Studies
8555 16 St, Suite 500, Silver Spring, MD 20910
Tel: 301-588-1800 *Toll Free Tel:* 800-296-7840 *Fax:* 301-588-2049
E-mail: excellence@ncss.org; publications@ncss.org
Web Site: www.socialstudies.org
Key Personnel
Exec Dir: Susan Griffin *E-mail:* sgriffin@ncss.org
Dir, Meetings & Exhibits: David Bailor *Tel:* 301-588-1800 ext 109 *E-mail:* dbailor@ncss.org
Dir, Pubns: Michael Simpson *Tel:* 301-588-1800 ext 105 *E-mail:* msimpson@ncss.org
External Rel Council Communs Dir: Ana Post *Tel:* 301-588-1800 ext 114 *E-mail:* apost@ncss.org
Prog Mgr: Prema Cordeiro *Tel:* 301-588-1800 ext 106 *E-mail:* pcordeiro@ncss.org
Established: 1974
Annual award established by National Council for the Social Studies to recognize the most distinguished nonfiction books for young readers which depict ethnicity in the US. Eligible books deal with the experiences of one or more racial/ethnic minority groups in the US. Publisher must provide copy of each title for submission requirements.
Award: One elementary (K-6) & one middle level (5-8), one secondary (7-12) annual award, runner-up books designated Woodson Honor Books, seals are now available to publishers $.25 each for less than 1,000 & less for larger quantities
Closing Date: Annually, Sept 30
Presented: Awards Reception, NCSS Annual Conference

Word Works Washington Prize
The Word Works
Adirondack Community College, Dearlove Hall, 640 Bay Rd, Queensbury, NY 12804
Mailing Address: PO Box 42164, Washington, DC 20015
Fax: 301-581-9443
E-mail: editor@wordworksbooks.org
Web Site: www.wordworksbooks.org
Key Personnel
Pres & Chpn of Bd of Dirs: Karren L Alenier
Pres: Nancy White
Established: 1974
Annual prize for an unpublished ms of poetry. Submission may be made by any living American or Canadian writer. Include 2 title pages, one with & one without name, address, telephone number & e-mail. No entry form is re-

quired. Online submissions available. Submissions should be 48-64 pages, in English; please attach $25 entry fee, acknowledgment page & brief bio. Business sized SASE mandatory with entry. Visit web site for guidelines.
Award: $1,500 & publication
Closing Date: March 15

World Fantasy Awards
World Fantasy Awards Association
PO Box 43, Mukilteo, WA 98275-0043
Web Site: www.worldfantasy.org
Key Personnel
Pres: Peter Dennis Pautz *E-mail:* sfexecsec@gmail.com
To acknowledge excellence in fantasy writing & art.
Award: Trophy (bust of H P Lovecraft)
Closing Date: June 1
Presented: World Fantasy Convention, Halloween weekend

World's Best Short-Short Story Contest
The Southeast Review
Florida State University, Dept of English, Tallahassee, FL 32306
E-mail: southeastreview@gmail.com
Web Site: www.southeastreview.org
Key Personnel
Ed: Erin Hoover
Established: 1986
Best 500 word (max) previously unpublished short, short story. All entries will be considered for publication. $16 entry fee for up to 3 stories.
Other Sponsor(s): FSU English Dept's Creative Writing Program
Award: $500
Closing Date: Annually in March

Write Now
Indiana Repertory Theatre Inc
140 W Washington St, Indianapolis, IN 46204-3465
Tel: 317-635-5277 *Fax:* 317-236-0767
E-mail: info@writenow.co
Web Site: www.writenow.co
Key Personnel
Founder: Dorothy Webb *E-mail:* dwebb@irtlive.com
Artistic Dir: Janet Allen *Tel:* 317-635-5277 ext 4800
Established: 1988
Biennial workshop to encourage writers to create artistic theatrical scripts for young audiences. A collaboration between Childsplay & Indiana Repertory Theatre.
Other Sponsor(s): Doris Duke Charitable Foundation
Award: $1,000, development workshop & rehearsed reading (up to 4 winners); certificates for semi-finalists & excerpts read at symposium
Closing Date: July 31, 2016
Presented: Spring 2017

Writer in Residence
Idaho Commission on the Arts
2410 N Old Penitentiary Rd, Boise, ID 83712
Mailing Address: PO Box 83720, Boise, ID 83720-0008
Tel: 208-334-2119 *Toll Free Tel:* 800-ART-FUND (278-3863 within Idaho) *Fax:* 208-334-2488
E-mail: info@arts.idaho.gov
Web Site: www.arts.idaho.gov
Key Personnel
Lit Dir: Cort Conley *Tel:* 208-334-2119 ext 108 *E-mail:* cort.conley@arts.idaho.gov
Open only to residents of Idaho; must have resided in Idaho at least one year. Triennial award for artistic excellence. Recipient tours state & does readings (4 sites annually for 3-year appointment).
Award: $10,000 plus travel expenses (distributed over 3 yr term)
Closing Date: Jan
Presented: Trienially in July

The Writer Magazine/Emily Dickinson Award
Poetry Society of America (PSA)
15 Gramercy Park, New York, NY 10003
Tel: 212-254-9628 *Fax:* 212-673-2352
Web Site: www.poetrysociety.org
Key Personnel
Pres: Ruth Kaplan
Exec Dir: Alice Quinn
Deputy Dir: Brett Fletcher Lauer *E-mail:* brett@poetrysociety.org
Progs Dir: Charif Shanahan *E-mail:* charif@poetrysociety.org
Established: 1971
For a poem inspired by Dickinson (though not necessarily in her style), not to exceed 30 lines. Open to society members only. Send No 10 SASE for guidelines, or visit web site.
Award: $250
Closing Date: Annually, Oct-Dec
Presented: Annual Awards Ceremony, New York, NY, Annually in Spring

Writer's Digest Writing Competition
Writer's Digest Books
Imprint of F+W, A Content + eCommerce Company
10151 Carver Rd, Suite 200, Blue Ash, OH 45242
Tel: 513-531-2690 *Fax:* 513-531-0798
E-mail: writing-competition@fwmedia.com; writersdigest@fwmedia.com (edit)
Web Site: www.writersdigest.com
Key Personnel
Cust Serv: Nicole Florence
Established: 1931
Originally, unpublished mss in 10 categories: Inspirational writing (spiritual/religious); memoirs/personal essay; magazine feature article; genre short story (mystery, romance, etc); mainstream/literary short story; rhyming poetry; non- rhyming poetry; stage play; television/movie script & children's young adult fiction. Poems are $15 for the first entry; $10 for each additional poem submitted in the same online session. All other entries are $25 for the first ms; $15 for each additional ms submitted in the same online session. Refer to web site for current information.
Award: Trip to New York for the Writer's Digest Conference to meet with editors or agents (grand prize); cash, reference books & subscriptions. Refer to web site for current information
Closing Date: Annually in May
Presented: Annually in Oct

Writers-Editors Network International Writing Competition
Florida Freelance Writers Association
Affiliate of Cassell Network of Writers
45 Main St, North Stratford, NH 03590
Mailing Address: PO Box A, North Stratford, NH 03590
Tel: 603-922-8338 *Fax:* 603-922-8339
E-mail: contest@writers-editors.com
Web Site: www.writers-editors.com; www.ffwamembers.com
Key Personnel
Exec Dir: Dana K Cassell *E-mail:* dana@writers-editors.com
Established: 1984
Fiction, nonfiction, juvenile & poetry.
Award: Cash & certificate
Closing Date: Annually, March 15
Presented: Annually, May 31

Writers Guild of America Awards
Writers Guild of America, West (WGAW)
7000 W Third St, Los Angeles, CA 90048
Tel: 323-951-4000; 323-782-4569 *Fax:* 323-782-4800
Web Site: www.wga.org
Key Personnel
Pres: Christopher Keyser
VP: Howard Rodman
Secy & Treas: Carl Gottlieb
Awards: Jennifer Burt
Established: 1948
Annual, any eligible film exhibited for one week during calendar year; original screenplay; adapted screenplay. TV & radio awards. Only members can enter.
Award: Statuette
Closing Date: Annually, Sept 30
Presented: Annual Writer's Guild Award Show, Annually in Feb

Writers' League of Texas Book Awards
Writers' League of Texas (WLT)
611 S Congress Ave, Suite 200 A-3, Austin, TX 78704
Tel: 512-499-8914
E-mail: wlt@writersleague.org
Web Site: www.writersleague.org
Key Personnel
Prog Dir: Jennifer Ziegler *E-mail:* jennifer@writersleague.org
Established: 1991
Members of the Writers' League of Texas annually recognize outstanding books (fiction, nonfiction, poetry & literary prose, children's long & children's short) published in the year prior to presentation. Membership is not required. See web site for complete submission details.
Other Sponsor(s): University Co-op
Award: $1,000 each award, commemorative award & appearance at the Texas Book Festival
Closing Date: Annually, late Feb
Presented: Autumn

Writers' Trust Engel/Findley Prize
The Writers' Trust of Canada
460 Richmond St W, Suite 600, Toronto, ON M5V 1Y1, Canada
Tel: 416-504-8222 *Toll Free Tel:* 877-906-6548 *Fax:* 416-504-9090
E-mail: info@writerstrust.com
Web Site: www.writerstrust.com
Key Personnel
Exec Dir: Mary Osborne *Tel:* 416-504-8222 ext 244
Established: 1986
Presented to a Canadian writer in mid-career. Writers are judged on their body of work-no less than 3 works of literary merit which are predominantly fiction rather than a single book. All Canadian writers are considered.
Award: $25,000
Presented: The Writers' Trust Awards, Toronto, ON, CN, Annually in Nov

The Writers Trust/McClelland & Stewart Journey Prize
The Writers' Trust of Canada
460 Richmond St W, Suite 600, Toronto, ON M5V 1Y1, Canada
Tel: 416-504-8222 *Toll Free Tel:* 877-906-6548 *Fax:* 416-504-9090
E-mail: info@writerstrust.com
Web Site: www.writerstrust.com
Key Personnel
Exec Dir: Mary Osborne *Tel:* 416-504-8222 ext 244
Established: 1988
Awarded to a new & developing writer of distinction for a short story published in a Canadian literary publication.

Other Sponsor(s): James A Michener (donation of his Canadian royalty earnings from his novel *Journey*)
Award: $10,000 (winner), $2,500 (finalists)
Presented: The Writers' Trust Awards, Toronto, ON, CN, Annually in Nov

WritersWeekly.com's 24-Hour Short Story Contest
WritersWeekly
5726 Cortez Rd, Suite 349, Bradenton, FL 34210
Fax: 305-768-0261
Web Site: www.writersweekly.com
Key Personnel
Publr: Angela Hoy *E-mail:* angela@writersweekly.com
Held quarterly & limited to 500 entrants. You must be entered in the contest before the topic is posted in order to submit your story. Late stories are disqualified. Entry fee $5.
Award: $300 (1st prize), $250 (2nd place), $200 (3rd place); All winners will receive publication of their story on the WritersWeekly.com web site & 1 Freelance Income Kit. There will be 30 honorable mentions
Closing Date: 24 hours after contest start

Wyoming Arts Council Literature Fellowships
Wyoming Arts Council
Division of Wyoming Department of Parks & Cultural Resources
2320 Capitol Ave, Cheyenne, WY 82002
Tel: 307-777-5234 *Fax:* 307-777-5499
Web Site: wyoarts.state.wy.us
Key Personnel
Literary, Visual & Performing Arts Specialist: Michael Shay *Tel:* 307-777-5234 *E-mail:* mshay@state.wy.us
Arts Council Mgr: Rita Basom *Tel:* 307-777-7473 *E-mail:* rbasom@state.wy.us
Established: 1986
Awarded annually for the most exciting new creative writing by Wyoming residents. Blind judges & one juror.
Award: $3,000 (three)
Closing Date: June 29
Presented: Casper College Literary Conference, Autumn

Yale Series of Younger Poets
Yale University Press
302 Temple St, New Haven, CT 06511
Mailing Address: PO Box 209040, New Haven, CT 06520-9040
Tel: 203-432-0960 *Fax:* 203-432-0948
Web Site: www.yalebooks.com
Key Personnel
Edit Dir: Christopher Rogers
Asst Ed, History: Erica Hanson
Established: 1919
Awarded annually for poetry mss, 48-64 pages, by early-career American poets who have not previously had a volume of verse published. Submission fee $25. Visit web site for further details.
Award: Publication & royalties
Closing Date: Oct 1-Nov 15

YALSA/VOYA Research Grant, see Frances Henne YALSA/VOYA Research Grant

Anne & Philip Yandle Best Article Award
British Columbia Historical Federation
PO Box 5254, Sta B, Victoria, BC V8R 6N4, Canada
E-mail: info@bchistory.ca; recognition@bchistory.ca
Web Site: www.bchistory.ca
Key Personnel
Pres: Gary Mitchell *E-mail:* president@bchistory.ca
Dir: Shannon Bettles
Awarded annually to the author of an article published in *British Columbia History* that best enhances knowledge of the history of British Columbia & provides enjoyable reading. Judging is based upon subject development, writing skill, freshness of material & its appeal to a general readership interested in all aspects of the history of the province. To be eligible, the article must have appeared in *British Columbia History*.
Award: $250 cash prize & certificate
Closing Date: Dec 31
Presented: Annual Awards Banquet

YES New Play Festival
Northern Kentucky University
205 FA Theatre Dept, Nunn Dr, Highland Heights, KY 41099-1007
Tel: 859-572-6303 *Fax:* 859-572-6057
Key Personnel
Proj Dir: Prof Sandra Forman *E-mail:* forman@nku.edu
Established: 1983
New play contest (biennial).
Award: $500 honoraria, travel & housing for 3 different playwrights to attend fully produced premiers of their plays
Closing Date: Plays accepted May 1-Sept 30 in even-numbered year prior to year of presentation
Presented: April 2017

The Young Adult Book Award
Canadian Library Association-CLA (Association Canadienne des bibliotheques)
1150 Morrison Dr, Suite 400, Ottawa, ON K2H 8S9, Canada
Tel: 613-232-9625 *Fax:* 613-563-9895
E-mail: info@cla.ca
Web Site: www.cla.ca
Key Personnel
Exec Dir: Valoree McKay *Tel:* 613-232-9625 ext 306 *E-mail:* vmckay@cla.ca
Mgr, Mktg & Communs: Judy Green *Tel:* 613-232-9625 ext 322 *E-mail:* jgreen@cla.ca
Established: 1980
Awarded to the author of an outstanding English language Canadian book which appeals to young adults between the ages of 13 & 18. Author must be citizen or resident of CN.
Award: $1,000, cheque & plaques
Closing Date: Annually, Dec 31
Presented: CLA National Conference

Young Lions Fiction Award
New York Public Library
Office of Development, Rm 73, 11 W 40 St, New York, NY 10018
Tel: 212-930-0887 *Fax:* 212-930-0983
E-mail: younglions@nypl.org
Web Site: www.nypl.org
Key Personnel
Assoc Mgr, Young Lions Fiction Award: Isabel Yordan
Established: 2001
Given annually to an American writer age 35 or younger for either a novel or collection of short stories.
Award: $10,000
Closing Date: Aug
Presented: The New York Public Library, May

Phyllis Smart-Young Poetry Prize
The Madison Review
University of Wisconsin, 6193 Helen C White Hall, English Dept, 600 N Park St, Madison, WI 53706
Tel: 608-263-0566
E-mail: madisonrevw@gmail.com
Web Site: www.english.wisc.edu/madisonreview
Key Personnel
Chmn Dept: Prof Thomas Schaub *E-mail:* thschaub@wisc.edu
Faculty Advisor & Prog Coord: Ronald Kuka *E-mail:* rfkuka@wisc.edu
Mss must be previously unpublished & should be double-spaced with standard 1 inch margins & 12-pt font. There is a maximum of 15 pages for combined 3 poems. Only 1 submission is allowed per person per contest. Entry fee $10.
Award: $1,000 & publication in the fall issue of The Madison Review
Closing Date: Feb 1 (postmark)
Presented: Winner announced annually in March

youngARTS
National Foundation for Advancement in the Arts
2100 Biscayne Blvd, Miami, FL 33137
Tel: 305-377-1140 *Toll Free Tel:* 800-970-ARTS (970-2787) *Fax:* 305-377-1149
E-mail: info@nfaa.org
Web Site: www.youngarts.org
Key Personnel
CEO & Pres (NFAA): Christina De Paul *E-mail:* cdepaul@youngarts.org
Dir, Prodns: Roberta B Fliss *Tel:* 305-377-1140 ext 1700 *E-mail:* rfliss@youngarts.org
Established: 1981
Annual cash award & scholarship opportunities for 17-18 year old artists with demonstrated talent in dance, jazz, cinematic arts, music, photography, theater, visual arts, voice & writing. Registration fee: $35.
Award: Up to $10,000 in individual awards with potential for Presidential Scholar in the Arts Award
Closing Date: Annually, Oct 9
Presented: Alumni Performance & Awards Ceremony, The Olympia Theater at the Gunsman Center for the Performing Arts, Miami, FL, Annually in Jan

The Youth Honor Awards
Skipping Stones Inc
166 W 12 Ave, Eugene, OR 97401
Mailing Address: PO Box 3939, Eugene, OR 97403
Tel: 541-342-4956
E-mail: info@skippingstones.org
Web Site: www.skippingstones.org
Key Personnel
Exec Ed: Arun N Toke *E-mail:* editor@skippingstones.org
Established: 1993
Recognizes 10 creative & artistic works (writing, art, photo, essays, etc) by young people that promote multicultural & nature awareness. Entry fee $5. Everyone who enters the awards program receives the Autumn issue with 10 winners & a few noteworthy entries for free.
Award: Ten winners published in our Autumn issue annually & receive an Honor Award Certificate, a subscription to *Skipping Stones* & five nature +/or multicultural books
Closing Date: Annually, June 25
Presented: Winners announced in Autumn issue of *Skipping Stones*

Morton Dauwen Zabel Award
American Academy of Arts & Letters
633 W 155 St, New York, NY 10032
Tel: 212-368-5900 *Fax:* 212-491-4615
E-mail: academy@artsandletters.org
Web Site: www.artsandletters.org
Key Personnel
Exec Dir: Virginia Dajani
Biennial award given in rotation to a poet, writer of fiction, or critic, of progressive, original & experimental tendencies.
Award: $10,000

Anna Zornio Memorial Children's Theatre Playwriting Award
University of New Hampshire Department of Theatre & Dance
D22 Paul Creative Arts Center, 30 Academic Way, Durham, NH 03824
Tel: 603-862-2919 *Fax:* 603-862-0298
Web Site: cola.unh.edu/theatre-dance/resource/zornio
Key Personnel
Admin Mgr: Michael Wood *Tel:* 603-862-3038
E-mail: mike.wood@unh.edu
Chair, Dept of Theatre & Dance: David Kaye
Established: 1980
Award for well written play or musical appropriate for young audiences, PreK-12.
Award: Cash award, up to $500 & play underwritten & produced by the UNH Theatre Department
Closing Date: March 1, 2017
Presented: University of New Hampshire, Durham, NH, Winner announced Nov 2017

Books & Magazines for the Trade

Reference Books for the Trade

All-in-One Media Contacts Directory
Published by Gebbie Press Inc
PO Box 1000, New Paltz, NY 12561-0017
Tel: 845-255-7560 *Toll Free Fax:* 888-345-2790
E-mail: gebbiepress@pipeline.com
Web Site: www.gebbieinc.com
Key Personnel
Pres: Mark Gebbie
Published in three sections. The Daily & Weekly Newspaper Directory section lists contact information for all US daily & weekly newspapers, including Black & Spanish language papers. The Radio & Television Directory section includes, radio & TV stations including Black & Spanish language stations & the Trade & Consumer Directory section includes a comprehensive listing of magazines available in various formats.
Annual (print version).
44th ed, 2015: 462 pp, $165 print, $395 online application or text files
ISBN(s): 978-0-692-30285-9

Almanac of Famous People
Published by Gale
Division of Cengage Learning
27500 Drake Rd, Farmington Hills, MI 48331-3535
SAN: 213-4373
Tel: 248-699-4253 *Toll Free Tel:* 800-877-4253 *Fax:* 248-699-8062 *Toll Free Fax:* 800-414-5043 (orders)
E-mail: gale.galeord@cengage.com
Web Site: www.gale.cengage.com
Key Personnel
Ed: Jennifer Mossman
A guide to sources of biographical information on more than 30,000 prominent persons, past & present, famous & infamous, who are of popular interest. Entries include basic personal data for quick identifications, plus citations to material appearing in biographical sources. Vol 2 indexes the entries chronologically by year & day of birth & death, geographically using places of birth & death, alphabetically by occupation.
10th ed, 2011: 3,000 pp, $267/set
ISBN(s): 978-1-4144-4548-9

American Book Prices Current
Published by Bancroft Parkman Inc
PO Box 1236, Washington, CT 06793-0236
Tel: 860-868-7408; 212-737-2715 *Fax:* 860-868-0080
E-mail: abpc@snet.net
Web Site: www.bookpricescurrent.com
Key Personnel
Publr: Daniel J Leab
Exec Ed: Katharine Kyes Leab
Research price guide detailing prices realized at auction in the USA & abroad in the world of books, mss, autographs, maps, broadsides & charts. Also the proprietor of a series of databases dealing with the prices realized at auction of books recording missing books & mss. Now on CD-ROM only.
1,100 pp, Online price: libr or dealer $595, others $800, update $198.90
ISBN(s): 978-0-914022-38-1

American Book Publishing Record® Annual
Published by Grey House Publishing Inc™
4919 Rte 22, Amenia, NY 12501
Mailing Address: PO Box 56, Amenia, NY 12501-0056
Tel: 518-789-8700 *Toll Free Tel:* 800-562-2139 *Fax:* 518-789-0556
E-mail: books@greyhouse.com
Web Site: www.greyhouse.com
Provides immediate access to the 73,000 cataloging records for the entire previous year, for books published or distributed in the US.
Annual.
2015, $700/2 vol set
ISBN(s): 978-1-61925-628-6 (2 vol set)

American Book Trade Directory
Published by Information Today, Inc
121 Chanlon Rd, Suite G-20, New Providence, NJ 07974-2195
Toll Free Tel: 800-824-2470 *Fax:* 813-855-2309
E-mail: custserv@infotoday.com
Key Personnel
Mgr, Tampa Edit Opers: Debra James *Tel:* 800-824-2470 ext 222 *E-mail:* djames@infotoday.com
Comprehensive directory of over 16,200 booksellers & wholesalers in the US & Canada, arranged by state/province & city; includes information on sidelines, appraisers, auctioneers & dealers in foreign-language books.
Annual.
61st ed, 2015-2016: 1,330 pp, $399
ISBN(s): 978-1-57387-503-5

American Ethnic Writers
Published by Grey House Publishing Inc™
2 University Plaza, Suite 310, Hackensack, NJ 07601
SAN: 208-838X
Tel: 201-968-0500 *Toll Free Tel:* 800-221-1592 *Fax:* 201-968-0511
E-mail: csr@salempress.com
Web Site: salempress.com
Includes summary descriptions of the writer's significance, associated ethnicities, birth/death dates, biography & thorough analysis of the writer's works.
Sept 2008, $217/3 vol set
ISBN(s): 978-1-58765-462-6; 978-1-58765-466-4 (ebook)

American Library Directory
Published by Information Today, Inc
121 Chanlon Road, Suite G-20, New Providence, NJ 07974-2195
Tel: 908-795-3755 *Toll Free Tel:* 800-300-9868 (cust serv); 800-409-4929 (ext 0278) *Fax:* 908-219-0192
E-mail: custserv@infotoday.com
Web Site: www.americanlibrarydirectory.com
Key Personnel
Mng Ed: Stephen L Torpie *Tel:* 908-219-0278 *E-mail:* storpie@infotoday.com
Comprehensive directory of over 31,000 libraries (public, academic & special) throughout the US & CN. Also includes listings of library schools, networks, consortia & state library agencies. Automation & database system vendor information, as well as URLs for libraries & e-mails for library personnel included. Entries arranged geographically. Personnel Index section arranged alphabetically.
Annual.
68th ed, 2015-2016: 4,078 pp, $399/2 vol set cloth
ISBN(s): 978-1-57387-504-2 (2 vol set)

American Reference Books Annual
Published by Libraries Unlimited
Imprint of ABC-CLIO
130 Cremona Dr, Santa Barbara, CA 93117
Mailing Address: PO Box 1911, Santa Barbara, CA 93116-1911
Tel: 805-968-1911 *Toll Free Tel:* 800-368-6868 *Fax:* 805-685-9685 *Toll Free Fax:* 866-270-3856
E-mail: customerservice@abc-clio.com
Web Site: www.abc-clio.com
Key Personnel
Assoc Ed: Shannon Graff Hysell
The premier sources of information for the library & information community for more than 3 decades. Includes descriptive & evaluative entries for recent reference publications. Reviews by subject experts of materials from more than 300 publishers & in nearly 500 subject areas. ARBA assists in answering everyday reference questions & in building a reference collection. Also available online.
Annual.
Vol 46, 2015: 600 pp, $155
ISBN(s): 978-1-4408-3756-2

An Author's Guide to Children's Book Promotion
Published by Raab Associates Inc

730 Yale Ave, Swarthmore, PA 19081
Tel: 914-241-2117
E-mail: info@raabassociates.com
Web Site: www.raabassociates.com
Key Personnel
Partner: Susan Raab
Provides authors & illustrators with the tools they need to get their books into the hands of key decision-makers: teachers, librarians, booksellers & reviewers. The book features a detailed directory of key associations, children's book information sources & trade & educational publications.
11th ed (rev), 2011: 87 pp, $14.95
ISBN(s): 978-096212-118-0

The Art & Science of Book Publishing
Published by Ohio University Press
215 Columbus Rd, Suite 101, Athens, OH 45701-1373
Fax: 740-593-4536
Web Site: www.ohioswallow.com
Key Personnel
Dir: Gillian Berchowitz *Tel:* 740-593-1159 *E-mail:* berchowi@ohio.edu
Author: Herbert S Bailey, Jr
Introduction to basics of book publishing.
1993 ed: 234 pp, $14.95 paper
First published 1970
ISBN(s): 978-0-8214-0970-1

The Association of American University Presses Directory
Published by Association of American University Presses (AAUP)
28 W 36 St, Suite 602, New York, NY 10018
Tel: 212-989-1010 *Toll Free Tel:* 800-621-2736 (orders) *Fax:* 773-702-7212 (orders); 212-989-0275
E-mail: info@aaupnet.org
Web Site: www.aaupnet.org
Key Personnel
Exec Dir: Peter Berkery *Tel:* 212-989-1010 ext 29 *E-mail:* pberkery@aaupnet.org
Dir of Mktg & Communs: Brenna McLaughlin *Tel:* 518-436-3586 *E-mail:* bmclaughlin@aaupnet.org
Off Mgr & Program Administrator: Kim Miller *Tel:* 212-989-1010 ext 26 *E-mail:* kmiller@aaupnet.org
A detailed introduction to the structure & staff of the AAUP & to the publishing programs & personnel of member presses.
Annual.
2015: 265 pp, $30 print, $30 full-access digital, $7 30-day access digital
ISBN(s): 978-0-945103-33-2 (print); 978-0-945103-34-9 (digital)

Authors, Copyright, and Publishing in the Digital Era
Published by IGI Global
701 E Chocolate Ave, Hershey, PA 17033-1240
Tel: 717-533-8845 (ext 100) *Toll Free Tel:* 866-342-6657 *Fax:* 717-533-8661
E-mail: cust@igi-global.com
Web Site: www.igi-global.com
2014: 262 pp, $195
ISBN(s): 978-1-4666-5214-9; 978-1-4666-5215-6 (ebook)

AV Market Place (AVMP)
Published by Information Today, Inc
121 Chanlon Rd, Suite G-20, New Providence, NJ 07974-2195
Tel: 908-795-3755 *Toll Free Tel:* 800-409-4929; 800-300-9868 (cust serv) *Fax:* 908-219-0192
E-mail: custserv@infotoday.com
Key Personnel
Mng Ed: Karen Hallard *Tel:* 908-219-0277 *E-mail:* khallard@infotoday.com
A comprehensive directory of the AV market, listing the activities of almost 5,100 manufacturers, distributors & production service companies & over 1,250 products & services. Heavily indexed. Also contains information on related associations, state & local film & television commissions, awards & festivals, periodicals, reference books & AV-oriented conferences & exhibits. Covers all 50 states plus Canada.
Annual.
43rd ed, 2015: 1,450 pp, $329.50 paper
ISBN(s): 978-1-57387-502-8

Awards & Prizes Online
Published by The Children's Book Council (CBC)
54 W 39 St, 14th fl, New York, NY 10018
Tel: 212-966-1990 *Toll Free Fax:* 888-807-9355 (orders only)
E-mail: cbc.info@cbcbooks.org; awardsandprizes@cbcbooks.org
Web Site: www.cbcbooks.org
Key Personnel
Exec Dir: Jon Colman *E-mail:* jon.colman@cbcbooks.org
Communs Dir: Nicole Deming *E-mail:* nicole.deming@cbcbooks.org
Lists over 300 major US, British Commonwealth & international children's & young adult book awards; for teachers, librarians & universities with English, library or education schools teaching children's literature or creative writing. Includes indices, appendix & a list of information resources.
$150 online

Banned in the USA: A Reference Guide to Book Censorship in Schools & Public Libraries Revised & Expanded Edition
Published by Greenwood Press
Imprint of ABC-CLIO
130 Cremona Dr, Suite C, Santa Barbara, CA 93117
Mailing Address: PO Box 1911, Santa Barbara, CA 93116-1911
Tel: 805-968-1911 *Toll Free Tel:* 800-368-6868 *Fax:* 805-685-9685 *Toll Free Fax:* 866-270-3856
E-mail: customerservice@abc-clio.com
Web Site: www.abc-clio.com
Key Personnel
Dir, Edit-Print: Anthony Chiffolo
Author: Herbert N Foerstel
Foerstel's book is the perfect book to hand to students writing papers on censorship or anyone doing research on the subject.
2002: 328 pp, $72 hardcover
ISBN(s): 978-0-313-31166-6

Be the Media
Published by Natural E Creative Group LLC
1110 Jericho Tpke, 2nd fl, New Hyde Park, NY 11040
Tel: 516-488-1143 *Fax:* 516-488-4111
E-mail: info@bethemedia.com
Web Site: www.bethemedia.com
1st ed: 536 pp, $34.95 US
First published 2009
ISBN(s): 978-0-9760814-5-6

Biography and Genealogy Master Index
Published by Gale
Division of Cengage Learning
27500 Drake Rd, Farmington Hills, MI 48331-3535
SAN: 213-4373
Tel: 248-699-4253 *Toll Free Tel:* 800-877-4253 *Fax:* 248-699-8074 *Toll Free Fax:* 800-414-5043 (orders)
E-mail: gale.galeord@cengage.com
Web Site: www.gale.cengage.com
Key Personnel
Ed: Jennifer Mossman
Provides more than 17 million citations compiled from more than 5,000 editions & volumes for approximately 1,700 current & retrospective biographical sources. Available online, updated twice annually.

Book Blitz, Getting Your Book in the News
Published by Best Sellers
7456 Evergreen Dr, Goleta, CA 93117
Tel: 805-968-8567 *Fax:* 805-968-8567
Key Personnel
Author: Barbara Gaughen *E-mail:* bgaughenmu@aol.com; Ernest Weckbaugh
A hands-on publicity guide for authors; 60 steps for instant book success.
1996: 268 pp, $12.95
ISBN(s): 978-1-881474-02-9

Book Fairs: An Exhibiting Guide for Publishers
Published by Para Publishing LLC
PO Box 8206-240, Santa Barbara, CA 93118-8206
SAN: 215-8981
Tel: 805-968-7277 *Toll Free Tel:* 800-727-2782 *Fax:* 805-968-1379
E-mail: info@parapublishing.com
Web Site: www.parapublishing.com
Key Personnel
Owner & Publr: Dan Poynter *E-mail:* danpoynter@parapublishing.com
5th ed, 2012: 96 pp, $7.95 paper
First published 1981
ISBN(s): 978-0-915516-43-8

Book Fulfillment: Order Entry, Picking, Packing and Shipping
Published by Para Publishing LLC
PO Box 8206-240, Santa Barbara, CA 93118-8206
SAN: 215-8981
Tel: 805-968-7277 *Toll Free Tel:* 800-727-2782 *Fax:* 805-968-1379
E-mail: info@parapublishing.com
Web Site: www.parapublishing.com
Key Personnel
Owner & Publr: Dan Poynter *E-mail:* danpoynter@parapublishing.com
How to set up your publishing company & run your shipping department.
11th ed, 2011: 43 pp, $19.95 paper
ISBN(s): 978-1-56860-037-6

Book Marketing: A New Approach
Published by Para Publishing LLC
PO Box 8206-240, Santa Barbara, CA 93118-8206
SAN: 215-8981
Tel: 805-968-7277 *Toll Free Tel:* 800-727-2782 *Fax:* 805-968-1379
E-mail: info@parapublishing.com
Web Site: www.parapublishing.com
Key Personnel
Owner & Publr: Dan Poynter *E-mail:* danpoynter@parapublishing.com
How to sell books to bookstores, libraries & non-traditional markets.
14th ed: 76 pp, $14.95 paper

Book Review Digest
Published by Grey House Publishing Inc™
4919 Rte 22, Amenia, NY 12501
Mailing Address: PO Box 56, Amenia, NY 12501-0056
Tel: 518-789-8700 *Toll Free Tel:* 800-562-2139 *Fax:* 518-789-0556
E-mail: books@greyhouse.com
Web Site: www.greyhouse.com

Concise critical evaluations, including citations & excerpts from book reviews, from more than 95 selected American, British & Canadian periodicals.
Annual.
Jan 2015 (2014 annual cumulation), $695
ISBN(s): 978-1-61925-279-0

Book Review Index
Published by Gale
Division of Cengage Learning
27500 Drake Rd, Farmington Hills, MI 48331-3535
SAN: 213-4373
Tel: 248-699-4253 *Toll Free Tel:* 800-877-4253 *Fax:* 248-699-8074 *Toll Free Fax:* 800-414-5043 (orders)
E-mail: gale.galeord@cengage.com
Web Site: www.gale.cengage.com
Key Personnel
Ed: Dana Ferguson
Provides review citations for approximately 600 publications. Available as 3 issue subscription or as an annual cumulation.
1,230 pp, $469.99
ISBN(s): 978-1-57302-292-7 (2014 cumulation)

Bookbinding Materials & Techniques 1700-1920
Published by Canadian Bookbinders and Book Artists Guild (CBBAG)
80 Ward St, Suite 207, Toronto, ON M6H 4A6, Canada
Tel: 416-581-1071
E-mail: cbbag@cbbag.ca
Web Site: www.cbbag.ca
Key Personnel
Author: Margaret Lock
160 pp, $20
First published 2003
ISBN(s): 978-0-9695091-9-6

Bookman's Price Index
Published by Gale
Unit of Cengage Learning
27500 Drake Rd, Farmington Hills, MI 48331-3535
SAN: 213-4373
Tel: 248-699-4253 *Toll Free Tel:* 800-877-4253 *Fax:* 248-699-8075 *Toll Free Fax:* 800-414-5043 (orders)
E-mail: gale.galeord@cengage.com
Web Site: www.gale.cengage.com
Key Personnel
Ed: Jeffrey Wilson
A guide to the prices & availability of more rare or out-of-print antiquarian books as offered for sale in the catalogs of leading book dealers in the US, UK & Canada. Each volume lists approximately 15,000 titles. Volumes do not supersede previous volumes. Each volume covers catalogs from the previous 4-6 months. Each entry includes title, author, edition, year published, physical description (size, binding, illustrations), condition of the book & price.
Vol. 95-96, 2012, $625/vol
First published 1964
ISBN(s): 978-1-4144-0661-9 (vol 95); 978-1-4144-4565-6 (vol 96)

Books in Print®
Published by Grey House Publishing Inc™
4919 Rte 22, Amenia, NY 12501
Mailing Address: PO Box 56, Amenia, NY 12501-0056
Tel: 518-789-8700 *Toll Free Tel:* 800-562-2139 *Fax:* 518-789-0556
E-mail: books@greyhouse.com
Web Site: www.greyhouse.com
Serves the library & book trade communities as the definitive bibliographic resource. Features more than 450,000 new titles & more than 500,000 new ISBNs, to offer unparalleled coverage of the full range of books currently published or distributed in the US.
Annual.
2015-2016: 18,000 pp, $1,325/7 vol set
ISBN(s): 978-1-61925-643-9 (7 vol set)

Books in Print® Supplement
Published by Grey House Publishing Inc™
4919 Rte 22, Amenia, NY 12501
Mailing Address: PO Box 56, Amenia, NY 12501-0056
Tel: 518-789-8700 *Toll Free Tel:* 800-562-2139 *Fax:* 518-789-0556
E-mail: books@greyhouse.com
Web Site: www.greyhouse.com
This essential mid-year supplement to *Books In Print*® provides the latest book publishing updates for the past six months. This resource is crucial in ensuring that libraries & bookstores have access to the most accurate information throughout the year.
Annual.
2014-2015: 8,400 pp, $760/3 vol set
ISBN(s): 978-1-61925-621-7 (3 vol set)

Books Out Loud™: Bowker's Guide to Audiobooks
Published by Grey House Publishing Inc™
4919 Rte 22, Amenia, NY 12501
Mailing Address: PO Box 56, Amenia, NY 12501-0056
Tel: 518-789-8700 *Toll Free Tel:* 800-562-2139 *Fax:* 518-789-0556
E-mail: books@greyhouse.com
Web Site: www.greyhouse.com
Must-have collection development & reference tool for your library or bookstore. Offers bibliographic information on over 154,000 audiobooks.
Annual.
2015: 5,800 pp, $480/2 vol set
ISBN(s): 978-1-61925-618-7 (2 vol set)

BookStats
Published by Book Industry Study Group Inc (BISG)
145 W 45 St, Suite 601, New York, NY 10036
Tel: 646-336-7141 *Fax:* 646-336-6214
E-mail: info@bisg.org; info@bookstats.org
Web Site: https://www.bisg.org/publications/bookstats; www.bisg.org; www.bookstats.org
Key Personnel
Proj Mgr, Standards & Best Practices: Julie Morris *Tel:* 646-336-7141 ext 14 *E-mail:* julie@bisg.org
Statistics of book sales by market.
Joint venture with Association of American Publishers (AAP). See https://www.bisg.org/publications/bookstats for all availability & price options. Volume 4 is the final volume in this series.
Vol 4, 2014, PDF Summary Overview (10-15 pp): free membs, $49 nonmembs; single-user PDF Annual Report (60-70 pp): $249 membs, $449 nonmembs

Breathing Life Into Your Characters
Published by Writer's Digest Books
Imprint of F+W, A Content + eCommerce Company
10151 Carver Rd, Suite 200, Blue Ash, OH 45242
Tel: 513-531-2690 *Fax:* 513-531-0798
E-mail: writersdigest@fwmedia.com (edit)
Web Site: www.writersdigest.com; www.writersdigestshop.com
Key Personnel
Publr & Edit Dir: Phil Sexton *E-mail:* phillip.sexton@fwcommunity.com
Learn techniques to help you tap into your own stories & emotions.
256 pp, $11.24
First published 2003
ISBN(s): 978-1-58297-597-9

Business & Legal Forms for Authors & Self-Publishers
Published by Allworth Press
Imprint of Skyhorse Publishing Inc
307 W 36 St, 11th fl, New York, NY 10018
Tel: 212-643-6816 *Fax:* 212-643-6819
Web Site: www.allworth.com
Key Personnel
Founder & Publr: Tad Crawford
E-mail: crawford@allworth.com
Busn Mgr: Marrissa Jones *E-mail:* mjones@skyhorsepublishing.com
Contains 25 ready-to-use forms, negotiation checklist, extra tear-out forms & forms on CD-ROM.
3rd ed, 2005: 160 pp, $29.95 (includes CD-ROM)
ISBN(s): 978-1-58115-395-8

Business Letters for Publishers: Creative Correspondence Outlines
Published by Para Publishing LLC
PO Box 8206-240, Santa Barbara, CA 93118-8206
SAN: 215-8981
Tel: 805-968-7277 *Toll Free Tel:* 800-727-2782 *Fax:* 805-968-1379
E-mail: info@parapublishing.com
Web Site: www.parapublishing.com
Key Personnel
Owner & Publr: Dan Poynter
E-mail: danpoynter@parapublishing.com
A collection of form letters conforming to publishing-industry procedures, designed to save time in drafting letters for sales, promotion, collections & other daily problems on disk.
82 pp, $29.95 electronic version
ISBN(s): 978-0-915516-47-6

Cabell's Directory of Publishing Opportunities in Accounting
Published by Cabell Publishing Co
PO Box 5428, Beaumont, TX 77726-5428
Tel: 409-898-0575; 409-291-2936 (orders) *Fax:* 409-866-9554
E-mail: orders@cabells.com
Web Site: www.cabells.com
Key Personnel
Founder & Pres: David Cabell *E-mail:* dave@cabells.com
COO & Exec Mng Ed: Twyla George
E-mail: twyla@cabells.com
Exec Dir & Sr Ed: Lacey Earle *E-mail:* lacey@cabells.com
Online directory of information on over 273 journals in accounting.
First published 1978

Cabell's Directory of Publishing Opportunities in Business - College/Library Set
Published by Cabell Publishing Co
PO Box 5428, Beaumont, TX 77726-5428
Tel: 409-898-0575; 409-291-2936 (orders) *Fax:* 409-866-9554
E-mail: orders@cabells.com
Web Site: www.cabells.com
Key Personnel
Founder & Pres: David Cabell *E-mail:* dave@cabells.com
COO & Exec Mng Ed: Twyla George
E-mail: twyla@cabells.com
Exec Dir & Sr Ed: Lacey Earle *E-mail:* lacey@cabells.com
Online directory of information on over 2,522 academic journals in business.
First published 1978

Cabell's Directory of Publishing Opportunities in Computer Science-Business Information Systems
Published by Cabell Publishing Co
PO Box 5428, Beaumont, TX 77726-5428
Tel: 409-898-0575; 409-291-2936 (orders)
Fax: 409-866-9554
E-mail: orders@cabells.com
Web Site: www.cabells.com
Key Personnel
Founder & Pres: David Cabell *E-mail:* dave@cabells.com
COO & Exec Mng Ed: Twyla George
E-mail: twyla@cabells.com
Exec Dir & Sr Ed: Lacey Earle *E-mail:* lacey@cabells.com
Information on over 181 journals in computer science & business information systems.

Cabell's Directory of Publishing Opportunities in Economics & Finance
Published by Cabell Publishing Co
PO Box 5428, Beaumont, TX 77726-5428
Tel: 409-898-0575; 409-291-2936 (orders)
Fax: 409-866-9554
E-mail: orders@cabells.com
Web Site: www.cabells.com
Key Personnel
Founder & Pres: David Cabell *E-mail:* dave@cabells.com
COO & Exec Mng Ed: Twyla George
E-mail: twyla@cabells.com
Exec Dir & Sr Ed: Lacey Earle *E-mail:* lacey@cabells.com
Online directory of information on over 839 journals in economics & finance.
First published 1978

Cabell's Directory of Publishing Opportunities in Education, Curriculum & Methods
Published by Cabell Publishing Co
PO Box 5428, Beaumont, TX 77726-5428
Tel: 409-898-0575; 409-291-2936 (orders)
Fax: 409-866-9554
E-mail: orders@cabells.com
Web Site: www.cabells.com
Key Personnel
Founder & Pres: David Cabell *E-mail:* dave@cabells.com
COO & Exec Mng Ed: Twyla George
E-mail: twyla@cabells.com
Exec Dir & Sr Ed: Lacey Earle *E-mail:* lacey@cabells.com
Online indexes of over 490 journals on 28 different topic areas related to educational curriculum & methods.
First published 1981

Cabell's Directory of Publishing Opportunities in Education Set
Published by Cabell Publishing Co
PO Box 5428, Beaumont, TX 77726-5428
Tel: 409-898-0575; 409-291-2936 (orders)
Fax: 409-866-9554
E-mail: orders@cabells.com
Web Site: www.cabells.com
Key Personnel
Founder & Pres: David Cabell *E-mail:* dave@cabells.com
COO & Exec Mng Ed: Twyla George
E-mail: twyla@cabells.com
Exec Dir & Sr Ed: Lacey Earle *E-mail:* lacey@cabells.com
Information on over 1,000 journals in education. Electronic version only.
First published 2009

Cabell's Directory of Publishing Opportunities in Educational Psychology & Administration
Published by Cabell Publishing Co
PO Box 5428, Beaumont, TX 77726-5428
Tel: 409-898-0575; 409-291-2936 (orders)
Fax: 409-866-9554
E-mail: orders@cabells.com
Web Site: www.cabells.com
Key Personnel
Founder & Pres: David Cabell *E-mail:* dave@cabells.com
COO & Exec Mng Ed: Twyla George
E-mail: twyla@cabells.com
Exec Dir & Sr Ed: Lacey Earle *E-mail:* lacey@cabells.com
Online indexes of over 360 journals on 28 different topic areas related to educational psychology & administration.
First published 1981

Cabell's Directory of Publishing Opportunities in Educational Technology & Library Science
Published by Cabell Publishing Co
PO Box 5428, Beaumont, TX 77726-5428
Tel: 409-898-0575; 409-291-2936 (orders)
Fax: 409-866-9554
E-mail: orders@cabells.com
Web Site: www.cabells.com
Key Personnel
Founder & Pres: David Cabell *E-mail:* dave@cabells.com
COO & Exec Mng Ed: Twyla George
E-mail: twyla@cabells.com
Exec Dir & Sr Ed: Lacey Earle *E-mail:* lacey@cabells.com
Online directory of information on over 200 journals in educational technology & library science.
First published 2007

Cabell's Directory of Publishing Opportunities in Health Administration
Published by Cabell Publishing Co
PO Box 5428, Beaumont, TX 77726-5428
Tel: 409-898-0575; 409-291-2936 (orders)
Fax: 409-866-9554
E-mail: orders@cabells.com
Web Site: www.cabells.com
Key Personnel
Founder & Pres: David Cabell *E-mail:* dave@cabells.com
COO & Exec Mng Ed: Twyla George
E-mail: twyla@cabells.com
Exec Dir & Sr Ed: Lacey Earle *E-mail:* lacey@cabells.com
Information on 208 journals listed in health administration.
First published 2010

Cabell's Directory of Publishing Opportunities in Management
Published by Cabell Publishing Co
PO Box 5428, Beaumont, TX 77726-5428
Tel: 409-898-0575; 409-291-2936 (orders)
Fax: 409-866-9554
E-mail: orders@cabells.com
Web Site: www.cabells.com
Key Personnel
Founder & Pres: David Cabell *E-mail:* dave@cabells.com
COO & Exec Mng Ed: Twyla George
E-mail: twyla@cabells.com
Exec Dir & Sr Ed: Lacey Earle *E-mail:* lacey@cabells.com
Online directory of information on over 1,150 journals in management.
First published 1978

Cabell's Directory of Publishing Opportunities in Marketing
Published by Cabell Publishing Co
PO Box 5428, Beaumont, TX 77726-5428
Tel: 409-898-0575; 409-291-2936 (orders)
Fax: 409-866-9554
E-mail: orders@cabells.com
Web Site: www.cabells.com
Key Personnel
Founder & Pres: David Cabell *E-mail:* dave@cabells.com
COO & Exec Mng Ed: Twyla George
E-mail: twyla@cabells.com
Exec Dir & Sr Ed: Lacey Earle *E-mail:* lacey@cabells.com
Online directory of information on over 261 journals in marketing.
First published 1978

Cabell's Directory of Publishing Opportunities in Nursing
Published by Cabell Publishing Co
PO Box 5428, Beaumont, TX 77726-5428
Tel: 409-898-0575; 409-291-2936 (orders)
Fax: 409-866-9554
E-mail: orders@cabells.com
Web Site: www.cabells.com
Key Personnel
Founder & Pres: David Cabell *E-mail:* dave@cabells.com
COO & Exec Mng Ed: Twyla George
E-mail: twyla@cabells.com
Exec Dir & Sr Ed: Lacey Earle *E-mail:* lacey@cabells.com
Information on over 181 academic journals in nursing. Electronic version only.
First published 2010

Cabell's Directory of Publishing Opportunities in Psychology & Psychiatry
Published by Cabell Publishing Co
PO Box 5428, Beaumont, TX 77726-5428
Tel: 409-898-0575; 409-291-2936 (orders)
Fax: 409-866-9554
E-mail: orders@cabells.com
Web Site: www.cabells.com
Key Personnel
Founder & Pres: David Cabell *E-mail:* dave@cabells.com
COO & Exec Mng Ed: Twyla George
E-mail: twyla@cabells.com
Exec Dir & Sr Ed: Lacey Earle *E-mail:* lacey@cabells.com
Online directory of information on 600 journals listed in psychology & psychiatry.
First published 2002

Catholic Press Directory
Published by Catholic Press Association of the United States & Canada
205 W Monroe St, Suite 470, Chicago, IL 60606
Tel: 312-380-6789 *Fax:* 312-361-0256
E-mail: cathjourn@catholicpress.org
Web Site: www.catholicpress.org
Key Personnel
Exec Dir: Timothy M Walter *E-mail:* twalter@catholicpress.org
Opers Analyst: Barbara Mastrolia
Proj Asst: Elise Freed-Brown
Complete listings of more than 600 Catholic newspapers, magazines, newsletters & foreign language publications in the USA & CN. Also includes Catholic book & general publishers; Diocesan directories & media services.
Annual.
2015: 132 pp, $80

CCOD, see Consultants & Consulting Organizations Directory

Chicago Guide to Preparing Electronic Manuscripts
Published by University of Chicago Press
1427 E 60 St, Chicago, IL 60637-2954
SAN: 202-5280
Tel: 773-702-7700 *Toll Free Tel:* 800-621-2736 (orders) *Fax:* 773-702-9756
E-mail: marketing@press.uchicago.edu; custserv@press.uchicago.edu
Web Site: www.press.uchicago.edu

Key Personnel
Exec Ed: Susan Bielstein *Tel:* 773-702-7633
E-mail: smb1@uchicago.edu
A practical guide for authors & publishers who use computer disks & tapes for typesetting.
1987: 151 pp, $40 cloth, $15 paper
ISBN(s): 978-0-226-10392-1 (cloth); 978-0-226-10393-8 (paper)

The Chicago Manual of Style
Published by University of Chicago Press
1427 E 60 St, Chicago, IL 60637-2954
SAN: 202-5280
Tel: 773-702-7700; 773-753-3347 (cust serv, online ed - outside US & CN) *Toll Free Tel:* 800-621-2736 (orders); 877-705-1878 (cust serv, online ed - outside US & CN) *Fax:* 773-702-9756
E-mail: custserv@press.uchicago.edu; marketing@press.uchicago.edu; cmoshelpdesk@press.uchicago.edu
Web Site: www.press.uchicago.edu; www.chicagomanualofstyle.org
Key Personnel
Sr Ed: David Morrow
Style manual for authors, editors & copywriters. Revised every 10 years.
15th ed, revised & expanded, 2003: 984 pp, $55 cloth, $60 CD-ROM
ISBN(s): 978-0-226-10403-4 (cloth); 978-0-226-10404-1 (CD-ROM)

Children's Books in Print®
Published by Grey House Publishing Inc™
4919 Rte 22, Amenia, NY 12501
Mailing Address: PO Box 56, Amenia, NY 12501-0056
Tel: 518-789-8700 *Toll Free Tel:* 800-562-2139 *Fax:* 518-789-0556
E-mail: books@greyhouse.com
Web Site: www.greyhouse.com
Vital resource for locating children's & young adult titles in the US, offering immediate access to over 250,000 children's books from over 18,000 US publishers.
Annual.
2015: 3,500 pp, $605/2 vol set
ISBN(s): 978-1-61925-385-8 (2 vol set)

Children's Core Collection
Published by Grey House Publishing Inc™
4919 Rte 22, Amenia, NY 12501
Mailing Address: PO Box 56, Amenia, NY 12501-0056
Tel: 518-789-8700 *Toll Free Tel:* 800-562-2139 *Fax:* 518-789-0556
E-mail: books@greyhouse.com
Web Site: www.greyhouse.com
Guide to approximately 12,000 books, covering fiction & nonfiction works, story collections, picture books, graphic novels & magazines recommended for readers from preschool through grade 6.
22nd ed, Nov 2015: 2,500 pp, $240/2 vol set
ISBN(s): 978-1-61925-705-4 (2 vol set)

Children's Literature Review
Published by Gale
Unit of Cengage Learning
27500 Drake Rd, Farmington Hills, MI 48331-3535
SAN: 213-4373
Tel: 248-699-4253 *Toll Free Tel:* 800-877-4253 *Fax:* 248-699-8054 *Toll Free Fax:* 800-414-5043 (orders)
E-mail: gale.galeord@cengage.com
Web Site: www.gale.cengage.com
Key Personnel
Ed: Jelena Krstovic
Provides full texts from criticism on authors & illustrators of books for children & young adults. Includes indexes to titles, authors & nationality. A cumulative title index to the entire series is published seperately (included in subscription). Illustrations & photographs are included. Also available as an ebook.

Children's Writer's Word Book
Published by Writer's Digest Books
Imprint of F+W, A Content + eCommerce Company
10151 Carver Rd, Suite 200, Blue Ash, OH 45242
Tel: 513-531-2690 *Toll Free Tel:* 800-289-0963 *Fax:* 513-531-0798
E-mail: writersdigest@fwmedia.com (edit)
Web Site: www.writersdigest.com; www.writersdigestshop.com
Key Personnel
Publr & Edit Dir: Phil Sexton *E-mail:* phillip.sexton@fwcommunity.com
Handy reference book to be used along with your dictionary or thesaurus. Gives guidelines for sentence length, word usage & theme at each reading level.
2nd ed: 352 pp, $11.48
First published 1999
ISBN(s): 978-1-58297-413-2

Christian Book Writers' Marketing Guide
Published by Joy Publishing Co
Division of California Clock Co
PO Box 9901, Fountain Valley, CA 92708
Tel: 714-545-4321 *Toll Free Tel:* 800-454-8228 *Fax:* 714-708-2099
E-mail: mail@joypublishing.com
Web Site: www.joypublishing.com
Key Personnel
Pres: Woody Young *E-mail:* woody@joypublishing.com
Info on publishers (books & periodicals).
2001: 273 pp, $19.95
ISBN(s): 973-0-939513-00-0

Classics of Science Fiction & Fantasy Literature
Published by Grey House Publishing Inc™
2 University Plaza, Suite 310, Hackensack, NJ 07601
SAN: 208-838X
Tel: 201-968-0500 *Toll Free Tel:* 800-221-1592 *Fax:* 201-968-0511
E-mail: csr@salempress.com
Web Site: salempress.com
Plot summaries & analyses of 180 major books & series in the genres of science fiction & fantasy.
March 2002, $130/2 vol set
ISBN(s): 978-1-58765-050-5; 978-1-58765-183-0 (ebook)

Communicating Ideas: The Politics of Publishing in a Post-Industrial Society
Published by Transaction Publishers Inc
10 Corporate Place S, Piscataway, NJ 08854
Mailing Address: 1247 State Rd, Princeton, NJ 08540
Tel: 732-445-2280 *Fax:* 732-445-3138
Web Site: www.transactionpub.com
View of publishing in America & abroad. Addresses the political implications of scholarly communication in the era of the new computerized technology. This title was originally published by Oxford University Press.
3rd ed, 2010: 356 pp, $27.95 (2nd ed) paper
First published 1988
ISBN(s): 978-0-88738-898-9 (2nd ed)

The Complete Directory of Large Print Books & Serials™
Published by Grey House Publishing Inc™
4919 Rte 22, Amenia, NY 12501
Mailing Address: PO Box 56, Amenia, NY 12501-0056
Tel: 518-789-8700 *Toll Free Tel:* 800-562-2139 *Fax:* 518-789-0556
E-mail: books@greyhouse.com
Web Site: www.greyhouse.com
Important resource for building a large print books or serials collection containing detailed data on over 32,000 large print active titles.
2013: 2,600 pp, $475
ISBN(s): 978-1-16925-053-6

The Complete Guide to Book Marketing
Published by Allworth Press
Subsidiary of Allworth Communications Inc
Imprint of Skyhorse Publishing Inc
307 W 36 St, 11th fl, New York, NY 10018
Tel: 212-643-6816 *Fax:* 212-643-6819
Web Site: www.allworth.com
Key Personnel
Founder & Publr: Tad Crawford
E-mail: crawford@allworth.com
Busn Mgr: Marrissa Jones *E-mail:* mjones@skyhorsepublishing.com
Author: David Cole
Comprehensive resource book covering all aspects of book marketing.
2004 (rev): 256 pp, $19.95
ISBN(s): 978-1-58115-322-4

The Complete Guide to Book Publicity
Published by Allworth Press
Imprint of Skyhorse Publishing Inc
307 W 36 St, 11th fl, New York, NY 10018
Tel: 212-643-6816 *Fax:* 212-643-6819
Web Site: www.allworth.com
Key Personnel
Founder & Publr: Tad Crawford
E-mail: crawford@allworth.com
Busn Mgr: Marrissa Jones *E-mail:* mjones@skyhorsepublishing.com
Author: Jodee Blanco
A comprehensive resource book covering all aspects of book publicity.
2nd ed, 2004: 304 pp, $19.95
ISBN(s): 978-1-58115-349-1

The Complete Guide to Self-Publishing
Published by Writer's Digest Books
Imprint of F+W, A Content + eCommerce Company
10151 Carver Rd, Suite 200, Blue Ash, OH 45242
Tel: 513-531-2690 *Toll Free Tel:* 800-289-0963 *Fax:* 513-531-0798
E-mail: writersdigest@fwmedia.com (edit)
Web Site: www.writersdigest.com; www.writersdigestshop.com
Key Personnel
Publr & Edit Dir: Phil Sexton *E-mail:* phillip.sexton@fwcommunity.com
Everything you need to write, publish, promote & sell your book.
5th ed: 576 pp, $16.32 paper
First published 1991
ISBN(s): 978-1-58297-711-8

The Complete Guide to Successful Publishing
Published by Cardoza Publishing
808 S Main St, Las Vegas, NV 89101
Tel: 702-870-7200 *Toll Free Tel:* 800-577-WINS (577-9467)
E-mail: info@cardozabooks.com; cardozabooks@aol.com
Web Site: www.cardozabooks.com
Key Personnel
Publr & Author: Avery Cardoza
This step-by-step guide shows beginning & established publishers how to successfully produce professional-looking books that not only look good, but sell in the open market; readers learn how to find & develop ideas; set up the busi-

ness from the ground up; design & layout a book; find authors, work contracts & negotiate deals; get distribution; expand a publishing company into a large enterprise & more.
3rd ed, April 2003: 416 pp, $12.97 paper
First published 1995
ISBN(s): 978-1-58042-097-6

The Complete Handbook of Novel Writing
Published by Writer's Digest Books
Imprint of F+W, A Content + eCommerce Company
10151 Carver Rd, Suite 200, Blue Ash, OH 45242
Tel: 513-531-2690 *Toll Free Tel:* 800-289-0963 *Fax:* 513-531-0798
E-mail: writersdigest@fwmedia.com (edit)
Web Site: www.writersdigest.com; www.writersdigestshop.com
Key Personnel
Publr & Edit Dir: Phil Sexton *E-mail:* phillip.sexton@fwcommunity.com
Everything you need to know about creating & selling your work.
1st ed: 400 pp, $7.20
First published 2002
ISBN(s): 978-1-58297-159-9

Complete Television, Radio & Cable Industry Directory
Published by Grey House Publishing Inc™
4919 Rte 22, Amenia, NY 12501
Mailing Address: PO Box 56, Amenia, NY 12501-0056
Tel: 518-789-8700 *Toll Free Tel:* 800-562-2139 *Fax:* 518-789-0556
E-mail: books@greyhouse.com
Web Site: www.greyhouse.com
Data & industry contacts on over 20,000 US & Canadian stations & organizations in the field: Television, Radio & Cable Stations, Programming Services & Technological Solutions, Brokers & Professional Services, Associations, Events, Education, Awards, Law & Regulation & Government Agencies.
2015: 2,000 pp, $350
ISBN(s): 978-1-61925-287-5

Complete Video Directory™
Published by Grey House Publishing Inc™
4919 Rte 22, Amenia, NY 12501
Mailing Address: PO Box 56, Amenia, NY 12501-0056
Tel: 518-789-8700 *Toll Free Tel:* 800-562-2139 *Fax:* 518-789-0556
E-mail: books@greyhouse.com
Web Site: www.greyhouse.com
Extensive listing of currently available entertainment titles along with education & special interest videos for home, school & business. Annual.
March 2015: 7,900 pp, $720/4-vol set
ISBN(s): 978-1-61925-631-6

Concise Dictionary of American Literary Biography
Published by Gale
Unit of Cengage Learning
27500 Drake Rd, Farmington Hills, MI 48331-3535
SAN: 213-4373
Tel: 248-699-4253 *Toll Free Tel:* 800-877-4253 *Fax:* 248-699-8070 *Toll Free Fax:* 800-414-5043 (orders)
E-mail: gale.galeord@cengage.com
Web Site: www.gale.cengage.com
Organized chronologically, this set covers only the American authors most frequently studied in high school & college literature courses, extracts & fully updates essays in their entirety from the much larger Dictionary of Literary Biography series. A one volume supplement highlighting Modern American Writers is available seperately.
Volumes include: *Colonization to the American Renaissance, 1640-1865*
Realism, Naturalism & Local Color, 1865-1917
The Twenties, 1917-1929
The Age of Maturity, 1929-1941
The New Consciousness, 1941-1968
Broadening Views, 1968-1988
Supplement: Modern American Writers.
2,506 pp, $799/6 vol set
First published 1987
ISBN(s): 978-0-8103-1818-2 (6 vol set)

Concise Dictionary of British Literary Biography
Published by Gale
Unit of Cengage Learning
27500 Drake Rd, Farmington Hills, MI 48331-3535
SAN: 213-4373
Tel: 248-699-4253 *Toll Free Tel:* 800-347-4253 *Fax:* 248-699-8070 *Toll Free Fax:* 800-414-5043 (orders)
E-mail: gale.galeord@cengage.com
Web Site: www.gale.cengage.com
Illustrated set provides thorough coverage of major British literary figures of all eras. Vol 1: *Writers of the Middle Ages & Renaissance Before 1660*; Vol 2: *Writers of the Restoration & 18th Century 1660-1789*; Vol 3: *Writers of the Romantic Period 1789-1832*; Vol 4: *Victorian Writers, 1832-1890*; Vol 5: *Late Victorian & Edwardian Writers, 1890-1914*; Vol 6: *Modern Writers, 1914-1945*; Vol 7: *Writers After World War II, 1945-1960*; Vol 8: *Contemporary Writers, 1960-Present.*
1991: 24,000 pp, $1086/8 vol set
ISBN(s): 978-0-8103-7980-0

Concise Major 21st-Century Writers
Published by Gale
Division of Cengage Learning
27500 Drake Rd, Farmington Hills, MI 48331-3535
SAN: 213-4373
Tel: 248-699-4253 *Toll Free Tel:* 800-347-4253 *Fax:* 248-699-8070 *Toll Free Fax:* 800-414-5043 (orders)
E-mail: gale.galeord@cengage.com
Web Site: www.gale.cengage.com
Highlights 21st century authors.
2006: 4,000 pp, $728 hardcover
ISBN(s): 978-0-7876-7539-4

Consultants & Consulting Organizations Directory
Published by Gale
Unit of Cengage Learning
27500 Drake Rd, Farmington Hills, MI 48331-3535
SAN: 213-4373
Tel: 248-699-4253 *Toll Free Tel:* 800-877-4253 *Fax:* 248-699-8069 *Toll Free Fax:* 800-414-5043 (orders)
E-mail: gale.galeord@cengage.com
Web Site: www.gale.cengage.com
Key Personnel
Ed: Julie A Gough *E-mail:* julie.gough@cengage.com
Important details, including services offered, full contact information, date founded & principal business executives. More than 26,000 firms & individuals listed are arranged in subject sections under 14 general fields of consulting activity ranging from agriculture to marketing. More than 400 specialties are represented, including finance, computers, fund raising & others.
$1392

Contemporary Authors
Published by Gale
Unit of Cengage Learning
27500 Drake Rd, Farmington Hills, MI 48331-3535
SAN: 213-4373
Tel: 248-699-4253 *Toll Free Tel:* 800-877-4253 *Fax:* 248-699-8070 *Toll Free Fax:* 800-414-5043 (orders)
E-mail: gale.galeord@cengage.com
Web Site: www.gale.cengage.com
Find biographical information on more than 130,000 modern novelists, poets, playwrights, nonfiction writers, journalists & motion picture & television scriptwriters. A softcover cumulative index is published twice per year (included in subscription).

Contemporary Literary Criticism
Published by Gale
Unit of Cengage Learning
27500 Drake Rd, Farmington Hills, MI 48331-3535
SAN: 213-4373
Tel: 248-699-4253 *Toll Free Tel:* 800-877-4253 *Fax:* 248-699-8054 *Toll Free Fax:* 800-414-5043 (orders)
E-mail: gale.galeord@cengage.com
Web Site: www.gale.cengage.com
Key Personnel
Ed: Jeffrey Hunter
Full or excerpted texts from criticism & evaluations of about 6-8 major modern authors. Over 200 vols in print covering over 3,000 authors. *Cumulative Title Index* is published seperately.

Copy Editing
Published by Cambridge University Press
32 Avenue of the Americas, New York, NY 10013-2473
SAN: 200-206X
Tel: 212-924-3900 *Fax:* 212-691-3239
E-mail: newyork@cambridge.org
Web Site: www.cambridge.org/us
Key Personnel
Author: Judith Butcher
Edit Asst: David Jones *Tel:* 212-924-3900 ext 5072 *E-mail:* djou@cabridge.org
Copy Editing covers all aspects of the editorial process involved in converting an author's ms to the printed page. It covers the basics from how to mark a ms for the designer & typesetter, through the ground rules of house style & consistency, to how to read & correct proofs.
4th ed, 2006: 558 pp, $107
ISBN(s): 978-521-84713-1

Copyediting: A Practical Guide
Published by Axzo Press
Division of Thomson Learning
PO Box 25690, Rochester, NY 14625
Toll Free Tel: 888-534-5556 *Toll Free Fax:* 888-715-0220
E-mail: customerservice@axzopress.com
Web Site: www.axzopress.com
For authors, publishing personnel, writers, editors, journalists, teachers, desktop publishing & computer software workers.
3rd ed, 2001: 328 pp, $24.95
Returns: Axzo Press Distribution Center, One Executive Pkwy, Minster, OH 45865
ISBN(s): 978-1-56052-608-7

Critical Insights: Authors
Published by Grey House Publishing Inc™
2 University Plaza, Suite 310, Hackensack, NJ 07601
SAN: 208-838X
Tel: 201-968-0500 *Toll Free Tel:* 800-221-1592 *Fax:* 201-968-0511
E-mail: csr@salempress.com
Web Site: salempress.com

Key Personnel
Ed, Mario Vargas Llosa: Juan De Castro
Ed, Tim O'Brien: Robert C Evans
Ed, David Foster Wallace: Philip Coleman
Each volume contains 300 pages & includes: General bibliography, chronology of author's life, complete list of author's works, publication dates of works, detailed bio of the editor & general subject index. Volume published April 2014: *Mario Vargas Llosa*.
Volumes published Jan-Feb 2015: *Tim O'Brien David Foster Wallace*.
$95/vol (includes online access)
ISBN(s): 978-1-61925-401-5 (Mario Vargas Llosa); 978-1-61925-402-2 (Mario Vargas Llosa ebook); 978-1-61925-421-3 (Tim O'Brien); 978-1-61925-422-0 (Tim O'Brien ebook); 978-1-61925-513-5 (David Foster Wallace); 978-1-61925-514-2 (David Foster Wallace ebook)

Critical Insights: Themes
Published by Grey House Publishing Inc™
2 University Plaza, Suite 310, Hackensack, NJ 07601
SAN: 208-838X
Tel: 201-968-0500 *Toll Free Tel:* 800-221-1592 *Fax:* 201-968-0511
E-mail: csr@salempress.com
Web Site: salempress.com
Each volume contains 300 pages & explores a popular literary theme.
Volumes published Jan-Nov 2014:
The American Comic Book
The American Multicultural Identity
The American Thriller
Contemporary Canadian Fiction
Gender, Sex & Sexuality
The Graphic Novel
Magical Realism
Political Fiction
Russia's Golden Age
The Slave Narrative
Violence in Literature.
Volumes published Jan-Nov 2015:
American Creative Non-Fiction
American Short Story
Gay & Lesbian Literature
Virginia Woolf & 20th Century Women Writers
The Woman Warrior.
300 pp, $95/vol (includes online access)
ISBN(s): 978-1-61925-220-2 (The American Thriller); 978-1-61925-221-9 (The American Thriller ebook); 978-1-61925-222-6 (Russia's Golden Age); 978-1-61925-223-3 (Russia's Golden Age ebook); 978-1-61925-226-4 (The American Comic Book); 978-1-61925-227-1 (The American Comic Book ebook); 978-1-61925-262-2 (The Graphic Novel); 978-1-61925-263-9 (The Graphic Novel ebook); 978-1-61925-397-1 (The Slave Narrative); 978-1-61925-398-8 (The Slave Narrative ebook); 978-1-61925-399-5 (The Woman Warrior); 978-1-61925-400-8 (The Woman Warrior ebook); 978-1-61925-403-9 (Gender, Sex & Sexuality); 978-1-61925-404-6 (Gender, Sex & Sexuality ebook); 978-1-61925-407-7 (The American Multicultural Identity); 978-1-61925-408-4 (The American Multicultural Identity ebook); 978-1-61925-409-1 (Violence in Literature); 978-1-61925-410-7 (Violence in Literature ebook); 978-1-61925-411-4 (Political Fiction); 978-1-61925-412-1 (Political Fiction ebook); 978-1-61925-413-8 (Magical Realism); 978-1-61925-414-5 (Magical Realism ebook); 978-1-61925-415-2 (Contemporary Canadian Fiction); 978-1-61925-416-9 (Contemporary Canadian Fiction ebook); 978-1-61925-417-6 (American Creative Non-Fiction); 978-1-61925-418-3 (American Creative Non-Fiction ebook); 978-1-61925-419-0 (Virginia Woolf & 20th Century Women Writers); 978-1-61925-420-6 (Virginia Woolf & 20th Century Women Writers ebook); 978-1-61925-423-7 (Gay & Lesbian Literature); 978-1-61925-424-4 (Gay & Lesbian Literature ebook); 978-1-61925-425-1 (American Short Story); 978-1-61925-426-8 (American Short Story ebook)

Critical Insights: Works
Published by Grey House Publishing Inc™
2 University Plaza, Suite 310, Hackensack, NJ 07601
SAN: 208-838X
Tel: 201-968-0500 *Toll Free Tel:* 800-221-1592 *Fax:* 201-968-0511
E-mail: csr@salempress.com
Web Site: salempress.com
Key Personnel
Ed, The Awakening & Moby-Dick: Robert C Evans
Ed, Brave New World: M Keith Booker
Ed, Jane Eyre: Katie R Peel
Ed, Fahrenheit 451: Rafeeq O McGiveron
Ed, Midnight's Children: Joel Kuortti
Ed, The Poetry of Baudelaire: Tom Hubbard
Ed, Harry Potter: M Katherine Grimes; Lana A Whited
Ed, The Sound and the Fury: Taylor Hagood
Ed, War and Peace: Brett Cooke
Each essay is 5,000 words in length & offers comprehensive, in-depth coverage of a single work. Each volume is 300 pages & contains 16-18 essays that break down the work from several different perspectives & includes a brief biography of the author.
Volumes published Jan-April 2014:
The Awakening
Brave New World by Aldous Huxley
Midnight's Children by Salman Rushdie
The Poetry of Baudelaire
The Sound and the Fury by William Faulkner
War and Peace by Leo Tolstoy.
Volume published Aug 2014:
Moby Dick by Herman Melville.
Volumes published March-April 2015:
Harry Potter by J K Rowling
Little Women by Louisa May Alcott.
$95/vol (includes online access)
ISBN(s): 978-1-58765-519-7 (Harry Potter); 978-1-58765-520-3 (Harry Potter ebook); 978-1-61825-405-3 (Moby-Dick); 978-1-61925-218-9 (Jane Eyre); 978-1-61925-219-6 (Jane Eyre ebook); 978-1-61925-228-8 (The Awakening); 978-1-61925-229-5 (The Awakening ebook); 978-1-61925-238-7 (Brave New World); 978-1-61925-239-4 (Brave New World ebook); 978-1-61925-389-6 (Midnight's Children); 978-1-61925-390-2 (Midnight's Children ebook); 978-1-61925-391-9 (The Sound and the Fury); 978-1-61925-392-6 (The Sound and the Fury ebook); 978-1-61925-393-3 (War and Peace); 978-1-61925-394-0 (War and Peace ebook); 978-1-61925-395-7 (The Poetry of Baudelaire); 978-1-61925-396-4 (The Poetry of Baudelaire ebook); 978-1-61925-406-0 (Moby-Dick ebook); 978-1-61925-427-5 (Little Women); 978-1-61925-428-2 (Little Women ebook)

Critical Survey of Drama
Published by Grey House Publishing Inc™
2 University Plaza, Suite 310, Hackensack, NJ 07601
SAN: 208-838X
Tel: 201-968-0500 *Toll Free Tel:* 800-221-1592 *Fax:* 201-968-0511
E-mail: csr@salempress.com
Web Site: salempress.com
Key Personnel
Ed: Carl Rollyson
Contains 602 essays that discuss both individual dramatists & overview topics. Also contains a listing of major dramatic awards, time line of drama history, glossary & bibliography.
2nd ed (rev), 2003: 4,662 pp, $499/8 vol set
ISBN(s): 978-1-58765-102-1 (8 vol set)

Critical Survey of Graphic Novels: Heroes & Superheroes
Published by Grey House Publishing Inc™
2 University Plaza, Suite 310, Hackensack, NJ 07601
SAN: 208-838X
Tel: 201-968-0500 *Toll Free Tel:* 800-221-1592 *Fax:* 201-968-0511
E-mail: csr@salempress.com
Web Site: salempress.com
Key Personnel
Ed: Bart H Beaty; Stephen Weiner
Provides in-depth insight into over 130 of the most popular & studied graphic novels. Arranged alphabetically.
April 2012: 800 pp, $295/2 vol set (includes online access)
ISBN(s): 978-1-58765-865-5 (2 vol set); 978-1-58765-869-3 (ebook)

Critical Survey of Graphic Novels: History, Theme & Technique
Published by Grey House Publishing Inc™
2 University Plaza, Suite 310, Hackensack, NJ 07601
SAN: 208-838X
Tel: 201-968-0500 *Toll Free Tel:* 800-221-1592 *Fax:* 201-968-0511
E-mail: csr@salempress.com
Web Site: salempress.com
Key Personnel
Ed: Bart H Beaty; Stephen Weiner
Contains over 70 essays covering themes & concepts of graphic novels, including genres, time periods, foreign language traditions, social relevance & craftsmanship such as penciling & inking.
Oct 2012: 400 pp, $195 (includes online access)
ISBN(s): 978-1-58765-957-7; 978-1-58765-958-4 (ebook)

Critical Survey of Graphic Novels: Independents & Underground Classics
Published by Grey House Publishing Inc™
2 University Plaza, Suite 310, Hackensack, NJ 07601
SAN: 208-838X
Tel: 201-968-0500 *Toll Free Tel:* 800-221-1592 *Fax:* 201-968-0511
E-mail: csr@salempress.com
Web Site: salempress.com
Key Personnel
Ed: Bart H Beaty; Stephen Weiner
215 essays covering graphic novels & core comics series, focusing on the independents & underground genre.
May 2012: 1,200 pp, $395/3 vol set (includes online access)
ISBN(s): 978-1-58765-950-8 (3 vol set); 978-1-58765-954-6 (ebook set)

Critical Survey of Graphic Novels: Manga
Published by Grey House Publishing Inc™
2 University Plaza, Suite 310, Hackensack, NJ 07601
SAN: 208-838X
Tel: 201-968-0500 *Toll Free Tel:* 800-221-1592 *Fax:* 201-968-0511
E-mail: csr@salempress.com
Web Site: salempress.com
Key Personnel
Ed: Bart H Beaty; Stephen Weiner
Provides in-depth insight for over 65 of the most popular manga graphic novels, ranging from metaseries to stand-alone books.
Sept 2012: 400 pp, $195 (includes online access)
ISBN(s): 978-1-58765-955-3; 978-1-58765-956-0 (ebook)

Critical Survey of Long Fiction
Published by Grey House Publishing Inc™

2 University Plaza, Suite 310, Hackensack, NJ 07601
SAN: 208-838X
Tel: 201-968-0500 *Toll Free Tel:* 800-221-1592 *Fax:* 201-968-0511
E-mail: csr@salempress.com
Web Site: salempress.com
Key Personnel
Ed: Carl Rollyson
581 original author essays as well as 97 new ones arranged alphabetically by author providing in-depth overviews of major authors in long fiction, both English language & foreign language.
Every 5-7 yrs.
4th ed, Jan 2010: 6,056 pp, $995/10 vol set (includes online access)
First published 1983
ISBN(s): 978-1-58765-535-7 (10 vol set); 978-1-58765-546-3 (ebook set)

Critical Survey of Mystery & Detective Fiction
Published by Grey House Publishing Inc™
2 University Plaza, Suite 310, Hackensack, NJ 07601
SAN: 208-838X
Tel: 201-968-0500 *Toll Free Tel:* 800-221-1592 *Fax:* 201-968-0511
E-mail: csr@salempress.com
Web Site: salempress.com
Key Personnel
Ed: Carl Rollyson
Provides detailed analyses of the lives & writings of major contributors to mystery & detective fiction.
Jan 2008 (rev): 2,388 pp, $399/5 vol set
ISBN(s): 978-1-58765-397-1 (5 vol set); 978-1-58765-444-2 (ebook set)

Critical Survey of Mythology & Folklore: Heroes & Heroines
Published by Grey House Publishing Inc™
2 University Plaza, Suite 310, Hackensack, NJ 07601
SAN: 208-838X
Tel: 201-968-0500 *Toll Free Tel:* 800-221-1592 *Fax:* 201-968-0511
E-mail: csr@salempress.com
Web Site: salempress.com
Covers a diverse range of countries & cultures, as well as important retellings in the modern tradition. Articles cover: *Birth & Prophecy*, *The Host of Heroines*, *The Culture Hero*, *Trial & Quest*, *Myth & Monstrosity*, *Survey of Myth & Folklore*.
Oct 2013: 516 pp, $175 (includes online access)
ISBN(s): 978-1-61925-181-6; 978-1-61925-186-1 (ebook)

Critical Survey of Mythology & Folklore: Love, Sexuality & Desire
Published by Grey House Publishing Inc™
2 University Plaza, Suite 310, Hackensack, NJ 07601
SAN: 208-838X
Tel: 201-968-0500 *Toll Free Tel:* 800-221-1592 *Fax:* 201-968-0511
E-mail: csr@salempress.com
Web Site: salempress.com
Each title examines familiar & unfamiliar myths, from a diverse range of countries & cultures as well as important retellings in the modern tradition. Topics covered include *Gods & Mortals in Love*, *The Myth of the Second Half*, *Animal Wives & Husbands*, *Modern Tales & Myths*, *Forbidden Love*, *Love Unrequited*, *The Lover's Quest*.
Jan 2013: 984 pp, $295/2 vol set (includes online access)
ISBN(s): 978-1-4298-3765-1 (2 vol set); 978-1-4298-3768-2 (ebook set)

Critical Survey of Mythology & Folklore: World Mythology
Published by Grey House Publishing Inc™
2 University Plaza, Suite 310, Hackensack, NJ 07601
SAN: 208-838X
Tel: 201-968-0500 *Toll Free Tel:* 800-221-1592 *Fax:* 201-968-0511
E-mail: csr@salempress.com
Web Site: salempress.com
Presents articles on myths, folktales, legends & other traditional literature. Covers a diverse range of authors, countries & cultures that spans the globe. Articles begin with a summary that offers readers the major actions & characters in the tale followed by an analysis of the important cultural & social interpretations of the author & myth.
Dec 2013: 326 pp, $175 (includes online access)
ISBN(s): 978-1-61925-182-3; 978-1-61925-187-8 (ebook)

Critical Survey of Poetry
Published by Grey House Publishing Inc™
2 University Plaza, Suite 310, Hackensack, NJ 07601
SAN: 208-838X
Tel: 201-968-0500 *Toll Free Tel:* 800-221-1592 *Fax:* 201-968-0511
E-mail: csr@salempress.com
Web Site: salempress.com
An in-depth resource covering 843 poets throughout history & the world. Organized into 5 subsets by geography & essay type.
American Poets, 4 vol set, 2,414 pp, $495.
British, Irish & Commonwealth Poets, 3 vol set, 1,470 pp, $395.
European Poets, 3 vol set, 1,262 pp, $395.
World Poets, 1 vol, 442 pp, $150.
Topical Essays, 2 vol set, 924 pp, $295.
Cumulative Indexes, 1 vol, 266 pp, free with purchase of more than one subset.
4th ed, Jan 2011: 6,778 pp, $1,295/14 vol set (includes online access)
First published 2002
ISBN(s): 978-1-58765-582-1 (14 vol set); 978-1-58765-583-8 (American Poets set); 978-1-58765-588-3 (British, Irish & Commonwealth Poets set); 978-1-58765-592-0 (American Poets ebook set); 978-1-58765-593-7 (ebook entire set); 978-1-58765-755-9 (British, Irish & Commonwealth Poets ebook set); 978-1-58765-756-6 (European Poets set); 978-1-58765-760-3 (European Poets ebook set); 978-1-58765-761-0 (World Poets); 978-1-58765-762-7 (World Poets ebook); 978-1-58765-763-4 (Topical Essays set); 978-1-58765-766-5 (Topical Essays ebook set); 978-1-58765-767-2 (Cumulative Indexes)

Critical Survey of Shakespeare's Sonnets
Published by Grey House Publishing Inc™
2 University Plaza, Suite 310, Hackensack, NJ 07601
SAN: 208-838X
Tel: 201-968-0500 *Toll Free Tel:* 800-221-1592 *Fax:* 201-968-0511
E-mail: csr@salempress.com
Web Site: salempress.com
Collection of 25 essays on the Sonnets written by William Shakespeare, each providing an in-depth critical analysis of its historical significance, literary technique & discusses its meaning to a contemporary audience.
July 2014: 355 pp, $95 (includes online access)
ISBN(s): 978-1-61925-499-2; 978-1-61925-500-5 (ebook)

Critical Survey of Short Fiction
Published by Grey House Publishing Inc™
2 University Plaza, Suite 310, Hackensack, NJ 07601
SAN: 208-838X
Tel: 201-968-0500 *Toll Free Tel:* 800-221-1592 *Fax:* 201-968-0511
E-mail: csr@salempress.com
Web Site: salempress.com
Key Personnel
Ed: Charles E May
625 essays providing in-depth overviews of short story writers throughout history & the world. Organized into 5 subsets by geography & essay type.
American Writers, 4 vol set, 1,600 pp, $495.
British, Irish & Commonwealth Writers, 2 vol set, 800 pp, $295.
European Writers, 1 vol, 400 pp, $175.
World Writers, 1 vol, 400 pp, $175.
Topical Essays, 1 vol, 400 pp, $175.
Cumulative Indexes, 1 vol, 400 pp, free with purchase of more than one subset.
Every 5-7 yrs.
4th ed, Jan 2012: 4,000 pp, $995/10 vol set (includes online access)
First published 2001
ISBN(s): 978-1-58765-789-4 (10 vol set); 978-1-58765-790-0 (American Writers set); 978-1-58765-795-5 (British, Irish & Commonwealth Writers set); 978-1-58765-798-6 (European Writers); 978-1-58765-799-3 (World Writers); 978-1-58765-800-6 (Topical Essays); 978-1-58765-803-7 (Cumulative Indexes); 978-1-58765-804-4 (ebook entire set); 978-1-58765-805-1 (American Writers ebook set); 978-1-58765-807-5 (European Writers ebook); 978-1-58765-808-2 (World Writers ebook); 978-1-58765-809-9 (Topical Essays ebook); 987-1-58765-806-8 (British, Irish & Commonwealth Writers ebook set)

Current Biography Cumulative Index 1946-2013
Published by Grey House Publishing Inc™
4919 Rte 22, Amenia, NY 12501
Mailing Address: PO Box 56, Amenia, NY 12501-0056
Tel: 518-789-8700 *Toll Free Tel:* 800-562-2139 *Fax:* 518-789-0556
E-mail: books@greyhouse.com
Web Site: www.greyhouse.com
Name & profession indexes to late issues in which biographies appear in *Current Biography Yearbook*.
Feb 2014: 800 pp, $199
ISBN(s): 978-1-61925-472-5

Current Biography Yearbook
Published by Grey House Publishing Inc™
4919 Rte 22, Amenia, NY 12501
Mailing Address: PO Box 56, Amenia, NY 12501-0056
Tel: 518-789-8700 *Toll Free Tel:* 800-562-2139 *Fax:* 518-789-0556
E-mail: books@greyhouse.com
Web Site: www.greyhouse.com
Compilation of 175 up-to-date, contemporary profiles of accomplished & rising stars of politics, industry, entertainment & the arts from the US & around the world.
Annual.
Dec 2015: 750 pp, $199/yr, $350/2 yrs, $480/3 yrs
ISBN(s): 978-1-61925-707-8

Cyclopedia of Literary Characters
Published by Grey House Publishing Inc™
2 University Plaza, Suite 310, Hackensack, NJ 07601
SAN: 208-838X
Tel: 201-968-0500 *Toll Free Tel:* 800-221-1592 *Fax:* 201-968-0511
E-mail: csr@salempress.com
Web Site: salempress.com
Provides critical descriptions of more than 29,000 major characters that appear in 3,500 important works of literature. New to this edition are 600

characters published in popular works of fiction from 2000 to 2013.
5th ed, Feb 2015: 2,700 pp, $455/5 vol set (includes online access)
ISBN(s): 978-1-61925-497-8 (5 vol set); 978-1-61925-498-5 (ebook set)

Dictionary of Literary Biography
Published by Gale
Unit of Cengage Learning
27500 Drake Rd, Farmington Hills, MI 48331-3535
SAN: 213-4373
Tel: 248-699-4253 *Toll Free Tel:* 800-877-4253 *Fax:* 248-699-8070 *Toll Free Fax:* 800-414-5043 (orders)
E-mail: gale.galeord@cengage.com
Web Site: www.gale.cengage.com
Multivolume series; each volume focuses on a specific literary movement or period. Series aims to encompass all who have contributed to literary history from the Elizabethan Era to 20th century English, American, Canadian, French & German literature, drama & history. Major biographical & critical essays are presented for the most important figures of each era. Each essay includes a career chronology, list of publications & a bibliography of works by & about the subject. Produced by Bruccoli, Clark & Layman for Gale. Also available online.

Dictionary of Modern English Usage
Published by Oxford University Press USA
198 Madison Ave, New York, NY 10016
SAN: 202-5892
Toll Free Tel: 800-451-7556 (orders) *Fax:* 212-726-6453
E-mail: orders.us@oup.com
Web Site: www.oup.com/us
Key Personnel
Author: H W Fowler
2010 (Dec): 832 pp, $17.95
First published 2009
ISBN(s): 978-0-19-958589-2

Direct Marketing Market Place® (DMMP)
Published by National Register Publishing
Division of Marquis Who's Who LLC
430 Mountain Ave, Suite 400, New Providence, NJ 07974
Toll Free Tel: 800-473-7020 *Fax:* 908-673-1189 (cust serv)
E-mail: NRPeditorial@marquiswhoswho.com (edit); NRPsales@marquiswhoswho.com (sales)
Web Site: www.nationalregisterpub.com
A comprehensive source of direct marketing, listing over 17,500 key personnel & over 8,800 leading direct marketing companies, suppliers & creative sources.
Annual.
2016 ed, $365 paper
ISBN(s): 978-0-87217-045-2

Directories in Print
Published by Gale
Unit of Cengage Learning
27500 Drake Rd, Farmington Hills, MI 48331-3535
SAN: 213-4373
Tel: 248-699-4253 *Toll Free Tel:* 800-877-4253 *Fax:* 248-699-8074 *Toll Free Fax:* 800-414-5043 (orders)
E-mail: gale.galeord@cengage.com
Web Site: www.gale.cengage.com
Key Personnel
Ed: Matthew Miskelly *Tel:* 248-699-4253 ext 1744 *E-mail:* matthew.miskelly@cengage.com
Annotated guide to approximately 16,000 directories, rosters, lists & guides of all kinds. Contains completely updated entries, plus many new entries, including principal business & institutional directories from more than 80 countries. *DIP*-supplement, approximately 775 new entries. Also available online.
Annual.
37th ed, 2015: 2,374 pp, $1,059 print
ISBN(s): 978-1-57302-542-3 (2 vol set)

A Directory of American Poets & Writers
Published by Poets & Writers Inc
90 Broad St, Suite 2100, New York, NY 10004
Tel: 212-226-3586 *Fax:* 212-226-3963
E-mail: directory@pw.org
Web Site: www.pw.org/directory
Key Personnel
Exec Dir: Elliot Figman
Asst Online Ed: Evan Smith Rakoff
Names, addresses, telephone numbers & e-mail addresses of over 9,000 contemporary American writers & poets. Available online only.
Free

The Directory of Business Information Resources
Published by Grey House Publishing Inc™
4919 Rte 22, Amenia, NY 12501
Mailing Address: PO Box 56, Amenia, NY 12501-0056
Tel: 518-789-8700 *Toll Free Tel:* 800-562-2139 *Fax:* 518-789-0556
E-mail: books@greyhouse.com
Web Site: www.greyhouse.com
Source for contacts in 98 business areas. The over 20,000 detailed, informative entries include contact names, phone & fax numbers, web sites & e-mail addresses along with descriptions, membership information, ordering details & more.
Annual.
Jan 2015: 2,500 pp, $495 busn, $195 acad & lib (includes online access)
ISBN(s): 978-1-61925-547-0

The Directory of Mail Order Catalogs
Published by Grey House Publishing Inc™
4919 Rte 22, Amenia, NY 12501
Mailing Address: PO Box 56, Amenia, NY 12501-0056
Tel: 518-789-8700 *Toll Free Tel:* 800-562-2139 *Fax:* 518-789-0556
E-mail: books@greyhouse.com
Web Site: www.greyhouse.com
Complete listing of direct-to-consumer & business-to-business mail order catalogs, including detailed contact information.
Annual.
Feb 2015: 1,200 pp, $450, $250 acad & lib (includes online access)
First published 1981
ISBN(s): 978-1-61925-286-8

Directory of Mailing List Companies
Published by Todd Publications
1388 Sabal Palm Dr, Boca Raton, FL 33432
SAN: 207-0804
Tel: 561-910-0440 *Fax:* 561-910-0440
E-mail: toddpub@yahoo.com
Key Personnel
Ed/Publr: Barry Klein
Provides alphabetically, with addresses, phone numbers & zip codes, the names of more than 1100 list companies, specialists & brokers, together with their managers' names & telephones & other pertinent information.
18th ed, 2014: 150 pp, $95 paperback
ISBN(s): 978-0-87340-024-4

Directory of Poetry Publishers
Published by Dustbooks
PO Box 100, Paradise, CA 95967-0100
SAN: 204-1871
Tel: 530-877-6110 *Fax:* 530-877-0222
E-mail: publisher@dustbooks.com; info@dustbooks.com
Web Site: www.dustbooks.com
Key Personnel
Publr: Kathleen Glanville
Ed: Neil McIntyre
Information on more than 1,900 book & magazine publishers of poetry worldwide, including university presses & e-zines.
Annual (CD-ROM), continuously (online).
31st ed, 2015-2016, $21 CD-ROM, $65 CD-ROM (3 directories), $49.95 online (4 directories)
ISBN(s): 978-1-935742-37-1 (CD-ROM)

Directory of Small Press/Magazine Editors & Publishers
Published by Dustbooks
PO Box 100, Paradise, CA 95967-0100
SAN: 204-1871
Tel: 530-877-6110 *Fax:* 530-877-0222
E-mail: publisher@dustbooks.com; info@dustbooks.com
Web Site: www.dustbooks.com
Key Personnel
Publr: Kathleen Glanville
Ed: Neil McIntyre
Names & numbers guide to the small press & magazine industry.
Annual (CD-ROM), continuously (online).
46th ed, 2015-2016, $21 CD-ROM, $65 CD-ROM (3 directories), $49.95 online (4 directories)
ISBN(s): 978-1-935742-35-7 (CD-ROM)

Directory of Special Libraries & Information Centers
Published by Gale
Unit of Cengage Learning
27500 Drake Rd, Farmington Hills, MI 48331-3535
SAN: 213-4373
Tel: 248-699-4253 *Toll Free Tel:* 800-877-4253 *Fax:* 248-699-8075 *Toll Free Fax:* 800-414-5043 (orders)
E-mail: gale.galeord@cengage.com
Web Site: www.gale.cengage.com
Key Personnel
Ed: Matthew Miskelly *Tel:* 248-699-4253 ext 1744 *E-mail:* matthew.miskelly@cengage.com
Vol 1, in three parts, provides detailed contact & descriptive info on subject-specific resource collections maintained by various government agencies, businesses, publishers, educational & nonprofit organizations & associations around the world. Vol 2 contains geographical & personnel indexes.
39th ed, $1,533
ISBN(s): 978-1-4144-5874-8

Do-It-Yourself Book Publicity Kit
Published by Open Horizons Publishing Co
PO Box 2887, Taos, NM 87571
Tel: 575-751-3398 *Fax:* 575-751-3100
E-mail: info@bookmarket.com
Web Site: www.bookmarket.com
Key Personnel
Publr & Ed: John Kremer *E-mail:* johnkremer@bookmarket.com
How to write a news release, put together a media kit, get reviews, schedule interviews & get on-going national publicity.
2008: 256 pp, $30

Drama Criticism
Published by Gale
Unit of Cengage Learning
27500 Drake Rd, Farmington Hills, MI 48331-3535
SAN: 213-4373
Tel: 248-699-4253 *Toll Free Tel:* 800-877-4253 *Fax:* 248-699-8070 *Toll Free Fax:* 800-414-5043 (orders)
E-mail: gale.galeord@cengage.com

Web Site: www.gale.cengage.com
Wide variety of critical, biographical & bibliographical information on major plays & playwrights from all time periods. Substantial excerpts from significant commentary on the more widely-studied dramatists.

Dynamic Characters
Published by Writer's Digest Books
Imprint of F+W, A Content + eCommerce Company
10151 Carver Rd, Suite 200, Blue Ash, OH 45242
Tel: 513-531-2690 *Toll Free Tel:* 800-289-0963 *Fax:* 513-531-0798
E-mail: writersdigest@fwmedia.com (edit)
Web Site: www.writersdigest.com; www.writersdigestshop.com
Key Personnel
Publr & Edit Dir: Phil Sexton *E-mail:* phillip.sexton@fwcommunity.com
Explores the fundamental relationship between characterization & plot.
1st ed: 272 pp, $11.39 paper
First published 2004
ISBN(s): 978-0-89879-815-9 (hardcover); 978-1-58297-319-7 (paper)

E-Publishing and Digital Libraries: Legal and Organizational Issues
Published by IGI Global
701 E Chocolate Ave, Hershey, PA 17033-1240
Tel: 717-533-8845 (ext 100) *Toll Free Tel:* 866-342-6657 *Fax:* 717-533-8661
E-mail: cust@igi-global.com
Web Site: www.igi-global.com
2011: 552 pp, $180
ISBN(s): 978-1-60960-031-0; 978-1-60960-033-4 (ebook)

EFA On-Line Directory
Published by Editorial Freelancers Association (EFA)
71 W 23 St, 4th fl, New York, NY 10010-4102
Tel: 212-929-5400 *Toll Free Tel:* 866-929-5425 *Fax:* 212-929-5439 *Toll Free Fax:* 866-929-5439
E-mail: info@the-efa.org; office@the-efa.org
Web Site: www.the-efa.org
Key Personnel
Exec: William P Keenan, Jr; J P Partland
National, nonprofit professional organization comprising editors, writers, indexers, proofreaders, researchers, translators & other self-employed workers in the publishing industry. Online directory searchable by skills, subject matter, expertise & location. Members may post descriptions of services, resumes & contact information. Clients can directly hire the freelance help they need.
2,300 pp, free (online)
ISBN(s): 978-1-880407-13-4

El-Hi Textbooks & Serials in Print®
Published by Grey House Publishing Inc™
4919 Rte 22, Amenia, NY 12501
Mailing Address: PO Box 56, Amenia, NY 12501-0056
Tel: 518-789-8700 *Toll Free Tel:* 800-562-2139 *Fax:* 518-789-0556
E-mail: books@greyhouse.com
Web Site: www.greyhouse.com
Includes the in-print titles of publishers of textbooks & related materials. Coverage includes over 195,000 elementary, junior high & high school textbooks from over 17,000 publishers worldwide.
Annual.
143rd ed, 2015: 4,000 pp, $540/2 vol set
ISBN(s): 978-1-61925-625-5 (2 vol set)

The Elements of Style
Published by Pearson Arts & Sciences
Division of Pearson Education
330 Hudson St, 9th fl, New York, NY 10013-1048
Tel: 917-981-2200
Web Site: www.pearsonhighered.com
Key Personnel
Author: William Strunk; E B White
50th Anniversary, 2008: 105 pp, $19.95
First published 2008
ISBN(s): 978-0-205-63264-0 (cloth)

Encyclopedia of Associations, National Organizations of the US
Published by Gale
Unit of Cengage Learning
27500 Drake Rd, Farmington Hills, MI 48331-3535
SAN: 213-4373
Tel: 248-699-4253 *Toll Free Tel:* 800-877-4253 *Fax:* 248-699-8075 *Toll Free Fax:* 800-414-5043 (orders)
E-mail: gale.galeord@cengage.com
Web Site: www.gale.cengage.com
Key Personnel
Ed: Tara Atterberry *E-mail:* tara.atterberry@cengage.com
A guide to 25,048 US nonprofit membership organizations of national & international scope; includes trade & professional associations, social welfare & public affairs organizations, religious organizations, sports & hobby groups with voluntary members. Detailed entries furnish association name & complete contact information. This information is not duplicated anywhere in Encyclopedia of Associations. Name & keyword indexes accompany each volume. *Geographic & Executive Indexes* are available as a separate volume. A supplement is published between volumes.

Fiction Core Collection
Published by Grey House Publishing Inc™
4919 Rte 22, Amenia, NY 12501
Mailing Address: PO Box 56, Amenia, NY 12501-0056
Tel: 518-789-8700 *Toll Free Tel:* 800-562-2139 *Fax:* 518-789-0556
E-mail: books@greyhouse.com
Web Site: www.greyhouse.com
Recommends novels, novellas & story collections for the general adult audience. Guide to over 8,000 books plus review sources & other professional aids for librarians.
17th ed, Feb 2014: 1,300 pp, $295
ISBN(s): 978-0-8242-1234-6

45 Master Characters
Published by Writer's Digest Books
Imprint of F+W, A Content + eCommerce Company
10151 Carver Rd, Suite 200, Blue Ash, OH 45242
Tel: 513-531-2690 *Toll Free Tel:* 800-289-0963 *Fax:* 513-531-0798
E-mail: writersdigest@fwmedia.com (edit)
Web Site: www.writersdigest.com; www.writersdigestshop.com
Key Personnel
Publr & Edit Dir: Phil Sexton *E-mail:* phillip.sexton@fwcommunity.com
Gives all the information you need to develop believable characters that resonate with every reader.
304 pp, $10.19 paper
First published 2001
ISBN(s): 978-1-58297-522-1

Gale Directory of Databases
Published by Gale
Unit of Cengage Learning
27500 Drake Rd, Farmington Hills, MI 48331-3535
SAN: 213-4373
Tel: 248-699-4253 *Toll Free Tel:* 800-347-4253 *Fax:* 248-699-8074 *Toll Free Fax:* 800-414-5043 (orders)
E-mail: gale.galeord@cengage.com
Web Site: www.gale.cengage.com
Key Personnel
Ed: Julie A Gough *E-mail:* julie.gough@cengage.com
Current information about more than 18,000 databases available worldwide in a variety of formats.
37th ed, 2014, $794/6 vol set paper
ISBN(s): 978-1-4144-7832-6 (6 vol set)

Gale Directory of Publications & Broadcast Media
Published by Gale
Unit of Cengage Learning
27500 Drake Rd, Farmington Hills, MI 48331-3535
SAN: 213-4373
Tel: 248-699-4253 *Toll Free Tel:* 800-877-4253 *Fax:* 248-699-8075 *Toll Free Fax:* 800-414-5043 (orders)
E-mail: gale.galeord@cengage.com
Web Site: www.gale.cengage.com
Key Personnel
Ed: Matthew Miskelly *Tel:* 248-699-4253 ext 1744 *E-mail:* matthew.miskelly@cengage.com
This media directory contains thousands of listings for radio & television stations & cable companies. Print media entries list: address, phone & fax numbers & e-mail addresses, key personnel, including feature editors. Broadcast media entries: address, phone & fax numbers, e-mail addresses; key personnel, owner information, station call letter & channel, hours of operation; networks carries & more.
151st ed, 2015, $1494 hardcover
ISBN(s): 978-1-4144-8796-0

General Issues in Literacy/Illiteracy in the World: A Bibliography
Published by Greenwood Press
Imprint of ABC-CLIO
130 Cremona Dr, Suite C, Santa Barbara, CA 93117
Mailing Address: PO Box 1911, Santa Barbara, CA 93116-1911
Tel: 805-968-1911 *Toll Free Tel:* 800-368-6868 *Fax:* 805-685-9685 *Toll Free Fax:* 866-270-3856
E-mail: customerservice@abc-clio.com
Web Site: www.abc-clio.com
Key Personnel
Dir, Edit-Print: Anthony Chiffolo
Author: William Eller; John Hladczuk; Sharon Hladczuk
Literacy-illiteracy; bibliography.
1st ed, 1990: 435 pp, $106.95 hardbound
ISBN(s): 978-0-313-27327-8

Getting Into Print: The Decision-Making Process in Scholarly Publishing
Published by University of Chicago Press
1427 E 60 St, Chicago, IL 60637-2954
SAN: 202-5280
Tel: 773-702-7700 *Toll Free Tel:* 800-621-2736 (orders) *Fax:* 773-702-9756
E-mail: custserv@press.uchicago.edu; marketing@press.uchicago.edu
Web Site: www.press.uchicago.edu
Key Personnel
Dir: Garrett P Kiely *Tel:* 773-702-8878 *E-mail:* gkiely@uchicago.edu
Exploration of two scholarly publishing companies & how editors select titles they sponsor.
1988: 282 pp, $38 cloth, $28 paper
ISBN(s): 978-0-226-67705-7 (cloth)

Grammatically Correct
Published by Writer's Digest Books
Imprint of F+W, A Content + eCommerce Company
10151 Carver Rd, Suite 200, Blue Ash, OH 45242
Tel: 513-531-2690 *Toll Free Tel:* 800-289-0963 *Fax:* 513-531-0798
E-mail: writersdigest@fwmedia.com (edit)
Web Site: www.writersdigest.com; www.writersdigestshop.com
Key Personnel
Publr & Edit Dir: Phil Sexton *E-mail:* phillip.sexton@fwcommunity.com
Easy to use, quick reference & most of all, comprehensive.
2nd ed: 352 pp, $11.98 paper
First published 1997
ISBN(s): 978-1-58297-616-7

Grants & Awards
Published by PEN American Center
Affiliate of PEN International
588 Broadway, Suite 303, New York, NY 10012
Tel: 212-334-1660 *Fax:* 212-334-2181
E-mail: info@pen.org
Web Site: www.pen.org
Key Personnel
Exec Dir: Suzanne Nossel
Pres: Andrew Solomon
Website Ed: Antonio Aiello *Tel:* 212-334-1660 ext 114 *E-mail:* antonio@pen.org
Database with nearly 15,000 domestic & foreign grants, literary awards, fellowships & residencies.
Online annual subn: free for membs; $12 nonmembs, 200 instns

A Guide to Academic Writing
Published by Praeger
Imprint of ABC-CLIO
130 Cremona Dr, Suite C, Santa Barbara, CA 93117
Mailing Address: PO Box 1911, Santa Barbara, CA 93116-1911
Tel: 805-968-1911 *Toll Free Tel:* 800-368-6868 *Fax:* 805-685-9685 *Toll Free Fax:* 866-270-3856
E-mail: custserv@abc-clio.com
Web Site: www.abc-clio.com
Key Personnel
Dir, Edit-Print: Anthony Chiffolo
Author: Jeffery A Cantor
A comprehensive guide to academic writing & publishing.
200 pp, $26.95 paper, $96 hardcover
ISBN(s): 978-0-275-94660-9 (paper); 978-0-313-29017-6 (hardcover)

Guide to American & International Directories
Published by Todd Publications
1388 Sabal Palm Dr, Boca Raton, FL 33432
SAN: 207-0804
Tel: 561-910-0440 *Fax:* 561-910-0440
E-mail: toddpub@yahoo.com
Key Personnel
Ed/Publr: Barry Klein
Complete information on more than 12,000 directories, covering more than 300 trade, educational & professional categories. Index.
Annual.
25th ed, 2016: 660 pp
ISBN(s): 978-0-873400-398

2015 Guide to Literary Agents
Published by Writer's Digest Books
Imprint of F+W, A Content + eCommerce Company
10151 Carver Rd, Suite 200, Blue Ash, OH 45242
Tel: 513-531-2690 *Toll Free Tel:* 800-289-0963 *Fax:* 513-531-0798
E-mail: writersdigest@fwmedia.com (edit)
Web Site: www.writersdigest.com; www.writersdigestshop.com
Key Personnel
Publr & Edit Dir: Phil Sexton *E-mail:* phillip.sexton@fwcommunity.com
Author: Chuck Sambuchino
Annual.
24th ed, 2015: 368 pp, $29.99 paper (retail)
ISBN(s): 978-1-59963-843-0

Guide to Writers Conferences & Writing Workshops
Published by ShawGuides
PO Box 61569, Staten Island, NY 61569
Tel: 718-874-3311
E-mail: writing@shawguides.com
Web Site: shawguides.com
Key Personnel
Pres: Ron Janorkar
Online directory of conferences, seminars, workshops & retreats. Includes information about dates, facilities, faculty, writing specialties, daily activities, tuition, accommodations, refund policies, handicapped accessibility, nearby attractions. Includes information on organizations (dues, benefits, activities). Contents indexed by location (covers 50 states & 11 countries); specialties (nine genres); availability of college credit, continuing education credit & scholarships; writing contests, college writing programs. Available at writing.shawguides.com.

How to Get Your Book Published Free in Minutes & Marketed Worldwide in Days
Published by Communication Unlimited
185 Shevelin Rd, Novato, CA 94947
Tel: 415-884-2941 *Toll Free Tel:* 800-563-1454 *Fax:* 415-883-5707
E-mail: gordon@gordonburgett.com
Web Site: www.gordonburgett.com
Key Personnel
Pres: Gordon Burgett *E-mail:* glburgett@aol.com
How-to information, step-by-step process & detailed examples of "ancillary" publishing.
1st ed, 2010: 208 pp, $15 paper, $10 digital download
ISBN(s): 978-0-9826635-0-9 (digital download); 978-0-9826635-1-6 (print)

How to Publish & Market Your Own Book as an Independent African Heritage Book Publisher
Published by ECA Associates Press
PO Box 15004, Chesapeake, VA 23328-0004
Tel: 757-547-5542 *Fax:* 757-547-5542 (call first)
E-mail: eca@bellsmill.net
Key Personnel
Pres: Dr E Curtis Alexander
Ed: Dr Mwalimu I Mwadilifu
1st ed: 140 pp, $15.95
ISBN(s): 978-0-938818-09-0

How to Write a Book Proposal
Published by Writer's Digest Books
Imprint of F+W, A Content + eCommerce Company
10151 Carver Rd, Suite 200, Blue Ash, OH 45242
Tel: 513-531-2690 *Toll Free Tel:* 800-289-0963 *Fax:* 513-531-0798
E-mail: writersdigest@fwmedia.com (edit)
Web Site: www.writersdigest.com; www.writersdigestshop.com
Key Personnel
Publr & Edit Dir: Phil Sexton *E-mail:* phillip.sexton@fwcommunity.com
Details how the industry works, where it's headed & how you can be part of it.
4th: 336 pp, $11.99 paper
First published 2003
ISBN(s): 978-1-58297-702-7

Hudson's Washington News Media Contacts Directory
Published by Grey House Publishing Inc™
4919 Rte 22, Amenia, NY 12501
Mailing Address: PO Box 56, Amenia, NY 12501-0056
Tel: 518-789-8700 *Toll Free Tel:* 800-562-2139 *Fax:* 518-789-0556
E-mail: books@greyhouse.com
Web Site: www.greyhouse.com
Comprehensive listing of 4,000 news media sources in Washington, DC.
Annual.
Feb 2015: 400 pp, $289, online database available (see web site for quote)
ISBN(s): 978-1-61925-575-3

Index to Legal Periodicals & Books
Published by Grey House Publishing Inc™
4919 Rte 22, Amenia, NY 12501
Mailing Address: PO Box 56, Amenia, NY 12501-0056
Tel: 518-789-8700 *Toll Free Tel:* 800-562-2139 *Fax:* 518-789-0556
E-mail: books@greyhouse.com
Web Site: www.greyhouse.com
A cumulative author-subject index to legal publications with a table of cases & statutes & listing of book reviews.
Feb 2015 (2014 annual cumulation): 3,000 pp, $695
ISBN(s): 978-1-61925-297-4

Indexing from A to Z
Published by Grey House Publishing Inc™
4919 Rte 22, Amenia, NY 12501
Mailing Address: PO Box 56, Amenia, NY 12501-0056
Tel: 518-789-8700 *Toll Free Tel:* 800-562-2139 *Fax:* 518-789-0556
E-mail: books@greyhouse.com
Web Site: www.greyhouse.com
Includes the latest national & international standards & recommended practices pertaining to indexes & indexing.
2nd ed, 1996: 569 pp, $80
First published 1991
ISBN(s): 978-0-8242-0882-0

International Directory of Little Magazines & Small Presses
Published by Dustbooks
PO Box 100, Paradise, CA 95967-0100
SAN: 204-1871
Tel: 530-877-6110 *Fax:* 530-877-0222
E-mail: publisher@dustbooks.com; info@dustbooks.com
Web Site: www.dustbooks.com
Key Personnel
Publr: Kathleen Glanville
Ed: Neil McIntyre
For libraries & writers; 4,000 small book & magazine publishers with full data.
Annual (CD-ROM), continuously (online).
51st ed, 2015-2016, $30 CD-ROM, $65 CD-ROM (3 directories), $49.95 online (4 directories)
ISBN(s): 978-1-935742-34-0 (CD-ROM)

International Literary Market Place (ILMP)
Published by Information Today, Inc
121 Chanlon Rd, Suite G-20, New Providence, NJ 07974-2195
Tel: 908-795-3755 *Toll Free Tel:* 800-409-4929; 800-300-9868 (cust serv) *Fax:* 908-219-0192
E-mail: custserv@infotoday.com
Web Site: www.literarymarketplace.com
Key Personnel
Mng Ed: Karen Hallard *Tel:* 908-219-0277 *E-mail:* khallard@infotoday.com
A comprehensive directory of current data on the book trade in over 175 countries outside

the US & Canada, with over 9,700 publishers & over 3,300 book organizations, including agents, booksellers & library associations. Includes information basic to conducting business in each country. The US & Canada are covered by *Literary Market Place*. Web version, which includes *Literary Market Place*, also available.
Annual.
49th ed, 2016: 1,906 pp, $299.50 paper, $399.50 online subn
ISBN(s): 978-1-57387-507-3

Introduction to Literary Context
Published by Grey House Publishing Inc™
2 University Plaza, Suite 310, Hackensack, NJ 07601
SAN: 208-838X
Tel: 201-968-0500 *Toll Free Tel:* 800-221-1592 *Fax:* 201-968-0511
E-mail: csr@salempress.com
Web Site: salempress.com
Each volume contains 300 pages & explores literary content. Each essay examines works through the following categories: content synopsis, religious context, historical context, societal context, biographic context, scientific & technological context. Includes discussion questions, essay ideas, works cited, bibliography & index.
Volumes published April-Dec 2014:
American Poetry of the 20th Century
English Literature
Plays
World Literature.
$165/vol (includes online access)
ISBN(s): 978-1-61925-483-1 (World Literature); 978-1-61925-484-8 (World Literature ebook); 978-1-61925-485-5 (English Literature); 978-1-61925-486-2 (English Literature ebook); 978-1-61925-713-9 (American Poetry of the 20th Century); 978-1-61925-714-6 (American Poetry of the 20th Century ebook); 978-1-61925-715-3 (Plays); 978-1-61925-716-0 (Plays ebook)

Is There a Book Inside You?
Published by Para Publishing LLC
PO Box 8206-240, Santa Barbara, CA 93118-8206
SAN: 215-8981
Tel: 805-968-7277 *Toll Free Tel:* 800-727-2782 *Fax:* 805-968-1379
E-mail: info@parapublishing.com
Web Site: www.parapublishing.com
Key Personnel
Owner & Publr: Dan Poynter *E-mail:* danpoynter@parapublishing.com
Author: Mindy Bingham
A step-by-step formula for researching & writing a book. How to find & work with collaborators.
5th ed, 1999: 236 pp, $14.95 paper
First published 1985
ISBN(s): 978-1-56860-046-8

Jeff Herman's Guide to Book Publishers, Editors and Literary Agents: Who They Are, What They Want, How to Win Them Over
Published by New World Library
Division of Whatever Publishing Inc
14 Pamaron Way, Novato, CA 94949
SAN: 211-8777
Tel: 415-884-2100 *Toll Free Tel:* 800-972-6657; 800-227-3900 (ext 52, retail orders) *Fax:* 415-884-2199
Web Site: www.newworldlibrary.com
Key Personnel
Author: Jeff Herman
Writing/reference book. Directory of publishers (US, University, CN) & US literary agents. Includes interviews with editors & agents as well as additional information on submitting material to the publishing industry.
Annual.
25th ed, 2015: 1,104 pp, $29.99 paper
First published 1990
ISBN(s): 978-1-4022-43370

The Joy of Publishing!
Published by Open Horizons Publishing Co
PO Box 2887, Taos, NM 87571
Tel: 575-751-3398 *Fax:* 575-751-3100
E-mail: info@bookmarket.com
Web Site: www.bookmarket.com
Key Personnel
Publr & Ed: John Kremer *E-mail:* johnkremer@bookmarket.com
Fascinating facts, anecdotes, curiosities & historic origins about books & authors, editors & publishers, bookmaking & bookselling.
2000: 256 pp, $29.99 (hardcover), $19.95 (Internet special)
First published 1996
ISBN(s): 978-0-912411-47-7

Jump Start Your Book Sales: A Money-Making Guide for Authors, Independent Publishers & Small Presses
Published by Communication Creativity
4542 Melbourne Way, Highlands Ranch, CO 80130
Tel: 720-344-4388 *Toll Free Fax:* 866-685-0307
Web Site: www.selfpublishingresources.com (bookstore)
Key Personnel
Pres: Sue Collier *E-mail:* sue@selfpublishingresources.com
Sales & Ad Mgr: Doug Collier *E-mail:* doug@selfpublishingresources.com
Creative & money-making marketing ideas for authors & publishers.
1st ed, 1999: 358 pp, $19.95 paper
ISBN(s): 978-0-918880-41-3

Keys to Great Writing
Published by Writer's Digest Books
Imprint of F+W, A Content + eCommerce Company
10151 Carver Rd, Suite 200, Blue Ash, OH 45242
Tel: 513-531-2690 *Toll Free Tel:* 800-289-0963 *Fax:* 513-531-0798
E-mail: writersdigest@fwmedia.com (edit)
Web Site: www.writersdigest.com; www.writersdigestshop.com
Key Personnel
Publr & Edit Dir: Phil Sexton *E-mail:* phillip.sexton@fwcommunity.com
From grammar to revision strategies.
1st ed: 240 pp, $8.24 paper
ISBN(s): 978-1-58297-492-7

Law Books & Serials in Print™
Published by Grey House Publishing Inc™
4919 Rte 22, Amenia, NY 12501
Mailing Address: PO Box 56, Amenia, NY 12501-0056
Tel: 518-789-8700 *Toll Free Tel:* 800-562-2139 *Fax:* 518-789-0556
E-mail: books@greyhouse.com
Web Site: www.greyhouse.com
Provides immediate access to current legal books, serials & multimedia publications. Offers data on 90,000 titles, including print & non-print materials & over 20,000 serials entries from domestic & international publishers.
Annual.
2015: 3,900 pp, $1,400/3 vol set
ISBN(s): 978-1-61925-639-2 (3 vol set)

The Library & Book Trade Almanac
Published by Information Today, Inc
121 Chanlon Rd, Suite G-20, New Providence, NJ 07974-2195
Tel: 908-795-3755 *Toll Free Tel:* 800-409-4929; 800-300-9868 (cust serv) *Fax:* 908-219-0192
E-mail: custserv@infotoday.com
Key Personnel
Ed: Dave Bogart *E-mail:* bogart@bogartandbarr.com
Almanac of US library & book trade statistics, standards, programs & major events of the year, as well as international statistics & developments. Includes lists of library & literary awards & prizes, notable books, library schools, scholarship sources; directory of book trade & library associations at state, regional, national & international levels; employment sources; calendar of events.
Annual.
60th ed, 2015: 740 pp, $279 hardbound
ISBN(s): 978-1-57387-505-9

Literary Market Place (LMP)
Published by Information Today, Inc
121 Chanlon Rd, Suite G-20, New Providence, NJ 07974-2195
Tel: 908-795-3755 *Toll Free Tel:* 800-409-4929; 800-300-9868 (cust serv) *Fax:* 908-219-0192
E-mail: custserv@infotoday.com
Web Site: www.literarymarketplace.com
Key Personnel
Mng Ed: Karen Hallard *Tel:* 908-219-0277 *E-mail:* khallard@infotoday.com
Directory of over 26,000 companies & individuals in US & Canadian publishing. Areas covered include book publishers; associations; book trade events; courses, conferences & contests; agents & agencies; services & suppliers; direct-mail promotion; review, selection & reference; radio & television; wholesale, export & import & book manufacturing. A two-volume set, each containing two alphabetical names & numbers indexes, one for key companies listed & one for individuals. The rest of the world is covered by *International Literary Market Place*. Web version, which also includes *International Literary Market Place*, also available.
Annual.
76th ed, 2016: 1,750 pp, $399.50/2 vol set paper, $399.50 online subn
ISBN(s): 978-1-57387-509-7 (2 vol set)

Magazines for Libraries
Published by ProQuest LLC
Subsidiary of Cambridge Information Group Inc
630 Central Ave, New Providence, NJ 07974
E-mail: core_service@proquest.com
Web Site: www.proquest.com (publr); www.serialssolutions.com
Key Personnel
Gen Ed: Cheryl LaGuardia
Creator: Bill Katz
A critically annotated guide to magazine selection for public, college, school & special libraries, with approximately 6,000 periodicals critically evaluated by more than 200 subject specialists & classified under more than 160 subject headings. Includes journals (print & electronic) & newspapers.
23rd ed, 2015, $990 cloth
First published 1969
ISBN(s): 978-1-60030-651-8

Magill's Literary Annual
Published by Grey House Publishing Inc™
2 University Plaza, Suite 310, Hackensack, NJ 07601
SAN: 208-838X
Tel: 201-968-0500 *Toll Free Tel:* 800-221-1592 *Fax:* 201-968-0511
E-mail: csr@salempress.com
Web Site: salempress.com

Offers over 150 major examples of serious literature published during the previous calendar year, covering the best of the best in fiction & nonfiction.
Annual.
June 2015: 686 pp, $195/2 vol set (includes online access)
First published 1954
ISBN(s): 978-1-61925-685-9 (2 vol set); 978-1-61925-686-6 (ebook set)

Magill's Survey of American Literature
Published by Grey House Publishing Inc™
2 University Plaza, Suite 310, Hackensack, NJ 07601
SAN: 208-838X
Tel: 201-968-0500 *Toll Free Tel:* 800-221-1592 *Fax:* 201-968-0511
E-mail: csr@salempress.com
Web Site: salempress.com
Key Personnel
Ed: Steven G Kellman
Profiles of over 300 major US & Canadian authors of fiction, drama, nonfiction, young adult literature & poetry, accompanied by analysis of their significant works.
Sept 2006: 2,904 pp, $499/6 vol set
First published 1991
ISBN(s): 978-1-58765-285-1 (6 vol set)

Magill's Survey of World Literature
Published by Grey House Publishing Inc™
2 University Plaza, Suite 310, Hackensack, NJ 07601
SAN: 208-838X
Tel: 201-968-0500 *Toll Free Tel:* 800-221-1592 *Fax:* 201-968-0511
E-mail: csr@salempress.com
Web Site: salempress.com
Key Personnel
Ed: Steven G Kellman
Profiles of major authors of fiction, drama, poetry, novels, short stories, poems, nonfiction & essays, each with sections on biography & analysis of the author's most important works.
Jan 2009 (rev): 3,032 pp, $499/6 vol set
ISBN(s): 978-1-58765-431-2 (6 vol set); 978-1-58765-446-6 (ebook set)

Mail Order Business Directory
Published by Todd Publications
1388 Sabal Palm Dr, Boca Raton, FL 33432
SAN: 207-0804
Tel: 561-910-0440 *Fax:* 561-910-0440
E-mail: toddpub@yahoo.com
Key Personnel
Ed/Publr: Barry Klein
Contains the names of the 5,500 most active mail order catalogs, listed by 40 product categories with Alphabetical Index & Merchandise Category Index.
35th ed, 2016: 470 pp, $195 paperback
ISBN(s): 978-0-873400-374

Managing the Publishing Process: An Annotated Bibliography
Published by Greenwood Press
Imprint of ABC-CLIO
130 Cremona Dr, Suite C, Santa Barbara, CA 93117
Mailing Address: PO Box 1911, Santa Barbara, CA 93116-1911
Tel: 805-968-1911 *Toll Free Tel:* 800-368-6868 *Fax:* 805-685-9685 *Toll Free Fax:* 866-270-3856
E-mail: customerservice@abc-clio.com
Web Site: www.abc-clio.com
Key Personnel
Dir, Edit-Print: Anthony Chiffolo
Author: Bruce Speck
Cites & annotates more than 1200 books & articles on how to manage the publishing process.
1995: 360 pp, $122 hardcover
ISBN(s): 978-0-313-27956-0

Manufacturing Standards & Specifications for (El-Hi) Textbooks (MSST)
Published by State Instructional Materials Review Administrators (SIMRA)
2 Armand Beach Dr, Suite 1-B, Palm Coast, FL 32137
Tel: 386-986-4552 *Fax:* 386-986-4553
E-mail: info@bmibook.com
Web Site: www.bmibook.org
Key Personnel
Admin & Tech Dir, ACTS: Daniel N Bach
The official Advisory Commission on Textbook Specifications (ACTS) publication detailing the approved guidelines for the manufacture of elementary & high school textbooks.
Aug 2009: 92 pp, $35 looseleaf bound, adhesive bound or CD/per copy

The Marshall Plan for Getting Your Novel Published
Published by Writer's Digest Books
Imprint of F+W, A Content + eCommerce Company
10151 Carver Rd, Suite 200, Blue Ash, OH 45242
Tel: 513-531-2690 *Toll Free Tel:* 800-289-0963 *Fax:* 513-531-0798
E-mail: writersdigest@fwmedia.com (edit)
Web Site: www.writersdigest.com; www.writersdigestshop.com
Key Personnel
Publr & Edit Dir: Phil Sexton *E-mail:* phillip.sexton@fwcommunity.com
Learn how to find a hook, create a conflict, develop a protagonist & set things in motion.
1st ed: 240 pp, $10.18 paper
First published 1998
ISBN(s): 978-1-58297-062-2 (paperback)

Masterplots
Published by Grey House Publishing Inc™
2 University Plaza, Suite 310, Hackensack, NJ 07601
SAN: 208-838X
Tel: 201-968-0500 *Toll Free Tel:* 800-221-1592 *Fax:* 201-968-0511
E-mail: csr@salempress.com
Web Site: salempress.com
Key Personnel
Ed: Laurence W Mazzeno
Fundamental reference data, plot synopses & critical evaluations of the most important works in all genres throughout history & around the world.
4th ed (rev), Nov 2010: 6,848 pp, $1,200/12 vol set (includes online access)
First published 1976
ISBN(s): 978-1-58765-568-5 (12 vol set)

Masterplots II: African American Literature
Published by Grey House Publishing Inc™
2 University Plaza, Suite 310, Hackensack, NJ 07601
SAN: 208-838X
Tel: 201-968-0500 *Toll Free Tel:* 800-221-1592 *Fax:* 201-968-0511
E-mail: csr@salempress.com
Web Site: salempress.com
Key Personnel
Ed: Tyrone Williams
Essays on individual titles by great novelists, playwrights, memoirists, historians, poets, short story writers, essayists & orators.
Dec 2008 (rev): 2,160 pp, $404/4 vol set
ISBN(s): 978-1-58765-438-1 (4 vol set); 978-1-58765-447-3 (ebook set)

Masterplots II: Christian Literature
Published by Grey House Publishing Inc™
2 University Plaza, Suite 310, Hackensack, NJ 07601
SAN: 208-838X
Tel: 201-968-0500 *Toll Free Tel:* 800-221-1592 *Fax:* 201-968-0511
E-mail: csr@salempress.com
Web Site: salempress.com
Key Personnel
Ed: John K Roth
Covers over 500 classic & contemporary works of Christian fiction, nonfiction, poetry & drama, providing a plot summary, analysis of Christian themes & an annotated bibliography for each title.
Sept 2007: 2,100 pp, $385/4 vol set
ISBN(s): 978-1-58765-379-7 (4 vol set); 978-1-58765-413-8 (ebook set)

Masterplots II: Drama Series
Published by Grey House Publishing Inc™
2 University Plaza, Suite 310, Hackensack, NJ 07601
SAN: 208-838X
Tel: 201-968-0500 *Toll Free Tel:* 800-221-1592 *Fax:* 201-968-0511
E-mail: csr@salempress.com
Web Site: salempress.com
Key Personnel
Ed: Christian H Moe
Covers plays by important 20th century playwrights. No other *Masterplots* covers these 345 plays.
Sept 2003 (rev): 1,850 pp, $404/4 vol set
ISBN(s): 978-1-58765-116-8 (4 vol set)

Masterplots II: Short Story Series
Published by Grey House Publishing Inc™
2 University Plaza, Suite 310, Hackensack, NJ 07601
SAN: 208-838X
Tel: 201-968-0500 *Toll Free Tel:* 800-221-1592 *Fax:* 201-968-0511
E-mail: csr@salempress.com
Web Site: salempress.com
Key Personnel
Ed: Charles E May
Penetrating discussions of the content, themes, structure & techniques of 1,490 stories by writers from around the world.
2nd ed (rev), Jan 2004: 5,170 pp, $599/8 vol set
ISBN(s): 978-1-58765-140-3 (8 vol set)

Medical & Health Care Books & Serials in Print™
Published by Grey House Publishing Inc™
4919 Rte 22, Amenia, NY 12501
Mailing Address: PO Box 56, Amenia, NY 12501-0056
Tel: 518-789-8700 *Toll Free Tel:* 800-562-2139 *Fax:* 518-789-0556
E-mail: books@greyhouse.com
Web Site: www.greyhouse.com
Provides immediate access to the highly specialized publishing activity in the health sciences & allied health fields.
Annual.
45th ed, March 2015: 6,300 pp, $680/2 vol set
ISBN(s): 978-1-61925-636-1 (2 vol set)

Middle & Junior High School Core Collection
Published by Grey House Publishing Inc™
4919 Rte 22, Amenia, NY 12501
Mailing Address: PO Box 56, Amenia, NY 12501-0056
Tel: 518-789-8700 *Toll Free Tel:* 800-562-2139 *Fax:* 518-789-0556
E-mail: books@greyhouse.com
Web Site: www.greyhouse.com
Guide to over 10,000 fiction & nonfiction books recommended for children & young adolescents, grades 5-9.

12th ed, Dec 2015: 1,500 pp, $295
ISBN(s): 978-1-61925-706-1

MLRC 50-State Survey: Employment Libel & Privacy Law
Published by Media Law Resource Center Inc
North Tower, 20th fl, 520 Eighth Ave, New York, NY 10018
Tel: 212-337-0200 *Fax:* 212-337-9893
E-mail: medialaw@medialaw.org
Web Site: www.medialaw.org
Key Personnel
Exec Dir: Sandra Baron
Easy-to-use compendiums of the law in all US jurisdictions, state & federal, used by journalists, lawyers, judges & law schools nationwide. Each state's chapter, prepared by experts in that jurisdiction, is presented in a uniform outline format & updated & published annually.
Jan.
$245

MLRC 50-State Survey: Media Libel Law
Published by Media Law Resource Center Inc
North Tower, 20th fl, 520 Eighth Ave, New York, NY 10018
Tel: 212-337-0200 *Fax:* 212-337-9893
E-mail: medialaw@medialaw.org
Web Site: www.medialaw.org
Key Personnel
Exec Dir: Sandra Baron
Easy-to-use compendiums of the law in all US jurisdictions, state & federal, used by journalists, lawyers, judges & law schools nationwide. Each state's chapter, prepared by experts in that jurisdiction, is presented in a uniform outline format & updated & published annually.
Nov.
1,500 pp, $245

MLRC 50-State Survey: Media Privacy & Related Law
Published by Media Law Resource Center Inc
North Tower, 20th fl, 520 Eighth Ave, New York, NY 10018
Tel: 212-337-0200 *Fax:* 212-337-9893
E-mail: medialaw@medialaw.org
Web Site: www.medialaw.org
Key Personnel
Exec Dir: Sandra Baron
Easy-to-use compendiums of the law in all US jurisdictions, state & federal, used by journalists, lawyers, judges & law schools nationwide. Each state's chapter, prepared by experts in that jurisdiction, is presented in a uniform outline format & is updated & published annually.
June.
$245

National Trade and Professional Associations of the United States
Published by Columbia Books & Information Services
4340 East-West Hwy, Suite 300, Bethesda, MD 20814
Tel: 240-235-0266 *Toll Free Tel:* 888-265-0600 (cust serv) *Fax:* 202-464-1775
E-mail: info@columbiabooks.com
Web Site: www.columbiabooks.com
Key Personnel
Dir of Sales & Mktg: Brittany Carter *Tel:* 240-235-0270 *E-mail:* bcarter@columbiabooks.com
Covers over 7,800 trade associations, professional societies & labor unions with national memberships with such data as chief executive, size of membership & staff, budget, telephone, facsimile number, e-mail address, publications, meeting data & historical background. Includes indexes by subject, geography, budget, acronym, chief executive officer & annual meeting location. Also available online at www.associationexecs.com.
Annual.
50th ed, 2015, $299 paper
First published 1965
ISBN(s): 978-0-910416-67-2

The New York Times Manual of Style & Usage
Published by Three Rivers Press
Division of Random House Inc
1745 Broadway, New York, NY 10019
Tel: 212-782-9000 *Toll Free Tel:* 800-733-3000 (cust serv)
Web Site: www.randomhouse.com
Key Personnel
Author: William G Connolly; Allan M Siegal
Revised Edition 2002, $16.95
ISBN(s): 978-0-8129-6389-2

Niche Publishing: Publish Profitably Every Time
Published by Communication Unlimited
185 Shevelin Rd, Novato, CA 94947
Tel: 415-884-2941 *Toll Free Tel:* 800-563-1454 *Fax:* 415-883-5707
E-mail: gordon@gordonburgett.com
Web Site: www.gordonburgett.com
Key Personnel
Pres & Ed: Gordon Burgett *E-mail:* glburgett@aol.com
How-to information, step-by-step process & detailed example of niche publishing.
2008: 208 pp, $15 paper, $10 digital download
First published 2008
ISBN(s): 978-0-979629-525

Nineteenth-Century Literature Criticism
Published by Gale
Unit of Cengage Learning
27500 Drake Rd, Farmington Hills, MI 48331-3535
SAN: 213-4373
Tel: 248-699-4253 *Toll Free Tel:* 800-877-4253 *Fax:* 248-699-8054 *Toll Free Fax:* 800-414-5043 (orders)
E-mail: gale.galeord@cengage.com
Web Site: www.gale.cengage.com
Key Personnel
Ed: Kathy Darrow
Online directory with critical overviews of poets, novelists, short story writers, playwrights, philosophers & other creative writers, who died between 1800 & 1899. Most critical essays are full text.

No More Rejections
Published by Writer's Digest Books
Imprint of F+W, A Content + eCommerce Company
10151 Carver Rd, Suite 200, Blue Ash, OH 45242
Tel: 513-531-2690 *Toll Free Tel:* 800-289-0963 *Fax:* 513-531-0798
E-mail: writersdigest@fwmedia.com (edit)
Web Site: www.writersdigest.com; www.writersdigestshop.com
Key Personnel
Publr & Edit Dir: Phil Sexton *E-mail:* phillip.sexton@fwcommunity.com
Secrets to writing a ms that sells. Thinking up original ideas, moving your story forward, developing characters with character, etc.
1st ed: 272 pp, $4.99
First published 2004
ISBN(s): 978-1-58297-285-5 (hardcover)

Notable African American Writers
Published by Grey House Publishing Inc™
2 University Plaza, Suite 310, Hackensack, NJ 07601
SAN: 208-838X
Tel: 201-968-0500 *Toll Free Tel:* 800-221-1592 *Fax:* 201-968-0511
E-mail: csr@salempress.com
Web Site: salempress.com
Contains 80 essays on important African American writers in all genres.
April 2006, $217/3 vol set
ISBN(s): 978-1-58765-272-1 (3 vol set); 978-1-58765-362-9 (ebook set)

Notable American Novelists
Published by Grey House Publishing Inc™
2 University Plaza, Suite 310, Hackensack, NJ 07601
SAN: 208-838X
Tel: 201-968-0500 *Toll Free Tel:* 800-221-1592 *Fax:* 201-968-0511
E-mail: csr@salempress.com
Web Site: salempress.com
Presents biographical sketches & analytical overviews of 145 of the best known American & Canadian writers of long fiction that are studied in the core curricula of high school & undergraduate literature studies.
Aug 2007, $217/3 vol set
ISBN(s): 978-1-58765-393-3 (3 vol set); 978-1-58765-410-7 (ebook set)

Notable Playwrights
Published by Grey House Publishing Inc™
2 University Plaza, Suite 310, Hackensack, NJ 07601
SAN: 208-838X
Tel: 201-968-0500 *Toll Free Tel:* 800-221-1592 *Fax:* 201-968-0511
E-mail: csr@salempress.com
Web Site: salempress.com
Biographical sketches & critical studies of 106 of the best known dramatists, from the development of drama in ancient Greece & Rome to European, American, Asian & African writers of today.
Aug 2004, $217/3 vol set
ISBN(s): 978-1-58765-195-3 (3 vol set); 978-1-58765-316-2 (ebook set)

O'Dwyer's Directory of Public Relations Firms
Published by O'Dwyer Co
271 Madison Ave, Rm 600, New York, NY 10016
Tel: 212-679-2471 *Toll Free Tel:* 866-395-7710 *Fax:* 212-683-2750
Web Site: www.odwyerpr.com
Key Personnel
Publr & Ed-in-Chief: Jack O'Dwyer *E-mail:* jack@odwyerpr.com
A listing of more than 1,400 PR firms in the US & overseas.
Annual.
45th ed, 2015: 330 pp, $95
First published 1970

100 Things Every Writer Needs to Know
Published by Perigee Books
Imprint of Penguin Group (USA) LLC
375 Hudson St, New York, NY 10014
SAN: 282-5074
Tel: 212-366-2000 *Fax:* 212-366-2365
Web Site: www.penguin.com; us.penguingroup.com
Key Personnel
Publr: John Duff
Ed-in-Chief: Marian Lizzi
Author: Scott Edelstein
256 pp, $14.95
First published 1996
ISBN(s): 978-0-399-52508-7

1001 Ways to Market Your Books
Published by Open Horizons Publishing Co
PO Box 2887, Taos, NM 87571
Tel: 575-751-3398 *Fax:* 575-751-3100
E-mail: info@bookmarket.com
Web Site: www.bookmarket.com

Key Personnel
Publr & Ed: John Kremer *E-mail:* johnkremer@bookmarket.com
Outlines more than 1,000 different ways to market books. Uses many real-life examples describing how other publishers market their books. Includes planning & design, advertising & distribution, subsidiary rights & spinoffs.
6th ed, 2008: 704 pp, $27.95 paper
ISBN(s): 978-0-912411-49-X (paper)

1,001 Tips for Writers: Words of Wisdom About Writing, Getting Published, and Living the Literary Life
Published by North Ridge Books
PO Box 2832, Rancho Mirage, CA 92270
Tel: 760-321-1977
E-mail: nrbooks@aol.com
Web Site: www.1001tipsforwriters.com
Key Personnel
Ed: William A Gordon
1,001 Tips for Writers is a quotation book offering "Words of Wisdom About Writing, Getting Published, and Living the Literary Life." The book quotes literary greats; working writers, publishers, editors on subjects such as "How to Get Traditionally Published," "Self-Publishing," "Book Publicity," & writing history, humor, novels, & journalism.
1st ed, 2014, $15.95 paperback, $8.95 ebook
ISBN(s): 978-0-937813-09-6 (ebook); 978-0-937813-10-2 (paperback)

Photographer's Market
Published by F+W, A Content + eCommerce Company
10151 Carver Rd, Suite 200, Blue Ash, OH 45242
Tel: 513-531-2690 *Toll Free Tel:* 855-842-5267 (cust serv) *Fax:* 513-891-7153
E-mail: photomarket@fwmedia.com
Web Site: www.artistsmarketonline.com
Key Personnel
Sr Content Developer: Mary Burzlaff Bostic
More than 1,500 listings of photo buyers with complete contact information; for freelance & stock photographers.
Annual.
38th ed, 2015: 688 pp, $34.99
ISBN(s): 978-1-4403-3567-2

Play Index
Published by H W Wilson
2 University Plaza, Suite 310, Hackensack, NJ 07601
Tel: 201-968-0500 *Toll Free Tel:* 800-221-1592 *Fax:* 201-968-0511
E-mail: information@ebscohost.com
Web Site: www.ebscohost.com/wilson
Key Personnel
VP, Cataloging & Gen Ref Servs: Joseph Miller, MLS, PhD
Online publication including some 31,000 plays published from 1949 to the present as well as over 600 monologues.
Contact for price information

The Pocket Muse
Published by Writer's Digest Books
Imprint of F+W, A Content + eCommerce Company
10151 Carver Rd, Suite 200, Blue Ash, OH 45242
Tel: 513-531-2690 *Toll Free Tel:* 800-289-0963 *Fax:* 513-531-0798
E-mail: writersdigest@fwmedia.com (edit)
Web Site: www.writersdigest.com; www.writersdigestshop.com
Key Personnel
Publr & Edit Dir: Phil Sexton *E-mail:* phillip.sexton@fwcommunity.com
Unique ideas for overcoming writer's block, creativity boosters, revision tips & more.
2004: 256 pp, $7.78 paper
ISBN(s): 978-1-58297-322-7

Poetry Criticism
Published by Gale
Unit of Cengage Learning
27500 Drake Rd, Farmington Hills, MI 48331-3535
SAN: 213-4373
Tel: 248-699-4253 *Toll Free Tel:* 800-347-4253 *Fax:* 248-699-8070 *Toll Free Fax:* 800-414-5043 (orders)
E-mail: gale.galeord@cengage.com
Web Site: www.gale.cengage.com
Online directory covering four-eight major poets from all eras. Provides intro author biographical sketch, primary bibliography. annotated full text & excerpted criticism with additional readings.

Poets' Encyclopedia
Published by Unmuzzled Ox Press
105 Hudson St, New York, NY 10013
Tel: 212-226-7170
Key Personnel
Ed: Michael Andre *E-mail:* mandreox@yahoo.com
Author: W H Auden; Dan Berrigan; John Cage; Allen Ginsberg
World's basic knowledge transformed by 225 poets, artists, musicians & novelists.
1st ed, 1979: 310 pp, $75 cloth, $40 paper
ISBN(s): 978-0-934450-02-7 (cloth); 978-0-934450-03-4 (paper)

Poet's Market
Published by Writer's Digest Books
Imprint of F+W, A Content + eCommerce Company
10151 Carver Rd, Suite 200, Blue Ash, OH 45242
Tel: 513-531-2690 *Toll Free Tel:* 800-289-0963 *Fax:* 513-531-0798
E-mail: writersdigest@fwmedia.com (edit)
Web Site: www.writersdigest.com; www.writersdigestshop.com
Key Personnel
Publr & Edit Dir: Phil Sexton *E-mail:* phillip.sexton@fwcommunity.com
Where & how to get poetry published; 1,800 US & international publisher listings, also includes contests & awards, writing colonies, organizations, conferences, workshops & publications useful to poets. Also available as ebook.
Annual.
2015: 512 pp, $29.99 paper or ebook
ISBN(s): 978-1-59963-844-7 (print); 978-1-59963-854-6 (ebook)

Professional Writing: Processes, Strategies & Tips for Publishing in Education Journals
Published by Krieger Publishing Co
1725 Krieger Dr, Malabar, FL 32950
SAN: 202-6562
Tel: 321-724-9542 *Toll Free Tel:* 800-724-0025 *Fax:* 321-951-3671
E-mail: info@krieger-publishing.com
Web Site: www.krieger-publishing.com
Key Personnel
Author: Roger Hiemstra
Ad Mgr: Cheryl Stanton
Provides insights, tips, strategies & recommendations for publishing in educational periodicals.
1994: 152 pp, $27.50 cloth
First published 1993
ISBN(s): 978-0-89464-660-7

Public Library Core Collection: Nonfiction
Published by Grey House Publishing Inc™
4919 Rte 22, Amenia, NY 12501
Mailing Address: PO Box 56, Amenia, NY 12501-0056
Tel: 518-789-8700 *Toll Free Tel:* 800-562-2139 *Fax:* 518-789-0556
E-mail: books@greyhouse.com
Web Site: www.greyhouse.com
Recommends reference & nonfiction books for the general adult audience. Guide to over 9,000 books, plus review sources & other professional aids for librarians & media specialists.
15th ed, Feb 2015: 2,500 pp, $420
ISBN(s): 978-1-61925-473-2

Publish, Don't Perish: The Scholar's Guide to Academic Writing & Publishing
Published by Praeger
Imprint of ABC-CLIO
130 Cremona Dr, Suite C, Santa Barbara, CA 93117
Mailing Address: PO Box 1911, Santa Barbara, CA 93116-1911
Tel: 805-968-1911 *Toll Free Tel:* 800-368-6868 *Fax:* 805-685-9685 *Toll Free Fax:* 866-270-3856
E-mail: custserv@abc-clio.com
Web Site: www.abc-clio.com
Key Personnel
Dir, Edit-Print: Anthony Chiffolo
Author: Joseph M Moxley
Expressing a strongly positive view of the value of academic publishing that reaches far beyond what is implied by the book title, Moxley offers informed suggestions to faculty members for conceiving, developing & publishing scholarly documents as books or journal articles.
224 pp, $27.95 paper, $80 hardcover
First published 1992
ISBN(s): 978-0-275-94453-6 (paper); 978-0-313-27735-1 (hardcover)

Publishers Directory
Published by Gale
Unit of Cengage Learning
27500 Drake Rd, Farmington Hills, MI 48331-3535
SAN: 213-4373
Tel: 248-699-4253 *Toll Free Tel:* 800-877-4253 *Fax:* 248-699-8074 *Toll Free Fax:* 800-414-5043 (orders)
E-mail: gale.galeord@cengage.com
Web Site: www.gale.cengage.com
Key Personnel
Ed: Verne Thompson
Contains over 30,000 US & Canadian publishers, distributors & wholesalers. Organizations listed are major publishing companies, small presses, special interest groups, museums, societies in the arts, science technology, history & genealogy, divisions within universities that issue field specific publications, religious institutions, government agencies & electronic & database publishers.
Annual.
40th ed, 2015: 2,191 pp, $790 (3 vol set)
ISBN(s): 978-1-57302-511-9 (3 vol set)

Publishers, Distributors & Wholesalers of the United States™
Published by Grey House Publishing Inc™
4919 Rte 22, Amenia, NY 12501
Mailing Address: PO Box 56, Amenia, NY 12501-0056
Tel: 518-789-8700 *Toll Free Tel:* 800-562-2139 *Fax:* 518-789-0556
E-mail: books@greyhouse.com
Web Site: www.greyhouse.com
Two information-packed volumes offering detailed data on 186,000 active US publishers, distributors, associations, software producers, video producers & manufacturers, audio cas-

sette producers & museums with publishing programs.
Annual.
2015: 5,400 pp, $635/2 vol set hardcover
ISBN(s): 978-1-61925-382-7 (2 vol set)

Publishers' International ISBN Directory
Published by De Gruyter Saur
Imprint of Walter de Gruyter GmbH & Co KG
Genthiner Str 13, 10785 Berlin, Germany
Tel: (030) 260 05-0 *Fax:* (030) 260 05-251
E-mail: info@degruyter.com
Web Site: www.degruyter.com
Seven volume set containing the names of more than 1,000,000 active publishing houses & more than 1,100,000 ISBN prefixes from 221 countries & territories.
Annual.
41st ed, 2015: 8,380 pp
ISBN(s): 978-3-11-0337365 (7-vol set)

Publishing as a Vocation: Studies of an Old Occupation in a New Technological Era
Published by Transaction Publishers Inc
10 Corporate Place S, Piscataway, NJ 08854
Mailing Address: 1247 State Rd, Princeton, NJ 08540
Tel: 732-445-2280 *Fax:* 732-445-3138
Web Site: www.transactionpub.com
Places publishing in America in its political & commercial setting. Addresses the political implications of scholary communication in the era of new computerized technology. Examines problems of political theory in the context of property rights versus the presumed right to know & the special strains involved in publishing as commerce versus information as a public trust.
1st ed, 2010: 167 pp, $37.95 paper
First published 2010
ISBN(s): 978-1-4128-1110-1

Publishing Contracts, Sample Agreements for Book Publishers on Disk
Published by Para Publishing LLC
PO Box 8206-240, Santa Barbara, CA 93118-8206
SAN: 215-8981
Tel: 805-968-7277 *Toll Free Tel:* 800-727-2782 *Fax:* 805-968-1379
E-mail: info@parapublishing.com
Web Site: www.parapublishing.com
Key Personnel
Owner & Publr: Dan Poynter
E-mail: danpoynter@parapublishing.com
Author: Charles Kent, Esq
22 different contracts covering every aspect of book publishing on disk, ready for computer customizing & printout.
5th ed, 2006: 127 pp, $29.95 disk
ISBN(s): 978-0-915516-46-9

Publishing for the PreK-12 Market
Published by Simba Information
Division of Market Research.com
1266 E Main St, Suite 700, Stamford, CT 06902
SAN: 210-2021
Tel: 203-325-8193 *Toll Free Tel:* 888-297-4622 (cust serv)
E-mail: customerservice@simbainformation.com
Web Site: www.simbainformation.com
Key Personnel
Sr Analyst/Mng Ed: Kathy Mickey
Prodn Coord: Farah Pierre
Up-to-date descriptions & statistics on enrollments, demographic trends, in several categories; publishers' sales, forecasts, expenditures & profiles of the leading publishers in the K-12 market place.
Annual.
2014-2015: 186 pp, $3,450 print, $3,250 online, $3,850 online & print

Publishing in the Information Age: A New Management Framework for the Digital Era
Published by Praeger
Imprint of ABC-CLIO
130 Cremona Dr, Suite C, Santa Barbara, CA 93117
Mailing Address: PO Box 1911, Santa Barbara, CA 93116-1911
Tel: 805-968-1911 *Toll Free Tel:* 800-368-6868 *Fax:* 805-685-9685 *Toll Free Fax:* 866-270-3856
E-mail: custserv@abc-clio.com
Web Site: www.abc-clio.com
Key Personnel
Dir, Edit-Print: Anthony Chiffolo
Author: Douglas M Eisenhart
A comprehensive single-volume study of the transformations underway in the publishing industry attributable to the penetration of digital information technologies & how publishers can benefit from them.
$39.95 paper, $119 hardcover
First published 1999
ISBN(s): 978-0-275-95696-7 (paper); 978-0-89930-847-0 (hardcover)

The Reference Shelf: Graphic Novels and Comic Books
Published by Grey House Publishing Inc™
4919 Rte 22, Amenia, NY 12501
Mailing Address: PO Box 56, Amenia, NY 12501-0056
Tel: 518-789-8700 *Toll Free Tel:* 800-562-2139 *Fax:* 518-789-0556
E-mail: books@greyhouse.com
Web Site: www.greyhouse.com
Explores the origins, development & future of comic books & graphic novels.
Nov 2010: 200 pp, $60
ISBN(s): 978-0-8242-1100-4

Research Centers Directory
Published by Gale
Unit of Cengage Learning
27500 Drake Rd, Farmington Hills, MI 48331-3535
SAN: 213-4373
Tel: 248-699-4253 *Toll Free Tel:* 800-877-4253 *Fax:* 248-699-8075 *Toll Free Fax:* 800-414-5043 (orders)
E-mail: gale.galeord@cengage.com
Web Site: www.gale.cengage.com
Key Personnel
Ed: Matthew Miskelly *Tel:* 248-699-4253 ext 1744 *E-mail:* matthew.miskelly@cengage.com; Sonya Hill
Directory describes more than 15,700 University affiliated & other nonprofit research centers in the US & Canada. Indexes: subject, geographic, personal name & master, including sponsoring organization, research center name & keywords.
44th ed, 2014: 2,600 pp, $1175/5 vol set
ISBN(s): 978-1-4144-9231-5 (5 vol set)

Sears List of Subject Headings
Published by Grey House Publishing Inc™
4919 Rte 22, Amenia, NY 12501
Mailing Address: PO Box 56, Amenia, NY 12501-0056
Tel: 518-789-8700 *Toll Free Tel:* 800-562-2139 *Fax:* 518-789-0556
E-mail: books@greyhouse.com
Web Site: www.greyhouse.com
Standard thesaurus of subject terminology for small & medium-sized libraries. Also includes "Principles of the Sears List", a 23-page insert outlining theoretical foundations of the *Sears List* & the general principles of subject cataloging.
21st ed, April 2014: 850 pp, $165
First published 1923
ISBN(s): 978-1-61925-190-8

Sears: Lista de Encabezamientos de Materia
Published by Grey House Publishing Inc™
4919 Rte 22, Amenia, NY 12501
Mailing Address: PO Box 56, Amenia, NY 12501-0056
Tel: 518-789-8700 *Toll Free Tel:* 800-562-2139 *Fax:* 518-789-0556
E-mail: books@greyhouse.com
Web Site: www.greyhouse.com
Sears List of Subject Headings adapted for the Spanish language.
June 2010: 800 pp, $150
ISBN(s): 978-0-8242-1058-8

The Self-Publishing Manual: How to Write, Print & Sell Your Own Book
Published by Para Publishing LLC
PO Box 8206-240, Santa Barbara, CA 93118-8206
SAN: 215-8981
Tel: 805-968-7277 *Toll Free Tel:* 800-727-2782 *Fax:* 805-968-1379
E-mail: info@parapublishing.com
Web Site: www.parapublishing.com
Key Personnel
Owner & Publr: Dan Poynter
E-mail: danpoynter@parapublishing.com
Founded: 1979
16th ed, 2009: 471 pp, $19.95 paper
First published 1979
ISBN(s): 978-1-56860-134-2

Senior High Core Collection
Published by Grey House Publishing Inc™
4919 Rte 22, Amenia, NY 12501
Mailing Address: PO Box 56, Amenia, NY 12501-0056
Tel: 518-789-8700 *Toll Free Tel:* 800-562-2139 *Fax:* 518-789-0556
E-mail: books@greyhouse.com
Web Site: www.greyhouse.com
Guide to over 10,000 fiction & nonfiction books recommended for adolescents & young adults, grades 9-12.
19th ed, Aug 2014: 1,500 pp, $295
ISBN(s): 978-0-8242-1244-5

Shakespearean Criticism
Published by Gale
Unit of Cengage Learning
27500 Drake Rd, Farmington Hills, MI 48331-3535
SAN: 213-4373
Tel: 248-699-4253 *Toll Free Tel:* 800-877-4253 *Fax:* 248-699-8070 *Toll Free Fax:* 800-414-5043 (orders)
E-mail: gale.galeord@cengage.com
Web Site: www.gale.cengage.com
Thematically arranged essays from 1960 to the present of commentary on Shakespeare's plays & poems. Illustrated series provides support to students & teachers at high school & college levels. Beginning with Vol 60, presents topic entries that analyze various themes of Shakespeare's works. Each volume has a cumulative character index, a topic index & a topic index arranged by play title.

Short Story Criticism
Published by Gale
Unit of Cengage Learning
27500 Drake Rd, Farmington Hills, MI 48331-3535
SAN: 213-4373
Tel: 248-699-4253 *Toll Free Tel:* 800-877-4253 *Fax:* 248-699-8070 *Toll Free Fax:* 800-414-5043 (orders)
E-mail: gale.galeord@cengage.com
Web Site: www.gale.cengage.com

Series presenting critical views on the most widely studied writers of short fiction. Each volume includes overview of four to eight short story writers & a chronological historical survey of the critical response to his or her work. Most critical essays are full text.

Short Story Index
Published by Grey House Publishing Inc™
4919 Rte 22, Amenia, NY 12501
Mailing Address: PO Box 56, Amenia, NY 12501-0056
Tel: 518-789-8700 *Toll Free Tel:* 800-562-2139 *Fax:* 518-789-0556
E-mail: books@greyhouse.com
Web Site: www.greyhouse.com
Indexing coverage of short stories written in or translated into English & published in collections, covering all styles & genres-from classics to experimental fiction.
Annual.
Jan 2015 (2014 annual cumulation): 260 pp, $295
ISBN(s): 978-1-61925-429-9

Short Story Writers
Published by Grey House Publishing Inc™
2 University Plaza, Suite 310, Hackensack, NJ 07601
SAN: 208-838X
Tel: 201-968-0500 *Toll Free Tel:* 800-221-1592 *Fax:* 201-968-0511
E-mail: csr@salempress.com
Web Site: salempress.com
Key Personnel
Ed: Charles May
Covers 146 of the most frequently taught, read & researched short fiction writers studied in schools & colleges.
Oct 2007: 1,164 pp, $217/3 vol set
ISBN(s): 978-1-58765-389-6 (3 vol set); 978-1-58765-411-4 (ebook set)

The Small Press Record of Books in Print
Published by Dustbooks
PO Box 100, Paradise, CA 95967-0100
SAN: 204-1871
Tel: 530-877-6110 *Fax:* 530-877-0222
E-mail: publisher@dustbooks.com; info@dustbooks.com
Web Site: www.dustbooks.com
Key Personnel
Publr: Kathleen Glanville
Ed: Neil McIntyre
More than 43,400 titles from more than 5,000 small, independent, educational & self-publishers worldwide.
41st ed, $37.95 CD-ROM, $49.95 online (4 directories)
ISBN(s): 978-1-935742-36-4 (CD-ROM)

Software and Intellectual Property Protection: Copyright and Patent Issues for Computer and Legal Professionals
Published by Praeger
Imprint of ABC-CLIO
130 Cremona Dr, Suite C, Santa Barbara, CA 93117
Mailing Address: PO Box 1911, Santa Barbara, CA 93116-1911
Tel: 805-968-1911 *Toll Free Tel:* 800-368-6868 *Fax:* 805-685-9685 *Toll Free Fax:* 866-270-3856
E-mail: custserv@abc-clio.com
Web Site: www.abc-clio.com
Key Personnel
Dir, Edit-Print: Anthony Chiffolo
Author: Bernard A Galler
A succinct, readable survey of the critical issues & cases in copyright & patent law applied to computer software, intended for computer professionals, academics & lawyers.
224 pp, $119 hardcover
ISBN(s): 978-0-89930-974-3

Something About the Author
Published by Gale
Unit of Cengage Learning
27500 Drake Rd, Farmington Hills, MI 48331-3535
SAN: 213-4373
Tel: 248-699-4253 *Toll Free Tel:* 800-877-4253 *Fax:* 248-699-8070 *Toll Free Fax:* 800-414-5043 (orders)
E-mail: gale.galeord@cengage.com
Web Site: www.gale.cengage.com
Heavily illustrated child-oriented reference tool. Each volume contains biographies on about 75 juvenile & young adult authors & illustrators. The series covers more than 12,000 authors. Entries include personal & career data, literary sidelights, complete bibliographies, critical comments & author portraits & book illustrations. A cumulative author index is included in each odd-numbered volume.

Standard Periodical Directory
Published by Oxbridge® Communications Inc
39 W 29 St, Suite 301, New York, NY 10001
Tel: 212-741-0231 *Toll Free Tel:* 800-955-0231 *Fax:* 212-633-2938
E-mail: info@oxbridge.com
Web Site: www.oxbridge.com
Key Personnel
CEO: Louis Hagood
Pres: Patricia Hagood
Over 63,000 US & Canadian periodicals arranged by subject matter into 262 classifications & indexed by title. Listings include publishing company, address, telephone number; names of editor, publisher, ad director; annotations; frequency, circulation, advertising & subscription rates; year established; trim size, print method, page count.
Annually in Jan.
38th ed, 2015: 2,167 pp, $1,995 hardcover, $995 digital, $1,995 single user CD-ROM, $2,995 print & CD-ROM
First published 1964
ISBN(s): 978-1-891783-63-0 (print)

Subject Guide to Books in Print®
Published by Grey House Publishing Inc™
4919 Rte 22, Amenia, NY 12501
Mailing Address: PO Box 56, Amenia, NY 12501-0056
Tel: 518-789-8700 *Toll Free Tel:* 800-562-2139 *Fax:* 518-789-0556
E-mail: books@greyhouse.com
Web Site: www.greyhouse.com
Master subject reference to titles, authors, publishers, wholesalers & distributors in the US.
Annual.
59th ed, 2015-2016: 15,400 pp, $970/6 vol set
ISBN(s): 978-1-61925-651-4 (6 vol set)

Subject Guide to Children's Books in Print®
Published by Grey House Publishing Inc™
4919 Rte 22, Amenia, NY 12501
Mailing Address: PO Box 56, Amenia, NY 12501-0056
Tel: 518-789-8700 *Toll Free Tel:* 800-562-2139 *Fax:* 518-789-0556
E-mail: books@greyhouse.com
Web Site: www.greyhouse.com
A natural complement to *Children's Books in Print®* & valuable tool when expanding children's literature collections & new curriculum areas. Coverage includes over 350,000 titles classified under 9,500 Library of Congress subject headings.
Annual.
45th ed, 2015: 2,900 pp, $460
ISBN(s): 978-1-61925-388-9

Survey of Compensation & Personnel Practices in the Publishing Industry
Published by Association of American Publishers (AAP)
71 Fifth Ave, 2nd fl, New York, NY 10003-3004
Tel: 212-255-0200 *Fax:* 212-255-7007
Web Site: publishers.org
Key Personnel
Pres & CEO: Tom Allen *E-mail:* tallen@publishers.org
VP: Tina Jordan *Tel:* 212-255-0275 *E-mail:* tjordan@publishers.org
VP & Exec Dir, Prof & Scholarly Publg: John Tagler *Tel:* 212-255-1407 *E-mail:* jtagler@publishers.org
Gen Coun & VP, Govt Aff: Allan R Adler *Tel:* 202-220-4544 *E-mail:* adler@publishers.org
Exec Dir, PreK-12 Learning Group: Jay Diskey *Tel:* 202-220-4549 *E-mail:* jdiskey@publishers.org
Survey report contains salary & personnel practices information for more than 120 benchmark jobs in the publishing industry.
Annual.
220 pp, Varies based on participation, company site & AAP membership status

Tenth Book of Junior Authors & Illustrators
Published by Grey House Publishing Inc™
4919 Rte 22, Amenia, NY 12501
Mailing Address: PO Box 56, Amenia, NY 12501-0056
Tel: 518-789-8700 *Toll Free Tel:* 800-562-2139 *Fax:* 518-789-0556
E-mail: books@greyhouse.com
Web Site: www.greyhouse.com
Biographical profiles of over 180 award-winning authors & illustrators who represent the rich variety & multicultural nature of children's literature today.
Nov 2008: 850 pp, $120
First published 1934
ISBN(s): 978-0-8242-1066-3

Training Guide to Frontline Bookselling
Published by Paz & Associates
1417 Sadler Rd, PMB 274, Fernandina Beach, FL 32034
Tel: 904-277-2664 *Fax:* 904-261-6742
E-mail: mkaufman@pazbookbiz.com
Web Site: www.pazbookbiz.com
Key Personnel
Partner: Donna Paz Kaufman *E-mail:* dpaz@pazbookbiz.com
12 chapters on all aspects of bookstore operations, includes trainers outline.
4th ed, Jan 2014: 125 pp, $189 plus shipping

Travel Writer's Guide
Published by Communication Unlimited
185 Shevelin Rd, Novato, CA 94947
Tel: 415-884-2941 *Toll Free Tel:* 800-563-1454 *Fax:* 415-883-5707
E-mail: gordon@gordonburgett.com
Web Site: www.gordonburgett.com
Key Personnel
Pres: Gordon Burgett *E-mail:* glburgett@aol.com
Writing/reference.
3rd ed (rev), updated 2005: 376 pp, $15 paper, $10 digital download
ISBN(s): 978-0-9708621-1-3

Travel Writing
Published by Writer's Digest Books
Imprint of F+W, A Content + eCommerce Company
10151 Carver Rd, Suite 200, Blue Ash, OH 45242
Tel: 513-531-2690 *Toll Free Tel:* 800-289-0963 *Fax:* 513-531-0798
E-mail: writersdigest@fwmedia.com (edit)

Web Site: www.writersdigest.com; www.writersdigestshop.com
Key Personnel
Publr & Edit Dir: Phil Sexton *E-mail:* phillip.sexton@fwcommunity.com
How to write engagingly about your travels, whether in journals for your own pleasure or articles for publications.
2nd ed, 2005: 320 pp, $8.24 paper
First published 2000
ISBN(s): 978-1-58297-381-4

TRUMATCH Colorfinder
Published by TRUMATCH Inc
122 Mill Pond Lane, Water Mill, NY 11976
Mailing Address: PO Box 501, Water Mill, NY 11976-0501
Tel: 631-204-9100 *Toll Free Tel:* 800-TRU-9100 (878-9100, US & CN)
E-mail: info@trumatch.com
Web Site: www.trumatch.com
Key Personnel
Pres: Steven J Abramson
VP: Jane E Nichols *E-mail:* janen@trumatch.com
Digital guides for 4-color printing.
$85 paper for coated ed or uncoated ed

Twentieth-Century Literary Criticism
Published by Gale
Unit of Cengage Learning
27500 Drake Rd, Farmington Hills, MI 48331-3535
SAN: 213-4373
Tel: 248-699-4253 *Toll Free Tel:* 800-347-4253 *Fax:* 248-699-8054 *Toll Free Fax:* 800-414-5043 (orders)
E-mail: gale.galeord@cengage.com
Web Site: www.gale.cengage.com
Key Personnel
Ed: Linda Pavlovski
Presents overviews of authors & furnishes full texts from representative criticism on the great novelists, poets & playwrights of the period 1900-1999. Every fourth volume covers literary topics including major literary movements, trends & other topics related to 20th century literature.

20 Master Plots
Published by Writer's Digest Books
Imprint of F+W, A Content + eCommerce Company
10151 Carver Rd, Suite 200, Blue Ash, OH 45242
Tel: 513-531-2690 *Toll Free Tel:* 800-289-0963 *Fax:* 513-531-0798
E-mail: writersdigest@fwmedia.com (edit)
Web Site: www.writersdigest.com; www.writersdigestshop.com
Key Personnel
Publr & Edit Dir: Phil Sexton *E-mail:* phillip.sexton@fwcommunity.com
How to take timeless storytelling structures & make them immediate, now, for fiction that's universal in how it speaks to the reader's heart.
1st ed: 288 pp, $10.04 paper
First published 2003
ISBN(s): 987-1-59963-537-8

Ulrich's Periodicals Directory
Published by ProQuest LLC
Subsidiary of Cambridge Information Group Inc
630 Central Ave, New Providence, NJ 07974
Tel: 908-795-3659 (edit) *Toll Free Tel:* 800-346-6049 (Ulrich's hotline, US only)
E-mail: ulrichs@proquest.com; core_service@proquest.com (orders)
Web Site: www.ulrichsweb.com; www.proquest.com (publr)
Key Personnel
Edit Mgr: Ewa Kowalska
Four-volume set, arranged by subject classification, includes periodicals, newsletters, newspapers, annuals & irregular serials published worldwide. Also available online.
Annual.
54th ed, 2016: 11,750 pp, $2,635/4 vol set
First published 1932
ISBN(s): 978-1-60030-653-3 (4 vol set)

Walden's Paper Catalog
Published by Walden-Mott Corp
225 N Franklin Tpke, Ramsey, NJ 07446-1600
Tel: 201-818-8630 *Fax:* 201-818-8720
E-mail: info@papercatalog.com
Web Site: www.papercatalog.com
Key Personnel
Ed: Alfred F Walden *Tel:* 201-818-8630 ext 11
National directory of fine printing & writing papers. Alphabetical listing of brand names, their characteristics along with merchants that carry those manufacturers' grades. Sections: "Brand Name Index", "Paper Distributors", "Papers by Grade" & "How to Buy Paper".
2 issues/yr.
$85/yr
First published 1914

Walden's Paper Handbook
Published by Walden-Mott Corp
225 N Franklin Tpke, Ramsey, NJ 07446-1600
Tel: 201-818-8630 *Fax:* 201-818-8720
E-mail: info@papercatalog.com
Web Site: www.waldenmott.com
Key Personnel
Ed: Alfred F Walden *Tel:* 201-818-8630 ext 11
Pulp & paper industry pocket guide.
5th ed: 277 pp, $25

Word Painting
Published by Writer's Digest Books
Imprint of F+W, A Content + eCommerce Company
10151 Carver Rd, Suite 200, Blue Ash, OH 45242
Tel: 513-531-2690 *Toll Free Tel:* 800-289-0963 *Fax:* 513-531-0798
E-mail: writersdigest@fwmedia.com (edit)
Web Site: www.writersdigest.com; www.writersdigestshop.com
Key Personnel
Publr & Edit Dir: Phil Sexton *E-mail:* phillip.sexton@fwcommunity.com
Combines direct instruction with intriguing word exercises to teach you how to "paint" evocative descriptions that capture the images of your mind's eye & improve your writing.
1st ed: 256 pp, $8.34 paper
First published 2000
ISBN(s): 978-1-58297-025-7

World Authors 2000-2005
Published by Grey House Publishing Inc™
4919 Rte 22, Amenia, NY 12501
Mailing Address: PO Box 56, Amenia, NY 12501-0056
Tel: 518-789-8700 *Toll Free Tel:* 800-562-2139 *Fax:* 518-789-0556
E-mail: books@greyhouse.com
Web Site: www.greyhouse.com
Covers some 300 novelists, poets, dramatists, essayists, scientists, biographers & other authors whose books, published 2000 through 2005, represent the dawn of a new millenium of great literature.
Jan 2007: 800 pp, $170
ISBN(s): 978-0-8242-1077-9

World Literature Criticism: A Selection of Major Authors from Gale's Literary Criticism - Supplement
Published by Gale
Unit of Cengage Learning
27500 Drake Rd, Farmington Hills, MI 48331-3535
SAN: 213-4373
Tel: 248-699-4253 *Toll Free Tel:* 800-877-4253 *Fax:* 248-699-8070 *Toll Free Fax:* 800-414-5043 (orders)
E-mail: gale.galeord@cengage.com
Web Site: www.gale.cengage.com
Updated supplement listing 20th Century authors collection of their biographical data, criticisms, list of principal works, historical survey of critical response to the author's works & sources for further study. Three indexes consist of authors, nationality & titles.
1997 supplement still in print.
961 pp, $231/2 vol set
ISBN(s): 978-07876-1696-0

The Writer's Complete Fantasy Reference
Published by Writer's Digest Books
Imprint of F+W, A Content + eCommerce Company
10151 Carver Rd, Suite 200, Blue Ash, OH 45242
Tel: 513-531-2690 *Toll Free Tel:* 800-289-0963 *Fax:* 513-531-0798
E-mail: writersdigest@fwmedia.com (edit)
Web Site: www.writersdigest.com; www.writersdigestshop.com
Key Personnel
Publr & Edit Dir: Phil Sexton *E-mail:* phillip.sexton@fwcommunity.com
Reveals the facts behind the fantasy, giving you the details you need to make your fiction vibrant, captivating & original.
304 pp, $10.79 paper
First published 2000
ISBN(s): 978-1-58297-026-4

The Writer's Guide to Character Traits
Published by Writer's Digest Books
Imprint of F+W, A Content + eCommerce Company
10151 Carver Rd, Suite 200, Blue Ash, OH 45242
Tel: 513-531-2690 *Toll Free Tel:* 800-289-0963 *Fax:* 513-531-0798
E-mail: writersdigest@fwmedia.com (edit)
Web Site: www.writersdigest.com; www.writersdigestshop.com
Key Personnel
Publr & Edit Dir: Phil Sexton *E-mail:* phillip.sexton@fwcommunity.com
Profiles the mental, emotional & physical qualities of dozens of different personality types.
384 pp, $11.43 paper
First published 1999
ISBN(s): 978-1-58297-390-6

The Writer's Guide to Crafting Stories for Children
Published by Writer's Digest Books
Imprint of F+W, A Content + eCommerce Company
10151 Carver Rd, Suite 200, Blue Ash, OH 45242
Tel: 513-531-2690 *Toll Free Tel:* 800-289-0963 *Fax:* 513-531-0798
E-mail: writersdigest@fwmedia.com (edit)
Web Site: www.writersdigest.com; www.writersdigestshop.com
Key Personnel
Publr & Edit Dir: Phil Sexton *E-mail:* phillip.sexton@fwcommunity.com
Insightful advice for mastering storytelling basics with dozens of examples that illustrate a variety of plot-building techniques.
1st ed: 192 pp, $10.67
First published 2001
ISBN(s): 978-1-58297-052-3

The Writer's Idea Book 10th Anniversary Edition
Published by Writer's Digest Books
Imprint of F+W, A Content + eCommerce Company
10151 Carver Rd, Suite 200, Blue Ash, OH 45242
Tel: 513-531-2690 *Toll Free Tel:* 800-289-0963 *Fax:* 513-531-0798
E-mail: writersdigest@fwmedia.com (edit)
Web Site: www.writersdigest.com; www.writersdigestshop.com
Key Personnel
Publr & Edit Dir: Phil Sexton *E-mail:* phillip.sexton@fwcommunity.com
Helps you to jump-start your creativity & develop original ideas.
1st ed: 352 pp, $13.39 paper
First published 2002
ISBN(s): 978-1-59963-386-2

Writer's Market
Published by Writer's Digest Books
Imprint of F+W, A Content + eCommerce Company
10151 Carver Rd, Suite 200, Blue Ash, OH 45242
Tel: 513-531-2690 *Toll Free Tel:* 800-289-0963 *Fax:* 513-531-0798
E-mail: writersdigest@fwmedia.com (edit)
Web Site: www.writersmarket.com; www.fwmedia.com; www.writersdigestshop.com; www.writersdigestshop.com
Key Personnel
Publr & Edit Dir: Phil Sexton *E-mail:* phillip.sexton@fwcommunity.com
Lists more than 4,000 places where freelance writers can sell articles, books, novels, stories, fillers & scripts.
Annual.
2016 ed: 896 pp, $29.99 paper regular ed, $49.99 paper deluxe ed (includes online)
ISBN(s): 978-1-59963-937-6 (regular ed); 978-1-59963-942-0 (deluxe ed)

The Writer's Market Guide to Getting Published
Published by Writer's Digest Books
Imprint of F+W, A Content + eCommerce Company
10151 Carver Rd, Suite 200, Blue Ash, OH 45242
Tel: 513-531-2690 *Toll Free Tel:* 800-289-0963 *Fax:* 513-531-0798
E-mail: writersdigest@fwmedia.com (edit)
Web Site: www.writersdigest.com; www.writersdigestshop.com
Key Personnel
Publr & Edit Dir: Phil Sexton *E-mail:* phillip.sexton@fwcommunity.com
Sound information on professional writing issues, focusing on everything from contracts to creativity.
3rd ed, March 2010: 368 pp, $10.99 paper
First published 2004
ISBN(s): 978-1-58297-608-2

Writer's Yearbook
Published by F+W, A Content + eCommerce Company
10151 Carver Rd, Suite 200, Blue Ash, OH 45242
Tel: 513-531-2690
E-mail: writersdigest@fwmedia.com
Web Site: www.writersdigest.com
Key Personnel
Ed: Jessica Strawser *E-mail:* jessica.strawser@fwcommunity.com
Includes lists of book & magazine article markets & how-to articles on writing & publishing.
Annual.
72 pp, $6.99 paper
First published 1990

Writing Creative Nonfiction
Published by Writer's Digest Books
Imprint of F+W, A Content + eCommerce Company
10151 Carver Rd, Suite 200, Blue Ash, OH 45242
Tel: 513-531-2690 *Toll Free Tel:* 800-289-0963 *Fax:* 513-531-0798
E-mail: writersdigest@fwmedia.com (edit)
Web Site: www.writersdigest.com; www.writersdigestshop.com
Key Personnel
Publr & Edit Dir: Phil Sexton *E-mail:* phillip.sexton@fwcommunity.com
More than thirty essays examining every key element of the craft, from researching ideas & structuring the story, to reportage & personal reflection.
400 pp, $12.70 paper
First published 2001
ISBN(s): 978-1-884910-50-0

Writing Down the Bones: Freeing the Writer Within
Published by Shambhala Publications Inc
Horticultural Hall, 300 Massachusetts Ave, Boston, MA 02115
SAN: 203-2481
Tel: 617-424-0030; 978-829-2599 (intl callers) *Toll Free Tel:* 888-424-2329 (cust serv); 866-424-0030 (off) *Fax:* 617-236-1563
E-mail: editorialdept@shambhala.com
Web Site: www.shambhala.com
Key Personnel
Owner & EVP: Sara Bercholz
Pres: Nikko Odiseos
Publr: Julie Saidenberg
Mng Ed: Liz Shaw
Author: Natalie Goldberg
Brings together Zen meditation & writing.
224 pp, $14 paper; $18.95 hardcover
First published 2005
ISBN(s): 978-1-59030-261-3 (paperback); 978-1-59030-794-6 (hardcover); 987-0-8348-2113-2 (ebook)

Writing Life Stories
Published by Writer's Digest Books
Imprint of F+W, A Content + eCommerce Company
10151 Carver Rd, Suite 200, Blue Ash, OH 45242
Tel: 513-531-2690 *Toll Free Tel:* 800-289-0963 *Fax:* 513-531-0798
E-mail: writersdigest@fwmedia.com (edit)
Web Site: www.writersdigest.com; www.writersdigestshop.com
Key Personnel
Publr & Edit Dir: Phil Sexton *E-mail:* phillip.sexton@fwcommunity.com
How to capture your own experiences & turn them into personal essays & book-length memoirs.
304 pp, $11.10 paper
First published 1998
ISBN(s): 978-1-58297-527-6

Writing Mysteries
Published by Writer's Digest Books
Imprint of F+W, A Content + eCommerce Company
10151 Carver Rd, Suite 200, Blue Ash, OH 45242
Tel: 513-531-2690 *Toll Free Tel:* 800-289-0963 *Fax:* 513-531-0798
E-mail: writersdigest@fwmedia.com (edit)
Web Site: www.writersdigest.com; www.writersdigestshop.com
Key Personnel
Publr & Edit Dir: Phil Sexton *E-mail:* phillip.sexton@fwcommunity.com
How to piece a perfect mystery together & create realistic stories that are taut, immediate & tense.
2nd ed: 256 pp, $11.43 paper
First published 2002
ISBN(s): 978-1-58297-102-5

Writing the Breakout Novel
Published by Writer's Digest Books
Imprint of F+W, A Content + eCommerce Company
10151 Carver Rd, Suite 200, Blue Ash, OH 45242
Tel: 513-531-2690 *Fax:* 513-531-0798
Web Site: www.writersdigest.com; www.writersdigestshop.com
Key Personnel
Publr & Edit Dir: Phil Sexton *E-mail:* phillip.sexton@fwcommunity.com
How to take your prose to the next level & write a breakout novel.
1st ed: 256 pp, $9.34 paper
First published 2001
ISBN(s): 978-1-58297-182-7

Yearbook of Experts, Authorities & Spokespersons
Published by Broadcast Interview Source Inc
2500 Wisconsin Ave NW, Suite 949, Washington, DC 20007-4132
Tel: 202-333-5000 *Fax:* 202-342-5411
E-mail: expertclick@gmail.com
Web Site: www.expertclick.com
Key Personnel
Publr & Ed: Mitchell P Davis *Tel:* 203-333-4904 *E-mail:* mitchell@yearbookofexperts.com
Listings of contacts at publishers, trade associations & public interest groups that welcome media contacts; for both print & broadcast journalist use. Also available online.
Annual.
31st ed, 2015: 274 pp
ISBN(s): 978-0-934333-95-5

You Can Write Children's Books Workbook
Published by Writer's Digest Books
Imprint of F+W, A Content + eCommerce Company
10151 Carver Rd, Suite 200, Blue Ash, OH 45242
Tel: 513-531-2690 *Toll Free Tel:* 800-289-0963 *Fax:* 513-531-0798
E-mail: writersdigest@fwmedia.com (edit)
Web Site: www.writersdigest.com; www.writersdigestshop.com
Key Personnel
Publr & Edit Dir: Phil Sexton *E-mail:* phillip.sexton@fwcommunity.com
Provides hands-on instruction for finishing a ms, preparing it for publication & getting it published.
1st ed: 144 pp, $8.98 paper
First published 2004
ISBN(s): 978-1-58297-248-0

Magazines for the Trade

The magazines listed have been selected because they are published specifically for the book trade industry (apart from book review and index journals, which are listed in **Book Review & Index Journals & Services** in volume 2) or because they are widely used in the industry for reference. Also included in this section are literary journals.

For a comprehensive international directory of periodicals, see *Ulrich's Periodicals Directory* (ProQuest LLC, 630 Central Avenue, New Providence, NJ 07974), which lists magazines by subject and includes notations indicating those that carry book reviews. See also the *International Directory of Little Magazines & Small Presses* (Dustbooks, PO Box 100, Paradise, CA 95967).

Writer's Digest (F+W, A Content & eCommerce Company, 10151 Carver Road, Suite 200, Blue Ash, OH 45242) publishes detailed magazine lists in certain issues. *Writer's Market* (Writer's Digest Books, 10151 Carver Road, Suite 200, Blue Ash, OH 45242) contains classified lists of writers' markets.

Advertising Age
Published by Crain Communications
Subsidiary of Crain Communications Inc
711 Third Ave, New York, NY 10017-4036
Tel: 212-210-0100 *Fax:* 212-210-0200 (NY)
E-mail: AdAgeEditor@adage.com
Web Site: adage.com
Subscription Address: 1155 Gratiot Ave, Detroit, MI 48207 *Tel:* 313-446-1665 *Fax:* 313-446-6777 *E-mail:* AdAgeSubscriptions@adage.com
Key Personnel
VP, Publg: Allison P Arden *Tel:* 212-210-0794 *E-mail:* aarden@adage.com
Ed-in-Chief, New York: Rance Crain *E-mail:* rcrain@crain.com
Exec Ed: Judann Pollack *Tel:* 212-210-0458 *E-mail:* jpollack@adage.com
Ed: Abbey Klaasen *E-mail:* aklaasen@adage.com
Covers advertising in business, media, trade newspapers & magazines. Also available online.
First published 1930
Frequency: Weekly
Circulation: 58,000
$4.99/issue
ISSN: 0001-8899 (print); 1557-7414 (online)

Adweek
Published by Prometheus Global Media LLC
770 Broadway, 15th fl, New York, NY 10003
Tel: 212-493-4100 *Fax:* 646-654-5637
E-mail: info@adweek.com
Web Site: www.adweek.com
Key Personnel
Edit Dir: Michael Wolff
Exec Ed: James Cooper
Mng Ed: Hillary Frey
Deputy Ed: Chip Bayers
Creative Dir: Nick Mrozowski
First published 1978
Frequency: 44 issues/yr
$149/yr print or digital
ISSN: 1549-9553

American Journalism Review
Published by The Phillip Merrill College of Journalism
Division of University of Maryland Foundation
University of Maryland, 1117 Journalism Bldg, College Park, MD 20742-7111
Tel: 301-405-8803 *Fax:* 301-405-8323
E-mail: editor@ajr.umd.edu
Web Site: www.ajr.org
Key Personnel
Pres: Kevin Klose
SVP & Ed: Rem Rieder
Edited for & by people working in the media & communications industry. Critiques journalism in all forms; including newspapers, TV, magazines, radio, cable TV, First Amendment issues & government regulation. Features book reviews, profiles, columns & news stories.
First published 1977
Frequency: Quarterly
Avg pages per issue: 72
Circulation: 25,000
ISSN: 1067-8654

American Poetry Review
University of the Arts (UARTS), Hamilton Hall, 320 S Broad St, Rm 313, Philadelphia, PA 19102-4901
Tel: 215-717-6801 *Fax:* 215-717-6805
Web Site: www.aprweb.org
Key Personnel
Busn Mgr: Michael Duffy
Ed: David Bonanno *E-mail:* dbonanno@aprweb.org; Elizabeth Scanlon *E-mail:* escanlon@aprweb.org
Poetry, general essays, fiction, translations, columns & interviews.
First published 1972
Book Use: Excerpts & serial rights, reviews
Frequency: 6 issues/yr
Avg pages per issue: 48
Circulation: 8,000
$4.50/issue, $25/yr
ISSN: 0360-3709
Ad Rates: Full page $950
Ad Closing Date(s): 45 days prior

The American Spectator
Published by The American Spectator Foundation
933 N Kenmore St, Suite 405, Arlington, VA 22201
Tel: 703-807-2011 *Toll Free Tel:* 800-524-3469
E-mail: editor@spectator.org
Web Site: www.spectator.org
Subscription Address: PO Box 171, Congers, NY 10920-0171
Key Personnel
Ed-in-Chief: R Emmett Tyrrell, Jr
Edit Dir: Wladyslaw Pleszczynski
Exec Dir: Donald Rieck *E-mail:* rieckd@spectator.org
Offers a unique blend of news reporting, social & political comment, humor pieces & cultural essays on the issues of the day.
First published 1924
Book Use: Book review section
Frequency: 10 issues/yr
Avg pages per issue: 82
Circulation: 50,000
$5.95/issue, $39/yr US, $59/yr, $109/2 yrs CN & elsewhere
ISSN: 0148-8414
Trim Size: 8 3/8 x 10 1/2
Ad Rates: 4-color full page $2,795; B&W full page $2,395
Ad Closing Date(s): 1st of each month

ANQ: A Quarterly Journal of Short Articles, Notes & Reviews
Published by Taylor & Francis Inc
325 Chestnut St, Suite 800, Philadelphia, PA 20036-1802
Tel: 215-625-8900 (ext 4) *Toll Free Tel:* 800-354-1420 (cust serv) *Fax:* 215-625-2940
E-mail: customer.service@taylorandfrancis.com
Web Site: www.tandfonline.com; www.routledge.com
Key Personnel
Global Publg Dir, Journals: Leon Heward-Mills
Ed: Sandro Jung *E-mail:* sandro.jung@ugent.be
English & American literature for an academic & library audience.
First published 1987
Book Use: Reviews
Frequency: Quarterly
Avg pages per issue: 64
Circulation: 500
$80/yr indivs (print & online), $204/yr instns (online only), $233/yr instns (print & online)
ISSN: 0895-769X
Trim Size: 6 x 9
Ad Rates: Full page $550; 1/2 page $350
Ad Closing Date(s): Winter Dec 1, Spring March 21, Summer June 18, Fall Sept 19

The Artist's Magazine
Published by F+W, A Content + eCommerce Company
10151 Carver Rd, Suite 200, Blue Ash, OH 45242
Tel: 513-531-2690 *Fax:* 513-513-2696
E-mail: tamedit@fwmedia.com
Web Site: www.theartistsnetwork.com/the-artists-magazine
Subscription Address: 700 Estate St, Iola, WI 54990 *Toll Free Tel:* 800-258-0929
Key Personnel
Ed-in-Chief: Maureen Bloomfield
Mng Ed: Christine McHugh
Art instruction & advice for the working artist.
First published 1984
Book Use: Occasional book reviews (art-related titles only)
Frequency: 10 issues/yr
Avg pages per issue: 100
Circulation: 140,000
$20.96/yr US, $30.96 CN & foreign
ISSN: 0741-3351
Trim Size: 7 3/4 x 10 3/4

AudioFile®
Published by AudioFile® Publications Inc
37 Silver St, Portland, ME 04101
Mailing Address: PO Box 109, Portland, ME 04112-0109
Tel: 207-774-7563 *Toll Free Tel:* 800-506-1212 *Fax:* 207-775-3744
E-mail: info@audiofilemagazine.com; editorial@audiofilemagazine.com
Web Site: www.audiofilemagazine.com
Key Personnel
Publr & Ed: Robin F Whitten *E-mail:* robin@audiofilemagazine.com
Fin Offr: Patricia E Stickney *E-mail:* pat@audiofilemagazine.com

Mng Ed: Jennifer M Dowell *E-mail:* jennifer@audiofilemagazine.com
Review Ed: Elizabeth K Dodge *E-mail:* edodge@maine.edu
Art Dir: Jennifer Steele
Web Mgr: Mark Mattos *E-mail:* mark@audiofilemagazine.com
Web Admin: MaryBeth Walz *E-mail:* webadmin@audiofilemagazine.com
Asst Ed: Allison Adams
Edit Asst: Andrea Jackson-Darling; Kate Menendez
Cust Serv: Casey McManamy
For people who love audiobooks, is indispensable for anyone who enjoys spoken-word audio. We review nearly 400 audio books every 60 days, feature narrator & author profiles & award exceptional performances with AudioFile's Earphone Awards.
First published 1992
Frequency: Bimonthly
Avg pages per issue: 72
Circulation: 15,000
$6 US, $8 CN
ISSN: 1063-0244
Avg reviews per issue: 400
Trim Size: 8 3/8 x 10 7/8
Ad Rates: Full page $3,100

Authorship
Published by National Writers Association
10940 S Parker Rd, Suite 508, Parker, CO 80134
Tel: 303-841-0246
E-mail: natlwritersassn@hotmail.com
Web Site: www.nationalwriters.com
Key Personnel
Exec Dir & Ed: Sandy Whelchel *E-mail:* authorsandy@hotmail.com
Only take submissions dealing with writing. Also available online.
Book Use: Review books for writers (in-house staff)
Frequency: Quarterly
Avg pages per issue: 28
Circulation: 8,000
$20/yr
ISSN: 1092-9347

Book Business
Published by North American Publishing Co (NAPCO)
1500 Spring Garden St, 12th fl, Philadelphia, PA 19130
Tel: 215-238-5300; 215-238-5338 (cust serv)
E-mail: magazinecs@napco.com
Web Site: www.bookbusinessmag.com
Key Personnel
Publr: Matt Steinmetz
Ed-in-Chief: Brian Howard
Mng Ed: Jim Sturdivant
Provides both strategic & practical information publishers need to stay ahead of market trends, confront change proactively & run their businesses successfully & profitably. Book Business provides forward thinking for senior-level trade, education, association, business, children's, STM, independent & other book publishing executives. Also avalable online.
First published 1998
Frequency: 6 issues/yr
Free to individuals who meet pre-established demographic criteria
ISSN: 1558-9889

Book Dealers World
Published by North American Bookdealers Exchange (NABE)
PO Box 606, Cottage Grove, OR 97424-0026
Tel: 541-942-7455
E-mail: bookdealersworld@bookmarketingprofits.com
Key Personnel
Exec Dir: Al Galasso
Book marketing, self-publishing, mail order.
First published 1980
Book Use: From NABE members
Frequency: Quarterly
Avg pages per issue: 32
Circulation: 10,000
$50/yr, sample $5
ISSN: 1098-8521

BookPage
Published by ProMotion Inc
2143 Belcourt Ave, Nashville, TN 37212
Tel: 615-292-8926 *Toll Free Tel:* 800-726-4242 *Fax:* 615-292-8249
Web Site: www.bookpage.com
Key Personnel
Pres & Publr: Michael A Zibart
Assoc Publr: Julia Steele *E-mail:* julia@bookpage.com
Subn Mgr: Elizabeth Herbert *Tel:* 615-292-8926 ext 34 *E-mail:* elizabeth@bookpage.com
Book reviews, author interviews; focus on general interest new releases. Monthly publication. Columns on romance, mystery, audio & paperback, plus individual reviews on books in all categories. Focus is completely on new releases; no backlist reviewed. HC & PB titles reviewed.
First published 1988
Book Use: Reviews
Frequency: Monthly
Avg pages per issue: 32
Circulation: 500,000

Bookselling This Week
Published by American Booksellers Association
333 Westchester Ave, Suite S202, White Plains, NY 10604
Tel: 914-406-7500 *Toll Free Tel:* 800-637-0037 *Fax:* 914-410-6297
E-mail: info@bookweb.org
Web Site: www.bookweb.org
Key Personnel
Dir, Content Devt: Rosemary Hawkins *Tel:* 914-406-7500 ext 7561 *E-mail:* rosemary@bookweb.org
Book industry news; ABA membership news. Available online only; no print edition.
Frequency: Weekly
Circulation: 10,000

Canadian Children's Book News
Published by Canadian Children's Book Centre
40 Orchard View Blvd, Suite 217, Toronto, ON M4R 1B9, Canada
Tel: 416-975-0010 *Fax:* 416-975-8970
E-mail: info@bookcentre.ca
Web Site: www.bookcentre.ca
Key Personnel
Ed: Gillian O'Reilly *E-mail:* gillian@bookcentre.ca
News, book reviews (only reviews books by Canadian authors & illustrators), author & illustrator profiles & information about the world of children's books in Canada. Visit website for media kit. CCBN is available with membership to the Canadian Children's Book Centre; also available in bulk subscriptions & on newsstands across Canada.
First published 1977
Frequency: 4 issues/yr
Avg pages per issue: 40
Circulation: 5,000
ISSN: 1705-7809
Trim Size: 8 1/8 x 10 7/8

Catholic Library World
Published by Catholic Library Association
8550 United Plaza Blvd, Suite 1001, Baton Rouge, LA 70809-2256
Tel: 225-408-4417
E-mail: cla2@cathla.org
Web Site: www.cathla.org
Key Personnel
Pres: Mary Kelleher *Tel:* 225-408-4417 *E-mail:* kellehm@stthom.edu
Gen Ed: Sigrid Kelsey *E-mail:* skelsey@lsu.edu
Articles, book & media reviews for library information professionals.
First published 1929
Book Use: Regularly publish reviews of books & other media
Frequency: Quarterly
Avg pages per issue: 90
Circulation: 1,100
Free to CLA membs, $100/yr nonmembs US, $125/yr + postage, back issues & single copies $25 + postage
ISSN: 0008-820X
Ad Rates: Full page $425; 2/3 page $360; 1/2 page $295; 1/3 page $230; 1/6 page $185; preferred space also available, color additional
Ad Closing Date(s): March issue, Jan 2; June issue, April 1; Sept issue, July 1; Dec issue, Oct 1

CBA Retailers+Resources
Published by CBA: The Association for Christian Retail
1365 Garden of the Gods Rd, Suite 105, Colorado Springs, CO 80907
Tel: 719-265-9895 *Toll Free Tel:* 800-252-1950 *Fax:* 719-272-3508
E-mail: info@cbaonline.org
Web Site: cbaonline.org
Key Personnel
Pres: Curtis Riskey *E-mail:* criskey@cbaonline.org
Trade publication for the Christian retail industry; official publication of Christian Booksellers Association.
First published 1968
Book Use: Review, bestseller lists
Frequency: Monthly
Circulation: 6,700
$7.50/issue membs, $9.50/issue nonmembs, $49.95/yr membs, $59.95/yr nonmembs
ISSN: 0006-7563

The Bulletin of the Center for Children's Books
Published by The Johns Hopkins University Press
2715 N Charles St, Baltimore, MD 21218-4363
SAN: 202-7348
Tel: 410-516-6900; 410-516-6987 (journal orders outside US & CN) *Toll Free Tel:* 800-548-1784 (journal orders) *Fax:* 410-516-6968; 410-516-3866 (journal orders)
E-mail: jrnlcirc@press.jhu.edu (journal orders)
Web Site: bccb.lis.illinois.edu
Subscription Address: PO Box 19966, Baltimore, MD 21211-0966
Key Personnel
Ed: Deborah Stevenson
For teachers, librarians, parents & booksellers.
First published 1947
Book Use: Reviews of children's & young adult books for teachers, librarians, parents & booksellers
Frequency: 11 issues/yr
Avg pages per issue: 40
Circulation: 6,500
$20/yr students, $55/yr indivs, $95/yr instns (print or online)
ISSN: 0008-9036

Christian Retailing
Published by Charisma Media
600 Rinehart Rd, Lake Mary, FL 32746
Tel: 407-333-0600 *Fax:* 407-333-7133
E-mail: christian.retailing@charismamedia.com
Web Site: www.charismamedia.com

Key Personnel
Mng Ed: Christine D Johnson *E-mail:* chris.johnson@charismamedia.com
News Ed: Eric Tiansay *E-mail:* eric.tiansay@charismamedia.com
A trade publication for the Christian retail market including industry news, books, music, inspirational gift & other market news, new releases & marketing & industry trends. Includes one supplement: Inspirational Gift Mart.
First published 1955
Book Use: News & reviews of New Releases
Frequency: Monthly
Avg pages per issue: 60
Circulation: 12,000
$40/yr, free to qualified retailers
ISSN: 0892-0281

The Chronicle of Higher Education
1255 23 St NW, Suite 700, Washington, DC 20037
Tel: 202-466-1000 *Fax:* 202-452-1033
E-mail: editor@chronicle.com
Web Site: chronicle.com
Key Personnel
Ed: Liz McMillan *E-mail:* liz.mcmillan@chronicle.com
Books Ed: Nina Ayoub *Tel:* 202-466-1020 *E-mail:* nina.ayoub@chronicle.com
Weekly newspaper covering higher education, including scholarly & publishing news.
First published 1966
Book Use: Articles on books of interest to an academic audience & on academic aspects of the publishing industry. Lists new books on higher education & new scholarly books; short & medium length excerpts from books on academic & literary issues
Frequency: Weekly (except for 2 issues in Dec & 1 in Aug)
Avg pages per issue: 100
Circulation: 350,000
$5.52/month print, $4.97/month digital ed
ISSN: 0009-5982

College & Research Libraries Journal
Published by Association of College & Research Libraries (ACRL)
Division of The American Library Association (ALA)
50 E Huron St, Chicago, IL 60611
Tel: 312-280-2516 *Toll Free Tel:* 800-545-2433 (ext 2516) *Fax:* 312-280-2520
E-mail: acrl@ala.org
Web Site: www.ala.org/acrl
Key Personnel
Ed-in-Chief: Joseph Branin *E-mail:* joseph.branin@kaust.edu.sa
Ed: Wendi Arant Kaspar
Prodn Ed: Dawn Mueller
Theory & research relevant to academic & research librarians. Check web site for submission information.
First published 1939
Book Use: Reviews
Frequency: Bimonthly
Avg pages per issue: 100
Circulation: 14,000
$75/yr nonmembs, $80/yr CN, $85/yr foreign
ISSN: 0010-0870

Columbia Journalism Review
Published by Columbia Graduate School of Journalism
Affiliate of Columbia University
Journalism Bldg, 2950 Broadway, New York, NY 10027
Tel: 212-854-1881; 212-854-2716 (busn) *Toll Free Tel:* 888-425-7782 (US subns) *Fax:* 212-854-8367
E-mail: cjr@columbia.edu
Web Site: www.cjr.org
Key Personnel
Acting Publr: Dennis Giza
Exec Ed: Mike Hoyt
Mng Ed: Brent Cunningham
Assoc Ed & Copy Mgr: Tom O'Neill
Monitors & assesses the performance of journalism in all forms.
First published 1961
Frequency: Bimonthly
Circulation: 30,000
$4.95/issue, $19.95/yr, $41.95/2 yrs
ISSN: 0010-194X

Connections
Published by Printing Industries of New England
5 Crystal Pond Rd, Southborough, MA 01772-1758
Tel: 508-804-4171 *Toll Free Tel:* 800-365-7463 *Fax:* 508-804-4119
Web Site: www.pine.org
Key Personnel
Pres & Publr: Tad Parker
Members only trade magazine for printing & graphic communication companies in New England.
First published 1938
Frequency: 6 issues/yr
Avg pages per issue: 48
Circulation: 1,200
Free to membs
ISSN: 0162-8771
Trim Size: 8 1/2 x 11
Ad Closing Date(s): Tenth of the month preceding publication

Editors' Association of Canada - Online Directory of Editors
Published by Editors' Association of Canada (Association canadienne des reviseurs)
27 Carlton St, Suite 502, Toronto, ON M5B 1L2, Canada
Tel: 416-975-1379 *Toll Free Tel:* 866-CAN-EDIT (226-3348) *Fax:* 416-975-1637
E-mail: info@editors.ca
Web Site: www.editors.ca
Key Personnel
Exec Dir: Carolyn L Burke *E-mail:* executivedirector@editors.ca
Communs Mgr: Michelle Ou *E-mail:* communications@editors.ca
Prof Devt Mgr: Helena Aalto *E-mail:* helena.aalto@editors.ca
Membership Coord: Lianne Zwarenstein
Online directory of descriptive listings of current association members indexed by specialty.

Educational Marketer
Published by Simba Information
Division of Market Research.com
1266 E Main St, Suite 700, Stamford, CT 06902
SAN: 210-2021
Tel: 203-325-8193 *Toll Free Tel:* 888-297-4622 (cust serv)
E-mail: customerservice@simbainformation.com
Web Site: www.simbainformation.com
Key Personnel
Sr Analyst/Mng Ed: Kathy Mickey
Analyst/Ed: Valerie Chernetskyy
Prodn Coord: Farah Pierre
Newsletter; reports on educational publishing field (el-hi & college): enrollments, demographics, funding, mergers & acquisitions, new product developments & personnel changes. For publishers, suppliers & dealers in the educational market.
First published 1968
Frequency: 24 issues/yr
Avg pages per issue: 8
$695/yr
ISSN: 1013-1806
Ad Rates: 4-color full page $1,650; 4-color 1/2 page $1,320; B&W full page $1,150; B&W 1/2 page $1,150
Ad Closing Date(s): 12 days before publication date

Electronic Education Report
Published by Simba Information
Division of Market Research.com
1266 E Main St, Suite 700, Stamford, CT 06902
SAN: 210-2021
Tel: 203-325-8193 *Toll Free Tel:* 888-297-4622 (cust serv)
E-mail: customerservice@simbainformation.com
Web Site: www.simbainformation.com
Key Personnel
Sr Analyst/Mng Ed: Kathy Mickey
Sr Analyst/Ed: Karen Meaney
Prodn Coord: Farah Pierre
Published twice each month to provide industry decision-makers with the problem-solving information they need to make prudent business decisions in a rapidly evolving, multi-billion dollar market. Technologies covered include hardware, software, multimedia/CD-ROM, integrated learning systems, video, distance learning, online services & educational videocassettes News coverage includes sales & distribution trends, company rankings & financial profiles, trademark & rights issues, strategic alliances & mergers, site licensing & networks, etc. Analyzes K-12. Readers are upper & middle management textbook & software publishers, software distributors, online service providers, video publishers & computer hardware manufacturers.
First published 1994
Frequency: 24 issues/yr
$650/yr PDF download
ISSN: 1077-9949
Trim Size: 8 1/2 x 11
Ad Rates: 4-color full page $1,320; 4-color 1/2 page $1,060; B&W full page $1,120; B&W 1/2 page $920

Event
Published by Douglas College
700 Royal Ave, New Westminster, BC V3M 5Z5, Canada
Mailing Address: PO Box 2503, New Westminster, BC V3L 5B2, Canada
Tel: 604-527-5293 *Fax:* 604-527-5095
E-mail: event@douglascollege.ca
Web Site: eventmags.com
Key Personnel
Ed: Elizabeth Bachinsky
Mng Ed: Ian Cockfield
Fiction Ed: Christine Dewar
Poetry Ed: Gillian Jerome
Reviews Ed: Susan Waserman
Literary journal. Occasionally publish unsol reviews but should query first. Publish mostly Canadian writers, but are open to anyone writing in English. Do not read mss in Jan, July, Aug & Dec. Buy fiction, poetry, creative nonfiction.
First published 1971
Frequency: 3 issues/yr
Avg pages per issue: 128
Circulation: 1,200
$11.95/issue, $39.95/yr US, $29.95/yr CN
ISSN: 0315-3770
Trim Size: 6 x 9
Ad Rates: Full page $200; 1/2 page $100
Ad Closing Date(s): March 15 (Summer), July 15 (Fall/Winter), Nov 15 (Spring)

Facilities Media Group
Published by Bedrock Communications Inc
152 Madison Ave, Suite 802, New York, NY 10016
Tel: 212-532-4150 *Fax:* 212-213-6382

Web Site: www.facilitiesonline.com
Key Personnel
Assoc Publr: Michael Caffin *Tel:* 212-532-4150 ext 103 *E-mail:* mcaffin@facilitiesonline.com
Edit Dir: Timothy Herrick *Tel:* 212-532-4150 ext 105
Monthly trade magazine chronicling the facility, event & convention marketplace.
First published 1991
Frequency: Monthly
Avg pages per issue: 48
Circulation: 30,303
$4.95/issue, $48/yr

Folio: The Magazine for Magazine Management
Published by Red 7 Media LLC
10 Norden Place, Norwalk, CT 06855
Tel: 203-854-6730 *Fax:* 203-854-6735
E-mail: folioedit@foliomag.com
Web Site: www.foliomag.com
Key Personnel
CEO & Pres: Kerry Smith *E-mail:* ksmith@red7media.com
Publr & Ed: Tony Silber *E-mail:* tsilber@foliomag.com
Group Creative Dir: Dan Trombetto
Ed: Bill Mickey
News & articles for the magazine publishing executive.
First published 1972
Book Use: Excerpts & condensations
Frequency: Monthly
Avg pages per issue: 60
Circulation: 8,500
$96/yr, $106/yr CN & Mexico, $116/yr elsewhere, $8/issue newsstand
ISSN: 0046-4333

Forecast
Published by Baker & Taylor Inc
2550 W Tyvola Rd, Suite 300, Charlotte, NC 28217
Mailing Address: PO Box 6885, Bridgewater, NJ 08807
Tel: 704-998-3100 *Toll Free Tel:* 800-775-1800 *Fax:* 704-998-3319
E-mail: btinfo@baker-taylor.com
Web Site: www.baker-taylor.com
Key Personnel
Prodn Coord: Donna Heffner *Tel:* 908-541-7412
Prepublication announcements for booksellers & librarians containing bibliographic data & descriptions of forthcoming adult hardcover future bestsellers, noteworthy midlist titles, university & independent press releases; includes spoken-word audio.
First published 1969
Frequency: Monthly
Avg pages per issue: 135
Circulation: 50,000
Free for those who qualify

ForeWord Reviews
Division of ForeWord Magazine Inc
425 Boardman Ave, Suite B, Traverse City, MI 49684
Tel: 231-933-3699 *Fax:* 231-933-3899
E-mail: sales@forewordreviews.com
Web Site: www.forewordreviews.com
Key Personnel
Publr: Victoria Sutherland *E-mail:* victoria@forewordreviews.com
Exec Ed: Howard Lovy *E-mail:* howard@forewordreviews.com
Mng Ed: Matt Sutherland *E-mail:* matt@forewordreviews.com
Ad Sales: Stacy Price *E-mail:* stacy@forewordreviews.com
Review journal of books from independent presses, university presses & self-publishers. Distributed to librarians & booksellers for collection development.
First published 1998
Frequency: Quarterly
Avg pages per issue: 64
Circulation: 15,000
$19.95/yr US, $39.95/yr CN, $59.95/yr foreign (print), $9.99/yr (online)
ISSN: 1099-2642
Trim Size: 8 1/2 x 11
Ad Rates: B&W full page $2,257, 1/2 page $1,349
Ad Closing Date(s): 3 weeks prior to issue date

Gateway Journalism Review/St Louis Journalism Review
Published by St Louis Journalism Review (SJR)
Communications Bldg, 1100 Lincoln Dr, Mail Code 6601, Carbondale, IL 62901
Tel: 618-536-3361
E-mail: gatewayjr@siu.edu
Web Site: gatewayjr.org
Key Personnel
Publr: William Freivogel
Media critic of press & broadcasting - particularly of St Louis region & the Midwest, but also nationally.
First published 1970
Book Use: Book review & excerpts
Frequency: Quarterly
Avg pages per issue: 36
Circulation: 1,250
$32/yr, $50/2 yrs
ISSN: 0036-2972
Trim Size: 8 1/2 x 11
Ad Closing Date(s): 20th of each month

Geist
Published by The Geist Foundation
201-111 W Hastings St, Vancouver, BC V6B 1H4, Canada
Tel: 604-681-9161 *Toll Free Tel:* 888-GEIST-EH (434-7834) *Fax:* 604-677-6319
E-mail: geist@geist.com
Web Site: www.geist.com
Key Personnel
Publr: Stephen Osborne
Sr Ed: Mary Schendlinger
Canadian ideas & culture with a strong literary focus & a sense of humor. Must have Canadian angle (content or author residency). No e-mail submissions.
First published 1990
Frequency: Quarterly
Avg pages per issue: 72
Circulation: 7,000
$27/yr US & foreign, $21/yr CN, $47 2/yrs US & foreign, $35 2/yrs CN, $62 3/yrs US & foreign, $44 3/yrs CN
ISSN: 1181-6554
Ad Rates: Full page $970; 2/3 page $735; 1/2 page $685; 1/3 page $425; 1/6 page $270; ad rates decrease with frequent advertisement

Graphic Monthly
Published by North Island Publishing Ltd
1606 Sedlescomb Dr, Suite 8, Mississauga, ON L4X 1M6, Canada
Tel: 905-625-7070 *Toll Free Tel:* 800-331-7408 (US only) *Fax:* 905-625-4856
Web Site: www.graphicmonthly.ca
Key Personnel
Ed: Filomena Tamburri *Tel:* 905-625-7070 ext 258 *E-mail:* ftamburri@graphicmonthly.ca
Publr: Alexander Donald *Tel:* 905-625-7070 ext 230 *E-mail:* s.donald@northisland.ca
Graphic, printing info.
First published 1980
Frequency: Bimonthly
Avg pages per issue: 60
Circulation: 10,500
Free to qualified Canadian businesses
ISSN: 0227-2806

Guild of Book Workers Newsletter
Published by Guild of Book Workers
521 Fifth Ave, 17th fl, New York, NY 10175
Tel: 212-292-4444
Web Site: www.guildofbookworkers.org
Key Personnel
Pres: Mark Andersson *Tel:* 520-682-7241 *E-mail:* president@guildofbookworkers.org
VP: Bexx Caswell *E-mail:* vicepresident@guildofbookworkers.org
Newsletter Ed: Cindy Haller *E-mail:* newsletter@guildofbookworkers.org
Secy: Catherine Burkhard *Tel:* 214-363-7946 *E-mail:* secretary@guildofbookworkers.org
Treas: Alicia Bailey *E-mail:* treasurer@guildofbookworkers.org
Articles, calendar of activities related to the book arts.
Frequency: Bimonthly
Avg pages per issue: 15
Circulation: 900
Free with membership

The Horn Book Guide
Published by Horn Book Inc
300 The Fenway, Suite P-311, Palace Road Bldg, Boston, MA 02115
Tel: 617-278-0225 *Toll Free Tel:* 888-628-0225 *Fax:* 617-278-6062
E-mail: info@hbook.com
Web Site: www.hbook.com
Subscription Address: 7585 Industrial Pkwy, Plain City, OH 43064 *Tel:* 614-873-7954 *Fax:* 614-873-7135
Key Personnel
VP, Mktg: Andrew Thorne *Tel:* 614-873-7956 *E-mail:* athorne@mediasourceinc.com
Dir, Content Strategy & Audience Devt, Media Source: Guy LeCharles Gonzalez *E-mail:* glgonzalez@mediasourceinc.com
Ed-in-Chief: Roger Sutton
Exec Ed: Kitty Flynn *E-mail:* kflynn@hbook.com
Prodn Mgr & Designer: Lolly Robinson *Tel:* 617-628-0225 ext 226 *E-mail:* lrobinson@hbook.com
Brief, critical reviews of nearly every hardcover trade children's & young adult book published in the US.
First published 1990
Book Use: Subject, series, reissues, new editions, author/illustrator & title indexes
Frequency: Semiannual
Avg pages per issue: 288
Circulation: 2,600
$35/issue, $60/yr
ISSN: 1044-405X
Trim Size: 8 3/8 x 11 1/16
Ad Rates: Color covers 2 & 3 $1690/each; color cover 4 $1740; B&W full page $1690
Ad Closing Date(s): Feb 1 for Spring issue, Aug 1 for Fall issue

The Horn Book Magazine
Published by Horn Book Inc
300 The Fenway, Suite P-311, Palace Road Bldg, Boston, MA 02115
Tel: 617-278-0225 *Toll Free Tel:* 888-628-0225 *Fax:* 617-278-6062
E-mail: info@hbook.com
Web Site: www.hbook.com
Subscription Address: 7585 Industrial Pkwy, Plain City, OH 43064 *Tel:* 614-873-7954 *Fax:* 614-873-7135
Key Personnel
VP, Mktg: Andrew Thorne *Tel:* 614-873-7956 *E-mail:* athorne@mediasourceinc.com
Dir, Content Strategy & Audience Devt, Media Source: Guy LeCharles Gonzalez *E-mail:* glgonzalez@mediasourceinc.com

Ed-in-Chief: Roger Sutton
Exec Ed: Martha V Parravano *E-mail:* mvp@hbook.com
Sr Ed: Elissa Gershowitz *E-mail:* egershowitz@hbook.com
Prodn Mgr & Designer: Lolly Robinson *Tel:* 617-628-0225 ext 226 *E-mail:* lrobinson@hbook.com
Children's literature journal featuring reviews, articles, essays, columns, interviews with children's book authors & illustrators, current announcements.
First published 1924
Book Use: Reviews & occasional excerpts
Frequency: Bimonthly
Avg pages per issue: 128
Circulation: 8,500
$72/yr
ISSN: 0018-5078
Trim Size: 6 x 9
Ad Rates: Color covers 2, 3 & 4 $2,577/each; full page interior $2,150
Ad Closing Date(s): 2 months before pub date

Independent Publisher
Published by Jenkins Group Inc
1129 Woodmere Ave, Suite B, Traverse City, MI 49686
Tel: 231-933-0445 *Toll Free Tel:* 800-706-4636 *Fax:* 231-933-0448
Web Site: www.independentpublisher.com
Key Personnel
CEO: Jerrold R Jenkins *Tel:* 231-933-0445 ext 1008 *E-mail:* jrj@bookpublishing.com
COO & Pres: James Kalajian *Tel:* 231-933-0445 ext 1006 *E-mail:* jjk@bookpublishing.com
Mng Ed, Independent Publisher Online: Jim Barnes *E-mail:* jimb@bookpublishing.com
Article topics relevant to the business of independent book publishing & retailing, including marketing, book awards, promotion & distribution. Available online since 2000.
First published 1983
Book Use: Featured reviews & individual reviews from independently published works of the current year
Frequency: Monthly
Avg pages per issue: 80
Circulation: 10,000
Free online; sent monthly via e-mail
ISSN: 1098-5735
Avg reviews per issue: 40

Information Today
Published by Information Today, Inc
143 Old Marlton Pike, Medford, NJ 08055-8750
Tel: 609-654-6266 *Toll Free Tel:* 800-300-9868 (cust serv) *Fax:* 609-654-4309
E-mail: custserv@infotoday.com
Web Site: www.infotoday.com/IT/default.asp
Key Personnel
Publr/Pres & CEO: Thomas H Hogan
Ed: Donovan Griffin *E-mail:* dgriffin@infotoday.com
For users & producers of digital information services.
First published 1983
Frequency: 10 issues/yr
Avg pages per issue: 32
Circulation: 8,000
$99.95/yr, $188/2yrs, $288/3yrs US; $128/yr, $241/2 yrs, $369/3 yrs CN & Mexico; $143 yr, $269/2 yrs, $412/3 yrs other; agencies $2 less
ISSN: 8755-6286
Trim Size: 9 1/2 x 11 3/4
Ad Rates: See web site for complete details

Inkwell
Published by Manhattanville College
2900 Purchase St, Purchase, NY 10577
Tel: 914-323-7239 *Fax:* 914-323-3122
E-mail: inkwell@mville.edu
Web Site: www.inkwelljournal.org
Key Personnel
Ed-in-Chief: Tanya M Beltram
Staffed by faculty & graduate students of the writing program, we are dedicated to providing a forum for emerging writers & to publishing high quality poems & short stories in a literary journal that also features nonfiction, artwork, essays & interviews on writing by established figures & yearly competitions in poetry & fiction. For our submission guidelines, see our web site.
First published 1995
Frequency: Semiannual (Spring & Fall)
Avg pages per issue: 150
Circulation: 500
$10
ISSN: 1085-0287
Trim Size: 8 1/2 x 5 1/2

InPrint
Published by New Jersey Press Association
810 Bear Tavern Rd, Suite 307, West Trenton, NJ 08628
Tel: 609-406-0600 *Fax:* 609-406-0300
E-mail: njpress@njpa.org
Web Site: www.njpa.org
Key Personnel
Communs Mgr: Catherine Langley *Tel:* 609-406-0600 ext 17 *E-mail:* clangley@njpa.org
News of the NJ newspaper industry.
First published 1990
Book Use: No columns or frequent articles about books, no book review
Frequency: 5 issues/yr
Avg pages per issue: 16
Circulation: 1,300
$12/yr
ISSN: 1067-5132

International Journal of Instructional Media (IJIM)
Published by Westwood Press Inc
Subsidiary of CAL Industries
118 Five Mile River Rd, Darien, CT 06820
Tel: 203-656-8680
Web Site: www.adprima.com/ijim.htm
Key Personnel
Exec Ed: Dr Phillip J Sleeman *Tel:* 860-875-5484 *E-mail:* plsleeman@aol.com
Assoc Ed: Linda B Sleeman
Media Reviews: Dr John G Flores
Articles about programs in computer technology; computer mediated; communications including the Internet; distance education, including the Internet, ITV, video & audio conferencing; instructional media & technology; telecommunications; interactive video, videodisc & software applications; instructional media management; instructional development & systems; media research & evaluation; media research & communications. Guidelines on the web site.
First published 1973
Book Use: Media reviews, book & technology forums
Frequency: Quarterly
Avg pages per issue: 130
Circulation: 1,325
$225/yr (plus $20 shipping), $225/yr CN & elsewhere (plus $40 shipping)
ISSN: 0092-1815

Journal of International Marketing
Published by American Marketing Association
311 S Wacker Dr, Suite 5800, Chicago, IL 60606
Tel: 312-542-9000 *Toll Free Tel:* 800-AMA-1150 (262-1150) *Fax:* 312-542-9001
E-mail: info@ama.org
Web Site: www.ama.org
Key Personnel
CEO: Dennis Dunlap *E-mail:* ceo@ama.org
Ad Sales Dir: Richard Ballschmiede *Tel:* 312-542-9076 *E-mail:* rballschmiede@ama.org
Mng Ed: Christopher Bartone *Tel:* 312-542-9000 ext 9029 *E-mail:* cbartone@ama.org
Tech Ed: Andy Seagram
Ed: David A Griffith
Timely insights from executives along with reports on new trends & tactics. Each issue also features analysis of the latest marketing theories, in-depth articles by practitioners & coverage of new methods.
Frequency: Quarterly
Avg pages per issue: 144
Circulation: 1,300
$55/yr AMA membs, $120/yr indivs US, $126.75/yr indivs CN, $150/yr indivs foreign, $235/yr instns US, print/online combo rates available. Visit www.marketingpower.com for more options
ISSN: 1069-031X

Journal of Marketing
Published by American Marketing Association
311 S Wacker Dr, Suite 5800, Chicago, IL 60606
Tel: 312-542-9000 *Toll Free Tel:* 800-AMA-1150 (262-1150) *Fax:* 312-542-9001
E-mail: info@ama.org
Web Site: www.ama.org
Key Personnel
CEO: Dennis Dunlap *E-mail:* ceo@ama.org
Ad Sales Dir: Richard Ballschmiede *Tel:* 312-542-9076 *E-mail:* rballschmiede@ama.org
Mng Ed: Christopher Bartone *Tel:* 312-542-9000 ext 9029 *E-mail:* cbartone@ama.org
Tech Ed: Andy Seagram
Ed: Gary L Frazier *Tel:* 213-740-5032 *E-mail:* frazier@marshall.usc.edu
Thought-provoking, in-depth articles covering vital aspects of the marketing industry. You'll find original research on all aspects of marketing & you'll appreciate how the journal bridges the gap between theory & application.
First published 1936
Book Use: Some reviews & excerpts
Frequency: 6 times/yr
Avg pages per issue: 144
Circulation: 8,200
$60/yr membs, $135/yr indivs, $375/yr corps & instns, online & print/online combo rates available. Visit www.marketingpower.com/publications for more information
ISSN: 0022-2429

Journal of Marketing Research
Published by American Marketing Association
311 S Wacker Dr, Suite 5800, Chicago, IL 60606
Tel: 312-542-9000 *Toll Free Tel:* 800-AMA-1150 (262-1150) *Fax:* 312-542-9001
E-mail: info@ama.org
Web Site: www.ama.org
Key Personnel
CEO: Dennis Dunlap *E-mail:* ceo@ama.org
Ad Sales Dir: Richard Ballschmiede *Tel:* 312-542-9076 *E-mail:* rballschmiede@ama.org
Mng Ed: Christopher Bartone *Tel:* 312-542-9000 ext 9029 *E-mail:* cbartone@ama.org
Ed: Tulin Erdem *Tel:* 212-998-0404 *E-mail:* terdem@stern.nyu.edu
For the latest thinking in marketing research. The journal covers a wide range of marketing-research concepts, methods & applications. You'll read about new techniques; contributions to knowledge based on experimental methods; & developments in related fields that have a bearing on marketing research.
First published 1963
Book Use: Some reviews
Frequency: 6 times/yr
Avg pages per issue: 128
Circulation: 4,400
$60/yr membs, $135/yr indivs US, $141.75/yr indivs CN, $180/yr indivs foreign, $375/yr instns US, $393.75/yr instns CN, $420/yr instns for-

eign; online & print/online combo rates available. Visit www.marketingpower.com/publications for more options
ISSN: 0022-2437

Journal of Scholarly Publishing
Published by University of Toronto Press Journals Division
Division of University of Toronto Press Inc
5201 Dufferin St, Toronto, ON M3H 5T8, Canada
Tel: 416-667-7810 *Toll Free Tel:* 800-221-9985 (CN) *Fax:* 416-667-7881
E-mail: journals@utpress.utoronto.ca
Web Site: www.utpjournals.com
Key Personnel
VP, Journals, Univ of Toronto Press: Anne Marie Corrigan *Tel:* 416-667-7777 ext 7838 *E-mail:* acorrigan@utpress.utoronto.ca
Ed: Tom Radko
Ad & Mktg Coord: Audrey Greenwood *Tel:* 416-667-7777 ext 7766 *E-mail:* agreenwood@utpress.utoronto.ca
Articles on the writing, publication & use of serious nonfiction addressed to scholars, authors, publishers, reviewers, editors & librarians.
First published 1969
Book Use: Reviews of books relating to publishing
Frequency: Quarterly
Avg pages per issue: 64
Circulation: 800
$130/yr instns, $45/yr indivs, $40/yr membs; online version $115 instns, $35 indivs, $30 membs
ISSN: 1198-9742
Trim Size: 6 x 9
Ad Rates: Full page $350; 1/2 page $250; inside back cover $370; outside back cover $420; frequency discount; 30% 4 consecutive insertions, 20% for 3 & 10% for 2 inserts

Journalism & Mass Communication Quarterly
Published by SAGE Publications
2455 Teller Rd, Thousand Oaks, CA 91320
Toll Free Tel: 800-818-7243 *Toll Free Fax:* 800-583-2665
E-mail: journals@sagepub.com
Web Site: www.sagepub.com
Key Personnel
Ed: Daniel Riffe
Research in journalism & mass communication.
First published 1924
Frequency: Quarterly
Avg pages per issue: 1,000
Circulation: 5,000
$155 indiv, $294 instl, $300 instl (print & electronic); single issue $50 indiv, $81 instns
ISSN: 1077-6990 (print); 2161-430X (online)

The Kenyon Review
Subsidiary of Kenyon College
Finn House, 102 W Wiggin St, Gambier, OH 43022
Tel: 740-427-5208 *Fax:* 740-427-5417
E-mail: kenyonreview@kenyon.edu
Web Site: www.kenyonreview.org
Key Personnel
Mng Ed: Abigail Wadsworth Serfass *Tel:* 740-427-5389 *E-mail:* serfassam@kenyon.edu
Ed: David Lynn
Fiction, poetry, essays, book reviews, drama. See web site for details.
First published 1939
Book Use: Reviews of 12 books
Frequency: 6 issues/yr
Avg pages per issue: 120
Circulation: 7,500
$10/issue, $30/yr, $50/2 yrs, $70/3 yrs
ISSN: 0163-075X
Trim Size: 6 1/8 x 10
Ad Rates: Full page $375
Ad Closing Date(s): Nov 10, Jan 10, March 10, May 10, July 10, Sept 10

Knowledge Quest
Published by American Association of School Librarians
Division of The American Library Association (ALA)
50 E Huron St, Chicago, IL 60611
Tel: 312-944-6780 *Toll Free Tel:* 800-545-2433 *Fax:* 312-280-5276
E-mail: aasl@ala.org
Web Site: www.ala.org/aasl/kq
Key Personnel
Mng Ed, Knowledge Quest: Meg Featheringham *Tel:* 312-280-1396
Devoted to offering substantive information to assist in building-level library media specialists, supervisors, library educators & other decision makers concerned with the development of school library media programs & services. Articles address the integration of theory & practice in school librarianship & new developments in education, learning theory & relevant disciplines.
First published 1997
Frequency: 5 issues/yr
Avg pages per issue: 80
Circulation: 10,000
$12/issue, $50/yr nonmembs US, $60/yr nonmembs foreign
ISSN: 1094-9046

Library Journal
Published by Media Source Inc
160 Varick St, 11th fl, New York, NY 10013
Tel: 646-380-0752 *Toll Free Tel:* 800-588-1030 *Fax:* 646-380-0756
E-mail: ljinfo@mediasourceinc.com
Web Site: lj.libraryjournal.com
Subscription Address: PO Box 5881, Harlan, IA 51593 *Tel:* 515-247-2984 (outside US) *E-mail:* ljcustserv@cds-global.com
Key Personnel
Dir, Content & Digital Prod Devt: Guy Le Charles Gonzalez
Mng Ed: Bette-Lee Fox *Tel:* 646-380-0717 *E-mail:* blfox@mediasourceinc.com
Reviews are written & edited specifically to assess the value of a book for the library collection. Also, review DVDs, audiobook CDs, magazines, databases & web sites.
First published 1876
Book Use: Reviews, news
Frequency: Semimonthly (exc monthly during Jan, July, Aug & Dec)
Avg pages per issue: 144
Circulation: 18,000
$157.99/yr US, $199.99/yr CN & Mexico, $259.99/yr foreign
ISSN: 0363-0277

Library Media Connection: The Professional Magazine for School Library Media & Technology Specialists
Published by Linworth Publishing
Imprint of Libraries Unlimited
PO Box 292114, Kettering, OH 45429
Toll Free Tel: 800-607-4410 *Fax:* 937-890-0221
E-mail: lmc@librarymediaconnection.com
Web Site: www.librarymediaconnection.com
Key Personnel
Pres & Publr: Marlene Woo-Lun
Mng Ed: Wendy Medvetz *E-mail:* wmedvetz@librarymediaconnection.com
Ed: Gail Dickinson
K-12 school librarians & educators. See web site for information regarding ad rates & ad closing dates.
First published 1982
Book Use: Reviews; articles written by school librarians
Frequency: 7 issues/school yr
Avg pages per issue: 96
Circulation: 17,000
$69/yr
ISSN: 0731-4388

The Library Quarterly
Published by The University of Chicago Press, Journals Div
University of Maryland, College of Information Studies, 4105 Hornbake Bldg, South Wing, College Park, MD 20742
Tel: 310-405-3267 *Fax:* 301-314-9145
E-mail: lq@press.uchicago.edu
Web Site: www.journals.uchicago.edu
Subscription Address: PO Box 37005, Chicago, IL 60637
Key Personnel
Ed: John Carlo Bertot; Paul Jaeger
Reviews Section Ed: Leah Kim Gannett
Library & information science & related subjects.
First published 1931
Book Use: Reviews
Frequency: Quarterly
Avg pages per issue: 128
Circulation: 1,018
$17/issue indiv, $54/issue instns, $49/yr indivs combined print & online, $177/yr instns combined print & online
ISSN: 0024-2519
Ad Rates: Full page $607

Locus: The Magazine of the Science Fiction & Fantasy Field
Published by Locus Science Fiction Foundation Inc
PO Box 13305, Oakland, CA 94661-0305
Tel: 510-339-9196; 510-339-9198 *Fax:* 510-339-9198
E-mail: locus@locusmag.com
Web Site: www.locusmag.com
Key Personnel
Ed-in-Chief: Liza Groen Trombi
Mng Ed: Kirsten Gong-Wong
Includes news, awards, interviews & annual analysis of the science fiction field, monthly bestseller list & a complete monthly listing of new publications. Primarily a trade magazine for science fiction professionals, booksellers & libraries.
First published 1968
Book Use: Reviews
Frequency: Monthly
Avg pages per issue: 88
Circulation: 7,000
$6.95/issue, $60/yr indivs, $64/yr libs
ISSN: 0047-4959
Trim Size: 8 3/8 x 10 7/8
Ad Rates: B&W full page $1,000

Marketing Management Magazine
Published by American Marketing Association
311 S Wacker Dr, Suite 5800, Chicago, IL 60606
Tel: 312-542-9000 *Toll Free Tel:* 800-AMA-1150 (262-1150) *Fax:* 312-542-9001
E-mail: info@ama.org
Web Site: www.ama.org
Key Personnel
CEO: Dennis Dunlap *E-mail:* ceo@ama.org
Ad Sales Dir: Richard Ballschmiede *Tel:* 312-542-9076 *E-mail:* rballschmiede@ama.org
Dir of Publg, Journals: Christopher Bartone *Tel:* 312-542-9029 *E-mail:* cbartone@ama.org
Ed-in-Chief: Gordon Wyner *E-mail:* gwyner@comcast.net
Focuses on strategic issues that marketing managers face every day. Covers brand management, CRM, product innovation, ROI, marketing effectiveness & B2B – to help managers keep pace with this rapidly changing field.

Frequency: 6 times/yr
Avg pages per issue: 55
Circulation: 12,000
$60/yr membs, $105/yr indivs US, $110.25/yr indivs CN, $150/yr indivs foreign, $135/yr instns US. See www.marketingpower.com/publications for more options
ISSN: 1061-3846

Marketing Research: A Magazine of Management & Applications
Published by American Marketing Association
311 S Wacker Dr, Suite 5800, Chicago, IL 60606
Tel: 312-542-9000 *Toll Free Tel:* 800-AMA-1150 (262-1150) *Fax:* 312-542-9001
E-mail: info@ama.org
Web Site: www.ama.org
Key Personnel
Ad Sales Dir: Richard Ballschmiede *Tel:* 312-542-9076 *E-mail:* rballschmiede@ama.org
Mng Ed, Magazines & E-newsletters: Mary M Flory *E-mail:* mflory@ama.org
Each issue offers thought-provoking analyses of the latest trends & methodologies in marketing research applications & management. Written in clear, concise language with a focus on practical application, *Marketing Research* clearly shows how marketing research strategies affect real-world businesses.
First published 1989
Book Use: Book & software reviews in each issue
Frequency: Quarterly
Avg pages per issue: 45
Circulation: 4,300
$55/yr AMA membs, $100/yr indivs US, $135/yr corps & instns US. Visit www.marketingpower.com/publications for more options
ISSN: 1040-8460
Ad Rates: Contact Ad Sales Dir for more information

The Masthead
Published by Association of Opinion Journalists (AOJ)
2301 Vanderbilt Place, VU Sta B 351669, Nashville, TN 37235-1669
Tel: 717-703-3015 *Fax:* 717-703-3014
E-mail: opinionjounalists@gmail.com
Web Site: www.opinionjournalists.org
Key Personnel
Pres: Miriam Pepper *Tel:* 816-234-4421 *E-mail:* mpepper@kcstar.com
All aspects of the work of professional opinion writers in all media, from determining editorial policy to writing, design & production.
First published 1948
Book Use: Reviews (select)
Frequency: Quarterly
Avg pages per issue: 36
Free online
ISSN: 0025-5122

Medical Reference Services Quarterly
Published by Routledge/Taylor & Francis
Member of Taylor & Francis Group
325 Chestnut St, Suite 800, Philadelphia, PA 19106
Toll Free Tel: 800-354-1420 (press 4) *Fax:* 215-625-2940
Web Site: www.tandfonline.com
Key Personnel
Ed: M Sandra Wood
Working tool journal for medical & health sciences librarians. Regularly publishes practice-oriented articles relating to medical reference services with an emphasis on online search services.
First published 1982
Book Use: Reviews
Frequency: Quarterly
Avg pages per issue: 116
Indiv: print & online $135, online only $125; Instns: print & online $523, online only $458
ISSN: 0276-3869 (print); 1540-9597 (online)

Mergers & Acquisitions
Published by Source Media
One State Street Plaza, 27th fl, New York, NY 10004
Tel: 212-803-6051 *Toll Free Tel:* 888-807-8667
E-mail: custserv@sourcemedia.com
Web Site: www.themiddlemarket.com
Key Personnel
Ed-in-Chief: Mary Kathleen Flynn *Tel:* 212-803-8708 *E-mail:* marykathleen.flynn@sourcemedia.com
Professional journal; covers the latest trends & influences impacting the buying & selling of businesses. Articles cover how to make money, save money & avoid disaster in the constantly changing merger & acquisition environment.
First published 1965
Frequency: Monthly
Avg pages per issue: 56
Circulation: 16,900
$995/yr, free 2 week trial available
ISSN: 0026-0010

MLQ (Modern Language Quarterly): A Journal of Literary History
Published by Duke University Press
University of Washington, English Dept, Box 354330, Seattle, WA 98195-4430
Tel: 206-543-6827 *Fax:* 206-685-2673
E-mail: mlq@u.washington.edu
Web Site: www.mlq.washington.edu; www.dukeupress.edu
Subscription Address: Duke University Press, Box 90660, Durham, NC 27708-0660 *Tel:* 919-687-3653 *E-mail:* subscriptions@dukeupress.edu
Key Personnel
Academic Ed: Marshall Brown
Acqs Ed, Journals: Erich Staib *Tel:* 919-687-3664
Edit/Admin Mgr, Journals: Rob Dilworth
Asst Ed: Heather Arvidson
Scholarly articles on literary history.
First published 1940
Book Use: Reviews
Frequency: Quarterly
Avg pages per issue: 130
Circulation: 1,350
$259/yr instns (print only); $226/yr instns (electronic); $266/yr instns (print & electronic); $35/yr indivs; $18/yr students add $12 postage & 7% GST for CN; $16 postage for outside US & CN
ISSN: 0026-7929 (print); 1527-1943 (online)
Ad Rates: B&W full page $250; B&W 1/2 page $175

Network
Published by The International Women's Writing Guild (IWWG)
274 Madison Ave, Suite 1202, New York, NY 10016
Tel: 917-720-6959
E-mail: iwwgquestions@gmail.com
Web Site: www.iwwg.org
Key Personnel
Dir of Opers/Ed & Art Dir: Kristin Rath
Member News, Regional Clusters, Correspondence Corner, Letters to the Editor, Environmental, Special Offerings, Profile of Guild Member, several hundred opportunities for publication & submission in every issue.
First published 1978
Frequency: Quarterly
Avg pages per issue: 32
Circulation: 3,000
$25; digital version free to membs

New Millennium Writings
4021 Garden Dr, Knoxville, TN 37918
Tel: 865-254-4880
E-mail: npf@nationalpress.org
Web Site: www.newmillenniumwritings.com
Key Personnel
Publr & Ed: Alexis Williams Carr *E-mail:* alexis.williams@hotmail.com
Contains fiction, poetry & creative nonfiction by both emerging & well known writers. Regularly features profiles, interviews & essay on famous writers. Also includes writing tips & commentary by the editor.
First published 1996

News & Tech, see Newspapers & Technology

Newspapers & Technology
Published by Conley Magazines LLC
1623 Blake St, Mezzanine, Denver, CO 80202-1053
Tel: 303-575-9595 *Fax:* 303-575-9555
E-mail: letters@newsandtech.com
Web Site: www.newsandtech.com
Key Personnel
Publr: Mary L Van Meter *E-mail:* vanmeternt@aol.com
Ed-in-Chief: Tara McMeekin *E-mail:* tmcmeekin@newsandtech.com
Trade publication for newspaper publishers & department managers involved in applying & integrating technology. Written by industry experts who provide regular coverage of the following departments: prepress, press, postpress & new media.
First published 1988
Frequency: 6 issues/yr
Avg pages per issue: 48
Circulation: 15,000
Free to qualified personnel
ISSN: 1052-5572

North Carolina Literary Review (NCLR)
Published by East Carolina University & North Carolina Literary & Historical Association
East Carolina University, English Dept, ECU Mailstop 555 English, Greenville, NC 27858-4353
Tel: 252-328-1537 *Fax:* 252-328-4889
E-mail: ncluser@ecu.edu
Web Site: www.nclr.ecu.edu
Key Personnel
Ed: Margaret Bauer *E-mail:* bauerm@ecu.edu
Sr Assoc Ed: Lorraine Hale Robinson *E-mail:* robinsonlo@ecu.edu
Articles, essays, interviews, fiction/poetry by & about North Carolina writers & literature, culture & history.
First published 1992
Book Use: Excerpts from forthcoming books; essay reviews only - 2 or more books treated thematically
Frequency: Annual
Avg pages per issue: 200
Circulation: 650 + bookstore sales
$15/issue, $25/2 yr subn, $25/yr instn, $50/issue foreign, $50/yr subn foreign
ISSN: 1063-0724
Ad Rates: Full page $250; 1/2 page $150; 1/4 page $100
Ad Closing Date(s): Feb 1

Poetics Today
Published by Duke University Press
905 W Main St, Suite 18B, Durham, NC 27701
SAN: 201-3436
Mailing Address: PO Box 90660, Durham, NC 27708-0660
Tel: 919-688-5134 *Toll Free Tel:* 888-651-0122 (US) *Fax:* 919-688-2615 *Toll Free Fax:* 888-651-0124
E-mail: subscriptions@dukeupress.edu
Web Site: www.dukeupress.edu

Key Personnel
CFO: Norris Langley
Edit/Admin Mgr, Journals: Rob Dilworth
Mgr, Cust Rel, Sales & Journals Mktg: Cason Lynley *E-mail:* jrnl_mktg_mgr@dukeupress.edu
Academic Ed: Meir Sternberg
Assoc Ed: Robert J Griffin
Asst Ed: Orly Lubin
Academics Exhibits & Publicity Coord: Emma Boyer
Book Use: Book reviews
Frequency: Quarterly
Avg pages per issue: 200
Circulation: 800
$40/yr indiv, $20/yr students (with photocopy of ID) $280/yr instns print only, $261/electronic only, $299/yr instns print & electronic
ISSN: 0333-5372 (print); 1527-5507 (online)
Ad Rates: B&W full page $250, B&W 1/2 page $200

Poetry
Published by Poetry Foundation
61 W Superior St, Chicago, IL 60654
Tel: 312-787-7070 *Fax:* 312-787-6650
E-mail: editors@poetrymagazine.org
Web Site: www.poetryfoundation.org/poetrymagazine
Subscription Address: PO Box 421141, Palm Coast, FL 32142-1141
Key Personnel
Ed: Don Share
Poetry, essays & book reviews. Complete submission guidelines can be found on the web site.
First published 1912
Frequency: Monthly
Avg pages per issue: 90
Circulation: 26,000
US: $3.75/issue, $35/yr indivs, $38/yr instns; Foreign: $47/yr indivs, $50/yr instns
ISSN: 0032-2032
Trim Size: 5 1/2 x 9
Ad Rates: Full page $800, 1/2 page $500, 1/4 page $375
Ad Closing Date(s): 15th of the 3rd month before issue date

Poets & Writers Magazine
Published by Poets & Writers Inc
90 Broad St, Suite 2100, New York, NY 10004
Tel: 212-226-3586 *Fax:* 212-226-3963
E-mail: editor@pw.org
Web Site: www.pw.org
Key Personnel
Edit Dir: Mary Gannon
Ed: Kevin Larimer
News for & about the contemporary literary community in the US. Pertinent articles, grants & awards, publishing opportunities, essays, interviews with writers.
First published 1973
Book Use: First serial, excerpts, author interviews
Frequency: Bimonthly
Avg pages per issue: 132
Circulation: 60,000
$5.95/issue, $19.95/yr
ISSN: 0891-6136

Print
Published by F+W, A Content + eCommerce Company
10151 Carver Rd, Suite 200, Blue Ash, OH 45242-4760
Tel: 212-447-1400 *Fax:* 212-447-5231
E-mail: info@printmag.com
Web Site: www.printmag.com
Subscription Address: PO Box 420235, Palm Coast, FL 32142-0235 *Tel:* 386-246-3361 *Toll Free Tel:* 877-860-9145 *E-mail:* print@palmcoastd.com
Key Personnel
Ed-in-Chief: Zachary Petit
Art Dir: Adam Ladd
Sales Dir: Elayne Recupero *Tel:* 267-247-5874 *E-mail:* elayne.recupero@gmail.com
Graphic design & visual communication for the creators of this material.
First published 1940
Book Use: Reviews
Frequency: 4 issues/yr
Avg pages per issue: 112
Circulation: 50,000
$40/yr US, 55/yr CN, $81/yr foreign; $19.95/yr digital
ISSN: 445-120

PRISM international
Published by University of British Columbia
Creative Writing Program UBC, 1866 Main Mall, Buch E-462, Vancouver, BC V6T 1Z1, Canada
Tel: 778-822-2514 *Fax:* 778-822-3616
E-mail: prismcirculation@gmail.com
Web Site: www.prismmagazine.ca
Key Personnel
Exec Ed, Circ: Jennifer Lori
Exec Ed, Promos: Claire Matthews
First published 1959
Frequency: Quarterly
Avg pages per issue: 90
Circulation: 1,200
$13/issue at newsstand; indivs: $35/yr, $55/2 yrs
Trim Size: 6 x 9
Ad Rates: Full page interior $220 (1 issue), $700 (1 yr, 4 issues); 1/2 page interior $160 (1 issue), $500 (1 yr, 4 issues); pre-printed inserts $50/100

Professional Photographer
Published by PPA Publications & Events Inc
229 Peachtree St NE, Suite 2200, Atlanta, GA 30303
Tel: 404-522-8600 *Toll Free Tel:* 800-786-6277 *Fax:* 404-614-6406
Web Site: www.ppa.com; www.ppmag.com
Key Personnel
Dir of Pubns: Jane Gaboury *E-mail:* jgaboury@ppa.com
Illustrated feature articles about photographers, business & photographic techniques & trends; for practicing professional photographers (portrait, wedding, commercial, illustration, freelance, industrial, biomedical & scientific).
First published 1907
Frequency: Monthly
Avg pages per issue: 80
Circulation: 31,000 paid
$19.95/yr (digital), $29.95/yr US (digital & print combo), $45.95/yr CN (digital & print combo), $35.95/yr CN (print)

ProtoView
Published by Ringgold Inc
5739 NE Sumner St, Portland, OR 97218
Tel: 503-281-9230 *Fax:* 503-287-4485
E-mail: info@protoview.com
Web Site: www.protoview.com
Key Personnel
Ed: Eithne O'Leyne *E-mail:* eithne.oleyne@ringgold.com
Subscription database incorporating reference & research & *SciTech Book News*. Abstracts, bibliographic & expanded metadata on scholary works in all media. ProtoView content licensed to Discovery channels, including vendors & related products owned by Baker & Taylor, ProQuest, Gale/Cengage, Powells & others.
ISSN: 2372-3424

Publishers Weekly
Published by PWxyz LLC
71 W 23 St, Suite 1608, New York, NY 10010
Tel: 212-377-5500 *Fax:* 212-377-2733
Web Site: www.publishersweekly.com
Subscription Address: PO Box 16957, North Hollywood, CA 91615-6957 *Tel:* 818-487-2069 *Toll Free Tel:* 800-278-2991 *Fax:* 818-487-4550 *E-mail:* pw@pubservice.com
Key Personnel
Pres: George Slowik, Jr *E-mail:* george@publishersweekly.com
Publr: Cevin Bryerman *Tel:* 212-377-5703 *E-mail:* cbryerman@publishersweekly.com
Edit Dir: Jim Milliot *Tel:* 212-377-5705 *E-mail:* jmilliot@publishersweekly.com
Reviews Dir: Louisa Ermelino *E-mail:* lermelino@publishersweekly.com
Exec Ed: Jonathan Segura *E-mail:* jsegura@publishersweekly.com
Mng Ed: Dan Berchenko *E-mail:* dberchenko@publishersweekly.com
News Dir: Rachel Deahl *E-mail:* rdeahl@publishersweekly.com
Sr Writer: Andrew R Albanese *E-mail:* aalbanese@publishersweekly.com
Sr Ed: Mark Rotella *E-mail:* mrotella@publishersweekly.com
Sr News Ed: Calvin Reid *E-mail:* creid@publishersweekly.com
News Ed: Clare Swanson *E-mail:* cswanson@publishersweekly.com
Children's Book Ed: Diane Roback *E-mail:* roback@publishersweekly.com
Children's Reviews Ed: John A Sellers *E-mail:* jsellers@publishersweekly.com
Assoc Ed, Children's Books: Natasha Gilmore *E-mail:* ngilmore@publishersweekly.com
Asst Ed, Children's Books: Matia Burnett *E-mail:* mburnett@publishersweekly.com
Features Ed: Carolyn Juris *E-mail:* cjuris@publishersweekly.com
Religion Reviews Ed: Seth Satterlee *E-mail:* ssatterlee@publishersweekly.com
Religion News Ed: Emma Koonse *E-mail:* ekoonse@publishersweekly.com
Sr Religion Ed: Lynn Garrett *E-mail:* lgarrett@publishersweekly.com
Deputy Reviews Ed: Gabe Habash
Sr Reviews Ed: Peter Cannon *E-mail:* pcannon@publishersweekly.com; Rose Fox *E-mail:* rfox@publishersweekly.com
Reviews Ed: Alex Crowley; Annie Coreno; Everett Jones
BookLife Ed: Adam Boretz *E-mail:* aboretz@publishersweekly.com
Copy Ed: Ivan Anderson *E-mail:* ianderson@publishersweekly.com
VP, Busn Devt: Carl Pritzkat *E-mail:* cpritzkat@publishersweekly.com
Digital Busn Mgr: Seth Dellon *E-mail:* sdellon@publishersweekly.com
Mktg/Licensing Mgr: Christi Cassidy *E-mail:* ccassidy@publishersweekly.com
Dir, Digital Opers: Craig Teicher *E-mail:* cteicher@publishersweekly.com
Bookselling Ed: Judith Rosen *Tel:* 617-876-2469 *E-mail:* jrosen@publishersweekly.com
Art Dir: Clive Chiu *E-mail:* cchiu@publishersweekly.com
VP, Opers: Patrick Turner *E-mail:* Patrick@publishersweekly.com
News for the book trade.
First published 1872
Book Use: Reviews, excerpts, news, features & statistics
Frequency: Weekly (51 issues/yr)
Avg pages per issue: 112
Circulation: 16,000+ subscribers
$8/issue, $249.99/yr US, $299.99/yr CN, $399.99 yr/foreign, $209/yr digital
ISSN: 0000-0019 (print); 2150-4000 (digital)
Trim Size: 7 7/8 x 10 1/2

Publishing Executive
Published by North American Publishing Co (NAPCO)

1500 Spring Garden St, 12th fl, Philadelphia, PA 19130
Tel: 215-238-5300; 215-238-5338 (cust serv)
E-mail: magazinecs@napco.com
Web Site: www.pubexec.com
Key Personnel
Publr: Matt Steinmetz
Mng Ed: Jim Sturdivant
Contrib Ed: Brian Howard
For publishing executives in b-to-b, consumer, association & government magazine publishing...how-to articles on business management, manufacturing, production & workflow.
First published 1987
Frequency: 6 issues/yr
Avg pages per issue: 60
Circulation: 14,000
Free qualified/controlled circulation
ISSN: 1048-3055

Publishing Poynters
Published by Para Publishing LLC
PO Box 8206-240, Santa Barbara, CA 93118-8206
SAN: 215-8981
Tel: 805-968-7277 *Toll Free Tel:* 800-727-2782 *Fax:* 805-968-1379
E-mail: info@parapublishing.com
Web Site: www.parapublishing.com
Key Personnel
Owner & Publr: Dan Poynter
E-mail: danpoynter@parapublishing.com
Book & information marketing news & ideas.
First published 1986
Book Use: Review copies on book publishing accepted
Frequency: 6 issues/yr
Avg pages per issue: 20
Circulation: 21,000
$9.95/2 yrs, free e-mail
ISSN: 1530-5694

Quill & Quire
Published by St Joseph Communications
111 Queen St E, Suite 320, Toronto, ON M5C 1S2, Canada
Tel: 416-364-3333 *Fax:* 416-595-5415
Web Site: www.quillandquire.com
Key Personnel
Publr: Alison Jones *Tel:* 416-364-3333 ext 3119
E-mail: ajones@quillandquire.com
Ed: Sue Carter
Articles & features on book selling, publishing & Canadian libraries for writers, booksellers, publishers & librarians. Includes section, *Books for Young People*, with news & reviews of children's books & authors; review section for books for adults.
First published 1935
Book Use: Reviews
Frequency: 10 issues/yr
Avg pages per issue: 56
Circulation: 4,500
$79.50/yr CN, $130/2 yrs CN, $125/yr outside CN
ISSN: 0033-6491

Quill & Scroll
Published by Quill and Scroll Society
University of Iowa, School of Journalism, E346 Adler Journalism Bldg, Iowa City, IA 52242
Tel: 319-335-3457 *Fax:* 319-335-3989
E-mail: quill-scroll@uiowa.edu
Web Site: quillandscroll.org
Key Personnel
Exec Dir & Publr: Vanessa Shelton
E-mail: vanessa-shelton@uiowa.edu
Circ Mgr: Judy M Hauge
Scholastic journalism publishing, editing, writing, design, legal, ethics, broadcast & multimedia production.
First published 1926
Frequency: Semiannual during school yr
Avg pages per issue: 24
Circulation: 9,300
$5/issue, $17/yr, $30/2 yrs
ISSN: 0033-6505

Quill Magazine
Published by The Society of Professional Journalists (SPJ)
Eugene S Pulliam National Journalism Ctr, 3909 N Meridian St, Indianapolis, IN 46208
Tel: 317-927-8000 *Fax:* 317-920-4789
E-mail: spj@spj.org
Web Site: www.spj.org/quill.asp; www.spj.org
Key Personnel
Ed: Scott Leadingham *Tel:* 317-927-8000 ext 211
E-mail: sleadingham@spj.com
Examines the issues, changes & trends that influence the journalism profession.
Book Use: Book reviews
Frequency: 6 issues/yr
Circulation: 10,500
$75/yr, free for membs
ISSN: 0033-6475

Radio-TV Interview Report
Published by Bradley Communications Corp
390 Reed Rd, Broomall, PA 19008
Tel: 484-477-4220 *Toll Free Tel:* 800-989-1400 (ext 408) *Fax:* 610-541-0281
E-mail: info@rtir.com
Web Site: www.rtir.com; www.rtironline.com
Key Personnel
Publr: Steve Harrison
Lists authors, experts, celebrities, entrepreneurs & others available for radio & TV appearances.
Frequency: Biweekly
Circulation: 4,000
Free to qualified personnel

Reference & User Services Quarterly (RUSQ)
Published by Reference & User Services Association
Division of The American Library Association (ALA)
50 E Huron St, Chicago, IL 60611
SAN: 201-0062
Tel: 312-280-4395 *Toll Free Tel:* 800-545-2433 *Fax:* 312-280-5273
E-mail: rusa@ala.org
Web Site: www.ala.org/rusa
Key Personnel
Exec Dir: Susan Hornung
First published 1960
Frequency: Quarterly
Avg pages per issue: 100
Circulation: 3,825 paid
$25/issue, $65/yr US, $70/yr CN & Mexico, $75/yr foreign
ISSN: 1094-9054

Reference Desk
Published by International Encyclopedia Society
3689 Campbell Ct, Yorktown Heights, NY 10598
Tel: 914-962-3287
Key Personnel
Pres & Ed: George Thomas Kurian
E-mail: gtkurian@aol.com
Articles on reference book publishing; reviews; quarterly record of reference books; publisher profiles.
First published 1991
Book Use: Book reviews; Index of publications
Frequency: Quarterly
Avg pages per issue: 32
Circulation: 902
$29/yr
ISSN: 1055-4777
Trim Size: 8 1/2 x 11
Ad Rates: Full page $300; 1/2 page $175
Ad Closing Date(s): March 30, June 30, Sept 30, Dec 30

Rosebud Magazine
Published by Rosebud Inc
PO Box 459, Cambridge, WI 53523
Tel: 608-423-9780
Web Site: www.rsbd.net
Key Personnel
Publr & Mng Ed: Roderick Clark
E-mail: jrodclark@rsbd.net
Short story, poetry & nonfiction.
First published 1993
Book Use: Excerpts
Frequency: 3 issues/yr
Avg pages per issue: 136
Circulation: 6,000
$6.95/issue, $20/yr, $35/2yrs
ISSN: 1072-1681

Sales & Marketing Management Magazine
Published by Mach1 Business Media LLC
27020 Noble Rd, Excelsior, MN 55331
Mailing Address: PO Box 247, Excelsior, MN 55331-0247
Tel: 952-401-1283 *Fax:* 952-401-7899
Web Site: www.salesandmarketing.com
Key Personnel
Pres & Publr: Mike Murrell *Tel:* 952-401-1283
E-mail: mike@salesandmarketing.com
Ed-in-Chief: Paul Nolan *Tel:* 763-350-3411
E-mail: paul@salesandmarketing.com
Mktg Mgr: Vicki Blomquist *E-mail:* vicki@salesandmarketing.com
Print & online magazine providing information on major marketing, sales & management trends.
First published 1918
Book Use: Reviews
Frequency: Updated 2-3 times a week
Avg pages per issue: 36
Circulation: 25,000 print
Free online. Print free to qualified recipients. Otherwise $48 US; $67 CN; $146 other countries
ISSN: 0163-7517
Trim Size: 8 x 10 3/4
Ad Rates: 2-page spread: $13,995 (1x), $13,695 (3x), $13,265 (6x); full page: $8,995 (1x), $8,695 (3x), $8,265 (6x); half page $6,075 (1x), $5,765 (3x), $5,460 (6x)
Ad Closing Date(s): See media kit online

School Library Journal
Published by Media Source Inc
160 Varick St, 11th fl, New York, NY 10013
Tel: 646-380-0752 *Toll Free Tel:* 800-588-1030 *Fax:* 646-380-0757
Web Site: www.slj.com; www.facebook.com/schoollibraryjournal; twitter.com/#!/sljournal
Subscription Address: PO Box 5881, Harlan, IA 51593 *Tel:* 515-247-2984 (outside US)
Key Personnel
Dir, Content & Digital Prod Devt: Guy Le Charles Gonzalez
Edit Dir, Lib Journals: Rebecca T Miller
Mng Ed: Phyllis Levy Mandell *Tel:* 646-380-0733
E-mail: pmandell@mediasourceinc.com
Articles about library service to children & young adults; reviews of new books & multimedia products for children & young adults by school & public librarians.
First published 1954
Book Use: Reviews
Frequency: 15 issues/yr
Avg pages per issue: 115
Circulation: 38,000
$11/issue newsstand, $136.99/yr US, $199.99/yr CN, $259.99/yr foreign
ISSN: 0362-8930

School Selection Guide
Published by Baker & Taylor Inc

2550 W Tyvola Rd, Suite 300, Charlotte, NC 28217
Mailing Address: PO Box 6885, Bridgewater, NJ 08807
Tel: 704-998-3100 *Toll Free Tel:* 800-775-1800 *Fax:* 704-998-3319
E-mail: btinfo@baker-taylor.com
Web Site: www.baker-taylor.com
Key Personnel
Prodn Coord: Donna Heffner *Tel:* 908-541-7412
Recommended & high-demand titles for school libraries; available in print & on the web page.
Book Use: Selection for recommendation
Frequency: 3 issues/yr
Avg pages per issue: 200
Circulation: 50,000
Free

Science & Technology Libraries
Published by Routledge/Taylor & Francis
Member of Taylor & Francis Group
325 Chestnut St, Suite 800, Philadelphia, PA 19106
Toll Free Tel: 800-354-1420 (press 4) *Fax:* 215-625-2940
Web Site: www.tandfonline.com
Key Personnel
Ed-in-Chief: Tony Stankus
Topics relevant to management, operations, collections, services & staffing of specialized libraries in science & technology fields. Also available online.
First published 1980
Book Use: Reviews
Frequency: Quarterly
Avg pages per issue: 105
Circulation: 343
Indiv: print & online or print only $140, online only $130; Instns: print & online $602, online only $527
ISSN: 0194-262X (print); 1541-1109 (online)

Scroll Original Artist Magazine
Published by Scroll Publications Inc
646 Saint Vrain Ave, Las Animas, CO 81054
Tel: 719-469-4847
E-mail: scrollpubl@outlook.com
Web Site: www.scrolloriginalartistmagazine.com; twitter.com/scrollpublinc
Key Personnel
Pres & Publr: Cherylann Gray
Original works by original people from all over the world.
First published 2000
Frequency: 6 issues/yr
Circulation: 3,700
$9.95/issue, $54.50/yr
Ad Rates: $3 per CR inch
Ad Closing Date(s): 15th of every month

The Serials Librarian
Published by Routledge/Taylor & Francis
Member of Taylor & Francis Group
325 Chestnut St, Suite 800, Philadelphia, PA 19106
Toll Free Tel: 800-354-1420 (press 4) *Fax:* 215-625-2940
Web Site: www.tandfonline.com
Key Personnel
Ed: Louise Cole; Andrew Shroyer
Serials librarianship in academic, public, medical, law & other special libraries.
First published 1976
Book Use: Reviews
Frequency: Quarterly
Avg pages per issue: 124
Circulation: 712
Indiv: print & online $270, online only $245; Instns: print & online $1,018, online only $891
ISSN: 0361-526X (print); 1541-1095 (online)

The Small Press Book Review
Division of Greenfield Press
PO Box 176, Southport, CT 06890-0176
Tel: 203-332-7629 *Fax:* 203-332-7629
Key Personnel
Publr & Ed: Henry Berry
E-mail: henryberryinct@gmail.com
Electronic publication with book reviews for online users. Not copywrited, so can be downloaded by anyone. Finished books only; no galleys. Books in all categories, including university press books. Reviews of selected books appear 2-4 months after submission.
First published 1985
Book Use: Book reviews
Frequency: Monthly
Circulation: Internet
Free to online users

subTerrain Magazine
Published by sub-TERRAIN Literary Collective Society
PO Box 3008, MPO, Vancouver, BC V6B 3X5, Canada
Tel: 604-876-8710 *Fax:* 604-879-2667
E-mail: subter@portal.ca
Web Site: www.subterrain.ca
Key Personnel
Contact: Brian Kaufman
Literary magazine with the motto "Strong Words for a Polite Nation".
First published 1988
Frequency: 3 issues/yr
Avg pages per issue: 68
Circulation: 3,000
$7/issue US, $8 issue/CN; $18/yr, $32/2 yrs (US & CN)
ISSN: 0840-7533
Trim Size: 8 1/2 x 11
Ad Rates: Back cover-color $900; inside front/back cover $800; inside full page color $847; 1/2 page color $575. Prices in Canadian dollars. For other sizes & B&W rates, visit www.subterrain.ca
Ad Closing Date(s): Feb 13, May 30, Oct 15

Subtext
Published by Open Book Publishing Inc
90 Holmes Ave, Darien, CT 06820
Mailing Address: PO Box 2228, Darien, CT 06820
Tel: 203-316-8008 *Fax:* 203-975-8469
E-mail: odasan@aol.com
Web Site: www.subtext.net
Key Personnel
Founder & Publr: Stephanie Oda; Glenn Sanislo
News & analysis on the book publishing & selling business, domestic & international.
First published 1995
Frequency: Biweekly
Avg pages per issue: 8
$499/yr

Wag's Revue
2865 W Lyndale St, Suite 1, Chicago, IL 60647
E-mail: editors@wagsrevue.com
Web Site: www.wagsrevue.com
Key Personnel
Mng & Essays Ed: Sandra Allen *Tel:* 415-806-2698 *E-mail:* sandra@wagsrevue.com
Fiction Ed: William Litton *Tel:* 919-475-2497 *E-mail:* willylitt@wagsrevue.com
Poetry Ed: William Guzzardi *Tel:* 919-619-0673 *E-mail:* willguzzo@wagsrevue.com
Interface Developer: John Herr *E-mail:* john@wagsrevue.com
Online only literary quarterly of fiction, poetry, essays & interviews. Release full, carefully edited issues, presenting content on a book-like page with the Internet's freedoms, creating something entirely new. All issues can be read for free online or downloaded at our web site. Submissions accepted from Dec 1-April 1 & July 1-Oct 1. We ask for first serial rights only, all other rights are retained by the author; no paper submissions. Refer to www.wagsrevue.com/submit.php.
First published 2009
Frequency: Quarterly
Avg pages per issue: 140
Free

The Wordsworth Circle
Published by New York University, Department of English
19 University Place, Rm 536, New York, NY 10003
Tel: 212-998-8812 *Fax:* 212-995-4019
Web Site: www.nyu.edu/gsas/dept/english/journal/wordsworth/
Key Personnel
Ed: Marilyn Gaull *E-mail:* mg49@nyu.edu
Peer-reviewed essays on all areas of British Romanticism.
First published 1970
Frequency: Quarterly
Avg pages per issue: 64
Circulation: 2,200
$25/yr, $40/2 yrs, $60/3 yrs
ISSN: 0043-8006

World Literature Today
Published by University of Oklahoma
630 Parrington Oval, Suite 110, Norman, OK 73019-4033
Tel: 405-325-4531 *Fax:* 405-325-7495
E-mail: wlt@ou.edu
Web Site: www.worldliteraturetoday.org
Key Personnel
Exec Dir: Robert Con Davis-Undiano
Brings you the whole world in every issue-covering over sixty of the world's literatures. With interviews, new poetry & fiction, lively essays on writers & regional trends, authors on books that changed their lives, travel writing, a column on children's literature & international book reviews, there is no better window to what is happening in world literature & culture. Also available online.
First published 1927
Frequency: 6 issues/yr
Avg pages per issue: 82
Circulation: 4,000
$6.95/issue, $30/yr indiv, $60/yr CN & elsewhere, $135/yr instn, $205/yr instn CN & elsewhere
ISSN: 0196-3570 (print); 1945-8134 (online)
Ad Rates: Full page $500; 1/2 page $350; inside cover (front or back) $700; back cover $1000

The Writer
Published by Madavor Media LLC
25 Braintree Hill Office Park, Suite 404, Braintree, MA 02184
Tel: 617-706-9110 (cust serv) *Toll Free Tel:* 800-437-5828 (cust serv) *Fax:* 617-536-0102
E-mail: info@madavor.com
Web Site: www.writermag.com
Key Personnel
Editor-in-Chief: Alicia Anstead *Tel:* 617-315-9153 *E-mail:* aanstead@writermag.com
Mng Ed: Aubrey Everett *Tel:* 617-706-9077 *E-mail:* aeverett@madavor.com
Instructional articles on fiction, nonfiction & freelance writing, plus markets for ms sales. See guidelines on web site. Accept unsol mss.
First published 1887
Book Use: Regular book review section
Frequency: Monthly
Avg pages per issue: 60
Circulation: 30,000
$6.95/issue, $32.95/yr US, $42.95/yr CN, $44.95/yr elsewhere
ISSN: 0043-9517 (print); 2163-0046 (online)

Writer's Digest Magazine
Published by F+W, A Content + eCommerce Company
10151 Carver Rd, Suite 200, Blue Ash, OH 45242
Tel: 513-531-2690 *Fax:* 513-891-7153
E-mail: writersdigest@fwmedia.com
Web Site: www.writersdigest.com
Subscription Address: PO Box 421365, Palm Coast, FL 32142-7104
Key Personnel
Ed: Jessica Strawser *E-mail:* jessica.strawser@fwcommunity.com
A publication focused on the craft & business of writing. No mail or phone queries. Submit full ms or pitch to writersdigest@fwmedia.com. No attachments.
First published 1920
Book Use: Excerpts, profiles of authors, tips & techniques
Frequency: 8 issues/yr
Avg pages per issue: 72
Circulation: 100,000
$19.96/yr US, $29.96/yr CN, $31.96/yr foreign
ISSN: 0043-9525
Trim Size: 7 3/4 x 10 1/2

Company Index

Included in this index are the names, addresses, telecommunication numbers and electronic addresses of the organizations included in this volume of *LMP*. Entries also include the page number(s) on which the listings appear.

Sections not represented in this index are **Imprints, Subsidiaries & Distributors; Calendar of Book Trade & Promotional Events; Reference Books for the Trade** and **Magazines for the Trade.**

A Better Be Write Publishing LLC, 9001 Ridge Hill St, Kernersville, NC 27284 *Tel:* 336-354-7173 *Fax:* 336-993-2497 *E-mail:* profin@triad.rr.com *Web Site:* www.abetterbewrite.com, pg 1

A+ English LLC/Book-Editing.com/Book Editing Associates, PO Box 1369, Mansfield, TX 76063 *Tel:* 469-789-3030 *E-mail:* editingnetwork@gmail.com *Web Site:* www.editing-writing.com; www.book-editing.com; www.HelpWithStatistics; www.apawriting.com; childrensbookeditors.com; dissertationeditor.com, pg 519

A-R Editions Inc, 1600 Aspen Commons, Suite 100, Middleton, WI 53562 *Tel:* 608-836-9000 *Toll Free Tel:* 800-736-0070 (North America book orders only) *Fax:* 608-831-8200 *E-mail:* info@areditions.com; orders@areditions.com *Web Site:* www.areditions.com, pg 1

A Westport Wordsmith, 101 Winfield St, Norwalk, CT 06855 *Tel:* 203-939-9484 *E-mail:* pj104daily@aol.com, pg 519

AAA Books Unlimited, 88 Greenbriar E Dr, Deerfield, IL 60015 *Tel:* 847-444-1220 *Fax:* 847-607-8335 *Web Site:* www.aaabooksunlimited.com, pg 539

AAA Photos, 401 Ocean Dr, Unit 804, Miami Beach, FL 33139 *Tel:* 305-534-0804 *Web Site:* www.photosphotos.net, pg 519

AAAI Press, 2275 E Bayshore Rd, Suite 160, Palo Alto, CA 94303 *Tel:* 650-328-3123 *Fax:* 650-321-4457 *E-mail:* publications14@aaai.org *Web Site:* www.aaaipress.org; www.aaai.org, pg 1

AACC International, 3340 Pilot Knob Rd, St Paul, MN 55121 *Tel:* 651-454-7250 *Fax:* 651-454-0766 *E-mail:* aacc@scisoc.org *Web Site:* www.aaccnet.org, pg 1

AAH Graphics Inc, 9293 Fort Valley Rd, Fort Valley, VA 22652-2020 *Tel:* 540-933-6211 *Fax:* 540-933-6523 *E-mail:* srhunter@aahgraphics.com *Web Site:* www.aahgraphics.com, pg 519

The Aaland Agency, PO Box 849, Inyokern, CA 93527-0849 *Tel:* 760-384-3910 *Web Site:* www.the-aaland-agency.com, pg 539

AAP PreK-12 Learning Group, 325 Chestnut St, Suite 1110, Philadelphia, PA 19106 *Tel:* 267-351-4310 *Fax:* 267-351-4317 *E-mail:* prek12learning@publishers.org *Web Site:* www.aepweb.org, pg 593

AAPG (American Association of Petroleum Geologists), 1444 S Boulder Ave, Tulsa, OK 74119 *Tel:* 918-584-2555 *Toll Free Tel:* 800-364-AAPG (364-2274) *Fax:* 918-580-2665 *Toll Free Fax:* 800-898-2274 *E-mail:* info@aapg.org *Web Site:* www.aapg.org, pg 1

Aaron-Spear, PO Box 42, Brooksville, ME 04617 *Tel:* 207-326-8764, pg 519

AAUP Book, Jacket & Journal Design Show, 28 W 36 St, Suite 602, New York, NY 10018 *Tel:* 212-989-1010 *Fax:* 212-989-0275 *E-mail:* info@aaupnet.org *Web Site:* www.aaupnet.org, pg 665

ABAC/ALAC, 368 Dalhousie St, Suite 301, Ottawa, ON K1N 7G3, Canada *Tel:* 416-364-2376 *E-mail:* info@abac.org *Web Site:* www.abac.org, pg 593

Abaris Books, 64 Wall St, Norwalk, CT 06850 *Tel:* 203-838-8402 *Fax:* 203-857-0730 *E-mail:* abaris@abarisbooks.com *Web Site:* abarisbooks.com, pg 2

Abbeville Press, 137 Varick St, Suite 504, New York, NY 10013-1105 *Tel:* 212-366-5585 *Toll Free Tel:* 800-ARTBOOK (278-2665); 800-343-4499 (orders) *Fax:* 212-366-6966 *Toll Free Fax:* 800-351-5073 (orders) *E-mail:* abbeville@abbeville.com; sales@abbeville.com; marketing@abbeville.com; rights@abbeville.com *Web Site:* www.abbeville.com, pg 2

Abbeville Publishing Group, 137 Varick St, Suite 504, New York, NY 10013 *Tel:* 212-366-5585 *Toll Free Tel:* 800-ART-BOOK (278-2665) *Fax:* 212-366-6966 *E-mail:* abbeville@abbeville.com; marketing@abbeville.com; sales@abbeville.com; rights@abbeville.com *Web Site:* www.abbeville.com, pg 2

ABC-CLIO, 130 Cremona Dr, Santa Barbara, CA 93117 *Tel:* 805-968-1911 *Toll Free Tel:* 800-368-6868 *Fax:* 805-685-9685 *Toll Free Fax:* 866-270-3856 *E-mail:* sales@abc-clio.com; customerservice@abc-clio.com *Web Site:* www.abc-clio.com, pg 2

ABDO Publishing Group, 8000 W 78 St, Suite 310, Edina, MN 55439 *Tel:* 952-831-2120 *Toll Free Tel:* 800-800-1312 *Toll Free Fax:* 800-862-3480 *E-mail:* customerservice@abdopublishing.com *Web Site:* abdopublishing.com, pg 2

Dominick Abel Literary Agency Inc, 146 W 82 St, Suite 1-A, New York, NY 10024 *Tel:* 212-877-0710 *Fax:* 212-595-3133 *E-mail:* agency@dalainc.com *Web Site:* www.dalainc.com, pg 539

Aberdeen Bay, 6285 Gentle Lane, Alexandria, VA 22310 *Tel:* 703-473-1392 *E-mail:* editor@aberdeenbay.com *Web Site:* www.aberdeenbay.com, pg 2

Abingdon Press, 201 Eighth Ave S, Nashville, TN 37203-3919 *Tel:* 615-749-6000 (academic books) *Toll Free Tel:* 800-251-3320 *Fax:* 615-749-6056 (academic books) *Toll Free Fax:* 800-836-7802 (orders) *E-mail:* orders@abingdonpress.com *Web Site:* www.abingdonpress.com, pg 2

About Books Inc, 1001 Taurus Dr, Colorado Springs, CO 80906 *Tel:* 719-632-8226 *Fax:* 719-213-2602 *Web Site:* www.about-books.com, pg 519

Abrams Artists Agency, 275 Seventh Ave, 26th fl, New York, NY 10001 *Tel:* 646-486-4600 *Fax:* 646-486-2358 *E-mail:* literary@abramsartny.com *Web Site:* www.abramsartists.com, pg 539

Harry N Abrams Inc, 115 W 18 St, 6th fl, New York, NY 10011 *Tel:* 212-206-7715 *Toll Free Tel:* 800-345-1359 *Fax:* 212-519-1210 *E-mail:* abrams@abramsbooks.com *Web Site:* www.abramsbooks.com, pg 2

Abrams Learning Trends, 16310 Bratton Lane, Suite 250, Austin, TX 78728-2403 *Toll Free Tel:* 800-227-9120 *Toll Free Fax:* 800-737-3322 *E-mail:* customerservice@abramslearningtrends.com (orders, cust serv); contactus@abramslearningtrends.com *Web Site:* www.abramslearningtrends.com (orders, cust serv), pg 3

Absey & Co Inc, 23011 Northcrest Dr, Spring, TX 77389 *Tel:* 281-257-2340 *Toll Free Tel:* 888-41-ABSEY (412-2739) *Fax:* 281-251-4676 *E-mail:* info@absey.biz *Web Site:* www.absey.biz, pg 3

ABZ First Book Poetry Prize, PO Box 2746, Huntington, WV 25727-2746 *Tel:* 304-638-5701 *E-mail:* abzpoetry@gmail.com *Web Site:* abzpress.sharepoint.com, pg 665

Acacia House Publishing Services Ltd, 51 Chestnut Ave, Brantford, ON N3T 4C3, Canada *Tel:* 519-752-0978 *Fax:* 519-752-8349, pg 539

Academic Press, 225 Wyman St, Waltham, MA 02144 *Tel:* 781-663-5200 *Fax:* 781-663-2262 *Web Site:* store.elsevier.com/Academic-Press, pg 3

Academica Press LLC, PO Box 60728, Cambridge Sta, Palo Alto, CA 94306 *Tel:* 650-329-0685 *Fax:* 650-329-0685 *E-mail:* academicapress@aol.com *Web Site:* www.academicapress.com, pg 3

Academy Chicago, 378 Park Ave, Suite 1E, Glencoe, IL 60022 *Tel:* 847-786-4224 *E-mail:* editors@academychicago.com *Web Site:* www.chicagoreviewpress.com, pg 3

The Academy of American Poets Inc, 75 Maiden Lane, Suite 901, New York, NY 10038 *Tel:* 212-274-0343 *Fax:* 212-274-9427 *E-mail:* academy@poets.org *Web Site:* www.poets.org, pg 593

Academy of Motion Picture Arts & Sciences (AMPAS), 8949 Wilshire Blvd, Beverly Hills, CA 90211 *Tel:* 310-247-3000 *Fax:* 310-859-9619 *E-mail:* ampas@oscars.org *Web Site:* www.oscars.org, pg 593

Academy of Nutrition & Dietetics, 120 S Riverside Plaza, Suite 2000, Chicago, IL 60606-6995 *Tel:* 312-899-0040 (ext 5000) *Toll Free Tel:* 800-877-1600 *E-mail:* sales@eatright.org *Web Site:* www.eatright.org, pg 3

Acanthus Publishing, 180 Lincoln St, 3rd fl, Boston, MA 02111 *Tel:* 617-230-2167 *Fax:* 617-995-0893 *E-mail:* info@acanthuspublishing.com *Web Site:* www.acanthuspublishing.com, pg 4

Access Copyright, The Canadian Copyright Licensing Agency, 56 Wellesley St W, Suite 401A, Toronto, ON M5S 2S3, Canada *Tel:* 416-868-1620 *Toll Free Tel:* 800-893-5777 *Fax:* 416-868-1621 *E-mail:* info@accesscopyright.ca *Web Site:* www.accesscopyright.ca, pg 593

Access Editorial Services, 1133 Broadway, Suite 528, New York, NY 10010 *Tel:* 212-255-7306 *E-mail:* wiseword@juno.com, pg 519

Acclaim Film Script Competition, 300 Central Ave, Suite 501, St Petersburg, FL 33701 *Web Site:* acclaimscripts.com, pg 665

Acclaim TV Script Competition, 300 Central Ave, Suite 501, St Petersburg, FL 33701 *Web Site:* acclaimscripts.com, pg 665

Accuity, 4709 W Golf Rd, Skokie, IL 60076 *Tel:* 847-676-9600 *Toll Free Tel:* 800-321-3373 *Fax:* 847-933-8101 *E-mail:* custserv@accuity.com; sales@accuity.com *Web Site:* www.accuity.com, pg 4

Accurate Writing & More, 16 Barstow Lane, Hadley, MA 01035 *Tel:* 413-586-2388 *Web Site:* www.accuratewriting.com; www.business-for-a-better-world.com; www.greenandprofitable.com; www.makinggreensexy.com; frugalmarketing.com; www.frugalfun.com; www.twitter.com/shelhorowitz, pg 519

Alice B Acheson's Workshops for Writers, Illustrators & Photographers, PO Box 735, Friday Harbor, WA 98250 *Tel:* 360-378-2815 *E-mail:* aliceba7@gmail.com, pg 649

Milton Acorn Poetry Award, 115 Richmond St, Charlottetown, PE C1A 1H7, Canada *Tel:* 902-368-4410 *Toll Free Tel:* 888-734-2784 *Fax:* 902-368-4418 *E-mail:* peiwritersguild@gmail.com *Web Site:* www.peiwritersguild.com, pg 665

Acres USA, 4029 Guadalupe St, Austin, TX 78751 *Tel:* 512-892-4400 *Toll Free Tel:* 800-355-5313 *Fax:* 512-892-4448 *E-mail:* orders@acresusa.com; editor@acresusa.com; info@acresusa.com *Web Site:* www.acresusa.com, pg 4

ACTA Press, 2509 Dieppe Ave SW, Bldg B6, Suite 101, Calgary, AB T3E 7J9, Canada *Tel:* 403-288-1195 *Fax:* 403-247-6851 *E-mail:* journals@actapress.com; publish@actapress.com; sales@actapress.com *Web Site:* www.actapress.com, pg 471

ACTA Publications, 4848 N Clark St, Chicago, IL 60640 *Tel:* 773-271-1030 *Toll Free Tel:* 800-397-2282 *Fax:* 773-271-7399 *Toll Free Fax:* 800-397-0079 *E-mail:* info@actapublications.com *Web Site:* www.actapublications.com, pg 4

ACU Press, 1626 Campus Ct, Abilene, TX 79601 *Tel:* 325-674-2720 *Toll Free Tel:* 877-816-4455 *Fax:* 325-674-6471 *Web Site:* www.acupressbooks.com; www.leafwoodpublishers.com, pg 4

Adams & Ambrose Publishing, PO Box 259684, Madison, WI 53725-9684 *Tel:* 608-257-5700 *Fax:* 608-257-5700 *E-mail:* info@adamsambrose.com, pg 4

Herbert Baxter Adams Prize, 400 "A" St SE, Washington, DC 20003 *Tel:* 202-544-2422 *Fax:* 202-544-8307 *E-mail:* awards@historians.org *Web Site:* www.historians.org, pg 665

Adams Media, 57 Littlefield St, Avon, MA 02322 *Tel:* 508-427-7100 *Fax:* 508-427-6790 *E-mail:* orders@adamsmedia.com *Web Site:* www.adamsmedia.com, pg 4

Adams-Pomeroy Press, 103 N Jackson St, Albany, WI 53502 *Tel:* 608-862-3645 *Toll Free Tel:* 877-862-3645 *Fax:* 608-862-3647 *E-mail:* adamspomeroy@tds.net, pg 507

ADASI Publishing Co, 13 Riverdale Ave, Dover, NH 03820-4698 *Tel:* 603-866-9426 *E-mail:* info@adasi.com *Web Site:* www.adasi.com, pg 4

Jane Addams Children's Book Award, 777 United Nations Plaza, 6th fl, New York, NY 10017 *Tel:* 212-682-8830 *E-mail:* japa@igc.org *Web Site:* www.janeaddamspeace.org, pg 665

Addicus Books Inc, PO Box 45327, Omaha, NE 68145 *Tel:* 402-330-7493 *Fax:* 402-330-1707 *E-mail:* info@addicusbooks.com; addicusbks@aol.com *Web Site:* www.addicusbooks.com, pg 4

J Adel Art & Design, 586 Ramapo Rd, Teaneck, NJ 07666 *Tel:* 201-836-2606 *E-mail:* jadelnj@aol.com, pg 519

Adirondack Mountain Club (ADK), 814 Goggins Rd, Lake George, NY 12845-4117 *Tel:* 518-668-4447 *Toll Free Tel:* 800-395-8080 *Fax:* 518-668-3746 *E-mail:* info@adk.org *Web Site:* www.adk.org, pg 5

Adler Publishing Inc, 46937 Monarch Dr, Parker, CO 80138 *Tel:* 303-660-2158 *Toll Free Tel:* 800-660-5107 (sales & orders) *E-mail:* customerservice@adlerpublishing.com; orders@4wdbooks.com *Web Site:* www.adlerpublishing.com, pg 5

Advance Publishing Inc, 6950 Fulton St, Houston, TX 77022 *Tel:* 713-695-0600 *Toll Free Tel:* 800-917-9630 *Fax:* 713-695-8585 *E-mail:* info@advancepublishing.com *Web Site:* www.advancepublishing.com, pg 5

Adventure House, 914 Laredo Rd, Silver Spring, MD 20901 *Tel:* 301-754-1589 *Web Site:* www.adventurehouse.com, pg 5

Adventure Publications, 820 Cleveland St, Cambridge, MN 55008 *Tel:* 763-689-9800 *Toll Free Tel:* 800-678-7006 *Fax:* 763-689-9039 *Toll Free Fax:* 877-374-9016 *E-mail:* custservice@adventurepublications.net; orders@adventurepublications.net *Web Site:* www.adventurepublications.net, pg 5

Adventures Unlimited Press (AUP), One Adventure Place, Kempton, IL 60946 *Tel:* 815-253-6390 *Fax:* 815-253-6300 *E-mail:* auphq@frontiernet.net; info@adventuresunlimitedpress.com *Web Site:* www.adventuresunlimitedpress.com, pg 5

Advertising Research Foundation (ARF), 432 Park Ave S, 6th fl, New York, NY 10016-8013 *Tel:* 212-751-5656 *Fax:* 212-319-5265 *E-mail:* info@thearf.org; jar@thearf.org (edit) *Web Site:* www.thearf.org, pg 593

Aegean Publishing Co, PO Box 6790, Santa Barbara, CA 93160 *Tel:* 805-964-6669 *Fax:* 805-683-4798 *E-mail:* info@aegeanpublishing.com *Web Site:* aegeanpublishing.com, pg 5

AEI (Atchity Entertainment International Inc), 9601 Wilshire Blvd, Unit 1202, Beverly Hills, CA 90210 *Tel:* 323-932-0407 *Fax:* 323-932-0321 *E-mail:* submissions@aeionline.com *Web Site:* www.aeionline.com, pg 540

The AEI Press, 1150 17 St NW, Washington, DC 20036 *Tel:* 202-862-5800 *Fax:* 202-862-7177 *Web Site:* www.aei.org, pg 5

AEIOU Inc, 894 Piermont Ave, Piermont, NY 10968 *Tel:* 845-680-5380, pg 519

AFB Press, 2 Penn Plaza, Suite 1102, New York, NY 10121 *Tel:* 212-502-7600 *Toll Free Tel:* 800-232-5463; 800-232-3044 (orders) *Fax:* 917-210-3979; 412-741-0609 (orders) *Toll Free Fax:* 888-545-8331 *E-mail:* press@afb.net; afbpress@afb.net; afbinfo@afb.net; afborder@afb.net (orders) *Web Site:* www.afb.org, pg 5

AFCP's Annual Awards, 7445 Morgan Rd, Suite 103, Liverpool, NY 13090 *Toll Free Tel:* 877-203-2327 *Fax:* 781-459-7770 *E-mail:* afcp@afcp.org *Web Site:* www.afcp.org, pg 665

Africa World Press Inc, 541 W Ingham Ave, Suite B, Trenton, NJ 08638 *Tel:* 609-695-3200 *Fax:* 609-695-6466 *E-mail:* customerservice@africaworldpressbooks.com *Web Site:* www.africaworldpressbooks.com, pg 6

African American Images, PO Box 1799, Chicago Heights, IL 60412 *Tel:* 708-672-4909 (cust serv) *Toll Free Tel:* 800-552-1991 (orders) *Fax:* 708-672-0466 *E-mail:* customersvc@africanamericanimages.com *Web Site:* www.africanamericanimages.com, pg 6

Africana Homestead Legacy Publishers Inc, 811 Church Rd, Suite 105, Cherry Hill, NJ 08002 *Tel:* 856-773-0694 *Fax:* 856-486-1135 *E-mail:* customer-service@ahlpub.com; sales@ahlpub.com; editors@ahlpub.com *Web Site:* www.ahlpub.com, pg 6

AFS Wordstead, 1062 Vallee-a-Josaphat, Lac-des-Iles, QC J0W 1J0, Canada *Tel:* 819-597-4072 *Fax:* 819-597-4547 *Web Site:* www.wordstead.com, pg 519

Agatha Awards, PO Box 8007, Gaithersburg, MD 20898-8007 *E-mail:* malicedomesticpr@gmail.com *Web Site:* www.malicedomestic.org, pg 665

Ageless Press, 3759 Collins St, Sarasota, FL 34232 *Tel:* 941-365-1367 *Fax:* 941-365-1367 *E-mail:* irishope@comcast.net, pg 6

Agency Chicago, 332 S Michigan Ave, Suite 1032, No A600, Chicago, IL 60604 *E-mail:* ernsant@aol.com, pg 540

Agent's Ink, PO Box 4956, Fresno, CA 93744-4956 *Tel:* 559-438-1883 *Fax:* 559-438-8289 *Web Site:* agents-ink.com, pg 540

Aggiornamento Award, 8550 United Plaza Blvd, Suite 1001, Baton Rouge, LA 70809-2256 *Tel:* 225-408-4417 *E-mail:* cla2@cathla.org *Web Site:* www.cathla.org, pg 665

AHA Press, 155 N Wacker Dr, Suite 400, Chicago, IL 60606 *Tel:* 312-893-6800 *Toll Free Tel:* 800-821-2039 *Fax:* 312-422-4500 *Toll Free Fax:* 866-516-5817 (orders) *Web Site:* www.healthforum.com, pg 6

The Ahearn Agency Inc, 2021 Pine St, New Orleans, LA 70118 *Tel:* 504-861-8395 *Fax:* 504-866-6434 *Web Site:* www.ahearnagency.com, pg 540

Ahsahta Press, Boise State University, Mail Stop 1525, 1910 University Dr, Boise, ID 83725-1525 *Tel:* 208-426-3134 *E-mail:* ahsahta@boisestate.edu *Web Site:* ahsahtapress.org, pg 6

AIC Publications, PO Box 181467, Arlington, TX 76002-1467 *E-mail:* submissions@aicpublications.com *Web Site:* aicpublications.com, pg 507

AICPA Professional Publications, 220 Leigh Farm Rd, Durham, NC 27707 *Tel:* 919-402-4500 *Toll Free Tel:* 888-777-7077 *Fax:* 919-402-4505 *Toll Free Fax:* 800-362-5066 *E-mail:* acquisitions@aicpa.org; service@aicpa.org *Web Site:* www.aicpa.org, pg 6

AIGA 50 Books/50 Covers, 233 Broadway, 17th fl, New York, NY 10279 *Tel:* 212-807-1990 *Fax:* 212-807-1799 *E-mail:* competitions@aiga.org *Web Site:* www.aiga.org, pg 665

AIGA, the professional association for design, 233 Broadway, 17th fl, New York, NY 10279 *Tel:* 212-807-1990 *Fax:* 212-807-1799 *E-mail:* general@aiga.org *Web Site:* www.aiga.org, pg 593

AIMS Education Foundation, 1595 S Chestnut Ave, Fresno, CA 93702-4706 *Tel:* 559-255-4094 *Toll Free Tel:* 888-733-2467 *Fax:* 559-255-6396 *E-mail:* aimsed@aimsedu.org *Web Site:* www.aimsedu.org, pg 6

Air Conditioning Contractors of America, 2800 Shirlington Rd, Suite 300, Arlington, VA 22206 *Tel:* 703-824-8851 *Toll Free Tel:* 888-290-2220 *Fax:* 703-575-8107 *Web Site:* www.acca.org, pg 6

Aitken Alexander Associates LLC, 30 Vandam St, Suite 5A, New York, NY 10013 *Tel:* 212-929-4100 *Web Site:* www.aitkenalexander.co.uk, pg 540

AJL Judaica Bibliography Award, PO Box 1118, Teaneck, NJ 07666 *Tel:* 201-371-3255 *E-mail:* ajlibs@osu.edu *Web Site:* www.jewishlibraries.org, pg 666

AJL Judaica Reference Award, PO Box 1118, Teaneck, NJ 07666 *Tel:* 201-371-3255 *E-mail:* ajlibs@osu.edu *Web Site:* www.jewishlibraries.org, pg 666

AJL Scholarship, PO Box 1118, Teaneck, NJ 07666 *Web Site:* www.jewishlibraries.org, pg 666

AK Press Distribution, 674-A 23 St, Oakland, CA 94612 *Tel:* 510-208-1700 *Fax:* 510-208-1701 *E-mail:* info@akpress.org; sales@akpress.org; orders@akpress.org *Web Site:* www.akpress.org, pg 7

Akashic Books, 232 Third St, Suite A-115, Brooklyn, NY 11215 *Tel:* 718-643-9193 *Fax:* 718-643-9195 *E-mail:* info@akashicbooks.com *Web Site:* www.akashicbooks.com, pg 7

AKC Publications Fiction Contest, 260 Madison Ave, New York, NY 10016 *Web Site:* www.akc.org/pubs/fictioncontest, pg 666

Akin & Randolph Agency, Literary Div, One Gateway Ctr, Suite 2600, Newark, NJ 07102 *Tel:* 973-353-8409; 973-623-6834 *Fax:* 973-353-8417 *E-mail:* info@akinandrandolph.com *Web Site:* www.akinandrandolph.com, pg 540

Akron Poetry Prize, The University of Akron Press, 120 E Mill St, Suite 415, Akron, OH 44308 *Tel:* 330-972-6953 *Fax:* 330-972-8364 *E-mail:* uapress@uakron.edu *Web Site:* www.uakron.edu/uapress/akron-poetry-prize, pg 666

Alabama Artists Fellowship Awards, 201 Monroe St, Suite 110, Montgomery, AL 36130-1800 *Tel:* 334-242-4076 *Fax:* 334-240-3269, pg 666

Alaska Native Language Center, PO Box 757680, Fairbanks, AK 99775-7680 *Tel:* 907-474-7874 *Fax:* 907-474-6586 *E-mail:* uaf-aknativelang@alaska.edu (orders) *Web Site:* www.uaf.edu/anlc, pg 7

Alazar Press, 201 Orchard Lane, Carrboro, NC 27510 *Tel:* 919-274-0653 *E-mail:* alazar.press@gmail.com *Web Site:* www.alazar-press.com, pg 507

Albert Whitman & Co, 250 S Northwest Hwy, Suite 320, Park Ridge, IL 60068 *Tel:* 847-232-2800 *Toll Free Tel:* 800-255-7675 *Fax:* 847-581-0039 *E-mail:* mail@awhitmanco.com *Web Site:* www.albertwhitman.com, pg 7

Alberta Book Awards, 10523 100 Ave, Edmonton, AB T5J 0A8, Canada *Tel:* 780-424-5060 *Fax:* 780-424-7943 *E-mail:* info@bookpublishers.ab.ca *Web Site:* www.bookpublishers.ab.ca, pg 666

Rodelinde Albrecht, PO Box 444, Lenox Dale, MA 01242-0444 *Tel:* 413-243-4350 *E-mail:* rodelinde@gmail.com, pg 519

American Association of University Women Award for Juvenile Literature, 4610 Mail Service Ctr, Raleigh, NC 27699-4610 *Tel:* 919-807-7290 *Fax:* 919-733-8807, pg 667

American Atheist Press, PO Box 158, Cranford, NJ 07016 *Tel:* 908-276-7300 *Fax:* 908-276-7402 *Web Site:* www.atheists.org, pg 11

American Auto Racing Writers & Broadcasters, 922 N Pass Ave, Burbank, CA 91505 *Tel:* 818-842-7005 *Fax:* 818-842-7020, pg 594

American Bar Association, 321 N Clark St, Chicago, IL 60654 *Tel:* 312-988-5000 *Toll Free Tel:* 800-285-2221 (orders) *Fax:* 312-988-6281 *E-mail:* orders@abanet.org *Web Site:* shop.americanbar.org, pg 11

American Bible Society, 1865 Broadway, New York, NY 10023-7505 *Tel:* 212-408-1200 *Toll Free Tel:* 800-322-4253; 888-596-6296 *Fax:* 212-408-1512 *E-mail:* info@americanbible.org *Web Site:* www.americanbible.org, pg 11

American Book Award, The Raymond House, 655 13 St, Suite 302, Oakland, CA 94612 *Tel:* 510-268-9775 *E-mail:* info@beforecolumbusfoundation.com *Web Site:* www.beforecolumbusfoundation.com, pg 667

American Book Producers Association (ABPA), 31 W Eighth St, 2nd fl, New York, NY 10011 *Tel:* 212-675-1363 *Fax:* 212-675-1364 *E-mail:* office@abpaonline.org *Web Site:* www.abpaonline.org, pg 594

American Booksellers Association, 333 Westchester Ave, Suite S202, White Plains, NY 10604 *Tel:* 914-406-7500 *Toll Free Tel:* 800-637-0037 *Fax:* 914-410-6297 *E-mail:* info@bookweb.org *Web Site:* www.bookweb.org, pg 594

American Business Media, 675 Third Ave, 22nd fl, New York, NY 10017-5704 *Tel:* 212-661-6360 *Fax:* 212-370-0736 *E-mail:* info@abmmail.com *Web Site:* www.americanbusinessmedia.com, pg 594

American Carriage House Publishing, PO Box 1130, Nevada City, CA 95959 *Tel:* 530-432-8860 *Toll Free Tel:* 866-986-2665 *Fax:* 530-432-7379 *E-mail:* editor@carriagehousepublishing.com *Web Site:* www.americancarriagehousepublishing.com, pg 11

American Catholic Press (ACP), 16565 S State St, South Holland, IL 60473 *Tel:* 708-331-5485 *Fax:* 708-331-5484 *E-mail:* acp@acpress.org *Web Site:* www.acpress.org, pg 11

The American Ceramic Society, 600 N Cleveland Ave, Suite 210, Westerville, OH 43082 *Tel:* 240-646-7054 *Toll Free Tel:* 866-721-3322 *Fax:* 240-396-5637 *E-mail:* customerservice@ceramics.org *Web Site:* ceramics.org, pg 11

The American Chemical Society, 1155 16 St NW, Washington, DC 20036 *Tel:* 202-872-4600 *Toll Free Tel:* 800-227-5558 (US) *Fax:* 202-872-6067 *E-mail:* help@acs.org *Web Site:* www.acs.org, pg 12

American Christian Writers, PO Box 110390, Nashville, TN 37222-0390 *Tel:* 615-331-8668 *Toll Free Tel:* 800-21-WRITE (219-7483) *E-mail:* acwriters@aol.com *Web Site:* regaforder.wordpress.com, pg 594

American Civil Liberties Union, 125 Broad St, 18th fl, New York, NY 10004 *Tel:* 212-549-2500 *E-mail:* media@aclu.org *Web Site:* www.aclu.org, pg 594

American College, 270 S Bryn Mawr Ave, Bryn Mawr, PA 19010 *Tel:* 610-526-1000 *Toll Free Tel:* 888-263-7265 *Fax:* 610-526-1310 *Web Site:* www.theamericancollege.edu, pg 12

American College of Physician Executives, 400 N Ashley Dr, Suite 400, Tampa, FL 33602 *Tel:* 813-287-2000 *Toll Free Tel:* 800-562-8088 *Fax:* 813-287-8993 *E-mail:* acpe@acpe.org *Web Site:* www.acpe.org, pg 12

American College of Surgeons, 633 N Saint Clair St, Chicago, IL 60611-3211 *Tel:* 312-202-5000 *Fax:* 312-202-5001 *E-mail:* postmaster@facs.org *Web Site:* www.facs.org, pg 12

American Correctional Association, 206 N Washington St, Suite 200, Alexandria, VA 22314 *Tel:* 703-224-0000 *Toll Free Tel:* 800-222-5646 *Fax:* 703-224-0179 *Web Site:* www.aca.org, pg 12

American Council on Education, One Dupont Circle NW, Washington, DC 20036 *Tel:* 202-939-9300; 301-632-6757 (orders) *Fax:* 202-939-9302 *E-mail:* pubs@acenet.edu *Web Site:* www.acenet.edu, pg 12

American Council on Education, One Dupont Circle NW, Washington, DC 20036 *Tel:* 202-939-9300 *Fax:* 202-939-9302 *Web Site:* www.acenet.edu, pg 594

American Counseling Association, 6101 Stevenson Ave, Suite 600, Alexandria, VA 22304 *Tel:* 703-823-9800 (ext 222, book orders) *Toll Free Tel:* 800-422-2648 (ext 222, book orders); 800-347-6647 *Fax:* 703-823-0252 *Toll Free Fax:* 800-473-2329 *E-mail:* membership@counseling.org (book orders) *Web Site:* www.counseling.org, pg 12

American Diabetes Association, 1701 N Beauregard St, Alexandria, VA 22311 *Toll Free Tel:* 800-342-2383 *E-mail:* booksinfo@diabetes.org *Web Site:* www.diabetes.org, pg 12

American Federation of Arts, 305 E 47 St, 10th fl, New York, NY 10017 *Tel:* 212-988-7700 *Toll Free Tel:* 800-232-0270 *Fax:* 212-861-2487 *E-mail:* pubinfo@afaweb.org *Web Site:* www.afaweb.org, pg 12

American Federation of Astrologers Inc, 6535 S Rural Rd, Tempe, AZ 85283-3746 *Tel:* 480-838-1751 *Toll Free Tel:* 888-301-7630 *Fax:* 480-838-8293 *Web Site:* www.astrologers.com, pg 12

American Fisheries Society, 5410 Grosvenor Lane, Suite 110, Bethesda, MD 20814-2199 *Tel:* 301-897-8616; 703-661-1570 (book orders) *Fax:* 301-897-8096; 703-996-1010 (book orders) *E-mail:* main@fisheries.org *Web Site:* www.fisheries.org, pg 12

American Forest Paper Association (AF&PA), 1101 "K" St NW, Suite 700, Washington, DC 20005 *Tel:* 202-463-2700 *E-mail:* info@afandpa.org *Web Site:* www.afandpa.org, pg 595

American Geophysical Union (AGU), 2000 Florida Ave NW, Washington, DC 20009 *Tel:* 202-462-6900 *Toll Free Tel:* 800-966-2481 (North America) *Fax:* 202-328-0566 *E-mail:* service@agu.org *Web Site:* www.agu.org, pg 13

American Geosciences Institute (AGI), 4220 King St, Alexandria, VA 22302-1502 *Tel:* 703-379-2480 (ext 246) *Fax:* 703-379-7563 *E-mail:* pubs@agiweb.org *Web Site:* www.agiweb.org, pg 13

American Girl Publishing, 8400 Fairway Place, Middleton, WI 53562 *Tel:* 608-836-4848; 608-831-5210 (outside US & CN) *Toll Free Tel:* 800-233-0264; 800-360-1861; 800-845-0005 (US & CN) *Fax:* 608-836-1999 *Web Site:* www.americangirl.com, pg 13

American Historical Association (AHA), 400 "A" St SE, Washington, DC 20003 *Tel:* 202-544-2422 *Fax:* 202-544-8307 *E-mail:* aha@historians.org; awards@historians.org; info@historians.org *Web Site:* www.historians.org, pg 13

American Illustration/American Photography, 15 E 32 St, 7th fl, New York, NY 10016 *Tel:* 212-470-0302 *Fax:* 212-532-2064 *E-mail:* info@ai-ap.com *Web Site:* www.ai-ap.com, pg 667

American Industrial Hygiene Association - AIHA, 3141 Fairview Park Dr, Suite 777, Falls Church, VA 22042 *Tel:* 703-849-8888 *Fax:* 703-207-3561 *E-mail:* infonet@aiha.org *Web Site:* www.aiha.org, pg 13

American Institute for Economic Research (AIER), 250 Division St, Great Barrington, MA 01230 *Tel:* 413-528-1216 *Toll Free Tel:* 888-528-1216 (orders) *E-mail:* info@aier.org, pg 13

American Institute of Aeronautics & Astronautics (AIAA), 1801 Alexander Bell Dr, Suite 500, Reston, VA 20191-4344 *Tel:* 703-264-7500 *Toll Free Tel:* 800-639-AIAA (639-2422) *Fax:* 703-264-7551 *E-mail:* custserv@aiaa.org *Web Site:* www.aiaa.org, pg 13

American Institute of Chemical Engineers (AIChE), 120 Wall St, 23rd fl, New York, NY 10005-4020 *Tel:* 203-702-7660 *Toll Free Tel:* 800-242-4363 *Fax:* 203-775-5177 *E-mail:* customerservice@aiche.org *Web Site:* www.aiche.org, pg 13

American Institute of Physics, 1305 Walt Whitman Rd, Suite 300, Melville, NY 11747 *Tel:* 516-576-2200; 301-209-3165 (orders) *Fax:* 301-209-0882 (orders) *E-mail:* aipinfo@aip.org *Web Site:* www.aip.org, pg 13

American Jewish Committee (AJC), Jacob Blaustein Bldg, 165 E 56 St, New York, NY 10022 *Tel:* 212-751-4000; 212-891-1456 (membership) *Fax:* 212-891-1450 *Web Site:* www.ajc.org, pg 595

American Law Institute, 4025 Chestnut St, Philadelphia, PA 19104-3099 *Tel:* 215-243-1600 *Toll Free Tel:* 800-253-6397 *Fax:* 215-243-1664 *Web Site:* www.ali.org, pg 14

American Law Institute Continuing Legal Education (ALI CLE), 4025 Chestnut St, Philadelphia, PA 19104 *Tel:* 215-243-1600 *Toll Free Tel:* 800-CLE-NEWS (253-6397) *Fax:* 215-243-1664; 215-243-1683 *Web Site:* www.ali-cle.org, pg 14

The American Library Association (ALA), 50 E Huron St, Chicago, IL 60611 *Tel:* 312-944-6780 *Toll Free Tel:* 800-545-2433 *Fax:* 312-280-5275 *E-mail:* editionsmarketing@ala.org *Web Site:* www.alastore.ala.org, pg 14

The American Library Association (ALA), 50 E Huron St, Chicago, IL 60611 *Tel:* 312-944-6780; 312-280-4299 (memb & cust serv) *Toll Free Tel:* 800-545-2433 *Fax:* 312-440-9374 *E-mail:* ala@ala.org; customerservice@ala.org *Web Site:* www.ala.org, pg 595

American Literacy Council, 1441 Mariposa Ave, Boulder, CO 80302 *Tel:* 303-440-7385 *Web Site:* www.americanliteracy.com, pg 595

American Literary Translators Association (ALTA), 900 E Seventh St, PMB 266, Bloomington, IN 47405-3201 *Tel:* 972-883-2093 *Fax:* 972-883-6303 *Web Site:* www.literarytranslators.org, pg 595

American Management Association (AMA), 1601 Broadway, New York, NY 10019 *Tel:* 212-586-8100 *Toll Free Tel:* 877-566-9441 *Fax:* 212-903-8168; 518-891-0368 *E-mail:* customerservice@amanet.org *Web Site:* www.amanet.org, pg 595

American Map Corp, 36-36 33 St, 4th fl, Long Island City, NY 11106 *Tel:* 718-784-0055 *Toll Free Tel:* 888-774-7979 *Fax:* 718-784-0640 (admin); 718-784-1216 (sales & orders) *E-mail:* info@kappamapgroup.com *Web Site:* www.kappamapgroup.com, pg 14

American Marketing Association, 311 S Wacker Dr, Suite 5800, Chicago, IL 60606 *Tel:* 312-542-9000 *Toll Free Tel:* 800-AMA-1150 (262-1150) *Fax:* 312-542-9001 *E-mail:* info@ama.org *Web Site:* www.ama.org, pg 14, 595

American Mathematical Society, 201 Charles St, Providence, RI 02904-2294 *Tel:* 401-455-4000 *Toll Free Tel:* 800-321-4267 *Fax:* 401-331-3842; 401-455-4046 (cust serv) *E-mail:* ams@ams.org; cust-serv@ams.org *Web Site:* www.ams.org, pg 14

American Medical Association, AMA Plaza, 330 N Wabash, Suite 39300, Chicago, IL 60611-5885 *Tel:* 312-464-5000 *Toll Free Tel:* 800-621-8335 *Fax:* 312-464-4184 *Web Site:* www.ama-assn.org, pg 14, 595

American Medical Writers Association (AMWA), 30 W Gude Dr, Suite 525, Rockville, MD 20850-4357 *Tel:* 240-238-0940 *Fax:* 301-294-9006 *E-mail:* amwa@amwa.org *Web Site:* www.amwa.org, pg 595

American Numismatic Society, 75 Varick St, 11th fl, New York, NY 10013 *Tel:* 212-571-4470 *Fax:* 212-571-4479 *E-mail:* ans@numismatics.org; orders@numismatics.org *Web Site:* www.numismatics.org, pg 14

The American Occupational Therapy Association Inc (AOTA), 4720 Montgomery Lane, Suite 200, Bethesda, MD 20814-3449 *Tel:* 301-652-6611 *Toll Free Tel:* 800-377-8555 (TDD); 877-404-AOTA

(404-2682, orders) *Fax:* 301-652-7711; 770-238-0414 (orders) *E-mail:* aotacustomerservice@pbd.com *Web Site:* www.aota.org; store.aota.org, pg 14

American Philosophical Society, 104 S Fifth St, Philadelphia, PA 19106 *Tel:* 215-440-3425 *Fax:* 215-440-3450 *E-mail:* dianepub@comcast.net *Web Site:* www.amphilsoc.org, pg 15

American Political Science Association, 1527 New Hampshire Ave NW, Washington, DC 20036-1203 *Tel:* 202-483-2512 *Fax:* 202-483-2657 *E-mail:* apsa@apsanet.org *Web Site:* www.apsanet.org, pg 595

American Press, 60 State St, Suite 700, Boston, MA 02109 *Tel:* 617-247-0022 *E-mail:* americanpress@flash.net *Web Site:* www.americanpresspublishers.com, pg 15

American Printing History Association, PO Box 4519, Grand Central Sta, New York, NY 10163 *Tel:* 202-544-2422 *E-mail:* secretary@printinghistory.org *Web Site:* printinghistory.org, pg 596

American Printing History Association Award, PO Box 4519, Grand Central Sta, New York, NY 10163 *Tel:* 202-544-2422 *Web Site:* printinghistory.org, pg 667

American Printing House for the Blind Inc, 1839 Frankfort Ave, Louisville, KY 40206 *Tel:* 502-895-2405 *Toll Free Tel:* 800-223-1839 (cust serv) *Fax:* 502-899-2274 *E-mail:* info@aph.org *Web Site:* www.aph.org; shop.aph.org, pg 15

American Products Publishing Co, 8260 SW Nimbus Ave, Beaverton, OR 97008 *Tel:* 503-672-7502 *Toll Free Tel:* 800-668-8181 *Fax:* 503-672-7104 *E-mail:* info@american-products.com *Web Site:* www.american-products.com, pg 15

American Program Bureau Inc, 313 Washington St, Suite 225, Newton, MA 02458 *Tel:* 617-965-6600 *Toll Free Tel:* 800-225-4575 *Fax:* 617-965-6610 *E-mail:* apb@apbspeakers.com *Web Site:* www.apbspeakers.com, pg 587

American Psychiatric Publishing (APP), 1000 Wilson Blvd, Suite 1825, Arlington, VA 22209 *Tel:* 703-907-7322 *Toll Free Tel:* 800-368-5777 *Fax:* 703-907-1091 *E-mail:* appi@psych.org *Web Site:* www.appi.org; www.psychiatryonline.org, pg 15

American Psychological Association, 750 First St NE, Washington, DC 20002-4242 *Tel:* 202-336-5510 *Toll Free Tel:* 800-374-2721 *Fax:* 202-336-5502 *E-mail:* order@apa.org *Web Site:* www.apa.org/books, pg 15

American Psychological Association, 750 First St NE, Washington, DC 20002-4242 *Tel:* 202-336-5500 *Toll Free Tel:* 800-374-2721 *E-mail:* order@apa.org *Web Site:* www.apa.org, pg 596

American Public Human Services Association, 1133 19 St NW, Suite 400, Washington, DC 20036 *Tel:* 202-682-0100 *Fax:* 202-289-6555 *Web Site:* www.aphsa.org, pg 596

American Public Works Association (APWA), 2345 Grand Blvd, Suite 700, Kansas City, MO 64108-2625 *Tel:* 816-472-6100 *Toll Free Tel:* 800-848-APWA (848-2792) *Fax:* 816-472-1610 *Web Site:* www.apwa.net, pg 15

American Quilter's Society, 5801 Kentucky Dam Rd, Paducah, KY 42003-9323 *Tel:* 270-898-7903 *Toll Free Tel:* 800-626-5420 (orders) *Fax:* 270-898-1173 *E-mail:* orders@americanquilter.com *Web Site:* www.americanquilter.com, pg 15

American Society for Indexing Inc (ASI), 1628 E Southern Ave, Suite 9-223, Tempe, AZ 85282 *Tel:* 480-245-6750 *E-mail:* info@asindexing.org *Web Site:* www.asindexing.org, pg 596

American Society for Nondestructive Testing, 1711 Arlingate Lane, Columbus, OH 43228-0518 *Tel:* 614-274-6003 *Toll Free Tel:* 800-222-2768 *Fax:* 614-274-6899 *Web Site:* www.asnt.org, pg 15

American Society for Quality (ASQ), 600 N Plankinton Ave, Milwaukee, WI 53203 *Tel:* 414-272-8575 *Toll Free Tel:* 800-248-1946 (US & CN); 800-514-1564 (Mexico) *Fax:* 414-272-1734 *E-mail:* help@asq.org *Web Site:* www.asq.org, pg 16

American Society of Agricultural & Biological Engineers (ASABE), 2950 Niles Rd, St Joseph, MI 49085-9659 *Tel:* 269-429-0300 *Toll Free Tel:* 800-371-2723 *Fax:* 269-429-3852 *E-mail:* hq@asabe.org *Web Site:* www.asabe.org, pg 16

American Society of Agronomy, 5585 Guilford Rd, Madison, WI 53711-1086 *Tel:* 608-273-8080 *Fax:* 608-273-2021 *E-mail:* headquarters@sciencesocieties.org *Web Site:* www.agronomy.org, pg 16

American Society of Civil Engineers (ASCE), 1801 Alexander Bell Dr, Reston, VA 20191-4400 *Tel:* 703-295-6300 *Toll Free Tel:* 800-548-2723 *Fax:* 703-295-6278 *E-mail:* marketing@asce.org *Web Site:* www.asce.org, pg 16

American Society of Composers, Authors & Publishers (ASCAP), 1900 Broadway, New York City, NY 10023 *Tel:* 212-621-6000 *Toll Free Tel:* 800-952-7227 *Fax:* 212-612-8453 *E-mail:* info@ascap.com *Web Site:* www.ascap.com, pg 596

American Society of Health-System Pharmacists (ASHP), 7272 Wisconsin Ave, Bethesda, MD 20814 *Tel:* 301-657-3000; 301-664-8700 *Toll Free Tel:* 866-279-0681 (orders) *Fax:* 301-657-1251 (orders) *E-mail:* custserv@ashp.org *Web Site:* www.ashp.org, pg 16

American Society of Journalists and Authors (ASJA), 1501 Broadway, Suite 403, New York, NY 10036 *Tel:* 212-997-0947 *Fax:* 212-937-2315 *Web Site:* asja.org, pg 596

American Society of Journalists and Authors Annual Writers Conference, 1501 Broadway, Suite 403, New York, NY 10036 *Tel:* 212-997-0947 *Fax:* 212-937-2315 *Web Site:* asja.org, pg 649

American Society of Magazine Editors (ASME), 757 Third Ave, 11th fl, New York, NY 10017 *Tel:* 212-872-3700 *Fax:* 212-906-0128 *E-mail:* asme@magazine.org *Web Site:* www.magazine.org/asme, pg 596

American Society of Mechanical Engineers (ASME), 2 Park Ave, New York, NY 10016-5990 *Tel:* 212-591-7000 *Toll Free Tel:* 800-843-2763 (cust serv-US, CN & Mexico) *Fax:* 212-591-7674; 973-882-8113 (cust serv); 973-882-1717 (orders & inquiries) *E-mail:* infocentral@asme.org *Web Site:* www.asme.org, pg 16

American Society of Media Photographers (ASMP), 150 N Second St, Philadelphia, PA 19106 *Tel:* 215-451-2767 *Fax:* 215-451-0880 *E-mail:* info@asmp.org *Web Site:* asmp.org, pg 596

American Society of Plant Taxonomists, University of Wyoming, Dept of Botany 3165, 1000 E University Ave, Laramie, WY 82071 *Tel:* 307-766-2556 *Fax:* 307-766-2851 *E-mail:* aspt@uwyo.edu *Web Site:* www.aspt.net, pg 16

American Sociological Association (ASA), 1430 "K" St NW, Suite 600, Washington, DC 20005-4701 *Tel:* 202-383-9005 *Fax:* 202-638-0882 *E-mail:* customer@asanet.org *Web Site:* www.asanet.org, pg 596

American Speech-Language-Hearing Association (ASHA), 2200 Research Blvd, Rockville, MD 20850-3289 *Tel:* 301-296-5700 *Toll Free Tel:* 800-638-8255 (nonmembs); 800-498-2071 (membs) *Fax:* 301-296-5777; 301-296-8580 *E-mail:* actioncenter@asha.org *Web Site:* www.asha.org, pg 597

American Technical Publishers Inc, 10100 Orland Pkwy, Suite 200, Orland Park, IL 60467-5756 *Toll Free Tel:* 800-323-3471 *Fax:* 708-957-1101 *E-mail:* service@atplearning.com; order@atplearning.com *Web Site:* www.atplearning.com, pg 16

American Translators Association (ATA), 225 Reinekers Lane, Suite 590, Alexandria, VA 22314 *Tel:* 703-683-6100 *Fax:* 703-683-6122 *E-mail:* ata@atanet.org *Web Site:* www.atanet.org, pg 597

American Water Works Association (AWWA), 6666 W Quincy Ave, Denver, CO 80235 *Tel:* 303-794-7711 *Toll Free Tel:* 800-926-7337 *Fax:* 303-347-0804 *Web Site:* www.awwa.org, pg 17

Amherst Media Inc, 175 Rano St, Suite 200, Buffalo, NY 14207 *Tel:* 716-874-4450 *Toll Free Tel:* 800-622-3278 *Fax:* 716-874-4508 *E-mail:* marketing@amherstmedia.com *Web Site:* www.amherstmedia.com, pg 17

Amicus, PO Box 1329, Mankato, MN 56002 *Tel:* 507-388-9357 *Fax:* 507-388-1779 *E-mail:* info@amicuspublishing.us; orders@amicuspublishing.us *Web Site:* www.amicuspublishing.us, pg 17

AMMO Books LLC, 1313 Foothill Blvd, La Canada, CA 91011 *Tel:* 323-223-AMMO (223-2666) *Fax:* 323-978-4200 *E-mail:* weborders@ammobooks.com; orders@ammobooks.com *Web Site:* ammobooks.com, pg 17

Ampersand Group, 12 Morenz Terr, Kanata, ON K2K 3G9, Canada *Tel:* 613-435-5066, pg 519

Ampersand Inc/Professional Publishing Services, 1050 N State St, Chicago, IL 60610 *Tel:* 312-280-8905 *Fax:* 312-944-1582 *E-mail:* info@ampersandworks.com *Web Site:* www.ampersandworks.com, pg 17

AMS Press Inc, Brooklyn Navy Yard, 63 Flushing Ave, Unit 221, Brooklyn, NY 11205-1005 *Tel:* 718-875-8100 *Fax:* 718-875-3800 *E-mail:* editorial@amspressinc.com; orders@amspressinc.com *Web Site:* www.amspressinc.com, pg 17

Betsy Amster Literary Enterprises, 6312 SW Capitol Hwy, No 503, Portland, OR 97239 *Tel:* 503-496-4007 *E-mail:* rights@amsterlit.com (rts inquiries); b.amster.assistant@gmail.com (adult book queries); b.amster.kidsbooks@gmail.com (children & young adult book queries) *Web Site:* www.amsterlit.com, pg 540

Marcia Amsterdam Agency, 41 W 82 St, Suite 9A, New York, NY 10024-5613 *Tel:* 212-873-4945, pg 541

AMWA Annual Conference, 30 W Gude Dr, Suite 525, Rockville, MD 20850-4357 *Tel:* 240-238-0940 *Fax:* 301-294-9006 *E-mail:* amwa@amwa.org *Web Site:* www.amwa.org, pg 649

AMWA Medical Book Awards, 30 W Gude Dr, Suite 525, Rockville, MD 20850-4357 *Tel:* 240-238-0940 *Fax:* 301-294-9006 *E-mail:* amwa@amwa.org *Web Site:* www.amwa.org, pg 667

The Amy Award, 90 Broad St, Suite 2100, New York, NY 10004 *Tel:* 212-226-3586 *Fax:* 212-226-3963 *E-mail:* admin@pw.org *Web Site:* www.pw.org, pg 667

Amy Writing Awards, PO Box 16091, Lansing, MI 48901-6091 *Tel:* 517-323-6233 *Toll Free Tel:* 877-727-4262 *Fax:* 517-321-2572 *E-mail:* amyawards@worldmag.com *Web Site:* www.worldmag.com/amyawards, pg 667

Joyce L Ananian, 25 Forest Circle, Waltham, MA 02452-4719 *Tel:* 781-894-4330 *E-mail:* jlananian@hotmail.com, pg 520

Anaphora Literary Press, 1803 Tree Hill Pkwy, Stone Mountain, GA 30088 *Tel:* 470-289-6395 *Web Site:* anaphoraliterary.com, pg 17

Anchor Group Publishing, PO Box 551, Flushing, MI 48433 *E-mail:* anchorgrouppublishing@gmail.com *Web Site:* anchorgrouppublishing.com, pg 17

Ancient Faith Publishing, 2747 Bond St, University Park, IL 60484 *Tel:* 219-728-2216 *Toll Free Tel:* 800-967-7377 *Toll Free Fax:* 866-599-5208 *E-mail:* info@ancientfaith.com; orders@ancientfaith.com *Web Site:* www.ancientfaith.com/publishing, pg 17

Hans Christian Andersen Award, c/o V Ellis Vance, 5503 N El Adobe Dr, Fresno, CA 93711-2363 *Tel:* 559-351-6119 *E-mail:* executive.director@usbby.org *Web Site:* www.usbby.org, pg 667

Barbara S Anderson, 706 W Davis Ave, Ann Arbor, MI 48103-4855 *Tel:* 734-995-0125 *E-mail:* bsa328@earthlink.net, pg 520

Denice A Anderson, 210 E Church St, Clinton, MI 49236 *Tel:* 517-456-4990 *Fax:* 517-456-4990 *E-mail:* deniceanderson@frontier.com, pg 520

Jim Anderson, 77 S Second St, Brooklyn, NY 11249 *Tel:* 718-388-1083 *E-mail:* jim.and@att.net, pg 520

Anderson Literary Management LLC, 244 Fifth Ave, 11th fl, New York, NY 10001 *Tel:* 212-645-6045 *Fax:* 212-741-1936 *E-mail:* info@andersonliterary.com *Web Site:* www.andersonliterary.com, pg 541

Patricia Anderson PhD, Literary Consultant, 1489 Marine Dr, Suite 515, West Vancouver, BC V7T 1B8, Canada *Tel:* 604-740-0805 *E-mail:* query@helpingyougetpublished.com; patriciaanderson@helpingyougetpublished.com *Web Site:* www.helpingyougetpublished.com, pg 520

Sara Anderson Children's Books, PO Box 47182, Seattle, WA 98146 *Tel:* 206-285-1520 *Web Site:* www.saranderson.com, pg 17

Andrews McMeel Publishing LLC, 1130 Walnut St, Kansas City, MO 64106-2109 *Toll Free Tel:* 800-851-8923; 800-943-9839 (cust serv) *Toll Free Fax:* 800-943-9831 (orders) *Web Site:* www.andrewsmcmeel.com, pg 18

Andrews University Press, Sutherland House, 8360 W Campus Circle Dr, Berrien Springs, MI 49104-1700 *Tel:* 269-471-6915; 269-471-6134 (orders) *Toll Free Tel:* 800-467-6369 (Visa, MC & American Express orders only) *Fax:* 269-471-6224 *E-mail:* aupo@andrews.edu *Web Site:* www.universitypress.andrews.edu, pg 18

Andy Ross Literary Agency, 767 Santa Ray Ave, Oakland, CA 94610 *Tel:* 510-238-8965 *E-mail:* andyrossagency@hotmail.com *Web Site:* www.andyrossagency.com, pg 541

Angel City Press, 2118 Wilshire Blvd, Suite 880, Santa Monica, CA 90403 *Tel:* 310-395-9982 *Toll Free Tel:* 800-949-8039 *Fax:* 310-395-3353 *E-mail:* info@angelcitypress.com *Web Site:* www.angelcitypress.com, pg 18

Angel Editing Services, PO Box 752, Mountain Ranch, CA 95246 *Tel:* 209-728-8364 *E-mail:* info@stephaniemarohn.com *Web Site:* www.stephaniemarohn.com, pg 520

Angels Editorial Services, 1630 Main St, Suite 41, Coventry, CT 06238 *Tel:* 860-742-5279 *E-mail:* angelsus@aol.com, pg 520

Angelus Press, 2915 Forest Ave, Kansas City, MO 64109 *Tel:* 816-753-3150 *Toll Free Tel:* 800-966-7337 *Fax:* 816-753-3557 *E-mail:* support@angeluspress.org *Web Site:* www.angeluspress.org, pg 18

Anhinga Press, PO Box 3665, Tallahassee, FL 32315 *Tel:* 850-577-0745 *E-mail:* info@anhinga.org *Web Site:* www.anhinga.org; www.facebook.com/anhingapress, pg 18

Animal Media Group LLC, 100 First Ave, Suite 1100, Pittsburgh, PA 15222-1519 *Tel:* 412-566-5656 *Fax:* 412-566-5656 *E-mail:* info@animalmediagroup.com *Web Site:* www.animalmediagroup.com, pg 18

The Anisfield-Wolf Book Awards, 1422 Euclid Ave, Suite 1300, Cleveland, OH 44115 *Tel:* 216-861-3810 *Fax:* 216-861-1729 *E-mail:* awinfo@clevefdn.org *Web Site:* www.anisfield-wolf.org; www.clevelandfoundation.org, pg 667

R Ross Annett Award for Children's Literature, 11759 Groat Rd, Edmonton, AB T5M 3K6, Canada *Tel:* 780-422-8174 *Toll Free Tel:* 800-665-5354 (AB only) *Fax:* 780-422-2663 (attn WGA) *E-mail:* mail@writersguild.ab.ca *Web Site:* www.writersguild.ab.ca, pg 667

Annick Press Ltd, 15 Patricia Ave, Toronto, ON M2M 1H9, Canada *Tel:* 416-221-4802 *Fax:* 416-221-8400 *E-mail:* annickpress@annickpress.com *Web Site:* www.annickpress.com, pg 471

Annual Off Off Broadway Short Play Festival, 235 Park Ave S, 5th fl, New York, NY 10003 *Tel:* 212-206-8990 *Toll Free Tel:* 866-598-8449 *Fax:* 212-206-1429 *E-mail:* oobfestival@samuelfrench.com *Web Site:* oob.samuelfrench.com; www.samuelfrench.com, pg 668

Annual Reviews, 4139 El Camino Way, Palo Alto, CA 94306 *Tel:* 650-493-4400 *Toll Free Tel:* 800-523-8635 *Fax:* 650-424-0910; 650-855-9815 *E-mail:* service@annualreviews.org *Web Site:* www.annualreviews.org, pg 18

ANR Publications University of California, 1301 S 46 St, Bldg 478 - MC 3580, Richmond, CA 94804 *Tel:* 510-665-2195 (cust serv) *Toll Free Tel:* 800-994-8849 *Fax:* 510-665-3427 *E-mail:* anrcatalog@ucdavis.edu *Web Site:* anrcatalog.ucanr.edu, pg 18

Anthony Awards, 605 Third Ave, 16th fl, New York, NY 10158 *Tel:* 917-670-9645 *Web Site:* www.bouchercon.info, pg 668

Antioch Writers' Workshop, 900 Dayton St, Yellow Springs, OH 45387 *Tel:* 937-769-1803 *E-mail:* info@antiochwritersworkshop.com *Web Site:* www.antiochwritersworkshop.com, pg 649

Antiquarian Booksellers' Association of America, 20 W 44 St, Suite 507, New York, NY 10036 *Tel:* 212-944-8291 *Fax:* 212-944-8293 *E-mail:* hq@abaa.org *Web Site:* www.abaa.org, pg 597

Antique Collectors' Club Ltd, 116 Pleasant St, Suite 18, East Hampton, MA 01027 *Tel:* 413-529-0861 *Toll Free Tel:* 800-252-5231 *Fax:* 413-529-0862 *E-mail:* sales@antiquecc.com *Web Site:* www.antiquecollectorsclub.com; www.accdistribution.com, pg 18

Antique Trader, c/o Krause Publications, 700 E State St, Iola, WI 54990-0001 *Tel:* 715-445-2214 *Toll Free Tel:* 888-457-2873 *Fax:* 715-445-4087 *Web Site:* www.krausebooks.com, pg 19

Antrim House, 21 Goodrich Rd, Simsbury, CT 06070-1804 *Tel:* 860-217-0023 *E-mail:* eds@antrimhousebooks.com *Web Site:* www.antrimhousebooks.com, pg 19

Anvil Press Publishers, 278 E First Ave, Vancouver, BC V5T 1A6, Canada *Tel:* 604-876-8710 *Fax:* 604-879-2667 *E-mail:* info@anvilpress.com *Web Site:* www.anvilpress.com, pg 471

AOCS Press, 2710 S Boulder Dr, Urbana, IL 61802-6996 *Tel:* 217-359-2344 *Fax:* 217-351-8091 *E-mail:* general@aocs.org *Web Site:* www.aocs.org, pg 19

APA Planners Press, 205 N Michigan Ave, Suite 1200, Chicago, IL 60601 *Tel:* 312-431-9100 *Fax:* 312-786-6700 *E-mail:* customerservice@planning.org *Web Site:* www.planning.org, pg 19

APA Talent & Literary Agency, 405 S Beverly Dr, Beverly Hills, CA 90212 *Tel:* 310-888-4200 *Fax:* 310-888-4242 *Web Site:* www.apa-agency.com, pg 541

Aperture Books, 547 W 27 St, 4th fl, New York, NY 10001 *Tel:* 212-505-5555 *Toll Free Tel:* 800-929-2323 *Fax:* 212-979-7759 *E-mail:* info@aperture.org *Web Site:* www.aperture.org, pg 19

The Apex Press, 4501 Forbes Blvd, Suite 200, Lanham, MD 20706 *Tel:* 301-459-3366 *Toll Free Tel:* 800-462-6420 *Toll Free Fax:* 800-388-4450 *E-mail:* customercare@rowman.com, pg 19

The Apocryphile Press, 1700 Shattuck Ave, Suite 81, Berkeley, CA 94709 *Tel:* 510-290-4349 *E-mail:* apocryphile@earthlink.net *Web Site:* www.apocryphile.org, pg 19

Apogee Press, 2308 Sixth St, Berkeley, CA 94710 *E-mail:* editors.apogee@gmail.com *Web Site:* www.apogeepress.com, pg 19

Apollo Managed Care Inc, 1651 Foothill Blvd, Santa Ana, CA 92705 *Tel:* 805-969-2606 *Fax:* 805-969-3749 *E-mail:* info@apollomanagedcare.com *Web Site:* www.apollomanagedcare.com, pg 19

APPA: The Association of Higher Education Facilities Officers, 1643 Prince St, Alexandria, VA 22314-2818 *Tel:* 703-684-1446 *Fax:* 703-549-2772 *Web Site:* www.appa.org, pg 19

Appalachian Mountain Club Books, 5 Joy St, Boston, MA 02108 *Tel:* 617-523-0655 *Toll Free Tel:* 800-262-4455 (orders) *Fax:* 617-523-0722 *E-mail:* amcbooks@outdoors.org *Web Site:* www.outdoors.org, pg 20

Appalachian Trail Conservancy, 799 Washington St, Harpers Ferry, WV 25425 *Tel:* 304-535-6331 *Toll Free Tel:* 888-287-8673 (orders only) *Fax:* 304-535-2667 *E-mail:* info@appalachiantrail.org *Web Site:* www.appalachiantrail.org; www.atctrailstore.org, pg 20

Appalachian Writers' Workshop, 71 Center St, Hindman, KY 41822 *Tel:* 606-785-5475 *Fax:* 606-785-3499 *E-mail:* info@hindmansettlement.org *Web Site:* www.hindmansettlement.org, pg 649

Applause Theatre & Cinema Books, 33 Plymouth St, Suite 302, Montclair, NJ 07042 *Tel:* 973-337-5034 *Toll Free Tel:* 800-637-2852 *Fax:* 973-337-5227 *E-mail:* info@applausepub.com *Web Site:* www.applausepub.com, pg 20

The Applegate/Jackson/Parks Future Teacher Scholarship, 5211 Port Royal Rd, Suite 510, Springfield, VA 22151 *Tel:* 703-321-9606 *Fax:* 703-321-7143 *E-mail:* research@nilrr.org *Web Site:* www.nilrr.org, pg 668

Appletree Press Inc, 151 Good Counsel Dr, Suite 125, Mankato, MN 56001 *Tel:* 507-345-4848 *Toll Free Tel:* 800-322-5679 *Fax:* 507-345-3002 *E-mail:* eatwell@hickorytech.net *Web Site:* www.appletreepress.com; www.appletree-press.com; www.letscookhealthymeals.com; www.appletree-press.us, pg 20

Applewood Books Inc, One River Rd, Carlisle, MA 01741 *Tel:* 781-271-0055 *Toll Free Tel:* 800-277-5312 (orders) *Fax:* 781-271-0056 *E-mail:* bookorder@awb.com; customercare@awb.com *Web Site:* www.awb.com, pg 20

Appraisal Institute, 200 W Madison, Suite 1500, Chicago, IL 60606 *Tel:* 312-335-4100 *Toll Free Tel:* 888-756-4624 *Fax:* 312-335-4400 *Web Site:* www.appraisalinstitute.org, pg 20

Apprentice Shop Books LLC, 18 Wentworth Dr, Bedford, NH 03110 *Tel:* 603-472-8741 *Fax:* 603-472-2323 *E-mail:* info@apprenticeshopbooks.com *Web Site:* www.apprenticeshopbooks.com, pg 20

Apress Media LLC, 233 Spring St, New York, NY 10013 *Tel:* 212-460-1500 *Fax:* 212-460-1575 *E-mail:* editorial@apress.com *Web Site:* www.apress.com, pg 20

APS PRESS, 3340 Pilot Knob Rd, St Paul, MN 55121 *Tel:* 651-454-7250 *Toll Free Tel:* 800-328-7560 *Fax:* 651-454-0766 *E-mail:* aps@scisoc.org *Web Site:* www.shopapspress.org, pg 21

Aptara Inc, 3110 Fairview Park Dr, Suite 900, Falls Church, VA 22042 *Tel:* 703-352-0001 *E-mail:* info@aptaracorp.com *Web Site:* www.aptaracorp.com, pg 520

Aqua Quest Publications Inc, 486 Bayville Rd, Locust Valley, NY 11560-1209 *Tel:* 516-759-0476 *Toll Free Tel:* 800-933-8989 *Fax:* 516-759-4519 *E-mail:* info@aquaquest.com *Web Site:* www.aquaquest.com, pg 21

Aquila Communications Inc, 2642 Diab St, Montreal, QC H4S 1E8, Canada *Tel:* 514-338-1065 *Toll Free Tel:* 800-667-7071 *Fax:* 514-338-1948 *Toll Free Fax:* 866-338-1948 *E-mail:* orders@aquilacommunications.com *Web Site:* www.aquilacommunications.com; aquilacommunications.net, pg 471

Arbordale Publishing, 612 Johnnie Dodds Blvd, Suite A2, Mount Pleasant, SC 29464 *Tel:* 843-971-6722 *Toll Free Tel:* 877-243-3457 *Fax:* 843-216-3804 *E-mail:* customerservice@arbordalepublishing.com; info@arbordalepublishing.com *Web Site:* www.arbordalepublishing.com, pg 21

The May Hill Arbuthnot Honor Lecture Award, 50 E Huron St, Chicago, IL 60611-2795 *Tel:* 312-280-2163 *Toll Free Tel:* 800-545-2433 *Fax:* 312-440-9374 *E-mail:* alsc@ala.org *Web Site:* www.ala.org/alsc, pg 668

Arbutus Press, 2364 Pinehurst Trail, Traverse City, MI 49696 *Tel:* 231-946-7240 *E-mail:* info@arbutuspress.com *Web Site:* www.arbutuspress.com, pg 21

Arcade Publishing Inc, 307 W 36 St, 11th fl, New York, NY 10018 *Tel:* 212-643-6816 *Fax:* 212-643-6819 *E-mail:* info@skyhorsepublishing.com (subs & foreign rts) *Web Site:* www.arcadepub.com, pg 21

Arcadia, 31 Lake Place N, Danbury, CT 06810 *Tel:* 203-797-0993 *E-mail:* arcadialit@sbcglobal.net, pg 541

Arcadia Publishing Inc, 420 Wando Park Blvd, Mount Pleasant, SC 29464 *Tel:* 843-853-2070 *Toll Free Tel:* 888-313-2665 (orders only) *Fax:* 843-853-0044 *E-mail:* sales@arcadiapublishing.com *Web Site:* www.arcadiapublishing.com, pg 21

Archon Editorial LLC, 815 King St, Suite 204, Alexandria, VA 22314 *Tel:* 703-838-1650, pg 520

Arden Press Inc, PO Box 418, Denver, CO 80201-0418 *Tel:* 303-697-6766 *Fax:* 303-697-3443 *E-mail:* ardenpress@msn.com, pg 21

Ardent Media Inc, 522 E 82 St, Suite 1, New York, NY 10028 *Tel:* 212-861-1501 *Fax:* 212-861-0998 *E-mail:* ivyboxer@aol.com; ardentmedia@hotmail.com, pg 21

ARE Press, 215 67 St, Virginia Beach, VA 23451 *Tel:* 757-428-3588 *Toll Free Tel:* 800-333-4499 *Fax:* 757-491-0689 *Web Site:* www.edgarcayce.org, pg 22

Ariadne Press, 270 Goins Ct, Riverside, CA 92507 *Tel:* 951-684-9202 *Fax:* 951-779-0449 *E-mail:* ariadnepress@aol.com *Web Site:* www.ariadnebooks.com, pg 22

Ariel Press, 3854 Mason Rd, Canal Winchester, OH 43110 *Toll Free Tel:* 800-336-7769 *E-mail:* lig201@lightariel.com *Web Site:* www.lightariel.com, pg 22

Ariel Starr Productions Inc, PO Box 575, Woodstock, NY 12498 *Tel:* 201-784-9148 *E-mail:* arielstarrprod@aol.com *Web Site:* arielstarrprod.wix.com/arielstarr, pg 22

The Arion Press, The Presidio, 1802 Hays St, San Francisco, CA 94129 *Tel:* 415-668-2542 *Fax:* 415-668-2550 *E-mail:* arionpress@arionpress.com *Web Site:* www.arionpress.com, pg 22

Arizona State University, Creative Writing Program, 851 S Cady Mall, Rm 542, Tempe, AZ 85287-0302 *Tel:* 480-965-3528 *Fax:* 480-965-3451 *Web Site:* www.asu.edu/clas/english/creativewriting, pg 659

Arkansas Diamond Primary Book Award, Arkansas State Library, Suite 100, 900 W Capitol Ave, Little Rock, AR 72201-3108 *Tel:* 501-682-2860 *Fax:* 501-682-1693 *Web Site:* www.library.arkansas.gov; www.library.arkansas.gov, pg 668

Arkansas State University Graphic Communications Program, PO Box 1930, Dept of Journalism & Graphic Communications, State University, AR 72467-1930 *Tel:* 870-972-3114 *Fax:* 870-972-3321 *Web Site:* www.astate.edu, pg 659

Arkansas Writers' Conference, 13005 Misty Creek Dr, Little Rock, AR 72211 *Tel:* 501-224-5823 *Fax:* 501-224-5823 *Web Site:* www.arkansaswritersconference.org, pg 649

Arkham House Publishers Inc, PO Box 546, Sauk City, WI 53583 *Tel:* 608-643-4500 *Fax:* 608-643-5043 *E-mail:* sales@arkhamhouse.com *Web Site:* www.arkhamhouse.com, pg 22

Aro Book Publishing Co, 130 S 800 W, Salt Lake City, UT 84104-1120 *Tel:* 801-953-1760 (office); 801-637-9115 (cell) *Fax:* 801-419-0125 *E-mail:* arobook@yahoo.com *Web Site:* www.arobookpublishing.com, pg 22

Jason Aronson Inc, 4501 Forbes Blvd, Suite 200, Lanham, MD 20706 *Tel:* 301-459-3366 *Toll Free Tel:* 800-462-6420 (orders) *Fax:* 301-429-5748 *Web Site:* www.rowman.com, pg 22

Arsenal Pulp Press, 211 E Georgia St, No 202, Vancouver, BC V6A 1Z6, Canada *Tel:* 604-687-4233 *Toll Free Tel:* 888-600-PULP (600-7857) *Fax:* 604-687-4283 *E-mail:* info@arsenalpulp.com *Web Site:* www.arsenalpulp.com, pg 471

Art Image Publications, PO Box 160, Derby Line, VT 05830 *Toll Free Tel:* 800-361-2598 *Toll Free Fax:* 800-559-2598 *E-mail:* info@artimagepublications.com; customer.service@artimagepublications.com *Web Site:* www.artimagepublications.com, pg 22

The Art Institute of Chicago, 111 S Michigan Ave, Chicago, IL 60603-6404 *Tel:* 312-443-3600; 312-443-3540 (pubns) *Fax:* 312-443-1334 (pubns) *Web Site:* www.artic.edu; www.artinstituteshop.org, pg 22

Art of Living, PrimaMedia Inc, 1250 Bethlehem Pike, Suite 241, Hatfield, PA 19440 *Tel:* 215-660-5045 *E-mail:* primamedia4@yahoo.com, pg 22

ArtAge Publications, PO Box 19955, Portland, OR 97280 *Tel:* 503-246-3000 *Toll Free Tel:* 800-858-4998 *Fax:* 503-246-3006 *Web Site:* www.seniortheatre.com, pg 23

Arte Publico Press, University of Houston, Bldg 19, Rm 10, 4902 Gulf Fwy, Houston, TX 77204-2004 *Tel:* 713-743-2998 (sales) *Toll Free Tel:* 800-633-2783 *Fax:* 713-743-2847 (sales) *E-mail:* appinfo@uh.edu; bkorders@uh.edu, pg 23

Artech House Inc, 685 Canton St, Norwood, MA 02062 *Tel:* 781-769-9750 *Toll Free Tel:* 800-225-9977 *Fax:* 781-769-6334 *E-mail:* artech@artechhouse.com *Web Site:* www.artechhouse.com, pg 23

Artisan Books, 225 Varick St, New York, NY 10014-4381 *Tel:* 212-254-5900 *Toll Free Tel:* 800-722-7202 *Fax:* 212-677-6692 *E-mail:* artisaninfo@artisanbooks.com *Web Site:* www.workman.com/artisanbooks, pg 23

Artisan Bookworks, 921 S Third Ave, No 8, Sequim, WA 98382 *Tel:* 425-954-5277 *E-mail:* books@artisanbookworks.com *Web Site:* www.artisanbookworks.com, pg 23

Artist Grants, 711 E Wells Ave, Pierre, SD 57501-3369 *Tel:* 605-773-3301 *Fax:* 605-773-5977 *E-mail:* sdac@state.sd.us *Web Site:* www.artscouncil.sd.gov/grants, pg 668

Artist-in-Residence Program, 649 rue Queen, 2nd fl, Fredericton, NB E3B 1C3, Canada *Tel:* 506-444-4444 *Toll Free Tel:* 866-460-ARTS (460-2787) *Fax:* 506-444-5543 *E-mail:* nbabcanb@artsnb.ca *Web Site:* www.artsnb.ca, pg 668

Artist Projects Grants, 417 W Roosevelt St, Phoenix, AZ 85003-1326 *Tel:* 602-771-6501 *Fax:* 602-256-0282 *E-mail:* info@azarts.gov *Web Site:* www.azarts.gov, pg 668

Artists & Writers Summer Fellowships, 435 Ellis Hollow Creek Rd, Ithaca, NY 14850 *Tel:* 607-539-3146 *E-mail:* artscolony@saltonstall.org *Web Site:* www.saltonstall.org, pg 649

Artists Associates, 4416 La Jolla Dr, Bradenton, FL 34210-3927 *Tel:* 941-756-8445, pg 583

Artists' Fellowships, 20 Jay St, 7th fl, Brooklyn, NY 11201 *Tel:* 212-366-6900 *Fax:* 212-366-1778 *E-mail:* info@nyfa.org *Web Site:* www.nyfa.org, pg 668

Arts & Letters Awards, 633 W 155 St, New York, NY 10032 *Tel:* 212-368-5900 *Fax:* 212-491-4615 *E-mail:* academy@artsandletters.org *Web Site:* www.artsandletters.org, pg 668

Arts Scholarships, 649 rue Queen, 2nd fl, Fredericton, NB E3B 1C3, Canada *Tel:* 506-444-4444 *Toll Free Tel:* 866-460-ARTS (460-2787) *Fax:* 506-444-5543 *E-mail:* nbabcanb@artsnb.ca *Web Site:* www.artsnb.ca, pg 668

Artworks Illustration, PO Box 453, New York, NY 10156 *Tel:* 212-239-4946 *E-mail:* artworksillustration@earthlink.net *Web Site:* www.artworksillustration.com, pg 583

ASCD, 1703 N Beauregard St, Alexandria, VA 22311-1714 *Tel:* 703-578-9600 *Toll Free Tel:* 800-933-2723 *Fax:* 703-575-5400 *E-mail:* member@ascd.org *Web Site:* www.ascd.org, pg 23

Ascend Books LLC, 12710 Pflumm Rd, Suite 200, Olathe, KS 66062 *Tel:* 913-948-5500 *Web Site:* www.ascendbooks.com, pg 23

Ascension Press, PO Box 1990, West Chester, PA 19380 *Tel:* 610-696-7795 (ext 207, edit); 484-875-4550 (admin) *Toll Free Tel:* 800-376-0520 (sales & cust serv) *E-mail:* info@ascensionpress.com *Web Site:* ascensionpress.com, pg 24

ASCP Press, 33 W Monroe St, Suite 1600, Chicago, IL 60603 *Tel:* 312-541-4999 *Toll Free Tel:* 800-267-2727 *Fax:* 312-541-4998 *Web Site:* www.ascp.org, pg 24

ASCSA Publications, American School of Classical Studies at Athens, 6-8 Charlton St, Princeton, NJ 08540-5232 *Tel:* 609-683-0800 *Fax:* 609-924-0578 *Web Site:* www.ascsa.edu.gr/publications, pg 24

ASET - The Neurodiagnostic Society, 402 E Bannister Rd, Suite A, Kansas City, KS 64131-3019 *Tel:* 816-931-1120 *Fax:* 816-931-1145 *E-mail:* info@aset.org *Web Site:* www.aset.org, pg 24

ASF Translation Awards, Scandinavia House, 58 Park Ave, New York, NY 10016 *Tel:* 212-879-9779 *Fax:* 212-686-2115 *E-mail:* grants@amscan.org *Web Site:* www.amscan.org, pg 668

Ash Tree Publishing, PO Box 64, Woodstock, NY 12498 *Tel:* 845-246-8081 *Fax:* 845-246-8081 *E-mail:* info@ashtreepublishing.com *Web Site:* www.ashtreepublishing.com, pg 24

Ashgate Publishing Co, 110 Cherry St, Suite 3-1, Burlington, VT 05401-3818 *Tel:* 802-865-7641 *Toll Free Tel:* 800-535-9544 *Fax:* 802-865-7847 *E-mail:* ashgate.online@ashgate.com *Web Site:* www.ashgate.com, pg 24

Ashland Creek Press, 2305 Ashland St, Suite C417, Ashland, OR 97520 *Tel:* 760-300-3620 *E-mail:* editors@ashlandcreekpress.com *Web Site:* www.ashlandcreekpress.com, pg 24

Ashland Poetry Press, Ashland University, 401 College Ave, Ashland, OH 44805 *Tel:* 419-289-5957 *Fax:* 419-289-5255 *E-mail:* app@ashland.edu *Web Site:* www.ashland.edu/aupoetry, pg 24

Asian American Literary Awards, 110-112 W 27 St, Suite 600, New York, NY 10001 *Tel:* 212-494-0061 *E-mail:* desk@aaww.org *Web Site:* aaww.org/curation/asian-american-literary-awards, pg 669

Asian American Writers' Workshop, 110-112 W 27 St, Suite 600, New York, NY 10001 *Tel:* 212-494-0061 *E-mail:* desk@aaww.org *Web Site:* aaww.org, pg 597

ASIS International, 1625 Prince St, Alexandria, VA 22314 *Tel:* 703-519-6200 *Fax:* 703-519-6299 *E-mail:* asis@asisonline.org *Web Site:* www.asisonline.org, pg 25

ASJA Freelance Writer Search, 355 Lexington Ave, 15th fl, New York, NY 10017 *Tel:* 212-997-0947 *E-mail:* asjaoffice@asja.org *Web Site:* www.freelancewritersearch.com, pg 520

Aslan Publishing, 857 Post Rd, Suite 302, Fairfield, CT 06824 *Tel:* 203-372-0300; 203-374-6224 *Fax:* 203-374-4766 *E-mail:* information@aslanpublishing.com *Web Site:* www.aslanpublishing.com, pg 25

ASM International, 9639 Kinsman Rd, Materials Park, OH 44073-0002 *Tel:* 440-338-5151 *Toll Free Tel:* 800-336-5152; 800-368-9800 (Europe) *Fax:* 440-338-4634 *E-mail:* memberservicecenter@asminternational.org *Web Site:* asmcommunity.asminternational.org, pg 25

ASM Press, 1752 "N" St NW, Washington, DC 20036-2904 *Tel:* 202-737-3600 *Toll Free Tel:* 800-546-2416 *Fax:* 202-942-9342 *E-mail:* books@asmusa.org *Web Site:* estore.asm.org, pg 25

Aspatore Books, 610 Opperman Dr, Eagan, MN 55123 *Tel:* 651-687-7000 *Toll Free Tel:* 866-ASPATORE (277-2867); 888-728-7677; 800-328-4880 *E-mail:* customerservice@thomsonreuters.com *Web Site:* legalsolutions.thomsonreuters.com; www.aspatore.com, pg 25

Aspen Summer Words Writing Retreat & Literary Festival, 110 E Hallam St, Suite 116, Aspen, CO 81611 *Tel:* 970-925-3122 *Fax:* 970-920-5700 *E-mail:* awfinfo@aspenwriters.org *Web Site:* www.aspenwriters.org, pg 649

Aspen Writers' Foundation, 110 E Hallam St, Suite 116, Aspen, CO 81611 *Tel:* 970-925-3122 *Fax:* 970-920-5700 *E-mail:* awfinfo@aspenwriters.org *Web Site:* www.aspenwriters.org, pg 597

Associated Business Writers of America Inc, 10940 S Parker Rd, Suite 508, Parker, CO 80134 *Tel:* 303-841-0246 *E-mail:* natlwritersassn@hotmail.com *Web Site:* www.nationalwriters.com, pg 597

Associated Editors, 27 W 96 St, New York, NY 10025 *Tel:* 212-662-9703, pg 520

Associated Press Broadcast, 1100 13 St NW, Suite 700, Washington, DC 20005 *Tel:* 202-641-9000 *Toll Free Tel:* 800-821-4747 *Fax:* 202-370-2710 *E-mail:* info@ap.org *Web Site:* www.ap.org, pg 597

Associated University Presses, 10 Schalks Crossing Rd, Suite 501-330, Plainsboro, NJ 08536 *Tel:* 609-269-8094 *Fax:* 609-269-8096 *E-mail:* aup440@aol.com, pg 25

Association des Libraires du Quebec (ALQ), 407 St-Laurent, bureau 801, Montreal, QC H2Y 2Y5, Canada *Tel:* 514-526-3349 *Fax:* 514-526-3340 *E-mail:* info@alq.qc.ca *Web Site:* www.alq.qc.ca, pg 597

Association for Computing Machinery, 2 Penn Plaza, Suite 701, New York, NY 10121-0701 *Tel:* 212-626-0500 *Toll Free Tel:* 800-342-6626 *Fax:* 212-944-1318 *E-mail:* acmhelp@acm.org *Web Site:* www.acm.org, pg 25

Association for Information & Image Management International (AIIM), 1100 Wayne Ave, Suite 1100, Silver Spring, MD 20910 *Tel:* 301-587-8202 *Toll Free Tel:* 800-477-2446 *Fax:* 301-587-2711 *E-mail:* aiim@aiim.org; info@aiim.org *Web Site:* www.aiim.org, pg 597

Association for Information Science & Technology (ASIS&T), 8555 16 St, Suite 850, Silver Spring, MD 20910 *Tel:* 301-495-0900 *Fax:* 301-495-0810 *E-mail:* asis@asis.org *Web Site:* www.asis.org, pg 25, 597

Association for Talent Development (ATD), 1640 King St, Box 1443, Alexandria, VA 22313-1443 *Tel:* 703-683-8100 *Toll Free Tel:* 800-628-2783 *Fax:* 703-299-8723; 703-683-1523 (cust care) *E-mail:* customercare@td.org *Web Site:* www.astd.org; www.td.org, pg 25

The Association for Women In Communications, 3337 Duke St, Alexandria, VA 22314 *Tel:* 703-370-7436 *Fax:* 703-342-4311 *E-mail:* info@womcom.org *Web Site:* www.womcom.org, pg 649

Association Media & Publishing (AM&P), 12100 Sunset Hills Rd, Suite 130, Reston, VA 20190 *Tel:* 703-234-4063 *Fax:* 703-435-4390 *E-mail:* info@associationmediaandpublishing.org *Web Site:* associationmediaandpublishing.org, pg 598

Association Nationale des Editeurs de Livres, 2514 boul Rosemont, Montreal, QC H1Y 1K4, Canada *Tel:* 514-273-8130 *Toll Free Tel:* 866-900-ANEL (900-2635) *E-mail:* info@anel.qc.ca *Web Site:* www.anel.qc.ca, pg 598

Association of American Editorial Cartoonists, 3899 N Front St, Harrisburg, PA 17110 *Tel:* 717-703-3003 *Fax:* 717-703-3008 *E-mail:* aaec@pa-news.org *Web Site:* www.editorialcartoonists.com, pg 598

Association of American Publishers (AAP), 71 Fifth Ave, 2nd fl, New York, NY 10003-3004 *Tel:* 212-255-0200 *Fax:* 212-255-7007 *E-mail:* info@publishers.org *Web Site:* publishers.org, pg 598

Association of American University Presses (AAUP), 28 W 36 St, Suite 602, New York, NY 10018 *Tel:* 212-989-1010 *Fax:* 212-989-0275 *E-mail:* info@aaupnet.org *Web Site:* www.aaupnet.org, pg 598

Association of Authors' Representatives Inc, 302A W 12 St, No 122, New York, NY 10014 *Tel:* 212-840-5770 *E-mail:* administrator@aaronline.org *Web Site:* www.aaronline.org, pg 598

Association of Book Publishers of British Columbia, 600-402 W Pender St, Vancouver, BC V6B 1T6, Canada *Tel:* 604-684-0228 *Fax:* 604-684-5788 *E-mail:* admin@books.bc.ca *Web Site:* www.books.bc.ca, pg 598

Association of Canadian Publishers (ACP), 174 Spadina Ave, Suite 306, Toronto, ON M5T 2C2, Canada *Tel:* 416-487-6116 *Fax:* 416-487-8815 *E-mail:* admin@canbook.org *Web Site:* publishers.ca, pg 598

Association of Canadian University Presses, 10 St Mary St, Suite 700, Toronto, ON M4Y 2W8, Canada *Tel:* 416-978-2239 ext 237 *Fax:* 416-978-4738 *Web Site:* www.acup.ca, pg 598

Association of Catholic Publishers Inc, 4725 Dorsey Hall Dr, Suite A, PMB 709, Elliott City, MD 21042 *Tel:* 410-988-2926 *Fax:* 410-571-4946 *Web Site:* www.catholicsread.org; www.catholicpublishers.org; www.midatlanticcongress.org, pg 598

Association of College & Research Libraries (ACRL), 50 E Huron St, Chicago, IL 60611 *Tel:* 312-280-2523 *Toll Free Tel:* 800-545-2433 (ext 2523) *Fax:* 312-280-2520 *E-mail:* acrl@ala.org *Web Site:* www.ala.org/acrl, pg 26

Association of College & University Printers (ACUP), PO Box 285, Carrabelle, FL 32322 *Tel:* 850-570-5241 *Web Site:* www.acup-edu.org, pg 599

The Association of English-Language Publishers of Quebec-AELAQ (Association des Editeurs de Langue Anglaise du Quebec), Atwater Library, 1200 Atwater Ave, Suite 3, Westmount, QC H3Z 1X4, Canada *Tel:* 514-932-5633 *E-mail:* admin@aelaq.org *Web Site:* aelaq.org, pg 599

Association of Free Community Papers (AFCP), 7445 Morgan Rd, Suite 103, Liverpool, NY 13090 *Toll Free Tel:* 877-203-2327 *Fax:* 781-459-7770 *E-mail:* afcp@afcp.org *Web Site:* www.afcp.org, pg 599

Association of Jewish Libraries (AJL) Inc, PO Box 1118, Teaneck, NJ 07666 *Tel:* 201-371-3255 *E-mail:* info@jewishlibraries.org *Web Site:* www.jewishlibraries.org, pg 599

Association of Manitoba Book Publishers, 100 Arthur St, Suite 404, Winnipeg, MB R3B 1H3, Canada *Tel:* 204-947-3335 *Fax:* 204-956-4689 *E-mail:* ambp@mts.net *Web Site:* ambp.ca, pg 599

The Association of Medical Illustrators (AMI), 201 E Main St, Suite 1405, Lexington, KY 40507 *Toll Free Tel:* 866-393-4264 *Fax:* 859-514-9166 *E-mail:* hq@ami.org *Web Site:* www.ami.org, pg 599

Association of Opinion Journalists (AOJ), 2301 Vanderbilt Place, VU Sta B 351669, Nashville, TN 37235-1669 *E-mail:* opinionjounalists@gmail.com *Web Site:* www.opinionjournalists.org, pg 599

Association of Publishers for Special Sales (APSS), PO Box 715, Avon, CT 06001-0715 *Tel:* 860-675-1344 *Web Site:* www.spannet.org, pg 599

Association of Research Libraries, 21 Dupont Circle NW, Suite 800, Washington, DC 20036 *Tel:* 202-296-2296 *Fax:* 202-872-0884 *E-mail:* arlhq@arl.org *Web Site:* www.arl.org, pg 26

Association of School Business Officials International, 11401 N Shore Dr, Reston, VA 20190 *Tel:* 703-478-0405 *Toll Free Tel:* 866-682-2729 *Fax:* 703-708-7060 *E-mail:* asboreq@asbointl.org; asbosba@asbointl.org *Web Site:* www.asbointl.org, pg 26

Association of Writers & Writing Programs (AWP), George Mason University, 4400 University Dr, MSN 1E3, Fairfax, VA 22030 *Tel:* 703-993-4301 *Fax:* 703-993-4302 *E-mail:* awp@awpwriter.org *Web Site:* www.awpwriter.org, pg 599

Association pour l'Avancement des Sciences et des Techniques de la Documentation, 2065 rue Parthenais, Bureau 387, Montreal, QC H2K 3T1, Canada *Tel:* 514-281-5012 *Fax:* 514-281-8219 *E-mail:* info@asted.org *Web Site:* www.asted.org, pg 472, 599, 649

Asta Publications LLC, PO Box 1735, Stockbridge, GA 30281 *Tel:* 678-814-1320 *Toll Free Tel:* 800-482-4190 *Fax:* 678-814-1370 *E-mail:* info@astapublications.com *Web Site:* www.astapublications.com, pg 26

ASTM International, 100 Barr Harbor Dr, West Conshohocken, PA 19428-2959 *Tel:* 610-832-9500; 610-832-9585 (intl) *Toll Free Tel:* 877-909-2786 (sales & cust support) *Fax:* 610-832-9555 *E-mail:* service@astm.org *Web Site:* www.astm.org, pg 26

Astor Indexers, 256 Blue Ridge Dr, Canadensis, PA 18325 *Tel:* 570-595-2336; 570-534-8951 (cell), pg 520

Astragal Press, 5995 149 St W, Suite 105, Apple Valley, MN 55124 *Tel:* 952-469-6699 *Toll Free Tel:* 866-543-3045 *Fax:* 952-469-1968 *Toll Free Fax:* 800-330-6232 *E-mail:* info@finneyco.com *Web Site:* www.astragalpress.com, pg 26

The Astronomical Society of the Pacific, 390 Ashton Ave, San Francisco, CA 94112 *Tel:* 415-337-1100 *Toll Free Tel:* 800-335-2624 *Fax:* 415-337-5205 *Web Site:* www.astrosociety.org, pg 26

Athabasca University Press, Edmonton Learning Ctr, Peace Hills Trust Tower, 1200, 10011-109 St, Edmonton, AB T5J 3S8, Canada *Tel:* 780-497-3412 *Fax:* 780-421-3298 *E-mail:* aupress@athabascau.ca *Web Site:* www.aupress.ca, pg 472

Athenaeum of Philadelphia Literary Award, 219 S Sixth St, Philadelphia, PA 19106 *Tel:* 215-925-2688 *Fax:* 215-925-3755 *Web Site:* www.philaathenaeum.org, pg 669

Athletic Guide Publishing, PO Box 1050, Flagler Beach, FL 32136 *Tel:* 386-439-2050 *Toll Free Tel:* 800-255-1050 *E-mail:* flaglernet@gmail.com *Web Site:* www.athleticguidepublishing.com, pg 26

Atlantic Center for the Arts Artists-in-Residence Program, 1414 Art Center Ave, New Smyrna Beach, FL 32168 *Tel:* 386-427-6975 *Toll Free Tel:* 800-393-6975 *Fax:* 386-427-5669 *E-mail:* program@atlanticcenterforthearts.org *Web Site:* www.atlanticcenterforthearts.org, pg 649

Atlantic Law Book Co, 22 Grassmere Ave, West Hartford, CT 06110-1215 *Tel:* 860-231-9300 *Toll Free Tel:* 800-259-5534 *Fax:* 860-231-9242 *E-mail:* atlanticlawbooks@aol.com *Web Site:* www.atlanticlawbooks.com, pg 26

Atlantic Poetry Prize, 1113 Marginal Rd, Halifax, NS B3H 4P7, Canada *Tel:* 902-423-8116 *Fax:* 902-422-0881 *E-mail:* contact@writers.ns.ca *Web Site:* writers.ns.ca, pg 669

Atlantic Public Art Funders (APAF) Creative Residency, 649 rue Queen, 2nd fl, Fredericton, NB E3B 1C3, Canada *Tel:* 506-444-4444 *Toll Free Tel:* 866-460-ARTS (460-2787) *Fax:* 506-444-5543 *E-mail:* nbabcanb@artsnb.ca *Web Site:* www.artsnb.ca, pg 669

Atlantic Publishing Group Inc, 1405 SW Sixth Ave, Ocala, FL 34471 *Tel:* 352-622-1825 *Toll Free Tel:* 800-814-1132 *Fax:* 352-622-1875 *E-mail:* sales@atlantic-pub.com *Web Site:* www.atlantic-pub.com, pg 26

Atria Books, 1230 Avenue of the Americas, New York, NY 10020 *Tel:* 212-698-7000 *Fax:* 212-698-7007 *Web Site:* www.simonandschuster.com, pg 26

Atwood Publishing, PO Box 3185, Madison, WI 53704 *Tel:* 608-242-7101 *Toll Free Tel:* 888-242-7101 *Fax:* 608-242-7102 *E-mail:* customerservice@atwoodpublishing.com *Web Site:* www.atwoodpublishing.com, pg 27

Audrey Owen, 494 Eaglecrest Dr, Gibsons, BC V0N 1V8, Canada *E-mail:* editor@writershelper.com *Web Site:* www.writershelper.com, pg 521

Augsburg Fortress Publishers, Publishing House of the Evangelical Lutheran Church in America, 510 Marquette Ave S, Minneapolis, MN 55402 *Tel:* 612-330-3300 *Toll Free Tel:* 800-426-0115 (ext 639, subns); 800-328-4648 (orders) *Fax:* 612-330-3455 *E-mail:* info@augsburgfortress.org; copyright@augsburgfortress.org (reprint permission requests); customercare@augsburgfortress.org *Web Site:* www.augsburgfortress.org, pg 27

August House Inc, 3500 Piedmont Rd NE, Suite 310, Atlanta, GA 30305 *Tel:* 404-442-4420 *Toll Free Tel:* 800-284-8784 *Fax:* 404-442-4435 *E-mail:* ahinfo@augusthouse.com *Web Site:* www.augusthouse.com, pg 27

Aum Publications, 86-10 Parsons Blvd, Jamaica, NY 11432-3314 *Tel:* 347-744-3199, pg 27

Barefoot Books, 2067 Massachusetts Ave, 5th fl, Cambridge, MA 02140 *Tel:* 617-576-0660 *Toll Free Tel:* 866-215-1756 (cust serv); 866-417-2369 (orders) *Fax:* 617-576-0049 *E-mail:* help@barefootbooks.com *Web Site:* www.barefootbooks.com, pg 30

The Barnabas Agency, PO Box 3113, Corsicana, TX 75110-3113 *Toll Free Tel:* 800-927-0517 *E-mail:* info@barnabasagency.com *Web Site:* www.barnabasagency.com, pg 587

Barnes & Noble Writers for Writers Award, 90 Broad St, Suite 2100, New York, NY 10004 *Tel:* 212-226-3586 *Fax:* 212-226-3963 *E-mail:* admin@pw.org *Web Site:* www.pw.org, pg 670

Kathleen Barnes, 238 W Fourth St, Suite 3-C, New York, NY 10014 *Tel:* 212-924-8084 *E-mail:* kbarnes@compasscommunications.org, pg 521

Barnhardt & Ashe Publishing Inc, 444 Brickell Ave, Suite 51, PMB 432, Miami, FL 33131 *Toll Free Tel:* 800-283-6360 (orders) *E-mail:* barnhardtashe@aol.com *Web Site:* barnhardtashepublishing.com, pg 31

Baror International Inc, PO Box 868, Armonk, NY 10504-0868 *Tel:* 914-273-9199 *Fax:* 914-273-5058 *Web Site:* www.barorint.com, pg 542

Barranca Press, 1450 Couse St, No 10, Taos, NM 87571 *Tel:* 575-613-1026 *E-mail:* editor@barrancapress.com *Web Site:* www.barrancapress.com, pg 31

Loretta Barrett Books Inc, 220 E 23 St, 11th fl, New York, NY 10010 *Tel:* 212-242-3420 *E-mail:* query@lorettabarrettbooks.com *Web Site:* www.lorettabarrettbooks.com, pg 542

Melinda Barrett, 37915 Sundance Dr, Coarsegold, CA 93614 *Tel:* 559-641-0944 *E-mail:* mbarrett_3@netzero.net, pg 521

Barricade Books Inc, 2037 LeMoine Ave, Fort Lee, NJ 07024 *Tel:* 201-944-7600 *E-mail:* customerservice@barricadebooks.com *Web Site:* www.barricadebooks.com, pg 31

Barringer Publishing, 3259 Sundance Circle, Naples, FL 34109 *Tel:* 239-514-7364 *E-mail:* schlesadv@gmail.com *Web Site:* www.barringerpublishing.com, pg 31

Barron's Educational Series Inc, 250 Wireless Blvd, Hauppauge, NY 11788 *Tel:* 631-434-3311 *Toll Free Tel:* 800-645-3476 *Fax:* 631-434-3723 *E-mail:* barrons@barronseduc.com *Web Site:* www.barronseduc.com, pg 31

James P Barry Ohioana Award for Editorial Excellence, 274 E First Ave, Suite 300, Columbus, OH 43201 *Tel:* 614-466-3831 *Fax:* 614-728-6974 *E-mail:* ohioana@ohioana.org *Web Site:* www.ohioana.org, pg 670

Barrytown/Station Hill Press, 120 Station Hill Rd, Barrytown, NY 12507 *Tel:* 845-758-5293 *E-mail:* publishers@stationhill.org *Web Site:* www.stationhill.org, pg 31

Diana Barth, 535 W 51 St, Suite 3-A, New York, NY 10019 *Tel:* 212-307-5465 *E-mail:* diabarth@juno.com, pg 521

Anita Bartholomew, 8535 SE 92 Ave, Portland, OR 97266 *Tel:* 941-358-0495 *E-mail:* anita@anitabartholomew.com *Web Site:* www.anitabartholomew.com, pg 521

Bartleby Press, 8926 Baltimore St, No 858, Savage, MD 20763 *Tel:* 301-725-3906 *Toll Free Tel:* 800-953-9929 *Fax:* 667-309-6993 *E-mail:* inquiries@bartlebythepublisher.com *Web Site:* www.bartlebythepublisher.com, pg 31

Basic Books, 250 W 57 St, 15th fl, New York, NY 10107 *Tel:* 212-340-8164; 212-340-8136 *Fax:* 212-340-8135 *E-mail:* perseus.promos@perseusbooks.com *Web Site:* www.basicbooks.com; perseusbooks.com, pg 31

Basic Health Publications Inc, 28812 Top of the World Dr, Laguna Beach, CA 92651 *Tel:* 949-715-7327 *Toll Free Tel:* 800-575-8890 (orders) *Fax:* 949-715-7328 *E-mail:* info@basichealthpub.com *Web Site:* www.basichealthpub.com, pg 32

Baskerville Publishers Poetry Award, Texas Christian University, Dept of English, TCU Box 297270, Fort Worth, TX 76129 *Tel:* 817-257-5907 *Fax:* 817-257-7709 *E-mail:* descant@tcu.edu *Web Site:* www.descant.tcu.edu, pg 670

The Mildred L Batchelder Award, 50 E Huron St, Chicago, IL 60611-2795 *Tel:* 312-280-2163 *Toll Free Tel:* 800-545-2433 *Fax:* 312-440-9374 *E-mail:* alsc@ala.org *Web Site:* www.ala.org/alsc, pg 670

Mark E Battersby, PO Box 527, Ardmore, PA 19003 *Tel:* 610-924-9157 *Fax:* 610-924-9159 *E-mail:* mebatt12@earthlink.net, pg 521

Bay Tree Publishing LLC, 1400 Pinnacle Ct, Suite 406, Point Richmond, CA 94801 *Tel:* 510-236-1475 *Toll Free Fax:* 866-552-7329 *Web Site:* www.baytreepublish.com, pg 32

Bayeux Arts Inc, 119 Stratton Crescent SW, Calgary, AB T3H 1T7, Canada *Tel:* 403-249-2477 *E-mail:* mail@bayeux.com *Web Site:* bayeux.com, pg 472

Baylor University Press, Baylor University, One Bear Place, Waco, TX 76798-7363 *Tel:* 254-710-3164 *Fax:* 254-710-3440 *Web Site:* www.baylorpress.com, pg 32

Baylor University, Writing Program, One Bear Place, Unit 97404, Waco, TX 76798-7404 *Tel:* 254-710-1768 *Fax:* 254-710-3894 *Web Site:* www.baylor.edu, pg 659

Baywood Publishing Co Inc, 26 Austin Ave, Amityville, NY 11701 *Tel:* 631-691-1270 *Toll Free Tel:* 800-638-7819 *Fax:* 631-691-1770 *E-mail:* baywood@baywood.com *Web Site:* www.baywood.com, pg 32

The BC Book Prizes, 207 W Hastings St, Suite 901, Vancouver, BC V6B 1H7, Canada *Tel:* 604-687-2405 *Fax:* 604-687-2435 *E-mail:* info@bcbookprizes.ca *Web Site:* www.bcbookprizes.ca, pg 670

BCFL, 4806 Martinique Way, Naples, FL 34119 *Tel:* 908-447-3553 *Fax:* 239-596-8611 *E-mail:* BCFLGroup@gmail.com *Web Site:* judgingfloraldesign.com, pg 507

BCHF Historial Writing Competition, PO Box 5254, Sta B, Victoria, BC V8R 6N4, Canada *E-mail:* writing@bchistory.ca *Web Site:* www.bchistory.ca, pg 670

Beach Lloyd Publishers LLC, 40 Cabot Dr, Wayne, PA 19087-5619 *Tel:* 610-407-9107 *Fax:* 775-254-0633 *E-mail:* beachlloyd@erols.com *Web Site:* www.beachlloyd.com, pg 32

Beacon Hill Press of Kansas City, PO Box 419527, Kansas City, MO 64141-6527 *Tel:* 816-931-1900 *Toll Free Tel:* 800-877-0700 (cust serv) *Fax:* 816-753-4071 *Web Site:* www.beaconhillbooks.com, pg 32

Beacon Press, 24 Farnsworth St, Boston, MA 02210-1409 *Tel:* 617-742-2110 *Fax:* 617-723-3097; 617-742-2290 *Web Site:* www.beacon.org, pg 32

Bear & Co Inc, One Park St, Rochester, VT 05767 *Tel:* 802-767-3174 *Toll Free Tel:* 800-932-3277 *Fax:* 802-767-3726 *E-mail:* customerservice@InnerTraditions.com *Web Site:* InnerTraditions.com, pg 33

James Beard Foundation Book Awards, Office of Awards, 6 W 18 St, 10th fl, New York, NY 10011 *Tel:* 212-627-1111 (ext 563) *Web Site:* www.jamesbeard.org/awards, pg 670

Bearport Publishing Co Inc, 45 W 21 St, Suite 3B, New York, NY 10010 *Tel:* 212-337-8577 *Toll Free Tel:* 877-337-8577 *Fax:* 212-337-8557 *Toll Free Fax:* 866-337-8557 *E-mail:* service@bearportpublishing.com; info@bearportpublishing.com *Web Site:* www.bearportpublishing.com, pg 33

Beaufort Books, 27 W 20 St, Suite 1102, New York, NY 10011 *Tel:* 212-727-0222 *Fax:* 212-727-0195 *E-mail:* info@beaufortbooks.com *Web Site:* www.beaufortbooks.com, pg 33

Beaver Wood Associates, 655 Alstead Center Rd, Alstead, NH 03602 *Tel:* 603-835-7900 *Web Site:* www.beaverwood.com, pg 521

Beaver's Pond Press Inc, 7108 Ohms Lane, Edina, MN 55439 *Tel:* 952-829-8818 *E-mail:* info@beaverspondpress.com *Web Site:* www.beaverspondpress.com, pg 33

Bedford/St Martin's, 75 Arlington St, Boston, MA 02116 *Tel:* 617-399-4000 *Toll Free Tel:* 800-779-7440 *Fax:* 617-426-8582 *Web Site:* www.bedfordstmartins.com, pg 33

Beekman Books Inc, 300 Old All Angels Hill Rd, Wappingers Falls, NY 12590 *Tel:* 845-297-2690 *Fax:* 845-297-1002 *E-mail:* beekmanbooks@yahoo.com *Web Site:* www.beekmanbooks.com, pg 33

George Louis Beer Prize, 400 "A" St SE, Washington, DC 20003 *Tel:* 202-544-2422 *Fax:* 202-544-8307 *E-mail:* awards@historians.org *Web Site:* www.historians.org, pg 671

Before Columbus Foundation, The Raymond House, 655 13 St, Suite 302, Oakland, CA 94612 *Tel:* 510-268-9775 *E-mail:* info@beforecolumbusfoundation.com *Web Site:* www.beforecolumbusfoundation.com, pg 600

Begell House Inc Publishers, 50 North St, Danbury, CT 06810 *Tel:* 203-456-6161 *Fax:* 203-456-6167 *E-mail:* orders@begellhouse.com *Web Site:* www.begellhouse.com, pg 33

Behrman House Inc, 11 Edison Place, Springfield, NJ 07081 *Tel:* 973-379-7200 *Toll Free Tel:* 800-221-2755 *Fax:* 973-379-7280 *E-mail:* behrmanhouse@gmail.com; customersupport@behrmanhouse.com *Web Site:* www.behrmanhouse.com, pg 33

Frederic C Beil Publisher Inc, 609 Whitaker St, Savannah, GA 31401 *Tel:* 912-233-2446 *E-mail:* editor@beil.com *Web Site:* www.beil.com, pg 34

Beliveau Editeur, 920, rue Jean-Neveu, Longueuil, QC J4G 2M1, Canada *Tel:* 450-679-1933; 514-253-0403 *Fax:* 450-679-6648 *E-mail:* info@beliveauediteur.com *Web Site:* www.beliveauediteur.com, pg 472

Bell Springs Publishing, PO Box 1240, Willits, CA 95490-1240 *Tel:* 707-459-6372 *E-mail:* publisher@bellsprings.com *Web Site:* bellsprings.com; aboutpinball.com, pg 34

Bella Books, PO Box 10543, Tallahassee, FL 32302 *Tel:* 850-576-2370 *Toll Free Tel:* 800-729-4992 *Fax:* 850-576-3498 *E-mail:* info@bellabooks.com; orders@bellabooks.com; ebooks@bellabooks.com *Web Site:* www.bellabooks.com, pg 34

Bellagio Press, 5501 Kincross Lane, Charlotte, NC 28277 *Web Site:* bellagiopress.com, pg 34

BelleBooks, PO Box 300921, Memphis, TN 38130 *Tel:* 901-344-9024 *Fax:* 901-344-9068 *E-mail:* bellebooks@bellebooks.com, pg 34

Bellerophon Books, PO Box 21307, Santa Barbara, CA 93121-1307 *Tel:* 805-965-7034 *Toll Free Tel:* 800-253-9943 *Fax:* 805-965-8286 *E-mail:* sales.bellerophon@gmail.com *Web Site:* www.bellerophonbooks.com, pg 34

Belltown Media, PO Box 980985, Houston, TX 77098 *Tel:* 713-344-1956 *Fax:* 713-583-7956 *E-mail:* subs@linuxjournal.com *Web Site:* www.belltownmedia.com, pg 34

The Pura Belpre Award, 50 E Huron St, Chicago, IL 60611-2795 *Tel:* 312-280-2163 *Toll Free Tel:* 800-545-2433 *Fax:* 312-440-9374 *E-mail:* alsc@ala.org *Web Site:* www.ala.org/alsc, pg 671

Ben Yehuda Press, 122 Ayers Ct, No 1B, Teaneck, NJ 07666 *Tel:* 201-836-0180 *Fax:* 201-917-1278 *E-mail:* orders@benyehudapress.com; yudel@benyehudapress.com *Web Site:* www.benyehudapress.com, pg 34

BenBella Books Inc, 10300 N Central Expwy, Suite 400, Dallas, TX 75231 *Tel:* 214-750-3600 *Fax:* 214-750-3645 *E-mail:* feedback@benbellabooks.com *Web Site:* www.benbellabooks.com; www.smartpopbooks.com, pg 34

R James Bender Publishing, PO Box 23456, San Jose, CA 95153-3456 *Tel:* 408-225-5777 *Fax:* 408-225-4739 *Web Site:* www.bender-publishing.com, pg 34

Birch Brook Press, PO Box 81, Delhi, NY 13753-0081 *Tel:* 607-746-7453 (book sales & prodn) *Fax:* 607-746-7453 *E-mail:* birchbrook@copper.net *Web Site:* www.birchbrookpress.info, pg 37

George T Bisel Co Inc, 710 S Washington Sq, Philadelphia, PA 19106-3519 *Tel:* 215-922-5760 *Toll Free Tel:* 800-247-3526 *Fax:* 215-922-2235 *E-mail:* gbisel@bisel.com *Web Site:* www.bisel.com, pg 37

Bisk Education, 9417 Princess Palm Ave, Suite 400, Tampa, FL 33619 *Tel:* 813-621-6200 *Toll Free Tel:* 800-280-9718 (cust serv) *E-mail:* customerservice@bisk.com *Web Site:* www.bisk.com, pg 37

Bitingduck Press LLC, 1262 Sunnyoaks Circle, Altadena, CA 91001 *Tel:* 626-679-2494; 626-507-8033 *E-mail:* notifications@bitingduckpress.com *Web Site:* bitingduckpress.com, pg 37

BizBest Media Corp, 860 Via de la Paz, Suite E3B, Pacific Palisades, CA 90272 *E-mail:* press@bizbest.com *Web Site:* www.bizbest.com, pg 38

BJU Press, 1700 Wade Hampton Blvd, Greenville, SC 29614-0062 *Tel:* 864-770-1317; 864-242-5100 *Toll Free Tel:* 800-845-5731 *E-mail:* bjupinfo@bjupress.com *Web Site:* www.bjupress.com, pg 38

BkMk Press - University of Missouri-Kansas City, University House, 5101 Rockhill Rd, Kansas City, MO 64110-2499 *Tel:* 816-235-2558 *Fax:* 816-235-2611 *E-mail:* bkmk@umkc.edu *Web Site:* www.umkc.edu/bkmk, pg 38

Black Classic Press, 3921 Vero Rd, Suite F, Baltimore, MD 21203-3414 *Tel:* 410-242-6954 *Toll Free Tel:* 800-476-8870 *Fax:* 410-242-6959 *E-mail:* email@blackclassicbooks.com; blackclassicpress@yahoo.com *Web Site:* www.blackclassicbooks.com; www.bcpdigital.com, pg 38

David Black Agency, 335 Adams St, 27th fl, Suite 2707, Brooklyn, NY 11201 *Tel:* 718-852-5500 *Fax:* 718-852-5539 *Web Site:* www.davidblackagency.com, pg 542

Black Dome Press Corp, 649 Delaware Ave, Delmar, NY 12054 *Tel:* 518-439-6512 *Fax:* 518-439-1309 *E-mail:* blackdomep@aol.com *Web Site:* www.blackdomepress.com, pg 38

Black Heron Press, PO Box 13396, Mill Creek, WA 98082-1396 *Tel:* 425-355-4929 *Fax:* 425-355-4929 *Web Site:* blackheronpress.com, pg 38

Irma S & James H Black Award, 610 W 112 St, New York, NY 10025 *Tel:* 212-875-4458 *Fax:* 212-875-4558 *E-mail:* ccl@bankstreet.edu *Web Site:* www.bankstreet.edu/center-childrens-literature, pg 672

Black Mountain Press, PO Box 9907, Asheville, NC 28815 *Tel:* 828-273-3332 *Web Site:* www.theblackmountainpress.com, pg 38

Black Rabbit Books, 515 N Riverfront Dr, Suite 200, Mankato, MN 56001 *Tel:* 507-388-1609 *Fax:* 507-388-1364 *E-mail:* info@blackrabbitbooks.com; orders@blackrabbitbooks.com *Web Site:* www.blackrabbitbooks.com, pg 38

Black Rose Books Ltd, CP 35788 Succ Leo Pariseau, Montreal, QC H2X 0A4, Canada *Tel:* 514-844-4076 *Toll Free Tel:* 800-565-9523 (orders) *Fax:* 514-849-1956 *Toll Free Fax:* 800-221-9985 (orders) *E-mail:* info@blackrosebooks.net *Web Site:* www.blackrosebooks.net, pg 472

Black Warrior Review Fiction, Nonfiction & Poetry Contest, Office of Student Media, University of Alabama, Tuscaloosa, AL 35486-0027 *Tel:* 205-348-4518 *Web Site:* www.bwr.ua.edu, pg 672

Christopher Blackburn, 16 Purple Sageway, Toronto, ON M2H 2Z5, Canada *Tel:* 416-491-4857 *E-mail:* cblackburn@rogers.com, pg 521

The Blackburn Press, PO Box 287, Caldwell, NJ 07006-0287 *Tel:* 973-228-7077 *Fax:* 973-228-7276 *Web Site:* www.blackburnpress.com, pg 38

John F Blair Publisher, 1406 Plaza Dr, Winston-Salem, NC 27103 *Tel:* 336-768-1374 *Toll Free Tel:* 800-222-9796 *Fax:* 336-768-9194 *Web Site:* www.blairpub.com, pg 39

Neltje Blanchan Memorial Award, 2320 Capitol Ave, Cheyenne, WY 82002 *Tel:* 307-777-5234 *Fax:* 307-777-5499 *Web Site:* wyoarts.state.wy.us, pg 672

Bleecker Street Associates Inc, 217 Thompson St, Suite 519, New York, NY 10012 *Tel:* 212-677-4492 *Fax:* 212-388-0001, pg 542

Theodore C Blegen Award, 701 William Vickers Ave, Durham, NC 27701-3162 *Tel:* 919-682-9319 *Fax:* 919-682-2349 *Web Site:* www.foresthistory.org, pg 672

Bloch Publishing Co, 10030 E W Pappy Rd, PMB 0015, Jacksonville, FL 32259 *Tel:* 904-880-7302 *Fax:* 904-880-7307 *E-mail:* info@blochpub.com *Web Site:* www.blochpub.com, pg 39

Blockbuster Plots for Writers Retreat, PO Box 1402, Capitola, CA 95010 *Tel:* 408-482-4678 *E-mail:* contact@blockbusterplots.com *Web Site:* www.blockbusterplots.com, pg 650

Blood Moon Productions Ltd, 75 Saint Marks Place, Staten Island, NY 10301-1606 *Tel:* 718-556-9410 *E-mail:* editors@bloodmoonproductions.com *Web Site:* bloodmoonproductions.com, pg 39

Bloom Ink, 3497 Bennington Ct, Bloomfield Hills, MI 48301 *Tel:* 248-291-0370 *E-mail:* info@bloomwriting.com *Web Site:* www.bloomwriting.com, pg 521

Susan P Bloom Children's Book Discovery Award, MIT, 14N-221A, 77 Massachusetts Ave, Cambridge, MA 02139 *Tel:* 617-324-1729 *E-mail:* pen-newengland@mit.edu *Web Site:* www.pen-ne.org/susan-p-bloom-award, pg 673

Bloom's Literary Criticism, 132 W 31 St, 17th fl, New York, NY 10001 *Toll Free Tel:* 800-322-8755 *Toll Free Fax:* 800-678-3633 *E-mail:* custserv@factsonfile.com *Web Site:* www.infobasepublishing.com, pg 39

Bloomsbury Academic, 1385 Broadway, 5th fl, New York, NY 10018 *Tel:* 212-419-5300 *Web Site:* www.bloomsbury.com, pg 39

Bloomsbury Publishing Inc, 1385 Broadway, 5th fl, New York, NY 10018 *Tel:* 212-419-5300 *E-mail:* marketingusa@bloomsbury.com; adultpublicityusa@bloomsbury.com; askacademic@bloomsbury.com *Web Site:* www.bloomsbury.com, pg 39

Heidi Blough, Book Indexer, 502 Tanager Rd, St Augustine, FL 32086 *Tel:* 904-797-6572 *E-mail:* indexing@heidiblough.com *Web Site:* www.heidiblough.com, pg 521

Blue & Ude Writers' Services, 4249 Nuthatch Way, Clinton, WA 98236 *Tel:* 360-341-1630 *E-mail:* blueyude@whidbey.com *Web Site:* www.blueudewritersservices.com, pg 522

Blue Apple Books, 515 Valley St, Suite 170, Maplewood, NJ 07040 *Tel:* 973-763-8191 *Toll Free Tel:* 800-283-3572 (orders) *Fax:* 973-763-5944 *E-mail:* info@blueapplebooks.com *Web Site:* blueapplebooks.com, pg 40

Blue Bike Books, 11919 125 St, Edmonton, AB T5L 0S3, Canada *Tel:* 780-951-0032 *E-mail:* info@bluebikebooks.com *Web Site:* www.bluebikebooks.com, pg 473

Blue Book Publications Inc, 8009 34 Ave S, Suite 250, Minneapolis, MN 55425 *Tel:* 952-854-5229 *Toll Free Tel:* 800-877-4867 *Fax:* 925-853-1486 *E-mail:* support@bluebookinc.com *Web Site:* www.bluebookofgunvalues.com; www.bluebookofguitarvalues.com, pg 40

Blue Crane Books, PO Box 380291, Cambridge, MA 02238 *Tel:* 617-926-8989 *Fax:* 617-926-0982 *E-mail:* bluecrane@arrow1.com, pg 40

Blue Dolphin Publishing Inc, 13340-D Grass Valley Ave, Grass Valley, CA 95945 *Tel:* 530-477-1503 *Toll Free Tel:* 800-643-0765 (orders) *Fax:* 530-477-8342 *E-mail:* bdolphin@bluedolphinpublishing.com *Web Site:* www.bluedolphinpublishing.com, pg 40

Blue Mountain Arts Inc, 2905 Wilderness Place, Boulder, CO 80301 *Tel:* 303-449-0536 *Toll Free Tel:* 800-525-0642 *Fax:* 303-417-6472 *Toll Free Fax:* 800-545-8573 *E-mail:* info@sps.com *Web Site:* www.sps.com, pg 40

Blue Note Publications Inc, 721 North Dr, Suite D, Melbourne, FL 32934 *Tel:* 321-799-2583 *Toll Free Tel:* 800-624-0401 (orders) *Fax:* 321-799-1942 *E-mail:* bluenotepress@gmail.com *Web Site:* www.bluenotebooks.com, pg 40

Blue Poppy Press, 1990 57 Ct, Unit A, Boulder, CO 80301 *Tel:* 303-447-8372 *Toll Free Tel:* 800-487-9296 *Fax:* 303-245-8362 *E-mail:* info@bluepoppy.com *Web Site:* www.bluepoppy.com, pg 40

Blue Rider Press, 375 Hudson St, New York, NY 10014 *Tel:* 212-366-2000 *E-mail:* blueriderpublicity@us.penguingroup.com, pg 40

BlueBridge, PO Box 601, Katonah, NY 10536 *Tel:* 914-301-5901 *Web Site:* www.bluebridgebooks.com, pg 41

Bluestocking Press, 3045 Sacramento St, No 1014, Placerville, CA 95667-1014 *Tel:* 530-622-8586 *Toll Free Tel:* 800-959-8586 *Fax:* 530-642-9222 *E-mail:* customerservice@bluestockingpress.com; orders@bluestockingpress.com *Web Site:* www.bluestockingpress.com, pg 41

BMI®, 7 World Trade Ctr, 250 Greenwich St, New York, NY 10007-0030 *Tel:* 212-586-2000; 212-220-3000 *Toll Free Tel:* 888-689-5264 (sales); 800-925-8451 (cust rel) *Fax:* 212-246-2163 *E-mail:* foundation@bmi.com *Web Site:* www.bmi.com, pg 600

BNA Books, 1801 S Bell St, Arlington, VA 22202 *Tel:* 732-476-6397 *Toll Free Tel:* 800-372-1033; 800-960-1220 *Fax:* 732-346-1624 *E-mail:* books@bna.com *Web Site:* www.bnabooks.com, pg 41

BNi Building News, 990 Park Center Dr, Suite E, Vista, CA 92081-8352 *Tel:* 760-734-1113 *Toll Free Tel:* 888-BNI-BOOK (264-2665) *Web Site:* www.bnibooks.com, pg 41

BOA Editions Ltd, 250 N Goodman St, Suite 306, Rochester, NY 14607 *Tel:* 585-546-3410 *Fax:* 585-546-3913 *E-mail:* contact@boaeditions.org *Web Site:* www.boaeditions.org, pg 41

BoardSource, 750 Ninth St NW, Suite 650, Washington, DC 20001-4793 *Tel:* 202-349-2500 *Toll Free Tel:* 877-892-6273 *Fax:* 202-349-2599 *E-mail:* members@boardsource.org *Web Site:* www.boardsource.org, pg 41

Reid Boates Literary Agency, 69 Cooks Crossroad, Pittstown, NJ 08867-0328 *Tel:* 908-797-8087 *E-mail:* reid.boates@gmail.com, pg 542

The James Boatwright III Prize for Poetry, Washington & Lee University, Mattingly House, 204 W Washington St, Lexington, VA 24450-2116 *Tel:* 540-458-8765 *E-mail:* shenandoah@wlu.edu *Web Site:* shenandoahliterary.org; shenandoah.wlu.edu, pg 673

Frederick Bock Prize, 444 N Michigan Ave, Suite 1850, Chicago, IL 60611-4034 *Tel:* 312-787-7070 *Fax:* 312-787-6650 *E-mail:* editors@poetrymagazine.org *Web Site:* www.poetryfoundation.org, pg 673

George Bogin Memorial Award, 15 Gramercy Park, New York, NY 10003 *Tel:* 212-254-9628 *Fax:* 212-673-2352 *Web Site:* www.poetrysociety.org, pg 673

Bogle International Library Travel Fund, 50 E Huron St, Chicago, IL 60611-2795 *Tel:* 312-280-3201 *Toll Free Tel:* 800-545-2433 (ext 3201) *Fax:* 312-280-4392 *E-mail:* intl@ala.org *Web Site:* www.ala.org, pg 673

Editions du Bois-de-Coulonge, 1140 Ave de Montigny, Sillery, QC G1S 3T7, Canada *Tel:* 418-683-6332 *Web Site:* www.ebc.qc.ca, pg 473

Bolchazy-Carducci Publishers Inc, 1570 Baskin Rd, Mundelein, IL 60060 *Tel:* 847-526-4344 *Toll Free Tel:* 800-392-6453 *Fax:* 847-526-2867 *E-mail:* info@bolchazy.com; orders@bolchazy.com *Web Site:* www.bolchazy.com, pg 41

Bold Strokes Books Inc, PO Box 249, Valley Falls, NY 12185 *Tel:* 518-677-5127 *Fax:* 518-677-5291 *E-mail:* bsb@boldstrokesbooks.com *Web Site:* www.boldstrokesbooks.com, pg 41

Laura Day Boggs Bolling Memorial, 1194 Hume Rd, Hume, VA 22639-1806 *E-mail:* poetryinva@aol.com *Web Site:* www.poetrysocietyofvirginia.org, pg 673

Bonasa Press, PO Box 340, Crosby, ND 58730 *Tel:* 701-965-3974 *E-mail:* new@bonasapress.com (inquiries) *Web Site:* www.bonasapress.com, pg 42

Alison Bond Literary Agency, 171 W 79 St, No 143, New York, NY 10024, pg 543

Bond Literary Agency, 4340 E Kentucky Ave, Suite 471, Denver, CO 80246 *Tel:* 303-781-9305 *E-mail:* queries@bondliteraryagency.com *Web Site:* bondliteraryagency.com, pg 543

Bondfire Books, 7680 Goddard St, Suite 220, Colorado Springs, CO 80920 *Tel:* 719-260-7080 *Web Site:* www.bondfirebooks.com, pg 42

Book & Periodical Council (BPC), 192 Spadina Ave, Suite 107, Toronto, ON M5T 2C2, Canada *Tel:* 416-975-9366 *Fax:* 416-975-1839 *E-mail:* info@thebpc.ca *Web Site:* www.thebpc.ca, pg 600

Book Industry Guild of New York, PO Box 2001, New York, NY 10113-2001 *E-mail:* admin@bookindustryguildofny.org *Web Site:* www.bookindustryguildofny.org, pg 600

Book Industry Study Group Inc (BISG), 145 W 45 St, Suite 601, New York, NY 10036 *Tel:* 646-336-7141 *Fax:* 646-336-6214 *E-mail:* info@bisg.org *Web Site:* www.bisg.org, pg 600

Book Manufacturers' Institute Inc (BMI), 2 Armand Beach Dr, Suite 1B, Palm Coast, FL 32137-2612 *Tel:* 386-986-4552 *Fax:* 386-986-4553 *E-mail:* info@bmibook.com *Web Site:* www.bmibook.org, pg 600

Book Marketing Works LLC, 50 Lovely St (Rte 177), Avon, CT 06001 *Tel:* 860-675-1344 *Web Site:* www.bookmarketingworks.com, pg 42

Book Peddlers, 18330 Minnetonka Blvd, Deephaven, MN 55391 *Tel:* 952-544-1154 *Fax:* 206-339-6913 *E-mail:* bookpeddlers@aol.com *Web Site:* www.bookpeddlers.com, pg 42

Book Publicists of Southern California, 714 Crescent Dr, Beverly Hills, CA 90210 *Tel:* 323-461-3921 *Fax:* 323-461-0917 *Web Site:* www.bookpublicists.org, pg 600

The Book Publishers Association of Alberta (BPAA), 10523 100 Ave, Edmonton, AB T5J 0A8, Canada *Tel:* 780-424-5060 *Fax:* 780-424-7943 *E-mail:* info@bookpublishers.ab.ca *Web Site:* www.bookpublishers.ab.ca, pg 601

Book Publishing Co, 415 Farm Rd, Summertown, TN 38483 *Tel:* 931-964-3571 *Fax:* 931-964-3518 *E-mail:* info@bookpubco.com *Web Site:* www.bookpubco.com, pg 42

Book Sales Inc, 142 W 36 St, 4th fl, New York, NY 10018 *Tel:* 212-779-4971; 212-779-4972 *Toll Free Tel:* 866-483-5456 *Fax:* 212-779-6058 *E-mail:* sales@quartous.com; customerservice@quartous.com *Web Site:* www.booksalesusa.com, pg 42

The Book Tree, 3316 Adams Ave, Suite A, San Diego, CA 92116 *Tel:* 619-280-1263 *Toll Free Tel:* 800-700-8733 (orders) *Fax:* 619-280-1285 *E-mail:* orders@thebooktree.com; titles@thebooktree.com; info@thebooktree.com *Web Site:* thebooktree.com, pg 42

Bookbuilders of Boston, 115 Webster Woods Lane, North Andover, MA 01845 *Tel:* 781-378-1361 *Fax:* 419-821-2171 *E-mail:* office@bbboston.org *Web Site:* www.bbboston.org, pg 601

BookCrafters LLC, Box C, Convent Station, NJ 07961 *Tel:* 973-984-7880 *Web Site:* bookcraftersllc.com, pg 522

BookEnds LLC, 136 Long Hill Rd, Gillette, NJ 07933 *Web Site:* www.bookends-inc.com, pg 543

Bookhaven Press LLC, 302 Scenic Ct, Moon Township, PA 15108 *Tel:* 412-494-6926 *E-mail:* info@bookhavenpress.com; orders@bookhavenpress.com *Web Site:* bookhavenpress.com, pg 42

BookLogix, 1264 Old Alpharetta Rd, Alpharetta, GA 30005 *Tel:* 470-239-8547 *Toll Free Fax:* 888-564-7890 *E-mail:* sales@booklogix.com *Web Site:* www.booklogix.com, pg 42

Bookmakers Ltd, 32 Parkview Ave, Wolfville, NS B4P 2K8, Canada *Tel:* 902-697-2569 *Web Site:* bookmakersltd.com, pg 583

The Bookmill, 501 Palisades Dr, No 315, Pacific Palisades, CA 90272-2848 *Tel:* 310-459-0190 *E-mail:* thebookmill1@verizon.net *Web Site:* www.thebookmill.us, pg 522

Books & Such, 52 Mission Circle, Suite 122, PMB 170, Santa Rosa, CA 95409-5370 *Tel:* 707-538-4184 *Web Site:* booksandsuch.com, pg 543

Books for a Better Life Awards, 733 Third Ave, 3rd fl, New York, NY 10017 *Tel:* 212-463-7787 *Toll Free Tel:* 800-344-4867 *Fax:* 212-986-7981 *Web Site:* www.nationalmssociety.org, pg 673

Books for Asia, 2490 Verna Ct, San Leandro, CA 94577 *E-mail:* booksforasia@asiafound.org *Web Site:* booksforasia.org, pg 623

Books for Everybody, 111 Queen St E, Suite 320, Toronto, ON M5C 1S2, Canada *Tel:* 416-364-3333 *Toll Free Tel:* 888-360-6658 *Fax:* 416-595-5415, pg 601

Books In Motion, 9922 E Montgomery, Suite 31, Spokane Valley, WA 99206 *Tel:* 509-922-1646 *Toll Free Tel:* 800-752-3199 *Fax:* 509-922-1445 *E-mail:* info@booksinmotion.com *Web Site:* www.booksinmotion.com, pg 42

Books on Tape®, 1745 Broadway, New York, NY 10019 *Toll Free Tel:* 800-733-3000 (cust serv) *Toll Free Fax:* 800-940-7046 *Web Site:* www.booksontape.com, pg 43

Books We Love Ltd, 192 Lakeside Greens Dr, Chestermere, AB T1X 1C2, Canada *Tel:* 403-710-4869 *E-mail:* bookswelove@shaw.ca, pg 473

BookStop Literary Agency LLC, 67 Meadow View Rd, Orinda, CA 94563 *E-mail:* info@bookstopliterary.com *Web Site:* www.bookstopliterary.com, pg 543

Boom! Studios, 5670 Wilshire Blvd, Suite 450, Los Angeles, CA 90036 *Web Site:* www.boom-studios.com, pg 43

Georges Borchardt Inc, 136 E 57 St, New York, NY 10022 *Tel:* 212-753-5785 *E-mail:* georges@gbagency.com *Web Site:* www.gbagency.com, pg 543

Borealis Press Ltd, 8 Mohawk Crescent, Nepean, ON K2H 7G6, Canada *Tel:* 613-829-0150 *Toll Free Tel:* 877-696-2585 *Fax:* 613-829-7783 *E-mail:* drt@borealispress.com *Web Site:* www.borealispress.com, pg 473

Boson Books, 1262 Sunnyoaks Circle, Altadena, CA 91001 *Tel:* 626-507-8033; 626-395-2405 *Web Site:* www.bosonbooks.com; bitingduckpress.com, pg 43

Boston Authors Club Inc, 33 Brayton Rd, Brighton, MA 02135 *Tel:* 617-783-1357 *E-mail:* bostonauthors@aol.com *Web Site:* www.bostonauthorsclub.org, pg 601

Boston Globe-Horn Book Award, 300 The Fenway, Boston, MA 02115-5820 *Tel:* 617-628-0225 *Toll Free Tel:* 800-325-1170; 888-628-0225 *Fax:* 617-278-6062 *E-mail:* info@hbook.com *Web Site:* www.hbook.com, pg 673

Boston Informatics, 35 Byard Lane, Westborough, MA 01581 *Tel:* 508-366-8176 *Web Site:* www.bostoninformatics.com, pg 522

The Boston Mills Press, 50 Staples Ave, Unit 1, Richmond Hill, ON L4B 0A7, Canada *Tel:* 416-499-8412 *Toll Free Tel:* 800-387-6192 *Fax:* 416-499-8313 *Toll Free Fax:* 800-450-0391 *E-mail:* service@fireflybooks.com *Web Site:* www.fireflybooks.com, pg 473

Boston Road Communications, 227 Boston Rd, Groton, MA 01450-1959 *Tel:* 978-448-8133 *Web Site:* www.bostonrdcom.com, pg 522

Boston University, 236 Bay State Rd, Boston, MA 02215 *Tel:* 617-353-2510 *Fax:* 617-353-3653 *E-mail:* crwr@bu.edu *Web Site:* www.bu.edu/writing, pg 659

The Boston Word Works, PO Box 56419, Sherman Oaks, CA 91413-1419 *Tel:* 818-904-9088 *Fax:* 818-787-1431, pg 522

Bottom Dog Press, 813 Seneca Ave, Huron, OH 44839 *Tel:* 419-433-3573 *Fax:* 419-616-3966 *Web Site:* smithdocs.net, pg 43

Boulevard Magazine Short Fiction Contest for Emerging Writers, 6614 Clayton Rd, PMB 325, Richmond Heights, MO 63117 *Tel:* 314-862-2643 *Web Site:* www.boulevardmagazine.org, pg 673

Bound to Stay Bound Books Scholarship, 50 E Huron St, Chicago, IL 60611-2795 *Tel:* 312-280-2163 *Toll Free Tel:* 800-545-2433 *Fax:* 312-440-9374 *E-mail:* alsc@ala.org *Web Site:* www.ala.org/alsc, pg 673

Amber Bowerman Memorial Travel Writing Award, 11759 Groat Rd, Edmonton, AB T5M 3K6, Canada *Tel:* 780-422-8174 *Toll Free Tel:* 800-665-5354 (AB only) *Fax:* 780-422-2663 (attn WGA) *E-mail:* mail@writersguild.ab.ca *Web Site:* www.writersguild.ab.ca, pg 673

Eddie Bowers Publishing Co Inc, PO Box 130, Peosta, IA 52068-0130 *Tel:* 563-582-8333 *Toll Free Tel:* 800-747-2411 *Fax:* 563-582-8555 *E-mail:* eddiebowerspub@aol.com *Web Site:* www.eddiebowerspublishing.com, pg 43

R R Bowker LLC, 630 Central Ave, New Providence, NJ 07974 *Tel:* 908-286-1090 *Toll Free Tel:* 888-269-5372 (edit & cust serv, press 2 for returns) *Fax:* 908-219-0098; (020) 7832 1710 (UK for intl) *Toll Free Fax:* 877-337-7015 (US & CN) *E-mail:* orders@proquest.com (dom orders); customer_service@proquest.co.uk (intl) *Web Site:* www.bowker.com, pg 43

Bowling Green State University, Creative Writing Program, Dept of English, 211 East Hall, Bowling Green, OH 43403 *Tel:* 419-372-2576 *Fax:* 419-372-0333 *Web Site:* www.bgsu.edu/departments/creative-writing, pg 659

Boydell & Brewer Inc, 668 Mount Hope Ave, Rochester, NY 14620-2731 *Tel:* 585-275-0419 *Fax:* 585-271-8778 *E-mail:* boydell@boydellusa.net *Web Site:* www.boydellandbrewer.com, pg 43

Boyds Mills Press, 815 Church St, Honesdale, PA 18431 *Tel:* 570-253-1164 *Toll Free Tel:* 800-490-5111 *Fax:* 570-253-0179 *E-mail:* contact@boydsmillspress.com *Web Site:* www.boydsmillspress.com, pg 43

Boynton/Cook Publishers, 361 Hanover St, Portsmouth, NH 03801-3912 *Tel:* 603-431-7894 *Toll Free Tel:* 800-225-5800 *Fax:* 603-431-2214 *Toll Free Fax:* 877-231-6980 *E-mail:* custserv@heinemann.com *Web Site:* www.heinemann.com/boyntoncook, pg 44

Boys Town Press, 14100 Crawford St, Boys Town, NE 68010 *Tel:* 402-498-1320 *Toll Free Tel:* 800-282-6657 *Fax:* 402-498-1310 *E-mail:* btpress@boystown.org *Web Site:* www.boystownpress.org, pg 44

BPA Worldwide, 100 Beard Sawmill Rd, 6th fl, Shelton, CT 06484 *Tel:* 203-447-2800 *Fax:* 203-447-2900 *E-mail:* info@bpaww.com *Web Site:* www.bpaww.com, pg 601

BPS Books, 42 Donalda Crescent, Toronto, ON M1S 1N7, Canada *Tel:* 416-609-2004 *Fax:* 416-609-2936 *Web Site:* www.bpsbooks.com, pg 473

Bradford Literary Agency, 5694 Mission Center Rd, Suite 347, San Diego, CA 92108 *Tel:* 619-521-1201 *E-mail:* queries@bradfordlit.com *Web Site:* www.bradfordlit.com, pg 543

Bradford Publishing Co, 1743 Wazee St, Denver, CO 80202 *Tel:* 303-292-2590 *Toll Free Tel:* 800-446-2831 *Fax:* 303-298-5014 *E-mail:* marketing@bradfordpublishing.com; customerservice@bradfordpublishing.com *Web Site:* www.bradfordpublishing.com, pg 44

Barbara Bradley Prize, 2 Farrar St, Cambridge, MA 02138 *Tel:* 617-744-6034 *E-mail:* contests@nepoetryclub.org *Web Site:* www.nepoetryclub.org, pg 673

BradyGames, 800 E 96 St, 3rd fl, Indianapolis, IN 46240 *Tel:* 317-428-3000 *Toll Free Tel:* 800-545-5912; 800-571-5840 (cust serv) *E-mail:* bradyquestions@pearsoned.com *Web Site:* www.bradygames.com, pg 44

bradylit, 81 Town Farm Hill, Hartland Four Corners, VT 05049 *Tel:* 802-436-2455, pg 522

BrainStorm Poetry Contest for Mental Health Consumers, 36 Elgin St, 2nd fl, Sudbury, ON P3C 5B4, Canada *Tel:* 705-222-6472 (ext 303) *E-mail:* openminds@nisa.on.ca *Web Site:* www.openmindsquarterly.com, pg 674

Branden Books, PO Box 812094, Wellesley, MA 02482-0013 *Tel:* 781-235-3347 *E-mail:* branden@brandenbooks.com *Web Site:* www.brandenbooks.com, pg 44

Brandt & Hochman Literary Agents Inc, 1501 Broadway, Suite 2310, New York, NY 10036 *Tel:* 212-840-5760 *Fax:* 212-840-5776 *Web Site:* brandthochman.com, pg 544

The Joan Brandt Agency, 788 Wesley Dr NW, Atlanta, GA 30305 *Tel:* 404-351-8877 *Fax:* 404-351-0068, pg 544

Brandylane Publishers Inc, 5 S First St, Richmond, VA 23219 *Tel:* 804-644-3090 *Fax:* 804-644-3092 *Web Site:* brandylanepublishers.com, pg 44

Michael Braude Award, 633 W 155 St, New York, NY 10032 *Tel:* 212-368-5900 *Fax:* 212-491-4615 *E-mail:* academy@artsandletters.org *Web Site:* www.artsandletters.org, pg 674

Brault & Bouthillier, 700 ave Beaumont, Montreal, QC H3N 1V5, Canada *Tel:* 514-273-9186 *Toll Free Tel:* 800-361-0378 *Fax:* 514-273-8627 *Toll Free Fax:* 800-361-0378 *E-mail:* ventes@bb.ca *Web Site:* bb.ca, pg 473

Barbara Braun Associates Inc, 7 E 14 St, Suite 19F, New York, NY 10003 *Tel:* 212-604-9023 *Web Site:* www.barbarabraunagency.com, pg 544

George Braziller Inc, 277 Broadway, Suite 708, New York, NY 10007 *Tel:* 212-260-9256 *Fax:* 212-267-3165 *E-mail:* editorial@georgebraziller.com *Web Site:* www.georgebraziller.com, pg 44

Bread Loaf Writers' Conference, 5525 Middlebury College, 14 Old Chapel Rd, Middlebury, VT 05753 *Tel:* 802-443-5286 *Fax:* 802-443-2087 *E-mail:* blwc@middlebury.edu *Web Site:* www.middlebury.edu/blwc, pg 650

Breakaway Books, PO Box 24, Halcottsville, NY 12438-0024 *Tel:* 607-326-4805 *E-mail:* breakawaybooks@gmail.com *Web Site:* www.breakawaybooks.com, pg 44

Breakthrough Publications Inc, 3 Iroquois St, Barn, Emmaus, PA 18049 *Toll Free Tel:* 800-824-5001 (ext 12) *Fax:* 610-928-4064 *E-mail:* dot@booksonhorses.com; ruth@booksonhorses.com *Web Site:* www.booksonhorses.com, pg 44

Breakwater Books Ltd, One Stamp's Lane, St John's, NL A1C 6E6, Canada *Tel:* 709-722-6680 *Toll Free Tel:* 800-563-3333 (orders) *Fax:* 709-753-0708 *E-mail:* info@breakwaterbooks.com; orders@breakwaterbooks.com *Web Site:* www.breakwaterbooks.com, pg 473

Nicholas Brealey Publishing, 20 Park Plaza, Suite 610, Boston, MA 02116 *Tel:* 617-523-3801 *Toll Free Tel:* 888-BREALEY (273-2539) *Fax:* 617-523-3708 *E-mail:* info@nicholasbrealey.com *Web Site:* www.nicholasbrealey.com, pg 44

James Henry Breasted Prize, 400 "A" St SE, Washington, DC 20003 *Tel:* 202-544-2422 *Fax:* 202-544-8307 *E-mail:* awards@historians.org *Web Site:* www.historians.org, pg 674

Brenner Information Group, 9282 Samantha Ct, San Diego, CA 92129 *Tel:* 858-538-0093 *Toll Free Tel:* 800-811-4337 (orders) *E-mail:* brenner@brennerbooks.com; sales@brennerbooks.com *Web Site:* www.brennerbooks.com, pg 45

Brentwood Christian Press, 4000 Beallwood Ave, Columbus, GA 31904 *Toll Free Tel:* 800-334-8861 *E-mail:* brentwood@aol.com *Web Site:* www.brentwoodbooks.com, pg 45

Brethren Press, 1451 Dundee Ave, Elgin, IL 60120 *Tel:* 847-742-5100 *Toll Free Tel:* 800-323-8039 *Toll Free Fax:* 800-667-8188 *E-mail:* brethrenpress@brethren.org *Web Site:* www.brethrenpress.com, pg 45

Brewers Publications, 1372 Spruce St, Boulder, CO 80302 *Tel:* 303-447-0816 *Toll Free Tel:* 888-822-6273 (CN & US) *Fax:* 303-447-2825 *E-mail:* info@brewersassociation.org *Web Site:* www.brewersassociation.org, pg 45

The Briar Cliff Review Fiction, Poetry & Creative Nonfiction Contest, 3303 Rebecca St, Sioux City, IA 51104-2100 *Tel:* 712-279-1651 *Fax:* 712-279-5486 *Web Site:* www.briarcliff.edu/bcreview, pg 674

Brick Books, Box 20081, 431 Boler Rd, London, ON N6K 4G6, Canada *Tel:* 519-657-8579 *E-mail:* brick.books@sympatico.ca *Web Site:* www.brickbooks.ca, pg 473

Brick Road Poetry Book Contest, 513 Broadway, Columbus, GA 31901 *Tel:* 706-649-3080 *Web Site:* brickroadpoetrypress.com, pg 674

Brick Tower Press, 1230 Park Ave, New York, NY 10128 *Tel:* 212-427-7139 *Toll Free Tel:* 800-68-BRICK (682-7425) *E-mail:* bricktower@aol.com *Web Site:* www.bricktowerpress.com, pg 45

BrickHouse Books Inc, 306 Suffolk Rd, Baltimore, MD 21218 *Tel:* 410-235-7690 *Fax:* 410-235-7690 *Web Site:* www.brickhousebooks.wordpress.com, pg 45

Bridge-Logos Inc, Bldg 200, Suite 220, 17750 NW 115 Ave, Alachua, FL 32615 *Tel:* 386-462-2525 *Toll Free Tel:* 800-631-5802 (orders) *Fax:* 386-462-2535 *Toll Free Fax:* 800-935-6467 *E-mail:* customerservice@bridgelogos.com; info@bridgelogos.com *Web Site:* www.bridgelogos.com, pg 45

Bridge Publications Inc, 5600 E Olympic Blvd, Commerce City, CA 90022 *Tel:* 323-888-6200 *Toll Free Tel:* 800-722-1733 *Fax:* 323-888-6202 *E-mail:* info@bridgepub.com *Web Site:* www.bridgepub.com, pg 45

Bridge to Asia, 1505 Juanita Way, Berkeley, CA 94702-1103 *Tel:* 510-665-3998 *E-mail:* asianet@bridge.org *Web Site:* www.bridge.org, pg 623

Brigantine Media, 211 North Ave, St Johnsbury, VT 05819 *Tel:* 802-751-8802 *Fax:* 802-751-8804 *Web Site:* brigantinemedia.com, pg 46

M Courtney Briggs Esq, Authors Representative, Chase Tower, 28th fl, 100 N Broadway Ave, Oklahoma City, OK 73102, pg 544

Bright Connections Media, A World Book Encyclopedia Company, 233 N Michigan Ave, Suite 2000, Chicago, IL 60601 *Tel:* 312-729-5800 *Fax:* 312-729-5610 *Web Site:* www.brightconnectionsmedia.com, pg 46

Brill Inc, 2 Liberty Sq, 11th fl, Boston, MA 02109 *Tel:* 617-263-2323 *Toll Free Tel:* 800-962-4406 *Fax:* 617-263-2324 *E-mail:* cs@brillusa.com *Web Site:* www.brill.com, pg 46

Brilliance Audio, 1704 Eaton Dr, Grand Haven, MI 49417 *Tel:* 616-846-5256 *Toll Free Tel:* 800-648-2312 (orders only) *Fax:* 616-846-0630 *E-mail:* customerservice@brillianceaudio.com *Web Site:* www.brillianceaudio.com, pg 46

Brindle & Glass Publishing Ltd, 1075 Pendergast St, Suite 103, Victoria, BC V8V 0A1, Canada *Tel:* 250-360-0829 *Fax:* 250-386-0829 *E-mail:* info@brindleandglass.com *Web Site:* www.brindleandglass.com, pg 474

Bristol Park Books, 252 W 38 St, Suite 206, New York, NY 10018 *Tel:* 212-842-0700 *Fax:* 212-842-1771 *E-mail:* info@bristolparkbooks.com *Web Site:* bristolparkbooks.com, pg 46

Brittingham & Pollak Prizes in Poetry, Dept of English, 600 N Park St, Madison, WI 53706 *Web Site:* www.wisc.edu/wisconsinpress, pg 674

Broadview Press, 280 Perry St, Unit 5, Peterborough, ON K9J 2J4, Canada *Tel:* 705-743-8990 *Fax:* 705-743-8353 *E-mail:* customerservice@broadviewpress.com *Web Site:* www.broadviewpress.com, pg 474

Brockman Inc, 260 Fifth Ave, 10th fl, New York, NY 10001 *Tel:* 212-935-8900 *Fax:* 212-935-5535 *E-mail:* rights@brockman.com *Web Site:* www.brockman.com, pg 544

Broden Books LLC, 3824 Sunset Dr, Spring Park, MN 55384 *Tel:* 952-471-1066 *E-mail:* media@brodenbooks.com *Web Site:* www.brodenbooks.com, pg 46

Broken Jaw Press Inc, Box 596, Sta A, Fredericton, NB E3B 5A6, Canada *Tel:* 506-454-5127 *Fax:* 506-454-5134 *E-mail:* editors@brokenjaw.com *Web Site:* www.brokenjaw.com, pg 474

Brookes Publishing Co Inc, PO Box 10624, Baltimore, MD 21285-0624 *Tel:* 410-337-9580 (outside US & CN) *Toll Free Tel:* 800-638-3775 (US & CN) *Fax:* 410-337-8539 *E-mail:* custserv@brookespublishing.com *Web Site:* www.brookespublishing.com, pg 46

Brookhaven Press, 2004 Kramer St, La Crosse, WI 54603 *Tel:* 608-781-0850 *Toll Free Tel:* 800-236-0850 *Fax:* 608-781-3883 *E-mail:* brookhaven@nmt.com *Web Site:* www.brookhavenpress.com, pg 46

The Brookings Institution Press, 1775 Massachusetts Ave NW, Washington, DC 20036-2188 *Tel:* 202-536-3600 *Toll Free Tel:* 800-537-5487 *Fax:* 202-536-3623 *E-mail:* permissions@brookings.edu *Web Site:* www.brookings.edu, pg 47

Brookline Books, 8 Trumbull Rd, Suite B-001, Northampton, MA 01060 *Tel:* 603-669-7032 (orders) *Toll Free Tel:* 800-666-2665 (orders) *Fax:* 413-584-6184 *E-mail:* brbooks@yahoo.com, pg 47

Brooklyn Publishers LLC, PO Box 248, Cedar Rapids, IA 52406 *Tel:* 319-368-8012 *Toll Free Tel:* 888-473-8521 *Fax:* 319-368-8011 *E-mail:* customerservice@brookpub.com; editor@brookpub.com *Web Site:* www.brookpub.com, pg 47

Broquet Inc, 97-B, Montee des Bouleaux, St-Constant, QC J5A 1A9, Canada *Tel:* 450-638-3338 *Fax:* 450-638-4338 *E-mail:* info@broquet.qc.ca *Web Site:* www.broquet.qc.ca, pg 474

The Heywood Broun Award, 501 Third St NW, 6th fl, Washington, DC 20001-2797 *Tel:* 202-434-7177; 202-434-7162 (The Guild Reporter) *Fax:* 202-434-1472 *Web Site:* www.newsguild.org, pg 674

Brown Books Publishing Group, 16250 Knoll Trail, Suite 205, Dallas, TX 75248 *Tel:* 972-381-0009 *Fax:* 972-248-4336 *E-mail:* publishing@brownbooks.com *Web Site:* www.brownbooks.com, pg 47

Curtis Brown Ltd, 10 Astor Place, New York, NY 10003 *Tel:* 212-473-5400 *Web Site:* www.curtisbrown.com, pg 544

John Nicholas Brown Prize, 104 Mount Auburn St, 5th fl, Cambridge, MA 02138 *Tel:* 617-491-1622 *Fax:* 617-492-3303 *E-mail:* speculum@medievalacademy.org *Web Site:* www.medievalacademy.org, pg 674

Karen Brown's Guides Inc, 16 E Third Ave, Suite 9, San Mateo, CA 94401 *Tel:* 650-342-9117 *Fax:* 650-342-9153 *Web Site:* www.karenbrown.com, pg 47

Marie Brown Associates, 412 W 154 St, New York, NY 10032 *Tel:* 212-939-9725 *Fax:* 212-939-9728 *E-mail:* mbrownlit@aol.com, pg 544

Browne & Miller Literary Associates, 410 S Michigan Ave, Suite 460, Chicago, IL 60605 *Tel:* 312-922-3063 *E-mail:* mail@browneandmiller.com *Web Site:* www.browneandmiller.com, pg 544

Brush Education Inc, 6531 111 St, Edmonton, AB T6H 4R5, Canada *Tel:* 780-989-0910 *Toll Free Tel:* 855-283-0900 *Fax:* 780-989-0930 *Toll Free Fax:* 855-283-6947 *E-mail:* contact@brusheducation.ca *Web Site:* www.brusheducation.ca, pg 474

Don Buchwald & Associates Inc, 10 E 44 St, New York, NY 10017 *Tel:* 212-867-1200 *Fax:* 212-867-2434 *E-mail:* info@buchwald.com *Web Site:* www.buchwald.com, pg 545

Howard Buck Agency, 80 Eighth Ave, Suite 1107, New York, NY 10011 *Tel:* 212-924-9093, pg 545

Bucknell Seminar for Younger Poets, Bucknell University, Bucknell Hall, Moore Ave, Lewisburg, PA 17837 *Tel:* 570-577-1853 *Fax:* 570-577-1885 *E-mail:* stadlercenter@bucknell.edu *Web Site:* www.bucknell.edu/stadlercenter, pg 650

Bucknell University Press, 6 Taylor Hall, Bucknell University, Lewisburg, PA 17837 *Tel:* 570-577-3674 *E-mail:* universitypress@bucknell.edu *Web Site:* www.bucknell.edu/universitypress, pg 47

Judith Buckner Literary Agency, 12721 Hart St, North Hollywood, CA 91605 *Tel:* 818-982-8202 *Fax:* 818-764-6844, pg 545

Georges Bugnet Award for Fiction, 11759 Groat Rd, Edmonton, AB T5M 3K6, Canada *Tel:* 780-422-8174 *Toll Free Tel:* 800-665-5354 (AB only) *Fax:* 780-422-2663 (attn WGA) *E-mail:* mail@writersguild.ab.ca *Web Site:* www.writersguild.ab.ca, pg 674

BuilderBooks.com, 1201 15 St NW, Washington, DC 20005 *Tel:* 202-822-0200 *Toll Free Tel:* 800-223-2665 *Fax:* 202-266-8096 (edit) *E-mail:* builderbooks@nahb.com *Web Site:* www.builderbooks.com, pg 47

The Bukowski Agency Ltd, 14 Prince Arthur Ave, Suite 202, Toronto, ON M5R 1A9, Canada *Tel:* 416-928-6728 *Fax:* 416-963-9978 *E-mail:* info@bukowskiagency.com *Web Site:* www.bukowskiagency.com, pg 545

Bull Publishing Co, PO Box 1377, Boulder, CO 80306 *Tel:* 303-545-6350 *Toll Free Tel:* 800-676-2855 *Fax:* 303-545-6354 *E-mail:* bullpublishing@msn.com *Web Site:* www.bullpub.com, pg 47

Bunker Hill Publishing, 285 River Rd, Piermont, NH 03779 *Tel:* 603-272-9221 *Fax:* 603-283-7240 *E-mail:* mail@bunkerhillpublishing.com *Web Site:* www.bunkerhillpublishing.com, pg 47

Bureau of Economic Geology, University of Texas at Austin, 10100 Burnet Rd, Bldg 130, Austin, TX 78758 *Tel:* 512-471-1534 *Fax:* 512-471-0140 *E-mail:* pubsales@beg.utexas.edu *Web Site:* www.beg.utexas.edu, pg 48

Burford Books, 101 E State St, No 301, Ithaca, NY 14850 *Tel:* 607-319-4373 *Fax:* 607-319-4373 *Toll Free Fax:* 866-212-7750 *E-mail:* info@burfordbooks.com *Web Site:* www.burfordbooks.com, pg 48

Hilary R Burke, 59 Sparks St, Ottawa, ON K1P 6C3, Canada *Tel:* 613-237-4658 *E-mail:* hburke99@yahoo.com, pg 522

Burns Archive Press, 140 E 38 St, New York, NY 10016 *Tel:* 212-889-1938 *Fax:* 212-481-9113 *E-mail:* info@burnsarchive.com *Web Site:* www.burnsarchive.com, pg 48

Burns Entertainment & Sports Marketing, 820 Davis St, Suite 222, Evanston, IL 60201 *Tel:* 847-866-9400 *Fax:* 847-491-9778 *E-mail:* burnsl@burnsent.com *Web Site:* burnsent.com, pg 587

Burnside Review Fiction Chapbook Competition, PO Box 1782, Portland, OR 97207 *Web Site:* burnsidereview.org, pg 674

The John Burroughs List of Nature Books for Young Readers, 15 W 77 St, New York, NY 10024 *Tel:* 212-769-5169 *Fax:* 212-313-7182 *Web Site:* research.amnh.org/burroughs, pg 674

John Burroughs Medal, 15 W 77 St, New York, NY 10024 *Tel:* 212-769-5169 *Fax:* 212-313-7182 *Web Site:* research.amnh.org/burroughs, pg 674

John Burroughs Outstanding Published Nature Essay Award, 15 W 77 St, New York, NY 10024 *Tel:* 212-769-5169 *Fax:* 212-313-7182 *Web Site:* research.amnh.org/burroughs, pg 675

Business & Legal Resources Inc, 100 Winners Circle, Suite 300, Brentwood, TN 37027 *Tel:* 860-510-0100 *Toll Free Tel:* 800-727-5257 *E-mail:* service@blr.com *Web Site:* www.blr.com, pg 48

Business Expert Press, 222 E 46 St, New York, NY 10017-2906 *Tel:* 630-207-5927 *E-mail:* charlene.kronstadt@businessexpertpress.com *Web Site:* www.businessexpertpress.com, pg 48

Business Forms Management Association (BFMA), 1147 Fleetwood Ave, Madison, WI 53716 *Toll Free Tel:* 888-367-3078 *E-mail:* bfma@bfma.org *Web Site:* www.bfma.org, pg 601

Business Marketing Association (BMA), 708 Third Ave, New York, NY 10017 *Tel:* 212-697-5950 *Fax:* 212-687-7310 *E-mail:* info@marketing.org *Web Site:* www.marketing.org, pg 601

Business Research Services Inc, 4641 Montgomery Ave, Suite 208, Bethesda, MD 20814 *Tel:* 301-229-5561 *Toll Free Tel:* 800-845-8420 *Toll Free Fax:* 877-516-0818 *E-mail:* brspubs@sba8a.com *Web Site:* www.sba8a.com; www.setasidealert.com, pg 48

Butte Publications Inc, PO Box 1328, Hillsboro, OR 97123-1328 *Tel:* 503-648-9791 *Toll Free Tel:* 866-312-8883 *Fax:* 503-693-9526 *Toll Free Fax:* 866-412-8883 (orders only) *E-mail:* service@buttepublications.com *Web Site:* www.buttepublications.com, pg 48

Byer-Sprinzeles Agency, 5800 Arlington Ave, Suite 16-C, Riverdale, NY 10471 *Tel:* 718-543-9399 *Web Site:* www.maggiebyersprinzeles.com, pg 583

Sheree Bykofsky Associates Inc, PO Box 706, Brigantine, NJ 08203 *E-mail:* submitbee@aol.com *Web Site:* www.shereebee.com, pg 545

Bywater Books, PO Box 3671, Ann Arbor, MI 48106-3671 *Tel:* 734-662-8815 *Web Site:* bywaterbooks.com, pg 48

BZ/Rights & Permissions Inc, 145 W 86 St, New York, NY 10024 *Tel:* 212-924-3000 *Fax:* 212-924-2525 *E-mail:* info@bzrights.com *Web Site:* www.bzrights.com, pg 522

C & T Publishing Inc, 1651 Challenge Dr, Concord, CA 94520-5206 *Tel:* 925-677-0377 *Toll Free Tel:* 800-284-1114 *Fax:* 925-677-0373 *E-mail:* support@ctpub.com *Web Site:* www.ctpub.com, pg 48

CAA Award for Fiction, 6 West St N, Suite 203, Orillia, ON L3V 5B8, Canada *Tel:* 705-325-3926 *Toll Free Tel:* 866-216-6222 *E-mail:* admin@canadianauthors.org *Web Site:* www.canadianauthors.org, pg 675

CAA Emerging Writer Award, 6 West St N, Suite 203, Orillia, ON L3V 5B8, Canada *Tel:* 705-325-3926 *Toll Free Tel:* 866-216-6222 *E-mail:* admin@canadianauthors.org *Web Site:* www.canadianauthors.org, pg 675

CAA Lela Common Award for Canadian History, 6 West St N, Suite 203, Orillia, ON L3V 5B8, Canada *Tel:* 705-325-3926 *Toll Free Tel:* 866-216-6222 *E-mail:* admin@canadianauthors.org *Web Site:* www.canadianauthors.org, pg 675

CAA Poetry Award, 6 West St N, Suite 203, Orillia, ON L3V 5B8, Canada *Tel:* 705-325-3926 *Toll Free Tel:* 866-216-6222 *E-mail:* admin@canadianauthors.org *Web Site:* www.canadianauthors.org, pg 675

Gerald Cable Book Award, PO Box 3541, Eugene, OR 97403 *Tel:* 541-344-5060 *E-mail:* sfrpress@earthlink.net *Web Site:* www.silverfishreviewpress.com, pg 675

Caissa Editions, PO Box 151, Yorklyn, DE 19736-0151 *Tel:* 302-239-4608 *Web Site:* www.chessbookstore.com, pg 48

The Randolph Caldecott Medal, 50 E Huron St, Chicago, IL 60611-2795 *Tel:* 312-280-2163 *Toll Free Tel:* 800-545-2433 *Fax:* 312-440-9374 *E-mail:* alsc@ala.org *Web Site:* www.ala.org/alsc, pg 675

California Book Awards, 595 Market St, San Francisco, CA 94105 *Tel:* 415-597-6700 *Fax:* 415-597-6729 *E-mail:* bookawards@commonwealthclub.org *Web Site:* www.commonwealthclub.org/bookawards, pg 675

California Writers Exchange Award, 90 Broad St, Suite 2100, New York, NY 10004 *Tel:* 212-226-3586 *Fax:* 212-226-3963 *E-mail:* admin@pw.org *Web Site:* www.pw.org, pg 675

Callawind Publications Inc, 3551 St Charles Blvd, Suite 179, Kirkland, QC H9H 3C4, Canada *Tel:* 514-685-9109 *E-mail:* info@callawind.com *Web Site:* www.callawind.com, pg 474

Cambridge Educational, 132 W 31 St, 17th fl, New York, NY 10001 *Toll Free Tel:* 800-322-8755 *Fax:* 609-671-0266 *Toll Free Fax:* 800-329-6687 *E-mail:* custserve@infobaselearning.com *Web Site:* www.infobasepublishing.com, pg 48

Cambridge Literary Associates, 135 Beach Rd, Unit C-3, Salisbury, MA 01952 *Tel:* 978-499-0374 *Fax:* 978-499-9774 *Web Site:* www.cambridgeliterary.com, pg 545

Cambridge University Press, 32 Avenue of the Americas, New York, NY 10013-2473 *Tel:* 212-924-3900; 212-337-5000 *Fax:* 212-691-3239 *E-mail:* newyork@cambridge.org *Web Site:* www.cambridge.org/us, pg 49

Camino Books Inc, PO Box 59026, Philadelphia, PA 19102-9026 *Tel:* 215-413-1917 *Fax:* 215-413-3255 *E-mail:* camino@caminobooks.com *Web Site:* www.caminobooks.com, pg 49

Joe Pendleton Campbell Narrative Contest, 1194 Hume Rd, Hume, VA 22639-1806 *E-mail:* poetryinva@aol.com *Web Site:* www.poetrysocietyofvirginia.org, pg 675

John W Campbell Memorial Award, University of Kansas, Wescoe Hall, Rm 3001, Dept of English, 1445 Jayhawk Blvd, Lawrence, KS 66045-7590 *Tel:* 785-864-3380 *Fax:* 785-864-1159 *Web Site:* www.ku.edu/~sfcenter; ku.edu/campbell.htm, pg 675

Campfield & Campfield Publishing, 6521 Cutler St, Philadelphia, PA 19126 *Toll Free Tel:* 888-518-2440 *Fax:* 215-224-6696 *E-mail:* info@campfieldspublishing.com *Web Site:* www.campfieldspublishing.com, pg 49

Canada Council for the Arts (Conseil des arts du Canada), 150 Elgin St, Ottawa, ON K1P 1L4, Canada *Tel:* 613-566-4414 *Toll Free Tel:* 800-263-5588 (CN only) *Fax:* 613-566-4390 *E-mail:* info@canadacouncil.ca *Web Site:* www.canadacouncil.ca, pg 601

Canada Law Book®, One Corporate Plaza, 2075 Kennedy Rd, Toronto, ON M1T 3V4, Canada *Tel:* 416-609-3800 (cust rel & orders) *Toll Free Tel:* 800-387-5351 (cust rel, CN & US only); 800-347-5164 (cust rel & orders, CN & US) *Fax:* 416-298-5082 (cust rel & orders, Toronto) *Toll Free Fax:* 877-750-9041 (cust rel & orders, CN only) *E-mail:* carswell.customerrelations@thomsonreuters.com; carswell.orders@thomsonreuters.com *Web Site:* www.canadalawbook.ca; www.carswell.com, pg 474

Canadian Authors Association (CAA), 6 West St N, Suite 203, Orillia, ON L3V 5B8, Canada *Tel:* 705-325-3926 *Toll Free Tel:* 866-216-6222 *E-mail:* admin@canadianauthors.org *Web Site:* www.canadianauthors.org, pg 601

Canadian Bible Society, 10 Carnforth Rd, Toronto, ON M4A 2S4, Canada *Tel:* 416-757-4171 *Toll Free Tel:* 866-946-1711 *Fax:* 416-757-3376 *E-mail:* custserv@biblesociety.ca *Web Site:* www.biblescanada.com; www.biblesociety.ca, pg 474

Canadian Bookbinders and Book Artists Guild (CBBAG), 80 Ward St, Suite 207, Toronto, ON M6H 4A6, Canada *Tel:* 416-581-1071 *E-mail:* cbbag@cbbag.ca *Web Site:* www.cbbag.ca, pg 601

Canadian Booksellers Association (CBA), 1881 Yonge St, Suite 800, Toronto, ON M4S 3C4, Canada *Tel:* 416-922-6678 *Toll Free Tel:* 888-373-8245 *Toll Free Fax:* 877-790-4271 *E-mail:* info@retailcouncil.org *Web Site:* www.retailcouncil.org, pg 601

Canadian Cataloguing in Publication Program, Library & Archives Canada, 395 Wellington St, Ottawa, ON K1A 0N4, Canada *Tel:* 819-994-6881 *Toll Free Tel:* 866-578-7777 (CN) *Fax:* 819-934-6777 *E-mail:* cip@lac-bac.gc.ca *Web Site:* www.collectionscanada.gc.ca/cip/index-e.html, pg 602

Canadian Children's Book Centre, 40 Orchard View Blvd, Suite 217, Toronto, ON M4R 1B9, Canada *Tel:* 416-975-0010 *Fax:* 416-975-8970 *E-mail:* info@bookcentre.ca *Web Site:* www.bookcentre.ca, pg 602

Canadian Circumpolar Institute (CCI) Press, University of Alberta, Ring House 2, Edmonton, AB T6G 2E1, Canada *Tel:* 780-492-3662 *Fax:* 780-492-0719 *Web Site:* www.uap.ualberta.ca, pg 475

Canadian Council on Social Development (Conseil canadien de developpement social), 190 O'Connor St, Suite 100, Ottawa, ON K2P 2R3, Canada *Tel:* 613-236-8977 *Fax:* 613-236-2750 *E-mail:* info@ccsd.ca *Web Site:* www.ccsd.ca, pg 475

Canadian Education Association (Association canadienne d'education), 119 Spadina Ave, Suite 705, Toronto, ON M5V 2L1, Canada *Tel:* 416-591-6300 *Toll Free Tel:* 866-803-9549 *Fax:* 416-591-5345 *E-mail:* info@cea-ace.ca *Web Site:* www.cea-ace.ca, pg 602

Canadian Energy Research Institute, 3512 33 St NW, Suite 150, Calgary, AB T2L 2A6, Canada *Tel:* 403-282-1231 *Fax:* 403-284-4181 *E-mail:* info@ceri.ca *Web Site:* www.ceri.ca, pg 475

Canadian Institute for Studies in Publishing, Simon Fraser University at Harbour Centre, 515 W Hastings St, Suite 3576, Vancouver, BC V6B 5K3, Canada *Tel:* 778-782-5242 *Fax:* 778-782-5239 *E-mail:* ccsp-info@sfu.ca *Web Site:* publishing.sfu.ca, pg 602

Canadian Institute of Chartered Accountants-CICA (L'Institut Canadien des Comptables Agrees), 277 Wellington St W, Toronto, ON M5V 3H2, Canada *Tel:* 416-977-3222 *Toll Free Tel:* 800-268-3793 (CN orders) *Fax:* 416-977-8585 *E-mail:* orders@cica.ca *Web Site:* www.cpacanada.ca, pg 475

Canadian Institute of Resources Law (L'Institut canadien du droit des ressources), Faculty of Law, University of Calgary, 2500 University Dr NW, MFH 3353, Calgary, AB T2N 1N4, Canada *Tel:* 403-220-3200 *Fax:* 403-282-6182 *E-mail:* cirl@ucalgary.ca *Web Site:* www.cirl.ca, pg 475

Canadian Institute of Ukrainian Studies Press, University of Toronto, 256 McCaul St, Rm 308, Toronto, ON M5T 1W5, Canada *Tel:* 416-978-6934 *Fax:* 416-978-2672 *E-mail:* cius@ualberta.ca *Web Site:* www.ciuspress.com, pg 475

Canadian ISBN Agency, Library & Archives Canada, 395 Wellington St, Ottawa, ON K1A 0N4, Canada *Tel:* 613-996-5115 *Toll Free Tel:* 866-578-7777 (CN & US) *Fax:* 613-995-6274 *E-mail:* isbn@lac-bac.gc.ca *Web Site:* www.collectionscanada.gc.ca/ciss-ssci/index-e.html, pg 602

Canadian Library Association-CLA (Association Canadienne des bibliotheques), 1150 Morrison Dr, Suite 400, Ottawa, ON K2H 8S9, Canada *Tel:* 613-232-9625 *Fax:* 613-563-9895 *E-mail:* info@cla.ca *Web Site:* www.cla.ca, pg 602

Canadian Museum of History (Musee Canadien de l'Histoire), 100 Laurier St, Gatineau, QC K1A 0M8, Canada *Tel:* 819-776-7000 *Toll Free Tel:* 800-555-5621 (North American orders only) *Fax:* 819-776-7187 *Web Site:* www.historymuseum.ca, pg 475

Canadian Newspaper Association, 890 Yonge St, Suite 200, Toronto, ON M4W 3P4, Canada *Tel:* 416-923-3567; 416-482-1090 *Toll Free Tel:* 877-305-2262 *Fax:* 416-923-7206; 416-482-1908 *E-mail:* info@newspaperscanada.ca *Web Site:* www.newspaperscanada.ca, pg 602

Canadian Poetry Press, Dept of English, University of Western Ontario, London, ON N6A 3K7, Canada *Tel:* 519-661-2111 (ext 85813); 519-661-2111 (ext 85834) *Fax:* 519-661-3776 *E-mail:* canadianpoetry@uwo.ca *Web Site:* canadianpoetry.org, pg 475

Canadian Publishers' Council (CPC), 250 Merton St, Suite 203, Toronto, ON M4S 1B1, Canada *Tel:* 416-322-7011 *Fax:* 416-322-6999 *Web Site:* www.pubcouncil.ca, pg 602

Canadian Scholars' Press Inc, 425 Adelaide St W, Suite 200, Toronto, ON M5V 3C1, Canada *Tel:* 416-929-2774 *Toll Free Tel:* 800-463-1998 *Fax:* 416-929-1926 *E-mail:* info@cspi.org; editorial@cspi.org; orders@cspi.org *Web Site:* www.cspi.org; womenspress.cspi.org, pg 475

Canadian Society of Children's Authors Illustrators & Performers (CANSCAIP), 720 Bathurst St, Suite 503, Toronto, ON M5S 2R4, Canada *Tel:* 416-515-1559 *E-mail:* office@canscaip.org *Web Site:* www.canscaip.org, pg 602

The Canadian Writers' Foundation Inc (La Fondation des Ecrivains Canadiens), PO Box 13281, Kanata Sta, Ottawa, ON K2K 1X4, Canada *Tel:* 613-256-6937 *Fax:* 613-256-5457 *E-mail:* info@canadianwritersfoundation.org *Web Site:* www.canadianwritersfoundation.org, pg 623

Candlewick Press, 99 Dover St, Somerville, MA 02144-2825 *Tel:* 617-661-3330 *Fax:* 617-661-0565 *E-mail:* bigbear@candlewick.com; salesinfo@candlewick.com *Web Site:* www.candlewick.com, pg 49

Canon Law Society of America, Hecker Ctr, Suite 111, 3025 Fourth St NE, Washington, DC 20017-1102 *Tel:* 202-832-2350 *Fax:* 202-832-2331 *E-mail:* coordinator@clsa.org; info@clsa.org *Web Site:* www.clsa.org, pg 49

Cantos Para Todos, 4749 Hillcrest St, Bel Aire, KS 67226 *Tel:* 316-239 6477 *Web Site:* www.cantos.org, pg 49

Cape Breton University Press Inc (CBU Press), 1250 Grand Lake Rd, Sydney, NS B1M 1A2, Canada *Tel:* 902-563-1604 (orders & cust serv) *Fax:* 902-563-1177 *E-mail:* cbu_press@cbu.ca *Web Site:* cbup.ca, pg 476

Annual Cape Cod Writers' Center Conference, 919 Main St, Osterville, MA 02655 *Tel:* 508-420-0200 *E-mail:* writers@capecodwriterscenter.org *Web Site:* www.capecodwriterscenter.org, pg 650

Capital Enquiry Inc, 1034 Emerald Bay Rd, No 435, South Lake Tahoe, CA 96150 *Tel:* 916-442-1434 *Toll Free Tel:* 800-922-7486 *Fax:* 916-244-2704 *E-mail:* info@capenq.com *Web Site:* www.govbuddy.com, pg 49

Alexander Patterson Cappon Prize for Fiction, UMKC, University House, 5101 Rockhill Rd, Kansas City, MO 64110-2499 *Tel:* 816-235-1169 *Fax:* 816-235-2611 *E-mail:* newletters@umkc.edu *Web Site:* www.newletters.org, pg 675

Dorothy Churchill Cappon Prize for the Essay, UMKC, University House, 5101 Rockhill Rd, Kansas City, MO 64110-2499 *Tel:* 816-235-1169 *Fax:* 816-235-2611 *E-mail:* newletters@umkc.edu *Web Site:* www.newletters.org, pg 675

Capstone Publishers™, 1710 Roe Crest Dr, North Mankato, MN 56003 *Toll Free Tel:* 800-747-4992 (cust serv) *Toll Free Fax:* 888-262-0705 *Web Site:* www.capstonepress.com, pg 49

Captain Fiddle Music & Publications, 94 Wiswall Rd, Lee, NH 03861 *Tel:* 603-659-2658 *E-mail:* cfiddle@tiac.net *Web Site:* captainfiddle.com, pg 49

Captus Press Inc, 1600 Steeles Ave W, Units 14 & 15, Concord, ON L4K 4M2, Canada *Tel:* 416-736-5537 *Fax:* 416-736-5793 *E-mail:* info@captus.com *Web Site:* www.captus.com, pg 476

Caravan Books, 6946 E Stevens Rd, Cave Creek, AZ 85331-8677 *Tel:* 480-575-9945 *E-mail:* sfandr@msn.com *Web Site:* www.scholarsbooklist.com, pg 49

Cardiotext Publishing, 3405 W 44 St, Minneapolis, MN 55410 *Tel:* 612-925-2053 *Fax:* 612-922-7556 *E-mail:* info@cardiotextpublishing.com *Web Site:* www.cardiotextpublishing.com, pg 50

Cardoza Publishing, 808 S Main St, Las Vegas, NV 89101 *Tel:* 702-870-7200 *Toll Free Tel:* 800-577-WINS (577-9467) *E-mail:* cardozabooks@aol.com; info@cardozabooks.com *Web Site:* www.cardozabooks.com, pg 50

The Career Press Inc, 12 Parish Dr, Wayne, NJ 07470 *Tel:* 201-848-0310 *Toll Free Tel:* 800-CAREER-1 (227-3371) *Fax:* 201-848-1727 *E-mail:* sales@careerpress.com *Web Site:* www.careerpress.com, pg 50

Caribe Betania Editores, PO Box 141000, Nashville, TN 37214-1000 *Tel:* 615-902-1893 *Fax:* 615-883-9376 *Web Site:* www.caribebetania.com, pg 50

Carlisle Press - Walnut Creek, 2673 Township Rd 421, Sugarcreek, OH 44681 *Tel:* 330-852-1900 *Toll Free Tel:* 800-852-4482 *Fax:* 330-852-3285, pg 50

Andrew Carnegie Medals for Excellence in Fiction & Nonfiction, 50 E Huron St, Chicago, IL 60611 *Tel:* 312-944-6780 *Toll Free Tel:* 800-545-2433 *Fax:* 312-440-9374 *E-mail:* ala@ala.org *Web Site:* www.ala.org/awardsgrants/carnegieadult, pg 676

Carnegie Mellon University Press, 5032 Forbes Ave, Pittsburgh, PA 15289-1021 *Tel:* 412-268-2861 *Fax:* 412-268-8706 *E-mail:* carnegiemellonuniversitypress@gmail.com *Web Site:* www.cmu.edu/universitypress, pg 50

Carnegie-Whitney Award, 50 E Huron St, Chicago, IL 60611 *Tel:* 312-280-5416 *Toll Free Tel:* 800-545-2433 *Fax:* 312-280-5275; 312-440-9379 *Web Site:* www.ala.org, pg 676

Carolina Academic Press, 700 Kent St, Durham, NC 27701 *Tel:* 919-489-7486 *Toll Free Tel:* 800-489-7486 *Fax:* 919-493-5668 *E-mail:* cap@cap-press.com *Web Site:* www.cap-press.com; www.caplaw.com, pg 50

Carolrhoda Books, 241 First Ave N, Minneapolis, MN 55401 *Tel:* 612-332-3344 *Toll Free Tel:* 800-328-4929 *Fax:* 612-332-7615 *Toll Free Fax:* 800-332-1132 *E-mail:* info@lernerbooks.com *Web Site:* www.lernerbooks.com, pg 50

Carolrhoda Lab™, 241 First Ave N, Minneapolis, MN 55401 *Tel:* 612-332-3344 *Toll Free Tel:* 800-328-4929 *Fax:* 612-332-7615 *Toll Free Fax:* 800-332-1132 (US) *E-mail:* info@lernerbooks.com *Web Site:* www.lernerbooks.com, pg 50

Carpe Indexum, 364 Woodbine Ave, Syracuse, NY 13206-3324 *Tel:* 315-431-4949 *E-mail:* info@carpeindexum.com *Web Site:* www.carpeindexum.com, pg 522

Carroll Publishing, 4701 Sangamore Rd, Suite S-155, Bethesda, MD 20816 *Tel:* 301-263-9800 *Toll Free Tel:* 800-336-4240 *Fax:* 301-263-9801 *E-mail:* info@carrollpub.com; customersvc@carrollpub.com *Web Site:* www.carrollpublishing.com, pg 51

R E Carsch, MS-Consultant, 1453 Rhode Island St, San Francisco, CA 94107-3248 *Tel:* 415-641-1095 *E-mail:* recarsch@mzinfo.com *Web Site:* www.mzinfo.com, pg 522

Anne Carson Associates, 3323 Nebraska Ave NW, Washington, DC 20016 *Tel:* 202-244-6679, pg 522

Carson-Dellosa Publishing LLC, PO Box 35665, Greensboro, NC 27425-5665 *Tel:* 336-632-0084 *Toll Free Tel:* 800-321-0943 *Fax:* 336-632-0087 *Toll Free Fax:* 800-535-2669 *E-mail:* custsvc@carsondellosa.com *Web Site:* www.carsondellosa.com, pg 51

Carswell, One Corporate Plaza, 2075 Kennedy Rd, Toronto, ON M1T 3V4, Canada *Tel:* 416-298-5141; 416-609-3800 *Toll Free Tel:* 800-387-5164 (CN & US) *Fax:* 416-298-5094; 416-298-5082 *Toll Free Fax:* 877-750-9041 (CN only) *E-mail:* carswell.customerrelations@thomsonreuters.com; carswell.orders@thomsonreuters.com *Web Site:* www.carswell.com, pg 476

Carol Cartaino, 2000 Flat Run Rd, Seaman, OH 45679 *Tel:* 937-764-1303 *Fax:* 937-764-1303 *E-mail:* cartaino@aol.com, pg 522

CarTech Inc, 39966 Grand Ave, North Branch, MN 55056 *Tel:* 651-277-1200 *Toll Free Tel:* 800-551-4754 *Fax:* 651-277-1203 *E-mail:* info@cartechbooks.com *Web Site:* www.cartechbooks.com, pg 51

The Carter Prize For The Essay, Washington & Lee University, Mattingly House, 204 W Washington St, Lexington, VA 24450-2116 *Tel:* 540-458-8765 *E-mail:* shenandoah@wlu.edu *Web Site:* shenandoahliterary.org; shenandoah.wlu.edu, pg 676

Claudia Caruana, PO Box 654, Murray Hill Sta, New York, NY 10016 *Tel:* 516-488-5815 *E-mail:* ccaruana29@hotmail.com, pg 522

Maria Carvainis Agency Inc, Rockefeller Center, 1270 Avenue of the Americas, Suite 2320, New York, NY 10020 *Tel:* 212-245-6365 *Fax:* 212-245-7196 *E-mail:* mca@mariacarvainisagency.com *Web Site:* mariacarvainisagency.com, pg 545

Casa Bautista de Publicaciones, 7000 Alabama Ave, El Paso, TX 79904 *Tel:* 915-566-9656 *Toll Free Tel:* 800-755-5958 (cust serv & orders) *Fax:* 915-562-6502; 915-565-9008 (orders) *E-mail:* orders@editorialmh.org *Web Site:* www.editorialmh.org, pg 51

Cascade Pass Inc, 4223 Glencoe Ave, Suite C-105, Marina Del Rey, CA 90292-8801 *Tel:* 310-305-0210 *Toll Free Tel:* 888-837-0704 *Fax:* 310-305-7850 *Web Site:* www.cascadepass.com, pg 51

Casemate Publishers & Book Distributors LLC, 908 Darby Rd, Havertown, PA 19083 *Tel:* 610-853-9131 *Fax:* 610-853-9146 *E-mail:* casemate@casematepublishing.com *Web Site:* www.casematepublishing.com, pg 51

Angela M Casey, 42 Nathaniel Blvd, Delmar, NY 12054 *Tel:* 518-729-2693 *E-mail:* casey.angela.m@gmail.com, pg 522

Castiglia Literary Agency, 1155 Camino Del Mar, Suite 510, Del Mar, CA 92014 *Tel:* 858-755-8761 *Fax:* 858-755-7063 *Web Site:* www.castiglialiteraryagency.com, pg 545

Castle Connolly Medical Ltd, 42 W 24 St, 2nd fl, New York, NY 10010 *Tel:* 212-367-8400 *Fax:* 212-367-0964 *Web Site:* www.castleconnolly.com, pg 51

Catalyst Communication Arts, 94 Chuparrosa Dr, San Luis Obispo, CA 93401 *Tel:* 805-235-2351 *Fax:* 805-543-7140 *Web Site:* www.sonsieconroy.com, pg 522

Catalyst Creative Services, 619 Marion Plaza, Palo Alto, CA 94301-4251 *Tel:* 650-325-1500 *E-mail:* afriendlyghostwriter@gmail.com *Web Site:* www.catalystcreative.us, pg 523

Catholic Book Awards, 205 W Monroe St, Suite 470, Chicago, IL 60606 *Tel:* 312-380-6789 *Fax:* 312-361-0256 *E-mail:* cathjourn@catholicpress.org *Web Site:* www.catholicpress.org, pg 676

Catholic Book Publishing Corp, 77 West End Rd, Totowa, NJ 07512 *Tel:* 973-890-2400 *Toll Free Tel:* 877-228-2665 *Fax:* 973-890-2410 *E-mail:* info@catholicbookpublishing.com *Web Site:* www.catholicbookpublishing.com, pg 51

The Catholic Health Association of the United States, 4455 Woodson Rd, St Louis, MO 63134-3797 *Tel:* 314-427-2500 *Fax:* 314-427-0029 *E-mail:* servicecenter@chausa.org *Web Site:* www.chausa.org, pg 52

Catholic Library Association, 8550 United Plaza Blvd, Suite 1001, Baton Rouge, LA 70809-2256 *Tel:* 225-408-4417 *E-mail:* cla2@cathla.org *Web Site:* www.cathla.org, pg 602

Catholic Press Association of the United States & Canada, 205 W Monroe St, Suite 470, Chicago, IL 60606 *Tel:* 312-380-6789 *Fax:* 312-361-0256 *E-mail:* cathjourn@catholicpress.org *Web Site:* www.catholicpress.org, pg 602

Catholic Press Awards, 205 W Monroe St, Suite 470, Chicago, IL 60606 *Tel:* 312-380-6789 *Fax:* 312-361-0256 *E-mail:* cathjourn@catholicpress.org *Web Site:* www.catholicpress.org, pg 676

The Catholic University of America Press, 240 Leahy Hall, 620 Michigan Ave NE, Washington, DC 20064 *Tel:* 202-319-5052 *Toll Free Tel:* 800-537-5487 (orders only) *Fax:* 202-319-4985 *E-mail:* cua-press@cua.edu *Web Site:* cuapress.cua.edu, pg 52

Cato Institute, 1000 Massachusetts Ave NW, Washington, DC 20001-5403 *Tel:* 202-842-0200 *Toll Free Tel:* 800-767-1241 *Fax:* 202-842-3490 *E-mail:* catostore@cato.org *Web Site:* www.cato.org, pg 52

Jeanne Cavelos Editorial Services, PO Box 75, Mont Vernon, NH 03057 *Tel:* 603-673-6234 *Web Site:* jeannecavelos.com, pg 523

Caxton Press, 312 Main St, Caldwell, ID 83605-3299 *Tel:* 208-459-7421 *Toll Free Tel:* 800-657-6465 *Fax:* 208-459-7450 *E-mail:* publish@caxtonpress.com *Web Site:* www.caxtonpress.com, pg 52

CBA: The Association for Christian Retail, 1365 Garden of the Gods Rd, Suite 105, Colorado Springs, CO 80907 *Tel:* 719-265-9895 *Toll Free Tel:* 800-252-1950 *Fax:* 719-272-3508 *E-mail:* info@cbaonline.org *Web Site:* cbaonline.org, pg 602

CCAB Inc, One Concorde Gate, Suite 800, Toronto, ON M3C 3N6, Canada *Tel:* 416-487-2418 *Fax:* 416-487-6405 *E-mail:* info@bpaww.com *Web Site:* www.bpaww.com, pg 603

CCH, a Wolters Kluwer business, 2700 Lake Cook Rd, Riverwoods, IL 60015 *Tel:* 847-267-7000 *Web Site:* www.cch.com, pg 52

CDL Press, PO Box 34454, Bethesda, MD 20827 *Tel:* 301-762-2066 *Fax:* 253-484-5542 *E-mail:* cdlpress@erols.com *Web Site:* www.cdlpress.com, pg 52

CeciBooks Editorial & Publishing Consultation, 7057 26 Ave NW, Seattle, WA 98117 *Tel:* 206-706-9565 *E-mail:* cecibooks@gmail.com *Web Site:* www.cecibooks.com, pg 523

Cedar Fort Inc, 2373 W 700 S, Springville, UT 84663 *Tel:* 801-489-4084 *Toll Free Tel:* 800-SKY-BOOK (759-2665) *Fax:* 801-489-1097 *Toll Free Fax:* 800-388-3727 *Web Site:* cedarfort.com, pg 52

Cedar Grove Books, 2215 High Point Dr, Carrollton, TX 75007 *Tel:* 415-364-8292 *Fax:* 415-276-9858 *E-mail:* queries@cedargrovebooks.com *Web Site:* www.cedargrovebooks.com, pg 52

Cedar Tree Books, PO Box 4256, Wilmington, DE 19807 *Tel:* 302-998-4171 *Fax:* 302-998-4185 *E-mail:* books@ctpress.com *Web Site:* www.cedartreebooks.com, pg 52

CEF Press, 17482 State Hwy M, Warrenton, MO 63383-0348 *Tel:* 636-456-4321 *Toll Free Tel:* 800-748-7710 (cust serv); 800-300-4033 (USA ministries) *Fax:* 636-456-9935 *E-mail:* cefexecutiveoffices@cefonline.com *Web Site:* www.cefonline.com, pg 52

Celebra, 375 Hudson St, New York, NY 10014 *Tel:* 212-366-2000 *Fax:* 212-366-2889, pg 53

Celebrity Profiles Publishing, PO Box 344, Stony Brook, NY 11790 *Tel:* 631-862-8555 *Fax:* 631-862-0139 *E-mail:* celebpro4@aol.com *Web Site:* www.richardgrudens.com; richardgrudensblog.blogspot.com, pg 53

Cengage Learning, 20 Channel Center St, Boston, MA 02210 *Tel:* 617-289-7700 *Toll Free Tel:* 800-354-9706 *Fax:* 617-289-7844 *Toll Free Fax:* 800-487-8488 *E-mail:* esales@cengage.com *Web Site:* www.cengage.com, pg 53

The Center for Book Arts, 28 W 27 St, 3rd fl, New York, NY 10001 *Tel:* 212-481-0295 *E-mail:* info@centerforbookarts.org *Web Site:* www.centerforbookarts.org, pg 603

The Center for Book Arts, 28 W 27 St, 3rd fl, New York, NY 10001 *Tel:* 212-481-0295 *Toll Free Fax:* 866-708-8994 *E-mail:* info@centerforbookarts.org *Web Site:* www.centerforbookarts.org, pg 659

Center for Creative Leadership LLC, One Leadership Place, Greensboro, NC 27410-9427 *Tel:* 336-545-2810; 336-288-7210 *Fax:* 336-282-3284 *E-mail:* info@ccl.org *Web Site:* www.ccl.org/publications, pg 53

Center for East Asian Studies (CEAS), Western Washington University, 516 High St, Bellingham, WA 98225 *Tel:* 360-650-3339 *Fax:* 360-650-6110 *E-mail:* easpress@wwu.edu *Web Site:* www.wwu.edu/eas, pg 53

The Center for Exhibition Industry Research (CEIR), 12700 Park Central Dr, Suite 308, Dallas, TX 75251 *Tel:* 972-687-9242 *Fax:* 972-692-6020 *E-mail:* info@ceir.org *Web Site:* www.ceir.org, pg 603

The Center for Fiction, 17 E 47 St, New York, NY 10017 *Tel:* 212-755-6710 *Fax:* 212-826-0831 *E-mail:* info@centerforfiction.org *Web Site:* centerforfiction.org/awards, pg 603

Center for Futures Education Inc, 345 Erie St, Grove City, PA 16127 *Tel:* 724-458-5860 *Fax:* 724-458-5962 *E-mail:* info@thectr.com *Web Site:* www.thectr.com, pg 53

The Center for Learning, 10200 Jefferson Blvd, Culver City, CA 90232 *Tel:* 310-839-2436 *Toll Free Tel:* 800-421-4246 *Fax:* 310-839-2249 *Toll Free Fax:* 800-944-5432 *E-mail:* customerservice@centerforlearning.org *Web Site:* www.centerforlearning.org, pg 53

Center for Publishing Departmental Scholarships, Midtown Ctr, Rm 429, 11 W 42 St, New York, NY 10036 *Tel:* 212-992-3232 *Fax:* 212-992-3233 *E-mail:* pub.center@nyu.edu; ms.publishing@nyu.edu *Web Site:* www.scps.nyu.edu, pg 676

The Center for the Book in the Library of Congress, The Library of Congress, 101 Independence Ave SE, Washington, DC 20540-4920 *Tel:* 202-707-5221 *Fax:* 202-707-0269 *E-mail:* cfbook@loc.gov *Web Site:* www.read.gov; www.read.gov/cfb, pg 603

Center for the Collaborative Classroom, 1250 53 St, Suite 3, Emeryville, CA 94608 *Tel:* 510-533-0213 *Toll Free Tel:* 800-666-7270 *Fax:* 510-464-3670 *E-mail:* info@collaborativeclassroom.org; clientsupport@collaborativeclassroom.org *Web Site:* www.collaborativeclassroom.org, pg 53

Center for Women Policy Studies, 4620 N Park Ave, Suite 302W, Chevy Chase, MD 20815 *Tel:* 301-986-0795 *E-mail:* cwps@centerwomenpolicy.org *Web Site:* www.centerwomenpolicy.org, pg 53

Centering Corp, 7230 Maple St, Omaha, NE 68134 *Tel:* 402-553-1200 *Toll Free Tel:* 866-218-0101 *Fax:* 402-553-0507 *E-mail:* orders@centering.org *Web Site:* www.centering.org, pg 54

Centerstream Publishing LLC, PO Box 17878, Anaheim Hills, CA 92817-7878 *Tel:* 714-779-9390 *E-mail:* centerstrm@aol.com *Web Site:* www.centerstream-usa.com, pg 54

Central Conference of American Rabbis/CCAR Press, 355 Lexington Ave, 18th fl, New York, NY 10017 *Tel:* 212-972-3636 *E-mail:* info@ccarnet.org *Web Site:* www.ccarpress.org, pg 54

Central European University Press, 224 W 57 St, New York, NY 10019 *Web Site:* www.ceupress.com, pg 54

Central Recovery Press (CRP), 3321 N Buffalo Dr, Suite 275, Las Vegas, NV 89129 *Tel:* 702-868-5830 *Fax:* 702-868-5831 *E-mail:* info@centralrecovery.com *Web Site:* centralrecoverypress.com, pg 54

Centre for Reformation & Renaissance Studies (CRRS), 71 Queen's Park Crescent E, Toronto, ON M5S 1K7, Canada *Tel:* 416-585-4465 *Fax:* 416-585-4430 (attn: CRRS) *E-mail:* crrs.publications@utoronto.ca *Web Site:* crrs.ca, pg 476

Centre Franco-Ontarien de Ressources en Alphabetisation (Centre FORA), 450 Notre Dame Ave, Suite 0103, Sudbury, ON P3C 5K8, Canada *Tel:* 705-524-3672 *Toll Free Tel:* 888-814-4422 (orders, CN only) *Fax:* 705-524-8535 *E-mail:* info@centrefora.on.ca *Web Site:* www.centrefora.on.ca, pg 476

The Century Foundation, One Whitehall St, 15 fl, New York, NY 10004 *Tel:* 212-452-7700 *Fax:* 212-535-7534 *E-mail:* info@tcf.org *Web Site:* www.tcf.org, pg 623

The Century Foundation Press, One Whitehall St, 15th fl, New York, NY 10004 *Tel:* 212-452-7700 *Fax:* 212-535-7534 *E-mail:* info@tcf.org *Web Site:* www.tcf.org, pg 54

Chain Store Guide (CSG), 10117 Princess Palm Ave, Suite 375, Tampa, FL 33610 *Tel:* 813-627-6957 *Toll Free Tel:* 800-927-9292 (orders) *Fax:* 813-627-6888 *E-mail:* info@csgis.com *Web Site:* www.csgis.com, pg 54

Chalice Press, 483 E Lockwood Ave, Suite 100, St Louis, MO 63119 *Tel:* 314-231-8500 *Toll Free Tel:* 800-366-3383 *Fax:* 314-231-8524; 770-280-4039 (orders) *E-mail:* customerservice@chalicepress.com *Web Site:* www.chalicepress.com, pg 54

Jane Chambers Playwriting Award, Georgetown University, 108 David Performing Arts Ctr, Box 571063, 37 & "O" St, NW, Washington, DC 20057-1063 *Tel:* 202-687-1327 *Web Site:* www.athe.org/?page=Jane_Chambers, pg 676

The Alfred & Fay Chandler Book Award, c/o Harvard Business School, Connell House 301A, Boston, MA 02163 *Tel:* 617-495-1003 *Fax:* 617-495-2705 *E-mail:* bhr@hbs.edu *Web Site:* www.hbs.edu/businesshistory/fellowships, pg 676

G S Sharat Chandra Prize for Short Fiction, University House, 5101 Rockhill Rd, Kansas City, MO 64110-2499 *Tel:* 816-235-2558 *Fax:* 816-235-2611 *E-mail:* bkmk@umkc.edu *Web Site:* www.umkc.edu/bkmk, pg 676

Channel Photographics, 980 Lincoln Ave, Suite 200-B, San Rafael, CA 94901 *Tel:* 415-456-2934 *Fax:* 415-456-4124 *Web Site:* www.channelphotographics.com, pg 55

Chaosium Inc, 22568 Mission Blvd, Suite 423, Hayward, CA 94541-5116 *Tel:* 510-583-1000 *Fax:* 510-583-1101 *Web Site:* www.chaosium.com, pg 55

Chapter One Fiction Competition, 1738 Hone Ave, Bronx, NY 10461-1486 *Tel:* 718-931-9500 *Fax:* 718-409-6445 *E-mail:* info@bronxarts.org *Web Site:* www.bronxarts.org, pg 676

Character Publishing, 6340 Kiln Delisle Rd, Unit F, Pass Christian, MS 39571 *Tel:* 228-234-7651 *Fax:* 228-222-3321 *Web Site:* www.characterpublishing.org, pg 55

Charisma Media, 600 Rinehart Rd, Lake Mary, FL 32746 *Tel:* 407-333-0600 (all imprints) *Toll Free Tel:* 800-283-8494 (Charisma Media, Siloam Press, Creation House); 800-665-1468 *Fax:* 407-333-7100 (all imprints) *E-mail:* charisma@charismamedia.com *Web Site:* www.charismamedia.com, pg 55

CharismaLife Publishers, 600 Rinehart Rd, Lake Mary, FL 32746 *Tel:* 407-333-0600 *Toll Free Tel:* 800-451-4598 *Fax:* 407-333-7100 *E-mail:* charismalife@charismamedia.com *Web Site:* www.charismamedia.com, pg 55

Chariton Review Short Fiction Prize, 100 E Normal Ave, Kirksville, MO 63501-4221 *Tel:* 660-785-7336 *Toll Free Tel:* 800-916-6802 *Fax:* 660-785-4480 *E-mail:* tsup@truman.edu *Web Site:* tsup.truman.edu, pg 676

The Charles Press, Publishers, 230 N 21 St, Suite 202, Philadelphia, PA 19103 *Tel:* 215-561-2786 *Fax:* 215-561-0191 *E-mail:* mail@charlespresspub.com *Web Site:* www.charlespresspub.com, pg 55

Charles River Media, 20 Channel Center St, Boston, MA 02210 *Toll Free Tel:* 800-354-9706 *Toll Free Fax:* 800-487-8488 *E-mail:* crminfo@cengage.com *Web Site:* www.cengage.com; www.delmarlearning.com/charlesriver, pg 55

Charles Scribner's Sons®, 27500 Drake Rd, Farmington Hills, MI 48331-3535 *Toll Free Tel:* 800-877-4253 *Toll Free Fax:* 800-414-5043 *E-mail:* gale.galeord@cengage.com *Web Site:* www.gale.com/scribners, pg 55

Charlesbridge Publishing Inc, 85 Main St, Watertown, MA 02472 *Tel:* 617-926-0329 *Toll Free Tel:* 800-225-3214 *Fax:* 617-926-5720 *Toll Free Fax:* 800-926-5775 *E-mail:* books@charlesbridge.com *Web Site:* www.charlesbridge.com, pg 55

The Charlton Press, 5845 Yonge St, PO Box 69509, North York, ON M2M 4K3, Canada *Tel:* 416-488-1418 *Toll Free Tel:* 800-442-6042 (North America) *Fax:* 416-488-4656 *Toll Free Fax:* 800-442-1542 (North America) *E-mail:* chpress@charltonpress.com *Web Site:* www.charltonpress.com, pg 476

Chautauqua Writers' Workshop, PO Box 28, Chautauqua, NY 14722-0408 *Tel:* 716-357-6316; 716-357-6250 *Toll Free Tel:* 800-836-ARTS (836-2787) *Fax:* 716-269-7444 *Web Site:* writers.ciweb.org, pg 650

Margaret Cheasebro, 246 Rd 2900, Aztec, NM 87410 *Tel:* 505-334-2869 *E-mail:* margaretcheasebro@yahoo.com *Web Site:* www.wordsandwellness.com, pg 523

Jane Chelius Literary Agency Inc, 548 Second St, Brooklyn, NY 11215 *Tel:* 718-499-0236; 718-499-0714 *Fax:* 718-832-7335 *E-mail:* queries@janechelius.com; rights@janechelius.com *Web Site:* www.janechelius.com, pg 545

Chelsea Green Publishing Co, 85 N Main St, Suite 120, White River Junction, VT 05001 *Tel:* 802-295-6300 *Toll Free Tel:* 800-639-4099 (cust serv, consumer & trade orders) *Fax:* 802-295-6444 *Web Site:* www.chelseagreen.com, pg 56

Chelsea House Publishers, 132 W 31 St, 17th fl, New York, NY 10001 *Tel:* 212-967-8800 *Toll Free Tel:* 800-322-8755 *Fax:* 917-339-0325 *Toll Free Fax:* 800-678-3633 *E-mail:* custserv@factsonfile.com *Web Site:* www.infobasepublishing.com; www.infobaselearning.com, pg 56

ChemTec Publishing, 38 Earswick Dr, Toronto, ON M1E 1C6, Canada *Tel:* 416-265-2603 *Fax:* 416-265-1399 *E-mail:* orderdesk@chemtec.org *Web Site:* www.chemtec.org, pg 477

Cheneliere Education Inc, 5800, rue St Denis, bureau 900, Montreal, QC H2S 3L5, Canada *Tel:* 514-273-1066 *Toll Free Tel:* 800-565-5531 *Fax:* 514-276-0324 *Toll Free Fax:* 800-814-0324 *E-mail:* info@cheneliere.ca *Web Site:* www.cheneliere.ca, pg 477

Cheng & Tsui Co Inc, 25 West St, 2nd fl, Boston, MA 02111-1213 *Tel:* 617-988-2401 *Toll Free Tel:* 800-554-1963 *Fax:* 617-426-3669; 617-556-8964 *E-mail:* service@cheng-tsui.com; orders@cheng-tsui.com *Web Site:* www.cheng-tsui.com, pg 56

Ruth Chernia, 198 Victor Ave, Toronto, ON M4K 1B2, Canada *Tel:* 416-466-0164 *E-mail:* rchernia@editors.ca; rchernia@sympatico.ca, pg 523

Cherry Hill Publishing LLC, 24344 Del Amo Rd, Ramona, CA 92065 *Tel:* 858-829-5550 *Toll Free Tel:* 800-407-1072 *Fax:* 760-203-1200 *E-mail:* operations@cherryhillpublishing.com; sales@cherryhillpublishing.com *Web Site:* www.cherryhillpublishing.com, pg 56

Linda Chester Literary Agency, 630 Fifth Ave, Suite 2000, New York, NY 10111 *Tel:* 212-218-3350 *Fax:* 212-218-3343 *E-mail:* submissions@lindachester.com *Web Site:* www.lindachester.com, pg 546

Chestnut Publishing Group Inc, 44 Stubbs Dr, Suite 207, Toronto, ON M2L 2R3, Canada *Tel:* 416-224-5824 *Fax:* 416-224-0595 *Web Site:* www.chestnutpublishing.com, pg 477

Chicago Review Press, 814 N Franklin St, Chicago, IL 60610 *Tel:* 312-337-0747 *Toll Free Tel:* 800-888-4741 *Fax:* 312-337-5110 *E-mail:* frontdesk@chicagoreviewpress.com *Web Site:* www.chicagoreviewpress.com, pg 56

Chicago Women in Publishing, PO Box 268107, Chicago, IL 60626 *Tel:* 773-508-0351 *Fax:* 435-604-6049 *E-mail:* info@cwip.org *Web Site:* www.cwip.org, pg 603

Child Welfare League of America (CWLA), 1726 "M" St, Suite 500, Washington, DC 20036 *Tel:* 202-688-4200 *Fax:* 202-833-1689 *E-mail:* cwla@cwla.org *Web Site:* www.cwla.org/publications, pg 56

Children's & Teen Choice Book Awards, 54 W 39 St, 14th fl, New York, NY 10018 *Tel:* 212-966-1990 *E-mail:* cbc.info@cbcbooks.org *Web Site:* ccbookawards.com; www.cbcbooks.org, pg 676

The Children's Book Council (CBC), 54 W 39 St, 14th fl, New York, NY 10018 *Tel:* 212-966-1990 *Toll Free Fax:* 888-807-9355 (orders only) *E-mail:* cbc.info@cbcbooks.org *Web Site:* www.cbcbooks.org, pg 603

Children's Book Press, 95 Madison Ave, Suite 1205, New York, NY 10016 *Tel:* 212-779-4400 *Fax:* 212-683-1894 *E-mail:* general@leeandlow.com; orders@leeandlow.com; sales@leeandlow.com *Web Site:* www.leeandlow.com, pg 57

Children's Literature Association Article Award, 1301 W 22 St, Suite 202, Oak Brook, IL 60523 *Tel:* 630-571-4520 *Fax:* 708-876-5598 *E-mail:* info@childlitassn.org *Web Site:* www.childlitassn.org, pg 677

Children's Literature Association Beiter Graduate Student Research Grants, 1301 W 22 St, Suite 202, Oak Brook, IL 60523 *Tel:* 630-571-4520 *Fax:* 708-876-5598 *E-mail:* info@childlitassn.org *Web Site:* www.childlitassn.org, pg 677

Children's Literature Association Book Award, 1301 W 22 St, Suite 202, Oak Brook, IL 60523 *Tel:* 630-571-4520 *Fax:* 708-876-5598 *E-mail:* info@childlitassn.org *Web Site:* www.childlitassn.org, pg 677

Children's Sequoyah Book Award, 300 Hardy Dr, Edmond, OK 73013 *Tel:* 405-525-5100 *Fax:* 405-525-5103 *Web Site:* www.oklibs.org, pg 677

Faith Childs Literary Agency Inc, 111 John St, Suite 1620, New York, NY 10038 *Tel:* 212-995-9600 *Web Site:* faithchildsliteraryagency.com, pg 546

Child's Play®, 250 Minot Ave, Auburn, ME 04210 *Tel:* 207-784-7252 *Toll Free Tel:* 800-639-6404 *Fax:* 207-784-7358 *Toll Free Fax:* 800-854-6989 *E-mail:* chpmaine@aol.com; cplay@earthlink.net *Web Site:* www.childs-play.com, pg 57

The Child's World Inc, 1980 Lookout Dr, North Mankato, MN 56003-1705 *Tel:* 507-385-1044 *Toll Free Tel:* 800-599-READ (599-7323) *Toll Free Fax:* 888-320-2329 *E-mail:* sales@childsworld.com *Web Site:* childsworld.com, pg 57

Childswork/Childsplay LLC, 303 Crossway Park Dr, Woodbury, NY 11797 *Toll Free Tel:* 800-962-1141 (cust serv) *Toll Free Fax:* 800-262-1886 (orders) *Web Site:* www.childswork.com, pg 57

China Books, 360 Swift Ave, Suite 48, South San Francisco, CA 94080 *Tel:* 650-872-7076 *Toll Free Tel:* 800-818-2017 (US only) *Fax:* 650-872-7808 *E-mail:* info@chinabooks.com *Web Site:* www.chinabooks.com, pg 57

Chinese Connection Agency, 67 Banksville Rd, Armonk, NY 10504 *Tel:* 914-765-0296 *Fax:* 914-765-0297 *E-mail:* info@yaollc.com *Web Site:* www.yaollc.com, pg 546

Chosen Books, 11400 Hampshire Ave S, Bloomington, MN 55438-2852 *Tel:* 616-676-9185 *Toll Free Tel:* 800-877-2665 (orders only) *Fax:* 616-676-9573 *Toll Free Fax:* 800-398-3111 (orders only) *Web Site:* bakerpublishinggroup.com/chosen, pg 57

Chouette Publishing, 1001 Lenoir St, Suite B-238, Montreal, QC H4C 2Z6, Canada *Tel:* 514-925-3325 *Fax:* 514-925-3323 *E-mail:* info@editions-chouette.com *Web Site:* www.chouette-publishing.com, pg 477

Christian Liberty Press, 502 W Euclid Ave, Arlington Heights, IL 60004-5402 *Tel:* 847-259-4444 *Toll Free Tel:* 800-832-2741 (cust serv) *Fax:* 847-259-2941 *E-mail:* custserv@christianlibertypress.com *Web Site:* www.shopchristianliberty.com, pg 57

Christian Light Publications Inc, 1051 Mount Clinton Pike, Harrisonburg, VA 22802 *Tel:* 540-434-1003 *Toll Free Tel:* 800-776-0478 *Fax:* 540-433-8896 *E-mail:* info@clp.org; orders@clp.org *Web Site:* www.clp.org, pg 57

Christian Schools International, 3350 E Paris Ave SE, Grand Rapids, MI 49512-3054 *Tel:* 616-957-1070 *Toll Free Tel:* 800-635-8288 *Fax:* 616-957-5022 *E-mail:* info@csionline.org *Web Site:* www.csionline.org, pg 57

The Christian Science Publishing Society, 210 Massachusetts Ave, Boston, MA 02115 *Tel:* 617-450-2000 *Toll Free Tel:* 800-288-7090 *Fax:* 617-450-7334 *E-mail:* contact@csps.com *Web Site:* christianscience.com, pg 57

The Christopher Awards, 5 Hanover Sq, 22nd fl, New York, NY 10004-2751 *Tel:* 212-759-4050 *Toll Free Tel:* 888-298-4050 (orders) *Fax:* 212-838-5073 *E-mail:* mail@christophers.org *Web Site:* www.christophers.org, pg 677

William F Christopher Publication Services, Kensington No 237, 1580 Geary Rd, Walnut Creek, CA 94597-2744 *Tel:* 925-943-5584 *Fax:* 925-943-5594 *E-mail:* wfcmgmt.innovations@yahoo.com, pg 546

Chronicle Books LLC, 680 Second St, San Francisco, CA 94107 *Tel:* 415-537-4200 *Toll Free Tel:* 800-759-0190 (cust serv) *Fax:* 415-537-4460 *Toll Free Fax:* 800-858-7787 (orders); 800-286-9471 (cust serv) *E-mail:* frontdesk@chroniclebooks.com *Web Site:* www.chroniclebooks.com, pg 57

John Ciardi Prize for Poetry, University House, 5101 Rockhill Rd, Kansas City, MO 64110-2499 *Tel:* 816-235-2558 *Fax:* 816-235-2611 *E-mail:* bkmk@umkc.edu *Web Site:* www.umkc.edu/bkmk, pg 677

Cider Mill Press Book Publishers LLC, 12 Spring St, Kennebunkport, ME 04046 *Tel:* 207-967-8232 *Fax:* 207-967-8233 *Web Site:* www.cidermillpress.com, pg 58

Cinco Puntos Press, 701 Texas Ave, El Paso, TX 79901 *Tel:* 915-838-1625 *Toll Free Tel:* 800-566-9072 *Fax:* 915-838-1635 *E-mail:* info@cincopuntos.com *Web Site:* www.cincopuntos.com, pg 58

Cine/Lit Representation, PO Box 802918, Santa Clarita, CA 91380-2918 *Tel:* 661-513-0268 *E-mail:* cinelit@att.net, pg 546

Circlet Press Inc, 39 Hurlbut St, Cambridge, MA 02138 *Toll Free Tel:* 800-729-6423 *E-mail:* circletintern@gmail.com *Web Site:* www.circlet.com, pg 58

Cistercian Publications, Saint John's Abbey, PO Box 7500, Collegeville, MN 56321 *Tel:* 320-363-2213 *Toll Free Tel:* 800-436-8431 *Fax:* 320-363-3299 *Toll Free Fax:* 800-445-5899 *E-mail:* sales@litpress.org *Web Site:* www.cistercianpublications.org, pg 58

City & Regional Magazine Association, 1970 E Grand Ave, Suite 330, El Segundo, CA 90245 *Tel:* 310-364-0193 *Fax:* 310-364-0196 *E-mail:* admin@citymag.org *Web Site:* www.citymag.org, pg 603

City Lights Publishers, 261 Columbus Ave, San Francisco, CA 94133 *Tel:* 415-362-8193 *Fax:* 415-362-4921 *E-mail:* staff@citylights.com *Web Site:* www.citylights.com, pg 58

The City of Calgary W O Mitchell Book Prize, 11759 Groat Rd, Edmonton, AB T5M 3K6, Canada *Tel:* 780-422-8174 *Toll Free Tel:* 800-665-5354 (AB only) *Fax:* 780-422-2663 (attn WGA) *E-mail:* mail@writersguild.ab.ca *Web Site:* www.writersguild.ab.ca, pg 677

City of Vancouver Book Award, Woodward's Heritage Bldg, Suite 501, 111 W Hastings St, Vancouver, BC V6B 1H4, Canada *Tel:* 604-871-6634 *Fax:* 604-871-6005 *E-mail:* culture@vancouver.ca *Web Site:* vancouver.ca/bookaward, pg 677

CLA Book of the Year for Children Award, 1150 Morrison Dr, Suite 1100, Ottawa, ON K2H 8S9, Canada *Tel:* 613-232-9625 *Fax:* 613-563-9895 *E-mail:* info@cla.ca *Web Site:* www.cla.ca, pg 677

The Clarion Awards, 3337 Duke St, Alexandria, VA 22314 *Tel:* 703-370-7436 *Fax:* 703-342-4311 *E-mail:* clarion@womcom.org *Web Site:* www.womcom.org, pg 677

Clarion Books, 215 Park Ave S, New York, NY 10003 *Tel:* 212-420-5889 *Toll Free Tel:* 800-225-3362 (orders) *Fax:* 212-420-5855 *Toll Free Fax:* 800-634-7568 (orders) *Web Site:* www.hmhco.com, pg 59

The Clarion Science Fiction & Fantasy Writers' Workshop, Dept of Literature, Mail Code 0410, UC San Diego, 9500 Gilman Dr, La Jolla, CA 92093-0410 *Tel:* 858-534-2115 *E-mail:* clarion@ucsd.edu *Web Site:* clarion.ucsd.edu, pg 650

Clarity Press Inc, 2625 Piedmont Rd NE, Suite 56, Atlanta, GA 30324 *Toll Free Tel:* 877-613-1495 (edit) *Toll Free Fax:* 877-613-7868 *E-mail:* claritypress@usa.net (foreign rts & perms) *Web Site:* www.claritypress.com, pg 59

Wm Clark Associates, 186 Fifth Ave, 2nd fl, New York, NY 10010 *Tel:* 212-675-2784 *Fax:* 347-649-9262 *E-mail:* general@wmclark.com *Web Site:* www.wmclark.com, pg 546

Class Action Ink, 1300 NE 16 Ave, Suite 712, Portland, OR 97232-1483 *Tel:* 503-280-2448 *E-mail:* pam@classactionink.com *Web Site:* www.classactionink.com, pg 507

Classical Academic Press, 2151 Market St, Camp Hill, PA 17011 *Tel:* 717-730-0711 *Fax:* 717-730-0721 *E-mail:* office@classicalsubjects.com *Web Site:* www.classicalsubjects.com, pg 59

Page Davidson Clayton Prize for Emerging Poets, University of Michigan, 0576 Rackham Bldg, 915 E Washington St, Ann Arbor, MI 48109-1070 *Tel:* 734-764-9265 *E-mail:* mqr@umich.edu *Web Site:* www.umich.edu/~mqr, pg 677

CLC Ministries, 701 Pennsylvania Ave, Fort Washington, PA 19034 *Tel:* 215-542-1240 *Toll Free Tel:* 800-659-1240 *Fax:* 215-542-7580 *E-mail:* orders@clcpublications.com *Web Site:* www.clcpublications.com, pg 59

Clear Concepts, 1329 Federal Ave, Suite 6, Los Angeles, CA 90025 *Tel:* 310-473-5453, pg 523

Clear Light Publishers, 823 Don Diego Ave, Santa Fe, NM 87505 *Tel:* 505-989-9590 *Toll Free Tel:* 800-253-2747 (orders) *Fax:* 505-989-9519 *E-mail:* market@clearlightbooks.com *Web Site:* www.clearlightbooks.com, pg 59

Clearfield Co Inc, 3600 Clipper Mill Rd, Suite 260, Baltimore, MD 21211 *Tel:* 410-837-8271 *Toll Free Tel:* 800-296-6687 (orders & cust serv) *Fax:* 410-752-8492 *E-mail:* sales@genealogical.com *Web Site:* www.genealogical.com, pg 59

Cleis Press, 2246 Sixth St, Berkeley, CA 94710 *Tel:* 510-845-8000 *Toll Free Tel:* 800-780-2279 (US) *Fax:* 510-845-8001 *E-mail:* orders@cleispress.com *Web Site:* www.cleispress.com; www.vivaeditions.com, pg 59

Clements Publishing, 6021 Yonge St, Suite 213, Toronto, ON M2M 3W2, Canada *Tel:* 647-477-2509 *Fax:* 647-477-2058 *E-mail:* info@clementspublishing.com *Web Site:* www.clementspublishing.com, pg 477

Clerical Plus, 97 Blueberry Lane, Shelton, CT 06484 *Tel:* 203-225-0879 *Fax:* 203-225-0879 *E-mail:* clericalplus@aol.com *Web Site:* www.clericalplus.net, pg 523

Clerisy Press, 306 Greenup St, Covington, KY 41011 *Tel:* 859-815-7200 *Toll Free Tel:* 800-913-9563 *Fax:* 859-291-9111 *E-mail:* info@clerisypress.com *Web Site:* www.clerisypress.com, pg 59

Cleveland State University Poetry Center Prizes, 2121 Euclid Ave, Cleveland, OH 44115-2214 *Tel:* 216-687-3986 *Fax:* 216-687-6943 *E-mail:* poetrycenter@csuohio.edu *Web Site:* www.csuohio.edu/poetrycenter, pg 678

David H Clift Scholarship, 50 E Huron St, Chicago, IL 60611 *Toll Free Tel:* 800-545-2433 (ext 4279) *Fax:* 312-280-3256 *E-mail:* scholarships@ala.org *Web Site:* www.ala.org/scholarships, pg 678

Clinical Laboratory & Standards Institute (CLSI), 950 W Valley Rd, Suite 2500, Wayne, PA 19087 *Tel:* 610-688-0100 *Toll Free Tel:* 877-447-1888 (orders) *Fax:* 610-688-0700 *E-mail:* customerservice@clsi.org *Web Site:* www.clsi.org, pg 59

Close Up Publishing, 1330 Braddock Place, Suite 400, Alexandria, VA 22314 *Tel:* 703-706-3300 *Toll Free Tel:* 800-CLOSE-UP (256-7387) *Fax:* 703-706-3564 *E-mail:* info@closeup.org *Web Site:* www.closeup.org, pg 60

Closson Press, 257 Delilah St, Apollo, PA 15613-1933 *Tel:* 724-337-4482 *Fax:* 724-337-9484 *E-mail:* clossonpress@comcast.net *Web Site:* www.clossonpress.com, pg 60

Clotilde's Secretarial & Management Services, PO Box 871926, New Orleans, LA 70187 *Tel:* 504-242-2912; 504-800-4853 (cell) *E-mail:* elcsy58@aol.com; elcsy58@att.net, pg 523

Dwight Clough, 1223 W Main St, No 228, Sun Prairie, WI 53590 *Tel:* 608-834-8291 *E-mail:* lmp@dwightclough.com *Web Site:* dwightclough.com, pg 523

CN Times Books, 501 Fifth Ave, Suite 1708, New York, NY 10017 *Tel:* 212-867-8666 *Web Site:* cntimesbooks.com, pg 60

Coach House Books, 80 bpNichol Lane, Toronto, ON M5S 3J4, Canada *Tel:* 416-979-2217 *Toll Free Tel:* 800-367-6360 (outside Toronto) *Fax:* 416-977-1158 *E-mail:* mail@chbooks.com *Web Site:* www.chbooks.com, pg 477

Coaches Choice, 514 Airport Way, Monterey, CA 93940 *Toll Free Tel:* 888-229-5745 *Fax:* 831-372-6075 *E-mail:* info@coacheschoice.com *Web Site:* www.coacheschoice.com, pg 60

Coachlight Press LLC, 1704 Craig's Store Rd, Afton, VA 22920-2017 *Tel:* 434-823-1692 *E-mail:* sales@coachlightpress.com *Web Site:* www.coachlightpress.com, pg 60

Coal Hill Review Poetry Chapbook Contest, c/o Autumn House Press, PO Box 60100, Pittsburgh, PA 15211 *E-mail:* reviewcoalhill@gmail.com *Web Site:* www.coalhillreview.com, pg 678

Coastside Editorial, PO Box 181, Moss Beach, CA 94038 *E-mail:* bevjoe@pacific.net, pg 523

Codhill Press, One Arden Lane, New Paltz, NY 12561 *E-mail:* codhillpress@aol.com *Web Site:* www.codhill.com, pg 60

CODiE Awards, 1090 Vermont Ave NW, 6th fl, Washington, DC 20005-4095 *Tel:* 202-289-7442 *Fax:* 202-289-7097 *E-mail:* info@siia.net *Web Site:* www.siia.net, pg 678

Coe College Playwriting Festival, 1220 First Ave NE, Cedar Rapids, IA 52402 *Tel:* 319-399-8624 *Fax:* 319-399-8557 *Web Site:* www.theatre.coe.edu; www.coe.edu/academics/theatrearts/theatrearts_playwritingfestival, pg 678

Coffee House Press, 79 13 Ave NE, Suite 110, Minneapolis, MN 55413 *Tel:* 612-338-0125 *Fax:* 612-338-4004 *E-mail:* info@coffeehousepress.org *Web Site:* coffeehousepress.org, pg 60

Cognizant Communication Corp, 18 Peekskill Hollow Rd, Putnam Valley, NY 10597-3213 *Tel:* 845-603-6440; 845-603-6441 (warehouse & orders) *Fax:* 845-603-6442 *E-mail:* inquiries@cognizantcommunication.com; sales@cognizantcommunication.com *Web Site:* www.cognizantcommunication.com, pg 60

Carla Furstenberg Cohen Literary Prize, 1322 Holly St NW, Washington, DC 20012, pg 678

Morton N Cohen Award for a Distinguished Edition of Letters, 26 Broadway, 3rd fl, New York, NY 10004-1789 *Tel:* 646-576-5141 *Fax:* 646-458-0030 *E-mail:* awards@mla.org *Web Site:* www.mla.org, pg 678

Robert L Cohen, 182-12 Horace Harding Expwy, Suite 2M, Fresh Meadows, NY 11365 *Tel:* 718-762-1195 *Toll Free Tel:* 866-EDITING (334-8464) *E-mail:* wordsmith@sterlingmp.com *Web Site:* www.rlcwordsandmusic.com; www.linkedin.com/in/robertcohen17, pg 523

The Victor Cohn Prize for Excellence in Medical Science Reporting, PO Box 910, Hedgesville, WV 25427 *Tel:* 304-754-6786 *Web Site:* www.casw.org, pg 678

Cold Spring Harbor Laboratory Press, 500 Sunnyside Blvd, Woodbury, NY 11797-2924 *Tel:* 516-422-4100 *Toll Free Tel:* 800-843-4388 *Fax:* 516-422-4097; 516-422-4092 (submissions) *E-mail:* cshpress@cshl.edu *Web Site:* www.cshlpress.com, pg 60

Collector Grade Publications Inc, PO Box 1046, Cobourg, ON K9A 4W5, Canada *Tel:* 905-342-3434 *Fax:* 905-342-3688 *E-mail:* info@collectorgrade.com *Web Site:* www.collectorgrade.com, pg 477

College & University Professional Association for Human Resources (CUPA-HR), 1811 Commons Point Dr, Knoxville, TN 37932 *Tel:* 865-637-7673 *Toll Free Tel:* 877-CUPA-HR4 (287-2474) *Fax:* 865-637-7674 *E-mail:* communications@cupahr.org *Web Site:* www.cupahr.org/publications, pg 60

The College Board, 250 Vesey St, New York, NY 10281 *Tel:* 212-713-8000 *Web Site:* www.collegeboard.com, pg 61

College of Liberal & Professional Studies, University of Pennsylvania, 3440 Market St, Suite 100, Philadelphia, PA 19104-3335 *Tel:* 215-898-7326 *Fax:* 215-573-2053 *E-mail:* lps@sas.upenn.edu *Web Site:* www.sas.upenn.edu; www.sas.upenn.edu/lps, pg 659

College Publishing, 12309 Lynwood Dr, Glen Allen, VA 23059 *Tel:* 804-364-8410 *Toll Free Tel:* 800-827-0723 *Fax:* 804-364-8408 *E-mail:* collegepub@mindspring.com *Web Site:* www.collegepublishing.us, pg 61

Collier Associates, 37 Marina Gardens Dr, Palm Beach Gardens, FL 33410 *Tel:* 561-514-6548 *Fax:* 561-799-4067 *E-mail:* dmccabooks@gmail.com, pg 546

John M Collier Award for Forest History Journalism, 701 William Vickers Ave, Durham, NC 27701-3162 *Tel:* 919-682-9319 *Fax:* 919-682-2349 *Web Site:* www.foresthistory.org, pg 678

Frances Collin Literary Agent, PO Box 33, Wayne, PA 19087 *E-mail:* queries@francescollin.com *Web Site:* www.francescollin.com, pg 546

Carr P Collins Award, c/o 7748 Hwy 290 W, Austin, TX 78736-3202 *Tel:* 512-683-5640 *E-mail:* president@texasinstituteofletters.org *Web Site:* www.texasinstituteofletters.org, pg 678

The Winston Collins/Descant Prize for Best Canadian Poem, 50 Baldwin St, Toronto, ON M5T 1L4, Canada *Tel:* 416-593-2557 *Fax:* 416-593-9362 *E-mail:* info@descant.ca *Web Site:* www.descant.ca, pg 678

The Colonial Williamsburg Foundation, PO Box 1776, Williamsburg, VA 23187-1776 *Tel:* 757-229-1000 *Toll Free Tel:* 800-HISTORY (447-8679) *Fax:* 757-220-7325 *E-mail:* cwres@cwf.org; geninfo@cwf.org *Web Site:* www.colonialwilliamsburg.org/publications, pg 61

Colorado Authors' League, PO Box 24905, Denver, CO 80224 *Web Site:* coloradoauthors.org, pg 603

Colorado Book Awards, 7935 E Prentice Ave, Suite 450, Greenwood Village, CO 80111 *Tel:* 303-894-7951 (ext 21) *Fax:* 303-864-9361 *E-mail:* info@coloradohumanities.org *Web Site:* www.coloradohumanities.org, pg 678

Betsy Colquitt Award for Poetry, Texas Christian University, Dept of English, TCU Box 297270, Fort Worth, TX 76129 *Tel:* 817-257-5907 *Fax:* 817-257-7709 *E-mail:* descant@tcu.edu *Web Site:* www.descant.tcu.edu, pg 678

Columbia Books & Information Services, 4340 East-West Hwy, Suite 300, Bethesda, MD 20814 *Tel:* 240-235-0266 *Toll Free Tel:* 888-265-0600 (cust serv) *Fax:* 202-464-1775 *E-mail:* info@columbiabooks.com *Web Site:* www.columbiabooks.com; www.lobbyists.info; www.associationexecs.com, pg 61

Columbia Publishing Course at Columbia University, 2950 Broadway, MC 3801, New York, NY 10027 *Tel:* 212-854-1898 *Fax:* 212-854-7618 *E-mail:* publishing@jrn.columbia.edu *Web Site:* www.journalism.columbia.edu/publishing, pg 659

Columbia University Press, 61 W 62 St, New York, NY 10023 *Tel:* 212-459-0600 *Toll Free Tel:* 800-944-8648 *Fax:* 212-459-3678 *E-mail:* cup_book@columbia.edu (orders & cust serv) *Web Site:* cup.columbia.edu, pg 61

Columbia University School of the Arts, Creative Writing Program, 617 Kent Hall, New York, NY 10027 *Tel:* 212-854-3774 *Fax:* 212-854-7704 *E-mail:* writingprogram@columbia.edu *Web Site:* www.columbia.edu/cu/writing, pg 659

Comex Systems Inc, 101 Pleasant Hill Rd, Chester, NJ 07930 *Tel:* 973-543-2862 *Toll Free Tel:* 800-543-6959 *Fax:* 973-543-9644 *E-mail:* mail@comexsystems.com *Web Site:* www.comexsystems.com, pg 61

Committee On Scholarly Editions, c/o Modern Language Association of America, 26 Broadway, 3rd fl, New York, NY 10004-1789 *Tel:* 646-576-5044 *Fax:* 646-458-0030 *Web Site:* www.mla.org, pg 603

Common Courage Press, One Red Barn Rd, Monroe, ME 04951 *Tel:* 207-525-0900 *Toll Free Tel:* 800-497-3207 *Fax:* 207-525-3068 *Web Site:* www.commoncouragepress.com, pg 62

Commonwealth Editions, One River Rd, Carlisle, MA 01741 *Tel:* 781-271-0055 *Toll Free Tel:* 800-277-5312 *Fax:* 781-271-0056 *E-mail:* customercare@awb.com *Web Site:* www.awb.com, pg 62

Community of Literary Magazines & Presses (CLMP), 154 Christopher St, Suite 3C, New York, NY 10014-9110 *Tel:* 212-741-9110 *Fax:* 212-741-9112 *E-mail:* info@clmp.org *Web Site:* www.clmp.org, pg 603

Company's Coming Publishing Ltd, 87 E Pender St, Vancouver, BC V6A 1S9, Canada *Tel:* 780-450-6223 (orders & inquiries) *Toll Free Tel:* 800-661-9017 (CN); 800-518-3541 (US) *Fax:* 780-450-1857 *E-mail:* info@companyscoming.com *Web Site:* www.companyscoming.com, pg 477

Concordia Publishing House, 3558 S Jefferson Ave, St Louis, MO 63118-3968 *Tel:* 314-268-1000; 314-268-1268 (bookshop) *Toll Free Tel:* 800-325-3040 (cust serv) *Toll Free Fax:* 800-490-9889 (cust serv) *E-mail:* order@cph.org *Web Site:* www.cph.org, pg 62

The Conference Board Inc, 845 Third Ave, New York, NY 10022-6679 *Tel:* 212-759-0900; 212-339-0345 (cust serv) *Fax:* 212-980-7014; 212-836-9740 (cust serv) *E-mail:* info@conference-board.org *Web Site:* www.conference-board.org, pg 62

Conference on Poetry, 158 Ridge Rd, Franconia, NH 03580 *Tel:* 603-823-5510 *E-mail:* frost@frostplace.org *Web Site:* www.frostplace.org, pg 650

Don Congdon Associates Inc, 110 William St, Suite 2202, New York, NY 10038-3914 *Tel:* 212-645-1229 *Fax:* 212-727-2688 *E-mail:* dca@doncongdon.com *Web Site:* www.doncongdon.com, pg 546

Connecticut Authors & Publishers Association (CAPA), PO Box 715, Avon, CT 06001-0715 *Tel:* 203-729-5335 *Fax:* 203-729-5335 *Web Site:* www.aboutcapa.com, pg 604

Miles Conrad Memorial Lecture, 801 Compass Way, Suite 201, Annapolis, MD 21401 *Tel:* 443-221-2980 *Fax:* 443-221-2981 *E-mail:* nfais@nfais.org *Web Site:* www.nfais.org, pg 679

Constance Rooke Creative Non-Fiction Prize, University of Victoria, Box 1700, Sta CSC, Victoria, BC V8W 2Y2, Canada *Tel:* 250-721-8524 *Fax:* 250-472-5051 *E-mail:* malahat@uvic.ca *Web Site:* malahatreview.ca, pg 679

Consumer Press, 13326 SW 28 St, Suite 102, Fort Lauderdale, FL 33330-1102 *Tel:* 954-370-9153 *Fax:* 954-472-1008 *E-mail:* info@consumerpress.com *Web Site:* www.consumerpress.com, pg 62

Consumertronics, PO Box 23097, Albuquerque, NM 87192 *Tel:* 505-321-1034 *E-mail:* wizguru@consumertronics.net *Web Site:* www.consumertronics.net, pg 62

Contemporary Publishing Co of Raleigh Inc, 5849 Lease Lane, Raleigh, NC 27617 *Tel:* 919-851-8221 *Fax:* 919-851-6666 *E-mail:* questions@contemporarypublishing.com *Web Site:* www.contemporarypublishing.com, pg 62

Continental AfrikaPublishers, 182 Stribling Circle, Spartanburg, SC 29301 *Tel:* 864-576-7992 *Fax:* 864-576-7992 *E-mail:* afrikalion@aol.com; profafrikadzatadeku@facebook.com; profafrikadzatadeku@yahoo.com; afrikapharaoh@gmail.com *Web Site:* www.afrikacentricity.com, pg 62

The Continuing Legal Education Society of British Columbia (CLEBC), 500-1155 W Pender St, Vancouver, BC V6E 2P4, Canada *Tel:* 604-669-3544; 604-893-2121 (cust serv) *Toll Free Tel:* 800-663-0437 (CN) *Fax:* 604-669-9260 *E-mail:* custserv@cle.bc.ca *Web Site:* www.cle.bc.ca, pg 478

David C Cook, 4050 Lee Vance View, Colorado Springs, CO 80918 *Tel:* 719-536-0100 *Toll Free Tel:* 800-708-5550; 800-323-7543 (orders & cust serv) *Toll Free Fax:* 800-430-0726 (cust serv) *Web Site:* www.davidccook.com, pg 62

James Fenimore Cooper Prize, 603 Fayerweather, MC 2538, New York, NY 10027 *Tel:* 212-854-6495 *E-mail:* amhistsociety@columbia.edu *Web Site:* sah.columbia.edu, pg 679

The Doe Coover Agency, PO Box 668, Winchester, MA 01890 *Tel:* 781-721-6000 *Fax:* 781-721-6727 *E-mail:* info@doecooveragency.com *Web Site:* www.doecooveragency.com, pg 547

Copley Custom Textbooks, 530 Great Rd, Acton, MA 01720 *Tel:* 978-263-9090 *Toll Free Tel:* 800-562-2147 *Fax:* 978-263-9190 *E-mail:* publish@copleycustom.com; textbook@copleypublishing.com *Web Site:* www.xanedu.com/copley, pg 62

Copper Canyon Press, Fort Worden State Park, Bldg 313, Port Townsend, WA 98368 *Tel:* 360-385-4925 *Toll Free Tel:* 877-501-1393 (orders) *Fax:* 360-385-4985 *E-mail:* poetry@coppercanyonpress.org *Web Site:* www.coppercanyonpress.org, pg 63

Copywriter's Council of America (CCA), CCA Bldg, 7 Putter Lane, Middle Island, NY 11953-1920 *Tel:* 631-924-3888 *Fax:* 631-924-8555 *E-mail:* cca4dmcopy@gmail.com *Web Site:* www.AndrewLinickDirectMarketing.com/Copywriters-Council.html; www.NewWorldPressBooks.com, pg 63

Copywriter's Council of America (CCA), CCA Bldg, 7 Putter Lane, Middle Island, NY 11953-1920 *Tel:* 631-924-8555 *Fax:* 631-924-8555 *E-mail:* cca4dmcopy@gmail.com *Web Site:* www.AndrewLinickDirectMarketing.com/Copywriters-Council.html; www.NewWorldPressBooks.com, pg 523, 604

Corbett Gordon Co, 6 Fort Rachel Place, Mystic, CT 06355 *Tel:* 860-536-4108 *Fax:* 860-536-3732 *E-mail:* corbettgordon@comcast.net, pg 523

Cordon d' Or - Gold Ribbon International Annual Cook Book & Culinary Arts Culinary Academy Awards, 7312 Sixth Ave N, St Petersburg, FL 33710 *Tel:* 727-347-2437 *E-mail:* cordondor@aol.com; culinaryparadise@aol.com *Web Site:* www.cordondorcuisine.com; www.florida-americasculinaryparadise.com, pg 679

Albert B Corey Prize, c/o American Historical Association, 400 "A" St SE, Washington, DC 20003-3889 *Tel:* 202-544-2422 *Fax:* 202-544-8307 *E-mail:* cha-shc@cha-shc.ca *Web Site:* www.historians.org/prizes; www.cha-shc.ca, pg 679

Cormorant Books Inc, 10 St Mary St, Suite 615, Toronto, ON M4Y-1P6, Canada *Tel:* 416-925-8887 *E-mail:* info@cormorantbooks.com *Web Site:* www.cormorantbooks.com, pg 478

Cornell & McCarthy LLC, 2-D Cross Hwy, Westport, CT 06880 *Tel:* 203-454-4210 *E-mail:* contact@cmartreps.com *Web Site:* www.cmartreps.com, pg 583

Cornell Maritime Press Inc, 4880 Lower Valley Rd, Atglen, PA 19310 *Tel:* 610-593-1777 *Fax:* 610-593-2002 *E-mail:* info@schifferbooks.com *Web Site:* www.cmptp.com, pg 63

Cornell University Press, Sage House, 512 E State St, Ithaca, NY 14850 *Tel:* 607-277-2338 *Fax:* 607-277-2374 *E-mail:* cupressinfo@cornell.edu; cupress-sales@cornell.edu *Web Site:* www.cornellpress.cornell.edu, pg 63

Cornell University Southeast Asia Program Publications, 213 Kahin Ctr, 640 Stewart Ave, Ithaca, NY 14850 *Tel:* 607-255-4359 *Fax:* 607-255-4359 *E-mail:* seappublications@cornell.edu *Web Site:* seapeinaudi.cornell.edu/southeastasia/publications, pg 64

Cornerstone Book Publishers, PO Box 24652, New Orleans, LA 70184 *E-mail:* info@cornerstonepublishers.com *Web Site:* www.cornerstonepublishers.com, pg 64

Corporation for Public Broadcasting (CPB), 401 Ninth St NW, Washington, DC 20004-2129 *Tel:* 202-879-9600 *Web Site:* www.cpb.org, pg 604

Corporation of Professional Librarians of Quebec, 1453, rue Beaubien Est, Bureau 215, Montreal, QC H2G 3C6, Canada *Tel:* 514-845-3327 *Fax:* 514-845-1618 *E-mail:* info@cbpq.qc.ca *Web Site:* www.cbpq.qc.ca, pg 604

Cortina Institute of Languages, 9 Hollyhock Rd, Wilton, CT 06897 *Tel:* 203-762-2510 *Toll Free Tel:* 800-245-2145 *Fax:* 203-762-2514 *Web Site:* www.cortina-languages.com, pg 64

Cortina Learning International Inc (CLI), 9 Hollyhock Rd, Wilton, CT 06897 *Tel:* 203-762-2510 *Toll Free Tel:* 800-245-2145 *Fax:* 203-762-2514 *E-mail:* info@cortinalearning.com *Web Site:* www.cortinalearning.com, pg 64

Corwin, a Sage Co, 2455 Teller Rd, Thousand Oaks, CA 91320 *Tel:* 805-499-9734 *Toll Free Tel:* 800-233-9936 *Fax:* 805-499-5323 *Toll Free Fax:* 800-417-2466 *E-mail:* info@corwin.com; order@corwin.com *Web Site:* www.corwin.com, pg 64

Cosimo Inc, Old Chelsea Sta, PO Box 416, New York, NY 10011-0416 *Tel:* 212-989-3616 *Fax:* 212-989-3662 *E-mail:* info@cosimobooks.com *Web Site:* www.cosimobooks.com, pg 64

Coteau Books, 2517 Victoria Ave, Regina, SK S4P 0T2, Canada *Tel:* 306-777-0170 *Toll Free Tel:* 800-440-4471 (CN only) *Fax:* 306-522-5152 *E-mail:* coteau@coteaubooks.com *Web Site:* www.coteaubooks.com, pg 478

Cotsen Institute of Archaeology Press, 308 Charles E Young Dr N, Fowler A163, Box 951510, Los Angeles, CA 90024 *Tel:* 310-206-9384 *Fax:* 310-206-4723 *E-mail:* ioapubs@ioa.ucla.edu *Web Site:* www.ioa.ucla.edu, pg 64

Cottonwood Press, University of Kansas, Kansas Union, Rm 400, 1301 Jayhawk Blvd, Lawrence, KS 66045 *Tel:* 785-864-4520 *Web Site:* www.englishcw.ku.edu/cottonwood, pg 64

Council for Advancement & Support of Education (CASE), 1307 New York Ave NW, Suite 1000, Washington, DC 20005-4701 *Tel:* 202-328-CASE (328-2273) *Fax:* 202-387-4973 *E-mail:* membersupportcenter@case.org *Web Site:* www.case.org, pg 604

Council for Exceptional Children (CEC), 2900 Crystal Dr, Suite 1000, Arlington, VA 22201 *Toll Free Tel:* 888-232-7733 (memb servs); 866-509-0219 *Fax:* 703-264-9494 *E-mail:* service@cec.sped.org *Web Site:* www.cec.sped.org, pg 64

Council for Research in Values & Philosophy (RVP), The Catholic University of America, Gibbons Hall, Rm B-12, 620 Michigan Ave NE, Washington, DC 20064 *Tel:* 202-319-6089 *Fax:* 202-319-6089 *E-mail:* cua-rvp@cua.edu *Web Site:* www.crvp.org, pg 64

Council for the Advancement of Science Writing (CASW), PO Box 910, Hedgesville, WV 25427 *Tel:* 304-754-6786 *Web Site:* www.casw.org, pg 604

Council Oak Books LLC, 2822 Van Ness Ave, San Francisco, CA 94109 *Tel:* 415-931-7700 *Toll Free Tel:* 888-275-2596 *E-mail:* marketing@counciloakbooks.com *Web Site:* www.counciloakbooks.com, pg 65

Council of State Governments, 2760 Research Park Dr, Lexington, KY 40511 *Tel:* 859-244-8000 *Toll Free Tel:* 800-800-1910 *Fax:* 859-244-8001 *E-mail:* sales@csg.org *Web Site:* www.csg.org; www.csgstore.org, pg 65

Council on Foreign Relations Press, The Harold Pratt House, 58 E 68 St, New York, NY 10065 *Tel:* 212-434-9400 *Fax:* 212-434-9800 *E-mail:* publications@cfr.org *Web Site:* www.cfr.org, pg 65

Council on Social Work Education (CSWE), 1701 Duke St, Suite 200, Alexandria, VA 22314-3457 *Tel:* 703-683-8080 *Fax:* 703-683-8493 *E-mail:* publications@cswe.org; info@cswe.org *Web Site:* www.cswe.org, pg 65

Counterpath Press, 613 22 St, Denver, CO 80205 *E-mail:* counterpath@counterpathpress.org; editors@counterpathpress.org *Web Site:* www.counterpathpress.org, pg 65

Counterpoint Press LLC, 1919 Fifth St, Berkeley, CA 94710 *Tel:* 510-704-0230 *Fax:* 510-704-0268 *E-mail:* info@counterpointpress.com *Web Site:* counterpointpress.com; www.sierraclub.org/books; softskull.com, pg 65

Country Music Foundation Press, 222 Fifth Ave S, Nashville, TN 37203 *Tel:* 615-416-2001 *Fax:* 615-255-2245 *E-mail:* info@countrymusichalloffame.com *Web Site:* www.countrymusichalloffame.com, pg 65

The Countryman Press, c/o W W Norton & Co Inc, 500 Fifth Ave, New York, NY 10110 *Tel:* 212-354-5500 *Fax:* 212-869-0856 *E-mail:* countrymanpress@wwnorton.com *Web Site:* www.countrymanpress.com, pg 65

Course Crafters Inc, 116 Pleasant Valley Rd, Amesbury, MA 01913 *Tel:* 978-372-3446 *E-mail:* info@coursecrafters.com *Web Site:* www.coursecrafters.com, pg 523

La Courte Echelle, 160, rue St-Viateur E, bureau 404, Montreal, QC H2T 1A8, Canada *Tel:* 514-274-2004 *Fax:* 514-270-4160 *E-mail:* info@courteechelle.com *Web Site:* www.courteechelle.com, pg 478

Covenant Communications Inc, 920 E State Rd, Suite F, American Fork, UT 84003-0416 *Tel:* 801-756-1041 *E-mail:* info@covenant-lds.com *Web Site:* www.covenant-lds.com, pg 66

Coyote Press, PO Box 3377, Salinas, CA 93912-3377 *Tel:* 831-422-4912 *Fax:* 831-422-4913 *E-mail:* orders@coyotepress.com *Web Site:* www.coyotepress.com, pg 66

CPSA Prize in Comparative Politics, 260 rue Dalhousie St, Suite 204, Ottawa, ON K1N 7E4, Canada *Tel:* 613-562-1202 *Fax:* 613-241-0019 *E-mail:* cpsa-acsp@cpsa-acsp.ca *Web Site:* www.cpsa-acsp.ca, pg 679

CPSA Prize in International Relations, 260 rue Dalhousie St, Suite 204, Ottawa, ON K1N 7E4, Canada *Tel:* 613-562-1202 *Fax:* 613-241-0019 *E-mail:* cpsa-acsp@cpsa-acsp.ca *Web Site:* www.cpsa-acsp.ca, pg 679

CQ Press, 2300 "N" St NW, Suite 800, Washington, DC 20037 *Tel:* 202-729-1900 *Toll Free Tel:* 866-4CQ-PRESS (427-7737) *Fax:* 202-729-1923 *Toll Free Fax:* 800-380-3810 *E-mail:* customerservice@cqpress.com; librarysales@cqpress.com *Web Site:* www.cqpress.com, pg 66

Crabtree Publishing Co, 350 Fifth Ave, 59th fl, PMB 59051, New York, NY 10118 *Tel:* 212-496-5040 *Toll Free Tel:* 800-387-7650 *Toll Free Fax:* 800-355-7166 *E-mail:* custserv@crabtreebooks.com *Web Site:* www.crabtreebooks.com, pg 66

Crabtree Publishing Co Ltd, 616 Welland Ave, St Catharines, ON L2M-5V6, Canada *Tel:* 905-682-5221 *Toll Free Tel:* 800-387-7650 *Fax:* 905-682-7166 *Toll Free Fax:* 800-355-7166 *E-mail:* custserv@crabtreebooks.com; sales@crabtreebooks.com; orders@crabtreebooks.com *Web Site:* www.crabtreebooks.com, pg 478

Craftsman Book Co, 6058 Corte Del Cedro, Carlsbad, CA 92011 *Tel:* 760-438-7828 *Toll Free Tel:* 800-829-8123 *Fax:* 760-438-0398 *Web Site:* www.craftsman-book.com, pg 66

Craven Design Inc, 1202 Lexington Ave, Box 242, New York, NY 10028 *Tel:* 212-288-1022 *Fax:* 212-249-9910 *E-mail:* cravendesign@mac.com *Web Site:* www.cravendesignstudios.com, pg 583

The Crazyhorse Fiction Prize, College of Charleston, Dept of English, 66 George St, Charleston, SC 29424 *Tel:* 843-953-7740 *Fax:* 843-953-7740 *E-mail:* crazyhorse@cofc.edu *Web Site:* crazyhorse.cofc.edu/prizes, pg 679

CRC Press LLC, 6000 Broken Sound Pkwy NW, Suite 300, Boca Raton, FL 33487 *Tel:* 561-994-0555 *Toll Free Tel:* 800-272-7737 (orders) *Toll Free Fax:* 800-643-9428 (sales); 800-374-3401 (orders) *E-mail:* orders@crcpress.com; orders@taylorandfrancis.com *Web Site:* www.crcpress.com, pg 66

Creation Grant Program, 649 rue Queen, 2nd fl, Fredericton, NB E3B 1C3, Canada *Tel:* 506-444-4444 *Toll Free Tel:* 866-460-ARTS (460-2787) *Fax:* 506-444-5543 *E-mail:* nbabcanb@artsnb.ca *Web Site:* www.artsnb.ca, pg 679

Creative Arts of Ventura, PO Box 684, Ventura, CA 93002-0684 *Tel:* 805-643-4160; 805-654-1927 *Web Site:* www.sculpture-museum.com, pg 583

The Creative Co, PO Box 227, Mankato, MN 56002 *Tel:* 507-388-6273 *Toll Free Tel:* 800-445-6209 *Fax:* 507-388-2746 *E-mail:* info@thecreativecompany.us; orders@thecreativecompany.us *Web Site:* www.thecreativecompany.us, pg 66

Creative Freelancers Inc, PO Box 366, Tallevast, FL 34270 *Toll Free Tel:* 800-398-9544 *Web Site:* www.freelancers1.com, pg 524

Creative Homeowner, 1970 Broad St, East Petersburg, PA 17520 *Tel:* 717-560-4703 *Toll Free Tel:* 800-475-9112 *Fax:* 717-560-4702 *Toll Free Fax:* 888-369-2885 *E-mail:* customerservice@foxchapelpublishing.com; sales@foxchapelpublishing.com *Web Site:* www.foxchapelpublishing.com/home-and-garden/creative-homeowner, pg 66

Creative Inspirations Inc, 6203 Old Springville Rd, Pinson, AL 35126 *Web Site:* www.manuscriptcritique.com, pg 524

Creative Writing Day & Workshops, 335 Cummings St, Abingdon, VA 24210 *Tel:* 276-623-5266 *Fax:* 276-676-3076 *E-mail:* vhf@eva.org *Web Site:* www.vahighlandsfestival.org, pg 650

CreativeWell Inc, PO Box 3130, Memorial Sta, Upper Montclair, NJ 07043 *Tel:* 973-783-7575 *Toll Free Tel:* 800-743-9182 *Fax:* 973-783-7530 *E-mail:* info@creativewell.com *Web Site:* www.creativewell.com, pg 547, 587

Crichton & Associates Inc, 6940 Carroll Ave, Takoma Park, MD 20912 *Tel:* 301-495-9663 *E-mail:* cricht1@aol.com *Web Site:* www.crichton-associates.com, pg 547

Cricket Cottage Publishing LLC, 4409 Hoffner Ave, Unit 127, Orlando, FL 32812 *Tel:* 407-255-7785 *E-mail:* cricketcottage@att.net *Web Site:* www.thecricketpublishing.com, pg 67

Crickhollow Books, 3147 S Pennsylvania Ave, Milwaukee, WI 53207 *Tel:* 414-294-4319 *E-mail:* info@crickhollowbooks.com *Web Site:* www.crickhollowbooks.com, pg 67

Cross-Cultural Communications, 239 Wynsum Ave, Merrick, NY 11566-4725 *Tel:* 516-868-5635 *Fax:* 516-379-1901 *E-mail:* info@cross-culturalcommunications.com; cccbarkan@optonline.net; cccpoetry@aol.com *Web Site:* www.cross-culturalcommunications.com, pg 67

Ruth C Cross, 196 Melrose St, Unit 52, Brattleboro, VT 05301 *Tel:* 802-579-1368, pg 524

Crossquarter Publishing Group, PO Box 23749, Santa Fe, NM 87502 *Tel:* 505-690-3923 *Fax:* 214-975-9715 *E-mail:* sales@crossquarter.com; info@crossquarter.com *Web Site:* www.crossquarter.com, pg 67

The Crossroad Publishing Co, 831 Chestnut Ridge Rd, Chestnut Ridge, NY 10977 *Tel:* 845-517-0180 *Toll Free Tel:* 800-888-4741 (orders) *Fax:* 845-517-0181 *E-mail:* office@crossroadpublishing.com *Web Site:* www.CrossroadPublishing.com, pg 67

Crossway, 1300 Crescent St, Wheaton, IL 60187 *Tel:* 630-682-4300 *Toll Free Tel:* 800-635-7993 (orders); 800-543-1659 (cust serv) *Fax:* 630-682-4785 *E-mail:* info@crossway.org *Web Site:* www.crossway.org, pg 67

Crown House Publishing Co LLC, 6 Trowbridge Dr, Bethel, CT 06801 *Tel:* 203-778-1300 *Toll Free Tel:* 877-925-1213 (cust serv); 866-272-8497 *Fax:* 203-778-9100 *E-mail:* info@chpus.com *Web Site:* www.crownhousepublishing.com, pg 67

Crown Publishing Group, c/o Penguin Random House Inc, 1745 Broadway, New York, NY 10019 *Tel:* 212-782-9000 *Toll Free Tel:* 888-264-1745 *Fax:* 212-940-7408 *E-mail:* crownosm@penguinrandomhouse.com *Web Site:* crownpublishing.com, pg 68

Crumb Elbow Publishing, PO Box 294, Rhododendron, OR 97049-0294 *Tel:* 503-622-4798, pg 68

Crystal Clarity Publishers, 14618 Tyler Foote Rd, Nevada City, CA 95959 *Tel:* 530-478-7600 *Toll Free Tel:* 800-424-1055 *Fax:* 530-478-7610 *E-mail:* clarity@crystalclarity.com *Web Site:* www.crystalclarity.com, pg 68

Crystal Productions, 5320 Carpinteria Ave, Suite K, Carpinteria, CA 93013-2107 *Tel:* 847-657-8144 *Toll Free Tel:* 800-255-8629 *Fax:* 847-657-8149 *Toll Free Fax:* 800-657-8149 *E-mail:* custserv@crystalproductions.com *Web Site:* www.crystalproductions.com, pg 68

Crystal Publishers Inc, 3460 Lost Hills Dr, Las Vegas, NV 89122 *Tel:* 702-434-3037 *Fax:* 702-434-3037 *Web Site:* www.crystalpub.com, pg 69

CS International Literary Agency, 43 W 39 St, New York, NY 10018 *Tel:* 212-921-1610; 212-391-9208 *E-mail:* query@csliterary.com; csliterary08@gmail.com *Web Site:* www.csliterary.com, pg 524

The CSIS Press, 1616 Rhode Island Ave, Washington, DC 20036 *Tel:* 202-887-0200 *Fax:* 202-775-3199 *E-mail:* books@csis.org *Web Site:* www.csis.org, pg 69

CSLI Publications, Stanford University, Cordura Hall, 220 Panama St, Stanford, CA 94305-4115 *Tel:* 650-723-1839 *Fax:* 650-725-2166 *E-mail:* pubs@csli.stanford.edu *Web Site:* cslipublications.stanford.edu, pg 69

CTB/McGraw-Hill, 20 Ryan Ranch Rd, Monterey, CA 93940-5703 *Tel:* 831-393-0700 *Toll Free Tel:* 800-538-9547 *Fax:* 831-393-7825 *Toll Free Fax:* 800-282-0266 *Web Site:* www.ctb.com, pg 69

Cultural Studies & Analysis, 1123 Montrose St, Philadelphia, PA 19147-3721 *Tel:* 215-592-8544 *Fax:* 215-413-9041 *E-mail:* info@culturalanalysis.com *Web Site:* www.culturalanalysis.com, pg 524

Cumberland House, 1935 Brookdale Rd, Suite 139, Naperville, IL 60563 *Tel:* 630-961-3900 *Toll Free Tel:* 800-43-BRIGHT (432-7444) *Fax:* 630-961-2168 *E-mail:* info@sourcebooks.com *Web Site:* www.sourcebooks.com, pg 69

Cummings & Hathaway Publishers, 395 Atlantic Ave, East Rockaway, NY 11518 *Tel:* 516-593-3607 *Fax:* 516-593-1401, pg 69

Cunningham Commission for Youth Theatre, 2135 N Kenmore Ave, Chicago, IL 60614-4100 *Tel:* 773-325-7932 *Fax:* 773-325-7920 *Web Site:* theatreschool.depaul.edu, pg 679

CUNY Journalism Press, 219 W 40 St, New York, NY 10018 *Tel:* 646-758-7824 *Fax:* 646-758-7809 *Web Site:* www.journalism.cuny.edu; press.journalism.cuny.edu, pg 69

Cup of Tea Books, PO Box 21133, Columbus, OH 43221 *Tel:* 614-264-5588 *E-mail:* sales@pagespringpublishing.com *Web Site:* www.cupofteabooks.com, pg 69

Richard Curtis Associates Inc, 171 E 74 St, 2nd fl, New York, NY 10021 *Tel:* 212-772-7363 *Fax:* 212-772-7393 *Web Site:* www.curtisagency.com, pg 547

Karen & Philip Cushman Late Bloomer Award, 4727 Wilshire Blvd, Suite 301, Los Angeles, CA 90010 *Tel:* 323-782-1010 *Fax:* 323-782-1892 *E-mail:* grants@scbwi.org *Web Site:* www.scbwi.org, pg 680

CWA/SCA Canada, 2200 Prince of Wales Dr, Suite 301, Ottawa, ON K2E 6Z9, Canada *Tel:* 613-820-9777 *Toll Free Tel:* 877-486-4292 *Fax:* 613-820-8188 *E-mail:* info@cwa-scacanada.ca *Web Site:* www.cwa-scacanada.ca, pg 604

Cycle Publishing LLC, 1282 Seventh Ave, San Francisco, CA 94122-2526 *Tel:* 415-665-8214 *Fax:* 415-753-8572 *Web Site:* www.cyclepublishing.com, pg 69

Cyclotour Guide Books, 160 Harvard St, Rochester, NY 14607-3174 *Tel:* 585-244-6157 *E-mail:* cyclotour@cyclotour.com *Web Site:* www.cyclotour.com, pg 69

Cypress House, 155 Cypress St, Fort Bragg, CA 95437 *Tel:* 707-964-9520 *Toll Free Tel:* 800-773-7782 *Fax:* 707-964-7531 *E-mail:* cypresshouse@cypresshouse.com *Web Site:* www.cypresshouse.com, pg 69, 524

Da Capo Press & Lifelong Books, 44 Farnsworth St, 3rd fl, Boston, MA 02210 *Tel:* 617-252-5200 *Toll Free Tel:* 800-343-4499 (orders) *Fax:* 617-252-5285 *Web Site:* www.perseusbooksgroup.com/dacapo, pg 69

Dalkey Archive Press, University of Houston-Victoria, 3007 N Ben Wilson, Victoria, TX 77901 *E-mail:* contact@dalkeyarchive.com *Web Site:* www.dalkeyarchive.com, pg 70

Damron Co, PO Box 422458, San Francisco, CA 94142-2458 *Tel:* 415-255-0404 *Toll Free Tel:* 800-462-6654 *Fax:* 415-703-9049 *E-mail:* info@damron.com *Web Site:* www.damron.com, pg 70

Dana Awards, Literary Competition, 200 Fosseway Dr, Greensboro, NC 27455 *Tel:* 336-644-8028 *E-mail:* danaawards@gmail.com *Web Site:* www.danaawards.com, pg 680

Robert Dana-Anhinga Prize for Poetry, PO Box 3665, Tallahassee, FL 32315 *Tel:* 850-577-0745 *E-mail:* info@anhinga.org *Web Site:* www.anhinga.org, pg 680

The Danahy Fiction Prize, University of Tampa Press, 401 W Kennedy Blvd, Tampa, FL 33606 *Tel:* 813-253-6266 *E-mail:* utpress@ut.edu *Web Site:* tampareview.ut.edu, pg 680

Dancing Dakini Press, 77 Morning Sun Dr, Sedona, AZ 86336 *Tel:* 928-852-0129 *E-mail:* editor@dancingdakinipress.com *Web Site:* www.dancingdakinipress.com, pg 70

Dancing Lemur Press LLC, PO Box 383, Pikeville, NC 27863-0383 *Tel:* 919-273-0939 *E-mail:* inquiries@dancinglemurpressllc.com *Web Site:* www.dancinglemurpressllc.com, pg 70

John Daniel & Co, PO Box 2790, McKinleyville, CA 95519-2790 *Tel:* 707-839-3495 *Toll Free Tel:* 800-662-8351 *Fax:* 707-839-3242 *E-mail:* dandd@danielpublishing.com *Web Site:* www.danielpublishing.com, pg 70

John M Daniel Literary Services, PO Box 2790, McKinleyville, CA 95519 *Tel:* 707-839-3495 *Fax:* 707-839-3242 *E-mail:* jmd@danielpublishing.com *Web Site:* www.danielpublishing.com/litserv.htm, pg 524

Benjamin H Danks Award, 633 W 155 St, New York, NY 10032 *Tel:* 212-368-5900 *Fax:* 212-491-4615 *E-mail:* academy@artsandletters.org *Web Site:* www.artsandletters.org, pg 680

Dante University of America Press Inc, PO Box 812158, Wellesley, MA 02482-0014 *Tel:* 781-235-3634 *E-mail:* danteu@danteuniversity.org *Web Site:* www.danteuniversity.org/books, pg 70

Darhansoff & Verrill, 236 W 26 St, Suite 802, New York, NY 10001-6736 *Tel:* 917-305-1300 *Fax:* 917-305-1400 *E-mail:* info@dvagency.com *Web Site:* www.dvagency.com, pg 547

Dark Horse Comics, 10956 SE Main St, Milwaukie, OR 97222 *Tel:* 503-652-8815 *Fax:* 503-654-9440 *E-mail:* dhcomics@darkhorse.com *Web Site:* www.darkhorse.com, pg 70

Darla Bruno Writer & Editor, PO Box 243, Madison, NJ 07940 *E-mail:* editor@darlabruno.com *Web Site:* www.darlabruno.com, pg 524

The Dartnell Corporation, 2222 Sedwick Dr, Durham, NC 27713 *Toll Free Tel:* 800-223-8720; 800-472-0148 (cust serv) *Fax:* 585-292-4392 *Toll Free Fax:* 800-508-2592 *E-mail:* customerservice@dartnellcorp.com *Web Site:* www.dartnellcorp.com, pg 70

The Darwin Press Inc, PO Box 2202, Princeton, NJ 08543 *Tel:* 609-737-1349 *Fax:* 609-737-0929 *E-mail:* books@darwinpress.com *Web Site:* www.darwinpress.com, pg 70

Data Trace Publishing Co (DTP), 110 West Rd, Suite 227, Towson, MD 21204-2316 *Tel:* 410-494-4994 *Toll Free Tel:* 800-342-0454 (orders only) *Fax:* 410-494-0515 *E-mail:* info@datatrace.com; salesandmarketing@datatrace.com; editorial@datatrace.com; info@datatrace.com *Web Site:* www.datatrace.com, pg 70

Database Directories, 588 Dufferin Ave, London, ON N6B 2A4, Canada *Tel:* 519-433-1666 *Fax:* 519-430-1131 *E-mail:* mail@databasedirectory.com *Web Site:* www.databasedirectory.com, pg 478

May Davenport Publishers, 26313 Purissima Rd, Los Altos Hills, CA 94022 *Tel:* 650-947-1275 *Fax:* 650-947-1373 *E-mail:* mdbooks@earthlink.net *Web Site:* www.maydavenportpublishers.org, pg 71

Suzanne B Davidson, 8084 N 44 St, Brown Deer, WI 53223 *Tel:* 414-355-6640 *E-mail:* davidson@milwpc.com, pg 524

Davies-Black Publishing, 53 State St, Boston, MA 02109 *Tel:* 617-523-3801 *Fax:* 617-523-3708 *E-mail:* info@nicholasbrealey.com *Web Site:* www.nicholasbrealey.com, pg 71

The Davies Group Publishers, PO Box 440140, Aurora, CO 80044-0140 *Tel:* 303-750-8374 *Fax:* 303-337-0952 *E-mail:* info@thedaviesgrouppublishers.com; daviesgroup@msn.com (orders) *Web Site:* www.thedaviesgrouppublishers.com, pg 71

Davies Publishing Inc, 32 S Raymond Ave, Suites 4 & 5, Pasadena, CA 91105-1961 *Tel:* 626-792-3046 *Toll Free Tel:* 877-792-0005 *Fax:* 626-792-5308 *E-mail:* info@daviespublishing.com *Web Site:* daviespublishing.com, pg 71

F A Davis Co, 1915 Arch St, Philadelphia, PA 19103 *Tel:* 215-568-2270; 215-440-3001 *Toll Free Tel:* 800-523-4049 *Fax:* 215-568-5065; 215-440-3016 *E-mail:* info@fadavis.com; orders@fadavis.com *Web Site:* www.fadavis.com, pg 71

Watson Davis & Helen Miles Davis Prize, 440 Geddes Hall, Notre Dame, IN 46556 *Tel:* 574-631-1194 *Fax:* 574-631-1533 *E-mail:* info@hssonline.org *Web Site:* www.hssonline.org, pg 680

DAW Books Inc, 375 Hudson St, New York, NY 10014 *Tel:* 212-366-2096 *Fax:* 212-366-2090 *E-mail:* daw@penguinrandomhouse.com *Web Site:* us.penguingroup.com; www.dawbooks.com, pg 71

The Dawn Horse Press, 10336 Loch Lomond Rd, No 305, Middletown, CA 95461 *Tel:* 707-928-6590 *Toll Free Tel:* 877-770-0772 *Fax:* 707-928-6590 *E-mail:* dhp@adidam.org *Web Site:* www.dawnhorsepress.com, pg 71

Dawn Publications Inc, 12402 Bitney Springs Rd, Nevada City, CA 95959 *Tel:* 530-274-7775 *Toll Free Tel:* 800-545-7475 *Fax:* 530-274-7778 *E-mail:* nature@dawnpub.com; orders@dawnpub.com *Web Site:* www.dawnpub.com, pg 71

DawnSignPress, 6130 Nancy Ridge Dr, San Diego, CA 92121-3223 *Tel:* 858-625-0600 *Toll Free Tel:* 800-549-5350 *Fax:* 858-625-2336 *E-mail:* info@dawnsign.com *Web Site:* www.dawnsign.com, pg 71

Liza Dawson Associates, 350 Seventh Ave, Suite 2003, New York, NY 10001 *Tel:* 212-465-9071 *Fax:* 212-947-0460 *Web Site:* www.lizadawsonassociates.com, pg 547

Day Owl Press Corp, 201 W Ocean Ave, Unit 3574, Lantana, FL 33465 *Toll Free Tel:* 888-806-6981 *Toll Free Fax:* 866-854-4375 *E-mail:* info@dayowl.net *Web Site:* www.dayowl.net, pg 72

Dayton Literary Peace Prize, 25 Harman Terr, Dayton, OH 45419 *Tel:* 937-298-5072 *Web Site:* daytonliterarypeaceprize.org, pg 680

Dayton Playhouse FutureFest, 1301 E Siebenthaler Ave, Dayton, OH 45414 *Tel:* 937-424-8477 *Fax:* 937-424-0062 *E-mail:* dp_futurefest@yahoo.com *Web Site:* www.daytonplayhouse.com, pg 680

dbS Productions, PO Box 94, Charlottesville, VA 22902 *Tel:* 434-293-5502 *Toll Free Tel:* 800-745-1581 *Fax:* 434-293-5502 *E-mail:* info@dbs-sar.com *Web Site:* www.dbs-sar.com, pg 72

DC Canada Education Publishing (DCCED), 180 Metcalfe St, Suite 204, Ottawa, ON K2P 1P5, Canada *Tel:* 613-565-8885 *Toll Free Tel:* 888-565-0262 *Fax:* 613-565-8881 *E-mail:* info@dc-canada.ca *Web Site:* www.dc-canada.ca, pg 478

DC Entertainment, 2900 Alameda, Burbank, CA 91505 *Toll Free Tel:* 800-887-6789 *E-mail:* dccomics@cambeywest.com *Web Site:* www.dcentertainment.com; www.dccomics.com; www.madmag.com, pg 72

DC Press LLC, 750 Powderhorn Circle, Lake Mary, FL 32746 *Tel:* 407-688-1156 *Toll Free Tel:* 877-203-1895 *Web Site:* www.dcpressbooks.com, pg 72

Walter De Gruyter Inc, 125 Pearl St, 3rd fl, Boston, MA 02110 *Tel:* 857-284-7073 *Fax:* 857-284-7358 *E-mail:* service@degruyter.com *Web Site:* www.degruyter.com, pg 72

J de S Associates Inc, 9 Shagbark Rd, South Norwalk, CT 06854 *Tel:* 203-838-7571 *Fax:* 203-866-2713 *Web Site:* www.jdesassociates.com, pg 547

De Vorss & Co, 553 Constitution Ave, Camarillo, CA 93012-8510 *Tel:* 805-322-9010 *Toll Free Tel:* 800-843-5743 *Fax:* 805-322-9011 *E-mail:* service@devorss.com *Web Site:* www.devorss.com, pg 72

Deadline Club, c/o Salmagundi Club, 47 Fifth Ave, New York, NY 10003 *Tel:* 646-481-7584 *E-mail:* info@deadlineclub.org *Web Site:* www.deadlineclub.org, pg 604

Deborah Wolfe Ltd, 731 N 24 St, Philadelphia, PA 19130 *Tel:* 215-232-6666 *Fax:* 215-232-6585 *E-mail:* info@illustrationonline.com *Web Site:* www.illustrationonline.com, pg 583

Decent Hill Publishers LLC, 6100 Oak Tree Blvd, Suite 200, Cleveland, OH 44131 *Toll Free Tel:* 866-688-5325 *Toll Free Fax:* 866-688-5325 *E-mail:* support@decenthill.com *Web Site:* www.decenthill.com, pg 72

The Jennifer DeChiara Literary Agency, 31 E 32 St, Suite 300, New York, NY 10016 *Tel:* 212-481-8484 (ext 362) *Fax:* 212-481-9582 *Web Site:* www.jdlit.com, pg 547

Decker Intellectual Properties Publisher, 69 John St S, Suite 310, Hamilton, ON L8N 2B9, Canada *Tel:* 905-522-8526 *Toll Free Tel:* 855-647-6511 (CN & US) *Fax:* 905-522-9273 *E-mail:* customercare@deckerip.com *Web Site:* www.deckerpublishing.com, pg 478

DeFiore and Company, LLC, 47 E 19 St, 3rd fl, New York, NY 10003 *Tel:* 212-925-7744 *Fax:* 212-925-9803 *E-mail:* submissions@defioreandco.com; info@defioreandco.com *Web Site:* www.defioreandco.com, pg 548

Delaware Division of the Arts, Carvel State Off Bldg, 4th fl, 820 N French St, Wilmington, DE 19801 *Tel:* 302-577-8278 *Fax:* 302-577-6561 *E-mail:* delarts@state.de.us *Web Site:* www.artsdel.org, pg 680

Joelle Delbourgo Associates Inc, 101 Park St, Montclair, NJ 07042 *Tel:* 973-773-0836 (call only during standard business hours) *Web Site:* www.delbourgo.com, pg 548

DeLorme Publishing Co Inc, 2 DeLorme Dr, Yarmouth, ME 04096 *Tel:* 207-846-7000; 207-846-7111 (sales) *Toll Free Tel:* 800-561-5105; 800-511-2459 (cust serv) *Fax:* 207-846-7051 *Toll Free Fax:* 800-575-2244 *E-mail:* reseller@delorme.com *Web Site:* www.delorme.com, pg 72

Delphi Books, 216 Landings Ct, Lee's Summit, MO 64064 *E-mail:* delphibks@yahoo.com *Web Site:* www.delphibooks.us, pg 72

Delphinium Books, PO Box 703, Harrison, NY 10528 *Tel:* 917-301-7496 (e-mail first) *E-mail:* contactform@delphiniumbooks.com *Web Site:* www.delphiniumbooks.com, pg 73

Delta Publishing Co, 1400 Miller Pkwy, McHenry, IL 60050-7030 *Tel:* 815-363-3582 *Toll Free Tel:* 800-323-8270 (orders) *Fax:* 815-363-2948 *Toll Free Fax:* 800-909-9901 *E-mail:* custsvc@deltapublishing.com *Web Site:* www.deltapublishing.com, pg 73

Rick DeMarinis Short Story Award, PO Box 2414, Durango, CO 81302 *Tel:* 970-903-7914 *E-mail:* cutthroatmag@gmail.com *Web Site:* www.cutthroatmag.com, pg 680

Demos Medical Publishing, 11 W 42 St, 15th fl, New York, NY 10036 *Tel:* 212-683-0072 *E-mail:* info@demosmedpub.com; orderdept@demosmedical.com; editorial@demosmedical.com *Web Site:* www.demosmedical.com, pg 73

Der-Hovanessian Translation Prize, 2 Farrar St, Cambridge, MA 02138 *Tel:* 617-744-6034 *E-mail:* contests@nepoetryclub.org *Web Site:* www.nepoetryclub.org, pg 680

Deseret Book Co, 57 W South Temple, Salt Lake City, UT 84101-1511 *Tel:* 801-517-3369 *Toll Free Tel:* 800-453-4532 (orders); 888-846-7302 (orders) *Fax:* 801-517-3126 *E-mail:* service@deseretbook.com *Web Site:* www.deseretbook.com, pg 73

DEStech Publications Inc, 439 N Duke St, Lancaster, PA 17602-4967 *Tel:* 717-290-1660 *Toll Free Tel:* 877-500-4337 *Fax:* 717-509-6100 *E-mail:* info@destechpub.com *Web Site:* www.destechpub.com, pg 73

Destiny Image Inc, 167 Walnut Bottom Rd, Shippensburg, PA 17257-0310 *Tel:* 717-532-3040 *Toll Free Tel:* 800-722-6774 (orders only) *Fax:* 717-532-9291 *Web Site:* www.destinyimage.com, pg 73

Dewey Publications Inc, 1840 Wilson Blvd, Suite 203, Arlington, VA 22201 *Tel:* 703-524-1355 *Fax:* 703-524-1463 *E-mail:* deweypublications@gmail.com *Web Site:* www.deweypub.com, pg 73

Dharma Publishing, 35788 Hauser Bridge Rd, Cazadero, CA 95421 *Tel:* 707-847-3717 *Toll Free Tel:* 800-873-4276 *Fax:* 707-847-3380 *E-mail:* contact@dharmapublishing.com; customerservice@dharmapublishing.com *Web Site:* www.dharmapublishing.com, pg 73

Alice Fay Di Castagnola Award, 15 Gramercy Park, New York, NY 10003 *Tel:* 212-254-9628 *Fax:* 212-673-2352 *Web Site:* www.poetrysociety.org, pg 680

Christina Di Martino Literary Services, 139 Sandpiper Ave, Royal Palm Beach, FL 33411 *Tel:* 212-996-9086 *E-mail:* writealotmail@gmail.com, pg 524

diacriTech Inc, 667 Boylston St, 5th fl, Boston, MA 02116 *Tel:* 617-236-7500 *Fax:* 617-848-2938 *Web Site:* www.diacritech.com, pg 524

Diagram Essay Contest, University of Arizona, ML-445, PO Box 210067, Tucson, AZ 85721 *E-mail:* editor@thediagram.com *Web Site:* www.thediagram.com/contest.html, pg 680

Dial Books for Young Readers, 345 Hudson St, New York, NY 10014 *Tel:* 212-366-2000 *Fax:* 212-414-3396 *E-mail:* online@penguinputnam.com *Web Site:* www.penguinputnam.com; us.penguingroup.com, pg 73

Diane Publishing Co, 330 Pusey Ave, Suite 3 (rear), Collingdale, PA 19023-0617 *Tel:* 610-461-6200 *Toll Free Tel:* 800-782-3833 *Fax:* 610-461-6130 *Web Site:* www.dianepublishing.net, pg 74

Philip K Dick Award, PO Box 3447, Hoboken, NJ 07030 *Tel:* 201-876-2551 *Web Site:* www.philipkdickaward.org, pg 681

D4EO Literary Agency, 7 Indian Valley Rd, Weston, CT 06883 *Tel:* 203-544-7180 *Fax:* 203-544-7160 *Web Site:* www.d4eoliteraryagency.com, pg 548

Sandra Dijkstra Literary Agency, 1155 Camino del Mar, PMB 515, Del Mar, CA 92014-2605 *E-mail:* queries@dijkstraagency.com *Web Site:* dijkstraagency.com, pg 548

Annie Dillard Award for Creative Nonfiction, Mail Stop 9053, Western Washington University, Bellingham, WA 98225 *Tel:* 360-650-4863 *E-mail:* bhreview@wwu.edu *Web Site:* www.bhreview.org, pg 681

Gordon W Dillon/Richard C Peterson Memorial Essay Prize, Fairfield Tropical Botanic Gardens, 10901 Old Cutler Rd, Coral Gables, FL 33156 *Tel:* 305-740-2010 *Fax:* 305-740-2011 *E-mail:* theaos@aos.org *Web Site:* www.aos.org, pg 681

Direct Marketing Association (DMA), 1120 Avenue of the Americas, New York, NY 10036-6700 *Tel:* 212-768-7277 *Fax:* 212-302-6714 *E-mail:* memberservices@the-dma.org *Web Site:* thedma.org, pg 74, 604

Discover Great New Writers Award, 122 Fifth Ave, New York, NY 10011 *Web Site:* www.barnesandnoble.com, pg 681

"Discovery"/Boston Review Poetry Contest, 1395 Lexington Ave, New York, NY 10128 *Tel:* 212-415-5760 *E-mail:* unterberg@92y.org *Web Site:* www.92y.org/discovery, pg 681

Discovery House Publishers, 3000 Kraft Ave SE, Grand Rapids, MI 49512 *Tel:* 616-942-2803 *Toll Free Tel:* 800-653-8333 (cust serv) *E-mail:* support@dhp.org *Web Site:* www.dhp.org, pg 74

Disney-Hyperion Books, 1101 Flower St, Glendale, CA 91201 *Web Site:* books.disney.com, pg 74

Disney Press, 1101 Flower St, Glendale, CA 91201 *Web Site:* books.disney.com, pg 74

Disney Publishing Worldwide, 1101 Flower St, Glendale, CA 91201 *Web Site:* books.disney.com, pg 74

Dissertation.com, 23331 Water Circle, Boca Raton, FL 33486-8540 *Tel:* 561-750-4344 *Toll Free Tel:* 800-636-8329 *Fax:* 561-750-6797 *Web Site:* www.dissertation.com, pg 74

Distinguished Book Award, c/o Governance Off, 1430 "K" St NW, Suite 600, Washington, DC 20005 *Tel:* 202-383-9005 *Fax:* 202-638-0882 *E-mail:* governance@asanet.org *Web Site:* www.asanet.org, pg 681

Diversion Books, 443 Park Ave S, Suite 1008, New York, NY 10016 *Tel:* 212-961-6390 *E-mail:* info@diversionbooks.com *Web Site:* www.diversionbooks.com, pg 74

Djerassi Resident Artists Program, 2325 Bear Gulch Rd, Woodside, CA 94062 *Tel:* 650-747-1250 *Fax:* 650-747-0105 *E-mail:* drap@djerassi.org *Web Site:* www.djerassi.org, pg 650

DK Publishing, 345 Hudson St, 2nd fl, New York, NY 10014 *Tel:* 646-674-4000 *Toll Free Tel:* 877-342-5357 (cust serv) *Web Site:* us.dk.com, pg 75

DK Research Inc, 14 Mohegan Lane, Commack, NY 11725 *Tel:* 631-543-5537 *Fax:* 631-543-5549 *Web Site:* www.dkresearchinc.com, pg 524

Do It Now Foundation, PO Box 27568, Tempe, AZ 85285-7568 *Tel:* 480-736-0599 *Fax:* 480-736-0771 *E-mail:* e-mail@doitnow.org; orders@doitnow.org *Web Site:* www.doitnow.org, pg 75

Do-It-Yourself Legal Publishers, 1588 Remsen Ave, Brooklyn, NY 11236 *Tel:* 718-684-4769 *Fax:* 718-684-4769 *E-mail:* ba07102@yahoo.com, pg 75

Documentation Grant Program, 649 rue Queen, 2nd fl, Fredericton, NB E3B 1C3, Canada *Tel:* 506-444-4444 *Toll Free Tel:* 866-460-ARTS (460-2787) *Fax:* 506-444-5543 *E-mail:* nbabcanb@artsnb.ca *Web Site:* www.artsnb.ca, pg 681

Blake Dodd Prize, 633 W 155 St, New York, NY 10032 *Tel:* 212-368-5900 *Fax:* 212-491-4615 *E-mail:* academy@artsandletters.org *Web Site:* www.artsandletters.org, pg 681

Dog Writers' Association of America Inc (DWAA), 66 Adams St, Jamestown, NY 14701 *Tel:* 716-484-6155 *E-mail:* dogwriter@windstream.net *Web Site:* www.dwaa.org, pg 604

Dog Writers' Association of America Inc (DWAA) Annual Writing Competition, 2243 Kelmscott Ct, Westlake Village, CA 91361 *Tel:* 805-418-7899 *Fax:* 831-374-9231 *E-mail:* dogwriter@windstream.net *Web Site:* www.dwaa.org, pg 681

Dogwise Publishing, 403 S Mission St, Wenatchee, WA 98801 *Tel:* 509-663-9115 *Toll Free Tel:* 800-776-2665 *E-mail:* mail@dogwise.com *Web Site:* www.dogwise.com, pg 75

The Christopher Doheny Award, 17 E 47 St, New York, NY 10017 *Tel:* 212-755-6710 *Fax:* 212-826-0831 *E-mail:* doheny@centerforfiction.org; info@centerforfiction.org *Web Site:* www.centerforfiction.org/awards/the-christopher-doheny-award, pg 681

Tom Doherty Associates, LLC, 175 Fifth Ave, 14th fl, New York, NY 10010 *Tel:* 646-307-5151 *Toll Free Tel:* 800-455-0340 *Fax:* 212-388-0191 *E-mail:* firstname.lastname@tor.com *Web Site:* www.tor-forge.com, pg 75

Dominie Press, 145 S Mount Zion Rd, Lebanon, IN 46052 *Tel:* 765-483-6500 *Toll Free Tel:* 800-321-3106 (Pearson Cust Serv); 800-848-9500 *Toll Free Fax:* 877-260-2530 *Web Site:* www.pearsonschool.com, pg 75

Donadio & Olson Inc, 121 W 27 St, Suite 704, New York, NY 10001 *Tel:* 212-691-8077 *Fax:* 212-633-2837 *E-mail:* mail@donadio.com *Web Site:* donadio.com, pg 548

Janis A Donnaud & Associates Inc, 525 Broadway, 2nd fl, New York, NY 10012 *Tel:* 212-431-2663 *Fax:* 212-431-2667 *E-mail:* jdonnaud@aol.com, pg 548

The Donning Company Publishers, 184 Business Park Dr, Suite 206, Virginia Beach, VA 23462 *Tel:* 757-497-1789 *Toll Free Tel:* 800-296-8572 *Fax:* 757-497-2542 *Web Site:* www.donning.com, pg 75

Jim Donovan Literary, 5635 SMU Blvd, Suite 201, Dallas, TX 75206 *Tel:* 214-696-9411 *E-mail:* jdlqueries@sbcglobal.net, pg 549

Dordt College Press, 498 Fourth Ave NE, Sioux Center, IA 51250-1606 *Tel:* 712-722-6420 *Toll Free Tel:* 800-343-6738 *Fax:* 712-722-1198 *E-mail:* dordtpress@dordt.edu; bookstore@dordt.edu *Web Site:* www.dordt.edu, pg 75

Dorland Health, 4 Choke Cherry Rd, 2nd fl, Rockville, MD 20850 *Tel:* 301-354-2000 *Toll Free Tel:* 855-225-5341 *Fax:* 301-287-2535 *E-mail:* customer@decisionhealth.com *Web Site:* www.dorlandhealth.com, pg 75

Dorothy Canfield Fisher Children's Book Award, 109 State St, Montpelier, VT 05609-0601 *Tel:* 802-828-6954 *Fax:* 802-828-1481 *E-mail:* cbec@state.vt.us *Web Site:* www.dcfaward.org; libraries.vermont.gov/libraries, pg 682

Dorrance Publishing Co Inc, 585 Alpha Dr, Suite 103, Pittsburgh, PA 15238 *Toll Free Tel:* 800-695-9599; 800-788-7654 (gen cust orders) *Fax:* 412-288-1786 *E-mail:* dorrinfo@dorrancepublishing.com; redleadbookorders@dorrancepublishing.com; bookorders@rosedogbooks.com *Web Site:* www.dorrancepublishing.com, pg 75

Dorset House Publishing Co Inc, 3143 Broadway, Suite 2-B, New York, NY 10027 *Tel:* 212-620-4053 *Toll Free Tel:* 800-DHBOOKS (342-6657, orders only) *Fax:* 212-727-1044 *E-mail:* info@dorsethouse.com *Web Site:* www.dorsethouse.com, pg 76

Dorset Prize, PO Box 1767, North Adams, MA 01247 *Tel:* 413-664-9611 *Fax:* 413-664-9711 *E-mail:* info@tupelopress.org *Web Site:* www.tupelopress.org, pg 682

John Dos Passos Prize for Literature, Dept of English & Modern Languages, 201 High St, Farmville, VA 23909 *Tel:* 434-395-2155 *Fax:* 434-395-2145, pg 682

Double Dragon Publishing Inc, 1-5762 Hwy 7 E, Markham, ON L3P 7Y4, Canada *Tel:* 603-778-7191 *E-mail:* info@double-dragon-ebooks.com; sales@double-dragon-ebooks.com *Web Site:* www.double-dragon-ebooks.com, pg 479

Double Play, 303 Hillcrest Rd, Belton, MO 64012-1852 *Tel:* 816-651-7118, pg 524

Doubleday Canada, One Toronto St, Suite 300, Toronto, ON M5C 2V6, Canada *Tel:* 416-364-4449 *Fax:* 416-364-6863 *Web Site:* www.randomhouse.ca, pg 479

Frank Nelson Doubleday Memorial Award, 2320 Capitol Ave, Cheyenne, WY 82002 *Tel:* 307-777-5234 *Fax:* 307-777-5499 *Web Site:* wyoarts.state.wy.us, pg 682

Doubleday/Nan A Talese, c/o Penguin Random House Inc, 1745 Broadway, New York, NY 10019 *Tel:* 212-751-2600 *Fax:* 212-572-2662 *E-mail:* ddaypub@randomhouse.com *Web Site:* knopfdoubleday.com, pg 76

Douglas & McIntyre (2013) Ltd, 4437 Rondeview Rd, Madeira Park, BC V0N 2H1, Canada *Toll Free Tel:* 800-667-2988 *E-mail:* info@douglas-mcintyre.com *Web Site:* www.douglas-mcintyre.com, pg 479

Dover Publications Inc, 31 E Second St, Mineola, NY 11501-3852 *Tel:* 516-294-7000 *Toll Free Tel:* 800-223-3130 (orders) *Fax:* 516-742-6953 *E-mail:* rights@doverpublications.com; service@doverpublications.com *Web Site:* store.doverdirect.com; www.doverpublications.com, pg 76

Down East Books, 680 Commercial St (US Rte 1), Rockport, ME 04856 *Tel:* 207-594-9544 *Toll Free Tel:* 800-685-7962 (US only orders); 800-766-1670 *E-mail:* editorial@downeast.com *Web Site:* www.downeast.com, pg 76

Down The Shore Publishing Corp, 106 Stafford Forge Rd, West Creek, NJ 08092 *Tel:* 609-812-5076 *Fax:* 609-812-5098 *E-mail:* dtsbooks@comcast.net; info@down-the-shore.com *Web Site:* www.down-the-shore.com, pg 76

Doyen Literary Services Inc, 1931 660 St, Newell, IA 50568 *Web Site:* www.barbaradoyen.com, pg 549

Dragon Door Publications, 5 E Country Rd B, Suite 3, Little Canada, MN 55117 *Tel:* 651-487-2180 *Toll Free Tel:* 800-899-5111 (orders & cust serv) *E-mail:* support@dragondoor.com *Web Site:* www.dragondoor.com, pg 76

Dragonfairy Press, 2107 N Decatur Rd, Suite 211, Decatur, GA 30033 *Tel:* 404-955-8150 *E-mail:* info@dragonfairypress.com *Web Site:* www.dragonfairypress.com, pg 76

Dramatic Publishing Co, 311 Washington St, Woodstock, IL 60098-3308 *Tel:* 815-338-7170 *Toll Free Tel:* 800-448-7469 *Fax:* 815-338-8981 *Toll Free Fax:* 800-334-5302 *E-mail:* plays@dramaticpublishing.com; customerservice@dpcplays.com *Web Site:* www.dramaticpublishing.com, pg 76

Dramatists Play Service Inc, 440 Park Ave S, New York, NY 10016 *Tel:* 212-683-8960 *Fax:* 212-213-1539 *E-mail:* postmaster@dramatists.com; orders@dramatists.com; publications@dramatists.com *Web Site:* www.dramatists.com, pg 76

Dreaming Publications LLC, 1938 Old Balsam Rd, Waynesville, NC 28786 *Tel:* 828-423-0226 *E-mail:* dreamingpublications@gmail.com *Web Site:* dreamingpublications.com, pg 507

Dreaming Robot Press, 1214 San Francisco Ave, Las Vegas, NM 87701 *Tel:* 505-264-3830 *E-mail:* books@dreamingrobotpress.com *Web Site:* dreamingrobotpress.com, pg 77

Dreamscape Media LLC, 6940 Hall St, Holland, OH 43528 *Tel:* 419-867-6965 *Toll Free Tel:* 877-983-7326 *E-mail:* info@dreamscapeab.com *Web Site:* www.dreamscapeab.com, pg 77

Drennan Communications, 6 Robin Lane, East Kingston, NH 03827 *Tel:* 603-642-8002 *Fax:* 603-642-8002, pg 524

Drennan Literary Agency, 6 Robin Lane, East Kingston, NH 03827 *Tel:* 603-642-8002 *Fax:* 603-642-8002, pg 549

Carleton Drewry Memorial, 1194 Hume Rd, Hume, VA 22639-1806 *E-mail:* poetryinva@aol.com *Web Site:* www.poetrysocietyofvirginia.org, pg 682

Saint Katharine Drexel Award, 8550 United Plaza Blvd, Suite 1001, Baton Rouge, LA 70809-2256 *Tel:* 225-408-4417 *E-mail:* cla2@cathla.org *Web Site:* www.cathla.org, pg 682

Drummond Books, 2111 Cleveland St, Evanston, IL 60202 *Tel:* 847-302-2534 *E-mail:* drummondbooks@gmail.com, pg 524

Drury University One-Act Play Competition, 900 N Benton Ave, Springfield, MO 65802-3344 *Tel:* 417-873-6821 *Web Site:* www.drury.edu, pg 682

Dubuque Fine Arts Players Annual One Act Play Festival, PO Box 1160, Dubuque, IA 52004-1160 *Tel:* 563-588-3438 *E-mail:* contact@dbqoneacts.org *Web Site:* www.dbqoneacts.org, pg 682

Dufour Editions Inc, PO Box 7, Chester Springs, PA 19425 *Tel:* 610-458-5005 *Fax:* 610-458-7103 *E-mail:* info@dufoureditions.com *Web Site:* www.dufoureditions.com, pg 77

Duke University Press, 905 W Main St, Suite 18B, Durham, NC 27701 *Tel:* 919-688-5134 *Toll Free Tel:* 888-651-0122 (US) *Fax:* 919-688-2615 *Toll Free Fax:* 888-651-0124 *E-mail:* orders@dukeupress.edu; permissions@dukeupress.edu *Web Site:* www.dukeupress.edu, pg 77

Dumbarton Oaks, 1703 32 St NW, Washington, DC 20007 *Tel:* 202-339-6400 *Fax:* 202-339-6401; 202-298-8407 *E-mail:* doaksbooks@doaks.org *Web Site:* www.doaks.org, pg 77

Dun & Bradstreet, 103 JFK Pkwy, Short Hills, NJ 07078 *Tel:* 973-921-5500 *Toll Free Tel:* 800-526-0651; 800-234-3867 (cust serv) *E-mail:* custserv@dnb.com *Web Site:* www.dnb.com, pg 77

Dundurn Press Ltd, 3 Church St, Suite 500, Toronto, ON M5E 1M2, Canada *Tel:* 416-214-5544 *Fax:* 416-214-5556 *E-mail:* info@dundurn.com *Web Site:* www.dundurn.com, pg 479

Dunham Literary Inc, 110 William St, Suite 2202, New York, NY 10038 *Tel:* 212-929-0994 *Web Site:* dunhamlit.com, pg 549

Dunhill Publishing, 18340 Sonoma Hwy, Sonoma, CA 95476 *Tel:* 707-939-0570 *Fax:* 707-938-3515 *E-mail:* dunhill@vom.com *Web Site:* www.dunhillpublishing.com, pg 77

John H Dunning Prize in United States History, 400 "A" St SE, Washington, DC 20003 *Tel:* 202-544-2422 *Fax:* 202-544-8307 *E-mail:* awards@historians.org *Web Site:* www.historians.org, pg 682

Dunow, Carlson & Lerner Literary Agency Inc, 27 W 20 St, Suite 1107, New York, NY 10011 *Tel:* 212-645-7606 *E-mail:* mail@dclagency.com *Web Site:* www.dclagency.com, pg 549

Dupree, Miller & Associates Inc, 100 Highland Park Village, Suite 350, Dallas, TX 75205 *Tel:* 214-559-2665 *Fax:* 214-559-7243 *E-mail:* editorial@dupreemiller.com *Web Site:* www.dupreemiller.com, pg 549

Duquesne University Press, 600 Forbes Ave, Pittsburgh, PA 15282 *Tel:* 412-396-6610 *Fax:* 412-396-5984 *E-mail:* dupress@duq.edu *Web Site:* www.dupress.duq.edu, pg 77

Dustbooks, PO Box 100, Paradise, CA 95967-0100 *Tel:* 530-877-6110 *Fax:* 530-877-0222 *E-mail:* publisher@dustbooks.com; info@dustbooks.com *Web Site:* www.dustbooks.com, pg 77

Dutton, 375 Hudson St, New York, NY 10014 *Tel:* 212-366-2000 *Fax:* 212-366-2262 *E-mail:* online@penguinputnam.com *Web Site:* www.penguinputnam.com; us.penguingroup.com, pg 78

Dutton Children's Books, 345 Hudson St, New York, NY 10014 *Tel:* 212-366-2000 *E-mail:* online@penguinputnam.com *Web Site:* www.penguinputnam.com; us.penguingroup.com, pg 78

DWJ BOOKS LLC, 46 Cliff Dr, Sag Harbor, NY 11963 *Tel:* 631-899-4500 *E-mail:* info@dwjbooks.com *Web Site:* www.dwjbooks.com, pg 524

DynaMinds Publishing®, PO Box 106, Johnston, IA 50131 *Tel:* 515-991-5315 *Web Site:* www.dynamindspublishing.com, pg 78

Dystel & Goderich Literary Management, One Union Sq W, Suite 904, New York, NY 10003 *Tel:* 212-627-9100 *Fax:* 212-627-9313 *Web Site:* www.dystel.com, pg 549

Eagan Press, 3340 Pilot Knob Rd, St Paul, MN 55121 *Tel:* 651-454-7250 *Toll Free Tel:* 800-328-7560 *Fax:* 651-454-0766 *E-mail:* aacc@scisoc.org *Web Site:* www.aaccnet.org, pg 78

Eagle's View Publishing, 6756 North Fork Rd, Liberty, UT 84310 *Tel:* 801-393-4555; 801-745-0905 (edit) *Fax:* 801-745-0903 (edit); 801-393-4647 *E-mail:* sales@eaglefeathertrading.com *Web Site:* www.eaglesviewpub.com, pg 78

Eakin Press, PO Box 331779, Fort Worth, TX 76163 *Tel:* 817-344-7036 *Toll Free Tel:* 888-982-8270 *Fax:* 817-344-7036 *Web Site:* www.eakinpress.com, pg 78

Earth Edit, PO Box 114, Maiden Rock, WI 54750 *Tel:* 715-448-3009, pg 525

East Asian Legal Studies Program (EALSP), 500 W Baltimore St, Suite 411, Baltimore, MD 21201-1786 *Tel:* 410-706-3870 *Fax:* 410-706-1516 *E-mail:* eastasia@law.umaryland.edu *Web Site:* www.law.umaryland.edu/programs/international/eastasia, pg 78

East Mountain Editing Services, PO Box 1895, Tijeras, NM 87059-1895 *Tel:* 505-281-8422 *Web Site:* www.spanishindexing.com, pg 525

East West Discovery Press, PO Box 3585, Manhattan Beach, CA 90266 *Tel:* 310-545-3730 *Fax:* 310-545-3731 *E-mail:* info@eastwestdiscovery.com *Web Site:* www.eastwestdiscovery.com, pg 78

EastBridge, 70 New Canaan Ave, Norwalk, CT 06850 *Tel:* 203-855-9125 *Fax:* 203-857-0730 *E-mail:* asia@eastbridgebooks.org; ask@eastbridgebooks.org *Web Site:* www.eastbridgebooks.org, pg 78

Eastland Press, 1240 Activity Dr, Suite D, Vista, CA 92081 *Tel:* 206-217-0204 (edit); 760-598-9695 (orders) *Toll Free Tel:* 800-453-3278 (orders) *Fax:* 760-598-6083 (orders) *Toll Free Fax:* 800-241-3329 (orders) *E-mail:* info@eastlandpress.com; orders@eastlandpress.com (credit card orders only) *Web Site:* www.eastlandpress.com, pg 78

Easy Money Press, 5419 87 St, Lubbock, TX 79424 *Tel:* 806-543-5215 *E-mail:* easymoneypress@yahoo.com, pg 78

Eaton Literary Associates Literary Awards, PO Box 49795, Sarasota, FL 34230-6795 *Tel:* 941-366-6589 *Fax:* 941-365-4679 *E-mail:* eatonlit@aol.com *Web Site:* www.eatonliterary.com, pg 682

Ecopress, 5995 149 St W, Suite 105, Apple Valley, MN 55124 *Tel:* 952-469-6699 *Toll Free Tel:* 800-846-7027 *Fax:* 952-469-1968 *Toll Free Fax:* 800-330-6232 *E-mail:* info@finneyco.com *Web Site:* www.ecopress.com, pg 79

Ecrits des Forges, 992-A rue Royale, Trois-Rivieres, QC G9A 4H9, Canada *Tel:* 819-840-8492 *E-mail:* ecritsdesforges@gmail.com *Web Site:* www.ecritsdesforges.com, pg 479

ECS Publishing Corp, 615 Concord St, Framingham, MA 01702 *Tel:* 508-620-7400 *Fax:* 508-620-7401 *E-mail:* office@ecspub.com *Web Site:* ecspublishing.com, pg 79

ECW Press, 665 Gerrard St E, Toronto, ON M4M 1Y2, Canada *Tel:* 416-694-3348 *Fax:* 416-698-9906 *E-mail:* info@ecwpress.com *Web Site:* www.ecwpress.com, pg 479

EDC Publishing, 10302 E 55 Place, Tulsa, OK 74146-6515 *Tel:* 918-622-4522 *Toll Free Tel:* 800-475-4522 *Fax:* 918-665-7919 *Toll Free Fax:* 800-743-5660 *E-mail:* edc@edcpub.com *Web Site:* www.edcpub.com, pg 79

Edda USA, 373 Park Ave S, 6th fl, New York, NY 10016 *Tel:* 646-755-9210 *Web Site:* eddausa.com, pg 79

Anne Edelstein Literary Agency LLC, 404 Riverside Dr, New York, NY 10025 *Tel:* 212-414-4923 *E-mail:* info@aeliterary.com; rights@aeliterary.com *Web Site:* www.aeliterary.com, pg 549

Edelstein Prize, Univ of Virginia, Dept of Science, Tech & Society, PO Box 400744, Charlottesville, VA 22904-4744 *Tel:* 434-987-6230 *Fax:* 434-975-2190 (attention: SHOT) *E-mail:* shot@virginia.edu *Web Site:* www.shot.jhu.edu, pg 682

EDGE Science Fiction & Fantasy Publishing, PO Box 1714, Sta M, Calgary, AB T2P 2L7, Canada *Tel:* 403-254-0160 *Web Site:* www.edgewebsite.com, pg 479

Edgewise Press Inc, 24 Fifth Ave, Suite 224, New York, NY 10011 *Tel:* 212-982-4818 *Fax:* 212-982-1364 *E-mail:* epinc@mindspring.com *Web Site:* www.edgewisepress.org, pg 79

ediciones Lerner, 241 First Ave N, Minneapolis, MN 55401 *Tel:* 612-332-3344 *Toll Free Tel:* 800-328-4929 *Fax:* 612-332-7615 *Toll Free Fax:* 800-332-1132 *E-mail:* info@lernerbooks.com *Web Site:* www.lernerbooks.com, pg 79

EditAndPublishYourBook.com, PO Box 2965, Nantucket, MA 02584-2965 *E-mail:* michaeltheauthor@yahoo.com *Web Site:* www.editandpublishyourbook.com, pg 525

Edit Etc, 20 Rock Harbor Rd, Orleans, MA 02653 *Tel:* 914-715-5849 *E-mail:* atkedit@cs.com *Web Site:* www.anntkeene.com, pg 525

Edit Resource LLC, 3578-E Hartsel Dr, Suite 387, Colorado Springs, CO 80920 *Tel:* 719-290-0757 *E-mail:* info@editresource.com (main) *Web Site:* www.editresource.com (main); www.inspirationalghostwriting.com, pg 525

EditAmerica, 115 Jacobs Creek Rd, Ewing, NJ 08628 *Tel:* 609-882-5852 *Web Site:* www.editamerica.com; www.linkedin.com/in/PaulaPlantier, pg 525

Editcetera, 2034 Blake St, Suite 5, Berkeley, CA 94704 *Tel:* 510-849-1110 *Fax:* 510-900-6141 *E-mail:* info@editcetera.com *Web Site:* www.editcetera.com, pg 525

EditCraft Editorial Services, 422 Pine St, Grass Valley, CA 95945 *Tel:* 530-263-3688 *Web Site:* www.editcraft.com, pg 525

Les Editions Alire, CP 67, Succursale B, Quebec, QC G1K 7A1, Canada *Tel:* 418-835-4441 *Fax:* 418-838-4443 *E-mail:* info@alire.com *Web Site:* www.alire.com, pg 479

Les Editions Caractere, 5800, rue St-Denis, bureau 900, Montreal, QC H2S 3L5, Canada *Tel:* 514-273-1066 *Fax:* 514-276-0324 *E-mail:* caractere@tc.tc *Web Site:* www.editionscaractere.com, pg 479

editions CERES Ltd/Le Moyen Francais, CP 1089, Succursale B, Maison de la Poste, Montreal, QC H3B 3K9, Canada *Tel:* 514-937-7138 *Fax:* 514-937-9875 *E-mail:* editionsceres@gmail.com *Web Site:* www.editionsceres.ca, pg 480

Editions de la Pleine Lune, 223 34 Ave, Lachine, QC H8T 1Z4, Canada *Tel:* 514-634-7954 *Fax:* 514-637-6366 *E-mail:* editpllune@videotron.ca *Web Site:* www.pleinelune.qc.ca, pg 480

Les Editions de l'Hexagone, 1010 rue de la Gauchetiere E, Montreal, QC H2L 2N5, Canada *Tel:* 514-523-7993 *Fax:* 514-282-7530 *Web Site:* www.edhexagone.com, pg 480

Les Editions de Mortagne, CP 116, Boucherville, QC J4B 5E6, Canada *Tel:* 450-641-2387 *Fax:* 450-655-6092 *E-mail:* info@editionsdemortagne.com *Web Site:* www.editionsdemortagne.com, pg 480

Editions Marcel Didier Inc, 1815, ave De Lorimier, Montreal, QC H2K 3W6, Canada *Tel:* 514-523-1523 *Toll Free Tel:* 800-361-1664 (Ontario to Maritimes) *Fax:* 514-523-5955 *E-mail:* marceldidier@hurtubisehmh.com *Web Site:* www.marceldidier.com, pg 480

Les Editions du Ble, 340 Provencher Blvd, St Boniface, MB R2H 0G7, Canada *Tel:* 204-237-8200 *Fax:* 204-233-8182 *E-mail:* direction@editionsduble.ca *Web Site:* ble.avoslivres.ca, pg 480

Les Editions du Boreal, 4447, rue St-Denis, Montreal, QC H2J 2L2, Canada *Tel:* 514-287-7401 *Fax:* 514-287-7664 *E-mail:* boreal@editionsboreal.qc.ca *Web Site:* www.editionsboreal.qc.ca, pg 480

Editions du CHU Sainte-Justine, 3175, chemin de la Cote-Sainte-Catherine, Montreal, QC H3T 1C5, Canada *Tel:* 514-345-4671 *Fax:* 514-345-4631 *E-mail:* edition.hsj@ssss.gouv.qc.ca *Web Site:* www.editions-chu-sainte-justine.org, pg 480

Les Editions du CRAM Inc, 1030, Cherrier, bureau 205, Montreal, QC H2L 1H9, Canada *Tel:* 514-598-8547 *Fax:* 514-598-8788 *E-mail:* service@editionscram.com *Web Site:* www.editionscram.com, pg 481

Les Editions du Noroit, 4609 rue D'Iberville, espace 202, Montreal, QC H2H 2L9, Canada *Tel:* 514-727-0005 *E-mail:* lenoroit@lenoroit.com *Web Site:* www.lenoroit.com, pg 481

Les Editions du Remue-Menage, La Maison Parent-Roback, 110 rue Ste-Therese, bureau 501, Montreal, QC H2Y 1E6, Canada *Tel:* 514-876-0097 *Fax:* 514-876-7951 *E-mail:* info@editions-rm.ca *Web Site:* www.editions-rm.ca, pg 481

Les Editions du Septentrion, 1300 Maguire Ave, Sillery, QC G1T 1Z3, Canada *Tel:* 418-688-3556 *Fax:* 418-527-4978 *E-mail:* info@septentrion.qc.ca *Web Site:* www.septentrion.qc.ca, pg 481

Les Editions du Vermillon, 305, rue St-Patrick, Ottawa, ON K1N 5K4, Canada *Tel:* 613-241-4032 *Fax:* 613-241-3109 *E-mail:* leseditionsduvermillon@rogers.com *Web Site:* www.leseditionsduvermillon.ca, pg 481

Les Editions Fides, 7333 place des Roseraies, bureau 100, Anjou, QC H1M 2X6, Canada *Tel:* 514-745-4290 *Fax:* 514-745-4299 *E-mail:* editions@groupefides.com *Web Site:* www.editionsfides.com, pg 481

Editions FouLire, 4339, rue des Becassines, Quebec, QC G1G 1V5, Canada *Tel:* 418-628-4029 *Toll Free Tel:* 877-628-4029 (CN & US) *Fax:* 418-628-4801 *E-mail:* info@foulire.com; edition@foulire.com *Web Site:* www.foulire.com, pg 481

Les Editions Ganesha Inc, CP 484, succursale d'Youville, Montreal, QC H2P 2W1, Canada *Tel:* 450-641-2395 *E-mail:* courriel@editions-ganesha.qc.ca *Web Site:* www.editions-ganesha.qc.ca, pg 481

Les Editions Goelette Inc, 1350 Marie-Victorin, St-Bruno-de-Montarville, Quebec, QC J3V 6B9, Canada *Tel:* 450-653-1337 *Toll Free Tel:* 800-463-4961 *Fax:* 450-653-9924 *E-mail:* info@boutiquegoelette.com *Web Site:* www.editionsgoelette.com, pg 481

Les Editions Heritage Inc, 1101, ave Victoria, St-Lambert, QC J4R 1P8, Canada *Tel:* 514-875-0327 *Toll Free Tel:* 800-561-3737 *Fax:* 450-672-5448, pg 482

Editions Hurtubise, 1815, ave De Lorimier, Montreal, QC H2K 3W6, Canada *Tel:* 514-523-1523 *Toll Free Tel:* 800-361-1664 *Fax:* 514-523-9969 *Web Site:* www.editionshurtubise.com, pg 482

Les Editions JCL, 930, rue Jacques-Cartier E, Chicoutimi, QC G7H 7K9, Canada *Tel:* 418-696-0536 *Fax:* 418-696-3132 *E-mail:* jcl@jcl.qc.ca *Web Site:* www.jcl.qc.ca, pg 482

Editions Le Dauphin Blanc Inc, 825, boul Lebourgneuf, Suite 125, Quebec, QC G2J 0B9, Canada *Tel:* 418-845-4045 *Fax:* 418-845-1933 *E-mail:* info@dauphinblanc.com *Web Site:* www.dauphinblanc.com, pg 482

Editions Marie-France, 9900 Ave des Laurentides, Montreal, QC H1H 4V1, Canada *Tel:* 514-329-3700 *Toll Free Tel:* 800-563-6644 (CN) *Fax:* 514-329-0630 *E-mail:* editions@marie-france.qc.ca *Web Site:* www.marie-france.qc.ca, pg 482

Editions Mediaspaul, 3965, blvd Henri-Bourassa E, Montreal, QC H1H 1L1, Canada *Tel:* 514-322-7341 *Fax:* 514-322-4281 *E-mail:* editeur@mediaspaul.ca *Web Site:* mediaspaul.ca, pg 482

Editions Michel Quintin, 4770 rue Foster, Waterloo, QC J0E 2N0, Canada *Tel:* 450-539-3774 *Fax:* 450-539-4905 *E-mail:* info@editionsmichelquintin.ca *Web Site:* www.editionsmichelquintin.ca, pg 482

Editions MultiMondes, 930 rue Pouliot, Quebec, QC G1V 3N9, Canada *Tel:* 418-651-3885 *Toll Free Tel:* 800-840-3029 *Fax:* 418-651-6822 *Toll Free Fax:* 888-303-5931 *E-mail:* multimondes@multim.com *Web Site:* www.multim.com, pg 482

Editions Orphee Inc, 1240 Clubview Blvd N, Columbus, OH 43235-1226 *Tel:* 614-846-9517 *Fax:* 614-846-9794 *E-mail:* sales@editionsorphee.com *Web Site:* www.editionsorphee.com, pg 79

Les Editions Phidal Inc, 5740 Ferrier, Montreal, QC H4P 1M7, Canada *Tel:* 514-738-0202 *Toll Free Tel:* 800-738-7349 *Fax:* 514-738-5102 *E-mail:* info@phidal.com; customer@phidal.com (sales & export), pg 482

Les Editions Pierre Tisseyre, 155, rue Maurice, Rosemere, QC J7A 2S8, Canada *Tel:* 514-335-0777 *Fax:* 514-335-6723 *E-mail:* info@edtisseyre.ca *Web Site:* www.tisseyre.ca, pg 482

Editions Trecarre, La Tourelle, Bureau 800, 1055, Blvd Rene-Levesque E, Montreal, QC H2L 4S5, Canada *Tel:* 514-849-5259 *Fax:* 514-849-1388 *Web Site:* www.edtrecarre.com, pg 483

Les Editions Un Monde Different, 3905 Isabelle, bureau 101, Brossard, QC J4Y 2R2, Canada *Tel:* 450-656-2660 *Toll Free Tel:* 800-443-2582 *Fax:* 450-659-9328 *E-mail:* info@umd.ca *Web Site:* www.umd.ca, pg 483

Les Editions Vents d'Ouest, 109, rue Wright, bureau 202, Gatineau, QC J8X 2G7, Canada *Tel:* 819-770-6377 *Fax:* 819-770-0559 *E-mail:* info@ventsdouest.ca *Web Site:* www.ventsdouest.ca, pg 483

Les Editions XYZ inc, 1815, ave De Lorimier, Montreal, QC H2K 3W6, Canada *Tel:* 514-525-2170 *Fax:* 514-525-7537 *E-mail:* info@editionsxyz.com *Web Site:* www.editionsxyz.com, pg 483

Editions Yvon Blais, 137 John, CP 180, Cowansville, QC J2K 3H6, Canada *Tel:* 450-266-1086 *Toll Free Tel:* 800-363-3047 *Fax:* 450-263-9256 *E-mail:* editionsyvonblais.commentaires@thomsonreuters.com; editionsyvonblais.commandes@thomsonreuters.com (cust serv) *Web Site:* www.editionsyvonblais.qc.ca, pg 483

Editorial Bautista Independiente, 3417 Kenilworth Blvd, Sebring, FL 33870-4469 *Tel:* 863-382-6350 *Toll Free Tel:* 800-398-7187 (US) *Fax:* 863-382-8650 *E-mail:* info@ebi-bmm.org; ebiweb@ebi-bmm.org *Web Site:* www.ebi-bmm.org, pg 79

The Editorial Dept LLC, 7650 E Broadway, Suite 308, Tucson, AZ 85710 *Tel:* 520-546-9992 *Fax:* 520-979-3408 *E-mail:* admin@editorialdepartment.com *Web Site:* www.editorialdepartment.com, pg 525

Editorial Freelancers Association (EFA), 71 W 23 St, 4th fl, New York, NY 10010-4102 *Tel:* 212-929-5400 *Toll Free Tel:* 866-929-5425 *Fax:* 212-929-5439 *Toll Free Fax:* 866-929-5439 *E-mail:* office@the-efa.org *Web Site:* www.the-efa.org, pg 605

Editorial Portavoz, 2450 Oak Industrial Dr NE, Grand Rapids, MI 49505 *Toll Free Tel:* 877-733-2607 (ext 206) *Fax:* 616-493-1790 *E-mail:* portavoz@portavoz.com *Web Site:* www.portavoz.com, pg 79

Editors' Association of Canada (Association canadienne des reviseurs), 27 Carlton St, Suite 502, Toronto, ON M5B 1L2, Canada *Tel:* 416-975-1379 *Toll Free Tel:* 866-CAN-EDIT (226-3348) *Fax:* 416-975-1637 *E-mail:* info@editors.ca; info@reviseurs.ca *Web Site:* www.editors.ca; www.reviseurs.ca, pg 605

The Editors Circle, 462 Grove St, Montclair, NJ 07043 *Tel:* 973-783-5082 *E-mail:* query@theeditorscircle.com *Web Site:* www.theeditorscircle.com, pg 525

Education Awards of Excellence, 200 Deer Run Rd, Sewickley, PA 15143-2324 *Tel:* 412-259-1705 *Toll Free Tel:* 800-910-4283 (ext 705) *Fax:* 412-749-9890 *E-mail:* printing@printing.org *Web Site:* www.printing.org/educationaward, pg 682

Education Writers Association (EWA), 3516 Connecticut Ave NW, Washington, DC 20008-2401 *Tel:* 202-452-9830 *Fax:* 202-452-9837 *E-mail:* ewa@ewa.org *Web Site:* www.ewa.org, pg 605

Education Writers Association Workshops, 3516 Connecticut Ave NW, Washington, DC 20008-2401 *Tel:* 202-452-9830 *Fax:* 202-452-9837 *E-mail:* ewa@ewa.org *Web Site:* www.ewa.org, pg 650

Educational Book & Media Association (EBMA), 37 Main St, Suite 203, Warrenton, VA 20186 *Tel:* 540-318-7770 *Fax:* 202-962-3939 *E-mail:* info@edupaperback.org *Web Site:* www.edupaperback.org, pg 605

Educational Design Services LLC, 5750 Bou Ave, Suite 1508, North Bethesda, MD 20852 *Tel:* 301-881-8611 *Web Site:* www.educationaldesignservices.com, pg 550

Educational Directories Inc (EDI), 1025 W Wise Rd, Suite 101, Schaumburg, IL 60193 *Tel:* 847-891-1250 *Toll Free Tel:* 800-357-6183 *Fax:* 847-891-0945 *E-mail:* info@ediusa.com *Web Site:* www.ediusa.com, pg 79

Educational Impressions Inc, 785 Franklin Ave, Franklin Lakes, NJ 07417 *Tel:* 201-644-0908 *Toll Free Tel:* 800-451-7450 *Fax:* 201-644-0907 *Web Site:* www.edimpressions.com; www.awpeller.com, pg 79

Educational Insights, 152 W Walnut St, Suite 201, Gardena, CA 90248 *Toll Free Tel:* 800-995-4436 *Toll Free Fax:* 888-892-8731 *E-mail:* cs@educationalinsights.com *Web Site:* www.educationalinsights.com, pg 80

Educators Award, PO Box 1589, Austin, TX 78767-1589 *Tel:* 512-478-5748 *Toll Free Tel:* 888-762-4685 *Fax:* 512-478-3961 *E-mail:* societyexec@dkg.org *Web Site:* www.dkg.org, pg 683

Educator's International Press Inc (EIP), 756 Linderman Ave, Kingston, NY 12401 *Tel:* 518-334-0276 *Fax:* 703-661-1547 *E-mail:* info@edint.com *Web Site:* edint.presswarehouse.com, pg 80

Educators Progress Service Inc, 214 Center St, Randolph, WI 53956 *Tel:* 920-326-3126 *Toll Free Tel:* 888-951-4469 *Fax:* 920-326-3127 *E-mail:* epsinc@centurytel.net, pg 80

Edupress Inc, 4810 Forrest Run Rd, Madison, WI 53704 *Toll Free Tel:* 800-835-7978 *Toll Free Fax:* 800-558-9332 *E-mail:* edupressdealers@edupress.com *Web Site:* www.edupress.com, pg 80

Margaret A Edwards Award, 50 E Huron St, Chicago, IL 60611 *Tel:* 312-280-4390 *Toll Free Tel:* 800-545-2433 *Fax:* 312-280-5276 *E-mail:* yalsa@ala.org *Web Site:* www.ala.org/yalsa/edwards, pg 683

Edwin Markham Prize for Poetry, San Jose State University, English Dept, One Washington Sq, San Jose, CA 95192-0090 *Tel:* 408-924-4441 *Web Site:* www.reedmag.org, pg 683

EEI Communications, 6301 Ivy Lane, Suite 250, Greenbelt, MD 20770 *Tel:* 410-309-8200 *Fax:* 410-630-3980 *E-mail:* info@eeicom.com *Web Site:* www.eeicom.com, pg 525, 659

Wm B Eerdmans Publishing Co, 2140 Oak Industrial Dr NE, Grand Rapids, MI 49505 *Tel:* 616-459-4591 *Toll Free Tel:* 800-253-7521 *Fax:* 616-459-6540 *E-mail:* customerservice@eerdmans.com; sales@eerdmans.com *Web Site:* www.eerdmans.com, pg 80

The Maureen Egen Writers Exchange Award, 90 Broad St, Suite 2100, New York, NY 10004 *Tel:* 212-226-3586 *Fax:* 212-226-3963 *E-mail:* admin@pw.org *Web Site:* www.pw.org, pg 683

Wilfrid Eggleston Award for Nonfiction, 11759 Groat Rd, Edmonton, AB T5M 3K6, Canada *Tel:* 780-422-8174 *Toll Free Tel:* 800-665-5354 (AB only) *Fax:* 780-422-2663 (attn WGA) *E-mail:* mail@writersguild.ab.ca *Web Site:* www.writersguild.ab.ca, pg 683

Diane Eickhoff, 3808 Genessee St, Kansas City, MO 64111 *Tel:* 816-561-6693 *E-mail:* diane.eickhoff@gmail.com, pg 525

Eisenbrauns Inc, PO Box 275, Winona Lake, IN 46590-0275 *Tel:* 574-269-2011 *Fax:* 574-269-6788 *E-mail:* customer_service@eisenbrauns.com; publisher@eisenbrauns.com *Web Site:* www.eisenbrauns.com, pg 80

The Lisa Ekus Group LLC, 57 North St, Hatfield, MA 01038 *Tel:* 413-247-9325 *Fax:* 413-247-9873 *E-mail:* lisaekus@lisaekus.com *Web Site:* lisaekus.com, pg 550

The Lisa Ekus Group LLC, 57 North St, Hatfield, MA 01038 *Tel:* 413-247-9325 *Fax:* 413-247-9873 *Web Site:* lisaekus.com, pg 660

Elderberry Press Inc, 1393 Old Homestead Dr, Oakland, OR 97462-9690 *Tel:* 541-459-6043 *Web Site:* www.elderberrypress.com, pg 80

The Electrochemical Society (ECS), 65 S Main St, Bldg D, Pennington, NJ 08534-2839 *Tel:* 609-737-1902 *Fax:* 609-737-2743 *E-mail:* publications@electrochem.org; customerservice@electrochem.org *Web Site:* www.electrochem.org, pg 80

Edward Elgar Publishing Inc, The William Pratt House, 9 Dewey Ct, Northampton, MA 01060-3815 *Tel:* 413-584-5551 *Toll Free Tel:* 800-390-3149 (orders) *Fax:* 413-584-9933 *E-mail:* elgarinfo@e-elgar.com; elgarsales@e-elgar.com; elgarsubmissions@e-elgar.com (edit) *Web Site:* www.e-elgar.com; www.elgaronline.com (ebooks & journals), pg 80

T S Eliot Prize for Poetry, 100 E Normal Ave, Kirksville, MO 63501-4221 *Tel:* 660-785-7336 *Toll Free Tel:* 800-916-6802 *Fax:* 660-785-4480 *E-mail:* tsup@truman.edu *Web Site:* tsup.truman.edu, pg 683

eLit Awards, 1129 Woodmere Ave, Suite B, Traverse City, MI 49686 *Tel:* 231-933-0445 *Toll Free Tel:* 800-706-4636 *Fax:* 231-933-0448 *E-mail:* info@elitawards.com *Web Site:* www.elitawards.com, pg 683

Elite Books, PO Box 442, Fulton, CA 95439 *Tel:* 707-525-9292 *Toll Free Fax:* 800-330-9798 *E-mail:* books@authorspublishing.com *Web Site:* www.elitebooksonline.com, pg 81

Ethan Ellenberg Literary Agency, 548 Broadway, Suite 5-E, New York, NY 10012 *Tel:* 212-431-4554 *E-mail:* agent@ethanellenberg.com *Web Site:* www.ethanellenberg.com, pg 550

Ellery Queen Award, 1140 Broadway, Suite 1507, New York, NY 10001 *Tel:* 212-888-8171 *Fax:* 212-888-8107 *E-mail:* mwa@mysterywriters.org *Web Site:* www.mysterywriters.org, pg 683

Elliott Prize, 104 Mount Auburn St, 5th fl, Cambridge, MA 02138 *Tel:* 617-491-1622 *Fax:* 617-492-3303 *E-mail:* speculum@medievalacademy.org *Web Site:* www.medievalacademy.org, pg 683

Nicholas Ellison Agency, 55 Fifth Ave, 15th fl, New York, NY 10003 *Tel:* 212-206-5600 *Fax:* 212-463-8718 *Web Site:* greenburger.com/agent/nick-ellison, pg 550

Ellora's Cave, 1056 Home Ave, Akron, OH 44310-3302 *Tel:* 330-253-3521 *E-mail:* service@ellorascave.com; comments@ellorascave.com *Web Site:* www.ellorascave.com, pg 81

Irene Elmer, 2806 Cherry St, Berkeley, CA 94705-2310 *Tel:* 510-841-0466 *E-mail:* ielmer@earthlink.net, pg 525

ELS Editions, University of Victoria, Dept of English, PO Box 1700, Sta CSC, Victoria, BC V8W 2Y2, Canada *Tel:* 250-721-7236 *Fax:* 250-721-6498 *E-mail:* els@uvic.ca *Web Site:* english.uvic.ca/els, pg 483

Elsevier Engineering Information (Ei), 360 Park Ave S, New York, NY 10010-1710 *Tel:* 212-989-5800 *Toll Free Tel:* 800-221-1044 *Fax:* 212-633-6380 *E-mail:* eicustomersupport@elsevier.com *Web Site:* www.ei.org, pg 81

Elsevier, Health Sciences Division, 1600 John F Kennedy Blvd, Suite 1800, Philadelphia, PA 19103-2899 *Tel:* 215-239-3900 *Toll Free Tel:* 800-523-1649 *Fax:* 215-239-3990 *Web Site:* www.elsevierhealth.com, pg 81

Elsevier Inc, 225 Wyman St, Waltham, MA 02144 *Tel:* 781-663-5200 *Fax:* 781-663-2262 *E-mail:* bookscustomerservice-usa@elsevier.com *Web Site:* www.elsevier.com, pg 81

Elva Resa Publishing, 8362 Tamarack Village, Suite 119-106, St Paul, MN 55125 *Tel:* 651-357-8770 *Fax:* 501-641-0777 *E-mail:* staff@elvaresa.com *Web Site:* www.elvaresa.com; www.almalittle.com, pg 81

Catherine C Elverston ELS, 9 Red Bay Lane, Kitty Hawk, NC 27949-3307 *Tel:* 352-222-0625 (cell) *E-mail:* celverston@gmail.com, pg 525

R Elwell Indexing, 193 Main St, Cold Spring, NY 10516 *Tel:* 845-667-1036 *E-mail:* ruth.elwell@yahoo.com, pg 525

EMC Publishing LLC, 875 Montreal Way, St Paul, MN 55102 *Tel:* 651-290-2800 (corp) *Toll Free Tel:* 800-328-1452 *Toll Free Fax:* 800-328-4564 *E-mail:* educate@emcp.com *Web Site:* www.emcp.com, pg 81

Emerald Books, PO Box 55787, Seattle, WA 98155 *Tel:* 425-771-1153 *Toll Free Tel:* 800-922-2143 *Fax:* 425-775-2383 *E-mail:* books@ywampublishing.com *Web Site:* www.ywampublishing.com, pg 81

Emerging Playwright Award, 555 Eighth Ave, Suite 1800, New York, NY 10018 *Tel:* 212-421-1380 *Fax:* 212-421-1387 *E-mail:* urbanstage@aol.com, pg 683

Emerson College Department of Writing, Literature & Publishing, 180 Tremont St, 10th fl, Boston, MA 02116 *Tel:* 617-824-8750 *Fax:* 617-824-7856 *Web Site:* www.emerson.edu, pg 660

Emerson College Literary Publishing Certificate Program, Dept of Professional Studies, 120 Boylston St, Boston, MA 02116-8750 *Tel:* 617-824-8280 *Fax:* 617-824-8158 *E-mail:* continuing@emerson.edu *Web Site:* www.emerson.edu/ce, pg 650

The Ralph Waldo Emerson Award, 1606 New Hampshire Ave NW, Washington, DC 20009 *Tel:* 202-265-3808 *Fax:* 202-986-1601 *E-mail:* awards@pbk.org *Web Site:* www.pbk.org/bookawards, pg 683

Emmaus Road Publishing Inc, 1468 Parkview Cir, Steubenville, OH 43952 *Tel:* 740-283-2880 (outside US) *Toll Free Tel:* 800-398-5470 (orders) *Fax:* 740-283-4011 (orders) *E-mail:* questions@emmausroad.org *Web Site:* www.emmausroad.org, pg 81

Emond Montgomery Publications Ltd, 60 Shaftesbury Ave, Toronto, ON M4T 1A3, Canada *Tel:* 416-975-3925 *Toll Free Tel:* 888-837-0815 *Fax:* 416-975-3924 *E-mail:* orders@emp.ca *Web Site:* www.emp.ca, pg 483

Empire Press Media/Avant-Guide, 244 Fifth Ave, Suite 2053, New York, NY 10001-7604 *Tel:* 917-512-3881 *Fax:* 212-202-7757 *E-mail:* info@avantguide.com; communications@avantguide.com; editor@avantguide.com *Web Site:* www.avantguide.com, pg 82

Empire Publishing Service, PO Box 1344, Studio City, CA 91614-0344 *Tel:* 818-784-8918 *E-mail:* empirepubsvc@att.net *Web Site:* www.ppeps.com, pg 82

Empire State Award for Excellence in Literature for Young People, 6021 State Farm Rd, Guilderland, NY 12084 *Tel:* 518-432-6952 *Toll Free Tel:* 800-252-6952 *Fax:* 518-427-1697 *E-mail:* info@nyla.org *Web Site:* www.nyla.org, pg 684

Enchanted Lion Books, 351 Van Brunt St, Ground fl-Gallery, Brooklyn, NY 11231 *Tel:* 646-785-9272 *E-mail:* enchantedlion@gmail.com *Web Site:* www.enchantedlionbooks.com, pg 82

Encounter Books, 900 Broadway, Suite 601, New York, NY 10003 *Tel:* 212-871-6310 *Toll Free Tel:* 800-786-3839 *Fax:* 212-871-6311 *E-mail:* publicity@encounterbooks.com *Web Site:* www.encounterbooks.com, pg 82

Encyclopaedia Britannica Inc, 331 N La Salle St, Chicago, IL 60654 *Tel:* 312-347-7159 (all other countries) *Toll Free Tel:* 800-323-1229 (US & CN) *Fax:* 312-294-2104 *E-mail:* editor@eb.com *Web Site:* www.eb.com; www.britannica.com, pg 82

Energy Information Administration (EIA), 1000 Independence Ave SW, Washington, DC 20585 *Tel:* 202-586-8800 *Fax:* 202-586-0727 *E-mail:* infoctr@eia.doe.gov *Web Site:* www.eia.doe.gov, pg 82

Energy Psychology Press, 1490 Mark West Springs Rd, Santa Rosa, CA 95404 *Tel:* 707-237-6951 *Toll Free Fax:* 800-330-9798 *E-mail:* books@authorspublishing.com *Web Site:* www.energypsychologypress.com; www.elitebooksonline.com, pg 82

Enfield Publishing & Distribution Co, 234 May St, Enfield, NH 03748 *Tel:* 603-632-7377 *Fax:* 603-632-5611 *E-mail:* info@enfieldbooks.com *Web Site:* www.enfieldbooks.com, pg 82

Elaine P English PLLC, 4710 41 St NW, Suite D, Washington, DC 20016 *Tel:* 202-362-5190 *Fax:* 202-362-5192 *E-mail:* foreignrights@elaineenglish.com *Web Site:* www.elaineenglish.com, pg 551

Enigma Books, 12 E 86 St, New York, NY 10028 *Tel:* 646-246-8010 *E-mail:* editor@enigmabooks.com *Web Site:* www.enigmabooks.com, pg 83

Enough Said, 3959 NW 29 Lane, Gainesville, FL 32606 *Tel:* 352-262-2971 *Fax:* 352-372-5747 (call first) *E-mail:* enoughsaid@cox.net *Web Site:* users.navi.net/~heathlynn, pg 525

Enslow Publishing LLC, 101 W 23 St, Suite 240, New York, NY 10011 *Tel:* 908-771-9400 *Toll Free Tel:* 800-398-2504 *Fax:* 908-771-0925 *Toll Free Fax:* 877-980-4454 *E-mail:* customerservice@enslow.com *Web Site:* www.enslow.com, pg 83

Entangled Publishing, 2614 S Timberline Rd, Suite 109, Fort Collins, CO 80525 *Tel:* 724-208-7888 (sales) *E-mail:* publisher@entangledpublishing.com *Web Site:* www.entangledpublishing.com, pg 83

Entomological Society of America, 3 Park Place, Suite 307, Annapolis, MD 21401-3722 *Tel:* 301-731-4535 *Fax:* 301-731-4538 *E-mail:* esa@entsoc.org *Web Site:* www.entsoc.org, pg 83

Environmental Law Institute, 1730 "M" St NW, Suite 700, Washington, DC 20036 *Tel:* 202-939-3800 *Toll Free Tel:* 800-433-5120 *Fax:* 202-939-3868 *E-mail:* law@eli.org *Web Site:* www.eli.org, pg 83

Epicenter Press Inc, 6524 NE 181 St, Suite 2, Kenmore, WA 98028 *Tel:* 425-485-6822 (edit, mktg, busn off) *Fax:* 425-481-8253 *E-mail:* info@epicenterpress.com *Web Site:* www.epicenterpress.com, pg 83

Epicomm, 1800 Diagonal Rd, Suite 320, Alexandria, VA 22314-2862 *Tel:* 703-836-9200 *E-mail:* webmaster@epicomm.org *Web Site:* epicomm.org, pg 605

EPS/School Specialty Literacy & Intervention, 625 Mount Auburn St, 3rd fl, Cambridge, MA 02138-3039 *Toll Free Tel:* 800-225-5750 *Toll Free Fax:* 888-440-2665 *E-mail:* customerservice.eps@schoolspecialty.com *Web Site:* eps.schoolspecialty.com, pg 83

Norma Epstein Foundation, 15 King's College Circle, UC 173, Toronto, ON M5S 3H7, Canada *Tel:* 416-978-8083 *Fax:* 416-971-2027 *Web Site:* www.utoronto.ca, pg 684

Ericson Books, 1614 Redbud St, Nacogdoches, TX 75965-2936 *Tel:* 936-564-3625 *Fax:* 936-552-8999 *E-mail:* kissinkuzzins@suddenlink.net *Web Site:* www.ericsonbooks.com, pg 83

The Ernest Sandeen & Richard Sullivan Prizes in Fiction & Poetry, 356 O'Shaughnessy Hall, Notre Dame, IN 46556 *Tel:* 574-631-7526 *Fax:* 574-631-4795 *E-mail:* creativewriting@nd.edu *Web Site:* creativewriting.nd.edu, pg 684

Erskine J Poetry Prize, PO Box 22161, Baltimore, MD 21203 *Web Site:* www.smartishpace.com, pg 684

Felicia Eth Literary Representation, 555 Bryant St, Suite 350, Palo Alto, CA 94301 *Tel:* 415-970-9717 *E-mail:* feliciaeth.literary@gmail.com *Web Site:* www.ethliterary.com, pg 551

Etruscan Press, Wilkes University, 84 W South St, Wilkes-Barre, PA 18766 *Tel:* 570-408-4546 *Fax:* 570-408-3333 *E-mail:* books@etruscanpress.org *Web Site:* www.etruscanpress.org, pg 84

Europa Editions, 214 W 29 St, Suite 1003, New York, NY 10001 *Tel:* 212-868-6844 *Fax:* 212-868-6845 *E-mail:* info@europaeditions.com *Web Site:* www.europaeditions.com, pg 84

European Masterpieces, 103 Walker Way, Newark, DE 19711 *Tel:* 302-453-8695 *Fax:* 302-453-8601 *E-mail:* text@linguatextltd.com *Web Site:* www.europeanmasterpieces.com, pg 84

Evan-Moor Educational Publishers, 18 Lower Ragsdale Dr, Monterey, CA 93940-5746 *Tel:* 831-649-5901 *Toll Free Tel:* 800-777-4362 (orders) *Fax:* 831-649-6256 *Toll Free Fax:* 800-777-4332 (orders) *E-mail:* sales@evan-moor.com; marketing@evan-moor.com *Web Site:* www.evan-moor.com, pg 84

Evangelical Christian Publishers Association (ECPA), 9633 S 48 St, Suite 195, Phoenix, AZ 85044-5697 *Tel:* 480-966-3998 *Fax:* 480-966-1944 *E-mail:* info@ecpa.org *Web Site:* www.ecpa.org, pg 605

Evangelical Press Association (EPA), PO Box 20198, El Cajon, CA 92021 *Toll Free Tel:* 888-311-1731 *E-mail:* info@evangelicalpress.com *Web Site:* www.evangelicalpress.com, pg 605

David W & Beatrice C Evans Biography & Handcart Awards, 0735 Old Main Hill, Logan, UT 84322-0735 *Tel:* 435-797-0299 *Fax:* 435-797-1092 *E-mail:* mwc@usu.edu *Web Site:* mountainwest.usu.edu, pg 684

M Evans & Company, c/o Rowman & Littlefield Publishing Group, 4501 Forbes Blvd, Suite 200, Lanham, MD 20706 *Tel:* 301-459-3366 *Fax:* 301-429-5748 *Web Site:* rowman.com, pg 84

Mary Evans Inc, 242 E Fifth St, New York, NY 10003-8501 *Tel:* 212-979-0880 *Fax:* 212-979-5344 *E-mail:* info@maryevansinc.com *Web Site:* www.maryevansinc.com, pg 551

Evergreen Pacific Publishing Ltd, 4204 Russell Rd, Suite M, Mukilteo, WA 98275-5424 *Tel:* 425-493-1451 *Fax:* 425-493-1453 *E-mail:* sales@evergreenpacific.com *Web Site:* www.evergreenpacific.com, pg 84

Everything Goes Media LLC, PO Box 1524, Milwaukee, WI 53201 *Tel:* 312-226-8400 *E-mail:* info@everythinggoesmedia.com *Web Site:* www.everythinggoesmedia.com, pg 84

Excalibur Publications, PO Box 89667, Tucson, AZ 85752-9667 *Tel:* 520-575-9057 *E-mail:* excaliburpublications@centurylink.net, pg 84

EXCEL Awards, 12100 Sunset Hills Rd, Suite 130, Reston, VA 20190 *Tel:* 703-234-4063 *Fax:* 703-435-4390 *E-mail:* info@associationmediaandpublishing.org *Web Site:* associationmediaandpublishing.org, pg 684

Excelsior Editions, 22 Corporate Woods Blvd, 3rd fl, Albany, NY 12211-2504 *Tel:* 518-472-5000 *Toll Free Tel:* 866-430-7869 *Fax:* 518-472-5038 *E-mail:* info@sunypress.edu *Web Site:* www.sunypress.edu, pg 84

The Experiment, 220 East 23 St, Suite 301, New York, NY 10010-4674 *Tel:* 212-889-1659 *E-mail:* info@theexperimentpublishing.com *Web Site:* www.theexperimentpublishing.com, pg 85

Eye in the Ear Children's Audio, 5 Crescent St, Portland, ME 04102 *Toll Free Tel:* 855-99-STORY (997-8679) *Fax:* 207-699-1380 (attn: Laurence Kelly) *E-mail:* info@eyeintheear.com *Web Site:* www.eyeintheear.com, pg 85

Facts On File, 132 W 31 St, 17th fl, New York, NY 10001 *Tel:* 212-967-8800 *Toll Free Tel:* 800-322-8755 *Toll Free Fax:* 800-678-3633 *E-mail:* custserv@factsonfile.com *Web Site:* infobasepublishing.com, pg 85

Fair Winds Press, 100 Cummings Ctr, Suite 406-L, Beverly, MA 01915 *Tel:* 978-282-9590 *Fax:* 978-282-7765 *E-mail:* sales@quartos.com *Web Site:* www.quartoknows.com, pg 85

John K Fairbank Prize in East Asian History, 400 "A" St SE, Washington, DC 20003 *Tel:* 202-544-2422 *Fax:* 202-544-8307 *E-mail:* awards@historians.org *Web Site:* www.historians.org, pg 684

Fairchild Books, 1385 Broadway, 5th fl, New York, NY 10018 *Tel:* 212-419-5300 *Toll Free Tel:* 800-932-4724; 888-330-8477 (orders) *Fax:* 212-704-5975 *Web Site:* bloomsbury.com/us/academic/fairchildbooks, pg 85

Fairleigh Dickinson University Press, M-GH2-01, 285 Madison Ave, Madison, NJ 07940 *Tel:* 973-443-8564 *Fax:* 974-443-8364 *E-mail:* fdupress@fdu.edu *Web Site:* www.fdupress.org, pg 85

Tom Fairley Award for Editorial Excellence, 27 Carlton St, Suite 502, Toronto, ON M5B 1L2, Canada *Tel:* 416-975-1379 *Toll Free Tel:* 866-CAN-EDIT (226-3348) *Fax:* 416-975-1637 *E-mail:* fairley_award@editors.ca *Web Site:* www.editors.ca; www.reviseurs.ca, pg 684

The Fairmont Press Inc, 700 Indian Trail, Lilburn, GA 30047 *Tel:* 770-925-9388 *Fax:* 770-381-9865 *Web Site:* www.fairmontpress.com, pg 85

Fairwinds Press, PO Box 668, Lions Bay, BC V0N 2E0, Canada *Tel:* 604-913-0649 *E-mail:* orders@fairwinds-press.com *Web Site:* www.fairwinds-press.com, pg 483

Faith Alive Christian Resources, 1700 28 St SE, Grand Rapids, MI 49508-1407 *Tel:* 616-224-0728 *Toll Free Tel:* 800-333-8300 *Toll Free Fax:* 888-642-8606 *E-mail:* info@faithaliveresources.org; sales@faithaliveresources.org; orders@faithaliveresources.org *Web Site:* www.faithaliveresources.org, pg 85

Faith & Fellowship Publishing, 1020 W Alcott Ave, Fergus Falls, MN 56537 *Tel:* 218-736-7357 *Toll Free Tel:* 800-332-9232 *E-mail:* clb@clba.org *Web Site:* www.clba.org, pg 86

Faith Library Publications, PO Box 50126, Tulsa, OK 74150-0126 *Tel:* 918-258-1588 (ext 2218) *Toll Free Tel:* 888-258-0999 (orders) *Fax:* 918-872-7710 (orders) *E-mail:* flp@rhema.org *Web Site:* www.rhema.org/store, pg 86

Faithlife Corp, 1313 Commercial St, Bellingham, WA 98225 *Tel:* 360-527-1700 *Toll Free Tel:* 800-875-6467 *Fax:* 360-527-1707 *E-mail:* sales@faithlife.com; customerservice@faithlife.com *Web Site:* www.faithlife.com, pg 86

FaithWalk Publishing, 5450 N Dixie Hwy, Lima, OH 45807 *Tel:* 419-227-1818 *Toll Free Tel:* 800-537-1030 (orders: non-bookstore mkts) *Fax:* 419-224-9184 *E-mail:* orders@csspub.com *Web Site:* www.faithwalkpub.com, pg 86

Family Matters, PO Box 80430, Portland, OR 97280-1430 *Tel:* 503-221-0836 *Fax:* 503-221-0837 *E-mail:* editors@glimmertrain.org *Web Site:* www.glimmertrain.org, pg 684

F+W, A Content + eCommerce Company, 10151 Carver Rd, Suite 200, Blue Ash, OH 45242 *Tel:* 513-531-2690 *Toll Free Tel:* 800-289-0963 (trade accts); 800-258-0929 (orders) *E-mail:* contact_us@fwmedia.com *Web Site:* www.fwcommunity.com, pg 86

Far Horizons Award for Poetry, University of Victoria, Box 1700, Sta CSC, Victoria, BC V8W 2Y2, Canada *Tel:* 250-721-8524 *Fax:* 250-472-5051 *E-mail:* malahat@uvic.ca *Web Site:* www.malahatreview.ca, pg 685

Far Horizons Award for Short Fiction, University of Victoria, Box 1700, Sta CSC, Victoria, BC V8W 2Y2, Canada *Tel:* 250-721-8524 *Fax:* 250-472-5051 *E-mail:* malahat@uvic.ca *Web Site:* www.malahatreview.ca, pg 685

Farber Literary Agency Inc, 14 E 75 St, New York, NY 10021 *Tel:* 212-861-7075 *Fax:* 212-861-7076 *E-mail:* farberlit@gmail.com, pg 551

Norma Farber First Book Award, 15 Gramercy Park, New York, NY 10003 *Tel:* 212-254-9628 *Fax:* 212-673-2352 *Web Site:* www.poetrysociety.org, pg 685

Farrar, Straus & Giroux Books for Young Readers, 175 Fifth Ave, 7th fl, New York, NY 10010 *Tel:* 646-307-5151 *Fax:* 646-438-6150 *Web Site:* us.macmillan.com/mackids.aspx, pg 86

Farrar, Straus & Giroux, LLC, 18 W 18 St, New York, NY 10011 *Tel:* 212-741-6900 *E-mail:* fsg.publicity@fsgbooks.com *Web Site:* us.macmillan.com/fsg.aspx, pg 86

Farrar Writing & Editing, 4638 Manchester Rd, Mound, MN 55364 *Tel:* 952-472-6874 *Fax:* 952-472-6874 (call first) *Web Site:* www.writeandedit.net, pg 526

Farris Literary Agency Inc, PO Box 570069, Dallas, TX 75357-0069 *Tel:* 972-203-8804 *E-mail:* farris1@airmail.net *Web Site:* www.farrisliterary.com, pg 551

Father & Son Publishing Inc, 4909 N Monroe St, Tallahassee, FL 32303-7015 *Tel:* 850-562-2612 *Toll Free Tel:* 800-741-2712 (orders only) *Fax:* 850-562-0916 *Web Site:* www.fatherson.com, pg 87

Favorable Impressions, 9 Elm Park Blvd, Pleasant Ridge, MI 48069 *Tel:* 248-544-2421 *Web Site:* www.favimp.com, pg 87

The FC2 Catherine Doctorow Innovative Fiction Prize, c/o Dept of English, Langs & Commun Bldg, 255 S Central Campus Dr, Rm 3500, Salt Lake City, UT 84112-0494 *Tel:* 773-702-7000 *Web Site:* www.fc2.org/prizes.html, pg 685

FC&A Publishing, 103 Clover Green, Peachtree City, GA 30269 *Tel:* 770-487-6307 *Toll Free Tel:* 800-226-8024 *Fax:* 770-631-4357 *E-mail:* customer_service@fca.com *Web Site:* www.fca.com, pg 87

Federal Bar Association, 1220 N Filmore St, Suite 444, Arlington, VA 22201 *Tel:* 571-481-9100 *Fax:* 571-481-9090 *E-mail:* fba@fedbar.org *Web Site:* www.fedbar.org, pg 87

Federal Street Press, 25-13 Old Kings Hwy N, No 277, Darien, CT 06820 *Tel:* 203-852-1280 *Toll Free Tel:* 877-886-2830 *Fax:* 203-852-1389 *E-mail:* sales@federalstreetpress.com *Web Site:* www.federalstreetpress.com, pg 87

Federation of BC Writers, PO Box 16028, 617 Belmont St, New Westminster, BC V3M 6W6, Canada *E-mail:* info@bcwriters.ca *Web Site:* bcwriters.ca, pg 605

Feigenbaum Publishing Consultants Inc, 61 Bounty Lane, Jericho, NY 11753 *Tel:* 516-647-8314 (cell) *Fax:* 516-935-0507 *E-mail:* readrover5@aol.com, pg 551

Betsy Feist Resources, 140 E 81 St, Unit 8-G, New York, NY 10028-1875 *Tel:* 212-861-2014 *E-mail:* bfresources@rcn.com, pg 526

Feldheim Publishers (Philipp Feldheim Inc), 208 Airport Executive Park, Nanuet, NY 10954 *Tel:* 845-356-2282 *Toll Free Tel:* 800-237-7149 (orders) *Fax:* 845-425-1908 *E-mail:* sales@feldheim.com *Web Site:* www.feldheim.com, pg 87

Fellowship & Scholarship Program for Writers, Middlebury College, Middlebury, VT 05753 *Tel:* 802-443-5286 *Fax:* 802-443-2087 *E-mail:* blwc@middlebury.edu *Web Site:* www.middlebury.edu/blwc, pg 685

Fellowship Program, One Capital Hill, 3rd fl, Providence, RI 02908 *Tel:* 401-222-3880 *Fax:* 401-222-3018 *Web Site:* www.arts.ri.gov, pg 685

Fellowships for Creative & Performing Artists & Writers, 185 Salisbury St, Worcester, MA 01609-1634 *Tel:* 508-755-5221 *Fax:* 508-753-3311 *Web Site:* www.americanantiquarian.org, pg 685

Fellowships for Historical Research, 185 Salisbury St, Worcester, MA 01609-1634 *Tel:* 508-471-2131 *Fax:* 508-754-9069 *Web Site:* www.americanantiquarian.org, pg 685

Jerry Felsen, 3960 NW 196 St, Miami Gardens, FL 33055-1869 *Tel:* 305-625-5012 *E-mail:* jfelsen0@att.net *Web Site:* beatthemarket.org, pg 526

The Feminist Press at The City University of New York, 365 Fifth Ave, Suite 5406, New York, NY 10016 *Tel:* 212-817-7915 *Fax:* 212-817-1593 *E-mail:* info@feministpress.org *Web Site:* www.feministpress.org, pg 87

Fence Books, University at Albany, Science Library 320, 1400 Washington Ave, Albany, NY 12222 *Tel:* 518-591-8162 *E-mail:* fence.fencebooks@gmail.com *Web Site:* www.fenceportal.org, pg 87

Fence Modern Poets Series, University at Albany, Science Library 320, 1400 Washington Ave, Albany, NY 12222 *Tel:* 518-591-8162 *E-mail:* fence.fencebooks@gmail.com *Web Site:* www.fenceportal.org, pg 685

Shubert Fendrich Memorial Playwriting Contest, PO Box 4267, Englewood, CO 80155-4267 *Tel:* 303-779-4035 *Toll Free Tel:* 800-333-7262 *Fax:* 303-779-4315 *E-mail:* playwrights@pioneerdrama.com *Web Site:* www.pioneerdrama.com, pg 685

Robert L Fenton PC; Entertainment Attorney & Literary Agent, 31800 Northwestern Hwy, Suite 204, Farmington Hills, MI 48334 *Tel:* 248-855-8780 *Fax:* 248-855-3302 *Web Site:* www.robertlfenton.com, pg 551

Feral House, 1240 W Sims Way, Suite 124, Port Townsend, WA 98368 *Tel:* 323-666-3311 *Fax:* 323-297-4331 *E-mail:* info@feralhouse.com *Web Site:* feralhouse.com, pg 87

Ferguson Publishing, 132 W 31 St, 17th fl, New York, NY 10001 *Tel:* 212-967-8800 *Toll Free Tel:* 800-322-8755 *Fax:* 917-339-0323 *Toll Free Fax:* 800-678-3633 *E-mail:* custserv@factsonfile.com *Web Site:* infobasepublishing.com, pg 88

Fernwood Publishing, 32 Oceanvista Lane, Black Point, NS B0J 1B0, Canada *Tel:* 902-857-1388 *Fax:* 902-857-1328 *E-mail:* info@fernpub.ca; roseway@fernpub.ca *Web Site:* fernwoodpublishing.ca, pg 483

Howard Fertig, Publisher, 80 E 11 St, New York, NY 10003 *Tel:* 212-982-7922 *Fax:* 212-982-1099 *E-mail:* enquiries@hfertigbooks.com; orders@hfertigbooks.com *Web Site:* www.hfertigbooks.com, pg 88

Fiction Collective Two Inc (FC2), c/o Dept of English, Langs & Commun Bldg, 255 S Central Campus Dr, Rm 3500, Salt Lake City, UT 84112-0494 *Tel:* 773-702-7000 *E-mail:* fc2.cmu@gmail.com *Web Site:* www.fc2.org/prizes.html, pg 88

Fiction Open, PO Box 80430, Portland, OR 97280-1430 *Tel:* 503-221-0836 *Fax:* 503-221-0837 *E-mail:* editors@glimmertrain.org *Web Site:* www.glimmertrain.org, pg 685

The Field Poetry Prize, 50 N Professor St, Oberlin, OH 44074-1091 *Tel:* 440-775-8408 *Fax:* 440-775-8124 *E-mail:* oc.press@oberlin.edu *Web Site:* www.oberlin.edu/ocpress; www.oberlin.edu/ocpress/prize.htm (guidelines), pg 685

Fifth Estate Publishing, 2795 County Hwy 57, Blounstville, AL 35031 *Toll Free Tel:* 855-299-2160 *E-mail:* fifth-estate@hotmail.com *Web Site:* fifthestatepub.com, pg 88

Fifth House Publishers, 195 Allstate Pkwy, Markham, ON L3R 4T8, Canada *Tel:* 905-477-9700 *Toll Free Tel:* 800-387-9776 *Toll Free Fax:* 800-260-9777 *E-mail:* godwit@fitzhenry.ca; bookinfo@fitzhenry.ca (cust serv) *Web Site:* www.fitzhenry.ca/fifthhouse.aspx, pg 484

Film-Video Publications/Circus Source Publications, 7944 Capistrano Ave, West Hills, CA 91304 *Tel:* 818-340-0175 *Fax:* 818-340-6620 *E-mail:* circussource@aol.com, pg 88

Filsinger & Company Ltd, 288 W 12 St, Suite 2R, New York, NY 10014 *Tel:* 212-243-7421 *E-mail:* filsingercompany@gmail.com *Web Site:* www.filsingerco.com, pg 507

Filter Press LLC, PO Box 95, Palmer Lake, CO 80133 *Tel:* 719-481-2420 *Toll Free Tel:* 888-570-2663 *Fax:* 719-481-2420 *E-mail:* info@filterpressbooks.com; orders@filterpressbooks.com *Web Site:* filterpressbooks.com, pg 88

Financial Executives Research Foundation Inc (FERF), West Tower, 7th fl, 1250 Headquarters Plaza, Morristown, NJ 07960-6837 *Tel:* 973-765-1000 *Fax:* 973-765-1023 *Web Site:* www.financialexecutives.org, pg 88

Financial Times Press, 225 River St, Hoboken, NJ 07030-4772 *Tel:* 201-236-7000 *Toll Free Tel:* 800-922-0579 (orders) *Web Site:* www.ftpress.com, pg 88

Fine Arts Work Center in Provincetown, 24 Pearl St, Provincetown, MA 02657 *Tel:* 508-487-9960 *Fax:* 508-487-8873 *E-mail:* general@fawc.org *Web Site:* www.fawc.org, pg 685

Fine Creative Media, Inc, 322 Eighth Ave, 15th fl, New York, NY 10001 *Tel:* 212-595-3500 *Fax:* 212-595-3779, pg 88

Fine Wordworking, PO Box 3041, Monterey, CA 93942-3041 *Tel:* 831-375-6278 *E-mail:* info@finewordworking.com *Web Site:* marilynch.com, pg 526

FineEdge.com LLC, 14004 Biz Point Lane, Anacortes, WA 98221 *Tel:* 360-299-8500 *Fax:* 360-299-0535 *E-mail:* pub@fineedge.com; orders@fineedge.com *Web Site:* www.fineedge.com, pg 89

FinePrint Literary Management, 115 W 29 St, 3rd fl, New York, NY 10001 *Tel:* 212-279-1282 *Web Site:* www.fineprintlit.com, pg 551

Finney Company Inc, 5995 149 St W, Suite 105, Apple Valley, MN 55124 *Tel:* 952-469-6699 *Toll Free Tel:* 800-846-7027 *Fax:* 952-469-1968 *Toll Free Fax:* 800-330-6232 *E-mail:* info@finneyco.com *Web Site:* www.finneyco.com, pg 89

Doug Fir Fiction Award, 240 N Broadway, Suite 112, Portland, OR 97227 *E-mail:* bear@orlo.org *Web Site:* www.orlo.org, pg 686

Fire Engineering Books & Videos, 1421 S Sheridan Rd, Tulsa, OK 74112 *Tel:* 918-931-9410 *Toll Free Tel:* 800-752-9764 *Fax:* 918-931-9555 *E-mail:* sales@pennwell.com *Web Site:* www.pennwellbooks.com, pg 89

Firecracker Awards, 154 Christopher St, Suite 3C, New York, NY 10014-9110 *Tel:* 212-741-9110 *Fax:* 212-741-9112 *E-mail:* info@clmp.org *Web Site:* www.clmp.org/firecracker, pg 686

Firefall Editions, 27 Bath St, Lido Beach, NY 11561 *Tel:* 510-549-2461 *E-mail:* fire@firefallmedia.com *Web Site:* www.firefallmedia.com, pg 89

Firefly Books Ltd, 50 Staples Ave, Unit 1, Richmond Hill, ON L4B 0A7, Canada *Tel:* 416-499-8412 *Toll Free Tel:* 800-387-6192 (CN); 800-387-5085 (US) *Fax:* 416-499-8313 *Toll Free Fax:* 800-450-0391 (CN); 800-565-6034 (US) *E-mail:* service@fireflybooks.com *Web Site:* www.fireflybooks.com, pg 484

First Avenue Editions, 241 First Ave N, Minneapolis, MN 55401 *Tel:* 612-332-3344 *Toll Free Tel:* 800-328-4929 *Fax:* 612-332-7615 *Toll Free Fax:* 800-332-1132 *E-mail:* info@lernerbooks.com *Web Site:* www.lernerbooks.com, pg 89

The Fischer-Harbage Agency Inc, 540 President St, 3rd fl, Brooklyn, NY 11215 *Tel:* 212-695-7105 *E-mail:* info@fischerharbage.com *Web Site:* www.fischerharbage.com, pg 552

The Fischer Ross Group Inc, 75 Holly Hill Lane, Suite 100, Greenwich, CT 06830 *Tel:* 203-622-4950 *Fax:* 203-531-4132 *E-mail:* frgstaff@frg-speakers.com *Web Site:* www.frg-speakers.com, pg 587

Fitzhenry & Whiteside Limited, 195 Allstate Pkwy, Markham, ON L3R 4T8, Canada *Tel:* 905-477-9700 *Toll Free Tel:* 800-387-9776 *Fax:* 905-477-2834 *Toll Free Fax:* 800-260-9777 *E-mail:* bookinfo@fitzhenry.ca; godwit@fitzhenry.ca *Web Site:* www.fitzhenry.ca, pg 484

Five Star Dragonfly Book Awards, 4696 W Tyson St, Chandler, AZ 85226-2903 *Tel:* 480-940-8182 *Fax:* 480-940-8787 *E-mail:* info@fivestarpublications.com *Web Site:* www.FiveStarBookAwards.com; www.FiveStarPublications.com, pg 686

Five Star Publications Inc, 4696 W Tyson St, Chandler, AZ 85226-2903 *Tel:* 480-940-8182 *Fax:* 480-940-8787 *E-mail:* fivestarpublications@gmail.com *Web Site:* www.FiveStarPublications.com; www.FiveStarBookAwards.com; www.AuthorsandExperts.com, pg 89

Five Star Publishing & Marketing Secrets, 4696 W Tyson St, Chandler, AZ 85226-2903 *Tel:* 480-940-8182 *Fax:* 480-940-8787 *E-mail:* info@fivestarpublications.com *Web Site:* www.FiveStarPublications.com, pg 650

FJH Music Co Inc, 2525 Davie Rd, Suite 360, Fort Lauderdale, FL 33317-7424 *Tel:* 954-382-6061 *Toll Free Tel:* 800-262-8744 *Fax:* 954-382-3073 *E-mail:* custserv@fjhmusic.com; sales@fjhmusic.com *Web Site:* www.fjhmusic.com, pg 89

The Flaherty-Dunnan First Novel Prize, 17 E 47 St, New York, NY 10017 *Tel:* 212-755-6710 *Fax:* 212-826-0831 *E-mail:* info@centerforfiction.org *Web Site:* centerforfiction.org/awards, pg 686

Flammarion Quebec, 375 Ave Laurier W, Montreal, QC H2V 2K3, Canada *Tel:* 514-277-8807 *Fax:* 514-278-2085 *E-mail:* info@flammarion.qc.ca *Web Site:* www.flammarion.qc.ca, pg 484

Flanker Press Ltd, 1243 Kenmount Rd, Unit A, Paradise, NL A1L 0V8, Canada *Tel:* 709-739-4477 *Toll Free Tel:* 866-739-4420 *Fax:* 709-739-4420 *E-mail:* info@flankerpress.com *Web Site:* www.flankerpress.com, pg 484

Flannery Literary, 1140 Wickfield Ct, Naperville, IL 60563 *Tel:* 630-428-2682 *Web Site:* flanneryliterary.com, pg 552

Flashlight Press, 527 Empire Blvd, Brooklyn, NY 11225 *Tel:* 718-288-8300 *Fax:* 718-972-6307 *E-mail:* editor@flashlightpress.com *Web Site:* www.flashlightpress.com, pg 89

Norma Fleck Award for Canadian Children's Non-Fiction, 40 Orchard View Blvd, Suite 217, Toronto, ON M4R 1B9, Canada *Tel:* 416-975-0010 *Fax:* 416-975-8970 *E-mail:* info@bookcentre.ca *Web Site:* www.bookcentre.ca, pg 686

FleetSeek, 6190 Powers Ferry Rd, Suite 320, Atlanta, GA 30339 *Tel:* 540-899-9872 *Toll Free Tel:* 888-ONLY-TTS (665-9887) *Fax:* 540-899-1948 *E-mail:* fleetseek@fleetseek.com *Web Site:* www.fleetseek.com, pg 89

Peter Fleming Agency, PO Box 458, Pacific Palisades, CA 90272 *Tel:* 310-454-1373 *E-mail:* peterfleming@earthlink.net, pg 552

Florida Academic Press, PO Box 357425, Gainesville, FL 32635 *Tel:* 352-332-5104 *E-mail:* fapress@gmail.com *Web Site:* www.florida-academic-press.com, pg 89

Florida Authors & Publishers Association Inc (FAPA), PO Box 915822, Longwood, FL 32791 *E-mail:* member.services@floridapublishersassociation.com *Web Site:* www.floridapublishersassociation.com, pg 605

Florida Freelance Writers Association, 45 Main St, North Stratford, NH 03590 *Tel:* 603-922-8338 *Fax:* 603-922-8339 *E-mail:* ffwa@writers-editors.com; info@writers-editors.com *Web Site:* www.writers-editors.com; www.ffwamembers.com, pg 605

Florida Individual Artist Fellowships, 500 S Bronough St, Tallahassee, FL 32399-0250 *Tel:* 850-245-6470 *Fax:* 850-245-6497 *E-mail:* info@florida-arts.org *Web Site:* www.florida-arts.org, pg 686

Florida Outdoor Writers Association Inc, 24 NW 33 Ct, Suite A, Gainesville, FL 32607 *Tel:* 352-284-1763 *E-mail:* info@fowa.org *Web Site:* www.fowa.org, pg 605

Florida Writers Association Conference, PO Box 66069, St Pete Beach, FL 33736-6069 *Web Site:* www.floridawriters.net, pg 651

Florida Writers Association Inc, PO Box 66069, St Pete Beach, FL 33736-6069 *Web Site:* www.floridawriters.net, pg 606

Flying Pen Press LLC, 1416 S Newport St, Denver, CO 80224 *Tel:* 303-375-0499 *Fax:* 303-375-0499 *E-mail:* directory@flyingpenpress.com *Web Site:* www.flyingpenpress.com, pg 90

Focus, PO Box 44937, Indianapolis, IN 46244-0937 *Tel:* 317-635-9250 *Fax:* 317-635-9292 *E-mail:* customer@hackettpublishing.com; editorial@hackettpublishing.com *Web Site:* focusbookstore.com, pg 90

Focus on the Family, 8605 Explorer Dr, Colorado Springs, CO 80920-1051 *Tel:* 719-531-5181 *Toll Free Tel:* 800-A-FAMILY (232-6459) *Fax:* 719-531-3424 *Web Site:* www.focusonthefamily.com; www.facebook.com/focusonthefamily, pg 90

Focus Strategic Communications Inc, 2474 Waterford St, Oakville, ON L6L 5E6, Canada *Tel:* 905-825-8757 *Toll Free Tel:* 866-263-6287 *Fax:* 905-825-5724 *Toll Free Fax:* 866-613-6287 *E-mail:* info@focussc.com *Web Site:* www.focussc.com, pg 526

Fodor's Travel Publications, 1745 Broadway, 15th fl, New York, NY 10019 *Toll Free Tel:* 800-733-3000 *E-mail:* fodorspublicity@randomhouse.com; editors@fodors.com *Web Site:* www.fodors.com, pg 90

Sheldon Fogelman Agency Inc, 10 E 40 St, Suite 3205, New York, NY 10016 *Tel:* 212-532-7250 *Fax:* 212-685-8939 *E-mail:* info@sheldonfogelmanagency.com *Web Site:* sheldonfogelmanagency.com, pg 552

Foil & Specialty Effects Association (FSEA), 2150 SW Westport Dr, Suite 101, Topeka, KS 66614 *Tel:* 785-271-5816 *Fax:* 785-271-6404 *E-mail:* info@fsea.com; fseamail@fsea.com *Web Site:* www.fsea.com, pg 606

The Foley Literary Agency, 34 E 38 St, Suite 1B, New York, NY 10016 *Tel:* 212-686-6930, pg 552

Folio Literary Management LLC, The Film Center Bldg, 630 Ninth Ave, Suite 1101, New York, NY 10036 *Tel:* 212-400-1494 *Fax:* 212-967-0977 *Web Site:* www.foliolit.com, pg 552

Folklore Publishing, 11717-9B Ave NW, Unit 2, Edmonton, AB T6J 7B7, Canada *Tel:* 780-435-2376 *Fax:* 780-435-0674 *E-mail:* submissions@folklorepublishing.com (ms submissions) *Web Site:* www.folklorepublishing.com, pg 484

La Fondation Emile Nelligan, 100, rue Sherbrooke, Montreal, QC H2X 1C3, Canada *Tel:* 514-278-4657 *Fax:* 514-278-1943 *E-mail:* info@fondation-nelligan.org *Web Site:* www.fondation-nelligan.org, pg 606

Fons Vitae, 49 Mockingbird Valley Dr, Louisville, KY 40207-1366 *Tel:* 502-897-3641 *Fax:* 502-893-7373 *E-mail:* fonsvitaeky@aol.com *Web Site:* www.fonsvitae.com, pg 90

Fordham University, Graduate School of Business Administration, Gabelli School of Business, 441 E Fordham Rd, Hughes Hall, Rm 516, Bronx, NY 10458 *Tel:* 718-817-1894 *Web Site:* www.bnet.fordham.edu, pg 660

Fordham University, Graduate School of Business Administration, 113 W 60 St, New York, NY 10023 *Fax:* 212-636-7076 *Web Site:* www.bnet.fordham.edu, pg 686

Fordham University Press, 2546 Belmont Ave, University Box L, Bronx, NY 10458 *Tel:* 718-817-4795 *Fax:* 718-817-4785 *Web Site:* www.fordhampress.com, pg 90

ForeWord Reviews Book of the Year Awards, 425 Boardman Ave, Suite B, Traverse City, MI 49684 *Tel:* 231-933-3699 *Fax:* 231-933-3899 *Web Site:* www.bookoftheyearawards.com, pg 686

Morris D Forkosch Prize, 400 "A" St SE, Washington, DC 20003 *Tel:* 202-544-2422 *Fax:* 202-544-8307 *E-mail:* awards@historians.org *Web Site:* www.historians.org, pg 686

E M Forster Award, 633 W 155 St, New York, NY 10032 *Tel:* 212-368-5900 *Fax:* 212-491-4615 *E-mail:* academy@artsandletters.org *Web Site:* www.artsandletters.org, pg 687

Fort Ross Inc - International Representation for Artists, 26 Arthur Place, Yonkers, NY 10701 *Tel:* 914-375-6448 *Web Site:* www.fortrossinc.com, pg 552

Fort Ross Inc - International Representation for Artists, 26 Arthur Place, Yonkers, NY 10701 *Tel:* 914-375-6448; 718-775-8340 *Web Site:* www.fortrossinc.com, pg 583

Fort Ross Inc Russian-American Publishing Projects, 26 Arthur Place, Yonkers, NY 10701 *Tel:* 914-375-6448 *Web Site:* www.fortrossinc.com, pg 90

49th Parallel Poetry Award, Mail Stop 9053, Western Washington University, Bellingham, WA 98225 *Tel:* 360-650-4863 *E-mail:* bhreview@wwu.edu *Web Site:* www.bhreview.org, pg 687

The Forum Press Inc, 3100 W Warner Ave, Suite 7, Santa Ana, CA 92704 *Tel:* 323-244-3938 *E-mail:* theforumpress@cs.com *Web Site:* www.theforumpress.com, pg 91

Forum Publishing Co, 383 E Main St, Centerport, NY 11721 *Tel:* 631-754-5000 *Toll Free Tel:* 800-635-7654 *Fax:* 631-754-0630 *E-mail:* forumpublishing@aol.com *Web Site:* www.forum123.com, pg 91

Forward Movement, 412 Sycamore St, Cincinnati, OH 45202-4110 *Tel:* 513-721-6659 *Toll Free Tel:* 800-543-1813 *Fax:* 513-721-0729 (orders) *E-mail:* orders@forwardmovement.org (orders & cust serv) *Web Site:* www.forwardmovement.org, pg 91

Foster City International Writers Contest, 650 Shell Blvd, Foster City, CA 94404 *Tel:* 650-286-3386 *E-mail:* fostercity_writers@yahoo.com *Web Site:* www.fostercity.org, pg 687

Foster Travel Publishing, PO Box 5715, Berkeley, CA 94705 *Tel:* 510-549-2202 *Web Site:* www.fostertravel.com, pg 526

Walter Foster Publishing Inc, 6 Orchard Rd, Suite 100, Lake Forest, CA 92630 *Tel:* 949-380-7510 *Toll Free Tel:* 800-426-0099; 800-759-0190 (orders) *Fax:* 949-380-7575 *E-mail:* walterfoster@quartous.com *Web Site:* www.quartous.com, pg 91

Foto Expression International (Toronto), 266 Charlotte St, Suite 297, Peterborough, ON K9J 2V4, Canada *Tel:* 705-745-5770 *E-mail:* operations@fotopressnews.org *Web Site:* www.fotopressnews.org, pg 583

The Foundation Center, 32 Old Slip, 24th fl, New York, NY 10005-3500 *Tel:* 212-620-4230 *Toll Free Tel:* 800-424-9836 *Fax:* 212-807-3677 *E-mail:* customerservice@foundationcenter.org *Web Site:* foundationcenter.org, pg 91

Foundation Press, c/o West Academic Publishing, 444 Cedar St, Suite 700, St Paul, MN 55101 *Toll Free Tel:* 877-888-1330 *E-mail:* customerservice@westacademic.com *Web Site:* www.westacademic.com, pg 91

Foundation Publications, 900 S Euclid St, La Habra, CA 90631 *Tel:* 714-879-2286 *Toll Free Tel:* 800-257-6272 *Fax:* 714-535-2164 *E-mail:* info@foundationpublications.com *Web Site:* www.foundationpublications.com, pg 91

4A's (American Association of Advertising Agencies), 1065 Avenue of the Americas, 16th fl, New York, NY 10018 *Tel:* 212-682-2500 *Web Site:* www.aaaa.org, pg 606

Fox Chapel Publishing Co Inc, 1970 Broad St, East Petersburg, PA 17520 *Tel:* 717-560-4703 *Toll Free Tel:* 800-457-9112 *Fax:* 717-560-4702 *E-mail:* customerservice@foxchapelpublishing.com *Web Site:* www.foxchapelpublishing.com, pg 91

Dixon Ryan Fox Manuscript Prize, 5798 State Hwy 80, Cooperstown, NY 13326 *Tel:* 607-547-1480 *Fax:* 607-547-1405, pg 687

Fox Run Press LLC, 7840 Bullet Rd, Peyton, OH 80831 *Tel:* 719-482-4035 *Fax:* 719-623-0254 *E-mail:* info@foxrunpress.com *Web Site:* www.foxrunpress.com, pg 91

FPMI Solutions Inc, 689 Discovery Dr, Suite 300, Huntsville, AL 35806 *Toll Free Tel:* 888-644-3764 *E-mail:* info@fpmi.com *Web Site:* www.fpmisolutions.com; www.fpmi.com, pg 91

Frances Henne YALSA/VOYA Research Grant, 50 E Huron St, Chicago, IL 60611 *Tel:* 312-280-4390 *Toll Free Tel:* 800-545-2433 *Fax:* 312-280-5276 *E-mail:* yalsa@ala.org *Web Site:* www.ala.org/yalsa, pg 687

H E Francis Award Short Story Competition, UAH Huntsville Dept of English, Morton Hall 222, Huntsville, AL 35899 *Web Site:* www.uah.edu/la/departments/english/h-e-francis-contest, pg 687

Franciscan Media, 28 W Liberty St, Cincinnati, OH 45202 *Tel:* 513-241-5615 *Toll Free Tel:* 800-488-0488 *Fax:* 513-241-0399 *E-mail:* books@americancatholic.org *Web Site:* www.americancatholic.org; www.franciscanmedia.org, pg 92

Sandi Frank, 8 Fieldcrest Ct, Cortlandt Manor, NY 10567 *Tel:* 914-739-7088 *E-mail:* sfrankmail@aol.com, pg 526

Franklin, Beedle & Associates Inc, 2154 NE Broadway, Suite 100, Portland, OR 97232 *Tel:* 503-284-6348 *Toll Free Tel:* 800-322-2665 *Fax:* 503-625-4434 *Web Site:* www.fbeedle.com, pg 92

Lynn C Franklin Associates Ltd, 1350 Broadway, Suite 2015, New York, NY 10018 *Tel:* 212-868-6311 *Fax:* 212-868-6312 *E-mail:* agency@franklinandsiegal.com, pg 552

The Fraser Institute, 1770 Burrard St, 4th fl, Vancouver, BC V6J 3G7, Canada *Tel:* 604-688-0221 *Toll Free Tel:* 800-665-3558 *Fax:* 604-688-8539 *E-mail:* info@fraserinstitute.org; sales@fraserinstitute.org *Web Site:* www.fraserinstitute.org, pg 485

Soeurette Diehl Fraser Translation Award, c/o 7748 Hwy 290 W, Austin, TX 78736-3202 *Tel:* 512-683-5640 *E-mail:* president@texasinstituteofletters.org *Web Site:* www.texasinstituteofletters.org, pg 687

Frederick Fell Publishers Inc, 2131 Hollywood Blvd, Suite 305, Hollywood, FL 33020 *Tel:* 954-925-5242 *E-mail:* fellpub@aol.com (admin only) *Web Site:* www.fellpub.com, pg 92

Jeanne Fredericks Literary Agency Inc, 221 Benedict Hill Rd, New Canaan, CT 06840 *Tel:* 203-972-3011 *Fax:* 203-972-3011 *E-mail:* jeanne.fredericks@gmail.com (no unsol attachments) *Web Site:* jeannefredericks.com, pg 552

Free Spirit Publishing Inc, 217 Fifth Ave N, Suite 200, Minneapolis, MN 55401-1299 *Tel:* 612-338-2068 *Toll Free Tel:* 800-735-7323 *Fax:* 612-337-5050 *Toll Free Fax:* 866-419-5199 *E-mail:* help4kids@freespirit.com *Web Site:* www.freespirit.com, pg 92

George Freedley Memorial Award, Roundabout Theatre Co, 231 W 39 St, Suite 1200, New York, NY 10018 *Tel:* 212-719-9393 (ext 351) *E-mail:* info@tla-online.org; tlabookawards@gmail.com *Web Site:* www.tla-online.org, pg 687

Robert A Freedman Dramatic Agency Inc, 1501 Broadway, Suite 2310, New York, NY 10036 *Tel:* 212-840-5760 *Fax:* 212-840-5776, pg 553

The Don Freeman Memorial Grant-In-Aid, 4727 Wilshire Blvd, Suite 301, Los Angeles, CA 90010 *Tel:* 323-782-1010; 310-403-0675 (cell) *Fax:* 323-782-1892 *E-mail:* membership@scbwi.org; scbwi@scbwi.org *Web Site:* www.scbwi.org, pg 687

W H Freeman, 41 Madison Ave, 37th fl, New York, NY 10010 *Tel:* 212-576-9400 *Fax:* 212-689-2383 *Web Site:* www.whfreeman.com, pg 92

The French-American Foundation & Florence Gould Foundation Annual Translation Prize, 28 W 44 St, Suite 1420, New York, NY 10036 *Tel:* 212-829-8800 *Fax:* 212-829-8810 *E-mail:* translation@frenchamerican.org *Web Site:* www.frenchamerican.org, pg 687

Samuel French Inc, 235 Park Ave S, 5th fl, New York, NY 10003 *Tel:* 212-206-8990 *Toll Free Tel:* 866-598-8449 *Fax:* 212-206-1429 *E-mail:* info@samuelfrench.com; publications@samuelfrench.com *Web Site:* www.samuelfrench.com, pg 92

Samuel French Inc, 235 Park Ave S, 5th fl, New York, NY 10003 *Tel:* 212-206-8990 *Toll Free Tel:* 866-598-8449 *Fax:* 212-206-1429 *E-mail:* info@samuelfrench.com *Web Site:* www.samuelfrench.com, pg 553

Fresh Air Books, 1908 Grand Ave, Nashville, TN 37212 *Tel:* 615-340-7200 *Toll Free Tel:* 800-972-0433 (orders) *Web Site:* books.upperroom.org, pg 93

Fresh Fish Award for Emerging Writers, Haymarket Sq, 208-223 Duckworth St, St John's, NL A1C 6N1, Canada *Tel:* 709-739-5215 *E-mail:* wanl@nf.aibn.com *Web Site:* wanl.ca, pg 687

Sarah Jane Freymann Literary Agency LLC, 59 W 71 St, Suite 9-B, New York, NY 10023 *Tel:* 212-362-9277 *E-mail:* submissions@sarahjanefreymann.com *Web Site:* www.sarahjanefreymann.com, pg 553

Fredrica S Friedman & Co Inc, 136 E 57 St, 14th fl, New York, NY 10022 *Tel:* 212-829-9600 *Fax:* 212-829-9669 *E-mail:* info@fredricafriedman.com; submissions@fredricafriedman.com *Web Site:* www.fredricafriedman.com, pg 553

Friends of American Writers Awards, 506 Rose Ave, Des Plaines, IL 60016 *Tel:* 847-827-8339 *Web Site:* www.fawchicago.org, pg 688

Friends United Press, 101 Quaker Hill Dr, Richmond, IN 47374 *Tel:* 765-962-7573 *Fax:* 765-966-1293 *E-mail:* friendspress@fum.org; orders@fum.org *Web Site:* shop.fum.org, pg 93

Frog Books, 2526 Martin Luther King Jr Way, Berkeley, CA 94704 *Tel:* 510-549-4270 *Fax:* 510-549-4276 *E-mail:* customerservice@northatlanticbooks.com *Web Site:* www.northatlanticbooks.com, pg 93

Fromer Editorial Services, 1606 Noyes Dr, Silver Spring, MD 20910-2224 *Tel:* 301-585-8827, pg 526

Candice Fuhrman Literary Agency, 10 Cypress Hollow Dr, Tiburon, CA 94920 *Tel:* 415-383-1014 *E-mail:* candicef@pacbell.net, pg 553

Fulbright Scholar Program, 1400 "K" St NW, Washington, DC 20005 *Tel:* 202-686-4000 *Fax:* 202-362-3442 *E-mail:* scholars@iie.org *Web Site:* www.iie.org/cies, pg 688

Fulcrum Publishing Inc, 4690 Table Mountain Dr, Suite 100, Golden, CO 80403 *Tel:* 303-277-1623 *Toll Free Tel:* 800-992-2908 *Fax:* 303-279-7111 *Toll Free Fax:* 800-726-7112 *E-mail:* info@fulcrumbooks.com; orders@fulcrumbooks.com *Web Site:* www.fulcrumbooks.com, pg 93

Fun in the Sun Conference, PO Box 480211, Fort Lauderdale, FL 33348 *E-mail:* frwfuninthesun@yahoo.com *Web Site:* www.frwriters.org/fun-in-the-sun-conference/; frwfuninthesunmain.blogspot.com/; www.frwriters.org, pg 651

FurnitureCore, 1389 Peachtree St NE, Suite 310, Atlanta, GA 30309 *Tel:* 404-961-3734 *Toll Free Tel:* 800-826-8868 *Fax:* 404-961-3749 *E-mail:* info@furniturecore.com *Web Site:* www.furniturecore.com, pg 93

Future Horizons Inc, 721 W Abram St, Arlington, TX 76013 *Tel:* 817-277-0727 *Toll Free Tel:* 800-489-0727 *Fax:* 817-277-2270 *E-mail:* info@fhautism.com *Web Site:* www.fhautism.com, pg 93

Gabriele Rico Creative Nonfiction Challenge, San Jose State University, English Dept, One Washington Sq, San Jose, CA 95192-0090 *Tel:* 408-924-4441 *Web Site:* www.reedmag.org, pg 688

Gaetan Morin Editeur, 5800, rue St-Denis, bureau 900, Montreal, QC H2S 3L5, Canada *Tel:* 514-273-1066 *Toll Free Tel:* 800-565-5531 *Fax:* 514-276-0324 *Toll Free Fax:* 800-814-0324 *E-mail:* info@cheneliere.ca *Web Site:* www.cheneliere.ca, pg 485

Gagosian Gallery, 980 Madison Ave, New York, NY 10075 *Tel:* 212-744-2313 *Fax:* 212-772-7962 *E-mail:* newyork@gagosian.com *Web Site:* www.gagosian.com, pg 93

Lewis Galantiere Translation Award, 225 Reinekers Lane, Suite 590, Alexandria, VA 22314 *Tel:* 703-683-6100 *Fax:* 703-683-6122 *E-mail:* ata@atanet.org *Web Site:* www.atanet.org, pg 688

Galaxy Press, 7051 Hollywood Blvd, Suite 200, Hollywood, CA 90028 *Tel:* 323-466-7815 *Toll Free Tel:* 877-8GALAXY (842-5299) *E-mail:* customers@galaxypress.com; info@galaxypress.com *Web Site:* www.galaxypress.com, pg 93

Galde Press Inc, PO Box 460, Lakeville, MN 55044 *Tel:* 952-891-5991 *Toll Free Tel:* 800-777-3454 *Web Site:* www.galdepress.com, pg 93

Gale, 27500 Drake Rd, Farmington Hills, MI 48331-3535 *Tel:* 248-699-4253 *Toll Free Tel:* 800-877-4253 *Fax:* 248-699-8049 *Toll Free Fax:* 800-414-5043 (orders) *E-mail:* gale.salesassistance@cengage.com *Web Site:* www.gale.cengage.com, pg 94

Galen Press Ltd, PO Box 64400-WB, Tucson, AZ 85728-4400 *Tel:* 520-577-8363 *Fax:* 520-529-6459 *E-mail:* sales@galenpress.com *Web Site:* www.galenpress.com, pg 94

Gallaudet University Press, 800 Florida Ave NE, Washington, DC 20002-3695 *Tel:* 202-651-5488; 773-568-1550 (orders) *Toll Free Tel:* 800-621-2736 (orders) *Fax:* 202-651-5489; 773-660-2235 (orders) *Toll Free Fax:* 800-621-8476 (orders) *E-mail:* gupress@gallaudet.edu *Web Site:* gupress.gallaudet.edu, pg 94

Gallery Books, 1230 Avenue of the Americas, New York, NY 10020 *Toll Free Tel:* 800-456-6798 *Fax:* 212-698-7284 *E-mail:* consumer.customerservice@simonandschuster.com *Web Site:* www.simonsays.com, pg 94

Diane Gallo, 49 Hilton St, Gilbertsville, NY 13776 *Tel:* 607-783-2386 *Fax:* 607-783-2386 *E-mail:* dgallo@stny.rr.com *Web Site:* www.dianegallo.com, pg 526

Gallopade International Inc, 611 Hwy 74 S, Suite 2000, Peachtree City, GA 30269 *Tel:* 770-631-4222 *Toll Free Tel:* 800-536-2GET (536-2438) *Fax:* 770-631-4810 *Toll Free Fax:* 800-871-2979 *E-mail:* customerservice@gallopade.com *Web Site:* www.gallopade.com, pg 94

Gannon University's High School Poetry Contest, Gannon University, Dept of English, 109 University Sq, Erie, PA 16541 *Tel:* 814-871-7504 *Web Site:* www.gannon.edu/departmental/english/poetry.asp, pg 688

The Garamond Agency Inc, 12 Horton St, Newburyport, MA 01950 *E-mail:* query@garamondagency.com *Web Site:* www.garamondagency.com, pg 553

Garden Writers Association, 7809 FM 179, Shallowater, TX 79363-3637 *Tel:* 806-832-1870 *Fax:* 806-832-5244 *E-mail:* info@gardenwriters.org *Web Site:* www.gardenwriters.org, pg 606

Gareth Stevens Publishing, 111 E 14 St, Suite 349, New York, NY 10003 *Toll Free Tel:* 800-542-2595 *Toll Free Fax:* 877-542-2596 (cust serv) *E-mail:* customerservice@gspub.com *Web Site:* garethstevens.com, pg 94

Garland Science Publishing, 711 Third Ave, 8th fl, New York, NY 10017 *Tel:* 212-216-7800; 212-281-4487 *Fax:* 212-947-3027 *E-mail:* science@garland.com *Web Site:* www.garlandscience.com, pg 94

Francois-Xavier Garneau Medal, 130 Albert St, Suite 501, Ottawa, ON K1P 5G4, Canada *Tel:* 613-233-7885 *Fax:* 613-565-5445 *E-mail:* cha-shc@cha-shc.ca *Web Site:* www.cha-shc.ca, pg 688

Max Gartenberg Literary Agency, 912 N Pennsylvania Ave, Yardley, PA 19067 *Tel:* 215-295-9230 *Web Site:* www.maxgartenberg.com, pg 553

Alfred C Gary Memorial, 1194 Hume Rd, Hume, VA 22639-1806 *E-mail:* poetryinva@aol.com *Web Site:* www.poetrysocietyofvirginia.org, pg 688

The Gary-Paul Agency, 1549 Main St, Stratford, CT 06615 *Tel:* 203-345-6167 *Web Site:* www.thegarypaulagency.com; www.nutmegpictures.com, pg 526

John Gassner Memorial Playwriting Award, 215 Knob Hill Dr, Hamden, CT 06518 *Tel:* 617-851-8535 *Fax:* 203-288-5938 *E-mail:* mail@netconline.org *Web Site:* www.netconline.org, pg 688

Gatekeeper Press, 3971 Hoover Rd, Suite 77, Columbus, OH 43123-2839 *Toll Free Tel:* 866-535-0913 *Fax:* 216-403-1314 *E-mail:* info@gatekeeperpress.com *Web Site:* www.gatekeeperpress.com, pg 95

Gateways Books & Tapes, PO Box 370, Nevada City, CA 95959 *Tel:* 530-271-2239 *Toll Free Tel:* 800-869-0658 *Fax:* 530-272-0184 *E-mail:* info@gatewaysbooksandtapes.com *Web Site:* gatewaysbooksandtapes.com; www.retrosf.com (Retro Science Fiction Imprint), pg 95

Gault Millau Inc/Gayot Publications, 4311 Wilshire Blvd, Suite 405, Los Angeles, CA 90010 *Tel:* 323-965-3529 *Fax:* 323-936-2883 *E-mail:* info@gayot.com *Web Site:* www.gayot.com, pg 95

The Christian Gauss Award, 1606 New Hampshire Ave NW, Washington, DC 20009 *Tel:* 202-265-3808 *Fax:* 202-986-1601 *E-mail:* awards@pbk.org *Web Site:* www.pbk.org/bookawards, pg 688

Gauthier Publications Inc, PO Box 806241, St Clair Shores, MI 48080 *Tel:* 313-458-7141 *Fax:* 586-279-1515 *E-mail:* info@gauthierpublications.com *Web Site:* www.gauthierpublications.com, pg 95

The Gaylactic Spectrum Awards, PO Box 73602, Washington, DC 20056-3602 *Tel:* 202-483-6369 *Web Site:* www.spectrumawards.org, pg 688

Gaylord College of Journalism & Mass Communication, Professional Writing Program, c/o University of Oklahoma, 395 W Lindsey St, Rm 3534, Norman, OK 73019-0270 *Tel:* 405-325-2721 *Fax:* 405-325-7565 *Web Site:* www.ou.edu/gaylord, pg 660

Fred Gebhart, PO Box 111, Gold Hill, OR 97525 *Tel:* 541-855-8975 *E-mail:* fgebhart@pobox.com *Web Site:* www.fredgebhart.com, pg 526

Gefen Books, c/o Storch, 255 Central Ave, B-206, Lawrence, NY 11559 *Tel:* 516-593-1234 *Toll Free Tel:* 800-477-5257 *Fax:* 516-295-2739 *E-mail:* gefenny@gefenpublishing.com; info@gefenpublishing.com *Web Site:* www.gefenpublishing.com; www.israelbooks.com, pg 95

Lionel Gelber Prize, University of Toronto, Munk School of Global Affairs, One Devonshire Place, Toronto, ON M5S 3K7, Canada *Tel:* 416-946-8901 *Fax:* 416-946-8915 *E-mail:* events.munk@utoronto.ca *Web Site:* munkschool.utoronto.ca/gelber/; www.facebook.com/GelberPrize, pg 688

Gelfman/Schneider/ICM, 850 Seventh Ave, Suite 903, New York, NY 10019 *Tel:* 212-245-1993 *Fax:* 212-245-8678 *E-mail:* mail@gelfmanschneider.com *Web Site:* gelfmanschneider.com, pg 553

The Gell Center of the Finger Lakes, 740 University Ave, Rochester, NY 14607-1259 *Tel:* 585-473-2590 *Fax:* 585-442-9333 *Web Site:* www.wab.org, pg 651

Gelles-Cole Literary Enterprises, 135 John Joy Rd, Woodstock, NY 12498-0341 *Tel:* 845-679-2452 *Web Site:* www.literaryenterprises.com, pg 526

Gem Guides Book Co, 1275 W Ninth St, Upland, CA 91786 *Tel:* 626-855-1611 *Toll Free Tel:* 800-824-5118 (orders) *Fax:* 626-855-1610 *E-mail:* info@gemguidesbooks.com *Web Site:* www.gemguidesbooks.com, pg 95

Genealogical Publishing Co, 3600 Clipper Mill Rd, Suite 260, Baltimore, MD 21211 *Tel:* 410-837-8271 *Toll Free Tel:* 800-296-6687 *Fax:* 410-752-8492 *Toll Free Fax:* 800-599-9561 *E-mail:* sales@genealogical.com; info@genealogical.com *Web Site:* www.genealogical.com, pg 95

General Store Publishing House (GSPH), 499 O'Brien Rd, Renfrew, ON K7V 3Z3, Canada *Tel:* 613-599-2064 *Toll Free Tel:* 800-465-6072 *E-mail:* orders@gsph.com; submissions@gsph.com *Web Site:* www.gsph.com, pg 485

Genesis Press Inc, PO Box 101, Columbus, MS 39701 *Toll Free Tel:* 888-463-4461 (orders only) *Web Site:* www.genesis-press.com, pg 95

Geological Society of America (GSA), 3300 Penrose Place, Boulder, CO 80301-1806 *Tel:* 303-357-1000 *Fax:* 303-357-1070 *E-mail:* pubs@geosociety.org (prodn); editing@geosociety.org (edit) *Web Site:* www.geosociety.org, pg 96

GeoLytics Inc, 3322 Rte 22, Suite 806, Branchburg, NJ 08876 *Tel:* 908-707-1505 *Toll Free Tel:* 800-577-6717 *Fax:* 908-707-1595 *E-mail:* support@geolytics.com; questions@geolytics.com *Web Site:* www.geolytics.com, pg 96

Georgetown Review Literary Prize, Box 227, 400 E College St, Georgetown, KY 40324 *Tel:* 502-863-8079 *E-mail:* gtownreview@georgetowncollege.edu *Web Site:* georgetownreview.georgetowncollege.edu, pg 688

Georgetown University Press, 3240 Prospect St NW, Suite 250, Washington, DC 20007 *Tel:* 202-687-5889 (busn) *Fax:* 202-687-6340 (edit) *E-mail:* gupress@georgetown.edu *Web Site:* press.georgetown.edu, pg 96

The Gersh Agency (TGA), 41 Madison Ave, 33rd fl, New York, NY 10010 *Tel:* 212-997-1818 *E-mail:* info@gershla.com *Web Site:* www.gershagency.com, pg 553

Leo Gershoy Award, 400 "A" St SE, Washington, DC 20003 *Tel:* 202-544-2422 *Fax:* 202-544-8307 *E-mail:* awards@historians.org *Web Site:* www.historians.org, pg 689

Nancy C Gerth PhD, 1431 Harlan's Trail, Sagle, ID 83860 *Tel:* 208-304-9066 *E-mail:* docnangee@nancygerth.com *Web Site:* www.nancygerth.com, pg 526

Gestalt Journal Press, PO Box 278, Gouldsboro, ME 04607-0278 *Tel:* 207-404-9954 *Fax:* 207-510-4889 *E-mail:* press@gestalt.org *Web Site:* www.gestaltjournalpress.com, pg 96

Getty Publications, 1200 Getty Center Dr, Suite 500, Los Angeles, CA 90049-1682 *Tel:* 310-440-7365 *Toll Free Tel:* 800-223-3431 (orders) *Fax:* 310-440-7758 *E-mail:* pubsinfo@getty.edu *Web Site:* www.getty.edu/publications, pg 96

GGP Publishing Inc, 105 Calvert St, Suite 201, Harrison, NY 10528-3138 *Tel:* 914-834-8896 *Fax:* 914-834-7566 *Web Site:* www.GGPPublishing.com, pg 526, 553

GIA Publications Inc, 7404 S Mason Ave, Chicago, IL 60638 *Tel:* 708-496-3800 *Toll Free Tel:* 800-GIA-1358 (442-1358) *Fax:* 708-496-3828 *E-mail:* custserv@giamusic.com *Web Site:* www.giamusic.com, pg 96

Gibbs Smith Publisher, 1877 E Gentile St, Layton, UT 84041 *Tel:* 801-544-9800 *Toll Free Tel:* 800-748-5439; 800-835-4993 (orders) *Fax:* 801-544-5582 *Toll Free Fax:* 800-213-3023 (orders only) *E-mail:* info@gibbs-smith.com; tradeorders@gibbs-smith.com *Web Site:* www.gibbs-smith.com, pg 96

Gifted Education Press, 10201 Yuma Ct, Manassas, VA 20109 *Tel:* 703-369-5017 *Web Site:* www.giftededpress.com, pg 97

Sheri Gilbert, 123 Van Voorhis Ave, Rochester, NY 14617 *Tel:* 585-342-0331 *E-mail:* gilbert@permissionseditor.com *Web Site:* permissionseditor.com, pg 527

Giller Prize, 543 Logan Ave, Toronto, ON M4K 3B6, Canada *Web Site:* www.scotiabankgillerprize.ca, pg 689

Gilpin Publishing, PO Box 597, Alliston, ON L9R 1V7, Canada *Tel:* 705-424-6507 *Toll Free Tel:* 800-867-3281 *Fax:* 705-424-6507 *E-mail:* mail@gilpin.ca *Web Site:* www.gilpin.ca, pg 485

Gingko Press Inc, 1321 Fifth St, Berkeley, CA 94710 *Tel:* 510-898-1195 *Fax:* 510-898-1196 *E-mail:* books@gingkopress.com *Web Site:* www.gingkopress.com, pg 97

Allen Ginsberg Poetry Award, One College Blvd, Paterson, NJ 07505-1179 *Tel:* 973-684-6555 *Fax:* 973-523-6085 *Web Site:* www.pccc.edu/poetry, pg 689

Gival Press, 5200 N First St, Arlington, VA 22203 *Tel:* 703-351-0079 *Fax:* 703-351-0079 (call first) *E-mail:* givalpress@yahoo.com *Web Site:* www.givalpress.com, pg 97

Gival Press Novel Award, PO Box 3812, Arlington, VA 22203 *Tel:* 703-351-0079 *Fax:* 703-351-0079 (call first) *E-mail:* givalpress@yahoo.com *Web Site:* www.givalpress.com, pg 689

Gival Press Oscar Wilde Award, PO Box 3812, Arlington, VA 22203 *Tel:* 703-351-0079 *Fax:* 703-351-0079 (call first) *E-mail:* givalpress@yahoo.com *Web Site:* www.givalpress.com, pg 689

Gival Press Poetry Award, PO Box 3812, Arlington, VA 22203 *Tel:* 703-351-0079 *Fax:* 703-351-0079 (call first) *E-mail:* givalpress@yahoo.com *Web Site:* www.givalpress.com, pg 689

Gival Press Short Story Award, PO Box 3812, Arlington, VA 22203 *Tel:* 703-351-0079 *Fax:* 703-351-0079 (call first) *E-mail:* givalpress@yahoo.com *Web Site:* www.givalpress.com, pg 689

John Glassco Translation Prize, Concordia University, LB 601, 1455 De Maisonneuve West, Montreal, QC H3G 1M8, Canada *Tel:* 514-848-2424 (ext 8702) *E-mail:* info@attlc-ltac.org *Web Site:* www.attlc-ltac.org, pg 689

GLCA New Writers Awards, 535 W William St, Suite 301, Ann Arbor, MI 48103 *Tel:* 734-661-2350 *Fax:* 734-661-2349 *Web Site:* www.glca.org, pg 689

Susan Gleason, 325 Riverside Dr, Suite 41, New York, NY 10025 *Tel:* 212-662-3876 *Fax:* 212-864-3298 *E-mail:* sgleasonliteraryagent@gmail.com, pg 554

The Danuta Gleed Literary Award, 600-460 Richmond St W, Toronto, ON M5V 1Y1, Canada *Tel:* 416-703-8982 *Fax:* 416-504-9090 *E-mail:* info@writersunion.ca *Web Site:* www.writersunion.ca, pg 689

The Glen Workshop, 3307 Third Ave W, Seattle, WA 98119 *Tel:* 206-281-2988 *Fax:* 206-281-2979 *E-mail:* glenworkshop@imagejournal.org *Web Site:* www.imagejournal.org/page/events/the-glen-workshop, pg 651

Glenbridge Publishing Ltd, 19923 E Long Ave, Centennial, CO 80016-1969 *Tel:* 720-870-8381 *Toll Free Tel:* 800-986-4135 (orders) *Fax:* 720-230-1209 *E-mail:* glenbridge10@gmail.com *Web Site:* www.glenbridgepublishing.com, pg 97

Peter Glenn Publications, 306 NE Second St, 2nd fl, Delray Beach, FL 33483 *Tel:* 561-404-4290 *Fax:* 561-892-5786 *Web Site:* pgdirect.com, pg 97

Glimmer Train Press Inc, PO Box 80430, Portland, OR 97280-1430 *Tel:* 503-221-0836 *Fax:* 503-221-0837 *E-mail:* editors@glimmertrain.org *Web Site:* www.glimmertrain.org, pg 97

Glitterati Inc, 630 Ninth Ave, Suite 603, New York, NY 10036 *Tel:* 212-362-9119 *Fax:* 646-607-4433 *E-mail:* info@glitteratiincorporated.com *Web Site:* glitteratiincorporated.com, pg 97

Global Authors Publications (GAP), 38 Bluegrass, Middleberg, FL 32068 *Tel:* 904-425-1608 *E-mail:* gapbook@yahoo.com *Web Site:* globalauthorspublications.com, pg 97

Global Ebook Awards, PO Box 8206-240, Santa Barbara, CA 93118-8206 *Tel:* 805-968-7277 *Fax:* 805-968-1379 *Web Site:* globalebookawards.com, pg 689

Global Lion Intellectual Property Management Inc, PO Box 669238, Pompano Beach, FL 33066 *Tel:* 754-222-6948 *Fax:* 754-222-6948 *E-mail:* queriesgloballionmgt@gmail.com *Web Site:* www.globallionmanagement.com, pg 554

Global Publishing, Sales & Distribution, 980 Lincoln Ave, Suite 200 B, San Rafael, CA 94901 *Tel:* 415-456-2934 *Fax:* 415-456-4124 *Web Site:* www.globalpsd.com, pg 97

Global Training Center Inc, 550 S Mesa Hills Dr, Suite E4, El Paso, TX 79912 *Tel:* 915-534-7900 *Toll Free Tel:* 800-860-5030 *Fax:* 915-534-7903 *E-mail:* contact@globaltrainingcenter.com *Web Site:* www.globaltrainingcenter.com, pg 97

The Globe Pequot Press, 246 Goose Lane, Guilford, CT 06437 *Tel:* 203-458-4500 *Toll Free Tel:* 800-243-0495 (orders only); 888-249-7586 (cust serv) *Fax:* 203-458-4601 *Toll Free Fax:* 800-820-2329 (orders & cust serv) *E-mail:* editorial@globepequot.com; info@rowman.com; orders@rowman.com *Web Site:* rowman.com, pg 98

Globo Libros Literary Agency, 402 E 64 St, Suite 6-C, New York, NY 10065 *Tel:* 212-888-4655 *Web Site:* www.globo-libros.com; publishersmarketplace.com/members/dstockwell, pg 554

David R Godine Publisher Inc, 15 Court Sq, Suite 320, Boston, MA 02108-4715 *Tel:* 617-451-9600 *Fax:* 617-350-0250 *E-mail:* info@godine.com *Web Site:* www.godine.com, pg 98

Krista Goering Literary Agency LLC, 3514 Clinton Pkwy, Suite A-404, Lawrence, KS 66047 *Tel:* 785-841-0634 *Fax:* 785-841-8500 *E-mail:* query@kristagoering.com *Web Site:* www.kristagoering.com, pg 554

Gold Eagle, 225 Duncan Mill Rd, 4th fl, Don Mills, ON M3B 3K9, Canada *Tel:* 416-445-5860 *Toll Free Tel:* 888-432-4879 *Fax:* 416-445-8655; 416-445-8736 *E-mail:* readgoldeagle@hotmail.com; customerservice@harlequin.com *Web Site:* www.harlequin.com, pg 485

Gold Leaf Press, 3670 Morrissey Ave, Warren, MI 48091 *Tel:* 313-331-3571 *Web Site:* www.goldleafpress.com, pg 527

Gold Medal, 633 W 155 St, New York, NY 10032 *Tel:* 212-368-5900 *Fax:* 212-491-4615 *E-mail:* academy@artsandletters.org *Web Site:* www.artsandletters.org, pg 689

Golden Cylindar Awards, 8281 Pine Lake Rd, Denver, NC 28037 *Tel:* 201-523-6042 *Fax:* 201-523-6048 *E-mail:* gaa@gaa.org *Web Site:* www.gaa.org, pg 689

Golden Kite Awards, 4727 Wilshire Blvd, Suite 301, Los Angeles, CA 90010 *Tel:* 323-782-1010; 310-403-0675 (cell) *Fax:* 323-782-1892 *E-mail:* scbwi@scbwi.org; membership@scbwi.org *Web Site:* www.scbwi.org, pg 689

Golden Meteorite Press, 11919 82 St NW, Suite 103, Edmonton, AB T5B 2W4, Canada *Tel:* 780-378-0063 *Fax:* 780-378-0063, pg 485

Golden Rose Award, 2 Farrar St, Cambridge, MA 02138 *Tel:* 617-744-6034 *E-mail:* contests@nepoetryclub.org *Web Site:* www.nepoetryclub.org, pg 690

Golden West Cookbooks, 5738 N Central Ave, Phoenix, AZ 85012-1316 *Tel:* 602-234-1574 *Toll Free Tel:* 800-521-9221 *Fax:* 602-234-3062 *E-mail:* info@americantravelerpress.com *Web Site:* www.americantravelerpress.com, pg 98

Goldfarb & Associates, 721 Gibbon St, Alexandria, VA 22314 *Tel:* 202-466-3030 *Fax:* 703-836-5644 *E-mail:* rglawlit@gmail.com *Web Site:* www.ronaldgoldfarb.com, pg 554

Frances Goldin Literary Agency, Inc, 57 E 11 St, Suite 5-B, New York, NY 10003 *Tel:* 212-777-0047 *Fax:* 212-228-1660 *E-mail:* agency@goldinlit.com *Web Site:* www.goldinlit.com, pg 554

Donald Goldstein, 1500 E 17 St, Brooklyn, NY 11230 *Tel:* 718-375-9346 *E-mail:* dgoldsbkyn@aol.com, pg 527

Laurence Goldstein Poetry Prize, University of Michigan, 0576 Rackham Bldg, 915 E Washington St, Ann Arbor, MI 48109-1070 *Tel:* 734-764-9265 *E-mail:* mqr@umich.edu *Web Site:* www.umich.edu/~mqr, pg 690

Gollehon Press Inc, 3655 Glenn Dr SE, Grand Rapids, MI 49546 *Tel:* 616-949-3515 *Fax:* 616-949-8674 *Web Site:* www.gollehonbooks.com, pg 98

Goodheart-Willcox Publisher, 18604 W Creek Dr, Tinley Park, IL 60477-6243 *Tel:* 708-687-5000 *Toll Free Tel:* 800-323-0440 *Fax:* 708-468-8692 *Toll Free Fax:* 888-409-3900 *E-mail:* custserv@g-w.com; orders@g-w.com *Web Site:* www.g-w.com, pg 98

Goodman Associates, 500 West End Ave, New York, NY 10024 *Tel:* 212-873-4806, pg 554

Irene Goodman Literary Agency, 27 W 24 St, Suite 700B, New York, NY 10010 *Tel:* 212-604-0330 *E-mail:* queries@irenegoodman.com *Web Site:* www.irenegoodman.com, pg 554

Robert M Goodman, 140 West End Ave, Unit 11-J, New York, NY 10023 *Tel:* 917-439-1097 *E-mail:* bobbybgood@gmail.com, pg 527

Sasha Goodman Agency Inc, 6680 Colgate Ave, Los Angeles, CA 90048 *Tel:* 310-387-0242 *Fax:* 323-653-3457 *E-mail:* ukseg@sbcglobal.net, pg 555

Goose Lane Editions, 500 Beaverbrook Ct, Suite 330, Fredericton, NB E3B 5X4, Canada *Tel:* 506-450-4251 *Toll Free Tel:* 888-926-8377 *Fax:* 506-459-4991 *E-mail:* info@gooselane.com; customerservice@gooselane.com *Web Site:* www.gooselane.com, pg 485

Goose River Press, 3400 Friendship Rd, Waldoboro, ME 04572-6337 *Tel:* 207-832-6665 *E-mail:* gooseriverpress@roadrunner.com *Web Site:* gooseriverpress.com, pg 98

Goosebottom Books, 543 Trinidad Lane, Foster City, CA 94404 *Tel:* 650-204-4076 *Toll Free Fax:* 888-407-5286 *E-mail:* info@goosebottombooks.com *Web Site:* goosebottombooks.com, pg 98

P M Gordon Associates Inc, 2115 Wallace St, Philadelphia, PA 19130 *Tel:* 215-769-2525 *E-mail:* pmga@pond1.net *Web Site:* www.pmgordon.com, pg 527

Gorgias Press LLC, PO Box 6939, Piscataway, NJ 08854-6939 *Tel:* 732-885-8900 *Fax:* 732-885-8908 *E-mail:* helpdesk@gorgiaspress.com *Web Site:* www.gorgiaspress.com, pg 99

Gospel Publishing House (GPH), 1445 Boonville Ave, Springfield, MO 65802 *Tel:* 417-862-2781; 417-831-8000 (outside US) *Toll Free Tel:* 800-641-4310 *Fax:* 417-863-1874; 417-862-5881 *Toll Free Fax:* 800-328-0294 *E-mail:* custsrvreps@ag.org *Web Site:* www.gospelpublishing.com, pg 99

Gotham Literary Agency, 170 E 83 St, New York, NY 10028 *Tel:* 212-249-2615, pg 555

Gotham Writers' Workshop, 555 Eighth Ave, Suite 1402, New York, NY 10018-4358 *Tel:* 212-974-8377 *Toll Free Tel:* 877-974-8377 *E-mail:* office@write.org *Web Site:* www.writingclasses.com, pg 651

C+S Gottfried, 619 Cricklewood Dr, State College, PA 16803 *Tel:* 814-237-2580 *Web Site:* www.lookoutnow.com/index2.html, pg 527

Sherry Gottlieb, 4900 Dunes St, Oxnard, CA 93035 *Tel:* 805-382-3425 *E-mail:* writer@wordservices.com *Web Site:* www.wordservices.com, pg 527

Government of Canada Publications, Publishing & Depository Services, Public Works & Government Services Canada, Ottawa, ON K1A 0S5, Canada *Tel:* 613-941-5995 *Toll Free Tel:* 800-635-7943 *Fax:* 613-954-5779 *Toll Free Fax:* 800-565-7757 *E-mail:* publications@tpsgc-pwgsc.gc.ca *Web Site:* publications.gc.ca, pg 485

Governor General's Literary Awards, 150 Elgin St, Ottawa, ON K1P 1L4, Canada *Tel:* 613-566-4414 *Toll Free Tel:* 800-263-5588 (CN only) *Fax:* 613-566-4390 *E-mail:* info@canadacouncil.ca *Web Site:* canadacouncil.ca/en/council/prizes, pg 690

The Gracies®, 1250 24 St NW, Suite 300, Washington, DC 20037 *Tel:* 202-750-3664 *Fax:* 202-750-3664 *E-mail:* info@allwomeninmedia.org *Web Site:* allwomeninmedia.org, pg 690

Doug Grad Literary Agency Inc, 68 Jay St, Suite W11, Brooklyn, NY 11201-1189 *Tel:* 718-788-6067 *E-mail:* query@dgliterary.com *Web Site:* www.dgliterary.com, pg 555

The Graduate Group/Booksellers, 86 Norwood Rd, West Hartford, CT 06117-2236 *Tel:* 860-233-2330 *Fax:* 860-233-2330 *E-mail:* graduategroup@hotmail.com *Web Site:* www.graduategroup.com, pg 99

Graham Agency, 250 W 57 St, Suite 2430, New York, NY 10107 *Tel:* 212-489-7730, pg 555

Grand Central Publishing, 1290 Avenue of the Americas, New York, NY 10019 *Tel:* 212-364-1100 *Web Site:* www.hachettebookgroup.com, pg 99

Grand Master Award, 1140 Broadway, Suite 1507, New York, NY 10001 *Tel:* 212-888-8171 *Fax:* 212-888-8107 *E-mail:* mwa@mysterywriters.org *Web Site:* www.mysterywriters.org, pg 690

Donald M Grant Publisher Inc, PO Box 187, Hampton Falls, NH 03844-0187 *Tel:* 603-778-7191 *Fax:* 603-778-7191 *E-mail:* office@grantbooks.com *Web Site:* secure.grantbooks.com, pg 99

Grants for Literary Artists, 649 rue Queen, 2nd fl, Fredericton, NB E3B 1C3, Canada *Tel:* 506-444-4444 *Toll Free Tel:* 866-460-ARTS (460-2787) *Fax:* 506-444-5543 *E-mail:* nbabcanb@artsnb.ca *Web Site:* www.artsnb.ca, pg 690

The Graphic Artists Guild Inc, 32 Broadway, Suite 1114, New York, NY 10004 *Tel:* 212-791-3400 *Fax:* 212-791-0333 *Web Site:* www.graphicartistsguild.org, pg 606, 660

Graphic Arts Association, 1210 Northbrook Dr, Suite 200, Trevose, PA 19053 *Tel:* 215-396-2300 *Fax:* 215-396-9890 *E-mail:* gaa@gaaonline.org *Web Site:* www.gaa1900.com, pg 660

Graphic Arts Books, 7820 NE Holman St, Suite B-9, Portland, OR 97218 *Tel:* 503-254-5591 *Fax:* 503-254-5609 *E-mail:* info-ga@graphicartsbooks.com *Web Site:* www.graphicartsbooks.com, pg 99

Graphic Arts Education & Research Foundation (GAERF), 1899 Preston White Dr, Reston, VA 20191 *Tel:* 703-264-7200 *Toll Free Tel:* 866-381-9839 *Fax:* 703-620-3165 *E-mail:* gaerf@npes.org *Web Site:* www.gaerf.org, pg 623

Graphic Arts Show Company (GASC), 1899 Preston White Dr, Reston, VA 20191 *Tel:* 703-264-7200 *Fax:* 703-620-9187 *E-mail:* info@gasc.org *Web Site:* www.gasc.org, pg 606

Graphic Universe™, 241 First Ave N, Minneapolis, MN 55401 *Tel:* 612-332-3344 *Toll Free Tel:* 800-328-4929 *Fax:* 612-332-7615 *Toll Free Fax:* 800-332-1132 *E-mail:* info@lernerbooks.com *Web Site:* www.lernerbooks.com, pg 99

Graphic World Publishing Services, 11687 Adie Rd, St Louis, MO 63043 *Tel:* 314-567-9854 *Fax:* 314-567-7178 *E-mail:* quote@gwinc.com *Web Site:* www.gwinc.com, pg 527

Gravure Association of the Americas Inc, 8281 Pine Lake Rd, Denver, NC 28037 *Tel:* 201-523-6042 *Fax:* 201-523-6048 *E-mail:* gaa@gaa.org *Web Site:* www.gaa.org, pg 606

Gray & Company Publishers, 1588 E 40 St, Suite 3A, Cleveland, OH 44103 *Tel:* 216-431-2665 *Toll Free Tel:* 800-915-3609 *E-mail:* sales@grayco.com; editorial@grayco.com; support@grayco.com; publicity@grayco.com *Web Site:* www.grayco.com, pg 99

James H Gray Award for Short Nonfiction, 11759 Groat Rd, Edmonton, AB T5M 3K6, Canada *Tel:* 780-422-8174 *Toll Free Tel:* 800-665-5354 (AB only) *Fax:* 780-422-2663 (attn WGA) *E-mail:* mail@writersguild.ab.ca *Web Site:* www.writersguild.ab.ca, pg 690

Ashley Grayson Literary Agency, 1342 W 18 St, San Pedro, CA 90732 *Tel:* 310-548-4672 *E-mail:* graysonagent@earthlink.net; rights@graysonagency.com *Web Site:* graysonagency.com/blog/, pg 555

Graywolf Press, 250 Third Ave N, Suite 600, Minneapolis, MN 55401 *Tel:* 651-641-0077 *Fax:* 651-641-0036 *E-mail:* wolves@graywolfpress.org *Web Site:* www.graywolfpress.org, pg 99

Great Lakes Graphics Association, W232 N2950 Roundy Circle E, Pewaukee, WI 53072 *Tel:* 262-522-2210 *Toll Free Tel:* 855-522-2210 *Fax:* 262-522-2211 *E-mail:* admin@piw.org *Web Site:* www.piw.org, pg 606

Great Potential Press Inc, 1325 N Wilmot Ave, Suite 300, Tucson, AZ 85712 *Tel:* 520-777-6161 *Fax:* 520-777-6217 *Web Site:* www.greatpotentialpress.com, pg 100

Great Quotations Inc, 1410 Brook Dr, Downers Grove, IL 60515 *Tel:* 630-985-2628 *Toll Free Tel:* 800-830-3020 *Fax:* 630-985-2610 *E-mail:* info@greatquotationsinc.com *Web Site:* www.greatquotationsinc.com, pg 100

Great Source Education Group, 181 Ballardvale St, Wilmington, MA 01887 *Toll Free Tel:* 800-289-4490 *Toll Free Fax:* 800-289-3994; 800-269-5232 *Web Site:* www.hmhco.com, pg 100

Greater Talent Network Inc, 437 Fifth Ave, New York, NY 10016 *Tel:* 212-645-4200 *Toll Free Tel:* 800-326-4211 *Fax:* 212-627-1471 *E-mail:* info@greatertalent.com *Web Site:* www.greatertalent.com, pg 587

Green Dragon Books, 2875 S Ocean Blvd, Suite 200, Palm Beach, FL 33480 *Tel:* 561-533-6231 *Toll Free Tel:* 800-874-8844 *Fax:* 561-533-6233 *Toll Free Fax:* 888-874-8844 *E-mail:* info@greendragonbooks.com *Web Site:* greendragonbooks.com, pg 100

Green Integer, 6210 Wilshire Blvd, Suite 211, Los Angeles, CA 90048 *Tel:* 323-857-1115 *Fax:* 323-857-0143 *Web Site:* www.greeninteger.com, pg 100

The Green Rose Prize in Poetry, c/o Western Michigan University, 1903 W Michigan Ave, Kalamazoo, MI 49008-5463 *Tel:* 269-387-8185 *Fax:* 269-387-2562 *E-mail:* new-issues@wmich.edu *Web Site:* www.wmich.edu/newissues/sub-guide.html, pg 690

Sanford J Greenburger Associates Inc, 55 Fifth Ave, New York, NY 10003 *Tel:* 212-206-5600 *Fax:* 212-463-8718 *Web Site:* greenburger.com; www.sjga.com/, pg 555

Greenhaven Press®, 27500 Drake Rd, Farmington Hills, MI 48331 *Toll Free Tel:* 800-877-GALE (877-4253 - cust serv & orders) *Toll Free Fax:* 800-414-5043 (orders only) *E-mail:* gale.customerservice@cengage.com; gale.galeord@cengage.com *Web Site:* www.gale.cengage.com/greenhaven, pg 100

Paul Greenland Editorial Services, 9184 Longfellow Lane, Machesney Park, IL 61115 *Tel:* 815-540-0911 *Web Site:* www.paulgreenland.com, pg 527

Greenleaf Book Group LLC, Three Park Place, 4005 Banister Lane, Suite B, Austin, TX 78704 *Tel:* 512-891-6100 *Toll Free Tel:* 800-932-5420 *Fax:* 512-891-6150 *E-mail:* contact@greenleafbookgroup.com *Web Site:* www.greenleafbookgroup.com, pg 100

Greenwoman Publishing LLC, 1823 W Pikes Peak Ave, Colorado Springs, CO 80904-3844 *Tel:* 719-473-9237 *Fax:* 719-473-9237 *Web Site:* www.greenwomanpublishing.com, pg 100

Greenwood Research Books & Software, PO Box 12102, Wichita, KS 67277-2102 *Tel:* 316-214-5103 *Web Site:* greenray4ever.com (ordering), pg 100

Bess Gresham Memorial, 1194 Hume Rd, Hume, VA 22639-1806 *E-mail:* poetryinva@aol.com *Web Site:* www.poetrysocietyofvirginia.org, pg 690

Rosemary F Gretton, 1029 El Capitan Dr, Danville, CA 94526 *Tel:* 925-336-0003 *Fax:* 925-336-0003 *E-mail:* rgretton@lyricism.ca *Web Site:* www.lyricism.ca, pg 527

Grey House Publishing Inc™, 4919 Rte 22, Amenia, NY 12501 *Tel:* 518-789-8700 *Toll Free Tel:* 800-562-2139 *Fax:* 518-789-0556 *E-mail:* books@greyhouse.com; customerservice@greyhouse.com *Web Site:* www.greyhouse.com, pg 101

Greystone Books Ltd, 343 Railway St, Suite 201, Vancouver, BC V6A 1A4, Canada *Tel:* 604-875-1550 *Fax:* 604-875-1556 *E-mail:* info@greystonebooks.com *Web Site:* www.greystonebooks.com, pg 486

Joan K Griffitts Indexing, 3909 W 71 St, Indianapolis, IN 46268-2257 *Tel:* 317-297-7312 *E-mail:* jkgriffitts@gmail.com *Web Site:* www.joankgriffittsindexing.com, pg 527

Jill Grinberg Literary Management LLC, 392 Vanderbilt Ave, Brooklyn, NY 11238 *Tel:* 212-620-5883 *E-mail:* info@jillgrinbergliterary.com *Web Site:* www.jillgrinbergliterary.com, pg 555

Jill Grosjean Literary Agency, 1390 Millstone Rd, Sag Harbor, NY 11963 *Tel:* 631-725-7419 *Fax:* 631-725-8632 *E-mail:* JillLit310@aol.com, pg 555

Laura Gross Literary Agency Ltd, PO Box 610326, Newton Highlands, MA 02461 *Tel:* 617-964-2977 *Fax:* 617-964-3023 *E-mail:* query@lg-la.com *Web Site:* www.lg-la.com, pg 555

Grosset & Dunlap, 345 Hudson St, New York, NY 10014 *Tel:* 212-366-2000 *Web Site:* www.penguinrandomhouse.com, pg 101

Judith S Grossman, 715 Cherry Circle, Wynnewood, PA 19096 *Tel:* 610-642-0906 *E-mail:* stogiz@aol.com, pg 527

Groundwood Books, 110 Spadina Ave, Suite 801, Toronto, ON M5V 2K4, Canada *Tel:* 416-363-4343 *Fax:* 416-363-1017 *E-mail:* genmail@groundwoodbooks.com *Web Site:* www.houseofanansi.com, pg 486

Group Publishing Inc, 1515 Cascade Ave, Loveland, CO 80538 *Tel:* 970-669-3836 *Toll Free Tel:* 800-447-1070 *Fax:* 970-292-4373 *E-mail:* info@group.com *Web Site:* www.group.com, pg 101

Groupe Educalivres Inc, 955, rue Bergar, Laval, QC H7L 4Z6, Canada *Tel:* 514-334-8466 *Toll Free Tel:* 800-567-3671 (info serv) *Fax:* 514-334-8387 *E-mail:* infoservice@grandduc.com *Web Site:* www.educalivres.com, pg 486

Groupe Modulo, c/o TC Media Books Inc, 5800 St Denis St, Suite 900, Montreal, QC H2S 3L5, Canada *Tel:* 514-273-1066 *Toll Free Tel:* 800-565-5531 *Fax:* 514-276-0234 *Toll Free Fax:* 800-814-0324 *Web Site:* www.groupemodulo.com, pg 486

Groupe Sogides Inc, 955 rue Amherst, Montreal, QC H2L 3K4, Canada *Tel:* 514-523-1182 *Fax:* 514-597-0370 *Web Site:* www.sogides.com, pg 486

Grove Atlantic Inc, 154 W 14 St, 12th fl, New York, NY 10011 *Tel:* 212-614-7850 *Toll Free Tel:* 800-521-0178 *Fax:* 212-614-7886 *E-mail:* info@groveatlantic.com *Web Site:* www.groveatlantic.com, pg 101

Gryphon Editions, PO Box 241823, Omaha, NE 68124 *Tel:* 402-298-5385 (intl) *Toll Free Tel:* 888-655-0134 (US & CN) *E-mail:* customerservice@gryphoneditions.com *Web Site:* www.gryphoneditions.com, pg 101

Gryphon House Inc, 6848 Leon's Way, Lewisville, NC 27023 *Toll Free Tel:* 800-638-0928 *Toll Free Fax:* 877-638-7576 *E-mail:* info@ghbooks.com *Web Site:* www.gryphonhouse.com, pg 101

Carol Guenzi Agents Inc, 865 Delaware St, Denver, CO 80204 *Tel:* 303-820-2599 *Toll Free Tel:* 800-417-5120 *Fax:* 303-820-2598 *E-mail:* info@artagent.com; art@artagent.com *Web Site:* www.artagent.com, pg 583

Guerin Editeur Ltee, 4501 rue Drolet, Montreal, QC H2T 2G2, Canada *Tel:* 514-842-3481 *Fax:* 514-842-4923 *Web Site:* www.guerin-editeur.qc.ca, pg 486

Guernica Editions Inc, 1569 Heritage Way, Oakville, ON L6M 2Z7, Canada *Fax:* 416-576-9403 *E-mail:* info@guernicaeditions.com *Web Site:* guernicaeditions.com, pg 486

John Simon Guggenheim Memorial Foundation, 90 Park Ave, New York, NY 10016 *Tel:* 212-687-4470 *Fax:* 212-697-3248 *E-mail:* fellowships@gf.org *Web Site:* www.gf.org, pg 623

Guggenheim-Lehrman Prize in Military History, 25 W 53 St, New York, NY 10019 *Tel:* 646-428-0971 *Fax:* 646-428-0981 *E-mail:* info@hfg.org *Web Site:* www.hfg.org/prize/main.htm, pg 690

Guideposts Book & Inspirational Media, 16 E 34 St, 12th fl, New York, NY 10016 *Tel:* 212-251-8100 *Toll Free Tel:* 800-431-2344 (cust serv) *Fax:* 212-684-0689 *E-mail:* gpsprod@cdsfulfillment.com *Web Site:* guideposts.org, pg 102

Guild of Book Workers, 521 Fifth Ave, 17th fl, New York, NY 10175 *Tel:* 212-292-4444 *E-mail:* communications@guildofbookworkers.org *Web Site:* www.guildofbookworkers.org, pg 606

The Guilford Press, 72 Spring St, New York, NY 10012 *Tel:* 212-431-9800 *Toll Free Tel:* 800-365-7006 *Fax:* 212-966-6708 *E-mail:* info@guilford.com *Web Site:* www.guilford.com, pg 102

Gulf Publishing Co, 2 Greenway Plaza, Suite 1020, Houston, TX 77046 *Tel:* 713-529-4301 *Fax:* 713-520-4433 *E-mail:* store@gulfpub.com *Web Site:* www.gulfpub.com, pg 102

The Charlotte Gusay Literary Agency, 10532 Blythe Ave, Los Angeles, CA 90064 *Tel:* 310-559-0831 *Fax:* 310-559-2639 *E-mail:* gusay1@ca.rr.com (queries only) *Web Site:* www.gusay.com, pg 555, 583

Hachai Publishing, 527 Empire Blvd, Brooklyn, NY 11225 *Tel:* 718-633-0100 *Fax:* 718-633-0103 *E-mail:* info@hachai.com *Web Site:* www.hachai.com, pg 102

Hachette Audio, 1290 Avenue of the Americas, New York, NY 10019 *Tel:* 212-364-1100, pg 102

Hachette Book Group, 1290 Avenue of the Americas, New York, NY 10019 *Tel:* 212-364-1100 *Toll Free Tel:* 800-759-0190 (cust serv) *Fax:* 212-364-0933 (intl orders) *Toll Free Fax:* 800-286-9471 (cust serv) *Web Site:* www.HachetteBookGroup.com, pg 102

Hachette Books, 1290 Avenue of the Americas, New York, NY 10019 *Tel:* 212-364-1100 *Web Site:* www.hachettebookgroup.com, pg 102

Hachette Nashville, 12 Cadillac Dr, Suite 480, Brentwood, TN 37027 *Tel:* 615-221-0996 *Fax:* 615-221-0962 *Web Site:* www.hachettebookgroup.com, pg 103

Hackett Publishing Co Inc, 3333 Massachusetts Ave, Indianapolis, IN 46218 *Tel:* 317-635-9250 (orders & cust serv) *Fax:* 317-635-9292 *Toll Free Fax:* 800-783-9213 *E-mail:* customer@hackettpublishing.com *Web Site:* www.hackettpublishing.com, pg 103

Hackmatack Children's Choice Book Award, PO Box 34055, Scotia Square RPO, Halifax, NS B3J 3S1, Canada *Tel:* 902-424-3774 *Fax:* 902-424-0613 *E-mail:* hackmatack@hackmatack.ca *Web Site:* www.hackmatack.ca, pg 690

Hackney Literary Awards, 1305 Second Ave N, Suite 103, Birmingham, AL 35203 *E-mail:* info@hackneyliteraryawards.org *Web Site:* www.hackneyliteraryawards.org, pg 691

Lisa Hagan Literary, 110 Martin Dr, Bracey, VA 23919 *Tel:* 434-636-4138 *E-mail:* LisaHaganLiterary@yahoo.com *Web Site:* www.publishersmarketplace.com/members/LisaHagan/, pg 556

Hagstrom Map, 1800 Lovering Ave, Wilmington, DE 19806 *Toll Free Tel:* 800-432-MAPS (432-6277) *Toll Free Fax:* 888-210-9654 *Web Site:* rockfordpublishing.com, pg 103

Haights Cross Communications®, 136 Madison Ave, 8th fl, New York, NY 10016 *Tel:* 212-209-0500 *Fax:* 212-209-0501 *E-mail:* info@haightscross.com *Web Site:* www.haightscross.com, pg 103

Hal Leonard Books, 33 Plymouth St, Suite 302, Montclair, NJ 07042 *Toll Free Tel:* 800-637-2852 *E-mail:* info@halleonardbooks.com; custserv@halleonardbooks.com *Web Site:* www.halleonardbooks.com, pg 103

Hal Leonard Corp, 7777 W Bluemound Rd, Milwaukee, WI 53213 *Tel:* 414-774-3630 *Toll Free Tel:* 800-524-4425 *Fax:* 414-774-3259 *E-mail:* halinfo@halleonard.com *Web Site:* www.halleonard.com, pg 103

Sarah Josepha Hale Award, 58 N Main, Newport, NH 03773 *Tel:* 603-863-3430 *E-mail:* rfl@newport.lib.nh.us *Web Site:* www.newport.lib.nh.us, pg 691

Loretta Dunn Hall Memorial, 1194 Hume Rd, Hume, VA 22639-1806 *E-mail:* poetryinva@aol.com *Web Site:* www.poetrysocietyofvirginia.org, pg 691

The Mitchell J Hamilburg Agency, 149 S Barrington Ave, Suite 732, Los Angeles, CA 90049 *Tel:* 310-471-4024 *Fax:* 310-471-9588, pg 556

Hamilton Books, 4501 Forbes Blvd, Suite 200, Lanham, MD 20706 *Tel:* 301-459-3366 *Toll Free Tel:* 800-462-6420 (cust serv) *Fax:* 301-429-5748 *Toll Free Fax:* 800-388-4550 (cust serv), pg 103

Hamilton College, English/Creative Writing, English/Creative Writing Dept, 198 College Hill Rd, Clinton, NY 13323 *Tel:* 315-859-4370 *Fax:* 315-859-4390 *E-mail:* english@hamilton.edu *Web Site:* www.hamilton.edu, pg 660

Hamilton Stone Editions, PO Box 43, Maplewood, NJ 07040 *Tel:* 973-378-8361 *E-mail:* hstone@hamiltonstone.org *Web Site:* www.hamiltonstone.org, pg 104

Hampton Press Inc, 307 Seventh Ave, Suite 506, New York, NY 10001 *Tel:* 646-638-3800 *Toll Free Tel:* 800-894-8955 *Fax:* 646-638-3802 *E-mail:* hamptonpr1@aol.com *Web Site:* www.hamptonpress.com, pg 104

Hampton Roads Publishing Co, 65 Parker St, Suite 7, Newburyport, MA 01950-4600 *Tel:* 978-465-0504 *Toll Free Tel:* 800-423-7087 (orders) *Fax:* 978-465-0243 *Toll Free Fax:* 877-337-3309 *E-mail:* orders@rwwbooks.com *Web Site:* redwheelweiser.com, pg 104

Hancock House Publishers, 4550 Birch Bay Lynden Rd, Suite 104, Blaine, WA 98230-5005 *Tel:* 604-538-1114 *Toll Free Tel:* 800-938-1114 *Fax:* 604-538-2262 *Toll Free Fax:* 800-983-2262 *E-mail:* sales@hancockhouse.com *Web Site:* www.hancockhouse.com, pg 104

Hancock House Publishers Ltd, 19313 Zero Ave, Surrey, BC V3S 9R9, Canada *Tel:* 604-538-1114 *Toll Free Tel:* 800-938-1114 *Fax:* 604-538-2262 *Toll Free Fax:* 800-983-2262 *E-mail:* sales@hancockhouse.com *Web Site:* www.hancockhouse.com, pg 487

Handprint Books Inc, 413 Sixth Ave, Brooklyn, NY 11215-3310 *Tel:* 718-768-3696 *Toll Free Tel:* 800-722-6657 (orders) *Fax:* 718-369-0844 *Toll Free Fax:* 800-858-7787 (orders) *E-mail:* info@handprintbooks.com *Web Site:* www.handprintbooks.com, pg 104

Handy Andy Prize, 1194 Hume Rd, Hume, VA 22639-1806 *E-mail:* poetryinva@aol.com *Web Site:* www.poetrysocietyofvirginia.org, pg 691

Hanging Loose Press, 231 Wyckoff St, Brooklyn, NY 11217 *Tel:* 347-529-4738 *Fax:* 347-227-8215 *E-mail:* print225@aol.com *Web Site:* www.hangingloosepress.com, pg 104

Hannacroix Creek Books Inc, 1127 High Ridge Rd, No 110-B, Stamford, CT 06905-1203 *Tel:* 203-968-8098 *Fax:* 203-968-0193 *E-mail:* hannacroix@aol.com *Web Site:* www.hannacroixcreekbooks.com, pg 104

Hanser Publications LLC, 6915 Valley Ave, Cincinnati, OH 45244-3029 *Tel:* 513-527-8977 *Toll Free Tel:* 800-950-8977; 877-751-5052 (orders) *Fax:* 513-534-7803 *Toll Free Fax:* 800-527-8801 *E-mail:* info@hanserpublications.com *Web Site:* www.hanserpublications.com, pg 104

Harbour Publishing Co Ltd, 4437 Rondeview Rd, Madeira Park, BC V0N 2H0, Canada *Tel:* 604-883-2730 *Toll Free Tel:* 800-667-2988 *Fax:* 604-883-9451 *E-mail:* info@harbourpublishing.com *Web Site:* www.harbourpublishing.com, pg 487

Harcourt Achieve, 6277 Sea Harbor Dr, Orlando, FL 32887 *Tel:* 407-345-2000 *Toll Free Tel:* 800-531-5015 (cust serv/orders) *Toll Free Fax:* 800-699-9459 (cust serv/orders) *Web Site:* www.harcourtachieve.com, pg 104

Harcourt Inc, 6277 Sea Harbor Dr, Orlando, FL 32887 *Tel:* 407-345-2000 *Toll Free Tel:* 800-225-5425 (cust serv/orders) *Toll Free Fax:* 800-269-5232 (cust serv/orders) *Web Site:* www.hmhco.com, pg 104

Hard Shell Word Factory, 6457 Glenway Ave, No 109, Cincinnati, OH 45211 *Toll Free Tel:* 888-232-0808 *Toll Free Fax:* 888-460-4752 *E-mail:* inquiry@mundania.com *Web Site:* www.mundania.com, pg 105

Clarence H Haring Prize, 400 "A" St SE, Washington, DC 20003 *Tel:* 202-544-2422 *Fax:* 202-544-8307 *E-mail:* awards@historians.org *Web Site:* www.historians.org, pg 691

Joy Harjo Poetry Award, PO Box 2414, Durango, CO 81302 *Tel:* 970-903-7914 *E-mail:* cutthroatmag@gmail.com *Web Site:* www.cutthroatmag.com, pg 691

Harlequin Enterprises Ltd, 233 Broadway, Suite 1001, New York, NY 10279 *Tel:* 212-553-4200 *Fax:* 212-227-8969 *E-mail:* CustomerService@harlequin.com *Web Site:* www.harlequin.com, pg 105

Harlequin Enterprises Ltd, 225 Duncan Mill Rd, Don Mills, ON M3B 3K9, Canada *Tel:* 416-445-5860 *Toll Free Tel:* 888-432-4879; 800-370-5838 (ebook inquiries) *E-mail:* customerservice@harlequin.com *Web Site:* www.harlequin.com, pg 487

HarperCollins Canada Ltd, 2 Bloor St E, 20th fl, Toronto, ON M4W 1A8, Canada *Tel:* 416-975-9334 *Fax:* 416-975-9884 *E-mail:* hcorder@harpercollins.com *Web Site:* www.harpercollins.ca, pg 487

HarperCollins Children's Books, 195 Broadway, New York, NY 10007 *Tel:* 212-207-7000 *Web Site:* www.harpercollins.com/childrens, pg 105

HarperCollins General Books Group, 195 Broadway, New York, NY 10007 *Tel:* 212-207-7000 *Web Site:* www.harpercollins.com, pg 105

HarperCollins Publishers, 195 Broadway, New York, NY 10007 *Tel:* 212-207-7000 *Fax:* 212-207-7145 *Web Site:* www.harpercollins.com, pg 106

HarperCollins Publishers Sales, 195 Broadway, New York, NY 10007 *Fax:* 212-207-7000 *Web Site:* www.harpercollins.com, pg 106

Harper's Magazine Foundation, 666 Broadway, 11th fl, New York, NY 10012 *Tel:* 212-420-5720 *Toll Free Tel:* 800-444-4653 *Fax:* 212-228-5889 *E-mail:* harpers@harpers.org *Web Site:* www.harpers.org, pg 106

Aurand Harris Memorial Playwriting Award, 215 Knob Hill Dr, Hamden, CT 06518 *Tel:* 617-851-8535 *Fax:* 203-288-5938 *E-mail:* mail@netconline.org *Web Site:* www.netconline.org, pg 691

The Joy Harris Literary Agency Inc, 381 Park Ave S, Suite 428, New York, NY 10016 *Tel:* 212-924-6269 *Fax:* 212-725-5275 *E-mail:* contact@jhlitagent.com *Web Site:* www.joyharrisliterary.com, pg 556

Harrison House Publishers, 7498 E 46 Place, Tulsa, OK 74145 *Tel:* 918-523-5700 *Toll Free Tel:* 800-888-4126 *Toll Free Fax:* 800-830-5688 *Web Site:* www.harrisonhouse.com, pg 106

Hartline Literary Agency LLC, 123 Queenston Dr, Pittsburgh, PA 15235 *Web Site:* www.hartlineliterary.com, pg 556

Hartman Publishing Inc, 1313 Iron Ave SW, Albuquerque, NM 87102 *Tel:* 505-291-1274 *Toll Free Tel:* 800-999-9534 *Fax:* 505-291-1284 *Toll Free Fax:* 800-474-6106 *E-mail:* orders@hartmanonline.com; help@hartmanonline.com *Web Site:* www.hartmanonline.com, pg 106

Harvard Art Museums, 32 Quincy St, Cambridge, MA 02138 *Tel:* 617-495-1440; 617-496-6529 (edit) *Fax:* 617-495-9985 *E-mail:* am_shop@harvard.edu *Web Site:* www.harvardartmuseums.org, pg 106

Harvard Business Review Press, 300 N Beacon St, Watertown, MA 02472 *Tel:* 617-783-7400 *Fax:* 617-783-7489 *E-mail:* custserv@hbsp.harvard.edu *Web Site:* www.harvardbusiness.org, pg 106

The Harvard Common Press, 535 Albany St, Boston, MA 02118 *Tel:* 617-423-5803 *Toll Free Tel:* 888-657-3755 *Fax:* 617-695-9794 *E-mail:* orders@harvardcommonpress.com; info@harvardcommonpress.com *Web Site:* www.harvardcommonpress.com, pg 107

Harvard Education Publishing Group, 8 Story St, 1st fl, Cambridge, MA 02138 *Tel:* 617-495-3432 *Toll Free Tel:* 800-513-0763 (subns); 888-437-1437 (orders) *Fax:* 617-496-3584; 978-348-1233 (orders) *E-mail:* hepg@harvard.edu *Web Site:* www.hepg.org, pg 107

Harvard Square Editions, 2152 Beachwood Terr, Hollywood, CA 90068 *Tel:* 323-469-8932 *Fax:* 323-469-8932 *Web Site:* harvardsquareeditions.org, pg 107

Harvard Summer Writing Program, 51 Brattle St, Dept S760, Cambridge, MA 02138-3722 *Tel:* 617-495-4024 *Fax:* 617-495-9176 *E-mail:* summer@hudce.harvard.edu *Web Site:* www.summer.harvard.edu, pg 651

Harvard Ukrainian Research Institute, 34 Kirkland St, Cambridge, MA 02138 *Tel:* 617-495-4053 *Fax:* 617-495-8097 *E-mail:* huri@fas.harvard.edu *Web Site:* www.huri.harvard.edu, pg 107

Harvard University Press, 79 Garden St, Cambridge, MA 02138-1499 *Tel:* 617-495-2600; 401-531-2800 (intl orders) *Toll Free Tel:* 800-405-1619 (orders) *Fax:* 617-495-5898 (general); 617-496-4677 (edit & rts); 401-531-2801 (intl orders) *Toll Free Fax:* 800-406-9145 (orders) *E-mail:* contact_hup@harvard.edu *Web Site:* www.hup.harvard.edu, pg 107

Harvest Hill Press, PO Box 55, Salisbury Cove, ME 04672-0055 *Tel:* 207-288-8900 *E-mail:* shop@harvesthillpress.com *Web Site:* www.harvesthillpress.com, pg 107

Harvest House Publishers Inc, 990 Owen Loop N, Eugene, OR 97402-9173 *Tel:* 541-343-0123 *Toll Free Tel:* 888-501-6991 *Fax:* 541-342-6410 *E-mail:* admin@harvesthousepublishers.com *Web Site:* harvesthousepublishers.com, pg 107

Haskins Medal Award, 104 Mount Auburn St, 5th fl, Cambridge, MA 02138 *Tel:* 617-491-1622 *Fax:* 617-492-3303 *E-mail:* speculum@medievalacademy.org *Web Site:* www.medievalacademy.org, pg 691

Hatherleigh Press Ltd, 62545 State Hwy 10, Hobart, NY 13788 *E-mail:* info@hatherleighpress.com; publicity@hatherleighpress.com *Web Site:* www.hatherleighpress.com, pg 108

John Hawkins and Associates Inc, 71 W 23 St, Suite 1600, New York, NY 10010 *Tel:* 212-807-7040 *E-mail:* jha@jhalit.com *Web Site:* jhalit.com, pg 556

Hay House Inc, 2776 Loker Ave W, Carlsbad, CA 92010 *Tel:* 760-431-7695 (ext 2, intl) *Toll Free Tel:* 800-654-5126 (ext 2, US) *Toll Free Fax:* 800-650-5115 *E-mail:* info@hayhouse.com; editorial@hayhouse.com *Web Site:* www.hayhouse.com, pg 108

Friedrich Hayek Lecture & Book Prize, 52 Vanderbilt Ave, New York, NY 10017 *Tel:* 212-599-7000 *Fax:* 212-599-3494 *Web Site:* www.manhattan-institute.org, pg 691

Haynes Manuals Inc, 861 Lawrence Dr, Newbury Park, CA 91320 *Tel:* 805-498-6703 *Toll Free Tel:* 800-4-HAYNES (442-9637) *Fax:* 805-498-2867 *E-mail:* cstn@haynes.com *Web Site:* www.haynes.com, pg 108

Hazelden Publishing, 15251 Pleasant Valley Rd, Center City, MN 55012-0011 *Tel:* 651-213-4200 *Toll Free Tel:* 800-257-7810 *Fax:* 651-213-4590 *E-mail:* info@hazelden.org *Web Site:* www.hazelden.org, pg 108

HCPro Inc, 75 Sylvan St, Suite A-101, Danvers, MA 01923 *Toll Free Tel:* 800-650-6787 *Toll Free Fax:* 800-785-9212 *E-mail:* customerservice@hcpro.com *Web Site:* www.hcpro.com, pg 108

Headlands Center for the Arts Residency for Writers, 944 Fort Barry, Sausalito, CA 94965 *Tel:* 415-331-2787 *Fax:* 415-331-3857 *Web Site:* www.headlands.org, pg 691

Health Administration Press, One N Franklin St, Suite 1700, Chicago, IL 60606-3491 *Tel:* 312-424-2800 *Fax:* 312-424-0014 *E-mail:* hap1@ache.org *Web Site:* www.ache.org/publications (orders), pg 108

Health Communications Inc, 3201 SW 15 St, Deerfield Beach, FL 33442 *Tel:* 954-360-0909 *Toll Free Tel:* 800-851-9100; 800-441-5569 (cust serv & orders) *Fax:* 954-360-0034 *Toll Free Fax:* 800-424-7652 (cust serv & orders) *Web Site:* www.hcibooks.com, pg 108

Health Forum Inc, 155 N Wacker Dr, Suite 400, Chicago, IL 60606 *Tel:* 312-893-6800 *Toll Free Tel:* 800-242-2626 *Fax:* 312-422-4500 *E-mail:* hfcustsvc@healthforum.com *Web Site:* www.ahaonlinestore.com; www.healthforum.com, pg 109

Health Professions Press, 409 Washington Ave, Suite 500, Towson, MD 21204 *Tel:* 410-337-9585 *Toll Free Tel:* 888-337-8808 *Fax:* 410-337-8539 *E-mail:* custserv@healthpropress.com *Web Site:* www.healthpropress.com, pg 109

Health Research Books, 62 Seventh St, Pomeroy, WA 99347 *Tel:* 509-843-2385 *Toll Free Tel:* 888-844-2386 *Fax:* 509-843-2387 *E-mail:* publish@pomeroy-wa.com *Web Site:* www.healthresearchbooks.com, pg 109

Heart and Mind Press LLC, 3135 E Palo Verde Dr, Phoenix, AZ 85016 *Tel:* 602-790-4009 *E-mail:* info@heartandmindpress.com *Web Site:* heartandmindpress.com, pg 507

Heartland Prize, 435 N Michigan Ave, Suite 1100, Chicago, IL 60611, pg 691

HeartMath LLC, 14700 W Park Ave, Boulder Creek, CA 95006 *Tel:* 831-338-8700 *Toll Free Tel:* 800-450-9111 *Fax:* 831-338-9861 *E-mail:* inquiry@heartmath.com *Web Site:* www.heartmath.com, pg 109

Hearts & Tummies Cookbook Co, 3544 Blakslee St, Wever, IA 52658 *Tel:* 319-372-7480 *Toll Free Tel:* 800-571-2665 *Fax:* 319-372-7485 *E-mail:* quixotepress@gmail.com; heartsntummies@gmail.com *Web Site:* www.heartsntummies.com, pg 109

Anne Hebenstreit, 20 Tip Top Way, Berkeley Heights, NJ 07922 *Tel:* 908-665-0536, pg 527

Hebrew Union College Press, 3101 Clifton Ave, Cincinnati, OH 45220 *Tel:* 513-221-1875 *Fax:* 513-221-0321 *Web Site:* press.huc.edu, pg 109

Hedgebrook Master Class Retreat Series, PO Box 1231, Freeland, WA 98249 *Tel:* 360-321-4786 *Fax:* 360-321-2171 *E-mail:* hedgebrook@hedgebrook.org *Web Site:* www.hedgebrook.org; www.facebook.com/hedgebrook, pg 651

Hedgebrook VORTEXT, PO Box 1231, Freeland, WA 98249 *Tel:* 360-321-4786 *Fax:* 360-321-2171 *E-mail:* hedgebrook@hedgebrook.org *Web Site:* www.hedgebrook.org; www.facebook.com/hedgebrook, pg 651

Hedgebrook Winter Salon, PO Box 1231, Freeland, WA 98249 *Tel:* 360-321-4786 *Fax:* 360-321-2171 *E-mail:* hedgebrook@hedgebrook.org *Web Site:* www.hedgebrook.org; www.facebook.com/hedgebrook, pg 651

Hedgebrook Writers in Residence Program, PO Box 1231, Freeland, WA 98249 *Tel:* 360-321-4786 *Fax:* 360-321-2171 *E-mail:* hedgebrook@hedgebrook.org *Web Site:* www.hedgebrook.org; www.facebook.com/hedgebrook, pg 651

Heian, 1393 Solono Ave, Albany, CA 94706 *Tel:* 510-524-8732 *Toll Free Fax:* 888-411-8527 *E-mail:* sbp@stonebridge.com *Web Site:* www.stonebridge.com, pg 109

Heimburger House Publishing Co, 7236 W Madison St, Forest Park, IL 60130 *Tel:* 708-366-1973 *Fax:* 708-366-1973 *E-mail:* info@heimburgerhouse.com *Web Site:* www.heimburgerhouse.com, pg 109

William S Hein & Co Inc, 2350 N Forest Rd, Getzville, NY 14068 *Tel:* 716-882-2600 *Toll Free Tel:* 800-828-7571 *Fax:* 716-883-8100 *E-mail:* mail@wshein.com; marketing@wshein.com *Web Site:* www.wshein.com, pg 109

Heinemann, 361 Hanover St, Portsmouth, NH 03801-3912 *Tel:* 603-431-7894 *Toll Free Tel:* 800-225-5800 (US) *Fax:* 603-431-2214 *Toll Free Fax:* 877-231-6980 (US) *E-mail:* custserv@heinemann.com *Web Site:* www.heinemann.com, pg 110

Drue Heinz Literature Prize, 7500 Thomas Blvd, Pittsburgh, PA 15260 *Tel:* 412-383-2456 *Fax:* 412-383-2466 *E-mail:* info@upress.pitt.edu *Web Site:* www.upress.pitt.edu, pg 691

Hellgate Press, PO Box 3531, Ashland, OR 97520 *Tel:* 541-973-5154 *Toll Free Tel:* 800-795-4059 *E-mail:* sales@hellgatepress.com *Web Site:* www.hellgatepress.com, pg 110

Helm Book Publishing, 3437 Huntington Place Dr, Sarasota, FL 34237 *Tel:* 727-623-5014 *Web Site:* www.helmbookpublishing.com, pg 110

Helm Editorial Services, 707 SW Eighth Way, Fort Lauderdale, FL 33315 *Tel:* 954-525-5626 *E-mail:* lynnehelm12@aol.com, pg 527

The Hemingway Foundation/PEN Award, MIT, 14N-221A, 77 Massachusetts Ave, Cambridge, MA 02139 *Tel:* 617-324-1729 *E-mail:* pen-newengland@mit.edu *Web Site:* www.pen-ne.org, pg 692

Cecil Hemley Memorial Award, 15 Gramercy Park, New York, NY 10003 *Tel:* 212-254-9628 *Fax:* 212-673-2352 *Web Site:* www.poetrysociety.org, pg 692

Hendrickson Publishers Inc, PO Box 3473, Peabody, MA 01961-3473 *Tel:* 978-532-6546 *Toll Free Tel:* 800-358-3111 *Fax:* 978-573-8111 *E-mail:* orders@hendrickson.com *Web Site:* www.hendrickson.com, pg 110

Henrico Theatre Company One-Act Playwriting Competition, PO Box 90775, Richmond, VA 23273-0775 *Tel:* 804-501-5138 *Fax:* 804-501-5284, pg 692

Her Own Words LLC, PO Box 5264, Madison, WI 53705-0264 *Tel:* 608-271-7083 *Fax:* 608-271-0209 *Web Site:* www.herownwords.com; www.nontraditionalcareers.com, pg 110

Herald Press, 1251 Virginia Ave, Harrisonburg, VA 22802-2434 *Toll Free Tel:* 800-245-7894 (orders-US); 800-631-6535 (orders-CN) *Toll Free Fax:* 877-271-0760 *E-mail:* info@MennoMedia.org *Web Site:* www.heraldpress.com; store.mennomedia.org, pg 110

Herald Press, 50 Kent Ave, Suite 204, Kitchener, ON N2G 3R1, Canada *Tel:* 519-747-5722 (US) *Toll Free Tel:* 800-631-6535 (CN) *Fax:* 519-747-5721 *E-mail:* hpcan@mpn.net *Web Site:* www.heraldpress.com, pg 487

Herald Publishing House, 1001 W Walnut St, Independence, MO 64051 *Tel:* 816-521-3015 *Toll Free Tel:* 800-767-8181 *Fax:* 816-521-3066 *E-mail:* sales@heraldhouse.org *Web Site:* www.heraldhouse.org, pg 110

Heritage Books Inc, 5810 Ruatan St, Berwyn Heights, MD 20740 *Toll Free Tel:* 800-876-6103 *Toll Free Fax:* 800-876-6103 *E-mail:* orders@heritagebooks.com; submissions@heritagebooks.com *Web Site:* www.heritagebooks.com, pg 110

The Heritage Foundation, 214 Massachusetts Ave NE, Washington, DC 20002-4999 *Tel:* 202-546-4400 *Toll Free Tel:* 800-544-4843 *Fax:* 202-546-8328 *E-mail:* info@heritage.org *Web Site:* www.heritage.org, pg 110, 623

Heritage House Publishing Co Ltd, 1075 Pendergast St, No 103, Victoria, BC V8V 0A1, Canada *Tel:* 250-360-0829 *Fax:* 250-386-0829 *E-mail:* heritage@heritagehouse.ca *Web Site:* www.heritagehouse.ca, pg 487

Herman Agency, 350 Central Park W, Apt 4I, New York, NY 10025 *Tel:* 212-749-4907 *Web Site:* www.hermanagencyinc.com, pg 583

The Jeff Herman Agency LLC, 29 Park St, Stockbridge, MA 01262 *Tel:* 413-298-0077 *Fax:* 413-298-8188 *E-mail:* submissions@jeffherman.com *Web Site:* www.jeffherman.com, pg 556

Brodie Herndon Memorial, 1194 Hume Rd, Hume, VA 22639-1806 *E-mail:* poetryinva@aol.com *Web Site:* www.poetrysocietyofvirginia.org, pg 692

Susan Herner Rights Agency Inc, 10 Upper Shad Rd, Pound Ridge, NY 10576 *Tel:* 914-234-2864 *Fax:* 914-234-2866 *E-mail:* sherneragency@optonline.net, pg 556

Herr's Indexing Service, 76-340 Kealoha St, Kailua Kona, HI 96740 *Tel:* 808-365-4348 *E-mail:* lindahallinger@gmail.com *Web Site:* www.herrsindexing.com, pg 527

Carl Hertzog Award for Excellence in Book Design, c/o Dir of the Library, University of Texas at El Paso, University Library, El Paso, TX 79968-0582 *Tel:* 915-747-5683 *Fax:* 915-747-5345 *Web Site:* libraryweb.utep.edu/about/hertzog_call.php, pg 692

Heuer Publishing LLC, PO Box 248, Cedar Rapids, IA 52406 *Tel:* 319-368-8008 *Toll Free Tel:* 800-950-7529 *Fax:* 319-368-8011 *E-mail:* editor@hitplays.com; customerservice@hitplays.com *Web Site:* www.hitplays.com, pg 110

Les Heures bleues, 560 Mercier, St-Lambert, QC J4P 1Z5, Canada *Tel:* 450-671-7718 *Fax:* 450-671-7718 *E-mail:* info@heuresbleues.com *Web Site:* www.heuresbleues.com, pg 488

Hewitt Homeschooling Resources, 2103 Main St, Washougal, WA 98671 *Tel:* 360-835-8708 *Toll Free Tel:* 800-348-1750 *Fax:* 360-835-8697 *E-mail:* sales@hewitthomeschooling.com *Web Site:* hewitthomeschooling.com, pg 111

Heyday Books, 1633 University Ave, Berkeley, CA 94703 *Tel:* 510-549-3564 *Fax:* 510-549-1889 *E-mail:* heyday@heydaybooks.com; orders@heydaybooks.com *Web Site:* heydaybooks.com, pg 111

Hi Willow Research & Publishing, 123 E Second Ave, Suite 1106, Salt Lake City, UT 84103 *Tel:* 801-532-1165 *E-mail:* sales@lmcsource.com *Web Site:* www.lmcsource.com; www.davidvl.org, pg 111

Hidden River Arts Playwriting Award, PO Box 63927, Philadelphia, PA 19147 *Tel:* 610-764-0813 *E-mail:* hiddenriverarts@gmail.com *Web Site:* www.hiddenriverarts.org, pg 692

Higginson Book Co, 10 Colonial Rd, Salem, MA 01970 *Tel:* 978-745-7170 *Fax:* 978-745-8025 *Web Site:* www.higginsonbooks.com, pg 111

High Plains Press, PO Box 123, Glendo, WY 82213 *Toll Free Tel:* 800-552-7819 *Fax:* 307-735-4590 *E-mail:* editor@highplainspress.com *Web Site:* highplainspress.com, pg 111

High Tide Press, 301 Veterans Pkwy, New Lenox, IL 60451 *Web Site:* cherryhillhightide.com/high-tide-press/, pg 111

Highland Summer Writers' Conference, PO Box 7014, Radford University, Radford, VA 24142 *Tel:* 540-831-5366; 540-831-6152 *Fax:* 540-831-5951 *Web Site:* www.radford.edu/~arsc, pg 651

Highlights for Children, 1800 Watermark Dr, Columbus, OH 43215 *Tel:* 614-486-0631 *Toll Free Tel:* 800-962-3661 (Highlights Club cust serv); 800-255-9517 (Highlights Magazine cust serv) *Web Site:* www.highlights.com, pg 111

Highlights for Children Fiction Contest, 803 Church St, Honesdale, PA 18431 *Tel:* 570-253-1080 *Fax:* 570-251-7847 *E-mail:* eds@highlights.com *Web Site:* www.highlights.com, pg 692

Hill & Wang, 18 W 18 St, New York, NY 10011 *Tel:* 212-741-6900 *Fax:* 212-633-9385 *E-mail:* fsg.publicity@fsgbooks.com; fsg.editorial@fsgbooks.com; sales@fsgbooks.com *Web Site:* us.macmillan.com/hillandwang.aspx, pg 111

Hill Nadell Literary Agency, 8899 Beverly Blvd, Suite 805, Los Angeles, CA 90048 *Tel:* 310-860-9605 *Fax:* 310-860-9672 *E-mail:* queries@hillnadell.com; rights@hillnadell.com (rts & perms) *Web Site:* www.hillnadell.com, pg 556

The Tony Hillerman Prize, 1063 Willow Way, Santa Fe, NM 87507 *Tel:* 505-471-1565 *E-mail:* wordharvest@wordharvest.com *Web Site:* www.wordharvest.com, pg 692

Hillman Prizes in Journalism, 12 W 31 St, 12th fl, New York, NY 10001 *Tel:* 646-448-6413 *Web Site:* www.hillmanfoundation.org, pg 692

Hillsdale College Press, 33 E College St, Hillsdale, MI 49242 *Tel:* 517-437-7341 *Toll Free Tel:* 800-437-2268 *Fax:* 517-437-3923 *E-mail:* news@hillsdale.edu *Web Site:* www.hillsdale.edu, pg 111

Hillsdale Educational Publishers Inc, 39 North St, Hillsdale, MI 49242 *Tel:* 517-437-3179 *Fax:* 517-437-0531 *E-mail:* davestory@aol.com *Web Site:* www.hillsdalepublishers.com; michbooks.com, pg 111

Hilton Publishing, 1630 45 St, Suite 103, Munster, IN 46321 *Tel:* 219-922-4868 *Fax:* 219-924-6811 *E-mail:* info@hiltonpub.com; orders@hiltonpub.com *Web Site:* www.hiltonpub.com, pg 111

Himalayan Institute Press, 952 Bethany Tpke, Honesdale, PA 18431 *Tel:* 570-253-5551 *Toll Free Tel:* 800-822-4547 *E-mail:* info@himalayaninstitute.org *Web Site:* www.himalayaninstitute.org, pg 112

Hippocrene Books Inc, 171 Madison Ave, New York, NY 10016 *Tel:* 212-685-4373 *Fax:* 212-779-9338 *E-mail:* info@hippocrenebooks.com; orderdept@hippocrenebooks.com (orders) *Web Site:* www.hippocrenebooks.com, pg 112

L Anne Hirschel DDS, 5990 Highgate Ave, East Lansing, MI 48823 *Tel:* 517-333-1748 *E-mail:* alicerichard@comcast.net, pg 527

The Historic New Orleans Collection, 533 Royal St, New Orleans, LA 70130 *Tel:* 504-523-4662 *Fax:* 504-598-7108 *E-mail:* wrc@hnoc.org *Web Site:* www.hnoc.org, pg 112

Historical Novel Society North American Conference, 400 Dark Star Ct, Fairbanks, AK 99709 *Tel:* 217-581-7538 *Fax:* 217-581-7534 *Web Site:* www.historicalnovelsociety.org, pg 651

History Publishing Co LLC, PO Box 700, Palisades, NY 10964 *Tel:* 845-398-8161 *E-mail:* info@historypublishingco.com *Web Site:* www.historypublishingco.com, pg 112

W D Hoard & Sons Co, 28 W Milwaukee Ave, Fort Atkinson, WI 53538 *Tel:* 920-563-5551 *Fax:* 920-563-7298 *E-mail:* hdbooks@hoards.com; editors@hoards.com *Web Site:* www.hoards.com; www.hoardprinting.com, pg 112

Hobar Publications, 5995 149 St W, Suite 105, Apple Valley, MN 55124 *Tel:* 952-469-6699 *Toll Free Tel:* 800-846-7027 *Fax:* 952-469-1968 *Toll Free Fax:* 800-330-6232 *E-mail:* info@finneyco.com *Web Site:* www.finney-hobar.com, pg 112

Hobbes End Publishing LLC, PO Box 193, Aubrey, TX 76227 *Web Site:* hobbesendpublishing.com, pg 112

Hobblebush Books, 17-A Old Milford Rd, Brookline, NH 03033 *Tel:* 603-672-4317 *Fax:* 603-672-4317 *E-mail:* hobblebush@charter.net; info@hobblebush.com *Web Site:* www.hobblebush.com, pg 112

Eric Hoffer Award for Independent Books, PO Box 11, Titusville, NJ 08560 *Fax:* 609-964-1718 *E-mail:* info@hofferaward.com *Web Site:* www.hofferaward.com, pg 692

Eric Hoffer Award for Short Prose, PO Box 11, Titusville, NJ 08560 *Fax:* 609-964-1718 *E-mail:* info@hofferaward.com *Web Site:* www.hofferaward.com, pg 692

Hofstra University, English Dept, 204 Mason Hall, Hempstead, NY 11549 *Tel:* 516-463-5454 *Web Site:* www.hofstra.edu, pg 660

The Barbara Hogenson Agency Inc, 165 West End Ave, Suite 19-C, New York, NY 10023 *Tel:* 212-874-8084 *Fax:* 212-595-6748 *E-mail:* bhogenson@aol.com, pg 557

Hogrefe Publishing, 38 Chauncy St, Suite 1002, Boston, MA 02111 *Toll Free Tel:* 866-823-4726 *Fax:* 617-354-6875 *E-mail:* publishing@hogrefe.com *Web Site:* www.hogrefe.com, pg 112

Hohm Press, PO Box 4410, Chino Valley, AZ 86323 *Tel:* 928-636-3331 *Toll Free Tel:* 800-381-2700 *Fax:* 928-636-7519 *E-mail:* hppublisher@cableone.net; hohmpresseditor@gmail.com *Web Site:* www.hohmpress.com, pg 113

Bess Hokin Prize, 444 N Michigan Ave, Suite 1850, Chicago, IL 60611-4034 *Tel:* 312-787-7070 *Fax:* 312-787-6650 *E-mail:* editors@poetrymagazine.org *Web Site:* www.poetryfoundation.org, pg 692

Holiday House Inc, 425 Madison Ave, New York, NY 10017 *Tel:* 212-688-0085 *Fax:* 212-421-6134 *E-mail:* holiday@holidayhouse.com *Web Site:* www.holidayhouse.com, pg 113

Hollins University-Jackson Center for Creative Writing, PO Box 9677, Roanoke, VA 24020 *Tel:* 540-362-6317 *Fax:* 540-362-6097 *E-mail:* creative.writing@hollins.edu *Web Site:* www.hollins.edu, pg 660

Hollym International Corp, 18 Donald Place, Elizabeth, NJ 07208 *Tel:* 908-353-1655 *Fax:* 908-353-0255 *E-mail:* contact@hollym.com *Web Site:* www.hollym.com, pg 113

Hollywood Film Archive, 8391 Beverly Blvd, Los Angeles, CA 90048 *Tel:* 323-655-4968 *Web Site:* hfarchive.com, pg 113

Burnham Holmes, 182 Lakeview Hill Rd, Poultney, VT 05764-9179 *Tel:* 802-287-9707 *Fax:* 802-287-9707 (computer fax/modem) *E-mail:* burnham.holmes@castleton.edu, pg 527

Henry Holmes Literary Agent/Book Publicist/Marketing Consultant, PO Box 433, Swansea, MA 02777 *Tel:* 508-672-2258 *E-mail:* henryholmesandassociates@yahoo.com, pg 527, 557

Holmes Publishing Group LLC, PO Box 2370, Sequim, WA 98382 *Tel:* 360-681-2900 *E-mail:* holmespub@fastmail.fm *Web Site:* www.jdholmes.com, pg 113

Henry Holt and Company, LLC, 175 Fifth Ave, New York, NY 10010 *Tel:* 646-307-5151 *Toll Free Tel:* 888-330-8477 (orders) *Fax:* 646-307-5285 *E-mail:* firstname.lastname@hholt.com *Web Site:* www.henryholt.com, pg 113

Holy Cow! Press, PO Box 3170, Mount Royal Sta, Duluth, MN 55803 *Tel:* 218-724-1653 *E-mail:* holycow@holycowpress.org *Web Site:* www.holycowpress.org, pg 113

Holy Cross Orthodox Press, 50 Goddard Ave, Brookline, MA 02445 *Tel:* 617-731-3500; 617-850-1200 *Fax:* 617-850-1460 *E-mail:* info@hchc.edu *Web Site:* www.hchc.edu, pg 114

Homa & Sekey Books, 140 E Ridgewood Ave, Paramus, NJ 07652 *Tel:* 201-261-8810 *Toll Free Tel:* 800-870-HOMA (870-4662 orders) *Fax:* 201-261-8890 *E-mail:* info@homabooks.com *Web Site:* www.homabooks.com, pg 114

Homestead Publishing, Box 193, Moose, WY 83012-0193 *Tel:* 307-733-6248 *Fax:* 307-733-6248 *E-mail:* orders@homesteadpublishing.net *Web Site:* www.homesteadpublishing.net, pg 114

Honickman First Book Prize, University of the Arts (UARTS), Hamilton Hall, 320 S Broad St, Rm 313, Philadelphia, PA 19102-4901 *Tel:* 215-717-6801 *Fax:* 215-717-6805 *Web Site:* www.aprweb.org, pg 692

Hoover Institution Press, Stanford University, 434 Galvez Mall, Stanford, CA 94305-6003 *Tel:* 650-725-7146; 650-723-3373 *Toll Free Tel:* 800-935-2882 *Fax:* 650-723-8626 *E-mail:* hooverpress@stanford.edu *Web Site:* www.hoover.org; www.hooverpress.org, pg 114

Hoover's Inc, 5800 Airport Blvd, Austin, TX 78752 *Tel:* 512-374-4500 *Toll Free Tel:* 866-486-8666 *Fax:* 512-374-4501 *Web Site:* www.hoovers.com, pg 114

Hope Publishing Co, 380 S Main Place, Carol Stream, IL 60188 *Tel:* 630-665-3200 *Toll Free Tel:* 800-323-1049 *Fax:* 630-665-2552 *E-mail:* hope@hopepublishing.com *Web Site:* www.hopepublishing.com, pg 114

Hope Street Publishing, PO Box 2705, Philadelphia, PA 19120 *E-mail:* contact@hopestreetpublishing.com *Web Site:* www.hopestreetpublishing.com, pg 114

Horizon Publishers & Distributors Inc, 191 N 650 E, Bountiful, UT 84010-3628 *Tel:* 801-292-7102 *E-mail:* ldshorizonpublishers1@gmail.com *Web Site:* www.ldshorizonpublishers.com, pg 114

Hornfischer Literary Management LP, PO Box 50544, Austin, TX 78763 *Tel:* 512-472-0011 *E-mail:* queries@hornfischerlit.com *Web Site:* www.hornfischerlit.com, pg 557

Horror Writers Association (HWA), 244 Fifth Ave, Suite 2767, New York, NY 10001 *E-mail:* hwa@horror.org *Web Site:* horror.org, pg 606

Hospital & Healthcare Compensation Service, 3 Post Rd, Suite 3, Oakland, NJ 07436 *Tel:* 201-405-0075 *Fax:* 201-405-2110 *E-mail:* allinfo@hhcsinc.com *Web Site:* www.hhcsinc.com, pg 114

Host Publications, 3408 West Ave, Austin, TX 78705 *Tel:* 512-236-1290 *Fax:* 512-236-1208 *Web Site:* www.hostpublications.com, pg 114

Firman Houghton Prize, 2 Farrar St, Cambridge, MA 02138 *Tel:* 617-744-6034 *E-mail:* contests@nepoetryclub.org *Web Site:* www.nepoetryclub.org, pg 693

Houghton Mifflin Harcourt, 222 Berkeley St, Boston, MA 02116 *Tel:* 617-351-5000 *Toll Free Tel:* 800-225-5425 (K-12 educ materials); 800-323-9540 (assessment materials); 877-219-1537 (SkillsTutor); 888-242-6747 (Destination; Earobics; Edmark; Learning Village; Riverdeep); 800-225-3362 (Houghton Mifflin Harcourt Trade & Reference Publishers) *Toll Free Fax:* 800-269-5232 *E-mail:* customerservice@hmhpub.com *Web Site:* www.hmhco.com, pg 114

Houghton Mifflin Harcourt K-12 Publishers, 222 Berkeley St, Boston, MA 02116 *Tel:* 617-351-5000 *Toll Free Tel:* 800-225-5425 (cust serv) *Web Site:* www.hmhco.com/educators; www.hmhco.com, pg 115

Houghton Mifflin Harcourt School Publishers, 9205 Southport Center Loop, Orlando, FL 32819 *Tel:* 407-345-2000 *Toll Free Tel:* 800-225-5425 (cust serv)

Fax: 407-345-3016 (cust serv) *Toll Free Fax:* 800-874-6418; 800-269-5232 (cust serv) *Web Site:* www.hmhco.com, pg 115

Houghton Mifflin Harcourt Trade & Reference Division, 222 Berkeley St, Boston, MA 02116 *Tel:* 617-351-5000 *Toll Free Tel:* 800-225-3362 *Web Site:* www.hmhco.com, pg 115

House of Anansi Press Inc, 110 Spadina Ave, Suite 801, Toronto, ON M5V 2K4, Canada *Tel:* 416-363-4343 *Fax:* 416-363-1017 *E-mail:* customerservice@houseofanansi.com *Web Site:* www.houseofanansi.com, pg 488

House of Collectibles, 1745 Broadway, New York, NY 10019 *Tel:* 212-782-9000 *Web Site:* www.houseofcollectibles.randomhouse.com; www.randomhouse.com, pg 116

House to House Publications, 11 Toll Gate Rd, Lititz, PA 17543 *Tel:* 717-627-1996 *Toll Free Tel:* 800-848-5892 *Fax:* 717-627-4004 *E-mail:* h2hp@dcfi.org *Web Site:* www.dcfi.org, pg 116

Housing Assistance Council, 1025 Vermont Ave NW, Suite 606, Washington, DC 20005 *Tel:* 202-842-8600 *Fax:* 202-347-3441 *E-mail:* hac@ruralhome.org *Web Site:* www.ruralhome.org, pg 116

How to be Published Workshops, c/o Creative Inspirations Inc, PO Box 362, Clay, AL 35048 *E-mail:* mgteach352@gmail.com *Web Site:* www.writing2sell.com, pg 652

Howard Books, 216 Centerview Dr, Suite 303, Brentwood, TN 37027 *Tel:* 615-873-2080 *Fax:* 615-370-3834 *E-mail:* howardbooks@simonandschuster.com (info) *Web Site:* www.howardpublishing.com, pg 116

Amelia Frances Howard-Gibbon Illustrator's Award, 1150 Morrison Dr, Suite 400, Ottawa, ON K2H 8S9, Canada *Tel:* 613-232-9625 *Fax:* 613-563-9895 *E-mail:* info@cla.ca *Web Site:* www.cla.ca, pg 693

Tom Howard/John H Reid Fiction & Essay Contest, 351 Pleasant St, PMB 222, Northampton, MA 01060-3961 *Tel:* 413-320-1847 *Toll Free Tel:* 866-WINWRIT (946-9748) *Fax:* 413-280-0539 *Web Site:* www.winningwriters.com, pg 693

Tom Howard/Margaret Reid Poetry Contest, 351 Pleasant St, PMB 222, Northampton, MA 01060-3961 *Tel:* 413-320-1847 *Toll Free Tel:* 866-WINWRIT (946-9748) *Fax:* 413-280-0539 *Web Site:* www.winningwriters.com, pg 693

C D Howe Institute, 67 Yonge St, Suite 300, Toronto, ON M5E 1J8, Canada *Tel:* 416-865-1904 *Fax:* 416-865-1866 *E-mail:* cdhowe@cdhowe.org *Web Site:* www.cdhowe.org, pg 488

Julia Ward Howe Book Awards, 33 Brayton Rd, Brighton, MA 02135 *Tel:* 617-783-1357 *E-mail:* bostonauthors@aol.com *Web Site:* www.bostonauthorsclub.org, pg 693

The William Dean Howells Medal, 633 W 155 St, New York, NY 10032 *Tel:* 212-368-5900 *Fax:* 212-491-4615 *E-mail:* academy@artsandletters.org *Web Site:* www.artsandletters.org, pg 693

HPBooks, 375 Hudson St, New York, NY 10014 *Tel:* 212-366-2000 *E-mail:* online@penguinputnam.com *Web Site:* www.penguinputnam.com; us.penguingroup.com, pg 116

HRD Press, 22 Amherst Rd, Amherst, MA 01002-9709 *Tel:* 413-253-3488 *Toll Free Tel:* 800-822-2801 *Fax:* 413-253-3490 *E-mail:* info@hrdpress.com; customerservice@hrdpress.com *Web Site:* www.hrdpress.com, pg 116

L Ron Hubbard's Writers of the Future Contest, PO Box 1630, Los Angeles, CA 90078 *Tel:* 323-466-3310 *Fax:* 323-466-6474 *E-mail:* contests@authorservicesinc.com *Web Site:* www.writersofthefuture.com, pg 693

Hudson Hills Press LLC, 116 Pleasant St, Suite 049, Easthampton, MA 01027 *Tel:* 413-527-6450 *E-mail:* artbooks@hudsonhills.com; editorial@hudsonhills.com (submissions) *Web Site:* www.hudsonhills.com, pg 116

Hudson Institute, 1015 15 St NW, 6th fl, Washington, DC 20005 *Tel:* 202-974-2400 *Fax:* 202-974-2410 *E-mail:* info@hudson.org *Web Site:* www.hudson.org, pg 116

Monica Hughes Award for Science Fiction & Fantasy, 40 Orchard View Blvd, Suite 217, Toronto, ON M4R 1B9, Canada *Tel:* 416-975-0010 *Fax:* 416-975-8970 *E-mail:* info@bookcentre.ca *Web Site:* www.bookcentre.ca, pg 693

Lynda Hull Memorial Poetry Prize, College of Charleston, Dept of English, 66 George St, Charleston, SC 29424 *Tel:* 843-953-7740 *Fax:* 843-953-7740 *E-mail:* crazyhorse@cofc.edu *Web Site:* crazyhorse.cofc.edu/prizes, pg 693

Human Kinetics Inc, 1607 N Market St, Champaign, IL 61820 *Tel:* 217-351-5076 *Toll Free Tel:* 800-747-4457 *Fax:* 217-351-1549 (orders/cust serv) *E-mail:* info@hkusa.com *Web Site:* www.humankinetics.com, pg 116

Human Rights Watch, 350 Fifth Ave, 34th fl, New York, NY 10118-3299 *Tel:* 212-290-4700 *Fax:* 212-736-1300 *E-mail:* hrwnyc@hrw.org *Web Site:* www.hrw.org, pg 117

Humanix Books LLC, PO Box 20989, West Palm Beach, FL 33416 *Tel:* 561-459-5997 *Toll Free Tel:* 855-371-7810 *Fax:* 561-241-6448 *Toll Free Fax:* 855-371-7809 *E-mail:* info@humanixbooks.com *Web Site:* www.humanixbooks.com, pg 117

Hunter Publishing Inc, 222 Clematis St, West Palm Beach, FL 33401 *Tel:* 561-835-2022 *Web Site:* guidestotheworld.com, pg 117

Huntington Library Press, 1151 Oxford Rd, San Marino, CA 91108 *Tel:* 626-405-2172 *Fax:* 626-585-0794 *E-mail:* booksales@huntington.org *Web Site:* www.huntington.org, pg 117

Huntington Press Publishing, 3665 Procyon St, Las Vegas, NV 89103-1907 *Tel:* 702-252-0655 *Toll Free Tel:* 800-244-2224 *Fax:* 702-252-0675 *E-mail:* sales@huntingtonpress.com *Web Site:* www.huntingtonpress.com, pg 117

Hurston/Wright Award for College Writers, 12138 Central Ave, Suite 209, Bowie, MD 20721 *Tel:* 301-459-2108 *Fax:* 301-277-1262 *E-mail:* info@hurstonwright.org *Web Site:* www.hurstonwright.org, pg 693

Hurston/Wright Legacy Awards, 12138 Central Ave, Suite 209, Bowie, MD 20721 *Tel:* 301-459-2108 *Fax:* 301-277-1262 *E-mail:* info@hurstonwright.org *Web Site:* www.hurstonwright.org, pg 693

Hurston/Wright Writer's Week, 12138 Central Ave, Suite 209, Bowie, MD 20721 *Tel:* 301-459-2108 *Fax:* 301-277-1262 *E-mail:* info@hurstonwright.org *Web Site:* www.hurstonwright.org, pg 652

Hutton Publishing, 140D Heritage Village, Southbury, CT 06488 *Tel:* 203-558-4478 *E-mail:* huttonbooks@hotmail.com *Web Site:* www.huttonpublishing.com, pg 117

I-5 Publishing LLC, 3 Burroughs, Irvine, CA 92618 *Tel:* 949-855-8822 *Toll Free Tel:* 888-738-2665 *Fax:* 949-458-3856 *Web Site:* www.i5publishing.com, pg 117

IACP Cookbook Awards, 1221 Avenue of the Americas, 42nd fl, New York, NY 10020 *Tel:* 646-358-4957 *Toll Free Tel:* 866-358-4951 *Toll Free Fax:* 866-358-2524 *E-mail:* info@iacp.com *Web Site:* www.iacp.com, pg 694

Ibex Publishers, PO Box 30087, Bethesda, MD 20824 *Tel:* 301-718-8188 *Toll Free Tel:* 888-718-8188 *Fax:* 301-907-8707 *E-mail:* info@ibexpub.com *Web Site:* www.ibexpublishers.com, pg 117

IBFD North America Inc (International Bureau of Fiscal Documentation), 8100 Boone Blvd, Suite 210, Vienna, VA 22182 *Tel:* 703-442-7757 *Fax:* 703-442-7758 *Web Site:* www.ibfd.org, pg 118

The Ibsen Society of America, University of California, Dept of Scandinavian, 6303 Dwinelle Hall, No 2690, Berkeley, CA 94720-2690 *Tel:* 510-642-4484 *Fax:* 510-642-6220 *Web Site:* www.ibsensociety.liu.edu, pg 607

ICM Lecture Division, 730 Fifth Ave, New York, NY 10019 *Tel:* 212-556-5600 *Fax:* 212-556-5665 *Web Site:* www.icmtalent.com, pg 587

ICM Partners, 730 Fifth Ave, New York, NY 10019 *Tel:* 212-556-5600 *Web Site:* www.icmtalent.com, pg 557

ICM/Sagalyn, 1250 Connecticut Ave, 7th fl, Washington, DC 20036 *Tel:* 202-419-1525 *E-mail:* query@sagalyn.com *Web Site:* www.sagalyn.com, pg 557

Iconografix Inc, 2017 O'Neil Rd, Hudson, WI 54016 *Tel:* 715-381-9755 *Toll Free Tel:* 800-289-3504 (orders only) *Fax:* 715-381-9756 *E-mail:* info@iconografixinc.com *Web Site:* www.iconografixinc.com, pg 118

Idaho Center for the Book, Boise State University, 1910 University Dr, Boise, ID 83725 *Tel:* 208-426-1000 *Toll Free Tel:* 800-992-8398 (outside ID) *Web Site:* www.boisestatebooks.com (orders), pg 118

The Idaho Prize for Poetry, 105 Lost Horse Lane, Sandpoint, ID 83864 *Tel:* 208-255-4410 *Fax:* 208-255-1560 *E-mail:* losthorsepress@mindspring.com *Web Site:* www.losthorsepress.org, pg 694

IDEAlliance®, 1600 Duke St, Suite 420, Alexandria, VA 22314 *Tel:* 703-837-1070 *Fax:* 703-837-1072 *E-mail:* registrar@idealliance.org *Web Site:* www.idealliance.org, pg 607

Ideals Publications, a Guideposts Co, 6100 Tower Circle, Suite 210, Franklin, TN 37067 *Tel:* 615-932-7600 *Toll Free Tel:* 800-586-2572 (cust serv) *Fax:* 615-781-1447 *Web Site:* www.idealsbooks.com, pg 118

Idyll Arbor Inc, 39129 264 Ave SE, Enumclaw, WA 98022 *Tel:* 360-825-7797 *Fax:* 360-825-5670 *E-mail:* sales@idyllarbor.com *Web Site:* www.idyllarbor.com, pg 118

Idyllwild Arts Summer Workshops, 52500 Temecula Dr, Idyllwild, CA 92549-0038 *Tel:* 951-659-2171 *Fax:* 951-659-4552 *E-mail:* summer@idyllwildarts.org *Web Site:* www.idyllwildarts.org/writersweek, pg 652

IEEE Computer Society, 2001 "L" St NW, Suite 700, Washington, DC 20036-4928 *Tel:* 202-371-0101 *Toll Free Tel:* 800-272-6657 (memb info) *Fax:* 202-728-9614 *E-mail:* help@computer.org *Web Site:* www.computer.org, pg 118

IEEE Press, 445 Hoes Lane, Piscataway, NJ 08854 *Tel:* 732-981-0060 *Fax:* 732-562-1746 *E-mail:* pressbooks@ieee.org (proposals & info) *Web Site:* www.ieee.org/press, pg 118

IET USA Inc, 379 Thornall St, Edison, NJ 08837 *Tel:* 732-321-5575 *Fax:* 732-321-5702 *E-mail:* ietusa@theiet.org *Web Site:* www.theiet.org, pg 118

Ignatius Press, 1348 Tenth Ave, San Francisco, CA 94122-2304 *Toll Free Tel:* 800-651-1531 (orders); 888-615-3186 (cust serv) *E-mail:* info@ignatius.com *Web Site:* www.ignatius.com, pg 118

IHS Jane's, 110 N Royal St, Suite 200, Alexandria, VA 22314-1651 *Tel:* 703-683-3700 *Toll Free Tel:* 800-824-0768 (sales) *Fax:* 703-836-0297 *Toll Free Fax:* 800-836-0297 *E-mail:* customercare@ihs.com *Web Site:* www.ihs.com, pg 119

IHS Press, 222 W 21 St, Suite F-122, Norfolk, VA 23517 *Toll Free Tel:* 877-447-7737 *Toll Free Fax:* 877-447-7737 *E-mail:* info@ihspress.com; tradesales@ihspress.com (wholesale sales); order@ihspress.com *Web Site:* www.ihspress.com, pg 119

ILA Children's & Young Adults' Book Awards, 800 Barksdale Rd, Newark, DE 19711-3204 *Tel:* 302-731-1600 *Toll Free Tel:* 800-336-7323 (US & CN) *Fax:* 302-731-1057 *E-mail:* committees@reading.org *Web Site:* www.literacyworldwide.org; www.reading.org, pg 694

Illinois State Museum Society, 502 S Spring St, Springfield, IL 62706-5000 *Tel:* 217-782-7386 *Fax:* 217-782-1254 *E-mail:* editor@museum.state.il.us *Web Site:* www.museum.state.il.us, pg 119

Illuminating Engineering Society of North America (IES), 120 Wall St, 17th fl, New York, NY 10005-4001 *Tel:* 212-248-5000 *Fax:* 212-248-5017; 212-248-5018 *E-mail:* ies@ies.org *Web Site:* www.ies.org, pg 119

Illumination Book Awards, 1129 Woodmere Ave, Suite B, Traverse City, MI 49686 *Tel:* 231-933-0445 *Toll Free Tel:* 800-706-4636 *Fax:* 231-933-0448 *E-mail:* awards@bookpublishing.com *Web Site:* www.illuminationawards.com, pg 694

Imagefinders Inc, 6101 Utah Ave NW, Washington, DC 20015 *Tel:* 202-244-4456 *Fax:* 202-244-3237, pg 528

Imagination Publishing Group, PO Box 1304, Dunedin, FL 34697 *Toll Free Tel:* 888-701-6481 *Fax:* 727-361-0584 *E-mail:* info@imaginationpublishinggroup.com *Web Site:* www.imaginationpublishinggroup.com, pg 119

Imago Press, 3710 E Edison St, Tucson, AZ 85716 *Tel:* 520-444-2265 *Web Site:* www.oasisjournal.org, pg 119

ImaJinn Books Inc, PO Box 74274, Phoenix, AZ 85087-4274 *Tel:* 623-236-3361 *Toll Free Tel:* 877-625-3592 (US & CN) *E-mail:* orders@imajinnbooks.com; editors@imajinnbooks.com *Web Site:* www.imajinnbooks.com, pg 119

Immedium, 535 Rockdale Dr, San Francisco, CA 94127 *Tel:* 415-452-8546 *Fax:* 360-937-6272 *E-mail:* orders@immedium.com; sales@immedium.com *Web Site:* www.immedium.com, pg 119

John Phillip Immroth Memorial Award, 50 E Huron St; Chicago, IL 60611 *Tel:* 312-280-4223 *Toll Free Tel:* 800-545-2433 *Fax:* 312-280-4227 *E-mail:* oif@ala.org *Web Site:* www.ala.org/ifrt, pg 694

Impact Publications/Development Concepts Inc, 9104 Manassas Dr, Suite N, Manassas Park, VA 20111-5211 *Tel:* 703-361-7300 *Toll Free Tel:* 800-361-1055 (cust serv) *Fax:* 703-335-9486 *E-mail:* query@impactpublications.com *Web Site:* www.impactpublications.com; www.ishoparoundtheworld.com; www.veteransworld.com; www.middleeasttravellover.com, pg 119

Impact Publishers Inc, PO Box 6016, Atascadero, CA 93423-6016 *Tel:* 805-466-5917 (opers & admin offs) *Toll Free Tel:* 800-246-7228 (orders) *Fax:* 805-466-5919 (opers & admin offs) *E-mail:* info@impactpublishers.com *Web Site:* www.impactpublishers.com; www.bibliotherapy.com, pg 119

In-Plant Printing & Mailing Association (IPMA), 455 S Sam Barr Dr, Suite 203, Kearney, MO 64060 *Tel:* 816-919-1691 *E-mail:* ipmainfo@ipma.org *Web Site:* www.ipma.org, pg 607

In the Garden Publishing, 7525 Paragon Rd, No 752252, Dayton, OH 45459 *Tel:* 937-317-0859 *E-mail:* editor@inthegardenpublishing.com *Web Site:* www.inthegardenpublishing.com, pg 120

Incentive Publications by World Book, 233 N Michigan Ave, Suite 2000, Chicago, IL 60601 *Toll Free Tel:* 800-967-5325 *E-mail:* incentive@worldbook.com *Web Site:* www.incentivepublications.com, pg 120

Inclusion Press International, 47 Indian Trail, Toronto, ON M6R 1Z8, Canada *Tel:* 416-658-5363 *Fax:* 416-658-5067 *E-mail:* inclusionpress@inclusion.com *Web Site:* www.inclusion.com, pg 488

The Independent Book Publishers Association (IBPA), 1020 Manhattan Beach Blvd, Suite 204, Manhattan Beach, CA 90266 *Tel:* 310-546-1818 *Fax:* 310-546-3939 *E-mail:* info@ibpa-online.org *Web Site:* www.ibpa-online.org, pg 607

Independent Information Publications, 3357 21 St, San Francisco, CA 94110 *Tel:* 415-643-8600 *E-mail:* sharisteiner@gmail.com *Web Site:* www.movedoc.com, pg 120

Independent Institute, 100 Swan Way, Oakland, CA 94621-1428 *Tel:* 510-632-1366 *Toll Free Tel:* 800-927-8733 *Fax:* 510-568-6040 *E-mail:* orders@independent.org *Web Site:* www.independent.org, pg 120

The Independent Publisher Book Awards, 1129 Woodmere Ave, Suite B, Traverse City, MI 49686 *Tel:* 231-933-0445 *Toll Free Tel:* 800-706-4636 *Fax:* 231-933-0448 *E-mail:* awards@bookpublishing.com *Web Site:* www.independentpublisher.com/ipland/ipawards.php, pg 694

Independent Writers of Chicago (IWOC), 332 S Michigan Ave, Suite 1032, Chicago, IL 60604 *Toll Free Tel:* 800-804-IWOC (804-4962) *E-mail:* info@iwoc.org *Web Site:* www.iwoc.org, pg 607

IndexEmpire Indexing Services, 16740 Orville Wright Dr, Riverside, CA 92518 *Tel:* 951-697-2819 *E-mail:* indexempire@gmail.com, pg 528

Indexing by the Book, PO Box 12513, Tucson, AZ 85732-2513 *Tel:* 520-750-8439 *E-mail:* indextran@cox.net *Web Site:* www.indexingbythebook.com, pg 528

Indiana Historical Society Press (IHS Press), 450 W Ohio St, Indianapolis, IN 46202-3269 *Tel:* 317-232-1882; 317-234-0026 (orders); 317-234-2716 (edit) *Toll Free Tel:* 800-447-1830 (orders) *Fax:* 317-234-0562 (orders); 317-233-0857 (edit) *E-mail:* ihspress@indianahistory.org; orders@indianahistory.org (orders) *Web Site:* www.indianahistory.org; shop.indianahistory.org (orders), pg 120

Indiana Review Fiction Prize, Ballantine Hall 465, 1020 E Kirkwood Ave, Bloomington, IN 47405 *Tel:* 812-855-3439 *E-mail:* inreview@indiana.edu *Web Site:* indianareview.org, pg 694

Indiana University African Studies Program, Indiana University, 221 Woodburn Hall, Bloomington, IN 47405 *Tel:* 812-855-8284 *Fax:* 812-855-6734 *E-mail:* afrist@indiana.edu *Web Site:* www.indiana.edu/~afrist, pg 120

Indiana University Press, Herman B Wells Library 350, 1320 E Tenth St, Bloomington, IN 47405-3907 *Tel:* 812-855-8817 *Toll Free Tel:* 800-842-6796 (orders only) *Fax:* 812-855-7931; 812-855-8507 *E-mail:* iupress@indiana.edu; iuporder@indiana.edu (orders) *Web Site:* www.iupress.indiana.edu, pg 120

Indiana University Writers' Conference, 464 Ballantine Hall, Dept of English, 1020 E Kirkwood Ave, Bloomington, IN 47405 *Tel:* 812-855-1877 *Fax:* 812-855-9535 *E-mail:* writecon@indiana.edu *Web Site:* www.indiana.edu/~writecon/, pg 652

IndieReader Discovery Awards, PO Box 43121, Montclair, NJ 07043 *Web Site:* indiereader.com/irda, pg 694

Indies Choice Book Awards, 333 Westchester Ave, Suite S202, White Plains, NY 10604 *Tel:* 914-406-7500 *Toll Free Tel:* 800-637-0037 *Fax:* 914-410-6297 *Web Site:* www.bookweb.org, pg 694

Individual Artist Awards, 175 W Ostend St, Suite E, Baltimore, MD 21230 *Tel:* 410-767-6555 *Fax:* 410-333-1062 *E-mail:* msac@msac.org *Web Site:* www.msac.org, pg 694

Individual Artist Fellowships, 1004 Farnam, Plaza Level, Omaha, NE 68102 *Tel:* 402-595-2122 *Toll Free Tel:* 800-341-4067 *Fax:* 402-595-2334 *Web Site:* www.nebraskaartscouncil.org, pg 695

Individual Artist Fellowships, 25 State House Sta, 193 State St, Augusta, ME 04333-0025 *Tel:* 207-287-2726 *Fax:* 207-287-2725 *Web Site:* mainearts.maine.gov, pg 695

Individual Artist's Fellowships in Literature, 1800 Gervais St, Columbia, SC 29201 *Tel:* 803-734-8696 *Fax:* 803-734-8526 *E-mail:* info@arts.sc.gov *Web Site:* www.southcarolinaarts.com, pg 695

Individual Excellence Awards, 30 E Broad St, 33rd fl, Columbus, OH 43215 *Tel:* 614-466-2613 *Fax:* 614-466-4494 *Web Site:* www.oac.state.oh.us, pg 695

Industrial Press Inc, 32 Haviland St, Unit 2C, Norwalk, CT 06854 *Tel:* 212-889-6330 *Toll Free Tel:* 888-528-7852 *Fax:* 212-545-8327 *E-mail:* info@industrialpress.com *Web Site:* new.industrialpress.com, pg 121

Information Age Publishing Inc, PO Box 79049, Charlotte, NC 28271-7047 *Tel:* 704-752-9125 *Fax:* 704-752-9113 *E-mail:* infoage@infoagepub.com *Web Site:* www.infoagepub.com, pg 121

Information Gatekeepers Inc, 1340 Soldiers Field Rd, Suite 2, Boston, MA 02135 *Tel:* 617-782-5033 *Fax:* 617-507-8338 *E-mail:* info@igigroup.com *Web Site:* www.igigroup.com, pg 121

Information Today, Inc, 143 Old Marlton Pike, Medford, NJ 08055-8750 *Tel:* 609-654-6266 *Toll Free Tel:* 800-300-9868 (cust serv) *Fax:* 609-654-4309 *E-mail:* custserv@infotoday.com *Web Site:* www.infotoday.com, pg 121

Infosources Publishing, 140 Norma Rd, Teaneck, NJ 07666 *Tel:* 201-836-7072 *Web Site:* www.infosourcespub.com, pg 121

Infusionmedia, 140 N Eighth St, Suite 214, The Apothecary, Lincoln, NE 68508-1353 *Tel:* 402-477-2065 *E-mail:* info@infusionmediadesign.com *Web Site:* www.infusionmediadesign.com, pg 508

Ingalls Publishing Group Inc (IPG), PO Box 2500, Banner Elk, NC 28604 *Tel:* 828-297-6884 *Fax:* 828-297-6880 *E-mail:* sales@ingallspublishinggroup.com *Web Site:* www.ingallspublishinggroup.com, pg 121

Ink Smith Publishing, PO Box 1086, Glendora, CA 91016 *Tel:* 626-415-7179 *Web Site:* ink-smith.com, pg 121

Inkwater Press, 6750 SW Franklin St, Suite A, Portland, OR 97223 *Tel:* 503-968-6777 *Fax:* 503-968-6779 *E-mail:* orders@inkwaterbooks.com *Web Site:* www.inkwater.com, pg 121

InkWell Management, 521 Fifth Ave, 26th fl, New York, NY 10175 *Tel:* 212-922-3500 *Fax:* 212-922-0535 *E-mail:* info@inkwellmanagement.com; submissions@inkwellmanagement.com *Web Site:* inkwellmanagement.com, pg 557

Inner Traditions International Ltd, One Park St, Rochester, VT 05767 *Tel:* 802-767-3174 *Toll Free Tel:* 800-246-8648 *Fax:* 802-767-3726 *E-mail:* customerservice@InnerTraditions.com *Web Site:* www.InnerTraditions.com, pg 122

Innis-Gerin Medal, Walter House, 282 Somerset W, Ottawa, ON K2P 0J6, Canada *Tel:* 613-991-6990 (ext 106) *Fax:* 613-991-6996 *E-mail:* nominations@rsc-src.ca *Web Site:* www.rsc-src.ca, pg 695

innovativeKids®, 50 Washington St, Suite 201, Norwalk, CT 06854 *Tel:* 203-838-6400 *E-mail:* info@innovativekids.com *Web Site:* www.innovativekids.com, pg 122

InScribe Christian Writers' Fellowship (ICWF), PO Box 6201, Wetaskiwin, AB T9A 2E9, Canada *E-mail:* inscribe.mail@gmail.com *Web Site:* inscribe.org, pg 607

Insight Editions, 800 "A" St, San Rafael, CA 94901 *Tel:* 415-526-1370 *Toll Free Tel:* 800-809-3792 *Toll Free Fax:* 866-509-0515 *E-mail:* info@insighteditions.com *Web Site:* www.insighteditions.com, pg 122

Insomniac Press, 520 Princess Ave, London, ON N6B 2B8, Canada *Tel:* 416-504-6270 *Web Site:* www.insomniacpress.com, pg 488

Inspiring Every Child dba Illumination Arts Publishing, 13023 NE Hwy 99, Suite 7-8, Vancouver, WA 98686 *Tel:* 425-968-5097 *Fax:* 425-968-5634 *E-mail:* liteinfo@illumin.com *Web Site:* www.illumin.com, pg 122

The Institute for Cooperation on Adult Education (Institut de Cooperation pour l'Education des Adultes-ICEA), 55, ave du Mont-Royal Ouest, Bureau 303, Montreal, QC H2T 2S6, Canada *Tel:* 514-948-2044 *Fax:* 514-948-2046 *E-mail:* icae@icea.qc.ca *Web Site:* www.icea.qc.ca, pg 607

Institute for Research on Public Policy (IRPP), 1470 Peel St, No 200, Montreal, QC H3A 1T1, Canada *Tel:* 514-985-2461 *Fax:* 514-985-2559 *E-mail:* irpp@irpp.org *Web Site:* www.irpp.org, pg 488

Institute of Continuing Legal Education, 1020 Greene St, Ann Arbor, MI 48109-1444 *Tel:* 734-764-0533 *Toll Free Tel:* 877-229-4350 *Fax:* 734-763-2412 *Toll Free Fax:* 877-229-4351 *E-mail:* icle@umich.edu *Web Site:* www.icle.org, pg 122

Institute of Environmental Sciences and Technology - IEST, 2340 S Arlington Heights Rd, Suite 620, Arlington Heights, IL 60005-4510 *Tel:* 847-981-0100 *Fax:* 847-981-4130 *E-mail:* publications@iest.org *Web Site:* www.iest.org, pg 122

Institute of Governmental Studies, 109 Moses Hall, No 2370, Berkeley, CA 94720-2370 *Tel:* 510-642-1428 *Fax:* 510-642-3020; 510-642-5537 (orders) *E-mail:* igspress@berkeley.edu *Web Site:* www.igs.berkeley.edu, pg 122

Institute of Intergovernmental Relations, Queen's University, Robert Sutherland Hall, Rm 301, Kingston, ON K7L 3N6, Canada *Tel:* 613-533-2080 *Fax:* 613-533-6868 *E-mail:* iigr@queensu.ca *Web Site:* www.queensu.ca/iigr, pg 488

Institute of Jesuit Sources (IJS), 3601 Lindell Blvd, St Louis, MO 63108 *Tel:* 314-633-4622 *Fax:* 314-633-4623 *E-mail:* ijs@jesuitsources.com *Web Site:* www.jesuitsources.com, pg 122

Institute of Mathematical Geography, 1964 Boulder Dr, Ann Arbor, MI 48104 *Tel:* 734-975-0246 *E-mail:* image@imagenet.org *Web Site:* www.imagenet.com, pg 123

Institute of Police Technology & Management, University Ctr, 12000 Alumni Dr, Jacksonville, FL 32224-2678 *Tel:* 904-620-4786 *Fax:* 904-620-2453 *E-mail:* info@iptm.org; orders@iptm.org *Web Site:* www.iptm.org, pg 123

Institute of Psychological Research, Inc., 76 Ave, Mozart W, Montreal, QC H2S 1C4, Canada *Tel:* 514-382-3000 *Toll Free Tel:* 800-363-7800 *Fax:* 514-382-3007 *Toll Free Fax:* 888-382-3007 *E-mail:* info@irpcanada.com *Web Site:* www.irpcanada.com, pg 488

Institute of Public Administration of Canada, 1075 Bay St, Suite 401, Toronto, ON M5S 2B1, Canada *Tel:* 416-924-8787 *Fax:* 416-924-4992 *E-mail:* ntl@ipac.ca *Web Site:* www.ipac.ca; www.iapc.ca, pg 489

Institute of Puerto Rican Culture National Literary Awards, PO Box 9024184, San Juan, PR 00902-4184 *Tel:* 787-724-0700 *Fax:* 787-724-8393 *Web Site:* www.icp.gobierno.pr, pg 695

The Institutes™, 720 Providence Rd, Suite 100, Malvern, PA 19355-3433 *Tel:* 610-644-2100 *Toll Free Tel:* 800-644-2101 *Fax:* 610-640-9576 *E-mail:* customerservice@theinstitutes.org *Web Site:* www.theinstitutes.org, pg 123

Integra Software Services Inc, 1110 Jorie Blvd, Suite 200, Oak Brook, IL 60523 *Tel:* 630-586-2579 *Fax:* 630-586-2599 *E-mail:* marketing@integra.co.in *Web Site:* www.integra.co.in, pg 528

Inter-American Development Bank, 1300 New York Ave NW, Washington, DC 20577 *Tel:* 202-623-1000 *Fax:* 202-623-3096 *E-mail:* pic@iadb.org *Web Site:* www.iadb.org/pub, pg 123

Inter American Press Association (IAPA), Jules Dubois Bldg, 1801 SW Third Ave, Miami, FL 33129 *Tel:* 305-634-2465 *Fax:* 305-635-2272 *E-mail:* info@sipiapa.org *Web Site:* www.sipiapa.org, pg 607

Inter-University Consortium for Political & Social Research (ICPSR), 330 Packard St, Ann Arbor, MI 48104 *Tel:* 734-647-5000 *Fax:* 734-647-8200 *E-mail:* netmail@icpsr.umich.edu *Web Site:* www.icpsr.umich.edu, pg 123

Intercultural Development Research Association (IDRA), 5815 Callaghan Rd, Suite 101, San Antonio, TX 78228 *Tel:* 210-444-1710 *Fax:* 210-444-1714 *E-mail:* contact@idra.org *Web Site:* www.idra.org, pg 123

Intercultural Press Inc, 20 Park Plaza, Suite 610, Boston, MA 02116 *Tel:* 617-523-3801 *Toll Free Tel:* 888-273-2539 *Fax:* 617-523-3708 *E-mail:* info@interculturalpress.com *Web Site:* nicholasbrealey.com, pg 123

InterLicense Ltd, 110 Country Club Dr, Suite A, Mill Valley, CA 94941 *Tel:* 415-381-9780 *Fax:* 415-381-6485 *E-mail:* interlicense@sbcglobal.net; ilicense@aol.com, pg 557

Interlink Publishing Group Inc, 46 Crosby St, Northampton, MA 01060 *Tel:* 413-582-7054 *Toll Free Tel:* 800-238-LINK (238-5465) *Fax:* 413-582-7057 *E-mail:* info@interlinkbooks.com *Web Site:* www.interlinkbooks.com, pg 123

Intermediate Sequoyah Book Award, 300 Hardy Dr, Edmond, OK 73013 *Tel:* 405-525-5100 *Fax:* 405-525-5103 *Web Site:* www.oklibs.org, pg 695

International Association of Business Communicators (IABC), 601 Montgomery St, Suite 1900, San Francisco, CA 94111 *Tel:* 415-544-4700 *Toll Free Tel:* 800-776-4222 (US & CN) *Fax:* 415-544-4747 *E-mail:* leader_centre@iabc.com *Web Site:* www.iabc.com, pg 607

International Association of Crime Writers Inc, North American Branch, 243 Fifth Ave, Suite 537, New York, NY 10016 *Tel:* 212-243-8966 *Fax:* 815-361-1477 *E-mail:* info@crimewritersna.org *Web Site:* www.crimewritersna.org, pg 607

International Book Centre Inc, 2391 Auburn Rd, Shelby Township, MI 48317 *Tel:* 586-254-7230 *Fax:* 586-254-7230 *E-mail:* ibc@ibcbooks.com *Web Site:* www.ibcbooks.com, pg 123

International City/County Management Association (ICMA), 777 N Capitol St NE, Suite 500, Washington, DC 20002-4201 *Tel:* 202-289-4262 *Toll Free Tel:* 800-745-8780 *Fax:* 202-962-3500 *E-mail:* customerservice@icma.org *Web Site:* icma.org, pg 123

International Code Council Inc, 5360 Workman Mill Rd, Whittier, CA 90601-2256 *Tel:* 562-699-0541 *Toll Free Tel:* 888-422-7233 *Fax:* 562-908-5524; 562-699-8031 *E-mail:* es@icc-es.org *Web Site:* www.iccsafe.org, pg 124

International Council of Shopping Centers (ICSC), 1221 Avenue of the Americas, 41st fl, New York, NY 10020-1099 *Tel:* 646-728-3800 *Fax:* 732-694-1755 *E-mail:* icsc@icsc.org *Web Site:* www.icsc.org, pg 124

International Development Research Centre (IDRC), 150 Kent St, Ottawa, ON K1P 0B2, Canada *Tel:* 613-236-6163 *Fax:* 613-238-7230 *E-mail:* info@idrc.ca *Web Site:* www.idrc.ca, pg 489

International Encyclopedia Society, 3689 Campbell Ct, Yorktown Heights, NY 10598 *Tel:* 914-962-3287 *Fax:* 914-962-3287, pg 607

International Entertainment Bureau, 3612 N Washington Blvd, Indianapolis, IN 46205-3592 *Tel:* 317-926-7566 *E-mail:* ieb@prodigy.net, pg 587

International Food Policy Research Institute, 2033 "K" St NW, Washington, DC 20006-1002 *Tel:* 202-862-5600 *Fax:* 202-467-4439 *E-mail:* ifpri@cgiar.org *Web Site:* www.ifpri.org, pg 124

International Foundation of Employee Benefit Plans, 18700 W Bluemound Rd, Brookfield, WI 53045 *Tel:* 262-786-6700 *Toll Free Tel:* 888-334-3327 *Fax:* 262-786-8780 *E-mail:* editor@ifebp.org *Web Site:* www.ifebp.org, pg 124

The International Institute of Islamic Thought, 500 Grove St, Suite 200, Herndon, VA 20170 *Tel:* 703-471-1133 *Fax:* 703-471-3922 *E-mail:* iiit@iiit.org *Web Site:* www.iiit.org, pg 124

International Latino Book Awards, 3445 Catalina Dr, Carlsbad, CA 92010 *Tel:* 760-434-1223 *Fax:* 760-434-7476 *E-mail:* kirk@whisler.com *Web Site:* www.lbff.us, pg 695

International Linguistics Corp, Learnables, 12220 Blue Ridge Blvd, Suite G, Grandview, MO 64030 *Tel:* 816-765-8855 *Toll Free Tel:* 800-237-1830 (orders) *Fax:* 816-765-2855 *E-mail:* learnables@sbcglobal.net *Web Site:* www.learnables.com, pg 124

International Literacy Association (ILA), 800 Barksdale Rd, Newark, DE 19711-3204 *Tel:* 302-731-1600 *Toll Free Tel:* 800-336-7323 (US & CN) *Fax:* 302-731-1057 *E-mail:* customerservice@reading.org *Web Site:* www.literacyworldwide.org; www.reading.org, pg 124, 608

International Monetary Fund (IMF), Editorial & Publications Division, 700 19 St NW, HQ1-7-124, Washington, DC 20431 *Tel:* 202-623-7430 *Fax:* 202-623-7201 *E-mail:* publications@imf.org *Web Site:* www.imfbookstore.org; elibrary.imf.org (online collection), pg 124

International Poetry Competition, PO Box 8248, Atlanta, GA 31106 *E-mail:* atlanta.review@yahoo.com *Web Site:* www.atlantareview.com, pg 695

International Press of Boston Inc, 387 Somerville Ave, Somerville, MA 02143 *Tel:* 617-623-3016 *Fax:* 617-623-3101 *E-mail:* ipb-info@intlpress.com; ipb-orders@intlpress.com *Web Site:* www.intlpress.com, pg 124

International Publishers Co Inc, 235 W 23 St, New York, NY 10011 *Tel:* 212-366-9816 *Fax:* 212-366-9820 *E-mail:* service@intpubnyc.com *Web Site:* www.intpubnyc.com, pg 124

International Research Center for Energy & Economic Development, 850 Willowbrook Rd, Boulder, CO 80302 *Tel:* 303-442-4014 *Fax:* 303-442-5042 *E-mail:* info@iceed.org *Web Site:* www.iceed.org, pg 124

International Risk Management Institute Inc, 12222 Merit Dr, Suite 1600, Dallas, TX 75251-2266 *Tel:* 972-960-7693 *Fax:* 972-371-5120 *E-mail:* info27@irmi.com *Web Site:* www.irmi.com, pg 125

International Society for Technology in Education, 180 W Eighth Ave, Suite 300, Eugene, OR 97401-2916 *Tel:* 541-302-3777 (intl) *Toll Free Tel:* 800-336-5191 (US & CN) *Fax:* 541-302-3778 *E-mail:* iste@iste.org *Web Site:* www.iste.org; www.iste.org/bookstore (orders); www.isteconference.org, pg 125

International Society of Automation (ISA), 67 T W Alexander Dr, Research Triangle Park, NC 27709-0185 *Tel:* 919-549-8411 *Fax:* 919-549-8288 *E-mail:* info@isa.org *Web Site:* www.isa.org, pg 125

International Society of Weekly Newspaper Editors, Missouri Southern State University, 3950 E Newman Rd, Joplin, MO 64801-1595 *Tel:* 417-625-9736 *Fax:* 417-659-4445 *Web Site:* www.iswne.org, pg 608

International Standard Book Numbering (ISBN) US Agency, A Cambridge Information Group Co, 630 Central Ave, New Providence, NJ 07974 *Toll Free Tel:* 877-310-7333 *Fax:* 908-219-0188 *E-mail:* isbn-san@bowker.com *Web Site:* www.isbn.org, pg 608

International Titles, 931 E 56 St, Austin, TX 78751-1724 *Tel:* 512-909-2447 *Web Site:* www.internationaltitles.com, pg 557

International Transactions Inc, 28 Alope Way, Gila, NM 88038 *Tel:* 845-373-9696 *Fax:* 480-393-5162 *E-mail:* info@intltrans.com *Web Site:* www.intltrans.com, pg 557

International Wealth Success Inc, PO Box 186, Merrick, NY 11566-0186 *Tel:* 516-766-5850 *Toll Free Tel:* 800-323-0548 *Fax:* 516-766-5919 *E-mail:* admin@iwsmoney.com *Web Site:* www.iwsmoney.com, pg 125

The International Women's Writing Guild (IWWG), 274 Madison Ave, Suite 1202, New York, NY 10016 *Tel:* 917-720-6959 *E-mail:* iwwgquestions@gmail.com *Web Site:* www.iwwg.org, pg 608

Internet Alliance (IA), 1615 "L" St NW, Suite 1100, Washington, DC 20036-5624 *Tel:* 202-861-2407 *Web Site:* www.internetalliance.org, pg 608

InterTech™ Technology Awards, 200 Deer Run Rd, Sewickley, PA 15143-2324 *Tel:* 412-259-1782 *Toll Free Tel:* 800-910-4283 (ext 782) *Fax:* 412-741-2311 *E-mail:* intertechaward@printing.org *Web Site:* www.printing.org/intertechawards, pg 695

InterVarsity Press, 430 Plaza Dr, Westmont, IL 60559-1234 *Tel:* 630-734-4000 *Toll Free Tel:* 800-843-9487 *Fax:* 630-734-4200 *E-mail:* email@ivpress.com *Web Site:* www.ivpress.com, pg 125

Interweave Press LLC, 201 E Fourth St, Loveland, CO 80537 *Toll Free Tel:* 800-272-2193; 800-289-0963 *Fax:* 970-613-4656 *Toll Free Fax:* 888-590-4082 *Web Site:* www.interweave.com, pg 125

The Intrepid Traveler, 152 Staltonstall Pkwy (rear entrance), East Haven, CT 06512 *Tel:* 203-469-0214 *E-mail:* admin@intrepidtraveler.com *Web Site:* www.intrepidtraveler.com, pg 125

Investigative Reporters & Editors, Missouri School of Journalism, 141 Neff Annex, Columbia, MO 65211 *Tel:* 573-882-2042 *Fax:* 573-882-5431 *E-mail:* info@ire.org *Web Site:* www.ire.org, pg 608

IODE Jean Throop Book Award, 9-45 Frid St, Hamilton, ON L8P 4M3, Canada *Tel:* 905-522-9537 *Fax:* 905-522-3637 *E-mail:* iodeontario@bellnet.ca *Web Site:* www.iodeontario.ca, pg 695

IODE Violet Downey Book Award, 40 Orchard View Blvd, Suite 219, Toronto, ON M4R 1B9, Canada *Tel:* 416-487-4416 *Toll Free Tel:* 866-827-7428 *Fax:* 416-487-4417 *E-mail:* iodecanada@bellnet.ca *Web Site:* www.iode.ca, pg 695

Iowa Poetry Prize, 119 W Park Rd, 100 Kuhl House, Iowa City, IA 52242-1000 *Tel:* 319-335-2000 *Fax:* 319-335-2055 *E-mail:* uipress@uiowa.edu *Web Site:* www.uiowapress.org, pg 695

The Iowa Review Award, 308 EPB, Iowa City, IA 52242-1408 *E-mail:* iowa-review@uiowa.edu *Web Site:* www.iowareview.org, pg 696

The Iowa Short Fiction Award, 102 Dey House, 507 N Clinton St, Iowa City, IA 52242-1000 *Tel:* 319-335-0416 *Fax:* 319-335-0420 *Web Site:* www.uiowapress.org/authors/iowa-short-fiction.htm, pg 696

Iowa Short Fiction Awards, 119 W Park Rd, 100 Kuhl House, Iowa City, IA 52242-1000 *Tel:* 319-335-2000 *Fax:* 319-335-2055 *E-mail:* uipress@uiowa.edu *Web Site:* www.uiowapress.org, pg 696

Iowa Summer Writing Festival, 250 Continuing Educ Facility, University of Iowa, Iowa City, IA 52242 *Tel:* 319-335-4160 *E-mail:* iswfestival@uiowa.edu *Web Site:* iowasummerwritingfestival.org, pg 652

Iron Gate Publishing, PO Box 999, Niwot, CO 80544 *Tel:* 303-530-2551 *Fax:* 303-530-5273 *E-mail:* editor@irongate.com *Web Site:* www.irongate.com, pg 125

Irwin Law Inc, 14 Duncan St, Suite 206, Toronto, ON M5H 3G8, Canada *Tel:* 416-862-7690 *Toll Free Tel:* 888-314-9014 *Fax:* 416-862-9236 *Web Site:* www.irwinlaw.com, pg 489

ISI Books, 3901 Centerville Rd, Wilmington, DE 19807-1938 *Tel:* 302-652-4600 *Toll Free Tel:* 800-526-7022 *Fax:* 302-652-1760 *E-mail:* info@isi.org; isibooks@isi.org *Web Site:* www.isibooks.org, pg 125

Island Press, 2000 "M" St NW, Suite 650, Washington, DC 20036 *Tel:* 202-232-7933 *Toll Free Tel:* 800-828-1302 *Fax:* 202-234-1328 *E-mail:* info@islandpress.org *Web Site:* www.islandpress.org, pg 126

Italica Press, 595 Main St, Suite 605, New York, NY 10044 *Tel:* 917-371-0563 *E-mail:* info@italicapress.com *Web Site:* www.italicapress.com, pg 126

ITMB Publishing Ltd, 12300 Bridgeport Rd, Richmond, BC V6V 1J5, Canada *Tel:* 604-273-1400 *Fax:* 604-273-1488 *E-mail:* itmb@itmb.com *Web Site:* www.itmb.com, pg 489

iUniverse, 1663 Liberty Dr, Bloomington, IN 47403 *Toll Free Tel:* 800-AUTHORS (288-4677) *Fax:* 812-355-4085 *Web Site:* www.iuniverse.com, pg 126

Richard Ivey School of Business, Ivey Business School at Western University, 1255 Western Rd, London, ON N6G 0N1, Canada *Tel:* 519-661-3206; 519-661-3208 *Toll Free Tel:* 800-649-6355 *Fax:* 519-661-3485; 519-661-3882 *E-mail:* cases@ivey.uwo.ca *Web Site:* www.iveycases.com; www.ivey.uwo.ca, pg 489

The Ivy League of Artists Inc, 7 Coventry Rd, Livingston, NJ 07039-5105 *Tel:* 973-992-4048 *Fax:* 973-992-4049 *E-mail:* ilartists@comcast.net, pg 584

JABberwocky Literary Agency Inc, 49 W 45 St, 12th fl, New York, NY 10036 *Tel:* 917-388-3010 *Fax:* 917-388-2998 *Web Site:* www.awfulagent.com, pg 558

Jackie White Memorial National Children's Playwriting Contest, 1400 Forum Blvd, 1C No 214, Columbia, MO 65203 *E-mail:* jwmcontest@cectheatre.org *Web Site:* www.cectheatre.org, pg 696

Joseph Henry Jackson Literary Award, One Embarcadero Ctr, Suite 1400, San Francisco, CA 94111 *Tel:* 415-733-8500 *Fax:* 415-477-2783 *E-mail:* info@sff.org *Web Site:* www.sff.org, pg 696

Melanie Jackson Agency LLC, 41 W 72 St, Suite 3F, New York, NY 10023 *Tel:* 212-873-3373, pg 558

The Jackson Poetry Prize, 90 Broad St, Suite 2100, New York, NY 10004 *Tel:* 212-226-3586 *Fax:* 212-226-3963 *E-mail:* admin@pw.org *Web Site:* www.pw.org, pg 696

Jain Publishing Co, PO Box 3523, Fremont, CA 94539 *Tel:* 510-659-8272 *Fax:* 510-659-0501 *E-mail:* mail@jainpub.com *Web Site:* www.jainpub.com, pg 126

James Peter Associates Inc, PO Box 358, New Canaan, CT 06840 *Tel:* 203-972-1070 *Web Site:* www.jamespeterassociates.com, pg 558

J Franklin Jameson Fellowship in American History, 400 "A" St SE, Washington, DC 20003 *Tel:* 202-544-2422 *Fax:* 202-544-8307 *E-mail:* awards@historians.org *Web Site:* www.historians.org, pg 696

Jamestown Prize, Swem Library, Ground fl, 400 Landrum Dr, Williamsburg, VA 23185 *Tel:* 757-221-1114 *Fax:* 757-221-1047 *E-mail:* ieahc1@wm.edu *Web Site:* oieahc.wm.edu, pg 696

Jan Williams Indexing Services, 300 Dartmouth College Hwy, Lyme, NH 03768-3207 *Tel:* 603-795-4924 *Web Site:* www.janwilliamsindexing.com, pg 528

Janklow & Nesbit Associates, 445 Park Ave, New York, NY 10022 *Tel:* 212-421-1700 *Fax:* 212-980-3671 *E-mail:* info@janklow.com *Web Site:* www.janklowandnesbit.com, pg 558

Janus Literary Agency, PO Box 837, Methuen, MA 01844 *Tel:* 978-273-4227 *E-mail:* janusliteraryagency@gmail.com *Web Site:* janusliteraryagency.com, pg 558

Japan-US Friendship Commission Translation Prize, Columbia University, 507 Kent Hall, MC3920, New York, NY 10027 *Tel:* 212-854-5036 *Fax:* 212-854-4019 *Web Site:* www.keenecenter.org, pg 696

JayJo Books LLC, One Huntington Quadrangle, Suite 1N03, Melville, NY 11747 *Tel:* 516-496-4863 *Toll Free Tel:* 800-999-6884 *Fax:* 516-496-4050 *Toll Free Fax:* 800-262-1886 *E-mail:* jayjobooks@guidance-group.com *Web Site:* www.guidance-group.com; www.jayjo.com, pg 126

Jefferson Cup Award, c/o Virginia Library Association (VLA), PO Box 56312, Virginia Beach, VA 23456 *Tel:* 757-689-0594 *Fax:* 757-447-3478 *Web Site:* www.vla.org, pg 696

Jellinek & Murray Literary Agency, 47-231 Kamakoi Rd, Kaneohe, HI 96744 *Tel:* 808-239-8451, pg 558

Jenkins Group Inc, 1129 Woodmere Ave, Suite B, Traverse City, MI 49686 *Tel:* 231-933-0445 *Toll Free Tel:* 800-706-4636 *Fax:* 231-933-0448 *E-mail:* info@bookpublishing.com *Web Site:* www.bookpublishing.com, pg 528

Carolyn Jenks Agency, 30 Cambridge Park Dr, Suite 3140, Cambridge, MA 02140 *Tel:* 617-354-5099 *Fax:* 617-354-5099 *E-mail:* queries@carolynjenksagency.com (submissions) *Web Site:* www.carolynjenksagency.com, pg 558

Jentel Artist Residency Program, 130 Lower Piney Rd, Banner, WY 82832 *Tel:* 307-737-2311 *Fax:* 307-737-2305 *E-mail:* jentel@jentelarts.org *Web Site:* www.jentelarts.org, pg 652

Jerome Award, 8550 United Plaza Blvd, Suite 1001, Baton Rouge, LA 70809-2256 *Tel:* 225-408-4417 *E-mail:* cla2@cathla.org *Web Site:* www.cathla.org, pg 697

Jerome Fellowship, 2301 Franklin Ave E, Minneapolis, MN 55406-1099 *Tel:* 612-332-7481 *Fax:* 612-332-6037 *E-mail:* info@pwcenter.org *Web Site:* www.pwcenter.org, pg 697

JET Literary Associates Inc, 941 Calle Mejia, Suite 507, Santa Fe, NM 87501 *Tel:* 212-971-2494 (NY voice mail); 505-780-0721 *E-mail:* query@jetliterary.com *Web Site:* www.jetliterary.wordpress.com, pg 558

Jewel Box Theatre Playwriting Competition, 3700 N Walker, Oklahoma City, OK 73118-7031 *Tel:* 405-521-1786 *Web Site:* jewelboxtheatre.org, pg 697

Jewish Book Council, 520 Eighth Ave, 4th fl, New York, NY 10018 *Tel:* 212-201-2920 *Fax:* 212-532-4952 *E-mail:* jbc@jewishbooks.org *Web Site:* www.jewishbookcouncil.org, pg 608

Jewish Lights Publishing, Sunset Farm Offices, Rte 4, Woodstock, VT 05091 *Tel:* 802-457-4000 *Toll Free Tel:* 800-962-4544 (orders only) *Fax:* 802-457-4004 *E-mail:* sales@jewishlights.com *Web Site:* www.jewishlights.com, pg 126

Jewish Publication Society, 2100 Arch St, Philadelphia, PA 19103 *Tel:* 215-832-0600 *Toll Free Tel:* 800-234-3151 *Fax:* 215-568-2017 *Web Site:* www.jps.org, pg 126

JFE Editorial, 8425 Doreen Ave, Fort Worth, TX 76116-4922 *Tel:* 817-560-7018, pg 528

Jhpiego, 1615 Thames St, Baltimore, MD 21231-3492 *Tel:* 410-537-1800 *Fax:* 410-537-1473 *E-mail:* info@jhpiego.net *Web Site:* www.jhpiego.org, pg 126

The Jim Henson Co, 1416 N La Brea Ave, Hollywood, CA 90028 *Tel:* 323-802-1500 *Fax:* 323-802-1825 *Web Site:* www.henson.com, pg 127

JIST Publishing, 875 Montreal Way, St Paul, MN 55102 *Toll Free Tel:* 800-328-1452 *Toll Free Fax:* 800-328-4564 *E-mail:* educate@emcp.com *Web Site:* jist.emcp.com, pg 127

JL Communications, 10205 Green Holly Terr, Silver Spring, MD 20902 *Tel:* 301-593-0640, pg 528

JMW Group Inc, One West Ave, Suite 219, Larchmont, NY 10538 *Tel:* 914-834-7800 *Fax:* 914-834-7824 *E-mail:* info@jmwgroup.net *Web Site:* jmwgroup.net, pg 558

The JOC Group Inc, 2 Penn Plaza E, Newark, NJ 07105 *Tel:* 973-776-8660 *Web Site:* www.joc.com, pg 127

Jody Rein Books Inc, 7741 S Ash Ct, Centennial, CO 80122 *Tel:* 303-694-9386 *Web Site:* www.jodyreinbooks.com, pg 558

John Deere Publishing, 5440 Corporate Park Dr, Davenport, IA 52807 *Toll Free Tel:* 800-522-7448 (orders) *Fax:* 563-355-3690 *E-mail:* johndeerepublishing@johndeere.com *Web Site:* www.johndeere.com/publications, pg 127

John Steinbeck Short Story Award, San Jose State University, English Dept, One Washington Sq, San Jose, CA 95192-0090 *Tel:* 408-924-4441 *Web Site:* www.reedmag.org, pg 697

The Johns Hopkins University Press, 2715 N Charles St, Baltimore, MD 21218-4363 *Tel:* 410-516-6900; 410-516-6987 (journal orders outside US & CN) *Toll Free Tel:* 800-537-5487 (book orders & cust serv); 800-548-1784 (journal orders) *Fax:* 410-516-6968; 410-516-3866 (journal orders) *E-mail:* hfscustserv@press.jhu.edu (cust serv); jrnlcirc@press.jhu.edu (journal orders) *Web Site:* www.press.jhu.edu; muse.jhu.edu, pg 127

Johnson Books, 3005 Center Green Dr, Suite 225, Boulder, CO 80301 *Tel:* 303-443-9766 *Toll Free Tel:* 800-258-5830 *Fax:* 303-443-9687 *E-mail:* books@bigearthpublishing.com *Web Site:* www.bigearthpublishing.com; www.johnsonbooks.com, pg 127

Cliff Johnson & Associates, 10867 Fruitland Dr, Studio City, CA 91604 *Tel:* 818-761-5665 *Fax:* 818-761-9501 *E-mail:* quest543@yahoo.com, pg 528

Jones & Bartlett Learning LLC, 5 Wall St, Burlington, MA 01803 *Tel:* 978-443-5000 *Toll Free Tel:* 800-832-0034 *Fax:* 978-443-8000 *E-mail:* info@jblearning.com *Web Site:* www.jblearning.com, pg 128

E-mail: custserv@kindredproductions.com; kindred@mbchurches.ca *Web Site:* www.kindredproductions.com, pg 489

Coretta Scott King Book Awards, 50 E Huron St, Chicago, IL 60611 *Toll Free Tel:* 800-545-2433 *E-mail:* olos@ala.org *Web Site:* www.ala.org/emiert/cskbookawards, pg 698

Jessica Kingsley Publishers Inc, 400 Market St, Suite 400, Philadelphia, PA 19106 *Tel:* 215-922-1161 *Toll Free Tel:* 866-416-1078 (cust serv) *Fax:* 215-922-1474 *E-mail:* orders@jkp.com; hello.usa@jkp.com *Web Site:* www.jkp.com, pg 131

Kinship Books, 305 Cedar Heights Rd, Rhinebeck, NY 12572 *Tel:* 845-876-4592 (orders) *E-mail:* kinship@hvc.rr.com *Web Site:* www.kinshipny.com, pg 131

Kirchoff/Wohlberg Inc, 897 Boston Post Rd, Madison, CT 06443 *Tel:* 203-245-7308 *Fax:* 203-245-3218 *Web Site:* www.kirchoffwohlberg.com, pg 559

Kirk House Publishers, PO Box 390759, Minneapolis, MN 55439 *Tel:* 952-835-1828 *Toll Free Tel:* 888-696-1828 *Fax:* 952-835-2613 *E-mail:* publisher@kirkhouse.com *Web Site:* www.kirkhouse.com, pg 131

Kirkbride Bible Co Inc, 1102 Deloss St, Indianapolis, IN 46203 *Tel:* 317-633-1900 *Toll Free Tel:* 800-428-4385 *Fax:* 317-633-1444 *E-mail:* sales@kirkbride.com; info@kirkbride.com *Web Site:* www.kirkbride.com, pg 131

Kirkus Prize, 65 W 36 St, Suite 700, New York, NY 10018 *Web Site:* www.kirkusreviews.com/prize, pg 698

Kiva Publishing Inc, 10 Bella Loma, Santa Fe, NM 87506 *Tel:* 909-896-0518 *E-mail:* kivapub@aol.com *Web Site:* www.kivapub.com, pg 131

Harvey Klinger Inc, 300 W 55 St, Suite 11V, New York, NY 10019 *Tel:* 212-581-7068 *Fax:* 212-315-3823 *E-mail:* queries@harveyklinger.com *Web Site:* www.harveyklinger.com, pg 560

Klutz, 568 Broadway, Suite 503, New York, NY 10012 *Tel:* 212-343-6360 *Fax:* 212-343-6366 *E-mail:* sales@klutz.com *Web Site:* store.scholastic.com, pg 131

Wolters Kluwer Law & Business, 76 Ninth Ave, 7th fl, New York, NY 10011-5201 *Tel:* 212-771-0600; 301-698-7100 (cust serv outside US) *Toll Free Tel:* 800-234-1660 (cust serv) *E-mail:* customer.service@wolterskluwer.com; sales@kluwerlaw.com *Web Site:* www.wklawbusiness.com, pg 131

Kneerim & Williams Agency, 90 Canal St, Boston, MA 02114 *Tel:* 617-303-1650 *Web Site:* www.kwblit.com, pg 560

The Knight Agency Inc, 570 East Ave, Madison, GA 30650 *E-mail:* submissions@knightagency.net *Web Site:* www.knightagency.net, pg 560

The Knight-Risser Prize for Western Environmental Journalism, Stanford University, 450 Serra Mall, Bldg 120, Rm 424, Stanford, CA 94305 *Tel:* 650-721-5955 *Fax:* 650-725-6154 *E-mail:* knightrisserprize@lists.stanford.edu *Web Site:* knightrisser.stanford.edu, pg 698

Theodore Knight PhD, RockCliff Farm, 40 Old Louisquisset Pike, Unit 101A, North Smithfield, RI 02896 *Tel:* 401-597-6982 *E-mail:* tedknight1@cox.net, pg 529

Knightville Poetry Contest, PO Box 5101, Hanover, NH 03755 *E-mail:* info@newguardreview.com *Web Site:* www.newguardreview.com, pg 698

Allen A Knoll Publishers, 200 W Victoria St, Santa Barbara, CA 93101-3627 *Tel:* 805-564-3377 *Toll Free Tel:* 800-777-7623 *Fax:* 805-966-6657 *E-mail:* bookinfo@knollpublishers.com *Web Site:* www.knollpublishers.com, pg 132

Alfred A Knopf/Everyman's Library, c/o Random House Inc, 1745 Broadway, New York, NY 10019 *Tel:* 212-751-2600 *Toll Free Tel:* 800-638-6460 *Fax:* 212-572-2593 *Web Site:* www.knopfdoubleday.com, pg 132

Knopf Canada, One Toronto St, Suite 300, Toronto, ON M5C 2V6, Canada *Tel:* 416-364-4449 *Toll Free Tel:* 888-523-9292 *Fax:* 416-364-6863 *Web Site:* www.randomhouse.ca, pg 490

Kodansha USA Inc, 451 Park Ave S, 7th fl, New York, NY 10016 *Tel:* 917-322-6200 *Fax:* 212-935-6929 *E-mail:* info@kodansha-usa.com *Web Site:* www.kodanshausa.com, pg 132

Bill Koehnlein, 236 E Fifth St, New York, NY 10003-8545 *Tel:* 212-674-9145 *E-mail:* koehnlein.bill@gmail.com, pg 529

E M Koeppel Short Fiction Award, PO Box 140310, Gainesville, FL 32614 *Tel:* 352-338-7778 *E-mail:* contact@writecorner.com *Web Site:* www.writecorner.com, pg 698

Barry R Koffler, Featherside, 14 Ginger Rd, High Falls, NY 12440 *Tel:* 845-687-9851 *E-mail:* barkof@feathersite.com, pg 529

Kogan Page Publishers, 1518 Walnut St, Suite 1100, Philadelphia, PA 19102 *Tel:* 215-928-9112 *Fax:* 215-928-9113 *E-mail:* info@koganpage.com *Web Site:* www.koganpageusa.com, pg 132

Paul Kohner Agency, 9300 Wilshire Blvd, Suite 555, Beverly Hills, CA 90212 *Tel:* 310-550-1060 *Fax:* 310-276-1083, pg 560

Koho Pono LLC, 15024 SE Pinegrove Loop, Clackamas, OR 97015 *Tel:* 503-723-7392 *Toll Free Tel:* 800-937-8000 (orders) *Toll Free Fax:* 800-876-0186 (orders) *E-mail:* info@kohopono.com; orders@ingrambook.com *Web Site:* kohopono.com, pg 132

KOK Edit, 15 Hare Lane, East Setauket, NY 11733-3606 *Tel:* 631-997-8191 *Fax:* 631-474-9849 *E-mail:* editor@kokedit.com *Web Site:* www.kokedit.com; twitter.com/kokedit; www.facebook.com/k.omooreklopf; www.linkedin.com/in/kokedit; www.editor-mom.blogspot.com, pg 529

Konecky & Konecky LLC, 72 Ayers Point Rd, Old Saybrook, CT 06475 *Tel:* 860-388-0878 *Fax:* 860-388-0273 *Web Site:* www.koneckyandkonecky.com, pg 132

Linda Konner Literary Agency, 10 W 15 St, Suite 1918, New York, NY 10011 *Tel:* 212-691-3419 *Fax:* 212-691-0935 *Web Site:* www.lindakonnerliteraryagency.com, pg 560

Elaine Koster Literary Agency LLC, 55 Central Park West, Suite 6, New York, NY 10023 *Tel:* 212-362-9488 *Fax:* 212-712-0164, pg 560

Barbara S Kouts Literary Agency LLC, PO Box 560, Bellport, NY 11713 *Tel:* 631-286-1278 *Fax:* 631-286-1538 *E-mail:* bkouts@aol.com, pg 561

Katherine Singer Kovacs Prize, 26 Broadway, 3rd fl, New York, NY 10004-1789 *Tel:* 646-576-5141 *Fax:* 646-458-0030 *E-mail:* awards@mla.org *Web Site:* www.mla.org, pg 698

Kraft & Kraft, 40 Memorial Hwy, Apt 23-C, New Rochelle, NY 10801 *Tel:* 914-319-3320 *Web Site:* www.erickraft.com, pg 529

Eileen Kramer, 336 Great Rd, Stow, MA 01775 *Tel:* 978-897-4121 *E-mail:* kramer@tiac.net *Web Site:* www.ekramer.com, pg 529

HJ Kramer Inc, PO Box 1082, Tiburon, CA 94920 *Tel:* 415-884-2100 (ext 10) *Toll Free Tel:* 800-972-6657 *Fax:* 415-435-5364 *E-mail:* hjkramer@jps.net *Web Site:* www.hjkramer.com; www.newworldlibrary.com, pg 133

Michael Kraus Research Grant in History, 400 "A" St SE, Washington, DC 20003 *Tel:* 202-544-2422 *Fax:* 202-544-8307 *E-mail:* awards@historians.org *Web Site:* www.historians.org, pg 698

Krause Publications Inc, 700 E State St, Iola, WI 54990 *Tel:* 715-445-2214 *Toll Free Tel:* 800-258-0929 (cust serv); 888-457-2873 (orders) *Fax:* 715-445-4087 *E-mail:* bookorders@krause.com *Web Site:* www.krausebooks.com, pg 133

Kregel Publications, 2450 Oak Industrial Dr NE, Grand Rapids, MI 49505 *Tel:* 616-451-4775 *Toll Free Tel:* 800-733-2607 *Fax:* 616-451-9330 *E-mail:* kregelbooks@kregel.com *Web Site:* www.kregel.com, pg 133

Stuart Krichevsky Literary Agency Inc, 381 Park Ave South, Suite 428, New York, NY 10016 *Tel:* 212-725-5288 *Fax:* 212-725-5275 *E-mail:* query@skagency.com *Web Site:* skagency.com, pg 561

Krieger Publishing Co, 1725 Krieger Dr, Malabar, FL 32950 *Tel:* 321-724-9542 *Toll Free Tel:* 800-724-0025 *Fax:* 321-951-3671 *E-mail:* info@krieger-publishing.com *Web Site:* www.krieger-publishing.com, pg 133

Eddie Kritzer Productions, 1112 Montana Ave, Suite 449, Santa Monica, CA 90403 *Tel:* 310-702-5356 *Fax:* 310-394-5770 *E-mail:* producedby@aol.com *Web Site:* eddiekritzer.com, pg 587

The Robert Kroetsch City of Edmonton Book Prize, 11759 Groat Rd, Edmonton, AB T5M 3K6, Canada *Tel:* 780-422-8174 *Toll Free Tel:* 800-665-5354 (AB only) *Fax:* 780-422-2663 (attn WGA) *E-mail:* mail@writersguild.ab.ca *Web Site:* www.writersguild.ab.ca, pg 698

Edite Kroll Literary Agency Inc, 20 Cross St, Saco, ME 04072 *Tel:* 207-283-8797 *Fax:* 207-283-8799, pg 561

Lynn C Kronzek & Richard A Flom, 145 S Glenoaks Blvd, Suite 240, Burbank, CA 91502 *Tel:* 818-768-7688 *Fax:* 818-768-7648, pg 529

KTAV Publishing House Inc, 888 Newark Ave, Jersey City, NJ 07306 *Tel:* 201-963-9524 *Fax:* 201-963-0102 *E-mail:* orders@ktav.com *Web Site:* www.ktav.com, pg 133

Kumarian Press, 1800 30 St, Suite 314, Boulder, CO 80301 *Tel:* 303-444-6684 *Toll Free Tel:* 800-232-0223 (orders only) *Fax:* 303-444-0824 *E-mail:* questions@rienner.com *Web Site:* www.kpbooks.com, pg 133

Polly Kummel, 624 Boardman Rd, Aiken, SC 29803 *Tel:* 803-641-6831 *E-mail:* editor@amazinphrasin.com; pollyk1@msn.com *Web Site:* www.amazinphrasin.com, pg 529

Kumon Publishing North America, 300 Frank Burr Blvd, Suite 6, Teaneck, NJ 07666 *Tel:* 201-836-2105 *Fax:* 201-836-1559 *E-mail:* books@kumon.com *Web Site:* www.kumonbooks.com, pg 133

Kumu Kahua/UHM Theatre & Dance Department Playwriting Contest, 46 Merchant St, Honolulu, HI 96813 *Tel:* 808-536-4441 (box off); 808-536-4222 *Fax:* 808-536-4226 *E-mail:* kumukahuatheatre@hawaiiantel.net *Web Site:* www.kumukahua.org, pg 699

George Kurian Reference Books, 3689 Campbell Ct, Yorktown Heights, NY 10598 *Tel:* 914-962-3287 *Fax:* 914-962-3287, pg 133

The LA Literary Agency, PO Box 46370, Los Angeles, CA 90046 *Tel:* 323-654-5288 *E-mail:* laliteraryagency@mac.com; mail@laliteraryagency.com *Web Site:* www.laliteraryagency.com, pg 561

Lachina Publishing Services Inc, 3793 S Green Rd, Cleveland, OH 44122 *Tel:* 216-292-7959 *E-mail:* info@lachina.com *Web Site:* www.lachina.com, pg 529

Lynne Lackenbach Editorial Services, 31 Pillsbury Rd, East Hampstead, NH 03826 *Tel:* 603-329-8133 *E-mail:* lynnelack@gmail.com, pg 529

LadybugPress, 16964 Columbia River Dr, Sonora, CA 95370 *Tel:* 209-694-8340 *Toll Free Tel:* 888-892-5000 *Fax:* 209-694-8916 *E-mail:* ladybugpress@ladybugbooks.com *Web Site:* www.ladybugbooks.com, pg 133

Lake Claremont Press, PO Box 711, Chicago, IL 60690 *Tel:* 312-226-8400 *Fax:* 312-226-8420 *Web Site:* www.lakeclaremont.com, pg 133

Lake Superior Port Cities Inc, 310 E Superior St, Suite 125, Duluth, MN 55802 *Tel:* 218-722-5002 *Toll Free Tel:* 888-BIG-LAKE (244-5253) *Fax:* 218-722-4096 *E-mail:* reader@lakesuperior.com *Web Site:* www.lakesuperior.com, pg 134

LAMA Books, 2381 Sleepy Hollow Ave, Hayward, CA 94545-3429 *Tel:* 510-785-1091 *Toll Free Tel:* 888-452-6244 *Fax:* 510-785-1099 *Web Site:* www.lamabooks.com, pg 134

W Kaye Lamb Award, PO Box 5254, Sta B, Victoria, BC V8R 6N4, Canada *E-mail:* essays@bchistory.ca *Web Site:* www.bchistory.ca, pg 699

Lambda Literary Awards (Lammys), 5482 Wilshire Blvd, No 1595, Los Angeles, CA 90036 *Tel:* 323-643-4281 *Fax:* 323-643-4281 *E-mail:* info@lambdaliterary.org *Web Site:* www.lambdaliterary.org, pg 699

Peter Lampack Agency Inc, 350 Fifth Ave, Suite 5300, New York, NY 10118 *Tel:* 212-687-9106 *Fax:* 212-687-9109 *Web Site:* www.peterlampackagency.com, pg 561

Gerald Lampert Memorial Award, 192 Spadina Ave, Suite 312, Toronto, ON M5T 2C2, Canada *Tel:* 416-504-1657 *Fax:* 416-504-0096 *E-mail:* readings@poets.ca *Web Site:* poets.ca, pg 699

Lanahan Publishers Inc, 324 Hawthorne Rd, Baltimore, MD 21210-2303 *Tel:* 410-366-2434 *Toll Free Tel:* 866-345-1949 *Fax:* 410-366-8798 *E-mail:* lanahan@aol.com *Web Site:* www.lanahanpublishers.com, pg 134

Land on Demand, 20 Long Crescent Dr, Bristol, VA 24201 *Tel:* 423-366-0513 *E-mail:* landondemand@gmail.com *Web Site:* boblandedits.blogspot.com, pg 529

Landauer Corp, 3100 101 St, Suite A, Urbandale, IA 50322 *Tel:* 515-287-2144 *Toll Free Tel:* 800-557-2144 *Fax:* 515-276-5102 *E-mail:* info@landauercorp.com *Web Site:* www.landauercorp.com, pg 134

Peter Lang Publishing Inc, 29 Broadway, 18th fl, New York, NY 10006-3223 *Tel:* 212-647-7706 *Toll Free Tel:* 800-770-5264 (cust serv) *Fax:* 212-647-7707 *Web Site:* www.peterlang.com, pg 134

LangMarc Publishing, PO Box 90488, Austin, TX 78709-0488 *Tel:* 512-394-0989 *Toll Free Tel:* 800-864-1648 (orders) *Fax:* 512-394-0829 *E-mail:* langmarc@booksails.com *Web Site:* www.langmarc.com, pg 134

Langum Prize in American Historical Fiction, 2809 Berkeley Dr, Birmingham, AL 35242 *Tel:* 205-726-2424 *Fax:* 205-726-4216 *Web Site:* www.langumtrust.org, pg 699

Langum Prize in American Legal History or Biography, 2809 Berkeley Dr, Birmingham, AL 35242 *Tel:* 205-726-2424 *Fax:* 205-726-4216 *E-mail:* langumtrust@gmail.com *Web Site:* www.langumtrust.org, pg 699

Lannan Literary Awards & Fellowships, 313 Read St, Santa Fe, NM 87501-2628 *Tel:* 505-986-8160 *Fax:* 505-986-8195 *E-mail:* info@lannan.org *Web Site:* www.lannan.org, pg 699

Lantern Books, 128 Second Place, Garden Suite, Brooklyn, NY 11231 *Tel:* 212-414-2275 *E-mail:* editorial@lanternbooks.com; info@lanternmedia.net *Web Site:* lanternbooks.presswarehouse.com/Home/home.aspx, pg 134

Laredo Publishing Co Inc, 465 Westview Ave, Englewood, NJ 07631 *Tel:* 201-408-4048 *Fax:* 201-408-5011 *E-mail:* info@laredopublishing.com *Web Site:* www.laredopublishing.com, pg 134

Lark Crafts, 1166 Avenue of the Americas, New York, NY 10036 *Tel:* 212-532-7160 *E-mail:* customerservice@sterlingpublishing.com *Web Site:* larkcrafts.com; www.sterlingpublishing.com, pg 134

Michael Larsen/Elizabeth Pomada Literary Agents, 1029 Jones St, San Francisco, CA 94109 *Tel:* 415-673-0939 *E-mail:* larsenpoma@aol.com *Web Site:* www.larsenpomada.com, pg 561

Larson Publications, 4936 State Rte 414, Burdett, NY 14818 *Tel:* 607-546-9342 *Toll Free Tel:* 800-828-2197 *Fax:* 607-546-9344 *E-mail:* custserv@larsonpublications.com *Web Site:* www.larsonpublications.com, pg 134

Lasaria Creative Publishing, 4094 Majestic Lane, Suite 352, Fairfax, VA 22033 *E-mail:* info@lasariacreative.com *Web Site:* www.lasariacreative.com, pg 135

Latin American Literary Review Press, PO Box 7530, Pittsburgh, PA 15213 *Tel:* 412-824-7903 *E-mail:* lalrp.editor@gmail.com *Web Site:* www.lalrp.org, pg 135

Laughing Elephant, 3645 Interlake N, Seattle, WA 98103 *Tel:* 206-447-9229 *Toll Free Tel:* 800-354-0400 *Fax:* 206-447-9189 *E-mail:* support@laughingelephant.com *Web Site:* www.laughingelephant.com, pg 135

Laurier Books Ltd, PO Box 8493, Ottawa, ON K1G 3H9, Canada *Tel:* 613-738-2163 *Toll Free Fax:* 855-736-9160 *E-mail:* laurierbooks@yahoo.com, pg 490

Law School Admission Council, 662 Penn St, Newtown, PA 18940 *Tel:* 215-968-1101 *E-mail:* lsacaccounts@lsac.org *Web Site:* www.lsac.org, pg 135

Law Tribune Books, 201 Ann Uccello St, 4th fl, Hartford, CT 06103 *Tel:* 860-527-7900 *Fax:* 860-527-7433 *E-mail:* lawtribune@alm.com *Web Site:* www.ctlawtribune.com, pg 135

The Lawbook Exchange Ltd, 33 Terminal Ave, Clark, NJ 07066-1321 *Tel:* 732-382-1800 *Toll Free Tel:* 800-422-6686 *Fax:* 732-382-1887 *E-mail:* law@lawbookexchange.com *Web Site:* www.lawbookexchange.com, pg 135

Lawrence Foundation Prize, University of Michigan, 0576 Rackham Bldg, 915 E Washington St, Ann Arbor, MI 48109-1070 *Tel:* 734-764-9265 *E-mail:* mqr@umich.edu *Web Site:* www.umich.edu/~mqr, pg 699

Merloyd Lawrence Inc, 102 Chestnut St, Boston, MA 02108 *Tel:* 617-523-5895 *Fax:* 617-252-5285, pg 135

Lawyers & Judges Publishing Co Inc, 917 N Swan Rd, Suite 300, Tucson, AZ 85711 *Tel:* 520-323-1500 *Toll Free Tel:* 800-209-7109 *Fax:* 520-323-0055 *Toll Free Fax:* 800-330-8795 *E-mail:* sales@lawyersandjudges.com *Web Site:* www.lawyersandjudges.com, pg 135

Sarah Lazin Books, 121 W 27 St, Suite 704, New York, NY 10001 *Tel:* 212-989-5757 *Fax:* 212-989-1393 *Web Site:* lazinbooks.com, pg 561

Stephen Leacock Memorial Medal for Humour, RR2, 4223 Line 12 N, Coldwater, ON L0K 1E0, Canada *Tel:* 705-835-3218 *Fax:* 705-835-5171 *Web Site:* www.leacock.ca, pg 699

Leadership Directories, 1407 Broadway, Suite 318, New York, NY 10018 *Tel:* 212-627-4140 *Fax:* 212-645-0931 *E-mail:* info@leadershipdirectories.com *Web Site:* www.leadershipdirectories.com, pg 135

Leadership Ministries Worldwide/OBR, 3755 Pilot Point, Chattanooga, TN 37416 *Tel:* 423-855-2181 *Toll Free Tel:* 800-987-8790 *Fax:* 423-855-8616 *E-mail:* info@outlinebible.org *Web Site:* www.outlinebible.org, pg 135

Leaf Storm Press, PO Box 4670, Santa Fe, NM 87502-4670 *Tel:* 505-216-6155 *E-mail:* leafstormpress@gmail.com *Web Site:* leafstormpress.com, pg 136

The League of Canadian Poets, 192 Spadina Ave, Suite 312, Toronto, ON M5T 2C2, Canada *Tel:* 416-504-1657 *Fax:* 416-504-0096 *Web Site:* poets.ca, pg 608

League of Vermont Writers, PO Box 172, Underhill Center, VT 05490 *Tel:* 802-349-7475 *E-mail:* lvw@leaguevtwriters.org *Web Site:* www.leagueofvermontwriters.org, pg 608

League of Women Voters of the United States, 1730 "M" St NW, Suite 1000, Washington, DC 20036-4508 *Tel:* 202-429-1965 *Fax:* 202-429-0854; 202-429-4343 *E-mail:* lwv@lwv.org *Web Site:* www.lwv.org, pg 608

Leaping Dog Press/Asylum Arts Press, PO Box 90473, Raleigh, NC 27675-0473 *Tel:* 919-809-9045 *E-mail:* sales@leapingdogpress.com *Web Site:* www.leapingdogpress.com, pg 136

THE Learning Connection®, 4100 Silverstar Rd, Suite D, Orlando, FL 32808 *Tel:* 407-292-2125 *Toll Free Tel:* 800-218-8489 *Fax:* 407-292-2123 *E-mail:* tlc@tlconnection.com *Web Site:* www.tlconnection.com, pg 136

Learning Links Inc, PO Box 326, Cranbury, NJ 08512 *Tel:* 516-437-9071 *Toll Free Tel:* 800-724-2616 *Fax:* 516-437-5392 *E-mail:* info@learninglinks.com *Web Site:* www.learninglinks.com, pg 136

The Learning Source Ltd, 644 Tenth St, Brooklyn, NY 11215 *Tel:* 718-768-0231 (ext 10) *Fax:* 718-369-3467 *E-mail:* info@learningsourceltd.com *Web Site:* www.learningsourceltd.com, pg 529

LearningExpress LLC, 2 Rector St, 26th fl, New York, NY 10006 *Tel:* 212-995-2566 *Toll Free Tel:* 800-295-9556 (ext 2) *Fax:* 212-995-5512 *E-mail:* customerservice@learningexpressllc.com (cust serv) *Web Site:* www.learningexpressllc.com, pg 136

The Ned Leavitt Agency, 70 Wooster St, Suite 4-F, New York, NY 10012 *Tel:* 212-334-0999 *Web Site:* www.nedleavittagency.com, pg 561

Lectorum Publications Inc, 205 Chubb Ave, Lyndhurst, NJ 07071 *Toll Free Tel:* 800-345-5946 *Fax:* 201-559-2201 *Toll Free Fax:* 877-532-8676 *E-mail:* lectorum@lectorum.com *Web Site:* www.lectorum.com, pg 136

Lederer Books, 6120 Day Long Lane, Clarksville, MD 21029 *Tel:* 410-531-6644 *Toll Free Tel:* 800-410-7367 (orders) *Fax:* 410-531-9440 *E-mail:* lederer@messianicjewish.net; customerservice@messianicjewish.net *Web Site:* www.messianicjewish.net, pg 136

The Ledge Press Fiction Awards Competition, 40 Maple Ave, Bellport, NY 11713 *E-mail:* info@theledgemagazine.com *Web Site:* theledgemagazine.com, pg 699

The Ledge Press Poetry Awards Competition, 40 Maple Ave, Bellport, NY 11713 *E-mail:* info@theledgemagazine.com *Web Site:* theledgemagazine.com, pg 699

The Ledge Press Poetry Chapbook Competition, 40 Maple Ave, Bellport, NY 11713 *E-mail:* info@theledgemagazine.com *Web Site:* theledgemagazine.com, pg 699

Lee & Low Books Inc, 95 Madison Ave, New York, NY 10016 *Tel:* 212-779-4400 *Toll Free Tel:* 888-320-3190 (ext 28, orders only) *Fax:* 212-683-1894 (orders only); 212-532-6035 *E-mail:* general@leeandlow.com *Web Site:* www.leeandlow.com, pg 136

Harper Lee Prize for Legal Fiction, 101 Paul Bryant Dr, Tuscaloosa, AL 35487 *Tel:* 205-348-5195 *Web Site:* www.law.ua.edu/programs/harper-lee-prize-for-legal-fiction, pg 699

Left Coast Press Inc, 1630 N Main St, Suite 400, Walnut Creek, CA 94596 *Tel:* 925-935-3380 *Fax:* 925-935-2916 *E-mail:* explore@lcoastpress.com *Web Site:* www.lcoastpress.com, pg 136

Lehigh University Press, B-040 Christmas-Saucon Hall, 14 E Packer Ave, Bethlehem, PA 18015 *Tel:* 610-758-3933 *Fax:* 610-758-6331 *E-mail:* inlup@lehigh.edu *Web Site:* inpress.sites.lehigh.edu, pg 137

Leilah Publications, 510 E University Dr, No 3413, Tempe, AZ 85281 *Tel:* 847-275-1657 *E-mail:* leilah@leilahpublications.com *Web Site:* facebook.com/leilahpublications, pg 137

Leisure Arts Inc, 104 Champs Blvd, Suite 100, Maumelle, AR 72113 *Tel:* 501-868-8800 *Toll Free Tel:* 800-643-8030 *Fax:* 501-868-8748 *Web Site:* www.leisurearts.com, pg 137

Waldo G Leland Prize, 400 "A" St SE, Washington, DC 20003 *Tel:* 202-544-2422 *Fax:* 202-544-8307 *E-mail:* awards@historians.org *Web Site:* www.historians.org, pg 700

Vincent Lemieux Prize, 260 rue Dalhousie St, Suite 204, Ottawa, ON K1N 7E4, Canada *Tel:* 613-562-1202 *Fax:* 613-241-0019 *E-mail:* cpsa-acsp@cpsa-acsp.ca *Web Site:* www.cpsa-acsp.ca, pg 700

Lemon Grove Press, 1158 26 St, Suite 502, Santa Monica, CA 90403 *Tel:* 310-471-1740 *Fax:* 310-476-7627 *E-mail:* info@lemongrovepress.com *Web Site:* www.thetakechargepatient.com, pg 508

Debra Lemonds, PO Box 5516, Pasadena, CA 91117-0516 *Tel:* 626-844-9363 *E-mail:* dlemonds@earthlink.net, pg 529

The Lentz Leadership Institute, 7124 Glyndon Trail NW, Albuquerque, NM 87114 *Tel:* 702-719-9214 *E-mail:* orders@lentzleadership.com *Web Site:* www.lentzleadership.com; www.refractivethinker.com, pg 137

John Leonard Award, 160 Varick St, 11th fl, New York, NY 10013 *E-mail:* info@bookcritics.org *Web Site:* bookcritics.org, pg 700

Leopold-Hidy Award, 701 William Vickers Ave, Durham, NC 27701-3162 *Tel:* 919-682-9319 *Fax:* 919-682-2349 *Web Site:* www.foresthistory.org, pg 700

Elizabeth J Leppman, 631 Worcester Dr, Lexington, KY 40503 *Tel:* 859-245-4325 *Fax:* 859-245-4325 *E-mail:* ejleppman@windstream.net, pg 529

Lerner Publications, 241 First Ave N, Minneapolis, MN 55401 *Tel:* 612-332-3344 *Toll Free Tel:* 800-328-4929 *Fax:* 612-332-7615 *Toll Free Fax:* 800-332-1132 *E-mail:* info@lernerbooks.com *Web Site:* www.lernerbooks.com, pg 137

Lerner Publishing Group Inc, 241 First Ave N, Minneapolis, MN 55401 *Tel:* 612-332-3344 *Toll Free Tel:* 800-328-4929 *Fax:* 612-332-7615 *Toll Free Fax:* 800-332-1132 *E-mail:* info@lernerbooks.com *Web Site:* www.lernerbooks.com, pg 137

LernerClassroom, 241 First Ave N, Minneapolis, MN 55401 *Tel:* 612-332-3344 *Toll Free Tel:* 800-328-4929 *Fax:* 612-332-7615 *Toll Free Fax:* 800-332-1132 *E-mail:* info@lernerbooks.com *Web Site:* www.lernerbooks.com, pg 137

Lessiter Publications, 16655 W Wisconsin Ave, Brookfield, WI 53005 *Tel:* 262-782-4480 *Toll Free Tel:* 800-645-8455 *Fax:* 262-782-1252 *E-mail:* info@lesspub.com *Web Site:* www.lesspub.com, pg 138

Letterbox/Papyrus of London Publishers USA, 10501 Broom Hill Dr, Suite 1-F, Las Vegas, NV 89134-7339 *Tel:* 702-256-3838 *E-mail:* lb27383@cox.net, pg 138

Level 4 Press Inc, 13518 Jamul Dr, Jamul, CA 91935-1635 *Fax:* 619-374-7311 *E-mail:* sales@level4press.com *Web Site:* www.level4press.com, pg 138

Fenia & Yaakov Leviant Memorial Prize in Yiddish Studies, 26 Broadway, 3rd fl, New York, NY 10004-1789 *Tel:* 646-576-5141 *Fax:* 646-458-0030 *E-mail:* awards@mla.org *Web Site:* www.mla.org, pg 700

Harry Levin Prize, University of South Carolina, Dept of Languages, Literature & Cultures, Rm 813-A, 1620 College St, Columbia, SC 29208 *Tel:* 803-777-3021 *Fax:* 803-777-3041 *E-mail:* info@acla.org *Web Site:* www.acla.org/awards/harry-levin-prize; www.acla.org, pg 700

Levine|Greenberg|Rostan Literary Agency Inc, 307 Seventh Ave, Suite 2407, New York, NY 10001 *Tel:* 212-337-0934 *Fax:* 212-337-0948 *Web Site:* lgrliterary.com, pg 561

Levinson Prize, 444 N Michigan Ave, Suite 1850, Chicago, IL 60611-4034 *Tel:* 312-787-7070 *Fax:* 312-787-6650 *E-mail:* editors@poetrymagazine.org *Web Site:* www.poetryfoundation.org, pg 700

Levis Reading Prize, PO Box 842005, Richmond, VA 23284-2005 *Tel:* 804-828-1331 *Fax:* 804-828-8684 *Web Site:* english.vcu.edu/mfa/levis/, pg 700

Levy Creative Management LLC, 425 E 58 St, Suite 37F, New York, NY 10022 *Tel:* 212-687-6463 *Fax:* 212-661-4839 *E-mail:* info@levycreative.com *Web Site:* www.levycreative.com, pg 584

Lexington Books, 4501 Forbes Blvd, Suite 200, Lanham, MD 20706 *Tel:* 301-459-3366 *Fax:* 301-429-5749 *Web Site:* www.lexingtonbooks.com, pg 138

LexisNexis®, 701 E Water St, Charlottesville, VA 22902 *Tel:* 434-972-7600 *Toll Free Tel:* 800-446-3410 *Fax:* 434-961-5576 *E-mail:* customer.support@lexisnexis.com *Web Site:* www.lexisnexis.com, pg 138

LexisNexis® Canada Inc, 123 Commerce Valley Dr E, Suite 700, Markham, ON L3T 7W8, Canada *Tel:* 905-479-2665 *Toll Free Tel:* 800-668-6481; 800-387-0899 (cust care) *Fax:* 905-479-2826 *Toll Free Fax:* 800-461-3275 *E-mail:* orders@lexisnexis.ca; service@lexisnexis.ca (cust serv) *Web Site:* www.lexisnexis.ca, pg 490

LexisNexis® Matthew Bender®, 630 Central Ave, New Providence, NJ 07974 *Tel:* 908-464-6800 *Web Site:* bender.lexisnexis.com, pg 138

Liberty Fund Inc, 8335 Allison Pointe Trail, Suite 300, Indianapolis, IN 46250-1684 *Tel:* 317-842-0880 *Toll Free Tel:* 800-955-8335; 800-866-3520; 800-368-7897 ext 6069 (cust serv) *Fax:* 317-577-9067; 317-579-6060 (cust serv); 708-534-7803 *E-mail:* books@libertyfund.org; info@libertyfund.org *Web Site:* www.libertyfund.org, pg 138

Libraries Unlimited, 130 Cremona Dr, Santa Barbara, CA 93117 *Tel:* 805-968-1911 *Toll Free Tel:* 800-368-6868 *Fax:* 805-685-9685 *Toll Free Fax:* 866-270-3856 *E-mail:* customerservice@abc-clio.com *Web Site:* www.abc-clio.com, pg 138

Library Association of Alberta (LAA), 80 Baker Crescent NW, Calgary, AB T2L 1R4, Canada *Tel:* 403-284-5818 *Toll Free Tel:* 877-522-5550 *Fax:* 403-282-6646 *E-mail:* info@laa.ca *Web Site:* www.laa.ca, pg 608

Library Binding Council, 4440 PGA Blvd, Suite 600, Palm Beach Gardens, FL 33410 *Tel:* 561-745-6821 *Toll Free Fax:* 800-837-7321 *E-mail:* info@lbibinders.org *Web Site:* www.lbibinders.org, pg 608

The Library of America, 14 E 60 St, New York, NY 10022-1006 *Tel:* 212-308-3360 *Fax:* 212-750-8352 *E-mail:* info@loa.org *Web Site:* www.loa.org, pg 138

Library of American Broadcasting (LAB), University of Maryland, Hornbake Library, College Park, MD 20742 *Tel:* 301-405-9212 *Web Site:* www.lib.umd.edu/special/collections/massmedia/about-us, pg 608

Library of Congress Literacy Awards, 101 Independence Ave SE, Washington, DC 20540-1400 *Tel:* 202-707-5221 (Center for the Book) *Fax:* 202-707-0269 *Web Site:* www.read.gov/literacyawards, pg 700

Library of Congress Prize for American Fiction, 101 Independence Ave SE, Washington, DC 20540-1400 *Tel:* 202-707-5221 (Center for the Book) *Web Site:* www.loc.gov, pg 700

Libris Award for Author of the Year, 1881 Yonge St, Suite 800, Toronto, ON M4S 3C4, Canada *Tel:* 416-922-6678 *Toll Free Tel:* 888-373-8245 *Fax:* 416-467-7886 *E-mail:* info@retailcouncil.org *Web Site:* www.retailcouncil.org, pg 700

Libris Children's Picture Book of the Year, 1881 Yonge St, Suite 800, Toronto, ON M4S 3C4, Canada *Tel:* 416-922-6678 *Toll Free Tel:* 888-373-8245 *Fax:* 416-467-7886 *E-mail:* info@retailcouncil.org *Web Site:* www.retailcouncil.org, pg 700

Libris Distributor of the Year, 1881 Yonge St, Suite 800, Toronto, ON M4S 3C4, Canada *Tel:* 416-922-6678 *Toll Free Tel:* 888-373-8245 *Fax:* 416-467-7886 *E-mail:* info@retailcouncil.org *Web Site:* www.retailcouncil.org, pg 701

Libris Editor of the Year, 1881 Yonge St, Suite 800, Toronto, ON M4S 3C4, Canada *Tel:* 416-922-6678 *Toll Free Tel:* 888-373-8245 *Fax:* 416-467-7886 *E-mail:* info@retailcouncil.org *Web Site:* www.retailcouncil.org, pg 701

Libris Fiction Book of the Year, 1881 Yonge St, Suite 800, Toronto, ON M4S 3C4, Canada *Tel:* 416-922-6678 *Toll Free Tel:* 888-373-8245 *Fax:* 416-467-7886 *E-mail:* info@retailcouncil.org *Web Site:* www.retailcouncil.org, pg 701

Libris Publisher of the Year, 1881 Yonge St, Suite 800, Toronto, ON M4S 3C4, Canada *Tel:* 416-922-6678 *Toll Free Tel:* 888-373-8245 *Fax:* 416-467-7886 *E-mail:* info@retailcouncil.org *Web Site:* www.retailcouncil.org, pg 701

Libris Sales Rep of the Year, 1881 Yonge St, Suite 800, Toronto, ON M4S 3C4, Canada *Tel:* 416-922-6678 *Toll Free Tel:* 888-373-8245 *Fax:* 416-467-7886 *E-mail:* info@retailcouncil.org *Web Site:* www.retailcouncil.org, pg 701

Libris Small Press Publisher of the Year, 1881 Yonge St, Suite 800, Toronto, ON M4S 3C4, Canada *Tel:* 416-922-6678 *Toll Free Tel:* 888-373-8245 *Fax:* 416-467-7886 *E-mail:* info@retailcouncil.org *Web Site:* www.retailcouncil.org, pg 701

Lidec Inc, 4501, rue Drolet, Montreal, QC H2T 2G2, Canada *Tel:* 514-843-5991 *Toll Free Tel:* 800-350-5991 (CN only) *Fax:* 514-843-5252 *E-mail:* lidec@lidec.qc.ca *Web Site:* www.lidec.qc.ca, pg 490

Robert Lieberman Agency, 475 Nelson Rd, Ithaca, NY 14850 *Tel:* 607-273-8801 *Web Site:* www.kewgardensmovie.com/CUPeople/users/rhl10, pg 562

Mary Ann Liebert Inc, 140 Huguenot St, 3rd fl, New Rochelle, NY 10801-5215 *Tel:* 914-740-2100 *Toll Free Tel:* 800-654-3237 *Fax:* 914-740-2101 *E-mail:* info@liebertpub.com *Web Site:* www.liebertonline.com, pg 139

The Lieutenant-Governor's Awards for High Achievement in the Arts, 649 rue Queen, 2nd fl, Fredericton, NB E3B 1C3, Canada *Tel:* 506-444-4444 *Toll Free Tel:* 866-460-ARTS (460-2787) *Fax:* 506-444-5543 *E-mail:* nbabcanb@artsnb.ca *Web Site:* www.artsnb.ca, pg 701

Life Cycle Books, PO Box 799, Fort Collins, CO 80522 *Toll Free Tel:* 800-214-5849 *Toll Free Fax:* 888-690-8532 *E-mail:* orders@lifecyclebooks.com; support@lifecyclebooks.com *Web Site:* www.lifecyclebooks.com, pg 139

Life Cycle Books Ltd, 1085 Bellamy Rd N, Suite 20, Toronto, ON M1H 3C7, Canada *Tel:* 416-690-5860 *Toll Free Tel:* 866-880-5860 *Toll Free Fax:* 866-260-8172 *E-mail:* orders@lifecyclebooks.com; billing@lifecyclebooks.com; support@lifecyclebooks.com *Web Site:* www.lifecyclebooks.com, pg 490

Light-Beams Publishing, 10 Toon Lane, Lee, NH 03861 *Tel:* 603-659-1300 *E-mail:* info@light-beams.com *Web Site:* www.light-beams.com, pg 139

Light Publications, Hope Artiste Village, 1005 Main St, Suite 1212, Pawtucket, RI 02806 *Tel:* 401-484-0228 *E-mail:* info@lightpublications.com *Web Site:* lightpublications.com, pg 139

Light Technology Publishing, 4030 E Huntington Dr, Flagstaff, AZ 86004 *Tel:* 928-526-1345 *Toll Free Tel:* 800-450-0985 *Fax:* 928-714-1132 *E-mail:* publishing@lighttechnology.net *Web Site:* www.lighttechnology.com, pg 139

Lighthouse Publishing of the Carolinas, 2333 Barton Oaks Dr, Raleigh, NC 27614-7940 *Tel:* 919-562-8439 *E-mail:* lighthousepublishingcarolinas@gmail.com *Web Site:* lighthousepublishingofthecarolinas.com, pg 139

Ligonier Valley Writers Conference, PO Box B, Ligonier, PA 15658-1602 *Tel:* 724-238-3692, pg 652

Liguori Publications, One Liguori Dr, Liguori, MO 63057-1000 *Tel:* 636-464-2500 *Toll Free Tel:* 866-848-2492; 800-325-9521 *Fax:* 636-464-8449 *Toll Free Fax:* 800-325-9526 (sales) *E-mail:* liguori@liguori.org (sales & cust serv) *Web Site:* www.liguori.org/contact-us.html, pg 139

Ruth Lilly Poetry Prize, 61 W Superior St, Chicago, IL 60654 *Tel:* 312-787-7070 *Fax:* 312-787-6650 *E-mail:* editors@poetrymagazine.org *Web Site:* poetrymagazine.org, pg 701

Limelight Editions, 33 Plymouth St, Suite 302, Montclair, NJ 07042 *Tel:* 973-337-5034 *Fax:* 973-337-5227 *Web Site:* limelighteditions.com, pg 139

Linden Publishing Co Inc, 2006 S Mary St, Fresno, CA 93721 *Tel:* 559-233-6633 *Toll Free Tel:* 800-345-4447 (orders) *Fax:* 559-233-6933 *Web Site:* lindenpub.com, pg 139

Lindgren & Smith, 888C Eighth Ave, No 329, New York, NY 10019 *Tel:* 212-397-7330 *E-mail:* info@lindgrensmith.com *Web Site:* lindgrensmith.com, pg 584

Lindisfarne Books, 610 Main St, Great Barrington, MA 01230 *Tel:* 413-528-8233 *Fax:* 413-528-8826 *E-mail:* service@steinerbooks.org *Web Site:* www.steinerbooks.org, pg 139

Lindquist & Vennum Prize for Poetry, 1011 Washington Ave S, Suite 300, Minneapolis, MN 55415-1246 *Tel:* 612-332-3192 *Toll Free Tel:* 800-520-6455 *Fax:* 612-215-2550 *Web Site:* www.milkweed.org, pg 701

LinguaText Ltd, 103 Walker Way, Newark, DE 19711 *Tel:* 302-453-8695 *Fax:* 302-453-8601 *Web Site:* www.linguatextltd.com, pg 140

Linguistic Society of America, 1325 18 St NW, Suite 211, Washington, DC 20036-6501 *Tel:* 202-835-1714 *Fax:* 202-835-1717 *E-mail:* lsa@lsadc.org *Web Site:* www.linguisticsociety.org, pg 609

Andrew S Linick PhD, The Copyologist®, Linick Bldg, 7 Putter Lane, Middle Island, NY 11953 *Tel:* 631-924-3888 *Fax:* 631-924-8555 *E-mail:* linickgroup@gmail.com *Web Site:* www.AndrewLinickDirectMarketing.com/The-Copyologist.html; www.NewWorldPressBooks.com, pg 529

The Linick Group Inc, Linick Bldg, 7 Putter Lane, Middle Island, NY 11953 *Tel:* 631-924-3888; 631-924-8555 *Fax:* 631-924-8555 *E-mail:* linickgroup@gmail.com; andrew@AskLinick.com *Web Site:* www.AndrewLinickDirectMarketing.com/Publishers-Advice.html; www.NewWorldPressBooks.com, pg 140

Linworth Publishing, 130 Cremona Dr, Santa Barbara, CA 93117 *Tel:* 805-968-1911 *Toll Free Tel:* 800-368-6868 *Fax:* 805-685-9685 *Toll Free Fax:* 866-270-3856 *E-mail:* customerservice@abc-clio.com *Web Site:* www.abc-clio.com, pg 140

Elliot Linzer, 126-10 Powells Cove Blvd, College Point, NY 11356 *Tel:* 718-353-1261 *Fax:* 814-253-1261 *E-mail:* elinzer@juno.com, pg 529

Joseph W Lippincott Award, 50 E Huron St, Chicago, IL 60611 *Tel:* 312-280-3247 *Toll Free Tel:* 800-545-2433 (ext 3247) *Fax:* 312-944-3897 *E-mail:* awards@ala.org *Web Site:* www.ala.org, pg 701

Lippincott Williams & Wilkins, 333 Seventh Ave, New York, NY 10001 *Toll Free Tel:* 800-950-2035 *E-mail:* orders@lww.com *Web Site:* www.lww.com, pg 140

E Trina Lipton, 60 E Eighth St, Suite 15-F, New York, NY 10003 *Tel:* 212-674-5558 (call first, messages); 917-327-6886 (cell) *Fax:* 212-674-3523 *E-mail:* trinalipton@hotmail.com, pg 529

Listen & Live Audio Inc, PO Box 817, Roseland, NJ 07068-0817 *Tel:* 201-558-9000 *Toll Free Tel:* 800-653-9400 (orders) *Fax:* 201-558-9800 *Web Site:* www.listenandlive.com, pg 140

LITA/Christian Larew Memorial Scholarship in Library & Information Technology, c/o American Library Association, 50 E Huron St, Chicago, IL 60611-2795 *Toll Free Tel:* 800-545-2433 (ext 4270) *Fax:* 312-280-3257 *E-mail:* lita@ala.org *Web Site:* www.ala.org/lita, pg 702

LITA/LSSI Minority Scholarship in Library & Information Technology, c/o American Library Association, 50 E Huron St, Chicago, IL 60611-2795 *Toll Free Tel:* 800-545-2433 (ext 4270) *Fax:* 312-280-3257 *E-mail:* lita@ala.org *Web Site:* www.ala.org/lita, pg 702

LITA/OCLC Minority Scholarship in Library & Information Technology, c/o American Library Association, 50 E Huron St, Chicago, IL 60611-2795 *Toll Free Tel:* 800-545-2433 (ext 4270) *Fax:* 312-280-3257 *E-mail:* lita@ala.org *Web Site:* www.ala.org/lita, pg 702

Literary & Creative Artists Inc, 3543 Albemarle St NW, Washington, DC 20008-4213 *Tel:* 202-362-4688 *Fax:* 202-362-8875 *E-mail:* lca9643@lcadc.com (queries, no attachments) *Web Site:* www.lcadc.com, pg 562

Literary Artists Representatives, 575 West End Ave, Suite GRC, New York, NY 10024-2711 *Tel:* 212-679-7788 *Fax:* 212-595-2098 *E-mail:* litartists@aol.com, pg 562

Literary Management Group LLC, 16970 San Carlos Blvd, Suite 160-100, Fort Myers, FL 33908 *Tel:* 615-812-4445 *Web Site:* www.literarymanagementgroup.com, pg 562

The Literary Press Group of Canada, 425 Adelaide St W, Suite 700, Toronto, ON M5V 3C1, Canada *Tel:* 416-483-1321 *Fax:* 416-483-2510 *Web Site:* www.lpg.ca, pg 609

Literary Translation Projects, 400 Seventh St SW, Washington, DC 20506-0001 *Tel:* 202-682-5400; 202-682-5496 (Voice/TTY); 202-682-5034 (lit fellowships hotline) *Fax:* 202-682-5609; 202-682-5610 *E-mail:* litfellowships@arts.gov *Web Site:* www.arts.gov; www.nea.gov, pg 702

Literary Translators' Association of Canada, Concordia University, LB 601, 1455 De Maisonneuve West, Montreal, QC H3G 1M8, Canada *Tel:* 514-848-2424 (ext 8702) *E-mail:* info@attlc-ltac.org *Web Site:* www.attlc-ltac.org, pg 609

Literature Fellowship, 2410 N Old Penitentiary Rd, Boise, ID 83712 *Tel:* 208-334-2119 *Toll Free Tel:* 800-ART-FUND (278-3863 within Idaho) *Fax:* 208-334-2488 *E-mail:* info@arts.idaho.gov *Web Site:* www.arts.idaho.gov, pg 702

Little Bee Books, 853 Broadway, Suite 2014, New York, NY 10003 *E-mail:* info@littlebeebooks.com *Web Site:* www.littlebeebooks.com, pg 140

Little, Brown and Company, 1290 Avenue of the Americas, New York, NY 10019 *Tel:* 212-364-1100 *Fax:* 212-364-0952 *E-mail:* firstname.lastname@hbgusa.com *Web Site:* www.HachetteBookGroup.com, pg 141

Little, Brown Books for Young Readers, 1290 Avenue of the Americas, New York, NY 10019 *Tel:* 212-364-1100 *Toll Free Tel:* 800-759-0190 (cust serv) *Web Site:* www.HachetteBookGroup.com, pg 141

Little Chicago Editorial Services, 154 Natural Tpke, Ripton, VT 05766 *Tel:* 802-388-9782 *Web Site:* andreachesman.com, pg 530

The Little Entrepreneur, c/o Harper-Arrington, 18701 Grand River, Suite 105, Detroit, MI 48223 *Toll Free Tel:* 888-435-9234 *Fax:* 248-281-0373 *E-mail:* info@harperarringtonmedia.com *Web Site:* www.thelittlee.com, pg 141

Littleton-Griswold Prize in American Law & Society, 400 "A" St SE, Washington, DC 20003 *Tel:* 202-544-2422 *Fax:* 202-544-8307 *E-mail:* awards@historians.org *Web Site:* www.historians.org, pg 702

Littleton-Griswold Research Grants, 400 "A" St SE, Washington, DC 20003 *Tel:* 202-544-2422 *Fax:* 202-544-8307 *E-mail:* awards@historians.org *Web Site:* www.historians.org, pg 702

Liturgical Press, PO Box 7500, St John's Abbey, Collegeville, MN 56321-7500 *Tel:* 320-363-2213 *Toll Free Tel:* 800-858-5450 *Fax:* 320-363-3299 *Toll Free Fax:* 800-445-5899 *E-mail:* sales@litpress.org *Web Site:* www.litpress.org, pg 141

Liturgy Training Publications, 3949 S Racine Ave, Chicago, IL 60609-2523 *Tel:* 773-579-4900 *Toll Free Tel:* 800-933-1800 (US & CN only orders) *Fax:* 773-579-4929 *Toll Free Fax:* 800-933-7094 (US & CN only orders) *E-mail:* orders@ltp.org *Web Site:* www.ltp.org, pg 141

The Live Oak Press LLC, PO Box 60036, Palo Alto, CA 94306-0036 *Tel:* 650-853-0197 *Fax:* 815-366-8205 *E-mail:* info@liveoakpress.com *Web Site:* www.liveoakpress.com, pg 141

Livestock Publications Council, 910 Currie St, Fort Worth, TX 76107 *Tel:* 817-336-1130 *Fax:* 817-232-4820 *Web Site:* www.livestockpublications.com, pg 609

Living Language, c/o Random House Inc, 1745 Broadway, New York, NY 10019 *Tel:* 212-782-9000 *Toll Free Tel:* 800-733-3000 (orders) *Toll Free Fax:* 800-659-2436 *E-mail:* livinglanguage@randomhouse.com *Web Site:* www.livinglanguage.com, pg 142

Living Now Book Awards, 1129 Woodmere Ave, Suite B, Traverse City, MI 49686 *Tel:* 231-933-0445 *Toll Free Tel:* 800-706-4636 *Fax:* 231-933-0448 *E-mail:* awards@bookpublishing.com *Web Site:* www.livingnowawards.com, pg 702

Living Stream Ministry (LSM), 2431 W La Palma Ave, Anaheim, CA 92801 *Tel:* 714-991-4681 *Fax:* 714-236-6005 *E-mail:* books@lsm.org *Web Site:* www.lsm.org, pg 142

Livingston Press, University of West Alabama, Sta 22, Livingston, AL 35470 *Tel:* 205-652-3470 *Web Site:* www.livingstonpress.uwa.edu, pg 142

Livres Canada Books, One Nicholas, Suite 504, Ottawa, ON K1N 7B7, Canada *Tel:* 613-562-2324 *Fax:* 613-562-2329 *E-mail:* info@livrescanadabooks.com *Web Site:* www.livrescanadabooks.com, pg 609

Llewellyn Publications, 2143 Wooddale Dr, Woodbury, MN 55125 *Tel:* 651-291-1970 *Toll Free Tel:* 800-843-6666 *Fax:* 651-291-1908 *E-mail:* publicity@llewellyn.com *Web Site:* www.llewellyn.com, pg 142

The Local History Co, 112 N Woodland Rd, Pittsburgh, PA 15232-2849 *Tel:* 412-362-2294 *Toll Free Tel:* 866-362-0789 (orders) *Fax:* 412-362-8192 *E-mail:* info@thelocalhistorycompany.com; sales@thelocalhistorycompany.com *Web Site:* www.thelocalhistorycompany.com, pg 142

Locks Art Publications/Locks Gallery, 600 Washington Sq S, Philadelphia, PA 19106 *Tel:* 215-629-1000 *E-mail:* info@locksgallery.com *Web Site:* www.locksgallery.com, pg 142

Locus Awards, PO Box 13305, Oakland, CA 94661-0305 *Tel:* 510-339-9196 *Fax:* 510-339-9198 *E-mail:* locus@locusmag.com *Web Site:* www.locusmag.com, pg 702

The Gerald Loeb Awards, Gold Hall, Suite B-305, 110 Westwood Plaza, Los Angeles, CA 90095-1481 *Tel:* 310-825-4478 *Fax:* 310-825-4479 *E-mail:* loeb@anderson.ucla.edu *Web Site:* www.loeb.anderson.ucla.edu, pg 702

Loft-Mentor Series in Poetry & Creative Prose, Open Book, Suite 200, 1011 Washington Ave S, Minneapolis, MN 55415 *Tel:* 612-215-2575 *Fax:* 612-215-2576 *E-mail:* loft@loft.org *Web Site:* www.loft.org, pg 702

Loft Press Inc, 9293 Fort Valley Rd, Fort Valley, VA 22652 *Tel:* 540-933-6210 *Fax:* 540-933-6523 *E-mail:* Books@LoftPress.com, pg 142

Logos Press, 3909 Witmer Rd, Suite 416, Niagara Falls, NY 14305 *Fax:* 815-346-3514 *E-mail:* info@logos-press.com *Web Site:* www.logos-press.com, pg 142

The Jack London Award, Box 17897, Encino, CA 91416-7897 *E-mail:* cwcsfv@gmail.com, pg 703

Lone Pine Publishing, 2311 96 St, Edmonton, AB T6N 1G3, Canada *Tel:* 780-433-9333 *Toll Free Tel:* 800-661-9017 *Fax:* 780-433-9646 *Toll Free Fax:* 800-424-7173 *E-mail:* info@lonepinepublishing.com *Web Site:* www.lonepinepublishing.com, pg 490

Lonely Planet, 150 Linden St, Oakland, CA 94607 *Tel:* 510-893-8555 *Toll Free Tel:* 800-275-8555 (orders) *Fax:* 510-893-8572 *E-mail:* info@lonelyplanet.com *Web Site:* www.lonelyplanet.com, pg 142

Long River Press, 360 Swift Ave, Suite 48, South San Francisco, CA 94080 *Tel:* 650-872-7718 (ext 312) *Fax:* 650-872-7808 *E-mail:* info@longriverpress.com *Web Site:* www.chinabooks.com, pg 142

Looseleaf Law Publications Inc, 43-08 162 St, Flushing, NY 11358 *Tel:* 718-359-5559 *Toll Free Tel:* 800-647-5547 *Fax:* 718-539-0941 *E-mail:* info@looseleaf.com *Web Site:* www.looseleaflaw.com, pg 143

Judy Lopez Memorial Award For Children's Literature, 1225 Selby Ave, Los Angeles, CA 90024 *Tel:* 310-474-9917 *Fax:* 310-474-6436 *Web Site:* www.wnba-books.org/la; www.judylopezbookaward.org, pg 703

Lorenz Educational Press, 501 E Third St, Dayton, OH 45402 *Tel:* 937-228-6118 *Toll Free Tel:* 800-444-1144 *Fax:* 937-223-2042 *E-mail:* lep@lorenz.com *Web Site:* www.lorenzeducationalpress.com, pg 143

James Lorimer & Co Ltd, Publishers, 317 Adelaide St W, Suite 1002, Toronto, ON M5V 1P9, Canada *Tel:* 416-362-4762 *Fax:* 416-362-3939 *Web Site:* www.lorimer.ca, pg 490

Los Angeles Times Book Prizes, 202 W First St, Los Angeles, CA 90012 *Tel:* 213-237-5775 *Toll Free Tel:* 800-528-4637 *Fax:* 213-237-7679 *Web Site:* www.latimesbookprizes.com, pg 703

Lost Classics Book Company LLC, 411 N Wales Dr, Lake Wales, FL 33853-3881 *Tel:* 863-632-1981 (edit off) *E-mail:* mgeditor@lostclassicsbooks.com *Web Site:* www.lostclassicsbooks.com, pg 143

Lost Horse Press, 105 Lost Horse Lane, Sandpoint, ID 83864 *Tel:* 208-255-4410 *E-mail:* losthorsepress@mindspring.com *Web Site:* www.losthorsepress.org, pg 143

Lott Representatives, PO Box 3607, New York, NY 10163 *Tel:* 212-755-5737 *Web Site:* www.lottreps.com, pg 584

Lotus Press, PO Box 325, Twin Lakes, WI 53181-0325 *Tel:* 262-889-8561 *Toll Free Tel:* 800-824-6396 (orders) *Fax:* 262-889-8591 *E-mail:* lotuspress@lotuspress.com *Web Site:* www.lotuspress.com, pg 143

Louise Louis/Emily F Bourne Student Poetry Award, 15 Gramercy Park, New York, NY 10003 *Tel:* 212-254-9628 *Fax:* 212-673-2352 *Web Site:* www.poetrysociety.org, pg 703

Louisiana State University Creative Writing Program MFA, English Dept, 260 Allen Hall, Baton Rouge, LA 70803 *Tel:* 225-578-5922 *Fax:* 225-578-4129 *Web Site:* www.lsu.edu; www.english.lsu.edu/dept/programs/grad/creative_writing, pg 660

Louisiana State University Press, 338 Johnston Hall, Baton Rouge, LA 70803 *Tel:* 225-578-6294 *Fax:* 225-578-6461 *E-mail:* lsupress@lsu.edu *Web Site:* lsupress.org, pg 143

Louisville Grawemeyer Award in Religion, 1044 Alta Vista Rd, Louisville, KY 40205-1798 *Tel:* 502-895-3411 *Toll Free Tel:* 800-264-1839 *Fax:* 502-894-2286 *E-mail:* grawemeyer@lpts.edu *Web Site:* www.grawemeyer.org, pg 703

Love Creek Annual Short Play Festival, 2144 45 Ave, Long Island City, NY 11101 *Tel:* 718-786-9397 *E-mail:* lovecreekle@aol.com; squaank@yahoo.com (submissions), pg 703

Love Inspired Books, 233 Broadway, Suite 1001, New York, NY 10279 *Tel:* 212-553-4200 *Fax:* 212-227-8969 *E-mail:* customer_service@harlequin.ca *Web Site:* www.harlequin.com, pg 143

Love Publishing Co, 9101 E Kenyon Ave, Suite 2200, Denver, CO 80237 *Tel:* 303-221-7333 *Toll Free Tel:* 877-240-6396 *Fax:* 303-221-7444 *E-mail:* lpc@lovepublishing.com *Web Site:* www.lovepublishing.com, pg 143

Loving Healing Press Inc, 5145 Pontiac Trail, Ann Arbor, MI 48105 *Tel:* 734-417-4266 *Toll Free Tel:* 888-761-6268 (US & CN) *Fax:* 734-663-6861 *E-mail:* info@lovinghealing.com; info@lhpress.com *Web Site:* www.lovinghealing.com; www.modernhistorypress.com (imprint), pg 143

James Russell Lowell Prize, 26 Broadway, 3rd fl, New York, NY 10004-1789 *Tel:* 646-576-5141 *Fax:* 646-458-0030 *E-mail:* awards@mla.org *Web Site:* www.mla.org, pg 703

Lowenstein Associates Inc, 115 E 23 St, 4th fl, New York, NY 10010 *Tel:* 212-206-1630 *Fax:* 212-727-0280 *E-mail:* assistant@bookhaven.com (queries, no attachments) *Web Site:* www.lowensteinassociates.com, pg 562

Pat Lowther Memorial Award, 192 Spadina Ave, Suite 312, Toronto, ON M5T 2C2, Canada *Tel:* 416-504-1657 *Fax:* 416-504-0096 *E-mail:* readings@poets.ca *Web Site:* poets.ca, pg 703

Loyola Press, 3441 N Ashland Ave, Chicago, IL 60657 *Tel:* 773-281-1818 *Toll Free Tel:* 800-621-1008 *Fax:* 773-281-0555 (cust serv); 773-281-4129 (edit) *E-mail:* customerservice@loyolapress.com *Web Site:* www.loyolapress.com, pg 144

LPD Press, 925 Salamanca NW, Los Ranchos de Albuquerque, NM 87107-5647 *Tel:* 505-344-9382 *Fax:* 505-345-5129 *E-mail:* info@nmsantos.com *Web Site:* nmsantos.com, pg 144

LRP Publications, 360 Hiatt Dr, Palm Beach Gardens, FL 33418 *Tel:* 561-622-6520 *Toll Free Tel:* 800-341-7874 *Fax:* 561-622-2423 *E-mail:* custserve@lrp.com *Web Site:* www.lrp.com, pg 144

LRS, 19146 Van Ness Ave, Torrance, CA 90501 *Tel:* 310-354-2610 *Toll Free Tel:* 800-255-5002 *Fax:* 310-354-2601 *E-mail:* largeprintsb@aol.com *Web Site:* lrs-largeprint.com, pg 144

Lucent Books®, 27500 Drake Rd, Farmington Hills, MI 48331 *Tel:* 248-699-4253 *Fax:* 248-699-8004 *E-mail:* gale.customerservice@cengage.com *Web Site:* solutions.cengage.com/greenhaven, pg 144

Lucky Marble Books, 2671 Bristol Rd, Columbus, OH 43221 *Tel:* 614-264-5588 *E-mail:* sales@pagespringpublishing.com *Web Site:* www.luckymarblebooks.com, pg 144

Jeremiah Ludington Award, 37 Main St, Suite 203, Warrenton, VA 20186 *Tel:* 540-318-7770 *Fax:* 202-962-3939 *E-mail:* info@edupaperback.org *Web Site:* www.edupaperback.org, pg 703

Lugus Publications, 28 Industrial St, Studio 203, Toronto, ON M4G 1Y9, Canada *Tel:* 416-467-0924 *Web Site:* www.thestudio203.com, pg 490

Lumina Datamatics, 4 Collins Ave, Plymouth, MA 02360 *Tel:* 508-746-0300 *Fax:* 508-746-3233 *E-mail:* info@luminadatamatics.com *Web Site:* luminadatamatics.com, pg 530

Luminis Books Inc, 1950 E Greyhound Pass, Suite 18, PMB 280, Carmel, IN 46033 *Tel:* 317-840-5838 *E-mail:* editor@luminisbooks.com *Web Site:* www.luminisbooks.com, pg 144

Luna Bisonte Prods, 137 Leland Ave, Columbus, OH 43214 *Tel:* 614-846-4126 *Web Site:* www.johnmbennett.net; www.lulu.com/spotlight/lunabisonteprods, pg 144

Lush Triumphant Literary Awards, PO Box 3008, MPO, Vancouver, BC V6B 3X5, Canada *Tel:* 604-876-8710 *Fax:* 604-879-2667 *E-mail:* subter@portal.ca *Web Site:* www.subterrain.ca, pg 703

Lutheran Braille Workers Inc, 13471 California St, Yucaipa, CA 92399 *Tel:* 909-795-8977 *Fax:* 909-795-8970 *E-mail:* lbw@lbwinc.org *Web Site:* www.lbwinc.org, pg 144

Lyceum Books Inc, 5758 S Blackstone Ave, Chicago, IL 60637 *Tel:* 773-643-1902 *Fax:* 773-643-1903 *E-mail:* lyceum@lyceumbooks.com *Web Site:* www.lyceumbooks.com, pg 144

Lyndon B Johnson School of Public Affairs, University of Texas at Austin, 2315 Red River St, Austin, TX 78712-1536 *Tel:* 512-471-3200 *Fax:* 512-471-4697 *E-mail:* lbjdeansoffice@austin.utexas.edu *Web Site:* www.utexas.edu/lbj, pg 144

Lynx House Press, 420 W 24 St, Spokane, WA 99203 *Tel:* 509-624-4894 *E-mail:* lynxhousepress@gmail.com *Web Site:* www.lynxhousepress.org, pg 144

Elizabeth Lyon, 3530 E Game Farm Rd, No 39, Springfield, OR 97477 *Tel:* 541-357-4181 *E-mail:* elyon123@comcast.net *Web Site:* www.elizabethlyon.com, pg 530

Thomas J Lyon Book Award in Western American Literary and Cultural Studies, PO Box 6815, Logan, UT 84341 *Web Site:* www.westernlit.org/thomas-j-lyon-book-award-in-western-american-literary-and-cultural-studies/; www.westernlit.org, pg 703

The Lyons Press, 246 Goose Lane, Guilford, CT 06437 *Tel:* 203-458-4500 *Fax:* 203-458-4668 *E-mail:* info@rowman.com *Web Site:* www.lyonspress.com; rowman.com, pg 144

Lyric Poetry Award, 15 Gramercy Park, New York, NY 10003 *Tel:* 212-254-9628 *Fax:* 212-673-2352 *Web Site:* www.poetrysociety.org, pg 704

Lyric Poetry Prizes, PO Box 110, Jericho, VT 05465 *Tel:* 802-899-3993 *Fax:* 802-899-3993 *E-mail:* themuse@thelyricmagazine.com *Web Site:* thelyricmagazine.com, pg 704

Donald Maass Literary Agency, 121 W 27 St, Suite 801, New York, NY 10001 *Tel:* 212-727-8383 *Fax:* 212-727-3271 *E-mail:* info@maassagency.com *Web Site:* www.maassagency.com, pg 562

Macavity Award, 7155 Marlborough Terr, Berkeley, CA 94705 *Tel:* 510-845-3600 *Web Site:* www.mysteryreaders.org, pg 704

Gina Maccoby Literary Agency, PO Box 60, Chappaqua, NY 10514-0060 *Tel:* 914-238-5630 *E-mail:* query@maccobylit.com *Web Site:* www.publishersmarketplace.com/members/GinaMaccoby, pg 562

Sir John A Macdonald Prize, 130 Albert St, Suite 501, Ottawa, ON K1P 5G4, Canada *Tel:* 613-233-7885 *Fax:* 613-565-5445 *E-mail:* cha-shc@cha-shc.ca *Web Site:* www.cha-shc.ca, pg 704

MacDowell Fellowships, 100 High St, Peterborough, NH 03458 *Tel:* 603-924-3886 *Fax:* 603-924-9142 *E-mail:* info@macdowellcolony.org; admissions@macdowellcolony.org *Web Site:* www.macdowellcolony.org, pg 704

Machigonne Fiction Contest, PO Box 5101, Hanover, NH 03755 *E-mail:* info@newguardreview.com *Web Site:* www.newguardreview.com, pg 704

Macmillan, 175 Fifth Ave, New York, NY 10010 *Tel:* 646-307-5151 *Fax:* 212-420-9314 *E-mail:* firstname.lastname@macmillan.com *Web Site:* www.macmillan.com, pg 145

Macmillan Audio, 175 Fifth Ave, New York, NY 10010 *Tel:* 646-307-5151 *Toll Free Tel:* 888-330-8477 (cust serv) *Fax:* 917-534-0980 *Web Site:* www.macmillanaudio.com, pg 145

Macmillan Higher Education, 41 Madison Ave, 37th fl, New York, NY 10010 *Tel:* 212-576-9400 *Fax:* 212-689-2383 *Web Site:* www.macmillanhighered.com, pg 145

Macmillan Reference USA™, 12 Lunar Dr, Woodbridge, CT 06525 *Tel:* 203-397-2600 *Toll Free Tel:* 800-444-0799 *Fax:* 203-397-8296 *Web Site:* www.gale.cengage.com/macmillan/, pg 145

C B MacPherson Prize, 260 rue Dalhousie St, Suite 204, Ottawa, ON K1N 7E4, Canada *Tel:* 613-562-1202 *Fax:* 613-241-0019 *E-mail:* cpsa-acsp@cpsa-acsp.ca *Web Site:* www.cpsa-acsp.ca, pg 704

Madison Press Books, 155 Edward St, Suite 1, Aurora, ON L4G 1W3, Canada *Tel:* 905-841-9300 *E-mail:* info@madisonpressbooks.com *Web Site:* www.madisonpressbooks.com, pg 490

Madonna House Publications, RR 2, 2888 Dafoe Rd, Combermere, ON K0J 1L0, Canada *Tel:* 613-756-3728 *Toll Free Tel:* 888-703-7110 *Fax:* 613-756-0103 *Toll Free Fax:* 877-717-2888 *E-mail:* publications@madonnahouse.org *Web Site:* www.madonnahouse.org/publications, pg 491

Magazine Merit Awards, 4727 Wilshire Blvd, Suite 301, Los Angeles, CA 90010 *Tel:* 323-782-1010; 310-403-0675 (cell) *Fax:* 323-782-1892 *E-mail:* membership@scbwi.org; scbwi@scbwi.org *Web Site:* www.scbwi.org, pg 704

The Magazine of the Year Award, 27 Union Sq W, Suite 207, New York, NY 10003 *Tel:* 212-223-3332 *Fax:* 212-223-5880 *E-mail:* mail@spd.org *Web Site:* www.spd.org, pg 704

Magazines Canada (MC), 425 Adelaide St W, Suite 700, Toronto, ON M5V 3C1, Canada *Tel:* 416-504-0274 *Fax:* 416-504-0437 *E-mail:* info@magazinescanada.ca *Web Site:* www.magazinescanada.ca/development/magnet, pg 609

Mage Publishers Inc, 1408 35 St NW, Washington, DC 20007 *Tel:* 202-342-1642 *Fax:* 202-342-9269 *Web Site:* www.mage.com, pg 145

Magic Hill Press LLC, 144 Magic Hill Rd, Hinesburg, VT 05461 *Tel:* 802-482-3287 *E-mail:* MagicHillPress@gmail.com *Web Site:* www.MagicHillPress.com, pg 508

The Magni Co, 7106 Wellington Point Rd, McKinney, TX 75070 *Tel:* 972-540-2050 *Fax:* 972-540-1057 *E-mail:* sales@magnico.com; info@magnico.com *Web Site:* www.magnico.com, pg 145

Maharishi University of Management Press, 1000 N Fourth St, Dept 1155, Fairfield, IA 52557-1155 *Tel:* 641-472-1101 *Toll Free Tel:* 800-831-6523 *Fax:* 641-472-1122 *E-mail:* mumpress@mum.edu *Web Site:* www.mumpress.com, pg 145

Maine Writers & Publishers Alliance, 314 Forest Ave, Rm 318, Portland, ME 04101 *Tel:* 207-228-8263 *Fax:* 207-228-8150 *E-mail:* info@mainewriters.org *Web Site:* mainewriters.org, pg 609

Maine Writers Conference at Ocean Park, 14 Temple Ave, Ocean Park, ME 04063 *Tel:* 401-598-1424 *E-mail:* www.opa@oceanpark.org *Web Site:* www.oceanpark.org, pg 652

Maisonneuve Press, 6423 Adelphi Rd, Hyattsville, MD 20782 *Tel:* 301-277-7505 *Fax:* 301-277-2467 *Web Site:* www.maisonneuvepress.com, pg 145

J Russell Major Prize, 400 "A" St SE, Washington, DC 20003 *Tel:* 202-544-2422 *Fax:* 202-544-8307 *E-mail:* awards@historians.org *Web Site:* www.historians.org, pg 704

Malahat Review Long Poem Prize, University of Victoria, Box 1700, Sta CSC, Victoria, BC V8W 2Y2, Canada *Tel:* 250-721-8524 *Fax:* 250-472-5051 *E-mail:* malahat@uvic.ca *Web Site:* www.malahatreview.ca, pg 704

Gene E & Adele R Malott Prize for Recording Community Activism, 2809 Berkeley Dr, Birmingham, AL 35242 *Tel:* 205-726-2424 *Fax:* 205-726-4216 *E-mail:* langumtrust@gmail.com *Web Site:* www.langumtrust.org, pg 705

Management Advisory Services & Publications (MASP), PO Box 81151, Wellesley Hills, MA 02481-0001 *Tel:* 781-235-2895 *Fax:* 781-235-5446 *E-mail:* info@masp.com *Web Site:* www.masp.com, pg 145

Management Concepts Inc, 8230 Leesburg Pike, Suite 800, Vienna, VA 22182 *Tel:* 703-790-9595 *Toll Free Tel:* 800 506-4450 *Fax:* 703-790-1371 *E-mail:* info@managementconcepts.com *Web Site:* www.managementconcepts.com, pg 146

Management Sciences for Health, 200 Rivers Edge Dr, Medford, MA 02155 *Tel:* 617-250-9500 *Fax:* 617-250-9090 *E-mail:* bookstore@msh.org *Web Site:* www.msh.org, pg 146

Mandala Earth, 800 "A" St, San Rafael, CA 94901 *Tel:* 415-526-1370 *Toll Free Fax:* 866-509-0515 *E-mail:* info@mandalapublishing.com *Web Site:* www.mandalaeartheditions.com, pg 146

Manhattan Publishing Co, 670 White Plains Rd, Scarsdale, NY 10583 *Tel:* 914-472-4650 *Fax:* 914-472-4316 *E-mail:* coe@manhattanpublishing.com *Web Site:* www.manhattanpublishing.com, pg 146

Manhattanville College Master of Arts in Writing Program, 2900 Purchase St, Purchase, NY 10577 *Tel:* 914-323-5239 *Fax:* 914-323-3122 *Web Site:* www.mville.edu/writing, pg 660

Manic D Press Inc, 250 Banks St, San Francisco, CA 94110 *Tel:* 415-648-8288 *E-mail:* info@manicdpress.com *Web Site:* www.manicdpress.com, pg 146

Manitoba Arts Council, 525-93 Lombard Ave, Winnipeg, MB R3B 3B1, Canada *Tel:* 204-945-2237 *Toll Free Tel:* 866-994-2787 *Fax:* 204-945-5925 *E-mail:* info@artscouncil.mb.ca *Web Site:* artscouncil.mb.ca, pg 609

The Manitoba Writers' Guild Inc, 218-100 Arthur St, Winnipeg, MB R3B 1H3, Canada *Tel:* 204-944-8013 *E-mail:* info@mbwriter.mb.ca *Web Site:* www.mbwriter.mb.ca, pg 609

Carol Mann Agency, 55 Fifth Ave, New York, NY 10003 *Tel:* 212-206-5635 *Fax:* 212-675-4809 *E-mail:* submissions@carolmannagency.com *Web Site:* www.carolmannagency.com, pg 563

Margaret Mann Citation, 50 E Huron St, Chicago, IL 60611 *Tel:* 312-280-5037 *Toll Free Tel:* 800-545-2433 *Fax:* 312-280-5033 *E-mail:* alcts@ala.org *Web Site:* www.ala.org/alcts, pg 705

Phyllis Manner, 17 Springdale Rd, New Rochelle, NY 10804 *Tel:* 914-834-4707 *Fax:* 914-834-4707 *E-mail:* pmanner@aol.com, pg 530

Manning Publications Co, PO Box 761, Shelter Island, NY 11964 *Tel:* 203-626-1510 *E-mail:* sales@manning.com; support@manning.com (cust serv) *Web Site:* www.manning.com, pg 146

Freya Manston Associates Inc, 145 W 58 St, New York, NY 10019 *Tel:* 212-247-3075, pg 563

Manus & Associates Literary Agency Inc, 425 Sherman Ave, Suite 200, Palo Alto, CA 94306 *Tel:* 650-470-5151 *Fax:* 650-470-5159 *E-mail:* manuslit@manuslit.com *Web Site:* www.manuslit.com, pg 563

Many Voices Fellowships, 2301 Franklin Ave E, Minneapolis, MN 55406-1099 *Tel:* 612-332-7481 *Fax:* 612-332-6037 *E-mail:* info@pwcenter.org *Web Site:* www.pwcenter.org, pg 705

MapEasy Inc, PO Box 80, Wainscott, NY 11975-0080 *Tel:* 631-537-6213 *Toll Free Tel:* 888-627-3279 *Fax:* 631-537-4541 *E-mail:* info@mapeasy.com *Web Site:* www.mapeasy.com, pg 146

MAR*CO Products Inc, 1443 Old York Rd, Warminster, PA 18974 *Tel:* 215-956-0313 *Toll Free Tel:* 800-448-2197 *Fax:* 215-956-9041 *E-mail:* help@marcoproducts.com *Web Site:* www.marcoproducts.com, pg 147

Marathon Press, 1500 Square Turn Blvd, Norfolk, NE 68701 *Tel:* 402-371-5040 *Toll Free Tel:* 800-228-0629 *Fax:* 402-371-9382 *Web Site:* www.marathonpress.com, pg 147

March Tenth Inc, 24 Hillside Terr, Montvale, NJ 07645 *Tel:* 201-387-6551 *Fax:* 201-387-6552 *Web Site:* www.marchtenthinc.com, pg 563

Denise Marcil Literary Agency LLC, 483 Westover Rd, Stamford, CT 06902 *Tel:* 203-327-9970 *Fax:* 203-327-9970 *E-mail:* dmla@denisemarcilagency.com *Web Site:* www.denisemarcilagency.com, pg 563

Danny Marcus Word Worker, 62 Washington St, Suite 2, Marblehead, MA 01945-3553 *Tel:* 781-631-3886; 781-290-9174 (cell) *Fax:* 781-631-3886 *E-mail:* emildanelle@yahoo.com, pg 530

Maren Green Publishing Inc, 5630 Memorial Ave N, Suite 3, Oak Park Heights, MN 55082 *Tel:* 651-439-4500 *Toll Free Tel:* 800-287-1512 *Fax:* 651-439-4532 *E-mail:* info@marengreen.com *Web Site:* www.marengreen.com, pg 147

Marfield Prize, 2017 "I" St NW, Washington, DC 20006-1804 *E-mail:* award@artsclubofwashington.org *Web Site:* artsclubofwashington.org, pg 705

Marian Library Medal, 300 College Park, Dayton, OH 45469-1390 *Tel:* 937-229-4214 *Fax:* 937-229-4258 *Web Site:* campus.udayton.edu/mary/mlmedal.html, pg 705

Marick Press, PO Box 36253, Grosse Pointe Farms, MI 48236 *Tel:* 313-407-9236 *E-mail:* orders@marickpress.com *Web Site:* www.marickpress.com, pg 147

Marick Press Poetry Prize Competition, PO Box 36253, Grosse Pointe Farms, MI 48236 *Tel:* 313-407-9236 *Web Site:* www.marickpress.com, pg 705

Marine Education Textbooks, 124 N Van Ave, Houma, LA 70363-5895 *Tel:* 985-879-3866 *Fax:* 985-879-3911 *E-mail:* email@marineeducationtextbooks.com *Web Site:* www.marineeducationtextbooks.com, pg 147

Marine Techniques Publishing, 126 Western Ave, Suite 266, Augusta, ME 04330-7249 *Tel:* 207-622-7984 *E-mail:* info@marinetechpublishing.com; sales@marinetechpublishing.com *Web Site:* marinetechpublishing.com; www.groups.yahoo.com/group/marinetechniquespublishing, pg 147

Marion Street Press LLC, 4207 SE Woodstock Blvd, No 168, Portland, OR 97206 *Tel:* 503-888-4624 *Toll Free Fax:* 866-571-8359 *E-mail:* marionbooks@outlook.com *Web Site:* www.marionstreetpress.com, pg 147

Maritime Writers' Workshops, PO Box 4400, Fredericton, NB E3B 5A3, Canada *Tel:* 506-458-7106 *Toll Free Tel:* 866-599-4646 *Fax:* 506-458-5012 *E-mail:* extend@unb.ca *Web Site:* www.unb.ca/cel, pg 652

Markowski International Publishers, One Oakglade Circle, Hummelstown, PA 17036-9525 *Tel:* 717-566-0468 *E-mail:* info@possibilitypress.com *Web Site:* www.possibilitypress.com; www.aeronauticalpublishers.com, pg 147

Markson Thoma Literary Agency Inc, 44 Greenwich Ave, New York, NY 10011 *Tel:* 212-243-8480 *Fax:* 212-691-9014 *E-mail:* info@marksonthoma.com *Web Site:* www.marksonthoma.com, pg 563

Mildred Marmur Associates Ltd, 2005 Palmer Ave, PMB 127, Larchmont, NY 10538 *Tel:* 914-834-1170 *Fax:* 914-833-1175 *E-mail:* marmur@westnet.com, pg 563

Marquette University Press, 1415 W Wisconsin Ave, Milwaukee, WI 53233 *Tel:* 414-288-1564 *Toll Free Tel:* 800-247-6553 (cust serv) *Fax:* 414-288-7813 *Web Site:* www.marquette.edu/mupress, pg 147

Marquis Who's Who LLC, 430 Mountain Ave, Suite 400, New Providence, NJ 07974 *Tel:* 908-673-1000 *Toll Free Tel:* 800-473-7020 *Fax:* 908-673-1189 (cust serv); 908-673-1179 (edit) *E-mail:* info@marquiswhoswho.com; customerservice@marquiswhoswho.com (cust serv, sales) *Web Site:* www.marquiswhoswho.com, pg 148

Morton Marr Poetry Prize, PO Box 750374, Dallas, TX 75275-0374 *Fax:* 214-768-1408 *E-mail:* swr@mail.smu.edu *Web Site:* www.smu.edu/southwestreview, pg 705

Helen & Howard R Marraro Prize in Italian History, 400 "A" St SE, Washington, DC 20003 *Tel:* 202-544-2422 *Fax:* 202-544-8307 *E-mail:* awards@historians.org *Web Site:* www.historians.org, pg 705

Howard R Marraro Prize, 26 Broadway, 3rd fl, New York, NY 10004-1789 *Tel:* 646-576-5141 *Fax:* 646-458-0030 *E-mail:* awards@mla.org *Web Site:* www.mla.org, pg 705

Marriage Transformation LLC, PO Box 249, Harrison, TN 37341 *Tel:* 423-599-0153 *Web Site:* www.marriagetransformation.com, pg 148

Marsal Lyon Literary Agency LLC, 665 San Rodolfo Dr, Suite 124, PMB 121, Solana Beach, CA 92075 *Tel:* 760-814-8507 *Web Site:* www.marsallyonliteraryagency.com, pg 563

Marshall & Swift, 777 S Figueroa St, 12th fl, Los Angeles, CA 90017 *Tel:* 213-683-9000 *Toll Free Tel:* 800-544-2678 *Fax:* 213-683-9043 *E-mail:* csinquiry@marshallswift.com *Web Site:* www.marshallswift.com, pg 148

Marshall Cavendish Corp, 99 White Plains Rd, Tarrytown, NY 10591-9001 *Tel:* 914-332-8888 *Toll Free Tel:* 800-821-9881 *Fax:* 914-332-8102 *E-mail:* mce@marshallcavendish.com *Web Site:* www.mceducation.us, pg 148

The Evan Marshall Agency, One Pacio Ct, Roseland, NJ 07068-1121 *Tel:* 973-287-6216 *Fax:* 973-488-7910, pg 564

The Martell Agency, 1350 Avenue of the Americas, Suite 1205, New York, NY 10019 *Tel:* 212-317-2672 *Web Site:* www.themartellagency.com, pg 564

Martin Literary Management, 7683 SE 27 St, No 307, Mercer Island, WA 98040 *Tel:* 206-466-1773 (no queries) *Fax:* 206-466-1774 *Web Site:* www.martinliterarymanagement.com, pg 564

Martin-McLean Literary Associates LLC, 5023 W 120 Ave, Suite 228, Broomfield, CO 80020 *Tel:* 303-465-2056 *Fax:* 303-465-2057 *E-mail:* martinmcleanlit@aol.com *Web Site:* www.martinmcleanlit.com; www.mcleanlit.com, pg 564

Martindale LLC, 121 Chanlon Rd, 1st fl, New Providence, NJ 07974 *Tel:* 908-464-6800 *Toll Free Tel:* 800-526-4902 *Fax:* 908-464-3553 *E-mail:* info@martindale.com *Web Site:* www.martindale.com, pg 148

Martingale®, 19021 120 Ave NE, Suite 102, Bothell, WA 98011 *Tel:* 425-483-3313 *Toll Free Tel:* 800-426-3126 *Fax:* 425-486-7596 *E-mail:* info@martingale-pub.com *Web Site:* www.martingale-pub.com, pg 148

Maryland Historical Society, 201 W Monument St, Baltimore, MD 21201 *Tel:* 410-685-3750 *Fax:* 410-385-2105 *Web Site:* www.mdhs.org, pg 148

Maryland History Press, PO Box 206, Fruitland, MD 21826-0206 *Tel:* 410-742-2682 *E-mail:* sales@marylandhistorypress.com *Web Site:* www.marylandhistorypress.com, pg 148

Marymark Press, 45-08 Old Millstone Dr, East Windsor, NJ 08520 *Tel:* 609-443-0646, pg 148

Mason Crest Publishers, 450 Parkway Dr, Suite D, Broomall, PA 19008 *Tel:* 610-543-6200 *Toll Free Tel:* 866-MCP-BOOK (627-2665) *Fax:* 610-543-3878 *Web Site:* www.masoncrest.com, pg 149

Massachusetts Book Awards, Simons College - GSLIS, 300 The Fenway, Boston, MA 02115 *Tel:* 617-521-2719 *Fax:* 617-521-3035 *E-mail:* bookawards@massbook.org *Web Site:* www.massbook.org, pg 705

Massachusetts College of Art & Design Writing Children's Literature, 621 Huntington Ave, Boston, MA 02115 *Tel:* 617-879-7200 *Fax:* 617-879-7171 *E-mail:* ce@massart.edu *Web Site:* www.massart.edu/ce, pg 661

The Massachusetts Historical Society, 1154 Boylston St, Boston, MA 02215-3695 *Tel:* 617-536-1608 *Fax:* 617-859-0074 *E-mail:* publications@masshist.org *Web Site:* www.masshist.org, pg 149

Massachusetts Institute of Technology Libraries, 77 Massachusetts Ave, Bldg 14-S, Rm 0551, Cambridge, MA 02139-4307 *Tel:* 617-253-5671 *Web Site:* libraries.mit.edu/docs, pg 149

Master Books, PO Box 726, Green Forest, AR 72638-0726 *Tel:* 870-438-5288 *Fax:* 870-438-5120 *E-mail:* submissions@newleafpress.net *Web Site:* www.nlpg.com, pg 149

Master Point Press, 331 Douglas Ave, Toronto, ON M5M 1H2, Canada *Tel:* 416-781-0351 *Fax:* 416-781-1831 *E-mail:* info@masterpointpress.com *Web Site:* www.masterpointpress.com; www.ebooksbridge.com (ebook sales), pg 491

Masters Literary Awards, PO Box 17897, Encino, CA 91416-7897 *Tel:* 818-377-4006 *E-mail:* titan91416@yahoo.com, pg 705

Materials Research Society, 506 Keystone Dr, Warrendale, PA 15086-7537 *Tel:* 724-779-3003 *Fax:* 724-779-8313 *E-mail:* info@mrs.org *Web Site:* www.mrs.org, pg 149

Math Solutions®, One Harbor Dr, Suite 101, Sausalito, CA 94965 *Tel:* 415-332-4181 *Toll Free Tel:* 800-868-9092 *Fax:* 415-331-1931 *Toll Free Fax:* 877-942-8837 *E-mail:* info@mathsolutions.com; orders@mathsolutions.com *Web Site:* www.mathsolutions.com, pg 149

Math Teachers Press Inc, 4850 Park Glen Rd, Minneapolis, MN 55416 *Tel:* 952-545-6535 *Toll Free Tel:* 800-852-2435 *Fax:* 952-546-7502 *E-mail:* info@movingwithmath.com *Web Site:* www.movingwithmath.com, pg 149

The Mathematical Association of America, 1529 18 St NW, Washington, DC 20036-1358 *Tel:* 202-387-5200 *Toll Free Tel:* 800-741-9415 *Fax:* 202-265-2384 *E-mail:* maahq@maa.org *Web Site:* www.maa.org, pg 149

Amy Mathers Teen Book Award, 40 Orchard View Blvd, Suite 217, Toronto, ON M4R 1B9, Canada *Tel:* 416-975-0010 *Fax:* 416-975-8970 *E-mail:* info@bookcentre.ca *Web Site:* www.bookcentre.ca, pg 706

Joy Matkowski, 212 Ridge Hill Rd, Mechanicsburg, PA 17050 *Tel:* 717-620-8881 *E-mail:* jmatkowski1@comcast.net, pg 530

Harold Matson Co Inc, 276 Fifth Ave, New York, NY 10001 *Tel:* 212-679-4490 *Fax:* 212-545-1224, pg 564

Matt Cohen Prize: In Celebration of a Writing Life, 460 Richmond St W, Suite 600, Toronto, ON M5V 1Y1, Canada *Tel:* 416-504-8222 *Toll Free Tel:* 877-906-6548 *Fax:* 416-504-9090 *E-mail:* info@writerstrust.com *Web Site:* www.writerstrust.com, pg 706

Mature Women Scholarship Grant - Art/Letters/Music, c/o National Pen Women-Scholarship, Pen Arts Bldg, 1300 17 St NW, Washington, DC 20036-1973 *Tel:* 202-785-1997 *Fax:* 202-452-8868 *E-mail:* contact@nlapw.org *Web Site:* www.nlapw.org, pg 706

Maven House Press, 4 Snead Ct, Palmyra, VA 22963 *Tel:* 610-883-7988 *Toll Free Fax:* 888-894-3403 *E-mail:* info@mavenhousepress.com *Web Site:* mavenhousepress.com, pg 149

Peter Mayeux, 8148 Regent Dr, Lincoln, NE 68507-3366 *Tel:* 402-466-8547 *E-mail:* pm41923@windstream.net, pg 530

Mazda Publishers Inc, One Park Plaza, Suite 600, Irvine, CA 92614 *Tel:* 714-751-5252 *Fax:* 714-751-4805 *E-mail:* mazdapub@aol.com *Web Site:* www.mazdapub.com, pg 149

Maxim Mazumdar New Play Competition, One Curtain Up Alley, Buffalo, NY 14202-1911 *Tel:* 716-852-2600 *E-mail:* publicrelations@alleyway.com *Web Site:* alleyway.com, pg 706

MB Artists, 775 Sixth Ave, Suite 6, New York, NY 10001 *Tel:* 212-689-7830 *Fax:* 212-689-7829 *Web Site:* www.mbartists.com, pg 584

McBooks Press Inc, ID Booth Bldg, 520 N Meadow St, Ithaca, NY 14850 *Tel:* 607-272-2114 *Fax:* 607-273-6068 *E-mail:* mcbooks@mcbooks.com *Web Site:* www.mcbooks.com, pg 150

Margret McBride Literary Agency, PO Box 9128, La Jolla, CA 92038 *Tel:* 858-454-1550 *E-mail:* staff@mcbridelit.com *Web Site:* www.mcbrideliterary.com, pg 564

Janet B McCabe Poetry Prize, 1041 N Taft Hill Rd, Fort Collins, CO 80521 *Tel:* 970-449-2726 *E-mail:* editor@ruminatemagazine.org *Web Site:* www.ruminatemagazine.com, pg 706

E J McCarthy Agency, 405 Maple St, Suite A, Mill Valley, CA 94941 *Tel:* 415-383-6639 *Fax:* 415-383-6639 *E-mail:* ejmagency@gmail.com *Web Site:* www.publishersmarketplace.com/members/ejmccarthy, pg 565

Gerard McCauley Agency Inc, PO Box 844, Katonah, NY 10536-0844 *Tel:* 914-232-5700, pg 565

McClanahan Publishing House Inc, 107 W Main, Princeton, KY 42445 *Tel:* 270-963-9005 *E-mail:* books@kybooks.com *Web Site:* kybooks.com, pg 150

Anita D McClellan Associates, 464 Common St, Suite 142, Belmont, MA 02478-2704 *Tel:* 617-575-9203 *Fax:* 617-315-8983 *E-mail:* adm@anitamcclellan.com *Web Site:* www.anitamcclellan.com, pg 530, 565

McClelland & Stewart Ltd, One Toronto St, Toronto, ON M5C 2V6, Canada *Tel:* 416-364-4449 *Fax:* 416-957-1587 *E-mail:* editorial@mcclelland.com *Web Site:* www.mcclelland.com, pg 491

McCutchan Publishing Corp, 2694 Ohart Rd, Richmond, CA 94806 *Tel:* 510-758-5510 *Toll Free Tel:* 800-227-1540 *Fax:* 510-758-6078 *E-mail:* mccutchanpublish@sbcglobal.net *Web Site:* www.mccutchanpublishing.com, pg 150

The McDonald & Woodward Publishing Co, 695 Tall Oaks Dr, Newark, OH 43055 *Tel:* 740-641-2691 *Toll Free Tel:* 800-233-8787 *Fax:* 740-641-2692 *E-mail:* mwpubco@mwpubco.com *Web Site:* www.mwpubco.com, pg 150

McFarland, 960 NC Hwy 88 W, Jefferson, NC 28640 *Tel:* 336-246-4460 *Toll Free Tel:* 800-253-2187 (orders) *Fax:* 336-246-5018; 336-246-4403 (orders) *E-mail:* info@mcfarlandpub.com *Web Site:* www.mcfarlandpub.com, pg 150

McGill-Queen's University Press, 1010 Sherbrooke W, Suite 1720, Montreal, QC H3A 2R7, Canada *Tel:* 514-398-3750 *Fax:* 514-398-4333 *E-mail:* mqup@mqup.ca *Web Site:* www.mqup.ca, pg 491

John H McGinnis Memorial Award, PO Box 750374, Dallas, TX 75275-0374 *Fax:* 214-768-1408 *E-mail:* swr@mail.smu.edu *Web Site:* www.smu.edu/southwestreview, pg 706

Harold W McGraw Jr - Prize in Education, 1221 Avenue of the Americas, 47th fl, New York, NY 10020-1095 *Tel:* 212-904-2000; 212-512-2000 *Fax:* 212-512-3611 *Web Site:* www.mhfi.com, pg 706

McGraw-Hill Career Education, 1333 Burr Ridge Pkwy, Burr Ridge, IL 60527 *Tel:* 630-789-4000 *Toll Free Tel:* 800-338-3987 (cust serv) *Fax:* 630-789-5523; 614-755-5645 (cust serv) *Web Site:* www.mhhe.com, pg 150

McGraw-Hill Contemporary Learning Series, 501 Bell St, Dubuque, IA 52001 *Toll Free Tel:* 800-243-6532 *Web Site:* www.mhcls.com, pg 150

McGraw-Hill Create, 501 Bell St, Dubuque, IA 52001 *Tel:* 563-584-6000 *Fax:* 563-584-6600 *E-mail:* first_last@mcgraw-hill.com *Web Site:* www.mhhe.com, pg 150

McGraw-Hill Education, 2 Penn Plaza, New York, NY 10121-2298 *Tel:* 212-904-2000 *E-mail:* customer.service@mcgraw-hill.com *Web Site:* www.mheducation.com; www.mheducation.com/custserv.html, pg 151

McGraw-Hill Financial, 1221 Avenue of the Americas, 50th fl, New York, NY 10020 *Tel:* 212-512-2000 *Web Site:* www.mhfi.com, pg 151

McGraw-Hill Higher Education, 1333 Burr Ridge Pkwy, Burr Ridge, IL 60527 *Tel:* 630-789-4000 *Toll Free Tel:* 800-338-3987 (cust serv) *Fax:* 614-755-5645 (cust serv) *Web Site:* www.mhhe.com, pg 151

McGraw-Hill Humanities, Social Sciences, Languages, 2 Penn Plaza, 21st fl, New York, NY 10121 *Tel:* 212-904-2000 *Toll Free Tel:* 800-338-3987 (cust serv) *Fax:* 614-755-5645 (cust serv) *Web Site:* www.mhhe.com, pg 151

McGraw-Hill International Publishing Group, 2 Penn Plaza, New York, NY 10121 *Tel:* 212-904-2000 *Web Site:* www.mcgraw-hill.com, pg 151

McGraw-Hill/Irwin, 1333 Burr Ridge Pkwy, Burr Ridge, IL 60527 *Tel:* 630-789-4000 *Toll Free Tel:* 800-338-3987 (cust serv) *Fax:* 630-789-6942; 614-755-5645 (cust serv) *Web Site:* www.mhhe.com, pg 152

McGraw-Hill Professional, 1221 Avenue of the Americas, New York, NY 10020 *Tel:* 212-512-2000 *Web Site:* www.mhprofessional.com, pg 152

McGraw-Hill Ryerson Limited, 300 Water St, Whitby, ON L1N 9B6, Canada *Tel:* 905-430-5000 *Toll Free Tel:* 800-565-5758 (cust serv) *Fax:* 905-430-5020 *Toll Free Fax:* 800-463-5885 *Web Site:* www.mheducation.ca, pg 491

McGraw-Hill School Education Group, 8787 Orion Place, Columbus, OH 43240 *Tel:* 614-430-4000 *Toll Free Tel:* 800-848-1567 *Web Site:* www.mheducation.com, pg 152

McGraw-Hill Science, Engineering, Mathematics, 501 Bell St, Dubuque, IA 52001 *Tel:* 563-584-6000 *Toll Free Tel:* 800-338-3987 (cust serv) *Fax:* 614-755-5645 (cust serv) *Web Site:* www.mhhe.com, pg 152

McHugh's Rights/Permissions Workshop™, PO Box 170665, Milwaukee, WI 53217-8056 *Tel:* 414-351-3056 *E-mail:* jack@johnbmchugh.com *Web Site:* www.johnbmchugh.com, pg 652

McIntosh & Otis Inc, 353 Lexington Ave, New York, NY 10016-0900 *Tel:* 212-687-7400 *Fax:* 212-687-6894 *E-mail:* info@mcintoshandotis.com *Web Site:* www.mcintoshandotis.com, pg 565

McKnight Artist Fellowship for Writers, Open Book, Suite 200, 1011 Washington Ave S, Minneapolis, MN 55415 *Tel:* 612-215-2575 *Fax:* 612-215-2576 *E-mail:* loft@loft.org *Web Site:* www.loft.org, pg 706

McKnight Fellowships for Playwrights, 2301 Franklin Ave E, Minneapolis, MN 55406-1099 *Tel:* 612-332-7481 *Fax:* 612-332-6037 *E-mail:* info@pwcenter.org *Web Site:* www.pwcenter.org, pg 706

McKnight National Residency & Commission, 2301 Franklin Ave E, Minneapolis, MN 55406-1099 *Tel:* 612-332-7481 *Fax:* 612-332-6037 *E-mail:* info@pwcenter.org *Web Site:* www.pwcenter.org, pg 706

Mid-List Press, 6524 Brownlee Dr, Nashville, TN 37205-3038 *Tel:* 615-822-3777 *Fax:* 612-823-8387 *E-mail:* guide@midlist.org *Web Site:* www.midlist.org, pg 156

Susan T Middleton, 366-A Norton Hill Rd, Ashfield, MA 01330-9601 *Tel:* 413-628-4039 *E-mail:* smiddle@crocker.com, pg 531

Midmarch Arts Press, 300 Riverside Dr, New York, NY 10025-5239 *Tel:* 212-666-6990 *Web Site:* midmarchartspress.org, pg 156

Midnight Marquee Press Inc, 9721 Britinay Lane, Baltimore, MD 21234 *Tel:* 410-665-1198 *E-mail:* mmarquee@aol.com *Web Site:* www.midmar.com, pg 156

Midwest Independent Booksellers Association (MIBA), 2355 Louisiana Ave N, Suite A, Golden Valley, MN 55427-3646 *Tel:* 763-544-2993 *Toll Free Tel:* 800-784-7522 *Fax:* 612-354-5728 *E-mail:* info@midwestbooksellers.org *Web Site:* midwestbooksellers.org, pg 610

MidWest Plan Service (MWPS), Iowa State University, 122 Davidson Hall, Ames, IA 50011-3080 *Tel:* 515-294-4337 *Toll Free Tel:* 800-562-3618 *Fax:* 515-294-9589 *E-mail:* mwps@iastate.edu *Web Site:* www.mwps.org, pg 156

Midwest Publishing Association (MPA), 275 N York St, Suite 401, Elmhurst, IL 60126 *Tel:* 630-833-4220 *Fax:* 630-563-9181 *E-mail:* info@midwestpublish.org *Web Site:* www.midwestpublish.org, pg 610

Midwest Publishing Association Webinars, 310 W Lake St, Suite 111, Elmhurst, IL 60126 *Tel:* 630-833-4220 *Fax:* 630-563-9181 *E-mail:* info@midwestpublish.org *Web Site:* www.midwestpublish.org, pg 661

Midwest Travel Writers Association, 902 S Randall Rd, Suite C311, St Charles, IL 60174 *Toll Free Tel:* 888-551-8184 *E-mail:* admin@mtwa.org *Web Site:* www.mtwa.org, pg 610

Mighty Media Press, 1201 Currie Ave, Minneapolis, MN 55403 *Tel:* 612-455-0252 *Fax:* 612-338-4817 *E-mail:* info@mightymedia.com *Web Site:* www.mightymediapress.com, pg 156

Mike Murach & Associates Inc, 4340 N Knoll Ave, Fresno, CA 93722 *Tel:* 559-440-9071 *Toll Free Tel:* 800-221-5528 *Fax:* 559-440-0963 *E-mail:* murachbooks@murach.com *Web Site:* www.murach.com, pg 156

Milady, Executive Woods, 5 Maxwell Dr, Clifton Park, NY 12065-2919 *Tel:* 518-348-2300 *Toll Free Tel:* 800-998-7498 *Fax:* 518-373-6309 *Web Site:* milady.cengage.com, pg 156

Robert J Milch, 9 Millbrook Dr, Stony Brook, NY 11790-2914 *Tel:* 631-689-8546 *Fax:* 631-689-8546 *E-mail:* milchedit@aol.com, pg 531

Kenneth W Mildenberger Prize, 26 Broadway, 3rd fl, New York, NY 10004-1789 *Tel:* 646-576-5141 *Fax:* 646-458-0030 *E-mail:* awards@mla.org *Web Site:* www.mla.org, pg 707

Military Info Publishing, PO Box 41211, Plymouth, MN 55442 *Tel:* 763-533-8627 *Fax:* 763-533-8627 *E-mail:* publisher@military-info.com *Web Site:* www.military-info.com, pg 157

Military Living Publications, 333 Maple Ave E, Suite 3130, Vienna, VA 22180-4717 *Tel:* 703-237-0203 (ext 1) *Toll Free Tel:* 877-363-4677 (ext 1) *Fax:* 703-997-8861 *E-mail:* customerservice@militaryliving.com *Web Site:* www.militaryliving.com, pg 157

Milkweed Editions, 1011 Washington Ave S, Suite 300, Minneapolis, MN 55415-1246 *Tel:* 612-332-3192 *Toll Free Tel:* 800-520-6455 *Fax:* 612-215-2550 *Web Site:* www.milkweed.org, pg 157

Milkweed National Fiction Prize, 1011 Washington Ave S, Suite 300, Minneapolis, MN 55415-1246 *Tel:* 612-332-3192 *Toll Free Tel:* 800-520-6455 *Fax:* 612-215-2550 *E-mail:* submissions@milkweed.org *Web Site:* www.milkweed.org, pg 707

Mill Mountain Theatre, Center in the Square, 2nd fl, One Market Sq SE, Roanoke, VA 24011-1437 *Tel:* 540-224-1250 (ext 7307) *Web Site:* www.millmountain.org, pg 707

Millbrook Press, 241 First Ave N, Minneapolis, MN 55401 *Tel:* 612-332-3344 *Toll Free Tel:* 800-328-4929 (US only) *Fax:* 612-332-7615 *Toll Free Fax:* 800-332-1132, pg 157

The Miller Agency Inc, 630 Ninth Ave, Suite 1102, New York, NY 10036 *Tel:* 212-206-0913 *Fax:* 212-206-1473, pg 566

Richard K Miller Associates, 4132 Atlanta Hwy, Suite 110, Loganville, GA 30052 *Tel:* 404-276-3376 *Toll Free Tel:* 888-928-RKMA (928-7562) *Toll Free Fax:* 877-928-7562 *Web Site:* rkma.com, pg 157

Robert Miller Gallery, 524 W 26 St, New York, NY 10001 *Tel:* 212-366-4774 *Fax:* 212-366-4454 *E-mail:* rmg@robertmillergallery.com *Web Site:* www.robertmillergallery.com, pg 157

Stephen M Miller Inc, 15727 S Madison Dr, Olathe, KS 66062 *Tel:* 913-768-7997 *Web Site:* www.stephenmillerbooks.com, pg 531

Milliken Publishing Co, 501 E Third St, Dayton, OH 45402 *Tel:* 937-228-6118 *Toll Free Tel:* 800-444-1144 *Fax:* 937-223-2042 *E-mail:* order@lorenz.com *Web Site:* www.lorenz.educationalpress.com, pg 157

Kathleen Mills Editorial Services, PO Box 214, Chardon, OH 44024 *Tel:* 440-285-4347 *E-mail:* mills_edit@yahoo.com, pg 531

Milner Award, One Margaret Mitchell Sq NW, Atlanta, GA 30303 *Tel:* 404-730-1865 *E-mail:* info@themilneraward.org *Web Site:* www.themilneraward.org, pg 707

Milton Dorfman Poetry Prize, 308 W Bloomfield St, Rome, NY 13440 *Tel:* 315-336-1040 *Fax:* 315-336-1090 *E-mail:* racc2@cnymail.com *Web Site:* www.romeart.org, pg 708

The Minerals, Metals & Materials Society (TMS), 184 Thorn Hill Rd, Warrendale, PA 15086 *Tel:* 724-776-9000 *Toll Free Tel:* 800-759-4867 *Fax:* 724-776-3770 *E-mail:* publications@tms.org (orders) *Web Site:* www.tms.org (orders), pg 157

Miniature Book Society Inc, 702 Rosecrans St, San Diego, CA 92106-3013 *Tel:* 619-226-4441 *Fax:* 619-226-4441 *E-mail:* minibook@cox.net *Web Site:* www.mbs.org, pg 610

Minnesota Book Awards, Degree of Honor Bldg, 325 Cedar St, Suite 555, St Paul, MN 55101-1055 *Tel:* 651-222-3242 *Fax:* 651-222-1988 *E-mail:* friends@thefriends.org *Web Site:* thefriends.org/events/mnba, pg 708

Minnesota Historical Society Press, 345 Kellogg Blvd W, St Paul, MN 55102-1906 *Tel:* 651-259-3205; 651-259-3000 *Toll Free Tel:* 800-621-2736 (warehouse) *Fax:* 651-297-1345 *Toll Free Fax:* 800-621-8476 (warehouse) *E-mail:* info-mnhspress@mnhs.org *Web Site:* www.mnhs.org/mnhspress, pg 157

Mississippi Review Prize, 118 College Dr, Box 5144, Hattiesburg, MS 39406-0001 *E-mail:* msreview@usm.edu *Web Site:* www.usm.edu/mississippi-review/contest.html, pg 708

Mississippi Review/University of Southern Mississippi, Center for Writers, 118 College Dr 5144, Hattiesburg, MS 39406-0001 *Tel:* 601-266-5600 *Fax:* 601-266-5757 *Web Site:* www.usm.edu/english/c4w.html; www.usm.edu/english/mississippireview.html, pg 661

Mississippi River Creative Writing Workshop, 720 Fourth Ave S, B-151, Rm 100, St Cloud, MN 56301-4498 *Tel:* 320-308-4947 *Fax:* 320-308-5524 *Web Site:* www.stcloudstate.edu, pg 652

MIT List Visual Arts Center, MIT E 15-109, 20 Ames St, Cambridge, MA 02139 *Tel:* 617-253-4400; 617-253-4680 *Fax:* 617-258-7265 *E-mail:* mlinga@mit.edu *Web Site:* listart.mit.edu, pg 157

The MIT Press, 55 Hayward St, Cambridge, MA 02142 *Tel:* 617-253-5255 *Toll Free Tel:* 800-207-8354 (orders) *Fax:* 617-258-6779; 617-577-1545 (orders) *Web Site:* mitpress.mit.edu, pg 158

Mitchell Lane Publishers Inc, PO Box 196, Hockessin, DE 19707 *Tel:* 302-234-9426 *Toll Free Tel:* 800-814-5484 *Fax:* 302-234-4742 *Toll Free Fax:* 866-834-4164 *E-mail:* orders@mitchelllane.com *Web Site:* www.mitchelllane.com, pg 158

MLA Prize for a Bibliography, Archive or Digital Project, 26 Broadway, 3rd fl, New York, NY 10004-1789 *Tel:* 646-576-5141 *Fax:* 646-458-0030 *E-mail:* awards@mla.org *Web Site:* www.mla.org, pg 708

MLA Prize for a First Book, 26 Broadway, 3rd fl, New York, NY 10004-1789 *Tel:* 646-576-5141 *Fax:* 646-458-0030 *E-mail:* awards@mla.org *Web Site:* www.mla.org, pg 708

MLA Prize for a Scholarly Edition, 26 Broadway, 3rd fl, New York, NY 10004-1789 *Tel:* 646-576-5141 *Fax:* 646-458-0030 *E-mail:* awards@mla.org *Web Site:* www.mla.org, pg 708

MLA Prize for Independent Scholars, 26 Broadway, 3rd fl, New York, NY 10004-1789 *Tel:* 646-576-5141 *Fax:* 646-458-0030 *E-mail:* awards@mla.org *Web Site:* www.mla.org, pg 708

MLA Prize for Studies in Native American Literatures, Cultures & Languages, 26 Broadway, 3rd fl, New York, NY 10004-1789 *Tel:* 646-576-5141 *Fax:* 646-458-0030 *E-mail:* awards@mla.org *Web Site:* www.mla.org, pg 708

MLA Prize in United States Latina & Latino & Chicano & Chicano Literary & Cultural Studies, 26 Broadway, 3rd fl, New York, NY 10004-1789 *Tel:* 646-576-5141 *Fax:* 646-458-0030 *E-mail:* awards@mla.org *Web Site:* www.mla.org, pg 708

Mobility International USA, 132 E Broadway, Suite 343, Eugene, OR 97401 *Tel:* 541-343-1284 *Fax:* 541-343-6812 *E-mail:* info@miusa.org *Web Site:* www.miusa.org, pg 158

Sondra Mochson, 18 Overlook Dr, Port Washington, NY 11050 *Tel:* 516-883-0961, pg 531

Modern Language Association of America (MLA), 26 Broadway, 3rd fl, New York, NY 10004-1789 *Tel:* 646-576-5000 *Fax:* 646-458-0030 *Web Site:* www.mla.org, pg 158

Modern Language Association of America (MLA), 26 Broadway, 3rd fl, New York, NY 10004-1789 *Tel:* 646-576-5000 *Fax:* 646-458-0030 *E-mail:* convention@mla.org *Web Site:* www.mla.org, pg 610

Modern Memoirs, 34 Main St, No 9, Amherst, MA 01002-2367 *Tel:* 413-253-2353 *Web Site:* www.modernmemoirs.com, pg 158

Modern Publishing, 155 E 55 St, New York, NY 10022 *Tel:* 212-826-0850 *Fax:* 212-759-9069 *Web Site:* www.modernpublishing.com, pg 158

Modus Vivendi Publishing Inc, 55, rue Jean-Talon Ouest, 2e etage, Montreal, QC H2R 2W8, Canada *Tel:* 514-272-0433 *Fax:* 514-272-7234 *E-mail:* info@groupemodus.com *Web Site:* www.groupemodus.com, pg 491

The Monacelli Press, 236 W 27 St, 4th fl, New York, NY 10001 *Tel:* 212-229-9925 *E-mail:* contact@monacellipress.com *Web Site:* www.monacellipress.com, pg 158

Mondial, 203 W 107 St, Suite 6-C, New York, NY 10025 *Tel:* 646-807-8031 *Fax:* 208-361-2863 *E-mail:* contact@mondialbooks.com *Web Site:* www.mondialbooks.com, pg 159

Mondo Publishing, 200 Sherwood Ave, Farmingdale, NY 11735 *Tel:* 212-268-3560 *Toll Free Tel:* 888-88-MONDO (886-6636) *Toll Free Fax:* 888-532-4492 *E-mail:* info@mondopub.com *Web Site:* www.mondopub.com, pg 159

Money Market Directories, 401 E Market St, Charlottesville, VA 22902 *Tel:* 434-977-1450 *Toll Free Tel:* 800-446-2810 *Fax:* 434-979-9962 *Web Site:* www.mmdwebaccess.com, pg 159

The Mongolia Society Inc, Indiana University, 322 Goodbody Hall, 1011 E Third St, Bloomington, IN 47405-7005 *Tel:* 812-855-4078 *Fax:* 812-855-4078 *E-mail:* monsoc@indiana.edu *Web Site:* www.mongoliasociety.org, pg 159

Monkfish Book Publishing Co, 22 E Market St, Suite 304, Rhinebeck, NY 12572 *Tel:* 845-876-4861 *E-mail:* monkfish@monkfishpublishing.com *Web Site:* www.monkfishpublishing.com, pg 159

The Montana Council for Indian Education, 1240 Burlington Ave, Billings, MT 59102-4224 *Tel:* 406-652-7598 (AM); 406-248-3465 (PM) *Fax:* 406-248-1297 *E-mail:* cie@cie-mt.org *Web Site:* www.cie-mt.org, pg 159

Montana Historical Society Press, Capitol Complex, 225 N Roberts St, Helena, MT 59620 *Tel:* 406-444-0090 (edit); 406-444-2890 (ordering/mktg); 406-444-2694 *Toll Free Tel:* 800-243-9900 *Fax:* 406-444-2696 (ordering/mktg) *Web Site:* www.montanahistoricalsociety.org, pg 159

Montemayor Press, 663 Hyland Hill Rd, Washington, VT 05675 *Tel:* 802-883-5081 *E-mail:* montepress@aol.com *Web Site:* www.montemayorpress.com, pg 159

Lucy Maud Montgomery Literature for Children Prize, 115 Richmond St, Charlottetown, PE C1A 1H7, Canada *Tel:* 902-368-4410 *Toll Free Tel:* 888-734-2784 *Fax:* 902-368-4418 *E-mail:* peiwritersguild@gmail.com *Web Site:* www.peiwritersguild.com, pg 708

Monthly Review Press, 146 W 29 St, Suite 6W, New York, NY 10001 *Tel:* 212-691-2555 *Toll Free Tel:* 800-670-9499 *Fax:* 212-727-3676 *E-mail:* mreview@igc.org *Web Site:* www.MonthlyReview.org, pg 159

Montreal-Contacts/The Rights Agency, 1350 Sherbrooke St E, Suite 1, Montreal, QC H2L 1M4, Canada *Tel:* 514-400-7075 *Fax:* 514-400-1045 *Web Site:* www.montreal-contacts.com/?lang=en, pg 566

Moody Publishers, 820 N La Salle Blvd, Chicago, IL 60610 *Tel:* 312-329-4000 *Toll Free Tel:* 800-678-8812 (cust serv) *Fax:* 312-329-2019 *Web Site:* www.moodypublishers.com, pg 159

Cenie H Moon Prize, 1194 Hume Rd, Hume, VA 22639-1806 *E-mail:* poetryinva@aol.com *Web Site:* www.poetrysocietyofvirginia.org, pg 708

Moonbeam Children's Book Awards, 1129 Woodmere Ave, Suite B, Traverse City, MI 49686 *Tel:* 231-933-0445 *Toll Free Tel:* 800-706-4636 *Fax:* 231-933-0448 *E-mail:* info@moonbeamawards.com *Web Site:* www.moonbeamawards.com, pg 709

Moonstone Press LLC, 4816 Carrington Circle, Sarasota, FL 34243 *Tel:* 301-765-1081 *Fax:* 301-765-0510 *E-mail:* mazeprod@erols.com *Web Site:* www.moonstonepress.net, pg 508

Jenny McKean Moore Writer-in-Washington, English Dept, Rome Hall, 801 22 St NW, Suite 760, Washington, DC 20052 *Tel:* 202-994-6180 *Fax:* 202-994-7915 *E-mail:* engldept@gwu.edu *Web Site:* www.gwu.edu/~english; departments.columbian.gwu.edu/english/openings (position details), pg 709

Moore Literary Agency, 10 State St, Suite 210, Newburyport, MA 01950 *Tel:* 978-465-9015 *Fax:* 978-465-6653, pg 566

Moose Hide Books, 684 Walls Rd, Prince Township, ON P6A 6K4, Canada *Tel:* 705-779-3331 *Fax:* 705-779-3331 *E-mail:* mooseenterprises@on.aibn.com *Web Site:* www.moosehidebooks.com, pg 492

Morehouse Publishing, 19 E 34 St, New York, NY 10016 *Tel:* 212-592-1800 *Toll Free Tel:* 800-672-1789 (retail orders only); 800-251-3320 (wholesale orders only) *Web Site:* www.morehousepublishing.com; www.churchpublishing.org, pg 160

Morgan Gaynin Inc, 149 Madison Ave, Suite 1140, New York, NY 10016 *Tel:* 212-475-0440 *E-mail:* info@morgangaynin.com *Web Site:* www.morgangaynin.com, pg 584

Morgan James Publishing, 5 Penn Plaza, 23rd fl, New York, NY 10001 *Tel:* 212-655-5470 *Toll Free Tel:* 800-485-4943 *Fax:* 516-908-4496 *E-mail:* csauer@morganjamespublishing.com *Web Site:* www.morganjamespublishing.com, pg 160

Morgan Kaufmann, 225 Wyman St, Waltham, MA 02451 *Toll Free Tel:* 866-607-1417 *Fax:* 619-699-6310 *Web Site:* www.mkp.com, pg 160

Morgan Reynolds Publishing, 620 S Elm St, Suite 387, Greensboro, NC 27406 *Tel:* 336-275-1311 *Toll Free Tel:* 800-535-1504 *Fax:* 336-275-1152 *Toll Free Fax:* 800-535-5725 *E-mail:* editorial@morganreynolds.com *Web Site:* www.morganreynolds.com, pg 160

Howard Morhaim Literary Agency Inc, 30 Pierrepont St, Brooklyn, NY 11201-3371 *Tel:* 718-222-8400 *Fax:* 718-222-5056 *E-mail:* info@morhaimliterary.com *Web Site:* www.morhaimliterary.com, pg 566

Morning Sun Books Inc, PO Box 326, Kutztown, PA 19530-0326 *Tel:* 610-683-8566 *Fax:* 610-683-3287 *E-mail:* sales.morningsunbooks@gmail.com (Sales) *Web Site:* www.morningsunbooks.com, pg 160

Ottoline Morrell Prize, University at Albany, Science Library 320, 1400 Washington Ave, Albany, NY 12222 *Tel:* 518-591-8162 *E-mail:* fence.fencebooks@gmail.com *Web Site:* www.fenceportal.org, pg 709

The William C Morris YA Debut Award, 50 E Huron St, Chicago, IL 60611 *Tel:* 312-280-4390 *Toll Free Tel:* 800-545-2433 (ext 4390) *Fax:* 312-280-5276 *E-mail:* yalsa@ala.org *Web Site:* www.ala.org/yalsa/morris, pg 709

William Morris Society in the United States Fellowships, PO Box 53263, Washington, DC 20009 *E-mail:* us@morrissociety.org *Web Site:* www.morrissociety.org, pg 709

Henry Morrison Inc, PO Box 235, Bedford Hills, NY 10507-0235 *Tel:* 914-666-3500 *Fax:* 914-241-7846 *E-mail:* hmorrison1@aol.com, pg 566

Morton Publishing Co, 925 W Kenyon Ave, Unit 12, Englewood, CO 80110 *Tel:* 303-761-4805 *Fax:* 303-762-9923 *E-mail:* contact@morton-pub.com *Web Site:* www.morton-pub.com, pg 160

Mosaic Press, 4500 Witmer Industrial Estates, PMB 145, Niagara Falls, NY 14305-1386 *Tel:* 905-825-2130 *Fax:* 905-825-2130 *E-mail:* info@mosaic-press.com *Web Site:* www.mosaic-press.com, pg 160

George L Mosse Prize, 400 "A" St SE, Washington, DC 20003 *Tel:* 202-544-2422 *Fax:* 202-544-8307 *E-mail:* awards@historians.org *Web Site:* www.historians.org, pg 709

Most Significant Scholarly Book Award, c/o 7748 Hwy 290 W, Austin, TX 78736-3202 *Tel:* 512-683-5640 *E-mail:* president@texasinstituteofletters.org *Web Site:* www.texasinstituteofletters.org, pg 709

Motion Picture Association of America Inc (MPAA), 1600 "I" St NW, Washington, DC 20006 *Tel:* 202-293-1966 *Fax:* 202-296-7410 *E-mail:* contactus@mpaa.org *Web Site:* www.mpaa.org, pg 610

Frank Luther Mott-Kappa Tau Alpha Research Award, University of Missouri, School of Journalism, 76 Gannett Hall, Columbia, MO 65211-1200 *Tel:* 573-882-7685 *Fax:* 573-884-1720 *E-mail:* umcjourkta@missouri.edu *Web Site:* www.kappataualpha.org, pg 709

Sheila Margaret Motton Prize, 2 Farrar St, Cambridge, MA 02138 *Tel:* 617-744-6034 *E-mail:* contests@nepoetryclub.org *Web Site:* www.nepoetryclub.org, pg 709

Mt Chocorua Writing Workshop, PO Box 2280, Conway, NH 03818-2280 *Tel:* 603-447-2280 *E-mail:* reservations@worldfellowship.org *Web Site:* www.worldfellowship.org, pg 652

Mount Hermon Christian Writers Conference, c/o Mount Hermon Association Inc, 37 Conference Dr, Felton, CA 95018 *Tel:* 831-335-4466 *Toll Free Tel:* 888-MH-CAMPS (642-2677 - registration) *Fax:* 831-335-9218 *E-mail:* info@mounthermon.org *Web Site:* www.mounthermon.org/writers, pg 653

Mount Olive College Press, 634 Henderson St, Mount Olive, NC 28365 *Tel:* 252-286-6851 *Fax:* 919-658-7180 *Web Site:* www.umo.edu, pg 160

Mountain n' Air Books, 2947-A Honolulu Ave, La Crescenta, CA 91214 *Tel:* 818-248-9345 *Toll Free Tel:* 800-446-9696 *Toll Free Fax:* 800-303-5578 *Web Site:* www.mountain-n-air.com, pg 160

Mountain Press Publishing Co, 1301 S Third W, Missoula, MT 59801 *Tel:* 406-728-1900 *Toll Free Tel:* 800-234-5308 *Fax:* 406-728-1635 *E-mail:* info@mtnpress.com *Web Site:* www.mountain-press.com, pg 160

Mountain Writers Series, 2804 SE 27 Ave, Suite 2, Portland, OR 97202 *Tel:* 503-232-4517 *Fax:* 503-232-4517 *E-mail:* pdxmws@mountainwriters.org *Web Site:* www.mountainwriters.org, pg 653

The Mountaineers Books, 1001 SW Klickitat Way, Suite 201, Seattle, WA 98134 *Tel:* 206-223-6303 *Toll Free Tel:* 800-553-4453 *Fax:* 206-223-6306 *Toll Free Fax:* 800-568-7604 *E-mail:* mbooks@mountaineersbooks.org *Web Site:* www.mountaineersbooks.org, pg 161

De Gruyter Mouton, 121 High St, 3rd fl, Boston, MA 02110 *Tel:* 857-284-7073 *Fax:* 857-284-7358 *E-mail:* degruytermail@presswarehouse.com (orders & claims) *Web Site:* www.degruyter.com, pg 161

Movable Type Management, 244 Madison Ave, Suite 334, New York, NY 10016 *Tel:* 646-431-6134 *Fax:* 646-810-5757 *Web Site:* www.mtmgmt.net, pg 566

Move Books, PO Box 183, Beacon Falls, CT 06403 *Web Site:* www.move-books.com, pg 508

Moznaim Publishing Corp, 4304 12 Ave, Brooklyn, NY 11219 *Tel:* 718-438-7680 *Fax:* 718-438-1305 *E-mail:* sales@moznaim.com *Web Site:* www.moznaim.com, pg 161

MPA Midwest Publishing Award Show, 275 N York St, Suite 401, Elmhurst, IL 60126 *Tel:* 630-833-4220 *Fax:* 630-563-9181 *E-mail:* info@midwestpublish.org *Web Site:* www.midwestpublish.org, pg 709

MPA - The Association of Magazine Media, 757 Third Ave, 11th fl, New York, NY 10012 *Tel:* 212-872-3700 *Fax:* 212-888-4217 *Web Site:* www.magazine.org, pg 610

MRTS, PO Box 874402, Tempe, AZ 85287-4402 *Tel:* 480-727-6503 *Toll Free Tel:* 800-621-2736 (orders) *Fax:* 480-965-1681 *Toll Free Fax:* 800-621-8476 (orders) *E-mail:* mrts@asu.edu *Web Site:* www.acmrs.org/pubs, pg 161

Mary Mueller, 516 Bartram Rd, Moorestown, NJ 08057 *Tel:* 856-778-4769 *E-mail:* mamam49@aol.com, pg 531

Multicultural Publications Inc, 936 Slosson St, Akron, OH 44320 *Tel:* 330-865-9578 *Fax:* 330-865-9578 *E-mail:* multiculturalpub@prodigy.net *Web Site:* www.multiculturalpub.net, pg 161

Multimedia Larga, 900 S Boardman Dr, No G72, Gallup, NM 87301, pg 161

Erika Mumford Prize, 2 Farrar St, Cambridge, MA 02138 *Tel:* 617-744-6034 *E-mail:* contests@nepoetryclub.org *Web Site:* www.nepoetryclub.org, pg 709

Mundania Press LLC, 6457 Glenway Ave, Suite 109, Cincinnati, OH 45211-5222 *Tel:* 513-490-2822 *Fax:* 513-598-9220 *Toll Free Fax:* 888-460-4752 *E-mail:* books@mundania.com; inquiry@mundania.com *Web Site:* www.mundania.com, pg 161

Municipal Analysis Services Inc, PO Box 13453, Austin, TX 78711-3453 *Tel:* 512-327-3328 *E-mail:* munilysis@gmail.com *Web Site:* sites.google.com/site/gregmichels/home, pg 161

The Museum of Modern Art (MoMA), 11 W 53 St, New York, NY 10019 *Tel:* 212-708-9443 *Fax:* 212-333-6575 *E-mail:* moma_publications@moma.org *Web Site:* www.moma.org, pg 162

Museum of New Mexico Press, 725 Camino Lejo, Suite C, Santa Fe, NM 87505 *Tel:* 505-476-1155; 505-272-7777 (orders) *Toll Free Tel:* 800-249-7737 (orders) *Fax:* 505-476-1156 *Toll Free Fax:* 800-622-8667 (orders) *Web Site:* www.mnmpress.org, pg 162

Music Publishers Association (MPA), 243 Fifth Ave, Suite 236, New York, NY 10016 *Tel:* 212-327-4044 *E-mail:* admin@mpa.org *Web Site:* www.mpa.org, pg 610

Mutual Publishing, 1215 Center St, Suite 210, Honolulu, HI 96816 *Tel:* 808-732-1709 *Fax:* 808-734-4094 *E-mail:* info@mutualpublishing.com *Web Site:* www.mutualpublishing.com, pg 162

MWG Writer Workshops, PO Box 3845, Meridian, MS 39303-3845 *Tel:* 601-880-1089 *Web Site:* www.mississippiwritersguild.com, pg 653

Mystery Writers of America (MWA), 1140 Broadway, Suite 1507, New York, NY 10001 *Tel:* 212-888-8171 *E-mail:* mwa@mysterywriters.org *Web Site:* www.mysterywriters.org, pg 610

Mystery Writers of America Workshops, 1140 Broadway, Suite 1507, New York, NY 10001 *Tel:* 212-888-8171 *E-mail:* mwa@mysterywriters.org *Web Site:* www.mysterywriters.org, pg 653

Mystic Seaport Museum Inc, PO Box 6000, Mystic, CT 06355-0990 *Tel:* 860-572-5302; 860-572-0711 (visitor serv) *Toll Free Tel:* 800-248-1066 (wholesale orders only); 800-331-2665 (retail orders only) *Fax:* 860-572-5321 *E-mail:* info@mysticseaport.org *Web Site:* www.mysticseaport.org, pg 162

Mythopoeic Awards, Oklahoma State University, 306 Edmon Low Library, Stillwater, OK 74078 *Tel:* 405-744-9773 *E-mail:* awards@mythsoc.org *Web Site:* www.mythsoc.org, pg 710

NACE International, 1440 S Creek Dr, Houston, TX 77084-4906 *Tel:* 281-228-6200 *Toll Free Tel:* 800-797-NACE (797-6223) *Fax:* 281-228-6300 *E-mail:* firstservice@nace.org *Web Site:* www.nace.org, pg 162

Jean V Naggar Literary Agency Inc (JVNLA), 216 E 75 St, Suite 1-E, New York, NY 10021 *Tel:* 212-794-1082 *E-mail:* jvnla@jvnla.com *Web Site:* www.jvnla.com, pg 566

NAL, 375 Hudson St, New York, NY 10014 *Tel:* 212-366-2000 *E-mail:* online@penguinputnam.com *Web Site:* www.penguinputnam.com; us.penguingroup.com, pg 162

Napa Valley Writers' Conference, Upper Valley Campus, 1088 College Ave, St Helena, CA 94574 *Tel:* 707-967-2900 (ext 1611) *Fax:* 707-967-2909 *E-mail:* writecon@napavalley.edu *Web Site:* www.napawritersconf.org, pg 653

Narada Press, 3165-133 Weber St N, Waterloo, ON N2J 3G9, Canada *Tel:* 519-886-1969, pg 492

The Narrative Press, 2041 E "A" St, Torrington, WY 82240 *Tel:* 307-532-3495 *Fax:* 307-532-3495 *E-mail:* service@narrativepress.com *Web Site:* www.narrativepress.com, pg 162

NASW Press, 750 First St NE, Suite 700, Washington, DC 20002 *Tel:* 202-408-8600 *Fax:* 203-336-8312 *E-mail:* press@naswdc.org *Web Site:* www.naswpress.org, pg 162

Nataraj Books, 7967 Twist Lane, Springfield, VA 22153 *Tel:* 703-455-4996 *Fax:* 703-455-4001 *E-mail:* nataraj@erols.com; orders@natarajbooks.com *Web Site:* www.natarajbooks.com, pg 163

Nation Books, 116 E 16 St, 8th fl, New York, NY 10003 *Tel:* 212–822–0250 *Fax:* 212-253-5356 *E-mail:* submissions@nationbooks.org *Web Site:* www.nationbooks.org, pg 163

National Academies Press (NAP), Lockbox 285, 500 Fifth St NW, Washington, DC 20001 *Tel:* 202-334-3313 *Toll Free Tel:* 888-624-8373 (cust serv) *Fax:* 202-334-2451 (cust serv); 202-334-2793 (mktg dept) *E-mail:* customer_service@nap.edu *Web Site:* www.nap.edu, pg 163

The National Alliance Research Academy, 3630 N Hills Dr, Austin, TX 78755 *Tel:* 512-345-7932 *Toll Free Tel:* 800-633-2165 *Fax:* 512-349-6194 *E-mail:* alliance@scic.com *Web Site:* www.scis.com/academy, pg 163

National Association for Music Education (NAfME), 1806 Robert Fulton Dr, Reston, VA 20191 *Tel:* 703-860-4000 *Toll Free Tel:* 800-462-6420 (orders & returns); 800-336-3768 *Fax:* 703-860-1531 *Web Site:* www.menc.org; www.nafme.org, pg 163

National Association of Black Journalists (NABJ), 1100 Knight Hall, Suite 3100, College Park, MD 20742 *Tel:* 301-405-0248 *Fax:* 301-314-1714 *E-mail:* nabj@nabj.org *Web Site:* www.nabj.org, pg 611

National Association of Broadcasters (NAB), 1771 "N" St NW, Washington, DC 20036 *Tel:* 202-429-5300 *Fax:* 202-429-4199 *E-mail:* nab@nab.org *Web Site:* www.nab.org, pg 163, 611

National Association of College Stores (NACS), 500 E Lorain St, Oberlin, OH 44074 *Tel:* 440-775-7777 *Toll Free Tel:* 800-622-7498 *Fax:* 440-775-4769 *Web Site:* www.nacs.org, pg 611

National Association of Hispanic Publications Inc (NAHP), 529 14 St NW, Suite 1126, Washington, DC 20045 *Tel:* 202-662-7250 *Web Site:* www.nahp.org, pg 611

National Association of Independent Publishers Representatives, 111 E 14 St, PMB 157, New York, NY 10003 *Tel:* 267-546-6561 *Toll Free Tel:* 888-624-7779 *Web Site:* naipr.org, pg 611

National Association of Insurance Commissioners, 2301 McGee St, Suite 800, Kansas City, MO 64108-2662 *Tel:* 816-842-3600; 816-783-8300 (cust serv) *Fax:* 816-783-8175; 816-460-7593 (cust serv) *E-mail:* prodserv@naic.org *Web Site:* www.naic.org, pg 163

National Association of Printing Ink Manufacturers (NAPIM), 15 Technology Pkwy S, Peachtree Corners, GA 30092 *Tel:* 770-209-7289 *Fax:* 678-680-4920; 770-209-7217 *E-mail:* napim@napim.org *Web Site:* www.napim.org, pg 611

National Association of Real Estate Editors (NAREE), 1003 NW Sixth Terr, Boca Raton, FL 33486-3455 *Tel:* 561-391-3599 *Fax:* 561-391-0099 *Web Site:* www.naree.org, pg 611

National Association of Science Writers (NASW), PO Box 7905, Berkeley, CA 94707 *Tel:* 510-647-9500 *Web Site:* www.nasw.org, pg 611

National Association of Secondary School Principals (NASSP), 1904 Association Dr, Reston, VA 20191-1537 *Tel:* 703-860-0200 *Toll Free Tel:* 800-253-7746 *Fax:* 703-476-5432 *E-mail:* membership@principals.org; sales@principals.org; publications2@nassp.org (communs & devt) *Web Site:* www.principals.org, pg 163

National Awards for Education Reporting, 3516 Connecticut Ave NW, Washington, DC 20008-2401 *Tel:* 202-452-9830 *Fax:* 202-452-9837 *E-mail:* ewa@ewa.org *Web Site:* www.ewa.org, pg 710

National Book Awards, 90 Broad St, Suite 604, New York, NY 10004 *Tel:* 212-685-0261 *Fax:* 212-213-6570 *E-mail:* nationalbook@nationalbook.org *Web Site:* www.nationalbook.org, pg 710

National Book Co, PO Box 8795, Portland, OR 97207-8795 *Tel:* 503-228-6345 *Fax:* 810-885-5811 *E-mail:* info@eralearning.com *Web Site:* www.eralearning.com, pg 163

National Braille Press, 88 St Stephen St, Boston, MA 02115-4302 *Tel:* 617-266-6160 *Toll Free Tel:* 800-548-7323 (cust serv); 888-965-8965 *Fax:* 617-437-0456 *E-mail:* orders@nbp.org *Web Site:* www.nbp.org, pg 164

The National Business Book Award, c/o Freedman & Associates Inc, 121 Richmond St W, Suite 605, Toronto, ON M5H 2K1, Canada *Tel:* 416-868-4739 *Web Site:* www.nbbaward.com, pg 710

National Cartoonists Society (NCS), 341 N Maitland Ave, Suite 260, Maitland, FL 32751 *Tel:* 407-647-8839 *Fax:* 407-629-2502 *E-mail:* info@reuben.org *Web Site:* www.reuben.org, pg 611

National Catholic Educational Association, 1005 N Glebe Rd, Suite 525, Arlington, VA 22201 *Tel:* 571-257-0010 *Toll Free Tel:* 800-711-6232 *Fax:* 703-243-0025 *E-mail:* nceaadmin@ncea.org *Web Site:* www.ncea.org, pg 164

National Center for Children in Poverty, 215 W 125 St, 3rd fl, New York, NY 10027 *Tel:* 646-284-9600 *Fax:* 646-284-9623 *E-mail:* info@nccp.org *Web Site:* www.nccp.org, pg 164

National Center For Employee Ownership (NCEO), 1736 Franklin St, 8th fl, Oakland, CA 94612-3445 *Tel:* 510-208-1300 *Fax:* 510-272-9510 *E-mail:* customerservice@nceo.org *Web Site:* www.nceo.org, pg 164

National Coalition Against Censorship (NCAC), 19 Fulton St, Suite 407, New York, NY 10038 *Tel:* 212-807-6222 *Fax:* 212-807-6245 *E-mail:* ncac@ncac.org *Web Site:* www.ncac.org, pg 611

National Coalition for Literacy (NCL), PO Box 2932, Washington, DC 20013-2932 *E-mail:* ncl@ncladvocacy.org *Web Site:* www.national-coalition-literacy.org, pg 611

National Communication Association, 1765 "N" St NW, Washington, DC 20036 *Tel:* 202-464-4622 *Fax:* 202-464-4600 *E-mail:* inbox@natcom.org *Web Site:* www.natcom.org, pg 612

National Conference for Community & Justice, 820A Prospect Hill Rd, Windsor, CT 06095 *Tel:* 860-683-1039 *Fax:* 860-683-1409 *E-mail:* info@nccj.org *Web Site:* www.nccj.org, pg 612

National Conference of State Legislatures (NCSL), 7700 E First Place, Denver, CO 80230 *Tel:* 303-364-7700 *Fax:* 303-364-7800 *E-mail:* books@ncsl.org *Web Site:* www.ncsl.org, pg 164

National Council of Teachers of English (NCTE), 1111 W Kenyon Rd, Urbana, IL 61801-1096 *Tel:* 217-328-3870 *Toll Free Tel:* 877-369-6283 (cust serv) *Fax:* 217-328-9645 *E-mail:* orders@ncte.org *Web Site:* www.ncte.org, pg 164

National Council of Teachers of English (NCTE), 1111 W Kenyon Rd, Urbana, IL 61801-1096 *Tel:* 217-328-3870 *Toll Free Tel:* 877-369-6283 (cust serv) *Fax:* 217-328-9645 *E-mail:* public_info@ncte.org *Web Site:* www.ncte.org, pg 612

National Council of Teachers of Mathematics (NCTM), 1906 Association Dr, Reston, VA 20191-1502 *Tel:* 703-620-9840 *Toll Free Tel:* 800-235-7566 *Fax:* 703-476-2970 *E-mail:* nctm@nctm.org *Web Site:* www.nctm.org, pg 164

National Council on Radiation Protection & Measurements (NCRP), 7910 Woodmont Ave, Suite 400, Bethesda, MD 20814-3095 *Tel:* 301-657-2652 *Toll Free Tel:* 800-229-2652 *Fax:* 301-907-8768 *E-mail:* ncrppubs@ncrponline.org *Web Site:* www.ncrponline.org; www.ncrppublications.org, pg 164

National Crime Prevention Council, 2001 Jefferson Davis Hwy, Suite 901, Arlington, VA 22202 *Tel:* 202-466-6272 *Fax:* 202-296-1356 *E-mail:* ncpc@fulfills.org (orders) *Web Site:* www.ncpc.org, pg 164

National Education Association (NEA), 1201 16 St NW, Washington, DC 20036-3290 *Tel:* 202-833-4000 *Fax:* 202-822-7974 *Web Site:* www.nea.org, pg 164, 612

The National Endowment for the Arts, Nancy Hanks Ctr, Rm 703, 1100 Pennsylvania Ave NW, Washington, DC 20506-0001 *Tel:* 202-682-5400 *Web Site:* www.arts.gov; www.nea.gov, pg 623

National Endowment for the Humanities, Mellon Foundation & Folger Long-term Fellowships, c/o Fellowship Committee, 201 E Capitol St SE, Washington, DC 20003 *Tel:* 202-544-4600 *Fax:* 202-544-4623 *E-mail:* institute@folger.edu *Web Site:* www.folger.edu, pg 710

National Federation of Advanced Information Services (NFAIS), 801 Compass Way, Suite 201, Annapolis, MD 21401 *Tel:* 443-221-2980 *Fax:* 443-221-2981 *E-mail:* nfais@nfais.org *Web Site:* www.nfais.org, pg 612

National Federation of Press Women Inc (NFPW), PO Box 5556, Arlington, VA 22205-0798 *Tel:* 703-237-9804 *Fax:* 703-237-9808 *E-mail:* presswomen@aol.com *Web Site:* www.nfpw.org, pg 612

National Federation of State Poetry Societies Annual Poetry Contest, 1375 Green Meadows Way, Ashland, OR 97520 *E-mail:* contestchair@nfsps.com *Web Site:* www.nfsps.com, pg 710

National Freedom of Information Coalition (NFOIC), 101C Reynolds Journalism Institute, Columbia, MO 65211 *Tel:* 573-882-4856 *Web Site:* nfoic.org, pg 612

National Gallery of Art, Fourth St & Pennsylvania Ave NW, Washington, DC 20565 *Tel:* 202-737-4215; 202-842-6480 *Fax:* 202-842-6733 *E-mail:* casva@nga.gov *Web Site:* www.nga.gov, pg 164

National Gallery of Canada, The Bookstore, 380 Sussex Dr, Ottawa, ON K1N 9N4, Canada *Tel:* 613-990-0962 (mail order sales) *Fax:* 613-990-1972 *E-mail:* ngcbook@gallery.ca *Web Site:* www.national.gallery.ca, pg 492

National Geographic Books, 1145 17 St NW, Washington, DC 20036-4688 *Tel:* 202-857-7000 *Fax:* 202-857-7670 *Web Site:* books.nationalgeographic.com/books, pg 165

National Geographic Learning, One Lower Ragsdale Dr, Bldg 1, Suite 200, Monterey, CA 93940 *Tel:* 831-625-3666 *Web Site:* www.ngl.cengage.com, pg 165

National Geographic Society, 1145 17 St NW, Washington, DC 20036-4688 *Tel:* 202-857-7000 *Fax:* 202-429-5727 *Web Site:* www.nationalgeographic.com, pg 165

National Golf Foundation, 1150 S US Hwy One, Suite 401, Jupiter, FL 33477 *Tel:* 561-744-6006 *Toll Free Tel:* 888-275-4643 *Fax:* 561-744-6107 *E-mail:* general@ngf.org *Web Site:* www.ngf.org, pg 165

National Information Standards Organization, 3600 Clipper Mill Rd, Suite 302, Baltimore, MD 21211 *Tel:* 301-654-2512 *Fax:* 410-685-5278 *E-mail:* nisohq@niso.org *Web Site:* www.niso.org, pg 165, 612

National Institute for Trial Advocacy (NITA), 1685 38 St, Suite 200, Boulder, CO 80301-2735 *Tel:* 720-890-4860 *Toll Free Tel:* 877-648-2632; 800-225-6482 (orders & returns) *Fax:* 720-890-7069 *E-mail:* info@nita.org *Web Site:* www.nita.org, pg 165

National Jewish Book Award-Children's & Young Adult Literature, 520 Eighth Ave, 4th fl, New York, NY 10018 *Tel:* 212-201-2920 *Fax:* 212-532-4952 *E-mail:* jbc@jewishbooks.org *Web Site:* www.jewishbookcouncil.org, pg 710

National Jewish Book Award-Contemporary Jewish Life & Practice, 520 Eighth Ave, 4th fl, New York, NY 10018 *Tel:* 212-201-2920 *Fax:* 212-532-4952 *E-mail:* jbc@jewishbooks.org *Web Site:* www.jewishbookcouncil.org, pg 710

National Jewish Book Award-History, 520 Eighth Ave, 4th fl, New York, NY 10018 *Tel:* 212-201-2920 *Fax:* 212-532-4952 *E-mail:* jbc@jewishbooks.org *Web Site:* www.jewishbookcouncil.org, pg 710

National Jewish Book Award-Illustrated Children's Book, 520 Eighth Ave, 4th fl, New York, NY 10018 *Tel:* 212-201-2920 *Fax:* 212-532-4952 *E-mail:* jbc@jewishbooks.org *Web Site:* www.jewishbookcouncil.org, pg 710

National Jewish Book Award-Modern Jewish Thought & Experience, 520 Eighth Ave, 4th fl, New York, NY 10018 *Tel:* 212-201-2920 *Fax:* 212-532-4952 *E-mail:* jbc@jewishbooks.org *Web Site:* www.jewishbookcouncil.org, pg 710

National Jewish Book Award-Scholarship, 520 Eighth Ave, 4th fl, New York, NY 10018 *Tel:* 212-201-2920 *Fax:* 212-532-4952 *E-mail:* jbc@jewishbooks.org *Web Site:* www.jewishbookcouncil.org, pg 710

National Jewish Book Awards, 520 Eighth Ave, 4th fl, New York, NY 10018 *Tel:* 212-201-2920 *Fax:* 212-532-4952 *E-mail:* jbc@jewishbooks.org *Web Site:* www.jewishbookcouncil.org, pg 710

National League of American Pen Women, c/o National Pen Women-Scholarship, Pen Arts Bldg, 1300 17 St NW, Washington, DC 20036-1973 *Tel:* 202-785-1997 *Fax:* 202-452-8868 *E-mail:* contact@nlapw.org *Web Site:* www.nlapw.org, pg 612

National League of Cities, 1301 Pennsylvania Ave NW, Washington, DC 20004-1763 *Tel:* 202-626-3100 *Fax:* 202-626-3043 *E-mail:* info@nlc.org *Web Site:* www.nlc.org, pg 165

National Learning Corp, 212 Michael Dr, Syosset, NY 11791 *Tel:* 516-921-8888 *Toll Free Tel:* 800-632-8888 *Fax:* 516-921-8743 *E-mail:* info@passbooks.com *Web Site:* www.passbooks.com, pg 165

National Magazine Awards, 2300 Yonge St, Suite 1600, Toronto, ON M4P 1E4, Canada *Tel:* 416-939-6200 *E-mail:* staff@magazine-awards.com *Web Site:* www.magazine-awards.com; https://twitter.com/magawards, pg 711

National Music Publishers' Association (NMPA), 975 "F" St NW, Suite 315, Washington, DC 20004 *Tel:* 202-393-6672 *Fax:* 202-393-6673 *E-mail:* pr@nmpa.org *Web Site:* www.nmpa.org, pg 613

National Newspaper Association, 309 S Providence Rd, Columbia, MO 65203-4267 *Tel:* 573-777-4980 *Fax:* 573-777-4985 *E-mail:* nna@nna.org *Web Site:* nnaweb.org, pg 613

National Newspaper Publishers Association (NNPA), 1816 12 St NW, Washington, DC 20009 *Tel:* 202-588-8764 *Fax:* 202-588-8960 *E-mail:* info@nnpa.org *Web Site:* www.nnpa.org; www.blackpressusa.com, pg 613

National Notary Association (NNA), 9350 De Soto Ave, Chatsworth, CA 91311 *Tel:* 818-739-4000 *Toll Free Tel:* 800-876-6827 *Toll Free Fax:* 800-833-1211 *E-mail:* nna@nationalnotary.org *Web Site:* www.nationalnotary.org, pg 165

National One-Act Playwriting Competition, 600 Wolfe St, Alexandria, VA 22314 *Tel:* 703-683-5778 *Fax:* 703-683-1378 *E-mail:* asklta@thelittletheatre.com *Web Site:* www.thelittletheatre.com, pg 711

National Outdoor Book Awards, 921 S Eighth Ave, Stop 8128, Pocatello, ID 83209-8128 *Tel:* 208-282-3912 *Fax:* 208-282-2127 *Web Site:* www.noba-web.org, pg 711

National Park Service Media Services, 67 Mather Place, Harpers Ferry, WV 25425 *Tel:* 304-535-5050 *Fax:* 304-535-6176 *Web Site:* www.nps.gov/hfc, pg 165

National Poetry Series Open Competition, 57 Mountain Ave, Princeton, NJ 08540 *Tel:* 609-430-0999 *Fax:* 609-430-9933 *Web Site:* www.pw.org/content/open_competition, pg 711

National Press Club (NPC), 529 14 St NW, 13th fl, Washington, DC 20045 *Tel:* 202-662-7500 *Fax:* 202-662-7569 *E-mail:* infocenter@npcpress.org *Web Site:* www.press.org, pg 613

National Press Club of Canada Foundation Inc, 17 York St, Suite 201, Ottawa, ON K1N 9J6, Canada *E-mail:* info@pressclubcanada.ca *Web Site:* pressclubcanada.ca, pg 613

National Press Foundation, 1211 Connecticut Ave NW, Suite 310, Washington, DC 20036 *Tel:* 202-663-7280 *Web Site:* nationalpress.org, pg 613

National Press Photographers Association Inc (NPPA), 3200 Croasdaile Dr, Suite 306, Durham, NC 27705 *Tel:* 919-383-7246 *Fax:* 919-383-7261 *E-mail:* info@nppa.org *Web Site:* www.nppa.org, pg 613

National Register Publishing, 430 Mountain Ave, Suite 400, New Providence, NJ 07974 *Toll Free Tel:* 800-473-7020 *Fax:* 908-673-1189 (cust serv) *E-mail:* NRPeditorial@marquiswhoswho.com (edit); NRPsales@marquiswhoswho.com (sales) *Web Site:* www.nationalregisterpub.com, pg 166

National Resource Center for Youth Services (NRCYS), Schusterman Ctr, Bldg 4W, 4502 E 41 St, Tulsa, OK 74135-2512 *Tel:* 918-660-3700 *Toll Free Tel:* 800-274-2687 *Fax:* 918-660-3737 *Web Site:* www.nrcys.ou.edu, pg 166

National Science Teachers Association (NSTA), 1840 Wilson Blvd, Arlington, VA 22201-3000 *Tel:* 703-312-9205 *Toll Free Tel:* 800-277-5300 (orders) *Toll Free Fax:* 888-433-0526 (orders) *E-mail:* orders@nsta.org; publisher@nsta.org (general info) *Web Site:* www.nsta.org/store, pg 166

National Society of Newspaper Columnists (NSNC), PO Box 411532, San Francisco, CA 94141 *Tel:* 415-488-NCNC (488-6762) *Fax:* 484-297-0336 *Web Site:* www.columnists.com, pg 613

National Society of Newspaper Columnists Annual Conference, 1345 Fillmore St, Suite 507, San Francisco, CA 94115 *Tel:* 415-488-NCNC (488-6762) *Toll Free Tel:* 866-440-NSNC (440-6762) *Fax:* 484-297-0336 *Toll Free Fax:* 866-635-5759 *Web Site:* www.columnists.com, pg 653

National Ten-Minute Play Contest, 316 W Main St, Louisville, KY 40202-4218 *Tel:* 502-584-1265 *Web Site:* actorstheatre.org/national-ten-minute-play-contest/, pg 711

National Translation Award, 900 E Seventh St, PMB 266, Bloomington, IN 47405-3201 *Web Site:* www.literarytranslators.org, pg 711

The National Underwriter Co, 5081 Olympic Blvd, Erlanger, KY 41018-3164 *Tel:* 859-692-2100 *Toll Free Tel:* 800-543-0874 *Fax:* 859-692-2289 *E-mail:* customerservice@nuco.com *Web Site:* www.nationalunderwriter.com, pg 166

National Writers Association, 10940 S Parker Rd, Suite 508, Parker, CO 80134 *Tel:* 303-841-0246 *E-mail:* natlwritersassn@hotmail.com *Web Site:* www.nationalwriters.com, pg 613

National Writers Association Novel Contest, 10940 S Parker Rd, Suite 508, Parker, CO 80134 *Tel:* 303-841-0246 *E-mail:* natlwritersassn@hotmail.com *Web Site:* www.nationalwriters.com, pg 711

National Writers Union/UAW Local 1981, 256 W 38 St, Suite 703, New York, NY 10018 *Tel:* 212-254-0279 *Fax:* 212-254-0673 *E-mail:* nwu@nwu.org *Web Site:* www.nwu.org/, pg 613

The Nautical & Aviation Publishing Co of America Inc, 845-A Lowcountry Blvd, Mount Pleasant, SC 29464 *Tel:* 843-856-0561 *Fax:* 843-856-3164 *Web Site:* www.nauticalandaviation.com, pg 166

Nautilus Awards, 378 Bromley Dr, Eastsound, WA 98245 *Tel:* 360-376-2001 *Web Site:* www.nautilusbookawards.com, pg 711

Naval Institute Press, 291 Wood Rd, Annapolis, MD 21402-5034 *Tel:* 410-268-6110 *Toll Free Tel:* 800-233-8764 *Fax:* 410-295-1084; 410-571-1703 (cust serv) *E-mail:* webmaster@navalinstitute.org; customer@navalinstitute.org (cust serv); trade@usni.org *Web Site:* www.nip.org; www.usni.org, pg 166

NavPress Publishing Group, 3820 N 30 St, Colorado Springs, CO 80904 *Tel:* 719-548-9222 *Toll Free Tel:* 800-366-7788 *Toll Free Fax:* 800-343-3902 *E-mail:* customerservice@navpress.com *Web Site:* www.navpress.com, pg 166

NBM Publishing Inc, 160 Broadway, E Wing, Suite 700, New York, NY 10038 *Tel:* 646-559-4681 *Toll Free Tel:* 800-886-1223 *Fax:* 212-643-1545 *E-mail:* admin@nbmpub.com *Web Site:* www.nbmpub.com, pg 166

NEA Literature Fellowships, 400 Seventh St SW, Washington, DC 20506-0001 *Tel:* 202-682-5400; 202-682-5496 (Voice/TTY); 202-682-5034 (lit fellowships hotline) *Fax:* 202-682-5609; 202-682-5610 *E-mail:* litfellowships@arts.gov *Web Site:* www.arts.gov; www.nea.gov, pg 711

Neal-Schuman Publishers Inc, 100 William St, Suite 2004, New York, NY 10038 *Tel:* 212-925-8650 *Toll Free Tel:* 866-NS-BOOKS (672-6657) *Fax:* 212-219-8916 *Toll Free Fax:* 877-231-6980 *E-mail:* info@neal-schuman.com *Web Site:* www.neal-schuman.com, pg 166

NeDeo Press, PO Box 668, Robbins, NC 27325 *Web Site:* www.nedeopress.com, pg 167

Neibauer Press & ChurchSupplier.com, 20 Industrial Dr, Warminster, PA 18974 *Tel:* 215-322-6200 *Toll Free Tel:* 800-322-6203 *Fax:* 215-322-2495 *E-mail:* sales@neibauer.com; sales@churchsupplier.com *Web Site:* www.churchsupplier.com, pg 167

Nina Neimark Editorial Services, 543 Third St, Brooklyn, NY 11215 *Tel:* 718-499-6804 *E-mail:* pneimark@hotmail.com, pg 531

Nelligan Prize for Short Fiction, Colorado State Univ, Dept of English, Ctr for Literary Publg, 9105 Campus Delivery, Fort Collins, CO 80523-9105 *Tel:* 970-491-5449 *E-mail:* creview@colostate.edu *Web Site:* nelliganprize.colostate.edu, pg 711

BK Nelson Inc Lecture Bureau, 1565 Paseo Vida, Palm Springs, CA 92264 *Tel:* 760-778-8800 *Fax:* 760-778-6242 *E-mail:* bknelson4@cs.com *Web Site:* www.bknelson.com; www.bknelsonlecturebureau.com; www.nelsonbookmovielecture.com; www.bknelsonmovieproduction.com, pg 587

BK Nelson Inc Literary Agency, 1565 Paseo Vida, Palm Springs, CA 92264 *Tel:* 760-778-8800 *Fax:* 760-778-6242 *E-mail:* bknelson4@cs.com *Web Site:* www.bknelson.com; www.bknelsonlecturebureau.com; www.nelsonbookmovielecture.com; www.bknelsonmovieproduction.com, pg 566

Nelson Education Ltd, 1120 Birchmount Rd, Scarborough, ON M1K 5G4, Canada *Tel:* 416-752-9100 *Toll Free Tel:* 800-268-2222 (cust serv) *Fax:* 416-752-8101 *Toll Free Fax:* 800-430-4445 *E-mail:* peopleandengagement@nelson.com *Web Site:* www.nelson.com, pg 492

Nelson Literary Agency LLC, 1732 Wazee St, Suite 207, Denver, CO 80202-1284 *Tel:* 303-292-2805 *E-mail:* query@nelsonagency.com *Web Site:* www.nelsonagency.com, pg 566

Howard Nemerov Sonnet Award, 21 Osborne Terr, Wayne, NJ 07470 *Web Site:* theformalist.evansville.edu/home.htm, pg 711

The Pablo Neruda Prize for Poetry, Nimrod International Journal, 800 S Tucker Dr, Tulsa, OK 74104 *Tel:* 918-631-3080 *Fax:* 918-631-3033 *E-mail:* nimrod@utulsa.edu *Web Site:* www.utulsa.edu/nimrod, pg 711

Nesbitt Graphics Inc, 555 Virginia Dr, Fort Washington, PA 19034 *Tel:* 215-591-9125 *Fax:* 215-591-9093 *Web Site:* cenveopublisherservices.com, pg 531

Neustadt International Prize for Literature, c/o University of Oklahoma, 630 Parrington Oval, Suite 110, Norman, OK 73019-4033 *Tel:* 405-325-4531 *Fax:* 405-325-7495 *Web Site:* www.worldliteraturetoday.org, pg 712

Allan Nevins Prize, 603 Fayerweather, MC 2538, New York, NY 10027 *Tel:* 212-854-6495 *E-mail:* amhistsociety@columbia.edu *Web Site:* sah.columbia.edu, pg 712

New Author Publishing, 4 E Fulford Place, Brockville, ON K6V 2Z8, Canada *Tel:* 613-865-7471 *Web Site:* www.newauthorpublishing.com, pg 492

New Canaan Publishing Co LLC, 2384 N Hwy 341, Rossville, GA 30741 *Tel:* 423-285-8672 *E-mail:* djm@newcanaanpublishing.com *Web Site:* www.newcanaanpublishing.com, pg 167

New City Press, 202 Comforter Blvd, Hyde Park, NY 12538 *Tel:* 845-229-0335 *Toll Free Tel:* 800-462-5980 (orders only) *Fax:* 845-229-0351 *E-mail:* info@newcitypress.com *Web Site:* www.newcitypress.com, pg 167

New Concepts Publishing, 106-A W Hill Ave, Valdosta, GA 31636 *E-mail:* service@newconceptspublishing.com; submissions@newconceptspublishing.com *Web Site:* www.newconceptspublishing.com, pg 167

New Dimensions Publishing, 11248 N 11 St, Phoenix, AZ 85020 *Tel:* 602-861-2631 *Toll Free Tel:* 800-736-7367 *Fax:* 602-944-1235 *E-mail:* info@thedream.com *Web Site:* www.thedream.com, pg 167

New Directions Publishing Corp, 80 Eighth Ave, New York, NY 10011 *Tel:* 212-255-0230 *Fax:* 212-255-0231 *E-mail:* newdirections@ndbooks.com; editorial@ndbooks.com *Web Site:* ndbooks.com, pg 167

New England Book Awards, 1955 Massachusetts Ave, Cambridge, MA 02140 *Tel:* 617-547-3642 *Fax:* 617-547-3759 *Web Site:* www.newenglandbooks.org/bookawards, pg 712

New England Independent Booksellers Association Inc (NEIBA), 1955 Massachusetts Ave, Cambridge, MA 02140 *Web Site:* www.newenglandbooks.org, pg 613

New England Poetry Club, 2 Farrar St, Cambridge, MA 02138 *Tel:* 617-744-6034 *E-mail:* info@nepoetryclub.org *Web Site:* www.nepoetryclub.org, pg 613

New England Publishing Associates Inc, One Carver Place, Lawrenceville, NJ 08648 *Tel:* 860-973-2439 *Web Site:* www.nepagency.com, pg 567

New Forums Press Inc, 1018 S Lewis St, Stillwater, OK 74074 *Tel:* 405-372-6158 *Toll Free Tel:* 800-606-3766 *Fax:* 405-377-2237 *E-mail:* submissions@newforums.com *Web Site:* www.newforums.com, pg 167

New Hampshire Literary Awards, 2500 N River Rd, Manchester, NH 03106 *Tel:* 603-314-7980 *Fax:* 603-314-7981 *E-mail:* info@nhwritersproject.org *Web Site:* www.nhwritersproject.org, pg 712

New Hampshire Writers' Project, 2500 N River Rd, Manchester, NH 03106 *Tel:* 603-314-7980 *Fax:* 603-314-7981 *E-mail:* info@nhwritersproject.org *Web Site:* www.nhwritersproject.org, pg 613

New Harbinger Publications Inc, 5674 Shattuck Ave, Oakland, CA 94609 *Tel:* 510-652-0215 *Toll Free Tel:* 800-748-6273 (orders only) *Fax:* 510-652-5472 *Toll Free Fax:* 800-652-1613 *E-mail:* nhhelp@newharbinger.com; customerservice@newharbinger.com *Web Site:* www.newharbinger.com, pg 167

New Horizon Press, PO Box 669, Far Hills, NJ 07931-0669 *Tel:* 908-604-6311 *Toll Free Tel:* 800-533-7978 (orders only) *Fax:* 908-604-6330 *E-mail:* nhp@newhorizonpressbooks.com *Web Site:* www.newhorizonpressbooks.com, pg 167

New Issues Poetry & Prose, c/o Western Michigan University, 1903 W Michigan Ave, Kalamazoo, MI 49008-5463 *Tel:* 269-387-8185 *Fax:* 269-387-2562 *E-mail:* new-issues@wmich.edu *Web Site:* www.wmich.edu/newissues, pg 168

New Issues Poetry Prize, c/o Western Michigan University, 1903 W Michigan Ave, Kalamazoo, MI 49008-5463 *Tel:* 269-387-8185 *Fax:* 269-387-2562 *E-mail:* new-issues@wmich.edu *Web Site:* www.wmich.edu/newissues, pg 712

New Jersey Council for the Humanities Book Award, 28 W State St, 6th fl, Trenton, NJ 08608 *Tel:* 609-695-4838 *Toll Free Tel:* 888-FYI-NJCH (394-6524) *Fax:* 609-695-4929 *E-mail:* njch@njch.org *Web Site:* www.njch.org, pg 712

New Leaf Press Inc, 3142 Hwy 103 N, Green Forest, AR 72638-2233 *Tel:* 870-438-5288 *Toll Free Tel:* 800-999-3777 *Fax:* 870-438-5120 *E-mail:* submissions@newleafpress.net *Web Site:* www.nlpg.com, pg 168

New Letters Literary Awards, UMKC, University House, 5101 Rockhill Rd, Kansas City, MO 64110-2499 *Tel:* 816-235-1169 *Fax:* 816-235-2611 *E-mail:* newletters@umkc.edu *Web Site:* www.newletters.org, pg 712

New Letters Prize for Poetry, UMKC, University House, 5101 Rockhill Rd, Kansas City, MO 64110-2499 *Tel:* 816-235-1169 *Fax:* 816-235-2611 *E-mail:* newletters@umkc.edu *Web Site:* www.newletters.org, pg 712

New Mexico Book Association (NMBA), 1219 Luisa St, Suite 1, Santa Fe, NM 87505 *Tel:* 505-660-6357 *E-mail:* admin@nmbook.org *Web Site:* www.nmbook.org, pg 614

New Millennium Awards for Fiction, Poetry & Nonfiction, 4021 Garden Dr, Knoxville, TN 37918 *Tel:* 865-254-4880 *Web Site:* www.newmillenniumwritings.com, pg 712

The New Press, 38 Greene St, 4th fl, New York, NY 10013 *Tel:* 212-629-8802 *Toll Free Tel:* 800-343-4489 (orders) *Fax:* 212-629-8617 *Toll Free Fax:* 800-351-5073 (orders) *E-mail:* newpress@thenewpress.com *Web Site:* www.thenewpress.com, pg 168

New Readers Press, 1320 Jamesville Ave, Syracuse, NY 13210 *Tel:* 315-422-9121 *Toll Free Tel:* 800-448-8878 *Fax:* 315-422-6369 *Toll Free Fax:* 866-894-2100 *E-mail:* nrp@proliteracy.org *Web Site:* www.newreaderspress.com, pg 168

New Rivers Press, c/o Minnesota State University Moorhead, 1104 Seventh Ave S, Moorhead, MN 56563 *Tel:* 218-477-5870 *Fax:* 218-477-2236 *E-mail:* nrp@mnstate.edu *Web Site:* www.newriverspress.com; www.mnstate.edu/newriverspress, pg 168

New Star Books Ltd, 107-3477 Commercial St, Vancouver, BC V5N 4E8, Canada *Tel:* 604-738-9429 *Fax:* 604-738-9332 *E-mail:* info@newstarbooks.com *Web Site:* www.newstarbooks.com, pg 492

New Strategist Publications Inc, 120 W State St, 4th fl, Ithaca, NY 14850 *Tel:* 607-273-0913 *Toll Free Tel:* 800-848-0842 *Fax:* 607-277-5009 *E-mail:* demographics@newstrategist.com *Web Site:* newstrategist.com, pg 168

New Win Publishing, 9682 Telstar Ave, Suite 110, El Monte, CA 91731 *Tel:* 626-448-3448 *Fax:* 626-602-3817 *E-mail:* info@academiclearningcompany.com *Web Site:* www.newwinpublishing.com; www.wbusinessbooks.com/, pg 168

New Women's Voices Chapbook Competition, PO Box 1626, Georgetown, KY 40324 *Tel:* 859-514-8966 *E-mail:* finishingbooks@aol.com; flpbookstore@aol.com *Web Site:* www.finishinglinepress.com, pg 712

New World Library, 14 Pamaron Way, Novato, CA 94949 *Tel:* 415-884-2100 *Toll Free Tel:* 800-227-3900 (ext 52, retail orders); 800-972-6657 *Fax:* 415-884-2199 *E-mail:* escort@newworldlibrary.com *Web Site:* www.newworldlibrary.com, pg 168

New World Publishing (Canada), PO Box 36075, Halifax, NS B3J 3S9, Canada *Tel:* 902-576-2055 (inquiries) *Toll Free Tel:* 877-211-3334 (orders) *Fax:* 902-576-2095 *Web Site:* www.newworldpublishing.com, pg 492

New York Academy of Sciences, 7 World Trade, 40th fl, 250 Greenwich St, New York, NY 10007-2157 *Tel:* 212-298-8600 *Toll Free Tel:* 800-843-6927 *Fax:* 212-298-3644 *E-mail:* nyas@nyas.org; publications@nyas.org *Web Site:* www.nyas.org, pg 169

The New York Botanical Garden Press, 2900 Southern Blvd, Bronx, NY 10458-5126 *Tel:* 718-817-8721 *Fax:* 718-817-8842 *E-mail:* nybgpress@nybg.org *Web Site:* www.nybgpress.org, pg 169

New York City Book Awards, 53 E 79 St, New York, NY 10075 *Tel:* 212-288-6900 *Fax:* 212-744-5832 *E-mail:* events@nysoclib.org *Web Site:* www.nysoclib.org, pg 712

New York City College of Technology, 300 Jay St, Brooklyn, NY 11201 *Tel:* 718-260-5500 *Fax:* 718-260-5198 *E-mail:* connect@citytech.cuny.edu *Web Site:* www.citytech.cuny.edu, pg 661

New York Media Works, 112 Franklin St, New York, NY 10013 *Tel:* 646-369-5681 *Fax:* 646-810-4033 *E-mail:* info@nymediaworks.com *Web Site:* www.nymediaworks.com, pg 508

New York Public Library, Publications Off, 2nd fl, 188 Madison Ave, New York, NY 10016-4314 *Tel:* 917-275-6975 *Web Site:* www.nypl.org, pg 169

The New York Public Library Helen Bernstein Book Award for Excellence in Journalism, Stephen A Schwarzman Bldg, Fifth Ave at 42 St, South Court Bldg, 3rd fl, New York, NY 10018-2788 *Tel:* 212-930-0876 *Web Site:* www.nypl.org, pg 713

New York State Bar Association, One Elk St, Albany, NY 12207 *Tel:* 518-463-3200 *Toll Free Tel:* 800-582-2452 *Fax:* 518-487-5517 *Web Site:* www.nysba.org, pg 169

New York State Edith Wharton Citation of Merit for Fiction Writers, University at Albany, SL 320, Albany, NY 12222 *Tel:* 518-442-5620 *Fax:* 518-442-5621 *E-mail:* writers@uamail.albany.edu *Web Site:* www.albany.edu/writers-inst, pg 713

New York State Walt Whitman Citation of Merit for Poets, University at Albany, SL 320, Albany, NY 12222 *Tel:* 518-442-5620 *Fax:* 518-442-5621 *E-mail:* writers@uamail.albany.edu *Web Site:* www.albany.edu/writers-inst, pg 713

New York State Writers Institute, University at Albany, Science Library 320, Albany, NY 12222 *Tel:* 518-442-5620 *Fax:* 518-442-5621 *E-mail:* writers@uamail.albany.edu *Web Site:* www.albany.edu/writers-inst, pg 653

New York University, Center for Publishing, Midtown Ctr, Rm 429, 11 W 42 St, New York, NY 10036 *Tel:* 212-992-3232 *Fax:* 212-992-3233 *E-mail:* pub.center@nyu.edu *Web Site:* www.scps.nyu.edu/publishing, pg 661

New York University Press, 838 Broadway, 3rd fl, New York, NY 10003-4812 *Tel:* 212-998-2575 (edit) *Toll Free Tel:* 800-996-6987 (orders) *Fax:* 212-995-3833 (orders) *E-mail:* information@nyupress.org; customerservice@nyupress.org; orders@nyupress.org *Web Site:* www.nyupress.org, pg 169

John Newbery Medal, 50 E Huron St, Chicago, IL 60611-2795 *Tel:* 312-280-2163 *Toll Free Tel:* 800-545-2433 *Fax:* 312-440-9374 *E-mail:* alsc@ala.org *Web Site:* www.ala.org/alsc, pg 713

Newbury Street Press, 101 Newbury St, Boston, MA 02116 *Tel:* 617-536-5740 *Toll Free Tel:* 888-296-3447 (NEHGS membership) *Fax:* 617-536-7307 *E-mail:* sales@nehgs.org *Web Site:* www.newenglandancestors.org, pg 169

NeWest Press, 8540 109 St, No 201, Edmonton, AB T6G 1E6, Canada *Tel:* 780-432-9427 *Toll Free Tel:* 866-796-5473 *Fax:* 780-433-3179 *E-mail:* info@newestpress.com; orders@newestpress.com *Web Site:* www.newestpress.com, pg 492

Newfoundland and Labrador Book Awards, Haymarket Sq, 208-223 Duckworth St, St John's, NL A1C 6N1, Canada *Tel:* 709-739-5215 *E-mail:* wanl@nf.aibn.com *Web Site:* wanl.ca, pg 713

Newgen North America Inc, 2714 Bee Cave Rd, Suite 201, Austin, TX 78746 *Tel:* 512-478-5341 *Fax:* 512-476-4756 *Web Site:* www.newgen.co, pg 531

NewSouth Books, 105 S Court St, Montgomery, AL 36104 *Tel:* 334-834-3556 *Fax:* 334-834-3557 *E-mail:* info@newsouthbooks.com *Web Site:* www.newsouthbooks.com, pg 169

Newspaper Association of America (NAA), 4401 Wilson Blvd, Suite 900, Arlington, VA 22203 *Tel:* 571-366-1000 *Web Site:* www.naa.org, pg 614

The Newspaper Guild, 501 Third St NW, 6th fl, Washington, DC 20001-2797 *Tel:* 202-434-7177; 202-434-7162 (The Guild Reporter) *Fax:* 202-434-1472 *E-mail:* guild@cwa-union.org *Web Site:* www.newsguild.org, pg 614

Sue Newton, 1385 Cypress Point Lane, Suite 202, Ventura, CA 93003 *Tel:* 805-553-8087 *E-mail:* sue.edit@gmail.com, pg 531

Don & Gee Nicholl Fellowships in Screenwriting, 1313 Vine St, Hollywood, CA 90028 *Tel:* 310-247-3010 *Fax:* 310-247-3794 *E-mail:* nicholl@oscars.org *Web Site:* www.oscars.org/nicholl, pg 713

Donald Nicholson-Smith, 50 Plaza St E, Brooklyn, NY 11238 *Tel:* 718-636-4732 *E-mail:* mnr.dns@verizon.net, pg 531

Nightingale-Conant, 6245 W Howard St, Niles, IL 60714 *Tel:* 847-647-0306 *Toll Free Tel:* 800-572-2770; 800-557-1660 (sales); 800-560-6081 (cust serv) *Fax:* 847-647-7145; 847-647-9143 (sales) *E-mail:* distributordivision@nightingale.com (orders) *Web Site:* www.nightingale.com, pg 169

Nilgiri Press, 3600 Tomales Rd, Tomales, CA 94971 *Tel:* 707-878-2369 *E-mail:* info@easwaran.org *Web Site:* www.easwaran.org, pg 169

Nimbus Publishing Ltd, 3731 Mackintosh St, Halifax, NS B3K 5A5, Canada *Tel:* 902-455-4286; 902-454-7404 *Toll Free Tel:* 800-NIMBUS9 (646-2879) *Fax:* 902-455-5440 *Toll Free Fax:* 888-253-3133 *E-mail:* customerservice@nimbus.ca *Web Site:* www.nimbus.ca, pg 492

John Frederick Nims Memorial Prize, 444 N Michigan Ave, Suite 1850, Chicago, IL 60611-4034 *Tel:* 312-787-7070 *Fax:* 312-787-6650 *E-mail:* editors@poetrymagazine.org *Web Site:* www.poetryfoundation.org, pg 713

NK Publications Inc, PO Box 1735, Radio City Sta, New York, NY 10101-1735 *E-mail:* info@nkpublications.com *Web Site:* www.nkpublications.com, pg 170

No Frills Buffalo, 119 Dorchester Rd, Buffalo, NY 14213 *Tel:* 716-510-0520 *E-mail:* contact@nofrillsbuffalo.com *Web Site:* www.nofrillsbuffalo.com, pg 170

No Starch Press Inc, 245 Eighth St, San Francisco, CA 94103 *Tel:* 415-863-9900 *Toll Free Tel:* 800-420-7240 *Fax:* 415-863-9950 *E-mail:* info@nostarch.com *Web Site:* www.nostarch.com, pg 170

Regula Noetzli Literary Agent, 2344 County Rte 83, Pine Plains, NY 12567 *Tel:* 518-398-6260 *E-mail:* regula@taconic.net; regula@sheedylit.com, pg 567

The Betsy Nolan Literary Agency, 214 W 29 St, Suite 1002, New York, NY 10001 *Tel:* 212-967-8200 *Fax:* 212-967-7292 *E-mail:* dblehr@cs.com, pg 567

NOLO, 950 Parker St, Berkeley, CA 94710 *Web Site:* www.nolo.com, pg 170

The Noontide Press, PO Box 2719, Newport Beach, CA 92659-1319 *Tel:* 714-593-9725 *Fax:* 714-593-9731 *E-mail:* orders@noontidepress.com *Web Site:* www.noontidepress.com, pg 170

Norilana Books, PO Box 209, Highgate Center, VT 05459-0209 *E-mail:* service@norilana.com *Web Site:* www.norilana.com, pg 170

North American Agricultural Journalists (NAAJ), 6434 Hurta Lane, Bryan, TX 77808 *Tel:* 979-845-2872 *Web Site:* www.naaj.net, pg 614

North American Bookdealers Exchange (NABE), PO Box 606, Cottage Grove, OR 97424-0026 *Tel:* 541-942-7455 *E-mail:* nabe@bookmarketingprofits.com *Web Site:* www.bookmarketingprofits.com, pg 614

North American Snowsports Journalists Association, 11728 SE Madison St, Portland, OR 97216-3849 *Tel:* 503-255-3771 *Fax:* 503-255-3771 *Web Site:* www.nasja.org, pg 614

North Atlantic Books, 2526 Martin Luther King Jr Way, Berkeley, CA 94704 *Tel:* 510-549-4270 *Fax:* 510-549-4276 *Web Site:* www.northatlanticbooks.com, pg 170

North Carolina Arts Council Writers Fellowships, 109 E Jones St, Raleigh, NC 27601 *Tel:* 919-807-6500 *Fax:* 919-807-6532 *E-mail:* ncarts@ncdcr.gov *Web Site:* www.ncarts.org, pg 713

North Carolina Office of Archives & History, Historical Publications Section, 4622 Mail Service Ctr, Raleigh, NC 27699-4622 *Tel:* 919-733-7442 (ext 225) *Fax:* 919-733-1439 *Web Site:* www.ncpublications.com; nc-historical-publications.stores.yahoo.net (online store), pg 170

North Carolina Writers' Network, PO Box 21591, Winston-Salem, NC 27120-1591 *Tel:* 336-293-8844 *Web Site:* www.ncwriters.org, pg 614

North Carolina Writers' Network Annual Fall Conference, PO Box 21591, Winston-Salem, NC 27120-1591 *Tel:* 336-293-8844 *E-mail:* mail@ncwriters.org *Web Site:* www.ncwriters.org, pg 653

North Country Books Inc, 220 Lafayette St, Utica, NY 13502-4312 *Tel:* 315-735-4877 *Toll Free Tel:* 800-342-7409 (orders) *Fax:* 315-738-4342 *E-mail:* ncbooks@verizon.net *Web Site:* www.northcountrybooks.com, pg 170

North Country Press, 126 Main St, Unity, ME 04988 *Tel:* 207-948-2208 *Fax:* 207-948-9000 *E-mail:* info@northcountrypress.com *Web Site:* www.northcountrypress.com, pg 170

North Point Press, 18 W 18 St, 8th fl, New York, NY 10011 *Tel:* 212-741-6900 *Toll Free Tel:* 888-330-8477 *Fax:* 212-633-9385 *Web Site:* www.fsgbooks.com, pg 171

North River Press Publishing Corp, 27 Rosseter St, Great Barrington, MA 01230 *Tel:* 413-528-0034 *Toll Free Tel:* 800-486-2665 *Fax:* 413-528-3163 *Toll Free Fax:* 800-BOOK-FAX (266-5329) *E-mail:* info@northriverpress.com *Web Site:* www.northriverpress.com, pg 171

The North-South Institute (Institut Nord-Sud), 100 Argyle Ave, Suite 200, Ottawa, ON K2P 1B6, Canada *Tel:* 613-241-3535 *Fax:* 613-241-7435 *E-mail:* nsi@nsi-ins.ca *Web Site:* www.nsi-ins.ca, pg 493

North Star Press of Saint Cloud Inc, PO Box 451, St Cloud, MN 56302-0451 *Tel:* 320-558-9062 *Toll Free Tel:* 888-820-1636 *Fax:* 320-558-9063 *E-mail:* info@northstarpress.com *Web Site:* www.northstarpress.com, pg 171

Northeast-Midwest Institute, 50 "F" St NW, Suite 950, Washington, DC 20001 *Tel:* 202-544-5200 *Fax:* 202-544-0043 *E-mail:* info@nemw.org *Web Site:* www.nemw.org, pg 171

Northeast Texas Community College Annual Writers Conference, Continuing Education, PO Box 1307, Mount Pleasant, TX 75456-1307 *Tel:* 903-434-8134 *Toll Free Tel:* 800-870-0142 *Fax:* 903-572-6712 *Web Site:* www.ntcc.edu, pg 653

Northeastern Graphic Inc, 33 Crystal Bay Ct, Palm Coast, FL 32137 *Tel:* 386-246-9942 *E-mail:* contact@northeasterngraphic.com *Web Site:* www.northeasterngraphic.com, pg 531

Northern California Book Awards, c/o Poetry Flash, 1450 Fourth St, Suite 4, Berkeley, CA 94710 *Tel:* 510-525-5476 *Fax:* 510-525-6752 *E-mail:* editor@poetryflash.org *Web Site:* www.poetryflash.org/ncba.html, pg 713

Northern California Independent Booksellers Association (NCIBA), The Presidio, 1007 General Kennedy Ave, San Francisco, CA 94129 *Tel:* 415-561-7686 *Fax:* 415-561-7685 *E-mail:* office@nciba.com *Web Site:* www.nciba.com, pg 614

Northern California Translators Association, 2261 Market St, Suite 160, San Francisco, CA 94114-1600 *Tel:* 510-845-8712 *E-mail:* administrator@ncta.org *Web Site:* www.ncta.org, pg 614

Northern Canada Evangelical Mission (NCEM), PO Box 3030, Prince Albert, SK S6V 7V4, Canada *Tel:* 306-764-3388 *Fax:* 306-764-3390 *E-mail:* ncem@ncem.ca *Web Site:* www.ncem.ca, pg 493

Northern Illinois University Press, 2280 Bethany Rd, DeKalb, IL 60115 *Tel:* 815-753-1826; 815-753-1075 *Fax:* 815-753-1845 *Web Site:* www.niupress.niu.edu, pg 171

Northstone Publishing, 485 Beaver Lake Rd, Kelowna, BC V4V 1S5, Canada *Tel:* 250-766-2778 *Toll Free Tel:* 800-299-2926; 800-663-2775 (orders) *Fax:* 250-766-2736 *Toll Free Fax:* 888-841-9991 *E-mail:* info@woodlakebooks.com *Web Site:* www.woodlakebooks.com, pg 493

Northwest Independent Editors Guild, PO Box 1630, Snoqualmie, WA 98065 *E-mail:* info@edsguild.org *Web Site:* www.edsguild.org, pg 614

Northwest Territories Public Library Services, 75 Woodland Dr, Hay River, NT X0E 1G1, Canada *Tel:* 867-874-6531 *Toll Free Tel:* 866-297-0232 (CN) *Fax:* 867-874-3321 *Web Site:* www.nwtpls.gov.nt.ca, pg 614

Northwest Writers & Publishers Association (NWPA), 21860 Willamette Dr, West Linn, OR 97068 *Web Site:* northwestwriterspublishers.weebly.com, pg 615

Northwestern University Press, 629 Noyes St, Evanston, IL 60208-4210 *Tel:* 847-491-2046 *Toll Free Tel:* 800-621-2736 (orders only) *Fax:* 847-491-8150 *E-mail:* nupress@northwestern.edu *Web Site:* www.nupress.northwestern.edu, pg 171

W W Norton & Company Inc, 500 Fifth Ave, New York, NY 10110-0017 *Tel:* 212-354-5500 *Toll Free Tel:* 800-233-4830 (orders & cust serv) *Fax:* 212-869-0856 *Toll Free Fax:* 800-458-6515 *Web Site:* www.wwnorton.com, pg 171

Norwood House Press, PO Box 316598, Chicago, IL 60631 *Tel:* 773-467-0837 *Toll Free Tel:* 866-565-2900 *Fax:* 773-467-9686 *Toll Free Fax:* 866-565-2901 *E-mail:* customerservice@norwoodhousepress.com *Web Site:* www.norwoodhousepress.com, pg 172

Notable Wisconsin Authors, 4610 S Biltmore Lane, Madison, WI 53718 *Tel:* 608-245-3640 *Fax:* 608-245-3646 *Web Site:* www.wla.lib.wi.us, pg 713

Nova Press, 9058 Lloyd Place, West Hollywood, CA 90069 *Tel:* 310-275-3513 *Toll Free Tel:* 800-949-6175 *Fax:* 310-281-5629 *E-mail:* novapress@aol.com *Web Site:* www.novapress.net, pg 172

Nova Science Publishers Inc, 400 Oser Ave, Suite 1600, Hauppauge, NY 11788-3619 *Tel:* 631-231-7269 *Fax:* 631-231-8175 *E-mail:* main@novapublishers.com *Web Site:* www.novapublishers.com, pg 172

Novalis Publishing, 10 Lower Spadina Ave, Suite 400, Toronto, ON M5V 2Z2, Canada *Tel:* 416-363-3303 *Toll Free Tel:* 877-702-7773 *Fax:* 416-363-9409 *Toll Free Fax:* 877-702-7775 *E-mail:* books@novalis.ca *Web Site:* www.novalis.ca, pg 493

Novella Prize, University of Victoria, Box 1700, Sta CSC, Victoria, BC V8W 2Y2, Canada *Tel:* 250-721-8524 *Fax:* 250-472-5051 *E-mail:* malahat@uvic.ca *Web Site:* www.malahatreview.ca, pg 713

Wanda Nowak Creative Illustrators Agency, 231 E 76 St, Suite 5-D, New York, NY 10021 *Tel:* 212-535-0438 *E-mail:* wanda@wandanow.com *Web Site:* www.wandanow.com, pg 584

NPES The Association for Suppliers of Printing, Publishing & Converting Technologies, 1899 Preston White Dr, Reston, VA 20191 *Tel:* 703-264-7200 *Fax:* 703-620-0994 *E-mail:* npes@npes.org *Web Site:* www.npes.org, pg 615

NPTA Alliance, 330 N Wabash Ave, Suite 2000, Chicago, IL 60611 *Tel:* 312-321-4092 *Toll Free Tel:* 800-355-NPTA (355-6782) *Fax:* 312-673-6736 *Web Site:* www.gonpta.com, pg 615

nSight Inc, One Van de Graaff Dr, Suite 202, Burlington, MA 01803 *Tel:* 781-273-6300 *Fax:* 781-273-6301 *Web Site:* www.nsightworks.com, pg 531

NSK Neustadt Prize for Children's Literature, c/o University of Oklahoma, 630 Parrington Oval, Suite 110, Norman, OK 73019-4033 *Tel:* 405-325-4531 *Fax:* 405-325-7495 *Web Site:* www.worldliteraturetoday.org, pg 714

Nuestras Voces National Playwriting Competition, 138 E 27 St, New York, NY 10016 *Tel:* 212-225-9950 *Fax:* 212-225-9085 *Web Site:* www.repertorio.org, pg 714

nursesbooks.org, The Publishing Program of ANA, 8515 Georgia Ave, Suite 400, Silver Spring, MD 20910-3492 *Tel:* 301-628-5000 *Toll Free Tel:* 800-924-9053; 800-637-0323 (orders) *Fax:* 301-628-5001 *E-mail:* anp@ana.org *Web Site:* www.nursesbooks.org; www.nursingworld.org, pg 172

Nystrom Herff Jones Education Division, 4719 W 62 St, Indianapolis, IN 46268-2593 *Tel:* 317-612-3901 *Toll Free Tel:* 800-621-8086 (cust serv) *Fax:* 317-329-3305 *E-mail:* info@nystromnet.com *Web Site:* www.nystromnet.com, pg 172

OAG Worldwide, 3025 Highland Pkwy, Suite 200, Downers Grove, IL 60515-5561 *Tel:* 630-515-5300 *Toll Free Tel:* 800-342-5624 (cust serv) *Fax:* 630-515-3251 *E-mail:* contactus@oag.com *Web Site:* www.oag.com, pg 172

Oak Knoll Press, 310 Delaware St, New Castle, DE 19720 *Tel:* 302-328-7232 *Toll Free Tel:* 800-996-2556 *Fax:* 302-328-7274 *E-mail:* oakknoll@oakknoll.com *Web Site:* www.oakknoll.com, pg 172

Oak Tree Press, 1820 W Lacey Blvd, Suite 220, Hanford, CA 93230 *Tel:* 217-824-6500 *E-mail:* publisher@oaktreebooks.com; info@oaktreebooks.com; query@oaktreebooks.com; pressdept@oaktreebooks.com; bookorders@oaktreebooks.com *Web Site:* www.oaktreebooks.com; www.otpblog.blogspot.com, pg 173

Oaklea Press, 41 Old Mill Rd, Richmond, VA 23226-3111 *Tel:* 804-308-3906 *Fax:* 804-980-7057 *Web Site:* oakleapress.com, pg 173

Oakstone Publishing LLC, 100 Corporate Pkwy, Suite 600, Birmingham, AL 35242 *Toll Free Tel:* 800-633-4743 *Fax:* 205-995-1926 *E-mail:* service@oakstonemedical.com *Web Site:* www.oakstonepublishing.com; www.cmeonly.com; www.cdeonly.com, pg 173

Harold Ober Associates Inc, 425 Madison Ave, New York, NY 10017 *Tel:* 212-759-8600 *Fax:* 212-759-9428 *Web Site:* www.haroldober.com, pg 567

Oberlin College Press, 50 N Professor St, Oberlin, OH 44074-1091 *Tel:* 440-775-8408 *Fax:* 440-775-8124 *E-mail:* oc.press@oberlin.edu *Web Site:* www.oberlin.edu/ocpress, pg 173

Oberon Press, 145 Spruce St, Suite 205, Ottawa, ON K1R 6P1, Canada *Tel:* 613-238-3275 *Fax:* 613-238-3275 *E-mail:* oberon@sympatico.ca *Web Site:* www.oberonpress.ca, pg 493

Objective Entertainment, 609 Greenwich St, 6th fl, New York, NY 10014 *Tel:* 212-431-5454 *Fax:* 917-464-6394 *Web Site:* www.objectiveent.com, pg 567

Eli M Oboler Memorial Award, 50 E Huron St, Chicago, IL 60611 *Tel:* 312-280-4223 *Toll Free Tel:* 800-545-2433 *Fax:* 312-280-4227 *E-mail:* oif@ala.org *Web Site:* www.ala.org/ifrt, pg 714

Ocean Press, 511 Avenue of the Americas, Suite 96, New York, NY 10011-8436 *Tel:* 212-260-3690 *E-mail:* info@oceanbooks.com.au; orders@oceanbooks.com.au (orders only) *Web Site:* www.oceanbooks.com.au, pg 173

Ocean Publishing, PO Box 1080, Flagler Beach, FL 32136-1080 *Tel:* 386-517-1600 *E-mail:* publisher@oceanpublishing.org *Web Site:* www.oceanpublishing.org, pg 173

Ocean Tree Books, 1325 Cerro Gordo Rd, Santa Fe, NM 87501 *Tel:* 505-983-1412 *Fax:* 505-983-0899 *Web Site:* www.oceantree.com, pg 173

Oceanview Publishing, CEO Center at Mediterranean Plaza, Suite 120-G, 595 Bay Isles Rd, Longboat Key, FL 34228 *Tel:* 941-387-8500 *Fax:* 941-387-0039 *Web Site:* www.oceanviewpub.com, pg 173

The Flannery O'Connor Award for Short Fiction, Main Library, 3rd fl, 320 S Jackson St, Athens, GA 30602 *Fax:* 706-542-2558 *Web Site:* www.ugapress.org, pg 714

Frank O'Connor Prize for Fiction, Texas Christian University, Dept of English, TCU Box 297270, Fort Worth, TX 76129 *Tel:* 817-257-5907 *Fax:* 817-257-7709 *E-mail:* descant@tcu.edu *Web Site:* www.descant.tcu.edu, pg 714

OCP, 5536 NE Hassalo St, Portland, OR 97213 *Tel:* 503-281-1191 *Toll Free Tel:* 800-548-8749 *Fax:* 503-282-3486 *Toll Free Fax:* 800-843-8181 *E-mail:* liturgy@ocp.org *Web Site:* www.ocp.org, pg 173

Octane Press, 808 Kinney Ave, Austin, TX 78704 *Tel:* 512-334-9441 *Fax:* 512-852-4737 *E-mail:* info@octanepress.com *Web Site:* www.octanepress.com, pg 174

Scott O'Dell Award for Historical Fiction, c/o Horn Book Inc, 56 Roland St, Suite 200, Boston, MA 02129 *Tel:* 617-628-8471 *Toll Free Tel:* 800-325-1170 *Web Site:* www.scottodell.com/odellaward.html, pg 714

Odyssey Books, 2421 Redwood Ct, Longmont, CO 80503-8155 *Tel:* 720-494-1473 *Fax:* 720-494-1471 *E-mail:* books@odysseybooks.net *Web Site:* cilettipublishinggroup.com, pg 174

Odyssey: The Summer Fantasy Writing Workshop, PO Box 75, Mont Vernon, NH 03057 *Tel:* 603-673-6234 *Fax:* 603-673-6234 *Web Site:* www.odysseyworkshop.org, pg 653

Dayne Ogilvie Prize, 460 Richmond St W, Suite 600, Toronto, ON M5V 1Y1, Canada *Tel:* 416-504-8222 *Toll Free Tel:* 877-906-6548 *Fax:* 416-504-9090 *E-mail:* info@writerstrust.com *Web Site:* www.writerstrust.com, pg 714

Howard O'Hagan Award for Short Story, 11759 Groat Rd, Edmonton, AB T5M 3K6, Canada *Tel:* 780-422-8174 *Toll Free Tel:* 800-665-5354 (AB only) *Fax:* 780-422-2663 (attn WGA) *E-mail:* mail@writersguild.ab.ca *Web Site:* www.writersguild.ab.ca, pg 714

Ohio Genealogical Society, 611 State Rte 97 W, Bellville, OH 44813-8813 *Tel:* 419-886-1903 *Fax:* 419-886-0092 *E-mail:* ogs@ogs.org *Web Site:* www.ogs.org, pg 174

Ohio State University Foreign Language Publications, 198 Hagerty Hall, 1775 College Rd, Columbus, OH 43210-1340 *Tel:* 614-292-3838 *Toll Free Tel:* 800-678-6999 *Fax:* 614-688-3355 *E-mail:* flpubs@osu.edu *Web Site:* www.flpubs.osu.edu, pg 174

Ohio State University Press, 180 Pressey Hall, 1070 Carmack Rd, Columbus, OH 43210-1002 *Tel:* 614-292-6930 *Fax:* 614-292-2065 *Toll Free Fax:* 800-621-8476 *E-mail:* info@osupress.org *Web Site:* ohiostatepress.org, pg 174

Ohio University, English Dept, Creative Writing Program, Ohio University, English Dept, Ellis Hall, Athens, OH 45701 *Tel:* 740-593-2838 (English Dept) *Fax:* 740-593-2832 *E-mail:* english.department@ohio.edu *Web Site:* english.ohiou.edu, pg 662

Ohio University Press, 215 Columbus Rd, Suite 101, Athens, OH 45701-1373 *Fax:* 740-593-4536 *Web Site:* www.ohioswallow.com, pg 174

Ohioana Award for Children's Literature-Alice Louise Wood Memorial, 274 E First Ave, Suite 300, Columbus, OH 43201 *Tel:* 614-466-3831 *Fax:* 614-728-6974 *E-mail:* ohioana@ohioana.org *Web Site:* www.ohioana.org, pg 714

Ohioana Book Awards, 274 E First Ave, Suite 300, Columbus, OH 43201 *Tel:* 614-466-3831 *Fax:* 614-728-6974 *E-mail:* ohioana@ohioana.org *Web Site:* www.ohioana.org, pg 714

Ohioana Career Award, 274 E First Ave, Suite 300, Columbus, OH 43201 *Tel:* 614-466-3831 *Fax:* 614-728-6974 *E-mail:* ohioana@ohioana.org *Web Site:* www.ohioana.org, pg 714

Ohioana Citations, 274 E First Ave, Suite 300, Columbus, OH 43201 *Tel:* 614-466-3831 *Fax:* 614-728-6974 *E-mail:* ohioana@ohioana.org *Web Site:* www.ohioana.org, pg 715

Ohioana Pegasus Award, 274 E First Ave, Suite 300, Columbus, OH 43201 *Tel:* 614-466-3831 *Fax:* 614-728-6974 *E-mail:* ohioana@ohioana.org *Web Site:* www.ohioana.org, pg 715

Ohioana Poetry Award-Memorial to Helen & Laura Krout, 274 E First Ave, Suite 300, Columbus, OH 43201 *Tel:* 614-466-3831 *Fax:* 614-728-6974 *E-mail:* ohioana@ohioana.org *Web Site:* www.ohioana.org, pg 715

Ohioana Walter Rumsey Marvin Grant, 274 E First Ave, Suite 300, Columbus, OH 43201 *Tel:* 614-466-3831 *Fax:* 614-728-6974 *E-mail:* ohioana@ohioana.org *Web Site:* www.ohioana.org, pg 715

Old Barn Enterprises Inc, 600 Kelly Rd, Carthage, NC 28327 *Tel:* 910-947-2587 *Fax:* 480-287-9017 *E-mail:* jeffandpam@nynphotoschool.com *Web Site:* www.nynphotoschool.com, pg 174

Olde & Oppenheim Publishers, 3219 N Margate Place, Chandler, AZ 85224 *E-mail:* olde_oppenheim@hotmail.com *Web Site:* oldeandoppenheimpublishers.com, pg 174

Veronica Oliva, 304 Lily St, San Francisco, CA 94102-5608 *Tel:* 415-337-7707 *E-mail:* veronicaoliva@sbcglobal.net, pg 532

The Oliver Press Inc, Charlotte Sq, 5707 W 36 St, Minneapolis, MN 55416-2510 *Tel:* 952-926-8981 *Toll Free Tel:* 800-8-OLIVER (865-4837) *Fax:* 952-926-8965 *E-mail:* orders@oliverpress.com *Web Site:* www.oliverpress.com, pg 174

Chris O'Malley Fiction Prize, University of Wisconsin, 6193 Helen C White Hall, English Dept, 600 N Park St, Madison, WI 53706 *Tel:* 608-263-0566 *E-mail:* madisonrevw@gmail.com *Web Site:* www.english.wisc.edu/madisonreview, pg 715

OMNI Publishers Inc, 29131 Bulverde Rd, San Antonio, TX 78260 *Tel:* 210-778-4437 *Fax:* 830-438-4645 *Web Site:* www.omnipublishers.com; www.educatorethicsseries.com, pg 174

Omnibus Press, 257 Park Ave S, 20th fl, New York, NY 10010 *Tel:* 212-254-2100 *Toll Free Tel:* 800-431-7187 *Fax:* 212-254-2013 *Toll Free Fax:* 800-345-6842 *E-mail:* info-us@omnibuspress.com *Web Site:* www.omnibuspress.com; www.musicsales.com, pg 174

Omnidawn Publishing, 1632 Elm Ave, Richmond, CA 94805-1614 *Tel:* 510-237-5472 *Toll Free Tel:* 800-792-4957 *Fax:* 510-232-8525 *E-mail:* manager@omnidawn.com *Web Site:* www.omnidawn.com, pg 175

Omnigraphics Inc, 155 W Congress, Suite 200, Detroit, MI 48226 *Tel:* 313-961-1340 *Toll Free Tel:* 800-234-1340 (cust serv) *Fax:* 313-961-1383 *Toll Free Fax:* 800-875-1340 (cust serv) *E-mail:* info@omnigraphics.com *Web Site:* www.omnigraphics.com, pg 175

Omohundro Institute of Early American History & Culture (OIEAHC), Swem Library, Ground fl, 400 Landrum Dr, Williamsburg, VA 23185 *Tel:* 757-221-1110 *Fax:* 757-221-1047 *E-mail:* ieahc1@wm.edu *Web Site:* oieahc.wm.edu, pg 175

One Act Play Depot, 618 Memorial Dr, PO Box 335, Spiritwood, SK S0J 2M0, Canada *E-mail:* plays@oneactplays.net; orders@oneactplays.net *Web Site:* oneactplays.net, pg 493

OneSource, 300 Baker Ave, Concord, MA 01742 *Tel:* 978-318-4300 *Toll Free Tel:* 866-354-6936 *Fax:* 978-318-4690 *E-mail:* sales@onesource.com *Web Site:* www.onesource.com, pg 175

Online Training Solutions Inc (OTSI), 2217 152 Ave NE, Redmond, WA 98052 *Toll Free Tel:* 888-308-6874 *Toll Free Fax:* 888-308-6875 *E-mail:* biz@otsi.com *Web Site:* www.otsi.com, pg 175

Ontario Book Publishers Organization (OBPO), 20 Maud St, No 401, Toronto, ON M5V 2M5, Canada *Tel:* 416-536-7584 *Fax:* 416-536-7692 *Web Site:* obpo.ca, pg 615

Ontario Library Association, 2 Toronto St, 3rd fl, Toronto, ON M5C 2B6, Canada *Tel:* 416-363-3388 *Toll Free Tel:* 866-873-9867 *Fax:* 416-941-9581 *E-mail:* info@accessola.com *Web Site:* www.accessola.com, pg 615

Oolichan Books, PO Box 2278, Fernie, BC V0B 1M0, Canada *Tel:* 250-423-6113 *E-mail:* info@oolichan.com *Web Site:* www.oolichan.com, pg 493

Ooligan Press, Portland State University, 369 Neuberger Hall, 724 SW Harrison St, Portland, OR 97201 *Tel:* 503-725-9748 *Fax:* 503-725-3561 *E-mail:* ooligan@ooliganpress.pdx.edu *Web Site:* ooligan.pdx.edu, pg 175

Open Chapbook Competition, PO Box 1626, Georgetown, KY 40324 *Tel:* 859-514-8966 *E-mail:* finishingbooks@aol.com; flpbookstore@aol.com *Web Site:* www.finishinglinepress.com, pg 715

Open Court, 70 E Lake St, Suite 300, Chicago, IL 60601 *Tel:* 312-701-1720 *Toll Free Tel:* 800-815-2280 (orders only) *Fax:* 312-701-1728 *E-mail:* opencourt@caruspub.com *Web Site:* www.opencourtbooks.com, pg 175

Open Horizons Publishing Co, PO Box 2887, Taos, NM 87571 *Tel:* 575-751-3398 *Fax:* 575-751-3100 *E-mail:* info@bookmarket.com *Web Site:* www.bookmarket.com, pg 175

Open Road Publishing, 32 Turkey Lane, Cold Spring Harbor, NY 11724 *Tel:* 631-692-7172 *E-mail:* jopenroad@aol.com *Web Site:* www.openroadguides.com, pg 175

Open Season Awards, University of Victoria, Box 1700, Sta CSC, Victoria, BC V8W 2Y2, Canada *Tel:* 250-721-8524 *Fax:* 250-472-5051 *E-mail:* malahat@uvic.ca *Web Site:* malahatreview.ca, pg 715

Opie Prize, Ohio State Univ, Mershon Ctr, 1501 Neil Ave, Columbus, OH 43201-2602 *Tel:* 614-292-3375 *Fax:* 614-292-2407 *Web Site:* www.afsnet.org/aboutAFS/AFSprizes.cfm, pg 715

OPIS/STALSBY Directories & Databases, 3349 Hwy 138, Bldg D, Suite D, Wall, NJ 07719 *Tel:* 732-901-8800 *Toll Free Tel:* 800-275-0950 *Toll Free Fax:* 800-450-5864 *E-mail:* opisstalsbylistings@opisnet.com *Web Site:* www.opisnet.com, pg 175

The Optical Society (OSA), 2010 Massachusetts Ave NW, Washington, DC 20036-1023 *Tel:* 202-223-8130 *Toll Free Tel:* 800-766-4672 *E-mail:* custserv@osa.org *Web Site:* www.osa.org, pg 175

Optometric Extension Program Foundation, 1921 E Carnegie Ave, Suite 3-L, Santa Ana, CA 92705-5510 *Tel:* 949-250-8070 *Fax:* 949-250-8157 *E-mail:* oep@oep.org *Web Site:* www.oepf.org, pg 176

OptumInsight™, 12125 Technology Dr, Eden Prairie, MN 55334 *Tel:* 952-833-7100 *Toll Free Tel:* 888-445-8745; 800-765-6713 *Fax:* 952-833-7201 *E-mail:* insight@optum.com *Web Site:* www.optuminsight.com, pg 176

Orange Frazer Press Inc, 37 1/2 W Main St, Wilmington, OH 45177 *Tel:* 937-382-3196 *Toll Free Tel:* 800-852-9332 (orders) *Fax:* 937-383-3159 *E-mail:* ofrazer@erinet.com *Web Site:* www.orangefrazer.com, pg 176

Orbis Books, Price Bldg, Box 302, Maryknoll, NY 10545-0302 *Tel:* 914-941-7636 *Toll Free Tel:* 800-258-5838 (orders) *Fax:* 914-941-7005 *E-mail:* orbisbooks@maryknoll.org *Web Site:* www.orbisbooks.com, pg 176

Orbit, 1290 Avenue of the Americas, New York, NY 10019 *Tel:* 212-364-1100 *Toll Free Tel:* 800-759-0190 *Web Site:* www.orbitbooks.net, pg 176

Orca Book Publishers, PO Box 468, Custer, WA 98240-0468 *Tel:* 250-380-1229 *Toll Free Tel:* 800-210-5277 *Fax:* 250-380-1892 *Toll Free Fax:* 877-408-1551 *E-mail:* orca@orcabook.com *Web Site:* www.orcabook.com, pg 176

Orchard Publications, 39510 Paseo Padre Pkwy, Suite 315, Fremont, CA 94538 *Tel:* 510-792-6077 *Fax:* 510-792-6097 *E-mail:* info@orchardpublications.com; orchard@orchardpublications.com *Web Site:* www.orchardpublications.com, pg 176

Orchises Press, PO Box 320533, Alexandria, VA 22320-4533 *Tel:* 703-683-1243 *Web Site:* mason.gmu.edu/~lathbury/, pg 176

Ordre des traducteurs, terminologues et interpretes agrees du quebec, 2021 Union Ave, Suite 1108, Montreal, QC H3A 2S9, Canada *Tel:* 514-845-4411 *Toll Free Tel:* 800-265-4815 *Fax:* 514-845-9903 *E-mail:* info@ottiaq.org *Web Site:* www.ottiaq.org, pg 615

Oregon Book Awards, 925 SW Washington St, Portland, OR 97205 *Tel:* 503-227-2583 *Fax:* 503-241-4256 *E-mail:* la@literary-arts.org *Web Site:* www.literary-arts.org, pg 715

Oregon Christian Writers (OCW), 1075 Willow Lake Rd N, Keizer, OR 97303 *Tel:* 503-393-3356 *E-mail:* contact@oregonchristianwriters.org *Web Site:* www.oregonchristianwriters.org, pg 615

Oregon Christian Writers Coaching Conference, 1075 Willow Lake Rd N, Keizer, OR 97303 *Tel:* 503-393-3356 *E-mail:* contact@oregonchristianwriters.org *Web Site:* www.oregonchristianwriters.org, pg 653

Oregon Christian Writers Seminar, 1075 Willow Lake Rd N, Keizer, OR 97303 *Tel:* 503-393-3356 *E-mail:* contact@oregonchristianwriters.org *Web Site:* www.oregonchristianwriters.org, pg 653

Oregon State University Press, 121 The Valley Library, Corvallis, OR 97331-4501 *Tel:* 541-737-3166 *Toll Free Tel:* 800-621-2736 (orders) *Web Site:* osupress.oregonstate.edu, pg 177

O'Reilly Media Inc, 1005 Gravenstein Hwy N, Sebastopol, CA 95472 *Tel:* 707-827-7000; 707-827-7019 *Toll Free Tel:* 800-998-9938; 800-889-8969 *Fax:* 707-829-0104; 707-824-8268 *E-mail:* orders@oreilly.com *Web Site:* www.oreilly.com, pg 177

Organization for Economic Cooperation & Development, 2001 "L" St NW, Suite 650, Washington, DC 20036-4922 *Tel:* 202-785-6323 *Toll Free Tel:* 800-456-6323 (dist ctr/pubns orders) *Fax:* 202-785-0350 *E-mail:* washington.contact@oecd.org *Web Site:* www.oecdwash.org; www.oecd.org, pg 177

Oriental Institute Publications, 1155 E 58 St, Chicago, IL 60637 *Tel:* 773-702-5967 *Fax:* 773-702-9853 *E-mail:* oi-publications@uchicago.edu; oi-museum@uchicago.edu; oi-administration@uchicago.edu *Web Site:* oi.uchicago.edu, pg 177

Orientation to the Graphic Arts, 200 Deer Run Rd, Sewickley, PA 15143-2324 *Tel:* 412-259-1711 *Toll Free Tel:* 800-910-4283 *Fax:* 412-741-2311 *E-mail:* printing@printing.org *Web Site:* www.printing.org, pg 653

The Original Falcon Press, 1753 E Broadway Rd, No 101-277, Tempe, AZ 85282 *Tel:* 602-708-1409 *E-mail:* info@originalfalcon.com *Web Site:* www.originalfalcon.com, pg 177

Original Publications, PO Box 236, Old Beth Page, NY 11804 *Tel:* 516-605-0547 *Toll Free Tel:* 888-622-8581 *Fax:* 516-605-0549 *E-mail:* originalpub@aol.com *Web Site:* www.occult1.com, pg 178

ORO editions, 31 Commercial Blvd, Suite F, Novato, CA 94949 *Tel:* 415-883-3300 *Fax:* 415-883-3309 *E-mail:* info@oroeditions.com *Web Site:* www.oroeditions.com, pg 178

George Orwell Award, 1111 W Kenyon Rd, Urbana, IL 61801-1096 *Tel:* 217-328-3870 *Toll Free Tel:* 877-369-6283 (cust serv) *Fax:* 217-328-0977 *E-mail:* publiclangawards@ncte.org *Web Site:* www.ncte.org, pg 715

Fifi Oscard Agency Inc, 110 W 40 St, 16th fl, New York, NY 10018 *Tel:* 212-764-1100 *Fax:* 212-840-5019 *E-mail:* agency@fifioscard.com *Web Site:* fifioscard.com, pg 567

Osprey Publishing Inc, 4301 21 St, Suite 220B, Long Island City, NY 11101 *Tel:* 718-433-4402 *Fax:* 718-433-4497 *E-mail:* ospreyusa@ospreypublishing.com *Web Site:* www.ospreypublishing.com, pg 178

Other Press LLC, 2 Park Ave, 24th fl, New York, NY 10016 *Tel:* 212-414-0054 *Toll Free Tel:* 877-843-6843 *Fax:* 212-414-0939 *E-mail:* editor@otherpress.com; rights@otherpress.com *Web Site:* www.otherpress.com, pg 178

OTTN Publishing, 16 Risler St, Stockton, NJ 08559 *Tel:* 609-397-4005 *Toll Free Tel:* 866-356-6886 *Fax:* 609-397-4007 *E-mail:* inquiries@ottnpublishing.com *Web Site:* www.ottnpublishing.com, pg 178

Our Sunday Visitor Publishing, 200 Noll Plaza, Huntington, IN 46750 *Tel:* 260-356-8400 *Toll Free Tel:* 800-348-2440 (orders) *Fax:* 260-356-8472 *Toll Free Fax:* 800-498-6709 *E-mail:* osvbooks@osv.com (book orders) *Web Site:* www.osv.com, pg 178

OUT OF YOUR MIND...AND INTO THE MARKETPLACE™, 13381 White Sand Dr, Tustin, CA 92780-4565 *Tel:* 714-544-0248 *Toll Free Tel:* 800-419-1513 *Fax:* 714-730-1414 *Web Site:* www.business-plan.com, pg 178

Outdoor Writers Association of America Annual Conference, 615 Oak St, Suite 201, Missoula, MT 59801 *Tel:* 406-728-7434 *Fax:* 406-728-7445 *E-mail:* info@owaa.org *Web Site:* www.owaa.org, pg 653

The Overlook Press, 141 Wooster St, Suite 4-B, New York, NY 10012 *Tel:* 212-673-2210; 845-679-6838 (orders & dist) *Fax:* 212-673-2296 *E-mail:* sales@overlookny.com (orders) *Web Site:* www.overlookpress.com, pg 178

The Overmountain Press, PO Box 1261, Johnson City, TN 37605-1261 *Tel:* 423-926-2691 *Toll Free Tel:* 800-992-2691 (orders) *Fax:* 423-232-1252 *E-mail:* orders@overmtn.com *Web Site:* www.overmtn.com, pg 179

Overseas Press Club of America (OPC), 40 W 45 St, New York, NY 10036 *Tel:* 212-626-9220 *Fax:* 212-626-9210 *Web Site:* www.opcofamerica.org, pg 615

Richard C Owen Publishers Inc, PO Box 585, Katonah, NY 10536-0585 *Tel:* 914-232-3903 *Toll Free Tel:* 800-336-5588 *Fax:* 914-232-3977 *Web Site:* www.rcowen.com, pg 179

Owl About Books Publisher Inc, 1632 Royalwood Circle, Joshua, TX 76058 *Tel:* 682-553-9078 *Fax:* 817-558-8983 *E-mail:* owlaboutbooks@gmail.com *Web Site:* www.owlaboutbooks.com, pg 179

Owlkids Books Inc, 10 Lower Spadina Ave, Suite 400, Toronto, ON M5V 2Z2, Canada *Tel:* 416-340-2700 *Fax:* 416-340-9769 *E-mail:* owlkids@owlkids.com *Web Site:* www.owlkidsbooks.com, pg 493

Frank L & Harriet C Owsley Award, University of Georgia, Dept of History, Athens, GA 30602-1602 *Tel:* 706-542-8848 *Fax:* 706-542-2455 *Web Site:* sha.uga.edu, pg 715

Oxbridge® Communications Inc, 39 W 29 St, Suite 301, New York, NY 10001 *Tel:* 212-741-0231 *Toll Free Tel:* 800-955-0231 *Fax:* 212-633-2938 *E-mail:* info@oxbridge.com *Web Site:* www.oxbridge.com, pg 179

Oxford University Press USA, 198 Madison Ave, New York, NY 10016 *Tel:* 212-726-6000 *Toll Free Tel:* 800-451-7556 (orders); 800-445-9714 (cust serv) *Fax:* 919-677-1303 *E-mail:* custserv.us@oup.com *Web Site:* www.oup.com/us, pg 179

Oxmoor House, 2100 Lakeshore Dr, Birmingham, AL 35209 *Tel:* 205-445-6000 *Toll Free Tel:* 800-366-4712; 888-891-8935 (cust serv); 800-765-6400 (orders) *Web Site:* www.oxmoorhouse.com, pg 179

Oyster River Press, 36 Oyster River Rd, Durham, NH 03824-3029 *Tel:* 603-868-5006 *E-mail:* oysterriverpress@comcast.net *Web Site:* www.oysterriverpress.com, pg 532

Ozark Creative Writers Inc Annual Conference, PO Box 9076, Fayetteville, AR 72703 *Tel:* 479-751-7246 *E-mail:* ozarkcreativewriters1@gmail.com *Web Site:* www.ozarkcreativewriters.org, pg 653

Ozark Mountain Publishing Inc, PO Box 754, Huntsville, AR 72740-0754 *Tel:* 479-738-2348 *Toll Free Tel:* 800-935-0045 *Fax:* 479-738-2448 *E-mail:* info@ozarkmt.com *Web Site:* www.ozarkmt.com, pg 179

Ozark Publishing Inc, PO Box 228, Prairie Grove, AR 72753-0228 *Tel:* 479-595-9522 *Toll Free Tel:* 800-321-5671 *Fax:* 479-846-2843 *E-mail:* srg304@yahoo.com *Web Site:* www.ozarkpublishing.us, pg 179

P & R Publishing Co, 1102 Marble Hill Rd, Phillipsburg, NJ 08865 *Tel:* 908-454-0505 *Toll Free Tel:* 800-631-0094 *Fax:* 908-859-2390 *E-mail:* sales@prpbooks.com; info@prpbooks.com *Web Site:* www.prpbooks.com, pg 180

P S M J Resources Inc, 10 Midland Ave, Newton, MA 02458 *Tel:* 617-965-0055 *Toll Free Tel:* 800-537-7765 *Fax:* 617-965-5152 *E-mail:* info@psmj.com *Web Site:* www.psmj.com, pg 180

Pace University, Master of Science in Publishing, Dept of Publishing, Rm 805-E, 551 Fifth Ave, New York, NY 10176 *Tel:* 212-346-1431 *Toll Free Tel:* 877-284-7670 *Fax:* 212-346-1165 *Web Site:* www.pace.edu/dyson/mspub, pg 662

Pace University Press, Dept of Publishing, Rm 805-E, 551 Fifth Ave, New York, NY 10176 *Tel:* 212-346-1417 *Fax:* 212-346-1165 *Web Site:* www.pace.edu/press, pg 180

Pacific Educational Press, c/o University of British Columbia, Faculty of Education, 411-2389 Health Sciences Mall, Vancouver, BC V6T 1Z4, Canada *Tel:* 604-822-5385 *Fax:* 604-822-6603 *E-mail:* pep.admin@ubc.ca; pep.sales@ubc.ca *Web Site:* www.pacificedpress.educ.ubc.ca, pg 494

Pacific Northwest Book Awards, 338 W 11 Ave, Unit 108, Eugene, OR 97401 *Tel:* 541-683-4363 *Fax:* 541-683-3910 *E-mail:* info@pnba.org *Web Site:* www.pnba.org, pg 715

Pacific Northwest Booksellers Association, 338 W 11 Ave, Unit 108, Eugene, OR 97401 *Tel:* 541-683-4363 *Toll Free Tel:* 800-353-6764 *Fax:* 541-683-3910 *E-mail:* info@pnba.org *Web Site:* www.pnba.org, pg 615

Pacific Northwest Children's Book Conference, 615 SW Harrison St, Portland, OR 97201 *Tel:* 503-725-9786 *Toll Free Tel:* 800-547-8887 (ext 9786) *Fax:* 503-725-5599 *Web Site:* www.pdx.edu/ceed/childrens-book-conference, pg 654

Pacific Northwest Young Reader's Choice Award, Vancouver Mall Community Library, 8700 NE Vancouver Mall Dr, Suite 285, Vancouver, WA 98662 *Tel:* 360-892-8256 *Web Site:* www.pnla.org/yrca, pg 716

Pacific Press Publishing Association, 1350 N Kings Rd, Nampa, ID 83687-3193 *Tel:* 208-465-2500 *Toll Free Tel:* 800-447-7377 *Fax:* 208-465-2531 *Web Site:* www.pacificpress.com, pg 180

Pacific Printing Industries Association, 6825 SW Sandburg St, Portland, OR 97223 *Tel:* 503-221-3944 *Toll Free Tel:* 877-762-7742 *Fax:* 503-221-5691 *E-mail:* info@ppiassociation.org *Web Site:* www.ppiassociation.org, pg 615

Pacific Publishing Services, PO Box 1150, Capitola, CA 95010-1150 *Tel:* 831-476-8284 *Fax:* 831-476-8294 *E-mail:* pacpubs@attglobal.net, pg 532

PAGE International Screenwriting Awards, 7510 Sunset Blvd, Suite 610, Hollywood, CA 90046 *E-mail:* info@pageawards.com *Web Site:* www.pageawards.com, pg 716

Paintbox Press, 275 Madison Ave, Suite 600, New York, NY 10016 *Tel:* 212-878-6610 *Fax:* 212-202-6157 *E-mail:* info@paintboxpress.com *Web Site:* www.paintboxpress.com, pg 180

Painted Hills Publishing, 16500 Dakota Ridge Rd, Longmont, CO 80503 *Tel:* 303-823-6642 *Fax:* 303-825-5119 *E-mail:* cw@livingimagescjw.com *Web Site:* www.wildhoofbeats.com; www.horsephotographyworkshops.com, pg 508

Painted Pony Inc, 3 Ethete Rd, Fort Washakie, WY 82514 *Tel:* 307-335-7330 *Toll Free Tel:* 877-253-3824 *Fax:* 307-335-7332 *E-mail:* ppi@wrdf.org *Web Site:* www.paintedponyinc.com, pg 180

Painted-Words Inc, 310 W 97 St, Suite 24, New York, NY 10025 *Tel:* 212-663-2311 *Fax:* 212-663-2891 *E-mail:* info@painted-words.com *Web Site:* www.painted-words.com, pg 584

Dobie Paisano Fellowship Program, Graduate School, 110 Inner Campus Dr, Stop G0400, Austin, TX 78712-0710 *Fax:* 512-471-7620 *Web Site:* www.utexas.edu/ogs/Paisano, pg 716

Paladin Press, 5540 Central Ave, Suite 20, Boulder, CO 80301 *Tel:* 303-443-7250 *Toll Free Tel:* 800-392-2400 *Fax:* 303-442-8741 *E-mail:* service@paladin-press.com *Web Site:* www.paladin-press.com, pg 180

Palgrave Macmillan, 175 Fifth Ave, Suite 200, New York, NY 10010 *Tel:* 646-307-5151 *Fax:* 212-777-6359 *E-mail:* firstname.lastname@palgrave-usa.com *Web Site:* us.macmillan.com/Palgrave.aspx, pg 180

Palimpsest Press, 1171 Eastlawn Ave, Windsor, ON N8S 3J1, Canada *Tel:* 519-563-9981 *E-mail:* info@palimpsestpress.ca *Web Site:* www.palimpsestpress.ca, pg 494

Palladium Books Inc, 39074 Webb Ct, Westland, MI 48185 *Tel:* 734-721-2903 (orders) *Fax:* 734-721-1238 *Web Site:* www.palladiumbooks.com, pg 180

Palm Island Press, 411 Truman Ave, Key West, FL 33040 *Tel:* 305-296-3102 *E-mail:* pipress2@gmail.com, pg 181

Palm Springs Writers Guild, PO Box 947, Rancho Mirage, CA 92270-0947 *Web Site:* www.palmspringswritersguild.org, pg 615

Palmetto Bug Books, 121 N Hibiscus Dr, Miami Beach, FL 33139 *Tel:* 305-531-9813 *Fax:* 305-604-1516 *E-mail:* palmettobugbooks@gmail.com, pg 181

Pangaea Publications, 226 Wheeler St S, St Paul, MN 55105-1927 *Tel:* 651-226-2032 *Fax:* 651-226-2032 *E-mail:* info@pangaea.org *Web Site:* pangaea.org, pg 181

Karen L Pangallo, 27 Buffum St, Salem, MA 01970 *Tel:* 978-744-8796 *E-mail:* pangallo@noblenet.org, pg 532

Panoptic Enterprises, PO Box 11220, Burke, VA 22009-1220 *Tel:* 703-451-5953 *Toll Free Tel:* 800-594-4766 *Fax:* 703-451-5953 *E-mail:* panoptic@fedgovcontracts.com *Web Site:* www.fedgovcontracts.com, pg 181

Mildred & Albert Panowski Playwriting Award, Forest Roberts Theatre, 1401 Presque Isle Ave, Marquette, MI 49855-5364 *Tel:* 906-227-2553 *Fax:* 906-227-2567 *E-mail:* theatre@nmu.edu *Web Site:* www.nmu.edu/theatre, pg 716

Pantheon Books/Schocken Books, c/o Random House Inc, 1745 Broadway, New York, NY 10019 *Tel:* 212-751-2600 *Toll Free Tel:* 800-638-6460 *Fax:* 212-572-6030, pg 181

Pants On Fire Press, 2062 Harbor Cove Way, Winter Garden, FL 34787 *Tel:* 863-546-0760 *E-mail:* submission@pantsonfirepress.com *Web Site:* www.pantsonfirepress.com, pg 181

Papercutz, 160 Broadway, E Wing, Suite 700, New York, NY 10038 *Tel:* 646-559-4681 *Toll Free Tel:* 800-886-1223 *Fax:* 212-643-1545 *E-mail:* papercutz@papercutz.com *Web Site:* www.papercutz.com, pg 181

Para Publishing LLC, PO Box 8206-240, Santa Barbara, CA 93118-8206 *Tel:* 805-968-7277 *Toll Free Tel:* 800-727-2782 *Fax:* 805-968-1379 *Web Site:* www.parapublishing.com, pg 181

Parabola Books, 20 W 20 St, 2nd fl, New York, NY 10011 *Tel:* 212-822-8806 *Toll Free Tel:* 800-592-2521 (subns) *Fax:* 212-822-8823 *E-mail:* info@parabola.org *Web Site:* www.parabola.org, pg 181

Parachute Publishing LLC, 322 Eighth Ave, Suite 702, New York, NY 10001 *Tel:* 212-691-1421 *Fax:* 212-647-9650 *Web Site:* www.parachutepublishing.com, pg 182

Paraclete Press Inc, 36 Southern Eagle Cartway, Brewster, MA 02631 *Tel:* 508-255-4685 *Toll Free Tel:* 800-451-5006 *Fax:* 508-255-5705 *E-mail:* mail@paracletepress.com *Web Site:* www.paracletepress.com, pg 182

Paradigm Publications, 202 Bendix Dr, Taos, NM 87571 *Tel:* 575-758-7758 *Toll Free Tel:* 800-873-3946 (US); 888-873-3947 (CN) *Fax:* 575-758-7768 *Web Site:* www.paradigm-pubs.com; www.redwingbooks.com, pg 182

Paradigm Publishers, 5589 Arapahoe Ave, Suite 206A, Boulder, CO 80303 *Tel:* 303-245-9054 *Web Site:* www.paradigmpublishers.com, pg 182

Paradise Cay Publications Inc, 550 S "G" St, Suite 1, Arcata, CA 95521 *Tel:* 707-822-9063 *Toll Free Tel:* 800-736-4509 *Fax:* 707-822-9163 *E-mail:* info@paracay.com *Web Site:* www.paracay.com, pg 182

Paragon House, 3600 Labore Rd, Suite 1, St Paul, MN 55110-4144 *Tel:* 651-644-3087 *Toll Free Tel:* 800-447-3709 *Fax:* 651-644-0997 *E-mail:* paragon@paragonhouse.com *Web Site:* www.paragonhouse.com, pg 182

Parallax Press, 2236-B Sixth St, Berkeley, CA 94710 *Tel:* 510-525-0101 *Toll Free Tel:* 800-863-5290 (orders) *Fax:* 510-525-7129 *E-mail:* info@parallax.org *Web Site:* www.parallax.org, pg 182

Paramount Market Publishing Inc, 950 Danby Rd, Suite 136, Ithaca, NY 14850 *Tel:* 607-275-8100 *Toll Free Tel:* 888-787-8100 *Fax:* 607-275-8101 *E-mail:* editors@paramountbooks.com *Web Site:* www.paramountbooks.com, pg 182

Parenting Press Inc, 13751 Lake City Way NE, Suite 110, Seattle, WA 98125 *Tel:* 206-364-2900 *Toll Free Tel:* 800-99-BOOKS (992-6657) *Fax:* 206-364-0702 *E-mail:* office@parentingpress.com; marketing@parentingpress.com *Web Site:* www.parentingpress.com, pg 183

Park Genealogical Books, PO Box 130968, Roseville, MN 55113-0968 *Tel:* 651-488-4416 *Fax:* 651-488-2653 *Web Site:* www.parkbooks.com, pg 183

Park Place Publications, 591 Lighthouse Ave, Suite 10, Pacific Grove, CA 93950 *Tel:* 831-649-6640 *E-mail:* publishingbiz@sbcglobal.net *Web Site:* www.parkplacepublications.com, pg 183

Francis Parkman Prize, 603 Fayerweather, MC 2538, New York, NY 10027 *Tel:* 212-854-6495 *E-mail:* amhistsociety@columbia.edu *Web Site:* sah.columbia.edu, pg 716

The Richard Parks Agency, PO Box 693, Salem, NY 12865 *Tel:* 518-854-9466 *Fax:* 518-854-9466 *E-mail:* rp@richardparksagency.com *Web Site:* www.richardparksagency.com, pg 567

Parlay Press, 301 Central Ave, No 311, Hilton Head, SC 29926 *Toll Free Fax:* 888-301-3116 *E-mail:* mail@parlaypress.com *Web Site:* www.parlaypress.com, pg 183

Parmenides Publishing, 3753 Howard Hughes Pkwy, Suite 200, Las Vegas, NV 89169 *Tel:* 702-892-3934 *Fax:* 702-892-3939 *E-mail:* info@parmenides.com *Web Site:* www.parmenides.com, pg 183

Parsons School of Design, Continuing Education, 66 Fifth Ave, New York, NY 10011 *Tel:* 212-229-8933 *Fax:* 212-229-5970 *E-mail:* ceinformation@newschool.edu; academy@newschool.edu *Web Site:* www.parsons.edu/ce, pg 662

Pastoral Press, 5536 NE Hassalo, Portland, OR 97213-3638 *Tel:* 503-281-1191 *Toll Free Tel:* 800-548-8749 *Fax:* 503-282-3486 *Toll Free Fax:* 800-462-7329 *E-mail:* liturgy@ocp.org *Web Site:* www.ocp.org, pg 183

The Paterson Fiction Prize, One College Blvd, Paterson, NJ 07505-1179 *Tel:* 973-684-6555 *Fax:* 973-523-6085 *Web Site:* www.pccc.edu/poetry, pg 716

The Paterson Poetry Prize, One College Blvd, Paterson, NJ 07505-1179 *Tel:* 973-684-6555 *Fax:* 973-523-6085 *Web Site:* www.pccc.edu/poetry, pg 716

The Paterson Prize for Books for Young People, One College Blvd, Paterson, NJ 07505-1179 *Tel:* 973-684-6555 *Fax:* 973-523-6085 *Web Site:* www.pccc.edu/poetry, pg 716

Path Press Inc, 1229 Emerson St, Evanston, IL 60201 *Tel:* 847-492-0177 *E-mail:* pathpressinc@aol.com, pg 183

Pathfinder Publishing Inc, 120 S Houghton Rd, Suite 138, Tucson, AZ 85748 *Tel:* 520-647-0158 *Toll Free Tel:* 800-977-2282 *Fax:* 520-647-0160 *Web Site:* www.pathfinderpublishing.com, pg 183

Kathi J Paton Literary Agency, Box 2236, Radio City Sta, New York, NY 10101-2236 *Tel:* 212-265-6586 *Fax:* 908-647-2117 *E-mail:* kjplitbiz@optonline.net *Web Site:* www.patonliterary.com, pg 567

Patria Press Inc, PO Box 752, Carmel, IN 46082 *Tel:* 317-577-1321 *Fax:* 413-215-8030 *E-mail:* moreinfo@patriapress.com *Web Site:* www.patriapress.com; www.facebook.com/YoungPatriotsBooks; twitter.com/#!/kidsbios, pg 183

Diane Patrick, 140 Carver Loop, No 21A, Bronx, NY 10475-2954 *E-mail:* dpatrickediting@aol.com *Web Site:* www.dianepatrick.net, pg 532

The Alicia Patterson Foundation Fellowship Program, 1100 Vermont Ave, Suite 900, Washington, DC 20005 *Tel:* 202-393-5995 *Fax:* 301-951-8512 *E-mail:* info@aliciapatterson.org *Web Site:* www.aliciapatterson.org, pg 716

Paul Dry Books, 1616 Walnut St, Suite 808, Philadelphia, PA 19103 *Tel:* 215-231-9939 *Fax:* 215-231-9942 *E-mail:* editor@pauldrybooks.com *Web Site:* www.pauldrybooks.com, pg 184

Pauline Books & Media, 50 St Paul's Ave, Boston, MA 02130 *Tel:* 617-522-8911 *Toll Free Tel:* 800-876-4463 (orders); 800-836-9723 (cust serv) *Fax:* 617-541-9805 *E-mail:* editorial@paulinemedia.com (ms submissions); orderentry@pauline.org (cust serv) *Web Site:* www.pauline.org, pg 184

Paulines Editions, 5610 rue Beaubien est, Montreal, QC H1T 1X5, Canada *Tel:* 514-253-5610 *Fax:* 514-253-1907 *E-mail:* fsp-paulines@videotron.ca *Web Site:* www.editions.paulines.qc.ca, pg 494

Paulist Press, 997 Macarthur Blvd, Mahwah, NJ 07430-9990 *Tel:* 201-825-7300 *Toll Free Tel:* 800-218-1903 *Fax:* 201-825-8345 *Toll Free Fax:* 800-836-3161 *E-mail:* info@paulistpress.com *Web Site:* www.paulistpress.com, pg 184

Peabody Museum Press, 11 Divinity Ave, Cambridge, MA 02138 *Tel:* 617-495-4255 *Fax:* 617-495-7535 *E-mail:* peapub@fas.harvard.edu *Web Site:* www.peabody.harvard.edu/publications, pg 184

Peace Hill Press, 18021 The Glebe Lane, Charles City, VA 23030 *Tel:* 804-829-5043 *Toll Free Tel:* 877-322-3445 (orders) *Fax:* 804-829-5704 *E-mail:* info@peacehillpress.com *Web Site:* www.peacehillpress.com, pg 184

Peachpit Press, 1249 Eighth St, Berkeley, CA 94710 *Tel:* 510-524-2178 *Toll Free Tel:* 800-283-9444 *Fax:* 510-524-2221 *E-mail:* info@peachpit.com *Web Site:* www.peachpit.com, pg 184

Peachtree Publishers, 1700 Chattahoochee Ave, Atlanta, GA 30318-2112 *Tel:* 404-876-8761 *Toll Free Tel:* 800-241-0113 *Fax:* 404-875-2578 *Toll Free Fax:* 800-875-8909 *E-mail:* hello@peachtree-online.com *Web Site:* www.peachtree-online.com, pg 184

Peanut Butter & Jelly Press LLC, PO Box 590239, Newton, MA 02459-0002 *Tel:* 617-630-0945 *Fax:* 617-630-0945 (call first) *E-mail:* info@pbjpress.com *Web Site:* www.publishinggame.com; www.pbjpress.com, pg 184

Pearson Arts & Sciences, 330 Hudson St, 9th fl, New York, NY 10013-1048 *Tel:* 917-981-2200 *Web Site:* www.pearsonhighered.com, pg 184

Pearson Benjamin Cummings, 1301 Sansome St, San Francisco, CA 94111-1122 *Tel:* 415-402-2500 *Toll Free Tel:* 800-922-0579 (orders) *Fax:* 415-402-2590 *E-mail:* question@aol.com *Web Site:* www.pearsonhighered.com, pg 184

Pearson Business Publishing, 225 River St, Hoboken, NJ 07030-4772 *Tel:* 201-236-7000 *Web Site:* www.pearsonhighered.com, pg 185

Pearson Career, Health, Education & Technology, 225 River St, Hoboken, NJ 07030-4772 *Tel:* 201-236-7000 *Fax:* 201-236-7755, pg 185

Pearson Education, 225 River St, Hoboken, NJ 07030-4772 *Tel:* 201-236-7000 *Fax:* 201-236-6549 *E-mail:* communications@pearsoned.com *Web Site:* www.pearsoned.com, pg 185

Pearson Education Canada, 26 Prince Andrew Place, Don Mills, ON M3C 2T8, Canada *Tel:* 416-447-5101 *Toll Free Tel:* 800-263-9965 *Fax:* 416-443-0948 *Toll Free Fax:* 800-263-7733; 888-465-0536 *Web Site:* www.pearsoned.ca, pg 494

Pearson Education International Group, 225 River St, Hoboken, NJ 07030-4772 *Tel:* 201-236-7000, pg 185

Pearson ELT, 10 Bank St, 9th fl, White Plains, NY 10606-1951 *Tel:* 914-287-8000 *Web Site:* www.pearsonelt.com, pg 185

Pearson ERPI, 5757 rue Cypihot, St-Laurent, QC H4S 1R3, Canada *Tel:* 514-334-2690 *Toll Free Tel:* 800-263-3678 *Fax:* 514-334-4720 *Toll Free Fax:* 800-643-4720 *E-mail:* erpidlm@erpi.com *Web Site:* www.erpi.com; pearsonplc.ca, pg 494

Pearson Higher Education, 225 River St, Hoboken, NJ 07030-4772 *Tel:* 201-236-7000 *Fax:* 201-236-3381 *Web Site:* www.pearsonhighered.com, pg 185

Pearson Humanities & Social Sciences, 225 River St, Hoboken, NJ 07030-4772 *Tel:* 201-236-7000 *Fax:* 201-236-3400, pg 185

Pearson Learning Solutions, 501 Boyleston St, Suite 900, Boston, MA 02116 *Tel:* 617-848-6300 *Toll Free Tel:* 800-428-4466 (orders) *Fax:* 617-848-6358 *E-mail:* pcp@pearsoncustom.com *Web Site:* www.pearsoned.com, pg 185

Pearson School, 225 River St, Hoboken, NJ 07030-4772 *Tel:* 201-236-7000 *Web Site:* www.pearsonschool.com, pg 185

Pearson Scott Foresman, 1900 E Lake Ave, Glenview, IL 60025 *Tel:* 847-729-3000 *Toll Free Tel:* 800-535-4391 (Midwest) *Fax:* 847-729-8910 *Web Site:* www.pearsonschool.com, pg 185

William Peden Prize in Fiction, 357 McReynolds Hall, Columbia, MO 65211 *Tel:* 573-882-4474 *Toll Free Tel:* 800-949-2505 *Fax:* 573-884-4671 *E-mail:* question@moreview.com *Web Site:* www.missourireview.com, pg 716

T H Peek Publisher, PO Box 7406, Ann Arbor, MI 48107 *Tel:* 734-222-8205 *Fax:* 734-661-0136 *E-mail:* info@thpeekpublisher.com *Web Site:* www.thpeekpublisher.com, pg 185

Peel Productions Inc, 9415 NE Woodridge St, Vancouver, WA 98664 *Tel:* 360-326-8003 *Toll Free Tel:* 800-345-6665 *Web Site:* www.peelbooks.com, pg 185

Pelican Publishing Co, 1000 Burmaster St, Gretna, LA 70053-2246 *Tel:* 504-368-1175 *Toll Free Tel:* 800-843-1724 *Fax:* 504-368-1195 *E-mail:* sales@pelicanpub.com (sales); office@pelicanpub.com (permission); promo@pelicanpub.com (publicity) *Web Site:* www.pelicanpub.com, pg 185

Pema Browne Ltd, 71 Pine Rd, Woodbourne, NY 12788 *E-mail:* ppbltd@optonline.net *Web Site:* www.pemabrowneltd.com, pg 567

Pembroke Publishers Ltd, 538 Hood Rd, Markham, ON L3R 3K9, Canada *Tel:* 905-477-0650 *Toll Free Tel:* 800-997-9807 *Fax:* 905-477-3691 *Toll Free Fax:* 800-339-5568 *Web Site:* www.pembrokepublishers.com, pg 494

Pemmican Publications Inc, 150 Henry Ave, Winnipeg, MB R3B 0J7, Canada *Tel:* 204-589-6346 *Fax:* 204-589-2063 *E-mail:* pemmican@pemmican.mb.ca *Web Site:* www.pemmican.mb.ca, pg 494

PEN American Center, 588 Broadway, Suite 303, New York, NY 10012 *Tel:* 212-334-1660 *Fax:* 212-334-2181 *E-mail:* info@pen.org *Web Site:* www.pen.org, pg 615

The PEN Award for Poetry in Translation, 588 Broadway, Suite 303, New York, NY 10012 *Tel:* 212-334-1660 *Fax:* 212-334-2181 *E-mail:* awards@pen.org *Web Site:* www.pen.org, pg 716

PEN/Bellwether Prize for Socially Engaged Fiction, 588 Broadway, Suite 303, New York, NY 10012 *Tel:* 212-334-1660 *E-mail:* awards@pen.org *Web Site:* www.pen.org, pg 717

PEN Canada, 24 Ryerson Ave, Suite 301, Toronto, ON M5T 2P3, Canada *Tel:* 416-703-8448 *Fax:* 416-703-3870 *E-mail:* queries@pencanada.ca *Web Site:* www.pencanada.ca, pg 616

PEN Center USA, PO Box 6037, Beverly Hills, CA 90212 *Tel:* 323-424-4939 *Fax:* 323-424-4944 *E-mail:* pen@penusa.org *Web Site:* www.penusa.org, pg 616

PEN Center USA Literary Awards, 269 S Beverly Dr, Suite 1163, Beverly Hills, CA 90212 *Tel:* 323-424-4939 *Fax:* 323-424-4944 *E-mail:* awards@penusa.org *Web Site:* www.penusa.org, pg 717

PEN/Diamonstein-Spielvogel Award for the Art of the Essay, 588 Broadway, Suite 303, New York, NY 10012 *Tel:* 212-334-1660 *E-mail:* awards@pen.org *Web Site:* www.pen.org/literary-awards, pg 717

PEN/E O Wilson Literary Science Writing Award, 588 Broadway, Suite 303, New York, NY 10012 *Tel:* 212-334-1660 *E-mail:* awards@pen.org *Web Site:* www.pen.org/literary-awards, pg 717

PEN/ESPN Award for Literary Sports Writing, 588 Broadway, Suite 303, New York, NY 10012 *Tel:* 212-334-1660 *E-mail:* awards@pen.org *Web Site:* www.pen.org/literary-awards, pg 717

PEN/ESPN Lifetime Achievement Award for Literary Sports Writing, 588 Broadway, Suite 303, New York, NY 10012 *Tel:* 212-334-1660 *E-mail:* awards@pen.org *Web Site:* www.pen.org/literary-awards, pg 717

PEN/Faulkner Award for Fiction, Folger Shakespeare Library, 201 E Capitol St SE, Washington, DC 20003 *Tel:* 202-898-9063 *Fax:* 202-675-0360 *Web Site:* www.penfaulkner.org, pg 717

PEN/Fusion Emerging Writers Prize, 588 Broadway, Suite 303, New York, NY 10012 *Tel:* 212-334-1660 *E-mail:* awards@pen.org *Web Site:* www.pen.org/literary-awards, pg 717

PEN/Jacqueline Bograd Weld Award for Biography, 588 Broadway, Suite 303, New York, NY 10012 *Tel:* 212-334-1660 *E-mail:* awards@pen.org *Web Site:* www.pen.org/literary-awards, pg 717

PEN/Joyce Osterweil Award for Poetry, 588 Broadway, Suite 303, New York, NY 10012 *Tel:* 212-334-1660 *E-mail:* awards@pen.org *Web Site:* www.pen.org, pg 717

PEN New England, MIT, 14N-221A, 77 Massachusetts Ave, Cambridge, MA 02139 *Tel:* 617-324-1729 *E-mail:* pen-newengland@mit.edu *Web Site:* www.pen-ne.org, pg 616

PEN/O. Henry Prize Stories, University of Texas at Austin, One University Sta B5000, Austin, TX 78712 *Tel:* 512-572-2428 *Web Site:* www.ohenryprizestories.com, pg 717

PEN Open Book Award, 588 Broadway, Suite 303, New York, NY 10012 *Tel:* 212-334-1660 *E-mail:* awards@pen.org *Web Site:* www.pen.org/literary-awards, pg 717

PEN/Phyllis Naylor Working Writer Fellowship, 588 Broadway, Suite 303, New York, NY 10012 *Tel:* 212-334-1660 *Fax:* 212-334-2181 *E-mail:* awards@pen.org *Web Site:* www.pen.org, pg 717

PEN/Ralph Manheim Medal for Translation, 588 Broadway, Suite 303, New York, NY 10012 *Tel:* 212-334-1660 *Fax:* 212-334-2181 *E-mail:* awards@pen.org *Web Site:* www.pen.org, pg 718

PEN/Robert Bingham Prize for Debut Fiction, 588 Broadway, Suite 303, New York, NY 10012 *Tel:* 212-334-1660 *Fax:* 212-334-2181 *E-mail:* awards@pen.org *Web Site:* www.pen.org, pg 718

PEN/Steven Kroll Award for Picture Book Writing, 588 Broadway, Suite 303, New York, NY 10012 *Tel:* 212-334-1660 *E-mail:* awards@pen.org *Web Site:* www.pen.org/literary-awards, pg 718

PEN Translation Prize, 588 Broadway, Suite 303, New York, NY 10012 *Tel:* 212-334-1660 *Fax:* 212-334-2181 *E-mail:* awards@pen.org *Web Site:* www.pen.org, pg 718

PEN/Voelcker Award, 588 Broadway, Suite 303, New York, NY 10012 *Tel:* 212-334-1660 *E-mail:* awards@pen.org *Web Site:* www.pen.org/literary-awards, pg 718

PEN Writers' Emergency Fund, 588 Broadway, Suite 303, New York, NY 10012 *Tel:* 212-334-1660 *Fax:* 212-334-2181 *Web Site:* www.pen.org, pg 718

Pendragon Press, 52 White Hill Lane, Hillsdale, NY 12529-5839 *Tel:* 518-325-6100 *Toll Free Tel:* 877-656-6381 (orders) *Fax:* 518-325-6102 *E-mail:* editor@pendragonpress.com *Web Site:* www.pendragonpress.com, pg 185

Penfield Books, 215 Brown St, Iowa City, IA 52245 *Tel:* 319-337-9998 *Toll Free Tel:* 800-728-9998 *Fax:* 319-351-6846 *E-mail:* penfield@penfieldbooks.com *Web Site:* www.penfieldbooks.com, pg 185

Penguin Books, 375 Hudson St, New York, NY 10014 *Tel:* 212-366-2000 *E-mail:* online@penguinputnam.com *Web Site:* www.penguinputnam.com; www.penguinclassics.com; us.penguingroup.com, pg 186

Penguin Group (Canada), 90 Eglinton Ave E, Suite 700, Toronto, ON M4P 2Y3, Canada *Tel:* 416-925-2249 *Fax:* 416-925-0068 *E-mail:* customerservicescanada@penguinrandomhouse.com *Web Site:* penguinrandomhouse.ca, pg 494

Penguin Group (USA) LLC, a Penguin Random House company, 375 Hudson St, New York, NY 10014 *Tel:* 212-366-2000 *Toll Free Tel:* 800-847-5515 (inside sales); 800-631-8571 (cust serv) *Fax:* 212-366-2666; 607-775-4829 (inside sales) *E-mail:* online@us.penguingroup.com *Web Site:* www.penguin.com; us.penguingroup.com, pg 186

Penguin Group (USA) LLC Sales, 375 Hudson St, New York, NY 10014 *Tel:* 212-366-2000 *E-mail:* online@penguinputnam.com *Web Site:* us.penguingroup.com, pg 186

The Penguin Press, 375 Hudson St, New York, NY 10014, pg 187

Penguin Random House Audio, 1745 Broadway, New York, NY 10019 *E-mail:* audio@randomhouse.com *Web Site:* www.randomhouse.com/audio, pg 187

Penguin Random House Canada Limited, 320 Front St W, Suite 1400, Toronto, ON M5V 3B6, Canada *Tel:* 416-364-4449 *Toll Free Tel:* 888-523-9292 (cust serv) *Fax:* 416-364-6863; 416-364-6653 (subs rts) *Web Site:* penguinrandomhouse.ca, pg 495

Penguin Random House Inc, 1745 Broadway, New York, NY 10019 *Tel:* 212-782-9000 *Toll Free Tel:* 800-726-0600 *Web Site:* www.randomhouse.com, pg 187

Penguin Random House Speakers Bureau, 1745 Broadway, Mail Drop 13-1, New York, NY 10019 *Tel:* 212-572-2013 *E-mail:* speakers@penguinrandomhouse.com *Web Site:* www.prhspeakers.com, pg 587

Penguin Young Readers Group, 345 Hudson St, New York, NY 10014 *Tel:* 212-366-2000 *E-mail:* online@penguinputnam.com *Web Site:* www.penguinputnam.com; us.penguingroup.com, pg 187

Peninsula Publishing, 26666 Birch Hill Way, Los Altos Hills, CA 94022 *Tel:* 650-948-2511 *Fax:* 650-948-5004 *E-mail:* sales@peninsulapublishing.com *Web Site:* www.peninsulapublishing.com, pg 188

Pennsylvania Historical & Museum Commission, Commonwealth Keystone Bldg, 400 North St, Harrisburg, PA 17120-0053 *Tel:* 717-783-2618 *Toll Free Tel:* 800-747-7790 *Fax:* 717-787-8312 *E-mail:* ra-pabookstore@state.pa.us *Web Site:* www.pabookstore.com; www.phmc.state.pa.us, pg 188

Pennsylvania State Data Center, Penn State Harrisburg, 777 W Harrisburg Pike, Middletown, PA 17057-4898 *Tel:* 717-948-6336 *Fax:* 717-948-6754 *E-mail:* pasdc@psu.edu *Web Site:* pasdc.hbg.psu.edu, pg 188

The Pennsylvania State University Press, University Support Bldg 1, Suite C, 820 N University Dr, University Park, PA 16802-1003 *Tel:* 814-865-1327 *Toll Free Tel:* 800-326-9180 *Fax:* 814-863-1408 *Toll Free Fax:* 877-778-2665 *E-mail:* info@psupress.org *Web Site:* www.psupress.org, pg 188

PennWell Books, 1421 S Sheridan Rd, Tulsa, OK 74112 *Tel:* 918-831-9410 *Toll Free Tel:* 800-752-9764 *Fax:* 918-831-9555 *E-mail:* sales@pennwell.com *Web Site:* www.pennwellbooks.com, pg 188

Pennwriters Conference, 5706 Sonoma Ridge, Missouri City, TX 77459 *Web Site:* www.pennwriters.org, pg 654

Pentecostal Publishing House, 8855 Dunn Rd, Hazelwood, MO 63042 *Tel:* 314-837-7300 *Fax:* 314-336-1803 *E-mail:* pphordersdept@upci.org (orders) *Web Site:* www.pentecostalpublishing.com, pg 188

Penton Media, 9800 Metcalf Ave, Overland Park, KS 66212 *Tel:* 913-967-1719 *Toll Free Tel:* 800-262-1954 (cust serv) *Fax:* 913-967-1901 *Toll Free Fax:* 800-633-6219 *E-mail:* bookorders@penton.com *Web Site:* www.buypenton.com, pg 188

Peoples Education Inc, 299 Market St, Suite 240, Saddle Brook, NJ 07663 *Tel:* 201-712-0090 *Toll Free Tel:* 800-822-1080 *Fax:* 201-712-0045 *Web Site:* www.peopleseducation.com; www.peoplescollegeprep.com; www.measuringuplive.com, pg 188

PeopleSpeak, 25260-I La Paz Rd, Suite 1, Laguna Hills, CA 92653 *Tel:* 949-581-6190 *Fax:* 949-581-4958 *E-mail:* pplspeak@att.net *Web Site:* www.detailsplease.com/peoplespeak, pg 532

Rebecca Pepper, 434 NE Floral Place, Portland, OR 97232 *Tel:* 503-236-5802 *E-mail:* rpepper@rpepper.net, pg 532

Per Annum Inc, 555 Eighth Ave, Suite 203, New York, NY 10018 *Tel:* 212-647-8700 *Toll Free Tel:* 800-548-1108 *Fax:* 212-647-8716 *E-mail:* info@perannum.com *Web Site:* www.perannum.com, pg 189

Peradam Press, PO Box 6, North San Juan, CA 95960-0006 *Tel:* 530-292-4266 *Fax:* 530-292-4266 *E-mail:* peradam@earthlink.net, pg 189

Dan Peragine Literary Agency, 227 Beechwood Ave, Bogota, NJ 07603 *Tel:* 201-390-0468 *E-mail:* dpliterary@aol.com, pg 567

Perfection Learning Corp, 2680 Berkshire Pkwy, Clive, IA 50325 *Tel:* 515-278-0133 *Toll Free Tel:* 800-762-2999 *Fax:* 515-278-2980 *Web Site:* perfectionlearning.com, pg 189

Perigee Books, 375 Hudson St, New York, NY 10014 *Tel:* 212-366-2000 *Fax:* 212-366-2365 *E-mail:* perigeebooks@us.penguingroup.com *Web Site:* www.penguin.com, pg 189

Periodical & Book Association of America Inc (PBAA), 481 Eighth Ave, Suite 526, New York, NY 10001 *Tel:* 212-563-6502 *Fax:* 212-563-4098 *Web Site:* www.pbaa.net, pg 616

Maxwell E Perkins Award, 17 E 47 St, New York, NY 10017 *Tel:* 212-755-6710 *Fax:* 212-826-0831 *E-mail:* info@centerforfiction.org *Web Site:* www.centerforfiction.org/awards/perkins, pg 718

The Permanent Press, 4170 Noyac Rd, Sag Harbor, NY 11963 *Tel:* 631-725-1101 *Fax:* 631-725-8215 *E-mail:* info@thepermanentpress.com *Web Site:* www.thepermanentpress.com, pg 189

The Permissions Group Inc, 1247 Milwaukee Ave, Suite 303, Glenview, IL 60025 *Tel:* 847-635-6550 *Toll Free Tel:* 800-374-7985 *Fax:* 847-635-6968 *E-mail:* info@permissionsgroup.com *Web Site:* www.permissionsgroup.com, pg 532

Persea Books, 277 Broadway, Suite 708, New York, NY 10007 *Tel:* 212-260-9256 *Fax:* 212-267-3165 *E-mail:* info@perseabooks.com *Web Site:* www.perseabooks.com, pg 189

The Perseus Books Group, 387 Park Ave S, 12th fl, New York, NY 10016 *Tel:* 212-340-8100 *Toll Free Tel:* 800-343-4499 (cust serv) *Fax:* 212-340-8105 *Web Site:* www.perseusbooksgroup.com, pg 189

Perugia Press Prize for a First or Second Book by a Woman, PO Box 60364, Florence, MA 01062 *Web Site:* www.perugiapress.com, pg 718

Peter Pauper Press, Inc, 202 Mamaroneck Ave, White Plains, NY 10601-5376 *Tel:* 914-681-0144 *Fax:* 914-681-0389 *E-mail:* customerservice@peterpauper.com; orders@peterpauper.com *Web Site:* www.peterpauper.com, pg 189

Elsa Peterson Ltd, 41 East Ave, Norwalk, CT 06851-3919 *Tel:* 203-846-8331 *E-mail:* epltd@earthlink.net, pg 532

Peterson Institute for International Economics (PIIE), 1750 Massachusetts Ave NW, Washington, DC 20036-1903 *Tel:* 202-328-9000 *Toll Free Tel:* 800-522-9139 (orders) *Fax:* 202-328-5432; 202-659-3225 *E-mail:* orders@petersoninstitute.org *Web Site:* www.petersoninstitute.org, pg 190

Peterson's, a Nelnet Company, Princeton Pike Corporate Ctr, 2000 Lenox Dr, Lawrenceville, NJ 08648 *Tel:* 609-896-1800 *E-mail:* sales@petersons.com *Web Site:* www.petersons.com, pg 190

Petroleum Extension Service (PETEX), University of Texas at Austin-PETEX, One University Sta, R8100, Austin, TX 78712-1100 *Tel:* 512-471-5940 *Toll Free Tel:* 800-687-4132 *Fax:* 512-471-9410 *Toll Free Fax:* 800-687-7839 *E-mail:* plach@www.utex.edu; petex@www.utexas.edu *Web Site:* www.utexas.edu/ce/petex, pg 190

Evelyn Walters Pettit, 114 S Park Ave, Suite E, Winter Park, FL 32789-7012 *Tel:* 407-620-0131 (cell); 407-644-1711 *Fax:* 407-644-1711 *E-mail:* bookseller@brandywinebooks.com, pg 532

Stephen Pevner Inc, 382 Lafayette St, Suite 8, New York, NY 10003 *Tel:* 212-674-8403 *Fax:* 212-529-3692 *E-mail:* spidevelopment@gmail.com, pg 567

Pfizer Award, 440 Geddes Hall, Notre Dame, IN 46556 *Tel:* 574-631-1194 *Fax:* 574-631-1533 *E-mail:* info@hssonline.org *Web Site:* www.hssonline.org, pg 718

Pflaum Publishing Group, 2621 Dryden Rd, Suite 300, Dayton, OH 45439 *Tel:* 937-293-1415 *Toll Free Tel:* 800-543-4383; 800-523-4625 (sales) *Fax:* 937-293-1310 *Toll Free Fax:* 800-370-4450 *E-mail:* service@pflaum.com *Web Site:* pflaum.com, pg 190

Phaidon Press Inc, 180 Varick St, 14th fl, New York, NY 10014 *Tel:* 212-652-5400 *Toll Free Tel:* 800-759-0190 (cust serv) *Fax:* 212-652-5410 *Toll Free Fax:* 800-286-9471 (cust serv) *E-mail:* ussales@phaidon.com *Web Site:* www.phaidon.com, pg 190

James D Phelan Literary Award, One Embarcadero Ctr, Suite 1400, San Francisco, CA 94111 *Tel:* 415-733-8500 *Fax:* 415-477-2783 *E-mail:* info@sff.org *Web Site:* www.sff.org, pg 718

Phi Beta Kappa Award in Science, 1606 New Hampshire Ave NW, Washington, DC 20009 *Tel:* 202-265-3808 *Fax:* 202-986-1601 *E-mail:* awards@pbk.org *Web Site:* www.pbk.org/bookawards, pg 718

Phi Delta Kappa International®, 320 W Eighth St, Suite 216, Bloomington, IN 47404 *Tel:* 812-339-1156 *Toll Free Tel:* 800-766-1156 *Fax:* 812-339-0018 *E-mail:* customerservice@pdkintl.org *Web Site:* www.pdkintl.org, pg 190

Philadelphia Museum of Art, 2525 Pennsylvania Ave, Philadelphia, PA 19130 *Tel:* 215-684-7250 *Fax:* 215-235-8715 *Web Site:* www.philamuseum.org, pg 190

Philadelphia Writers' Conference, PO Box 7171, Elkins Park, PA 19027-0171 *Tel:* 215-782-3288 *Fax:* 215-782-3288 *E-mail:* info@pwcwriters.org *Web Site:* pwcwriters.org, pg 654

Meredith Phillips, 4127 Old Adobe Rd, Palo Alto, CA 94306 *Tel:* 650-857-9555 *E-mail:* mphillips0743@comcast.net, pg 532

Philomel, 345 Hudson St, New York, NY 10014 *Tel:* 212-366-2000, pg 191

Philosophical Library Inc, 275 Central Park W, Suite 12D, New York, NY 10024 *Tel:* 212-886-1873 *Fax:* 212-873-6070 *E-mail:* editors@philosophicallibrary.com *Web Site:* philosophicallibrary.com, pg 191

Philosophy Documentation Center, PO Box 7147, Charlottesville, VA 22906-7147 *Tel:* 434-220-3300 *Toll Free Tel:* 800-444-2419 *Fax:* 434-220-3301 *E-mail:* order@pdcnet.org *Web Site:* www.pdcnet.org, pg 191

Phoenix Society for Burn Survivors, 1835 R W Berends Dr SW, Grand Rapids, MI 49519 *Tel:* 616-458-2773 *Toll Free Tel:* 800-888-BURN (888-2876) *Fax:* 616-458-2831 *E-mail:* info@phoenix-society.org *Web Site:* www.phoenix-society.org, pg 191

PhotoEdit Inc, 3505 Cadillac Ave, Suite P-101, Costa Mesa, CA 92626 *Toll Free Tel:* 800-860-2098 *Fax:* 714-434-5937 *Toll Free Fax:* 800-804-3707 *E-mail:* sales@photoeditinc.com *Web Site:* www.photoeditinc.com, pg 532

Photographic Society of America® (PSA®), 8241 S Walker Ave, Suite 104, Oklahoma City, OK 73139 *Tel:* 405-843-1437 *Toll Free Tel:* 855-PSA-INFO (855-772-4636) *Fax:* 405-843-1438 *E-mail:* hq@psa-photo.org *Web Site:* www.psa-photo.org, pg 616

Piano Press, 1425 Ocean Ave, Suite 5, Del Mar, CA 92014 *Tel:* 619-884-1401 *Fax:* 858-755-1104 *E-mail:* pianopress@pianopress.com *Web Site:* www.pianopress.com, pg 191

Picador, 175 Fifth Ave, 19th fl, New York, NY 10010 *Tel:* 646-307-5151 *Fax:* 212-253-9627 *E-mail:* firstname.lastname@picadorusa.com *Web Site:* www.picadorusa.com, pg 191

Alison Picard Literary Agent, PO Box 2000, Cotuit, MA 02635 *Tel:* 508-477-7192 *Fax:* 508-477-7192 (call first) *E-mail:* ajpicard@aol.com, pg 568

Picasso Project, 1109 Geary Blvd, San Francisco, CA 94109 *Tel:* 415-292-6500 *Fax:* 415-292-6594 *E-mail:* editeur@earthlink.net (editorial); picasso@art-books.com (orders) *Web Site:* www.art-books.com, pg 191

Piccadilly Books Ltd, PO Box 25203, Colorado Springs, CO 80936-5203 *Tel:* 719-550-9887 *E-mail:* orders@piccadillybooks.com *Web Site:* www.piccadillybooks.com, pg 191

Robert J Pickering Award for Playwriting Excellence, 89 Division, Coldwater, MI 49036 *E-mail:* j7eden@aol.com *Web Site:* www.branchcct.org, pg 719

Picton Press, 814 E Elkcam Circle, Marco Island, FL 34145-2558 *Tel:* 239-970-2442 *E-mail:* sales@pictonpress.com (orders) *Web Site:* www.pictonpress.com, pg 191

Pictorial Histories Publishing Co, 521 Bickford St, Missoula, MT 59801 *Tel:* 406-549-8488 *Toll Free Tel:* 888-763-8350 *Fax:* 406-728-9280 *E-mail:* phpc@montana.com *Web Site:* www.pictorialhistoriespublishing.com, pg 191

Pictures & Words Editorial Services, 3100 "B" Ave, Anacortes, WA 98221 *Tel:* 360-293-8476 *E-mail:* editor@picturesandwords.com *Web Site:* www.picturesandwords.com/words, pg 532

Pie in the Sky Publishing LLC, 8031 E Phillips Circle, Centennial, CO 80112 *Tel:* 303-773-0851 *Fax:* 303-773-0851 *E-mail:* pieintheskypublishing@msn.com *Web Site:* www.pieintheskypublishing.com, pg 191

Pieces of Learning, 1990 Market Rd, Marion, IL 62959-8976 *Tel:* 618-964-9426 *Toll Free Tel:* 800-729-5137 *Toll Free Fax:* 800-844-0455 *E-mail:* piecesoflearning@verizon.net *Web Site:* www.piecesoflearning.com, pg 191

Lorne Pierce Medal, Walter House, 282 Somerset W, Ottawa, ON K2P 0J6, Canada *Tel:* 613-991-6990 (ext 106) *Fax:* 613-991-6996 *E-mail:* nominations@rsc-src.ca *Web Site:* www.rsc-src.ca, pg 719

The Pilgrim Press/United Church Press, 700 Prospect Ave, Cleveland, OH 44115-1100 *Toll Free Tel:* 800-537-3394 (cust serv-indivs); 800-654-5129 (cust serv-commercial accts) *Fax:* 216-736-2206 (orders) *E-mail:* proposals@thepilgrimpress.com *Web Site:* www.thepilgrimpress.com; www.unitedchurchpress.com, pg 192

Pilgrim Publications, PO Box 66, Pasadena, TX 77501-0066 *Tel:* 713-477-4261 *Fax:* 713-477-7561 *E-mail:* pilgrimpub@aol.com *Web Site:* members.aol.com/pilgrimpub/; www.pilgrimpublications.com, pg 192

Pima Writers' Workshop, Pima College West Campus, 2202 W Anklam Rd, Tucson, AZ 85709-0170 *Tel:* 520-206-6084 *Fax:* 520-206-6020 *Web Site:* www.pima.edu, pg 654

Pimlico/Aurous Inc, PO Box 20490, New York, NY 10017 *Tel:* 212-628-9729 *Fax:* 212-535-7861, pg 568

The Pinch Writing Awards in Fiction, University of Memphis, English Dept, 435 Patterson Hall, Memphis, TN 38152 *Tel:* 901-678-4190 *Fax:* 901-678-2226 *E-mail:* editor@thepinchjournal.com *Web Site:* www.thepinchjournal.com, pg 719

The Pinch Writing Awards in Poetry, University of Memphis, English Dept, 435 Patterson Hall, Memphis, TN 38152 *Tel:* 901-678-4190 *Fax:* 901-678-2226 *E-mail:* editor@thepinchjournal.com *Web Site:* www.thepinchjournal.com, pg 719

Caroline Pincus Book Midwife, 101 Wool St, San Francisco, CA 94110 *Tel:* 415-516-6206 *E-mail:* cpincus100@sbcglobal.net, pg 532

Marilyn Pincus, 1320 W Bloomington Place, Tucson, AZ 85755 *Tel:* 520-742-6699 *E-mail:* MPscribe@aol.com *Web Site:* www.marilynpincus.info, pg 532

Pinder Lane & Garon-Brooke Associates Ltd, 159 W 53 St, New York, NY 10019 *Tel:* 212-489-0880 *Fax:* 212-489-7104 *E-mail:* pinderlanegaronbrooke@gmail.com *Web Site:* www.pinderlaneandgaronbrooke.com, pg 568

Pine Forge Press, 2455 Teller Rd, Thousand Oaks, CA 91320 *Tel:* 805-499-4224; 805-499-9774 (orders) *Fax:* 805-499-0871 (orders) *E-mail:* info@sagepub.com *Web Site:* www.sagepub.com; www.pineforge.com, pg 192

Pineapple Press Inc, PO Box 3889, Sarasota, FL 34230-3889 *Tel:* 941-706-2507 *Toll Free Tel:* 866-766-3850 (orders) *Fax:* 941-706-2509 *Toll Free Fax:* 800-838-1149 (orders) *E-mail:* info@pineapplepress.com; customer.service@ingrampublisherservices.com *Web Site:* www.pineapplepress.com, pg 192

Pioneer Publishing Co, Hwy 82 E, Carrolton, MS 38917 *Tel:* 662-237-6010 *E-mail:* pioneerse@tecinfo.com *Web Site:* www.pioneersoutheast.com, pg 192

Pippin Press, 229 E 85 St, New York, NY 10028 *Tel:* 212-288-4920 *Fax:* 908-237-2407, pg 192

Pippin Properties Inc, 110 W 40 St, Suite 1704, New York, NY 10018 *Tel:* 212-338-9310 *Fax:* 212-338-9579 *E-mail:* info@pippinproperties.com *Web Site:* www.pippinproperties.com; www.facebook.com/pippinproperties, pg 568

Pippin Publishing, 5201 Dufferin St, Toronto, ON M3H 5T8, Canada *Tel:* 416-667-8731; 426-667-7791 (CN warehouse) *Toll Free Tel:* 800-565-9523 (CN warehouse) *Fax:* 416-667-7832 *Toll Free Fax:* 800-221-9985 (CN warehouse) *E-mail:* utpbooks@utpress.utoronto.ca (CN warehouse) *Web Site:* www.utpguidancecentre.com, pg 495

PJD Publications Ltd, PO Box 966, Westbury, NY 11590-0966 *Tel:* 516-626-0650 *Fax:* 516-626-4456 *Web Site:* www.pjdonline.com, pg 192

Planert Creek Press, E4843 395 Ave, Menomonie, WI 54751 *Tel:* 715-235-4110 *E-mail:* publisher@planertcreekpress.com *Web Site:* www.planertcreekpress.com, pg 192

Platinum Press LLC, 281 Hicks St, Brooklyn Heights, NY 11201 *Tel:* 718-875-5065 *Fax:* 718-875-5065, pg 192

Platypus Media LLC, 725 Eighth St SE, Washington, DC 20003 *Tel:* 202-546-1674 *Toll Free Tel:* 877-PLATYPS (752-8977) *Fax:* 202-546-2356 *E-mail:* info@platypusmedia.com *Web Site:* www.platypusmedia.com, pg 192

Playboy College Fiction Contest, 9346 Civic Center Dr, Suite 300, Beverly Hills, CA 90210-3604 *Web Site:* playboymagazine.submittable.com/submit, pg 719

Players Press Inc, PO Box 1132, Studio City, CA 91614-0132 *Tel:* 818-789-4980 *E-mail:* playerspress@att.net *Web Site:* www.ppeps.com, pg 193

Playhouse Publishing, PO Box 1962, Cleveland, OH 44106 *Tel:* 330-926-1313 *Fax:* 330-475-8579 *E-mail:* info@picturemepress.com *Web Site:* www.picturemepress.com, pg 193

Playwright Discovery Award, 818 Connecticut Ave NW, Suite 600, Washington, DC 20006 *Tel:* 202-628-2800 *Toll Free Tel:* 800-933-8721 *Fax:* 202-429-0868 *Web Site:* www.vsarts.org/playwrightdiscovery, pg 719

Playwrights Guild of Canada, 401 Richmond St W, Suite 350, Toronto, ON M5V 3A8, Canada *Tel:* 416-703-0201 *Fax:* 416-703-0059 *E-mail:* info@playwrightsguild.ca *Web Site:* www.playwrightsguild.ca, pg 616

Playwrights Project, 3675 Ruffin Rd, Suite 330, San Diego, CA 92123 *Tel:* 858-384-2970 *Fax:* 858-384-2974 *E-mail:* write@playwrightsproject.org *Web Site:* www.playwrightsproject.org, pg 719

Pleasure Boat Studio: A Literary Press, 201 W 89 St, New York, NY 10024 *Tel:* 212-362-8563 *Fax:* 413-677-0085 *E-mail:* pleasboat@nyc.rr.com *Web Site:* www.pleasureboatstudio.com, pg 193

Plexus Publishing, Inc, 143 Old Marlton Pike, Medford, NJ 08055 *Tel:* 609-654-6500 *Fax:* 609-654-4309 *E-mail:* info@plexuspublishing.com *Web Site:* www.plexuspublishing.com, pg 193

The Plimpton Prize, 544 W 27 St, New York, NY 10001 *Tel:* 212-343-1333 *Fax:* 212-343-1988 *E-mail:* queries@theparisreview.org *Web Site:* www.theparisreview.org, pg 719

Plough Publishing House, 151 Bowne Dr, Walden, NY 12586-2832 *Tel:* 845-572-3455 *Toll Free Tel:* 800-521-8011 *Fax:* 845-572-3472 *E-mail:* info@plough.com *Web Site:* www.plough.com, pg 193

Ploughshares, Emerson College, 120 Boylston St, Boston, MA 02116 *Tel:* 617-824-3757 *E-mail:* pshares@pshares.org *Web Site:* www.pshares.org, pg 193

Plowshare Media, 405 Vincente Way, La Jolla, CA 92037 *E-mail:* sales@plowsharemedia.com *Web Site:* plowsharemedia.com, pg 193

Plum Tree Books, 2151 Market St, Camp Hill, PA 17011 *Tel:* 717-730-0711 *Fax:* 717-730-0721 *E-mail:* info@classicalsubjects.com *Web Site:* www.plumtreebooks.com, pg 193

Plume, 375 Hudson St, New York, NY 10014 *Tel:* 212-366-2000 *Fax:* 212-366-2666 *E-mail:* online@penguinputnam.com *Web Site:* www.penguinputnam.com; us.penguingroup.com, pg 193

Plunkett Research Ltd, PO Drawer 541737, Houston, TX 77254-1737 *Tel:* 713-932-0000 *Fax:* 713-932-7080 *E-mail:* customersupport@plunkettresearch.com *Web Site:* www.plunkettresearch.com, pg 193

Plutarch Award, PO Box 33020, Santa Fe, NM 87594 *Tel:* 505-983-4671 *Web Site:* biographersinternational.org, pg 719

PNWA Literary Contest, 1420 NW Gilman Blvd, Suite 2, PMB 2717, Issaquah, WA 98027 *Tel:* 425-673-2665 *E-mail:* pnwa@pnwa.org *Web Site:* www.pnwa.org, pg 719

PNWA - a writer's resource, 1420 NW Gilman Blvd, Suite 2, PMB 2717, Issaquah, WA 98027 *Tel:* 425-673-2665 *Fax:* 425-961-0768 *E-mail:* pnwa@pnwa.org *Web Site:* www.pnwa.org, pg 616

J P Pochron Writer for Hire, 830 Lake Orchid Circle, No 203, Vero Beach, FL 32962 *Tel:* 772-569-2967 *E-mail:* hotwriter15@hotmail.com, pg 532

Pocket Press Inc, PO Box 25124, Portland, OR 97298-0124 *Toll Free Tel:* 888-237-2110 *Toll Free Fax:* 877-643-3732 *E-mail:* sales@pocketpressinc.com *Web Site:* www.pocketpressinc.com, pg 194

Pocol Press, 6023 Pocol Dr, Clifton, VA 20124-1333 *Tel:* 703-830-5862 *E-mail:* chrisandtom@erols.com *Web Site:* www.pocolpress.com, pg 194

Edgar Allan Poe Awards®, 1140 Broadway, Suite 1507, New York, NY 10001 *Tel:* 212-888-8171 *E-mail:* mwa@mysterywriters.org *Web Site:* www.mysterywriters.org, pg 719

Edgar Allan Poe Memorial, 1194 Hume Rd, Hume, VA 22639-1806 *E-mail:* poetryinva@aol.com *Web Site:* www.poetrysocietyofvirginia.org, pg 719

A Poem With a Point of View, 1194 Hume Rd, Hume, VA 22639-1806 *E-mail:* poetryinva@aol.com *Web Site:* www.poetrysocietyofvirginia.org, pg 719

Poetry Book Contest, PO Box 910456, Lexington, KY 40591-0456 *Web Site:* www.accents-publishing.com/contest.html, pg 720

Poetry Center Book Award, 1600 Holloway Ave, San Francisco, CA 94132 *Tel:* 415-338-2227 *Fax:* 415-338-0966 *E-mail:* poetry@sfsu.edu *Web Site:* www.sfsu.edu/~poetry, pg 720

Poetry Chapbook Contest, 1935 Penfield Rd, Penfield, NY 14526 *Tel:* 585-383-0812 *E-mail:* palettesnquills@gmail.com *Web Site:* www.palettesnquills.com, pg 720

Poetry Flash Reading Series, 1450 Fourth St, Suite 4, Berkeley, CA 94710 *Tel:* 510-525-5476 *Fax:* 510-525-6752 *E-mail:* editor@poetryflash.org *Web Site:* www.poetryflash.org, pg 654

Poetry Society of America (PSA), 15 Gramercy Park, New York, NY 10003 *Tel:* 212-254-9628 *Fax:* 212-673-2352 *Web Site:* www.poetrysociety.org, pg 616

Poets & Writers Inc, 90 Broad St, Suite 2100, New York, NY 10004 *Tel:* 212-226-3586 *Fax:* 212-226-3963 *E-mail:* admin@pw.org *Web Site:* www.pw.org, pg 616

Pogo Press Inc, 5995 149 St W, Suite 105, Apple Valley, MN 55124 *Tel:* 952-469-6699 *Toll Free Tel:* 800-846-7027 *Fax:* 952-469-1968 *Toll Free Fax:* 800-330-6232 *E-mail:* info@finneyco.com *Web Site:* www.pogopress.com, pg 194

Pointed Leaf Press, 136 Baxter St, New York, NY 10013 *Tel:* 212-941-1800 *Fax:* 212-941-1822 *E-mail:* info@pointedleafpress.com *Web Site:* www.pointedleafpress.com, pg 194

Poirot & Co Literary Agency, 3887 Nimbus Rd, Longmont, CO 80503 *Tel:* 303-494-0668 *Fax:* 303-494-9396 *E-mail:* poirotco@comcast.net, pg 568

Poisoned Pen Press, 6962 E First Ave, Suite 103, Scottsdale, AZ 85251 *Tel:* 480-945-3375 *Toll Free Tel:* 800-421-3976 *Fax:* 480-949-1707 *E-mail:* info@poisonedpenpress.com *Web Site:* www.poisonedpenpress.com, pg 194

Polar Bear & Co, 8 Brook St, Solon, ME 04979 *Tel:* 207-643-2795 *Web Site:* www.polarbearandco.com, pg 194

Polebridge Press, c/o Willamette University, 900 State St, Salem, OR 97301 *Tel:* 503-375-5323 *E-mail:* orders@westarinstitute.org *Web Site:* www.polebridgepress.com, pg 194

Wendy Polhemus-Annibell, PO Box 464, Peconic, NY 11958 *Tel:* 631-276-0684 *E-mail:* wannibell@gmail.com; wannibel@suffolk.lib.ny.us, pg 532

Police Executive Research Forum, 1120 Connecticut Ave NW, Suite 930, Washington, DC 20036 *Tel:* 202-466-7820 *Fax:* 202-466-7826 *E-mail:* perf@policeforum.org *Web Site:* www.policeforum.org, pg 194

Polis Books, 1201 Hudson St, No 211S, Hoboken, NJ 07030 *E-mail:* info@polisbooks.com; submissions@polisbooks.com *Web Site:* www.polisbooks.com; facebook.com/PolisBooks; twitter.com/PolisBooks, pg 194

The George Polk Awards, The Brooklyn Campus, One University Plaza, Brooklyn, NY 11201-5372 *Tel:* 718-488-1009; 718-488-1115 *Web Site:* www.liu.edu/polk, pg 720

Pom Inc, 18-15 215 St, Bayside, NY 11360 *Tel:* 516-487-3441, pg 568

Pomegranate Communications Inc, 19018 NE Portal Way, Portland, OR 97230 *Tel:* 503-328-6500 *Toll Free Tel:* 800-227-1428 *Fax:* 503-328-9330 *Toll Free Fax:* 800-848-4376 *E-mail:* contactus@pomegranate.com *Web Site:* www.pomegranate.com, pg 195

Pontifical Institute of Mediaeval Studies, Department of Publications, 59 Queen's Park Crescent E, Toronto, ON M5S 2C4, Canada *Tel:* 416-926-7142 *Fax:* 416-926-7292 *Web Site:* www.pims.ca, pg 495

Porcupine's Quill Inc, 68 Main St, Erin, ON N0B 1T0, Canada *Tel:* 519-833-9158 *Fax:* 519-833-9845 *E-mail:* pql@sentex.net *Web Site:* porcupinesquill.ca, pg 495

Port Townsend Writers' Conference, 223 Battery Way, Port Townsend, WA 98368 *Tel:* 360-385-3102 *Toll Free Tel:* 800-733-3608 (ticket off) *Fax:* 360-385-2470 *E-mail:* info@centrum.org *Web Site:* www.centrum.org, pg 654

Portage & Main Press, 318 McDermot, Suite 100, Winnipeg, MB R3A 0A2, Canada *Tel:* 204-987-3500 *Toll Free Tel:* 800-667-9673 *Fax:* 204-947-0080 *Toll Free Fax:* 866-734-8477 *E-mail:* books@portageandmainpress.com *Web Site:* www.portageandmainpress.com, pg 495

Katherine Anne Porter Award, 633 W 155 St, New York, NY 10032 *Tel:* 212-368-5900 *Fax:* 212-491-4615 *E-mail:* academy@artsandletters.org *Web Site:* www.artsandletters.org, pg 720

Katherine Anne Porter Prize for Fiction, Nimrod International Journal, 800 S Tucker Dr, Tulsa, OK 74104 *Tel:* 918-631-3080 *Fax:* 918-631-3033 *E-mail:* nimrod@utulsa.edu *Web Site:* www.utulsa.edu/nimrod, pg 720

Portfolio, 375 Hudson St, New York, NY 10014, pg 195

Portfolio Solutions LLC, 136 Jameson Hill Rd, Clinton Corners, NY 12514 *Tel:* 845-266-1001 *Web Site:* www.portfoliosolutionsllc.com, pg 584

Potomac Books Inc, 22841 Quicksilver Dr, Dulles, VA 20166 *Tel:* 703-661-1548 *Fax:* 703-661-1547 *E-mail:* pbimail@presswarehouse.com *Web Site:* www.potomacbooksinc.com, pg 195

Clarkson Potter Publishers, c/o Random House Inc, 1745 Broadway, New York, NY 10019 *Tel:* 212-782-9000 *Toll Free Tel:* 888-264-1745 *Fax:* 212-572-6181 *Web Site:* www.clarksonpotter.com; www.randomhouse.com/crown/clarksonpotter, pg 195

Pottersfield Press, 83 Leslie Rd, East Lawrencetown, NS B2Z 1P8, Canada *Toll Free Fax:* 888-253-3133 *Web Site:* www.pottersfieldpress.com, pg 495

powerHouse Books, 37 Main St, Brooklyn, NY 11201 *Tel:* 212-604-9074 *Fax:* 212-366-5247 *E-mail:* info@powerhousebooks.com *Web Site:* www.powerhousebooks.com, pg 195

The Poynor Group, 13454 Yorktown Dr, Bowie, MD 20715 *Tel:* 301-805-6788, pg 568

Practice Management Information Corp (PMIC), 4727 Wilshire Blvd, Suite 300, Los Angeles, CA 90010 *Tel:* 323-954-0224 *Fax:* 323-954-0253 *Toll Free Fax:* 800-633-6556 (orders) *E-mail:* orders@medicalbookstore.com; customer.service@pmiconline.com *Web Site:* www.pmiconline.com, pg 195

Practising Law Institute, 1177 Avenue of the Americas, New York, NY 10036 *Tel:* 212-824-5700 *Toll Free Tel:* 800-260-4PLI (260-4754, cust serv) *Fax:* 212-265-4742 (intl) *Toll Free Fax:* 800-321-0093 (local) *E-mail:* info@pli.edu (cust serv) *Web Site:* www.pli.edu, pg 195

Prairie Schooner Annual Strousse Award, University of Nebraska, 123 Andrews Hall, 625 N 14 St, Lincoln, NE 68508 *Tel:* 402-472-0911 *Fax:* 402-472-9771 *E-mail:* prairieschooner@unl.edu *Web Site:* prairieschooner.unl.edu, pg 720

Prairie Schooner Bernice Slote Award, University of Nebraska, 123 Andrews Hall, 625 N 14 St, Lincoln, NE 68508 *Tel:* 402-472-0911 *E-mail:* prairieschooner@unl.edu *Web Site:* prairieschooner.unl.edu, pg 720

Prairie Schooner Book Prize Contest in Fiction, University of Nebraska, 123 Andrews Hall, 625 N 14 St, Lincoln, NE 68508 *Tel:* 402-472-0911 *Fax:* 402-472-9771 *E-mail:* psbookprize@unl.edu *Web Site:* prairieschooner.unl.edu, pg 720

Prairie Schooner Book Prize Contest in Poetry, University of Nebraska, 123 Andrews Hall, 625 N 14 St, Lincoln, NE 68508 *Tel:* 402-472-0911 *Fax:* 402-472-9771 *E-mail:* psbookprize@unl.edu *Web Site:* prairieschooner.unl.edu, pg 720

Prairie Schooner Edward Stanley Award, University of Nebraska, 123 Andrews Hall, 625 N 14 St, Lincoln, NE 68508 *Tel:* 402-472-0911 *Fax:* 402-472-9771 *E-mail:* prairieschooner@unl.edu *Web Site:* prairieschooner.unl.edu, pg 720

Prairie Schooner Glenna Luschei Award, University of Nebraska, 123 Andrews Hall, 625 N 14 St, Lincoln, NE 68508 *Tel:* 402-472-0911 *Fax:* 402-472-9771 *E-mail:* prairieschooner@unl.edu *Web Site:* prairieschooner.unl.edu, pg 721

Prairie Schooner Hugh J Luke Award, University of Nebraska, 123 Andrews Hall, 625 N 14 St, Lincoln, NE 68508 *Tel:* 402-472-0911 *Fax:* 402-472-9771 *E-mail:* prairieschooner@unl.edu *Web Site:* prairieschooner.unl.edu, pg 721

Prairie Schooner Jane Geske Award, University of Nebraska, 123 Andrews Hall, 625 N 14 St, Lincoln, NE 68508 *Tel:* 402-472-0911 *Fax:* 402-472-9771 *E-mail:* prairieschooner@unl.edu *Web Site:* prairieschooner.unl.edu, pg 721

Prairie Schooner Lawrence Foundation Award, University of Nebraska, 123 Andrews Hall, 625 N 14 St, Lincoln, NE 68508 *Tel:* 402-472-0911 *Fax:* 402-472-9771 *E-mail:* prairieschooner@unl.edu *Web Site:* prairieschooner.unl.edu, pg 721

Prairie Schooner Virginia Faulkner Award for Excellence in Writing, University of Nebraska, 123 Andrews Hall, 625 N 14 St, Lincoln, NE 68508 *Tel:* 402-472-0911 *Fax:* 402-472-9771 *E-mail:* prairieschooner@unl.edu *Web Site:* prairieschooner.unl.edu, pg 721

PrairieView Press, PO Box 460, Rosenort, MB R0G-1W0, Canada *Tel:* 204-327-6543 *Toll Free Tel:* 800-477-7377 *Fax:* 204-327-6544 *Web Site:* www.prairieviewpress.com, pg 496

Prayer Book Press Inc, 1363 Fairfield Ave, Bridgeport, CT 06605 *Tel:* 203-384-2284 *Fax:* 203-579-9109, pg 196

PRB Productions, 963 Peralta Ave, Albany, CA 94706-2144 *Tel:* 510-526-0722 *Fax:* 510-527-4763 *E-mail:* prbprdns@aol.com *Web Site:* www.prbmusic.com, pg 196

Premier Print Awards, 200 Deer Run Rd, Sewickley, PA 15143-2324 *Tel:* 412-741-6860 *Toll Free Tel:* 800-910-4283 *Fax:* 412-741-2311 *E-mail:* printing@printing.org *Web Site:* www.printing.org/premierprint, pg 721

Prentice Hall Press, 375 Hudson St, New York, NY 10014 *Tel:* 212-366-2000 *Fax:* 212-366-2666, pg 196

Linn Prentis Literary, 6830 NE Bothell Way, PMB 496, Kenmore, WA 98028 *Tel:* 212-876-8557 *Fax:* 206-984-0837 *E-mail:* linn@linnprentis.com *Web Site:* www.linnprentis.com, pg 568

PREP Publishing, 3528 Turnberry Circle, Fayetteville, NC 28303 *Tel:* 910-483-6611 *Toll Free Tel:* 800-533-2814 *E-mail:* preppub@aol.com *Web Site:* www.prep-pub.com, pg 196

Presbyterian Publishing Corp (PPC), 100 Witherspoon St, Louisville, KY 40202 *Tel:* 502-569-5000 *Toll Free Tel:* 800-523-1631 (US only) *Fax:* 502-569-5113 *E-mail:* ppcmail@presbypub.com *Web Site:* www.ppcbooks.com, pg 196

The Press at California State University, Fresno, 2380 E Keats, M/S MB 99, Fresno, CA 93740-8024 *Tel:* 559-278-3056 *Fax:* 559-278-6758 *E-mail:* press@csufresno.edu *Web Site:* shop.thepressatcsufresno.com; thepressatcsufresno.com, pg 196

Les Presses de l'Universite du Quebec, 2875 blvd Laurier, Suite 450, Quebec, QC G1V 2M2, Canada *Tel:* 418-657-4399 *Fax:* 418-657-2096 *E-mail:* puq@puq.ca *Web Site:* www.puq.ca, pg 496

Les Presses De L'Universite Laval, 2180, Chemin Ste-Foy, 1st fl, Quebec, QC G1V 0A6, Canada *Tel:* 418-656-2803 *Fax:* 418-656-3305 *E-mail:* presses@pul.ulaval.ca *Web Site:* www.pulaval.com, pg 496

Prestel Publishing, 900 Broadway, Suite 603, New York, NY 10003 *Tel:* 212-995-2720 *Toll Free Tel:* 888-463-6110 (cust serv) *Fax:* 212-995-2733 *E-mail:* sales@prestel-usa.com *Web Site:* www.prestel.com, pg 196

Prevention Products & Services Inc dba The Bureau for At-Risk Youth, PO Box 170, Farmingville, NY 11738 *Toll Free Tel:* 800-99YOUTH (999-6884) *Fax:* 631-389-2511 *Web Site:* www.at-risk.com, pg 196

Derek Price/Rod Webster Prize Award, 440 Geddes Hall, Notre Dame, IN 46556 *Tel:* 574-631-1194 *Fax:* 574-631-1533 *E-mail:* info@hssonline.org *Web Site:* www.hssonline.org, pg 721

Price Stern Sloan, 345 Hudson St, New York, NY 10014 *Tel:* 212-366-2000 *E-mail:* online@penguinputnam.com *Web Site:* www.penguinputnam.com; us.penguingroup.com, pg 196

Price World Publishing, 3971 Hoover Rd, Suite 77, Columbus, OH 43123-2839 *Toll Free Tel:* 888-234-6896 *Fax:* 216-803-0350 *E-mail:* info@priceworldpublishing.com *Web Site:* www.priceworldpublishing.com, pg 196

The Aaron M Priest Literary Agency Inc, 708 Third Ave, 23rd fl, New York, NY 10017-4201 *Tel:* 212-818-0344 *Fax:* 212-573-9417 *E-mail:* info@aaronpriest.com *Web Site:* www.aaronpriest.com, pg 568

Prima Games, 3000 Lava Ridge Ct, Roseville, CA 95661 *Tel:* 916-787-7000 *Fax:* 916-787-7001 *Web Site:* www.primagames.com, pg 196

Primary Research Group Inc, 2753 Broadway, Suite 156, New York, NY 10025 *Tel:* 212-736-2316 *Fax:* 212-412-9097 *E-mail:* primaryresearchgroup@gmail.com *Web Site:* www.primaryresearch.com, pg 197

Princeton Architectural Press, 37 E Seventh St, New York, NY 10003 *Tel:* 212-995-9620 *Toll Free Tel:* 800-722-6657 (dist); 800-759-0190 (sales) *Fax:* 212-995-9454 *E-mail:* sales@papress.com *Web Site:* www.papress.com, pg 197

Princeton Book Co Publishers, 614 Rte 130, Hightstown, NJ 08520 *Tel:* 609-426-0602 *Toll Free Tel:* 800-220-7149 *Fax:* 609-426-1344 *E-mail:* pbc@dancehorizons.com; elysian@princetonbookcompany.com *Web Site:* www.dancehorizons.com, pg 197

The Princeton Review, c/o Random House Inc, 1745 Broadway, New York, NY 10019 *Toll Free Tel:* 800-733-3000 *Fax:* 212-782-9682 *E-mail:* princetonreview@randomhouse.com *Web Site:* www.princetonreview.com, pg 197

Princeton University Press, 41 William St, Princeton, NJ 08540-5237 *Tel:* 609-258-4900 *Toll Free Tel:* 800-777-4726 (orders) *Fax:* 609-258-6305 *Toll Free Fax:* 800-999-1958 *E-mail:* orders@cpfsinc.com *Web Site:* press.princeton.edu, pg 197

Print Industries Market Information & Research Organization, 1899 Preston White Dr, Reston, VA 20191 *Tel:* 703-264-7200 *Fax:* 703-620-0994 *E-mail:* npes@npes.org *Web Site:* www.primir.org; www.npes.org/primirresearch/primir.aspx, pg 616

Printing & Graphics Association MidAtlantic (PGAMA), 9685 Gerwig Lane, Suite A, Columbia, MD 21046-1520 *Tel:* 410-319-0900 *Toll Free Tel:* 877-319-0906 *Fax:* 410-319-0905 *E-mail:* info@pgama.com *Web Site:* www.pgama.com, pg 616

Printing Association of Florida Inc (PAF), 6250 Hazeltine National Dr, Suite 114, Orlando, FL 32822 *Tel:* 407-240-8009 *Toll Free Tel:* 800-331-0461 *Fax:* 407-240-8333 *Web Site:* www.flprint.org, pg 616

Printing Brokerage/Buyers Association International (PBBA), 1530 Locust St, Mezzanine 124, Philadelphia, PA 19102 *Tel:* 215-821-6581 *E-mail:* contactus@pbba.org *Web Site:* pbba.org, pg 616

Printing Industries of America, 200 Deer Run Rd, Sewickley, PA 15143-2324 *Tel:* 412-741-6860; 412-259-1770 *E-mail:* membercentral@printing.org (orders) *Web Site:* www.printing.org, pg 197

Printing Industries of America, 200 Deer Run Rd, Sewickley, PA 15143-2324 *Tel:* 412-741-6860 *Toll Free Tel:* 800-910-4283 *Fax:* 412-741-2311 *E-mail:* printing@printing.org *Web Site:* www.printing.org, pg 617

Printing Industry Association of the South (PIAS), 305 Plus Park Blvd, Nashville, TN 37217 *Tel:* 615-366-1094 *Fax:* 615-366-4192 *E-mail:* info@pias.org *Web Site:* www.pias.org, pg 617

Michael L Printz Award, 50 E Huron St, Chicago, IL 60611 *Tel:* 312-280-4390 *Toll Free Tel:* 800-545-2433 *Fax:* 312-280-5276 *E-mail:* yalsa@ala.org *Web Site:* www.ala.org/yalsa/printz, pg 721

Prise de Parole Inc, 109 Elm St, Suite 205, Sudbury, ON P3C 1T4, Canada *Tel:* 705-675-6491 *Fax:* 705-673-1817 *E-mail:* info@prisedeparole.ca *Web Site:* www.prisedeparole.ca, pg 496

PRISM international Literary Non-Fiction Contest, University of British Columbia, Buch E462, 1866 Main Mall, Vancouver, BC V6T 1Z1, Canada *Tel:* 778-822-2514 *Fax:* 778-822-3616 *E-mail:* prismwritingcontest@gmail.com *Web Site:* www.prismmagazine.ca, pg 721

PRISM international Poetry Contest, University of British Columbia, Buch E462, 1866 Main Mall, Vancouver, BC V6T 1Z1, Canada *Tel:* 778-822-2514 *Fax:* 778-822-3616 *E-mail:* prismwritingcontest@gmail.com *Web Site:* www.prismmagazine.ca, pg 721

PRISM international Short Fiction Contest, University of British Columbia, Buch E462, 1866 Main Mall, Vancouver, BC V6T 1Z1, Canada *Tel:* 778-822-2514 *Fax:* 778-822-3616 *E-mail:* prismwritingcontest@gmail.com *Web Site:* www.prismmagazine.ca, pg 721

Pritzker Literature Award for Lifetime Achievement in Military Writing, Pritzker Military Museum & Library, 104 S Michigan Ave, Suite 525, Chicago, IL 60603 *Tel:* 312-374-9390 *Fax:* 312-374-9394 *E-mail:* info@pritzkermilitary.org *Web Site:* www.pritzkermilitary.org, pg 721

Privacy Journal, PO Box 28577, Providence, RI 02908 *Tel:* 401-274-7861 *Fax:* 401-274-4747 *E-mail:* orders@privacyjournal.net *Web Site:* www.privacyjournal.net, pg 197

Prix Alvine-Belisle, 2065 rue Parthenais, Bureau 387, Montreal, QC H2K 3T1, Canada *Tel:* 514-281-5012 *Fax:* 514-281-8219 *E-mail:* info@asted.org *Web Site:* www.asted.org, pg 722

Prix Emile-Nelligan, 100, rue Sherbrooke, Montreal, QC H2X 1C3, Canada *Tel:* 514-278-4657 *Toll Free Tel:* 888-849-8540 *Fax:* 514-278-1943 *E-mail:* info@fondation-nelligan.org *Web Site:* www.fondation-nelligan.org, pg 722

PRO-ED Inc, 8700 Shoal Creek Blvd, Austin, TX 78757-6897 *Tel:* 512-451-3246 *Toll Free Tel:* 800-897-3202 *Fax:* 512-451-8542 *Toll Free Fax:* 800-397-7633 *E-mail:* general@proedinc.com *Web Site:* www.proedinc.com, pg 198

Pro Lingua Associates Inc, 74 Cotton Mill Hill, Suite A-315, Brattleboro, VT 05301 *Tel:* 802-257-7779 *Toll Free Tel:* 800-366-4775 *Fax:* 802-257-5117 *E-mail:* info@prolinguaassociates.com *Web Site:* www.prolinguaassociates.com, pg 198

ProChain Press, 3460 Commission Ct, No 301, Lake Ridge, VA 22192 *Tel:* 703-490-8821 *Fax:* 703-494-1414 *E-mail:* publishing@prochain.com *Web Site:* prochain.com, pg 508

Productive Publications, 7-B Pleasant Blvd, Unit 1210, Toronto, ON M4T 1K2, Canada *Tel:* 416-483-0634 *Toll Free Tel:* 877-879-2669 (orders) *Fax:* 416-322-7434 *E-mail:* productivepublications@rogers.com *Web Site:* www.productivepublications.ca, pg 496

Productivity Press, c/o Routledge, 711 Third Ave, New York, NY 10017 *Tel:* 212-216-7800 *Toll Free Tel:* 800-634-7064 (orders) *Fax:* 212-563-2269 *Toll Free Fax:* 800-248-4724 (orders) *E-mail:* info@productivitypress.com; orders@taylorandfrancis.com *Web Site:* www.productivitypress.com, pg 198

Professional Communications Inc, 20968 State Rd 22, Caddo, OK 74729 *Tel:* 580-367-9838 *Toll Free Tel:* 800-337-9838 *Fax:* 580-367-9989 *E-mail:* info@pcibooks.com *Web Site:* www.pcibooks.com, pg 198

The Professional Education Group Inc (PEG), 12401 Minnetonka Blvd, Suite 200, Minnetonka, MN 55305-3994 *Tel:* 952-933-9990 *Toll Free Tel:* 800-229-2531 *Fax:* 952-933-7784 *E-mail:* orders@proedgroup.com *Web Site:* www.proedgroup.com, pg 198

Professional Publications Inc (PPI), 1250 Fifth Ave, Belmont, CA 94002 *Tel:* 650-593-9119 *Fax:* 650-592-4519 *E-mail:* info@ppi2pass.com *Web Site:* ppi2pass.com; feprep.com, pg 198

Professional Resource Press, 1958 Barber Rd, Sarasota, FL 34240 *Tel:* 941-343-9601 *Toll Free Tel:* 800-443-3364 (orders & cust serv) *Fax:* 941-343-9201 *Toll Free Fax:* 866-804-4843 (orders only) *E-mail:* cs.prpress@gmail.com *Web Site:* www.prpress.com, pg 198

The Professional Writer, 175 W 12 St, Suite 6D, New York, NY 10011 *Tel:* 212-414-0188; 917-658-1946 (cell) *E-mail:* paul@theprofessionalwriter.com *Web Site:* www.theprofessionalwriter.com, pg 532

Professional Writers Association of Canada (PWAC), 215 Spadina Ave, Suite 130, Toronto, ON M5T 2C7, Canada *Tel:* 416-504-1645 *E-mail:* info@pwac.ca *Web Site:* pwac.ca; www.writers.ca, pg 617

Progressive Press, 3716 37 St, San Diego, CA 92105-2409 *Tel:* 619-892-7781 *Fax:* 619-892-7781 *E-mail:* info@progressivepress.com *Web Site:* www.progressivepress.com, pg 198

Prometheus Awards, 650 Castro St, Suite 120-433, Mountain View, CA 94041 *Tel:* 650-968-6319 *E-mail:* info@lfs.org *Web Site:* www.lfs.org, pg 722

Prometheus Books, 59 John Glenn Dr, Amherst, NY 14228-2119 *Tel:* 716-691-0133 *Toll Free Tel:* 800-421-0351 *Fax:* 716-691-0137 *E-mail:* marketing@prometheusbooks.com; editorial@prometheusbooks.com *Web Site:* www.prometheusbooks.com, pg 199

Pronk Media Inc, PO Box 340, Beaverton, ON L0K 1A0, Canada *Tel:* 416-441-3760 *E-mail:* info@pronk.com *Web Site:* www.pronk.com, pg 532

Proofed to Perfection Editing Services, 4018 Summer Lane, Hillsborough, NC 27278 *Tel:* 919-732-8565 *E-mail:* inquiries@proofedtoperfection.com *Web Site:* www.proofedtoperfection.com, pg 533

ProQuest LLC, 789 E Eisenhower Pkwy, Ann Arbor, MI 48108-3218 *Tel:* 734-761-4700 *Toll Free Tel:* 800-521-0600 *Fax:* 734-975-6486 *Toll Free Fax:* 800-864-0019 *E-mail:* info@proquest.com *Web Site:* www.proquest.com, pg 199

PROSE Awards, 71 Fifth Ave, 2nd fl, New York, NY 10003-3004 *Tel:* 212-255-0200 *Fax:* 212-255-7007 *Web Site:* www.proseawards.com; publishers.org, pg 722

Prospect Agency, 285 Fifth Ave, PMB 445, Brooklyn, NY 11215 *Tel:* 718-788-3217 *Fax:* 718-360-9582 *Web Site:* www.prospectagency.com, pg 568

Prospect Park Books, 2359 Lincoln Ave, Altadena, CA 91001 *Tel:* 626-793-9796 *E-mail:* info@prospectparkbooks.com *Web Site:* www.prospectparkbooks.com, pg 199

ProStar Publications Inc, 3 Church Circle, Suite 109, Annapolis, MD 21401 *Tel:* 310-280-1010 *Toll Free Tel:* 800-481-6277 *Fax:* 310-280-1025 *Toll Free Fax:* 800-487-6277 *E-mail:* editor@prostarpublications.com *Web Site:* www.prostarpublications.com, pg 199

Protestant Church-Owned Publishers Association, 6631 Westbury Oaks Ct, Springfield, VA 22152 *Tel:* 703-220-5989 *Web Site:* www.pcpaonline.org, pg 617

The PRS Group Inc, 6320 Fly Rd, Suite 102, East Syracuse, NY 13057-9358 *Tel:* 315-431-0511 *Fax:* 315-431-0200 *E-mail:* custserv@prsgroup.com *Web Site:* www.prsgroup.com, pg 199

Prufrock Press, PO Box 8813, Waco, TX 76714-8813 *Tel:* 254-756-3337 *Toll Free Tel:* 800-998-2208 *Fax:* 254-756-3339 *Toll Free Fax:* 800-240-0333 *E-mail:* info@prufrock.com *Web Site:* www.prufrock.com, pg 199

Psychological Assessment Resources Inc (PAR), 16204 N Florida Ave, Lutz, FL 33549 *Tel:* 813-968-3003; 813-449-4065 *Toll Free Tel:* 800-331-8378 *Fax:* 813-968-2598; 813-961-2196 *Toll Free Fax:* 800-727-9329 *E-mail:* custsup@parinc.com *Web Site:* www4.parinc.com, pg 199

Psychology Press, 711 Third Ave, 8th fl, New York, NY 10017 *Tel:* 212-216-7800 *Toll Free Tel:* 800-634-7064 *Fax:* 212-563-2269 *Web Site:* www.psypress.com, pg 199

Public Citizen, 1600 20 St NW, Washington, DC 20009 *Tel:* 202-588-1000 *Fax:* 202-588-7798 *E-mail:* public_citizen@citizen.org *Web Site:* www.citizen.org, pg 200

Public Relations Society of America, 33 Maiden Lane, 11th fl, New York, NY 10038-5150 *Tel:* 212-460-1400 *Fax:* 212-995-0757 *Web Site:* www.prsa.org, pg 617

Public Scholar Program, 400 Seventh St SW, Washington, DC 20506 *Tel:* 202-606-8200 *E-mail:* publicscholar@neh.gov *Web Site:* www.neh.gov/grants/research, pg 722

PublicAffairs, 250 W 57 St, Suite 1321, New York, NY 10107 *Tel:* 212-397-6666 *Toll Free Tel:* 800-343-4499 (orders) *Fax:* 212-397-4277 *E-mail:* publicaffairs@perseusbooks.com *Web Site:* www.publicaffairsbooks.com, pg 200

Publication Consultants, 8370 Eleusis Dr, Anchorage, AK 99502 *Tel:* 907-349-2424 *Fax:* 907-349-2426 *E-mail:* books@publicationconsultants.com *Web Site:* www.publicationconsultants.com, pg 200

Les Publications du Quebec, 1000, rte de l'Eqalise, Bureau 500, Quebec, QC G1V 3V9, Canada *Tel:* 418-643-5150 *Toll Free Tel:* 800-463-2100 (Quebec province only) *Fax:* 418-643-6177 *Toll Free Fax:* 800-561-3479 *E-mail:* publicationsduquebec@cspq.gouv.qc.ca *Web Site:* www.publicationsduquebec.gouv.qc.ca, pg 496

Publications International Ltd, 7373 N Cicero Ave, Lincolnwood, IL 60712 *Tel:* 847-676-3470 *Fax:* 847-676-3671 *E-mail:* customer_service@pubint.com *Web Site:* www.pilbooks.com, pg 200

Publishers Association of the West (PubWest), 17501 Hill Way, Lake Oswego, OR 97035 *Tel:* 503-901-9865 *Web Site:* pubwest.org, pg 617

Publishers' Graphics Inc, 231 Judd Rd, Easton, CT 06612-1025 *Tel:* 203-445-1511 *Fax:* 203-445-1411 *E-mail:* sales@publishersgraphics.com *Web Site:* www.publishersgraphics.com, pg 584

Publishers Information Bureau (PIB)®, 757 Third Ave, 11th fl, New York, NY 10017 *Tel:* 212-872-3745; 212-872-3700 (MPA) *E-mail:* infocenter@magazine.org *Web Site:* www.magazine.org, pg 617

Publishing Certificate Program at City College, Division of Humanities NAC 5225, City College of New York, New York, NY 10031 *Tel:* 212-650-7925 *Fax:* 212-650-7912 *E-mail:* ccnypub@aol.com *Web Site:* www.ccny.cuny.edu/publishing_certificate/index.html, pg 662

The Publishing Game, PO Box 590239, Newton, MA 02459-0002 *Tel:* 617-630-0945 *Fax:* 617-630-0945 (call first) *E-mail:* info@publishinggame.com; workshops@publishinggame.com *Web Site:* www.publishinggame.com, pg 654

Publishing Professionals Network, 9328 Elk Grove, Suite 105-250, Elk Grove, CA 95624 *Tel:* 415-279-2334 *E-mail:* operations@pubpronetwork.org *Web Site:* www.pubpronetwork.org, pg 617

Publishing Resources Inc, 425 Carr 693, PMB 160, Dorado, PR 00646 *Tel:* 787-626-0607 *Toll Free Fax:* 866-547-3005 *E-mail:* pri@chevako.net *Web Site:* www.publishingresources.net, pg 533

Publishing Services, 525 E 86 St, Suite 8-E, New York, NY 10028 *Tel:* 212-535-6248 *Fax:* 212-988-1999 *E-mail:* publishingservices@mac.com, pg 533, 568

Publishing Synthesis Ltd, 39 Crosby St, New York, NY 10013 *Tel:* 212-219-0135 *Fax:* 212-219-0136 *E-mail:* mainmail@pubsyn.com *Web Site:* www.pubsyn.com, pg 533

The Publishing Triangle Literary Awards, 332 Bleecker St, Suite D-36, New York, NY 10014 *E-mail:* publishingtriangle@gmail.com *Web Site:* www.publishingtriangle.org, pg 722

PubWest Book Design Awards, 17501 Hill Way, Lake Oswego, OR 97035 *Tel:* 503-901-9865 *Fax:* 602-234-3062 *Web Site:* pubwest.org, pg 722

Puddingstone Literary, Authors' Agents, 11 Mabro Dr, Denville, NJ 07834-9607 *Tel:* 973-366-3622, pg 569

Puffin Books, 345 Hudson St, New York, NY 10014 *Tel:* 212-366-2000 *E-mail:* online@penguinputnam.com *Web Site:* www.penguinputnam.com; us.penguingroup.com, pg 200

Pulitzer Prizes, 709 Journalism Bldg, Columbia University, 2950 Broadway, New York, NY 10027 *Tel:* 212-854-3841 *Fax:* 212-854-3342 *E-mail:* pulitzer@pulitzer.org *Web Site:* www.pulitzer.org, pg 722

Purdue University Press, Stewart Ctr 370, 504 W State St, West Lafayette, IN 47907-2058 *Tel:* 765-494-2038 *Fax:* 765-496-2442 *E-mail:* pupress@purdue.edu *Web Site:* www.thepress.purdue.edu, pg 200

Pureplay Press, 195 26 Ave, No 2, San Francisco, CA 94121 *Tel:* 310-597-0328 *E-mail:* info@pureplaypress.com *Web Site:* www.pureplaypress.com, pg 200

Purich Publishing Ltd, PO Box 23032, Market Mall Postal Outlet, Saskatoon, SK S7J 5H3, Canada *Tel:* 306-373-5311 *Fax:* 306-373-5315 *E-mail:* purich@sasktel.net *Web Site:* www.purichpublishing.com, pg 496

Purple House Press, 8100 US Hwy 62 E, Cynthiana, KY 41031 *Tel:* 859-235-9970 *Web Site:* www.purplehousepress.com, pg 200

Purple Mountain Press Ltd, 1060 Main St, Fleischmanns, NY 12430 *Tel:* 845-254-4062 *Toll Free Tel:* 800-325-2665 (orders) *Fax:* 845-254-4476 *E-mail:* purple@catskill.net *Web Site:* www.catskill.net/purple, pg 201

Purple Pomegranate Productions, 60 Haight St, San Francisco, CA 94102 *Tel:* 415-864-2600 *Fax:* 415-552-8325 *E-mail:* sf@jewsforjesus.org *Web Site:* www.jewsforjesus.org, pg 201

Pushcart Press, PO Box 380, Wainscott, NY 11975-0380 *Tel:* 631-324-9300, pg 201

Pushcart Prize: Best of the Small Presses, PO Box 380, Wainscott, NY 11975-0380 *Tel:* 631-324-9300, pg 722

Putnam Berkley Audio, 375 Hudson St, New York, NY 10014 *Tel:* 212-366-2000 *Fax:* 212-366-2666 *E-mail:* online@penguinputnam.com *Web Site:* www.penguinputnam.com; us.penguingroup.com, pg 201

The Putnam Publishing Group, 375 Hudson St, New York, NY 10014 *Tel:* 212-366-2000 *Toll Free Tel:* 800-631-8571 *Fax:* 212-366-2643 *E-mail:* online@penguinputnam.com *Web Site:* www.penguinputnam.com; us.penguingroup.com, pg 201

GP Putnam's Sons (Children's), 345 Hudson St, New York, NY 10014 *Tel:* 212-366-2000 *Fax:* 212-414-3393 *E-mail:* online@penguinputnam.com *Web Site:* us.penguingroup.com, pg 201

GP Putnam's Sons (Hardcover), 375 Hudson St, New York, NY 10014 *Tel:* 212-366-2000 *E-mail:* online@penguinputnam.com *Web Site:* us.penguingroup.com, pg 201

PNWA Writers Conference, 1420 NW Gilman Blvd, Suite 2, PMB 2717, Issaquah, WA 98027 *Tel:* 425-673-2665 *E-mail:* pnwa@pnwa.org *Web Site:* www.pnwa.org, pg 654

Pyncheon House, 6 University Dr, Suite 105, Amherst, MA 01002, pg 201

QA International (QAI), 329 De la Commune W, 3rd fl, Montreal, QC H2Y 2E1, Canada *Tel:* 514-499-3000 *Fax:* 514-499-3010 *Web Site:* www.qa-international.com, pg 496

Robert Quackenbush's Children's Book Writing & Illustration Workshops, 223 E 78 St, New York, NY 10075 *Tel:* 212-744-3822 *E-mail:* rqstudios@aol.com *Web Site:* www.rquackenbush.com, pg 654

Quackenworth Publishing, PO Box 4747, Culver City, CA 90231-4747 *Tel:* 310-945-5634 *Toll Free Tel:* 888-701-4991 *Fax:* 310-945-5709 *Toll Free Fax:* 888-892-6339 *E-mail:* info@quackenworth.com *Web Site:* www.quackenworth.com; www.wittybittybunch.com, pg 201

Quail Ridge Press, 101 Brooks Dr, Brandon, MS 39042 *Tel:* 601-825-2063 *Toll Free Tel:* 800-343-1583 *Fax:* 601-825-3091 *Toll Free Fax:* 800-864-1082 *E-mail:* info@quailridge.com *Web Site:* quailridge.com, pg 201

Quality Medical Publishing Inc, 2248 Welsch Industrial Ct, St Louis, MO 63146-4222 *Tel:* 314-878-7808 *Toll Free Tel:* 800-348-7808 *Fax:* 314-878-9937 *E-mail:* qmp@qmp.com *Web Site:* www.qmp.com, pg 201

The Quarasan Group Inc, 405 W Superior St, Chicago, IL 60654 *Tel:* 312-981-2500 *E-mail:* info@quarasan.com *Web Site:* www.quarasan.com, pg 533

Quarto Publishing Group USA Inc, 400 First Ave N, Suite 300, Minneapolis, MN 55401 *Tel:* 612-344-8100 *Toll Free Tel:* 800-328-0590 (sales); 800-458-0454 *Fax:* 612-344-8691 *E-mail:* sales@creativepub.com *Web Site:* quartoknows.com, pg 201

Quattro Books Inc, Centre for Social Innovation, 2nd fl, 720 Bathurst St, Toronto, ON M5S 2R4, Canada *Tel:* 647-748-7484 *E-mail:* info@quattrobooks.ca *Web Site:* www.quattrobooks.ca, pg 496

Quebec Dans Le Monde, 335, rue Saint-Joseph E, bureau 600, Quebec, QC G1K 3B4, Canada *Tel:* 418-659-5540 *Fax:* 418-659-4143 *E-mail:* info@quebecmonde.com *Web Site:* www.quebecmonde.com, pg 497

Quebec Writers' Federation (QWF), 1200 Atwater Ave, Suite 3, Westmount, QC H3Z 1X4, Canada *Tel:* 514-933-0878 *E-mail:* info@qwf.org *Web Site:* www.qwf.org, pg 617

Quicksilver Productions, PO Box 340, Ashland, OR 97520-0012 *Tel:* 541-482-5343 *Toll Free Fax:* 888-974-6462 *E-mail:* celestialcalendars@email.com *Web Site:* www.quicksilverproductions.com, pg 202

Quincannon Publishing Group, PO Box 8100, Glen Ridge, NJ 07028-8100 *Tel:* 973-380-9942 *E-mail:* editors@quincannongroup.com *Web Site:* www.quincannongroup.com, pg 202

Quintessence Publishing Co Inc, 4350 Chandler Dr, Hanover Park, IL 60133 *Tel:* 630-736-3600 *Toll Free Tel:* 800-621-0387 *Fax:* 630-736-3633 *E-mail:* contact@quintbook.com; service@quintbook.com *Web Site:* www.quintpub.com, pg 202

Quirk Books, 215 Church St, Philadelphia, PA 19106 *Tel:* 215-627-3581 *Fax:* 215-627-5220 *E-mail:* general@quirkbooks.com *Web Site:* www.quirkbooks.com, pg 202

Quite Specific Media Group Ltd, 7373 Pyramid Place, Hollywood, CA 90046 *Tel:* 323-851-5797 *Fax:* 323-851-5798 *E-mail:* info@quitespecificmedia.com *Web Site:* www.quitespecificmedia.com, pg 202

Quixote Press, 3544 Black St, Wever, IA 52658 *Tel:* 319-372-7480 *Toll Free Tel:* 800-571-2665 *Fax:* 319-372-7485 *E-mail:* heartsntummies@gmail.com; potpress@gmail.com, pg 202

QWF Literary Awards, 1200 Atwater Ave, Suite 3, Westmount, QC H3Z 1X4, Canada *Tel:* 514-933-0878 *E-mail:* info@qwf.org *Web Site:* www.qwf.org, pg 722

Susan Rabiner Literary Agency Inc, 315 W 39 St, Suite 1501, New York, NY 10018-3907 *Web Site:* RabinerLit.com, pg 569

Miriam Rachimi Memorial, 1194 Hume Rd, Hume, VA 22639-1806 *E-mail:* poetryinva@aol.com *Web Site:* www.poetrysocietyofvirginia.org, pg 722

Rada Press Inc, One Richdale Ave, Unit 10, Cambridge, MA 02140 *Tel:* 651-645-3304 *E-mail:* info@radapress.com *Web Site:* www.radapress.com, pg 202

Radcliffe Fellowship, 8 Garden St, Cambridge, MA 02138 *Tel:* 617-496-1324 (application office) *Fax:* 617-495-8136 *Web Site:* www.radcliffe.harvard.edu, pg 723

Thomas Head Raddall Atlantic Fiction Award, 1113 Marginal Rd, Halifax, NS B3H 4P7, Canada *Tel:* 902-423-8116 *Fax:* 902-422-0881 *E-mail:* contact@writers.ns.ca *Web Site:* www.writers.ns.ca, pg 723

Radix Press, 11715 Bandlon Dr, Houston, TX 77072 *Tel:* 281-879-5688 *Web Site:* www.specialforcesbooks.com, pg 202

Jane Rafal Editing Associates, 325 Forest Ridge Dr, Scottsville, VA 24590 *Tel:* 434-286-6949, pg 533

The Ragan Old North State Award Cup for Nonfiction, 4610 Mail Service Ctr, Raleigh, NC 27699-4610 *Tel:* 919-807-7290 *Fax:* 919-733-8807 *Web Site:* www.history.ncdcr.gov/affiliates/lit-hist/awards/awards.htm, pg 723

Rainbow Books Inc, PO Box 430, Highland City, FL 33846 *Tel:* 863-648-4420 *Fax:* 863-647-5951 *E-mail:* info@rainbowbooksinc.com *Web Site:* www.rainbowbooksinc.com, pg 202

Rainbow Publishers, PO Box 261129, San Diego, CA 92196 *Tel:* 858-277-1167 *Toll Free Tel:* 800-323-7337 *Toll Free Fax:* 800-331-0297 *E-mail:* info@rainbowpublishers.com; editor@rainbowpublishers.com (edit dept) *Web Site:* www.rainbowpublishers.com, pg 203

Raines & Raines, 103 Kenyon Rd, Medusa, NY 12120 *Tel:* 518-239-8311 *Fax:* 518-239-6029, pg 569

Raiziss/de Palchi Fellowship, 75 Maiden Lane, Suite 901, New York, NY 10038 *Tel:* 212-274-0343 *Fax:* 212-274-9427 *E-mail:* academy@poets.org *Web Site:* www.poets.org, pg 723

Sir Walter Raleigh Award for Fiction, 4610 Mail Service Ctr, Raleigh, NC 27699-4610 *Tel:* 919-807-7290 *Fax:* 919-733-8807, pg 723

Jerry Ralya, 7909 Vt Rte 14, Craftsbury Common, VT 05827 *Tel:* 802-586-7514 *E-mail:* jerryralya@gmail.com, pg 533

Ram Publishing Co, 1881 W State St, Garland, TX 75042 *Tel:* 972-494-6151 *Toll Free Tel:* 800-527-4011 *Fax:* 972-494-1881 *E-mail:* sales@garrett.com *Web Site:* www.garrett.com, pg 203

RAND Corp, 1776 Main St, Santa Monica, CA 90407-2138 *Tel:* 310-393-0411 *Fax:* 310-393-4818 *Web Site:* www.rand.org, pg 203

Rand McNally, 9855 Woods Dr, Skokie, IL 60077 *Tel:* 847-329-8100 *Toll Free Tel:* 800-678-7263 *Fax:* 847-329-6139 *E-mail:* ctsales@randmcnally.com; mediarelations@randmcnally.com *Web Site:* www.randmcnally.com, pg 203

Peter E Randall Publisher, 5 Greenleaf Woods Dr, Suite 102, Portsmouth, NH 03801 *Tel:* 603-431-5667 *Fax:* 603-431-3566 *E-mail:* media@perpublisher.com *Web Site:* www.perpublisher.com, pg 203

Random House Children's Books, 1745 Broadway, New York, NY 10019 *Tel:* 212-782-9000 *Toll Free Tel:* 800-200-3552 *Fax:* 212-782-9452 *Web Site:* randomhousekids.com, pg 203

Random House Large Print, 1745 Broadway, New York, NY 10019 *Tel:* 212-782-9000 *Fax:* 212-782-9484, pg 204

Random House Publishing Group, 1745 Broadway, New York, NY 10019 *Toll Free Tel:* 800-200-3552 *Web Site:* atrandom.com, pg 204

Random House Reference/Random House Puzzles & Games/House of Collectibles, 1745 Broadway, New York, NY 10019 *Toll Free Tel:* 800-733-3000 *Toll Free Fax:* 800-659-2436 *E-mail:* words@random.com; puzzles@random.com, pg 204

Ransom Note Press, 143 E Ridgewood Ave, Box 419, Ridgewood, NJ 07451 *Tel:* 201-835-2790 *E-mail:* editorial@ransomnotepress.com *Web Site:* www.ransomnotepress.com, pg 508

Gerald & Cullen Rapp, 420 Lexington Ave, New York, NY 10170 *Tel:* 212-889-3337 *Fax:* 212-889-3341 *E-mail:* info@rappart.com *Web Site:* www.rappart.com, pg 584

Rattapallax Press, 217 Thompson St, Suite 353, New York, NY 10012 *E-mail:* info@rattapallax.com *Web Site:* www.rattapallax.com, pg 204

Raven Award, 1140 Broadway, Suite 1507, New York, NY 10001 *Tel:* 212-888-8171 *Fax:* 212-888-8107 *E-mail:* mwa@mysterywriters.org *Web Site:* www.mysterywriters.org, pg 723

Raven Productions Inc, PO Box 188, Ely, MN 55731 *Tel:* 218-365-3375 *Fax:* 678-306-3375 *E-mail:* raven@ravenwords.com; order@ravenwords.com *Web Site:* www.ravenwords.com, pg 205

Raven Publishing Inc, 125 Cherry Creek Rd, Norris, MT 59745 *Tel:* 406-685-3545 *Toll Free Tel:* 866-685-3545 *Fax:* 406-685-3599 *E-mail:* info@ravenpublishing.net *Web Site:* www.ravenpublishing.net, pg 205

Raven Tree Press, 1400 Miller Pkwy, McHenry, IL 60050-7030 *Tel:* 815-363-3582 *Toll Free Tel:* 800-323-8270; 877-256-0579 *Fax:* 815-363-2948 *Toll Free Fax:* 800-909-9901 *E-mail:* raven@raventreepress.com; raven@deltapublishing.com *Web Site:* www.raventreepress.com, pg 205

Ravenhawk™ Books, 8364 E Balfour Place, Tucson, AZ 85710 *Tel:* 520-296-4491 *Fax:* 520-296-4491 *E-mail:* ravenhawk6dof@yahoo.com *Web Site:* 6dofsolutions.com, pg 205

Charlotte Cecil Raymond, Literary Agent, 32 Bradlee Rd, Marblehead, MA 01945 *Tel:* 781-631-6722 *Fax:* 781-631-6722 *E-mail:* raymondliterary@gmail.com, pg 569

Rayve Productions Inc, PO Box 726, Windsor, CA 95492 *Tel:* 707-838-6200 *Toll Free Tel:* 800-852-4890 *Fax:* 707-838-2220 *E-mail:* rayvepro@aol.com *Web Site:* www.rayveproductions.com; www.foodandwinebooks.com, pg 205

Razorbill, 345 Hudson St, New York, NY 10014 *Tel:* 212-366-2000, pg 205

RBC Bronwen Wallace Award for Emerging Writers, 460 Richmond St W, Suite 600, Toronto, ON M5V 1Y1, Canada *Tel:* 416-504-8222 *Toll Free Tel:* 877-906-6548 *Fax:* 416-504-9090 *E-mail:* info@writerstrust.com *Web Site:* www.writerstrust.com, pg 723

The Rea Award for the Short Story, 53 W Church Hill Rd, Washington, CT 06794 *Web Site:* reaaward.org, pg 723

Reader's Digest Association Canada ULC (Selection du Reader's Digest Canada SRL), 1100 Rene Levesque Blvd W, Montreal, QC H3B 5H5, Canada *Tel:* 514-940-0751 *Toll Free Tel:* 866-236-7789 (cust serv) *Fax:* 514-940-3637 *E-mail:* erdcustserv@cdsfulfillment.com *Web Site:* www.readersdigest.ca, pg 497

The Reader's Digest Association Inc, 750 Third Ave, New York, NY 10017 *Tel:* 914-238-1000; 646-293-6284 *Toll Free Tel:* 800-310-6261 (cust serv) *Fax:* 914-238-4559 *Web Site:* www.rd.com; www.rda.com, pg 205

Reader's Digest General Books, Reader's Digest Rd, Pleasantville, NY 10570-7000 *Tel:* 914-238-1000 *Toll Free Tel:* 800-304-2807 (cust serv) *Fax:* 914-244-7436, pg 205

Reader's Digest Trade Books, 44 S Broadway, White Plains, NY 10601 *Tel:* 914-244-7503 *Fax:* 914-244-4841 *Web Site:* www.rd.com, pg 205

Reader's Digest USA Select Editions, 44 S Broadway, 7th fl, White Plains, NY 10601 *Tel:* 914-238-1000 *Toll Free Tel:* 800-304-2807 (cust serv) *Fax:* 914-831-1560 *Web Site:* www.rda.com/readers-digest-select-editions, pg 205

The Reading Component, 3900 Parkview Lane, 3B, Irvine, CA 92612-2003 *Tel:* 949-387-6330, pg 533

Recorded Books LLC, 270 Skipjack Rd, Prince Frederick, MD 20678 *Tel:* 410-535-5590 *Toll Free Tel:* 800-638-1304; 877-732-2898 *Fax:* 410-535-5499 *E-mail:* customerservice@recordedbooks.com *Web Site:* www.recordedbooks.com, pg 206

Red Chair Press, PO Box 333, South Egremont, MA 01258-0333 *Toll Free Tel:* 888-327-2141 (ext 110) *Toll Free Fax:* 888-533-4037 *E-mail:* info@redchairpress.com *Web Site:* www.redchairpress.com, pg 206

Red Deer Press Inc, 195 Allstate Pkwy, Markham, ON L3R 4T8, Canada *Tel:* 905-477-9700 *Toll Free Tel:* 800-387-9776 (orders) *Fax:* 905-477-2834 *Toll Free Fax:* 800-260-9777 (orders) *E-mail:* rdp@reddeerpress.com; bookinfo@fitzhenry.ca *Web Site:* www.reddeerpress.com, pg 497

Red Dust Inc, 1148 Fifth Ave, New York, NY 10128 *Tel:* 212-348-4388 *Web Site:* www.reddustbooks.com, pg 206

Red Hen Press, PO Box 40820, Pasadena, CA 91114 *Tel:* 626-356-4760 *Fax:* 626-356-9974 *Web Site:* www.redhen.org, pg 206

Red Moon Press, PO Box 2461, Winchester, VA 22604-1661 *Tel:* 540-722-2156 *Web Site:* www.redmoonpress.com, pg 206

Red Rock Press, 331 W 57 St, Suite 175, New York, NY 10019 *Tel:* 212-362-8304 *Fax:* 212-362-6216 *E-mail:* info@redrockpress.com *Web Site:* www.redrockpress.com, pg 206

Red Sea Press Inc, 541 W Ingham Ave, Suite B, Trenton, NJ 08638 *Tel:* 609-695-3200 *Fax:* 609-695-6466 *E-mail:* customerservice@africaworldpressbooks.com *Web Site:* www.africaworldpressbooks.com, pg 206

Red Wheel/Weiser/Conari, 65 Parker St, Suite 7, Newburyport, MA 01950 *Tel:* 978-465-0504 *Toll Free Tel:* 800-423-7087 (orders) *Fax:* 978-465-0243 *E-mail:* info@rwwbooks.com *Web Site:* www.redwheelweiser.com, pg 206

RedBone Press, PO Box 15571, Washington, DC 20003 *Tel:* 202-667-0392 *Fax:* 301-588-0588 *E-mail:* info@redbonepress.com *Web Site:* www.redbonepress.com, pg 206

Redleaf Press, 10 Yorkton Ct, St Paul, MN 55117 *Tel:* 651-641-0508 *Toll Free Tel:* 800-423-8309 *Toll Free Fax:* 800-641-0115 *Web Site:* www.redleafpress.org, pg 206

Robert D Reed Publishers, PO Box 1992, Bandon, OR 97411-1192 *Tel:* 541-347-9882 *Fax:* 541-347-9883 *E-mail:* 4bobreed@msn.com *Web Site:* www.rdrpublishers.com, pg 207

Robert F Reed Technology Medal, 200 Deer Run Rd, Sewickley, PA 15143-2324 *Tel:* 412-259-1705 *Toll Free Tel:* 800-910-4283 (ext 705) *Fax:* 412-749-9890 *E-mail:* printing@printing.org *Web Site:* www.printing.org/reedaward, pg 723

Reedswain Inc, 88 Wells Rd, Spring City, PA 19475 *Tel:* 610-495-9578 *Toll Free Tel:* 800-331-5191 *Fax:* 610-495-6632 *E-mail:* orders@reedswain.com *Web Site:* www.reedswain.com, pg 207

Rees Literary Agency, 14 Beacon St, Suite 710, Boston, MA 02108 *Tel:* 617-227-9014 *Fax:* 617-227-8762 *E-mail:* reesagency@reesagency.com *Web Site:* reesagency.com, pg 569

The Re-evaluation Counseling Communities, 719 Second Ave N, Seattle, WA 98109 *Tel:* 206-284-0311 *Fax:* 206-284-8429 *E-mail:* ircc@rc.org *Web Site:* www.rc.org, pg 207

Referee Books, 2017 Lathrop Ave, Racine, WI 53405 *Tel:* 262-632-8855 *Toll Free Tel:* 800-733-6100 *Fax:* 262-632-5460 *E-mail:* questions@referee.com *Web Site:* www.referee.com, pg 207

Reference Publications Inc, 218 Saint Clair River Dr, Algonac, MI 48001 *Tel:* 810-794-5722 *Fax:* 810-794-7463 *E-mail:* referencepub@sbcglobal.net, pg 207

Reference Service Press, 5000 Windplay Dr, Suite 4, El Dorado Hills, CA 95762-9319 *Tel:* 916-939-9620 *Fax:* 916-939-9626 *E-mail:* info@rspfunding.com *Web Site:* www.rspfunding.com, pg 207

ReferencePoint Press Inc, 17150 Via del Campo, Suite 205, San Diego, CA 92127 *Tel:* 858-618-1314 *Toll Free Tel:* 888-479-6436 *Fax:* 858-618-1730 *E-mail:* orders@referencepointpress.com *Web Site:* www.referencepointpress.com, pg 207

Reformation Heritage Books, 2965 Leonard St NE, Grand Rapids, MI 49525 *Tel:* 616-977-0889 *Fax:* 616-285-3246 *E-mail:* orders@heritagebooks.org *Web Site:* www.heritagebooks.org, pg 207

Regal Books, 1957 Eastman Ave, Ventura, CA 93003 *Tel:* 805-644-9721 *Toll Free Tel:* 800-446-7735 (orders) *Web Site:* www.regalbooks.com; www.gospellight.com, pg 207

Regal Crest Enterprises LLC, 229 Sheridan Loop, Belton, TX 76513 *Tel:* 409-527-1188 *Toll Free Fax:* 866-294-9628 *E-mail:* info@regalcrestbooks.biz *Web Site:* www.regalcrest.biz, pg 207

Regina Medal Award, 8550 United Plaza Blvd, Suite 1001, Baton Rouge, LA 70809-2256 *Tel:* 225-408-4417 *E-mail:* cla2@cathla.org *Web Site:* www.cathla.org, pg 723

Regnery Publishing Inc, 300 New Jersey Ave NW, Washington, DC 20001 *Tel:* 202-216-0600 *Toll Free Tel:* 888-219-4747 *Fax:* 202-216-0612 *Web Site:* www.regnery.com, pg 208

Regular Baptist Press, 1300 N Meacham Rd, Schaumburg, IL 60173-4806 *Tel:* 847-843-1600 *Toll Free Tel:* 800-727-4440 (orders only); 888-588-1600 *Fax:* 847-843-3757 *E-mail:* rbp@garbc.org *Web Site:* www.regularbaptistpress.org, pg 208

Kerry Reilly: Representatives, 1826 Asheville Place, Charlotte, NC 28203 *Tel:* 704-372-6007 *E-mail:* kerry@reillyreps.com *Web Site:* www.reillyreps.com, pg 584

ReIMAGINE the MAGIC Annual Summer Conference, 274 Madison Ave, Suite 1202, New York, NY 10016 *Tel:* 917-720-6959 *E-mail:* iwwgquestions@gmail.com *Web Site:* www.iwwg.org, pg 654

Marian Reiner, 71 Disbrow Lane, New Rochelle, NY 10804 *Tel:* 914-235-7808 *Fax:* 914-576-1432 *E-mail:* mreinerlit@aol.com, pg 569

Nathan Reingold Prize, 440 Geddes Hall, Notre Dame, IN 46556 *Tel:* 574-631-1194 *Fax:* 574-631-1533 *E-mail:* info@hssonline.org *Web Site:* www.hssonline.org, pg 723

Renaissance House, 465 Westview Ave, Englewood, NJ 07631 *Tel:* 201-408-4048 *Fax:* 201-408-5011 *E-mail:* info@renaissancehouse.net *Web Site:* www.renaissancehouse.net, pg 208

Renaissance House, 465 Westview Ave, Englewood, NJ 07631 *Tel:* 201-408-4048 *Fax:* 201-408-5011 *E-mail:* laredo@renaissancehouse.net; info@renaissancehouse.net *Web Site:* www.renaissancehouse.net, pg 584

Renaissance Literary & Talent, PO Box 17379, Beverly Hills, CA 90209 *Tel:* 323-848-8305 *Fax:* 424-298-2588 *E-mail:* query@renaissancemgmt.net *Web Site:* www.facebook.com/RenaissanceLiteraryTalent, pg 569

The Amy Rennert Agency Inc, 1550 Tiburon Blvd, Suite 302, Tiburon, CA 94920 *Tel:* 415-789-8955 *E-mail:* queries@amyrennert.com *Web Site:* amyrennert.com, pg 569

Arthur Rense Prize, 633 W 155 St, New York, NY 10032 *Tel:* 212-368-5900 *Fax:* 212-491-4615 *E-mail:* academy@artsandletters.org *Web Site:* www.artsandletters.org, pg 723

Reporters Committee for Freedom of the Press, 1101 Wilson Blvd, Suite 1100, Arlington, VA 22209-1817 *Tel:* 703-807-2100 *Toll Free Tel:* 800-336-4243 *Fax:* 703-807-2109 *E-mail:* info@rcfp.org *Web Site:* www.rcfp.org, pg 617

Research & Education Association (REA), 61 Ethel Rd W, Piscataway, NJ 08854 *Tel:* 732-819-8880 *Fax:* 732-819-8808 (orders) *E-mail:* info@rea.com *Web Site:* www.rea.com, pg 208

Research Press, 2612 N Mattis Ave, Champaign, IL 61822 *Tel:* 217-352-3273 *Toll Free Tel:* 800-519-2707 *Fax:* 217-352-1221 *E-mail:* rp@researchpress.com; orders@researchpress.com *Web Site:* www.researchpress.com, pg 208

Research Research, 240 E 27 St, Suite 20-K, New York, NY 10016-9238 *Tel:* 212-779-9540 *Fax:* 212-779-9540 *E-mail:* ehtac@msn.com, pg 533

Residency, 454 E Hill Rd, Austerlitz, NY 12017 *Tel:* 518-392-3103; 518-392-4144 *E-mail:* apply@millaycolony.org *Web Site:* www.millaycolony.org, pg 723

Resilient Publishing, 406 S Third St, Boise, ID 83702 *Tel:* 208-258-9544 *E-mail:* submissions@resilientpublishing.com *Web Site:* www.resilientpublishing.com, pg 208

Resource Publications Inc, 160 E Virginia St, Suite 170, San Jose, CA 95112-5876 *Tel:* 408-286-8505 *Fax:* 408-287-8748 *E-mail:* orders@rpinet.com *Web Site:* www.rpinet.com, pg 208

Revell, PO Box 6287, Grand Rapids, MI 49516-6287 *Tel:* 616-676-9185 *Toll Free Tel:* 800-877-2665; 800-679-1957 *Fax:* 616-676-9573 *Web Site:* www.revellbooks.com, pg 208

Review & Herald Publishing Association, 55 W Oak Ridge Dr, Hagerstown, MD 21740 *Tel:* 301-393-3000 *Toll Free Tel:* 800-234-7630 *Fax:* 301-393-4055 (edit); 301-393-3222 (book div) *E-mail:* editorial@rhpa.org *Web Site:* www.reviewandherald.com, pg 208

Rhemalda Publishing, PO Box 1790, Moses Lake, WA 98837 *E-mail:* editor@rhemalda.com; customer_service@rhemalda.com *Web Site:* rhemalda.com, pg 208

Jodie Rhodes Literary Agency, 8840 Villa La Jolla Dr, Suite 315, La Jolla, CA 92037 *E-mail:* jrhodesl@san.rr.com, pg 569

The Harold U Ribalow Prize, 40 Wall St, New York, NY 10005-1387 *Tel:* 212-451-6286 *Fax:* 212-451-6257 *E-mail:* magtemp3@hadassah.org *Web Site:* www.hadassah.org/magazine, pg 724

Evelyn Richardson Memorial Literary Trust Award, 1113 Marginal Rd, Halifax, NS B3H 4P7, Canada *Tel:* 902-423-8116 *Fax:* 902-422-0881 *E-mail:* contact@writers.ns.ca *Web Site:* writers.ns.ca, pg 724

The Ridenhour Book Prize, 116 E 16 St, 8th fl, New York, NY 10003 *Tel:* 212-822-0250 *Fax:* 212-253-5356 *E-mail:* ridenhour@nationinstitute.org *Web Site:* www.ridenhour.org, pg 724

The Ridenhour Courage Prize, 116 E 16 St, 8th fl, New York, NY 10003 *Tel:* 212-822-0250 *Fax:* 212-253-5356 *E-mail:* ridenhour@nationinstitute.org *Web Site:* www.ridenhour.org, pg 724

The Ridenhour Prize for Truth-Telling, 116 E 16 St, 8th fl, New York, NY 10003 *Tel:* 212-822-0250 *Fax:* 212-253-5356 *E-mail:* ridenhour@nationinstitute.org *Web Site:* www.ridenhour.org, pg 724

Lynne Rienner Publishers Inc, 1800 30 St, Suite 314, Boulder, CO 80301 *Tel:* 303-444-6684 *Fax:* 303-444-0824 *E-mail:* questions@rienner.com; cservice@rienner.com *Web Site:* www.rienner.com, pg 208

John R Riina Literary Agency, 1055 W Joppa Rd, Unit 651, Towson, MD 21204-3777 *Tel:* 410-296-1499, pg 570

The Angela Rinaldi Literary Agency, PO Box 7877, Beverly Hills, CA 90212-7877 *Tel:* 310-842-7665 *Fax:* 310-837-8143 *E-mail:* info@rinaldiliterary.com (submissions) *Web Site:* www.rinaldiliterary.com, pg 570

Gwen Pharis Ringwood Award for Drama, 11759 Groat Rd, Edmonton, AB T5M 3K6, Canada *Tel:* 780-422-8174 *Toll Free Tel:* 800-665-5354 (AB only) *Fax:* 780-422-2663 (attn WGA) *E-mail:* mail@writersguild.ab.ca *Web Site:* www.writersguild.ab.ca, pg 724

Rio Nuevo Publishers, 451 N Bonita Ave, Tucson, AZ 85745 *Tel:* 520-623-9558 *Toll Free Tel:* 800-969-9558 *Fax:* 520-624-5888 *Toll Free Fax:* 800-715-5888 *E-mail:* info@rionuevo.com (cust serv) *Web Site:* www.rionuevo.com, pg 209

Rising Sun Publishing, PO Box 70906, Marietta, GA 30007-0906 *Tel:* 770-518-0369 *Toll Free Tel:* 800-524-2813 *Fax:* 770-587-0862 *E-mail:* info@rspublishing.com *Web Site:* www.rspublishing.com, pg 209

Ann Rittenberg Literary Agency Inc, 15 Maiden Lane, Suite 206, New York, NY 10038 *Tel:* 212-684-6936 *Fax:* 212-684-6929 *E-mail:* info@rittlit.com *Web Site:* www.rittlit.com, pg 570

Jack D Rittenhouse Award, 17501 Hill Way, Lake Oswego, OR 97035 *Tel:* 503-901-9865 *Web Site:* pubwest.org, pg 724

Judith Riven Literary Agent LLC, 250 W 16 St, Suite 4F, New York, NY 10011 *Tel:* 212-255-1009 *Fax:* 212-255-8547 *E-mail:* rivenlitqueries@gmail.com *Web Site:* rivenlit.com, pg 533, 570

Rivendell Books, PO Box 29348, St Louis, MO 63126-0348 *Tel:* 314-609-6534 *E-mail:* butch@rivendellbooks.com *Web Site:* www.rivendellbooks.com, pg 509

River City Publishing LLC, 1719 Mulberry St, Montgomery, AL 36106 *Tel:* 334-265-6753 *Fax:* 334-265-8880 *E-mail:* sales@rivercitypublishing.com *Web Site:* www.rivercitypublishing.com, pg 209

Riverdale Avenue Books (RAB), 5676 Riverdale Ave, Bronx, NY 10471 *Tel:* 212-279-6418 *Web Site:* www.riverdaleavebooks.com, pg 209

Riverhead Books (Hardcover), 375 Hudson St, New York, NY 10014 *Tel:* 212-366-2000 *E-mail:* online@penguinputnam.com *Web Site:* www.penguinputnam.com; us.penguingroup.com, pg 209

Riverhead Books (Trade Paperback), 375 Hudson St, New York, NY 10014 *Tel:* 212-366-2000 *E-mail:* online@penguinputnam.com *Web Site:* www.penguinputnam.com; us.penguingroup.com, pg 209

Riverside Literary Agency, 41 Simon Keets Rd, Leyden, MA 01337 *Tel:* 413-772-0067 *Fax:* 413-772-0969 *E-mail:* rivlit@sover.net *Web Site:* www.riversideliteraryagency.com, pg 570

Riverside Publishing, 3800 Golf Rd, Suite 200, Rolling Meadows, IL 60008 *Tel:* 630-467-7000 *Toll Free Tel:* 800-323-9540 *Fax:* 630-467-7192 (cust serv) *E-mail:* rpc_customer_service@hmhpub.com (cust serv) *Web Site:* www.riversidepublishing.com, pg 209

Rizzoli International Publications Inc, 300 Park Ave S, 4th fl, New York, NY 10010-5399 *Tel:* 212-387-3400 *Toll Free Tel:* 800-522-6657 (orders only) *Fax:* 212-387-3535 *E-mail:* publicity@rizzoliusa.com *Web Site:* www.rizzoliusa.com, pg 209

RLR Associates Ltd, 7 W 51 St, New York, NY 10019 *Tel:* 212-541-8641 *Fax:* 212-262-7084 *Web Site:* www.rlrassociates.net, pg 570

RMA, 85 Lincoln St, 1st fl, Meriden, CT 06451 *Tel:* 718-434-1893 *Web Site:* www.ricia.com, pg 570

The RoadRunner Press, 124 NW 32 St, Oklahoma City, OK 73118 *Tel:* 405-524-6205 *Fax:* 405-524-6312 *E-mail:* info@theroadrunnerpress.com; orders@theroadrunnerpress.com *Web Site:* www.theroadrunnerpress.com, pg 210

Roanoke-Chowan Award for Poetry, 4610 Mail Service Ctr, Raleigh, NC 27699-4610 *Tel:* 919-807-7290 *Fax:* 919-733-8807 *Web Site:* www.history.ncdcr.gov/affiliates/lit-hist/awards/awards.htm, pg 724

The Roanoke Review Fiction Contest, 221 College Lane, Salem, VA 24153 *E-mail:* review@roanoke.edu *Web Site:* roanokereview.wordpress.com, pg 724

Roaring Brook Press, 175 Fifth Ave, New York, NY 10010 *Tel:* 646-307-5151 *Web Site:* us.macmillan.com/roaringbrookpressaspx, pg 210

Roaring Forties Press, 1053 Santa Fe Ave, Berkeley, CA 94706 *Tel:* 510-527-5461 *E-mail:* info@roaringfortiespress.com *Web Site:* www.roaringfortiespress.com, pg 210

B J Robbins Literary Agency, 5130 Bellaire Ave, North Hollywood, CA 91607 *E-mail:* robbinsliterary@gmail.com, pg 570

The Roberts Group, 12803 Eastview Curve, Apple Valley, MN 55124 *Tel:* 952-322-4005 *E-mail:* info@editorialservice.com *Web Site:* www.editorialservice.com, pg 533

Rochester Institute of Technology, School of Print Media, 69 Lomb Memorial Dr, Rochester, NY 14623-5603 *Tel:* 585-475-2728; 585-475-5336 *Fax:* 585-475-5336 *E-mail:* spmofc@rit.edu *Web Site:* cias.rit.edu/printmedia, pg 662

James A Rock & Co Publishers, 900 S Irby St, Suite 508, Florence, SC 29501 *Toll Free Tel:* 800-411-2230 *Fax:* 843-395-5975 *E-mail:* jrock@rockpublishing.com *Web Site:* rockpublishing.com, pg 210

RockBench Publishing Corp, 6101 Stillmeadow Dr, Nashville, TN 37211-6518 *Tel:* 615-831-2277 *Fax:* 615-831-2212 *E-mail:* info@rockbench.com *Web Site:* www.rockbench.com, pg 210

The Rockefeller University Press, 1114 First Ave, 3rd fl, New York, NY 10065-8325 *Tel:* 212-327-7938 *Fax:* 212-327-8587 *E-mail:* rupress@rockefeller.edu *Web Site:* www.rupress.org, pg 210

Rockmill & Company, 647 Warren St, Brooklyn, NY 11217 *E-mail:* agentrockmill@yahoo.com, pg 570

Rocky Mountain Book Award, PO Box 42, Lethbridge, AB T1J 3Y3, Canada *Tel:* 403-381-7164 *E-mail:* rockymountainbookaward@shaw.ca *Web Site:* rmba.lethsd.ab.ca, pg 724

Rocky Mountain Books Ltd (RMB), 103-1075 Pendergast St, Victoria, BC V8V 0A1, Canada *Tel:* 250-360-0829 *Fax:* 250-386-0829 *Web Site:* www.rmbooks.com, pg 497

Rocky Mountain Mineral Law Foundation, 9191 Sheridan Blvd, Suite 203, Westminister, CO 80031 *Tel:* 303-321-8100 *Fax:* 303-321-7657 *E-mail:* info@rmmlf.org *Web Site:* www.rmmlf.org, pg 210

Rocky River Publishers LLC, PO Box 1679, Shepherdstown, WV 25443-1679 *Tel:* 304-876-1868 *Fax:* 304-263-2949 *E-mail:* rockyriverpublishers@citlink.net *Web Site:* www.rockyriver.com, pg 210

Rod & Staff Publishers Inc, Hwy 172, Crockett, KY 41413 *Tel:* 606-522-4348 *Fax:* 606-522-4896 *Toll Free Fax:* 800-643-1244 (ordering in US), pg 210

Rodale Inc, 400 S Tenth St, Emmaus, PA 18098 *Tel:* 610-967-5171 *Web Site:* www.rodaleinc.com, pg 210

Rogers Writers' Trust Fiction Prize, 460 Richmond St W, Suite 600, Toronto, ON M5V 1Y1, Canada *Tel:* 416-504-8222 *Toll Free Tel:* 877-906-6548 *Fax:* 416-504-9090 *E-mail:* info@writerstrust.com *Web Site:* www.writerstrust.com, pg 724

Linda Roghaar Literary Agency LLC, 133 High Point Dr, Amherst, MA 01002 *Tel:* 413-256-1921 *E-mail:* contact@lindaroghaar.com *Web Site:* www.lindaroghaar.com, pg 570

Sami Rohr Prize for Jewish Literature, 520 Eighth Ave, 4th fl, New York, NY 10018 *Tel:* 212-201-2920 *Fax:* 212-532-4952 *E-mail:* jbc@jewishbooks.org *Web Site:* www.jewishbookcouncil.org, pg 724

The Roistacher Literary Agency, 545 W 111 St, Suite 7-J, New York, NY 10025 *Tel:* 212-222-1405, pg 571

Roman Catholic Books, PO Box 2286, Fort Collins, CO 80522-2286 *Tel:* 970-490-2735 *Fax:* 904-212-1287 *Web Site:* www.booksforcatholics.com, pg 211

Romance Writers of America®, 14615 Benfer Rd, Houston, TX 77069 *Tel:* 832-717-5200 *Fax:* 832-717-5201 *E-mail:* info@rwa.org *Web Site:* www.rwa.org, pg 618

Romance Writers of America Annual Conference, 14615 Benfer Rd, Houston, TX 77069 *Tel:* 832-717-5200 *Fax:* 832-717-5201 *E-mail:* info@rwa.org *Web Site:* www.rwa.org, pg 654

Romance Writers of America Awards, 14615 Benfer Rd, Houston, TX 77069 *Tel:* 832-717-5200 *Fax:* 832-717-5201 *E-mail:* info@rwa.org *Web Site:* www.rwa.org, pg 724

Roncorp Music, PO Box 517, Glenmoore, PA 19343 *Tel:* 610-942-2370 *Fax:* 610-942-0660 *E-mail:* info@nemusicpub.com *Web Site:* www.nemusicpub.com, pg 211

Ronin Publishing Inc, PO Box 22900, Oakland, CA 94609 *Tel:* 510-420-3669 *Fax:* 510-420-3672 *E-mail:* ronin@roninpub.com *Web Site:* www.roninpub.com, pg 211

Ronsdale Press Ltd, 3350 W 21 Ave, Vancouver, BC V6S 1G7, Canada *Tel:* 604-738-4688 *Fax:* 604-731-4548 *E-mail:* ronsdale@shaw.ca *Web Site:* ronsdalepress.com, pg 497

Peter Rooney, 332 Bleecker St, PMB X-6, New York, NY 10014-2980 *Tel:* 917-376-1792 *Fax:* 212-226-8047 *E-mail:* magnetix@ix.netcom.com *Web Site:* www.magneticreports.com, pg 533

Robert Rose Inc, 120 Eglinton Ave E, Suite 800, Toronto, ON M4P 1E2, Canada *Tel:* 416-322-6552 *Fax:* 416-322-6936 *Web Site:* www.robertrose.ca, pg 497

Rosemont College, Graduate Publg Prog, 1400 Montgomery Ave, Rosemont, PA 19010 *Tel:* 610-527-0200 (ext 2336) *Fax:* 610-526-2964 *Web Site:* www.rosemont.edu, pg 662

The Rosen Publishing Group Inc, 29 E 21 St, New York, NY 10010 *Tel:* 212-777-3017 *Toll Free Tel:* 800-237-9932 *Toll Free Fax:* 888-436-4643 *E-mail:* info@rosenpub.com *Web Site:* www.rosenpublishing.com, pg 211

Dorothy Sargent Rosenberg Poetry Prizes, PO Box 2306, Orinda, CA 94563 *Web Site:* www.dorothyprizes.org, pg 725

The Rosenberg Group, 23 Lincoln Ave, Marblehead, MA 01945 *Tel:* 781-990-1341 *Fax:* 781-990-1344 *Web Site:* www.rosenberggroup.com, pg 571

Rita Rosenkranz Literary Agency, 440 West End Ave, Suite 15D, New York, NY 10024-5358 *Tel:* 212-873-6333 *Fax:* 212-873-5225 *Web Site:* www.ritarosenkranzliteraryagency.com, pg 571

Rosenthal Family Foundation Awards, 633 W 155 St, New York, NY 10032 *Tel:* 212-368-5900 *Fax:* 212-491-4615 *E-mail:* academy@artsandletters.org *Web Site:* www.artsandletters.org, pg 725

Rosenthal Represents, 3850 Eddingham Ave, Calabasas, CA 91302 *Tel:* 818-222-5445 *Fax:* 818-222-5650 *E-mail:* eliselicenses@earthlink.net *Web Site:* www.rosenthalrepresents.com, pg 584

Ross Books, PO Box 4340, Berkeley, CA 94704-0340 *Tel:* 510-841-2474 *Fax:* 510-295-2531 *E-mail:* sales@rossbooks.com *Web Site:* www.rossbooks.com, pg 211

Ross Publishing LLC, 392 Central Park W, Suite 20-C, New York, NY 10025-5878 *Tel:* 212-765-8200 *E-mail:* info@rosspub.com *Web Site:* www.rosspub.com, pg 211

Margaret W Rossiter History of Women in Science Prize, 440 Geddes Hall, Notre Dame, IN 46556 *Tel:* 574-631-1194 *Fax:* 574-631-1533 *E-mail:* info@hssonline.org *Web Site:* www.hssonline.org, pg 725

Lois Roth Award, 26 Broadway, 3rd fl, New York, NY 10004-1789 *Tel:* 646-576-5141 *Fax:* 646-458-0030 *E-mail:* awards@mla.org *Web Site:* www.mla.org, pg 725

Rothstein Publishing, 4 Arapaho Rd, Brookfield, CT 06804-3104 *Tel:* 203-740-7400 *Toll Free Tel:* 888-768-4783 *Fax:* 203-740-7401 *E-mail:* info@rothstein.com *Web Site:* www.rothstein.com; www.rothsteinpublishing.com, pg 211

Jane Rotrosen Agency LLC, 318 E 51 St, New York, NY 10022 *Tel:* 212-593-4330 *Fax:* 212-935-6985 *Web Site:* janerotrosen.com, pg 571

Rough Guides, 375 Hudson St, New York, NY 10014 *Toll Free Tel:* 800-631-8571 *E-mail:* mail@roughguides.com *Web Site:* www.roughguides.com, pg 211

The Rough Notes Co Inc, 11690 Technology Dr, Carmel, IN 46032-5600 *Tel:* 317-582-1600 *Toll Free Tel:* 800-428-4384 (cust serv) *Fax:* 317-816-1000 *Toll Free Fax:* 800-321-1909 *E-mail:* rnc@roughnotes.com *Web Site:* www.roughnotes.com, pg 211

Routledge/Taylor & Francis, 711 Third Ave, 8th fl, New York, NY 10017 *Tel:* 212-216-7800 *Toll Free Tel:* 800-634-7064 (orders) *Fax:* 212-564-7854 *Web Site:* www.routledge.com, pg 211

Damaris Rowland, 115 Elm St, Unit 7b, Hatfield, MA 01038-3808 *Tel:* 413-247-6011 *E-mail:* nicholerowland5@mac.com, pg 571

Rowman & Littlefield Publishers Inc, 4501 Forbes Blvd, Suite 200, Lanham, MD 20706 *Tel:* 301-459-3366 *Toll Free Tel:* 800-462-6420 (cust serv) *Fax:* 301-429-5748 *Web Site:* www.rowmanlittlefield.com, pg 212

Dick Rowson, 4701 Connecticut Ave NW, Suite 503, Washington, DC 20008 *Tel:* 202-244-8104 *E-mail:* rcrowson2@aol.com, pg 533

Royal Fireworks Press, PO Box 399, Unionville, NY 10988 *Fax:* 845-726-3824 *E-mail:* mail@rfwp.com *Web Site:* www.rfwp.com, pg 212

Royal Ontario Museum Press, 100 Queen's Park, Toronto, ON M5S 2C6, Canada *Tel:* 416-586-8000 *Fax:* 416-586-5642 *E-mail:* info@rom.on.ca *Web Site:* www.rom.on.ca, pg 497

Royce Carlton Inc, 866 United Nations Plaza, Suite 587, New York, NY 10017-1880 *Tel:* 212-355-7700 *Toll Free Tel:* 800-LECTURE (532-8873) *Fax:* 212-888-8659 *E-mail:* info@roycecarlton.com *Web Site:* www.roycecarlton.com, pg 588

Lexi Rudnitsky Poetry Prize, 277 Broadway, Suite 708, New York, NY 10007 *Tel:* 212-260-9256 *Fax:* 212-267-3165 *E-mail:* info@perseabooks.com *Web Site:* www.perseabooks.com, pg 725

William B Ruggles Journalism Scholarship, 5211 Port Royal Rd, Suite 510, Springfield, VA 22151 *Tel:* 703-321-9606 *Fax:* 703-321-7143 *E-mail:* research@nilrr.org *Web Site:* www.nilrr.org, pg 725

Running Press Book Publishers, 2300 Chestnut St, Philadelphia, PA 19103-4399 *Tel:* 215-567-5080 *Toll Free Tel:* 800-343-4499 (cust serv & orders) *Fax:* 215-568-2919 *Toll Free Fax:* 800-453-2884 (cust serv & orders) *E-mail:* perseus.promos@perseusbooks.com *Web Site:* www.runningpress.com, pg 212

Russell Sage Foundation, 112 E 64 St, New York, NY 10065 *Tel:* 212-750-6000 *Toll Free Tel:* 800-524-6401 *Fax:* 212-371-4761 *E-mail:* info@rsage.org *Web Site:* www.russellsage.org, pg 212

Russian Information Service Inc, PO Box 567, Montpelier, VT 05601 *Tel:* 802-223-4955 *E-mail:* editors@russianlife.com *Web Site:* www.russianlife.com, pg 212

Rutgers University Press, 106 Somerset St, 3rd fl, New Brunswick, NJ 08901 *Tel:* 848-445-7762 *Toll Free Tel:* 800-848-6224 (orders only) *Fax:* 732-745-4935 (acqs, edit, mktg, perms & prodn) *Toll Free Fax:* 800-272-6817 (fulfillment) *Web Site:* rutgerspress.rutgers.edu, pg 212

The Cornelius Ryan Award, 40 W 45 St, New York, NY 10036 *Tel:* 212-626-9220 *Fax:* 212-626-9210 *Web Site:* www.opcofamerica.org, pg 725

Regina Ryan Books, 251 Central Park W, Suite 7-D, New York, NY 10024 *Tel:* 212-787-5589 *E-mail:* queries@reginaryanbooks.com *Web Site:* www.reginaryanbooks.com, pg 571

Sachem Publishing Associates Inc, 402 W Lyon Farm Dr, Greenwich, CT 06831 *Tel:* 203-813-3077 *Fax:* 203-531-2879 *E-mail:* sachempub@optonline.net, pg 533

Saddleback Educational Publishing, 3120-A Pullman St, Costa Mesa, CA 92626 *Tel:* 714-640-5200 *Toll Free Tel:* 888-SDLBACK (735-2225); 800-637-8715 *Fax:* 714-640-5297 *Toll Free Fax:* 888-734-4010 *E-mail:* contact@sdlback.com *Web Site:* www.sdlback.com, pg 213

William H Sadlier Inc, 9 Pine St, New York, NY 10005 *Tel:* 212-227-2120 *Toll Free Tel:* 800-221-5175 (cust serv) *Fax:* 212-312-6080 *E-mail:* customerservice@sadlier.com *Web Site:* www.sadlier.com, pg 213

SAE (Society of Automotive Engineers International), 400 Commonwealth Dr, Warrendale, PA 15096-0001 *Tel:* 724-776-4841; 724-776-4970 (outside US & CN) *Toll Free Tel:* 877-606-7323 (cust serv) *Fax:* 724-776-0790 (cust serv) *E-mail:* publications@sae.org; customerservice@sae.org *Web Site:* www.sae.org, pg 213

Safari Press, 15621 Chemical Lane, Bldg B, Huntington Beach, CA 92649 *Tel:* 714-894-9080 *Toll Free Tel:* 800-451-4788 *Fax:* 714-894-4949 *E-mail:* info@safaripress.com *Web Site:* www.safaripress.com, pg 213

Safer Society Foundation Inc, 29 Union St, Brandon, VT 05733 *Tel:* 802-247-3132 *Fax:* 802-247-4233 *E-mail:* info@safersociety.org *Web Site:* www.safersociety.org, pg 213

Sagamore Publishing LLC, 1807 Federal Dr, Urbana, IL 61801 *Tel:* 217-359-5940 *Toll Free Tel:* 800-327-5557 (orders) *Fax:* 217-359-5975 *E-mail:* books@sagamorepub.com *Web Site:* www.sagamorepub.com, pg 213

SAGE Publications, 2455 Teller Rd, Thousand Oaks, CA 91320 *Toll Free Tel:* 800-818-7243 *Toll Free Fax:* 800-583-2665 *E-mail:* info@sagepub.com *Web Site:* www.sagepub.com, pg 214

St Andrews College Press, 1700 Dogwood Mile, Laurinburg, NC 28352-5598 *Tel:* 910-277-5310 *Fax:* 910-277-5020 *E-mail:* press@sapc.edu *Web Site:* www.sapc.edu/sapress, pg 214

St Augustine's Press Inc, PO Box 2285, South Bend, IN 46680-2285 *Tel:* 574-291-3500 *Toll Free Tel:* 888-997-4994 *Fax:* 574-291-3700 *Web Site:* www.staugustine.net, pg 214

Saint Herman Press, 10 Beegum Gorge Rd, Platina, CA 96076 *Tel:* 530-352-4430 *Fax:* 530-352-4432 *E-mail:* stherman@stherman.com *Web Site:* www.stherman.com, pg 214

St James Press®, 27500 Drake Rd, Farmington Hills, MI 48331-3535 *Tel:* 248-699-4253 *Toll Free Tel:* 800-877-4253 (orders) *Fax:* 248-699-8035 *Toll Free Fax:* 800-414-5043 (orders) *E-mail:* gale.galeord@cengage.com *Web Site:* www.gale.cengage.com, pg 214

Guy Saint-Jean Editeur Inc, 3440 Blvd Industriel, Laval, QC H7L 4R9, Canada *Tel:* 450-663-1777 *Fax:* 450-663-6666 *E-mail:* info@saint-jeanediteur.com *Web Site:* www.saint-jeanediteur.com, pg 498

Saint Johann Press, 315 Schraalenburgh Rd, Haworth, NJ 07641 *Tel:* 201-387-1529 *Fax:* 201-501-0698 *Web Site:* www.stjohannpress.com, pg 214

St Joseph's University Press, 5600 City Ave, Philadelphia, PA 19131-1395 *Tel:* 610-660-3402 *Fax:* 610-660-3412 *E-mail:* sjupress@sju.edu *Web Site:* www.sjupress.com, pg 214

Saint Louis Literary Award, Pius XII Memorial Library, 3650 Lindell Blvd, St Louis, MO 63108 *Tel:* 314-977-3100 *Fax:* 314-977-3587 *E-mail:* slula@slu.edu *Web Site:* www.slu.edu/libraries/associates, pg 725

St Martin's Press, LLC, 175 Fifth Ave, New York, NY 10010 *Tel:* 646-307-5151 *Fax:* 212-420-9314 *E-mail:* firstname.lastname@macmillan.com *Web Site:* www.stmartins.com, pg 214

Saint Mary's Press, 702 Terrace Heights, Winona, MN 55987-1318 *Tel:* 507-457-7900 *Toll Free Tel:* 800-533-8095 *Fax:* 507-457-7990 *Toll Free Fax:* 800-344-9225 *E-mail:* smpress@smp.org *Web Site:* www.smp.org, pg 215

Saint Nectarios Press, 10300 Ashworth Ave N, Seattle, WA 98133-9410 *Tel:* 206-522-4471 *Toll Free Tel:* 800-643-4233 *Fax:* 206-523-0550 *E-mail:* orders@stnectariospress.com *Web Site:* www.stnectariospress.com, pg 215

St Pauls, 2187 Victory Blvd, Staten Island, NY 10314-6603 *Tel:* 718-761-0047 (edit & prodn); 718-698-2759 (mktg & billing) *Toll Free Tel:* 800-343-2522 *Fax:* 718-761-0057 *E-mail:* sales@stpauls.us; marketing@stpauls.us *Web Site:* www.stpauls.us, pg 215

Sts Judes imPress, 5537 Waterman Blvd, Suite 2-W, St Louis, MO 63112 *Tel:* 314-454-0064 *E-mail:* stjudes1@att.net, pg 215

Salem Press Inc, 2 University Plaza, Suite 310, Hackensack, NJ 07601 *Tel:* 201-968-0500 *Toll Free Tel:* 800-221-1592; 800-221-1592 *Fax:* 201-968-0511 *E-mail:* csr@salempress.com *Web Site:* salempress.com, pg 215

Salina Bookshelf Inc, 3120 N Caden Ct, Suite 4, Flagstaff, AZ 86004 *Toll Free Tel:* 877-527-0070 *Fax:* 928-526-0386 *Web Site:* www.salinabookshelf.com, pg 215

Barbara S Salz LLC Photo Research, 127 Prospect Place, South Orange, NJ 07079 *Tel:* 973-762-6486 *E-mail:* bsalz.photo@gmail.com, pg 533

Salzman International, 1751 Charles Ave, Arcata, CA 95521 *Tel:* 415-285-8267; 212-997-0115 (NY) *Fax:* 707-822-5500 *Web Site:* www.salzint.com, pg 584

Samhain Publishing Ltd, 11821 Mason Montgomery Rd, Suite 4-B, Cincinnati, OH 45249 *Tel:* 513-453-4688 *Fax:* 513-583-0191 *E-mail:* support@samhainpublishing.com *Web Site:* www.samhainpublishing.com, pg 215

SAMS Technical Publishing LLC, 9850 E 30 St, Indianapolis, IN 46229 *Tel:* 317-396-5336 *Toll Free Tel:* 800-428-7267 *Fax:* 317-489-3406 *Toll Free Fax:* 800-552-3910 *E-mail:* customercare@samswebsite.com *Web Site:* www.samswebsite.com, pg 216

Paul Samuelson, 117 Oak Dr, San Rafael, CA 94901 *Tel:* 415-459-5352; 415-517-0700 (cell) *Fax:* 415-459-5352 *E-mail:* paul@storywrangler.com *Web Site:* www.storywrangler.com, pg 533

San Diego Christian Writers' Guild Conference, PO Box 270403, San Diego, CA 92198 *Tel:* 760-294-3269 *Fax:* 760-294-3269 *E-mail:* info@sandiegocwg.org *Web Site:* www.sandiegocwg.org, pg 654

San Diego State University Press, Arts & Letters 283, 5500 Campanile Dr, San Diego, CA 92182-6020 *Tel:* 619-594-6220 (orders) *Web Site:* sdsupress.sdsu.edu, pg 216

San Francisco Writers Conference, 1029 Jones St, San Francisco, CA 94109 *Tel:* 415-673-0939 *E-mail:* sfwriterscon@aol.com *Web Site:* www.sfwriters.org, pg 654

San Francisco Writers Contest (SFWC), 1029 Jones St, San Francisco, CA 94109 *Tel:* 415-673-0939 *E-mail:* sfwriterscon@aol.com *Web Site:* www.sfwriters.org, pg 725

The Carl Sandburg Literary Awards, 20 N Michigan Ave, Suite 520, Chicago, IL 60602 *Tel:* 312-201-9830 *Fax:* 312-201-9833 *Web Site:* www.cplfoundation.org, pg 725

Victoria Sanders & Associates LLC, 241 Avenue of the Americas, Suite 11-H, New York, NY 10014 *Tel:* 212-633-8811 *Fax:* 212-633-0525 *E-mail:* queriesvsa@gmail.com *Web Site:* www.victoriasanders.com, pg 571

Ada Sanderson Memorial, 1194 Hume Rd, Hume, VA 22639-1806 *E-mail:* poetryinva@aol.com *Web Site:* www.poetrysocietyofvirginia.org, pg 725

Sandhills Writers' Series, Dept of Communications & Professional Writing, 2500 Walton Way, Augusta, GA 30904 *Tel:* 706-667-4437 *Fax:* 706-667-4770 *Web Site:* www.sandhills.aug.edu, pg 654

Sandlapper Publishing Inc, 1281 Amelia St NE, Orangeburg, SC 29115-5475 *Tel:* 803-531-1658 *Toll Free Tel:* 800-849-7263 (orders only) *Fax:* 803-534-5223 *Toll Free Fax:* 800-337-9420 *E-mail:* sales@sandlapperpublishing.com *Web Site:* www.sandlapperpublishing.com, pg 216

Mari Sandoz Award, PO Box 21756, Lincoln, NE 68542-1756 *E-mail:* nebraskalibraries@gmail.com *Web Site:* www.nebraskalibraries.org, pg 725

Ivan Sandrof Lifetime Achievement Award, 160 Varick St, 11th fl, New York, NY 10013 *E-mail:* info@bookcritics.org; membership@bookcritics.org (nominations from membs) *Web Site:* bookcritics.org, pg 725

Santa Barbara Book Promotion Workshop, PO Box 8206-240, Santa Barbara, CA 93118-8206 *Tel:* 805-968-7277 *Toll Free Tel:* 800-727-2782 *Fax:* 805-968-1379 *E-mail:* info@parapublishing.com *Web Site:* www.parapublishing.com, pg 655

Santa Monica Press LLC, 215 S Hwy 101, Suite 110, Solana Beach, CA 92075 *Tel:* 858-793-1890 *Toll Free Tel:* 800-784-9553 *Fax:* 858-777-0444 *E-mail:* books@santamonicapress.com *Web Site:* www.santamonicapress.com, pg 216

Santillana USA Publishing Co Inc, 2023 NW 84 Ave, Doral, FL 33122 *Tel:* 305-591-9522 *Toll Free Tel:* 800-245-8584 *Fax:* 305-591-9145 *Toll Free Fax:* 888-248-9518 *E-mail:* customerservice@santillanausa.com *Web Site:* www.santillanausa.com; www.alfaguara.net, pg 216

Sara Jordan Publishing, RPO Lakeport Box 28105, St Catharines, ON L2N 7P8, Canada *Tel:* 905-938-5050 *Toll Free Tel:* 800-567-7733 *Fax:* 905-938-9970 *Toll Free Fax:* 800-229-3855 *Web Site:* www.sara-jordan.com, pg 498

Sarabande Books Inc, 2234 Dundee Rd, Suite 200, Louisville, KY 40205 *Tel:* 502-458-4028 *Fax:* 502-458-4065 *E-mail:* info@sarabandebooks.org *Web Site:* www.sarabandebooks.org, pg 216

William Saroyan International Prize for Writing, Administrator, Saroyan Prize Committee, Stanford University Libraries, 557 Escondido Mall, Stanford, CA 94305-6004 *Tel:* 650-736-9538 *Web Site:* library.stanford.edu, pg 725

May Sarton Award, 2 Farrar St, Cambridge, MA 02138 *Tel:* 617-744-6034 *E-mail:* contests@nepoetryclub.org *Web Site:* www.nepoetryclub.org, pg 726

SAS Publishing, 100 SAS Campus Dr, Cary, NC 27513-2414 *Tel:* 919-677-8000 *Fax:* 919-677-4444 *E-mail:* saspress@sas.com *Web Site:* www.sas.com/publishing, pg 216

Saskatchewan Arts Board, 1355 Broad St, Regina, SK S4R 7V1, Canada *Tel:* 306-787-4056 *Toll Free Tel:* 800-667-7526 (Saskatchewan only) *Fax:* 306-787-4199 *E-mail:* info@artsboard.sk.ca *Web Site:* www.artsboard.sk.ca, pg 618

Sasquatch Books, 1904 S Main St, Suite 710, Seattle, WA 98101 *Tel:* 206-467-4300 *Toll Free Tel:* 800-775-0817 *Fax:* 206-467-4301 *E-mail:* custserv@sasquatchbooks.com *Web Site:* www.sasquatchbooks.com, pg 217

Saturnalia Books Poetry Prize, 105 Woodside Rd, Ardmore, PA 19003 *Tel:* 267-278-9541 *E-mail:* info@saturnaliabooks.com *Web Site:* www.saturnaliabooks.com, pg 726

SATW Foundation Lowell Thomas Travel Journalism Competition, 306 Summer Hill Dr, Fredericksburg, TX 78654 *Tel:* 713-973-9985 *E-mail:* awards@satwf.com *Web Site:* www.satwfoundation.org, pg 726

Satya House Publications, 22 Turkey St, Hardwick, MA 01037 *Tel:* 413-477-8743 *E-mail:* info@satyahouse.com; orders@satyahouse.com *Web Site:* www.satyahouse.com, pg 217

Savant Books & Publications LLC, 2630 Kapiolani Blvd, Suite 1601, Honolulu, HI 96826 *Tel:* 808-941-3927 *Fax:* 808-941-3927 *E-mail:* savantbooks@gmail.com *Web Site:* www.savantbooksandpublications.com, pg 217

SBL Press, The Luce Ctr, Suite 350, 825 Houston Mill Rd, Atlanta, GA 30329 *Tel:* 404-727-3100 *Fax:* 404-727-3101 (corp) *E-mail:* sbl@sbl-site.org *Web Site:* www.sbl-site.org, pg 217

Aldo & Jeanne Scaglione Prize for a Translation of a Literary Work, 26 Broadway, 3rd fl, New York, NY 10004-1789 *Tel:* 646-576-5141 *Fax:* 646-458-0030 *E-mail:* awards@mla.org *Web Site:* www.mla.org, pg 726

Aldo & Jeanne Scaglione Prize for a Translation of a Scholarly Study of Literature, 26 Broadway, 3rd fl, New York, NY 10004-1789 *Tel:* 646-576-5141 *Fax:* 646-458-0030 *E-mail:* awards@mla.org *Web Site:* www.mla.org, pg 726

Aldo & Jeanne Scaglione Prize for Comparative Literary Studies, 26 Broadway, 3rd fl, New York, NY 10004-1789 *Tel:* 646-576-5141 *Fax:* 646-458-0030 *E-mail:* awards@mla.org *Web Site:* www.mla.org, pg 726

Aldo & Jeanne Scaglione Prize for French & Francophone Studies, 26 Broadway, 3rd fl, New York, NY 10004-1789 *Tel:* 646-576-5141 *Fax:* 646-458-0030 *E-mail:* awards@mla.org *Web Site:* www.mla.org, pg 726

Aldo & Jeanne Scaglione Prize for Italian Studies, 26 Broadway, 3rd fl, New York, NY 10004-1789 *Tel:* 646-576-5141 *Fax:* 646-458-0030 *E-mail:* awards@mla.org *Web Site:* www.mla.org, pg 726

Aldo & Jeanne Scaglione Prize for Studies in Germanic Languages & Literatures, 26 Broadway, 3rd fl, New York, NY 10004-1789 *Tel:* 646-576-5141 *Fax:* 646-458-0030 *E-mail:* awards@mla.org *Web Site:* www.mla.org, pg 726

Aldo & Jeanne Scaglione Prize for Studies in Slavic Languages & Literatures, 26 Broadway, 3rd fl, New York, NY 10004-1789 *Tel:* 646-576-5141 *E-mail:* awards@mla.org *Web Site:* www.mla.org, pg 726

Aldo & Jeanne Scaglione Publication Award for a Manuscript in Italian Literary Studies, 26 Broadway, 3rd fl, New York, NY 10004-1789 *Tel:* 646-576-5141 *Fax:* 646-458-0030 *E-mail:* awards@mla.org *Web Site:* www.mla.org, pg 726

Jack Scagnetti Talent & Literary Agency, 5136 Vineland Ave, North Hollywood, CA 91601 *Tel:* 818-762-3871, pg 571

William Sanders Scarborough Prize, 26 Broadway, 3rd fl, New York, NY 10004-1789 *Tel:* 646-576-5141 *Fax:* 646-458-0030 *E-mail:* awards@mla.org *Web Site:* www.mla.org, pg 727

Scarecrow Press Inc, 4501 Forbes Blvd, Suite 200, Lanham, MD 20706 *Tel:* 301-459-3366 *Fax:* 301-429-5748 *Web Site:* www.scarecrowpress.com, pg 217

SCBWI Work-In-Progress Grants, 4727 Wilshire Blvd, Suite 301, Los Angeles, CA 90010 *Tel:* 323-782-1010; 310-403-0675 (cell) *Fax:* 323-782-1892 *E-mail:* membership@scbwi.org; scbwi@scbwi.org *Web Site:* www.scbwi.org, pg 727

Scepter Publishers, PO Box 1391, New York, NY 10802 *Tel:* 212-354-0670 *Toll Free Tel:* 800-322-8773 *Fax:* 212-354-0736 *Web Site:* www.scepterpublishers.org, pg 217

William D Schaeffer Environmental Award, 200 Deer Run Rd, Sewickley, PA 15143-2324 *Tel:* 412-259-1705 *Toll Free Tel:* 800-910-4283 (ext 705) *Fax:* 412-749-9890 *E-mail:* printing@printing.org *Web Site:* www.printing.org/page/3783, pg 727

Schaffner Press, PO Box 41567, Tucson, AZ 85717 *E-mail:* tim@schaffnerpress.com *Web Site:* www.schaffnerpress.com, pg 217

C J Scheiner Books, 275 Linden Blvd, Suite B-2, Brooklyn, NY 11226 *Tel:* 718-469-1089 *Fax:* 718-469-1089, pg 533

Schiavone Literary Agency Inc, 236 Trails End, West Palm Beach, FL 33413-2135 *Tel:* 561-966-9294 *Fax:* 561-966-9294 *E-mail:* profschia@aol.com *Web Site:* www.publishersmarketplace.com/members/profschia, pg 571

Schiel & Denver Book Publishers, 10685-B Hazelhurst Dr, Suite 8575, Houston, TX 77043 *Tel:* 832-699-0264 *Toll Free Tel:* 888-629-4449 *Toll Free Fax:* 888-224-2721 *E-mail:* enquiries@schieldenver.com *Web Site:* www.schieldenver.com, pg 217

Schiffer Publishing Ltd, 4880 Lower Valley Rd, Atglen, PA 19310 *Tel:* 610-593-1777 *Fax:* 610-593-2002 *E-mail:* schifferbk@aol.com *Web Site:* www.schifferbooks.com, pg 217

Schirmer Trade Books, 180 Madison Ave, 24th fl, New York, NY 10016 *Tel:* 212-254-2100 *Toll Free Tel:* 800-431-7187 (orders) *Fax:* 212-254-2013 *Web Site:* www.musicsales.com, pg 218

Schlager Group Inc, 325 N Saint Paul, Suite 3425, Dallas, TX 75201 *Toll Free Tel:* 888-416-5727 *Fax:* 214-347-9469 *E-mail:* info@schlagergroup.com *Web Site:* www.schlagergroup.com, pg 218

Wendy Schmalz Agency, 402 Union St, Unit 831, Hudson, NY 12534 *Tel:* 518-672-7697 *E-mail:* wendy@schmalzagency.com *Web Site:* www.schmalzagency.com, pg 572

Harold Schmidt Literary Agency, 415 W 23 St, Suite 6-F, New York, NY 10011 *Tel:* 212-727-7473, pg 572

Bernadotte E Schmitt Grants, 400 "A" St SE, Washington, DC 20003 *Tel:* 202-544-2422 *Fax:* 202-544-8307 *E-mail:* awards@historians.org *Web Site:* www.historians.org, pg 727

Scholars' Facsimiles & Reprints, 6946 E Stevens Rd, Cave Creek, AZ 85331-8677 *Tel:* 480-575-9945 *E-mail:* sfandr@msn.com *Web Site:* www.scholarsbooklist.com, pg 218

Scholastic Canada Ltd, 604 King St W, Toronto, ON M5V 1E1, Canada *Tel:* 905-887-7323 *Toll Free Tel:* 800-268-3860 (CN) *Toll Free Fax:* 866-387-4944 *E-mail:* custserve@scholastic.ca *Web Site:* www.scholastic.ca, pg 498

Scholastic Education, 524 Broadway, New York, NY 10012 *Tel:* 212-343-6100 *Fax:* 212-343-6189 *Web Site:* www.scholastic.com, pg 218

Scholastic Inc, 557 Broadway, New York, NY 10012 *Tel:* 212-343-6100 *Toll Free Tel:* 800-scholastic *Web Site:* www.scholastic.com, pg 218

Scholastic International, 557 Broadway, New York, NY 10012 *Tel:* 212-343-6100; 646-330-5288 (intl cust serv) *Toll Free Tel:* 800-SCHOLASTIC (800-724-6527) *Fax:* 646-837-7878 *E-mail:* international@scholastic.com, pg 218

Scholastic Library/National Library Week Grant, 50 E Huron St, Chicago, IL 60611 *Tel:* 312-280-2148 *Toll Free Tel:* 800-545-2433 (ext 2148) *Fax:* 312-280-5274 *Web Site:* www.ala.org/nlwgrant, pg 727

Scholastic Trade Division, 557 Broadway, New York, NY 10012 *Tel:* 212-343-6100; 212-343-4685 (export sales) *Fax:* 212-343-4714 (export sales) *Web Site:* www.scholastic.com, pg 219

Scholium International Inc, 151 Cow Neck Rd, Port Washington, NY 11050 *Tel:* 516-767-7171 *E-mail:* info@scholium.com *Web Site:* www.scholium.com, pg 219

Schonfeld & Associates Inc, 1931 Lynn Circle, Libertyville, IL 60048 *Tel:* 847-816-4870 *Toll Free Tel:* 800-205-0030 *Fax:* 847-816-4872 *E-mail:* saiinfo@saibooks.com *Web Site:* www.saibooks.com, pg 219

School for Advanced Research Press, 660 Garcia St, Santa Fe, NM 87505 *Tel:* 505-954-7206 *Toll Free Tel:* 888-390-6070 *Fax:* 505-954-7241 *E-mail:* press@sarsf.org *Web Site:* sarpress.sarweb.org, pg 219

School Guide Publications, 210 North Ave, New Rochelle, NY 10801 *Tel:* 914-632-1220 *Toll Free Tel:* 800-433-7771 *Fax:* 914-632-3412 *E-mail:* info@religiousministries.com *Web Site:* www.graduateguide.com; www.schoolguides.com; www.religiousministries.com, pg 219

School of Government, University of North Carolina, CB 3330, Chapel Hill, NC 27599-3330 *Tel:* 919-966-4119 *Fax:* 919-962-2709 *Web Site:* www.sog.unc.edu, pg 219

School of Visual Arts, 209 E 23 St, New York, NY 10010-3994 *Tel:* 212-592-2100 *Fax:* 212-592-2116 *Web Site:* www.sva.edu, pg 662

School Zone Publishing Co, 1819 Industrial Dr, Grand Haven, MI 49417 *Tel:* 616-846-5030 *Toll Free Tel:* 800-253-0564 *Fax:* 616-846-6181 *Toll Free Fax:* 800-550-4618 (orders only) *Web Site:* www.schoolzone.com, pg 219

Schoolhouse Indexing, 10-B Parade Ground Rd, Etna, NH 03750 *Tel:* 603-643-1617 *Web Site:* schoolhouseindexing.com, pg 534

Schoolhouse Network Inc, PO Box 17676, Fountain Hills, AZ 85269 *Tel:* 973-206-1389 *E-mail:* info@schoolhousenetwork.com *Web Site:* www.schoolhousenetwork.com, pg 534

Schreiber Publishing Inc, PO Box 4193, Rockville, MD 20849 *Tel:* 301-725-3906 *Toll Free Tel:* 800-296-1961 (sales) *Fax:* 301-725-0333 (orders) *E-mail:* schreiberpublishing@comcast.net *Web Site:* schreiberlanguage.com; shengold.com, pg 219

Schroeder Indexing Services, 23 Camilla Pink Ct, Bluffton, SC 29909 *Tel:* 843-705-9779 *E-mail:* sanindex@schroederindexing.com *Web Site:* www.schroederindexing.com, pg 534

Franklin L Schulaner, PO Box 507, Kealakekua, HI 96750-0507 *Tel:* 808-322-3785 *E-mail:* fschulaner@hawaii.rr.com, pg 534

Susan Schulman Literary Agency LLC, 454 W 44 St, New York, NY 10036 *Tel:* 212-713-1633 *Fax:* 212-581-8830, pg 572

Sherri Schultz/Words with Grace, 1916 Pike Place, Suite 12, No 118, Seattle, WA 98101 *Tel:* 415-297-5708 *E-mail:* WordsWithGraceEditorial@gmail.com *Web Site:* www.wordswithgrace.com, pg 534

The Schuna Group Inc, 1503 Briarknoll Dr, Arden Hills, MN 55112 *Tel:* 651-631-8480 *Web Site:* www.schunagroup.com, pg 584

A E Schwartz & Associates, 13 Conversation Way, Stoughton, MA 02072 *Tel:* 781-436-5033 *E-mail:* info@aeschwartz.com *Web Site:* aeschwartz.com, pg 572

Laurens R Schwartz, Esquire, 5 E 22 St, Suite 15-D, New York, NY 10010-5325 *Tel:* 212-228-2614, pg 572

Ruth & Sylvia Schwartz Children's Book Award, c/o Ontario Arts Council, 151 Bloor St W, 5th fl, Toronto, ON M5S 1T6, Canada *Tel:* 416-961-1660 *Toll Free Tel:* 800-387-0058 (ON) *Fax:* 416-961-7447 *E-mail:* info@arts.on.ca *Web Site:* www.arts.on.ca, pg 727

Science & Humanities Press, 63 Summit Point, St Charles, MO 63301-0571 *Tel:* 636-394-4950 *Web Site:* sciencehumanitiespress.com; beachhousebooks.com; macroprintbooks.com; earlyeditionsbooks.com; heuristicsbooks.com, pg 219

Science Fiction & Fantasy Writers of America Inc (SFWA), PO Box 3238, Enfield, CT 06083-3238 *E-mail:* office@sfwa.org *Web Site:* www.sfwa.org, pg 618

Science Fiction Writers Workshop, University of Kansas, Wescoe Hall, Rm 3001, Dept of English, 1445 Jayhawk Blvd, Lawrence, KS 66045-7590 *Tel:* 785-864-3380 *Fax:* 785-864-1159 *Web Site:* www.ku.edu/~sfcenter, pg 655

Science in Society Journalism Awards, PO Box 7905, Berkeley, CA 94707 *Tel:* 510-647-9500 *Web Site:* www.nasw.org, pg 727

Science, Naturally!™, 725 Eighth St SE, Washington, DC 20003 *Tel:* 202-465-4798 *Toll Free Tel:* 866-724-9876 *Fax:* 202-558-2132 *E-mail:* info@sciencenaturally.com *Web Site:* www.sciencenaturally.com, pg 219

Science Publishers Inc, PO Box 699, Enfield, NH 03748-0699 *Tel:* 603-632-7377 *Fax:* 603-632-5611 *E-mail:* info@scipub.net *Web Site:* www.scipub.net, pg 220

ScienceThrillers Media, PO Box 601392, Sacramento, CA 95860-1392 *Tel:* 916-712-3334 *E-mail:* query@sciencethrillersmedia.com *Web Site:* www.sciencethrillersmedia.com, pg 220

Scobre Press Corp, 2255 Calle Clara, La Jolla, CA 92037 *Toll Free Tel:* 877-726-2734 *Fax:* 858-551-1232 *E-mail:* info@scobre.com *Web Site:* www.scobre.com, pg 220

Scott Publishing Co, 911 S Vandemark Rd, Sidney, OH 45365 *Tel:* 937-498-0802 *Toll Free Tel:* 800-572-6885 (cust serv) *Fax:* 937-498-0807 *Toll Free Fax:* 800-488-5349 *E-mail:* cuserv@amospress.com *Web Site:* www.amosadvantage.com, pg 220

S©ott Treimel NY, 434 Lafayette St, New York, NY 10003-6943 *Tel:* 212-505-8353 *E-mail:* general@scotttreimelny.com *Web Site:* scotttreimelny.com; scotttreimelny.blogspot.com, pg 572

Scovil Galen Ghosh Literary Agency Inc, 276 Fifth Ave, Suite 708, New York, NY 10001 *Tel:* 212-679-8686 *Fax:* 212-679-6710 *E-mail:* info@sgglit.com *Web Site:* www.sgglit.com, pg 572

Scribendi Inc, 405 Riverview Dr, Chatham, ON N7M 0N3, Canada *Tel:* 519-351-1626 (cust serv) *Fax:* 519-354-0192 *E-mail:* customerservice@scribendi.com *Web Site:* www.scribendi.com, pg 534

Scribes & Scribblers Writing Camps for Kids, 110 E Hallam St, Suite 116, Aspen, CO 81611 *Tel:* 970-925-3122 *Fax:* 970-920-5700 *E-mail:* awfinfo@aspenwriters.org *Web Site:* www.aspenwriters.org, pg 655

Scribner, 1230 Avenue of the Americas, New York, NY 10020, pg 220

Scripta Humanistica Publishing International, 1383 Kersey Lane, Potomac, MD 20854 *Tel:* 301-294-7949 *Fax:* 301-424-9584 *E-mail:* info@scriptahumanistica.com *Web Site:* www.scriptahumanistica.com, pg 220

The Scriptural Research & Publishing Co Inc, 344 E Johnson Ave, Cheshire, CT 06410 *Tel:* 203-272-1780 *Fax:* 203-272-2296 *E-mail:* src1@srpublish.org *Web Site:* www.scripturalresearch.com, pg 220

Scurlock Publishing Co Inc, 1293 Myrtle Springs Rd, Texarkana, TX 75503 *Tel:* 903-832-4726 *Toll Free Tel:* 800-228-6389 (US & CN) *Fax:* 903-831-3177 *E-mail:* custserv@scurlockpublishing.com *Web Site:* muzzleloadermag.com; www.scurlockpublishing.com, pg 220

SDP Publishing Solutions LLC, 36 Captain's Way, East Bridgewater, MA 02333 *Tel:* 617-775-0656 *Web Site:* www.sdppublishingsolutions.com, pg 534

SDSU Writers' Conference, 5250 Campanile Dr, Rm 2503, San Diego, CA 92182-1920 *Tel:* 619-594-5821 *Fax:* 619-594-8566 *E-mail:* sdsuwritersconference@mail.sdsu.edu *Web Site:* www.neverstoplearning.net/writers, pg 655

Seal Books, One Toronto St, Suite 300, Toronto, ON M5C 2V6, Canada *Tel:* 416-364-4449 *Toll Free Tel:* 888-523-9292 (order desk) *Fax:* 416-364-6863 *Web Site:* www.randomhouse.ca, pg 498

Seal Press, 1700 Fourth St, Berkeley, CA 94710 *Tel:* 510-595-3664 *Fax:* 510-595-4228 *Web Site:* www.sealpress.com, pg 221

Search Institute Press®, The Banks Bldg, Suite 125, 615 First Ave NE, Minneapolis, MN 55413 *Tel:* 612-376-8955 *Toll Free Tel:* 800-888-7828 *Fax:* 612-692-5553 *E-mail:* si@search-institute.org *Web Site:* www.search-institute.org, pg 221

Hank Searls, Box 1877, 4435 Holly Lane NW, Gig Harbor, WA 98335 *Tel:* 253-851-9896 *Fax:* 253-851-9897 *E-mail:* hanksearls@comcast.net, pg 534

Hank Searls Authors Workshop, 4435 Holly Lane NW, Gig Harbor, WA 98335 *Tel:* 253-851-9896 *Fax:* 253-851-9897 *E-mail:* hanksearls@comcast.net, pg 655

Second Chance Press, 4170 Noyac Rd, Sag Harbor, NY 11963 *Tel:* 631-725-1101 *E-mail:* info@thepermanentpress.com *Web Site:* www.thepermanentpress.com, pg 221

Second Story Press, 20 Maud St, Suite 401, Toronto, ON M5V 2M5, Canada *Tel:* 416-537-7850 *Fax:* 416-537-0588 *E-mail:* info@secondstorypress.ca *Web Site:* secondstorypress.ca, pg 498

See-More's Workshop, 325 West End Ave, Suite 12-B, New York, NY 10023 *Tel:* 212-724-0677 *Fax:* 212-724-0767 *E-mail:* sbt@shadowboxtheatre.org *Web Site:* www.shadowboxtheatre.org, pg 221

See-More's Workshop Arts & Education Workshops, 325 West End Ave, Suite 12-B, New York, NY 10023 *Tel:* 212-724-0677 *Fax:* 212-724-0767 *E-mail:* sbt@shadowboxtheatre.org *Web Site:* www.shadowboxtheatre.org, pg 655

See Sharp Press, PO Box 1731, Tucson, AZ 85702-1731 *Tel:* 520-338-2151 *E-mail:* info@seesharppress.com *Web Site:* www.seesharppress.com, pg 221

Seedling Publications Inc, 520 E Bainbridge St, Elizabethtown, PA 17022 *Toll Free Tel:* 800-233-0759 *Toll Free Fax:* 888-834-1303 *E-mail:* info@continentalpress.com *Web Site:* www.continentalpress.com, pg 221

SelectBooks Inc, One Union Sq W, Suite 909, New York, NY 10003 *Tel:* 212-206-1997 *Fax:* 212-206-3815 *E-mail:* info@selectbooks.com *Web Site:* www.selectbooks.com, pg 221

Self-Counsel Press Ltd, 4152 Meridian St, Suite 105-471, Bellingham, WA 98226 *Toll Free Tel:* 800-663-3007 *E-mail:* orders@self-counsel.com *Web Site:* www.self-counsel.com, pg 221

Self-Realization Fellowship Publishers, 3208 Humboldt St, Los Angeles, CA 90031 *Tel:* 323-276-6002 *Toll Free Tel:* 888-773-8680 *Fax:* 323-927-1624 *Web Site:* www.srfpublishers.org, pg 222

Lynn Seligman, 400 Highland Ave, Upper Montclair, NJ 07043 *Tel:* 973-783-3631 *Fax:* 973-783-3691 *E-mail:* seliglit@aol.com, pg 572

Edythea Ginis Selman Literary Agency Inc, 14 Washington Place, New York, NY 10003 *Tel:* 212-473-1874 *Fax:* 212-473-1875, pg 572

Richard Selman, 14 Washington Place, New York, NY 10003 *Tel:* 212-473-1874 *Fax:* 212-473-1875, pg 534

Alexa Selph, 4300 McClatchey Circle, Atlanta, GA 30342 *Tel:* 404-256-3717 *E-mail:* lexa101@aol.com, pg 534

Sentient Publications LLC, 1113 Spruce St, Boulder, CO 80302 *Tel:* 303-443-2188 *Fax:* 303-381-2538 *E-mail:* contact@sentientpublications.com *Web Site:* www.sentientpublications.com, pg 222

The Robert S Sergeant Memorial, 1194 Hume Rd, Hume, VA 22639-1806 *E-mail:* poetryinva@aol.com *Web Site:* www.poetrysocietyofvirginia.org, pg 727

Serindia Publications, PO Box 10335, Chicago, IL 60610-0335 *Tel:* 312-664-5531 *Fax:* 312-664-4389 *E-mail:* info@serindia.com *Web Site:* www.serindia.com, pg 222

Seven Footer Kids, 247 W 30 St, 11th fl, New York, NY 10001-2824 *Tel:* 212-710-9340 *Fax:* 212-710-9344 *E-mail:* info@sevenfooter.com *Web Site:* www.sevenfooterpress.com, pg 222

Seven Footer Press, 247 W 30 St, 2nd fl, New York, NY 10001-2824 *Tel:* 212-710-9340 *Fax:* 212-710-9344 *E-mail:* info@sevenfooter.com *Web Site:* www.sevenfooterpress.com, pg 222

Seven Locks Press, 3100 W Warner Ave, Suite 8, Santa Ana, CA 97204 *E-mail:* sevenlocks@aol.com *Web Site:* www.sevenlockspublishing.com, pg 222

Seven Stories Press, 140 Watts St, New York, NY 10013 *Tel:* 212-226-8760 *Toll Free Tel:* 800-733-3000 (orders) *Fax:* 212-226-1411 *E-mail:* info@sevenstories.com *Web Site:* www.sevenstories.com, pg 222

1765 Productions, PO Box 4151, Fairfax, VA 22124-8151 *Tel:* 703-242-1734 *Fax:* 703-242-1734 *E-mail:* 1765productions@gmail.com, pg 222

Seventh Avenue Literary Agency, 2052 124 St, South Surrey, BC V4A 9K3, Canada *Tel:* 604-538-7252 *Fax:* 604-538-7252 *E-mail:* info@seventhavenuelit.com *Web Site:* www.seventhavenuelit.com, pg 572

Sewanee Writers' Conference, Stamler Ctr, 119 Gailor Hall, 735 University Ave, Sewanee, TN 37383-1000 *Tel:* 931-598-1141 *E-mail:* swc@sewanee.edu *Web Site:* www.sewaneewriters.org, pg 655

Mary Sue Seymour, 475 Miner Street Rd, Canton, NY 13617 *Tel:* 315-386-1831 *Web Site:* www.theseymouragency.com, pg 573

SF Canada, 7433 E River Rd, Washago, ON L0K 2B0, Canada *Web Site:* www.sfcanada.org, pg 618

SFWA Nebula Awards, PO Box 3238, Enfield, CT 06083-3238 *E-mail:* office@sfwa.org *Web Site:* www.sfwa.org, pg 727

Shadow Mountain, PO Box 30178, Salt Lake City, UT 84130 *Tel:* 801-534-1515 *Fax:* 801-517-3474 *E-mail:* submissions@shadowmountain.com *Web Site:* shadowmountain.com, pg 222

Shambhala Publications Inc, Horticultural Hall, 300 Massachusetts Ave, Boston, MA 02115 *Tel:* 617-424-0030 *Toll Free Tel:* 866-424-0030 (off); 888-424-2329 (cust serv) *Fax:* 617-236-1563 *E-mail:* customercare@shambhala.com *Web Site:* www.shambhala.com, pg 223

M E Sharpe Inc, 80 Business Park Dr, Suite 202, Armonk, NY 10504 *Tel:* 914-273-1800 *Toll Free Tel:* 800-541-6563 *Fax:* 914-273-2106 *E-mail:* info@mesharpe.com *Web Site:* www.mesharpe.com, pg 223

Shaughnessy Cohen Prize for Political Writing, 460 Richmond St W, Suite 600, Toronto, ON M5V 1Y1, Canada *Tel:* 416-504-8222 *Toll Free Tel:* 877-906-6548 *Fax:* 416-504-9090 *E-mail:* info@writerstrust.com *Web Site:* www.writerstrust.com, pg 727

Mina P Shaughnessy Prize, 26 Broadway, 3rd fl, New York, NY 10004-1789 *Tel:* 646-576-5141 *Fax:* 646-458-0030 *E-mail:* awards@mla.org *Web Site:* www.mla.org, pg 727

Charlotte Sheedy Literary Agency Inc, 928 Broadway, Suite 901, New York, NY 10010 *Tel:* 212-780-9800 *Web Site:* www.sheedylit.com, pg 573

Sheffield Publishing Co, 9009 Antioch Rd, Salem, WI 53168 *Tel:* 262-843-2281 *Fax:* 262-843-3683 *E-mail:* info@spcbooks.com *Web Site:* www.spcbooks.com, pg 223

Barry Sheinkopf, c/o The Writing Ctr, 601 Palisade Ave, Englewood Cliffs, NJ 07632 *Tel:* 201-567-4017 *Fax:* 201-567-7202 *E-mail:* bsheinkopf@optonline.net, pg 534

Shenanigan Books, 84 River Rd, Summit, NJ 07901 *Tel:* 908-219-4275 *Fax:* 908-219-4485 *E-mail:* info@shenaniganbooks.com *Web Site:* www.shenaniganbooks.com, pg 223

Shen's Books, 1547 Palos Verdes Mall, Unit 291, Walnut Creek, CA 94597 *Tel:* 925-262-8108 *Toll Free Tel:* 800-456-6660 *Fax:* 925-415-6136 *Toll Free Fax:* 888-269-9092 *E-mail:* info@shens.com *Web Site:* www.shens.com, pg 223

The Shepard Agency, 73 Kingswood Dr, Bethel, CT 06801 *Tel:* 203-790-4230; 203-790-1780 *Fax:* 203-798-2924 *E-mail:* shepardagcy@mindspring.com, pg 573

Shepard Publications, PO Box 280, Friday Harbor, WA 98250 *Web Site:* www.shepardpub.com, pg 223

The Robert E Shepard Agency, 4804 Laurel Canyon Blvd, Box 592, Valley Village, CA 91607-3717 *Web Site:* www.shepardagency.com, pg 573

Sherman Asher Publishing, 126 Candelario St, Santa Fe, NM 87501 *Tel:* 505-988-7214 *E-mail:* westernedge@santa-fe.net *Web Site:* www.shermanasher.com; www.westernedgepress.com, pg 223

Ken Sherman & Associates, 1275 N Hayworth, Suite 103, Los Angeles, CA 90046 *Tel:* 310-273-8840 *E-mail:* kenshermanassociates@gmail.com *Web Site:* www.kenshermanassociates.com, pg 573

Wendy Sherman Associates Inc, 27 W 24 St, Suite 700-B, New York, NY 10010 *Tel:* 212-279-9027 *E-mail:* submissions@wsherman.com *Web Site:* www.wsherman.com, pg 573

Sheron Enterprises Inc, 1035 S Carley Ct, North Bellmore, NY 11710 *Tel:* 516-783-5885 *E-mail:* contact@longislandbookpublisher.com *Web Site:* www.longislandbookpublisher.com, pg 223

Shields Publications, PO Box 669, Eagle River, WI 54521-0669 *Tel:* 715-479-4810 *Fax:* 715-479-3905 *E-mail:* wormbooks@wormbooks.com *Web Site:* www.wormbooks.com, pg 223

J Gordon Shillingford Publishing Inc, PO Box 86, RPO Corydon Ave, Winnipeg, MB R3M 3S3, Canada *Tel:* 204-779-6967 *Web Site:* www.jgshillingford.com, pg 498

Monika Shoffman-Graves, 70 Transylvania Ave, Key Largo, FL 33037 *Tel:* 305-451-1462 *Fax:* 305-451-1462 *E-mail:* keysmobill@earthlink.net; mograv@gmail.com, pg 534

Shoreline Press, 23 Ste-Anne, Ste-Anne-de-Bellevue, QC H9X 1L1, Canada *Tel:* 514-457-5733 *E-mail:* info@shorelinepress.ca *Web Site:* shorelinepress.ca, pg 499

Short Prose Competition for Developing Writers, 600-460 Richmond St W, Toronto, ON M5V 1Y1, Canada *Tel:* 416-703-8982 *Fax:* 416-504-9090 *E-mail:* info@writersunion.ca *Web Site:* www.writersunion.ca, pg 728

Short Story Award, 115 Richmond St, Charlottetown, PE C1A 1H7, Canada *Tel:* 902-368-4410 *Toll Free Tel:* 888-734-2784 *Fax:* 902-368-4418 *E-mail:* peiwritersguild@gmail.com *Web Site:* www.peiwritersguild.com, pg 728

Short Story Award for New Writers, PO Box 80430, Portland, OR 97280-1430 *Tel:* 503-221-0836 *Fax:* 503-221-0837 *E-mail:* editors@glimmertrain.org *Web Site:* www.glimmertrain.org, pg 728

Show What You Know® Publishing, A Lorenz Company, 501 E Third St, Dayton, OH 45402 *Tel:* 614-764-1211; 937-228-6118 *Toll Free Tel:* 877-PASSING (727-7464) *Fax:* 937-233-2042 *E-mail:* info@swykonline.com *Web Site:* www.swykonline.com; www.lorenzeducationalpress.com, pg 224

Edwin "Bud" Shrake Award for Best Short Nonfiction, c/o 7748 Hwy 290 W, Austin, TX 78736-3202 *Tel:* 512-683-5640 *E-mail:* president@texasinstituteofletters.org *Web Site:* www.texasinstituteofletters.org, pg 728

Robert F Sibert Informational Book Award, 50 E Huron St, Chicago, IL 60611-2795 *Tel:* 312-280-2163 *Toll Free Tel:* 800-545-2433 *Fax:* 312-440-9374 *E-mail:* alsc@ala.org *Web Site:* www.ala.org/alsc, pg 728

Side by Side Literary Productions Inc, 145 E 35 St, Suite 7FE, New York, NY 10016 *Tel:* 646-442-2905 *Fax:* 212-888-3650 *Web Site:* sidebysidelit.com, pg 573

Rosalie Siegel, International Literary Agent Inc, One Abey Dr, Pennington, NJ 08534 *Tel:* 609-737-1007 *Fax:* 609-737-3708 *Web Site:* www.rosaliesiegel.com, pg 573

Sierra Club Books, 85 Second St, 2nd fl, San Francisco, CA 94105 *Tel:* 415-977-5500 *Fax:* 415-977-5794 *E-mail:* books.publishing@sierraclub.org *Web Site:* www.sierraclubbooks.org, pg 224

Siglio, 2432 Medlow Ave, Los Angeles, CA 90041 *Tel:* 310-857-6935 *Fax:* 310-728-6844 *E-mail:* publisher@sigliopress.com *Web Site:* sigliopress.com, pg 224

Signalman Publishing, 3700 Commerce Blvd, Kissimmee, FL 34741 *Tel:* 407-504-4103 *Toll Free Tel:* 888-907-4423 *E-mail:* info@signalmanpublishing.com *Web Site:* www.signalmanpublishing.com, pg 224

Signature Books Publishing LLC, 564 W 400 N, Salt Lake City, UT 84116-3411 *Tel:* 801-531-1483 *Fax:* 801-531-1488 *E-mail:* people@signaturebooks.com *Web Site:* www.signaturebooks.com; www.signaturebookslibrary.org, pg 224

Signature Editions, RPO Corydon, PO Box 206, Winnipeg, MB R3M 3S7, Canada *Tel:* 204-779-7803 *Fax:* 204-779-6970 *E-mail:* signature@allstream.net; orders@signature-editions.com *Web Site:* www.signature-editions.com, pg 499

SIL International, 7500 W Camp Wisdom Rd, Dallas, TX 75236-5629 *Tel:* 972-708-7400 *Fax:* 972-708-7350 *E-mail:* publications_intl@sil.org *Web Site:* www.ethnologue.com; www.sil.org, pg 224

Silicon Press, 25 Beverly Rd, Summit, NJ 07901 *Tel:* 908-273-8919 *Fax:* 908-273-6149 *E-mail:* info@silicon-press.com *Web Site:* www.silicon-press.com, pg 224

Silman-James Press, 3624 Shannon Rd, Los Angeles, CA 90027 *Tel:* 323-661-9922 *Toll Free Tel:* 877-SJP-BOOK (757-2665) *Fax:* 323-661-9933 *E-mail:* info@silmanjamespress.com *Web Site:* www.silmanjamespress.com, pg 224

Silver Gavel Awards, 321 N Clark St, Chicago, IL 60654 *Tel:* 312-988-5733 *Toll Free Tel:* 800-285-2221 (orders) *Fax:* 312-988-5494 *Web Site:* www.abanow.org; www.americanbar.org, pg 728

Silver Leaf Books LLC, 13 Temi Rd, Holliston, MA 01746 *E-mail:* sales@silverleafbooks.com; editor@silverleafbooks.com; customerservice@silverleafbooks.com *Web Site:* www.silverleafbooks.com, pg 224

Silver Moon Press, 400 E 85 St, New York, NY 10028 *Toll Free Tel:* 800-874-3320 *Fax:* 212-988-8112 *E-mail:* mail@silvermoonpress.com *Web Site:* www.silvermoonpress.com, pg 224

SilverHouse Books, 555 NE 15 St, Suite 2-i, Miami, FL 33132 *Tel:* 305-747-1258 *E-mail:* info@silverhousebooks.com *Web Site:* www.silverhousebooks.com, pg 224

Simba Information, 1266 E Main St, Suite 700, Stamford, CT 06902 *Tel:* 203-325-8193 *Toll Free Tel:* 888-297-4622 (cust serv) *E-mail:* customerservice@simbainformation.com *Web Site:* www.simbainformation.com, pg 224

Simcha Press, 3201 SW 15 St, Deerfield Beach, FL 33442-8190 *Tel:* 954-360-0909 ext 212 *Toll Free Tel:* 800-851-9100 ext 212 *Toll Free Fax:* 800-424-7652 *E-mail:* simchapress@hcibooks.com *Web Site:* www.hcibooks.com, pg 225

Francis B Simkins Award, University of Georgia, Dept of History, Athens, GA 30602-1602 *Tel:* 706-542-8848 *Fax:* 706-542-2455 *Web Site:* sha.uga.edu, pg 728

The John Simmons Short Fiction Award, 102 Dey House, 507 N Clinton St, Iowa City, IA 52242-1000 *Tel:* 319-335-0416 *Fax:* 319-335-0420, pg 728

Simon & Pierre Publishing Co Ltd, 3 Church St, Suite 500, Toronto, ON M5E 1M2, Canada *Tel:* 416-214-5544 *Fax:* 416-214-5556 *E-mail:* info@dundurn.com *Web Site:* www.dundurn.com, pg 499

Simon & Schuster, 1230 Avenue of the Americas, New York, NY 10020 *Tel:* 212-698-7000 *Toll Free Tel:* 800-223-2348 (cust serv); 800-223-2336 (orders) *Toll Free Fax:* 800-943-9831 (orders) *Web Site:* www.simonandschuster.com, pg 225

Simon & Schuster Audio, 1230 Avenue of the Americas, New York, NY 10020 *Web Site:* audio.simonandschuster.com, pg 225

Simon & Schuster Canada, 166 King St E, Suite 300, Toronto, ON M5A 1J3, Canada *Tel:* 647-427-8882 *Toll Free Tel:* 800-387-0446; 800-268-3216 (orders) *Fax:* 647-430-9446 *Toll Free Fax:* 888-849-8151 (orders) *E-mail:* info@simonandschuster.ca *Web Site:* www.simonandschuster.ca, pg 499

Simon & Schuster Children's Publishing, 1230 Avenue of the Americas, New York, NY 10020 *Tel:* 212-698-7000 *Web Site:* KIDS.SimonandSchuster.com; TEEN.SimonandSchuster.com; simonandschuster.net; simonandschuster.biz, pg 225

Simon & Schuster Digital, 1230 Avenue of the Americas, New York, NY 10020 *Tel:* 212-698-7547 *Web Site:* www.simonandschuster.com; kids.simonandschuster.com; www.simonandschuster.ca; www.simonandschuster.co.uk; www.simonandschuster.net; www.simonandschuster.biz; www.tipsoncareerandmoney.com; www.tipsonhealthyliving.com; www.tipsonhomeandstyle.com; www.tipsonlifeandlove.com; www.offtheshelf.com; www.simonandschuster.com/teen, pg 225

Simon & Schuster, Inc, 1230 Avenue of the Americas, New York, NY 10020 *Tel:* 212-698-7000 *Fax:* 212-698-7007 *E-mail:* firstname.lastname@simonandschuster.com *Web Site:* www.simonandschuster.com, pg 225

Simon & Schuster Sales Division, 1230 Avenue of the Americas, New York, NY 10020 *Tel:* 212-698-7000, pg 226

Charlie May Simon Children's Book Award, Arkansas State Library, Suite 100, 900 W Capitol Ave, Little Rock, AR 72201-3108 *Tel:* 501-682-2860 *Fax:* 501-682-1693 *Web Site:* www.library.arkansas.gov, pg 728

Simply Read Books, 501-5525 West Blvd, Vancouver, BC V6M 3W6, Canada *Tel:* 604-727-2960 *E-mail:* go@simplyreadbooks.com *Web Site:* www.simplyreadbooks.com, pg 499

Sinauer Associates Inc, 23 Plumtree Rd, Sunderland, MA 01375 *Tel:* 413-549-4300 *Fax:* 413-549-1118 *E-mail:* publish@sinauer.com; orders@sinauer.com *Web Site:* www.sinauer.com, pg 226

Six Gallery Press, PO Box 90145, Pittsburgh, PA 15224-0545 *Web Site:* www.sixgallerypress.com, pg 227

Skandisk Inc, 6667 W Old Shakapee Rd, Suite 109, Bloomington, MN 55438-2622 *Tel:* 952-829-8998 *Toll Free Tel:* 800-468-2424 *Fax:* 952-829-8992 *E-mail:* tomten@skandisk.com *Web Site:* www.skandisk.com, pg 227

SkillPath Publications, PO Box 2768, Mission, KS 66201-2768 *Tel:* 913-362-3900 *Toll Free Tel:* 800-873-7545 *Fax:* 913-362-4241 *E-mail:* customercare@skillpath.net; products@skillpath.net *Web Site:* www.skillpath.com, pg 227

Skinner House Books, c/o Unitarian Universalist Assn, 24 Farnsworth St, Boston, MA 02210-1409 *Tel:* 617-742-2100 *Fax:* 617-948-6466 *E-mail:* skinnerhouse@uua.org *Web Site:* www.skinnerhouse.org, pg 227

Skipping Stones Honor Awards, 166 W 12 Ave, Eugene, OR 97401 *Tel:* 541-342-4956 *E-mail:* info@skippingstones.org *Web Site:* www.skippingstones.org, pg 728

Irene Skolnick Literary Agency, 27 W 20 St, Suite 305, New York, NY 10011 *Tel:* 212-727-3648 *Fax:* 212-352-2059 *E-mail:* office@skolnickliterary.com (queries) *Web Site:* www.skolnickagency.com, pg 573

Sky Oaks Productions Inc, 19544 Sky Oaks Way, Los Gatos, CA 95030 *Tel:* 408-395-7600 *Fax:* 408-395-8440 *E-mail:* tprworld@aol.com *Web Site:* www.tpr-world.com, pg 227

Sky Pony Press, 307 W 36 St, 11th fl, New York, NY 10018 *Tel:* 212-643-6816 *Fax:* 212-643-6819 *E-mail:* skypony@skyhorsepublishing.com; submissions@skyhorsepublishing.com; info@skyhorsepublishing.com *Web Site:* www.skyponypress.com, pg 227

Sky Publishing, 90 Sherman St, Cambridge, MA 02140 *Tel:* 617-864-7360 *Toll Free Tel:* 866-644-1377 *Fax:* 617-864-6117 *E-mail:* info@skyandtelescope.com *Web Site:* www.skyandtelescope.com, pg 227

SkyLight Paths Publishing, Sunset Farm Offices, Rte 4, Woodstock, VT 05091 *Tel:* 802-457-4000 *Toll Free Tel:* 800-962-4544 *Fax:* 802-457-4004 *E-mail:* sales@skylightpaths.com *Web Site:* www.skylightpaths.com, pg 227

Slack Incorporated, 6900 Grove Rd, Thorofare, NJ 08086-9447 *Tel:* 856-848-1000 *Toll Free Tel:* 800-257-8290 *Fax:* 856-848-6091 *E-mail:* sales@slackinc.com *Web Site:* www.slackbooks.com, pg 227

SLC Enterprises Inc, 332 S Michigan Ave, No 1032-C216, Chicago, IL 60604 *Tel:* 616-942-2665 (answering serv & voice mail) *E-mail:* scasari1@hotmail.com, pg 573

Sleeping Bear Press™, 315 Eisenhower Pkwy, Suite 200, Ann Arbor, MI 48108 *Toll Free Tel:* 800-487-2323 *Fax:* 734-794-0004 *E-mail:* sleepingbearpress@cengage.com *Web Site:* www.sleepingbearpress.com, pg 227

Slipdown Mountain Publications LLC, 28151 Quarry Lake Rd, Lake Linden, MI 49945 *Tel:* 906-523-4118 *Toll Free Tel:* 866-341-3705 *Toll Free Fax:* 866-341-3705 *E-mail:* books@jacobsvillebooks.com *Web Site:* www.jacobsvillebooks.com, pg 228

Slipstream Annual Poetry Chapbook Contest, PO Box 2071, Dept W-1, Niagara Falls, NY 14301 *Web Site:* www.slipstreampress.org, pg 728

Beverley Slopen Literary Agency, 131 Bloor St W, Suite 711, Toronto, ON M5S 1S3, Canada *Tel:* 416-964-9598 *Fax:* 416-921-7726 *Web Site:* www.slopenagency.com, pg 574

Small Beer Press, 150 Pleasant St, No 306, Easthampton, MA 01027 *Tel:* 413-203-1636 *Fax:* 413-203-1636 *E-mail:* info@smallbeerpress.com *Web Site:* smallbeerpress.com, pg 228

Small Business Advisors Inc, 11 Franklin Ave, Hewlett, NY 11557 *Tel:* 516-374-1387; 914-260-1027 *Fax:* 516-374-1175; 720-294-3202 *E-mail:* info@smallbusinessadvice.com *Web Site:* www.smallbusinessadvice.com, pg 228

Small Publishers, Artists & Writers Network (SPAWN), 323 E Matilija St, Suite 110, PMB 123, Ojai, CA 93023 *Tel:* 805-646-3045 *Fax:* 805-640-8213 *E-mail:* execdir@spawn.org *Web Site:* www.spawn.org, pg 618

Donald Smiley Prize, 260 rue Dalhousie St, Suite 204, Ottawa, ON K1N 7E4, Canada *Tel:* 613-562-1202 *Fax:* 613-241-0019 *E-mail:* cpsa-acsp@cpsa-acsp.ca *Web Site:* www.cpsa-acsp.ca, pg 729

Smith & Kraus Publishers Inc, 40 Walch Dr, Portland, ME 04103 *Tel:* 207-523-2585 *Toll Free Tel:* 877-668-8680 *Fax:* 207-699-3698 *E-mail:* editor@smithandkraus.com *Web Site:* www.smithandkraus.com, pg 228

Helen C Smith Memorial Award, c/o 7748 Hwy 290 W, Austin, TX 78736-3202 *Tel:* 512-683-5640 *E-mail:* president@texasinstituteofletters.org *Web Site:* www.texasinstituteofletters.org, pg 729

The Jeffrey E Smith Editors' Prize, 357 McReynolds Hall, Columbia, MO 65211 *Tel:* 573-882-4474 *Toll Free Tel:* 800-949-2505 *Fax:* 573-884-4671 *Web Site:* www.missourireview.com, pg 729

M Lee Smith Publishers LLC, 5201 Virginia Way, Brentwood, TN 37027 *Tel:* 615-373-7517 *Toll Free Tel:* 800-274-6774 *Fax:* 615-373-5183 *E-mail:* custserv@mleesmith.com *Web Site:* www.mleesmith.com, pg 228

Roger W Smith, 59-67 58 Rd, Maspeth, NY 11378-3211 *Tel:* 718-416-1334 *E-mail:* roger.smith106@verizon.net, pg 534

Steve Smith Autosports, PO Box 11631, Santa Ana, CA 92711-1631 *Tel:* 714-639-7681 *Fax:* 714-639-9741 *Web Site:* www.stevesmithautosports.com, pg 228

Valerie Smith, Literary Agent, 1746 Rte 44-55, Modena, NY 12548 *Tel:* 845-883-5848, pg 574

Smithsonian Scholarly Press, Aerospace Bldg, 704-A, MRC 957, Washington, DC 20013 *Tel:* 202-633-3017 *Fax:* 202-633-6877 *E-mail:* schol_press@si.edu *Web Site:* www.scholarlypress.si.edu, pg 228

Smyth & Helwys Publishing Inc, 6316 Peake Rd, Macon, GA 31210-3960 *Tel:* 478-757-0564 *Toll Free Tel:* 800-747-3016 (orders only); 800-568-1248 (orders only) *Fax:* 478-757-1305 *E-mail:* information@helwys.com *Web Site:* www.helwys.com, pg 228

Michael Snell Literary Agency, PO Box 1206, Truro, MA 02666-1206 *Tel:* 508-349-3718 *Web Site:* www.michaelsnellagency.com, pg 574

Kay Snow Literary Contest, 2108 Buck St, West Linn, OR 97068 *Tel:* 503-305-6729 *Fax:* 503-344-6174 *E-mail:* wilwrite@willamettewriters.com *Web Site:* www.willamettewriters.com, pg 729

Snow Lion Publications Inc, 300 Massachusetts Ave, Boston, MA 02115 *Tel:* 617-236-0030 *Fax:* 617-236-1563 *E-mail:* customercare@shambhala.com *Web Site:* www.shambhala.com/snowlion, pg 228

Sobel Weber Associates Inc, 146 E 19 St, New York, NY 10003-2404 *Tel:* 212-420-8585 *Fax:* 212-505-1017 *E-mail:* info@sobelweber.com *Web Site:* www.sobelweber.com, pg 574

Social Sciences & Humanities Research Council of Canada (SSHRC), 350 Albert St, Ottawa, ON K1P 6G4, Canada *Tel:* 613-992-0691 *E-mail:* research@sshrc-crsh.gc.ca *Web Site:* www.sshrc.ca, pg 618

Society for Features Journalism (SFJ), University of Maryland, Philip Merrill College of Journalism, 1100 Knight Hall, College Park, MD 20742 *Tel:* 301-314-2631 *Fax:* 301-314-9166 *Web Site:* featuresjournalism.org, pg 618

Society for Human Resource Management (SHRM), 1800 Duke St, Alexandria, VA 22314 *Tel:* 703-548-3440 *Toll Free Tel:* 800-444-5006 (orders) *Fax:* 703-535-6490 *E-mail:* shrm@shrm.org; shrmstore@shrm.org *Web Site:* www.shrm.org, pg 228

Society for Industrial & Applied Mathematics, 3600 Market St, 6th fl, Philadelphia, PA 19104-2688 *Tel:* 215-382-9800 *Toll Free Tel:* 800-447-7426 *Fax:* 215-386-7999 *E-mail:* siambooks@siam.org *Web Site:* www.siam.org, pg 228

Society for Mining, Metallurgy & Exploration, 12999 E Adam Aircraft Circle, Englewood, CO 80112 *Tel:* 303-948-4200 *Toll Free Tel:* 800-763-3132 *Fax:* 303-973-3845 *E-mail:* cs@smenet.org *Web Site:* www.smenet.org, pg 229

Society for Scholarly Publishing (SSP), 10200 W 44 Ave, Suite 304, Wheat Ridge, CO 80033-2840 *Tel:* 303-422-3914 *Fax:* 720-881-6101 *E-mail:* info@sspnet.org *Web Site:* www.sspnet.org, pg 618

Society for Technical Communication, 9401 Lee Hwy, Suite 300, Fairfax, VA 22031 *Tel:* 703-522-4114 *Fax:* 703-522-2075 *E-mail:* stc@stc.org *Web Site:* www.stc.org, pg 618

Society for Technical Communication's Annual Conference, 9401 Lee Hwy, Suite 300, Fairfax, VA 22031 *Tel:* 703-522-4114 *Fax:* 703-522-2075 *E-mail:* stc@stc.org *Web Site:* www.stc.org, pg 655

Society for the History of Authorship, Reading & Publishing Inc (SHARP), c/o The Johns Hopkins University Press, Journals Publishing Div, PO Box 19966, Baltimore, MD 21211-0966 *Tel:* 410-516-6987 *Toll Free Tel:* 800-548-1784 *Fax:* 410-516-3866 *E-mail:* members@sharpweb.org *Web Site:* www.sharpweb.org, pg 618

Society of American Archivists, 17 N State St, Suite 1425, Chicago, IL 60602-4061 *Tel:* 312-606-0722 *Toll Free Tel:* 866-722-7858 *Fax:* 312-606-0728 *E-mail:* info@archivists.org *Web Site:* www.archivists.org, pg 229

Society of American Business Editors & Writers Inc (SABEW), Walter Cronkite School of Journalism & Mass Communication, Arizona State University, 555 N Central Ave, Suite 406 E, Phoenix, AZ 85004-1248 *Tel:* 602-496-7862 *Fax:* 602-496-7041 *E-mail:* sabew@sabew.org *Web Site:* sabew.org, pg 619

Society of American Travel Writers (SATW), 11950 W Lake Park Dr, Suite 320, Milwaukee, WI 53224-3049 *Tel:* 414-359-1625 *Fax:* 414-359-1671 *E-mail:* info@satw.org *Web Site:* www.satw.org, pg 619

Society of Children's Book Writers and Illustrators (SCBWI), 4727 Wilshire Blvd, Suite 301, Los Angeles, CA 90010 *Tel:* 323-782-1010 *Fax:* 323-782-1892 *E-mail:* membership@scbwi.org; scbwi@scbwi.org *Web Site:* www.scbwi.org, pg 619

Society of Environmental Toxicology & Chemistry, 229 S Baylen St, 2nd fl, Pensacola, FL 32502 *Tel:* 850-469-1500 *Fax:* 850-469-9778 *E-mail:* setac@setac.org *Web Site:* www.setac.org, pg 229

Society of Exploration Geophysicists, 8801 S Yale Ave, Tulsa, OK 74137 *Tel:* 918-497-5500 *Fax:* 918-497-5557 *E-mail:* web@seg.org *Web Site:* www.seg.org, pg 229

Society of Illustrators (SI), 128 E 63 St, New York, NY 10065 *Tel:* 212-838-2560 *Fax:* 212-838-2561 *E-mail:* info@societyillustrators.org *Web Site:* www.societyillustrators.org, pg 619

Society of Manufacturing Engineers, One SME Dr, Dearborn, MI 48121 *Tel:* 313-425-3000 *Toll Free Tel:* 800-733-4763 (cust serv) *Fax:* 313-425-3400 *E-mail:* publications@sme.org *Web Site:* www.sme.org, pg 229

The Society of Midland Authors (SMA), PO Box 10419, Chicago, IL 60610 *E-mail:* info@midlandauthors.com *Web Site:* www.midlandauthors.com, pg 619

The Society of Midland Authors Awards, 530 Michigan Ave, Evanston, IL 60202 *E-mail:* info@midlandauthors.com *Web Site:* www.midlandauthors.com, pg 729

Society of Motion Picture & Television Engineers® (SMPTE®), 3 Barker Ave, 5th fl, White Plains, NY 10601 *Tel:* 914-761-1100 *Fax:* 914-761-3115 *Web Site:* www.smpte.org, pg 619

The Society of Naval Architects & Marine Engineers, 601 Pavonia Ave, Jersey City, NJ 07306-2907 *Tel:* 201-798-4800 *Toll Free Tel:* 800-798-2188 *Fax:* 201-798-4975 *Web Site:* www.sname.org, pg 229

The Society of Southwestern Authors (SSA), PO Box 30355, Tucson, AZ 85751-0355 *Tel:* 520-546-9382 *Web Site:* www.ssa-az.org, pg 619

The Society of Southwestern Authors Writing Contest, PO Box 30355, Tucson, AZ 85751-0355 *Tel:* 520-546-9382 *Fax:* 520-751-7877 *E-mail:* info@ssa-az.org *Web Site:* www.ssa-az.org, pg 729

Software & Information Industry Association (SIIA), 1090 Vermont Ave NW, 6th fl, Washington, DC 20005-4095 *Tel:* 202-289-7442 *Fax:* 202-289-7097 *Web Site:* www.siia.net, pg 619

Soho Press Inc, 853 Broadway, New York, NY 10003 *Tel:* 212-260-1900 *Fax:* 212-260-1902 *E-mail:* soho@sohopress.com; publicity@sohopress.com *Web Site:* www.sohopress.com, pg 229

Soil Science Society of America, 5585 Guilford Rd, Madison, WI 53711-5801 *Tel:* 608-273-8080 *Fax:* 608-273-2021 *E-mail:* headquarters@soils.org *Web Site:* www.soils.org, pg 229

Solano Press Books, PO Box 773, Point Arena, CA 95468 *Tel:* 707-884-4508 *Toll Free Tel:* 800-931-9373 *Fax:* 707-884-4109 *E-mail:* spbooks@solano.com *Web Site:* www.solano.com, pg 229

Solid Gold Marketing Design Workshops, PO Box 2373, La Mesa, CA 91943-2373 *Tel:* 858-569-6555 *Toll Free Tel:* 800-932-0973 *Web Site:* www.sparklepresentations.com, pg 655

Jodi Solomon Speakers Bureau, 295 Huntington Ave, Suite 211, Boston, MA 02115 *Tel:* 617-266-3450 *Fax:* 617-266-5660 *E-mail:* jodi@jodisolomon.biz *Web Site:* www.jodisolomonspeakers.com, pg 588

Solution Tree, 555 N Morton St, Bloomington, IN 47404 *Tel:* 812-336-7700 *Toll Free Tel:* 800-733-6786 *Fax:* 812-336-7790 *E-mail:* info@solution-tree.com *Web Site:* www.solution-tree.com, pg 230

SOM Publishing, 163 Moon Valley Rd, Windyville, MO 65783 *Tel:* 417-345-8411 *Fax:* 417-345-6668 *E-mail:* som@som.org; dreamschool@dreamschool.org *Web Site:* www.som.org; www.dreamschool.org, pg 230

Somerset Hall Press, 416 Commonwealth Ave, Suite 612, Boston, MA 02215 *Tel:* 617-236-5126 *E-mail:* info@somersethallpress.com *Web Site:* www.somersethallpress.com, pg 230

Soncino Press Ltd, 123 Ditmas Ave, Brooklyn, NY 11218 *Tel:* 718-972-6200 *Toll Free Tel:* 800-972-6201 *Fax:* 718-972-6204 *E-mail:* info@soncino.com *Web Site:* www.soncino.com, pg 230

Sophia Institute Press®, 522 Donald St, Unit 3, Bedford, NH 03110 *Tel:* 603-836-5505 *Toll Free Tel:* 800-888-9344 *Fax:* 603-641-8108 *Toll Free Fax:* 888-288-2259 *E-mail:* orders@sophiainstitute.com *Web Site:* www.sophiainstitute.com, pg 230

Sophie Kerr Prize, c/o College Relations Off, 300 Washington Ave, Chestertown, MD 21620 *Tel:* 410-778-2800 *Toll Free Tel:* 800-422-1782 *Fax:* 410-810-7150 *Web Site:* www.washcoll.edu, pg 729

Sopris West Educational Services, 17855 Dallas Pkwy, Suite 400, Dallas, TX 75287 *Tel:* 303-651-2829 *Toll Free Tel:* 800-547-6747 *Fax:* 303-776-5934 *Toll Free Fax:* 888-819-7767 *E-mail:* customerservice@sopriswest.com *Web Site:* www.sopriswest.com, pg 230

Soul Mate Publishing, PO Box 24, Macedon, NY 14502 *Tel:* 585-598-4791 *E-mail:* submissions@soulmatepublishing.com *Web Site:* www.soulmatepublishing.com, pg 230

Gordon Soules Book Publishers Ltd, 1359 Amble Side Lane, West Vancouver, BC V7T 2Y9, Canada *Tel:* 604-922-6588 *Fax:* 604-922-6574 *E-mail:* books@gordonsoules.com *Web Site:* www.gordonsoules.com, pg 499

Sound Feelings Publishing, 18375 Ventura Blvd, No 8000, Tarzana, CA 91356 *Tel:* 818-757-0600 *E-mail:* information@soundfeelings.com *Web Site:* www.soundfeelings.com, pg 230

Sounds True Inc, 413 S Arthur Ave, Louisville, CO 80027 *Tel:* 303-665-3151 *Toll Free Tel:* 800-333-9185 *E-mail:* customerservice@soundstrue.com *Web Site:* www.soundstrue.com, pg 230

Sourcebooks Inc, 1935 Brookdale Rd, Suite 139, Naperville, IL 60563 *Tel:* 630-961-3900 *Toll Free Tel:* 800-432-7444 *Fax:* 630-961-2168 *E-mail:* info@sourcebooks.com; customersupport@sourcebooks.com *Web Site:* www.sourcebooks.com, pg 230

Sourced Media Books, 29 Via Regalo, San Clemente, CA 92673 *Tel:* 949-813-0182 *E-mail:* info@sourcedmediabooks.com *Web Site:* sourcedmediabooks.com, pg 231

South Carolina Bar, Continuing Legal Education Div, 950 Taylor St, Columbia, SC 29201 *Tel:* 803-799-6653 *Toll Free Tel:* 800-768-7787 *Fax:* 803-799-4118 *E-mail:* scbar-info@scbar.org *Web Site:* www.scbar.org, pg 231

South Dakota Historical Society Press, 900 Governors Dr, Pierre, SD 57501 *Tel:* 605-773-6009 *Fax:* 605-773-6041 *E-mail:* info@sdshspress.com *Web Site:* sdshspress.com, pg 231

South End Press, PO Box 382132, Cambridge, MA 02238 *Tel:* 718-874-0089 *Toll Free Fax:* 800-960-0078 *E-mail:* southend@southendpress.org; info@southendpress.org *Web Site:* www.southendpress.org, pg 231

South Platte Press, PO Box 163, David City, NE 68632-0163 *Tel:* 402-367-3554 *E-mail:* railroads@windstream.net *Web Site:* www.southplattepress.net, pg 231

Southampton Writers' Conference, 239 Montauk Hwy, Southampton, NY 11968 *Tel:* 631-632-5007 *E-mail:* southamptonwriters@notes.cc.sunysb.edu *Web Site:* www.stonybrook.edu/writers, pg 655

Southeast Review Narrative Nonfiction Contest, Florida State University, Dept of English, Tallahassee, FL 32306 *E-mail:* southeastreview@gmail.com *Web Site:* www.southeastreview.org, pg 729

Southeast Review's Gearhart Poetry Contest, Florida State University, Dept of English, Tallahassee, FL 32306 *E-mail:* southeastreview@gmail.com *Web Site:* www.southeastreview.org, pg 729

Southeastern Theatre Conference New Play Project, 1175 Revolution Mill Dr, Suite 14, Greensboro, NC 27405 *Tel:* 336-272-3645 *Fax:* 336-272-8810 *E-mail:* info@setc.org *Web Site:* www.setc.org, pg 729

Southern Books Competition, PO Box 950, Rex, GA 30273 *Tel:* 678-466-4334 *Fax:* 678-466-4349 *Web Site:* selaonline.org, pg 729

Southern California Writers' Conference, 18160 Cottonwood Rd, Suite 260, Sunriver, OR 97707 *Tel:* 619-303-8185 *Fax:* 619-906-7462 *E-mail:* msg@writersconference.com *Web Site:* www.writersconference.com, pg 655

Southern Historical Press Inc, 375 W Broad St, Greenville, SC 29601 *Tel:* 864-233-2346 *Toll Free Tel:* 800-233-0152 *Fax:* 864-233-2349, pg 231

Southern Illinois University Press, 1915 University Press Dr, SIUC Mail Code 6806, Carbondale, IL 62901-4323 *Tel:* 618-453-2281 *Fax:* 618-453-1221 *E-mail:* custserv@press.uchicago.edu; rights@siu.edu *Web Site:* www.siupress.com, pg 231

Southern Independent Booksellers Alliance, 3806 Yale Ave, Columbia, SC 29205 *Tel:* 803-994-9530 *Fax:* 309-410-0211 *E-mail:* info@sibaweb.com *Web Site:* www.sibaweb.com, pg 619

Southern Playwrights Competition, 700 Pelham Rd N, Jacksonville, AL 36265-1602 *Tel:* 256-782-5498 *Fax:* 256-782-5441 *Web Site:* www.jsu.edu/english/southpla.html, pg 730

Terry Southern Prize, 544 W 27 St, New York, NY 10001 *Tel:* 212-343-1333 *Fax:* 212-343-1988 *E-mail:* queries@theparisreview.org *Web Site:* www.theparisreview.org, pg 730

SouthWest Writers Conference Series, 3200 Carlisle Blvd NE, Suite 114, Albuquerque, NM 87110-1663 *Tel:* 505-830-6034 *E-mail:* swwriters@juno.com *Web Site:* www.southwestwriters.com, pg 655

Sovereign Award for Writing, Woodbine Sales Pavilion, 555 Rexdale Blvd, Rexdale, ON M9W 5L2, Canada *Tel:* 416-675-7756 *Fax:* 416-675-6378 *E-mail:* jockeyclub@bellnet.ca *Web Site:* www.jockeyclubcanada.com, pg 730

The Sow's Ear Poetry Prize & The Sow's Ear Chapbook Prize, 1748 Cave Ridge Rd, Mount Jackson, VA 22842 *E-mail:* sepoetryreview@gmail.com *Web Site:* sows-ear.kitenet.net, pg 730

Soyinfo Center, PO Box 234, Lafayette, CA 94549-0234 *Tel:* 925-283-2991 *E-mail:* info@soyinfocenter.com *Web Site:* www.soyinfocenter.com, pg 231

Spark Award, 4727 Wilshire Blvd, Suite 301, Los Angeles, CA 90010 *Tel:* 323-782-1010 *Fax:* 323-782-1892 *E-mail:* grants@scbwi.org *Web Site:* www.scbwi.org, pg 730

Special Libraries Association (SLA), 331 S Patrick St, Alexandria, VA 22314-3501 *Tel:* 703-647-4900 *Fax:* 703-647-4901 *Web Site:* www.sla.org, pg 619

Specialized Information Publishers Association (SIPA), 1090 Vermont Ave NW, 6th fl, Washington, DC 20005-4095 *Web Site:* www.sipaonline.com, pg 619

Specialty Graphic Imaging Association, 10015 Main St, Fairfax, VA 22031-3489 *Tel:* 703-385-1335 *Toll Free Tel:* 888-385-3588 *Fax:* 703-273-0456 *E-mail:* sgia@sgia.org *Web Site:* www.sgia.org, pg 620

Specialty Press Inc, 300 NW 70 Ave, Suite 102, Plantation, FL 33317 *Tel:* 954-792-8100 *Toll Free Tel:* 800-233-9273 *Fax:* 954-792-8545 *E-mail:* websales@addwarehouse.com *Web Site:* addwarehouse.com, pg 231

Spectrum Literary Agency, 320 Central Park W, Suite 1-D, New York, NY 10025 *Tel:* 212-362-4323 *Fax:* 212-362-4562 *Web Site:* www.spectrumliteraryagency.com, pg 574

SPIE, 1000 20 St, Bellingham, WA 98225-6705 *Tel:* 360-676-3290 *Toll Free Tel:* 888-504-8171 *Fax:* 360-647-1445 *E-mail:* spie@spie.org *Web Site:* www.spie.org, pg 231

The Spieler Agency, 27 W 20 St, Suite 305, New York, NY 10011 *Tel:* 212-757-4439 *Fax:* 212-333-2019 *E-mail:* spieleragency@spieleragency.com, pg 574

Spinsters Ink, PO Box 242, Midway, FL 32343 *E-mail:* info@spinstersink.com; editorialdirector@spinstersink.com *Web Site:* www.spinstersink.com, pg 232

Philip G Spitzer Literary Agency Inc, 50 Talmage Farm Lane, East Hampton, NY 11937 *Tel:* 631-329-3650 *Fax:* 631-329-3651 *Web Site:* www.spitzeragency.com, pg 574

Spizzirri Publishing Inc, PO Box 9397, Rapid City, SD 57709-9397 *Tel:* 605-348-2749 *Toll Free Tel:* 800-325-9819 *Fax:* 605-348-6251 *Toll Free Fax:* 800-322-9819 *E-mail:* spizzpub@aol.com *Web Site:* www.spizzirri.com, pg 232

Sport Books Publisher, 212 Robert St (side basement door), Toronto, ON M5S 2K7, Canada *Tel:* 416-323-9438 *Fax:* 416-966-9022 *E-mail:* sbp@sportbookspub.com; kbp@sportbookspub.com *Web Site:* www.sportbookspub.com, pg 499

John Spray Mystery Award, 40 Orchard View Blvd, Suite 217, Toronto, ON M4R 1B9, Canada *Tel:* 416-975-0010 *Fax:* 416-975-8970 *E-mail:* info@bookcentre.ca *Web Site:* www.bookcentre.ca, pg 730

Spring Time Writers Creative Writing & Journaling Workshop, PO Box 512, Lyons, CO 80540-0512 *Tel:* 303-823-0997 *E-mail:* writers@springtimewriters.com *Web Site:* www.springtimewriters.com, pg 655

Springer, 233 Spring St, New York, NY 10013-1578 *Tel:* 212-460-1500 *Toll Free Tel:* 800-SPRINGER (777-4643) *Fax:* 212-460-1575 *E-mail:* service-ny@springer.com *Web Site:* www.springer.com, pg 232

Springer Publishing Co, 11 W 42 St, 15th fl, New York, NY 10036-8002 *Tel:* 212-431-4370 *Toll Free Tel:* 877-687-7476 *Fax:* 212-941-7842 *E-mail:* marketing@

The Story Prize, 41 Watchung Plaza, No 384, Montclair, NJ 07042 *Tel:* 973-932-0324 *E-mail:* info@thestoryprize.org *Web Site:* www.thestoryprize.org, pg 731

Storybook Arts Inc, 414 Poplar Hill Rd, Dover Plains, NY 12522 *Tel:* 845-877-3305 *Web Site:* www.storybookartsinc.com, pg 584

Elizabeth Matchett Stover Memorial Award, PO Box 750374, Dallas, TX 75275-0374 *Fax:* 214-768-1408 *E-mail:* swr@mail.smu.edu *Web Site:* www.smu.edu/southwestreview, pg 731

Strata Publishing Inc, PO Box 1303, State College, PA 16804 *Tel:* 814-234-8545 *Fax:* 814-238-7222 *E-mail:* stratapub@stratapub.com *Web Site:* www.stratapub.com, pg 236

Strategic Book Publishing & Rights Agency (SBPRA), 12620 FM 1960, Suite A-4507, Houston, TX 77065 *Toll Free Tel:* 888-808-6190 *Web Site:* www.sbpra.com, pg 237

Strategic Media Books LLC, 782 Wofford St, Rock Hill, SC 29730 *Tel:* 803-366-5440 *E-mail:* contact@strategicmediabooks.com *Web Site:* strategicmediabooks.com, pg 237

Straus Literary, 319 Lafayette St, Suite 220, New York, NY 10012 *Tel:* 646-843-9950 *Fax:* 646-390-3320 *Web Site:* www.strausliterary.com, pg 575

Robin Straus Agency Inc, 229 E 79 St, Suite 5A, New York, NY 10075 *Tel:* 212-472-3282 *E-mail:* info@robinstrausagency.com *Web Site:* www.robinstrausagency.com, pg 576

Stress Free Kids®, 2561 Chimney Springs Dr, Marietta, GA 30062 *Toll Free Tel:* 800-841-4204 *Toll Free Fax:* 866-302-2759 *E-mail:* media@stressfreekids.com *Web Site:* www.stressfreekids.com, pg 237

Marianne Strong Literary Agency, 65 E 96 St, New York, NY 10128 *Tel:* 212-249-1000 *Fax:* 212-831-3241 *Web Site:* stronglit.com, pg 576

Strothman Agency LLC, 63 E Ninth St, 10X, New York, NY 10003 *E-mail:* info@strothmanagency.com *Web Site:* www.strothmanagency.com, pg 576

The Jesse Stuart Foundation (JSF), 1645 Winchester Ave, Ashland, KY 41101 *Tel:* 606-326-1667 *Fax:* 606-325-2519 *E-mail:* jsf@jsfbooks.com *Web Site:* www.jsfbooks.com, pg 237

Studio Fun International Inc, 44 S Broadway, White Plains, NY 10601 *Tel:* 914-238-1000 *Toll Free Tel:* 800-934-0977 *Web Site:* www.rdtradepublishing.com, pg 237

Jessamy Stursberg Poetry Contest for Youth, 192 Spadina Ave, Suite 312, Toronto, ON M5T 2C2, Canada *Tel:* 416-504-1657 *Fax:* 416-504-0096 *E-mail:* readings@poets.ca *Web Site:* www.youngpoets.ca; poets.ca, pg 731

Stylus Publishing LLC, 22883 Quicksilver Dr, Sterling, VA 20166-2012 *Tel:* 703-661-1504 (edit & sales) *Toll Free Tel:* 800-232-0223 (orders & cust serv) *Fax:* 703-661-1547 *E-mail:* stylusmail@presswarehouse.com (orders & cust serv); stylusinfo@styluspub.com *Web Site:* www.styluspub.com, pg 237

Success Advertising & Publishing, 3419 Dunham Rd, Warsaw, NY 14569 *Tel:* 585-786-5663, pg 237

Sudden Fiction Contest, c/o ASUC Publications, Univ of California, 10-B Eshleman Hall, Berkeley, CA 94720-4500 *E-mail:* bfictionreview@yahoo.com *Web Site:* www.ocf.berkeley.edu/~bfr/, pg 731

Vivian Sudhalter, 1202 Loma Dr, No 117, Ojai, CA 93023 *Tel:* 805-640-9737 *E-mail:* vivians09@att.net, pg 535

The Sugarman Family Award for Jewish Children's Literature, Irwin P Edlavitch Bldg, 1529 16 St NW, Washington, DC 20036 *Tel:* 202-518-9400 *Fax:* 202-518-9420 *Web Site:* www.washingtondcjcc.org, pg 731

Ronald Sukenick American Book Review Innovative Fiction Prize, c/o Dept of English, Langs & Commun Bldg, 255 S Central Campus Dr, Rm 3500, Salt Lake City, UT 84112-0494 *Tel:* 773-702-7000 *Web Site:* www.fc2.org/prizes.html, pg 731

Sumach Press, 425 Adelaide St W, Suite 200, Toronto, ON M5V 3C1, Canada *Tel:* 416-929-2964 *Fax:* 416-929-1926 *E-mail:* info@threeoclockpress.com *Web Site:* www.threeoclockpress.com, pg 500

Summa Publications, PO Box 660725, Birmingham, AL 35266-0725 *Tel:* 205-822-0463 *Fax:* 205-822-0463 *Web Site:* summapub2.googlepages.com, pg 237

The Summer Experience, 601 Spadina Crescent E, Suite 718, Saskatoon, SK S7K 3G8, Canada *Tel:* 306-652-7395 *Fax:* 306-244-0255 *E-mail:* sage.hill@sasktel.net *Web Site:* www.sagehillwriting.ca, pg 656

Summer Writers Program, CE, 250 Hofstra University, Hempstead, NY 11549-2500 *Tel:* 516-463-7200 *Fax:* 516-463-4833 *E-mail:* ce@hofstra.edu *Web Site:* ce.hofstra.edu, pg 656

Summer Writing Seminar, 7 E Pasture Rd, Aquinnah, MA 02535 *Tel:* 954-242-2903 *Web Site:* mvicw.com, pg 656

Hollis Summers Poetry Prize, 215 Columbus Rd, Suite 101, Athens, OH 45701-1373 *Web Site:* www.ohioswallow.com/poetry_prize, pg 731

Summerthought Publishing, PO Box 2309, Banff, AB T1L 1C1, Canada *Tel:* 403-762-0535 *Fax:* 403-762-3095 *Toll Free Fax:* 800-762-3095 (orders) *E-mail:* info@summerthought.com; sales@summerthought.com *Web Site:* summerthought.com, pg 500

Summertime Publications Inc, 7502 E Berridge Lane, Scottsdale, AZ 85250 *Tel:* 480-409-1554 *E-mail:* handell@summertimepublications.com *Web Site:* www.summertimepublications.com, pg 237

Summit University Press, 63 Summit Way, Gardiner, MT 59030-9314 *Tel:* 406-848-9742; 406-848-9500 *Toll Free Tel:* 800-245-5445 (retail orders) *Fax:* 406-848-9650 *Toll Free Fax:* 800-221-8307 *E-mail:* info@summituniversitypress.com *Web Site:* www.summituniversitypress.com, pg 237

Sun Publishing Company, PO Box 5588, Santa Fe, NM 87502-5588 *Tel:* 505-471-5177; 505-473-4161 *Toll Free Tel:* 877-849-0051 *Fax:* 505-473-4458 *E-mail:* info@sunbooks.com *Web Site:* www.sunbooks.com, pg 238

Sunbelt Publications Inc, 1256 Fayette St, El Cajon, CA 92020-1511 *Tel:* 619-258-4911 *Toll Free Tel:* 800-626-6579 (cust serv) *Fax:* 619-258-4916 *E-mail:* service@sunbeltpub.com; info@sunbeltpub.com *Web Site:* www.sunbeltbooks.com, pg 238

Sunburst Digital Inc, 3150 W Higgins Rd, Suite 140, Hoffman Estates, IL 60169 *Toll Free Tel:* 800-321-7511 *Toll Free Fax:* 888-800-3028 *E-mail:* service@sunburst.com; sales@sunburst.com *Web Site:* sunburst.com; edresources.com, pg 238

Sundance/Newbridge Publishing, 33 Boston Post Rd W, Suite 440, Marlborough, MA 01752 *Toll Free Tel:* 888-200-2720; 800-343-8204 (Sundance cust serv & orders); 800-867-0307 (Newbridge cust serv & orders) *Toll Free Fax:* 800-456-2419 (orders) *E-mail:* info@sundancepub.com; info@newbridgeonline.com *Web Site:* www.sundancepub.com; www.newbridgeonline.com, pg 238

Sunrise River Press, 39966 Grand Ave, North Branch, MN 55056 *Tel:* 651-277-1400 *Toll Free Tel:* 800-895-4585 *Fax:* 651-277-1203 *E-mail:* info@sunriseriverpress.com; sales@sunriseriverpress.com *Web Site:* www.sunriseriverpress.com, pg 238

Sunstone Press, PO Box 2321, Santa Fe, NM 87504-2321 *Tel:* 505-988-4418 *Toll Free Tel:* 800-243-5644 *Fax:* 505-988-1025 (orders only) *Web Site:* www.sunstonepress.com, pg 238

Surrey Books, 1328 Greenleaf St, Evanston, IL 60202 *Tel:* 847-475-4457 *Toll Free Tel:* 800-326-4430 *Web Site:* agatepublishing.com/surrey, pg 238

Susquehanna University, Department of English, 514 University Ave, Selinsgrove, PA 17870 *Tel:* 570-372-0101, pg 662

Susquehanna University Press, 514 University Ave, Selinsgrove, PA 17870 *Tel:* 570-372-4175 *Fax:* 570-372-4021 *E-mail:* supress@susqu.edu, pg 238

Fraser Sutherland, 39 Helena Ave, Toronto, ON M6G 2H3, Canada *Tel:* 416-652-5735 *E-mail:* rodfrasers@gmail.com, pg 535

Swagger Literary Agency, 601 Shenandoah Valley Dr, Front Royal, VA 22630 *Tel:* 540-636-7076 *E-mail:* swaggerlit@gmail.com *Web Site:* www.swaggerliterary.com, pg 576

Swallow Press, 215 Columbus Rd, Suite 101, Athens, OH 45701-1373 *Fax:* 740-593-4536 *Web Site:* www.ohioswallow.com, pg 239

Swan Isle Press, 11030 S Langley Ave, Chicago, IL 60628 *Tel:* 773-728-3780 (edit); 773-702-7000 (cust serv) *Toll Free Tel:* 800-621-2736 (cust serv) *Fax:* 773-702-7212 (cust serv) *Toll Free Fax:* 800-621-8476 (cust serv) *E-mail:* info@swanislepress.com *Web Site:* www.swanislepress.com, pg 239

Carolyn Swayze Literary Agency Ltd, 7360 137 St, Suite 319, Surrey, BC V3W 1A3, Canada *Tel:* 604-503-3895 *E-mail:* reception@swayzeagency.com *Web Site:* www.swayzeagency.com, pg 576

Swedenborg Foundation, 320 N Church St, West Chester, PA 19380 *Tel:* 610-430-3222 *Toll Free Tel:* 800-355-3222 (cust serv) *Fax:* 610-430-7982 *E-mail:* info@swedenborg.com *Web Site:* www.swedenborg.com, pg 239

May Swenson Poetry Award, 3078 Old Main Hill, Logan, UT 84322-3078 *Tel:* 435-797-1362 *Fax:* 435-797-0313 *Web Site:* www.usupress.org, pg 731

SYBEX Inc, 111 River St, Hoboken, NJ 07030-5774 *Tel:* 201-748-6000 *Fax:* 201-748-6088 *E-mail:* info@wiley.com *Web Site:* www.sybex.com; www.wiley.com, pg 239

Sydney Taylor Book Awards, PO Box 1118, Teaneck, NJ 07666 *Tel:* 973-744-3836 *E-mail:* chair@sydneytaylorbookaward.org *Web Site:* www.sydneytaylorbookaward.org, pg 731

Sydney Taylor Manuscript Award, 204 Park St, Montclair, NJ 07042 *E-mail:* stmacajl@aol.com *Web Site:* www.jewishlibraries.org, pg 731

Charles S Sydnor Award, University of Georgia, Dept of History, Athens, GA 30602-1602 *Tel:* 706-542-8848 *Fax:* 706-542-2455 *Web Site:* sha.uga.edu, pg 731

Synapse Information Resources Inc, 1247 Taft Ave, Endicott, NY 13760 *Tel:* 607-748-4145 *Toll Free Tel:* 888-SYN-CHEM (796-2436) *Fax:* 607-786-3966 *E-mail:* salesinfo@synapseinfo.com *Web Site:* www.synapseinfo.com, pg 239

Synaxis Press, 37323 Hawkins Rd, Dewdney, BC V0M 1H0, Canada *Tel:* 604-826-9336 *E-mail:* synaxis@new-ostrog.org *Web Site:* synaxispress.ca, pg 500

SynergEbooks, 948 New Hwy 7, Columbia, TN 38401 *Tel:* 931-548-2494 *E-mail:* synergebooks@aol.com *Web Site:* www.synergebooks.com, pg 239

Syracuse University Creative Writing Program, 401 Hall of Languages, Syracuse, NY 13244-1170 *Tel:* 315-443-2173 *Fax:* 315-443-3660 *Web Site:* english.syr.edu/creative_writing; www.syr.edu, pg 662

Syracuse University Press, 621 Skytop Rd, Suite 110, Syracuse, NY 13244-5290 *Tel:* 315-443-5534 *Toll Free Tel:* 800-365-8929 (cust serv) *Fax:* 315-443-5545 *E-mail:* supress@syr.edu *Web Site:* syracuseuniversitypress.syr.edu, pg 239

Syracuse University, SI Newhouse School of Public Communications, 215 University Place, Syracuse, NY 13244-2100 *Tel:* 315-443-3627 *Fax:* 315-443-3946 *E-mail:* newhouse@syr.edu *Web Site:* newhouse.syr.edu, pg 662

Robert E Tabian/Literary Agent, 229 Paterson Ave, Suite 2, East Rutherford, NJ 07073 *Tel:* 631-987-2293 *Fax:* 201-438-1327 *E-mail:* retlit@mindspring.com, pg 576

Tachyon Publications, 1459 18 St, No 139, San Francisco, CA 94107 *Tel:* 415-285-5615 *E-mail:* tachyon@tachyonpublications.com *Web Site:* www.tachyonpublications.com, pg 240

Tag & Label Manufacturers Institute Inc (TLMI), One Blackburn Ctr, Gloucester, MA 01930 *Tel:* 978-282-1400 *Fax:* 978-282-3238 *E-mail:* office@tlmi.com *Web Site:* tlmi.com, pg 620

Tahrike Tarsile Qur'an Inc, 80-08 51 Ave, Elmhurst, NY 11373 *Tel:* 718-446-6472 *Fax:* 718-446-4370 *E-mail:* read@koranusa.org *Web Site:* www.koranusa.org, pg 240

The Tampa Review Prize for Poetry, University of Tampa Press, 401 W Kennedy Blvd, Tampa, FL 33606 *Tel:* 813-253-6266 *E-mail:* utpress@ut.edu *Web Site:* tampareview.ut.edu, pg 731

TAN Books, PO Box 410487, Charlotte, NC 28241 *Toll Free Tel:* 800-437-5876 *Fax:* 815-226-7770 *E-mail:* customerservice@tanbooks.com *Web Site:* tanbooks.benedictpress.com; benedictpress.com, pg 240

T&T Clark International, 1385 Broadway, 5th fl, New York, NY 10018 *Tel:* 212-953-5858 *Toll Free Tel:* 800-561-7704 (orders) *Fax:* 212-953-5944 *Web Site:* www.continuumbooks.com, pg 240

Tanglewood Press, PO Box 3009, Terre Haute, IN 47803 *Tel:* 812-877-9488; 412-741-1579 (orders) *Toll Free Tel:* 800-836-4994 (orders) *Fax:* 412-741-0609 (orders) *Web Site:* www.tanglewoodbooks.com, pg 240

Tantor Media Inc, 2 Business Park, Old Saybrook, CT 06475 *Toll Free Tel:* 877-782-6867 *Toll Free Fax:* 888-782-7821 *Web Site:* www.tantor.com, pg 240

Taos Summer Writers' Conference, One University of New Mexico, Albuquerque, NM 87131-0001 *Tel:* 505-277-5572 *E-mail:* taosconf@unm.edu *Web Site:* taosconf.unm.edu, pg 656

Tapestry Press Ltd, 19 Nashoba Rd, Littleton, MA 01460 *Tel:* 978-486-0200 *Toll Free Tel:* 800-535-2007 *Fax:* 978-486-0244 *E-mail:* publish@tapestrypress.com *Web Site:* www.tapestrypress.com, pg 240

Taplinger Publishing Co Inc, PO Box 175, Marlboro, NJ 07746-0175 *Tel:* 305-256-7880 *Fax:* 305-256-7816 *E-mail:* taplingerpub@yahoo.com (rts & perms, edit, corp only), pg 240

Jeremy P Tarcher, 375 Hudson St, New York, NY 10014 *Tel:* 212-366-2000 *E-mail:* online@penguinputnam.com *Web Site:* www.penguinputnam.com; us.penguingroup.com, pg 240

Taschen America, 6671 Sunset Blvd, Suite 1508, Los Angeles, CA 90028 *Tel:* 323-463-4441 *Toll Free Tel:* 888-TASCHEN (827-2436) *Fax:* 323-463-4442 *E-mail:* contact-us@taschen.com *Web Site:* www.taschen.com, pg 241

The Taunton Press Inc, 63 S Main St, Newtown, CT 06470 *Tel:* 203-426-8171 *Toll Free Tel:* 800-477-8727 (cust serv); 800-888-8286 (orders) *Fax:* 203-426-3434 *E-mail:* booksales@taunton.com *Web Site:* www.taunton.com, pg 241

Taylor & Francis Inc, 325 Chestnut St, Suite 800, Philadelphia, PA 20036-1802 *Tel:* 215-625-8900 *Toll Free Tel:* 800-354-1420 *Fax:* 215-625-2940 *E-mail:* customer.service@taylorandfrancis.com *Web Site:* www.taylorandfrancis.com, pg 241

The Charles Taylor Prize, 26 Berkeley St, Toronto, ON M5A 2W3, Canada *Tel:* 416-901-9314 *E-mail:* rbctaylorprize@gmail.com *Web Site:* thecharlestaylorprize.ca, pg 731

Taylor-Dth Publishing, 108 Caribe Isle, Novato, CA 94949 *Tel:* 415-299-1087 *Web Site:* www.taylor-dth.com, pg 241

Rennie Taylor & Alton Blakeslee Fellowships in Science Writing, PO Box 910, Hedgesville, WV 25427 *Tel:* 304-754-6786 *Web Site:* www.casw.org, pg 731

TCP Press, Legacy Ctr, 9 Lobraico Lane, Whitchurch-Stouffville, ON L4A 7X5, Canada *Tel:* 905-640-8914 *Toll Free Tel:* 800-772-7765 *E-mail:* tcp@tcpnow.com *Web Site:* www.tcppress.com, pg 500

TD Canadian Children's Literature Award, 40 Orchard View Blvd, Suite 217, Toronto, ON M4R 1B9, Canada *Tel:* 416-975-0010 *Fax:* 416-975-8970 *E-mail:* info@bookcentre.ca *Web Site:* www.bookcentre.ca, pg 732

Teach Me Tapes Inc, 6016 Blue Circle Dr, Minnetonka, MN 55343 *Tel:* 952-933-8086 *Toll Free Tel:* 800-456-4656 *Fax:* 952-933-0512 *E-mail:* marie@teachmetapes.com *Web Site:* www.teachmetapes.com, pg 241

Teacher Created Resources Inc, 6421 Industry Way, Westminster, CA 92683 *Tel:* 714-891-7895 *Toll Free Tel:* 800-662-4321; 888-343-4335 *Fax:* 714-892-0283 *Toll Free Fax:* 800-525-1254 *E-mail:* custserv@teachercreated.com *Web Site:* www.teachercreated.com, pg 241

Teachers & Writers Collaborative, 520 Eighth Ave, Suite 2020, New York, NY 10018-4165 *Tel:* 212-691-6590 *Toll Free Tel:* 888-BOOKS-TW (266-5789) *Fax:* 212-675-0171 *E-mail:* info@twc.org *Web Site:* www.twc.org, pg 620

Teachers College Press, 1234 Amsterdam Ave, New York, NY 10027 *Tel:* 212-678-3929 *Toll Free Tel:* 800-575-6566 *Fax:* 212-678-4149; 802-864-7626 *E-mail:* tcpress@tc.columbia.edu; tcp.orders@aidcvt.com (orders) *Web Site:* www.teacherscollegepress.com, pg 241

Teacher's Discovery, 2741 Paldan Dr, Auburn Hills, MI 48326 *Toll Free Tel:* 800-832-2437 *Toll Free Fax:* 800-287-4509 *E-mail:* foreignlanguage@teachersdiscovery.com, pg 242

Teachers of English to Speakers of Other Languages Inc (TESOL), 1925 Ballenger Ave, Alexandria, VA 22314-6820 *Tel:* 703-836-0774 *Toll Free Tel:* 888-547-3369 *Fax:* 703-836-7864 *E-mail:* info@tesol.org *Web Site:* www.tesol.org, pg 242

Teaching & Learning Co, 501 E Third St, Dayton, OH 45402 *Tel:* 937-228-6118 *Toll Free Tel:* 800-444-1144 *Fax:* 937-223-2042 *E-mail:* info@lorenz.com, pg 242

Teaching Strategies, 7101 Wisconsin Ave, Suite 700, Bethesda, MD 20814 *Tel:* 301-634-0818 *Toll Free Tel:* 800-637-3652 *Fax:* 301-657-0250 *E-mail:* customerrelations@teachingstrategies.com *Web Site:* www.teachingstrategies.com, pg 242

Technical Association of the Pulp & Paper Industry (TAPPI), 15 Technology Pkwy S, Suite 115, Peachtree Corners, GA 30092 *Tel:* 770-446-1400 *Toll Free Tel:* 800-332-8686 (US); 800-446-9431 (CN) *Fax:* 770-446-6947 *E-mail:* memberconnection@tappi.org *Web Site:* www.tappi.org, pg 620

Television Academy, 5220 Lankershim Blvd, North Hollywood, CA 91601-3109 *Tel:* 818-754-2800 *Fax:* 818-761-2827 *Web Site:* www.emmys.com, pg 620

Temple University Press, 1852 N Tenth St, Philadelphia, PA 19122-6099 *Tel:* 215-926-2140 *Toll Free Tel:* 800-621-2736 *Fax:* 215-926-2141 *E-mail:* tempress@temple.edu *Web Site:* www.temple.edu/tempress, pg 242

Templegate Publishers, 302 E Adams St, Springfield, IL 62701 *Tel:* 217-522-3353 (edit & sales); 217-522-3354 (billing) *Toll Free Tel:* 800-367-4844 (orders only) *Fax:* 217-522-3362 *E-mail:* wisdom@templegate.com; orders@templegate.com (sales) *Web Site:* www.templegate.com, pg 242

Templeton Press, 300 Conshohocken State Rd, Suite 550, West Conshohocken, PA 19428 *Tel:* 484-531-8380 *Fax:* 484-531-8382 *E-mail:* tpinfo@templetonpress.org *Web Site:* www.templetonpress.org, pg 242

Temporal Mechanical Press, 6760 Hwy 7, Estes Park, CO 80517-6404 *Tel:* 970-586-4706 *E-mail:* enosmillscbn@earthlink.net *Web Site:* www.enosmills.com, pg 242

Ten Speed Press, 2625 Alcatraz Ave, Unit 505, Berkeley, CA 94705 *Tel:* 510-285-3000 *Toll Free Tel:* 800-841-BOOK (841-2665) *E-mail:* csorders@randomhouse.com *Web Site:* crownpublishing.com/imprint/ten-speed-press, pg 243

Tennessee Arts Commission Fellowships, 401 Charlotte Ave, Nashville, TN 37243-0780 *Tel:* 615-741-1701 *Toll Free Tel:* 800-848-0299 *Fax:* 615-741-8559 *Web Site:* www.tn.gov/arts, pg 732

Teora USA LLC, 505 Hampton Park Blvd, Unit G, Capitol Heights, MD 20743 *Tel:* 301-986-6990 *Toll Free Tel:* 800-974-2105 *Fax:* 301-350-5480 *Toll Free Fax:* 800-358-3754 *E-mail:* 2010@teora.com *Web Site:* www.teora.com, pg 243

Tessler Literary Agency LLC, 27 W 20 St, Suite 1003, New York, NY 10011 *Tel:* 212-242-0466 *Fax:* 212-242-2366 *Web Site:* www.tessleragency.com, pg 577

Teton NewMedia, 90 E Simpson, Suite 110, Jackson, WY 83001 *Tel:* 307-732-0028 *Toll Free Tel:* 877-306-9793 *Fax:* 307-734-0841 *E-mail:* sales@tetonnm.com *Web Site:* www.tetonnm.com, pg 243

Tetra Press, 3001 Commerce St, Blacksburg, VA 24060 *Tel:* 540-951-5400 *Toll Free Tel:* 800-526-0650 *Fax:* 540-951-5415 *E-mail:* consumer@tetra-fish.com *Web Site:* www.tetra-fish.com, pg 243

Texas A&M University Press, John H Lindsey Bldg, Lewis St, 4354 TAMU, College Station, TX 77843-4354 *Tel:* 979-845-1436 *Toll Free Tel:* 800-826-8911 (orders) *Fax:* 979-847-8752 *Toll Free Fax:* 888-617-2421 (orders) *E-mail:* tampress@tamu.edu *Web Site:* www.tamupress.com, pg 243

The Texas Bluebonnet Award, 3355 Bee Cave Rd, Suite 401, Austin, TX 78746 *Tel:* 512-328-1518 *Toll Free Tel:* 800-580-2852 *Fax:* 512-328-8852 *Web Site:* www.txla.org, pg 732

Texas Christian University Press, 3000 Sandage Ave, Fort Worth, TX 76109 *Tel:* 817-257-7822 *Toll Free Tel:* 800-826-8911 *Fax:* 817-257-5075 *Web Site:* www.prs.tcu.edu, pg 243

Texas Institute of Letters (TIL), c/o 7748 Hwy 290 W, Austin, TX 78736-3202 *E-mail:* president@texasinstituteofletters.org; secretary@texasinstituteofletters.org *Web Site:* www.texasinstituteofletters.org, pg 620

Texas Institute of Letters Awards, c/o 7748 Hwy 290 W, Austin, TX 78736-3202 *Tel:* 512-683-5640 *E-mail:* president@texasinstituteofletters.org *Web Site:* www.texasinstituteofletters.org, pg 732

Texas State Historical Association, Stovall Hall 175, 1400 W Highland St, Denton, TX 76203 *Tel:* 940-369-5200 *Fax:* 940-369-5248 *Web Site:* www.tshaonline.org, pg 243

Texas Tech University Press, 2903 Fourth St, Suite 201, Lubbock, TX 79409 *Tel:* 806-742-2982 *Toll Free Tel:* 800-832-4042 *Fax:* 806-742-2979 *E-mail:* ttup@ttu.edu *Web Site:* www.ttupress.org, pg 243

University of Texas Press, 2100 Comal St, Austin, TX 78722 *Tel:* 512-471-7233 *Fax:* 512-232-7178 *E-mail:* utpress@uts.cc.utexas.edu *Web Site:* www.utexaspress.com, pg 244

Texas Western Press, c/o University of Texas at El Paso, 500 W University Ave, El Paso, TX 79968-0633 *Tel:* 915-747-5688 *Toll Free Tel:* 800-488-3798 (orders only) *Fax:* 915-747-7515 *E-mail:* twpress@utep.edu *Web Site:* twp.utep.edu, pg 244

Textbook Writers Associates Inc, 25 Crescent St, Suite 733, Waltham, MA 02453 *Tel:* 781-209-0051 *Fax:* 781-899-2084 *Web Site:* www.textbookwriters.com, pg 535

TFH Publications Inc, One TFH Plaza, Third & Union Aves, Neptune City, NJ 07753 *Tel:* 732-988-8400 *Toll Free Tel:* 800-631-2188 *Fax:* 732-776-8763 *E-mail:* info@tfh.com *Web Site:* www.tfh.com, pg 244

Thames & Hudson, 500 Fifth Ave, New York, NY 10110 *Tel:* 212-354-3763 *Toll Free Tel:* 800-233-4830 *Fax:* 212-398-1252 *E-mail:* bookinfo@thames.wwnorton.com *Web Site:* www.thamesandhudsonusa.com, pg 244

The Society of Professional Journalists (SPJ), Eugene S Pulliam National Journalism Ctr, 3909 N Meridian St, Indianapolis, IN 46208 *Tel:* 317-927-8000 *Fax:* 317-920-4789 *E-mail:* spj@spj.org *Web Site:* www.spj.org, pg 620

Theatre Communications Group, 520 Eighth Ave, 24th fl, New York, NY 10018-4156 *Tel:* 212-609-5900 *Fax:* 212-609-5901 *E-mail:* tcg@tcg.org *Web Site:* www.tcg.org, pg 244

Theosophical Publishing House/Quest Books, 306 W Geneva Rd, Wheaton, IL 60187 *Tel:* 630-665-0130 (ext 347) *Toll Free Tel:* 800-669-9425 (ext 347) *Fax:* 630-665-8791 *E-mail:* customerservice@questbooks.net *Web Site:* www.questbooks.net, pg 244

Theosophical University Press, PO Box C, Pasadena, CA 91109-7107 *Tel:* 626-798-3378 *E-mail:* tupress@theosociety.org *Web Site:* www.theosociety.org, pg 244

Theytus Books Ltd, RR 2, Green Mountain Rd, Site 50, Comp 8, Lot 45, Penticton, BC V2A 6J7, Canada *Tel:* 250-493-7181 *Fax:* 250-493-5302 *E-mail:* order@theytus.com *Web Site:* www.theytus.com, pg 500

Thieme Medical Publishers Inc, 333 Seventh Ave, 18th fl, New York, NY 10001 *Tel:* 212-760-0888 *Toll Free Tel:* 800-782-3488 *Fax:* 212-947-1112 *E-mail:* customerservice@thieme.com *Web Site:* www.thieme.com, pg 245

Thinkers' Press Inc, 1524 Le Claire St, Davenport, IA 52803 *Tel:* 563-271-6657 *E-mail:* info@chessbutler.com *Web Site:* www.thinkerspressinc.com, pg 245

Third World Press, 7822 S Dobson Ave, Chicago, IL 60619 *Tel:* 773-651-0700 *Fax:* 773-651-7286 *E-mail:* twpress3@aol.com *Web Site:* www.thirdworldpressbooks.com, pg 245

Thistledown Press, 410 Second Ave, Saskatoon, SK S7N 2C3, Canada *Tel:* 306-244-1722 *Fax:* 306-244-1762 *E-mail:* tdpress@thistledownpress.com; editorial@thistledownpress.com; marketing@thistledownpress.com *Web Site:* www.thistledownpress.com, pg 500

Thodestool Fiction Editing, 40 McDougall Rd, Waterloo, ON N2L 2W5, Canada *Web Site:* www.thodestool.com, pg 535

Charles C Thomas Publisher Ltd, 2600 S First St, Springfield, IL 62704 *Tel:* 217-789-8980 *Toll Free Tel:* 800-258-8980 *Fax:* 217-789-9130 *E-mail:* books@ccthomas.com *Web Site:* www.ccthomas.com, pg 245

Thomas Geale Publications Inc, PO Box 370540, Montara, CA 94037-0540 *Tel:* 650-728-5219 *Toll Free Tel:* 800-554-5457 *Fax:* 650-728-0918 *E-mail:* justthink@comcast.net, pg 245

Thomas Nelson, 501 Nelson Place, Nashville, TN 37214 *Tel:* 615-889-9000 *Toll Free Tel:* 800-251-4000 *Fax:* 615-902-1548 *E-mail:* publicity@thomasnelson.com *Web Site:* www.thomasnelson.com, pg 245

Thomas Publications, 3245 Fairfield Rd, Gettysburg, PA 17325 *Tel:* 717-642-6600 *Toll Free Tel:* 800-840-6782 *Fax:* 717-642-5555 *E-mail:* info@thomaspublications.com *Web Site:* www.thomaspublications.com, pg 245

Thompson Educational Publishing Inc, 20 Ripley Ave, Toronto, ON M6S 3N9, Canada *Tel:* 416-766-2763 (admin & orders) *Toll Free Tel:* 877-366-2763 *Fax:* 416-766-0398 (admin & orders) *E-mail:* info@thompsonbooks.com *Web Site:* www.thompsonbooks.com, pg 501

Thompson Mill Press LLC, 2865 S Eagle Rd, No 368, Newtown, PA 18940 *Tel:* 215-431-1424 *E-mail:* bob.regan@thompsonmillpress.com *Web Site:* www.thompsonmillpress.com; www.KobeeManatee.com, pg 509

Thomson Reuters Westlaw™, 610 Opperman Dr, Eagan, MN 55123 *Tel:* 651-687-7000 *Toll Free Tel:* 800-328-9352 (sales); 800-328-4880 (cust serv) *Fax:* 651-687-7302 *Web Site:* www.westlawnext.com; store.westlaw.com, pg 245

Thorndike Press, 10 Water St, Suite 310, Waterville, ME 04901 *Toll Free Tel:* 800-233-1244 (ext 4, cust serv/orders) *Toll Free Fax:* 800-558-4676 (orders) *E-mail:* gale.printorders@cengage.com; international@cengage.com (cust orders outside US & CN) *Web Site:* thorndike.gale.com, pg 245

Susan Thornton, 6090 Liberty Ave, Vermilion, OH 44089 *Tel:* 440-967-1757 *E-mail:* allenthornton@earthlink.net, pg 535

3-Day Novel Contest, 201-111 W Hastings St, Vancouver, BC V6B 1H4, Canada *E-mail:* info@3daynovel.com *Web Site:* www.3daynovel.com, pg 732

3 Seas Literary Agency, PO Box 8571, Madison, WI 53708 *Tel:* 608-834-9317, pg 577

Three Wishes Publishing Company, 26500 W Agoura Rd, Suite 102-754, Calabasas, CA 91302 *Tel:* 818-878-0902 *Fax:* 818-878-1805 *E-mail:* Alva710@aol.com *Web Site:* www.threewishespublishing.com, pg 509

ThunderStone Books, 6575 Horse Dr, Las Vegas, NV 89131 *E-mail:* info@thunderstonebooks.com *Web Site:* www.thunderstonebooks.com, pg 246

Thurber Prize for American Humor, 77 Jefferson Ave, Columbus, OH 43215 *Tel:* 614-464-1032 *Fax:* 614-280-3645 *E-mail:* thurberhouse@thurberhouse.org *Web Site:* www.thurberhouse.org, pg 732

Tide-mark Press, 22 Prestige Park Circle, East Hartford, CT 06108-1917 *Tel:* 860-310-3370 *Toll Free Tel:* 800-338-2508 *Fax:* 860-310-3654 *E-mail:* customerservice@tide-mark.com *Web Site:* www.tidemarkpress.com, pg 246

Tiger Tales, 5 River Rd, Suite 128, Wilton, CT 06897 *Tel:* 920-387-2333 *Fax:* 920-387-9994 *Web Site:* www.tigertalesbooks.com, pg 246

Tilbury House Publishers, 12 Starr St, Thomaston, ME 04861 *Tel:* 207-582-1899 *Toll Free Tel:* 800-582-1899 (orders) *Fax:* 207-582-8227 *E-mail:* tilbury@tilburyhouse.com *Web Site:* www.tilburyhouse.com, pg 246

Timber Press Inc, 133 SW Second Ave, Suite 450, Portland, OR 97204 *Tel:* 503-227-2878 *Toll Free Tel:* 800-327-5680 *Fax:* 503-227-3070 *E-mail:* info@timberpress.com *Web Site:* www.timberpress.com, pg 246

Time Being Books, 10411 Clayton Rd, Suites 201-203, St Louis, MO 63131 *Tel:* 314-432-1771 *Fax:* 314-432-7939 *E-mail:* tbbooks@sbcglobal.net *Web Site:* www.timebeing.com, pg 246

James Tiptree Jr Award, 680 66 St, Oakland, CA 94609 *Tel:* 510-658-7176 *E-mail:* info@tiptree.org *Web Site:* tiptree.org, pg 732

TJ Publishers Inc, PO Box 702701, Dallas, TX 75370 *Toll Free Tel:* 800-999-1168 *Fax:* 972-416-0944 *E-mail:* TJPubinc@aol.com, pg 509

The Toby Press LLC, PO Box 8531, New Milford, CT 06776-8531 *Tel:* 203-830-8508 *Fax:* 203-830-8512 *E-mail:* toby@tobypress.com *Web Site:* korenpub.com/toby/intusd/, pg 246

Todd Publications, 1388 Sabal Palm Dr, Boca Raton, FL 33432 *Tel:* 561-910-0440 *Fax:* 561-910-0440 *E-mail:* toddpub@yahoo.com, pg 246

The Tomasino Agency Inc, 70 Chestnut St, Dobbs Ferry, NY 10522 *Tel:* 914-674-9659 *Fax:* 914-693-0381 *E-mail:* info@tomasinoagency.com *Web Site:* www.tomasinoagency.com, pg 577

Tommy Nelson, 501 Nelson Place, Nashville, TN 37214 *Tel:* 615-889-9000; 615-902-1485 (cust serv) *Toll Free Tel:* 800-251-4000 *Fax:* 615-391-5225 *Web Site:* www.tommynelson.com, pg 247

Tony Hillerman Writers Conference, 1063 Willow Way, Santa Fe, NM 87507 *Tel:* 505-471-1565 *E-mail:* wordharvest@wordharvest.com *Web Site:* www.wordharvest.com, pg 656

Top of the Mountain Publishing, PO Box 2244, Pinellas Park, FL 33780-2244 *Tel:* 727-391-3958 *E-mail:* tag@abcinfo.com; info@abcinfo.com *Web Site:* abcinfo.com; www.topofthemountain.com, pg 247

Top Publications Ltd, 12221 Merit Dr, Suite 950, Dallas, TX 75251 *Tel:* 972-628-6414 *Fax:* 972-233-0713 *E-mail:* info@toppub.com *Web Site:* toppub.com, pg 247

Torah Aura Productions, 4423 Fruitland Ave, Los Angeles, CA 90058 *Tel:* 323-585-7312 *Toll Free Tel:* 800-238-6724 *Fax:* 323-585-0327 *E-mail:* misrad@torahaura.com; orders@torahaura.com *Web Site:* www.torahaura.com, pg 247

Torah Umesorah Publications, 620 Foster Ave, Brooklyn, NY 11230 *Tel:* 718-259-1223 *Fax:* 718-259-1795 *E-mail:* publications@torah-umesorah.org, pg 247

Toronto Book Awards, c/o Toronto Arts & Culture, City Hall, 9E, 100 Queen St W, Toronto, ON M5H 2N2, Canada *Web Site:* www.toronto.ca/book_awards, pg 732

Tortuga Press, 2777 Yulupa Ave, PMB 181, Santa Rosa, CA 95405 *Tel:* 707-544-4720 *Toll Free Tel:* 866-4TORTUGA (486-7884) *Fax:* 707-544-5609 *E-mail:* info@tortugapress.com *Web Site:* www.tortugapress.com, pg 247

TotalRecall Publications Inc, 1103 Middlecreek, Friendswood, TX 77546 *Tel:* 281-992-3131 *E-mail:* sales@totalrecallpress.com *Web Site:* www.totalrecallpress.com, pg 247

Touchstone, 1230 Avenue of the Americas, New York, NY 10020, pg 247

TouchWood Editions, 103-1075 Pendergast St, Victoria, BC V8V 0A1, Canada *Tel:* 250-360-0829 *Fax:* 250-386-0829 *E-mail:* info@touchwoodeditions.com *Web Site:* www.touchwoodeditions.com, pg 501

Tower Publishing Co, 588 Saco Rd, Standish, ME 04084 *Tel:* 207-642-5400 *Toll Free Tel:* 800-969-8693 *Fax:* 207-264-3870 *E-mail:* info@towerpub.com *Web Site:* www.towerpub.com, pg 247

Townson Publishing Co Ltd, PO Box 1404, Sta A, Vancouver, BC V6C 2P7, Canada *Tel:* 604-886-0594 (CN) *E-mail:* townsonpublishing@gmail.com *Web Site:* generalpublishing.co.uk, pg 501

Towson University Prize for Literature, English Dept, 8000 York Rd, Towson, MD 21252 *Tel:* 410-704-2000 *Fax:* 410-704-3999 *Web Site:* www.towson.edu/english, pg 732

Tracks Publishing, 140 Brightwood Ave, Chula Vista, CA 91910 *Tel:* 619-476-7125 *Toll Free Tel:* 800-443-3570 *Fax:* 619-476-8173 *E-mail:* tracks@cox.net *Web Site:* www.startupsports.com, pg 247

Tradewind Books, 202-1807 Maritime Mews, Vancouver, BC V6H 3W7, Canada *Tel:* 604-662-4405 *E-mail:* tradewindbooks@yahoo.com *Web Site:* www.tradewindbooks.com, pg 501

Trafalgar Square Books, 388 Howe Hill Rd, North Pomfret, VT 05053 *Tel:* 802-457-1911 *Toll Free Tel:* 800-423-4525 *Fax:* 802-457-1913 *E-mail:* contact@trafalgarbooks.com *Web Site:* www.trafalgarbooks.com; www.horseandriderbooks.com, pg 248

Trafford, 1663 Liberty Dr, Bloomington, IN 47403 *Toll Free Tel:* 888-232-4444 *E-mail:* customersupport@trafford.com *Web Site:* www.trafford.com, pg 248

Trails Books, 3005 Center Green Dr, Suite 225, Boulder, CO 80301 *Tel:* 303-541-1506 *Toll Free Tel:* 800-258-5830 *E-mail:* books@bigearthpublishing.com *Web Site:* www.trailsbooks.com, pg 248

Training Resource Network Inc (TRN), PO Box 439, St Augustine, FL 32085-0439 *Tel:* 904-823-9800 (cust serv) *Toll Free Tel:* 800-280-7010 (orders) *Fax:* 904-823-3554 *E-mail:* customerservice@trninc.com *Web Site:* www.trn-store.com, pg 248

Tralco-Lingo Fun, 3909 Witmer Rd, Suite 856, Niagara Falls, NY 14305 *Tel:* 905-575-5717 *Toll Free Tel:* 888-487-2526 *Fax:* 905-575-1783 *Toll Free Fax:* 866-487-2527 *E-mail:* contact@tralco.com *Web Site:* www.tralco.com, pg 248

Trans-Atlantic Publications Inc, 311 Bainbridge St, Philadelphia, PA 19147 *Tel:* 215-925-5083 *Fax:* 215-925-1912 *Web Site:* www.transatlanticpub.com; www.businesstitles.com, pg 248

Trans Tech Publications, c/o Enfield Distribution Co, 234 May St, Enfield, NH 03748 *Tel:* 603-632-7377 *Fax:* 603-632-5611 *E-mail:* usa-ttp@ttp.net; info@enfieldbooks.com *Web Site:* www.ttp.net, pg 248

Transaction Publishers Inc, 10 Corporate Place S, 35 Berrue Circle, Piscataway, NJ 08854 *Tel:* 732-445-2280; 732-445-1245 (orders) *Toll Free Tel:* 888-999-6778 (dist ctr) *Fax:* 732-445-3138 *E-mail:* trans@transactionpub.com; orders@transactionpub.om *Web Site:* www.transactionpub.com, pg 248

Transatlantic Agency, 2 Bloor St E, Suite 3500, Toronto, ON M4W 1A8, Canada *Tel:* 416-488-9214 *E-mail:* info@transatlanticagency.com *Web Site:* www.transatlanticagency.com, pg 577

Transcontinental Music Publications, 633 Third Ave, New York, NY 10017 *Tel:* 212-650-4101; 212-650-4120 *Toll Free Tel:* 888-489-8242 (orders) *Fax:* 212-650-4119 *E-mail:* tmp@urj.org; press@urj.org *Web Site:* www.transcontinentalmusic.com, pg 248

Transportation Research Board, 500 Fifth St NW, Washington, DC 20001 *Tel:* 202-334-2934; 202-334-3213 (orders); 202-334-3072 (subns) *Fax:* 202-334-2519 *E-mail:* trbsales@nas.edu *Web Site:* trb.org, pg 249

Travel Keys, PO Box 160691, Sacramento, CA 95816-0691 *Tel:* 916-452-5200 *Fax:* 916-452-5200, pg 249

Travelers' Tales, 2320 Bowdoin St, Palo Alto, CA 94306 *Tel:* 650-462-2110 *Fax:* 650-462-6305 *E-mail:* ttales@travelerstales.com *Web Site:* www.travelerstales.com, pg 249

Treasure Bay Inc, PO Box 119, Novato, CA 94948 *Tel:* 415-884-2888 *Fax:* 415-884-2840 *E-mail:* webothread@comcast.net *Web Site:* www.webothread.com, pg 249

Treehaus Communications Inc, 906 W Loveland Ave, Loveland, OH 45140 *Tel:* 513-683-5716 *Toll Free Tel:* 800-638-4287 (orders) *Fax:* 513-683-2882 (orders) *E-mail:* treehaus@treehaus1.com *Web Site:* www.treehaus1.com, pg 249

Triad Publishing Co, PO Box 13355, Gainesville, FL 32604 *Tel:* 352-373-5800 *Fax:* 352-373-1488 *Toll Free Fax:* 800-854-4947 *E-mail:* orders@triadpublishing.com *Web Site:* www.triadpublishing.com, pg 249

TriadaUS Literary Agency, PO Box 561, Sewickley, PA 15143 *Tel:* 412-401-3376 *Fax:* 412-749-0842 *Web Site:* www.triadaus.com, pg 577

Trident Inc, 885 Pierce Butler Rte, St Paul, MN 55104 *Tel:* 651-638-0077 *Fax:* 651-638-0084 *E-mail:* info@atlas-games.com *Web Site:* www.atlas-games.com, pg 249

Trident Media Group LLC, 41 Madison Ave, 36th fl, New York, NY 10010 *Tel:* 212-333-1511 *E-mail:* info@tridentmediagroup.com; press@tridentmediagroup.com *Web Site:* www.tridentmediagroup.com, pg 577

Trillium Book Award/Prix Trillium, South Tower, Suite 501, 175 Bloor St E, Toronto, ON M4W 3R8, Canada *Tel:* 416-314-6858 (ext 698) *Fax:* 416-314-6876 *E-mail:* trillium23@omdc.on.ca *Web Site:* www.omdc.on.ca, pg 732

The Trinity Foundation, PO Box 68, Unicoi, TN 37692-0068 *Tel:* 423-743-0199 *Fax:* 423-743-2005 *Web Site:* www.trinityfoundation.org, pg 249

Trinity University Press, One Trinity Place, San Antonio, TX 78212-7200 *Tel:* 210-999-8884 *Fax:* 210-999-8838 *E-mail:* books@trinity.edu *Web Site:* www.tupress.org, pg 249

TripBuilder Media Inc, 180 Post Rd E, Suite 200, Westport, CT 06880 *Tel:* 203-227-1255 *Toll Free Tel:* 800-525-9745 *Fax:* 203-227-1257 *E-mail:* info@tripbuildermedia.com *Web Site:* www.tripbuildermedia.com, pg 249

TriQuarterly Books, 629 Noyes St, Evanston, IL 60201 *Toll Free Tel:* 800-621-2736 (orders only) *Fax:* 847-467-2096 *E-mail:* nupress@northwestern.edu *Web Site:* www.nupress.northwestern.edu, pg 249

TRISTAN Publishing, 2355 Louisiana Ave, Minneapolis, MN 55427 *Tel:* 763-545-1383 *Toll Free Tel:* 866-545-1383 *Fax:* 763-545-1387 *E-mail:* info@tristanpublishing.com *Web Site:* www.tristanpublishing.com, pg 250

Triumph Books, 814 N Franklin St, Chicago, IL 60610 *Toll Free Tel:* 800-888-4741 (orders only) *Fax:* 312-280-5470 *Web Site:* www.triumphbooks.com, pg 250

Triumph Learning LLC, 136 Madison Ave, 7th fl, New York, NY 10016 *Tel:* 212-652-0200 *Toll Free Tel:* 800-338-6519 (cust serv) *Toll Free Fax:* 866-805-5723 *E-mail:* info@triumphlearning.com; customerservice@triumphlearning.com *Web Site:* www.triumphlearning.com, pg 250

Harry S Truman Book Award, 500 W US Hwy 24, Independence, MO 64050 *Tel:* 816-268-8200 *Toll Free Tel:* 800-833-1225 *Web Site:* trumanlibraryinstitute.org, pg 732

Truman State University Press, 100 E Normal Ave, Kirksville, MO 63501-4221 *Tel:* 660-785-7336 *Toll Free Tel:* 800-916-6802 *Fax:* 660-785-4480 *E-mail:* tsup@truman.edu *Web Site:* tsup.truman.edu, pg 250

Trustus Playwrights' Festival, 520 Lady St, Columbia, SC 29201 *Tel:* 803-254-9732 *Fax:* 803-771-9153 *E-mail:* trustus@trustus.org *Web Site:* www.trustus.org, pg 732

TSAR Publications, PO Box 6996, Sta A, Toronto, ON M5W 1X7, Canada *Tel:* 416-483-7191 *Fax:* 416-486-0706 *E-mail:* inquiries@tsarbooks.com *Web Site:* www.tsarbooks.com, pg 501

TSG Publishing Foundation Inc, 28641 N 63 Place, Cave Creek, AZ 85331 *Tel:* 480-502-1909 *Fax:* 480-502-0713 *E-mail:* info@tsgfoundation.org *Web Site:* www.tsgfoundation.org, pg 250

Tudor Publishers Inc, 3109 Shady Lawn Dr, Greensboro, NC 27408 *Tel:* 336-288-5395 *E-mail:* tudorpublishers@triad.rr.com, pg 250

The Tuesday Agency, 132 1/2 E Washington St, Iowa City, IA 52240 *Tel:* 319-338-7080 *E-mail:* trinity@tuesdayagency.com *Web Site:* tuesdayagency.com, pg 588

Kate Tufts Discovery Award, Harper East, Unit B-7, 160 E Tenth St, Claremont, CA 91711-6165 *Tel:* 909-621-8974 *E-mail:* tufts@cgu.edu *Web Site:* www.cgu.edu/tufts, pg 733

Kingsley Tufts Poetry Award, Harper East, Unit B-7, 160 E Tenth St, Claremont, CA 91711-6165 *Tel:* 909-621-8974 *E-mail:* tufts@cgu.edu *Web Site:* www.cgu.edu/tufts, pg 733

Christina A Tugeau Artist Agency LLC, 3009 Margaret Jones Lane, Williamsburg, VA 23185 *Tel:* 757-221-0666; 917-434-3141 *E-mail:* chris@catugeau.com *Web Site:* www.catugeau.com, pg 585

Tugeau 2 Inc, 2231 Grandview Ave, Cleveland Heights, OH 44106 *Tel:* 216-707-0854 *Fax:* 216-795-8404 *Web Site:* www.tugeau2.com, pg 585

Tughra Books, 345 Clifton Ave, Clifton, NJ 07011 *Tel:* 973-777-2704 *Fax:* 973-457-7334 *E-mail:* info@tughrabooks.com *Web Site:* www.tughrabooks.com, pg 250

Tumblehome Learning Inc, PO Box 171386, Boston, MA 02117 *E-mail:* info@tumblehomelearning.com *Web Site:* www.tumblehomelearning.com, pg 250

Tundra Books, One Toronto St, Suite 300, Toronto, ON M5C 2V6, Canada *Tel:* 416-364-4449 *Toll Free Tel:* 888-523-9292 (orders); 800-588-1074 *Fax:* 416-598-0247 *Toll Free Fax:* 888-562-9924 (orders) *E-mail:* tundra@mcclelland.com *Web Site:* www.tundrabooks.com, pg 501

Tupelo Press Inc, PO Box 1767, North Adams, MA 01247 *Tel:* 413-664-9611 *Fax:* 413-664-9711 *E-mail:* info@tupelopress.org *Web Site:* www.tupelopress.org, pg 250

Tupelo Press Poetry Contest for First or Second Books of Poetry, PO Box 1767, North Adams, MA 01247 *Tel:* 413-664-9611 *Fax:* 413-664-9711 *E-mail:* info@tupelopress.org *Web Site:* www.tupelopress.org, pg 733

Tupelo Press Snowbound Series Chapbook Award, PO Box 1767, North Adams, MA 01247 *Tel:* 413-664-9611 *Fax:* 413-664-9711 *E-mail:* info@tupelopress.org *Web Site:* www.tupelopress.org, pg 733

Turner Publishing Co, 200 Fourth Ave N, Suite 950, Nashville, TN 37219 *Tel:* 615-255-BOOK (255-2665) *Fax:* 615-255-5081 *E-mail:* marketing@turnerpublishing.com; submissions@turnerpublishing.com *Web Site:* www.turnerpublishing.com, pg 250

Turnstone Press, Artspace Bldg, 206-100 Arthur St, Winnipeg, MB R3B 1H3, Canada *Tel:* 204-947-1555 *Toll Free Tel:* 888-363-7718 *Fax:* 204-942-1556 *E-mail:* info@turnstonepress.com *Web Site:* www.turnstonepress.com, pg 502

Turtle Point Press, 233 Broadway, Rm 946, New York, NY 10279 *Tel:* 212-945-6622 *E-mail:* countomega@aol.com *Web Site:* www.turtlepointpress.com, pg 251

The Tusculum Review Prize for Fiction, 60 Shiloh Rd, PO Box 5113, Greeneville, TN 37743 *Web Site:* www.tusculum.edu/tusculumreview, pg 733

Tuttle Publishing, Airport Business Park, 364 Innovation Dr, North Clarendon, VT 05759-9436 *Tel:* 802-773-8930 *Toll Free Tel:* 800-526-2778 *Fax:* 802-773-6993 *Toll Free Fax:* 800-FAX-TUTL *E-mail:* info@tuttlepublishing.com *Web Site:* www.tuttlepublishing.com, pg 251

Tuxedo Press, 546 E Springville Rd, Carlisle, PA 17015 *Tel:* 717-258-9733 *Fax:* 717-243-0074 *E-mail:* info@tuxedo-press.com *Web Site:* tuxedo-press.com, pg 251

Twayne Publishers™, 27500 Drake Rd, Farmington Hills, MI 48331-3535 *Tel:* 248-699-4253 *Toll Free Tel:* 800-877-4253; 800-363-4253 *Toll Free Fax:* 800-414-5043 *E-mail:* gale.galeord@cengage.com *Web Site:* www.gale.com, pg 251

Twenty-First Century Books, 241 First Ave N, Minneapolis, MN 55401 *Tel:* 612-332-3344 *Toll Free Tel:* 800-328-4929 *Fax:* 612-332-7615 *Toll Free Fax:* 800-332-1132 *E-mail:* info@lernerbooks.com *Web Site:* www.lernerbooks.com, pg 251

The 25 Most "Censored" Stories Annual, PO Box 571, Cotati, CA 94931 *Tel:* 707-874-2695 *Web Site:* www.projectcensored.org, pg 733

Twenty-Third Publications, One Montauk Ave, Suite 200, New London, CT 06320 *Tel:* 860-437-3012 *Toll Free Tel:* 800-321-0411 (orders) *Toll Free Fax:* 800-572-0788 *E-mail:* 23ppweb@bayard-inc.com *Web Site:* www.twentythirdpublications.com, pg 251

Twilight Times Books, PO Box 3340, Kingsport, TN 37664-0340 *Tel:* 423-323-0183 *Fax:* 423-323-0183 *E-mail:* publisher@twilighttimes.com *Web Site:* www.twilighttimesbooks.com, pg 251

Twin Oaks Indexing, 138 Twin Oaks Rd, Suite W, Louisa, VA 23093 *Tel:* 540-894-5126 *Web Site:* www.twinoakscommunity.org, pg 535

Two Thousand Three Associates, 4180 Saxon Dr, New Smyrna Beach, FL 32169 *Tel:* 386-690-2503 *E-mail:* ttta1@att.net *Web Site:* www.twothousandthree.com, pg 251

2M Communications Ltd, 19 W 21 St, Suite 501, New York, NY 10010 *Tel:* 212-741-1509 *Fax:* 212-691-4460 *Web Site:* www.2mcommunications.com, pg 578

Tyndale House Publishers Inc, 351 Executive Dr, Carol Stream, IL 60188 *Tel:* 630-668-8300 *Toll Free Tel:* 800-323-9400 *Web Site:* www.tyndale.com, pg 252

Type & Archetype Press, 846 Dupont Rd, Suite-C, Charleston, SC 29407 *Tel:* 843-406-9113 *Toll Free Tel:* 800-447-8973 *Fax:* 843-406-9118 *E-mail:* info@typetemperament.com *Web Site:* www.typetemperament.com; typenewsletter.com, pg 252

UCI Extension Writers' Program, PO Box 6050, Irvine, CA 92616-6050 *Tel:* 949-824-5990 *Fax:* 949-824-3651 *Web Site:* www.unex.uci.edu, pg 656

UCLA Fowler Museum of Cultural History, PO Box 951549, Los Angeles, CA 90095-1549 *Tel:* 310-825-4361 *Fax:* 310-206-7007 *Web Site:* www.fmch.ucla.edu, pg 252

UCLA Latin American Center Publications, UCLA Latin American Institute, 10343 Bunche Hall, Los Angeles, CA 90095 *Tel:* 310-825-4571 *Fax:* 310-206-6859 *E-mail:* latinamctr@international.ucla.edu *Web Site:* www.international.ucla.edu/lai, pg 252

Ucross Foundation Residency Program, 30 Big Red Lane, Clearmont, WY 82835 *Tel:* 307-737-2291 *Fax:* 307-737-2322 *E-mail:* info@ucross.org *Web Site:* www.ucrossfoundation.org, pg 733

Ugly Duckling Presse, The Old American Can Factory, 232 Third St, Suite E002, Brooklyn, NY 11215 *Tel:* 347-948-5170 *E-mail:* udp_mailbox@yahoo.com; info@uglyducklingpresse.org *Web Site:* www.uglyducklingpresse.org, pg 252

ULI-The Urban Land Institute, 1025 Thomas Jefferson St NW, Suite 500-W, Washington, DC 20007-5201 *Tel:* 202-624-7000; 410-626-7505 (cust serv outside US) *Toll Free Tel:* 800-321-5011 (cust serv) *Fax:* 202-624-7140; 410-626-7147 (orders only) *Toll Free Fax:* 800-248-4585 *E-mail:* bookstore@uli.org; customerservice@uli.org *Web Site:* www.uli.org, pg 252

Ultramarine Publishing Co Inc, 12 Washington Ave, Hastings-on-Hudson, NY 10706 *Tel:* 914-478-1339, pg 252

Ulysses Press, PO Box 3440, Berkeley, CA 94703-0440 *Tel:* 510-601-8301 *Toll Free Tel:* 800-377-2542 *Fax:* 510-601-8307 *E-mail:* ulysses@ulyssespress.com *Web Site:* www.ulyssespress.com, pg 252

Ulysses Travel Guides, 4176 Rue St-Denis, Montreal, QC H2W 2M5, Canada *Tel:* 514-843-9447 (bookstore); 514-843-9882 (ext 2232) *Toll Free Tel:* 800-748-9171 *Fax:* 514-843-9448 *E-mail:* info@ulysses.ca; st-denis@ulysses.ca *Web Site:* www.ulyssesguides.com, pg 502

Unarius Academy of Science Publications, 145 S Magnolia Ave, El Cajon, CA 92020-4522 *Tel:* 619-444-7062 *Toll Free Tel:* 800-475-7062 *Fax:* 619-444-9637 *E-mail:* uriel@unarius.org *Web Site:* www.unarius.org, pg 252

Unicor Medical Inc, 4160 Carmichael Rd, Montgomery, AL 36106 *Tel:* 334-260-8150 *Toll Free Tel:* 800-825-7421 *Toll Free Fax:* 800-305-8030 *E-mail:* sales@unicormed.com *Web Site:* www.unicormed.com, pg 253

Unicorn Writers' Conference, 17 Church Hill Rd, Redding, CT 06896 *Tel:* 203-938-7405 *Fax:* 203-938-7405 *E-mail:* unicornwritersconference@gmail.com *Web Site:* unicornwritersconference.com, pg 656

Editorial Unilit, 8167 NW 84 St, Medley, FL 33166 *Tel:* 305-592-6136 *Toll Free Tel:* 800-767-7726 *Fax:* 305-592-0087 *E-mail:* info@editorialunilit.com; customerservice@editorialunilit.com *Web Site:* www.editorialunilit.com, pg 253

The United Educators Inc, 900 N Shore Dr, Suite 279, Lake Bluff, IL 60044-2210 *Tel:* 847-234-3700 *Toll Free Tel:* 800-323-5875 *Fax:* 847-234-8705 *E-mail:* unitededucators@yahoo.com *Web Site:* www.theunitededucatorsinc.com, pg 253

United for Libraries, 109 S 13 St, Suite 117B, Philadelphia, PA 19107 *Tel:* 312-280-2161 *Toll Free Tel:* 800-545-2433 (ext 2161) *Fax:* 215-545-3821 *E-mail:* united@ala.org *Web Site:* www.ala.org/united, pg 620

United Nations Association of the United States of America, 1750 Pennsylvania Ave NW, Suite 300, Washington, DC 20006 *Tel:* 202-887-9040 *Fax:* 202-887-9021 *Web Site:* www.unausa.org, pg 620

United Nations Publications, 300 E 42 St, 9th fl, New York, NY 10017 *Tel:* 703-661-1571 *Fax:* 703-996-1010 *E-mail:* publications@un.org *Web Site:* un.org/publications, pg 253

United States Holocaust Memorial Museum, 100 Raoul Wallenberg Place SW, Washington, DC 20024-2126 *Tel:* 202-314-7837; 202-488-6144 (orders) *Toll Free Tel:* 800-259-9998 (orders) *Fax:* 202-479-9726; 202-488-0438 (orders) *E-mail:* cahs_publications@ushmm.org *Web Site:* www.ushmm.org, pg 253

United States Institute of Peace Press, 2301 Constitution Ave NW, Washington, DC 20037 *Tel:* 202-457-1700 (edit); 703-661-1590 (cust serv) *Toll Free Tel:* 800-868-8064 (cust serv) *Fax:* 202-429-6063; 703-661-1501 (cust serv) *Web Site:* bookstore.usip.org, pg 253

United States Pharmacopeia, 12601 Twinbrook Pkwy, Rockville, MD 20852-1790 *Tel:* 301-881-0666 *Toll Free Tel:* 800-227-8772 *Fax:* 301-816-8237 (mktg) *E-mail:* marketing@usp.org *Web Site:* www.usp.org, pg 253

United States Tennis Association, 70 W Red Oak Lane, White Plains, NY 10604 *Tel:* 914-696-7000 *Fax:* 914-696-7027 *Web Site:* www.usta.com, pg 254

United Synagogue Book Service, 820 Second Ave, New York, NY 10017 *Tel:* 212-533-7800 *Toll Free Tel:* 800-594-5617 (warehouse only) *Fax:* 212-253-5422 *E-mail:* booksvc@uscj.org *Web Site:* secure.uscj.org/bookservice, pg 254

United Talent Agency, 9336 Civic Center Dr, Beverly Hills, CA 90210 *Tel:* 310-273-6700 *Fax:* 310-247-1111 *Web Site:* www.unitedtalent.com, pg 578

Univelt Inc, 740 Metcalf St, No 13 & 15, Escondido, CA 92025 *Tel:* 760-746-4005 *Fax:* 760-746-3139 *E-mail:* sales@univelt.com *Web Site:* www.univelt.com; www.astronautical.org, pg 254

Universal-Publishers Inc, 23331 Water Circle, Boca Raton, FL 33486-8540 *Tel:* 561-750-4344 *Toll Free Tel:* 800-636-8329 *Fax:* 561-750-6797 *Web Site:* www.universal-publishers.com, pg 254

Universe Publishing, 300 Park Ave S, 4th fl, New York, NY 10010 *Tel:* 212-387-3400 *Fax:* 212-387-3535 *Web Site:* www.rizzoliusa.com, pg 254

University Council for Educational Administration, The University of Texas at Austin, Dept of Educ Admin, Coll of Educ, One University Sta, D-5400, Austin, TX 78712-0374 *Tel:* 512-475-8592 *Fax:* 512-471-5974 *E-mail:* ucea.org@gmail.com *Web Site:* www.ucea.org, pg 254

University of Alabama Press, 200 Hackberry Lane, 2nd fl, Tuscaloosa, AL 35487 *Tel:* 205-348-5180 *Fax:* 205-348-9201 *Web Site:* www.uapress.ua.edu, pg 254

University of Alabama Program in Creative Writing, PO Box 870244, Tuscaloosa, AL 35487-0244 *Tel:* 205-348-5065 *Fax:* 205-348-1388 *E-mail:* english@ua.edu *Web Site:* www.as.ua.edu/english, pg 663

University of Alaska Press, 794 University Ave, Suite 220, Fairbanks, AK 99709 *Tel:* 907-474-5831 *Toll Free Tel:* 888-252-6657 (US only) *Fax:* 907-474-5502 *E-mail:* fypress@uaf.edu *Web Site:* www.uaf.edu/uapress, pg 254

University of Alberta Press, Ring House 2, Edmonton, AB T6G 2E1, Canada *Tel:* 780-492-3662 *Fax:* 780-492-0719 *Web Site:* www.uap.ualberta.ca, pg 502

The University of Arizona Press, 1510 E University Blvd, Tucson, AZ 85721 *Tel:* 520-621-1441 *Toll Free Tel:* 800-426-3797 (orders) *Fax:* 520-621-8899 *Toll Free Fax:* 800-426-3797 *E-mail:* uap@uapress.arizona.edu *Web Site:* www.uapress.arizona.edu, pg 254

The University of Arkansas Press, McIlroy House, 105 N McIlroy Ave, Fayetteville, AR 72701 *Tel:* 479-575-3246 *Toll Free Tel:* 800-626-0090 *Fax:* 479-575-6044 *E-mail:* uapress@uark.edu *Web Site:* www.uapress.com, pg 255

University of Baltimore - Yale Gordon College of Arts & Sciences, Ampersand Institute for Words & Images, 1420 N Charles St, Baltimore, MD 21201-5779 *Tel:* 410-837-6022 *Fax:* 410-837-6029 *E-mail:* scd@ubalt.edu *Web Site:* www.ubalt.edu, pg 663

University of British Columbia Press, 2029 West Mall, Vancouver, BC V6T 1Z2, Canada *Tel:* 604-822-5959 *Toll Free Tel:* 877-377-9378 *Fax:* 604-822-6083 *Toll Free Fax:* 800-668-0821 *E-mail:* frontdesk@ubcpress.ca *Web Site:* www.ubcpress.ca, pg 502

University of Calgary Press, 2500 University Dr NW, Calgary, AB T2N 1N4, Canada *Tel:* 403-220-7578 *Fax:* 403-282-0085 *E-mail:* ucpress@ucalgary.ca *Web Site:* uofcpress.com, pg 503

University of California Extension Professional Sequence in Copyediting & Courses in Publishing, 1995 University Ave, Suite 110, Berkeley, CA 94720-7000 *Tel:* 510-642-6362 *Fax:* 510-643-0216 *E-mail:* letters@unex.berkeley.edu *Web Site:* www.unex.berkeley.edu, pg 663

University of California Institute on Global Conflict & Cooperation, 9500 Gilman Dr, MC 0518, La Jolla, CA 92093-0518 *Tel:* 858-534-3352 *Fax:* 858-534-7655 *E-mail:* igcc-cp@ucsd.edu *Web Site:* www-igcc.ucsd.edu, pg 255

University of California Press, 2120 Berkeley Way, Berkeley, CA 94704-1012 *Tel:* 510-642-4247 *Fax:* 510-643-7127 *E-mail:* askucp@ucpress.edu (books); customerservice@ucpressjournals.com *Web Site:* www.ucpress.edu, pg 255

University of Chicago, Graham School of General Studies, 1427 E 60 St, Chicago, IL 60637 *Tel:* 773-702-1722 *Fax:* 773-702-6814 *Web Site:* www.grahamschool.uchicago.edu, pg 663

University of Chicago Press, 1427 E 60 St, Chicago, IL 60637-2954 *Tel:* 773-702-7700; 773-702-7600 *Toll Free Tel:* 800-621-2736 (orders) *Fax:* 773-702-9756; 773-660-2235 (orders); 773-702-2708 *E-mail:* custserv@press.uchicago.edu; marketing@press.uchicago.edu *Web Site:* www.press.uchicago.edu, pg 255

The University of Connecticut, The Realities of Publishing, CLAS, 215 Glenbrook Rd, Unit 4025, Storrs, CT 06269-4025 *Tel:* 860-486-2141 *Web Site:* web.uconn.edu/english291, pg 663

University of Delaware Press, 200A Morris Library, 181 S College Ave, Newark, DE 19717-5267 *Tel:* 302-831-1149 *Fax:* 302-831-6549 *E-mail:* ud-press@udel.edu *Web Site:* library.udel.edu/udpress, pg 256

University of Denver Publishing Institute, 2000 E Asbury Ave, Denver, CO 80208 *Tel:* 303-871-2570 *Fax:* 303-871-2501 *Web Site:* www.du.edu/publishinginstitute, pg 663

University of Georgia Press, Main Library, 3rd fl, 320 S Jackson St, Athens, GA 30602 *Tel:* 706-369-6130 *Fax:* 706-542-2558; 706-369-6162 *E-mail:* books@ugapress.uga.edu (orders) *Web Site:* www.ugapress.org, pg 256

University of Hawaii Press, 2840 Kolowalu St, Honolulu, HI 96822 *Tel:* 808-956-8255 *Toll Free Tel:* 888-UHPRESS (847-7377) *Fax:* 808-988-6052 *Toll Free Fax:* 800-650-7811 *E-mail:* uhpbooks@hawaii.edu *Web Site:* www.uhpress.hawaii.edu, pg 256

University of Houston Creative Writing Program, 229 Roy Cullen Bldg, Houston, TX 77204-5008 *Tel:* 713-743-2255 *Fax:* 713-743-3697 *E-mail:* cwp@uh.edu *Web Site:* www.uh.edu/cwp, pg 663

University of Illinois at Chicago, Program for Writers, College of Liberal Arts & Sciences, 2027 University Hall, 601 S Morgan St, Chicago, IL 60607-7120 *Tel:* 312-413-2200 (Eng Dept) *Fax:* 312-413-1005 *Web Site:* www.uic.edu, pg 663

University of Illinois, Department of Journalism, Gregory Hall, Rm 120-A, 810 S Wright St, Urbana, IL 61801 *Tel:* 217-333-0709 *Fax:* 217-333-7931 *E-mail:* journ@uiuc.edu *Web Site:* www.comm.uiuc.edu, pg 663

University of Illinois Press, 1325 S Oak St, MC-566, Champaign, IL 61820-6903 *Tel:* 217-333-0950 *Fax:* 217-244-8082 *E-mail:* uipress@uillinois.edu; journals@uillinois.edu *Web Site:* www.press.uillinois.edu, pg 256

University of Iowa Press, 119 W Park Rd, 100 Kuhl House, Iowa City, IA 52242-1000 *Tel:* 319-335-2000 *Toll Free Tel:* 800-621-2736 (orders only) *Fax:* 319-335-2055 *Toll Free Fax:* 800-621-8476 (orders only) *E-mail:* uipress@uiowa.edu *Web Site:* www.uiowapress.org, pg 256

University of Iowa, Writer's Workshop, 102 Dey House, 507 N Clinton St, Iowa City, IA 52242-1000 *Tel:* 319-335-0416 *Fax:* 319-335-0420, pg 733

University of Iowa, Writers' Workshop, Graduate Creative Writing Program, 102 Dey House, 507 N Clinton St, Iowa City, IA 52242-1000 *Tel:* 319-335-0416 *Fax:* 319-335-0420 *Web Site:* writersworkshop.uiowa.edu, pg 663

University of Louisiana at Lafayette Press, PO Box 40831, UL, Lafayette, LA 70504-0831 *Tel:* 337-482-6027 *Fax:* 337-482-6028 *E-mail:* cls@louisiana.edu *Web Site:* www.ulpress.org, pg 256

University of Manitoba Press, University of Manitoba, 301 St Johns College, 92 Dysart Rd, Winnipeg, MB R3T 2M5, Canada *Tel:* 204-474-9495 *Fax:* 204-474-7566 *E-mail:* uofmpress@umanitoba.ca *Web Site:* uofmpress.ca, pg 503

University of Massachusetts Press, East Experiment Sta, 671 N Pleasant St, Amherst, MA 01003 *Tel:* 413-545-2217 *Fax:* 413-545-1226 *E-mail:* info@umpress.umass.edu *Web Site:* www.umass.edu/umpress, pg 257

University of Michigan Center for Japanese Studies, 1007 E Huron St, Ann Arbor, MI 48104-1690 *Tel:* 734-647-8885 *Fax:* 734-647-8886 *E-mail:* ii.cjspubs@umich.edu *Web Site:* www.cjspubs.lsa.umich.edu, pg 257

University of Michigan Press, 839 Greene St, Ann Arbor, MI 48104-3209 *Tel:* 734-764-4388 *Fax:* 734-615-1540 *E-mail:* esladmin@umich.edu *Web Site:* www.press.umich.edu, pg 257

University of Minnesota Press, 111 Third Ave S, Suite 290, Minneapolis, MN 55401-2520 *Tel:* 612-627-1970 *Fax:* 612-627-1980 *E-mail:* ump@umn.edu *Web Site:* www.upress.umn.edu, pg 257

University of Missouri-Kansas City, New Letters Weekend Writers Conference, College of Arts & Sciences, Continuing Education Div, 5300 Rockhill Rd, Kansas City, MO 64110 *Tel:* 816-235-2736 *Fax:* 816-235-5279 *Web Site:* www.umkc.edu, pg 663

University of Missouri Press, 2910 Le Mone Blvd, Columbia, MO 65201 *Tel:* 573-882-7641 *Toll Free Tel:* 800-621-2736 (orders) *Fax:* 573-884-4498 *Web Site:* press.umsystem.edu, pg 257

University of Montana, Environmental Writing Institute, Environmental Studies, University of Montana, Missoula, MT 59812 *Tel:* 406-243-2904 *Fax:* 406-243-6090 *Web Site:* www.umt.edu/ewi, pg 663

University of Nebraska at Omaha Center for Public Affairs Research, CPACS Bldg, Rm 108, 6001 Dodge St, Omaha, NE 68182 *Tel:* 402-554-2134 *Web Site:* www.unomaha.edu/cpar, pg 257

University of Nebraska Press, 1111 Lincoln Mall, Lincoln, NE 68588-0630 *Tel:* 402-472-3581; 919-966-7449 (cust serv & foreign orders) *Toll Free Tel:* 800-848-6224 (cust serv & US orders) *Fax:* 402-472-6214; 919-962-2704 (cust serv & foreign orders) *Toll Free Fax:* 800-526-2617 (cust serv & US orders) *E-mail:* pressmail@unl.edu *Web Site:* www.nebraskapress.unl.edu, pg 257

University of Nevada Press, University of Nevada, M/S 0166, Reno, NV 89557-0166 *Tel:* 775-784-6573 *Fax:* 775-784-6200 *Web Site:* www.unpress.nevada.edu, pg 258

University of New Mexico, One University of New Mexico, Albuquerque, NM 87131-0001 *Tel:* 505-277-2346; 505-272-7777 (cust serv) *Toll Free Tel:* 800-249-7737 (orders only) *Fax:* 505-277-3343; 505-272-7778 (cust serv) *Toll Free Fax:* 800-622-8667 (orders only) *E-mail:* unmpress@unm.edu; custserv@upress.unm.edu (order dept) *Web Site:* unmpress.com, pg 258

The University of North Carolina Press, 116 S Boundary St, Chapel Hill, NC 27514-3808 *Tel:* 919-966-3561 *Fax:* 919-966-3829 *E-mail:* uncpress@unc.edu *Web Site:* www.uncpress.unc.edu, pg 258

University of North Texas Press, Stovall Hall, Suite 174, 1400 Highland St, Denton, TX 76201 *Tel:* 940-565-2142 *Fax:* 940-565-4590 *Web Site:* www.unt.edu/untpress, pg 258

University of Notre Dame Press, 310 Flanner Hall, Notre Dame, IN 46556 *Tel:* 574-631-6346 *Fax:* 574-631-8148 *E-mail:* undpress@nd.edu *Web Site:* www.undpress.nd.edu, pg 258

University of Oklahoma Press, 2800 Venture Dr, Norman, OK 73069-8216 *Tel:* 405-325-2000 *Toll Free Tel:* 800-627-7377 (orders) *Fax:* 405-364-5798 (orders) *Toll Free Fax:* 800-735-0476 (orders) *E-mail:* presscs@ou.edu *Web Site:* www.oupress.com, pg 258

University of Ottawa Press (Les Presses de l'Université d'Ottawa), 542 King Edward Ave, Ottawa, ON K1N 6N5, Canada *Tel:* 613-562-5246 *Fax:* 613-562-5247 *E-mail:* puo-oup@uottawa.ca *Web Site:* www.press.uottawa.ca, pg 503

University of Pennsylvania Museum of Archaeology & Anthropology, 3260 South St, Philadelphia, PA 19104-6324 *Tel:* 215-898-5723 *Fax:* 215-573-2497 *E-mail:* info@pennmuseum.org; publications@pennmuseum.org *Web Site:* www.penn.museum, pg 259

University of Pennsylvania Press, 3905 Spruce St, Philadelphia, PA 19104 *Tel:* 215-898-6261 *Fax:* 215-898-0404 *E-mail:* custserv@pobox.upenn.edu *Web Site:* www.pennpress.org, pg 259

University of Pittsburgh Press, 7500 Thomas Blvd, Pittsburgh, PA 15260 *Tel:* 412-383-2456 *Fax:* 412-383-2466 *E-mail:* info@upress.pitt.edu *Web Site:* www.upress.pitt.edu, pg 259

University of Puerto Rico Press, Edificio La Editorial (level 2), Carr No 1, KM 12.0, Jardin Botanico Norte, San Juan, PR 00927 *Tel:* 787-250-0435; 787-250-0550 *Toll Free Tel:* 877-338-7788 *Fax:* 787-753-9116 *E-mail:* info@laeditorialupr.com *Web Site:* www.laeditorialupr.com, pg 259

University of Regina Press, 2 Research Dr, Suite 246, Regina, SK S4S 7H9, Canada *Tel:* 306-585-4758 *Toll Free Tel:* 866-874-2257 *Fax:* 306-585-4699 *E-mail:* uofrpress@uregina.ca *Web Site:* uofrpress.ca, pg 503

University of Rochester Press, 668 Mount Hope Ave, Rochester, NY 14620-2731 *Tel:* 585-275-0419 *Fax:* 585-271-8778 *E-mail:* boydell@boydellusa.net *Web Site:* www.urpress.com, pg 259

University of South Carolina Press, 1600 Hampton St, Suite 544, Columbia, SC 29208 *Tel:* 803-777-5245 *Toll Free Tel:* 800-768-2500 (orders) *Fax:* 803-777-0160 *Toll Free Fax:* 800-868-0740 (orders) *Web Site:* www.sc.edu/uscpress, pg 259

University of Southern California, Master of Professional Writing Program, Mark Taper Hall, THH 355, 3501 Trousedale Pkwy, Los Angeles, CA 90089-0355 *Tel:* 213-740-3252 *Fax:* 213-740-5002 *E-mail:* mpw@college.usc.edu *Web Site:* college.usc.edu/mpw, pg 664

University of Tennessee Press, 110 Conference Center Bldg, 600 Henley St, Knoxville, TN 37996-4108 *Tel:* 865-974-3321 *Toll Free Tel:* 800-621-2736 (orders) *Fax:* 865-974-3724 *Toll Free Fax:* 800-621-8476 (orders) *E-mail:* custserv@utpress.org *Web Site:* www.utpress.org, pg 260

University of Texas at Arlington School of Urban & Public Affairs, 511 University Hall, 5th fl, 601 S Nedderman Dr, Arlington, TX 76010 *Tel:* 817-272-3071 *Fax:* 817-272-3415 *E-mail:* supa@uta.edu *Web Site:* www.uta.edu/supa, pg 260

University of Texas at Austin, Creative Writing Program, Dept of English, PAR 108, One University Sta, Mailcode B5000, Austin, TX 78712-1164 *Tel:* 512-471-5132; 512-471-4991 *Fax:* 512-471-4909 *Web Site:* www.utexas.edu/cola/depts/english/creative-writing, pg 664

University of Texas at El Paso, Department of Creative Writing, MFA/Department of Creative Writing, Liberal Arts 415 UTEP, 500 W University Ave, El Paso, TX 79968-9991 *Tel:* 915-747-5713 *Fax:* 915-747-5523 *Web Site:* www.utep.edu/cw, pg 664

University of Toronto Press, 10 St Mary St, Suite 700, Toronto, ON M4Y 2W8, Canada *Tel:* 416-978-2239 *Fax:* 416-978-4738 *E-mail:* info@utpress.utoronto.ca *Web Site:* www.utpress.utoronto.ca; www.utppublishing.com, pg 504

The University of Utah Press, J Willard Marriott Library, Suite 5400, 295 S 1500 E, Salt Lake City, UT 84112-0860 *Tel:* 801-581-6771 *Toll Free Tel:* 800-621-2736 (orders) *Fax:* 801-581-3365 *Toll Free Fax:* 800-621-8471 *E-mail:* info@upress.utah.edu *Web Site:* www.uofupress.com, pg 260

The University of Virginia Press, PO Box 400318, Charlottesville, VA 22904-4318 *Tel:* 434-924-3468 (cust serv); 434-924-3469 (cust serv) *Toll Free Tel:* 800-831-3406 (orders) *Fax:* 434-982-2655 *Toll Free Fax:* 877-288-6400 *E-mail:* vapress@virginia.edu *Web Site:* www.upress.virginia.edu, pg 260

University of Washington Press, 433 Brooklyn Ave NE, Seattle, WA 98195-9570 *Tel:* 206-543-4050 *Toll Free Tel:* 800-537-5487 (orders) *Fax:* 206-543-3932; 410-516-6998 (orders) *E-mail:* uwpress@u.washington.edu *Web Site:* www.washington.edu/uwpress/, pg 260

University of Wisconsin Press, 1930 Monroe St, 3rd fl, Madison, WI 53711-2059 *Tel:* 608-263-0668 *Toll Free Tel:* 800-621-2736 (orders) *Fax:* 608-263-1173 *Toll Free Fax:* 800-621-2736 (orders) *E-mail:* uwiscpress@uwpress.wisc.edu (main off) *Web Site:* www.wisc.edu/wisconsinpress, pg 260

University of Wisconsin-Madison Continuing Studies, 21 N Park St, 7th fl, Madison, WI 53715 *Tel:* 608-262-1156 *E-mail:* info@dsc.wisc.edu *Web Site:* continuingstudies.wisc.edu, pg 664

University Press of America Inc, 4501 Forbes Blvd, Suite 200, Lanham, MD 20706 *Tel:* 301-459-3366 *Toll Free Tel:* 800-462-6420 *Fax:* 301-429-5748 *Toll Free Fax:* 800-338-4550 *Web Site:* www.univpress.com, pg 261

University Press of Colorado, 5589 Arapahoe Ave, Suite 206-C, Boulder, CO 80303 *Tel:* 720-406-8849 *Toll Free Tel:* 800-621-2736 (orders) *Fax:* 720-406-3443 *Web Site:* www.upcolorado.com, pg 261

University Press of Florida, 15 NW 15 St, Gainesville, FL 32603-2079 *Tel:* 352-392-1351 *Toll Free Tel:* 800-226-3822 (orders only) *Fax:* 352-392-0590 *Toll Free Fax:* 800-680-1955 (orders only) *E-mail:* info@upf.com *Web Site:* www.upf.com, pg 261

University Press of Kansas, 2502 Westbrooke Circle, Lawrence, KS 66045-4444 *Tel:* 785-864-4154; 785-864-4155 (orders) *Fax:* 785-864-4586 *E-mail:* upress@ku.edu; upkorders@ku.edu (orders) *Web Site:* www.kansaspress.ku.edu, pg 261

The University Press of Kentucky, 663 S Limestone St, Lexington, KY 40508-4008 *Tel:* 859-257-8400 *Fax:* 859-257-8481 *Web Site:* www.kentuckypress.com, pg 261

University Press of Mississippi, 3825 Ridgewood Rd, Jackson, MS 39211-6492 *Tel:* 601-432-6205 *Toll Free Tel:* 800-737-7788 (orders & cust serv) *Fax:* 601-432-6217 *E-mail:* press@mississippi.edu *Web Site:* www.upress.state.ms.us, pg 261

University Press of New England, One Court St, Suite 250, Lebanon, NH 03766 *Tel:* 603-448-1533 *Toll Free Tel:* 800-421-1561 (orders only) *Fax:* 603-448-7006; 603-643-1540 *E-mail:* university.press@dartmouth.edu *Web Site:* www.upne.com, pg 262

University Publishing Group, 6 Public Sq, Suite 206, Hagerstown, MD 21740 *Tel:* 240-420-0036 *Toll Free Tel:* 800-654-8188 *Fax:* 240-718-7100 *E-mail:* editorial@upgbooks.com; orders@upgbooks.com; sales@upgbooks.com *Web Site:* www.upgbooks.com, pg 262

University Publishing House, PO Box 1664, Mannford, OK 74044 *Tel:* 918-865-4726 *E-mail:* upub3@juno.com *Web Site:* www.universitypublishinghouse.net, pg 262

University Science Books, 20 Edgeshill Rd, Mill Valley, CA 94941 *Tel:* 415-332-5390 *Fax:* 415-332-5390 *E-mail:* univscibks@igc.org *Web Site:* www.uscibooks.com, pg 262

UnKnownTruths.com Publishing Co, 8815 Conroy Windermere Rd, Suite 190, Orlando, FL 32835 *Tel:* 407-929-9207 *Fax:* 407-876-3933 *E-mail:* info@unknowntruths.com *Web Site:* unknowntruths.com, pg 262

Unlimited Publishing LLC, PO Box 99, Nashville, IN 47448 *Tel:* 206-666-5484 *E-mail:* acquisitions@unlimitedpublishing.com *Web Site:* www.unlimitedpublishing.com, pg 263

UNO Press, University of New Orleans Metro College, Educ Bldg, Suite 210, 2000 Lakeshore Dr, New Orleans, LA 70148 *Tel:* 504-280-7457 *Fax:* 504-280-7317 *E-mail:* unopress@uno.edu *Web Site:* unopress.org, pg 263

Unveiled Media LLC, PO Box 930463, Verona, WI 53593 *Tel:* 707-986-8345 *Web Site:* www.unveiledmedia.com, pg 263

The Voices Summer Writing Workshops, c/o Community Initiatives Inc, 354 Pine St, Suite 700, San Francisco, CA 94104 *Toll Free Tel:* 866-202-6152 *E-mail:* info@voicesatvona.org *Web Site:* www.voicesatvona.org, pg 656

Volcano Press, 21496 National St, Volcano, CA 95689 *Tel:* 209-296-7989 *Toll Free Tel:* 800-879-9636 *Fax:* 209-296-4515 *E-mail:* sales@volcanopress.com *Web Site:* www.volcanopress.com, pg 266

Ludwig von Mises Institute, 518 W Magnolia Ave, Auburn, AL 36832 *Tel:* 334-321-2100 *Fax:* 334-321-2119 *E-mail:* info@mises.org *Web Site:* www.mises.org, pg 266

Harold D Vursell Memorial Award, 633 W 155 St, New York, NY 10032 *Tel:* 212-368-5900 *Fax:* 212-491-4615 *E-mail:* academy@artsandletters.org *Web Site:* www.artsandletters.org, pg 734

Wadsworth Publishing, 20 Davis Dr, Belmont, CA 94002 *Tel:* 650-595-2350 *Fax:* 650-592-3022 *Toll Free Fax:* 800-522-4923 *Web Site:* www.cengage.com, pg 266

Wag's Revue Writers' Contest, 2865 W Lyndale St, Suite 1, Chicago, IL 60647 *E-mail:* editors@wagsrevue.com *Web Site:* www.wagsrevue.com, pg 734

Wake Forest University Press, A5 Tribble Hall, Wake Forest University, Winston-Salem, NC 27109 *Tel:* 336-758-5448 *Fax:* 336-758-5636 *E-mail:* wfupress@wfu.edu *Web Site:* www.wfu.edu/wfupress, pg 266

Walch Education, 40 Walch Dr, Portland, ME 04103-1286 *Tel:* 207-772-2846 *Toll Free Tel:* 800-558-2846 *Fax:* 207-772-3105 *Toll Free Fax:* 888-991-5755 *E-mail:* customerservice@walch.com *Web Site:* www.walch.com, pg 266

Wales Literary Agency Inc, 1508 Tenth Ave E, No 401, Seattle, WA 98102 *Tel:* 206-284-7114 *E-mail:* waleslit@waleslit.com *Web Site:* www.waleslit.com, pg 578

Richard Wall Memorial Award, Roundabout Theatre Co, 231 W 39 St, Suite 1200, New York, NY 10018 *Tel:* 212-719-9393 (ext 351) *E-mail:* info@tla-online.org; tlabookawards@gmail.com *Web Site:* www.tla-online.org, pg 734

Wallace Literary Agency Inc, 229 E 79 St, No 5A, New York, NY 10075 *Tel:* 212-472-3282 *Fax:* 212-472-3833 *E-mail:* info@wallaceliteraryagency.com, pg 578

Edward Lewis Wallant Book Award, 3 Brighton Rd, West Hartford, CT 06117 *Tel:* 860-232-1421, pg 734

Wambtac Communications, 1512 E Santa Clara Ave, Santa Ana, CA 92705 *Tel:* 714-954-0580 *Toll Free Tel:* 800-641-3936 *E-mail:* wambtac@wambtac.com *Web Site:* www.wambtac.com; claudiasuzanne.com (prof servs), pg 535

Ward & Balkin Agency, Inc, 30 Brock Way, South Hadley, MA 01075 *Tel:* 413-322-8697 *Web Site:* www.wardbalkin.com, pg 578

Frederick Warne, 345 Hudson St, New York, NY 10014 *Tel:* 212-366-2000 *Web Site:* www.penguinrandomhouse.com, pg 267

Warner Press, 1201 E Fifth St, Anderson, IN 46018 *Tel:* 765-644-7721 *Toll Free Tel:* 800-741-7721 (orders) *Fax:* 765-640-8005 *Toll Free Fax:* 800-347-6411 *E-mail:* wporders@warnerpress.org *Web Site:* www.warnerpress.org, pg 267

Warren Communications News Inc, 2115 Ward Ct NW, Washington, DC 20037 *Tel:* 202-872-9200 *Toll Free Tel:* 800-771-9202 *Fax:* 202-293-3435; 202-318-8350 *E-mail:* info@warren-news.com; newsroom@warren-news.com *Web Site:* www.warren-news.com, pg 267

Warren Wilson College, MFA Program for Writers, 701 Warren Wilson Rd, Swannanoa, NC 28778 *Tel:* 828-771-3717 *Fax:* 828-771-7005 *E-mail:* mfa@warren-wilson.edu *Web Site:* www.warren-wilson.edu/~mfa, pg 664

Warwick Associates, 18340 Sonoma Hwy, Sonoma, CA 95476 *Tel:* 707-939-9212 *Fax:* 707-938-3515 *E-mail:* warwick@vom.com *Web Site:* www.warwickassociates.com, pg 578

George Washington Book Prize, 101 S Water St, Chestertown, MD 21620 *Tel:* 410-810-7165 *Fax:* 410-810-7175 *Web Site:* starrcenter.washcoll.edu/gw_book_prize, pg 734

Washington State University Press, Cooper Publications Bldg, Grimes Way, Pullman, WA 99164 *Tel:* 509-335-3518; 509-335-7880 (order fulfillment) *Toll Free Tel:* 800-354-7360 *Fax:* 509-335-8568 *E-mail:* wsupress@wsu.edu *Web Site:* wsupress.wsu.edu, pg 267

Water Environment Federation, 601 Wythe St, Alexandria, VA 22314-1994 *Tel:* 703-684-2400 *Toll Free Tel:* 800-666-0206 *Fax:* 703-684-2492 *E-mail:* csc@wef.org (cust serv) *Web Site:* www.wef.org, pg 267

Water Resources Publications LLC, PO Box 630026, Highlands Ranch, CO 80163-0026 *Tel:* 720-873-0171 *Toll Free Tel:* 800-736-2405 *Fax:* 720-873-0173 *Toll Free Fax:* 800-616-1971 *E-mail:* info@wrpllc.com *Web Site:* www.wrpllc.com, pg 267

Water Row Press, PO Box 438, Sudbury, MA 01776 *Tel:* 508-485-8515 *Fax:* 508-229-0885 *E-mail:* contact@waterrowbooks.com *Web Site:* www.waterrowbooks.com, pg 267

WaterBrook Multnomah Publishing Group, 12265 Oracle Blvd, Suite 200, Colorado Springs, CO 80921 *Tel:* 719-590-4999 *Toll Free Tel:* 800-603-7051 (orders) *Fax:* 719-590-8977 *Toll Free Fax:* 800-294-5686 (orders) *E-mail:* info@waterbrookmultnomah.com *Web Site:* waterbrookmultnomah.com, pg 267

Watermark Publishing, 1088 Bishop St, Suite 310, Honolulu, HI 96813 *Tel:* 808-587-7766 *Toll Free Tel:* 866-900-BOOK (900-2665) *Fax:* 808-521-3461 *E-mail:* info@bookshawaii.net *Web Site:* www.bookshawaii.net, pg 267

Waterside Productions Inc, 2055 Oxford Ave, Cardiff, CA 92007 *Tel:* 760-632-9190 *Fax:* 760-632-9295 *E-mail:* admin@waterside.com *Web Site:* www.waterside.com, pg 579

Watkins/Loomis Agency Inc, PO Box 20925, New York, NY 10025 *Tel:* 212-532-0080 *Fax:* 646-383-2449 *E-mail:* assistant@watkinsloomis.com *Web Site:* www.watkinsloomis.com, pg 579

Watson-Guptill Publications, c/o Random House Inc, 1745 Broadway, New York, NY 10019 *Tel:* 212-782-9000 *Fax:* 212-940-7381 *E-mail:* crownbiz@randomhouse.com *Web Site:* www.randomhouse.com/crown/watsonguptill, pg 268

Watson Publishing International LLC, PO Box 1240, Sagamore Beach, MA 02562-1240 *Tel:* 508-888-9113 *Fax:* 508-888-3733 *E-mail:* orders@watsonpublishing.com; orders@shpusa.com *Web Site:* www.shpusa.com; www.watsonpublishing.com, pg 268

The Robert Watson Literary Prizes in Fiction & Poetry, MFA Writing Program, The Greensboro Review, UNC-Greensboro, 3302 MHRA Bldg, Greensboro, NC 27402-6170 *Tel:* 336-334-5459 *Fax:* 336-256-1470 *Web Site:* www.greensbororeview.org, pg 734

Waveland Press Inc, 4180 IL Rte 83, Suite 101, Long Grove, IL 60047-9580 *Tel:* 847-634-0081 *Fax:* 847-634-9501 *E-mail:* info@waveland.com *Web Site:* www.waveland.com, pg 268

Waverly Place Literary Agency, 189 Waverly Place, Unit 4, New York, NY 10014-3135 *Tel:* 212-925-3721 *E-mail:* waverlyplaceliterary@aol.com *Web Site:* www.waverlyplaceliterary.com; twitter.com/waverlyplacelit, pg 579

Waxman Leavell Literary Agency, 443 Park Ave S, No 1004, New York, NY 10016 *Tel:* 212-675-5556 *Fax:* 212-675-1381 *Web Site:* www.waxmanleavell.com, pg 579

Wayne State University Press, Leonard N Simons Bldg, 4809 Woodward Ave, Detroit, MI 48201-1309 *Tel:* 313-577-6120 *Toll Free Tel:* 800-978-7323 *Fax:* 313-577-6131 *Web Site:* www.wsupress.wayne.edu, pg 268

Wayside Publishing, 11 Jan Sebastian Dr, Suite 5, Sandwich, MA 02563 *Tel:* 508-833-5096 *Toll Free Tel:* 888-302-2519 *Fax:* 508-833-6284 *E-mail:* wayside@sprintmail.com *Web Site:* www.waysidepublishing.com, pg 268

Web Offset Association (WOA), 200 Deer Run Rd, Sewickley, PA 15143 *Tel:* 412-741-6860 *Toll Free Tel:* 800-910-4283 *Fax:* 412-741-2311 *E-mail:* printing@printing.org *Web Site:* www.printing.org/page/3419, pg 621

Weigl Educational Publishers Ltd, 6325 Tenth St SE, Calgary, AB T2H 2Z9, Canada *Tel:* 403-233-7747 *Toll Free Tel:* 800-668-0766 *Fax:* 403-233-7769 *Toll Free Fax:* 866-449-3445 *E-mail:* info@weigl.com; orders@weigl.com *Web Site:* www.weigl.ca; av2books.com, pg 504

Cherry Weiner Literary Agency, 925 Oak Bluff Ct, Dacula, GA 30019-6660 *Tel:* 732-446-2096 *Fax:* 732-792-0506 *E-mail:* cherry8486@aol.com, pg 579

The Weingel-Fidel Agency, 310 E 46 St, Suite 21-E, New York, NY 10017 *Tel:* 212-599-2959 *Fax:* 212-286-1986 *E-mail:* queries@theweingel-fidelagency.com, pg 579

Anne Jones Weitzer, 60 Sutton Place South, Suite 9-B South, New York, NY 10022-4168 *Tel:* 212-758-8149 *E-mail:* 47dehaven@msn.com; enamel@yahoo.com, pg 535

Welcome Books®, 300 Park Ave S, New York, NY 10010 *Tel:* 212-387-3400 *Web Site:* www.rizzoliusa.com, pg 268

Welcome Rain Publishers LLC, 217 Thompson St, Suite 473, New York, NY 10012 *Tel:* 212-686-1909 *Web Site:* welcomerain.com, pg 268

Rene Wellek Prize, University of South Carolina, Dept of Languages, Literature & Cultures, Rm 813-A, 1620 College St, Columbia, SC 29208 *Tel:* 803-777-3021 *Fax:* 803-777-3041 *E-mail:* info@acla.org *Web Site:* www.acla.org/awards/rene-wellek-prize; www.acla.org, pg 734

Wellington Press, 9601-30 Miccosukee Rd, Tallahassee, FL 32309 *E-mail:* peacegames@aol.com *Web Site:* www.peacegames.com, pg 268

Wellness Institute/Self Help Books LLC, 515 W North St, Pass Christian, MS 39571-2605 *Tel:* 228-452-0770 *Fax:* 228-452-0775, pg 268

WendyLynn & Co, 504 Wilson Rd, Annapolis, MD 21401 *Tel:* 410-224-2729; 410-507-1059 *Web Site:* wendylynn.com, pg 585

Wergle Flomp Humor Poetry Contest, 351 Pleasant St, PMB 222, Northampton, MA 01060-3961 *Tel:* 413-320-1847 *Toll Free Tel:* 866-WINWRIT (946-9748) *Fax:* 413-280-0539 *Web Site:* www.winningwriters.com, pg 735

Eliot Werner Publications Inc, 31 Willow Lane, Clinton Corners, NY 12514 *Tel:* 845-266-4241 *Fax:* 845-266-3317 *E-mail:* eliotwerner@optonline.net *Web Site:* www.eliotwerner.com, pg 268

Toby Wertheim, 240 E 76 St, New York, NY 10021 *Tel:* 212-472-8587 *E-mail:* tobywertheim@yahoo.com, pg 535

Wescott Cove Publishing Co, 1227 S Florida Ave, Rockledge, FL 32955 *Tel:* 321-690-2224 *Fax:* 321-690-0853 *E-mail:* customerservice@farhorizonsmedia.com *Web Site:* www.farhorizonsmedia.com, pg 268

Wesley-Logan Prize, 400 "A" St SE, Washington, DC 20003 *Tel:* 202-544-2422 *Fax:* 202-544-8307 *E-mail:* awards@historians.org *Web Site:* www.historians.org, pg 735

Wesleyan Publishing House, 13300 Olio Rd, Fishers, IN 46037 *Tel:* 317-774-3853 *Toll Free Tel:* 800-493-7539 *Fax:* 317-774-3865 *Toll Free Fax:* 800-788-3535 *E-mail:* wph@wesleyan.org *Web Site:* www.wesleyan.org/wph, pg 269

Wesleyan University Press, 215 Long Lane, Middletown, CT 06459-0433 *Tel:* 860-685-7711 *Fax:* 860-685-7712 *Web Site:* www.wesleyan.edu/wespress, pg 269

John Wiley & Sons Inc Scientific, Technical, Medical & Scholarly (STMS), 111 River St, Hoboken, NJ 07030 *Tel:* 201-748-6000 *Toll Free Tel:* 800-225-5945 (cust serv) *Fax:* 201-748-6088 *E-mail:* info@wiley.com *Web Site:* www.wiley.com, pg 272

Wilfrid Laurier University Press, 255 King St N, Suite 401, Waterloo, ON N2J 4V2, Canada *Tel:* 519-884-0710 (ext 6124) *Toll Free Tel:* 866-836-5551 (CN & US) *Fax:* 519-725-1399 *E-mail:* press@wlu.ca *Web Site:* www.wlupress.wlu.ca, pg 505

Wilkinson Studios Inc, 1121 E Main St, Suite 310, St Charles, IL 60174 *Tel:* 630-549-0504 *Web Site:* www.wilkinsonstudios.com, pg 585

Willamette Writers, 2108 Buck St, West Linn, OR 97068 *Tel:* 503-305-6729 *Fax:* 503-344-6174 *E-mail:* wilwrite@willamettewriters.com *Web Site:* www.willamettewriters.com, pg 621

Willamette Writers' Conference, 2108 Buck St, West Linn, OR 97068 *Tel:* 503-305-6729 *Fax:* 503-344-6174 *E-mail:* wilwrite@willamettewriters.com *Web Site:* www.willamettewriters.com, pg 656

William Carey Library Publishers, 1605 E Elizabeth St, Pasadena, CA 91104 *Tel:* 626-720-8210 *Toll Free Tel:* 866-732-6657 (orders & cust serv) *E-mail:* assistant@wclbooks.com *Web Site:* www.missionbooks.org, pg 272

William Flanagan Memorial Creative Persons Center, 14 Harrison St, New York, NY 10013 *Tel:* 212-226-2020 *Fax:* 212-226-5551 *E-mail:* info@albeefoundation.org *Web Site:* www.albeefoundation.org, pg 736

Williams & Company Book Publishers, 1317 Pine Ridge Dr, Savannah, GA 31406 *Tel:* 912-352-0404 *E-mail:* bookpub@comcast.net *Web Site:* www.pubmart.com, pg 272

Oscar Williams/Gene Derwood Award, 909 Third Ave, New York, NY 10022 *Tel:* 212-686-0010 *Fax:* 212-532-8528 *E-mail:* info@nycommunitytrust.org *Web Site:* www.nycommunitytrust.org, pg 736

William Carlos Williams Award, 15 Gramercy Park, New York, NY 10003 *Tel:* 212-254-9628 *Fax:* 212-673-2352 *Web Site:* www.poetrysociety.org, pg 736

Willow Creek Press, 9931 Hwy 70 W, Minocqua, WI 54548 *Tel:* 715-358-7010 *Toll Free Tel:* 800-850-9453 *Fax:* 715-358-2807 *E-mail:* info@willowcreekpress.com *Web Site:* www.willowcreekpress.com, pg 272

Wilshire Book Co, 9731 Variel Ave, Chatsworth, CA 91311-4315 *Tel:* 818-700-1522 *Fax:* 818-700-1527 *E-mail:* sales@mpowers.com *Web Site:* www.mpowers.com, pg 272

Gary Wilson Award for Short Fiction, Texas Christian University, Dept of English, TCU Box 297270, Fort Worth, TX 76129 *Tel:* 817-257-5907 *Fax:* 817-257-7709 *E-mail:* descant@tcu.edu *Web Site:* www.descant.tcu.edu, pg 736

H W Wilson, 2 University Plaza, Suite 310, Hackensack, NJ 07601 *Tel:* 201-968-0500 *Toll Free Tel:* 800-221-1592 *Fax:* 201-968-0511 *E-mail:* info@hwwilsoninprint.com; csr@hwwilsoninprint.com; information@ebscohost.com *Web Site:* www.hwwilsoninprint.com; www.ebscohost.com/wilson, pg 273

H W Wilson Co Indexing Award, 1628 E Southern Ave, Suite 9-223, Tempe, AZ 85282 *Tel:* 480-245-6750 *E-mail:* info@asindexing.org *Web Site:* www.asindexing.org, pg 736

H W Wilson Foundation, 10 Estes St, Ipswich, MA 01938 *Tel:* 978-356-6500 *Toll Free Tel:* 800-653-2726 (US & CN) *Fax:* 978-356-6565 *E-mail:* information@ebscohost.com *Web Site:* www.ebscohost.com, pg 623

The H W Wilson Library Staff Development Grant, 50 E Huron St, Chicago, IL 60611 *Tel:* 312-280-3247 *Toll Free Tel:* 800-545-2433 (ext 3247) *Fax:* 312-944-3897; 312-440-9379 *E-mail:* awards@ala.org *Web Site:* www.ala.org, pg 736

Wimbledon Music Inc & Trigram Music Inc, 1801 Century Park E, Suite 2400, Los Angeles, CA 90067 *Tel:* 310-556-9683 *Fax:* 310-277-1278 *E-mail:* irishmex127@gmail.com *Web Site:* www.wimbtri.net, pg 273

Wimmer Cookbooks, 4650 Shelby Air Dr, Memphis, TN 38118 *Tel:* 901-362-8900 *Toll Free Tel:* 800-363-1771 *E-mail:* wimmer@wimmerco.com *Web Site:* www.wimmerco.com, pg 273

Wind Canyon Books, PO Box 7035, Stockton, CA 95267 *Tel:* 209-956-1600 *Toll Free Tel:* 800-952-7007 *Fax:* 209-956-9424 *Toll Free Fax:* 888-289-7086 *E-mail:* books@windcanyonbooks.com *Web Site:* www.windcanyonbooks.com, pg 273

Herbert Warren Wind Book Award, 77 Liberty Corner Rd, Far Hills, NJ 07931-0708 *Tel:* 908-234-2300 *Fax:* 908-470-5013 *Web Site:* www.usga.org, pg 736

Windbreak House Writing Retreat, PO Box 169, Hermosa, SD 57744-0169 *Tel:* 605-255-4064 *E-mail:* info@windbreakhouse.com *Web Site:* www.windbreakhouse.com, pg 656

Windham-Campbell Prizes, Beinecke Library, 121 Whitney Ave, Suite 102, New Haven, CT 06510-1242 *Fax:* 203-432-9033 *Web Site:* windhamcampbell.org, pg 736

Windhaven®, 466 Rte 10, Orford, NH 03777 *Tel:* 603-483-0929 *E-mail:* info@windhaven.com *Web Site:* www.windhaven.com, pg 535

Windsor Books, 260 Montauk Hwy, Suite 5, Bayshore, NY 11706 *Tel:* 631-665-6688 *Toll Free Tel:* 800-321-5934 *E-mail:* windsor.books@att.net *Web Site:* www.windsorpublishing.com, pg 273

Windward Publishing, 5995 149 St W, Suite 105, Apple Valley, MN 55124 *Tel:* 952-469-6699 *Toll Free Tel:* 800-846-7027 *Fax:* 952-469-1968 *Toll Free Fax:* 800-330-6232 *E-mail:* info@finneyco.com *Web Site:* www.finneyco.com, pg 273

The Wine Appreciation Guild Ltd, 360 Swift Ave, Suites 30 & 34, South San Francisco, CA 94080 *Tel:* 650-866-3020 *Toll Free Tel:* 800-231-9463 *Fax:* 650-866-3513 *E-mail:* info@wineappreciation.com *Web Site:* www.wineappreciation.com, pg 273

Wings Press, 627 E Guenther, San Antonio, TX 78210-1134 *Tel:* 210-271-7805 *Fax:* 210-271-7805 *E-mail:* press@wingspress.com *Web Site:* www.wingspress.com, pg 273

WingSpread Publishers, 2020 State Rd, Camp Hill, PA 17011 *Tel:* 717-761-7044 *Toll Free Tel:* 800-884-4571 *Fax:* 717-761-7273 *E-mail:* customerservice@echurchdepot.com *Web Site:* wingspreadpublishers.com, pg 273

The Laurence L & Thomas Winship/PEN New England Award, MIT, 14N-221A, 77 Massachusetts Ave, Cambridge, MA 02139 *Tel:* 617-324-1729 *E-mail:* pen-ne@lesley.edu *Web Site:* www.pen-ne.org, pg 737

Justin Winsor Prize for Library History Essay, 50 E Huron St, Chicago, IL 60611 *Tel:* 312-280-4283 *Toll Free Tel:* 800-545-2433 (ext 4283) *Fax:* 312-280-4392 *Web Site:* www.ala.org, pg 737

Winter Words Apres Ski for the Mind, 110 E Hallam St, Suite 116, Aspen, CO 81611 *Tel:* 970-925-3122 *Fax:* 970-920-5700 *E-mail:* awfinfo@aspenwriters.org *Web Site:* www.aspenwriters.org, pg 656

Winters Publishing, 705 E Washington St, Greensburg, IN 47240 *Tel:* 812-663-4948 *Toll Free Tel:* 800-457-3230 *Fax:* 812-663-4948 *E-mail:* winterspublishing@gmail.com *Web Site:* www.winterspublishing.com, pg 273

Winterthur Museum & Country Estate, 5105 Kennett Pike, Wilmington, DE 19735 *Tel:* 302-888-4663 *Toll Free Tel:* 800-448-3883 *Fax:* 302-888-4950 *Web Site:* www.winterthur.org, pg 274

Wisconsin Annual Fall Conferencee, PO Box 259303, Madison, WI 53725 *Tel:* 608-278-0692 *Web Site:* www.scbwi.org; www.scbwi-wi.com, pg 657

Wisconsin Department of Public Instruction, 125 S Webster St, Madison, WI 53703 *Tel:* 608-266-2188 *Toll Free Tel:* 800-441-4563 *Fax:* 608-267-9110 *E-mail:* pubsales@dpi.state.wi.us *Web Site:* www.dpi.wi.gov/pubsales, pg 274

Wisdom Publications Inc, 199 Elm St, Somerville, MA 02144 *Tel:* 617-776-7416 *Toll Free Tel:* 800-272-4050 (orders) *Fax:* 617-776-7841 *E-mail:* info@wisdompubs.org *Web Site:* www.wisdompubs.org, pg 274

Wish Publishing, PO Box 10337, Terre Haute, IN 47801-0337 *Web Site:* www.wishpublishing.com, pg 274

Wittenborn Art Books, 1109 Geary Blvd, San Francisco, CA 94109 *Tel:* 415-292-6500 *Toll Free Tel:* 800-660-6403 *Fax:* 415-292-6594 *E-mail:* wittenborn@art-books.com *Web Site:* www.art-books.com, pg 274

Wizards of the Coast LLC, 1600 Lind Ave SW, Renton, WA 98057-3305 *Tel:* 425-226-6500 *Web Site:* company.wizards.com, pg 274

WLA Literary Award, 4610 S Biltmore Lane, Madison, WI 53718 *Tel:* 608-245-3640 *Fax:* 608-245-3646 *Web Site:* www.wla.lib.wi.us, pg 737

WME, 1325 Avenue of the Americas, New York, NY 10019 *Tel:* 212-586-5100 *Fax:* 212-246-3583 *E-mail:* wma@interport.net *Web Site:* www.wma.com, pg 579

WNBA Pannell Award for Excellence in Children's Bookselling, 435 W 23 St, Suite 8-C, New York, NY 10011 *Tel:* 212-242-6930 *E-mail:* pannellaward@gmail.com *Web Site:* www.wnba-books.org; www.NationalReadingGroupMonth.org; www.wnba-books.org/awards, pg 737

Alan Wofsy Fine Arts, 1109 Geary Blvd, San Francisco, CA 94109 *Tel:* 415-292-6500 *Toll Free Tel:* 800-660-6403 *Fax:* 415-292-6594 (off & cust serv); 510-251-1840 (acctg) *E-mail:* order@art-books.com (orders); editeur@earthlink.net (edit); beauxarts@earthlink.net (cust serv) *Web Site:* www.art-books.com, pg 274

Wolf Pirate Project Inc, 337 Lost Lake Dr, Divide, CO 80814 *Tel:* 305-333-3186 *E-mail:* contact@wolfpiratebooks.com; workshop@wolfpiratebooks.com *Web Site:* www.wolf-pirate.com, pg 535

Thomas Wolfe Fiction Prize, PO Box 21591, Winston-Salem, NC 27120-1591 *E-mail:* mail@ncwriters.org *Web Site:* www.ncwriters.org, pg 737

Nancy Wolff, 125 Gates Ave, No 14, Montclair, NJ 07042 *Tel:* 973-746-7415 *E-mail:* wolffindex@aol.com, pg 536

Tobias Wolff Award for Fiction, Mail Stop 9053, Western Washington University, Bellingham, WA 98225 *Tel:* 360-650-4863 *E-mail:* bhreview@wwu.edu *Web Site:* www.bhreview.org, pg 737

Wolters Kluwer Ltd, 90 Sheppard Ave E, Suite 300, Toronto, ON M2N 6X1, Canada *Tel:* 416-224-2224 *Toll Free Tel:* 800-268-4522 (CN & US cust serv) *Fax:* 416-224-2243 *Toll Free Fax:* 800-461-4131 *E-mail:* cservice@cch.ca (cust serv) *Web Site:* www.cch.ca, pg 505

Wolters Kluwer US Corp, 2700 Lake Cook Rd, Riverwoods, IL 60015 *Tel:* 847-267-7000 *Fax:* 847-580-5192 *Web Site:* www.wolterskluwer.com, pg 274

Women Who Write Inc, PO Box 652, Madison, NJ 07940-0652 *E-mail:* info@womenwhowrite.org *Web Site:* womenwhowrite.org, pg 621

Women's National Book Association Award, PO Box 237, FDR Sta, New York, NY 10150-0231 *Tel:* 212-208-4629 *Fax:* 212-208-4629 *E-mail:* publicity@bookbuzz.com *Web Site:* www.wnba-books.org; www.NationalReadingGroupMonth.org, pg 737

Women's National Book Association Inc, PO Box 237, FDR Sta, New York, NY 10150-0231 *Tel:* 212-208-4629 *Fax:* 212-208-4629 *E-mail:* publicity@bookbuzz.com; info@wnba-books.org *Web Site:* www.wnba-books.org; www.NationalReadingGroupMonth.org, pg 621

The J Howard & Barbara M J Wood Prize, 444 N Michigan Ave, Suite 1850, Chicago, IL 60611-4034 *Tel:* 312-787-7070 *Fax:* 312-787-6650 *E-mail:* editors@poetrymagazine.org *Web Site:* www.poetryfoundation.org, pg 737

Wood Lake Publishing Inc, 485 Beaver Lake Rd, Kelowna, BC V4V 1S5, Canada *Tel:* 250-766-2778 *Toll Free Tel:* 800-663-2775 (orders & cust serv) *Fax:* 250-766-2736 *Toll Free Fax:* 888-841-9991 (orders & cust serv) *E-mail:* info@woodlake.com; customerservice@woodlake.com *Web Site:* www.woodlakebooks.com, pg 505

Woodbine House, 6510 Bells Mill Rd, Bethesda, MD 20817 *Tel:* 301-897-3570 *Toll Free Tel:* 800-843-7323 *Fax:* 301-897-5838 *E-mail:* info@woodbinehouse.com *Web Site:* www.woodbinehouse.com, pg 274

Woodland Publishing Inc, 515 S 700 E, Suite 2D, Salt Lake City, UT 84102 *Toll Free Tel:* 800-277-3243 *Fax:* 801-334-1913 *E-mail:* info@woodlandpublishing.com *Web Site:* www.woodlandpublishing.com, pg 275

Woodrow Wilson Center Press, One Woodrow Wilson Plaza, 1300 Pennsylvania Ave NW, Washington, DC 20004-3027 *Tel:* 202-691-4000 *Fax:* 202-691-4001 *Web Site:* wilsoncenter.org, pg 275

Carter G Woodson Book Awards, 8555 16 St, Suite 500, Silver Spring, MD 20910 *Tel:* 301-588-1800 *Toll Free Tel:* 800-296-7840 *Fax:* 301-588-2049 *E-mail:* excellence@ncss.org; publications@ncss.org *Web Site:* www.socialstudies.org, pg 737

WoodstockArts, PO Box 1342, Woodstock, NY 12498 *Tel:* 845-679-8111 *E-mail:* info@woodstockarts.com *Web Site:* www.woodstockarts.com, pg 275

Word Works Washington Prize, Adirondack Community College, Dearlove Hall, 640 Bay Rd, Queensbury, NY 12804 *Fax:* 301-581-9443 *E-mail:* editor@wordworksbooks.org *Web Site:* www.wordworksbooks.org, pg 737

WordCo Indexing Services Inc, 49 Church St, Norwich, CT 06360 *Tel:* 860-886-2532 *Toll Free Tel:* 877-WORDCO-3 (967-3263) *Fax:* 860-886-1155 *E-mail:* office@wordco.com *Web Site:* www.wordco.com, pg 536

WordForce Communications, 35 Ormskirk Ave, Suite 805, Toronto, ON M6S 1A8, Canada *Tel:* 416-534-9881 *E-mail:* info@wordforce.ca *Web Site:* www.wordforce.ca, pg 536

Words into Print, 57 Prince St, Suite 4R, New York, NY 10012 *Tel:* 212-741-1393 *Fax:* 419-441-1393 *E-mail:* query@wordsintoprint.org *Web Site:* www.wordsintoprint.org, pg 536

WordWitlox, 70 Grainger Crescent, Ajax, ON L1T 4Y6, Canada *Tel:* 647-505-9673 *Web Site:* www.wordwitlox.com, pg 536

Workers Compensation Research Institute, 955 Massachusetts Ave, Cambridge, MA 02139 *Tel:* 617-661-9274 *Fax:* 617-661-9284 *E-mail:* wcri@wcrinet.org *Web Site:* www.wcrinet.org, pg 275

Working With Words, 9720 SW Eagle Ct, Beaverton, OR 97008 *Tel:* 503-644-4317 *E-mail:* editor@zzz.com, pg 536

Workman Publishing Co Inc, 225 Varick St, 9th fl, New York, NY 10014-4381 *Tel:* 212-254-5900 *Toll Free Tel:* 800-722-7202 *Fax:* 212-254-8098 *E-mail:* info@workman.com *Web Site:* www.workman.com, pg 275

World Almanac®, 132 W 31 St, New York, NY 10001 *Toll Free Tel:* 800-322-8755 *E-mail:* almanac@factsonfile.com *Web Site:* www.worldalmanac.com, pg 275

World Bank Publications, Office of the Publisher, 1818 "H" St NW, U-11-1104, Washington, DC 20433 *Tel:* 202-458-4497 *Toll Free Tel:* 800-645-7247 (cust serv) *Fax:* 202-522-2631; 202-614-1237 *E-mail:* books@worldbank.org; pubrights@worldbank.org (foreign rts) *Web Site:* www.worldbank.org/publications; publications.worldbank.org, pg 275

World Book Inc, 233 N Michigan, Suite 2000, Chicago, IL 60601 *Tel:* 312-729-5800 *Toll Free Tel:* 800-967-5325 (consumer sales, US); 800-463-8845 (consumer sales, CN); 800-975-3250 (school & lib sales, US); 800-837-5365 (school & lib sales, CN); 866-866-5200 (web sales) *Fax:* 312-729-5600; 312-729-5606 *Toll Free Fax:* 800-433-9330 (school & lib sales, US); 888-690-4002 (school lib sales, CN) *Web Site:* www.worldbook.com, pg 276

World Citizens, PO Box 131, Mill Valley, CA 94942-0131 *Tel:* 415-380-8020 *Toll Free Tel:* 800-247-6553 (orders only), pg 276

World Class Speakers & Entertainers, 5200 Kanan Rd, Suite 210, Agoura Hills, CA 91301 *Tel:* 818-991-5400 *E-mail:* wcse@wcspeakers.com *Web Site:* www.wcspeakers.com, pg 588

World Fantasy Awards, PO Box 43, Mukilteo, WA 98275-0043 *Web Site:* www.worldfantasy.org, pg 738

World Resources Institute, 10 "G" St NE, Suite 800, Washington, DC 20002 *Tel:* 202-729-7600 *Fax:* 202-729-7610 *Web Site:* www.wri.org, pg 276

World Scientific Publishing Co Inc, 27 Warren St, Suite 401-402, Hackensack, NJ 07601 *Tel:* 201-487-9655 *Toll Free Tel:* 800-227-7562 *Fax:* 201-487-9656 *Toll Free Fax:* 888-977-2665 *E-mail:* wspc@wspc.com *Web Site:* www.wspc.com, pg 276

World Trade Press, 800 Lindberg Lane, Suite 190, Petaluma, CA 94952 *Tel:* 707-778-1124 *Toll Free Tel:* 800-833-8586 *Fax:* 707-778-1329 *Web Site:* www.worldtradepress.com, pg 276

World Vision Resources, 800 W Chestnut Ave, Monrovia, CA 91016-3198 *Tel:* 626-303-8811; 909-463-2998 (intl orders) *Toll Free Tel:* 800-777-7752 (US only) *Fax:* 909-463-2999 *E-mail:* wvresources@worldvision.org *Web Site:* www.worldvisionresources.com, pg 276

World's Best Short-Short Story Contest, Florida State University, Dept of English, Tallahassee, FL 32306 *E-mail:* southeastreview@gmail.com *Web Site:* www.southeastreview.org, pg 738

WorldTariff, 220 Montgomery St, Suite 448, San Francisco, CA 94104-3410 *Tel:* 415-391-7501; 415-591-6666 *Toll Free Tel:* 800-556-9334 *Fax:* 415-391-7537 (Fax/Modem) *Web Site:* www.worldtariff.com; ftn.fedex.com/wtonline, pg 276

Worldwide Library, 225 Duncan Mill Rd, Don Mills, ON M3B 3K9, Canada *Tel:* 416-445-5860 *Toll Free Tel:* 888-432-4879 *Fax:* 416-445-8655; 416-445-8736 *E-mail:* customerservice@harlequin.com *Web Site:* www.harlequin.com, pg 505

Worth Publishers, 41 Madison Ave, 37th fl, New York, NY 10010 *Tel:* 212-576-9400 *Fax:* 212-561-8281 *Web Site:* www.worthpub.com, pg 276

Worthy & James Publishing, PO Box 362015, Milpitas, CA 95036 *Tel:* 408-945-3963 *E-mail:* worthy1234@sbcglobal.net; mail@worthyjames.com *Web Site:* www.worthyjames.com, pg 509

Wright Group/McGraw-Hill, 8787 Orion Place, Columbus, OH 43240 *Tel:* 614-430-4000 *Toll Free Tel:* 800-537-4740, pg 276

Wright Information Indexing Services, PO Box 658, Sandia Park, NM 87047 *Tel:* 505-281-2600 *Web Site:* www.wrightinformation.com, pg 536

Write Bloody Publishing, 2306 E Cesar Chavez, Suite 103, Austin, TX 78706 *E-mail:* writebloody@gmail.com *Web Site:* writebloody.com, pg 276

Write for Success (WFS), PO Box 292153, Los Angeles, CA 90029-8653 *Tel:* 323-356-8833 *E-mail:* writeforsuccess@yahoo.com *Web Site:* www.write-for-success.com, pg 536

Write Now, 140 W Washington St, Indianapolis, IN 46204-3465 *Tel:* 317-635-5277 *Fax:* 317-236-0767 *E-mail:* info@writenow.co *Web Site:* www.writenow.co, pg 738

Write on the Sound Writers' Conference, 700 Main St, Edmonds, WA 98020 *Tel:* 425-771-0228 *Fax:* 425-771-0253 *E-mail:* wots@edmondswa.gov *Web Site:* www.writeonthesound.com, pg 657

Write Stuff Enterprises LLC, 1001 S Andrews Ave, Suite 120, Fort Lauderdale, FL 33316 *Tel:* 954-462-6657 *Toll Free Tel:* 800-900-2665 *Fax:* 954-462-6023 *E-mail:* legends@writestuffbooks.com *Web Site:* www.writestuffbooks.com, pg 277

The Write Way, 3048 Horizon Lane, Suite 1102, Naples, FL 34109 *Tel:* 239-273-9145 *E-mail:* darekane@gmail.com, pg 536

WriteLife LLC, 2323 S 171 St, Suite 202, Omaha, NE 68130 *Tel:* 402-934-1412 *Toll Free Tel:* 877-974-8354 *E-mail:* info@writelife.com *Web Site:* www.writelife.com; www.facebook.com/WriteLife; twitter.com/WriteLifeLLC, pg 277

Writer in Residence, 2410 N Old Penitentiary Rd, Boise, ID 83712 *Tel:* 208-334-2119 *Toll Free Tel:* 800-ART-FUND (278-3863 within Idaho) *Fax:* 208-334-2488 *E-mail:* info@arts.idaho.gov *Web Site:* www.arts.idaho.gov, pg 738

The Writer Magazine/Emily Dickinson Award, 15 Gramercy Park, New York, NY 10003 *Tel:* 212-254-9628 *Fax:* 212-673-2352 *Web Site:* www.poetrysociety.org, pg 738

Writers' Alliance of Newfoundland & Labrador, Haymarket Sq, 223 Duckworth St, Suite 208, St John's, NL A1C 6N1, Canada *Tel:* 709-739-5215 *Toll Free Tel:* 866-739-5215 *E-mail:* wanl@nf.aibn.com *Web Site:* wanl.ca, pg 621

Writers Anonymous Inc, 1302 E Coronado Rd, Phoenix, AZ 85006 *Tel:* 602-256-2830 *Fax:* 602-256-2830 *Web Site:* writersanonymousinc.blogspot.com, pg 536

Writer's AudioShop, 1316 Overland Stage Rd, Dripping Springs, TX 78620 *Tel:* 512-264-7067 *Fax:* 512-264-7067 *E-mail:* wrtaudshop@aol.com *Web Site:* www.writersaudio.com, pg 277

The Writers' Colony at Dairy Hollow, 515 Spring St, Eureka Springs, AR 72632 *Tel:* 479-253-7444 *E-mail:* director@writerscolony.org *Web Site:* www.writerscolony.org, pg 657

Writer's Digest Books, 10151 Carver Rd, Suite 200, Blue Ash, OH 45242 *Tel:* 513-531-2690 *Toll Free Tel:* 800-289-0963 *E-mail:* writersdigest@fwmedia.com (edit) *Web Site:* www.writersdigest.com, pg 277

Writer's Digest University, 10151 Carver Rd, Suite 200, Blue Ash, OH 45242-4760 *Tel:* 513-531-2690 *Toll Free Tel:* 800-759-0963 *Fax:* 513-531-0798 *E-mail:* contact_us@fwmedia.com *Web Site:* www.writersonlineworkshops.com, pg 664

Writer's Digest Writing Competition, 10151 Carver Rd, Suite 200, Blue Ash, OH 45242 *Tel:* 513-531-2690 *Fax:* 513-531-0798 *E-mail:* writing-competition@fwmedia.com; writersdigest@fwmedia.com (edit) *Web Site:* www.writersdigest.com, pg 738

Writers-Editors Network International Writing Competition, 45 Main St, North Stratford, NH 03590 *Tel:* 603-922-8338 *Fax:* 603-922-8339 *E-mail:* contest@writers-editors.com *Web Site:* www.writers-editors.com; www.ffwamembers.com, pg 738

Writers' Federation of Nova Scotia, 1113 Marginal Rd, Halifax, NS B3H 4P7, Canada *Tel:* 902-423-8116 *Fax:* 902-422-0881 *E-mail:* contact@writers.ns.ca *Web Site:* writers.ns.ca, pg 621

Writers' Guild of Alberta, 11759 Groat Rd, Edmonton, AB T5M 3K6, Canada *Tel:* 780-422-8174 *Toll Free Tel:* 800-665-5354 (AB only) *Fax:* 780-422-2663 (attn WGA) *E-mail:* mail@writersguild.ab.ca *Web Site:* www.writersguild.ab.ca, pg 621

Writers Guild of America Awards, 7000 W Third St, Los Angeles, CA 90048 *Tel:* 323-951-4000; 323-782-4569 *Fax:* 323-782-4800 *Web Site:* www.wga.org, pg 738

Writers Guild of America, East (WGAE), 250 Hudson St, Suite 700, New York, NY 10013 *Tel:* 212-767-7800 *Fax:* 212-582-1909 *Web Site:* www.wgaeast.org, pg 621

Writers Guild of America, West (WGAW), 7000 W Third St, Los Angeles, CA 90048 *Tel:* 323-951-4000 *Toll Free Tel:* 800-548-4532 *Fax:* 323-782-4800 *Web Site:* www.wga.org, pg 621

Writers House, 21 W 26 St, New York, NY 10010 *Tel:* 212-685-2400 *Fax:* 212-685-1781 *Web Site:* www.writershouse.com, pg 580

Robert Zolnerzak, 101 Clark St, Unit 20-K, Brooklyn, NY 11201 *Tel:* 718-522-0591 *E-mail:* bobzolnerzak@verizon.net, pg 537

Zondervan, 3900 Sparks Dr, Grand Rapids, MI 49546 *Tel:* 616-698-6900 *Toll Free Tel:* 800-226-1122; 800-727-1309 (retail orders) *Fax:* 616-698-3350 *Toll Free Fax:* 800-698-3256 (retail orders) *E-mail:* zinfo@zondervan.com *Web Site:* www.zondervan.com, pg 280

Zone Books dba Urzone Inc, 1226 Prospect Ave, Brooklyn, NY 11218 *Tel:* 718-686-0048 *Toll Free Tel:* 800-405-1619 (orders & cust serv) *Fax:* 718-686-9045 *Toll Free Fax:* 800-406-9145 (orders) *E-mail:* orders@triliteral.org *Web Site:* www.zonebooks.org, pg 280

Anna Zornio Memorial Children's Theatre Playwriting Award, D22 Paul Creative Arts Center, 30 Academic Way, Durham, NH 03824 *Tel:* 603-862-2919 *Fax:* 603-862-0298 *Web Site:* cola.unh.edu/theatre-dance/resource/zornio, pg 740

ZOVA Books, PO Box 21833, Long Beach, CA 90801 *Tel:* 805-426-9682 *Fax:* 562-394-9568 *Web Site:* www.zovabooks.com, pg 280

Zumaya Publications LLC, 3209 S IH 35, Suite 1086, Austin, TX 78741 *Tel:* 512-402-5298 *Fax:* 253-660-2009 *E-mail:* acquisitions@zumayapublications.com *Web Site:* www.zumayapublications.com, pg 280

Personnel Index

Included in this index are the personnel included in the entries in this volume of *LMP*, along with the page number(s) on which they appear. Not included in this index are those individuals associated with listings in the **Calendar of Book Trade & Promotional Events; Reference Books for the Trade** and **Magazines for the Trade** sections. Also, personnel associated with secondary addresses within listings (such as branch offices, sales offices, editorial offices, etc.) are not included.

Aalto, Helena, Canadian Society of Children's Authors Illustrators & Performers (CANSCAIP), 720 Bathurst St, Suite 503, Toronto, ON M5S 2R4, Canada *Tel:* 416-515-1559 *E-mail:* office@canscaip.org *Web Site:* www.canscaip.org, pg 602

Aalto, Helena, Tom Fairley Award for Editorial Excellence, 27 Carlton St, Suite 502, Toronto, ON M5B 1L2, Canada *Tel:* 416-975-1379 *Toll Free Tel:* 866-CAN-EDIT (226-3348) *Fax:* 416-975-1637 *E-mail:* fairley_award@editors.ca *Web Site:* www.editors.ca; www.reviseurs.ca, pg 684

Aardema, John, Sourcebooks Inc, 1935 Brookdale Rd, Suite 139, Naperville, IL 60563 *Tel:* 630-961-3900 *Toll Free Tel:* 800-432-7444 *Fax:* 630-961-2168 *E-mail:* info@sourcebooks.com; customersupport@sourcebooks.com *Web Site:* www.sourcebooks.com, pg 230

Aaronson, Deborah, Phaidon Press Inc, 180 Varick St, 14th fl, New York, NY 10014 *Tel:* 212-652-5400 *Toll Free Tel:* 800-759-0190 (cust serv) *Fax:* 212-652-5410 *Toll Free Fax:* 800-286-9471 (cust serv) *E-mail:* ussales@phaidon.com *Web Site:* www.phaidon.com, pg 190

Aballe, Sabrina, Holiday House Inc, 425 Madison Ave, New York, NY 10017 *Tel:* 212-688-0085 *Fax:* 212-421-6134 *E-mail:* holiday@holidayhouse.com *Web Site:* www.holidayhouse.com, pg 113

Abbots, Jennifer, Harlequin Enterprises Ltd, 233 Broadway, Suite 1001, New York, NY 10279 *Tel:* 212-553-4200 *Fax:* 212-227-8969 *E-mail:* CustomerService@harlequin.com *Web Site:* www.harlequin.com, pg 105

Abbott, George, AFB Press, 2 Penn Plaza, Suite 1102, New York, NY 10121 *Tel:* 212-502-7600 *Toll Free Tel:* 800-232-5463; 800-232-3044 (orders) *Fax:* 917-210-3979; 412-741-0609 (orders) *Toll Free Fax:* 888-545-8331 *E-mail:* press@afb.net; afbpress@afb.net; afbinfo@afb.net; afborder@afb.net (orders) *Web Site:* www.afb.org, pg 5

Abbott, Stephen E, Maine Writers & Publishers Alliance, 314 Forest Ave, Rm 318, Portland, ME 04101 *Tel:* 207-228-8263 *Fax:* 207-228-8150 *E-mail:* info@mainewriters.org *Web Site:* mainewriters.org, pg 609

Abdo, Jim, ABDO Publishing Group, 8000 W 78 St, Suite 310, Edina, MN 55439 *Tel:* 952-831-2120 *Toll Free Tel:* 800-800-1312 *Toll Free Fax:* 800-862-3480 *E-mail:* customerservice@abdopublishing.com *Web Site:* abdopublishing.com, pg 2

Abdo, Paul, ABDO Publishing Group, 8000 W 78 St, Suite 310, Edina, MN 55439 *Tel:* 952-831-2120 *Toll Free Tel:* 800-800-1312 *Toll Free Fax:* 800-862-3480 *E-mail:* customerservice@abdopublishing.com *Web Site:* abdopublishing.com, pg 2

Abdulhamid, Abusolayman, The International Institute of Islamic Thought, 500 Grove St, Suite 200, Herndon, VA 20170 *Tel:* 703-471-1133 *Fax:* 703-471-3922 *E-mail:* iiit@iiit.org *Web Site:* www.iiit.org, pg 124

Abe, Carol, University of Hawaii Press, 2840 Kolowalu St, Honolulu, HI 96822 *Tel:* 808-956-8255 *Toll Free Tel:* 888-UHPRESS (847-7377) *Fax:* 808-988-6052 *Toll Free Fax:* 800-650-7811 *E-mail:* uhpbooks@hawaii.edu *Web Site:* www.uhpress.hawaii.edu, pg 256

Abel, Dominick, Dominick Abel Literary Agency Inc, 146 W 82 St, Suite 1-A, New York, NY 10024 *Tel:* 212-877-0710 *Fax:* 212-595-3133 *E-mail:* agency@dalainc.com *Web Site:* www.dalainc.com, pg 539

Abernathy, Charlotte, National Federation of State Poetry Societies Annual Poetry Contest, 1375 Green Meadows Way, Ashland, OR 97520 *E-mail:* contestchair@nfsps.com *Web Site:* www.nfsps.com, pg 710

Abfier, Mel, StarGroup International Inc, 1194 Old Dixie Hwy, Suite 201, West Palm Beach, FL 33413 *Tel:* 561-547-0667 *Fax:* 561-843-8530 *E-mail:* info@stargroupinternational.com *Web Site:* www.stargroupinternational.com, pg 234

Abkemeier, Laurie, DeFiore and Company, LLC, 47 E 19 St, 3rd fl, New York, NY 10003 *Tel:* 212-925-7744 *Fax:* 212-925-9803 *E-mail:* submissions@defioreandco.com; info@defioreandco.com *Web Site:* www.defioreandco.com, pg 548

Ablaza, Christina, Stegner Fellowship, Stanford Creative Writing Program, Dept of English, Stanford, CA 94305-2087 *Tel:* 650-723-0011 *Fax:* 650-723-3679 *Web Site:* creativewriting.stanford.edu, pg 730

Ableman, Brian, The Learning Source Ltd, 644 Tenth St, Brooklyn, NY 11215 *Tel:* 718-768-0231 (ext 10) *Fax:* 718-369-3467 *E-mail:* info@learningsourceltd.com *Web Site:* www.learningsourceltd.com, pg 529

Abraham, Ben, Urban Land Institute, 1025 Thomas Jefferson St NW, Suite 500-W, Washington, DC 20007 *Tel:* 202-624-7000 *Toll Free Tel:* 800-321-5011 (cust serv) *Fax:* 410-626-7140 *E-mail:* bookstore@uli.org; customerservice@uli.org *Web Site:* www.uli.org/books, pg 263

Abramo, Lauren E, Dystel & Goderich Literary Management, One Union Sq W, Suite 904, New York, NY 10003 *Tel:* 212-627-9100 *Fax:* 212-627-9313 *Web Site:* www.dystel.com, pg 549

Abrams, Joanne, Square One Publishers Inc, 115 Herricks Rd, Garden City Park, NY 11040 *Tel:* 516-535-2010 *Toll Free Tel:* 877-900-BOOK (900-2665) *Fax:* 516-535-2014 *E-mail:* sq1publish@aol.com *Web Site:* www.squareonepublishers.com, pg 232

Abrams, Liesa, Simon & Schuster Children's Publishing, 1230 Avenue of the Americas, New York, NY 10020 *Tel:* 212-698-7000 *Web Site:* KIDS.SimonandSchuster.com; TEEN.SimonandSchuster.com; simonandschuster.net; simonandschuster.biz, pg 225

Abrams, Robert E, Abbeville Publishing Group, 137 Varick St, Suite 504, New York, NY 10013 *Tel:* 212-366-5585 *Toll Free Tel:* 800-ART-BOOK (278-2665) *Fax:* 212-366-6966 *E-mail:* abbeville@abbeville.com; marketing@abbeville.com; sales@abbeville.com; rights@abbeville.com *Web Site:* www.abbeville.com, pg 2

Abreu, Carmen, Blue Note Publications Inc, 721 North Dr, Suite D, Melbourne, FL 32934 *Tel:* 321-799-2583 *Toll Free Tel:* 800-624-0401 (orders) *Fax:* 321-799-1942 *E-mail:* bluenotepress@gmail.com *Web Site:* www.bluenotebooks.com, pg 40

Acevedo, Amanda, Houghton Mifflin Harcourt Trade & Reference Division, 222 Berkeley St, Boston, MA 02116 *Tel:* 617-351-5000 *Toll Free Tel:* 800-225-3362 *Web Site:* www.hmhco.com, pg 115

Acheson, Alice B, Alice B Acheson's Workshops for Writers, Illustrators & Photographers, PO Box 735, Friday Harbor, WA 98250 *Tel:* 360-378-2815 *E-mail:* aliceba7@gmail.com, pg 649

Acheson, Alison, Tradewind Books, 202-1807 Maritime Mews, Vancouver, BC V6H 3W7, Canada *Tel:* 604-662-4405 *E-mail:* tradewindbooks@yahoo.com *Web Site:* www.tradewindbooks.com, pg 501

Acland, Marigold, Cambridge University Press, 32 Avenue of the Americas, New York, NY 10013-2473 *Tel:* 212-924-3900; 212-337-5000 *Fax:* 212-691-3239 *E-mail:* newyork@cambridge.org *Web Site:* www.cambridge.org/us, pg 49

Acocella, Amy, Gryphon House Inc, 6848 Leon's Way, Lewisville, NC 27023 *Toll Free Tel:* 800-638-0928 *Toll Free Fax:* 877-638-7576 *E-mail:* info@ghbooks.com *Web Site:* www.gryphonhouse.com, pg 101

Acton, Amy, Phoenix Society for Burn Survivors, 1835 R W Berends Dr SW, Grand Rapids, MI 49519 *Tel:* 616-458-2773 *Toll Free Tel:* 800-888-BURN (888-2876) *Fax:* 616-458-2831 *E-mail:* info@phoenix-society.org *Web Site:* www.phoenix-society.org, pg 191

Adamo, John, Random House Children's Books, 1745 Broadway, New York, NY 10019 *Tel:* 212-782-9000 *Toll Free Tel:* 800-200-3552 *Fax:* 212-782-9452 *Web Site:* randomhousekids.com, pg 203

Adams, Barry, Temple University Press, 1852 N Tenth St, Philadelphia, PA 19122-6099 *Tel:* 215-926-2140 *Toll Free Tel:* 800-621-2736 *Fax:* 215-926-2141 *E-mail:* tempress@temple.edu *Web Site:* www.temple.edu/tempress, pg 242

Adams, Ben, PublicAffairs, 250 W 57 St, Suite 1321, New York, NY 10107 *Tel:* 212-397-6666 *Toll Free Tel:* 800-343-4499 (orders) *Fax:* 212-397-4277 *E-mail:* publicaffairs@perseusbooks.com *Web Site:* www.publicaffairsbooks.com, pg 200

Adams, Beth, Howard Books, 216 Centerview Dr, Suite 303, Brentwood, TN 37027 *Tel:* 615-873-2080 *Fax:* 615-370-3834 *E-mail:* howardbooks@simonandschuster.com (info) *Web Site:* www.howardpublishing.com, pg 116

Adams, Chuck, Algonquin Books, 400 Silver Cedar Ct, Suite 300, Chapel Hill, NC 27514-1585 *Tel:* 919-967-0108 *Fax:* 919-933-0272 *E-mail:* inquiry@algonquin.com *Web Site:* www.workman.com/algonquin, pg 8

Adams, Haydn, The Graphic Artists Guild Inc, 32 Broadway, Suite 1114, New York, NY 10004 *Tel:* 212-791-3400 *Fax:* 212-791-0333 *Web Site:* www.graphicartistsguild.org, pg 606, 660

Adams, Jennifer, Clinical Laboratory & Standards Institute (CLSI), 950 W Valley Rd, Suite 2500, Wayne, PA 19087 *Tel:* 610-688-0100 *Toll Free Tel:* 877-447-1888 (orders) *Fax:* 610-688-0700 *E-mail:* customerservice@clsi.org *Web Site:* www.clsi.org, pg 59

Adams, John T III, Association Media & Publishing (AM&P), 12100 Sunset Hills Rd, Suite 130, Reston, VA 20190 *Tel:* 703-234-4063 *Fax:* 703-435-4390 *E-mail:* info@associationmediaandpublishing.org *Web Site:* associationmediaandpublishing.org, pg 598

Adams, John T III, EXCEL Awards, 12100 Sunset Hills Rd, Suite 130, Reston, VA 20190 *Tel:* 703-234-4063 *Fax:* 703-435-4390 *E-mail:* info@associationmediaandpublishing.org *Web Site:* associationmediaandpublishing.org, pg 684

Adams, Katie Henderson, W W Norton & Company Inc, 500 Fifth Ave, New York, NY 10110-0017 *Tel:* 212-354-5500 *Toll Free Tel:* 800-233-4830 (orders & cust serv) *Fax:* 212-869-0856 *Toll Free Fax:* 800-458-6515 *Web Site:* www.wwnorton.com, pg 172

Adams, Kelli, Counterpoint Press LLC, 1919 Fifth St, Berkeley, CA 94710 *Tel:* 510-704-0230 *Fax:* 510-704-0268 *E-mail:* info@counterpointpress.com *Web Site:* counterpointpress.com; www.sierraclub.org/books; softskull.com, pg 65

Adams, Lauren, Random House Children's Books, 1745 Broadway, New York, NY 10019 *Tel:* 212-782-9000 *Toll Free Tel:* 800-200-3552 *Fax:* 212-782-9452 *Web Site:* randomhousekids.com, pg 204

Adams, Lisa, The Garamond Agency Inc, 12 Horton St, Newburyport, MA 01950 *E-mail:* query@garamondagency.com *Web Site:* www.garamondagency.com, pg 553

Adams, Mark Wayne, Florida Authors & Publishers Association Inc (FAPA), PO Box 915822, Longwood, FL 32791 *E-mail:* member.services@floridapublishersassociation.com *Web Site:* www.floridapublishersassociation.com, pg 605

Adams, Martha, Leisure Arts Inc, 104 Champs Blvd, Suite 100, Maumelle, AR 72113 *Tel:* 501-868-8800 *Toll Free Tel:* 800-643-8030 *Fax:* 501-868-8748 *Web Site:* www.leisurearts.com, pg 137

Adams, Matthew, Between the Lines (BTL), 401 Richmond St W, No 277, Toronto, ON M5V 3A8, Canada *Tel:* 416-535-9914 *Toll Free Tel:* 800-718-7201 *Fax:* 416-535-1484 *E-mail:* info@btlbooks.com *Web Site:* btlbooks.com, pg 472

Adams, Dr Michael, Dobie Paisano Fellowship Program, Graduate School, 110 Inner Campus Dr, Stop G0400, Austin, TX 78712-0710 *Fax:* 512-471-7620 *Web Site:* www.utexas.edu/ogs/Paisano, pg 716

Adams, Michael W, University of Texas at Austin, Creative Writing Program, Dept of English, PAR 108, One University Sta, Mailcode B5000, Austin, TX 78712-1164 *Tel:* 512-471-5132; 512-471-4991 *Fax:* 512-471-4909 *Web Site:* www.utexas.edu/cola/depts/english/creative-writing, pg 664

Adams, Michele, 4A's (American Association of Advertising Agencies), 1065 Avenue of the Americas, 16th fl, New York, NY 10018 *Tel:* 212-682-2500 *Web Site:* www.aaaa.org, pg 606

Adams, Phillip, The Summer Experience, 601 Spadina Crescent E, Suite 718, Saskatoon, SK S7K 3G8, Canada *Tel:* 306-652-7395 *Fax:* 306-244-0255 *E-mail:* sage.hill@sasktel.net *Web Site:* www.sagehillwriting.ca, pg 656

Adams, Steven, American Institute for Economic Research (AIER), 250 Division St, Great Barrington, MA 01230 *Tel:* 413-528-1216 *Toll Free Tel:* 888-528-1216 (orders) *E-mail:* info@aier.org, pg 13

Adams, Susan, Addicus Books Inc, PO Box 45327, Omaha, NE 68145 *Tel:* 402-330-7493 *Fax:* 402-330-1707 *E-mail:* info@addicusbooks.com; addicusbks@aol.com *Web Site:* www.addicusbooks.com, pg 4

Adams, Terry, Little, Brown and Company, 1290 Avenue of the Americas, New York, NY 10019 *Tel:* 212-364-1100 *Fax:* 212-364-0952 *E-mail:* firstname.lastname@hbgusa.com *Web Site:* www.HachetteBookGroup.com, pg 141

Adams, William, Public Scholar Program, 400 Seventh St SW, Washington, DC 20506 *Tel:* 202-606-8200 *E-mail:* publicscholar@neh.gov *Web Site:* www.neh.gov/grants/research, pg 722

Adams, William, University of South Carolina Press, 1600 Hampton St, Suite 544, Columbia, SC 29208 *Tel:* 803-777-5245 *Toll Free Tel:* 800-768-2500 (orders) *Fax:* 803-777-0160 *Toll Free Fax:* 800-868-0740 (orders) *Web Site:* www.sc.edu/uscpress, pg 260

Addicott, Lori, WaterBrook Multnomah Publishing Group, 12265 Oracle Blvd, Suite 200, Colorado Springs, CO 80921 *Tel:* 719-590-4999 *Toll Free Tel:* 800-603-7051 (orders) *Fax:* 719-590-8977 *Toll Free Fax:* 800-294-5686 (orders) *E-mail:* info@waterbrookmultnomah.com *Web Site:* waterbrookmultnomah.com, pg 267

Adel, Judith, J Adel Art & Design, 586 Ramapo Rd, Teaneck, NJ 07666 *Tel:* 201-836-2606 *E-mail:* jadelnj@aol.com, pg 519

Aders-Weremczuk, Coco, Federation of BC Writers, PO Box 16028, 617 Belmont St, New Westminster, BC V3M 6W6, Canada *E-mail:* info@bcwriters.ca *Web Site:* bcwriters.ca, pg 605

Adjemian, Robert, Vedanta Press, 1946 Vedanta Place, Hollywood, CA 90068 *Tel:* 323-960-1736 *Toll Free Tel:* 800-816-2242 *E-mail:* info@vedanta.com *Web Site:* www.vedanta.com, pg 265

Adkins, David, Council of State Governments, 2760 Research Park Dr, Lexington, KY 40511 *Tel:* 859-244-8000 *Toll Free Tel:* 800-800-1910 *Fax:* 859-244-8001 *E-mail:* sales@csg.org *Web Site:* www.csg.org; www.csgstore.org, pg 65

Adler, Allan R, Association of American Publishers (AAP), 71 Fifth Ave, 2nd fl, New York, NY 10003-3004 *Tel:* 212-255-0200 *Fax:* 212-255-7007 *E-mail:* info@publishers.org *Web Site:* publishers.org, pg 598

Adler, Ellen, The New Press, 38 Greene St, 4th fl, New York, NY 10013 *Tel:* 212-629-8802 *Toll Free Tel:* 800-343-4489 (orders) *Fax:* 212-629-8617 *Toll Free Fax:* 800-351-5073 (orders) *E-mail:* newpress@thenewpress.com *Web Site:* www.thenewpress.com, pg 168

Adler, Laina, HarperCollins General Books Group, 195 Broadway, New York, NY 10007 *Tel:* 212-207-7000 *Web Site:* www.harpercollins.com, pg 105

Adler, William K, Reader's Digest General Books, Reader's Digest Rd, Pleasantville, NY 10570-7000 *Tel:* 914-238-1000 *Toll Free Tel:* 800-304-2807 (cust serv) *Fax:* 914-244-7436, pg 205

Adler-Kozak, Mary, National Association of College Stores (NACS), 500 E Lorain St, Oberlin, OH 44074 *Tel:* 440-775-7777 *Toll Free Tel:* 800-622-7498 *Fax:* 440-775-4769 *Web Site:* www.nacs.org, pg 611

Agbonlahor, Etinosa, Touchstone, 1230 Avenue of the Americas, New York, NY 10020, pg 247

Agnew, Tim, Concordia Publishing House, 3558 S Jefferson Ave, St Louis, MO 63118-3968 *Tel:* 314-268-1000; 314-268-1268 (bookshop) *Toll Free Tel:* 800-325-3040 (cust serv) *Toll Free Fax:* 800-490-9889 (cust serv) *E-mail:* order@cph.org *Web Site:* www.cph.org, pg 62

Agree, Peter A, University of Pennsylvania Press, 3905 Spruce St, Philadelphia, PA 19104 *Tel:* 215-898-6261 *Fax:* 215-898-0404 *E-mail:* custserv@pobox.upenn.edu *Web Site:* www.pennpress.org, pg 259

Aguilar, Enrique, Paulist Press, 997 Macarthur Blvd, Mahwah, NJ 07430-9990 *Tel:* 201-825-7300 *Toll Free Tel:* 800-218-1903 *Fax:* 201-825-8345 *Toll Free Fax:* 800-836-3161 *E-mail:* info@paulistpress.com *Web Site:* www.paulistpress.com, pg 184

Aguilo, Maria Jesus, Berrett-Koehler Publishers Inc, 1333 Broadway, Suite 1000, Oakland, CA 94612 *Tel:* 510-817-2277 *Fax:* 510-817-2278 *E-mail:* bkpub@bkpub.com *Web Site:* www.bkconnection.com, pg 35

Ahearn, Pamela G, The Ahearn Agency Inc, 2021 Pine St, New Orleans, LA 70118 *Tel:* 504-861-8395 *Fax:* 504-866-6434 *Web Site:* www.ahearnagency.com, pg 540

Ahern, G Thomas, Capstone Publishers™, 1710 Roe Crest Dr, North Mankato, MN 56003 *Toll Free Tel:* 800-747-4992 (cust serv) *Toll Free Fax:* 888-262-0705 *Web Site:* www.capstonepress.com, pg 49

Ahlquist, Susan, Second Chance Press, 4170 Noyac Rd, Sag Harbor, NY 11963 *Tel:* 631-725-1101 *E-mail:* info@thepermanentpress.com *Web Site:* www.thepermanentpress.com, pg 221

Ahmad, Ibrahim, Akashic Books, 232 Third St, Suite A-115, Brooklyn, NY 11215 *Tel:* 718-643-9193 *Fax:* 718-643-9195 *E-mail:* info@akashicbooks.com *Web Site:* www.akashicbooks.com, pg 7

Ahuja, Parveen, Kapp Books LLC, 3602 Rocky Meadow Ct, Fairfax, VA 22033 *Tel:* 703-261-9171 *Fax:* 703-621-7162 *E-mail:* info@kappbooks.com *Web Site:* www.kappbooks.com, pg 129

Aielli, Michelle, Hachette Books, 1290 Avenue of the Americas, New York, NY 10019 *Tel:* 212-364-1100 *Web Site:* www.hachettebookgroup.com, pg 102

Akers, Terrie, Other Press LLC, 2 Park Ave, 24th fl, New York, NY 10016 *Tel:* 212-414-0054 *Toll Free Tel:* 877-843-6843 *Fax:* 212-414-0939 *E-mail:* editor@otherpress.com; rights@otherpress.com *Web Site:* www.otherpress.com, pg 178

Akin, Wanda M, Akin & Randolph Agency, Literary Div, One Gateway Ctr, Suite 2600, Newark, NJ 07102 *Tel:* 973-353-8409; 973-623-6834 *Fax:* 973-353-8417 *E-mail:* info@akinandrandolph.com *Web Site:* www.akinandrandolph.com, pg 540

Akoury-Ross, Lisa, SDP Publishing Solutions LLC, 36 Captain's Way, East Bridgewater, MA 02333 *Tel:* 617-775-0656 *Web Site:* www.sdppublishingsolutions.com, pg 534

Al-Hillal, Ms Semareh, Kids Can Press Ltd, 25 Dockside Dr, Toronto, ON M5A 0B5, Canada *Tel:* 416-479-7000 *Toll Free Tel:* 800-265-0884 *Fax:* 416-960-5437 *E-mail:* info@kidscan.com; customerservice@kidscan.com *Web Site:* www.kidscanpress.com; www.kidscanpress.ca, pg 489

Al-Yemany, Riyad, The International Institute of Islamic Thought, 500 Grove St, Suite 200, Herndon, VA 20170 *Tel:* 703-471-1133 *Fax:* 703-471-3922 *E-mail:* iiit@iiit.org *Web Site:* www.iiit.org, pg 124

Alain, Louise, Les Editions Alire, CP 67, Succursale B, Quebec, QC G1K 7A1, Canada *Tel:* 418-835-4441 *Fax:* 418-838-4443 *E-mail:* info@alire.com *Web Site:* www.alire.com, pg 479

Alain, Marc, Modus Vivendi Publishing Inc, 55, rue Jean-Talon Ouest, 2e etage, Montreal, QC H2R 2W8, Canada *Tel:* 514-272-0433 *Fax:* 514-272-7234 *E-mail:* info@groupemodus.com *Web Site:* www.groupemodus.com, pg 491

Alan, Yusuf, Tughra Books, 345 Clifton Ave, Clifton, NJ 07011 *Tel:* 973-777-2704 *Fax:* 973-457-7334 *E-mail:* info@tughrabooks.com *Web Site:* www.tughrabooks.com, pg 250

Albanese, Frank, HarperCollins Publishers, 195 Broadway, New York, NY 10007 *Tel:* 212-207-7000 *Fax:* 212-207-7145 *Web Site:* www.harpercollins.com, pg 106

Albanese, Frank, HarperCollins Publishers Sales, 195 Broadway, New York, NY 10007 *Fax:* 212-207-7000 *Web Site:* www.harpercollins.com, pg 106

Albee, Edward, William Flanagan Memorial Creative Persons Center, 14 Harrison St, New York, NY 10013 *Tel:* 212-226-2020 *Fax:* 212-226-5551 *E-mail:* info@albeefoundation.org *Web Site:* www.albeefoundation.org, pg 736

Albers, Wes, Southern California Writers' Conference, 18160 Cottonwood Rd, Suite 260, Sunriver, OR 97707 *Tel:* 619-303-8185 *Fax:* 619-906-7462 *E-mail:* msg@writersconference.com *Web Site:* www.writersconference.com, pg 655

Alberti, Milena, Random House Publishing Group, 1745 Broadway, New York, NY 10019 *Toll Free Tel:* 800-200-3552 *Web Site:* atrandom.com, pg 204

Alberti, Robert E, Impact Publishers Inc, PO Box 6016, Atascadero, CA 93423-6016 *Tel:* 805-466-5917 (opers & admin offs) *Toll Free Tel:* 800-246-7228 (orders) *Fax:* 805-466-5919 (opers & admin offs) *E-mail:* info@impactpublishers.com *Web Site:* www.impactpublishers.com; www.bibliotherapy.com, pg 119

Albi, Mary, Phaidon Press Inc, 180 Varick St, 14th fl, New York, NY 10014 *Tel:* 212-652-5400 *Toll Free Tel:* 800-759-0190 (cust serv) *Fax:* 212-652-5410 *Toll Free Fax:* 800-286-9471 (cust serv) *E-mail:* ussales@phaidon.com *Web Site:* www.phaidon.com, pg 190

Albrecht, Ms Geri, Heuer Publishing LLC, PO Box 248, Cedar Rapids, IA 52406 *Tel:* 319-368-8008 *Toll Free Tel:* 800-950-7529 *Fax:* 319-368-8011 *E-mail:* editor@hitplays.com; customerservice@hitplays.com *Web Site:* www.hitplays.com, pg 111

Alcala, Rosa, University of Texas at El Paso, Department of Creative Writing, MFA/Department of Creative Writing, Liberal Arts 415 UTEP, 500 W University Ave, El Paso, TX 79968-9991 *Tel:* 915-747-5713 *Fax:* 915-747-5523 *Web Site:* www.utep.edu/cw, pg 664

Alcantara, Anitra, Ten Speed Press, 2625 Alcatraz Ave, Unit 505, Berkeley, CA 94705 *Tel:* 510-285-3000 *Toll Free Tel:* 800-841-BOOK (841-2665) *E-mail:* csorders@randomhouse.com *Web Site:* crownpublishing.com/imprint/ten-speed-press, pg 243

Alcid, Edmond, Moose Hide Books, 684 Walls Rd, Prince Township, ON P6A 6K4, Canada *Tel:* 705-779-3331 *Fax:* 705-779-3331 *E-mail:* mooseenterprises@on.aibn.com *Web Site:* www.moosehidebooks.com, pg 492

Alden, Laura, Judson Press, 588 N Gulph Rd, King of Prussia, PA 19406 *Toll Free Tel:* 800-458-3766 *Fax:* 610-768-2107 *Web Site:* www.judsonpress.com, pg 128

Alderson, Martha, Blockbuster Plots for Writers Retreat, PO Box 1402, Capitola, CA 95010 *Tel:* 408-482-4678 *E-mail:* contact@blockbusterplots.com *Web Site:* www.blockbusterplots.com, pg 650

Aldis, Sherri, Harry N Abrams Inc, 115 W 18 St, 6th fl, New York, NY 10011 *Tel:* 212-206-7715 *Toll Free Tel:* 800-345-1359 *Fax:* 212-519-1210 *E-mail:* abrams@abramsbooks.com *Web Site:* www.abramsbooks.com, pg 3

Aldis, Sherri, United Nations Publications, 300 E 42 St, 9th fl, New York, NY 10017 *Tel:* 703-661-1571 *Fax:* 703-996-1010 *E-mail:* publications@un.org *Web Site:* un.org/publications, pg 253

Alenier, Karren L, Word Works Washington Prize, Adirondack Community College, Dearlove Hall, 640 Bay Rd, Queensbury, NY 12804 *Fax:* 301-581-9443 *E-mail:* editor@wordworksbooks.org *Web Site:* www.wordworksbooks.org, pg 737

Alesse, Craig, Amherst Media Inc, 175 Rano St, Suite 200, Buffalo, NY 14207 *Tel:* 716-874-4450 *Toll Free Tel:* 800-622-3278 *Fax:* 716-874-4508 *E-mail:* marketing@amherstmedia.com *Web Site:* www.amherstmedia.com, pg 17

Alewel, Rex, Marathon Press, 1500 Square Turn Blvd, Norfolk, NE 68701 *Tel:* 402-371-5040 *Toll Free Tel:* 800-228-0629 *Fax:* 402-371-9382 *Web Site:* www.marathonpress.com, pg 147

Alexander, Britta, The Ned Leavitt Agency, 70 Wooster St, Suite 4-F, New York, NY 10012 *Tel:* 212-334-0999 *Web Site:* www.nedleavittagency.com, pg 561

Alexander, Caitlin, Random House Publishing Group, 1745 Broadway, New York, NY 10019 *Toll Free Tel:* 800-200-3552 *Web Site:* atrandom.com, pg 204

Alexander, Heather, Pippin Properties Inc, 110 W 40 St, Suite 1704, New York, NY 10018 *Tel:* 212-338-9310 *Fax:* 212-338-9579 *E-mail:* info@pippinproperties.com *Web Site:* www.pippinproperties.com; www.facebook.com/pippinproperties, pg 568

Alexander, Lawrence, Polebridge Press, c/o Willamette University, 900 State St, Salem, OR 97301 *Tel:* 503-375-5323 *E-mail:* orders@westarinstitute.org *Web Site:* www.polebridgepress.com, pg 194

Alexander, Michael, Red Wheel/Weiser/Conari, 65 Parker St, Suite 7, Newburyport, MA 01950 *Tel:* 978-465-0504 *Toll Free Tel:* 800-423-7087 (orders) *Fax:* 978-465-0243 *E-mail:* info@rwwbooks.com *Web Site:* www.redwheelweiser.com, pg 206

Alexander, Neil M, Abingdon Press, 201 Eighth Ave S, Nashville, TN 37203-3919 *Tel:* 615-749-6000 (academic books) *Toll Free Tel:* 800-251-3320 *Fax:* 615-749-6056 (academic books) *Toll Free Fax:* 800-836-7802 (orders) *E-mail:* orders@abingdonpress.com *Web Site:* www.abingdonpress.com, pg 2

Alexander, Pamela, Oberlin College Press, 50 N Professor St, Oberlin, OH 44074-1091 *Tel:* 440-775-8408 *Fax:* 440-775-8124 *E-mail:* oc.press@oberlin.edu *Web Site:* www.oberlin.edu/ocpress, pg 173

Alexander, Patrick, The Pennsylvania State University Press, University Support Bldg 1, Suite C, 820 N University Dr, University Park, PA 16802-1003 *Tel:* 814-865-1327 *Toll Free Tel:* 800-326-9180 *Fax:* 814-863-1408 *Toll Free Fax:* 877-778-2665 *E-mail:* info@psupress.org *Web Site:* www.psupress.org, pg 188

Alexander, Ms Sandy, University Press of Mississippi, 3825 Ridgewood Rd, Jackson, MS 39211-6492 *Tel:* 601-432-6205 *Toll Free Tel:* 800-737-7788 (orders & cust serv) *Fax:* 601-432-6217 *E-mail:* press@mississippi.edu *Web Site:* www.upress.state.ms.us, pg 262

Alexander, Shara, Harlequin Enterprises Ltd, 233 Broadway, Suite 1001, New York, NY 10279 *Tel:* 212-553-4200 *Fax:* 212-227-8969 *E-mail:* CustomerService@harlequin.com *Web Site:* www.harlequin.com, pg 105

Alexander, Susanne, Goose Lane Editions, 500 Beaverbrook Ct, Suite 330, Fredericton, NB E3B 5X4, Canada *Tel:* 506-450-4251 *Toll Free Tel:* 888-926-8377 *Fax:* 506-459-4991 *E-mail:* info@gooselane.com; customerservice@gooselane.com *Web Site:* www.gooselane.com, pg 485

Alexander, Susanne M, Marriage Transformation LLC, PO Box 249, Harrison, TN 37341 *Tel:* 423-599-0153 *Web Site:* www.marriagetransformation.com, pg 148

Alexander, Tracy, McLaren Memorial Comedy Play Writing Competition, 2000 W Wadley Ave, Midland, TX 79705 *Tel:* 432-682-2544 *E-mail:* tracy@mctmidland.org *Web Site:* www.mctmidland.org, pg 707

Algar, Liza, Chronicle Books LLC, 680 Second St, San Francisco, CA 94107 *Tel:* 415-537-4200 *Toll Free Tel:* 800-759-0190 (cust serv) *Fax:* 415-537-4460 *Toll Free Fax:* 800-858-7787 (orders); 800-286-9471 (cust serv) *E-mail:* frontdesk@chroniclebooks.com *Web Site:* www.chroniclebooks.com, pg 57

Alguire, Julie, Crabtree Publishing Co, 350 Fifth Ave, 59th fl, PMB 59051, New York, NY 10118 *Tel:* 212-496-5040 *Toll Free Tel:* 800-387-7650 *Toll Free Fax:* 800-355-7166 *E-mail:* custserv@crabtreebooks.com *Web Site:* www.crabtreebooks.com, pg 66

Alguire, Julie, Crabtree Publishing Co Ltd, 616 Welland Ave, St Catharines, ON L2M-5V6, Canada *Tel:* 905-682-5221 *Toll Free Tel:* 800-387-7650 *Fax:* 905-682-7166 *Toll Free Fax:* 800-355-7166 *E-mail:* custserv@crabtreebooks.com; sales@crabtreebooks.com; orders@crabtreebooks.com *Web Site:* www.crabtreebooks.com, pg 478

Ali, Kazim, Oberlin College Press, 50 N Professor St, Oberlin, OH 44074-1091 *Tel:* 440-775-8408 *Fax:* 440-775-8124 *E-mail:* oc.press@oberlin.edu *Web Site:* www.oberlin.edu/ocpress, pg 173

Ali, Liaquat, Kazi Publications Inc, 3023 W Belmont Ave, Chicago, IL 60618 *Tel:* 773-267-7001 *Fax:* 773-267-7002 *E-mail:* info@kazi.org *Web Site:* www.kazi.org, pg 130

Alighieri, Christian, Ransom Note Press, 143 E Ridgewood Ave, Box 419, Ridgewood, NJ 07451 *Tel:* 201-835-2790 *E-mail:* editorial@ransomnotepress.com *Web Site:* www.ransomnotepress.com, pg 509

Alioto, Domenica, Crown Publishing Group, c/o Penguin Random House Inc, 1745 Broadway, New York, NY 10019 *Tel:* 212-782-9000 *Toll Free Tel:* 888-264-1745 *Fax:* 212-940-7408 *E-mail:* crownosm@penguinrandomhouse.com *Web Site:* crownpublishing.com, pg 68

Aliotti, Tracee, International Society for Technology in Education, 180 W Eighth Ave, Suite 300, Eugene, OR 97401-2916 *Tel:* 541-302-3777 (intl) *Toll Free Tel:* 800-336-5191 (US & CN) *Fax:* 541-302-3778 *E-mail:* iste@iste.org *Web Site:* www.iste.org; www.iste.org/bookstore (orders); www.isteconference.org, pg 125

Allan, Dr John R, Institute of Intergovernmental Relations, Queen's University, Robert Sutherland Hall, Rm 301, Kingston, ON K7L 3N6, Canada *Tel:* 613-533-2080 *Fax:* 613-533-6868 *E-mail:* iigr@queensu.ca *Web Site:* www.queensu.ca/iigr, pg 488

Allan, Richard, The Aaland Agency, PO Box 849, Inyokern, CA 93527-0849 *Tel:* 760-384-3910 *Web Site:* www.the-aaland-agency.com, pg 539

Allberry, Debra, Warren Wilson College, MFA Program for Writers, 701 Warren Wilson Rd, Swannanoa, NC 28778 *Tel:* 828-771-3717 *Fax:* 828-771-7005 *E-mail:* mfa@warren-wilson.edu *Web Site:* www.warren-wilson.edu/~mfa, pg 664

Allday, Liana, Stewart, Tabori & Chang, 115 W 18 St, 6th fl, New York, NY 10011 *Tel:* 212-519-1200 *Fax:* 212-519-1210 *Web Site:* www.abramsbooks.com, pg 236

Allen, Christopher, Summit University Press, 63 Summit Way, Gardiner, MT 59030-9314 *Tel:* 406-848-9742; 406-848-9500 *Toll Free Tel:* 800-245-5445 (retail orders) *Fax:* 406-848-9650 *Toll Free Fax:* 800-221-8307 *E-mail:* info@summituniversitypress.com *Web Site:* www.summituniversitypress.com, pg 238

Allen, Inge, Crystal Publishers Inc, 3460 Lost Hills Dr, Las Vegas, NV 89122 *Tel:* 702-434-3037 *Fax:* 702-434-3037 *Web Site:* www.crystalpub.com, pg 69

Allen, Janet, Write Now, 140 W Washington St, Indianapolis, IN 46204-3465 *Tel:* 317-635-5277 *Fax:* 317-236-0767 *E-mail:* info@writenow.co *Web Site:* www.writenow.co, pg 738

Allen, Jennifer, Educational Book & Media Association (EBMA), 37 Main St, Suite 203, Warrenton, VA 20186 *Tel:* 540-318-7770 *Fax:* 202-962-3939 *E-mail:* info@edupaperback.org *Web Site:* www.edupaperback.org, pg 605

Allen, Keith, The Optical Society (OSA), 2010 Massachusetts Ave NW, Washington, DC 20036-1023 *Tel:* 202-223-8130 *Toll Free Tel:* 800-766-4672 *E-mail:* custserv@osa.org *Web Site:* www.osa.org, pg 175

Allen, Dr Leonard, ACU Press, 1626 Campus Ct, Abilene, TX 79601 *Tel:* 325-674-2720 *Toll Free Tel:* 877-816-4455 *Fax:* 325-674-6471 *Web Site:* www.acupressbooks.com; www.leafwoodpublishers.com, pg 4

Allen, Linda, Linda Allen Literary Agency, 1949 Green St, Suite 5, San Francisco, CA 94123 *Tel:* 415-921-6437, pg 540

Allen, Marc, New World Library, 14 Pamaron Way, Novato, CA 94949 *Tel:* 415-884-2100 *Toll Free Tel:* 800-227-3900 (ext 52, retail orders); 800-972-6657 *Fax:* 415-884-2199 *E-mail:* escort@newworldlibrary.com *Web Site:* www.newworldlibrary.com, pg 168

Allen, Mitch, Left Coast Press Inc, 1630 N Main St, Suite 400, Walnut Creek, CA 94596 *Tel:* 925-935-3380 *Fax:* 925-935-2916 *E-mail:* explore@lcoastpress.com *Web Site:* www.lcoastpress.com, pg 136

Allen, Rebecca, Texas Christian University Press, 3000 Sandage Ave, Fort Worth, TX 76109 *Tel:* 817-257-7822 *Toll Free Tel:* 800-826-8911 *Fax:* 817-257-5075 *Web Site:* www.prs.tcu.edu, pg 243

Allen, Robert, Macmillan Audio, 175 Fifth Ave, New York, NY 10010 *Tel:* 646-307-5151 *Toll Free Tel:* 888-330-8477 (cust serv) *Fax:* 917-534-0980 *Web Site:* www.macmillanaudio.com, pg 145

Allen, Ron, International Risk Management Institute Inc, 12222 Merit Dr, Suite 1600, Dallas, TX 75251-2266 *Tel:* 972-960-7693 *Fax:* 972-371-5120 *E-mail:* info27@irmi.com *Web Site:* www.irmi.com, pg 125

Allen, Sandra, Wag's Revue Writers' Contest, 2865 W Lyndale St, Suite 1, Chicago, IL 60647 *E-mail:* editors@wagsrevue.com *Web Site:* www.wagsrevue.com, pg 734

Allen, Tom, Association of American Publishers (AAP), 71 Fifth Ave, 2nd fl, New York, NY 10003-3004 *Tel:* 212-255-0200 *Fax:* 212-255-7007 *E-mail:* info@publishers.org *Web Site:* publishers.org, pg 598

Allen, Tom, Sterling Publishing Co Inc, 1166 Avenue of the Americas, 17th fl, New York, NY 10036 *Tel:* 212-532-7160 *Toll Free Tel:* 800-367-9692 *Fax:* 212-213-2495 *Web Site:* www.sterlingpublishing.com, pg 235

Allen-Crowley, Mary, ANR Publications University of California, 1301 S 46 St, Bldg 478 - MC 3580, Richmond, CA 94804 *Tel:* 510-665-2195 (cust serv)

Toll Free Tel: 800-994-8849 *Fax:* 510-665-3427 *E-mail:* anrcatalog@ucdavis.edu *Web Site:* anrcatalog.ucanr.edu, pg 18

Aller, Gary, Gallaudet University Press, 800 Florida Ave NE, Washington, DC 20002-3695 *Tel:* 202-651-5488; 773-568-1550 (orders) *Toll Free Tel:* 800-621-2736 (orders) *Fax:* 202-651-5489; 773-660-2235 (orders) *Toll Free Fax:* 800-621-8476 (orders) *E-mail:* gupress@gallaudet.edu *Web Site:* gupress.gallaudet.edu, pg 94

Allin, Mark, John Wiley & Sons Inc, 111 River St, Hoboken, NJ 07030-5774 *Tel:* 201-748-6000 *Toll Free Tel:* 800-225-5945 (cust serv) *Fax:* 201-748-6088 *E-mail:* info@wiley.com *Web Site:* www.wiley.com, pg 272

Allison, Christine, City & Regional Magazine Association, 1970 E Grand Ave, Suite 330, El Segundo, CA 90245 *Tel:* 310-364-0193 *Fax:* 310-364-0196 *E-mail:* admin@citymag.org *Web Site:* www.citymag.org, pg 603

Allison, Kevin, Oxford University Press USA, 198 Madison Ave, New York, NY 10016 *Tel:* 212-726-6000 *Toll Free Tel:* 800-451-7556 (orders); 800-445-9714 (cust serv) *Fax:* 919-677-1303 *E-mail:* custserv.us@oup.com *Web Site:* www.oup.com/us, pg 179

Allison, Mark, Stackpole Books, 5067 Ritter Rd, Mechanicsburg, PA 17055 *Tel:* 717-796-0411 *Toll Free Tel:* 800-732-3669 *Fax:* 717-796-0412 *Web Site:* www.stackpolebooks.com, pg 233

Almack, David, CLC Ministries, 701 Pennsylvania Ave, Fort Washington, PA 19034 *Tel:* 215-542-1240 *Toll Free Tel:* 800-659-1240 *Fax:* 215-542-7580 *E-mail:* orders@clcpublications.com *Web Site:* www.clcpublications.com, pg 59

Almqvist, Johan, Chronicle Books LLC, 680 Second St, San Francisco, CA 94107 *Tel:* 415-537-4200 *Toll Free Tel:* 800-759-0190 (cust serv) *Fax:* 415-537-4460 *Toll Free Fax:* 800-858-7787 (orders); 800-286-9471 (cust serv) *E-mail:* frontdesk@chroniclebooks.com *Web Site:* www.chroniclebooks.com, pg 58

Almutawa, Shatha, American Historical Association (AHA), 400 "A" St SE, Washington, DC 20003 *Tel:* 202-544-2422 *Fax:* 202-544-8307 *E-mail:* aha@historians.org; awards@historians.org; info@historians.org *Web Site:* www.historians.org, pg 13

Alongi, Pietro, Pearson ELT, 10 Bank St, 9th fl, White Plains, NY 10606-1951 *Tel:* 914-287-8000 *Web Site:* www.pearsonelt.com, pg 185

Alperen, Jennifer, The Betsy Nolan Literary Agency, 214 W 29 St, Suite 1002, New York, NY 10001 *Tel:* 212-967-8200 *Fax:* 212-967-7292 *E-mail:* dblehr@cs.com, pg 567

Alps, Marisa, Harbour Publishing Co Ltd, 4437 Rondeview Rd, Madeira Park, BC V0N 2H0, Canada *Tel:* 604-883-2730 *Toll Free Tel:* 800-667-2988 *Fax:* 604-883-9451 *E-mail:* info@harbourpublishing.com *Web Site:* www.harbourpublishing.com, pg 487

Alter, George, Inter-University Consortium for Political & Social Research (ICPSR), 330 Packard St, Ann Arbor, MI 48104 *Tel:* 734-647-5000 *Fax:* 734-647-8200 *E-mail:* netmail@icpsr.umich.edu *Web Site:* www.icpsr.umich.edu, pg 123

Altman, David G, Center for Creative Leadership LLC, One Leadership Place, Greensboro, NC 27410-9427 *Tel:* 336-545-2810; 336-288-7210 *Fax:* 336-282-3284 *E-mail:* info@ccl.org *Web Site:* www.ccl.org/publications, pg 53

Altman, Elias, Zachary Shuster Harmsworth Agency, 1776 Broadway, Suite 1405, New York, NY 10019 *Tel:* 212-765-6900 *Fax:* 212-765-6490 *Web Site:* www.zshliterary.com, pg 580

Altshuler, Miriam, Miriam Altshuler Literary Agency, 53 Old Post Rd N, Red Hook, NY 12571 *Tel:* 845-758-9408 *Web Site:* www.miriamaltshulerliteraryagency.com, pg 540

Alvarado, Beth, Rick DeMarinis Short Story Award, PO Box 2414, Durango, CO 81302 *Tel:* 970-903-7914 *E-mail:* cutthroatmag@gmail.com *Web Site:* www.cutthroatmag.com, pg 680

Alvarado, Beth, Joy Harjo Poetry Award, PO Box 2414, Durango, CO 81302 *Tel:* 970-903-7914 *E-mail:* cutthroatmag@gmail.com *Web Site:* www.cutthroatmag.com, pg 691

Alvarez, Awilda, Hippocrene Books Inc, 171 Madison Ave, New York, NY 10016 *Tel:* 212-685-4373 *Fax:* 212-779-9338 *E-mail:* info@hippocrenebooks.com; orderdept@hippocrenebooks.com (orders) *Web Site:* www.hippocrenebooks.com, pg 112

Alvarez, Jessica, BookEnds LLC, 136 Long Hill Rd, Gillette, NJ 07933 *Web Site:* www.bookends-inc.com, pg 543

Alvarez, Lisa, Squaw Valley Community of Writers Summer Workshops, PO Box 1416, Nevada City, CA 95959 *Tel:* 530-470-8440 *E-mail:* info@squawvalleywriters.org *Web Site:* www.squawvalleywriters.org, pg 656

Alward, Kathy, Piano Press, 1425 Ocean Ave, Suite 5, Del Mar, CA 92014 *Tel:* 619-884-1401 *Fax:* 858-755-1104 *E-mail:* pianopress@pianopress.com *Web Site:* www.pianopress.com, pg 191

Amato, Frank W, Frank Amato Publications Inc, 4040 SE Wister St, Milwaukie, OR 97222 *Tel:* 503-653-8108 *Toll Free Tel:* 800-541-9498 *Fax:* 503-653-2766 *E-mail:* customerservice@amatobooks.com; info@amatobooks.com *Web Site:* www.amatobooks.com, pg 9

Amato, Nick S, Frank Amato Publications Inc, 4040 SE Wister St, Milwaukie, OR 97222 *Tel:* 503-653-8108 *Toll Free Tel:* 800-541-9498 *Fax:* 503-653-2766 *E-mail:* customerservice@amatobooks.com; info@amatobooks.com *Web Site:* www.amatobooks.com, pg 9

Amato, Tony F, Frank Amato Publications Inc, 4040 SE Wister St, Milwaukie, OR 97222 *Tel:* 503-653-8108 *Toll Free Tel:* 800-541-9498 *Fax:* 503-653-2766 *E-mail:* customerservice@amatobooks.com; info@amatobooks.com *Web Site:* www.amatobooks.com, pg 9

Ambrosio, Dan, Da Capo Press & Lifelong Books, 44 Farnsworth St, 3rd fl, Boston, MA 02210 *Tel:* 617-252-5200 *Toll Free Tel:* 800-343-4499 (orders) *Fax:* 617-252-5285 *Web Site:* www.perseusbooksgroup.com/dacapo, pg 69

Amendolara, Paula, Simon & Schuster Sales Division, 1230 Avenue of the Americas, New York, NY 10020 *Tel:* 212-698-7000, pg 226

Ames, Joanna, Canadian Publishers' Council (CPC), 250 Merton St, Suite 203, Toronto, ON M4S 1B1, Canada *Tel:* 416-322-7011 *Fax:* 416-322-6999 *Web Site:* www.pubcouncil.ca, pg 602

Ames, Michael, Vanderbilt University Press, 2014 Broadway, Suite 320, Nashville, TN 37203 *Tel:* 615-322-3585 *Toll Free Tel:* 800-627-7377 (orders only) *Fax:* 615-343-8823 *Toll Free Fax:* 800-735-0476 (orders only) *E-mail:* vupress@vanderbilt.edu *Web Site:* www.vanderbiltuniversitypress.com, pg 264

Ames, Steve, World Citizens, PO Box 131, Mill Valley, CA 94942-0131 *Tel:* 415-380-8020 *Toll Free Tel:* 800-247-6553 (orders only), pg 276

Amini, Christina, Chronicle Books LLC, 680 Second St, San Francisco, CA 94107 *Tel:* 415-537-4200 *Toll Free Tel:* 800-759-0190 (cust serv) *Fax:* 415-537-4460 *Toll Free Fax:* 800-858-7787 (orders); 800-286-9471 (cust serv) *E-mail:* frontdesk@chroniclebooks.com *Web Site:* www.chroniclebooks.com, pg 58

Amitie, Julie, Scholastic Trade Division, 557 Broadway, New York, NY 10012 *Tel:* 212-343-6100; 212-343-4685 (export sales) *Fax:* 212-343-4714 (export sales) *Web Site:* www.scholastic.com, pg 219

Amling, Eric, Darhansoff & Verrill, 236 W 26 St, Suite 802, New York, NY 10001-6736 *Tel:* 917-305-1300 *Fax:* 917-305-1400 *E-mail:* info@dvagency.com *Web Site:* www.dvagency.com, pg 547

Ammons-Longtin, Cheryl, Oxford University Press USA, 198 Madison Ave, New York, NY 10016 *Tel:* 212-726-6000 *Toll Free Tel:* 800-451-7556 (orders); 800-445-9714 (cust serv) *Fax:* 919-677-1303 *E-mail:* custserv.us@oup.com *Web Site:* www.oup.com/us, pg 179

Amoroso, Connie, Carnegie Mellon University Press, 5032 Forbes Ave, Pittsburgh, PA 15289-1021 *Tel:* 412-268-2861 *Fax:* 412-268-8706 *E-mail:* carnegiemellonuniversitypress@gmail.com *Web Site:* www.cmu.edu/universitypress, pg 50

Amour, Lucie, Visual Artists & Galleries Association Inc (VAGA), 111 Broadway, Suite 1006, New York, NY 10006 *Tel:* 212-736-6666 *Fax:* 212-736-6767 *E-mail:* info@vagarights.com *Web Site:* vagarights.com, pg 621

Amper, Julie, Holiday House Inc, 425 Madison Ave, New York, NY 10017 *Tel:* 212-688-0085 *Fax:* 212-421-6134 *E-mail:* holiday@holidayhouse.com *Web Site:* www.holidayhouse.com, pg 113

Amsden, Ariel, Poisoned Pen Press, 6962 E First Ave, Suite 103, Scottsdale, AZ 85251 *Tel:* 480-945-3375 *Toll Free Tel:* 800-421-3976 *Fax:* 480-949-1707 *E-mail:* info@poisonedpenpress.com *Web Site:* www.poisonedpenpress.com, pg 194

Amsel, Andrew, Prayer Book Press Inc, 1363 Fairfield Ave, Bridgeport, CT 06605 *Tel:* 203-384-2284 *Fax:* 203-579-9109, pg 196

Amster, Betsy, Betsy Amster Literary Enterprises, 6312 SW Capitol Hwy, No 503, Portland, OR 97239 *Tel:* 503-496-4007 *E-mail:* rights@amsterlit.com (rts inquiries); b.amster.assistant@gmail.com (adult book queries); b.amster.kidsbooks@gmail.com (children & young adult book queries) *Web Site:* www.amsterlit.com, pg 540

Amstuta, Nicolette, University Press of America Inc, 4501 Forbes Blvd, Suite 200, Lanham, MD 20706 *Tel:* 301-459-3366 *Toll Free Tel:* 800-462-6420 *Fax:* 301-429-5748 *Toll Free Fax:* 800-338-4550 *Web Site:* www.univpress.com, pg 261

Amstutz, Nicolette, Hamilton Books, 4501 Forbes Blvd, Suite 200, Lanham, MD 20706 *Tel:* 301-459-3366 *Toll Free Tel:* 800-462-6420 (cust serv) *Fax:* 301-429-5748 *Toll Free Fax:* 800-388-4550 (cust serv), pg 104

Amundsen, John, Coretta Scott King Book Awards, 50 E Huron St, Chicago, IL 60611 *Toll Free Tel:* 800-545-2433 *E-mail:* olos@ala.org *Web Site:* www.ala.org/emiert/cskbookawards, pg 698

Anastas, Greg, The Perseus Books Group, 387 Park Ave S, 12th fl, New York, NY 10016 *Tel:* 212-340-8100 *Toll Free Tel:* 800-343-4499 (cust serv) *Fax:* 212-340-8105 *Web Site:* www.perseusbooksgroup.com, pg 189

Anastas, Mara, Simon & Schuster Children's Publishing, 1230 Avenue of the Americas, New York, NY 10020 *Tel:* 212-698-7000 *Web Site:* KIDS.SimonandSchuster.com; TEEN.SimonandSchuster.com; simonandschuster.net; simonandschuster.biz, pg 225

Andersen, Peter, Doubleday/Nan A Talese, c/o Penguin Random House Inc, 1745 Broadway, New York, NY 10019 *Tel:* 212-751-2600 *Fax:* 212-572-2662 *E-mail:* ddaypub@randomhouse.com *Web Site:* knopfdoubleday.com, pg 76

Andersen, Peter, Alfred A Knopf/Everyman's Library, c/o Random House Inc, 1745 Broadway, New York, NY 10019 *Tel:* 212-751-2600 *Toll Free Tel:* 800-638-6460 *Fax:* 212-572-2593 *Web Site:* www.knopfdoubleday.com, pg 132

Andersen, Vicki, North American Snowsports Journalists Association, 11728 SE Madison St, Portland, OR 97216-3849 *Tel:* 503-255-3771 *Fax:* 503-255-3771 *Web Site:* www.nasja.org, pg 614

Andersen-Zantop, Ashley, Capstone Publishers™, 1710 Roe Crest Dr, North Mankato, MN 56003 *Toll Free Tel:* 800-747-4992 (cust serv) *Toll Free Fax:* 888-262-0705 *Web Site:* www.capstonepress.com, pg 49

Anderson, Alison, University of Pennsylvania Press, 3905 Spruce St, Philadelphia, PA 19104 *Tel:* 215-898-6261 *Fax:* 215-898-0404 *E-mail:* custserv@pobox.upenn.edu *Web Site:* www.pennpress.org, pg 259

Anderson, Andrea, Theodore C Blegen Award, 701 William Vickers Ave, Durham, NC 27701-3162 *Tel:* 919-682-9319 *Fax:* 919-682-2349 *Web Site:* www.foresthistory.org, pg 672

Anderson, Andrea, John M Collier Award for Forest History Journalism, 701 William Vickers Ave, Durham, NC 27701-3162 *Tel:* 919-682-9319 *Fax:* 919-682-2349 *Web Site:* www.foresthistory.org, pg 678

Anderson, Andrea, Leopold-Hidy Award, 701 William Vickers Ave, Durham, NC 27701-3162 *Tel:* 919-682-9319 *Fax:* 919-682-2349 *Web Site:* www.foresthistory.org, pg 700

Anderson, Andrea, Charles A Weyerhauser Book Award, 701 William Vickers Ave, Durham, NC 27701-3162 *Tel:* 919-682-9319 *Fax:* 919-682-2349 *Web Site:* www.foresthistory.org, pg 735

Anderson, Ann-Marie, Temple University Press, 1852 N Tenth St, Philadelphia, PA 19122-6099 *Tel:* 215-926-2140 *Toll Free Tel:* 800-621-2736 *Fax:* 215-926-2141 *E-mail:* tempress@temple.edu *Web Site:* www.temple.edu/tempress, pg 242

Anderson, Aubrey, Epicenter Press Inc, 6524 NE 181 St, Suite 2, Kenmore, WA 98028 *Tel:* 425-485-6822 (edit, mktg, busn off) *Fax:* 425-481-8253 *E-mail:* info@epicenterpress.com *Web Site:* www.epicenterpress.com, pg 83

Anderson, Barbara S, Barbara S Anderson, 706 W Davis Ave, Ann Arbor, MI 48103-4855 *Tel:* 734-995-0125 *E-mail:* bsa328@earthlink.net, pg 520

Anderson, Becky, Gollehon Press Inc, 3655 Glenn Dr SE, Grand Rapids, MI 49546 *Tel:* 616-949-3515 *Fax:* 616-949-8674 *Web Site:* www.gollehonbooks.com, pg 98

Anderson, Colleen, Balance Sports Publishing LLC, 195 Lucero Way, Portola Valley, CA 94028 *Tel:* 650-561-9586 *Fax:* 650-391-9850 *E-mail:* info@balancesportspublishing.com *Web Site:* www.balancesportspublishing.com, pg 30

Anderson, Colleen, SF Canada, 7433 E River Rd, Washago, ON L0K 2B0, Canada *Web Site:* www.sfcanada.org, pg 618

Anderson, Craig, Herald Press, 50 Kent Ave, Suite 204, Kitchener, ON N2G 3R1, Canada *Tel:* 519-747-5722 (US) *Toll Free Tel:* 800-631-6535 (CN) *Fax:* 519-747-5721 *E-mail:* hpcan@mpn.net *Web Site:* www.heraldpress.com, pg 487

Anderson, Duane, ACU Press, 1626 Campus Ct, Abilene, TX 79601 *Tel:* 325-674-2720 *Toll Free Tel:* 877-816-4455 *Fax:* 325-674-6471 *Web Site:* www.acupressbooks.com; www.leafwoodpublishers.com, pg 4

Anderson, Erik, University of Minnesota Press, 111 Third Ave S, Suite 290, Minneapolis, MN 55401-2520 *Tel:* 612-627-1970 *Fax:* 612-627-1980 *E-mail:* ump@umn.edu *Web Site:* www.upress.umn.edu, pg 257

Anderson, Gordon L, Paragon House, 3600 Labore Rd, Suite 1, St Paul, MN 55110-4144 *Tel:* 651-644-3087 *Toll Free Tel:* 800-447-3709 *Fax:* 651-644-0997 *E-mail:* paragon@paragonhouse.com *Web Site:* www.paragonhouse.com, pg 182

Anderson, Heather, De Gruyter Mouton, 121 High St, 3rd fl, Boston, MA 02110 *Tel:* 857-284-7073 *Fax:* 857-284-7358 *E-mail:* degruytermail@presswarehouse.com (orders & claims) *Web Site:* www.degruyter.com, pg 161

Anderson, Jon, Simon & Schuster Children's Publishing, 1230 Avenue of the Americas, New York, NY 10020 *Tel:* 212-698-7000 *Web Site:* KIDS.SimonandSchuster.com; TEEN.SimonandSchuster.com; simonandschuster.net; simonandschuster.biz, pg 225

Anderson, Jon, Simon & Schuster, Inc, 1230 Avenue of the Americas, New York, NY 10020 *Tel:* 212-698-7000 *Fax:* 212-698-7007 *E-mail:* firstname.lastname@simonandschuster.com *Web Site:* www.simonandschuster.com, pg 226

Anderson, Kathleen, Anderson Literary Management LLC, 244 Fifth Ave, 11th fl, New York, NY 10001 *Tel:* 212-645-6045 *Fax:* 212-741-1936 *E-mail:* info@andersonliterary.com *Web Site:* www.andersonliterary.com, pg 541

Anderson, Kent, Penguin Group (USA) LLC Sales, 375 Hudson St, New York, NY 10014 *Tel:* 212-366-2000 *E-mail:* online@penguinputnam.com *Web Site:* us.penguingroup.com, pg 186

Anderson, Kristin, Corwin, a Sage Co, 2455 Teller Rd, Thousand Oaks, CA 91320 *Tel:* 805-499-9734 *Toll Free Tel:* 800-233-9936 *Fax:* 805-499-5323 *Toll Free Fax:* 800-417-2466 *E-mail:* info@corwin.com; order@corwin.com *Web Site:* www.corwin.com, pg 64

Anderson, Liz, Houghton Mifflin Harcourt, 222 Berkeley St, Boston, MA 02116 *Tel:* 617-351-5000 *Toll Free Tel:* 800-225-5425 (K-12 educ materials); 800-323-9540 (assessment materials); 877-219-1537 (SkillsTutor); 888-242-6747 (Destination; Earobics; Edmark; Learning Village; Riverdeep); 800-225-3362 (Houghton Mifflin Harcourt Trade & Reference Publishers) *Toll Free Fax:* 800-269-5232 *E-mail:* customerservice@hmhpub.com *Web Site:* www.hmhco.com, pg 115

Anderson, Lydia, Wisdom Publications Inc, 199 Elm St, Somerville, MA 02144 *Tel:* 617-776-7416 *Toll Free Tel:* 800-272-4050 (orders) *Fax:* 617-776-7841 *E-mail:* info@wisdompubs.org *Web Site:* www.wisdompubs.org, pg 274

Anderson, Mary, University of Washington Press, 433 Brooklyn Ave NE, Seattle, WA 98195-9570 *Tel:* 206-543-4050 *Toll Free Tel:* 800-537-5487 (orders) *Fax:* 206-543-3932; 410-516-6998 (orders) *E-mail:* uwpress@u.washington.edu *Web Site:* www.washington.edu/uwpress/, pg 260

Anderson, Mary K, IODE Jean Throop Book Award, 9-45 Frid St, Hamilton, ON L8P 4M3, Canada *Tel:* 905-522-9537 *Fax:* 905-522-3637 *E-mail:* iodeontario@bellnet.ca *Web Site:* www.iodeontario.ca, pg 695

Anderson, Monty, Presbyterian Publishing Corp (PPC), 100 Witherspoon St, Louisville, KY 40202 *Tel:* 502-569-5000 *Toll Free Tel:* 800-523-1631 (US only) *Fax:* 502-569-5113 *E-mail:* ppcmail@presbypub.com *Web Site:* www.ppcbooks.com, pg 196

Anderson, Monty, Westminster John Knox Press (WJK), 100 Witherspoon St, Louisville, KY 40202-1396 *Tel:* 502-569-5052 *Toll Free Tel:* 800-227-2872 (US only) *Fax:* 502-569-8308 *Toll Free Fax:* 800-541-5113 (US & CN) *E-mail:* wjk@wjkbooks.com; customer_service@wjkbooks.com *Web Site:* www.wjkbooks.com, pg 269

Anderson, Dr Patricia PhD, Patricia Anderson PhD, Literary Consultant, 1489 Marine Dr, Suite 515, West Vancouver, BC V7T 1B8, Canada *Tel:* 604-740-0805 *E-mail:* query@helpingyougetpublished.com; patriciaanderson@helpingyougetpublished.com *Web Site:* www.helpingyougetpublished.com, pg 520

Anderson, Patricia PhD, Maryland Historical Society, 201 W Monument St, Baltimore, MD 21201 *Tel:* 410-685-3750 *Fax:* 410-385-2105 *Web Site:* www.mdhs.org, pg 148

Anderson, Robert, BNA Books, 1801 S Bell St, Arlington, VA 22202 *Tel:* 732-476-6397 *Toll Free Tel:* 800-372-1033; 800-960-1220 *Fax:* 732-346-1624 *E-mail:* books@bna.com *Web Site:* www.bnabooks.com, pg 41

Anderson, Sara, Sara Anderson Children's Books, PO Box 47182, Seattle, WA 98146 *Tel:* 206-285-1520 *Web Site:* www.saranderson.com, pg 17

Anderson, Shatera, University of Houston Creative Writing Program, 229 Roy Cullen Bldg, Houston, TX 77204-5008 *Tel:* 713-743-2255 *Fax:* 713-743-3697 *E-mail:* cwp@uh.edu *Web Site:* www.uh.edu/cwp, pg 663

Anderson, Steven, John M Collier Award for Forest History Journalism, 701 William Vickers Ave, Durham, NC 27701-3162 *Tel:* 919-682-9319 *Fax:* 919-682-2349 *Web Site:* www.foresthistory.org, pg 678

Anderson, William, Sagamore Publishing LLC, 1807 Federal Dr, Urbana, IL 61801 *Tel:* 217-359-5940 *Toll Free Tel:* 800-327-5557 (orders) *Fax:* 217-359-5975 *E-mail:* books@sagamorepub.com *Web Site:* www.sagamorepub.com, pg 213

Andersson, Mark, Guild of Book Workers, 521 Fifth Ave, 17th fl, New York, NY 10175 *Tel:* 212-292-4444 *E-mail:* communications@guildofbookworkers.org *Web Site:* www.guildofbookworkers.org, pg 606

Andonian, Mr Aramais, Blue Crane Books, PO Box 380291, Cambridge, MA 02238 *Tel:* 617-926-8989 *Fax:* 617-926-0982 *E-mail:* bluecrane@arrow1.com, pg 40

Andreadis, Tina, HarperCollins General Books Group, 195 Broadway, New York, NY 10007 *Tel:* 212-207-7000 *Web Site:* www.harpercollins.com, pg 105

Andreou, George, Alfred A Knopf/Everyman's Library, c/o Random House Inc, 1745 Broadway, New York, NY 10019 *Tel:* 212-751-2600 *Toll Free Tel:* 800-638-6460 *Fax:* 212-572-2593 *Web Site:* www.knopfdoubleday.com, pg 132

Andrew, Emily, University of British Columbia Press, 2029 West Mall, Vancouver, BC V6T 1Z2, Canada *Tel:* 604-822-5959 *Toll Free Tel:* 877-377-9378 *Fax:* 604-822-6083 *Toll Free Fax:* 800-668-0821 *E-mail:* frontdesk@ubcpress.ca *Web Site:* www.ubcpress.ca, pg 502

Andrewes, Lancelot, Wittenborn Art Books, 1109 Geary Blvd, San Francisco, CA 94109 *Tel:* 415-292-6500 *Toll Free Tel:* 800-660-6403 *Fax:* 415-292-6594 *E-mail:* wittenborn@art-books.com *Web Site:* www.art-books.com, pg 274

Andrews, Gaylen, Copywriter's Council of America (CCA), CCA Bldg, 7 Putter Lane, Middle Island, NY 11953-1920 *Tel:* 631-924-8555 *Fax:* 631-924-8555 *E-mail:* cca4dmcopy@gmail.com *Web Site:* www.AndrewLinickDirectMarketing.com/Copywriters-Council.html; www.NewWorldPressBooks.com, pg 604

Andrews, Hugh, Andrews McMeel Publishing LLC, 1130 Walnut St, Kansas City, MO 64106-2109 *Toll Free Tel:* 800-851-8923; 800-943-9839 (cust serv) *Toll Free Fax:* 800-943-9831 (orders) *Web Site:* www.andrewsmcmeel.com, pg 18

Andrews, Meredith, National Book Awards, 90 Broad St, Suite 604, New York, NY 10004 *Tel:* 212-685-0261 *Fax:* 212-213-6570 *E-mail:* nationalbook@nationalbook.org *Web Site:* www.nationalbook.org, pg 710

Andrews, Michael, Nelson Education Ltd, 1120 Birchmount Rd, Scarborough, ON M1K 5G4, Canada *Tel:* 416-752-9100 *Toll Free Tel:* 800-268-2222 (cust serv) *Fax:* 416-752-8101 *Toll Free Fax:* 800-430-4445 *E-mail:* peopleandengagement@nelson.com *Web Site:* www.nelson.com, pg 492

Andrews, Vaughn, Workman Publishing Co Inc, 225 Varick St, 9th fl, New York, NY 10014-4381 *Tel:* 212-254-5900 *Toll Free Tel:* 800-722-7202 *Fax:* 212-254-8098 *E-mail:* info@workman.com *Web Site:* www.workman.com, pg 275

Andrikanich, Chris, Gray & Company Publishers, 1588 E 40 St, Suite 3A, Cleveland, OH 44103 *Tel:* 216-431-2665 *Toll Free Tel:* 800-915-3609 *E-mail:* sales@grayco.com; editorial@grayco.com; support@grayco.com; publicity@grayco.com *Web Site:* www.grayco.com, pg 99

Anfuso, Dominick, Crown Publishing Group, c/o Penguin Random House Inc, 1745 Broadway, New York, NY 10019 *Tel:* 212-782-9000 *Toll Free Tel:* 888-264-1745 *Fax:* 212-940-7408 *E-mail:* crownosm@penguinrandomhouse.com *Web Site:* crownpublishing.com, pg 68

Angelilli, Chris, Random House Children's Books, 1745 Broadway, New York, NY 10019 *Tel:* 212-782-9000 *Toll Free Tel:* 800-200-3552 *Fax:* 212-782-9452 *Web Site:* randomhousekids.com, pg 203

Angell, Emily, Portfolio, 375 Hudson St, New York, NY 10014, pg 195

Angelo, Jim, The Mathematical Association of America, 1529 18 St NW, Washington, DC 20036-1358 *Tel:* 202-387-5200 *Toll Free Tel:* 800-741-9415 *Fax:* 202-265-2384 *E-mail:* maahq@maa.org *Web Site:* www.maa.org, pg 149

Angeloro, Nicole, Houghton Mifflin Harcourt Trade & Reference Division, 222 Berkeley St, Boston, MA 02116 *Tel:* 617-351-5000 *Toll Free Tel:* 800-225-3362 *Web Site:* www.hmhco.com, pg 115

Annis, Jay, The Taunton Press Inc, 63 S Main St, Newtown, CT 06470 *Tel:* 203-426-8171 *Toll Free Tel:* 800-477-8727 (cust serv); 800-888-8286 (orders) *Fax:* 203-426-3434 *E-mail:* booksales@taunton.com *Web Site:* www.taunton.com, pg 241

Anson-Turturro, Ginny, Penguin Young Readers Group, 345 Hudson St, New York, NY 10014 *Tel:* 212-366-2000 *E-mail:* online@penguinputnam.com *Web Site:* www.penguinputnam.com; us.penguingroup.com, pg 188

Anthony, Graham, August House Inc, 3500 Piedmont Rd NE, Suite 310, Atlanta, GA 30305 *Tel:* 404-442-4420 *Toll Free Tel:* 800-284-8784 *Fax:* 404-442-4435 *E-mail:* ahinfo@augusthouse.com *Web Site:* www.augusthouse.com, pg 27

Anthony, Dr Michelle, David C Cook, 4050 Lee Vance View, Colorado Springs, CO 80918 *Tel:* 719-536-0100 *Toll Free Tel:* 800-708-5550; 800-323-7543 (orders & cust serv) *Toll Free Fax:* 800-430-0726 (cust serv) *Web Site:* www.davidccook.com, pg 62

Antolos, Gianna, Crown Publishing Group, c/o Penguin Random House Inc, 1745 Broadway, New York, NY 10019 *Tel:* 212-782-9000 *Toll Free Tel:* 888-264-1745 *Fax:* 212-940-7408 *E-mail:* crownosm@penguinrandomhouse.com *Web Site:* crownpublishing.com, pg 68

Antonacci, Laura, Random House Children's Books, 1745 Broadway, New York, NY 10019 *Tel:* 212-782-9000 *Toll Free Tel:* 800-200-3552 *Fax:* 212-782-9452 *Web Site:* randomhousekids.com, pg 203

Antonetti, Martin, Bibliographical Society of America, PO Box 1537, Lenox Hill Sta, New York, NY 10021-0043 *Tel:* 212-452-2710 *Fax:* 212-452-2710 *E-mail:* bsa@bibsocamer.org *Web Site:* www.bibsocamer.org, pg 600

Antonson, Lori, The Axelrod Agency, 55 Main St, Chatham, NY 12037 *Tel:* 518-392-2100, pg 541

Antony, Jessica, Fernwood Publishing, 32 Oceanvista Lane, Black Point, NS B0J 1B0, Canada *Tel:* 902-857-1388 *Fax:* 902-857-1328 *E-mail:* info@fernpub.ca; roseway@fernpub.ca *Web Site:* fernwoodpublishing.ca, pg 483

Antony, Peter, The Metropolitan Museum of Art, 1000 Fifth Ave, New York, NY 10028 *Tel:* 212-879-5500; 212-570-3725 *Fax:* 212-396-5062 *E-mail:* editorial@metmuseum.org *Web Site:* www.metmuseum.org, pg 155

Antony, Wayne, Fernwood Publishing, 32 Oceanvista Lane, Black Point, NS B0J 1B0, Canada *Tel:* 902-857-1388 *Fax:* 902-857-1328 *E-mail:* info@fernpub.ca; roseway@fernpub.ca *Web Site:* fernwoodpublishing.ca, pg 483

Apelian, Bill, BJU Press, 1700 Wade Hampton Blvd, Greenville, SC 29614-0062 *Tel:* 864-770-1317; 864-242-5100 *Toll Free Tel:* 800-845-5731 *E-mail:* bjupinfo@bjupress.com *Web Site:* www.bjupress.com, pg 38

Apgar, Robert, New Jersey Council for the Humanities Book Award, 28 W State St, 6th fl, Trenton, NJ 08608 *Tel:* 609-695-4838 *Toll Free Tel:* 888-FYI-NJCH (394-6524) *Fax:* 609-695-4929 *E-mail:* njch@njch.org *Web Site:* www.njch.org, pg 712

Apollon, Karine, Scholastic Education, 524 Broadway, New York, NY 10012 *Tel:* 212-343-6100 *Fax:* 212-343-6189 *Web Site:* www.scholastic.com, pg 218

Appel, Celeste, Unarius Academy of Science Publications, 145 S Magnolia Ave, El Cajon, CA 92020-4522 *Tel:* 619-444-7062 *Toll Free Tel:* 800-475-7062 *Fax:* 619-444-9637 *E-mail:* uriel@unarius.org *Web Site:* www.unarius.org, pg 252

Appel, Fred, Princeton University Press, 41 William St, Princeton, NJ 08540-5237 *Tel:* 609-258-4900 *Toll Free Tel:* 800-777-4726 (orders) *Fax:* 609-258-6305 *Toll Free Fax:* 800-999-1958 *E-mail:* orders@cpfsinc.com *Web Site:* press.princeton.edu, pg 197

Appelbaum, David, Codhill Press, One Arden Lane, New Paltz, NY 12561 *E-mail:* codhillpress@aol.com *Web Site:* www.codhill.com, pg 60

Appling, Carol, University of Alabama Program in Creative Writing, PO Box 870244, Tuscaloosa, AL 35487-0244 *Tel:* 205-348-5065 *Fax:* 205-348-1388 *E-mail:* english@ua.edu *Web Site:* www.as.ua.edu/english, pg 663

Aquilina, Dianne, HarperCollins Canada Ltd, 2 Bloor St E, 20th fl, Toronto, ON M4W 1A8, Canada *Tel:* 416-975-9334 *Fax:* 416-975-9884 *E-mail:* hcorder@harpercollins.com *Web Site:* www.harpercollins.ca, pg 487

Arbaiza, Ingrid, Amber Quill Press LLC, PO Box 265, Indian Hills, CO 80454 *E-mail:* business@amberquill.com; customer_service@amberquill.com *Web Site:* www.amberquill.com, pg 10

Areheart, Shaye, Columbia Publishing Course at Columbia University, 2950 Broadway, MC 3801, New York, NY 10027 *Tel:* 212-854-1898 *Fax:* 212-854-7618 *E-mail:* publishing@jrn.columbia.edu *Web Site:* www.journalism.columbia.edu/publishing, pg 659

Arellano, Susan, Templeton Press, 300 Conshohocken State Rd, Suite 550, West Conshohocken, PA 19428 *Tel:* 484-531-8380 *Fax:* 484-531-8382 *E-mail:* tpinfo@templetonpress.org *Web Site:* www.templetonpress.org, pg 242

Arena, Michael, Deadline Club, c/o Salmagundi Club, 47 Fifth Ave, New York, NY 10003 *Tel:* 646-481-7584 *E-mail:* info@deadlineclub.org *Web Site:* www.deadlineclub.org, pg 604

Argentine, Jan, Cold Spring Harbor Laboratory Press, 500 Sunnyside Blvd, Woodbury, NY 11797-2924 *Tel:* 516-422-4100 *Toll Free Tel:* 800-843-4388 *Fax:* 516-422-4097; 516-422-4092 (submissions) *E-mail:* cshpress@cshl.edu *Web Site:* www.cshlpress.com, pg 60

Arlinghaus, Sandra Lach, Institute of Mathematical Geography, 1964 Boulder Dr, Ann Arbor, MI 48104 *Tel:* 734-975-0246 *E-mail:* image@imagenet.org *Web Site:* www.imagenet.com, pg 123

Arlington, William J, John Wiley & Sons Inc, 111 River St, Hoboken, NJ 07030-5774 *Tel:* 201-748-6000 *Toll Free Tel:* 800-225-5945 (cust serv) *Fax:* 201-748-6088 *E-mail:* info@wiley.com *Web Site:* www.wiley.com, pg 272

Armato, Doug, University of Minnesota Press, 111 Third Ave S, Suite 290, Minneapolis, MN 55401-2520 *Tel:* 612-627-1970 *Fax:* 612-627-1980 *E-mail:* ump@umn.edu *Web Site:* www.upress.umn.edu, pg 257

Armbruster, Bruce, University Science Books, 20 Edgeshill Rd, Mill Valley, CA 94941 *Tel:* 415-332-5390 *Fax:* 415-332-5390 *E-mail:* univscibks@igc.org *Web Site:* www.uscibooks.com, pg 262

Armbruster, Kathy, University Science Books, 20 Edgeshill Rd, Mill Valley, CA 94941 *Tel:* 415-332-5390 *Fax:* 415-332-5390 *E-mail:* univscibks@igc.org *Web Site:* www.uscibooks.com, pg 262

Armengol, Norma C, Casa Bautista de Publicaciones, 7000 Alabama Ave, El Paso, TX 79904 *Tel:* 915-566-9656 *Toll Free Tel:* 800-755-5958 (cust serv & orders) *Fax:* 915-562-6502; 915-565-9008 (orders) *E-mail:* orders@editorialmh.org *Web Site:* www.editorialmh.org, pg 51

Armstrong, Alicia, Police Executive Research Forum, 1120 Connecticut Ave NW, Suite 930, Washington, DC 20036 *Tel:* 202-466-7820 *Fax:* 202-466-7826 *E-mail:* perf@policeforum.org *Web Site:* www.policeforum.org, pg 194

Armstrong, Shane, Scholastic Inc, 557 Broadway, New York, NY 10012 *Tel:* 212-343-6100 *Toll Free Tel:* 800-scholastic *Web Site:* www.scholastic.com, pg 218

Armstrong, Shane, Scholastic International, 557 Broadway, New York, NY 10012 *Tel:* 212-343-6100; 646-330-5288 (intl cust serv) *Toll Free Tel:* 800-SCHOLASTIC (800-724-6527) *Fax:* 646-837-7878 *E-mail:* international@scholastic.com, pg 218

Arnold, Alex, HarperCollins Children's Books, 195 Broadway, New York, NY 10007 *Tel:* 212-207-7000 *Web Site:* www.harpercollins.com/childrens, pg 105

Arnold, Bill, SPIE, 1000 20 St, Bellingham, WA 98225-6705 *Tel:* 360-676-3290 *Toll Free Tel:* 888-504-8171 *Fax:* 360-647-1445 *E-mail:* spie@spie.org *Web Site:* www.spie.org, pg 231

Arnold, Carol, American Marketing Association, 311 S Wacker Dr, Suite 5800, Chicago, IL 60606 *Tel:* 312-542-9000 *Toll Free Tel:* 800-AMA-1150 (262-1150) *Fax:* 312-542-9001 *E-mail:* info@ama.org *Web Site:* www.ama.org, pg 595

Arnold, Courtney, Elite Books, PO Box 442, Fulton, CA 95439 *Tel:* 707-525-9292 *Toll Free Fax:* 800-330-9798 *E-mail:* books@authorspublishing.com *Web Site:* www.elitebooksonline.com, pg 81

Arnold, Courtney, Energy Psychology Press, 1490 Mark West Springs Rd, Santa Rosa, CA 95404 *Tel:* 707-237-6951 *Toll Free Fax:* 800-330-9798 *E-mail:* books@authorspublishing.com *Web Site:* www.energypsychologypress.com; www.elitebooksonline.com, pg 82

Arnold, David, CarTech Inc, 39966 Grand Ave, North Branch, MN 55056 *Tel:* 651-277-1200 *Toll Free Tel:* 800-551-4754 *Fax:* 651-277-1203 *E-mail:* info@cartechbooks.com *Web Site:* www.cartechbooks.com, pg 51

Arnovitz, Benton M, United States Holocaust Memorial Museum, 100 Raoul Wallenberg Place SW, Washington, DC 20024-2126 *Tel:* 202-314-7837; 202-488-6144 (orders) *Toll Free Tel:* 800-259-9998 (orders) *Fax:* 202-479-9726; 202-488-0438 (orders) *E-mail:* cahs_publications@ushmm.org *Web Site:* www.ushmm.org, pg 253

Arnow, Ann, Bridge Publications Inc, 5600 E Olympic Blvd, Commerce City, CA 90022 *Tel:* 323-888-6200 *Toll Free Tel:* 800-722-1733 *Fax:* 323-888-6202 *E-mail:* info@bridgepub.com *Web Site:* www.bridgepub.com, pg 45

Arnow, Don, Bridge Publications Inc, 5600 E Olympic Blvd, Commerce City, CA 90022 *Tel:* 323-888-6200 *Toll Free Tel:* 800-722-1733 *Fax:* 323-888-6202 *E-mail:* info@bridgepub.com *Web Site:* www.bridgepub.com, pg 45

Aron, Paul, The Colonial Williamsburg Foundation, PO Box 1776, Williamsburg, VA 23187-1776 *Tel:* 757-229-1000 *Toll Free Tel:* 800-HISTORY (447-8679) *Fax:* 757-220-7325 *E-mail:* cwres@cwf.org; geninfo@cwf.org *Web Site:* www.colonialwilliamsburg.org/publications, pg 61

Aronica, Lou, The Story Plant, PO Box 4331, Stamford, CT 06907 *Tel:* 203-722-7920 *E-mail:* thestoryplant@thestoryplant.com *Web Site:* www.thestoryplant.com, pg 236

Aronson, Michael A, Harvard University Press, 79 Garden St, Cambridge, MA 02138-1499 *Tel:* 617-495-2600; 401-531-2800 (intl orders) *Toll Free Tel:* 800-405-1619 (orders) *Fax:* 617-495-5898 (general); 617-496-4677 (edit & rts); 401-531-2801 (intl orders) *Toll Free Fax:* 800-406-9145 (orders) *E-mail:* contact_hup@harvard.edu *Web Site:* www.hup.harvard.edu, pg 107

Aronson, Rosa, Teachers of English to Speakers of Other Languages Inc (TESOL), 1925 Ballenger Ave, Alexandria, VA 22314-6820 *Tel:* 703-836-0774 *Toll Free Tel:* 888-547-3369 *Fax:* 703-836-7864 *E-mail:* info@tesol.org *Web Site:* www.tesol.org, pg 242

Arriaza, David, UCLA Latin American Center Publications, UCLA Latin American Institute, 10343 Bunche Hall, Los Angeles, CA 90095 *Tel:* 310-825-4571 *Fax:* 310-206-6859 *E-mail:* latinamctr@international.ucla.edu *Web Site:* www.international.ucla.edu/lai, pg 252

Arrington, Jay, The Little Entrepreneur, c/o Harper-Arrington, 18701 Grand River, Suite 105, Detroit, MI 48223 *Toll Free Tel:* 888-435-9234 *Fax:* 248-281-0373 *E-mail:* info@harperarringtonmedia.com *Web Site:* www.thelittlee.com, pg 141

Arrow, Kevin P, Graphic World Publishing Services, 11687 Adie Rd, St Louis, MO 63043 *Tel:* 314-567-9854 *Fax:* 314-567-7178 *E-mail:* quote@gwinc.com *Web Site:* www.gwinc.com, pg 527

Arsenault, Jessica, Bear & Co Inc, One Park St, Rochester, VT 05767 *Tel:* 802-767-3174 *Toll Free Tel:* 800-932-3277 *Fax:* 802-767-3726 *E-mail:* customerservice@InnerTraditions.com *Web Site:* InnerTraditions.com, pg 33

Arsenault, Jessica, Inner Traditions International Ltd, One Park St, Rochester, VT 05767 *Tel:* 802-767-3174 *Toll Free Tel:* 800-246-8648 *Fax:* 802-767-3726 *E-mail:* customerservice@InnerTraditions.com *Web Site:* www.InnerTraditions.com, pg 122

Arseneault, Brenda, McGraw-Hill Ryerson Limited, 300 Water St, Whitby, ON L1N 9B6, Canada *Tel:* 905-430-5000 *Toll Free Tel:* 800-565-5758 (cust serv) *Fax:* 905-430-5020 *Toll Free Fax:* 800-463-5885 *Web Site:* www.mheducation.ca, pg 491

Arthur, Julie, Adventure Publications, 820 Cleveland St, Cambridge, MN 55008 *Tel:* 763-689-9800 *Toll Free Tel:* 800-678-7006 *Fax:* 763-689-9039 *Toll Free Fax:* 877-374-9016 *E-mail:* custservice@adventurepublications.net; orders@adventurepublications.net *Web Site:* www.adventurepublications.net, pg 5

Arthur, Michael, Beekman Books Inc, 300 Old All Angels Hill Rd, Wappingers Falls, NY 12590 *Tel:* 845-297-2690 *Fax:* 845-297-1002 *E-mail:* beekmanbooks@yahoo.com *Web Site:* www.beekmanbooks.com, pg 33

Arthur, Reagan, Hachette Book Group, 1290 Avenue of the Americas, New York, NY 10019 *Tel:* 212-364-1100 *Toll Free Tel:* 800-759-0190 (cust serv) *Fax:* 212-364-0933 (intl orders) *Toll Free Fax:* 800-286-9471 (cust serv) *Web Site:* www.HachetteBookGroup.com, pg 102

Arthur, Reagan, Little, Brown and Company, 1290 Avenue of the Americas, New York, NY 10019 *Tel:* 212-364-1100 *Fax:* 212-364-0952 *E-mail:* firstname.lastname@hbgusa.com *Web Site:* www.HachetteBookGroup.com, pg 141

Ascher, David, Scholastic Trade Division, 557 Broadway, New York, NY 10012 *Tel:* 212-343-6100; 212-343-4685 (export sales) *Fax:* 212-343-4714 (export sales) *Web Site:* www.scholastic.com, pg 219

Ascher, James P, American Printing History Association, PO Box 4519, Grand Central Sta, New York, NY 10163 *Tel:* 202-544-2422 *E-mail:* secretary@printinghistory.org *Web Site:* printinghistory.org, pg 596

Ascher, James P, American Printing History Association Award, PO Box 4519, Grand Central Sta, New York, NY 10163 *Tel:* 202-544-2422 *Web Site:* printinghistory.org, pg 667

Ash, Irene, Synapse Information Resources Inc, 1247 Taft Ave, Endicott, NY 13760 *Tel:* 607-748-4145 *Toll Free Tel:* 888-SYN-CHEM (796-2436) *Fax:* 607-786-3966 *E-mail:* salesinfo@synapseinfo.com *Web Site:* www.synapseinfo.com, pg 239

Ash, Michael, Synapse Information Resources Inc, 1247 Taft Ave, Endicott, NY 13760 *Tel:* 607-748-4145 *Toll Free Tel:* 888-SYN-CHEM (796-2436) *Fax:* 607-786-3966 *E-mail:* salesinfo@synapseinfo.com *Web Site:* www.synapseinfo.com, pg 239

Asher, Virginia Lee, Sky Oaks Productions Inc, 19544 Sky Oaks Way, Los Gatos, CA 95030 *Tel:* 408-395-7600 *Fax:* 408-395-8440 *E-mail:* tprworld@aol.com *Web Site:* www.tpr-world.com, pg 227

Ashfield, Keith, Kogan Page Publishers, 1518 Walnut St, Suite 1100, Philadelphia, PA 19102 *Tel:* 215-928-9112 *Fax:* 215-928-9113 *E-mail:* info@koganpage.com *Web Site:* www.koganpageusa.com, pg 132

Ashley, Britt, Indiana Review Fiction Prize, Ballantine Hall 465, 1020 E Kirkwood Ave, Bloomington, IN 47405 *Tel:* 812-855-3439 *E-mail:* inreview@indiana.edu *Web Site:* indianareview.org, pg 694

Ashton, Stacy, Reader's Digest Trade Books, 44 S Broadway, White Plains, NY 10601 *Tel:* 914-244-7503 *Fax:* 914-244-4841 *Web Site:* www.rd.com, pg 205

Ashwood, Shana, LearningExpress LLC, 2 Rector St, 26th fl, New York, NY 10006 *Tel:* 212-995-2566 *Toll Free Tel:* 800-295-9556 (ext 2) *Fax:* 212-995-5512 *E-mail:* customerservice@learningexpressllc.com (cust serv) *Web Site:* www.learningexpressllc.com, pg 136

Asiaghi, Anthony, American Society of Mechanical Engineers (ASME), 2 Park Ave, New York, NY 10016-5990 *Tel:* 212-591-7000 *Toll Free Tel:* 800-843-2763 (cust serv-US, CN & Mexico) *Fax:* 212-591-7674; 973-882-8113 (cust serv); 973-882-1717 (orders & inquiries) *E-mail:* infocentral@asme.org *Web Site:* www.asme.org, pg 16

Aspey, Susan, Cengage Learning, 20 Channel Center St, Boston, MA 02210 *Tel:* 617-289-7700 *Toll Free Tel:* 800-354-9706 *Fax:* 617-289-7844 *Toll Free Fax:* 800-487-8488 *E-mail:* esales@cengage.com *Web Site:* www.cengage.com, pg 53

Assathiany, Pascal, Les Editions du Boreal, 4447, rue St-Denis, Montreal, QC H2J 2L2, Canada *Tel:* 514-287-7401 *Fax:* 514-287-7664 *E-mail:* boreal@editionsboreal.qc.ca *Web Site:* www.editionsboreal.qc.ca, pg 480

Assouad, Maya, Vehicule Press, PO Box 42094, CP Roy, Montreal, QC H2W-2T3, Canada *Tel:* 514-844-6073 *Fax:* 514-844-7543 *E-mail:* vp@vehiculepress.com; admin@vehiculepress.com *Web Site:* www.vehiculepress.com, pg 504

Aster, Howard, Mosaic Press, 4500 Witmer Industrial Estates, PMB 145, Niagara Falls, NY 14305-1386 *Tel:* 905-825-2130 *Fax:* 905-825-2130 *E-mail:* info@mosaic-press.com *Web Site:* www.mosaic-press.com, pg 160

Asteriou, Michael, The Apocryphile Press, 1700 Shattuck Ave, Suite 81, Berkeley, CA 94709 *Tel:* 510-290-4349 *E-mail:* apocryphile@earthlink.net *Web Site:* www.apocryphile.org, pg 19

Astor, Dave, National Society of Newspaper Columnists Annual Conference, 1345 Fillmore St, Suite 507, San Francisco, CA 94115 *Tel:* 415-488-NCNC (488-6762) *Toll Free Tel:* 866-440-NSNC (440-6762) *Fax:* 484-297-0336 *Toll Free Fax:* 866-635-5759 *Web Site:* www.columnists.com, pg 653

Atchity, Dr Kenneth, AEI (Atchity Entertainment International Inc), 9601 Wilshire Blvd, Unit 1202, Beverly Hills, CA 90210 *Tel:* 323-932-0407 *Fax:* 323-932-0321 *E-mail:* submissions@aeionline.com *Web Site:* www.aeionline.com, pg 540

Atchity, Kenneth PhD, The Writer's Lifeline Inc, 400 S Burnside Ave, Suite 11B, Los Angeles, CA 90036 *Tel:* 323-932-1685 *Fax:* 323-932-1220 *Web Site:* www.thewriterslifeline.com, pg 536

Athens, Phil, Resilient Publishing, 406 S Third St, Boise, ID 83702 *Tel:* 208-258-9544 *E-mail:* submissions@resilientpublishing.com *Web Site:* www.resilientpublishing.com, pg 208

Atkinson, Marisa, Graywolf Press, 250 Third Ave N, Suite 600, Minneapolis, MN 55401 *Tel:* 651-641-0077 *Fax:* 651-641-0036 *E-mail:* wolves@graywolfpress.org *Web Site:* www.graywolfpress.org, pg 100

Atkocaitis, John, Sundance/Newbridge Publishing, 33 Boston Post Rd W, Suite 440, Marlborough, MA 01752 *Toll Free Tel:* 888-200-2720; 800-343-8204 (Sundance cust serv & orders); 800-867-0307 (Newbridge cust serv & orders) *Toll Free Fax:* 800-456-2419 (orders) *E-mail:* info@sundancepub.com; info@newbridgeonline.com *Web Site:* www.sundancepub.com; www.newbridgeonline.com, pg 238

Atsma, Helen, Houghton Mifflin Harcourt Trade & Reference Division, 222 Berkeley St, Boston, MA 02116 *Tel:* 617-351-5000 *Toll Free Tel:* 800-225-3362 *Web Site:* www.hmhco.com, pg 115

Attebery, Gerilyn, Lonely Planet, 150 Linden St, Oakland, CA 94607 *Tel:* 510-893-8555 *Toll Free Tel:* 800-275-8555 (orders) *Fax:* 510-893-8572 *E-mail:* info@lonelyplanet.com *Web Site:* www.lonelyplanet.com, pg 142

Attfield, Hilary, West Virginia University Press, West Virginia University, PO Box 6295, Morgantown, WV 26506-6295 *Tel:* 304-293-8400 *Toll Free Tel:* 866-WVU-PRES (988-7737) *Fax:* 304-293-6585 *E-mail:* press@wvu.edu *Web Site:* www.wvupress.com, pg 269

Attlee, James, University of Chicago Press, 1427 E 60 St, Chicago, IL 60637-2954 *Tel:* 773-702-7700; 773-702-7600 *Toll Free Tel:* 800-621-2736 (orders) *Fax:* 773-702-9756; 773-660-2235 (orders); 773-702-2708 *E-mail:* custserv@press.uchicago.edu; marketing@press.uchicago.edu *Web Site:* www.press.uchicago.edu, pg 255

Attwood, Beth, Harlequin Enterprises Ltd, 233 Broadway, Suite 1001, New York, NY 10279 *Tel:* 212-553-4200 *Fax:* 212-227-8969 *E-mail:* CustomerService@harlequin.com *Web Site:* www.harlequin.com, pg 105

Attwood, Beth, Harlequin Enterprises Ltd, 225 Duncan Mill Rd, Don Mills, ON M3B 3K9, Canada *Tel:* 416-445-5860 *Toll Free Tel:* 888-432-4879; 800-370-5838 (ebook inquiries) *E-mail:* customerservice@harlequin.com *Web Site:* www.harlequin.com, pg 487

Atwan, Helene, Beacon Press, 24 Farnsworth St, Boston, MA 02210-1409 *Tel:* 617-742-2110 *Fax:* 617-723-3097; 617-742-2290 *Web Site:* www.beacon.org, pg 32

Atwan, Helene, The Hemingway Foundation/PEN Award, MIT, 14N-221A, 77 Massachusetts Ave, Cambridge, MA 02139 *Tel:* 617-324-1729 *E-mail:* pen-newengland@mit.edu *Web Site:* www.pen-ne.org, pg 692

Atwood, Dr Christopher, The Mongolia Society Inc, Indiana University, 322 Goodbody Hall, 1011 E Third St, Bloomington, IN 47405-7005 *Tel:* 812-855-4078 *Fax:* 812-855-4078 *E-mail:* monsoc@indiana.edu *Web Site:* www.mongoliasociety.org, pg 159

Audet, Janice, Harvard University Press, 79 Garden St, Cambridge, MA 02138-1499 *Tel:* 617-495-2600; 401-531-2800 (intl orders) *Toll Free Tel:* 800-405-1619 (orders) *Fax:* 617-495-5898 (general); 617-496-4677 (edit & rts); 401-531-2801 (intl orders) *Toll Free Fax:* 800-406-9145 (orders) *E-mail:* contact_hup@harvard.edu *Web Site:* www.hup.harvard.edu, pg 107

Auerbach, Karen, Kensington Publishing Corp, 119 W 40 St, New York, NY 10018 *Tel:* 212-407-1500 *Toll Free Tel:* 800-221-2647 *Fax:* 212-935-0699 *Web Site:* www.kensingtonbooks.com, pg 130

Aufmuth, Christopher, Michelin Maps & Guides, One Parkway S, Greenville, SC 29615-5022 *Tel:* 864-458-5565 *Fax:* 864-458-5665 *Toll Free Fax:* 866-297-0914; 888-773-7979 *E-mail:* orders@americanmap.com (orders) *Web Site:* www.michelintravel.com; www.michelinguide.com, pg 155

Augerbraun, Harold, National Book Awards, 90 Broad St, Suite 604, New York, NY 10004 *Tel:* 212-685-0261 *Fax:* 212-213-6570 *E-mail:* nationalbook@nationalbook.org *Web Site:* www.nationalbook.org, pg 710

August, Scott, Haights Cross Communications®, 136 Madison Ave, 8th fl, New York, NY 10016 *Tel:* 212-209-0500 *Fax:* 212-209-0501 *E-mail:* info@haightscross.com *Web Site:* www.haightscross.com, pg 103

Auh, Jin, The Wylie Agency Inc, 250 W 57 St, Suite 2114, New York, NY 10107 *Tel:* 212-246-0069 *Fax:* 212-586-8953 *E-mail:* mail@wylieagency.com *Web Site:* www.wylieagency.com, pg 580

Aujla, Simmi, Houghton Mifflin Harcourt Trade & Reference Division, 222 Berkeley St, Boston, MA 02116 *Tel:* 617-351-5000 *Toll Free Tel:* 800-225-3362 *Web Site:* www.hmhco.com, pg 115

Aulisio, Michael, Thomas Nelson, 501 Nelson Place, Nashville, TN 37214 *Tel:* 615-889-9000 *Toll Free Tel:* 800-251-4000 *Fax:* 615-902-1548 *E-mail:* publicity@thomasnelson.com *Web Site:* www.thomasnelson.com, pg 245

Ault, Charles, Temple University Press, 1852 N Tenth St, Philadelphia, PA 19122-6099 *Tel:* 215-926-2140 *Toll Free Tel:* 800-621-2736 *Fax:* 215-926-2141 *E-mail:* tempress@temple.edu *Web Site:* www.temple.edu/tempress, pg 242

Balliett, Will, Thames & Hudson, 500 Fifth Ave, New York, NY 10110 *Tel:* 212-354-3763 *Toll Free Tel:* 800-233-4830 *Fax:* 212-398-1252 *E-mail:* bookinfo@thames.wwnorton.com *Web Site:* www.thamesandhudsonusa.com, pg 244

Ballinger, Glenys, Ballinger Publishing, 41 N Jefferson St, Suite 402, Pensacola, FL 32502 *Tel:* 850-433-1166 *Fax:* 850-435-9174 *E-mail:* info@ballingerpublishing.com *Web Site:* www.ballingerpublishing.com, pg 30

Ballinger, Malcolm, Ballinger Publishing, 41 N Jefferson St, Suite 402, Pensacola, FL 32502 *Tel:* 850-433-1166 *Fax:* 850-435-9174 *E-mail:* info@ballingerpublishing.com *Web Site:* www.ballingerpublishing.com, pg 30

Ballinger, Peter R, PRB Productions, 963 Peralta Ave, Albany, CA 94706-2144 *Tel:* 510-526-0722 *Fax:* 510-527-4763 *E-mail:* prbprdns@aol.com *Web Site:* www.prbmusic.com, pg 196

Balmuth, Deborah, Storey Publishing LLC, 210 MASS MoCA Way, North Adams, MA 01247 *Tel:* 413-346-2100 *Toll Free Tel:* 800-441-5700 (orders); 800-793-9396 (edit) *Fax:* 413-346-2199; 413-346-2196 (edit) *E-mail:* sales@storey.com *Web Site:* www.storey.com, pg 236

Balotro, April, I-5 Publishing LLC, 3 Burroughs, Irvine, CA 92618 *Tel:* 949-855-8822 *Toll Free Tel:* 888-738-2665 *Fax:* 949-458-3856 *Web Site:* www.i5publishing.com, pg 117

Balsamo, Kathy, Pieces of Learning, 1990 Market Rd, Marion, IL 62959-8976 *Tel:* 618-964-9426 *Toll Free Tel:* 800-729-5137 *Toll Free Fax:* 800-844-0455 *E-mail:* piecesoflearning@verizon.net *Web Site:* www.piecesoflearning.com, pg 192

Balsamo, Stan, Pieces of Learning, 1990 Market Rd, Marion, IL 62959-8976 *Tel:* 618-964-9426 *Toll Free Tel:* 800-729-5137 *Toll Free Fax:* 800-844-0455 *E-mail:* piecesoflearning@verizon.net *Web Site:* www.piecesoflearning.com, pg 192

Balser, Frank, IDEAlliance®, 1600 Duke St, Suite 420, Alexandria, VA 22314 *Tel:* 703-837-1070 *Fax:* 703-837-1072 *E-mail:* registrar@idealliance.org *Web Site:* www.idealliance.org, pg 607

Balthazar, Martin, Les Editions de l'Hexagone, 1010 rue de la Gauchetiere E, Montreal, QC H2L 2N5, Canada *Tel:* 514-523-7993 *Fax:* 514-282-7530 *Web Site:* www.edhexagone.com, pg 480

Balthazar, Martin, VLB Editeur Inc, 1010, Rue de la Gauchetiere Est, Montreal, QC H2L 2N5, Canada *Tel:* 514-523-7993 *Fax:* 514-282-7530 *Web Site:* www.edvlb.com, pg 504

Balvenie, K, One Act Play Depot, 618 Memorial Dr, PO Box 335, Spiritwood, SK S0J 2M0, Canada *E-mail:* plays@oneactplays.net; orders@oneactplays.net *Web Site:* oneactplays.net, pg 493

Bamford, Christopher, Lindisfarne Books, 610 Main St, Great Barrington, MA 01230 *Tel:* 413-528-8233 *Fax:* 413-528-8826 *E-mail:* service@steinerbooks.org *Web Site:* www.steinerbooks.org, pg 139

Bamford, Christopher, SteinerBooks, 610 Main St, Great Barrington, MA 01230 *Tel:* 413-528-8233 *Fax:* 413-528-8826 *E-mail:* friends@steinerbooks.org *Web Site:* www.steinerbooks.org, pg 235

Bamundo, Claire, Harry N Abrams Inc, 115 W 18 St, 6th fl, New York, NY 10011 *Tel:* 212-206-7715 *Toll Free Tel:* 800-345-1359 *Fax:* 212-519-1210 *E-mail:* abrams@abramsbooks.com *Web Site:* www.abramsbooks.com, pg 3

Bandini, Lisa Kent, Center for the Collaborative Classroom, 1250 53 St, Suite 3, Emeryville, CA 94608 *Tel:* 510-533-0213 *Toll Free Tel:* 800-666-7270 *Fax:* 510-464-3670 *E-mail:* info@collaborativeclassroom.org; clientsupport@collaborativeclassroom.org *Web Site:* www.collaborativeclassroom.org, pg 53

Bandos, Kate, Bookhaven Press LLC, 302 Scenic Ct, Moon Township, PA 15108 *Tel:* 412-494-6926 *E-mail:* info@bookhavenpress.com; orders@bookhavenpress.com *Web Site:* bookhavenpress.com, pg 42

Banducci, Jo Anne, University of Nevada Press, University of Nevada, M/S 0166, Reno, NV 89557-0166 *Tel:* 775-784-6573 *Fax:* 775-784-6200 *Web Site:* www.unpress.nevada.edu, pg 258

Bane, Barbara S, NeDeo Press, PO Box 668, Robbins, NC 27325 *Web Site:* www.nedeopress.com, pg 167

Banis, Robert J, Science & Humanities Press, 63 Summit Point, St Charles, MO 63301-0571 *Tel:* 636-394-4950 *Web Site:* sciencehumanitiespress.com; beachhousebooks.com; macroprintbooks.com; earlyeditionsbooks.com; heuristicsbooks.com, pg 219

Bank, Josh, Alloy Entertainment LLC, 1700 Broadway, New York, NY 10019 *Web Site:* alloyentertainment.com, pg 8

Banker, Rhea, Pearson ELT, 10 Bank St, 9th fl, White Plains, NY 10606-1951 *Tel:* 914-287-8000 *Web Site:* www.pearsonelt.com, pg 185

Bankoff, Lisa, ICM Partners, 730 Fifth Ave, New York, NY 10019 *Tel:* 212-556-5600 *Web Site:* www.icmtalent.com, pg 557

Banks, Clare, Beullah Rose Poetry Prize, PO Box 22161, Baltimore, MD 21203 *Web Site:* www.smartishpace.com, pg 671

Banks, Jennifer, Yale University Press, 302 Temple St, New Haven, CT 06511-8909 *Tel:* 203-432-0960; 203-432-0966 (sales); 401-531-2800 (cust serv) *Toll Free Tel:* 800-405-1619 (cust serv) *Fax:* 203-432-0948; 203-432-8485 (sales); 401-531-2801 (cust serv) *Toll Free Fax:* 800-406-9145 (cust serv) *E-mail:* sales.press@yale.edu (sales); customer.care@trilateral.org (cust serv) *Web Site:* www.yalebooks.com; yalepress.yale.edu/yupbooks, pg 278

Bannon, Dr Joseph J Sr, Sagamore Publishing LLC, 1807 Federal Dr, Urbana, IL 61801 *Tel:* 217-359-5940 *Toll Free Tel:* 800-327-5557 (orders) *Fax:* 217-359-5975 *E-mail:* books@sagamorepub.com *Web Site:* www.sagamorepub.com, pg 213

Bannon, Peter L, Sagamore Publishing LLC, 1807 Federal Dr, Urbana, IL 61801 *Tel:* 217-359-5940 *Toll Free Tel:* 800-327-5557 (orders) *Fax:* 217-359-5975 *E-mail:* books@sagamorepub.com *Web Site:* www.sagamorepub.com, pg 213

Barathon, Marie-Pierre, Les Editions XYZ inc, 1815, ave De Lorimier, Montreal, QC H2K 3W6, Canada *Tel:* 514-525-2170 *Fax:* 514-525-7537 *E-mail:* info@editionsxyz.com *Web Site:* www.editionsxyz.com, pg 483

Barb, Patrick, Ten Speed Press, 2625 Alcatraz Ave, Unit 505, Berkeley, CA 94705 *Tel:* 510-285-3000 *Toll Free Tel:* 800-841-BOOK (841-2665) *E-mail:* csorders@randomhouse.com *Web Site:* crownpublishing.com/imprint/ten-speed-press, pg 243

Barbara, Stephen, InkWell Management, 521 Fifth Ave, 26th fl, New York, NY 10175 *Tel:* 212-922-3500 *Fax:* 212-922-0535 *E-mail:* info@inkwellmanagement.com; submissions@inkwellmanagement.com *Web Site:* inkwellmanagement.com, pg 557

Barbasa, Santos, University of Hawaii Press, 2840 Kolowalu St, Honolulu, HI 96822 *Tel:* 808-956-8255 *Toll Free Tel:* 888-UHPRESS (847-7377) *Fax:* 808-988-6052 *Toll Free Fax:* 800-650-7811 *E-mail:* uhpbooks@hawaii.edu *Web Site:* www.uhpress.hawaii.edu, pg 256

Barbee, Michael, Kalmbach Publishing Co, 21027 Crossroads Circle, Waukesha, WI 53186 *Tel:* 262-796-8776 *Toll Free Tel:* 800-533-6644 (cust serv & orders) *Fax:* 262-796-1615 (sales & cust serv); 262-798-6468 (edit) *E-mail:* customerservice@kalmbach.com *Web Site:* www.kalmbach.com; www.kalmbachstore.com, pg 129

Barber, A Richard, A Richard Barber/Peter Berinstein & Associates, 60 E Eighth St, Suite 21-N, New York, NY 10003 *Tel:* 212-737-7266 *Fax:* 860-927-3942 *E-mail:* barberrich@aol.com, pg 542

Barbour, Bruce R, Literary Management Group LLC, 16970 San Carlos Blvd, Suite 160-100, Fort Myers, FL 33908 *Tel:* 615-812-4445 *Web Site:* www.literarymanagementgroup.com, pg 562

Barbour, Matthew, Omnigraphics Inc, 155 W Congress, Suite 200, Detroit, MI 48226 *Tel:* 313-961-1340 *Toll Free Tel:* 800-234-1340 (cust serv) *Fax:* 313-961-1383 *Toll Free Fax:* 800-875-1340 (cust serv) *E-mail:* info@omnigraphics.com *Web Site:* www.omnigraphics.com, pg 175

Barbour, Wanda, American Industrial Hygiene Association - AIHA, 3141 Fairview Park Dr, Suite 777, Falls Church, VA 22042 *Tel:* 703-849-8888 *Fax:* 703-207-3561 *E-mail:* infonet@aiha.org *Web Site:* www.aiha.org, pg 13

Barcatta, Sabine, Thomas J Lyon Book Award in Western American Literary and Cultural Studies, PO Box 6815, Logan, UT 84341 *Web Site:* www.westernlit.org/thomas-j-lyon-book-award-in-western-american-literary-and-cultural-studies/; www.westernlit.org, pg 703

Barich, Steven, Alan Wofsy Fine Arts, 1109 Geary Blvd, San Francisco, CA 94109 *Tel:* 415-292-6500 *Toll Free Tel:* 800-660-6403 *Fax:* 415-292-6594 (off & cust serv); 510-251-1840 (acctg) *E-mail:* order@art-books.com (orders); editeur@earthlink.net (edit); beauxarts@earthlink.net (cust serv) *Web Site:* www.art-books.com, pg 274

Baril, Andre, Les Presses De L'Universite Laval, 2180, Chemin Ste-Foy, 1st fl, Quebec, QC G1V 0A6, Canada *Tel:* 418-656-2803 *Fax:* 418-656-3305 *E-mail:* presses@pul.ulaval.ca *Web Site:* www.pulaval.com, pg 496

Barkan, Bebe, Cross-Cultural Communications, 239 Wynsum Ave, Merrick, NY 11566-4725 *Tel:* 516-868-5635 *Fax:* 516-379-1901 *E-mail:* info@cross-culturalcommunications.com; cccbarkan@optonline.net; cccpoetry@aol.com *Web Site:* www.cross-culturalcommunications.com, pg 67

Barkan, Stanley H, Cross-Cultural Communications, 239 Wynsum Ave, Merrick, NY 11566-4725 *Tel:* 516-868-5635 *Fax:* 516-379-1901 *E-mail:* info@cross-culturalcommunications.com; cccbarkan@optonline.net; cccpoetry@aol.com *Web Site:* www.cross-culturalcommunications.com, pg 67

Barker, Clyde F, American Philosophical Society, 104 S Fifth St, Philadelphia, PA 19106 *Tel:* 215-440-3425 *Fax:* 215-440-3450 *E-mail:* dianepub@comcast.net *Web Site:* www.amphilsoc.org, pg 15

Barker, Laura, Crown Publishing Group, c/o Penguin Random House Inc, 1745 Broadway, New York, NY 10019 *Tel:* 212-782-9000 *Toll Free Tel:* 888-264-1745 *Fax:* 212-940-7408 *E-mail:* crownosm@penguinrandomhouse.com *Web Site:* crownpublishing.com, pg 68

Barker, Laura, WaterBrook Multnomah Publishing Group, 12265 Oracle Blvd, Suite 200, Colorado Springs, CO 80921 *Tel:* 719-590-4999 *Toll Free Tel:* 800-603-7051 (orders) *Fax:* 719-590-8977 *Toll Free Fax:* 800-294-5686 (orders) *E-mail:* info@waterbrookmultnomah.com *Web Site:* waterbrookmultnomah.com, pg 267

Barmash, Erica, Bloomsbury Publishing Inc, 1385 Broadway, 5th fl, New York, NY 10018 *Tel:* 212-419-5300 *E-mail:* marketingusa@bloomsbury.com; adultpublicityusa@bloomsbury.com; askacademic@bloomsbury.com *Web Site:* www.bloomsbury.com, pg 40

Barnes, Catherine, Oxford University Press USA, 198 Madison Ave, New York, NY 10016 *Tel:* 212-726-6000 *Toll Free Tel:* 800-451-7556 (orders); 800-445-9714 (cust serv) *Fax:* 919-677-1303 *E-mail:* custserv.us@oup.com *Web Site:* www.oup.com/us, pg 179

Barnes, Jacqueline, BuilderBooks.com, 1201 15 St NW, Washington, DC 20005 *Tel:* 202-822-0200 *Toll Free Tel:* 800-223-2665 *Fax:* 202-266-8096 (edit) *E-mail:* builderbooks@nahb.com *Web Site:* www.builderbooks.com, pg 47

Barnes, Janet, Bentley Publishers, 1734 Massachusetts Ave, Cambridge, MA 02138-1804 *Tel:* 617-547-4170 *Toll Free Tel:* 800-423-4595 *Fax:* 617-876-9235 *E-mail:* sales@bentleypublishers.com *Web Site:* www.bentleypublishers.com, pg 35

Barnes, Jim, Axiom Business Book Awards, 1129 Woodmere Ave, Suite B, Traverse City, MI 49686 *Tel:* 231-933-0445 *Toll Free Tel:* 800-706-4636 *Fax:* 231-933-0448 *E-mail:* info@axiomawards.com *Web Site:* www.axiomawards.com, pg 669

Barnes, Jim, Illumination Book Awards, 1129 Woodmere Ave, Suite B, Traverse City, MI 49686 *Tel:* 231-933-0445 *Toll Free Tel:* 800-706-4636 *Fax:* 231-933-0448 *E-mail:* awards@bookpublishing.com *Web Site:* www.illuminationawards.com, pg 694

Barnes, Jim, The Independent Publisher Book Awards, 1129 Woodmere Ave, Suite B, Traverse City, MI 49686 *Tel:* 231-933-0445 *Toll Free Tel:* 800-706-4636 *Fax:* 231-933-0448 *E-mail:* awards@bookpublishing.com *Web Site:* www.independentpublisher.com/ipland/ipawards.php, pg 694

Barnes, Jim, Jenkins Group Inc, 1129 Woodmere Ave, Suite B, Traverse City, MI 49686 *Tel:* 231-933-0445 *Toll Free Tel:* 800-706-4636 *Fax:* 231-933-0448 *E-mail:* info@bookpublishing.com *Web Site:* www.bookpublishing.com, pg 528

Barnes, Jim, Living Now Book Awards, 1129 Woodmere Ave, Suite B, Traverse City, MI 49686 *Tel:* 231-933-0445 *Toll Free Tel:* 800-706-4636 *Fax:* 231-933-0448 *E-mail:* awards@bookpublishing.com *Web Site:* www.livingnowawards.com, pg 702

Barnes, Jim, Moonbeam Children's Book Awards, 1129 Woodmere Ave, Suite B, Traverse City, MI 49686 *Tel:* 231-933-0445 *Toll Free Tel:* 800-706-4636 *Fax:* 231-933-0448 *E-mail:* info@moonbeamawards.com *Web Site:* www.moonbeamawards.com, pg 709

Barnes, Lisa, Penguin Random House Speakers Bureau, 1745 Broadway, Mail Drop 13-1, New York, NY 10019 *Tel:* 212-572-2013 *E-mail:* speakers@penguinrandomhouse.com *Web Site:* www.prhspeakers.com, pg 588

Barnes, Marcy, Beacon Press, 24 Farnsworth St, Boston, MA 02210-1409 *Tel:* 617-742-2110 *Fax:* 617-723-3097; 617-742-2290 *Web Site:* www.beacon.org, pg 32

Barnes, Shannon Howe, Marilyn Baillie Picture Book Award, 40 Orchard View Blvd, Suite 217, Toronto, ON M4R 1B9, Canada *Tel:* 416-975-0010 *Fax:* 416-975-8970 *E-mail:* info@bookcentre.ca *Web Site:* www.bookcentre.ca, pg 669

Barnes, Shannon Howe, The Geoffrey Bilson Award for Historical Fiction for Young People, 40 Orchard View Blvd, Suite 217, Toronto, ON M4R 1B9, Canada *Tel:* 416-975-0010 *Fax:* 416-975-8970 *E-mail:* info@bookcentre.ca *Web Site:* www.bookcentre.ca, pg 672

Barnes, Shannon Howe, Canadian Children's Book Centre, 40 Orchard View Blvd, Suite 217, Toronto, ON M4R 1B9, Canada *Tel:* 416-975-0010 *Fax:* 416-975-8970 *E-mail:* info@bookcentre.ca *Web Site:* www.bookcentre.ca, pg 602

Barnes, Shannon Howe, Norma Fleck Award for Canadian Children's Non-Fiction, 40 Orchard View Blvd, Suite 217, Toronto, ON M4R 1B9, Canada *Tel:* 416-975-0010 *Fax:* 416-975-8970 *E-mail:* info@bookcentre.ca *Web Site:* www.bookcentre.ca, pg 686

Barnes, Shannon Howe, Monica Hughes Award for Science Fiction & Fantasy, 40 Orchard View Blvd, Suite 217, Toronto, ON M4R 1B9, Canada *Tel:* 416-975-0010 *Fax:* 416-975-8970 *E-mail:* info@bookcentre.ca *Web Site:* www.bookcentre.ca, pg 693

Barnes, Shannon Howe, Amy Mathers Teen Book Award, 40 Orchard View Blvd, Suite 217, Toronto, ON M4R 1B9, Canada *Tel:* 416-975-0010 *Fax:* 416-975-8970 *E-mail:* info@bookcentre.ca *Web Site:* www.bookcentre.ca, pg 706

Barnes, Shannon Howe, John Spray Mystery Award, 40 Orchard View Blvd, Suite 217, Toronto, ON M4R 1B9, Canada *Tel:* 416-975-0010 *Fax:* 416-975-8970 *E-mail:* info@bookcentre.ca *Web Site:* www.bookcentre.ca, pg 730

Barnes, Shannon Howe, TD Canadian Children's Literature Award, 40 Orchard View Blvd, Suite 217, Toronto, ON M4R 1B9, Canada *Tel:* 416-975-0010 *Fax:* 416-975-8970 *E-mail:* info@bookcentre.ca *Web Site:* www.bookcentre.ca, pg 732

Barnett, Chrissie A, Southern California Writers' Conference, 18160 Cottonwood Rd, Suite 260, Sunriver, OR 97707 *Tel:* 619-303-8185 *Fax:* 619-906-7462 *E-mail:* msg@writersconference.com *Web Site:* www.writersconference.com, pg 655

Barnett, Katie, Clinical Laboratory & Standards Institute (CLSI), 950 W Valley Rd, Suite 2500, Wayne, PA 19087 *Tel:* 610-688-0100 *Toll Free Tel:* 877-447-1888 (orders) *Fax:* 610-688-0700 *E-mail:* customerservice@clsi.org *Web Site:* www.clsi.org, pg 59

Barnett, Marilyn, Workman Publishing Co Inc, 225 Varick St, 9th fl, New York, NY 10014-4381 *Tel:* 212-254-5900 *Toll Free Tel:* 800-722-7202 *Fax:* 212-254-8098 *E-mail:* info@workman.com *Web Site:* www.workman.com, pg 275

Barnett, Robin, Zondervan, 3900 Sparks Dr, Grand Rapids, MI 49546 *Tel:* 616-698-6900 *Toll Free Tel:* 800-226-1122; 800-727-1309 (retail orders) *Fax:* 616-698-3350 *Toll Free Fax:* 800-698-3256 (retail orders) *E-mail:* zinfo@zondervan.com *Web Site:* www.zondervan.com, pg 280

Barney, Stacey, GP Putnam's Sons (Children's), 345 Hudson St, New York, NY 10014 *Tel:* 212-366-2000 *Fax:* 212-414-3393 *E-mail:* online@penguinputnam.com *Web Site:* us.penguingroup.com, pg 201

Baron, Carole, Alfred A Knopf/Everyman's Library, c/o Random House Inc, 1745 Broadway, New York, NY 10019 *Tel:* 212-751-2600 *Toll Free Tel:* 800-638-6460 *Fax:* 212-572-2593 *Web Site:* www.knopfdoubleday.com, pg 132

Baron, Herman, Diane Publishing Co, 330 Pusey Ave, Suite 3 (rear), Collingdale, PA 19023-0617 *Tel:* 610-461-6200 *Toll Free Tel:* 800-782-3833 *Fax:* 610-461-6130 *Web Site:* www.dianepublishing.net, pg 74

Baror, Danny, Baror International Inc, PO Box 868, Armonk, NY 10504-0868 *Tel:* 914-273-9199 *Fax:* 914-273-5058 *Web Site:* www.barorint.com, pg 542

Baror-Shapiro, Heather, Baror International Inc, PO Box 868, Armonk, NY 10504-0868 *Tel:* 914-273-9199 *Fax:* 914-273-5058 *Web Site:* www.barorint.com, pg 542

Barot, Len, Bold Strokes Books Inc, PO Box 249, Valley Falls, NY 12185 *Tel:* 518-677-5127 *Fax:* 518-677-5291 *E-mail:* bsb@boldstrokesbooks.com *Web Site:* www.boldstrokesbooks.com, pg 41

Barr, Stephen, Writers House, 21 W 26 St, New York, NY 10010 *Tel:* 212-685-2400 *Fax:* 212-685-1781 *Web Site:* www.writershouse.com, pg 580

Barr, Wayne, Barron's Educational Series Inc, 250 Wireless Blvd, Hauppauge, NY 11788 *Tel:* 631-434-3311 *Toll Free Tel:* 800-645-3476 *Fax:* 631-434-3723 *E-mail:* barrons@barronseduc.com *Web Site:* www.barronseduc.com, pg 31

Barrales-Saylor, Kelly, Albert Whitman & Co, 250 S Northwest Hwy, Suite 320, Park Ridge, IL 60068 *Tel:* 847-232-2800 *Toll Free Tel:* 800-255-7675 *Fax:* 847-581-0039 *E-mail:* mail@awhitmanco.com *Web Site:* www.albertwhitman.com, pg 7

Barras, Lise, Pearson ERPI, 5757 rue Cypihot, St-Laurent, QC H4S 1R3, Canada *Tel:* 514-334-2690 *Toll Free Tel:* 800-263-3678 *Fax:* 514-334-4720 *Toll Free Fax:* 800-643-4720 *E-mail:* erpidlm@erpi.com *Web Site:* www.erpi.com; pearsonplc.ca, pg 494

Barrett, Lauren, Ohio State University Foreign Language Publications, 198 Hagerty Hall, 1775 College Rd, Columbus, OH 43210-1340 *Tel:* 614-292-3838 *Toll Free Tel:* 800-678-6999 *Fax:* 614-688-3355 *E-mail:* flpubs@osu.edu *Web Site:* www.flpubs.osu.edu, pg 174

Barrett, Sheila, Harvard University Press, 79 Garden St, Cambridge, MA 02138-1499 *Tel:* 617-495-2600; 401-531-2800 (intl orders) *Toll Free Tel:* 800-405-1619 (orders) *Fax:* 617-495-5898 (general); 617-496-4677 (edit & rts); 401-531-2801 (intl orders) *Toll Free Fax:* 800-406-9145 (orders) *E-mail:* contact_hup@harvard.edu *Web Site:* www.hup.harvard.edu, pg 107

Barrios, Gregg, Nona Balakian Citation for Excellence in Reviewing, 160 Varick St, 11th fl, New York, NY 10013 *E-mail:* info@bookcritics.org *Web Site:* bookcritics.org, pg 670

Barron, Manuel H, Barron's Educational Series Inc, 250 Wireless Blvd, Hauppauge, NY 11788 *Tel:* 631-434-3311 *Toll Free Tel:* 800-645-3476 *Fax:* 631-434-3723 *E-mail:* barrons@barronseduc.com *Web Site:* www.barronseduc.com, pg 31

Barrs, Michael, HarperCollins General Books Group, 195 Broadway, New York, NY 10007 *Tel:* 212-207-7000 *Web Site:* www.harpercollins.com, pg 105

Barry, Beth, Demos Medical Publishing, 11 W 42 St, 15th fl, New York, NY 10036 *Tel:* 212-683-0072 *E-mail:* info@demosmedpub.com; orderdept@demosmedical.com; editorial@demosmedical.com *Web Site:* www.demosmedical.com, pg 73

Barry, Graham, Chronicle Books LLC, 680 Second St, San Francisco, CA 94107 *Tel:* 415-537-4200 *Toll Free Tel:* 800-759-0190 (cust serv) *Fax:* 415-537-4460 *Toll Free Fax:* 800-858-7787 (orders); 800-286-9471 (cust serv) *E-mail:* frontdesk@chroniclebooks.com *Web Site:* www.chroniclebooks.com, pg 58

Barry, Patrick, Houghton Mifflin Harcourt, 222 Berkeley St, Boston, MA 02116 *Tel:* 617-351-5000 *Toll Free Tel:* 800-225-5425 (K-12 educ materials); 800-323-9540 (assessment materials); 877-219-1537 (SkillsTutor); 888-242-6747 (Destination; Earobics; Edmark; Learning Village; Riverdeep); 800-225-3362 (Houghton Mifflin Harcourt Trade & Reference Publishers) *Toll Free Fax:* 800-269-5232 *E-mail:* customerservice@hmhpub.com *Web Site:* www.hmhco.com, pg 115

Barry, Patrick, Houghton Mifflin Harcourt Trade & Reference Division, 222 Berkeley St, Boston, MA 02116 *Tel:* 617-351-5000 *Toll Free Tel:* 800-225-3362 *Web Site:* www.hmhco.com, pg 115

Barry, Sheila, Groundwood Books, 110 Spadina Ave, Suite 801, Toronto, ON M5V 2K4, Canada *Tel:* 416-363-4343 *Fax:* 416-363-1017 *E-mail:* genmail@groundwoodbooks.com *Web Site:* www.houseofanansi.com, pg 486

Barsan, Corinna, Grove Atlantic Inc, 154 W 14 St, 12th fl, New York, NY 10011 *Tel:* 212-614-7850 *Toll Free Tel:* 800-521-0178 *Fax:* 212-614-7886 *E-mail:* info@groveatlantic.com *Web Site:* www.groveatlantic.com, pg 101

Bartels, Lynn, Lucky Marble Books, 2671 Bristol Rd, Columbus, OH 43221 *Tel:* 614-264-5588 *E-mail:* sales@pagespringpublishing.com *Web Site:* www.luckymarblebooks.com, pg 144

Barth, Ilene, Red Rock Press, 331 W 57 St, Suite 175, New York, NY 10019 *Tel:* 212-362-8304 *Fax:* 212-362-6216 *E-mail:* info@redrockpress.com *Web Site:* www.redrockpress.com, pg 206

Barth, Richard, Red Rock Press, 331 W 57 St, Suite 175, New York, NY 10019 *Tel:* 212-362-8304 *Fax:* 212-362-6216 *E-mail:* info@redrockpress.com *Web Site:* www.redrockpress.com, pg 206

Barthelmes, Victoria, American Association of Blood Banks, 8101 Glenbrook Rd, Bethesda, MD 20814-2749 *Tel:* 301-907-6977 *Toll Free Tel:* 866-222-2498 (sales) *Fax:* 301-907-6895 *E-mail:* aabb@aabb.org; sales@aabb.org (ordering); publications1@aabb.org *Web Site:* www.aabb.org, pg 11

Bartholomew, Marie, Kids Can Press Ltd, 25 Dockside Dr, Toronto, ON M5A 0B5, Canada *Tel:* 416-479-7000 *Toll Free Tel:* 800-265-0884 *Fax:* 416-960-5437 *E-mail:* info@kidscan.com; customerservice@kidscan.com *Web Site:* www.kidscanpress.com; www.kidscanpress.ca, pg 489

Bartleson, Katelynn, Jessica Kingsley Publishers Inc, 400 Market St, Suite 400, Philadelphia, PA 19106 *Tel:* 215-922-1161 *Toll Free Tel:* 866-416-1078 (cust serv) *Fax:* 215-922-1474 *E-mail:* orders@jkp.com; hello.usa@jkp.com *Web Site:* www.jkp.com, pg 131

Bartlett, Danielle, HarperCollins General Books Group, 195 Broadway, New York, NY 10007 *Tel:* 212-207-7000 *Web Site:* www.harpercollins.com, pg 105

Bartlett, Katy, Thompson Educational Publishing Inc, 20 Ripley Ave, Toronto, ON M6S 3N9, Canada *Tel:* 416-766-2763 (admin & orders) *Toll Free Tel:* 877-366-2763 *Fax:* 416-766-0398 (admin & orders) *E-mail:* info@thompsonbooks.com *Web Site:* www.thompsonbooks.com, pg 501

Bartlett, Laura J, 4A's (American Association of Advertising Agencies), 1065 Avenue of the Americas, 16th fl, New York, NY 10018 *Tel:* 212-682-2500 *Web Site:* www.aaaa.org, pg 606

Bartok, Josh, Wisdom Publications Inc, 199 Elm St, Somerville, MA 02144 *Tel:* 617-776-7416 *Toll Free Tel:* 800-272-4050 (orders) *Fax:* 617-776-7841 *E-mail:* info@wisdompubs.org *Web Site:* www.wisdompubs.org, pg 274

Barton, John, Constance Rooke Creative Non-Fiction Prize, University of Victoria, Box 1700, Sta CSC, Victoria, BC V8W 2Y2, Canada *Tel:* 250-721-8524 *Fax:* 250-472-5051 *E-mail:* malahat@uvic.ca *Web Site:* malahatreview.ca, pg 679

Barton, John, Far Horizons Award for Poetry, University of Victoria, Box 1700, Sta CSC, Victoria, BC V8W 2Y2, Canada *Tel:* 250-721-8524 *Fax:* 250-472-5051 *E-mail:* malahat@uvic.ca *Web Site:* www.malahatreview.ca, pg 685

Barton, John, Far Horizons Award for Short Fiction, University of Victoria, Box 1700, Sta CSC, Victoria, BC V8W 2Y2, Canada *Tel:* 250-721-8524 *Fax:* 250-472-5051 *E-mail:* malahat@uvic.ca *Web Site:* www.malahatreview.ca, pg 685

Barton, John, Malahat Review Long Poem Prize, University of Victoria, Box 1700, Sta CSC, Victoria, BC V8W 2Y2, Canada *Tel:* 250-721-8524 *Fax:* 250-472-5051 *E-mail:* malahat@uvic.ca *Web Site:* www.malahatreview.ca, pg 704

Barton, John, Novella Prize, University of Victoria, Box 1700, Sta CSC, Victoria, BC V8W 2Y2, Canada *Tel:* 250-721-8524 *Fax:* 250-472-5051 *E-mail:* malahat@uvic.ca *Web Site:* www.malahatreview.ca, pg 714

Barton, John, Open Season Awards, University of Victoria, Box 1700, Sta CSC, Victoria, BC V8W 2Y2, Canada *Tel:* 250-721-8524 *Fax:* 250-472-5051 *E-mail:* malahat@uvic.ca *Web Site:* malahatreview.ca, pg 715

Barton, Rick, Leisure Arts Inc, 104 Champs Blvd, Suite 100, Maumelle, AR 72113 *Tel:* 501-868-8800 *Toll Free Tel:* 800-643-8030 *Fax:* 501-868-8748 *Web Site:* www.leisurearts.com, pg 137

Barton, Tim, Oxford University Press USA, 198 Madison Ave, New York, NY 10016 *Tel:* 212-726-6000 *Toll Free Tel:* 800-451-7556 (orders); 800-445-9714 (cust serv) *Fax:* 919-677-1303 *E-mail:* custserv.us@oup.com *Web Site:* www.oup.com/us, pg 179

Bartone, Christopher, American Marketing Association, 311 S Wacker Dr, Suite 5800, Chicago, IL 60606 *Tel:* 312-542-9000 *Toll Free Tel:* 800-AMA-1150 (262-1150) *Fax:* 312-542-9001 *E-mail:* info@ama.org *Web Site:* www.ama.org, pg 14, 595

Baruth, Ruth, W H Freeman, 41 Madison Ave, 37th fl, New York, NY 10010 *Tel:* 212-576-9400 *Fax:* 212-689-2383 *Web Site:* www.whfreeman.com, pg 92

Barz, Otto, YBK Publishers Inc, 39 Crosby St, New York, NY 10013 *Tel:* 212-219-0135 *Fax:* 212-219-0136 *E-mail:* info@ybkpublishers.com, pg 278

Barz, Otto H, Publishing Synthesis Ltd, 39 Crosby St, New York, NY 10013 *Tel:* 212-219-0135 *Fax:* 212-219-0136 *E-mail:* mainmail@pubsyn.com *Web Site:* www.pubsyn.com, pg 533

Barzinji, Dr Jamal, The International Institute of Islamic Thought, 500 Grove St, Suite 200, Herndon, VA 20170 *Tel:* 703-471-1133 *Fax:* 703-471-3922 *E-mail:* iiit@iiit.org *Web Site:* www.iiit.org, pg 124

Basch, Richard, Don Buchwald & Associates Inc, 10 E 44 St, New York, NY 10017 *Tel:* 212-867-1200 *Fax:* 212-867-2434 *E-mail:* info@buchwald.com *Web Site:* www.buchwald.com, pg 545

Base, Blaise, HarperCollins General Books Group, 195 Broadway, New York, NY 10007 *Tel:* 212-207-7000 *Web Site:* www.harpercollins.com, pg 105

Bashirrad, Avideh, Random House Publishing Group, 1745 Broadway, New York, NY 10019 *Toll Free Tel:* 800-200-3552 *Web Site:* atrandom.com, pg 204

Baskin, John, Orange Frazer Press Inc, 37 1/2 W Main St, Wilmington, OH 45177 *Tel:* 937-382-3196 *Toll Free Tel:* 800-852-9332 (orders) *Fax:* 937-383-3159 *E-mail:* ofrazer@erinet.com *Web Site:* www.orangefrazer.com, pg 176

Basmajian, Nancy, Ohio University Press, 215 Columbus Rd, Suite 101, Athens, OH 45701-1373 *Fax:* 740-593-4536 *Web Site:* www.ohioswallow.com, pg 174

Basmajian, Nancy, Swallow Press, 215 Columbus Rd, Suite 101, Athens, OH 45701-1373 *Fax:* 740-593-4536 *Web Site:* www.ohioswallow.com, pg 239

Basom, Rita, Neltje Blanchan Memorial Award, 2320 Capitol Ave, Cheyenne, WY 82002 *Tel:* 307-777-5234 *Fax:* 307-777-5499 *Web Site:* wyoarts.state.wy.us, pg 672

Basom, Rita, Frank Nelson Doubleday Memorial Award, 2320 Capitol Ave, Cheyenne, WY 82002 *Tel:* 307-777-5234 *Fax:* 307-777-5499 *Web Site:* wyoarts.state.wy.us, pg 682

Basom, Rita, Wyoming Arts Council Literature Fellowships, 2320 Capitol Ave, Cheyenne, WY 82002 *Tel:* 307-777-5234 *Fax:* 307-777-5499 *Web Site:* wyoarts.state.wy.us, pg 739

Bass, Jordan, McSweeney's Publishing, 849 Valencia St, San Francisco, CA 94110 *Tel:* 415-642-5609 (cust serv) *Web Site:* www.mcsweeneys.net, pg 152

Bassel, Katie, St Martin's Press, LLC, 175 Fifth Ave, New York, NY 10010 *Tel:* 646-307-5151 *Fax:* 212-420-9314 *E-mail:* firstname.lastname@macmillan.com *Web Site:* www.stmartins.com, pg 215

Bast, Laura, Cape Breton University Press Inc (CBU Press), 1250 Grand Lake Rd, Sydney, NS B1M 1A2, Canada *Tel:* 902-563-1604 (orders & cust serv) *Fax:* 902-563-1177 *E-mail:* cbu_press@cbu.ca *Web Site:* cbup.ca, pg 476

Bast, Tom, Triumph Books, 814 N Franklin St, Chicago, IL 60610 *Toll Free Tel:* 800-888-4741 (orders only) *Fax:* 312-280-5470 *Web Site:* www.triumphbooks.com, pg 250

Bastagli, Alessandra, Nation Books, 116 E 16 St, 8th fl, New York, NY 10003 *Tel:* 212–822–0250 *Fax:* 212-253-5356 *E-mail:* submissions@nationbooks.org *Web Site:* www.nationbooks.org, pg 163

Bastian, Donald G, BPS Books, 42 Donalda Crescent, Toronto, ON M1S 1N7, Canada *Tel:* 416-609-2004 *Fax:* 416-609-2936 *Web Site:* www.bpsbooks.com, pg 473

Batana, Rosario, Vernon Press, 1000 N West St, Suite 1200, Wilmington, DE 19801 *Tel:* 302-250-4440 *E-mail:* info@vernonpress.com *Web Site:* www.vernonpress.com, pg 265

Batcheller, Susan, Candlewick Press, 99 Dover St, Somerville, MA 02144-2825 *Tel:* 617-661-3330 *Fax:* 617-661-0565 *E-mail:* bigbear@candlewick.com; salesinfo@candlewick.com *Web Site:* www.candlewick.com, pg 49

Bateman, Lewis, Cambridge University Press, 32 Avenue of the Americas, New York, NY 10013-2473 *Tel:* 212-924-3900; 212-337-5000 *Fax:* 212-691-3239 *E-mail:* newyork@cambridge.org *Web Site:* www.cambridge.org/us, pg 49

Bates, Colleen Dunn, Prospect Park Books, 2359 Lincoln Ave, Altadena, CA 91001 *Tel:* 626-793-9796 *E-mail:* info@prospectparkbooks.com *Web Site:* www.prospectparkbooks.com, pg 199

Bates, Greg, Common Courage Press, One Red Barn Rd, Monroe, ME 04951 *Tel:* 207-525-0900 *Toll Free Tel:* 800-497-3207 *Fax:* 207-525-3068 *Web Site:* www.commoncouragepress.com, pg 62

Bates, Vicki, University of South Carolina Press, 1600 Hampton St, Suite 544, Columbia, SC 29208 *Tel:* 803-777-5245 *Toll Free Tel:* 800-768-2500 (orders) *Fax:* 803-777-0160 *Toll Free Fax:* 800-868-0740 (orders) *Web Site:* www.sc.edu/uscpress, pg 260

Batiz-Benet, Mercedes, Bayeux Arts Inc, 119 Stratton Crescent SW, Calgary, AB T3H 1T7, Canada *Tel:* 403-249-2477 *E-mail:* mail@bayeux.com *Web Site:* bayeux.com, pg 472

Batkie, Sara, The Christopher Doheny Award, 17 E 47 St, New York, NY 10017 *Tel:* 212-755-6710 *Fax:* 212-826-0831 *E-mail:* doheny@centerforfiction.org; info@centerforfiction.org *Web Site:* www.centerforfiction.org/awards/the-christopher-doheny-award, pg 681

Batkie, Sara, The Flaherty-Dunnan First Novel Prize, 17 E 47 St, New York, NY 10017 *Tel:* 212-755-6710 *Fax:* 212-826-0831 *E-mail:* info@centerforfiction.org *Web Site:* centerforfiction.org/awards, pg 686

Batkie, Sara, Maxwell E Perkins Award, 17 E 47 St, New York, NY 10017 *Tel:* 212-755-6710 *Fax:* 212-826-0831 *E-mail:* info@centerforfiction.org *Web Site:* www.centerforfiction.org/awards/perkins, pg 718

Batmanglij, Mohammad, Mage Publishers Inc, 1408 35 St NW, Washington, DC 20007 *Tel:* 202-342-1642 *Fax:* 202-342-9269 *Web Site:* www.mage.com, pg 145

Batmanglij, Najmieh, Mage Publishers Inc, 1408 35 St NW, Washington, DC 20007 *Tel:* 202-342-1642 *Fax:* 202-342-9269 *Web Site:* www.mage.com, pg 145

Battista, Dino, The University of North Carolina Press, 116 S Boundary St, Chapel Hill, NC 27514-3808 *Tel:* 919-966-3561 *Fax:* 919-966-3829 *E-mail:* uncpress@unc.edu *Web Site:* www.uncpress.unc.edu, pg 258

Battista, Garth, Breakaway Books, PO Box 24, Halcottsville, NY 12438-0024 *Tel:* 607-326-4805 *E-mail:* breakawaybooks@gmail.com *Web Site:* www.breakawaybooks.com, pg 44

Batura, Paul, Focus on the Family, 8605 Explorer Dr, Colorado Springs, CO 80920-1051 *Tel:* 719-531-5181 *Toll Free Tel:* 800-A-FAMILY (232-6459) *Fax:* 719-531-3424 *Web Site:* www.focusonthefamily.com; www.facebook.com/focusonthefamily, pg 90

Bauchner, Howard C MD, American Medical Association, AMA Plaza, 330 N Wabash, Suite 39300, Chicago, IL 60611-5885 *Tel:* 312-464-5000 *Toll Free Tel:* 800-621-8335 *Fax:* 312-464-4184 *Web Site:* www.ama-assn.org, pg 14

Bauer, Susan Wise, Peace Hill Press, 18021 The Glebe Lane, Charles City, VA 23030 *Tel:* 804-829-5043 *Toll Free Tel:* 877-322-3445 (orders) *Fax:* 804-829-5704 *E-mail:* info@peacehillpress.com *Web Site:* www.peacehillpress.com, pg 184

Bauerle, Chris, Sourcebooks Inc, 1935 Brookdale Rd, Suite 139, Naperville, IL 60563 *Tel:* 630-961-3900 *Toll Free Tel:* 800-432-7444 *Fax:* 630-961-2168 *E-mail:* info@sourcebooks.com; customersupport@sourcebooks.com *Web Site:* www.sourcebooks.com, pg 230

Bauers, William, Penguin Group (USA) LLC Sales, 375 Hudson St, New York, NY 10014 *Tel:* 212-366-2000 *E-mail:* online@penguinputnam.com *Web Site:* us.penguingroup.com, pg 187

Baughman, Kathy, ILA Children's & Young Adults' Book Awards, 800 Barksdale Rd, Newark, DE 19711-3204 *Tel:* 302-731-1600 *Toll Free Tel:* 800-336-7323 (US & CN) *Fax:* 302-731-1057 *E-mail:* committees@reading.org *Web Site:* www.literacyworldwide.org; www.reading.org, pg 694

Baughman, Kathy, International Literacy Association (ILA), 800 Barksdale Rd, Newark, DE 19711-3204 *Tel:* 302-731-1600 *Toll Free Tel:* 800-336-7323 (US & CN) *Fax:* 302-731-1057 *E-mail:* customerservice@reading.org *Web Site:* www.literacyworldwide.org; www.reading.org, pg 124, 608

Baum, Richard, New York Academy of Sciences, 7 World Trade, 40th fl, 250 Greenwich St, New York, NY 10007-2157 *Tel:* 212-298-8600 *Toll Free Tel:* 800-843-6927 *Fax:* 212-298-3644 *E-mail:* nyas@nyas.org; publications@nyas.org *Web Site:* www.nyas.org, pg 169

Free Tel: 888-264-1745 *Fax:* 212-940-7408 *E-mail:* crownosm@penguinrandomhouse.com *Web Site:* crownpublishing.com, pg 68

Beditz, Dr Joseph, National Golf Foundation, 1150 S US Hwy One, Suite 401, Jupiter, FL 33477 *Tel:* 561-744-6006 *Toll Free Tel:* 888-275-4643 *Fax:* 561-744-6107 *E-mail:* general@ngf.org *Web Site:* www.ngf.org, pg 165

Bednarik, Joseph, Copper Canyon Press, Fort Worden State Park, Bldg 313, Port Townsend, WA 98368 *Tel:* 360-385-4925 *Toll Free Tel:* 877-501-1393 (orders) *Fax:* 360-385-4985 *E-mail:* poetry@coppercanyonpress.org *Web Site:* www.coppercanyonpress.org, pg 63

Bedney, Steve, Book Industry Guild of New York, PO Box 2001, New York, NY 10113-2001 *E-mail:* admin@bookindustryguildofny.org *Web Site:* www.bookindustryguildofny.org, pg 600

Bedrick, Claudia, Enchanted Lion Books, 351 Van Brunt St, Ground fl-Gallery, Brooklyn, NY 11231 *Tel:* 646-785-9272 *E-mail:* enchantedlion@gmail.com *Web Site:* www.enchantedlionbooks.com, pg 82

Beecroft, Alexander, The Charles Bernheimer Prize, University of South Carolina, Dept of Languages, Literature & Cultures, Rm 813-A, 1620 College St, Columbia, SC 29208 *Tel:* 803-777-3021 *Fax:* 803-777-3041 *E-mail:* info@acla.org *Web Site:* www.acla.org, pg 671

Beecroft, Alexander, Harry Levin Prize, University of South Carolina, Dept of Languages, Literature & Cultures, Rm 813-A, 1620 College St, Columbia, SC 29208 *Tel:* 803-777-3021 *Fax:* 803-777-3041 *E-mail:* info@acla.org *Web Site:* www.acla.org/awards/harry-levin-prize; www.acla.org, pg 700

Beecroft, Alexander, Rene Wellek Prize, University of South Carolina, Dept of Languages, Literature & Cultures, Rm 813-A, 1620 College St, Columbia, SC 29208 *Tel:* 803-777-3021 *Fax:* 803-777-3041 *E-mail:* info@acla.org *Web Site:* www.acla.org/awards/rene-wellek-prize; www.acla.org, pg 735

Beeke, Joel R, Reformation Heritage Books, 2965 Leonard St NE, Grand Rapids, MI 49525 *Tel:* 616-977-0889 *Fax:* 616-285-3246 *E-mail:* orders@heritagebooks.org *Web Site:* www.heritagebooks.org, pg 207

Beeny, Martyn, University of Nebraska Press, 1111 Lincoln Mall, Lincoln, NE 68588-0630 *Tel:* 402-472-3581; 919-966-7449 (cust serv & foreign orders) *Toll Free Tel:* 800-848-6224 (cust serv & US orders) *Fax:* 402-472-6214; 919-962-2704 (cust serv & foreign orders) *Toll Free Fax:* 800-526-2617 (cust serv & US orders) *E-mail:* pressmail@unl.edu *Web Site:* www.nebraskapress.unl.edu, pg 257

Beers, Ron, Tyndale House Publishers Inc, 351 Executive Dr, Carol Stream, IL 60188 *Tel:* 630-668-8300 *Toll Free Tel:* 800-323-9400 *Web Site:* www.tyndale.com, pg 252

Beetham, Christopher, Zondervan, 3900 Sparks Dr, Grand Rapids, MI 49546 *Tel:* 616-698-6900 *Toll Free Tel:* 800-226-1122; 800-727-1309 (retail orders) *Fax:* 616-698-3350 *Toll Free Fax:* 800-698-3256 (retail orders) *E-mail:* zinfo@zondervan.com *Web Site:* www.zondervan.com, pg 280

Behar, Ann, Scovil Galen Ghosh Literary Agency Inc, 276 Fifth Ave, Suite 708, New York, NY 10001 *Tel:* 212-679-8686 *Fax:* 212-679-6710 *E-mail:* info@sgglit.com *Web Site:* www.sgglit.com, pg 572

Behm, Melissa A, Brookes Publishing Co Inc, PO Box 10624, Baltimore, MD 21285-0624 *Tel:* 410-337-9580 (outside US & CN) *Toll Free Tel:* 800-638-3775 (US & CN) *Fax:* 410-337-8539 *E-mail:* custserv@brookespublishing.com *Web Site:* www.brookespublishing.com, pg 46

Behm, Melissa A, Health Professions Press, 409 Washington Ave, Suite 500, Towson, MD 21204 *Tel:* 410-337-9585 *Toll Free Tel:* 888-337-8808 *Fax:* 410-337-8539 *E-mail:* custserv@healthpropress.com *Web Site:* www.healthpropress.com, pg 109

Behn, Robin, University of Alabama Program in Creative Writing, PO Box 870244, Tuscaloosa, AL 35487-0244 *Tel:* 205-348-5065 *Fax:* 205-348-1388 *E-mail:* english@ua.edu *Web Site:* www.as.ua.edu/english, pg 663

Behrman, David, Behrman House Inc, 11 Edison Place, Springfield, NJ 07081 *Tel:* 973-379-7200 *Toll Free Tel:* 800-221-2755 *Fax:* 973-379-7280 *E-mail:* behrmanhouse@gmail.com; customersupport@behrmanhouse.com *Web Site:* www.behrmanhouse.com, pg 33

Behroozi, Cyrus, The Brookings Institution Press, 1775 Massachusetts Ave NW, Washington, DC 20036-2188 *Tel:* 202-536-3600 *Toll Free Tel:* 800-537-5487 *Fax:* 202-536-3623 *E-mail:* permissions@brookings.edu *Web Site:* www.brookings.edu, pg 47

Beier, Elizabeth, St Martin's Press, LLC, 175 Fifth Ave, New York, NY 10010 *Tel:* 646-307-5151 *Fax:* 212-420-9314 *E-mail:* firstname.lastname@macmillan.com *Web Site:* www.stmartins.com, pg 215

Beil, Frederic C, Frederic C Beil Publisher Inc, 609 Whitaker St, Savannah, GA 31401 *Tel:* 912-233-2446 *E-mail:* editor@beil.com *Web Site:* www.beil.com, pg 34

Beilenson, Evelyn L, Peter Pauper Press, Inc, 202 Mamaroneck Ave, White Plains, NY 10601-5376 *Tel:* 914-681-0144 *Fax:* 914-681-0389 *E-mail:* customerservice@peterpauper.com; orders@peterpauper.com *Web Site:* www.peterpauper.com, pg 190

Beilenson, Laurence, Peter Pauper Press, Inc, 202 Mamaroneck Ave, White Plains, NY 10601-5376 *Tel:* 914-681-0144 *Fax:* 914-681-0389 *E-mail:* customerservice@peterpauper.com; orders@peterpauper.com *Web Site:* www.peterpauper.com, pg 190

Beiser, Martin, Words into Print, 57 Prince St, Suite 4R, New York, NY 10012 *Tel:* 212-741-1393 *Fax:* 419-441-1393 *E-mail:* query@wordsintoprint.org *Web Site:* www.wordsintoprint.org, pg 536

Beitzel, Tim, Kendall Hunt Publishing Co, 4050 Westmark Dr, Dubuque, IA 52002-2624 *Tel:* 563-589-1000 *Toll Free Tel:* 800-228-0810 (orders) *Fax:* 563-589-1046 *Toll Free Fax:* 800-772-9165 *E-mail:* orders@kendallhunt.com *Web Site:* www.kendallhunt.com, pg 130

Bejarano, Laura, Lectorum Publications Inc, 205 Chubb Ave, Lyndhurst, NJ 07071 *Toll Free Tel:* 800-345-5946 *Fax:* 201-559-2201 *Toll Free Fax:* 877-532-8676 *E-mail:* lectorum@lectorum.com *Web Site:* www.lectorum.com, pg 136

Belanger, Paul, Les Editions du Noroit, 4609 rue D'Iberville, espace 202, Montreal, QC H2H 2L9, Canada *Tel:* 514-727-0005 *E-mail:* lenoroit@lenoroit.com *Web Site:* www.lenoroit.com, pg 481

Belderis, Ina, Theosophical University Press, PO Box C, Pasadena, CA 91109-7107 *Tel:* 626-798-3378 *E-mail:* tupress@theosociety.org *Web Site:* www.theosociety.org, pg 244

Belfiglio, Brian, Scribner, 1230 Avenue of the Americas, New York, NY 10020, pg 220

Belfiglio, Brian, Touchstone, 1230 Avenue of the Americas, New York, NY 10020, pg 247

Belfus, Linda, Elsevier, Health Sciences Division, 1600 John F Kennedy Blvd, Suite 1800, Philadelphia, PA 19103-2899 *Tel:* 215-239-3900 *Toll Free Tel:* 800-523-1649 *Fax:* 215-239-3990 *Web Site:* www.elsevierhealth.com, pg 81

Belieu, Erin, Port Townsend Writers' Conference, 223 Battery Way, Port Townsend, WA 98368 *Tel:* 360-385-3102 *Toll Free Tel:* 800-733-3608 (ticket off) *Fax:* 360-385-2470 *E-mail:* info@centrum.org *Web Site:* www.centrum.org, pg 654

Beliveau, Mathieu, Beliveau Editeur, 920, rue Jean-Neveu, Longueuil, QC J4G 2M1, Canada *Tel:* 450-679-1933; 514-253-0403 *Fax:* 450-679-6648 *E-mail:* info@beliveauediteur.com *Web Site:* www.beliveauediteur.com, pg 472

Belkind, Myron, National Press Club (NPC), 529 14 St NW, 13th fl, Washington, DC 20045 *Tel:* 202-662-7500 *Fax:* 202-662-7569 *E-mail:* infocenter@npcpress.org *Web Site:* www.press.org, pg 613

Bell, Duncan, Columbia Books & Information Services, 4340 East-West Hwy, Suite 300, Bethesda, MD 20814 *Tel:* 240-235-0266 *Toll Free Tel:* 888-265-0600 (cust serv) *Fax:* 202-464-1775 *E-mail:* info@columbiabooks.com *Web Site:* www.columbiabooks.com; www.lobbyists.info; www.associationexecs.com, pg 61

Bell, Hannah, Schiel & Denver Book Publishers, 10685-B Hazelhurst Dr, Suite 8575, Houston, TX 77043 *Tel:* 832-699-0264 *Toll Free Tel:* 888-629-4449 *Toll Free Fax:* 888-224-2721 *E-mail:* enquiries@schieldenver.com *Web Site:* www.schieldenver.com, pg 217

Bell, Justin, Spectrum Literary Agency, 320 Central Park W, Suite 1-D, New York, NY 10025 *Tel:* 212-362-4323 *Fax:* 212-362-4562 *Web Site:* www.spectrumliteraryagency.com, pg 574

Bell, Merleyn, Neustadt International Prize for Literature, c/o University of Oklahoma, 630 Parrington Oval, Suite 110, Norman, OK 73019-4033 *Tel:* 405-325-4531 *Fax:* 405-325-7495 *Web Site:* www.worldliteraturetoday.org, pg 712

Bell, Merleyn, NSK Neustadt Prize for Children's Literature, c/o University of Oklahoma, 630 Parrington Oval, Suite 110, Norman, OK 73019-4033 *Tel:* 405-325-4531 *Fax:* 405-325-7495 *Web Site:* www.worldliteraturetoday.org, pg 714

Bellanca, Dr Patricia, Harvard Summer Writing Program, 51 Brattle St, Dept S760, Cambridge, MA 02138-3722 *Tel:* 617-495-4024 *Fax:* 617-495-9176 *E-mail:* summer@hudce.harvard.edu *Web Site:* www.summer.harvard.edu, pg 651

Belle, Linda, Jane Addams Children's Book Award, 777 United Nations Plaza, 6th fl, New York, NY 10017 *Tel:* 212-682-8830 *E-mail:* japa@igc.org *Web Site:* www.janeaddamspeace.org, pg 665

Bellet, Danny, The Pennsylvania State University Press, University Support Bldg 1, Suite C, 820 N University Dr, University Park, PA 16802-1003 *Tel:* 814-865-1327 *Toll Free Tel:* 800-326-9180 *Fax:* 814-863-1408 *Toll Free Fax:* 877-778-2665 *E-mail:* info@psupress.org *Web Site:* www.psupress.org, pg 188

Bellew, Ib, Bunker Hill Publishing, 285 River Rd, Piermont, NH 03779 *Tel:* 603-272-9221 *Fax:* 603-283-7240 *E-mail:* mail@bunkerhillpublishing.com *Web Site:* www.bunkerhillpublishing.com, pg 47

Bellitto, Christopher, Paulist Press, 997 Macarthur Blvd, Mahwah, NJ 07430-9990 *Tel:* 201-825-7300 *Toll Free Tel:* 800-218-1903 *Fax:* 201-825-8345 *Toll Free Fax:* 800-836-3161 *E-mail:* info@paulistpress.com *Web Site:* www.paulistpress.com, pg 184

Bellow, Adam, HarperCollins General Books Group, 195 Broadway, New York, NY 10007 *Tel:* 212-207-7000 *Web Site:* www.harpercollins.com, pg 105

Bellows, Melinda Gerosa, National Geographic Books, 1145 17 St NW, Washington, DC 20036-4688 *Tel:* 202-857-7000 *Fax:* 202-857-7670 *Web Site:* books.nationalgeographic.com/books, pg 165

Belton, Aislinn, Crown Publishing Group, c/o Penguin Random House Inc, 1745 Broadway, New York, NY 10019 *Tel:* 212-782-9000 *Toll Free Tel:* 888-264-1745 *Fax:* 212-940-7408 *E-mail:* crownosm@penguinrandomhouse.com *Web Site:* crownpublishing.com, pg 68

Bemis, Carol Stiles, W W Norton & Company Inc, 500 Fifth Ave, New York, NY 10110-0017 *Tel:* 212-354-5500 *Toll Free Tel:* 800-233-4830 (orders & cust serv) *Fax:* 212-869-0856 *Toll Free Fax:* 800-458-6515 *Web Site:* www.wwnorton.com, pg 171

Bemiss, Holly, Susan Rabiner Literary Agency Inc, 315 W 39 St, Suite 1501, New York, NY 10018-3907 *Web Site:* RabinerLit.com, pg 569

Benamou, Sharon, AJL Judaica Bibliography Award, PO Box 1118, Teaneck, NJ 07666 *Tel:* 201-371-3255 *E-mail:* ajlibs@osu.edu *Web Site:* www.jewishlibraries.org, pg 666

Benamou, Sharon, AJL Judaica Reference Award, PO Box 1118, Teaneck, NJ 07666 *Tel:* 201-371-3255 *E-mail:* ajlibs@osu.edu *Web Site:* www.jewishlibraries.org, pg 666

Benard, Mary, Skinner House Books, c/o Unitarian Universalist Assn, 24 Farnsworth St, Boston, MA 02210-1409 *Tel:* 617-742-2100 *Fax:* 617-948-6466 *E-mail:* skinnerhouse@uua.org *Web Site:* www.skinnerhouse.org, pg 227

Benatar, Raquel, Laredo Publishing Co Inc, 465 Westview Ave, Englewood, NJ 07631 *Tel:* 201-408-4048 *Fax:* 201-408-5011 *E-mail:* info@laredopublishing.com *Web Site:* www.laredopublishing.com, pg 134

Benatar, Raquel, Renaissance House, 465 Westview Ave, Englewood, NJ 07631 *Tel:* 201-408-4048 *Fax:* 201-408-5011 *E-mail:* info@renaissancehouse.net *Web Site:* www.renaissancehouse.net, pg 208

Bendell, Amy, HarperCollins General Books Group, 195 Broadway, New York, NY 10007 *Tel:* 212-207-7000 *Web Site:* www.harpercollins.com, pg 105

Bender, Robert, Simon & Schuster, 1230 Avenue of the Americas, New York, NY 10020 *Tel:* 212-698-7000 *Toll Free Tel:* 800-223-2348 (cust serv); 800-223-2336 (orders) *Toll Free Fax:* 800-943-9831 (orders) *Web Site:* www.simonandschuster.com, pg 225

Bender, Roger J, R James Bender Publishing, PO Box 23456, San Jose, CA 95153-3456 *Tel:* 408-225-5777 *Fax:* 408-225-4739 *Web Site:* www.bender-publishing.com, pg 34

Bendimerad, Soumeya, Writers House, 21 W 26 St, New York, NY 10010 *Tel:* 212-685-2400 *Fax:* 212-685-1781 *Web Site:* www.writershouse.com, pg 580

Benedict, Holly, Quincannon Publishing Group, PO Box 8100, Glen Ridge, NJ 07028-8100 *Tel:* 973-380-9942 *E-mail:* editors@quincannongroup.com *Web Site:* www.quincannongroup.com, pg 202

Benezra, Mark, Original Publications, PO Box 236, Old Beth Page, NY 11804 *Tel:* 516-605-0547 *Toll Free Tel:* 888-622-8581 *Fax:* 516-605-0549 *E-mail:* originalpub@aol.com *Web Site:* www.occult1.com, pg 178

Benjamin, Dan, Do-It-Yourself Legal Publishers, 1588 Remsen Ave, Brooklyn, NY 11236 *Tel:* 718-684-4769 *Fax:* 718-684-4769 *E-mail:* ba07102@yahoo.com, pg 75

Benjamin, Matthew, Touchstone, 1230 Avenue of the Americas, New York, NY 10020, pg 247

Benjey, Thomas R, Tuxedo Press, 546 E Springville Rd, Carlisle, PA 17015 *Tel:* 717-258-9733 *Fax:* 717-243-0074 *E-mail:* info@tuxedo-press.com *Web Site:* tuxedo-press.com, pg 251

Benka, Jennifer, The Academy of American Poets Inc, 75 Maiden Lane, Suite 901, New York, NY 10038 *Tel:* 212-274-0343 *Fax:* 212-274-9427 *E-mail:* academy@poets.org *Web Site:* www.poets.org, pg 593

Benka, Jennifer, Raiziss/de Palchi Fellowship, 75 Maiden Lane, Suite 901, New York, NY 10038 *Tel:* 212-274-0343 *Fax:* 212-274-9427 *E-mail:* academy@poets.org *Web Site:* www.poets.org, pg 723

Benka, Jennifer, Walt Whitman Award, 75 Maiden Lane, Suite 901, New York, NY 10038 *Tel:* 212-274-0343 *Fax:* 212-274-9427 *E-mail:* academy@poets.org *Web Site:* www.poets.org, pg 735

Benne, Susan, Antiquarian Booksellers' Association of America, 20 W 44 St, Suite 507, New York, NY 10036 *Tel:* 212-944-8291 *Fax:* 212-944-8293 *E-mail:* hq@abaa.org *Web Site:* www.abaa.org, pg 597

Benner, Deborah J, Goose River Press, 3400 Friendship Rd, Waldoboro, ME 04572-6337 *Tel:* 207-832-6665 *E-mail:* gooseriverpress@roadrunner.com *Web Site:* gooseriverpress.com, pg 98

Bennett, Barbara, Kensington Publishing Corp, 119 W 40 St, New York, NY 10018 *Tel:* 212-407-1500 *Toll Free Tel:* 800-221-2647 *Fax:* 212-935-0699 *Web Site:* www.kensingtonbooks.com, pg 130

Bennett, David, Transatlantic Agency, 2 Bloor St E, Suite 3500, Toronto, ON M4W 1A8, Canada *Tel:* 416-488-9214 *E-mail:* info@transatlanticagency.com *Web Site:* www.transatlanticagency.com, pg 577

Bennett, Elizabeth, Houghton Mifflin Harcourt Trade & Reference Division, 222 Berkeley St, Boston, MA 02116 *Tel:* 617-351-5000 *Toll Free Tel:* 800-225-3362 *Web Site:* www.hmhco.com, pg 115

Bennett, Jed, Penguin Young Readers Group, 345 Hudson St, New York, NY 10014 *Tel:* 212-366-2000 *E-mail:* online@penguinputnam.com *Web Site:* www.penguinputnam.com; us.penguingroup.com, pg 188

Bennett, John M, Luna Bisonte Prods, 137 Leland Ave, Columbus, OH 43214 *Tel:* 614-846-4126 *Web Site:* www.johnmbennett.net; www.lulu.com/spotlight/lunabisonteprods, pg 144

Bennett, Julie, Ten Speed Press, 2625 Alcatraz Ave, Unit 505, Berkeley, CA 94705 *Tel:* 510-285-3000 *Toll Free Tel:* 800-841-BOOK (841-2665) *E-mail:* csorders@randomhouse.com *Web Site:* crownpublishing.com/imprint/ten-speed-press, pg 243

Bennett, Lori, Nelson Literary Agency LLC, 1732 Wazee St, Suite 207, Denver, CO 80202-1284 *Tel:* 303-292-2805 *E-mail:* query@nelsonagency.com *Web Site:* www.nelsonagency.com, pg 566

Bennett, Lynn, Transatlantic Agency, 2 Bloor St E, Suite 3500, Toronto, ON M4W 1A8, Canada *Tel:* 416-488-9214 *E-mail:* info@transatlanticagency.com *Web Site:* www.transatlanticagency.com, pg 577

Bennett, Lyron, Sourcebooks Inc, 1935 Brookdale Rd, Suite 139, Naperville, IL 60563 *Tel:* 630-961-3900 *Toll Free Tel:* 800-432-7444 *Fax:* 630-961-2168 *E-mail:* info@sourcebooks.com; customersupport@sourcebooks.com *Web Site:* www.sourcebooks.com, pg 230

Bennett, Meagan, Phaidon Press Inc, 180 Varick St, 14th fl, New York, NY 10014 *Tel:* 212-652-5400 *Toll Free Tel:* 800-759-0190 (cust serv) *Fax:* 212-652-5410 *Toll Free Fax:* 800-286-9471 (cust serv) *E-mail:* ussales@phaidon.com *Web Site:* www.phaidon.com, pg 190

Bennett, Millicent, Simon & Schuster, 1230 Avenue of the Americas, New York, NY 10020 *Tel:* 212-698-7000 *Toll Free Tel:* 800-223-2348 (cust serv); 800-223-2336 (orders) *Toll Free Fax:* 800-943-9831 (orders) *Web Site:* www.simonandschuster.com, pg 225

Bennett, Sarah, The Countryman Press, c/o W W Norton & Co Inc, 500 Fifth Ave, New York, NY 10110 *Tel:* 212-354-5500 *Fax:* 212-869-0856 *E-mail:* countrymanpress@wwnorton.com *Web Site:* www.countrymanpress.com, pg 65

Bennett, Tina, WME, 1325 Avenue of the Americas, New York, NY 10019 *Tel:* 212-586-5100 *Fax:* 212-246-3583 *E-mail:* wma@interport.net *Web Site:* www.wma.com, pg 579

Bennett, Twila, Revell, PO Box 6287, Grand Rapids, MI 49516-6287 *Tel:* 616-676-9185 *Toll Free Tel:* 800-877-2665; 800-679-1957 *Fax:* 616-676-9573 *Web Site:* www.revellbooks.com, pg 208

Bennie, Dale, University of Oklahoma Press, 2800 Venture Dr, Norman, OK 73069-8216 *Tel:* 405-325-2000 *Toll Free Tel:* 800-627-7377 (orders) *Fax:* 405-364-5798 (orders) *Toll Free Fax:* 800-735-0476 (orders) *E-mail:* presscs@ou.edu *Web Site:* www.oupress.com, pg 258

Benoit, Emmanuel, Jouve North America Inc, 70 Landmark Hill Dr, Brattleboro, VT 05301 *Tel:* 802-254-6073 *Toll Free Tel:* 800-451-4328 *Fax:* 802-257-1511 *Web Site:* www.jouve.com, pg 528

Benoit, Michael J, Benoit & Associates, 279 S Schuyler Ave, Kankakee, IL 60901 *Tel:* 815-932-2582 *Fax:* 815-932-2594 *Web Site:* www.benoit-associates.com, pg 583

Bensaid, Barbara, US Games Systems Inc, 179 Ludlow St, Stamford, CT 06902 *Tel:* 203-353-8400 *Toll Free Tel:* 800-54-GAMES (544-2637) *Fax:* 203-353-8431 *E-mail:* info@usgamesinc.com *Web Site:* www.usgamesinc.com, pg 264

Bensky, Dan, Eastland Press, 1240 Activity Dr, Suite D, Vista, CA 92081 *Tel:* 206-217-0204 (edit); 760-598-9695 (orders) *Toll Free Tel:* 800-453-3278 (orders) *Fax:* 760-598-6083 (orders) *Toll Free Fax:* 800-241-3329 (orders) *E-mail:* info@eastlandpress.com; orders@eastlandpress.com (credit card orders only) *Web Site:* www.eastlandpress.com, pg 78

Benson, Ms Frances, Cornell University Press, Sage House, 512 E State St, Ithaca, NY 14850 *Tel:* 607-277-2338 *Fax:* 607-277-2374 *E-mail:* cupressinfo@cornell.edu; cupress-sales@cornell.edu *Web Site:* www.cornellpress.cornell.edu, pg 63

Benson, Ingrid, Integra Software Services Inc, 1110 Jorie Blvd, Suite 200, Oak Brook, IL 60523 *Tel:* 630-586-2579 *Fax:* 630-586-2599 *E-mail:* marketing@integra.co.in *Web Site:* www.integra.co.in, pg 528

Benson, Jack, Water Environment Federation, 601 Wythe St, Alexandria, VA 22314-1994 *Tel:* 703-684-2400 *Toll Free Tel:* 800-666-0206 *Fax:* 703-684-2492 *E-mail:* csc@wef.org (cust serv) *Web Site:* www.wef.org, pg 267

Benson, John W, BK Nelson Inc Lecture Bureau, 1565 Paseo Vida, Palm Springs, CA 92264 *Tel:* 760-778-8800 *Fax:* 760-778-6242 *E-mail:* bknelson4@cs.com *Web Site:* www.bknelson.com; www.bknelsonlecturebureau.com; www.nelsonbookmovielecture.com; www.bknelsonmovieproduction.com, pg 587

Benson, John W, BK Nelson Inc Literary Agency, 1565 Paseo Vida, Palm Springs, CA 92264 *Tel:* 760-778-8800 *Fax:* 760-778-6242 *E-mail:* bknelson4@cs.com *Web Site:* www.bknelson.com; www.bknelsonlecturebureau.com; www.nelsonbookmovielecture.com; www.bknelsonmovieproduction.com, pg 566

Benson, Stephanae, The Center for Learning, 10200 Jefferson Blvd, Culver City, CA 90232 *Tel:* 310-839-2436 *Toll Free Tel:* 800-421-4246 *Fax:* 310-839-2249 *Toll Free Fax:* 800-944-5432 *E-mail:* customerservice@centerforlearning.org *Web Site:* www.centerforlearning.org, pg 53

Bentley, D M R, Canadian Poetry Press, Dept of English, University of Western Ontario, London, ON N6A 3K7, Canada *Tel:* 519-661-2111 (ext 85813); 519-661-2111 (ext 85834) *Fax:* 519-661-3776 *E-mail:* canadianpoetry@uwo.ca *Web Site:* canadianpoetry.org, pg 475

Bentley, Michael, Bentley Publishers, 1734 Massachusetts Ave, Cambridge, MA 02138-1804 *Tel:* 617-547-4170 *Toll Free Tel:* 800-423-4595 *Fax:* 617-876-9235 *E-mail:* sales@bentleypublishers.com *Web Site:* www.bentleypublishers.com, pg 35

Bentley, Susan, Canadian Poetry Press, Dept of English, University of Western Ontario, London, ON N6A 3K7, Canada *Tel:* 519-661-2111 (ext 85813); 519-661-2111 (ext 85834) *Fax:* 519-661-3776 *E-mail:* canadianpoetry@uwo.ca *Web Site:* canadianpoetry.org, pg 475

Benton, Lori, Scholastic Trade Division, 557 Broadway, New York, NY 10012 *Tel:* 212-343-6100; 212-343-4685 (export sales) *Fax:* 212-343-4714 (export sales) *Web Site:* www.scholastic.com, pg 219

Benton, Thomas J, Direct Marketing Association (DMA), 1120 Avenue of the Americas, New York, NY 10036-6700 *Tel:* 212-768-7277 *Fax:* 212-302-6714 *E-mail:* memberservices@the-dma.org *Web Site:* thedma.org, pg 74, 604

Benvenuto, Kerri, Random House Children's Books, 1745 Broadway, New York, NY 10019 *Tel:* 212-782-9000 *Toll Free Tel:* 800-200-3552 *Fax:* 212-782-9452 *Web Site:* randomhousekids.com, pg 203

Bercholz, Ivan, Shambhala Publications Inc, Horticultural Hall, 300 Massachusetts Ave, Boston, MA 02115 *Tel:* 617-424-0030 *Toll Free Tel:* 866-424-0030 (off); 888-424-2329 (cust serv) *Fax:* 617-236-1563 *E-mail:* customercare@shambhala.com *Web Site:* www.shambhala.com, pg 223

Bercholz, Samuel, Shambhala Publications Inc, Horticultural Hall, 300 Massachusetts Ave, Boston, MA 02115 *Tel:* 617-424-0030 *Toll Free Tel:* 866-

424-0030 (off); 888-424-2329 (cust serv) *Fax:* 617-236-1563 *E-mail:* customercare@shambhala.com *Web Site:* www.shambhala.com, pg 223

Bercholz, Sara, Shambhala Publications Inc, Horticultural Hall, 300 Massachusetts Ave, Boston, MA 02115 *Tel:* 617-424-0030 *Toll Free Tel:* 866-424-0030 (off); 888-424-2329 (cust serv) *Fax:* 617-236-1563 *E-mail:* customercare@shambhala.com *Web Site:* www.shambhala.com, pg 223

Berchowitz, Gillian, Ohio University Press, 215 Columbus Rd, Suite 101, Athens, OH 45701-1373 *Fax:* 740-593-4536 *Web Site:* www.ohioswallow.com, pg 174

Berchowitz, Gillian, Hollis Summers Poetry Prize, 215 Columbus Rd, Suite 101, Athens, OH 45701-1373 *Web Site:* www.ohioswallow.com/poetry_prize, pg 731

Berchowitz, Gillian, Swallow Press, 215 Columbus Rd, Suite 101, Athens, OH 45701-1373 *Fax:* 740-593-4536 *Web Site:* www.ohioswallow.com, pg 239

Berchten, Rachel, University of California Press, 2120 Berkeley Way, Berkeley, CA 94704-1012 *Tel:* 510-642-4247 *Fax:* 510-643-7127 *E-mail:* askucp@ucpress.edu (books); customerservice@ucpressjournals.com *Web Site:* www.ucpress.edu, pg 255

Berens, Gayle, ULI-The Urban Land Institute, 1025 Thomas Jefferson St NW, Suite 500-W, Washington, DC 20007-5201 *Tel:* 202-624-7000; 410-626-7505 (cust serv outside US) *Toll Free Tel:* 800-321-5011 (cust serv) *Fax:* 202-624-7140; 410-626-7147 (orders only) *Toll Free Fax:* 800-248-4585 *E-mail:* bookstore@uli.org; customerservice@uli.org *Web Site:* www.uli.org, pg 252

Beresford, Lea, Bloomsbury Publishing Inc, 1385 Broadway, 5th fl, New York, NY 10018 *Tel:* 212-419-5300 *E-mail:* marketingusa@bloomsbury.com; adultpublicityusa@bloomsbury.com; askacademic@bloomsbury.com *Web Site:* www.bloomsbury.com, pg 40

Berg, Betsy, ICM Lecture Division, 730 Fifth Ave, New York, NY 10019 *Tel:* 212-556-5600 *Fax:* 212-556-5665 *Web Site:* www.icmtalent.com, pg 587

Berg, Jennifer, PAGE International Screenwriting Awards, 7510 Sunset Blvd, Suite 610, Hollywood, CA 90046 *E-mail:* info@pageawards.com *Web Site:* www.pageawards.com, pg 716

Berg, Patty, Crown Publishing Group, c/o Penguin Random House Inc, 1745 Broadway, New York, NY 10019 *Tel:* 212-782-9000 *Toll Free Tel:* 888-264-1745 *Fax:* 212-940-7408 *E-mail:* crownosm@penguinrandomhouse.com *Web Site:* crownpublishing.com, pg 68

Berge, Pablo Agrest, STOCKCERO Inc, 3785 NW 82 Ave, Suite 302, Doral, FL 33166 *Tel:* 305-722-7628 *Fax:* 305-477-5794 *E-mail:* academicservices@stockcero.com; sales@stockcero.com *Web Site:* www.stockcero.com, pg 236

Bergen, Glenn, University of Manitoba Press, University of Manitoba, 301 St Johns College, 92 Dysart Rd, Winnipeg, MB R3T 2M5, Canada *Tel:* 204-474-9495 *Fax:* 204-474-7566 *E-mail:* uofmpress@umanitoba.ca *Web Site:* uofmpress.ca, pg 503

Berger, Ellie, Scholastic Inc, 557 Broadway, New York, NY 10012 *Tel:* 212-343-6100 *Toll Free Tel:* 800-scholastic *Web Site:* www.scholastic.com, pg 218

Berger, Ellie, Scholastic Trade Division, 557 Broadway, New York, NY 10012 *Tel:* 212-343-6100; 212-343-4685 (export sales) *Fax:* 212-343-4714 (export sales) *Web Site:* www.scholastic.com, pg 219

Berger, Erin, Penguin Young Readers Group, 345 Hudson St, New York, NY 10014 *Tel:* 212-366-2000 *E-mail:* online@penguinputnam.com *Web Site:* www.penguinputnam.com; us.penguingroup.com, pg 188

Berger, Erin, Razorbill, 345 Hudson St, New York, NY 10014 *Tel:* 212-366-2000, pg 205

Berger, Dr John, Cambridge University Press, 32 Avenue of the Americas, New York, NY 10013-2473 *Tel:* 212-924-3900; 212-337-5000 *Fax:* 212-691-3239 *E-mail:* newyork@cambridge.org *Web Site:* www.cambridge.org/us, pg 49

Berger, Karen, Quality Medical Publishing Inc, 2248 Welsch Industrial Ct, St Louis, MO 63146-4222 *Tel:* 314-878-7808 *Toll Free Tel:* 800-348-7808 *Fax:* 314-878-9937 *E-mail:* qmp@qmp.com *Web Site:* www.qmp.com, pg 201

Berger, Mel, WME, 1325 Avenue of the Americas, New York, NY 10019 *Tel:* 212-586-5100 *Fax:* 212-246-3583 *E-mail:* wma@interport.net *Web Site:* www.wma.com, pg 579

Berger, Pat, Vandamere Press, 3580 Morris St N, St Petersburg, FL 33713 *Tel:* 727-556-0950 *Toll Free Tel:* 800-551-7776 *Fax:* 727-556-2560 *E-mail:* orders@vandamere.com *Web Site:* www.vandamere.com, pg 264

Berger, Shulamith, AJL Scholarship, PO Box 1118, Teaneck, NJ 07666 *Web Site:* www.jewishlibraries.org, pg 666

Berger, Stacie, F+W, A Content + eCommerce Company, 10151 Carver Rd, Suite 200, Blue Ash, OH 45242 *Tel:* 513-531-2690 *Toll Free Tel:* 800-289-0963 (trade accts); 800-258-0929 (orders) *E-mail:* contact_us@fwmedia.com *Web Site:* www.fwcommunity.com, pg 86

Bergeron, Amanda, HarperCollins General Books Group, 195 Broadway, New York, NY 10007 *Tel:* 212-207-7000 *Web Site:* www.harpercollins.com, pg 106

Bergeron, Catherine, The Johns Hopkins University Press, 2715 N Charles St, Baltimore, MD 21218-4363 *Tel:* 410-516-6900; 410-516-6987 (journal orders outside US & CN) *Toll Free Tel:* 800-537-5487 (book orders & cust serv); 800-548-1784 (journal orders) *Fax:* 410-516-6968; 410-516-3866 (journal orders) *E-mail:* hfscustserv@press.jhu.edu (cust serv); jrnlcirc@press.jhu.edu (journal orders) *Web Site:* www.press.jhu.edu; muse.jhu.edu, pg 127

Bergeron, Diane, Raven Tree Press, 1400 Miller Pkwy, McHenry, IL 60050-7030 *Tel:* 815-363-3582 *Toll Free Tel:* 800-323-8270; 877-256-0579 *Fax:* 815-363-2948 *Toll Free Fax:* 800-909-9901 *E-mail:* raven@raventreepress.com; raven@deltapublishing.com *Web Site:* www.raventreepress.com, pg 205

Bergeron, Elise, Les Editions du Remue-Menage, La Maison Parent-Roback, 110 rue Ste-Therese, bureau 501, Montreal, QC H2Y 1E6, Canada *Tel:* 514-876-0097 *Fax:* 514-876-7951 *E-mail:* info@editions-rm.ca *Web Site:* www.editions-rm.ca, pg 481

Bergey, Brad, National Association of Printing Ink Manufacturers (NAPIM), 15 Technology Pkwy S, Peachtree Corners, GA 30092 *Tel:* 770-209-7289 *Fax:* 678-680-4920; 770-209-7217 *E-mail:* napim@napim.org *Web Site:* www.napim.org, pg 611

Bergfeld, Ellen, American Society of Agronomy, 5585 Guilford Rd, Madison, WI 53711-1086 *Tel:* 608-273-8080 *Fax:* 608-273-2021 *E-mail:* headquarters@sciencesocieties.org *Web Site:* www.agronomy.org, pg 16

Bergfeld, Ellen, Soil Science Society of America, 5585 Guilford Rd, Madison, WI 53711-5801 *Tel:* 608-273-8080 *Fax:* 608-273-2021 *E-mail:* headquarters@soils.org *Web Site:* www.soils.org, pg 229

Bergh, Lily, Canadian Scholars' Press Inc, 425 Adelaide St W, Suite 200, Toronto, ON M5V 3C1, Canada *Tel:* 416-929-2774 *Toll Free Tel:* 800-463-1998 *Fax:* 416-929-1926 *E-mail:* info@cspi.org; editorial@cspi.org; orders@cspi.org *Web Site:* www.cspi.org; womenspress.cspi.org, pg 476

Berghahn, Dr Marion, Berghahn Books, 20 Jay St, Suite 512, Brooklyn, NY 11201 *Tel:* 212-233-6004 *Fax:* 212-233-6007 *E-mail:* info@berghahnbooks.com; salesus@berghahnbooks.com; editorial@journals.berghahnbooks.com *Web Site:* www.berghahnbooks.com, pg 35

Berghahn, Vivian, Berghahn Books, 20 Jay St, Suite 512, Brooklyn, NY 11201 *Tel:* 212-233-6004 *Fax:* 212-233-6007 *E-mail:* info@berghahnbooks.com; salesus@berghahnbooks.com; editorial@journals.berghahnbooks.com *Web Site:* www.berghahnbooks.com, pg 35

Bergkamp, Will, Augsburg Fortress Publishers, Publishing House of the Evangelical Lutheran Church in America, 510 Marquette Ave S, Minneapolis, MN 55402 *Tel:* 612-330-3300 *Toll Free Tel:* 800-426-0115 (ext 639, subns); 800-328-4648 (orders) *Fax:* 612-330-3455 *E-mail:* info@augsburgfortress.org; copyright@augsburgfortress.org (reprint permission requests); customercare@augsburgfortress.org *Web Site:* www.augsburgfortress.org, pg 27

Bergsten, C Fred, Peterson Institute for International Economics (PIIE), 1750 Massachusetts Ave NW, Washington, DC 20036-1903 *Tel:* 202-328-9000 *Toll Free Tel:* 800-522-9139 (orders) *Fax:* 202-328-5432; 202-659-3225 *E-mail:* orders@petersoninstitute.org *Web Site:* www.petersoninstitute.org, pg 190

Bergstrom, Jennifer, Gallery Books, 1230 Avenue of the Americas, New York, NY 10020 *Toll Free Tel:* 800-456-6798 *Fax:* 212-698-7284 *E-mail:* consumer.customerservice@simonandschuster.com *Web Site:* www.simonsays.com, pg 94

Berinstein, Peter, A Richard Barber/Peter Berinstein & Associates, 60 E Eighth St, Suite 21-N, New York, NY 10003 *Tel:* 212-737-7266 *Fax:* 860-927-3942 *E-mail:* barberrich@aol.com, pg 542

Berisford, John, McGraw-Hill Financial, 1221 Avenue of the Americas, 50th fl, New York, NY 10020 *Tel:* 212-512-2000 *Web Site:* www.mhfi.com, pg 151

Berkery, Peter, AAUP Book, Jacket & Journal Design Show, 28 W 36 St, Suite 602, New York, NY 10018 *Tel:* 212-989-1010 *Fax:* 212-989-0275 *E-mail:* info@aaupnet.org *Web Site:* www.aaupnet.org, pg 665

Berkery, Peter, Association of American University Presses (AAUP), 28 W 36 St, Suite 602, New York, NY 10018 *Tel:* 212-989-1010 *Fax:* 212-989-0275 *E-mail:* info@aaupnet.org *Web Site:* www.aaupnet.org, pg 598

Berkey, Jane Rotrosen, Jane Rotrosen Agency LLC, 318 E 51 St, New York, NY 10022 *Tel:* 212-593-4330 *Fax:* 212-935-6985 *Web Site:* janerotrosen.com, pg 571

Berki, Attila, Books for Everybody, 111 Queen St E, Suite 320, Toronto, ON M5C 1S2, Canada *Tel:* 416-364-3333 *Toll Free Tel:* 888-360-6658 *Fax:* 416-595-5415, pg 601

Berkman, Hilary, Candlewick Press, 99 Dover St, Somerville, MA 02144-2825 *Tel:* 617-661-3330 *Fax:* 617-661-0565 *E-mail:* bigbear@candlewick.com; salesinfo@candlewick.com *Web Site:* www.candlewick.com, pg 49

Berkower, Amy, Writers House, 21 W 26 St, New York, NY 10010 *Tel:* 212-685-2400 *Fax:* 212-685-1781 *Web Site:* www.writershouse.com, pg 580

Berkowitz, Rachel, Crown Publishing Group, c/o Penguin Random House Inc, 1745 Broadway, New York, NY 10019 *Tel:* 212-782-9000 *Toll Free Tel:* 888-264-1745 *Fax:* 212-940-7408 *E-mail:* crownosm@penguinrandomhouse.com *Web Site:* crownpublishing.com, pg 68

Berlack, Ken, Miles Conrad Memorial Lecture, 801 Compass Way, Suite 201, Annapolis, MD 21401 *Tel:* 443-221-2980 *Fax:* 443-221-2981 *E-mail:* nfais@nfais.org *Web Site:* www.nfais.org, pg 679

Berlack, Ken, National Federation of Advanced Information Services (NFAIS), 801 Compass Way, Suite 201, Annapolis, MD 21401 *Tel:* 443-221-2980 *Fax:* 443-221-2981 *E-mail:* nfais@nfais.org *Web Site:* www.nfais.org, pg 612

Berlin, Ann, John Wiley & Sons Inc Higher Education, 111 River St, Hoboken, NJ 07030-5774 *Tel:* 201-748-6000 *Toll Free Tel:* 800-225-5945 (cust serv) *Fax:* 201-748-6008 *E-mail:* info@wiley.com *Web Site:* www.wiley.com, pg 272

Berlow, Lawrence H, Berlow Technical Communications Inc, 9 Prairie Ave, Suffern, NY 10901 *E-mail:* bteccinc@yahoo.com, pg 521

Berman, Jeff, Warren Communications News Inc, 2115 Ward Ct NW, Washington, DC 20037 *Tel:* 202-872-9200 *Toll Free Tel:* 800-771-9202 *Fax:* 202-293-

3435; 202-318-8350 *E-mail:* info@warren-news.com; newsroom@warren-news.com *Web Site:* www.warren-news.com, pg 267

Berman, Sam, The Rough Notes Co Inc, 11690 Technology Dr, Carmel, IN 46032-5600 *Tel:* 317-582-1600 *Toll Free Tel:* 800-428-4384 (cust serv) *Fax:* 317-816-1000 *Toll Free Fax:* 800-321-1909 *E-mail:* rnc@roughnotes.com *Web Site:* www.roughnotes.com, pg 211

Bernard, Alec, Puddingstone Literary, Authors' Agents, 11 Mabro Dr, Denville, NJ 07834-9607 *Tel:* 973-366-3622, pg 569

Bernard, Andre, John Simon Guggenheim Memorial Foundation, 90 Park Ave, New York, NY 10016 *Tel:* 212-687-4470 *Fax:* 212-697-3248 *E-mail:* fellowships@gf.org *Web Site:* www.gf.org, pg 623

Bernard, Kimberly, Paulist Press, 997 Macarthur Blvd, Mahwah, NJ 07430-9990 *Tel:* 201-825-7300 *Toll Free Tel:* 800-218-1903 *Fax:* 201-825-8345 *Toll Free Fax:* 800-836-3161 *E-mail:* info@paulistpress.com *Web Site:* www.paulistpress.com, pg 184

Berner, Mary, MPA - The Association of Magazine Media, 757 Third Ave, 11th fl, New York, NY 10012 *Tel:* 212-872-3700 *Fax:* 212-888-4217 *Web Site:* www.magazine.org, pg 610

Berner, Mary, Publishers Information Bureau (PIB)®, 757 Third Ave, 11th fl, New York, NY 10017 *Tel:* 212-872-3745; 212-872-3700 (MPA) *E-mail:* infocenter@magazine.org *Web Site:* www.magazine.org, pg 617

Berner, Mary, Reader's Digest General Books, Reader's Digest Rd, Pleasantville, NY 10570-7000 *Tel:* 914-238-1000 *Toll Free Tel:* 800-304-2807 (cust serv) *Fax:* 914-244-7436, pg 205

Berner-Tobin, Julia, The Feminist Press at The City University of New York, 365 Fifth Ave, Suite 5406, New York, NY 10016 *Tel:* 212-817-7915 *Fax:* 212-817-1593 *E-mail:* info@feministpress.org *Web Site:* www.feministpress.org, pg 87

Bernfeld, Linda Rodriguez, Writers Workshop in Children's Literature, 125 E Merritt Island Causeway, Suite 209, Merritt Island, FL 32952 *Tel:* 321-338-7208 *Web Site:* florida.scbwi.org, pg 657

Bernier, Jean, Les Editions du Boreal, 4447, rue St-Denis, Montreal, QC H2J 2L2, Canada *Tel:* 514-287-7401 *Fax:* 514-287-7664 *E-mail:* boreal@editionsboreal.qc.ca *Web Site:* www.editionsboreal.qc.ca, pg 480

Bernstein, Barbara, Hampton Press Inc, 307 Seventh Ave, Suite 506, New York, NY 10001 *Tel:* 646-638-3800 *Toll Free Tel:* 800-894-8955 *Fax:* 646-638-3802 *E-mail:* hamptonpr1@aol.com *Web Site:* www.hamptonpress.com, pg 104

Bernstein, Laurie, Side by Side Literary Productions Inc, 145 E 35 St, Suite 7FE, New York, NY 10016 *Tel:* 646-442-2905 *Fax:* 212-888-3650 *Web Site:* sidebysidelit.com, pg 573

Bernstein, Meredith, Meredith Bernstein Literary Agency Inc, 2095 Broadway, Suite 505, New York, NY 10023 *Tel:* 212-799-1007 *Fax:* 212-799-1145 *E-mail:* MGoodBern@aol.com *Web Site:* www.meredithbernsteinliteraryagency.com, pg 542

Bernstein, Rachel, Random House Publishing Group, 1745 Broadway, New York, NY 10019 *Toll Free Tel:* 800-200-3552 *Web Site:* atrandom.com, pg 204

Bernstein, Teresa Young, The Perseus Books Group, 387 Park Ave S, 12th fl, New York, NY 10016 *Tel:* 212-340-8100 *Toll Free Tel:* 800-343-4499 (cust serv) *Fax:* 212-340-8105 *Web Site:* www.perseusbooksgroup.com, pg 189

Bernstein, Tracy, NAL, 375 Hudson St, New York, NY 10014 *Tel:* 212-366-2000 *E-mail:* online@penguinputnam.com *Web Site:* www.penguinputnam.com; us.penguingroup.com, pg 162

Berrios, Frank, Random House Children's Books, 1745 Broadway, New York, NY 10019 *Tel:* 212-782-9000 *Toll Free Tel:* 800-200-3552 *Fax:* 212-782-9452 *Web Site:* randomhousekids.com, pg 203

Berry, Eleanor, National Federation of State Poetry Societies Annual Poetry Contest, 1375 Green Meadows Way, Ashland, OR 97520 *E-mail:* contestchair@nfsps.com *Web Site:* www.nfsps.com, pg 710

Berry, Gail, Open Horizons Publishing Co, PO Box 2887, Taos, NM 87571 *Tel:* 575-751-3398 *Fax:* 575-751-3100 *E-mail:* info@bookmarket.com *Web Site:* www.bookmarket.com, pg 175

Berry, Michael, American Society for Quality (ASQ), 600 N Plankinton Ave, Milwaukee, WI 53203 *Tel:* 414-272-8575 *Toll Free Tel:* 800-248-1946 (US & CN); 800-514-1564 (Mexico) *Fax:* 414-272-1734 *E-mail:* help@asq.org *Web Site:* www.asq.org, pg 16

Berry, Nidhi, Crown Publishing Group, c/o Penguin Random House Inc, 1745 Broadway, New York, NY 10019 *Tel:* 212-782-9000 *Toll Free Tel:* 888-264-1745 *Fax:* 212-940-7408 *E-mail:* crownosm@penguinrandomhouse.com *Web Site:* crownpublishing.com, pg 68

Berry, Nidhi, Clarkson Potter Publishers, c/o Random House Inc, 1745 Broadway, New York, NY 10019 *Tel:* 212-782-9000 *Toll Free Tel:* 888-264-1745 *Fax:* 212-572-6181 *Web Site:* www.clarksonpotter.com; www.randomhouse.com/crown/clarksonpotter, pg 195

Berry, Nidhi, Ten Speed Press, 2625 Alcatraz Ave, Unit 505, Berkeley, CA 94705 *Tel:* 510-285-3000 *Toll Free Tel:* 800-841-BOOK (841-2665) *E-mail:* csorders@randomhouse.com *Web Site:* crownpublishing.com/imprint/ten-speed-press, pg 243

Berryhill, Ginny, Artist Projects Grants, 417 W Roosevelt St, Phoenix, AZ 85003-1326 *Tel:* 602-771-6501 *Fax:* 602-256-0282 *E-mail:* info@azarts.gov *Web Site:* www.azarts.gov, pg 668

Bershtel, Sara, Henry Holt and Company, LLC, 175 Fifth Ave, New York, NY 10010 *Tel:* 646-307-5151 *Toll Free Tel:* 888-330-8477 (orders) *Fax:* 646-307-5285 *E-mail:* firstname.lastname@hholt.com *Web Site:* www.henryholt.com, pg 113

Berteotti, Carol, Brookhaven Press, 2004 Kramer St, La Crosse, WI 54603 *Tel:* 608-781-0850 *Toll Free Tel:* 800-236-0850 *Fax:* 608-781-3883 *E-mail:* brookhaven@nmt.com *Web Site:* www.brookhavenpress.com, pg 47

Bertin, Joan E, National Coalition Against Censorship (NCAC), 19 Fulton St, Suite 407, New York, NY 10038 *Tel:* 212-807-6222 *Fax:* 212-807-6245 *E-mail:* ncac@ncac.org *Web Site:* www.ncac.org, pg 611

Bertoli, Monique, Les Editions du Vermillon, 305, rue St-Patrick, Ottawa, ON K1N 5K4, Canada *Tel:* 613-241-4032 *Fax:* 613-241-3109 *E-mail:* leseditionsduvermillon@rogers.com *Web Site:* www.leseditionsduvermillon.ca, pg 481

Berube, Patty, Northstone Publishing, 485 Beaver Lake Rd, Kelowna, BC V4V 1S5, Canada *Tel:* 250-766-2778 *Toll Free Tel:* 800-299-2926; 800-663-2775 (orders) *Fax:* 250-766-2736 *Toll Free Fax:* 888-841-9991 *E-mail:* info@woodlakebooks.com *Web Site:* www.woodlakebooks.com, pg 493

Berube, Patty, Wood Lake Publishing Inc, 485 Beaver Lake Rd, Kelowna, BC V4V 1S5, Canada *Tel:* 250-766-2778 *Toll Free Tel:* 800-663-2775 (orders & cust serv) *Fax:* 250-766-2736 *Toll Free Fax:* 888-841-9991 (orders & cust serv) *E-mail:* info@woodlake.com; customerservice@woodlake.com *Web Site:* www.woodlakebooks.com, pg 505

Bess, Benjamin E, Bess Press, 3565 Harding Ave, Honolulu, HI 96816 *Tel:* 808-734-7159 *Fax:* 808-732-3627 *E-mail:* customerservice@besspress.com *Web Site:* www.besspress.com, pg 36

Besse, Chris, Nelson Education Ltd, 1120 Birchmount Rd, Scarborough, ON M1K 5G4, Canada *Tel:* 416-752-9100 *Toll Free Tel:* 800-268-2222 (cust serv) *Fax:* 416-752-8101 *Toll Free Fax:* 800-430-4445 *E-mail:* peopleandengagement@nelson.com *Web Site:* www.nelson.com, pg 492

Besser, Jennifer, GP Putnam's Sons (Children's), 345 Hudson St, New York, NY 10014 *Tel:* 212-366-2000 *Fax:* 212-414-3393 *E-mail:* online@penguinputnam.com *Web Site:* us.penguingroup.com, pg 201

Bestall, May, Wolf Pirate Project Inc, 337 Lost Lake Dr, Divide, CO 80814 *Tel:* 305-333-3186 *E-mail:* contact@wolfpiratebooks.com; workshop@wolfpiratebooks.com *Web Site:* www.wolf-pirate.com, pg 535

Bestler, Emily, Atria Books, 1230 Avenue of the Americas, New York, NY 10020 *Tel:* 212-698-7000 *Fax:* 212-698-7007 *Web Site:* www.simonandschuster.com, pg 26

Betancourt, John, Wildside Press LLC, 414 Hungerford Dr, Suite 234, Rockville, MD 20850 *Tel:* 301-762-1305 *Fax:* 301-762-1306 *E-mail:* wildside@wildsidepress.com *Web Site:* www.wildsidebooks.com; www.wildsidemagazines.com; www.wildsidepress.com, pg 272

Bethel, Courtney, MacDowell Fellowships, 100 High St, Peterborough, NH 03458 *Tel:* 603-924-3886 *Fax:* 603-924-9142 *E-mail:* info@macdowellcolony.org; admissions@macdowellcolony.org *Web Site:* www.macdowellcolony.org, pg 704

Betsch, Carol, University of Massachusetts Press, East Experiment Sta, 671 N Pleasant St, Amherst, MA 01003 *Tel:* 413-545-2217 *Fax:* 413-545-1226 *E-mail:* info@umpress.umass.edu *Web Site:* www.umass.edu/umpress, pg 257

Bettinger, James R, The Knight-Risser Prize for Western Environmental Journalism, Stanford University, 450 Serra Mall, Bldg 120, Rm 424, Stanford, CA 94305 *Tel:* 650-721-5955 *Fax:* 650-725-6154 *E-mail:* knightrisserprize@lists.stanford.edu *Web Site:* knightrisser.stanford.edu, pg 698

Bettles, Shannon, Anne & Philip Yandle Best Article Award, PO Box 5254, Sta B, Victoria, BC V8R 6N4, Canada *E-mail:* info@bchistory.ca; recognition@bchistory.ca *Web Site:* www.bchistory.ca, pg 739

Betz, James L, George T Bisel Co Inc, 710 S Washington Sq, Philadelphia, PA 19106-3519 *Tel:* 215-922-5760 *Toll Free Tel:* 800-247-3526 *Fax:* 215-922-2235 *E-mail:* gbisel@bisel.com *Web Site:* www.bisel.com, pg 37

Betz, Paul, The University of North Carolina Press, 116 S Boundary St, Chapel Hill, NC 27514-3808 *Tel:* 919-966-3561 *Fax:* 919-966-3829 *E-mail:* uncpress@unc.edu *Web Site:* www.uncpress.unc.edu, pg 258

Beullac, Paul, B & B Publishing, 4823 Sherbrooke St W, Off 275, Westmount, QC H3Z 1G7, Canada *Tel:* 514-932-9466 *Fax:* 514-932-5929 *E-mail:* editions@ebbp.ca, pg 472

Bevington, Stan, Coach House Books, 80 bpNichol Lane, Toronto, ON M5S 3J4, Canada *Tel:* 416-979-2217 *Toll Free Tel:* 800-367-6360 (outside Toronto) *Fax:* 416-977-1158 *E-mail:* mail@chbooks.com *Web Site:* www.chbooks.com, pg 477

Bewick, Andrea, Napa Valley Writers' Conference, Upper Valley Campus, 1088 College Ave, St Helena, CA 94574 *Tel:* 707-967-2900 (ext 1611) *Fax:* 707-967-2909 *E-mail:* writecon@napavalley.edu *Web Site:* www.napawritersconf.org, pg 653

Bewley, Elizabeth, Houghton Mifflin Harcourt Trade & Reference Division, 222 Berkeley St, Boston, MA 02116 *Tel:* 617-351-5000 *Toll Free Tel:* 800-225-3362 *Web Site:* www.hmhco.com, pg 115

Beyers, Don, Novalis Publishing, 10 Lower Spadina Ave, Suite 400, Toronto, ON M5V 2Z2, Canada *Tel:* 416-363-3303 *Toll Free Tel:* 877-702-7773 *Fax:* 416-363-9409 *Toll Free Fax:* 877-702-7775 *E-mail:* books@novalis.ca *Web Site:* www.novalis.ca, pg 493

Bezalel, Lindsay Gordon, Avery, 375 Hudson St, New York, NY 10014 *Tel:* 212-366-2000 *Fax:* 212-366-2643 *E-mail:* online@penguinputnam.com *Web Site:* www.penguinputnam.com; us.penguingroup.com, pg 28

Bhatnagar, Supriya, Association of Writers & Writing Programs (AWP), George Mason University, 4400 University Dr, MSN 1E3, Fairfax, VA 22030 *Tel:* 703-993-4301 *Fax:* 703-993-4302 *E-mail:* awp@awpwriter.org *Web Site:* www.awpwriter.org, pg 599

Bhatnagar, Supriya, AWP Award Series, George Mason University, 4400 University Dr, MSN 1E3, Fairfax, VA 22030 *Tel:* 703-993-4301 *Fax:* 703-993-4302 *E-mail:* awp@awpwriter.org *Web Site:* www.awpwriter.org, pg 669

Bhattacharjee, Mala, Kensington Publishing Corp, 119 W 40 St, New York, NY 10018 *Tel:* 212-407-1500 *Toll Free Tel:* 800-221-2647 *Fax:* 212-935-0699 *Web Site:* www.kensingtonbooks.com, pg 130

Biagi, Laura, Jean V Naggar Literary Agency Inc (JVNLA), 216 E 75 St, Suite 1-E, New York, NY 10021 *Tel:* 212-794-1082 *E-mail:* jvnla@jvnla.com *Web Site:* www.jvnla.com, pg 566

Bial, Daniel, Daniel Bial Agency, 41 W 83 St, Suite 5-C, New York, NY 10024 *Tel:* 212-721-1786 *E-mail:* dbialagency@msn.com *Web Site:* www.danielbialagency.com, pg 542

Bial, Daniel, Daniel Bial & Associates, 41 W 83 St, Suite 5-C, New York, NY 10024 *Tel:* 212-721-1786 *E-mail:* dbialagency@msn.com *Web Site:* www.danielbialagency.com, pg 521

Bialer, Matt, Sanford J Greenburger Associates Inc, 55 Fifth Ave, New York, NY 10003 *Tel:* 212-206-5600 *Fax:* 212-463-8718 *Web Site:* greenburger.com; www.sjga.com/, pg 555

Bialosky, Jill, W W Norton & Company Inc, 500 Fifth Ave, New York, NY 10110-0017 *Tel:* 212-354-5500 *Toll Free Tel:* 800-233-4830 (orders & cust serv) *Fax:* 212-869-0856 *Toll Free Fax:* 800-458-6515 *Web Site:* www.wwnorton.com, pg 171

Bianchini, Brian, International Press of Boston Inc, 387 Somerville Ave, Somerville, MA 02143 *Tel:* 617-623-3016 *Fax:* 617-623-3101 *E-mail:* ipb-info@intlpress.com; ipb-orders@intlpress.com *Web Site:* www.intlpress.com, pg 124

Bianchini, Lori, National Council of Teachers of English (NCTE), 1111 W Kenyon Rd, Urbana, IL 61801-1096 *Tel:* 217-328-3870 *Toll Free Tel:* 877-369-6283 (cust serv) *Fax:* 217-328-9645 *E-mail:* public_info@ncte.org *Web Site:* www.ncte.org, pg 612

Bick, George, Doug Grad Literary Agency Inc, 68 Jay St, Suite W11, Brooklyn, NY 11201-1189 *Tel:* 718-788-6067 *E-mail:* query@dgliterary.com *Web Site:* www.dgliterary.com, pg 555

Bickerstaff, Patsy Anne, Laura Day Boggs Bolling Memorial, 1194 Hume Rd, Hume, VA 22639-1806 *E-mail:* poetryinva@aol.com *Web Site:* www.poetrysocietyofvirginia.org, pg 673

Bickerstaff, Patsy Anne, Joe Pendleton Campbell Narrative Contest, 1194 Hume Rd, Hume, VA 22639-1806 *E-mail:* poetryinva@aol.com *Web Site:* www.poetrysocietyofvirginia.org, pg 675

Bickerstaff, Patsy Anne, Carleton Drewry Memorial, 1194 Hume Rd, Hume, VA 22639-1806 *E-mail:* poetryinva@aol.com *Web Site:* www.poetrysocietyofvirginia.org, pg 682

Bickerstaff, Patsy Anne, Alfred C Gary Memorial, 1194 Hume Rd, Hume, VA 22639-1806 *E-mail:* poetryinva@aol.com *Web Site:* www.poetrysocietyofvirginia.org, pg 688

Bickerstaff, Patsy Anne, Bess Gresham Memorial, 1194 Hume Rd, Hume, VA 22639-1806 *E-mail:* poetryinva@aol.com *Web Site:* www.poetrysocietyofvirginia.org, pg 690

Bickerstaff, Patsy Anne, Loretta Dunn Hall Memorial, 1194 Hume Rd, Hume, VA 22639-1806 *E-mail:* poetryinva@aol.com *Web Site:* www.poetrysocietyofvirginia.org, pg 691

Bickerstaff, Patsy Anne, Handy Andy Prize, 1194 Hume Rd, Hume, VA 22639-1806 *E-mail:* poetryinva@aol.com *Web Site:* www.poetrysocietyofvirginia.org, pg 691

Bickerstaff, Patsy Anne, Brodie Herndon Memorial, 1194 Hume Rd, Hume, VA 22639-1806 *E-mail:* poetryinva@aol.com *Web Site:* www.poetrysocietyofvirginia.org, pg 692

Bickerstaff, Patsy Anne, Judah, Sarah, Grace & Tom Memorial, 1194 Hume Rd, Hume, VA 22639-1806 *E-mail:* poetryinva@aol.com *Web Site:* www.poetrysocietyofvirginia.org, pg 697

Bickerstaff, Patsy Anne, Cenie H Moon Prize, 1194 Hume Rd, Hume, VA 22639-1806 *E-mail:* poetryinva@aol.com *Web Site:* www.poetrysocietyofvirginia.org, pg 709

Bickerstaff, Patsy Anne, Edgar Allan Poe Memorial, 1194 Hume Rd, Hume, VA 22639-1806 *E-mail:* poetryinva@aol.com *Web Site:* www.poetrysocietyofvirginia.org, pg 719

Bickerstaff, Patsy Anne, A Poem With a Point of View, 1194 Hume Rd, Hume, VA 22639-1806 *E-mail:* poetryinva@aol.com *Web Site:* www.poetrysocietyofvirginia.org, pg 719

Bickerstaff, Patsy Anne, Miriam Rachimi Memorial, 1194 Hume Rd, Hume, VA 22639-1806 *E-mail:* poetryinva@aol.com *Web Site:* www.poetrysocietyofvirginia.org, pg 722

Bickerstaff, Patsy Anne, Ada Sanderson Memorial, 1194 Hume Rd, Hume, VA 22639-1806 *E-mail:* poetryinva@aol.com *Web Site:* www.poetrysocietyofvirginia.org, pg 725

Bickerstaff, Patsy Anne, The Robert S Sergeant Memorial, 1194 Hume Rd, Hume, VA 22639-1806 *E-mail:* poetryinva@aol.com *Web Site:* www.poetrysocietyofvirginia.org, pg 727

Bicknell, Liz, Candlewick Press, 99 Dover St, Somerville, MA 02144-2825 *Tel:* 617-661-3330 *Fax:* 617-661-0565 *E-mail:* bigbear@candlewick.com; salesinfo@candlewick.com *Web Site:* www.candlewick.com, pg 49

Biddinger, Mary, Akron Poetry Prize, The University of Akron Press, 120 E Mill St, Suite 415, Akron, OH 44308 *Tel:* 330-972-6953 *Fax:* 330-972-8364 *E-mail:* uapress@uakron.edu *Web Site:* www.uakron.edu/uapress/akron-poetry-prize, pg 666

Bider, Rich, Printing Association of Florida Inc (PAF), 6250 Hazeltine National Dr, Suite 114, Orlando, FL 32822 *Tel:* 407-240-8009 *Toll Free Tel:* 800-331-0461 *Fax:* 407-240-8333 *Web Site:* www.flprint.org, pg 616

Bidler, R M, editions CERES Ltd/Le Moyen Francais, CP 1089, Succursale B, Maison de la Poste, Montreal, QC H3B 3K9, Canada *Tel:* 514-937-7138 *Fax:* 514-937-9875 *E-mail:* editionsceres@gmail.com *Web Site:* www.editionsceres.ca, pg 480

Biehl, Michael, Write for Success (WFS), PO Box 292153, Los Angeles, CA 90029-8653 *Tel:* 323-356-8833 *E-mail:* writeforsuccess@yahoo.com *Web Site:* www.write-for-success.com, pg 536

Bieker, Mike, The University of Arkansas Press, McIlroy House, 105 N McIlroy Ave, Fayetteville, AR 72701 *Tel:* 479-575-3246 *Toll Free Tel:* 800-626-0090 *Fax:* 479-575-6044 *E-mail:* uapress@uark.edu *Web Site:* www.uapress.com, pg 255

Bielstein, Susan, University of Chicago Press, 1427 E 60 St, Chicago, IL 60637-2954 *Tel:* 773-702-7700; 773-702-7600 *Toll Free Tel:* 800-621-2736 (orders) *Fax:* 773-702-9756; 773-660-2235 (orders); 773-702-2708 *E-mail:* custserv@press.uchicago.edu; marketing@press.uchicago.edu *Web Site:* www.press.uchicago.edu, pg 255

Biesel, David, Saint Johann Press, 315 Schraalenburgh Rd, Haworth, NJ 07641 *Tel:* 201-387-1529 *Fax:* 201-501-0698 *Web Site:* www.stjohannpress.com, pg 214

Biesel, Diane, Saint Johann Press, 315 Schraalenburgh Rd, Haworth, NJ 07641 *Tel:* 201-387-1529 *Fax:* 201-501-0698 *Web Site:* www.stjohannpress.com, pg 214

Bigelow, Christopher, Zarahemla Books, 869 E 2680 N, Provo, UT 84604 *Tel:* 801-368-7374 *Fax:* 801-418-2081 *E-mail:* info@zarahemlabooks.com *Web Site:* zarahemlabooks.com, pg 279

Bijur, Vicky, Vicky Bijur Literary Agency, 333 West End Ave, Suite 5-B, New York, NY 10023 *Tel:* 212-580-4108 *E-mail:* queries@vickybijuragency.com *Web Site:* www.vickybijuragency.com, pg 542

Bilek, Jerry, Minnesota Historical Society Press, 345 Kellogg Blvd W, St Paul, MN 55102-1906 *Tel:* 651-259-3205; 651-259-3000 *Toll Free Tel:* 800-621-2736 (warehouse) *Fax:* 651-297-1345 *Toll Free Fax:* 800-621-8476 (warehouse) *E-mail:* info-mnhspress@mnhs.org *Web Site:* www.mnhs.org/mnhspress, pg 157

Billeter, Michelle, Woodland Publishing Inc, 515 S 700 E, Suite 2D, Salt Lake City, UT 84102 *Toll Free Tel:* 800-277-3243 *Fax:* 801-334-1913 *E-mail:* info@woodlandpublishing.com *Web Site:* www.woodlandpublishing.com, pg 275

Billings, Hyacinth, World Resources Institute, 10 "G" St NE, Suite 800, Washington, DC 20002 *Tel:* 202-729-7600 *Fax:* 202-729-7610 *Web Site:* www.wri.org, pg 276

Billingsley, Joseph, Pelican Publishing Co, 1000 Burmaster St, Gretna, LA 70053-2246 *Tel:* 504-368-1175 *Toll Free Tel:* 800-843-1724 *Fax:* 504-368-1195 *E-mail:* sales@pelicanpub.com (sales); office@pelicanpub.com (permission); promo@pelicanpub.com (publicity) *Web Site:* www.pelicanpub.com, pg 185

Billingsley, Sarah, Chronicle Books LLC, 680 Second St, San Francisco, CA 94107 *Tel:* 415-537-4200 *Toll Free Tel:* 800-759-0190 (cust serv) *Fax:* 415-537-4460 *Toll Free Fax:* 800-858-7787 (orders); 800-286-9471 (cust serv) *E-mail:* frontdesk@chroniclebooks.com *Web Site:* www.chroniclebooks.com, pg 58

Bilofski, Ellen, AFB Press, 2 Penn Plaza, Suite 1102, New York, NY 10121 *Tel:* 212-502-7600 *Toll Free Tel:* 800-232-5463; 800-232-3044 (orders) *Fax:* 917-210-3979; 412-741-0609 (orders) *Toll Free Fax:* 888-545-8331 *E-mail:* press@afb.net; afbpress@afb.net; afbinfo@afb.net; afborder@afb.net (orders) *Web Site:* www.afb.org, pg 5

Binder, Pam, PNWA Literary Contest, 1420 NW Gilman Blvd, Suite 2, PMB 2717, Issaquah, WA 98027 *Tel:* 425-673-2665 *E-mail:* pnwa@pnwa.org *Web Site:* www.pnwa.org, pg 719

Binder, Pam, PNWA - a writer's resource, 1420 NW Gilman Blvd, Suite 2, PMB 2717, Issaquah, WA 98027 *Tel:* 425-673-2665 *Fax:* 425-961-0768 *E-mail:* pnwa@pnwa.org *Web Site:* www.pnwa.org, pg 616

Binder, Pam, PNWA Writers Conference, 1420 NW Gilman Blvd, Suite 2, PMB 2717, Issaquah, WA 98027 *Tel:* 425-673-2665 *E-mail:* pnwa@pnwa.org *Web Site:* www.pnwa.org, pg 654

Bingham, Tony, Association for Talent Development (ATD), 1640 King St, Box 1443, Alexandria, VA 22313-1443 *Tel:* 703-683-8100 *Toll Free Tel:* 800-628-2783 *Fax:* 703-299-8723; 703-683-1523 (cust care) *E-mail:* customercare@td.org *Web Site:* www.astd.org; www.td.org, pg 25

Binney, Ann, Los Angeles Times Book Prizes, 202 W First St, Los Angeles, CA 90012 *Tel:* 213-237-5775 *Toll Free Tel:* 800-528-4637 *Fax:* 213-237-7679 *Web Site:* www.latimesbookprizes.com, pg 703

Binns, Beth, Woodbine House, 6510 Bells Mill Rd, Bethesda, MD 20817 *Tel:* 301-897-3570 *Toll Free Tel:* 800-843-7323 *Fax:* 301-897-5838 *E-mail:* info@woodbinehouse.com *Web Site:* www.woodbinehouse.com, pg 275

Binyominson, Yerachmiel, Hachai Publishing, 527 Empire Blvd, Brooklyn, NY 11225 *Tel:* 718-633-0100 *Fax:* 718-633-0103 *E-mail:* info@hachai.com *Web Site:* www.hachai.com, pg 102

Biolchini, Bob, PennWell Books, 1421 S Sheridan Rd, Tulsa, OK 74112 *Tel:* 918-831-9410 *Toll Free Tel:* 800-752-9764 *Fax:* 918-831-9555 *E-mail:* sales@pennwell.com *Web Site:* www.pennwellbooks.com, pg 188

Birckhead, Molly, HarperCollins General Books Group, 195 Broadway, New York, NY 10007 *Tel:* 212-207-7000 *Web Site:* www.harpercollins.com, pg 105

Boer, Faye, Folklore Publishing, 11717-9B Ave NW, Unit 2, Edmonton, AB T6J 7B7, Canada *Tel:* 780-435-2376 *Fax:* 780-435-0674 *E-mail:* submissions@folklorepublishing.com (ms submissions) *Web Site:* www.folklorepublishing.com, pg 484

Boers, Jack, Baker Books, PO Box 6287, Grand Rapids, MI 49516-6287 *Tel:* 616-676-9185 *Toll Free Tel:* 800-877-2665; 800-679-1957 *Fax:* 616-676-9573 *Toll Free Fax:* 800-398-3111 *Web Site:* www.bakerpublishinggroup.com, pg 29

Boersma, Karen, Owlkids Books Inc, 10 Lower Spadina Ave, Suite 400, Toronto, ON M5V 2Z2, Canada *Tel:* 416-340-2700 *Fax:* 416-340-9769 *E-mail:* owlkids@owlkids.com *Web Site:* www.owlkidsbooks.com, pg 493

Bogaards, Paul, Alfred A Knopf/Everyman's Library, c/o Random House Inc, 1745 Broadway, New York, NY 10019 *Tel:* 212-751-2600 *Toll Free Tel:* 800-638-6460 *Fax:* 212-572-2593 *Web Site:* www.knopfdoubleday.com, pg 132

Boggs, Amy, Donald Maass Literary Agency, 121 W 27 St, Suite 801, New York, NY 10001 *Tel:* 212-727-8383 *Fax:* 212-727-3271 *E-mail:* info@maassagency.com *Web Site:* www.maassagency.com, pg 562

Boggs, Marcus, Scarecrow Press Inc, 4501 Forbes Blvd, Suite 200, Lanham, MD 20706 *Tel:* 301-459-3366 *Fax:* 301-429-5748 *Web Site:* www.scarecrowpress.com, pg 217

Bogie, Patty, MPA - The Association of Magazine Media, 757 Third Ave, 11th fl, New York, NY 10012 *Tel:* 212-872-3700 *Fax:* 212-888-4217 *Web Site:* www.magazine.org, pg 610

Bohan, Dr Mark, InterTech™ Technology Awards, 200 Deer Run Rd, Sewickley, PA 15143-2324 *Tel:* 412-259-1782 *Toll Free Tel:* 800-910-4283 (ext 782) *Fax:* 412-741-2311 *E-mail:* intertechaward@printing.org *Web Site:* www.printing.org/intertechawards, pg 695

Boies, Kay, Children's Sequoyah Book Award, 300 Hardy Dr, Edmond, OK 73013 *Tel:* 405-525-5100 *Fax:* 405-525-5103 *Web Site:* www.oklibs.org, pg 677

Boies, Kay, Intermediate Sequoyah Book Award, 300 Hardy Dr, Edmond, OK 73013 *Tel:* 405-525-5100 *Fax:* 405-525-5103 *Web Site:* www.oklibs.org, pg 695

Boisseau, Michelle, BkMk Press - University of Missouri-Kansas City, University House, 5101 Rockhill Rd, Kansas City, MO 64110-2499 *Tel:* 816-235-2558 *Fax:* 816-235-2611 *E-mail:* bkmk@umkc.edu *Web Site:* www.umkc.edu/bkmk, pg 38

Boisseau, Michelle, G S Sharat Chandra Prize for Short Fiction, University House, 5101 Rockhill Rd, Kansas City, MO 64110-2499 *Tel:* 816-235-2558 *Fax:* 816-235-2611 *E-mail:* bkmk@umkc.edu *Web Site:* www.umkc.edu/bkmk, pg 676

Boisseau, Michelle, John Ciardi Prize for Poetry, University House, 5101 Rockhill Rd, Kansas City, MO 64110-2499 *Tel:* 816-235-2558 *Fax:* 816-235-2611 *E-mail:* bkmk@umkc.edu *Web Site:* www.umkc.edu/bkmk, pg 677

Boitnott, Sally, Pelican Publishing Co, 1000 Burmaster St, Gretna, LA 70053-2246 *Tel:* 504-368-1175 *Toll Free Tel:* 800-843-1724 *Fax:* 504-368-1195 *E-mail:* sales@pelicanpub.com (sales); office@pelicanpub.com (permission); promo@pelicanpub.com (publicity) *Web Site:* www.pelicanpub.com, pg 185

Bol, Bob, Baker Books, PO Box 6287, Grand Rapids, MI 49516-6287 *Tel:* 616-676-9185 *Toll Free Tel:* 800-877-2665; 800-679-1957 *Fax:* 616-676-9573 *Toll Free Fax:* 800-398-3111 *Web Site:* www.bakerpublishinggroup.com, pg 29

Bol, Robert, Revell, PO Box 6287, Grand Rapids, MI 49516-6287 *Tel:* 616-676-9185 *Toll Free Tel:* 800-877-2665; 800-679-1957 *Fax:* 616-676-9573 *Web Site:* www.revellbooks.com, pg 208

Bolan, Michael, European Masterpieces, 103 Walker Way, Newark, DE 19711 *Tel:* 302-453-8695 *Fax:* 302-453-8601 *E-mail:* text@linguatextltd.com *Web Site:* www.europeanmasterpieces.com, pg 84

Bolan, Michael, LinguaText Ltd, 103 Walker Way, Newark, DE 19711 *Tel:* 302-453-8695 *Fax:* 302-453-8601 *Web Site:* www.linguatextltd.com, pg 140

Bolchazy, Allan, Bolchazy-Carducci Publishers Inc, 1570 Baskin Rd, Mundelein, IL 60060 *Tel:* 847-526-4344 *Toll Free Tel:* 800-392-6453 *Fax:* 847-526-2867 *E-mail:* info@bolchazy.com; orders@bolchazy.com *Web Site:* www.bolchazy.com, pg 41

Bolchazy, Dr Marie Carducci PhD, Bolchazy-Carducci Publishers Inc, 1570 Baskin Rd, Mundelein, IL 60060 *Tel:* 847-526-4344 *Toll Free Tel:* 800-392-6453 *Fax:* 847-526-2867 *E-mail:* info@bolchazy.com; orders@bolchazy.com *Web Site:* www.bolchazy.com, pg 41

Boldrick, Penelope, Ignatius Press, 1348 Tenth Ave, San Francisco, CA 94122-2304 *Toll Free Tel:* 800-651-1531 (orders); 888-615-3186 (cust serv) *E-mail:* info@ignatius.com *Web Site:* www.ignatius.com, pg 118

Bolduc, Mary Jo, The American Library Association (ALA), 50 E Huron St, Chicago, IL 60611 *Tel:* 312-944-6780 *Toll Free Tel:* 800-545-2433 *Fax:* 312-280-5275 *E-mail:* editionsmarketing@ala.org *Web Site:* www.alastore.ala.org, pg 14

Bolduc, Mary Jo, Carnegie-Whitney Award, 50 E Huron St, Chicago, IL 60611 *Tel:* 312-280-5416 *Toll Free Tel:* 800-545-2433 *Fax:* 312-280-5275; 312-440-9379 *Web Site:* www.ala.org, pg 676

Bole, Angela, The Independent Book Publishers Association (IBPA), 1020 Manhattan Beach Blvd, Suite 204, Manhattan Beach, CA 90266 *Tel:* 310-546-1818 *Fax:* 310-546-3939 *E-mail:* info@ibpa-online.org *Web Site:* www.ibpa-online.org, pg 607

Bolen, Dave, Highlights for Children, 1800 Watermark Dr, Columbus, OH 43215 *Tel:* 614-486-0631 *Toll Free Tel:* 800-962-3661 (Highlights Club cust serv); 800-255-9517 (Highlights Magazine cust serv) *Web Site:* www.highlights.com, pg 111

Bolger, Loretta, Quincannon Publishing Group, PO Box 8100, Glen Ridge, NJ 07028-8100 *Tel:* 973-380-9942 *E-mail:* editors@quincannongroup.com *Web Site:* www.quincannongroup.com, pg 202

Bolinao, Mela, MB Artists, 775 Sixth Ave, Suite 6, New York, NY 10001 *Tel:* 212-689-7830 *Fax:* 212-689-7829 *Web Site:* www.mbartists.com, pg 584

Boling, John Mark, Grove Atlantic Inc, 154 W 14 St, 12th fl, New York, NY 10011 *Tel:* 212-614-7850 *Toll Free Tel:* 800-521-0178 *Fax:* 212-614-7886 *E-mail:* info@groveatlantic.com *Web Site:* www.groveatlantic.com, pg 101

Bolinger, Becke, Indiana Historical Society Press (IHS Press), 450 W Ohio St, Indianapolis, IN 46202-3269 *Tel:* 317-232-1882; 317-234-0026 (orders); 317-234-2716 (edit) *Toll Free Tel:* 800-447-1830 (orders) *Fax:* 317-234-0562 (orders); 317-233-0857 (edit) *E-mail:* ihspress@indianahistory.org; orders@indianahistory.org (orders) *Web Site:* www.indianahistory.org; shop.indianahistory.org (orders), pg 120

Bollas, George, Cortina Institute of Languages, 9 Hollyhock Rd, Wilton, CT 06897 *Tel:* 203-762-2510 *Toll Free Tel:* 800-245-2145 *Fax:* 203-762-2514 *Web Site:* www.cortina-languages.com, pg 64

Bollas, George, Cortina Learning International Inc (CLI), 9 Hollyhock Rd, Wilton, CT 06897 *Tel:* 203-762-2510 *Toll Free Tel:* 800-245-2145 *Fax:* 203-762-2514 *E-mail:* info@cortinalearning.com *Web Site:* www.cortinalearning.com, pg 64

Bollenbach, Ryan, Black Warrior Review Fiction, Nonfiction & Poetry Contest, Office of Student Media, University of Alabama, Tuscaloosa, AL 35486-0027 *Tel:* 205-348-4518 *Web Site:* www.bwr.ua.edu, pg 672

Boller, Katherine, Yale University Press, 302 Temple St, New Haven, CT 06511-8909 *Tel:* 203-432-0960; 203-432-0966 (sales); 401-531-2800 (cust serv) *Toll Free Tel:* 800-405-1619 (cust serv) *Fax:* 203-432-0948; 203-432-8485 (sales); 401-531-2801 (cust serv) *Toll Free Fax:* 800-406-9145 (cust serv) *E-mail:* sales.press@yale.edu (sales); customer.care@trilateral.org (cust serv) *Web Site:* www.yalebooks.com; yalepress.yale.edu/yupbooks, pg 278

Bolm, Jennifer, Adventures Unlimited Press (AUP), One Adventure Place, Kempton, IL 60946 *Tel:* 815-253-6390 *Fax:* 815-253-6300 *E-mail:* auphq@frontiernet.net; info@adventuresunlimitedpress.com *Web Site:* www.adventuresunlimitedpress.com, pg 5

Bolotin, Susan, Workman Publishing Co Inc, 225 Varick St, 9th fl, New York, NY 10014-4381 *Tel:* 212-254-5900 *Toll Free Tel:* 800-722-7202 *Fax:* 212-254-8098 *E-mail:* info@workman.com *Web Site:* www.workman.com, pg 275

Bolstad, Karen, Purich Publishing Ltd, PO Box 23032, Market Mall Postal Outlet, Saskatoon, SK S7J 5H3, Canada *Tel:* 306-373-5311 *Fax:* 306-373-5315 *E-mail:* purich@sasktel.net *Web Site:* www.purichpublishing.com, pg 496

Bolte, Lynda, Shields Publications, PO Box 669, Eagle River, WI 54521-0669 *Tel:* 715-479-4810 *Fax:* 715-479-3905 *E-mail:* wormbooks@wormbooks.com *Web Site:* www.wormbooks.com, pg 223

Bomberger, Rachel, Wm B Eerdmans Publishing Co, 2140 Oak Industrial Dr NE, Grand Rapids, MI 49505 *Tel:* 616-459-4591 *Toll Free Tel:* 800-253-7521 *Fax:* 616-459-6540 *E-mail:* customerservice@eerdmans.com; sales@eerdmans.com *Web Site:* www.eerdmans.com, pg 80

Bonacum, Leslie, CCH, a Wolters Kluwer business, 2700 Lake Cook Rd, Riverwoods, IL 60015 *Tel:* 847-267-7000 *Web Site:* www.cch.com, pg 52

Bonanno, Michelle, Houghton Mifflin Harcourt Trade & Reference Division, 222 Berkeley St, Boston, MA 02116 *Tel:* 617-351-5000 *Toll Free Tel:* 800-225-3362 *Web Site:* www.hmhco.com, pg 115

Bonaventura, Philip, Public Relations Society of America, 33 Maiden Lane, 11th fl, New York, NY 10038-5150 *Tel:* 212-460-1400 *Fax:* 212-995-0757 *Web Site:* www.prsa.org, pg 617

Boncottie, John, Antique Collectors' Club Ltd, 116 Pleasant St, Suite 18, East Hampton, MA 01027 *Tel:* 413-529-0861 *Toll Free Tel:* 800-252-5231 *Fax:* 413-529-0862 *E-mail:* sales@antiquecc.com *Web Site:* www.antiquecollectorsclub.com; www.accdistribution.com, pg 19

Bond, Alison M, Alison Bond Literary Agency, 171 W 79 St, No 143, New York, NY 10024, pg 543

Bond, John H, Slack Incorporated, 6900 Grove Rd, Thorofare, NJ 08086-9447 *Tel:* 856-848-1000 *Toll Free Tel:* 800-257-8290 *Fax:* 856-848-6091 *E-mail:* sales@slackinc.com *Web Site:* www.slackbooks.com, pg 227

Bond, Sandra, Bond Literary Agency, 4340 E Kentucky Ave, Suite 471, Denver, CO 80246 *Tel:* 303-781-9305 *E-mail:* queries@bondliteraryagency.com *Web Site:* bondliteraryagency.com, pg 543

Bonelli, Kristen, Ave Maria Press, PO Box 428, Notre Dame, IN 46556 *Tel:* 574-287-2831 *Toll Free Tel:* 800-282-1865 *Fax:* 574-239-2904 *Toll Free Fax:* 800-282-5681 *E-mail:* avemariapress.1@nd.edu *Web Site:* www.avemariapress.com, pg 28

Bonenberger, John, William H Sadlier Inc, 9 Pine St, New York, NY 10005 *Tel:* 212-227-2120 *Toll Free Tel:* 800-221-5175 (cust serv) *Fax:* 212-312-6080 *E-mail:* customerservice@sadlier.com *Web Site:* www.sadlier.com, pg 213

Bonenfant, Rene, Les Heures bleues, 560 Mercier, St-Lambert, QC J4P 1Z5, Canada *Tel:* 450-671-7718 *Fax:* 450-671-7718 *E-mail:* info@heuresbleues.com *Web Site:* www.heuresbleues.com, pg 488

Boni, Anne, The Center for the Book in the Library of Congress, The Library of Congress, 101 Independence Ave SE, Washington, DC 20540-4920 *Tel:* 202-707-5221 *Fax:* 202-707-0269 *E-mail:* cfbook@loc.gov *Web Site:* www.read.gov; www.read.gov/cfb, pg 603

Boni, Anne, Library of Congress Prize for American Fiction, 101 Independence Ave SE, Washington, DC 20540-1400 *Tel:* 202-707-5221 (Center for the Book) *Web Site:* www.loc.gov, pg 700

Bonifacio, Kris Anne, Media Coalition Inc, 19 Fulton St, Suite 407, New York, NY 10038 *Tel:* 212-587-4025 *Fax:* 212-587-2436 *E-mail:* info@mediacoalition.org *Web Site:* mediacoalition.org, pg 609

Bonk, Rich, Philadelphia Museum of Art, 2525 Pennsylvania Ave, Philadelphia, PA 19130 *Tel:* 215-684-7250 *Fax:* 215-235-8715 *Web Site:* www.philamuseum.org, pg 191

Bonner, Pat, International Foundation of Employee Benefit Plans, 18700 W Bluemound Rd, Brookfield, WI 53045 *Tel:* 262-786-6700 *Toll Free Tel:* 888-334-3327 *Fax:* 262-786-8780 *E-mail:* editor@ifebp.org *Web Site:* www.ifebp.org, pg 124

Bonoff, Steve, IDEAlliance®, 1600 Duke St, Suite 420, Alexandria, VA 22314 *Tel:* 703-837-1070 *Fax:* 703-837-1072 *E-mail:* registrar@idealliance.org *Web Site:* www.idealliance.org, pg 607

Booher, Jason, Blue Rider Press, 375 Hudson St, New York, NY 10014 *Tel:* 212-366-2000 *E-mail:* blueriderpublicity@us.penguingroup.com, pg 41

Boomer, Helen, Penguin Young Readers Group, 345 Hudson St, New York, NY 10014 *Tel:* 212-366-2000 *E-mail:* online@penguinputnam.com *Web Site:* www.penguinputnam.com; us.penguingroup.com, pg 188

Boomhower, Ray, Indiana Historical Society Press (IHS Press), 450 W Ohio St, Indianapolis, IN 46202-3269 *Tel:* 317-232-1882; 317-234-0026 (orders); 317-234-2716 (edit) *Toll Free Tel:* 800-447-1830 (orders) *Fax:* 317-234-0562 (orders); 317-233-0857 (edit) *E-mail:* ihspress@indianahistory.org; orders@indianahistory.org (orders) *Web Site:* www.indianahistory.org; shop.indianahistory.org (orders), pg 120

Boorstein, Amy, Crown Publishing Group, c/o Penguin Random House Inc, 1745 Broadway, New York, NY 10019 *Tel:* 212-782-9000 *Toll Free Tel:* 888-264-1745 *Fax:* 212-940-7408 *E-mail:* crownosm@penguinrandomhouse.com *Web Site:* crownpublishing.com, pg 68

Boot, Chris, Aperture Books, 547 W 27 St, 4th fl, New York, NY 10001 *Tel:* 212-505-5555 *Toll Free Tel:* 800-929-2323 *Fax:* 212-979-7759 *E-mail:* info@aperture.org *Web Site:* www.aperture.org, pg 19

Booth, Doris, Authorlink Press, 103 Guadalupe Dr, Irving, TX 75039-3334 *Tel:* 972-402-0101 *E-mail:* admin@authorlink.com *Web Site:* www.authorlink.com, pg 27

Booth, Jessica, The University of Utah Press, J Willard Marriott Library, Suite 5400, 295 S 1500 E, Salt Lake City, UT 84112-0860 *Tel:* 801-581-6771 *Toll Free Tel:* 800-621-2736 (orders) *Fax:* 801-581-3365 *Toll Free Fax:* 800-621-8471 *E-mail:* info@upress.utah.edu *Web Site:* www.uofupress.com, pg 260

Booth, Tom, Oregon State University Press, 121 The Valley Library, Corvallis, OR 97331-4501 *Tel:* 541-737-3166 *Toll Free Tel:* 800-621-2736 (orders) *Web Site:* osupress.oregonstate.edu, pg 177

Borchardt, Anne, Georges Borchardt Inc, 136 E 57 St, New York, NY 10022 *Tel:* 212-753-5785 *E-mail:* georges@gbagency.com *Web Site:* www.gbagency.com, pg 543

Borchardt, Georges, Georges Borchardt Inc, 136 E 57 St, New York, NY 10022 *Tel:* 212-753-5785 *E-mail:* georges@gbagency.com *Web Site:* www.gbagency.com, pg 543

Borchardt, Valerie, Georges Borchardt Inc, 136 E 57 St, New York, NY 10022 *Tel:* 212-753-5785 *E-mail:* georges@gbagency.com *Web Site:* www.gbagency.com, pg 543

Borchert, Scott, Monthly Review Press, 146 W 29 St, Suite 6W, New York, NY 10001 *Tel:* 212-691-2555 *Toll Free Tel:* 800-670-9499 *Fax:* 212-727-3676 *E-mail:* mreview@igc.org *Web Site:* www.MonthlyReview.org, pg 159

Borgenicht, David, Quirk Books, 215 Church St, Philadelphia, PA 19106 *Tel:* 215-627-3581 *Fax:* 215-627-5220 *E-mail:* general@quirkbooks.com *Web Site:* www.quirkbooks.com, pg 202

Borges, Michael, Empire State Award for Excellence in Literature for Young People, 6021 State Farm Rd, Guilderland, NY 12084 *Tel:* 518-432-6952 *Toll Free Tel:* 800-252-6952 *Fax:* 518-427-1697 *E-mail:* info@nyla.org *Web Site:* www.nyla.org, pg 684

Borland, Peter, Atria Books, 1230 Avenue of the Americas, New York, NY 10020 *Tel:* 212-698-7000 *Fax:* 212-698-7007 *Web Site:* www.simonandschuster.com, pg 26

Born, Bob, Pocket Press Inc, PO Box 25124, Portland, OR 97298-0124 *Toll Free Tel:* 888-237-2110 *Toll Free Fax:* 877-643-3732 *E-mail:* sales@pocketpressinc.com *Web Site:* www.pocketpressinc.com, pg 194

Borne, Joell Smith, Vanderbilt University Press, 2014 Broadway, Suite 320, Nashville, TN 37203 *Tel:* 615-322-3585 *Toll Free Tel:* 800-627-7377 (orders only) *Fax:* 615-343-8823 *Toll Free Fax:* 800-735-0476 (orders only) *E-mail:* vupress@vanderbilt.edu *Web Site:* www.vanderbiltuniversitypress.com, pg 264

Borodyanskaya, Yulia, Harry N Abrams Inc, 115 W 18 St, 6th fl, New York, NY 10011 *Tel:* 212-206-7715 *Toll Free Tel:* 800-345-1359 *Fax:* 212-519-1210 *E-mail:* abrams@abramsbooks.com *Web Site:* www.abramsbooks.com, pg 3

Borque, Paul, Twenty-Third Publications, One Montauk Ave, Suite 200, New London, CT 06320 *Tel:* 860-437-3012 *Toll Free Tel:* 800-321-0411 (orders) *Toll Free Fax:* 800-572-0788 *E-mail:* 23ppweb@bayard-inc.com *Web Site:* www.twentythirdpublications.com, pg 251

Borsecnik, Mary, J J Keller & Associates, Inc, 3003 Breezewood Lane, Neenah, WI 54957 *Tel:* 920-722-2848 *Toll Free Tel:* 877-564-2333 *Toll Free Fax:* 800-727-7516 *E-mail:* contactus@jjkeller.com; customerservice@jjkeller.com *Web Site:* www.jjkeller.com, pg 130

Borsics, Angelin, Clarkson Potter Publishers, c/o Random House Inc, 1745 Broadway, New York, NY 10019 *Tel:* 212-782-9000 *Toll Free Tel:* 888-264-1745 *Fax:* 212-572-6181 *Web Site:* www.clarksonpotter.com; www.randomhouse.com/crown/clarksonpotter, pg 195

Borski, Jill Zima, Florida Outdoor Writers Association Inc, 24 NW 33 Ct, Suite A, Gainesville, FL 32607 *Tel:* 352-284-1763 *E-mail:* info@fowa.org *Web Site:* www.fowa.org, pg 606

Bortz, Andrew, Bancroft Press, 3209 Bancroft Rd, Baltimore, MD 21215 *Tel:* 410-358-0658 *Fax:* 410-764-1967 *Web Site:* www.bancroftpress.com, pg 30

Bortz, Bruce L, Bancroft Press, 3209 Bancroft Rd, Baltimore, MD 21215 *Tel:* 410-358-0658 *Fax:* 410-764-1967 *Web Site:* www.bancroftpress.com, pg 30

Borzumato, Theresa M, Holiday House Inc, 425 Madison Ave, New York, NY 10017 *Tel:* 212-688-0085 *Fax:* 212-421-6134 *E-mail:* holiday@holidayhouse.com *Web Site:* www.holidayhouse.com, pg 113

Bosarge, Jerusha, Character Publishing, 6340 Kiln Delisle Rd, Unit F, Pass Christian, MS 39571 *Tel:* 228-234-7651 *Fax:* 228-222-3321 *Web Site:* www.characterpublishing.org, pg 55

Bosch, Sammy, Mighty Media Press, 1201 Currie Ave, Minneapolis, MN 55403 *Tel:* 612-455-0252 *Fax:* 612-338-4817 *E-mail:* info@mightymedia.com *Web Site:* www.mightymediapress.com, pg 156

Bost, Laura, University of Texas Press, 2100 Comal St, Austin, TX 78722 *Tel:* 512-471-7233 *Fax:* 512-232-7178 *E-mail:* utpress@uts.cc.utexas.edu *Web Site:* www.utexaspress.com, pg 244

Boston, Leslie Paul, The Boston Word Works, PO Box 56419, Sherman Oaks, CA 91413-1419 *Tel:* 818-904-9088 *Fax:* 818-787-1431, pg 522

Botsford, Marj, CWA/SCA Canada, 2200 Prince of Wales Dr, Suite 301, Ottawa, ON K2E 6Z9, Canada *Tel:* 613-820-9777 *Toll Free Tel:* 877-486-4292 *Fax:* 613-820-8188 *E-mail:* info@cwa-scacanada.ca *Web Site:* www.cwa-scacanada.ca, pg 604

Botton, Maury, The New Press, 38 Greene St, 4th fl, New York, NY 10013 *Tel:* 212-629-8802 *Toll Free Tel:* 800-343-4489 (orders) *Fax:* 212-629-8617 *Toll Free Fax:* 800-351-5073 (orders) *E-mail:* newpress@thenewpress.com *Web Site:* www.thenewpress.com, pg 168

Bottorff, Todd, Turner Publishing Co, 200 Fourth Ave N, Suite 950, Nashville, TN 37219 *Tel:* 615-255-BOOK (255-2665) *Fax:* 615-255-5081 *E-mail:* marketing@turnerpublishing.com; submissions@turnerpublishing.com *Web Site:* www.turnerpublishing.com, pg 250

Bottrell, Donna, The Wine Appreciation Guild Ltd, 360 Swift Ave, Suites 30 & 34, South San Francisco, CA 94080 *Tel:* 650-866-3020 *Toll Free Tel:* 800-231-9463 *Fax:* 650-866-3513 *E-mail:* info@wineappreciation.com *Web Site:* www.wineappreciation.com, pg 273

Botzman, Harvey, Cyclotour Guide Books, 160 Harvard St, Rochester, NY 14607-3174 *Tel:* 585-244-6157 *E-mail:* cyclotour@cyclotour.com *Web Site:* www.cyclotour.com, pg 69

Bouchard, Judith, Les Editions JCL, 930, rue Jacques-Cartier E, Chicoutimi, QC G7H 7K9, Canada *Tel:* 418-696-0536 *Fax:* 418-696-3132 *E-mail:* jcl@jcl.qc.ca *Web Site:* www.jcl.qc.ca, pg 482

Boucher, Jayme, Penguin Random House Speakers Bureau, 1745 Broadway, Mail Drop 13-1, New York, NY 10019 *Tel:* 212-572-2013 *E-mail:* speakers@penguinrandomhouse.com *Web Site:* www.prhspeakers.com, pg 587

Boucher, Johanne, Ordre des traducteurs, terminologues et interpretes agrees du quebec, 2021 Union Ave, Suite 1108, Montreal, QC H3A 2S9, Canada *Tel:* 514-845-4411 *Toll Free Tel:* 800-265-4815 *Fax:* 514-845-9903 *E-mail:* info@ottiaq.org *Web Site:* www.ottiaq.org, pg 615

Boughton, Simon, Macmillan, 175 Fifth Ave, New York, NY 10010 *Tel:* 646-307-5151 *Fax:* 212-420-9314 *E-mail:* firstname.lastname@macmillan.com *Web Site:* www.macmillan.com, pg 145

Boughton, Simon, Roaring Brook Press, 175 Fifth Ave, New York, NY 10010 *Tel:* 646-307-5151 *Web Site:* us.macmillan.com/roaringbrookpressaspx, pg 210

Boulder, Sharon, Top of the Mountain Publishing, PO Box 2244, Pinellas Park, FL 33780-2244 *Tel:* 727-391-3958 *E-mail:* tag@abcinfo.com; info@abcinfo.com *Web Site:* abcinfo.com; www.topofthemountain.com, pg 247

Boulerice, Yvan, Art Image Publications, PO Box 160, Derby Line, VT 05830 *Toll Free Tel:* 800-361-2598 *Toll Free Fax:* 800-559-2598 *E-mail:* info@artimagepublications.com; customer.service@artimagepublications.com *Web Site:* www.artimagepublications.com, pg 22

Boulle, Philippe, White Wolf Publishing Inc, 250 Ponce de Leon Ave, Suite 700, Decatur, GA 30030 *Tel:* 404-292-1819 *Toll Free Tel:* 800-454-9653 *E-mail:* questions@white-wolf.com *Web Site:* www.white-wolf.com, pg 271

Boultinghouse, Philis, Howard Books, 216 Centerview Dr, Suite 303, Brentwood, TN 37027 *Tel:* 615-873-2080 *Fax:* 615-370-3834 *E-mail:* howardbooks@simonandschuster.com (info) *Web Site:* www.howardpublishing.com, pg 116

Bourbon Ramirez, Melissa, Entangled Publishing, 2614 S Timberline Rd, Suite 109, Fort Collins, CO 80525 *Tel:* 724-208-7888 (sales) *E-mail:* publisher@entangledpublishing.com *Web Site:* www.entangledpublishing.com, pg 83

Bourdon, Pierre, Groupe Sogides Inc, 955 rue Amherst, Montreal, QC H2L 3K4, Canada *Tel:* 514-523-1182 *Fax:* 514-597-0370 *Web Site:* www.sogides.com, pg 486

Bourg, Chris, Massachusetts Institute of Technology Libraries, 77 Massachusetts Ave, Bldg 14-S, Rm 0551, Cambridge, MA 02139-4307 *Tel:* 617-253-5671 *Web Site:* libraries.mit.edu/docs, pg 149

Bourgault, Rochelle, Shambhala Publications Inc, Horticultural Hall, 300 Massachusetts Ave, Boston, MA 02115 *Tel:* 617-424-0030 *Toll Free Tel:* 866-

Bradford, Laura, Bradford Literary Agency, 5694 Mission Center Rd, Suite 347, San Diego, CA 92108 *Tel:* 619-521-1201 *E-mail:* queries@bradfordlit.com *Web Site:* www.bradfordlit.com, pg 543

Bradford, Maya, Harry N Abrams Inc, 115 W 18 St, 6th fl, New York, NY 10011 *Tel:* 212-206-7715 *Toll Free Tel:* 800-345-1359 *Fax:* 212-519-1210 *E-mail:* abrams@abramsbooks.com *Web Site:* www.abramsbooks.com, pg 3

Bradhering, Gary, MapEasy Inc, PO Box 80, Wainscott, NY 11975-0080 *Tel:* 631-537-6213 *Toll Free Tel:* 888-627-3279 *Fax:* 631-537-4541 *E-mail:* info@mapeasy.com *Web Site:* www.mapeasy.com, pg 146

Bradie, Ian R, Cambridge University Press, 32 Avenue of the Americas, New York, NY 10013-2473 *Tel:* 212-924-3900; 212-337-5000 *Fax:* 212-691-3239 *E-mail:* newyork@cambridge.org *Web Site:* www.cambridge.org/us, pg 49

Bradley, Cheryl, NASW Press, 750 First St NE, Suite 700, Washington, DC 20002 *Tel:* 202-408-8600 *Fax:* 203-336-8312 *E-mail:* press@naswdc.org *Web Site:* www.naswpress.org, pg 162

Bradley, Elizabeth, The Foundation Center, 32 Old Slip, 24th fl, New York, NY 10005-3500 *Tel:* 212-620-4230 *Toll Free Tel:* 800-424-9836 *Fax:* 212-807-3677 *E-mail:* customerservice@foundationcenter.org *Web Site:* foundationcenter.org, pg 91

Bradley, Fern Marshall, Chelsea Green Publishing Co, 85 N Main St, Suite 120, White River Junction, VT 05001 *Tel:* 802-295-6300 *Toll Free Tel:* 800-639-4099 (cust serv, consumer & trade orders) *Fax:* 802-295-6444 *Web Site:* www.chelseagreen.com, pg 56

Bradley, Joanna, Fresh Air Books, 1908 Grand Ave, Nashville, TN 37212 *Tel:* 615-340-7200 *Toll Free Tel:* 800-972-0433 (orders) *Web Site:* books.upperroom.org, pg 93

Bradley, Joanna, Upper Room Books, 1908 Grand Ave, Nashville, TN 37212 *Tel:* 615-340-7200 *Toll Free Tel:* 800-972-0433 *Fax:* 615-340-7266 *Web Site:* books.upperroom.org, pg 263

Bradley, Kevin J, Taylor & Francis Inc, 325 Chestnut St, Suite 800, Philadelphia, PA 20036-1802 *Tel:* 215-625-8900 *Toll Free Tel:* 800-354-1420 *Fax:* 215-625-2940 *E-mail:* customer.service@taylorandfrancis.com *Web Site:* www.taylorandfrancis.com, pg 241

Bradley, Linda, Learning Links Inc, PO Box 326, Cranbury, NJ 08512 *Tel:* 516-437-9071 *Toll Free Tel:* 800-724-2616 *Fax:* 516-437-5392 *E-mail:* info@learninglinks.com *Web Site:* www.learninglinks.com, pg 136

Bradley, Rosemary, Pearson Humanities & Social Sciences, 225 River St, Hoboken, NJ 07030-4772 *Tel:* 201-236-7000 *Fax:* 201-236-3400, pg 185

Bradley, Shaun, Transatlantic Agency, 2 Bloor St E, Suite 3500, Toronto, ON M4W 1A8, Canada *Tel:* 416-488-9214 *E-mail:* info@transatlanticagency.com *Web Site:* www.transatlanticagency.com, pg 577

Bradshaw, Alan, Palgrave Macmillan, 175 Fifth Ave, Suite 200, New York, NY 10010 *Tel:* 646-307-5151 *Fax:* 212-777-6359 *E-mail:* firstname.lastname@palgrave-usa.com *Web Site:* us.macmillan.com/Palgrave.aspx, pg 180

Brady, Lizz, Fine Creative Media, Inc, 322 Eighth Ave, 15th fl, New York, NY 10001 *Tel:* 212-595-3500 *Fax:* 212-595-3779, pg 88

Brady, Mackenzie, Charlotte Sheedy Literary Agency Inc, 928 Broadway, Suite 901, New York, NY 10010 *Tel:* 212-780-9800 *Web Site:* www.sheedylit.com, pg 573

Brady, Philip, Etruscan Press, Wilkes University, 84 W South St, Wilkes-Barre, PA 18766 *Tel:* 570-408-4546 *Fax:* 570-408-3333 *E-mail:* books@etruscanpress.org *Web Site:* www.etruscanpress.org, pg 84

Brady, Robert L, Business & Legal Resources Inc, 100 Winners Circle, Suite 300, Brentwood, TN 37027 *Tel:* 860-510-0100 *Toll Free Tel:* 800-727-5257 *E-mail:* service@blr.com *Web Site:* www.blr.com, pg 48

Brady, Sally R, bradylit, 81 Town Farm Hill, Hartland Four Corners, VT 05049 *Tel:* 802-436-2455, pg 522

Braeckel, Maria, Random House Publishing Group, 1745 Broadway, New York, NY 10019 *Toll Free Tel:* 800-200-3552 *Web Site:* atrandom.com, pg 204

Bragg, Judith K, Laura Day Boggs Bolling Memorial, 1194 Hume Rd, Hume, VA 22639-1806 *E-mail:* poetryinva@aol.com *Web Site:* www.poetrysocietyofvirginia.org, pg 673

Bragg, Judith K, Joe Pendleton Campbell Narrative Contest, 1194 Hume Rd, Hume, VA 22639-1806 *E-mail:* poetryinva@aol.com *Web Site:* www.poetrysocietyofvirginia.org, pg 675

Bragg, Judith K, Carleton Drewry Memorial, 1194 Hume Rd, Hume, VA 22639-1806 *E-mail:* poetryinva@aol.com *Web Site:* www.poetrysocietyofvirginia.org, pg 682

Bragg, Judith K, Alfred C Gary Memorial, 1194 Hume Rd, Hume, VA 22639-1806 *E-mail:* poetryinva@aol.com *Web Site:* www.poetrysocietyofvirginia.org, pg 688

Bragg, Judith K, Bess Gresham Memorial, 1194 Hume Rd, Hume, VA 22639-1806 *E-mail:* poetryinva@aol.com *Web Site:* www.poetrysocietyofvirginia.org, pg 690

Bragg, Judith K, Loretta Dunn Hall Memorial, 1194 Hume Rd, Hume, VA 22639-1806 *E-mail:* poetryinva@aol.com *Web Site:* www.poetrysocietyofvirginia.org, pg 691

Bragg, Judith K, Handy Andy Prize, 1194 Hume Rd, Hume, VA 22639-1806 *E-mail:* poetryinva@aol.com *Web Site:* www.poetrysocietyofvirginia.org, pg 691

Bragg, Judith K, Brodie Herndon Memorial, 1194 Hume Rd, Hume, VA 22639-1806 *E-mail:* poetryinva@aol.com *Web Site:* www.poetrysocietyofvirginia.org, pg 692

Bragg, Judith K, Judah, Sarah, Grace & Tom Memorial, 1194 Hume Rd, Hume, VA 22639-1806 *E-mail:* poetryinva@aol.com *Web Site:* www.poetrysocietyofvirginia.org, pg 697

Bragg, Judith K, Cenie H Moon Prize, 1194 Hume Rd, Hume, VA 22639-1806 *E-mail:* poetryinva@aol.com *Web Site:* www.poetrysocietyofvirginia.org, pg 709

Bragg, Judith K, Edgar Allan Poe Memorial, 1194 Hume Rd, Hume, VA 22639-1806 *E-mail:* poetryinva@aol.com *Web Site:* www.poetrysocietyofvirginia.org, pg 719

Bragg, Judith K, A Poem With a Point of View, 1194 Hume Rd, Hume, VA 22639-1806 *E-mail:* poetryinva@aol.com *Web Site:* www.poetrysocietyofvirginia.org, pg 719

Bragg, Judith K, Miriam Rachimi Memorial, 1194 Hume Rd, Hume, VA 22639-1806 *E-mail:* poetryinva@aol.com *Web Site:* www.poetrysocietyofvirginia.org, pg 722

Bragg, Judith K, Ada Sanderson Memorial, 1194 Hume Rd, Hume, VA 22639-1806 *E-mail:* poetryinva@aol.com *Web Site:* www.poetrysocietyofvirginia.org, pg 725

Bragg, Judith K, The Robert S Sergeant Memorial, 1194 Hume Rd, Hume, VA 22639-1806 *E-mail:* poetryinva@aol.com *Web Site:* www.poetrysocietyofvirginia.org, pg 727

Braithwaite, Jill, Carolrhoda Books, 241 First Ave N, Minneapolis, MN 55401 *Tel:* 612-332-3344 *Toll Free Tel:* 800-328-4929 *Fax:* 612-332-7615 *Toll Free Fax:* 800-332-1132 *E-mail:* info@lernerbooks.com *Web Site:* www.lernerbooks.com, pg 50

Braithwaite, Jill, Carolrhoda Lab™, 241 First Ave N, Minneapolis, MN 55401 *Tel:* 612-332-3344 *Toll Free Tel:* 800-328-4929 *Fax:* 612-332-7615 *Toll Free Fax:* 800-332-1132 (US) *E-mail:* info@lernerbooks.com *Web Site:* www.lernerbooks.com, pg 51

Braithwaite, Jill, ediciones Lerner, 241 First Ave N, Minneapolis, MN 55401 *Tel:* 612-332-3344 *Toll Free Tel:* 800-328-4929 *Fax:* 612-332-7615 *Toll Free Fax:* 800-332-1132 *E-mail:* info@lernerbooks.com *Web Site:* www.lernerbooks.com, pg 79

Braithwaite, Jill, First Avenue Editions, 241 First Ave N, Minneapolis, MN 55401 *Tel:* 612-332-3344 *Toll Free Tel:* 800-328-4929 *Fax:* 612-332-7615 *Toll Free Fax:* 800-332-1132 *E-mail:* info@lernerbooks.com *Web Site:* www.lernerbooks.com, pg 89

Braithwaite, Jill, Graphic Universe™, 241 First Ave N, Minneapolis, MN 55401 *Tel:* 612-332-3344 *Toll Free Tel:* 800-328-4929 *Fax:* 612-332-7615 *Toll Free Fax:* 800-332-1132 *E-mail:* info@lernerbooks.com *Web Site:* www.lernerbooks.com, pg 99

Braithwaite, Jill, Lerner Publications, 241 First Ave N, Minneapolis, MN 55401 *Tel:* 612-332-3344 *Toll Free Tel:* 800-328-4929 *Fax:* 612-332-7615 *Toll Free Fax:* 800-332-1132 *E-mail:* info@lernerbooks.com *Web Site:* www.lernerbooks.com, pg 137

Braithwaite, Jill, Lerner Publishing Group Inc, 241 First Ave N, Minneapolis, MN 55401 *Tel:* 612-332-3344 *Toll Free Tel:* 800-328-4929 *Fax:* 612-332-7615 *Toll Free Fax:* 800-332-1132 *E-mail:* info@lernerbooks.com *Web Site:* www.lernerbooks.com, pg 137

Braithwaite, Jill, LernerClassroom, 241 First Ave N, Minneapolis, MN 55401 *Tel:* 612-332-3344 *Toll Free Tel:* 800-328-4929 *Fax:* 612-332-7615 *Toll Free Fax:* 800-332-1132 *E-mail:* info@lernerbooks.com *Web Site:* www.lernerbooks.com, pg 137

Braithwaite, Jill, Millbrook Press, 241 First Ave N, Minneapolis, MN 55401 *Tel:* 612-332-3344 *Toll Free Tel:* 800-328-4929 (US only) *Fax:* 612-332-7615 *Toll Free Fax:* 800-332-1132, pg 157

Braithwaite, Jill, Twenty-First Century Books, 241 First Ave N, Minneapolis, MN 55401 *Tel:* 612-332-3344 *Toll Free Tel:* 800-328-4929 *Fax:* 612-332-7615 *Toll Free Fax:* 800-332-1132 *E-mail:* info@lernerbooks.com *Web Site:* www.lernerbooks.com, pg 251

Bramson, Ann, Workman Publishing Co Inc, 225 Varick St, 9th fl, New York, NY 10014-4381 *Tel:* 212-254-5900 *Toll Free Tel:* 800-722-7202 *Fax:* 212-254-8098 *E-mail:* info@workman.com *Web Site:* www.workman.com, pg 275

Branch, Justin, Greenleaf Book Group LLC, Three Park Place, 4005 Banister Lane, Suite B, Austin, TX 78704 *Tel:* 512-891-6100 *Toll Free Tel:* 800-932-5420 *Fax:* 512-891-6150 *E-mail:* contact@greenleafbookgroup.com *Web Site:* www.greenleafbookgroup.com, pg 100

Brand, Amy, The MIT Press, 55 Hayward St, Cambridge, MA 02142 *Tel:* 617-253-5255 *Toll Free Tel:* 800-207-8354 (orders) *Fax:* 617-258-6779; 617-577-1545 (orders) *Web Site:* mitpress.mit.edu, pg 158

Brand, Christopher, Crown Publishing Group, c/o Penguin Random House Inc, 1745 Broadway, New York, NY 10019 *Tel:* 212-782-9000 *Toll Free Tel:* 888-264-1745 *Fax:* 212-940-7408 *E-mail:* crownosm@penguinrandomhouse.com *Web Site:* crownpublishing.com, pg 68

Brand, Elaine, See-More's Workshop, 325 West End Ave, Suite 12-B, New York, NY 10023 *Tel:* 212-724-0677 *Fax:* 212-724-0767 *E-mail:* sbt@shadowboxtheatre.org *Web Site:* www.shadowboxtheatre.org, pg 221

Brand, Elaine, See-More's Workshop Arts & Education Workshops, 325 West End Ave, Suite 12-B, New York, NY 10023 *Tel:* 212-724-0677 *Fax:* 212-724-0767 *E-mail:* sbt@shadowboxtheatre.org *Web Site:* www.shadowboxtheatre.org, pg 655

Brand, Megan, University of British Columbia Press, 2029 West Mall, Vancouver, BC V6T 1Z2, Canada *Tel:* 604-822-5959 *Toll Free Tel:* 877-377-9378 *Fax:* 604-822-6083 *Toll Free Fax:* 800-668-0821 *E-mail:* frontdesk@ubcpress.ca *Web Site:* www.ubcpress.ca, pg 502

Brandel, Ms Dusty, American Auto Racing Writers & Broadcasters, 922 N Pass Ave, Burbank, CA 91505 *Tel:* 818-842-7005 *Fax:* 818-842-7020, pg 594

Brandenburgh, Greg, Red Wheel/Weiser/Conari, 65 Parker St, Suite 7, Newburyport, MA 01950 *Tel:* 978-465-0504 *Toll Free Tel:* 800-423-7087 (orders) *Fax:* 978-465-0243 *E-mail:* info@rwwbooks.com *Web Site:* www.redwheelweiser.com, pg 206

Brander, Jacob, Mesorah Publications Ltd, 4401 Second Ave, Brooklyn, NY 11232 *Tel:* 718-921-9000 *Toll Free Tel:* 800-637-6724 *Fax:* 718-680-1875 *E-mail:* artscroll@mesorah.com *Web Site:* www.artscroll.com; www.mesorah.com, pg 155

Brandhorst, Timothy, American Bar Association, 321 N Clark St, Chicago, IL 60654 *Tel:* 312-988-5000 *Toll Free Tel:* 800-285-2221 (orders) *Fax:* 312-988-6281 *E-mail:* orders@abanet.org *Web Site:* shop.americanbar.org, pg 11

Brandl, Gary, New City Press, 202 Comforter Blvd, Hyde Park, NY 12538 *Tel:* 845-229-0335 *Toll Free Tel:* 800-462-5980 (orders only) *Fax:* 845-229-0351 *E-mail:* info@newcitypress.com *Web Site:* www.newcitypress.com, pg 167

Brandreth, Dale, Caissa Editions, PO Box 151, Yorklyn, DE 19736-0151 *Tel:* 302-239-4608 *Web Site:* www.chessbookstore.com, pg 48

Brandt, Eric, The University of Virginia Press, PO Box 400318, Charlottesville, VA 22904-4318 *Tel:* 434-924-3468 (cust serv); 434-924-3469 (cust serv) *Toll Free Tel:* 800-831-3406 (orders) *Fax:* 434-982-2655 *Toll Free Fax:* 877-288-6400 *E-mail:* vapress@virginia.edu *Web Site:* www.upress.virginia.edu, pg 260

Brandt, Joan, The Joan Brandt Agency, 788 Wesley Dr NW, Atlanta, GA 30305 *Tel:* 404-351-8877 *Fax:* 404-351-0068, pg 544

Branham, Lorraine, Syracuse University, SI Newhouse School of Public Communications, 215 University Place, Syracuse, NY 13244-2100 *Tel:* 315-443-3627 *Fax:* 315-443-3946 *E-mail:* newhouse@syr.edu *Web Site:* newhouse.syr.edu, pg 662

Branham, Sarah, Atria Books, 1230 Avenue of the Americas, New York, NY 10020 *Tel:* 212-698-7000 *Fax:* 212-698-7007 *Web Site:* www.simonandschuster.com, pg 27

Brann, Helen, ICM Partners, 730 Fifth Ave, New York, NY 10019 *Tel:* 212-556-5600 *Web Site:* www.icmtalent.com, pg 557

Brants, Keith, Martingale®, 19021 120 Ave NE, Suite 102, Bothell, WA 98011 *Tel:* 425-483-3313 *Toll Free Tel:* 800-426-3126 *Fax:* 425-486-7596 *E-mail:* info@martingale-pub.com *Web Site:* www.martingale-pub.com, pg 148

Brashear, Amanda S, Samhain Publishing Ltd, 11821 Mason Montgomery Rd, Suite 4-B, Cincinnati, OH 45249 *Tel:* 513-453-4688 *Fax:* 513-583-0191 *E-mail:* support@samhainpublishing.com *Web Site:* www.samhainpublishing.com, pg 216

Brashear, Christina M, Samhain Publishing Ltd, 11821 Mason Montgomery Rd, Suite 4-B, Cincinnati, OH 45249 *Tel:* 513-453-4688 *Fax:* 513-583-0191 *E-mail:* support@samhainpublishing.com *Web Site:* www.samhainpublishing.com, pg 215

Braswell, Calandra, World Scientific Publishing Co Inc, 27 Warren St, Suite 401-402, Hackensack, NJ 07601 *Tel:* 201-487-9655 *Toll Free Tel:* 800-227-7562 *Fax:* 201-487-9656 *Toll Free Fax:* 888-977-2665 *E-mail:* wspc@wspc.com *Web Site:* www.wspc.com, pg 276

Bratcher, Joe W III, Host Publications, 3408 West Ave, Austin, TX 78705 *Tel:* 512-236-1290 *Fax:* 512-236-1208 *Web Site:* www.hostpublications.com, pg 114

Bratton, Chuck, EMC Publishing LLC, 875 Montreal Way, St Paul, MN 55102 *Tel:* 651-290-2800 (corp) *Toll Free Tel:* 800-328-1452 *Toll Free Fax:* 800-328-4564 *E-mail:* educate@emcp.com *Web Site:* www.emcp.com, pg 81

Brault, Carol, Dorland Health, 4 Choke Cherry Rd, 2nd fl, Rockville, MD 20850 *Tel:* 301-354-2000 *Toll Free Tel:* 855-225-5341 *Fax:* 301-287-2535 *E-mail:* customer@decisionhealth.com *Web Site:* www.dorlandhealth.com, pg 75

Brault, Yves, Brault & Bouthillier, 700 ave Beaumont, Montreal, QC H3N 1V5, Canada *Tel:* 514-273-9186 *Toll Free Tel:* 800-361-0378 *Fax:* 514-273-8627 *Toll Free Fax:* 800-361-0378 *E-mail:* ventes@bb.ca *Web Site:* bb.ca, pg 473

Braun, Barbara, Barbara Braun Associates Inc, 7 E 14 St, Suite 19F, New York, NY 10003 *Tel:* 212-604-9023 *Web Site:* www.barbarabraunagency.com, pg 544

Braun, Mary Elizabeth, Oregon State University Press, 121 The Valley Library, Corvallis, OR 97331-4501 *Tel:* 541-737-3166 *Toll Free Tel:* 800-621-2736 (orders) *Web Site:* osupress.oregonstate.edu, pg 177

Braunstein, Bruce, Book Publicists of Southern California, 714 Crescent Dr, Beverly Hills, CA 90210 *Tel:* 323-461-3921 *Fax:* 323-461-0917 *Web Site:* www.bookpublicists.org, pg 600

Braverman, Marianne, Andrew Carnegie Medals for Excellence in Fiction & Nonfiction, 50 E Huron St, Chicago, IL 60611 *Tel:* 312-944-6780 *Toll Free Tel:* 800-545-2433 *Fax:* 312-440-9374 *E-mail:* ala@ala.org *Web Site:* www.ala.org/awardsgrants/carnegieadult, pg 676

Braziller, George, George Braziller Inc, 277 Broadway, Suite 708, New York, NY 10007 *Tel:* 212-260-9256 *Fax:* 212-267-3165 *E-mail:* editorial@georgebraziller.com *Web Site:* www.georgebraziller.com, pg 44

Braziller, Karen, Persea Books, 277 Broadway, Suite 708, New York, NY 10007 *Tel:* 212-260-9256 *Fax:* 212-267-3165 *E-mail:* info@perseabooks.com *Web Site:* www.perseabooks.com, pg 189

Braziller, Karen, Lexi Rudnitsky Poetry Prize, 277 Broadway, Suite 708, New York, NY 10007 *Tel:* 212-260-9256 *Fax:* 212-267-3165 *E-mail:* info@perseabooks.com *Web Site:* www.perseabooks.com, pg 725

Braziller, Michael, George Braziller Inc, 277 Broadway, Suite 708, New York, NY 10007 *Tel:* 212-260-9256 *Fax:* 212-267-3165 *E-mail:* editorial@georgebraziller.com *Web Site:* www.georgebraziller.com, pg 44

Braziller, Michael, Persea Books, 277 Broadway, Suite 708, New York, NY 10007 *Tel:* 212-260-9256 *Fax:* 212-267-3165 *E-mail:* info@perseabooks.com *Web Site:* www.perseabooks.com, pg 189

Braziller, Michael, Lexi Rudnitsky Poetry Prize, 277 Broadway, Suite 708, New York, NY 10007 *Tel:* 212-260-9256 *Fax:* 212-267-3165 *E-mail:* info@perseabooks.com *Web Site:* www.perseabooks.com, pg 725

Brealey, Nicholas, Nicholas Brealey Publishing, 20 Park Plaza, Suite 610, Boston, MA 02116 *Tel:* 617-523-3801 *Toll Free Tel:* 888-BREALEY (273-2539) *Fax:* 617-523-3708 *E-mail:* info@nicholasbrealey.com *Web Site:* www.nicholasbrealey.com, pg 45

Brebner, Nicole, Harlequin Enterprises Ltd, 225 Duncan Mill Rd, Don Mills, ON M3B 3K9, Canada *Tel:* 416-445-5860 *Toll Free Tel:* 888-432-4879; 800-370-5838 (ebook inquiries) *E-mail:* customerservice@harlequin.com *Web Site:* www.harlequin.com, pg 487

Brechner, Michael, Cypress House, 155 Cypress St, Fort Bragg, CA 95437 *Tel:* 707-964-9520 *Toll Free Tel:* 800-773-7782 *Fax:* 707-964-7531 *E-mail:* cypresshouse@cypresshouse.com *Web Site:* www.cypresshouse.com, pg 69, 524

Brecker, Lora, Ascension Press, PO Box 1990, West Chester, PA 19380 *Tel:* 610-696-7795 (ext 207, edit); 484-875-4550 (admin) *Toll Free Tel:* 800-376-0520 (sales & cust serv) *E-mail:* info@ascensionpress.com *Web Site:* ascensionpress.com, pg 24

Breckler, Steven J PhD, American Psychological Association, 750 First St NE, Washington, DC 20002-4242 *Tel:* 202-336-5510 *Toll Free Tel:* 800-374-2721 *Fax:* 202-336-5502 *E-mail:* order@apa.org *Web Site:* www.apa.org/books, pg 15

Breckler, Steven J PhD, American Psychological Association, 750 First St NE, Washington, DC 20002-4242 *Tel:* 202-336-5500 *Toll Free Tel:* 800-374-2721 *E-mail:* order@apa.org *Web Site:* www.apa.org, pg 596

Breden, Cathy, The Center for Exhibition Industry Research (CEIR), 12700 Park Central Dr, Suite 308, Dallas, TX 75251 *Tel:* 972-687-9242 *Fax:* 972-692-6020 *E-mail:* info@ceir.org *Web Site:* www.ceir.org, pg 603

Breeden, Elizabeth, Simon & Schuster, 1230 Avenue of the Americas, New York, NY 10020 *Tel:* 212-698-7000 *Toll Free Tel:* 800-223-2348 (cust serv); 800-223-2336 (orders) *Toll Free Fax:* 800-943-9831 (orders) *Web Site:* www.simonandschuster.com, pg 225

Brehl, Joan, Alliance for Audited Media (AAM), Canadian Office, 151 Bloor St W, Suite 850, Toronto, ON M5S 1S4, Canada *Tel:* 416-962-5840 *Fax:* 416-962-5844 *Web Site:* www.auditmedia.com, pg 594

Breichner, William M, The Johns Hopkins University Press, 2715 N Charles St, Baltimore, MD 21218-4363 *Tel:* 410-516-6900; 410-516-6987 (journal orders outside US & CN) *Toll Free Tel:* 800-537-5487 (book orders & cust serv); 800-548-1784 (journal orders) *Fax:* 410-516-6968; 410-516-3866 (journal orders) *E-mail:* hfscustserv@press.jhu.edu (cust serv); jrnlcirc@press.jhu.edu (journal orders) *Web Site:* www.press.jhu.edu; muse.jhu.edu, pg 127

Breier, Davida, The Johns Hopkins University Press, 2715 N Charles St, Baltimore, MD 21218-4363 *Tel:* 410-516-6900; 410-516-6987 (journal orders outside US & CN) *Toll Free Tel:* 800-537-5487 (book orders & cust serv); 800-548-1784 (journal orders) *Fax:* 410-516-6968; 410-516-3866 (journal orders) *E-mail:* hfscustserv@press.jhu.edu (cust serv); jrnlcirc@press.jhu.edu (journal orders) *Web Site:* www.press.jhu.edu; muse.jhu.edu, pg 127

Breisacher, Ed, The Darwin Press Inc, PO Box 2202, Princeton, NJ 08543 *Tel:* 609-737-1349 *Fax:* 609-737-0929 *E-mail:* books@darwinpress.com *Web Site:* www.darwinpress.com, pg 70

Breivogel, Sarah, Crown Publishing Group, c/o Penguin Random House Inc, 1745 Broadway, New York, NY 10019 *Tel:* 212-782-9000 *Toll Free Tel:* 888-264-1745 *Fax:* 212-940-7408 *E-mail:* crownosm@penguinrandomhouse.com *Web Site:* crownpublishing.com, pg 68

Brendan, Stephen, Light Publications, Hope Artiste Village, 1005 Main St, Suite 1212, Pawtucket, RI 02806 *Tel:* 401-484-0228 *E-mail:* info@lightpublications.com *Web Site:* lightpublications.com, pg 139

Brennan, Kit, Signature Editions, RPO Corydon, PO Box 206, Winnipeg, MB R3M 3S7, Canada *Tel:* 204-779-7803 *Fax:* 204-779-6970 *E-mail:* signature@allstream.net; orders@signature-editions.com *Web Site:* www.signature-editions.com, pg 499

Brenner, Carol, Brenner Information Group, 9282 Samantha Ct, San Diego, CA 92129 *Tel:* 858-538-0093 *Toll Free Tel:* 800-811-4337 (orders) *E-mail:* brenner@brennerbooks.com; sales@brennerbooks.com *Web Site:* www.brennerbooks.com, pg 45

Brenner, Robert, Brenner Information Group, 9282 Samantha Ct, San Diego, CA 92129 *Tel:* 858-538-0093 *Toll Free Tel:* 800-811-4337 (orders) *E-mail:* brenner@brennerbooks.com; sales@brennerbooks.com *Web Site:* www.brennerbooks.com, pg 45

Brent, Barbara, Two Thousand Three Associates, 4180 Saxon Dr, New Smyrna Beach, FL 32169 *Tel:* 386-690-2503 *E-mail:* ttta1@att.net *Web Site:* www.twothousandthree.com, pg 252

Brent, T David, University of Chicago Press, 1427 E 60 St, Chicago, IL 60637-2954 *Tel:* 773-702-7700; 773-702-7600 *Toll Free Tel:* 800-621-2736 (orders) *Fax:* 773-702-9756; 773-660-2235 (orders); 773-702-2708 *E-mail:* custserv@press.uchicago.edu; marketing@press.uchicago.edu *Web Site:* www.press.uchicago.edu, pg 255

Breschini, Gary PhD, Coyote Press, PO Box 3377, Salinas, CA 93912-3377 *Tel:* 831-422-4912 *Fax:* 831-422-4913 *E-mail:* orders@coyotepress.com *Web Site:* www.coyotepress.com, pg 66

Breslin, Ramsay, Kelsey Street Press, 2824 Kelsey St, Berkeley, CA 94705 *Tel:* 510-845-2260 *Fax:* 510-548-9185 *E-mail:* info@kelseyst.com *Web Site:* www.kelseyst.com, pg 130

Breslof, Lisa, The John Burroughs List of Nature Books for Young Readers, 15 W 77 St, New York, NY 10024 *Tel:* 212-769-5169 *Fax:* 212-313-7182 *Web Site:* research.amnh.org/burroughs, pg 674

Breslof, Lisa, John Burroughs Medal, 15 W 77 St, New York, NY 10024 *Tel:* 212-769-5169 *Fax:* 212-313-7182 *Web Site:* research.amnh.org/burroughs, pg 674

Breslof, Lisa, John Burroughs Outstanding Published Nature Essay Award, 15 W 77 St, New York, NY 10024 *Tel:* 212-769-5169 *Fax:* 212-313-7182 *Web Site:* research.amnh.org/burroughs, pg 675

Bressler, Rachel, Plume, 375 Hudson St, New York, NY 10014 *Tel:* 212-366-2000 *Fax:* 212-366-2666 *E-mail:* online@penguinputnam.com *Web Site:* www.penguinputnam.com; us.penguingroup.com, pg 193

Brettschneider, Cathie, The University of Virginia Press, PO Box 400318, Charlottesville, VA 22904-4318 *Tel:* 434-924-3468 (cust serv); 434-924-3469 (cust serv) *Toll Free Tel:* 800-831-3406 (orders) *Fax:* 434-982-2655 *Toll Free Fax:* 877-288-6400 *E-mail:* vapress@virginia.edu *Web Site:* www.upress.virginia.edu, pg 260

Breunig, Kevin, Appalachian Mountain Club Books, 5 Joy St, Boston, MA 02108 *Tel:* 617-523-0655 *Toll Free Tel:* 800-262-4455 (orders) *Fax:* 617-523-0722 *E-mail:* amcbooks@outdoors.org *Web Site:* www.outdoors.org, pg 20

Brewer, Andrew, University of California Press, 2120 Berkeley Way, Berkeley, CA 94704-1012 *Tel:* 510-642-4247 *Fax:* 510-643-7127 *E-mail:* askucp@ucpress.edu (books); customerservice@ucpressjournals.com *Web Site:* www.ucpress.edu, pg 255

Brewer, Anne, St Martin's Press, LLC, 175 Fifth Ave, New York, NY 10010 *Tel:* 646-307-5151 *Fax:* 212-420-9314 *E-mail:* firstname.lastname@macmillan.com *Web Site:* www.stmartins.com, pg 215

Brewer, Leah, Jewish Lights Publishing, Sunset Farm Offices, Rte 4, Woodstock, VT 05091 *Tel:* 802-457-4000 *Toll Free Tel:* 800-962-4544 (orders only) *Fax:* 802-457-4004 *E-mail:* sales@jewishlights.com *Web Site:* www.jewishlights.com, pg 126

Breznay, Ron, Bram Stoker Awards®, 244 Fifth Ave, Suite 2767, New York, NY 10001 *E-mail:* hwa@horror.org *Web Site:* www.horror.org/awards/stokers.htm, pg 730

Bricker, Megan, The American Ceramic Society, 600 N Cleveland Ave, Suite 210, Westerville, OH 43082 *Tel:* 240-646-7054 *Toll Free Tel:* 866-721-3322 *Fax:* 240-396-5637 *E-mail:* customerservice@ceramics.org *Web Site:* ceramics.org, pg 11

Bridburg, Eve, Zachary Shuster Harmsworth Agency, 1776 Broadway, Suite 1405, New York, NY 10019 *Tel:* 212-765-6900 *Fax:* 212-765-6490 *Web Site:* www.zshliterary.com, pg 580

Bridges, Shirin Yim, Goosebottom Books, 543 Trinidad Lane, Foster City, CA 94404 *Tel:* 650-204-4076 *Toll Free Fax:* 888-407-5286 *E-mail:* info@goosebottombooks.com *Web Site:* goosebottombooks.com, pg 98

Bridgins, Sarah, Frances Goldin Literary Agency, Inc, 57 E 11 St, Suite 5-B, New York, NY 10003 *Tel:* 212-777-0047 *Fax:* 212-228-1660 *E-mail:* agency@goldinlit.com *Web Site:* www.goldinlit.com, pg 554

Briel, Barbara, Sourcebooks Inc, 1935 Brookdale Rd, Suite 139, Naperville, IL 60563 *Tel:* 630-961-3900 *Toll Free Tel:* 800-432-7444 *Fax:* 630-961-2168 *E-mail:* info@sourcebooks.com; customersupport@sourcebooks.com *Web Site:* www.sourcebooks.com, pg 230

Briere, Sylvie, Les Editions de l'Hexagone, 1010 rue de la Gauchetiere E, Montreal, QC H2L 2N5, Canada *Tel:* 514-523-7993 *Fax:* 514-282-7530 *Web Site:* www.edhexagone.com, pg 480

Briere, Sylvie, VLB Editeur Inc, 1010, Rue de la Gauchetiere Est, Montreal, QC H2L 2N5, Canada *Tel:* 514-523-7993 *Fax:* 514-282-7530 *Web Site:* www.edvlb.com, pg 504

Briesmaster, Allan, Quattro Books Inc, Centre for Social Innovation, 2nd fl, 720 Bathurst St, Toronto, ON M5S 2R4, Canada *Tel:* 647-748-7484 *E-mail:* info@quattrobooks.ca *Web Site:* www.quattrobooks.ca, pg 497

Briet, Eugenie, The French-American Foundation & Florence Gould Foundation Annual Translation Prize, 28 W 44 St, Suite 1420, New York, NY 10036 *Tel:* 212-829-8800 *Fax:* 212-829-8810 *E-mail:* translation@frenchamerican.org *Web Site:* www.frenchamerican.org, pg 687

Briggs, Barbara, University Press of New England, One Court St, Suite 250, Lebanon, NH 03766 *Tel:* 603-448-1533 *Toll Free Tel:* 800-421-1561 (orders only) *Fax:* 603-448-7006; 603-643-1540 *E-mail:* university.press@dartmouth.edu *Web Site:* www.upne.com, pg 262

Briggs, David, Philomel, 345 Hudson St, New York, NY 10014 *Tel:* 212-366-2000, pg 191

Briggs, David, GP Putnam's Sons (Children's), 345 Hudson St, New York, NY 10014 *Tel:* 212-366-2000 *Fax:* 212-414-3393 *E-mail:* online@penguinputnam.com *Web Site:* us.penguingroup.com, pg 201

Briggs, Harry, M E Sharpe Inc, 80 Business Park Dr, Suite 202, Armonk, NY 10504 *Tel:* 914-273-1800 *Toll Free Tel:* 800-541-6563 *Fax:* 914-273-2106 *E-mail:* info@mesharpe.com *Web Site:* www.mesharpe.com, pg 223

Briggs, John, Holiday House Inc, 425 Madison Ave, New York, NY 10017 *Tel:* 212-688-0085 *Fax:* 212-421-6134 *E-mail:* holiday@holidayhouse.com *Web Site:* www.holidayhouse.com, pg 113

Briggs, Laura, Potomac Books Inc, 22841 Quicksilver Dr, Dulles, VA 20166 *Tel:* 703-661-1548 *Fax:* 703-661-1547 *E-mail:* pbimail@presswarehouse.com *Web Site:* www.potomacbooksinc.com, pg 195

Briggs, M Courtney, M Courtney Briggs Esq, Authors Representative, Chase Tower, 28th fl, 100 N Broadway Ave, Oklahoma City, OK 73102, pg 544

Briggs, Michael, University Press of Kansas, 2502 Westbrooke Circle, Lawrence, KS 66045-4444 *Tel:* 785-864-4154; 785-864-4155 (orders) *Fax:* 785-864-4586 *E-mail:* upress@ku.edu; upkorders@ku.edu (orders) *Web Site:* www.kansaspress.ku.edu, pg 261

Bright, Harry, Maharishi University of Management Press, 1000 N Fourth St, Dept 1155, Fairfield, IA 52557-1155 *Tel:* 641-472-1101 *Toll Free Tel:* 800-831-6523 *Fax:* 641-472-1122 *E-mail:* mumpress@mum.edu *Web Site:* www.mumpress.com, pg 145

Brill, Calista, Roaring Brook Press, 175 Fifth Ave, New York, NY 10010 *Tel:* 646-307-5151 *Web Site:* us.macmillan.com/roaringbrookpressaspx, pg 210

Brill, L Chip, Peter Glenn Publications, 306 NE Second St, 2nd fl, Delray Beach, FL 33483 *Tel:* 561-404-4290 *Fax:* 561-892-5786 *Web Site:* pgdirect.com, pg 97

Brill, Paula, Between the Lines (BTL), 401 Richmond St W, No 277, Toronto, ON M5V 3A8, Canada *Tel:* 416-535-9914 *Toll Free Tel:* 800-718-7201 *Fax:* 416-535-1484 *E-mail:* info@btlbooks.com *Web Site:* btlbooks.com, pg 472

Brill, Randi S, The Quarasan Group Inc, 405 W Superior St, Chicago, IL 60654 *Tel:* 312-981-2500 *E-mail:* info@quarasan.com *Web Site:* www.quarasan.com, pg 533

Brinati, Teresa, Society of American Archivists, 17 N State St, Suite 1425, Chicago, IL 60602-4061 *Tel:* 312-606-0722 *Toll Free Tel:* 866-722-7858 *Fax:* 312-606-0728 *E-mail:* info@archivists.org *Web Site:* www.archivists.org, pg 229

Brine, Matthew, ProQuest LLC, 789 E Eisenhower Pkwy, Ann Arbor, MI 48108-3218 *Tel:* 734-761-4700 *Toll Free Tel:* 800-521-0600 *Fax:* 734-975-6486 *Toll Free Fax:* 800-864-0019 *E-mail:* info@proquest.com *Web Site:* www.proquest.com, pg 199

Brink, Matthew H, Butte Publications Inc, PO Box 1328, Hillsboro, OR 97123-1328 *Tel:* 503-648-9791 *Toll Free Tel:* 866-312-8883 *Fax:* 503-693-9526 *Toll Free Fax:* 866-412-8883 (orders only) *E-mail:* service@buttepublications.com *Web Site:* www.buttepublications.com, pg 48

Brinker, Spencer, Bearport Publishing Co Inc, 45 W 21 St, Suite 3B, New York, NY 10010 *Tel:* 212-337-8577 *Toll Free Tel:* 877-337-8577 *Fax:* 212-337-8557 *Toll Free Fax:* 866-337-8557 *E-mail:* service@bearportpublishing.com; info@bearportpublishing.com *Web Site:* www.bearportpublishing.com, pg 33

Brinley, Joseph F Jr, Woodrow Wilson Center Press, One Woodrow Wilson Plaza, 1300 Pennsylvania Ave NW, Washington, DC 20004-3027 *Tel:* 202-691-4000 *Fax:* 202-691-4001 *Web Site:* wilsoncenter.org, pg 275

Briseboas, Diane J, Canadian Booksellers Association (CBA), 1881 Yonge St, Suite 800, Toronto, ON M4S 3C4, Canada *Tel:* 416-922-6678 *Toll Free Tel:* 888-373-8245 *Toll Free Fax:* 877-790-4271 *E-mail:* info@retailcouncil.org *Web Site:* www.retailcouncil.org, pg 601

Briseboas, Diane J, Libris Award for Author of the Year, 1881 Yonge St, Suite 800, Toronto, ON M4S 3C4, Canada *Tel:* 416-922-6678 *Toll Free Tel:* 888-373-8245 *Fax:* 416-467-7886 *E-mail:* info@retailcouncil.org *Web Site:* www.retailcouncil.org, pg 700

Briseboas, Diane J, Libris Children's Picture Book of the Year, 1881 Yonge St, Suite 800, Toronto, ON M4S 3C4, Canada *Tel:* 416-922-6678 *Toll Free Tel:* 888-373-8245 *Fax:* 416-467-7886 *E-mail:* info@retailcouncil.org *Web Site:* www.retailcouncil.org, pg 700

Briseboas, Diane J, Libris Distributor of the Year, 1881 Yonge St, Suite 800, Toronto, ON M4S 3C4, Canada *Tel:* 416-922-6678 *Toll Free Tel:* 888-373-8245 *Fax:* 416-467-7886 *E-mail:* info@retailcouncil.org *Web Site:* www.retailcouncil.org, pg 701

Briseboas, Diane J, Libris Editor of the Year, 1881 Yonge St, Suite 800, Toronto, ON M4S 3C4, Canada *Tel:* 416-922-6678 *Toll Free Tel:* 888-373-8245 *Fax:* 416-467-7886 *E-mail:* info@retailcouncil.org *Web Site:* www.retailcouncil.org, pg 701

Briseboas, Diane J, Libris Fiction Book of the Year, 1881 Yonge St, Suite 800, Toronto, ON M4S 3C4, Canada *Tel:* 416-922-6678 *Toll Free Tel:* 888-373-8245 *Fax:* 416-467-7886 *E-mail:* info@retailcouncil.org *Web Site:* www.retailcouncil.org, pg 701

Briseboas, Diane J, Libris Publisher of the Year, 1881 Yonge St, Suite 800, Toronto, ON M4S 3C4, Canada *Tel:* 416-922-6678 *Toll Free Tel:* 888-373-8245 *Fax:* 416-467-7886 *E-mail:* info@retailcouncil.org *Web Site:* www.retailcouncil.org, pg 701

Briseboas, Diane J, Libris Sales Rep of the Year, 1881 Yonge St, Suite 800, Toronto, ON M4S 3C4, Canada *Tel:* 416-922-6678 *Toll Free Tel:* 888-373-8245 *Fax:* 416-467-7886 *E-mail:* info@retailcouncil.org *Web Site:* www.retailcouncil.org, pg 701

Briseboas, Diane J, Libris Small Press Publisher of the Year, 1881 Yonge St, Suite 800, Toronto, ON M4S 3C4, Canada *Tel:* 416-922-6678 *Toll Free Tel:* 888-373-8245 *Fax:* 416-467-7886 *E-mail:* info@retailcouncil.org *Web Site:* www.retailcouncil.org, pg 701

Briskin, Dennis Alan, Catalyst Creative Services, 619 Marion Plaza, Palo Alto, CA 94301-4251 *Tel:* 650-325-1500 *E-mail:* afriendlyghostwriter@gmail.com *Web Site:* www.catalystcreative.us, pg 523

Brissie, Gene, James Peter Associates Inc, PO Box 358, New Canaan, CT 06840 *Tel:* 203-972-1070 *Web Site:* www.jamespeterassociates.com, pg 558

Britson, Lowell, University of Pittsburgh Press, 7500 Thomas Blvd, Pittsburgh, PA 15260 *Tel:* 412-383-2456 *Fax:* 412-383-2466 *E-mail:* info@upress.pitt.edu *Web Site:* www.upress.pitt.edu, pg 259

Britton, Greg, The Johns Hopkins University Press, 2715 N Charles St, Baltimore, MD 21218-4363 *Tel:* 410-516-6900; 410-516-6987 (journal orders outside US & CN) *Toll Free Tel:* 800-537-5487 (book orders & cust serv); 800-548-1784 (journal

Brown, Cheri, Hackett Publishing Co Inc, 3333 Massachusetts Ave, Indianapolis, IN 46218 *Tel:* 317-635-9250 (orders & cust serv) *Fax:* 317-635-9292 *Toll Free Fax:* 800-783-9213 *E-mail:* customer@hackettpublishing.com *Web Site:* www.hackettpublishing.com, pg 103

Brown, Mr Chris, National Association of Broadcasters (NAB), 1771 "N" St NW, Washington, DC 20036 *Tel:* 202-429-5300 *Fax:* 202-429-4199 *E-mail:* nab@nab.org *Web Site:* www.nab.org, pg 163, 611

Brown, Derrick, Write Bloody Publishing, 2306 E Cesar Chavez, Suite 103, Austin, TX 78706 *E-mail:* writebloody@gmail.com *Web Site:* writebloody.com, pg 276

Brown, Douglas R, Atlantic Publishing Group Inc, 1405 SW Sixth Ave, Ocala, FL 34471 *Tel:* 352-622-1825 *Toll Free Tel:* 800-814-1132 *Fax:* 352-622-1875 *E-mail:* sales@atlantic-pub.com *Web Site:* www.atlantic-pub.com, pg 26

Brown, Janice W, The Pilgrim Press/United Church Press, 700 Prospect Ave, Cleveland, OH 44115-1100 *Toll Free Tel:* 800-537-3394 (cust serv-indivs); 800-654-5129 (cust serv-commercial accts) *Fax:* 216-736-2206 (orders) *E-mail:* proposals@thepilgrimpress.com *Web Site:* www.thepilgrimpress.com; www.unitedchurchpress.com, pg 192

Brown, Jennifer, Sudden Fiction Contest, c/o ASUC Publications, Univ of California, 10-B Eshleman Hall, Berkeley, CA 94720-4500 *E-mail:* bfictionreview@yahoo.com *Web Site:* www.ocf.berkeley.edu/~bfr/, pg 731

Brown, Jennifer M, Random House Children's Books, 1745 Broadway, New York, NY 10019 *Tel:* 212-782-9000 *Toll Free Tel:* 800-200-3552 *Fax:* 212-782-9452 *Web Site:* randomhousekids.com, pg 203

Brown, Jessica, Crown Publishing Group, c/o Penguin Random House Inc, 1745 Broadway, New York, NY 10019 *Tel:* 212-782-9000 *Toll Free Tel:* 888-264-1745 *Fax:* 212-940-7408 *E-mail:* crownosm@penguinrandomhouse.com *Web Site:* crownpublishing.com, pg 68

Brown, Kate, Yale University Press, 302 Temple St, New Haven, CT 06511-8909 *Tel:* 203-432-0960; 203-432-0966 (sales); 401-531-2800 (cust serv) *Toll Free Tel:* 800-405-1619 (cust serv) *Fax:* 203-432-0948; 203-432-8485 (sales); 401-531-2801 (cust serv) *Toll Free Fax:* 800-406-9145 (cust serv) *E-mail:* sales.press@yale.edu (sales); customer.care@trilateral.org (cust serv) *Web Site:* www.yalebooks.com; yalepress.yale.edu/yupbooks, pg 278

Brown, Katy, Ten Speed Press, 2625 Alcatraz Ave, Unit 505, Berkeley, CA 94705 *Tel:* 510-285-3000 *Toll Free Tel:* 800-841-BOOK (841-2665) *E-mail:* csorders@randomhouse.com *Web Site:* crownpublishing.com/imprint/ten-speed-press, pg 243

Brown, Kent, Dramatic Publishing Co, 311 Washington St, Woodstock, IL 60098-3308 *Tel:* 815-338-7170 *Toll Free Tel:* 800-448-7469 *Fax:* 815-338-8981 *Toll Free Fax:* 800-334-5302 *E-mail:* plays@dramaticpublishing.com; customerservice@dpcplays.com *Web Site:* www.dramaticpublishing.com, pg 76

Brown, Kent L Jr, The Writing for Children Founders Workshops, 814 Court St, Honesdale, PA 18431 *Tel:* 570-253-1192 *Fax:* 570-253-0179 *E-mail:* jolloyd@highlightsfoundation.org *Web Site:* www.highlightsfoundation.org, pg 657

Brown, Laurie, Houghton Mifflin Harcourt Trade & Reference Division, 222 Berkeley St, Boston, MA 02116 *Tel:* 617-351-5000 *Toll Free Tel:* 800-225-3362 *Web Site:* www.hmhco.com, pg 115

Brown, Linda, American Society of Plant Taxonomists, University of Wyoming, Dept of Botany 3165, 1000 E University Ave, Laramie, WY 82071 *Tel:* 307-766-2556 *Fax:* 307-766-2851 *E-mail:* aspt@uwyo.edu *Web Site:* www.aspt.net, pg 16

Brown, Lindsay, Beyond Words Publishing Inc, 20827 NW Cornell Rd, Suite 500, Hillsboro, OR 97124-9808 *Tel:* 503-531-8700 *Fax:* 503-531-8773 *E-mail:* info@beyondword.com *Web Site:* www.beyondword.com, pg 36

Brown, Lucia, The Feminist Press at The City University of New York, 365 Fifth Ave, Suite 5406, New York, NY 10016 *Tel:* 212-817-7915 *Fax:* 212-817-1593 *E-mail:* info@feministpress.org *Web Site:* www.feministpress.org, pg 87

Brown, Marian, Blue Rider Press, 375 Hudson St, New York, NY 10014 *Tel:* 212-366-2000 *E-mail:* blueriderpublicity@us.penguingroup.com, pg 41

Brown, Marian, Plume, 375 Hudson St, New York, NY 10014 *Tel:* 212-366-2000 *Fax:* 212-366-2666 *E-mail:* online@penguinputnam.com *Web Site:* www.penguinputnam.com; us.penguingroup.com, pg 193

Brown, Marie D, Marie Brown Associates, 412 W 154 St, New York, NY 10032 *Tel:* 212-939-9725 *Fax:* 212-939-9728 *E-mail:* mbrownlit@aol.com, pg 544

Brown, Marty, Oregon State University Press, 121 The Valley Library, Corvallis, OR 97331-4501 *Tel:* 541-737-3166 *Toll Free Tel:* 800-621-2736 (orders) *Web Site:* osupress.oregonstate.edu, pg 177

Brown, Merle, Harry N Abrams Inc, 115 W 18 St, 6th fl, New York, NY 10011 *Tel:* 212-206-7715 *Toll Free Tel:* 800-345-1359 *Fax:* 212-519-1210 *E-mail:* abrams@abramsbooks.com *Web Site:* www.abramsbooks.com, pg 3

Brown, Milli, Brown Books Publishing Group, 16250 Knoll Trail, Suite 205, Dallas, TX 75248 *Tel:* 972-381-0009 *Fax:* 972-248-4336 *E-mail:* publishing@brownbooks.com *Web Site:* www.brownbooks.com, pg 47

Brown, Ray, WorldTariff, 220 Montgomery St, Suite 448, San Francisco, CA 94104-3410 *Tel:* 415-391-7501; 415-591-6666 *Toll Free Tel:* 800-556-9334 *Fax:* 415-391-7537 (Fax/Modem) *Web Site:* www.worldtariff.com; ftn.fedex.com/wtonline, pg 276

Brown, Richard PhD, Georgetown University Press, 3240 Prospect St NW, Suite 250, Washington, DC 20007 *Tel:* 202-687-5889 (busn) *Fax:* 202-687-6340 (edit) *E-mail:* gupress@georgetown.edu *Web Site:* press.georgetown.edu, pg 96

Brown, Rose E, Clerical Plus, 97 Blueberry Lane, Shelton, CT 06484 *Tel:* 203-225-0879 *Fax:* 203-225-0879 *E-mail:* clericalplus@aol.com *Web Site:* www.clericalplus.net, pg 523

Brown, Sam, Guernica Editions Inc, 1569 Heritage Way, Oakville, ON L6M 2Z7, Canada *Fax:* 416-576-9403 *E-mail:* info@guernicaeditions.com *Web Site:* guernicaeditions.com, pg 486

Brown, Sheila, Apprentice Shop Books LLC, 18 Wentworth Dr, Bedford, NH 03110 *Tel:* 603-472-8741 *Fax:* 603-472-2323 *E-mail:* info@apprenticeshopbooks.com *Web Site:* www.apprenticeshopbooks.com, pg 20

Brown, Sherri L, Atlantic Publishing Group Inc, 1405 SW Sixth Ave, Ocala, FL 34471 *Tel:* 352-622-1825 *Toll Free Tel:* 800-814-1132 *Fax:* 352-622-1875 *E-mail:* sales@atlantic-pub.com *Web Site:* www.atlantic-pub.com, pg 26

Brown, Stephanie, Vandamere Press, 3580 Morris St N, St Petersburg, FL 33713 *Tel:* 727-556-0950 *Toll Free Tel:* 800-551-7776 *Fax:* 727-556-2560 *E-mail:* orders@vandamere.com *Web Site:* www.vandamere.com, pg 264

Brown, Stephen, Random House Children's Books, 1745 Broadway, New York, NY 10019 *Tel:* 212-782-9000 *Toll Free Tel:* 800-200-3552 *Fax:* 212-782-9452 *Web Site:* randomhousekids.com, pg 204

Brown, Susan, Macmillan Higher Education, 41 Madison Ave, 37th fl, New York, NY 10010 *Tel:* 212-576-9400 *Fax:* 212-689-2383 *Web Site:* www.macmillanhighered.com, pg 145

Brown, Therese, Association of Catholic Publishers Inc, 4725 Dorsey Hall Dr, Suite A, PMB 709, Elliott City, MD 21042 *Tel:* 410-988-2926 *Fax:* 410-571-4946 *Web Site:* www.catholicsread.org; www.catholicpublishers.org; www.midatlanticcongress.org, pg 598

Browne, Dwight, University of Missouri Press, 2910 Le Mone Blvd, Columbia, MO 65201 *Tel:* 573-882-7641 *Toll Free Tel:* 800-621-2736 (orders) *Fax:* 573-884-4498 *Web Site:* press.umsystem.edu, pg 257

Browne, Pema, Pema Browne Ltd, 71 Pine Rd, Woodbourne, NY 12788 *E-mail:* ppbltd@optonline.net *Web Site:* www.pemabrowneltd.com, pg 567

Browne, Perry, Pema Browne Ltd, 71 Pine Rd, Woodbourne, NY 12788 *E-mail:* ppbltd@optonline.net *Web Site:* www.pemabrowneltd.com, pg 567

Browne, Renni, The Editorial Dept LLC, 7650 E Broadway, Suite 308, Tucson, AZ 85710 *Tel:* 520-546-9992 *Fax:* 520-979-3408 *E-mail:* admin@editorialdepartment.com *Web Site:* www.editorialdepartment.com, pg 525

Browne, Ross, The Editorial Dept LLC, 7650 E Broadway, Suite 308, Tucson, AZ 85710 *Tel:* 520-546-9992 *Fax:* 520-979-3408 *E-mail:* admin@editorialdepartment.com *Web Site:* www.editorialdepartment.com, pg 525

Browning, Niki, Mundania Press LLC, 6457 Glenway Ave, Suite 109, Cincinnati, OH 45211-5222 *Tel:* 513-490-2822 *Fax:* 513-598-9220 *Toll Free Fax:* 888-460-4752 *E-mail:* books@mundania.com; inquiry@mundania.com *Web Site:* www.mundania.com, pg 161

Brownoff, Alan, University of Alberta Press, Ring House 2, Edmonton, AB T6G 2E1, Canada *Tel:* 780-492-3662 *Fax:* 780-492-0719 *Web Site:* www.uap.ualberta.ca, pg 502

Bruce, Sandra, Milady, Executive Woods, 5 Maxwell Dr, Clifton Park, NY 12065-2919 *Tel:* 518-348-2300 *Toll Free Tel:* 800-998-7498 *Fax:* 518-373-6309 *Web Site:* milady.cengage.com, pg 156

Brueggeman, George, Haynes Manuals Inc, 861 Lawrence Dr, Newbury Park, CA 91320 *Tel:* 805-498-6703 *Toll Free Tel:* 800-4-HAYNES (442-9637) *Fax:* 805-498-2867 *E-mail:* cstn@haynes.com *Web Site:* www.haynes.com, pg 108

Brugger, Deborah, Saint Johann Press, 315 Schraalenburgh Rd, Haworth, NJ 07641 *Tel:* 201-387-1529 *Fax:* 201-501-0698 *Web Site:* www.stjohannpress.com, pg 214

Brumley, Mark, Ignatius Press, 1348 Tenth Ave, San Francisco, CA 94122-2304 *Toll Free Tel:* 800-651-1531 (orders); 888-615-3186 (cust serv) *E-mail:* info@ignatius.com *Web Site:* www.ignatius.com, pg 118

Brumwell, Barbara, LexisNexis® Canada Inc, 123 Commerce Valley Dr E, Suite 700, Markham, ON L3T 7W8, Canada *Tel:* 905-479-2665 *Toll Free Tel:* 800-668-6481; 800-387-0899 (cust care) *Fax:* 905-479-2826 *Toll Free Fax:* 800-461-3275 *E-mail:* orders@lexisnexis.ca; service@lexisnexis.ca (cust serv) *Web Site:* www.lexisnexis.ca, pg 490

Brunette, Paul, Concordia Publishing House, 3558 S Jefferson Ave, St Louis, MO 63118-3968 *Tel:* 314-268-1000; 314-268-1268 (bookshop) *Toll Free Tel:* 800-325-3040 (cust serv) *Toll Free Fax:* 800-490-9889 (cust serv) *E-mail:* order@cph.org *Web Site:* www.cph.org, pg 62

Brunke, Pamela, Salem Press Inc, 2 University Plaza, Suite 310, Hackensack, NJ 07601 *Tel:* 201-968-0500 *Toll Free Tel:* 800-221-1592; 800-221-1592 *Fax:* 201-968-0511 *E-mail:* csr@salempress.com *Web Site:* salempress.com, pg 215

Brunn, Jennifer, Harry N Abrams Inc, 115 W 18 St, 6th fl, New York, NY 10011 *Tel:* 212-206-7715 *Toll Free Tel:* 800-345-1359 *Fax:* 212-519-1210 *E-mail:* abrams@abramsbooks.com *Web Site:* www.abramsbooks.com, pg 3

Brunner, Br Richard C, St Pauls, 2187 Victory Blvd, Staten Island, NY 10314-6603 *Tel:* 718-761-0047 (edit & prodn); 718-698-2759 (mktg & billing) *Toll Free Tel:* 800-343-2522 *Fax:* 718-761-0057 *E-mail:* sales@stpauls.us; marketing@stpauls.us *Web Site:* www.stpauls.us, pg 215

Bruns, Erica, Bright Connections Media, A World Book Encyclopedia Company, 233 N Michigan Ave, Suite 2000, Chicago, IL 60601 *Tel:* 312-729-5800 *Fax:* 312-729-5610 *Web Site:* www.brightconnectionsmedia.com, pg 46

Brunsek, Judy, Owlkids Books Inc, 10 Lower Spadina Ave, Suite 400, Toronto, ON M5V 2Z2, Canada *Tel:* 416-340-2700 *Fax:* 416-340-9769 *E-mail:* owlkids@owlkids.com *Web Site:* www.owlkidsbooks.com, pg 493

Bruscia, Kenneth E, Barcelona Publishers, 27602 Bogen Rd, New Braunfels, TX 78132-3873 *Tel:* 830-980-6422 *E-mail:* barcelonapublishers@gvtc.com; barcelonapublishers@ware-pak.com (orders) *Web Site:* www.barcelonapublishers.com, pg 30

Bryan, Heather, Nimbus Publishing Ltd, 3731 Mackintosh St, Halifax, NS B3K 5A5, Canada *Tel:* 902-455-4286; 902-454-7404 *Toll Free Tel:* 800-NIMBUS9 (646-2879) *Fax:* 902-455-5440 *Toll Free Fax:* 888-253-3133 *E-mail:* customerservice@nimbus.ca *Web Site:* www.nimbus.ca, pg 493

Bryan, Nancy, University of Texas Press, 2100 Comal St, Austin, TX 78722 *Tel:* 512-471-7233 *Fax:* 512-232-7178 *E-mail:* utpress@uts.cc.utexas.edu *Web Site:* www.utexaspress.com, pg 244

Bryant, Del R, BMI®, 7 World Trade Ctr, 250 Greenwich St, New York, NY 10007-0030 *Tel:* 212-586-2000; 212-220-3000 *Toll Free Tel:* 888-689-5264 (sales); 800-925-8451 (cust rel) *Fax:* 212-246-2163 *E-mail:* foundation@bmi.com *Web Site:* www.bmi.com, pg 600

Bryant, L J, Wildflower Press, Oakbrook Press, 3301 S Valley Dr, Rapid City, SD 57703 *Tel:* 605-381-6385 *Fax:* 605-343-8733 *E-mail:* info@wildflowerpress.org; bookorder@wildflowerpress.org *Web Site:* www.wildflowerpress.org, pg 271

Bryant, Tommy, Creative Writing Day & Workshops, 335 Cummings St, Abingdon, VA 24210 *Tel:* 276-623-5266 *Fax:* 276-676-3076 *E-mail:* vhf@eva.org *Web Site:* www.vahighlandsfestival.org, pg 650

Bryerose, Cathy C, Regal Crest Enterprises LLC, 229 Sheridan Loop, Belton, TX 76513 *Tel:* 409-527-1188 *Toll Free Fax:* 866-294-9628 *E-mail:* info@regalcrestbooks.biz *Web Site:* www.regalcrest.biz, pg 207

Buchwald, Don, Don Buchwald & Associates Inc, 10 E 44 St, New York, NY 10017 *Tel:* 212-867-1200 *Fax:* 212-867-2434 *E-mail:* info@buchwald.com *Web Site:* www.buchwald.com, pg 545

Buck, Howard, Howard Buck Agency, 80 Eighth Ave, Suite 1107, New York, NY 10011 *Tel:* 212-924-9093, pg 545

Buck, Susan, Coteau Books, 2517 Victoria Ave, Regina, SK S4P 0T2, Canada *Tel:* 306-777-0170 *Toll Free Tel:* 800-440-4471 (CN only) *Fax:* 306-522-5152 *E-mail:* coteau@coteaubooks.com *Web Site:* www.coteaubooks.com, pg 478

Buckbee, Alana, Crown Publishing Group, c/o Penguin Random House Inc, 1745 Broadway, New York, NY 10019 *Tel:* 212-782-9000 *Toll Free Tel:* 888-264-1745 *Fax:* 212-940-7408 *E-mail:* crownosm@penguinrandomhouse.com *Web Site:* crownpublishing.com, pg 68

Buckles, Kristen, The University of Arizona Press, 1510 E University Blvd, Tucson, AZ 85721 *Tel:* 520-621-1441 *Toll Free Tel:* 800-426-3797 (orders) *Fax:* 520-621-8899 *Toll Free Fax:* 800-426-3797 *E-mail:* uap@uapress.arizona.edu *Web Site:* www.uapress.arizona.edu, pg 255

Buckley, Carol, Piano Press, 1425 Ocean Ave, Suite 5, Del Mar, CA 92014 *Tel:* 619-884-1401 *Fax:* 858-755-1104 *E-mail:* pianopress@pianopress.com *Web Site:* www.pianopress.com, pg 191

Buckley, Cicely, Oyster River Press, 36 Oyster River Rd, Durham, NH 03824-3029 *Tel:* 603-868-5006 *E-mail:* oysterriverpress@comcast.net *Web Site:* www.oysterriverpress.com, pg 532

Buckley, Kerri, Harlequin Enterprises Ltd, 233 Broadway, Suite 1001, New York, NY 10279 *Tel:* 212-553-4200 *Fax:* 212-227-8969 *E-mail:* CustomerService@harlequin.com *Web Site:* www.harlequin.com, pg 105

Buckley, Paul, Penguin Books, 375 Hudson St, New York, NY 10014 *Tel:* 212-366-2000 *E-mail:* online@penguinputnam.com *Web Site:* www.penguinputnam.com; www.penguinclassics.com; us.penguingroup.com, pg 186

Buckley, Paul, Viking, 375 Hudson St, New York, NY 10014 *Tel:* 212-366-2000 *E-mail:* online@penguinputnam.com *Web Site:* www.penguinputnam.com; us.penguingroup.com, pg 265

Buckner, Judith, Judith Buckner Literary Agency, 12721 Hart St, North Hollywood, CA 91605 *Tel:* 818-982-8202 *Fax:* 818-764-6844, pg 545

Buckner, Richard, Beacon Hill Press of Kansas City, PO Box 419527, Kansas City, MO 64141-6527 *Tel:* 816-931-1900 *Toll Free Tel:* 800-877-0700 (cust serv) *Fax:* 816-753-4071 *Web Site:* www.beaconhillbooks.com, pg 32

Budnick, Philip, Penguin Group (USA) LLC, a Penguin Random House company, 375 Hudson St, New York, NY 10014 *Tel:* 212-366-2000 *Toll Free Tel:* 800-847-5515 (inside sales); 800-631-8571 (cust serv) *Fax:* 212-366-2666; 607-775-4829 (inside sales) *E-mail:* online@us.penguingroup.com *Web Site:* www.penguin.com; us.penguingroup.com, pg 186

Buevich, Alina, Chronicle Books LLC, 680 Second St, San Francisco, CA 94107 *Tel:* 415-537-4200 *Toll Free Tel:* 800-759-0190 (cust serv) *Fax:* 415-537-4460 *Toll Free Fax:* 800-858-7787 (orders); 800-286-9471 (cust serv) *E-mail:* frontdesk@chroniclebooks.com *Web Site:* www.chroniclebooks.com, pg 58

Bufe, Charles, See Sharp Press, PO Box 1731, Tucson, AZ 85702-1731 *Tel:* 520-338-2151 *E-mail:* info@seesharppress.com *Web Site:* www.seesharppress.com, pg 221

Buffaloe, Christine, Lemon Grove Press, 1158 26 St, Suite 502, Santa Monica, CA 90403 *Tel:* 310-471-1740 *Fax:* 310-476-7627 *E-mail:* info@lemongrovepress.com *Web Site:* www.thetakechargepatient.com, pg 508

Bui, Francoise, Random House Children's Books, 1745 Broadway, New York, NY 10019 *Tel:* 212-782-9000 *Toll Free Tel:* 800-200-3552 *Fax:* 212-782-9452 *Web Site:* randomhousekids.com, pg 203

Bukovietski, Alexander, Wm B Eerdmans Publishing Co, 2140 Oak Industrial Dr NE, Grand Rapids, MI 49505 *Tel:* 616-459-4591 *Toll Free Tel:* 800-253-7521 *Fax:* 616-459-6540 *E-mail:* customerservice@eerdmans.com; sales@eerdmans.com *Web Site:* www.eerdmans.com, pg 80

Bukowski, Denise, The Bukowski Agency Ltd, 14 Prince Arthur Ave, Suite 202, Toronto, ON M5R 1A9, Canada *Tel:* 416-928-6728 *Fax:* 416-963-9978 *E-mail:* info@bukowskiagency.com *Web Site:* www.bukowskiagency.com, pg 545

Bulger, Joe, Simon & Schuster, Inc, 1230 Avenue of the Americas, New York, NY 10020 *Tel:* 212-698-7000 *Fax:* 212-698-7007 *E-mail:* firstname.lastname@simonandschuster.com *Web Site:* www.simonandschuster.com, pg 226

Bulger, Terrilee, Nimbus Publishing Ltd, 3731 Mackintosh St, Halifax, NS B3K 5A5, Canada *Tel:* 902-455-4286; 902-454-7404 *Toll Free Tel:* 800-NIMBUS9 (646-2879) *Fax:* 902-455-5440 *Toll Free Fax:* 888-253-3133 *E-mail:* customerservice@nimbus.ca *Web Site:* www.nimbus.ca, pg 493

Bull, James, Bull Publishing Co, PO Box 1377, Boulder, CO 80306 *Tel:* 303-545-6350 *Toll Free Tel:* 800-676-2855 *Fax:* 303-545-6354 *E-mail:* bullpublishing@msn.com *Web Site:* www.bullpub.com, pg 47

Bullas, Roslyn, North Atlantic Books, 2526 Martin Luther King Jr Way, Berkeley, CA 94704 *Tel:* 510-549-4270 *Fax:* 510-549-4276 *Web Site:* www.northatlanticbooks.com, pg 170

Buller, Bob, SBL Press, The Luce Ctr, Suite 350, 825 Houston Mill Rd, Atlanta, GA 30329 *Tel:* 404-727-3100 *Fax:* 404-727-3101 (corp) *E-mail:* sbl@sbl-site.org *Web Site:* www.sbl-site.org, pg 217

Bullock, Karen, Meriwether Publishing, c/o Pioneer Drama Service, 9707-A E Easter Lane, Englewood, CO 80112 *Tel:* 303-779-4035 *Toll Free Tel:* 800-333-7262 *Fax:* 303-779-4315 *E-mail:* wholesale@pioneerdrama.com *Web Site:* www.pioneerdrama.com, pg 155

Bumps, Susan, North Atlantic Books, 2526 Martin Luther King Jr Way, Berkeley, CA 94704 *Tel:* 510-549-4270 *Fax:* 510-549-4276 *Web Site:* www.northatlanticbooks.com, pg 170

Bunch, Cindy, InterVarsity Press, 430 Plaza Dr, Westmont, IL 60559-1234 *Tel:* 630-734-4000 *Toll Free Tel:* 800-843-9487 *Fax:* 630-734-4200 *E-mail:* email@ivpress.com *Web Site:* www.ivpress.com, pg 125

Bunch, Rick, CEF Press, 17482 State Hwy M, Warrenton, MO 63383-0348 *Tel:* 636-456-4321 *Toll Free Tel:* 800-748-7710 (cust serv); 800-300-4033 (USA ministries) *Fax:* 636-456-9935 *E-mail:* cefexecutiveoffices@cefonline.com *Web Site:* www.cefonline.com, pg 53

Bunker, Jane, Northwestern University Press, 629 Noyes St, Evanston, IL 60208-4210 *Tel:* 847-491-2046 *Toll Free Tel:* 800-621-2736 (orders only) *Fax:* 847-491-8150 *E-mail:* nupress@northwestern.edu *Web Site:* www.nupress.northwestern.edu, pg 171

Bunker, Jane, TriQuarterly Books, 629 Noyes St, Evanston, IL 60201 *Toll Free Tel:* 800-621-2736 (orders only) *Fax:* 847-467-2096 *E-mail:* nupress@northwestern.edu *Web Site:* www.nupress.northwestern.edu, pg 249

Bunn, Anne, The MIT Press, 55 Hayward St, Cambridge, MA 02142 *Tel:* 617-253-5255 *Toll Free Tel:* 800-207-8354 (orders) *Fax:* 617-258-6779; 617-577-1545 (orders) *Web Site:* mitpress.mit.edu, pg 158

Bunner, Bruce, AuthorHouse, 1663 Liberty Dr, Bloomington, IN 47403 *Tel:* 812-339-6000 (outside US) *Toll Free Tel:* 888-519-5121 *E-mail:* authorsupport@authorhouse.com *Web Site:* www.authorhouse.com, pg 27

Bunzel, Mark, FineEdge.com LLC, 14004 Biz Point Lane, Anacortes, WA 98221 *Tel:* 360-299-8500 *Fax:* 360-299-0535 *E-mail:* pub@fineedge.com; orders@fineedge.com *Web Site:* www.fineedge.com, pg 89

Burch, Martin, Ocean Tree Books, 1325 Cerro Gordo Rd, Santa Fe, NM 87501 *Tel:* 505-983-1412 *Fax:* 505-983-0899 *Web Site:* www.oceantree.com, pg 173

Burch, Renee C, Wildlife Education Ltd, 2418 Noyes St, Evanston, IL 60201 *Toll Free Tel:* 800-477-5034 *E-mail:* owls5@zoobooks.com; helpdesk@zoobooks.com *Web Site:* www.zoobooks.com; wildlife-ed.com, pg 272

Burford, Peter, Burford Books, 101 E State St, No 301, Ithaca, NY 14850 *Tel:* 607-319-4373 *Fax:* 607-319-4373 *Toll Free Fax:* 866-212-7750 *E-mail:* info@burfordbooks.com *Web Site:* www.burfordbooks.com, pg 48

Burgauer, Steve, Prometheus Awards, 650 Castro St, Suite 120-433, Mountain View, CA 94041 *Tel:* 650-968-6319 *E-mail:* info@lfs.org *Web Site:* www.lfs.org, pg 722

Burgess, Angela R, IEEE Computer Society, 2001 "L" St NW, Suite 700, Washington, DC 20036-4928 *Tel:* 202-371-0101 *Toll Free Tel:* 800-272-6657 (memb info) *Fax:* 202-728-9614 *E-mail:* help@computer.org *Web Site:* www.computer.org, pg 118

Burgess, Kathy, University Press of Mississippi, 3825 Ridgewood Rd, Jackson, MS 39211-6492 *Tel:* 601-432-6205 *Toll Free Tel:* 800-737-7788 (orders & cust serv) *Fax:* 601-432-6217 *E-mail:* press@mississippi.edu *Web Site:* www.upress.state.ms.us, pg 262

Burgess, Marsha P, ALSC BWI/Summer Reading Program Grant, 50 E Huron St, Chicago, IL 60611-2795 *Tel:* 312-280-2163 *Toll Free Tel:* 800-545-2433 *Fax:* 312-440-9374 *E-mail:* alsc@ala.org *Web Site:* www.ala.org/alsc, pg 667

Burgess, Marsha P, The May Hill Arbuthnot Honor Lecture Award, 50 E Huron St, Chicago, IL 60611-2795 *Tel:* 312-280-2163 *Toll Free Tel:* 800-545-2433 *Fax:* 312-440-9374 *E-mail:* alsc@ala.org *Web Site:* www.ala.org/alsc, pg 668

Burgess, Marsha P, The Mildred L Batchelder Award, 50 E Huron St, Chicago, IL 60611-2795 *Tel:* 312-280-2163 *Toll Free Tel:* 800-545-2433 *Fax:* 312-440-9374 *E-mail:* alsc@ala.org *Web Site:* www.ala.org/alsc, pg 670

Burgess, Marsha P, The Pura Belpre Award, 50 E Huron St, Chicago, IL 60611-2795 *Tel:* 312-280-2163 *Toll Free Tel:* 800-545-2433 *Fax:* 312-440-9374 *E-mail:* alsc@ala.org *Web Site:* www.ala.org/alsc, pg 671

Burgess, Marsha P, Bound to Stay Bound Books Scholarship, 50 E Huron St, Chicago, IL 60611-2795 *Tel:* 312-280-2163 *Toll Free Tel:* 800-545-2433 *Fax:* 312-440-9374 *E-mail:* alsc@ala.org *Web Site:* www.ala.org/alsc, pg 673

Burgess, Marsha P, The Randolph Caldecott Medal, 50 E Huron St, Chicago, IL 60611-2795 *Tel:* 312-280-2163 *Toll Free Tel:* 800-545-2433 *Fax:* 312-440-9374 *E-mail:* alsc@ala.org *Web Site:* www.ala.org/alsc, pg 675

Burgess, Marsha P, Frederic G Melcher Scholarship, 50 E Huron St, Chicago, IL 60611-2795 *Tel:* 312-280-2163 *Toll Free Tel:* 800-545-2433 *Fax:* 312-440-9374 *E-mail:* alsc@ala.org *Web Site:* www.ala.org/alsc, pg 707

Burgess, Marsha P, John Newbery Medal, 50 E Huron St, Chicago, IL 60611-2795 *Tel:* 312-280-2163 *Toll Free Tel:* 800-545-2433 *Fax:* 312-440-9374 *E-mail:* alsc@ala.org *Web Site:* www.ala.org/alsc, pg 713

Burgess, Marsha P, Robert F Sibert Informational Book Award, 50 E Huron St, Chicago, IL 60611-2795 *Tel:* 312-280-2163 *Toll Free Tel:* 800-545-2433 *Fax:* 312-440-9374 *E-mail:* alsc@ala.org *Web Site:* www.ala.org/alsc, pg 728

Burgess, Marsha P, The Laura Ingalls Wilder Medal, 50 E Huron St, Chicago, IL 60611-2795 *Tel:* 312-280-2163 *Toll Free Tel:* 800-545-2433 *Fax:* 312-440-9374 *E-mail:* alsc@ala.org *Web Site:* www.ala.org/alsc, pg 736

Burgin, Richard, Boulevard Magazine Short Fiction Contest for Emerging Writers, 6614 Clayton Rd, PMB 325, Richmond Heights, MO 63117 *Tel:* 314-862-2643 *Web Site:* www.boulevardmagazine.org, pg 673

Burgos, Rachel, AAP PreK-12 Learning Group, 325 Chestnut St, Suite 1110, Philadelphia, PA 19106 *Tel:* 267-351-4310 *Fax:* 267-351-4317 *E-mail:* prek12learning@publishers.org *Web Site:* www.aepweb.org, pg 593

Burk, Dale A, Stoneydale Press Publishing Co, 523 Main St, Stevensville, MT 59870-2839 *Tel:* 406-777-2729 *Toll Free Tel:* 800-735-7006 *Fax:* 406-777-2521 *Web Site:* www.stoneydale.com, pg 236

Burke, Carolyn L, Editors' Association of Canada (Association canadienne des reviseurs), 27 Carlton St, Suite 502, Toronto, ON M5B 1L2, Canada *Tel:* 416-975-1379 *Toll Free Tel:* 866-CAN-EDIT (226-3348) *Fax:* 416-975-1637 *E-mail:* info@editors.ca; info@reviseurs.ca *Web Site:* www.editors.ca; www.reviseurs.ca, pg 605

Burke, Carolyn L, Tom Fairley Award for Editorial Excellence, 27 Carlton St, Suite 502, Toronto, ON M5B 1L2, Canada *Tel:* 416-975-1379 *Toll Free Tel:* 866-CAN-EDIT (226-3348) *Fax:* 416-975-1637 *E-mail:* fairley_award@editors.ca *Web Site:* www.editors.ca; www.reviseurs.ca, pg 684

Burke, Charlie, Bentley Publishers, 1734 Massachusetts Ave, Cambridge, MA 02138-1804 *Tel:* 617-547-4170 *Toll Free Tel:* 800-423-4595 *Fax:* 617-876-9235 *E-mail:* sales@bentleypublishers.com *Web Site:* www.bentleypublishers.com, pg 35

Burke, Colleen, Binghamton University Creative Writing Program, c/o Dept of English, PO Box 6000, Binghamton, NY 13902-6000 *Tel:* 607-777-2168 *Fax:* 607-777-2408 *E-mail:* cwpro@binghamton.edu *Web Site:* english.binghamton.edu/cwpro, pg 659

Burke, Craig, Berkley Books, 375 Hudson St, New York, NY 10014 *Tel:* 212-366-2000 *Fax:* 212-366-2666 *E-mail:* online@penguinputnam.com *Web Site:* www.penguinputnam.com; us.penguingroup.com, pg 35

Burke, Craig, Berkley Publishing Group, 375 Hudson St, New York, NY 10014 *Tel:* 212-366-2000 *Fax:* 212-366-2385 *E-mail:* online@penguinputnam.com *Web Site:* us.penguingroup.com, pg 35

Burke, Craig, NAL, 375 Hudson St, New York, NY 10014 *Tel:* 212-366-2000 *E-mail:* online@penguinputnam.com *Web Site:* www.penguinputnam.com; us.penguingroup.com, pg 162

Burke, Darius, Pomegranate Communications Inc, 19018 NE Portal Way, Portland, OR 97230 *Tel:* 503-328-6500 *Toll Free Tel:* 800-227-1428 *Fax:* 503-328-9330 *Toll Free Fax:* 800-848-4376 *E-mail:* contactus@pomegranate.com *Web Site:* www.pomegranate.com, pg 195

Burke, Kate, Da Capo Press & Lifelong Books, 44 Farnsworth St, 3rd fl, Boston, MA 02210 *Tel:* 617-252-5200 *Toll Free Tel:* 800-343-4499 (orders) *Fax:* 617-252-5285 *Web Site:* www.perseusbooksgroup.com/dacapo, pg 69

Burke, Katie, Pomegranate Communications Inc, 19018 NE Portal Way, Portland, OR 97230 *Tel:* 503-328-6500 *Toll Free Tel:* 800-227-1428 *Fax:* 503-328-9330 *Toll Free Fax:* 800-848-4376 *E-mail:* contactus@pomegranate.com *Web Site:* www.pomegranate.com, pg 195

Burke, Lori, Grosset & Dunlap, 345 Hudson St, New York, NY 10014 *Tel:* 212-366-2000 *Web Site:* www.penguinrandomhouse.com, pg 101

Burke, Lori, Penguin Young Readers Group, 345 Hudson St, New York, NY 10014 *Tel:* 212-366-2000 *E-mail:* online@penguinputnam.com *Web Site:* www.penguinputnam.com; us.penguingroup.com, pg 188

Burke, Louise, Gallery Books, 1230 Avenue of the Americas, New York, NY 10020 *Toll Free Tel:* 800-456-6798 *Fax:* 212-698-7284 *E-mail:* consumer.customerservice@simonandschuster.com *Web Site:* www.simonsays.com, pg 94

Burke, Louise, Simon & Schuster, Inc, 1230 Avenue of the Americas, New York, NY 10020 *Tel:* 212-698-7000 *Fax:* 212-698-7007 *E-mail:* firstname.lastname@simonandschuster.com *Web Site:* www.simonandschuster.com, pg 226

Burke, Michele, Random House Children's Books, 1745 Broadway, New York, NY 10019 *Tel:* 212-782-9000 *Toll Free Tel:* 800-200-3552 *Fax:* 212-782-9452 *Web Site:* randomhousekids.com, pg 203

Burke, Penny, Rutgers University Press, 106 Somerset St, 3rd fl, New Brunswick, NJ 08901 *Tel:* 848-445-7762 *Toll Free Tel:* 800-848-6224 (orders only) *Fax:* 732-745-4935 (acqs, edit, mktg, perms & prodn) *Toll Free Fax:* 800-272-6817 (fulfillment) *Web Site:* rutgerspress.rutgers.edu, pg 213

Burke, Thomas F, Pomegranate Communications Inc, 19018 NE Portal Way, Portland, OR 97230 *Tel:* 503-328-6500 *Toll Free Tel:* 800-227-1428 *Fax:* 503-328-9330 *Toll Free Fax:* 800-848-4376 *E-mail:* contactus@pomegranate.com *Web Site:* www.pomegranate.com, pg 195

Burke, Vincent J, The Johns Hopkins University Press, 2715 N Charles St, Baltimore, MD 21218-4363 *Tel:* 410-516-6900; 410-516-6987 (journal orders outside US & CN) *Toll Free Tel:* 800-537-5487 (book orders & cust serv); 800-548-1784 (journal orders) *Fax:* 410-516-6968; 410-516-3866 (journal orders) *E-mail:* hfscustserv@press.jhu.edu (cust serv); jrnlcirc@press.jhu.edu (journal orders) *Web Site:* www.press.jhu.edu; muse.jhu.edu, pg 127

Burke, William, Cummings & Hathaway Publishers, 395 Atlantic Ave, East Rockaway, NY 11518 *Tel:* 516-593-3607 *Fax:* 516-593-1401, pg 69

Burkhard, Catherine, Guild of Book Workers, 521 Fifth Ave, 17th fl, New York, NY 10175 *Tel:* 212-292-4444 *E-mail:* communications@guildofbookworkers.org *Web Site:* www.guildofbookworkers.org, pg 606

Burkholder, Bruce, Editorial Bautista Independiente, 3417 Kenilworth Blvd, Sebring, FL 33870-4469 *Tel:* 863-382-6350 *Toll Free Tel:* 800-398-7187 (US) *Fax:* 863-382-8650 *E-mail:* info@ebi-bmm.org; ebiweb@ebi-bmm.org *Web Site:* www.ebi-bmm.org, pg 79

Burkle, Sharon, Random House Children's Books, 1745 Broadway, New York, NY 10019 *Tel:* 212-782-9000 *Toll Free Tel:* 800-200-3552 *Fax:* 212-782-9452 *Web Site:* randomhousekids.com, pg 203

Burkman, Sarah, Newspaper Association of America (NAA), 4401 Wilson Blvd, Suite 900, Arlington, VA 22203 *Tel:* 571-366-1000 *Web Site:* www.naa.org, pg 614

Burkot, Rachel, Harlequin Enterprises Ltd, 225 Duncan Mill Rd, Don Mills, ON M3B 3K9, Canada *Tel:* 416-445-5860 *Toll Free Tel:* 888-432-4879; 800-370-5838 (ebook inquiries) *E-mail:* customerservice@harlequin.com *Web Site:* www.harlequin.com, pg 487

Burks, Meredith, Penguin Group (USA) LLC, a Penguin Random House company, 375 Hudson St, New York, NY 10014 *Tel:* 212-366-2000 *Toll Free Tel:* 800-847-5515 (inside sales); 800-631-8571 (cust serv) *Fax:* 212-366-2666; 607-775-4829 (inside sales) *E-mail:* online@us.penguingroup.com *Web Site:* www.penguin.com; us.penguingroup.com, pg 186

Burks, Meredith, Viking, 375 Hudson St, New York, NY 10014 *Tel:* 212-366-2000 *E-mail:* online@penguinputnam.com *Web Site:* www.penguinputnam.com; us.penguingroup.com, pg 265

Burley, Rachel, John Wiley & Sons Inc, 111 River St, Hoboken, NJ 07030-5774 *Tel:* 201-748-6000 *Toll Free Tel:* 800-225-5945 (cust serv) *Fax:* 201-748-6088 *E-mail:* info@wiley.com *Web Site:* www.wiley.com, pg 272

Burmeister-Brown, Susan, Family Matters, PO Box 80430, Portland, OR 97280-1430 *Tel:* 503-221-0836 *Fax:* 503-221-0837 *E-mail:* editors@glimmertrain.org *Web Site:* www.glimmertrain.org, pg 684

Burmeister-Brown, Susan, Fiction Open, PO Box 80430, Portland, OR 97280-1430 *Tel:* 503-221-0836 *Fax:* 503-221-0837 *E-mail:* editors@glimmertrain.org *Web Site:* www.glimmertrain.org, pg 685

Burmeister-Brown, Susan, Glimmer Train Press Inc, PO Box 80430, Portland, OR 97280-1430 *Tel:* 503-221-0836 *Fax:* 503-221-0837 *E-mail:* editors@glimmertrain.org *Web Site:* www.glimmertrain.org, pg 97

Burmeister-Brown, Susan, Short Story Award for New Writers, PO Box 80430, Portland, OR 97280-1430 *Tel:* 503-221-0836 *Fax:* 503-221-0837 *E-mail:* editors@glimmertrain.org *Web Site:* www.glimmertrain.org, pg 728

Burmeister-Brown, Susan, Very Short Fiction Award, PO Box 80430, Portland, OR 97280-1430 *Tel:* 503-221-0836 *Fax:* 503-221-0837 *E-mail:* editors@glimmertrain.org *Web Site:* www.glimmertrain.org, pg 734

Burn, Dr Geoffrey R H, Stanford University Press, 1450 Page Mill Rd, Palo Alto, CA 94304-1124 *Tel:* 650-723-9434 *Fax:* 650-725-3457 *E-mail:* info@sup.org *Web Site:* www.sup.org, pg 233

Burnett, Sheila, Rowman & Littlefield Publishers Inc, 4501 Forbes Blvd, Suite 200, Lanham, MD 20706 *Tel:* 301-459-3366 *Toll Free Tel:* 800-462-6420 (cust serv) *Fax:* 301-429-5748 *Web Site:* www.rowmanlittlefield.com, pg 212

Burnett, Sheila, Scarecrow Press Inc, 4501 Forbes Blvd, Suite 200, Lanham, MD 20706 *Tel:* 301-459-3366 *Fax:* 301-429-5748 *Web Site:* www.scarecrowpress.com, pg 217

Burnett, Terry, South Carolina Bar, Continuing Legal Education Div, 950 Taylor St, Columbia, SC 29201 *Tel:* 803-799-6653 *Toll Free Tel:* 800-768-7787 *Fax:* 803-799-4118 *E-mail:* scbar-info@scbar.org *Web Site:* www.scbar.org, pg 231

Byl, Craig, American Institute of Aeronautics & Astronautics (AIAA), 1801 Alexander Bell Dr, Suite 500, Reston, VA 20191-4344 *Tel:* 703-264-7500 *Toll Free Tel:* 800-639-AIAA (639-2422) *Fax:* 703-264-7551 *E-mail:* custserv@aiaa.org *Web Site:* www.aiaa.org, pg 13

Byler, Josh, Herald Press, 1251 Virginia Ave, Harrisonburg, VA 22802-2434 *Toll Free Tel:* 800-245-7894 (orders-US); 800-631-6535 (orders-CN) *Toll Free Fax:* 877-271-0760 *E-mail:* info@MennoMedia.org *Web Site:* www.heraldpress.com; store.mennomedia.org, pg 110

Bynum, Robert C, Travel Keys, PO Box 160691, Sacramento, CA 95816-0691 *Tel:* 916-452-5200 *Fax:* 916-452-5200, pg 249

Byram, John W, University of New Mexico, One University of New Mexico, Albuquerque, NM 87131-0001 *Tel:* 505-277-2346; 505-272-7777 (cust serv) *Toll Free Tel:* 800-249-7737 (orders only) *Fax:* 505-277-3343; 505-272-7778 (cust serv) *Toll Free Fax:* 800-622-8667 (orders only) *E-mail:* unmpress@unm.edu; custserv@upress.unm.edu (order dept) *Web Site:* unmpress.com, pg 258

Byrd, Bobby, Cinco Puntos Press, 701 Texas Ave, El Paso, TX 79901 *Tel:* 915-838-1625 *Toll Free Tel:* 800-566-9072 *Fax:* 915-838-1635 *E-mail:* info@cincopuntos.com *Web Site:* www.cincopuntos.com, pg 58

Byrd, John, Cinco Puntos Press, 701 Texas Ave, El Paso, TX 79901 *Tel:* 915-838-1625 *Toll Free Tel:* 800-566-9072 *Fax:* 915-838-1635 *E-mail:* info@cincopuntos.com *Web Site:* www.cincopuntos.com, pg 58

Byrd, Lee, Cinco Puntos Press, 701 Texas Ave, El Paso, TX 79901 *Tel:* 915-838-1625 *Toll Free Tel:* 800-566-9072 *Fax:* 915-838-1635 *E-mail:* info@cincopuntos.com *Web Site:* www.cincopuntos.com, pg 58

Byrns, Bob, Paulist Press, 997 Macarthur Blvd, Mahwah, NJ 07430-9990 *Tel:* 201-825-7300 *Toll Free Tel:* 800-218-1903 *Fax:* 201-825-8345 *Toll Free Fax:* 800-836-3161 *E-mail:* info@paulistpress.com *Web Site:* www.paulistpress.com, pg 184

Cabasin, Linda, Fodor's Travel Publications, 1745 Broadway, 15th fl, New York, NY 10019 *Toll Free Tel:* 800-733-3000 *E-mail:* fodorspublicity@randomhouse.com; editors@fodors.com *Web Site:* www.fodors.com, pg 90

Cabezas, Sue, Applewood Books Inc, One River Rd, Carlisle, MA 01741 *Tel:* 781-271-0055 *Toll Free Tel:* 800-277-5312 (orders) *Fax:* 781-271-0056 *E-mail:* bookorder@awb.com; customercare@awb.com *Web Site:* www.awb.com, pg 20

Cabin, John, Vandamere Press, 3580 Morris St N, St Petersburg, FL 33713 *Tel:* 727-556-0950 *Toll Free Tel:* 800-551-7776 *Fax:* 727-556-2560 *E-mail:* orders@vandamere.com *Web Site:* www.vandamere.com, pg 264

Cabrera, Tommy, Crown Publishing Group, c/o Penguin Random House Inc, 1745 Broadway, New York, NY 10019 *Tel:* 212-782-9000 *Toll Free Tel:* 888-264-1745 *Fax:* 212-940-7408 *E-mail:* crownosm@penguinrandomhouse.com *Web Site:* crownpublishing.com, pg 68

Cady, Donald, Wesleyan Publishing House, 13300 Olio Rd, Fishers, IN 46037 *Tel:* 317-774-3853 *Toll Free Tel:* 800-493-7539 *Fax:* 317-774-3865 *Toll Free Fax:* 800-788-3535 *E-mail:* wph@wesleyan.org *Web Site:* www.wesleyan.org/wph, pg 269

Cahill, Brendan, Penguin Random House Inc, 1745 Broadway, New York, NY 10019 *Tel:* 212-782-9000 *Toll Free Tel:* 800-726-0600 *Web Site:* www.randomhouse.com, pg 187

Cahill, Kerry, The Johns Hopkins University Press, 2715 N Charles St, Baltimore, MD 21218-4363 *Tel:* 410-516-6900; 410-516-6987 (journal orders outside US & CN) *Toll Free Tel:* 800-537-5487 (book orders & cust serv); 800-548-1784 (journal orders) *Fax:* 410-516-6968; 410-516-3866 (journal orders) *E-mail:* hfscustserv@press.jhu.edu (cust serv); jrnlcirc@press.jhu.edu (journal orders) *Web Site:* www.press.jhu.edu; muse.jhu.edu, pg 127

Cahoon, Nancy Stauffer, Nancy Stauffer Associates, 30 Corbin Dr, Suite 1203, Darien, CT 06820 *Tel:* 203-202-2500 *Web Site:* publishersmarketplace.com/members/nstauffer; staufferliterary.com, pg 575

Cain, Karen, Standard Publishing, 8805 Governors Hill Dr, Suite 400, Cincinnati, OH 45249 *Tel:* 513-931-4050 *Toll Free Tel:* 800-543-1353 *Fax:* 513-931-0950 *Toll Free Fax:* 877-867-5751 *E-mail:* customerservice@standardpub.com *Web Site:* www.standardpub.com, pg 233

Calamia, Joseph, Yale University Press, 302 Temple St, New Haven, CT 06511-8909 *Tel:* 203-432-0960; 203-432-0966 (sales); 401-531-2800 (cust serv) *Toll Free Tel:* 800-405-1619 (cust serv) *Fax:* 203-432-0948; 203-432-8485 (sales); 401-531-2801 (cust serv) *Toll Free Fax:* 800-406-9145 (cust serv) *E-mail:* sales.press@yale.edu (sales); customer.care@trilateral.org (cust serv) *Web Site:* www.yalebooks.com; yalepress.yale.edu/yupbooks, pg 278

Calarco, Catherine, HeartMath LLC, 14700 W Park Ave, Boulder Creek, CA 95006 *Tel:* 831-338-8700 *Toll Free Tel:* 800-450-9111 *Fax:* 831-338-9861 *E-mail:* inquiry@heartmath.com *Web Site:* www.heartmath.com, pg 109

Calder, Kent, Texas State Historical Association, Stovall Hall 175, 1400 W Highland St, Denton, TX 76203 *Tel:* 940-369-5200 *Fax:* 940-369-5248 *Web Site:* www.tshaonline.org, pg 243

Caldwell, Amy, Beacon Press, 24 Farnsworth St, Boston, MA 02210-1409 *Tel:* 617-742-2110 *Fax:* 617-723-3097; 617-742-2290 *Web Site:* www.beacon.org, pg 32

Caldwell, Linda, The Writers' Colony at Dairy Hollow, 515 Spring St, Eureka Springs, AR 72632 *Tel:* 479-253-7444 *E-mail:* director@writerscolony.org *Web Site:* www.writerscolony.org, pg 657

Caldwell, Madeline, Alfred A Knopf/Everyman's Library, c/o Random House Inc, 1745 Broadway, New York, NY 10019 *Tel:* 212-751-2600 *Toll Free Tel:* 800-638-6460 *Fax:* 212-572-2593 *Web Site:* www.knopfdoubleday.com, pg 132

Calicchio, Rosemary, William H Sadlier Inc, 9 Pine St, New York, NY 10005 *Tel:* 212-227-2120 *Toll Free Tel:* 800-221-5175 (cust serv) *Fax:* 212-312-6080 *E-mail:* customerservice@sadlier.com *Web Site:* www.sadlier.com, pg 213

Calistro, Paddy, Angel City Press, 2118 Wilshire Blvd, Suite 880, Santa Monica, CA 90403 *Tel:* 310-395-9982 *Toll Free Tel:* 800-949-8039 *Fax:* 310-395-3353 *E-mail:* info@angelcitypress.com *Web Site:* www.angelcitypress.com, pg 18

Call, Jerry, Time Being Books, 10411 Clayton Rd, Suites 201-203, St Louis, MO 63131 *Tel:* 314-432-1771 *Fax:* 314-432-7939 *E-mail:* tbbooks@sbcglobal.net *Web Site:* www.timebeing.com, pg 246

Call, Pat, Wadsworth Publishing, 20 Davis Dr, Belmont, CA 94002 *Tel:* 650-595-2350 *Fax:* 650-592-3022 *Toll Free Fax:* 800-522-4923 *Web Site:* www.cengage.com, pg 266

Call, Susan, Jossey-Bass, One Montgomery St, Suite 1200, San Francisco, CA 94104 *Tel:* 415-433-1740 *Toll Free Tel:* 800-956-7739 *Fax:* 415-433-0499 (edit/mktg) *Web Site:* www.josseybass.com; www.pfeiffer.com, pg 128

Callahan, Allison, Gallery Books, 1230 Avenue of the Americas, New York, NY 10020 *Toll Free Tel:* 800-456-6798 *Fax:* 212-698-7284 *E-mail:* consumer.customerservice@simonandschuster.com *Web Site:* www.simonsays.com, pg 94

Callahan, Jack, McGraw-Hill Financial, 1221 Avenue of the Americas, 50th fl, New York, NY 10020 *Tel:* 212-512-2000 *Web Site:* www.mhfi.com, pg 151

Callahan, Kevin, HarperCollins General Books Group, 195 Broadway, New York, NY 10007 *Tel:* 212-207-7000 *Web Site:* www.harpercollins.com, pg 105

Callahan, Kimberly R, Frank Amato Publications Inc, 4040 SE Wister St, Milwaukie, OR 97222 *Tel:* 503-653-8108 *Toll Free Tel:* 800-541-9498 *Fax:* 503-653-2766 *E-mail:* customerservice@amatobooks.com; info@amatobooks.com *Web Site:* www.amatobooks.com, pg 9

Callahan, Laurie, New Directions Publishing Corp, 80 Eighth Ave, New York, NY 10011 *Tel:* 212-255-0230 *Fax:* 212-255-0231 *E-mail:* newdirections@ndbooks.com; editorial@ndbooks.com *Web Site:* ndbooks.com, pg 167

Callahan, Pat, University of South Carolina Press, 1600 Hampton St, Suite 544, Columbia, SC 29208 *Tel:* 803-777-5245 *Toll Free Tel:* 800-768-2500 (orders) *Fax:* 803-777-0160 *Toll Free Fax:* 800-868-0740 (orders) *Web Site:* www.sc.edu/uscpress, pg 259

Callahan, William, InkWell Management, 521 Fifth Ave, 26th fl, New York, NY 10175 *Tel:* 212-922-3500 *Fax:* 212-922-0535 *E-mail:* info@inkwellmanagement.com; submissions@inkwellmanagement.com *Web Site:* inkwellmanagement.com, pg 557

Callaway, MaryKatherine, Louisiana State University Press, 338 Johnston Hall, Baton Rouge, LA 70803 *Tel:* 225-578-6294 *Fax:* 225-578-6461 *E-mail:* lsupress@lsu.edu *Web Site:* lsupress.org, pg 143

Callery, Maryann, Plowshare Media, 405 Vincente Way, La Jolla, CA 92037 *E-mail:* sales@plowsharemedia.com *Web Site:* plowsharemedia.com, pg 193

Callison, Richard, Random House Publishing Group, 1745 Broadway, New York, NY 10019 *Toll Free Tel:* 800-200-3552 *Web Site:* atrandom.com, pg 204

Calvi, Paul, Annual Reviews, 4139 El Camino Way, Palo Alto, CA 94306 *Tel:* 650-493-4400 *Toll Free Tel:* 800-523-8635 *Fax:* 650-424-0910; 650-855-9815 *E-mail:* service@annualreviews.org *Web Site:* www.annualreviews.org, pg 18

Calvo, Roque J, The Electrochemical Society (ECS), 65 S Main St, Bldg D, Pennington, NJ 08534-2839 *Tel:* 609-737-1902 *Fax:* 609-737-2743 *E-mail:* publications@electrochem.org; customerservice@electrochem.org *Web Site:* www.electrochem.org, pg 80

Camacho, Linda, Prospect Agency, 285 Fifth Ave, PMB 445, Brooklyn, NY 11215 *Tel:* 718-788-3217 *Fax:* 718-360-9582 *Web Site:* www.prospectagency.com, pg 568

Camacho, Linda, Random House Children's Books, 1745 Broadway, New York, NY 10019 *Tel:* 212-782-9000 *Toll Free Tel:* 800-200-3552 *Fax:* 212-782-9452 *Web Site:* randomhousekids.com, pg 204

Camardi, Ben, Harold Matson Co Inc, 276 Fifth Ave, New York, NY 10001 *Tel:* 212-679-4490 *Fax:* 212-545-1224, pg 564

Cambell, Cloves C Jr, National Newspaper Publishers Association (NNPA), 1816 12 St NW, Washington, DC 20009 *Tel:* 202-588-8764 *Fax:* 202-588-8960 *E-mail:* info@nnpa.org *Web Site:* www.nnpa.org; www.blackpressusa.com, pg 613

Cambridge, Barbara, National Council of Teachers of English (NCTE), 1111 W Kenyon Rd, Urbana, IL 61801-1096 *Tel:* 217-328-3870 *Toll Free Tel:* 877-369-6283 (cust serv) *Fax:* 217-328-9645 *E-mail:* orders@ncte.org *Web Site:* www.ncte.org, pg 164

Cambridge, Barbara, National Council of Teachers of English (NCTE), 1111 W Kenyon Rd, Urbana, IL 61801-1096 *Tel:* 217-328-3870 *Toll Free Tel:* 877-369-6283 (cust serv) *Fax:* 217-328-9645 *E-mail:* public_info@ncte.org *Web Site:* www.ncte.org, pg 612

Cameron, Claire, Bull Publishing Co, PO Box 1377, Boulder, CO 80306 *Tel:* 303-545-6350 *Toll Free Tel:* 800-676-2855 *Fax:* 303-545-6354 *E-mail:* bullpublishing@msn.com *Web Site:* www.bullpub.com, pg 47

Cameron, Hamish, University of Toronto Press, 10 St Mary St, Suite 700, Toronto, ON M4Y 2W8, Canada *Tel:* 416-978-2239 *Fax:* 416-978-4738 *E-mail:* info@utpress.utoronto.ca *Web Site:* www.utpress.utoronto.ca; www.utppublishing.com, pg 504

Cameron, Kimberley, Kimberley Cameron & Associates, 1550 Tiburon Blvd, Suite 704, Tiburon, CA 94920 *Tel:* 415-789-9191 *Fax:* 415-789-9177 *E-mail:* info@kimberleycameron.com *Web Site:* www.kimberleycameron.com, pg 559

Cameron, Laura, Flanker Press Ltd, 1243 Kenmount Rd, Unit A, Paradise, NL A1L 0V8, Canada *Tel:* 709-739-4477 *Toll Free Tel:* 866-739-4420 *Fax:* 709-739-4420 *E-mail:* info@flankerpress.com *Web Site:* www.flankerpress.com, pg 484

Cameron, Linda, University of Alberta Press, Ring House 2, Edmonton, AB T6G 2E1, Canada *Tel:* 780-492-3662 *Fax:* 780-492-0719 *Web Site:* www.uap.ualberta.ca, pg 502

Cameron, Ronald, The Institute for Cooperation on Adult Education (Institut de Cooperation pour l'Education des Adultes-ICEA), 55, ave du Mont-Royal Ouest, Bureau 303, Montreal, QC H2T 2S6, Canada *Tel:* 514-948-2044 *Fax:* 514-948-2046 *E-mail:* icae@icea.qc.ca *Web Site:* www.icea.qc.ca, pg 607

Cameron, Skyla Dawn, Mundania Press LLC, 6457 Glenway Ave, Suite 109, Cincinnati, OH 45211-5222 *Tel:* 513-490-2822 *Fax:* 513-598-9220 *Toll Free Fax:* 888-460-4752 *E-mail:* books@mundania.com; inquiry@mundania.com *Web Site:* www.mundania.com, pg 161

Camp, Aaron, Crossway, 1300 Crescent St, Wheaton, IL 60187 *Tel:* 630-682-4300 *Toll Free Tel:* 800-635-7993 (orders); 800-543-1659 (cust serv) *Fax:* 630-682-4785 *E-mail:* info@crossway.org *Web Site:* www.crossway.org, pg 67

Campana, Piya, Harlequin Enterprises Ltd, 225 Duncan Mill Rd, Don Mills, ON M3B 3K9, Canada *Tel:* 416-445-5860 *Toll Free Tel:* 888-432-4879; 800-370-5838 (ebook inquiries) *E-mail:* customerservice@harlequin.com *Web Site:* www.harlequin.com, pg 487

Campaniolo, Jennifer, Nicholas Brealey Publishing, 20 Park Plaza, Suite 610, Boston, MA 02116 *Tel:* 617-523-3801 *Toll Free Tel:* 888-BREALEY (273-2539) *Fax:* 617-523-3708 *E-mail:* info@nicholasbrealey.com *Web Site:* www.nicholasbrealey.com, pg 45

Campany, Rebecca, The Brookings Institution Press, 1775 Massachusetts Ave NW, Washington, DC 20036-2188 *Tel:* 202-536-3600 *Toll Free Tel:* 800-537-5487 *Fax:* 202-536-3623 *E-mail:* permissions@brookings.edu *Web Site:* www.brookings.edu, pg 47

Campbell, Abigail, Association of Writers & Writing Programs (AWP), George Mason University, 4400 University Dr, MSN 1E3, Fairfax, VA 22030 *Tel:* 703-993-4301 *Fax:* 703-993-4302 *E-mail:* awp@awpwriter.org *Web Site:* www.awpwriter.org, pg 599

Campbell, Beth, BookEnds LLC, 136 Long Hill Rd, Gillette, NJ 07933 *Web Site:* www.bookends-inc.com, pg 543

Campbell, Bruce, Capital Enquiry Inc, 1034 Emerald Bay Rd, No 435, South Lake Tahoe, CA 96150 *Tel:* 916-442-1434 *Toll Free Tel:* 800-922-7486 *Fax:* 916-244-2704 *E-mail:* info@capenq.com *Web Site:* www.govbuddy.com, pg 49

Campbell, Colin G, The Colonial Williamsburg Foundation, PO Box 1776, Williamsburg, VA 23187-1776 *Tel:* 757-229-1000 *Toll Free Tel:* 800-HISTORY (447-8679) *Fax:* 757-220-7325 *E-mail:* cwres@cwf.org; geninfo@cwf.org *Web Site:* www.colonialwilliamsburg.org/publications, pg 61

Campbell, Corey, Arizona State University, Creative Writing Program, 851 S Cady Mall, Rm 542, Tempe, AZ 85287-0302 *Tel:* 480-965-3528 *Fax:* 480-965-3451 *Web Site:* www.asu.edu/clas/english/creativewriting, pg 659

Campbell, Jane, Chosen Books, 11400 Hampshire Ave S, Bloomington, MN 55438-2852 *Tel:* 616-676-9185 *Toll Free Tel:* 800-877-2665 (orders only) *Fax:* 616-676-9573 *Toll Free Fax:* 800-398-3111 (orders only) *Web Site:* bakerpublishinggroup.com/chosen, pg 57

Campbell, Jennie, Water Resources Publications LLC, PO Box 630026, Highlands Ranch, CO 80163-0026 *Tel:* 720-873-0171 *Toll Free Tel:* 800-736-2405 *Fax:* 720-873-0173 *Toll Free Fax:* 800-616-1971 *E-mail:* info@wrpllc.com *Web Site:* www.wrpllc.com, pg 267

Campbell, Kristina, NASW Press, 750 First St NE, Suite 700, Washington, DC 20002 *Tel:* 202-408-8600 *Fax:* 203-336-8312 *E-mail:* press@naswdc.org *Web Site:* www.naswpress.org, pg 162

Campbell, Lakisha, BuilderBooks.com, 1201 15 St NW, Washington, DC 20005 *Tel:* 202-822-0200 *Toll Free Tel:* 800-223-2665 *Fax:* 202-266-8096 (edit) *E-mail:* builderbooks@nahb.com *Web Site:* www.builderbooks.com, pg 47

Campbell, Logan, Pearson Higher Education, 225 River St, Hoboken, NJ 07030-4772 *Tel:* 201-236-7000 *Fax:* 201-236-3381 *Web Site:* www.pearsonhighered.com, pg 185

Campbell, Marie, Transatlantic Agency, 2 Bloor St E, Suite 3500, Toronto, ON M4W 1A8, Canada *Tel:* 416-488-9214 *E-mail:* info@transatlanticagency.com *Web Site:* www.transatlanticagency.com, pg 577

Campbell, Marilyn A, Rutgers University Press, 106 Somerset St, 3rd fl, New Brunswick, NJ 08901 *Tel:* 848-445-7762 *Toll Free Tel:* 800-848-6224 (orders only) *Fax:* 732-745-4935 (acqs, edit, mktg, perms & prodn) *Toll Free Fax:* 800-272-6817 (fulfillment) *Web Site:* rutgerspress.rutgers.edu, pg 213

Campbell, Michael O, Lone Pine Publishing, 2311 96 St, Edmonton, AB T6N 1G3, Canada *Tel:* 780-433-9333 *Toll Free Tel:* 800-661-9017 *Fax:* 780-433-9646 *Toll Free Fax:* 800-424-7173 *E-mail:* info@lonepinepublishing.com *Web Site:* www.lonepinepublishing.com, pg 490

Campbell, Thomas P, The Metropolitan Museum of Art, 1000 Fifth Ave, New York, NY 10028 *Tel:* 212-879-5500; 212-570-3725 *Fax:* 212-396-5062 *E-mail:* editorial@metmuseum.org *Web Site:* www.metmuseum.org, pg 155

Campfield, Charlene M, Campfield & Campfield Publishing, 6521 Cutler St, Philadelphia, PA 19126 *Toll Free Tel:* 888-518-2440 *Fax:* 215-224-6696 *E-mail:* info@campfieldspublishing.com *Web Site:* www.campfieldspublishing.com, pg 49

Campfield, Leon V Sr, Campfield & Campfield Publishing, 6521 Cutler St, Philadelphia, PA 19126 *Toll Free Tel:* 888-518-2440 *Fax:* 215-224-6696 *E-mail:* info@campfieldspublishing.com *Web Site:* www.campfieldspublishing.com, pg 49

Campi, Dr Alicia, The Mongolia Society Inc, Indiana University, 322 Goodbody Hall, 1011 E Third St, Bloomington, IN 47405-7005 *Tel:* 812-855-4078 *Fax:* 812-855-4078 *E-mail:* monsoc@indiana.edu *Web Site:* www.mongoliasociety.org, pg 159

Campion, Emma Boys, Ten Speed Press, 2625 Alcatraz Ave, Unit 505, Berkeley, CA 94705 *Tel:* 510-285-3000 *Toll Free Tel:* 800-841-BOOK (841-2665) *E-mail:* csorders@randomhouse.com *Web Site:* crownpublishing.com/imprint/ten-speed-press, pg 243

Campion, Owen, Our Sunday Visitor Publishing, 200 Noll Plaza, Huntington, IN 46750 *Tel:* 260-356-8400 *Toll Free Tel:* 800-348-2440 (orders) *Fax:* 260-356-8472 *Toll Free Fax:* 800-498-6709 *E-mail:* osvbooks@osv.com (book orders) *Web Site:* www.osv.com, pg 178

Campling, Neil, Aptara Inc, 3110 Fairview Park Dr, Suite 900, Falls Church, VA 22042 *Tel:* 703-352-0001 *E-mail:* info@aptaracorp.com *Web Site:* www.aptaracorp.com, pg 520

Campo, Gigi, Avery, 375 Hudson St, New York, NY 10014 *Tel:* 212-366-2000 *Fax:* 212-366-2643 *E-mail:* online@penguinputnam.com *Web Site:* www.penguinputnam.com; us.penguingroup.com, pg 28

Campo, Gigi, Penguin Group (USA) LLC, a Penguin Random House company, 375 Hudson St, New York, NY 10014 *Tel:* 212-366-2000 *Toll Free Tel:* 800-847-5515 (inside sales); 800-631-8571 (cust serv) *Fax:* 212-366-2666; 607-775-4829 (inside sales) *E-mail:* online@us.penguingroup.com *Web Site:* www.penguin.com; us.penguingroup.com, pg 186

Campo, Joan, Art of Living, PrimaMedia Inc, 1250 Bethlehem Pike, Suite 241, Hatfield, PA 19440 *Tel:* 215-660-5045 *E-mail:* primamedia4@yahoo.com, pg 23

Campoli, Leila, The Stonesong Press LLC, 270 W 39 St, No 201, New York, NY 10018 *Tel:* 212-929-4600 *E-mail:* editors@stonesong.com *Web Site:* www.stonesong.com, pg 575

Campos, Alexander, The Center for Book Arts, 28 W 27 St, 3rd fl, New York, NY 10001 *Tel:* 212-481-0295 *E-mail:* info@centerforbookarts.org *Web Site:* www.centerforbookarts.org, pg 603

Campos, Alexander, The Center for Book Arts, 28 W 27 St, 3rd fl, New York, NY 10001 *Tel:* 212-481-0295 *Toll Free Fax:* 866-708-8994 *E-mail:* info@centerforbookarts.org *Web Site:* www.centerforbookarts.org, pg 659

Canavan, Susan, Houghton Mifflin Harcourt Trade & Reference Division, 222 Berkeley St, Boston, MA 02116 *Tel:* 617-351-5000 *Toll Free Tel:* 800-225-3362 *Web Site:* www.hmhco.com, pg 115

Cancio, Jose, Periodical & Book Association of America Inc (PBAA), 481 Eighth Ave, Suite 526, New York, NY 10001 *Tel:* 212-563-6502 *Fax:* 212-563-4098 *Web Site:* www.pbaa.net, pg 616

Candido, Arthur, Scholium International Inc, 151 Cow Neck Rd, Port Washington, NY 11050 *Tel:* 516-767-7171 *E-mail:* info@scholium.com *Web Site:* www.scholium.com, pg 219

Candido, Elena M, Scholium International Inc, 151 Cow Neck Rd, Port Washington, NY 11050 *Tel:* 516-767-7171 *E-mail:* info@scholium.com *Web Site:* www.scholium.com, pg 219

Canell, Pam, University of Washington Press, 433 Brooklyn Ave NE, Seattle, WA 98195-9570 *Tel:* 206-543-4050 *Toll Free Tel:* 800-537-5487 (orders) *Fax:* 206-543-3932; 410-516-6998 (orders) *E-mail:* uwpress@u.washington.edu *Web Site:* www.washington.edu/uwpress/, pg 260

Canfield, Doug, The Mountaineers Books, 1001 SW Klickitat Way, Suite 201, Seattle, WA 98134 *Tel:* 206-223-6303 *Toll Free Tel:* 800-553-4453 *Fax:* 206-223-6306 *Toll Free Fax:* 800-568-7604 *E-mail:* mbooks@mountaineersbooks.org *Web Site:* www.mountaineersbooks.org, pg 161

Canfield, Thomas, Starcrafts LLC, 334-A Calef Hwy, Epping, NH 03042 *Tel:* 603-734-4300 *Toll Free Tel:* 866-953-8458 (24/7 message ctr) *Fax:* 603-734-4311 *E-mail:* astrosales@astrocom.com; starcrafts@comcast.net *Web Site:* www.astrocom.com; starcraftspublishing.com; acspublications.com, pg 234

Cangelosi, Allegra, Northeast-Midwest Institute, 50 "F" St NW, Suite 950, Washington, DC 20001 *Tel:* 202-544-5200 *Fax:* 202-544-0043 *E-mail:* info@nemw.org *Web Site:* www.nemw.org, pg 171

Cannon, Chad, Thomas Nelson, 501 Nelson Place, Nashville, TN 37214 *Tel:* 615-889-9000 *Toll Free Tel:* 800-251-4000 *Fax:* 615-902-1548 *E-mail:* publicity@thomasnelson.com *Web Site:* www.thomasnelson.com, pg 245

Cannon, Dolores, Ozark Mountain Publishing Inc, PO Box 754, Huntsville, AR 72740-0754 *Tel:* 479-738-2348 *Toll Free Tel:* 800-935-0045 *Fax:* 479-738-2448 *E-mail:* info@ozarkmt.com *Web Site:* www.ozarkmt.com, pg 179

Cannon, Pamela, Random House Publishing Group, 1745 Broadway, New York, NY 10019 *Toll Free Tel:* 800-200-3552 *Web Site:* atrandom.com, pg 204

Cannon, Tim, Houghton Mifflin Harcourt, 222 Berkeley St, Boston, MA 02116 *Tel:* 617-351-5000 *Toll Free Tel:* 800-225-5425 (K-12 educ materials); 800-323-9540 (assessment materials); 877-219-1537 (SkillsTutor); 888-242-6747 (Destination; Earobics; Edmark; Learning Village; Riverdeep); 800-225-3362 (Houghton Mifflin Harcourt Trade & Reference Publishers) *Toll Free Fax:* 800-269-5232 *E-mail:* customerservice@hmhpub.com *Web Site:* www.hmhco.com, pg 115

Cantor, Carrie, Joelle Delbourgo Associates Inc, 101 Park St, Montclair, NJ 07042 *Tel:* 973-773-0836 (call only during standard business hours) *Web Site:* www.delbourgo.com, pg 548

Cantor, Eric, JIST Publishing, 875 Montreal Way, St Paul, MN 55102 *Toll Free Tel:* 800-328-1452 *Toll Free Fax:* 800-328-4564 *E-mail:* educate@emcp.com *Web Site:* jist.emcp.com, pg 127

Cantor, Jacqueline, Berkley Books, 375 Hudson St, New York, NY 10014 *Tel:* 212-366-2000 *Fax:* 212-366-2666 *E-mail:* online@penguinputnam.com *Web Site:* www.penguinputnam.com; us.penguingroup.com, pg 35

Cantor, Jacqueline, Berkley Publishing Group, 375 Hudson St, New York, NY 10014 *Tel:* 212-366-2000 *Fax:* 212-366-2385 *E-mail:* online@penguinputnam.com *Web Site:* us.penguingroup.com, pg 35

Canuel, Ron, Canadian Education Association (Association canadienne d'education), 119 Spadina Ave, Suite 705, Toronto, ON M5V 2L1, Canada *Tel:* 416-591-6300 *Toll Free Tel:* 866-803-9549 *Fax:* 416-591-5345 *E-mail:* info@cea-ace.ca *Web Site:* www.cea-ace.ca, pg 602

Canzoneri, Jennifer, BenBella Books Inc, 10300 N Central Expwy, Suite 400, Dallas, TX 75231 *Tel:* 214-750-3600 *Fax:* 214-750-3645 *E-mail:* feedback@benbellabooks.com *Web Site:* www.benbellabooks.com; www.smartpopbooks.com, pg 34

Capik, Gloria A, Paulist Press, 997 Macarthur Blvd, Mahwah, NJ 07430-9990 *Tel:* 201-825-7300 *Toll Free Tel:* 800-218-1903 *Fax:* 201-825-8345 *Toll Free Fax:* 800-836-3161 *E-mail:* info@paulistpress.com *Web Site:* www.paulistpress.com, pg 184

Caplan, David, Little, Brown Books for Young Readers, 1290 Avenue of the Americas, New York, NY 10019 *Tel:* 212-364-1100 *Toll Free Tel:* 800-759-0190 (cust serv) *Web Site:* www.HachetteBookGroup.com, pg 141

Capobiano, John, Society of Illustrators (SI), 128 E 63 St, New York, NY 10065 *Tel:* 212-838-2560 *Fax:* 212-838-2561 *E-mail:* info@societyillustrators.org *Web Site:* www.societyillustrators.org, pg 619

Cappabianca, Rosemarie, McGraw-Hill Education, 2 Penn Plaza, New York, NY 10121-2298 *Tel:* 212-904-2000 *E-mail:* customer.service@mcgraw-hill.com *Web Site:* www.mheducation.com; www.mheducation.com/custserv.html, pg 151

Capps, Karen, Concordia Publishing House, 3558 S Jefferson Ave, St Louis, MO 63118-3968 *Tel:* 314-268-1000; 314-268-1268 (bookshop) *Toll Free Tel:* 800-325-3040 (cust serv) *Toll Free Fax:* 800-490-9889 (cust serv) *E-mail:* order@cph.org *Web Site:* www.cph.org, pg 62

Capron, Elise, Sandra Dijkstra Literary Agency, 1155 Camino del Mar, PMB 515, Del Mar, CA 92014-2605 *E-mail:* queries@dijkstraagency.com *Web Site:* dijkstraagency.com, pg 548

Caputo, Nicole, Basic Books, 250 W 57 St, 15th fl, New York, NY 10107 *Tel:* 212-340-8164; 212-340-8136 *Fax:* 212-340-8135 *E-mail:* perseus.promos@perseusbooks.com *Web Site:* www.basicbooks.com; perseusbooks.com, pg 31

Caratozzolo, Marie, Square One Publishers Inc, 115 Herricks Rd, Garden City Park, NY 11040 *Tel:* 516-535-2010 *Toll Free Tel:* 877-900-BOOK (900-2665) *Fax:* 516-535-2014 *E-mail:* sq1publish@aol.com *Web Site:* www.squareonepublishers.com, pg 232

Carberry, Tara, Trident Media Group LLC, 41 Madison Ave, 36th fl, New York, NY 10010 *Tel:* 212-333-1511 *E-mail:* info@tridentmediagroup.com; press@tridentmediagroup.com *Web Site:* www.tridentmediagroup.com, pg 578

Carbone, Becky, Global Ebook Awards, PO Box 8206-240, Santa Barbara, CA 93118-8206 *Tel:* 805-968-7277 *Fax:* 805-968-1379 *Web Site:* globalebookawards.com, pg 689

Carbone, Becky, Para Publishing LLC, PO Box 8206-240, Santa Barbara, CA 93118-8206 *Tel:* 805-968-7277 *Toll Free Tel:* 800-727-2782 *Fax:* 805-968-1379 *Web Site:* www.parapublishing.com, pg 181

Carbone, Courtney, Random House Children's Books, 1745 Broadway, New York, NY 10019 *Tel:* 212-782-9000 *Toll Free Tel:* 800-200-3552 *Fax:* 212-782-9452 *Web Site:* randomhousekids.com, pg 204

Carbone, Linda, Words into Print, 57 Prince St, Suite 4R, New York, NY 10012 *Tel:* 212-741-1393 *Fax:* 419-441-1393 *E-mail:* query@wordsintoprint.org *Web Site:* www.wordsintoprint.org, pg 536

Carder, Sara, Jeremy P Tarcher, 375 Hudson St, New York, NY 10014 *Tel:* 212-366-2000 *E-mail:* online@penguinputnam.com *Web Site:* www.penguinputnam.com; us.penguingroup.com, pg 240

Cardinal, Chyla, Rocky Mountain Books Ltd (RMB), 103-1075 Pendergast St, Victoria, BC V8V 0A1, Canada *Tel:* 250-360-0829 *Fax:* 250-386-0829 *Web Site:* www.rmbooks.com, pg 497

Cardona, Moses, John Hawkins and Associates Inc, 71 W 23 St, Suite 1600, New York, NY 10010 *Tel:* 212-807-7040 *E-mail:* jha@jhalit.com *Web Site:* jhalit.com, pg 556

Cardoza, Avery, Cardoza Publishing, 808 S Main St, Las Vegas, NV 89101 *Tel:* 702-870-7200 *Toll Free Tel:* 800-577-WINS (577-9467) *E-mail:* cardozabooks@aol.com; info@cardozabooks.com *Web Site:* www.cardozabooks.com, pg 50

Carey, Brooke, Avery, 375 Hudson St, New York, NY 10014 *Tel:* 212-366-2000 *Fax:* 212-366-2643 *E-mail:* online@penguinputnam.com *Web Site:* www.penguinputnam.com; us.penguingroup.com, pg 28

Carey, Brooke, Penguin Group (USA) LLC, a Penguin Random House company, 375 Hudson St, New York, NY 10014 *Tel:* 212-366-2000 *Toll Free Tel:* 800-847-5515 (inside sales); 800-631-8571 (cust serv) *Fax:* 212-366-2666; 607-775-4829 (inside sales) *E-mail:* online@us.penguingroup.com *Web Site:* www.penguin.com; us.penguingroup.com, pg 186

Carey, Jennifer, Mountain Press Publishing Co, 1301 S Third W, Missoula, MT 59801 *Tel:* 406-728-1900 *Toll Free Tel:* 800-234-5308 *Fax:* 406-728-1635 *E-mail:* info@mtnpress.com *Web Site:* www.mountain-press.com, pg 160

Carey, Mary Ann, Paulist Press, 997 Macarthur Blvd, Mahwah, NJ 07430-9990 *Tel:* 201-825-7300 *Toll Free Tel:* 800-218-1903 *Fax:* 201-825-8345 *Toll Free Fax:* 800-836-3161 *E-mail:* info@paulistpress.com *Web Site:* www.paulistpress.com, pg 184

Cargill, Noreen, Bread Loaf Writers' Conference, 5525 Middlebury College, 14 Old Chapel Rd, Middlebury, VT 05753 *Tel:* 802-443-5286 *Fax:* 802-443-2087 *E-mail:* blwc@middlebury.edu *Web Site:* www.middlebury.edu/blwc, pg 650

Cargill, Noreen, Fellowship & Scholarship Program for Writers, Middlebury College, Middlebury, VT 05753 *Tel:* 802-443-5286 *Fax:* 802-443-2087 *E-mail:* blwc@middlebury.edu *Web Site:* www.middlebury.edu/blwc, pg 685

Carispat, Gia, Art of Living, PrimaMedia Inc, 1250 Bethlehem Pike, Suite 241, Hatfield, PA 19440 *Tel:* 215-660-5045 *E-mail:* primamedia4@yahoo.com, pg 23

Carkhuff, Robert W, HRD Press, 22 Amherst Rd, Amherst, MA 01002-9709 *Tel:* 413-253-3488 *Toll Free Tel:* 800-822-2801 *Fax:* 413-253-3490 *E-mail:* info@hrdpress.com; customerservice@hrdpress.com *Web Site:* www.hrdpress.com, pg 116

Carland-Adams, Bethany, F+W, A Content + eCommerce Company, 10151 Carver Rd, Suite 200, Blue Ash, OH 45242 *Tel:* 513-531-2690 *Toll Free Tel:* 800-289-0963 (trade accts); 800-258-0929 (orders) *E-mail:* contact_us@fwmedia.com *Web Site:* www.fwcommunity.com, pg 86

Carleton, Emily, St Martin's Press, LLC, 175 Fifth Ave, New York, NY 10010 *Tel:* 646-307-5151 *Fax:* 212-420-9314 *E-mail:* firstname.lastname@macmillan.com *Web Site:* www.stmartins.com, pg 215

Carlisle, Michael, InkWell Management, 521 Fifth Ave, 26th fl, New York, NY 10175 *Tel:* 212-922-3500 *Fax:* 212-922-0535 *E-mail:* info@inkwellmanagement.com; submissions@inkwellmanagement.com *Web Site:* inkwellmanagement.com, pg 557

Carlisle, Roy M, Independent Institute, 100 Swan Way, Oakland, CA 94621-1428 *Tel:* 510-632-1366 *Toll Free Tel:* 800-927-8733 *Fax:* 510-568-6040 *E-mail:* orders@independent.org *Web Site:* www.independent.org, pg 120

Carlough, Rosemary Kane, AMACOM Books, 1601 Broadway, New York, NY 10019-7420 *Tel:* 212-586-8100 *Toll Free Tel:* 800-250-5308 (cust serv) *Fax:* 212-903-8083; 518-891-2372 (orders) *E-mail:* pubs_cust_serv@amanet.org *Web Site:* www.amacombooks.org, pg 9

Carlson, Ann, Scott O'Dell Award for Historical Fiction, c/o Horn Book Inc, 56 Roland St, Suite 200, Boston, MA 02129 *Tel:* 617-628-8471 *Toll Free Tel:* 800-325-1170 *Web Site:* www.scottodell.com/odellaward.html, pg 714

Carlson, Bernie, Edelstein Prize, Univ of Virginia, Dept of Science, Tech & Society, PO Box 400744, Charlottesville, VA 22904-4744 *Tel:* 434-987-6230 *Fax:* 434-975-2190 (attention: SHOT) *E-mail:* shot@virginia.edu *Web Site:* www.shot.jhu.edu, pg 682

Carlson, Bruce, Hearts & Tummies Cookbook Co, 3544 Blakslee St, Wever, IA 52658 *Tel:* 319-372-7480 *Toll Free Tel:* 800-571-2665 *Fax:* 319-372-7485 *E-mail:* quixotepress@gmail.com; heartsntummies@gmail.com *Web Site:* www.heartsntummies.com, pg 109

Carlson, Bruce, Quixote Press, 3544 Black St, Wever, IA 52658 *Tel:* 319-372-7480 *Toll Free Tel:* 800-571-2665 *Fax:* 319-372-7485 *E-mail:* heartsntummies@gmail.com; potpress@gmail.com, pg 202

Carlson, Carolyn, Viking, 375 Hudson St, New York, NY 10014 *Tel:* 212-366-2000 *E-mail:* online@penguinputnam.com *Web Site:* www.penguinputnam.com; us.penguingroup.com, pg 265

Carlson, Dale, Bick Publishing House, 16 Marion Rd, Branford, CT 06405 *Tel:* 203-208-5253 *Fax:* 203-208-5253 *E-mail:* bickpubhse@aol.com *Web Site:* www.bickpubhouse.com, pg 37

Carlson, Hannah, Bick Publishing House, 16 Marion Rd, Branford, CT 06405 *Tel:* 203-208-5253 *Fax:* 203-208-5253 *E-mail:* bickpubhse@aol.com *Web Site:* www.bickpubhouse.com, pg 37

Carlson, Jennifer, Dunow, Carlson & Lerner Literary Agency Inc, 27 W 20 St, Suite 1107, New York, NY 10011 *Tel:* 212-645-7606 *E-mail:* mail@dclagency.com *Web Site:* www.dclagency.com, pg 549

Carlson, John, Chronicle Books LLC, 680 Second St, San Francisco, CA 94107 *Tel:* 415-537-4200 *Toll Free Tel:* 800-759-0190 (cust serv) *Fax:* 415-537-4460 *Toll Free Fax:* 800-858-7787 (orders); 800-286-9471 (cust serv) *E-mail:* frontdesk@chroniclebooks.com *Web Site:* www.chroniclebooks.com, pg 58

Carlson, Linda, Parenting Press Inc, 13751 Lake City Way NE, Suite 110, Seattle, WA 98125 *Tel:* 206-364-2900 *Toll Free Tel:* 800-99-BOOKS (992-6657) *Fax:* 206-364-0702 *E-mail:* office@parentingpress.com; marketing@parentingpress.com *Web Site:* www.parentingpress.com, pg 183

Carlson, Lynn, Harper's Magazine Foundation, 666 Broadway, 11th fl, New York, NY 10012 *Tel:* 212-420-5720 *Toll Free Tel:* 800-444-4653 *Fax:* 212-228-5889 *E-mail:* harpers@harpers.org *Web Site:* www.harpers.org, pg 106

Carlson, Stephen T, Upper Access Inc, 87 Upper Access Rd, Hinesburg, VT 05461 *Tel:* 802-482-2988 *Toll Free Tel:* 800-310-8320 (orders) *Fax:* 802-417-3002 *E-mail:* info@upperaccess.com *Web Site:* www.upperaccess.com, pg 263

Carlson, Tara Singh, GP Putnam's Sons (Hardcover), 375 Hudson St, New York, NY 10014 *Tel:* 212-366-2000 *E-mail:* online@penguinputnam.com *Web Site:* us.penguingroup.com, pg 201

Carlton, Kirsten, Waxman Leavell Literary Agency, 443 Park Ave S, No 1004, New York, NY 10016 *Tel:* 212-675-5556 *Fax:* 212-675-1381 *Web Site:* www.waxmanleavell.com, pg 579

Carman, Bill, Canadian Museum of History (Musee Canadien de l'Histoire), 100 Laurier St, Gatineau, QC K1A 0M8, Canada *Tel:* 819-776-7000 *Toll Free Tel:* 800-555-5621 (North American orders only) *Fax:* 819-776-7187 *Web Site:* www.historymuseum.ca, pg 475

Carmen, Pamela, Callawind Publications Inc, 3551 St Charles Blvd, Suite 179, Kirkland, QC H9H 3C4, Canada *Tel:* 514-685-9109 *E-mail:* info@callawind.com *Web Site:* www.callawind.com, pg 474

Carney, Paul T, Fons Vitae, 49 Mockingbird Valley Dr, Louisville, KY 40207-1366 *Tel:* 502-897-3641 *Fax:* 502-893-7373 *E-mail:* fonsvitaeky@aol.com *Web Site:* www.fonsvitae.com, pg 90

Carola, Leslie, American Book Producers Association (ABPA), 31 W Eighth St, 2nd fl, New York, NY 10011 *Tel:* 212-675-1363 *Fax:* 212-675-1364 *E-mail:* office@abpaonline.org *Web Site:* www.abpaonline.org, pg 594

Caron, Mia, La Courte Echelle, 160, rue St-Viateur E, bureau 404, Montreal, QC H2T 1A8, Canada *Tel:* 514-274-2004 *Fax:* 514-270-4160 *E-mail:* info@courteechelle.com *Web Site:* www.courteechelle.com, pg 478

Carosi, Chris, City Lights Publishers, 261 Columbus Ave, San Francisco, CA 94133 *Tel:* 415-362-8193 *Fax:* 415-362-4921 *E-mail:* staff@citylights.com *Web Site:* www.citylights.com, pg 58

Carpenter, Ann, Jane Addams Children's Book Award, 777 United Nations Plaza, 6th fl, New York, NY 10017 *Tel:* 212-682-8830 *E-mail:* japa@igc.org *Web Site:* www.janeaddamspeace.org, pg 665

Carpenter, Ken, Houghton Mifflin Harcourt Trade & Reference Division, 222 Berkeley St, Boston, MA 02116 *Tel:* 617-351-5000 *Toll Free Tel:* 800-225-3362 *Web Site:* www.hmhco.com, pg 115

Carpenter, Manzanita, Bear & Co Inc, One Park St, Rochester, VT 05767 *Tel:* 802-767-3174 *Toll Free Tel:* 800-932-3277 *Fax:* 802-767-3726 *E-mail:* customerservice@InnerTraditions.com *Web Site:* InnerTraditions.com, pg 33

Carpenter, Manzanita, Inner Traditions International Ltd, One Park St, Rochester, VT 05767 *Tel:* 802-767-3174 *Toll Free Tel:* 800-246-8648 *Fax:* 802-767-3726 *E-mail:* customerservice@InnerTraditions.com *Web Site:* www.InnerTraditions.com, pg 122

Carpenter, Todd, National Information Standards Organization, 3600 Clipper Mill Rd, Suite 302, Baltimore, MD 21211 *Tel:* 301-654-2512 *Fax:* 410-685-5278 *E-mail:* nisohq@niso.org *Web Site:* www.niso.org, pg 165, 612

Carr, Alexis Williams, New Millennium Awards for Fiction, Poetry & Nonfiction, 4021 Garden Dr, Knoxville, TN 37918 *Tel:* 865-254-4880 *Web Site:* www.newmillenniumwritings.com, pg 712

Carr, David, University of Manitoba Press, University of Manitoba, 301 St Johns College, 92 Dysart Rd, Winnipeg, MB R3T 2M5, Canada *Tel:* 204-474-9495 *Fax:* 204-474-7566 *E-mail:* uofmpress@umanitoba.ca *Web Site:* uofmpress.ca, pg 503

Carr, Gale, Parmenides Publishing, 3753 Howard Hughes Pkwy, Suite 200, Las Vegas, NV 89169 *Tel:* 702-892-3934 *Fax:* 702-892-3939 *E-mail:* info@parmenides.com *Web Site:* www.parmenides.com, pg 183

Carr, Julie, Counterpath Press, 613 22 St, Denver, CO 80205 *E-mail:* counterpath@counterpathpress.org; editors@counterpathpress.org *Web Site:* www.counterpathpress.org, pg 65

Carr, Lloyd, New York City College of Technology, 300 Jay St, Brooklyn, NY 11201 *Tel:* 718-260-5500 *Fax:* 718-260-5198 *E-mail:* connect@citytech.cuny.edu *Web Site:* www.citytech.cuny.edu, pg 661

Carr, Rosalyn, University of Alabama Press, 200 Hackberry Lane, 2nd fl, Tuscaloosa, AL 35487 *Tel:* 205-348-5180 *Fax:* 205-348-9201 *Web Site:* www.uapress.ua.edu, pg 254

Carr, Shida, Touchstone, 1230 Avenue of the Americas, New York, NY 10020, pg 247

Carriere, Nicholle, Blue Bike Books, 11919 125 St, Edmonton, AB T5L 0S3, Canada *Tel:* 780-951-0032 *E-mail:* info@bluebikebooks.com *Web Site:* www.bluebikebooks.com, pg 473

Carrigan, Bob, Dun & Bradstreet, 103 JFK Pkwy, Short Hills, NJ 07078 *Tel:* 973-921-5500 *Toll Free Tel:* 800-526-0651; 800-234-3867 (cust serv) *E-mail:* custserv@dnb.com *Web Site:* www.dnb.com, pg 77

Carrigan, Henry, Northwestern University Press, 629 Noyes St, Evanston, IL 60208-4210 *Tel:* 847-491-2046 *Toll Free Tel:* 800-621-2736 (orders only) *Fax:* 847-491-8150 *E-mail:* nupress@northwestern.edu *Web Site:* www.nupress.northwestern.edu, pg 171

Carrillo, Nica, Coffee House Press, 79 13 Ave NE, Suite 110, Minneapolis, MN 55413 *Tel:* 612-338-0125 *Fax:* 612-338-4004 *E-mail:* info@coffeehousepress.org *Web Site:* coffeehousepress.org, pg 60

Carroll, Allison, Harlequin Enterprises Ltd, 233 Broadway, Suite 1001, New York, NY 10279 *Tel:* 212-553-4200 *Fax:* 212-227-8969 *E-mail:* CustomerService@harlequin.com *Web Site:* www.harlequin.com, pg 105

Carroll, Katie, Franciscan Media, 28 W Liberty St, Cincinnati, OH 45202 *Tel:* 513-241-5615 *Toll Free Tel:* 800-488-0488 *Fax:* 513-241-0399 *E-mail:* books@americancatholic.org *Web Site:* www.americancatholic.org; www.franciscanmedia.org, pg 92

Carroll, Kent, Europa Editions, 214 W 29 St, Suite 1003, New York, NY 10001 *Tel:* 212-868-6844 *Fax:* 212-868-6845 *E-mail:* info@europaeditions.com *Web Site:* www.europaeditions.com, pg 84

Carroll, Lisa, Allen A Knoll Publishers, 200 W Victoria St, Santa Barbara, CA 93101-3627 *Tel:* 805-564-3377 *Toll Free Tel:* 800-777-7623 *Fax:* 805-966-6657 *E-mail:* bookinfo@knollpublishers.com *Web Site:* www.knollpublishers.com, pg 132

Carroll, Michael, The Edna Staebler Award for Creative Non-Fiction, Office of the Dean, Faculty of Arts, 75 University Ave W, Waterloo, ON N2L 3C5, Canada *Tel:* 519-884-1970 (ext 3891) *Fax:* 519-884-8854, pg 730

Carroll, Patrick, Princeton University Press, 41 William St, Princeton, NJ 08540-5237 *Tel:* 609-258-4900 *Toll Free Tel:* 800-777-4726 (orders) *Fax:* 609-258-6305 *Toll Free Fax:* 800-999-1958 *E-mail:* orders@cpfsinc.com *Web Site:* press.princeton.edu, pg 197

Carroll, Sydney, Sinauer Associates Inc, 23 Plumtree Rd, Sunderland, MA 01375 *Tel:* 413-549-4300 *Fax:* 413-549-1118 *E-mail:* publish@sinauer.com; orders@sinauer.com *Web Site:* www.sinauer.com, pg 226

Carroll-Hackett, Mary, John Dos Passos Prize for Literature, Dept of English & Modern Languages, 201 High St, Farmville, VA 23909 *Tel:* 434-395-2155 *Fax:* 434-395-2145, pg 682

Carson, Anne Conover, Anne Carson Associates, 3323 Nebraska Ave NW, Washington, DC 20016 *Tel:* 202-244-6679, pg 522

Carson, Carol, Alfred A Knopf/Everyman's Library, c/o Random House Inc, 1745 Broadway, New York, NY 10019 *Tel:* 212-751-2600 *Toll Free Tel:* 800-638-6460 *Fax:* 212-572-2593 *Web Site:* www.knopfdoubleday.com, pg 132

Carson, Cheryl, University of Tennessee Press, 110 Conference Center Bldg, 600 Henley St, Knoxville, TN 37996-4108 *Tel:* 865-974-3321 *Toll Free Tel:* 800-621-2736 (orders) *Fax:* 865-974-3724 *Toll Free Fax:* 800-621-8476 (orders) *E-mail:* custserv@utpress.org *Web Site:* www.utpress.org, pg 260

Carson, Dina C, Iron Gate Publishing, PO Box 999, Niwot, CO 80544 *Tel:* 303-530-2551 *Fax:* 303-530-5273 *E-mail:* editor@irongate.com *Web Site:* www.irongate.com, pg 125

Carson, Ken, Cengage Learning, 20 Channel Center St, Boston, MA 02210 *Tel:* 617-289-7700 *Toll Free Tel:* 800-354-9706 *Fax:* 617-289-7844 *Toll Free Fax:* 800-487-8488 *E-mail:* esales@cengage.com *Web Site:* www.cengage.com, pg 53

Carson, Dr Luke, ELS Editions, University of Victoria, Dept of English, PO Box 1700, Sta CSC, Victoria, BC V8W 2Y2, Canada *Tel:* 250-721-7236 *Fax:* 250-721-6498 *E-mail:* els@uvic.ca *Web Site:* english.uvic.ca/els, pg 483

Carstanjen, Lee Ann, Wayside Publishing, 11 Jan Sebastian Dr, Suite 5, Sandwich, MA 02563 *Tel:* 508-833-5096 *Toll Free Tel:* 888-302-2519 *Fax:* 508-833-6284 *E-mail:* wayside@sprintmail.com *Web Site:* www.waysidepublishing.com, pg 268

Carstens, Sarah, Rizzoli International Publications Inc, 300 Park Ave S, 4th fl, New York, NY 10010-5399 *Tel:* 212-387-3400 *Toll Free Tel:* 800-522-6657 (orders only) *Fax:* 212-387-3535 *E-mail:* publicity@rizzoliusa.com *Web Site:* www.rizzoliusa.com, pg 209

Carswell, Christine, Chronicle Books LLC, 680 Second St, San Francisco, CA 94107 *Tel:* 415-537-4200 *Toll Free Tel:* 800-759-0190 (cust serv) *Fax:* 415-537-4460 *Toll Free Fax:* 800-858-7787 (orders); 800-286-9471 (cust serv) *E-mail:* frontdesk@chroniclebooks.com *Web Site:* www.chroniclebooks.com, pg 57

Carter, Dr Allyson, The University of Arizona Press, 1510 E University Blvd, Tucson, AZ 85721 *Tel:* 520-621-1441 *Toll Free Tel:* 800-426-3797 (orders) *Fax:* 520-621-8899 *Toll Free Fax:* 800-426-3797 *E-mail:* uap@uapress.arizona.edu *Web Site:* www.uapress.arizona.edu, pg 255

Carter, Brittany, Columbia Books & Information Services, 4340 East-West Hwy, Suite 300, Bethesda, MD 20814 *Tel:* 240-235-0266 *Toll Free Tel:* 888-265-0600 (cust serv) *Fax:* 202-464-1775 *E-mail:* info@columbiabooks.com *Web Site:* www.columbiabooks.com; www.lobbyists.info; www.associationexecs.com, pg 61

Carter, Charles Cuykendall, American Printing History Association, PO Box 4519, Grand Central Sta, New York, NY 10163 *Tel:* 202-544-2422 *E-mail:* secretary@printinghistory.org *Web Site:* printinghistory.org, pg 596

Carter, Cherie, UnKnownTruths.com Publishing Co, 8815 Conroy Windermere Rd, Suite 190, Orlando, FL 32835 *Tel:* 407-929-9207 *Fax:* 407-876-3933 *E-mail:* info@unknowntruths.com *Web Site:* unknowntruths.com, pg 262

Carter, Deborah, Waverly Place Literary Agency, 189 Waverly Place, Unit 4, New York, NY 10014-3135 *Tel:* 212-925-3721 *E-mail:* waverlyplaceliterary@aol.com *Web Site:* www.waverlyplaceliterary.com; twitter.com/waverlyplacelit, pg 579

Carter, Eryn, Hampton Roads Publishing Co, 65 Parker St, Suite 7, Newburyport, MA 01950-4600 *Tel:* 978-465-0504 *Toll Free Tel:* 800-423-7087 (orders) *Fax:* 978-465-0243 *Toll Free Fax:* 877-337-3309 *E-mail:* orders@rwwbooks.com *Web Site:* redwheelweiser.com, pg 104

Carter, Jamie, Bookbuilders of Boston, 115 Webster Woods Lane, North Andover, MA 01845 *Tel:* 781-378-1361 *Fax:* 419-821-2171 *E-mail:* office@bbboston.org *Web Site:* www.bbboston.org, pg 601

Carter, Jill, Crossway, 1300 Crescent St, Wheaton, IL 60187 *Tel:* 630-682-4300 *Toll Free Tel:* 800-635-7993 (orders); 800-543-1659 (cust serv) *Fax:* 630-682-4785 *E-mail:* info@crossway.org *Web Site:* www.crossway.org, pg 67

Carvainis, Maria, Maria Carvainis Agency Inc, Rockefeller Center, 1270 Avenue of the Americas, Suite 2320, New York, NY 10020 *Tel:* 212-245-6365 *Fax:* 212-245-7196 *E-mail:* mca@mariacarvainisagency.com *Web Site:* mariacarvainisagency.com, pg 545

Carvalho, Julia, Chronicle Books LLC, 680 Second St, San Francisco, CA 94107 *Tel:* 415-537-4200 *Toll Free Tel:* 800-759-0190 (cust serv) *Fax:* 415-537-4460 *Toll Free Fax:* 800-858-7787 (orders); 800-286-9471 (cust serv) *E-mail:* frontdesk@chroniclebooks.com *Web Site:* www.chroniclebooks.com, pg 58

Carver, Holly, University of Iowa Press, 119 W Park Rd, 100 Kuhl House, Iowa City, IA 52242-1000 *Tel:* 319-335-2000 *Toll Free Tel:* 800-621-2736

Cavelos, Jeanne, Jeanne Cavelos Editorial Services, PO Box 75, Mont Vernon, NH 03057 *Tel:* 603-673-6234 *Web Site:* jeannecavelos.com, pg 523

Cavelos, Jeanne, Odyssey: The Summer Fantasy Writing Workshop, PO Box 75, Mont Vernon, NH 03057 *Tel:* 603-673-6234 *Fax:* 603-673-6234 *Web Site:* www.odysseyworkshop.org, pg 653

Cazares, Yolanda, Chronicle Books LLC, 680 Second St, San Francisco, CA 94107 *Tel:* 415-537-4200 *Toll Free Tel:* 800-759-0190 (cust serv) *Fax:* 415-537-4460 *Toll Free Fax:* 800-858-7787 (orders); 800-286-9471 (cust serv) *E-mail:* frontdesk@chroniclebooks.com *Web Site:* www.chroniclebooks.com, pg 58

Ceballos, Kelly, League of Women Voters of the United States, 1730 "M" St NW, Suite 1000, Washington, DC 20036-4508 *Tel:* 202-429-1965 *Fax:* 202-429-0854; 202-429-4343 *E-mail:* lwv@lwv.org *Web Site:* www.lwv.org, pg 608

Cebik, Stephen, Yale University Press, 302 Temple St, New Haven, CT 06511-8909 *Tel:* 203-432-0960; 203-432-0966 (sales); 401-531-2800 (cust serv) *Toll Free Tel:* 800-405-1619 (cust serv) *Fax:* 203-432-0948; 203-432-8485 (sales); 401-531-2801 (cust serv) *Toll Free Fax:* 800-406-9145 (cust serv) *E-mail:* sales.press@yale.edu (sales); customer.care@trilateral.org (cust serv) *Web Site:* www.yalebooks.com; yalepress.yale.edu/yupbooks, pg 278

Cech, Scott, American Council on Education, One Dupont Circle NW, Washington, DC 20036 *Tel:* 202-939-9300; 301-632-6757 (orders) *Fax:* 202-939-9302 *E-mail:* pubs@acenet.edu *Web Site:* www.acenet.edu, pg 12

Cecka, Melanie, Random House Children's Books, 1745 Broadway, New York, NY 10019 *Tel:* 212-782-9000 *Toll Free Tel:* 800-200-3552 *Fax:* 212-782-9452 *Web Site:* randomhousekids.com, pg 203

Cegielski, Stephanie, Public Relations Society of America, 33 Maiden Lane, 11th fl, New York, NY 10038-5150 *Tel:* 212-460-1400 *Fax:* 212-995-0757 *Web Site:* www.prsa.org, pg 617

Cekola, Kim, Michigan Municipal League, 1675 Green Rd, Ann Arbor, MI 48105 *Tel:* 734-662-3246 *Toll Free Tel:* 800-653-2483 *Fax:* 734-663-4496 *Web Site:* www.mml.org, pg 155

Cella, Joe, Book Sales Inc, 142 W 36 St, 4th fl, New York, NY 10018 *Tel:* 212-779-4971; 212-779-4972 *Toll Free Tel:* 866-483-5456 *Fax:* 212-779-6058 *E-mail:* sales@quartous.com; customerservice@quartous.com *Web Site:* www.booksalesusa.com, pg 42

Centrello, Gina, Penguin Random House Inc, 1745 Broadway, New York, NY 10019 *Tel:* 212-782-9000 *Toll Free Tel:* 800-726-0600 *Web Site:* www.randomhouse.com, pg 187

Centrello, Gina, Random House Publishing Group, 1745 Broadway, New York, NY 10019 *Toll Free Tel:* 800-200-3552 *Web Site:* atrandom.com, pg 204

Cepler, Julie, Crown Publishing Group, c/o Penguin Random House Inc, 1745 Broadway, New York, NY 10019 *Tel:* 212-782-9000 *Toll Free Tel:* 888-264-1745 *Fax:* 212-940-7408 *E-mail:* crownosm@penguinrandomhouse.com *Web Site:* crownpublishing.com, pg 68

Cerasoli, Lisa, The Writer's Lifeline Inc, 400 S Burnside Ave, Suite 11B, Los Angeles, CA 90036 *Tel:* 323-932-1685 *Fax:* 323-932-1220 *Web Site:* www.thewriterslifeline.com, pg 536

Cerbone, Will, Fordham University Press, 2546 Belmont Ave, University Box L, Bronx, NY 10458 *Tel:* 718-817-4795 *Fax:* 718-817-4785 *Web Site:* www.fordhampress.com, pg 90

Cercone, Philip, McGill-Queen's University Press, 1010 Sherbrooke W, Suite 1720, Montreal, QC H3A 2R7, Canada *Tel:* 514-398-3750 *Fax:* 514-398-4333 *E-mail:* mqup@mqup.ca *Web Site:* www.mqup.ca, pg 491

Ceres, Diana, Greenleaf Book Group LLC, Three Park Place, 4005 Banister Lane, Suite B, Austin, TX 78704 *Tel:* 512-891-6100 *Toll Free Tel:* 800-932-5420 *Fax:* 512-891-6150 *E-mail:* contact@greenleafbookgroup.com *Web Site:* www.greenleafbookgroup.com, pg 100

Cerruti, Laura, University of California Press, 2120 Berkeley Way, Berkeley, CA 94704-1012 *Tel:* 510-642-4247 *Fax:* 510-643-7127 *E-mail:* askucp@ucpress.edu (books); customerservice@ucpressjournals.com *Web Site:* www.ucpress.edu, pg 255

Cerullo, John, Amadeus Press/Hal Leonard Performing Arts Publishing Group, 33 Plymouth St, Suite 302, Montclair, NJ 07042 *Tel:* 973-337-5034 *Toll Free Tel:* 800-524-4425 *E-mail:* info@halleonardbooks.com *Web Site:* www.amadeuspress.com; www.halleonardbooks.com, pg 9

Cerullo, John, Applause Theatre & Cinema Books, 33 Plymouth St, Suite 302, Montclair, NJ 07042 *Tel:* 973-337-5034 *Toll Free Tel:* 800-637-2852 *Fax:* 973-337-5227 *E-mail:* info@applausepub.com *Web Site:* www.applausepub.com, pg 20

Cerullo, John, Backbeat Books, 33 Plymouth St, Suite 302, Montclair, NJ 07042 *Tel:* 973-337-5034 *Toll Free Tel:* 800-637-2852 (Music Dispatch) *Fax:* 973-337-5227 *Web Site:* www.backbeatbooks.com, pg 29

Cerullo, John, Hal Leonard Books, 33 Plymouth St, Suite 302, Montclair, NJ 07042 *Toll Free Tel:* 800-637-2852 *E-mail:* info@halleonardbooks.com; custserv@halleonardbooks.com *Web Site:* www.halleonardbooks.com, pg 103

Cerullo, John, Limelight Editions, 33 Plymouth St, Suite 302, Montclair, NJ 07042 *Tel:* 973-337-5034 *Fax:* 973-337-5227 *Web Site:* limelighteditions.com, pg 139

Chaban, Enid, Random House Children's Books, 1745 Broadway, New York, NY 10019 *Tel:* 212-782-9000 *Toll Free Tel:* 800-200-3552 *Fax:* 212-782-9452 *Web Site:* randomhousekids.com, pg 203

Chabert, Sally, Irene Skolnick Literary Agency, 27 W 20 St, Suite 305, New York, NY 10011 *Tel:* 212-727-3648 *Fax:* 212-352-2059 *E-mail:* office@skolnickliterary.com (queries) *Web Site:* www.skolnickagency.com, pg 573

Chacon, Daniel, University of Texas at El Paso, Department of Creative Writing, MFA/Department of Creative Writing, Liberal Arts 415 UTEP, 500 W University Ave, El Paso, TX 79968-9991 *Tel:* 915-747-5713 *Fax:* 915-747-5523 *Web Site:* www.utep.edu/cw, pg 664

Chadwell, Faye, Oregon State University Press, 121 The Valley Library, Corvallis, OR 97331-4501 *Tel:* 541-737-3166 *Toll Free Tel:* 800-621-2736 (orders) *Web Site:* osupress.oregonstate.edu, pg 177

Chait, Mark, HarperCollins General Books Group, 195 Broadway, New York, NY 10007 *Tel:* 212-207-7000 *Web Site:* www.harpercollins.com, pg 105

Chalfant, Sarah, The Wylie Agency Inc, 250 W 57 St, Suite 2114, New York, NY 10107 *Tel:* 212-246-0069 *Fax:* 212-586-8953 *E-mail:* mail@wylieagency.com *Web Site:* www.wylieagency.com, pg 580

Chalifoux, Ed, Printing Industry Association of the South (PIAS), 305 Plus Park Blvd, Nashville, TN 37217 *Tel:* 615-366-1094 *Fax:* 615-366-4192 *E-mail:* info@pias.org *Web Site:* www.pias.org, pg 617

Chalker, Bob, NACE International, 1440 S Creek Dr, Houston, TX 77084-4906 *Tel:* 281-228-6200 *Toll Free Tel:* 800-797-NACE (797-6223) *Fax:* 281-228-6300 *E-mail:* firstservice@nace.org *Web Site:* www.nace.org, pg 162

Challender, Gary, Books In Motion, 9922 E Montgomery, Suite 31, Spokane Valley, WA 99206 *Tel:* 509-922-1646 *Toll Free Tel:* 800-752-3199 *Fax:* 509-922-1445 *E-mail:* info@booksinmotion.com *Web Site:* www.booksinmotion.com, pg 42

Challice, John, Oxford University Press USA, 198 Madison Ave, New York, NY 10016 *Tel:* 212-726-6000 *Toll Free Tel:* 800-451-7556 (orders); 800-445-9714 (cust serv) *Fax:* 919-677-1303 *E-mail:* custserv.us@oup.com *Web Site:* www.oup.com/us, pg 179

Challman, Roger, TRISTAN Publishing, 2355 Louisiana Ave, Minneapolis, MN 55427 *Tel:* 763-545-1383 *Toll Free Tel:* 866-545-1383 *Fax:* 763-545-1387 *E-mail:* info@tristanpublishing.com *Web Site:* www.tristanpublishing.com, pg 250

Chambers, Andrea L, New York University, Center for Publishing, Midtown Ctr, Rm 429, 11 W 42 St, New York, NY 10036 *Tel:* 212-992-3232 *Fax:* 212-992-3233 *E-mail:* pub.center@nyu.edu *Web Site:* www.scps.nyu.edu/publishing, pg 661

Chambers, Jennifer, In-Plant Printing & Mailing Association (IPMA), 455 S Sam Barr Dr, Suite 203, Kearney, MO 64060 *Tel:* 816-919-1691 *E-mail:* ipmainfo@ipma.org *Web Site:* www.ipma.org, pg 607

Chambers, Lewis R, Bethel Agency, PO Box 21043, Park West Sta, New York, NY 10025 *Tel:* 212-864-4510 *E-mail:* bethelagcy@aol.com, pg 542

Chambers, Nathaniel, National Association of Black Journalists (NABJ), 1100 Knight Hall, Suite 3100, College Park, MD 20742 *Tel:* 301-405-0248 *Fax:* 301-314-1714 *E-mail:* nabj@nabj.org *Web Site:* www.nabj.org, pg 611

Chambliss, Thom, Pacific Northwest Book Awards, 338 W 11 Ave, Unit 108, Eugene, OR 97401 *Tel:* 541-683-4363 *Fax:* 541-683-3910 *E-mail:* info@pnba.org *Web Site:* www.pnba.org, pg 715

Chambliss, Thom, Pacific Northwest Booksellers Association, 338 W 11 Ave, Unit 108, Eugene, OR 97401 *Tel:* 541-683-4363 *Toll Free Tel:* 800-353-6764 *Fax:* 541-683-3910 *E-mail:* info@pnba.org *Web Site:* www.pnba.org, pg 615

Chamenko, Tiffany, Information Today, Inc, 143 Old Marlton Pike, Medford, NJ 08055-8750 *Tel:* 609-654-6266 *Toll Free Tel:* 800-300-9868 (cust serv) *Fax:* 609-654-4309 *E-mail:* custserv@infotoday.com *Web Site:* www.infotoday.com, pg 121

Chamichian, Ani, The Experiment, 220 East 23 St, Suite 301, New York, NY 10010-4674 *Tel:* 212-889-1659 *E-mail:* info@theexperimentpublishing.com *Web Site:* www.theexperimentpublishing.com, pg 85

Chan, James, The Perseus Books Group, 387 Park Ave S, 12th fl, New York, NY 10016 *Tel:* 212-340-8100 *Toll Free Tel:* 800-343-4499 (cust serv) *Fax:* 212-340-8105 *Web Site:* www.perseusbooksgroup.com, pg 189

Chan, Stephanie, Columbia Publishing Course at Columbia University, 2950 Broadway, MC 3801, New York, NY 10027 *Tel:* 212-854-1898 *Fax:* 212-854-7618 *E-mail:* publishing@jrn.columbia.edu *Web Site:* www.journalism.columbia.edu/publishing, pg 659

Chan, Wayne, National Society of Newspaper Columnists Annual Conference, 1345 Fillmore St, Suite 507, San Francisco, CA 94115 *Tel:* 415-488-NCNC (488-6762) *Toll Free Tel:* 866-440-NSNC (440-6762) *Fax:* 484-297-0336 *Toll Free Fax:* 866-635-5759 *Web Site:* www.columnists.com, pg 653

Chance, Rachel, The American Library Association (ALA), 50 E Huron St, Chicago, IL 60611 *Tel:* 312-944-6780 *Toll Free Tel:* 800-545-2433 *Fax:* 312-280-5275 *E-mail:* editionsmarketing@ala.org *Web Site:* www.alastore.ala.org, pg 14

Chanda, Justin, Simon & Schuster Children's Publishing, 1230 Avenue of the Americas, New York, NY 10020 *Tel:* 212-698-7000 *Web Site:* KIDS.SimonandSchuster.com; TEEN.SimonandSchuster.com; simonandschuster.net; simonandschuster.biz, pg 225

Chandlee, Chad M, Kendall Hunt Publishing Co, 4050 Westmark Dr, Dubuque, IA 52002-2624 *Tel:* 563-589-1000 *Toll Free Tel:* 800-228-0810 (orders) *Fax:* 563-589-1046 *Toll Free Fax:* 800-772-9165 *E-mail:* orders@kendallhunt.com *Web Site:* www.kendallhunt.com, pg 130

Chandler, Beth, University of Missouri Press, 2910 Le Mone Blvd, Columbia, MO 65201 *Tel:* 573-882-7641 *Toll Free Tel:* 800-621-2736 (orders) *Fax:* 573-884-4498 *Web Site:* press.umsystem.edu, pg 257

Cherullo, Helen, The Mountaineers Books, 1001 SW Klickitat Way, Suite 201, Seattle, WA 98134 *Tel:* 206-223-6303 *Toll Free Tel:* 800-553-4453 *Fax:* 206-223-6306 *Toll Free Fax:* 800-568-7604 *E-mail:* mbooks@mountaineersbooks.org *Web Site:* www.mountaineersbooks.org, pg 161

Chesman, Andrea, Little Chicago Editorial Services, 154 Natural Tpke, Ripton, VT 05766 *Tel:* 802-388-9782 *Web Site:* andreachesman.com, pg 530

Chester, Linda, Linda Chester Literary Agency, 630 Fifth Ave, Suite 2000, New York, NY 10111 *Tel:* 212-218-3350 *Fax:* 212-218-3343 *E-mail:* submissions@lindachester.com *Web Site:* www.lindachester.com, pg 546

Cheuse, Sonya, HarperCollins General Books Group, 195 Broadway, New York, NY 10007 *Tel:* 212-207-7000 *Web Site:* www.harpercollins.com, pg 105

Chevako, Anne W, Publishing Resources Inc, 425 Carr 693, PMB 160, Dorado, PR 00646 *Tel:* 787-626-0607 *Toll Free Fax:* 866-547-3005 *E-mail:* pri@chevako.net *Web Site:* www.publishingresources.net, pg 533

Chevako, Jay A, Publishing Resources Inc, 425 Carr 693, PMB 160, Dorado, PR 00646 *Tel:* 787-626-0607 *Toll Free Fax:* 866-547-3005 *E-mail:* pri@chevako.net *Web Site:* www.publishingresources.net, pg 533

Chevako, Ronald J, Publishing Resources Inc, 425 Carr 693, PMB 160, Dorado, PR 00646 *Tel:* 787-626-0607 *Toll Free Fax:* 866-547-3005 *E-mail:* pri@chevako.net *Web Site:* www.publishingresources.net, pg 533

Childers, Kimberly B, Indiana University Press, Herman B Wells Library 350, 1320 E Tenth St, Bloomington, IN 47405-3907 *Tel:* 812-855-8817 *Toll Free Tel:* 800-842-6796 (orders only) *Fax:* 812-855-7931; 812-855-8507 *E-mail:* iupress@indiana.edu; iuporder@indiana.edu (orders) *Web Site:* www.iupress.indiana.edu, pg 120

Childress, David H, Adventures Unlimited Press (AUP), One Adventure Place, Kempton, IL 60946 *Tel:* 815-253-6390 *Fax:* 815-253-6300 *E-mail:* auphq@frontiernet.net; info@adventuresunlimitedpress.com *Web Site:* www.adventuresunlimitedpress.com, pg 5

Childs, Faith Hampton, Faith Childs Literary Agency Inc, 111 John St, Suite 1620, New York, NY 10038 *Tel:* 212-995-9600 *Web Site:* faithchildsliteraryagency.com, pg 546

Childs, Jim, The Globe Pequot Press, 246 Goose Lane, Guilford, CT 06437 *Tel:* 203-458-4500 *Toll Free Tel:* 800-243-0495 (orders only); 888-249-7586 (cust serv) *Fax:* 203-458-4601 *Toll Free Fax:* 800-820-2329 (orders & cust serv) *E-mail:* editorial@globepequot.com; info@rowman.com; orders@rowman.com *Web Site:* rowman.com, pg 98

Childs, Jim, Rowman & Littlefield Publishers Inc, 4501 Forbes Blvd, Suite 200, Lanham, MD 20706 *Tel:* 301-459-3366 *Toll Free Tel:* 800-462-6420 (cust serv) *Fax:* 301-429-5748 *Web Site:* www.rowmanlittlefield.com, pg 212

Childs, Kate, Random House Publishing Group, 1745 Broadway, New York, NY 10019 *Toll Free Tel:* 800-200-3552 *Web Site:* atrandom.com, pg 204

Childs, Maren, Crown Publishing Group, c/o Penguin Random House Inc, 1745 Broadway, New York, NY 10019 *Tel:* 212-782-9000 *Toll Free Tel:* 888-264-1745 *Fax:* 212-940-7408 *E-mail:* crownosm@penguinrandomhouse.com *Web Site:* crownpublishing.com, pg 68

Chin Aleong, Anne B, Mary Ann Liebert Inc, 140 Huguenot St, 3rd fl, New Rochelle, NY 10801-5215 *Tel:* 914-740-2100 *Toll Free Tel:* 800-654-3237 *Fax:* 914-740-2101 *E-mail:* info@liebertpub.com *Web Site:* www.liebertonline.com, pg 139

Chin, Brenda, BelleBooks, PO Box 300921, Memphis, TN 38130 *Tel:* 901-344-9024 *Fax:* 901-344-9068 *E-mail:* bellebooks@bellebooks.com, pg 34

Chin, Kristine, American Institute of Chemical Engineers (AIChE), 120 Wall St, 23rd fl, New York, NY 10005-4020 *Tel:* 203-702-7660 *Toll Free Tel:* 800-242-4363 *Fax:* 203-775-5177 *E-mail:* customerservice@aiche.org *Web Site:* www.aiche.org, pg 13

Chin, Oliver, Immedium, 535 Rockdale Dr, San Francisco, CA 94127 *Tel:* 415-452-8546 *Fax:* 360-937-6272 *E-mail:* orders@immedium.com; sales@immedium.com *Web Site:* www.immedium.com, pg 119

Chinski, Eric, Farrar, Straus & Giroux, LLC, 18 W 18 St, New York, NY 10011 *Tel:* 212-741-6900 *E-mail:* fsg.publicity@fsgbooks.com *Web Site:* us.macmillan.com/fsg.aspx, pg 86

Chipponeri, Kelli, Chronicle Books LLC, 680 Second St, San Francisco, CA 94107 *Tel:* 415-537-4200 *Toll Free Tel:* 800-759-0190 (cust serv) *Fax:* 415-537-4460 *Toll Free Fax:* 800-858-7787 (orders); 800-286-9471 (cust serv) *E-mail:* frontdesk@chroniclebooks.com *Web Site:* www.chroniclebooks.com, pg 58

Chirico, Anthony, Doubleday/Nan A Talese, c/o Penguin Random House Inc, 1745 Broadway, New York, NY 10019 *Tel:* 212-751-2600 *Fax:* 212-572-2662 *E-mail:* ddaypub@randomhouse.com *Web Site:* knopfdoubleday.com, pg 76

Chirico, Anthony, Alfred A Knopf/Everyman's Library, c/o Random House Inc, 1745 Broadway, New York, NY 10019 *Tel:* 212-751-2600 *Toll Free Tel:* 800-638-6460 *Fax:* 212-572-2593 *Web Site:* www.knopfdoubleday.com, pg 132

Chirico, Tony, Penguin Random House Inc, 1745 Broadway, New York, NY 10019 *Tel:* 212-782-9000 *Toll Free Tel:* 800-726-0600 *Web Site:* www.randomhouse.com, pg 187

Chiusano, Mark, Vintage & Anchor Books, c/o Random House Inc, 1745 Broadway, New York, NY 10019 *Tel:* 212-572-2420 *E-mail:* vintageanchorpublicity@randomhouse.com *Web Site:* vintage-anchor.knopfdoubleday.com, pg 266

Chmiel, Barbara R, The Blackburn Press, PO Box 287, Caldwell, NJ 07006-0287 *Tel:* 973-228-7077 *Fax:* 973-228-7276 *Web Site:* www.blackburnpress.com, pg 39

Cho, Alino, Random House Publishing Group, 1745 Broadway, New York, NY 10019 *Toll Free Tel:* 800-200-3552 *Web Site:* atrandom.com, pg 204

Cho, Barbara, Little Bee Books, 853 Broadway, Suite 2014, New York, NY 10003 *E-mail:* info@littlebeebooks.com *Web Site:* www.littlebeebooks.com, pg 140

Cho, Tom, Princeton Architectural Press, 37 E Seventh St, New York, NY 10003 *Tel:* 212-995-9620 *Toll Free Tel:* 800-722-6657 (dist); 800-759-0190 (sales) *Fax:* 212-995-9454 *E-mail:* sales@papress.com *Web Site:* www.papress.com, pg 197

Chodosh, Ellen, New York University Press, 838 Broadway, 3rd fl, New York, NY 10003-4812 *Tel:* 212-998-2575 (edit) *Toll Free Tel:* 800-996-6987 (orders) *Fax:* 212-995-3833 (orders) *E-mail:* information@nyupress.org; customerservice@nyupress.org; orders@nyupress.org *Web Site:* www.nyupress.org, pg 169

Chong, Anita, McClelland & Stewart Ltd, One Toronto St, Toronto, ON M5C 2V6, Canada *Tel:* 416-364-4449 *Fax:* 416-957-1587 *E-mail:* editorial@mcclelland.com *Web Site:* www.mcclelland.com, pg 491

Chong, Michele, Michael Wiese Productions, 12400 Ventura Blvd, No 1111, Studio City, CA 91604 *Tel:* 818-379-8799 *Toll Free Tel:* 800-833-5738 (orders) *Fax:* 818-986-3408 *E-mail:* mwpsales@mwp.com; fulfillment@portcity.com *Web Site:* www.mwp.com, pg 271

Choron, Harry, March Tenth Inc, 24 Hillside Terr, Montvale, NJ 07645 *Tel:* 201-387-6551 *Fax:* 201-387-6552 *Web Site:* www.marchtenthinc.com, pg 563

Choron, Sandra, March Tenth Inc, 24 Hillside Terr, Montvale, NJ 07645 *Tel:* 201-387-6551 *Fax:* 201-387-6552 *Web Site:* www.marchtenthinc.com, pg 563

Chorpenning, Rev Joseph F, St Joseph's University Press, 5600 City Ave, Philadelphia, PA 19131-1395 *Tel:* 610-660-3402 *Fax:* 610-660-3412 *E-mail:* sjupress@sju.edu *Web Site:* www.sjupress.com, pg 214

Choteborsky, Mary, Crown Publishing Group, c/o Penguin Random House Inc, 1745 Broadway, New York, NY 10019 *Tel:* 212-782-9000 *Toll Free Tel:* 888-264-1745 *Fax:* 212-940-7408 *E-mail:* crownosm@penguinrandomhouse.com *Web Site:* crownpublishing.com, pg 68

Chotiner-Gardiner, Miriam, Crown Publishing Group, c/o Penguin Random House Inc, 1745 Broadway, New York, NY 10019 *Tel:* 212-782-9000 *Toll Free Tel:* 888-264-1745 *Fax:* 212-940-7408 *E-mail:* crownosm@penguinrandomhouse.com *Web Site:* crownpublishing.com, pg 68

Chou, Arthur, New Win Publishing, 9682 Telstar Ave, Suite 110, El Monte, CA 91731 *Tel:* 626-448-3448 *Fax:* 626-602-3817 *E-mail:* info@academiclearningcompany.com *Web Site:* www.newwinpublishing.com; www.wbusinessbooks.com/, pg 168

Chou, Shelly, Agency Chicago, 332 S Michigan Ave, Suite 1032, No A600, Chicago, IL 60604 *E-mail:* ernsant@aol.com, pg 540

Choyce, Lesley, Pottersfield Press, 83 Leslie Rd, East Lawrencetown, NS B2Z 1P8, Canada *Toll Free Fax:* 888-253-3133 *Web Site:* www.pottersfieldpress.com, pg 495

Chrichton, John, Bibliographical Society of America, PO Box 1537, Lenox Hill Sta, New York, NY 10021-0043 *Tel:* 212-452-2710 *Fax:* 212-452-2710 *E-mail:* bsa@bibsocamer.org *Web Site:* www.bibsocamer.org, pg 600

Chrisman, Ronald, University of North Texas Press, Stovall Hall, Suite 174, 1400 Highland St, Denton, TX 76201 *Tel:* 940-565-2142 *Fax:* 940-565-4590 *Web Site:* www.unt.edu/untpress, pg 258

Christian, Rick, Bondfire Books, 7680 Goddard St, Suite 220, Colorado Springs, CO 80920 *Tel:* 719-260-7080 *Web Site:* www.bondfirebooks.com, pg 42

Christiansen, Gayla, Texas A&M University Press, John H Lindsey Bldg, Lewis St, 4354 TAMU, College Station, TX 77843-4354 *Tel:* 979-845-1436 *Toll Free Tel:* 800-826-8911 (orders) *Fax:* 979-847-8752 *Toll Free Fax:* 888-617-2421 (orders) *E-mail:* tampress@tamu.edu *Web Site:* www.tamupress.com, pg 243

Christiansen, Hillary, Palm Springs Writers Guild, PO Box 947, Rancho Mirage, CA 92270-0947 *Web Site:* www.palmspringswritersguild.org, pg 615

Christianson, Julie, University of California Press, 2120 Berkeley Way, Berkeley, CA 94704-1012 *Tel:* 510-642-4247 *Fax:* 510-643-7127 *E-mail:* askucp@ucpress.edu (books); customerservice@ucpressjournals.com *Web Site:* www.ucpress.edu, pg 255

Christmas, Bobbie, Zebra Communications, 230 Deerchase Dr, Woodstock, GA 30188-4438 *Tel:* 770-924-0528 *Web Site:* www.zebraeditor.com, pg 537

Christofferson, Andrea, University of Wisconsin Press, 1930 Monroe St, 3rd fl, Madison, WI 53711-2059 *Tel:* 608-263-0668 *Toll Free Tel:* 800-621-2736 (orders) *Fax:* 608-263-1173 *Toll Free Fax:* 800-621-2736 (orders) *E-mail:* uwiscpress@uwpress.wisc.edu (main off) *Web Site:* www.wisc.edu/wisconsinpress, pg 260

Christopher, Rob, The American Library Association (ALA), 50 E Huron St, Chicago, IL 60611 *Tel:* 312-944-6780 *Toll Free Tel:* 800-545-2433 *Fax:* 312-280-5275 *E-mail:* editionsmarketing@ala.org *Web Site:* www.alastore.ala.org, pg 14

Christopher, William F (Bill), William F Christopher Publication Services, Kensington No 237, 1580 Geary Rd, Walnut Creek, CA 94597-2744 *Tel:* 925-943-5584 *Fax:* 925-943-5594 *E-mail:* wfcmgmt.innovations@yahoo.com, pg 546

Chromy, Adam, Movable Type Management, 244 Madison Ave, Suite 334, New York, NY 10016 *Tel:* 646-431-6134 *Fax:* 646-810-5757 *Web Site:* www.mtmgmt.net, pg 566

Chu, Elaine, Immedium, 535 Rockdale Dr, San Francisco, CA 94127 *Tel:* 415-452-8546 *Fax:* 360-937-6272 *E-mail:* orders@immedium.com; sales@immedium.com *Web Site:* www.immedium.com, pg 119

Chu, Lily, Captus Press Inc, 1600 Steeles Ave W, Units 14 & 15, Concord, ON L4K 4M2, Canada *Tel:* 416-736-5537 *Fax:* 416-736-5793 *E-mail:* info@captus.com *Web Site:* www.captus.com, pg 476

Chu, Lynn, Writers' Representatives LLC, 116 W 14 St, 11th fl, New York, NY 10011-7305 *Tel:* 212-620-9009 *Fax:* 212-620-0023 *E-mail:* transom@writersreps.com *Web Site:* www.writersreps.com, pg 580

Chun, Stephanie, University of Hawaii Press, 2840 Kolowalu St, Honolulu, HI 96822 *Tel:* 808-956-8255 *Toll Free Tel:* 888-UHPRESS (847-7377) *Fax:* 808-988-6052 *Toll Free Fax:* 800-650-7811 *E-mail:* uhpbooks@hawaii.edu *Web Site:* www.uhpress.hawaii.edu, pg 256

Chung, Christopher, University of Chicago Press, 1427 E 60 St, Chicago, IL 60637-2954 *Tel:* 773-702-7700; 773-702-7600 *Toll Free Tel:* 800-621-2736 (orders) *Fax:* 773-702-9756; 773-660-2235 (orders); 773-702-2708 *E-mail:* custserv@press.uchicago.edu; marketing@press.uchicago.edu *Web Site:* www.press.uchicago.edu, pg 255

Church, Dawson, Elite Books, PO Box 442, Fulton, CA 95439 *Tel:* 707-525-9292 *Toll Free Fax:* 800-330-9798 *E-mail:* books@authorspublishing.com *Web Site:* www.elitebooksonline.com, pg 81

Church, Dawson, Energy Psychology Press, 1490 Mark West Springs Rd, Santa Rosa, CA 95404 *Tel:* 707-237-6951 *Toll Free Fax:* 800-330-9798 *E-mail:* books@authorspublishing.com *Web Site:* www.energypsychologypress.com; www.elitebooksonline.com, pg 82

Church, Doug, Pacific Press Publishing Association, 1350 N Kings Rd, Nampa, ID 83687-3193 *Tel:* 208-465-2500 *Toll Free Tel:* 800-447-7377 *Fax:* 208-465-2531 *Web Site:* www.pacificpress.com, pg 180

Churchward, Aubrey, Holiday House Inc, 425 Madison Ave, New York, NY 10017 *Tel:* 212-688-0085 *Fax:* 212-421-6134 *E-mail:* holiday@holidayhouse.com *Web Site:* www.holidayhouse.com, pg 113

Churko, Helen, Royce Carlton Inc, 866 United Nations Plaza, Suite 587, New York, NY 10017-1880 *Tel:* 212-355-7700 *Toll Free Tel:* 800-LECTURE (532-8873) *Fax:* 212-888-8659 *E-mail:* info@roycecarlton.com *Web Site:* www.roycecarlton.com, pg 588

Cianfarani, Nick, New City Press, 202 Comforter Blvd, Hyde Park, NY 12538 *Tel:* 845-229-0335 *Toll Free Tel:* 800-462-5980 (orders only) *Fax:* 845-229-0351 *E-mail:* info@newcitypress.com *Web Site:* www.newcitypress.com, pg 167

Ciccone, Patti, Midwest Travel Writers Association, 902 S Randall Rd, Suite C311, St Charles, IL 60174 *Toll Free Tel:* 888-551-8184 *E-mail:* admin@mtwa.org *Web Site:* www.mtwa.org, pg 610

Ciecierski, Andrea, Stylus Publishing LLC, 22883 Quicksilver Dr, Sterling, VA 20166-2012 *Tel:* 703-661-1504 (edit & sales) *Toll Free Tel:* 800-232-0223 (orders & cust serv) *Fax:* 703-661-1547 *E-mail:* stylusmail@presswarehouse.com (orders & cust serv); stylusinfo@styluspub.com *Web Site:* www.styluspub.com, pg 237

Cihlar, James, The Backwaters Press, 3502 N 52 St, Omaha, NE 68104-3506 *Tel:* 402-451-4052 *E-mail:* thebackwaterspress@gmail.com *Web Site:* www.thebackwaterspress.org, pg 29

Ciletti, Barbara, Odyssey Books, 2421 Redwood Ct, Longmont, CO 80503-8155 *Tel:* 720-494-1473 *Fax:* 720-494-1471 *E-mail:* books@odysseybooks.net *Web Site:* cilettipublishinggroup.com, pg 174

Cilurso, Ed, Taylor & Francis Inc, 325 Chestnut St, Suite 800, Philadelphia, PA 20036-1802 *Tel:* 215-625-8900 *Toll Free Tel:* 800-354-1420 *Fax:* 215-625-2940 *E-mail:* customer.service@taylorandfrancis.com *Web Site:* www.taylorandfrancis.com, pg 241

Cimina, Dominique, Random House Children's Books, 1745 Broadway, New York, NY 10019 *Tel:* 212-782-9000 *Toll Free Tel:* 800-200-3552 *Fax:* 212-782-9452 *Web Site:* randomhousekids.com, pg 203

Ciminera, Siobhan, Simon & Schuster Children's Publishing, 1230 Avenue of the Americas, New York, NY 10020 *Tel:* 212-698-7000 *Web Site:* KIDS.SimonandSchuster.com; TEEN.SimonandSchuster.com; simonandschuster.net; simonandschuster.biz, pg 225

Cimino, Antoinette, Springer, 233 Spring St, New York, NY 10013-1578 *Tel:* 212-460-1500 *Toll Free Tel:* 800-SPRINGER (777-4643) *Fax:* 212-460-1575 *E-mail:* service-ny@springer.com *Web Site:* www.springer.com, pg 232

Ciommo, Dave, EPS/School Specialty Literacy & Intervention, 625 Mount Auburn St, 3rd fl, Cambridge, MA 02138-3039 *Toll Free Tel:* 800-225-5750 *Toll Free Fax:* 888-440-2665 *E-mail:* customerservice.eps@schoolspecialty.com *Web Site:* eps.schoolspecialty.com, pg 83

Ciotola, Andrew, Bucknell Seminar for Younger Poets, Bucknell University, Bucknell Hall, Moore Ave, Lewisburg, PA 17837 *Tel:* 570-577-1853 *Fax:* 570-577-1885 *E-mail:* stadlercenter@bucknell.edu *Web Site:* www.bucknell.edu/stadlercenter, pg 650

Circosta, Karey, Ave Maria Press, PO Box 428, Notre Dame, IN 46556 *Tel:* 574-287-2831 *Toll Free Tel:* 800-282-1865 *Fax:* 574-239-2904 *Toll Free Fax:* 800-282-5681 *E-mail:* avemariapress.1@nd.edu *Web Site:* www.avemariapress.com, pg 28

Cirillo, Andrea, Jane Rotrosen Agency LLC, 318 E 51 St, New York, NY 10022 *Tel:* 212-593-4330 *Fax:* 212-935-6985 *Web Site:* janerotrosen.com, pg 571

Cizek, Nick, The Experiment, 220 East 23 St, Suite 301, New York, NY 10010-4674 *Tel:* 212-889-1659 *E-mail:* info@theexperimentpublishing.com *Web Site:* www.theexperimentpublishing.com, pg 85

Clague, Sue A, The Montana Council for Indian Education, 1240 Burlington Ave, Billings, MT 59102-4224 *Tel:* 406-652-7598 (AM); 406-248-3465 (PM) *Fax:* 406-248-1297 *E-mail:* cie@cie-mt.org *Web Site:* www.cie-mt.org, pg 159

Clain, Judy, Little, Brown and Company, 1290 Avenue of the Americas, New York, NY 10019 *Tel:* 212-364-1100 *Fax:* 212-364-0952 *E-mail:* firstname.lastname@hbgusa.com *Web Site:* www.HachetteBookGroup.com, pg 141

Clark, Barbara, Amber Quill Press LLC, PO Box 265, Indian Hills, CO 80454 *E-mail:* business@amberquill.com; customer_service@amberquill.com *Web Site:* www.amberquill.com, pg 10

Clark, Becky Brasington, The Johns Hopkins University Press, 2715 N Charles St, Baltimore, MD 21218-4363 *Tel:* 410-516-6900; 410-516-6987 (journal orders outside US & CN) *Toll Free Tel:* 800-537-5487 (book orders & cust serv); 800-548-1784 (journal orders) *Fax:* 410-516-6968; 410-516-3866 (journal orders) *E-mail:* hfscustserv@press.jhu.edu (cust serv); jrnlcirc@press.jhu.edu (journal orders) *Web Site:* www.press.jhu.edu; muse.jhu.edu, pg 127

Clark, Curtis L, University of Alabama Press, 200 Hackberry Lane, 2nd fl, Tuscaloosa, AL 35487 *Tel:* 205-348-5180 *Fax:* 205-348-9201 *Web Site:* www.uapress.ua.edu, pg 254

Clark, Denise, University of Washington Press, 433 Brooklyn Ave NE, Seattle, WA 98195-9570 *Tel:* 206-543-4050 *Toll Free Tel:* 800-537-5487 (orders) *Fax:* 206-543-3932; 410-516-6998 (orders) *E-mail:* uwpress@u.washington.edu *Web Site:* www.washington.edu/uwpress/, pg 260

Clark, Ginger, Curtis Brown Ltd, 10 Astor Place, New York, NY 10003 *Tel:* 212-473-5400 *Web Site:* www.curtisbrown.com, pg 544

Clark, James C, Penguin Group (USA) LLC, a Penguin Random House company, 375 Hudson St, New York, NY 10014 *Tel:* 212-366-2000 *Toll Free Tel:* 800-847-5515 (inside sales); 800-631-8571 (cust serv) *Fax:* 212-366-2666; 607-775-4829 (inside sales) *E-mail:* online@us.penguingroup.com *Web Site:* www.penguin.com; us.penguingroup.com, pg 186

Clark, Jim, The Robert Watson Literary Prizes in Fiction & Poetry, MFA Writing Program, The Greensboro Review, UNC-Greensboro, 3302 MHRA Bldg, Greensboro, NC 27402-6170 *Tel:* 336-334-5459 *Fax:* 336-256-1470 *Web Site:* www.greensbororeview.org, pg 734

Clark, June, FinePrint Literary Management, 115 W 29 St, 3rd fl, New York, NY 10001 *Tel:* 212-279-1282 *Web Site:* www.fineprintlit.com, pg 551

Clark, Kevin, American Public Works Association (APWA), 2345 Grand Blvd, Suite 700, Kansas City, MO 64108-2625 *Tel:* 816-472-6100 *Toll Free Tel:* 800-848-APWA (848-2792) *Fax:* 816-472-1610 *Web Site:* www.apwa.net, pg 15

Clark, Dr Laurel, SOM Publishing, 163 Moon Valley Rd, Windyville, MO 65783 *Tel:* 417-345-8411 *Fax:* 417-345-6668 *E-mail:* som@som.org; dreamschool@dreamschool.org *Web Site:* www.som.org; www.dreamschool.org, pg 230

Clark, Michiko, Pantheon Books/Schocken Books, c/o Random House Inc, 1745 Broadway, New York, NY 10019 *Tel:* 212-751-2600 *Toll Free Tel:* 800-638-6460 *Fax:* 212-572-6030, pg 181

Clark, Raymond C, Pro Lingua Associates Inc, 74 Cotton Mill Hill, Suite A-315, Brattleboro, VT 05301 *Tel:* 802-257-7779 *Toll Free Tel:* 800-366-4775 *Fax:* 802-257-5117 *E-mail:* info@prolinguaassociates.com *Web Site:* www.prolinguaassociates.com, pg 198

Clark, Sarah, Yale University Press, 302 Temple St, New Haven, CT 06511-8909 *Tel:* 203-432-0960; 203-432-0966 (sales); 401-531-2800 (cust serv) *Toll Free Tel:* 800-405-1619 (cust serv) *Fax:* 203-432-0948; 203-432-8485 (sales); 401-531-2801 (cust serv) *Toll Free Fax:* 800-406-9145 (cust serv) *E-mail:* sales.press@yale.edu (sales); customer.care@trilateral.org (cust serv) *Web Site:* www.yalebooks.com; yalepress.yale.edu/yupbooks, pg 278

Clark, Shaqunia, Stylus Publishing LLC, 22883 Quicksilver Dr, Sterling, VA 20166-2012 *Tel:* 703-661-1504 (edit & sales) *Toll Free Tel:* 800-232-0223 (orders & cust serv) *Fax:* 703-661-1547 *E-mail:* stylusmail@presswarehouse.com (orders & cust serv); stylusinfo@styluspub.com *Web Site:* www.styluspub.com, pg 237

Clark, Steve, Standard Publishing, 8805 Governors Hill Dr, Suite 400, Cincinnati, OH 45249 *Tel:* 513-931-4050 *Toll Free Tel:* 800-543-1353 *Fax:* 513-931-0950 *Toll Free Fax:* 877-867-5751 *E-mail:* customerservice@standardpub.com *Web Site:* www.standardpub.com, pg 233

Clark, William, Wm Clark Associates, 186 Fifth Ave, 2nd fl, New York, NY 10010 *Tel:* 212-675-2784 *Fax:* 347-649-9262 *E-mail:* general@wmclark.com *Web Site:* www.wmclark.com, pg 546

Clark, Zina, Coretta Scott King Book Awards, 50 E Huron St, Chicago, IL 60611 *Toll Free Tel:* 800-545-2433 *E-mail:* olos@ala.org *Web Site:* www.ala.org/emiert/cskbookawards, pg 698

Clarke, Anne, Orbit, 1290 Avenue of the Americas, New York, NY 10019 *Tel:* 212-364-1100 *Toll Free Tel:* 800-759-0190 *Web Site:* www.orbitbooks.net, pg 176

Clarke, Chandra, Scribendi Inc, 405 Riverview Dr, Chatham, ON N7M 0N3, Canada *Tel:* 519-351-1626 (cust serv) *Fax:* 519-354-0192 *E-mail:* customerservice@scribendi.com *Web Site:* www.scribendi.com, pg 534

Clarke, Erin, Random House Children's Books, 1745 Broadway, New York, NY 10019 *Tel:* 212-782-9000 *Toll Free Tel:* 800-200-3552 *Fax:* 212-782-9452 *Web Site:* randomhousekids.com, pg 203

Clarke, Harold, Reader's Digest Trade Books, 44 S Broadway, White Plains, NY 10601 *Tel:* 914-244-7503 *Fax:* 914-244-4841 *Web Site:* www.rd.com, pg 205

Clarke, Harold, Reader's Digest USA Select Editions, 44 S Broadway, 7th fl, White Plains, NY 10601 *Tel:* 914-238-1000 *Toll Free Tel:* 800-304-2807 (cust serv) *Fax:* 914-831-1560 *Web Site:* www.rda.com/readers-digest-select-editions, pg 205

Clarke, Harold, Studio Fun International Inc, 44 S Broadway, White Plains, NY 10601 *Tel:* 914-238-1000 *Toll Free Tel:* 800-934-0977 *Web Site:* www.rdtradepublishing.com, pg 237

Clarke, Meghan, Taschen America, 6671 Sunset Blvd, Suite 1508, Los Angeles, CA 90028 *Tel:* 323-463-4441 *Toll Free Tel:* 888-TASCHEN (827-2436) *Fax:* 323-463-4442 *E-mail:* contact-us@taschen.com *Web Site:* www.taschen.com, pg 241

Clarke, Mia Barkan, Cross-Cultural Communications, 239 Wynsum Ave, Merrick, NY 11566-4725 *Tel:* 516-868-5635 *Fax:* 516-379-1901 *E-mail:* info@cross-culturalcommunications.com; cccbarkan@optonline.net; cccpoetry@aol.com *Web Site:* www.cross-culturalcommunications.com, pg 67

Clarke, Vicky, Utah Geological Survey, 1594 W North Temple, Suite 3110, Salt Lake City, UT 84116-3154 *Tel:* 801-537-3300 *Toll Free Tel:* 888-UTAH-MAP (882-4627 bookstore) *Fax:* 801-537-3400 *E-mail:* geostore@utah.gov *Web Site:* geology.utah.gov, pg 264

Classic, Lesley, Database Directories, 588 Dufferin Ave, London, ON N6B 2A4, Canada *Tel:* 519-433-1666 *Fax:* 519-430-1131 *E-mail:* mail@databasedirectory.com *Web Site:* www.databasedirectory.com, pg 478

Clay, Carolyn, Day Owl Press Corp, 201 W Ocean Ave, Unit 3574, Lantana, FL 33465 *Toll Free Tel:* 888-806-6981 *Toll Free Fax:* 866-854-4375 *E-mail:* info@dayowl.net *Web Site:* www.dayowl.net, pg 72

Clayton, Douglas, Harvard Education Publishing Group, 8 Story St, 1st fl, Cambridge, MA 02138 *Tel:* 617-495-3432 *Toll Free Tel:* 800-513-0763 (subns); 888-437-1437 (orders) *Fax:* 617-496-3584; 978-348-1233 (orders) *E-mail:* hepg@harvard.edu *Web Site:* www.hepg.org, pg 107

Clayton, Keith, Random House Publishing Group, 1745 Broadway, New York, NY 10019 *Toll Free Tel:* 800-200-3552 *Web Site:* atrandom.com, pg 204

Clayton, Patricia Mulrane, Peter Lang Publishing Inc, 29 Broadway, 18th fl, New York, NY 10006-3223 *Tel:* 212-647-7706 *Toll Free Tel:* 800-770-5264 (cust serv) *Fax:* 212-647-7707 *Web Site:* www.peterlang.com, pg 134

Clayton, Susan, American Correctional Association, 206 N Washington St, Suite 200, Alexandria, VA 22314 *Tel:* 703-224-0000 *Toll Free Tel:* 800-222-5646 *Fax:* 703-224-0179 *Web Site:* www.aca.org, pg 12

Cleary, Amy, Chronicle Books LLC, 680 Second St, San Francisco, CA 94107 *Tel:* 415-537-4200 *Toll Free Tel:* 800-759-0190 (cust serv) *Fax:* 415-537-4460 *Toll Free Fax:* 800-858-7787 (orders); 800-286-9471 (cust serv) *E-mail:* frontdesk@chroniclebooks.com *Web Site:* www.chroniclebooks.com, pg 58

Cleary, Donald W, Jane Rotrosen Agency LLC, 318 E 51 St, New York, NY 10022 *Tel:* 212-593-4330 *Fax:* 212-935-6985 *Web Site:* janerotrosen.com, pg 571

Cleland, Lucy, Kneerim & Williams Agency, 90 Canal St, Boston, MA 02114 *Tel:* 617-303-1650 *Web Site:* www.kwblit.com, pg 560

Clemens, Michael, Blue Dolphin Publishing Inc, 13340-D Grass Valley Ave, Grass Valley, CA 95945 *Tel:* 530-477-1503 *Toll Free Tel:* 800-643-0765 (orders) *Fax:* 530-477-8342 *E-mail:* bdolphin@bluedolphinpublishing.com *Web Site:* www.bluedolphinpublishing.com, pg 40

Clemens, Paul M, Blue Dolphin Publishing Inc, 13340-D Grass Valley Ave, Grass Valley, CA 95945 *Tel:* 530-477-1503 *Toll Free Tel:* 800-643-0765 (orders) *Fax:* 530-477-8342 *E-mail:* bdolphin@bluedolphinpublishing.com *Web Site:* www.bluedolphinpublishing.com, pg 40

Clemente, Stephen, Peterson's, a Nelnet Company, Princeton Pike Corporate Ctr, 2000 Lenox Dr, Lawrenceville, NJ 08648 *Tel:* 609-896-1800 *E-mail:* sales@petersons.com *Web Site:* www.petersons.com, pg 190

Clements, Caley, Canadian Scholars' Press Inc, 425 Adelaide St W, Suite 200, Toronto, ON M5V 3C1, Canada *Tel:* 416-929-2774 *Toll Free Tel:* 800-463-1998 *Fax:* 416-929-1926 *E-mail:* info@cspi.org; editorial@cspi.org; orders@cspi.org *Web Site:* www.cspi.org; womenspress.cspi.org, pg 476

Clements, Pamela, Abingdon Press, 201 Eighth Ave S, Nashville, TN 37203-3919 *Tel:* 615-749-6000 (academic books) *Toll Free Tel:* 800-251-3320 *Fax:* 615-749-6056 (academic books) *Toll Free Fax:* 800-836-7802 (orders) *E-mail:* orders@abingdonpress.com *Web Site:* www.abingdonpress.com, pg 2

Clements, Rob, Clements Publishing, 6021 Yonge St, Suite 213, Toronto, ON M2M 3W2, Canada *Tel:* 647-477-2509 *Fax:* 647-477-2058 *E-mail:* info@clementspublishing.com *Web Site:* www.clementspublishing.com, pg 477

Clementson, Elizabeth, W W Norton & Company Inc, 500 Fifth Ave, New York, NY 10110-0017 *Tel:* 212-354-5500 *Toll Free Tel:* 800-233-4830 (orders & cust serv) *Fax:* 212-869-0856 *Toll Free Fax:* 800-458-6515 *Web Site:* www.wwnorton.com, pg 172

Clemons, G Scott, Bibliographical Society of America, PO Box 1537, Lenox Hill Sta, New York, NY 10021-0043 *Tel:* 212-452-2710 *Fax:* 212-452-2710 *E-mail:* bsa@bibsocamer.org *Web Site:* www.bibsocamer.org, pg 600

Clermont, Marie-Andree, Les Editions Pierre Tisseyre, 155, rue Maurice, Rosemere, QC J7A 2S8, Canada *Tel:* 514-335-0777 *Fax:* 514-335-6723 *E-mail:* info@edtisseyre.ca *Web Site:* www.tisseyre.ca, pg 483

Cleveland, Marisa, Mary Sue Seymour, 475 Miner Street Rd, Canton, NY 13617 *Tel:* 315-386-1831 *Web Site:* www.theseymouragency.com, pg 573

Cleveland, Rob, August House Inc, 3500 Piedmont Rd NE, Suite 310, Atlanta, GA 30305 *Tel:* 404-442-4420 *Toll Free Tel:* 800-284-8784 *Fax:* 404-442-4435 *E-mail:* ahinfo@augusthouse.com *Web Site:* www.augusthouse.com, pg 27

Clifford, Carla, Penguin Group (USA) LLC Sales, 375 Hudson St, New York, NY 10014 *Tel:* 212-366-2000 *E-mail:* online@penguinputnam.com *Web Site:* us.penguingroup.com, pg 187

Clifford, Christina, Harlequin Enterprises Ltd, 225 Duncan Mill Rd, Don Mills, ON M3B 3K9, Canada *Tel:* 416-445-5860 *Toll Free Tel:* 888-432-4879; 800-370-5838 (ebook inquiries) *E-mail:* customerservice@harlequin.com *Web Site:* www.harlequin.com, pg 487

Clift, Jeremy, International Monetary Fund (IMF), Editorial & Publications Division, 700 19 St NW, HQ1-7-124, Washington, DC 20431 *Tel:* 202-623-7430 *Fax:* 202-623-7201 *E-mail:* publications@imf.org *Web Site:* www.imfbookstore.org; elibrary.imf.org (online collection), pg 124

Cline, Susan, Nelson Education Ltd, 1120 Birchmount Rd, Scarborough, ON M1K 5G4, Canada *Tel:* 416-752-9100 *Toll Free Tel:* 800-268-2222 (cust serv) *Fax:* 416-752-8101 *Toll Free Fax:* 800-430-4445 *E-mail:* peopleandengagement@nelson.com *Web Site:* www.nelson.com, pg 492

Clingham, Greg, Bucknell University Press, 6 Taylor Hall, Bucknell University, Lewisburg, PA 17837 *Tel:* 570-577-3674 *E-mail:* universitypress@bucknell.edu *Web Site:* www.bucknell.edu/universitypress, pg 47

Clockel, William, Educator's International Press Inc (EIP), 756 Linderman Ave, Kingston, NY 12401 *Tel:* 518-334-0276 *Fax:* 703-661-1547 *E-mail:* info@edint.com *Web Site:* edint.presswarehouse.com, pg 80

Cloidt, Kim, Independent Institute, 100 Swan Way, Oakland, CA 94621-1428 *Tel:* 510-632-1366 *Toll Free Tel:* 800-927-8733 *Fax:* 510-568-6040 *E-mail:* orders@independent.org *Web Site:* www.independent.org, pg 120

Close, Amanda, Random House Publishing Group, 1745 Broadway, New York, NY 10019 *Toll Free Tel:* 800-200-3552 *Web Site:* atrandom.com, pg 204

Close, Ann, Alfred A Knopf/Everyman's Library, c/o Random House Inc, 1745 Broadway, New York, NY 10019 *Tel:* 212-751-2600 *Toll Free Tel:* 800-638-6460 *Fax:* 212-572-2593 *Web Site:* www.knopfdoubleday.com, pg 132

Close, Megan, Keller Media Inc, 578 Washington Blvd, No 745, Marina del Rey, CA 90292 *Toll Free Tel:* 800-278-8706 *E-mail:* query@kellermedia.com *Web Site:* kellermedia.com/query, pg 559

Close, Tim, David C Cook, 4050 Lee Vance View, Colorado Springs, CO 80918 *Tel:* 719-536-0100 *Toll Free Tel:* 800-708-5550; 800-323-7543 (orders & cust serv) *Toll Free Fax:* 800-430-0726 (cust serv) *Web Site:* www.davidccook.com, pg 62

Closson, Bob, Closson Press, 257 Delilah St, Apollo, PA 15613-1933 *Tel:* 724-337-4482 *Fax:* 724-337-9484 *E-mail:* clossonpress@comcast.net *Web Site:* www.clossonpress.com, pg 60

Closson, Marietta, Closson Press, 257 Delilah St, Apollo, PA 15613-1933 *Tel:* 724-337-4482 *Fax:* 724-337-9484 *E-mail:* clossonpress@comcast.net *Web Site:* www.clossonpress.com, pg 60

Cloutier, Suzanne, University of Ottawa Press (Les Presses de l'Université d'Ottawa), 542 King Edward Ave, Ottawa, ON K1N 6N5, Canada *Tel:* 613-562-5246 *Fax:* 613-562-5247 *E-mail:* puo-oup@uottawa.ca *Web Site:* www.press.uottawa.ca, pg 503

Clurman, Robert, United Synagogue Book Service, 820 Second Ave, New York, NY 10017 *Tel:* 212-533-7800 *Toll Free Tel:* 800-594-5617 (warehouse only) *Fax:* 212-253-5422 *E-mail:* booksvc@uscj.org *Web Site:* secure.uscj.org/bookservice, pg 254

Clute, Sharla, State University of New York Press, 22 Corporate Woods Blvd, 3rd fl, Albany, NY 12211-2504 *Tel:* 518-472-5000 *Toll Free Tel:* 877-204-6073 (orders) *Fax:* 518-472-5038 *Toll Free Fax:* 877-204-6074 (orders) *E-mail:* suny@presswarehouse.com (orders); info@sunypress.edu (edit off) *Web Site:* www.sunypress.edu, pg 234

Coakley, Lena, Canadian Society of Children's Authors Illustrators & Performers (CANSCAIP), 720 Bathurst St, Suite 503, Toronto, ON M5S 2R4, Canada *Tel:* 416-515-1559 *E-mail:* office@canscaip.org *Web Site:* www.canscaip.org, pg 602

Coalson, Lance, Father & Son Publishing Inc, 4909 N Monroe St, Tallahassee, FL 32303-7015 *Tel:* 850-562-2612 *Toll Free Tel:* 800-741-2712 (orders only) *Fax:* 850-562-0916 *Web Site:* www.fatherson.com, pg 87

Coan, Cynthia J, Indexing by the Book, PO Box 12513, Tucson, AZ 85732-2513 *Tel:* 520-750-8439 *E-mail:* indextran@cox.net *Web Site:* www.indexingbythebook.com, pg 528

Coates, Damani, Black Classic Press, 3921 Vero Rd, Suite F, Baltimore, MD 21203-3414 *Tel:* 410-242-6954 *Toll Free Tel:* 800-476-8870 *Fax:* 410-242-6959 *E-mail:* email@blackclassicbooks.com; blackclassicpress@yahoo.com *Web Site:* www.blackclassicbooks.com; www.bcpdigital.com, pg 38

Coates, Laraine, University of British Columbia Press, 2029 West Mall, Vancouver, BC V6T 1Z2, Canada *Tel:* 604-822-5959 *Toll Free Tel:* 877-377-9378 *Fax:* 604-822-6083 *Toll Free Fax:* 800-668-0821 *E-mail:* frontdesk@ubcpress.ca *Web Site:* www.ubcpress.ca, pg 502

Coates, W Paul, Black Classic Press, 3921 Vero Rd, Suite F, Baltimore, MD 21203-3414 *Tel:* 410-242-6954 *Toll Free Tel:* 800-476-8870 *Fax:* 410-242-6959 *E-mail:* email@blackclassicbooks.com; blackclassicpress@yahoo.com *Web Site:* www.blackclassicbooks.com; www.bcpdigital.com, pg 38

Cobb, David, The University Press of Kentucky, 663 S Limestone St, Lexington, KY 40508-4008 *Tel:* 859-257-8400 *Fax:* 859-257-8481 *Web Site:* www.kentuckypress.com, pg 261

Cobb, Kiara, Glitterati Inc, 630 Ninth Ave, Suite 603, New York, NY 10036 *Tel:* 212-362-9119 *Fax:* 646-607-4433 *E-mail:* info@glitteratiincorporated.com *Web Site:* glitteratiincorporated.com, pg 97

Coburn, Tristram, Tilbury House Publishers, 12 Starr St, Thomaston, ME 04861 *Tel:* 207-582-1899 *Toll Free Tel:* 800-582-1899 (orders) *Fax:* 207-582-8227 *E-mail:* tilbury@tilburyhouse.com *Web Site:* www.tilburyhouse.com, pg 246

Cochran, Angela, American Society of Civil Engineers (ASCE), 1801 Alexander Bell Dr, Reston, VA 20191-4400 *Tel:* 703-295-6300 *Toll Free Tel:* 800-548-2723 *Fax:* 703-295-6278 *E-mail:* marketing@asce.org *Web Site:* www.asce.org, pg 16

Cochran, Heather, Television Academy, 5220 Lankershim Blvd, North Hollywood, CA 91601-3109 *Tel:* 818-754-2800 *Fax:* 818-761-2827 *Web Site:* www.emmys.com, pg 620

Cochran, Marnie, Random House Publishing Group, 1745 Broadway, New York, NY 10019 *Toll Free Tel:* 800-200-3552 *Web Site:* atrandom.com, pg 204

Cochran, Terry, Sunbelt Publications Inc, 1256 Fayette St, El Cajon, CA 92020-1511 *Tel:* 619-258-4911 *Toll Free Tel:* 800-626-6579 (cust serv) *Fax:* 619-258-4916 *E-mail:* service@sunbeltpub.com; info@sunbeltpub.com *Web Site:* www.sunbeltbooks.com, pg 238

Cochran, Tracy, Parabola Books, 20 W 20 St, 2nd fl, New York, NY 10011 *Tel:* 212-822-8806 *Toll Free Tel:* 800-592-2521 (subns) *Fax:* 212-822-8823 *E-mail:* info@parabola.org *Web Site:* www.parabola.org, pg 181

Cochrane, Hank, Penguin Group (USA) LLC Sales, 375 Hudson St, New York, NY 10014 *Tel:* 212-366-2000 *E-mail:* online@penguinputnam.com *Web Site:* us.penguingroup.com, pg 186

Cochrane, Kristin, Doubleday Canada, One Toronto St, Suite 300, Toronto, ON M5C 2V6, Canada *Tel:* 416-364-4449 *Fax:* 416-364-6863 *Web Site:* www.randomhouse.ca, pg 479

Cochrane, Kristin, Knopf Canada, One Toronto St, Suite 300, Toronto, ON M5C 2V6, Canada *Tel:* 416-364-4449 *Toll Free Tel:* 888-523-9292 *Fax:* 416-364-6863 *Web Site:* www.randomhouse.ca, pg 490

Cochrane, Kristin, Penguin Random House Canada Limited, 320 Front St W, Suite 1400, Toronto, ON M5V 3B6, Canada *Tel:* 416-364-4449 *Toll Free Tel:* 888-523-9292 (cust serv) *Fax:* 416-364-6863; 416-364-6653 (subs rts) *Web Site:* penguinrandomhouse.ca, pg 495

Cochrane, Kristin, Seal Books, One Toronto St, Suite 300, Toronto, ON M5C 2V6, Canada *Tel:* 416-364-4449 *Toll Free Tel:* 888-523-9292 (order desk) *Fax:* 416-364-6863 *Web Site:* www.randomhouse.ca, pg 498

Cochrell, Christie, Stanford University Press, 1450 Page Mill Rd, Palo Alto, CA 94304-1124 *Tel:* 650-723-9434 *Fax:* 650-725-3457 *E-mail:* info@sup.org *Web Site:* www.sup.org, pg 233

Cocks, Pamela, Tudor Publishers Inc, 3109 Shady Lawn Dr, Greensboro, NC 27408 *Tel:* 336-288-5395 *E-mail:* tudorpublishers@triad.rr.com, pg 250

Coe, Karen, United States Holocaust Memorial Museum, 100 Raoul Wallenberg Place SW, Washington, DC 20024-2126 *Tel:* 202-314-7837; 202-488-6144 (orders) *Toll Free Tel:* 800-259-9998 (orders) *Fax:* 202-479-9726; 202-488-0438 (orders) *E-mail:* cahs_publications@ushmm.org *Web Site:* www.ushmm.org, pg 253

Coffey, Darla Spence PhD, Council on Social Work Education (CSWE), 1701 Duke St, Suite 200, Alexandria, VA 22314-3457 *Tel:* 703-683-8080 *Fax:* 703-683-8493 *E-mail:* publications@cswe.org; info@cswe.org *Web Site:* www.cswe.org, pg 65

Coffin, Christina, Yale University Press, 302 Temple St, New Haven, CT 06511-8909 *Tel:* 203-432-0960; 203-432-0966 (sales); 401-531-2800 (cust serv) *Toll Free Tel:* 800-405-1619 (cust serv) *Fax:* 203-432-0948; 203-432-8485 (sales); 401-531-2801 (cust serv) *Toll Free Fax:* 800-406-9145 (cust serv) *E-mail:* sales.press@yale.edu (sales); customer.care@trilateral.org (cust serv) *Web Site:* www.yalebooks.com; yalepress.yale.edu/yupbooks, pg 278

Coghlan, Jennifer, BradyGames, 800 E 96 St, 3rd fl, Indianapolis, IN 46240 *Tel:* 317-428-3000 *Toll Free Tel:* 800-545-5912; 800-571-5840 (cust serv) *E-mail:* bradyquestions@pearsoned.com *Web Site:* www.bradygames.com, pg 44

Coglianese, Diana, Alfred A Knopf/Everyman's Library, c/o Random House Inc, 1745 Broadway, New York, NY 10019 *Tel:* 212-751-2600 *Toll Free Tel:* 800-638-6460 *Fax:* 212-572-2593 *Web Site:* www.knopfdoubleday.com, pg 132

Coglianese, Diana, Pantheon Books/Schocken Books, c/o Random House Inc, 1745 Broadway, New York, NY 10019 *Tel:* 212-751-2600 *Toll Free Tel:* 800-638-6460 *Fax:* 212-572-6030, pg 181

Cohan, Darcy, HarperCollins General Books Group, 195 Broadway, New York, NY 10007 *Tel:* 212-207-7000 *Web Site:* www.harpercollins.com, pg 105

Cohen, Adam, Tom Howard/John H Reid Fiction & Essay Contest, 351 Pleasant St, PMB 222, Northampton, MA 01060-3961 *Tel:* 413-320-1847 *Toll Free Tel:* 866-WINWRIT (946-9748) *Fax:* 413-280-0539 *Web Site:* www.winningwriters.com, pg 693

Cohen, Adam, Tom Howard/Margaret Reid Poetry Contest, 351 Pleasant St, PMB 222, Northampton, MA 01060-3961 *Tel:* 413-320-1847 *Toll Free Tel:* 866-WINWRIT (946-9748) *Fax:* 413-280-0539 *Web Site:* www.winningwriters.com, pg 693

Cohen, Adam, Wergle Flomp Humor Poetry Contest, 351 Pleasant St, PMB 222, Northampton, MA 01060-3961 *Tel:* 413-320-1847 *Toll Free Tel:* 866-WINWRIT (946-9748) *Fax:* 413-280-0539 *Web Site:* www.winningwriters.com, pg 735

Cohen, Barbara, Oxford University Press USA, 198 Madison Ave, New York, NY 10016 *Tel:* 212-726-6000 *Toll Free Tel:* 800-451-7556 (orders); 800-445-9714 (cust serv) *Fax:* 919-677-1303 *E-mail:* custserv.us@oup.com *Web Site:* www.oup.com/us, pg 179

Cohen, Brett, Quirk Books, 215 Church St, Philadelphia, PA 19106 *Tel:* 215-627-3581 *Fax:* 215-627-5220 *E-mail:* general@quirkbooks.com *Web Site:* www.quirkbooks.com, pg 202

Cohen, Carmela, Barricade Books Inc, 2037 LeMoine Ave, Fort Lee, NJ 07024 *Tel:* 201-944-7600 *E-mail:* customerservice@barricadebooks.com *Web Site:* www.barricadebooks.com, pg 31

Cohen, Christine M, Virginia Kidd Agency Inc, 538 E Harford St, PO Box 278, Milford, PA 18337 *Tel:* 570-296-6205 *Web Site:* vk-agency.com, pg 559

Cohen, Craig, powerHouse Books, 37 Main St, Brooklyn, NY 11201 *Tel:* 212-604-9074 *Fax:* 212-366-5247 *E-mail:* info@powerhousebooks.com *Web Site:* www.powerhousebooks.com, pg 195

Cohen, Debbie, Columbia Books & Information Services, 4340 East-West Hwy, Suite 300, Bethesda, MD 20814 *Tel:* 240-235-0266 *Toll Free Tel:* 888-265-0600 (cust serv) *Fax:* 202-464-1775 *E-mail:* info@columbiabooks.com *Web Site:* www.columbiabooks.com; www.lobbyists.info; www.associationexecs.com, pg 61

Cohen, Dr Emily-Jane, Stanford University Press, 1450 Page Mill Rd, Palo Alto, CA 94304-1124 *Tel:* 650-723-9434 *Fax:* 650-725-3457 *E-mail:* info@sup.org *Web Site:* www.sup.org, pg 233

Cohen, Herbert J, Platinum Press LLC, 281 Hicks St, Brooklyn Heights, NY 11201 *Tel:* 718-875-5065 *Fax:* 718-875-5065, pg 192

Cohen, Jeremy, Jerome Fellowship, 2301 Franklin Ave E, Minneapolis, MN 55406-1099 *Tel:* 612-332-7481 *Fax:* 612-332-6037 *E-mail:* info@pwcenter.org *Web Site:* www.pwcenter.org, pg 697

Cohen, Jeremy, Many Voices Fellowships, 2301 Franklin Ave E, Minneapolis, MN 55406-1099 *Tel:* 612-332-7481 *Fax:* 612-332-6037 *E-mail:* info@pwcenter.org *Web Site:* www.pwcenter.org, pg 705

Cohen, Jeremy, McKnight Fellowships for Playwrights, 2301 Franklin Ave E, Minneapolis, MN 55406-1099 *Tel:* 612-332-7481 *Fax:* 612-332-6037 *E-mail:* info@pwcenter.org *Web Site:* www.pwcenter.org, pg 706

Cohen, Jeremy, McKnight National Residency & Commission, 2301 Franklin Ave E, Minneapolis, MN 55406-1099 *Tel:* 612-332-7481 *Fax:* 612-332-6037 *E-mail:* info@pwcenter.org *Web Site:* www.pwcenter.org, pg 706

Cohen, Jonathan, Kensington Publishing Corp, 119 W 40 St, New York, NY 10018 *Tel:* 212-407-1500 *Toll Free Tel:* 800-221-2647 *Fax:* 212-935-0699 *Web Site:* www.kensingtonbooks.com, pg 130

Cohen, Judith, Cascade Pass Inc, 4223 Glencoe Ave, Suite C-105, Marina Del Rey, CA 90292-8801 *Tel:* 310-305-0210 *Toll Free Tel:* 888-837-0704 *Fax:* 310-305-7850 *Web Site:* www.cascadepass.com, pg 51

Cohen, Katia Segre, GeoLytics Inc, 3322 Rte 22, Suite 806, Branchburg, NJ 08876 *Tel:* 908-707-1505 *Toll Free Tel:* 800-577-6717 *Fax:* 908-707-1595 *E-mail:* support@geolytics.com; questions@geolytics.com *Web Site:* www.geolytics.com, pg 96

Cohen, Kelly, The Optical Society (OSA), 2010 Massachusetts Ave NW, Washington, DC 20036-1023 *Tel:* 202-223-8130 *Toll Free Tel:* 800-766-4672 *E-mail:* custserv@osa.org *Web Site:* www.osa.org, pg 175

Cohen, Larry, National Society of Newspaper Columnists Annual Conference, 1345 Fillmore St, Suite 507, San Francisco, CA 94115 *Tel:* 415-488-NCNC (488-6762) *Toll Free Tel:* 866-440-NSNC (440-6762) *Fax:* 484-297-0336 *Toll Free Fax:* 866-635-5759 *Web Site:* www.columnists.com, pg 653

Cohen, Linda, AICPA Professional Publications, 220 Leigh Farm Rd, Durham, NC 27707 *Tel:* 919-402-4500 *Toll Free Tel:* 888-777-7077 *Fax:* 919-402-4505 *Toll Free Fax:* 800-362-5066 *E-mail:* acquisitions@aicpa.org; service@aicpa.org *Web Site:* www.aicpa.org, pg 6

Cohen, Lord, Alan Wofsy Fine Arts, 1109 Geary Blvd, San Francisco, CA 94109 *Tel:* 415-292-6500 *Toll Free Tel:* 800-660-6403 *Fax:* 415-292-6594 (off & cust serv); 510-251-1840 (acctg) *E-mail:* order@art-books.com (orders); editeur@earthlink.net (edit); beauxarts@earthlink.net (cust serv) *Web Site:* www.art-books.com, pg 274

Cohen, Louis, Mason Crest Publishers, 450 Parkway Dr, Suite D, Broomall, PA 19008 *Tel:* 610-543-6200 *Toll Free Tel:* 866-MCP-BOOK (627-2665) *Fax:* 610-543-3878 *Web Site:* www.masoncrest.com, pg 149

Cohen, M, Players Press Inc, PO Box 1132, Studio City, CA 91614-0132 *Tel:* 818-789-4980 *E-mail:* playerspress@att.net *Web Site:* www.ppeps.com, pg 193

Cohen, Mark E, CDL Press, PO Box 34454, Bethesda, MD 20827 *Tel:* 301-762-2066 *Fax:* 253-484-5542 *E-mail:* cdlpress@erols.com *Web Site:* www.cdlpress.com, pg 52

Cohen, Michael R, Puddingstone Literary, Authors' Agents, 11 Mabro Dr, Denville, NJ 07834-9607 *Tel:* 973-366-3622, pg 569

Cohen, Mo, Gingko Press Inc, 1321 Fifth St, Berkeley, CA 94710 *Tel:* 510-898-1195 *Fax:* 510-898-1196 *E-mail:* books@gingkopress.com *Web Site:* www.gingkopress.com, pg 97

Cohen, Mort, Riverside Publishing, 3800 Golf Rd, Suite 200, Rolling Meadows, IL 60008 *Tel:* 630-467-7000 *Toll Free Tel:* 800-323-9540 *Fax:* 630-467-7192 (cust serv) *E-mail:* rpc_customer_service@hmhpub.com (cust serv) *Web Site:* www.riversidepublishing.com, pg 209

Cohen, Nan, Napa Valley Writers' Conference, Upper Valley Campus, 1088 College Ave, St Helena, CA 94574 *Tel:* 707-967-2900 (ext 1611) *Fax:* 707-967-2909 *E-mail:* writecon@napavalley.edu *Web Site:* www.napawritersconf.org, pg 653

Cohen, Paul, Monkfish Book Publishing Co, 22 E Market St, Suite 304, Rhinebeck, NY 12572 *Tel:* 845-876-4861 *E-mail:* monkfish@monkfishpublishing.com *Web Site:* www.monkfishpublishing.com, pg 159

Cohen, Peter, Houghton Mifflin Harcourt, 222 Berkeley St, Boston, MA 02116 *Tel:* 617-351-5000 *Toll Free Tel:* 800-225-5425 (K-12 educ materials); 800-323-9540 (assessment materials); 877-219-1537 (SkillsTutor); 888-242-6747 (Destination; Earobics; Edmark; Learning Village; Riverdeep); 800-225-3362 (Houghton Mifflin Harcourt Trade

Collier, Michael, Bread Loaf Writers' Conference, 5525 Middlebury College, 14 Old Chapel Rd, Middlebury, VT 05753 *Tel:* 802-443-5286 *Fax:* 802-443-2087 *E-mail:* blwc@middlebury.edu *Web Site:* www.middlebury.edu/blwc, pg 650

Collier, Michael, Fellowship & Scholarship Program for Writers, Middlebury College, Middlebury, VT 05753 *Tel:* 802-443-5286 *Fax:* 802-443-2087 *E-mail:* blwc@middlebury.edu *Web Site:* www.middlebury.edu/blwc, pg 685

Collier, Theresa, Bloomsbury Publishing Inc, 1385 Broadway, 5th fl, New York, NY 10018 *Tel:* 212-419-5300 *E-mail:* marketingusa@bloomsbury.com; adultpublicityusa@bloomsbury.com; askacademic@bloomsbury.com *Web Site:* www.bloomsbury.com, pg 40

Collignon, Kimberly, Data Trace Publishing Co (DTP), 110 West Rd, Suite 227, Towson, MD 21204-2316 *Tel:* 410-494-4994 *Toll Free Tel:* 800-342-0454 (orders only) *Fax:* 410-494-0515 *E-mail:* info@datatrace.com; salesandmarketing@datatrace.com; editorial@datatrace.com; info@datatrace.com *Web Site:* www.datatrace.com, pg 70

Collin, Frances, Frances Collin Literary Agent, PO Box 33, Wayne, PA 19087 *E-mail:* queries@francescollin.com *Web Site:* www.francescollin.com, pg 546

Collins, Allison Janse, Health Communications Inc, 3201 SW 15 St, Deerfield Beach, FL 33442 *Tel:* 954-360-0909 *Toll Free Tel:* 800-851-9100; 800-441-5569 (cust serv & orders) *Fax:* 954-360-0034 *Toll Free Fax:* 800-424-7652 (cust serv & orders) *Web Site:* www.hcibooks.com, pg 108

Collins, Anne, Knopf Canada, One Toronto St, Suite 300, Toronto, ON M5C 2V6, Canada *Tel:* 416-364-4449 *Toll Free Tel:* 888-523-9292 *Fax:* 416-364-6863 *Web Site:* www.randomhouse.ca, pg 490

Collins, Christy, White Cloud Press, 300 E Hersey St, Suite 11, Ashland, OR 97520 *Tel:* 541-488-6415 *Toll Free Tel:* 800-380-8286 *Fax:* 541-482-7708 *E-mail:* info@whitecloudpress.com *Web Site:* www.whitecloudpress.com, pg 270

Collins, JoAnn, International Transactions Inc, 28 Alope Way, Gila, NM 88038 *Tel:* 845-373-9696 *Fax:* 480-393-5162 *E-mail:* info@intltrans.com *Web Site:* www.intltrans.com, pg 557

Collins, Jonathan, ProQuest LLC, 789 E Eisenhower Pkwy, Ann Arbor, MI 48108-3218 *Tel:* 734-761-4700 *Toll Free Tel:* 800-521-0600 *Fax:* 734-975-6486 *Toll Free Fax:* 800-864-0019 *E-mail:* info@proquest.com *Web Site:* www.proquest.com, pg 199

Collins, Kate, Random House Publishing Group, 1745 Broadway, New York, NY 10019 *Toll Free Tel:* 800-200-3552 *Web Site:* atrandom.com, pg 204

Collins, Martha, Oberlin College Press, 50 N Professor St, Oberlin, OH 44074-1091 *Tel:* 440-775-8408 *Fax:* 440-775-8124 *E-mail:* oc.press@oberlin.edu *Web Site:* www.oberlin.edu/ocpress, pg 173

Collins, Nate, Samuel French Inc, 235 Park Ave S, 5th fl, New York, NY 10003 *Tel:* 212-206-8990 *Toll Free Tel:* 866-598-8449 *Fax:* 212-206-1429 *E-mail:* info@samuelfrench.com; publications@samuelfrench.com *Web Site:* www.samuelfrench.com, pg 92

Collins, Nate, Samuel French Inc, 235 Park Ave S, 5th fl, New York, NY 10003 *Tel:* 212-206-8990 *Toll Free Tel:* 866-598-8449 *Fax:* 212-206-1429 *E-mail:* info@samuelfrench.com *Web Site:* www.samuelfrench.com, pg 553

Collins, Randall, Leadership Ministries Worldwide/OBR, 3755 Pilot Point, Chattanooga, TN 37416 *Tel:* 423-855-2181 *Toll Free Tel:* 800-987-8790 *Fax:* 423-855-8616 *E-mail:* info@outlinebible.org *Web Site:* www.outlinebible.org, pg 135

Collins, Teresa Wells, The University Press of Kentucky, 663 S Limestone St, Lexington, KY 40508-4008 *Tel:* 859-257-8400 *Fax:* 859-257-8481 *Web Site:* www.kentuckypress.com, pg 261

Colman, Jon, Children's & Teen Choice Book Awards, 54 W 39 St, 14th fl, New York, NY 10018 *Tel:* 212-966-1990 *E-mail:* cbc.info@cbcbooks.org *Web Site:* ccbookawards.com; www.cbcbooks.org, pg 677

Colman, Jon, The Children's Book Council (CBC), 54 W 39 St, 14th fl, New York, NY 10018 *Tel:* 212-966-1990 *Toll Free Fax:* 888-807-9355 (orders only) *E-mail:* cbc.info@cbcbooks.org *Web Site:* www.cbcbooks.org, pg 603

Colom, Wilbur O, Genesis Press Inc, PO Box 101, Columbus, MS 39701 *Toll Free Tel:* 888-463-4461 (orders only) *Web Site:* www.genesis-press.com, pg 95

Colton, Tim, Carolina Academic Press, 700 Kent St, Durham, NC 27701 *Tel:* 919-489-7486 *Toll Free Tel:* 800-489-7486 *Fax:* 919-493-5668 *E-mail:* cap@cap-press.com *Web Site:* www.cap-press.com; www.caplaw.com, pg 50

Columbari, Bari, Pastoral Press, 5536 NE Hassalo, Portland, OR 97213-3638 *Tel:* 503-281-1191 *Toll Free Tel:* 800-548-8749 *Fax:* 503-282-3486 *Toll Free Fax:* 800-462-7329 *E-mail:* liturgy@ocp.org *Web Site:* www.ocp.org, pg 183

Columbus, Nadia, Nova Science Publishers Inc, 400 Oser Ave, Suite 1600, Hauppauge, NY 11788-3619 *Tel:* 631-231-7269 *Fax:* 631-231-8175 *E-mail:* main@novapublishers.com *Web Site:* www.novapublishers.com, pg 172

Colvin, Andrea, Andrews McMeel Publishing LLC, 1130 Walnut St, Kansas City, MO 64106-2109 *Toll Free Tel:* 800-851-8923; 800-943-9839 (cust serv) *Toll Free Fax:* 800-943-9831 (orders) *Web Site:* www.andrewsmcmeel.com, pg 18

Colvin, Rod, Addicus Books Inc, PO Box 45327, Omaha, NE 68145 *Tel:* 402-330-7493 *Fax:* 402-330-1707 *E-mail:* info@addicusbooks.com; addicusbks@aol.com *Web Site:* www.addicusbooks.com, pg 4

Colvin, Theresa, Individual Artist Awards, 175 W Ostend St, Suite E, Baltimore, MD 21230 *Tel:* 410-767-6555 *Fax:* 410-333-1062 *E-mail:* msac@msac.org *Web Site:* www.msac.org, pg 694

Comacchio, Blaire, Wilfrid Laurier University Press, 255 King St N, Suite 401, Waterloo, ON N2J 4V2, Canada *Tel:* 519-884-0710 (ext 6124) *Toll Free Tel:* 866-836-5551 (CN & US) *Fax:* 519-725-1399 *E-mail:* press@wlu.ca *Web Site:* www.wlupress.wlu.ca, pg 505

Combs, Michele, Carpe Indexum, 364 Woodbine Ave, Syracuse, NY 13206-3324 *Tel:* 315-431-4949 *E-mail:* info@carpeindexum.com *Web Site:* www.carpeindexum.com, pg 522

Combs, Misty, Money Market Directories, 401 E Market St, Charlottesville, VA 22902 *Tel:* 434-977-1450 *Toll Free Tel:* 800-446-2810 *Fax:* 434-979-9962 *Web Site:* www.mmdwebaccess.com, pg 159

Comfort, Anna, Harbour Publishing Co Ltd, 4437 Rondeview Rd, Madeira Park, BC V0N 2H0, Canada *Tel:* 604-883-2730 *Toll Free Tel:* 800-667-2988 *Fax:* 604-883-9451 *E-mail:* info@harbourpublishing.com *Web Site:* www.harbourpublishing.com, pg 487

Commella, Victoria, HarperCollins General Books Group, 195 Broadway, New York, NY 10007 *Tel:* 212-207-7000 *Web Site:* www.harpercollins.com, pg 105

Comrie, Tim, YMAA Publication Center, PO Box 480, Wolfeboro, NH 03894 *Tel:* 603-569-7988 *Toll Free Tel:* 800-669-8892 *Fax:* 603-569-1889 *E-mail:* ymaa@aol.com *Web Site:* www.ymaa.com, pg 278

Conant, Vic, Nightingale-Conant, 6245 W Howard St, Niles, IL 60714 *Tel:* 847-647-0306 *Toll Free Tel:* 800-572-2770; 800-557-1660 (sales); 800-560-6081 (cust serv) *Fax:* 847-647-7145; 847-647-9143 (sales) *E-mail:* distributordivision@nightingale.com (orders) *Web Site:* www.nightingale.com, pg 169

Conary, Lori, Shubert Fendrich Memorial Playwriting Contest, PO Box 4267, Englewood, CO 80155-4267 *Tel:* 303-779-4035 *Toll Free Tel:* 800-333-7262 *Fax:* 303-779-4315 *E-mail:* playwrights@pioneerdrama.com *Web Site:* www.pioneerdrama.com, pg 685

Conaway, Dan, Writers House, 21 W 26 St, New York, NY 10010 *Tel:* 212-685-2400 *Fax:* 212-685-1781 *Web Site:* www.writershouse.com, pg 580

Concepcion, Cristina, Don Congdon Associates Inc, 110 William St, Suite 2202, New York, NY 10038-3914 *Tel:* 212-645-1229 *Fax:* 212-727-2688 *E-mail:* dca@doncongdon.com *Web Site:* www.doncongdon.com, pg 546

Conde, Sidney, St Martin's Press, LLC, 175 Fifth Ave, New York, NY 10010 *Tel:* 646-307-5151 *Fax:* 212-420-9314 *E-mail:* firstname.lastname@macmillan.com *Web Site:* www.stmartins.com, pg 214

Condit, Carl Daniel, Sunstone Press, PO Box 2321, Santa Fe, NM 87504-2321 *Tel:* 505-988-4418 *Toll Free Tel:* 800-243-5644 *Fax:* 505-988-1025 (orders only) *Web Site:* www.sunstonepress.com, pg 238

Condon, Alicia, Kensington Publishing Corp, 119 W 40 St, New York, NY 10018 *Tel:* 212-407-1500 *Toll Free Tel:* 800-221-2647 *Fax:* 212-935-0699 *Web Site:* www.kensingtonbooks.com, pg 130

Condon, Phil, University of Montana, Environmental Writing Institute, Environmental Studies, University of Montana, Missoula, MT 59812 *Tel:* 406-243-2904 *Fax:* 406-243-6090 *Web Site:* www.umt.edu/ewi, pg 663

Condron, Dr Barbara, SOM Publishing, 163 Moon Valley Rd, Windyville, MO 65783 *Tel:* 417-345-8411 *Fax:* 417-345-6668 *E-mail:* som@som.org; dreamschool@dreamschool.org *Web Site:* www.som.org; www.dreamschool.org, pg 230

Conescu, Nancy, Dial Books for Young Readers, 345 Hudson St, New York, NY 10014 *Tel:* 212-366-2000 *Fax:* 212-414-3396 *E-mail:* online@penguinputnam.com *Web Site:* www.penguinputnam.com; us.penguingroup.com, pg 74

Congdon, Michael, Don Congdon Associates Inc, 110 William St, Suite 2202, New York, NY 10038-3914 *Tel:* 212-645-1229 *Fax:* 212-727-2688 *E-mail:* dca@doncongdon.com *Web Site:* www.doncongdon.com, pg 546

Conine, Nancy, Transaction Publishers Inc, 10 Corporate Place S, 35 Berrue Circle, Piscataway, NJ 08854 *Tel:* 732-445-2280; 732-445-1245 (orders) *Toll Free Tel:* 888-999-6778 (dist ctr) *Fax:* 732-445-3138 *E-mail:* trans@transactionpub.com; orders@transactionpub.om *Web Site:* www.transactionpub.com, pg 248

Conis, Kym, Foil & Specialty Effects Association (FSEA), 2150 SW Westport Dr, Suite 101, Topeka, KS 66614 *Tel:* 785-271-5816 *Fax:* 785-271-6404 *E-mail:* info@fsea.com; fseamail@fsea.com *Web Site:* www.fsea.com, pg 606

Conley, Charlie, DeLorme Publishing Co Inc, 2 DeLorme Dr, Yarmouth, ME 04096 *Tel:* 207-846-7000; 207-846-7111 (sales) *Toll Free Tel:* 800-561-5105; 800-511-2459 (cust serv) *Fax:* 207-846-7051 *Toll Free Fax:* 800-575-2244 *E-mail:* reseller@delorme.com *Web Site:* www.delorme.com, pg 72

Conley, Cort, Literature Fellowship, 2410 N Old Penitentiary Rd, Boise, ID 83712 *Tel:* 208-334-2119 *Toll Free Tel:* 800-ART-FUND (278-3863 within Idaho) *Fax:* 208-334-2488 *E-mail:* info@arts.idaho.gov *Web Site:* www.arts.idaho.gov, pg 702

Conley, Cort, Writer in Residence, 2410 N Old Penitentiary Rd, Boise, ID 83712 *Tel:* 208-334-2119 *Toll Free Tel:* 800-ART-FUND (278-3863 within Idaho) *Fax:* 208-334-2488 *E-mail:* info@arts.idaho.gov *Web Site:* www.arts.idaho.gov, pg 738

Conley, Susan, Arden Press Inc, PO Box 418, Denver, CO 80201-0418 *Tel:* 303-697-6766 *Fax:* 303-697-3443 *E-mail:* ardenpress@msn.com, pg 21

Conley, Tricia, The Penguin Press, 375 Hudson St, New York, NY 10014, pg 187

Conley, Tricia, Portfolio, 375 Hudson St, New York, NY 10014, pg 195

Conley, Tricia, Viking, 375 Hudson St, New York, NY 10014 *Tel:* 212-366-2000 *E-mail:* online@penguinputnam.com *Web Site:* www.penguinputnam.com; us.penguingroup.com, pg 265

1Z1, Canada *Tel:* 778-822-2514 *Fax:* 778-822-3616 *E-mail:* prismwritingcontest@gmail.com *Web Site:* www.prismmagazine.ca, pg 721

Cormier, Dominique Bernier, PRISM international Short Fiction Contest, University of British Columbia, Buch E462, 1866 Main Mall, Vancouver, BC V6T 1Z1, Canada *Tel:* 778-822-2514 *Fax:* 778-822-3616 *E-mail:* prismwritingcontest@gmail.com *Web Site:* www.prismmagazine.ca, pg 721

Cormier, Stephane, Prise de Parole Inc, 109 Elm St, Suite 205, Sudbury, ON P3C 1T4, Canada *Tel:* 705-675-6491 *Fax:* 705-673-1817 *E-mail:* info@prisedeparole.ca *Web Site:* www.prisedeparole.ca, pg 496

Cornack, Shelley, Norma Epstein Foundation, 15 King's College Circle, UC 173, Toronto, ON M5S 3H7, Canada *Tel:* 416-978-8083 *Fax:* 416-971-2027 *Web Site:* www.utoronto.ca, pg 684

Cornejo, Tony, Mel Bay Publications Inc, 4 Industrial Dr, Pacific, MO 63069-0066 *Tel:* 636-257-3970 *Toll Free Tel:* 800-863-5229 *Fax:* 636-257-5062 *Toll Free Fax:* 800-660-9818 *E-mail:* email@melbay.com *Web Site:* www.melbay.com, pg 154

Cornelius, Vicki, Blue Mountain Arts Inc, 2905 Wilderness Place, Boulder, CO 80301 *Tel:* 303-449-0536 *Toll Free Tel:* 800-525-0642 *Fax:* 303-417-6472 *Toll Free Fax:* 800-545-8573 *E-mail:* info@sps.com *Web Site:* www.sps.com, pg 40

Cornell du Houx, Paul, Polar Bear & Co, 8 Brook St, Solon, ME 04979 *Tel:* 207-643-2795 *Web Site:* www.polarbearandco.com, pg 194

Cornell, Merial, Cornell & McCarthy LLC, 2-D Cross Hwy, Westport, CT 06880 *Tel:* 203-454-4210 *E-mail:* contact@cmartreps.com *Web Site:* www.cmartreps.com, pg 583

Corngold, Sally Marshall, Optometric Extension Program Foundation, 1921 E Carnegie Ave, Suite 3-L, Santa Ana, CA 92705-5510 *Tel:* 949-250-8070 *Fax:* 949-250-8157 *E-mail:* oep@oep.org *Web Site:* www.oepf.org, pg 176

Corpus, Angela, Walter Foster Publishing Inc, 6 Orchard Rd, Suite 100, Lake Forest, CA 92630 *Tel:* 949-380-7510 *Toll Free Tel:* 800-426-0099; 800-759-0190 (orders) *Fax:* 949-380-7575 *E-mail:* walterfoster@quartous.com *Web Site:* www.quartous.com, pg 91

Corrado, Susan, Naval Institute Press, 291 Wood Rd, Annapolis, MD 21402-5034 *Tel:* 410-268-6110 *Toll Free Tel:* 800-233-8764 *Fax:* 410-295-1084; 410-571-1703 (cust serv) *E-mail:* webmaster@navalinstitute.org; customer@navalinstitute.org (cust serv); trade@usni.org *Web Site:* www.nip.org; www.usni.org, pg 166

Corral, Rodrigo, Farrar, Straus & Giroux, LLC, 18 W 18 St, New York, NY 10011 *Tel:* 212-741-6900 *E-mail:* fsg.publicity@fsgbooks.com *Web Site:* us.macmillan.com/fsg.aspx, pg 86

Correa, Alex, Lectorum Publications Inc, 205 Chubb Ave, Lyndhurst, NJ 07071 *Toll Free Tel:* 800-345-5946 *Fax:* 201-559-2201 *Toll Free Fax:* 877-532-8676 *E-mail:* lectorum@lectorum.com *Web Site:* www.lectorum.com, pg 136

Correa, Nick, Cambridge University Press, 32 Avenue of the Americas, New York, NY 10013-2473 *Tel:* 212-924-3900; 212-337-5000 *Fax:* 212-691-3239 *E-mail:* newyork@cambridge.org *Web Site:* www.cambridge.org/us, pg 49

Correia, Peter R III, National Resource Center for Youth Services (NRCYS), Schusterman Ctr, Bldg 4W, 4502 E 41 St, Tulsa, OK 74135-2512 *Tel:* 918-660-3700 *Toll Free Tel:* 800-274-2687 *Fax:* 918-660-3737 *Web Site:* www.nrcys.ou.edu, pg 166

Corrigan, Anne Marie, University of Toronto Press, 10 St Mary St, Suite 700, Toronto, ON M4Y 2W8, Canada *Tel:* 416-978-2239 *Fax:* 416-978-4738 *E-mail:* info@utpress.utoronto.ca *Web Site:* www.utpress.utoronto.ca; www.utppublishing.com, pg 504

Corrin, Dean, Cunningham Commission for Youth Theatre, 2135 N Kenmore Ave, Chicago, IL 60614-4100 *Tel:* 773-325-7932 *Fax:* 773-325-7920 *Web Site:* theatreschool.depaul.edu, pg 679

Cosgrove, Jay, Yale University Press, 302 Temple St, New Haven, CT 06511-8909 *Tel:* 203-432-0960; 203-432-0966 (sales); 401-531-2800 (cust serv) *Toll Free Tel:* 800-405-1619 (cust serv) *Fax:* 203-432-0948; 203-432-8485 (sales); 401-531-2801 (cust serv) *Toll Free Fax:* 800-406-9145 (cust serv) *E-mail:* sales.press@yale.edu (sales); customer.care@trilateral.org (cust serv) *Web Site:* www.yalebooks.com; yalepress.yale.edu/yupbooks, pg 278

Cosseboom, Joel, University of Hawaii Press, 2840 Kolowalu St, Honolulu, HI 96822 *Tel:* 808-956-8255 *Toll Free Tel:* 888-UHPRESS (847-7377) *Fax:* 808-988-6052 *Toll Free Fax:* 800-650-7811 *E-mail:* uhpbooks@hawaii.edu *Web Site:* www.uhpress.hawaii.edu, pg 256

Costantini MFA, Lana, Center for the Collaborative Classroom, 1250 53 St, Suite 3, Emeryville, CA 94608 *Tel:* 510-533-0213 *Toll Free Tel:* 800-666-7270 *Fax:* 510-464-3670 *E-mail:* info@collaborativeclassroom.org; clientsupport@collaborativeclassroom.org *Web Site:* www.collaborativeclassroom.org, pg 53

Costanzo, Gerald, Carnegie Mellon University Press, 5032 Forbes Ave, Pittsburgh, PA 15289-1021 *Tel:* 412-268-2861 *Fax:* 412-268-8706 *E-mail:* carnegiemellonuniversitypress@gmail.com *Web Site:* www.cmu.edu/universitypress, pg 50

Costella, Andrea, W W Norton & Company Inc, 500 Fifth Ave, New York, NY 10110-0017 *Tel:* 212-354-5500 *Toll Free Tel:* 800-233-4830 (orders & cust serv) *Fax:* 212-869-0856 *Toll Free Fax:* 800-458-6515 *Web Site:* www.wwnorton.com, pg 172

Costello, James C, Springer Publishing Co, 11 W 42 St, 15th fl, New York, NY 10036-8002 *Tel:* 212-431-4370 *Toll Free Tel:* 877-687-7476 *Fax:* 212-941-7842 *E-mail:* marketing@springerpub.com; cs@springerpub.com (orders); editorial@springerpub.com *Web Site:* www.springerpub.com, pg 232

Costello, John, The MIT Press, 55 Hayward St, Cambridge, MA 02142 *Tel:* 617-253-5255 *Toll Free Tel:* 800-207-8354 (orders) *Fax:* 617-258-6779; 617-577-1545 (orders) *Web Site:* mitpress.mit.edu, pg 158

Coster, Candace, BHTG - Competition for Youth Theatre Marilyn Hall Awards, PO Box 148, Beverly Hills, CA 90213 *Tel:* 310-273-3390 *Web Site:* www.beverlyhillstheatreguild.com, pg 672

Coster, Candace, BHTG - Julie Harris Playwright Award Competition, PO Box 148, Beverly Hills, CA 90213 *Tel:* 310-273-3390 *Web Site:* www.beverlyhillstheatreguild.com, pg 672

Costopulos, Nancy, American Marketing Association, 311 S Wacker Dr, Suite 5800, Chicago, IL 60606 *Tel:* 312-542-9000 *Toll Free Tel:* 800-AMA-1150 (262-1150) *Fax:* 312-542-9001 *E-mail:* info@ama.org *Web Site:* www.ama.org, pg 595

Cota, Tammy, Internet Alliance (IA), 1615 "L" St NW, Suite 1100, Washington, DC 20036-5624 *Tel:* 202-861-2407 *Web Site:* www.internetalliance.org, pg 608

Cote, Marc, Cormorant Books Inc, 10 St Mary St, Suite 615, Toronto, ON M4Y-1P6, Canada *Tel:* 416-925-8887 *E-mail:* info@cormorantbooks.com *Web Site:* www.cormorantbooks.com, pg 478

Cotter, Kelly, Standard Publishing Corp, 155 Federal St, 13th fl, Boston, MA 02110 *Tel:* 617-457-0600 *Toll Free Tel:* 800-682-5759 *Fax:* 617-457-0608 *Web Site:* www.spcpub.com, pg 233

Cottle, Anna, Cine/Lit Representation, PO Box 802918, Santa Clarita, CA 91380-2918 *Tel:* 661-513-0268 *E-mail:* cinelit@att.net, pg 546

Cottrell, Sophie, Hachette Book Group, 1290 Avenue of the Americas, New York, NY 10019 *Tel:* 212-364-1100 *Toll Free Tel:* 800-759-0190 (cust serv) *Fax:* 212-364-0933 (intl orders) *Toll Free Fax:* 800-286-9471 (cust serv) *Web Site:* www.HachetteBookGroup.com, pg 102

Cotts, Diane, University of Oklahoma Press, 2800 Venture Dr, Norman, OK 73069-8216 *Tel:* 405-325-2000 *Toll Free Tel:* 800-627-7377 (orders) *Fax:* 405-364-5798 (orders) *Toll Free Fax:* 800-735-0476 (orders) *E-mail:* presscs@ou.edu *Web Site:* www.oupress.com, pg 258

Cottter, Glenda, The University of Utah Press, J Willard Marriott Library, Suite 5400, 295 S 1500 E, Salt Lake City, UT 84112-0860 *Tel:* 801-581-6771 *Toll Free Tel:* 800-621-2736 (orders) *Fax:* 801-581-3365 *Toll Free Fax:* 800-621-8471 *E-mail:* info@upress.utah.edu *Web Site:* www.uofupress.com, pg 260

Couch, Peg, Fox Chapel Publishing Co Inc, 1970 Broad St, East Petersburg, PA 17520 *Tel:* 717-560-4703 *Toll Free Tel:* 800-457-9112 *Fax:* 717-560-4702 *E-mail:* customerservice@foxchapelpublishing.com *Web Site:* www.foxchapelpublishing.com, pg 91

Coughlan, Robert, Capstone Publishers™, 1710 Roe Crest Dr, North Mankato, MN 56003 *Toll Free Tel:* 800-747-4992 (cust serv) *Toll Free Fax:* 888-262-0705 *Web Site:* www.capstonepress.com, pg 49

Coumbis, Alex, Random House Publishing Group, 1745 Broadway, New York, NY 10019 *Toll Free Tel:* 800-200-3552 *Web Site:* atrandom.com, pg 204

Counihan, Claire, Holiday House Inc, 425 Madison Ave, New York, NY 10017 *Tel:* 212-688-0085 *Fax:* 212-421-6134 *E-mail:* holiday@holidayhouse.com *Web Site:* www.holidayhouse.com, pg 113

Coupe, Carla, Wildside Press LLC, 414 Hungerford Dr, Suite 234, Rockville, MD 20850 *Tel:* 301-762-1305 *Fax:* 301-762-1306 *E-mail:* wildside@wildsidepress.com *Web Site:* www.wildsidebooks.com; www.wildsidemagazines.com; www.wildsidepress.com, pg 272

Court, Kathryn, Penguin Books, 375 Hudson St, New York, NY 10014 *Tel:* 212-366-2000 *E-mail:* online@penguinputnam.com *Web Site:* www.penguinputnam.com; www.penguinclassics.com; us.penguingroup.com, pg 186

Court, Kathryn, Penguin Group (USA) LLC, a Penguin Random House company, 375 Hudson St, New York, NY 10014 *Tel:* 212-366-2000 *Toll Free Tel:* 800-847-5515 (inside sales); 800-631-8571 (cust serv) *Fax:* 212-366-2666; 607-775-4829 (inside sales) *E-mail:* online@us.penguingroup.com *Web Site:* www.penguin.com; us.penguingroup.com, pg 186

Court, Kathryn, Plume, 375 Hudson St, New York, NY 10014 *Tel:* 212-366-2000 *Fax:* 212-366-2666 *E-mail:* online@penguinputnam.com *Web Site:* www.penguinputnam.com; us.penguingroup.com, pg 193

Courtier, Jon, S©ott Treimel NY, 434 Lafayette St, New York, NY 10003-6943 *Tel:* 212-505-8353 *E-mail:* general@scotttreimelny.com *Web Site:* scotttreimelny.com; scotttreimelny.blogspot.com, pg 572

Cousineau, Helene, Pearson ERPI, 5757 rue Cypihot, St-Laurent, QC H4S 1R3, Canada *Tel:* 514-334-2690 *Toll Free Tel:* 800-263-3678 *Fax:* 514-334-4720 *Toll Free Fax:* 800-643-4720 *E-mail:* erpidlm@erpi.com *Web Site:* www.erpi.com; pearsonplc.ca, pg 494

Cousineau, Lea, The Institute for Cooperation on Adult Education (Institut de Cooperation pour l'Education des Adultes-ICEA), 55, ave du Mont-Royal Ouest, Bureau 303, Montreal, QC H2T 2S6, Canada *Tel:* 514-948-2044 *Fax:* 514-948-2046 *E-mail:* icae@icea.qc.ca *Web Site:* www.icea.qc.ca, pg 607

Coutu, Caroline, Les Editions Goelette Inc, 1350 Marie-Victorin, St-Bruno-de-Montarville, Quebec, QC J3V 6B9, Canada *Tel:* 450-653-1337 *Toll Free Tel:* 800-463-4961 *Fax:* 450-653-9924 *E-mail:* info@boutiquegoelette.com *Web Site:* www.editionsgoelette.com, pg 481

Coutu, Dawn, New Hampshire Literary Awards, 2500 N River Rd, Manchester, NH 03106 *Tel:* 603-314-7980 *Fax:* 603-314-7981 *E-mail:* info@nhwritersproject.org *Web Site:* www.nhwritersproject.org, pg 712

Coutu, Susy, Editions du CHU Sainte-Justine, 3175, chemin de la Cote-Sainte-Catherine, Montreal, QC H3T 1C5, Canada *Tel:* 514-345-4671 *Fax:* 514-345-4631 *E-mail:* edition.hsj@ssss.gouv.qc.ca *Web Site:* www.editions-chu-sainte-justine.org, pg 481

Covell, John S, The MIT Press, 55 Hayward St, Cambridge, MA 02142 *Tel:* 617-253-5255 *Toll Free Tel:* 800-207-8354 (orders) *Fax:* 617-258-6779; 617-577-1545 (orders) *Web Site:* mitpress.mit.edu, pg 158

Covert, Brenda, Ambassador International, 427 Wade Hampton Blvd, Greenville, SC 29609 *Tel:* 864-235-2434 *Toll Free Tel:* 800-209-8570 *Fax:* 864-235-2491 *E-mail:* info@emeraldhouse.com; publisher@emeraldhouse.com (ms submissions); sales@emeraldhouse.com (orders/order inquiries) *Web Site:* ambassador-international.com; www.facebook.com/AmbassadorIntl; twitter.com/ambassadorintl, pg 10

Covey, Bill, CBA: The Association for Christian Retail, 1365 Garden of the Gods Rd, Suite 105, Colorado Springs, CO 80907 *Tel:* 719-265-9895 *Toll Free Tel:* 800-252-1950 *Fax:* 719-272-3508 *E-mail:* info@cbaonline.org *Web Site:* cbaonline.org, pg 603

Cowles, Lauren, Cambridge University Press, 32 Avenue of the Americas, New York, NY 10013-2473 *Tel:* 212-924-3900; 212-337-5000 *Fax:* 212-691-3239 *E-mail:* newyork@cambridge.org *Web Site:* www.cambridge.org/us, pg 49

Cowlin, Scott, Peachpit Press, 1249 Eighth St, Berkeley, CA 94710 *Tel:* 510-524-2178 *Toll Free Tel:* 800-283-9444 *Fax:* 510-524-2221 *E-mail:* info@peachpit.com *Web Site:* www.peachpit.com, pg 184

Cox, Beth, McFarland, 960 NC Hwy 88 W, Jefferson, NC 28640 *Tel:* 336-246-4460 *Toll Free Tel:* 800-253-2187 (orders) *Fax:* 336-246-5018; 336-246-4403 (orders) *E-mail:* info@mcfarlandpub.com *Web Site:* www.mcfarlandpub.com, pg 150

Cox, Clare, Rowman & Littlefield Publishers Inc, 4501 Forbes Blvd, Suite 200, Lanham, MD 20706 *Tel:* 301-459-3366 *Toll Free Tel:* 800-462-6420 (cust serv) *Fax:* 301-429-5748 *Web Site:* www.rowmanlittlefield.com, pg 212

Cox, Clare, Scarecrow Press Inc, 4501 Forbes Blvd, Suite 200, Lanham, MD 20706 *Tel:* 301-459-3366 *Fax:* 301-429-5748 *Web Site:* www.scarecrowpress.com, pg 217

Cox, Clare, University Press of America Inc, 4501 Forbes Blvd, Suite 200, Lanham, MD 20706 *Tel:* 301-459-3366 *Toll Free Tel:* 800-462-6420 *Fax:* 301-429-5748 *Toll Free Fax:* 800-338-4550 *Web Site:* www.univpress.com, pg 261

Cox, Jon, Painted Pony Inc, 3 Ethete Rd, Fort Washakie, WY 82514 *Tel:* 307-335-7330 *Toll Free Tel:* 877-253-3824 *Fax:* 307-335-7332 *E-mail:* ppi@wrdf.org *Web Site:* www.paintedponyinc.com, pg 180

Cox, Jonathan, Simon & Schuster, 1230 Avenue of the Americas, New York, NY 10020 *Tel:* 212-698-7000 *Toll Free Tel:* 800-223-2348 (cust serv); 800-223-2336 (orders) *Toll Free Fax:* 800-943-9831 (orders) *Web Site:* www.simonandschuster.com, pg 225

Cox, Merrilee, Society for Features Journalism (SFJ), University of Maryland, Philip Merrill College of Journalism, 1100 Knight Hall, College Park, MD 20742 *Tel:* 301-314-2631 *Fax:* 301-314-9166 *Web Site:* featuresjournalism.org, pg 618

Cox, Ron, Kamehameha Publishing, 567 S King St, Suite 118, Honolulu, HI 96813 *Tel:* 808-534-8205 *Fax:* 808-541-5305 *E-mail:* publishing@ksbe.edu *Web Site:* kamehamehapublishing.org, pg 129

Cox, Tom, Whitaker House, 1030 Hunt Valley Circle, New Kensington, PA 15068 *Tel:* 724-334-7000 *Fax:* 724-334-1200 *E-mail:* publisher@whitakerhouse.com *Web Site:* www.whitakerhouse.com, pg 270

Coyle, Lily, Beaver's Pond Press Inc, 7108 Ohms Lane, Edina, MN 55439 *Tel:* 952-829-8818 *E-mail:* info@beaverspondpress.com *Web Site:* www.beaverspondpress.com, pg 33

Coyne, Christopher, Marshall Cavendish Corp, 99 White Plains Rd, Tarrytown, NY 10591-9001 *Tel:* 914-332-8888 *Toll Free Tel:* 800-821-9881 *Fax:* 914-332-8102 *E-mail:* mce@marshallcavendish.com *Web Site:* www.mceducation.us, pg 148

Coyne, Frank, George T Bisel Co Inc, 710 S Washington Sq, Philadelphia, PA 19106-3519 *Tel:* 215-922-5760 *Toll Free Tel:* 800-247-3526 *Fax:* 215-922-2235 *E-mail:* gbisel@bisel.com *Web Site:* www.bisel.com, pg 37

Coyne, Mary, Penguin Random House Speakers Bureau, 1745 Broadway, Mail Drop 13-1, New York, NY 10019 *Tel:* 212-572-2013 *E-mail:* speakers@penguinrandomhouse.com *Web Site:* www.prhspeakers.com, pg 587

Coyne, Rachel, FinePrint Literary Management, 115 W 29 St, 3rd fl, New York, NY 10001 *Tel:* 212-279-1282 *Web Site:* www.fineprintlit.com, pg 551

Craane, Isle, BookStop Literary Agency LLC, 67 Meadow View Rd, Orinda, CA 94563 *E-mail:* info@bookstopliterary.com *Web Site:* www.bookstopliterary.com, pg 543

Crabtree, Andrea, Crabtree Publishing Co, 350 Fifth Ave, 59th fl, PMB 59051, New York, NY 10118 *Tel:* 212-496-5040 *Toll Free Tel:* 800-387-7650 *Toll Free Fax:* 800-355-7166 *E-mail:* custserv@crabtreebooks.com *Web Site:* www.crabtreebooks.com, pg 66

Crabtree, Andrea, Crabtree Publishing Co Ltd, 616 Welland Ave, St Catharines, ON L2M-5V6, Canada *Tel:* 905-682-5221 *Toll Free Tel:* 800-387-7650 *Fax:* 905-682-7166 *Toll Free Fax:* 800-355-7166 *E-mail:* custserv@crabtreebooks.com; sales@crabtreebooks.com; orders@crabtreebooks.com *Web Site:* www.crabtreebooks.com, pg 478

Crabtree, Danielle, Crown Publishing Group, c/o Penguin Random House Inc, 1745 Broadway, New York, NY 10019 *Tel:* 212-782-9000 *Toll Free Tel:* 888-264-1745 *Fax:* 212-940-7408 *E-mail:* crownosm@penguinrandomhouse.com *Web Site:* crownpublishing.com, pg 68

Crabtree, Peter A, Crabtree Publishing Co, 350 Fifth Ave, 59th fl, PMB 59051, New York, NY 10118 *Tel:* 212-496-5040 *Toll Free Tel:* 800-387-7650 *Toll Free Fax:* 800-355-7166 *E-mail:* custserv@crabtreebooks.com *Web Site:* www.crabtreebooks.com, pg 66

Crabtree, Peter A, Crabtree Publishing Co Ltd, 616 Welland Ave, St Catharines, ON L2M-5V6, Canada *Tel:* 905-682-5221 *Toll Free Tel:* 800-387-7650 *Fax:* 905-682-7166 *Toll Free Fax:* 800-355-7166 *E-mail:* custserv@crabtreebooks.com; sales@crabtreebooks.com; orders@crabtreebooks.com *Web Site:* www.crabtreebooks.com, pg 478

Crabtree, Tamara, Abingdon Press, 201 Eighth Ave S, Nashville, TN 37203-3919 *Tel:* 615-749-6000 (academic books) *Toll Free Tel:* 800-251-3320 *Fax:* 615-749-6056 (academic books) *Toll Free Fax:* 800-836-7802 (orders) *E-mail:* orders@abingdonpress.com *Web Site:* www.abingdonpress.com, pg 2

Craft, Baird, Jones McClure Publishing, 3131 Eastside St, Suite 300, Houston, TX 77098 *Tel:* 713-335-8200 *Toll Free Tel:* 800-626-6667 *Fax:* 713-335-8201 *E-mail:* comments@jonesmcclure.com *Web Site:* www.jonesmcclure.com, pg 128

Craft, Tonaya, Copper Canyon Press, Fort Worden State Park, Bldg 313, Port Townsend, WA 98368 *Tel:* 360-385-4925 *Toll Free Tel:* 877-501-1393 (orders) *Fax:* 360-385-4985 *E-mail:* poetry@coppercanyonpress.org *Web Site:* www.coppercanyonpress.org, pg 63

Cragin, Sally, Barbara Bradley Prize, 2 Farrar St, Cambridge, MA 02138 *Tel:* 617-744-6034 *E-mail:* contests@nepoetryclub.org *Web Site:* www.nepoetryclub.org, pg 673

Cragin, Sally, Der-Hovanessian Translation Prize, 2 Farrar St, Cambridge, MA 02138 *Tel:* 617-744-6034 *E-mail:* contests@nepoetryclub.org *Web Site:* www.nepoetryclub.org, pg 680

Cragin, Sally, Golden Rose Award, 2 Farrar St, Cambridge, MA 02138 *Tel:* 617-744-6034 *E-mail:* contests@nepoetryclub.org *Web Site:* www.nepoetryclub.org, pg 690

Cragin, Sally, Firman Houghton Prize, 2 Farrar St, Cambridge, MA 02138 *Tel:* 617-744-6034 *E-mail:* contests@nepoetryclub.org *Web Site:* www.nepoetryclub.org, pg 693

Cragin, Sally, Sheila Margaret Motton Prize, 2 Farrar St, Cambridge, MA 02138 *Tel:* 617-744-6034 *E-mail:* contests@nepoetryclub.org *Web Site:* www.nepoetryclub.org, pg 709

Cragin, Sally, Erika Mumford Prize, 2 Farrar St, Cambridge, MA 02138 *Tel:* 617-744-6034 *E-mail:* contests@nepoetryclub.org *Web Site:* www.nepoetryclub.org, pg 710

Cragin, Sally, New England Poetry Club, 2 Farrar St, Cambridge, MA 02138 *Tel:* 617-744-6034 *E-mail:* info@nepoetryclub.org *Web Site:* www.nepoetryclub.org, pg 613

Cragin, Sally, May Sarton Award, 2 Farrar St, Cambridge, MA 02138 *Tel:* 617-744-6034 *E-mail:* contests@nepoetryclub.org *Web Site:* www.nepoetryclub.org, pg 726

Cragin, Sally, Daniel Varoujan Award, 2 Farrar St, Cambridge, MA 02138 *Tel:* 617-744-6034 *E-mail:* contests@nepoetryclub.org *Web Site:* www.nepoetryclub.org, pg 733

Crago, Jonathan, McGill-Queen's University Press, 1010 Sherbrooke W, Suite 1720, Montreal, QC H3A 2R7, Canada *Tel:* 514-398-3750 *Fax:* 514-398-4333 *E-mail:* mqup@mqup.ca *Web Site:* www.mqup.ca, pg 491

Crahan, Eric, Princeton University Press, 41 William St, Princeton, NJ 08540-5237 *Tel:* 609-258-4900 *Toll Free Tel:* 800-777-4726 (orders) *Fax:* 609-258-6305 *Toll Free Fax:* 800-999-1958 *E-mail:* orders@cpfsinc.com *Web Site:* press.princeton.edu, pg 197

Craig, Bryce H, P & R Publishing Co, 1102 Marble Hill Rd, Phillipsburg, NJ 08865 *Tel:* 908-454-0505 *Toll Free Tel:* 800-631-0094 *Fax:* 908-859-2390 *E-mail:* sales@prpbooks.com; info@prpbooks.com *Web Site:* www.prpbooks.com, pg 180

Craig, Jo Ann, Harold W McGraw Jr - Prize in Education, 1221 Avenue of the Americas, 47th fl, New York, NY 10020-1095 *Tel:* 212-904-2000; 212-512-2000 *Fax:* 212-512-3611 *Web Site:* www.mhfi.com, pg 706

Craigo-Snell, Shannon, Louisville Grawemeyer Award in Religion, 1044 Alta Vista Rd, Louisville, KY 40205-1798 *Tel:* 502-895-3411 *Toll Free Tel:* 800-264-1839 *Fax:* 502-894-2286 *E-mail:* grawemeyer@lpts.edu *Web Site:* www.grawemeyer.org, pg 703

Crane, Edward H, Cato Institute, 1000 Massachusetts Ave NW, Washington, DC 20001-5403 *Tel:* 202-842-0200 *Toll Free Tel:* 800-767-1241 *Fax:* 202-842-3490 *E-mail:* catostore@cato.org *Web Site:* www.cato.org, pg 52

Cranfill, Jennifer, Morton Marr Poetry Prize, PO Box 750374, Dallas, TX 75275-0374 *Fax:* 214-768-1408 *E-mail:* swr@mail.smu.edu *Web Site:* www.smu.edu/southwestreview, pg 705

Cranfill, Jennifer, John H McGinnis Memorial Award, PO Box 750374, Dallas, TX 75275-0374 *Fax:* 214-768-1408 *E-mail:* swr@mail.smu.edu *Web Site:* www.smu.edu/southwestreview, pg 706

Cranfill, Jennifer, The David Nathan Meyerson Prize for Fiction, PO Box 750374, Dallas, TX 75275-0374 *Fax:* 214-768-1408 *E-mail:* swr@mail.smu.edu *Web Site:* www.smu.edu/southwestreview, pg 707

Cranfill, Jennifer, Elizabeth Matchett Stover Memorial Award, PO Box 750374, Dallas, TX 75275-0374 *Fax:* 214-768-1408 *E-mail:* swr@mail.smu.edu *Web Site:* www.smu.edu/southwestreview, pg 731

Cranford, Garry, Flanker Press Ltd, 1243 Kenmount Rd, Unit A, Paradise, NL A1L 0V8, Canada *Tel:* 709-739-4477 *Toll Free Tel:* 866-739-4420 *Fax:* 709-739-4420 *E-mail:* info@flankerpress.com *Web Site:* www.flankerpress.com, pg 484

Cranford, Jerry, Flanker Press Ltd, 1243 Kenmount Rd, Unit A, Paradise, NL A1L 0V8, Canada *Tel:* 709-739-4477 *Toll Free Tel:* 866-739-4420 *Fax:* 709-739-4420 *E-mail:* info@flankerpress.com *Web Site:* www.flankerpress.com, pg 484

Crary, Elizabeth, Parenting Press Inc, 13751 Lake City Way NE, Suite 110, Seattle, WA 98125 *Tel:* 206-364-2900 *Toll Free Tel:* 800-99-BOOKS (992-6657) *Fax:* 206-364-0702 *E-mail:* office@parentingpress.com; marketing@parentingpress.com *Web Site:* www.parentingpress.com, pg 183

Crary, Jonathan, Zone Books dba Urzone Inc, 1226 Prospect Ave, Brooklyn, NY 11218 *Tel:* 718-686-0048 *Toll Free Tel:* 800-405-1619 (orders & cust serv) *Fax:* 718-686-9045 *Toll Free Fax:* 800-406-9145 (orders) *E-mail:* orders@triliteral.org *Web Site:* www.zonebooks.org, pg 280

Craven, Kim, Oxford University Press USA, 198 Madison Ave, New York, NY 10016 *Tel:* 212-726-6000 *Toll Free Tel:* 800-451-7556 (orders); 800-445-9714 (cust serv) *Fax:* 919-677-1303 *E-mail:* custserv.us@oup.com *Web Site:* www.oup.com/us, pg 179

Craven, Robert H Jr, F A Davis Co, 1915 Arch St, Philadelphia, PA 19103 *Tel:* 215-568-2270; 215-440-3001 *Toll Free Tel:* 800-523-4049 *Fax:* 215-568-5065; 215-440-3016 *E-mail:* info@fadavis.com; orders@fadavis.com *Web Site:* www.fadavis.com, pg 71

Craven, Robert H Sr, F A Davis Co, 1915 Arch St, Philadelphia, PA 19103 *Tel:* 215-568-2270; 215-440-3001 *Toll Free Tel:* 800-523-4049 *Fax:* 215-568-5065; 215-440-3016 *E-mail:* info@fadavis.com; orders@fadavis.com *Web Site:* www.fadavis.com, pg 71

Craven, Victoria, The Monacelli Press, 236 W 27 St, 4th fl, New York, NY 10001 *Tel:* 212-229-9925 *E-mail:* contact@monacellipress.com *Web Site:* www.monacellipress.com, pg 159

Crawford, Ann H, Geological Society of America (GSA), 3300 Penrose Place, Boulder, CO 80301-1806 *Tel:* 303-357-1000 *Fax:* 303-357-1070 *E-mail:* pubs@geosociety.org (prodn); editing@geosociety.org (edit) *Web Site:* www.geosociety.org, pg 96

Crawford, Betty Anne, The Jennifer DeChiara Literary Agency, 31 E 32 St, Suite 300, New York, NY 10016 *Tel:* 212-481-8484 (ext 362) *Fax:* 212-481-9582 *Web Site:* www.jdlit.com, pg 547

Crawford, Ingrid, North American Bookdealers Exchange (NABE), PO Box 606, Cottage Grove, OR 97424-0026 *Tel:* 541-942-7455 *E-mail:* nabe@bookmarketingprofits.com *Web Site:* www.bookmarketingprofits.com, pg 614

Crawford, Kristen, Arcadia Publishing Inc, 420 Wando Park Blvd, Mount Pleasant, SC 29464 *Tel:* 843-853-2070 *Toll Free Tel:* 888-313-2665 (orders only) *Fax:* 843-853-0044 *E-mail:* sales@arcadiapublishing.com *Web Site:* www.arcadiapublishing.com, pg 21

Crawford, Mark, MC2 Solutions LLC, 5101 Violet Lane, Madison, WI 53714 *Tel:* 608-240-4959, pg 530

Crawford, Tad, Allworth Press, 307 W 36 St, 11th fl, New York, NY 10018 *Tel:* 212-643-6816 *Fax:* 212-643-6819 *Web Site:* www.allworth.com, pg 8

Crawford, William R Sr, Military Living Publications, 333 Maple Ave E, Suite 3130, Vienna, VA 22180-4717 *Tel:* 703-237-0203 (ext 1) *Toll Free Tel:* 877-363-4677 (ext 1) *Fax:* 703-997-8861 *E-mail:* customerservice@militaryliving.com *Web Site:* www.militaryliving.com, pg 157

Crawley, Sandy, Professional Writers Association of Canada (PWAC), 215 Spadina Ave, Suite 130, Toronto, ON M5T 2C7, Canada *Tel:* 416-504-1645 *E-mail:* info@pwac.ca *Web Site:* pwac.ca; www.writers.ca, pg 617

Creamer, Stacy, Hachette Books, 1290 Avenue of the Americas, New York, NY 10019 *Tel:* 212-364-1100 *Web Site:* www.hachettebookgroup.com, pg 102

Crean, Patrick, HarperCollins Canada Ltd, 2 Bloor St E, 20th fl, Toronto, ON M4W 1A8, Canada *Tel:* 416-975-9334 *Fax:* 416-975-9884 *E-mail:* hcorder@harpercollins.com *Web Site:* www.harpercollins.ca, pg 487

Creehan, Tara, Chronicle Books LLC, 680 Second St, San Francisco, CA 94107 *Tel:* 415-537-4200 *Toll Free Tel:* 800-759-0190 (cust serv) *Fax:* 415-537-4460 *Toll Free Fax:* 800-858-7787 (orders); 800-286-9471 (cust serv) *E-mail:* frontdesk@chroniclebooks.com *Web Site:* www.chroniclebooks.com, pg 58

Crevier, Yvonne, University of Massachusetts Press, East Experiment Sta, 671 N Pleasant St, Amherst, MA 01003 *Tel:* 413-545-2217 *Fax:* 413-545-1226 *E-mail:* info@umpress.umass.edu *Web Site:* www.umass.edu/umpress, pg 257

Crewe, Jennifer, Columbia University Press, 61 W 62 St, New York, NY 10023 *Tel:* 212-459-0600 *Toll Free Tel:* 800-944-8648 *Fax:* 212-459-3678 *E-mail:* cup_book@columbia.edu (orders & cust serv) *Web Site:* cup.columbia.edu, pg 61

Crews, Shaquona, Princeton University Press, 41 William St, Princeton, NJ 08540-5237 *Tel:* 609-258-4900 *Toll Free Tel:* 800-777-4726 (orders) *Fax:* 609-258-6305 *Toll Free Fax:* 800-999-1958 *E-mail:* orders@cpfsinc.com *Web Site:* press.princeton.edu, pg 197

Crichton, Sha-Shana, Crichton & Associates Inc, 6940 Carroll Ave, Takoma Park, MD 20912 *Tel:* 301-495-9663 *E-mail:* cricht1@aol.com *Web Site:* www.crichton-associates.com, pg 547

Criler, Andrew, Christian Light Publications Inc, 1051 Mount Clinton Pike, Harrisonburg, VA 22802 *Tel:* 540-434-1003 *Toll Free Tel:* 800-776-0478 *Fax:* 540-433-8896 *E-mail:* info@clp.org; orders@clp.org *Web Site:* www.clp.org, pg 57

Crilly, Donna, Paulist Press, 997 Macarthur Blvd, Mahwah, NJ 07430-9990 *Tel:* 201-825-7300 *Toll Free Tel:* 800-218-1903 *Fax:* 201-825-8345 *Toll Free Fax:* 800-836-3161 *E-mail:* info@paulistpress.com *Web Site:* www.paulistpress.com, pg 184

Crim, Michele, Crown Publishing Group, c/o Penguin Random House Inc, 1745 Broadway, New York, NY 10019 *Tel:* 212-782-9000 *Toll Free Tel:* 888-264-1745 *Fax:* 212-940-7408 *E-mail:* crownosm@penguinrandomhouse.com *Web Site:* crownpublishing.com, pg 68

Crim, Michele, Ten Speed Press, 2625 Alcatraz Ave, Unit 505, Berkeley, CA 94705 *Tel:* 510-285-3000 *Toll Free Tel:* 800-841-BOOK (841-2665) *E-mail:* csorders@randomhouse.com *Web Site:* crownpublishing.com/imprint/ten-speed-press, pg 243

Crippen, Cynthia, AEIOU Inc, 894 Piermont Ave, Piermont, NY 10968 *Tel:* 845-680-5380, pg 519

Crisp, Laura, Vintage & Anchor Books, c/o Random House Inc, 1745 Broadway, New York, NY 10019 *Tel:* 212-572-2420 *E-mail:* vintageanchorpublicity@randomhouse.com *Web Site:* vintage-anchor.knopfdoubleday.com, pg 266

Crist, Connie, Warner Press, 1201 E Fifth St, Anderson, IN 46018 *Tel:* 765-644-7721 *Toll Free Tel:* 800-741-7721 (orders) *Fax:* 765-640-8005 *Toll Free Fax:* 800-347-6411 *E-mail:* wporders@warnerpress.org *Web Site:* www.warnerpress.org, pg 267

Crist, Steve, AMMO Books LLC, 1313 Foothill Blvd, La Canada, CA 91011 *Tel:* 323-223-AMMO (223-2666) *Fax:* 323-978-4200 *E-mail:* weborders@ammobooks.com; orders@ammobooks.com *Web Site:* ammobooks.com, pg 17

Cristofaro, Joe, Groupe Educalivres Inc, 955, rue Bergar, Laval, QC H7L 4Z6, Canada *Tel:* 514-334-8466 *Toll Free Tel:* 800-567-3671 (info serv) *Fax:* 514-334-8387 *E-mail:* infoservice@grandduc.com *Web Site:* www.educalivres.com, pg 486

Criswell, Andrew Sr, CBA: The Association for Christian Retail, 1365 Garden of the Gods Rd, Suite 105, Colorado Springs, CO 80907 *Tel:* 719-265-9895 *Toll Free Tel:* 800-252-1950 *Fax:* 719-272-3508 *E-mail:* info@cbaonline.org *Web Site:* cbaonline.org, pg 603

Crocco, Kathy, MAR*CO Products Inc, 1443 Old York Rd, Warminster, PA 18974 *Tel:* 215-956-0313 *Toll Free Tel:* 800-448-2197 *Fax:* 215-956-9041 *E-mail:* help@marcoproducts.com *Web Site:* www.marcoproducts.com, pg 147

Croce, Mr Carmen R, St Joseph's University Press, 5600 City Ave, Philadelphia, PA 19131-1395 *Tel:* 610-660-3402 *Fax:* 610-660-3412 *E-mail:* sjupress@sju.edu *Web Site:* www.sjupress.com, pg 214

Crocker, Amanda, Between the Lines (BTL), 401 Richmond St W, No 277, Toronto, ON M5V 3A8, Canada *Tel:* 416-535-9914 *Toll Free Tel:* 800-718-7201 *Fax:* 416-535-1484 *E-mail:* info@btlbooks.com *Web Site:* btlbooks.com, pg 472

Crocker, Harry W III, Regnery Publishing Inc, 300 New Jersey Ave NW, Washington, DC 20001 *Tel:* 202-216-0600 *Toll Free Tel:* 888-219-4747 *Fax:* 202-216-0612 *Web Site:* www.regnery.com, pg 208

Crockett, Barbara, Standard Publishing Corp, 155 Federal St, 13th fl, Boston, MA 02110 *Tel:* 617-457-0600 *Toll Free Tel:* 800-682-5759 *Fax:* 617-457-0608 *Web Site:* www.spcpub.com, pg 233

Croft, Charles R, Kalmbach Publishing Co, 21027 Crossroads Circle, Waukesha, WI 53186 *Tel:* 262-796-8776 *Toll Free Tel:* 800-533-6644 (cust serv & orders) *Fax:* 262-796-1615 (sales & cust serv); 262-798-6468 (edit) *E-mail:* customerservice@kalmbach.com *Web Site:* www.kalmbach.com; www.kalmbachstore.com, pg 129

Croft, Diane, National Braille Press, 88 St Stephen St, Boston, MA 02115-4302 *Tel:* 617-266-6160 *Toll Free Tel:* 800-548-7323 (cust serv); 888-965-8965 *Fax:* 617-437-0456 *E-mail:* orders@nbp.org *Web Site:* www.nbp.org, pg 164

Crone, Jeanie M, EDC Publishing, 10302 E 55 Place, Tulsa, OK 74146-6515 *Tel:* 918-622-4522 *Toll Free Tel:* 800-475-4522 *Fax:* 918-665-7919 *Toll Free Fax:* 800-743-5660 *E-mail:* edc@edcpub.com *Web Site:* www.edcpub.com, pg 79

Cronin, Denise, Random House Publishing Group, 1745 Broadway, New York, NY 10019 *Toll Free Tel:* 800-200-3552 *Web Site:* atrandom.com, pg 204

Cronin, Denise, Viking Children's Books, 345 Hudson St, New York, NY 10014 *Tel:* 212-366-2000 *E-mail:* online@penguinputnam.com *Web Site:* www.penguinputnam.com; us.penguingroup.com, pg 265

Cronin, John, The Johns Hopkins University Press, 2715 N Charles St, Baltimore, MD 21218-4363 *Tel:* 410-516-6900; 410-516-6987 (journal orders outside US & CN) *Toll Free Tel:* 800-537-5487 (book orders & cust serv); 800-548-1784 (journal orders) *Fax:* 410-516-6968; 410-516-3866 (journal orders) *E-mail:* hfscustserv@press.jhu.edu (cust serv); jrnlcirc@press.jhu.edu (journal orders) *Web Site:* www.press.jhu.edu; muse.jhu.edu, pg 127

Cronin, Thomas, St Martin's Press, LLC, 175 Fifth Ave, New York, NY 10010 *Tel:* 646-307-5151 *Fax:* 212-420-9314 *E-mail:* firstname.lastname@macmillan.com *Web Site:* www.stmartins.com, pg 214

Cronk, Kevin, Fox Run Press LLC, 7840 Bullet Rd, Peyton, OH 80831 *Tel:* 719-482-4035 *Fax:* 719-623-0254 *E-mail:* info@foxrunpress.com *Web Site:* www.foxrunpress.com, pg 91

Cronshaw, Francine, East Mountain Editing Services, PO Box 1895, Tijeras, NM 87059-1895 *Tel:* 505-281-8422 *Web Site:* www.spanishindexing.com, pg 525

Cronyn, Melissa, National Park Service Media Services, 67 Mather Place, Harpers Ferry, WV 25425 *Tel:* 304-535-5050 *Fax:* 304-535-6176 *Web Site:* www.nps.gov/hfc, pg 166

Crooks, Cathie, University of Alberta Press, Ring House 2, Edmonton, AB T6G 2E1, Canada *Tel:* 780-492-3662 *Fax:* 780-492-0719 *Web Site:* www.uap.ualberta.ca, pg 502

Crooks, Jaye, University of Baltimore - Yale Gordon College of Arts & Sciences, Ampersand Institute for Words & Images, 1420 N Charles St, Baltimore, MD 21201-5779 *Tel:* 410-837-6022 *Fax:* 410-837-6029 *E-mail:* scd@ubalt.edu *Web Site:* www.ubalt.edu, pg 663

Cropsey, Marvin, Abingdon Press, 201 Eighth Ave S, Nashville, TN 37203-3919 *Tel:* 615-749-6000 (academic books) *Toll Free Tel:* 800-251-3320 *Fax:* 615-749-6056 (academic books) *Toll Free Fax:* 800-836-7802 (orders) *E-mail:* orders@abingdonpress.com *Web Site:* www.abingdonpress.com, pg 2

Crosby, Calvin, Northern California Independent Booksellers Association (NCIBA), The Presidio, 1007 General Kennedy Ave, San Francisco, CA 94129 *Tel:* 415-561-7686 *Fax:* 415-561-7685 *E-mail:* office@nciba.com *Web Site:* www.nciba.com, pg 614

Crosby, Jeff, InterVarsity Press, 430 Plaza Dr, Westmont, IL 60559-1234 *Tel:* 630-734-4000 *Toll Free Tel:* 800-843-9487 *Fax:* 630-734-4200 *E-mail:* email@ivpress.com *Web Site:* www.ivpress.com, pg 125

Crosby, Lori R, Duquesne University Press, 600 Forbes Ave, Pittsburgh, PA 15282 *Tel:* 412-396-6610 *Fax:* 412-396-5984 *E-mail:* dupress@duq.edu *Web Site:* www.dupress.duq.edu, pg 77

Cross, Claudia, Folio Literary Management LLC, The Film Center Bldg, 630 Ninth Ave, Suite 1101, New York, NY 10036 *Tel:* 212-400-1494 *Fax:* 212-967-0977 *Web Site:* www.foliolit.com, pg 552

Cross, Jamie, Math Solutions®, One Harbor Dr, Suite 101, Sausalito, CA 94965 *Tel:* 415-332-4181 *Toll Free Tel:* 800-868-9092 *Fax:* 415-331-1931 *Toll Free Fax:* 877-942-8837 *E-mail:* info@mathsolutions.com; orders@mathsolutions.com *Web Site:* www.mathsolutions.com, pg 149

Cross, John C Esq, Standard Publishing Corp, 155 Federal St, 13th fl, Boston, MA 02110 *Tel:* 617-457-0600 *Toll Free Tel:* 800-682-5759 *Fax:* 617-457-0608 *Web Site:* www.spcpub.com, pg 233

Cross, William K, The Charlton Press, 5845 Yonge St, PO Box 69509, North York, ON M2M 4K3, Canada *Tel:* 416-488-1418 *Toll Free Tel:* 800-442-6042 (North America) *Fax:* 416-488-4656 *Toll Free Fax:* 800-442-1542 (North America) *E-mail:* chpress@charltonpress.com *Web Site:* www.charltonpress.com, pg 476

Crosse, Ann Mehan, Society for Scholarly Publishing (SSP), 10200 W 44 Ave, Suite 304, Wheat Ridge, CO 80033-2840 *Tel:* 303-422-3914 *Fax:* 720-881-6101 *E-mail:* info@sspnet.org *Web Site:* www.sspnet.org, pg 618

Crossley, Guy, M Lee Smith Publishers LLC, 5201 Virginia Way, Brentwood, TN 37027 *Tel:* 615-373-7517 *Toll Free Tel:* 800-274-6774 *Fax:* 615-373-5183 *E-mail:* custserv@mleesmith.com *Web Site:* www.mleesmith.com, pg 228

Croteau, Marie, Wolters Kluwer Ltd, 90 Sheppard Ave E, Suite 300, Toronto, ON M2N 6X1, Canada *Tel:* 416-224-2224 *Toll Free Tel:* 800-268-4522 (CN & US cust serv) *Fax:* 416-224-2243 *Toll Free Fax:* 800-461-4131 *E-mail:* cservice@cch.ca (cust serv) *Web Site:* www.cch.ca, pg 505

Crouch, Anthony, University of California Press, 2120 Berkeley Way, Berkeley, CA 94704-1012 *Tel:* 510-642-4247 *Fax:* 510-643-7127 *E-mail:* askucp@ucpress.edu (books); customerservice@ucpressjournals.com *Web Site:* www.ucpress.edu, pg 255

Crouch, Lori, Education Writers Association (EWA), 3516 Connecticut Ave NW, Washington, DC 20008-2401 *Tel:* 202-452-9830 *Fax:* 202-452-9837 *E-mail:* ewa@ewa.org *Web Site:* www.ewa.org, pg 605

Crouchet, Mike, Cardiotext Publishing, 3405 W 44 St, Minneapolis, MN 55410 *Tel:* 612-925-2053 *Fax:* 612-922-7556 *E-mail:* info@cardiotextpublishing.com *Web Site:* www.cardiotextpublishing.com, pg 50

Crow, Dennis, Maisonneuve Press, 6423 Adelphi Rd, Hyattsville, MD 20782 *Tel:* 301-277-7505 *Fax:* 301-277-2467 *Web Site:* www.maisonneuvepress.com, pg 145

Crowe, Sara, Harvey Klinger Inc, 300 W 55 St, Suite 11V, New York, NY 10019 *Tel:* 212-581-7068 *Fax:* 212-315-3823 *E-mail:* queries@harveyklinger.com *Web Site:* www.harveyklinger.com, pg 560

Crowley, James M, Society for Industrial & Applied Mathematics, 3600 Market St, 6th fl, Philadelphia, PA 19104-2688 *Tel:* 215-382-9800 *Toll Free Tel:* 800-447-7426 *Fax:* 215-386-7999 *E-mail:* siambooks@siam.org *Web Site:* www.siam.org, pg 228

Crowley, Louise, Vermont College of Fine Arts, MFA in Writing Program, 36 College St, Montpelier, VT 05602 *Tel:* 802-828-8840; 802-828-8839 *Toll Free Tel:* 866-934-VCFA (934-8232) *Fax:* 802-828-8649 *Web Site:* www.vcfa.edu, pg 664

Crowther, Duane S, Horizon Publishers & Distributors Inc, 191 N 650 E, Bountiful, UT 84010-3628 *Tel:* 801-292-7102 *E-mail:* ldshorizonpublishers1@gmail.com *Web Site:* www.ldshorizonpublishers.com, pg 114

Crowther, Jean D, Horizon Publishers & Distributors Inc, 191 N 650 E, Bountiful, UT 84010-3628 *Tel:* 801-292-7102 *E-mail:* ldshorizonpublishers1@gmail.com *Web Site:* www.ldshorizonpublishers.com, pg 114

Crum, Erin, HarperCollins Publishers, 195 Broadway, New York, NY 10007 *Tel:* 212-207-7000 *Fax:* 212-207-7145 *Web Site:* www.harpercollins.com, pg 106

Crumly, Chuck, University of California Press, 2120 Berkeley Way, Berkeley, CA 94704-1012 *Tel:* 510-642-4247 *Fax:* 510-643-7127 *E-mail:* askucp@ucpress.edu (books); customerservice@ucpressjournals.com *Web Site:* www.ucpress.edu, pg 255

Crumpacker, Caroline, Residency, 454 E Hill Rd, Austerlitz, NY 12017 *Tel:* 518-392-3103; 518-392-4144 *E-mail:* apply@millaycolony.org *Web Site:* www.millaycolony.org, pg 723

Cruz, Ricky, US Games Systems Inc, 179 Ludlow St, Stamford, CT 06902 *Tel:* 203-353-8400 *Toll Free Tel:* 800-54-GAMES (544-2637) *Fax:* 203-353-8431 *E-mail:* info@usgamesinc.com *Web Site:* www.usgamesinc.com, pg 264

Cryer, Bruce, HeartMath LLC, 14700 W Park Ave, Boulder Creek, CA 95006 *Tel:* 831-338-8700 *Toll Free Tel:* 800-450-9111 *Fax:* 831-338-9861 *E-mail:* inquiry@heartmath.com *Web Site:* www.heartmath.com, pg 109

Cubberley, William, Practising Law Institute, 1177 Avenue of the Americas, New York, NY 10036 *Tel:* 212-824-5700 *Toll Free Tel:* 800-260-4PLI (260-4754, cust serv) *Fax:* 212-265-4742 (intl) *Toll Free Fax:* 800-321-0093 (local) *E-mail:* info@pli.edu (cust serv) *Web Site:* www.pli.edu, pg 195

Cull, Mark E, Red Hen Press, PO Box 40820, Pasadena, CA 91114 *Tel:* 626-356-4760 *Fax:* 626-356-9974 *Web Site:* www.redhen.org, pg 206

Cullen, Dan, American Booksellers Association, 333 Westchester Ave, Suite S202, White Plains, NY 10604 *Tel:* 914-406-7500 *Toll Free Tel:* 800-637-0037 *Fax:* 914-410-6297 *E-mail:* info@bookweb.org *Web Site:* www.bookweb.org, pg 594

Cullen, Darcy, University of British Columbia Press, 2029 West Mall, Vancouver, BC V6T 1Z2, Canada *Tel:* 604-822-5959 *Toll Free Tel:* 877-377-9378 *Fax:* 604-822-6083 *Toll Free Fax:* 800-668-0821 *E-mail:* frontdesk@ubcpress.ca *Web Site:* www.ubcpress.ca, pg 502

Culliford, Craig, Crabtree Publishing Co, 350 Fifth Ave, 59th fl, PMB 59051, New York, NY 10118 *Tel:* 212-496-5040 *Toll Free Tel:* 800-387-7650 *Toll Free Fax:* 800-355-7166 *E-mail:* custserv@crabtreebooks.com *Web Site:* www.crabtreebooks.com, pg 66

Culliford, Craig, Crabtree Publishing Co Ltd, 616 Welland Ave, St Catharines, ON L2M-5V6, Canada *Tel:* 905-682-5221 *Toll Free Tel:* 800-387-7650 *Fax:* 905-682-7166 *Toll Free Fax:* 800-355-7166 *E-mail:* custserv@crabtreebooks.com; sales@crabtreebooks.com; orders@crabtreebooks.com *Web Site:* www.crabtreebooks.com, pg 478

Cullinane, Mary, Houghton Mifflin Harcourt, 222 Berkeley St, Boston, MA 02116 *Tel:* 617-351-5000 *Toll Free Tel:* 800-225-5425 (K-12 educ materials); 800-323-9540 (assessment materials); 877-219-1537 (SkillsTutor); 888-242-6747 (Destination; Earobics; Edmark; Learning Village; Riverdeep); 800-225-3362 (Houghton Mifflin Harcourt Trade & Reference Publishers) *Toll Free Fax:* 800-269-5232 *E-mail:* customerservice@hmhpub.com *Web Site:* www.hmhco.com, pg 115

Cully, Christine French, Highlights for Children, 1800 Watermark Dr, Columbus, OH 43215 *Tel:* 614-486-0631 *Toll Free Tel:* 800-962-3661 (Highlights Club cust serv); 800-255-9517 (Highlights Magazine cust serv) *Web Site:* www.highlights.com, pg 111

Cully, Lynn, Kensington Publishing Corp, 119 W 40 St, New York, NY 10018 *Tel:* 212-407-1500 *Toll Free Tel:* 800-221-2647 *Fax:* 212-935-0699 *Web Site:* www.kensingtonbooks.com, pg 130

Culp, Rick, Pearson School, 225 River St, Hoboken, NJ 07030-4772 *Tel:* 201-236-7000 *Web Site:* www.pearsonschool.com, pg 185

Cumberland, Brian, Faith Library Publications, PO Box 50126, Tulsa, OK 74150-0126 *Tel:* 918-258-1588 (ext 2218) *Toll Free Tel:* 888-258-0999 (orders) *Fax:* 918-872-7710 (orders) *E-mail:* flp@rhema.org *Web Site:* www.rhema.org/store, pg 86

Cummings, Mary, Betsy Amster Literary Enterprises, 6312 SW Capitol Hwy, No 503, Portland, OR 97239 *Tel:* 503-496-4007 *E-mail:* rights@amsterlit.com (rts inquiries); b.amster.assistant@gmail.com (adult book queries); b.amster.kidsbooks@gmail.com (children & young adult book queries) *Web Site:* www.amsterlit.com, pg 540

Cummings, Mary, Diversion Books, 443 Park Ave S, Suite 1008, New York, NY 10016 *Tel:* 212-961-6390 *E-mail:* info@diversionbooks.com *Web Site:* www.diversionbooks.com, pg 74

Cummings, Pat, The Authors League Fund, 31 E 32 St, 7th fl, New York, NY 10016 *Tel:* 212-268-1208 *Fax:* 212-564-5363 *E-mail:* staff@authorsleaguefund.org *Web Site:* www.authorsleaguefund.org, pg 599

Cunningham, Emily, The Penguin Press, 375 Hudson St, New York, NY 10014, pg 187

Cunningham, Kay, Psychological Assessment Resources Inc (PAR), 16204 N Florida Ave, Lutz, FL 33549 *Tel:* 813-968-3003; 813-449-4065 *Toll Free Tel:* 800-331-8378 *Fax:* 813-968-2598; 813-961-2196 *Toll Free Fax:* 800-727-9329 *E-mail:* custsup@parinc.com *Web Site:* www4.parinc.com, pg 199

Cunningham, Michael, Health Administration Press, One N Franklin St, Suite 1700, Chicago, IL 60606-3491 *Tel:* 312-424-2800 *Fax:* 312-424-0014 *E-mail:* hap1@ache.org *Web Site:* www.ache.org/publications (orders), pg 108

Cunningham, Tammy, LearningExpress LLC, 2 Rector St, 26th fl, New York, NY 10006 *Tel:* 212-995-2566 *Toll Free Tel:* 800-295-9556 (ext 2) *Fax:* 212-995-5512 *E-mail:* customerservice@learningexpressllc.com (cust serv) *Web Site:* www.learningexpressllc.com, pg 136

Cuocci, Kerri, Sterling Publishing Co Inc, 1166 Avenue of the Americas, 17th fl, New York, NY 10036 *Tel:* 212-532-7160 *Toll Free Tel:* 800-367-9692 *Fax:* 212-213-2495 *Web Site:* www.sterlingpublishing.com, pg 235

Curr, Judith, Atria Books, 1230 Avenue of the Americas, New York, NY 10020 *Tel:* 212-698-7000 *Fax:* 212-698-7007 *Web Site:* www.simonandschuster.com, pg 26

Curr, Judith, Simon & Schuster, Inc, 1230 Avenue of the Americas, New York, NY 10020 *Tel:* 212-698-7000 *Fax:* 212-698-7007 *E-mail:* firstname.lastname@simonandschuster.com *Web Site:* www.simonandschuster.com, pg 226

Curran, Katherine, American Diabetes Association, 1701 N Beauregard St, Alexandria, VA 22311 *Toll Free Tel:* 800-342-2383 *E-mail:* booksinfo@diabetes.org *Web Site:* www.diabetes.org, pg 12

Curran, Randall, The Reader's Digest Association Inc, 750 Third Ave, New York, NY 10017 *Tel:* 914-238-1000; 646-293-6284 *Toll Free Tel:* 800-310-6261 (cust serv) *Fax:* 914-238-4559 *Web Site:* www.rd.com; www.rda.com, pg 205

Currans-Sheehan, Tricia, The Briar Cliff Review Fiction, Poetry & Creative Nonfiction Contest, 3303 Rebecca St, Sioux City, IA 51104-2100 *Tel:* 712-279-1651 *Fax:* 712-279-5486 *Web Site:* www.briarcliff.edu/bcreview, pg 674

Curren, Vincent, Corporation for Public Broadcasting (CPB), 401 Ninth St NW, Washington, DC 20004-2129 *Tel:* 202-879-9600 *Web Site:* www.cpb.org, pg 604

Curry, Brendan, W W Norton & Company Inc, 500 Fifth Ave, New York, NY 10110-0017 *Tel:* 212-354-5500 *Toll Free Tel:* 800-233-4830 (orders & cust serv) *Fax:* 212-869-0856 *Toll Free Fax:* 800-458-6515 *Web Site:* www.wwnorton.com, pg 172

Curry, C, Golden Meteorite Press, 11919 82 St NW, Suite 103, Edmonton, AB T5B 2W4, Canada *Tel:* 780-378-0063 *Fax:* 780-378-0063, pg 485

Curry, Michael, Donald Maass Literary Agency, 121 W 27 St, Suite 801, New York, NY 10001 *Tel:* 212-727-8383 *Fax:* 212-727-3271 *E-mail:* info@maassagency.com *Web Site:* www.maassagency.com, pg 562

Curtin, Thomas, Waveland Press Inc, 4180 IL Rte 83, Suite 101, Long Grove, IL 60047-9580 *Tel:* 847-634-0081 *Fax:* 847-634-9501 *E-mail:* info@waveland.com *Web Site:* www.waveland.com, pg 268

Curtis, Anthony, Huntington Press Publishing, 3665 Procyon St, Las Vegas, NV 89103-1907 *Tel:* 702-252-0655 *Toll Free Tel:* 800-244-2224 *Fax:* 702-252-0675 *E-mail:* sales@huntingtonpress.com *Web Site:* www.huntingtonpress.com, pg 117

Curtis, Carolyn, Pacific Press Publishing Association, 1350 N Kings Rd, Nampa, ID 83687-3193 *Tel:* 208-465-2500 *Toll Free Tel:* 800-447-7377 *Fax:* 208-465-2531 *Web Site:* www.pacificpress.com, pg 180

Curtis, Mary E, Transaction Publishers Inc, 10 Corporate Place S, 35 Berrue Circle, Piscataway, NJ 08854 *Tel:* 732-445-2280; 732-445-1245 (orders) *Toll Free Tel:* 888-999-6778 (dist ctr) *Fax:* 732-445-3138 *E-mail:* trans@transactionpub.com; orders@transactionpub.om *Web Site:* www.transactionpub.com, pg 248

Curtis, Nancy, High Plains Press, PO Box 123, Glendo, WY 82213 *Toll Free Tel:* 800-552-7819 *Fax:* 307-735-4590 *E-mail:* editor@highplainspress.com *Web Site:* highplainspress.com, pg 111

Curtis, Richard, Richard Curtis Associates Inc, 171 E 74 St, 2nd fl, New York, NY 10021 *Tel:* 212-772-7363 *Fax:* 212-772-7393 *Web Site:* www.curtisagency.com, pg 547

Curtis, William F PhD, Springer, 233 Spring St, New York, NY 10013-1578 *Tel:* 212-460-1500 *Toll Free Tel:* 800-SPRINGER (777-4643) *Fax:* 212-460-1575 *E-mail:* service-ny@springer.com *Web Site:* www.springer.com, pg 232

Cusack, John, St Martin's Press, LLC, 175 Fifth Ave, New York, NY 10010 *Tel:* 646-307-5151 *Fax:* 212-420-9314 *E-mail:* firstname.lastname@macmillan.com *Web Site:* www.stmartins.com, pg 214

Cusack, Leigh Ann, Greenhaven Press®, 27500 Drake Rd, Farmington Hills, MI 48331 *Toll Free Tel:* 800-877-GALE (877-4253 - cust serv & orders) *Toll Free Fax:* 800-414-5043 (orders only) *E-mail:* gale.customerservice@cengage.com; gale.galeord@cengage.com *Web Site:* www.gale.cengage.com/greenhaven, pg 100

Cussen, David M, Pineapple Press Inc, PO Box 3889, Sarasota, FL 34230-3889 *Tel:* 941-706-2507 *Toll Free Tel:* 866-766-3850 (orders) *Fax:* 941-706-2509 *Toll Free Fax:* 800-838-1149 (orders) *E-mail:* info@pineapplepress.com; customer.service@ingrampublisherservices.com *Web Site:* www.pineapplepress.com, pg 192

Cussen, June, Pineapple Press Inc, PO Box 3889, Sarasota, FL 34230-3889 *Tel:* 941-706-2507 *Toll Free Tel:* 866-766-3850 (orders) *Fax:* 941-706-2509 *Toll Free Fax:* 800-838-1149 (orders) *E-mail:* info@pineapplepress.com; customer.service@ingrampublisherservices.com *Web Site:* www.pineapplepress.com, pg 192

Cutler, Jean, Pennsylvania Historical & Museum Commission, Commonwealth Keystone Bldg, 400 North St, Harrisburg, PA 17120-0053 *Tel:* 717-783-2618 *Toll Free Tel:* 800-747-7790 *Fax:* 717-787-8312 *E-mail:* ra-pabookstore@state.pa.us *Web Site:* www.pabookstore.com; www.phmc.state.pa.us, pg 188

Cutler, Thomas, Naval Institute Press, 291 Wood Rd, Annapolis, MD 21402-5034 *Tel:* 410-268-6110 *Toll Free Tel:* 800-233-8764 *Fax:* 410-295-1084; 410-571-1703 (cust serv) *E-mail:* webmaster@navalinstitute.org; customer@navalinstitute.org (cust serv); trade@usni.org *Web Site:* www.nip.org; www.usni.org, pg 166

Cywinski, David, Hal Leonard Corp, 7777 W Bluemound Rd, Milwaukee, WI 53213 *Tel:* 414-774-3630 *Toll Free Tel:* 800-524-4425 *Fax:* 414-774-3259 *E-mail:* halinfo@halleonard.com *Web Site:* www.halleonard.com, pg 103

Czik, Alex, Crown Publishing Group, c/o Penguin Random House Inc, 1745 Broadway, New York, NY 10019 *Tel:* 212-782-9000 *Toll Free Tel:* 888-264-1745 *Fax:* 212-940-7408 *E-mail:* crownosm@penguinrandomhouse.com *Web Site:* crownpublishing.com, pg 68

D'Acierno, Amanda, Books on Tape®, 1745 Broadway, New York, NY 10019 *Toll Free Tel:* 800-733-3000 (cust serv) *Toll Free Fax:* 800-940-7046 *Web Site:* www.booksontape.com, pg 43

D'Acierno, Amanda, Fodor's Travel Publications, 1745 Broadway, 15th fl, New York, NY 10019 *Toll Free Tel:* 800-733-3000 *E-mail:* fodorspublicity@randomhouse.com; editors@fodors.com *Web Site:* www.fodors.com, pg 90

D'Acierno, Amanda, Living Language, c/o Random House Inc, 1745 Broadway, New York, NY 10019 *Tel:* 212-782-9000 *Toll Free Tel:* 800-733-3000 (orders) *Toll Free Fax:* 800-659-2436 *E-mail:* livinglanguage@randomhouse.com *Web Site:* www.livinglanguage.com, pg 142

D'Acierno, Amanda, Penguin Random House Audio, 1745 Broadway, New York, NY 10019 *E-mail:* audio@randomhouse.com *Web Site:* www.randomhouse.com/audio, pg 187

D'Acierno, Amanda, Random House Reference/Random House Puzzles & Games/House of Collectibles, 1745 Broadway, New York, NY 10019 *Toll Free Tel:* 800-733-3000 *Toll Free Fax:* 800-659-2436 *E-mail:* words@random.com; puzzles@random.com, pg 204

D'Agnes, Glenn, Workman Publishing Co Inc, 225 Varick St, 9th fl, New York, NY 10014-4381 *Tel:* 212-254-5900 *Toll Free Tel:* 800-722-7202 *Fax:* 212-254-8098 *E-mail:* info@workman.com *Web Site:* www.workman.com, pg 275

D'Amato, Sally-Ann, Society of Motion Picture & Television Engineers® (SMPTE®), 3 Barker Ave, 5th fl, White Plains, NY 10601 *Tel:* 914-761-1100 *Fax:* 914-761-3115 *Web Site:* www.smpte.org, pg 619

D'Ambrosi, Dean, Epicomm, 1800 Diagonal Rd, Suite 320, Alexandria, VA 22314-2862 *Tel:* 703-836-9200 *E-mail:* webmaster@epicomm.org *Web Site:* epicomm.org, pg 605

D'Andrea, Deborah, Playhouse Publishing, PO Box 1962, Cleveland, OH 44106 *Tel:* 330-926-1313 *Fax:* 330-475-8579 *E-mail:* info@picturemepress.com *Web Site:* www.picturemepress.com, pg 193

d'Arbonne, Jessica, University Press of Colorado, 5589 Arapahoe Ave, Suite 206-C, Boulder, CO 80303 *Tel:* 720-406-8849 *Toll Free Tel:* 800-621-2736 (orders) *Fax:* 720-406-3443 *Web Site:* www.upcolorado.com, pg 261

D'Auria, Don, Samhain Publishing Ltd, 11821 Mason Montgomery Rd, Suite 4-B, Cincinnati, OH 45249 *Tel:* 513-453-4688 *Fax:* 513-583-0191 *E-mail:* support@samhainpublishing.com *Web Site:* www.samhainpublishing.com, pg 216

D'Auria, Heather, Yale University Press, 302 Temple St, New Haven, CT 06511-8909 *Tel:* 203-432-0960; 203-432-0966 (sales); 401-531-2800 (cust serv) *Toll Free Tel:* 800-405-1619 (cust serv) *Fax:* 203-432-0948; 203-432-8485 (sales); 401-531-2801 (cust serv) *Toll Free Fax:* 800-406-9145 (cust serv) *E-mail:* sales.press@yale.edu (sales); customer.care@trilateral.org (cust serv) *Web Site:* www.yalebooks.com; yalepress.yale.edu/yupbooks, pg 278

D'Erasmo, Stacey, Columbia University School of the Arts, Creative Writing Program, 617 Kent Hall, New York, NY 10027 *Tel:* 212-854-3774 *Fax:* 212-854-7704 *E-mail:* writingprogram@columbia.edu *Web Site:* www.columbia.edu/cu/writing, pg 659

D'Esmond, Kate, HarperCollins Publishers, 195 Broadway, New York, NY 10007 *Tel:* 212-207-7000 *Fax:* 212-207-7145 *Web Site:* www.harpercollins.com, pg 106

d'Urso, Gilberto, Mountain n' Air Books, 2947-A Honolulu Ave, La Crescenta, CA 91214 *Tel:* 818-248-9345 *Toll Free Tel:* 800-446-9696 *Toll Free Fax:* 800-303-5578 *Web Site:* www.mountain-n-air.com, pg 160

d'Urso, Mary K, Mountain n' Air Books, 2947-A Honolulu Ave, La Crescenta, CA 91214 *Tel:* 818-248-9345 *Toll Free Tel:* 800-446-9696 *Toll Free Fax:* 800-303-5578 *Web Site:* www.mountain-n-air.com, pg 160

DaCunha, Joanne, F A Davis Co, 1915 Arch St, Philadelphia, PA 19103 *Tel:* 215-568-2270; 215-440-3001 *Toll Free Tel:* 800-523-4049 *Fax:* 215-568-5065; 215-440-3016 *E-mail:* info@fadavis.com; orders@fadavis.com *Web Site:* www.fadavis.com, pg 71

Dadah, Jordan, Wildflower Press, Oakbrook Press, 3301 S Valley Dr, Rapid City, SD 57703 *Tel:* 605-381-6385 *Fax:* 605-343-8733 *E-mail:* info@wildflowerpress.org; bookorder@wildflowerpress.org *Web Site:* www.wildflowerpress.org, pg 271

Dages, Emmett, CRC Press LLC, 6000 Broken Sound Pkwy NW, Suite 300, Boca Raton, FL 33487 *Tel:* 561-994-0555 *Toll Free Tel:* 800-272-7737 (orders) *Toll Free Fax:* 800-643-9428 (sales); 800-374-3401 (orders) *E-mail:* orders@crcpress.com; orders@taylorandfrancis.com *Web Site:* www.crcpress.com, pg 66

Dages, Emmett, Garland Science Publishing, 711 Third Ave, 8th fl, New York, NY 10017 *Tel:* 212-216-7800; 212-281-4487 *Fax:* 212-947-3027 *E-mail:* science@garland.com *Web Site:* www.garlandscience.com, pg 95

Daghesty, Amany El-Ameera, Leilah Publications, 510 E University Dr, No 3413, Tempe, AZ 85281 *Tel:* 847-275-1657 *E-mail:* leilah@leilahpublications.com *Web Site:* facebook.com/leilahpublications, pg 137

Dahl, Brad, Brilliance Audio, 1704 Eaton Dr, Grand Haven, MI 49417 *Tel:* 616-846-5256 *Toll Free Tel:* 800-648-2312 (orders only) *Fax:* 616-846-0630 *E-mail:* customerservice@brillianceaudio.com *Web Site:* www.brillianceaudio.com, pg 46

Dahl, Corey, Royal Ontario Museum Press, 100 Queen's Park, Toronto, ON M5S 2C6, Canada *Tel:* 416-586-8000 *Fax:* 416-586-5642 *E-mail:* info@rom.on.ca *Web Site:* www.rom.on.ca, pg 497

Dahl, Kristine, ICM Partners, 730 Fifth Ave, New York, NY 10019 *Tel:* 212-556-5600 *Web Site:* www.icmtalent.com, pg 557

Dahlgren, Kari, University of California Press, 2120 Berkeley Way, Berkeley, CA 94704-1012 *Tel:* 510-642-4247 *Fax:* 510-643-7127 *E-mail:* askucp@ucpress.edu (books); customerservice@ucpressjournals.com *Web Site:* www.ucpress.edu, pg 255

Dailey, Pam, Bucknell University Press, 6 Taylor Hall, Bucknell University, Lewisburg, PA 17837 *Tel:* 570-577-3674 *E-mail:* universitypress@bucknell.edu *Web Site:* www.bucknell.edu/universitypress, pg 47

Daillak, Jonathan, The Gerald Loeb Awards, Gold Hall, Suite B-305, 110 Westwood Plaza, Los Angeles, CA 90095-1481 *Tel:* 310-825-4478 *Fax:* 310-825-4479 *E-mail:* loeb@anderson.ucla.edu *Web Site:* www.loeb.anderson.ucla.edu, pg 702

Daily, Peggy, A Westport Wordsmith, 101 Winfield St, Norwalk, CT 06855 *Tel:* 203-939-9484 *E-mail:* pj104daily@aol.com, pg 519

Dajani, Virginia, Arts & Letters Awards, 633 W 155 St, New York, NY 10032 *Tel:* 212-368-5900 *Fax:* 212-491-4615 *E-mail:* academy@artsandletters.org *Web Site:* www.artsandletters.org, pg 668

Dajani, Virginia, Award of Merit, 633 W 155 St, New York, NY 10032 *Tel:* 212-368-5900 *Fax:* 212-491-4615 *E-mail:* academy@artsandletters.org *Web Site:* www.artsandletters.org, pg 669

Dajani, Virginia, Michael Braude Award, 633 W 155 St, New York, NY 10032 *Tel:* 212-368-5900 *Fax:* 212-491-4615 *E-mail:* academy@artsandletters.org *Web Site:* www.artsandletters.org, pg 674

Dajani, Virginia, Benjamin H Danks Award, 633 W 155 St, New York, NY 10032 *Tel:* 212-368-5900 *Fax:* 212-491-4615 *E-mail:* academy@artsandletters.org *Web Site:* www.artsandletters.org, pg 680

Dajani, Virginia, Blake Dodd Prize, 633 W 155 St, New York, NY 10032 *Tel:* 212-368-5900 *Fax:* 212-491-4615 *E-mail:* academy@artsandletters.org *Web Site:* www.artsandletters.org, pg 681

Dajani, Virginia, E M Forster Award, 633 W 155 St, New York, NY 10032 *Tel:* 212-368-5900 *Fax:* 212-491-4615 *E-mail:* academy@artsandletters.org *Web Site:* www.artsandletters.org, pg 687

Dajani, Virginia, Gold Medal, 633 W 155 St, New York, NY 10032 *Tel:* 212-368-5900 *Fax:* 212-491-4615 *E-mail:* academy@artsandletters.org *Web Site:* www.artsandletters.org, pg 689

Dajani, Virginia, The William Dean Howells Medal, 633 W 155 St, New York, NY 10032 *Tel:* 212-368-5900 *Fax:* 212-491-4615 *E-mail:* academy@artsandletters.org *Web Site:* www.artsandletters.org, pg 693

Dajani, Virginia, Sue Kaufman Prize for First Fiction, 633 W 155 St, New York, NY 10032 *Tel:* 212-368-5900 *Fax:* 212-491-4615 *E-mail:* academy@artsandletters.org *Web Site:* www.artsandletters.org, pg 697

Dajani, Virginia, Addison M Metcalf Award in Literature, 633 W 155 St, New York, NY 10032 *Tel:* 212-368-5900 *Fax:* 212-491-4615 *E-mail:* academy@artsandletters.org *Web Site:* www.artsandletters.org, pg 707

Dajani, Virginia, Katherine Anne Porter Award, 633 W 155 St, New York, NY 10032 *Tel:* 212-368-5900 *Fax:* 212-491-4615 *E-mail:* academy@artsandletters.org *Web Site:* www.artsandletters.org, pg 720

Dajani, Virginia, Arthur Rense Prize, 633 W 155 St, New York, NY 10032 *Tel:* 212-368-5900 *Fax:* 212-491-4615 *E-mail:* academy@artsandletters.org *Web Site:* www.artsandletters.org, pg 723

Dajani, Virginia, Rosenthal Family Foundation Awards, 633 W 155 St, New York, NY 10032 *Tel:* 212-368-5900 *Fax:* 212-491-4615 *E-mail:* academy@artsandletters.org *Web Site:* www.artsandletters.org, pg 725

Dajani, Virginia, John Updike Award, 633 W 155 St, New York, NY 10032 *Tel:* 212-368-5900 *Fax:* 212-491-4615 *E-mail:* academy@artsandletters.org *Web Site:* www.artsandletters.org, pg 733

Dajani, Virginia, Harold D Vursell Memorial Award, 633 W 155 St, New York, NY 10032 *Tel:* 212-368-5900 *Fax:* 212-491-4615 *E-mail:* academy@artsandletters.org *Web Site:* www.artsandletters.org, pg 734

Dajani, Virginia, E B White Award, 633 W 155 St, New York, NY 10032 *Tel:* 212-368-5900 *Fax:* 212-491-4615 *E-mail:* academy@artsandletters.org *Web Site:* www.artsandletters.org, pg 735

Dajani, Virginia, Thornton Wilder Prize for Translation, 633 W 155 St, New York, NY 10032 *Tel:* 212-368-5900 *Fax:* 212-491-4615 *E-mail:* academy@artsandletters.org *Web Site:* www.artsandletters.org, pg 736

Dajani, Virginia, Morton Dauwen Zabel Award, 633 W 155 St, New York, NY 10032 *Tel:* 212-368-5900 *Fax:* 212-491-4615 *E-mail:* academy@artsandletters.org *Web Site:* www.artsandletters.org, pg 739

Dalbotten, Albee, Chronicle Books LLC, 680 Second St, San Francisco, CA 94107 *Tel:* 415-537-4200 *Toll Free Tel:* 800-759-0190 (cust serv) *Fax:* 415-537-4460 *Toll Free Fax:* 800-858-7787 (orders); 800-286-9471 (cust serv) *E-mail:* frontdesk@chroniclebooks.com *Web Site:* www.chroniclebooks.com, pg 58

Daley, Patrick, Scholastic Education, 524 Broadway, New York, NY 10012 *Tel:* 212-343-6100 *Fax:* 212-343-6189 *Web Site:* www.scholastic.com, pg 218

Dallaire, Michel, La Fondation Emile Nelligan, 100, rue Sherbrooke, Montreal, QC H2X 1C3, Canada *Tel:* 514-278-4657 *Fax:* 514-278-1943 *E-mail:* info@fondation-nelligan.org *Web Site:* www.fondation-nelligan.org, pg 606

Dallaire, Michel, Prix Emile-Nelligan, 100, rue Sherbrooke, Montreal, QC H2X 1C3, Canada *Tel:* 514-278-4657 *Toll Free Tel:* 888-849-8540 *Fax:* 514-278-1943 *E-mail:* info@fondation-nelligan.org *Web Site:* www.fondation-nelligan.org, pg 722

Dallanegra-Sanger, Joy, American Booksellers Association, 333 Westchester Ave, Suite S202, White Plains, NY 10604 *Tel:* 914-406-7500 *Toll Free Tel:* 800-637-0037 *Fax:* 914-410-6297 *E-mail:* info@bookweb.org *Web Site:* www.bookweb.org, pg 594

Dalton, Heather, Living Language, c/o Random House Inc, 1745 Broadway, New York, NY 10019 *Tel:* 212-782-9000 *Toll Free Tel:* 800-733-3000 (orders) *Toll Free Fax:* 800-659-2436 *E-mail:* livinglanguage@randomhouse.com *Web Site:* www.livinglanguage.com, pg 142

Dalton, Heather, Penguin Random House Audio, 1745 Broadway, New York, NY 10019 *E-mail:* audio@randomhouse.com *Web Site:* www.randomhouse.com/audio, pg 187

Daly, Emma, Human Rights Watch, 350 Fifth Ave, 34th fl, New York, NY 10118-3299 *Tel:* 212-290-4700 *Fax:* 212-736-1300 *E-mail:* hrwnyc@hrw.org *Web Site:* www.hrw.org, pg 117

Daly, Frank W, H W Wilson, 2 University Plaza, Suite 310, Hackensack, NJ 07601 *Tel:* 201-968-0500 *Toll Free Tel:* 800-221-1592 *Fax:* 201-968-0511 *E-mail:* info@hwwilsoninprint.com; csr@hwwilsoninprint.com; information@ebscohost.com *Web Site:* www.hwwilsoninprint.com; www.ebscohost.com/wilson, pg 273

Daly, Michelle, Thistledown Press, 410 Second Ave, Saskatoon, SK S7N 2C3, Canada *Tel:* 306-244-1722 *Fax:* 306-244-1762 *E-mail:* tdpress@thistledownpress.com; editorial@thistledownpress.com; marketing@thistledownpress.com *Web Site:* www.thistledownpress.com, pg 500

Daly, Patrick, Banner of Truth, 63 E Louther St, Carlisle, PA 17013 *Tel:* 717-249-5747 *Toll Free Tel:* 800-263-8085 (orders) *Fax:* 717-249-0604 *E-mail:* info@banneroftruth.org *Web Site:* www.banneroftruth.co.uk; www.banneroftruth.org, pg 30

Daly, Peter H, Naval Institute Press, 291 Wood Rd, Annapolis, MD 21402-5034 *Tel:* 410-268-6110 *Toll Free Tel:* 800-233-8764 *Fax:* 410-295-1084; 410-571-1703 (cust serv) *E-mail:* webmaster@navalinstitute.org; customer@navalinstitute.org (cust serv); trade@usni.org *Web Site:* www.nip.org; www.usni.org, pg 166

Damiani, Prof Bruno M, Scripta Humanistica Publishing International, 1383 Kersey Lane, Potomac, MD 20854 *Tel:* 301-294-7949 *Fax:* 301-424-9584 *E-mail:* info@scriptahumanistica.com *Web Site:* www.scriptahumanistica.com, pg 220

Damp, Dennis V, Bookhaven Press LLC, 302 Scenic Ct, Moon Township, PA 15108 *Tel:* 412-494-6926 *E-mail:* info@bookhavenpress.com; orders@bookhavenpress.com *Web Site:* bookhavenpress.com, pg 42

Danaczko, Melissa Ann, Doubleday/Nan A Talese, c/o Penguin Random House Inc, 1745 Broadway, New York, NY 10019 *Tel:* 212-751-2600 *Fax:* 212-572-2662 *E-mail:* ddaypub@randomhouse.com *Web Site:* knopfdoubleday.com, pg 76

Danahy, Kevin, Artech House Inc, 685 Canton St, Norwood, MA 02062 *Tel:* 781-769-9750 *Toll Free Tel:* 800-225-9977 *Fax:* 781-769-6334 *E-mail:* artech@artechhouse.com *Web Site:* www.artechhouse.com, pg 23

Dane, Steve, Brill Inc, 2 Liberty Sq, 11th fl, Boston, MA 02109 *Tel:* 617-263-2323 *Toll Free Tel:* 800-962-4406 *Fax:* 617-263-2324 *E-mail:* cs@brillusa.com *Web Site:* www.brill.com, pg 46

Daneman, Kathy, Community of Literary Magazines & Presses (CLMP), 154 Christopher St, Suite 3C, New York, NY 10014-9110 *Tel:* 212-741-9110 *Fax:* 212-741-9112 *E-mail:* info@clmp.org *Web Site:* www.clmp.org, pg 603

Daneman, Kathy, Firecracker Awards, 154 Christopher St, Suite 3C, New York, NY 10014-9110 *Tel:* 212-741-9110 *Fax:* 212-741-9112 *E-mail:* info@clmp.org *Web Site:* www.clmp.org/firecracker, pg 686

Danforth, Randi, Cotsen Institute of Archaeology Press, 308 Charles E Young Dr N, Fowler A163, Box 951510, Los Angeles, CA 90024 *Tel:* 310-206-9384 *Fax:* 310-206-4723 *E-mail:* ioapubs@ioa.ucla.edu *Web Site:* www.ioa.ucla.edu, pg 64

Danforth, Scott, University of Tennessee Press, 110 Conference Center Bldg, 600 Henley St, Knoxville, TN 37996-4108 *Tel:* 865-974-3321 *Toll Free Tel:* 800-621-2736 (orders) *Fax:* 865-974-3724 *Toll Free Fax:* 800-621-8476 (orders) *E-mail:* custserv@utpress.org *Web Site:* www.utpress.org, pg 260

Dang, Mei, DC Canada Education Publishing (DCCED), 180 Metcalfe St, Suite 204, Ottawa, ON K2P 1P5, Canada *Tel:* 613-565-8885 *Toll Free Tel:* 888-565-0262 *Fax:* 613-565-8881 *E-mail:* info@dc-canada.ca *Web Site:* www.dc-canada.ca, pg 478

Daniel, Annie, Paradigm Publishers, 5589 Arapahoe Ave, Suite 206A, Boulder, CO 80303 *Tel:* 303-245-9054 *Web Site:* www.paradigmpublishers.com, pg 182

Daniel, John, John Daniel & Co, PO Box 2790, McKinleyville, CA 95519-2790 *Tel:* 707-839-3495 *Toll Free Tel:* 800-662-8351 *Fax:* 707-839-3242 *E-mail:* dandd@danielpublishing.com *Web Site:* www.danielpublishing.com, pg 70

Daniel, John M, John M Daniel Literary Services, PO Box 2790, McKinleyville, CA 95519 *Tel:* 707-839-3495 *Fax:* 707-839-3242 *E-mail:* jmd@danielpublishing.com *Web Site:* www.danielpublishing.com/litserv.htm, pg 524

Daniel, Martha, Juvenile Literary Awards/Young People's Literature Awards, 506 Rose Ave, Des Plaines, IL 60016 *Tel:* 847-827-8339 *Web Site:* www.fawchicago.org, pg 697

Daniel, Susan, John Daniel & Co, PO Box 2790, McKinleyville, CA 95519-2790 *Tel:* 707-839-3495 *Toll Free Tel:* 800-662-8351 *Fax:* 707-839-3242 *E-mail:* dandd@danielpublishing.com *Web Site:* www.danielpublishing.com, pg 70

Daniel, Tina, Human Kinetics Inc, 1607 N Market St, Champaign, IL 61820 *Tel:* 217-351-5076 *Toll Free Tel:* 800-747-4457 *Fax:* 217-351-1549 (orders/cust serv) *E-mail:* info@hkusa.com *Web Site:* www.humankinetics.com, pg 117

Daniels, Diana, Mason Crest Publishers, 450 Parkway Dr, Suite D, Broomall, PA 19008 *Tel:* 610-543-6200 *Toll Free Tel:* 866-MCP-BOOK (627-2665) *Fax:* 610-543-3878 *Web Site:* www.masoncrest.com, pg 149

Danielson, Krista, Ecopress, 5995 149 St W, Suite 105, Apple Valley, MN 55124 *Tel:* 952-469-6699 *Toll Free Tel:* 800-846-7027 *Fax:* 952-469-1968 *Toll Free Fax:* 800-330-6232 *E-mail:* info@finneyco.com *Web Site:* www.ecopress.com, pg 79

Danielson, Krista, Finney Company Inc, 5995 149 St W, Suite 105, Apple Valley, MN 55124 *Tel:* 952-469-6699 *Toll Free Tel:* 800-846-7027 *Fax:* 952-469-1968 *Toll Free Fax:* 800-330-6232 *E-mail:* info@finneyco.com *Web Site:* www.finneyco.com, pg 89

Danielson, Krista, Hobar Publications, 5995 149 St W, Suite 105, Apple Valley, MN 55124 *Tel:* 952-469-6699 *Toll Free Tel:* 800-846-7027 *Fax:* 952-469-1968 *Toll Free Fax:* 800-330-6232 *E-mail:* info@finneyco.com *Web Site:* www.finney-hobar.com, pg 112

Danielson, Krista, Pogo Press Inc, 5995 149 St W, Suite 105, Apple Valley, MN 55124 *Tel:* 952-469-6699 *Toll Free Tel:* 800-846-7027 *Fax:* 952-469-1968 *Toll Free Fax:* 800-330-6232 *E-mail:* info@finneyco.com *Web Site:* www.pogopress.com, pg 194

Danielson, Krista, Windward Publishing, 5995 149 St W, Suite 105, Apple Valley, MN 55124 *Tel:* 952-469-6699 *Toll Free Tel:* 800-846-7027 *Fax:* 952-469-1968 *Toll Free Fax:* 800-330-6232 *E-mail:* info@finneyco.com *Web Site:* www.finneyco.com, pg 273

Dann, Jordan, Teachers & Writers Collaborative, 520 Eighth Ave, Suite 2020, New York, NY 10018-4165 *Tel:* 212-691-6590 *Toll Free Tel:* 888-BOOKS-TW (266-5789) *Fax:* 212-675-0171 *E-mail:* info@twc.org *Web Site:* www.twc.org, pg 620

Dannis, Joe, DawnSignPress, 6130 Nancy Ridge Dr, San Diego, CA 92121-3223 *Tel:* 858-625-0600 *Toll Free Tel:* 800-549-5350 *Fax:* 858-625-2336 *E-mail:* info@dawnsign.com *Web Site:* www.dawnsign.com, pg 72

Dano, Yvette, Penguin Group (USA) LLC, a Penguin Random House company, 375 Hudson St, New York, NY 10014 *Tel:* 212-366-2000 *Toll Free Tel:* 800-847-5515 (inside sales); 800-631-8571 (cust serv) *Fax:* 212-366-2666; 607-775-4829 (inside sales) *E-mail:* online@us.penguingroup.com *Web Site:* www.penguin.com; us.penguingroup.com, pg 186

Dardick, Simon, Vehicule Press, PO Box 42094, CP Roy, Montreal, QC H2W-2T3, Canada *Tel:* 514-844-6073 *Fax:* 514-844-7543 *E-mail:* vp@vehiculepress.com; admin@vehiculepress.com *Web Site:* www.vehiculepress.com, pg 504

Darhansoff, Liz, Darhansoff & Verrill, 236 W 26 St, Suite 802, New York, NY 10001-6736 *Tel:* 917-305-1300 *Fax:* 917-305-1400 *E-mail:* info@dvagency.com *Web Site:* www.dvagency.com, pg 547

Dark, Larry, The Story Prize, 41 Watchung Plaza, No 384, Montclair, NJ 07042 *Tel:* 973-932-0324 *E-mail:* info@thestoryprize.org *Web Site:* www.thestoryprize.org, pg 731

Darksmith, Rebekah, University of California Press, 2120 Berkeley Way, Berkeley, CA 94704-1012 *Tel:* 510-642-4247 *Fax:* 510-643-7127 *E-mail:* askucp@ucpress.edu (books); customerservice@ucpressjournals.com *Web Site:* www.ucpress.edu, pg 255

Darling, Abigail, Laughing Elephant, 3645 Interlake N, Seattle, WA 98103 *Tel:* 206-447-9229 *Toll Free Tel:* 800-354-0400 *Fax:* 206-447-9189 *E-mail:* support@laughingelephant.com *Web Site:* www.laughingelephant.com, pg 135

Darling, Christina, Laughing Elephant, 3645 Interlake N, Seattle, WA 98103 *Tel:* 206-447-9229 *Toll Free Tel:* 800-354-0400 *Fax:* 206-447-9189 *E-mail:* support@laughingelephant.com *Web Site:* www.laughingelephant.com, pg 135

Darling, Harold, Laughing Elephant, 3645 Interlake N, Seattle, WA 98103 *Tel:* 206-447-9229 *Toll Free Tel:* 800-354-0400 *Fax:* 206-447-9189 *E-mail:* support@laughingelephant.com *Web Site:* www.laughingelephant.com, pg 135

Darling, Karen Merikangas, University of Chicago Press, 1427 E 60 St, Chicago, IL 60637-2954 *Tel:* 773-702-7700; 773-702-7600 *Toll Free Tel:* 800-621-2736 (orders) *Fax:* 773-702-9756; 773-660-2235 (orders); 773-702-2708 *E-mail:* custserv@press.uchicago.edu; marketing@press.uchicago.edu *Web Site:* www.press.uchicago.edu, pg 255

Darnton, John, The George Polk Awards, The Brooklyn Campus, One University Plaza, Brooklyn, NY 11201-5372 *Tel:* 718-488-1009; 718-488-1115 *Web Site:* www.liu.edu/polk, pg 720

Dattorre, Michael, Ash Tree Publishing, PO Box 64, Woodstock, NY 12498 *Tel:* 845-246-8081 *Fax:* 845-246-8081 *E-mail:* info@ashtreepublishing.com *Web Site:* www.ashtreepublishing.com, pg 24

Dauber, Mira Pomerantz, Jewish Book Council, 520 Eighth Ave, 4th fl, New York, NY 10018 *Tel:* 212-201-2920 *Fax:* 212-532-4952 *E-mail:* jbc@jewishbooks.org *Web Site:* www.jewishbookcouncil.org, pg 608

Daulton, Sue, Penguin Random House Audio, 1745 Broadway, New York, NY 10019 *E-mail:* audio@randomhouse.com *Web Site:* www.randomhouse.com/audio, pg 187

Dave, Rishi, Dun & Bradstreet, 103 JFK Pkwy, Short Hills, NJ 07078 *Tel:* 973-921-5500 *Toll Free Tel:* 800-526-0651; 800-234-3867 (cust serv) *E-mail:* custserv@dnb.com *Web Site:* www.dnb.com, pg 77

Davenport, Elaine, Writer's AudioShop, 1316 Overland Stage Rd, Dripping Springs, TX 78620 *Tel:* 512-264-7067 *Fax:* 512-264-7067 *E-mail:* wrtaudshop@aol.com *Web Site:* www.writersaudio.com, pg 277

Davenport, May, May Davenport Publishers, 26313 Purissima Rd, Los Altos Hills, CA 94022 *Tel:* 650-947-1275 *Fax:* 650-947-1373 *E-mail:* mdbooks@earthlink.net *Web Site:* www.maydavenportpublishers.org, pg 71

David, Jack, ECW Press, 665 Gerrard St E, Toronto, ON M4M 1Y2, Canada *Tel:* 416-694-3348 *Fax:* 416-698-9906 *E-mail:* info@ecwpress.com *Web Site:* www.ecwpress.com, pg 479

David, Kim, McGraw-Hill Higher Education, 1333 Burr Ridge Pkwy, Burr Ridge, IL 60527 *Tel:* 630-789-4000 *Toll Free Tel:* 800-338-3987 (cust serv) *Fax:* 614-755-5645 (cust serv) *Web Site:* www.mhhe.com, pg 151

David, Kim, McGraw-Hill Humanities, Social Sciences, Languages, 2 Penn Plaza, 21st fl, New York, NY 10121 *Tel:* 212-904-2000 *Toll Free Tel:* 800-338-3987 (cust serv) *Fax:* 614-755-5645 (cust serv) *Web Site:* www.mhhe.com, pg 151

David, Kim, McGraw-Hill/Irwin, 1333 Burr Ridge Pkwy, Burr Ridge, IL 60527 *Tel:* 630-789-4000 *Toll Free Tel:* 800-338-3987 (cust serv) *Fax:* 630-789-6942; 614-755-5645 (cust serv) *Web Site:* www.mhhe.com, pg 152

David, Kim, McGraw-Hill Science, Engineering, Mathematics, 501 Bell St, Dubuque, IA 52001 *Tel:* 563-584-6000 *Toll Free Tel:* 800-338-3987 (cust serv) *Fax:* 614-755-5645 (cust serv) *Web Site:* www.mhhe.com, pg 152

Davidson, Christine, Emond Montgomery Publications Ltd, 60 Shaftesbury Ave, Toronto, ON M4T 1A3, Canada *Tel:* 416-975-3925 *Toll Free Tel:* 888-837-0815 *Fax:* 416-975-3924 *E-mail:* orders@emp.ca *Web Site:* www.emp.ca, pg 483

Davidson, Scott, McGraw-Hill Career Education, 1333 Burr Ridge Pkwy, Burr Ridge, IL 60527 *Tel:* 630-789-4000 *Toll Free Tel:* 800-338-3987 (cust serv) *Fax:* 630-789-5523; 614-755-5645 (cust serv) *Web Site:* www.mhhe.com, pg 150

Davies, Mr Glyn, Rothstein Publishing, 4 Arapaho Rd, Brookfield, CT 06804-3104 *Tel:* 203-740-7400 *Toll Free Tel:* 888-768-4783 *Fax:* 203-740-7401 *E-mail:* info@rothstein.com *Web Site:* www.rothstein.com; www.rothsteinpublishing.com, pg 211

Davies, Jocelyn, HarperCollins Children's Books, 195 Broadway, New York, NY 10007 *Tel:* 212-207-7000 *Web Site:* www.harpercollins.com/childrens, pg 105

Davies, Michael, Davies Publishing Inc, 32 S Raymond Ave, Suites 4 & 5, Pasadena, CA 91105-1961 *Tel:* 626-792-3046 *Toll Free Tel:* 877-792-0005 *Fax:* 626-792-5308 *E-mail:* info@daviespublishing.com *Web Site:* daviespublishing.com, pg 71

Davies, Shannon, Texas A&M University Press, John H Lindsey Bldg, Lewis St, 4354 TAMU, College Station, TX 77843-4354 *Tel:* 979-845-1436 *Toll Free Tel:* 800-826-8911 (orders) *Fax:* 979-847-8752 *Toll Free Fax:* 888-617-2421 (orders) *E-mail:* tampress@tamu.edu *Web Site:* www.tamupress.com, pg 243

Davis, Aida, American Institute of Aeronautics & Astronautics (AIAA), 1801 Alexander Bell Dr, Suite 500, Reston, VA 20191-4344 *Tel:* 703-264-7500 *Toll Free Tel:* 800-639-AIAA (639-2422) *Fax:* 703-264-7551 *E-mail:* custserv@aiaa.org *Web Site:* www.aiaa.org, pg 13

Davis, Dr Alan, New Rivers Press, c/o Minnesota State University Moorhead, 1104 Seventh Ave S, Moorhead, MN 56563 *Tel:* 218-477-5870 *Fax:* 218-477-2236 *E-mail:* nrp@mnstate.edu *Web Site:* www.newriverspress.com; www.mnstate.edu/newriverspress, pg 168

Davis, Carol Prud'homme, See-More's Workshop Arts & Education Workshops, 325 West End Ave, Suite 12-B, New York, NY 10023 *Tel:* 212-724-0677 *Fax:* 212-724-0767 *E-mail:* sbt@shadowboxtheatre.org *Web Site:* www.shadowboxtheatre.org, pg 655

Davis, Chris, The American Occupational Therapy Association Inc (AOTA), 4720 Montgomery Lane, Suite 200, Bethesda, MD 20814-3449 *Tel:* 301-652-6611 *Toll Free Tel:* 800-377-8555 (TDD); 877-404-AOTA (404-2682, orders) *Fax:* 301-652-7711; 770-238-0414 (orders) *E-mail:* aotacustomerservice@pbd.com *Web Site:* www.aota.org; store.aota.org, pg 15

Davis, Dawn, Atria Books, 1230 Avenue of the Americas, New York, NY 10020 *Tel:* 212-698-7000 *Fax:* 212-698-7007 *Web Site:* www.simonandschuster.com, pg 26

Davis, Dawn, HarperCollins General Books Group, 195 Broadway, New York, NY 10007 *Tel:* 212-207-7000 *Web Site:* www.harpercollins.com, pg 105

Davis, Dina, Harlequin Enterprises Ltd, 233 Broadway, Suite 1001, New York, NY 10279 *Tel:* 212-553-4200 *Fax:* 212-227-8969 *E-mail:* CustomerService@harlequin.com *Web Site:* www.harlequin.com, pg 105

Davis, Emily, Crown Publishing Group, c/o Penguin Random House Inc, 1745 Broadway, New York, NY 10019 *Tel:* 212-782-9000 *Toll Free Tel:* 888-264-1745 *Fax:* 212-940-7408 *E-mail:* crownosm@penguinrandomhouse.com *Web Site:* crownpublishing.com, pg 68

Davis, Gary, The Learning Source Ltd, 644 Tenth St, Brooklyn, NY 11215 *Tel:* 718-768-0231 (ext 10) *Fax:* 718-369-3467 *E-mail:* info@learningsourceltd.com *Web Site:* www.learningsourceltd.com, pg 529

Davis, H Leigh, BradyGames, 800 E 96 St, 3rd fl, Indianapolis, IN 46240 *Tel:* 317-428-3000 *Toll Free Tel:* 800-545-5912; 800-571-5840 (cust serv) *E-mail:* bradyquestions@pearsoned.com *Web Site:* www.bradygames.com, pg 44

Davis, J Madison, Gaylord College of Journalism & Mass Communication, Professional Writing Program, c/o University of Oklahoma, 395 W Lindsey St, Rm 3534, Norman, OK 73019-0270 *Tel:* 405-325-2721 *Fax:* 405-325-7565 *Web Site:* www.ou.edu/gaylord, pg 660

Davis, J Madison, International Association of Crime Writers Inc, North American Branch, 243 Fifth Ave, Suite 537, New York, NY 10016 *Tel:* 212-243-8966 *Fax:* 815-361-1477 *E-mail:* info@crimewritersna.org *Web Site:* www.crimewritersna.org, pg 607

Davis, James B, Practice Management Information Corp (PMIC), 4727 Wilshire Blvd, Suite 300, Los Angeles, CA 90010 *Tel:* 323-954-0224 *Fax:* 323-954-0253 *Toll Free Fax:* 800-633-6556 (orders) *E-mail:* orders@medicalbookstore.com; customer.service@pmiconline.com *Web Site:* www.pmiconline.com, pg 195

Davis, Janet, Health Administration Press, One N Franklin St, Suite 1700, Chicago, IL 60606-3491 *Tel:* 312-424-2800 *Fax:* 312-424-0014 *E-mail:* hap1@ache.org *Web Site:* www.ache.org/publications (orders), pg 108

Davis, Jill, The American Library Association (ALA), 50 E Huron St, Chicago, IL 60611 *Tel:* 312-944-6780 *Toll Free Tel:* 800-545-2433 *Fax:* 312-280-5275 *E-mail:* editionsmarketing@ala.org *Web Site:* www.alastore.ala.org, pg 14

Davis, John, Central Recovery Press (CRP), 3321 N Buffalo Dr, Suite 275, Las Vegas, NV 89129 *Tel:* 702-868-5830 *Fax:* 702-868-5831 *E-mail:* info@centralrecovery.com *Web Site:* centralrecoverypress.com, pg 54

Davis, Kara, Lantern Books, 128 Second Place, Garden Suite, Brooklyn, NY 11231 *Tel:* 212-414-2275 *E-mail:* editorial@lanternbooks.com; info@lanternmedia.net *Web Site:* lanternbooks.presswarehouse.com/Home/home.aspx, pg 134

Davis, Ken, Lone Pine Publishing, 2311 96 St, Edmonton, AB T6N 1G3, Canada *Tel:* 780-433-9333 *Toll Free Tel:* 800-661-9017 *Fax:* 780-433-9646 *Toll Free Fax:* 800-424-7173 *E-mail:* info@lonepinepublishing.com *Web Site:* www.lonepinepublishing.com, pg 490

Davis, Kendall, WaterBrook Multnomah Publishing Group, 12265 Oracle Blvd, Suite 200, Colorado Springs, CO 80921 *Tel:* 719-590-4999 *Toll Free Tel:* 800-603-7051 (orders) *Fax:* 719-590-

Tel: 800-621-2736 (orders) *Fax:* 801-581-3365 *Toll Free Fax:* 800-621-8471 *E-mail:* info@upress.utah.edu *Web Site:* www.uofupress.com, pg 260

de Alteriis, Antoinette, Pelican Publishing Co, 1000 Burmaster St, Gretna, LA 70053-2246 *Tel:* 504-368-1175 *Toll Free Tel:* 800-843-1724 *Fax:* 504-368-1195 *E-mail:* sales@pelicanpub.com (sales); office@pelicanpub.com (permission); promo@pelicanpub.com (publicity) *Web Site:* www.pelicanpub.com, pg 185

De Angelis, Sylvia, Les Editions Pierre Tisseyre, 155, rue Maurice, Rosemere, QC J7A 2S8, Canada *Tel:* 514-335-0777 *Fax:* 514-335-6723 *E-mail:* info@edtisseyre.ca *Web Site:* www.tisseyre.ca, pg 482

De Boer, Rebecca, University of Notre Dame Press, 310 Flanner Hall, Notre Dame, IN 46556 *Tel:* 574-631-6346 *Fax:* 574-631-8148 *E-mail:* undpress@nd.edu *Web Site:* www.undpress.nd.edu, pg 258

de Buerba, Jose, World Bank Publications, Office of the Publisher, 1818 "H" St NW, U-11-1104, Washington, DC 20433 *Tel:* 202-458-4497 *Toll Free Tel:* 800-645-7247 (cust serv) *Fax:* 202-522-2631; 202-614-1237 *E-mail:* books@worldbank.org; pubrights@worldbank.org (foreign rts) *Web Site:* www.worldbank.org/publications; publications.worldbank.org, pg 275

De Cairns, Brendan, PEN Canada, 24 Ryerson Ave, Suite 301, Toronto, ON M5T 2P3, Canada *Tel:* 416-703-8448 *Fax:* 416-703-3870 *E-mail:* queries@pencanada.ca *Web Site:* www.pencanada.ca, pg 616

De Carlo, Janet, Storybook Arts Inc, 414 Poplar Hill Rd, Dover Plains, NY 12522 *Tel:* 845-877-3305 *Web Site:* www.storybookartsinc.com, pg 584

de Flon, Nancy, Paulist Press, 997 Macarthur Blvd, Mahwah, NJ 07430-9990 *Tel:* 201-825-7300 *Toll Free Tel:* 800-218-1903 *Fax:* 201-825-8345 *Toll Free Fax:* 800-836-3161 *E-mail:* info@paulistpress.com *Web Site:* www.paulistpress.com, pg 184

de Groot, Ali, Modern Memoirs, 34 Main St, No 9, Amherst, MA 01002-2367 *Tel:* 413-253-2353 *Web Site:* www.modernmemoirs.com, pg 158

de Guzman, Beth, Grand Central Publishing, 1290 Avenue of the Americas, New York, NY 10019 *Tel:* 212-364-1100 *Web Site:* www.hachettebookgroup.com, pg 99

de Jackmo, Nicole, Quirk Books, 215 Church St, Philadelphia, PA 19106 *Tel:* 215-627-3581 *Fax:* 215-627-5220 *E-mail:* general@quirkbooks.com *Web Site:* www.quirkbooks.com, pg 202

De Jackmo, Nicole, Quirk Books, 215 Church St, Philadelphia, PA 19106 *Tel:* 215-627-3581 *Fax:* 215-627-5220 *E-mail:* general@quirkbooks.com *Web Site:* www.quirkbooks.com, pg 202

de la Campa, Cecelia, Writers House, 21 W 26 St, New York, NY 10010 *Tel:* 212-685-2400 *Fax:* 212-685-1781 *Web Site:* www.writershouse.com, pg 580

de la Cuesta, Barbara, Birch Brook Press, PO Box 81, Delhi, NY 13753-0081 *Tel:* 607-746-7453 (book sales & prodn) *Fax:* 607-746-7453 *E-mail:* birchbrook@copper.net *Web Site:* www.birchbrookpress.info, pg 37

de la Hoz, Cindy, Running Press Book Publishers, 2300 Chestnut St, Philadelphia, PA 19103-4399 *Tel:* 215-567-5080 *Toll Free Tel:* 800-343-4499 (cust serv & orders) *Fax:* 215-568-2919 *Toll Free Fax:* 800-453-2884 (cust serv & orders) *E-mail:* perseus.promos@perseusbooks.com *Web Site:* www.runningpress.com, pg 212

de la Rosa, Denise, Palgrave Macmillan, 175 Fifth Ave, Suite 200, New York, NY 10010 *Tel:* 646-307-5151 *Fax:* 212-777-6359 *E-mail:* firstname.lastname@palgrave-usa.com *Web Site:* us.macmillan.com/Palgrave.aspx, pg 180

de Menil, Joy, Viking, 375 Hudson St, New York, NY 10014 *Tel:* 212-366-2000 *E-mail:* online@penguinputnam.com *Web Site:* www.penguinputnam.com; us.penguingroup.com, pg 265

De Mers, Martin, Algora Publishing, 222 Riverside Dr, 16th fl, New York, NY 10025-6809 *Tel:* 212-678-0232 *Fax:* 212-666-3682 *E-mail:* editors@algora.com *Web Site:* www.algora.com, pg 8

De Mier, Chrissy, Morton Publishing Co, 925 W Kenyon Ave, Unit 12, Englewood, CO 80110 *Tel:* 303-761-4805 *Fax:* 303-762-9923 *E-mail:* contact@morton-pub.com *Web Site:* www.morton-pub.com, pg 160

de Pablos, Jaime, Vintage & Anchor Books, c/o Random House Inc, 1745 Broadway, New York, NY 10019 *Tel:* 212-572-2420 *E-mail:* vintageanchorpublicity@randomhouse.com *Web Site:* vintage-anchor.knopfdoubleday.com, pg 266

De Pasture, Andrea, New Concepts Publishing, 106-A W Hill Ave, Valdosta, GA 31636 *E-mail:* service@newconceptspublishing.com; submissions@newconceptspublishing.com *Web Site:* www.newconceptspublishing.com, pg 167

De Pasture, Madris, New Concepts Publishing, 106-A W Hill Ave, Valdosta, GA 31636 *E-mail:* service@newconceptspublishing.com; submissions@newconceptspublishing.com *Web Site:* www.newconceptspublishing.com, pg 167

De Paul, Christina, youngARTS, 2100 Biscayne Blvd, Miami, FL 33137 *Tel:* 305-377-1140 *Toll Free Tel:* 800-970-ARTS (970-2787) *Fax:* 305-377-1149 *E-mail:* info@nfaa.org *Web Site:* www.youngarts.org, pg 739

de Pree-Kajfez, Ariane, Stanford University Press, 1450 Page Mill Rd, Palo Alto, CA 94304-1124 *Tel:* 650-723-9434 *Fax:* 650-725-3457 *E-mail:* info@sup.org *Web Site:* www.sup.org, pg 233

de Rooy, Yolanda, Pearson Humanities & Social Sciences, 225 River St, Hoboken, NJ 07030-4772 *Tel:* 201-236-7000 *Fax:* 201-236-3400, pg 185

De Silva, Devni, University of British Columbia Press, 2029 West Mall, Vancouver, BC V6T 1Z2, Canada *Tel:* 604-822-5959 *Toll Free Tel:* 877-377-9378 *Fax:* 604-822-6083 *Toll Free Fax:* 800-668-0821 *E-mail:* frontdesk@ubcpress.ca *Web Site:* www.ubcpress.ca, pg 502

De Souza, Kathleen, Mary Ann Liebert Inc, 140 Huguenot St, 3rd fl, New Rochelle, NY 10801-5215 *Tel:* 914-740-2100 *Toll Free Tel:* 800-654-3237 *Fax:* 914-740-2101 *E-mail:* info@liebertpub.com *Web Site:* www.liebertonline.com, pg 139

De Spelder, Lynne Ann, Pacific Publishing Services, PO Box 1150, Capitola, CA 95010-1150 *Tel:* 831-476-8284 *Fax:* 831-476-8294 *E-mail:* pacpubs@attglobal.net, pg 532

de Spoelberch, Jacques, J de S Associates Inc, 9 Shagbark Rd, South Norwalk, CT 06854 *Tel:* 203-838-7571 *Fax:* 203-866-2713 *Web Site:* www.jdesassociates.com, pg 547

De Vinney, Karen, University of North Texas Press, Stovall Hall, Suite 174, 1400 Highland St, Denton, TX 76201 *Tel:* 940-565-2142 *Fax:* 940-565-4590 *Web Site:* www.unt.edu/untpress, pg 258

De Vivo, Frank, Practising Law Institute, 1177 Avenue of the Americas, New York, NY 10036 *Tel:* 212-824-5700 *Toll Free Tel:* 800-260-4PLI (260-4754, cust serv) *Fax:* 212-265-4742 (intl) *Toll Free Fax:* 800-321-0093 (local) *E-mail:* info@pli.edu (cust serv) *Web Site:* www.pli.edu, pg 195

De Voll, Julie, Harvard Business Review Press, 300 N Beacon St, Watertown, MA 02472 *Tel:* 617-783-7400 *Fax:* 617-783-7489 *E-mail:* custserv@hbsp.harvard.edu *Web Site:* www.harvardbusiness.org, pg 106

De Vos, Sarah, Fire Engineering Books & Videos, 1421 S Sheridan Rd, Tulsa, OK 74112 *Tel:* 918-931-9410 *Toll Free Tel:* 800-752-9764 *Fax:* 918-931-9555 *E-mail:* sales@pennwell.com *Web Site:* www.pennwellbooks.com, pg 89

De Wit, Dave, Moody Publishers, 820 N La Salle Blvd, Chicago, IL 60610 *Tel:* 312-329-4000 *Toll Free Tel:* 800-678-8812 (cust serv) *Fax:* 312-329-2019 *Web Site:* www.moodypublishers.com, pg 159

De Witt, Marjorie, Other Press LLC, 2 Park Ave, 24th fl, New York, NY 10016 *Tel:* 212-414-0054 *Toll Free Tel:* 877-843-6843 *Fax:* 212-414-0939 *E-mail:* editor@otherpress.com; rights@otherpress.com *Web Site:* www.otherpress.com, pg 178

De Wolf, James S, The MIT Press, 55 Hayward St, Cambridge, MA 02142 *Tel:* 617-253-5255 *Toll Free Tel:* 800-207-8354 (orders) *Fax:* 617-258-6779; 617-577-1545 (orders) *Web Site:* mitpress.mit.edu, pg 158

Deal, Barbara, Copywriter's Council of America (CCA), CCA Bldg, 7 Putter Lane, Middle Island, NY 11953-1920 *Tel:* 631-924-8555 *Fax:* 631-924-8555 *E-mail:* cca4dmcopy@gmail.com *Web Site:* www.AndrewLinickDirectMarketing.com/Copywriters-Council.html; www.NewWorldPressBooks.com, pg 523, 604

Deale, Chip, National Press Photographers Association Inc (NPPA), 3200 Croasdaile Dr, Suite 306, Durham, NC 27705 *Tel:* 919-383-7246 *Fax:* 919-383-7261 *E-mail:* info@nppa.org *Web Site:* www.nppa.org, pg 613

Dean, Keisha, The Magazine of the Year Award, 27 Union Sq W, Suite 207, New York, NY 10003 *Tel:* 212-223-3332 *Fax:* 212-223-5880 *E-mail:* mail@spd.org *Web Site:* www.spd.org, pg 704

Dean, Mary Catherine, Abingdon Press, 201 Eighth Ave S, Nashville, TN 37203-3919 *Tel:* 615-749-6000 (academic books) *Toll Free Tel:* 800-251-3320 *Fax:* 615-749-6056 (academic books) *Toll Free Fax:* 800-836-7802 (orders) *E-mail:* orders@abingdonpress.com *Web Site:* www.abingdonpress.com, pg 2

Dean, Tom, Zondervan, 3900 Sparks Dr, Grand Rapids, MI 49546 *Tel:* 616-698-6900 *Toll Free Tel:* 800-226-1122; 800-727-1309 (retail orders) *Fax:* 616-698-3350 *Toll Free Fax:* 800-698-3256 (retail orders) *E-mail:* zinfo@zondervan.com *Web Site:* www.zondervan.com, pg 280

Dear, Sandra, Penguin Group (USA) LLC Sales, 375 Hudson St, New York, NY 10014 *Tel:* 212-366-2000 *E-mail:* online@penguinputnam.com *Web Site:* us.penguingroup.com, pg 186

DeBoer, John, Copley Custom Textbooks, 530 Great Rd, Acton, MA 01720 *Tel:* 978-263-9090 *Toll Free Tel:* 800-562-2147 *Fax:* 978-263-9190 *E-mail:* publish@copleycustom.com; textbook@copleypublishing.com *Web Site:* www.xanedu.com/copley, pg 63

Deboer, Kathleen, Organization for Economic Cooperation & Development, 2001 "L" St NW, Suite 650, Washington, DC 20036-4922 *Tel:* 202-785-6323 *Toll Free Tel:* 800-456-6323 (dist ctr/pubns orders) *Fax:* 202-785-0350 *E-mail:* washington.contact@oecd.org *Web Site:* www.oecdwash.org; www.oecd.org, pg 177

deBoer, Margaret, Houghton Mifflin Harcourt School Publishers, 9205 Southport Center Loop, Orlando, FL 32819 *Tel:* 407-345-2000 *Toll Free Tel:* 800-225-5425 (cust serv) *Fax:* 407-345-3016 (cust serv) *Toll Free Fax:* 800-874-6418; 800-269-5232 (cust serv) *Web Site:* www.hmhco.com, pg 115

DeBold, Kathleen, Lambda Literary Awards (Lammys), 5482 Wilshire Blvd, No 1595, Los Angeles, CA 90036 *Tel:* 323-643-4281 *Fax:* 323-643-4281 *E-mail:* info@lambdaliterary.org *Web Site:* www.lambdaliterary.org, pg 699

Decalo, Prof Sam, Florida Academic Press, PO Box 357425, Gainesville, FL 32635 *Tel:* 352-332-5104 *E-mail:* fapress@gmail.com *Web Site:* www.florida-academic-press.com, pg 90

DeChiara, Jennifer, The Jennifer DeChiara Literary Agency, 31 E 32 St, Suite 300, New York, NY 10016 *Tel:* 212-481-8484 (ext 362) *Fax:* 212-481-9582 *Web Site:* www.jdlit.com, pg 547

Decker, Kate Delano-Condax, Resilient Publishing, 406 S Third St, Boise, ID 83702 *Tel:* 208-258-9544 *E-mail:* submissions@resilientpublishing.com *Web Site:* www.resilientpublishing.com, pg 208

Decker, Ryan, Decker Intellectual Properties Publisher, 69 John St S, Suite 310, Hamilton, ON L8N 2B9, Canada *Tel:* 905-522-8526 *Toll Free Tel:* 855-647-6511 (CN & US) *Fax:* 905-522-9273 *E-mail:* customercare@deckerip.com *Web Site:* www.deckerpublishing.com, pg 478

Doornbos, Cris, David C Cook, 4050 Lee Vance View, Colorado Springs, CO 80918 *Tel:* 719-536-0100 *Toll Free Tel:* 800-708-5550; 800-323-7543 (orders & cust serv) *Toll Free Fax:* 800-430-0726 (cust serv) *Web Site:* www.davidccook.com, pg 62

Doremus, Morgan, Sourcebooks Inc, 1935 Brookdale Rd, Suite 139, Naperville, IL 60563 *Tel:* 630-961-3900 *Toll Free Tel:* 800-432-7444 *Fax:* 630-961-2168 *E-mail:* info@sourcebooks.com; customersupport@sourcebooks.com *Web Site:* www.sourcebooks.com, pg 230

Dorff, Patricia, Council on Foreign Relations Press, The Harold Pratt House, 58 E 68 St, New York, NY 10065 *Tel:* 212-434-9400 *Fax:* 212-434-9800 *E-mail:* publications@cfr.org *Web Site:* www.cfr.org, pg 65

Dorfman, Debra, Scholastic Trade Division, 557 Broadway, New York, NY 10012 *Tel:* 212-343-6100; 212-343-4685 (export sales) *Fax:* 212-343-4714 (export sales) *Web Site:* www.scholastic.com, pg 219

Dorfman, Larry, Capstone Publishers™, 1710 Roe Crest Dr, North Mankato, MN 56003 *Toll Free Tel:* 800-747-4992 (cust serv) *Toll Free Fax:* 888-262-0705 *Web Site:* www.capstonepress.com, pg 49

Dorfman, Peter, Wimbledon Music Inc & Trigram Music Inc, 1801 Century Park E, Suite 2400, Los Angeles, CA 90067 *Tel:* 310-556-9683 *Fax:* 310-277-1278 *E-mail:* irishmex127@gmail.com *Web Site:* www.wimbtri.net, pg 273

Dorman, Dr Jessica, The Historic New Orleans Collection, 533 Royal St, New Orleans, LA 70130 *Tel:* 504-523-4662 *Fax:* 504-598-7108 *E-mail:* wrc@hnoc.org *Web Site:* www.hnoc.org, pg 112

Dorman, Mark, McGraw-Hill Education, 2 Penn Plaza, New York, NY 10121-2298 *Tel:* 212-904-2000 *E-mail:* customer.service@mcgraw-hill.com *Web Site:* www.mheducation.com; www.mheducation.com/custserv.html, pg 151

Dorman, Mark, McGraw-Hill International Publishing Group, 2 Penn Plaza, New York, NY 10121 *Tel:* 212-904-2000 *Web Site:* www.mcgraw-hill.com, pg 152

Dorman, Pamela, Viking, 375 Hudson St, New York, NY 10014 *Tel:* 212-366-2000 *E-mail:* online@penguinputnam.com *Web Site:* www.penguinputnam.com; us.penguingroup.com, pg 265

Dorning, Matthew, Ancient Faith Publishing, 2747 Bond St, University Park, IL 60484 *Tel:* 219-728-2216 *Toll Free Tel:* 800-967-7377 *Toll Free Fax:* 866-599-5208 *E-mail:* info@ancientfaith.com; orders@ancientfaith.com *Web Site:* www.ancientfaith.com/publishing, pg 17

Dorr, Sharron, Theosophical Publishing House/Quest Books, 306 W Geneva Rd, Wheaton, IL 60187 *Tel:* 630-665-0130 (ext 347) *Toll Free Tel:* 800-669-9425 (ext 347) *Fax:* 630-665-8791 *E-mail:* customerservice@questbooks.net *Web Site:* www.questbooks.net, pg 244

Dorrance, Samuel R, Potomac Books Inc, 22841 Quicksilver Dr, Dulles, VA 20166 *Tel:* 703-661-1548 *Fax:* 703-661-1547 *E-mail:* pbimail@presswarehouse.com *Web Site:* www.potomacbooksinc.com, pg 195

Dosik, Anita, APPA: The Association of Higher Education Facilities Officers, 1643 Prince St, Alexandria, VA 22314-2818 *Tel:* 703-684-1446 *Fax:* 703-549-2772 *Web Site:* www.appa.org, pg 20

Doten, Mark, Soho Press Inc, 853 Broadway, New York, NY 10003 *Tel:* 212-260-1900 *Fax:* 212-260-1902 *E-mail:* soho@sohopress.com; publicity@sohopress.com *Web Site:* www.sohopress.com, pg 229

Dotto, Gabriel, Michigan State University Press (MSU Press), 1405 S Harrison Rd, Suite 25, East Lansing, MI 48823 *Tel:* 517-355-9543 *Fax:* 517-432-2611 *Toll Free Fax:* 800-678-2120 *E-mail:* msupress@msu.edu *Web Site:* www.msupress.msu.edu, pg 156

Dougan, Clark, University of Massachusetts Press, East Experiment Sta, 671 N Pleasant St, Amherst, MA 01003 *Tel:* 413-545-2217 *Fax:* 413-545-1226 *E-mail:* info@umpress.umass.edu *Web Site:* www.umass.edu/umpress, pg 257

Dougherty, Adria, Sterling Publishing Co Inc, 1166 Avenue of the Americas, 17th fl, New York, NY 10036 *Tel:* 212-532-7160 *Toll Free Tel:* 800-367-9692 *Fax:* 212-213-2495 *Web Site:* www.sterlingpublishing.com, pg 235

Dougherty, Peter, Princeton University Press, 41 William St, Princeton, NJ 08540-5237 *Tel:* 609-258-4900 *Toll Free Tel:* 800-777-4726 (orders) *Fax:* 609-258-6305 *Toll Free Fax:* 800-999-1958 *E-mail:* orders@cpfsinc.com *Web Site:* press.princeton.edu, pg 197

Doughten, Kevin, Crown Publishing Group, c/o Penguin Random House Inc, 1745 Broadway, New York, NY 10019 *Tel:* 212-782-9000 *Toll Free Tel:* 888-264-1745 *Fax:* 212-940-7408 *E-mail:* crownosm@penguinrandomhouse.com *Web Site:* crownpublishing.com, pg 68

Douglas, Alecia, McIntosh & Otis Inc, 353 Lexington Ave, New York, NY 10016-0900 *Tel:* 212-687-7400 *Fax:* 212-687-6894 *E-mail:* info@mcintoshandotis.com *Web Site:* www.mcintoshandotis.com, pg 565

Douglas, Deron, Double Dragon Publishing Inc, 1-5762 Hwy 7 E, Markham, ON L3P 7Y4, Canada *Tel:* 603-778-7191 *E-mail:* info@double-dragon-ebooks.com; sales@double-dragon-ebooks.com *Web Site:* www.double-dragon-ebooks.com, pg 479

Douglas, Diana R, Self-Counsel Press Ltd, 4152 Meridian St, Suite 105-471, Bellingham, WA 98226 *Toll Free Tel:* 800-663-3007 *E-mail:* orders@self-counsel.com *Web Site:* www.self-counsel.com, pg 221

Douglas, Sarah L, Abrams Artists Agency, 275 Seventh Ave, 26th fl, New York, NY 10001 *Tel:* 646-486-4600 *Fax:* 646-486-2358 *E-mail:* literary@abramsartny.com *Web Site:* www.abramsartists.com, pg 539

Douglas, Tyler, Self-Counsel Press Ltd, 4152 Meridian St, Suite 105-471, Bellingham, WA 98226 *Toll Free Tel:* 800-663-3007 *E-mail:* orders@self-counsel.com *Web Site:* www.self-counsel.com, pg 221

Douvris, Mara, Institute of Environmental Sciences and Technology - IEST, 2340 S Arlington Heights Rd, Suite 620, Arlington Heights, IL 60005-4510 *Tel:* 847-981-0100 *Fax:* 847-981-4130 *E-mail:* publications@iest.org *Web Site:* www.iest.org, pg 122

Dove, Veronica, Bernan, 4501 Forbes Blvd, Suite 200, Lanham, MD 20706 *Tel:* 301-459-7666 (cust serv & orders) *Fax:* 301-459-0056 *E-mail:* customercare@bernan.com *Web Site:* www.bernan.com, pg 35

Dowden, C James, City & Regional Magazine Association, 1970 E Grand Ave, Suite 330, El Segundo, CA 90245 *Tel:* 310-364-0193 *Fax:* 310-364-0196 *E-mail:* admin@citymag.org *Web Site:* www.citymag.org, pg 603

Dowdy, Eric, Group Publishing Inc, 1515 Cascade Ave, Loveland, CO 80538 *Tel:* 970-669-3836 *Toll Free Tel:* 800-447-1070 *Fax:* 970-292-4373 *E-mail:* info@group.com *Web Site:* www.group.com, pg 101

Dowen, Joyce, American Academy of Environmental Engineers & Scientists™, 147 Old Solomons Island Rd, Suite 303, Annapolis, MD 21401 *Tel:* 410-266-3311 *Fax:* 410-266-7653 *E-mail:* info@aaees.org *Web Site:* www.aaees.org, pg 10

Dowling, Michael, Bogle International Library Travel Fund, 50 E Huron St, Chicago, IL 60611-2795 *Tel:* 312-280-3201 *Toll Free Tel:* 800-545-2433 (ext 3201) *Fax:* 312-280-4392 *E-mail:* intl@ala.org *Web Site:* www.ala.org, pg 673

Downes, Terry, Disney Publishing Worldwide, 1101 Flower St, Glendale, CA 91201 *Web Site:* books.disney.com, pg 74

Downey, Alessandra, Lynne Rienner Publishers Inc, 1800 30 St, Suite 314, Boulder, CO 80301 *Tel:* 303-444-6684 *Fax:* 303-444-0824 *E-mail:* questions@rienner.com; cservice@rienner.com *Web Site:* www.rienner.com, pg 209

Downey, Floann, West Virginia University Press, West Virginia University, PO Box 6295, Morgantown, WV 26506-6295 *Tel:* 304-293-8400 *Toll Free Tel:* 866-WVU-PRES (988-7737) *Fax:* 304-293-6585 *E-mail:* press@wvu.edu *Web Site:* www.wvupress.com, pg 269

Downs, Toddie, Northwest Independent Editors Guild, PO Box 1630, Snoqualmie, WA 98065 *E-mail:* info@edsguild.org *Web Site:* www.edsguild.org, pg 614

Doyel, Jade, Tyndale House Publishers Inc, 351 Executive Dr, Carol Stream, IL 60188 *Tel:* 630-668-8300 *Toll Free Tel:* 800-323-9400 *Web Site:* www.tyndale.com, pg 252

Doyen, Barb J, Doyen Literary Services Inc, 1931 660 St, Newell, IA 50568 *Web Site:* www.barbaradoyen.com, pg 549

Doyle, Kathy, St Martin's Press, LLC, 175 Fifth Ave, New York, NY 10010 *Tel:* 646-307-5151 *Fax:* 212-420-9314 *E-mail:* firstname.lastname@macmillan.com *Web Site:* www.stmartins.com, pg 215

Doyle, Linda, Trails Books, 3005 Center Green Dr, Suite 225, Boulder, CO 80301 *Tel:* 303-541-1506 *Toll Free Tel:* 800-258-5830 *E-mail:* books@bigearthpublishing.com *Web Site:* www.trailsbooks.com, pg 248

Doyle, Patricia, Barron's Educational Series Inc, 250 Wireless Blvd, Hauppauge, NY 11788 *Tel:* 631-434-3311 *Toll Free Tel:* 800-645-3476 *Fax:* 631-434-3723 *E-mail:* barrons@barronseduc.com *Web Site:* www.barronseduc.com, pg 31

Doyle-Kimball, Mary, National Association of Real Estate Editors (NAREE), 1003 NW Sixth Terr, Boca Raton, FL 33486-3455 *Tel:* 561-391-3599 *Fax:* 561-391-0099 *Web Site:* www.naree.org, pg 611

Dozier, Laura, Harry N Abrams Inc, 115 W 18 St, 6th fl, New York, NY 10011 *Tel:* 212-206-7715 *Toll Free Tel:* 800-345-1359 *Fax:* 212-519-1210 *E-mail:* abrams@abramsbooks.com *Web Site:* www.abramsbooks.com, pg 3

Drake, David, Crown Publishing Group, c/o Penguin Random House Inc, 1745 Broadway, New York, NY 10019 *Tel:* 212-782-9000 *Toll Free Tel:* 888-264-1745 *Fax:* 212-940-7408 *E-mail:* crownosm@penguinrandomhouse.com *Web Site:* crownpublishing.com, pg 68

Dreesen, Robert, Cambridge University Press, 32 Avenue of the Americas, New York, NY 10013-2473 *Tel:* 212-924-3900; 212-337-5000 *Fax:* 212-691-3239 *E-mail:* newyork@cambridge.org *Web Site:* www.cambridge.org/us, pg 49

Dreher, Dwayne, Coteau Books, 2517 Victoria Ave, Regina, SK S4P 0T2, Canada *Tel:* 306-777-0170 *Toll Free Tel:* 800-440-4471 (CN only) *Fax:* 306-522-5152 *E-mail:* coteau@coteaubooks.com *Web Site:* www.coteaubooks.com, pg 478

Drehs, Shana, Sourcebooks Inc, 1935 Brookdale Rd, Suite 139, Naperville, IL 60563 *Tel:* 630-961-3900 *Toll Free Tel:* 800-432-7444 *Fax:* 630-961-2168 *E-mail:* info@sourcebooks.com; customersupport@sourcebooks.com *Web Site:* www.sourcebooks.com, pg 230

Dreibelbis, Dana, Rutgers University Press, 106 Somerset St, 3rd fl, New Brunswick, NJ 08901 *Tel:* 848-445-7762 *Toll Free Tel:* 800-848-6224 (orders only) *Fax:* 732-745-4935 (acqs, edit, mktg, perms & prodn) *Toll Free Fax:* 800-272-6817 (fulfillment) *Web Site:* rutgerspress.rutgers.edu, pg 213

Dreiblatt, Ian, Seven Stories Press, 140 Watts St, New York, NY 10013 *Tel:* 212-226-8760 *Toll Free Tel:* 800-733-3000 (orders) *Fax:* 212-226-1411 *E-mail:* info@sevenstories.com *Web Site:* www.sevenstories.com, pg 222

Dreier, Eliza, Carol Mann Agency, 55 Fifth Ave, New York, NY 10003 *Tel:* 212-206-5635 *Fax:* 212-675-4809 *E-mail:* submissions@carolmannagency.com *Web Site:* www.carolmannagency.com, pg 563

Drennan, Christina L, Drennan Communications, 6 Robin Lane, East Kingston, NH 03827 *Tel:* 603-642-8002 *Fax:* 603-642-8002, pg 524

Drennan, Christina L, Drennan Literary Agency, 6 Robin Lane, East Kingston, NH 03827 *Tel:* 603-642-8002 *Fax:* 603-642-8002, pg 549

Dukes, Paul, Psychology Press, 711 Third Ave, 8th fl, New York, NY 10017 *Tel:* 212-216-7800 *Toll Free Tel:* 800-634-7064 *Fax:* 212-563-2269 *Web Site:* www.psypress.com, pg 200

Dulaney, Kristin, Little, Brown Books for Young Readers, 1290 Avenue of the Americas, New York, NY 10019 *Tel:* 212-364-1100 *Toll Free Tel:* 800-759-0190 (cust serv) *Web Site:* www.HachetteBookGroup.com, pg 141

Dumanis, Michael, Cleveland State University Poetry Center Prizes, 2121 Euclid Ave, Cleveland, OH 44115-2214 *Tel:* 216-687-3986 *Fax:* 216-687-6943 *E-mail:* poetrycenter@csuohio.edu *Web Site:* www.csuohio.edu/poetrycenter, pg 678

Dunbar, Linda, John Wiley & Sons Inc, 111 River St, Hoboken, NJ 07030-5774 *Tel:* 201-748-6000 *Toll Free Tel:* 800-225-5945 (cust serv) *Fax:* 201-748-6088 *E-mail:* info@wiley.com *Web Site:* www.wiley.com, pg 272

Duncan, Michael, Cambridge University Press, 32 Avenue of the Americas, New York, NY 10013-2473 *Tel:* 212-924-3900; 212-337-5000 *Fax:* 212-691-3239 *E-mail:* newyork@cambridge.org *Web Site:* www.cambridge.org/us, pg 49

Dungan, Thomas F III, Management Concepts Inc, 8230 Leesburg Pike, Suite 800, Vienna, VA 22182 *Tel:* 703-790-9595 *Toll Free Tel:* 800 506-4450 *Fax:* 703-790-1371 *E-mail:* info@managementconcepts.com *Web Site:* www.managementconcepts.com, pg 146

Dunham, C Ryan, David C Cook, 4050 Lee Vance View, Colorado Springs, CO 80918 *Tel:* 719-536-0100 *Toll Free Tel:* 800-708-5550; 800-323-7543 (orders & cust serv) *Toll Free Fax:* 800-430-0726 (cust serv) *Web Site:* www.davidccook.com, pg 62

Dunham, Courtney, Basic Health Publications Inc, 28812 Top of the World Dr, Laguna Beach, CA 92651 *Tel:* 949-715-7327 *Toll Free Tel:* 800-575-8890 (orders) *Fax:* 949-715-7328 *E-mail:* info@basichealthpub.com *Web Site:* www.basichealthpub.com, pg 32

Dunham, Gary, Indiana University Press, Herman B Wells Library 350, 1320 E Tenth St, Bloomington, IN 47405-3907 *Tel:* 812-855-8817 *Toll Free Tel:* 800-842-6796 (orders only) *Fax:* 812-855-7931; 812-855-8507 *E-mail:* iupress@indiana.edu; iuporder@indiana.edu (orders) *Web Site:* www.iupress.indiana.edu, pg 120

Dunlap, Dennis, American Marketing Association, 311 S Wacker Dr, Suite 5800, Chicago, IL 60606 *Tel:* 312-542-9000 *Toll Free Tel:* 800-AMA-1150 (262-1150) *Fax:* 312-542-9001 *E-mail:* info@ama.org *Web Site:* www.ama.org, pg 14, 595

Dunlap, Ellen S, American Antiquarian Society (AAS), 185 Salisbury St, Worcester, MA 01609-1634 *Tel:* 508-755-5221 *Fax:* 508-753-3311 *E-mail:* library@americanantiquarian.org *Web Site:* www.americanantiquarian.org, pg 594

Dunn, Aimee Parent, Palimpsest Press, 1171 Eastlawn Ave, Windsor, ON N8S 3J1, Canada *Tel:* 519-563-9981 *E-mail:* info@palimpsestpress.ca *Web Site:* www.palimpsestpress.ca, pg 494

Dunn, Craig A, Wesleyan Publishing House, 13300 Olio Rd, Fishers, IN 46037 *Tel:* 317-774-3853 *Toll Free Tel:* 800-493-7539 *Fax:* 317-774-3865 *Toll Free Fax:* 800-788-3535 *E-mail:* wph@wesleyan.org *Web Site:* www.wesleyan.org/wph, pg 269

Dunn, Heather, The Society of Professional Journalists (SPJ), Eugene S Pulliam National Journalism Ctr, 3909 N Meridian St, Indianapolis, IN 46208 *Tel:* 317-927-8000 *Fax:* 317-920-4789 *E-mail:* spj@spj.org *Web Site:* www.spj.org, pg 620

Dunn, Karen, Child Welfare League of America (CWLA), 1726 "M" St, Suite 500, Washington, DC 20036 *Tel:* 202-688-4200 *Fax:* 202-833-1689 *E-mail:* cwla@cwla.org *Web Site:* www.cwla.org/publications, pg 56

Dunn, Kathy, Penguin Random House Speakers Bureau, 1745 Broadway, Mail Drop 13-1, New York, NY 10019 *Tel:* 212-572-2013 *E-mail:* speakers@penguinrandomhouse.com *Web Site:* www.prhspeakers.com, pg 587

Dunn, Peter, Abrams Learning Trends, 16310 Bratton Lane, Suite 250, Austin, TX 78728-2403 *Toll Free Tel:* 800-227-9120 *Toll Free Fax:* 800-737-3322 *E-mail:* customerservice@abramslearningtrends.com (orders, cust serv); contactus@abramslearningtrends.com *Web Site:* www.abramslearningtrends.com (orders, cust serv), pg 3

Dunn, Ronald, Wadsworth Publishing, 20 Davis Dr, Belmont, CA 94002 *Tel:* 650-595-2350 *Fax:* 650-592-3022 *Toll Free Fax:* 800-522-4923 *Web Site:* www.cengage.com, pg 266

Dunn, Stephen P, W W Norton & Company Inc, 500 Fifth Ave, New York, NY 10110-0017 *Tel:* 212-354-5500 *Toll Free Tel:* 800-233-4830 (orders & cust serv) *Fax:* 212-869-0856 *Toll Free Fax:* 800-458-6515 *Web Site:* www.wwnorton.com, pg 171

Dunne, Thomas, St Martin's Press, LLC, 175 Fifth Ave, New York, NY 10010 *Tel:* 646-307-5151 *Fax:* 212-420-9314 *E-mail:* firstname.lastname@macmillan.com *Web Site:* www.stmartins.com, pg 214

Dunow, Henry, Dunow, Carlson & Lerner Literary Agency Inc, 27 W 20 St, Suite 1107, New York, NY 10011 *Tel:* 212-645-7606 *E-mail:* mail@dclagency.com *Web Site:* www.dclagency.com, pg 549

Dunphy, Dr Joan S, New Horizon Press, PO Box 669, Far Hills, NJ 07931-0669 *Tel:* 908-604-6311 *Toll Free Tel:* 800-533-7978 (orders only) *Fax:* 908-604-6330 *E-mail:* nhp@newhorizonpressbooks.com *Web Site:* www.newhorizonpressbooks.com, pg 168

Dunton, David, Harvey Klinger Inc, 300 W 55 St, Suite 11V, New York, NY 10019 *Tel:* 212-581-7068 *Fax:* 212-315-3823 *E-mail:* queries@harveyklinger.com *Web Site:* www.harveyklinger.com, pg 560

Dunton, James R, The CSIS Press, 1616 Rhode Island Ave, Washington, DC 20036 *Tel:* 202-887-0200 *Fax:* 202-775-3199 *E-mail:* books@csis.org *Web Site:* www.csis.org, pg 69

DuPont, Charles, Alan Wofsy Fine Arts, 1109 Geary Blvd, San Francisco, CA 94109 *Tel:* 415-292-6500 *Toll Free Tel:* 800-660-6403 *Fax:* 415-292-6594 (off & cust serv); 510-251-1840 (acctg) *E-mail:* order@art-books.com (orders); editeur@earthlink.net (edit); beauxarts@earthlink.net (cust serv) *Web Site:* www.art-books.com, pg 274

Duquet, Michel, Francois-Xavier Garneau Medal, 130 Albert St, Suite 501, Ottawa, ON K1P 5G4, Canada *Tel:* 613-233-7885 *Fax:* 613-565-5445 *E-mail:* cha-shc@cha-shc.ca *Web Site:* www.cha-shc.ca, pg 688

Duquet, Michel, Sir John A Macdonald Prize, 130 Albert St, Suite 501, Ottawa, ON K1P 5G4, Canada *Tel:* 613-233-7885 *Fax:* 613-565-5445 *E-mail:* cha-shc@cha-shc.ca *Web Site:* www.cha-shc.ca, pg 704

Duquette, Lise, La Courte Echelle, 160, rue St-Viateur E, bureau 404, Montreal, QC H2T 1A8, Canada *Tel:* 514-274-2004 *Fax:* 514-270-4160 *E-mail:* info@courteechelle.com *Web Site:* www.courteechelle.com, pg 478

Durakis, Tom, American Bible Society, 1865 Broadway, New York, NY 10023-7505 *Tel:* 212-408-1200 *Toll Free Tel:* 800-322-4253; 888-596-6296 *Fax:* 212-408-1512 *E-mail:* info@americanbible.org *Web Site:* www.americanbible.org, pg 11

Durbin, Dean, Wadsworth Publishing, 20 Davis Dr, Belmont, CA 94002 *Tel:* 650-595-2350 *Fax:* 650-592-3022 *Toll Free Fax:* 800-522-4923 *Web Site:* www.cengage.com, pg 266

Durbin, Jon, W W Norton & Company Inc, 500 Fifth Ave, New York, NY 10110-0017 *Tel:* 212-354-5500 *Toll Free Tel:* 800-233-4830 (orders & cust serv) *Fax:* 212-869-0856 *Toll Free Fax:* 800-458-6515 *Web Site:* www.wwnorton.com, pg 171

Durepos, Joseph, Loyola Press, 3441 N Ashland Ave, Chicago, IL 60657 *Tel:* 773-281-1818 *Toll Free Tel:* 800-621-1008 *Fax:* 773-281-0555 (cust serv); 773-281-4129 (edit) *E-mail:* customerservice@loyolapress.com *Web Site:* www.loyolapress.com, pg 144

Durham, Anne, AFB Press, 2 Penn Plaza, Suite 1102, New York, NY 10121 *Tel:* 212-502-7600 *Toll Free Tel:* 800-232-5463; 800-232-3044 (orders) *Fax:* 917-210-3979; 412-741-0609 (orders) *Toll Free Fax:* 888-545-8331 *E-mail:* press@afb.net; afbpress@afb.net; afbinfo@afb.net; afborder@afb.net (orders) *Web Site:* www.afb.org, pg 5

Durham, Rusty, StarGroup International Inc, 1194 Old Dixie Hwy, Suite 201, West Palm Beach, FL 33413 *Tel:* 561-547-0667 *Fax:* 561-843-8530 *E-mail:* info@stargroupinternational.com *Web Site:* www.stargroupinternational.com, pg 234

Duval, Nathalie, Alexander Street Press LLC, 3212 Duke St, Alexandria, VA 22314 *Tel:* 703-212-8520 *Toll Free Tel:* 800-889-5937 *Fax:* 703-940-6584 *E-mail:* sales@alexanderstreet.com; marketing@alexanderstreet.com; info@alexanderstreet.com *Web Site:* alexanderstreet.com, pg 7

Duvall, Donna, Paladin Press, 5540 Central Ave, Suite 20, Boulder, CO 80301 *Tel:* 303-443-7250 *Toll Free Tel:* 800-392-2400 *Fax:* 303-442-8741 *E-mail:* service@paladin-press.com *Web Site:* www.paladin-press.com, pg 180

DuVall, Jennifer, Schiavone Literary Agency Inc, 236 Trails End, West Palm Beach, FL 33413-2135 *Tel:* 561-966-9294 *Fax:* 561-966-9294 *E-mail:* profschia@aol.com *Web Site:* www.publishersmarketplace.com/members/profschia, pg 571

Dworkin, Brooke, Disney Press, 1101 Flower St, Glendale, CA 91201 *Web Site:* books.disney.com, pg 74

Dworkin, Sharon, Prayer Book Press Inc, 1363 Fairfield Ave, Bridgeport, CT 06605 *Tel:* 203-384-2284 *Fax:* 203-579-9109, pg 196

Dwyer, Cecelia, North Star Press of Saint Cloud Inc, PO Box 451, St Cloud, MN 56302-0451 *Tel:* 320-558-9062 *Toll Free Tel:* 888-820-1636 *Fax:* 320-558-9063 *E-mail:* info@northstarpress.com *Web Site:* www.northstarpress.com, pg 171

Dwyer, Corinne A, North Star Press of Saint Cloud Inc, PO Box 451, St Cloud, MN 56302-0451 *Tel:* 320-558-9062 *Toll Free Tel:* 888-820-1636 *Fax:* 320-558-9063 *E-mail:* info@northstarpress.com *Web Site:* www.northstarpress.com, pg 171

Dwyer, Peter, Cistercian Publications, Saint John's Abbey, PO Box 7500, Collegeville, MN 56321 *Tel:* 320-363-2213 *Toll Free Tel:* 800-436-8431 *Fax:* 320-363-3299 *Toll Free Fax:* 800-445-5899 *E-mail:* sales@litpress.org *Web Site:* www.cistercianpublications.org, pg 58

Dwyer, Peter, Liturgical Press, PO Box 7500, St John's Abbey, Collegeville, MN 56321-7500 *Tel:* 320-363-2213 *Toll Free Tel:* 800-858-5450 *Fax:* 320-363-3299 *Toll Free Fax:* 800-445-5899 *E-mail:* sales@litpress.org *Web Site:* www.litpress.org, pg 141

Dwyer, Mr Terry, Xlibris Corp, 1663 Liberty Dr, Suite 200, Bloomington, IN 47403 *Toll Free Tel:* 888-795-4274 *Fax:* 610-915-0294 *E-mail:* info@xlibris.com *Web Site:* www.xlibris.com, pg 277

Dye, Skip, Books on Tape®, 1745 Broadway, New York, NY 10019 *Toll Free Tel:* 800-733-3000 (cust serv) *Toll Free Fax:* 800-940-7046 *Web Site:* www.booksontape.com, pg 43

Dye, Skip, Crown Publishing Group, c/o Penguin Random House Inc, 1745 Broadway, New York, NY 10019 *Tel:* 212-782-9000 *Toll Free Tel:* 888-264-1745 *Fax:* 212-940-7408 *E-mail:* crownosm@penguinrandomhouse.com *Web Site:* crownpublishing.com, pg 68

Dye, Skip, Penguin Random House Inc, 1745 Broadway, New York, NY 10019 *Tel:* 212-782-9000 *Toll Free Tel:* 800-726-0600 *Web Site:* www.randomhouse.com, pg 187

Dyer, Alison, Fresh Fish Award for Emerging Writers, Haymarket Sq, 208-223 Duckworth St, St John's, NL A1C 6N1, Canada *Tel:* 709-739-5215 *E-mail:* wanl@nf.aibn.com *Web Site:* wanl.ca, pg 688

Dyer, Alison, Newfoundland and Labrador Book Awards, Haymarket Sq, 208-223 Duckworth St, St John's, NL A1C 6N1, Canada *Tel:* 709-739-5215 *E-mail:* wanl@nf.aibn.com *Web Site:* wanl.ca, pg 713

Dyer, Alison, Writers' Alliance of Newfoundland & Labrador, Haymarket Sq, 223 Duckworth St, Suite 208, St John's, NL A1C 6N1, Canada *Tel:* 709-739-5215 *Toll Free Tel:* 866-739-5215 *E-mail:* wanl@nf.aibn.com *Web Site:* wanl.ca, pg 621

Dyer, Ann, IODE Violet Downey Book Award, 40 Orchard View Blvd, Suite 219, Toronto, ON M4R 1B9, Canada *Tel:* 416-487-4416 *Toll Free Tel:* 866-827-7428 *Fax:* 416-487-4417 *E-mail:* iodecanada@bellnet.ca *Web Site:* www.iode.ca, pg 695

Dyer, Gordon, McGraw-Hill International Publishing Group, 2 Penn Plaza, New York, NY 10121 *Tel:* 212-904-2000 *Web Site:* www.mcgraw-hill.com, pg 152

Dyke, George, Earth Edit, PO Box 114, Maiden Rock, WI 54750 *Tel:* 715-448-3009, pg 525

Dykstra, LeeAnna, Broadview Press, 280 Perry St, Unit 5, Peterborough, ON K9J 2J4, Canada *Tel:* 705-743-8990 *Fax:* 705-743-8353 *E-mail:* customerservice@broadviewpress.com *Web Site:* www.broadviewpress.com, pg 474

Dynak, Sharon, Ucross Foundation Residency Program, 30 Big Red Lane, Clearmont, WY 82835 *Tel:* 307-737-2291 *Fax:* 307-737-2322 *E-mail:* info@ucross.org *Web Site:* www.ucrossfoundation.org, pg 733

Dyson, Peter, American Society of Media Photographers (ASMP), 150 N Second St, Philadelphia, PA 19106 *Tel:* 215-451-2767 *Fax:* 215-451-0880 *E-mail:* info@asmp.org *Web Site:* asmp.org, pg 596

Dyssegaard, Elisabeth, St Martin's Press, LLC, 175 Fifth Ave, New York, NY 10010 *Tel:* 646-307-5151 *Fax:* 212-420-9314 *E-mail:* firstname.lastname@macmillan.com *Web Site:* www.stmartins.com, pg 215

Dystel, Jane, Dystel & Goderich Literary Management, One Union Sq W, Suite 904, New York, NY 10003 *Tel:* 212-627-9100 *Fax:* 212-627-9313 *Web Site:* www.dystel.com, pg 549

Eagle, Jane, National Notary Association (NNA), 9350 De Soto Ave, Chatsworth, CA 91311 *Tel:* 818-739-4000 *Toll Free Tel:* 800-876-6827 *Toll Free Fax:* 800-833-1211 *E-mail:* nna@nationalnotary.org *Web Site:* www.nationalnotary.org, pg 165

Eagle, Sara, Alfred A Knopf/Everyman's Library, c/o Random House Inc, 1745 Broadway, New York, NY 10019 *Tel:* 212-751-2600 *Toll Free Tel:* 800-638-6460 *Fax:* 212-572-2593 *Web Site:* www.knopfdoubleday.com, pg 132

Eaker, Noah, Random House Publishing Group, 1745 Broadway, New York, NY 10019 *Toll Free Tel:* 800-200-3552 *Web Site:* atrandom.com, pg 204

Eakin, Wendy, Dorset House Publishing Co Inc, 3143 Broadway, Suite 2-B, New York, NY 10027 *Tel:* 212-620-4053 *Toll Free Tel:* 800-DHBOOKS (342-6657, orders only) *Fax:* 212-727-1044 *E-mail:* info@dorsethouse.com *Web Site:* www.dorsethouse.com, pg 76

Eanes, Russ, Herald Press, 1251 Virginia Ave, Harrisonburg, VA 22802-2434 *Toll Free Tel:* 800-245-7894 (orders-US); 800-631-6535 (orders-CN) *Toll Free Fax:* 877-271-0760 *E-mail:* info@MennoMedia.org *Web Site:* www.heraldpress.com; store.mennomedia.org, pg 110

Early, Brighton, Sudden Fiction Contest, c/o ASUC Publications, Univ of California, 10-B Eshleman Hall, Berkeley, CA 94720-4500 *E-mail:* bfictionreview@yahoo.com *Web Site:* www.ocf.berkeley.edu/~bfr/, pg 731

Easley, Thomas J, American Medical Association, AMA Plaza, 330 N Wabash, Suite 39300, Chicago, IL 60611-5885 *Tel:* 312-464-5000 *Toll Free Tel:* 800-621-8335 *Fax:* 312-464-4184 *Web Site:* www.ama-assn.org, pg 14, 595

Easter, Eric, Akin & Randolph Agency, Literary Div, One Gateway Ctr, Suite 2600, Newark, NJ 07102 *Tel:* 973-353-8409; 973-623-6834 *Fax:* 973-353-8417 *E-mail:* info@akinandrandolph.com *Web Site:* www.akinandrandolph.com, pg 540

Eastman-Mullins, Andrea, Alexander Street Press LLC, 3212 Duke St, Alexandria, VA 22314 *Tel:* 703-212-8520 *Toll Free Tel:* 800-889-5937 *Fax:* 703-940-6584 *E-mail:* sales@alexanderstreet.com; marketing@alexanderstreet.com; info@alexanderstreet.com *Web Site:* alexanderstreet.com, pg 7

Easton, Emily, Penguin Random House Inc, 1745 Broadway, New York, NY 10019 *Tel:* 212-782-9000 *Toll Free Tel:* 800-726-0600 *Web Site:* www.randomhouse.com, pg 187

Easton, Emily, Random House Children's Books, 1745 Broadway, New York, NY 10019 *Tel:* 212-782-9000 *Toll Free Tel:* 800-200-3552 *Fax:* 212-782-9452 *Web Site:* randomhousekids.com, pg 203

Eaton, Brenda, Interlink Publishing Group Inc, 46 Crosby St, Northampton, MA 01060 *Tel:* 413-582-7054 *Toll Free Tel:* 800-238-LINK (238-5465) *Fax:* 413-582-7057 *E-mail:* info@interlinkbooks.com *Web Site:* www.interlinkbooks.com, pg 123

Eaton, Dena, Bitingduck Press LLC, 1262 Sunnyoaks Circle, Altadena, CA 91001 *Tel:* 626-679-2494; 626-507-8033 *E-mail:* notifications@bitingduckpress.com *Web Site:* bitingduckpress.com, pg 38

Eaton, Jonathan, Tilbury House Publishers, 12 Starr St, Thomaston, ME 04861 *Tel:* 207-582-1899 *Toll Free Tel:* 800-582-1899 (orders) *Fax:* 207-582-8227 *E-mail:* tilbury@tilburyhouse.com *Web Site:* www.tilburyhouse.com, pg 246

Eaton, Ralph A, Eaton Literary Associates Literary Awards, PO Box 49795, Sarasota, FL 34230-6795 *Tel:* 941-366-6589 *Fax:* 941-365-4679 *E-mail:* eatonlit@aol.com *Web Site:* www.eatonliterary.com, pg 682

Eaton, Sandi, Chelsea Green Publishing Co, 85 N Main St, Suite 120, White River Junction, VT 05001 *Tel:* 802-295-6300 *Toll Free Tel:* 800-639-4099 (cust serv, consumer & trade orders) *Fax:* 802-295-6444 *Web Site:* www.chelseagreen.com, pg 56

Ebershoff, David, Random House Publishing Group, 1745 Broadway, New York, NY 10019 *Toll Free Tel:* 800-200-3552 *Web Site:* atrandom.com, pg 204

Ebro, Casey, McGraw-Hill Professional, 1221 Avenue of the Americas, New York, NY 10020 *Tel:* 212-512-2000 *Web Site:* www.mhprofessional.com, pg 152

Eckenrode, Dr Joseph, DEStech Publications Inc, 439 N Duke St, Lancaster, PA 17602-4967 *Tel:* 717-290-1660 *Toll Free Tel:* 877-500-4337 *Fax:* 717-509-6100 *E-mail:* info@destechpub.com *Web Site:* www.destechpub.com, pg 73

Ecker, Sarah, ASET - The Neurodiagnostic Society, 402 E Bannister Rd, Suite A, Kansas City, KS 64131-3019 *Tel:* 816-931-1120 *Fax:* 816-931-1145 *E-mail:* info@aset.org *Web Site:* www.aset.org, pg 24

Eckert, Carolyn, Storey Publishing LLC, 210 MASS MoCA Way, North Adams, MA 01247 *Tel:* 413-346-2100 *Toll Free Tel:* 800-441-5700 (orders); 800-793-9396 (edit) *Fax:* 413-346-2199; 413-346-2196 (edit) *E-mail:* sales@storey.com *Web Site:* www.storey.com, pg 236

Ecklebarger, David, Editorial Unilit, 8167 NW 84 St, Medley, FL 33166 *Tel:* 305-592-6136 *Toll Free Tel:* 800-767-7726 *Fax:* 305-592-0087 *E-mail:* info@editorialunilit.com; customerservice@editorialunilit.com *Web Site:* www.editorialunilit.com, pg 253

Eckmair, Leigh, Birch Brook Press, PO Box 81, Delhi, NY 13753-0081 *Tel:* 607-746-7453 (book sales & prodn) *Fax:* 607-746-7453 *E-mail:* birchbrook@copper.net *Web Site:* www.birchbrookpress.info, pg 37

Eckstut, Arielle, Levine|Greenberg|Rostan Literary Agency Inc, 307 Seventh Ave, Suite 2407, New York, NY 10001 *Tel:* 212-337-0934 *Fax:* 212-337-0948 *Web Site:* lgrliterary.com, pg 561

Eddy, Susan, Mondo Publishing, 200 Sherwood Ave, Farmingdale, NY 11735 *Tel:* 212-268-3560 *Toll Free Tel:* 888-88-MONDO (886-6636) *Toll Free Fax:* 888-532-4492 *E-mail:* info@mondopub.com *Web Site:* www.mondopub.com, pg 159

Edelson, Libby, HarperCollins General Books Group, 195 Broadway, New York, NY 10007 *Tel:* 212-207-7000 *Web Site:* www.harpercollins.com, pg 105

Edelson, Samantha, Macmillan Audio, 175 Fifth Ave, New York, NY 10010 *Tel:* 646-307-5151 *Toll Free Tel:* 888-330-8477 (cust serv) *Fax:* 917-534-0980 *Web Site:* www.macmillanaudio.com, pg 145

Edelstein, Anne, Anne Edelstein Literary Agency LLC, 404 Riverside Dr, New York, NY 10025 *Tel:* 212-414-4923 *E-mail:* info@aeliterary.com; rights@aeliterary.com *Web Site:* www.aeliterary.com, pg 549

Eden, Katriena, Cedar Fort Inc, 2373 W 700 S, Springville, UT 84663 *Tel:* 801-489-4084 *Toll Free Tel:* 800-SKY-BOOK (759-2665) *Fax:* 801-489-1097 *Toll Free Fax:* 800-388-3727 *Web Site:* cedarfort.com, pg 52

Eder, Elsa, Northern California Independent Booksellers Association (NCIBA), The Presidio, 1007 General Kennedy Ave, San Francisco, CA 94129 *Tel:* 415-561-7686 *Fax:* 415-561-7685 *E-mail:* office@nciba.com *Web Site:* www.nciba.com, pg 614

Edgar, Blake, University of California Press, 2120 Berkeley Way, Berkeley, CA 94704-1012 *Tel:* 510-642-4247 *Fax:* 510-643-7127 *E-mail:* askucp@ucpress.edu (books); customerservice@ucpressjournals.com *Web Site:* www.ucpress.edu, pg 255

Edgecombe, Lindsay, Levine|Greenberg|Rostan Literary Agency Inc, 307 Seventh Ave, Suite 2407, New York, NY 10001 *Tel:* 212-337-0934 *Fax:* 212-337-0948 *Web Site:* lgrliterary.com, pg 561

Edinger, Lynn, National Newspaper Association, 309 S Providence Rd, Columbia, MO 65203-4267 *Tel:* 573-777-4980 *Fax:* 573-777-4985 *E-mail:* nna@nna.org *Web Site:* nnaweb.org, pg 613

Edmonds-Merritt, Valerie A, LITA/Christian Larew Memorial Scholarship in Library & Information Technology, c/o American Library Association, 50 E Huron St, Chicago, IL 60611-2795 *Toll Free Tel:* 800-545-2433 (ext 4270) *Fax:* 312-280-3257 *E-mail:* lita@ala.org *Web Site:* www.ala.org/lita, pg 702

Edmonds-Merritt, Valerie A, LITA/LSSI Minority Scholarship in Library & Information Technology, c/o American Library Association, 50 E Huron St, Chicago, IL 60611-2795 *Toll Free Tel:* 800-545-2433 (ext 4270) *Fax:* 312-280-3257 *E-mail:* lita@ala.org *Web Site:* www.ala.org/lita, pg 702

Edmonds-Merritt, Valerie A, LITA/OCLC Minority Scholarship in Library & Information Technology, c/o American Library Association, 50 E Huron St, Chicago, IL 60611-2795 *Toll Free Tel:* 800-545-2433 (ext 4270) *Fax:* 312-280-3257 *E-mail:* lita@ala.org *Web Site:* www.ala.org/lita, pg 702

Edmunds, Page, Workman Publishing Co Inc, 225 Varick St, 9th fl, New York, NY 10014-4381 *Tel:* 212-254-5900 *Toll Free Tel:* 800-722-7202 *Fax:* 212-254-8098 *E-mail:* info@workman.com *Web Site:* www.workman.com, pg 275

Edwards, Adrianna, Focus Strategic Communications Inc, 2474 Waterford St, Oakville, ON L6L 5E6, Canada *Tel:* 905-825-8757 *Toll Free Tel:* 866-263-6287 *Fax:* 905-825-5724 *Toll Free Fax:* 866-613-6287 *E-mail:* info@focussc.com *Web Site:* www.focussc.com, pg 526

Edwards, Barrie, Omnibus Press, 257 Park Ave S, 20th fl, New York, NY 10010 *Tel:* 212-254-2100 *Toll Free Tel:* 800-431-7187 *Fax:* 212-254-2013 *Toll Free Fax:* 800-345-6842 *E-mail:* info-us@omnibuspress.com *Web Site:* www.omnibuspress.com; www.musicsales.com, pg 174

Edwards, Barrie, Schirmer Trade Books, 180 Madison Ave, 24th fl, New York, NY 10016 *Tel:* 212-254-2100 *Toll Free Tel:* 800-431-7187 (orders) *Fax:* 212-254-2013 *Web Site:* www.musicsales.com, pg 218

Edwards, Brittany, Houghton Mifflin Harcourt Trade & Reference Division, 222 Berkeley St, Boston, MA 02116 *Tel:* 617-351-5000 *Toll Free Tel:* 800-225-3362 *Web Site:* www.hmhco.com, pg 115

Edwards, Carol, Teachers of English to Speakers of Other Languages Inc (TESOL), 1925 Ballenger Ave, Alexandria, VA 22314-6820 *Tel:* 703-836-0774 *Toll Free Tel:* 888-547-3369 *Fax:* 703-836-7864 *E-mail:* info@tesol.org *Web Site:* www.tesol.org, pg 242

Edwards, Ellen, NAL, 375 Hudson St, New York, NY 10014 *Tel:* 212-366-2000 *E-mail:* online@penguinputnam.com *Web Site:* www.penguinputnam.com; us.penguingroup.com, pg 162

Edwards, Karen Gray, American Sociological Association (ASA), 1430 "K" St NW, Suite 600, Washington, DC 20005-4701 *Tel:* 202-383-9005 *Fax:* 202-638-0882 *E-mail:* customer@asanet.org *Web Site:* www.asanet.org, pg 596

Edwards, Kate, Association of Canadian Publishers (ACP), 174 Spadina Ave, Suite 306, Toronto, ON M5T 2C2, Canada *Tel:* 416-487-6116 *Fax:* 416-487-8815 *E-mail:* admin@canbook.org *Web Site:* publishers.ca, pg 598

Edwards, Kathy, Ohio State University Press, 180 Pressey Hall, 1070 Carmack Rd, Columbus, OH 43210-1002 *Tel:* 614-292-6930 *Fax:* 614-292-2065 *Toll Free Fax:* 800-621-8476 *E-mail:* info@osupress.org *Web Site:* ohiostatepress.org, pg 174

Edwards, Katya, The Guilford Press, 72 Spring St, New York, NY 10012 *Tel:* 212-431-9800 *Toll Free Tel:* 800-365-7006 *Fax:* 212-966-6708 *E-mail:* info@guilford.com *Web Site:* www.guilford.com, pg 102

Edwards, Mary Jane, Jentel Artist Residency Program, 130 Lower Piney Rd, Banner, WY 82832 *Tel:* 307-737-2311 *Fax:* 307-737-2305 *E-mail:* jentel@jentelarts.org *Web Site:* www.jentelarts.org, pg 652

Edwards, Melissa, The Aaron M Priest Literary Agency Inc, 708 Third Ave, 23rd fl, New York, NY 10017-4201 *Tel:* 212-818-0344 *Fax:* 212-573-9417 *E-mail:* info@aaronpriest.com *Web Site:* www.aaronpriest.com, pg 568

Edwards, Ron, Focus Strategic Communications Inc, 2474 Waterford St, Oakville, ON L6L 5E6, Canada *Tel:* 905-825-8757 *Toll Free Tel:* 866-263-6287 *Fax:* 905-825-5724 *Toll Free Fax:* 866-613-6287 *E-mail:* info@focussc.com *Web Site:* www.focussc.com, pg 526

Edwards, S, Baywood Publishing Co Inc, 26 Austin Ave, Amityville, NY 11701 *Tel:* 631-691-1270 *Toll Free Tel:* 800-638-7819 *Fax:* 631-691-1770 *E-mail:* baywood@baywood.com *Web Site:* www.baywood.com, pg 32

Eerdmans, Anita, Wm B Eerdmans Publishing Co, 2140 Oak Industrial Dr NE, Grand Rapids, MI 49505 *Tel:* 616-459-4591 *Toll Free Tel:* 800-253-7521 *Fax:* 616-459-6540 *E-mail:* customerservice@eerdmans.com; sales@eerdmans.com *Web Site:* www.eerdmans.com, pg 80

Eerdmans, William B Jr, Wm B Eerdmans Publishing Co, 2140 Oak Industrial Dr NE, Grand Rapids, MI 49505 *Tel:* 616-459-4591 *Toll Free Tel:* 800-253-7521 *Fax:* 616-459-6540 *E-mail:* customerservice@eerdmans.com; sales@eerdmans.com *Web Site:* www.eerdmans.com, pg 80

Efting, Brad, Paladin Press, 5540 Central Ave, Suite 20, Boulder, CO 80301 *Tel:* 303-443-7250 *Toll Free Tel:* 800-392-2400 *Fax:* 303-442-8741 *E-mail:* service@paladin-press.com *Web Site:* www.paladin-press.com, pg 180

Egan, Debra, Fulbright Scholar Program, 1400 "K" St NW, Washington, DC 20005 *Tel:* 202-686-4000 *Fax:* 202-362-3442 *E-mail:* scholars@iie.org *Web Site:* www.iie.org/cies, pg 688

Egan, Rachel, McGraw-Hill Create, 501 Bell St, Dubuque, IA 52001 *Tel:* 563-584-6000 *Fax:* 563-584-6600 *E-mail:* first_last@mcgraw-hill.com *Web Site:* www.mhhe.com, pg 150

Egan-Miller, Danielle, Browne & Miller Literary Associates, 410 S Michigan Ave, Suite 460, Chicago, IL 60605 *Tel:* 312-922-3063 *E-mail:* mail@browneandmiller.com *Web Site:* www.browneandmiller.com, pg 544

Ehart, Kimberly, Red Wheel/Weiser/Conari, 65 Parker St, Suite 7, Newburyport, MA 01950 *Tel:* 978-465-0504 *Toll Free Tel:* 800-423-7087 (orders) *Fax:* 978-465-0243 *E-mail:* info@rwwbooks.com *Web Site:* www.redwheelweiser.com, pg 206

Ehle, Robert, Stanford University Press, 1450 Page Mill Rd, Palo Alto, CA 94304-1124 *Tel:* 650-723-9434 *Fax:* 650-725-3457 *E-mail:* info@sup.org *Web Site:* www.sup.org, pg 233

Ehrenclou, Martine, Lemon Grove Press, 1158 26 St, Suite 502, Santa Monica, CA 90403 *Tel:* 310-471-1740 *Fax:* 310-476-7627 *E-mail:* info@lemongrovepress.com *Web Site:* www.thetakechargepatient.com, pg 508

Ehrenhaft, Dan, HarperCollins Children's Books, 195 Broadway, New York, NY 10007 *Tel:* 212-207-7000 *Web Site:* www.harpercollins.com/childrens, pg 105

Ehrentraut, Krista, Move Books, PO Box 183, Beacon Falls, CT 06403 *Web Site:* www.move-books.com, pg 508

Eis, Arlene L, Infosources Publishing, 140 Norma Rd, Teaneck, NJ 07666 *Tel:* 201-836-7072 *Web Site:* www.infosourcespub.com, pg 121

Eisemann, Patricia, Henry Holt and Company, LLC, 175 Fifth Ave, New York, NY 10010 *Tel:* 646-307-5151 *Toll Free Tel:* 888-330-8477 (orders) *Fax:* 646-307-5285 *E-mail:* firstname.lastname@hholt.com *Web Site:* www.henryholt.com, pg 113

Eisenberg, Michael, Boyds Mills Press, 815 Church St, Honesdale, PA 18431 *Tel:* 570-253-1164 *Toll Free Tel:* 800-490-5111 *Fax:* 570-253-0179 *E-mail:* contact@boydsmillspress.com *Web Site:* www.boydsmillspress.com, pg 43

Eisenberg, Michael, Highlights for Children, 1800 Watermark Dr, Columbus, OH 43215 *Tel:* 614-486-0631 *Toll Free Tel:* 800-962-3661 (Highlights Club cust serv); 800-255-9517 (Highlights Magazine cust serv) *Web Site:* www.highlights.com, pg 111

Eisenbraun, James E, Eisenbrauns Inc, PO Box 275, Winona Lake, IN 46590-0275 *Tel:* 574-269-2011 *Fax:* 574-269-6788 *E-mail:* customer_service@eisenbrauns.com; publisher@eisenbrauns.com *Web Site:* www.eisenbrauns.com, pg 80

Eisenhardt, Gae, Azro Press, 1704 Llano St B, PMB 342, Santa Fe, NM 87505 *Tel:* 505-989-3272 *Fax:* 505-989-3832 *E-mail:* books@azropress.com *Web Site:* www.azropress.com, pg 29

Eisenstein, Ken, American Program Bureau Inc, 313 Washington St, Suite 225, Newton, MA 02458 *Tel:* 617-965-6600 *Toll Free Tel:* 800-225-4575 *Fax:* 617-965-6610 *E-mail:* apb@apbspeakers.com *Web Site:* www.apbspeakers.com, pg 587

Eiynck, Sandra, Liturgical Press, PO Box 7500, St John's Abbey, Collegeville, MN 56321-7500 *Tel:* 320-363-2213 *Toll Free Tel:* 800-858-5450 *Fax:* 320-363-3299 *Toll Free Fax:* 800-445-5899 *E-mail:* sales@litpress.org *Web Site:* www.litpress.org, pg 141

Ekroth, Angela, Paulist Press, 997 Macarthur Blvd, Mahwah, NJ 07430-9990 *Tel:* 201-825-7300 *Toll Free Tel:* 800-218-1903 *Fax:* 201-825-8345 *Toll Free Fax:* 800-836-3161 *E-mail:* info@paulistpress.com *Web Site:* www.paulistpress.com, pg 184

Ekstrom, Rachel, Irene Goodman Literary Agency, 27 W 24 St, Suite 700B, New York, NY 10010 *Tel:* 212-604-0330 *E-mail:* queries@irenegoodman.com *Web Site:* www.irenegoodman.com, pg 554

Ekus, Lisa, The Lisa Ekus Group LLC, 57 North St, Hatfield, MA 01038 *Tel:* 413-247-9325 *Fax:* 413-247-9873 *E-mail:* lisaekus@lisaekus.com *Web Site:* lisaekus.com, pg 550

Ekus, Lisa, The Lisa Ekus Group LLC, 57 North St, Hatfield, MA 01038 *Tel:* 413-247-9325 *Fax:* 413-247-9873 *Web Site:* lisaekus.com, pg 660

Ekus, Sally, The Lisa Ekus Group LLC, 57 North St, Hatfield, MA 01038 *Tel:* 413-247-9325 *Fax:* 413-247-9873 *E-mail:* lisaekus@lisaekus.com *Web Site:* lisaekus.com, pg 550

Ekus, Sally, The Lisa Ekus Group LLC, 57 North St, Hatfield, MA 01038 *Tel:* 413-247-9325 *Fax:* 413-247-9873 *Web Site:* lisaekus.com, pg 660

El Mallakh, Dorothea H, International Research Center for Energy & Economic Development, 850 Willowbrook Rd, Boulder, CO 80302 *Tel:* 303-442-4014 *Fax:* 303-442-5042 *E-mail:* info@iceed.org *Web Site:* www.iceed.org, pg 124

El Mallakh, Helen, International Research Center for Energy & Economic Development, 850 Willowbrook Rd, Boulder, CO 80302 *Tel:* 303-442-4014 *Fax:* 303-442-5042 *E-mail:* info@iceed.org *Web Site:* www.iceed.org, pg 125

Elancheran, Maran, Newgen North America Inc, 2714 Bee Cave Rd, Suite 201, Austin, TX 78746 *Tel:* 512-478-5341 *Fax:* 512-476-4756 *Web Site:* www.newgen.co, pg 531

Elbe, Susan, John Wiley & Sons Inc Higher Education, 111 River St, Hoboken, NJ 07030-5774 *Tel:* 201-748-6000 *Toll Free Tel:* 800-225-5945 (cust serv) *Fax:* 201-748-6008 *E-mail:* info@wiley.com *Web Site:* www.wiley.com, pg 272

Elblonk, Matthew, DeFiore and Company, LLC, 47 E 19 St, 3rd fl, New York, NY 10003 *Tel:* 212-925-7744 *Fax:* 212-925-9803 *E-mail:* submissions@defioreandco.com; info@defioreandco.com *Web Site:* www.defioreandco.com, pg 548

Eldemir, Mollie, Sierra Club Books, 85 Second St, 2nd fl, San Francisco, CA 94105 *Tel:* 415-977-5500 *Fax:* 415-977-5794 *E-mail:* books.publishing@sierraclub.org *Web Site:* www.sierraclubbooks.org, pg 224

Elder, Jo-Anne, John Glassco Translation Prize, Concordia University, LB 601, 1455 De Maisonneuve West, Montreal, QC H3G 1M8, Canada *Tel:* 514-848-2424 (ext 8702) *E-mail:* info@attlc-ltac.org *Web Site:* www.attlc-ltac.org, pg 689

Elder, Jo-Anne, Literary Translators' Association of Canada, Concordia University, LB 601, 1455 De Maisonneuve West, Montreal, QC H3G 1M8, Canada *Tel:* 514-848-2424 (ext 8702) *E-mail:* info@attlc-ltac.org *Web Site:* www.attlc-ltac.org, pg 609

Elfenbein, Reed, John Wiley & Sons Inc Scientific, Technical, Medical & Scholarly (STMS), 111 River St, Hoboken, NJ 07030 *Tel:* 201-748-6000 *Toll Free Tel:* 800-225-5945 (cust serv) *Fax:* 201-748-6088 *E-mail:* info@wiley.com *Web Site:* www.wiley.com, pg 272

Elias, Che, Six Gallery Press, PO Box 90145, Pittsburgh, PA 15224-0545 *Web Site:* www.sixgallerypress.com, pg 227

Elias, Maria, Disney-Hyperion Books, 1101 Flower St, Glendale, CA 91201 *Web Site:* books.disney.com, pg 74

Elias-Rowley, Kristen, University of Nebraska Press, 1111 Lincoln Mall, Lincoln, NE 68588-0630 *Tel:* 402-472-3581; 919-966-7449 (cust serv & foreign orders) *Toll Free Tel:* 800-848-6224 (cust serv & US orders) *Fax:* 402-472-6214; 919-962-2704 (cust serv & foreign orders) *Toll Free Fax:* 800-526-2617 (cust serv & US orders) *E-mail:* pressmail@unl.edu *Web Site:* www.nebraskapress.unl.edu, pg 257

Elinsky, Rachel, HarperCollins Publishers, 195 Broadway, New York, NY 10007 *Tel:* 212-207-7000 *Fax:* 212-207-7145 *Web Site:* www.harpercollins.com, pg 106

Ellen, Joan, World Citizens, PO Box 131, Mill Valley, CA 94942-0131 *Tel:* 415-380-8020 *Toll Free Tel:* 800-247-6553 (orders only), pg 276

Ellenberg, Ethan, Ethan Ellenberg Literary Agency, 548 Broadway, Suite 5-E, New York, NY 10012 *Tel:* 212-431-4554 *E-mail:* agent@ethanellenberg.com *Web Site:* www.ethanellenberg.com, pg 550

Eller, Linda, Educators Award, PO Box 1589, Austin, TX 78767-1589 *Tel:* 512-478-5748 *Toll Free Tel:* 888-762-4685 *Fax:* 512-478-3961 *E-mail:* societyexec@dkg.org *Web Site:* www.dkg.org, pg 683

Ellerbeck, Brian, Teachers College Press, 1234 Amsterdam Ave, New York, NY 10027 *Tel:* 212-678-3929 *Toll Free Tel:* 800-575-6566 *Fax:* 212-678-4149; 802-864-7626 *E-mail:* tcpress@tc.columbia.edu; tcp.orders@aidcvt.com (orders) *Web Site:* www.teacherscollegepress.com, pg 241

Elliot, Marie, W Kaye Lamb Award, PO Box 5254, Sta B, Victoria, BC V8R 6N4, Canada *E-mail:* essays@bchistory.ca *Web Site:* www.bchistory.ca, pg 699

Elliot, Nick, Random House Children's Books, 1745 Broadway, New York, NY 10019 *Tel:* 212-782-9000 *Toll Free Tel:* 800-200-3552 *Fax:* 212-782-9452 *Web Site:* randomhousekids.com, pg 204

Elliot, Steve, Morgan Kaufmann, 225 Wyman St, Waltham, MA 02451 *Toll Free Tel:* 866-607-1417 *Fax:* 619-699-6310 *Web Site:* www.mkp.com, pg 160

Elliott, Brad, Dufour Editions Inc, PO Box 7, Chester Springs, PA 19425 *Tel:* 610-458-5005 *Fax:* 610-458-7103 *E-mail:* info@dufoureditions.com *Web Site:* www.dufoureditions.com, pg 77

Elliott, Jennifer, International Linguistics Corp, Learnables, 12220 Blue Ridge Blvd, Suite G, Grandview, MO 64030 *Tel:* 816-765-8855 *Toll Free Tel:* 800-237-1830 (orders) *Fax:* 816-765-2855 *E-mail:* learnables@sbcglobal.net *Web Site:* www.learnables.com, pg 124

Elliott, Stephanie, Wesleyan University Press, 215 Long Lane, Middletown, CT 06459-0433 *Tel:* 860-685-7711 *Fax:* 860-685-7712 *Web Site:* www.wesleyan.edu/wespress, pg 269

Elliott, Stephen P, Sachem Publishing Associates Inc, 402 W Lyon Farm Dr, Greenwich, CT 06831 *Tel:* 203-813-3077 *Fax:* 203-531-2879 *E-mail:* sachempub@optonline.net, pg 533

Ellis, Elaina, Copper Canyon Press, Fort Worden State Park, Bldg 313, Port Townsend, WA 98368 *Tel:* 360-385-4925 *Toll Free Tel:* 877-501-1393 (orders) *Fax:* 360-385-4985 *E-mail:* poetry@coppercanyonpress.org *Web Site:* www.coppercanyonpress.org, pg 63

Ellis, Jane, University Science Books, 20 Edgeshill Rd, Mill Valley, CA 94941 *Tel:* 415-332-5390 *Fax:* 415-332-5390 *E-mail:* univscibks@igc.org *Web Site:* www.uscibooks.com, pg 262

Ellis, Kirk, Spur Awards, 271 CR 219, Encampment, WY 82325 *Tel:* 307-329-8942 *Fax:* 307-327-5465 *E-mail:* wwa.moulton@gmail.com *Web Site:* westernwriters.org, pg 730

Ellis, Kirk, Western Writers of America Inc (WWA), 271 CR 219, Encampment, WY 82325 *Tel:* 307-329-8942 *Fax:* 307-327-5465 *Web Site:* westernwriters.org, pg 621

Ellis, Mercury, Chronicle Books LLC, 680 Second St, San Francisco, CA 94107 *Tel:* 415-537-4200 *Toll Free Tel:* 800-759-0190 (cust serv) *Fax:* 415-537-4460 *Toll Free Fax:* 800-858-7787 (orders); 800-286-9471 (cust serv) *E-mail:* frontdesk@chroniclebooks.com *Web Site:* www.chroniclebooks.com, pg 58

Ellison, Nicholas, Nicholas Ellison Agency, 55 Fifth Ave, 15th fl, New York, NY 10003 *Tel:* 212-206-5600 *Fax:* 212-463-8718 *Web Site:* greenburger.com/agent/nick-ellison, pg 551

Ellison, Nicholas, Sanford J Greenburger Associates Inc, 55 Fifth Ave, New York, NY 10003 *Tel:* 212-206-5600 *Fax:* 212-463-8718 *Web Site:* greenburger.com; www.sjga.com/, pg 555

Ellsberg, Robert, Orbis Books, Price Bldg, Box 302, Maryknoll, NY 10545-0302 *Tel:* 914-941-7636 *Toll Free Tel:* 800-258-5838 (orders) *Fax:* 914-941-7005 *E-mail:* orbisbooks@maryknoll.org *Web Site:* www.orbisbooks.com, pg 176

Ellsworth, Sherri, Sinauer Associates Inc, 23 Plumtree Rd, Sunderland, MA 01375 *Tel:* 413-549-4300 *Fax:* 413-549-1118 *E-mail:* publish@sinauer.com; orders@sinauer.com *Web Site:* www.sinauer.com, pg 226

Ellwood, Nancy, DK Publishing, 345 Hudson St, 2nd fl, New York, NY 10014 *Tel:* 646-674-4000 *Toll Free Tel:* 877-342-5357 (cust serv) *Web Site:* us.dk.com, pg 75

Elnan, Hannah, Sasquatch Books, 1904 S Main St, Suite 710, Seattle, WA 98101 *Tel:* 206-467-4300 *Toll Free Tel:* 800-775-0817 *Fax:* 206-467-4301 *E-mail:* custserv@sasquatchbooks.com *Web Site:* www.sasquatchbooks.com, pg 217

Elsbree, Amy, National League of Cities, 1301 Pennsylvania Ave NW, Washington, DC 20004-1763 *Tel:* 202-626-3100 *Fax:* 202-626-3043 *E-mail:* info@nlc.org *Web Site:* www.nlc.org, pg 165

Elson, Shellie, National Council of Teachers of English (NCTE), 1111 W Kenyon Rd, Urbana, IL 61801-1096 *Tel:* 217-328-3870 *Toll Free Tel:* 877-369-6283 (cust serv) *Fax:* 217-328-9645 *E-mail:* orders@ncte.org *Web Site:* www.ncte.org, pg 164

Elson, Shellie, National Council of Teachers of English (NCTE), 1111 W Kenyon Rd, Urbana, IL 61801-1096 *Tel:* 217-328-3870 *Toll Free Tel:* 877-369-6283 (cust serv) *Fax:* 217-328-9645 *E-mail:* public_info@ncte.org *Web Site:* www.ncte.org, pg 612

Eltman, Kerry, Fox Chapel Publishing Co Inc, 1970 Broad St, East Petersburg, PA 17520 *Tel:* 717-560-4703 *Toll Free Tel:* 800-457-9112 *Fax:* 717-560-4702 *E-mail:* customerservice@foxchapelpublishing.com *Web Site:* www.foxchapelpublishing.com, pg 91

Elwell, Jake, Harold Ober Associates Inc, 425 Madison Ave, New York, NY 10017 *Tel:* 212-759-8600 *Fax:* 212-759-9428 *Web Site:* www.haroldober.com, pg 567

Elwell, James, Tyndale House Publishers Inc, 351 Executive Dr, Carol Stream, IL 60188 *Tel:* 630-668-8300 *Toll Free Tel:* 800-323-9400 *Web Site:* www.tyndale.com, pg 252

Elwell, Morgan, Kensington Publishing Corp, 119 W 40 St, New York, NY 10018 *Tel:* 212-407-1500 *Toll Free Tel:* 800-221-2647 *Fax:* 212-935-0699 *Web Site:* www.kensingtonbooks.com, pg 130

Emerick, Ken, Individual Excellence Awards, 30 E Broad St, 33rd fl, Columbus, OH 43215 *Tel:* 614-466-2613 *Fax:* 614-466-4494 *Web Site:* www.oac.state.oh.us, pg 695

Emmrich, Terry, University of Wisconsin Press, 1930 Monroe St, 3rd fl, Madison, WI 53711-2059 *Tel:* 608-263-0668 *Toll Free Tel:* 800-621-2736 (orders) *Fax:* 608-263-1173 *Toll Free Fax:* 800-621-2736 (orders) *E-mail:* uwiscpress@uwpress.wisc.edu (main off) *Web Site:* www.wisc.edu/wisconsinpress, pg 260

Emond, D Paul, Emond Montgomery Publications Ltd, 60 Shaftesbury Ave, Toronto, ON M4T 1A3, Canada *Tel:* 416-975-3925 *Toll Free Tel:* 888-837-0815 *Fax:* 416-975-3924 *E-mail:* orders@emp.ca *Web Site:* www.emp.ca, pg 483

Enderlin, Jennifer, St Martin's Press, LLC, 175 Fifth Ave, New York, NY 10010 *Tel:* 646-307-5151 *Fax:* 212-420-9314 *E-mail:* firstname.lastname@macmillan.com *Web Site:* www.stmartins.com, pg 214

Eng, Kenneth, Macmillan, 175 Fifth Ave, New York, NY 10010 *Tel:* 646-307-5151 *Fax:* 212-420-9314 *E-mail:* firstname.lastname@macmillan.com *Web Site:* www.macmillan.com, pg 145

Engel, Carrie, The Brookings Institution Press, 1775 Massachusetts Ave NW, Washington, DC 20036-2188 *Tel:* 202-536-3600 *Toll Free Tel:* 800-537-5487 *Fax:* 202-536-3623 *E-mail:* permissions@brookings.edu *Web Site:* www.brookings.edu, pg 47

Engel, Deborah, Houghton Mifflin Harcourt Trade & Reference Division, 222 Berkeley St, Boston, MA 02116 *Tel:* 617-351-5000 *Toll Free Tel:* 800-225-3362 *Web Site:* www.hmhco.com, pg 115

Engel, Jacqueline, Penguin Young Readers Group, 345 Hudson St, New York, NY 10014 *Tel:* 212-366-2000 *E-mail:* online@penguinputnam.com *Web Site:* www.penguinputnam.com; us.penguingroup.com, pg 187

Engel, Margaret, The Alicia Patterson Foundation Fellowship Program, 1100 Vermont Ave, Suite 900, Washington, DC 20005 *Tel:* 202-393-5995 *Fax:* 301-951-8512 *E-mail:* info@aliciapatterson.org *Web Site:* www.aliciapatterson.org, pg 716

Engel Steinberg, Jackie, Penguin Group (USA) LLC Sales, 375 Hudson St, New York, NY 10014 *Tel:* 212-366-2000 *E-mail:* online@penguinputnam.com *Web Site:* us.penguingroup.com, pg 186

Engelhardt, James, University of Alaska Press, 794 University Ave, Suite 220, Fairbanks, AK 99709 *Tel:* 907-474-5831 *Toll Free Tel:* 888-252-6657 (US only) *Fax:* 907-474-5502 *E-mail:* fypress@uaf.edu *Web Site:* www.uaf.edu/uapress, pg 254

Engelman, Ralph, The George Polk Awards, The Brooklyn Campus, One University Plaza, Brooklyn, NY 11201-5372 *Tel:* 718-488-1009; 718-488-1115 *Web Site:* www.liu.edu/polk, pg 720

Engelsma, Jonathan, Reformation Heritage Books, 2965 Leonard St NE, Grand Rapids, MI 49525 *Tel:* 616-977-0889 *Fax:* 616-285-3246 *E-mail:* orders@heritagebooks.org *Web Site:* www.heritagebooks.org, pg 207

Englander, Amanda, Crown Publishing Group, c/o Penguin Random House Inc, 1745 Broadway, New York, NY 10019 *Tel:* 212-782-9000 *Toll Free Tel:* 888-264-1745 *Fax:* 212-940-7408 *E-mail:* crownosm@penguinrandomhouse.com *Web Site:* crownpublishing.com, pg 68

Engles, Eric W PhD, EditCraft Editorial Services, 422 Pine St, Grass Valley, CA 95945 *Tel:* 530-263-3688 *Web Site:* www.editcraft.com, pg 525

English, Elaine, Elaine P English PLLC, 4710 41 St NW, Suite D, Washington, DC 20016 *Tel:* 202-362-5190 *Fax:* 202-362-5192 *E-mail:* foreignrights@elaineenglish.com *Web Site:* www.elaineenglish.com, pg 551

Engracia, Judith, Liza Dawson Associates, 350 Seventh Ave, Suite 2003, New York, NY 10001 *Tel:* 212-465-9071 *Fax:* 212-947-0460 *Web Site:* www.lizadawsonassociates.com, pg 547

Engstrand, Vida, Kensington Publishing Corp, 119 W 40 St, New York, NY 10018 *Tel:* 212-407-1500 *Toll Free Tel:* 800-221-2647 *Fax:* 212-935-0699 *Web Site:* www.kensingtonbooks.com, pg 130

Engstrom, Krister, Random House Children's Books, 1745 Broadway, New York, NY 10019 *Tel:* 212-782-9000 *Toll Free Tel:* 800-200-3552 *Fax:* 212-782-9452 *Web Site:* randomhousekids.com, pg 204

Ensign, Rebecca J, Gold Leaf Press, 3670 Morrissey Ave, Warren, MI 48091 *Tel:* 313-331-3571 *Web Site:* www.goldleafpress.com, pg 527

Enslow, Brian D, Enslow Publishing LLC, 101 W 23 St, Suite 240, New York, NY 10011 *Tel:* 908-771-9400 *Toll Free Tel:* 800-398-2504 *Fax:* 908-771-0925 *Toll Free Fax:* 877-980-4454 *E-mail:* customerservice@enslow.com *Web Site:* www.enslow.com, pg 83

Enslow, Mark, Enslow Publishing LLC, 101 W 23 St, Suite 240, New York, NY 10011 *Tel:* 908-771-9400 *Toll Free Tel:* 800-398-2504 *Fax:* 908-771-0925 *Toll Free Fax:* 877-980-4454 *E-mail:* customerservice@enslow.com *Web Site:* www.enslow.com, pg 83

Ensor, Kendra, Rand McNally, 9855 Woods Dr, Skokie, IL 60077 *Tel:* 847-329-8100 *Toll Free Tel:* 800-678-7263 *Fax:* 847-329-6139 *E-mail:* ctsales@randmcnally.com; mediarelations@randmcnally.com *Web Site:* www.randmcnally.com, pg 203

Entrekin, Morgan, Grove Atlantic Inc, 154 W 14 St, 12th fl, New York, NY 10011 *Tel:* 212-614-7850 *Toll Free Tel:* 800-521-0178 *Fax:* 212-614-7886 *E-mail:* info@groveatlantic.com *Web Site:* www.groveatlantic.com, pg 101

Epler, Barbara, New Directions Publishing Corp, 80 Eighth Ave, New York, NY 10011 *Tel:* 212-255-0230 *Fax:* 212-255-0231 *E-mail:* newdirections@ndbooks.com; editorial@ndbooks.com *Web Site:* ndbooks.com, pg 167

Epstein, Don R, Greater Talent Network Inc, 437 Fifth Ave, New York, NY 10016 *Tel:* 212-645-4200 *Toll Free Tel:* 800-326-4211 *Fax:* 212-627-1471 *E-mail:* info@greatertalent.com *Web Site:* www.greatertalent.com, pg 587

Epstein, Leslie, Boston University, 236 Bay State Rd, Boston, MA 02215 *Tel:* 617-353-2510 *Fax:* 617-353-3653 *E-mail:* crwr@bu.edu *Web Site:* www.bu.edu/writing, pg 659

Epstein, Linda, The Jennifer DeChiara Literary Agency, 31 E 32 St, Suite 300, New York, NY 10016 *Tel:* 212-481-8484 (ext 362) *Fax:* 212-481-9582 *Web Site:* www.jdlit.com, pg 547

Epstein, Richard, Atlantic Law Book Co, 22 Grassmere Ave, West Hartford, CT 06110-1215 *Tel:* 860-231-9300 *Toll Free Tel:* 800-259-5534 *Fax:* 860-231-9242 *E-mail:* atlanticlawbooks@aol.com *Web Site:* www.atlanticlawbooks.com, pg 26

Erickson, Leslie, University of British Columbia Press, 2029 West Mall, Vancouver, BC V6T 1Z2, Canada *Tel:* 604-822-5959 *Toll Free Tel:* 877-377-9378 *Fax:* 604-822-6083 *Toll Free Fax:* 800-668-0821 *E-mail:* frontdesk@ubcpress.ca *Web Site:* www.ubcpress.ca, pg 502

Erickson, Tim, RAND Corp, 1776 Main St, Santa Monica, CA 90407-2138 *Tel:* 310-393-0411 *Fax:* 310-393-4818 *Web Site:* www.rand.org, pg 203

Ericson, Carolyn Reeves, Ericson Books, 1614 Redbud St, Nacogdoches, TX 75965-2936 *Tel:* 936-564-3625 *Fax:* 936-552-8999 *E-mail:* kissinkuzzins@suddenlink.net *Web Site:* www.ericsonbooks.com, pg 84

Erikson, Anna, The Creative Co, PO Box 227, Mankato, MN 56002 *Tel:* 507-388-6273 *Toll Free Tel:* 800-445-6209 *Fax:* 507-388-2746 *E-mail:* info@thecreativecompany.us; orders@thecreativecompany.us *Web Site:* www.thecreativecompany.us, pg 66

Erlacher, Bill, Artists Associates, 4416 La Jolla Dr, Bradenton, FL 34210-3927 *Tel:* 941-756-8445, pg 583

Erlandson, Greg, Our Sunday Visitor Publishing, 200 Noll Plaza, Huntington, IN 46750 *Tel:* 260-356-8400 *Toll Free Tel:* 800-348-2440 (orders) *Fax:* 260-356-8472 *Toll Free Fax:* 800-498-6709 *E-mail:* osvbooks@osv.com (book orders) *Web Site:* www.osv.com, pg 178

Ernest, James, Wm B Eerdmans Publishing Co, 2140 Oak Industrial Dr NE, Grand Rapids, MI 49505 *Tel:* 616-459-4591 *Toll Free Tel:* 800-253-7521 *Fax:* 616-459-6540 *E-mail:* customerservice@eerdmans.com; sales@eerdmans.com *Web Site:* www.eerdmans.com, pg 80

Ernst, Christopher R, Artech House Inc, 685 Canton St, Norwood, MA 02062 *Tel:* 781-769-9750 *Toll Free Tel:* 800-225-9977 *Fax:* 781-769-6334 *E-mail:* artech@artechhouse.com *Web Site:* www.artechhouse.com, pg 23

Ernst, Megan, Bloomsbury Publishing Inc, 1385 Broadway, 5th fl, New York, NY 10018 *Tel:* 212-419-5300 *E-mail:* marketingusa@bloomsbury.com; adultpublicityusa@bloomsbury.com; askacademic@bloomsbury.com *Web Site:* www.bloomsbury.com, pg 40

Ero, Lauren, AMWA Annual Conference, 30 W Gude Dr, Suite 525, Rockville, MD 20850-4357 *Tel:* 240-238-0940 *Fax:* 301-294-9006 *E-mail:* amwa@amwa.org *Web Site:* www.amwa.org, pg 649

Erochina, Barbara, Gerald Lampert Memorial Award, 192 Spadina Ave, Suite 312, Toronto, ON M5T 2C2, Canada *Tel:* 416-504-1657 *Fax:* 416-504-0096 *E-mail:* readings@poets.ca *Web Site:* poets.ca, pg 699

Erochina, Barbara, The League of Canadian Poets, 192 Spadina Ave, Suite 312, Toronto, ON M5T 2C2, Canada *Tel:* 416-504-1657 *Fax:* 416-504-0096 *Web Site:* poets.ca, pg 608

Erochina, Barbara, Pat Lowther Memorial Award, 192 Spadina Ave, Suite 312, Toronto, ON M5T 2C2, Canada *Tel:* 416-504-1657 *Fax:* 416-504-0096 *E-mail:* readings@poets.ca *Web Site:* poets.ca, pg 703

Erochina, Barbara, Jessamy Stursberg Poetry Contest for Youth, 192 Spadina Ave, Suite 312, Toronto, ON M5T 2C2, Canada *Tel:* 416-504-1657 *Fax:* 416-504-0096 *E-mail:* readings@poets.ca *Web Site:* www.youngpoets.ca; poets.ca, pg 731

Errico, Kristin, Harlequin Enterprises Ltd, 233 Broadway, Suite 1001, New York, NY 10279 *Tel:* 212-553-4200 *Fax:* 212-227-8969 *E-mail:* CustomerService@harlequin.com *Web Site:* www.harlequin.com, pg 105

Esagui, Dr Veronica, Northwest Writers & Publishers Association (NWPA), 21860 Willamette Dr, West Linn, OR 97068 *Web Site:* northwestwriterspublishers.weebly.com, pg 615

Esco, Melinda, Texas Christian University Press, 3000 Sandage Ave, Fort Worth, TX 76109 *Tel:* 817-257-7822 *Toll Free Tel:* 800-826-8911 *Fax:* 817-257-5075 *Web Site:* www.prs.tcu.edu, pg 243

Escobar, Nicole, New Hampshire Literary Awards, 2500 N River Rd, Manchester, NH 03106 *Tel:* 603-314-7980 *Fax:* 603-314-7981 *E-mail:* info@nhwritersproject.org *Web Site:* www.nhwritersproject.org, pg 712

Escobedo, Eddie Jr, National Association of Hispanic Publications Inc (NAHP), 529 14 St NW, Suite 1126, Washington, DC 20045 *Tel:* 202-662-7250 *Web Site:* www.nahp.org, pg 611

Eselgroth, Spring, Society of American Business Editors & Writers Inc (SABEW), Walter Cronkite School of Journalism & Mass Communication, Arizona State University, 555 N Central Ave, Suite 406 E, Phoenix, AZ 85004-1248 *Tel:* 602-496-7862 *Fax:* 602-496-7041 *E-mail:* sabew@sabew.org *Web Site:* sabew.org, pg 619

Esersky, Gareth, Carol Mann Agency, 55 Fifth Ave, New York, NY 10003 *Tel:* 212-206-5635 *Fax:* 212-675-4809 *E-mail:* submissions@carolmannagency.com *Web Site:* www.carolmannagency.com, pg 563

Eskelsen, Lily, National Education Association (NEA), 1201 16 St NW, Washington, DC 20036-3290 *Tel:* 202-833-4000 *Fax:* 202-822-7974 *Web Site:* www.nea.org, pg 164, 612

Essary, Loris, International Titles, 931 E 56 St, Austin, TX 78751-1724 *Tel:* 512-909-2447 *Web Site:* www.internationaltitles.com, pg 557

Essary, Loris, Quincannon Publishing Group, PO Box 8100, Glen Ridge, NJ 07028-8100 *Tel:* 973-380-9942 *E-mail:* editors@quincannongroup.com *Web Site:* www.quincannongroup.com, pg 202

Estep, Ida Esq, Dog Writers' Association of America Inc (DWAA), 66 Adams St, Jamestown, NY 14701 *Tel:* 716-484-6155 *E-mail:* dogwriter@windstream.net *Web Site:* www.dwaa.org, pg 604

Estep, Ida Esq, Dog Writers' Association of America Inc (DWAA) Annual Writing Competition, 2243 Kelmscott Ct, Westlake Village, CA 91361 *Tel:* 805-418-7899 *Fax:* 831-374-9231 *E-mail:* dogwriter@windstream.net *Web Site:* www.dwaa.org, pg 681

Esterman, Laura, Paradigm Publishers, 5589 Arapahoe Ave, Suite 206A, Boulder, CO 80303 *Tel:* 303-245-9054 *Web Site:* www.paradigmpublishers.com, pg 182

Estes, Jack, Pleasure Boat Studio: A Literary Press, 201 W 89 St, New York, NY 10024 *Tel:* 212-362-8563 *Fax:* 413-677-0085 *E-mail:* pleasboat@nyc.rr.com *Web Site:* www.pleasureboatstudio.com, pg 193

Estremera, Estefeni, The Guilford Press, 72 Spring St, New York, NY 10012 *Tel:* 212-431-9800 *Toll Free Tel:* 800-365-7006 *Fax:* 212-966-6708 *E-mail:* info@guilford.com *Web Site:* www.guilford.com, pg 102

Estridge, Holli, Texas A&M University Press, John H Lindsey Bldg, Lewis St, 4354 TAMU, College Station, TX 77843-4354 *Tel:* 979-845-1436 *Toll Free Tel:* 800-826-8911 (orders) *Fax:* 979-847-8752 *Toll Free Fax:* 888-617-2421 (orders) *E-mail:* tampress@tamu.edu *Web Site:* www.tamupress.com, pg 243

Estrin, Heidi, AJL Judaica Bibliography Award, PO Box 1118, Teaneck, NJ 07666 *Tel:* 201-371-3255 *E-mail:* ajlibs@osu.edu *Web Site:* www.jewishlibraries.org, pg 666

Estrin, Heidi, AJL Judaica Reference Award, PO Box 1118, Teaneck, NJ 07666 *Tel:* 201-371-3255 *E-mail:* ajlibs@osu.edu *Web Site:* www.jewishlibraries.org, pg 666

Estrin, Heidi, Association of Jewish Libraries (AJL) Inc, PO Box 1118, Teaneck, NJ 07666 *Tel:* 201-371-3255 *E-mail:* info@jewishlibraries.org *Web Site:* www.jewishlibraries.org, pg 599

Estrin, Heidi, Sydney Taylor Book Awards, PO Box 1118, Teaneck, NJ 07666 *Tel:* 973-744-3836 *E-mail:* chair@sydneytaylorbookaward.org *Web Site:* www.sydneytaylorbookaward.org, pg 731

Etcheson, Amy, Southern Illinois University Press, 1915 University Press Dr, SIUC Mail Code 6806, Carbondale, IL 62901-4323 *Tel:* 618-453-2281 *Fax:* 618-453-1221 *E-mail:* custserv@press.uchicago.edu; rights@siu.edu *Web Site:* www.siupress.com, pg 231

Eth, Felicia, Felicia Eth Literary Representation, 555 Bryant St, Suite 350, Palo Alto, CA 94301 *Tel:* 415-970-9717 *E-mail:* feliciaeth.literary@gmail.com *Web Site:* www.ethliterary.com, pg 551

Etra, Judith, Whittier Publications Inc, 3115 Long Beach Rd, Oceanside, NY 11572 *Tel:* 516-432-8120 *Toll Free Tel:* 800-897-TEXT (897-8398) *Fax:* 516-889-0341 *E-mail:* info@whitbooks.com, pg 271

Eubanks, Debra, American Psychiatric Publishing (APP), 1000 Wilson Blvd, Suite 1825, Arlington, VA 22209 *Tel:* 703-907-7322 *Toll Free Tel:* 800-368-5777 *Fax:* 703-907-1091 *E-mail:* appi@psych.org *Web Site:* www.appi.org; www.psychiatryonline.org, pg 15

Eulau, Dennis, Simon & Schuster, Inc, 1230 Avenue of the Americas, New York, NY 10020 *Tel:* 212-698-7000 *Fax:* 212-698-7007 *E-mail:* firstname.lastname@simonandschuster.com *Web Site:* www.simonandschuster.com, pg 226

Evans, Alyn, Watson-Guptill Publications, c/o Random House Inc, 1745 Broadway, New York, NY 10019 *Tel:* 212-782-9000 *Fax:* 212-940-7381 *E-mail:* crownbiz@randomhouse.com *Web Site:* www.randomhouse.com/crown/watsonguptill, pg 268

Evans, Anne Matlack, Napa Valley Writers' Conference, Upper Valley Campus, 1088 College Ave, St Helena, CA 94574 *Tel:* 707-967-2900 (ext 1611) *Fax:* 707-967-2909 *E-mail:* writecon@napavalley.edu *Web Site:* www.napawritersconf.org, pg 653

Evans, Christopher, PRISM international Literary Non-Fiction Contest, University of British Columbia, Buch E462, 1866 Main Mall, Vancouver, BC V6T 1Z1, Canada *Tel:* 778-822-2514 *Fax:* 778-822-3616 *E-mail:* prismwritingcontest@gmail.com *Web Site:* www.prismmagazine.ca, pg 721

Evans, Christopher, PRISM international Poetry Contest, University of British Columbia, Buch E462, 1866 Main Mall, Vancouver, BC V6T 1Z1, Canada *Tel:* 778-822-2514 *Fax:* 778-822-3616 *E-mail:* prismwritingcontest@gmail.com *Web Site:* www.prismmagazine.ca, pg 721

Evans, Christopher, PRISM international Short Fiction Contest, University of British Columbia, Buch E462, 1866 Main Mall, Vancouver, BC V6T 1Z1, Canada *Tel:* 778-822-2514 *Fax:* 778-822-3616 *E-mail:* prismwritingcontest@gmail.com *Web Site:* www.prismmagazine.ca, pg 721

Evans, Claire Lewis, University of Alabama Press, 200 Hackberry Lane, 2nd fl, Tuscaloosa, AL 35487 *Tel:* 205-348-5180 *Fax:* 205-348-9201 *Web Site:* www.uapress.ua.edu, pg 254

Evans, Elaine, Standard International Media Holdings, 568 Ninth St S, Suite 201, Naples, FL 34102-7336 *Tel:* 239-248-5550 *Fax:* 239-649-5832 *Toll Free Fax:* 866-948-7883 *E-mail:* sales@standardinternationalmedia.com *Web Site:* www.standardinternationalmedia.com, pg 233

Evans, Elizabeth, Jean V Naggar Literary Agency Inc (JVNLA), 216 E 75 St, Suite 1-E, New York, NY 10021 *Tel:* 212-794-1082 *E-mail:* jvnla@jvnla.com *Web Site:* www.jvnla.com, pg 566

Farley-Chevrier, Francis, Prix Alvine-Belisle, 2065 rue Parthenais, Bureau 387, Montreal, QC H2K 3T1, Canada *Tel:* 514-281-5012 *Fax:* 514-281-8219 *E-mail:* info@asted.org *Web Site:* www.asted.org, pg 722

Farlow, Martha, The University of Virginia Press, PO Box 400318, Charlottesville, VA 22904-4318 *Tel:* 434-924-3468 (cust serv); 434-924-3469 (cust serv) *Toll Free Tel:* 800-831-3406 (orders) *Fax:* 434-982-2655 *Toll Free Fax:* 877-288-6400 *E-mail:* vapress@virginia.edu *Web Site:* www.upress.virginia.edu, pg 260

Farmer, Brad, Gibbs Smith Publisher, 1877 E Gentile St, Layton, UT 84041 *Tel:* 801-544-9800 *Toll Free Tel:* 800-748-5439; 800-835-4993 (orders) *Fax:* 801-544-5582 *Toll Free Fax:* 800-213-3023 (orders only) *E-mail:* info@gibbs-smith.com; tradeorders@gibbs-smith.com *Web Site:* www.gibbs-smith.com, pg 96

Farmer, Brent, Charlesbridge Publishing Inc, 85 Main St, Watertown, MA 02472 *Tel:* 617-926-0329 *Toll Free Tel:* 800-225-3214 *Fax:* 617-926-5720 *Toll Free Fax:* 800-926-5775 *E-mail:* books@charlesbridge.com *Web Site:* www.charlesbridge.com, pg 55

Farmer, Chris, University of Texas Press, 2100 Comal St, Austin, TX 78722 *Tel:* 512-471-7233 *Fax:* 512-232-7178 *E-mail:* utpress@uts.cc.utexas.edu *Web Site:* www.utexaspress.com, pg 244

Farmer, Daryl, Visiting Writers Series, English Dept, PO Box 755720, Fairbanks, AK 99775-5720 *Tel:* 907-474-7193 *Fax:* 907-474-5247 *E-mail:* faengl@uaf.edu *Web Site:* www.alaska.edu/english, pg 656

Farmer, Gary, American Association for Vocational Instructional Materials, 220 Smithonia Rd, Winterville, GA 30683 *Tel:* 706-742-5355 *Fax:* 706-742-7005 *E-mail:* sales@aavim.com *Web Site:* www.aavim.com, pg 11

Farnol, Jane, Astor Indexers, 256 Blue Ridge Dr, Canadensis, PA 18325 *Tel:* 570-595-2336; 570-534-8951 (cell), pg 520

Farnsworth, David, Casemate Publishers & Book Distributors LLC, 908 Darby Rd, Havertown, PA 19083 *Tel:* 610-853-9131 *Fax:* 610-853-9146 *E-mail:* casemate@casematepublishing.com *Web Site:* www.casematepublishing.com, pg 51

Farnsworth, Sarah, Casemate Publishers & Book Distributors LLC, 908 Darby Rd, Havertown, PA 19083 *Tel:* 610-853-9131 *Fax:* 610-853-9146 *E-mail:* casemate@casematepublishing.com *Web Site:* www.casematepublishing.com, pg 51

Farr, Jeff, Old Barn Enterprises Inc, 600 Kelly Rd, Carthage, NC 28327 *Tel:* 910-947-2587 *Fax:* 480-287-9017 *E-mail:* jeffandpam@nynphotoschool.com *Web Site:* www.nynphotoschool.com, pg 174

Farrace, Bob, National Association of Secondary School Principals (NASSP), 1904 Association Dr, Reston, VA 20191-1537 *Tel:* 703-860-0200 *Toll Free Tel:* 800-253-7746 *Fax:* 703-476-5432 *E-mail:* membership@principals.org; sales@principals.org; publications2@nassp.org (communs & devt) *Web Site:* www.principals.org, pg 163

Farranto, Amy, Northern Illinois University Press, 2280 Bethany Rd, DeKalb, IL 60115 *Tel:* 815-753-1826; 815-753-1075 *Fax:* 815-753-1845 *Web Site:* www.niupress.niu.edu, pg 171

Farrar, Amy E, Farrar Writing & Editing, 4638 Manchester Rd, Mound, MN 55364 *Tel:* 952-472-6874 *Fax:* 952-472-6874 (call first) *Web Site:* www.writeandedit.net, pg 526

Farrin, Cassandra, Polebridge Press, c/o Willamette University, 900 State St, Salem, OR 97301 *Tel:* 503-375-5323 *E-mail:* orders@westarinstitute.org *Web Site:* www.polebridgepress.com, pg 194

Farris, Michael D, Farris Literary Agency Inc, PO Box 570069, Dallas, TX 75357-0069 *Tel:* 972-203-8804 *E-mail:* farris1@airmail.net *Web Site:* www.farrisliterary.com, pg 551

Farris, Susan Morgan, Farris Literary Agency Inc, PO Box 570069, Dallas, TX 75357-0069 *Tel:* 972-203-8804 *E-mail:* farris1@airmail.net *Web Site:* www.farrisliterary.com, pg 551

Fastiggi, Ray, The Rockefeller University Press, 1114 First Ave, 3rd fl, New York, NY 10065-8325 *Tel:* 212-327-7938 *Fax:* 212-327-8587 *E-mail:* rupress@rockefeller.edu *Web Site:* www.rupress.org, pg 210

Fauci, Julia, Northern Illinois University Press, 2280 Bethany Rd, DeKalb, IL 60115 *Tel:* 815-753-1826; 815-753-1075 *Fax:* 815-753-1845 *Web Site:* www.niupress.niu.edu, pg 171

Fauley, Tim, Orange Frazer Press Inc, 37 1/2 W Main St, Wilmington, OH 45177 *Tel:* 937-382-3196 *Toll Free Tel:* 800-852-9332 (orders) *Fax:* 937-383-3159 *E-mail:* ofrazer@erinet.com *Web Site:* www.orangefrazer.com, pg 176

Faulkner, Cassandra, Blue Book Publications Inc, 8009 34 Ave S, Suite 250, Minneapolis, MN 55425 *Tel:* 952-854-5229 *Toll Free Tel:* 800-877-4867 *Fax:* 925-853-1486 *E-mail:* support@bluebookinc.com *Web Site:* www.bluebookofgunvalues.com; www.bluebookofguitarvalues.com, pg 40

Faulkner, Donald, New York State Edith Wharton Citation of Merit for Fiction Writers, University at Albany, SL 320, Albany, NY 12222 *Tel:* 518-442-5620 *Fax:* 518-442-5621 *E-mail:* writers@uamail.albany.edu *Web Site:* www.albany.edu/writers-inst, pg 713

Faulkner, Donald, New York State Walt Whitman Citation of Merit for Poets, University at Albany, SL 320, Albany, NY 12222 *Tel:* 518-442-5620 *Fax:* 518-442-5621 *E-mail:* writers@uamail.albany.edu *Web Site:* www.albany.edu/writers-inst, pg 713

Faulkner, Donald, New York State Writers Institute, University at Albany, Science Library 320, Albany, NY 12222 *Tel:* 518-442-5620 *Fax:* 518-442-5621 *E-mail:* writers@uamail.albany.edu *Web Site:* www.albany.edu/writers-inst, pg 653

Fausset, Katherine, Curtis Brown Ltd, 10 Astor Place, New York, NY 10003 *Tel:* 212-473-5400 *Web Site:* www.curtisbrown.com, pg 544

Faust, Jessica H, BookEnds LLC, 136 Long Hill Rd, Gillette, NJ 07933 *Web Site:* www.bookends-inc.com, pg 543

Faust, Rudy, Northwestern University Press, 629 Noyes St, Evanston, IL 60208-4210 *Tel:* 847-491-2046 *Toll Free Tel:* 800-621-2736 (orders only) *Fax:* 847-491-8150 *E-mail:* nupress@northwestern.edu *Web Site:* www.nupress.northwestern.edu, pg 171

Favreau, Marc, The New Press, 38 Greene St, 4th fl, New York, NY 10013 *Tel:* 212-629-8802 *Toll Free Tel:* 800-343-4489 (orders) *Fax:* 212-629-8617 *Toll Free Fax:* 800-351-5073 (orders) *E-mail:* newpress@thenewpress.com *Web Site:* www.thenewpress.com, pg 168

Faxel, Tammy, Brilliance Audio, 1704 Eaton Dr, Grand Haven, MI 49417 *Tel:* 616-846-5256 *Toll Free Tel:* 800-648-2312 (orders only) *Fax:* 616-846-0630 *E-mail:* customerservice@brillianceaudio.com *Web Site:* www.brillianceaudio.com, pg 46

Faxel, Tammy, Dreamscape Media LLC, 6940 Hall St, Holland, OH 43528 *Tel:* 419-867-6965 *Toll Free Tel:* 877-983-7326 *E-mail:* info@dreamscapeab.com *Web Site:* www.dreamscapeab.com, pg 77

Feal, Rosemary G, Modern Language Association of America (MLA), 26 Broadway, 3rd fl, New York, NY 10004-1789 *Tel:* 646-576-5000 *Fax:* 646-458-0030 *Web Site:* www.mla.org, pg 158

Feal, Rosemary G, Modern Language Association of America (MLA), 26 Broadway, 3rd fl, New York, NY 10004-1789 *Tel:* 646-576-5000 *Fax:* 646-458-0030 *E-mail:* convention@mla.org *Web Site:* www.mla.org, pg 610

Featherstone, Craig, B&H Publishing Group, One Lifeway Plaza, Nashville, TN 37234-0114 *Tel:* 615-251-2520 *Fax:* 615-251-5004 *Web Site:* www.bhpublishinggroup.com, pg 30

Feazel, R Michael, Warren Communications News Inc, 2115 Ward Ct NW, Washington, DC 20037 *Tel:* 202-872-9200 *Toll Free Tel:* 800-771-9202 *Fax:* 202-293-3435; 202-318-8350 *E-mail:* info@warren-news.com; newsroom@warren-news.com *Web Site:* www.warren-news.com, pg 267

Febus, Fernando, Lectorum Publications Inc, 205 Chubb Ave, Lyndhurst, NJ 07071 *Toll Free Tel:* 800-345-5946 *Fax:* 201-559-2201 *Toll Free Fax:* 877-532-8676 *E-mail:* lectorum@lectorum.com *Web Site:* www.lectorum.com, pg 136

Fedorko, Lauren, DWJ BOOKS LLC, 46 Cliff Dr, Sag Harbor, NY 11963 *Tel:* 631-899-4500 *E-mail:* info@dwjbooks.com *Web Site:* www.dwjbooks.com, pg 524

Feehan, Kristen, Penguin Group (USA) LLC Sales, 375 Hudson St, New York, NY 10014 *Tel:* 212-366-2000 *E-mail:* online@penguinputnam.com *Web Site:* us.penguingroup.com, pg 186

Feher, Michel, Zone Books dba Urzone Inc, 1226 Prospect Ave, Brooklyn, NY 11218 *Tel:* 718-686-0048 *Toll Free Tel:* 800-405-1619 (orders & cust serv) *Fax:* 718-686-9045 *Toll Free Fax:* 800-406-9145 (orders) *E-mail:* orders@triliteral.org *Web Site:* www.zonebooks.org, pg 280

Feher-Gurewich, Judith, Other Press LLC, 2 Park Ave, 24th fl, New York, NY 10016 *Tel:* 212-414-0054 *Toll Free Tel:* 877-843-6843 *Fax:* 212-414-0939 *E-mail:* editor@otherpress.com; rights@otherpress.com *Web Site:* www.otherpress.com, pg 178

Fehr, Don, Trident Media Group LLC, 41 Madison Ave, 36th fl, New York, NY 10010 *Tel:* 212-333-1511 *E-mail:* info@tridentmediagroup.com; press@tridentmediagroup.com *Web Site:* www.tridentmediagroup.com, pg 577

Feigenbaum, Laurie, Feigenbaum Publishing Consultants Inc, 61 Bounty Lane, Jericho, NY 11753 *Tel:* 516-647-8314 (cell) *Fax:* 516-935-0507 *E-mail:* readrover5@aol.com, pg 551

Feinberg, Joan, Macmillan Higher Education, 41 Madison Ave, 37th fl, New York, NY 10010 *Tel:* 212-576-9400 *Fax:* 212-689-2383 *Web Site:* www.macmillanhighered.com, pg 145

Feist, Betsy, Betsy Feist Resources, 140 E 81 St, Unit 8-G, New York, NY 10028-1875 *Tel:* 212-861-2014 *E-mail:* bfresources@rcn.com, pg 526

Feiwel, Jean, Macmillan, 175 Fifth Ave, New York, NY 10010 *Tel:* 646-307-5151 *Fax:* 212-420-9314 *E-mail:* firstname.lastname@macmillan.com *Web Site:* www.macmillan.com, pg 145

Feld, Rachel, Random House Children's Books, 1745 Broadway, New York, NY 10019 *Tel:* 212-782-9000 *Toll Free Tel:* 800-200-3552 *Fax:* 212-782-9452 *Web Site:* randomhousekids.com, pg 203

Felder, David W PhD, Wellington Press, 9601-30 Miccosukee Rd, Tallahassee, FL 32309 *E-mail:* peacegames@aol.com *Web Site:* www.peacegames.com, pg 268

Feldheim, Yitzchak, Feldheim Publishers (Philipp Feldheim Inc), 208 Airport Executive Park, Nanuet, NY 10954 *Tel:* 845-356-2282 *Toll Free Tel:* 800-237-7149 (orders) *Fax:* 845-425-1908 *E-mail:* sales@feldheim.com *Web Site:* www.feldheim.com, pg 87

Feldman, Gwen, Silman-James Press, 3624 Shannon Rd, Los Angeles, CA 90027 *Tel:* 323-661-9922 *Toll Free Tel:* 877-SJP-BOOK (757-2665) *Fax:* 323-661-9933 *E-mail:* info@silmanjamespress.com *Web Site:* www.silmanjamespress.com, pg 224

Feldman, Jennifer, Marshall Cavendish Corp, 99 White Plains Rd, Tarrytown, NY 10591-9001 *Tel:* 914-332-8888 *Toll Free Tel:* 800-821-9881 *Fax:* 914-332-8102 *E-mail:* mce@marshallcavendish.com *Web Site:* www.mceducation.us, pg 148

Feldman, Ronit, Doubleday/Nan A Talese, c/o Penguin Random House Inc, 1745 Broadway, New York, NY 10019 *Tel:* 212-751-2600 *Fax:* 212-572-2662 *E-mail:* ddaypub@randomhouse.com *Web Site:* knopfdoubleday.com, pg 76

Feldman, Steven, United States Holocaust Memorial Museum, 100 Raoul Wallenberg Place SW, Washington, DC 20024-2126 *Tel:* 202-314-7837; 202-488-6144 (orders) *Toll Free Tel:* 800-259-

9998 (orders) *Fax:* 202-479-9726; 202-488-0438 (orders) *E-mail:* cahs_publications@ushmm.org *Web Site:* www.ushmm.org, pg 253

Feldman, Tim, International Society of Automation (ISA), 67 T W Alexander Dr, Research Triangle Park, NC 27709-0185 *Tel:* 919-549-8411 *Fax:* 919-549-8288 *E-mail:* info@isa.org *Web Site:* www.isa.org, pg 125

Feldmann, Sharon, Mel Bay Publications Inc, 4 Industrial Dr, Pacific, MO 63069-0066 *Tel:* 636-257-3970 *Toll Free Tel:* 800-863-5229 *Fax:* 636-257-5062 *Toll Free Fax:* 800-660-9818 *E-mail:* email@melbay.com *Web Site:* www.melbay.com, pg 154

Felgar, Catherine, HarperCollins General Books Group, 195 Broadway, New York, NY 10007 *Tel:* 212-207-7000 *Web Site:* www.harpercollins.com, pg 105

Feller, Sally, Spry Publishing, 2500 S State St, Ann Arbor, MI 48104 *Tel:* 734-913-1700 *Toll Free Tel:* 877-722-2264 *Fax:* 734-913-1249 *E-mail:* info@sprypub.com *Web Site:* www.sprypub.com, pg 232

Felt, Robert L, Paradigm Publications, 202 Bendix Dr, Taos, NM 87571 *Tel:* 575-758-7758 *Toll Free Tel:* 800-873-3946 (US); 888-873-3947 (CN) *Fax:* 575-758-7768 *Web Site:* www.paradigm-pubs.com; www.redwingbooks.com, pg 182

Felus, Allison, Chicago Review Press, 814 N Franklin St, Chicago, IL 60610 *Tel:* 312-337-0747 *Toll Free Tel:* 800-888-4741 *Fax:* 312-337-5110 *E-mail:* frontdesk@chicagoreviewpress.com *Web Site:* www.chicagoreviewpress.com, pg 56

Fendrich, Debra, Meriwether Publishing, c/o Pioneer Drama Service, 9707-A E Easter Lane, Englewood, CO 80112 *Tel:* 303-779-4035 *Toll Free Tel:* 800-333-7262 *Fax:* 303-779-4315 *E-mail:* wholesale@pioneerdrama.com *Web Site:* www.pioneerdrama.com, pg 155

Fendrich, Steven, Meriwether Publishing, c/o Pioneer Drama Service, 9707-A E Easter Lane, Englewood, CO 80112 *Tel:* 303-779-4035 *Toll Free Tel:* 800-333-7262 *Fax:* 303-779-4315 *E-mail:* wholesale@pioneerdrama.com *Web Site:* www.pioneerdrama.com, pg 155

Feng, Kelly, China Books, 360 Swift Ave, Suite 48, South San Francisco, CA 94080 *Tel:* 650-872-7076 *Toll Free Tel:* 800-818-2017 (US only) *Fax:* 650-872-7808 *E-mail:* info@chinabooks.com *Web Site:* www.chinabooks.com, pg 57

Fenn, Jordan, McClelland & Stewart Ltd, One Toronto St, Toronto, ON M5C 2V6, Canada *Tel:* 416-364-4449 *Fax:* 416-957-1587 *E-mail:* editorial@mcclelland.com *Web Site:* www.mcclelland.com, pg 491

Fenton, Carter, Morton Publishing Co, 925 W Kenyon Ave, Unit 12, Englewood, CO 80110 *Tel:* 303-761-4805 *Fax:* 303-762-9923 *E-mail:* contact@morton-pub.com *Web Site:* www.morton-pub.com, pg 160

Fenton, Robert L, Robert L Fenton PC; Entertainment Attorney & Literary Agent, 31800 Northwestern Hwy, Suite 204, Farmington Hills, MI 48334 *Tel:* 248-855-8780 *Fax:* 248-855-3302 *Web Site:* www.robertlfenton.com, pg 551

Fenza, David W, Association of Writers & Writing Programs (AWP), George Mason University, 4400 University Dr, MSN 1E3, Fairfax, VA 22030 *Tel:* 703-993-4301 *Fax:* 703-993-4302 *E-mail:* awp@awpwriter.org *Web Site:* www.awpwriter.org, pg 599

Fenza, David W, AWP Award Series, George Mason University, 4400 University Dr, MSN 1E3, Fairfax, VA 22030 *Tel:* 703-993-4301 *Fax:* 703-993-4302 *E-mail:* awp@awpwriter.org *Web Site:* www.awpwriter.org, pg 669

Feresten, Nancy Laties, National Geographic Books, 1145 17 St NW, Washington, DC 20036-4688 *Tel:* 202-857-7000 *Fax:* 202-857-7670 *Web Site:* books.nationalgeographic.com/books, pg 165

Ferguson, David, Morton Publishing Co, 925 W Kenyon Ave, Unit 12, Englewood, CO 80110 *Tel:* 303-761-4805 *Fax:* 303-762-9923 *E-mail:* contact@morton-pub.com *Web Site:* www.morton-pub.com, pg 160

Ferland, Sylvie, Les Publications du Quebec, 1000, rte de l'Eqalise, Bureau 500, Quebec, QC G1V 3V9, Canada *Tel:* 418-643-5150 *Toll Free Tel:* 800-463-2100 (Quebec province only) *Fax:* 418-643-6177 *Toll Free Fax:* 800-561-3479 *E-mail:* publicationsduquebec@cspq.gouv.qc.ca *Web Site:* www.publicationsduquebec.gouv.qc.ca, pg 496

Fernald, Bob, Down East Books, 680 Commercial St (US Rte 1), Rockport, ME 04856 *Tel:* 207-594-9544 *Toll Free Tel:* 800-685-7962 (US only orders); 800-766-1670 *E-mail:* editorial@downeast.com *Web Site:* www.downeast.com, pg 76

Fernald, Tom, Chronicle Books LLC, 680 Second St, San Francisco, CA 94107 *Tel:* 415-537-4200 *Toll Free Tel:* 800-759-0190 (cust serv) *Fax:* 415-537-4460 *Toll Free Fax:* 800-858-7787 (orders); 800-286-9471 (cust serv) *E-mail:* frontdesk@chroniclebooks.com *Web Site:* www.chroniclebooks.com, pg 57

Fernandez, Mercedes, Kensington Publishing Corp, 119 W 40 St, New York, NY 10018 *Tel:* 212-407-1500 *Toll Free Tel:* 800-221-2647 *Fax:* 212-935-0699 *Web Site:* www.kensingtonbooks.com, pg 130

Fernandez, Oliva, Pearson ELT, 10 Bank St, 9th fl, White Plains, NY 10606-1951 *Tel:* 914-287-8000 *Web Site:* www.pearsonelt.com, pg 185

Fernandez-Williams, Sherrie, Loft-Mentor Series in Poetry & Creative Prose, Open Book, Suite 200, 1011 Washington Ave S, Minneapolis, MN 55415 *Tel:* 612-215-2575 *Fax:* 612-215-2576 *E-mail:* loft@loft.org *Web Site:* www.loft.org, pg 703

Fernando, Mark, National Communication Association, 1765 "N" St NW, Washington, DC 20036 *Tel:* 202-464-4622 *Fax:* 202-464-4600 *E-mail:* inbox@natcom.org *Web Site:* www.natcom.org, pg 612

Feron, Carrie, HarperCollins General Books Group, 195 Broadway, New York, NY 10007 *Tel:* 212-207-7000 *Web Site:* www.harpercollins.com, pg 105

Ferrara, Moe, BookEnds LLC, 136 Long Hill Rd, Gillette, NJ 07933 *Web Site:* www.bookends-inc.com, pg 543

Ferrari, Nick, American Society of Mechanical Engineers (ASME), 2 Park Ave, New York, NY 10016-5990 *Tel:* 212-591-7000 *Toll Free Tel:* 800-843-2763 (cust serv-US, CN & Mexico) *Fax:* 212-591-7674; 973-882-8113 (cust serv); 973-882-1717 (orders & inquiries) *E-mail:* infocentral@asme.org *Web Site:* www.asme.org, pg 16

Ferrari-Adler, Jofie, Simon & Schuster, 1230 Avenue of the Americas, New York, NY 10020 *Tel:* 212-698-7000 *Toll Free Tel:* 800-223-2348 (cust serv); 800-223-2336 (orders) *Toll Free Fax:* 800-943-9831 (orders) *Web Site:* www.simonandschuster.com, pg 225

Ferraro, Leslie, Disney Publishing Worldwide, 1101 Flower St, Glendale, CA 91201 *Web Site:* books.disney.com, pg 74

Ferri, Sandra Ozzola, Europa Editions, 214 W 29 St, Suite 1003, New York, NY 10001 *Tel:* 212-868-6844 *Fax:* 212-868-6845 *E-mail:* info@europaeditions.com *Web Site:* www.europaeditions.com, pg 84

Ferri, Sandro, Europa Editions, 214 W 29 St, Suite 1003, New York, NY 10001 *Tel:* 212-868-6844 *Fax:* 212-868-6845 *E-mail:* info@europaeditions.com *Web Site:* www.europaeditions.com, pg 84

Ferrier, Patrick, McGraw-Hill Ryerson Limited, 300 Water St, Whitby, ON L1N 9B6, Canada *Tel:* 905-430-5000 *Toll Free Tel:* 800-565-5758 (cust serv) *Fax:* 905-430-5020 *Toll Free Fax:* 800-463-5885 *Web Site:* www.mheducation.ca, pg 491

Ferro, Alden, Yale University Press, 302 Temple St, New Haven, CT 06511-8909 *Tel:* 203-432-0960; 203-432-0966 (sales); 401-531-2800 (cust serv) *Toll Free Tel:* 800-405-1619 (cust serv) *Fax:* 203-432-0948; 203-432-8485 (sales); 401-531-2801 (cust serv) *Toll Free Fax:* 800-406-9145 (cust serv) *E-mail:* sales.press@yale.edu (sales); customer.care@trilateral.org (cust serv) *Web Site:* www.yalebooks.com; yalepress.yale.edu/yupbooks, pg 278

Ferron, Michel, Les Editions Un Monde Different, 3905 Isabelle, Bureau 101, Brossard, QC J4Y 2R2, Canada *Tel:* 450-656-2660 *Toll Free Tel:* 800-443-2582 *Fax:* 450-659-9328 *E-mail:* info@umd.ca *Web Site:* www.umd.ca, pg 483

Fertig, Howard, Howard Fertig, Publisher, 80 E 11 St, New York, NY 10003 *Tel:* 212-982-7922 *Fax:* 212-982-1099 *E-mail:* enquiries@hfertigbooks.com; orders@hfertigbooks.com *Web Site:* www.hfertigbooks.com, pg 88

Fessio SJ, Fr Joseph, Ignatius Press, 1348 Tenth Ave, San Francisco, CA 94122-2304 *Toll Free Tel:* 800-651-1531 (orders); 888-615-3186 (cust serv) *E-mail:* info@ignatius.com *Web Site:* www.ignatius.com, pg 118

Fessler, Amanda, PubWest Book Design Awards, 17501 Hill Way, Lake Oswego, OR 97035 *Tel:* 503-901-9865 *Fax:* 602-234-3062 *Web Site:* pubwest.org, pg 722

Fessler, Bill, Golden West Cookbooks, 5738 N Central Ave, Phoenix, AZ 85012-1316 *Tel:* 602-234-1574 *Toll Free Tel:* 800-521-9221 *Fax:* 602-234-3062 *E-mail:* info@americantravelerpress.com *Web Site:* www.americantravelerpress.com, pg 98

Fetterman, Bonny, The Editors Circle, 462 Grove St, Montclair, NJ 07043 *Tel:* 973-783-5082 *E-mail:* query@theeditorscircle.com *Web Site:* www.theeditorscircle.com, pg 525

Feuer, Lisa, Random House Publishing Group, 1745 Broadway, New York, NY 10019 *Toll Free Tel:* 800-200-3552 *Web Site:* atrandom.com, pg 204

Feulner, Megan, Other Press LLC, 2 Park Ave, 24th fl, New York, NY 10016 *Tel:* 212-414-0054 *Toll Free Tel:* 877-843-6843 *Fax:* 212-414-0939 *E-mail:* editor@otherpress.com; rights@otherpress.com *Web Site:* www.otherpress.com, pg 178

Ficarra, Elise, Poetry Center Book Award, 1600 Holloway Ave, San Francisco, CA 94132 *Tel:* 415-338-2227 *Fax:* 415-338-0966 *E-mail:* poetry@sfsu.edu *Web Site:* www.sfsu.edu/~poetry, pg 720

Fichtelberg, Joseph PhD, Hofstra University, English Dept, 204 Mason Hall, Hempstead, NY 11549 *Tel:* 516-463-5454 *Web Site:* www.hofstra.edu, pg 660

Fidler, Patricia, Yale University Press, 302 Temple St, New Haven, CT 06511-8909 *Tel:* 203-432-0960; 203-432-0966 (sales); 401-531-2800 (cust serv) *Toll Free Tel:* 800-405-1619 (cust serv) *Fax:* 203-432-0948; 203-432-8485 (sales); 401-531-2801 (cust serv) *Toll Free Fax:* 800-406-9145 (cust serv) *E-mail:* sales.press@yale.edu (sales); customer.care@trilateral.org (cust serv) *Web Site:* www.yalebooks.com; yalepress.yale.edu/yupbooks, pg 278

Field, Alexander, Crown Publishing Group, c/o Penguin Random House Inc, 1745 Broadway, New York, NY 10019 *Tel:* 212-782-9000 *Toll Free Tel:* 888-264-1745 *Fax:* 212-940-7408 *E-mail:* crownosm@penguinrandomhouse.com *Web Site:* crownpublishing.com, pg 68

Field, Alexander, WaterBrook Multnomah Publishing Group, 12265 Oracle Blvd, Suite 200, Colorado Springs, CO 80921 *Tel:* 719-590-4999 *Toll Free Tel:* 800-603-7051 (orders) *Fax:* 719-590-8977 *Toll Free Fax:* 800-294-5686 (orders) *E-mail:* info@waterbrookmultnomah.com *Web Site:* waterbrookmultnomah.com, pg 267

Field, Ty, Jones & Bartlett Learning LLC, 5 Wall St, Burlington, MA 01803 *Tel:* 978-443-5000 *Toll Free Tel:* 800-832-0034 *Fax:* 978-443-8000 *E-mail:* info@jblearning.com *Web Site:* www.jblearning.com, pg 128

Fielder, John, Westcliffe Publishers Inc, 3360 Mitchell Lane, Suite E, Boulder, CO 80301 *Toll Free Tel:* 800-258-5830 *Fax:* 303-443-9687 *E-mail:* books@bigearthpublishing.com *Web Site:* www.bigearthpublishing.com/westcliffe-publishers, pg 269

Fields, Allyson, Rutgers University Press, 106 Somerset St, 3rd fl, New Brunswick, NJ 08901 *Tel:* 848-445-7762 *Toll Free Tel:* 800-848-6224 (orders only) *Fax:* 732-745-4935 (acqs, edit, mktg, perms & prodn) *Toll Free Fax:* 800-272-6817 (fulfillment) *Web Site:* rutgerspress.rutgers.edu, pg 213

Fields, Monique, Harper Lee Prize for Legal Fiction, 101 Paul Bryant Dr, Tuscaloosa, AL 35487 *Tel:* 205-348-5195 *Web Site:* www.law.ua.edu/programs/harper-lee-prize-for-legal-fiction, pg 700

Fields, Tyler, Perigee Books, 375 Hudson St, New York, NY 10014 *Tel:* 212-366-2000 *Fax:* 212-366-2365 *E-mail:* perigeebooks@us.penguingroup.com *Web Site:* www.penguin.com, pg 189

Fields, Tyler, Jeremy P Tarcher, 375 Hudson St, New York, NY 10014 *Tel:* 212-366-2000 *E-mail:* online@penguinputnam.com *Web Site:* www.penguinputnam.com; us.penguingroup.com, pg 240

Fiels, Keith Michael, The American Library Association (ALA), 50 E Huron St, Chicago, IL 60611 *Tel:* 312-944-6780; 312-280-4299 (memb & cust serv) *Toll Free Tel:* 800-545-2433 *Fax:* 312-440-9374 *E-mail:* ala@ala.org; customerservice@ala.org *Web Site:* www.ala.org, pg 595

Fife, Bruce, Piccadilly Books Ltd, PO Box 25203, Colorado Springs, CO 80936-5203 *Tel:* 719-550-9887 *E-mail:* orders@piccadillybooks.com *Web Site:* www.piccadillybooks.com, pg 191

Figman, Elliot, Poets & Writers Inc, 90 Broad St, Suite 2100, New York, NY 10004 *Tel:* 212-226-3586 *Fax:* 212-226-3963 *E-mail:* admin@pw.org *Web Site:* www.pw.org, pg 616

Figueira, Sarah George, ASCSA Publications, American School of Classical Studies at Athens, 6-8 Charlton St, Princeton, NJ 08540-5232 *Tel:* 609-683-0800 *Fax:* 609-924-0578 *Web Site:* www.ascsa.edu.gr/publications, pg 24

Files, Meg, Pima Writers' Workshop, Pima College West Campus, 2202 W Anklam Rd, Tucson, AZ 85709-0170 *Tel:* 520-206-6084 *Fax:* 520-206-6020 *Web Site:* www.pima.edu, pg 654

Filion, Annie, Editions Hurtubise, 1815, ave De Lorimier, Montreal, QC H2K 3W6, Canada *Tel:* 514-523-1523 *Toll Free Tel:* 800-361-1664 *Fax:* 514-523-9969 *Web Site:* www.editionshurtubise.com, pg 482

Filling, Gregory, Pippin Press, 229 E 85 St, New York, NY 10028 *Tel:* 212-288-4920 *Fax:* 908-237-2407, pg 192

Filppi, Julie, OUT OF YOUR MIND...AND INTO THE MARKETPLACE™, 13381 White Sand Dr, Tustin, CA 92780-4565 *Tel:* 714-544-0248 *Toll Free Tel:* 800-419-1513 *Fax:* 714-730-1414 *Web Site:* www.business-plan.com, pg 178

Filsinger, Cheryl, Filsinger & Company Ltd, 288 W 12 St, Suite 2R, New York, NY 10014 *Tel:* 212-243-7421 *E-mail:* filsingercompany@gmail.com *Web Site:* www.filsingerco.com, pg 507

Filucci, Sierra, University of California Press, 2120 Berkeley Way, Berkeley, CA 94704-1012 *Tel:* 510-642-4247 *Fax:* 510-643-7127 *E-mail:* askucp@ucpress.edu (books); customerservice@ucpressjournals.com *Web Site:* www.ucpress.edu, pg 255

Finan, Bill, The Brookings Institution Press, 1775 Massachusetts Ave NW, Washington, DC 20036-2188 *Tel:* 202-536-3600 *Toll Free Tel:* 800-537-5487 *Fax:* 202-536-3623 *E-mail:* permissions@brookings.edu *Web Site:* www.brookings.edu, pg 47

Findlay, Ben, Coffee House Press, 79 13 Ave NE, Suite 110, Minneapolis, MN 55413 *Tel:* 612-338-0125 *Fax:* 612-338-4004 *E-mail:* info@coffeehousepress.org *Web Site:* coffeehousepress.org, pg 60

Fine, Celeste, Sterling Lord Literistic Inc, 65 Bleecker St, New York, NY 10012 *Tel:* 212-780-6050 *Fax:* 212-780-6095 *E-mail:* info@sll.com *Web Site:* www.sll.com, pg 575

Fine, Glenn, Clinical Laboratory & Standards Institute (CLSI), 950 W Valley Rd, Suite 2500, Wayne, PA 19087 *Tel:* 610-688-0100 *Toll Free Tel:* 877-447-1888 (orders) *Fax:* 610-688-0700 *E-mail:* customerservice@clsi.org *Web Site:* www.clsi.org, pg 59

Fine, Michael J, Fine Creative Media, Inc, 322 Eighth Ave, 15th fl, New York, NY 10001 *Tel:* 212-595-3500 *Fax:* 212-595-3779, pg 88

Fine, Steven, Fine Creative Media, Inc, 322 Eighth Ave, 15th fl, New York, NY 10001 *Tel:* 212-595-3500 *Fax:* 212-595-3779, pg 88

Finegan, Patrick G Jr, 1765 Productions, PO Box 4151, Fairfax, VA 22124-8151 *Tel:* 703-242-1734 *Fax:* 703-242-1734 *E-mail:* 1765productions@gmail.com, pg 222

Fingerhut, Benjamin, St Augustine's Press Inc, PO Box 2285, South Bend, IN 46680-2285 *Tel:* 574-291-3500 *Toll Free Tel:* 888-997-4994 *Fax:* 574-291-3700 *Web Site:* www.staugustine.net, pg 214

Fingerhut, Bruce, St Augustine's Press Inc, PO Box 2285, South Bend, IN 46680-2285 *Tel:* 574-291-3500 *Toll Free Tel:* 888-997-4994 *Fax:* 574-291-3700 *Web Site:* www.staugustine.net, pg 214

Finkel, Allison, The Perseus Books Group, 387 Park Ave S, 12th fl, New York, NY 10016 *Tel:* 212-340-8100 *Toll Free Tel:* 800-343-4499 (cust serv) *Fax:* 212-340-8105 *Web Site:* www.perseusbooksgroup.com, pg 189

Finkel, Erica, Harry N Abrams Inc, 115 W 18 St, 6th fl, New York, NY 10011 *Tel:* 212-206-7715 *Toll Free Tel:* 800-345-1359 *Fax:* 212-519-1210 *E-mail:* abrams@abramsbooks.com *Web Site:* www.abramsbooks.com, pg 3

Finkelman, Jamie, W W Norton & Company Inc, 500 Fifth Ave, New York, NY 10110-0017 *Tel:* 212-354-5500 *Toll Free Tel:* 800-233-4830 (orders & cust serv) *Fax:* 212-869-0856 *Toll Free Fax:* 800-458-6515 *Web Site:* www.wwnorton.com, pg 172

Finkelstein, Roxanne, Harlequin Enterprises Ltd, 225 Duncan Mill Rd, Don Mills, ON M3B 3K9, Canada *Tel:* 416-445-5860 *Toll Free Tel:* 888-432-4879; 800-370-5838 (ebook inquiries) *E-mail:* customerservice@harlequin.com *Web Site:* www.harlequin.com, pg 487

Finley, Doug, Wolters Kluwer Ltd, 90 Sheppard Ave E, Suite 300, Toronto, ON M2N 6X1, Canada *Tel:* 416-224-2224 *Toll Free Tel:* 800-268-4522 (CN & US cust serv) *Fax:* 416-224-2243 *Toll Free Fax:* 800-461-4131 *E-mail:* cservice@cch.ca (cust serv) *Web Site:* www.cch.ca, pg 505

Finman, Stephanie, The Martell Agency, 1350 Avenue of the Americas, Suite 1205, New York, NY 10019 *Tel:* 212-317-2672 *Web Site:* www.themartellagency.com, pg 564

Finn, Candace, Clarion Books, 215 Park Ave S, New York, NY 10003 *Tel:* 212-420-5889 *Toll Free Tel:* 800-225-3362 (orders) *Fax:* 212-420-5855 *Toll Free Fax:* 800-634-7568 (orders) *Web Site:* www.hmhco.com, pg 59

Finn, Candace, Houghton Mifflin Harcourt Trade & Reference Division, 222 Berkeley St, Boston, MA 02116 *Tel:* 617-351-5000 *Toll Free Tel:* 800-225-3362 *Web Site:* www.hmhco.com, pg 115

Finn, Frank, Columbia Books & Information Services, 4340 East-West Hwy, Suite 300, Bethesda, MD 20814 *Tel:* 240-235-0266 *Toll Free Tel:* 888-265-0600 (cust serv) *Fax:* 202-464-1775 *E-mail:* info@columbiabooks.com *Web Site:* www.columbiabooks.com; www.lobbyists.info; www.associationexecs.com, pg 61

Finn, Lydia, Random House Children's Books, 1745 Broadway, New York, NY 10019 *Tel:* 212-782-9000 *Toll Free Tel:* 800-200-3552 *Fax:* 212-782-9452 *Web Site:* randomhousekids.com, pg 203

Finnes, Kristl, WriteLife LLC, 2323 S 171 St, Suite 202, Omaha, NE 68130 *Tel:* 402-934-1412 *Toll Free Tel:* 877-974-8354 *E-mail:* info@writelife.com *Web Site:* www.writelife.com; www.facebook.com/WriteLife; twitter.com/WriteLifeLLC, pg 277

Finsterbusch, Marty, National Coalition for Literacy (NCL), PO Box 2932, Washington, DC 20013-2932 *E-mail:* ncl@ncladvocacy.org *Web Site:* www.national-coalition-literacy.org, pg 611

Firestone-Teeter, Naomi, Jewish Book Council, 520 Eighth Ave, 4th fl, New York, NY 10018 *Tel:* 212-201-2920 *Fax:* 212-532-4952 *E-mail:* jbc@jewishbooks.org *Web Site:* www.jewishbookcouncil.org, pg 608

Firestone-Teeter, Naomi, National Jewish Book Award-Children's & Young Adult Literature, 520 Eighth Ave, 4th fl, New York, NY 10018 *Tel:* 212-201-2920 *Fax:* 212-532-4952 *E-mail:* jbc@jewishbooks.org *Web Site:* www.jewishbookcouncil.org, pg 710

Firestone-Teeter, Naomi, National Jewish Book Award-Contemporary Jewish Life & Practice, 520 Eighth Ave, 4th fl, New York, NY 10018 *Tel:* 212-201-2920 *Fax:* 212-532-4952 *E-mail:* jbc@jewishbooks.org *Web Site:* www.jewishbookcouncil.org, pg 710

Firestone-Teeter, Naomi, National Jewish Book Award-History, 520 Eighth Ave, 4th fl, New York, NY 10018 *Tel:* 212-201-2920 *Fax:* 212-532-4952 *E-mail:* jbc@jewishbooks.org *Web Site:* www.jewishbookcouncil.org, pg 710

Firestone-Teeter, Naomi, National Jewish Book Award-Illustrated Children's Book, 520 Eighth Ave, 4th fl, New York, NY 10018 *Tel:* 212-201-2920 *Fax:* 212-532-4952 *E-mail:* jbc@jewishbooks.org *Web Site:* www.jewishbookcouncil.org, pg 710

Firestone-Teeter, Naomi, National Jewish Book Award-Modern Jewish Thought & Experience, 520 Eighth Ave, 4th fl, New York, NY 10018 *Tel:* 212-201-2920 *Fax:* 212-532-4952 *E-mail:* jbc@jewishbooks.org *Web Site:* www.jewishbookcouncil.org, pg 710

Firestone-Teeter, Naomi, National Jewish Book Award-Scholarship, 520 Eighth Ave, 4th fl, New York, NY 10018 *Tel:* 212-201-2920 *Fax:* 212-532-4952 *E-mail:* jbc@jewishbooks.org *Web Site:* www.jewishbookcouncil.org, pg 710

Firestone-Teeter, Naomi, National Jewish Book Awards, 520 Eighth Ave, 4th fl, New York, NY 10018 *Tel:* 212-201-2920 *Fax:* 212-532-4952 *E-mail:* jbc@jewishbooks.org *Web Site:* www.jewishbookcouncil.org, pg 710

Firestone-Teeter, Naomi, Sami Rohr Prize for Jewish Literature, 520 Eighth Ave, 4th fl, New York, NY 10018 *Tel:* 212-201-2920 *Fax:* 212-532-4952 *E-mail:* jbc@jewishbooks.org *Web Site:* www.jewishbookcouncil.org, pg 724

Firing, Rob, HarperCollins Canada Ltd, 2 Bloor St E, 20th fl, Toronto, ON M4W 1A8, Canada *Tel:* 416-975-9334 *Fax:* 416-975-9884 *E-mail:* hcorder@harpercollins.com *Web Site:* www.harpercollins.ca, pg 487

Fischbach, Christopher, Coffee House Press, 79 13 Ave NE, Suite 110, Minneapolis, MN 55413 *Tel:* 612-338-0125 *Fax:* 612-338-4004 *E-mail:* info@coffeehousepress.org *Web Site:* coffeehousepress.org, pg 60

Fischer, Amy-Lynn, University of California Press, 2120 Berkeley Way, Berkeley, CA 94704-1012 *Tel:* 510-642-4247 *Fax:* 510-643-7127 *E-mail:* askucp@ucpress.edu (books); customerservice@ucpressjournals.com *Web Site:* www.ucpress.edu, pg 255

Fischer, Craig, Police Executive Research Forum, 1120 Connecticut Ave NW, Suite 930, Washington, DC 20036 *Tel:* 202-466-7820 *Fax:* 202-466-7826 *E-mail:* perf@policeforum.org *Web Site:* www.policeforum.org, pg 194

Fischer, Grada, The Fischer Ross Group Inc, 75 Holly Hill Lane, Suite 100, Greenwich, CT 06830 *Tel:* 203-622-4950 *Fax:* 203-531-4132 *E-mail:* frgstaff@frg-speakers.com *Web Site:* www.frg-speakers.com, pg 587

Fischer, Shannon, Purple Pomegranate Productions, 60 Haight St, San Francisco, CA 94102 *Tel:* 415-864-2600 *Fax:* 415-552-8325 *E-mail:* sf@jewsforjesus.org *Web Site:* www.jewsforjesus.org, pg 201

Fischer, Steven, New England Book Awards, 1955 Massachusetts Ave, Cambridge, MA 02140 *Tel:* 617-547-3642 *Fax:* 617-547-3759 *Web Site:* www.newenglandbooks.org/bookawards, pg 712

Fischer, Steven, New England Independent Booksellers Association Inc (NEIBA), 1955 Massachusetts Ave, Cambridge, MA 02140 *Web Site:* www.newenglandbooks.org, pg 613

Fischer, Tom, Timber Press Inc, 133 SW Second Ave, Suite 450, Portland, OR 97204 *Tel:* 503-227-2878 *Toll Free Tel:* 800-327-5680 *Fax:* 503-227-3070 *E-mail:* info@timberpress.com *Web Site:* www.timberpress.com, pg 246

Fischer-Harbage, Ryan, The Fischer-Harbage Agency Inc, 540 President St, 3rd fl, Brooklyn, NY 11215 *Tel:* 212-695-7105 *E-mail:* info@fischerharbage.com *Web Site:* www.fischerharbage.com, pg 552

Fisher, Brad, The Charles Press, Publishers, 230 N 21 St, Suite 202, Philadelphia, PA 19103 *Tel:* 215-561-2786 *Fax:* 215-561-0191 *E-mail:* mail@charlespresspub.com *Web Site:* www.charlespresspub.com, pg 55

Fisher, Curtis, Diane Publishing Co, 330 Pusey Ave, Suite 3 (rear), Collingdale, PA 19023-0617 *Tel:* 610-461-6200 *Toll Free Tel:* 800-782-3833 *Fax:* 610-461-6130 *Web Site:* www.dianepublishing.net, pg 74

Fisher, Elizabeth, Levine|Greenberg|Rostan Literary Agency Inc, 307 Seventh Ave, Suite 2407, New York, NY 10001 *Tel:* 212-337-0934 *Fax:* 212-337-0948 *Web Site:* lgrliterary.com, pg 561

Fisher, Jenna, BOA Editions Ltd, 250 N Goodman St, Suite 306, Rochester, NY 14607 *Tel:* 585-546-3410 *Fax:* 585-546-3913 *E-mail:* contact@boaeditions.org *Web Site:* www.boaeditions.org, pg 41

Fisher, John, Templegate Publishers, 302 E Adams St, Springfield, IL 62701 *Tel:* 217-522-3353 (edit & sales); 217-522-3354 (billing) *Toll Free Tel:* 800-367-4844 (orders only) *Fax:* 217-522-3362 *E-mail:* wisdom@templegate.com; orders@templegate.com (sales) *Web Site:* www.templegate.com, pg 242

Fisher, Lynn, University of Toronto Press, 10 St Mary St, Suite 700, Toronto, ON M4Y 2W8, Canada *Tel:* 416-978-2239 *Fax:* 416-978-4738 *E-mail:* info@utpress.utoronto.ca *Web Site:* www.utpress.utoronto.ca; www.utppublishing.com, pg 504

Fisher, Maurice D, Gifted Education Press, 10201 Yuma Ct, Manassas, VA 20109 *Tel:* 703-369-5017 *Web Site:* www.giftededpress.com, pg 97

Fisher, Melissa, Vermont College of Fine Arts MFA in Writing for Children & Young Adults Program, 36 College St, Montpelier, VT 05602 *Tel:* 802-828-8637; 802-828-8696 *Toll Free Tel:* 866-934-VCFA (934-8232) *Fax:* 802-828-8649 *Web Site:* www.vcfa.edu, pg 664

Fisher, Stephen, Don Buchwald & Associates Inc, 10 E 44 St, New York, NY 10017 *Tel:* 212-867-1200 *Fax:* 212-867-2434 *E-mail:* info@buchwald.com *Web Site:* www.buchwald.com, pg 545

Fisher, Tracy, WME, 1325 Avenue of the Americas, New York, NY 10019 *Tel:* 212-586-5100 *Fax:* 212-246-3583 *E-mail:* wma@interport.net *Web Site:* www.wma.com, pg 579

Fishmann, Megan, Counterpoint Press LLC, 1919 Fifth St, Berkeley, CA 94710 *Tel:* 510-704-0230 *Fax:* 510-704-0268 *E-mail:* info@counterpointpress.com *Web Site:* counterpointpress.com; www.sierraclub.org/books; softskull.com, pg 65

Fisk, Karen, Juniper Prize for Fiction, East Experiment Sta, 671 N Pleasant St, Amherst, MA 01003 *Tel:* 413-545-2217 *Fax:* 413-545-1226 *E-mail:* info@umpress.umass.edu *Web Site:* www.umass.edu/umpress; www.umass.edu/umpress/content/juniper-literary-prize-series, pg 697

Fisk, Karen, Juniper Prize for Poetry, East Experiment Sta, 671 N Pleasant St, Amherst, MA 01003 *Tel:* 413-545-2217 *Fax:* 413-545-1226 *E-mail:* info@umpress.umass.edu *Web Site:* www.umass.edu/umpress; www.umass.edu/umpress/content/juniper-literary-prize-series, pg 697

Fisk, Karen, University of Massachusetts Press, East Experiment Sta, 671 N Pleasant St, Amherst, MA 01003 *Tel:* 413-545-2217 *Fax:* 413-545-1226 *E-mail:* info@umpress.umass.edu *Web Site:* www.umass.edu/umpress, pg 257

Fisk, Raymond G, Down The Shore Publishing Corp, 106 Stafford Forge Rd, West Creek, NJ 08092 *Tel:* 609-812-5076 *Fax:* 609-812-5098 *E-mail:* dtsbooks@comcast.net; info@down-the-shore.com *Web Site:* www.down-the-shore.com, pg 76

Fiske, Robert Hartwell, Vocabula Communications Co, 5-A Holbrook Ct, Rockport, MA 01966 *Tel:* 978-309-8730 *E-mail:* info@vocabula.com *Web Site:* www.vocabula.com; www.vocabula.com/dailyvocabula.asp (Daily Vocabula), pg 535

Fisketjon, Gary, Alfred A Knopf/Everyman's Library, c/o Random House Inc, 1745 Broadway, New York, NY 10019 *Tel:* 212-751-2600 *Toll Free Tel:* 800-638-6460 *Fax:* 212-572-2593 *Web Site:* www.knopfdoubleday.com, pg 132

Fitch, Ann, Tuxedo Press, 546 E Springville Rd, Carlisle, PA 17015 *Tel:* 717-258-9733 *Fax:* 717-243-0074 *E-mail:* info@tuxedo-press.com *Web Site:* tuxedo-press.com, pg 251

Fitterling, Michael Alan, Lost Classics Book Company LLC, 411 N Wales Dr, Lake Wales, FL 33853-3881 *Tel:* 863-632-1981 (edit off) *E-mail:* mgeditor@lostclassicsbooks.com *Web Site:* www.lostclassicsbooks.com, pg 143

Fitzgerald, Brenda, The University of Virginia Press, PO Box 400318, Charlottesville, VA 22904-4318 *Tel:* 434-924-3468 (cust serv); 434-924-3469 (cust serv) *Toll Free Tel:* 800-831-3406 (orders) *Fax:* 434-982-2655 *Toll Free Fax:* 877-288-6400 *E-mail:* vapress@virginia.edu *Web Site:* www.upress.virginia.edu, pg 260

Fitzgerald, Lance, Crown Publishing Group, c/o Penguin Random House Inc, 1745 Broadway, New York, NY 10019 *Tel:* 212-782-9000 *Toll Free Tel:* 888-264-1745 *Fax:* 212-940-7408 *E-mail:* crownosm@penguinrandomhouse.com *Web Site:* crownpublishing.com, pg 68

Fitzgerald, Megan, Bread Loaf Writers' Conference, 5525 Middlebury College, 14 Old Chapel Rd, Middlebury, VT 05753 *Tel:* 802-443-5286 *Fax:* 802-443-2087 *E-mail:* blwc@middlebury.edu *Web Site:* www.middlebury.edu/blwc, pg 650

Fitzgerald, Michelle, Palgrave Macmillan, 175 Fifth Ave, Suite 200, New York, NY 10010 *Tel:* 646-307-5151 *Fax:* 212-777-6359 *E-mail:* firstname.lastname@palgrave-usa.com *Web Site:* us.macmillan.com/Palgrave.aspx, pg 180

Fitzgerald, Patrick, Columbia University Press, 61 W 62 St, New York, NY 10023 *Tel:* 212-459-0600 *Toll Free Tel:* 800-944-8648 *Fax:* 212-459-3678 *E-mail:* cup_book@columbia.edu (orders & cust serv) *Web Site:* cup.columbia.edu, pg 61

Fitzgerald, Susan Kelly, Kinship Books, 305 Cedar Heights Rd, Rhinebeck, NY 12572 *Tel:* 845-876-4592 (orders) *E-mail:* kinship@hvc.rr.com *Web Site:* www.kinshipny.com, pg 131

Fitzhenry, Sharon, Fitzhenry & Whiteside Limited, 195 Allstate Pkwy, Markham, ON L3R 4T8, Canada *Tel:* 905-477-9700 *Toll Free Tel:* 800-387-9776 *Fax:* 905-477-2834 *Toll Free Fax:* 800-260-9777 *E-mail:* bookinfo@fitzhenry.ca; godwit@fitzhenry.ca *Web Site:* www.fitzhenry.ca, pg 484

Fitzpatrick, Megan, Hachette Audio, 1290 Avenue of the Americas, New York, NY 10019 *Tel:* 212-364-1100, pg 102

Fiyak-Burkley, Michele, University Press of Florida, 15 NW 15 St, Gainesville, FL 32603-2079 *Tel:* 352-392-1351 *Toll Free Tel:* 800-226-3822 (orders only) *Fax:* 352-392-0590 *Toll Free Fax:* 800-680-1955 (orders only) *E-mail:* info@upf.com *Web Site:* www.upf.com, pg 261

Fjestad, S P, Blue Book Publications Inc, 8009 34 Ave S, Suite 250, Minneapolis, MN 55425 *Tel:* 952-854-5229 *Toll Free Tel:* 800-877-4867 *Fax:* 925-853-1486 *E-mail:* support@bluebookinc.com *Web Site:* www.bluebookofgunvalues.com; www.bluebookofguitarvalues.com, pg 40

Flach, Andrew, Hatherleigh Press Ltd, 62545 State Hwy 10, Hobart, NY 13788 *E-mail:* info@hatherleighpress.com; publicity@hatherleighpress.com *Web Site:* www.hatherleighpress.com, pg 108

Flamand, Jacques, Les Editions du Vermillon, 305, rue St-Patrick, Ottawa, ON K1N 5K4, Canada *Tel:* 613-241-4032 *Fax:* 613-241-3109 *E-mail:* leseditionsduvermillon@rogers.com *Web Site:* www.leseditionsduvermillon.ca, pg 481

Flamini, Michael, St Martin's Press, LLC, 175 Fifth Ave, New York, NY 10010 *Tel:* 646-307-5151 *Fax:* 212-420-9314 *E-mail:* firstname.lastname@macmillan.com *Web Site:* www.stmartins.com, pg 215

Flanagan, John F, Goodheart-Willcox Publisher, 18604 W Creek Dr, Tinley Park, IL 60477-6243 *Tel:* 708-687-5000 *Toll Free Tel:* 800-323-0440 *Fax:* 708-468-8692 *Toll Free Fax:* 888-409-3900 *E-mail:* custserv@g-w.com; orders@g-w.com *Web Site:* www.g-w.com, pg 98

Flanagan, Marty, Ideals Publications, a Guideposts Co, 6100 Tower Circle, Suite 210, Franklin, TN 37067 *Tel:* 615-932-7600 *Toll Free Tel:* 800-586-2572 (cust serv) *Fax:* 615-781-1447 *Web Site:* www.idealsbooks.com, pg 118

Flanagin, Annette, American Medical Association, AMA Plaza, 330 N Wabash, Suite 39300, Chicago, IL 60611-5885 *Tel:* 312-464-5000 *Toll Free Tel:* 800-621-8335 *Fax:* 312-464-4184 *Web Site:* www.ama-assn.org, pg 14

Flanders, Lorene, Southern Books Competition, PO Box 950, Rex, GA 30273 *Tel:* 678-466-4334 *Fax:* 678-466-4349 *Web Site:* selaonline.org, pg 729

Flanders, Margaret, Judy Lopez Memorial Award For Children's Literature, 1225 Selby Ave, Los Angeles, CA 90024 *Tel:* 310-474-9917 *Fax:* 310-474-6436 *Web Site:* www.wnba-books.org/la; www.judylopezbookaward.org, pg 703

Flanders, Tony, Sky Publishing, 90 Sherman St, Cambridge, MA 02140 *Tel:* 617-864-7360 *Toll Free Tel:* 866-644-1377 *Fax:* 617-864-6117 *E-mail:* info@skyandtelescope.com *Web Site:* www.skyandtelescope.com, pg 227

Flannery, Jennifer, Flannery Literary, 1140 Wickfield Ct, Naperville, IL 60563 *Tel:* 630-428-2682 *Web Site:* flanneryliterary.com, pg 552

Flashman, Melissa, Trident Media Group LLC, 41 Madison Ave, 36th fl, New York, NY 10010 *Tel:* 212-333-1511 *E-mail:* info@tridentmediagroup.com; press@tridentmediagroup.com *Web Site:* www.tridentmediagroup.com, pg 577

Flavin, Laura, Touchstone, 1230 Avenue of the Americas, New York, NY 10020, pg 247

Flax, Margery, Mystery Writers of America (MWA), 1140 Broadway, Suite 1507, New York, NY 10001 *Tel:* 212-888-8171 *E-mail:* mwa@mysterywriters.org *Web Site:* www.mysterywriters.org, pg 610

Flax, Margery, Mystery Writers of America Workshops, 1140 Broadway, Suite 1507, New York, NY 10001 *Tel:* 212-888-8171 *E-mail:* mwa@mysterywriters.org *Web Site:* www.mysterywriters.org, pg 653

Flax, Margery, Edgar Allan Poe Awards®, 1140 Broadway, Suite 1507, New York, NY 10001 *Tel:* 212-888-8171 *E-mail:* mwa@mysterywriters.org *Web Site:* www.mysterywriters.org, pg 719

Flaxman, Jill, Crown Publishing Group, c/o Penguin Random House Inc, 1745 Broadway, New York, NY 10019 *Tel:* 212-782-9000 *Toll Free Tel:* 888-264-1745 *Fax:* 212-940-7408 *E-mail:* crownosm@penguinrandomhouse.com *Web Site:* crownpublishing.com, pg 68

Fleck, Robert III, Oak Knoll Press, 310 Delaware St, New Castle, DE 19720 *Tel:* 302-328-7232 *Toll Free Tel:* 800-996-2556 *Fax:* 302-328-7274 *E-mail:* oakknoll@oakknoll.com *Web Site:* www.oakknoll.com, pg 172

Fleck, Robert D, Oak Knoll Press, 310 Delaware St, New Castle, DE 19720 *Tel:* 302-328-7232 *Toll Free Tel:* 800-996-2556 *Fax:* 302-328-7274 *E-mail:* oakknoll@oakknoll.com *Web Site:* www.oakknoll.com, pg 172

Fleck-Nisbet, Andrea, Workman Publishing Co Inc, 225 Varick St, 9th fl, New York, NY 10014-4381 *Tel:* 212-254-5900 *Toll Free Tel:* 800-722-7202 *Fax:* 212-254-8098 *E-mail:* info@workman.com *Web Site:* www.workman.com, pg 275

Fleet, Jani, Signature Books Publishing LLC, 564 W 400 N, Salt Lake City, UT 84116-3411 *Tel:* 801-531-1483 *Fax:* 801-531-1488 *E-mail:* people@signaturebooks.com *Web Site:* www.signaturebooks.com; www.signaturebookslibrary.org, pg 224

Flegal, Diana, Hartline Literary Agency LLC, 123 Queenston Dr, Pittsburgh, PA 15235 *Web Site:* www.hartlineliterary.com, pg 556

Fleischer, Chip, Steerforth Press, 45 Lyme Rd, Suite 208, Hanover, NH 03755-1222 *Tel:* 603-643-4787 *Fax:* 603-643-4788 *E-mail:* info@steerforth.com *Web Site:* www.steerforth.com, pg 234

Fleischer, Elizabeth, Materials Research Society, 506 Keystone Dr, Warrendale, PA 15086-7537 *Tel:* 724-779-3003 *Fax:* 724-779-8313 *E-mail:* info@mrs.org *Web Site:* www.mrs.org, pg 149

Fleishman, Samuel, Literary Artists Representatives, 575 West End Ave, Suite GRC, New York, NY 10024-2711 *Tel:* 212-679-7788 *Fax:* 212-595-2098 *E-mail:* litartists@aol.com, pg 562

Fleming, Connie, Oakstone Publishing LLC, 100 Corporate Pkwy, Suite 600, Birmingham, AL 35242 *Toll Free Tel:* 800-633-4743 *Fax:* 205-995-1926 *E-mail:* service@oakstonemedical.com *Web Site:* www.oakstonepublishing.com; www.cmeonly.com; www.cdeonly.com, pg 173

Fleming, Dr Deborah, Ashland Poetry Press, Ashland University, 401 College Ave, Ashland, OH 44805 *Tel:* 419-289-5957 *Fax:* 419-289-5255 *E-mail:* app@ashland.edu *Web Site:* www.ashland.edu/aupoetry, pg 24

Fleming, James, C D Howe Institute, 67 Yonge St, Suite 300, Toronto, ON M5E 1J8, Canada *Tel:* 416-865-1904 *Fax:* 416-865-1866 *E-mail:* cdhowe@cdhowe.org *Web Site:* www.cdhowe.org, pg 488

Fleming, Katherine, Fodor's Travel Publications, 1745 Broadway, 15th fl, New York, NY 10019 *Toll Free Tel:* 800-733-3000 *E-mail:* fodorspublicity@randomhouse.com; editors@fodors.com *Web Site:* www.fodors.com, pg 90

Fleming, Margo Beth, Stanford University Press, 1450 Page Mill Rd, Palo Alto, CA 94304-1124 *Tel:* 650-723-9434 *Fax:* 650-725-3457 *E-mail:* info@sup.org *Web Site:* www.sup.org, pg 233

Fleming, Peter, Peter Fleming Agency, PO Box 458, Pacific Palisades, CA 90272 *Tel:* 310-454-1373 *E-mail:* peterfleming@earthlink.net, pg 552

Fleming, Sue, Simon & Schuster Digital, 1230 Avenue of the Americas, New York, NY 10020 *Tel:* 212-698-7547 *Web Site:* www.simonandschuster.com; kids.simonandschuster.com; www.simonandschuster.ca; www.simonandschuster.co.uk; www.simonandschuster.net; www.simonandschuster.biz; www.tipsoncareerandmoney.com; www.tipsonhealthyliving.com; www.tipsonhomeandstyle.com; www.tipsonlifeandlove.com; www.offtheshelf.com; www.simonandschuster.com/teen, pg 225

Fletcher, JT, Northeast-Midwest Institute, 50 "F" St NW, Suite 950, Washington, DC 20001 *Tel:* 202-544-5200 *Fax:* 202-544-0043 *E-mail:* info@nemw.org *Web Site:* www.nemw.org, pg 171

Fletcher, Kate, Candlewick Press, 99 Dover St, Somerville, MA 02144-2825 *Tel:* 617-661-3330 *Fax:* 617-661-0565 *E-mail:* bigbear@candlewick.com; salesinfo@candlewick.com *Web Site:* www.candlewick.com, pg 49

Fletcher, Robert, Strategic Book Publishing & Rights Agency (SBPRA), 12620 FM 1960, Suite A-4507, Houston, TX 77065 *Toll Free Tel:* 888-808-6190 *Web Site:* www.sbpra.com, pg 237

Fletcher, Sharon, NASW Press, 750 First St NE, Suite 700, Washington, DC 20002 *Tel:* 202-408-8600 *Fax:* 203-336-8312 *E-mail:* press@naswdc.org *Web Site:* www.naswpress.org, pg 162

Fletcher, Stephanie, Houghton Mifflin Harcourt Trade & Reference Division, 222 Berkeley St, Boston, MA 02116 *Tel:* 617-351-5000 *Toll Free Tel:* 800-225-3362 *Web Site:* www.hmhco.com, pg 115

Fletcher, Susan, AAP PreK-12 Learning Group, 325 Chestnut St, Suite 1110, Philadelphia, PA 19106 *Tel:* 267-351-4310 *Fax:* 267-351-4317 *E-mail:* prek12learning@publishers.org *Web Site:* www.aepweb.org, pg 593

Fletty, Eric, Technical Association of the Pulp & Paper Industry (TAPPI), 15 Technology Pkwy S, Suite 115, Peachtree Corners, GA 30092 *Tel:* 770-446-1400 *Toll Free Tel:* 800-332-8686 (US); 800-446-9431 (CN) *Fax:* 770-446-6947 *E-mail:* memberconnection@tappi.org *Web Site:* www.tappi.org, pg 620

Fleury, Amy, McNeese State University, Writing Program, PO Box 92655, Lake Charles, LA 70609-0001 *Tel:* 337-475-5325; 337-475-5327 *Web Site:* www.mcneese.edu.com; www.mfa.mcneese.edu, pg 661

Fleury, Kathleen, Down East Books, 680 Commercial St (US Rte 1), Rockport, ME 04856 *Tel:* 207-594-9544 *Toll Free Tel:* 800-685-7962 (US only orders); 800-766-1670 *E-mail:* editorial@downeast.com *Web Site:* www.downeast.com, pg 76

Flickinger, Mike, Ascension Press, PO Box 1990, West Chester, PA 19380 *Tel:* 610-696-7795 (ext 207, edit); 484-875-4550 (admin) *Toll Free Tel:* 800-376-0520 (sales & cust serv) *E-mail:* info@ascensionpress.com *Web Site:* ascensionpress.com, pg 24

Flight, Nancy, Greystone Books Ltd, 343 Railway St, Suite 201, Vancouver, BC V6A 1A4, Canada *Tel:* 604-875-1550 *Fax:* 604-875-1556 *E-mail:* info@greystonebooks.com *Web Site:* www.greystonebooks.com, pg 486

Fliss, Roberta B, youngARTS, 2100 Biscayne Blvd, Miami, FL 33137 *Tel:* 305-377-1140 *Toll Free Tel:* 800-970-ARTS (970-2787) *Fax:* 305-377-1149 *E-mail:* info@nfaa.org *Web Site:* www.youngarts.org, pg 739

Flora, Debi, About Books Inc, 1001 Taurus Dr, Colorado Springs, CO 80906 *Tel:* 719-632-8226 *Fax:* 719-213-2602 *Web Site:* www.about-books.com, pg 519

Flora, Scott, About Books Inc, 1001 Taurus Dr, Colorado Springs, CO 80906 *Tel:* 719-632-8226 *Fax:* 719-213-2602 *Web Site:* www.about-books.com, pg 519

Florence, Nicole, Writer's Digest Writing Competition, 10151 Carver Rd, Suite 200, Blue Ash, OH 45242 *Tel:* 513-531-2690 *Fax:* 513-531-0798 *E-mail:* writing-competition@fwmedia.com; writersdigest@fwmedia.com (edit) *Web Site:* www.writersdigest.com, pg 738

Florio, Marie, Gallery Books, 1230 Avenue of the Americas, New York, NY 10020 *Toll Free Tel:* 800-456-6798 *Fax:* 212-698-7284 *E-mail:* consumer.customerservice@simonandschuster.com *Web Site:* www.simonsays.com, pg 94

Florio, Marie, Simon & Schuster, 1230 Avenue of the Americas, New York, NY 10020 *Tel:* 212-698-7000 *Toll Free Tel:* 800-223-2348 (cust serv); 800-223-2336 (orders) *Toll Free Fax:* 800-943-9831 (orders) *Web Site:* www.simonandschuster.com, pg 225

Flounders, Emer, Harlequin Enterprises Ltd, 233 Broadway, Suite 1001, New York, NY 10279 *Tel:* 212-553-4200 *Fax:* 212-227-8969 *E-mail:* CustomerService@harlequin.com *Web Site:* www.harlequin.com, pg 105

Flower, Lauren, HarperCollins Children's Books, 195 Broadway, New York, NY 10007 *Tel:* 212-207-7000 *Web Site:* www.harpercollins.com/childrens, pg 105

Flower, Richard, World Book Inc, 233 N Michigan, Suite 2000, Chicago, IL 60601 *Tel:* 312-729-5800 *Toll Free Tel:* 800-967-5325 (consumer sales, US); 800-463-8845 (consumer sales, CN); 800-975-3250 (school & lib sales, US); 800-837-5365 (school & lib sales, CN); 866-866-5200 (web sales) *Fax:* 312-729-5600; 312-729-5606 *Toll Free Fax:* 800-433-9330 (school & lib sales, US); 888-690-4002 (school lib sales, CN) *Web Site:* www.worldbook.com, pg 276

Floyd, Chriscynethia, David C Cook, 4050 Lee Vance View, Colorado Springs, CO 80918 *Tel:* 719-536-0100 *Toll Free Tel:* 800-708-5550; 800-323-7543 (orders & cust serv) *Toll Free Fax:* 800-430-0726 (cust serv) *Web Site:* www.davidccook.com, pg 62

Floyd, Raymond, The Perseus Books Group, 387 Park Ave S, 12th fl, New York, NY 10016 *Tel:* 212-340-8100 *Toll Free Tel:* 800-343-4499 (cust serv) *Fax:* 212-340-8105 *Web Site:* www.perseusbooksgroup.com, pg 189

Floyd, Steve, August House Inc, 3500 Piedmont Rd NE, Suite 310, Atlanta, GA 30305 *Tel:* 404-442-4420 *Toll Free Tel:* 800-284-8784 *Fax:* 404-442-4435 *E-mail:* ahinfo@augusthouse.com *Web Site:* www.augusthouse.com, pg 27

Flum, Caitie, Liza Dawson Associates, 350 Seventh Ave, Suite 2003, New York, NY 10001 *Tel:* 212-465-9071 *Fax:* 212-947-0460 *Web Site:* www.lizadawsonassociates.com, pg 547

Flum, David, Rutgers University Press, 106 Somerset St, 3rd fl, New Brunswick, NJ 08901 *Tel:* 848-445-7762 *Toll Free Tel:* 800-848-6224 (orders only) *Fax:* 732-745-4935 (acqs, edit, mktg, perms & prodn) *Toll Free Fax:* 800-272-6817 (fulfillment) *Web Site:* rutgerspress.rutgers.edu, pg 213

Flynn, Daniel, Excelsior Editions, 22 Corporate Woods Blvd, 3rd fl, Albany, NY 12211-2504 *Tel:* 518-472-5000 *Toll Free Tel:* 866-430-7869 *Fax:* 518-472-5038 *E-mail:* info@sunypress.edu *Web Site:* www.sunypress.edu, pg 84

Flynn, Daniel, State University of New York Press, 22 Corporate Woods Blvd, 3rd fl, Albany, NY 12211-2504 *Tel:* 518-472-5000 *Toll Free Tel:* 877-204-6073 (orders) *Fax:* 518-472-5038 *Toll Free Fax:* 877-204-6074 (orders) *E-mail:* suny@presswarehouse.com (orders); info@sunypress.edu (edit off) *Web Site:* www.sunypress.edu, pg 234

Flynn, Jacquie, Joelle Delbourgo Associates Inc, 101 Park St, Montclair, NJ 07042 *Tel:* 973-773-0836 (call only during standard business hours) *Web Site:* www.delbourgo.com, pg 548

Flynn, Katherine, Kneerim & Williams Agency, 90 Canal St, Boston, MA 02114 *Tel:* 617-303-1650 *Web Site:* www.kwblit.com, pg 560

Flynn, Robert T, Getty Publications, 1200 Getty Center Dr, Suite 500, Los Angeles, CA 90049-1682 *Tel:* 310-440-7365 *Toll Free Tel:* 800-223-3431 (orders) *Fax:* 310-440-7758 *E-mail:* pubsinfo@getty.edu *Web Site:* www.getty.edu/publications, pg 96

Flynn, Thomas M, The National Underwriter Co, 5081 Olympic Blvd, Erlanger, KY 41018-3164 *Tel:* 859-692-2100 *Toll Free Tel:* 800-543-0874 *Fax:* 859-692-2289 *E-mail:* customerservice@nuco.com *Web Site:* www.nationalunderwriter.com, pg 166

Fochetta, Frank, Studio Fun International Inc, 44 S Broadway, White Plains, NY 10601 *Tel:* 914-238-1000 *Toll Free Tel:* 800-934-0977 *Web Site:* www.rdtradepublishing.com, pg 237

Fogelberg, Paul A, The Professional Education Group Inc (PEG), 12401 Minnetonka Blvd, Suite 200, Minnetonka, MN 55305-3994 *Tel:* 952-933-9990 *Toll Free Tel:* 800-229-2531 *Fax:* 952-933-7784 *E-mail:* orders@proedgroup.com *Web Site:* www.proedgroup.com, pg 198

Fogelman, Sheldon, Sheldon Fogelman Agency Inc, 10 E 40 St, Suite 3205, New York, NY 10016 *Tel:* 212-532-7250 *Fax:* 212-685-8939 *E-mail:* info@sheldonfogelmanagency.com *Web Site:* sheldonfogelmanagency.com, pg 552

Fogelson, Aliza, Clarkson Potter Publishers, c/o Random House Inc, 1745 Broadway, New York, NY 10019 *Tel:* 212-782-9000 *Toll Free Tel:* 888-264-1745 *Fax:* 212-572-6181 *Web Site:* www.clarksonpotter.com; www.randomhouse.com/crown/clarksonpotter, pg 195

Fogle, Linda Haines, University of South Carolina Press, 1600 Hampton St, Suite 544, Columbia, SC 29208 *Tel:* 803-777-5245 *Toll Free Tel:* 800-768-2500 (orders) *Fax:* 803-777-0160 *Toll Free Fax:* 800-868-0740 (orders) *Web Site:* www.sc.edu/uscpress, pg 259

Folan, Ellen, Crown Publishing Group, c/o Penguin Random House Inc, 1745 Broadway, New York, NY 10019 *Tel:* 212-782-9000 *Toll Free Tel:* 888-264-1745 *Fax:* 212-940-7408 *E-mail:* crownosm@penguinrandomhouse.com *Web Site:* crownpublishing.com, pg 68

Foley, Joan, The Foley Literary Agency, 34 E 38 St, Suite 1B, New York, NY 10016 *Tel:* 212-686-6930, pg 552

Foley, Leanne, Manitoba Arts Council, 525-93 Lombard Ave, Winnipeg, MB R3B 3B1, Canada *Tel:* 204-945-2237 *Toll Free Tel:* 866-994-2787 *Fax:* 204-945-5925 *E-mail:* info@artscouncil.mb.ca *Web Site:* artscouncil.mb.ca, pg 609

Foley, Margaret, Royal Fireworks Press, PO Box 399, Unionville, NY 10988 *Fax:* 845-726-3824 *E-mail:* mail@rfwp.com *Web Site:* www.rfwp.com, pg 212

Foley, Taylor, Houghton Mifflin Harcourt Trade & Reference Division, 222 Berkeley St, Boston, MA 02116 *Tel:* 617-351-5000 *Toll Free Tel:* 800-225-3362 *Web Site:* www.hmhco.com, pg 115

Foley-Mendelssohn, Dierdre, The Plimpton Prize, 544 W 27 St, New York, NY 10001 *Tel:* 212-343-1333 *Fax:* 212-343-1988 *E-mail:* queries@theparisreview.org *Web Site:* www.theparisreview.org, pg 719

Folino, Alison, Random House Children's Books, 1745 Broadway, New York, NY 10019 *Tel:* 212-782-9000 *Toll Free Tel:* 800-200-3552 *Fax:* 212-782-9452 *Web Site:* randomhousekids.com, pg 204

Follmer, David C, Lyceum Books Inc, 5758 S Blackstone Ave, Chicago, IL 60637 *Tel:* 773-643-1902 *Fax:* 773-643-1903 *E-mail:* lyceum@lyceumbooks.com *Web Site:* www.lyceumbooks.com, pg 144

Foltys, Karen, Martingale®, 19021 120 Ave NE, Suite 102, Bothell, WA 98011 *Tel:* 425-483-3313 *Toll Free Tel:* 800-426-3126 *Fax:* 425-486-7596 *E-mail:* info@martingale-pub.com *Web Site:* www.martingale-pub.com, pg 148

Folz, Robert, Visuals Unlimited, 27 Meadow Dr, Hollis, NH 03049 *Tel:* 603-465-3340 *Fax:* 603-465-3360 *E-mail:* staff@visualsunlimited.com *Web Site:* visualsunlimited.com, pg 535

Folz, Shelly, Visuals Unlimited, 27 Meadow Dr, Hollis, NH 03049 *Tel:* 603-465-3340 *Fax:* 603-465-3360 *E-mail:* staff@visualsunlimited.com *Web Site:* visualsunlimited.com, pg 535

Fontana, Frank, Dover Publications Inc, 31 E Second St, Mineola, NY 11501-3852 *Tel:* 516-294-7000 *Toll Free Tel:* 800-223-3130 (orders) *Fax:* 516-742-6953 *E-mail:* rights@doverpublications.com; service@doverpublications.com *Web Site:* store.doverdirect.com; www.doverpublications.com, pg 76

Fontana, John, Doubleday/Nan A Talese, c/o Penguin Random House Inc, 1745 Broadway, New York, NY 10019 *Tel:* 212-751-2600 *Fax:* 212-572-2662 *E-mail:* ddaypub@randomhouse.com *Web Site:* knopfdoubleday.com, pg 76

Fontanarosa, Phil B MD, American Medical Association, AMA Plaza, 330 N Wabash, Suite 39300, Chicago, IL 60611-5885 *Tel:* 312-464-5000 *Toll Free Tel:* 800-621-8335 *Fax:* 312-464-4184 *Web Site:* www.ama-assn.org, pg 14

Fonte, Brittany, Eric Hoffer Award for Short Prose, PO Box 11, Titusville, NJ 08560 *Fax:* 609-964-1718 *E-mail:* info@hofferaward.com *Web Site:* www.hofferaward.com, pg 692

Fontecchio, Mike, Ascension Press, PO Box 1990, West Chester, PA 19380 *Tel:* 610-696-7795 (ext 207, edit); 484-875-4550 (admin) *Toll Free Tel:* 800-376-0520 (sales & cust serv) *E-mail:* info@ascensionpress.com *Web Site:* ascensionpress.com, pg 24

Fontille, Brigitte, Canada Council for the Arts (Conseil des arts du Canada), 150 Elgin St, Ottawa, ON K1P 1L4, Canada *Tel:* 613-566-4414 *Toll Free Tel:* 800-263-5588 (CN only) *Fax:* 613-566-4390 *E-mail:* info@canadacouncil.ca *Web Site:* www.canadacouncil.ca, pg 601

Foo, Bill, Other Press LLC, 2 Park Ave, 24th fl, New York, NY 10016 *Tel:* 212-414-0054 *Toll Free Tel:* 877-843-6843 *Fax:* 212-414-0939 *E-mail:* editor@otherpress.com; rights@otherpress.com *Web Site:* www.otherpress.com, pg 178

Foot, Doug, Knopf Canada, One Toronto St, Suite 300, Toronto, ON M5C 2V6, Canada *Tel:* 416-364-4449 *Toll Free Tel:* 888-523-9292 *Fax:* 416-364-6863 *Web Site:* www.randomhouse.ca, pg 490

Foot, Doug, Seal Books, One Toronto St, Suite 300, Toronto, ON M5C 2V6, Canada *Tel:* 416-364-4449 *Toll Free Tel:* 888-523-9292 (order desk) *Fax:* 416-364-6863 *Web Site:* www.randomhouse.ca, pg 498

Foot, Douglas, Doubleday Canada, One Toronto St, Suite 300, Toronto, ON M5C 2V6, Canada *Tel:* 416-364-4449 *Fax:* 416-364-6863 *Web Site:* www.randomhouse.ca, pg 479

Foot, Douglas, Penguin Random House Canada Limited, 320 Front St W, Suite 1400, Toronto, ON M5V 3B6, Canada *Tel:* 416-364-4449 *Toll Free Tel:* 888-523-9292 (cust serv) *Fax:* 416-364-6863; 416-364-6653 (subs rts) *Web Site:* penguinrandomhouse.ca, pg 495

Ford, Gregory L, Ugly Duckling Presse, The Old American Can Factory, 232 Third St, Suite E002, Brooklyn, NY 11215 *Tel:* 347-948-5170 *E-mail:* udp_mailbox@yahoo.com; info@uglyducklingpresse.org *Web Site:* www.uglyducklingpresse.org, pg 252

Ford, June, JFE Editorial, 8425 Doreen Ave, Fort Worth, TX 76116-4922 *Tel:* 817-560-7018, pg 528

Forde, Carolyn, Westwood Creative Artists Ltd, 94 Harbord St, Toronto, ON M5S 1G6, Canada *Tel:* 416-964-3302 *Fax:* 416-975-9209 *E-mail:* wca_office@wcaltd.com *Web Site:* www.wcaltd.com, pg 579

Forde, Michelle, Kensington Publishing Corp, 119 W 40 St, New York, NY 10018 *Tel:* 212-407-1500 *Toll Free Tel:* 800-221-2647 *Fax:* 212-935-0699 *Web Site:* www.kensingtonbooks.com, pg 130

Forde, Tony, PublicAffairs, 250 W 57 St, Suite 1321, New York, NY 10107 *Tel:* 212-397-6666 *Toll Free Tel:* 800-343-4499 (orders) *Fax:* 212-397-4277 *E-mail:* publicaffairs@perseusbooks.com *Web Site:* www.publicaffairsbooks.com, pg 200

Forder, Reg A, American Christian Writers, PO Box 110390, Nashville, TN 37222-0390 *Tel:* 615-331-8668 *Toll Free Tel:* 800-21-WRITE (219-7483) *E-mail:* acwriters@aol.com *Web Site:* regaforder.wordpress.com, pg 594

Forder, Reg A, Writers Mentoring Retreat, PO Box 110390, Nashville, TN 37222-0390 *Tel:* 615-331-8668 *Toll Free Tel:* 800-21-WRITE (219-7483) *E-mail:* acwriters@aol.com *Web Site:* regaforder.wordpress.com/mentoring; regaforder.wordpress.com, pg 657

Forest, Marsha, Inclusion Press International, 47 Indian Trail, Toronto, ON M6R 1Z8, Canada *Tel:* 416-658-5363 *Fax:* 416-658-5067 *E-mail:* inclusionpress@inclusion.com *Web Site:* www.inclusion.com, pg 488

Forest, Susan, Science Fiction & Fantasy Writers of America Inc (SFWA), PO Box 3238, Enfield, CT 06083-3238 *E-mail:* office@sfwa.org *Web Site:* www.sfwa.org, pg 618

Forest, Susan, SFWA Nebula Awards, PO Box 3238, Enfield, CT 06083-3238 *E-mail:* office@sfwa.org *Web Site:* www.sfwa.org, pg 727

Forland, Emily, Brandt & Hochman Literary Agents Inc, 1501 Broadway, Suite 2310, New York, NY 10036 *Tel:* 212-840-5760 *Fax:* 212-840-5776 *Web Site:* brandthochman.com, pg 544

Forman, Mark, Light-Beams Publishing, 10 Toon Lane, Lee, NH 03861 *Tel:* 603-659-1300 *E-mail:* info@light-beams.com *Web Site:* www.light-beams.com, pg 139

Forman, Prof Sandra, YES New Play Festival, 205 FA Theatre Dept, Nunn Dr, Highland Heights, KY 41099-1007 *Tel:* 859-572-6303 *Fax:* 859-572-6057, pg 739

Forman, Stephen A, W W Norton & Company Inc, 500 Fifth Ave, New York, NY 10110-0017 *Tel:* 212-354-5500 *Toll Free Tel:* 800-233-4830 (orders & cust serv) *Fax:* 212-869-0856 *Toll Free Fax:* 800-458-6515 *Web Site:* www.wwnorton.com, pg 171

Formica, Ron, Tantor Media Inc, 2 Business Park, Old Saybrook, CT 06475 *Toll Free Tel:* 877-782-6867 *Toll Free Fax:* 888-782-7821 *Web Site:* www.tantor.com, pg 240

Forner, Alison, Simon & Schuster, 1230 Avenue of the Americas, New York, NY 10020 *Tel:* 212-698-7000 *Toll Free Tel:* 800-223-2348 (cust serv); 800-223-2336 (orders) *Toll Free Fax:* 800-943-9831 (orders) *Web Site:* www.simonandschuster.com, pg 225

Forrer, David, InkWell Management, 521 Fifth Ave, 26th fl, New York, NY 10175 *Tel:* 212-922-3500 *Fax:* 212-922-0535 *E-mail:* info@inkwellmanagement.com; submissions@inkwellmanagement.com *Web Site:* inkwellmanagement.com, pg 557

Forrest, Iris, Ageless Press, 3759 Collins St, Sarasota, FL 34232 *Tel:* 941-365-1367 *Fax:* 941-365-1367 *E-mail:* irishope@comcast.net, pg 6

Forrey, Scott, The Urban Institute, 2100 "M" St NW, Washington, DC 20037 *Tel:* 202-833-7200 *Web Site:* www.urban.org, pg 263

Forrie, Allan, Thistledown Press, 410 Second Ave, Saskatoon, SK S7N 2C3, Canada *Tel:* 306-244-1722 *Fax:* 306-244-1762 *E-mail:* tdpress@thistledownpress.com; editorial@thistledownpress.com; marketing@thistledownpress.com *Web Site:* www.thistledownpress.com, pg 500

Forrie, Jackie, Thistledown Press, 410 Second Ave, Saskatoon, SK S7N 2C3, Canada *Tel:* 306-244-1722 *Fax:* 306-244-1762 *E-mail:* tdpress@thistledownpress.com; editorial@thistledownpress.com; marketing@thistledownpress.com *Web Site:* www.thistledownpress.com, pg 500

Forrister, Brad, M Lee Smith Publishers LLC, 5201 Virginia Way, Brentwood, TN 37027 *Tel:* 615-373-7517 *Toll Free Tel:* 800-274-6774 *Fax:* 615-373-5183 *E-mail:* custserv@mleesmith.com *Web Site:* www.mleesmith.com, pg 228

Forsa, Bethlam, Houghton Mifflin Harcourt, 222 Berkeley St, Boston, MA 02116 *Tel:* 617-351-5000 *Toll Free Tel:* 800-225-5425 (K-12 educ materials); 800-323-9540 (assessment materials); 877-219-1537 (SkillsTutor); 888-242-6747 (Destination; Earobics; Edmark; Learning Village; Riverdeep); 800-225-3362 (Houghton Mifflin Harcourt Trade & Reference Publishers) *Toll Free Fax:* 800-269-5232 *E-mail:* customerservice@hmhpub.com *Web Site:* www.hmhco.com, pg 115

Forsberg, Jennie, ABDO Publishing Group, 8000 W 78 St, Suite 310, Edina, MN 55439 *Tel:* 952-831-2120 *Toll Free Tel:* 800-800-1312 *Toll Free Fax:* 800-862-3480 *E-mail:* customerservice@abdopublishing.com *Web Site:* abdopublishing.com, pg 2

Forsyth, Elliot, ProQuest LLC, 789 E Eisenhower Pkwy, Ann Arbor, MI 48108-3218 *Tel:* 734-761-4700 *Toll Free Tel:* 800-521-0600 *Fax:* 734-975-6486 *Toll Free Fax:* 800-864-0019 *E-mail:* info@proquest.com *Web Site:* www.proquest.com, pg 199

Forsythe, Kelly, Copper Canyon Press, Fort Worden State Park, Bldg 313, Port Townsend, WA 98368 *Tel:* 360-385-4925 *Toll Free Tel:* 877-501-1393 (orders) *Fax:* 360-385-4985 *E-mail:* poetry@coppercanyonpress.org *Web Site:* www.coppercanyonpress.org, pg 63

Forte, Fran, The New Press, 38 Greene St, 4th fl, New York, NY 10013 *Tel:* 212-629-8802 *Toll Free Tel:* 800-343-4489 (orders) *Fax:* 212-629-8617 *Toll Free Fax:* 800-351-5073 (orders) *E-mail:* newpress@thenewpress.com *Web Site:* www.thenewpress.com, pg 168

Forte, Jeffrey L, Law Tribune Books, 201 Ann Uccello St, 4th fl, Hartford, CT 06103 *Tel:* 860-527-7900 *Fax:* 860-527-7433 *E-mail:* lawtribune@alm.com *Web Site:* www.ctlawtribune.com, pg 135

Francis, Mary C, University of California Press, 2120 Berkeley Way, Berkeley, CA 94704-1012 *Tel:* 510-642-4247 *Fax:* 510-643-7127 *E-mail:* askucp@ucpress.edu (books); customerservice@ucpressjournals.com *Web Site:* www.ucpress.edu, pg 255

Francis, Paul, American Society of Mechanical Engineers (ASME), 2 Park Ave, New York, NY 10016-5990 *Tel:* 212-591-7000 *Toll Free Tel:* 800-843-2763 (cust serv-US, CN & Mexico) *Fax:* 212-591-7674; 973-882-8113 (cust serv); 973-882-1717 (orders & inquiries) *E-mail:* infocentral@asme.org *Web Site:* www.asme.org, pg 16

Francis, Therese, Crossquarter Publishing Group, PO Box 23749, Santa Fe, NM 87502 *Tel:* 505-690-3923 *Fax:* 214-975-9715 *E-mail:* sales@crossquarter.com; info@crossquarter.com *Web Site:* www.crossquarter.com, pg 67

Franco, Jimmy, Grand Central Publishing, 1290 Avenue of the Americas, New York, NY 10019 *Tel:* 212-364-1100 *Web Site:* www.hachettebookgroup.com, pg 99

Frank, Charlotte, McGraw-Hill Education, 2 Penn Plaza, New York, NY 10121-2298 *Tel:* 212-904-2000 *E-mail:* customer.service@mcgraw-hill.com *Web Site:* www.mheducation.com; www.mheducation.com/custserv.html, pg 151

Frank, Cynthia, Cypress House, 155 Cypress St, Fort Bragg, CA 95437 *Tel:* 707-964-9520 *Toll Free Tel:* 800-773-7782 *Fax:* 707-964-7531 *E-mail:* cypresshouse@cypresshouse.com *Web Site:* www.cypresshouse.com, pg 69, 524

Frank, Daniel, Pantheon Books/Schocken Books, c/o Random House Inc, 1745 Broadway, New York, NY 10019 *Tel:* 212-751-2600 *Toll Free Tel:* 800-638-6460 *Fax:* 212-572-6030, pg 181

Frank, Jerry, Vandamere Press, 3580 Morris St N, St Petersburg, FL 33713 *Tel:* 727-556-0950 *Toll Free Tel:* 800-551-7776 *Fax:* 727-556-2560 *E-mail:* orders@vandamere.com *Web Site:* www.vandamere.com, pg 264

Frankel, David, The Museum of Modern Art (MoMA), 11 W 53 St, New York, NY 10019 *Tel:* 212-708-9443 *Fax:* 212-333-6575 *E-mail:* moma_publications@moma.org *Web Site:* www.moma.org, pg 162

Frankl, Beth, Shambhala Publications Inc, Horticultural Hall, 300 Massachusetts Ave, Boston, MA 02115 *Tel:* 617-424-0030 *Toll Free Tel:* 866-424-0030 (off); 888-424-2329 (cust serv) *Fax:* 617-236-1563 *E-mail:* customercare@shambhala.com *Web Site:* www.shambhala.com, pg 223

Franklin, Lynn C, Lynn C Franklin Associates Ltd, 1350 Broadway, Suite 2015, New York, NY 10018 *Tel:* 212-868-6311 *Fax:* 212-868-6312 *E-mail:* agency@franklinandsiegal.com, pg 552

Franklin, Robert, McFarland, 960 NC Hwy 88 W, Jefferson, NC 28640 *Tel:* 336-246-4460 *Toll Free Tel:* 800-253-2187 (orders) *Fax:* 336-246-5018; 336-246-4403 (orders) *E-mail:* info@mcfarlandpub.com *Web Site:* www.mcfarlandpub.com, pg 150

Franklin, Wayne, The University of Connecticut, The Realities of Publishing, CLAS, 215 Glenbrook Rd, Unit 4025, Storrs, CT 06269-4025 *Tel:* 860-486-2141 *Web Site:* web.uconn.edu/english291, pg 663

Frantz, Kristen, Berrett-Koehler Publishers Inc, 1333 Broadway, Suite 1000, Oakland, CA 94612 *Tel:* 510-817-2277 *Fax:* 510-817-2278 *E-mail:* bkpub@bkpub.com *Web Site:* www.bkconnection.com, pg 35

Franzak, George, Rowman & Littlefield Publishers Inc, 4501 Forbes Blvd, Suite 200, Lanham, MD 20706 *Tel:* 301-459-3366 *Toll Free Tel:* 800-462-6420 (cust serv) *Fax:* 301-429-5748 *Web Site:* www.rowmanlittlefield.com, pg 212

Franzak, George, University Press of America Inc, 4501 Forbes Blvd, Suite 200, Lanham, MD 20706 *Tel:* 301-459-3366 *Toll Free Tel:* 800-462-6420 *Fax:* 301-429-5748 *Toll Free Fax:* 800-338-4550 *Web Site:* www.univpress.com, pg 261

Fraser, Caroline, Houghton Mifflin Harcourt, 222 Berkeley St, Boston, MA 02116 *Tel:* 617-351-5000 *Toll Free Tel:* 800-225-5425 (K-12 educ materials); 800-323-9540 (assessment materials); 877-219-1537 (SkillsTutor); 888-242-6747 (Destination; Earobics; Edmark; Learning Village; Riverdeep); 800-225-3362 (Houghton Mifflin Harcourt Trade & Reference Publishers) *Toll Free Fax:* 800-269-5232 *E-mail:* customerservice@hmhpub.com *Web Site:* www.hmhco.com, pg 115

Fraser, Simon, DK Publishing, 345 Hudson St, 2nd fl, New York, NY 10014 *Tel:* 646-674-4000 *Toll Free Tel:* 877-342-5357 (cust serv) *Web Site:* us.dk.com, pg 75

Fraser, Stephen, The Jennifer DeChiara Literary Agency, 31 E 32 St, Suite 300, New York, NY 10016 *Tel:* 212-481-8484 (ext 362) *Fax:* 212-481-9582 *Web Site:* www.jdlit.com, pg 547

Fraser-Bub, MacKenzie, Trident Media Group LLC, 41 Madison Ave, 36th fl, New York, NY 10010 *Tel:* 212-333-1511 *E-mail:* info@tridentmediagroup.com; press@tridentmediagroup.com *Web Site:* www.tridentmediagroup.com, pg 577

Frazier, Felicia, Penguin Group (USA) LLC, a Penguin Random House company, 375 Hudson St, New York, NY 10014 *Tel:* 212-366-2000 *Toll Free Tel:* 800-847-5515 (inside sales); 800-631-8571 (cust serv) *Fax:* 212-366-2666; 607-775-4829 (inside sales) *E-mail:* online@us.penguingroup.com *Web Site:* www.penguin.com; us.penguingroup.com, pg 186

Frazier, Felicia, Penguin Group (USA) LLC Sales, 375 Hudson St, New York, NY 10014 *Tel:* 212-366-2000 *E-mail:* online@penguinputnam.com *Web Site:* us.penguingroup.com, pg 186

Frazier, Felicia, Penguin Young Readers Group, 345 Hudson St, New York, NY 10014 *Tel:* 212-366-2000 *E-mail:* online@penguinputnam.com *Web Site:* www.penguinputnam.com; us.penguingroup.com, pg 187

Frazier, Warren, John Hawkins and Associates Inc, 71 W 23 St, Suite 1600, New York, NY 10010 *Tel:* 212-807-7040 *E-mail:* jha@jhalit.com *Web Site:* jhalit.com, pg 556

Frazin, Rhona, The Carl Sandburg Literary Awards, 20 N Michigan Ave, Suite 520, Chicago, IL 60602 *Tel:* 312-201-9830 *Fax:* 312-201-9833 *Web Site:* www.cplfoundation.org, pg 725

Frechette, Christopher, Paulist Press, 997 Macarthur Blvd, Mahwah, NJ 07430-9990 *Tel:* 201-825-7300 *Toll Free Tel:* 800-218-1903 *Fax:* 201-825-8345 *Toll Free Fax:* 800-836-3161 *E-mail:* info@paulistpress.com *Web Site:* www.paulistpress.com, pg 184

Frechette, Jacques, Guy Saint-Jean Editeur Inc, 3440 Blvd Industriel, Laval, QC H7L 4R9, Canada *Tel:* 450-663-1777 *Fax:* 450-663-6666 *E-mail:* info@saint-jeanediteur.com *Web Site:* www.saint-jeanediteur.com, pg 498

Freda, Kristin, Irma S & James H Black Award, 610 W 112 St, New York, NY 10025 *Tel:* 212-875-4458 *Fax:* 212-875-4558 *E-mail:* ccl@bankstreet.edu *Web Site:* www.bankstreet.edu/center-childrens-literature, pg 672

Fredell, Eric, Software & Information Industry Association (SIIA), 1090 Vermont Ave NW, 6th fl, Washington, DC 20005-4095 *Tel:* 202-289-7442 *Fax:* 202-289-7097 *Web Site:* www.siia.net, pg 619

Frederick, Holly, Curtis Brown Ltd, 10 Astor Place, New York, NY 10003 *Tel:* 212-473-5400 *Web Site:* www.curtisbrown.com, pg 544

Frederick, Margaretta S, William Morris Society in the United States Fellowships, PO Box 53263, Washington, DC 20009 *E-mail:* us@morrissociety.org *Web Site:* www.morrissociety.org, pg 709

Fredericks, Jeanne, Jeanne Fredericks Literary Agency Inc, 221 Benedict Hill Rd, New Canaan, CT 06840 *Tel:* 203-972-3011 *Fax:* 203-972-3011 *E-mail:* jeanne.fredericks@gmail.com (no unsol attachments) *Web Site:* jeannefredericks.com, pg 553

Fredrickson, Jordan, Arbordale Publishing, 612 Johnnie Dodds Blvd, Suite A2, Mount Pleasant, SC 29464 *Tel:* 843-971-6722 *Toll Free Tel:* 877-243-3457 *Fax:* 843-216-3804 *E-mail:* customerservice@arbordalepublishing.com; info@arbordalepublishing.com *Web Site:* www.arbordalepublishing.com, pg 21

Free, Liz, John Hawkins and Associates Inc, 71 W 23 St, Suite 1600, New York, NY 10010 *Tel:* 212-807-7040 *E-mail:* jha@jhalit.com *Web Site:* jhalit.com, pg 556

Freedman, Josie, ICM Partners, 730 Fifth Ave, New York, NY 10019 *Tel:* 212-556-5600 *Web Site:* www.icmtalent.com, pg 557

Freedman, Rana, Lonely Planet, 150 Linden St, Oakland, CA 94607 *Tel:* 510-893-8555 *Toll Free Tel:* 800-275-8555 (orders) *Fax:* 510-893-8572 *E-mail:* info@lonelyplanet.com *Web Site:* www.lonelyplanet.com, pg 142

Freedman, Robert A, Robert A Freedman Dramatic Agency Inc, 1501 Broadway, Suite 2310, New York, NY 10036 *Tel:* 212-840-5760 *Fax:* 212-840-5776, pg 553

Freeland, Abby, West Virginia University Press, West Virginia University, PO Box 6295, Morgantown, WV 26506-6295 *Tel:* 304-293-8400 *Toll Free Tel:* 866-WVU-PRES (988-7737) *Fax:* 304-293-6585 *E-mail:* press@wvu.edu *Web Site:* www.wvupress.com, pg 269

Freeland, Ronald, Judson Press, 588 N Gulph Rd, King of Prussia, PA 19406 *Toll Free Tel:* 800-458-3766 *Fax:* 610-768-2107 *Web Site:* www.judsonpress.com, pg 128

Freeman, Darla, Kensington Publishing Corp, 119 W 40 St, New York, NY 10018 *Tel:* 212-407-1500 *Toll Free Tel:* 800-221-2647 *Fax:* 212-935-0699 *Web Site:* www.kensingtonbooks.com, pg 130

Freeman, Katharine, Riverhead Books (Hardcover), 375 Hudson St, New York, NY 10014 *Tel:* 212-366-2000 *E-mail:* online@penguinputnam.com *Web Site:* www.penguinputnam.com; us.penguingroup.com, pg 209

Freeman-Slade, Jessica, Clarkson Potter Publishers, c/o Random House Inc, 1745 Broadway, New York, NY 10019 *Tel:* 212-782-9000 *Toll Free Tel:* 888-264-1745 *Fax:* 212-572-6181 *Web Site:* www.clarksonpotter.com; www.randomhouse.com/crown/clarksonpotter, pg 195

Freeny, Phyllis Jones, Professional Communications Inc, 20968 State Rd 22, Caddo, OK 74729 *Tel:* 580-367-9838 *Toll Free Tel:* 800-337-9838 *Fax:* 580-367-9989 *E-mail:* info@pcibooks.com *Web Site:* www.pcibooks.com, pg 198

Freese, Rich, Recorded Books LLC, 270 Skipjack Rd, Prince Frederick, MD 20678 *Tel:* 410-535-5590 *Toll Free Tel:* 800-638-1304; 877-732-2898 *Fax:* 410-535-5499 *E-mail:* customerservice@recordedbooks.com *Web Site:* www.recordedbooks.com, pg 206

Freet, Roger, HarperCollins General Books Group, 195 Broadway, New York, NY 10007 *Tel:* 212-207-7000 *Web Site:* www.harpercollins.com, pg 105

Freilach, David, MIT List Visual Arts Center, MIT E 15-109, 20 Ames St, Cambridge, MA 02139 *Tel:* 617-253-4400; 617-253-4680 *Fax:* 617-258-7265 *E-mail:* mlinga@mit.edu *Web Site:* listart.mit.edu, pg 157

French, Tiffany, The Pilgrim Press/United Church Press, 700 Prospect Ave, Cleveland, OH 44115-1100 *Toll Free Tel:* 800-537-3394 (cust serv-indivs); 800-654-5129 (cust serv-commercial accts) *Fax:* 216-736-2206 (orders) *E-mail:* proposals@thepilgrimpress.com *Web Site:* www.thepilgrimpress.com; www.unitedchurchpress.com, pg 192

Frerich, Stephanie, Penguin Group (USA) LLC, a Penguin Random House company, 375 Hudson St, New York, NY 10014 *Tel:* 212-366-2000 *Toll Free Tel:* 800-847-5515 (inside sales); 800-631-8571 (cust serv) *Fax:* 212-366-2666; 607-775-4829 (inside sales) *E-mail:* online@us.penguingroup.com *Web Site:* www.penguin.com; us.penguingroup.com, pg 186

Frerich, Stephanie, Portfolio, 375 Hudson St, New York, NY 10014, pg 195

Frese, Alan, Pippin Press, 229 E 85 St, New York, NY 10028 *Tel:* 212-288-4920 *Fax:* 908-237-2407, pg 192

Fulle, Nan, Minnesota Historical Society Press, 345 Kellogg Blvd W, St Paul, MN 55102-1906 *Tel:* 651-259-3205; 651-259-3000 *Toll Free Tel:* 800-621-2736 (warehouse) *Fax:* 651-297-1345 *Toll Free Fax:* 800-621-8476 (warehouse) *E-mail:* info-mnhspress@mnhs.org *Web Site:* www.mnhs.org/mnhspress, pg 157

Fuller, Barbara, Editcetera, 2034 Blake St, Suite 5, Berkeley, CA 94704 *Tel:* 510-849-1110 *Fax:* 510-900-6141 *E-mail:* info@editcetera.com *Web Site:* www.editcetera.com, pg 525

Fuller, Dale, Parabola Books, 20 W 20 St, 2nd fl, New York, NY 10011 *Tel:* 212-822-8806 *Toll Free Tel:* 800-592-2521 (subns) *Fax:* 212-822-8823 *E-mail:* info@parabola.org *Web Site:* www.parabola.org, pg 182

Fuller, Diana, Squaw Valley Community of Writers Summer Workshops, PO Box 1416, Nevada City, CA 95959 *Tel:* 530-470-8440 *E-mail:* info@squawvalleywriters.org *Web Site:* www.squawvalleywriters.org, pg 656

Fuller, Mila, National Council of Teachers of English (NCTE), 1111 W Kenyon Rd, Urbana, IL 61801-1096 *Tel:* 217-328-3870 *Toll Free Tel:* 877-369-6283 (cust serv) *Fax:* 217-328-9645 *E-mail:* orders@ncte.org *Web Site:* www.ncte.org, pg 164

Fuller, Mila, National Council of Teachers of English (NCTE), 1111 W Kenyon Rd, Urbana, IL 61801-1096 *Tel:* 217-328-3870 *Toll Free Tel:* 877-369-6283 (cust serv) *Fax:* 217-328-9645 *E-mail:* public_info@ncte.org *Web Site:* www.ncte.org, pg 612

Fuller, Molly, Coffee House Press, 79 13 Ave NE, Suite 110, Minneapolis, MN 55413 *Tel:* 612-338-0125 *Fax:* 612-338-4004 *E-mail:* info@coffeehousepress.org *Web Site:* coffeehousepress.org, pg 60

Fuller, Dr Renee PhD, Ball-Stick-Bird Publications Inc, PO Box 429, Williamstown, MA 01267-0429 *Tel:* 413-664-0002 *Fax:* 413-664-0002 *E-mail:* info@ballstickbird.com *Web Site:* www.ballstickbird.com, pg 30

Fumich, Jita, Folio Literary Management LLC, The Film Center Bldg, 630 Ninth Ave, Suite 1101, New York, NY 10036 *Tel:* 212-400-1494 *Fax:* 212-967-0977 *Web Site:* www.foliolit.com, pg 552

Fund, Ken, Quarto Publishing Group USA Inc, 400 First Ave N, Suite 300, Minneapolis, MN 55401 *Tel:* 612-344-8100 *Toll Free Tel:* 800-328-0590 (sales); 800-458-0454 *Fax:* 612-344-8691 *E-mail:* sales@creativepub.com *Web Site:* quartoknows.com, pg 201

Funk, Susan, Mystic Seaport Museum Inc, PO Box 6000, Mystic, CT 06355-0990 *Tel:* 860-572-5302; 860-572-0711 (visitor serv) *Toll Free Tel:* 800-248-1066 (wholesale orders only); 800-331-2665 (retail orders only) *Fax:* 860-572-5321 *E-mail:* info@mysticseaport.org *Web Site:* www.mysticseaport.org, pg 162

Furbacher, Michelle, Whitecap Books Ltd, 314 W Cordova St, Suite 210, Vancouver, BC V6B 1E8, Canada *Tel:* 604-681-6181 *Toll Free Tel:* 800-387-9776 *Toll Free Fax:* 800-260-9777 *Web Site:* www.whitecap.ca, pg 505

Furbush, Jake, The MIT Press, 55 Hayward St, Cambridge, MA 02142 *Tel:* 617-253-5255 *Toll Free Tel:* 800-207-8354 (orders) *Fax:* 617-258-6779; 617-577-1545 (orders) *Web Site:* mitpress.mit.edu, pg 158

Furman, Laura, PEN/O. Henry Prize Stories, University of Texas at Austin, One University Sta B5000, Austin, TX 78712 *Tel:* 512-572-2428 *Web Site:* www.ohenryprizestories.com, pg 717

Furman, Laura, University of Texas at Austin, Creative Writing Program, Dept of English, PAR 108, One University Sta, Mailcode B5000, Austin, TX 78712-1164 *Tel:* 512-471-5132; 512-471-4991 *Fax:* 512-471-4909 *Web Site:* www.utexas.edu/cola/depts/english/creative-writing, pg 664

Furnish, Ben, BkMk Press - University of Missouri-Kansas City, University House, 5101 Rockhill Rd, Kansas City, MO 64110-2499 *Tel:* 816-235-2558 *Fax:* 816-235-2611 *E-mail:* bkmk@umkc.edu *Web Site:* www.umkc.edu/bkmk, pg 38

Furnish, Ben, G S Sharat Chandra Prize for Short Fiction, University House, 5101 Rockhill Rd, Kansas City, MO 64110-2499 *Tel:* 816-235-2558 *Fax:* 816-235-2611 *E-mail:* bkmk@umkc.edu *Web Site:* www.umkc.edu/bkmk, pg 676

Furnish, Ben, John Ciardi Prize for Poetry, University House, 5101 Rockhill Rd, Kansas City, MO 64110-2499 *Tel:* 816-235-2558 *Fax:* 816-235-2611 *E-mail:* bkmk@umkc.edu *Web Site:* www.umkc.edu/bkmk, pg 677

Furr, Patti, FaithWalk Publishing, 5450 N Dixie Hwy, Lima, OH 45807 *Tel:* 419-227-1818 *Toll Free Tel:* 800-537-1030 (orders: non-bookstore mkts) *Fax:* 419-224-9184 *E-mail:* orders@csspub.com *Web Site:* www.faithwalkpub.com, pg 86

Fusting, Donald W, Lanahan Publishers Inc, 324 Hawthorne Rd, Baltimore, MD 21210-2303 *Tel:* 410-366-2434 *Toll Free Tel:* 866-345-1949 *Fax:* 410-366-8798 *E-mail:* lanahan@aol.com *Web Site:* www.lanahanpublishers.com, pg 134

Futter, Deb, Grand Central Publishing, 1290 Avenue of the Americas, New York, NY 10019 *Tel:* 212-364-1100 *Web Site:* www.hachettebookgroup.com, pg 99

G'Schwind, Stephanie, Nelligan Prize for Short Fiction, Colorado State Univ, Dept of English, Ctr for Literary Publg, 9105 Campus Delivery, Fort Collins, CO 80523-9105 *Tel:* 970-491-5449 *E-mail:* creview@colostate.edu *Web Site:* nelliganprize.colostate.edu, pg 711

Ga, Ellie, Ugly Duckling Presse, The Old American Can Factory, 232 Third St, Suite E002, Brooklyn, NY 11215 *Tel:* 347-948-5170 *E-mail:* udp_mailbox@yahoo.com; info@uglyducklingpresse.org *Web Site:* www.uglyducklingpresse.org, pg 252

Gabel, Claudia, HarperCollins Children's Books, 195 Broadway, New York, NY 10007 *Tel:* 212-207-7000 *Web Site:* www.harpercollins.com/childrens, pg 105

Gadd, Laurence, North River Press Publishing Corp, 27 Rosseter St, Great Barrington, MA 01230 *Tel:* 413-528-0034 *Toll Free Tel:* 800-486-2665 *Fax:* 413-528-3163 *Toll Free Fax:* 800-BOOK-FAX (266-5329) *E-mail:* info@northriverpress.com *Web Site:* www.northriverpress.com, pg 171

Gadiraju, Raju, Oxford University Press USA, 198 Madison Ave, New York, NY 10016 *Tel:* 212-726-6000 *Toll Free Tel:* 800-451-7556 (orders); 800-445-9714 (cust serv) *Fax:* 919-677-1303 *E-mail:* custserv.us@oup.com *Web Site:* www.oup.com/us, pg 179

Gadney, Alan, Film-Video Publications/Circus Source Publications, 7944 Capistrano Ave, West Hills, CA 91304 *Tel:* 818-340-0175 *Fax:* 818-340-6620 *E-mail:* circussource@aol.com, pg 88

Gadney, Nancy, Film-Video Publications/Circus Source Publications, 7944 Capistrano Ave, West Hills, CA 91304 *Tel:* 818-340-0175 *Fax:* 818-340-6620 *E-mail:* circussource@aol.com, pg 88

Gage, Michael, Kirkbride Bible Co Inc, 1102 Deloss St, Indianapolis, IN 46203 *Tel:* 317-633-1900 *Toll Free Tel:* 800-428-4385 *Fax:* 317-633-1444 *E-mail:* sales@kirkbride.com; info@kirkbride.com *Web Site:* www.kirkbride.com, pg 131

Gagen, Sheila, EEI Communications, 6301 Ivy Lane, Suite 250, Greenbelt, MD 20770 *Tel:* 410-309-8200 *Fax:* 410-630-3980 *E-mail:* info@eeicom.com *Web Site:* www.eeicom.com, pg 525, 660

Gagnon, Debbie, Reader's Digest Trade Books, 44 S Broadway, White Plains, NY 10601 *Tel:* 914-244-7503 *Fax:* 914-244-4841 *Web Site:* www.rd.com, pg 205

Gagnon, Jean-Marc, Editions MultiMondes, 930 rue Pouliot, Quebec, QC G1V 3N9, Canada *Tel:* 418-651-3885 *Toll Free Tel:* 800-840-3029 *Fax:* 418-651-6822 *Toll Free Fax:* 888-303-5931 *E-mail:* multimondes@multim.com *Web Site:* www.multim.com, pg 482

Gagnon, Manon, La Fondation Emile Nelligan, 100, rue Sherbrooke, Montreal, QC H2X 1C3, Canada *Tel:* 514-278-4657 *Fax:* 514-278-1943 *E-mail:* info@fondation-nelligan.org *Web Site:* www.fondation-nelligan.org, pg 606

Gagnon, Manon, Prix Emile-Nelligan, 100, rue Sherbrooke, Montreal, QC H2X 1C3, Canada *Tel:* 514-278-4657 *Toll Free Tel:* 888-849-8540 *Fax:* 514-278-1943 *E-mail:* info@fondation-nelligan.org *Web Site:* www.fondation-nelligan.org, pg 722

Gagnon, Matt, Boom! Studios, 5670 Wilshire Blvd, Suite 450, Los Angeles, CA 90036 *Web Site:* www.boom-studios.com, pg 43

Galassi, Donna, Avalon Travel Publishing, 1700 Fourth St, Berkeley, CA 94710 *Tel:* 510-595-3664 *Fax:* 510-809-3777 *Web Site:* www.avalontravelbooks.com, pg 28

Galassi, Jonathan, Farrar, Straus & Giroux, LLC, 18 W 18 St, New York, NY 10011 *Tel:* 212-741-6900 *E-mail:* fsg.publicity@fsgbooks.com *Web Site:* us.macmillan.com/fsg.aspx, pg 86

Galassi, Jonathan, Macmillan, 175 Fifth Ave, New York, NY 10010 *Tel:* 646-307-5151 *Fax:* 212-420-9314 *E-mail:* firstname.lastname@macmillan.com *Web Site:* www.macmillan.com, pg 145

Galasso, Al, North American Bookdealers Exchange (NABE), PO Box 606, Cottage Grove, OR 97424-0026 *Tel:* 541-942-7455 *E-mail:* nabe@bookmarketingprofits.com *Web Site:* www.bookmarketingprofits.com, pg 614

Galat, Danielle, New World Library, 14 Pamaron Way, Novato, CA 94949 *Tel:* 415-884-2100 *Toll Free Tel:* 800-227-3900 (ext 52, retail orders); 800-972-6657 *Fax:* 415-884-2199 *E-mail:* escort@newworldlibrary.com *Web Site:* www.newworldlibrary.com, pg 168

Galbraith, Judy, Free Spirit Publishing Inc, 217 Fifth Ave N, Suite 200, Minneapolis, MN 55401-1299 *Tel:* 612-338-2068 *Toll Free Tel:* 800-735-7323 *Fax:* 612-337-5050 *Toll Free Fax:* 866-419-5199 *E-mail:* help4kids@freespirit.com *Web Site:* www.freespirit.com, pg 92

Galde, Phyllis, Galde Press Inc, PO Box 460, Lakeville, MN 55044 *Tel:* 952-891-5991 *Toll Free Tel:* 800-777-3454 *Web Site:* www.galdepress.com, pg 94

Gale, David, Simon & Schuster Children's Publishing, 1230 Avenue of the Americas, New York, NY 10020 *Tel:* 212-698-7000 *Web Site:* KIDS.SimonandSchuster.com; TEEN.SimonandSchuster.com; simonandschuster.net; simonandschuster.biz, pg 225

Gale, Kate, Red Hen Press, PO Box 40820, Pasadena, CA 91114 *Tel:* 626-356-4760 *Fax:* 626-356-9974 *Web Site:* www.redhen.org, pg 206

Gale, Meighan, Zone Books dba Urzone Inc, 1226 Prospect Ave, Brooklyn, NY 11218 *Tel:* 718-686-0048 *Toll Free Tel:* 800-405-1619 (orders & cust serv) *Fax:* 718-686-9045 *Toll Free Fax:* 800-406-9145 (orders) *E-mail:* orders@triliteral.org *Web Site:* www.zonebooks.org, pg 280

Galen, Russell, Scovil Galen Ghosh Literary Agency Inc, 276 Fifth Ave, Suite 708, New York, NY 10001 *Tel:* 212-679-8686 *Fax:* 212-679-6710 *E-mail:* info@sgglit.com *Web Site:* www.sgglit.com, pg 572

Gales, Kate, Simon & Schuster, 1230 Avenue of the Americas, New York, NY 10020 *Tel:* 212-698-7000 *Toll Free Tel:* 800-223-2348 (cust serv); 800-223-2336 (orders) *Toll Free Fax:* 800-943-9831 (orders) *Web Site:* www.simonandschuster.com, pg 225

Gall, John, Harry N Abrams Inc, 115 W 18 St, 6th fl, New York, NY 10011 *Tel:* 212-206-7715 *Toll Free Tel:* 800-345-1359 *Fax:* 212-519-1210 *E-mail:* abrams@abramsbooks.com *Web Site:* www.abramsbooks.com, pg 3

Gallagher, Amy, North River Press Publishing Corp, 27 Rosseter St, Great Barrington, MA 01230 *Tel:* 413-528-0034 *Toll Free Tel:* 800-486-2665 *Fax:* 413-528-3163 *Toll Free Fax:* 800-BOOK-FAX (266-5329) *E-mail:* info@northriverpress.com *Web Site:* www.northriverpress.com, pg 171

Gallagher, Charles, The Perseus Books Group, 387 Park Ave S, 12th fl, New York, NY 10016 *Tel:* 212-340-8100 *Toll Free Tel:* 800-343-4499 (cust serv) *Fax:* 212-340-8105 *Web Site:* www.perseusbooksgroup.com, pg 189

Garretson, Jessie, Penguin Random House Speakers Bureau, 1745 Broadway, Mail Drop 13-1, New York, NY 10019 *Tel:* 212-572-2013 *E-mail:* speakers@penguinrandomhouse.com *Web Site:* www.prhspeakers.com, pg 588

Garretson, Robin, Success Advertising & Publishing, 3419 Dunham Rd, Warsaw, NY 14569 *Tel:* 585-786-5663, pg 237

Garrett, Edward, Macmillan, 175 Fifth Ave, New York, NY 10010 *Tel:* 646-307-5151 *Fax:* 212-420-9314 *E-mail:* firstname.lastname@macmillan.com *Web Site:* www.macmillan.com, pg 145

Garrett, Michael, Creative Inspirations Inc, 6203 Old Springville Rd, Pinson, AL 35126 *Web Site:* www.manuscriptcritique.com, pg 524

Garrett, Michael, How to be Published Workshops, c/o Creative Inspirations Inc, PO Box 362, Clay, AL 35048 *E-mail:* mgteach352@gmail.com *Web Site:* www.writing2sell.com, pg 652

Garrett, Phil, Epicenter Press Inc, 6524 NE 181 St, Suite 2, Kenmore, WA 98028 *Tel:* 425-485-6822 (edit, mktg, busn off) *Fax:* 425-481-8253 *E-mail:* info@epicenterpress.com *Web Site:* www.epicenterpress.com, pg 83

Garrick, Kate, The Karpfinger Agency, 357 W 20 St, New York, NY 10011-3379 *Tel:* 212-691-2690 *Fax:* 212-691-7129 *E-mail:* info@karpfinger.com (no queries or submissions) *Web Site:* karpfinger.com, pg 559

Garrido, Dr Marta, Merit Publishing International Inc, 6839 Villas Dr S, Boca Raton, FL 33433 *Tel:* 561-350-0329; 561-697-1116 (orders) *E-mail:* merituk@aol.com; meritpi@aol.com *Web Site:* www.meritpublishing.com, pg 154

Garrison, Deborah, Alfred A Knopf/Everyman's Library, c/o Random House Inc, 1745 Broadway, New York, NY 10019 *Tel:* 212-751-2600 *Toll Free Tel:* 800-638-6460 *Fax:* 212-572-2593 *Web Site:* www.knopfdoubleday.com, pg 132

Garrison, Deborah, Pantheon Books/Schocken Books, c/o Random House Inc, 1745 Broadway, New York, NY 10019 *Tel:* 212-751-2600 *Toll Free Tel:* 800-638-6460 *Fax:* 212-572-6030, pg 181

Garrison, Jessica, Dial Books for Young Readers, 345 Hudson St, New York, NY 10014 *Tel:* 212-366-2000 *Fax:* 212-414-3396 *E-mail:* online@penguinputnam.com *Web Site:* www.penguinputnam.com; us.penguingroup.com, pg 74

Garstein, Stacey, Markus Wiener Publishers Inc, 231 Nassau St, Princeton, NJ 08542 *Tel:* 609-921-1141 *Fax:* 609-921-1140 *E-mail:* publisher@markuswiener.com *Web Site:* www.markuswiener.com, pg 271

Garton, Keith, Red Chair Press, PO Box 333, South Egremont, MA 01258-0333 *Toll Free Tel:* 888-327-2141 (ext 110) *Toll Free Fax:* 888-533-4037 *E-mail:* info@redchairpress.com *Web Site:* www.redchairpress.com, pg 206

Garvey, Elaine, Templegate Publishers, 302 E Adams St, Springfield, IL 62701 *Tel:* 217-522-3353 (edit & sales); 217-522-3354 (billing) *Toll Free Tel:* 800-367-4844 (orders only) *Fax:* 217-522-3362 *E-mail:* wisdom@templegate.com; orders@templegate.com (sales) *Web Site:* www.templegate.com, pg 242

Garvey, Thomas M, Templegate Publishers, 302 E Adams St, Springfield, IL 62701 *Tel:* 217-522-3353 (edit & sales); 217-522-3354 (billing) *Toll Free Tel:* 800-367-4844 (orders only) *Fax:* 217-522-3362 *E-mail:* wisdom@templegate.com; orders@templegate.com (sales) *Web Site:* www.templegate.com, pg 242

Garych, Leslie, Scholastic Trade Division, 557 Broadway, New York, NY 10012 *Tel:* 212-343-6100; 212-343-4685 (export sales) *Fax:* 212-343-4714 (export sales) *Web Site:* www.scholastic.com, pg 219

Garza, Jennifer, Random House Publishing Group, 1745 Broadway, New York, NY 10019 *Toll Free Tel:* 800-200-3552 *Web Site:* atrandom.com, pg 204

Gaterud, Abbey, Ooligan Press, Portland State University, 369 Neuberger Hall, 724 SW Harrison St, Portland, OR 97201 *Tel:* 503-725-9748 *Fax:* 503-725-3561 *E-mail:* ooligan@ooliganpress.pdx.edu *Web Site:* ooligan.pdx.edu, pg 175

Gates, Henry Louis Jr, The Anisfield-Wolf Book Awards, 1422 Euclid Ave, Suite 1300, Cleveland, OH 44115 *Tel:* 216-861-3810 *Fax:* 216-861-1729 *E-mail:* awinfo@clevefdn.org *Web Site:* www.anisfield-wolf.org; www.clevelandfoundation.org, pg 667

Gates, Jaym, Science Fiction & Fantasy Writers of America Inc (SFWA), PO Box 3238, Enfield, CT 06083-3238 *E-mail:* office@sfwa.org *Web Site:* www.sfwa.org, pg 618

Gates, Jennifer, Zachary Shuster Harmsworth Agency, 1776 Broadway, Suite 1405, New York, NY 10019 *Tel:* 212-765-6900 *Fax:* 212-765-6490 *Web Site:* www.zshliterary.com, pg 580

Gates, Rob, The Gaylactic Spectrum Awards, PO Box 73602, Washington, DC 20056-3602 *Tel:* 202-483-6369 *Web Site:* www.spectrumawards.org, pg 688

Gates, Roberta, Friends of American Writers Awards, 506 Rose Ave, Des Plaines, IL 60016 *Tel:* 847-827-8339 *Web Site:* www.fawchicago.org, pg 688

Gates, Roberta, Juvenile Literary Awards/Young People's Literature Awards, 506 Rose Ave, Des Plaines, IL 60016 *Tel:* 847-827-8339 *Web Site:* www.fawchicago.org, pg 697

Gates, Tracy, Viking Children's Books, 345 Hudson St, New York, NY 10014 *Tel:* 212-366-2000 *E-mail:* online@penguinputnam.com *Web Site:* www.penguinputnam.com; us.penguingroup.com, pg 265

Gatland, Steve, MDR, A D&B Co, 6 Armstrong Rd, Suite 301, Shelton, CT 06484 *Tel:* 203-926-4800 *Toll Free Tel:* 800-333-8802 *Fax:* 203-225-4603 *Toll Free Fax:* 866-532-7097 *E-mail:* mdrinfo@dnb.com *Web Site:* schooldata.com, pg 152

Gatt, Michelle, Slack Incorporated, 6900 Grove Rd, Thorofare, NJ 08086-9447 *Tel:* 856-848-1000 *Toll Free Tel:* 800-257-8290 *Fax:* 856-848-6091 *E-mail:* sales@slackinc.com *Web Site:* www.slackbooks.com, pg 227

Gatten, Dave, Pacific Press Publishing Association, 1350 N Kings Rd, Nampa, ID 83687-3193 *Tel:* 208-465-2500 *Toll Free Tel:* 800-447-7377 *Fax:* 208-465-2531 *Web Site:* www.pacificpress.com, pg 180

Gaudioso, Angela, Resilient Publishing, 406 S Third St, Boise, ID 83702 *Tel:* 208-258-9544 *E-mail:* submissions@resilientpublishing.com *Web Site:* www.resilientpublishing.com, pg 208

Gauthier, Daniel J, Gauthier Publications Inc, PO Box 806241, St Clair Shores, MI 48080 *Tel:* 313-458-7141 *Fax:* 586-279-1515 *E-mail:* info@gauthierpublications.com *Web Site:* www.gauthierpublications.com, pg 95

Gauthier, Elizabeth, Gauthier Publications Inc, PO Box 806241, St Clair Shores, MI 48080 *Tel:* 313-458-7141 *Fax:* 586-279-1515 *E-mail:* info@gauthierpublications.com *Web Site:* www.gauthierpublications.com, pg 95

Gauthier, Jen, Greystone Books Ltd, 343 Railway St, Suite 201, Vancouver, BC V6A 1A4, Canada *Tel:* 604-875-1550 *Fax:* 604-875-1556 *E-mail:* info@greystonebooks.com *Web Site:* www.greystonebooks.com, pg 486

Gauthier, Mark, H W Wilson, 2 University Plaza, Suite 310, Hackensack, NJ 07601 *Tel:* 201-968-0500 *Toll Free Tel:* 800-221-1592 *Fax:* 201-968-0511 *E-mail:* info@hwwilsoninprint.com; csr@hwwilsoninprint.com; information@ebscohost.com *Web Site:* www.hwwilsoninprint.com; www.ebscohost.com/wilson, pg 273

Gautier, Donna, Bloomsbury Publishing Inc, 1385 Broadway, 5th fl, New York, NY 10018 *Tel:* 212-419-5300 *E-mail:* marketingusa@bloomsbury.com; adultpublicityusa@bloomsbury.com; askacademic@bloomsbury.com *Web Site:* www.bloomsbury.com, pg 40

Gauvin, Rod, ProQuest LLC, 789 E Eisenhower Pkwy, Ann Arbor, MI 48108-3218 *Tel:* 734-761-4700 *Toll Free Tel:* 800-521-0600 *Fax:* 734-975-6486 *Toll Free Fax:* 800-864-0019 *E-mail:* info@proquest.com *Web Site:* www.proquest.com, pg 199

Gavin, Tara, Kensington Publishing Corp, 119 W 40 St, New York, NY 10018 *Tel:* 212-407-1500 *Toll Free Tel:* 800-221-2647 *Fax:* 212-935-0699 *Web Site:* www.kensingtonbooks.com, pg 130

Gayles, Jia, The Knight Agency Inc, 570 East Ave, Madison, GA 30650 *E-mail:* submissions@knightagency.net *Web Site:* www.knightagency.net, pg 560

Gaynin, Gail, Morgan Gaynin Inc, 149 Madison Ave, Suite 1140, New York, NY 10016 *Tel:* 212-475-0440 *E-mail:* info@morgangaynin.com *Web Site:* www.morgangaynin.com, pg 584

Gayot, Alain, Gault Millau Inc/Gayot Publications, 4311 Wilshire Blvd, Suite 405, Los Angeles, CA 90010 *Tel:* 323-965-3529 *Fax:* 323-936-2883 *E-mail:* info@gayot.com *Web Site:* www.gayot.com, pg 95

Gayot, Andre, Gault Millau Inc/Gayot Publications, 4311 Wilshire Blvd, Suite 405, Los Angeles, CA 90010 *Tel:* 323-965-3529 *Fax:* 323-936-2883 *E-mail:* info@gayot.com *Web Site:* www.gayot.com, pg 95

Gazlay, Laura, The Library of America, 14 E 60 St, New York, NY 10022-1006 *Tel:* 212-308-3360 *Fax:* 212-750-8352 *E-mail:* info@loa.org *Web Site:* www.loa.org, pg 139

Gazzolo, Paul, Gale, 27500 Drake Rd, Farmington Hills, MI 48331-3535 *Tel:* 248-699-4253 *Toll Free Tel:* 800-877-4253 *Fax:* 248-699-8049 *Toll Free Fax:* 800-414-5043 (orders) *E-mail:* gale.salesassistance@cengage.com *Web Site:* www.gale.cengage.com, pg 94

Geale, Nancy L, Thomas Geale Publications Inc, PO Box 370540, Montara, CA 94037-0540 *Tel:* 650-728-5219 *Toll Free Tel:* 800-554-5457 *Fax:* 650-728-0918 *E-mail:* justthink@comcast.net, pg 245

Geary, Judith, Ingalls Publishing Group Inc (IPG), PO Box 2500, Banner Elk, NC 28604 *Tel:* 828-297-6884 *Fax:* 828-297-6880 *E-mail:* sales@ingallspublishinggroup.com *Web Site:* www.ingallspublishinggroup.com, pg 121

Geary, William III, Bisk Education, 9417 Princess Palm Ave, Suite 400, Tampa, FL 33619 *Tel:* 813-621-6200 *Toll Free Tel:* 800-280-9718 (cust serv) *E-mail:* customerservice@bisk.com *Web Site:* www.bisk.com, pg 37

Geck, Steve, Sourcebooks Inc, 1935 Brookdale Rd, Suite 139, Naperville, IL 60563 *Tel:* 630-961-3900 *Toll Free Tel:* 800-432-7444 *Fax:* 630-961-2168 *E-mail:* info@sourcebooks.com; customersupport@sourcebooks.com *Web Site:* www.sourcebooks.com, pg 230

Gee, Connie, BePuzzled, 2030 Harrison St, San Francisco, CA 94110 *Tel:* 415-503-1600 *Toll Free Tel:* 800-347-4818 *Fax:* 415-503-0085 *E-mail:* info@ugames.com *Web Site:* www.ugames.com, pg 35

Geer, David, Samuel French Inc, 235 Park Ave S, 5th fl, New York, NY 10003 *Tel:* 212-206-8990 *Toll Free Tel:* 866-598-8449 *Fax:* 212-206-1429 *E-mail:* info@samuelfrench.com; publications@samuelfrench.com *Web Site:* www.samuelfrench.com, pg 92

Geers, Torsten, Cengage Learning, 20 Channel Center St, Boston, MA 02210 *Tel:* 617-289-7700 *Toll Free Tel:* 800-354-9706 *Fax:* 617-289-7844 *Toll Free Fax:* 800-487-8488 *E-mail:* esales@cengage.com *Web Site:* www.cengage.com, pg 53

Gehani, Indu, Silicon Press, 25 Beverly Rd, Summit, NJ 07901 *Tel:* 908-273-8919 *Fax:* 908-273-6149 *E-mail:* info@silicon-press.com *Web Site:* www.silicon-press.com, pg 224

Gehringer, Richard, Columbia University Press, 61 W 62 St, New York, NY 10023 *Tel:* 212-459-0600 *Toll Free Tel:* 800-944-8648 *Fax:* 212-459-3678 *E-mail:* cup_book@columbia.edu (orders & cust serv) *Web Site:* cup.columbia.edu, pg 61

Geiger, Ellen, Frances Goldin Literary Agency, Inc, 57 E 11 St, Suite 5-B, New York, NY 10003 *Tel:* 212-777-0047 *Fax:* 212-228-1660 *E-mail:* agency@goldinlit.com *Web Site:* www.goldinlit.com, pg 554

Geiger, Rachel, Chronicle Books LLC, 680 Second St, San Francisco, CA 94107 *Tel:* 415-537-4200 *Toll Free Tel:* 800-759-0190 (cust serv) *Fax:* 415-537-4460 *Toll Free Fax:* 800-858-7787 (orders); 800-286-9471 (cust serv) *E-mail:* frontdesk@chroniclebooks.com *Web Site:* www.chroniclebooks.com, pg 58

Geissler, Cynara, Arsenal Pulp Press, 211 E Georgia St, No 202, Vancouver, BC V6A 1Z6, Canada *Tel:* 604-687-4233 *Toll Free Tel:* 888-600-PULP (600-7857) *Fax:* 604-687-4283 *E-mail:* info@arsenalpulp.com *Web Site:* www.arsenalpulp.com, pg 471

Geist, Ken, Scholastic Trade Division, 557 Broadway, New York, NY 10012 *Tel:* 212-343-6100; 212-343-4685 (export sales) *Fax:* 212-343-4714 (export sales) *Web Site:* www.scholastic.com, pg 219

Gelb, Eric, Small Business Advisors Inc, 11 Franklin Ave, Hewlett, NY 11557 *Tel:* 516-374-1387; 914-260-1027 *Fax:* 516-374-1175; 720-294-3202 *E-mail:* info@smallbusinessadvice.com *Web Site:* www.smallbusinessadvice.com, pg 228

Gelb, Joe, Small Business Advisors Inc, 11 Franklin Ave, Hewlett, NY 11557 *Tel:* 516-374-1387; 914-260-1027 *Fax:* 516-374-1175; 720-294-3202 *E-mail:* info@smallbusinessadvice.com *Web Site:* www.smallbusinessadvice.com, pg 228

Gelbman, Leslie, Berkley Books, 375 Hudson St, New York, NY 10014 *Tel:* 212-366-2000 *Fax:* 212-366-2666 *E-mail:* online@penguinputnam.com *Web Site:* www.penguinputnam.com; us.penguingroup.com, pg 35

Gelbman, Leslie, Berkley Publishing Group, 375 Hudson St, New York, NY 10014 *Tel:* 212-366-2000 *Fax:* 212-366-2385 *E-mail:* online@penguinputnam.com *Web Site:* us.penguingroup.com, pg 35

Gelbman, Leslie, Penguin Group (USA) LLC, a Penguin Random House company, 375 Hudson St, New York, NY 10014 *Tel:* 212-366-2000 *Toll Free Tel:* 800-847-5515 (inside sales); 800-631-8571 (cust serv) *Fax:* 212-366-2666; 607-775-4829 (inside sales) *E-mail:* online@us.penguingroup.com *Web Site:* www.penguin.com; us.penguingroup.com, pg 186

Gelbman, Leslie, GP Putnam's Sons (Hardcover), 375 Hudson St, New York, NY 10014 *Tel:* 212-366-2000 *E-mail:* online@penguinputnam.com *Web Site:* us.penguingroup.com, pg 201

Gelfand, Dr Sergei, American Mathematical Society, 201 Charles St, Providence, RI 02904-2294 *Tel:* 401-455-4000 *Toll Free Tel:* 800-321-4267 *Fax:* 401-331-3842; 401-455-4046 (cust serv) *E-mail:* ams@ams.org; cust-serv@ams.org *Web Site:* www.ams.org, pg 14

Gelfman, Jane, Gelfman/Schneider/ICM, 850 Seventh Ave, Suite 903, New York, NY 10019 *Tel:* 212-245-1993 *Fax:* 212-245-8678 *E-mail:* mail@gelfmanschneider.com *Web Site:* gelfmanschneider.com, pg 553

Gelineau, Christine, Binghamton University Creative Writing Program, c/o Dept of English, PO Box 6000, Binghamton, NY 13902-6000 *Tel:* 607-777-2168 *Fax:* 607-777-2408 *E-mail:* cwpro@binghamton.edu *Web Site:* english.binghamton.edu/cwpro, pg 659

Geller, Sandra R, Practising Law Institute, 1177 Avenue of the Americas, New York, NY 10036 *Tel:* 212-824-5700 *Toll Free Tel:* 800-260-4PLI (260-4754, cust serv) *Fax:* 212-265-4742 (intl) *Toll Free Fax:* 800-321-0093 (local) *E-mail:* info@pli.edu (cust serv) *Web Site:* www.pli.edu, pg 195

Gelles-Cole, Sandi, Gelles-Cole Literary Enterprises, 135 John Joy Rd, Woodstock, NY 12498-0341 *Tel:* 845-679-2452 *Web Site:* www.literaryenterprises.com, pg 526

Gelsomino, Tara, F+W, A Content + eCommerce Company, 10151 Carver Rd, Suite 200, Blue Ash, OH 45242 *Tel:* 513-531-2690 *Toll Free Tel:* 800-289-0963 (trade accts); 800-258-0929 (orders) *E-mail:* contact_us@fwmedia.com *Web Site:* www.fwcommunity.com, pg 86

Geltzeiler, Michael S, Reader's Digest General Books, Reader's Digest Rd, Pleasantville, NY 10570-7000 *Tel:* 914-238-1000 *Toll Free Tel:* 800-304-2807 (cust serv) *Fax:* 914-244-7436, pg 205

Gelwicks, Maureen, Educational Book & Media Association (EBMA), 37 Main St, Suite 203, Warrenton, VA 20186 *Tel:* 540-318-7770 *Fax:* 202-962-3939 *E-mail:* info@edupaperback.org *Web Site:* www.edupaperback.org, pg 605

Gelwicks, Maureen, Jeremiah Ludington Award, 37 Main St, Suite 203, Warrenton, VA 20186 *Tel:* 540-318-7770 *Fax:* 202-962-3939 *E-mail:* info@edupaperback.org *Web Site:* www.edupaperback.org, pg 703

Gemignani, Nathan D, Cornell University Press, Sage House, 512 E State St, Ithaca, NY 14850 *Tel:* 607-277-2338 *Fax:* 607-277-2374 *E-mail:* cupressinfo@cornell.edu; cupress-sales@cornell.edu *Web Site:* www.cornellpress.cornell.edu, pg 63

Geneste, Mark, Dun & Bradstreet, 103 JFK Pkwy, Short Hills, NJ 07078 *Tel:* 973-921-5500 *Toll Free Tel:* 800-526-0651; 800-234-3867 (cust serv) *E-mail:* custserv@dnb.com *Web Site:* www.dnb.com, pg 77

Genet, Pascal, Les Editions XYZ inc, 1815, ave De Lorimier, Montreal, QC H2K 3W6, Canada *Tel:* 514-525-2170 *Fax:* 514-525-7537 *E-mail:* info@editionsxyz.com *Web Site:* www.editionsxyz.com, pg 483

Genna, Victoria, Farrar, Straus & Giroux, LLC, 18 W 18 St, New York, NY 10011 *Tel:* 212-741-6900 *E-mail:* fsg.publicity@fsgbooks.com *Web Site:* us.macmillan.com/fsg.aspx, pg 86

Genna, Victoria, Hill & Wang, 18 W 18 St, New York, NY 10011 *Tel:* 212-741-6900 *Fax:* 212-633-9385 *E-mail:* fsg.publicity@fsgbooks.com; fsg.editorial@fsgbooks.com; sales@fsgbooks.com *Web Site:* us.macmillan.com/hillandwang.aspx, pg 111

Gentel, Gary, Houghton Mifflin Harcourt, 222 Berkeley St, Boston, MA 02116 *Tel:* 617-351-5000 *Toll Free Tel:* 800-225-5425 (K-12 educ materials); 800-323-9540 (assessment materials); 877-219-1537 (SkillsTutor); 888-242-6747 (Destination; Earobics; Edmark; Learning Village; Riverdeep); 800-225-3362 (Houghton Mifflin Harcourt Trade & Reference Publishers) *Toll Free Fax:* 800-269-5232 *E-mail:* customerservice@hmhpub.com *Web Site:* www.hmhco.com, pg 115

Gentel, Gary, Houghton Mifflin Harcourt Trade & Reference Division, 222 Berkeley St, Boston, MA 02116 *Tel:* 617-351-5000 *Toll Free Tel:* 800-225-3362 *Web Site:* www.hmhco.com, pg 115

Gentillo, Eileen, Simon & Schuster Sales Division, 1230 Avenue of the Americas, New York, NY 10020 *Tel:* 212-698-7000, pg 226

Gentry, Robert B, E M Koeppel Short Fiction Award, PO Box 140310, Gainesville, FL 32614 *Tel:* 352-338-7778 *E-mail:* contact@writecorner.com *Web Site:* www.writecorner.com, pg 698

George, Bob, FurnitureCore, 1389 Peachtree St NE, Suite 310, Atlanta, GA 30309 *Tel:* 404-961-3734 *Toll Free Tel:* 800-826-8868 *Fax:* 404-961-3749 *E-mail:* info@furniturecore.com *Web Site:* www.furniturecore.com, pg 93

George, Keyleigh, Crown Publishing Group, c/o Penguin Random House Inc, 1745 Broadway, New York, NY 10019 *Tel:* 212-782-9000 *Toll Free Tel:* 888-264-1745 *Fax:* 212-940-7408 *E-mail:* crownosm@penguinrandomhouse.com *Web Site:* crownpublishing.com, pg 68

George, Lee Anne, Association of Research Libraries, 21 Dupont Circle NW, Suite 800, Washington, DC 20036 *Tel:* 202-296-2296 *Fax:* 202-872-0884 *E-mail:* arlhq@arl.org *Web Site:* www.arl.org, pg 26

George, Patricia, Association of School Business Officials International, 11401 N Shore Dr, Reston, VA 20190 *Tel:* 703-478-0405 *Toll Free Tel:* 866-682-2729 *Fax:* 703-708-7060 *E-mail:* asboreq@asbointl.org; asbosba@asbointl.org *Web Site:* www.asbointl.org, pg 26

Geraghty, Joe, Close Up Publishing, 1330 Braddock Place, Suite 400, Alexandria, VA 22314 *Tel:* 703-706-3300 *Toll Free Tel:* 800-CLOSE-UP (256-7387) *Fax:* 703-706-3564 *E-mail:* info@closeup.org *Web Site:* www.closeup.org, pg 60

Geraghty, Kate, Macmillan Higher Education, 41 Madison Ave, 37th fl, New York, NY 10010 *Tel:* 212-576-9400 *Fax:* 212-689-2383 *Web Site:* www.macmillanhighered.com, pg 145

Gerardi, Jan, Random House Children's Books, 1745 Broadway, New York, NY 10019 *Tel:* 212-782-9000 *Toll Free Tel:* 800-200-3552 *Fax:* 212-782-9452 *Web Site:* randomhousekids.com, pg 203

Gerbasi, Catherine, Portage & Main Press, 318 McDermot, Suite 100, Winnipeg, MB R3A 0A2, Canada *Tel:* 204-987-3500 *Toll Free Tel:* 800-667-9673 *Fax:* 204-947-0080 *Toll Free Fax:* 866-734-8477 *E-mail:* books@portageandmainpress.com *Web Site:* www.portageandmainpress.com, pg 495

Gericke, Carla, New Hampshire Literary Awards, 2500 N River Rd, Manchester, NH 03106 *Tel:* 603-314-7980 *Fax:* 603-314-7981 *E-mail:* info@nhwritersproject.org *Web Site:* www.nhwritersproject.org, pg 712

German, Donna, Arbordale Publishing, 612 Johnnie Dodds Blvd, Suite A2, Mount Pleasant, SC 29464 *Tel:* 843-971-6722 *Toll Free Tel:* 877-243-3457 *Fax:* 843-216-3804 *E-mail:* customerservice@arbordalepublishing.com; info@arbordalepublishing.com *Web Site:* www.arbordalepublishing.com, pg 21

German, Mr Lee, Arbordale Publishing, 612 Johnnie Dodds Blvd, Suite A2, Mount Pleasant, SC 29464 *Tel:* 843-971-6722 *Toll Free Tel:* 877-243-3457 *Fax:* 843-216-3804 *E-mail:* customerservice@arbordalepublishing.com; info@arbordalepublishing.com *Web Site:* www.arbordalepublishing.com, pg 21

Gerrain, Dawn, Milady, Executive Woods, 5 Maxwell Dr, Clifton Park, NY 12065-2919 *Tel:* 518-348-2300 *Toll Free Tel:* 800-998-7498 *Fax:* 518-373-6309 *Web Site:* milady.cengage.com, pg 156

Gerrish, Debbie, Women Who Write Inc, PO Box 652, Madison, NJ 07940-0652 *E-mail:* info@womenwhowrite.org *Web Site:* womenwhowrite.org, pg 621

Gerrish, Nancy, McGraw-Hill Ryerson Limited, 300 Water St, Whitby, ON L1N 9B6, Canada *Tel:* 905-430-5000 *Toll Free Tel:* 800-565-5758 (cust serv) *Fax:* 905-430-5020 *Toll Free Fax:* 800-463-5885 *Web Site:* www.mheducation.ca, pg 491

Gersch, Michael, ProQuest LLC, 789 E Eisenhower Pkwy, Ann Arbor, MI 48108-3218 *Tel:* 734-761-4700 *Toll Free Tel:* 800-521-0600 *Fax:* 734-975-6486 *Toll Free Fax:* 800-864-0019 *E-mail:* info@proquest.com *Web Site:* www.proquest.com, pg 199

Gershenowitz, Deborah, New York University Press, 838 Broadway, 3rd fl, New York, NY 10003-4812 *Tel:* 212-998-2575 (edit) *Toll Free Tel:* 800-996-6987 (orders) *Fax:* 212-995-3833 (orders) *E-mail:* information@nyupress.org; customerservice@nyupress.org; orders@nyupress.org *Web Site:* www.nyupress.org, pg 169

Gerstle, Dan, Basic Books, 250 W 57 St, 15th fl, New York, NY 10107 *Tel:* 212-340-8164; 212-340-8136 *Fax:* 212-340-8135 *E-mail:* perseus.promos@perseusbooks.com *Web Site:* www.basicbooks.com; perseusbooks.com, pg 31

Gerth, Anne, InterVarsity Press, 430 Plaza Dr, Westmont, IL 60559-1234 *Tel:* 630-734-4000 *Toll Free Tel:* 800-843-9487 *Fax:* 630-734-4200 *E-mail:* email@ivpress.com *Web Site:* www.ivpress.com, pg 125

Gerth, Rob, The Electrochemical Society (ECS), 65 S Main St, Bldg D, Pennington, NJ 08534-2839 *Tel:* 609-737-1902 *Fax:* 609-737-2743 *E-mail:* publications@electrochem.org; customerservice@electrochem.org *Web Site:* www.electrochem.org, pg 80

Gervais, Debbie, DC Canada Education Publishing (DCCED), 180 Metcalfe St, Suite 204, Ottawa, ON K2P 1P5, Canada *Tel:* 613-565-8885 *Toll Free Tel:* 888-565-0262 *Fax:* 613-565-8881 *E-mail:* info@dc-canada.ca *Web Site:* www.dc-canada.ca, pg 478

Gervasio, Janet, HarperCollins Publishers, 195 Broadway, New York, NY 10007 *Tel:* 212-207-7000 *Fax:* 212-207-7145 *Web Site:* www.harpercollins.com, pg 106

Gerwitz, Elaine, Dog Writers' Association of America Inc (DWAA), 66 Adams St, Jamestown, NY 14701 *Tel:* 716-484-6155 *E-mail:* dogwriter@windstream.net *Web Site:* www.dwaa.org, pg 604

Gerwitz, Elaine, Dog Writers' Association of America Inc (DWAA) Annual Writing Competition, 2243 Kelmscott Ct, Westlake Village, CA 91361 *Tel:* 805-418-7899 *Fax:* 831-374-9231 *E-mail:* dogwriter@windstream.net *Web Site:* www.dwaa.org, pg 681

Gesford, Mary, University Publishing Group, 6 Public Sq, Suite 206, Hagerstown, MD 21740 *Tel:* 240-420-0036 *Toll Free Tel:* 800-654-8188 *Fax:* 240-718-7100 *E-mail:* editorial@upgbooks.com; orders@upgbooks.com; sales@upgbooks.com *Web Site:* www.upgbooks.com, pg 262

Getek, Lauren Marie, Milton Dorfman Poetry Prize, 308 W Bloomfield St, Rome, NY 13440 *Tel:* 315-336-1040 *Fax:* 315-336-1090 *E-mail:* racc2@cnymail.com *Web Site:* www.romeart.org, pg 708

Gethers, Peter, Penguin Random House Inc, 1745 Broadway, New York, NY 10019 *Tel:* 212-782-9000 *Toll Free Tel:* 800-726-0600 *Web Site:* www.randomhouse.com, pg 187

Ghavami, Parvaneh, ADASI Publishing Co, 13 Riverdale Ave, Dover, NH 03820-4698 *Tel:* 603-866-9426 *E-mail:* info@adasi.com *Web Site:* www.adasi.com, pg 4

Ghazarian, Ms Salpi H, Blue Crane Books, PO Box 380291, Cambridge, MA 02238 *Tel:* 617-926-8989 *Fax:* 617-926-0982 *E-mail:* bluecrane@arrow1.com, pg 40

Ghione, Yvette, Kids Can Press Ltd, 25 Dockside Dr, Toronto, ON M5A 0B5, Canada *Tel:* 416-479-7000 *Toll Free Tel:* 800-265-0884 *Fax:* 416-960-5437 *E-mail:* info@kidscan.com; customerservice@kidscan.com *Web Site:* www.kidscanpress.com; www.kidscanpress.ca, pg 489

Ghose, Zulfikar A, University of Texas at Austin, Creative Writing Program, Dept of English, PAR 108, One University Sta, Mailcode B5000, Austin, TX 78712-1164 *Tel:* 512-471-5132; 512-471-4991 *Fax:* 512-471-4909 *Web Site:* www.utexas.edu/cola/depts/english/creative-writing, pg 664

Ghoura, Judy, Fitzhenry & Whiteside Limited, 195 Allstate Pkwy, Markham, ON L3R 4T8, Canada *Tel:* 905-477-9700 *Toll Free Tel:* 800-387-9776 *Fax:* 905-477-2834 *Toll Free Fax:* 800-260-9777 *E-mail:* bookinfo@fitzhenry.ca; godwit@fitzhenry.ca *Web Site:* www.fitzhenry.ca, pg 484

Ghoura, Judy, Red Deer Press Inc, 195 Allstate Pkwy, Markham, ON L3R 4T8, Canada *Tel:* 905-477-9700 *Toll Free Tel:* 800-387-9776 (orders) *Fax:* 905-477-2834 *Toll Free Fax:* 800-260-9777 (orders) *E-mail:* rdp@reddeerpress.com; bookinfo@fitzhenry.ca *Web Site:* www.reddeerpress.com, pg 497

Giagnocavo, Alan, Fox Chapel Publishing Co Inc, 1970 Broad St, East Petersburg, PA 17520 *Tel:* 717-560-4703 *Toll Free Tel:* 800-457-9112 *Fax:* 717-560-4702 *E-mail:* customerservice@foxchapelpublishing.com *Web Site:* www.foxchapelpublishing.com, pg 91

Giarratano, Matt, Penguin Books, 375 Hudson St, New York, NY 10014 *Tel:* 212-366-2000 *E-mail:* online@penguinputnam.com *Web Site:* www.penguinputnam.com; www.penguinclassics.com; us.penguingroup.com, pg 186

Giarratano, Matt, Plume, 375 Hudson St, New York, NY 10014 *Tel:* 212-366-2000 *Fax:* 212-366-2666 *E-mail:* online@penguinputnam.com *Web Site:* www.penguinputnam.com; us.penguingroup.com, pg 193

Gibbons, Melissa, William H Sadlier Inc, 9 Pine St, New York, NY 10005 *Tel:* 212-227-2120 *Toll Free Tel:* 800-221-5175 (cust serv) *Fax:* 212-312-6080 *E-mail:* customerservice@sadlier.com *Web Site:* www.sadlier.com, pg 213

Gibbs, Naomi, Houghton Mifflin Harcourt Trade & Reference Division, 222 Berkeley St, Boston, MA 02116 *Tel:* 617-351-5000 *Toll Free Tel:* 800-225-3362 *Web Site:* www.hmhco.com, pg 115

Gibney, Bob, Cengage Learning, 20 Channel Center St, Boston, MA 02210 *Tel:* 617-289-7700 *Toll Free Tel:* 800-354-9706 *Fax:* 617-289-7844 *Toll Free Fax:* 800-487-8488 *E-mail:* esales@cengage.com *Web Site:* www.cengage.com, pg 53

Gibson, Bethany, Goose Lane Editions, 500 Beaverbrook Ct, Suite 330, Fredericton, NB E3B 5X4, Canada *Tel:* 506-450-4251 *Toll Free Tel:* 888-926-8377 *Fax:* 506-459-4991 *E-mail:* info@gooselane.com; customerservice@gooselane.com *Web Site:* www.gooselane.com, pg 485

Gibson, George, Bloomsbury Publishing Inc, 1385 Broadway, 5th fl, New York, NY 10018 *Tel:* 212-419-5300 *E-mail:* marketingusa@bloomsbury.com; adultpublicityusa@bloomsbury.com; askacademic@bloomsbury.com *Web Site:* www.bloomsbury.com, pg 40

Gibson, Jack, International Risk Management Institute Inc, 12222 Merit Dr, Suite 1600, Dallas, TX 75251-2266 *Tel:* 972-960-7693 *Fax:* 972-371-5120 *E-mail:* info27@irmi.com *Web Site:* www.irmi.com, pg 125

Gibson, Maggie, Random House Children's Books, 1745 Broadway, New York, NY 10019 *Tel:* 212-782-9000 *Toll Free Tel:* 800-200-3552 *Fax:* 212-782-9452 *Web Site:* randomhousekids.com, pg 204

Gibson, Phil, National Press Club of Canada Foundation Inc, 17 York St, Suite 201, Ottawa, ON K1N 9J6, Canada *E-mail:* info@pressclubcanada.ca *Web Site:* pressclubcanada.ca, pg 613

Gibson, William, Premier Print Awards, 200 Deer Run Rd, Sewickley, PA 15143-2324 *Tel:* 412-741-6860 *Toll Free Tel:* 800-910-4283 *Fax:* 412-741-2311 *E-mail:* printing@printing.org *Web Site:* www.printing.org/premierprint, pg 721

Giddens, Mary, SteinerBooks, 610 Main St, Great Barrington, MA 01230 *Tel:* 413-528-8233 *Fax:* 413-528-8826 *E-mail:* friends@steinerbooks.org *Web Site:* www.steinerbooks.org, pg 235

Gifford, James M PhD, The Jesse Stuart Foundation (JSF), 1645 Winchester Ave, Ashland, KY 41101 *Tel:* 606-326-1667 *Fax:* 606-325-2519 *E-mail:* jsf@jsfbooks.com *Web Site:* www.jsfbooks.com, pg 237

Giffuni, Cathe, Research Research, 240 E 27 St, Suite 20-K, New York, NY 10016-9238 *Tel:* 212-779-9540 *Fax:* 212-779-9540 *E-mail:* ehtac@msn.com, pg 533

Giganti, Edward J, The Catholic Health Association of the United States, 4455 Woodson Rd, St Louis, MO 63134-3797 *Tel:* 314-427-2500 *Fax:* 314-427-0029 *E-mail:* servicecenter@chausa.org *Web Site:* www.chausa.org, pg 52

Giglierano, Emily, Vintage & Anchor Books, c/o Random House Inc, 1745 Broadway, New York, NY 10019 *Tel:* 212-572-2420 *E-mail:* vintageanchorpublicity@randomhouse.com *Web Site:* vintage-anchor.knopfdoubleday.com, pg 266

Gilbert, Christina, Bloomsbury Publishing Inc, 1385 Broadway, 5th fl, New York, NY 10018 *Tel:* 212-419-5300 *E-mail:* marketingusa@bloomsbury.com; adultpublicityusa@bloomsbury.com; askacademic@bloomsbury.com *Web Site:* www.bloomsbury.com, pg 39

Gilbert, Deborah, Soul Mate Publishing, PO Box 24, Macedon, NY 14502 *Tel:* 585-598-4791 *E-mail:* submissions@soulmatepublishing.com *Web Site:* www.soulmatepublishing.com, pg 230

Gilbert, Jennifer G, Galen Press Ltd, PO Box 64400-WB, Tucson, AZ 85728-4400 *Tel:* 520-577-8363 *Fax:* 520-529-6459 *E-mail:* sales@galenpress.com *Web Site:* www.galenpress.com, pg 94

Gilbert, Jon, Seven Stories Press, 140 Watts St, New York, NY 10013 *Tel:* 212-226-8760 *Toll Free Tel:* 800-733-3000 (orders) *Fax:* 212-226-1411 *E-mail:* info@sevenstories.com *Web Site:* www.sevenstories.com, pg 222

Gilbert, Sheila E, DAW Books Inc, 375 Hudson St, New York, NY 10014 *Tel:* 212-366-2096 *Fax:* 212-366-2090 *E-mail:* daw@penguinrandomhouse.com *Web Site:* us.penguingroup.com; www.dawbooks.com, pg 71

Gilbride, Tara, Penguin Group (USA) LLC, a Penguin Random House company, 375 Hudson St, New York, NY 10014 *Tel:* 212-366-2000 *Toll Free Tel:* 800-847-5515 (inside sales); 800-631-8571 (cust serv) *Fax:* 212-366-2666; 607-775-4829 (inside sales) *E-mail:* online@us.penguingroup.com *Web Site:* www.penguin.com; us.penguingroup.com, pg 186

Gilbride, Tara, Portfolio, 375 Hudson St, New York, NY 10014, pg 195

Gildred, Becca, Down East Books, 680 Commercial St (US Rte 1), Rockport, ME 04856 *Tel:* 207-594-9544 *Toll Free Tel:* 800-685-7962 (US only orders); 800-766-1670 *E-mail:* editorial@downeast.com *Web Site:* www.downeast.com, pg 76

Gilewicz, John, Adirondack Mountain Club (ADK), 814 Goggins Rd, Lake George, NY 12845-4117 *Tel:* 518-668-4447 *Toll Free Tel:* 800-395-8080 *Fax:* 518-668-3746 *E-mail:* info@adk.org *Web Site:* www.adk.org, pg 5

Gill, Craig, University Press of Mississippi, 3825 Ridgewood Rd, Jackson, MS 39211-6492 *Tel:* 601-432-6205 *Toll Free Tel:* 800-737-7788 (orders & cust serv) *Fax:* 601-432-6217 *E-mail:* press@mississippi.edu *Web Site:* www.upress.state.ms.us, pg 262

Gillan, Maria, Binghamton University Creative Writing Program, c/o Dept of English, PO Box 6000, Binghamton, NY 13902-6000 *Tel:* 607-777-2168 *Fax:* 607-777-2408 *E-mail:* cwpro@binghamton.edu *Web Site:* english.binghamton.edu/cwpro, pg 659

Gillan, Maria Mazziotti, Binghamton University John Gardner Fiction Book Award, Dept of English, General Literature & Rhetoric, Library N, Rm 1149, Vestal Pkwy E, Binghamton, NY 13902 *Tel:* 607-777-2713 *Web Site:* www2.binghamton.edu/english/creative-writing, pg 672

Gillan, Maria Mazziotti, Binghamton University Milt Kessler Poetry Book Award, Dept of English, General Literature & Rhetoric, Library N, Rm 1149, Vestal Pkwy E, Binghamton, NY 13902 *Tel:* 607-777-2713 *Web Site:* www2.binghamton.edu/english/creative-writing, pg 672

Gillan, Maria Mazziotti, Allen Ginsberg Poetry Award, One College Blvd, Paterson, NJ 07505-1179 *Tel:* 973-684-6555 *Fax:* 973-523-6085 *Web Site:* www.pccc.edu/poetry, pg 689

Gillan, Maria Mazziotti, The Paterson Fiction Prize, One College Blvd, Paterson, NJ 07505-1179 *Tel:* 973-684-6555 *Fax:* 973-523-6085 *Web Site:* www.pccc.edu/poetry, pg 716

Gillan, Maria Mazziotti, The Paterson Poetry Prize, One College Blvd, Paterson, NJ 07505-1179 *Tel:* 973-684-6555 *Fax:* 973-523-6085 *Web Site:* www.pccc.edu/poetry, pg 716

Gillan, Maria Mazziotti, The Paterson Prize for Books for Young People, One College Blvd, Paterson, NJ 07505-1179 *Tel:* 973-684-6555 *Fax:* 973-523-6085 *Web Site:* www.pccc.edu/poetry, pg 716

Gillespie, Christine, Alfred A Knopf/Everyman's Library, c/o Random House Inc, 1745 Broadway, New York, NY 10019 *Tel:* 212-751-2600 *Toll Free Tel:* 800-638-6460 *Fax:* 212-572-2593 *Web Site:* www.knopfdoubleday.com, pg 132

Gillespie, Christine, Pantheon Books/Schocken Books, c/o Random House Inc, 1745 Broadway, New York, NY 10019 *Tel:* 212-751-2600 *Toll Free Tel:* 800-638-6460 *Fax:* 212-572-6030, pg 181

Gillespie, Jennie, San Diego Christian Writers' Guild Conference, PO Box 270403, San Diego, CA 92198 *Tel:* 760-294-3269 *Fax:* 760-294-3269 *E-mail:* info@sandiegocwg.org *Web Site:* www.sandiegocwg.org, pg 654

Gillespie, Robert, San Diego Christian Writers' Guild Conference, PO Box 270403, San Diego, CA 92198 *Tel:* 760-294-3269 *Fax:* 760-294-3269 *E-mail:* info@sandiegocwg.org *Web Site:* www.sandiegocwg.org, pg 654

Gilliam, Ashley, Scribner, 1230 Avenue of the Americas, New York, NY 10020, pg 220

Gillies, Paige, Publishers' Graphics Inc, 231 Judd Rd, Easton, CT 06612-1025 *Tel:* 203-445-1511 *Fax:* 203-445-1411 *E-mail:* sales@publishersgraphics.com *Web Site:* www.publishersgraphics.com, pg 584

Gilligan, Rev Michael PhD, American Catholic Press (ACP), 16565 S State St, South Holland, IL 60473 *Tel:* 708-331-5485 *Fax:* 708-331-5484 *E-mail:* acp@acpress.org *Web Site:* www.acpress.org, pg 11

Gilliland, Hap, The Montana Council for Indian Education, 1240 Burlington Ave, Billings, MT 59102-4224 *Tel:* 406-652-7598 (AM); 406-248-3465 (PM) *Fax:* 406-248-1297 *E-mail:* cie@cie-mt.org *Web Site:* www.cie-mt.org, pg 159

Gillis, Karen, St Martin's Press, LLC, 175 Fifth Ave, New York, NY 10010 *Tel:* 646-307-5151 *Fax:* 212-420-9314 *E-mail:* firstname.lastname@macmillan.com *Web Site:* www.stmartins.com, pg 214

Gilliss, Sonya, Fitzhenry & Whiteside Limited, 195 Allstate Pkwy, Markham, ON L3R 4T8, Canada *Tel:* 905-477-9700 *Toll Free Tel:* 800-387-9776 *Fax:* 905-477-2834 *Toll Free Fax:* 800-260-9777 *E-mail:* bookinfo@fitzhenry.ca; godwit@fitzhenry.ca *Web Site:* www.fitzhenry.ca, pg 484

Gilliss, Sonya, Red Deer Press Inc, 195 Allstate Pkwy, Markham, ON L3R 4T8, Canada *Tel:* 905-477-9700 *Toll Free Tel:* 800-387-9776 (orders) *Fax:* 905-477-2834 *Toll Free Fax:* 800-260-9777 (orders) *E-mail:* rdp@reddeerpress.com; bookinfo@fitzhenry.ca *Web Site:* www.reddeerpress.com, pg 497

Gilly, Holly, Human Kinetics Inc, 1607 N Market St, Champaign, IL 61820 *Tel:* 217-351-5076 *Toll Free Tel:* 800-747-4457 *Fax:* 217-351-1549 (orders/cust serv) *E-mail:* info@hkusa.com *Web Site:* www.humankinetics.com, pg 117

Gilman, Dana S, J J Keller & Associates, Inc, 3003 Breezewood Lane, Neenah, WI 54957 *Tel:* 920-722-2848 *Toll Free Tel:* 877-564-2333 *Toll Free Fax:* 800-727-7516 *E-mail:* contactus@jjkeller.com; customerservice@jjkeller.com *Web Site:* www.jjkeller.com, pg 130

Gilmer, E J, Amber Quill Press LLC, PO Box 265, Indian Hills, CO 80454 *E-mail:* business@amberquill.com; customer_service@amberquill.com *Web Site:* www.amberquill.com, pg 10

Gilo, Jessica, Houghton Mifflin Harcourt, 222 Berkeley St, Boston, MA 02116 *Tel:* 617-351-5000 *Toll Free Tel:* 800-225-5425 (K-12 educ materials); 800-323-9540 (assessment materials); 877-219-1537 (SkillsTutor); 888-242-6747 (Destination; Earobics; Edmark; Learning Village; Riverdeep); 800-225-3362 (Houghton Mifflin Harcourt Trade & Reference Publishers) *Toll Free Fax:* 800-269-5232 *E-mail:* customerservice@hmhpub.com *Web Site:* www.hmhco.com, pg 115

Gilpin, R Wayne, Future Horizons Inc, 721 W Abram St, Arlington, TX 76013 *Tel:* 817-277-0727 *Toll Free Tel:* 800-489-0727 *Fax:* 817-277-2270 *E-mail:* info@fhautism.com *Web Site:* www.fhautism.com, pg 93

Gilpin, Wayne, Gilpin Publishing, PO Box 597, Alliston, ON L9R 1V7, Canada *Tel:* 705-424-6507 *Toll Free Tel:* 800-867-3281 *Fax:* 705-424-6507 *E-mail:* mail@gilpin.ca *Web Site:* www.gilpin.ca, pg 485

Gilson, Kristin, Puffin Books, 345 Hudson St, New York, NY 10014 *Tel:* 212-366-2000 *E-mail:* online@penguinputnam.com *Web Site:* www.penguinputnam.com; us.penguingroup.com, pg 200

Gimbel, Despina P, New York University Press, 838 Broadway, 3rd fl, New York, NY 10003-4812 *Tel:* 212-998-2575 (edit) *Toll Free Tel:* 800-996-6987 (orders) *Fax:* 212-995-3833 (orders) *E-mail:* information@nyupress.org; customerservice@nyupress.org; orders@nyupress.org *Web Site:* www.nyupress.org, pg 169

Gingerich, Amy, Herald Press, 1251 Virginia Ave, Harrisonburg, VA 22802-2434 *Toll Free Tel:* 800-245-7894 (orders-US); 800-631-6535 (orders-CN) *Toll Free Fax:* 877-271-0760 *E-mail:* info@MennoMedia.org *Web Site:* www.heraldpress.com; store.mennomedia.org, pg 110

Gingerich, Amy, Herald Press, 50 Kent Ave, Suite 204, Kitchener, ON N2G 3R1, Canada *Tel:* 519-747-5722 (US) *Toll Free Tel:* 800-631-6535 (CN) *Fax:* 519-747-5721 *E-mail:* hpcan@mpn.net *Web Site:* www.heraldpress.com, pg 487

Gingerich, Amy, MennoMedia, 1251 Virginia Ave, Harrisonburg, VA 22802-2434 *Toll Free Tel:* 800-245-7894 (orders & cust serv US); 800-631-6535 (orders & cust serv CN) *Web Site:* www.mennomedia.org, pg 154

Gingras, Dominique, Les Presses De L'Universite Laval, 2180, Chemin Ste-Foy, 1st fl, Quebec, QC G1V 0A6, Canada *Tel:* 418-656-2803 *Fax:* 418-656-3305 *E-mail:* presses@pul.ulaval.ca *Web Site:* www.pulaval.com, pg 496

Gingrich, Jessica, WaterBrook Multnomah Publishing Group, 12265 Oracle Blvd, Suite 200, Colorado Springs, CO 80921 *Tel:* 719-590-4999 *Toll Free Tel:* 800-603-7051 (orders) *Fax:* 719-590-8977 *Toll Free Fax:* 800-294-5686 (orders) *E-mail:* info@waterbrookmultnomah.com *Web Site:* waterbrookmultnomah.com, pg 267

Ginna, Peter, The Center for Fiction, 17 E 47 St, New York, NY 10017 *Tel:* 212-755-6710 *Fax:* 212-826-0831 *E-mail:* info@centerforfiction.org *Web Site:* centerforfiction.org/awards, pg 603

Ginsberg, Peter L, Curtis Brown Ltd, 10 Astor Place, New York, NY 10003 *Tel:* 212-473-5400 *Web Site:* www.curtisbrown.com, pg 544

Ginsburg, Susan, Writers House, 21 W 26 St, New York, NY 10010 *Tel:* 212-685-2400 *Fax:* 212-685-1781 *Web Site:* www.writershouse.com, pg 580

Giordano, Steve, Society of American Travel Writers (SATW), 11950 W Lake Park Dr, Suite 320, Milwaukee, WI 53224-3049 *Tel:* 414-359-1625 *Fax:* 414-359-1671 *E-mail:* info@satw.org *Web Site:* www.satw.org, pg 619

Giovanniello, Thomas J Jr, Down East Books, 680 Commercial St (US Rte 1), Rockport, ME 04856 *Tel:* 207-594-9544 *Toll Free Tel:* 800-685-7962 (US only orders); 800-766-1670 *E-mail:* editorial@downeast.com *Web Site:* www.downeast.com, pg 76

Giovinazzo, Elena, Pippin Properties Inc, 110 W 40 St, Suite 1704, New York, NY 10018 *Tel:* 212-338-9310 *Fax:* 212-338-9579 *E-mail:* info@pippinproperties.com *Web Site:* www.pippinproperties.com; www.facebook.com/pippinproperties, pg 568

Gipson, Scott, Caxton Press, 312 Main St, Caldwell, ID 83605-3299 *Tel:* 208-459-7421 *Toll Free Tel:* 800-657-6465 *Fax:* 208-459-7450 *E-mail:* publish@caxtonpress.com *Web Site:* www.caxtonpress.com, pg 52

Girard, Guylaine, Les Editions Fides, 7333 place des Roseraies, bureau 100, Anjou, QC H1M 2X6, Canada *Tel:* 514-745-4290 *Fax:* 514-745-4299 *E-mail:* editions@groupefides.com *Web Site:* www.editionsfides.com, pg 481

Giron, Robert L, Gival Press, 5200 N First St, Arlington, VA 22203 *Tel:* 703-351-0079 *Fax:* 703-351-0079 (call first) *E-mail:* givalpress@yahoo.com *Web Site:* www.givalpress.com, pg 97

Giron, Robert L, Gival Press Novel Award, PO Box 3812, Arlington, VA 22203 *Tel:* 703-351-0079 *Fax:* 703-351-0079 (call first) *E-mail:* givalpress@yahoo.com *Web Site:* www.givalpress.com, pg 689

Giron, Robert L, Gival Press Oscar Wilde Award, PO Box 3812, Arlington, VA 22203 *Tel:* 703-351-0079 *Fax:* 703-351-0079 (call first) *E-mail:* givalpress@yahoo.com *Web Site:* www.givalpress.com, pg 689

Giron, Robert L, Gival Press Poetry Award, PO Box 3812, Arlington, VA 22203 *Tel:* 703-351-0079 *Fax:* 703-351-0079 (call first) *E-mail:* givalpress@yahoo.com *Web Site:* www.givalpress.com, pg 689

Giron, Robert L, Gival Press Short Story Award, PO Box 3812, Arlington, VA 22203 *Tel:* 703-351-0079 *Fax:* 703-351-0079 (call first) *E-mail:* givalpress@yahoo.com *Web Site:* www.givalpress.com, pg 689

Giroux, Greg, Bartleby Press, 8926 Baltimore St, No 858, Savage, MD 20763 *Tel:* 301-725-3906 *Toll Free Tel:* 800-953-9929 *Fax:* 667-309-6993 *E-mail:* inquiries@bartlebythepublisher.com *Web Site:* www.bartlebythepublisher.com, pg 31

Giroux, Greg, Schreiber Publishing Inc, PO Box 4193, Rockville, MD 20849 *Tel:* 301-725-3906 *Toll Free Tel:* 800-296-1961 (sales) *Fax:* 301-725-0333 (orders) *E-mail:* schreiberpublishing@comcast.net *Web Site:* schreiberlanguage.com; shengold.com, pg 219

Giroux, Laura, United Nations Association of the United States of America, 1750 Pennsylvania Ave NW, Suite 300, Washington, DC 20006 *Tel:* 202-887-9040 *Fax:* 202-887-9021 *Web Site:* www.unausa.org, pg 620

Giroux, Steve, Teacher's Discovery, 2741 Paldan Dr, Auburn Hills, MI 48326 *Toll Free Tel:* 800-832-2437 *Toll Free Fax:* 800-287-4509 *E-mail:* foreignlanguage@teachersdiscovery.com, pg 242

Girsch, Laurie, Professional Resource Press, 1958 Barber Rd, Sarasota, FL 34240 *Tel:* 941-343-9601 *Toll Free Tel:* 800-443-3364 (orders & cust serv) *Fax:* 941-343-9201 *Toll Free Fax:* 866-804-4843 (orders only) *E-mail:* cs.prpress@gmail.com *Web Site:* www.prpress.com, pg 198

Gisonny, Karen, The New York Public Library Helen Bernstein Book Award for Excellence in Journalism, Stephen A Schwarzman Bldg, Fifth Ave at 42 St, South Court Bldg, 3rd fl, New York, NY 10018-2788 *Tel:* 212-930-0876 *Web Site:* www.nypl.org, pg 713

Gissinger-Rivera, Beth, Adams Media, 57 Littlefield St, Avon, MA 02322 *Tel:* 508-427-7100 *Fax:* 508-427-6790 *E-mail:* orders@adamsmedia.com *Web Site:* www.adamsmedia.com, pg 4

Gissler, Sig, Pulitzer Prizes, 709 Journalism Bldg, Columbia University, 2950 Broadway, New York, NY 10027 *Tel:* 212-854-3841 *Fax:* 212-854-3342 *E-mail:* pulitzer@pulitzer.org *Web Site:* www.pulitzer.org, pg 722

Giusio, Dana, Tom Doherty Associates, LLC, 175 Fifth Ave, 14th fl, New York, NY 10010 *Tel:* 646-307-5151 *Toll Free Tel:* 800-455-0340 *Fax:* 212-388-0191 *E-mail:* firstname.lastname@tor.com *Web Site:* www.tor-forge.com, pg 75

Gladney, Dave, AAP PreK-12 Learning Group, 325 Chestnut St, Suite 1110, Philadelphia, PA 19106 *Tel:* 267-351-4310 *Fax:* 267-351-4317 *E-mail:* prek12learning@publishers.org *Web Site:* www.aepweb.org, pg 593

Gladstone, Bill, Waterside Productions Inc, 2055 Oxford Ave, Cardiff, CA 92007 *Tel:* 760-632-9190 *Fax:* 760-632-9295 *E-mail:* admin@waterside.com *Web Site:* www.waterside.com, pg 579

Gladysz, Thomas, The Arion Press, The Presidio, 1802 Hays St, San Francisco, CA 94129 *Tel:* 415-668-2542 *Fax:* 415-668-2550 *E-mail:* arionpress@arionpress.com *Web Site:* www.arionpress.com, pg 22

Glanville, Kathleen, Dustbooks, PO Box 100, Paradise, CA 95967-0100 *Tel:* 530-877-6110 *Fax:* 530-877-0222 *E-mail:* publisher@dustbooks.com; info@dustbooks.com *Web Site:* www.dustbooks.com, pg 78

Glaser, Rebecca, Amicus, PO Box 1329, Mankato, MN 56002 *Tel:* 507-388-9357 *Fax:* 507-388-1779 *E-mail:* info@amicuspublishing.us; orders@amicuspublishing.us *Web Site:* www.amicuspublishing.us, pg 17

Glasner, Lynne, Associated Editors, 27 W 96 St, New York, NY 10025 *Tel:* 212-662-9703, pg 520

Glass, Erica, Penguin Group (USA) LLC, a Penguin Random House company, 375 Hudson St, New York, NY 10014 *Tel:* 212-366-2000 *Toll Free Tel:* 800-

Goldstein, Gary, Kensington Publishing Corp, 119 W 40 St, New York, NY 10018 *Tel:* 212-407-1500 *Toll Free Tel:* 800-221-2647 *Fax:* 212-935-0699 *Web Site:* www.kensingtonbooks.com, pg 130

Goldstein, Jeff, Trans-Atlantic Publications Inc, 311 Bainbridge St, Philadelphia, PA 19147 *Tel:* 215-925-5083 *Fax:* 215-925-1912 *Web Site:* www.transatlanticpub.com; www.businesstitles.com, pg 248

Golembiewski, Joan, American Academy of Orthopaedic Surgeons (AAOS), 6300 N River Rd, Rosemont, IL 60018-4262 *Tel:* 847-823-7186 *Toll Free Tel:* 800-346-2267 *Fax:* 847-823-8125 *E-mail:* custserv@aaos.org *Web Site:* www.aaos.org, pg 10

Gollehon, John T, Gollehon Press Inc, 3655 Glenn Dr SE, Grand Rapids, MI 49546 *Tel:* 616-949-3515 *Fax:* 616-949-8674 *Web Site:* www.gollehonbooks.com, pg 98

Gollehon, Kathy, Gollehon Press Inc, 3655 Glenn Dr SE, Grand Rapids, MI 49546 *Tel:* 616-949-3515 *Fax:* 616-949-8674 *Web Site:* www.gollehonbooks.com, pg 98

Gollogly, Eugene, Lindisfarne Books, 610 Main St, Great Barrington, MA 01230 *Tel:* 413-528-8233 *Fax:* 413-528-8826 *E-mail:* service@steinerbooks.org *Web Site:* www.steinerbooks.org, pg 139

Gollogly, Gene, Lantern Books, 128 Second Place, Garden Suite, Brooklyn, NY 11231 *Tel:* 212-414-2275 *E-mail:* editorial@lanternbooks.com; info@lanternmedia.net *Web Site:* lanternbooks.presswarehouse.com/Home/home.aspx, pg 134

Gollogly, Gene, SteinerBooks, 610 Main St, Great Barrington, MA 01230 *Tel:* 413-528-8233 *Fax:* 413-528-8826 *E-mail:* friends@steinerbooks.org *Web Site:* www.steinerbooks.org, pg 235

Gollub, Matthew, Tortuga Press, 2777 Yulupa Ave, PMB 181, Santa Rosa, CA 95405 *Tel:* 707-544-4720 *Toll Free Tel:* 866-4TORTUGA (486-7884) *Fax:* 707-544-5609 *E-mail:* info@tortugapress.com *Web Site:* www.tortugapress.com, pg 247

Golob, Paul, Henry Holt and Company, LLC, 175 Fifth Ave, New York, NY 10010 *Tel:* 646-307-5151 *Toll Free Tel:* 888-330-8477 (orders) *Fax:* 646-307-5285 *E-mail:* firstname.lastname@hholt.com *Web Site:* www.henryholt.com, pg 113

Golomb, Susan, Writers House, 21 W 26 St, New York, NY 10010 *Tel:* 212-685-2400 *Fax:* 212-685-1781 *Web Site:* www.writershouse.com, pg 580

Golski, Sara, Chronicle Books LLC, 680 Second St, San Francisco, CA 94107 *Tel:* 415-537-4200 *Toll Free Tel:* 800-759-0190 (cust serv) *Fax:* 415-537-4460 *Toll Free Fax:* 800-858-7787 (orders); 800-286-9471 (cust serv) *E-mail:* frontdesk@chroniclebooks.com *Web Site:* www.chroniclebooks.com, pg 58

Golski, Sara, Ten Speed Press, 2625 Alcatraz Ave, Unit 505, Berkeley, CA 94705 *Tel:* 510-285-3000 *Toll Free Tel:* 800-841-BOOK (841-2665) *E-mail:* csorders@randomhouse.com *Web Site:* crownpublishing.com/imprint/ten-speed-press, pg 243

Gomberg, David, Seven Footer Kids, 247 W 30 St, 11th fl, New York, NY 10001-2824 *Tel:* 212-710-9340 *Fax:* 212-710-9344 *E-mail:* info@sevenfooter.com *Web Site:* www.sevenfooterpress.com, pg 222

Gomberg, David, Seven Footer Press, 247 W 30 St, 2nd fl, New York, NY 10001-2824 *Tel:* 212-710-9340 *Fax:* 212-710-9344 *E-mail:* info@sevenfooter.com *Web Site:* www.sevenfooterpress.com, pg 222

Goncharenko, Kathy, Scholastic Canada Ltd, 604 King St W, Toronto, ON M5V 1E1, Canada *Tel:* 905-887-7323 *Toll Free Tel:* 800-268-3860 (CN) *Toll Free Fax:* 866-387-4944 *E-mail:* custserve@scholastic.ca *Web Site:* www.scholastic.ca, pg 498

Gong Stewart, Mrs Shane, University Press of Mississippi, 3825 Ridgewood Rd, Jackson, MS 39211-6492 *Tel:* 601-432-6205 *Toll Free Tel:* 800-737-7788 (orders & cust serv) *Fax:* 601-432-6217 *E-mail:* press@mississippi.edu *Web Site:* www.upress.state.ms.us, pg 262

Gong, Wakeford, Pureplay Press, 195 26 Ave, No 2, San Francisco, CA 94121 *Tel:* 310-597-0328 *E-mail:* info@pureplaypress.com *Web Site:* www.pureplaypress.com, pg 200

Gong-Wong, Kirsten, Locus Awards, PO Box 13305, Oakland, CA 94661-0305 *Tel:* 510-339-9196 *Fax:* 510-339-9198 *E-mail:* locus@locusmag.com *Web Site:* www.locusmag.com, pg 702

Gonneville, Michel, La Fondation Emile Nelligan, 100, rue Sherbrooke, Montreal, QC H2X 1C3, Canada *Tel:* 514-278-4657 *Fax:* 514-278-1943 *E-mail:* info@fondation-nelligan.org *Web Site:* www.fondation-nelligan.org, pg 606

Gonneville, Michel, Prix Emile-Nelligan, 100, rue Sherbrooke, Montreal, QC H2X 1C3, Canada *Tel:* 514-278-4657 *Toll Free Tel:* 888-849-8540 *Fax:* 514-278-1943 *E-mail:* info@fondation-nelligan.org *Web Site:* www.fondation-nelligan.org, pg 722

Gonzales, Gail, Rodale Inc, 400 S Tenth St, Emmaus, PA 18098 *Tel:* 610-967-5171 *Web Site:* www.rodaleinc.com, pg 210

Gonzales, Kimberly, Fun in the Sun Conference, PO Box 480211, Fort Lauderdale, FL 33348 *E-mail:* frwfuninthesun@yahoo.com *Web Site:* www.frwriters.org/fun-in-the-sun-conference/; frwfuninthesunmain.blogspot.com/; www.frwriters.org, pg 651

Gonzalez, Diana, Consumer Press, 13326 SW 28 St, Suite 102, Fort Lauderdale, FL 33330-1102 *Tel:* 954-370-9153 *Fax:* 954-472-1008 *E-mail:* info@consumerpress.com *Web Site:* www.consumerpress.com, pg 62

Gonzalez, Neil, Greenleaf Book Group LLC, Three Park Place, 4005 Banister Lane, Suite B, Austin, TX 78704 *Tel:* 512-891-6100 *Toll Free Tel:* 800-932-5420 *Fax:* 512-891-6150 *E-mail:* contact@greenleafbookgroup.com *Web Site:* www.greenleafbookgroup.com, pg 100

Gonzalez, Nellie, Arte Publico Press, University of Houston, Bldg 19, Rm 10, 4902 Gulf Fwy, Houston, TX 77204-2004 *Tel:* 713-743-2998 (sales) *Toll Free Tel:* 800-633-2783 *Fax:* 713-743-2847 (sales) *E-mail:* appinfo@uh.edu; bkorders@uh.edu, pg 23

Gooch, Emily, Arbordale Publishing, 612 Johnnie Dodds Blvd, Suite A2, Mount Pleasant, SC 29464 *Tel:* 843-971-6722 *Toll Free Tel:* 877-243-3457 *Fax:* 843-216-3804 *E-mail:* customerservice@arbordalepublishing.com; info@arbordalepublishing.com *Web Site:* www.arbordalepublishing.com, pg 21

Good, Kyle, Scholastic Inc, 557 Broadway, New York, NY 10012 *Tel:* 212-343-6100 *Toll Free Tel:* 800-scholastic *Web Site:* www.scholastic.com, pg 218

Good, Lou Anne, House to House Publications, 11 Toll Gate Rd, Lititz, PA 17543 *Tel:* 717-627-1996 *Toll Free Tel:* 800-848-5892 *Fax:* 717-627-4004 *E-mail:* h2hp@dcfi.org *Web Site:* www.dcfi.org, pg 116

Goodfriend, Cathy, Macmillan, 175 Fifth Ave, New York, NY 10010 *Tel:* 646-307-5151 *Fax:* 212-420-9314 *E-mail:* firstname.lastname@macmillan.com *Web Site:* www.macmillan.com, pg 145

Goodman, Arnold P, Goodman Associates, 500 West End Ave, New York, NY 10024 *Tel:* 212-873-4806, pg 554

Goodman, Christie, Intercultural Development Research Association (IDRA), 5815 Callaghan Rd, Suite 101, San Antonio, TX 78228 *Tel:* 210-444-1710 *Fax:* 210-444-1714 *E-mail:* contact@idra.org *Web Site:* www.idra.org, pg 123

Goodman, Eleanor, The Pennsylvania State University Press, University Support Bldg 1, Suite C, 820 N University Dr, University Park, PA 16802-1003 *Tel:* 814-865-1327 *Toll Free Tel:* 800-326-9180 *Fax:* 814-863-1408 *Toll Free Fax:* 877-778-2665 *E-mail:* info@psupress.org *Web Site:* www.psupress.org, pg 188

Goodman, Elise Simon, Goodman Associates, 500 West End Ave, New York, NY 10024 *Tel:* 212-873-4806, pg 554

Goodman, Irene, Irene Goodman Literary Agency, 27 W 24 St, Suite 700B, New York, NY 10010 *Tel:* 212-604-0330 *E-mail:* queries@irenegoodman.com *Web Site:* www.irenegoodman.com, pg 554

Goodman, Peter, Heian, 1393 Solono Ave, Albany, CA 94706 *Tel:* 510-524-8732 *Toll Free Fax:* 888-411-8527 *E-mail:* sbp@stonebridge.com *Web Site:* www.stonebridge.com, pg 109

Goodman, Peter, Stone Bridge Press Inc, 1393 Solano Ave, Suite C, Albany, CA 94706 *Tel:* 510-524-8732 *Toll Free Tel:* 800-947-7271 (orders) *Fax:* 510-524-8711 *E-mail:* sbp@stonebridge.com; sbpedit@stonebridge.com *Web Site:* www.stonebridge.com, pg 236

Goodman, Robert White, The Johns Hopkins University Press, 2715 N Charles St, Baltimore, MD 21218-4363 *Tel:* 410-516-6900; 410-516-6987 (journal orders outside US & CN) *Toll Free Tel:* 800-537-5487 (book orders & cust serv); 800-548-1784 (journal orders) *Fax:* 410-516-6968; 410-516-3866 (journal orders) *E-mail:* hfscustserv@press.jhu.edu (cust serv); jrnlcirc@press.jhu.edu (journal orders) *Web Site:* www.press.jhu.edu; muse.jhu.edu, pg 127

Goodman, Sasha, Sasha Goodman Agency Inc, 6680 Colgate Ave, Los Angeles, CA 90048 *Tel:* 310-387-0242 *Fax:* 323-653-3457 *E-mail:* ukseg@sbcglobal.net, pg 555

Goodnough, Doris, Orbis Books, Price Bldg, Box 302, Maryknoll, NY 10545-0302 *Tel:* 914-941-7636 *Toll Free Tel:* 800-258-5838 (orders) *Fax:* 914-941-7005 *E-mail:* orbisbooks@maryknoll.org *Web Site:* www.orbisbooks.com, pg 176

Goodrich, David, American Printing History Association, PO Box 4519, Grand Central Sta, New York, NY 10163 *Tel:* 202-544-2422 *E-mail:* secretary@printinghistory.org *Web Site:* printinghistory.org, pg 596

Goodson, Kara, Photographic Society of America® (PSA®), 8241 S Walker Ave, Suite 104, Oklahoma City, OK 73139 *Tel:* 405-843-1437 *Toll Free Tel:* 855-PSA-INFO (855-772-4636) *Fax:* 405-843-1438 *E-mail:* hq@psa-photo.org *Web Site:* www.psa-photo.org, pg 616

Goodspeed, Brianne, Chelsea Green Publishing Co, 85 N Main St, Suite 120, White River Junction, VT 05001 *Tel:* 802-295-6300 *Toll Free Tel:* 800-639-4099 (cust serv, consumer & trade orders) *Fax:* 802-295-6444 *Web Site:* www.chelseagreen.com, pg 56

Goodwin, Bryan, Greenleaf Book Group LLC, Three Park Place, 4005 Banister Lane, Suite B, Austin, TX 78704 *Tel:* 512-891-6100 *Toll Free Tel:* 800-932-5420 *Fax:* 512-891-6150 *E-mail:* contact@greenleafbookgroup.com *Web Site:* www.greenleafbookgroup.com, pg 100

Goodwin, John, Galaxy Press, 7051 Hollywood Blvd, Suite 200, Hollywood, CA 90028 *Tel:* 323-466-7815 *Toll Free Tel:* 877-8GALAXY (842-5299) *E-mail:* customers@galaxypress.com; info@galaxypress.com *Web Site:* www.galaxypress.com, pg 93

Goody, Margo, Macmillan Audio, 175 Fifth Ave, New York, NY 10010 *Tel:* 646-307-5151 *Toll Free Tel:* 888-330-8477 (cust serv) *Fax:* 917-534-0980 *Web Site:* www.macmillanaudio.com, pg 145

Goossen, Chad, PrairieView Press, PO Box 460, Rosenort, MB R0G-1W0, Canada *Tel:* 204-327-6543 *Toll Free Tel:* 800-477-7377 *Fax:* 204-327-6544 *Web Site:* www.prairieviewpress.com, pg 496

Goossen, Chester, PrairieView Press, PO Box 460, Rosenort, MB R0G-1W0, Canada *Tel:* 204-327-6543 *Toll Free Tel:* 800-477-7377 *Fax:* 204-327-6544 *Web Site:* www.prairieviewpress.com, pg 496

Gordon, Annette, Clarity Press Inc, 2625 Piedmont Rd NE, Suite 56, Atlanta, GA 30324 *Toll Free Tel:* 877-613-1495 (edit) *Toll Free Fax:* 877-613-7868 *E-mail:* claritypress@usa.net (foreign rts & perms) *Web Site:* www.claritypress.com, pg 59

Gordon, Clayton, Illuminating Engineering Society of North America (IES), 120 Wall St, 17th fl, New York, NY 10005-4001 *Tel:* 212-248-5000 *Fax:* 212-248-5017; 212-248-5018 *E-mail:* ies@ies.org *Web Site:* www.ies.org, pg 119

Gouzoules, Leon, Firefly Books Ltd, 50 Staples Ave, Unit 1, Richmond Hill, ON L4B 0A7, Canada *Tel:* 416-499-8412 *Toll Free Tel:* 800-387-6192 (CN); 800-387-5085 (US) *Fax:* 416-499-8313 *Toll Free Fax:* 800-450-0391 (CN); 800-565-6034 (US) *E-mail:* service@fireflybooks.com *Web Site:* www.fireflybooks.com, pg 484

Goyette, Sue, Writers' Federation of Nova Scotia, 1113 Marginal Rd, Halifax, NS B3H 4P7, Canada *Tel:* 902-423-8116 *Fax:* 902-422-0881 *E-mail:* contact@writers.ns.ca *Web Site:* writers.ns.ca, pg 621

Grad, Doug, Doug Grad Literary Agency Inc, 68 Jay St, Suite W11, Brooklyn, NY 11201-1189 *Tel:* 718-788-6067 *E-mail:* query@dgliterary.com *Web Site:* www.dgliterary.com, pg 555

Gradel, Melissa Ford, Poets & Writers Inc, 90 Broad St, Suite 2100, New York, NY 10004 *Tel:* 212-226-3586 *Fax:* 212-226-3963 *E-mail:* admin@pw.org *Web Site:* www.pw.org, pg 616

Grady, Cindy, WriteLife LLC, 2323 S 171 St, Suite 202, Omaha, NE 68130 *Tel:* 402-934-1412 *Toll Free Tel:* 877-974-8354 *E-mail:* info@writelife.com *Web Site:* www.writelife.com; www.facebook.com/WriteLife; twitter.com/WriteLifeLLC, pg 277

Grady, Lynn, HarperCollins General Books Group, 195 Broadway, New York, NY 10007 *Tel:* 212-207-7000 *Web Site:* www.harpercollins.com, pg 105

Grady, Thomas, Ave Maria Press, PO Box 428, Notre Dame, IN 46556 *Tel:* 574-287-2831 *Toll Free Tel:* 800-282-1865 *Fax:* 574-239-2904 *Toll Free Fax:* 800-282-5681 *E-mail:* avemariapress.1@nd.edu *Web Site:* www.avemariapress.com, pg 28

Graff, Emily, Simon & Schuster, 1230 Avenue of the Americas, New York, NY 10020 *Tel:* 212-698-7000 *Toll Free Tel:* 800-223-2348 (cust serv); 800-223-2336 (orders) *Toll Free Fax:* 800-943-9831 (orders) *Web Site:* www.simonandschuster.com, pg 225

Grafton, John, Dover Publications Inc, 31 E Second St, Mineola, NY 11501-3852 *Tel:* 516-294-7000 *Toll Free Tel:* 800-223-3130 (orders) *Fax:* 516-742-6953 *E-mail:* rights@doverpublications.com; service@doverpublications.com *Web Site:* store.doverdirect.com; www.doverpublications.com, pg 76

Graham, Alex, Council for Exceptional Children (CEC), 2900 Crystal Dr, Suite 1000, Arlington, VA 22201 *Toll Free Tel:* 888-232-7733 (memb servs); 866-509-0219 *Fax:* 703-264-9494 *E-mail:* service@cec.sped.org *Web Site:* www.cec.sped.org, pg 64

Graham, Bethany, Vanderbilt University Press, 2014 Broadway, Suite 320, Nashville, TN 37203 *Tel:* 615-322-3585 *Toll Free Tel:* 800-627-7377 (orders only) *Fax:* 615-343-8823 *Toll Free Fax:* 800-735-0476 (orders only) *E-mail:* vupress@vanderbilt.edu *Web Site:* www.vanderbiltuniversitypress.com, pg 264

Graham, Bonny, National Council of Teachers of English (NCTE), 1111 W Kenyon Rd, Urbana, IL 61801-1096 *Tel:* 217-328-3870 *Toll Free Tel:* 877-369-6283 (cust serv) *Fax:* 217-328-9645 *E-mail:* orders@ncte.org *Web Site:* www.ncte.org, pg 164

Graham, Earl, Graham Agency, 250 W 57 St, Suite 2430, New York, NY 10107 *Tel:* 212-489-7730, pg 555

Graham, Jennifer, Harry N Abrams Inc, 115 W 18 St, 6th fl, New York, NY 10011 *Tel:* 212-206-7715 *Toll Free Tel:* 800-345-1359 *Fax:* 212-519-1210 *E-mail:* abrams@abramsbooks.com *Web Site:* www.abramsbooks.com, pg 3

Graham, Jon, Bear & Co Inc, One Park St, Rochester, VT 05767 *Tel:* 802-767-3174 *Toll Free Tel:* 800-932-3277 *Fax:* 802-767-3726 *E-mail:* customerservice@InnerTraditions.com *Web Site:* InnerTraditions.com, pg 33

Graham, Jon, Inner Traditions International Ltd, One Park St, Rochester, VT 05767 *Tel:* 802-767-3174 *Toll Free Tel:* 800-246-8648 *Fax:* 802-767-3726 *E-mail:* customerservice@InnerTraditions.com *Web Site:* www.InnerTraditions.com, pg 122

Graham, Joseph, The American Chemical Society, 1155 16 St NW, Washington, DC 20036 *Tel:* 202-872-4600 *Toll Free Tel:* 800-227-5558 (US) *Fax:* 202-872-6067 *E-mail:* help@acs.org *Web Site:* www.acs.org, pg 12

Graham, Kassia, New York Media Works, 112 Franklin St, New York, NY 10013 *Tel:* 646-369-5681 *Fax:* 646-810-4033 *E-mail:* info@nymediaworks.com *Web Site:* www.nymediaworks.com, pg 508

Graham, Nan, Scribner, 1230 Avenue of the Americas, New York, NY 10020, pg 220

Graham, Phil, F+W, A Content + eCommerce Company, 10151 Carver Rd, Suite 200, Blue Ash, OH 45242 *Tel:* 513-531-2690 *Toll Free Tel:* 800-289-0963 (trade accts); 800-258-0929 (orders) *E-mail:* contact_us@fwmedia.com *Web Site:* www.fwcommunity.com, pg 86

Graham, Phil, Writer's Digest Books, 10151 Carver Rd, Suite 200, Blue Ash, OH 45242 *Tel:* 513-531-2690 *Toll Free Tel:* 800-289-0963 *E-mail:* writersdigest@fwmedia.com (edit) *Web Site:* www.writersdigest.com, pg 277

Graham, Rachel, National Geographic Books, 1145 17 St NW, Washington, DC 20036-4688 *Tel:* 202-857-7000 *Fax:* 202-857-7670 *Web Site:* books.nationalgeographic.com/books, pg 165

Graham, Stephanie, Sourcebooks Inc, 1935 Brookdale Rd, Suite 139, Naperville, IL 60563 *Tel:* 630-961-3900 *Toll Free Tel:* 800-432-7444 *Fax:* 630-961-2168 *E-mail:* info@sourcebooks.com; customersupport@sourcebooks.com *Web Site:* www.sourcebooks.com, pg 230

Graham, Wendy, Scholastic Canada Ltd, 604 King St W, Toronto, ON M5V 1E1, Canada *Tel:* 905-887-7323 *Toll Free Tel:* 800-268-3860 (CN) *Toll Free Fax:* 866-387-4944 *E-mail:* custserve@scholastic.ca *Web Site:* www.scholastic.ca, pg 498

Grahek, Greg, AACC International, 3340 Pilot Knob Rd, St Paul, MN 55121 *Tel:* 651-454-7250 *Fax:* 651-454-0766 *E-mail:* aacc@scisoc.org *Web Site:* www.aaccnet.org, pg 1

Grahek, Greg, APS PRESS, 3340 Pilot Knob Rd, St Paul, MN 55121 *Tel:* 651-454-7250 *Toll Free Tel:* 800-328-7560 *Fax:* 651-454-0766 *E-mail:* aps@scisoc.org *Web Site:* www.shopapspress.org, pg 21

Grahek, Greg, Eagan Press, 3340 Pilot Knob Rd, St Paul, MN 55121 *Tel:* 651-454-7250 *Toll Free Tel:* 800-328-7560 *Fax:* 651-454-0766 *E-mail:* aacc@scisoc.org *Web Site:* www.aaccnet.org, pg 78

Grain, Tim, Birch Brook Press, PO Box 81, Delhi, NY 13753-0081 *Tel:* 607-746-7453 (book sales & prodn) *Fax:* 607-746-7453 *E-mail:* birchbrook@copper.net *Web Site:* www.birchbrookpress.info, pg 37

Grainger, Jeremy, Rutgers University Press, 106 Somerset St, 3rd fl, New Brunswick, NJ 08901 *Tel:* 848-445-7762 *Toll Free Tel:* 800-848-6224 (orders only) *Fax:* 732-745-4935 (acqs, edit, mktg, perms & prodn) *Toll Free Fax:* 800-272-6817 (fulfillment) *Web Site:* rutgerspress.rutgers.edu, pg 213

Grajkowski, Michelle, 3 Seas Literary Agency, PO Box 8571, Madison, WI 53708 *Tel:* 608-834-9317, pg 577

Grall, Shirley, McGraw-Hill Create, 501 Bell St, Dubuque, IA 52001 *Tel:* 563-584-6000 *Fax:* 563-584-6600 *E-mail:* first_last@mcgraw-hill.com *Web Site:* www.mhhe.com, pg 150

Gramaglia, Maria Pia, Rizzoli International Publications Inc, 300 Park Ave S, 4th fl, New York, NY 10010-5399 *Tel:* 212-387-3400 *Toll Free Tel:* 800-522-6657 (orders only) *Fax:* 212-387-3535 *E-mail:* publicity@rizzoliusa.com *Web Site:* www.rizzoliusa.com, pg 209

Grames, Juliet, Soho Press Inc, 853 Broadway, New York, NY 10003 *Tel:* 212-260-1900 *Fax:* 212-260-1902 *E-mail:* soho@sohopress.com; publicity@sohopress.com *Web Site:* www.sohopress.com, pg 229

Granada, Lina, Brandt & Hochman Literary Agents Inc, 1501 Broadway, Suite 2310, New York, NY 10036 *Tel:* 212-840-5760 *Fax:* 212-840-5776 *Web Site:* brandthochman.com, pg 544

Granahan, Marcie, Miles Conrad Memorial Lecture, 801 Compass Way, Suite 201, Annapolis, MD 21401 *Tel:* 443-221-2980 *Fax:* 443-221-2981 *E-mail:* nfais@nfais.org *Web Site:* www.nfais.org, pg 679

Granahan, Marcie, National Federation of Advanced Information Services (NFAIS), 801 Compass Way, Suite 201, Annapolis, MD 21401 *Tel:* 443-221-2980 *Fax:* 443-221-2981 *E-mail:* nfais@nfais.org *Web Site:* www.nfais.org, pg 612

Grandstaff, Emily, The University of Virginia Press, PO Box 400318, Charlottesville, VA 22904-4318 *Tel:* 434-924-3468 (cust serv); 434-924-3469 (cust serv) *Toll Free Tel:* 800-831-3406 (orders) *Fax:* 434-982-2655 *Toll Free Fax:* 877-288-6400 *E-mail:* vapress@virginia.edu *Web Site:* www.upress.virginia.edu, pg 260

Granger, Heather, Law Tribune Books, 201 Ann Uccello St, 4th fl, Hartford, CT 06103 *Tel:* 860-527-7900 *Fax:* 860-527-7433 *E-mail:* lawtribune@alm.com *Web Site:* www.ctlawtribune.com, pg 135

Grant, Darlene, The Pilgrim Press/United Church Press, 700 Prospect Ave, Cleveland, OH 44115-1100 *Toll Free Tel:* 800-537-3394 (cust serv-indivs); 800-654-5129 (cust serv-commercial accts) *Fax:* 216-736-2206 (orders) *E-mail:* proposals@thepilgrimpress.com *Web Site:* www.thepilgrimpress.com; www.unitedchurchpress.com, pg 192

Grant, Donna, University of Regina Press, 2 Research Dr, Suite 246, Regina, SK S4S 7H9, Canada *Tel:* 306-585-4758 *Toll Free Tel:* 866-874-2257 *Fax:* 306-585-4699 *E-mail:* uofrpress@uregina.ca *Web Site:* uofrpress.ca, pg 503

Grant, Gavin J, Small Beer Press, 150 Pleasant St, No 306, Easthampton, MA 01027 *Tel:* 413-203-1636 *Fax:* 413-203-1636 *E-mail:* info@smallbeerpress.com *Web Site:* smallbeerpress.com, pg 228

Grant, Janet Kobobel, Books & Such, 52 Mission Circle, Suite 122, PMB 170, Santa Rosa, CA 95409-5370 *Tel:* 707-538-4184 *Web Site:* booksandsuch.com, pg 543

Grant, Jerome, Pearson Business Publishing, 225 River St, Hoboken, NJ 07030-4772 *Tel:* 201-236-7000 *Web Site:* www.pearsonhighered.com, pg 185

Grant, Penny, Sinauer Associates Inc, 23 Plumtree Rd, Sunderland, MA 01375 *Tel:* 413-549-4300 *Fax:* 413-549-1118 *E-mail:* publish@sinauer.com; orders@sinauer.com *Web Site:* www.sinauer.com, pg 226

Grantham, Charles E, Contemporary Publishing Co of Raleigh Inc, 5849 Lease Lane, Raleigh, NC 27617 *Tel:* 919-851-8221 *Fax:* 919-851-6666 *E-mail:* questions@contemporarypublishing.com *Web Site:* www.contemporarypublishing.com, pg 62

Grantham, Dean, Graphic World Publishing Services, 11687 Adie Rd, St Louis, MO 63043 *Tel:* 314-567-9854 *Fax:* 314-567-7178 *E-mail:* quote@gwinc.com *Web Site:* www.gwinc.com, pg 527

Granville, Shannon, Woodrow Wilson Center Press, One Woodrow Wilson Plaza, 1300 Pennsylvania Ave NW, Washington, DC 20004-3027 *Tel:* 202-691-4000 *Fax:* 202-691-4001 *Web Site:* wilsoncenter.org, pg 275

Grathwohl, Casper, Oxford University Press USA, 198 Madison Ave, New York, NY 10016 *Tel:* 212-726-6000 *Toll Free Tel:* 800-451-7556 (orders); 800-445-9714 (cust serv) *Fax:* 919-677-1303 *E-mail:* custserv.us@oup.com *Web Site:* www.oup.com/us, pg 179

Gratz, Mike, Olde & Oppenheim Publishers, 3219 N Margate Place, Chandler, AZ 85224 *E-mail:* olde_oppenheim@hotmail.com *Web Site:* oldeandoppenheimpublishers.com, pg 174

Grau, Julie, Random House Publishing Group, 1745 Broadway, New York, NY 10019 *Toll Free Tel:* 800-200-3552 *Web Site:* atrandom.com, pg 204

Grauman, Judith, The Guilford Press, 72 Spring St, New York, NY 10012 *Tel:* 212-431-9800 *Toll Free Tel:* 800-365-7006 *Fax:* 212-966-6708 *E-mail:* info@guilford.com *Web Site:* www.guilford.com, pg 102

Gray, Bob, Central Recovery Press (CRP), 3321 N Buffalo Dr, Suite 275, Las Vegas, NV 89129 *Tel:* 702-868-5830 *Fax:* 702-868-5831 *E-mail:* info@centralrecovery.com *Web Site:* centralrecoverypress.com, pg 54

Gray, Carolyn, The Manitoba Writers' Guild Inc, 218-100 Arthur St, Winnipeg, MB R3B 1H3, Canada *Tel:* 204-944-8013 *E-mail:* info@mbwriter.mb.ca *Web Site:* www.mbwriter.mb.ca, pg 609

Gray, Catherine Moreton, Business & Legal Resources Inc, 100 Winners Circle, Suite 300, Brentwood, TN 37027 *Tel:* 860-510-0100 *Toll Free Tel:* 800-727-5257 *E-mail:* service@blr.com *Web Site:* www.blr.com, pg 48

Gray, David, Gray & Company Publishers, 1588 E 40 St, Suite 3A, Cleveland, OH 44103 *Tel:* 216-431-2665 *Toll Free Tel:* 800-915-3609 *E-mail:* sales@grayco.com; editorial@grayco.com; support@grayco.com; publicity@grayco.com *Web Site:* www.grayco.com, pg 99

Gray, Jason, Association of Writers & Writing Programs (AWP), George Mason University, 4400 University Dr, MSN 1E3, Fairfax, VA 22030 *Tel:* 703-993-4301 *Fax:* 703-993-4302 *E-mail:* awp@awpwriter.org *Web Site:* www.awpwriter.org, pg 599

Gray, Jason, AWP Award Series, George Mason University, 4400 University Dr, MSN 1E3, Fairfax, VA 22030 *Tel:* 703-993-4301 *Fax:* 703-993-4302 *E-mail:* awp@awpwriter.org *Web Site:* www.awpwriter.org, pg 669

Gray, Jason, University of Wisconsin Press, 1930 Monroe St, 3rd fl, Madison, WI 53711-2059 *Tel:* 608-263-0668 *Toll Free Tel:* 800-621-2736 (orders) *Fax:* 608-263-1173 *Toll Free Fax:* 800-621-2736 (orders) *E-mail:* uwiscpress@uwpress.wisc.edu (main off) *Web Site:* www.wisc.edu/wisconsinpress, pg 260

Gray, Kevin, Trafford, 1663 Liberty Dr, Bloomington, IN 47403 *Toll Free Tel:* 888-232-4444 *E-mail:* customersupport@trafford.com *Web Site:* www.trafford.com, pg 248

Gray, Phil, Self-Realization Fellowship Publishers, 3208 Humboldt St, Los Angeles, CA 90031 *Tel:* 323-276-6002 *Toll Free Tel:* 888-773-8680 *Fax:* 323-927-1624 *Web Site:* www.srfpublishers.org, pg 222

Gray, Thomas, Upper Access Inc, 87 Upper Access Rd, Hinesburg, VT 05461 *Tel:* 802-482-2988 *Toll Free Tel:* 800-310-8320 (orders) *Fax:* 802-417-3002 *E-mail:* info@upperaccess.com *Web Site:* www.upperaccess.com, pg 263

Grayson, Ashley, Ashley Grayson Literary Agency, 1342 W 18 St, San Pedro, CA 90732 *Tel:* 310-548-4672 *E-mail:* graysonagent@earthlink.net; rights@graysonagency.com *Web Site:* graysonagency.com/blog/, pg 555

Grayson, Carolyn, Ashley Grayson Literary Agency, 1342 W 18 St, San Pedro, CA 90732 *Tel:* 310-548-4672 *E-mail:* graysonagent@earthlink.net; rights@graysonagency.com *Web Site:* graysonagency.com/blog/, pg 555

Graziadie, Claude, Statistics Canada, 150 Tunney's Pasture Driveway, Ottawa, ON K1A 0T6, Canada *Tel:* 514-283-8300 *Toll Free Tel:* 800-263-1136 (CN & US, gen inquiries); 800-267-6677 (prods & servs) *Toll Free Fax:* 877-287-4369 (orders) *E-mail:* infostats@statcan.gc.ca *Web Site:* statcan.gc.ca, pg 500

Grebenar, Sandy, Houghton Mifflin Harcourt Trade & Reference Division, 222 Berkeley St, Boston, MA 02116 *Tel:* 617-351-5000 *Toll Free Tel:* 800-225-3362 *Web Site:* www.hmhco.com, pg 115

Greber, Erika, Random House Publishing Group, 1745 Broadway, New York, NY 10019 *Toll Free Tel:* 800-200-3552 *Web Site:* atrandom.com, pg 204

Greco, Al, Carson-Dellosa Publishing LLC, PO Box 35665, Greensboro, NC 27425-5665 *Tel:* 336-632-0084 *Toll Free Tel:* 800-321-0943 *Fax:* 336-632-0087 *Toll Free Fax:* 800-535-2669 *E-mail:* custsvc@carsondellosa.com *Web Site:* www.carsondellosa.com, pg 51

Greco, Albert N, Fordham University, Graduate School of Business Administration, Gabelli School of Business, 441 E Fordham Rd, Hughes Hall, Rm 516, Bronx, NY 10458 *Tel:* 718-817-1894 *Web Site:* www.bnet.fordham.edu, pg 660

Greco, John, American Bible Society, 1865 Broadway, New York, NY 10023-7505 *Tel:* 212-408-1200 *Toll Free Tel:* 800-322-4253; 888-596-6296 *Fax:* 212-408-1512 *E-mail:* info@americanbible.org *Web Site:* www.americanbible.org, pg 11

Greco, Marilyn, Schoolhouse Network Inc, PO Box 17676, Fountain Hills, AZ 85269 *Tel:* 973-206-1389 *E-mail:* info@schoolhousenetwork.com *Web Site:* www.schoolhousenetwork.com, pg 534

Greeman, Amy, Storey Publishing LLC, 210 MASS MoCA Way, North Adams, MA 01247 *Tel:* 413-346-2100 *Toll Free Tel:* 800-441-5700 (orders); 800-793-9396 (edit) *Fax:* 413-346-2199; 413-346-2196 (edit) *E-mail:* sales@storey.com *Web Site:* www.storey.com, pg 236

Green, Anthony, Quackenworth Publishing, PO Box 4747, Culver City, CA 90231-4747 *Tel:* 310-945-5634 *Toll Free Tel:* 888-701-4991 *Fax:* 310-945-5709 *Toll Free Fax:* 888-892-6339 *E-mail:* info@quackenworth.com *Web Site:* www.quackenworth.com; www.wittybittybunch.com, pg 201

Green, Becky, Random House Children's Books, 1745 Broadway, New York, NY 10019 *Tel:* 212-782-9000 *Toll Free Tel:* 800-200-3552 *Fax:* 212-782-9452 *Web Site:* randomhousekids.com, pg 203

Green, Dan, Pom Inc, 18-15 215 St, Bayside, NY 11360 *Tel:* 516-487-3441, pg 568

Green, Eric, The Perseus Books Group, 387 Park Ave S, 12th fl, New York, NY 10016 *Tel:* 212-340-8100 *Toll Free Tel:* 800-343-4499 (cust serv) *Fax:* 212-340-8105 *Web Site:* www.perseusbooksgroup.com, pg 189

Green, Erin, Boys Town Press, 14100 Crawford St, Boys Town, NE 68010 *Tel:* 402-498-1320 *Toll Free Tel:* 800-282-6657 *Fax:* 402-498-1310 *E-mail:* btpress@boystown.org *Web Site:* www.boystownpress.org, pg 44

Green, Frank, Bard Society Fiction Writing Workshop, 3113 Crosby Lane, Jacksonville, FL 32216, pg 650

Green, George, America West Publishers, PO Box 599, Hayden, ID 83835 *Tel:* 775-885-0700 *Toll Free Tel:* 800-729-4131 *Web Site:* www.nohoax.com, pg 10

Green, James A, Greenwood Research Books & Software, PO Box 12102, Wichita, KS 67277-2102 *Tel:* 316-214-5103 *Web Site:* greenray4ever.com (ordering), pg 101

Green, Jane, PennWell Books, 1421 S Sheridan Rd, Tulsa, OK 74112 *Tel:* 918-831-9410 *Toll Free Tel:* 800-752-9764 *Fax:* 918-831-9555 *E-mail:* sales@pennwell.com *Web Site:* www.pennwellbooks.com, pg 188

Green, Judy, The Young Adult Book Award, 1150 Morrison Dr, Suite 400, Ottawa, ON K2H 8S9, Canada *Tel:* 613-232-9625 *Fax:* 613-563-9895 *E-mail:* info@cla.ca *Web Site:* www.cla.ca, pg 739

Green, Karen, Anvil Press Publishers, 278 E First Ave, Vancouver, BC V5T 1A6, Canada *Tel:* 604-876-8710 *Fax:* 604-879-2667 *E-mail:* info@anvilpress.com *Web Site:* www.anvilpress.com, pg 471

Green, Karen, The BC Book Prizes, 207 W Hastings St, Suite 901, Vancouver, BC V6B 1H7, Canada *Tel:* 604-687-2405 *Fax:* 604-687-2435 *E-mail:* info@bcbookprizes.ca *Web Site:* www.bcbookprizes.ca, pg 670

Green, Kate, Clarion Books, 215 Park Ave S, New York, NY 10003 *Tel:* 212-420-5889 *Toll Free Tel:* 800-225-3362 (orders) *Fax:* 212-420-5855 *Toll Free Fax:* 800-634-7568 (orders) *Web Site:* www.hmhco.com, pg 59

Green, Michael, Philomel, 345 Hudson St, New York, NY 10014 *Tel:* 212-366-2000, pg 191

Green, Nancy, The Monacelli Press, 236 W 27 St, 4th fl, New York, NY 10001 *Tel:* 212-229-9925 *E-mail:* contact@monacellipress.com *Web Site:* www.monacellipress.com, pg 159

Green, Spencer, Opie Prize, Ohio State Univ, Mershon Ctr, 1501 Neil Ave, Columbus, OH 43201-2602 *Tel:* 614-292-3375 *Fax:* 614-292-2407 *Web Site:* www.afsnet.org/aboutAFS/AFSprizes.cfm, pg 715

Green, Susan, Huntington Library Press, 1151 Oxford Rd, San Marino, CA 91108 *Tel:* 626-405-2172 *Fax:* 626-585-0794 *E-mail:* booksales@huntington.org *Web Site:* www.huntington.org, pg 117

Greenbaum, Arlynn, Authors Unlimited Inc, 31 E 32 St, Suite 300, New York, NY 10016 *Tel:* 212-481-8484 (ext 336) *Fax:* 212-481-9582 *Web Site:* www.authorsunlimited.com, pg 587

Greenberg, Annalee, Portage & Main Press, 318 McDermot, Suite 100, Winnipeg, MB R3A 0A2, Canada *Tel:* 204-987-3500 *Toll Free Tel:* 800-667-9673 *Fax:* 204-947-0080 *Toll Free Fax:* 866-734-8477 *E-mail:* books@portageandmainpress.com *Web Site:* www.portageandmainpress.com, pg 495

Greenberg, Daniel, Levine|Greenberg|Rostan Literary Agency Inc, 307 Seventh Ave, Suite 2407, New York, NY 10001 *Tel:* 212-337-0934 *Fax:* 212-337-0948 *Web Site:* lgrliterary.com, pg 561

Greenberg, Jeff, AAA Photos, 401 Ocean Dr, Unit 804, Miami Beach, FL 33139 *Tel:* 305-534-0804 *Web Site:* www.photosphotos.net, pg 519

Greenberg, Karen Matsu, American Book Producers Association (ABPA), 31 W Eighth St, 2nd fl, New York, NY 10011 *Tel:* 212-675-1363 *Fax:* 212-675-1364 *E-mail:* office@abpaonline.org *Web Site:* www.abpaonline.org, pg 594

Greenberg, Susannah, Women's National Book Association Award, PO Box 237, FDR Sta, New York, NY 10150-0231 *Tel:* 212-208-4629 *Fax:* 212-208-4629 *E-mail:* publicity@bookbuzz.com *Web Site:* www.wnba-books.org; www.NationalReadingGroupMonth.org, pg 737

Greenberg, Susannah, Women's National Book Association Inc, PO Box 237, FDR Sta, New York, NY 10150-0231 *Tel:* 212-208-4629 *Fax:* 212-208-4629 *E-mail:* publicity@bookbuzz.com; info@wnba-books.org *Web Site:* www.wnba-books.org; www.NationalReadingGroupMonth.org, pg 621

Greenberg, Zeke, Alan Wofsy Fine Arts, 1109 Geary Blvd, San Francisco, CA 94109 *Tel:* 415-292-6500 *Toll Free Tel:* 800-660-6403 *Fax:* 415-292-6594 (off & cust serv); 510-251-1840 (acctg) *E-mail:* order@art-books.com (orders); editeur@earthlink.net (edit); beauxarts@earthlink.net (cust serv) *Web Site:* www.art-books.com, pg 274

Greene, Alexander, Springer, 233 Spring St, New York, NY 10013-1578 *Tel:* 212-460-1500 *Toll Free Tel:* 800-SPRINGER (777-4643) *Fax:* 212-460-1575 *E-mail:* service-ny@springer.com *Web Site:* www.springer.com, pg 232

Greene, Anne, Wesleyan Writers Conference, c/o Wesleyan University, 294 High St, Middletown, CT 06459 *Tel:* 860-685-3604 *Fax:* 860-685-2441 *Web Site:* www.wesleyan.edu/writing/conference, pg 656

Greene, Deirdre, Roaring Forties Press, 1053 Santa Fe Ave, Berkeley, CA 94706 *Tel:* 510-527-5461 *E-mail:* info@roaringfortiespress.com *Web Site:* www.roaringfortiespress.com, pg 210

Greene, Grace Worcester, Dorothy Canfield Fisher Children's Book Award, 109 State St, Montpelier, VT 05609-0601 *Tel:* 802-828-6954 *Fax:* 802-828-1481 *E-mail:* cbec@state.vt.us *Web Site:* www.dcfaward.org; libraries.vermont.gov/libraries, pg 682

Greenfield, George M, CreativeWell Inc, PO Box 3130, Memorial Sta, Upper Montclair, NJ 07043 *Tel:* 973-783-7575 *Toll Free Tel:* 800-743-9182 *Fax:* 973-783-7530 *E-mail:* info@creativewell.com *Web Site:* www.creativewell.com, pg 547, 587

Greenhut, Carol, Schonfeld & Associates Inc, 1931 Lynn Circle, Libertyville, IL 60048 *Tel:* 847-816-4870 *Toll Free Tel:* 800-205-0030 *Fax:* 847-816-4872 *E-mail:* saiinfo@saibooks.com *Web Site:* www.saibooks.com, pg 219

Greenland, Paul R, Paul Greenland Editorial Services, 9184 Longfellow Lane, Machesney Park, IL 61115 *Tel:* 815-540-0911 *Web Site:* www.paulgreenland.com, pg 527

Greenleaf, Clint, Greenleaf Book Group LLC, Three Park Place, 4005 Banister Lane, Suite B, Austin, TX 78704 *Tel:* 512-891-6100 *Toll Free Tel:* 800-932-5420 *Fax:* 512-891-6150 *E-mail:* contact@greenleafbookgroup.com *Web Site:* www.greenleafbookgroup.com, pg 100

Greenleaf, Lisa, Apprentice Shop Books LLC, 18 Wentworth Dr, Bedford, NH 03110 *Tel:* 603-472-8741 *Fax:* 603-472-2323 *E-mail:* info@apprenticeshopbooks.com *Web Site:* www.apprenticeshopbooks.com, pg 20

Greenspan, Elizabeth, Society for Industrial & Applied Mathematics, 3600 Market St, 6th fl, Philadelphia, PA 19104-2688 *Tel:* 215-382-9800 *Toll Free Tel:* 800-447-7426 *Fax:* 215-386-7999 *E-mail:* siambooks@siam.org *Web Site:* www.siam.org, pg 229

Greenspan, Jackie, Mondo Publishing, 200 Sherwood Ave, Farmingdale, NY 11735 *Tel:* 212-268-3560 *Toll Free Tel:* 888-88-MONDO (886-6636) *Toll Free Fax:* 888-532-4492 *E-mail:* info@mondopub.com *Web Site:* www.mondopub.com, pg 159

Greenspan, Shari Dash, Flashlight Press, 527 Empire Blvd, Brooklyn, NY 11225 *Tel:* 718-288-8300 *Fax:* 718-972-6307 *E-mail:* editor@flashlightpress.com *Web Site:* www.flashlightpress.com, pg 89

Greenspan, Shari Dash, Urim Publications, c/o Lambda Publications Inc, 527 Empire Blvd, Brooklyn, NY 11225-3121 *Tel:* 718-972-5449 *Fax:* 718-972-6307 *E-mail:* publisher@urimpublications.com *Web Site:* urimpublications.com, pg 263

Greenstein, Ruth, Words into Print, 57 Prince St, Suite 4R, New York, NY 10012 *Tel:* 212-741-1393 *Fax:* 419-441-1393 *E-mail:* query@wordsintoprint.org *Web Site:* www.wordsintoprint.org, pg 536

Greer, Jessica, Other Press LLC, 2 Park Ave, 24th fl, New York, NY 10016 *Tel:* 212-414-0054 *Toll Free Tel:* 877-843-6843 *Fax:* 212-414-0939 *E-mail:* editor@otherpress.com; rights@otherpress.com *Web Site:* www.otherpress.com, pg 178

Gref, Emily, Lowenstein Associates Inc, 115 E 23 St, 4th fl, New York, NY 10010 *Tel:* 212-206-1630 *Fax:* 212-727-0280 *E-mail:* assistant@bookhaven.com (queries, no attachments) *Web Site:* www.lowensteinassociates.com, pg 562

Grefe, Richard, AIGA, the professional association for design, 233 Broadway, 17th fl, New York, NY 10279 *Tel:* 212-807-1990 *Fax:* 212-807-1799 *E-mail:* general@aiga.org *Web Site:* www.aiga.org, pg 593

Gregg, Richard, Phaidon Press Inc, 180 Varick St, 14th fl, New York, NY 10014 *Tel:* 212-652-5400 *Toll Free Tel:* 800-759-0190 (cust serv) *Fax:* 212-652-5410 *Toll Free Fax:* 800-286-9471 (cust serv) *E-mail:* ussales@phaidon.com *Web Site:* www.phaidon.com, pg 190

Gregoire, Pierre, Les Editions Vents d'Ouest, 109, rue Wright, bureau 202, Gatineau, QC J8X 2G7, Canada *Tel:* 819-770-6377 *Fax:* 819-770-0559 *E-mail:* info@ventsdouest.ca *Web Site:* www.ventsdouest.ca, pg 483

Gregory, Alexis, The Vendome Press, 1334 York Ave, 3rd fl, New York, NY 10021 *Tel:* 212-737-5297 *Fax:* 212-737-5340 *E-mail:* info@vendomepress.com *Web Site:* www.vendomepress.com, pg 265

Gregory, Debbie, Upper Room Books, 1908 Grand Ave, Nashville, TN 37212 *Tel:* 615-340-7200 *Toll Free Tel:* 800-972-0433 *Fax:* 615-340-7266 *Web Site:* books.upperroom.org, pg 263

Gregory, Evan, Ethan Ellenberg Literary Agency, 548 Broadway, Suite 5-E, New York, NY 10012 *Tel:* 212-431-4554 *E-mail:* agent@ethanellenberg.com *Web Site:* www.ethanellenberg.com, pg 550

Gregory, Kevin G, AuthorHouse, 1663 Liberty Dr, Bloomington, IN 47403 *Tel:* 812-339-6000 (outside US) *Toll Free Tel:* 888-519-5121 *E-mail:* authorsupport@authorhouse.com *Web Site:* www.authorhouse.com, pg 27

Gregory, Kevin G, iUniverse, 1663 Liberty Dr, Bloomington, IN 47403 *Toll Free Tel:* 800-AUTHORS (288-4677) *Fax:* 812-355-4085 *Web Site:* www.iuniverse.com, pg 126

Gregory, Kevin G, Xlibris Corp, 1663 Liberty Dr, Suite 200, Bloomington, IN 47403 *Toll Free Tel:* 888-795-4274 *Fax:* 610-915-0294 *E-mail:* info@xlibris.com *Web Site:* www.xlibris.com, pg 277

Gregory, Michael Steven, Southern California Writers' Conference, 18160 Cottonwood Rd, Suite 260, Sunriver, OR 97707 *Tel:* 619-303-8185 *Fax:* 619-906-7462 *E-mail:* msg@writersconference.com *Web Site:* www.writersconference.com, pg 655

Greig, Bill T III, Regal Books, 1957 Eastman Ave, Ventura, CA 93003 *Tel:* 805-644-9721 *Toll Free Tel:* 800-446-7735 (orders) *Web Site:* www.regalbooks.com; www.gospellight.com, pg 207

Grench, Charles, The University of North Carolina Press, 116 S Boundary St, Chapel Hill, NC 27514-3808 *Tel:* 919-966-3561 *Fax:* 919-966-3829 *E-mail:* uncpress@unc.edu *Web Site:* www.uncpress.unc.edu, pg 258

Grennan, Karen, SDP Publishing Solutions LLC, 36 Captain's Way, East Bridgewater, MA 02333 *Tel:* 617-775-0656 *Web Site:* www.sdppublishingsolutions.com, pg 534

Gress, Priti Chitnis, Hippocrene Books Inc, 171 Madison Ave, New York, NY 10016 *Tel:* 212-685-4373 *Fax:* 212-779-9338 *E-mail:* info@hippocrenebooks.com; orderdept@hippocrenebooks.com (orders) *Web Site:* www.hippocrenebooks.com, pg 112

Greuel, Greg, Wayside Publishing, 11 Jan Sebastian Dr, Suite 5, Sandwich, MA 02563 *Tel:* 508-833-5096 *Toll Free Tel:* 888-302-2519 *Fax:* 508-833-6284 *E-mail:* wayside@sprintmail.com *Web Site:* www.waysidepublishing.com, pg 268

Gribble, Julie, New York Media Works, 112 Franklin St, New York, NY 10013 *Tel:* 646-369-5681 *Fax:* 646-810-4033 *E-mail:* info@nymediaworks.com *Web Site:* www.nymediaworks.com, pg 508

Griebeler, Pat, Theosophical Publishing House/Quest Books, 306 W Geneva Rd, Wheaton, IL 60187 *Tel:* 630-665-0130 (ext 347) *Toll Free Tel:* 800-669-9425 (ext 347) *Fax:* 630-665-8791 *E-mail:* customerservice@questbooks.net *Web Site:* www.questbooks.net, pg 244

Griffes, Peter L, ProStar Publications Inc, 3 Church Circle, Suite 109, Annapolis, MD 21401 *Tel:* 310-280-1010 *Toll Free Tel:* 800-481-6277 *Fax:* 310-280-1025 *Toll Free Fax:* 800-487-6277 *E-mail:* editor@prostarpublications.com *Web Site:* www.prostarpublications.com, pg 199

Griffin, Courtney, Bloomsbury Publishing Inc, 1385 Broadway, 5th fl, New York, NY 10018 *Tel:* 212-419-5300 *E-mail:* marketingusa@bloomsbury.com; adultpublicityusa@bloomsbury.com; askacademic@bloomsbury.com *Web Site:* www.bloomsbury.com, pg 40

Griffin, Jean, Hachette Book Group, 1290 Avenue of the Americas, New York, NY 10019 *Tel:* 212-364-1100 *Toll Free Tel:* 800-759-0190 (cust serv) *Fax:* 212-364-0933 (intl orders) *Toll Free Fax:* 800-286-9471 (cust serv) *Web Site:* www.HachetteBookGroup.com, pg 102

Griffin, Jennifer, The Miller Agency Inc, 630 Ninth Ave, Suite 1102, New York, NY 10036 *Tel:* 212-206-0913 *Fax:* 212-206-1473, pg 566

Griffin, Jo Beth, Elsevier, Health Sciences Division, 1600 John F Kennedy Blvd, Suite 1800, Philadelphia, PA 19103-2899 *Tel:* 215-239-3900 *Toll Free Tel:* 800-523-1649 *Fax:* 215-239-3990 *Web Site:* www.elsevierhealth.com, pg 81

Griffin, John, National Geographic Society, 1145 17 St NW, Washington, DC 20036-4688 *Tel:* 202-857-7000 *Fax:* 202-429-5727 *Web Site:* www.nationalgeographic.com, pg 165

Griffin, Susan, Carter G Woodson Book Awards, 8555 16 St, Suite 500, Silver Spring, MD 20910 *Tel:* 301-588-1800 *Toll Free Tel:* 800-296-7840 *Fax:* 301-588-2049 *E-mail:* excellence@ncss.org; publications@ncss.org *Web Site:* www.socialstudies.org, pg 737

Griffiths, Jenese, AFB Press, 2 Penn Plaza, Suite 1102, New York, NY 10121 *Tel:* 212-502-7600 *Toll Free Tel:* 800-232-5463; 800-232-3044 (orders) *Fax:* 917-210-3979; 412-741-0609 (orders) *Toll Free Fax:* 888-545-8331 *E-mail:* press@afb.net; afbpress@afb.net; afbinfo@afb.net; afborder@afb.net (orders) *Web Site:* www.afb.org, pg 5

Griffor, Mariela, Marick Press, PO Box 36253, Grosse Pointe Farms, MI 48236 *Tel:* 313-407-9236 *E-mail:* orders@marickpress.com *Web Site:* www.marickpress.com, pg 147

Grilliot, Bob, JIST Publishing, 875 Montreal Way, St Paul, MN 55102 *Toll Free Tel:* 800-328-1452 *Toll Free Fax:* 800-328-4564 *E-mail:* educate@emcp.com *Web Site:* jist.emcp.com, pg 127

Grillo, Scott, McGraw-Hill Professional, 1221 Avenue of the Americas, New York, NY 10020 *Tel:* 212-512-2000 *Web Site:* www.mhprofessional.com, pg 152

Grima, Tony, National Braille Press, 88 St Stephen St, Boston, MA 02115-4302 *Tel:* 617-266-6160 *Toll Free Tel:* 800-548-7323 (cust serv); 888-965-8965 *Fax:* 617-437-0456 *E-mail:* orders@nbp.org *Web Site:* www.nbp.org, pg 164

Grimaldi, Dana, Harlequin Enterprises Ltd, 225 Duncan Mill Rd, Don Mills, ON M3B 3K9, Canada *Tel:* 416-445-5860 *Toll Free Tel:* 888-432-4879; 800-370-5838 (ebook inquiries) *E-mail:* customerservice@harlequin.com *Web Site:* www.harlequin.com, pg 487

Grimbleby, Jennifer, Kids Can Press Ltd, 25 Dockside Dr, Toronto, ON M5A 0B5, Canada *Tel:* 416-479-7000 *Toll Free Tel:* 800-265-0884 *Fax:* 416-960-5437 *E-mail:* info@kidscan.com; customerservice@kidscan.com *Web Site:* www.kidscanpress.com; www.kidscanpress.ca, pg 489

Grimes, Mark, American Academy of Pediatrics, 141 NW Point Blvd, Elk Grove Village, IL 60007-1098 *Tel:* 847-434-4000 *Toll Free Tel:* 888-227-1770 *Fax:* 847-434-8000 *E-mail:* pubs@aap.org *Web Site:* www.aap.org, pg 10

Grimm, Chris, Kensington Publishing Corp, 119 W 40 St, New York, NY 10018 *Tel:* 212-407-1500 *Toll Free Tel:* 800-221-2647 *Fax:* 212-935-0699 *Web Site:* www.kensingtonbooks.com, pg 130

Grimm, Katie, Don Congdon Associates Inc, 110 William St, Suite 2202, New York, NY 10038-3914 *Tel:* 212-645-1229 *Fax:* 212-727-2688 *E-mail:* dca@doncongdon.com *Web Site:* www.doncongdon.com, pg 546

Grimm, Sarah, GP Putnam's Sons (Hardcover), 375 Hudson St, New York, NY 10014 *Tel:* 212-366-2000 *E-mail:* online@penguinputnam.com *Web Site:* us.penguingroup.com, pg 201

Grimshaw, Sue, Penguin Random House Inc, 1745 Broadway, New York, NY 10019 *Tel:* 212-782-9000 *Toll Free Tel:* 800-726-0600 *Web Site:* www.randomhouse.com, pg 187

Grimshaw, Sue, Random House Publishing Group, 1745 Broadway, New York, NY 10019 *Toll Free Tel:* 800-200-3552 *Web Site:* atrandom.com, pg 204

Grinberg, Jill, Jill Grinberg Literary Management LLC, 392 Vanderbilt Ave, Brooklyn, NY 11238 *Tel:* 212-620-5883 *E-mail:* info@jillgrinbergliterary.com *Web Site:* www.jillgrinbergliterary.com, pg 555

Grisafi, Lora, Random House Children's Books, 1745 Broadway, New York, NY 10019 *Tel:* 212-782-9000 *Toll Free Tel:* 800-200-3552 *Fax:* 212-782-9452 *Web Site:* randomhousekids.com, pg 203

Grisebach, Rolf, Thames & Hudson, 500 Fifth Ave, New York, NY 10110 *Tel:* 212-354-3763 *Toll Free Tel:* 800-233-4830 *Fax:* 212-398-1252 *E-mail:* bookinfo@thames.wwnorton.com *Web Site:* www.thamesandhudsonusa.com, pg 244

Groban, Betsy, Houghton Mifflin Harcourt Trade & Reference Division, 222 Berkeley St, Boston, MA 02116 *Tel:* 617-351-5000 *Toll Free Tel:* 800-225-3362 *Web Site:* www.hmhco.com, pg 115

Groell, Anne, Random House Publishing Group, 1745 Broadway, New York, NY 10019 *Toll Free Tel:* 800-200-3552 *Web Site:* atrandom.com, pg 204

Gromling, Frank, Ocean Publishing, PO Box 1080, Flagler Beach, FL 32136-1080 *Tel:* 386-517-1600 *E-mail:* publisher@oceanpublishing.org *Web Site:* www.oceanpublishing.org, pg 173

Gros, Tobias, Octane Press, 808 Kinney Ave, Austin, TX 78704 *Tel:* 512-334-9441 *Fax:* 512-852-4737 *E-mail:* info@octanepress.com *Web Site:* www.octanepress.com, pg 174

Grosjean, Jill, Jill Grosjean Literary Agency, 1390 Millstone Rd, Sag Harbor, NY 11963 *Tel:* 631-725-7419 *Fax:* 631-725-8632 *E-mail:* JillLit310@aol.com, pg 555

Gross, Laura, Laura Gross Literary Agency Ltd, PO Box 610326, Newton Highlands, MA 02461 *Tel:* 617-964-2977 *Fax:* 617-964-3023 *E-mail:* query@lg-la.com *Web Site:* www.lg-la.com, pg 555

Grossberg, Aileen, Sydney Taylor Manuscript Award, 204 Park St, Montclair, NJ 07042 *E-mail:* stmacajl@aol.com *Web Site:* www.jewishlibraries.org, pg 731

Grossinger, Richard, Frog Books, 2526 Martin Luther King Jr Way, Berkeley, CA 94704 *Tel:* 510-549-4270 *Fax:* 510-549-4276 *E-mail:* customerservice@northatlanticbooks.com *Web Site:* www.northatlanticbooks.com, pg 93

Grossinger, Richard, North Atlantic Books, 2526 Martin Luther King Jr Way, Berkeley, CA 94704 *Tel:* 510-549-4270 *Fax:* 510-549-4276 *Web Site:* www.northatlanticbooks.com, pg 170

Grosskopf, Bill M, Newgen North America Inc, 2714 Bee Cave Rd, Suite 201, Austin, TX 78746 *Tel:* 512-478-5341 *Fax:* 512-476-4756 *Web Site:* www.newgen.co, pg 531

Grossman, Jim, American Historical Association (AHA), 400 "A" St SE, Washington, DC 20003 *Tel:* 202-544-2422 *Fax:* 202-544-8307 *E-mail:* aha@historians.org; awards@historians.org; info@historians.org *Web Site:* www.historians.org, pg 13

Grossman, Lawrence, American Jewish Committee (AJC), Jacob Blaustein Bldg, 165 E 56 St, New York, NY 10022 *Tel:* 212-751-4000; 212-891-1456 (membership) *Fax:* 212-891-1450 *Web Site:* www.ajc.org, pg 595

Grossman, Moshe, Feldheim Publishers (Philipp Feldheim Inc), 208 Airport Executive Park, Nanuet, NY 10954 *Tel:* 845-356-2282 *Toll Free Tel:* 800-237-7149 (orders) *Fax:* 845-425-1908 *E-mail:* sales@feldheim.com *Web Site:* www.feldheim.com, pg 87

Grossman, Sarah, Cornell University Southeast Asia Program Publications, 213 Kahin Ctr, 640 Stewart Ave, Ithaca, NY 14850 *Tel:* 607-255-4359 *Fax:* 607-255-4359 *E-mail:* seappublications@cornell.edu *Web Site:* seapeinaudi.cornell.edu/southeastasia/publications, pg 64

Grosz-Ngate, Maria, Indiana University African Studies Program, Indiana University, 221 Woodburn Hall, Bloomington, IN 47405 *Tel:* 812-855-8284 *Fax:* 812-855-6734 *E-mail:* afrist@indiana.edu *Web Site:* www.indiana.edu/~afrist, pg 120

Grote, Bill, BNi Building News, 990 Park Center Dr, Suite E, Vista, CA 92081-8352 *Tel:* 760-734-1113 *Toll Free Tel:* 888-BNI-BOOK (264-2665) *Web Site:* www.bnibooks.com, pg 41

Groton, John, Quarto Publishing Group USA Inc, 400 First Ave N, Suite 300, Minneapolis, MN 55401 *Tel:* 612-344-8100 *Toll Free Tel:* 800-328-0590 (sales); 800-458-0454 *Fax:* 612-344-8691 *E-mail:* sales@creativepub.com *Web Site:* quartoknows.com, pg 202

Grotz, Jennifer, Bread Loaf Writers' Conference, 5525 Middlebury College, 14 Old Chapel Rd, Middlebury, VT 05753 *Tel:* 802-443-5286 *Fax:* 802-443-2087 *E-mail:* blwc@middlebury.edu *Web Site:* www.middlebury.edu/blwc, pg 650

Grotz, Jennifer, Fellowship & Scholarship Program for Writers, Middlebury College, Middlebury, VT 05753 *Tel:* 802-443-5286 *Fax:* 802-443-2087 *E-mail:* blwc@middlebury.edu *Web Site:* www.middlebury.edu/blwc, pg 685

Grove, Alyssa Hickman, Utah Original Writing Competition, 617 E South Temple, Salt Lake City, UT 84102 *Tel:* 801-236-7555 *Fax:* 801-236-7556 *Web Site:* arts.utah.gov, pg 733

Grove, Susan Evans, The Society of Naval Architects & Marine Engineers, 601 Pavonia Ave, Jersey City, NJ 07306-2907 *Tel:* 201-798-4800 *Toll Free Tel:* 800-798-2188 *Fax:* 201-798-4975 *Web Site:* www.sname.org, pg 229

Grows, Penelope, Wilfrid Laurier University Press, 255 King St N, Suite 401, Waterloo, ON N2J 4V2, Canada *Tel:* 519-884-0710 (ext 6124) *Toll Free Tel:* 866-836-5551 (CN & US) *Fax:* 519-725-1399 *E-mail:* press@wlu.ca *Web Site:* www.wlupress.wlu.ca, pg 505

Grubb, Randell C, Theosophical University Press, PO Box C, Pasadena, CA 91109-7107 *Tel:* 626-798-3378 *E-mail:* tupress@theosociety.org *Web Site:* www.theosociety.org, pg 244

Grubb, Sara, Irene Goodman Literary Agency, 27 W 24 St, Suite 700B, New York, NY 10010 *Tel:* 212-604-0330 *E-mail:* queries@irenegoodman.com *Web Site:* www.irenegoodman.com, pg 554

Grudens, Richard, Celebrity Profiles Publishing, PO Box 344, Stony Brook, NY 11790 *Tel:* 631-862-8555 *Fax:* 631-862-0139 *E-mail:* celebpro4@aol.com *Web Site:* www.richardgrudens.com; richardgrudensblog.blogspot.com, pg 53

Gruenspecht, Ayelet, Crown Publishing Group, c/o Penguin Random House Inc, 1745 Broadway, New York, NY 10019 *Tel:* 212-782-9000 *Toll Free Tel:* 888-264-1745 *Fax:* 212-940-7408 *E-mail:* crownosm@penguinrandomhouse.com *Web Site:* crownpublishing.com, pg 68

Grumbach, Antonia, Whiting Writers' Awards, 1133 Avenue of the Americas, 22nd fl, New York, NY 10036-6710 *Tel:* 212-336-2138 *E-mail:* info@whitingfoundation.org *Web Site:* www.whitingfoundation.org, pg 735

Grunewald, Nancy, Washington State University Press, Cooper Publications Bldg, Grimes Way, Pullman, WA 99164 *Tel:* 509-335-3518; 509-335-7880 (order fulfillment) *Toll Free Tel:* 800-354-7360 *Fax:* 509-335-8568 *E-mail:* wsupress@wsu.edu *Web Site:* wsupress.wsu.edu, pg 267

Grusa, Jiri, PEN Writers' Emergency Fund, 588 Broadway, Suite 303, New York, NY 10012 *Tel:* 212-334-1660 *Fax:* 212-334-2181 *Web Site:* www.pen.org, pg 718

Guarin, Imelda, Marshall Cavendish Corp, 99 White Plains Rd, Tarrytown, NY 10591-9001 *Tel:* 914-332-8888 *Toll Free Tel:* 800-821-9881 *Fax:* 914-332-8102 *E-mail:* mce@marshallcavendish.com *Web Site:* www.mceducation.us, pg 148

Guarnaschelli, Maria, W W Norton & Company Inc, 500 Fifth Ave, New York, NY 10110-0017 *Tel:* 212-354-5500 *Toll Free Tel:* 800-233-4830 (orders & cust serv) *Fax:* 212-869-0856 *Toll Free Fax:* 800-458-6515 *Web Site:* www.wwnorton.com, pg 171

Guay, Marie-Noelle, Editions Yvon Blais, 137 John, CP 180, Cowansville, QC J2K 3H6, Canada *Tel:* 450-266-1086 *Toll Free Tel:* 800-363-3047 *Fax:* 450-263-9256 *E-mail:* editionsyvonblais.commentaires@thomsonreuters.com; editionsyvonblais.commandes@thomsonreuters.com (cust serv) *Web Site:* www.editionsyvonblais.qc.ca, pg 483

Gubins, Samuel, Annual Reviews, 4139 El Camino Way, Palo Alto, CA 94306 *Tel:* 650-493-4400 *Toll Free Tel:* 800-523-8635 *Fax:* 650-424-0910; 650-855-9815 *E-mail:* service@annualreviews.org *Web Site:* www.annualreviews.org, pg 18

Gudovitz, Neil, Waterside Productions Inc, 2055 Oxford Ave, Cardiff, CA 92007 *Tel:* 760-632-9190 *Fax:* 760-632-9295 *E-mail:* admin@waterside.com *Web Site:* www.waterside.com, pg 579

Guelker, Lorraine P, Frank Amato Publications Inc, 4040 SE Wister St, Milwaukie, OR 97222 *Tel:* 503-653-8108 *Toll Free Tel:* 800-541-9498 *Fax:* 503-653-2766 *E-mail:* customerservice@amatobooks.com; info@amatobooks.com *Web Site:* www.amatobooks.com, pg 9

Guenzel, Andrea L, The Electrochemical Society (ECS), 65 S Main St, Bldg D, Pennington, NJ 08534-2839 *Tel:* 609-737-1902 *Fax:* 609-737-2743 *E-mail:* publications@electrochem.org; customerservice@electrochem.org *Web Site:* www.electrochem.org, pg 80

Guenzi, Carol, Carol Guenzi Agents Inc, 865 Delaware St, Denver, CO 80204 *Tel:* 303-820-2599 *Toll Free Tel:* 800-417-5120 *Fax:* 303-820-2598 *E-mail:* info@artagent.com; art@artagent.com *Web Site:* www.artagent.com, pg 583

Guernsey, Sarah E, The Art Institute of Chicago, 111 S Michigan Ave, Chicago, IL 60603-6404 *Tel:* 312-443-3600; 312-443-3540 (pubns) *Fax:* 312-443-1334 (pubns) *Web Site:* www.artic.edu; www.artinstituteshop.org, pg 22

Guerra, Delin, Bogle International Library Travel Fund, 50 E Huron St, Chicago, IL 60611-2795 *Tel:* 312-280-3201 *Toll Free Tel:* 800-545-2433 (ext 3201) *Fax:* 312-280-4392 *E-mail:* intl@ala.org *Web Site:* www.ala.org, pg 673

Guerrieri, Pamela, Proofed to Perfection Editing Services, 4018 Summer Lane, Hillsborough, NC 27278 *Tel:* 919-732-8565 *E-mail:* inquiries@proofedtoperfection.com *Web Site:* www.proofedtoperfection.com, pg 533

Guerth, Jan-Erik, BlueBridge, PO Box 601, Katonah, NY 10536 *Tel:* 914-301-5901 *Web Site:* www.bluebridgebooks.com, pg 41

Guetebier, Amber, Red Wheel/Weiser/Conari, 65 Parker St, Suite 7, Newburyport, MA 01950 *Tel:* 978-465-0504 *Toll Free Tel:* 800-423-7087 (orders) *Fax:* 978-465-0243 *E-mail:* info@rwwbooks.com *Web Site:* www.redwheelweiser.com, pg 206

Guevara, Linda L, All About Kids Publishing, PO Box 159, Gilroy, CA 95020 *Tel:* 408-337-1866 *Fax:* 408-337-5192 *E-mail:* mail@aakp.com *Web Site:* www.aakp.com, pg 8

Guevara, Mike G, All About Kids Publishing, PO Box 159, Gilroy, CA 95020 *Tel:* 408-337-1866 *Fax:* 408-337-5192 *E-mail:* mail@aakp.com *Web Site:* www.aakp.com, pg 8

Guevin, John R, Biographical Publishing Co, 95 Sycamore Dr, Prospect, CT 06712-1011 *Tel:* 203-758-3661 *Fax:* 253-793-2618 *E-mail:* biopub@aol.com *Web Site:* www.biopub.us, pg 37

Guevremont, Diane, The North-South Institute (Institut Nord-Sud), 100 Argyle Ave, Suite 200, Ottawa, ON K2P 1B6, Canada *Tel:* 613-241-3535 *Fax:* 613-241-7435 *E-mail:* nsi@nsi-ins.ca *Web Site:* www.nsi-ins.ca, pg 493

Guibord, Maurice, BCHF Historial Writing Competition, PO Box 5254, Sta B, Victoria, BC V8R 6N4, Canada *E-mail:* writing@bchistory.ca *Web Site:* www.bchistory.ca, pg 670

Guido, Umberto III, Peter Glenn Publications, 306 NE Second St, 2nd fl, Delray Beach, FL 33483 *Tel:* 561-404-4290 *Fax:* 561-892-5786 *Web Site:* pgdirect.com, pg 97

Guidone, Kimberly, The Jennifer DeChiara Literary Agency, 31 E 32 St, Suite 300, New York, NY 10016 *Tel:* 212-481-8484 (ext 362) *Fax:* 212-481-9582 *Web Site:* www.jdlit.com, pg 547

Guilfoyle, Virginia, Federal Street Press, 25-13 Old Kings Hwy N, No 277, Darien, CT 06820 *Tel:* 203-852-1280 *Toll Free Tel:* 877-886-2830 *Fax:* 203-852-1389 *E-mail:* sales@federalstreetpress.com *Web Site:* www.federalstreetpress.com, pg 87

Guili, Lisa, Educational Insights, 152 W Walnut St, Suite 201, Gardena, CA 90248 *Toll Free Tel:* 800-995-4436 *Toll Free Fax:* 888-892-8731 *E-mail:* cs@educationalinsights.com *Web Site:* www.educationalinsights.com, pg 80

Guillemette-Bedard, Catherine, Ordre des traducteurs, terminologues et interpretes agrees du quebec, 2021 Union Ave, Suite 1108, Montreal, QC H3A 2S9,

Hackinson, Kevin, FJH Music Co Inc, 2525 Davie Rd, Suite 360, Fort Lauderdale, FL 33317-7424 *Tel:* 954-382-6061 *Toll Free Tel:* 800-262-8744 *Fax:* 954-382-3073 *E-mail:* custserv@fjhmusic.com; sales@fjhmusic.com *Web Site:* www.fjhmusic.com, pg 89

Hackinson, Kyle, FJH Music Co Inc, 2525 Davie Rd, Suite 360, Fort Lauderdale, FL 33317-7424 *Tel:* 954-382-6061 *Toll Free Tel:* 800-262-8744 *Fax:* 954-382-3073 *E-mail:* custserv@fjhmusic.com; sales@fjhmusic.com *Web Site:* www.fjhmusic.com, pg 89

Haddadian, Nola, International Development Research Centre (IDRC), 150 Kent St, Ottawa, ON K1P 0B2, Canada *Tel:* 613-236-6163 *Fax:* 613-238-7230 *E-mail:* info@idrc.ca *Web Site:* www.idrc.ca, pg 489

Haddock, Amy, WaterBrook Multnomah Publishing Group, 12265 Oracle Blvd, Suite 200, Colorado Springs, CO 80921 *Tel:* 719-590-4999 *Toll Free Tel:* 800-603-7051 (orders) *Fax:* 719-590-8977 *Toll Free Fax:* 800-294-5686 (orders) *E-mail:* info@waterbrookmultnomah.com *Web Site:* waterbrookmultnomah.com, pg 267

Haderer, Russell, BPA Worldwide, 100 Beard Sawmill Rd, 6th fl, Shelton, CT 06484 *Tel:* 203-447-2800 *Fax:* 203-447-2900 *E-mail:* info@bpaww.com *Web Site:* www.bpaww.com, pg 601

Hades, Brian, EDGE Science Fiction & Fantasy Publishing, PO Box 1714, Sta M, Calgary, AB T2P 2L7, Canada *Tel:* 403-254-0160 *Web Site:* www.edgewebsite.com, pg 479

Hadley, Candida, Fernwood Publishing, 32 Oceanvista Lane, Black Point, NS B0J 1B0, Canada *Tel:* 902-857-1388 *Fax:* 902-857-1328 *E-mail:* info@fernpub.ca; roseway@fernpub.ca *Web Site:* fernwoodpublishing.ca, pg 483

Hafftka, Michael, Six Gallery Press, PO Box 90145, Pittsburgh, PA 15224-0545 *Web Site:* www.sixgallerypress.com, pg 227

Hagan, Lisa, Lisa Hagan Literary, 110 Martin Dr, Bracey, VA 23919 *Tel:* 434-636-4138 *E-mail:* LisaHaganLiterary@yahoo.com *Web Site:* www.publishersmarketplace.com/members/LisaHagan/, pg 556

Hagan, Peter, Abrams Artists Agency, 275 Seventh Ave, 26th fl, New York, NY 10001 *Tel:* 646-486-4600 *Fax:* 646-486-2358 *E-mail:* literary@abramsartny.com *Web Site:* www.abramsartists.com, pg 539

Hagan, Peter, Dramatists Play Service Inc, 440 Park Ave S, New York, NY 10016 *Tel:* 212-683-8960 *Fax:* 212-213-1539 *E-mail:* postmaster@dramatists.com; orders@dramatists.com; publications@dramatists.com *Web Site:* www.dramatists.com, pg 77

Hagen, James, InterVarsity Press, 430 Plaza Dr, Westmont, IL 60559-1234 *Tel:* 630-734-4000 *Toll Free Tel:* 800-843-9487 *Fax:* 630-734-4200 *E-mail:* email@ivpress.com *Web Site:* www.ivpress.com, pg 125

Hagenberg, Mark, Perfection Learning Corp, 2680 Berkshire Pkwy, Clive, IA 50325 *Tel:* 515-278-0133 *Toll Free Tel:* 800-762-2999 *Fax:* 515-278-2980 *Web Site:* perfectionlearning.com, pg 189

Hagerbaumer, Samantha, HarperCollins Publishers, 195 Broadway, New York, NY 10007 *Tel:* 212-207-7000 *Fax:* 212-207-7145 *Web Site:* www.harpercollins.com, pg 106

Haggar, Darren, The Penguin Press, 375 Hudson St, New York, NY 10014, pg 187

Hagman, Lorri, University of Washington Press, 433 Brooklyn Ave NE, Seattle, WA 98195-9570 *Tel:* 206-543-4050 *Toll Free Tel:* 800-537-5487 (orders) *Fax:* 206-543-3932; 410-516-6998 (orders) *E-mail:* uwpress@u.washington.edu *Web Site:* www.washington.edu/uwpress/, pg 260

Hagood, Louis, Oxbridge® Communications Inc, 39 W 29 St, Suite 301, New York, NY 10001 *Tel:* 212-741-0231 *Toll Free Tel:* 800-955-0231 *Fax:* 212-633-2938 *E-mail:* info@oxbridge.com *Web Site:* www.oxbridge.com, pg 179

Hagood, Patricia, Oxbridge® Communications Inc, 39 W 29 St, Suite 301, New York, NY 10001 *Tel:* 212-741-0231 *Toll Free Tel:* 800-955-0231 *Fax:* 212-633-2938 *E-mail:* info@oxbridge.com *Web Site:* www.oxbridge.com, pg 179

Hague, Paige Stover Esq, Acanthus Publishing, 180 Lincoln St, 3rd fl, Boston, MA 02111 *Tel:* 617-230-2167 *Fax:* 617-995-0893 *E-mail:* info@acanthuspublishing.com *Web Site:* www.acanthuspublishing.com, pg 4

Hahn, Dr H George, Towson University Prize for Literature, English Dept, 8000 York Rd, Towson, MD 21252 *Tel:* 410-704-2000 *Fax:* 410-704-3999 *Web Site:* www.towson.edu/english, pg 732

Haidle, Micaela, McGraw-Hill Career Education, 1333 Burr Ridge Pkwy, Burr Ridge, IL 60527 *Tel:* 630-789-4000 *Toll Free Tel:* 800-338-3987 (cust serv) *Fax:* 630-789-5523; 614-755-5645 (cust serv) *Web Site:* www.mhhe.com, pg 150

Haigh, Liz, American Water Works Association (AWWA), 6666 W Quincy Ave, Denver, CO 80235 *Tel:* 303-794-7711 *Toll Free Tel:* 800-926-7337 *Fax:* 303-347-0804 *Web Site:* www.awwa.org, pg 17

Hairston, Ginia, WaterBrook Multnomah Publishing Group, 12265 Oracle Blvd, Suite 200, Colorado Springs, CO 80921 *Tel:* 719-590-4999 *Toll Free Tel:* 800-603-7051 (orders) *Fax:* 719-590-8977 *Toll Free Fax:* 800-294-5686 (orders) *E-mail:* info@waterbrookmultnomah.com *Web Site:* waterbrookmultnomah.com, pg 267

Halasz, Peter, SF Canada, 7433 E River Rd, Washago, ON L0K 2B0, Canada *Web Site:* www.sfcanada.org, pg 618

Hale, Charles, The MIT Press, 55 Hayward St, Cambridge, MA 02142 *Tel:* 617-253-5255 *Toll Free Tel:* 800-207-8354 (orders) *Fax:* 617-258-6779; 617-577-1545 (orders) *Web Site:* mitpress.mit.edu, pg 158

Hale, Nancy, Springer Publishing Co, 11 W 42 St, 15th fl, New York, NY 10036-8002 *Tel:* 212-431-4370 *Toll Free Tel:* 877-687-7476 *Fax:* 212-941-7842 *E-mail:* marketing@springerpub.com; cs@springerpub.com (orders); editorial@springerpub.com *Web Site:* www.springerpub.com, pg 232

Hales, Robert E MD, American Psychiatric Publishing (APP), 1000 Wilson Blvd, Suite 1825, Arlington, VA 22209 *Tel:* 703-907-7322 *Toll Free Tel:* 800-368-5777 *Fax:* 703-907-1091 *E-mail:* appi@psych.org *Web Site:* www.appi.org; www.psychiatryonline.org, pg 15

Haley, Annette Marie, Women's National Book Association Award, PO Box 237, FDR Sta, New York, NY 10150-0231 *Tel:* 212-208-4629 *Fax:* 212-208-4629 *E-mail:* publicity@bookbuzz.com *Web Site:* www.wnba-books.org; www.NationalReadingGroupMonth.org, pg 737

Haley, Ellen, CTB/McGraw-Hill, 20 Ryan Ranch Rd, Monterey, CA 93940-5703 *Tel:* 831-393-0700 *Toll Free Tel:* 800-538-9547 *Fax:* 831-393-7825 *Toll Free Fax:* 800-282-0266 *Web Site:* www.ctb.com, pg 69

Haley, Ellen, McGraw-Hill Education, 2 Penn Plaza, New York, NY 10121-2298 *Tel:* 212-904-2000 *E-mail:* customer.service@mcgraw-hill.com *Web Site:* www.mheducation.com; www.mheducation.com/custserv.html, pg 151

Haley, Elma, Arbordale Publishing, 612 Johnnie Dodds Blvd, Suite A2, Mount Pleasant, SC 29464 *Tel:* 843-971-6722 *Toll Free Tel:* 877-243-3457 *Fax:* 843-216-3804 *E-mail:* customerservice@arbordalepublishing.com; info@arbordalepublishing.com *Web Site:* www.arbordalepublishing.com, pg 21

Haley, Ryan, Ugly Duckling Presse, The Old American Can Factory, 232 Third St, Suite E002, Brooklyn, NY 11215 *Tel:* 347-948-5170 *E-mail:* udp_mailbox@yahoo.com; info@uglyducklingpresse.org *Web Site:* www.uglyducklingpresse.org, pg 252

Hall, Cindy, Pippin Publishing, 5201 Dufferin St, Toronto, ON M3H 5T8, Canada *Tel:* 416-667-8731; 426-667-7791 (CN warehouse) *Toll Free Tel:* 800-565-9523 (CN warehouse) *Fax:* 416-667-7832 *Toll Free Fax:* 800-221-9985 (CN warehouse) *E-mail:* utpbooks@utpress.utoronto.ca (CN warehouse) *Web Site:* www.utpguidancecentre.com, pg 495

Hall, Eric, The Rough Notes Co Inc, 11690 Technology Dr, Carmel, IN 46032-5600 *Tel:* 317-582-1600 *Toll Free Tel:* 800-428-4384 (cust serv) *Fax:* 317-816-1000 *Toll Free Fax:* 800-321-1909 *E-mail:* rnc@roughnotes.com *Web Site:* www.roughnotes.com, pg 211

Hall, Kevin, Society of American Business Editors & Writers Inc (SABEW), Walter Cronkite School of Journalism & Mass Communication, Arizona State University, 555 N Central Ave, Suite 406 E, Phoenix, AZ 85004-1248 *Tel:* 602-496-7862 *Fax:* 602-496-7041 *E-mail:* sabew@sabew.org *Web Site:* sabew.org, pg 619

Hall, Kit, Financial Executives Research Foundation Inc (FERF), West Tower, 7th fl, 1250 Headquarters Plaza, Morristown, NJ 07960-6837 *Tel:* 973-765-1000 *Fax:* 973-765-1023 *Web Site:* www.financialexecutives.org, pg 88

Hall, Laurie, US Government Publishing Office (GPO), Superintendent of Documents, 732 N Capitol St NW, Washington, DC 20401 *Tel:* 202-512-1800 *Toll Free Tel:* 866-512-1800 (orders) *Fax:* 202-512-2104 *E-mail:* contactcenter@gpo.gov *Web Site:* bookstore.gpo.gov (sales), pg 264

Hall, Linda, The Society of Professional Journalists (SPJ), Eugene S Pulliam National Journalism Ctr, 3909 N Meridian St, Indianapolis, IN 46208 *Tel:* 317-927-8000 *Fax:* 317-920-4789 *E-mail:* spj@spj.org *Web Site:* www.spj.org, pg 620

Hall, Marie, Fordham University Press, 2546 Belmont Ave, University Box L, Bronx, NY 10458 *Tel:* 718-817-4795 *Fax:* 718-817-4785 *Web Site:* www.fordhampress.com, pg 90

Hall, Megan, Athabasca University Press, Edmonton Learning Ctr, Peace Hills Trust Tower, 1200, 10011-109 St, Edmonton, AB T5J 3S8, Canada *Tel:* 780-497-3412 *Fax:* 780-421-3298 *E-mail:* aupress@athabascau.ca *Web Site:* www.aupress.ca, pg 472

Hall, Melissa, BOA Editions Ltd, 250 N Goodman St, Suite 306, Rochester, NY 14607 *Tel:* 585-546-3410 *Fax:* 585-546-3913 *E-mail:* contact@boaeditions.org *Web Site:* www.boaeditions.org, pg 41

Hall, Nancy, American Book Producers Association (ABPA), 31 W Eighth St, 2nd fl, New York, NY 10011 *Tel:* 212-675-1363 *Fax:* 212-675-1364 *E-mail:* office@abpaonline.org *Web Site:* www.abpaonline.org, pg 594

Hall, Mr Sidney Jr, Hobblebush Books, 17-A Old Milford Rd, Brookline, NH 03033 *Tel:* 603-672-4317 *Fax:* 603-672-4317 *E-mail:* hobblebush@charter.net; info@hobblebush.com *Web Site:* www.hobblebush.com, pg 112

Hall, Tanya, Greenleaf Book Group LLC, Three Park Place, 4005 Banister Lane, Suite B, Austin, TX 78704 *Tel:* 512-891-6100 *Toll Free Tel:* 800-932-5420 *Fax:* 512-891-6150 *E-mail:* contact@greenleafbookgroup.com *Web Site:* www.greenleafbookgroup.com, pg 100

Hall, Tina, Hamilton College, English/Creative Writing, English/Creative Writing Dept, 198 College Hill Rd, Clinton, NY 13323 *Tel:* 315-859-4370 *Fax:* 315-859-4390 *E-mail:* english@hamilton.edu *Web Site:* www.hamilton.edu, pg 660

Haller, Jennifer, Penguin Young Readers Group, 345 Hudson St, New York, NY 10014 *Tel:* 212-366-2000 *E-mail:* online@penguinputnam.com *Web Site:* www.penguinputnam.com; us.penguingroup.com, pg 187

Hallett, Flossie, W W Norton & Company Inc, 500 Fifth Ave, New York, NY 10110-0017 *Tel:* 212-354-5500 *Toll Free Tel:* 800-233-4830 (orders & cust serv) *Fax:* 212-869-0856 *Toll Free Fax:* 800-458-6515 *Web Site:* www.wwnorton.com, pg 172

Hallett, Heidi, Writers' Federation of Nova Scotia, 1113 Marginal Rd, Halifax, NS B3H 4P7, Canada *Tel:* 902-423-8116 *Fax:* 902-422-0881 *E-mail:* contact@writers.ns.ca *Web Site:* writers.ns.ca, pg 621

Hallett, Martha, Glitterati Inc, 630 Ninth Ave, Suite 603, New York, NY 10036 *Tel:* 212-362-9119 *Fax:* 646-607-4433 *E-mail:* info@glitteratiincorporated.com *Web Site:* glitteratiincorporated.com, pg 97

Halley, Brian, University of Massachusetts Press, East Experiment Sta, 671 N Pleasant St, Amherst, MA 01003 *Tel:* 413-545-2217 *Fax:* 413-545-1226 *E-mail:* info@umpress.umass.edu *Web Site:* www.umass.edu/umpress, pg 257

Hallinger, Linda Herr, Herr's Indexing Service, 76-340 Kealoha St, Kailua Kona, HI 96740 *Tel:* 808-365-4348 *E-mail:* lindahallinger@gmail.com *Web Site:* www.herrsindexing.com, pg 527

Hallock, Tom, Beacon Press, 24 Farnsworth St, Boston, MA 02210-1409 *Tel:* 617-742-2110 *Fax:* 617-723-3097; 617-742-2290 *Web Site:* www.beacon.org, pg 32

Halpern, Daniel, HarperCollins General Books Group, 195 Broadway, New York, NY 10007 *Tel:* 212-207-7000 *Web Site:* www.harpercollins.com, pg 105

Halpern, Eric, University of Pennsylvania Press, 3905 Spruce St, Philadelphia, PA 19104 *Tel:* 215-898-6261 *Fax:* 215-898-0404 *E-mail:* custserv@pobox.upenn.edu *Web Site:* www.pennpress.org, pg 259

Halseth, Kelly, Business Forms Management Association (BFMA), 1147 Fleetwood Ave, Madison, WI 53716 *Toll Free Tel:* 888-367-3078 *E-mail:* bfma@bfma.org *Web Site:* www.bfma.org, pg 601

Halverson, Amanda, Caxton Press, 312 Main St, Caldwell, ID 83605-3299 *Tel:* 208-459-7421 *Toll Free Tel:* 800-657-6465 *Fax:* 208-459-7450 *E-mail:* publish@caxtonpress.com *Web Site:* www.caxtonpress.com, pg 52

Halverson, Brianne, HarperCollins General Books Group, 195 Broadway, New York, NY 10007 *Tel:* 212-207-7000 *Web Site:* www.harpercollins.com, pg 105

Halverson, Pete, University Press of Mississippi, 3825 Ridgewood Rd, Jackson, MS 39211-6492 *Tel:* 601-432-6205 *Toll Free Tel:* 800-737-7788 (orders & cust serv) *Fax:* 601-432-6217 *E-mail:* press@mississippi.edu *Web Site:* www.upress.state.ms.us, pg 262

Halyard, Helen, Mehring Books Inc, PO Box 48377, Oak Park, MI 48237-5977 *Tel:* 248-967-2924 *Fax:* 248-967-3023 *E-mail:* sales@mehring.com *Web Site:* www.mehring.com, pg 154

Hamblen, Carol, The Johns Hopkins University Press, 2715 N Charles St, Baltimore, MD 21218-4363 *Tel:* 410-516-6900; 410-516-6987 (journal orders outside US & CN) *Toll Free Tel:* 800-537-5487 (book orders & cust serv); 800-548-1784 (journal orders) *Fax:* 410-516-6968; 410-516-3866 (journal orders) *E-mail:* hfscustserv@press.jhu.edu (cust serv); jrnlcirc@press.jhu.edu (journal orders) *Web Site:* www.press.jhu.edu; muse.jhu.edu, pg 127

Hames, Charles, New York University Press, 838 Broadway, 3rd fl, New York, NY 10003-4812 *Tel:* 212-998-2575 (edit) *Toll Free Tel:* 800-996-6987 (orders) *Fax:* 212-995-3833 (orders) *E-mail:* information@nyupress.org; customerservice@nyupress.org; orders@nyupress.org *Web Site:* www.nyupress.org, pg 169

Hamilburg, Michael, The Mitchell J Hamilburg Agency, 149 S Barrington Ave, Suite 732, Los Angeles, CA 90049 *Tel:* 310-471-4024 *Fax:* 310-471-9588, pg 556

Hamilton, Bonni, Hampton Roads Publishing Co, 65 Parker St, Suite 7, Newburyport, MA 01950-4600 *Tel:* 978-465-0504 *Toll Free Tel:* 800-423-7087 (orders) *Fax:* 978-465-0243 *Toll Free Fax:* 877-337-3309 *E-mail:* orders@rwwbooks.com *Web Site:* redwheelweiser.com, pg 104

Hamilton, Bonni, Red Wheel/Weiser/Conari, 65 Parker St, Suite 7, Newburyport, MA 01950 *Tel:* 978-465-0504 *Toll Free Tel:* 800-423-7087 (orders) *Fax:* 978-465-0243 *E-mail:* info@rwwbooks.com *Web Site:* www.redwheelweiser.com, pg 206

Hamilton, Carol, AAAI Press, 2275 E Bayshore Rd, Suite 160, Palo Alto, CA 94303 *Tel:* 650-328-3123 *Fax:* 650-321-4457 *E-mail:* publications14@aaai.org *Web Site:* www.aaaipress.org; www.aaai.org, pg 1

Hamilton, Dana, Harlequin Enterprises Ltd, 225 Duncan Mill Rd, Don Mills, ON M3B 3K9, Canada *Tel:* 416-445-5860 *Toll Free Tel:* 888-432-4879; 800-370-5838 (ebook inquiries) *E-mail:* customerservice@harlequin.com *Web Site:* www.harlequin.com, pg 487

Hamilton, David M, The Live Oak Press LLC, PO Box 60036, Palo Alto, CA 94306-0036 *Tel:* 650-853-0197 *Fax:* 815-366-8205 *E-mail:* info@liveoakpress.com *Web Site:* www.liveoakpress.com, pg 141

Hamilton, Emily, University of Minnesota Press, 111 Third Ave S, Suite 290, Minneapolis, MN 55401-2520 *Tel:* 612-627-1970 *Fax:* 612-627-1980 *E-mail:* ump@umn.edu *Web Site:* www.upress.umn.edu, pg 257

Hamilton, Julie, Insight Editions, 800 "A" St, San Rafael, CA 94901 *Tel:* 415-526-1370 *Toll Free Tel:* 800-809-3792 *Toll Free Fax:* 866-509-0515 *E-mail:* info@insighteditions.com *Web Site:* www.insighteditions.com, pg 122

Hamilton, Julie, Mandala Earth, 800 "A" St, San Rafael, CA 94901 *Tel:* 415-526-1370 *Toll Free Fax:* 866-509-0515 *E-mail:* info@mandalapublishing.com *Web Site:* www.mandalaeartheditions.com, pg 146

Hamilton, Michaela, Kensington Publishing Corp, 119 W 40 St, New York, NY 10018 *Tel:* 212-407-1500 *Toll Free Tel:* 800-221-2647 *Fax:* 212-935-0699 *Web Site:* www.kensingtonbooks.com, pg 130

Hamilton, Mike, AAAI Press, 2275 E Bayshore Rd, Suite 160, Palo Alto, CA 94303 *Tel:* 650-328-3123 *Fax:* 650-321-4457 *E-mail:* publications14@aaai.org *Web Site:* www.aaaipress.org; www.aaai.org, pg 1

Hamilton, Patricia, Park Place Publications, 591 Lighthouse Ave, Suite 10, Pacific Grove, CA 93950 *Tel:* 831-649-6640 *E-mail:* publishingbiz@sbcglobal.net *Web Site:* www.parkplacepublications.com, pg 183

Hamilton, Richard, XML Press, 24310 Moulton Pkwy, Suite O-175, Laguna Hills, CA 92637 *Tel:* 970-231-3624 *E-mail:* publisher@xmlpress.net *Web Site:* xmlpress.net, pg 277

Hamilton, Wade, Dayton Playhouse FutureFest, 1301 E Siebenthaler Ave, Dayton, OH 45414 *Tel:* 937-424-8477 *Fax:* 937-424-0062 *E-mail:* dp_futurefest@yahoo.com *Web Site:* www.daytonplayhouse.com, pg 680

Hamlin, Faith, Sanford J Greenburger Associates Inc, 55 Fifth Ave, New York, NY 10003 *Tel:* 212-206-5600 *Fax:* 212-463-8718 *Web Site:* greenburger.com; www.sjga.com/, pg 555

Hamlin, Kairi, Tanglewood Press, PO Box 3009, Terre Haute, IN 47803 *Tel:* 812-877-9488; 412-741-1579 (orders) *Toll Free Tel:* 800-836-4994 (orders) *Fax:* 412-741-0609 (orders) *Web Site:* www.tanglewoodbooks.com, pg 240

Hamm, Wanda K, Unicor Medical Inc, 4160 Carmichael Rd, Montgomery, AL 36106 *Tel:* 334-260-8150 *Toll Free Tel:* 800-825-7421 *Toll Free Fax:* 800-305-8030 *E-mail:* sales@unicormed.com *Web Site:* www.unicormed.com, pg 253

Hamma, Robert, Ave Maria Press, PO Box 428, Notre Dame, IN 46556 *Tel:* 574-287-2831 *Toll Free Tel:* 800-282-1865 *Fax:* 574-239-2904 *Toll Free Fax:* 800-282-5681 *E-mail:* avemariapress.1@nd.edu *Web Site:* www.avemariapress.com, pg 28

Hammack, Brice, Rutgers University Press, 106 Somerset St, 3rd fl, New Brunswick, NJ 08901 *Tel:* 848-445-7762 *Toll Free Tel:* 800-848-6224 (orders only) *Fax:* 732-745-4935 (acqs, edit, mktg, perms & prodn) *Toll Free Fax:* 800-272-6817 (fulfillment) *Web Site:* rutgerspress.rutgers.edu, pg 213

Hammer, Jacob, Samhain Publishing Ltd, 11821 Mason Montgomery Rd, Suite 4-B, Cincinnati, OH 45249 *Tel:* 513-453-4688 *Fax:* 513-583-0191 *E-mail:* support@samhainpublishing.com *Web Site:* www.samhainpublishing.com, pg 216

Hammer, Jennifer, New York University Press, 838 Broadway, 3rd fl, New York, NY 10003-4812 *Tel:* 212-998-2575 (edit) *Toll Free Tel:* 800-996-6987 (orders) *Fax:* 212-995-3833 (orders) *E-mail:* information@nyupress.org; customerservice@nyupress.org; orders@nyupress.org *Web Site:* www.nyupress.org, pg 169

Hammer, Steve, University of Missouri Press, 2910 Le Mone Blvd, Columbia, MO 65201 *Tel:* 573-882-7641 *Toll Free Tel:* 800-621-2736 (orders) *Fax:* 573-884-4498 *Web Site:* press.umsystem.edu, pg 257

Hammond, Dosier D, W W Norton & Company Inc, 500 Fifth Ave, New York, NY 10110-0017 *Tel:* 212-354-5500 *Toll Free Tel:* 800-233-4830 (orders & cust serv) *Fax:* 212-869-0856 *Toll Free Fax:* 800-458-6515 *Web Site:* www.wwnorton.com, pg 171

Hammond, Sarah, Trustus Playwrights' Festival, 520 Lady St, Columbia, SC 29201 *Tel:* 803-254-9732 *Fax:* 803-771-9153 *E-mail:* trustus@trustus.org *Web Site:* www.trustus.org, pg 732

Hamnes, Lisa, Skandisk Inc, 6667 W Old Shakapee Rd, Suite 109, Bloomington, MN 55438-2622 *Tel:* 952-829-8998 *Toll Free Tel:* 800-468-2424 *Fax:* 952-829-8992 *E-mail:* tomten@skandisk.com *Web Site:* www.skandisk.com, pg 227

Hamon, Donna L, Triad Publishing Co, PO Box 13355, Gainesville, FL 32604 *Tel:* 352-373-5800 *Fax:* 352-373-1488 *Toll Free Fax:* 800-854-4947 *E-mail:* orders@triadpublishing.com *Web Site:* www.triadpublishing.com, pg 249

Hampel, Matt, Bancroft Prizes, 517 Butler Library, Mail Code 1101, 535 W 114 St, New York, NY 10027 *Tel:* 212-854-4746 *Fax:* 212-854-9099 *Web Site:* www.columbia.edu/cu/lweb/eguides/amerihist/bancroft.html, pg 670

Hampton, Debra, John F Blair Publisher, 1406 Plaza Dr, Winston-Salem, NC 27103 *Tel:* 336-768-1374 *Toll Free Tel:* 800-222-9796 *Fax:* 336-768-9194 *Web Site:* www.blairpub.com, pg 39

Hamre, John J, The CSIS Press, 1616 Rhode Island Ave, Washington, DC 20036 *Tel:* 202-887-0200 *Fax:* 202-775-3199 *E-mail:* books@csis.org *Web Site:* www.csis.org, pg 69

Hamrick, Dave, University of Texas Press, 2100 Comal St, Austin, TX 78722 *Tel:* 512-471-7233 *Fax:* 512-232-7178 *E-mail:* utpress@uts.cc.utexas.edu *Web Site:* www.utexaspress.com, pg 244

Hamstra, Paul, Evergreen Pacific Publishing Ltd, 4204 Russell Rd, Suite M, Mukilteo, WA 98275-5424 *Tel:* 425-493-1451 *Fax:* 425-493-1453 *E-mail:* sales@evergreenpacific.com *Web Site:* www.evergreenpacific.com, pg 84

Hamza, Dr Mohamed H, ACTA Press, 2509 Dieppe Ave SW, Bldg B6, Suite 101, Calgary, AB T3E 7J9, Canada *Tel:* 403-288-1195 *Fax:* 403-247-6851 *E-mail:* journals@actapress.com; publish@actapress.com; sales@actapress.com *Web Site:* www.actapress.com, pg 471

Hamzah, M, AIC Publications, PO Box 181467, Arlington, TX 76002-1467 *E-mail:* submissions@aicpublications.com *Web Site:* aicpublications.com, pg 507

Hanas, Jim, HarperCollins General Books Group, 195 Broadway, New York, NY 10007 *Tel:* 212-207-7000 *Web Site:* www.harpercollins.com, pg 105

Hanas, Jim, HarperCollins Publishers, 195 Broadway, New York, NY 10007 *Tel:* 212-207-7000 *Fax:* 212-207-7145 *Web Site:* www.harpercollins.com, pg 106

Hancock, David, Hancock House Publishers, 4550 Birch Bay Lynden Rd, Suite 104, Blaine, WA 98230-5005 *Tel:* 604-538-1114 *Toll Free Tel:* 800-938-1114 *Fax:* 604-538-2262 *Toll Free Fax:* 800-983-2262 *E-mail:* sales@hancockhouse.com *Web Site:* www.hancockhouse.com, pg 104

Hancock, David, Hancock House Publishers Ltd, 19313 Zero Ave, Surrey, BC V3S 9R9, Canada *Tel:* 604-538-1114 *Toll Free Tel:* 800-938-1114 *Fax:* 604-538-2262 *Toll Free Fax:* 800-983-2262 *E-mail:* sales@hancockhouse.com *Web Site:* www.hancockhouse.com, pg 487

Hancock, David L, Morgan James Publishing, 5 Penn Plaza, 23rd fl, New York, NY 10001 *Tel:* 212-655-5470 *Toll Free Tel:* 800-485-4943 *Fax:* 516-908-4496 *E-mail:* csauer@morganjamespublishing.com *Web Site:* www.morganjamespublishing.com, pg 160

Handberg, Ryan, THE Learning Connection®, 4100 Silverstar Rd, Suite D, Orlando, FL 32808 *Tel:* 407-292-2125 *Toll Free Tel:* 800-218-8489 *Fax:* 407-292-2123 *E-mail:* tlc@tlconnection.com *Web Site:* www.tlconnection.com, pg 136

Hane, Erik, The Overlook Press, 141 Wooster St, Suite 4-B, New York, NY 10012 *Tel:* 212-673-2210; 845-679-6838 (orders & dist) *Fax:* 212-673-2296 *E-mail:* sales@overlookny.com (orders) *Web Site:* www.overlookpress.com, pg 178

Hanes, Peter, Flanker Press Ltd, 1243 Kenmount Rd, Unit A, Paradise, NL A1L 0V8, Canada *Tel:* 709-739-4477 *Toll Free Tel:* 866-739-4420 *Fax:* 709-739-4420 *E-mail:* info@flankerpress.com *Web Site:* www.flankerpress.com, pg 484

Hanesalo, Bruce A, Military Info Publishing, PO Box 41211, Plymouth, MN 55442 *Tel:* 763-533-8627 *Fax:* 763-533-8627 *E-mail:* publisher@military-info.com *Web Site:* www.military-info.com, pg 157

Hanford, Juliana, Kane Press Inc, 225 E 46 St, Suite 4D, New York, NY 10017-2924 *Tel:* 212-935-0246 *Web Site:* www.kanepress.com, pg 129

Hanger, Nancy C, Windhaven®, 466 Rte 10, Orford, NH 03777 *Tel:* 603-483-0929 *E-mail:* info@windhaven.com *Web Site:* www.windhaven.com, pg 535

Hanjian, Cassie, Waxman Leavell Literary Agency, 443 Park Ave S, No 1004, New York, NY 10016 *Tel:* 212-675-5556 *Fax:* 212-675-1381 *Web Site:* www.waxmanleavell.com, pg 579

Hankshaw, Hank, Two Thousand Three Associates, 4180 Saxon Dr, New Smyrna Beach, FL 32169 *Tel:* 386-690-2503 *E-mail:* ttta1@att.net *Web Site:* www.twothousandthree.com, pg 252

Hanna, Bill, Acacia House Publishing Services Ltd, 51 Chestnut Ave, Brantford, ON N3T 4C3, Canada *Tel:* 519-752-0978 *Fax:* 519-752-8349, pg 539

Hannan, Jack, McGill-Queen's University Press, 1010 Sherbrooke W, Suite 1720, Montreal, QC H3A 2R7, Canada *Tel:* 514-398-3750 *Fax:* 514-398-4333 *E-mail:* mqup@mqup.ca *Web Site:* www.mqup.ca, pg 491

Hannigan, Rosemarie, Research & Education Association (REA), 61 Ethel Rd W, Piscataway, NJ 08854 *Tel:* 732-819-8880 *Fax:* 732-819-8808 (orders) *E-mail:* info@rea.com *Web Site:* www.rea.com, pg 208

Hanning-Yu, Elizabeth, Allen A Knoll Publishers, 200 W Victoria St, Santa Barbara, CA 93101-3627 *Tel:* 805-564-3377 *Toll Free Tel:* 800-777-7623 *Fax:* 805-966-6657 *E-mail:* bookinfo@knollpublishers.com *Web Site:* www.knollpublishers.com, pg 132

Hanover, Kevin, Da Capo Press & Lifelong Books, 44 Farnsworth St, 3rd fl, Boston, MA 02210 *Tel:* 617-252-5200 *Toll Free Tel:* 800-343-4499 (orders) *Fax:* 617-252-5285 *Web Site:* www.perseusbooksgroup.com/dacapo, pg 69

Hansard, Patrick, American Psychiatric Publishing (APP), 1000 Wilson Blvd, Suite 1825, Arlington, VA 22209 *Tel:* 703-907-7322 *Toll Free Tel:* 800-368-5777 *Fax:* 703-907-1091 *E-mail:* appi@psych.org *Web Site:* www.appi.org; www.psychiatryonline.org, pg 15

Hansen, Anu, Purdue University Press, Stewart Ctr 370, 504 W State St, West Lafayette, IN 47907-2058 *Tel:* 765-494-2038 *Fax:* 765-496-2442 *E-mail:* pupress@purdue.edu *Web Site:* www.thepress.purdue.edu, pg 200

Hansen, Gary, Carolrhoda Books, 241 First Ave N, Minneapolis, MN 55401 *Tel:* 612-332-3344 *Toll Free Tel:* 800-328-4929 *Fax:* 612-332-7615 *Toll Free Fax:* 800-332-1132 *E-mail:* info@lernerbooks.com *Web Site:* www.lernerbooks.com, pg 50

Hansen, Gary, Carolrhoda Lab™, 241 First Ave N, Minneapolis, MN 55401 *Tel:* 612-332-3344 *Toll Free Tel:* 800-328-4929 *Fax:* 612-332-7615 *Toll Free Fax:* 800-332-1132 (US) *E-mail:* info@lernerbooks.com *Web Site:* www.lernerbooks.com, pg 51

Hansen, Gary, ediciones Lerner, 241 First Ave N, Minneapolis, MN 55401 *Tel:* 612-332-3344 *Toll Free Tel:* 800-328-4929 *Fax:* 612-332-7615 *Toll Free Fax:* 800-332-1132 *E-mail:* info@lernerbooks.com *Web Site:* www.lernerbooks.com, pg 79

Hansen, Gary, First Avenue Editions, 241 First Ave N, Minneapolis, MN 55401 *Tel:* 612-332-3344 *Toll Free Tel:* 800-328-4929 *Fax:* 612-332-7615 *Toll Free Fax:* 800-332-1132 *E-mail:* info@lernerbooks.com *Web Site:* www.lernerbooks.com, pg 89

Hansen, Gary, Graphic Universe™, 241 First Ave N, Minneapolis, MN 55401 *Tel:* 612-332-3344 *Toll Free Tel:* 800-328-4929 *Fax:* 612-332-7615 *Toll Free Fax:* 800-332-1132 *E-mail:* info@lernerbooks.com *Web Site:* www.lernerbooks.com, pg 99

Hansen, Gary, Lerner Publications, 241 First Ave N, Minneapolis, MN 55401 *Tel:* 612-332-3344 *Toll Free Tel:* 800-328-4929 *Fax:* 612-332-7615 *Toll Free Fax:* 800-332-1132 *E-mail:* info@lernerbooks.com *Web Site:* www.lernerbooks.com, pg 137

Hansen, Gary, Lerner Publishing Group Inc, 241 First Ave N, Minneapolis, MN 55401 *Tel:* 612-332-3344 *Toll Free Tel:* 800-328-4929 *Fax:* 612-332-7615 *Toll Free Fax:* 800-332-1132 *E-mail:* info@lernerbooks.com *Web Site:* www.lernerbooks.com, pg 137

Hansen, Gary, LernerClassroom, 241 First Ave N, Minneapolis, MN 55401 *Tel:* 612-332-3344 *Toll Free Tel:* 800-328-4929 *Fax:* 612-332-7615 *Toll Free Fax:* 800-332-1132 *E-mail:* info@lernerbooks.com *Web Site:* www.lernerbooks.com, pg 137

Hansen, Gary, Millbrook Press, 241 First Ave N, Minneapolis, MN 55401 *Tel:* 612-332-3344 *Toll Free Tel:* 800-328-4929 (US only) *Fax:* 612-332-7615 *Toll Free Fax:* 800-332-1132, pg 157

Hansen, Gary, Twenty-First Century Books, 241 First Ave N, Minneapolis, MN 55401 *Tel:* 612-332-3344 *Toll Free Tel:* 800-328-4929 *Fax:* 612-332-7615 *Toll Free Fax:* 800-332-1132 *E-mail:* info@lernerbooks.com *Web Site:* www.lernerbooks.com, pg 251

Hansen, Glenn J, BPA Worldwide, 100 Beard Sawmill Rd, 6th fl, Shelton, CT 06484 *Tel:* 203-447-2800 *Fax:* 203-447-2900 *E-mail:* info@bpaww.com *Web Site:* www.bpaww.com, pg 601

Hansen, Jill, ABDO Publishing Group, 8000 W 78 St, Suite 310, Edina, MN 55439 *Tel:* 952-831-2120 *Toll Free Tel:* 800-800-1312 *Toll Free Fax:* 800-862-3480 *E-mail:* customerservice@abdopublishing.com *Web Site:* abdopublishing.com, pg 2

Hansen, Karen, National Conference of State Legislatures (NCSL), 7700 E First Place, Denver, CO 80230 *Tel:* 303-364-7700 *Fax:* 303-364-7800 *E-mail:* books@ncsl.org *Web Site:* www.ncsl.org, pg 164

Hansen, Kathleen, Modern Language Association of America (MLA), 26 Broadway, 3rd fl, New York, NY 10004-1789 *Tel:* 646-576-5000 *Fax:* 646-458-0030 *Web Site:* www.mla.org, pg 158

Hansen, Michael, Cengage Learning, 20 Channel Center St, Boston, MA 02210 *Tel:* 617-289-7700 *Toll Free Tel:* 800-354-9706 *Fax:* 617-289-7844 *Toll Free Fax:* 800-487-8488 *E-mail:* esales@cengage.com *Web Site:* www.cengage.com, pg 53

Hansen, Mike, Hal Leonard Corp, 7777 W Bluemound Rd, Milwaukee, WI 53213 *Tel:* 414-774-3630 *Toll Free Tel:* 800-524-4425 *Fax:* 414-774-3259 *E-mail:* halinfo@halleonard.com *Web Site:* www.halleonard.com, pg 103

Hansen, Vaughne L, Virginia Kidd Agency Inc, 538 E Harford St, PO Box 278, Milford, PA 18337 *Tel:* 570-296-6205 *Web Site:* vk-agency.com, pg 559

Hanson, Andy, Illinois State Museum Society, 502 S Spring St, Springfield, IL 62706-5000 *Tel:* 217-782-7386 *Fax:* 217-782-1254 *E-mail:* editor@museum.state.il.us *Web Site:* www.museum.state.il.us, pg 119

Hanson, Erica, Yale Series of Younger Poets, 302 Temple St, New Haven, CT 06511 *Tel:* 203-432-0960 *Fax:* 203-432-0948 *Web Site:* www.yalebooks.com, pg 739

Hanson, Erica, Yale University Press, 302 Temple St, New Haven, CT 06511-8909 *Tel:* 203-432-0960; 203-432-0966 (sales); 401-531-2800 (cust serv) *Toll Free Tel:* 800-405-1619 (cust serv) *Fax:* 203-432-0948; 203-432-8485 (sales); 401-531-2801 (cust serv) *Toll Free Fax:* 800-406-9145 (cust serv) *E-mail:* sales.press@yale.edu (sales); customer.care@trilateral.org (cust serv) *Web Site:* www.yalebooks.com; yalepress.yale.edu/yupbooks, pg 278

Hanson, Kevin, Simon & Schuster Canada, 166 King St E, Suite 300, Toronto, ON M5A 1J3, Canada *Tel:* 647-427-8882 *Toll Free Tel:* 800-387-0446; 800-268-3216 (orders) *Fax:* 647-430-9446 *Toll Free Fax:* 888-849-8151 (orders) *E-mail:* info@simonandschuster.ca *Web Site:* www.simonandschuster.ca, pg 499

Hanson, Kevin, Simon & Schuster, Inc, 1230 Avenue of the Americas, New York, NY 10020 *Tel:* 212-698-7000 *Fax:* 212-698-7007 *E-mail:* firstname.lastname@simonandschuster.com *Web Site:* www.simonandschuster.com, pg 226

Hanson, Sarah, Sasquatch Books, 1904 S Main St, Suite 710, Seattle, WA 98101 *Tel:* 206-467-4300 *Toll Free Tel:* 800-775-0817 *Fax:* 206-467-4301 *E-mail:* custserv@sasquatchbooks.com *Web Site:* www.sasquatchbooks.com, pg 217

Hanson, Todd, Medical Physics Publishing Corp (MPP), 555 Helgesen Dr, Madison, WI 53718 *Tel:* 608-262-4021 *Toll Free Tel:* 800-442-5778 (cust serv) *E-mail:* mpp@medicalphysics.org *Web Site:* www.medicalphysics.org, pg 153

Hanstedt, Paul, The Roanoke Review Fiction Contest, 221 College Lane, Salem, VA 24153 *E-mail:* review@roanoke.edu *Web Site:* roanokereview.wordpress.com, pg 724

Haproff, David, Russell Sage Foundation, 112 E 64 St, New York, NY 10065 *Tel:* 212-750-6000 *Toll Free Tel:* 800-524-6401 *Fax:* 212-371-4761 *E-mail:* info@rsage.org *Web Site:* www.russellsage.org, pg 212

Har-zvi, Allison, Simon & Schuster, 1230 Avenue of the Americas, New York, NY 10020 *Tel:* 212-698-7000 *Toll Free Tel:* 800-223-2348 (cust serv); 800-223-2336 (orders) *Toll Free Fax:* 800-943-9831 (orders) *Web Site:* www.simonandschuster.com, pg 225

Harden, Mary, Dramatists Play Service Inc, 440 Park Ave S, New York, NY 10016 *Tel:* 212-683-8960 *Fax:* 212-213-1539 *E-mail:* postmaster@dramatists.com; orders@dramatists.com; publications@dramatists.com *Web Site:* www.dramatists.com, pg 77

Harding, Elizabeth, Curtis Brown Ltd, 10 Astor Place, New York, NY 10003 *Tel:* 212-473-5400 *Web Site:* www.curtisbrown.com, pg 544

Harding, Sandra, NAL, 375 Hudson St, New York, NY 10014 *Tel:* 212-366-2000 *E-mail:* online@penguinputnam.com *Web Site:* www.penguinputnam.com; us.penguingroup.com, pg 162

Hardman, Ron, Fox Run Press LLC, 7840 Bullet Rd, Peyton, OH 80831 *Tel:* 719-482-4035 *Fax:* 719-623-0254 *E-mail:* info@foxrunpress.com *Web Site:* www.foxrunpress.com, pg 91

Hardy, Lynn, Resilient Publishing, 406 S Third St, Boise, ID 83702 *Tel:* 208-258-9544 *E-mail:* submissions@resilientpublishing.com *Web Site:* www.resilientpublishing.com, pg 208

Hare, Robbie Anna, Goldfarb & Associates, 721 Gibbon St, Alexandria, VA 22314 *Tel:* 202-466-3030 *Fax:* 703-836-5644 *E-mail:* rglawlit@gmail.com *Web Site:* www.ronaldgoldfarb.com, pg 554

Harkins, Ann M, National Crime Prevention Council, 2001 Jefferson Davis Hwy, Suite 901, Arlington, VA 22202 *Tel:* 202-466-6272 *Fax:* 202-296-1356 *E-mail:* ncpc@fulfills.org (orders) *Web Site:* www.ncpc.org, pg 164

Harland, Cisco, Water Row Press, PO Box 438, Sudbury, MA 01776 *Tel:* 508-485-8515 *Fax:* 508-229-0885 *E-mail:* contact@waterrowbooks.com *Web Site:* www.waterrowbooks.com, pg 267

Harlow, Hannah, Houghton Mifflin Harcourt, 222 Berkeley St, Boston, MA 02116 *Tel:* 617-351-5000 *Toll Free Tel:* 800-225-5425 (K-12 educ materials); 800-323-9540 (assessment materials); 877-219-1537 (SkillsTutor); 888-242-6747 (Destination;

Harting, Laurie, Palgrave Macmillan, 175 Fifth Ave, Suite 200, New York, NY 10010 *Tel:* 646-307-5151 *Fax:* 212-777-6359 *E-mail:* firstname.lastname@palgrave-usa.com *Web Site:* us.macmillan.com/Palgrave.aspx, pg 180

Hartjens, Elisabeth M, Imagefinders Inc, 6101 Utah Ave NW, Washington, DC 20015 *Tel:* 202-244-4456 *Fax:* 202-244-3237, pg 528

Hartley, Glen, Writers' Representatives LLC, 116 W 14 St, 11th fl, New York, NY 10011-7305 *Tel:* 212-620-9009 *Fax:* 212-620-0023 *E-mail:* transom@writersreps.com *Web Site:* www.writersreps.com, pg 580

Hartley, John, Peter Pauper Press, Inc, 202 Mamaroneck Ave, White Plains, NY 10601-5376 *Tel:* 914-681-0144 *Fax:* 914-681-0389 *E-mail:* customerservice@peterpauper.com; orders@peterpauper.com *Web Site:* www.peterpauper.com, pg 190

Hartley, Rodger, South Dakota Historical Society Press, 900 Governors Dr, Pierre, SD 57501 *Tel:* 605-773-6009 *Fax:* 605-773-6041 *E-mail:* info@sdshspress.com *Web Site:* sdshspress.com, pg 231

Hartline, Connie, American Public Works Association (APWA), 2345 Grand Blvd, Suite 700, Kansas City, MO 64108-2625 *Tel:* 816-472-6100 *Toll Free Tel:* 800-848-APWA (848-2792) *Fax:* 816-472-1610 *Web Site:* www.apwa.net, pg 15

Hartman, Charles, National Council of Teachers of English (NCTE), 1111 W Kenyon Rd, Urbana, IL 61801-1096 *Tel:* 217-328-3870 *Toll Free Tel:* 877-369-6283 (cust serv) *Fax:* 217-328-9645 *E-mail:* orders@ncte.org *Web Site:* www.ncte.org, pg 164

Hartman, Dorothy, Herald Press, 50 Kent Ave, Suite 204, Kitchener, ON N2G 3R1, Canada *Tel:* 519-747-5722 (US) *Toll Free Tel:* 800-631-6535 (CN) *Fax:* 519-747-5721 *E-mail:* hpcan@mpn.net *Web Site:* www.heraldpress.com, pg 487

Hartman, Janell, The Newspaper Guild, 501 Third St NW, 6th fl, Washington, DC 20001-2797 *Tel:* 202-434-7177; 202-434-7162 (The Guild Reporter) *Fax:* 202-434-1472 *E-mail:* guild@cwa-union.org *Web Site:* www.newsguild.org, pg 614

Hartman, Mark, Hartman Publishing Inc, 1313 Iron Ave SW, Albuquerque, NM 87102 *Tel:* 505-291-1274 *Toll Free Tel:* 800-999-9534 *Fax:* 505-291-1284 *Toll Free Fax:* 800-474-6106 *E-mail:* orders@hartmanonline.com; help@hartmanonline.com *Web Site:* www.hartmanonline.com, pg 106

Hartman, William, Quintessence Publishing Co Inc, 4350 Chandler Dr, Hanover Park, IL 60133 *Tel:* 630-736-3600 *Toll Free Tel:* 800-621-0387 *Fax:* 630-736-3633 *E-mail:* contact@quintbook.com; service@quintbook.com *Web Site:* www.quintpub.com, pg 202

Hartnett, Laura, The Ralph Waldo Emerson Award, 1606 New Hampshire Ave NW, Washington, DC 20009 *Tel:* 202-265-3808 *Fax:* 202-986-1601 *E-mail:* awards@pbk.org *Web Site:* www.pbk.org/bookawards, pg 684

Hartnett, Laura, The Christian Gauss Award, 1606 New Hampshire Ave NW, Washington, DC 20009 *Tel:* 202-265-3808 *Fax:* 202-986-1601 *E-mail:* awards@pbk.org *Web Site:* www.pbk.org/bookawards, pg 688

Hartnett, Laura, Phi Beta Kappa Award in Science, 1606 New Hampshire Ave NW, Washington, DC 20009 *Tel:* 202-265-3808 *Fax:* 202-986-1601 *E-mail:* awards@pbk.org *Web Site:* www.pbk.org/bookawards, pg 718

Hartogh, Frances, Rocky Mountain Mineral Law Foundation, 9191 Sheridan Blvd, Suite 203, Westminister, CO 80031 *Tel:* 303-321-8100 *Fax:* 303-321-7657 *E-mail:* info@rmmlf.org *Web Site:* www.rmmlf.org, pg 210

Hartson, Kate, Hachette Nashville, 12 Cadillac Dr, Suite 480, Brentwood, TN 37027 *Tel:* 615-221-0996 *Fax:* 615-221-0962 *Web Site:* www.hachettebookgroup.com, pg 103

Harty, Pamela, The Knight Agency Inc, 570 East Ave, Madison, GA 30650 *E-mail:* submissions@knightagency.net *Web Site:* www.knightagency.net, pg 560

Harvey, Dr Alan, Stanford University Press, 1450 Page Mill Rd, Palo Alto, CA 94304-1124 *Tel:* 650-723-9434 *Fax:* 650-725-3457 *E-mail:* info@sup.org *Web Site:* www.sup.org, pg 233

Harvey, Damien, Quackenworth Publishing, PO Box 4747, Culver City, CA 90231-4747 *Tel:* 310-945-5634 *Toll Free Tel:* 888-701-4991 *Fax:* 310-945-5709 *Toll Free Fax:* 888-892-6339 *E-mail:* info@quackenworth.com *Web Site:* www.quackenworth.com; www.wittybittybunch.com, pg 201

Harwell, Andrew, HarperCollins Children's Books, 195 Broadway, New York, NY 10007 *Tel:* 212-207-7000 *Web Site:* www.harpercollins.com/childrens, pg 105

Harwell, Sarah C, Syracuse University Creative Writing Program, 401 Hall of Languages, Syracuse, NY 13244-1170 *Tel:* 315-443-2173 *Fax:* 315-443-3660 *Web Site:* english.syr.edu/creative_writing; www.syr.edu, pg 662

Harwood, Josh, Houghton Mifflin Harcourt Trade & Reference Division, 222 Berkeley St, Boston, MA 02116 *Tel:* 617-351-5000 *Toll Free Tel:* 800-225-3362 *Web Site:* www.hmhco.com, pg 115

Hasan, Syed, Springer, 233 Spring St, New York, NY 10013-1578 *Tel:* 212-460-1500 *Toll Free Tel:* 800-SPRINGER (777-4643) *Fax:* 212-460-1575 *E-mail:* service-ny@springer.com *Web Site:* www.springer.com, pg 232

Haskell, Arlo, Key West Literary Seminar, 718 Love Lane, Key West, FL 33040 *Toll Free Tel:* 888-293-9291 *E-mail:* mail@kwls.org *Web Site:* www.kwls.org, pg 652

Hass, Robert, Squaw Valley Community of Writers Summer Workshops, PO Box 1416, Nevada City, CA 95959 *Tel:* 530-470-8440 *E-mail:* info@squawvalleywriters.org *Web Site:* www.squawvalleywriters.org, pg 656

Hassan, Shannon, Marsal Lyon Literary Agency LLC, 665 San Rodolfo Dr, Suite 124, PMB 121, Solana Beach, CA 92075 *Tel:* 760-814-8507 *Web Site:* www.marsallyonliteraryagency.com, pg 563

Hasselberger, Rich, Berkley Books, 375 Hudson St, New York, NY 10014 *Tel:* 212-366-2000 *Fax:* 212-366-2666 *E-mail:* online@penguinputnam.com *Web Site:* www.penguinputnam.com; us.penguingroup.com, pg 35

Hasselberger, Rich, Berkley Publishing Group, 375 Hudson St, New York, NY 10014 *Tel:* 212-366-2000 *Fax:* 212-366-2385 *E-mail:* online@penguinputnam.com *Web Site:* us.penguingroup.com, pg 35

Hasselberger, Rich, Dutton, 375 Hudson St, New York, NY 10014 *Tel:* 212-366-2000 *Fax:* 212-366-2262 *E-mail:* online@penguinputnam.com *Web Site:* www.penguinputnam.com; us.penguingroup.com, pg 78

Hasselberger, Rich, NAL, 375 Hudson St, New York, NY 10014 *Tel:* 212-366-2000 *E-mail:* online@penguinputnam.com *Web Site:* www.penguinputnam.com; us.penguingroup.com, pg 162

Hasselberger, Rich, GP Putnam's Sons (Hardcover), 375 Hudson St, New York, NY 10014 *Tel:* 212-366-2000 *E-mail:* online@penguinputnam.com *Web Site:* us.penguingroup.com, pg 201

Hasselstrom, Linda M, Windbreak House Writing Retreat, PO Box 169, Hermosa, SD 57744-0169 *Tel:* 605-255-4064 *E-mail:* info@windbreakhouse.com *Web Site:* www.windbreakhouse.com, pg 656

Hassler, Kurt, Orbit, 1290 Avenue of the Americas, New York, NY 10019 *Tel:* 212-364-1100 *Toll Free Tel:* 800-759-0190 *Web Site:* www.orbitbooks.net, pg 176

Hassman, Chelsea, Random House Children's Books, 1745 Broadway, New York, NY 10019 *Tel:* 212-782-9000 *Toll Free Tel:* 800-200-3552 *Fax:* 212-782-9452 *Web Site:* randomhousekids.com, pg 204

Hasso, M (May) H, Boston Informatics, 35 Byard Lane, Westborough, MA 01581 *Tel:* 508-366-8176 *Web Site:* www.bostoninformatics.com, pg 522

Hastings, Deborah, Federal Street Press, 25-13 Old Kings Hwy N, No 277, Darien, CT 06820 *Tel:* 203-852-1280 *Toll Free Tel:* 877-886-2830 *Fax:* 203-852-1389 *E-mail:* sales@federalstreetpress.com *Web Site:* www.federalstreetpress.com, pg 87

Hastings, Katherine, Susquehanna University, Department of English, 514 University Ave, Selinsgrove, PA 17870 *Tel:* 570-372-0101, pg 662

Hatch, James C, Committee On Scholarly Editions, c/o Modern Language Association of America, 26 Broadway, 3rd fl, New York, NY 10004-1789 *Tel:* 646-576-5044 *Fax:* 646-458-0030 *Web Site:* www.mla.org, pg 603

Hatch, Ronald, Ronsdale Press Ltd, 3350 W 21 Ave, Vancouver, BC V6S 1G7, Canada *Tel:* 604-738-4688 *Fax:* 604-731-4548 *E-mail:* ronsdale@shaw.ca *Web Site:* ronsdalepress.com, pg 497

Hatch, Veronica, Ronsdale Press Ltd, 3350 W 21 Ave, Vancouver, BC V6S 1G7, Canada *Tel:* 604-738-4688 *Fax:* 604-731-4548 *E-mail:* ronsdale@shaw.ca *Web Site:* ronsdalepress.com, pg 497

Hatcher, Lori, Urban Land Institute, 1025 Thomas Jefferson St NW, Suite 500-W, Washington, DC 20007 *Tel:* 202-624-7000 *Toll Free Tel:* 800-321-5011 (cust serv) *Fax:* 410-626-7140 *E-mail:* bookstore@uli.org; customerservice@uli.org *Web Site:* www.uli.org/books, pg 263

Hatter, Richard W, John Simon Guggenheim Memorial Foundation, 90 Park Ave, New York, NY 10016 *Tel:* 212-687-4470 *Fax:* 212-697-3248 *E-mail:* fellowships@gf.org *Web Site:* www.gf.org, pg 623

Hatton, Valerie, Firefly Books Ltd, 50 Staples Ave, Unit 1, Richmond Hill, ON L4B 0A7, Canada *Tel:* 416-499-8412 *Toll Free Tel:* 800-387-6192 (CN); 800-387-5085 (US) *Fax:* 416-499-8313 *Toll Free Fax:* 800-450-0391 (CN); 800-565-6034 (US) *E-mail:* service@fireflybooks.com *Web Site:* www.fireflybooks.com, pg 484

Hauber, Janine, Sheldon Fogelman Agency Inc, 10 E 40 St, Suite 3205, New York, NY 10016 *Tel:* 212-532-7250 *Fax:* 212-685-8939 *E-mail:* info@sheldonfogelmanagency.com *Web Site:* sheldonfogelmanagency.com, pg 552

Haubner, Julianna, Simon & Schuster, 1230 Avenue of the Americas, New York, NY 10020 *Tel:* 212-698-7000 *Toll Free Tel:* 800-223-2348 (cust serv); 800-223-2336 (orders) *Toll Free Fax:* 800-943-9831 (orders) *Web Site:* www.simonandschuster.com, pg 225

Hauck, Michael T, DEStech Publications Inc, 439 N Duke St, Lancaster, PA 17602-4967 *Tel:* 717-290-1660 *Toll Free Tel:* 877-500-4337 *Fax:* 717-509-6100 *E-mail:* info@destechpub.com *Web Site:* www.destechpub.com, pg 73

Haughian, Karen, Signature Editions, RPO Corydon, PO Box 206, Winnipeg, MB R3M 3S7, Canada *Tel:* 204-779-7803 *Fax:* 204-779-6970 *E-mail:* signature@allstream.net; orders@signature-editions.com *Web Site:* www.signature-editions.com, pg 499

Haught, Robert, National Society of Newspaper Columnists Annual Conference, 1345 Fillmore St, Suite 507, San Francisco, CA 94115 *Tel:* 415-488-NCNC (488-6762) *Toll Free Tel:* 866-440-NSNC (440-6762) *Fax:* 484-297-0336 *Toll Free Fax:* 866-635-5759 *Web Site:* www.columnists.com, pg 653

Haupt, Jonathan, University of South Carolina Press, 1600 Hampton St, Suite 544, Columbia, SC 29208 *Tel:* 803-777-5245 *Toll Free Tel:* 800-768-2500 (orders) *Fax:* 803-777-0160 *Toll Free Fax:* 800-868-0740 (orders) *Web Site:* www.sc.edu/uscpress, pg 259

Haut, Judith, Random House Children's Books, 1745 Broadway, New York, NY 10019 *Tel:* 212-782-9000 *Toll Free Tel:* 800-200-3552 *Fax:* 212-782-9452 *Web Site:* randomhousekids.com, pg 203

Haven, Dr Stephen, Ashland Poetry Press, Ashland University, 401 College Ave, Ashland, OH 44805 *Tel:* 419-289-5957 *Fax:* 419-289-5255 *E-mail:* app@ashland.edu *Web Site:* www.ashland.edu/aupoetry, pg 24

Havlish, Sue, Vanderbilt University Press, 2014 Broadway, Suite 320, Nashville, TN 37203 *Tel:* 615-322-3585 *Toll Free Tel:* 800-627-7377 (orders only) *Fax:* 615-343-8823 *Toll Free Fax:* 800-735-0476 (orders only) *E-mail:* vupress@vanderbilt.edu *Web Site:* www.vanderbiltuniversitypress.com, pg 264

Hawk, David, Ten Speed Press, 2625 Alcatraz Ave, Unit 505, Berkeley, CA 94705 *Tel:* 510-285-3000 *Toll Free Tel:* 800-841-BOOK (841-2665) *E-mail:* csorders@randomhouse.com *Web Site:* crownpublishing.com/imprint/ten-speed-press, pg 243

Hawkins, Anne, John Hawkins and Associates Inc, 71 W 23 St, Suite 1600, New York, NY 10010 *Tel:* 212-807-7040 *E-mail:* jha@jhalit.com *Web Site:* jhalit.com, pg 556

Hawkins, Bob Jr, Harvest House Publishers Inc, 990 Owen Loop N, Eugene, OR 97402-9173 *Tel:* 541-343-0123 *Toll Free Tel:* 888-501-6991 *Fax:* 541-342-6410 *E-mail:* admin@harvesthousepublishers.com *Web Site:* harvesthousepublishers.com, pg 107

Hawkins, Drew, Canadian Scholars' Press Inc, 425 Adelaide St W, Suite 200, Toronto, ON M5V 3C1, Canada *Tel:* 416-929-2774 *Toll Free Tel:* 800-463-1998 *Fax:* 416-929-1926 *E-mail:* info@cspi.org; editorial@cspi.org; orders@cspi.org *Web Site:* www.cspi.org; womenspress.cspi.org, pg 476

Hawkins, Janet, Trillium Book Award/Prix Trillium, South Tower, Suite 501, 175 Bloor St E, Toronto, ON M4W 3R8, Canada *Tel:* 416-314-6858 (ext 698) *Fax:* 416-314-6876 *E-mail:* trillium23@omdc.on.ca *Web Site:* www.omdc.on.ca, pg 732

Hawkins, Luvenia J, National Council on Radiation Protection & Measurements (NCRP), 7910 Woodmont Ave, Suite 400, Bethesda, MD 20814-3095 *Tel:* 301-657-2652 *Toll Free Tel:* 800-229-2652 *Fax:* 301-907-8768 *E-mail:* ncrppubs@ncrponline.org *Web Site:* www.ncrponline.org; www.ncrppublications.org, pg 164

Hawkins, Valerie, The American Library Association (ALA), 50 E Huron St, Chicago, IL 60611 *Tel:* 312-944-6780; 312-280-4299 (memb & cust serv) *Toll Free Tel:* 800-545-2433 *Fax:* 312-440-9374 *E-mail:* ala@ala.org; customerservice@ala.org *Web Site:* www.ala.org, pg 595

Hawley, Marcy, Orange Frazer Press Inc, 37 1/2 W Main St, Wilmington, OH 45177 *Tel:* 937-382-3196 *Toll Free Tel:* 800-852-9332 (orders) *Fax:* 937-383-3159 *E-mail:* ofrazer@erinet.com *Web Site:* www.orangefrazer.com, pg 176

Hawley, Sarah, Orange Frazer Press Inc, 37 1/2 W Main St, Wilmington, OH 45177 *Tel:* 937-382-3196 *Toll Free Tel:* 800-852-9332 (orders) *Fax:* 937-383-3159 *E-mail:* ofrazer@erinet.com *Web Site:* www.orangefrazer.com, pg 176

Hay, Louise L, Hay House Inc, 2776 Loker Ave W, Carlsbad, CA 92010 *Tel:* 760-431-7695 (ext 2, intl) *Toll Free Tel:* 800-654-5126 (ext 2, US) *Toll Free Fax:* 800-650-5115 *E-mail:* info@hayhouse.com; editorial@hayhouse.com *Web Site:* www.hayhouse.com, pg 108

Hayden, Amy L, Seven Stories Press, 140 Watts St, New York, NY 10013 *Tel:* 212-226-8760 *Toll Free Tel:* 800-733-3000 (orders) *Fax:* 212-226-1411 *E-mail:* info@sevenstories.com *Web Site:* www.sevenstories.com, pg 222

Hayden, Cynthia, Lake Superior Port Cities Inc, 310 E Superior St, Suite 125, Duluth, MN 55802 *Tel:* 218-722-5002 *Toll Free Tel:* 888-BIG-LAKE (244-5253) *Fax:* 218-722-4096 *E-mail:* reader@lakesuperior.com *Web Site:* www.lakesuperior.com, pg 134

Hayden, Patrick Nielsen, Tom Doherty Associates, LLC, 175 Fifth Ave, 14th fl, New York, NY 10010 *Tel:* 646-307-5151 *Toll Free Tel:* 800-455-0340 *Fax:* 212-388-0191 *E-mail:* firstname.lastname@tor.com *Web Site:* www.tor-forge.com, pg 75

Hayden, Paul L, Lake Superior Port Cities Inc, 310 E Superior St, Suite 125, Duluth, MN 55802 *Tel:* 218-722-5002 *Toll Free Tel:* 888-BIG-LAKE (244-5253) *Fax:* 218-722-4096 *E-mail:* reader@lakesuperior.com *Web Site:* www.lakesuperior.com, pg 134

Hayden, Thomas K, National Notary Association (NNA), 9350 De Soto Ave, Chatsworth, CA 91311 *Tel:* 818-739-4000 *Toll Free Tel:* 800-876-6827 *Toll Free Fax:* 800-833-1211 *E-mail:* nna@nationalnotary.org *Web Site:* www.nationalnotary.org, pg 165

Haydis, Bill, Oxford University Press USA, 198 Madison Ave, New York, NY 10016 *Tel:* 212-726-6000 *Toll Free Tel:* 800-451-7556 (orders); 800-445-9714 (cust serv) *Fax:* 919-677-1303 *E-mail:* custserv.us@oup.com *Web Site:* www.oup.com/us, pg 179

Haydon, Roger, Cornell University Press, Sage House, 512 E State St, Ithaca, NY 14850 *Tel:* 607-277-2338 *Fax:* 607-277-2374 *E-mail:* cupressinfo@cornell.edu; cupress-sales@cornell.edu *Web Site:* www.cornellpress.cornell.edu, pg 63

Hayes, Kevin, Omnigraphics Inc, 155 W Congress, Suite 200, Detroit, MI 48226 *Tel:* 313-961-1340 *Toll Free Tel:* 800-234-1340 (cust serv) *Fax:* 313-961-1383 *Toll Free Fax:* 800-875-1340 (cust serv) *E-mail:* info@omnigraphics.com *Web Site:* www.omnigraphics.com, pg 175

Hayes, Regina, Viking Children's Books, 345 Hudson St, New York, NY 10014 *Tel:* 212-366-2000 *E-mail:* online@penguinputnam.com *Web Site:* www.penguinputnam.com; us.penguingroup.com, pg 265

Hayes, Ryan, Chronicle Books LLC, 680 Second St, San Francisco, CA 94107 *Tel:* 415-537-4200 *Toll Free Tel:* 800-759-0190 (cust serv) *Fax:* 415-537-4460 *Toll Free Fax:* 800-858-7787 (orders); 800-286-9471 (cust serv) *E-mail:* frontdesk@chroniclebooks.com *Web Site:* www.chroniclebooks.com, pg 58

Hayes, Todd, Oxford University Press USA, 198 Madison Ave, New York, NY 10016 *Tel:* 212-726-6000 *Toll Free Tel:* 800-451-7556 (orders); 800-445-9714 (cust serv) *Fax:* 919-677-1303 *E-mail:* custserv.us@oup.com *Web Site:* www.oup.com/us, pg 179

Hayes, William F, Poets & Writers Inc, 90 Broad St, Suite 2100, New York, NY 10004 *Tel:* 212-226-3586 *Fax:* 212-226-3963 *E-mail:* admin@pw.org *Web Site:* www.pw.org, pg 616

Hayford, Chuck, EastBridge, 70 New Canaan Ave, Norwalk, CT 06850 *Tel:* 203-855-9125 *Fax:* 203-857-0730 *E-mail:* asia@eastbridgebooks.org; ask@eastbridgebooks.org *Web Site:* www.eastbridgebooks.org, pg 78

Haynes, J, Haynes Manuals Inc, 861 Lawrence Dr, Newbury Park, CA 91320 *Tel:* 805-498-6703 *Toll Free Tel:* 800-4-HAYNES (442-9637) *Fax:* 805-498-2867 *E-mail:* cstn@haynes.com *Web Site:* www.haynes.com, pg 108

Haynes, John, American Institute of Physics, 1305 Walt Whitman Rd, Suite 300, Melville, NY 11747 *Tel:* 516-576-2200; 301-209-3165 (orders) *Fax:* 301-209-0882 (orders) *E-mail:* aipinfo@aip.org *Web Site:* www.aip.org, pg 13

Hays, Carisa, Crown Publishing Group, c/o Penguin Random House Inc, 1745 Broadway, New York, NY 10019 *Tel:* 212-782-9000 *Toll Free Tel:* 888-264-1745 *Fax:* 212-940-7408 *E-mail:* crownosm@penguinrandomhouse.com *Web Site:* crownpublishing.com, pg 68

Hays, Chris, Jackie White Memorial National Children's Playwriting Contest, 1400 Forum Blvd, 1C No 214, Columbia, MO 65203 *E-mail:* jwmcontest@cectheatre.org *Web Site:* www.cectheatre.org, pg 696

Hays, John, Bear & Co Inc, One Park St, Rochester, VT 05767 *Tel:* 802-767-3174 *Toll Free Tel:* 800-932-3277 *Fax:* 802-767-3726 *E-mail:* customerservice@InnerTraditions.com *Web Site:* InnerTraditions.com, pg 33

Hays, John, Inner Traditions International Ltd, One Park St, Rochester, VT 05767 *Tel:* 802-767-3174 *Toll Free Tel:* 800-246-8648 *Fax:* 802-767-3726 *E-mail:* customerservice@InnerTraditions.com *Web Site:* www.InnerTraditions.com, pg 122

Hays, Michael, McGraw-Hill Higher Education, 1333 Burr Ridge Pkwy, Burr Ridge, IL 60527 *Tel:* 630-789-4000 *Toll Free Tel:* 800-338-3987 (cust serv) *Fax:* 614-755-5645 (cust serv) *Web Site:* www.mhhe.com, pg 151

Hayskar, Bonnie, Pangaea Publications, 226 Wheeler St S, St Paul, MN 55105-1927 *Tel:* 651-226-2032 *Fax:* 651-226-2032 *E-mail:* info@pangaea.org *Web Site:* pangaea.org, pg 181

Hayward, Thomas, Professional Publications Inc (PPI), 1250 Fifth Ave, Belmont, CA 94002 *Tel:* 650-593-9119 *Fax:* 650-592-4519 *E-mail:* info@ppi2pass.com *Web Site:* ppi2pass.com; feprep.com, pg 198

Haywood, Samantha, Transatlantic Agency, 2 Bloor St E, Suite 3500, Toronto, ON M4W 1A8, Canada *Tel:* 416-488-9214 *E-mail:* info@transatlanticagency.com *Web Site:* www.transatlanticagency.com, pg 577

Heacock, Kait, The Feminist Press at The City University of New York, 365 Fifth Ave, Suite 5406, New York, NY 10016 *Tel:* 212-817-7915 *Fax:* 212-817-1593 *E-mail:* info@feministpress.org *Web Site:* www.feministpress.org, pg 87

Head, Albert B, Alabama Artists Fellowship Awards, 201 Monroe St, Suite 110, Montgomery, AL 36130-1800 *Tel:* 334-242-4076 *Fax:* 334-240-3269, pg 666

Healy, Nick, Capstone Publishers™, 1710 Roe Crest Dr, North Mankato, MN 56003 *Toll Free Tel:* 800-747-4992 (cust serv) *Toll Free Fax:* 888-262-0705 *Web Site:* www.capstonepress.com, pg 49

Healy, Sue, Leadership Directories, 1407 Broadway, Suite 318, New York, NY 10018 *Tel:* 212-627-4140 *Fax:* 212-645-0931 *E-mail:* info@leadershipdirectories.com *Web Site:* www.leadershipdirectories.com, pg 135

Heard, Janet, Davies Publishing Inc, 32 S Raymond Ave, Suites 4 & 5, Pasadena, CA 91105-1961 *Tel:* 626-792-3046 *Toll Free Tel:* 877-792-0005 *Fax:* 626-792-5308 *E-mail:* info@daviespublishing.com *Web Site:* daviespublishing.com, pg 71

Hearon, Todd, George Bennett Fellowship, Phillips Exeter Academy, Off of the Dean of Faculty, 20 Main St, Exeter, NH 03833-2460 *Tel:* 603-772-4311 *Fax:* 603-777-4384 *E-mail:* teaching_opportunities@exeter.edu *Web Site:* www.exeter.edu, pg 671

Heath, David, Redleaf Press, 10 Yorkton Ct, St Paul, MN 55117 *Tel:* 651-641-0508 *Toll Free Tel:* 800-423-8309 *Toll Free Fax:* 800-641-0115 *Web Site:* www.redleafpress.org, pg 206

Hebel, Brad, Columbia University Press, 61 W 62 St, New York, NY 10023 *Tel:* 212-459-0600 *Toll Free Tel:* 800-944-8648 *Fax:* 212-459-3678 *E-mail:* cup_book@columbia.edu (orders & cust serv) *Web Site:* cup.columbia.edu, pg 61

Hebert, Jean-Francois, Editions du CHU Sainte-Justine, 3175, chemin de la Cote-Sainte-Catherine, Montreal, QC H3T 1C5, Canada *Tel:* 514-345-4671 *Fax:* 514-345-4631 *E-mail:* edition.hsj@ssss.gouv.qc.ca *Web Site:* www.editions-chu-sainte-justine.org, pg 481

Hechler, Kay, United States Institute of Peace Press, 2301 Constitution Ave NW, Washington, DC 20037 *Tel:* 202-457-1700 (edit); 703-661-1590 (cust serv) *Toll Free Tel:* 800-868-8064 (cust serv) *Fax:* 202-429-6063; 703-661-1501 (cust serv) *Web Site:* bookstore.usip.org, pg 253

Hecker, J L, Stipes Publishing LLC, 204 W University, Champaign, IL 61820 *Tel:* 217-356-8391 *Fax:* 217-356-5753 *E-mail:* stipes01@sbcglobal.net *Web Site:* www.stipes.com, pg 236

Hecker, Mel, United States Holocaust Memorial Museum, 100 Raoul Wallenberg Place SW, Washington, DC 20024-2126 *Tel:* 202-314-7837; 202-488-6144 (orders) *Toll Free Tel:* 800-259-9998 (orders) *Fax:* 202-479-9726; 202-488-0438 (orders) *E-mail:* cahs_publications@ushmm.org *Web Site:* www.ushmm.org, pg 253

Hedden, Andrew, Scholastic Inc, 557 Broadway, New York, NY 10012 *Tel:* 212-343-6100 *Toll Free Tel:* 800-scholastic *Web Site:* www.scholastic.com, pg 218

Hedeen, Katrina, Boston Globe-Horn Book Award, 300 The Fenway, Boston, MA 02115-5820 *Tel:* 617-628-0225 *Toll Free Tel:* 800-325-1170; 888-628-0225 *Fax:* 617-278-6062 *E-mail:* info@hbook.com *Web Site:* www.hbook.com, pg 673

Hedger, Heidi, Interweave Press LLC, 201 E Fourth St, Loveland, CO 80537 *Toll Free Tel:* 800-272-2193; 800-289-0963 *Fax:* 970-613-4656 *Toll Free Fax:* 888-590-4082 *Web Site:* www.interweave.com, pg 125

Hedman, Susan Alvare, Hartman Publishing Inc, 1313 Iron Ave SW, Albuquerque, NM 87102 *Tel:* 505-291-1274 *Toll Free Tel:* 800-999-9534 *Fax:* 505-291-1284 *Toll Free Fax:* 800-474-6106 *E-mail:* orders@hartmanonline.com; help@hartmanonline.com *Web Site:* www.hartmanonline.com, pg 106

Heffron, Tom, Octane Press, 808 Kinney Ave, Austin, TX 78704 *Tel:* 512-334-9441 *Fax:* 512-852-4737 *E-mail:* info@octanepress.com *Web Site:* www.octanepress.com, pg 174

Heflin, Mark, American Illustration/American Photography, 15 E 32 St, 7th fl, New York, NY 10016 *Tel:* 212-470-0302 *Fax:* 212-532-2064 *E-mail:* info@ai-ap.com *Web Site:* www.ai-ap.com, pg 667

Hegeman, Ann, Rutgers University Press, 106 Somerset St, 3rd fl, New Brunswick, NJ 08901 *Tel:* 848-445-7762 *Toll Free Tel:* 800-848-6224 (orders only) *Fax:* 732-745-4935 (acqs, edit, mktg, perms & prodn) *Toll Free Fax:* 800-272-6817 (fulfillment) *Web Site:* rutgerspress.rutgers.edu, pg 213

Heiblum, Judy, Sterling Lord Literistic Inc, 65 Bleecker St, New York, NY 10012 *Tel:* 212-780-6050 *Fax:* 212-780-6095 *E-mail:* info@sll.com *Web Site:* www.sll.com, pg 575

Heider, Joe, John Wiley & Sons Inc Higher Education, 111 River St, Hoboken, NJ 07030-5774 *Tel:* 201-748-6000 *Toll Free Tel:* 800-225-5945 (cust serv) *Fax:* 201-748-6008 *E-mail:* info@wiley.com *Web Site:* www.wiley.com, pg 272

Heider, Joseph Sheridan, John Wiley & Sons Inc, 111 River St, Hoboken, NJ 07030-5774 *Tel:* 201-748-6000 *Toll Free Tel:* 800-225-5945 (cust serv) *Fax:* 201-748-6088 *E-mail:* info@wiley.com *Web Site:* www.wiley.com, pg 272

Heifetz, Merrilee, Writers House, 21 W 26 St, New York, NY 10010 *Tel:* 212-685-2400 *Fax:* 212-685-1781 *Web Site:* www.writershouse.com, pg 580

Heilman, Erica, Nicholas Brealey Publishing, 20 Park Plaza, Suite 610, Boston, MA 02116 *Tel:* 617-523-3801 *Toll Free Tel:* 888-BREALEY (273-2539) *Fax:* 617-523-3708 *E-mail:* info@nicholasbrealey.com *Web Site:* www.nicholasbrealey.com, pg 45

Heimberg, Justin, Seven Footer Kids, 247 W 30 St, 11th fl, New York, NY 10001-2824 *Tel:* 212-710-9340 *Fax:* 212-710-9344 *E-mail:* info@sevenfooter.com *Web Site:* www.sevenfooterpress.com, pg 222

Heimberg, Justin, Seven Footer Press, 247 W 30 St, 2nd fl, New York, NY 10001-2824 *Tel:* 212-710-9340 *Fax:* 212-710-9344 *E-mail:* info@sevenfooter.com *Web Site:* www.sevenfooterpress.com, pg 222

Heimbouch, Hollis, HarperCollins General Books Group, 195 Broadway, New York, NY 10007 *Tel:* 212-207-7000 *Web Site:* www.harpercollins.com, pg 105

Heimburger, Donald J, Heimburger House Publishing Co, 7236 W Madison St, Forest Park, IL 60130 *Tel:* 708-366-1973 *Fax:* 708-366-1973 *E-mail:* info@heimburgerhouse.com *Web Site:* www.heimburgerhouse.com, pg 109

Heimert, Laura, Basic Books, 250 W 57 St, 15th fl, New York, NY 10107 *Tel:* 212-340-8164; 212-340-8136 *Fax:* 212-340-8135 *E-mail:* perseus.promos@perseusbooks.com *Web Site:* www.basicbooks.com; perseusbooks.com, pg 31

Hein, Kristi, Pictures & Words Editorial Services, 3100 "B" Ave, Anacortes, WA 98221 *Tel:* 360-293-8476 *E-mail:* editor@picturesandwords.com *Web Site:* www.picturesandwords.com/words, pg 532

Hein, William S Jr, William S Hein & Co Inc, 2350 N Forest Rd, Getzville, NY 14068 *Tel:* 716-882-2600 *Toll Free Tel:* 800-828-7571 *Fax:* 716-883-8100 *E-mail:* mail@wshein.com; marketing@wshein.com *Web Site:* www.wshein.com, pg 109

Heineke, Mark, Getty Publications, 1200 Getty Center Dr, Suite 500, Los Angeles, CA 90049-1682 *Tel:* 310-440-7365 *Toll Free Tel:* 800-223-3431 (orders) *Fax:* 310-440-7758 *E-mail:* pubsinfo@getty.edu *Web Site:* www.getty.edu/publications, pg 96

Heinle, Charles, EPS/School Specialty Literacy & Intervention, 625 Mount Auburn St, 3rd fl, Cambridge, MA 02138-3039 *Toll Free Tel:* 800-225-5750 *Toll Free Fax:* 888-440-2665 *E-mail:* customerservice.eps@schoolspecialty.com *Web Site:* eps.schoolspecialty.com, pg 83

Heins, Julie, Johnson Books, 3005 Center Green Dr, Suite 225, Boulder, CO 80301 *Tel:* 303-443-9766 *Toll Free Tel:* 800-258-5830 *Fax:* 303-443-9687 *E-mail:* books@bigearthpublishing.com *Web Site:* www.bigearthpublishing.com; www.johnsonbooks.com, pg 128

Heinzelman, Kurt, University of Texas at Austin, Creative Writing Program, Dept of English, PAR 108, One University Sta, Mailcode B5000, Austin, TX 78712-1164 *Tel:* 512-471-5132; 512-471-4991 *Fax:* 512-471-4909 *Web Site:* www.utexas.edu/cola/depts/english/creative-writing, pg 664

Heise, Judy, Naval Institute Press, 291 Wood Rd, Annapolis, MD 21402-5034 *Tel:* 410-268-6110 *Toll Free Tel:* 800-233-8764 *Fax:* 410-295-1084; 410-571-1703 (cust serv) *E-mail:* webmaster@navalinstitute.org; customer@navalinstitute.org (cust serv); trade@usni.org *Web Site:* www.nip.org; www.usni.org, pg 166

Heiser, Christopher, University of Chicago Press, 1427 E 60 St, Chicago, IL 60637-2954 *Tel:* 773-702-7700; 773-702-7600 *Toll Free Tel:* 800-621-2736 (orders) *Fax:* 773-702-9756; 773-660-2235 (orders); 773-702-2708 *E-mail:* custserv@press.uchicago.edu; marketing@press.uchicago.edu *Web Site:* www.press.uchicago.edu, pg 255

Heiserman, Alice, American Correctional Association, 206 N Washington St, Suite 200, Alexandria, VA 22314 *Tel:* 703-224-0000 *Toll Free Tel:* 800-222-5646 *Fax:* 703-224-0179 *Web Site:* www.aca.org, pg 12

Held, Ivan, Dutton, 375 Hudson St, New York, NY 10014 *Tel:* 212-366-2000 *Fax:* 212-366-2262 *E-mail:* online@penguinputnam.com *Web Site:* www.penguinputnam.com; us.penguingroup.com, pg 78

Held, Ivan, Dutton Children's Books, 345 Hudson St, New York, NY 10014 *Tel:* 212-366-2000 *E-mail:* online@penguinputnam.com *Web Site:* www.penguinputnam.com; us.penguingroup.com, pg 78

Held, Ivan, Penguin Group (USA) LLC, a Penguin Random House company, 375 Hudson St, New York, NY 10014 *Tel:* 212-366-2000 *Toll Free Tel:* 800-847-5515 (inside sales); 800-631-8571 (cust serv) *Fax:* 212-366-2666; 607-775-4829 (inside sales) *E-mail:* online@us.penguingroup.com *Web Site:* www.penguin.com; us.penguingroup.com, pg 186

Held, Ivan, GP Putnam's Sons (Hardcover), 375 Hudson St, New York, NY 10014 *Tel:* 212-366-2000 *E-mail:* online@penguinputnam.com *Web Site:* us.penguingroup.com, pg 201

Held, Joe, The Reader's Digest Association Inc, 750 Third Ave, New York, NY 10017 *Tel:* 914-238-1000; 646-293-6284 *Toll Free Tel:* 800-310-6261 (cust serv) *Fax:* 914-238-4559 *Web Site:* www.rd.com; www.rda.com, pg 205

Helfand, Debra, Farrar, Straus & Giroux, LLC, 18 W 18 St, New York, NY 10011 *Tel:* 212-741-6900 *E-mail:* fsg.publicity@fsgbooks.com *Web Site:* us.macmillan.com/fsg.aspx, pg 86

Helgesen, Charles, The Oliver Press Inc, Charlotte Sq, 5707 W 36 St, Minneapolis, MN 55416-2510 *Tel:* 952-926-8981 *Toll Free Tel:* 800-8-OLIVER (865-4837) *Fax:* 952-926-8965 *E-mail:* orders@oliverpress.com *Web Site:* www.oliverpress.com, pg 174

Helgesen, Jeff, Research Press, 2612 N Mattis Ave, Champaign, IL 61822 *Tel:* 217-352-3273 *Toll Free Tel:* 800-519-2707 *Fax:* 217-352-1221 *E-mail:* rp@researchpress.com; orders@researchpress.com *Web Site:* www.researchpress.com, pg 208

Heller, Carol, Kent State University Press, 1118 University Library Bldg, 1125 Risman Dr, Kent, OH 44242 *Tel:* 330-672-7913; 419-281-1802 *Fax:* 330-672-3104 *E-mail:* ksupress@kent.edu *Web Site:* www.kentstateuniversitypress.com, pg 130

Heller, Chelsey, Zachary Shuster Harmsworth Agency, 1776 Broadway, Suite 1405, New York, NY 10019 *Tel:* 212-765-6900 *Fax:* 212-765-6490 *Web Site:* www.zshliterary.com, pg 580

Heller, Moshe, KTAV Publishing House Inc, 888 Newark Ave, Jersey City, NJ 07306 *Tel:* 201-963-9524 *Fax:* 201-963-0102 *E-mail:* orders@ktav.com *Web Site:* www.ktav.com, pg 133

Helm, Dianne, Helm Book Publishing, 3437 Huntington Place Dr, Sarasota, FL 34237 *Tel:* 727-623-5014 *Web Site:* www.helmbookpublishing.com, pg 110

Helmke, Juliet, American Federation of Arts, 305 E 47 St, 10th fl, New York, NY 10017 *Tel:* 212-988-7700 *Toll Free Tel:* 800-232-0270 *Fax:* 212-861-2487 *E-mail:* pubinfo@afaweb.org *Web Site:* www.afaweb.org, pg 12

Heltzel, Anne, Harry N Abrams Inc, 115 W 18 St, 6th fl, New York, NY 10011 *Tel:* 212-206-7715 *Toll Free Tel:* 800-345-1359 *Fax:* 212-519-1210 *E-mail:* abrams@abramsbooks.com *Web Site:* www.abramsbooks.com, pg 3

Helus, Eric, NavPress Publishing Group, 3820 N 30 St, Colorado Springs, CO 80904 *Tel:* 719-548-9222 *Toll Free Tel:* 800-366-7788 *Toll Free Fax:* 800-343-3902 *E-mail:* customerservice@navpress.com *Web Site:* www.navpress.com, pg 166

Helvey, Christopher, Eric Hoffer Award for Short Prose, PO Box 11, Titusville, NJ 08560 *Fax:* 609-964-1718 *E-mail:* info@hofferaward.com *Web Site:* www.hofferaward.com, pg 692

Hembree, Larry, Trustus Playwrights' Festival, 520 Lady St, Columbia, SC 29201 *Tel:* 803-254-9732 *Fax:* 803-771-9153 *E-mail:* trustus@trustus.org *Web Site:* www.trustus.org, pg 732

Hemlock, Katherine, BradyGames, 800 E 96 St, 3rd fl, Indianapolis, IN 46240 *Tel:* 317-428-3000 *Toll Free Tel:* 800-545-5912; 800-571-5840 (cust serv) *E-mail:* bradyquestions@pearsoned.com *Web Site:* www.bradygames.com, pg 44

Hemperly, Becky S, Candlewick Press, 99 Dover St, Somerville, MA 02144-2825 *Tel:* 617-661-3330 *Fax:* 617-661-0565 *E-mail:* bigbear@candlewick.com; salesinfo@candlewick.com *Web Site:* www.candlewick.com, pg 49

Hempstead, Andrew, Summerthought Publishing, PO Box 2309, Banff, AB T1L 1C1, Canada *Tel:* 403-762-0535 *Fax:* 403-762-3095 *Toll Free Fax:* 800-762-3095 (orders) *E-mail:* info@summerthought.com; sales@summerthought.com *Web Site:* summerthought.com, pg 500

Henahan, Julie, Individual Excellence Awards, 30 E Broad St, 33rd fl, Columbus, OH 43215 *Tel:* 614-466-2613 *Fax:* 614-466-4494 *Web Site:* www.oac.state.oh.us, pg 695

Henderson, Allison, Scholastic Education, 524 Broadway, New York, NY 10012 *Tel:* 212-343-6100 *Fax:* 212-343-6189 *Web Site:* www.scholastic.com, pg 218

Henderson, Bill, Pushcart Press, PO Box 380, Wainscott, NY 11975-0380 *Tel:* 631-324-9300, pg 201

Henderson, Bill, Pushcart Prize: Best of the Small Presses, PO Box 380, Wainscott, NY 11975-0380 *Tel:* 631-324-9300, pg 722

Henderson, Brian, Wilfrid Laurier University Press, 255 King St N, Suite 401, Waterloo, ON N2J 4V2, Canada *Tel:* 519-884-0710 (ext 6124) *Toll Free Tel:* 866-836-5551 (CN & US) *Fax:* 519-725-1399 *E-mail:* press@wlu.ca *Web Site:* www.wlupress.wlu.ca, pg 505

Henderson, Diane, Homestead Publishing, Box 193, Moose, WY 83012-0193 *Tel:* 307-733-6248 *Fax:* 307-733-6248 *E-mail:* orders@homesteadpublishing.net *Web Site:* www.homesteadpublishing.net, pg 114

Henderson, Homer, Parenting Press Inc, 13751 Lake City Way NE, Suite 110, Seattle, WA 98125 *Tel:* 206-364-2900 *Toll Free Tel:* 800-99-BOOKS (992-6657) *Fax:* 206-364-0702 *E-mail:* office@parentingpress.com; marketing@parentingpress.com *Web Site:* www.parentingpress.com, pg 183

Henderson, Joe, The Jim Henson Co, 1416 N La Brea Ave, Hollywood, CA 90028 *Tel:* 323-802-1500 *Fax:* 323-802-1825 *Web Site:* www.henson.com, pg 127

Henderson, Keith, The Association of English-Language Publishers of Quebec-AELAQ (Association des Editeurs de Langue Anglaise du Quebec), Atwater Library, 1200 Atwater Ave, Suite 3, Westmount, QC H3Z 1X4, Canada *Tel:* 514-932-5633 *E-mail:* admin@aelaq.org *Web Site:* aelaq.org, pg 599

Henderson, Paul, US Conference of Catholic Bishops, USCCB Publishing, 3211 Fourth St NE, Washington, DC 20017 *Tel:* 202-541-3090 *Toll Free Tel:* 800-235-8722 (orders only) *Fax:* 202-722-8709 *E-mail:* css@usccb.org; publications@usccb.org *Web Site:* www.usccbpublishing.org, pg 264

Hendrie, Caroline W, Education Writers Association (EWA), 3516 Connecticut Ave NW, Washington, DC 20008-2401 *Tel:* 202-452-9830 *Fax:* 202-452-9837 *E-mail:* ewa@ewa.org *Web Site:* www.ewa.org, pg 605

Hendrie, Caroline W, Education Writers Association Workshops, 3516 Connecticut Ave NW, Washington, DC 20008-2401 *Tel:* 202-452-9830 *Fax:* 202-452-9837 *E-mail:* ewa@ewa.org *Web Site:* www.ewa.org, pg 650

Hendrie, Caroline W, National Awards for Education Reporting, 3516 Connecticut Ave NW, Washington, DC 20008-2401 *Tel:* 202-452-9830 *Fax:* 202-452-9837 *E-mail:* ewa@ewa.org *Web Site:* www.ewa.org, pg 710

Henebry, Martha, American Association of Collegiate Registrars & Admissions Officers (AACRAO), One Dupont Circle NW, Suite 520, Washington, DC 20036 *Tel:* 202-293-9161 *Fax:* 202-872-8857 *Web Site:* www.aacrao.org, pg 11

Hengst, Linda R, James P Barry Ohioana Award for Editorial Excellence, 274 E First Ave, Suite 300, Columbus, OH 43201 *Tel:* 614-466-3831 *Fax:* 614-728-6974 *E-mail:* ohioana@ohioana.org *Web Site:* www.ohioana.org, pg 670

Hengst, Linda R, Ohioana Award for Children's Literature-Alice Louise Wood Memorial, 274 E First Ave, Suite 300, Columbus, OH 43201 *Tel:* 614-466-3831 *Fax:* 614-728-6974 *E-mail:* ohioana@ohioana.org *Web Site:* www.ohioana.org, pg 714

Hengst, Linda R, Ohioana Book Awards, 274 E First Ave, Suite 300, Columbus, OH 43201 *Tel:* 614-466-3831 *Fax:* 614-728-6974 *E-mail:* ohioana@ohioana.org *Web Site:* www.ohioana.org, pg 714

Hengst, Linda R, Ohioana Career Award, 274 E First Ave, Suite 300, Columbus, OH 43201 *Tel:* 614-466-3831 *Fax:* 614-728-6974 *E-mail:* ohioana@ohioana.org *Web Site:* www.ohioana.org, pg 715

Hengst, Linda R, Ohioana Citations, 274 E First Ave, Suite 300, Columbus, OH 43201 *Tel:* 614-466-3831 *Fax:* 614-728-6974 *E-mail:* ohioana@ohioana.org *Web Site:* www.ohioana.org, pg 715

Hengst, Linda R, Ohioana Pegasus Award, 274 E First Ave, Suite 300, Columbus, OH 43201 *Tel:* 614-466-3831 *Fax:* 614-728-6974 *E-mail:* ohioana@ohioana.org *Web Site:* www.ohioana.org, pg 715

Hengst, Linda R, Ohioana Poetry Award-Memorial to Helen & Laura Krout, 274 E First Ave, Suite 300, Columbus, OH 43201 *Tel:* 614-466-3831 *Fax:* 614-728-6974 *E-mail:* ohioana@ohioana.org *Web Site:* www.ohioana.org, pg 715

Hengst, Linda R, Ohioana Walter Rumsey Marvin Grant, 274 E First Ave, Suite 300, Columbus, OH 43201 *Tel:* 614-466-3831 *Fax:* 614-728-6974 *E-mail:* ohioana@ohioana.org *Web Site:* www.ohioana.org, pg 715

Henkin, Alyssa Eisner, Trident Media Group LLC, 41 Madison Ave, 36th fl, New York, NY 10010 *Tel:* 212-333-1511 *E-mail:* info@tridentmediagroup.com; press@tridentmediagroup.com *Web Site:* www.tridentmediagroup.com, pg 577

Henney, Eric, Princeton University Press, 41 William St, Princeton, NJ 08540-5237 *Tel:* 609-258-4900 *Toll Free Tel:* 800-777-4726 (orders) *Fax:* 609-258-6305 *Toll Free Fax:* 800-999-1958 *E-mail:* orders@cpfsinc.com *Web Site:* press.princeton.edu, pg 197

Henning, Richard, University Press of New England, One Court St, Suite 250, Lebanon, NH 03766 *Tel:* 603-448-1533 *Toll Free Tel:* 800-421-1561 (orders only) *Fax:* 603-448-7006; 603-643-1540 *E-mail:* university.press@dartmouth.edu *Web Site:* www.upne.com, pg 262

Henoch, Larissa, Health Communications Inc, 3201 SW 15 St, Deerfield Beach, FL 33442 *Tel:* 954-360-0909 *Toll Free Tel:* 800-851-9100; 800-441-5569 (cust serv & orders) *Fax:* 954-360-0034 *Toll Free Fax:* 800-424-7652 (cust serv & orders) *Web Site:* www.hcibooks.com, pg 108

Henry, Brian, Strata Publishing Inc, PO Box 1303, State College, PA 16804 *Tel:* 814-234-8545 *Fax:* 814-238-7222 *E-mail:* stratapub@stratapub.com *Web Site:* www.stratapub.com, pg 237

Henry, Christie, University of Chicago Press, 1427 E 60 St, Chicago, IL 60637-2954 *Tel:* 773-702-7700; 773-702-7600 *Toll Free Tel:* 800-621-2736 (orders) *Fax:* 773-702-9756; 773-660-2235 (orders); 773-702-2708 *E-mail:* custserv@press.uchicago.edu; marketing@press.uchicago.edu *Web Site:* www.press.uchicago.edu, pg 255

Henry, Claire, Fairchild Books, 1385 Broadway, 5th fl, New York, NY 10018 *Tel:* 212-419-5300 *Toll Free Tel:* 800-932-4724; 888-330-8477 (orders) *Fax:* 212-704-5975 *Web Site:* bloomsbury.com/us/academic/fairchildbooks, pg 85

Henry, Gray, Fons Vitae, 49 Mockingbird Valley Dr, Louisville, KY 40207-1366 *Tel:* 502-897-3641 *Fax:* 502-893-7373 *E-mail:* fonsvitaeky@aol.com *Web Site:* www.fonsvitae.com, pg 90

Henry, Jack, World Citizens, PO Box 131, Mill Valley, CA 94942-0131 *Tel:* 415-380-8020 *Toll Free Tel:* 800-247-6553 (orders only), pg 276

Henry, Karen, Bedford/St Martin's, 75 Arlington St, Boston, MA 02116 *Tel:* 617-399-4000 *Toll Free Tel:* 800-779-7440 *Fax:* 617-426-8582 *Web Site:* www.bedfordstmartins.com, pg 33

Henry, Lynn, Knopf Canada, One Toronto St, Suite 300, Toronto, ON M5C 2V6, Canada *Tel:* 416-364-4449 *Toll Free Tel:* 888-523-9292 *Fax:* 416-364-6863 *Web Site:* www.randomhouse.ca, pg 490

Henry, Ronna MD, American Medical Association, AMA Plaza, 330 N Wabash, Suite 39300, Chicago, IL 60611-5885 *Tel:* 312-464-5000 *Toll Free Tel:* 800-621-8335 *Fax:* 312-464-4184 *Web Site:* www.ama-assn.org, pg 14

Hensley, Alan, McGraw-Hill Career Education, 1333 Burr Ridge Pkwy, Burr Ridge, IL 60527 *Tel:* 630-789-4000 *Toll Free Tel:* 800-338-3987 (cust serv) *Fax:* 630-789-5523; 614-755-5645 (cust serv) *Web Site:* www.mhhe.com, pg 150

Hensley, Todd, C & T Publishing Inc, 1651 Challenge Dr, Concord, CA 94520-5206 *Tel:* 925-677-0377 *Toll Free Tel:* 800-284-1114 *Fax:* 925-677-0373 *E-mail:* support@ctpub.com *Web Site:* www.ctpub.com, pg 48

Hensley, Tony, C & T Publishing Inc, 1651 Challenge Dr, Concord, CA 94520-5206 *Tel:* 925-677-0377 *Toll Free Tel:* 800-284-1114 *Fax:* 925-677-0373 *E-mail:* support@ctpub.com *Web Site:* www.ctpub.com, pg 48

Henson, Brian, The Jim Henson Co, 1416 N La Brea Ave, Hollywood, CA 90028 *Tel:* 323-802-1500 *Fax:* 323-802-1825 *Web Site:* www.henson.com, pg 127

Henson, Gwen, American Society for Indexing Inc (ASI), 1628 E Southern Ave, Suite 9-223, Tempe, AZ 85282 *Tel:* 480-245-6750 *E-mail:* info@asindexing.org *Web Site:* www.asindexing.org, pg 596

Henson, Gwen, H W Wilson Co Indexing Award, 1628 E Southern Ave, Suite 9-223, Tempe, AZ 85282 *Tel:* 480-245-6750 *E-mail:* info@asindexing.org *Web Site:* www.asindexing.org, pg 736

Henson, Lisa Esq, The Jim Henson Co, 1416 N La Brea Ave, Hollywood, CA 90028 *Tel:* 323-802-1500 *Fax:* 323-802-1825 *Web Site:* www.henson.com, pg 127

Henson, Victoria, Westview Press, 2465 Central Ave, Boulder, CO 80301 *Tel:* 303-444-3541 *Fax:* 720-406-7336 *E-mail:* westview.orders@perseusbooks.com *Web Site:* www.perseusbooksgroup.com; www.westviewpress.com, pg 270

Herbert, Karen Brown, Karen Brown's Guides Inc, 16 E Third Ave, Suite 9, San Mateo, CA 94401 *Tel:* 650-342-9117 *Fax:* 650-342-9153 *Web Site:* www.karenbrown.com, pg 47

Herbert-Copley, Brent, Social Sciences & Humanities Research Council of Canada (SSHRC), 350 Albert St, Ottawa, ON K1P 6G4, Canada *Tel:* 613-992-0691 *E-mail:* research@sshrc-crsh.gc.ca *Web Site:* www.sshrc.ca, pg 618

Herbig, Alice, University of Washington Press, 433 Brooklyn Ave NE, Seattle, WA 98195-9570 *Tel:* 206-543-4050 *Toll Free Tel:* 800-537-5487 (orders) *Fax:* 206-543-3932; 410-516-6998 (orders) *E-mail:* uwpress@u.washington.edu *Web Site:* www.washington.edu/uwpress/, pg 260

Herbst, John, Indiana Historical Society Press (IHS Press), 450 W Ohio St, Indianapolis, IN 46202-3269 *Tel:* 317-232-1882; 317-234-0026 (orders); 317-234-2716 (edit) *Toll Free Tel:* 800-447-1830 (orders) *Fax:* 317-234-0562 (orders); 317-233-0857 (edit) *E-mail:* ihspress@indianahistory.org; orders@indianahistory.org (orders) *Web Site:* www.indianahistory.org; shop.indianahistory.org (orders), pg 120

Herder, Dr Gwendolin, The Crossroad Publishing Co, 831 Chestnut Ridge Rd, Chestnut Ridge, NY 10977 *Tel:* 845-517-0180 *Toll Free Tel:* 800-888-4741 (orders) *Fax:* 845-517-0181 *E-mail:* office@crossroadpublishing.com *Web Site:* www.CrossroadPublishing.com, pg 67

Hergenroeder, Jennifer, The Experiment, 220 East 23 St, Suite 301, New York, NY 10010-4674 *Tel:* 212-889-1659 *E-mail:* info@theexperimentpublishing.com *Web Site:* www.theexperimentpublishing.com, pg 85

Heritage, Barbara, Bibliographical Society of America, PO Box 1537, Lenox Hill Sta, New York, NY 10021-0043 *Tel:* 212-452-2710 *Fax:* 212-452-2710 *E-mail:* bsa@bibsocamer.org *Web Site:* www.bibsocamer.org, pg 600

Herits, Noreen, Random House Children's Books, 1745 Broadway, New York, NY 10019 *Tel:* 212-782-9000 *Toll Free Tel:* 800-200-3552 *Fax:* 212-782-9452 *Web Site:* randomhousekids.com, pg 203

Herits, Noreen, Workman Publishing Co Inc, 225 Varick St, 9th fl, New York, NY 10014-4381 *Tel:* 212-254-5900 *Toll Free Tel:* 800-722-7202 *Fax:* 212-254-8098 *E-mail:* info@workman.com *Web Site:* www.workman.com, pg 275

Hermalyn, Sarah, Harlequin Enterprises Ltd, 233 Broadway, Suite 1001, New York, NY 10279 *Tel:* 212-553-4200 *Fax:* 212-227-8969 *E-mail:* CustomerService@harlequin.com *Web Site:* www.harlequin.com, pg 105

Herman, Cheryl, Books on Tape®, 1745 Broadway, New York, NY 10019 *Toll Free Tel:* 800-733-3000 (cust serv) *Toll Free Fax:* 800-940-7046 *Web Site:* www.booksontape.com, pg 43

Herman, Gilles, Les Editions du Septentrion, 1300 Maguire Ave, Sillery, QC G1T 1Z3, Canada *Tel:* 418-688-3556 *Fax:* 418-527-4978 *E-mail:* info@septentrion.qc.ca *Web Site:* www.septentrion.qc.ca, pg 481

Higgins, Jeff, Dalkey Archive Press, University of Houston-Victoria, 3007 N Ben Wilson, Victoria, TX 77901 *E-mail:* contact@dalkeyarchive.com *Web Site:* www.dalkeyarchive.com, pg 70

Higgins, Ron, Gulf Publishing Co, 2 Greenway Plaza, Suite 1020, Houston, TX 77046 *Tel:* 713-529-4301 *Fax:* 713-520-4433 *E-mail:* store@gulfpub.com *Web Site:* www.gulfpub.com, pg 102

Higgins-Jacob, Coleen, John Simon Guggenheim Memorial Foundation, 90 Park Ave, New York, NY 10016 *Tel:* 212-687-4470 *Fax:* 212-697-3248 *E-mail:* fellowships@gf.org *Web Site:* www.gf.org, pg 623

Hilarian, Abbott, Saint Herman Press, 10 Beegum Gorge Rd, Platina, CA 96076 *Tel:* 530-352-4430 *Fax:* 530-352-4432 *E-mail:* stherman@stherman.com *Web Site:* www.stherman.com, pg 214

Hildebrand, Lloyd, Bridge-Logos Inc, Bldg 200, Suite 220, 17750 NW 115 Ave, Alachua, FL 32615 *Tel:* 386-462-2525 *Toll Free Tel:* 800-631-5802 (orders) *Fax:* 386-462-2535 *Toll Free Fax:* 800-935-6467 *E-mail:* customerservice@bridgelogos.com; info@bridgelogos.com *Web Site:* www.bridgelogos.com, pg 45

Hildreth, Mary Anne, Tower Publishing Co, 588 Saco Rd, Standish, ME 04084 *Tel:* 207-642-5400 *Toll Free Tel:* 800-969-8693 *Fax:* 207-264-3870 *E-mail:* info@towerpub.com *Web Site:* www.towerpub.com, pg 247

Hilferty, Daniel, Mason Crest Publishers, 450 Parkway Dr, Suite D, Broomall, PA 19008 *Tel:* 610-543-6200 *Toll Free Tel:* 866-MCP-BOOK (627-2665) *Fax:* 610-543-3878 *Web Site:* www.masoncrest.com, pg 149

Hill, Brandon, Ludwig von Mises Institute, 518 W Magnolia Ave, Auburn, AL 36832 *Tel:* 334-321-2100 *Fax:* 334-321-2119 *E-mail:* info@mises.org *Web Site:* www.mises.org, pg 266

Hill, David, Kregel Publications, 2450 Oak Industrial Dr NE, Grand Rapids, MI 49505 *Tel:* 616-451-4775 *Toll Free Tel:* 800-733-2607 *Fax:* 616-451-9330 *E-mail:* kregelbooks@kregel.com *Web Site:* www.kregel.com, pg 133

Hill, Frances, Emerging Playwright Award, 555 Eighth Ave, Suite 1800, New York, NY 10018 *Tel:* 212-421-1380 *Fax:* 212-421-1387 *E-mail:* urbanstage@aol.com, pg 683

Hill, Jamie, Books We Love Ltd, 192 Lakeside Greens Dr, Chestermere, AB T1X 1C2, Canada *Tel:* 403-710-4869 *E-mail:* bookswelove@shaw.ca, pg 473

Hill, Janet Muirhead, Raven Publishing Inc, 125 Cherry Creek Rd, Norris, MT 59745 *Tel:* 406-685-3545 *Toll Free Tel:* 866-685-3545 *Fax:* 406-685-3599 *E-mail:* info@ravenpublishing.net *Web Site:* www.ravenpublishing.net, pg 205

Hill, Joann, Disney-Hyperion Books, 1101 Flower St, Glendale, CA 91201 *Web Site:* books.disney.com, pg 74

Hill, Linda, Bella Books, PO Box 10543, Tallahassee, FL 32302 *Tel:* 850-576-2370 *Toll Free Tel:* 800-729-4992 *Fax:* 850-576-3498 *E-mail:* info@bellabooks.com; orders@bellabooks.com; ebooks@bellabooks.com *Web Site:* www.bellabooks.com, pg 34

Hill, Linda, Spinsters Ink, PO Box 242, Midway, FL 32343 *E-mail:* info@spinstersink.com; editorialdirector@spinstersink.com *Web Site:* www.spinstersink.com, pg 232

Hill, Michael, American Association of University Women Award for Juvenile Literature, 4610 Mail Service Ctr, Raleigh, NC 27699-4610 *Tel:* 919-807-7290 *Fax:* 919-733-8807, pg 667

Hill, Michael, Stephen Leacock Memorial Medal for Humour, RR2, 4223 Line 12 N, Coldwater, ON L0K 1E0, Canada *Tel:* 705-835-3218 *Fax:* 705-835-5171 *Web Site:* www.leacock.ca, pg 699

Hill, Michael, The Ragan Old North State Award Cup for Nonfiction, 4610 Mail Service Ctr, Raleigh, NC 27699-4610 *Tel:* 919-807-7290 *Fax:* 919-733-8807 *Web Site:* www.history.ncdcr.gov/affiliates/lit-hist/awards/awards.htm, pg 723

Hill, Michael, Sir Walter Raleigh Award for Fiction, 4610 Mail Service Ctr, Raleigh, NC 27699-4610 *Tel:* 919-807-7290 *Fax:* 919-733-8807, pg 723

Hill, Michael, Roanoke-Chowan Award for Poetry, 4610 Mail Service Ctr, Raleigh, NC 27699-4610 *Tel:* 919-807-7290 *Fax:* 919-733-8807 *Web Site:* www.history.ncdcr.gov/affiliates/lit-hist/awards/awards.htm, pg 724

Hill, Nancy, 4A's (American Association of Advertising Agencies), 1065 Avenue of the Americas, 16th fl, New York, NY 10018 *Tel:* 212-682-2500 *Web Site:* www.aaaa.org, pg 606

Hill, Richard, AHA Press, 155 N Wacker Dr, Suite 400, Chicago, IL 60606 *Tel:* 312-893-6800 *Toll Free Tel:* 800-821-2039 *Fax:* 312-422-4500 *Toll Free Fax:* 866-516-5817 (orders) *Web Site:* www.healthforum.com, pg 6

Hill, Richard, Association for Information Science & Technology (ASIS&T), 8555 16 St, Suite 850, Silver Spring, MD 20910 *Tel:* 301-495-0900 *Fax:* 301-495-0810 *E-mail:* asis@asis.org *Web Site:* www.asis.org, pg 25, 598

Hill, Rick, Health Forum Inc, 155 N Wacker Dr, Suite 400, Chicago, IL 60606 *Tel:* 312-893-6800 *Toll Free Tel:* 800-242-2626 *Fax:* 312-422-4500 *E-mail:* hfcustsvc@healthforum.com *Web Site:* www.ahaonlinestore.com; www.healthforum.com, pg 109

Hill, Sandy, Simon & Schuster, 1230 Avenue of the Americas, New York, NY 10020 *Tel:* 212-698-7000 *Toll Free Tel:* 800-223-2348 (cust serv); 800-223-2336 (orders) *Toll Free Fax:* 800-943-9831 (orders) *Web Site:* www.simonandschuster.com, pg 225

Hill, Stephanie, Whitecap Books Ltd, 314 W Cordova St, Suite 210, Vancouver, BC V6B 1E8, Canada *Tel:* 604-681-6181 *Toll Free Tel:* 800-387-9776 *Toll Free Fax:* 800-260-9777 *Web Site:* www.whitecap.ca, pg 505

Hill, Stephen W, Kiva Publishing Inc, 10 Bella Loma, Santa Fe, NM 87506 *Tel:* 909-896-0518 *E-mail:* kivapub@aol.com *Web Site:* www.kivapub.com, pg 131

Hillebrand, Donald, SAE (Society of Automotive Engineers International), 400 Commonwealth Dr, Warrendale, PA 15096-0001 *Tel:* 724-776-4841; 724-776-4970 (outside US & CN) *Toll Free Tel:* 877-606-7323 (cust serv) *Fax:* 724-776-0790 (cust serv) *E-mail:* publications@sae.org; customerservice@sae.org *Web Site:* www.sae.org, pg 213

Hillerman, Anne, The Tony Hillerman Prize, 1063 Willow Way, Santa Fe, NM 87507 *Tel:* 505-471-1565 *E-mail:* wordharvest@wordharvest.com *Web Site:* www.wordharvest.com, pg 692

Hillerman, Anne, Tony Hillerman Writers Conference, 1063 Willow Way, Santa Fe, NM 87507 *Tel:* 505-471-1565 *E-mail:* wordharvest@wordharvest.com *Web Site:* www.wordharvest.com, pg 656

Hilliard, Elbert, McLemore Prize, PO Box 571, Jackson, MS 39205-0571 *Tel:* 601-576-6850 *Fax:* 601-576-6975 *E-mail:* mhs@mdah.state.ms.us *Web Site:* www.mdah.state.ms.us, pg 707

Hilliard, Kathy, Andrews McMeel Publishing LLC, 1130 Walnut St, Kansas City, MO 64106-2109 *Toll Free Tel:* 800-851-8923; 800-943-9839 (cust serv) *Toll Free Fax:* 800-943-9831 (orders) *Web Site:* www.andrewsmcmeel.com, pg 18

Hillman, David, Simon & Schuster, Inc, 1230 Avenue of the Americas, New York, NY 10020 *Tel:* 212-698-7000 *Fax:* 212-698-7007 *E-mail:* firstname.lastname@simonandschuster.com *Web Site:* www.simonandschuster.com, pg 226

Hillman, Dennis, Kregel Publications, 2450 Oak Industrial Dr NE, Grand Rapids, MI 49505 *Tel:* 616-451-4775 *Toll Free Tel:* 800-733-2607 *Fax:* 616-451-9330 *E-mail:* kregelbooks@kregel.com *Web Site:* www.kregel.com, pg 133

Hillsman, Sally, American Sociological Association (ASA), 1430 "K" St NW, Suite 600, Washington, DC 20005-4701 *Tel:* 202-383-9005 *Fax:* 202-638-0882 *E-mail:* customer@asanet.org *Web Site:* www.asanet.org, pg 596

Himmel, Eric, Harry N Abrams Inc, 115 W 18 St, 6th fl, New York, NY 10011 *Tel:* 212-206-7715 *Toll Free Tel:* 800-345-1359 *Fax:* 212-519-1210 *E-mail:* abrams@abramsbooks.com *Web Site:* www.abramsbooks.com, pg 3

Hinchberger, Lara, McClelland & Stewart Ltd, One Toronto St, Toronto, ON M5C 2V6, Canada *Tel:* 416-364-4449 *Fax:* 416-957-1587 *E-mail:* editorial@mcclelland.com *Web Site:* www.mcclelland.com, pg 491

Hinds, John, Canadian Newspaper Association, 890 Yonge St, Suite 200, Toronto, ON M4W 3P4, Canada *Tel:* 416-923-3567; 416-482-1090 *Toll Free Tel:* 877-305-2262 *Fax:* 416-923-7206; 416-482-1908 *E-mail:* info@newspaperscanada.ca *Web Site:* www.newspaperscanada.ca, pg 602

Hine, Sam, Plough Publishing House, 151 Bowne Dr, Walden, NY 12586-2832 *Tel:* 845-572-3455 *Toll Free Tel:* 800-521-8011 *Fax:* 845-572-3472 *E-mail:* info@plough.com *Web Site:* www.plough.com, pg 193

Hines, Thomas M, Summa Publications, PO Box 660725, Birmingham, AL 35266-0725 *Tel:* 205-822-0463 *Fax:* 205-822-0463 *Web Site:* summapub2.googlepages.com, pg 237

Hines, Tom, J J Keller & Associates, Inc, 3003 Breezewood Lane, Neenah, WI 54957 *Tel:* 920-722-2848 *Toll Free Tel:* 877-564-2333 *Toll Free Fax:* 800-727-7516 *E-mail:* contactus@jjkeller.com; customerservice@jjkeller.com *Web Site:* www.jjkeller.com, pg 130

Hinkel, Nancy, Random House Children's Books, 1745 Broadway, New York, NY 10019 *Tel:* 212-782-9000 *Toll Free Tel:* 800-200-3552 *Fax:* 212-782-9452 *Web Site:* randomhousekids.com, pg 203

Hinkelman, Edward G, World Trade Press, 800 Lindberg Lane, Suite 190, Petaluma, CA 94952 *Tel:* 707-778-1124 *Toll Free Tel:* 800-833-8586 *Fax:* 707-778-1329 *Web Site:* www.worldtradepress.com, pg 276

Hinkley, John, Moody Publishers, 820 N La Salle Blvd, Chicago, IL 60610 *Tel:* 312-329-4000 *Toll Free Tel:* 800-678-8812 (cust serv) *Fax:* 312-329-2019 *Web Site:* www.moodypublishers.com, pg 159

Hinojosa-Smith, Rolando, University of Texas at Austin, Creative Writing Program, Dept of English, PAR 108, One University Sta, Mailcode B5000, Austin, TX 78712-1164 *Tel:* 512-471-5132; 512-471-4991 *Fax:* 512-471-4909 *Web Site:* www.utexas.edu/cola/depts/english/creative-writing, pg 664

Hinsch, Peter, Foundation Press, c/o West Academic Publishing, 444 Cedar St, Suite 700, St Paul, MN 55101 *Toll Free Tel:* 877-888-1330 *E-mail:* customerservice@westacademic.com *Web Site:* www.westacademic.com, pg 91

Hinsley, Erica, Alfred A Knopf/Everyman's Library, c/o Random House Inc, 1745 Broadway, New York, NY 10019 *Tel:* 212-751-2600 *Toll Free Tel:* 800-638-6460 *Fax:* 212-572-2593 *Web Site:* www.knopfdoubleday.com, pg 132

Hinz, Carol, Millbrook Press, 241 First Ave N, Minneapolis, MN 55401 *Tel:* 612-332-3344 *Toll Free Tel:* 800-328-4929 (US only) *Fax:* 612-332-7615 *Toll Free Fax:* 800-332-1132, pg 157

Hirashima, Steve, University of Hawaii Press, 2840 Kolowalu St, Honolulu, HI 96822 *Tel:* 808-956-8255 *Toll Free Tel:* 888-UHPRESS (847-7377) *Fax:* 808-988-6052 *Toll Free Fax:* 800-650-7811 *E-mail:* uhpbooks@hawaii.edu *Web Site:* www.uhpress.hawaii.edu, pg 256

Hirsch, Cheryl, Basic Health Publications Inc, 28812 Top of the World Dr, Laguna Beach, CA 92651 *Tel:* 949-715-7327 *Toll Free Tel:* 800-575-8890 (orders) *Fax:* 949-715-7328 *E-mail:* info@basichealthpub.com *Web Site:* www.basichealthpub.com, pg 32

Hirsch, Edward, John Simon Guggenheim Memorial Foundation, 90 Park Ave, New York, NY 10016 *Tel:* 212-687-4470 *Fax:* 212-697-3248 *E-mail:* fellowships@gf.org *Web Site:* www.gf.org, pg 623

Hitchcock, Elise, National Association of Printing Ink Manufacturers (NAPIM), 15 Technology Pkwy S, Peachtree Corners, GA 30092 *Tel:* 770-209-7289 *Fax:* 678-680-4920; 770-209-7217 *E-mail:* napim@napim.org *Web Site:* www.napim.org, pg 611

Hite, Robyn, Wimmer Cookbooks, 4650 Shelby Air Dr, Memphis, TN 38118 *Tel:* 901-362-8900 *Toll Free Tel:* 800-363-1771 *E-mail:* wimmer@wimmerco.com *Web Site:* www.wimmerco.com, pg 273

Hivnor, Maggie, University of Chicago Press, 1427 E 60 St, Chicago, IL 60637-2954 *Tel:* 773-702-7700; 773-702-7600 *Toll Free Tel:* 800-621-2736 (orders) *Fax:* 773-702-9756; 773-660-2235 (orders); 773-702-2708 *E-mail:* custserv@press.uchicago.edu; marketing@press.uchicago.edu *Web Site:* www.press.uchicago.edu, pg 255

Ho, Howard, University of Southern California, Master of Professional Writing Program, Mark Taper Hall, THH 355, 3501 Trousedale Pkwy, Los Angeles, CA 90089-0355 *Tel:* 213-740-3252 *Fax:* 213-740-5002 *E-mail:* mpw@college.usc.edu *Web Site:* college.usc.edu/mpw, pg 664

Hoak, Michael, Yale University Press, 302 Temple St, New Haven, CT 06511-8909 *Tel:* 203-432-0960; 203-432-0966 (sales); 401-531-2800 (cust serv) *Toll Free Tel:* 800-405-1619 (cust serv) *Fax:* 203-432-0948; 203-432-8485 (sales); 401-531-2801 (cust serv) *Toll Free Fax:* 800-406-9145 (cust serv) *E-mail:* sales.press@yale.edu (sales); customer.care@trilateral.org (cust serv) *Web Site:* www.yalebooks.com; yalepress.yale.edu/yupbooks, pg 278

Hoard, Trish, The Library of America, 14 E 60 St, New York, NY 10022-1006 *Tel:* 212-308-3360 *Fax:* 212-750-8352 *E-mail:* info@loa.org *Web Site:* www.loa.org, pg 139

Hoare, Steve, Black Dome Press Corp, 649 Delaware Ave, Delmar, NY 12054 *Tel:* 518-439-6512 *Fax:* 518-439-1309 *E-mail:* blackdomep@aol.com *Web Site:* www.blackdomepress.com, pg 38

Hoban, Kathryn, Holiday House Inc, 425 Madison Ave, New York, NY 10017 *Tel:* 212-688-0085 *Fax:* 212-421-6134 *E-mail:* holiday@holidayhouse.com *Web Site:* www.holidayhouse.com, pg 113

Hobeika, Joelle, Alloy Entertainment LLC, 1700 Broadway, New York, NY 10019 *Web Site:* alloyentertainment.com, pg 8

Hocherman, Riva, Henry Holt and Company, LLC, 175 Fifth Ave, New York, NY 10010 *Tel:* 646-307-5151 *Toll Free Tel:* 888-330-8477 (orders) *Fax:* 646-307-5285 *E-mail:* firstname.lastname@hholt.com *Web Site:* www.henryholt.com, pg 113

Hochman, Gail, Brandt & Hochman Literary Agents Inc, 1501 Broadway, Suite 2310, New York, NY 10036 *Tel:* 212-840-5760 *Fax:* 212-840-5776 *Web Site:* brandthochman.com, pg 544

Hochman, Sarah, Blue Rider Press, 375 Hudson St, New York, NY 10014 *Tel:* 212-366-2000 *E-mail:* blueriderpublicity@us.penguingroup.com, pg 41

Hodapp, Angie, Nelson Literary Agency LLC, 1732 Wazee St, Suite 207, Denver, CO 80202-1284 *Tel:* 303-292-2805 *E-mail:* query@nelsonagency.com *Web Site:* www.nelsonagency.com, pg 566

Hodell, Courtney, Whiting Writers' Awards, 1133 Avenue of the Americas, 22nd fl, New York, NY 10036-6710 *Tel:* 212-336-2138 *E-mail:* info@whitingfoundation.org *Web Site:* www.whitingfoundation.org, pg 735

Hodges, Joanne, National Council of Teachers of Mathematics (NCTM), 1906 Association Dr, Reston, VA 20191-1502 *Tel:* 703-620-9840 *Toll Free Tel:* 800-235-7566 *Fax:* 703-476-2970 *E-mail:* nctm@nctm.org *Web Site:* www.nctm.org, pg 164

Hodges, Peter, EMC Publishing LLC, 875 Montreal Way, St Paul, MN 55102 *Tel:* 651-290-2800 (corp) *Toll Free Tel:* 800-328-1452 *Toll Free Fax:* 800-328-4564 *E-mail:* educate@emcp.com *Web Site:* www.emcp.com, pg 81

Hodson, Brad, Horror Writers Association (HWA), 244 Fifth Ave, Suite 2767, New York, NY 10001 *E-mail:* hwa@horror.org *Web Site:* horror.org, pg 606

Hodson, Nancy, Cold Spring Harbor Laboratory Press, 500 Sunnyside Blvd, Woodbury, NY 11797-2924 *Tel:* 516-422-4100 *Toll Free Tel:* 800-843-4388 *Fax:* 516-422-4097; 516-422-4092 (submissions) *E-mail:* cshpress@cshl.edu *Web Site:* www.cshlpress.com, pg 60

Hodus, Brett, Scobre Press Corp, 2255 Calle Clara, La Jolla, CA 92037 *Toll Free Tel:* 877-726-2734 *Fax:* 858-551-1232 *E-mail:* info@scobre.com *Web Site:* www.scobre.com, pg 220

Hoehner, Jane, Wayne State University Press, Leonard N Simons Bldg, 4809 Woodward Ave, Detroit, MI 48201-1309 *Tel:* 313-577-6120 *Toll Free Tel:* 800-978-7323 *Fax:* 313-577-6131 *Web Site:* www.wsupress.wayne.edu, pg 268

Hoelzel, Christopher, Air Conditioning Contractors of America, 2800 Shirlington Rd, Suite 300, Arlington, VA 22206 *Tel:* 703-824-8851 *Toll Free Tel:* 888-290-2220 *Fax:* 703-575-8107 *Web Site:* www.acca.org, pg 6

Hoerdeman, Sara, Northern Illinois University Press, 2280 Bethany Rd, DeKalb, IL 60115 *Tel:* 815-753-1826; 815-753-1075 *Fax:* 815-753-1845 *Web Site:* www.niupress.niu.edu, pg 171

Hoesly, Sherry, The Permissions Group Inc, 1247 Milwaukee Ave, Suite 303, Glenview, IL 60025 *Tel:* 847-635-6550 *Toll Free Tel:* 800-374-7985 *Fax:* 847-635-6968 *E-mail:* info@permissionsgroup.com *Web Site:* www.permissionsgroup.com, pg 532

Hofeldt, Sara E, Tapestry Press Ltd, 19 Nashoba Rd, Littleton, MA 01460 *Tel:* 978-486-0200 *Toll Free Tel:* 800-535-2007 *Fax:* 978-486-0244 *E-mail:* publish@tapestrypress.com *Web Site:* www.tapestrypress.com, pg 240

Hoffman, Joan, School Zone Publishing Co, 1819 Industrial Dr, Grand Haven, MI 49417 *Tel:* 616-846-5030 *Toll Free Tel:* 800-253-0564 *Fax:* 616-846-6181 *Toll Free Fax:* 800-550-4618 (orders only) *Web Site:* www.schoolzone.com, pg 219

Hoffman, Randy, Captus Press Inc, 1600 Steeles Ave W, Units 14 & 15, Concord, ON L4K 4M2, Canada *Tel:* 416-736-5537 *Fax:* 416-736-5793 *E-mail:* info@captus.com *Web Site:* www.captus.com, pg 476

Hoffman, Scott, Folio Literary Management LLC, The Film Center Bldg, 630 Ninth Ave, Suite 1101, New York, NY 10036 *Tel:* 212-400-1494 *Fax:* 212-967-0977 *Web Site:* www.foliolit.com, pg 552

Hoffman, Shira, McIntosh & Otis Inc, 353 Lexington Ave, New York, NY 10016-0900 *Tel:* 212-687-7400 *Fax:* 212-687-6894 *E-mail:* info@mcintoshandotis.com *Web Site:* www.mcintoshandotis.com, pg 565

Hoffman, Stuart A, Star Publishing Co Inc, 650 El Camino Real, Redwood City, CA 94063 *Tel:* 650-591-3505 *Fax:* 650-591-3898 *E-mail:* mail@starpublishing.com *Web Site:* www.starpublishing.com, pg 234

Hoffmeister, Emmaline, Rhemalda Publishing, PO Box 1790, Moses Lake, WA 98837 *E-mail:* editor@rhemalda.com; customer_service@rhemalda.com *Web Site:* rhemalda.com, pg 208

Hoffmeister, Rhett, Rhemalda Publishing, PO Box 1790, Moses Lake, WA 98837 *E-mail:* editor@rhemalda.com; customer_service@rhemalda.com *Web Site:* rhemalda.com, pg 208

Hoffnagle, Jerry, Rizzoli International Publications Inc, 300 Park Ave S, 4th fl, New York, NY 10010-5399 *Tel:* 212-387-3400 *Toll Free Tel:* 800-522-6657 (orders only) *Fax:* 212-387-3535 *E-mail:* publicity@rizzoliusa.com *Web Site:* www.rizzoliusa.com, pg 209

Hofford, Amy, Brilliance Audio, 1704 Eaton Dr, Grand Haven, MI 49417 *Tel:* 616-846-5256 *Toll Free Tel:* 800-648-2312 (orders only) *Fax:* 616-846-0630 *E-mail:* customerservice@brillianceaudio.com *Web Site:* www.brillianceaudio.com, pg 46

Hogan, Mary S, Plexus Publishing, Inc, 143 Old Marlton Pike, Medford, NJ 08055 *Tel:* 609-654-6500 *Fax:* 609-654-4309 *E-mail:* info@plexuspublishing.com *Web Site:* www.plexuspublishing.com, pg 193

Hogan, Megan, Simon & Schuster, 1230 Avenue of the Americas, New York, NY 10020 *Tel:* 212-698-7000 *Toll Free Tel:* 800-223-2348 (cust serv); 800-223-2336 (orders) *Toll Free Fax:* 800-943-9831 (orders) *Web Site:* www.simonandschuster.com, pg 225

Hogan, Michelle, Our Sunday Visitor Publishing, 200 Noll Plaza, Huntington, IN 46750 *Tel:* 260-356-8400 *Toll Free Tel:* 800-348-2440 (orders) *Fax:* 260-356-8472 *Toll Free Fax:* 800-498-6709 *E-mail:* osvbooks@osv.com (book orders) *Web Site:* www.osv.com, pg 178

Hogan, Patrick, The American Library Association (ALA), 50 E Huron St, Chicago, IL 60611 *Tel:* 312-944-6780 *Toll Free Tel:* 800-545-2433 *Fax:* 312-280-5275 *E-mail:* editionsmarketing@ala.org *Web Site:* www.alastore.ala.org, pg 14

Hogan, Robin, CBA: The Association for Christian Retail, 1365 Garden of the Gods Rd, Suite 105, Colorado Springs, CO 80907 *Tel:* 719-265-9895 *Toll Free Tel:* 800-252-1950 *Fax:* 719-272-3508 *E-mail:* info@cbaonline.org *Web Site:* cbaonline.org, pg 603

Hogan, Thomas Jr, Information Today, Inc, 143 Old Marlton Pike, Medford, NJ 08055-8750 *Tel:* 609-654-6266 *Toll Free Tel:* 800-300-9868 (cust serv) *Fax:* 609-654-4309 *E-mail:* custserv@infotoday.com *Web Site:* www.infotoday.com, pg 121

Hogan, Thomas Jr, Plexus Publishing, Inc, 143 Old Marlton Pike, Medford, NJ 08055 *Tel:* 609-654-6500 *Fax:* 609-654-4309 *E-mail:* info@plexuspublishing.com *Web Site:* www.plexuspublishing.com, pg 193

Hogan, Thomas H Sr, Information Today, Inc, 143 Old Marlton Pike, Medford, NJ 08055-8750 *Tel:* 609-654-6266 *Toll Free Tel:* 800-300-9868 (cust serv) *Fax:* 609-654-4309 *E-mail:* custserv@infotoday.com *Web Site:* www.infotoday.com, pg 121

Hogan, Thomas H Sr, Plexus Publishing, Inc, 143 Old Marlton Pike, Medford, NJ 08055 *Tel:* 609-654-6500 *Fax:* 609-654-4309 *E-mail:* info@plexuspublishing.com *Web Site:* www.plexuspublishing.com, pg 193

Hoge, Steve, W W Norton & Company Inc, 500 Fifth Ave, New York, NY 10110-0017 *Tel:* 212-354-5500 *Toll Free Tel:* 800-233-4830 (orders & cust serv) *Fax:* 212-869-0856 *Toll Free Fax:* 800-458-6515 *Web Site:* www.wwnorton.com, pg 171

Hogeland, Kim, University Press of Kansas, 2502 Westbrooke Circle, Lawrence, KS 66045-4444 *Tel:* 785-864-4154; 785-864-4155 (orders) *Fax:* 785-864-4586 *E-mail:* upress@ku.edu; upkorders@ku.edu (orders) *Web Site:* www.kansaspress.ku.edu, pg 261

Hogenson, Barbara, The Barbara Hogenson Agency Inc, 165 West End Ave, Suite 19-C, New York, NY 10023 *Tel:* 212-874-8084 *Fax:* 212-595-6748 *E-mail:* bhogenson@aol.com, pg 557

Hoggard, James, Carr P Collins Award, c/o 7748 Hwy 290 W, Austin, TX 78736-3202 *Tel:* 512-683-5640 *E-mail:* president@texasinstituteofletters.org *Web Site:* www.texasinstituteofletters.org, pg 678

Hoggard, James, Soeurette Diehl Fraser Translation Award, c/o 7748 Hwy 290 W, Austin, TX 78736-3202 *Tel:* 512-683-5640 *E-mail:* president@texasinstituteofletters.org *Web Site:* www.texasinstituteofletters.org, pg 687

Hoggard, James, Jesse H Jones Award, c/o 7748 Hwy 290 W, Austin, TX 78736-3202 *Tel:* 512-683-5640 *E-mail:* president@texasinstituteofletters.org *Web Site:* www.texasinstituteofletters.org, pg 697

Hoggard, James, Most Significant Scholarly Book Award, c/o 7748 Hwy 290 W, Austin, TX 78736-3202 *Tel:* 512-683-5640 *E-mail:* president@texasinstituteofletters.org *Web Site:* www.texasinstituteofletters.org, pg 709

Hoggard, James, Edwin "Bud" Shrake Award for Best Short Nonfiction, c/o 7748 Hwy 290 W, Austin, TX 78736-3202 *Tel:* 512-683-5640 *E-mail:* president@texasinstituteofletters.org *Web Site:* www.texasinstituteofletters.org, pg 728

Hoggard, James, Helen C Smith Memorial Award, c/o 7748 Hwy 290 W, Austin, TX 78736-3202 *Tel:* 512-683-5640 *E-mail:* president@texasinstituteofletters.org *Web Site:* www.texasinstituteofletters.org, pg 729

Hoggard, James, Texas Institute of Letters (TIL), c/o 7748 Hwy 290 W, Austin, TX 78736-3202 *E-mail:* president@texasinstituteofletters.org; secretary@texasinstituteofletters.org *Web Site:* www.texasinstituteofletters.org, pg 620

Hoggard, James, Texas Institute of Letters Awards, c/o 7748 Hwy 290 W, Austin, TX 78736-3202 *Tel:* 512-683-5640 *E-mail:* president@texasinstituteofletters.org *Web Site:* www.texasinstituteofletters.org, pg 732

Hoggutt, Brenda Jo, University of Texas Press, 2100 Comal St, Austin, TX 78722 *Tel:* 512-471-7233 *Fax:* 512-232-7178 *E-mail:* utpress@uts.cc.utexas.edu *Web Site:* www.utexaspress.com, pg 244

Hogrebe, Christina, Jane Rotrosen Agency LLC, 318 E 51 St, New York, NY 10022 *Tel:* 212-593-4330 *Fax:* 212-935-6985 *Web Site:* janerotrosen.com, pg 571

Hohenadel, Liz, Riverhead Books (Hardcover), 375 Hudson St, New York, NY 10014 *Tel:* 212-366-2000 *E-mail:* online@penguinputnam.com *Web Site:* www.penguinputnam.com; us.penguingroup.com, pg 209

Hohman, David, Iconografix Inc, 2017 O'Neil Rd, Hudson, WI 54016 *Tel:* 715-381-9755 *Toll Free Tel:* 800-289-3504 (orders only) *Fax:* 715-381-9756 *E-mail:* info@iconografixinc.com *Web Site:* www.iconografixinc.com, pg 118

Hokanson, Sarah, Random House Children's Books, 1745 Broadway, New York, NY 10019 *Tel:* 212-782-9000 *Toll Free Tel:* 800-200-3552 *Fax:* 212-782-9452 *Web Site:* randomhousekids.com, pg 203

Holbert, Christine, The Idaho Prize for Poetry, 105 Lost Horse Lane, Sandpoint, ID 83864 *Tel:* 208-255-4410 *Fax:* 208-255-1560 *E-mail:* losthorsepress@mindspring.com *Web Site:* www.losthorsepress.org, pg 694

Holbert, Christine, Lost Horse Press, 105 Lost Horse Lane, Sandpoint, ID 83864 *Tel:* 208-255-4410 *E-mail:* losthorsepress@mindspring.com *Web Site:* www.losthorsepress.org, pg 143

Hold, William J, The National Alliance Research Academy, 3630 N Hills Dr, Austin, TX 78755 *Tel:* 512-345-7932 *Toll Free Tel:* 800-633-2165 *Fax:* 512-349-6194 *E-mail:* alliance@scic.com *Web Site:* www.scis.com/academy, pg 163

Hold, William T PhD, The National Alliance Research Academy, 3630 N Hills Dr, Austin, TX 78755 *Tel:* 512-345-7932 *Toll Free Tel:* 800-633-2165 *Fax:* 512-349-6194 *E-mail:* alliance@scic.com *Web Site:* www.scis.com/academy, pg 163

Holder, Jakob, William Flanagan Memorial Creative Persons Center, 14 Harrison St, New York, NY 10013 *Tel:* 212-226-2020 *Fax:* 212-226-5551 *E-mail:* info@albeefoundation.org *Web Site:* www.albeefoundation.org, pg 736

Holding, Brian, Human Kinetics Inc, 1607 N Market St, Champaign, IL 61820 *Tel:* 217-351-5076 *Toll Free Tel:* 800-747-4457 *Fax:* 217-351-1549 (orders/cust serv) *E-mail:* info@hkusa.com *Web Site:* www.humankinetics.com, pg 117

Holding, Hal, HPBooks, 375 Hudson St, New York, NY 10014 *Tel:* 212-366-2000 *E-mail:* online@penguinputnam.com *Web Site:* www.penguinputnam.com; us.penguingroup.com, pg 116

Holdridge, Jefferson, Wake Forest University Press, A5 Tribble Hall, Wake Forest University, Winston-Salem, NC 27109 *Tel:* 336-758-5448 *Fax:* 336-758-5636 *E-mail:* wfupress@wfu.edu *Web Site:* www.wfu.edu/wfupress, pg 266

Hollahan, Patricia, Medieval Institute Publications, WMU East Campus, 100-E Walwood Hall, Kalamazoo, MI 49008 *Tel:* 269-387-8755 (orders) *Fax:* 269-387-8750 *Web Site:* www.wmich.edu/medieval/mip, pg 153

Holland, Joyce, D4EO Literary Agency, 7 Indian Valley Rd, Weston, CT 06883 *Tel:* 203-544-7180 *Fax:* 203-544-7160 *Web Site:* www.d4eoliteraryagency.com, pg 548

Holland, Kevin, Air Conditioning Contractors of America, 2800 Shirlington Rd, Suite 300, Arlington, VA 22206 *Tel:* 703-824-8851 *Toll Free Tel:* 888-290-2220 *Fax:* 703-575-8107 *Web Site:* www.acca.org, pg 6

Holland, Lori, Springer, 233 Spring St, New York, NY 10013-1578 *Tel:* 212-460-1500 *Toll Free Tel:* 800-SPRINGER (777-4643) *Fax:* 212-460-1575 *E-mail:* service-ny@springer.com *Web Site:* www.springer.com, pg 232

Holland, Mark, Rocky Mountain Mineral Law Foundation, 9191 Sheridan Blvd, Suite 203, Westminister, CO 80031 *Tel:* 303-321-8100 *Fax:* 303-321-7657 *E-mail:* info@rmmlf.org *Web Site:* www.rmmlf.org, pg 210

Hollander, Elia, Feldheim Publishers (Philipp Feldheim Inc), 208 Airport Executive Park, Nanuet, NY 10954 *Tel:* 845-356-2282 *Toll Free Tel:* 800-237-7149 (orders) *Fax:* 845-425-1908 *E-mail:* sales@feldheim.com *Web Site:* www.feldheim.com, pg 87

Hollander, Michelle, Women Who Write Inc, PO Box 652, Madison, NJ 07940-0652 *E-mail:* info@womenwhowrite.org *Web Site:* womenwhowrite.org, pg 621

Hollaway, David, Quackenworth Publishing, PO Box 4747, Culver City, CA 90231-4747 *Tel:* 310-945-5634 *Toll Free Tel:* 888-701-4991 *Fax:* 310-945-5709 *Toll Free Fax:* 888-892-6339 *E-mail:* info@quackenworth.com *Web Site:* www.quackenworth.com; www.wittybittybunch.com, pg 201

Holliday, Sara, New York City Book Awards, 53 E 79 St, New York, NY 10075 *Tel:* 212-288-6900 *Fax:* 212-744-5832 *E-mail:* events@nysoclib.org *Web Site:* www.nysoclib.org, pg 713

Hollins, Pamela, Silver Gavel Awards, 321 N Clark St, Chicago, IL 60654 *Tel:* 312-988-5733 *Toll Free Tel:* 800-285-2221 (orders) *Fax:* 312-988-5494 *Web Site:* www.abanow.org; www.americanbar.org, pg 728

Hollman, Michael, The RoadRunner Press, 124 NW 32 St, Oklahoma City, OK 73118 *Tel:* 405-524-6205 *Fax:* 405-524-6312 *E-mail:* info@theroadrunnerpress.com; orders@theroadrunnerpress.com *Web Site:* www.theroadrunnerpress.com, pg 210

Holloway, J David, American Technical Publishers Inc, 10100 Orland Pkwy, Suite 200, Orland Park, IL 60467-5756 *Toll Free Tel:* 800-323-3471 *Fax:* 708-957-1101 *E-mail:* service@atplearning.com; order@atplearning.com *Web Site:* www.atplearning.com, pg 16

Holman, Tim, Hachette Book Group, 1290 Avenue of the Americas, New York, NY 10019 *Tel:* 212-364-1100 *Toll Free Tel:* 800-759-0190 (cust serv) *Fax:* 212-364-0933 (intl orders) *Toll Free Fax:* 800-286-9471 (cust serv) *Web Site:* www.HachetteBookGroup.com, pg 102

Holman, Tim, Orbit, 1290 Avenue of the Americas, New York, NY 10019 *Tel:* 212-364-1100 *Toll Free Tel:* 800-759-0190 *Web Site:* www.orbitbooks.net, pg 176

Holmberg, Martha, IACP Cookbook Awards, 1221 Avenue of the Americas, 42nd fl, New York, NY 10020 *Tel:* 646-358-4957 *Toll Free Tel:* 866-358-4951 *Toll Free Fax:* 866-358-2524 *E-mail:* info@iacp.com *Web Site:* www.iacp.com, pg 694

Holmes, Carol, R Ross Annett Award for Children's Literature, 11759 Groat Rd, Edmonton, AB T5M 3K6, Canada *Tel:* 780-422-8174 *Toll Free Tel:* 800-665-5354 (AB only) *Fax:* 780-422-2663 (attn WGA) *E-mail:* mail@writersguild.ab.ca *Web Site:* www.writersguild.ab.ca, pg 667

Holmes, Carol, Amber Bowerman Memorial Travel Writing Award, 11759 Groat Rd, Edmonton, AB T5M 3K6, Canada *Tel:* 780-422-8174 *Toll Free Tel:* 800-665-5354 (AB only) *Fax:* 780-422-2663 (attn WGA) *E-mail:* mail@writersguild.ab.ca *Web Site:* www.writersguild.ab.ca, pg 673

Holmes, Carol, Georges Bugnet Award for Fiction, 11759 Groat Rd, Edmonton, AB T5M 3K6, Canada *Tel:* 780-422-8174 *Toll Free Tel:* 800-665-5354 (AB only) *Fax:* 780-422-2663 (attn WGA) *E-mail:* mail@writersguild.ab.ca *Web Site:* www.writersguild.ab.ca, pg 674

Holmes, Carol, The City of Calgary W O Mitchell Book Prize, 11759 Groat Rd, Edmonton, AB T5M 3K6, Canada *Tel:* 780-422-8174 *Toll Free Tel:* 800-665-5354 (AB only) *Fax:* 780-422-2663 (attn WGA) *E-mail:* mail@writersguild.ab.ca *Web Site:* www.writersguild.ab.ca, pg 677

Holmes, Carol, Wilfrid Eggleston Award for Nonfiction, 11759 Groat Rd, Edmonton, AB T5M 3K6, Canada *Tel:* 780-422-8174 *Toll Free Tel:* 800-665-5354 (AB only) *Fax:* 780-422-2663 (attn WGA) *E-mail:* mail@writersguild.ab.ca *Web Site:* www.writersguild.ab.ca, pg 683

Holmes, Carol, James H Gray Award for Short Nonfiction, 11759 Groat Rd, Edmonton, AB T5M 3K6, Canada *Tel:* 780-422-8174 *Toll Free Tel:* 800-665-5354 (AB only) *Fax:* 780-422-2663 (attn WGA) *E-mail:* mail@writersguild.ab.ca *Web Site:* www.writersguild.ab.ca, pg 690

Holmes, Carol, The Robert Kroetsch City of Edmonton Book Prize, 11759 Groat Rd, Edmonton, AB T5M 3K6, Canada *Tel:* 780-422-8174 *Toll Free Tel:* 800-665-5354 (AB only) *Fax:* 780-422-2663 (attn WGA) *E-mail:* mail@writersguild.ab.ca *Web Site:* www.writersguild.ab.ca, pg 698

Holmes, Carol, Howard O'Hagan Award for Short Story, 11759 Groat Rd, Edmonton, AB T5M 3K6, Canada *Tel:* 780-422-8174 *Toll Free Tel:* 800-665-5354 (AB only) *Fax:* 780-422-2663 (attn WGA) *E-mail:* mail@writersguild.ab.ca *Web Site:* www.writersguild.ab.ca, pg 714

Holmes, Carol, Gwen Pharis Ringwood Award for Drama, 11759 Groat Rd, Edmonton, AB T5M 3K6, Canada *Tel:* 780-422-8174 *Toll Free Tel:* 800-665-5354 (AB only) *Fax:* 780-422-2663 (attn WGA) *E-mail:* mail@writersguild.ab.ca *Web Site:* www.writersguild.ab.ca, pg 724

Holmes, Carol, Stephan G Stephansson Award for Poetry, 11759 Groat Rd, Edmonton, AB T5M 3K6, Canada *Tel:* 780-422-8174 *Toll Free Tel:* 800-665-5354 (AB only) *Fax:* 780-422-2663 (attn WGA) *E-mail:* mail@writersguild.ab.ca *Web Site:* www.writersguild.ab.ca, pg 730

Holmes, Carol, Jon Whyte Memorial Essay Prize, 11759 Groat Rd, Edmonton, AB T5M 3K6, Canada *Tel:* 780-422-8174 *Toll Free Tel:* 800-665-5354 (AB only) *Fax:* 780-422-2663 (attn WGA) *E-mail:* mail@writersguild.ab.ca *Web Site:* www.writersguild.ab.ca, pg 736

Holmes, Carol, Writers' Guild of Alberta, 11759 Groat Rd, Edmonton, AB T5M 3K6, Canada *Tel:* 780-422-8174 *Toll Free Tel:* 800-665-5354 (AB only) *Fax:* 780-422-2663 (attn WGA) *E-mail:* mail@writersguild.ab.ca *Web Site:* www.writersguild.ab.ca, pg 621

Holmes, Henry, Henry Holmes Literary Agent/Book Publicist/Marketing Consultant, PO Box 433, Swansea, MA 02777 *Tel:* 508-672-2258 *E-mail:* henryholmesandassociates@yahoo.com, pg 527, 557

Holmes, J D, Holmes Publishing Group LLC, PO Box 2370, Sequim, WA 98382 *Tel:* 360-681-2900 *E-mail:* holmespub@fastmail.fm *Web Site:* www.jdholmes.com, pg 113

Holmes, Jack, The Johns Hopkins University Press, 2715 N Charles St, Baltimore, MD 21218-4363 *Tel:* 410-516-6900; 410-516-6987 (journal orders outside US & CN) *Toll Free Tel:* 800-537-5487 (book orders & cust serv); 800-548-1784 (journal orders) *Fax:* 410-516-6968; 410-516-3866 (journal orders) *E-mail:* hfscustserv@press.jhu.edu (cust serv); jrnlcirc@press.jhu.edu (journal orders) *Web Site:* www.press.jhu.edu; muse.jhu.edu, pg 127

Horler, Fred, Groundwood Books, 110 Spadina Ave, Suite 801, Toronto, ON M5V 2K4, Canada *Tel:* 416-363-4343 *Fax:* 416-363-1017 *E-mail:* genmail@groundwoodbooks.com *Web Site:* www.houseofanansi.com, pg 486

Horn, Leah, Western States Arts Federation, 1743 Wazee St, Suite 300, Denver, CO 80202 *Tel:* 303-629-1166 *Toll Free Tel:* 888-562-7232 *Fax:* 303-629-9717 *E-mail:* staff@westaf.org *Web Site:* www.westaf.org, pg 623

Hornby, Simon, Schiel & Denver Book Publishers, 10685-B Hazelhurst Dr, Suite 8575, Houston, TX 77043 *Tel:* 832-699-0264 *Toll Free Tel:* 888-629-4449 *Toll Free Fax:* 888-224-2721 *E-mail:* enquiries@schieldenver.com *Web Site:* www.schieldenver.com, pg 217

Horner, Christine, In the Garden Publishing, 7525 Paragon Rd, No 752252, Dayton, OH 45459 *Tel:* 937-317-0859 *E-mail:* editor@inthegardenpublishing.com *Web Site:* www.inthegardenpublishing.com, pg 120

Hornfischer, Jim, Hornfischer Literary Management LP, PO Box 50544, Austin, TX 78763 *Tel:* 512-472-0011 *E-mail:* queries@hornfischerlit.com *Web Site:* www.hornfischerlit.com, pg 557

Hornik, Lauri, Dial Books for Young Readers, 345 Hudson St, New York, NY 10014 *Tel:* 212-366-2000 *Fax:* 212-414-3396 *E-mail:* online@penguinputnam.com *Web Site:* www.penguinputnam.com; us.penguingroup.com, pg 74

Hornstein, Gabriel, AMS Press Inc, Brooklyn Navy Yard, 63 Flushing Ave, Unit 221, Brooklyn, NY 11205-1005 *Tel:* 718-875-8100 *Fax:* 718-875-3800 *E-mail:* editorial@amspressinc.com; orders@amspressinc.com *Web Site:* www.amspressinc.com, pg 17

Hornung, Susan, Andrew Carnegie Medals for Excellence in Fiction & Nonfiction, 50 E Huron St, Chicago, IL 60611 *Tel:* 312-944-6780 *Toll Free Tel:* 800-545-2433 *Fax:* 312-440-9374 *E-mail:* ala@ala.org *Web Site:* www.ala.org/awardsgrants/carnegieadult, pg 676

Hornyak, Kim, Jenkins Group Inc, 1129 Woodmere Ave, Suite B, Traverse City, MI 49686 *Tel:* 231-933-0445 *Toll Free Tel:* 800-706-4636 *Fax:* 231-933-0448 *E-mail:* info@bookpublishing.com *Web Site:* www.bookpublishing.com, pg 528

Horowitz, Beverly, Random House Children's Books, 1745 Broadway, New York, NY 10019 *Tel:* 212-782-9000 *Toll Free Tel:* 800-200-3552 *Fax:* 212-782-9452 *Web Site:* randomhousekids.com, pg 203

Horowitz, David, Media Coalition Inc, 19 Fulton St, Suite 407, New York, NY 10038 *Tel:* 212-587-4025 *Fax:* 212-587-2436 *E-mail:* info@mediacoalition.org *Web Site:* mediacoalition.org, pg 609

Horowitz, Mitchell, Jeremy P Tarcher, 375 Hudson St, New York, NY 10014 *Tel:* 212-366-2000 *E-mail:* online@penguinputnam.com *Web Site:* www.penguinputnam.com; us.penguingroup.com, pg 240

Horowitz, Shel, Accurate Writing & More, 16 Barstow Lane, Hadley, MA 01035 *Tel:* 413-586-2388 *Web Site:* www.accuratewriting.com; www.business-for-a-better-world.com; www.greenandprofitable.com; www.makinggreensexy.com; frugalmarketing.com; www.frugalfun.com; www.twitter.com/shelhorowitz, pg 519

Horowitz, Valerie, The Lawbook Exchange Ltd, 33 Terminal Ave, Clark, NJ 07066-1321 *Tel:* 732-382-1800 *Toll Free Tel:* 800-422-6686 *Fax:* 732-382-1887 *E-mail:* law@lawbookexchange.com *Web Site:* www.lawbookexchange.com, pg 135

Horton, Boe, ProQuest LLC, 789 E Eisenhower Pkwy, Ann Arbor, MI 48108-3218 *Tel:* 734-761-4700 *Toll Free Tel:* 800-521-0600 *Fax:* 734-975-6486 *Toll Free Fax:* 800-864-0019 *E-mail:* info@proquest.com *Web Site:* www.proquest.com, pg 199

Horton, David, Bethany House Publishers, 11400 Hampshire Ave S, Bloomington, MN 55438 *Tel:* 952-829-2500 *Toll Free Tel:* 800-877-2665 (orders) *Fax:* 952-829-2568 *Toll Free Fax:* 800-398-3111 (orders) *Web Site:* www.bethanyhouse.com; www.bakerpublishinggroup.com, pg 36

Horvath, Dave, Jason Aronson Inc, 4501 Forbes Blvd, Suite 200, Lanham, MD 20706 *Tel:* 301-459-3366 *Toll Free Tel:* 800-462-6420 (orders) *Fax:* 301-429-5748 *Web Site:* www.rowman.com, pg 22

Horvath, Dave, Lexington Books, 4501 Forbes Blvd, Suite 200, Lanham, MD 20706 *Tel:* 301-459-3366 *Fax:* 301-429-5749 *Web Site:* www.lexingtonbooks.com, pg 138

Horvath, Dave, University Press of America Inc, 4501 Forbes Blvd, Suite 200, Lanham, MD 20706 *Tel:* 301-459-3366 *Toll Free Tel:* 800-462-6420 *Fax:* 301-429-5748 *Toll Free Fax:* 800-338-4550 *Web Site:* www.univpress.com, pg 261

Horvit, Mark, Investigative Reporters & Editors, Missouri School of Journalism, 141 Neff Annex, Columbia, MO 65211 *Tel:* 573-882-2042 *Fax:* 573-882-5431 *E-mail:* info@ire.org *Web Site:* www.ire.org, pg 608

Horwege, Richard, The Donning Company Publishers, 184 Business Park Dr, Suite 206, Virginia Beach, VA 23462 *Tel:* 757-497-1789 *Toll Free Tel:* 800-296-8572 *Fax:* 757-497-2542 *Web Site:* www.donning.com, pg 75

Hoshijo, Amara, Soho Press Inc, 853 Broadway, New York, NY 10003 *Tel:* 212-260-1900 *Fax:* 212-260-1902 *E-mail:* soho@sohopress.com; publicity@sohopress.com *Web Site:* www.sohopress.com, pg 229

Hosier, Chad, The Society of Professional Journalists (SPJ), Eugene S Pulliam National Journalism Ctr, 3909 N Meridian St, Indianapolis, IN 46208 *Tel:* 317-927-8000 *Fax:* 317-920-4789 *E-mail:* spj@spj.org *Web Site:* www.spj.org, pg 620

Hosier, Erin, Dunow, Carlson & Lerner Literary Agency Inc, 27 W 20 St, Suite 1107, New York, NY 10011 *Tel:* 212-645-7606 *E-mail:* mail@dclagency.com *Web Site:* www.dclagency.com, pg 549

Hoskin, Christine, Schoolhouse Indexing, 10-B Parade Ground Rd, Etna, NH 03750 *Tel:* 603-643-1617 *Web Site:* schoolhouseindexing.com, pg 534

Hotchkiss, Erin, Harry N Abrams Inc, 115 W 18 St, 6th fl, New York, NY 10011 *Tel:* 212-206-7715 *Toll Free Tel:* 800-345-1359 *Fax:* 212-519-1210 *E-mail:* abrams@abramsbooks.com *Web Site:* www.abramsbooks.com, pg 3

Hotzler, Russell K PhD, New York City College of Technology, 300 Jay St, Brooklyn, NY 11201 *Tel:* 718-260-5500 *Fax:* 718-260-5198 *E-mail:* connect@citytech.cuny.edu *Web Site:* www.citytech.cuny.edu, pg 661

Houder, Daniel, Kennedy Information Inc, 24 Railroad St, Keene, NH 03431 *Tel:* 603-924-0900 *Toll Free Tel:* 800-531-0140 *Fax:* 603-357-8112 *E-mail:* customerservice@kennedyinfo.com *Web Site:* www.kennedyinfo.com, pg 130

Hough, Millie, Individual Artist's Fellowships in Literature, 1800 Gervais St, Columbia, SC 29201 *Tel:* 803-734-8696 *Fax:* 803-734-8526 *E-mail:* info@arts.sc.gov *Web Site:* www.southcarolinaarts.com, pg 695

Houghton, Daniel, Lonely Planet, 150 Linden St, Oakland, CA 94607 *Tel:* 510-893-8555 *Toll Free Tel:* 800-275-8555 (orders) *Fax:* 510-893-8572 *E-mail:* info@lonelyplanet.com *Web Site:* www.lonelyplanet.com, pg 142

Houghton, Harmon, Clear Light Publishers, 823 Don Diego Ave, Santa Fe, NM 87505 *Tel:* 505-989-9590 *Toll Free Tel:* 800-253-2747 (orders) *Fax:* 505-989-9519 *E-mail:* market@clearlightbooks.com *Web Site:* www.clearlightbooks.com, pg 59

Hourahan, Glenn, Air Conditioning Contractors of America, 2800 Shirlington Rd, Suite 300, Arlington, VA 22206 *Tel:* 703-824-8851 *Toll Free Tel:* 888-290-2220 *Fax:* 703-575-8107 *Web Site:* www.acca.org, pg 6

Hourigan, Katherine, Doubleday/Nan A Talese, c/o Penguin Random House Inc, 1745 Broadway, New York, NY 10019 *Tel:* 212-751-2600 *Fax:* 212-572-2662 *E-mail:* ddaypub@randomhouse.com *Web Site:* knopfdoubleday.com, pg 76

Hourigan, Katherine, Alfred A Knopf/Everyman's Library, c/o Random House Inc, 1745 Broadway, New York, NY 10019 *Tel:* 212-751-2600 *Toll Free Tel:* 800-638-6460 *Fax:* 212-572-2593 *Web Site:* www.knopfdoubleday.com, pg 132

House, Jackson, Townson Publishing Co Ltd, PO Box 1404, Sta A, Vancouver, BC V6C 2P7, Canada *Tel:* 604-886-0594 (CN) *E-mail:* townsonpublishing@gmail.com *Web Site:* generalpublishing.co.uk, pg 501

Householder, Stacy, National Conference of State Legislatures (NCSL), 7700 E First Place, Denver, CO 80230 *Tel:* 303-364-7700 *Fax:* 303-364-7800 *E-mail:* books@ncsl.org *Web Site:* www.ncsl.org, pg 164

Houser, Meghan, Crown Publishing Group, c/o Penguin Random House Inc, 1745 Broadway, New York, NY 10019 *Tel:* 212-782-9000 *Toll Free Tel:* 888-264-1745 *Fax:* 212-940-7408 *E-mail:* crownosm@penguinrandomhouse.com *Web Site:* crownpublishing.com, pg 68

Housley, Jim, Bloom's Literary Criticism, 132 W 31 St, 17th fl, New York, NY 10001 *Toll Free Tel:* 800-322-8755 *Toll Free Fax:* 800-678-3633 *E-mail:* custserv@factsonfile.com *Web Site:* www.infobasepublishing.com, pg 39

Housley, Jim, Chelsea House Publishers, 132 W 31 St, 17th fl, New York, NY 10001 *Tel:* 212-967-8800 *Toll Free Tel:* 800-322-8755 *Fax:* 917-339-0325 *Toll Free Fax:* 800-678-3633 *E-mail:* custserv@factsonfile.com *Web Site:* www.infobasepublishing.com; www.infobaselearning.com, pg 56

Housley, Jim, Facts On File, 132 W 31 St, 17th fl, New York, NY 10001 *Tel:* 212-967-8800 *Toll Free Tel:* 800-322-8755 *Toll Free Fax:* 800-678-3633 *E-mail:* custserv@factsonfile.com *Web Site:* infobasepublishing.com, pg 85

Housley, Jim, Ferguson Publishing, 132 W 31 St, 17th fl, New York, NY 10001 *Tel:* 212-967-8800 *Toll Free Tel:* 800-322-8755 *Fax:* 917-339-0323 *Toll Free Fax:* 800-678-3633 *E-mail:* custserv@factsonfile.com *Web Site:* infobasepublishing.com, pg 88

Houtz, Julie, ASCD, 1703 N Beauregard St, Alexandria, VA 22311-1714 *Tel:* 703-578-9600 *Toll Free Tel:* 800-933-2723 *Fax:* 703-575-5400 *E-mail:* member@ascd.org *Web Site:* www.ascd.org, pg 23

Hovemann, Glenn, Dawn Publications Inc, 12402 Bitney Springs Rd, Nevada City, CA 95959 *Tel:* 530-274-7775 *Toll Free Tel:* 800-545-7475 *Fax:* 530-274-7778 *E-mail:* nature@dawnpub.com; orders@dawnpub.com *Web Site:* www.dawnpub.com, pg 71

Hovey, Kim, Random House Publishing Group, 1745 Broadway, New York, NY 10019 *Toll Free Tel:* 800-200-3552 *Web Site:* atrandom.com, pg 204

Hoving, Allan, Tantor Media Inc, 2 Business Park, Old Saybrook, CT 06475 *Toll Free Tel:* 877-782-6867 *Toll Free Fax:* 888-782-7821 *Web Site:* www.tantor.com, pg 240

Howard, Assuanta, Asta Publications LLC, PO Box 1735, Stockbridge, GA 30281 *Tel:* 678-814-1320 *Toll Free Tel:* 800-482-4190 *Fax:* 678-814-1370 *E-mail:* info@astapublications.com *Web Site:* www.astapublications.com, pg 26

Howard, Brent, NAL, 375 Hudson St, New York, NY 10014 *Tel:* 212-366-2000 *E-mail:* online@penguinputnam.com *Web Site:* www.penguinputnam.com; us.penguingroup.com, pg 162

Howard, Elise, Algonquin Books, 400 Silver Cedar Ct, Suite 300, Chapel Hill, NC 27514-1585 *Tel:* 919-967-0108 *Fax:* 919-933-0272 *E-mail:* inquiry@algonquin.com *Web Site:* www.workman.com/algonquin, pg 8

Howard, Gerry, Doubleday/Nan A Talese, c/o Penguin Random House Inc, 1745 Broadway, New York, NY 10019 *Tel:* 212-751-2600 *Fax:* 212-572-2662 *E-mail:* ddaypub@randomhouse.com *Web Site:* knopfdoubleday.com, pg 76

Hudson, Ken, Schiel & Denver Book Publishers, 10685-B Hazelhurst Dr, Suite 8575, Houston, TX 77043 *Tel:* 832-699-0264 *Toll Free Tel:* 888-629-4449 *Toll Free Fax:* 888-224-2721 *E-mail:* enquiries@schieldenver.com *Web Site:* www.schieldenver.com, pg 217

Hudson, Suzan, Herald Publishing House, 1001 W Walnut St, Independence, MO 64051 *Tel:* 816-521-3015 *Toll Free Tel:* 800-767-8181 *Fax:* 816-521-3066 *E-mail:* sales@heraldhouse.org *Web Site:* www.heraldhouse.org, pg 110

Huelsing, Kristi, Coaches Choice, 514 Airport Way, Monterey, CA 93940 *Toll Free Tel:* 888-229-5745 *Fax:* 831-372-6075 *E-mail:* info@coacheschoice.com *Web Site:* www.coacheschoice.com, pg 60

Huey-Steiner, Kim, I-5 Publishing LLC, 3 Burroughs, Irvine, CA 92618 *Tel:* 949-855-8822 *Toll Free Tel:* 888-738-2665 *Fax:* 949-458-3856 *Web Site:* www.i5publishing.com, pg 117

Huff, Mickey, The 25 Most "Censored" Stories Annual, PO Box 571, Cotati, CA 94931 *Tel:* 707-874-2695 *Web Site:* www.projectcensored.org, pg 733

Hughes, Amy, Dunow, Carlson & Lerner Literary Agency Inc, 27 W 20 St, Suite 1107, New York, NY 10011 *Tel:* 212-645-7606 *E-mail:* mail@dclagency.com *Web Site:* www.dclagency.com, pg 549

Hughes, Andrew W, Doubleday/Nan A Talese, c/o Penguin Random House Inc, 1745 Broadway, New York, NY 10019 *Tel:* 212-751-2600 *Fax:* 212-572-2662 *E-mail:* ddaypub@randomhouse.com *Web Site:* knopfdoubleday.com, pg 76

Hughes, Andrew W, Alfred A Knopf/Everyman's Library, c/o Random House Inc, 1745 Broadway, New York, NY 10019 *Tel:* 212-751-2600 *Toll Free Tel:* 800-638-6460 *Fax:* 212-572-2593 *Web Site:* www.knopfdoubleday.com, pg 132

Hughes, Andy, Pantheon Books/Schocken Books, c/o Random House Inc, 1745 Broadway, New York, NY 10019 *Tel:* 212-751-2600 *Toll Free Tel:* 800-638-6460 *Fax:* 212-572-6030, pg 181

Hughes, Brigid, Graywolf Press, 250 Third Ave N, Suite 600, Minneapolis, MN 55401 *Tel:* 651-641-0077 *Fax:* 651-641-0036 *E-mail:* wolves@graywolfpress.org *Web Site:* www.graywolfpress.org, pg 100

Hughes, Connie, Lippincott Williams & Wilkins, 333 Seventh Ave, New York, NY 10001 *Toll Free Tel:* 800-950-2035 *E-mail:* orders@lww.com *Web Site:* www.lww.com, pg 140

Hughes, Doug, McGraw-Hill Contemporary Learning Series, 501 Bell St, Dubuque, IA 52001 *Toll Free Tel:* 800-243-6532 *Web Site:* www.mhcls.com, pg 150

Hughes, Doug, McGraw-Hill Higher Education, 1333 Burr Ridge Pkwy, Burr Ridge, IL 60527 *Tel:* 630-789-4000 *Toll Free Tel:* 800-338-3987 (cust serv) *Fax:* 614-755-5645 (cust serv) *Web Site:* www.mhhe.com, pg 151

Hughes, Doug, McGraw-Hill Humanities, Social Sciences, Languages, 2 Penn Plaza, 21st fl, New York, NY 10121 *Tel:* 212-904-2000 *Toll Free Tel:* 800-338-3987 (cust serv) *Fax:* 614-755-5645 (cust serv) *Web Site:* www.mhhe.com, pg 151

Hughes, Doug, McGraw-Hill/Irwin, 1333 Burr Ridge Pkwy, Burr Ridge, IL 60527 *Tel:* 630-789-4000 *Toll Free Tel:* 800-338-3987 (cust serv) *Fax:* 630-789-6942; 614-755-5645 (cust serv) *Web Site:* www.mhhe.com, pg 152

Hughes, Doug, McGraw-Hill Science, Engineering, Mathematics, 501 Bell St, Dubuque, IA 52001 *Tel:* 563-584-6000 *Toll Free Tel:* 800-338-3987 (cust serv) *Fax:* 614-755-5645 (cust serv) *Web Site:* www.mhhe.com, pg 152

Hughes, Georgia, New World Library, 14 Pamaron Way, Novato, CA 94949 *Tel:* 415-884-2100 *Toll Free Tel:* 800-227-3900 (ext 52, retail orders); 800-972-6657 *Fax:* 415-884-2199 *E-mail:* escort@newworldlibrary.com *Web Site:* www.newworldlibrary.com, pg 168

Hughes, Heather, Sleeping Bear Press™, 315 Eisenhower Pkwy, Suite 200, Ann Arbor, MI 48108 *Toll Free Tel:* 800-487-2323 *Fax:* 734-794-0004 *E-mail:* sleepingbearpress@cengage.com *Web Site:* www.sleepingbearpress.com, pg 228

Hughes, Jessie, W W Norton & Company Inc, 500 Fifth Ave, New York, NY 10110-0017 *Tel:* 212-354-5500 *Toll Free Tel:* 800-233-4830 (orders & cust serv) *Fax:* 212-869-0856 *Toll Free Fax:* 800-458-6515 *Web Site:* www.wwnorton.com, pg 172

Hughes, Larry, Simon & Schuster, 1230 Avenue of the Americas, New York, NY 10020 *Tel:* 212-698-7000 *Toll Free Tel:* 800-223-2348 (cust serv); 800-223-2336 (orders) *Toll Free Fax:* 800-943-9831 (orders) *Web Site:* www.simonandschuster.com, pg 225

Hughes, Nicki, Castle Connolly Medical Ltd, 42 W 24 St, 2nd fl, New York, NY 10010 *Tel:* 212-367-8400 *Fax:* 212-367-0964 *Web Site:* www.castleconnolly.com, pg 51

Hughes, Patrick, Central Recovery Press (CRP), 3321 N Buffalo Dr, Suite 275, Las Vegas, NV 89129 *Tel:* 702-868-5830 *Fax:* 702-868-5831 *E-mail:* info@centralrecovery.com *Web Site:* centralrecoverypress.com, pg 54

Huizenga, Alan, Tyndale House Publishers Inc, 351 Executive Dr, Carol Stream, IL 60188 *Tel:* 630-668-8300 *Toll Free Tel:* 800-323-9400 *Web Site:* www.tyndale.com, pg 252

Hulbert, Jonathan, Wadsworth Publishing, 20 Davis Dr, Belmont, CA 94002 *Tel:* 650-595-2350 *Fax:* 650-592-3022 *Toll Free Fax:* 800-522-4923 *Web Site:* www.cengage.com, pg 266

Hulburt, Stephen, Prestel Publishing, 900 Broadway, Suite 603, New York, NY 10003 *Tel:* 212-995-2720 *Toll Free Tel:* 888-463-6110 (cust serv) *Fax:* 212-995-2733 *E-mail:* sales@prestel-usa.com *Web Site:* www.prestel.com, pg 196

Hulkower, Lynda, Midmarch Arts Press, 300 Riverside Dr, New York, NY 10025-5239 *Tel:* 212-666-6990 *Web Site:* midmarchartspress.org, pg 156

Hull, Stephen, University Press of New England, One Court St, Suite 250, Lebanon, NH 03766 *Tel:* 603-448-1533 *Toll Free Tel:* 800-421-1561 (orders only) *Fax:* 603-448-7006; 603-643-1540 *E-mail:* university.press@dartmouth.edu *Web Site:* www.upne.com, pg 262

Hullinger, Margret S, BNA Books, 1801 S Bell St, Arlington, VA 22202 *Tel:* 732-476-6397 *Toll Free Tel:* 800-372-1033; 800-960-1220 *Fax:* 732-346-1624 *E-mail:* books@bna.com *Web Site:* www.bnabooks.com, pg 41

Hulsebosch, Betsy, Hachette Books, 1290 Avenue of the Americas, New York, NY 10019 *Tel:* 212-364-1100 *Web Site:* www.hachettebookgroup.com, pg 102

Hulsey, Dave, Indiana University Press, Herman B Wells Library 350, 1320 E Tenth St, Bloomington, IN 47405-3907 *Tel:* 812-855-8817 *Toll Free Tel:* 800-842-6796 (orders only) *Fax:* 812-855-7931; 812-855-8507 *E-mail:* iupress@indiana.edu; iuporder@indiana.edu (orders) *Web Site:* www.iupress.indiana.edu, pg 120

Hultenschmidt, Leah, Grand Central Publishing, 1290 Avenue of the Americas, New York, NY 10019 *Tel:* 212-364-1100 *Web Site:* www.hachettebookgroup.com, pg 99

Humby, Jeff, Samhain Publishing Ltd, 11821 Mason Montgomery Rd, Suite 4-B, Cincinnati, OH 45249 *Tel:* 513-453-4688 *Fax:* 513-583-0191 *E-mail:* support@samhainpublishing.com *Web Site:* www.samhainpublishing.com, pg 216

Humphrey, Harv, University of Notre Dame Press, 310 Flanner Hall, Notre Dame, IN 46556 *Tel:* 574-631-6346 *Fax:* 574-631-8148 *E-mail:* undpress@nd.edu *Web Site:* www.undpress.nd.edu, pg 258

Humphrey, John H, Journal of Roman Archaeology LLC, 95 Peleg Rd, Portsmouth, RI 02871 *Tel:* 401-683-1955 *Fax:* 401-683-1975 *E-mail:* jra@journalofromanarch.com *Web Site:* www.journalofromanarch.com, pg 128

Hundley, Amy, Grove Atlantic Inc, 154 W 14 St, 12th fl, New York, NY 10011 *Tel:* 212-614-7850 *Toll Free Tel:* 800-521-0178 *Fax:* 212-614-7886 *E-mail:* info@groveatlantic.com *Web Site:* www.groveatlantic.com, pg 101

Hung, Helena, Penguin Group (Canada), 90 Eglinton Ave E, Suite 700, Toronto, ON M4P 2Y3, Canada *Tel:* 416-925-2249 *Fax:* 416-925-0068 *E-mail:* customerservicescanada@penguinrandomhouse.com *Web Site:* penguinrandomhouse.ca, pg 494

Hunt, Lia, Princeton Architectural Press, 37 E Seventh St, New York, NY 10003 *Tel:* 212-995-9620 *Toll Free Tel:* 800-722-6657 (dist); 800-759-0190 (sales) *Fax:* 212-995-9454 *E-mail:* sales@papress.com *Web Site:* www.papress.com, pg 197

Hunt, Rebecca, Harlequin Enterprises Ltd, 233 Broadway, Suite 1001, New York, NY 10279 *Tel:* 212-553-4200 *Fax:* 212-227-8969 *E-mail:* CustomerService@harlequin.com *Web Site:* www.harlequin.com, pg 105

Hunt, Rebecca, HarperCollins General Books Group, 195 Broadway, New York, NY 10007 *Tel:* 212-207-7000 *Web Site:* www.harpercollins.com, pg 105

Hunt, Richard, Clerisy Press, 306 Greenup St, Covington, KY 41011 *Tel:* 859-815-7200 *Toll Free Tel:* 800-913-9563 *Fax:* 859-291-9111 *E-mail:* info@clerisypress.com *Web Site:* www.clerisypress.com, pg 59

Hunt, Steve, Michelin Maps & Guides, One Parkway S, Greenville, SC 29615-5022 *Tel:* 864-458-5565 *Fax:* 864-458-5665 *Toll Free Fax:* 866-297-0914; 888-773-7979 *E-mail:* orders@americanmap.com (orders) *Web Site:* www.michelintravel.com; www.michelinguide.com, pg 155

Hunter, Allison, Stuart Krichevsky Literary Agency Inc, 381 Park Ave South, Suite 428, New York, NY 10016 *Tel:* 212-725-5288 *Fax:* 212-725-5275 *E-mail:* query@skagency.com *Web Site:* skagency.com, pg 561

Hunter, Ann A, AAH Graphics Inc, 9293 Fort Valley Rd, Fort Valley, VA 22652-2020 *Tel:* 540-933-6211 *Fax:* 540-933-6523 *E-mail:* srhunter@aahgraphics.com *Web Site:* www.aahgraphics.com, pg 519

Hunter, Ann A, Loft Press Inc, 9293 Fort Valley Rd, Fort Valley, VA 22652 *Tel:* 540-933-6210 *Fax:* 540-933-6523 *E-mail:* Books@LoftPress.com, pg 142

Hunter, Kristy, The Knight Agency Inc, 570 East Ave, Madison, GA 30650 *E-mail:* submissions@knightagency.net *Web Site:* www.knightagency.net, pg 560

Hunter, Michael, Hunter Publishing Inc, 222 Clematis St, West Palm Beach, FL 33401 *Tel:* 561-835-2022 *Web Site:* guidestotheworld.com, pg 117

Hunter, Mike R, Cape Breton University Press Inc (CBU Press), 1250 Grand Lake Rd, Sydney, NS B1M 1A2, Canada *Tel:* 902-563-1604 (orders & cust serv) *Fax:* 902-563-1177 *E-mail:* cbu_press@cbu.ca *Web Site:* cbup.ca, pg 476

Hunter, Shelli, Richard Ivey School of Business, Ivey Business School at Western University, 1255 Western Rd, London, ON N6G 0N1, Canada *Tel:* 519-661-3206; 519-661-3208 *Toll Free Tel:* 800-649-6355 *Fax:* 519-661-3485; 519-661-3882 *E-mail:* cases@ivey.uwo.ca *Web Site:* www.iveycases.com; www.ivey.uwo.ca, pg 489

Hunter, Stephen R, Loft Press Inc, 9293 Fort Valley Rd, Fort Valley, VA 22652 *Tel:* 540-933-6210 *Fax:* 540-933-6523 *E-mail:* Books@LoftPress.com, pg 142

Huot, Mary, Houghton Mifflin Harcourt Trade & Reference Division, 222 Berkeley St, Boston, MA 02116 *Tel:* 617-351-5000 *Toll Free Tel:* 800-225-3362 *Web Site:* www.hmhco.com, pg 115

Hupping, Carol, Jewish Publication Society, 2100 Arch St, Philadelphia, PA 19103 *Tel:* 215-832-0600 *Toll Free Tel:* 800-234-3151 *Fax:* 215-568-2017 *Web Site:* www.jps.org, pg 126

Hurd, Charlie, CLC Ministries, 701 Pennsylvania Ave, Fort Washington, PA 19034 *Tel:* 215-542-1240 *Toll Free Tel:* 800-659-1240 *Fax:* 215-542-7580 *E-mail:* orders@clcpublications.com *Web Site:* www.clcpublications.com, pg 59

Impey, Alison, Random House Children's Books, 1745 Broadway, New York, NY 10019 *Tel:* 212-782-9000 *Toll Free Tel:* 800-200-3552 *Fax:* 212-782-9452 *Web Site:* randomhousekids.com, pg 203

Inabashitsi, Cynthia, Prise de Parole Inc, 109 Elm St, Suite 205, Sudbury, ON P3C 1T4, Canada *Tel:* 705-675-6491 *Fax:* 705-673-1817 *E-mail:* info@prisedeparole.ca *Web Site:* www.prisedeparole.ca, pg 496

Indrigo, Miranda, Harlequin Enterprises Ltd, 225 Duncan Mill Rd, Don Mills, ON M3B 3K9, Canada *Tel:* 416-445-5860 *Toll Free Tel:* 888-432-4879; 800-370-5838 (ebook inquiries) *E-mail:* customerservice@harlequin.com *Web Site:* www.harlequin.com, pg 487

Ingalls, Johanna, Akashic Books, 232 Third St, Suite A-115, Brooklyn, NY 11215 *Tel:* 718-643-9193 *Fax:* 718-643-9195 *E-mail:* info@akashicbooks.com *Web Site:* www.akashicbooks.com, pg 7

Ingalls, Robert, Ingalls Publishing Group Inc (IPG), PO Box 2500, Banner Elk, NC 28604 *Tel:* 828-297-6884 *Fax:* 828-297-6880 *E-mail:* sales@ingallspublishinggroup.com *Web Site:* www.ingallspublishinggroup.com, pg 121

Ingebretson, Krista, Anne Edelstein Literary Agency LLC, 404 Riverside Dr, New York, NY 10025 *Tel:* 212-414-4923 *E-mail:* info@aeliterary.com; rights@aeliterary.com *Web Site:* www.aeliterary.com, pg 549

Ingenito, Kim Thornton, Penguin Random House Speakers Bureau, 1745 Broadway, Mail Drop 13-1, New York, NY 10019 *Tel:* 212-572-2013 *E-mail:* speakers@penguinrandomhouse.com *Web Site:* www.prhspeakers.com, pg 587

Ingle, Stephen, WordCo Indexing Services Inc, 49 Church St, Norwich, CT 06360 *Tel:* 860-886-2532 *Toll Free Tel:* 877-WORDCO-3 (967-3263) *Fax:* 860-886-1155 *E-mail:* office@wordco.com *Web Site:* www.wordco.com, pg 536

Inglis, John, Cold Spring Harbor Laboratory Press, 500 Sunnyside Blvd, Woodbury, NY 11797-2924 *Tel:* 516-422-4100 *Toll Free Tel:* 800-843-4388 *Fax:* 516-422-4097; 516-422-4092 (submissions) *E-mail:* cshpress@cshl.edu *Web Site:* www.cshlpress.com, pg 60

Inkster, Tim, Porcupine's Quill Inc, 68 Main St, Erin, ON N0B 1T0, Canada *Tel:* 519-833-9158 *Fax:* 519-833-9845 *E-mail:* pql@sentex.net *Web Site:* porcupinesquill.ca, pg 495

Inman, Matt, Crown Publishing Group, c/o Penguin Random House Inc, 1745 Broadway, New York, NY 10019 *Tel:* 212-782-9000 *Toll Free Tel:* 888-264-1745 *Fax:* 212-940-7408 *E-mail:* crownosm@penguinrandomhouse.com *Web Site:* crownpublishing.com, pg 68

Inouye, Natalie, University of Southern California, Master of Professional Writing Program, Mark Taper Hall, THH 355, 3501 Trousedale Pkwy, Los Angeles, CA 90089-0355 *Tel:* 213-740-3252 *Fax:* 213-740-5002 *E-mail:* mpw@college.usc.edu *Web Site:* college.usc.edu/mpw, pg 664

Inshiqaq, Shanta, Rizzoli International Publications Inc, 300 Park Ave S, 4th fl, New York, NY 10010-5399 *Tel:* 212-387-3400 *Toll Free Tel:* 800-522-6657 (orders only) *Fax:* 212-387-3535 *E-mail:* publicity@rizzoliusa.com *Web Site:* www.rizzoliusa.com, pg 209

Inteli, Nancy, HarperCollins Children's Books, 195 Broadway, New York, NY 10007 *Tel:* 212-207-7000 *Web Site:* www.harpercollins.com/childrens, pg 105

Inwood, Johanna, WaterBrook Multnomah Publishing Group, 12265 Oracle Blvd, Suite 200, Colorado Springs, CO 80921 *Tel:* 719-590-4999 *Toll Free Tel:* 800-603-7051 (orders) *Fax:* 719-590-8977 *Toll Free Fax:* 800-294-5686 (orders) *E-mail:* info@waterbrookmultnomah.com *Web Site:* waterbrookmultnomah.com, pg 267

Ippolito, Marc, Burns Entertainment & Sports Marketing, 820 Davis St, Suite 222, Evanston, IL 60201 *Tel:* 847-866-9400 *Fax:* 847-491-9778 *E-mail:* burnsl@burnsent.com *Web Site:* burnsent.com, pg 587

Ireland, Elizabeth, Coffee House Press, 79 13 Ave NE, Suite 110, Minneapolis, MN 55413 *Tel:* 612-338-0125 *Fax:* 612-338-4004 *E-mail:* info@coffeehousepress.org *Web Site:* coffeehousepress.org, pg 60

Ireland, Pamela, BelleBooks, PO Box 300921, Memphis, TN 38130 *Tel:* 901-344-9024 *Fax:* 901-344-9068 *E-mail:* bellebooks@bellebooks.com, pg 34

Irgang, Mark, Belltown Media, PO Box 980985, Houston, TX 77098 *Tel:* 713-344-1956 *Fax:* 713-583-7956 *E-mail:* subs@linuxjournal.com *Web Site:* www.belltownmedia.com, pg 34

Irish-Underwood, Lesleigh, Kensington Publishing Corp, 119 W 40 St, New York, NY 10018 *Tel:* 212-407-1500 *Toll Free Tel:* 800-221-2647 *Fax:* 212-935-0699 *Web Site:* www.kensingtonbooks.com, pg 130

Irizarry Vizcarrondo, Jorge, Institute of Puerto Rican Culture National Literary Awards, PO Box 9024184, San Juan, PR 00902-4184 *Tel:* 787-724-0700 *Fax:* 787-724-8393 *Web Site:* www.icp.gobierno.pr, pg 695

Irvine, Dominique, Reference Publications Inc, 218 Saint Clair River Dr, Algonac, MI 48001 *Tel:* 810-794-5722 *Fax:* 810-794-7463 *E-mail:* referencepub@sbcglobal.net, pg 207

Irvine, Marie Aline, Reference Publications Inc, 218 Saint Clair River Dr, Algonac, MI 48001 *Tel:* 810-794-5722 *Fax:* 810-794-7463 *E-mail:* referencepub@sbcglobal.net, pg 207

Irwin-Diehl, Rebecca, Judson Press, 588 N Gulph Rd, King of Prussia, PA 19406 *Toll Free Tel:* 800-458-3766 *Fax:* 610-768-2107 *Web Site:* www.judsonpress.com, pg 128

Isaac, Joanne, American Numismatic Society, 75 Varick St, 11th fl, New York, NY 10013 *Tel:* 212-571-4470 *Fax:* 212-571-4479 *E-mail:* ans@numismatics.org; orders@numismatics.org *Web Site:* www.numismatics.org, pg 14

Isaacs, Suzanne Talbot, Ampersand Inc/Professional Publishing Services, 1050 N State St, Chicago, IL 60610 *Tel:* 312-280-8905 *Fax:* 312-944-1582 *E-mail:* info@ampersandworks.com *Web Site:* www.ampersandworks.com, pg 17

Isaacson, Dana, Random House Publishing Group, 1745 Broadway, New York, NY 10019 *Toll Free Tel:* 800-200-3552 *Web Site:* atrandom.com, pg 204

Iserson, Mary Lou, Galen Press Ltd, PO Box 64400-WB, Tucson, AZ 85728-4400 *Tel:* 520-577-8363 *Fax:* 520-529-6459 *E-mail:* sales@galenpress.com *Web Site:* www.galenpress.com, pg 94

Isherwood, Judith, Shoreline Press, 23 Ste-Anne, Ste-Anne-de-Bellevue, QC H9X 1L1, Canada *Tel:* 514-457-5733 *E-mail:* info@shorelinepress.ca *Web Site:* shorelinepress.ca, pg 499

Ison, Tara, Arizona State University, Creative Writing Program, 851 S Cady Mall, Rm 542, Tempe, AZ 85287-0302 *Tel:* 480-965-3528 *Fax:* 480-965-3451 *Web Site:* www.asu.edu/clas/english/creativewriting, pg 659

Israeli, Henry, Saturnalia Books Poetry Prize, 105 Woodside Rd, Ardmore, PA 19003 *Tel:* 267-278-9541 *E-mail:* info@saturnaliabooks.com *Web Site:* www.saturnaliabooks.com, pg 726

Israelite, David M, National Music Publishers' Association (NMPA), 975 "F" St NW, Suite 315, Washington, DC 20004 *Tel:* 202-393-6672 *Fax:* 202-393-6673 *E-mail:* pr@nmpa.org *Web Site:* www.nmpa.org, pg 613

Ivers, Mitchell, Gallery Books, 1230 Avenue of the Americas, New York, NY 10020 *Toll Free Tel:* 800-456-6798 *Fax:* 212-698-7284 *E-mail:* consumer.customerservice@simonandschuster.com *Web Site:* www.simonsays.com, pg 94

Iversen, Dr Kristen, The Pinch Writing Awards in Fiction, University of Memphis, English Dept, 435 Patterson Hall, Memphis, TN 38152 *Tel:* 901-678-4190 *Fax:* 901-678-2226 *E-mail:* editor@thepinchjournal.com *Web Site:* www.thepinchjournal.com, pg 719

Iversen, Dr Kristen, The Pinch Writing Awards in Poetry, University of Memphis, English Dept, 435 Patterson Hall, Memphis, TN 38152 *Tel:* 901-678-4190 *Fax:* 901-678-2226 *E-mail:* editor@thepinchjournal.com *Web Site:* www.thepinchjournal.com, pg 719

Iverson, Anne, Mountain Press Publishing Co, 1301 S Third W, Missoula, MT 59801 *Tel:* 406-728-1900 *Toll Free Tel:* 800-234-5308 *Fax:* 406-728-1635 *E-mail:* info@mtnpress.com *Web Site:* www.mountain-press.com, pg 160

Ivett, Claire, Da Capo Press & Lifelong Books, 44 Farnsworth St, 3rd fl, Boston, MA 02210 *Tel:* 617-252-5200 *Toll Free Tel:* 800-343-4499 (orders) *Fax:* 617-252-5285 *Web Site:* www.perseusbooksgroup.com/dacapo, pg 69

Jabbari, Dr Ahmad, Mazda Publishers Inc, One Park Plaza, Suite 600, Irvine, CA 92614 *Tel:* 714-751-5252 *Fax:* 714-751-4805 *E-mail:* mazdapub@aol.com *Web Site:* www.mazdapub.com, pg 150

Jackel, Lawrence, Waterside Productions Inc, 2055 Oxford Ave, Cardiff, CA 92007 *Tel:* 760-632-9190 *Fax:* 760-632-9295 *E-mail:* admin@waterside.com *Web Site:* www.waterside.com, pg 579

Jackolin, Jennifer, Waveland Press Inc, 4180 IL Rte 83, Suite 101, Long Grove, IL 60047-9580 *Tel:* 847-634-0081 *Fax:* 847-634-9501 *E-mail:* info@waveland.com *Web Site:* www.waveland.com, pg 268

Jackson, Bill, Workman Publishing Co Inc, 225 Varick St, 9th fl, New York, NY 10014-4381 *Tel:* 212-254-5900 *Toll Free Tel:* 800-722-7202 *Fax:* 212-254-8098 *E-mail:* info@workman.com *Web Site:* www.workman.com, pg 275

Jackson, Bobby L, Multicultural Publications Inc, 936 Slosson St, Akron, OH 44320 *Tel:* 330-865-9578 *Fax:* 330-865-9578 *E-mail:* multiculturalpub@prodigy.net *Web Site:* www.multiculturalpub.net, pg 161

Jackson, Carolyn, Second Story Press, 20 Maud St, Suite 401, Toronto, ON M5V 2M5, Canada *Tel:* 416-537-7850 *Fax:* 416-537-0588 *E-mail:* info@secondstorypress.ca *Web Site:* secondstorypress.ca, pg 498

Jackson, Chrissy, Florida Writers Association Conference, PO Box 66069, St Pete Beach, FL 33736-6069 *Web Site:* www.floridawriters.net, pg 651

Jackson, Chrissy, Florida Writers Association Inc, PO Box 66069, St Pete Beach, FL 33736-6069 *Web Site:* www.floridawriters.net, pg 606

Jackson, Christopher, Random House Publishing Group, 1745 Broadway, New York, NY 10019 *Toll Free Tel:* 800-200-3552 *Web Site:* atrandom.com, pg 204

Jackson, David B, Stanford University Press, 1450 Page Mill Rd, Palo Alto, CA 94304-1124 *Tel:* 650-723-9434 *Fax:* 650-725-3457 *E-mail:* info@sup.org *Web Site:* www.sup.org, pg 233

Jackson, Eleanor, Dunow, Carlson & Lerner Literary Agency Inc, 27 W 20 St, Suite 1107, New York, NY 10011 *Tel:* 212-645-7606 *E-mail:* mail@dclagency.com *Web Site:* www.dclagency.com, pg 549

Jackson, Heather, Crown Publishing Group, c/o Penguin Random House Inc, 1745 Broadway, New York, NY 10019 *Tel:* 212-782-9000 *Toll Free Tel:* 888-264-1745 *Fax:* 212-940-7408 *E-mail:* crownosm@penguinrandomhouse.com *Web Site:* crownpublishing.com, pg 68

Jackson, Jennifer, Doubleday/Nan A Talese, c/o Penguin Random House Inc, 1745 Broadway, New York, NY 10019 *Tel:* 212-751-2600 *Fax:* 212-572-2662 *E-mail:* ddaypub@randomhouse.com *Web Site:* knopfdoubleday.com, pg 76

Jackson, Jennifer, Alfred A Knopf/Everyman's Library, c/o Random House Inc, 1745 Broadway, New York, NY 10019 *Tel:* 212-751-2600 *Toll Free Tel:* 800-638-6460 *Fax:* 212-572-2593 *Web Site:* www.knopfdoubleday.com, pg 132

Jackson, Jennifer, Donald Maass Literary Agency, 121 W 27 St, Suite 801, New York, NY 10001 *Tel:* 212-727-8383 *Fax:* 212-727-3271 *E-mail:* info@maassagency.com *Web Site:* www.maassagency.com, pg 562

Jackson, Joe, University of Chicago Press, 1427 E 60 St, Chicago, IL 60637-2954 *Tel:* 773-702-7700; 773-702-7600 *Toll Free Tel:* 800-621-2736 (orders) *Fax:* 773-702-9756; 773-660-2235 (orders); 773-702-2708 *E-mail:* custserv@press.uchicago.edu; marketing@press.uchicago.edu *Web Site:* www.press.uchicago.edu, pg 255

Jackson, Judy, Northeast Texas Community College Annual Writers Conference, Continuing Education, PO Box 1307, Mount Pleasant, TX 75456-1307 *Tel:* 903-434-8134 *Toll Free Tel:* 800-870-0142 *Fax:* 903-572-6712 *Web Site:* www.ntcc.edu, pg 653

Jackson, Kate, HarperCollins Children's Books, 195 Broadway, New York, NY 10007 *Tel:* 212-207-7000 *Web Site:* www.harpercollins.com/childrens, pg 105

Jackson, Lauren, Harlequin Enterprises Ltd, 233 Broadway, Suite 1001, New York, NY 10279 *Tel:* 212-553-4200 *Fax:* 212-227-8969 *E-mail:* CustomerService@harlequin.com *Web Site:* www.harlequin.com, pg 105

Jackson, Marie Marr, United States Institute of Peace Press, 2301 Constitution Ave NW, Washington, DC 20037 *Tel:* 202-457-1700 (edit); 703-661-1590 (cust serv) *Toll Free Tel:* 800-868-8064 (cust serv) *Fax:* 202-429-6063; 703-661-1501 (cust serv) *Web Site:* bookstore.usip.org, pg 253

Jackson, Melanie, Melanie Jackson Agency LLC, 41 W 72 St, Suite 3F, New York, NY 10023 *Tel:* 212-873-3373, pg 558

Jackson, Patricia, Regnery Publishing Inc, 300 New Jersey Ave NW, Washington, DC 20001 *Tel:* 202-216-0600 *Toll Free Tel:* 888-219-4747 *Fax:* 202-216-0612 *Web Site:* www.regnery.com, pg 208

Jackson, Regina, Warner Press, 1201 E Fifth St, Anderson, IN 46018 *Tel:* 765-644-7721 *Toll Free Tel:* 800-741-7721 (orders) *Fax:* 765-640-8005 *Toll Free Fax:* 800-347-6411 *E-mail:* wporders@warnerpress.org *Web Site:* www.warnerpress.org, pg 267

Jacob, Chris, HeartMath LLC, 14700 W Park Ave, Boulder Creek, CA 95006 *Tel:* 831-338-8700 *Toll Free Tel:* 800-450-9111 *Fax:* 831-338-9861 *E-mail:* inquiry@heartmath.com *Web Site:* www.heartmath.com, pg 109

Jacob, Mary Ann, Texas A&M University Press, John H Lindsey Bldg, Lewis St, 4354 TAMU, College Station, TX 77843-4354 *Tel:* 979-845-1436 *Toll Free Tel:* 800-826-8911 (orders) *Fax:* 979-847-8752 *Toll Free Fax:* 888-617-2421 (orders) *E-mail:* tampress@tamu.edu *Web Site:* www.tamupress.com, pg 243

Jacobs, Andrea, The Globe Pequot Press, 246 Goose Lane, Guilford, CT 06437 *Tel:* 203-458-4500 *Toll Free Tel:* 800-243-0495 (orders only); 888-249-7586 (cust serv) *Fax:* 203-458-4601 *Toll Free Fax:* 800-820-2329 (orders & cust serv) *E-mail:* editorial@globepequot.com; info@rowman.com; orders@rowman.com *Web Site:* rowman.com, pg 98

Jacobs, Ben, Bloom's Literary Criticism, 132 W 31 St, 17th fl, New York, NY 10001 *Toll Free Tel:* 800-322-8755 *Toll Free Fax:* 800-678-3633 *E-mail:* custserv@factsonfile.com *Web Site:* www.infobasepublishing.com, pg 39

Jacobs, Ben, Chelsea House Publishers, 132 W 31 St, 17th fl, New York, NY 10001 *Tel:* 212-967-8800 *Toll Free Tel:* 800-322-8755 *Fax:* 917-339-0325 *Toll Free Fax:* 800-678-3633 *E-mail:* custserv@factsonfile.com *Web Site:* www.infobasepublishing.com; www.infobaselearning.com, pg 56

Jacobs, Ben, Facts On File, 132 W 31 St, 17th fl, New York, NY 10001 *Tel:* 212-967-8800 *Toll Free Tel:* 800-322-8755 *Toll Free Fax:* 800-678-3633 *E-mail:* custserv@factsonfile.com *Web Site:* infobasepublishing.com, pg 85

Jacobs, Ben, Ferguson Publishing, 132 W 31 St, 17th fl, New York, NY 10001 *Tel:* 212-967-8800 *Toll Free Tel:* 800-322-8755 *Fax:* 917-339-0323 *Toll Free Fax:* 800-678-3633 *E-mail:* custserv@factsonfile.com *Web Site:* infobasepublishing.com, pg 88

Jacobs, Ben, World Almanac®, 132 W 31 St, New York, NY 10001 *Toll Free Tel:* 800-322-8755 *E-mail:* almanac@factsonfile.com *Web Site:* www.worldalmanac.com, pg 275

Jacobs, Donald, Georgetown University Press, 3240 Prospect St NW, Suite 250, Washington, DC 20007 *Tel:* 202-687-5889 (busn) *Fax:* 202-687-6340 (edit) *E-mail:* gupress@georgetown.edu *Web Site:* press.georgetown.edu, pg 96

Jacobs, Farrin, Little, Brown Books for Young Readers, 1290 Avenue of the Americas, New York, NY 10019 *Tel:* 212-364-1100 *Toll Free Tel:* 800-759-0190 (cust serv) *Web Site:* www.HachetteBookGroup.com, pg 141

Jacobs, Laurence, Craftsman Book Co, 6058 Corte Del Cedro, Carlsbad, CA 92011 *Tel:* 760-438-7828 *Toll Free Tel:* 800-829-8123 *Fax:* 760-438-0398 *Web Site:* www.craftsman-book.com, pg 66

Jacobs, Lindy, Oregon Christian Writers (OCW), 1075 Willow Lake Rd N, Keizer, OR 97303 *Tel:* 503-393-3356 *E-mail:* contact@oregonchristianwriters.org *Web Site:* www.oregonchristianwriters.org, pg 615

Jacobs, Lindy, Oregon Christian Writers Coaching Conference, 1075 Willow Lake Rd N, Keizer, OR 97303 *Tel:* 503-393-3356 *E-mail:* contact@oregonchristianwriters.org *Web Site:* www.oregonchristianwriters.org, pg 653

Jacobs, Madeleine, The American Chemical Society, 1155 16 St NW, Washington, DC 20036 *Tel:* 202-872-4600 *Toll Free Tel:* 800-227-5558 (US) *Fax:* 202-872-6067 *E-mail:* help@acs.org *Web Site:* www.acs.org, pg 12

Jacobs, Michael, Harry N Abrams Inc, 115 W 18 St, 6th fl, New York, NY 10011 *Tel:* 212-206-7715 *Toll Free Tel:* 800-345-1359 *Fax:* 212-519-1210 *E-mail:* abrams@abramsbooks.com *Web Site:* www.abramsbooks.com, pg 3

Jacobs, Michael, Stewart, Tabori & Chang, 115 W 18 St, 6th fl, New York, NY 10011 *Tel:* 212-519-1200 *Fax:* 212-519-1210 *Web Site:* www.abramsbooks.com, pg 236

Jacobs, Nicki, Literary Translation Projects, 400 Seventh St SW, Washington, DC 20506-0001 *Tel:* 202-682-5400; 202-682-5496 (Voice/TTY); 202-682-5034 (lit fellowships hotline) *Fax:* 202-682-5609; 202-682-5610 *E-mail:* litfellowships@arts.gov *Web Site:* www.arts.gov; www.nea.gov, pg 702

Jacobs, Nicki, NEA Literature Fellowships, 400 Seventh St SW, Washington, DC 20506-0001 *Tel:* 202-682-5400; 202-682-5496 (Voice/TTY); 202-682-5034 (lit fellowships hotline) *Fax:* 202-682-5609; 202-682-5610 *E-mail:* litfellowships@arts.gov *Web Site:* www.arts.gov; www.nea.gov, pg 711

Jacobs, Robert H, Univelt Inc, 740 Metcalf St, No 13 & 15, Escondido, CA 92025 *Tel:* 760-746-4005 *Fax:* 760-746-3139 *E-mail:* sales@univelt.com *Web Site:* www.univelt.com; www.astronautical.org, pg 254

Jacobs, Valerie Seiling, Mews Books Ltd, 20 Bluewater Hill, Westport, CT 06880 *Tel:* 203-227-1836 *Fax:* 203-227-1144 *E-mail:* mewsbooks@aol.com, pg 565

Jacobsen, Jodi R, Sheffield Publishing Co, 9009 Antioch Rd, Salem, WI 53168 *Tel:* 262-843-2281 *Fax:* 262-843-3683 *E-mail:* info@spcbooks.com *Web Site:* www.spcbooks.com, pg 223

Jacobson, Gretchen, NACE International, 1440 S Creek Dr, Houston, TX 77084-4906 *Tel:* 281-228-6200 *Toll Free Tel:* 800-797-NACE (797-6223) *Fax:* 281-228-6300 *E-mail:* firstservice@nace.org *Web Site:* www.nace.org, pg 162

Jacobson, Kip, Blue Apple Books, 515 Valley St, Suite 170, Maplewood, NJ 07040 *Tel:* 973-763-8191 *Toll Free Tel:* 800-283-3572 (orders) *Fax:* 973-763-5944 *E-mail:* info@blueapplebooks.com *Web Site:* blueapplebooks.com, pg 40

Jacobson, Tina, The Barnabas Agency, PO Box 3113, Corsicana, TX 75110-3113 *Toll Free Tel:* 800-927-0517 *E-mail:* info@barnabasagency.com *Web Site:* www.barnabasagency.com, pg 587

Jacobson, Wendy, Martingale®, 19021 120 Ave NE, Suite 102, Bothell, WA 98011 *Tel:* 425-483-3313 *Toll Free Tel:* 800-426-3126 *Fax:* 425-486-7596 *E-mail:* info@martingale-pub.com *Web Site:* www.martingale-pub.com, pg 148

Jacoby, Judy, Doubleday/Nan A Talese, c/o Penguin Random House Inc, 1745 Broadway, New York, NY 10019 *Tel:* 212-751-2600 *Fax:* 212-572-2662 *E-mail:* ddaypub@randomhouse.com *Web Site:* knopfdoubleday.com, pg 76

Jade, Miranda, Imagination Publishing Group, PO Box 1304, Dunedin, FL 34697 *Toll Free Tel:* 888-701-6481 *Fax:* 727-361-0584 *E-mail:* info@imaginationpublishinggroup.com *Web Site:* www.imaginationpublishinggroup.com, pg 119

Jaffa, Molly, Folio Literary Management LLC, The Film Center Bldg, 630 Ninth Ave, Suite 1101, New York, NY 10036 *Tel:* 212-400-1494 *Fax:* 212-967-0977 *Web Site:* www.foliolit.com, pg 552

Jaffe, Gary, Linda Chester Literary Agency, 630 Fifth Ave, Suite 2000, New York, NY 10111 *Tel:* 212-218-3350 *Fax:* 212-218-3343 *E-mail:* submissions@lindachester.com *Web Site:* www.lindachester.com, pg 546

Jaffe, Susanne, Thurber Prize for American Humor, 77 Jefferson Ave, Columbus, OH 43215 *Tel:* 614-464-1032 *Fax:* 614-280-3645 *E-mail:* thurberhouse@thurberhouse.org *Web Site:* www.thurberhouse.org, pg 732

Jaffrey, Zareen, Simon & Schuster Children's Publishing, 1230 Avenue of the Americas, New York, NY 10020 *Tel:* 212-698-7000 *Web Site:* KIDS.SimonandSchuster.com; TEEN.SimonandSchuster.com; simonandschuster.net; simonandschuster.biz, pg 225

Jahns, Randy, Crossway, 1300 Crescent St, Wheaton, IL 60187 *Tel:* 630-682-4300 *Toll Free Tel:* 800-635-7993 (orders); 800-543-1659 (cust serv) *Fax:* 630-682-4785 *E-mail:* info@crossway.org *Web Site:* www.crossway.org, pg 67

Jain, Mukesh, Jain Publishing Co, PO Box 3523, Fremont, CA 94539 *Tel:* 510-659-8272 *Fax:* 510-659-0501 *E-mail:* mail@jainpub.com *Web Site:* www.jainpub.com, pg 126

Jaitly, Kay, Bellagio Press, 5501 Kincross Lane, Charlotte, NC 28277 *Web Site:* bellagiopress.com, pg 34

Jaksah, Joel, Hazelden Publishing, 15251 Pleasant Valley Rd, Center City, MN 55012-0011 *Tel:* 651-213-4200 *Toll Free Tel:* 800-257-7810 *Fax:* 651-213-4590 *E-mail:* info@hazelden.org *Web Site:* www.hazelden.org, pg 108

James, Angela, Harlequin Enterprises Ltd, 225 Duncan Mill Rd, Don Mills, ON M3B 3K9, Canada *Tel:* 416-445-5860 *Toll Free Tel:* 888-432-4879; 800-370-5838 (ebook inquiries) *E-mail:* customerservice@harlequin.com *Web Site:* www.harlequin.com, pg 487

James, Diane, Worthy & James Publishing, PO Box 362015, Milpitas, CA 95036 *Tel:* 408-945-3963 *E-mail:* worthy1234@sbcglobal.net; mail@worthyjames.com *Web Site:* www.worthyjames.com, pg 509

James, Gethin, Lugus Publications, 28 Industrial St, Studio 203, Toronto, ON M4G 1Y9, Canada *Tel:* 416-467-0924 *Web Site:* www.thestudio203.com, pg 490

James, Jacqueline, Lugus Publications, 28 Industrial St, Studio 203, Toronto, ON M4G 1Y9, Canada *Tel:* 416-467-0924 *Web Site:* www.thestudio203.com, pg 490

James, Jeff, Thomas Nelson, 501 Nelson Place, Nashville, TN 37214 *Tel:* 615-889-9000 *Toll Free Tel:* 800-251-4000 *Fax:* 615-902-1548 *E-mail:* publicity@thomasnelson.com *Web Site:* www.thomasnelson.com, pg 245

James, Selena, Kensington Publishing Corp, 119 W 40 St, New York, NY 10018 *Tel:* 212-407-1500 *Toll Free Tel:* 800-221-2647 *Fax:* 212-935-0699 *Web Site:* www.kensingtonbooks.com, pg 130

James, Tina, Harlequin Enterprises Ltd, 233 Broadway, Suite 1001, New York, NY 10279 *Tel:* 212-553-4200 *Fax:* 212-227-8969 *E-mail:* CustomerService@harlequin.com *Web Site:* www.harlequin.com, pg 105

James, Tina, Love Inspired Books, 233 Broadway, Suite 1001, New York, NY 10279 *Tel:* 212-553-4200 *Fax:* 212-227-8969 *E-mail:* customer_service@harlequin.ca *Web Site:* www.harlequin.com, pg 143

James-Gilboe, Lynda, ProQuest LLC, 789 E Eisenhower Pkwy, Ann Arbor, MI 48108-3218 *Tel:* 734-761-4700 *Toll Free Tel:* 800-521-0600 *Fax:* 734-975-6486 *Toll Free Fax:* 800-864-0019 *E-mail:* info@proquest.com *Web Site:* www.proquest.com, pg 199

Jamison, Mark, Magazines Canada (MC), 425 Adelaide St W, Suite 700, Toronto, ON M5V 3C1, Canada *Tel:* 416-504-0274 *Fax:* 416-504-0437 *E-mail:* info@magazinescanada.ca *Web Site:* www.magazinescanada.ca/development/magnet, pg 609

Jan, Kevin, Crown Publishing Group, c/o Penguin Random House Inc, 1745 Broadway, New York, NY 10019 *Tel:* 212-782-9000 *Toll Free Tel:* 888-264-1745 *Fax:* 212-940-7408 *E-mail:* crownosm@penguinrandomhouse.com *Web Site:* crownpublishing.com, pg 68

Janecke, Roger, Visible Ink Press®, 43311 Joy Rd, Suite 414, Canton, MI 48187-2075 *Tel:* 734-667-3211 *Fax:* 734-667-4311 *E-mail:* info@visibleink.com *Web Site:* www.visibleink.com, pg 266

Janes, Phil, Indiana Historical Society Press (IHS Press), 450 W Ohio St, Indianapolis, IN 46202-3269 *Tel:* 317-232-1882; 317-234-0026 (orders); 317-234-2716 (edit) *Toll Free Tel:* 800-447-1830 (orders) *Fax:* 317-234-0562 (orders); 317-233-0857 (edit) *E-mail:* ihspress@indianahistory.org; orders@indianahistory.org (orders) *Web Site:* www.indianahistory.org; shop.indianahistory.org (orders), pg 120

Janeway, Brant, St Martin's Press, LLC, 175 Fifth Ave, New York, NY 10010 *Tel:* 646-307-5151 *Fax:* 212-420-9314 *E-mail:* firstname.lastname@macmillan.com *Web Site:* www.stmartins.com, pg 214

Janik, Daniel S, Savant Books & Publications LLC, 2630 Kapiolani Blvd, Suite 1601, Honolulu, HI 96826 *Tel:* 808-941-3927 *Fax:* 808-941-3927 *E-mail:* savantbooks@gmail.com *Web Site:* www.savantbooksandpublications.com, pg 217

Janiszewski, Kerry, NAL, 375 Hudson St, New York, NY 10014 *Tel:* 212-366-2000 *E-mail:* online@penguinputnam.com *Web Site:* www.penguinputnam.com; us.penguingroup.com, pg 162

Janklow, Lucas W, Janklow & Nesbit Associates, 445 Park Ave, New York, NY 10022 *Tel:* 212-421-1700 *Fax:* 212-980-3671 *E-mail:* info@janklow.com *Web Site:* www.janklowandnesbit.com, pg 558

Janklow, Morton L, Janklow & Nesbit Associates, 445 Park Ave, New York, NY 10022 *Tel:* 212-421-1700 *Fax:* 212-980-3671 *E-mail:* info@janklow.com *Web Site:* www.janklowandnesbit.com, pg 558

Jannsohn, Aimee, The Pilgrim Press/United Church Press, 700 Prospect Ave, Cleveland, OH 44115-1100 *Toll Free Tel:* 800-537-3394 (cust serv-indivs); 800-654-5129 (cust serv-commercial accts) *Fax:* 216-736-2206 (orders) *E-mail:* proposals@thepilgrimpress.com *Web Site:* www.thepilgrimpress.com; www.unitedchurchpress.com, pg 192

Jansen, Gary, Crown Publishing Group, c/o Penguin Random House Inc, 1745 Broadway, New York, NY 10019 *Tel:* 212-782-9000 *Toll Free Tel:* 888-264-1745 *Fax:* 212-940-7408 *E-mail:* crownosm@penguinrandomhouse.com *Web Site:* crownpublishing.com, pg 68

Janson, Karen, Barefoot Books, 2067 Massachusetts Ave, 5th fl, Cambridge, MA 02140 *Tel:* 617-576-0660 *Toll Free Tel:* 866-215-1756 (cust serv); 866-417-2369 (orders) *Fax:* 617-576-0049 *E-mail:* help@barefootbooks.com *Web Site:* www.barefootbooks.com, pg 30

Janssen, Karl, University Press of Kansas, 2502 Westbrooke Circle, Lawrence, KS 66045-4444 *Tel:* 785-864-4154; 785-864-4155 (orders) *Fax:* 785-864-4586 *E-mail:* upress@ku.edu; upkorders@ku.edu (orders) *Web Site:* www.kansaspress.ku.edu, pg 261

Janssen, Peter, Macmillan, 175 Fifth Ave, New York, NY 10010 *Tel:* 646-307-5151 *Fax:* 212-420-9314 *E-mail:* firstname.lastname@macmillan.com *Web Site:* www.macmillan.com, pg 145

Janssen, Sarah, World Almanac®, 132 W 31 St, New York, NY 10001 *Toll Free Tel:* 800-322-8755 *E-mail:* almanac@factsonfile.com *Web Site:* www.worldalmanac.com, pg 275

Jantz, Stan, Regal Books, 1957 Eastman Ave, Ventura, CA 93003 *Tel:* 805-644-9721 *Toll Free Tel:* 800-446-7735 (orders) *Web Site:* www.regalbooks.com; www.gospellight.com, pg 207

Janus, CSP, Mark-David, Paulist Press, 997 Macarthur Blvd, Mahwah, NJ 07430-9990 *Tel:* 201-825-7300 *Toll Free Tel:* 800-218-1903 *Fax:* 201-825-8345 *Toll Free Fax:* 800-836-3161 *E-mail:* info@paulistpress.com *Web Site:* www.paulistpress.com, pg 184

Janusz, Julie, ProQuest LLC, 789 E Eisenhower Pkwy, Ann Arbor, MI 48108-3218 *Tel:* 734-761-4700 *Toll Free Tel:* 800-521-0600 *Fax:* 734-975-6486 *Toll Free Fax:* 800-864-0019 *E-mail:* info@proquest.com *Web Site:* www.proquest.com, pg 199

Jao, Jonathan, HarperCollins General Books Group, 195 Broadway, New York, NY 10007 *Tel:* 212-207-7000 *Web Site:* www.harpercollins.com, pg 105

Japikse, Carl, Ariel Press, 3854 Mason Rd, Canal Winchester, OH 43110 *Toll Free Tel:* 800-336-7769 *E-mail:* lig201@lightariel.com *Web Site:* www.lightariel.com, pg 22

Jaque, Cathy, The Karpfinger Agency, 357 W 20 St, New York, NY 10011-3379 *Tel:* 212-691-2690 *Fax:* 212-691-7129 *E-mail:* info@karpfinger.com (no queries or submissions) *Web Site:* karpfinger.com, pg 559

Jaquith, George, Wind Canyon Books, PO Box 7035, Stockton, CA 95267 *Tel:* 209-956-1600 *Toll Free Tel:* 800-952-7007 *Fax:* 209-956-9424 *Toll Free Fax:* 888-289-7086 *E-mail:* books@windcanyonbooks.com *Web Site:* www.windcanyonbooks.com, pg 273

Jaramillo, Raquel, Workman Publishing Co Inc, 225 Varick St, 9th fl, New York, NY 10014-4381 *Tel:* 212-254-5900 *Toll Free Tel:* 800-722-7202 *Fax:* 212-254-8098 *E-mail:* info@workman.com *Web Site:* www.workman.com, pg 275

Jarrad, Mary Beth, New York University Press, 838 Broadway, 3rd fl, New York, NY 10003-4812 *Tel:* 212-998-2575 (edit) *Toll Free Tel:* 800-996-6987 (orders) *Fax:* 212-995-3833 (orders) *E-mail:* information@nyupress.org; customerservice@nyupress.org; orders@nyupress.org *Web Site:* www.nyupress.org, pg 169

Jarvela, Allison, HarperCollins Publishers, 195 Broadway, New York, NY 10007 *Tel:* 212-207-7000 *Fax:* 212-207-7145 *Web Site:* www.harpercollins.com, pg 106

Jasmine, Michelle, Random House Publishing Group, 1745 Broadway, New York, NY 10019 *Toll Free Tel:* 800-200-3552 *Web Site:* atrandom.com, pg 204

Javsicas, Aaron, W W Norton & Company Inc, 500 Fifth Ave, New York, NY 10110-0017 *Tel:* 212-354-5500 *Toll Free Tel:* 800-233-4830 (orders & cust serv) *Fax:* 212-869-0856 *Toll Free Fax:* 800-458-6515 *Web Site:* www.wwnorton.com, pg 172

Jean-Francois, Jessica, National Press Foundation, 1211 Connecticut Ave NW, Suite 310, Washington, DC 20036 *Tel:* 202-663-7280 *Web Site:* nationalpress.org, pg 613

Jebb, Michaela, Storey Publishing LLC, 210 MASS MoCA Way, North Adams, MA 01247 *Tel:* 413-346-2100 *Toll Free Tel:* 800-441-5700 (orders); 800-793-9396 (edit) *Fax:* 413-346-2199; 413-346-2196 (edit) *E-mail:* sales@storey.com *Web Site:* www.storey.com, pg 236

Jeffrey, Douglas A, Hillsdale College Press, 33 E College St, Hillsdale, MI 49242 *Tel:* 517-437-7341 *Toll Free Tel:* 800-437-2268 *Fax:* 517-437-3923 *E-mail:* news@hillsdale.edu *Web Site:* www.hillsdale.edu, pg 111

Jeglinski, Melissa, The Knight Agency Inc, 570 East Ave, Madison, GA 30650 *E-mail:* submissions@knightagency.net *Web Site:* www.knightagency.net, pg 560

Jelen, Carole, Waterside Productions Inc, 2055 Oxford Ave, Cardiff, CA 92007 *Tel:* 760-632-9190 *Fax:* 760-632-9295 *E-mail:* admin@waterside.com *Web Site:* www.waterside.com, pg 579

Jellinek, Roger, Jellinek & Murray Literary Agency, 47-231 Kamakoi Rd, Kaneohe, HI 96744 *Tel:* 808-239-8451, pg 558

Jenkins, Jerrold R, Axiom Business Book Awards, 1129 Woodmere Ave, Suite B, Traverse City, MI 49686 *Tel:* 231-933-0445 *Toll Free Tel:* 800-706-4636 *Fax:* 231-933-0448 *E-mail:* info@axiomawards.com *Web Site:* www.axiomawards.com, pg 669

Jenkins, Jerrold R, eLit Awards, 1129 Woodmere Ave, Suite B, Traverse City, MI 49686 *Tel:* 231-933-0445 *Toll Free Tel:* 800-706-4636 *Fax:* 231-933-0448 *E-mail:* info@elitawards.com *Web Site:* www.elitawards.com, pg 683

Jenkins, Jerrold R, Illumination Book Awards, 1129 Woodmere Ave, Suite B, Traverse City, MI 49686 *Tel:* 231-933-0445 *Toll Free Tel:* 800-706-4636 *Fax:* 231-933-0448 *E-mail:* awards@bookpublishing.com *Web Site:* www.illuminationawards.com, pg 694

Jenkins, Jerrold R, The Independent Publisher Book Awards, 1129 Woodmere Ave, Suite B, Traverse City, MI 49686 *Tel:* 231-933-0445 *Toll Free Tel:* 800-706-4636 *Fax:* 231-933-0448 *E-mail:* awards@bookpublishing.com *Web Site:* www.independentpublisher.com/ipland/ipawards.php, pg 694

Jenkins, Jerrold R, Jenkins Group Inc, 1129 Woodmere Ave, Suite B, Traverse City, MI 49686 *Tel:* 231-933-0445 *Toll Free Tel:* 800-706-4636 *Fax:* 231-933-0448 *E-mail:* info@bookpublishing.com *Web Site:* www.bookpublishing.com, pg 528

Jenkins, Jerrold R, Living Now Book Awards, 1129 Woodmere Ave, Suite B, Traverse City, MI 49686 *Tel:* 231-933-0445 *Toll Free Tel:* 800-706-4636 *Fax:* 231-933-0448 *E-mail:* awards@bookpublishing.com *Web Site:* www.livingnowawards.com, pg 702

Jenkins, Jerrold R, Moonbeam Children's Book Awards, 1129 Woodmere Ave, Suite B, Traverse City, MI 49686 *Tel:* 231-933-0445 *Toll Free Tel:* 800-706-4636 *Fax:* 231-933-0448 *E-mail:* info@moonbeamawards.com *Web Site:* www.moonbeamawards.com, pg 709

Jenkins, John, The MIT Press, 55 Hayward St, Cambridge, MA 02142 *Tel:* 617-253-5255 *Toll Free Tel:* 800-207-8354 (orders) *Fax:* 617-258-6779; 617-577-1545 (orders) *Web Site:* mitpress.mit.edu, pg 158

Jenkins, Joyce, Northern California Book Awards, c/o Poetry Flash, 1450 Fourth St, Suite 4, Berkeley, CA 94710 *Tel:* 510-525-5476 *Fax:* 510-525-6752 *E-mail:* editor@poetryflash.org *Web Site:* www.poetryflash.org/ncba.html, pg 713

Jenkins, Joyce, Poetry Flash Reading Series, 1450 Fourth St, Suite 4, Berkeley, CA 94710 *Tel:* 510-525-5476 *Fax:* 510-525-6752 *E-mail:* editor@poetryflash.org *Web Site:* www.poetryflash.org, pg 654

Jenkinson, John, Workman Publishing Co Inc, 225 Varick St, 9th fl, New York, NY 10014-4381 *Tel:* 212-254-5900 *Toll Free Tel:* 800-722-7202 *Fax:* 212-254-8098 *E-mail:* info@workman.com *Web Site:* www.workman.com, pg 275

Jenks, Carolyn, Carolyn Jenks Agency, 30 Cambridge Park Dr, Suite 3140, Cambridge, MA 02140 *Tel:* 617-354-5099 *Fax:* 617-354-5099 *E-mail:* queries@carolynjenksagency.com (submissions) *Web Site:* www.carolynjenksagency.com, pg 558

Jenness, Morgan, Abrams Artists Agency, 275 Seventh Ave, 26th fl, New York, NY 10001 *Tel:* 646-486-4600 *Fax:* 646-486-2358 *E-mail:* literary@abramsartny.com *Web Site:* www.abramsartists.com, pg 539

Jennings, Sharon, Canadian Society of Children's Authors Illustrators & Performers (CANSCAIP), 720 Bathurst St, Suite 503, Toronto, ON M5S 2R4, Canada *Tel:* 416-515-1559 *E-mail:* office@canscaip.org *Web Site:* www.canscaip.org, pg 602

Jensen, Chris, IEEE Computer Society, 2001 "L" St NW, Suite 700, Washington, DC 20036-4928 *Tel:* 202-371-0101 *Toll Free Tel:* 800-272-6657 (memb info) *Fax:* 202-728-9614 *E-mail:* help@computer.org *Web Site:* www.computer.org, pg 118

Jensen, Connie, Saint Mary's Press, 702 Terrace Heights, Winona, MN 55987-1318 *Tel:* 507-457-7900 *Toll Free Tel:* 800-533-8095 *Fax:* 507-457-7990 *Toll Free Fax:* 800-344-9225 *E-mail:* smpress@smp.org *Web Site:* www.smp.org, pg 215

Jensen, Jack, Chronicle Books LLC, 680 Second St, San Francisco, CA 94107 *Tel:* 415-537-4200 *Toll Free Tel:* 800-759-0190 (cust serv) *Fax:* 415-537-4460 *Toll Free Fax:* 800-858-7787 (orders); 800-286-9471 (cust serv) *E-mail:* frontdesk@chroniclebooks.com *Web Site:* www.chroniclebooks.com, pg 57

Jensen, Neysa, SDP Publishing Solutions LLC, 36 Captain's Way, East Bridgewater, MA 02333 *Tel:* 617-775-0656 *Web Site:* www.sdppublishingsolutions.com, pg 534

Jensen, Renee, National Association of Insurance Commissioners, 2301 McGee St, Suite 800, Kansas City, MO 64108-2662 *Tel:* 816-842-3600; 816-783-8300 (cust serv) *Fax:* 816-783-8175; 816-460-7593 (cust serv) *E-mail:* prodserv@naic.org *Web Site:* www.naic.org, pg 163

Jerman, Alice, HarperCollins Children's Books, 195 Broadway, New York, NY 10007 *Tel:* 212-207-7000 *Web Site:* www.harpercollins.com/childrens, pg 105

Jewell, Caroline, ALSC BWI/Summer Reading Program Grant, 50 E Huron St, Chicago, IL 60611-2795 *Tel:* 312-280-2163 *Toll Free Tel:* 800-545-2433 *Fax:* 312-440-9374 *E-mail:* alsc@ala.org *Web Site:* www.ala.org/alsc, pg 667

Jewell, Caroline, The May Hill Arbuthnot Honor Lecture Award, 50 E Huron St, Chicago, IL 60611-2795 *Tel:* 312-280-2163 *Toll Free Tel:* 800-545-2433 *Fax:* 312-440-9374 *E-mail:* alsc@ala.org *Web Site:* www.ala.org/alsc, pg 668

Jewell, Caroline, The Mildred L Batchelder Award, 50 E Huron St, Chicago, IL 60611-2795 *Tel:* 312-280-2163 *Toll Free Tel:* 800-545-2433 *Fax:* 312-440-9374 *E-mail:* alsc@ala.org *Web Site:* www.ala.org/alsc, pg 670

Jewell, Caroline, The Pura Belpre Award, 50 E Huron St, Chicago, IL 60611-2795 *Tel:* 312-280-2163 *Toll Free Tel:* 800-545-2433 *Fax:* 312-440-9374 *E-mail:* alsc@ala.org *Web Site:* www.ala.org/alsc, pg 671

Jewell, Caroline, Bound to Stay Bound Books Scholarship, 50 E Huron St, Chicago, IL 60611-2795 *Tel:* 312-280-2163 *Toll Free Tel:* 800-545-2433 *Fax:* 312-440-9374 *E-mail:* alsc@ala.org *Web Site:* www.ala.org/alsc, pg 673

Jewell, Caroline, The Randolph Caldecott Medal, 50 E Huron St, Chicago, IL 60611-2795 *Tel:* 312-280-2163 *Toll Free Tel:* 800-545-2433 *Fax:* 312-440-9374 *E-mail:* alsc@ala.org *Web Site:* www.ala.org/alsc, pg 675

Jewell, Caroline, Frederic G Melcher Scholarship, 50 E Huron St, Chicago, IL 60611-2795 *Tel:* 312-280-2163 *Toll Free Tel:* 800-545-2433 *Fax:* 312-440-9374 *E-mail:* alsc@ala.org *Web Site:* www.ala.org/alsc, pg 707

Jewell, Caroline, John Newbery Medal, 50 E Huron St, Chicago, IL 60611-2795 *Tel:* 312-280-2163 *Toll Free Tel:* 800-545-2433 *Fax:* 312-440-9374 *E-mail:* alsc@ala.org *Web Site:* www.ala.org/alsc, pg 713

Jewell, Caroline, Robert F Sibert Informational Book Award, 50 E Huron St, Chicago, IL 60611-2795 *Tel:* 312-280-2163 *Toll Free Tel:* 800-545-2433 *Fax:* 312-440-9374 *E-mail:* alsc@ala.org *Web Site:* www.ala.org/alsc, pg 728

Jewell, Caroline, The Laura Ingalls Wilder Medal, 50 E Huron St, Chicago, IL 60611-2795 *Tel:* 312-280-2163 *Toll Free Tel:* 800-545-2433 *Fax:* 312-440-9374 *E-mail:* alsc@ala.org *Web Site:* www.ala.org/alsc, pg 736

Jewell, Wanda, Southern Independent Booksellers Alliance, 3806 Yale Ave, Columbia, SC 29205 *Tel:* 803-994-9530 *Fax:* 309-410-0211 *E-mail:* info@sibaweb.com *Web Site:* www.sibaweb.com, pg 619

Jewett, Marty, Truman State University Press, 100 E Normal Ave, Kirksville, MO 63501-4221 *Tel:* 660-785-7336 *Toll Free Tel:* 800-916-6802 *Fax:* 660-785-4480 *E-mail:* tsup@truman.edu *Web Site:* tsup.truman.edu, pg 250

Jimenez, Kathy, Santillana USA Publishing Co Inc, 2023 NW 84 Ave, Doral, FL 33122 *Tel:* 305-591-9522 *Toll Free Tel:* 800-245-8584 *Fax:* 305-591-9145 *Toll Free Fax:* 888-248-9518 *E-mail:* customerservice@santillanausa.com *Web Site:* www.santillanausa.com; www.alfaguara.net, pg 216

Jimenez, Martha, Hilton Publishing, 1630 45 St, Suite 103, Munster, IN 46321 *Tel:* 219-922-4868 *Fax:* 219-924-6811 *E-mail:* info@hiltonpub.com; orders@hiltonpub.com *Web Site:* www.hiltonpub.com, pg 111

Jimenez, Sandy, Publishers Information Bureau (PIB)®, 757 Third Ave, 11th fl, New York, NY 10017 *Tel:* 212-872-3745; 212-872-3700 (MPA) *E-mail:* infocenter@magazine.org *Web Site:* www.magazine.org, pg 617

Jimenez, Sophia, Simon & Schuster, 1230 Avenue of the Americas, New York, NY 10020 *Tel:* 212-698-7000 *Toll Free Tel:* 800-223-2348 (cust serv); 800-223-2336 (orders) *Toll Free Fax:* 800-943-9831 (orders) *Web Site:* www.simonandschuster.com, pg 225

Jin, Prof Ha, Boston University, 236 Bay State Rd, Boston, MA 02215 *Tel:* 617-353-2510 *Fax:* 617-353-3653 *E-mail:* crwr@bu.edu *Web Site:* www.bu.edu/writing, pg 659

Joanisse, Joanne, Government of Canada Publications, Publishing & Depository Services, Public Works & Government Services Canada, Ottawa, ON K1A 0S5, Canada *Tel:* 613-941-5995 *Toll Free Tel:* 800-635-7943 *Fax:* 613-954-5779 *Toll Free Fax:* 800-565-7757 *E-mail:* publications@tpsgc-pwgsc.gc.ca *Web Site:* publications.gc.ca, pg 485

Jodoin, Isabelle, Modus Vivendi Publishing Inc, 55, rue Jean-Talon Ouest, 2e etage, Montreal, QC H2R 2W8, Canada *Tel:* 514-272-0433 *Fax:* 514-272-7234 *E-mail:* info@groupemodus.com *Web Site:* www.groupemodus.com, pg 491

Joel, Jennifer, ICM Partners, 730 Fifth Ave, New York, NY 10019 *Tel:* 212-556-5600 *Web Site:* www.icmtalent.com, pg 557

Joel, Richard, Yeshiva University Press, 500 W 185 St, New York, NY 10033-3201 *Tel:* 212-960-5400 *Fax:* 212-960-0043 *Web Site:* www.yu.edu, pg 278

Johannesen, Jeremy, Empire State Award for Excellence in Literature for Young People, 6021 State Farm Rd, Guilderland, NY 12084 *Tel:* 518-432-6952 *Toll Free Tel:* 800-252-6952 *Fax:* 518-427-1697 *E-mail:* info@nyla.org *Web Site:* www.nyla.org, pg 684

Johanson, Leah, Simon & Schuster, 1230 Avenue of the Americas, New York, NY 10020 *Tel:* 212-698-7000 *Toll Free Tel:* 800-223-2348 (cust serv); 800-223-2336 (orders) *Toll Free Fax:* 800-943-9831 (orders) *Web Site:* www.simonandschuster.com, pg 225

Johns, Christopher, Tuttle Publishing, Airport Business Park, 364 Innovation Dr, North Clarendon, VT 05759-9436 *Tel:* 802-773-8930 *Toll Free Tel:* 800-526-2778 *Fax:* 802-773-6993 *Toll Free Fax:* 800-FAX-TUTL *E-mail:* info@tuttlepublishing.com *Web Site:* www.tuttlepublishing.com, pg 251

Johns, Jorun, Ariadne Press, 270 Goins Ct, Riverside, CA 92507 *Tel:* 951-684-9202 *Fax:* 951-779-0449 *E-mail:* ariadnepress@aol.com *Web Site:* www.ariadnebooks.com, pg 22

Johnson, Anna, The Glen Workshop, 3307 Third Ave W, Seattle, WA 98119 *Tel:* 206-281-2988 *Fax:* 206-281-2979 *E-mail:* glenworkshop@imagejournal.org *Web Site:* www.imagejournal.org/page/events/the-glen-workshop, pg 651

Johnson, Annette R, AllWrite Advertising & Publishing, 241 Peachtree St NE, Suite 400, Atlanta, GA 30303 *Tel:* 404-221-0703 *Fax:* 770-284-8986 *E-mail:* questions@allwritepublishing.com; support@allwritepublishing.com (orders & returns) *Web Site:* allwritepublishing.com, pg 8

Johnson, Annette R, AllWrite Advertising & Publishing, 241 Peachtree St NE, Suite 400, Atlanta, GA 30303 *Tel:* 404-221-0703 *Fax:* 770-284-8986 *E-mail:* questions@allwritepublishing.com *Web Site:* www.e-allwrite.com, pg 519

Johnson, Barry, Human Kinetics Inc, 1607 N Market St, Champaign, IL 61820 *Tel:* 217-351-5076 *Toll Free Tel:* 800-747-4457 *Fax:* 217-351-1549 (orders/cust serv) *E-mail:* info@hkusa.com *Web Site:* www.humankinetics.com, pg 117

Johnson, Bennett J, Path Press Inc, 1229 Emerson St, Evanston, IL 60201 *Tel:* 847-492-0177 *E-mail:* pathpressinc@aol.com, pg 183

Johnson, Bill, Kay Snow Literary Contest, 2108 Buck St, West Linn, OR 97068 *Tel:* 503-305-6729 *Fax:* 503-344-6174 *E-mail:* wilwrite@willamettewriters.com *Web Site:* www.willamettewriters.com, pg 729

Johnson, Bill, Willamette Writers, 2108 Buck St, West Linn, OR 97068 *Tel:* 503-305-6729 *Fax:* 503-344-6174 *E-mail:* wilwrite@willamettewriters.com *Web Site:* www.willamettewriters.com, pg 621

Johnson, Bill, Willamette Writers' Conference, 2108 Buck St, West Linn, OR 97068 *Tel:* 503-305-6729 *Fax:* 503-344-6174 *E-mail:* wilwrite@willamettewriters.com *Web Site:* www.willamettewriters.com, pg 656

Johnson, Billie, Oak Tree Press, 1820 W Lacey Blvd, Suite 220, Hanford, CA 93230 *Tel:* 217-824-6500 *E-mail:* publisher@oaktreebooks.com; info@oaktreebooks.com; query@oaktreebooks.com; pressdept@oaktreebooks.com; bookorders@oaktreebooks.com *Web Site:* www.oaktreebooks.com; www.otpblog.blogspot.com, pg 173

Johnson, Blanche, Wilderness Adventures Press Inc, 45 Buckskin Rd, Belgrade, MT 59714 *Tel:* 406-388-0112 *Toll Free Tel:* 866-400-2012 *E-mail:* books@wildadvpress.com *Web Site:* store.wildadvpress.com, pg 271

Johnson, Dr Brad, Northeast Texas Community College Annual Writers Conference, Continuing Education, PO Box 1307, Mount Pleasant, TX 75456-1307 *Tel:* 903-434-8134 *Toll Free Tel:* 800-870-0142 *Fax:* 903-572-6712 *Web Site:* www.ntcc.edu, pg 653

Johnson, Prof Brian, University of Illinois, Department of Journalism, Gregory Hall, Rm 120-A, 810 S Wright St, Urbana, IL 61801 *Tel:* 217-333-0709 *Fax:* 217-333-7931 *E-mail:* journ@uiuc.edu *Web Site:* www.comm.uiuc.edu, pg 663

Johnson, Brianne, Writers House, 21 W 26 St, New York, NY 10010 *Tel:* 212-685-2400 *Fax:* 212-685-1781 *Web Site:* www.writershouse.com, pg 580

Johnson, Caitlin, St Andrews College Press, 1700 Dogwood Mile, Laurinburg, NC 28352-5598 *Tel:* 910-277-5310 *Fax:* 910-277-5020 *E-mail:* press@sapc.edu *Web Site:* www.sapc.edu/sapress, pg 214

Johnson, Candace, Health Communications Inc, 3201 SW 15 St, Deerfield Beach, FL 33442 *Tel:* 954-360-0909 *Toll Free Tel:* 800-851-9100; 800-441-5569 (cust serv & orders) *Fax:* 954-360-0034 *Toll Free Fax:* 800-424-7652 (cust serv & orders) *Web Site:* www.hcibooks.com, pg 108

Johnson, Chuck, Wilderness Adventures Press Inc, 45 Buckskin Rd, Belgrade, MT 59714 *Tel:* 406-388-0112 *Toll Free Tel:* 866-400-2012 *E-mail:* books@wildadvpress.com *Web Site:* store.wildadvpress.com, pg 271

Johnson, Cindy, Solution Tree, 555 N Morton St, Bloomington, IN 47404 *Tel:* 812-336-7700 *Toll Free Tel:* 800-733-6786 *Fax:* 812-336-7790 *E-mail:* info@solution-tree.com *Web Site:* www.solution-tree.com, pg 230

Johnson, Cliff, Cliff Johnson & Associates, 10867 Fruitland Dr, Studio City, CA 91604 *Tel:* 818-761-5665 *Fax:* 818-761-9501 *E-mail:* quest543@yahoo.com, pg 528

Johnson, Connie, Double Play, 303 Hillcrest Rd, Belton, MO 64012-1852 *Tel:* 816-651-7118, pg 524

Johnson, Crissie, University of Alabama Press, 200 Hackberry Lane, 2nd fl, Tuscaloosa, AL 35487 *Tel:* 205-348-5180 *Fax:* 205-348-9201 *Web Site:* www.uapress.ua.edu, pg 254

Johnson, Darryl, SIL International, 7500 W Camp Wisdom Rd, Dallas, TX 75236-5629 *Tel:* 972-708-7400 *Fax:* 972-708-7350 *E-mail:* publications_intl@sil.org *Web Site:* www.ethnologue.com; www.sil.org, pg 224

Johnson, Diane E, Livestock Publications Council, 910 Currie St, Fort Worth, TX 76107 *Tel:* 817-336-1130 *Fax:* 817-232-4820 *Web Site:* www.livestockpublications.com, pg 609

Johnson, Eric, Redleaf Press, 10 Yorkton Ct, St Paul, MN 55117 *Tel:* 651-641-0508 *Toll Free Tel:* 800-423-8309 *Toll Free Fax:* 800-641-0115 *Web Site:* www.redleafpress.org, pg 206

Johnson, Gary, Markson Thoma Literary Agency Inc, 44 Greenwich Ave, New York, NY 10011 *Tel:* 212-243-8480 *Fax:* 212-691-9014 *E-mail:* info@marksonthoma.com *Web Site:* www.marksonthoma.com, pg 563

Johnson, George F, Information Age Publishing Inc, PO Box 79049, Charlotte, NC 28271-7047 *Tel:* 704-752-9125 *Fax:* 704-752-9113 *E-mail:* infoage@infoagepub.com *Web Site:* www.infoagepub.com, pg 121

Johnson, Halvard, Hamilton Stone Editions, PO Box 43, Maplewood, NJ 07040 *Tel:* 973-378-8361 *E-mail:* hstone@hamiltonstone.org *Web Site:* www.hamiltonstone.org, pg 104

Johnson, Harmony, University of British Columbia Press, 2029 West Mall, Vancouver, BC V6T 1Z2, Canada *Tel:* 604-822-5959 *Toll Free Tel:* 877-377-9378 *Fax:* 604-822-6083 *Toll Free Fax:* 800-668-0821 *E-mail:* frontdesk@ubcpress.ca *Web Site:* www.ubcpress.ca, pg 502

Johnson, Howard Jr, Edgewise Press Inc, 24 Fifth Ave, Suite 224, New York, NY 10011 *Tel:* 212-982-4818 *Fax:* 212-982-1364 *E-mail:* epinc@mindspring.com *Web Site:* www.edgewisepress.org, pg 79

Johnson, Jeff, Tyndale House Publishers Inc, 351 Executive Dr, Carol Stream, IL 60188 *Tel:* 630-668-8300 *Toll Free Tel:* 800-323-9400 *Web Site:* www.tyndale.com, pg 252

Johnson, Jenna, Houghton Mifflin Harcourt Trade & Reference Division, 222 Berkeley St, Boston, MA 02116 *Tel:* 617-351-5000 *Toll Free Tel:* 800-225-3362 *Web Site:* www.hmhco.com, pg 115

Johnson, Jennifer, Craftsman Book Co, 6058 Corte Del Cedro, Carlsbad, CA 92011 *Tel:* 760-438-7828 *Toll Free Tel:* 800-829-8123 *Fax:* 760-438-0398 *Web Site:* www.craftsman-book.com, pg 66

Johnson, John, Penfield Books, 215 Brown St, Iowa City, IA 52245 *Tel:* 319-337-9998 *Toll Free Tel:* 800-728-9998 *Fax:* 319-351-6846 *E-mail:* penfield@penfieldbooks.com *Web Site:* www.penfieldbooks.com, pg 186

Johnson, John, Wisconsin Department of Public Instruction, 125 S Webster St, Madison, WI 53703 *Tel:* 608-266-2188 *Toll Free Tel:* 800-441-4563 *Fax:* 608-267-9110 *E-mail:* pubsales@dpi.state.wi.us *Web Site:* www.dpi.wi.gov/pubsales, pg 274

Johnson, Joy, Centering Corp, 7230 Maple St, Omaha, NE 68134 *Tel:* 402-553-1200 *Toll Free Tel:* 866-218-0101 *Fax:* 402-553-0507 *E-mail:* orders@centering.org *Web Site:* www.centering.org, pg 54

Johnson, Karen, Martingale®, 19021 120 Ave NE, Suite 102, Bothell, WA 98011 *Tel:* 425-483-3313 *Toll Free Tel:* 800-426-3126 *Fax:* 425-486-7596 *E-mail:* info@martingale-pub.com *Web Site:* www.martingale-pub.com, pg 148

Johnson, Kent S, Highlights for Children, 1800 Watermark Dr, Columbus, OH 43215 *Tel:* 614-486-0631 *Toll Free Tel:* 800-962-3661 (Highlights Club cust serv); 800-255-9517 (Highlights Magazine cust serv) *Web Site:* www.highlights.com, pg 111

Johnson, Lars, Christian Liberty Press, 502 W Euclid Ave, Arlington Heights, IL 60004-5402 *Tel:* 847-259-4444 *Toll Free Tel:* 800-832-2741 (cust serv) *Fax:* 847-259-2941 *E-mail:* custserv@christianlibertypress.com *Web Site:* www.shopchristianliberty.com, pg 57

Johnson, Leslie, Graywolf Press, 250 Third Ave N, Suite 600, Minneapolis, MN 55401 *Tel:* 651-641-0077 *Fax:* 651-641-0036 *E-mail:* wolves@graywolfpress.org *Web Site:* www.graywolfpress.org, pg 100

Johnson, Lloyd, Double Play, 303 Hillcrest Rd, Belton, MO 64012-1852 *Tel:* 816-651-7118, pg 524

Johnson, Lynne, Spry Publishing, 2500 S State St, Ann Arbor, MI 48104 *Tel:* 734-913-1700 *Toll Free Tel:* 877-722-2264 *Fax:* 734-913-1249 *E-mail:* info@sprypub.com *Web Site:* www.sprypub.com, pg 232

Johnson, Mark, International Code Council Inc, 5360 Workman Mill Rd, Whittier, CA 90601-2256 *Tel:* 562-699-0541 *Toll Free Tel:* 888-422-7233 *Fax:* 562-908-5524; 562-699-8031 *E-mail:* es@icc-es.org *Web Site:* www.iccsafe.org, pg 124

Johnson, Marla, Neustadt International Prize for Literature, c/o University of Oklahoma, 630 Parrington Oval, Suite 110, Norman, OK 73019-4033 *Tel:* 405-325-4531 *Fax:* 405-325-7495 *Web Site:* www.worldliteraturetoday.org, pg 712

Johnson, Marla, NSK Neustadt Prize for Children's Literature, c/o University of Oklahoma, 630 Parrington Oval, Suite 110, Norman, OK 73019-4033 *Tel:* 405-325-4531 *Fax:* 405-325-7495 *Web Site:* www.worldliteraturetoday.org, pg 714

Johnson, Dr Marvin, Centering Corp, 7230 Maple St, Omaha, NE 68134 *Tel:* 402-553-1200 *Toll Free Tel:* 866-218-0101 *Fax:* 402-553-0507 *E-mail:* orders@centering.org *Web Site:* www.centering.org, pg 54

Johnson, Michael, Wadsworth Publishing, 20 Davis Dr, Belmont, CA 94002 *Tel:* 650-595-2350 *Fax:* 650-592-3022 *Toll Free Fax:* 800-522-4923 *Web Site:* www.cengage.com, pg 266

Johnson, Michelle, Neustadt International Prize for Literature, c/o University of Oklahoma, 630 Parrington Oval, Suite 110, Norman, OK 73019-4033 *Tel:* 405-325-4531 *Fax:* 405-325-7495 *Web Site:* www.worldliteraturetoday.org, pg 712

Johnson, Michelle, NSK Neustadt Prize for Children's Literature, c/o University of Oklahoma, 630 Parrington Oval, Suite 110, Norman, OK 73019-4033 *Tel:* 405-325-4531 *Fax:* 405-325-7495 *Web Site:* www.worldliteraturetoday.org, pg 714

Johnson, Patricia, Pantheon Books/Schocken Books, c/o Random House Inc, 1745 Broadway, New York, NY 10019 *Tel:* 212-751-2600 *Toll Free Tel:* 800-638-6460 *Fax:* 212-572-6030, pg 181

Johnson, Robin, Pentecostal Publishing House, 8855 Dunn Rd, Hazelwood, MO 63042 *Tel:* 314-837-7300 *Fax:* 314-336-1803 *E-mail:* pphordersdept@upci.org (orders) *Web Site:* www.pentecostalpublishing.com, pg 188

Johnson, Ronald, National Notary Association (NNA), 9350 De Soto Ave, Chatsworth, CA 91311 *Tel:* 818-739-4000 *Toll Free Tel:* 800-876-6827 *Toll Free Fax:* 800-833-1211 *E-mail:* nna@nationalnotary.org *Web Site:* www.nationalnotary.org, pg 165

Johnson, Shelly, Fox Run Press LLC, 7840 Bullet Rd, Peyton, OH 80831 *Tel:* 719-482-4035 *Fax:* 719-623-0254 *E-mail:* info@foxrunpress.com *Web Site:* www.foxrunpress.com, pg 91

Johnson, Sue, AVKO Educational Research Foundation Inc, 3084 Willard Rd, Birch Run, MI 48415-9404 *Tel:* 810-686-9283 (orders & billing) *Toll Free Tel:* 866-AVKO612 (285-6612) *Fax:* 810-686-1101 *E-mail:* info@avko.org (gen inquiry) *Web Site:* www.avko.org; www.avko.blogspot.org, pg 28

Johnson, Tashauna, PhotoEdit Inc, 3505 Cadillac Ave, Suite P-101, Costa Mesa, CA 92626 *Toll Free Tel:* 800-860-2098 *Fax:* 714-434-5937 *Toll Free Fax:* 800-804-3707 *E-mail:* sales@photoeditinc.com *Web Site:* www.photoeditinc.com, pg 532

Johnson, Terence MA, Scribendi Inc, 405 Riverview Dr, Chatham, ON N7M 0N3, Canada *Tel:* 519-351-1626 (cust serv) *Fax:* 519-354-0192 *E-mail:* customerservice@scribendi.com *Web Site:* www.scribendi.com, pg 534

Johnson, Thomas, University Press of New England, One Court St, Suite 250, Lebanon, NH 03766 *Tel:* 603-448-1533 *Toll Free Tel:* 800-421-1561 (orders only) *Fax:* 603-448-7006; 603-643-1540 *E-mail:* university.press@dartmouth.edu *Web Site:* www.upne.com, pg 262

Johnson, Thomas D, Business Research Services Inc, 4641 Montgomery Ave, Suite 208, Bethesda, MD 20814 *Tel:* 301-229-5561 *Toll Free Tel:* 800-845-8420 *Toll Free Fax:* 877-516-0818 *E-mail:* brspubs@sba8a.com *Web Site:* www.sba8a.com; www.setasidealert.com, pg 48

Johnson, Tildy Banker, Carolyn Jenks Agency, 30 Cambridge Park Dr, Suite 3140, Cambridge, MA 02140 *Tel:* 617-354-5099 *Fax:* 617-354-5099 *E-mail:* queries@carolynjenksagency.com (submissions) *Web Site:* www.carolynjenksagency.com, pg 558

Johnson, Valerie, Frederick Bock Prize, 444 N Michigan Ave, Suite 1850, Chicago, IL 60611-4034 *Tel:* 312-787-7070 *Fax:* 312-787-6650 *E-mail:* editors@poetrymagazine.org *Web Site:* www.poetryfoundation.org, pg 673

Johnson, Valerie, Bess Hokin Prize, 444 N Michigan Ave, Suite 1850, Chicago, IL 60611-4034 *Tel:* 312-787-7070 *Fax:* 312-787-6650 *E-mail:* editors@poetrymagazine.org *Web Site:* www.poetryfoundation.org, pg 692

Johnson, Valerie, Levinson Prize, 444 N Michigan Ave, Suite 1850, Chicago, IL 60611-4034 *Tel:* 312-787-7070 *Fax:* 312-787-6650 *E-mail:* editors@poetrymagazine.org *Web Site:* www.poetryfoundation.org, pg 700

Johnson, Valerie, John Frederick Nims Memorial Prize, 444 N Michigan Ave, Suite 1850, Chicago, IL 60611-4034 *Tel:* 312-787-7070 *Fax:* 312-787-6650 *E-mail:* editors@poetrymagazine.org *Web Site:* www.poetryfoundation.org, pg 713

Johnson, Valerie, The J Howard & Barbara M J Wood Prize, 444 N Michigan Ave, Suite 1850, Chicago, IL 60611-4034 *Tel:* 312-787-7070 *Fax:* 312-787-6650 *E-mail:* editors@poetrymagazine.org *Web Site:* www.poetryfoundation.org, pg 737

Johnson-LeBlanc, Linda, Judson Press, 588 N Gulph Rd, King of Prussia, PA 19406 *Toll Free Tel:* 800-458-3766 *Fax:* 610-768-2107 *Web Site:* www.judsonpress.com, pg 128

Johnston, Allyn, Simon & Schuster Children's Publishing, 1230 Avenue of the Americas, New York, NY 10020 *Tel:* 212-698-7000 *Web Site:* KIDS.SimonandSchuster.com; TEEN.SimonandSchuster.com; simonandschuster.net; simonandschuster.biz, pg 225

Johnston, Dillon, Wake Forest University Press, A5 Tribble Hall, Wake Forest University, Winston-Salem, NC 27109 *Tel:* 336-758-5448 *Fax:* 336-758-5636 *E-mail:* wfupress@wfu.edu *Web Site:* www.wfu.edu/wfupress, pg 266

Johnston, James, Random House Publishing Group, 1745 Broadway, New York, NY 10019 *Toll Free Tel:* 800-200-3552 *Web Site:* atrandom.com, pg 204

Johnston, Lisa Lyons, Kids Can Press Ltd, 25 Dockside Dr, Toronto, ON M5A 0B5, Canada *Tel:* 416-479-7000 *Toll Free Tel:* 800-265-0884 *Fax:* 416-960-

5437 *E-mail:* info@kidscan.com; customerservice@kidscan.com *Web Site:* www.kidscanpress.com; www.kidscanpress.ca, pg 489

Johnston, Suzanne M, Western Pennsylvania Genealogical Society, 4400 Forbes Ave, Pittsburgh, PA 15213-4080 *Tel:* 412-687-6811 (answering machine) *E-mail:* info@wpgs.org *Web Site:* www.wpgs.org, pg 269

Johovic, Kelley H, Drue Heinz Literature Prize, 7500 Thomas Blvd, Pittsburgh, PA 15260 *Tel:* 412-383-2456 *Fax:* 412-383-2466 *E-mail:* info@upress.pitt.edu *Web Site:* www.upress.pitt.edu, pg 691

Johovic, Kelley H, Agnes Lynch Starrett Poetry Prize, 7500 Thomas Blvd, Pittsburgh, PA 15260 *Tel:* 412-383-2456 *Fax:* 412-383-2466 *E-mail:* info@upress.pitt.edu *Web Site:* www.upress.pitt.edu, pg 730

Joiner, Leila, Imago Press, 3710 E Edison St, Tucson, AZ 85716 *Tel:* 520-444-2265 *Web Site:* www.oasisjournal.org, pg 119

Jolley, Marc, Mercer University Press, 368 Orange St, Macon, GA 31201 *Tel:* 478-301-2880 *Toll Free Tel:* 866-895-1472 *Fax:* 478-301-2585 *E-mail:* mupressorders@mercer.edu *Web Site:* www.mupress.org, pg 154

Jolly, Anjali V, The Perseus Books Group, 387 Park Ave S, 12th fl, New York, NY 10016 *Tel:* 212-340-8100 *Toll Free Tel:* 800-343-4499 (cust serv) *Fax:* 212-340-8105 *Web Site:* www.perseusbooksgroup.com, pg 189

Jonas, Darrell, PublicAffairs, 250 W 57 St, Suite 1321, New York, NY 10107 *Tel:* 212-397-6666 *Toll Free Tel:* 800-343-4499 (orders) *Fax:* 212-397-4277 *E-mail:* publicaffairs@perseusbooks.com *Web Site:* www.publicaffairsbooks.com, pg 200

Jones, Alice, Apogee Press, 2308 Sixth St, Berkeley, CA 94710 *E-mail:* editors.apogee@gmail.com *Web Site:* www.apogeepress.com, pg 19

Jones, Allison, Fairchild Books, 1385 Broadway, 5th fl, New York, NY 10018 *Tel:* 212-419-5300 *Toll Free Tel:* 800-932-4724; 888-330-8477 (orders) *Fax:* 212-704-5975 *Web Site:* bloomsbury.com/us/academic/fairchildbooks, pg 85

Jones, Amy, Harlequin Enterprises Ltd, 225 Duncan Mill Rd, Don Mills, ON M3B 3K9, Canada *Tel:* 416-445-5860 *Toll Free Tel:* 888-432-4879; 800-370-5838 (ebook inquiries) *E-mail:* customerservice@harlequin.com *Web Site:* www.harlequin.com, pg 487

Jones, Andrew, Emmaus Road Publishing Inc, 1468 Parkview Cir, Steubenville, OH 43952 *Tel:* 740-283-2880 (outside US) *Toll Free Tel:* 800-398-5470 (orders) *Fax:* 740-283-4011 (orders) *E-mail:* questions@emmausroad.org *Web Site:* www.emmausroad.org, pg 82

Jones, Ashley, Greenleaf Book Group LLC, Three Park Place, 4005 Banister Lane, Suite B, Austin, TX 78704 *Tel:* 512-891-6100 *Toll Free Tel:* 800-932-5420 *Fax:* 512-891-6150 *E-mail:* contact@greenleafbookgroup.com *Web Site:* www.greenleafbookgroup.com, pg 100

Jones, Ms Brett Hall, Squaw Valley Community of Writers Summer Workshops, PO Box 1416, Nevada City, CA 95959 *Tel:* 530-470-8440 *E-mail:* info@squawvalleywriters.org *Web Site:* www.squawvalleywriters.org, pg 656

Jones, Briony, University of New Mexico, One University of New Mexico, Albuquerque, NM 87131-0001 *Tel:* 505-277-2346; 505-272-7777 (cust serv) *Toll Free Tel:* 800-249-7737 (orders only) *Fax:* 505-277-3343; 505-272-7778 (cust serv) *Toll Free Fax:* 800-622-8667 (orders only) *E-mail:* unmpress@unm.edu; custserv@upress.unm.edu (order dept) *Web Site:* unmpress.com, pg 258

Jones, Candide, Wake Forest University Press, A5 Tribble Hall, Wake Forest University, Winston-Salem, NC 27109 *Tel:* 336-758-5448 *Fax:* 336-758-5636 *E-mail:* wfupress@wfu.edu *Web Site:* www.wfu.edu/wfupress, pg 266

Jones, Carrie, Greenleaf Book Group LLC, Three Park Place, 4005 Banister Lane, Suite B, Austin, TX 78704 *Tel:* 512-891-6100 *Toll Free Tel:* 800-932-5420 *Fax:* 512-891-6150 *E-mail:* contact@greenleafbookgroup.com *Web Site:* www.greenleafbookgroup.com, pg 100

Jones, Cathy, The Applegate/Jackson/Parks Future Teacher Scholarship, 5211 Port Royal Rd, Suite 510, Springfield, VA 22151 *Tel:* 703-321-9606 *Fax:* 703-321-7143 *E-mail:* research@nilrr.org *Web Site:* www.nilrr.org, pg 668

Jones, Cathy, William B Ruggles Journalism Scholarship, 5211 Port Royal Rd, Suite 510, Springfield, VA 22151 *Tel:* 703-321-9606 *Fax:* 703-321-7143 *E-mail:* research@nilrr.org *Web Site:* www.nilrr.org, pg 725

Jones, Christopher, Toronto Book Awards, c/o Toronto Arts & Culture, City Hall, 9E, 100 Queen St W, Toronto, ON M5H 2N2, Canada *Web Site:* www.toronto.ca/book_awards, pg 732

Jones, Diane, Standard Publishing, 8805 Governors Hill Dr, Suite 400, Cincinnati, OH 45249 *Tel:* 513-931-4050 *Toll Free Tel:* 800-543-1353 *Fax:* 513-931-0950 *Toll Free Fax:* 877-867-5751 *E-mail:* customerservice@standardpub.com *Web Site:* www.standardpub.com, pg 233

Jones, Diane W, The United Educators Inc, 900 N Shore Dr, Suite 279, Lake Bluff, IL 60044-2210 *Tel:* 847-234-3700 *Toll Free Tel:* 800-323-5875 *Fax:* 847-234-8705 *E-mail:* unitededucators@yahoo.com *Web Site:* www.theunitededucatorsinc.com, pg 253

Jones, Diem, The Voices Summer Writing Workshops, c/o Community Initiatives Inc, 354 Pine St, Suite 700, San Francisco, CA 94104 *Toll Free Tel:* 866-202-6152 *E-mail:* info@voicesatvona.org *Web Site:* www.voicesatvona.org, pg 656

Jones, Doug, HarperCollins Publishers Sales, 195 Broadway, New York, NY 10007 *Fax:* 212-207-7000 *Web Site:* www.harpercollins.com, pg 106

Jones, Eddie, Lighthouse Publishing of the Carolinas, 2333 Barton Oaks Dr, Raleigh, NC 27614-7940 *Tel:* 919-562-8439 *E-mail:* lighthousepublishingcarolinas@gmail.com *Web Site:* lighthousepublishingofthecarolinas.com, pg 139

Jones, Erin, Odyssey Books, 2421 Redwood Ct, Longmont, CO 80503-8155 *Tel:* 720-494-1473 *Fax:* 720-494-1471 *E-mail:* books@odysseybooks.net *Web Site:* cilettipublishinggroup.com, pg 174

Jones, Georgia, LadybugPress, 16964 Columbia River Dr, Sonora, CA 95370 *Tel:* 209-694-8340 *Toll Free Tel:* 888-892-5000 *Fax:* 209-694-8916 *E-mail:* ladybugpress@ladybugbooks.com *Web Site:* www.ladybugbooks.com, pg 133

Jones, Greg, Signature Books Publishing LLC, 564 W 400 N, Salt Lake City, UT 84116-3411 *Tel:* 801-531-1483 *Fax:* 801-531-1488 *E-mail:* people@signaturebooks.com *Web Site:* www.signaturebooks.com; www.signaturebookslibrary.org, pg 224

Jones, Hugh, Accuity, 4709 W Golf Rd, Skokie, IL 60076 *Tel:* 847-676-9600 *Toll Free Tel:* 800-321-3373 *Fax:* 847-933-8101 *E-mail:* custserv@accuity.com; sales@accuity.com *Web Site:* www.accuity.com, pg 4

Jones, James, Autism Asperger Publishing Co, 11209 Strang Line Rd, Lenexa, KS 66215 *Tel:* 913-897-1004 *Toll Free Tel:* 877-277-8254 *Fax:* 913-681-9473 *E-mail:* info@aapcpublishing.net *Web Site:* www.aapcpublishing.net, pg 28

Jones, Jennifer, Nilgiri Press, 3600 Tomales Rd, Tomales, CA 94971 *Tel:* 707-878-2369 *E-mail:* info@easwaran.org *Web Site:* www.easwaran.org, pg 170

Jones, Mr Jordan D, Leaping Dog Press/Asylum Arts Press, PO Box 90473, Raleigh, NC 27675-0473 *Tel:* 919-809-9045 *E-mail:* sales@leapingdogpress.com *Web Site:* www.leapingdogpress.com, pg 136

Jones, Keasley, Peachpit Press, 1249 Eighth St, Berkeley, CA 94710 *Tel:* 510-524-2178 *Toll Free Tel:* 800-283-9444 *Fax:* 510-524-2221 *E-mail:* info@peachpit.com *Web Site:* www.peachpit.com, pg 184

Jones, Keiko, Signature Books Publishing LLC, 564 W 400 N, Salt Lake City, UT 84116-3411 *Tel:* 801-531-1483 *Fax:* 801-531-1488 *E-mail:* people@signaturebooks.com *Web Site:* www.signaturebooks.com; www.signaturebookslibrary.org, pg 224

Jones, Linda, Andrews McMeel Publishing LLC, 1130 Walnut St, Kansas City, MO 64106-2109 *Toll Free Tel:* 800-851-8923; 800-943-9839 (cust serv) *Toll Free Fax:* 800-943-9831 (orders) *Web Site:* www.andrewsmcmeel.com, pg 18

Jones, Linda, Enfield Publishing & Distribution Co, 234 May St, Enfield, NH 03748 *Tel:* 603-632-7377 *Fax:* 603-632-5611 *E-mail:* info@enfieldbooks.com *Web Site:* www.enfieldbooks.com, pg 83

Jones, Linda, Science Publishers Inc, PO Box 699, Enfield, NH 03748-0699 *Tel:* 603-632-7377 *Fax:* 603-632-5611 *E-mail:* info@scipub.net *Web Site:* www.scipub.net, pg 220

Jones, Linda, Trans Tech Publications, c/o Enfield Distribution Co, 234 May St, Enfield, NH 03748 *Tel:* 603-632-7377 *Fax:* 603-632-5611 *E-mail:* usa-ttp@ttp.net; info@enfieldbooks.com *Web Site:* www.ttp.net, pg 248

Jones, Ling-Yen, Solano Press Books, PO Box 773, Point Arena, CA 95468 *Tel:* 707-884-4508 *Toll Free Tel:* 800-931-9373 *Fax:* 707-884-4109 *E-mail:* spbooks@solano.com *Web Site:* www.solano.com, pg 230

Jones, Lorena, Chronicle Books LLC, 680 Second St, San Francisco, CA 94107 *Tel:* 415-537-4200 *Toll Free Tel:* 800-759-0190 (cust serv) *Fax:* 415-537-4460 *Toll Free Fax:* 800-858-7787 (orders); 800-286-9471 (cust serv) *E-mail:* frontdesk@chroniclebooks.com *Web Site:* www.chroniclebooks.com, pg 58

Jones, Louis B, Squaw Valley Community of Writers Summer Workshops, PO Box 1416, Nevada City, CA 95959 *Tel:* 530-470-8440 *E-mail:* info@squawvalleywriters.org *Web Site:* www.squawvalleywriters.org, pg 656

Jones, Marjorie Gillette, Baldwin Literary Services, 935 Hayes St, Baldwin, NY 11510-4834 *Tel:* 516-546-8338 *Fax:* 516-546-8338, pg 521

Jones, Marrissa, Allworth Press, 307 W 36 St, 11th fl, New York, NY 10018 *Tel:* 212-643-6816 *Fax:* 212-643-6819 *Web Site:* www.allworth.com, pg 8

Jones, Melissa, Graphic Arts Association, 1210 Northbrook Dr, Suite 200, Trevose, PA 19053 *Tel:* 215-396-2300 *Fax:* 215-396-9890 *E-mail:* gaa@gaaonline.org *Web Site:* www.gaa1900.com, pg 660

Jones, Meryl, Craven Design Inc, 1202 Lexington Ave, Box 242, New York, NY 10028 *Tel:* 212-288-1022 *Fax:* 212-249-9910 *E-mail:* cravendesign@mac.com *Web Site:* www.cravendesignstudios.com, pg 583

Jones, Michael P, Crumb Elbow Publishing, PO Box 294, Rhododendron, OR 97049-0294 *Tel:* 503-622-4798, pg 68

Jones, Nikki, Health Research Books, 62 Seventh St, Pomeroy, WA 99347 *Tel:* 509-843-2385 *Toll Free Tel:* 888-844-2386 *Fax:* 509-843-2387 *E-mail:* publish@pomeroy-wa.com *Web Site:* www.healthresearchbooks.com, pg 109

Jones, Parneshia, Northwestern University Press, 629 Noyes St, Evanston, IL 60208-4210 *Tel:* 847-491-2046 *Toll Free Tel:* 800-621-2736 (orders only) *Fax:* 847-491-8150 *E-mail:* nupress@northwestern.edu *Web Site:* www.nupress.northwestern.edu, pg 171

Jones, Patsy, Hachette Nashville, 12 Cadillac Dr, Suite 480, Brentwood, TN 37027 *Tel:* 615-221-0996 *Fax:* 615-221-0962 *Web Site:* www.hachettebookgroup.com, pg 103

Jones, Peter, LRS, 19146 Van Ness Ave, Torrance, CA 90501 *Tel:* 310-354-2610 *Toll Free Tel:* 800-255-5002 *Fax:* 310-354-2601 *E-mail:* largeprintsb@aol.com *Web Site:* lrs-largeprint.com, pg 144

Jones, Tim, American Society for Nondestructive Testing, 1711 Arlingate Lane, Columbus, OH 43228-0518 *Tel:* 614-274-6003 *Toll Free Tel:* 800-222-2768 *Fax:* 614-274-6899 *Web Site:* www.asnt.org, pg 15

Jones, Tim, Harvard University Press, 79 Garden St, Cambridge, MA 02138-1499 *Tel:* 617-495-2600; 401-531-2800 (intl orders) *Toll Free Tel:* 800-405-1619 (orders) *Fax:* 617-495-5898 (general); 617-496-4677 (edit & rts); 401-531-2801 (intl orders) *Toll Free Fax:* 800-406-9145 (orders) *E-mail:* contact_hup@harvard.edu *Web Site:* www.hup.harvard.edu, pg 107

Jones, Todd, American Atheist Press, PO Box 158, Cranford, NJ 07016 *Tel:* 908-276-7300 *Fax:* 908-276-7402 *Web Site:* www.atheists.org, pg 11

Jones, Valerie, University Press of Mississippi, 3825 Ridgewood Rd, Jackson, MS 39211-6492 *Tel:* 601-432-6205 *Toll Free Tel:* 800-737-7788 (orders & cust serv) *Fax:* 601-432-6217 *E-mail:* press@mississippi.edu *Web Site:* www.upress.state.ms.us, pg 262

Jones, Winifred, Stellar Publishing, 2114 S Live Oak Pkwy, Wilmington, NC 28403 *Tel:* 910-269-7444 *Web Site:* www.stellar-publishing.com, pg 235

Jongsma, Jennifer, Annual Reviews, 4139 El Camino Way, Palo Alto, CA 94306 *Tel:* 650-493-4400 *Toll Free Tel:* 800-523-8635 *Fax:* 650-424-0910; 650-855-9815 *E-mail:* service@annualreviews.org *Web Site:* www.annualreviews.org, pg 18

Jonker, Rosie, Ann Rittenberg Literary Agency Inc, 15 Maiden Lane, Suite 206, New York, NY 10038 *Tel:* 212-684-6936 *Fax:* 212-684-6929 *E-mail:* info@rittlit.com *Web Site:* www.rittlit.com, pg 570

Jordan, Jim, Oxford University Press USA, 198 Madison Ave, New York, NY 10016 *Tel:* 212-726-6000 *Toll Free Tel:* 800-451-7556 (orders); 800-445-9714 (cust serv) *Fax:* 919-677-1303 *E-mail:* custserv.us@oup.com *Web Site:* www.oup.com/us, pg 179

Jordan, Sara, Sara Jordan Publishing, RPO Lakeport Box 28105, St Catharines, ON L2N 7P8, Canada *Tel:* 905-938-5050 *Toll Free Tel:* 800-567-7733 *Fax:* 905-938-9970 *Toll Free Fax:* 800-229-3855 *Web Site:* www.sara-jordan.com, pg 498

Jordan, Tina, Association of American Publishers (AAP), 71 Fifth Ave, 2nd fl, New York, NY 10003-3004 *Tel:* 212-255-0200 *Fax:* 212-255-7007 *E-mail:* info@publishers.org *Web Site:* publishers.org, pg 598

Joseph, Jennifer, Manic D Press Inc, 250 Banks St, San Francisco, CA 94110 *Tel:* 415-648-8288 *E-mail:* info@manicdpress.com *Web Site:* www.manicdpress.com, pg 146

Joseph, Kelly, House of Anansi Press Inc, 110 Spadina Ave, Suite 801, Toronto, ON M5V 2K4, Canada *Tel:* 416-363-4343 *Fax:* 416-363-1017 *E-mail:* customerservice@houseofanansi.com *Web Site:* www.houseofanansi.com, pg 488

Jost, David, Houghton Mifflin Harcourt Trade & Reference Division, 222 Berkeley St, Boston, MA 02116 *Tel:* 617-351-5000 *Toll Free Tel:* 800-225-3362 *Web Site:* www.hmhco.com, pg 115

Jourdane, Tom, AZ Books LLC, 320 Fifth Ave, New York, NY 10001 *Toll Free Tel:* 888-945-7723 *Toll Free Fax:* 888-945-7724 *Web Site:* www.azbooksusa.com, pg 29

Jowett, Barry, Cormorant Books Inc, 10 St Mary St, Suite 615, Toronto, ON M4Y-1P6, Canada *Tel:* 416-925-8887 *E-mail:* info@cormorantbooks.com *Web Site:* www.cormorantbooks.com, pg 478

Jowsey, Heather, Mehring Books Inc, PO Box 48377, Oak Park, MI 48237-5977 *Tel:* 248-967-2924 *Fax:* 248-967-3023 *E-mail:* sales@mehring.com *Web Site:* www.mehring.com, pg 154

Joyce, Jack, ITMB Publishing Ltd, 12300 Bridgeport Rd, Richmond, BC V6V 1J5, Canada *Tel:* 604-273-1400 *Fax:* 604-273-1488 *E-mail:* itmb@itmb.com *Web Site:* www.itmb.com, pg 489

Joyce, John, Joyce Media Inc, 3413 Soledad Canyon Rd, Acton, CA 93510-1974 *Tel:* 661-269-1169 *Fax:* 661-269-2139 *E-mail:* help@joycemediainc.com *Web Site:* www.joycemediainc.com, pg 128

Joyce, Robinson, Firefall Editions, 27 Bath St, Lido Beach, NY 11561 *Tel:* 510-549-2461 *E-mail:* fire@firefallmedia.com *Web Site:* www.firefallmedia.com, pg 89

Juarez, Benny, Ross Books, PO Box 4340, Berkeley, CA 94704-0340 *Tel:* 510-841-2474 *Fax:* 510-295-2531 *E-mail:* sales@rossbooks.com *Web Site:* www.rossbooks.com, pg 211

Jud, Brian, Association of Publishers for Special Sales (APSS), PO Box 715, Avon, CT 06001-0715 *Tel:* 860-675-1344 *Web Site:* www.spannet.org, pg 599

Jud, Brian, Book Marketing Works LLC, 50 Lovely St (Rte 177), Avon, CT 06001 *Tel:* 860-675-1344 *Web Site:* www.bookmarketingworks.com, pg 42

Jud, Brian, Connecticut Authors & Publishers Association (CAPA), PO Box 715, Avon, CT 06001-0715 *Tel:* 203-729-5335 *Fax:* 203-729-5335 *Web Site:* www.aboutcapa.com, pg 604

Judd, Darrell, Artech House Inc, 685 Canton St, Norwood, MA 02062 *Tel:* 781-769-9750 *Toll Free Tel:* 800-225-9977 *Fax:* 781-769-6334 *E-mail:* artech@artechhouse.com *Web Site:* www.artechhouse.com, pg 23

Judd, Edwin J, Jhpiego, 1615 Thames St, Baltimore, MD 21231-3492 *Tel:* 410-537-1800 *Fax:* 410-537-1473 *E-mail:* info@jhpiego.net *Web Site:* www.jhpiego.org, pg 126

Judson, Nancy, TripBuilder Media Inc, 180 Post Rd E, Suite 200, Westport, CT 06880 *Tel:* 203-227-1255 *Toll Free Tel:* 800-525-9745 *Fax:* 203-227-1257 *E-mail:* info@tripbuildermedia.com *Web Site:* www.tripbuildermedia.com, pg 249

Juenemann, Brian, Pacific Northwest Book Awards, 338 W 11 Ave, Unit 108, Eugene, OR 97401 *Tel:* 541-683-4363 *Fax:* 541-683-3910 *E-mail:* info@pnba.org *Web Site:* www.pnba.org, pg 715

Juenemann, Brian, Pacific Northwest Booksellers Association, 338 W 11 Ave, Unit 108, Eugene, OR 97401 *Tel:* 541-683-4363 *Toll Free Tel:* 800-353-6764 *Fax:* 541-683-3910 *E-mail:* info@pnba.org *Web Site:* www.pnba.org, pg 615

Julien, Ria, Frances Goldin Literary Agency, Inc, 57 E 11 St, Suite 5-B, New York, NY 10003 *Tel:* 212-777-0047 *Fax:* 212-228-1660 *E-mail:* agency@goldinlit.com *Web Site:* www.goldinlit.com, pg 554

Junior, Bobbi, InScribe Christian Writers' Fellowship (ICWF), PO Box 6201, Wetaskiwin, AB T9A 2E9, Canada *E-mail:* inscribe.mail@gmail.com *Web Site:* inscribe.org, pg 607

Junker, Lisa, Entomological Society of America, 3 Park Place, Suite 307, Annapolis, MD 21401-3722 *Tel:* 301-731-4535 *Fax:* 301-731-4538 *E-mail:* esa@entsoc.org *Web Site:* www.entsoc.org, pg 83

Juodaitis, Thomas W, The Trinity Foundation, PO Box 68, Unicoi, TN 37692-0068 *Tel:* 423-743-0199 *Fax:* 423-743-2005 *Web Site:* www.trinityfoundation.org, pg 249

Jusino, John, HarperCollins General Books Group, 195 Broadway, New York, NY 10007 *Tel:* 212-207-7000 *Web Site:* www.harpercollins.com, pg 105

Jutkowitz, Edward J, Camino Books Inc, PO Box 59026, Philadelphia, PA 19102-9026 *Tel:* 215-413-1917 *Fax:* 215-413-3255 *E-mail:* camino@caminobooks.com *Web Site:* www.caminobooks.com, pg 49

Jutras, Luc, Health Communications Inc, 3201 SW 15 St, Deerfield Beach, FL 33442 *Tel:* 954-360-0909 *Toll Free Tel:* 800-851-9100; 800-441-5569 (cust serv & orders) *Fax:* 954-360-0034 *Toll Free Fax:* 800-424-7652 (cust serv & orders) *Web Site:* www.hcibooks.com, pg 108

Kacian, Jim, Red Moon Press, PO Box 2461, Winchester, VA 22604-1661 *Tel:* 540-722-2156 *Web Site:* www.redmoonpress.com, pg 206

Kadetz, Stuart, Bhaktivedanta Book Trust (BBT), 9701 Venice Blvd, Suite 3, Los Angeles, CA 90034 *Tel:* 310-837-5283 *Toll Free Tel:* 800-927-4152 *Fax:* 310-837-1056 *E-mail:* store@krishna.com *Web Site:* www.krishna.com, pg 36

Kadin, Ellen, AMACOM Books, 1601 Broadway, New York, NY 10019-7420 *Tel:* 212-586-8100 *Toll Free Tel:* 800-250-5308 (cust serv) *Fax:* 212-903-8083; 518-891-2372 (orders) *E-mail:* pubs_cust_serv@amanet.org *Web Site:* www.amacombooks.org, pg 9

Kadish, Emily, Dramatists Play Service Inc, 440 Park Ave S, New York, NY 10016 *Tel:* 212-683-8960 *Fax:* 212-213-1539 *E-mail:* postmaster@dramatists.com; orders@dramatists.com; publications@dramatists.com *Web Site:* www.dramatists.com, pg 77

Kadushin, Raphael, University of Wisconsin Press, 1930 Monroe St, 3rd fl, Madison, WI 53711-2059 *Tel:* 608-263-0668 *Toll Free Tel:* 800-621-2736 (orders) *Fax:* 608-263-1173 *Toll Free Fax:* 800-621-2736 (orders) *E-mail:* uwiscpress@uwpress.wisc.edu (main off) *Web Site:* www.wisc.edu/wisconsinpress, pg 260

Kaemmer, Beverly, University of Minnesota Press, 111 Third Ave S, Suite 290, Minneapolis, MN 55401-2520 *Tel:* 612-627-1970 *Fax:* 612-627-1980 *E-mail:* ump@umn.edu *Web Site:* www.upress.umn.edu, pg 257

Kaemmerling, TeRessa, National Resource Center for Youth Services (NRCYS), Schusterman Ctr, Bldg 4W, 4502 E 41 St, Tulsa, OK 74135-2512 *Tel:* 918-660-3700 *Toll Free Tel:* 800-274-2687 *Fax:* 918-660-3737 *Web Site:* www.nrcys.ou.edu, pg 166

Kaeser, Scott, Tide-mark Press, 22 Prestige Park Circle, East Hartford, CT 06108-1917 *Tel:* 860-310-3370 *Toll Free Tel:* 800-338-2508 *Fax:* 860-310-3654 *E-mail:* customerservice@tide-mark.com *Web Site:* www.tidemarkpress.com, pg 246

Kaffel, Meredith, DeFiore and Company, LLC, 47 E 19 St, 3rd fl, New York, NY 10003 *Tel:* 212-925-7744 *Fax:* 212-925-9803 *E-mail:* submissions@defioreandco.com; info@defioreandco.com *Web Site:* www.defioreandco.com, pg 548

Kagan, Abby, Farrar, Straus & Giroux, LLC, 18 W 18 St, New York, NY 10011 *Tel:* 212-741-6900 *E-mail:* fsg.publicity@fsgbooks.com *Web Site:* us.macmillan.com/fsg.aspx, pg 86

Kagan, Heidi, Penguin Group (USA) LLC, a Penguin Random House company, 375 Hudson St, New York, NY 10014 *Tel:* 212-366-2000 *Toll Free Tel:* 800-847-5515 (inside sales); 800-631-8571 (cust serv) *Fax:* 212-366-2666; 607-775-4829 (inside sales) *E-mail:* online@us.penguingroup.com *Web Site:* www.penguin.com; us.penguingroup.com, pg 186

Kagan, Ute Wartenberg, American Numismatic Society, 75 Varick St, 11th fl, New York, NY 10013 *Tel:* 212-571-4470 *Fax:* 212-571-4479 *E-mail:* ans@numismatics.org; orders@numismatics.org *Web Site:* www.numismatics.org, pg 14

Kageff, Karl, Southern Illinois University Press, 1915 University Press Dr, SIUC Mail Code 6806, Carbondale, IL 62901-4323 *Tel:* 618-453-2281 *Fax:* 618-453-1221 *E-mail:* custserv@press.uchicago.edu; rights@siu.edu *Web Site:* www.siupress.com, pg 231

Kahan, Rachel, HarperCollins General Books Group, 195 Broadway, New York, NY 10007 *Tel:* 212-207-7000 *Web Site:* www.harpercollins.com, pg 105

Kahla, Keith, St Martin's Press, LLC, 175 Fifth Ave, New York, NY 10010 *Tel:* 646-307-5151 *Fax:* 212-420-9314 *E-mail:* firstname.lastname@macmillan.com *Web Site:* www.stmartins.com, pg 215

Kahn, Chris, Benjamin Franklin Awards™, 1020 Manhattan Beach Blvd, Suite 204, Manhattan Beach, CA 90266 *Tel:* 310-546-1818 *Fax:* 310-546-3939 *E-mail:* info@ibpa-online.org *Web Site:* www.ibpa-online.org; ibpabenjaminfranklinawards.com, pg 671

Kahn, Chris, The Independent Book Publishers Association (IBPA), 1020 Manhattan Beach Blvd, Suite 204, Manhattan Beach, CA 90266 *Tel:* 310-546-1818 *Fax:* 310-546-3939 *E-mail:* info@ibpa-online.org *Web Site:* www.ibpa-online.org, pg 607

Kahn, Jody, Brandt & Hochman Literary Agents Inc, 1501 Broadway, Suite 2310, New York, NY 10036 *Tel:* 212-840-5760 *Fax:* 212-840-5776 *Web Site:* brandthochman.com, pg 544

Kahn, Kenneth F, LRP Publications, 360 Hiatt Dr, Palm Beach Gardens, FL 33418 *Tel:* 561-622-6520 *Toll Free Tel:* 800-341-7874 *Fax:* 561-622-2423 *E-mail:* custserve@lrp.com *Web Site:* www.lrp.com, pg 144

Kahrizi, Camilia, Marilyn Baillie Picture Book Award, 40 Orchard View Blvd, Suite 217, Toronto, ON M4R 1B9, Canada *Tel:* 416-975-0010 *Fax:* 416-975-8970 *E-mail:* info@bookcentre.ca *Web Site:* www.bookcentre.ca, pg 669

Kahrizi, Camilia, The Geoffrey Bilson Award for Historical Fiction for Young People, 40 Orchard View Blvd, Suite 217, Toronto, ON M4R 1B9, Canada *Tel:* 416-975-0010 *Fax:* 416-975-8970 *E-mail:* info@bookcentre.ca *Web Site:* www.bookcentre.ca, pg 672

Kahrizi, Camilia, Canadian Children's Book Centre, 40 Orchard View Blvd, Suite 217, Toronto, ON M4R 1B9, Canada *Tel:* 416-975-0010 *Fax:* 416-975-8970 *E-mail:* info@bookcentre.ca *Web Site:* www.bookcentre.ca, pg 602

Kahrizi, Camilia, Norma Fleck Award for Canadian Children's Non-Fiction, 40 Orchard View Blvd, Suite 217, Toronto, ON M4R 1B9, Canada *Tel:* 416-975-0010 *Fax:* 416-975-8970 *E-mail:* info@bookcentre.ca *Web Site:* www.bookcentre.ca, pg 686

Kahrizi, Camilia, Monica Hughes Award for Science Fiction & Fantasy, 40 Orchard View Blvd, Suite 217, Toronto, ON M4R 1B9, Canada *Tel:* 416-975-0010 *Fax:* 416-975-8970 *E-mail:* info@bookcentre.ca *Web Site:* www.bookcentre.ca, pg 693

Kahrizi, Camilia, Amy Mathers Teen Book Award, 40 Orchard View Blvd, Suite 217, Toronto, ON M4R 1B9, Canada *Tel:* 416-975-0010 *Fax:* 416-975-8970 *E-mail:* info@bookcentre.ca *Web Site:* www.bookcentre.ca, pg 706

Kahrizi, Camilia, John Spray Mystery Award, 40 Orchard View Blvd, Suite 217, Toronto, ON M4R 1B9, Canada *Tel:* 416-975-0010 *Fax:* 416-975-8970 *E-mail:* info@bookcentre.ca *Web Site:* www.bookcentre.ca, pg 730

Kahrizi, Camilia, TD Canadian Children's Literature Award, 40 Orchard View Blvd, Suite 217, Toronto, ON M4R 1B9, Canada *Tel:* 416-975-0010 *Fax:* 416-975-8970 *E-mail:* info@bookcentre.ca *Web Site:* www.bookcentre.ca, pg 732

Kaiman, Ken, Basic Health Publications Inc, 28812 Top of the World Dr, Laguna Beach, CA 92651 *Tel:* 949-715-7327 *Toll Free Tel:* 800-575-8890 (orders) *Fax:* 949-715-7328 *E-mail:* info@basichealthpub.com *Web Site:* www.basichealthpub.com, pg 32

Kaiman, Ken, Square One Publishers Inc, 115 Herricks Rd, Garden City Park, NY 11040 *Tel:* 516-535-2010 *Toll Free Tel:* 877-900-BOOK (900-2665) *Fax:* 516-535-2014 *E-mail:* sq1publish@aol.com *Web Site:* www.squareonepublishers.com, pg 232

Kaire, Natalie, Stewart, Tabori & Chang, 115 W 18 St, 6th fl, New York, NY 10011 *Tel:* 212-519-1200 *Fax:* 212-519-1210 *Web Site:* www.abramsbooks.com, pg 236

Kaiser, Cecily, Phaidon Press Inc, 180 Varick St, 14th fl, New York, NY 10014 *Tel:* 212-652-5400 *Toll Free Tel:* 800-759-0190 (cust serv) *Fax:* 212-652-5410 *Toll Free Fax:* 800-286-9471 (cust serv) *E-mail:* ussales@phaidon.com *Web Site:* www.phaidon.com, pg 190

Kaiser, Debra, Lorenz Educational Press, 501 E Third St, Dayton, OH 45402 *Tel:* 937-228-6118 *Toll Free Tel:* 800-444-1144 *Fax:* 937-223-2042 *E-mail:* lep@lorenz.com *Web Site:* www.lorenzeducationalpress.com, pg 143

Kaiser, Debra, Milliken Publishing Co, 501 E Third St, Dayton, OH 45402 *Tel:* 937-228-6118 *Toll Free Tel:* 800-444-1144 *Fax:* 937-223-2042 *E-mail:* order@lorenz.com *Web Site:* www.lorenz.educationalpress.com, pg 157

Kaiser, Debra, Teaching & Learning Co, 501 E Third St, Dayton, OH 45402 *Tel:* 937-228-6118 *Toll Free Tel:* 800-444-1144 *Fax:* 937-223-2042 *E-mail:* info@lorenz.com, pg 242

Kaiser, Jackie, Westwood Creative Artists Ltd, 94 Harbord St, Toronto, ON M5S 1G6, Canada *Tel:* 416-964-3302 *Fax:* 416-975-9209 *E-mail:* wca_office@wcaltd.com *Web Site:* www.wcaltd.com, pg 579

Kaiser, Kathleen Sexton, Small Publishers, Artists & Writers Network (SPAWN), 323 E Matilija St, Suite 110, PMB 123, Ojai, CA 93023 *Tel:* 805-646-3045 *Fax:* 805-640-8213 *E-mail:* execdir@spawn.org *Web Site:* www.spawn.org, pg 618

Kaita, Melissa, Second Story Press, 20 Maud St, Suite 401, Toronto, ON M5V 2M5, Canada *Tel:* 416-537-7850 *Fax:* 416-537-0588 *E-mail:* info@secondstorypress.ca *Web Site:* secondstorypress.ca, pg 498

Kalajian, James, Axiom Business Book Awards, 1129 Woodmere Ave, Suite B, Traverse City, MI 49686 *Tel:* 231-933-0445 *Toll Free Tel:* 800-706-4636 *Fax:* 231-933-0448 *E-mail:* info@axiomawards.com *Web Site:* www.axiomawards.com, pg 669

Kalajian, James, eLit Awards, 1129 Woodmere Ave, Suite B, Traverse City, MI 49686 *Tel:* 231-933-0445 *Toll Free Tel:* 800-706-4636 *Fax:* 231-933-0448 *E-mail:* info@elitawards.com *Web Site:* www.elitawards.com, pg 683

Kalajian, James, Illumination Book Awards, 1129 Woodmere Ave, Suite B, Traverse City, MI 49686 *Tel:* 231-933-0445 *Toll Free Tel:* 800-706-4636 *Fax:* 231-933-0448 *E-mail:* awards@bookpublishing.com *Web Site:* www.illuminationawards.com, pg 694

Kalajian, James, The Independent Publisher Book Awards, 1129 Woodmere Ave, Suite B, Traverse City, MI 49686 *Tel:* 231-933-0445 *Toll Free Tel:* 800-706-4636 *Fax:* 231-933-0448 *E-mail:* awards@bookpublishing.com *Web Site:* www.independentpublisher.com/ipland/ipawards.php, pg 694

Kalajian, James, Jenkins Group Inc, 1129 Woodmere Ave, Suite B, Traverse City, MI 49686 *Tel:* 231-933-0445 *Toll Free Tel:* 800-706-4636 *Fax:* 231-933-0448 *E-mail:* info@bookpublishing.com *Web Site:* www.bookpublishing.com, pg 528

Kalajian, James, Living Now Book Awards, 1129 Woodmere Ave, Suite B, Traverse City, MI 49686 *Tel:* 231-933-0445 *Toll Free Tel:* 800-706-4636 *Fax:* 231-933-0448 *E-mail:* awards@bookpublishing.com *Web Site:* www.livingnowawards.com, pg 702

Kalajian, James, Moonbeam Children's Book Awards, 1129 Woodmere Ave, Suite B, Traverse City, MI 49686 *Tel:* 231-933-0445 *Toll Free Tel:* 800-706-4636 *Fax:* 231-933-0448 *E-mail:* info@moonbeamawards.com *Web Site:* www.moonbeamawards.com, pg 709

Kalajin, Audrey, Golden Rose Award, 2 Farrar St, Cambridge, MA 02138 *Tel:* 617-744-6034 *E-mail:* contests@nepoetryclub.org *Web Site:* www.nepoetryclub.org, pg 690

Kalajin, Audrey, New England Poetry Club, 2 Farrar St, Cambridge, MA 02138 *Tel:* 617-744-6034 *E-mail:* info@nepoetryclub.org *Web Site:* www.nepoetryclub.org, pg 613

Kalett, Alison, Princeton University Press, 41 William St, Princeton, NJ 08540-5237 *Tel:* 609-258-4900 *Toll Free Tel:* 800-777-4726 (orders) *Fax:* 609-258-6305 *Toll Free Fax:* 800-999-1958 *E-mail:* orders@cpfsinc.com *Web Site:* press.princeton.edu, pg 197

Kalish, Ilene, New York University Press, 838 Broadway, 3rd fl, New York, NY 10003-4812 *Tel:* 212-998-2575 (edit) *Toll Free Tel:* 800-996-6987 (orders) *Fax:* 212-995-3833 (orders) *E-mail:* information@nyupress.org; customerservice@nyupress.org; orders@nyupress.org *Web Site:* www.nyupress.org, pg 169

Kalk, Valentina, The Brookings Institution Press, 1775 Massachusetts Ave NW, Washington, DC 20036-2188 *Tel:* 202-536-3600 *Toll Free Tel:* 800-537-5487 *Fax:* 202-536-3623 *E-mail:* permissions@brookings.edu *Web Site:* www.brookings.edu, pg 47

Kalman, Ms Bobbie, Crabtree Publishing Co, 350 Fifth Ave, 59th fl, PMB 59051, New York, NY 10118 *Tel:* 212-496-5040 *Toll Free Tel:* 800-387-7650 *Toll Free Fax:* 800-355-7166 *E-mail:* custserv@crabtreebooks.com *Web Site:* www.crabtreebooks.com, pg 66

Kalman, Bobbie, Crabtree Publishing Co Ltd, 616 Welland Ave, St Catharines, ON L2M-5V6, Canada *Tel:* 905-682-5221 *Toll Free Tel:* 800-387-7650 *Fax:* 905-682-7166 *Toll Free Fax:* 800-355-7166 *E-mail:* custserv@crabtreebooks.com; sales@crabtreebooks.com; orders@crabtreebooks.com *Web Site:* www.crabtreebooks.com, pg 478

Kalogeridis, Carla, Association Media & Publishing (AM&P), 12100 Sunset Hills Rd, Suite 130, Reston, VA 20190 *Tel:* 703-234-4063 *Fax:* 703-435-4390 *E-mail:* info@associationmediaandpublishing.org *Web Site:* associationmediaandpublishing.org, pg 598

Kalonick, Jillian, United for Libraries, 109 S 13 St, Suite 117B, Philadelphia, PA 19107 *Tel:* 312-280-2161 *Toll Free Tel:* 800-545-2433 (ext 2161) *Fax:* 215-545-3821 *E-mail:* united@ala.org *Web Site:* www.ala.org/united, pg 620

Kals, Josie, Alfred A Knopf/Everyman's Library, c/o Random House Inc, 1745 Broadway, New York, NY 10019 *Tel:* 212-751-2600 *Toll Free Tel:* 800-638-6460 *Fax:* 212-572-2593 *Web Site:* www.knopfdoubleday.com, pg 132

Kalweit, Burk, American Academy of Environmental Engineers & Scientists™, 147 Old Solomons Island Rd, Suite 303, Annapolis, MD 21401 *Tel:* 410-266-3311 *Fax:* 410-266-7653 *E-mail:* info@aaees.org *Web Site:* www.aaees.org, pg 10

Kamil, Susan, Random House Publishing Group, 1745 Broadway, New York, NY 10019 *Toll Free Tel:* 800-200-3552 *Web Site:* atrandom.com, pg 204

Kamoroff, Bernard, Bell Springs Publishing, PO Box 1240, Willits, CA 95490-1240 *Tel:* 707-459-6372 *E-mail:* publisher@bellsprings.com *Web Site:* bellsprings.com; aboutpinball.com, pg 34

Kampmann, Eric M, Beaufort Books, 27 W 20 St, Suite 1102, New York, NY 10011 *Tel:* 212-727-0222 *Fax:* 212-727-0195 *E-mail:* info@beaufortbooks.com *Web Site:* www.beaufortbooks.com, pg 33

Kan, Susan, Perugia Press Prize for a First or Second Book by a Woman, PO Box 60364, Florence, MA 01062 *Web Site:* www.perugiapress.com, pg 718

Kanagy, Dave, Society for Mining, Metallurgy & Exploration, 12999 E Adam Aircraft Circle, Englewood, CO 80112 *Tel:* 303-948-4200 *Toll Free Tel:* 800-763-3132 *Fax:* 303-973-3845 *E-mail:* cs@smenet.org *Web Site:* www.smenet.org, pg 229

Kane, Joanne E, Kane Press Inc, 225 E 46 St, Suite 4D, New York, NY 10017-2924 *Tel:* 212-935-0246 *Web Site:* www.kanepress.com, pg 129

Kane, Roberta, The Write Way, 3048 Horizon Lane, Suite 1102, Naples, FL 34109 *Tel:* 239-273-9145 *E-mail:* darekane@gmail.com, pg 536

Kane, Sonia, Boydell & Brewer Inc, 668 Mount Hope Ave, Rochester, NY 14620-2731 *Tel:* 585-275-0419 *Fax:* 585-271-8778 *E-mail:* boydell@boydellusa.net *Web Site:* www.boydellandbrewer.com, pg 43

Kane, Tracey, Liguori Publications, One Liguori Dr, Liguori, MO 63057-1000 *Tel:* 636-464-2500 *Toll Free Tel:* 866-848-2492; 800-325-9521 *Fax:* 636-464-8449 *Toll Free Fax:* 800-325-9526 (sales) *E-mail:* liguori@liguori.org (sales & cust serv) *Web Site:* www.liguori.org/contact-us.html, pg 139

Kanellos, Nicolas, Arte Publico Press, University of Houston, Bldg 19, Rm 10, 4902 Gulf Fwy, Houston, TX 77204-2004 *Tel:* 713-743-2998 (sales) *Toll Free Tel:* 800-633-2783 *Fax:* 713-743-2847 (sales) *E-mail:* appinfo@uh.edu; bkorders@uh.edu, pg 23

Kaneski, Sean, Business Expert Press, 222 E 46 St, New York, NY 10017-2906 *Tel:* 630-207-5927 *E-mail:* charlene.kronstadt@businessexpertpress.com *Web Site:* www.businessexpertpress.com, pg 48

Kanya-Forstner, Martha, Doubleday Canada, One Toronto St, Suite 300, Toronto, ON M5C 2V6, Canada *Tel:* 416-364-4449 *Fax:* 416-364-6863 *Web Site:* www.randomhouse.ca, pg 479

Kapanyko, Chrystal, Printing Industries of America, 200 Deer Run Rd, Sewickley, PA 15143-2324 *Tel:* 412-741-6860 *Toll Free Tel:* 800-910-4283 *Fax:* 412-741-2311 *E-mail:* printing@printing.org *Web Site:* www.printing.org, pg 617

Kaplan, Deborah, Puffin Books, 345 Hudson St, New York, NY 10014 *Tel:* 212-366-2000 *E-mail:* online@penguinputnam.com *Web Site:* www.penguinputnam.com; us.penguingroup.com, pg 200

Kaplan, Genevieve, Kate Tufts Discovery Award, Harper East, Unit B-7, 160 E Tenth St, Claremont, CA 91711-6165 *Tel:* 909-621-8974 *E-mail:* tufts@cgu.edu *Web Site:* www.cgu.edu/tufts, pg 733

Kaplan, Genevieve, Kingsley Tufts Poetry Award, Harper East, Unit B-7, 160 E Tenth St, Claremont, CA 91711-6165 *Tel:* 909-621-8974 *E-mail:* tufts@cgu.edu *Web Site:* www.cgu.edu/tufts, pg 733

Kaplan, Howard, Silver Gavel Awards, 321 N Clark St, Chicago, IL 60654 *Tel:* 312-988-5733 *Toll Free Tel:* 800-285-2221 (orders) *Fax:* 312-988-5494 *Web Site:* www.abanow.org; www.americanbar.org, pg 728

Kaplan, Joyce, Kensington Publishing Corp, 119 W 40 St, New York, NY 10018 *Tel:* 212-407-1500 *Toll Free Tel:* 800-221-2647 *Fax:* 212-935-0699 *Web Site:* www.kensingtonbooks.com, pg 130

Kaplan, Lawrence D, Alaska Native Language Center, PO Box 757680, Fairbanks, AK 99775-7680 *Tel:* 907-474-7874 *Fax:* 907-474-6586 *E-mail:* uaf-aknativelang@alaska.edu (orders) *Web Site:* www.uaf.edu/anlc, pg 7

Kaplan, Linda, DeFiore and Company, LLC, 47 E 19 St, 3rd fl, New York, NY 10003 *Tel:* 212-925-7744 *Fax:* 212-925-9803 *E-mail:* submissions@defioreandco.com; info@defioreandco.com *Web Site:* www.defioreandco.com, pg 548

Kaplan, Rob, The Editors Circle, 462 Grove St, Montclair, NJ 07043 *Tel:* 973-783-5082 *E-mail:* query@theeditorscircle.com *Web Site:* www.theeditorscircle.com, pg 525

Kaplan, Ruth, George Bogin Memorial Award, 15 Gramercy Park, New York, NY 10003 *Tel:* 212-254-9628 *Fax:* 212-673-2352 *Web Site:* www.poetrysociety.org, pg 673

Kaplan, Ruth, Alice Fay Di Castagnola Award, 15 Gramercy Park, New York, NY 10003 *Tel:* 212-254-9628 *Fax:* 212-673-2352 *Web Site:* www.poetrysociety.org, pg 680

Kaplan, Ruth, Norma Farber First Book Award, 15 Gramercy Park, New York, NY 10003 *Tel:* 212-254-9628 *Fax:* 212-673-2352 *Web Site:* www.poetrysociety.org, pg 685

Kaplan, Ruth, Cecil Hemley Memorial Award, 15 Gramercy Park, New York, NY 10003 *Tel:* 212-254-9628 *Fax:* 212-673-2352 *Web Site:* www.poetrysociety.org, pg 692

Kaplan, Ruth, Louise Louis/Emily F Bourne Student Poetry Award, 15 Gramercy Park, New York, NY 10003 *Tel:* 212-254-9628 *Fax:* 212-673-2352 *Web Site:* www.poetrysociety.org, pg 703

Kaplan, Ruth, Lyric Poetry Award, 15 Gramercy Park, New York, NY 10003 *Tel:* 212-254-9628 *Fax:* 212-673-2352 *Web Site:* www.poetrysociety.org, pg 704

Kaplan, Ruth, Lucille Medwick Memorial Award, 15 Gramercy Park, New York, NY 10003 *Tel:* 212-254-9628 *Fax:* 212-673-2352 *Web Site:* www.poetrysociety.org, pg 707

Kaplan, Ruth, Poetry Society of America (PSA), 15 Gramercy Park, New York, NY 10003 *Tel:* 212-254-9628 *Fax:* 212-673-2352 *Web Site:* www.poetrysociety.org, pg 616

Kaplan, Ruth, William Carlos Williams Award, 15 Gramercy Park, New York, NY 10003 *Tel:* 212-254-9628 *Fax:* 212-673-2352 *Web Site:* www.poetrysociety.org, pg 736

Kaplan, Ruth, The Writer Magazine/Emily Dickinson Award, 15 Gramercy Park, New York, NY 10003 *Tel:* 212-254-9628 *Fax:* 212-673-2352 *Web Site:* www.poetrysociety.org, pg 738

Kaplan, Stuart R, US Games Systems Inc, 179 Ludlow St, Stamford, CT 06902 *Tel:* 203-353-8400 *Toll Free Tel:* 800-54-GAMES (544-2637) *Fax:* 203-353-8431 *E-mail:* info@usgamesinc.com *Web Site:* www.usgamesinc.com, pg 264

Kapoor, Prashant, Aptara Inc, 3110 Fairview Park Dr, Suite 900, Falls Church, VA 22042 *Tel:* 703-352-0001 *E-mail:* info@aptaracorp.com *Web Site:* www.aptaracorp.com, pg 520

Kapp, Debbie, Western Pennsylvania Genealogical Society, 4400 Forbes Ave, Pittsburgh, PA 15213-4080 *Tel:* 412-687-6811 (answering machine) *E-mail:* info@wpgs.org *Web Site:* www.wpgs.org, pg 269

Karagueuzian, Dikran, CSLI Publications, Stanford University, Cordura Hall, 220 Panama St, Stanford, CA 94305-4115 *Tel:* 650-723-1839 *Fax:* 650-725-2166 *E-mail:* pubs@csli.stanford.edu *Web Site:* cslipublications.stanford.edu, pg 69

Karchmar, Dorian, WME, 1325 Avenue of the Americas, New York, NY 10019 *Tel:* 212-586-5100 *Fax:* 212-246-3583 *E-mail:* wma@interport.net *Web Site:* www.wma.com, pg 579

Kardon, Julia, Mary Evans Inc, 242 E Fifth St, New York, NY 10003-8501 *Tel:* 212-979-0880 *Fax:* 212-979-5344 *E-mail:* info@maryevansinc.com *Web Site:* www.maryevansinc.com, pg 551

Kardys, Jan L, Unicorn Writers' Conference, 17 Church Hill Rd, Redding, CT 06896 *Tel:* 203-938-7405 *Fax:* 203-938-7405 *E-mail:* unicornwritersconference@gmail.com *Web Site:* unicornwritersconference.com, pg 656

Karimi, Joanne, Houghton Mifflin Harcourt, 222 Berkeley St, Boston, MA 02116 *Tel:* 617-351-5000 *Toll Free Tel:* 800-225-5425 (K-12 educ materials); 800-323-9540 (assessment materials); 877-219-1537 (SkillsTutor); 888-242-6747 (Destination; Earobics; Edmark; Learning Village; Riverdeep); 800-225-3362 (Houghton Mifflin Harcourt Trade & Reference Publishers) *Toll Free Fax:* 800-269-5232 *E-mail:* customerservice@hmhpub.com *Web Site:* www.hmhco.com, pg 115

Karl, Laraine, The Rockefeller University Press, 1114 First Ave, 3rd fl, New York, NY 10065-8325 *Tel:* 212-327-7938 *Fax:* 212-327-8587 *E-mail:* rupress@rockefeller.edu *Web Site:* www.rupress.org, pg 210

Karle, John, St Martin's Press, LLC, 175 Fifth Ave, New York, NY 10010 *Tel:* 646-307-5151 *Fax:* 212-420-9314 *E-mail:* firstname.lastname@macmillan.com *Web Site:* www.stmartins.com, pg 215

Karp, Jonathan, Simon & Schuster, 1230 Avenue of the Americas, New York, NY 10020 *Tel:* 212-698-7000 *Toll Free Tel:* 800-223-2348 (cust serv); 800-223-2336 (orders) *Toll Free Fax:* 800-943-9831 (orders) *Web Site:* www.simonandschuster.com, pg 225

Karp, Jonathan, Simon & Schuster, Inc, 1230 Avenue of the Americas, New York, NY 10020 *Tel:* 212-698-7000 *Fax:* 212-698-7007 *E-mail:* firstname.lastname@simonandschuster.com *Web Site:* www.simonandschuster.com, pg 226

Karper, Altie, Pantheon Books/Schocken Books, c/o Random House Inc, 1745 Broadway, New York, NY 10019 *Tel:* 212-751-2600 *Toll Free Tel:* 800-638-6460 *Fax:* 212-572-6030, pg 181

Karpfinger, Barney M, The Karpfinger Agency, 357 W 20 St, New York, NY 10011-3379 *Tel:* 212-691-2690 *Fax:* 212-691-7129 *E-mail:* info@karpfinger.com (no queries or submissions) *Web Site:* karpfinger.com, pg 559

Karre, Andrew, Carolrhoda Books, 241 First Ave N, Minneapolis, MN 55401 *Tel:* 612-332-3344 *Toll Free Tel:* 800-328-4929 *Fax:* 612-332-7615 *Toll Free Fax:* 800-332-1132 *E-mail:* info@lernerbooks.com *Web Site:* www.lernerbooks.com, pg 50

Karre, Andrew, Carolrhoda Lab™, 241 First Ave N, Minneapolis, MN 55401 *Tel:* 612-332-3344 *Toll Free Tel:* 800-328-4929 *Fax:* 612-332-7615 *Toll Free Fax:* 800-332-1132 (US) *E-mail:* info@lernerbooks.com *Web Site:* www.lernerbooks.com, pg 51

Karrel, Dean, John Wiley & Sons Inc Professional/Trade Group, 111 River St, Hoboken, NJ 07030 *Tel:* 201-748-6000 *Toll Free Tel:* 800-225-5945 (cust serv) *Fax:* 201-748-6088 *E-mail:* info@wiley.com *Web Site:* www.wiley.com, pg 272

Karris, Steven T, Orchard Publications, 39510 Paseo Padre Pkwy, Suite 315, Fremont, CA 94538 *Tel:* 510-792-6077 *Fax:* 510-792-6097 *E-mail:* info@orchardpublications.com; orchard@orchardpublications.com *Web Site:* www.orchardpublications.com, pg 176

Kartsaklis, Lee, Simon & Schuster, Inc, 1230 Avenue of the Americas, New York, NY 10020 *Tel:* 212-698-7000 *Fax:* 212-698-7007 *E-mail:* firstname.lastname@simonandschuster.com *Web Site:* www.simonandschuster.com, pg 226

Kartsev, Dr Vladimir, Fort Ross Inc Russian-American Publishing Projects, 26 Arthur Place, Yonkers, NY 10701 *Tel:* 914-375-6448 *Web Site:* www.fortrossinc.com, pg 90

Kartsev, Dr Vladimir P, Fort Ross Inc - International Representation for Artists, 26 Arthur Place, Yonkers, NY 10701 *Tel:* 914-375-6448 *Web Site:* www.fortrossinc.com, pg 552

Kartsev, Dr Vladimir P, Fort Ross Inc - International Representation for Artists, 26 Arthur Place, Yonkers, NY 10701 *Tel:* 914-375-6448; 718-775-8340 *Web Site:* www.fortrossinc.com, pg 583

Kasdin, Steve, Curtis Brown Ltd, 10 Astor Place, New York, NY 10003 *Tel:* 212-473-5400 *Web Site:* www.curtisbrown.com, pg 544

Kase, Josef, Letterbox/Papyrus of London Publishers USA, 10501 Broom Hill Dr, Suite 1-F, Las Vegas, NV 89134-7339 *Tel:* 702-256-3838 *E-mail:* lb27383@cox.net, pg 138

Kaser, Richard T, Information Today, Inc, 143 Old Marlton Pike, Medford, NJ 08055-8750 *Tel:* 609-654-6266 *Toll Free Tel:* 800-300-9868 (cust serv) *Fax:* 609-654-4309 *E-mail:* custserv@infotoday.com *Web Site:* www.infotoday.com, pg 121

Kasher, Robert, Database Directories, 588 Dufferin Ave, London, ON N6B 2A4, Canada *Tel:* 519-433-1666 *Fax:* 519-430-1131 *E-mail:* mail@databasedirectory.com *Web Site:* www.databasedirectory.com, pg 478

Kasius, Jennifer, Running Press Book Publishers, 2300 Chestnut St, Philadelphia, PA 19103-4399 *Tel:* 215-567-5080 *Toll Free Tel:* 800-343-4499 (cust serv & orders) *Fax:* 215-568-2919 *Toll Free Fax:* 800-453-2884 (cust serv & orders) *E-mail:* perseus.promos@perseusbooks.com *Web Site:* www.runningpress.com, pg 212

Kasparian, George Esq, Acanthus Publishing, 180 Lincoln St, 3rd fl, Boston, MA 02111 *Tel:* 617-230-2167 *Fax:* 617-995-0893 *E-mail:* info@acanthuspublishing.com *Web Site:* www.acanthuspublishing.com, pg 4

Kasper, Karl, Crabtree Publishing Co, 350 Fifth Ave, 59th fl, PMB 59051, New York, NY 10118 *Tel:* 212-496-5040 *Toll Free Tel:* 800-387-7650 *Toll Free Fax:* 800-355-7166 *E-mail:* custserv@crabtreebooks.com *Web Site:* www.crabtreebooks.com, pg 66

Kasper, Karl, Crabtree Publishing Co Ltd, 616 Welland Ave, St Catharines, ON L2M-5V6, Canada *Tel:* 905-682-5221 *Toll Free Tel:* 800-387-7650 *Fax:* 905-682-7166 *Toll Free Fax:* 800-355-7166 *E-mail:* custserv@crabtreebooks.com; sales@crabtreebooks.com; orders@crabtreebooks.com *Web Site:* www.crabtreebooks.com, pg 478

Kassahun, Senait, Red Sea Press Inc, 541 W Ingham Ave, Suite B, Trenton, NJ 08638 *Tel:* 609-695-3200 *Fax:* 609-695-6466 *E-mail:* customerservice@africaworldpressbooks.com *Web Site:* www.africaworldpressbooks.com, pg 206

Kastely, Jay, University of Houston Creative Writing Program, 229 Roy Cullen Bldg, Houston, TX 77204-5008 *Tel:* 713-743-2255 *Fax:* 713-743-3697 *E-mail:* cwp@uh.edu *Web Site:* www.uh.edu/cwp, pg 663

Kastenmeier, Edward, Vintage & Anchor Books, c/o Random House Inc, 1745 Broadway, New York, NY 10019 *Tel:* 212-572-2420 *E-mail:* vintageanchorpublicity@randomhouse.com *Web Site:* vintage-anchor.knopfdoubleday.com, pg 266

Kastner, Suzanne, Graphic World Publishing Services, 11687 Adie Rd, St Louis, MO 63043 *Tel:* 314-567-9854 *Fax:* 314-567-7178 *E-mail:* quote@gwinc.com *Web Site:* www.gwinc.com, pg 527

Kastning, Tess, nSight Inc, One Van de Graaff Dr, Suite 202, Burlington, MA 01803 *Tel:* 781-273-6300 *Fax:* 781-273-6301 *Web Site:* www.nsightworks.com, pg 531

Kasuga, Mika, Random House Publishing Group, 1745 Broadway, New York, NY 10019 *Toll Free Tel:* 800-200-3552 *Web Site:* atrandom.com, pg 204

Kater, Julia, The Association of English-Language Publishers of Quebec-AELAQ (Association des Editeurs de Langue Anglaise du Quebec), Atwater Library, 1200 Atwater Ave, Suite 3, Westmount, QC H3Z 1X4, Canada *Tel:* 514-932-5633 *E-mail:* admin@aelaq.org *Web Site:* aelaq.org, pg 599

Kathe, J, Amber Quill Press LLC, PO Box 265, Indian Hills, CO 80454 *E-mail:* business@amberquill.com; customer_service@amberquill.com *Web Site:* www.amberquill.com, pg 10

Katsoris, Nick, NK Publications Inc, PO Box 1735, Radio City Sta, New York, NY 10101-1735 *E-mail:* info@nkpublications.com *Web Site:* www.nkpublications.com, pg 170

Katz, David, Cascade Pass Inc, 4223 Glencoe Ave, Suite C-105, Marina Del Rey, CA 90292-8801 *Tel:* 310-305-0210 *Toll Free Tel:* 888-837-0704 *Fax:* 310-305-7850 *Web Site:* www.cascadepass.com, pg 51

Katz, David, Silver Moon Press, 400 E 85 St, New York, NY 10028 *Toll Free Tel:* 800-874-3320 *Fax:* 212-988-8112 *E-mail:* mail@silvermoonpress.com *Web Site:* www.silvermoonpress.com, pg 224

Katz, Laurie, Chelsea House Publishers, 132 W 31 St, 17th fl, New York, NY 10001 *Tel:* 212-967-8800 *Toll Free Tel:* 800-322-8755 *Fax:* 917-339-0325 *Toll Free Fax:* 800-678-3633 *E-mail:* custserv@factsonfile.com *Web Site:* www.infobasepublishing.com; www.infobaselearning.com, pg 56

Katz, Laurie, Facts On File, 132 W 31 St, 17th fl, New York, NY 10001 *Tel:* 212-967-8800 *Toll Free Tel:* 800-322-8755 *Toll Free Fax:* 800-678-3633 *E-mail:* custserv@factsonfile.com *Web Site:* infobasepublishing.com, pg 85

Katz, Laurie, Ferguson Publishing, 132 W 31 St, 17th fl, New York, NY 10001 *Tel:* 212-967-8800 *Toll Free Tel:* 800-322-8755 *Fax:* 917-339-0323 *Toll Free Fax:* 800-678-3633 *E-mail:* custserv@factsonfile.com *Web Site:* infobasepublishing.com, pg 88

Katz, Megan, Write for Success (WFS), PO Box 292153, Los Angeles, CA 90029-8653 *Tel:* 323-356-8833 *E-mail:* writeforsuccess@yahoo.com *Web Site:* www.write-for-success.com, pg 536

Katz, Michael, Tradewind Books, 202-1807 Maritime Mews, Vancouver, BC V6H 3W7, Canada *Tel:* 604-662-4405 *E-mail:* tradewindbooks@yahoo.com *Web Site:* www.tradewindbooks.com, pg 501

Katzenberger, Elaine, City Lights Publishers, 261 Columbus Ave, San Francisco, CA 94133 *Tel:* 415-362-8193 *Fax:* 415-362-4921 *E-mail:* staff@citylights.com *Web Site:* www.citylights.com, pg 58

Katzman, Julie T, Inter-American Development Bank, 1300 New York Ave NW, Washington, DC 20577 *Tel:* 202-623-1000 *Fax:* 202-623-3096 *E-mail:* pic@iadb.org *Web Site:* www.iadb.org/pub, pg 123

Katzman, Ken, Dover Publications Inc, 31 E Second St, Mineola, NY 11501-3852 *Tel:* 516-294-7000 *Toll Free Tel:* 800-223-3130 (orders) *Fax:* 516-742-6953 *E-mail:* rights@doverpublications.com; service@doverpublications.com *Web Site:* store.doverdirect.com; www.doverpublications.com, pg 76

Kauffman, Katie, The Re-evaluation Counseling Communities, 719 Second Ave N, Seattle, WA 98109 *Tel:* 206-284-0311 *Fax:* 206-284-8429 *E-mail:* ircc@rc.org *Web Site:* www.rc.org, pg 207

Kaufman, Andrew, Wayne State University Press, Leonard N Simons Bldg, 4809 Woodward Ave, Detroit, MI 48201-1309 *Tel:* 313-577-6120 *Toll Free Tel:* 800-978-7323 *Fax:* 313-577-6131 *Web Site:* www.wsupress.wayne.edu, pg 268

Kaufman, Brian, Anvil Press Publishers, 278 E First Ave, Vancouver, BC V5T 1A6, Canada *Tel:* 604-876-8710 *Fax:* 604-879-2667 *E-mail:* info@anvilpress.com *Web Site:* www.anvilpress.com, pg 471

Kaufman, Jason, Doubleday/Nan A Talese, c/o Penguin Random House Inc, 1745 Broadway, New York, NY 10019 *Tel:* 212-751-2600 *Fax:* 212-572-2662 *E-mail:* ddaypub@randomhouse.com *Web Site:* knopfdoubleday.com, pg 76

Kaufman, Lois, Peter Pauper Press, Inc, 202 Mamaroneck Ave, White Plains, NY 10601-5376 *Tel:* 914-681-0144 *Fax:* 914-681-0389 *E-mail:* customerservice@peterpauper.com; orders@peterpauper.com *Web Site:* www.peterpauper.com, pg 190

Kaufman, Shari, innovativeKids®, 50 Washington St, Suite 201, Norwalk, CT 06854 *Tel:* 203-838-6400 *E-mail:* info@innovativekids.com *Web Site:* www.innovativekids.com, pg 122

Kaufmann, Anne, FC&A Publishing, 103 Clover Green, Peachtree City, GA 30269 *Tel:* 770-487-6307 *Toll Free Tel:* 800-226-8024 *Fax:* 770-631-4357 *E-mail:* customer_service@fca.com *Web Site:* www.fca.com, pg 87

Kaufmann, Anthony S, Abaris Books, 64 Wall St, Norwalk, CT 06850 *Tel:* 203-838-8402 *Fax:* 203-857-0730 *E-mail:* abaris@abarisbooks.com *Web Site:* abarisbooks.com, pg 2

Kaufmann, Anthony S, EastBridge, 70 New Canaan Ave, Norwalk, CT 06850 *Tel:* 203-855-9125 *Fax:* 203-857-0730 *E-mail:* asia@eastbridgebooks.org; ask@eastbridgebooks.org *Web Site:* www.eastbridgebooks.org, pg 78

Kavaler, Ethan Matt, Centre for Reformation & Renaissance Studies (CRRS), 71 Queen's Park Crescent E, Toronto, ON M5S 1K7, Canada *Tel:* 416-585-4465 *Fax:* 416-585-4430 (attn: CRRS) *E-mail:* crrs.publications@utoronto.ca *Web Site:* crrs.ca, pg 476

Kavonic, Melissa, Bloomsbury Publishing Inc, 1385 Broadway, 5th fl, New York, NY 10018 *Tel:* 212-419-5300 *E-mail:* marketingusa@bloomsbury.com; adultpublicityusa@bloomsbury.com; askacademic@bloomsbury.com *Web Site:* www.bloomsbury.com, pg 40

Kawai, Colins, University of Hawaii Press, 2840 Kolowalu St, Honolulu, HI 96822 *Tel:* 808-956-8255 *Toll Free Tel:* 888-UHPRESS (847-7377) *Fax:* 808-988-6052 *Toll Free Fax:* 800-650-7811 *E-mail:* uhpbooks@hawaii.edu *Web Site:* www.uhpress.hawaii.edu, pg 256

Kay, Jeremy, Bartleby Press, 8926 Baltimore St, No 858, Savage, MD 20763 *Tel:* 301-725-3906 *Toll Free Tel:* 800-953-9929 *Fax:* 667-309-6993 *E-mail:* inquiries@bartlebythepublisher.com *Web Site:* www.bartlebythepublisher.com, pg 31

Kay, Jeremy, Schreiber Publishing Inc, PO Box 4193, Rockville, MD 20849 *Tel:* 301-725-3906 *Toll Free Tel:* 800-296-1961 (sales) *Fax:* 301-725-0333 (orders) *E-mail:* schreiberpublishing@comcast.net *Web Site:* schreiberlanguage.com; shengold.com, pg 219

Kaye, Bradley, The Mellen Poetry Press, 240 Portage Rd, Lewiston, NY 14092 *Tel:* 716-754-2266; 716-754-1400 (mktg); 716-754-2788 (order fulfillment) *Fax:* 716-754-4056; 716-754-1860 (fulfillment) *E-mail:* cservice@mellenpress.com *Web Site:* www.mellenpress.com, pg 154

Kaye, David, Anna Zornio Memorial Children's Theatre Playwriting Award, D22 Paul Creative Arts Center, 30 Academic Way, Durham, NH 03824 *Tel:* 603-862-2919 *Fax:* 603-862-0298 *Web Site:* cola.unh.edu/theatre-dance/resource/zornio, pg 740

Kaye, Terry, Behrman House Inc, 11 Edison Place, Springfield, NJ 07081 *Tel:* 973-379-7200 *Toll Free Tel:* 800-221-2755 *Fax:* 973-379-7280 *E-mail:* behrmanhouse@gmail.com; customersupport@behrmanhouse.com *Web Site:* www.behrmanhouse.com, pg 33

Kayne, Amy, Walch Education, 40 Walch Dr, Portland, ME 04103-1286 *Tel:* 207-772-2846 *Toll Free Tel:* 800-558-2846 *Fax:* 207-772-3105 *Toll Free Fax:* 888-991-5755 *E-mail:* customerservice@walch.com *Web Site:* www.walch.com, pg 266

Kean, Carla, Seal Books, One Toronto St, Suite 300, Toronto, ON M5C 2V6, Canada *Tel:* 416-364-4449 *Toll Free Tel:* 888-523-9292 (order desk) *Fax:* 416-364-6863 *Web Site:* www.randomhouse.ca, pg 498

Kean, Linda Griffin, International Monetary Fund (IMF), Editorial & Publications Division, 700 19 St NW, HQ1-7-124, Washington, DC 20431 *Tel:* 202-623-7430 *Fax:* 202-623-7201 *E-mail:* publications@imf.org *Web Site:* www.imfbookstore.org; elibrary.imf.org (online collection), pg 124

Keane, Christopher, American Geosciences Institute (AGI), 4220 King St, Alexandria, VA 22302-1502 *Tel:* 703-379-2480 (ext 246) *Fax:* 703-379-7563 *E-mail:* pubs@agiweb.org *Web Site:* www.agiweb.org, pg 13

Keane, Kathleen, The Johns Hopkins University Press, 2715 N Charles St, Baltimore, MD 21218-4363 *Tel:* 410-516-6900; 410-516-6987 (journal orders outside US & CN) *Toll Free Tel:* 800-537-5487 (book orders & cust serv); 800-548-1784 (journal orders) *Fax:* 410-516-6968; 410-516-3866 (journal orders) *E-mail:* hfscustserv@press.jhu.edu (cust serv); jrnlcirc@press.jhu.edu (journal orders) *Web Site:* www.press.jhu.edu; muse.jhu.edu, pg 127

Keane, Patrick, Hagstrom Map, 1800 Lovering Ave, Wilmington, DE 19806 *Toll Free Tel:* 800-432-MAPS (432-6277) *Toll Free Fax:* 888-210-9654 *Web Site:* rockfordpublishing.com, pg 103

Kecskemethy, Tom, American Academy of Political & Social Science, 202 S 36 St, Philadelphia, PA 19104-3806 *Tel:* 215-746-6500 *Fax:* 215-573-2667 *Web Site:* www.aapss.org, pg 594

Keefe, Laura, Bloomsbury Publishing Inc, 1385 Broadway, 5th fl, New York, NY 10018 *Tel:* 212-419-5300 *E-mail:* marketingusa@bloomsbury.com; adultpublicityusa@bloomsbury.com; askacademic@bloomsbury.com *Web Site:* www.bloomsbury.com, pg 40

Keegan, Kenneth, Omnidawn Publishing, 1632 Elm Ave, Richmond, CA 94805-1614 *Tel:* 510-237-5472 *Toll Free Tel:* 800-792-4957 *Fax:* 510-232-8525 *E-mail:* manager@omnidawn.com *Web Site:* www.omnidawn.com, pg 175

Keegan, Tom, Athletic Guide Publishing, PO Box 1050, Flagler Beach, FL 32136 *Tel:* 386-439-2050 *Toll Free Tel:* 800-255-1050 *E-mail:* flaglernet@gmail.com *Web Site:* www.athleticguidepublishing.com, pg 26

Keeler, Rev Roger H, Canon Law Society of America, Hecker Ctr, Suite 111, 3025 Fourth St NE, Washington, DC 20017-1102 *Tel:* 202-832-2350 *Fax:* 202-832-2331 *E-mail:* coordinator@clsa.org; info@clsa.org *Web Site:* www.clsa.org, pg 49

Keeley, Mary, Books & Such, 52 Mission Circle, Suite 122, PMB 170, Santa Rosa, CA 95409-5370 *Tel:* 707-538-4184 *Web Site:* booksandsuch.com, pg 543

Keeley, Tracy, Children's Sequoyah Book Award, 300 Hardy Dr, Edmond, OK 73013 *Tel:* 405-525-5100 *Fax:* 405-525-5103 *Web Site:* www.oklibs.org, pg 677

Keeley, Tracy, Intermediate Sequoyah Book Award, 300 Hardy Dr, Edmond, OK 73013 *Tel:* 405-525-5100 *Fax:* 405-525-5103 *Web Site:* www.oklibs.org, pg 695

Keeling, Judith, Texas Tech University Press, 2903 Fourth St, Suite 201, Lubbock, TX 79409 *Tel:* 806-742-2982 *Toll Free Tel:* 800-832-4042 *Fax:* 806-742-2979 *E-mail:* ttup@ttu.edu *Web Site:* www.ttupress.org, pg 243

Keenan, William P Jr, Editorial Freelancers Association (EFA), 71 W 23 St, 4th fl, New York, NY 10010-4102 *Tel:* 212-929-5400 *Toll Free Tel:* 866-929-5425 *Fax:* 212-929-5439 *Toll Free Fax:* 866-929-5439 *E-mail:* office@the-efa.org *Web Site:* www.the-efa.org, pg 605

Keene, Ann T, Edit Etc, 20 Rock Harbor Rd, Orleans, MA 02653 *Tel:* 914-715-5849 *E-mail:* atkedit@cs.com *Web Site:* www.anntkeene.com, pg 525

Keene, James A, Glenbridge Publishing Ltd, 19923 E Long Ave, Centennial, CO 80016-1969 *Tel:* 720-870-8381 *Toll Free Tel:* 800-986-4135 (orders) *Fax:* 720-230-1209 *E-mail:* glenbridge10@gmail.com *Web Site:* www.glenbridgepublishing.com, pg 97

Keene, Katie, University Press of Mississippi, 3825 Ridgewood Rd, Jackson, MS 39211-6492 *Tel:* 601-432-6205 *Toll Free Tel:* 800-737-7788 (orders & cust serv) *Fax:* 601-432-6217 *E-mail:* press@mississippi.edu *Web Site:* www.upress.state.ms.us, pg 262

Keene, Kristyn, ICM Partners, 730 Fifth Ave, New York, NY 10019 *Tel:* 212-556-5600 *Web Site:* www.icmtalent.com, pg 557

Keene, Mary B, Glenbridge Publishing Ltd, 19923 E Long Ave, Centennial, CO 80016-1969 *Tel:* 720-870-8381 *Toll Free Tel:* 800-986-4135 (orders) *Fax:* 720-230-1209 *E-mail:* glenbridge10@gmail.com *Web Site:* www.glenbridgepublishing.com, pg 97

Keener, Lamar, Evangelical Press Association (EPA), PO Box 20198, El Cajon, CA 92021 *Toll Free Tel:* 888-311-1731 *E-mail:* info@evangelicalpress.com *Web Site:* www.evangelicalpress.com, pg 605

Keesler, Darin, Picador, 175 Fifth Ave, 19th fl, New York, NY 10010 *Tel:* 646-307-5151 *Fax:* 212-253-9627 *E-mail:* firstname.lastname@picadorusa.com *Web Site:* www.picadorusa.com, pg 191

Kehnemui, Sharon, The AEI Press, 1150 17 St NW, Washington, DC 20036 *Tel:* 202-862-5800 *Fax:* 202-862-7177 *Web Site:* www.aei.org, pg 5

Kehren, Vanessa, Blue Rider Press, 375 Hudson St, New York, NY 10014 *Tel:* 212-366-2000 *E-mail:* blueriderpublicity@us.penguingroup.com, pg 41

Kehrer, Daniel, BizBest Media Corp, 860 Via de la Paz, Suite E3B, Pacific Palisades, CA 90272 *E-mail:* press@bizbest.com *Web Site:* www.bizbest.com, pg 38

Keim, Betty, Keim Publishing, 66 Main St, Suite 807, Yonkers, NY 10701 *Tel:* 917-655-7190, pg 528

Keim, Lisa, Atria Books, 1230 Avenue of the Americas, New York, NY 10020 *Tel:* 212-698-7000 *Fax:* 212-698-7007 *Web Site:* www.simonandschuster.com, pg 26

Keim, Lisa, Howard Books, 216 Centerview Dr, Suite 303, Brentwood, TN 37027 *Tel:* 615-873-2080 *Fax:* 615-370-3834 *E-mail:* howardbooks@simonandschuster.com (info) *Web Site:* www.howardpublishing.com, pg 116

Keith, Rebecca, National Book Awards, 90 Broad St, Suite 604, New York, NY 10004 *Tel:* 212-685-0261 *Fax:* 212-213-6570 *E-mail:* nationalbook@nationalbook.org *Web Site:* www.nationalbook.org, pg 710

Kelada, Mike, Aquila Communications Inc, 2642 Diab St, Montreal, QC H4S 1E8, Canada *Tel:* 514-338-1065 *Toll Free Tel:* 800-667-7071 *Fax:* 514-338-1948 *Toll Free Fax:* 866-338-1948 *E-mail:* orders@aquilacommunications.com *Web Site:* www.aquilacommunications.com; aquilacommunications.net, pg 471

Kelada, Sami, Aquila Communications Inc, 2642 Diab St, Montreal, QC H4S 1E8, Canada *Tel:* 514-338-1065 *Toll Free Tel:* 800-667-7071 *Fax:* 514-338-1948 *Toll Free Fax:* 866-338-1948 *E-mail:* orders@aquilacommunications.com *Web Site:* www.aquilacommunications.com; aquilacommunications.net, pg 471

Kelleher, Mary, Aggiornamento Award, 8550 United Plaza Blvd, Suite 1001, Baton Rouge, LA 70809-2256 *Tel:* 225-408-4417 *E-mail:* cla2@cathla.org *Web Site:* www.cathla.org, pg 665

Kelleher, Mary, Catholic Library Association, 8550 United Plaza Blvd, Suite 1001, Baton Rouge, LA 70809-2256 *Tel:* 225-408-4417 *E-mail:* cla2@cathla.org *Web Site:* www.cathla.org, pg 602

Kelleher, Mary, Saint Katharine Drexel Award, 8550 United Plaza Blvd, Suite 1001, Baton Rouge, LA 70809-2256 *Tel:* 225-408-4417 *E-mail:* cla2@cathla.org *Web Site:* www.cathla.org, pg 682

Kelleher, Mary, Jerome Award, 8550 United Plaza Blvd, Suite 1001, Baton Rouge, LA 70809-2256 *Tel:* 225-408-4417 *E-mail:* cla2@cathla.org *Web Site:* www.cathla.org, pg 697

Kelleher, Mary, Regina Medal Award, 8550 United Plaza Blvd, Suite 1001, Baton Rouge, LA 70809-2256 *Tel:* 225-408-4417 *E-mail:* cla2@cathla.org *Web Site:* www.cathla.org, pg 723

Kelleher, Michael, Windham-Campbell Prizes, Beinecke Library, 121 Whitney Ave, Suite 102, New Haven, CT 06510-1242 *Fax:* 203-432-9033 *Web Site:* windhamcampbell.org, pg 737

Kelleher, Roger, American Management Association (AMA), 1601 Broadway, New York, NY 10019 *Tel:* 212-586-8100 *Toll Free Tel:* 877-566-9441 *Fax:* 212-903-8168; 518-891-0368 *E-mail:* customerservice@amanet.org *Web Site:* www.amanet.org, pg 595

Kelleher, TJ, Basic Books, 250 W 57 St, 15th fl, New York, NY 10107 *Tel:* 212-340-8164; 212-340-8136 *Fax:* 212-340-8135 *E-mail:* perseus.promos@perseusbooks.com *Web Site:* www.basicbooks.com; perseusbooks.com, pg 31

Keller, Donald, Bright Connections Media, A World Book Encyclopedia Company, 233 N Michigan Ave, Suite 2000, Chicago, IL 60601 *Tel:* 312-729-5800 *Fax:* 312-729-5610 *Web Site:* www.brightconnectionsmedia.com, pg 46

Keller, Donald D, World Book Inc, 233 N Michigan, Suite 2000, Chicago, IL 60601 *Tel:* 312-729-5800 *Toll Free Tel:* 800-967-5325 (consumer sales, US); 800-463-8845 (consumer sales, CN); 800-975-3250 (school & lib sales, US); 800-837-5365 (school & lib sales, CN); 866-866-5200 (web sales) *Fax:* 312-729-5600; 312-729-5606 *Toll Free Fax:* 800-433-9330 (school & lib sales, US); 888-690-4002 (school lib sales, CN) *Web Site:* www.worldbook.com, pg 276

Keller, Gary D, Bilingual Press/Editorial Bilingue, Arizona State Univ, Hispanic Research Ctr, Tempe, AZ 85287-2702 *Tel:* 480-965-3867 *Toll Free Tel:* 866-965-3867 *Fax:* 480-965-0315 *E-mail:* brp@asu.edu *Web Site:* www.asu.edu/brp, pg 37

Keller, Holly, University of British Columbia Press, 2029 West Mall, Vancouver, BC V6T 1Z2, Canada *Tel:* 604-822-5959 *Toll Free Tel:* 877-377-9378 *Fax:* 604-822-6083 *Toll Free Fax:* 800-668-0821 *E-mail:* frontdesk@ubcpress.ca *Web Site:* www.ubcpress.ca, pg 502

Keller, Jim, J J Keller & Associates, Inc, 3003 Breezewood Lane, Neenah, WI 54957 *Tel:* 920-722-2848 *Toll Free Tel:* 877-564-2333 *Toll Free Fax:* 800-727-7516 *E-mail:* contactus@jjkeller.com; customerservice@jjkeller.com *Web Site:* www.jjkeller.com, pg 130

Keller, Karen, Orientation to the Graphic Arts, 200 Deer Run Rd, Sewickley, PA 15143-2324 *Tel:* 412-259-1711 *Toll Free Tel:* 800-910-4283 *Fax:* 412-741-2311 *E-mail:* printing@printing.org *Web Site:* www.printing.org, pg 653

Keller, Matthew A, Capstone Publishers™, 1710 Roe Crest Dr, North Mankato, MN 56003 *Toll Free Tel:* 800-747-4992 (cust serv) *Toll Free Fax:* 888-262-0705 *Web Site:* www.capstonepress.com, pg 49

Keller, Michael, Stanford University Press, 1450 Page Mill Rd, Palo Alto, CA 94304-1124 *Tel:* 650-723-9434 *Fax:* 650-725-3457 *E-mail:* info@sup.org *Web Site:* www.sup.org, pg 233

Keller, Robert L, J J Keller & Associates, Inc, 3003 Breezewood Lane, Neenah, WI 54957 *Tel:* 920-722-2848 *Toll Free Tel:* 877-564-2333 *Toll Free Fax:* 800-727-7516 *E-mail:* contactus@jjkeller.com; customerservice@jjkeller.com *Web Site:* www.jjkeller.com, pg 130

Keller, Rustin R, J J Keller & Associates, Inc, 3003 Breezewood Lane, Neenah, WI 54957 *Tel:* 920-722-2848 *Toll Free Tel:* 877-564-2333 *Toll Free Fax:* 800-727-7516 *E-mail:* contactus@jjkeller.com; customerservice@jjkeller.com *Web Site:* www.jjkeller.com, pg 130

Keller, Wendy, Keller Media Inc, 578 Washington Blvd, No 745, Marina del Rey, CA 90292 *Toll Free Tel:* 800-278-8706 *E-mail:* query@kellermedia.com *Web Site:* kellermedia.com/query, pg 559

Keller-Krikava, Marne, J J Keller & Associates, Inc, 3003 Breezewood Lane, Neenah, WI 54957 *Tel:* 920-722-2848 *Toll Free Tel:* 877-564-2333 *Toll Free Fax:* 800-727-7516 *E-mail:* contactus@jjkeller.com; customerservice@jjkeller.com *Web Site:* www.jjkeller.com, pg 130

Kelley, Allison, Romance Writers of America®, 14615 Benfer Rd, Houston, TX 77069 *Tel:* 832-717-5200 *Fax:* 832-717-5201 *E-mail:* info@rwa.org *Web Site:* www.rwa.org, pg 618

Kelley, Allison, Romance Writers of America Annual Conference, 14615 Benfer Rd, Houston, TX 77069 *Tel:* 832-717-5200 *Fax:* 832-717-5201 *E-mail:* info@rwa.org *Web Site:* www.rwa.org, pg 654

Kelley, Allison, Romance Writers of America Awards, 14615 Benfer Rd, Houston, TX 77069 *Tel:* 832-717-5200 *Fax:* 832-717-5201 *E-mail:* info@rwa.org *Web Site:* www.rwa.org, pg 724

Kelley, Annie, Random House Children's Books, 1745 Broadway, New York, NY 10019 *Tel:* 212-782-9000 *Toll Free Tel:* 800-200-3552 *Fax:* 212-782-9452 *Web Site:* randomhousekids.com, pg 203

Kelley, Lynn, Kane Miller Books, 4901 Morena Blvd, Suite 213, San Diego, CA 92117 *E-mail:* info@kanemiller.com *Web Site:* www.kanemiller.com, pg 129

Kelley, Pamela, University of Hawaii Press, 2840 Kolowalu St, Honolulu, HI 96822 *Tel:* 808-956-8255 *Toll Free Tel:* 888-UHPRESS (847-7377) *Fax:* 808-988-6052 *Toll Free Fax:* 800-650-7811 *E-mail:* uhpbooks@hawaii.edu *Web Site:* www.uhpress.hawaii.edu, pg 256

Kelley, Dr Suzzanne, New Rivers Press, c/o Minnesota State University Moorhead, 1104 Seventh Ave S, Moorhead, MN 56563 *Tel:* 218-477-5870 *Fax:* 218-477-2236 *E-mail:* nrp@mnstate.edu *Web Site:* www.newriverspress.com; www.mnstate.edu/newriverspress, pg 168

Kellman, Anthony, Sandhills Writers' Series, Dept of Communications & Professional Writing, 2500 Walton Way, Augusta, GA 30904 *Tel:* 706-667-4437 *Fax:* 706-667-4770 *Web Site:* www.sandhills.aug.edu, pg 654

Kellman, Steven, Ivan Sandrof Lifetime Achievement Award, 160 Varick St, 11th fl, New York, NY 10013 *E-mail:* info@bookcritics.org; membership@bookcritics.org (nominations from membs) *Web Site:* bookcritics.org, pg 725

Kelly, Barbara, PJD Publications Ltd, PO Box 966, Westbury, NY 11590-0966 *Tel:* 516-626-0650 *Fax:* 516-626-4456 *Web Site:* www.pjdonline.com, pg 192

Kelly, Burta, Ashgate Publishing Co, 110 Cherry St, Suite 3-1, Burlington, VT 05401-3818 *Tel:* 802-865-7641 *Toll Free Tel:* 800-535-9544 *Fax:* 802-865-7847 *E-mail:* ashgate.online@ashgate.com *Web Site:* www.ashgate.com, pg 24

Kelly, Charlotte, Other Press LLC, 2 Park Ave, 24th fl, New York, NY 10016 *Tel:* 212-414-0054 *Toll Free Tel:* 877-843-6843 *Fax:* 212-414-0939 *E-mail:* editor@otherpress.com; rights@otherpress.com *Web Site:* www.otherpress.com, pg 178

Kelly, Donna E, North Carolina Office of Archives & History, Historical Publications Section, 4622 Mail Service Ctr, Raleigh, NC 27699-4622 *Tel:* 919-733-7442 (ext 225) *Fax:* 919-733-1439 *Web Site:* www.ncpublications.com; nc-historical-publications.stores.yahoo.net (online store), pg 170

Kelly, Frances, Eye in the Ear Children's Audio, 5 Crescent St, Portland, ME 04102 *Toll Free Tel:* 855-99-STORY (997-8679) *Fax:* 207-699-1380 (attn: Laurence Kelly) *E-mail:* info@eyeintheear.com *Web Site:* www.eyeintheear.com, pg 85

Kelly, Jean Marie, HarperCollins Publishers, 195 Broadway, New York, NY 10007 *Tel:* 212-207-7000 *Fax:* 212-207-7145 *Web Site:* www.harpercollins.com, pg 106

Kelly, Kate, Morgan Gaynin Inc, 149 Madison Ave, Suite 1140, New York, NY 10016 *Tel:* 212-475-0440 *E-mail:* info@morgangaynin.com *Web Site:* www.morgangaynin.com, pg 584

Kelly, Kevin, Practising Law Institute, 1177 Avenue of the Americas, New York, NY 10036 *Tel:* 212-824-5700 *Toll Free Tel:* 800-260-4PLI (260-4754, cust serv) *Fax:* 212-265-4742 (intl) *Toll Free Fax:* 800-321-0093 (local) *E-mail:* info@pli.edu (cust serv) *Web Site:* www.pli.edu, pg 195

Kelly, Laurence A, Eye in the Ear Children's Audio, 5 Crescent St, Portland, ME 04102 *Toll Free Tel:* 855-99-STORY (997-8679) *Fax:* 207-699-1380 (attn: Laurence Kelly) *E-mail:* info@eyeintheear.com *Web Site:* www.eyeintheear.com, pg 85

Kelly, Neil K, F A Davis Co, 1915 Arch St, Philadelphia, PA 19103 *Tel:* 215-568-2270; 215-440-3001 *Toll Free Tel:* 800-523-4049 *Fax:* 215-568-5065; 215-440-3016 *E-mail:* info@fadavis.com; orders@fadavis.com *Web Site:* www.fadavis.com, pg 71

Kelly, Patricia, Crown Publishing Group, c/o Penguin Random House Inc, 1745 Broadway, New York, NY 10019 *Tel:* 212-782-9000 *Toll Free Tel:* 888-264-1745 *Fax:* 212-940-7408 *E-mail:* crownosm@penguinrandomhouse.com *Web Site:* crownpublishing.com, pg 68

Kelly, Patricia, Lonely Planet, 150 Linden St, Oakland, CA 94607 *Tel:* 510-893-8555 *Toll Free Tel:* 800-275-8555 (orders) *Fax:* 510-893-8572 *E-mail:* info@lonelyplanet.com *Web Site:* www.lonelyplanet.com, pg 142

Kelly, Robert, Goodheart-Willcox Publisher, 18604 W Creek Dr, Tinley Park, IL 60477-6243 *Tel:* 708-687-5000 *Toll Free Tel:* 800-323-0440 *Fax:* 708-468-8692 *Toll Free Fax:* 888-409-3900 *E-mail:* custserv@g-w.com; orders@g-w.com *Web Site:* www.g-w.com, pg 98

Kelly, Stephanie, Penguin Group (USA) LLC, a Penguin Random House company, 375 Hudson St, New York, NY 10014 *Tel:* 212-366-2000 *Toll Free Tel:* 800-847-5515 (inside sales); 800-631-8571 (cust serv) *Fax:* 212-366-2666; 607-775-4829 (inside sales) *E-mail:* online@us.penguingroup.com *Web Site:* www.penguin.com; us.penguingroup.com, pg 186

Kelly, Timothy T, National Geographic Society, 1145 17 St NW, Washington, DC 20036-4688 *Tel:* 202-857-7000 *Fax:* 202-429-5727 *Web Site:* www.nationalgeographic.com, pg 165

Kelly-Pye, Laurie, The Career Press Inc, 12 Parish Dr, Wayne, NJ 07470 *Tel:* 201-848-0310 *Toll Free Tel:* 800-CAREER-1 (227-3371) *Fax:* 201-848-1727 *E-mail:* sales@careerpress.com *Web Site:* www.careerpress.com, pg 50

Kelpner, Jennifer, Martingale®, 19021 120 Ave NE, Suite 102, Bothell, WA 98011 *Tel:* 425-483-3313 *Toll Free Tel:* 800-426-3126 *Fax:* 425-486-7596 *E-mail:* info@martingale-pub.com *Web Site:* www.martingale-pub.com, pg 148

Kelsey, Karla, Susquehanna University, Department of English, 514 University Ave, Selinsgrove, PA 17870 *Tel:* 570-372-0101, pg 662

Kelty, John, Copywriter's Council of America (CCA), CCA Bldg, 7 Putter Lane, Middle Island, NY 11953-1920 *Tel:* 631-924-3888 *Fax:* 631-924-8555 *E-mail:* cca4dmcopy@gmail.com *Web Site:* www.AndrewLinickDirectMarketing.com/Copywriters-Council.html; www.NewWorldPressBooks.com, pg 63

Kemp, Jaemellah, Naval Institute Press, 291 Wood Rd, Annapolis, MD 21402-5034 *Tel:* 410-268-6110 *Toll Free Tel:* 800-233-8764 *Fax:* 410-295-1084; 410-571-1703 (cust serv) *E-mail:* webmaster@navalinstitute.org; customer@navalinstitute.org (cust serv); trade@usni.org *Web Site:* www.nip.org; www.usni.org, pg 166

Kempker, Debra, Prima Games, 3000 Lava Ridge Ct, Roseville, CA 95661 *Tel:* 916-787-7000 *Fax:* 916-787-7001 *Web Site:* www.primagames.com, pg 196

Kempster, Rachel, DK Publishing, 345 Hudson St, 2nd fl, New York, NY 10014 *Tel:* 646-674-4000 *Toll Free Tel:* 877-342-5357 (cust serv) *Web Site:* us.dk.com, pg 75

Kenady, Anne, Chronicle Books LLC, 680 Second St, San Francisco, CA 94107 *Tel:* 415-537-4200 *Toll Free Tel:* 800-759-0190 (cust serv) *Fax:* 415-537-4460 *Toll Free Fax:* 800-858-7787 (orders); 800-286-9471 (cust serv) *E-mail:* frontdesk@chroniclebooks.com *Web Site:* www.chroniclebooks.com, pg 58

Kendall, Josh, Little, Brown and Company, 1290 Avenue of the Americas, New York, NY 10019 *Tel:* 212-364-1100 *Fax:* 212-364-0952 *E-mail:* firstname.lastname@hbgusa.com *Web Site:* www.HachetteBookGroup.com, pg 141

Keneston, Fran, State University of New York Press, 22 Corporate Woods Blvd, 3rd fl, Albany, NY 12211-2504 *Tel:* 518-472-5000 *Toll Free Tel:* 877-204-6073 (orders) *Fax:* 518-472-5038 *Toll Free Fax:* 877-204-6074 (orders) *E-mail:* suny@presswarehouse.com (orders); info@sunypress.edu (edit off) *Web Site:* www.sunypress.edu, pg 234

Kennedy, Christopher, Syracuse University Creative Writing Program, 401 Hall of Languages, Syracuse, NY 13244-1170 *Tel:* 315-443-2173 *Fax:* 315-443-3660 *Web Site:* english.syr.edu/creative_writing; www.syr.edu, pg 662

Kennedy, Daniel W, Whitehorse Press, 107 E Conway Rd, Center Conway, NH 03813-4012 *Tel:* 603-356-6556 *Toll Free Tel:* 800-531-1133 *Fax:* 603-356-6590 *E-mail:* customerservice@whitehorsepress.com *Web Site:* www.whitehorsebooks.com, pg 271

Kennedy, Frances, The Doe Coover Agency, PO Box 668, Winchester, MA 01890 *Tel:* 781-721-6000 *Fax:* 781-721-6727 *E-mail:* info@doecooveragency.com *Web Site:* www.doecooveragency.com, pg 547

Kennedy, Judith M, Whitehorse Press, 107 E Conway Rd, Center Conway, NH 03813-4012 *Tel:* 603-356-6556 *Toll Free Tel:* 800-531-1133 *Fax:* 603-356-6590 *E-mail:* customerservice@whitehorsepress.com *Web Site:* www.whitehorsebooks.com, pg 271

Kennedy, Lindsay, Random House Publishing Group, 1745 Broadway, New York, NY 10019 *Toll Free Tel:* 800-200-3552 *Web Site:* atrandom.com, pg 204

Kennedy, Lorie, Young People's Press Inc (YPPI), 1527 Reed Ave, San Diego, CA 92109 *Tel:* 619-992-3258 (orders) *Toll Free Tel:* 800-231-9774 *E-mail:* admin@youngpeoplespress.com *Web Site:* www.youngpeoplespress.com, pg 279

Kennedy, Mary, Institute of Intergovernmental Relations, Queen's University, Robert Sutherland Hall, Rm 301, Kingston, ON K7L 3N6, Canada *Tel:* 613-533-2080 *Fax:* 613-533-6868 *E-mail:* iigr@queensu.ca *Web Site:* www.queensu.ca/iigr, pg 488

Kennedy, Megan, Rough Guides, 375 Hudson St, New York, NY 10014 *Toll Free Tel:* 800-631-8571 *E-mail:* mail@roughguides.com *Web Site:* www.roughguides.com, pg 211

Kennedy, Paul, F+W, A Content + eCommerce Company, 10151 Carver Rd, Suite 200, Blue Ash, OH 45242 *Tel:* 513-531-2690 *Toll Free Tel:* 800-289-0963 (trade accts); 800-258-0929 (orders) *E-mail:* contact_us@fwmedia.com *Web Site:* www.fwcommunity.com, pg 86

Kennedy, Shane, Lone Pine Publishing, 2311 96 St, Edmonton, AB T6N 1G3, Canada *Tel:* 780-433-9333 *Toll Free Tel:* 800-661-9017 *Fax:* 780-433-9646 *Toll Free Fax:* 800-424-7173 *E-mail:* info@lonepinepublishing.com *Web Site:* www.lonepinepublishing.com, pg 490

Kennedy, Tara, Oxford University Press USA, 198 Madison Ave, New York, NY 10016 *Tel:* 212-726-6000 *Toll Free Tel:* 800-451-7556 (orders); 800-445-9714 (cust serv) *Fax:* 919-677-1303 *E-mail:* custserv.us@oup.com *Web Site:* www.oup.com/us, pg 179

Kennedy, Terry, The Robert Watson Literary Prizes in Fiction & Poetry, MFA Writing Program, The Greensboro Review, UNC-Greensboro, 3302 MHRA Bldg, Greensboro, NC 27402-6170 *Tel:* 336-334-5459 *Fax:* 336-256-1470 *Web Site:* www.greensbororeview.org, pg 734

Kennedy, William, New York State Edith Wharton Citation of Merit for Fiction Writers, University at Albany, SL 320, Albany, NY 12222 *Tel:* 518-442-5620 *Fax:* 518-442-5621 *E-mail:* writers@uamail.albany.edu *Web Site:* www.albany.edu/writers-inst, pg 713

Kennedy, William, New York State Walt Whitman Citation of Merit for Poets, University at Albany, SL 320, Albany, NY 12222 *Tel:* 518-442-5620 *Fax:* 518-442-5621 *E-mail:* writers@uamail.albany.edu *Web Site:* www.albany.edu/writers-inst, pg 713

Kennedy, William, New York State Writers Institute, University at Albany, Science Library 320, Albany, NY 12222 *Tel:* 518-442-5620 *Fax:* 518-442-5621 *E-mail:* writers@uamail.albany.edu *Web Site:* www.albany.edu/writers-inst, pg 653

Kenney, Philip, Bisk Education, 9417 Princess Palm Ave, Suite 400, Tampa, FL 33619 *Tel:* 813-621-6200 *Toll Free Tel:* 800-280-9718 (cust serv) *E-mail:* customerservice@bisk.com *Web Site:* www.bisk.com, pg 37

Kenney, Verne, David C Cook, 4050 Lee Vance View, Colorado Springs, CO 80918 *Tel:* 719-536-0100 *Toll Free Tel:* 800-708-5550; 800-323-7543 (orders & cust serv) *Toll Free Fax:* 800-430-0726 (cust serv) *Web Site:* www.davidccook.com, pg 62

Kenney, Verne, Zondervan, 3900 Sparks Dr, Grand Rapids, MI 49546 *Tel:* 616-698-6900 *Toll Free Tel:* 800-226-1122; 800-727-1309 (retail orders) *Fax:* 616-698-3350 *Toll Free Fax:* 800-698-3256 (retail orders) *E-mail:* zinfo@zondervan.com *Web Site:* www.zondervan.com, pg 280

Kenniff, Thomas, National Press Photographers Association Inc (NPPA), 3200 Croasdaile Dr, Suite 306, Durham, NC 27705 *Tel:* 919-383-7246 *Fax:* 919-383-7261 *E-mail:* info@nppa.org *Web Site:* www.nppa.org, pg 613

Kenny, Julia, Dunow, Carlson & Lerner Literary Agency Inc, 27 W 20 St, Suite 1107, New York, NY 10011 *Tel:* 212-645-7606 *E-mail:* mail@dclagency.com *Web Site:* www.dclagency.com, pg 549

Kenny, Leslie, Heritage House Publishing Co Ltd, 1075 Pendergast St, No 103, Victoria, BC V8V 0A1, Canada *Tel:* 250-360-0829 *Fax:* 250-386-0829 *E-mail:* heritage@heritagehouse.ca *Web Site:* www.heritagehouse.ca, pg 487

Kenny, Maryanne, The Blackburn Press, PO Box 287, Caldwell, NJ 07006-0287 *Tel:* 973-228-7077 *Fax:* 973-228-7276 *Web Site:* www.blackburnpress.com, pg 39

Kenshole, Fiona, Transatlantic Agency, 2 Bloor St E, Suite 3500, Toronto, ON M4W 1A8, Canada *Tel:* 416-488-9214 *E-mail:* info@transatlanticagency.com *Web Site:* www.transatlanticagency.com, pg 577

Kent, Amy, Wm B Eerdmans Publishing Co, 2140 Oak Industrial Dr NE, Grand Rapids, MI 49505 *Tel:* 616-459-4591 *Toll Free Tel:* 800-253-7521 *Fax:* 616-459-6540 *E-mail:* customerservice@eerdmans.com; sales@eerdmans.com *Web Site:* www.eerdmans.com, pg 80

Kent, Emily, SDP Publishing Solutions LLC, 36 Captain's Way, East Bridgewater, MA 02333 *Tel:* 617-775-0656 *Web Site:* www.sdppublishingsolutions.com, pg 534

Kent, Rachel, Books & Such, 52 Mission Circle, Suite 122, PMB 170, Santa Rosa, CA 95409-5370 *Tel:* 707-538-4184 *Web Site:* booksandsuch.com, pg 543

Kent, Rachel, New York Media Works, 112 Franklin St, New York, NY 10013 *Tel:* 646-369-5681 *Fax:* 646-810-4033 *E-mail:* info@nymediaworks.com *Web Site:* www.nymediaworks.com, pg 508

Kentwell, Richard, Reedswain Inc, 88 Wells Rd, Spring City, PA 19475 *Tel:* 610-495-9578 *Toll Free Tel:* 800-331-5191 *Fax:* 610-495-6632 *E-mail:* orders@reedswain.com *Web Site:* www.reedswain.com, pg 207

Kephart, Sheri, Easy Money Press, 5419 87 St, Lubbock, TX 79424 *Tel:* 806-543-5215 *E-mail:* easymoneypress@yahoo.com, pg 79

Kepler, James, Independent Writers of Chicago (IWOC), 332 S Michigan Ave, Suite 1032, Chicago, IL 60604 *Toll Free Tel:* 800-804-IWOC (804-4962) *E-mail:* info@iwoc.org *Web Site:* www.iwoc.org, pg 607

Kepner, Mr Chris, Victoria Sanders & Associates LLC, 241 Avenue of the Americas, Suite 11-H, New York, NY 10014 *Tel:* 212-633-8811 *Fax:* 212-633-0525 *E-mail:* queriesvsa@gmail.com *Web Site:* www.victoriasanders.com, pg 571

Kerber, Heather, Beaver's Pond Press Inc, 7108 Ohms Lane, Edina, MN 55439 *Tel:* 952-829-8818 *E-mail:* info@beaverspondpress.com *Web Site:* www.beaverspondpress.com, pg 33

Kerber, Michael, Red Wheel/Weiser/Conari, 65 Parker St, Suite 7, Newburyport, MA 01950 *Tel:* 978-465-0504 *Toll Free Tel:* 800-423-7087 (orders) *Fax:* 978-465-0243 *E-mail:* info@rwwbooks.com *Web Site:* www.redwheelweiser.com, pg 206

Kerber, Tom, Beaver's Pond Press Inc, 7108 Ohms Lane, Edina, MN 55439 *Tel:* 952-829-8818 *E-mail:* info@beaverspondpress.com *Web Site:* www.beaverspondpress.com, pg 33

Kerfoot, Karen, The Continuing Legal Education Society of British Columbia (CLEBC), 500-1155 W Pender St, Vancouver, BC V6E 2P4, Canada *Tel:* 604-669-3544; 604-893-2121 (cust serv) *Toll Free Tel:* 800-663-0437 (CN) *Fax:* 604-669-9260 *E-mail:* custserv@cle.bc.ca *Web Site:* www.cle.bc.ca, pg 478

Kerkstra, Allen R, Zondervan, 3900 Sparks Dr, Grand Rapids, MI 49546 *Tel:* 616-698-6900 *Toll Free Tel:* 800-226-1122; 800-727-1309 (retail orders) *Fax:* 616-698-3350 *Toll Free Fax:* 800-698-3256 (retail orders) *E-mail:* zinfo@zondervan.com *Web Site:* www.zondervan.com, pg 280

Kern, Athena, Natasha Kern Literary Agency Inc, PO Box 1069, White Salmon, WA 98672 *Tel:* 509-493-3803 *E-mail:* agent@natashakern.com *Web Site:* www.natashakern.com, pg 559

Kern, Natasha, Natasha Kern Literary Agency Inc, PO Box 1069, White Salmon, WA 98672 *Tel:* 509-493-3803 *E-mail:* agent@natashakern.com *Web Site:* www.natashakern.com, pg 559

Kerner, Aaron, David R Godine Publisher Inc, 15 Court Sq, Suite 320, Boston, MA 02108-4715 *Tel:* 617-451-9600 *Fax:* 617-350-0250 *E-mail:* info@godine.com *Web Site:* www.godine.com, pg 98

Kerner, Diane, Scholastic Canada Ltd, 604 King St W, Toronto, ON M5V 1E1, Canada *Tel:* 905-887-7323 *Toll Free Tel:* 800-268-3860 (CN) *Toll Free Fax:* 866-387-4944 *E-mail:* custserve@scholastic.ca *Web Site:* www.scholastic.ca, pg 498

Kerns, Samuel, American Forest Paper Association (AF&PA), 1101 "K" St NW, Suite 700, Washington, DC 20005 *Tel:* 202-463-2700 *E-mail:* info@afandpa.org *Web Site:* www.afandpa.org, pg 595

Kerr, Elisabeth, W W Norton & Company Inc, 500 Fifth Ave, New York, NY 10110-0017 *Tel:* 212-354-5500 *Toll Free Tel:* 800-233-4830 (orders & cust serv) *Fax:* 212-869-0856 *Toll Free Fax:* 800-458-6515 *Web Site:* www.wwnorton.com, pg 171

Kerr, Karen, Cornell University Press, Sage House, 512 E State St, Ithaca, NY 14850 *Tel:* 607-277-2338 *Fax:* 607-277-2374 *E-mail:* cupressinfo@cornell.edu; cupress-sales@cornell.edu *Web Site:* www.cornellpress.cornell.edu, pg 63

Kerr, Marianne, Oakstone Publishing LLC, 100 Corporate Pkwy, Suite 600, Birmingham, AL 35242 *Toll Free Tel:* 800-633-4743 *Fax:* 205-995-1926 *E-mail:* service@oakstonemedical.com *Web Site:* www.oakstonepublishing.com; www.cmeonly.com; www.cdeonly.com, pg 173

Kerrion, Jade, Florida Writers Association Conference, PO Box 66069, St Pete Beach, FL 33736-6069 *Web Site:* www.floridawriters.net, pg 651

Kerrion, Jade, Florida Writers Association Inc, PO Box 66069, St Pete Beach, FL 33736-6069 *Web Site:* www.floridawriters.net, pg 606

Kessinger, Roger A, Kessinger Publishing LLC, PO Box 1404, Whitefish, MT 59937 *E-mail:* books@kessingerpub.com *Web Site:* www.kessinger.net, pg 131

Kessler, Erika, Contemporary Publishing Co of Raleigh Inc, 5849 Lease Lane, Raleigh, NC 27617 *Tel:* 919-851-8221 *Fax:* 919-851-6666 *E-mail:* questions@contemporarypublishing.com *Web Site:* www.contemporarypublishing.com, pg 62

Kessler, Joseph I, World Class Speakers & Entertainers, 5200 Kanan Rd, Suite 210, Agoura Hills, CA 91301 *Tel:* 818-991-5400 *E-mail:* wcse@wcspeakers.com *Web Site:* www.wcspeakers.com, pg 588

Kessler, Robert J, Pendragon Press, 52 White Hill Lane, Hillsdale, NY 12529-5839 *Tel:* 518-325-6100 *Toll Free Tel:* 877-656-6381 (orders) *Fax:* 518-325-6102 *E-mail:* editor@pendragonpress.com *Web Site:* www.pendragonpress.com, pg 185

Kestin, Lynn, Random House Children's Books, 1745 Broadway, New York, NY 10019 *Tel:* 212-782-9000 *Toll Free Tel:* 800-200-3552 *Fax:* 212-782-9452 *Web Site:* randomhousekids.com, pg 203

Ketchersid, Sarah, Candlewick Press, 99 Dover St, Somerville, MA 02144-2825 *Tel:* 617-661-3330 *Fax:* 617-661-0565 *E-mail:* bigbear@candlewick.com; salesinfo@candlewick.com *Web Site:* www.candlewick.com, pg 49

Ketchum, Kaitlin, Ten Speed Press, 2625 Alcatraz Ave, Unit 505, Berkeley, CA 94705 *Tel:* 510-285-3000 *Toll Free Tel:* 800-841-BOOK (841-2665) *E-mail:* csorders@randomhouse.com *Web Site:* crownpublishing.com/imprint/ten-speed-press, pg 243

Kettler, CJ, Houghton Mifflin Harcourt, 222 Berkeley St, Boston, MA 02116 *Tel:* 617-351-5000 *Toll Free Tel:* 800-225-5425 (K-12 educ materials); 800-323-9540 (assessment materials); 877-219-1537 (SkillsTutor); 888-242-6747 (Destination; Earobics; Edmark; Learning Village; Riverdeep); 800-225-3362 (Houghton Mifflin Harcourt Trade & Reference Publishers) *Toll Free Fax:* 800-269-5232 *E-mail:* customerservice@hmhpub.com *Web Site:* www.hmhco.com, pg 115

Kettner, Christine, Clarion Books, 215 Park Ave S, New York, NY 10003 *Tel:* 212-420-5889 *Toll Free Tel:* 800-225-3362 (orders) *Fax:* 212-420-5855 *Toll Free Fax:* 800-634-7568 (orders) *Web Site:* www.hmhco.com, pg 59

Ketz, Louise B, Louise B Ketz Agency, 414 E 78 St, Suite 1-B, New York, NY 10075 *Tel:* 212-249-0668 *E-mail:* ketzagency@aol.com, pg 559

Kevin, Brian, Down East Books, 680 Commercial St (US Rte 1), Rockport, ME 04856 *Tel:* 207-594-9544 *Toll Free Tel:* 800-685-7962 (US only orders); 800-766-1670 *E-mail:* editorial@downeast.com *Web Site:* www.downeast.com, pg 76

Keyishian, Harry, Fairleigh Dickinson University Press, M-GH2-01, 285 Madison Ave, Madison, NJ 07940 *Tel:* 973-443-8564 *Fax:* 974-443-8364 *E-mail:* fdupress@fdu.edu *Web Site:* www.fdupress.org, pg 85

Keyser, Christopher, Writers Guild of America Awards, 7000 W Third St, Los Angeles, CA 90048 *Tel:* 323-951-4000; 323-782-4569 *Fax:* 323-782-4800 *Web Site:* www.wga.org, pg 738

Keyser, Christopher, Writers Guild of America, West (WGAW), 7000 W Third St, Los Angeles, CA 90048 *Tel:* 323-951-4000 *Toll Free Tel:* 800-548-4532 *Fax:* 323-782-4800 *Web Site:* www.wga.org, pg 621

Khalfan, Aun Ali, Tahrike Tarsile Qur'an Inc, 80-08 51 Ave, Elmhurst, NY 11373 *Tel:* 718-446-6472 *Fax:* 718-446-4370 *E-mail:* read@koranusa.org *Web Site:* www.koranusa.org, pg 240

Khalil, Maha, The Perseus Books Group, 387 Park Ave S, 12th fl, New York, NY 10016 *Tel:* 212-340-8100 *Toll Free Tel:* 800-343-4499 (cust serv) *Fax:* 212-340-8105 *Web Site:* www.perseusbooksgroup.com, pg 189

Khan, Ms Lakin, Napa Valley Writers' Conference, Upper Valley Campus, 1088 College Ave, St Helena, CA 94574 *Tel:* 707-967-2900 (ext 1611) *Fax:* 707-967-2909 *E-mail:* writecon@napavalley.edu *Web Site:* www.napawritersconf.org, pg 653

Khan, Roohana, Palgrave Macmillan, 175 Fifth Ave, Suite 200, New York, NY 10010 *Tel:* 646-307-5151 *Fax:* 212-777-6359 *E-mail:* firstname.lastname@palgrave-usa.com *Web Site:* us.macmillan.com/Palgrave.aspx, pg 180

Kharbanda, Sanj, Houghton Mifflin Harcourt Trade & Reference Division, 222 Berkeley St, Boston, MA 02116 *Tel:* 617-351-5000 *Toll Free Tel:* 800-225-3362 *Web Site:* www.hmhco.com, pg 115

Khatib, Kate, AK Press Distribution, 674-A 23 St, Oakland, CA 94612 *Tel:* 510-208-1700 *Fax:* 510-208-1701 *E-mail:* info@akpress.org; sales@akpress.org; orders@akpress.org *Web Site:* www.akpress.org, pg 7

Kheradi, Cyrus, Random House Publishing Group, 1745 Broadway, New York, NY 10019 *Toll Free Tel:* 800-200-3552 *Web Site:* atrandom.com, pg 204

Kheradi, Irene, Simon & Schuster, Inc, 1230 Avenue of the Americas, New York, NY 10020 *Tel:* 212-698-7000 *Fax:* 212-698-7007 *E-mail:* firstname.lastname@simonandschuster.com *Web Site:* www.simonandschuster.com, pg 226

Kichler, Florrie Binford, Patria Press Inc, PO Box 752, Carmel, IN 46082 *Tel:* 317-577-1321 *Fax:* 413-215-8030 *E-mail:* moreinfo@patriapress.com *Web Site:* www.patriapress.com; www.facebook.com/YoungPatriotsBooks; twitter.com/#!/kidsbios, pg 183

Kidd, Kenneth, Children's Literature Association Beiter Graduate Student Research Grants, 1301 W 22 St, Suite 202, Oak Brook, IL 60523 *Tel:* 630-571-4520 *Fax:* 708-876-5598 *E-mail:* info@childlitassn.org *Web Site:* www.childlitassn.org, pg 677

Kidd, Nancy PhD, National Communication Association, 1765 "N" St NW, Washington, DC 20036 *Tel:* 202-464-4622 *Fax:* 202-464-4600 *E-mail:* inbox@natcom.org *Web Site:* www.natcom.org, pg 612

Kiefer, Emily, Westminster John Knox Press (WJK), 100 Witherspoon St, Louisville, KY 40202-1396 *Tel:* 502-569-5052 *Toll Free Tel:* 800-227-2872 (US only) *Fax:* 502-569-8308 *Toll Free Fax:* 800-541-5113 (US & CN) *E-mail:* wjk@wjkbooks.com; customer_service@wjkbooks.com *Web Site:* www.wjkbooks.com, pg 269

Kiefer, Kim, Houghton Mifflin Harcourt Trade & Reference Division, 222 Berkeley St, Boston, MA 02116 *Tel:* 617-351-5000 *Toll Free Tel:* 800-225-3362 *Web Site:* www.hmhco.com, pg 115

Kielbicki, Eugenia, Puddingstone Literary, Authors' Agents, 11 Mabro Dr, Denville, NJ 07834-9607 *Tel:* 973-366-3622, pg 569

Kiely, Garrett P, University of Chicago Press, 1427 E 60 St, Chicago, IL 60637-2954 *Tel:* 773-702-7700; 773-702-7600 *Toll Free Tel:* 800-621-2736 (orders) *Fax:* 773-702-9756; 773-660-2235 (orders); 773-702-2708 *E-mail:* custserv@press.uchicago.edu; marketing@press.uchicago.edu *Web Site:* www.press.uchicago.edu, pg 255

Kier, Mary Alice, Cine/Lit Representation, PO Box 802918, Santa Clarita, CA 91380-2918 *Tel:* 661-513-0268 *E-mail:* cinelit@att.net, pg 546

Kietlinski, Teresa, Prospect Agency, 285 Fifth Ave, PMB 445, Brooklyn, NY 11215 *Tel:* 718-788-3217 *Fax:* 718-360-9582 *Web Site:* www.prospectagency.com, pg 568

Kilburg, Kathy, McGraw-Hill Create, 501 Bell St, Dubuque, IA 52001 *Tel:* 563-584-6000 *Fax:* 563-584-6600 *E-mail:* first_last@mcgraw-hill.com *Web Site:* www.mhhe.com, pg 150

Kilburn, Donald, Pearson Learning Solutions, 501 Boyleston St, Suite 900, Boston, MA 02116 *Tel:* 617-848-6300 *Toll Free Tel:* 800-428-4466 (orders) *Fax:* 617-848-6358 *E-mail:* pcp@pearsoncustom.com *Web Site:* www.pearsoned.com, pg 185

Kilcur, Patrick, Motion Picture Association of America Inc (MPAA), 1600 "I" St NW, Washington, DC 20006 *Tel:* 202-293-1966 *Fax:* 202-296-7410 *E-mail:* contactus@mpaa.org *Web Site:* www.mpaa.org, pg 610

Kiley, Gus, Zone Books dba Urzone Inc, 1226 Prospect Ave, Brooklyn, NY 11218 *Tel:* 718-686-0048 *Toll Free Tel:* 800-405-1619 (orders & cust serv) *Fax:* 718-686-9045 *Toll Free Fax:* 800-406-9145 (orders) *E-mail:* orders@triliteral.org *Web Site:* www.zonebooks.org, pg 280

Kilgras, Heidi, Random House Children's Books, 1745 Broadway, New York, NY 10019 *Tel:* 212-782-9000 *Toll Free Tel:* 800-200-3552 *Fax:* 212-782-9452 *Web Site:* randomhousekids.com, pg 203

Kilkelly, Mary Beth, Random House Children's Books, 1745 Broadway, New York, NY 10019 *Tel:* 212-782-9000 *Toll Free Tel:* 800-200-3552 *Fax:* 212-782-9452 *Web Site:* randomhousekids.com, pg 203

Killam, Ray, Business Forms Management Association (BFMA), 1147 Fleetwood Ave, Madison, WI 53716 *Toll Free Tel:* 888-367-3078 *E-mail:* bfma@bfma.org *Web Site:* www.bfma.org, pg 601

Killeen, Valerie, Central Recovery Press (CRP), 3321 N Buffalo Dr, Suite 275, Las Vegas, NV 89129 *Tel:* 702-868-5830 *Fax:* 702-868-5831 *E-mail:* info@centralrecovery.com *Web Site:* centralrecoverypress.com, pg 54

Killoh, Kathy, Athabasca University Press, Edmonton Learning Ctr, Peace Hills Trust Tower, 1200, 10011-109 St, Edmonton, AB T5J 3S8, Canada *Tel:* 780-497-3412 *Fax:* 780-421-3298 *E-mail:* aupress@athabascau.ca *Web Site:* www.aupress.ca, pg 472

Kilmartin, Kerry, University of British Columbia Press, 2029 West Mall, Vancouver, BC V6T 1Z2, Canada *Tel:* 604-822-5959 *Toll Free Tel:* 877-377-9378 *Fax:* 604-822-6083 *Toll Free Fax:* 800-668-0821 *E-mail:* frontdesk@ubcpress.ca *Web Site:* www.ubcpress.ca, pg 502

Kim, Charles R, The Museum of Modern Art (MoMA), 11 W 53 St, New York, NY 10019 *Tel:* 212-708-9443 *Fax:* 212-333-6575 *E-mail:* moma_publications@moma.org *Web Site:* www.moma.org, pg 162

Kim, Emily Sylvan, Prospect Agency, 285 Fifth Ave, PMB 445, Brooklyn, NY 11215 *Tel:* 718-788-3217 *Fax:* 718-360-9582 *Web Site:* www.prospectagency.com, pg 568

Kim, Gail, Judy Lopez Memorial Award For Children's Literature, 1225 Selby Ave, Los Angeles, CA 90024 *Tel:* 310-474-9917 *Fax:* 310-474-6436 *Web Site:* www.wnba-books.org/la; www.judylopezbookaward.org, pg 703

Kim, Irene, Chronicle Books LLC, 680 Second St, San Francisco, CA 94107 *Tel:* 415-537-4200 *Toll Free Tel:* 800-759-0190 (cust serv) *Fax:* 415-537-4460 *Toll Free Fax:* 800-858-7787 (orders); 800-286-9471 (cust serv) *E-mail:* frontdesk@chroniclebooks.com *Web Site:* www.chroniclebooks.com, pg 58

Kim, Jean H, Stanford University Press, 1450 Page Mill Rd, Palo Alto, CA 94304-1124 *Tel:* 650-723-9434 *Fax:* 650-725-3457 *E-mail:* info@sup.org *Web Site:* www.sup.org, pg 233

Kim, Jisu, The Feminist Press at The City University of New York, 365 Fifth Ave, Suite 5406, New York, NY 10016 *Tel:* 212-817-7915 *Fax:* 212-817-1593 *E-mail:* info@feministpress.org *Web Site:* www.feministpress.org, pg 87

Kim, Kirby, Janklow & Nesbit Associates, 445 Park Ave, New York, NY 10022 *Tel:* 212-421-1700 *Fax:* 212-980-3671 *E-mail:* info@janklow.com *Web Site:* www.janklowandnesbit.com, pg 558

Kim, Linette, Bloomsbury Publishing Inc, 1385 Broadway, 5th fl, New York, NY 10018 *Tel:* 212-419-5300 *E-mail:* marketingusa@bloomsbury.com; adultpublicityusa@bloomsbury.com; askacademic@bloomsbury.com *Web Site:* www.bloomsbury.com, pg 40

Kim, Luenna H, National Society of Newspaper Columnists (NSNC), PO Box 411532, San Francisco, CA 94141 *Tel:* 415-488-NCNC (488-6762) *Fax:* 484-297-0336 *Web Site:* www.columnists.com, pg 613

Kim, Luenna H, National Society of Newspaper Columnists Annual Conference, 1345 Fillmore St, Suite 507, San Francisco, CA 94115 *Tel:* 415-488-NCNC (488-6762) *Toll Free Tel:* 866-440-NSNC (440-6762) *Fax:* 484-297-0336 *Toll Free Fax:* 866-635-5759 *Web Site:* www.columnists.com, pg 653

Kim, Sally, Chronicle Books LLC, 680 Second St, San Francisco, CA 94107 *Tel:* 415-537-4200 *Toll Free Tel:* 800-759-0190 (cust serv) *Fax:* 415-537-4460 *Toll Free Fax:* 800-858-7787 (orders); 800-286-9471 (cust serv) *E-mail:* frontdesk@chroniclebooks.com *Web Site:* www.chroniclebooks.com, pg 58

Kim, Sally, Touchstone, 1230 Avenue of the Americas, New York, NY 10020, pg 247

Kim, Stephanie, Houghton Mifflin Harcourt, 222 Berkeley St, Boston, MA 02116 *Tel:* 617-351-5000 *Toll Free Tel:* 800-225-5425 (K-12 educ materials); 800-323-9540 (assessment materials); 877-219-1537 (SkillsTutor); 888-242-6747 (Destination; Earobics; Edmark; Learning Village; Riverdeep); 800-225-3362 (Houghton Mifflin Harcourt Trade & Reference Publishers) *Toll Free Fax:* 800-269-5232 *E-mail:* customerservice@hmhpub.com *Web Site:* www.hmhco.com, pg 115

Kimball, David, National Association of Real Estate Editors (NAREE), 1003 NW Sixth Terr, Boca Raton, FL 33486-3455 *Tel:* 561-391-3599 *Fax:* 561-391-0099 *Web Site:* www.naree.org, pg 611

Kimball, James, Doubleday/Nan A Talese, c/o Penguin Random House Inc, 1745 Broadway, New York, NY 10019 *Tel:* 212-751-2600 *Fax:* 212-572-2662 *E-mail:* ddaypub@randomhouse.com *Web Site:* knopfdoubleday.com, pg 76

Kimball, James, Alfred A Knopf/Everyman's Library, c/o Random House Inc, 1745 Broadway, New York, NY 10019 *Tel:* 212-751-2600 *Toll Free Tel:* 800-638-6460 *Fax:* 212-572-2593 *Web Site:* www.knopfdoubleday.com, pg 132

Kimball, Roger, Encounter Books, 900 Broadway, Suite 601, New York, NY 10003 *Tel:* 212-871-6310 *Toll Free Tel:* 800-786-3839 *Fax:* 212-871-6311 *E-mail:* publicity@encounterbooks.com *Web Site:* www.encounterbooks.com, pg 82

Kimball, Tom, Signature Books Publishing LLC, 564 W 400 N, Salt Lake City, UT 84116-3411 *Tel:* 801-531-1483 *Fax:* 801-531-1488 *E-mail:* people@signaturebooks.com *Web Site:* www.signaturebooks.com; www.signaturebookslibrary.org, pg 224

Kimberling, Clint, University Press of Mississippi, 3825 Ridgewood Rd, Jackson, MS 39211-6492 *Tel:* 601-432-6205 *Toll Free Tel:* 800-737-7788 (orders & cust serv) *Fax:* 601-432-6217 *E-mail:* press@mississippi.edu *Web Site:* www.upress.state.ms.us, pg 262

Kimzey, Anne, Alabama Artists Fellowship Awards, 201 Monroe St, Suite 110, Montgomery, AL 36130-1800 *Tel:* 334-242-4076 *Fax:* 334-240-3269, pg 666

Kinard, Erin, Abrams Learning Trends, 16310 Bratton Lane, Suite 250, Austin, TX 78728-2403 *Toll Free Tel:* 800-227-9120 *Toll Free Fax:* 800-737-3322 *E-mail:* customerservice@abramslearningtrends.com (orders, cust serv); contactus@abramslearningtrends.com *Web Site:* www.abramslearningtrends.com (orders, cust serv), pg 3

Kincaid, Christen, New Women's Voices Chapbook Competition, PO Box 1626, Georgetown, KY 40324 *Tel:* 859-514-8966 *E-mail:* finishingbooks@aol.com; flpbookstore@aol.com *Web Site:* www.finishinglinepress.com, pg 712

Kincaid, Christen, Open Chapbook Competition, PO Box 1626, Georgetown, KY 40324 *Tel:* 859-514-8966 *E-mail:* finishingbooks@aol.com; flpbookstore@aol.com *Web Site:* www.finishinglinepress.com, pg 715

Kind, Rachel, Random House Publishing Group, 1745 Broadway, New York, NY 10019 *Toll Free Tel:* 800-200-3552 *Web Site:* atrandom.com, pg 204

King, Amy, Jason Aronson Inc, 4501 Forbes Blvd, Suite 200, Lanham, MD 20706 *Tel:* 301-459-3366 *Toll Free Tel:* 800-462-6420 (orders) *Fax:* 301-429-5748 *Web Site:* www.rowman.com, pg 22

King, Brenda, Yale University Press, 302 Temple St, New Haven, CT 06511-8909 *Tel:* 203-432-0960; 203-432-0966 (sales); 401-531-2800 (cust serv) *Toll Free Tel:* 800-405-1619 (cust serv) *Fax:* 203-432-0948; 203-432-8485 (sales); 401-531-2801 (cust serv) *Toll Free Fax:* 800-406-9145 (cust serv) *E-mail:* sales.press@yale.edu (sales); customer.care@trilateral.org (cust serv) *Web Site:* www.yalebooks.com; yalepress.yale.edu/yupbooks, pg 278

King, Brian, The University of Arkansas Press, McIlroy House, 105 N McIlroy Ave, Fayetteville, AR 72701 *Tel:* 479-575-3246 *Toll Free Tel:* 800-626-0090 *Fax:* 479-575-6044 *E-mail:* uapress@uark.edu *Web Site:* www.uapress.com, pg 255

King, Brian B, Appalachian Trail Conservancy, 799 Washington St, Harpers Ferry, WV 25425 *Tel:* 304-535-6331 *Toll Free Tel:* 888-287-8673 (orders only) *Fax:* 304-535-2667 *E-mail:* info@appalachiantrail.org *Web Site:* www.appalachiantrail.org; www.atctrailstore.org, pg 20

King, Darrell, Ellora's Cave, 1056 Home Ave, Akron, OH 44310-3302 *Tel:* 330-253-3521 *E-mail:* service@ellorascave.com; comments@ellorascave.com *Web Site:* www.ellorascave.com, pg 81

King, Eric, Warner Press, 1201 E Fifth St, Anderson, IN 46018 *Tel:* 765-644-7721 *Toll Free Tel:* 800-741-7721 (orders) *Fax:* 765-640-8005 *Toll Free Fax:* 800-347-6411 *E-mail:* wporders@warnerpress.org *Web Site:* www.warnerpress.org, pg 267

King, London, Random House Publishing Group, 1745 Broadway, New York, NY 10019 *Toll Free Tel:* 800-200-3552 *Web Site:* atrandom.com, pg 204

King, Margaret J PhD, Cultural Studies & Analysis, 1123 Montrose St, Philadelphia, PA 19147-3721 *Tel:* 215-592-8544 *Fax:* 215-413-9041 *E-mail:* info@culturalanalysis.com *Web Site:* www.culturalanalysis.com, pg 524

King, Patricia, Berkley Books, 375 Hudson St, New York, NY 10014 *Tel:* 212-366-2000 *Fax:* 212-366-2666 *E-mail:* online@penguinputnam.com *Web Site:* www.penguinputnam.com; us.penguingroup.com, pg 35

King, Patricia, Berkley Publishing Group, 375 Hudson St, New York, NY 10014 *Tel:* 212-366-2000 *Fax:* 212-366-2385 *E-mail:* online@penguinputnam.com *Web Site:* us.penguingroup.com, pg 35

King, Rachel, West Virginia University Press, West Virginia University, PO Box 6295, Morgantown, WV 26506-6295 *Tel:* 304-293-8400 *Toll Free Tel:* 866-WVU-PRES (988-7737) *Fax:* 304-293-6585 *E-mail:* press@wvu.edu *Web Site:* www.wvupress.com, pg 269

King, Stacy, Federal Bar Association, 1220 N Filmore St, Suite 444, Arlington, VA 22201 *Tel:* 571-481-9100 *Fax:* 571-481-9090 *E-mail:* fba@fedbar.org *Web Site:* www.fedbar.org, pg 87

King, Stephen, W W Norton & Company Inc, 500 Fifth Ave, New York, NY 10110-0017 *Tel:* 212-354-5500 *Toll Free Tel:* 800-233-4830 (orders & cust serv) *Fax:* 212-869-0856 *Toll Free Fax:* 800-458-6515 *Web Site:* www.wwnorton.com, pg 171

King, Terry, The Authors Registry Inc, 31 E 32 St, 7th fl, New York, NY 10016 *Tel:* 212-563-6920 *Fax:* 212-564-5363 *E-mail:* staff@authorsregistry.org *Web Site:* www.authorsregistry.org, pg 600

King, Vicki, Psychological Assessment Resources Inc (PAR), 16204 N Florida Ave, Lutz, FL 33549 *Tel:* 813-968-3003; 813-449-4065 *Toll Free Tel:* 800-331-8378 *Fax:* 813-968-2598; 813-961-2196 *Toll Free Fax:* 800-727-9329 *E-mail:* custsup@parinc.com *Web Site:* www4.parinc.com, pg 199

Kingra, Mr Mahinder S, Cornell University Press, Sage House, 512 E State St, Ithaca, NY 14850 *Tel:* 607-277-2338 *Fax:* 607-277-2374 *E-mail:* cupressinfo@cornell.edu; cupress-sales@cornell.edu *Web Site:* www.cornellpress.cornell.edu, pg 63

Kingsley, Jessica, Jessica Kingsley Publishers Inc, 400 Market St, Suite 400, Philadelphia, PA 19106 *Tel:* 215-922-1161 *Toll Free Tel:* 866-416-1078 (cust serv) *Fax:* 215-922-1474 *E-mail:* orders@jkp.com; hello.usa@jkp.com *Web Site:* www.jkp.com, pg 131

Kinkaid, Ashley McDonald, Phi Delta Kappa International®, 320 W Eighth St, Suite 216, Bloomington, IN 47404 *Tel:* 812-339-1156 *Toll Free Tel:* 800-766-1156 *Fax:* 812-339-0018 *E-mail:* customerservice@pdkintl.org *Web Site:* www.pdkintl.org, pg 190

Kinney, Andrew, Harvard University Press, 79 Garden St, Cambridge, MA 02138-1499 *Tel:* 617-495-2600; 401-531-2800 (intl orders) *Toll Free Tel:* 800-405-1619 (orders) *Fax:* 617-495-5898 (general); 617-496-4677 (edit & rts); 401-531-2801 (intl orders) *Toll Free Fax:* 800-406-9145 (orders) *E-mail:* contact_hup@harvard.edu *Web Site:* www.hup.harvard.edu, pg 107

Kinney, Erika, Brookes Publishing Co Inc, PO Box 10624, Baltimore, MD 21285-0624 *Tel:* 410-337-9580 (outside US & CN) *Toll Free Tel:* 800-638-3775 (US & CN) *Fax:* 410-337-8539 *E-mail:* custserv@brookespublishing.com *Web Site:* www.brookespublishing.com, pg 46

Kinney, Noreen, Cordon d' Or - Gold Ribbon International Annual Cook Book & Culinary Arts Culinary Academy Awards, 7312 Sixth Ave N, St Petersburg, FL 33710 *Tel:* 727-347-2437 *E-mail:* cordondor@aol.com; culinaryparadise@aol.com *Web Site:* www.cordondorcuisine.com; www.florida-americasculinaryparadise.com, pg 679

Kintigh, Cynthia, ANR Publications University of California, 1301 S 46 St, Bldg 478 - MC 3580, Richmond, CA 94804 *Tel:* 510-665-2195 (cust serv) *Toll Free Tel:* 800-994-8849 *Fax:* 510-665-3427 *E-mail:* anrcatalog@ucdavis.edu *Web Site:* anrcatalog.ucanr.edu, pg 18

Kintz, Dr Bruce G, Concordia Publishing House, 3558 S Jefferson Ave, St Louis, MO 63118-3968 *Tel:* 314-268-1000; 314-268-1268 (bookshop) *Toll Free Tel:* 800-325-3040 (cust serv) *Toll Free Fax:* 800-490-9889 (cust serv) *E-mail:* order@cph.org *Web Site:* www.cph.org, pg 62

Kiple, Cindy, InterVarsity Press, 430 Plaza Dr, Westmont, IL 60559-1234 *Tel:* 630-734-4000 *Toll Free Tel:* 800-843-9487 *Fax:* 630-734-4200 *E-mail:* email@ivpress.com *Web Site:* www.ivpress.com, pg 125

Kiraz, Christine PhD, Gorgias Press LLC, PO Box 6939, Piscataway, NJ 08854-6939 *Tel:* 732-885-8900 *Fax:* 732-885-8908 *E-mail:* helpdesk@gorgiaspress.com *Web Site:* www.gorgiaspress.com, pg 99

Kiraz, George Anton PhD, Gorgias Press LLC, PO Box 6939, Piscataway, NJ 08854-6939 *Tel:* 732-885-8900 *Fax:* 732-885-8908 *E-mail:* helpdesk@gorgiaspress.com *Web Site:* www.gorgiaspress.com, pg 99

Kirby, Judy, National Crime Prevention Council, 2001 Jefferson Davis Hwy, Suite 901, Arlington, VA 22202 *Tel:* 202-466-6272 *Fax:* 202-296-1356 *E-mail:* ncpc@fulfills.org (orders) *Web Site:* www.ncpc.org, pg 164

Kirchoff, Morris A, Kirchoff/Wohlberg Inc, 897 Boston Post Rd, Madison, CT 06443 *Tel:* 203-245-7308 *Fax:* 203-245-3218 *Web Site:* www.kirchoffwohlberg.com, pg 560

Kirk, Kara, Getty Publications, 1200 Getty Center Dr, Suite 500, Los Angeles, CA 90049-1682 *Tel:* 310-440-7365 *Toll Free Tel:* 800-223-3431 (orders) *Fax:* 310-440-7758 *E-mail:* pubsinfo@getty.edu *Web Site:* www.getty.edu/publications, pg 96

Kirk, Margaret, Copper Canyon Press, Fort Worden State Park, Bldg 313, Port Townsend, WA 98368 *Tel:* 360-385-4925 *Toll Free Tel:* 877-501-1393 (orders) *Fax:* 360-385-4985 *E-mail:* poetry@coppercanyonpress.org *Web Site:* www.coppercanyonpress.org, pg 63

Kirk, Robert, Princeton University Press, 41 William St, Princeton, NJ 08540-5237 *Tel:* 609-258-4900 *Toll Free Tel:* 800-777-4726 (orders) *Fax:* 609-258-6305 *Toll Free Fax:* 800-999-1958 *E-mail:* orders@cpfsinc.com *Web Site:* press.princeton.edu, pg 197

Kirk, Steve, John F Blair Publisher, 1406 Plaza Dr, Winston-Salem, NC 27103 *Tel:* 336-768-1374 *Toll Free Tel:* 800-222-9796 *Fax:* 336-768-9194 *Web Site:* www.blairpub.com, pg 39

Kirkley, Jeffrey E, Institute of Continuing Legal Education, 1020 Greene St, Ann Arbor, MI 48109-1444 *Tel:* 734-764-0533 *Toll Free Tel:* 877-229-4350 *Fax:* 734-763-2412 *Toll Free Fax:* 877-229-4351 *E-mail:* icle@umich.edu *Web Site:* www.icle.org, pg 122

Kirklin, Dan, Liberty Fund Inc, 8335 Allison Pointe Trail, Suite 300, Indianapolis, IN 46250-1684 *Tel:* 317-842-0880 *Toll Free Tel:* 800-955-8335; 800-866-3520; 800-368-7897 ext 6069 (cust serv) *Fax:* 317-577-9067; 317-579-6060 (cust serv); 708-534-7803 *E-mail:* books@libertyfund.org; info@libertyfund.org *Web Site:* www.libertyfund.org, pg 138

Kirkpatrick, Caitlin, Chronicle Books LLC, 680 Second St, San Francisco, CA 94107 *Tel:* 415-537-4200 *Toll Free Tel:* 800-759-0190 (cust serv) *Fax:* 415-537-4460 *Toll Free Fax:* 800-858-7787 (orders); 800-286-9471 (cust serv) *E-mail:* frontdesk@chroniclebooks.com *Web Site:* www.chroniclebooks.com, pg 58

Kirkpatrick, Kristin, University Press of Mississippi, 3825 Ridgewood Rd, Jackson, MS 39211-6492 *Tel:* 601-432-6205 *Toll Free Tel:* 800-737-7788 (orders & cust serv) *Fax:* 601-432-6217 *E-mail:* press@mississippi.edu *Web Site:* www.upress.state.ms.us, pg 262

Kirkpatrick, Rob, HarperCollins General Books Group, 195 Broadway, New York, NY 10007 *Tel:* 212-207-7000 *Web Site:* www.harpercollins.com, pg 105

Kirsch, Julie, Jason Aronson Inc, 4501 Forbes Blvd, Suite 200, Lanham, MD 20706 *Tel:* 301-459-3366 *Toll Free Tel:* 800-462-6420 (orders) *Fax:* 301-429-5748 *Web Site:* www.rowman.com, pg 22

Kirsch, Julie, Hamilton Books, 4501 Forbes Blvd, Suite 200, Lanham, MD 20706 *Tel:* 301-459-3366 *Toll Free Tel:* 800-462-6420 (cust serv) *Fax:* 301-429-5748 *Toll Free Fax:* 800-388-4550 (cust serv), pg 104

Kirsch, Julie, Lexington Books, 4501 Forbes Blvd, Suite 200, Lanham, MD 20706 *Tel:* 301-459-3366 *Fax:* 301-429-5749 *Web Site:* www.lexingtonbooks.com, pg 138

Kirsch, Julie, University Press of America Inc, 4501 Forbes Blvd, Suite 200, Lanham, MD 20706 *Tel:* 301-459-3366 *Toll Free Tel:* 800-462-6420 *Fax:* 301-429-5748 *Toll Free Fax:* 800-338-4550 *Web Site:* www.univpress.com, pg 261

Kirschbaum, Betsy, Water Row Press, PO Box 438, Sudbury, MA 01776 *Tel:* 508-485-8515 *Fax:* 508-229-0885 *E-mail:* contact@waterrowbooks.com *Web Site:* www.waterrowbooks.com, pg 267

Kirschen, Dan, ICM Partners, 730 Fifth Ave, New York, NY 10019 *Tel:* 212-556-5600 *Web Site:* www.icmtalent.com, pg 557

Kirshbaum, Larry, Waxman Leavell Literary Agency, 443 Park Ave S, No 1004, New York, NY 10016 *Tel:* 212-675-5556 *Fax:* 212-675-1381 *Web Site:* www.waxmanleavell.com, pg 579

Kirshenbaum, Binnie, Columbia University School of the Arts, Creative Writing Program, 617 Kent Hall, New York, NY 10027 *Tel:* 212-854-3774 *Fax:* 212-854-7704 *E-mail:* writingprogram@columbia.edu *Web Site:* www.columbia.edu/cu/writing, pg 659

Kirshner, Sandi, Cengage Learning, 20 Channel Center St, Boston, MA 02210 *Tel:* 617-289-7700 *Toll Free Tel:* 800-354-9706 *Fax:* 617-289-7844 *Toll Free Fax:* 800-487-8488 *E-mail:* esales@cengage.com *Web Site:* www.cengage.com, pg 53

Kirsten, Naomi, Chronicle Books LLC, 680 Second St, San Francisco, CA 94107 *Tel:* 415-537-4200 *Toll Free Tel:* 800-759-0190 (cust serv) *Fax:* 415-537-4460 *Toll Free Fax:* 800-858-7787 (orders); 800-286-9471 (cust serv) *E-mail:* frontdesk@chroniclebooks.com *Web Site:* www.chroniclebooks.com, pg 58

Kiser, Gayle, College & University Professional Association for Human Resources (CUPA-HR), 1811 Commons Point Dr, Knoxville, TN 37932 *Tel:* 865-637-7673 *Toll Free Tel:* 877-CUPA-HR4 (287-2474) *Fax:* 865-637-7674 *E-mail:* communications@cupahr.org *Web Site:* www.cupahr.org/publications, pg 61

Kiser, Kristin, Running Press Book Publishers, 2300 Chestnut St, Philadelphia, PA 19103-4399 *Tel:* 215-567-5080 *Toll Free Tel:* 800-343-4499 (cust serv & orders) *Fax:* 215-568-2919 *Toll Free Fax:* 800-453-2884 (cust serv & orders) *E-mail:* perseus.promos@perseusbooks.com *Web Site:* www.runningpress.com, pg 212

Kisiner, Andrea, Transportation Research Board, 500 Fifth St NW, Washington, DC 20001 *Tel:* 202-334-2934; 202-334-3213 (orders); 202-334-3072 (subns) *Fax:* 202-334-2519 *E-mail:* trbsales@nas.edu *Web Site:* trb.org, pg 249

Kissling, Mark, ST Media Group Book Division, 11262 Cornell Park Dr, Cincinnati, OH 45242 *Tel:* 513-421-2050 *Toll Free Tel:* 866-265-0954 *Fax:* 513-421-5144 *E-mail:* books@stmediagroup.com *Web Site:* www.stmediagroup.com, pg 233

Kissner, Matthew, John Wiley & Sons Inc, 111 River St, Hoboken, NJ 07030-5774 *Tel:* 201-748-6000 *Toll Free Tel:* 800-225-5945 (cust serv) *Fax:* 201-748-6088 *E-mail:* info@wiley.com *Web Site:* www.wiley.com, pg 272

Kistler, Steve, RAND Corp, 1776 Main St, Santa Monica, CA 90407-2138 *Tel:* 310-393-0411 *Fax:* 310-393-4818 *Web Site:* www.rand.org, pg 203

Kitchel Bellew, Carole, Bunker Hill Publishing, 285 River Rd, Piermont, NH 03779 *Tel:* 603-272-9221 *Fax:* 603-283-7240 *E-mail:* mail@bunkerhillpublishing.com *Web Site:* www.bunkerhillpublishing.com, pg 47

Kitchen, Sara, Bloomsbury Publishing Inc, 1385 Broadway, 5th fl, New York, NY 10018 *Tel:* 212-419-5300 *E-mail:* marketingusa@bloomsbury.com; adultpublicityusa@bloomsbury.com; askacademic@bloomsbury.com *Web Site:* www.bloomsbury.com, pg 40

Kitman, Taya, The Ridenhour Book Prize, 116 E 16 St, 8th fl, New York, NY 10003 *Tel:* 212-822-0250 *Fax:* 212-253-5356 *E-mail:* ridenhour@nationinstitute.org *Web Site:* www.ridenhour.org, pg 724

Kitman, Taya, The Ridenhour Courage Prize, 116 E 16 St, 8th fl, New York, NY 10003 *Tel:* 212-822-0250 *Fax:* 212-253-5356 *E-mail:* ridenhour@nationinstitute.org *Web Site:* www.ridenhour.org, pg 724

Kitman, Taya, The Ridenhour Prize for Truth-Telling, 116 E 16 St, 8th fl, New York, NY 10003 *Tel:* 212-822-0250 *Fax:* 212-253-5356 *E-mail:* ridenhour@nationinstitute.org *Web Site:* www.ridenhour.org, pg 724

Kittle, Barbara, Pearson Humanities & Social Sciences, 225 River St, Hoboken, NJ 07030-4772 *Tel:* 201-236-7000 *Fax:* 201-236-3400, pg 185

Kitz, Lois, George Washington Book Prize, 101 S Water St, Chestertown, MD 21620 *Tel:* 410-810-7165 *Fax:* 410-810-7175 *Web Site:* starrcenter.washcoll.edu/gw_book_prize, pg 734

Kjoller, Maria, Carolrhoda Books, 241 First Ave N, Minneapolis, MN 55401 *Tel:* 612-332-3344 *Toll Free Tel:* 800-328-4929 *Fax:* 612-332-7615 *Toll Free Fax:* 800-332-1132 *E-mail:* info@lernerbooks.com *Web Site:* www.lernerbooks.com, pg 50

hwwilsoninprint.com; information@ebscohost.com *Web Site:* www.hwwilsoninprint.com; www.ebscohost.com/wilson, pg 273

Kolb, Patricia A, M E Sharpe Inc, 80 Business Park Dr, Suite 202, Armonk, NY 10504 *Tel:* 914-273-1800 *Toll Free Tel:* 800-541-6563 *Fax:* 914-273-2106 *E-mail:* info@mesharpe.com *Web Site:* www.mesharpe.com, pg 223

Kolbe, Kimberly, The Green Rose Prize in Poetry, c/o Western Michigan University, 1903 W Michigan Ave, Kalamazoo, MI 49008-5463 *Tel:* 269-387-8185 *Fax:* 269-387-2562 *E-mail:* new-issues@wmich.edu *Web Site:* www.wmich.edu/newissues/sub-guide.html, pg 690

Kolbe, Kimberly, New Issues Poetry & Prose, c/o Western Michigan University, 1903 W Michigan Ave, Kalamazoo, MI 49008-5463 *Tel:* 269-387-8185 *Fax:* 269-387-2562 *E-mail:* new-issues@wmich.edu *Web Site:* www.wmich.edu/newissues, pg 168

Kolbe, Kimberly, New Issues Poetry Prize, c/o Western Michigan University, 1903 W Michigan Ave, Kalamazoo, MI 49008-5463 *Tel:* 269-387-8185 *Fax:* 269-387-2562 *E-mail:* new-issues@wmich.edu *Web Site:* www.wmich.edu/newissues, pg 712

Kolby, Jeff, Nova Press, 9058 Lloyd Place, West Hollywood, CA 90069 *Tel:* 310-275-3513 *Toll Free Tel:* 800-949-6175 *Fax:* 310-281-5629 *E-mail:* novapress@aol.com *Web Site:* www.novapress.net, pg 172

Kole, Mary, Movable Type Management, 244 Madison Ave, Suite 334, New York, NY 10016 *Tel:* 646-431-6134 *Fax:* 646-810-5757 *Web Site:* www.mtmgmt.net, pg 566

Kolen, Kerri, GP Putnam's Sons (Hardcover), 375 Hudson St, New York, NY 10014 *Tel:* 212-366-2000 *E-mail:* online@penguinputnam.com *Web Site:* us.penguingroup.com, pg 201

Kolendo, Kate, PROSE Awards, 71 Fifth Ave, 2nd fl, New York, NY 10003-3004 *Tel:* 212-255-0200 *Fax:* 212-255-7007 *Web Site:* www.proseawards.com; publishers.org, pg 722

Kolkman, Tammy, Covenant Communications Inc, 920 E State Rd, Suite F, American Fork, UT 84003-0416 *Tel:* 801-756-1041 *E-mail:* info@covenant-lds.com *Web Site:* www.covenant-lds.com, pg 66

Kollenbaum, Louise, The Amy Rennert Agency Inc, 1550 Tiburon Blvd, Suite 302, Tiburon, CA 94920 *Tel:* 415-789-8955 *E-mail:* queries@amyrennert.com *Web Site:* amyrennert.com, pg 569

Kolsrud, Kelli, International Foundation of Employee Benefit Plans, 18700 W Bluemound Rd, Brookfield, WI 53045 *Tel:* 262-786-6700 *Toll Free Tel:* 888-334-3327 *Fax:* 262-786-8780 *E-mail:* editor@ifebp.org *Web Site:* www.ifebp.org, pg 124

Komie, Michelle, Princeton University Press, 41 William St, Princeton, NJ 08540-5237 *Tel:* 609-258-4900 *Toll Free Tel:* 800-777-4726 (orders) *Fax:* 609-258-6305 *Toll Free Fax:* 800-999-1958 *E-mail:* orders@cpfsinc.com *Web Site:* press.princeton.edu, pg 197

Kondras, Holly, Wish Publishing, PO Box 10337, Terre Haute, IN 47801-0337 *Web Site:* www.wishpublishing.com, pg 274

Kondrick, Maureen, Marquette University Press, 1415 W Wisconsin Ave, Milwaukee, WI 53233 *Tel:* 414-288-1564 *Toll Free Tel:* 800-247-6553 (cust serv) *Fax:* 414-288-7813 *Web Site:* www.marquette.edu/mupress, pg 147

Konecke, Kaitlin, Health Professions Press, 409 Washington Ave, Suite 500, Towson, MD 21204 *Tel:* 410-337-9585 *Toll Free Tel:* 888-337-8808 *Fax:* 410-337-8539 *E-mail:* custserv@healthpropress.com *Web Site:* www.healthpropress.com, pg 109

Konecky, Edith, Hamilton Stone Editions, PO Box 43, Maplewood, NJ 07040 *Tel:* 973-378-8361 *E-mail:* hstone@hamiltonstone.org *Web Site:* www.hamiltonstone.org, pg 104

Konecky, Sean, Konecky & Konecky LLC, 72 Ayers Point Rd, Old Saybrook, CT 06475 *Tel:* 860-388-0878 *Fax:* 860-388-0273 *Web Site:* www.koneckyandkonecky.com, pg 132

Kong, Molly, Disney Press, 1101 Flower St, Glendale, CA 91201 *Web Site:* books.disney.com, pg 74

Konner, Linda, Linda Konner Literary Agency, 10 W 15 St, Suite 1918, New York, NY 10011 *Tel:* 212-691-3419 *Fax:* 212-691-0935 *Web Site:* www.lindakonnerliteraryagency.com, pg 560

Konowitch, Paul, Sundance/Newbridge Publishing, 33 Boston Post Rd W, Suite 440, Marlborough, MA 01752 *Toll Free Tel:* 888-200-2720; 800-343-8204 (Sundance cust serv & orders); 800-867-0307 (Newbridge cust serv & orders) *Toll Free Fax:* 800-456-2419 (orders) *E-mail:* info@sundancepub.com; info@newbridgeonline.com *Web Site:* www.sundancepub.com; www.newbridgeonline.com, pg 238

Konya, Heather, Association Media & Publishing (AM&P), 12100 Sunset Hills Rd, Suite 130, Reston, VA 20190 *Tel:* 703-234-4063 *Fax:* 703-435-4390 *E-mail:* info@associationmediaandpublishing.org *Web Site:* associationmediaandpublishing.org, pg 598

Konya, Heather, EXCEL Awards, 12100 Sunset Hills Rd, Suite 130, Reston, VA 20190 *Tel:* 703-234-4063 *Fax:* 703-435-4390 *E-mail:* info@associationmediaandpublishing.org *Web Site:* associationmediaandpublishing.org, pg 684

Koohi-Kamali, Farideh, Palgrave Macmillan, 175 Fifth Ave, Suite 200, New York, NY 10010 *Tel:* 646-307-5151 *Fax:* 212-777-6359 *E-mail:* firstname.lastname@palgrave-usa.com *Web Site:* us.macmillan.com/Palgrave.aspx, pg 180

Kooij, Nina, Pelican Publishing Co, 1000 Burmaster St, Gretna, LA 70053-2246 *Tel:* 504-368-1175 *Toll Free Tel:* 800-843-1724 *Fax:* 504-368-1195 *E-mail:* sales@pelicanpub.com (sales); office@pelicanpub.com (permission); promo@pelicanpub.com (publicity) *Web Site:* www.pelicanpub.com, pg 185

Koors, Patrick, Thomas Nelson, 501 Nelson Place, Nashville, TN 37214 *Tel:* 615-889-9000 *Toll Free Tel:* 800-251-4000 *Fax:* 615-902-1548 *E-mail:* publicity@thomasnelson.com *Web Site:* www.thomasnelson.com, pg 245

Kopb, Charles, The French-American Foundation & Florence Gould Foundation Annual Translation Prize, 28 W 44 St, Suite 1420, New York, NY 10036 *Tel:* 212-829-8800 *Fax:* 212-829-8810 *E-mail:* translation@frenchamerican.org *Web Site:* www.frenchamerican.org, pg 687

Kopelman, Charles, Abrams Artists Agency, 275 Seventh Ave, 26th fl, New York, NY 10001 *Tel:* 646-486-4600 *Fax:* 646-486-2358 *E-mail:* literary@abramsartny.com *Web Site:* www.abramsartists.com, pg 539

Kopp, David, Crown Publishing Group, c/o Penguin Random House Inc, 1745 Broadway, New York, NY 10019 *Tel:* 212-782-9000 *Toll Free Tel:* 888-264-1745 *Fax:* 212-940-7408 *E-mail:* crownosm@penguinrandomhouse.com *Web Site:* crownpublishing.com, pg 68

Kordic, Lara, Heritage House Publishing Co Ltd, 1075 Pendergast St, No 103, Victoria, BC V8V 0A1, Canada *Tel:* 250-360-0829 *Fax:* 250-386-0829 *E-mail:* heritage@heritagehouse.ca *Web Site:* www.heritagehouse.ca, pg 487

Korman, Keith, Raines & Raines, 103 Kenyon Rd, Medusa, NY 12120 *Tel:* 518-239-8311 *Fax:* 518-239-6029, pg 569

Korman, Tom, DK Publishing, 345 Hudson St, 2nd fl, New York, NY 10014 *Tel:* 646-674-4000 *Toll Free Tel:* 877-342-5357 (cust serv) *Web Site:* us.dk.com, pg 75

Korn, Adam, HarperCollins General Books Group, 195 Broadway, New York, NY 10007 *Tel:* 212-207-7000 *Web Site:* www.harpercollins.com, pg 105

Kornoelje, Kristin, Revell, PO Box 6287, Grand Rapids, MI 49516-6287 *Tel:* 616-676-9185 *Toll Free Tel:* 800-877-2665; 800-679-1957 *Fax:* 616-676-9573 *Web Site:* www.revellbooks.com, pg 208

Kortekamp, Jeanne, Franciscan Media, 28 W Liberty St, Cincinnati, OH 45202 *Tel:* 513-241-5615 *Toll Free Tel:* 800-488-0488 *Fax:* 513-241-0399 *E-mail:* books@americancatholic.org *Web Site:* www.americancatholic.org; www.franciscanmedia.org, pg 92

Korth, Bob, Standard Publishing, 8805 Governors Hill Dr, Suite 400, Cincinnati, OH 45249 *Tel:* 513-931-4050 *Toll Free Tel:* 800-543-1353 *Fax:* 513-931-0950 *Toll Free Fax:* 877-867-5751 *E-mail:* customerservice@standardpub.com *Web Site:* www.standardpub.com, pg 233

Kosiewska, Anthony, Scholastic Trade Division, 557 Broadway, New York, NY 10012 *Tel:* 212-343-6100; 212-343-4685 (export sales) *Fax:* 212-343-4714 (export sales) *Web Site:* www.scholastic.com, pg 219

Koski, Abby, Soho Press Inc, 853 Broadway, New York, NY 10003 *Tel:* 212-260-1900 *Fax:* 212-260-1902 *E-mail:* soho@sohopress.com; publicity@sohopress.com *Web Site:* www.sohopress.com, pg 229

Kosman, Phoebe, Harvard University Press, 79 Garden St, Cambridge, MA 02138-1499 *Tel:* 617-495-2600; 401-531-2800 (intl orders) *Toll Free Tel:* 800-405-1619 (orders) *Fax:* 617-495-5898 (general); 617-496-4677 (edit & rts); 401-531-2801 (intl orders) *Toll Free Fax:* 800-406-9145 (orders) *E-mail:* contact_hup@harvard.edu *Web Site:* www.hup.harvard.edu, pg 107

Kosmoski, Anne, Avery, 375 Hudson St, New York, NY 10014 *Tel:* 212-366-2000 *Fax:* 212-366-2643 *E-mail:* online@penguinputnam.com *Web Site:* www.penguinputnam.com; us.penguingroup.com, pg 28

Kosowski, Mary Beth, Mercer University Press, 368 Orange St, Macon, GA 31201 *Tel:* 478-301-2880 *Toll Free Tel:* 866-895-1472 *Fax:* 478-301-2585 *E-mail:* mupressorders@mercer.edu *Web Site:* www.mupress.org, pg 154

Kostman, Lynne, UCLA Fowler Museum of Cultural History, PO Box 951549, Los Angeles, CA 90095-1549 *Tel:* 310-825-4361 *Fax:* 310-206-7007 *Web Site:* www.fmch.ucla.edu, pg 252

Kosztolnyik, Karen, Gallery Books, 1230 Avenue of the Americas, New York, NY 10020 *Toll Free Tel:* 800-456-6798 *Fax:* 212-698-7284 *E-mail:* consumer.customerservice@simonandschuster.com *Web Site:* www.simonsays.com, pg 94

Kot, Rick, Viking, 375 Hudson St, New York, NY 10014 *Tel:* 212-366-2000 *E-mail:* online@penguinputnam.com *Web Site:* www.penguinputnam.com; us.penguingroup.com, pg 265

Kotchman, Katie, Don Congdon Associates Inc, 110 William St, Suite 2202, New York, NY 10038-3914 *Tel:* 212-645-1229 *Fax:* 212-727-2688 *E-mail:* dca@doncongdon.com *Web Site:* www.doncongdon.com, pg 546

Kottke, Erin, Graywolf Press, 250 Third Ave N, Suite 600, Minneapolis, MN 55401 *Tel:* 651-641-0077 *Fax:* 651-641-0036 *E-mail:* wolves@graywolfpress.org *Web Site:* www.graywolfpress.org, pg 100

Kouma, Cecelia, Playwrights Project, 3675 Ruffin Rd, Suite 330, San Diego, CA 92123 *Tel:* 858-384-2970 *Fax:* 858-384-2974 *E-mail:* write@playwrightsproject.org *Web Site:* www.playwrightsproject.org, pg 719

Koupal, Nancy Tystad, South Dakota Historical Society Press, 900 Governors Dr, Pierre, SD 57501 *Tel:* 605-773-6009 *Fax:* 605-773-6041 *E-mail:* info@sdshspress.com *Web Site:* sdshspress.com, pg 231

Kouts, Barbara S, Barbara S Kouts Literary Agency LLC, PO Box 560, Bellport, NY 11713 *Tel:* 631-286-1278 *Fax:* 631-286-1538 *E-mail:* bkouts@aol.com, pg 561

Kowalchuk, Tavia, HarperCollins General Books Group, 195 Broadway, New York, NY 10007 *Tel:* 212-207-7000 *Web Site:* www.harpercollins.com, pg 105

Kowalewski, Christina, Focus, PO Box 44937, Indianapolis, IN 46244-0937 *Tel:* 317-635-9250 *Fax:* 317-635-9292 *E-mail:* customer@hackettpublishing.com; editorial@hackettpublishing.com *Web Site:* focusbookstore.com, pg 90

Kowalewski, Christina, Hackett Publishing Co Inc, 3333 Massachusetts Ave, Indianapolis, IN 46218 *Tel:* 317-635-9250 (orders & cust serv) *Fax:* 317-635-9292 *Toll Free Fax:* 800-783-9213 *E-mail:* customer@hackettpublishing.com *Web Site:* www.hackettpublishing.com, pg 103

Kowaluk, Lucia, Black Rose Books Ltd, CP 35788 Succ Leo Pariseau, Montreal, QC H2X 0A4, Canada *Tel:* 514-844-4076 *Toll Free Tel:* 800-565-9523 (orders) *Fax:* 514-849-1956 *Toll Free Fax:* 800-221-9985 (orders) *E-mail:* info@blackrosebooks.net *Web Site:* www.blackrosebooks.net, pg 472

Kozlowski, Darrell, DWJ BOOKS LLC, 46 Cliff Dr, Sag Harbor, NY 11963 *Tel:* 631-899-4500 *E-mail:* info@dwjbooks.com *Web Site:* www.dwjbooks.com, pg 524

Krach, Elizabeth, Kimberley Cameron & Associates, 1550 Tiburon Blvd, Suite 704, Tiburon, CA 94920 *Tel:* 415-789-9191 *Fax:* 415-789-9177 *E-mail:* info@kimberleycameron.com *Web Site:* www.kimberleycameron.com, pg 559

Kracht, Ellen, Materials Research Society, 506 Keystone Dr, Warrendale, PA 15086-7537 *Tel:* 724-779-3003 *Fax:* 724-779-8313 *E-mail:* info@mrs.org *Web Site:* www.mrs.org, pg 149

Kracht, Peter, University of Pittsburgh Press, 7500 Thomas Blvd, Pittsburgh, PA 15260 *Tel:* 412-383-2456 *Fax:* 412-383-2466 *E-mail:* info@upress.pitt.edu *Web Site:* www.upress.pitt.edu, pg 259

Kraft, Eric, Kraft & Kraft, 40 Memorial Hwy, Apt 23-C, New Rochelle, NY 10801 *Tel:* 914-319-3320 *Web Site:* www.erickraft.com, pg 529

Kraft, Madeline, Kraft & Kraft, 40 Memorial Hwy, Apt 23-C, New Rochelle, NY 10801 *Tel:* 914-319-3320 *Web Site:* www.erickraft.com, pg 529

Kral, Steve, Society for Mining, Metallurgy & Exploration, 12999 E Adam Aircraft Circle, Englewood, CO 80112 *Tel:* 303-948-4200 *Toll Free Tel:* 800-763-3132 *Fax:* 303-973-3845 *E-mail:* cs@smenet.org *Web Site:* www.smenet.org, pg 229

Kramer, David, United Talent Agency, 9336 Civic Center Dr, Beverly Hills, CA 90210 *Tel:* 310-273-6700 *Fax:* 310-247-1111 *Web Site:* www.unitedtalent.com, pg 578

Kramer, Gary, Temple University Press, 1852 N Tenth St, Philadelphia, PA 19122-6099 *Tel:* 215-926-2140 *Toll Free Tel:* 800-621-2736 *Fax:* 215-926-2141 *E-mail:* tempress@temple.edu *Web Site:* www.temple.edu/tempress, pg 242

Kramer, Jill, Waterside Productions Inc, 2055 Oxford Ave, Cardiff, CA 92007 *Tel:* 760-632-9190 *Fax:* 760-632-9295 *E-mail:* admin@waterside.com *Web Site:* www.waterside.com, pg 579

Kramer, Linda, HJ Kramer Inc, PO Box 1082, Tiburon, CA 94920 *Tel:* 415-884-2100 (ext 10) *Toll Free Tel:* 800-972-6657 *Fax:* 415-435-5364 *E-mail:* hjkramer@jps.net *Web Site:* www.hjkramer.com; www.newworldlibrary.com, pg 133

Kramer, Sidney B, Mews Books Ltd, 20 Bluewater Hill, Westport, CT 06880 *Tel:* 203-227-1836 *Fax:* 203-227-1144 *E-mail:* mewsbooks@aol.com, pg 565

Kramer, Sydelle, Susan Rabiner Literary Agency Inc, 315 W 39 St, Suite 1501, New York, NY 10018-3907 *Web Site:* RabinerLit.com, pg 569

Krannich, Ronald PhD, Impact Publications/Development Concepts Inc, 9104 Manassas Dr, Suite N, Manassas Park, VA 20111-5211 *Tel:* 703-361-7300 *Toll Free Tel:* 800-361-1055 (cust serv) *Fax:* 703-335-9486 *E-mail:* query@impactpublications.com *Web Site:* www.impactpublications.com; www.ishoparoundtheworld.com; www.veteransworld.com; www.middleeasttravellover.com, pg 119

Kranz, Deb, Plexus Publishing, Inc, 143 Old Marlton Pike, Medford, NJ 08055 *Tel:* 609-654-6500 *Fax:* 609-654-4309 *E-mail:* info@plexuspublishing.com *Web Site:* www.plexuspublishing.com, pg 193

Kranz, Patricia, Overseas Press Club of America (OPC), 40 W 45 St, New York, NY 10036 *Tel:* 212-626-9220 *Fax:* 212-626-9210 *Web Site:* www.opcofamerica.org, pg 615

Kranz, Patricia, The Cornelius Ryan Award, 40 W 45 St, New York, NY 10036 *Tel:* 212-626-9220 *Fax:* 212-626-9210 *Web Site:* www.opcofamerica.org, pg 725

Kranzberg, Alena, The Sugarman Family Award for Jewish Children's Literature, Irwin P Edlavitch Bldg, 1529 16 St NW, Washington, DC 20036 *Tel:* 202-518-9400 *Fax:* 202-518-9420 *Web Site:* www.washingtondcjcc.org, pg 731

Krasner, Emily, Workman Publishing Co Inc, 225 Varick St, 9th fl, New York, NY 10014-4381 *Tel:* 212-254-5900 *Toll Free Tel:* 800-722-7202 *Fax:* 212-254-8098 *E-mail:* info@workman.com *Web Site:* www.workman.com, pg 275

Krasner, Justin, Workman Publishing Co Inc, 225 Varick St, 9th fl, New York, NY 10014-4381 *Tel:* 212-254-5900 *Toll Free Tel:* 800-722-7202 *Fax:* 212-254-8098 *E-mail:* info@workman.com *Web Site:* www.workman.com, pg 275

Krassner, Kaye, Association of Publishers for Special Sales (APSS), PO Box 715, Avon, CT 06001-0715 *Tel:* 860-675-1344 *Web Site:* www.spannet.org, pg 599

Krattenmaker, Kathleen, Philadelphia Museum of Art, 2525 Pennsylvania Ave, Philadelphia, PA 19130 *Tel:* 215-684-7250 *Fax:* 215-235-8715 *Web Site:* www.philamuseum.org, pg 191

Kraus, Jim, Tyndale House Publishers Inc, 351 Executive Dr, Carol Stream, IL 60188 *Tel:* 630-668-8300 *Toll Free Tel:* 800-323-9400 *Web Site:* www.tyndale.com, pg 252

Kraus, Marisa Smith, Smith & Kraus Publishers Inc, 40 Walch Dr, Portland, ME 04103 *Tel:* 207-523-2585 *Toll Free Tel:* 877-668-8680 *Fax:* 207-699-3698 *E-mail:* editor@smithandkraus.com *Web Site:* www.smithandkraus.com, pg 228

Krause, Bill, Llewellyn Publications, 2143 Wooddale Dr, Woodbury, MN 55125 *Tel:* 651-291-1970 *Toll Free Tel:* 800-843-6666 *Fax:* 651-291-1908 *E-mail:* publicity@llewellyn.com *Web Site:* www.llewellyn.com, pg 142

Krause, Chester L, Krause Publications Inc, 700 E State St, Iola, WI 54990 *Tel:* 715-445-2214 *Toll Free Tel:* 800-258-0929 (cust serv); 888-457-2873 (orders) *Fax:* 715-445-4087 *E-mail:* bookorders@krause.com *Web Site:* www.krausebooks.com, pg 133

Krause, Katrina, Houghton Mifflin Harcourt Trade & Reference Division, 222 Berkeley St, Boston, MA 02116 *Tel:* 617-351-5000 *Toll Free Tel:* 800-225-3362 *Web Site:* www.hmhco.com, pg 115

Kraut, Diane, DK Research Inc, 14 Mohegan Lane, Commack, NY 11725 *Tel:* 631-543-5537 *Fax:* 631-543-5549 *Web Site:* www.dkresearchinc.com, pg 524

Kravenas, Mary, Chicago Review Press, 814 N Franklin St, Chicago, IL 60610 *Tel:* 312-337-0747 *Toll Free Tel:* 800-888-4741 *Fax:* 312-337-5110 *E-mail:* frontdesk@chicagoreviewpress.com *Web Site:* www.chicagoreviewpress.com, pg 56

Kravitz, Jamie, Aspen Writers' Foundation, 110 E Hallam St, Suite 116, Aspen, CO 81611 *Tel:* 970-925-3122 *Fax:* 970-920-5700 *E-mail:* awfinfo@aspenwriters.org *Web Site:* www.aspenwriters.org, pg 597

Krawczyk, Andie, Candlewick Press, 99 Dover St, Somerville, MA 02144-2825 *Tel:* 617-661-3330 *Fax:* 617-661-0565 *E-mail:* bigbear@candlewick.com; salesinfo@candlewick.com *Web Site:* www.candlewick.com, pg 49

Krebs, Gary, Brilliance Audio, 1704 Eaton Dr, Grand Haven, MI 49417 *Tel:* 616-846-5256 *Toll Free Tel:* 800-648-2312 (orders only) *Fax:* 616-846-0630 *E-mail:* customerservice@brillianceaudio.com *Web Site:* www.brillianceaudio.com, pg 46

Kregel, James R, Editorial Portavoz, 2450 Oak Industrial Dr NE, Grand Rapids, MI 49505 *Toll Free Tel:* 877-733-2607 (ext 206) *Fax:* 616-493-1790 *E-mail:* portavoz@portavoz.com *Web Site:* www.portavoz.com, pg 79

Kregel, James R, Kregel Publications, 2450 Oak Industrial Dr NE, Grand Rapids, MI 49505 *Tel:* 616-451-4775 *Toll Free Tel:* 800-733-2607 *Fax:* 616-451-9330 *E-mail:* kregelbooks@kregel.com *Web Site:* www.kregel.com, pg 133

Kregel, Jerold W, Kregel Publications, 2450 Oak Industrial Dr NE, Grand Rapids, MI 49505 *Tel:* 616-451-4775 *Toll Free Tel:* 800-733-2607 *Fax:* 616-451-9330 *E-mail:* kregelbooks@kregel.com *Web Site:* www.kregel.com, pg 133

Krehbiel, Kenneth, National Council of Teachers of Mathematics (NCTM), 1906 Association Dr, Reston, VA 20191-1502 *Tel:* 703-620-9840 *Toll Free Tel:* 800-235-7566 *Fax:* 703-476-2970 *E-mail:* nctm@nctm.org *Web Site:* www.nctm.org, pg 164

Kreit, Eileen, Puffin Books, 345 Hudson St, New York, NY 10014 *Tel:* 212-366-2000 *E-mail:* online@penguinputnam.com *Web Site:* www.penguinputnam.com; us.penguingroup.com, pg 200

Kreiter, Lance, Boom! Studios, 5670 Wilshire Blvd, Suite 450, Los Angeles, CA 90036 *Web Site:* www.boom-studios.com, pg 43

Krell, Henry, Springer, 233 Spring St, New York, NY 10013-1578 *Tel:* 212-460-1500 *Toll Free Tel:* 800-SPRINGER (777-4643) *Fax:* 212-460-1575 *E-mail:* service-ny@springer.com *Web Site:* www.springer.com, pg 232

Kreloff, Elliot, Blue Apple Books, 515 Valley St, Suite 170, Maplewood, NJ 07040 *Tel:* 973-763-8191 *Toll Free Tel:* 800-283-3572 (orders) *Fax:* 973-763-5944 *E-mail:* info@blueapplebooks.com *Web Site:* blueapplebooks.com, pg 40

Kremer, John, Open Horizons Publishing Co, PO Box 2887, Taos, NM 87571 *Tel:* 575-751-3398 *Fax:* 575-751-3100 *E-mail:* info@bookmarket.com *Web Site:* www.bookmarket.com, pg 175

Krempa, Julie, Baywood Publishing Co Inc, 26 Austin Ave, Amityville, NY 11701 *Tel:* 631-691-1270 *Toll Free Tel:* 800-638-7819 *Fax:* 631-691-1770 *E-mail:* baywood@baywood.com *Web Site:* www.baywood.com, pg 32

Kresan, Dawn, Palimpsest Press, 1171 Eastlawn Ave, Windsor, ON N8S 3J1, Canada *Tel:* 519-563-9981 *E-mail:* info@palimpsestpress.ca *Web Site:* www.palimpsestpress.ca, pg 494

Kress, Steven, The Pennsylvania State University Press, University Support Bldg 1, Suite C, 820 N University Dr, University Park, PA 16802-1003 *Tel:* 814-865-1327 *Toll Free Tel:* 800-326-9180 *Fax:* 814-863-1408 *Toll Free Fax:* 877-778-2665 *E-mail:* info@psupress.org *Web Site:* www.psupress.org, pg 188

Kress-Russick, Michael, Wisconsin Annual Fall Conferencee, PO Box 259303, Madison, WI 53725 *Tel:* 608-278-0692 *Web Site:* www.scbwi.org; www.scbwi-wi.com, pg 657

Kretzer, Marilyn, Sterling Publishing Co Inc, 1166 Avenue of the Americas, 17th fl, New York, NY 10036 *Tel:* 212-532-7160 *Toll Free Tel:* 800-367-9692 *Fax:* 212-213-2495 *Web Site:* www.sterlingpublishing.com, pg 235

Kreuser, Joe, Bloomsbury Academic, 1385 Broadway, 5th fl, New York, NY 10018 *Tel:* 212-419-5300 *Web Site:* www.bloomsbury.com, pg 39

Krichevsky, Stuart, Stuart Krichevsky Literary Agency Inc, 381 Park Ave South, Suite 428, New York, NY 10016 *Tel:* 212-725-5288 *Fax:* 212-725-5275 *E-mail:* query@skagency.com *Web Site:* skagency.com, pg 561

Krieger, Donald E, Krieger Publishing Co, 1725 Krieger Dr, Malabar, FL 32950 *Tel:* 321-724-9542 *Toll Free Tel:* 800-724-0025 *Fax:* 321-951-3671 *E-mail:* info@krieger-publishing.com *Web Site:* www.krieger-publishing.com, pg 133

Krieger, Maxine D, Krieger Publishing Co, 1725 Krieger Dr, Malabar, FL 32950 *Tel:* 321-724-9542 *Toll Free Tel:* 800-724-0025 *Fax:* 321-951-3671 *E-mail:* info@krieger-publishing.com *Web Site:* www.krieger-publishing.com, pg 133

Krieger, Robert E, Krieger Publishing Co, 1725 Krieger Dr, Malabar, FL 32950 *Tel:* 321-724-9542 *Toll Free Tel:* 800-724-0025 *Fax:* 321-951-3671 *E-mail:* info@krieger-publishing.com *Web Site:* www.krieger-publishing.com, pg 133

Krienke, Mary, Sterling Lord Literistic Inc, 65 Bleecker St, New York, NY 10012 *Tel:* 212-780-6050 *Fax:* 212-780-6095 *E-mail:* info@sll.com *Web Site:* www.sll.com, pg 575

Krinsky, Santosh, Lotus Press, PO Box 325, Twin Lakes, WI 53181-0325 *Tel:* 262-889-8561 *Toll Free Tel:* 800-824-6396 (orders) *Fax:* 262-889-8591 *E-mail:* lotuspress@lotuspress.com *Web Site:* www.lotuspress.com, pg 143

Krishnan, Priyanka, Random House Publishing Group, 1745 Broadway, New York, NY 10019 *Toll Free Tel:* 800-200-3552 *Web Site:* atrandom.com, pg 204

Kriss, Miriam, Irene Goodman Literary Agency, 27 W 24 St, Suite 700B, New York, NY 10010 *Tel:* 212-604-0330 *E-mail:* queries@irenegoodman.com *Web Site:* www.irenegoodman.com, pg 554

Krissoff, Derek, West Virginia University Press, West Virginia University, PO Box 6295, Morgantown, WV 26506-6295 *Tel:* 304-293-8400 *Toll Free Tel:* 866-WVU-PRES (988-7737) *Fax:* 304-293-6585 *E-mail:* press@wvu.edu *Web Site:* www.wvupress.com, pg 269

Kritzer, Eddie, Eddie Kritzer Productions, 1112 Montana Ave, Suite 449, Santa Monica, CA 90403 *Tel:* 310-702-5356 *Fax:* 310-394-5770 *E-mail:* producedby@aol.com *Web Site:* eddiekritzer.com, pg 587

Kritzmacher, John, John Wiley & Sons Inc, 111 River St, Hoboken, NJ 07030-5774 *Tel:* 201-748-6000 *Toll Free Tel:* 800-225-5945 (cust serv) *Fax:* 201-748-6088 *E-mail:* info@wiley.com *Web Site:* www.wiley.com, pg 272

Krivda, David, Simon & Schuster Digital, 1230 Avenue of the Americas, New York, NY 10020 *Tel:* 212-698-7547 *Web Site:* www.simonandschuster.com; kids.simonandschuster.com; www.simonandschuster.ca; www.simonandschuster.co.uk; www.simonandschuster.net; www.simonandschuster.biz; www.tipsoncareerandmoney.com; www.tipsonhealthyliving.com; www.tipsonhomeandstyle.com; www.tipsonlifeandlove.com; www.offtheshelf.com; www.simonandschuster.com/teen, pg 225

Kroger, Rev Dan OFM, Franciscan Media, 28 W Liberty St, Cincinnati, OH 45202 *Tel:* 513-241-5615 *Toll Free Tel:* 800-488-0488 *Fax:* 513-241-0399 *E-mail:* books@americancatholic.org *Web Site:* www.americancatholic.org; www.franciscanmedia.org, pg 92

Krohn, Talia, Crown Publishing Group, c/o Penguin Random House Inc, 1745 Broadway, New York, NY 10019 *Tel:* 212-782-9000 *Toll Free Tel:* 888-264-1745 *Fax:* 212-940-7408 *E-mail:* crownosm@penguinrandomhouse.com *Web Site:* crownpublishing.com, pg 68

Kroll, Edite, Edite Kroll Literary Agency Inc, 20 Cross St, Saco, ME 04072 *Tel:* 207-283-8797 *Fax:* 207-283-8799, pg 561

Krones, Christine, Houghton Mifflin Harcourt Trade & Reference Division, 222 Berkeley St, Boston, MA 02116 *Tel:* 617-351-5000 *Toll Free Tel:* 800-225-3362 *Web Site:* www.hmhco.com, pg 115

Kronzek, Lynn C, Lynn C Kronzek & Richard A Flom, 145 S Glenoaks Blvd, Suite 240, Burbank, CA 91502 *Tel:* 818-768-7688 *Fax:* 818-768-7648, pg 529

Krovitz, Debbie, De Vorss & Co, 553 Constitution Ave, Camarillo, CA 93012-8510 *Tel:* 805-322-9010 *Toll Free Tel:* 800-843-5743 *Fax:* 805-322-9011 *E-mail:* service@devorss.com *Web Site:* www.devorss.com, pg 72

Krueger, Jo Ann, The Aaland Agency, PO Box 849, Inyokern, CA 93527-0849 *Tel:* 760-384-3910 *Web Site:* www.the-aaland-agency.com, pg 539

Krug, Susan, American Medical Writers Association (AMWA), 30 W Gude Dr, Suite 525, Rockville, MD 20850-4357 *Tel:* 240-238-0940 *Fax:* 301-294-9006 *E-mail:* amwa@amwa.org *Web Site:* www.amwa.org, pg 595

Krump, Emily, HarperCollins General Books Group, 195 Broadway, New York, NY 10007 *Tel:* 212-207-7000 *Web Site:* www.harpercollins.com, pg 106

Krumpe, Mr Kreig, Boyds Mills Press, 815 Church St, Honesdale, PA 18431 *Tel:* 570-253-1164 *Toll Free Tel:* 800-490-5111 *Fax:* 570-253-0179 *E-mail:* contact@boydsmillspress.com *Web Site:* www.boydsmillspress.com, pg 44

Krumpfer, Jorie, W W Norton & Company Inc, 500 Fifth Ave, New York, NY 10110-0017 *Tel:* 212-354-5500 *Toll Free Tel:* 800-233-4830 (orders & cust serv) *Fax:* 212-869-0856 *Toll Free Fax:* 800-458-6515 *Web Site:* www.wwnorton.com, pg 171

Krup, Agnes, Sanford J Greenburger Associates Inc, 55 Fifth Ave, New York, NY 10003 *Tel:* 212-206-5600 *Fax:* 212-463-8718 *Web Site:* greenburger.com; www.sjga.com/, pg 555

Krupin, Emily, Harlequin Enterprises Ltd, 233 Broadway, Suite 1001, New York, NY 10279 *Tel:* 212-553-4200 *Fax:* 212-227-8969 *E-mail:* CustomerService@harlequin.com *Web Site:* www.harlequin.com, pg 105

Kruse, Katrina, Houghton Mifflin Harcourt, 222 Berkeley St, Boston, MA 02116 *Tel:* 617-351-5000 *Toll Free Tel:* 800-225-5425 (K-12 educ materials); 800-323-9540 (assessment materials); 877-219-1537 (SkillsTutor); 888-242-6747 (Destination; Earobics; Edmark; Learning Village; Riverdeep); 800-225-3362 (Houghton Mifflin Harcourt Trade & Reference Publishers) *Toll Free Fax:* 800-269-5232 *E-mail:* customerservice@hmhpub.com *Web Site:* www.hmhco.com, pg 115

Krusinski, Anna, Hatherleigh Press Ltd, 62545 State Hwy 10, Hobart, NY 13788 *E-mail:* info@hatherleighpress.com; publicity@hatherleighpress.com *Web Site:* www.hatherleighpress.com, pg 108

Krysan, Alan, Astragal Press, 5995 149 St W, Suite 105, Apple Valley, MN 55124 *Tel:* 952-469-6699 *Toll Free Tel:* 866-543-3045 *Fax:* 952-469-1968 *Toll Free Fax:* 800-330-6232 *E-mail:* info@finneyco.com *Web Site:* www.astragalpress.com, pg 26

Krysan, Alan, Pogo Press Inc, 5995 149 St W, Suite 105, Apple Valley, MN 55124 *Tel:* 952-469-6699 *Toll Free Tel:* 800-846-7027 *Fax:* 952-469-1968 *Toll Free Fax:* 800-330-6232 *E-mail:* info@finneyco.com *Web Site:* www.pogopress.com, pg 194

Krysan, Alan E, Ecopress, 5995 149 St W, Suite 105, Apple Valley, MN 55124 *Tel:* 952-469-6699 *Toll Free Tel:* 800-846-7027 *Fax:* 952-469-1968 *Toll Free Fax:* 800-330-6232 *E-mail:* info@finneyco.com *Web Site:* www.ecopress.com, pg 79

Krysan, Alan E, Finney Company Inc, 5995 149 St W, Suite 105, Apple Valley, MN 55124 *Tel:* 952-469-6699 *Toll Free Tel:* 800-846-7027 *Fax:* 952-469-1968 *Toll Free Fax:* 800-330-6232 *E-mail:* info@finneyco.com *Web Site:* www.finneyco.com, pg 89

Krysan, Alan E, Hobar Publications, 5995 149 St W, Suite 105, Apple Valley, MN 55124 *Tel:* 952-469-6699 *Toll Free Tel:* 800-846-7027 *Fax:* 952-469-1968 *Toll Free Fax:* 800-330-6232 *E-mail:* info@finneyco.com *Web Site:* www.finney-hobar.com, pg 112

Krysan, Alan E, Windward Publishing, 5995 149 St W, Suite 105, Apple Valley, MN 55124 *Tel:* 952-469-6699 *Toll Free Tel:* 800-846-7027 *Fax:* 952-469-1968 *Toll Free Fax:* 800-330-6232 *E-mail:* info@finneyco.com *Web Site:* www.finneyco.com, pg 273

Kubie, Greg, Random House Publishing Group, 1745 Broadway, New York, NY 10019 *Toll Free Tel:* 800-200-3552 *Web Site:* atrandom.com, pg 204

Kubik, John Milan, Foto Expression International (Toronto), 266 Charlotte St, Suite 297, Peterborough, ON K9J 2V4, Canada *Tel:* 705-745-5770 *E-mail:* operations@fotopressnews.org *Web Site:* www.fotopressnews.org, pg 583

Kuehl, Kathy, The Guilford Press, 72 Spring St, New York, NY 10012 *Tel:* 212-431-9800 *Toll Free Tel:* 800-365-7006 *Fax:* 212-966-6708 *E-mail:* info@guilford.com *Web Site:* www.guilford.com, pg 102

Kuerbis, Lisa, Syracuse University Press, 621 Skytop Rd, Suite 110, Syracuse, NY 13244-5290 *Tel:* 315-443-5534 *Toll Free Tel:* 800-365-8929 (cust serv) *Fax:* 315-443-5545 *E-mail:* supress@syr.edu *Web Site:* syracuseuniversitypress.syr.edu, pg 239

Kuhatschek, Jack, Baker Books, PO Box 6287, Grand Rapids, MI 49516-6287 *Tel:* 616-676-9185 *Toll Free Tel:* 800-877-2665; 800-679-1957 *Fax:* 616-676-9573 *Toll Free Fax:* 800-398-3111 *Web Site:* www.bakerpublishinggroup.com, pg 29

Kuhn, Lauren, Crown Publishing Group, c/o Penguin Random House Inc, 1745 Broadway, New York, NY 10019 *Tel:* 212-782-9000 *Toll Free Tel:* 888-264-1745 *Fax:* 212-940-7408 *E-mail:* crownosm@penguinrandomhouse.com *Web Site:* crownpublishing.com, pg 68

Kuhne, Barbara, Pacific Educational Press, c/o University of British Columbia, Faculty of Education, 411-2389 Health Sciences Mall, Vancouver, BC V6T 1Z4, Canada *Tel:* 604-822-5385 *Fax:* 604-822-6603 *E-mail:* pep.admin@ubc.ca; pep.sales@ubc.ca *Web Site:* www.pacificedpress.educ.ubc.ca, pg 494

Kujichagulia, Phavia, Media Alliance, 2830 20 St, Suite 102, San Francisco, CA 94110 *Tel:* 415-746-9475 *E-mail:* information@media-alliance.org *Web Site:* www.media-alliance.org, pg 609

Kuka, Ronald, Chris O'Malley Fiction Prize, University of Wisconsin, 6193 Helen C White Hall, English Dept, 600 N Park St, Madison, WI 53706 *Tel:* 608-263-0566 *E-mail:* madisonrevw@gmail.com *Web Site:* www.english.wisc.edu/madisonreview, pg 715

Kuka, Ronald, Phyllis Smart-Young Poetry Prize, University of Wisconsin, 6193 Helen C White Hall, English Dept, 600 N Park St, Madison, WI 53706 *Tel:* 608-263-0566 *E-mail:* madisonrevw@gmail.com *Web Site:* www.english.wisc.edu/madisonreview, pg 739

Kulikowski, Katarzyna, W W Norton & Company Inc, 500 Fifth Ave, New York, NY 10110-0017 *Tel:* 212-354-5500 *Toll Free Tel:* 800-233-4830 (orders & cust serv) *Fax:* 212-869-0856 *Toll Free Fax:* 800-458-6515 *Web Site:* www.wwnorton.com, pg 172

Kull, Irene Imperio, Temple University Press, 1852 N Tenth St, Philadelphia, PA 19122-6099 *Tel:* 215-926-2140 *Toll Free Tel:* 800-621-2736 *Fax:* 215-926-2141 *E-mail:* tempress@temple.edu *Web Site:* www.temple.edu/tempress, pg 242

Kumangai, Miya, Touchstone, 1230 Avenue of the Americas, New York, NY 10020, pg 247

Kunde-Anderson, Mary Beth, Association of Catholic Publishers Inc, 4725 Dorsey Hall Dr, Suite A, PMB 709, Elliott City, MD 21042 *Tel:* 410-988-2926 *Fax:* 410-571-4946 *Web Site:* www.catholicsread.org; www.catholicpublishers.org; www.midatlanticcongress.org, pg 598

Kundert, Beth, McGraw-Hill Create, 501 Bell St, Dubuque, IA 52001 *Tel:* 563-584-6000 *Fax:* 563-584-6600 *E-mail:* first_last@mcgraw-hill.com *Web Site:* www.mhhe.com, pg 150

Kunjufu, Dr Jawanza PhD, African American Images, PO Box 1799, Chicago Heights, IL 60412 *Tel:* 708-672-4909 (cust serv) *Toll Free Tel:* 800-552-1991 (orders) *Fax:* 708-672-0466 *E-mail:* customersvc@africanamericanimages.com *Web Site:* www.africanamericanimages.com, pg 6

Kuny, Greg, American Psychiatric Publishing (APP), 1000 Wilson Blvd, Suite 1825, Arlington, VA 22209 *Tel:* 703-907-7322 *Toll Free Tel:* 800-368-5777 *Fax:* 703-907-1091 *E-mail:* appi@psych.org *Web Site:* www.appi.org; www.psychiatryonline.org, pg 15

Kunz, Jeannine, Society of Manufacturing Engineers, One SME Dr, Dearborn, MI 48121 *Tel:* 313-425-3000 *Toll Free Tel:* 800-733-4763 (cust serv) *Fax:* 313-425-3400 *E-mail:* publications@sme.org *Web Site:* www.sme.org, pg 229

Kuong, Jay, Management Advisory Services & Publications (MASP), PO Box 81151, Wellesley Hills, MA 02481-0001 *Tel:* 781-235-2895 *Fax:* 781-235-5446 *E-mail:* info@masp.com *Web Site:* www.masp.com, pg 145

Kurian, George Thomas, International Encyclopedia Society, 3689 Campbell Ct, Yorktown Heights, NY 10598 *Tel:* 914-962-3287 *Fax:* 914-962-3287, pg 607

Kurian, George Thomas, George Kurian Reference Books, 3689 Campbell Ct, Yorktown Heights, NY 10598 *Tel:* 914-962-3287 *Fax:* 914-962-3287, pg 133

Kurtz, Gretchen, Prometheus Books, 59 John Glenn Dr, Amherst, NY 14228-2119 *Tel:* 716-691-0133 *Toll Free Tel:* 800-421-0351 *Fax:* 716-691-0137 *E-mail:* marketing@prometheusbooks.com; editorial@prometheusbooks.com *Web Site:* www.prometheusbooks.com, pg 199

Kurtz, Jonathan, Prometheus Books, 59 John Glenn Dr, Amherst, NY 14228-2119 *Tel:* 716-691-0133 *Toll Free Tel:* 800-421-0351 *Fax:* 716-691-0137 *E-mail:* marketing@prometheusbooks.com; editorial@prometheusbooks.com *Web Site:* www.prometheusbooks.com, pg 199

Kurtz, Paul, Prometheus Books, 59 John Glenn Dr, Amherst, NY 14228-2119 *Tel:* 716-691-0133 *Toll Free Tel:* 800-421-0351 *Fax:* 716-691-0137 *E-mail:* marketing@prometheusbooks.com; editorial@prometheusbooks.com *Web Site:* www.prometheusbooks.com, pg 199

Kurtzman, Nellie, HarperCollins Children's Books, 195 Broadway, New York, NY 10007 *Tel:* 212-207-7000 *Web Site:* www.harpercollins.com/childrens, pg 105

Kusler, Jack, Addicus Books Inc, PO Box 45327, Omaha, NE 68145 *Tel:* 402-330-7493 *Fax:* 402-330-1707 *E-mail:* info@addicusbooks.com; addicusbks@aol.com *Web Site:* www.addicusbooks.com, pg 4

Kuster, Charles, DynaMinds Publishing®, PO Box 106, Johnston, IA 50131 *Tel:* 515-991-5315 *Web Site:* www.dynamindspublishing.com, pg 78

Kutsko, John F, SBL Press, The Luce Ctr, Suite 350, 825 Houston Mill Rd, Atlanta, GA 30329 *Tel:* 404-727-3100 *Fax:* 404-727-3101 (corp) *E-mail:* sbl@sbl-site.org *Web Site:* www.sbl-site.org, pg 217

Kuyper, Mark, Book Industry Study Group Inc (BISG), 145 W 45 St, Suite 601, New York, NY 10036 *Tel:* 646-336-7141 *Fax:* 646-336-6214 *E-mail:* info@bisg.org *Web Site:* www.bisg.org, pg 600

Kwon, DoEun, Kids Can Press Ltd, 25 Dockside Dr, Toronto, ON M5A 0B5, Canada *Tel:* 416-479-7000 *Toll Free Tel:* 800-265-0884 *Fax:* 416-960-5437 *E-mail:* info@kidscan.com; customerservice@kidscan.com *Web Site:* www.kidscanpress.com; www.kidscanpress.ca, pg 489

Kye-Casella, Maura, Don Congdon Associates Inc, 110 William St, Suite 2202, New York, NY 10038-3914 *Tel:* 212-645-1229 *Fax:* 212-727-2688 *E-mail:* dca@doncongdon.com *Web Site:* www.doncongdon.com, pg 546

Kyle, David, Saskatchewan Arts Board, 1355 Broad St, Regina, SK S4R 7V1, Canada *Tel:* 306-787-4056 *Toll Free Tel:* 800-667-7526 (Saskatchewan only) *Fax:* 306-787-4199 *E-mail:* info@artsboard.sk.ca *Web Site:* www.artsboard.sk.ca, pg 618

La Due, Holly, Prestel Publishing, 900 Broadway, Suite 603, New York, NY 10003 *Tel:* 212-995-2720 *Toll Free Tel:* 888-463-6110 (cust serv) *Fax:* 212-995-2733 *E-mail:* sales@prestel-usa.com *Web Site:* www.prestel.com, pg 196

La Fehr, Audrey, Kensington Publishing Corp, 119 W 40 St, New York, NY 10018 *Tel:* 212-407-1500 *Toll Free Tel:* 800-221-2647 *Fax:* 212-935-0699 *Web Site:* www.kensingtonbooks.com, pg 130

La Mattina, Elaine, White Pine Press, PO Box 236, Buffalo, NY 14201 *Tel:* 716-627-4665 *Fax:* 716-627-4665 *E-mail:* wpine@whitepine.org *Web Site:* www.whitepine.org, pg 270

La Norte, Gianna, University of Texas Press, 2100 Comal St, Austin, TX 78722 *Tel:* 512-471-7233 *Fax:* 512-232-7178 *E-mail:* utpress@uts.cc.utexas.edu *Web Site:* www.utexaspress.com, pg 244

La Pointe, Kathy, Broden Books LLC, 3824 Sunset Dr, Spring Park, MN 55384 *Tel:* 952-471-1066 *E-mail:* media@brodenbooks.com *Web Site:* www.brodenbooks.com, pg 46

La Rosa, Suzanne, NewSouth Books, 105 S Court St, Montgomery, AL 36104 *Tel:* 334-834-3556 *Fax:* 334-834-3557 *E-mail:* info@newsouthbooks.com *Web Site:* www.newsouthbooks.com, pg 169

La Rose, Charley, Association of Canadian University Presses, 10 St Mary St, Suite 700, Toronto, ON M4Y 2W8, Canada *Tel:* 416-978-2239 ext 237 *Fax:* 416-978-4738 *Web Site:* www.acup.ca, pg 598

La Salle, Peter N, University of Texas at Austin, Creative Writing Program, Dept of English, PAR 108, One University Sta, Mailcode B5000, Austin, TX 78712-1164 *Tel:* 512-471-5132; 512-471-4991 *Fax:* 512-471-4909 *Web Site:* www.utexas.edu/cola/depts/english/creative-writing, pg 664

La Via, Carmen, Fifi Oscard Agency Inc, 110 W 40 St, 16th fl, New York, NY 10018 *Tel:* 212-764-1100 *Fax:* 212-840-5019 *E-mail:* agency@fifioscard.com *Web Site:* fifioscard.com, pg 567

Labaqui, Joni, L Ron Hubbard's Writers of the Future Contest, PO Box 1630, Los Angeles, CA 90078 *Tel:* 323-466-3310 *Fax:* 323-466-6474 *E-mail:* contests@authorservicesinc.com *Web Site:* www.writersofthefuture.com, pg 693

Labbate, Alison, Wiley-Blackwell, Commerce Place, 350 Main St, Malden, MA 02148 *Tel:* 781-388-8200 *Fax:* 781-388-8210 *E-mail:* info@wiley.com *Web Site:* www.wiley.com, pg 272

Laberge, Isabelle, Editions Marcel Didier Inc, 1815, ave De Lorimier, Montreal, QC H2K 3W6, Canada *Tel:* 514-523-1523 *Toll Free Tel:* 800-361-1664 (Ontario to Maritimes) *Fax:* 514-523-5955 *E-mail:* marceldidier@hurtubisehmh.com *Web Site:* www.marceldidier.com, pg 480

LaBombard, Nicole, Rees Literary Agency, 14 Beacon St, Suite 710, Boston, MA 02108 *Tel:* 617-227-9014 *Fax:* 617-227-8762 *E-mail:* reesagency@reesagency.com *Web Site:* reesagency.com, pg 569

LaBore, Lindsey, Free Spirit Publishing Inc, 217 Fifth Ave N, Suite 200, Minneapolis, MN 55401-1299 *Tel:* 612-338-2068 *Toll Free Tel:* 800-735-7323 *Fax:* 612-337-5050 *Toll Free Fax:* 866-419-5199 *E-mail:* help4kids@freespirit.com *Web Site:* www.freespirit.com, pg 92

LaBounty, Kimberly, Midwest Publishing Association Webinars, 310 W Lake St, Suite 111, Elmhurst, IL 60126 *Tel:* 630-833-4220 *Fax:* 630-563-9181 *E-mail:* info@midwestpublish.org *Web Site:* www.midwestpublish.org, pg 661

Labov, Christine, Penguin Random House Speakers Bureau, 1745 Broadway, Mail Drop 13-1, New York, NY 10019 *Tel:* 212-572-2013 *E-mail:* speakers@penguinrandomhouse.com *Web Site:* www.prhspeakers.com, pg 588

Labrecque, Marise, Editions du CHU Sainte-Justine, 3175, chemin de la Cote-Sainte-Catherine, Montreal, QC H3T 1C5, Canada *Tel:* 514-345-4671 *Fax:* 514-345-4631 *E-mail:* edition.hsj@ssss.gouv.qc.ca *Web Site:* www.editions-chu-sainte-justine.org, pg 480

Lachapelle, Jean, Editions Marie-France, 9900 Ave des Laurentides, Montreal, QC H1H 4V1, Canada *Tel:* 514-329-3700 *Toll Free Tel:* 800-563-6644 (CN) *Fax:* 514-329-0630 *E-mail:* editions@marie-france.qc.ca *Web Site:* www.marie-france.qc.ca, pg 482

Lachina, Jeffrey A, Lachina Publishing Services Inc, 3793 S Green Rd, Cleveland, OH 44122 *Tel:* 216-292-7959 *E-mail:* info@lachina.com *Web Site:* www.lachina.com, pg 529

Lacombe, Joanne, Editions Marie-France, 9900 Ave des Laurentides, Montreal, QC H1H 4V1, Canada *Tel:* 514-329-3700 *Toll Free Tel:* 800-563-6644 (CN) *Fax:* 514-329-0630 *E-mail:* editions@marie-france.qc.ca *Web Site:* www.marie-france.qc.ca, pg 482

Lacy, Linda M, Carolina Academic Press, 700 Kent St, Durham, NC 27701 *Tel:* 919-489-7486 *Toll Free Tel:* 800-489-7486 *Fax:* 919-493-5668 *E-mail:* cap@cap-press.com *Web Site:* www.cap-press.com; www.caplaw.com, pg 50

Lacy, Natalie, Aspen Summer Words Writing Retreat & Literary Festival, 110 E Hallam St, Suite 116, Aspen, CO 81611 *Tel:* 970-925-3122 *Fax:* 970-920-5700 *E-mail:* awfinfo@aspenwriters.org *Web Site:* www.aspenwriters.org, pg 649

Lacy, Natalie, Winter Words Apres Ski for the Mind, 110 E Hallam St, Suite 116, Aspen, CO 81611 *Tel:* 970-925-3122 *Fax:* 970-920-5700 *E-mail:* awfinfo@aspenwriters.org *Web Site:* www.aspenwriters.org, pg 657

Ladd, Cheyenne, Impact Publishers Inc, PO Box 6016, Atascadero, CA 93423-6016 *Tel:* 805-466-5917 (opers & admin offs) *Toll Free Tel:* 800-246-7228 (orders) *Fax:* 805-466-5919 (opers & admin offs) *E-mail:* info@impactpublishers.com *Web Site:* www.impactpublishers.com; www.bibliotherapy.com, pg 119

LaDelle, Ebony, Simon & Schuster, 1230 Avenue of the Americas, New York, NY 10020 *Tel:* 212-698-7000 *Toll Free Tel:* 800-223-2348 (cust serv); 800-223-2336 (orders) *Toll Free Fax:* 800-943-9831 (orders) *Web Site:* www.simonandschuster.com, pg 225

LaFleur, Pat, Menasha Ridge Press Inc, 2204 First Ave S, Suite 102, Birmingham, AL 35233 *Tel:* 205-322-0439 *Toll Free Tel:* 888-604-4537 *Fax:* 205-326-1012 *E-mail:* info@menasharidge.com *Web Site:* www.menasharidge.com, pg 154

Lagace, Nettie, National Information Standards Organization, 3600 Clipper Mill Rd, Suite 302, Baltimore, MD 21211 *Tel:* 301-654-2512 *Fax:* 410-685-5278 *E-mail:* nisohq@niso.org *Web Site:* www.niso.org, pg 165, 612

LaGasse, Robert, Garden Writers Association, 7809 FM 179, Shallowater, TX 79363-3637 *Tel:* 806-832-1870 *Fax:* 806-832-5244 *E-mail:* info@gardenwriters.org *Web Site:* www.gardenwriters.org, pg 606

Lagunoff, Liza, Oscar Williams/Gene Derwood Award, 909 Third Ave, New York, NY 10022 *Tel:* 212-686-0010 *Fax:* 212-532-8528 *E-mail:* info@nycommunitytrust.org *Web Site:* www.nycommunitytrust.org, pg 736

Lahurd, Kristin, Coretta Scott King Book Awards, 50 E Huron St, Chicago, IL 60611 *Toll Free Tel:* 800-545-2433 *E-mail:* olos@ala.org *Web Site:* www.ala.org/emiert/cskbookawards, pg 698

Lai, Pauline, Captus Press Inc, 1600 Steeles Ave W, Units 14 & 15, Concord, ON L4K 4M2, Canada *Tel:* 416-736-5537 *Fax:* 416-736-5793 *E-mail:* info@captus.com *Web Site:* www.captus.com, pg 476

Laing, Bonnie, Pacific Press Publishing Association, 1350 N Kings Rd, Nampa, ID 83687-3193 *Tel:* 208-465-2500 *Toll Free Tel:* 800-447-7377 *Fax:* 208-465-2531 *Web Site:* www.pacificpress.com, pg 180

Laing, Glenn, American Society of Agricultural & Biological Engineers (ASABE), 2950 Niles Rd, St Joseph, MI 49085-9659 *Tel:* 269-429-0300 *Toll Free Tel:* 800-371-2723 *Fax:* 269-429-3852 *E-mail:* hq@asabe.org *Web Site:* www.asabe.org, pg 16

Lajeunesse, Danielle, Editions FouLire, 4339, rue des Becassines, Quebec, QC G1G 1V5, Canada *Tel:* 418-628-4029 *Toll Free Tel:* 877-628-4029 (CN & US) *Fax:* 418-628-4801 *E-mail:* info@foulire.com; edition@foulire.com *Web Site:* www.foulire.com, pg 481

Lake, Henry, The Professional Education Group Inc (PEG), 12401 Minnetonka Blvd, Suite 200, Minnetonka, MN 55305-3994 *Tel:* 952-933-9990 *Toll Free Tel:* 800-229-2531 *Fax:* 952-933-7784 *E-mail:* orders@proedgroup.com *Web Site:* www.proedgroup.com, pg 198

Lake, Kim, University Press of Florida, 15 NW 15 St, Gainesville, FL 32603-2079 *Tel:* 352-392-1351 *Toll Free Tel:* 800-226-3822 (orders only) *Fax:* 352-

392-0590 *Toll Free Fax:* 800-680-1955 (orders only) *E-mail:* info@upf.com *Web Site:* www.upf.com, pg 261

Lakin, Chuck, Zeig, Tucker & Theisen Inc, 3614 N 24 St, Phoenix, AZ 85016 *Tel:* 480-389-4342 *Toll Free Tel:* 800-666-2211 (orders) *Fax:* 602-944-8118 *E-mail:* marketing@zeigtucker.com *Web Site:* www.zeigtucker.com, pg 279

Lakosil, Natalie, Bradford Literary Agency, 5694 Mission Center Rd, Suite 347, San Diego, CA 92108 *Tel:* 619-521-1201 *E-mail:* queries@bradfordlit.com *Web Site:* www.bradfordlit.com, pg 543

LaLonde, Chantale, Scholastic Canada Ltd, 604 King St W, Toronto, ON M5V 1E1, Canada *Tel:* 905-887-7323 *Toll Free Tel:* 800-268-3860 (CN) *Toll Free Fax:* 866-387-4944 *E-mail:* custserve@scholastic.ca *Web Site:* www.scholastic.ca, pg 498

Lalwani, R, Laurier Books Ltd, PO Box 8493, Ottawa, ON K1G 3H9, Canada *Tel:* 613-738-2163 *Toll Free Fax:* 855-736-9160 *E-mail:* laurierbooks@yahoo.com, pg 490

Lam, Anna, Baker & Taylor/YALSA Conference Grants, 50 E Huron St, Chicago, IL 60611 *Tel:* 312-280-4390 *Toll Free Tel:* 800-545-2433 *Fax:* 312-280-5276; 312-664-7459 *E-mail:* yalsa@ala.org *Web Site:* www.ala.org/yalsa, pg 670

Lam, Anna, Margaret A Edwards Award, 50 E Huron St, Chicago, IL 60611 *Tel:* 312-280-4390 *Toll Free Tel:* 800-545-2433 *Fax:* 312-280-5276 *E-mail:* yalsa@ala.org *Web Site:* www.ala.org/yalsa/edwards, pg 683

Lam, Anna, Frances Henne YALSA/VOYA Research Grant, 50 E Huron St, Chicago, IL 60611 *Tel:* 312-280-4390 *Toll Free Tel:* 800-545-2433 *Fax:* 312-280-5276 *E-mail:* yalsa@ala.org *Web Site:* www.ala.org/yalsa, pg 687

Lam, Anna, Michael L Printz Award, 50 E Huron St, Chicago, IL 60611 *Tel:* 312-280-4390 *Toll Free Tel:* 800-545-2433 *Fax:* 312-280-5276 *E-mail:* yalsa@ala.org *Web Site:* www.ala.org/yalsa/printz, pg 721

Lam, Brian, Arsenal Pulp Press, 211 E Georgia St, No 202, Vancouver, BC V6A 1Z6, Canada *Tel:* 604-687-4233 *Toll Free Tel:* 888-600-PULP (600-7857) *Fax:* 604-687-4283 *E-mail:* info@arsenalpulp.com *Web Site:* www.arsenalpulp.com, pg 471

Lam, Francis, Clarkson Potter Publishers, c/o Random House Inc, 1745 Broadway, New York, NY 10019 *Tel:* 212-782-9000 *Toll Free Tel:* 888-264-1745 *Fax:* 212-572-6181 *Web Site:* www.clarksonpotter.com; www.randomhouse.com/crown/clarksonpotter, pg 195

Lamb, Beth, Vintage & Anchor Books, c/o Random House Inc, 1745 Broadway, New York, NY 10019 *Tel:* 212-572-2420 *E-mail:* vintageanchorpublicity@randomhouse.com *Web Site:* vintage-anchor.knopfdoubleday.com, pg 266

Lamb, Cynthia, Carnegie Mellon University Press, 5032 Forbes Ave, Pittsburgh, PA 15289-1021 *Tel:* 412-268-2861 *Fax:* 412-268-8706 *E-mail:* carnegiemellonuniversitypress@gmail.com *Web Site:* www.cmu.edu/universitypress, pg 50

Lamb, David, Scribner, 1230 Avenue of the Americas, New York, NY 10020, pg 220

Lamb, John D, Springfed Writers' Retreat, PO Box 304, Royal Oak, MI 48068-0304 *Tel:* 248-589-3913 *Web Site:* www.springfed.org, pg 655

Lamb, Paul, Howard Morhaim Literary Agency Inc, 30 Pierrepont St, Brooklyn, NY 11201-3371 *Tel:* 718-222-8400 *Fax:* 718-222-5056 *E-mail:* info@morhaimliterary.com *Web Site:* www.morhaimliterary.com, pg 566

Lamb, Wendy, Random House Children's Books, 1745 Broadway, New York, NY 10019 *Tel:* 212-782-9000 *Toll Free Tel:* 800-200-3552 *Fax:* 212-782-9452 *Web Site:* randomhousekids.com, pg 203

Lamba, Marie, The Jennifer DeChiara Literary Agency, 31 E 32 St, Suite 300, New York, NY 10016 *Tel:* 212-481-8484 (ext 362) *Fax:* 212-481-9582 *Web Site:* www.jdlit.com, pg 547

Lambert, Joan, Online Training Solutions Inc (OTSI), 2217 152 Ave NE, Redmond, WA 98052 *Toll Free Tel:* 888-308-6874 *Toll Free Fax:* 888-308-6875 *E-mail:* biz@otsi.com *Web Site:* www.otsi.com, pg 175

Lambert, Nancy, Harry N Abrams Inc, 115 W 18 St, 6th fl, New York, NY 10011 *Tel:* 212-206-7715 *Toll Free Tel:* 800-345-1359 *Fax:* 212-519-1210 *E-mail:* abrams@abramsbooks.com *Web Site:* www.abramsbooks.com, pg 3

Lambert, Patricia, David W & Beatrice C Evans Biography & Handcart Awards, 0735 Old Main Hill, Logan, UT 84322-0735 *Tel:* 435-797-0299 *Fax:* 435-797-1092 *E-mail:* mwc@usu.edu *Web Site:* mountainwest.usu.edu, pg 684

Lambeth, Pike, Foundation Publications, 900 S Euclid St, La Habra, CA 90631 *Tel:* 714-879-2286 *Toll Free Tel:* 800-257-6272 *Fax:* 714-535-2164 *E-mail:* info@foundationpublications.com *Web Site:* www.foundationpublications.com, pg 91

LaMee, Maurice, Aspen Writers' Foundation, 110 E Hallam St, Suite 116, Aspen, CO 81611 *Tel:* 970-925-3122 *Fax:* 970-920-5700 *E-mail:* awfinfo@aspenwriters.org *Web Site:* www.aspenwriters.org, pg 597

Lamm, Gigi, University of Pennsylvania Press, 3905 Spruce St, Philadelphia, PA 19104 *Tel:* 215-898-6261 *Fax:* 215-898-0404 *E-mail:* custserv@pobox.upenn.edu *Web Site:* www.pennpress.org, pg 259

Lamolinara, Guy, The Center for the Book in the Library of Congress, The Library of Congress, 101 Independence Ave SE, Washington, DC 20540-4920 *Tel:* 202-707-5221 *Fax:* 202-707-0269 *E-mail:* cfbook@loc.gov *Web Site:* www.read.gov; www.read.gov/cfb, pg 603

Lamolinara, Guy, Library of Congress Prize for American Fiction, 101 Independence Ave SE, Washington, DC 20540-1400 *Tel:* 202-707-5221 (Center for the Book) *Web Site:* www.loc.gov, pg 700

Lampack, Andrew, Peter Lampack Agency Inc, 350 Fifth Ave, Suite 5300, New York, NY 10118 *Tel:* 212-687-9106 *Fax:* 212-687-9109 *Web Site:* www.peterlampackagency.com, pg 561

Lampack, Peter A, Peter Lampack Agency Inc, 350 Fifth Ave, Suite 5300, New York, NY 10118 *Tel:* 212-687-9106 *Fax:* 212-687-9109 *Web Site:* www.peterlampackagency.com, pg 561

Lampe, Betsy, Rainbow Books Inc, PO Box 430, Highland City, FL 33846 *Tel:* 863-648-4420 *Fax:* 863-647-5951 *E-mail:* info@rainbowbooksinc.com *Web Site:* www.rainbowbooksinc.com, pg 202

Lampe, C Marzen, Rainbow Books Inc, PO Box 430, Highland City, FL 33846 *Tel:* 863-648-4420 *Fax:* 863-647-5951 *E-mail:* info@rainbowbooksinc.com *Web Site:* www.rainbowbooksinc.com, pg 202

Lamplough, Jack, The Overlook Press, 141 Wooster St, Suite 4-B, New York, NY 10012 *Tel:* 212-673-2210; 845-679-6838 (orders & dist) *Fax:* 212-673-2296 *E-mail:* sales@overlookny.com (orders) *Web Site:* www.overlookpress.com, pg 178

Lampo, David, Cato Institute, 1000 Massachusetts Ave NW, Washington, DC 20001-5403 *Tel:* 202-842-0200 *Toll Free Tel:* 800-767-1241 *Fax:* 202-842-3490 *E-mail:* catostore@cato.org *Web Site:* www.cato.org, pg 52

Lamprich, Ed, Pearson ELT, 10 Bank St, 9th fl, White Plains, NY 10606-1951 *Tel:* 914-287-8000 *Web Site:* www.pearsonelt.com, pg 185

Lamstein, Sarah, Julia Ward Howe Book Awards, 33 Brayton Rd, Brighton, MA 02135 *Tel:* 617-783-1357 *E-mail:* bostonauthors@aol.com *Web Site:* www.bostonauthorsclub.org, pg 693

Lamy, Patricia, Editions de la Pleine Lune, 223 34 Ave, Lachine, QC H8T 1Z4, Canada *Tel:* 514-634-7954 *Fax:* 514-637-6366 *E-mail:* editpllune@videotron.ca *Web Site:* www.pleinelune.qc.ca, pg 480

Lancaster, Brian, Africana Homestead Legacy Publishers Inc, 811 Church Rd, Suite 105, Cherry Hill, NJ 08002 *Tel:* 856-773-0694 *Fax:* 856-486-1135 *E-mail:* customer-service@ahlpub.com; sales@ahlpub.com; editors@ahlpub.com *Web Site:* www.ahlpub.com, pg 6

Lance, Dan, Kalmbach Publishing Co, 21027 Crossroads Circle, Waukesha, WI 53186 *Tel:* 262-796-8776 *Toll Free Tel:* 800-533-6644 (cust serv & orders) *Fax:* 262-796-1615 (sales & cust serv); 262-798-6468 (edit) *E-mail:* customerservice@kalmbach.com *Web Site:* www.kalmbach.com; www.kalmbachstore.com, pg 129

Lance, James, Cornell University Press, Sage House, 512 E State St, Ithaca, NY 14850 *Tel:* 607-277-2338 *Fax:* 607-277-2374 *E-mail:* cupressinfo@cornell.edu; cupress-sales@cornell.edu *Web Site:* www.cornellpress.cornell.edu, pg 63

Lance, Suzanne, New York State Walt Whitman Citation of Merit for Poets, University at Albany, SL 320, Albany, NY 12222 *Tel:* 518-442-5620 *Fax:* 518-442-5621 *E-mail:* writers@uamail.albany.edu *Web Site:* www.albany.edu/writers-inst, pg 713

Lance, Suzanne, New York State Writers Institute, University at Albany, Science Library 320, Albany, NY 12222 *Tel:* 518-442-5620 *Fax:* 518-442-5621 *E-mail:* writers@uamail.albany.edu *Web Site:* www.albany.edu/writers-inst, pg 653

Land, Bob, Land on Demand, 20 Long Crescent Dr, Bristol, VA 24201 *Tel:* 423-366-0513 *E-mail:* landondemand@gmail.com *Web Site:* boblandedits.blogspot.com, pg 529

Land, Dudley, McGraw-Hill Create, 501 Bell St, Dubuque, IA 52001 *Tel:* 563-584-6000 *Fax:* 563-584-6600 *E-mail:* first_last@mcgraw-hill.com *Web Site:* www.mhhe.com, pg 150

Landa, Anne, Walter Foster Publishing Inc, 6 Orchard Rd, Suite 100, Lake Forest, CA 92630 *Tel:* 949-380-7510 *Toll Free Tel:* 800-426-0099; 800-759-0190 (orders) *Fax:* 949-380-7575 *E-mail:* walterfoster@quartous.com *Web Site:* www.quartous.com, pg 91

Landau, David, Harvard Square Editions, 2152 Beachwood Terr, Hollywood, CA 90068 *Tel:* 323-469-8932 *Fax:* 323-469-8932 *Web Site:* harvardsquareeditions.org, pg 107

Landau, David, Pureplay Press, 195 26 Ave, No 2, San Francisco, CA 94121 *Tel:* 310-597-0328 *E-mail:* info@pureplaypress.com *Web Site:* www.pureplaypress.com, pg 200

Landauer, Jeramy, Landauer Corp, 3100 101 St, Suite A, Urbandale, IA 50322 *Tel:* 515-287-2144 *Toll Free Tel:* 800-557-2144 *Fax:* 515-276-5102 *E-mail:* info@landauercorp.com *Web Site:* www.landauercorp.com, pg 134

Landesman, Cliff, W W Norton & Company Inc, 500 Fifth Ave, New York, NY 10110-0017 *Tel:* 212-354-5500 *Toll Free Tel:* 800-233-4830 (orders & cust serv) *Fax:* 212-869-0856 *Toll Free Fax:* 800-458-6515 *Web Site:* www.wwnorton.com, pg 171

Landis, Sarah, HarperCollins Children's Books, 195 Broadway, New York, NY 10007 *Tel:* 212-207-7000 *Web Site:* www.harpercollins.com/childrens, pg 105

Landskroener, Marcia, Sophie Kerr Prize, c/o College Relations Off, 300 Washington Ave, Chestertown, MD 21620 *Tel:* 410-778-2800 *Toll Free Tel:* 800-422-1782 *Fax:* 410-810-7150 *Web Site:* www.washcoll.edu, pg 729

Landwehr, Kathy, Peachtree Publishers, 1700 Chattahoochee Ave, Atlanta, GA 30318-2112 *Tel:* 404-876-8761 *Toll Free Tel:* 800-241-0113 *Fax:* 404-875-2578 *Toll Free Fax:* 800-875-8909 *E-mail:* hello@peachtree-online.com *Web Site:* www.peachtree-online.com, pg 184

Lane, Connor, Lindquist & Vennum Prize for Poetry, 1011 Washington Ave S, Suite 300, Minneapolis, MN 55415-1246 *Tel:* 612-332-3192 *Toll Free Tel:* 800-520-6455 *Fax:* 612-215-2550 *Web Site:* www.milkweed.org, pg 701

Lane, Fr Edmund C, St Pauls, 2187 Victory Blvd, Staten Island, NY 10314-6603 *Tel:* 718-761-0047 (edit & prodn); 718-698-2759 (mktg & billing) *Toll Free*

Tel: 800-343-2522 *Fax:* 718-761-0057 *E-mail:* sales@stpauls.us; marketing@stpauls.us *Web Site:* www.stpauls.us, pg 215

Lane, Mary Ann, Harvard University Press, 79 Garden St, Cambridge, MA 02138-1499 *Tel:* 617-495-2600; 401-531-2800 (intl orders) *Toll Free Tel:* 800-405-1619 (orders) *Fax:* 617-495-5898 (general); 617-496-4677 (edit & rts); 401-531-2801 (intl orders) *Toll Free Fax:* 800-406-9145 (orders) *E-mail:* contact_hup@harvard.edu *Web Site:* www.hup.harvard.edu, pg 107

Lang, Amanda, Simon & Schuster, 1230 Avenue of the Americas, New York, NY 10020 *Tel:* 212-698-7000 *Toll Free Tel:* 800-223-2348 (cust serv); 800-223-2336 (orders) *Toll Free Fax:* 800-943-9831 (orders) *Web Site:* www.simonandschuster.com, pg 225

Lang, Amelia, Aperture Books, 547 W 27 St, 4th fl, New York, NY 10001 *Tel:* 212-505-5555 *Toll Free Tel:* 800-929-2323 *Fax:* 212-979-7759 *E-mail:* info@aperture.org *Web Site:* www.aperture.org, pg 19

Lange, April, W W Norton & Company Inc, 500 Fifth Ave, New York, NY 10110-0017 *Tel:* 212-354-5500 *Toll Free Tel:* 800-233-4830 (orders & cust serv) *Fax:* 212-869-0856 *Toll Free Fax:* 800-458-6515 *Web Site:* www.wwnorton.com, pg 171

Lange, Barbara, Society of Motion Picture & Television Engineers® (SMPTE®), 3 Barker Ave, 5th fl, White Plains, NY 10601 *Tel:* 914-761-1100 *Fax:* 914-761-3115 *Web Site:* www.smpte.org, pg 619

Lange, Heide, Sanford J Greenburger Associates Inc, 55 Fifth Ave, New York, NY 10003 *Tel:* 212-206-5600 *Fax:* 212-463-8718 *Web Site:* greenburger.com; www.sjga.com/, pg 555

Lange, Marty, McGraw-Hill Science, Engineering, Mathematics, 501 Bell St, Dubuque, IA 52001 *Tel:* 563-584-6000 *Toll Free Tel:* 800-338-3987 (cust serv) *Fax:* 614-755-5645 (cust serv) *Web Site:* www.mhhe.com, pg 152

Langille, Donald, Palm Island Press, 411 Truman Ave, Key West, FL 33040 *Tel:* 305-296-3102 *E-mail:* pipress2@gmail.com, pg 181

Langley, Norris, Duke University Press, 905 W Main St, Suite 18B, Durham, NC 27701 *Tel:* 919-688-5134 *Toll Free Tel:* 888-651-0122 (US) *Fax:* 919-688-2615 *Toll Free Fax:* 888-651-0124 *E-mail:* orders@dukeupress.edu; permissions@dukeupress.edu *Web Site:* www.dukeupress.edu, pg 77

Langlois, Dennis, Princeton University Press, 41 William St, Princeton, NJ 08540-5237 *Tel:* 609-258-4900 *Toll Free Tel:* 800-777-4726 (orders) *Fax:* 609-258-6305 *Toll Free Fax:* 800-999-1958 *E-mail:* orders@cpfsinc.com *Web Site:* press.princeton.edu, pg 197

Langman, Joe, Schiffer Publishing Ltd, 4880 Lower Valley Rd, Atglen, PA 19310 *Tel:* 610-593-1777 *Fax:* 610-593-2002 *E-mail:* schifferbk@aol.com *Web Site:* www.schifferbooks.com, pg 217

Langman, Lucy, Fons Vitae, 49 Mockingbird Valley Dr, Louisville, KY 40207-1366 *Tel:* 502-897-3641 *Fax:* 502-893-7373 *E-mail:* fonsvitaeky@aol.com *Web Site:* www.fonsvitae.com, pg 90

Langston, John, University Press of Mississippi, 3825 Ridgewood Rd, Jackson, MS 39211-6492 *Tel:* 601-432-6205 *Toll Free Tel:* 800-737-7788 (orders & cust serv) *Fax:* 601-432-6217 *E-mail:* press@mississippi.edu *Web Site:* www.upress.state.ms.us, pg 262

Langton, Dawn, Training Resource Network Inc (TRN), PO Box 439, St Augustine, FL 32085-0439 *Tel:* 904-823-9800 (cust serv) *Toll Free Tel:* 800-280-7010 (orders) *Fax:* 904-823-3554 *E-mail:* customerservice@trninc.com *Web Site:* www.trn-store.com, pg 248

Langum, David J Sr, Langum Prize in American Historical Fiction, 2809 Berkeley Dr, Birmingham, AL 35242 *Tel:* 205-726-2424 *Fax:* 205-726-4216 *Web Site:* www.langumtrust.org, pg 699

Langum, David J Sr, Langum Prize in American Legal History or Biography, 2809 Berkeley Dr, Birmingham, AL 35242 *Tel:* 205-726-2424 *Fax:* 205-726-4216 *E-mail:* langumtrust@gmail.com *Web Site:* www.langumtrust.org, pg 699

Langum, David J Sr, Gene E & Adele R Malott Prize for Recording Community Activism, 2809 Berkeley Dr, Birmingham, AL 35242 *Tel:* 205-726-2424 *Fax:* 205-726-4216 *E-mail:* langumtrust@gmail.com *Web Site:* www.langumtrust.org, pg 705

Lanick, Colleen, The MIT Press, 55 Hayward St, Cambridge, MA 02142 *Tel:* 617-253-5255 *Toll Free Tel:* 800-207-8354 (orders) *Fax:* 617-258-6779; 617-577-1545 (orders) *Web Site:* mitpress.mit.edu, pg 158

Lansing, Jim, OMNI Publishers Inc, 29131 Bulverde Rd, San Antonio, TX 78260 *Tel:* 210-778-4437 *Fax:* 830-438-4645 *Web Site:* www.omnipublishers.com; www.educatorethicsseries.com, pg 174

Lansing, Richard, Springer, 233 Spring St, New York, NY 10013-1578 *Tel:* 212-460-1500 *Toll Free Tel:* 800-SPRINGER (777-4643) *Fax:* 212-460-1575 *E-mail:* service-ny@springer.com *Web Site:* www.springer.com, pg 232

Lansing, Ruth, OMNI Publishers Inc, 29131 Bulverde Rd, San Antonio, TX 78260 *Tel:* 210-778-4437 *Fax:* 830-438-4645 *Web Site:* www.omnipublishers.com; www.educatorethicsseries.com, pg 174

Lansky, Bruce, Meadowbrook Press, 6110 Blue Circle Dr, Suite 237, Minnetonka, MN 55343 *Toll Free Tel:* 800-338-2232 *Fax:* 952-930-1940 *E-mail:* info@meadowbrookpress.com *Web Site:* www.meadowbrookpress.com, pg 153

Lansky, Vicki, Book Peddlers, 18330 Minnetonka Blvd, Deephaven, MN 55391 *Tel:* 952-544-1154 *Fax:* 206-339-6913 *E-mail:* bookpeddlers@aol.com *Web Site:* www.bookpeddlers.com, pg 42

Lape, Todd, University Press of Mississippi, 3825 Ridgewood Rd, Jackson, MS 39211-6492 *Tel:* 601-432-6205 *Toll Free Tel:* 800-737-7788 (orders & cust serv) *Fax:* 601-432-6217 *E-mail:* press@mississippi.edu *Web Site:* www.upress.state.ms.us, pg 262

Laperriere, Ginette, Guerin Editeur Ltee, 4501 rue Drolet, Montreal, QC H2T 2G2, Canada *Tel:* 514-842-3481 *Fax:* 514-842-4923 *Web Site:* www.guerin-editeur.qc.ca, pg 486

LaPolla, Sarah, Bradford Literary Agency, 5694 Mission Center Rd, Suite 347, San Diego, CA 92108 *Tel:* 619-521-1201 *E-mail:* queries@bradfordlit.com *Web Site:* www.bradfordlit.com, pg 543

Laporte, Janine, Doubleday Canada, One Toronto St, Suite 300, Toronto, ON M5C 2V6, Canada *Tel:* 416-364-4449 *Fax:* 416-364-6863 *Web Site:* www.randomhouse.ca, pg 479

Laporte, Janine, Knopf Canada, One Toronto St, Suite 300, Toronto, ON M5C 2V6, Canada *Tel:* 416-364-4449 *Toll Free Tel:* 888-523-9292 *Fax:* 416-364-6863 *Web Site:* www.randomhouse.ca, pg 490

Laporte, Janine, Penguin Random House Canada Limited, 320 Front St W, Suite 1400, Toronto, ON M5V 3B6, Canada *Tel:* 416-364-4449 *Toll Free Tel:* 888-523-9292 (cust serv) *Fax:* 416-364-6863; 416-364-6653 (subs rts) *Web Site:* penguinrandomhouse.ca, pg 495

Laporte, Janine, Seal Books, One Toronto St, Suite 300, Toronto, ON M5C 2V6, Canada *Tel:* 416-364-4449 *Toll Free Tel:* 888-523-9292 (order desk) *Fax:* 416-364-6863 *Web Site:* www.randomhouse.ca, pg 498

Laprairie, Dinah, BrainStorm Poetry Contest for Mental Health Consumers, 36 Elgin St, 2nd fl, Sudbury, ON P3C 5B4, Canada *Tel:* 705-222-6472 (ext 303) *E-mail:* openminds@nisa.on.ca *Web Site:* www.openmindsquarterly.com, pg 674

Laramie, Ben, Chronicle Books LLC, 680 Second St, San Francisco, CA 94107 *Tel:* 415-537-4200 *Toll Free Tel:* 800-759-0190 (cust serv) *Fax:* 415-537-4460 *Toll Free Fax:* 800-858-7787 (orders); 800-286-9471 (cust serv) *E-mail:* frontdesk@chroniclebooks.com *Web Site:* www.chroniclebooks.com, pg 58

Larcada, Marie Ellen, Teachers College Press, 1234 Amsterdam Ave, New York, NY 10027 *Tel:* 212-678-3929 *Toll Free Tel:* 800-575-6566 *Fax:* 212-678-4149; 802-864-7626 *E-mail:* tcpress@tc.columbia.edu; tcp.orders@aidcvt.com (orders) *Web Site:* www.teacherscollegepress.com, pg 241

Laredo, Sam, Laredo Publishing Co Inc, 465 Westview Ave, Englewood, NJ 07631 *Tel:* 201-408-4048 *Fax:* 201-408-5011 *E-mail:* info@laredopublishing.com *Web Site:* www.laredopublishing.com, pg 134

Laredo, Sam, Renaissance House, 465 Westview Ave, Englewood, NJ 07631 *Tel:* 201-408-4048 *Fax:* 201-408-5011 *E-mail:* info@renaissancehouse.net *Web Site:* www.renaissancehouse.net, pg 208

Largent, Marilyn, David C Cook, 4050 Lee Vance View, Colorado Springs, CO 80918 *Tel:* 719-536-0100 *Toll Free Tel:* 800-708-5550; 800-323-7543 (orders & cust serv) *Toll Free Fax:* 800-430-0726 (cust serv) *Web Site:* www.davidccook.com, pg 62

Larochelle, France, Guerin Editeur Ltee, 4501 rue Drolet, Montreal, QC H2T 2G2, Canada *Tel:* 514-842-3481 *Fax:* 514-842-4923 *Web Site:* www.guerin-editeur.qc.ca, pg 486

Larouche, Jean-Claude, Les Editions JCL, 930, rue Jacques-Cartier E, Chicoutimi, QC G7H 7K9, Canada *Tel:* 418-696-0536 *Fax:* 418-696-3132 *E-mail:* jcl@jcl.qc.ca *Web Site:* www.jcl.qc.ca, pg 482

Laroya, Colette, Hippocrene Books Inc, 171 Madison Ave, New York, NY 10016 *Tel:* 212-685-4373 *Fax:* 212-779-9338 *E-mail:* info@hippocrenebooks.com; orderdept@hippocrenebooks.com (orders) *Web Site:* www.hippocrenebooks.com, pg 112

Larsen, David, University of Manitoba Press, University of Manitoba, 301 St Johns College, 92 Dysart Rd, Winnipeg, MB R3T 2M5, Canada *Tel:* 204-474-9495 *Fax:* 204-474-7566 *E-mail:* uofmpress@umanitoba.ca *Web Site:* uofmpress.ca, pg 503

Larsen, Donna, Book Publicists of Southern California, 714 Crescent Dr, Beverly Hills, CA 90210 *Tel:* 323-461-3921 *Fax:* 323-461-0917 *Web Site:* www.bookpublicists.org, pg 600

Larsen, Elizabeth A, Tapestry Press Ltd, 19 Nashoba Rd, Littleton, MA 01460 *Tel:* 978-486-0200 *Toll Free Tel:* 800-535-2007 *Fax:* 978-486-0244 *E-mail:* publish@tapestrypress.com *Web Site:* www.tapestrypress.com, pg 240

Larsen, Emily, Book Industry Guild of New York, PO Box 2001, New York, NY 10113-2001 *E-mail:* admin@bookindustryguildofny.org *Web Site:* www.bookindustryguildofny.org, pg 600

Larsen, Michael, Michael Larsen/Elizabeth Pomada Literary Agents, 1029 Jones St, San Francisco, CA 94109 *Tel:* 415-673-0939 *E-mail:* larsenpoma@aol.com *Web Site:* www.larsenpomada.com, pg 561

Larsen, Michael, San Francisco Writers Conference, 1029 Jones St, San Francisco, CA 94109 *Tel:* 415-673-0939 *E-mail:* sfwriterscon@aol.com *Web Site:* www.sfwriters.org, pg 654

Larsen, Michael, San Francisco Writers Contest (SFWC), 1029 Jones St, San Francisco, CA 94109 *Tel:* 415-673-0939 *E-mail:* sfwriterscon@aol.com *Web Site:* www.sfwriters.org, pg 725

Larsen, Sven, Papercutz, 160 Broadway, E Wing, Suite 700, New York, NY 10038 *Tel:* 646-559-4681 *Toll Free Tel:* 800-886-1223 *Fax:* 212-643-1545 *E-mail:* papercutz@papercutz.com *Web Site:* www.papercutz.com, pg 181

Larsen, Todd, EMC Publishing LLC, 875 Montreal Way, St Paul, MN 55102 *Tel:* 651-290-2800 (corp) *Toll Free Tel:* 800-328-1452 *Toll Free Fax:* 800-328-4564 *E-mail:* educate@emcp.com *Web Site:* www.emcp.com, pg 81

Larson, Doran, Hamilton College, English/Creative Writing, English/Creative Writing Dept, 198 College Hill Rd, Clinton, NY 13323 *Tel:* 315-859-4370 *Fax:* 315-859-4390 *E-mail:* english@hamilton.edu *Web Site:* www.hamilton.edu, pg 660

Larson, Jeannette, Houghton Mifflin Harcourt Trade & Reference Division, 222 Berkeley St, Boston, MA 02116 *Tel:* 617-351-5000 *Toll Free Tel:* 800-225-3362 *Web Site:* www.hmhco.com, pg 115

LaSala, Erica, Harry N Abrams Inc, 115 W 18 St, 6th fl, New York, NY 10011 *Tel:* 212-206-7715 *Toll Free Tel:* 800-345-1359 *Fax:* 212-519-1210 *E-mail:* abrams@abramsbooks.com *Web Site:* www.abramsbooks.com, pg 3

LaSasso, Anthony, Bloomsbury Publishing Inc, 1385 Broadway, 5th fl, New York, NY 10018 *Tel:* 212-419-5300 *E-mail:* marketingusa@bloomsbury.com; adultpublicityusa@bloomsbury.com; askacademic@bloomsbury.com *Web Site:* www.bloomsbury.com, pg 40

Lasek, Ms Robin, Xlibris Corp, 1663 Liberty Dr, Suite 200, Bloomington, IN 47403 *Toll Free Tel:* 888-795-4274 *Fax:* 610-915-0294 *E-mail:* info@xlibris.com *Web Site:* www.xlibris.com, pg 277

Lasher, Eric, The LA Literary Agency, PO Box 46370, Los Angeles, CA 90046 *Tel:* 323-654-5288 *E-mail:* laliteraryagency@mac.com; mail@laliteraryagency.com *Web Site:* www.laliteraryagency.com, pg 561

Lasher, Maureen, The LA Literary Agency, PO Box 46370, Los Angeles, CA 90046 *Tel:* 323-654-5288 *E-mail:* laliteraryagency@mac.com; mail@laliteraryagency.com *Web Site:* www.laliteraryagency.com, pg 561

Lasky, Cynthia, Random House Publishing Group, 1745 Broadway, New York, NY 10019 *Toll Free Tel:* 800-200-3552 *Web Site:* atrandom.com, pg 204

Lasky, Karl, Ravenhawk™ Books, 8364 E Balfour Place, Tucson, AZ 85710 *Tel:* 520-296-4491 *Fax:* 520-296-4491 *E-mail:* ravenhawk6dof@yahoo.com *Web Site:* 6dofsolutions.com, pg 205

Lasner, Mark Samuels, William Morris Society in the United States Fellowships, PO Box 53263, Washington, DC 20009 *E-mail:* us@morrissociety.org *Web Site:* www.morrissociety.org, pg 709

Lassiter, Steve, APA Talent & Literary Agency, 405 S Beverly Dr, Beverly Hills, CA 90212 *Tel:* 310-888-4200 *Fax:* 310-888-4242 *Web Site:* www.apa-agency.com, pg 541

Last, Stanley, Fine Creative Media, Inc, 322 Eighth Ave, 15th fl, New York, NY 10001 *Tel:* 212-595-3500 *Fax:* 212-595-3779, pg 88

Latham, Adam, Sewanee Writers' Conference, Stamler Ctr, 119 Gailor Hall, 735 University Ave, Sewanee, TN 37383-1000 *Tel:* 931-598-1141 *E-mail:* swc@sewanee.edu *Web Site:* www.sewaneewriters.org, pg 655

Latham, Joyce Eileen, JL Communications, 10205 Green Holly Terr, Silver Spring, MD 20902 *Tel:* 301-593-0640, pg 528

Lathbury, Roger, Orchises Press, PO Box 320533, Alexandria, VA 22320-4533 *Tel:* 703-683-1243 *Web Site:* mason.gmu.edu/~lathbury/, pg 176

Latimer, Nicholas, Alfred A Knopf/Everyman's Library, c/o Random House Inc, 1745 Broadway, New York, NY 10019 *Tel:* 212-751-2600 *Toll Free Tel:* 800-638-6460 *Fax:* 212-572-2593 *Web Site:* www.knopfdoubleday.com, pg 132

Latour, Gilles, Canadian Education Association (Association canadienne d'education), 119 Spadina Ave, Suite 705, Toronto, ON M5V 2L1, Canada *Tel:* 416-591-6300 *Toll Free Tel:* 866-803-9549 *Fax:* 416-591-5345 *E-mail:* info@cea-ace.ca *Web Site:* www.cea-ace.ca, pg 602

Latshaw, Katherine, Folio Literary Management LLC, The Film Center Bldg, 630 Ninth Ave, Suite 1101, New York, NY 10036 *Tel:* 212-400-1494 *Fax:* 212-967-0977 *Web Site:* www.foliolit.com, pg 552

Lauber, Kimberly, Random House Children's Books, 1745 Broadway, New York, NY 10019 *Tel:* 212-782-9000 *Toll Free Tel:* 800-200-3552 *Fax:* 212-782-9452 *Web Site:* randomhousekids.com, pg 203

Lauer, Brett Fletcher, George Bogin Memorial Award, 15 Gramercy Park, New York, NY 10003 *Tel:* 212-254-9628 *Fax:* 212-673-2352 *Web Site:* www.poetrysociety.org, pg 673

Lauer, Brett Fletcher, Alice Fay Di Castagnola Award, 15 Gramercy Park, New York, NY 10003 *Tel:* 212-254-9628 *Fax:* 212-673-2352 *Web Site:* www.poetrysociety.org, pg 680

Lauer, Brett Fletcher, Norma Farber First Book Award, 15 Gramercy Park, New York, NY 10003 *Tel:* 212-254-9628 *Fax:* 212-673-2352 *Web Site:* www.poetrysociety.org, pg 685

Lauer, Brett Fletcher, Cecil Hemley Memorial Award, 15 Gramercy Park, New York, NY 10003 *Tel:* 212-254-9628 *Fax:* 212-673-2352 *Web Site:* www.poetrysociety.org, pg 692

Lauer, Brett Fletcher, Louise Louis/Emily F Bourne Student Poetry Award, 15 Gramercy Park, New York, NY 10003 *Tel:* 212-254-9628 *Fax:* 212-673-2352 *Web Site:* www.poetrysociety.org, pg 703

Lauer, Brett Fletcher, Lyric Poetry Award, 15 Gramercy Park, New York, NY 10003 *Tel:* 212-254-9628 *Fax:* 212-673-2352 *Web Site:* www.poetrysociety.org, pg 704

Lauer, Brett Fletcher, Lucille Medwick Memorial Award, 15 Gramercy Park, New York, NY 10003 *Tel:* 212-254-9628 *Fax:* 212-673-2352 *Web Site:* www.poetrysociety.org, pg 707

Lauer, Brett Fletcher, Poetry Society of America (PSA), 15 Gramercy Park, New York, NY 10003 *Tel:* 212-254-9628 *Fax:* 212-673-2352 *Web Site:* www.poetrysociety.org, pg 616

Lauer, Brett Fletcher, William Carlos Williams Award, 15 Gramercy Park, New York, NY 10003 *Tel:* 212-254-9628 *Fax:* 212-673-2352 *Web Site:* www.poetrysociety.org, pg 736

Lauer, Brett Fletcher, The Writer Magazine/Emily Dickinson Award, 15 Gramercy Park, New York, NY 10003 *Tel:* 212-254-9628 *Fax:* 212-673-2352 *Web Site:* www.poetrysociety.org, pg 738

Lauer, George, Venture Publishing Inc, 1999 Cato Ave, State College, PA 16801 *Tel:* 814-234-4561 *Fax:* 814-234-1651 *E-mail:* vpublish@venturepublish.com *Web Site:* www.venturepublish.com, pg 265

Lauer, Jack, Natasha Kern Literary Agency Inc, PO Box 1069, White Salmon, WA 98672 *Tel:* 509-493-3803 *E-mail:* agent@natashakern.com *Web Site:* www.natashakern.com, pg 559

Lauer, Valerie, Hanser Publications LLC, 6915 Valley Ave, Cincinnati, OH 45244-3029 *Tel:* 513-527-8977 *Toll Free Tel:* 800-950-8977; 877-751-5052 (orders) *Fax:* 513-534-7803 *Toll Free Fax:* 800-527-8801 *E-mail:* info@hanserpublications.com *Web Site:* www.hanserpublications.com, pg 104

Laughlin, Phil, The MIT Press, 55 Hayward St, Cambridge, MA 02142 *Tel:* 617-253-5255 *Toll Free Tel:* 800-207-8354 (orders) *Fax:* 617-258-6779; 617-577-1545 (orders) *Web Site:* mitpress.mit.edu, pg 158

Laur, Mary, University of Chicago Press, 1427 E 60 St, Chicago, IL 60637-2954 *Tel:* 773-702-7700; 773-702-7600 *Toll Free Tel:* 800-621-2736 (orders) *Fax:* 773-702-9756; 773-660-2235 (orders); 773-702-2708 *E-mail:* custserv@press.uchicago.edu; marketing@press.uchicago.edu *Web Site:* www.press.uchicago.edu, pg 255

Laurenzo, Diane, American Management Association (AMA), 1601 Broadway, New York, NY 10019 *Tel:* 212-586-8100 *Toll Free Tel:* 877-566-9441 *Fax:* 212-903-8168; 518-891-0368 *E-mail:* customerservice@amanet.org *Web Site:* www.amanet.org, pg 595

Lauterbach, Ellen, Marshall Cavendish Corp, 99 White Plains Rd, Tarrytown, NY 10591-9001 *Tel:* 914-332-8888 *Toll Free Tel:* 800-821-9881 *Fax:* 914-332-8102 *E-mail:* mce@marshallcavendish.com *Web Site:* www.mceducation.us, pg 148

Lavelle, Emily, PublicAffairs, 250 W 57 St, Suite 1321, New York, NY 10107 *Tel:* 212-397-6666 *Toll Free Tel:* 800-343-4499 (orders) *Fax:* 212-397-4277 *E-mail:* publicaffairs@perseusbooks.com *Web Site:* www.publicaffairsbooks.com, pg 200

Lavender, John, CRC Press LLC, 6000 Broken Sound Pkwy NW, Suite 300, Boca Raton, FL 33487 *Tel:* 561-994-0555 *Toll Free Tel:* 800-272-7737 (orders) *Toll Free Fax:* 800-643-9428 (sales); 800-374-3401 (orders) *E-mail:* orders@crcpress.com; orders@taylorandfrancis.com *Web Site:* www.crcpress.com, pg 66

Laventhall, Don, Harold Ober Associates Inc, 425 Madison Ave, New York, NY 10017 *Tel:* 212-759-8600 *Fax:* 212-759-9428 *Web Site:* www.haroldober.com, pg 567

Lavery, Brittany, Harlequin Enterprises Ltd, 225 Duncan Mill Rd, Don Mills, ON M3B 3K9, Canada *Tel:* 416-445-5860 *Toll Free Tel:* 888-432-4879; 800-370-5838 (ebook inquiries) *E-mail:* customerservice@harlequin.com *Web Site:* www.harlequin.com, pg 487

Lavigne, Guillaume, Les Editions du CRAM Inc, 1030, Cherrier, bureau 205, Montreal, QC H2L 1H9, Canada *Tel:* 514-598-8547 *Fax:* 514-598-8788 *E-mail:* service@editionscram.com *Web Site:* www.editionscram.com, pg 481

Lavigne, Pierre, Les Editions du CRAM Inc, 1030, Cherrier, bureau 205, Montreal, QC H2L 1H9, Canada *Tel:* 514-598-8547 *Fax:* 514-598-8788 *E-mail:* service@editionscram.com *Web Site:* www.editionscram.com, pg 481

Lavoie, Michel, Les Editions Vents d'Ouest, 109, rue Wright, bureau 202, Gatineau, QC J8X 2G7, Canada *Tel:* 819-770-6377 *Fax:* 819-770-0559 *E-mail:* info@ventsdouest.ca *Web Site:* www.ventsdouest.ca, pg 483

Lawrence, Brittany, AAP PreK-12 Learning Group, 325 Chestnut St, Suite 1110, Philadelphia, PA 19106 *Tel:* 267-351-4310 *Fax:* 267-351-4317 *E-mail:* prek12learning@publishers.org *Web Site:* www.aepweb.org, pg 593

Lawrence, Derek, PubWest Book Design Awards, 17501 Hill Way, Lake Oswego, OR 97035 *Tel:* 503-901-9865 *Fax:* 602-234-3062 *Web Site:* pubwest.org, pg 722

Lawrence, Eileen, Alexander Street Press LLC, 3212 Duke St, Alexandria, VA 22314 *Tel:* 703-212-8520 *Toll Free Tel:* 800-889-5937 *Fax:* 703-940-6584 *E-mail:* sales@alexanderstreet.com; marketing@alexanderstreet.com; info@alexanderstreet.com *Web Site:* alexanderstreet.com, pg 7

Lawrence, Jane, RockBench Publishing Corp, 6101 Stillmeadow Dr, Nashville, TN 37211-6518 *Tel:* 615-831-2277 *Fax:* 615-831-2212 *E-mail:* info@rockbench.com *Web Site:* www.rockbench.com, pg 210

Lawrence, Kristin Harpster, Wayne State University Press, Leonard N Simons Bldg, 4809 Woodward Ave, Detroit, MI 48201-1309 *Tel:* 313-577-6120 *Toll Free Tel:* 800-978-7323 *Fax:* 313-577-6131 *Web Site:* www.wsupress.wayne.edu, pg 268

Lawrence, Merloyd Ludington, Merloyd Lawrence Inc, 102 Chestnut St, Boston, MA 02108 *Tel:* 617-523-5895 *Fax:* 617-252-5285, pg 135

Lawrence, Michael, Orbis Books, Price Bldg, Box 302, Maryknoll, NY 10545-0302 *Tel:* 914-941-7636 *Toll Free Tel:* 800-258-5838 (orders) *Fax:* 914-941-7005 *E-mail:* orbisbooks@maryknoll.org *Web Site:* www.orbisbooks.com, pg 176

Lawrence, Nancy, Melcher Book Award, 25 Beacon St, Boston, MA 02108-2800 *Tel:* 617-948-4303 *Fax:* 617-367-3237 *E-mail:* info@uua.org *Web Site:* www.uua.org, pg 707

Lawrence, Priscilla, The Historic New Orleans Collection, 533 Royal St, New Orleans, LA 70130 *Tel:* 504-523-4662 *Fax:* 504-598-7108 *E-mail:* wrc@hnoc.org *Web Site:* www.hnoc.org, pg 112

Lawrence, Richard, Eaton Literary Associates Literary Awards, PO Box 49795, Sarasota, FL 34230-6795 *Tel:* 941-366-6589 *Fax:* 941-365-4679 *E-mail:* eatonlit@aol.com *Web Site:* www.eatonliterary.com, pg 682

Lawrence, Ron, Upper Access Inc, 87 Upper Access Rd, Hinesburg, VT 05461 *Tel:* 802-482-2988 *Toll Free Tel:* 800-310-8320 (orders) *Fax:* 802-417-3002 *E-mail:* info@upperaccess.com *Web Site:* www.upperaccess.com, pg 263

LeCates, Justine, Doubleday/Nan A Talese, c/o Penguin Random House Inc, 1745 Broadway, New York, NY 10019 *Tel:* 212-751-2600 *Fax:* 212-572-2662 *E-mail:* ddaypub@randomhouse.com *Web Site:* knopfdoubleday.com, pg 76

LeCates, Justine, Alfred A Knopf/Everyman's Library, c/o Random House Inc, 1745 Broadway, New York, NY 10019 *Tel:* 212-751-2600 *Toll Free Tel:* 800-638-6460 *Fax:* 212-572-2593 *Web Site:* www.knopfdoubleday.com, pg 132

LeCates, Justine, Pantheon Books/Schocken Books, c/o Random House Inc, 1745 Broadway, New York, NY 10019 *Tel:* 212-751-2600 *Toll Free Tel:* 800-638-6460 *Fax:* 212-572-6030, pg 181

Leckie, Ross, Goose Lane Editions, 500 Beaverbrook Ct, Suite 330, Fredericton, NB E3B 5X4, Canada *Tel:* 506-450-4251 *Toll Free Tel:* 888-926-8377 *Fax:* 506-459-4991 *E-mail:* info@gooselane.com; customerservice@gooselane.com *Web Site:* www.gooselane.com, pg 485

Leclerc, Dr Richard PhD, Editions du Bois-de-Coulonge, 1140 Ave de Montigny, Sillery, QC G1S 3T7, Canada *Tel:* 418-683-6332 *Web Site:* www.ebc.qc.ca, pg 473

Leczkowski, Jennifer, Running Press Book Publishers, 2300 Chestnut St, Philadelphia, PA 19103-4399 *Tel:* 215-567-5080 *Toll Free Tel:* 800-343-4499 (cust serv & orders) *Fax:* 215-568-2919 *Toll Free Fax:* 800-453-2884 (cust serv & orders) *E-mail:* perseus.promos@perseusbooks.com *Web Site:* www.runningpress.com, pg 212

Leder, Meg, Penguin Books, 375 Hudson St, New York, NY 10014 *Tel:* 212-366-2000 *E-mail:* online@penguinputnam.com *Web Site:* www.penguinputnam.com; www.penguinclassics.com; us.penguingroup.com, pg 186

Lee, Adam, Lasaria Creative Publishing, 4094 Majestic Lane, Suite 352, Fairfax, VA 22033 *E-mail:* info@lasariacreative.com *Web Site:* www.lasariacreative.com, pg 135

Lee, Ben, Fine Creative Media, Inc, 322 Eighth Ave, 15th fl, New York, NY 10001 *Tel:* 212-595-3500 *Fax:* 212-595-3779, pg 88

Lee, Benjamin, Dutton, 375 Hudson St, New York, NY 10014 *Tel:* 212-366-2000 *Fax:* 212-366-2262 *E-mail:* online@penguinputnam.com *Web Site:* www.penguinputnam.com; us.penguingroup.com, pg 78

Lee, Benjamin, Penguin Group (USA) LLC, a Penguin Random House company, 375 Hudson St, New York, NY 10014 *Tel:* 212-366-2000 *Toll Free Tel:* 800-847-5515 (inside sales); 800-631-8571 (cust serv) *Fax:* 212-366-2666; 607-775-4829 (inside sales) *E-mail:* online@us.penguingroup.com *Web Site:* www.penguin.com; us.penguingroup.com, pg 186

Lee, Benjamin, The Putnam Publishing Group, 375 Hudson St, New York, NY 10014 *Tel:* 212-366-2000 *Toll Free Tel:* 800-631-8571 *Fax:* 212-366-2643 *E-mail:* online@penguinputnam.com *Web Site:* www.penguinputnam.com; us.penguingroup.com, pg 201

Lee, Calee, Xist Publishing, PO Box 61593, Irvine, CA 92602 *Tel:* 949-478-2568 *E-mail:* info@xistpublishing.com *Web Site:* www.xistpublishing.com, pg 277

Lee, Jacob, Xist Publishing, PO Box 61593, Irvine, CA 92602 *Tel:* 949-478-2568 *E-mail:* info@xistpublishing.com *Web Site:* www.xistpublishing.com, pg 277

Lee, Jay, Marshall Cavendish Corp, 99 White Plains Rd, Tarrytown, NY 10591-9001 *Tel:* 914-332-8888 *Toll Free Tel:* 800-821-9881 *Fax:* 914-332-8102 *E-mail:* mce@marshallcavendish.com *Web Site:* www.mceducation.us, pg 148

Lee, Jill LeMin, Athenaeum of Philadelphia Literary Award, 219 S Sixth St, Philadelphia, PA 19106 *Tel:* 215-925-2688 *Fax:* 215-925-3755 *Web Site:* www.philaathenaeum.org, pg 669

Lee, Jim, DC Entertainment, 2900 Alameda, Burbank, CA 91505 *Toll Free Tel:* 800-887-6789 *E-mail:* dccomics@cambeywest.com *Web Site:* www.dcentertainment.com; www.dccomics.com; www.madmag.com, pg 72

Lee, Ken, Michael Wiese Productions, 12400 Ventura Blvd, No 1111, Studio City, CA 91604 *Tel:* 818-379-8799 *Toll Free Tel:* 800-833-5738 (orders) *Fax:* 818-986-3408 *E-mail:* mwpsales@mwp.com; fulfillment@portcity.com *Web Site:* www.mwp.com, pg 271

Lee, Linda, Master Point Press, 331 Douglas Ave, Toronto, ON M5M 1H2, Canada *Tel:* 416-781-0351 *Fax:* 416-781-1831 *E-mail:* info@masterpointpress.com *Web Site:* www.masterpointpress.com; www.ebooksbridge.com (ebook sales), pg 491

Lee, Linda, Princeton Architectural Press, 37 E Seventh St, New York, NY 10003 *Tel:* 212-995-9620 *Toll Free Tel:* 800-722-6657 (dist); 800-759-0190 (sales) *Fax:* 212-995-9454 *E-mail:* sales@papress.com *Web Site:* www.papress.com, pg 197

Lee, Lisa, Holiday House Inc, 425 Madison Ave, New York, NY 10017 *Tel:* 212-688-0085 *Fax:* 212-421-6134 *E-mail:* holiday@holidayhouse.com *Web Site:* www.holidayhouse.com, pg 113

Lee, Patrick, Crown Publishing Group, c/o Penguin Random House Inc, 1745 Broadway, New York, NY 10019 *Tel:* 212-782-9000 *Toll Free Tel:* 888-264-1745 *Fax:* 212-940-7408 *E-mail:* crownosm@penguinrandomhouse.com *Web Site:* crownpublishing.com, pg 68

Lee, Quinlan, WNBA Pannell Award for Excellence in Children's Bookselling, 435 W 23 St, Suite 8-C, New York, NY 10011 *Tel:* 212-242-6930 *E-mail:* pannellaward@gmail.com *Web Site:* www.wnba-books.org; www.NationalReadingGroupMonth.org; www.wnba-books.org/awards, pg 737

Lee, Ray, Master Point Press, 331 Douglas Ave, Toronto, ON M5M 1H2, Canada *Tel:* 416-781-0351 *Fax:* 416-781-1831 *E-mail:* info@masterpointpress.com *Web Site:* www.masterpointpress.com; www.ebooksbridge.com (ebook sales), pg 491

Lee, Ron, WaterBrook Multnomah Publishing Group, 12265 Oracle Blvd, Suite 200, Colorado Springs, CO 80921 *Tel:* 719-590-4999 *Toll Free Tel:* 800-603-7051 (orders) *Fax:* 719-590-8977 *Toll Free Fax:* 800-294-5686 (orders) *E-mail:* info@waterbrookmultnomah.com *Web Site:* waterbrookmultnomah.com, pg 267

Lee, Sonia, William Saroyan International Prize for Writing, Administrator, Saroyan Prize Committee, Stanford University Libraries, 557 Escondido Mall, Stanford, CA 94305-6004 *Tel:* 650-736-9538 *Web Site:* library.stanford.edu, pg 725

Lee, Spenser, Farrar, Straus & Giroux, LLC, 18 W 18 St, New York, NY 10011 *Tel:* 212-741-6900 *E-mail:* fsg.publicity@fsgbooks.com *Web Site:* us.macmillan.com/fsg.aspx, pg 86

Lee, Vance Jr, Penguin Group (USA) LLC Sales, 375 Hudson St, New York, NY 10014 *Tel:* 212-366-2000 *E-mail:* online@penguinputnam.com *Web Site:* us.penguingroup.com, pg 187

Leep, Jennifer, Revell, PO Box 6287, Grand Rapids, MI 49516-6287 *Tel:* 616-676-9185 *Toll Free Tel:* 800-877-2665; 800-679-1957 *Fax:* 616-676-9573 *Web Site:* www.revellbooks.com, pg 208

Lefebvre, Marie-Eve, Editions du CHU Sainte-Justine, 3175, chemin de la Cote-Sainte-Catherine, Montreal, QC H3T 1C5, Canada *Tel:* 514-345-4671 *Fax:* 514-345-4631 *E-mail:* edition.hsj@ssss.gouv.qc.ca *Web Site:* www.editions-chu-sainte-justine.org, pg 480

Lefevre, Delphine, Ecrits des Forges, 992-A rue Royale, Trois-Rivieres, QC G9A 4H9, Canada *Tel:* 819-840-8492 *E-mail:* ecritsdesforges@gmail.com *Web Site:* www.ecritsdesforges.com, pg 479

Leffmann, Laurel, Summertime Publications Inc, 7502 E Berridge Lane, Scottsdale, AZ 85250 *Tel:* 480-409-1554 *E-mail:* handell@summertimepublications.com *Web Site:* www.summertimepublications.com, pg 237

Lefkon, Wendy, Disney Press, 1101 Flower St, Glendale, CA 91201 *Web Site:* books.disney.com, pg 74

Legatt, Renee, Westview Press, 2465 Central Ave, Boulder, CO 80301 *Tel:* 303-444-3541 *Fax:* 720-406-7336 *E-mail:* westview.orders@perseusbooks.com *Web Site:* www.perseusbooksgroup.com; www.westviewpress.com, pg 270

Legault, Claude, Guerin Editeur Ltee, 4501 rue Drolet, Montreal, QC H2T 2G2, Canada *Tel:* 514-842-3481 *Fax:* 514-842-4923 *Web Site:* www.guerin-editeur.qc.ca, pg 486

Legault, Claude, Lidec Inc, 4501, rue Drolet, Montreal, QC H2T 2G2, Canada *Tel:* 514-843-5991 *Toll Free Tel:* 800-350-5991 (CN only) *Fax:* 514-843-5252 *E-mail:* lidec@lidec.qc.ca *Web Site:* www.lidec.qc.ca, pg 490

Legault, Ms Josee, Brault & Bouthillier, 700 ave Beaumont, Montreal, QC H3N 1V5, Canada *Tel:* 514-273-9186 *Toll Free Tel:* 800-361-0378 *Fax:* 514-273-8627 *Toll Free Fax:* 800-361-0378 *E-mail:* ventes@bb.ca *Web Site:* bb.ca, pg 473

Legault, Paul, Raiziss/de Palchi Fellowship, 75 Maiden Lane, Suite 901, New York, NY 10038 *Tel:* 212-274-0343 *Fax:* 212-274-9427 *E-mail:* academy@poets.org *Web Site:* www.poets.org, pg 723

Legault, Paul, Walt Whitman Award, 75 Maiden Lane, Suite 901, New York, NY 10038 *Tel:* 212-274-0343 *Fax:* 212-274-9427 *E-mail:* academy@poets.org *Web Site:* www.poets.org, pg 735

Leggett, John, Napa Valley Writers' Conference, Upper Valley Campus, 1088 College Ave, St Helena, CA 94574 *Tel:* 707-967-2900 (ext 1611) *Fax:* 707-967-2909 *E-mail:* writecon@napavalley.edu *Web Site:* www.napawritersconf.org, pg 653

LeGro, Hope J, Georgetown University Press, 3240 Prospect St NW, Suite 250, Washington, DC 20007 *Tel:* 202-687-5889 (busn) *Fax:* 202-687-6340 (edit) *E-mail:* gupress@georgetown.edu *Web Site:* press.georgetown.edu, pg 96

Lehman, Michelle, National Association of Broadcasters (NAB), 1771 "N" St NW, Washington, DC 20036 *Tel:* 202-429-5300 *Fax:* 202-429-4199 *E-mail:* nab@nab.org *Web Site:* www.nab.org, pg 163, 611

Lehman, Susannah, The Optical Society (OSA), 2010 Massachusetts Ave NW, Washington, DC 20036-1023 *Tel:* 202-223-8130 *Toll Free Tel:* 800-766-4672 *E-mail:* custserv@osa.org *Web Site:* www.osa.org, pg 175

Lehmann, Rachel, Edupress Inc, 4810 Forrest Run Rd, Madison, WI 53704 *Toll Free Tel:* 800-835-7978 *Toll Free Fax:* 800-558-9332 *E-mail:* edupressdealers@edupress.com *Web Site:* www.edupress.com, pg 80

Lehmann, Stephanie, Elaine Koster Literary Agency LLC, 55 Central Park West, Suite 6, New York, NY 10023 *Tel:* 212-362-9488 *Fax:* 212-712-0164, pg 560

Lehr, Donald, The Betsy Nolan Literary Agency, 214 W 29 St, Suite 1002, New York, NY 10001 *Tel:* 212-967-8200 *Fax:* 212-967-7292 *E-mail:* dblehr@cs.com, pg 567

Lehto, Bill, Polebridge Press, c/o Willamette University, 900 State St, Salem, OR 97301 *Tel:* 503-375-5323 *E-mail:* orders@westarinstitute.org *Web Site:* www.polebridgepress.com, pg 194

Leibovitch, Earl, Fitzhenry & Whiteside Limited, 195 Allstate Pkwy, Markham, ON L3R 4T8, Canada *Tel:* 905-477-9700 *Toll Free Tel:* 800-387-9776 *Fax:* 905-477-2834 *Toll Free Fax:* 800-260-9777 *E-mail:* bookinfo@fitzhenry.ca; godwit@fitzhenry.ca *Web Site:* www.fitzhenry.ca, pg 484

Leichum, Laura, Georgetown University Press, 3240 Prospect St NW, Suite 250, Washington, DC 20007 *Tel:* 202-687-5889 (busn) *Fax:* 202-687-6340 (edit) *E-mail:* gupress@georgetown.edu *Web Site:* press.georgetown.edu, pg 96

Leifer, Jaime, PublicAffairs, 250 W 57 St, Suite 1321, New York, NY 10107 *Tel:* 212-397-6666 *Toll Free Tel:* 800-343-4499 (orders) *Fax:* 212-397-4277 *E-mail:* publicaffairs@perseusbooks.com *Web Site:* www.publicaffairsbooks.com, pg 200

Leinberger, Anna, Berrett-Koehler Publishers Inc, 1333 Broadway, Suite 1000, Oakland, CA 94612 *Tel:* 510-817-2277 *Fax:* 510-817-2278 *E-mail:* bkpub@bkpub.com *Web Site:* www.bkconnection.com, pg 35

Lerner, Harry J, Millbrook Press, 241 First Ave N, Minneapolis, MN 55401 *Tel:* 612-332-3344 *Toll Free Tel:* 800-328-4929 (US only) *Fax:* 612-332-7615 *Toll Free Fax:* 800-332-1132, pg 157

Lerner, Harry J, Twenty-First Century Books, 241 First Ave N, Minneapolis, MN 55401 *Tel:* 612-332-3344 *Toll Free Tel:* 800-328-4929 *Fax:* 612-332-7615 *Toll Free Fax:* 800-332-1132 *E-mail:* info@lernerbooks.com *Web Site:* www.lernerbooks.com, pg 251

Lerner, Mark, MedBooks, 101 W Buckingham Rd, Richardson, TX 75081-4802 *Tel:* 972-643-1809 *Fax:* 972-643-1859 *E-mail:* medbooks@medbooks.com *Web Site:* www.medbooks.com, pg 153

Lerner, Mark, The Oliver Press Inc, Charlotte Sq, 5707 W 36 St, Minneapolis, MN 55416-2510 *Tel:* 952-926-8981 *Toll Free Tel:* 800-8-OLIVER (865-4837) *Fax:* 952-926-8965 *E-mail:* orders@oliverpress.com *Web Site:* www.oliverpress.com, pg 174

Lerner, Seth, Tom Doherty Associates, LLC, 175 Fifth Ave, 14th fl, New York, NY 10010 *Tel:* 646-307-5151 *Toll Free Tel:* 800-455-0340 *Fax:* 212-388-0191 *E-mail:* firstname.lastname@tor.com *Web Site:* www.tor-forge.com, pg 75

Lerner, Shannon, Business Forms Management Association (BFMA), 1147 Fleetwood Ave, Madison, WI 53716 *Toll Free Tel:* 888-367-3078 *E-mail:* bfma@bfma.org *Web Site:* www.bfma.org, pg 601

LeRoy, Yolanda, Charlesbridge Publishing Inc, 85 Main St, Watertown, MA 02472 *Tel:* 617-926-0329 *Toll Free Tel:* 800-225-3214 *Fax:* 617-926-5720 *Toll Free Fax:* 800-926-5775 *E-mail:* books@charlesbridge.com *Web Site:* www.charlesbridge.com, pg 55

Lesak, Susan, Host Publications, 3408 West Ave, Austin, TX 78705 *Tel:* 512-236-1290 *Fax:* 512-236-1208 *Web Site:* www.hostpublications.com, pg 114

Lesan, Susanna, Pearson Humanities & Social Sciences, 225 River St, Hoboken, NJ 07030-4772 *Tel:* 201-236-7000 *Fax:* 201-236-3400, pg 185

Lescaze, Alexandra, Hillman Prizes in Journalism, 12 W 31 St, 12th fl, New York, NY 10001 *Tel:* 646-448-6413 *Web Site:* www.hillmanfoundation.org, pg 692

Leschner, Alan I, American Association for the Advancement of Science (AAAS), 1200 New York Ave NW, Washington, DC 20005 *Tel:* 202-326-6400 *Web Site:* www.aaas.org, pg 594

Lesko, Marian, Agatha Awards, PO Box 8007, Gaithersburg, MD 20898-8007 *E-mail:* malicedomesticpr@gmail.com *Web Site:* www.malicedomestic.org, pg 665

Leslie, Nathan, Hamilton Stone Editions, PO Box 43, Maplewood, NJ 07040 *Tel:* 973-378-8361 *E-mail:* hstone@hamiltonstone.org *Web Site:* www.hamiltonstone.org, pg 104

Lessiter, Frank, Lessiter Publications, 16655 W Wisconsin Ave, Brookfield, WI 53005 *Tel:* 262-782-4480 *Toll Free Tel:* 800-645-8455 *Fax:* 262-782-1252 *E-mail:* info@lesspub.com *Web Site:* www.lesspub.com, pg 138

Lessiter, Mike, Lessiter Publications, 16655 W Wisconsin Ave, Brookfield, WI 53005 *Tel:* 262-782-4480 *Toll Free Tel:* 800-645-8455 *Fax:* 262-782-1252 *E-mail:* info@lesspub.com *Web Site:* www.lesspub.com, pg 138

Lessne, Donald L, Frederick Fell Publishers Inc, 2131 Hollywood Blvd, Suite 305, Hollywood, FL 33020 *Tel:* 954-925-5242 *E-mail:* fellpub@aol.com (admin only) *Web Site:* www.fellpub.com, pg 92

Letchworth, Lynne, Chalice Press, 483 E Lockwood Ave, Suite 100, St Louis, MO 63119 *Tel:* 314-231-8500 *Toll Free Tel:* 800-366-3383 *Fax:* 314-231-8524; 770-280-4039 (orders) *E-mail:* customerservice@chalicepress.com *Web Site:* www.chalicepress.com, pg 54

Letourneau, Helene, Association Nationale des Editeurs de Livres, 2514 boul Rosemont, Montreal, QC H1Y 1K4, Canada *Tel:* 514-273-8130 *Toll Free Tel:* 866-900-ANEL (900-2635) *E-mail:* info@anel.qc.ca *Web Site:* www.anel.qc.ca, pg 598

Lettice, Jenna, Random House Children's Books, 1745 Broadway, New York, NY 10019 *Tel:* 212-782-9000 *Toll Free Tel:* 800-200-3552 *Fax:* 212-782-9452 *Web Site:* randomhousekids.com, pg 204

Leung, Mona, McGraw-Hill Higher Education, 1333 Burr Ridge Pkwy, Burr Ridge, IL 60527 *Tel:* 630-789-4000 *Toll Free Tel:* 800-338-3987 (cust serv) *Fax:* 614-755-5645 (cust serv) *Web Site:* www.mhhe.com, pg 151

Levay, Rachael, University of Washington Press, 433 Brooklyn Ave NE, Seattle, WA 98195-9570 *Tel:* 206-543-4050 *Toll Free Tel:* 800-537-5487 (orders) *Fax:* 206-543-3932; 410-516-6998 (orders) *E-mail:* uwpress@u.washington.edu *Web Site:* www.washington.edu/uwpress/, pg 260

Levenberg, Rachel, HarperCollins Publishers Sales, 195 Broadway, New York, NY 10007 *Fax:* 212-207-7000 *Web Site:* www.harpercollins.com, pg 106

Leventhal, J P, Hachette Books, 1290 Avenue of the Americas, New York, NY 10019 *Tel:* 212-364-1100 *Web Site:* www.hachettebookgroup.com, pg 102

Leventhal, Josh, Minnesota Historical Society Press, 345 Kellogg Blvd W, St Paul, MN 55102-1906 *Tel:* 651-259-3205; 651-259-3000 *Toll Free Tel:* 800-621-2736 (warehouse) *Fax:* 651-297-1345 *Toll Free Fax:* 800-621-8476 (warehouse) *E-mail:* info-mnhspress@mnhs.org *Web Site:* www.mnhs.org/mnhspress, pg 157

Leverence, John, Television Academy, 5220 Lankershim Blvd, North Hollywood, CA 91601-3109 *Tel:* 818-754-2800 *Fax:* 818-761-2827 *Web Site:* www.emmys.com, pg 620

Leverton, Yossi, Hachai Publishing, 527 Empire Blvd, Brooklyn, NY 11225 *Tel:* 718-633-0100 *Fax:* 718-633-0103 *E-mail:* info@hachai.com *Web Site:* www.hachai.com, pg 102

Levesque, Brigit, Broquet Inc, 97-B, Montee des Bouleaux, St-Constant, QC J5A 1A9, Canada *Tel:* 450-638-3338 *Fax:* 450-638-4338 *E-mail:* info@broquet.qc.ca *Web Site:* www.broquet.qc.ca, pg 474

Levesque, Jennifer, Rodale Inc, 400 S Tenth St, Emmaus, PA 18098 *Tel:* 610-967-5171 *Web Site:* www.rodaleinc.com, pg 210

Levin, David, McGraw-Hill Education, 2 Penn Plaza, New York, NY 10121-2298 *Tel:* 212-904-2000 *E-mail:* customer.service@mcgraw-hill.com *Web Site:* www.mheducation.com; www.mheducation.com/custserv.html, pg 151

Levin, Janet, North Atlantic Books, 2526 Martin Luther King Jr Way, Berkeley, CA 94704 *Tel:* 510-549-4270 *Fax:* 510-549-4276 *Web Site:* www.northatlanticbooks.com, pg 170

Levine, Arthur A, Scholastic Trade Division, 557 Broadway, New York, NY 10012 *Tel:* 212-343-6100; 212-343-4685 (export sales) *Fax:* 212-343-4714 (export sales) *Web Site:* www.scholastic.com, pg 219

Levine, Deborah, The Jeff Herman Agency LLC, 29 Park St, Stockbridge, MA 01262 *Tel:* 413-298-0077 *Fax:* 413-298-8188 *E-mail:* submissions@jeffherman.com *Web Site:* www.jeffherman.com, pg 556

Levine, Ellen, Trident Media Group LLC, 41 Madison Ave, 36th fl, New York, NY 10010 *Tel:* 212-333-1511 *E-mail:* info@tridentmediagroup.com; press@tridentmediagroup.com *Web Site:* www.tridentmediagroup.com, pg 577

Levine, Ellie, Harry N Abrams Inc, 115 W 18 St, 6th fl, New York, NY 10011 *Tel:* 212-206-7715 *Toll Free Tel:* 800-345-1359 *Fax:* 212-519-1210 *E-mail:* abrams@abramsbooks.com *Web Site:* www.abramsbooks.com, pg 3

Levine, Harold, Aslan Publishing, 857 Post Rd, Suite 302, Fairfield, CT 06824 *Tel:* 203-372-0300; 203-374-6224 *Fax:* 203-374-4766 *E-mail:* information@aslanpublishing.com *Web Site:* www.aslanpublishing.com, pg 25

Levine, James, Levine|Greenberg|Rostan Literary Agency Inc, 307 Seventh Ave, Suite 2407, New York, NY 10001 *Tel:* 212-337-0934 *Fax:* 212-337-0948 *Web Site:* lgrliterary.com, pg 561

Levine, Jeanne, Financial Times Press, 225 River St, Hoboken, NJ 07030-4772 *Tel:* 201-236-7000 *Toll Free Tel:* 800-922-0579 (orders) *Web Site:* www.ftpress.com, pg 88

Levine, Jeffrey, Tupelo Press Inc, PO Box 1767, North Adams, MA 01247 *Tel:* 413-664-9611 *Fax:* 413-664-9711 *E-mail:* info@tupelopress.org *Web Site:* www.tupelopress.org, pg 250

Levine, Jonathan D, Prayer Book Press Inc, 1363 Fairfield Ave, Bridgeport, CT 06605 *Tel:* 203-384-2284 *Fax:* 203-579-9109, pg 196

Levine, Katie, HarperCollins Publishers, 195 Broadway, New York, NY 10007 *Tel:* 212-207-7000 *Fax:* 212-207-7145 *Web Site:* www.harpercollins.com, pg 106

Levine, Michael, Westwood Creative Artists Ltd, 94 Harbord St, Toronto, ON M5S 1G6, Canada *Tel:* 416-964-3302 *Fax:* 416-975-9209 *E-mail:* wca_office@wcaltd.com *Web Site:* www.wcaltd.com, pg 579

Levine, Reyna Abigale, National Press Foundation, 1211 Connecticut Ave NW, Suite 310, Washington, DC 20036 *Tel:* 202-663-7280 *Web Site:* nationalpress.org, pg 613

Levine, Ronn, Specialized Information Publishers Association (SIPA), 1090 Vermont Ave NW, 6th fl, Washington, DC 20005-4095 *Web Site:* www.sipaonline.com, pg 620

Levins, Michael S, innovativeKids®, 50 Washington St, Suite 201, Norwalk, CT 06854 *Tel:* 203-838-6400 *E-mail:* info@innovativekids.com *Web Site:* www.innovativekids.com, pg 122

Levinson, Diane, Princeton Architectural Press, 37 E Seventh St, New York, NY 10003 *Tel:* 212-995-9620 *Toll Free Tel:* 800-722-6657 (dist); 800-759-0190 (sales) *Fax:* 212-995-9454 *E-mail:* sales@papress.com *Web Site:* www.papress.com, pg 197

Levinson, Meagan Stacey, Princeton University Press, 41 William St, Princeton, NJ 08540-5237 *Tel:* 609-258-4900 *Toll Free Tel:* 800-777-4726 (orders) *Fax:* 609-258-6305 *Toll Free Fax:* 800-999-1958 *E-mail:* orders@cpfsinc.com *Web Site:* press.princeton.edu, pg 197

Levitan, Jeanie, Bear & Co Inc, One Park St, Rochester, VT 05767 *Tel:* 802-767-3174 *Toll Free Tel:* 800-932-3277 *Fax:* 802-767-3726 *E-mail:* customerservice@InnerTraditions.com *Web Site:* InnerTraditions.com, pg 33

Levitan, Jeanie, Inner Traditions International Ltd, One Park St, Rochester, VT 05767 *Tel:* 802-767-3174 *Toll Free Tel:* 800-246-8648 *Fax:* 802-767-3726 *E-mail:* customerservice@InnerTraditions.com *Web Site:* www.InnerTraditions.com, pg 122

Levithan, David, Scholastic Trade Division, 557 Broadway, New York, NY 10012 *Tel:* 212-343-6100; 212-343-4685 (export sales) *Fax:* 212-343-4714 (export sales) *Web Site:* www.scholastic.com, pg 219

Levitt, Sarah, Zachary Shuster Harmsworth Agency, 1776 Broadway, Suite 1405, New York, NY 10019 *Tel:* 212-765-6900 *Fax:* 212-765-6490 *Web Site:* www.zshliterary.com, pg 580

Levy, Michael, Corporation for Public Broadcasting (CPB), 401 Ninth St NW, Washington, DC 20004-2129 *Tel:* 202-879-9600 *Web Site:* www.cpb.org, pg 604

Levy, Roanie, Access Copyright, The Canadian Copyright Licensing Agency, 56 Wellesley St W, Suite 401A, Toronto, ON M5S 2S3, Canada *Tel:* 416-868-1620 *Toll Free Tel:* 800-893-5777 *Fax:* 416-868-1621 *E-mail:* info@accesscopyright.ca *Web Site:* www.accesscopyright.ca, pg 593

Lew, Cindy, Fine Creative Media, Inc, 322 Eighth Ave, 15th fl, New York, NY 10001 *Tel:* 212-595-3500 *Fax:* 212-595-3779, pg 88

Lewandoski, Joyce, University of Texas Press, 2100 Comal St, Austin, TX 78722 *Tel:* 512-471-7233 *Fax:* 512-232-7178 *E-mail:* utpress@uts.cc.utexas.edu *Web Site:* www.utexaspress.com, pg 244

Lewin, Arianne, GP Putnam's Sons (Children's), 345 Hudson St, New York, NY 10014 *Tel:* 212-366-2000 *Fax:* 212-414-3393 *E-mail:* online@penguinputnam.com *Web Site:* us.penguingroup.com, pg 201

Lewis, Alexandra, Cider Mill Press Book Publishers LLC, 12 Spring St, Kennebunkport, ME 04046 *Tel:* 207-967-8232 *Fax:* 207-967-8233 *Web Site:* www.cidermillpress.com, pg 58

Lewis, Beth A, Augsburg Fortress Publishers, Publishing House of the Evangelical Lutheran Church in America, 510 Marquette Ave S, Minneapolis, MN 55402 *Tel:* 612-330-3300 *Toll Free Tel:* 800-426-0115 (ext 639, subns); 800-328-4648 (orders) *Fax:* 612-330-3455 *E-mail:* info@augsburgfortress.org; copyright@augsburgfortress.org (reprint permission requests); customercare@augsburgfortress.org *Web Site:* www.augsburgfortress.org, pg 27

Lewis, BiBi, Ethan Ellenberg Literary Agency, 548 Broadway, Suite 5-E, New York, NY 10012 *Tel:* 212-431-4554 *E-mail:* agent@ethanellenberg.com *Web Site:* www.ethanellenberg.com, pg 550

Lewis, Brandi, Howard Books, 216 Centerview Dr, Suite 303, Brentwood, TN 37027 *Tel:* 615-873-2080 *Fax:* 615-370-3834 *E-mail:* howardbooks@simonandschuster.com (info) *Web Site:* www.howardpublishing.com, pg 116

Lewis, Brent, Harlequin Enterprises Ltd, 225 Duncan Mill Rd, Don Mills, ON M3B 3K9, Canada *Tel:* 416-445-5860 *Toll Free Tel:* 888-432-4879; 800-370-5838 (ebook inquiries) *E-mail:* customerservice@harlequin.com *Web Site:* www.harlequin.com, pg 487

Lewis, Brian, International Society for Technology in Education, 180 W Eighth Ave, Suite 300, Eugene, OR 97401-2916 *Tel:* 541-302-3777 (intl) *Toll Free Tel:* 800-336-5191 (US & CN) *Fax:* 541-302-3778 *E-mail:* iste@iste.org *Web Site:* www.iste.org; www.iste.org/bookstore (orders); www.isteconference.org, pg 125

Lewis, Daniel, The Overmountain Press, PO Box 1261, Johnson City, TN 37605-1261 *Tel:* 423-926-2691 *Toll Free Tel:* 800-992-2691 (orders) *Fax:* 423-232-1252 *E-mail:* orders@overmtn.com *Web Site:* www.overmtn.com, pg 179

Lewis, Dave, Baker Books, PO Box 6287, Grand Rapids, MI 49516-6287 *Tel:* 616-676-9185 *Toll Free Tel:* 800-877-2665; 800-679-1957 *Fax:* 616-676-9573 *Toll Free Fax:* 800-398-3111 *Web Site:* www.bakerpublishinggroup.com, pg 29

Lewis, Dave, Bethany House Publishers, 11400 Hampshire Ave S, Bloomington, MN 55438 *Tel:* 952-829-2500 *Toll Free Tel:* 800-877-2665 (orders) *Fax:* 952-829-2568 *Toll Free Fax:* 800-398-3111 (orders) *Web Site:* www.bethanyhouse.com; www.bakerpublishinggroup.com, pg 36

Lewis, David, Don Buchwald & Associates Inc, 10 E 44 St, New York, NY 10017 *Tel:* 212-867-1200 *Fax:* 212-867-2434 *E-mail:* info@buchwald.com *Web Site:* www.buchwald.com, pg 545

Lewis, Dottie, National Academies Press (NAP), Lockbox 285, 500 Fifth St NW, Washington, DC 20001 *Tel:* 202-334-3313 *Toll Free Tel:* 888-624-8373 (cust serv) *Fax:* 202-334-2451 (cust serv); 202-334-2793 (mktg dept) *E-mail:* customer_service@nap.edu *Web Site:* www.nap.edu, pg 163

Lewis, Jennifer, Gryphon House Inc, 6848 Leon's Way, Lewisville, NC 27023 *Toll Free Tel:* 800-638-0928 *Toll Free Fax:* 877-638-7576 *E-mail:* info@ghbooks.com *Web Site:* www.gryphonhouse.com, pg 101

Lewis, Kevin, Disney-Hyperion Books, 1101 Flower St, Glendale, CA 91201 *Web Site:* books.disney.com, pg 74

Lewis, Kitty, Brick Books, Box 20081, 431 Boler Rd, London, ON N6K 4G6, Canada *Tel:* 519-657-8579 *E-mail:* brick.books@sympatico.ca *Web Site:* www.brickbooks.ca, pg 473

Lewis, Kristen, Upper Access Inc, 87 Upper Access Rd, Hinesburg, VT 05461 *Tel:* 802-482-2988 *Toll Free Tel:* 800-310-8320 (orders) *Fax:* 802-417-3002 *E-mail:* info@upperaccess.com *Web Site:* www.upperaccess.com, pg 263

Lewis, Marc, Presbyterian Publishing Corp (PPC), 100 Witherspoon St, Louisville, KY 40202 *Tel:* 502-569-5000 *Toll Free Tel:* 800-523-1631 (US only) *Fax:* 502-569-5113 *E-mail:* ppcmail@presbypub.com *Web Site:* www.ppcbooks.com, pg 196

Lewis, Marc, Westminster John Knox Press (WJK), 100 Witherspoon St, Louisville, KY 40202-1396 *Tel:* 502-569-5052 *Toll Free Tel:* 800-227-2872 (US only) *Fax:* 502-569-8308 *Toll Free Fax:* 800-541-5113 (US & CN) *E-mail:* wjk@wjkbooks.com; customer_service@wjkbooks.com *Web Site:* www.wjkbooks.com, pg 269

Lewis, Molly, ZOVA Books, PO Box 21833, Long Beach, CA 90801 *Tel:* 805-426-9682 *Fax:* 562-394-9568 *Web Site:* www.zovabooks.com, pg 280

Lewis, Mrs Morgan, Florida Individual Artist Fellowships, 500 S Bronough St, Tallahassee, FL 32399-0250 *Tel:* 850-245-6470 *Fax:* 850-245-6497 *E-mail:* info@florida-arts.org *Web Site:* www.florida-arts.org, pg 686

Lewis, Nora, College of Liberal & Professional Studies, University of Pennsylvania, 3440 Market St, Suite 100, Philadelphia, PA 19104-3335 *Tel:* 215-898-7326 *Fax:* 215-573-2053 *E-mail:* lps@sas.upenn.edu *Web Site:* www.sas.upenn.edu; www.sas.upenn.edu/lps, pg 659

Lewis, Sherry, The Overmountain Press, PO Box 1261, Johnson City, TN 37605-1261 *Tel:* 423-926-2691 *Toll Free Tel:* 800-992-2691 (orders) *Fax:* 423-232-1252 *E-mail:* orders@overmtn.com *Web Site:* www.overmtn.com, pg 179

Lewis, Stacey, City Lights Publishers, 261 Columbus Ave, San Francisco, CA 94133 *Tel:* 415-362-8193 *Fax:* 415-362-4921 *E-mail:* staff@citylights.com *Web Site:* www.citylights.com, pg 58

Lewis, Sylvia, APA Planners Press, 205 N Michigan Ave, Suite 1200, Chicago, IL 60601 *Tel:* 312-431-9100 *Fax:* 312-786-6700 *E-mail:* customerservice@planning.org *Web Site:* www.planning.org, pg 19

Li, Cherlynne, Touchstone, 1230 Avenue of the Americas, New York, NY 10020, pg 247

Li, Johanna, Simon & Schuster, 1230 Avenue of the Americas, New York, NY 10020 *Tel:* 212-698-7000 *Toll Free Tel:* 800-223-2348 (cust serv); 800-223-2336 (orders) *Toll Free Fax:* 800-943-9831 (orders) *Web Site:* www.simonandschuster.com, pg 225

Li, Karen, Owlkids Books Inc, 10 Lower Spadina Ave, Suite 400, Toronto, ON M5V 2Z2, Canada *Tel:* 416-340-2700 *Fax:* 416-340-9769 *E-mail:* owlkids@owlkids.com *Web Site:* www.owlkidsbooks.com, pg 493

Li, Philip, The Century Foundation, One Whitehall St, 15 fl, New York, NY 10004 *Tel:* 212-452-7700 *Fax:* 212-535-7534 *E-mail:* info@tcf.org *Web Site:* www.tcf.org, pg 623

Li, Philip, The Century Foundation Press, One Whitehall St, 15th fl, New York, NY 10004 *Tel:* 212-452-7700 *Fax:* 212-535-7534 *E-mail:* info@tcf.org *Web Site:* www.tcf.org, pg 54

Libby, Lewis, Hudson Institute, 1015 15 St NW, 6th fl, Washington, DC 20005 *Tel:* 202-974-2400 *Fax:* 202-974-2410 *E-mail:* info@hudson.org *Web Site:* www.hudson.org, pg 116

Liberatore, Arlette, Society for Industrial & Applied Mathematics, 3600 Market St, 6th fl, Philadelphia, PA 19104-2688 *Tel:* 215-382-9800 *Toll Free Tel:* 800-447-7426 *Fax:* 215-386-7999 *E-mail:* siambooks@siam.org *Web Site:* www.siam.org, pg 229

Lichtenstadter, Jill, The Overlook Press, 141 Wooster St, Suite 4-B, New York, NY 10012 *Tel:* 212-673-2210; 845-679-6838 (orders & dist) *Fax:* 212-673-2296 *E-mail:* sales@overlookny.com (orders) *Web Site:* www.overlookpress.com, pg 178

Lieberman, Beth, The Editors Circle, 462 Grove St, Montclair, NJ 07043 *Tel:* 973-783-5082 *E-mail:* query@theeditorscircle.com *Web Site:* www.theeditorscircle.com, pg 525

Lieberman, Robert H, Robert Lieberman Agency, 475 Nelson Rd, Ithaca, NY 14850 *Tel:* 607-273-8801 *Web Site:* www.kewgardensmovie.com/CUPeople/users/rhl10, pg 562

Lieberman, Sarah, Simon & Schuster Audio, 1230 Avenue of the Americas, New York, NY 10020 *Web Site:* audio.simonandschuster.com, pg 225

Liebling, Sara, Disney-Hyperion Books, 1101 Flower St, Glendale, CA 91201 *Web Site:* books.disney.com, pg 74

Liebling, Sara, Disney Publishing Worldwide, 1101 Flower St, Glendale, CA 91201 *Web Site:* books.disney.com, pg 74

Liebmann, Nicholas, Saint Herman Press, 10 Beegum Gorge Rd, Platina, CA 96076 *Tel:* 530-352-4430 *Fax:* 530-352-4432 *E-mail:* stherman@stherman.com *Web Site:* www.stherman.com, pg 214

Liffring-Zug Bourret, Joan, Penfield Books, 215 Brown St, Iowa City, IA 52245 *Tel:* 319-337-9998 *Toll Free Tel:* 800-728-9998 *Fax:* 319-351-6846 *E-mail:* penfield@penfieldbooks.com *Web Site:* www.penfieldbooks.com, pg 186

Liggett, Diane, National Park Service Media Services, 67 Mather Place, Harpers Ferry, WV 25425 *Tel:* 304-535-5050 *Fax:* 304-535-6176 *Web Site:* www.nps.gov/hfc, pg 165

Light, Tan, The Literary Press Group of Canada, 425 Adelaide St W, Suite 700, Toronto, ON M5V 3C1, Canada *Tel:* 416-483-1321 *Fax:* 416-483-2510 *Web Site:* www.lpg.ca, pg 609

Ligon, Linda, Interweave Press LLC, 201 E Fourth St, Loveland, CO 80537 *Toll Free Tel:* 800-272-2193; 800-289-0963 *Fax:* 970-613-4656 *Toll Free Fax:* 888-590-4082 *Web Site:* www.interweave.com, pg 125

Likoff, Laurie, Bloom's Literary Criticism, 132 W 31 St, 17th fl, New York, NY 10001 *Toll Free Tel:* 800-322-8755 *Toll Free Fax:* 800-678-3633 *E-mail:* custserv@factsonfile.com *Web Site:* www.infobasepublishing.com, pg 39

Likoff, Laurie, Chelsea House Publishers, 132 W 31 St, 17th fl, New York, NY 10001 *Tel:* 212-967-8800 *Toll Free Tel:* 800-322-8755 *Fax:* 917-339-0325 *Toll Free Fax:* 800-678-3633 *E-mail:* custserv@factsonfile.com *Web Site:* www.infobasepublishing.com; www.infobaselearning.com, pg 56

Likoff, Laurie, Facts On File, 132 W 31 St, 17th fl, New York, NY 10001 *Tel:* 212-967-8800 *Toll Free Tel:* 800-322-8755 *Toll Free Fax:* 800-678-3633 *E-mail:* custserv@factsonfile.com *Web Site:* infobasepublishing.com, pg 85

Likoff, Laurie, Ferguson Publishing, 132 W 31 St, 17th fl, New York, NY 10001 *Tel:* 212-967-8800 *Toll Free Tel:* 800-322-8755 *Fax:* 917-339-0323 *Toll Free Fax:* 800-678-3633 *E-mail:* custserv@factsonfile.com *Web Site:* infobasepublishing.com, pg 88

Lima, Ashley, Ten Speed Press, 2625 Alcatraz Ave, Unit 505, Berkeley, CA 94705 *Tel:* 510-285-3000 *Toll Free Tel:* 800-841-BOOK (841-2665) *E-mail:* csorders@randomhouse.com *Web Site:* crownpublishing.com/imprint/ten-speed-press, pg 243

Limb, John, OCP, 5536 NE Hassalo St, Portland, OR 97213 *Tel:* 503-281-1191 *Toll Free Tel:* 800-548-8749 *Fax:* 503-282-3486 *Toll Free Fax:* 800-843-8181 *E-mail:* liturgy@ocp.org *Web Site:* www.ocp.org, pg 173

Limb, John, Pastoral Press, 5536 NE Hassalo, Portland, OR 97213-3638 *Tel:* 503-281-1191 *Toll Free Tel:* 800-548-8749 *Fax:* 503-282-3486 *Toll Free Fax:* 800-462-7329 *E-mail:* liturgy@ocp.org *Web Site:* www.ocp.org, pg 183

Limke, Fred, Franciscan Media, 28 W Liberty St, Cincinnati, OH 45202 *Tel:* 513-241-5615 *Toll Free Tel:* 800-488-0488 *Fax:* 513-241-0399 *E-mail:* books@americancatholic.org *Web Site:* www.americancatholic.org; www.franciscanmedia.org, pg 92

Lindeburg, Michael, Professional Publications Inc (PPI), 1250 Fifth Ave, Belmont, CA 94002 *Tel:* 650-593-9119 *Fax:* 650-592-4519 *E-mail:* info@ppi2pass.com *Web Site:* ppi2pass.com; feprep.com, pg 198

Lindeman, Susan, Pennsylvania Historical & Museum Commission, Commonwealth Keystone Bldg, 400 North St, Harrisburg, PA 17120-0053 *Tel:* 717-783-2618 *Toll Free Tel:* 800-747-7790 *Fax:* 717-787-8312 *E-mail:* ra-pabookstore@state.pa.us *Web Site:* www.pabookstore.com; www.phmc.state.pa.us, pg 188

Lindemer, Christine R, Boston Road Communications, 227 Boston Rd, Groton, MA 01450-1959 *Tel:* 978-448-8133 *Web Site:* www.bostonrdcom.com, pg 522

Linden, Judy, The Stonesong Press LLC, 270 W 39 St, No 201, New York, NY 10018 *Tel:* 212-929-4600 *E-mail:* editors@stonesong.com *Web Site:* www.stonesong.com, pg 575

Lindensmith, Chris, Bitingduck Press LLC, 1262 Sunnyoaks Circle, Altadena, CA 91001 *Tel:* 626-679-2494; 626-507-8033 *E-mail:* notifications@bitingduckpress.com *Web Site:* bitingduckpress.com, pg 38

Lindensmith, Chris, Boson Books, 1262 Sunnyoaks Circle, Altadena, CA 91001 *Tel:* 626-507-8033; 626-395-2405 *Web Site:* www.bosonbooks.com; bitingduckpress.com, pg 43

Lindensmith, Gretchen, Bitingduck Press LLC, 1262 Sunnyoaks Circle, Altadena, CA 91001 *Tel:* 626-679-2494; 626-507-8033 *E-mail:* notifications@bitingduckpress.com *Web Site:* bitingduckpress.com, pg 38

Linder, Bertram L, Educational Design Services LLC, 5750 Bou Ave, Suite 1508, North Bethesda, MD 20852 *Tel:* 301-881-8611 *Web Site:* www.educationaldesignservices.com, pg 550

Lindgren, Pat, Lindgren & Smith, 888C Eighth Ave, No 329, New York, NY 10019 *Tel:* 212-397-7330 *E-mail:* info@lindgrensmith.com *Web Site:* lindgrensmith.com, pg 584

Lindman, Chelsea, Sanford J Greenburger Associates Inc, 55 Fifth Ave, New York, NY 10003 *Tel:* 212-206-5600 *Fax:* 212-463-8718 *Web Site:* greenburger.com; www.sjga.com/, pg 555

Lindquist, Evert A, Institute of Public Administration of Canada, 1075 Bay St, Suite 401, Toronto, ON M5S 2B1, Canada *Tel:* 416-924-8787 *Fax:* 416-924-4992 *E-mail:* ntl@ipac.ca *Web Site:* www.ipac.ca; www.iapc.ca, pg 489

Lindquist, Gina, American Society of Civil Engineers (ASCE), 1801 Alexander Bell Dr, Reston, VA 20191-4400 *Tel:* 703-295-6300 *Toll Free Tel:* 800-548-2723 *Fax:* 703-295-6278 *E-mail:* marketing@asce.org *Web Site:* www.asce.org, pg 16

Lindsay, Diana, Sunbelt Publications Inc, 1256 Fayette St, El Cajon, CA 92020-1511 *Tel:* 619-258-4911 *Toll Free Tel:* 800-626-6579 (cust serv) *Fax:* 619-258-4916 *E-mail:* service@sunbeltpub.com; info@sunbeltpub.com *Web Site:* www.sunbeltbooks.com, pg 238

Lindsay, Elizabeth, Alfred A Knopf/Everyman's Library, c/o Random House Inc, 1745 Broadway, New York, NY 10019 *Tel:* 212-751-2600 *Toll Free Tel:* 800-638-6460 *Fax:* 212-572-2593 *Web Site:* www.knopfdoubleday.com, pg 132

Lindsay, Lowell, Sunbelt Publications Inc, 1256 Fayette St, El Cajon, CA 92020-1511 *Tel:* 619-258-4911 *Toll Free Tel:* 800-626-6579 (cust serv) *Fax:* 619-258-4916 *E-mail:* service@sunbeltpub.com; info@sunbeltpub.com *Web Site:* www.sunbeltbooks.com, pg 238

Lindsay, Nick, The MIT Press, 55 Hayward St, Cambridge, MA 02142 *Tel:* 617-253-5255 *Toll Free Tel:* 800-207-8354 (orders) *Fax:* 617-258-6779; 617-577-1545 (orders) *Web Site:* mitpress.mit.edu, pg 158

Lindsey, Charles, Hoover Institution Press, Stanford University, 434 Galvez Mall, Stanford, CA 94305-6003 *Tel:* 650-725-7146; 650-723-3373 *Toll Free Tel:* 800-935-2882 *Fax:* 650-723-8626 *E-mail:* hooverpress@stanford.edu *Web Site:* www.hoover.org; www.hooverpress.org, pg 114

Linebaugh, Andy, National Education Association (NEA), 1201 16 St NW, Washington, DC 20036-3290 *Tel:* 202-833-4000 *Fax:* 202-822-7974 *Web Site:* www.nea.org, pg 164

Ling, Alvina, Little, Brown Books for Young Readers, 1290 Avenue of the Americas, New York, NY 10019 *Tel:* 212-364-1100 *Toll Free Tel:* 800-759-0190 (cust serv) *Web Site:* www.HachetteBookGroup.com, pg 141

Ling, Yuyi, Tumblehome Learning Inc, PO Box 171386, Boston, MA 02117 *E-mail:* info@tumblehomelearning.com *Web Site:* www.tumblehomelearning.com, pg 250

Linick, Andrew S PhD, Copywriter's Council of America (CCA), CCA Bldg, 7 Putter Lane, Middle Island, NY 11953-1920 *Tel:* 631-924-3888 *Fax:* 631-924-8555 *E-mail:* cca4dmcopy@gmail.com *Web Site:* www.AndrewLinickDirectMarketing.com/Copywriters-Council.html; www.NewWorldPressBooks.com, pg 63

Linick, Andrew S PhD, Copywriter's Council of America (CCA), CCA Bldg, 7 Putter Lane, Middle Island, NY 11953-1920 *Tel:* 631-924-8555 *Fax:* 631-924-8555 *E-mail:* cca4dmcopy@gmail.com *Web Site:* www.AndrewLinickDirectMarketing.com/Copywriters-Council.html; www.NewWorldPressBooks.com, pg 523, 604

Linick, Andrew S PhD, Andrew S Linick PhD, The Copyologist®, Linick Bldg, 7 Putter Lane, Middle Island, NY 11953 *Tel:* 631-924-3888 *Fax:* 631-924-8555 *E-mail:* linickgroup@gmail.com *Web Site:* www.AndrewLinickDirectMarketing.com/The-Copyologist.html; www.NewWorldPressBooks.com, pg 529

Link, Kelly, Small Beer Press, 150 Pleasant St, No 306, Easthampton, MA 01027 *Tel:* 413-203-1636 *Fax:* 413-203-1636 *E-mail:* info@smallbeerpress.com *Web Site:* smallbeerpress.com, pg 228

Linka, Ruth, Brindle & Glass Publishing Ltd, 1075 Pendergast St, Suite 103, Victoria, BC V8V 0A1, Canada *Tel:* 250-360-0829 *Fax:* 250-386-0829 *E-mail:* info@brindleandglass.com *Web Site:* www.brindleandglass.com, pg 474

Linker, Damon, University of Pennsylvania Press, 3905 Spruce St, Philadelphia, PA 19104 *Tel:* 215-898-6261 *Fax:* 215-898-0404 *E-mail:* custserv@pobox.upenn.edu *Web Site:* www.pennpress.org, pg 259

Linn, Debra, Algonquin Books, 400 Silver Cedar Ct, Suite 300, Chapel Hill, NC 27514-1585 *Tel:* 919-967-0108 *Fax:* 919-933-0272 *E-mail:* inquiry@algonquin.com *Web Site:* www.workman.com/algonquin, pg 8

Linn, Donald, University of Chicago Press, 1427 E 60 St, Chicago, IL 60637-2954 *Tel:* 773-702-7700; 773-702-7600 *Toll Free Tel:* 800-621-2736 (orders) *Fax:* 773-702-9756; 773-660-2235 (orders); 773-702-2708 *E-mail:* custserv@press.uchicago.edu; marketing@press.uchicago.edu *Web Site:* www.press.uchicago.edu, pg 255

Linney, Mary, Dorothy Canfield Fisher Children's Book Award, 109 State St, Montpelier, VT 05609-0601 *Tel:* 802-828-6954 *Fax:* 802-828-1481 *E-mail:* cbec@state.vt.us *Web Site:* www.dcfaward.org; libraries.vermont.gov/libraries, pg 682

Linsky, Melissa L, Haights Cross Communications®, 136 Madison Ave, 8th fl, New York, NY 10016 *Tel:* 212-209-0500 *Fax:* 212-209-0501 *E-mail:* info@haightscross.com *Web Site:* www.haightscross.com, pg 103

Lintao, Eileen, Public Relations Society of America, 33 Maiden Lane, 11th fl, New York, NY 10038-5150 *Tel:* 212-460-1400 *Fax:* 212-995-0757 *Web Site:* www.prsa.org, pg 617

Lionetti, Kim, BookEnds LLC, 136 Long Hill Rd, Gillette, NJ 07933 *Web Site:* www.bookends-inc.com, pg 543

Liota, Dan, Davies Publishing Inc, 32 S Raymond Ave, Suites 4 & 5, Pasadena, CA 91105-1961 *Tel:* 626-792-3046 *Toll Free Tel:* 877-792-0005 *Fax:* 626-792-5308 *E-mail:* info@daviespublishing.com *Web Site:* daviespublishing.com, pg 71

Lipinski, Michelle, Stanford University Press, 1450 Page Mill Rd, Palo Alto, CA 94304-1124 *Tel:* 650-723-9434 *Fax:* 650-725-3457 *E-mail:* info@sup.org *Web Site:* www.sup.org, pg 233

Lipowski, Vicky, Begell House Inc Publishers, 50 North St, Danbury, CT 06810 *Tel:* 203-456-6161 *Fax:* 203-456-6167 *E-mail:* orders@begellhouse.com *Web Site:* www.begellhouse.com, pg 33

Lipp, Michelle, University of Calgary Press, 2500 University Dr NW, Calgary, AB T2N 1N4, Canada *Tel:* 403-220-7578 *Fax:* 403-282-0085 *E-mail:* ucpress@ucalgary.ca *Web Site:* uofcpress.com, pg 503

Lippel, Roz, Scribner, 1230 Avenue of the Americas, New York, NY 10020, pg 220

Lippert, Kevin C, Princeton Architectural Press, 37 E Seventh St, New York, NY 10003 *Tel:* 212-995-9620 *Toll Free Tel:* 800-722-6657 (dist); 800-759-0190 (sales) *Fax:* 212-995-9454 *E-mail:* sales@papress.com *Web Site:* www.papress.com, pg 197

Lippert, Megan, Hilton Publishing, 1630 45 St, Suite 103, Munster, IN 46321 *Tel:* 219-922-4868 *Fax:* 219-924-6811 *E-mail:* info@hiltonpub.com; orders@hiltonpub.com *Web Site:* www.hiltonpub.com, pg 111

Lippincott, John, Council for Advancement & Support of Education (CASE), 1307 New York Ave NW, Suite 1000, Washington, DC 20005-4701 *Tel:* 202-328-CASE (328-2273) *Fax:* 202-387-4973 *E-mail:* membersupportcenter@case.org *Web Site:* www.case.org, pg 604

Lippman, Barry, LearningExpress LLC, 2 Rector St, 26th fl, New York, NY 10006 *Tel:* 212-995-2566 *Toll Free Tel:* 800-295-9556 (ext 2) *Fax:* 212-995-5512 *E-mail:* customerservice@learningexpressllc.com (cust serv) *Web Site:* www.learningexpressllc.com, pg 136

Lipschultz, Margo, Harlequin Enterprises Ltd, 225 Duncan Mill Rd, Don Mills, ON M3B 3K9, Canada *Tel:* 416-445-5860 *Toll Free Tel:* 888-432-4879; 800-370-5838 (ebook inquiries) *E-mail:* customerservice@harlequin.com *Web Site:* www.harlequin.com, pg 487

Lipscombe, Trevor C, The Catholic University of America Press, 240 Leahy Hall, 620 Michigan Ave NE, Washington, DC 20064 *Tel:* 202-319-5052 *Toll Free Tel:* 800-537-5487 (orders only) *Fax:* 202-319-4985 *E-mail:* cua-press@cua.edu *Web Site:* cuapress.cua.edu, pg 52

Lipskar, Simon, Writers House, 21 W 26 St, New York, NY 10010 *Tel:* 212-685-2400 *Fax:* 212-685-1781 *Web Site:* www.writershouse.com, pg 580

Liss, Laurie, Sterling Lord Literistic Inc, 65 Bleecker St, New York, NY 10012 *Tel:* 212-780-6050 *Fax:* 212-780-6095 *E-mail:* info@sll.com *Web Site:* www.sll.com, pg 575

Liss-Levinson, William PhD, Castle Connolly Medical Ltd, 42 W 24 St, 2nd fl, New York, NY 10010 *Tel:* 212-367-8400 *Fax:* 212-367-0964 *Web Site:* www.castleconnolly.com, pg 51

Litchfield, Malcolm, Ohio State University Press, 180 Pressey Hall, 1070 Carmack Rd, Columbus, OH 43210-1002 *Tel:* 614-292-6930 *Fax:* 614-292-2065 *Toll Free Fax:* 800-621-8476 *E-mail:* info@osupress.org *Web Site:* ohiostatepress.org, pg 174

Lite, Lori, Stress Free Kids®, 2561 Chimney Springs Dr, Marietta, GA 30062 *Toll Free Tel:* 800-841-4204 *Toll Free Fax:* 866-302-2759 *E-mail:* media@stressfreekids.com *Web Site:* www.stressfreekids.com, pg 237

Lite, Rick, Stress Free Kids®, 2561 Chimney Springs Dr, Marietta, GA 30062 *Toll Free Tel:* 800-841-4204 *Toll Free Fax:* 866-302-2759 *E-mail:* media@stressfreekids.com *Web Site:* www.stressfreekids.com, pg 237

Lithgow, Angie, Turner Publishing Co, 200 Fourth Ave N, Suite 950, Nashville, TN 37219 *Tel:* 615-255-BOOK (255-2665) *Fax:* 615-255-5081 *E-mail:* marketing@turnerpublishing.com; submissions@turnerpublishing.com *Web Site:* www.turnerpublishing.com, pg 250

Littell, Amelie, St Martin's Press, LLC, 175 Fifth Ave, New York, NY 10010 *Tel:* 646-307-5151 *Fax:* 212-420-9314 *E-mail:* firstname.lastname@macmillan.com *Web Site:* www.stmartins.com, pg 215

Little, Caroline H, Newspaper Association of America (NAA), 4401 Wilson Blvd, Suite 900, Arlington, VA 22203 *Tel:* 571-366-1000 *Web Site:* www.naa.org, pg 614

Little, Joseph R, American Literacy Council, 1441 Mariposa Ave, Boulder, CO 80302 *Tel:* 303-440-7385 *Web Site:* www.americanliteracy.com, pg 595

Little, Nadine, University of Hawaii Press, 2840 Kolowalu St, Honolulu, HI 96822 *Tel:* 808-956-8255 *Toll Free Tel:* 888-UHPRESS (847-7377) *Fax:* 808-988-6052 *Toll Free Fax:* 800-650-7811 *E-mail:* uhpbooks@hawaii.edu *Web Site:* www.uhpress.hawaii.edu, pg 256

Littlefield, Alex, Houghton Mifflin Harcourt Trade & Reference Division, 222 Berkeley St, Boston, MA 02116 *Tel:* 617-351-5000 *Toll Free Tel:* 800-225-3362 *Web Site:* www.hmhco.com, pg 115

Littlefield, Barb, Thorndike Press, 10 Water St, Suite 310, Waterville, ME 04901 *Toll Free Tel:* 800-233-1244 (ext 4, cust serv/orders) *Toll Free Fax:* 800-558-4676 (orders) *E-mail:* gale.printorders@cengage.com; international@cengage.com (cust orders outside US & CN) *Web Site:* thorndike.gale.com, pg 245

Litton, William, Wag's Revue Writers' Contest, 2865 W Lyndale St, Suite 1, Chicago, IL 60647 *E-mail:* editors@wagsrevue.com *Web Site:* www.wagsrevue.com, pg 734

Litwack, Lisa, Gallery Books, 1230 Avenue of the Americas, New York, NY 10020 *Toll Free Tel:* 800-456-6798 *Fax:* 212-698-7284 *E-mail:* consumer.customerservice@simonandschuster.com *Web Site:* www.simonsays.com, pg 94

Liu, George, DC Canada Education Publishing (DCCED), 180 Metcalfe St, Suite 204, Ottawa, ON K2P 1P5, Canada *Tel:* 613-565-8885 *Toll Free Tel:* 888-565-0262 *Fax:* 613-565-8881 *E-mail:* info@dc-canada.ca *Web Site:* www.dc-canada.ca, pg 478

Liu, Ingsu, W W Norton & Company Inc, 500 Fifth Ave, New York, NY 10110-0017 *Tel:* 212-354-5500 *Toll Free Tel:* 800-233-4830 (orders & cust serv) *Fax:* 212-869-0856 *Toll Free Fax:* 800-458-6515 *Web Site:* www.wwnorton.com, pg 171

Liu, Newton, Bridge to Asia, 1505 Juanita Way, Berkeley, CA 94702-1103 *Tel:* 510-665-3998 *E-mail:* asianet@bridge.org *Web Site:* www.bridge.org, pg 623

Livesey, Magdalen B, Cortina Institute of Languages, 9 Hollyhock Rd, Wilton, CT 06897 *Tel:* 203-762-2510 *Toll Free Tel:* 800-245-2145 *Fax:* 203-762-2514 *Web Site:* www.cortina-languages.com, pg 64

Livesey, Magdalen B, Cortina Learning International Inc (CLI), 9 Hollyhock Rd, Wilton, CT 06897 *Tel:* 203-762-2510 *Toll Free Tel:* 800-245-2145 *Fax:* 203-762-2514 *E-mail:* info@cortinalearning.com *Web Site:* www.cortinalearning.com, pg 64

Lizotte, Donald, VLB Editeur Inc, 1010, Rue de la Gauchetiere Est, Montreal, QC H2L 2N5, Canada *Tel:* 514-523-7993 *Fax:* 514-282-7530 *Web Site:* www.edvlb.com, pg 504

Lizzi, Marian, Perigee Books, 375 Hudson St, New York, NY 10014 *Tel:* 212-366-2000 *Fax:* 212-366-2365 *E-mail:* perigeebooks@us.penguingroup.com *Web Site:* www.penguin.com, pg 189

Llosa, Genoveva, HarperCollins General Books Group, 195 Broadway, New York, NY 10007 *Tel:* 212-207-7000 *Web Site:* www.harpercollins.com, pg 105

Lloyd, Casey, Random House Children's Books, 1745 Broadway, New York, NY 10019 *Tel:* 212-782-9000 *Toll Free Tel:* 800-200-3552 *Fax:* 212-782-9452 *Web Site:* randomhousekids.com, pg 203

Lloyd, Dennis, University of Wisconsin Press, 1930 Monroe St, 3rd fl, Madison, WI 53711-2059 *Tel:* 608-263-0668 *Toll Free Tel:* 800-621-2736 (orders) *Fax:* 608-263-1173 *Toll Free Fax:* 800-621-2736 (orders) *E-mail:* uwiscpress@uwpress.wisc.edu (main off) *Web Site:* www.wisc.edu/wisconsinpress, pg 260

Lloyd, Kate, Scribner, 1230 Avenue of the Americas, New York, NY 10020, pg 220

Lloyd, Timothy, Opie Prize, Ohio State Univ, Mershon Ctr, 1501 Neil Ave, Columbus, OH 43201-2602 *Tel:* 614-292-3375 *Fax:* 614-292-2407 *Web Site:* www.afsnet.org/aboutAFS/AFSprizes.cfm, pg 715

Lloyd-Sidle, Elena, Fons Vitae, 49 Mockingbird Valley Dr, Louisville, KY 40207-1366 *Tel:* 502-897-3641 *Fax:* 502-893-7373 *E-mail:* fonsvitaeky@aol.com *Web Site:* www.fonsvitae.com, pg 90

Lo Brutto, Patrick, Philip K Dick Award, PO Box 3447, Hoboken, NJ 07030 *Tel:* 201-876-2551 *Web Site:* www.philipkdickaward.org, pg 681

Lo Frumento, John, American Society of Composers, Authors & Publishers (ASCAP), 1900 Broadway, New York City, NY 10023 *Tel:* 212-621-6000 *Toll Free Tel:* 800-952-7227 *Fax:* 212-612-8453 *E-mail:* info@ascap.com *Web Site:* www.ascap.com, pg 596

Lobdell, Jim, Balance Sports Publishing LLC, 195 Lucero Way, Portola Valley, CA 94028 *Tel:* 650-561-9586 *Fax:* 650-391-9850 *E-mail:* info@balancesportspublishing.com *Web Site:* www.balancesportspublishing.com, pg 29

Lobynko, Anastasia, AZ Books LLC, 320 Fifth Ave, New York, NY 10001 *Toll Free Tel:* 888-945-7723 *Toll Free Fax:* 888-945-7724 *Web Site:* www.azbooksusa.com, pg 29

Lochner, Wendy, Columbia University Press, 61 W 62 St, New York, NY 10023 *Tel:* 212-459-0600 *Toll Free Tel:* 800-944-8648 *Fax:* 212-459-3678 *E-mail:* cup_book@columbia.edu (orders & cust serv) *Web Site:* cup.columbia.edu, pg 61

Lockard, Eric, Salina Bookshelf Inc, 3120 N Caden Ct, Suite 4, Flagstaff, AZ 86004 *Toll Free Tel:* 877-527-0070 *Fax:* 928-526-0386 *Web Site:* www.salinabookshelf.com, pg 215

Locke, Charlene, Davies Publishing Inc, 32 S Raymond Ave, Suites 4 & 5, Pasadena, CA 91105-1961 *Tel:* 626-792-3046 *Toll Free Tel:* 877-792-0005 *Fax:* 626-792-5308 *E-mail:* info@daviespublishing.com *Web Site:* daviespublishing.com, pg 71

Locke, Terry, Loyola Press, 3441 N Ashland Ave, Chicago, IL 60657 *Tel:* 773-281-1818 *Toll Free Tel:* 800-621-1008 *Fax:* 773-281-0555 (cust serv); 773-281-4129 (edit) *E-mail:* customerservice@loyolapress.com *Web Site:* www.loyolapress.com, pg 144

Lockhart, Matt, Standard Publishing, 8805 Governors Hill Dr, Suite 400, Cincinnati, OH 45249 *Tel:* 513-931-4050 *Toll Free Tel:* 800-543-1353 *Fax:* 513-931-0950 *Toll Free Fax:* 877-867-5751 *E-mail:* customerservice@standardpub.com *Web Site:* www.standardpub.com, pg 233

Lockhart, Robert, University of Pennsylvania Press, 3905 Spruce St, Philadelphia, PA 19104 *Tel:* 215-898-6261 *Fax:* 215-898-0404 *E-mail:* custserv@pobox.upenn.edu *Web Site:* www.pennpress.org, pg 259

Lockley, Beth, Penguin Random House Canada Limited, 320 Front St W, Suite 1400, Toronto, ON M5V 3B6, Canada *Tel:* 416-364-4449 *Toll Free Tel:* 888-523-9292 (cust serv) *Fax:* 416-364-6863; 416-364-6653 (subs rts) *Web Site:* penguinrandomhouse.ca, pg 495

Locks, Sueyun, Locks Art Publications/Locks Gallery, 600 Washington Sq S, Philadelphia, PA 19106 *Tel:* 215-629-1000 *E-mail:* info@locksgallery.com *Web Site:* www.locksgallery.com, pg 142

Lockwood, Karen, Syracuse University Press, 621 Skytop Rd, Suite 110, Syracuse, NY 13244-5290 *Tel:* 315-443-5534 *Toll Free Tel:* 800-365-8929 (cust serv) *Fax:* 315-443-5545 *E-mail:* supress@syr.edu *Web Site:* syracuseuniversitypress.syr.edu, pg 239

Lodge, Anne, Stackpole Books, 5067 Ritter Rd, Mechanicsburg, PA 17055 *Tel:* 717-796-0411 *Toll Free Tel:* 800-732-3669 *Fax:* 717-796-0412 *Web Site:* www.stackpolebooks.com, pg 233

Lodi, Rachel, Penguin Young Readers Group, 345 Hudson St, New York, NY 10014 *Tel:* 212-366-2000 *E-mail:* online@penguinputnam.com *Web Site:* www.penguinputnam.com; us.penguingroup.com, pg 188

Lodwick, Kathleen, EastBridge, 70 New Canaan Ave, Norwalk, CT 06850 *Tel:* 203-855-9125 *Fax:* 203-857-0730 *E-mail:* asia@eastbridgebooks.org; ask@eastbridgebooks.org *Web Site:* www.eastbridgebooks.org, pg 78

Loeb, Sharon, McGraw-Hill/Irwin, 1333 Burr Ridge Pkwy, Burr Ridge, IL 60527 *Tel:* 630-789-4000 *Toll Free Tel:* 800-338-3987 (cust serv) *Fax:* 630-789-6942; 614-755-5645 (cust serv) *Web Site:* www.mhhe.com, pg 152

Loedel, Daniel, Scribner, 1230 Avenue of the Americas, New York, NY 10020, pg 220

Loeding, Deborah V, H W Wilson, 2 University Plaza, Suite 310, Hackensack, NJ 07601 *Tel:* 201-968-0500 *Toll Free Tel:* 800-221-1592 *Fax:* 201-968-0511 *E-mail:* info@hwwilsoninprint.com; csr@hwwilsoninprint.com; information@ebscohost.com *Web Site:* www.hwwilsoninprint.com; www.ebscohost.com/wilson, pg 273

Loehnen, Ben, Simon & Schuster, 1230 Avenue of the Americas, New York, NY 10020 *Tel:* 212-698-7000 *Toll Free Tel:* 800-223-2348 (cust serv); 800-223-2336 (orders) *Toll Free Fax:* 800-943-9831 (orders) *Web Site:* www.simonandschuster.com, pg 225

Loehr, Julie L, Michigan State University Press (MSU Press), 1405 S Harrison Rd, Suite 25, East Lansing, MI 48823 *Tel:* 517-355-9543 *Fax:* 517-432-2611 *Toll Free Fax:* 800-678-2120 *E-mail:* msupress@msu.edu *Web Site:* www.msupress.msu.edu, pg 156

Loehr, Mallory, Random House Children's Books, 1745 Broadway, New York, NY 10019 *Tel:* 212-782-9000 *Toll Free Tel:* 800-200-3552 *Fax:* 212-782-9452 *Web Site:* randomhousekids.com, pg 203

Loertscher, David V, Hi Willow Research & Publishing, 123 E Second Ave, Suite 1106, Salt Lake City, UT 84103 *Tel:* 801-532-1165 *E-mail:* sales@lmcsource.com *Web Site:* www.lmcsource.com; www.davidvl.org, pg 111

Loerzel, Robert, The Society of Midland Authors (SMA), PO Box 10419, Chicago, IL 60610 *E-mail:* info@midlandauthors.com *Web Site:* www.midlandauthors.com, pg 619

Loerzel, Robert, The Society of Midland Authors Awards, 530 Michigan Ave, Evanston, IL 60202 *E-mail:* info@midlandauthors.com *Web Site:* www.midlandauthors.com, pg 729

Loesche, Kerri, Group Publishing Inc, 1515 Cascade Ave, Loveland, CO 80538 *Tel:* 970-669-3836 *Toll Free Tel:* 800-447-1070 *Fax:* 970-292-4373 *E-mail:* info@group.com *Web Site:* www.group.com, pg 101

Loewen, Darleen, PrairieView Press, PO Box 460, Rosenort, MB R0G-1W0, Canada *Tel:* 204-327-6543 *Toll Free Tel:* 800-477-7377 *Fax:* 204-327-6544 *Web Site:* www.prairieviewpress.com, pg 496

Loewenthal, Linda, David Black Agency, 335 Adams St, 27th fl, Suite 2707, Brooklyn, NY 11201 *Tel:* 718-852-5500 *Fax:* 718-852-5539 *Web Site:* www.davidblackagency.com, pg 542

Logan, Beverly, Pacific Press Publishing Association, 1350 N Kings Rd, Nampa, ID 83687-3193 *Tel:* 208-465-2500 *Toll Free Tel:* 800-447-7377 *Fax:* 208-465-2531 *Web Site:* www.pacificpress.com, pg 180

Logan, Emily, Houghton Mifflin Harcourt, 222 Berkeley St, Boston, MA 02116 *Tel:* 617-351-5000 *Toll Free Tel:* 800-225-5425 (K-12 educ materials); 800-323-9540 (assessment materials); 877-219-1537 (SkillsTutor); 888-242-6747 (Destination; Earobics; Edmark; Learning Village; Riverdeep); 800-225-3362 (Houghton Mifflin Harcourt Trade & Reference Publishers) *Toll Free Fax:* 800-269-5232 *E-mail:* customerservice@hmhpub.com *Web Site:* www.hmhco.com, pg 115

Loggia, Wendy, Random House Children's Books, 1745 Broadway, New York, NY 10019 *Tel:* 212-782-9000 *Toll Free Tel:* 800-200-3552 *Fax:* 212-782-9452 *Web Site:* randomhousekids.com, pg 203

Loh, Cindy, Bloomsbury Publishing Inc, 1385 Broadway, 5th fl, New York, NY 10018 *Tel:* 212-419-5300 *E-mail:* marketingusa@bloomsbury.com; adultpublicityusa@bloomsbury.com; askacademic@bloomsbury.com *Web Site:* www.bloomsbury.com, pg 40

Lohia, Shefali, Little Bee Books, 853 Broadway, Suite 2014, New York, NY 10003 *E-mail:* info@littlebeebooks.com *Web Site:* www.littlebeebooks.com, pg 140

Loiselle, Louise, Flammarion Quebec, 375 Ave Laurier W, Montreal, QC H2V 2K3, Canada *Tel:* 514-277-8807 *Fax:* 514-278-2085 *E-mail:* info@flammarion.qc.ca *Web Site:* www.flammarion.qc.ca, pg 484

Loney, Brian, Canadian Institute of Chartered Accountants-CICA (L'Institut Canadien des Comptables Agrees), 277 Wellington St W, Toronto, ON M5V 3H2, Canada *Tel:* 416-977-3222 *Toll Free Tel:* 800-268-3793 (CN orders) *Fax:* 416-977-8585 *E-mail:* orders@cica.ca *Web Site:* www.cpacanada.ca, pg 475

Long, Ben, Dancing Dakini Press, 77 Morning Sun Dr, Sedona, AZ 86336 *Tel:* 928-852-0129 *E-mail:* editor@dancingdakinipress.com *Web Site:* www.dancingdakinipress.com, pg 70

Long, Bob, Thinkers' Press Inc, 1524 Le Claire St, Davenport, IA 52803 *Tel:* 563-271-6657 *E-mail:* info@chessbutler.com *Web Site:* www.thinkerspressinc.com, pg 245

Long, Candace, Mature Women Scholarship Grant - Art/Letters/Music, c/o National Pen Women-Scholarship, Pen Arts Bldg, 1300 17 St NW, Washington, DC 20036-1973 *Tel:* 202-785-1997 *Fax:* 202-452-8868 *E-mail:* contact@nlapw.org *Web Site:* www.nlapw.org, pg 706

Long, Candace, National League of American Pen Women, c/o National Pen Women-Scholarship, Pen Arts Bldg, 1300 17 St NW, Washington, DC 20036-1973 *Tel:* 202-785-1997 *Fax:* 202-452-8868 *E-mail:* contact@nlapw.org *Web Site:* www.nlapw.org, pg 612

Long, Chris, Howard Books, 216 Centerview Dr, Suite 303, Brentwood, TN 37027 *Tel:* 615-873-2080 *Fax:* 615-370-3834 *E-mail:* howardbooks@simonandschuster.com (info) *Web Site:* www.howardpublishing.com, pg 116

Long, Christopher G, ISI Books, 3901 Centerville Rd, Wilmington, DE 19807-1938 *Tel:* 302-652-4600 *Toll Free Tel:* 800-526-7022 *Fax:* 302-652-1760 *E-mail:* info@isi.org; isibooks@isi.org *Web Site:* www.isibooks.org, pg 125

Long, Donna, HRD Press, 22 Amherst Rd, Amherst, MA 01002-9709 *Tel:* 413-253-3488 *Toll Free Tel:* 800-822-2801 *Fax:* 413-253-3490 *E-mail:* info@hrdpress.com; customerservice@hrdpress.com *Web Site:* www.hrdpress.com, pg 116

Long, Jennifer, Gallery Books, 1230 Avenue of the Americas, New York, NY 10020 *Toll Free Tel:* 800-456-6798 *Fax:* 212-698-7284 *E-mail:* consumer.customerservice@simonandschuster.com *Web Site:* www.simonsays.com, pg 94

Long, Karen R, The Anisfield-Wolf Book Awards, 1422 Euclid Ave, Suite 1300, Cleveland, OH 44115 *Tel:* 216-861-3810 *Fax:* 216-861-1729 *E-mail:* awinfo@clevefdn.org *Web Site:* www.anisfield-wolf.org; www.clevelandfoundation.org, pg 667

Longino, Karen, Howard Books, 216 Centerview Dr, Suite 303, Brentwood, TN 37027 *Tel:* 615-873-2080 *Fax:* 615-370-3834 *E-mail:* howardbooks@simonandschuster.com (info) *Web Site:* www.howardpublishing.com, pg 116

Longmeyer, Michael, Gallopade International Inc, 611 Hwy 74 S, Suite 2000, Peachtree City, GA 30269 *Tel:* 770-631-4222 *Toll Free Tel:* 800-536-2GET (536-2438) *Fax:* 770-631-4810 *Toll Free Fax:* 800-871-2979 *E-mail:* customerservice@gallopade.com *Web Site:* www.gallopade.com, pg 94

Longo, Edward, Recorded Books LLC, 270 Skipjack Rd, Prince Frederick, MD 20678 *Tel:* 410-535-5590 *Toll Free Tel:* 800-638-1304; 877-732-2898 *Fax:* 410-535-5499 *E-mail:* customerservice@recordedbooks.com *Web Site:* www.recordedbooks.com, pg 206

Longobardi, Cara, Empire State Award for Excellence in Literature for Young People, 6021 State Farm Rd, Guilderland, NY 12084 *Tel:* 518-432-6952 *Toll Free Tel:* 800-252-6952 *Fax:* 518-427-1697 *E-mail:* info@nyla.org *Web Site:* www.nyla.org, pg 684

Loomis, Gloria, Watkins/Loomis Agency Inc, PO Box 20925, New York, NY 10025 *Tel:* 212-532-0080 *Fax:* 646-383-2449 *E-mail:* assistant@watkinsloomis.com *Web Site:* www.watkinsloomis.com, pg 579

Loomis, Michael J, Graphic World Publishing Services, 11687 Adie Rd, St Louis, MO 63043 *Tel:* 314-567-9854 *Fax:* 314-567-7178 *E-mail:* quote@gwinc.com *Web Site:* www.gwinc.com, pg 527

Loose, Emily, Words into Print, 57 Prince St, Suite 4R, New York, NY 10012 *Tel:* 212-741-1393 *Fax:* 419-441-1393 *E-mail:* query@wordsintoprint.org *Web Site:* www.wordsintoprint.org, pg 536

Loosvelt, Derek, Vault.com Inc, 132 W 31 St, 17th fl, New York, NY 10001 *Tel:* 212-366-4212 *Toll Free Tel:* 800-535-2074 *Fax:* 212-366-6117 (cust serv) *E-mail:* editors@vault.com; customerservice@vault.com *Web Site:* www.vault.com, pg 265

Lopes, David, Gingko Press Inc, 1321 Fifth St, Berkeley, CA 94710 *Tel:* 510-898-1195 *Fax:* 510-898-1196 *E-mail:* books@gingkopress.com *Web Site:* www.gingkopress.com, pg 97

Lopez, Vanessa, Insight Editions, 800 "A" St, San Rafael, CA 94901 *Tel:* 415-526-1370 *Toll Free Tel:* 800-809-3792 *Toll Free Fax:* 866-509-0515 *E-mail:* info@insighteditions.com *Web Site:* www.insighteditions.com, pg 122

Lord, Sterling, Sterling Lord Literistic Inc, 65 Bleecker St, New York, NY 10012 *Tel:* 212-780-6050 *Fax:* 212-780-6095 *E-mail:* info@sll.com *Web Site:* www.sll.com, pg 575

Lore, Matthew, The Experiment, 220 East 23 St, Suite 301, New York, NY 10010-4674 *Tel:* 212-889-1659 *E-mail:* info@theexperimentpublishing.com *Web Site:* www.theexperimentpublishing.com, pg 85

Lorenz, Geoff, Show What You Know® Publishing, A Lorenz Company, 501 E Third St, Dayton, OH 45402 *Tel:* 614-764-1211; 937-228-6118 *Toll Free Tel:* 877-PASSING (727-7464) *Fax:* 937-233-2042 *E-mail:* info@swykonline.com *Web Site:* www.swykonline.com; www.lorenzeducationalpress.com, pg 224

Lorenz, Ken, Standard Publishing, 8805 Governors Hill Dr, Suite 400, Cincinnati, OH 45249 *Tel:* 513-931-4050 *Toll Free Tel:* 800-543-1353 *Fax:* 513-931-0950 *Toll Free Fax:* 877-867-5751 *E-mail:* customerservice@standardpub.com *Web Site:* www.standardpub.com, pg 233

Lorenz, Tom, Cottonwood Press, University of Kansas, Kansas Union, Rm 400, 1301 Jayhawk Blvd, Lawrence, KS 66045 *Tel:* 785-864-4520 *Web Site:* www.englishcw.ku.edu/cottonwood, pg 64

Lori, Jennifer, PRISM international Literary Non-Fiction Contest, University of British Columbia, Buch E462, 1866 Main Mall, Vancouver, BC V6T 1Z1, Canada *Tel:* 778-822-2514 *Fax:* 778-822-3616 *E-mail:* prismwritingcontest@gmail.com *Web Site:* www.prismmagazine.ca, pg 721

Lori, Jennifer, PRISM international Poetry Contest, University of British Columbia, Buch E462, 1866 Main Mall, Vancouver, BC V6T 1Z1, Canada *Tel:* 778-822-2514 *Fax:* 778-822-3616 *E-mail:* prismwritingcontest@gmail.com *Web Site:* www.prismmagazine.ca, pg 721

Lori, Jennifer, PRISM international Short Fiction Contest, University of British Columbia, Buch E462, 1866 Main Mall, Vancouver, BC V6T 1Z1, Canada *Tel:* 778-822-2514 *Fax:* 778-822-3616 *E-mail:* prismwritingcontest@gmail.com *Web Site:* www.prismmagazine.ca, pg 721

Lorimer, James, James Lorimer & Co Ltd, Publishers, 317 Adelaide St W, Suite 1002, Toronto, ON M5V 1P9, Canada *Tel:* 416-362-4762 *Fax:* 416-362-3939 *Web Site:* www.lorimer.ca, pg 490

Lotman, Lynda, A+ English LLC/Book-Editing.com/Book Editing Associates, PO Box 1369, Mansfield, TX 76063 *Tel:* 469-789-3030 *E-mail:* editingnetwork@gmail.com *Web Site:* www.editing-writing.com; www.book-editing.com; www.HelpWithStatistics; www.apawriting.com; childrensbookeditors.com; dissertationeditor.com, pg 519

Lotowycz, Randall, Workman Publishing Co Inc, 225 Varick St, 9th fl, New York, NY 10014-4381 *Tel:* 212-254-5900 *Toll Free Tel:* 800-722-7202 *Fax:* 212-254-8098 *E-mail:* info@workman.com *Web Site:* www.workman.com, pg 275

Lott, Peter, Lott Representatives, PO Box 3607, New York, NY 10163 *Tel:* 212-755-5737 *Web Site:* www.lottreps.com, pg 584

Lotto, Elizabeth, Gallery Books, 1230 Avenue of the Americas, New York, NY 10020 *Toll Free Tel:* 800-456-6798 *Fax:* 212-698-7284 *E-mail:* consumer.customerservice@simonandschuster.com *Web Site:* www.simonsays.com, pg 94

Lotz, Karen, Candlewick Press, 99 Dover St, Somerville, MA 02144-2825 *Tel:* 617-661-3330 *Fax:* 617-661-0565 *E-mail:* bigbear@candlewick.com; salesinfo@candlewick.com *Web Site:* www.candlewick.com, pg 49

Loudon, John, Yale University Press, 302 Temple St, New Haven, CT 06511-8909 *Tel:* 203-432-0960; 203-432-0966 (sales); 401-531-2800 (cust serv) *Toll Free Tel:* 800-405-1619 (cust serv) *Fax:* 203-432-0948; 203-432-8485 (sales); 401-531-2801 (cust serv) *Toll Free Fax:* 800-406-9145 (cust serv) *E-mail:* sales.press@yale.edu (sales); customer.care@trilateral.org (cust serv) *Web Site:* www.yalebooks.com; yalepress.yale.edu/yupbooks, pg 278

Loughlin, Thomas G, American Society of Mechanical Engineers (ASME), 2 Park Ave, New York, NY 10016-5990 *Tel:* 212-591-7000 *Toll Free Tel:* 800-843-2763 (cust serv-US, CN & Mexico) *Fax:* 212-591-7674; 973-882-8113 (cust serv); 973-882-1717 (orders & inquiries) *E-mail:* infocentral@asme.org *Web Site:* www.asme.org, pg 16

Loughman, Kelly, Holiday House Inc, 425 Madison Ave, New York, NY 10017 *Tel:* 212-688-0085 *Fax:* 212-421-6134 *E-mail:* holiday@holidayhouse.com *Web Site:* www.holidayhouse.com, pg 113

Loughrey, Mary, Looseleaf Law Publications Inc, 43-08 162 St, Flushing, NY 11358 *Tel:* 718-359-5559 *Toll Free Tel:* 800-647-5547 *Fax:* 718-539-0941 *E-mail:* info@looseleaf.com *Web Site:* www.looseleaflaw.com, pg 143

Loughrey, Michael L, Looseleaf Law Publications Inc, 43-08 162 St, Flushing, NY 11358 *Tel:* 718-359-5559 *Toll Free Tel:* 800-647-5547 *Fax:* 718-539-0941 *E-mail:* info@looseleaf.com *Web Site:* www.looseleaflaw.com, pg 143

Louie, Karen, Harlequin Enterprises Ltd, 225 Duncan Mill Rd, Don Mills, ON M3B 3K9, Canada *Tel:* 416-445-5860 *Toll Free Tel:* 888-432-4879; 800-370-5838 (ebook inquiries) *E-mail:* customerservice@harlequin.com *Web Site:* www.harlequin.com, pg 487

Lourie, Dick, Hanging Loose Press, 231 Wyckoff St, Brooklyn, NY 11217 *Tel:* 347-529-4738 *Fax:* 347-227-8215 *E-mail:* print225@aol.com *Web Site:* www.hangingloosepress.com, pg 104

Lourie, Iven, Gateways Books & Tapes, PO Box 370, Nevada City, CA 95959 *Tel:* 530-271-2239 *Toll Free Tel:* 800-869-0658 *Fax:* 530-272-0184 *E-mail:* info@gatewaysbooksandtapes.com *Web Site:* www.gatewaysbooksandtapes.com; www.retrosf.com (Retro Science Fiction Imprint), pg 95

Lovaas, Eric, HarperCollins Publishers Sales, 195 Broadway, New York, NY 10007 *Fax:* 212-207-7000 *Web Site:* www.harpercollins.com, pg 106

Love, Hannah, University of California Press, 2120 Berkeley Way, Berkeley, CA 94704-1012 *Tel:* 510-642-4247 *Fax:* 510-643-7127 *E-mail:* askucp@ucpress.edu (books); customerservice@ucpressjournals.com *Web Site:* www.ucpress.edu, pg 255

Love, Robert, Square One Publishers Inc, 115 Herricks Rd, Garden City Park, NY 11040 *Tel:* 516-535-2010 *Toll Free Tel:* 877-900-BOOK (900-2665) *Fax:* 516-535-2014 *E-mail:* sq1publish@aol.com *Web Site:* www.squareonepublishers.com, pg 232

Love, Shelby, Mill Mountain Theatre, Center in the Square, 2nd fl, One Market Sq SE, Roanoke, VA 24011-1437 *Tel:* 540-224-1250 (ext 7307) *Web Site:* www.millmountain.org, pg 707

Love, Stanley F, Love Publishing Co, 9101 E Kenyon Ave, Suite 2200, Denver, CO 80237 *Tel:* 303-221-7333 *Toll Free Tel:* 877-240-6396 *Fax:* 303-221-7444 *E-mail:* lpc@lovepublishing.com *Web Site:* www.lovepublishing.com, pg 143

Lovegrove, Stephanie, Janet B McCabe Poetry Prize, 1041 N Taft Hill Rd, Fort Collins, CO 80521 *Tel:* 970-449-2726 *E-mail:* editor@ruminatemagazine.org *Web Site:* www.ruminatemagazine.com, pg 706

Lovegrove, Stephanie, William Van Dyke Short Story Prize, 1041 N Taft Hill Rd, Fort Collins, CO 80521 *Tel:* 970-449-2726 *E-mail:* editor@ruminatemagazine.org *Web Site:* www.ruminatemagazine.com, pg 733

Lovegrove, Stephanie, VanderMey Nonfiction Prize, 1041 N Taft Hill Rd, Fort Collins, CO 80521 *Tel:* 970-449-2726 *E-mail:* editor@ruminatemagazine.org *Web Site:* www.ruminatemagazine.com, pg 733

Lovell, Deborah, Taylor & Francis Inc, 325 Chestnut St, Suite 800, Philadelphia, PA 20036-1802 *Tel:* 215-625-8900 *Toll Free Tel:* 800-354-1420 *Fax:* 215-625-2940 *E-mail:* customer.service@taylorandfrancis.com *Web Site:* www.taylorandfrancis.com, pg 241

Lovett, Erin, W W Norton & Company Inc, 500 Fifth Ave, New York, NY 10110-0017 *Tel:* 212-354-5500 *Toll Free Tel:* 800-233-4830 (orders & cust serv) *Fax:* 212-869-0856 *Toll Free Fax:* 800-458-6515 *Web Site:* www.wwnorton.com, pg 171

Lovig, Grant, Company's Coming Publishing Ltd, 87 E Pender St, Vancouver, BC V6A 1S9, Canada *Tel:* 780-450-6223 (orders & inquiries) *Toll Free Tel:* 800-661-9017 (CN); 800-518-3541 (US) *Fax:* 780-450-1857 *E-mail:* info@companyscoming.com *Web Site:* www.companyscoming.com, pg 477

Lovito-Nelson, Joanne, University of Texas at Arlington School of Urban & Public Affairs, 511 University Hall, 5th fl, 601 S Nedderman Dr, Arlington, TX 76010 *Tel:* 817-272-3071 *Fax:* 817-272-3415 *E-mail:* supa@uta.edu *Web Site:* www.uta.edu/supa, pg 260

Low, Craig, Children's Book Press, 95 Madison Ave, Suite 1205, New York, NY 10016 *Tel:* 212-779-4400 *Fax:* 212-683-1894 *E-mail:* general@leeandlow.com; orders@leeandlow.com; sales@leeandlow.com *Web Site:* www.leeandlow.com, pg 57

Low, Craig, Lee & Low Books Inc, 95 Madison Ave, New York, NY 10016 *Tel:* 212-779-4400 *Toll Free Tel:* 888-320-3190 (ext 28, orders only) *Fax:* 212-683-1894 (orders only); 212-532-6035 *E-mail:* general@leeandlow.com *Web Site:* www.leeandlow.com, pg 136

Low, Jason, Lee & Low Books Inc, 95 Madison Ave, New York, NY 10016 *Tel:* 212-779-4400 *Toll Free Tel:* 888-320-3190 (ext 28, orders only) *Fax:* 212-683-1894 (orders only); 212-532-6035 *E-mail:* general@leeandlow.com *Web Site:* www.leeandlow.com, pg 136

Lowary, Nicole, Loretta Barrett Books Inc, 220 E 23 St, 11th fl, New York, NY 10010 *Tel:* 212-242-3420 *E-mail:* query@lorettabarrettbooks.com *Web Site:* www.lorettabarrettbooks.com, pg 542

Lowary, Nicole, Marianne Strong Literary Agency, 65 E 96 St, New York, NY 10128 *Tel:* 212-249-1000 *Fax:* 212-831-3241 *Web Site:* stronglit.com, pg 576

Lowe, Amy, Janet B McCabe Poetry Prize, 1041 N Taft Hill Rd, Fort Collins, CO 80521 *Tel:* 970-449-2726 *E-mail:* editor@ruminatemagazine.org *Web Site:* www.ruminatemagazine.com, pg 706

Lowe, Amy, William Van Dyke Short Story Prize, 1041 N Taft Hill Rd, Fort Collins, CO 80521 *Tel:* 970-449-2726 *E-mail:* editor@ruminatemagazine.org *Web Site:* www.ruminatemagazine.com, pg 733

Lowe, Amy, VanderMey Nonfiction Prize, 1041 N Taft Hill Rd, Fort Collins, CO 80521 *Tel:* 970-449-2726 *E-mail:* editor@ruminatemagazine.org *Web Site:* www.ruminatemagazine.com, pg 733

Lowenstein, Barbara, Lowenstein Associates Inc, 115 E 23 St, 4th fl, New York, NY 10010 *Tel:* 212-206-1630 *Fax:* 212-727-0280 *E-mail:* assistant@bookhaven.com (queries, no attachments) *Web Site:* www.lowensteinassociates.com, pg 562

Lowenstein, Carole, Random House Publishing Group, 1745 Broadway, New York, NY 10019 *Toll Free Tel:* 800-200-3552 *Web Site:* atrandom.com, pg 204

Lowes, Tara, Broadview Press, 280 Perry St, Unit 5, Peterborough, ON K9J 2J4, Canada *Tel:* 705-743-8990 *Fax:* 705-743-8353 *E-mail:* customerservice@broadviewpress.com *Web Site:* www.broadviewpress.com, pg 474

Lowry, Betty, Julia Ward Howe Book Awards, 33 Brayton Rd, Brighton, MA 02135 *Tel:* 617-783-1357 *E-mail:* bostonauthors@aol.com *Web Site:* www.bostonauthorsclub.org, pg 693

Lowry, Dr Samuel, Ambassador International, 427 Wade Hampton Blvd, Greenville, SC 29609 *Tel:* 864-235-2434 *Toll Free Tel:* 800-209-8570 *Fax:* 864-235-2491 *E-mail:* info@emeraldhouse.com; publisher@emeraldhouse.com (ms submissions); sales@emeraldhouse.com (orders/order inquiries) *Web Site:* ambassador-international.com; www.facebook.com/AmbassadorIntl; twitter.com/ambassadorintl, pg 10

Lowry, Timothy, Ambassador International, 427 Wade Hampton Blvd, Greenville, SC 29609 *Tel:* 864-235-2434 *Toll Free Tel:* 800-209-8570 *Fax:* 864-235-2491 *E-mail:* info@emeraldhouse.com; publisher@emeraldhouse.com (ms submissions); sales@emeraldhouse.com (orders/order inquiries) *Web Site:* ambassador-international.com; www.facebook.com/AmbassadorIntl; twitter.com/ambassadorintl, pg 10

Loyd, Lois, Reporters Committee for Freedom of the Press, 1101 Wilson Blvd, Suite 1100, Arlington, VA 22209-1817 *Tel:* 703-807-2100 *Toll Free Tel:* 800-336-4243 *Fax:* 703-807-2109 *E-mail:* info@rcfp.org *Web Site:* www.rcfp.org, pg 617

Lozar, Paula, New Mexico Book Association (NMBA), 1219 Luisa St, Suite 1, Santa Fe, NM 87505 *Tel:* 505-660-6357 *E-mail:* admin@nmbook.org *Web Site:* www.nmbook.org, pg 614

Lozo, Sarah, Boyds Mills Press, 815 Church St, Honesdale, PA 18431 *Tel:* 570-253-1164 *Toll Free Tel:* 800-490-5111 *Fax:* 570-253-0179 *E-mail:* contact@boydsmillspress.com *Web Site:* www.boydsmillspress.com, pg 44

Lu, Kitty, Cornell University Press, Sage House, 512 E State St, Ithaca, NY 14850 *Tel:* 607-277-2338 *Fax:* 607-277-2374 *E-mail:* cupressinfo@cornell.edu; cupress-sales@cornell.edu *Web Site:* www.cornellpress.cornell.edu, pg 63

Lu, Mei-li, XML Press, 24310 Moulton Pkwy, Suite O-175, Laguna Hills, CA 92637 *Tel:* 970-231-3624 *E-mail:* publisher@xmlpress.net *Web Site:* xmlpress.net, pg 277

Lubart, Dan, Hachette Book Group, 1290 Avenue of the Americas, New York, NY 10019 *Tel:* 212-364-1100 *Toll Free Tel:* 800-759-0190 (cust serv) *Fax:* 212-364-0933 (intl orders) *Toll Free Fax:* 800-286-9471 (cust serv) *Web Site:* www.HachetteBookGroup.com, pg 102

Lubrant, Trisha, Jewish Publication Society, 2100 Arch St, Philadelphia, PA 19103 *Tel:* 215-832-0600 *Toll Free Tel:* 800-234-3151 *Fax:* 215-568-2017 *Web Site:* www.jps.org, pg 126

Lucas, George, InkWell Management, 521 Fifth Ave, 26th fl, New York, NY 10175 *Tel:* 212-922-3500 *Fax:* 212-922-0535 *E-mail:* info@inkwellmanagement.com; submissions@inkwellmanagement.com *Web Site:* inkwellmanagement.com, pg 557

Lucas, LaBruce M S, Southern Historical Press Inc, 375 W Broad St, Greenville, SC 29601 *Tel:* 864-233-2346 *Toll Free Tel:* 800-233-0152 *Fax:* 864-233-2349, pg 231

Lucas, Wade, Penguin Random House Speakers Bureau, 1745 Broadway, Mail Drop 13-1, New York, NY 10019 *Tel:* 212-572-2013 *E-mail:* speakers@penguinrandomhouse.com *Web Site:* www.prhspeakers.com, pg 587

Lucchese, Iole, Scholastic Canada Ltd, 604 King St W, Toronto, ON M5V 1E1, Canada *Tel:* 905-887-7323 *Toll Free Tel:* 800-268-3860 (CN) *Toll Free Fax:* 866-387-4944 *E-mail:* custserve@scholastic.ca *Web Site:* www.scholastic.ca, pg 498

Lucchese, Iole, Scholastic Inc, 557 Broadway, New York, NY 10012 *Tel:* 212-343-6100 *Toll Free Tel:* 800-scholastic *Web Site:* www.scholastic.com, pg 218

Lucero, Seyan, Western States Arts Federation, 1743 Wazee St, Suite 300, Denver, CO 80202 *Tel:* 303-629-1166 *Toll Free Tel:* 888-562-7232 *Fax:* 303-629-9717 *E-mail:* staff@westaf.org *Web Site:* www.westaf.org, pg 623

Luchars, Alex, Industrial Press Inc, 32 Haviland St, Unit 2C, Norwalk, CT 06854 *Tel:* 212-889-6330 *Toll Free Tel:* 888-528-7852 *Fax:* 212-545-8327 *E-mail:* info@industrialpress.com *Web Site:* new.industrialpress.com, pg 121

Luciano, Jeannie, W W Norton & Company Inc, 500 Fifth Ave, New York, NY 10110-0017 *Tel:* 212-354-5500 *Toll Free Tel:* 800-233-4830 (orders & cust serv) *Fax:* 212-869-0856 *Toll Free Fax:* 800-458-6515 *Web Site:* www.wwnorton.com, pg 171

Lucido, Joe, Black Warrior Review Fiction, Nonfiction & Poetry Contest, Office of Student Media, University of Alabama, Tuscaloosa, AL 35486-0027 *Tel:* 205-348-4518 *Web Site:* www.bwr.ua.edu, pg 672

Luck, Carolyn, Althos Publishing, 1500 Piney Plains Rd, Suite 200, Carey, NC 27518 *Tel:* 919-557-2260 *Fax:* 919-557-2261 *E-mail:* info@althos.com *Web Site:* www.althosbooks.com, pg 9

Luderitz, Zoe, Candlewick Press, 99 Dover St, Somerville, MA 02144-2825 *Tel:* 617-661-3330 *Fax:* 617-661-0565 *E-mail:* bigbear@candlewick.com; salesinfo@candlewick.com *Web Site:* www.candlewick.com, pg 49

Luke, Gary, Sasquatch Books, 1904 S Main St, Suite 710, Seattle, WA 98101 *Tel:* 206-467-4300 *Toll Free Tel:* 800-775-0817 *Fax:* 206-467-4301 *E-mail:* custserv@sasquatchbooks.com *Web Site:* www.sasquatchbooks.com, pg 217

Lum, Robert, PRO-ED Inc, 8700 Shoal Creek Blvd, Austin, TX 78757-6897 *Tel:* 512-451-3246 *Toll Free Tel:* 800-897-3202 *Fax:* 512-451-8542 *Toll Free Fax:* 800-397-7633 *E-mail:* general@proedinc.com *Web Site:* www.proedinc.com, pg 198

Lum, Roxanne, Ignatius Press, 1348 Tenth Ave, San Francisco, CA 94122-2304 *Toll Free Tel:* 800-651-1531 (orders); 888-615-3186 (cust serv) *E-mail:* info@ignatius.com *Web Site:* www.ignatius.com, pg 118

Lumelsky, Irina, United Nations Publications, 300 E 42 St, 9th fl, New York, NY 10017 *Tel:* 703-661-1571 *Fax:* 703-996-1010 *E-mail:* publications@un.org *Web Site:* un.org/publications, pg 253

Lummis, Kristen, North American Snowsports Journalists Association, 11728 SE Madison St, Portland, OR 97216-3849 *Tel:* 503-255-3771 *Fax:* 503-255-3771 *Web Site:* www.nasja.org, pg 614

Lumpee, Cynthia, Psychological Assessment Resources Inc (PAR), 16204 N Florida Ave, Lutz, FL 33549 *Tel:* 813-968-3003; 813-449-4065 *Toll Free Tel:* 800-

331-8378 *Fax:* 813-968-2598; 813-961-2196 *Toll Free Fax:* 800-727-9329 *E-mail:* custsup@parinc.com *Web Site:* www4.parinc.com, pg 199

Lumsden, Carolyn, Association of Opinion Journalists (AOJ), 2301 Vanderbilt Place, VU Sta B 351669, Nashville, TN 37235-1669 *E-mail:* opinionjounalists@gmail.com *Web Site:* www.opinionjournalists.org, pg 599

Luna, Andrea, Police Executive Research Forum, 1120 Connecticut Ave NW, Suite 930, Washington, DC 20036 *Tel:* 202-466-7820 *Fax:* 202-466-7826 *E-mail:* perf@policeforum.org *Web Site:* www.policeforum.org, pg 194

Lund, Peder C, Paladin Press, 5540 Central Ave, Suite 20, Boulder, CO 80301 *Tel:* 303-443-7250 *Toll Free Tel:* 800-392-2400 *Fax:* 303-442-8741 *E-mail:* service@paladin-press.com *Web Site:* www.paladin-press.com, pg 180

Lund, Tom, Llewellyn Publications, 2143 Wooddale Dr, Woodbury, MN 55125 *Tel:* 651-291-1970 *Toll Free Tel:* 800-843-6666 *Fax:* 651-291-1908 *E-mail:* publicity@llewellyn.com *Web Site:* www.llewellyn.com, pg 142

Lunghi, Meghan, Merriam-Webster Inc, 47 Federal St, Springfield, MA 01102 *Tel:* 413-734-3134 *Toll Free Tel:* 800-828-1880 (orders & cust serv) *Fax:* 413-731-5979 (sales) *E-mail:* support@merriam-webster.com *Web Site:* www.merriam-webster.com, pg 155

Lunnie, Sarah, National Ten-Minute Play Contest, 316 W Main St, Louisville, KY 40202-4218 *Tel:* 502-584-1265 *Web Site:* actorstheatre.org/national-ten-minute-play-contest/, pg 711

Lunsford, Alexis, Penguin Group (USA) LLC Sales, 375 Hudson St, New York, NY 10014 *Tel:* 212-366-2000 *E-mail:* online@penguinputnam.com *Web Site:* us.penguingroup.com, pg 187

Lunzer, Bernard, The Newspaper Guild, 501 Third St NW, 6th fl, Washington, DC 20001-2797 *Tel:* 202-434-7177; 202-434-7162 (The Guild Reporter) *Fax:* 202-434-1472 *E-mail:* guild@cwa-union.org *Web Site:* www.newsguild.org, pg 614

Luongo, Rose, Brill Inc, 2 Liberty Sq, 11th fl, Boston, MA 02109 *Tel:* 617-263-2323 *Toll Free Tel:* 800-962-4406 *Fax:* 617-263-2324 *E-mail:* cs@brillusa.com *Web Site:* www.brill.com, pg 46

Luppino, Lynda, McGraw-Hill Professional, 1221 Avenue of the Americas, New York, NY 10020 *Tel:* 212-512-2000 *Web Site:* www.mhprofessional.com, pg 152

Lurie, Aimee, Sydney Taylor Book Awards, PO Box 1118, Teaneck, NJ 07666 *Tel:* 973-744-3836 *E-mail:* chair@sydneytaylorbookaward.org *Web Site:* www.sydneytaylorbookaward.org, pg 731

Lurie, David B, Japan-US Friendship Commission Translation Prize, Columbia University, 507 Kent Hall, MC3920, New York, NY 10027 *Tel:* 212-854-5036 *Fax:* 212-854-4019 *Web Site:* www.keenecenter.org, pg 696

Lurie, Stephanie Owens, Disney-Hyperion Books, 1101 Flower St, Glendale, CA 91201 *Web Site:* books.disney.com, pg 74

Lusardi, Alessandra, Rizzoli International Publications Inc, 300 Park Ave S, 4th fl, New York, NY 10010-5399 *Tel:* 212-387-3400 *Toll Free Tel:* 800-522-6657 (orders only) *Fax:* 212-387-3535 *E-mail:* publicity@rizzoliusa.com *Web Site:* www.rizzoliusa.com, pg 209

Lush, Janette, Penguin Group (Canada), 90 Eglinton Ave E, Suite 700, Toronto, ON M4P 2Y3, Canada *Tel:* 416-925-2249 *Fax:* 416-925-0068 *E-mail:* customerservicescanada@penguinrandomhouse.com *Web Site:* penguinrandomhouse.ca, pg 495

Luther, Kay, Ave Maria Press, PO Box 428, Notre Dame, IN 46556 *Tel:* 574-287-2831 *Toll Free Tel:* 800-282-1865 *Fax:* 574-239-2904 *Toll Free Fax:* 800-282-5681 *E-mail:* avemariapress.1@nd.edu *Web Site:* www.avemariapress.com, pg 28

Luttinger, Catherine, Darhansoff & Verrill, 236 W 26 St, Suite 802, New York, NY 10001-6736 *Tel:* 917-305-1300 *Fax:* 917-305-1400 *E-mail:* info@dvagency.com *Web Site:* www.dvagency.com, pg 547

Luttinger, Selma, Robert A Freedman Dramatic Agency Inc, 1501 Broadway, Suite 2310, New York, NY 10036 *Tel:* 212-840-5760 *Fax:* 212-840-5776, pg 553

Luttrell, Marsha, Mercer University Press, 368 Orange St, Macon, GA 31201 *Tel:* 478-301-2880 *Toll Free Tel:* 866-895-1472 *Fax:* 478-301-2585 *E-mail:* mupressorders@mercer.edu *Web Site:* www.mupress.org, pg 154

Luvaas, William, Joy Harjo Poetry Award, PO Box 2414, Durango, CO 81302 *Tel:* 970-903-7914 *E-mail:* cutthroatmag@gmail.com *Web Site:* www.cutthroatmag.com, pg 691

Lyman, Joe, Great Lakes Graphics Association, W232 N2950 Roundy Circle E, Pewaukee, WI 53072 *Tel:* 262-522-2210 *Toll Free Tel:* 855-522-2210 *Fax:* 262-522-2211 *E-mail:* admin@piw.org *Web Site:* www.piw.org, pg 606

Lynch, Catharine, GP Putnam's Sons (Hardcover), 375 Hudson St, New York, NY 10014 *Tel:* 212-366-2000 *E-mail:* online@penguinputnam.com *Web Site:* us.penguingroup.com, pg 201

Lynch, Chris, Simon & Schuster Audio, 1230 Avenue of the Americas, New York, NY 10020 *Web Site:* audio.simonandschuster.com, pg 225

Lynch, Chris, Simon & Schuster, Inc, 1230 Avenue of the Americas, New York, NY 10020 *Tel:* 212-698-7000 *Fax:* 212-698-7007 *E-mail:* firstname.lastname@simonandschuster.com *Web Site:* www.simonandschuster.com, pg 226

Lynch, Megan, HarperCollins General Books Group, 195 Broadway, New York, NY 10007 *Tel:* 212-207-7000 *Web Site:* www.harpercollins.com, pg 105

Lynch, Patrick, Oxford University Press USA, 198 Madison Ave, New York, NY 10016 *Tel:* 212-726-6000 *Toll Free Tel:* 800-451-7556 (orders); 800-445-9714 (cust serv) *Fax:* 919-677-1303 *E-mail:* custserv.us@oup.com *Web Site:* www.oup.com/us, pg 179

Lynch, William, ProChain Press, 3460 Commission Ct, No 301, Lake Ridge, VA 22192 *Tel:* 703-490-8821 *Fax:* 703-494-1414 *E-mail:* publishing@prochain.com *Web Site:* prochain.com, pg 508

Lynell, James, Multicultural Publications Inc, 936 Slosson St, Akron, OH 44320 *Tel:* 330-865-9578 *Fax:* 330-865-9578 *E-mail:* multiculturalpub@prodigy.net *Web Site:* www.multiculturalpub.net, pg 161

Lynley, Cason, Duke University Press, 905 W Main St, Suite 18B, Durham, NC 27701 *Tel:* 919-688-5134 *Toll Free Tel:* 888-651-0122 (US) *Fax:* 919-688-2615 *Toll Free Fax:* 888-651-0124 *E-mail:* orders@dukeupress.edu; permissions@dukeupress.edu *Web Site:* www.dukeupress.edu, pg 77

Lynn, Kira, Kane Miller Books, 4901 Morena Blvd, Suite 213, San Diego, CA 92117 *E-mail:* info@kanemiller.com *Web Site:* www.kanemiller.com, pg 129

Lyon, Kevan, Marsal Lyon Literary Agency LLC, 665 San Rodolfo Dr, Suite 124, PMB 121, Solana Beach, CA 92075 *Tel:* 760-814-8507 *Web Site:* www.marsallyonliteraryagency.com, pg 563

Lyons, Brad, Chalice Press, 483 E Lockwood Ave, Suite 100, St Louis, MO 63119 *Tel:* 314-231-8500 *Toll Free Tel:* 800-366-3383 *Fax:* 314-231-8524; 770-280-4039 (orders) *E-mail:* customerservice@chalicepress.com *Web Site:* www.chalicepress.com, pg 54

Lyons, Chris, Society for Technical Communication, 9401 Lee Hwy, Suite 300, Fairfax, VA 22031 *Tel:* 703-522-4114 *Fax:* 703-522-2075 *E-mail:* stc@stc.org *Web Site:* www.stc.org, pg 618

Lyons, Chris, Society for Technical Communication's Annual Conference, 9401 Lee Hwy, Suite 300, Fairfax, VA 22031 *Tel:* 703-522-4114 *Fax:* 703-522-2075 *E-mail:* stc@stc.org *Web Site:* www.stc.org, pg 655

Lyons, James E, University Press of America Inc, 4501 Forbes Blvd, Suite 200, Lanham, MD 20706 *Tel:* 301-459-3366 *Toll Free Tel:* 800-462-6420 *Fax:* 301-429-5748 *Toll Free Fax:* 800-338-4550 *Web Site:* www.univpress.com, pg 261

Lyons, Jed, Rowman & Littlefield Publishers Inc, 4501 Forbes Blvd, Suite 200, Lanham, MD 20706 *Tel:* 301-459-3366 *Toll Free Tel:* 800-462-6420 (cust serv) *Fax:* 301-429-5748 *Web Site:* www.rowmanlittlefield.com, pg 212

Lyons, Jed, Scarecrow Press Inc, 4501 Forbes Blvd, Suite 200, Lanham, MD 20706 *Tel:* 301-459-3366 *Fax:* 301-429-5748 *Web Site:* www.scarecrowpress.com, pg 217

Lyons, Jonathan, Curtis Brown Ltd, 10 Astor Place, New York, NY 10003 *Tel:* 212-473-5400 *Web Site:* www.curtisbrown.com, pg 544

Lyons, Krista, Seal Press, 1700 Fourth St, Berkeley, CA 94710 *Tel:* 510-595-3664 *Fax:* 510-595-4228 *Web Site:* www.sealpress.com, pg 221

Lyons, Michael, Tower Publishing Co, 588 Saco Rd, Standish, ME 04084 *Tel:* 207-642-5400 *Toll Free Tel:* 800-969-8693 *Fax:* 207-264-3870 *E-mail:* info@towerpub.com *Web Site:* www.towerpub.com, pg 247

Lyons, Pat, Dutton, 375 Hudson St, New York, NY 10014 *Tel:* 212-366-2000 *Fax:* 212-366-2262 *E-mail:* online@penguinputnam.com *Web Site:* www.penguinputnam.com; us.penguingroup.com, pg 78

Lyons, Pat, NAL, 375 Hudson St, New York, NY 10014 *Tel:* 212-366-2000 *E-mail:* online@penguinputnam.com *Web Site:* www.penguinputnam.com; us.penguingroup.com, pg 162

Lyons, Pat, Plume, 375 Hudson St, New York, NY 10014 *Tel:* 212-366-2000 *Fax:* 212-366-2666 *E-mail:* online@penguinputnam.com *Web Site:* www.penguinputnam.com; us.penguingroup.com, pg 193

Lyons, Tony, Arcade Publishing Inc, 307 W 36 St, 11th fl, New York, NY 10018 *Tel:* 212-643-6816 *Fax:* 212-643-6819 *E-mail:* info@skyhorsepublishing.com (subs & foreign rts) *Web Site:* www.arcadepub.com, pg 21

Lypen, Krestyna, Algonquin Books, 400 Silver Cedar Ct, Suite 300, Chapel Hill, NC 27514-1585 *Tel:* 919-967-0108 *Fax:* 919-933-0272 *E-mail:* inquiry@algonquin.com *Web Site:* www.workman.com/algonquin, pg 8

Ma, Amy, Immedium, 535 Rockdale Dr, San Francisco, CA 94127 *Tel:* 415-452-8546 *Fax:* 360-937-6272 *E-mail:* orders@immedium.com; sales@immedium.com *Web Site:* www.immedium.com, pg 119

Ma, Cindy, House of Anansi Press Inc, 110 Spadina Ave, Suite 801, Toronto, ON M5V 2K4, Canada *Tel:* 416-363-4343 *Fax:* 416-363-1017 *E-mail:* customerservice@houseofanansi.com *Web Site:* www.houseofanansi.com, pg 488

Maas, John, Sterling Lord Literistic Inc, 65 Bleecker St, New York, NY 10012 *Tel:* 212-780-6050 *Fax:* 212-780-6095 *E-mail:* info@sll.com *Web Site:* www.sll.com, pg 575

Maass, Donald, Donald Maass Literary Agency, 121 W 27 St, Suite 801, New York, NY 10001 *Tel:* 212-727-8383 *Fax:* 212-727-3271 *E-mail:* info@maassagency.com *Web Site:* www.maassagency.com, pg 562

Mabie, Van, Riverside Publishing, 3800 Golf Rd, Suite 200, Rolling Meadows, IL 60008 *Tel:* 630-467-7000 *Toll Free Tel:* 800-323-9540 *Fax:* 630-467-7192 (cust serv) *E-mail:* rpc_customer_service@hmhpub.com (cust serv) *Web Site:* www.riversidepublishing.com, pg 209

Mabry, John R, The Apocryphile Press, 1700 Shattuck Ave, Suite 81, Berkeley, CA 94709 *Tel:* 510-290-4349 *E-mail:* apocryphile@earthlink.net *Web Site:* www.apocryphile.org, pg 19

Macavage, Joe, HarperCollins General Books Group, 195 Broadway, New York, NY 10007 *Tel:* 212-207-7000 *Web Site:* www.harpercollins.com, pg 105

Macca, Joe, Scholastic International, 557 Broadway, New York, NY 10012 *Tel:* 212-343-6100; 646-330-5288 (intl cust serv) *Toll Free Tel:* 800-SCHOLASTIC (800-724-6527) *Fax:* 646-837-7878 *E-mail:* international@scholastic.com, pg 218

Maccarone, Grace, Holiday House Inc, 425 Madison Ave, New York, NY 10017 *Tel:* 212-688-0085 *Fax:* 212-421-6134 *E-mail:* holiday@holidayhouse.com *Web Site:* www.holidayhouse.com, pg 113

Macchiusi, Mary, Pembroke Publishers Ltd, 538 Hood Rd, Markham, ON L3R 3K9, Canada *Tel:* 905-477-0650 *Toll Free Tel:* 800-997-9807 *Fax:* 905-477-3691 *Toll Free Fax:* 800-339-5568 *Web Site:* www.pembrokepublishers.com, pg 494

Maccoby, Gina, Gina Maccoby Literary Agency, PO Box 60, Chappaqua, NY 10514-0060 *Tel:* 914-238-5630 *E-mail:* query@maccobylit.com *Web Site:* www.publishersmarketplace.com/members/GinaMaccoby, pg 562

MacDonald, Brian, University of Toronto Press, 10 St Mary St, Suite 700, Toronto, ON M4Y 2W8, Canada *Tel:* 416-978-2239 *Fax:* 416-978-4738 *E-mail:* info@utpress.utoronto.ca *Web Site:* www.utpress.utoronto.ca; www.utppublishing.com, pg 504

MacDonald, Brian A, National Braille Press, 88 St Stephen St, Boston, MA 02115-4302 *Tel:* 617-266-6160 *Toll Free Tel:* 800-548-7323 (cust serv); 888-965-8965 *Fax:* 617-437-0456 *E-mail:* orders@nbp.org *Web Site:* www.nbp.org, pg 164

MacDonald, David, The National Underwriter Co, 5081 Olympic Blvd, Erlanger, KY 41018-3164 *Tel:* 859-692-2100 *Toll Free Tel:* 800-543-0874 *Fax:* 859-692-2289 *E-mail:* customerservice@nuco.com *Web Site:* www.nationalunderwriter.com, pg 166

MacDonald, Jane, The MIT Press, 55 Hayward St, Cambridge, MA 02142 *Tel:* 617-253-5255 *Toll Free Tel:* 800-207-8354 (orders) *Fax:* 617-258-6779; 617-577-1545 (orders) *Web Site:* mitpress.mit.edu, pg 158

MacDonald, Leo, HarperCollins Canada Ltd, 2 Bloor St E, 20th fl, Toronto, ON M4W 1A8, Canada *Tel:* 416-975-9334 *Fax:* 416-975-9884 *E-mail:* hcorder@harpercollins.com *Web Site:* www.harpercollins.ca, pg 487

MacDonald, Nora, Random House Children's Books, 1745 Broadway, New York, NY 10019 *Tel:* 212-782-9000 *Toll Free Tel:* 800-200-3552 *Fax:* 212-782-9452 *Web Site:* randomhousekids.com, pg 204

MacDonald, Tim, David C Cook, 4050 Lee Vance View, Colorado Springs, CO 80918 *Tel:* 719-536-0100 *Toll Free Tel:* 800-708-5550; 800-323-7543 (orders & cust serv) *Toll Free Fax:* 800-430-0726 (cust serv) *Web Site:* www.davidccook.com, pg 62

MacFarlane, Fraser, One Act Play Depot, 618 Memorial Dr, PO Box 335, Spiritwood, SK S0J 2M0, Canada *E-mail:* plays@oneactplays.net; orders@oneactplays.net *Web Site:* oneactplays.net, pg 493

MacGowan, Melissa, National Freedom of Information Coalition (NFOIC), 101C Reynolds Journalism Institute, Columbia, MO 65211 *Tel:* 573-882-4856 *Web Site:* nfoic.org, pg 612

MacGregor, Rob, Crabtree Publishing Co Ltd, 616 Welland Ave, St Catharines, ON L2M-5V6, Canada *Tel:* 905-682-5221 *Toll Free Tel:* 800-387-7650 *Fax:* 905-682-7166 *Toll Free Fax:* 800-355-7166 *E-mail:* custserv@crabtreebooks.com; sales@crabtreebooks.com; orders@crabtreebooks.com *Web Site:* www.crabtreebooks.com, pg 478

MacGregor, Robert, Crabtree Publishing Co, 350 Fifth Ave, 59th fl, PMB 59051, New York, NY 10118 *Tel:* 212-496-5040 *Toll Free Tel:* 800-387-7650 *Toll Free Fax:* 800-355-7166 *E-mail:* custserv@crabtreebooks.com *Web Site:* www.crabtreebooks.com, pg 66

Machat, Joshua, Yale University Press, 302 Temple St, New Haven, CT 06511-8909 *Tel:* 203-432-0960; 203-432-0966 (sales); 401-531-2800 (cust serv) *Toll Free Tel:* 800-405-1619 (cust serv) *Fax:* 203-432-0948; 203-432-8485 (sales); 401-531-2801 (cust serv) *Toll Free Fax:* 800-406-9145 (cust serv) *E-mail:* sales.press@yale.edu (sales); customer.care@trilateral.org (cust serv) *Web Site:* www.yalebooks.com; yalepress.yale.edu/yupbooks, pg 278

Machinist, Alexandra, ICM Partners, 730 Fifth Ave, New York, NY 10019 *Tel:* 212-556-5600 *Web Site:* www.icmtalent.com, pg 557

Maciag, Thomas, Hachette Book Group, 1290 Avenue of the Americas, New York, NY 10019 *Tel:* 212-364-1100 *Toll Free Tel:* 800-759-0190 (cust serv) *Fax:* 212-364-0933 (intl orders) *Toll Free Fax:* 800-286-9471 (cust serv) *Web Site:* www.HachetteBookGroup.com, pg 102

MacIlwaine, Paula, American Water Works Association (AWWA), 6666 W Quincy Ave, Denver, CO 80235 *Tel:* 303-794-7711 *Toll Free Tel:* 800-926-7337 *Fax:* 303-347-0804 *Web Site:* www.awwa.org, pg 17

Macintosh, Adrienne, Harlequin Enterprises Ltd, 225 Duncan Mill Rd, Don Mills, ON M3B 3K9, Canada *Tel:* 416-445-5860 *Toll Free Tel:* 888-432-4879; 800-370-5838 (ebook inquiries) *E-mail:* customerservice@harlequin.com *Web Site:* www.harlequin.com, pg 487

MacIntyre, Mary, Canadian Bookbinders and Book Artists Guild (CBBAG), 80 Ward St, Suite 207, Toronto, ON M6H 4A6, Canada *Tel:* 416-581-1071 *E-mail:* cbbag@cbbag.ca *Web Site:* www.cbbag.ca, pg 601

MacIsaac, Bonnie, Howard Books, 216 Centerview Dr, Suite 303, Brentwood, TN 37027 *Tel:* 615-873-2080 *Fax:* 615-370-3834 *E-mail:* howardbooks@simonandschuster.com (info) *Web Site:* www.howardpublishing.com, pg 116

Mackeen, Alison, Sterling Lord Literistic Inc, 65 Bleecker St, New York, NY 10012 *Tel:* 212-780-6050 *Fax:* 212-780-6095 *E-mail:* info@sll.com *Web Site:* www.sll.com, pg 575

MacKenzie, Anne Marie, Cape Breton University Press Inc (CBU Press), 1250 Grand Lake Rd, Sydney, NS B1M 1A2, Canada *Tel:* 902-563-1604 (orders & cust serv) *Fax:* 902-563-1177 *E-mail:* cbu_press@cbu.ca *Web Site:* cbup.ca, pg 476

MacKenzie, Joanna, Browne & Miller Literary Associates, 410 S Michigan Ave, Suite 460, Chicago, IL 60605 *Tel:* 312-922-3063 *E-mail:* mail@browneandmiller.com *Web Site:* www.browneandmiller.com, pg 544

Mackenzie, Leslie, Grey House Publishing Inc™, 4919 Rte 22, Amenia, NY 12501 *Tel:* 518-789-8700 *Toll Free Tel:* 800-562-2139 *Fax:* 518-789-0556 *E-mail:* books@greyhouse.com; customerservice@greyhouse.com *Web Site:* www.greyhouse.com, pg 101

Mackey, Elliott, The Wine Appreciation Guild Ltd, 360 Swift Ave, Suites 30 & 34, South San Francisco, CA 94080 *Tel:* 650-866-3020 *Toll Free Tel:* 800-231-9463 *Fax:* 650-866-3513 *E-mail:* info@wineappreciation.com *Web Site:* www.wineappreciation.com, pg 273

Mackey, Zoe, Berrett-Koehler Publishers Inc, 1333 Broadway, Suite 1000, Oakland, CA 94612 *Tel:* 510-817-2277 *Fax:* 510-817-2278 *E-mail:* bkpub@bkpub.com *Web Site:* www.bkconnection.com, pg 35

Mackinnon, Emily, Nimbus Publishing Ltd, 3731 Mackintosh St, Halifax, NS B3K 5A5, Canada *Tel:* 902-455-4286; 902-454-7404 *Toll Free Tel:* 800-NIMBUS9 (646-2879) *Fax:* 902-455-5440 *Toll Free Fax:* 888-253-3133 *E-mail:* customerservice@nimbus.ca *Web Site:* www.nimbus.ca, pg 493

Mackinnon, Margo, IODE Jean Throop Book Award, 9-45 Frid St, Hamilton, ON L8P 4M3, Canada *Tel:* 905-522-9537 *Fax:* 905-522-3637 *E-mail:* iodeontario@bellnet.ca *Web Site:* www.iodeontario.ca, pg 695

Mackintosh, Teresa, CCH, a Wolters Kluwer business, 2700 Lake Cook Rd, Riverwoods, IL 60015 *Tel:* 847-267-7000 *Web Site:* www.cch.com, pg 52

Macklem, Ann, University of British Columbia Press, 2029 West Mall, Vancouver, BC V6T 1Z2, Canada *Tel:* 604-822-5959 *Toll Free Tel:* 877-377-9378 *Fax:* 604-822-6083 *Toll Free Fax:* 800-668-0821 *E-mail:* frontdesk@ubcpress.ca *Web Site:* www.ubcpress.ca, pg 502

Macklem, Michael, Oberon Press, 145 Spruce St, Suite 205, Ottawa, ON K1R 6P1, Canada *Tel:* 613-238-3275 *Fax:* 613-238-3275 *E-mail:* oberon@sympatico.ca *Web Site:* www.oberonpress.ca, pg 493

Macklem, Nicholas, Oberon Press, 145 Spruce St, Suite 205, Ottawa, ON K1R 6P1, Canada *Tel:* 613-238-3275 *Fax:* 613-238-3275 *E-mail:* oberon@sympatico.ca *Web Site:* www.oberonpress.ca, pg 493

Mackwood, Robert, Seventh Avenue Literary Agency, 2052 124 St, South Surrey, BC V4A 9K3, Canada *Tel:* 604-538-7252 *Fax:* 604-538-7252 *E-mail:* info@seventhavenuelit.com *Web Site:* www.seventhavenuelit.com, pg 572

MacLachlan, Christina, Wildflower Press, Oakbrook Press, 3301 S Valley Dr, Rapid City, SD 57703 *Tel:* 605-381-6385 *Fax:* 605-343-8733 *E-mail:* info@wildflowerpress.org; bookorder@wildflowerpress.org *Web Site:* www.wildflowerpress.org, pg 271

MacLachlan, Sarah, Groundwood Books, 110 Spadina Ave, Suite 801, Toronto, ON M5V 2K4, Canada *Tel:* 416-363-4343 *Fax:* 416-363-1017 *E-mail:* genmail@groundwoodbooks.com *Web Site:* www.houseofanansi.com, pg 486

MacLachlan, Sarah, House of Anansi Press Inc, 110 Spadina Ave, Suite 801, Toronto, ON M5V 2K4, Canada *Tel:* 416-363-4343 *Fax:* 416-363-1017 *E-mail:* customerservice@houseofanansi.com *Web Site:* www.houseofanansi.com, pg 488

Maclagan, Maral, Scholastic Canada Ltd, 604 King St W, Toronto, ON M5V 1E1, Canada *Tel:* 905-887-7323 *Toll Free Tel:* 800-268-3860 (CN) *Toll Free Fax:* 866-387-4944 *E-mail:* custserve@scholastic.ca *Web Site:* www.scholastic.ca, pg 498

MacLeod, Lauren E, Strothman Agency LLC, 63 E Ninth St, 10X, New York, NY 10003 *E-mail:* info@strothmanagency.com *Web Site:* www.strothmanagency.com, pg 576

MacLeod, Nancy, Short Prose Competition for Developing Writers, 600-460 Richmond St W, Toronto, ON M5V 1Y1, Canada *Tel:* 416-703-8982 *Fax:* 416-504-9090 *E-mail:* info@writersunion.ca *Web Site:* www.writersunion.ca, pg 728

MacMahon, Ted, Newbury Street Press, 101 Newbury St, Boston, MA 02116 *Tel:* 617-536-5740 *Toll Free Tel:* 888-296-3447 (NEHGS membership) *Fax:* 617-536-7307 *E-mail:* sales@nehgs.org *Web Site:* www.newenglandancestors.org, pg 169

MacMillan, Colleen, Annick Press Ltd, 15 Patricia Ave, Toronto, ON M2M 1H9, Canada *Tel:* 416-221-4802 *Fax:* 416-221-8400 *E-mail:* annickpress@annickpress.com *Web Site:* www.annickpress.com, pg 471

Macnair, Randal, Oolichan Books, PO Box 2278, Fernie, BC V0B 1M0, Canada *Tel:* 250-423-6113 *E-mail:* info@oolichan.com *Web Site:* www.oolichan.com, pg 493

MacNamara, Elisabeth, League of Women Voters of the United States, 1730 "M" St NW, Suite 1000, Washington, DC 20036-4508 *Tel:* 202-429-1965 *Fax:* 202-429-0854; 202-429-4343 *E-mail:* lwv@lwv.org *Web Site:* www.lwv.org, pg 608

MacNeil, Mary, The University of Virginia Press, PO Box 400318, Charlottesville, VA 22904-4318 *Tel:* 434-924-3468 (cust serv); 434-924-3469 (cust serv) *Toll Free Tel:* 800-831-3406 (orders) *Fax:* 434-982-2655 *Toll Free Fax:* 877-288-6400 *E-mail:* vapress@virginia.edu *Web Site:* www.upress.virginia.edu, pg 260

MacNevin, James, McGill-Queen's University Press, 1010 Sherbrooke W, Suite 1720, Montreal, QC H3A 2R7, Canada *Tel:* 514-398-3750 *Fax:* 514-398-4333 *E-mail:* mqup@mqup.ca *Web Site:* www.mqup.ca, pg 491

Macrides, Kristine, HarperCollins Publishers Sales, 195 Broadway, New York, NY 10007 *Fax:* 212-207-7000 *Web Site:* www.harpercollins.com, pg 106

Macris, Natalie, Solano Press Books, PO Box 773, Point Arena, CA 95468 *Tel:* 707-884-4508 *Toll Free Tel:* 800-931-9373 *Fax:* 707-884-4109 *E-mail:* spbooks@solano.com *Web Site:* www.solano.com, pg 230

MacRobert, Alan M, Sky Publishing, 90 Sherman St, Cambridge, MA 02140 *Tel:* 617-864-7360 *Toll Free Tel:* 866-644-1377 *Fax:* 617-864-6117 *E-mail:* info@skyandtelescope.com *Web Site:* www.skyandtelescope.com, pg 227

Madan, Neeti, Sterling Lord Literistic Inc, 65 Bleecker St, New York, NY 10012 *Tel:* 212-780-6050 *Fax:* 212-780-6095 *E-mail:* info@sll.com *Web Site:* www.sll.com, pg 575

Madan, Vineet, McGraw-Hill Education, 2 Penn Plaza, New York, NY 10121-2298 *Tel:* 212-904-2000 *E-mail:* customer.service@mcgraw-hill.com *Web Site:* www.mheducation.com; www.mheducation.com/custserv.html, pg 151

Madara, James L MD, American Medical Association, AMA Plaza, 330 N Wabash, Suite 39300, Chicago, IL 60611-5885 *Tel:* 312-464-5000 *Toll Free Tel:* 800-621-8335 *Fax:* 312-464-4184 *Web Site:* www.ama-assn.org, pg 14, 595

Madden, Kyla, McGill-Queen's University Press, 1010 Sherbrooke W, Suite 1720, Montreal, QC H3A 2R7, Canada *Tel:* 514-398-3750 *Fax:* 514-398-4333 *E-mail:* mqup@mqup.ca *Web Site:* www.mqup.ca, pg 491

Maddex, John, Ancient Faith Publishing, 2747 Bond St, University Park, IL 60484 *Tel:* 219-728-2216 *Toll Free Tel:* 800-967-7377 *Toll Free Fax:* 866-599-5208 *E-mail:* info@ancientfaith.com; orders@ancientfaith.com *Web Site:* www.ancientfaith.com/publishing, pg 17

Madhubuti, Haki R, Third World Press, 7822 S Dobson Ave, Chicago, IL 60619 *Tel:* 773-651-0700 *Fax:* 773-651-7286 *E-mail:* twpress3@aol.com *Web Site:* www.thirdworldpressbooks.com, pg 245

Madigan, Michael, Colorado Authors' League, PO Box 24905, Denver, CO 80224 *Web Site:* coloradoauthors.org, pg 603

Madonia, Nena, Dupree, Miller & Associates Inc, 100 Highland Park Village, Suite 350, Dallas, TX 75205 *Tel:* 214-559-2665 *Fax:* 214-559-7243 *E-mail:* editorial@dupreemiller.com *Web Site:* www.dupreemiller.com, pg 549

Madrus, Ingel, Gerald Lampert Memorial Award, 192 Spadina Ave, Suite 312, Toronto, ON M5T 2C2, Canada *Tel:* 416-504-1657 *Fax:* 416-504-0096 *E-mail:* readings@poets.ca *Web Site:* poets.ca, pg 699

Madrus, Ingel, The League of Canadian Poets, 192 Spadina Ave, Suite 312, Toronto, ON M5T 2C2, Canada *Tel:* 416-504-1657 *Fax:* 416-504-0096 *Web Site:* poets.ca, pg 608

Madrus, Ingel, Pat Lowther Memorial Award, 192 Spadina Ave, Suite 312, Toronto, ON M5T 2C2, Canada *Tel:* 416-504-1657 *Fax:* 416-504-0096 *E-mail:* readings@poets.ca *Web Site:* poets.ca, pg 703

Madrus, Ingel, Jessamy Stursberg Poetry Contest for Youth, 192 Spadina Ave, Suite 312, Toronto, ON M5T 2C2, Canada *Tel:* 416-504-1657 *Fax:* 416-504-0096 *E-mail:* readings@poets.ca *Web Site:* www.youngpoets.ca; poets.ca, pg 731

Mafchir, James, Sherman Asher Publishing, 126 Candelario St, Santa Fe, NM 87501 *Tel:* 505-988-7214 *E-mail:* westernedge@santa-fe.net *Web Site:* www.shermanasher.com; www.westernedgepress.com, pg 223

Magill, William H, The Reader's Digest Association Inc, 750 Third Ave, New York, NY 10017 *Tel:* 914-238-1000; 646-293-6284 *Toll Free Tel:* 800-310-6261 (cust serv) *Fax:* 914-238-4559 *Web Site:* www.rd.com; www.rda.com, pg 205

Magill, William H, Reader's Digest General Books, Reader's Digest Rd, Pleasantville, NY 10570-7000 *Tel:* 914-238-1000 *Toll Free Tel:* 800-304-2807 (cust serv) *Fax:* 914-244-7436, pg 205

Magno, Lisa Krebs, Benjamin Franklin Awards™, 1020 Manhattan Beach Blvd, Suite 204, Manhattan Beach, CA 90266 *Tel:* 310-546-1818 *Fax:* 310-546-3939 *E-mail:* info@ibpa-online.org *Web Site:* www.ibpa-online.org; ibpabenjaminfranklinawards.com, pg 671

Magno, Lisa Krebs, The Independent Book Publishers Association (IBPA), 1020 Manhattan Beach Blvd, Suite 204, Manhattan Beach, CA 90266 *Tel:* 310-546-1818 *Fax:* 310-546-3939 *E-mail:* info@ibpa-online.org *Web Site:* www.ibpa-online.org, pg 607

Magnus, Mary H, Health Professions Press, 409 Washington Ave, Suite 500, Towson, MD 21204 *Tel:* 410-337-9585 *Toll Free Tel:* 888-337-8808 *Fax:* 410-337-8539 *E-mail:* custserv@healthpropress.com *Web Site:* www.healthpropress.com, pg 109

Magnus, Dr Sandra, American Institute of Aeronautics & Astronautics (AIAA), 1801 Alexander Bell Dr, Suite 500, Reston, VA 20191-4344 *Tel:* 703-264-7500 *Toll Free Tel:* 800-639-AIAA (639-2422) *Fax:* 703-264-7551 *E-mail:* custserv@aiaa.org *Web Site:* www.aiaa.org, pg 13

Magnuson, James, University of Texas at Austin, Creative Writing Program, Dept of English, PAR 108, One University Sta, Mailcode B5000, Austin, TX 78712-1164 *Tel:* 512-471-5132; 512-471-4991 *Fax:* 512-471-4909 *Web Site:* www.utexas.edu/cola/depts/english/creative-writing, pg 664

Magoulias, Michael, University of Chicago Press, 1427 E 60 St, Chicago, IL 60637-2954 *Tel:* 773-702-7700; 773-702-7600 *Toll Free Tel:* 800-621-2736 (orders) *Fax:* 773-702-9756; 773-660-2235 (orders); 773-702-2708 *E-mail:* custserv@press.uchicago.edu; marketing@press.uchicago.edu *Web Site:* www.press.uchicago.edu, pg 255

Magowan, Mark, The Vendome Press, 1334 York Ave, 3rd fl, New York, NY 10021 *Tel:* 212-737-5297 *Fax:* 212-737-5340 *E-mail:* info@vendomepress.com *Web Site:* www.vendomepress.com, pg 265

Magruder, Munro, New World Library, 14 Pamaron Way, Novato, CA 94949 *Tel:* 415-884-2100 *Toll Free Tel:* 800-227-3900 (ext 52, retail orders); 800-972-6657 *Fax:* 415-884-2199 *E-mail:* escort@newworldlibrary.com *Web Site:* www.newworldlibrary.com, pg 168

Maguire, Julia, Random House Children's Books, 1745 Broadway, New York, NY 10019 *Tel:* 212-782-9000 *Toll Free Tel:* 800-200-3552 *Fax:* 212-782-9452 *Web Site:* randomhousekids.com, pg 203

Maguire, Kevin, Paulist Press, 997 Macarthur Blvd, Mahwah, NJ 07430-9990 *Tel:* 201-825-7300 *Toll Free Tel:* 800-218-1903 *Fax:* 201-825-8345 *Toll Free Fax:* 800-836-3161 *E-mail:* info@paulistpress.com *Web Site:* www.paulistpress.com, pg 184

Mahajan, Vinod, Nataraj Books, 7967 Twist Lane, Springfield, VA 22153 *Tel:* 703-455-4996 *Fax:* 703-455-4001 *E-mail:* nataraj@erols.com; orders@natarajbooks.com *Web Site:* www.natarajbooks.com, pg 163

Mahalek, Gina M, The University of North Carolina Press, 116 S Boundary St, Chapel Hill, NC 27514-3808 *Tel:* 919-966-3561 *Fax:* 919-966-3829 *E-mail:* uncpress@unc.edu *Web Site:* www.uncpress.unc.edu, pg 258

Mahaney, John, PublicAffairs, 250 W 57 St, Suite 1321, New York, NY 10107 *Tel:* 212-397-6666 *Toll Free Tel:* 800-343-4499 (orders) *Fax:* 212-397-4277 *E-mail:* publicaffairs@perseusbooks.com *Web Site:* www.publicaffairsbooks.com, pg 200

Maher, William, National Association of Insurance Commissioners, 2301 McGee St, Suite 800, Kansas City, MO 64108-2662 *Tel:* 816-842-3600; 816-783-8300 (cust serv) *Fax:* 816-783-8175; 816-460-7593 (cust serv) *E-mail:* prodserv@naic.org *Web Site:* www.naic.org, pg 163

Mahoney, Ann, International City/County Management Association (ICMA), 777 N Capitol St NE, Suite 500, Washington, DC 20002-4201 *Tel:* 202-289-4262 *Toll Free Tel:* 800-745-8780 *Fax:* 202-962-3500 *E-mail:* customerservice@icma.org *Web Site:* icma.org, pg 123

Mahoney, Anne Louise, Novalis Publishing, 10 Lower Spadina Ave, Suite 400, Toronto, ON M5V 2Z2, Canada *Tel:* 416-363-3303 *Toll Free Tel:* 877-702-7773 *Fax:* 416-363-9409 *Toll Free Fax:* 877-702-7775 *E-mail:* books@novalis.ca *Web Site:* www.novalis.ca, pg 493

Mahoney, Judy, Teach Me Tapes Inc, 6016 Blue Circle Dr, Minnetonka, MN 55343 *Tel:* 952-933-8086 *Toll Free Tel:* 800-456-4656 *Fax:* 952-933-0512 *E-mail:* marie@teachmetapes.com *Web Site:* www.teachmetapes.com, pg 241

Mahoney, Tyrrell, Chronicle Books LLC, 680 Second St, San Francisco, CA 94107 *Tel:* 415-537-4200 *Toll Free Tel:* 800-759-0190 (cust serv) *Fax:* 415-537-4460 *Toll Free Fax:* 800-858-7787 (orders); 800-286-9471 (cust serv) *E-mail:* frontdesk@chroniclebooks.com *Web Site:* www.chroniclebooks.com, pg 57

Mai, Andrea, Penguin Group (USA) LLC Sales, 375 Hudson St, New York, NY 10014 *Tel:* 212-366-2000 *E-mail:* online@penguinputnam.com *Web Site:* us.penguingroup.com, pg 187

Maillet, Neal, Berrett-Koehler Publishers Inc, 1333 Broadway, Suite 1000, Oakland, CA 94612 *Tel:* 510-817-2277 *Fax:* 510-817-2278 *E-mail:* bkpub@bkpub.com *Web Site:* www.bkconnection.com, pg 35

Maines, Kevin Murphy, New Women's Voices Chapbook Competition, PO Box 1626, Georgetown, KY 40324 *Tel:* 859-514-8966 *E-mail:* finishingbooks@aol.com; flpbookstore@aol.com *Web Site:* www.finishinglinepress.com, pg 712

Maines, Kevin Murphy, Open Chapbook Competition, PO Box 1626, Georgetown, KY 40324 *Tel:* 859-514-8966 *E-mail:* finishingbooks@aol.com; flpbookstore@aol.com *Web Site:* www.finishinglinepress.com, pg 715

Maines, Leah, New Women's Voices Chapbook Competition, PO Box 1626, Georgetown, KY 40324 *Tel:* 859-514-8966 *E-mail:* finishingbooks@aol.com; flpbookstore@aol.com *Web Site:* www.finishinglinepress.com, pg 712

Maines, Leah, Open Chapbook Competition, PO Box 1626, Georgetown, KY 40324 *Tel:* 859-514-8966 *E-mail:* finishingbooks@aol.com; flpbookstore@aol.com *Web Site:* www.finishinglinepress.com, pg 715

Mainhardt, Ricia, RMA, 85 Lincoln St, 1st fl, Meriden, CT 06451 *Tel:* 718-434-1893 *Web Site:* www.ricia.com, pg 570

Mainville, Lara, University of Ottawa Press (Les Presses de l'Université d'Ottawa), 542 King Edward Ave, Ottawa, ON K1N 6N5, Canada *Tel:* 613-562-5246 *Fax:* 613-562-5247 *E-mail:* puo-oup@uottawa.ca *Web Site:* www.press.uottawa.ca, pg 503

Mairs, Jane, Merriam-Webster Inc, 47 Federal St, Springfield, MA 01102 *Tel:* 413-734-3134 *Toll Free Tel:* 800-828-1880 (orders & cust serv) *Fax:* 413-731-5979 (sales) *E-mail:* support@merriam-webster.com *Web Site:* www.merriam-webster.com, pg 155

Maitland, Arnaud, Dharma Publishing, 35788 Hauser Bridge Rd, Cazadero, CA 95421 *Tel:* 707-847-3717 *Toll Free Tel:* 800-873-4276 *Fax:* 707-847-3380 *E-mail:* contact@dharmapublishing.com; customerservice@dharmapublishing.com *Web Site:* www.dharmapublishing.com, pg 73

Majczyk, Amy, RAND Corp, 1776 Main St, Santa Monica, CA 90407-2138 *Tel:* 310-393-0411 *Fax:* 310-393-4818 *Web Site:* www.rand.org, pg 203

Majer, Carrie, Basic Books, 250 W 57 St, 15th fl, New York, NY 10107 *Tel:* 212-340-8164; 212-340-8136 *Fax:* 212-340-8135 *E-mail:* perseus.promos@perseusbooks.com *Web Site:* www.basicbooks.com; perseusbooks.com, pg 31

Majuk, Irene, AMACOM Books, 1601 Broadway, New York, NY 10019-7420 *Tel:* 212-586-8100 *Toll Free Tel:* 800-250-5308 (cust serv) *Fax:* 212-903-8083; 518-891-2372 (orders) *E-mail:* pubs_cust_serv@amanet.org *Web Site:* www.amacombooks.org, pg 9

Majury, Yolanda, LexisNexis® Canada Inc, 123 Commerce Valley Dr E, Suite 700, Markham, ON L3T 7W8, Canada *Tel:* 905-479-2665 *Toll Free Tel:* 800-668-6481; 800-387-0899 (cust care) *Fax:* 905-479-2826 *Toll Free Fax:* 800-461-3275 *E-mail:* orders@lexisnexis.ca; service@lexisnexis.ca (cust serv) *Web Site:* www.lexisnexis.ca, pg 490

Makholm, Lauren, The Art Institute of Chicago, 111 S Michigan Ave, Chicago, IL 60603-6404 *Tel:* 312-443-3600; 312-443-3540 (pubns) *Fax:* 312-443-1334 (pubns) *Web Site:* www.artic.edu; www.artinstituteshop.org, pg 22

Marshall, Kate, University of California Press, 2120 Berkeley Way, Berkeley, CA 94704-1012 *Tel:* 510-642-4247 *Fax:* 510-643-7127 *E-mail:* askucp@ucpress.edu (books); customerservice@ucpressjournals.com *Web Site:* www.ucpress.edu, pg 255

Marshall, Len, HarperCollins General Books Group, 195 Broadway, New York, NY 10007 *Tel:* 212-207-7000 *Web Site:* www.harpercollins.com, pg 105

Marshall, Peter, W H Freeman, 41 Madison Ave, 37th fl, New York, NY 10010 *Tel:* 212-576-9400 *Fax:* 212-689-2383 *Web Site:* www.whfreeman.com, pg 92

Marsham, Nachie, Disney Press, 1101 Flower St, Glendale, CA 91201 *Web Site:* books.disney.com, pg 74

Marsolini, Maxine, Oregon Christian Writers (OCW), 1075 Willow Lake Rd N, Keizer, OR 97303 *Tel:* 503-393-3356 *E-mail:* contact@oregonchristianwriters.org *Web Site:* www.oregonchristianwriters.org, pg 615

Marsolini, Maxine, Oregon Christian Writers Seminar, 1075 Willow Lake Rd N, Keizer, OR 97303 *Tel:* 503-393-3356 *E-mail:* contact@oregonchristianwriters.org *Web Site:* www.oregonchristianwriters.org, pg 653

Marson, Amy, C & T Publishing Inc, 1651 Challenge Dr, Concord, CA 94520-5206 *Tel:* 925-677-0377 *Toll Free Tel:* 800-284-1114 *Fax:* 925-677-0373 *E-mail:* support@ctpub.com *Web Site:* www.ctpub.com, pg 48

Martel, Manon, Les Editions Un Monde Different, 3905 Isabelle, bureau 101, Brossard, QC J4Y 2R2, Canada *Tel:* 450-656-2660 *Toll Free Tel:* 800-443-2582 *Fax:* 450-659-9328 *E-mail:* info@umd.ca *Web Site:* www.umd.ca, pg 483

Martell, Alice Fried, The Martell Agency, 1350 Avenue of the Americas, Suite 1205, New York, NY 10019 *Tel:* 212-317-2672 *Web Site:* www.themartellagency.com, pg 564

Martens, Julie S, Human Kinetics Inc, 1607 N Market St, Champaign, IL 61820 *Tel:* 217-351-5076 *Toll Free Tel:* 800-747-4457 *Fax:* 217-351-1549 (orders/cust serv) *E-mail:* info@hkusa.com *Web Site:* www.humankinetics.com, pg 117

Martens, Patricia, Boys Town Press, 14100 Crawford St, Boys Town, NE 68010 *Tel:* 402-498-1320 *Toll Free Tel:* 800-282-6657 *Fax:* 402-498-1310 *E-mail:* btpress@boystown.org *Web Site:* www.boystownpress.org, pg 44

Martens, Rainer, Human Kinetics Inc, 1607 N Market St, Champaign, IL 61820 *Tel:* 217-351-5076 *Toll Free Tel:* 800-747-4457 *Fax:* 217-351-1549 (orders/cust serv) *E-mail:* info@hkusa.com *Web Site:* www.humankinetics.com, pg 116

Marthe, L, Laurier Books Ltd, PO Box 8493, Ottawa, ON K1G 3H9, Canada *Tel:* 613-738-2163 *Toll Free Fax:* 855-736-9160 *E-mail:* laurierbooks@yahoo.com, pg 490

Martin, Andrew, St Martin's Press, LLC, 175 Fifth Ave, New York, NY 10010 *Tel:* 646-307-5151 *Fax:* 212-420-9314 *E-mail:* firstname.lastname@macmillan.com *Web Site:* www.stmartins.com, pg 214

Martin, Barbara, Southern Illinois University Press, 1915 University Press Dr, SIUC Mail Code 6806, Carbondale, IL 62901-4323 *Tel:* 618-453-2281 *Fax:* 618-453-1221 *E-mail:* custserv@press.uchicago.edu; rights@siu.edu *Web Site:* www.siupress.com, pg 231

Martin, Betsy, Skinner House Books, c/o Unitarian Universalist Assn, 24 Farnsworth St, Boston, MA 02210-1409 *Tel:* 617-742-2100 *Fax:* 617-948-6466 *E-mail:* skinnerhouse@uua.org *Web Site:* www.skinnerhouse.org, pg 227

Martin, Brad, Doubleday Canada, One Toronto St, Suite 300, Toronto, ON M5C 2V6, Canada *Tel:* 416-364-4449 *Fax:* 416-364-6863 *Web Site:* www.randomhouse.ca, pg 479

Martin, Brad, Knopf Canada, One Toronto St, Suite 300, Toronto, ON M5C 2V6, Canada *Tel:* 416-364-4449 *Toll Free Tel:* 888-523-9292 *Fax:* 416-364-6863 *Web Site:* www.randomhouse.ca, pg 490

Martin, Brad, Penguin Random House Canada Limited, 320 Front St W, Suite 1400, Toronto, ON M5V 3B6, Canada *Tel:* 416-364-4449 *Toll Free Tel:* 888-523-9292 (cust serv) *Fax:* 416-364-6863; 416-364-6653 (subs rts) *Web Site:* penguinrandomhouse.ca, pg 495

Martin, Brad, Seal Books, One Toronto St, Suite 300, Toronto, ON M5C 2V6, Canada *Tel:* 416-364-4449 *Toll Free Tel:* 888-523-9292 (order desk) *Fax:* 416-364-6863 *Web Site:* www.randomhouse.ca, pg 498

Martin, Cynthia Parkinson, Research Press, 2612 N Mattis Ave, Champaign, IL 61822 *Tel:* 217-352-3273 *Toll Free Tel:* 800-519-2707 *Fax:* 217-352-1221 *E-mail:* rp@researchpress.com; orders@researchpress.com *Web Site:* www.researchpress.com, pg 208

Martin, Denny, Piano Press, 1425 Ocean Ave, Suite 5, Del Mar, CA 92014 *Tel:* 619-884-1401 *Fax:* 858-755-1104 *E-mail:* pianopress@pianopress.com *Web Site:* www.pianopress.com, pg 191

Martin, Emily, Harlequin Enterprises Ltd, 225 Duncan Mill Rd, Don Mills, ON M3B 3K9, Canada *Tel:* 416-445-5860 *Toll Free Tel:* 888-432-4879; 800-370-5838 (ebook inquiries) *E-mail:* customerservice@harlequin.com *Web Site:* www.harlequin.com, pg 487

Martin, Howard, HeartMath LLC, 14700 W Park Ave, Boulder Creek, CA 95006 *Tel:* 831-338-8700 *Toll Free Tel:* 800-450-9111 *Fax:* 831-338-9861 *E-mail:* inquiry@heartmath.com *Web Site:* www.heartmath.com, pg 109

Martin, James, Oxford University Press USA, 198 Madison Ave, New York, NY 10016 *Tel:* 212-726-6000 *Toll Free Tel:* 800-451-7556 (orders); 800-445-9714 (cust serv) *Fax:* 919-677-1303 *E-mail:* custserv.us@oup.com *Web Site:* www.oup.com/us, pg 179

Martin, Jehu, Money Market Directories, 401 E Market St, Charlottesville, VA 22902 *Tel:* 434-977-1450 *Toll Free Tel:* 800-446-2810 *Fax:* 434-979-9962 *Web Site:* www.mmdwebaccess.com, pg 159

Martin, Jennie Taylor, ARE Press, 215 67 St, Virginia Beach, VA 23451 *Tel:* 757-428-3588 *Toll Free Tel:* 800-333-4499 *Fax:* 757-491-0689 *Web Site:* www.edgarcayce.org, pg 22

Martin, John, Rod & Staff Publishers Inc, Hwy 172, Crockett, KY 41413 *Tel:* 606-522-4348 *Fax:* 606-522-4896 *Toll Free Fax:* 800-643-1244 (ordering in US), pg 210

Martin, Jynne, Riverhead Books (Hardcover), 375 Hudson St, New York, NY 10014 *Tel:* 212-366-2000 *E-mail:* online@penguinputnam.com *Web Site:* www.penguinputnam.com; us.penguingroup.com, pg 209

Martin, Katherine, Oxford University Press USA, 198 Madison Ave, New York, NY 10016 *Tel:* 212-726-6000 *Toll Free Tel:* 800-451-7556 (orders); 800-445-9714 (cust serv) *Fax:* 919-677-1303 *E-mail:* custserv.us@oup.com *Web Site:* www.oup.com/us, pg 179

Martin, Lesley, Aperture Books, 547 W 27 St, 4th fl, New York, NY 10001 *Tel:* 212-505-5555 *Toll Free Tel:* 800-929-2323 *Fax:* 212-979-7759 *E-mail:* info@aperture.org *Web Site:* www.aperture.org, pg 19

Martin, Lisa Ann PhD, Martin-McLean Literary Associates LLC, 5023 W 120 Ave, Suite 228, Broomfield, CO 80020 *Tel:* 303-465-2056 *Fax:* 303-465-2057 *E-mail:* martinmcleanlit@aol.com *Web Site:* www.martinmcleanlit.com; www.mcleanlit.com, pg 564

Martin, Marianne K, Bywater Books, PO Box 3671, Ann Arbor, MI 48106-3671 *Tel:* 734-662-8815 *Web Site:* bywaterbooks.com, pg 48

Martin, Matthew, Penguin Random House Inc, 1745 Broadway, New York, NY 10019 *Tel:* 212-782-9000 *Toll Free Tel:* 800-726-0600 *Web Site:* www.randomhouse.com, pg 187

Martin, Michael, University of Louisiana at Lafayette Press, PO Box 40831, UL, Lafayette, LA 70504-0831 *Tel:* 337-482-6027 *Fax:* 337-482-6028 *E-mail:* cls@louisiana.edu *Web Site:* www.ulpress.org, pg 256

Martin, Michele, Gallery Books, 1230 Avenue of the Americas, New York, NY 10020 *Toll Free Tel:* 800-456-6798 *Fax:* 212-698-7284 *E-mail:* consumer.customerservice@simonandschuster.com *Web Site:* www.simonsays.com, pg 94

Martin, Natasha, Crown Publishing Group, c/o Penguin Random House Inc, 1745 Broadway, New York, NY 10019 *Tel:* 212-782-9000 *Toll Free Tel:* 888-264-1745 *Fax:* 212-940-7408 *E-mail:* crownosm@penguinrandomhouse.com *Web Site:* crownpublishing.com, pg 68

Martin, Natasha, Clarkson Potter Publishers, c/o Random House Inc, 1745 Broadway, New York, NY 10019 *Tel:* 212-782-9000 *Toll Free Tel:* 888-264-1745 *Fax:* 212-572-6181 *Web Site:* www.clarksonpotter.com; www.randomhouse.com/crown/clarksonpotter, pg 195

Martin, Nathan, Destiny Image Inc, 167 Walnut Bottom Rd, Shippensburg, PA 17257-0310 *Tel:* 717-532-3040 *Toll Free Tel:* 800-722-6774 (orders only) *Fax:* 717-532-9291 *Web Site:* www.destinyimage.com, pg 73

Martin, Patrick, Prometheus Books, 59 John Glenn Dr, Amherst, NY 14228-2119 *Tel:* 716-691-0133 *Toll Free Tel:* 800-421-0351 *Fax:* 716-691-0137 *E-mail:* marketing@prometheusbooks.com; editorial@prometheusbooks.com *Web Site:* www.prometheusbooks.com, pg 199

Martin, Philip, Crickhollow Books, 3147 S Pennsylvania Ave, Milwaukee, WI 53207 *Tel:* 414-294-4319 *E-mail:* info@crickhollowbooks.com *Web Site:* www.crickhollowbooks.com, pg 67

Martin, Rux, Houghton Mifflin Harcourt Trade & Reference Division, 222 Berkeley St, Boston, MA 02116 *Tel:* 617-351-5000 *Toll Free Tel:* 800-225-3362 *Web Site:* www.hmhco.com, pg 115

Martin, Shari, University of British Columbia Press, 2029 West Mall, Vancouver, BC V6T 1Z2, Canada *Tel:* 604-822-5959 *Toll Free Tel:* 877-377-9378 *Fax:* 604-822-6083 *Toll Free Fax:* 800-668-0821 *E-mail:* frontdesk@ubcpress.ca *Web Site:* www.ubcpress.ca, pg 502

Martin, Sharlene, Martin Literary Management, 7683 SE 27 St, No 307, Mercer Island, WA 98040 *Tel:* 206-466-1773 (no queries) *Fax:* 206-466-1774 *Web Site:* www.martinliterarymanagement.com, pg 564

Martin, Stephen H, Oaklea Press, 41 Old Mill Rd, Richmond, VA 23226-3111 *Tel:* 804-308-3906 *Fax:* 804-980-7057 *Web Site:* oakleapress.com, pg 173

Martin, Wayne, North Carolina Arts Council Writers Fellowships, 109 E Jones St, Raleigh, NC 27601 *Tel:* 919-807-6500 *Fax:* 919-807-6532 *E-mail:* ncarts@ncdcr.gov *Web Site:* www.ncarts.org, pg 713

Martinelli, Theresa, Wayne State University Press, Leonard N Simons Bldg, 4809 Woodward Ave, Detroit, MI 48201-1309 *Tel:* 313-577-6120 *Toll Free Tel:* 800-978-7323 *Fax:* 313-577-6131 *Web Site:* www.wsupress.wayne.edu, pg 268

Martinez, Claudia, Vintage & Anchor Books, c/o Random House Inc, 1745 Broadway, New York, NY 10019 *Tel:* 212-572-2420 *E-mail:* vintageanchorpublicity@randomhouse.com *Web Site:* vintage-anchor.knopfdoubleday.com, pg 266

Martino, Alfred C, Listen & Live Audio Inc, PO Box 817, Roseland, NJ 07068-0817 *Tel:* 201-558-9000 *Toll Free Tel:* 800-653-9400 (orders) *Fax:* 201-558-9800 *Web Site:* www.listenandlive.com, pg 140

Martino, John B, The Catholic University of America Press, 240 Leahy Hall, 620 Michigan Ave NE, Washington, DC 20064 *Tel:* 202-319-5052 *Toll Free Tel:* 800-537-5487 (orders only) *Fax:* 202-319-4985 *E-mail:* cua-press@cua.edu *Web Site:* cuapress.cua.edu, pg 52

Martins, Tim H, Barbour Publishing Inc, 1810 Barbour Dr, Uhrichsville, OH 44683 *Tel:* 740-922-6045 *Fax:* 740-922-5948 *E-mail:* info@barbourbooks.com *Web Site:* www.barbourbooks.com, pg 30

Marton, Wayne, Tetra Press, 3001 Commerce St, Blacksburg, VA 24060 *Tel:* 540-951-5400 *Toll Free Tel:* 800-526-0650 *Fax:* 540-951-5415 *E-mail:* consumer@tetra-fish.com *Web Site:* www.tetra-fish.com, pg 243

Martone, Michael, University of Alabama Program in Creative Writing, PO Box 870244, Tuscaloosa, AL 35487-0244 *Tel:* 205-348-5065 *Fax:* 205-348-1388 *E-mail:* english@ua.edu *Web Site:* www.as.ua.edu/english, pg 663

Martone, Robert, F A Davis Co, 1915 Arch St, Philadelphia, PA 19103 *Tel:* 215-568-2270; 215-440-3001 *Toll Free Tel:* 800-523-4049 *Fax:* 215-568-5065; 215-440-3016 *E-mail:* info@fadavis.com; orders@fadavis.com *Web Site:* www.fadavis.com, pg 71

Marun, Serdar, Autism Asperger Publishing Co, 11209 Strang Line Rd, Lenexa, KS 66215 *Tel:* 913-897-1004 *Toll Free Tel:* 877-277-8254 *Fax:* 913-681-9473 *E-mail:* info@aapcpublishing.net *Web Site:* www.aapcpublishing.net, pg 28

Marven, Shannon, Dupree, Miller & Associates Inc, 100 Highland Park Village, Suite 350, Dallas, TX 75205 *Tel:* 214-559-2665 *Fax:* 214-559-7243 *E-mail:* editorial@dupreemiller.com *Web Site:* www.dupreemiller.com, pg 549

Marvin, Sally, Random House Publishing Group, 1745 Broadway, New York, NY 10019 *Toll Free Tel:* 800-200-3552 *Web Site:* atrandom.com, pg 204

Marwell, Josh, HarperCollins Publishers, 195 Broadway, New York, NY 10007 *Tel:* 212-207-7000 *Fax:* 212-207-7145 *Web Site:* www.harpercollins.com, pg 106

Marwell, Josh, HarperCollins Publishers Sales, 195 Broadway, New York, NY 10007 *Fax:* 212-207-7000 *Web Site:* www.harpercollins.com, pg 106

Marzan, Clarissa, Simon & Schuster, 1230 Avenue of the Americas, New York, NY 10020 *Tel:* 212-698-7000 *Toll Free Tel:* 800-223-2348 (cust serv); 800-223-2336 (orders) *Toll Free Fax:* 800-943-9831 (orders) *Web Site:* www.simonandschuster.com, pg 225

Marzano, Vincent, John Wiley & Sons Inc, 111 River St, Hoboken, NJ 07030-5774 *Tel:* 201-748-6000 *Toll Free Tel:* 800-225-5945 (cust serv) *Fax:* 201-748-6088 *E-mail:* info@wiley.com *Web Site:* www.wiley.com, pg 272

Masaryk, Hanna, Sanford J Greenburger Associates Inc, 55 Fifth Ave, New York, NY 10003 *Tel:* 212-206-5600 *Fax:* 212-463-8718 *Web Site:* greenburger.com; www.sjga.com/, pg 555

Masch, Travis, Parallax Press, 2236-B Sixth St, Berkeley, CA 94710 *Tel:* 510-525-0101 *Toll Free Tel:* 800-863-5290 (orders) *Fax:* 510-525-7129 *E-mail:* info@parallax.org *Web Site:* www.parallax.org, pg 182

Masciovecchio, Alison, Random House Publishing Group, 1745 Broadway, New York, NY 10019 *Toll Free Tel:* 800-200-3552 *Web Site:* atrandom.com, pg 204

Maslin, Ella, Random House Publishing Group, 1745 Broadway, New York, NY 10019 *Toll Free Tel:* 800-200-3552 *Web Site:* atrandom.com, pg 204

Masnik, Julia, Watkins/Loomis Agency Inc, PO Box 20925, New York, NY 10025 *Tel:* 212-532-0080 *Fax:* 646-383-2449 *E-mail:* assistant@watkinsloomis.com *Web Site:* www.watkinsloomis.com, pg 579

Mason, Alane, W W Norton & Company Inc, 500 Fifth Ave, New York, NY 10110-0017 *Tel:* 212-354-5500 *Toll Free Tel:* 800-233-4830 (orders & cust serv) *Fax:* 212-869-0856 *Toll Free Fax:* 800-458-6515 *Web Site:* www.wwnorton.com, pg 171

Mason, Jonathan, Don Buchwald & Associates Inc, 10 E 44 St, New York, NY 10017 *Tel:* 212-867-1200 *Fax:* 212-867-2434 *E-mail:* info@buchwald.com *Web Site:* www.buchwald.com, pg 545

Mason, Linda, MPA - The Association of Magazine Media, 757 Third Ave, 11th fl, New York, NY 10012 *Tel:* 212-872-3700 *Fax:* 212-888-4217 *Web Site:* www.magazine.org, pg 610

Mason, Linda, Publishers Information Bureau (PIB)®, 757 Third Ave, 11th fl, New York, NY 10017 *Tel:* 212-872-3745; 212-872-3700 (MPA) *E-mail:* infocenter@magazine.org *Web Site:* www.magazine.org, pg 617

Mason, Lizzy, Bloomsbury Publishing Inc, 1385 Broadway, 5th fl, New York, NY 10018 *Tel:* 212-419-5300 *E-mail:* marketingusa@bloomsbury.com; adultpublicityusa@bloomsbury.com; askacademic@bloomsbury.com *Web Site:* www.bloomsbury.com, pg 40

Mason, Val, The BC Book Prizes, 207 W Hastings St, Suite 901, Vancouver, BC V6B 1H7, Canada *Tel:* 604-687-2405 *Fax:* 604-687-2435 *E-mail:* info@bcbookprizes.ca *Web Site:* www.bcbookprizes.ca, pg 670

Maspeller, George, Quarto Publishing Group USA Inc, 400 First Ave N, Suite 300, Minneapolis, MN 55401 *Tel:* 612-344-8100 *Toll Free Tel:* 800-328-0590 (sales); 800-458-0454 *Fax:* 612-344-8691 *E-mail:* sales@creativepub.com *Web Site:* quartoknows.com, pg 201

Masry, Susan, Rizzoli International Publications Inc, 300 Park Ave S, 4th fl, New York, NY 10010-5399 *Tel:* 212-387-3400 *Toll Free Tel:* 800-522-6657 (orders only) *Fax:* 212-387-3535 *E-mail:* publicity@rizzoliusa.com *Web Site:* www.rizzoliusa.com, pg 209

Massey, Jeanne, Adler Publishing Inc, 46937 Monarch Dr, Parker, CO 80138 *Tel:* 303-660-2158 *Toll Free Tel:* 800-660-5107 (sales & orders) *E-mail:* customerservice@adlerpublishing.com; orders@4wdbooks.com *Web Site:* www.adlerpublishing.com, pg 5

Massey, Peter, Adler Publishing Inc, 46937 Monarch Dr, Parker, CO 80138 *Tel:* 303-660-2158 *Toll Free Tel:* 800-660-5107 (sales & orders) *E-mail:* customerservice@adlerpublishing.com; orders@4wdbooks.com *Web Site:* www.adlerpublishing.com, pg 5

Massicotte, Celine, Groupe Sogides Inc, 955 rue Amherst, Montreal, QC H2L 3K4, Canada *Tel:* 514-523-1182 *Fax:* 514-597-0370 *Web Site:* www.sogides.com, pg 486

Massov, Olga, Phaidon Press Inc, 180 Varick St, 14th fl, New York, NY 10014 *Tel:* 212-652-5400 *Toll Free Tel:* 800-759-0190 (cust serv) *Fax:* 212-652-5410 *Toll Free Fax:* 800-286-9471 (cust serv) *E-mail:* ussales@phaidon.com *Web Site:* www.phaidon.com, pg 190

Mastandrea, Damon, BioTechniques Books, 52 Vanderbilt Ave, 11th fl, New York, NY 10017 *Tel:* 212-520-2777 *Fax:* 212-520-2705 *Web Site:* www.biotechniques.com, pg 37

Masters, Charles J, The Society of Midland Authors (SMA), PO Box 10419, Chicago, IL 60610 *E-mail:* info@midlandauthors.com *Web Site:* www.midlandauthors.com, pg 619

Masters, Charles J, The Society of Midland Authors Awards, 530 Michigan Ave, Evanston, IL 60202 *E-mail:* info@midlandauthors.com *Web Site:* www.midlandauthors.com, pg 729

Masterson, Amanda, Bureau of Economic Geology, University of Texas at Austin, 10100 Burnet Rd, Bldg 130, Austin, TX 78758 *Tel:* 512-471-1534 *Fax:* 512-471-0140 *E-mail:* pubsales@beg.utexas.edu *Web Site:* www.beg.utexas.edu, pg 48

Mastrolia, Barbara, Catholic Book Awards, 205 W Monroe St, Suite 470, Chicago, IL 60606 *Tel:* 312-380-6789 *Fax:* 312-361-0256 *E-mail:* cathjourn@catholicpress.org *Web Site:* www.catholicpress.org, pg 676

Mastrolia, Barbara, Catholic Press Awards, 205 W Monroe St, Suite 470, Chicago, IL 60606 *Tel:* 312-380-6789 *Fax:* 312-361-0256 *E-mail:* cathjourn@catholicpress.org *Web Site:* www.catholicpress.org, pg 676

Matejovsky, Char, Polebridge Press, c/o Willamette University, 900 State St, Salem, OR 97301 *Tel:* 503-375-5323 *E-mail:* orders@westarinstitute.org *Web Site:* www.polebridgepress.com, pg 194

Mather, Nicholas, R Ross Annett Award for Children's Literature, 11759 Groat Rd, Edmonton, AB T5M 3K6, Canada *Tel:* 780-422-8174 *Toll Free Tel:* 800-665-5354 (AB only) *Fax:* 780-422-2663 (attn WGA) *E-mail:* mail@writersguild.ab.ca *Web Site:* www.writersguild.ab.ca, pg 667

Mather, Nicholas, Amber Bowerman Memorial Travel Writing Award, 11759 Groat Rd, Edmonton, AB T5M 3K6, Canada *Tel:* 780-422-8174 *Toll Free Tel:* 800-665-5354 (AB only) *Fax:* 780-422-2663 (attn WGA) *E-mail:* mail@writersguild.ab.ca *Web Site:* www.writersguild.ab.ca, pg 673

Mather, Nicholas, Georges Bugnet Award for Fiction, 11759 Groat Rd, Edmonton, AB T5M 3K6, Canada *Tel:* 780-422-8174 *Toll Free Tel:* 800-665-5354 (AB only) *Fax:* 780-422-2663 (attn WGA) *E-mail:* mail@writersguild.ab.ca *Web Site:* www.writersguild.ab.ca, pg 674

Mather, Nicholas, The City of Calgary W O Mitchell Book Prize, 11759 Groat Rd, Edmonton, AB T5M 3K6, Canada *Tel:* 780-422-8174 *Toll Free Tel:* 800-665-5354 (AB only) *Fax:* 780-422-2663 (attn WGA) *E-mail:* mail@writersguild.ab.ca *Web Site:* www.writersguild.ab.ca, pg 677

Mather, Nicholas, Wilfrid Eggleston Award for Nonfiction, 11759 Groat Rd, Edmonton, AB T5M 3K6, Canada *Tel:* 780-422-8174 *Toll Free Tel:* 800-665-5354 (AB only) *Fax:* 780-422-2663 (attn WGA) *E-mail:* mail@writersguild.ab.ca *Web Site:* www.writersguild.ab.ca, pg 683

Mather, Nicholas, James H Gray Award for Short Nonfiction, 11759 Groat Rd, Edmonton, AB T5M 3K6, Canada *Tel:* 780-422-8174 *Toll Free Tel:* 800-665-5354 (AB only) *Fax:* 780-422-2663 (attn WGA) *E-mail:* mail@writersguild.ab.ca *Web Site:* www.writersguild.ab.ca, pg 690

Mather, Nicholas, The Robert Kroetsch City of Edmonton Book Prize, 11759 Groat Rd, Edmonton, AB T5M 3K6, Canada *Tel:* 780-422-8174 *Toll Free Tel:* 800-665-5354 (AB only) *Fax:* 780-422-2663 (attn WGA) *E-mail:* mail@writersguild.ab.ca *Web Site:* www.writersguild.ab.ca, pg 698

Mather, Nicholas, Howard O'Hagan Award for Short Story, 11759 Groat Rd, Edmonton, AB T5M 3K6, Canada *Tel:* 780-422-8174 *Toll Free Tel:* 800-665-5354 (AB only) *Fax:* 780-422-2663 (attn WGA) *E-mail:* mail@writersguild.ab.ca *Web Site:* www.writersguild.ab.ca, pg 714

Mather, Nicholas, Gwen Pharis Ringwood Award for Drama, 11759 Groat Rd, Edmonton, AB T5M 3K6, Canada *Tel:* 780-422-8174 *Toll Free Tel:* 800-665-5354 (AB only) *Fax:* 780-422-2663 (attn WGA) *E-mail:* mail@writersguild.ab.ca *Web Site:* www.writersguild.ab.ca, pg 724

Mather, Nicholas, Stephan G Stephansson Award for Poetry, 11759 Groat Rd, Edmonton, AB T5M 3K6, Canada *Tel:* 780-422-8174 *Toll Free Tel:* 800-665-5354 (AB only) *Fax:* 780-422-2663 (attn WGA) *E-mail:* mail@writersguild.ab.ca *Web Site:* www.writersguild.ab.ca, pg 730

Mather, Nicholas, Jon Whyte Memorial Essay Prize, 11759 Groat Rd, Edmonton, AB T5M 3K6, Canada *Tel:* 780-422-8174 *Toll Free Tel:* 800-665-5354 (AB only) *Fax:* 780-422-2663 (attn WGA) *E-mail:* mail@writersguild.ab.ca *Web Site:* www.writersguild.ab.ca, pg 736

Mather, Nicholas, Writers' Guild of Alberta, 11759 Groat Rd, Edmonton, AB T5M 3K6, Canada *Tel:* 780-422-8174 *Toll Free Tel:* 800-665-5354 (AB only) *Fax:* 780-422-2663 (attn WGA) *E-mail:* mail@writersguild.ab.ca *Web Site:* www.writersguild.ab.ca, pg 621

Matherne, Todd, City & Regional Magazine Association, 1970 E Grand Ave, Suite 330, El Segundo, CA 90245 *Tel:* 310-364-0193 *Fax:* 310-364-0196 *E-mail:* admin@citymag.org *Web Site:* www.citymag.org, pg 603

Matheson, Ed, Ampersand Group, 12 Morenz Terr, Kanata, ON K2K 3G9, Canada *Tel:* 613-435-5066, pg 520

Matheson, Laurie, University of Illinois Press, 1325 S Oak St, MC-566, Champaign, IL 61820-6903 *Tel:* 217-333-0950 *Fax:* 217-244-8082 *E-mail:* uipress@uillinois.edu; journals@uillinois.edu *Web Site:* www.press.uillinois.edu, pg 256

Mathews, Allison, Shadow Mountain, PO Box 30178, Salt Lake City, UT 84130 *Tel:* 801-534-1515 *Fax:* 801-517-3474 *E-mail:* submissions@shadowmountain.com *Web Site:* shadowmountain.com, pg 222

Mathews, Lisa Vitarisi, Evan-Moor Educational Publishers, 18 Lower Ragsdale Dr, Monterey, CA 93940-5746 *Tel:* 831-649-5901 *Toll Free Tel:* 800-777-4362 (orders) *Fax:* 831-649-6256 *Toll Free Fax:* 800-777-4332 (orders) *E-mail:* sales@evan-moor.com; marketing@evan-moor.com *Web Site:* www.evan-moor.com, pg 84

Mathews, Richard, The Danahy Fiction Prize, University of Tampa Press, 401 W Kennedy Blvd, Tampa, FL 33606 *Tel:* 813-253-6266 *E-mail:* utpress@ut.edu *Web Site:* tampareview.ut.edu, pg 680

Mathews, Richard, The Tampa Review Prize for Poetry, University of Tampa Press, 401 W Kennedy Blvd, Tampa, FL 33606 *Tel:* 813-253-6266 *E-mail:* utpress@ut.edu *Web Site:* tampareview.ut.edu, pg 731

Mathieson, Tim, Faith & Fellowship Publishing, 1020 W Alcott Ave, Fergus Falls, MN 56537 *Tel:* 218-736-7357 *Toll Free Tel:* 800-332-9232 *E-mail:* clb@clba.org *Web Site:* www.clba.org, pg 86

Mathieu, James R, University of Pennsylvania Museum of Archaeology & Anthropology, 3260 South St, Philadelphia, PA 19104-6324 *Tel:* 215-898-5723 *Fax:* 215-573-2497 *E-mail:* info@pennmuseum.org; publications@pennmuseum.org *Web Site:* www.penn.museum, pg 259

Mathis, Catherine J, McGraw-Hill Education, 2 Penn Plaza, New York, NY 10121-2298 *Tel:* 212-904-2000 *E-mail:* customer.service@mcgraw-hill.com *Web Site:* www.mheducation.com; www.mheducation.com/custserv.html, pg 151

Mathoslah, Donna, Romance Writers of America®, 14615 Benfer Rd, Houston, TX 77069 *Tel:* 832-717-5200 *Fax:* 832-717-5201 *E-mail:* info@rwa.org *Web Site:* www.rwa.org, pg 618

Mathy, Mike, Society of American Travel Writers (SATW), 11950 W Lake Park Dr, Suite 320, Milwaukee, WI 53224-3049 *Tel:* 414-359-1625 *Fax:* 414-359-1671 *E-mail:* info@satw.org *Web Site:* www.satw.org, pg 619

Matlins, Stuart M, Jewish Lights Publishing, Sunset Farm Offices, Rte 4, Woodstock, VT 05091 *Tel:* 802-457-4000 *Toll Free Tel:* 800-962-4544 (orders only) *Fax:* 802-457-4004 *E-mail:* sales@jewishlights.com *Web Site:* www.jewishlights.com, pg 126

Matlins, Stuart M, SkyLight Paths Publishing, Sunset Farm Offices, Rte 4, Woodstock, VT 05091 *Tel:* 802-457-4000 *Toll Free Tel:* 800-962-4544 *Fax:* 802-457-4004 *E-mail:* sales@skylightpaths.com *Web Site:* www.skylightpaths.com, pg 227

Matloff, Robert, The Guilford Press, 72 Spring St, New York, NY 10012 *Tel:* 212-431-9800 *Toll Free Tel:* 800-365-7006 *Fax:* 212-966-6708 *E-mail:* info@guilford.com *Web Site:* www.guilford.com, pg 102

Matson, Jonathan, Harold Matson Co Inc, 276 Fifth Ave, New York, NY 10001 *Tel:* 212-679-4490 *Fax:* 212-545-1224, pg 564

Matson, Katinka, Brockman Inc, 260 Fifth Ave, 10th fl, New York, NY 10001 *Tel:* 212-935-8900 *Fax:* 212-935-5535 *E-mail:* rights@brockman.com *Web Site:* www.brockman.com, pg 544

Matson, Peter, Sterling Lord Literistic Inc, 65 Bleecker St, New York, NY 10012 *Tel:* 212-780-6050 *Fax:* 212-780-6095 *E-mail:* info@sll.com *Web Site:* www.sll.com, pg 575

Matthews, Claire, PRISM international Literary Non-Fiction Contest, University of British Columbia, Buch E462, 1866 Main Mall, Vancouver, BC V6T 1Z1, Canada *Tel:* 778-822-2514 *Fax:* 778-822-3616 *E-mail:* prismwritingcontest@gmail.com *Web Site:* www.prismmagazine.ca, pg 721

Matthews, Claire, PRISM international Poetry Contest, University of British Columbia, Buch E462, 1866 Main Mall, Vancouver, BC V6T 1Z1, Canada *Tel:* 778-822-2514 *Fax:* 778-822-3616 *E-mail:* prismwritingcontest@gmail.com *Web Site:* www.prismmagazine.ca, pg 721

Matthews, Claire, PRISM international Short Fiction Contest, University of British Columbia, Buch E462, 1866 Main Mall, Vancouver, BC V6T 1Z1, Canada *Tel:* 778-822-2514 *Fax:* 778-822-3616 *E-mail:* prismwritingcontest@gmail.com *Web Site:* www.prismmagazine.ca, pg 721

Matthews, Darryl R Sr, National Association of Black Journalists (NABJ), 1100 Knight Hall, Suite 3100, College Park, MD 20742 *Tel:* 301-405-0248 *Fax:* 301-314-1714 *E-mail:* nabj@nabj.org *Web Site:* www.nabj.org, pg 611

Matthews, Katherine, Lucky Marble Books, 2671 Bristol Rd, Columbus, OH 43221 *Tel:* 614-264-5588 *E-mail:* sales@pagespringpublishing.com *Web Site:* www.luckymarblebooks.com, pg 144

Mattingly, Laura Lee, Chronicle Books LLC, 680 Second St, San Francisco, CA 94107 *Tel:* 415-537-4200 *Toll Free Tel:* 800-759-0190 (cust serv) *Fax:* 415-537-4460 *Toll Free Fax:* 800-858-7787 (orders); 800-286-9471 (cust serv) *E-mail:* frontdesk@chroniclebooks.com *Web Site:* www.chroniclebooks.com, pg 58

Mattos, Dominic, T&T Clark International, 1385 Broadway, 5th fl, New York, NY 10018 *Tel:* 212-953-5858 *Toll Free Tel:* 800-561-7704 (orders) *Fax:* 212-953-5944 *Web Site:* www.continuumbooks.com, pg 240

Mattson, Stewart, Business Expert Press, 222 E 46 St, New York, NY 10017-2906 *Tel:* 630-207-5927 *E-mail:* charlene.kronstadt@businessexpertpress.com *Web Site:* www.businessexpertpress.com, pg 48

Mattson, Trilogy, Time Being Books, 10411 Clayton Rd, Suites 201-203, St Louis, MO 63131 *Tel:* 314-432-1771 *Fax:* 314-432-7939 *E-mail:* tbbooks@sbcglobal.net *Web Site:* www.timebeing.com, pg 246

Mattura, Cat, McGraw-Hill Create, 501 Bell St, Dubuque, IA 52001 *Tel:* 563-584-6000 *Fax:* 563-584-6600 *E-mail:* first_last@mcgraw-hill.com *Web Site:* www.mhhe.com, pg 150

Matuszak, Ashley, Ten Speed Press, 2625 Alcatraz Ave, Unit 505, Berkeley, CA 94705 *Tel:* 510-285-3000 *Toll Free Tel:* 800-841-BOOK (841-2665) *E-mail:* csorders@randomhouse.com *Web Site:* crownpublishing.com/imprint/ten-speed-press, pg 243

Matute, Silvia, Santillana USA Publishing Co Inc, 2023 NW 84 Ave, Doral, FL 33122 *Tel:* 305-591-9522 *Toll Free Tel:* 800-245-8584 *Fax:* 305-591-9145 *Toll Free Fax:* 888-248-9518 *E-mail:* customerservice@santillanausa.com *Web Site:* www.santillanausa.com; www.alfaguara.net, pg 216

Matwychuk, Paul, NeWest Press, 8540 109 St, No 201, Edmonton, AB T6G 1E6, Canada *Tel:* 780-432-9427 *Toll Free Tel:* 866-796-5473 *Fax:* 780-433-3179 *E-mail:* info@newestpress.com; orders@newestpress.com *Web Site:* www.newestpress.com, pg 492

Matysik, Julie, Sky Pony Press, 307 W 36 St, 11th fl, New York, NY 10018 *Tel:* 212-643-6816 *Fax:* 212-643-6819 *E-mail:* skypony@skyhorsepublishing.com; submissions@skyhorsepublishing.com; info@skyhorsepublishing.com *Web Site:* www.skyponypress.com, pg 227

Matysko, Harriet I, Mary Ann Liebert Inc, 140 Huguenot St, 3rd fl, New Rochelle, NY 10801-5215 *Tel:* 914-740-2100 *Toll Free Tel:* 800-654-3237 *Fax:* 914-740-2101 *E-mail:* info@liebertpub.com *Web Site:* www.liebertonline.com, pg 139

Mauer, Harry, Flashlight Press, 527 Empire Blvd, Brooklyn, NY 11225 *Tel:* 718-288-8300 *Fax:* 718-972-6307 *E-mail:* editor@flashlightpress.com *Web Site:* www.flashlightpress.com, pg 89

Mauer, Tzvi, Urim Publications, c/o Lambda Publications Inc, 527 Empire Blvd, Brooklyn, NY 11225-3121 *Tel:* 718-972-5449 *Fax:* 718-972-6307 *E-mail:* publisher@urimpublications.com *Web Site:* urimpublications.com, pg 263

Mauk, J T, The Perseus Books Group, 387 Park Ave S, 12th fl, New York, NY 10016 *Tel:* 212-340-8100 *Toll Free Tel:* 800-343-4499 (cust serv) *Fax:* 212-340-8105 *Web Site:* www.perseusbooksgroup.com, pg 189

Maurer, Rolf, New Star Books Ltd, 107-3477 Commercial St, Vancouver, BC V5N 4E8, Canada *Tel:* 604-738-9429 *Fax:* 604-738-9332 *E-mail:* info@newstarbooks.com *Web Site:* www.newstarbooks.com, pg 492

Maurin, Denise, Omnibus Press, 257 Park Ave S, 20th fl, New York, NY 10010 *Tel:* 212-254-2100 *Toll Free Tel:* 800-431-7187 *Fax:* 212-254-2013 *Toll Free Fax:* 800-345-6842 *E-mail:* info-us@omnibuspress.com *Web Site:* www.omnibuspress.com; www.musicsales.com, pg 174

Mausser, Therese, AMACOM Books, 1601 Broadway, New York, NY 10019-7420 *Tel:* 212-586-8100 *Toll Free Tel:* 800-250-5308 (cust serv) *Fax:* 212-903-8083; 518-891-2372 (orders) *E-mail:* pubs_cust_serv@amanet.org *Web Site:* www.amacombooks.org, pg 9

Mautner, Stephen, National Academies Press (NAP), Lockbox 285, 500 Fifth St NW, Washington, DC 20001 *Tel:* 202-334-3313 *Toll Free Tel:* 888-624-8373 (cust serv) *Fax:* 202-334-2451 (cust serv); 202-334-2793 (mktg dept) *E-mail:* customer_service@nap.edu *Web Site:* www.nap.edu, pg 163

Mavjee, Maya, Crown Publishing Group, c/o Penguin Random House Inc, 1745 Broadway, New York, NY 10019 *Tel:* 212-782-9000 *Toll Free Tel:* 888-264-1745 *Fax:* 212-940-7408 *E-mail:* crownosm@penguinrandomhouse.com *Web Site:* crownpublishing.com, pg 68

Mavjee, Maya, Penguin Random House Inc, 1745 Broadway, New York, NY 10019 *Tel:* 212-782-9000 *Toll Free Tel:* 800-726-0600 *Web Site:* www.randomhouse.com, pg 187

Mavreshko, Lana, Business Marketing Association (BMA), 708 Third Ave, New York, NY 10017 *Tel:* 212-697-5950 *Fax:* 212-687-7310 *E-mail:* info@marketing.org *Web Site:* www.marketing.org, pg 601

Max, P J, Easy Money Press, 5419 87 St, Lubbock, TX 79424 *Tel:* 806-543-5215 *E-mail:* easymoneypress@yahoo.com, pg 79

Maxick, Jill, Prometheus Books, 59 John Glenn Dr, Amherst, NY 14228-2119 *Tel:* 716-691-0133 *Toll Free Tel:* 800-421-0351 *Fax:* 716-691-0137 *E-mail:* marketing@prometheusbooks.com; editorial@prometheusbooks.com *Web Site:* www.prometheusbooks.com, pg 199

Maxwell, Linda, Blue Dolphin Publishing Inc, 13340-D Grass Valley Ave, Grass Valley, CA 95945 *Tel:* 530-477-1503 *Toll Free Tel:* 800-643-0765 (orders) *Fax:* 530-477-8342 *E-mail:* bdolphin@bluedolphinpublishing.com *Web Site:* www.bluedolphinpublishing.com, pg 40

Maxwell, Mitchell, The Story Plant, PO Box 4331, Stamford, CT 06907 *Tel:* 203-722-7920 *E-mail:* thestoryplant@thestoryplant.com *Web Site:* www.thestoryplant.com, pg 236

Maxwell, Nancy, Ariel Press, 3854 Mason Rd, Canal Winchester, OH 43110 *Toll Free Tel:* 800-336-7769 *E-mail:* lig201@lightariel.com *Web Site:* www.lightariel.com, pg 22

May, Brendan, Simon & Schuster Canada, 166 King St E, Suite 300, Toronto, ON M5A 1J3, Canada *Tel:* 647-427-8882 *Toll Free Tel:* 800-387-0446; 800-268-3216 (orders) *Fax:* 647-430-9446 *Toll Free Fax:* 888-849-8151 (orders) *E-mail:* info@simonandschuster.ca *Web Site:* www.simonandschuster.ca, pg 499

May, Christopher, Dufour Editions Inc, PO Box 7, Chester Springs, PA 19425 *Tel:* 610-458-5005 *Fax:* 610-458-7103 *E-mail:* info@dufoureditions.com *Web Site:* www.dufoureditions.com, pg 77

May, Duncan, Dufour Editions Inc, PO Box 7, Chester Springs, PA 19425 *Tel:* 610-458-5005 *Fax:* 610-458-7103 *E-mail:* info@dufoureditions.com *Web Site:* www.dufoureditions.com, pg 77

May, Linda, The Apex Press, 4501 Forbes Blvd, Suite 200, Lanham, MD 20706 *Tel:* 301-459-3366 *Toll Free Tel:* 800-462-6420 *Toll Free Fax:* 800-388-4450 *E-mail:* customercare@rowman.com, pg 19

May, Linda, Scarecrow Press Inc, 4501 Forbes Blvd, Suite 200, Lanham, MD 20706 *Tel:* 301-459-3366 *Fax:* 301-429-5748 *Web Site:* www.scarecrowpress.com, pg 217

May, Louise, Lee & Low Books Inc, 95 Madison Ave, New York, NY 10016 *Tel:* 212-779-4400 *Toll Free Tel:* 888-320-3190 (ext 28, orders only) *Fax:* 212-683-1894 (orders only); 212-532-6035 *E-mail:* general@leeandlow.com *Web Site:* www.leeandlow.com, pg 136

May, Theresa, University of Texas Press, 2100 Comal St, Austin, TX 78722 *Tel:* 512-471-7233 *Fax:* 512-232-7178 *E-mail:* utpress@uts.cc.utexas.edu *Web Site:* www.utexaspress.com, pg 244

Mayer, Christie, Dissertation.com, 23331 Water Circle, Boca Raton, FL 33486-8540 *Tel:* 561-750-4344 *Toll Free Tel:* 800-636-8329 *Fax:* 561-750-6797 *Web Site:* www.dissertation.com, pg 74

Mayer, Dariel, Vanderbilt University Press, 2014 Broadway, Suite 320, Nashville, TN 37203 *Tel:* 615-322-3585 *Toll Free Tel:* 800-627-7377 (orders only) *Fax:* 615-343-8823 *Toll Free Fax:* 800-735-0476 (orders only) *E-mail:* vupress@vanderbilt.edu *Web Site:* www.vanderbiltuniversitypress.com, pg 264

Mayer, Karen, Penguin Group (USA) LLC, a Penguin Random House company, 375 Hudson St, New York, NY 10014 *Tel:* 212-366-2000 *Toll Free Tel:* 800-847-5515 (inside sales); 800-631-8571 (cust serv) *Fax:* 212-366-2666; 607-775-4829 (inside sales) *E-mail:* online@us.penguingroup.com *Web Site:* www.penguin.com; us.penguingroup.com, pg 186

Mayer, Liese, Scribner, 1230 Avenue of the Americas, New York, NY 10020, pg 220

Mayer, Peter, The Overlook Press, 141 Wooster St, Suite 4-B, New York, NY 10012 *Tel:* 212-673-2210; 845-679-6838 (orders & dist) *Fax:* 212-673-2296 *E-mail:* sales@overlookny.com (orders) *Web Site:* www.overlookpress.com, pg 178

Mayer, Sr Sean Marie David, Pauline Books & Media, 50 St Paul's Ave, Boston, MA 02130 *Tel:* 617-522-8911 *Toll Free Tel:* 800-876-4463 (orders); 800-836-9723 (cust serv) *Fax:* 617-541-9805 *E-mail:* editorial@paulinemedia.com (ms submissions); orderentry@pauline.org (cust serv) *Web Site:* www.pauline.org, pg 184

Mayer, Tania, The Clarion Science Fiction & Fantasy Writers' Workshop, Dept of Literature, Mail Code 0410, UC San Diego, 9500 Gilman Dr, La Jolla, CA 92093-0410 *Tel:* 858-534-2115 *E-mail:* clarion@ucsd.edu *Web Site:* clarion.ucsd.edu, pg 650

Mayer, Tom, W W Norton & Company Inc, 500 Fifth Ave, New York, NY 10110-0017 *Tel:* 212-354-5500 *Toll Free Tel:* 800-233-4830 (orders & cust serv) *Fax:* 212-869-0856 *Toll Free Fax:* 800-458-6515 *Web Site:* www.wwnorton.com, pg 172

Mayers, Roy, Abrams Learning Trends, 16310 Bratton Lane, Suite 250, Austin, TX 78728-2403 *Toll Free Tel:* 800-227-9120 *Toll Free Fax:* 800-737-3322 *E-mail:* customerservice@abramslearningtrends.com (orders, cust serv); contactus@abramslearningtrends.com *Web Site:* www.abramslearningtrends.com (orders, cust serv), pg 3

Mayhew, Alice E, Simon & Schuster, 1230 Avenue of the Americas, New York, NY 10020 *Tel:* 212-698-7000 *Toll Free Tel:* 800-223-2348 (cust serv); 800-223-2336 (orders) *Toll Free Fax:* 800-943-9831 (orders) *Web Site:* www.simonandschuster.com, pg 225

Maynard, Audrey, Tilbury House Publishers, 12 Starr St, Thomaston, ME 04861 *Tel:* 207-582-1899 *Toll Free Tel:* 800-582-1899 (orders) *Fax:* 207-582-8227 *E-mail:* tilbury@tilburyhouse.com *Web Site:* www.tilburyhouse.com, pg 246

Maynard, Gary, The Gary-Paul Agency, 1549 Main St, Stratford, CT 06615 *Tel:* 203-345-6167 *Web Site:* www.thegarypaulagency.com; www.nutmegpictures.com, pg 526

Maynard, Jim, Quicksilver Productions, PO Box 340, Ashland, OR 97520-0012 *Tel:* 541-482-5343 *Toll Free Fax:* 888-974-6462 *E-mail:* celestialcalendars@email.com *Web Site:* www.quicksilverproductions.com, pg 202

Mayotte, Alain, Prise de Parole Inc, 109 Elm St, Suite 205, Sudbury, ON P3C 1T4, Canada *Tel:* 705-675-6491 *Fax:* 705-673-1817 *E-mail:* info@prisedeparole.ca *Web Site:* www.prisedeparole.ca, pg 496

Mays, Wendy, WendyLynn & Co, 504 Wilson Rd, Annapolis, MD 21401 *Tel:* 410-224-2729; 410-507-1059 *Web Site:* wendylynn.com, pg 585

Maze, Stephanie, Moonstone Press LLC, 4816 Carrington Circle, Sarasota, FL 34243 *Tel:* 301-765-1081 *Fax:* 301-765-0510 *E-mail:* mazeprod@erols.com *Web Site:* www.moonstonepress.net, pg 508

Mazer, Laura, Seal Press, 1700 Fourth St, Berkeley, CA 94710 *Tel:* 510-595-3664 *Fax:* 510-595-4228 *Web Site:* www.sealpress.com, pg 221

Mazia, Judith, Alan Wofsy Fine Arts, 1109 Geary Blvd, San Francisco, CA 94109 *Tel:* 415-292-6500 *Toll Free Tel:* 800-660-6403 *Fax:* 415-292-6594 (off & cust serv); 510-251-1840 (acctg) *E-mail:* order@art-books.com (orders); editeur@earthlink.net (edit); beauxarts@earthlink.net (cust serv) *Web Site:* www.art-books.com, pg 274

Mazur, Julie, Watson-Guptill Publications, c/o Random House Inc, 1745 Broadway, New York, NY 10019 *Tel:* 212-782-9000 *Fax:* 212-940-7381 *E-mail:* crownbiz@randomhouse.com *Web Site:* www.randomhouse.com/crown/watsonguptill, pg 268

Mazurkiewicz, Orchid, UCLA Latin American Center Publications, UCLA Latin American Institute, 10343 Bunche Hall, Los Angeles, CA 90095 *Tel:* 310-825-4571 *Fax:* 310-206-6859 *E-mail:* latinamctr@international.ucla.edu *Web Site:* www.international.ucla.edu/lai, pg 252

Mazza, Cris, University of Illinois at Chicago, Program for Writers, College of Liberal Arts & Sciences, 2027 University Hall, 601 S Morgan St, Chicago, IL 60607-7120 *Tel:* 312-413-2200 (Eng Dept) *Fax:* 312-413-1005 *Web Site:* www.uic.edu, pg 663

Mazza, Melissa, Paradigm Publishers, 5589 Arapahoe Ave, Suite 206A, Boulder, CO 80303 *Tel:* 303-245-9054 *Web Site:* www.paradigmpublishers.com, pg 182

McAdam, Elena Goranescu, McGill-Queen's University Press, 1010 Sherbrooke W, Suite 1720, Montreal, QC H3A 2R7, Canada *Tel:* 514-398-3750 *Fax:* 514-398-4333 *E-mail:* mqup@mqup.ca *Web Site:* www.mqup.ca, pg 491

McAdam, Matthew, The Johns Hopkins University Press, 2715 N Charles St, Baltimore, MD 21218-4363 *Tel:* 410-516-6900; 410-516-6987 (journal orders outside US & CN) *Toll Free Tel:* 800-537-5487 (book orders & cust serv); 800-548-1784 (journal orders) *Fax:* 410-516-6968; 410-516-3866 (journal orders) *E-mail:* hfscustserv@press.jhu.edu (cust serv); jrnlcirc@press.jhu.edu (journal orders) *Web Site:* www.press.jhu.edu; muse.jhu.edu, pg 127

McAdams, Heather, CN Times Books, 501 Fifth Ave, Suite 1708, New York, NY 10017 *Tel:* 212-867-8666 *Web Site:* cntimesbooks.com, pg 60

McAdams, Kevin, Schiavone Literary Agency Inc, 236 Trails End, West Palm Beach, FL 33413-2135 *Tel:* 561-966-9294 *Fax:* 561-966-9294 *E-mail:* profschia@aol.com *Web Site:* www.publishersmarketplace.com/members/profschia, pg 571

McAllister, Shawn, StarGroup International Inc, 1194 Old Dixie Hwy, Suite 201, West Palm Beach, FL 33413 *Tel:* 561-547-0667 *Fax:* 561-843-8530 *E-mail:* info@stargroupinternational.com *Web Site:* www.stargroupinternational.com, pg 234

McAloon, Hugh, Krause Publications Inc, 700 E State St, Iola, WI 54990 *Tel:* 715-445-2214 *Toll Free Tel:* 800-258-0929 (cust serv); 888-457-2873 (orders) *Fax:* 715-445-4087 *E-mail:* bookorders@krause.com *Web Site:* www.krausebooks.com, pg 133

McArdle, Moira, MDR, A D&B Co, 6 Armstrong Rd, Suite 301, Shelton, CT 06484 *Tel:* 203-926-4800 *Toll Free Tel:* 800-333-8802 *Fax:* 203-225-4603 *Toll Free Fax:* 866-532-7097 *E-mail:* mdrinfo@dnb.com *Web Site:* schooldata.com, pg 152

McAuley, Scott, Angel City Press, 2118 Wilshire Blvd, Suite 880, Santa Monica, CA 90403 *Tel:* 310-395-9982 *Toll Free Tel:* 800-949-8039 *Fax:* 310-395-3353 *E-mail:* info@angelcitypress.com *Web Site:* www.angelcitypress.com, pg 18

McAweeney, Terry, MFA Publications, 465 Huntington Ave, Boston, MA 02115 *Tel:* 617-369-4233 *Fax:* 617-369-3459 *Web Site:* www.mfa.org/publications, pg 155

McBeath, Kasey, Texas Tech University Press, 2903 Fourth St, Suite 201, Lubbock, TX 79409 *Tel:* 806-742-2982 *Toll Free Tel:* 800-832-4042 *Fax:* 806-742-2979 *E-mail:* ttup@ttu.edu *Web Site:* www.ttupress.org, pg 244

McBride, David, Oxford University Press USA, 198 Madison Ave, New York, NY 10016 *Tel:* 212-726-6000 *Toll Free Tel:* 800-451-7556 (orders); 800-445-9714 (cust serv) *Fax:* 919-677-1303 *E-mail:* custserv.us@oup.com *Web Site:* www.oup.com/us, pg 179

McBride, Gerilee, Arsenal Pulp Press, 211 E Georgia St, No 202, Vancouver, BC V6A 1Z6, Canada *Tel:* 604-687-4233 *Toll Free Tel:* 888-600-PULP (600-7857) *Fax:* 604-687-4283 *E-mail:* info@arsenalpulp.com *Web Site:* www.arsenalpulp.com, pg 471

McBride, Margret, Margret McBride Literary Agency, PO Box 9128, La Jolla, CA 92038 *Tel:* 858-454-1550 *E-mail:* staff@mcbridelit.com *Web Site:* www.mcbrideliterary.com, pg 564

McCabe, Don, AVKO Educational Research Foundation Inc, 3084 Willard Rd, Birch Run, MI 48415-9404 *Tel:* 810-686-9283 (orders & billing) *Toll Free Tel:* 866-AVKO612 (285-6612) *Fax:* 810-686-1101 *E-mail:* info@avko.org (gen inquiry) *Web Site:* www.avko.org; www.avko.blogspot.org, pg 28

McCabe, Kristin, American Association of Colleges for Teacher Education (AACTE), 1307 New York Ave NW, Suite 300, Washington, DC 20005 *Tel:* 202-293-2450 *Fax:* 202-457-8095 *E-mail:* aacte@aacte.org *Web Site:* www.aacte.org, pg 11

McCabe, Robert, AVKO Educational Research Foundation Inc, 3084 Willard Rd, Birch Run, MI 48415-9404 *Tel:* 810-686-9283 (orders & billing) *Toll Free Tel:* 866-AVKO612 (285-6612) *Fax:* 810-686-1101 *E-mail:* info@avko.org (gen inquiry) *Web Site:* www.avko.org; www.avko.blogspot.org, pg 28

McCaffery, Greg, BNA Books, 1801 S Bell St, Arlington, VA 22202 *Tel:* 732-476-6397 *Toll Free Tel:* 800-372-1033; 800-960-1220 *Fax:* 732-346-1624 *E-mail:* books@bna.com *Web Site:* www.bnabooks.com, pg 41

McCaffrey, Roger A, Roman Catholic Books, PO Box 2286, Fort Collins, CO 80522-2286 *Tel:* 970-490-2735 *Fax:* 904-212-1287 *Web Site:* www.booksforcatholics.com, pg 211

McCahon, Kristin, The Fraser Institute, 1770 Burrard St, 4th fl, Vancouver, BC V6J 3G7, Canada *Tel:* 604-688-0221 *Toll Free Tel:* 800-665-3558 *Fax:* 604-688-8539 *E-mail:* info@fraserinstitute.org; sales@fraserinstitute.org *Web Site:* www.fraserinstitute.org, pg 485

McCain, Rev Paul T, Concordia Publishing House, 3558 S Jefferson Ave, St Louis, MO 63118-3968 *Tel:* 314-268-1000; 314-268-1268 (bookshop) *Toll Free Tel:* 800-325-3040 (cust serv) *Toll Free Fax:* 800-490-9889 (cust serv) *E-mail:* order@cph.org *Web Site:* www.cph.org, pg 62

McCall, Jay, The Society of Southwestern Authors (SSA), PO Box 30355, Tucson, AZ 85751-0355 *Tel:* 520-546-9382 *Web Site:* www.ssa-az.org, pg 619

McCall, Michael, Country Music Foundation Press, 222 Fifth Ave S, Nashville, TN 37203 *Tel:* 615-416-2001 *Fax:* 615-255-2245 *E-mail:* info@countrymusichalloffame.com *Web Site:* www.countrymusichalloffame.com, pg 65

McCamant, Robert, American Printing History Association, PO Box 4519, Grand Central Sta, New York, NY 10163 *Tel:* 202-544-2422 *E-mail:* secretary@printinghistory.org *Web Site:* printinghistory.org, pg 596

McCamant, Robert, American Printing History Association Award, PO Box 4519, Grand Central Sta, New York, NY 10163 *Tel:* 202-544-2422 *Web Site:* printinghistory.org, pg 667

McCamley, Maren, Living Language, c/o Random House Inc, 1745 Broadway, New York, NY 10019 *Tel:* 212-782-9000 *Toll Free Tel:* 800-733-3000 (orders) *Toll Free Fax:* 800-659-2436 *E-mail:* livinglanguage@randomhouse.com *Web Site:* www.livinglanguage.com, pg 142

McCann, Peg, American Society of Agricultural & Biological Engineers (ASABE), 2950 Niles Rd, St Joseph, MI 49085-9659 *Tel:* 269-429-0300 *Toll Free Tel:* 800-371-2723 *Fax:* 269-429-3852 *E-mail:* hq@asabe.org *Web Site:* www.asabe.org, pg 16

McCardell, Michelle, Upstart Books™, 4810 Forest Run Rd, Madison, WI 53704 *Tel:* 608-241-1201 *Toll Free Tel:* 800-448-4887 (orders) *Toll Free Fax:* 800-448-5828 *E-mail:* custsvc@upstartpromotions.com *Web Site:* www.upstartbooks.com, pg 263

McCarren, William, National Press Club (NPC), 529 14 St NW, 13th fl, Washington, DC 20045 *Tel:* 202-662-7500 *Fax:* 202-662-7569 *E-mail:* infocenter@npcpress.org *Web Site:* www.press.org, pg 613

McCarter, Robert, Jodie Rhodes Literary Agency, 8840 Villa La Jolla Dr, Suite 315, La Jolla, CA 92037 *E-mail:* jrhodesl@san.rr.com, pg 569

McCarthy, Brian, The Library of America, 14 E 60 St, New York, NY 10022-1006 *Tel:* 212-308-3360 *Fax:* 212-750-8352 *E-mail:* info@loa.org *Web Site:* www.loa.org, pg 139

McCarthy, Dan, The Taunton Press Inc, 63 S Main St, Newtown, CT 06470 *Tel:* 203-426-8171 *Toll Free Tel:* 800-477-8727 (cust serv); 800-888-8286 (orders) *Fax:* 203-426-3434 *E-mail:* booksales@taunton.com *Web Site:* www.taunton.com, pg 241

McCarthy, Donna, Houghton Mifflin Harcourt Trade & Reference Division, 222 Berkeley St, Boston, MA 02116 *Tel:* 617-351-5000 *Toll Free Tel:* 800-225-3362 *Web Site:* www.hmhco.com, pg 115

McCarthy, E J, E J McCarthy Agency, 405 Maple St, Suite A, Mill Valley, CA 94941 *Tel:* 415-383-6639 *Fax:* 415-383-6639 *E-mail:* ejmagency@gmail.com *Web Site:* www.publishersmarketplace.com/members/ejmccarthy, pg 565

McCarthy, Genevieve, BioTechniques Books, 52 Vanderbilt Ave, 11th fl, New York, NY 10017 *Tel:* 212-520-2777 *Fax:* 212-520-2705 *Web Site:* www.biotechniques.com, pg 37

McCarthy, Jim, Dystel & Goderich Literary Management, One Union Sq W, Suite 904, New York, NY 10003 *Tel:* 212-627-9100 *Fax:* 212-627-9313 *Web Site:* www.dystel.com, pg 549

McCarthy, Juliana M, The Johns Hopkins University Press, 2715 N Charles St, Baltimore, MD 21218-4363 *Tel:* 410-516-6900; 410-516-6987 (journal orders outside US & CN) *Toll Free Tel:* 800-537-5487 (book orders & cust serv); 800-548-1784 (journal orders) *Fax:* 410-516-6968; 410-516-3866 (journal orders) *E-mail:* hfscustserv@press.jhu.edu (cust serv); jrnlcirc@press.jhu.edu (journal orders) *Web Site:* www.press.jhu.edu; muse.jhu.edu, pg 127

McCarthy, Pat, Cornell & McCarthy LLC, 2-D Cross Hwy, Westport, CT 06880 *Tel:* 203-454-4210 *E-mail:* contact@cmartreps.com *Web Site:* www.cmartreps.com, pg 583

McCarthy, Sabrina, The Perseus Books Group, 387 Park Ave S, 12th fl, New York, NY 10016 *Tel:* 212-340-8100 *Toll Free Tel:* 800-343-4499 (cust serv) *Fax:* 212-340-8105 *Web Site:* www.perseusbooksgroup.com, pg 189

McCarthy, Sarah, Center for Publishing Departmental Scholarships, Midtown Ctr, Rm 429, 11 W 42 St, New York, NY 10036 *Tel:* 212-992-3232 *Fax:* 212-992-3233 *E-mail:* pub.center@nyu.edu; ms.publishing@nyu.edu *Web Site:* www.scps.nyu.edu, pg 676

McCarthy, Sarah, New York University, Center for Publishing, Midtown Ctr, Rm 429, 11 W 42 St, New York, NY 10036 *Tel:* 212-992-3232 *Fax:* 212-992-3233 *E-mail:* pub.center@nyu.edu *Web Site:* www.scps.nyu.edu/publishing, pg 661

McCarthy, Vanessa, Centre for Reformation & Renaissance Studies (CRRS), 71 Queen's Park Crescent E, Toronto, ON M5S 1K7, Canada *Tel:* 416-585-4465 *Fax:* 416-585-4430 (attn: CRRS) *E-mail:* crrs.publications@utoronto.ca *Web Site:* crrs.ca, pg 476

McCaskey, Caitlin, Penguin Random House Speakers Bureau, 1745 Broadway, Mail Drop 13-1, New York, NY 10019 *Tel:* 212-572-2013 *E-mail:* speakers@penguinrandomhouse.com *Web Site:* www.prhspeakers.com, pg 588

McCauley, Gerard, Gerard McCauley Agency Inc, PO Box 844, Katonah, NY 10536-0844 *Tel:* 914-232-5700, pg 565

McCauley, Katie, American College of Surgeons, 633 N Saint Clair St, Chicago, IL 60611-3211 *Tel:* 312-202-5000 *Fax:* 312-202-5001 *E-mail:* postmaster@facs.org *Web Site:* www.facs.org, pg 12

McCauley, Kay, Pimlico/Aurous Inc, PO Box 20490, New York, NY 10017 *Tel:* 212-628-9729 *Fax:* 212-535-7861, pg 568

McCauley, Kirby, Pimlico/Aurous Inc, PO Box 20490, New York, NY 10017 *Tel:* 212-628-9729 *Fax:* 212-535-7861, pg 568

McCaull, June, The MIT Press, 55 Hayward St, Cambridge, MA 02142 *Tel:* 617-253-5255 *Toll Free Tel:* 800-207-8354 (orders) *Fax:* 617-258-6779; 617-577-1545 (orders) *Web Site:* mitpress.mit.edu, pg 158

McCay, Deanna, Syracuse University Press, 621 Skytop Rd, Suite 110, Syracuse, NY 13244-5290 *Tel:* 315-443-5534 *Toll Free Tel:* 800-365-8929 (cust serv) *Fax:* 315-443-5545 *E-mail:* supress@syr.edu *Web Site:* syracuseuniversitypress.syr.edu, pg 239

McClain, J Cameron, Cedar Grove Books, 2215 High Point Dr, Carrollton, TX 75007 *Tel:* 415-364-8292 *Fax:* 415-276-9858 *E-mail:* queries@cedargrovebooks.com *Web Site:* www.cedargrovebooks.com, pg 52

McClanahan, Pamela, Minnesota Historical Society Press, 345 Kellogg Blvd W, St Paul, MN 55102-1906 *Tel:* 651-259-3205; 651-259-3000 *Toll Free Tel:* 800-621-2736 (warehouse) *Fax:* 651-297-1345 *Toll Free Fax:* 800-621-8476 (warehouse) *E-mail:* info-mnhspress@mnhs.org *Web Site:* www.mnhs.org/mnhspress, pg 157

McClay, Ashley Pattison, The Putnam Publishing Group, 375 Hudson St, New York, NY 10014 *Tel:* 212-366-2000 *Toll Free Tel:* 800-631-8571 *Fax:* 212-366-2643 *E-mail:* online@penguinputnam.com *Web Site:* www.penguinputnam.com; us.penguingroup.com, pg 201

McClay, Ashley Pattison, GP Putnam's Sons (Hardcover), 375 Hudson St, New York, NY 10014 *Tel:* 212-366-2000 *E-mail:* online@penguinputnam.com *Web Site:* us.penguingroup.com, pg 201

McClellan, Anita, Anita D McClellan Associates, 464 Common St, Suite 142, Belmont, MA 02478-2704 *Tel:* 617-575-9203 *Fax:* 617-315-8983 *E-mail:* adm@anitamcclellan.com *Web Site:* www.anitamcclellan.com, pg 565

McClellan, Anita D, Anita D McClellan Associates, 464 Common St, Suite 142, Belmont, MA 02478-2704 *Tel:* 617-575-9203 *Fax:* 617-315-8983 *E-mail:* adm@anitamcclellan.com *Web Site:* www.anitamcclellan.com, pg 530

McClellan, Dennis, DC Press LLC, 750 Powderhorn Circle, Lake Mary, FL 32746 *Tel:* 407-688-1156 *Toll Free Tel:* 877-203-1895 *Web Site:* www.dcpressbooks.com, pg 72

McClelland, Anne, Book & Periodical Council (BPC), 192 Spadina Ave, Suite 107, Toronto, ON M5T 2C2, Canada *Tel:* 416-975-9366 *Fax:* 416-975-1839 *E-mail:* info@thebpc.ca *Web Site:* www.thebpc.ca, pg 600

McClure, Cameron, Donald Maass Literary Agency, 121 W 27 St, Suite 801, New York, NY 10001 *Tel:* 212-727-8383 *Fax:* 212-727-3271 *E-mail:* info@maassagency.com *Web Site:* www.maassagency.com, pg 562

McClure, Dr Donald E, American Mathematical Society, 201 Charles St, Providence, RI 02904-2294 *Tel:* 401-455-4000 *Toll Free Tel:* 800-321-4267 *Fax:* 401-331-3842; 401-455-4046 (cust serv) *E-mail:* ams@ams.org; cust-serv@ams.org *Web Site:* www.ams.org, pg 14

McClure, John, Signalman Publishing, 3700 Commerce Blvd, Kissimmee, FL 34741 *Tel:* 407-504-4103 *Toll Free Tel:* 888-907-4423 *E-mail:* info@signalmanpublishing.com *Web Site:* www.signalmanpublishing.com, pg 224

McClure, Urmila, Signalman Publishing, 3700 Commerce Blvd, Kissimmee, FL 34741 *Tel:* 407-504-4103 *Toll Free Tel:* 888-907-4423 *E-mail:* info@signalmanpublishing.com *Web Site:* www.signalmanpublishing.com, pg 224

McCollough, Aaron, University of Michigan Press, 839 Greene St, Ann Arbor, MI 48104-3209 *Tel:* 734-764-4388 *Fax:* 734-615-1540 *E-mail:* esladmin@umich.edu *Web Site:* www.press.umich.edu, pg 257

McCollum, Lauren, Chain Store Guide (CSG), 10117 Princess Palm Ave, Suite 375, Tampa, FL 33610 *Tel:* 813-627-6957 *Toll Free Tel:* 800-927-9292 (orders) *Fax:* 813-627-6888 *E-mail:* info@csgis.com *Web Site:* www.csgis.com, pg 54

McConkey, Jill, University of Manitoba Press, University of Manitoba, 301 St Johns College, 92 Dysart Rd, Winnipeg, MB R3T 2M5, Canada *Tel:* 204-474-9495 *Fax:* 204-474-7566 *E-mail:* uofmpress@umanitoba.ca *Web Site:* uofmpress.ca, pg 503

McConnell, Ami, Howard Books, 216 Centerview Dr, Suite 303, Brentwood, TN 37027 *Tel:* 615-873-2080 *Fax:* 615-370-3834 *E-mail:* howardbooks@simonandschuster.com (info) *Web Site:* www.howardpublishing.com, pg 116

McConnell, Christine, Margaret Mann Citation, 50 E Huron St, Chicago, IL 60611 *Tel:* 312-280-5037 *Toll Free Tel:* 800-545-2433 *Fax:* 312-280-5033 *E-mail:* alcts@ala.org *Web Site:* www.ala.org/alcts, pg 705

McConnell, David B, Hillsdale Educational Publishers Inc, 39 North St, Hillsdale, MI 49242 *Tel:* 517-437-3179 *Fax:* 517-437-0531 *E-mail:* davestory@aol.com *Web Site:* www.hillsdalepublishers.com; michbooks.com, pg 111

McConnell, Ted, Advertising Research Foundation (ARF), 432 Park Ave S, 6th fl, New York, NY 10016-8013 *Tel:* 212-751-5656 *Fax:* 212-319-5265 *E-mail:* info@thearf.org; jar@thearf.org (edit) *Web Site:* www.thearf.org, pg 593

McConville, Sarah, Harvard Business Review Press, 300 N Beacon St, Watertown, MA 02472 *Tel:* 617-783-7400 *Fax:* 617-783-7489 *E-mail:* custserv@hbsp.harvard.edu *Web Site:* www.harvardbusiness.org, pg 106

McCoy, Anne, Columbia University Press, 61 W 62 St, New York, NY 10023 *Tel:* 212-459-0600 *Toll Free Tel:* 800-944-8648 *Fax:* 212-459-3678 *E-mail:* cup_book@columbia.edu (orders & cust serv) *Web Site:* cup.columbia.edu, pg 61

McCoy, Beverly, Eisenbrauns Inc, PO Box 275, Winona Lake, IN 46590-0275 *Tel:* 574-269-2011 *Fax:* 574-269-6788 *E-mail:* customer_service@eisenbrauns.com; publisher@eisenbrauns.com *Web Site:* www.eisenbrauns.com, pg 80

McCoy, James, Iowa Poetry Prize, 119 W Park Rd, 100 Kuhl House, Iowa City, IA 52242-1000 *Tel:* 319-335-2000 *Fax:* 319-335-2055 *E-mail:* uipress@uiowa.edu *Web Site:* www.uiowapress.org, pg 695

McCoy, James, Iowa Short Fiction Awards, 119 W Park Rd, 100 Kuhl House, Iowa City, IA 52242-1000 *Tel:* 319-335-2000 *Fax:* 319-335-2055 *E-mail:* uipress@uiowa.edu *Web Site:* www.uiowapress.org, pg 696

McCoy, James, University of Iowa Press, 119 W Park Rd, 100 Kuhl House, Iowa City, IA 52242-1000 *Tel:* 319-335-2000 *Toll Free Tel:* 800-621-2736 (orders only) *Fax:* 319-335-2055 *Toll Free Fax:* 800-621-8476 (orders only) *E-mail:* uipress@uiowa.edu *Web Site:* www.uiowapress.org, pg 256

McCoy, Melody, Jhpiego, 1615 Thames St, Baltimore, MD 21231-3492 *Tel:* 410-537-1800 *Fax:* 410-537-1473 *E-mail:* info@jhpiego.net *Web Site:* www.jhpiego.org, pg 126

McCracken, Brad, Pauline Books & Media, 50 St Paul's Ave, Boston, MA 02130 *Tel:* 617-522-8911 *Toll Free Tel:* 800-876-4463 (orders); 800-836-9723 (cust serv) *Fax:* 617-541-9805 *E-mail:* editorial@paulinemedia.com (ms submissions); orderentry@pauline.org (cust serv) *Web Site:* www.pauline.org, pg 184

McCrae, Fiona, Graywolf Press, 250 Third Ave N, Suite 600, Minneapolis, MN 55401 *Tel:* 651-641-0077 *Fax:* 651-641-0036 *E-mail:* wolves@graywolfpress.org *Web Site:* www.graywolfpress.org, pg 100

McCreary, Courtney, University Press of Mississippi, 3825 Ridgewood Rd, Jackson, MS 39211-6492 *Tel:* 601-432-6205 *Toll Free Tel:* 800-737-7788 (orders & cust serv) *Fax:* 601-432-6217 *E-mail:* press@mississippi.edu *Web Site:* www.upress.state.ms.us, pg 262

McCreight, Tim, American Institute of Chemical Engineers (AIChE), 120 Wall St, 23rd fl, New York, NY 10005-4020 *Tel:* 203-702-7660 *Toll Free Tel:* 800-242-4363 *Fax:* 203-775-5177 *E-mail:* customerservice@aiche.org *Web Site:* www.aiche.org, pg 13

McCullough, Mark S, Wyndham Hall Press, 5050 Kerr Rd, Lima, OH 45806 *Tel:* 419-648-9124 *Toll Free Tel:* 866-895-0977 *Fax:* 419-648-9124; 413-208-2409 *E-mail:* whpbooks@wyndhamhallbooks.com; orders@wyndhamhallbooks.com *Web Site:* www.wyndhamhallpress.com, pg 277

McCullough, Michael, Duke University Press, 905 W Main St, Suite 18B, Durham, NC 27701 *Tel:* 919-688-5134 *Toll Free Tel:* 888-651-0122 (US) *Fax:* 919-688-2615 *Toll Free Fax:* 888-651-0124 *E-mail:* orders@dukeupress.edu; permissions@dukeupress.edu *Web Site:* www.dukeupress.edu, pg 77

McCullough, Robert, Penguin Random House Canada Limited, 320 Front St W, Suite 1400, Toronto, ON M5V 3B6, Canada *Tel:* 416-364-4449 *Toll Free Tel:* 888-523-9292 (cust serv) *Fax:* 416-364-6863; 416-364-6653 (subs rts) *Web Site:* penguinrandomhouse.ca, pg 495

McCully, Meredith, Beyond the Book, 222 Rosewood Dr, Danvers, MA 01923 *Tel:* 978-750-8400 *Fax:* 978-646-8600 *E-mail:* beyondthebook@copyright.com *Web Site:* www.copyright.com; beyondthebookcast.com, pg 650

McCune, Sara Miller, SAGE Publications, 2455 Teller Rd, Thousand Oaks, CA 91320 *Toll Free Tel:* 800-818-7243 *Toll Free Fax:* 800-583-2665 *E-mail:* info@sagepub.com *Web Site:* www.sagepub.com, pg 214

McCurdy, Wendy, Kensington Publishing Corp, 119 W 40 St, New York, NY 10018 *Tel:* 212-407-1500 *Toll Free Tel:* 800-221-2647 *Fax:* 212-935-0699 *Web Site:* www.kensingtonbooks.com, pg 130

McCutcheon, Clark, Jodie Rhodes Literary Agency, 8840 Villa La Jolla Dr, Suite 315, La Jolla, CA 92037 *E-mail:* jrhodesl@san.rr.com, pg 569

McDaniel, Clay, ProQuest LLC, 789 E Eisenhower Pkwy, Ann Arbor, MI 48108-3218 *Tel:* 734-761-4700 *Toll Free Tel:* 800-521-0600 *Fax:* 734-975-6486 *Toll Free Fax:* 800-864-0019 *E-mail:* info@proquest.com *Web Site:* www.proquest.com, pg 199

McDermott, Diana, M E Sharpe Inc, 80 Business Park Dr, Suite 202, Armonk, NY 10504 *Tel:* 914-273-1800 *Toll Free Tel:* 800-541-6563 *Fax:* 914-273-2106 *E-mail:* info@mesharpe.com *Web Site:* www.mesharpe.com, pg 223

McDermott, Kathleen, Harvard University Press, 79 Garden St, Cambridge, MA 02138-1499 *Tel:* 617-495-2600; 401-531-2800 (intl orders) *Toll Free Tel:* 800-405-1619 (orders) *Fax:* 617-495-5898 (general); 617-496-4677 (edit & rts); 401-531-2801 (intl orders) *Toll Free Fax:* 800-406-9145 (orders) *E-mail:* contact_hup@harvard.edu *Web Site:* www.hup.harvard.edu, pg 107

McDevitt, Jo-Ann, AAP PreK-12 Learning Group, 325 Chestnut St, Suite 1110, Philadelphia, PA 19106 *Tel:* 267-351-4310 *Fax:* 267-351-4317 *E-mail:* prek12learning@publishers.org *Web Site:* www.aepweb.org, pg 593

McDiarmid, Mark, Penguin Group (USA) LLC Sales, 375 Hudson St, New York, NY 10014 *Tel:* 212-366-2000 *E-mail:* online@penguinputnam.com *Web Site:* us.penguingroup.com, pg 187

McDonald, Alison, Gagosian Gallery, 980 Madison Ave, New York, NY 10075 *Tel:* 212-744-2313 *Fax:* 212-772-7962 *E-mail:* newyork@gagosian.com *Web Site:* www.gagosian.com, pg 93

McDonald, Caitlin, Sterling Lord Literistic Inc, 65 Bleecker St, New York, NY 10012 *Tel:* 212-780-6050 *Fax:* 212-780-6095 *E-mail:* info@sll.com *Web Site:* www.sll.com, pg 575

McDonald, Erroll, Pantheon Books/Schocken Books, c/o Random House Inc, 1745 Broadway, New York, NY 10019 *Tel:* 212-751-2600 *Toll Free Tel:* 800-638-6460 *Fax:* 212-572-6030, pg 181

McDonald, Jerry N, The McDonald & Woodward Publishing Co, 695 Tall Oaks Dr, Newark, OH 43055 *Tel:* 740-641-2691 *Toll Free Tel:* 800-233-8787 *Fax:* 740-641-2692 *E-mail:* mwpubco@mwpubco.com *Web Site:* www.mwpubco.com, pg 150

McDonald, Kathy, Bisk Education, 9417 Princess Palm Ave, Suite 400, Tampa, FL 33619 *Tel:* 813-621-6200 *Toll Free Tel:* 800-280-9718 (cust serv) *E-mail:* customerservice@bisk.com *Web Site:* www.bisk.com, pg 37

McDonald, Mary, American Philosophical Society, 104 S Fifth St, Philadelphia, PA 19106 *Tel:* 215-440-3425 *Fax:* 215-440-3450 *E-mail:* dianepub@comcast.net *Web Site:* www.amphilsoc.org, pg 15

McDonnell, Mark, Bloom's Literary Criticism, 132 W 31 St, 17th fl, New York, NY 10001 *Toll Free Tel:* 800-322-8755 *Toll Free Fax:* 800-678-3633 *E-mail:* custserv@factsonfile.com *Web Site:* www.infobasepublishing.com, pg 39

McDonnell, Mark, Cambridge Educational, 132 W 31 St, 17th fl, New York, NY 10001 *Toll Free Tel:* 800-322-8755 *Fax:* 609-671-0266 *Toll Free Fax:* 800-329-6687 *E-mail:* custserve@infobaselearning.com *Web Site:* www.infobasepublishing.com, pg 48

McDonnell, Mark, Chelsea House Publishers, 132 W 31 St, 17th fl, New York, NY 10001 *Tel:* 212-967-8800 *Toll Free Tel:* 800-322-8755 *Fax:* 917-339-0325 *Toll Free Fax:* 800-678-3633 *E-mail:* custserv@factsonfile.com *Web Site:* www.infobasepublishing.com; www.infobaselearning.com, pg 56

McDonnell, Mark, Facts On File, 132 W 31 St, 17th fl, New York, NY 10001 *Tel:* 212-967-8800 *Toll Free Tel:* 800-322-8755 *Toll Free Fax:* 800-678-3633 *E-mail:* custserv@factsonfile.com *Web Site:* infobasepublishing.com, pg 85

McDonnell, Mark, Ferguson Publishing, 132 W 31 St, 17th fl, New York, NY 10001 *Tel:* 212-967-8800 *Toll Free Tel:* 800-322-8755 *Fax:* 917-339-0323 *Toll Free Fax:* 800-678-3633 *E-mail:* custserv@factsonfile.com *Web Site:* infobasepublishing.com, pg 88

McDonnough, Paul A, Direct Marketing Association (DMA), 1120 Avenue of the Americas, New York, NY 10036-6700 *Tel:* 212-768-7277 *Fax:* 212-302-6714 *E-mail:* memberservices@the-dma.org *Web Site:* thedma.org, pg 604

McDonough, Aileen, SDP Publishing Solutions LLC, 36 Captain's Way, East Bridgewater, MA 02333 *Tel:* 617-775-0656 *Web Site:* www.sdppublishingsolutions.com, pg 534

McDonough, Gregory K, EEI Communications, 6301 Ivy Lane, Suite 250, Greenbelt, MD 20770 *Tel:* 410-309-8200 *Fax:* 410-630-3980 *E-mail:* info@eeicom.com *Web Site:* www.eeicom.com, pg 525, 660

McDonough, Katie, National Book Awards, 90 Broad St, Suite 604, New York, NY 10004 *Tel:* 212-685-0261 *Fax:* 212-213-6570 *E-mail:* nationalbook@nationalbook.org *Web Site:* www.nationalbook.org, pg 710

McDonough, Liz, University of California Extension Professional Sequence in Copyediting & Courses in Publishing, 1995 University Ave, Suite 110, Berkeley, CA 94720-7000 *Tel:* 510-642-6362 *Fax:* 510-643-0216 *E-mail:* letters@unex.berkeley.edu *Web Site:* www.unex.berkeley.edu, pg 663

McDuffie, John, American Psychiatric Publishing (APP), 1000 Wilson Blvd, Suite 1825, Arlington, VA 22209 *Tel:* 703-907-7322 *Toll Free Tel:* 800-368-5777 *Fax:* 703-907-1091 *E-mail:* appi@psych.org *Web Site:* www.appi.org; www.psychiatryonline.org, pg 15

McElvene, Clyde, Hurston/Wright Award for College Writers, 12138 Central Ave, Suite 209, Bowie, MD 20721 *Tel:* 301-459-2108 *Fax:* 301-277-1262 *E-mail:* info@hurstonwright.org *Web Site:* www.hurstonwright.org, pg 693

McElvene, Clyde, Hurston/Wright Legacy Awards, 12138 Central Ave, Suite 209, Bowie, MD 20721 *Tel:* 301-459-2108 *Fax:* 301-277-1262 *E-mail:* info@hurstonwright.org *Web Site:* www.hurstonwright.org, pg 694

McElvene, Clyde, Hurston/Wright Writer's Week, 12138 Central Ave, Suite 209, Bowie, MD 20721 *Tel:* 301-459-2108 *Fax:* 301-277-1262 *E-mail:* info@hurstonwright.org *Web Site:* www.hurstonwright.org, pg 652

McEvoy, Nion, Chronicle Books LLC, 680 Second St, San Francisco, CA 94107 *Tel:* 415-537-4200 *Toll Free Tel:* 800-759-0190 (cust serv) *Fax:* 415-537-4460 *Toll Free Fax:* 800-858-7787 (orders); 800-286-9471 (cust serv) *E-mail:* frontdesk@chroniclebooks.com *Web Site:* www.chroniclebooks.com, pg 57

McEvoy, William, The Guilford Press, 72 Spring St, New York, NY 10012 *Tel:* 212-431-9800 *Toll Free Tel:* 800-365-7006 *Fax:* 212-966-6708 *E-mail:* info@guilford.com *Web Site:* www.guilford.com, pg 102

McEwen, Rebecca, Fulcrum Publishing Inc, 4690 Table Mountain Dr, Suite 100, Golden, CO 80403 *Tel:* 303-277-1623 *Toll Free Tel:* 800-992-2908 *Fax:* 303-279-7111 *Toll Free Fax:* 800-726-7112 *E-mail:* info@fulcrumbooks.com; orders@fulcrumbooks.com *Web Site:* www.fulcrumbooks.com, pg 93

McFadden, Michael, Peter Lang Publishing Inc, 29 Broadway, 18th fl, New York, NY 10006-3223 *Tel:* 212-647-7706 *Toll Free Tel:* 800-770-5264 (cust serv) *Fax:* 212-647-7707 *Web Site:* www.peterlang.com, pg 134

McFadden, Wendy, Brethren Press, 1451 Dundee Ave, Elgin, IL 60120 *Tel:* 847-742-5100 *Toll Free Tel:* 800-323-8039 *Toll Free Fax:* 800-667-8188 *E-mail:* brethrenpress@brethren.org *Web Site:* www.brethrenpress.com, pg 45

McFarlane, Megan, Scholastic Library/National Library Week Grant, 50 E Huron St, Chicago, IL 60611 *Tel:* 312-280-2148 *Toll Free Tel:* 800-545-2433 (ext 2148) *Fax:* 312-280-5274 *Web Site:* www.ala.org/nlwgrant, pg 727

McFeely, W Drake, The Countryman Press, c/o W W Norton & Co Inc, 500 Fifth Ave, New York, NY 10110 *Tel:* 212-354-5500 *Fax:* 212-869-0856 *E-mail:* countrymanpress@wwnorton.com *Web Site:* www.countrymanpress.com, pg 65

McFeely, W Drake, W W Norton & Company Inc, 500 Fifth Ave, New York, NY 10110-0017 *Tel:* 212-354-5500 *Toll Free Tel:* 800-233-4830 (orders & cust serv) *Fax:* 212-869-0856 *Toll Free Fax:* 800-458-6515 *Web Site:* www.wwnorton.com, pg 171

McGahern, Liam, ABAC/ALAC, 368 Dalhousie St, Suite 301, Ottawa, ON K1N 7G3, Canada *Tel:* 416-364-2376 *E-mail:* info@abac.org *Web Site:* www.abac.org, pg 593

McGandy, Michael J, Cornell University Press, Sage House, 512 E State St, Ithaca, NY 14850 *Tel:* 607-277-2338 *Fax:* 607-277-2374 *E-mail:* cupressinfo@cornell.edu; cupress-sales@cornell.edu *Web Site:* www.cornellpress.cornell.edu, pg 63

McGarity, Todd, Hachette Book Group, 1290 Avenue of the Americas, New York, NY 10019 *Tel:* 212-364-1100 *Toll Free Tel:* 800-759-0190 (cust serv) *Fax:* 212-364-0933 (intl orders) *Toll Free Fax:* 800-286-9471 (cust serv) *Web Site:* www.HachetteBookGroup.com, pg 102

McGeagh, Ellen, Greenhaven Press®, 27500 Drake Rd, Farmington Hills, MI 48331 *Toll Free Tel:* 800-877-GALE (877-4253 - cust serv & orders) *Toll Free Fax:* 800-414-5043 (orders only) *E-mail:* gale.customerservice@cengage.com; gale.galeord@cengage.com *Web Site:* www.gale.cengage.com/greenhaven, pg 100

McGee, Colin, Jessica Kingsley Publishers Inc, 400 Market St, Suite 400, Philadelphia, PA 19106 *Tel:* 215-922-1161 *Toll Free Tel:* 866-416-1078 (cust serv) *Fax:* 215-922-1474 *E-mail:* orders@jkp.com; hello.usa@jkp.com *Web Site:* www.jkp.com, pg 131

McGee, Linda, Bearport Publishing Co Inc, 45 W 21 St, Suite 3B, New York, NY 10010 *Tel:* 212-337-8577 *Toll Free Tel:* 877-337-8577 *Fax:* 212-337-8557 *Toll Free Fax:* 866-337-8557 *E-mail:* service@bearportpublishing.com; info@bearportpublishing.com *Web Site:* www.bearportpublishing.com, pg 33

McGee, Mary, Fire Engineering Books & Videos, 1421 S Sheridan Rd, Tulsa, OK 74112 *Tel:* 918-931-9410 *Toll Free Tel:* 800-752-9764 *Fax:* 918-931-9555 *E-mail:* sales@pennwell.com *Web Site:* www.pennwellbooks.com, pg 89

McGee, Mary, PennWell Books, 1421 S Sheridan Rd, Tulsa, OK 74112 *Tel:* 918-831-9410 *Toll Free Tel:* 800-752-9764 *Fax:* 918-831-9555 *E-mail:* sales@pennwell.com *Web Site:* www.pennwellbooks.com, pg 188

McGeehon, Allison, Artisan Books, 225 Varick St, New York, NY 10014-4381 *Tel:* 212-254-5900 *Toll Free Tel:* 800-722-7202 *Fax:* 212-677-6692 *E-mail:* artisaninfo@artisanbooks.com *Web Site:* www.workman.com/artisanbooks, pg 23

McGeehon, Priscilla, Fairchild Books, 1385 Broadway, 5th fl, New York, NY 10018 *Tel:* 212-419-5300 *Toll Free Tel:* 800-932-4724; 888-330-8477 (orders) *Fax:* 212-704-5975 *Web Site:* bloomsbury.com/us/academic/fairchildbooks, pg 85

McGeehon, Priscilla, Westview Press, 2465 Central Ave, Boulder, CO 80301 *Tel:* 303-444-3541 *Fax:* 720-406-7336 *E-mail:* westview.orders@perseusbooks.com *Web Site:* www.perseusbooksgroup.com; www.westviewpress.com, pg 270

McGhee, Holly M, Pippin Properties Inc, 110 W 40 St, Suite 1704, New York, NY 10018 *Tel:* 212-338-9310 *Fax:* 212-338-9579 *E-mail:* info@pippinproperties.com *Web Site:* www.pippinproperties.com; www.facebook.com/pippinproperties, pg 568

McGill, Julia Lee, Melanie Jackson Agency LLC, 41 W 72 St, Suite 3F, New York, NY 10023 *Tel:* 212-873-3373, pg 558

McGinn, Patrick, Clinical Laboratory & Standards Institute (CLSI), 950 W Valley Rd, Suite 2500, Wayne, PA 19087 *Tel:* 610-688-0100 *Toll Free Tel:* 877-447-1888 (orders) *Fax:* 610-688-0700 *E-mail:* customerservice@clsi.org *Web Site:* www.clsi.org, pg 59

McGinnis, Claire, Riverhead Books (Hardcover), 375 Hudson St, New York, NY 10014 *Tel:* 212-366-2000 *E-mail:* online@penguinputnam.com *Web Site:* www.penguinputnam.com; us.penguingroup.com, pg 209

McGinnis, Meredith, W W Norton & Company Inc, 500 Fifth Ave, New York, NY 10110-0017 *Tel:* 212-354-5500 *Toll Free Tel:* 800-233-4830 (orders & cust serv) *Fax:* 212-869-0856 *Toll Free Fax:* 800-458-6515 *Web Site:* www.wwnorton.com, pg 171

McGonigle, Michele, Hachette Audio, 1290 Avenue of the Americas, New York, NY 10019 *Tel:* 212-364-1100, pg 102

McGowan, Matt, Frances Goldin Literary Agency, Inc, 57 E 11 St, Suite 5-B, New York, NY 10003 *Tel:* 212-777-0047 *Fax:* 212-228-1660 *E-mail:* agency@goldinlit.com *Web Site:* www.goldinlit.com, pg 554

McGowan, Tony, The Melville Society, Johns Hopkins University Press, PO Box 19966, Baltimore, MD 21211-0966 *Web Site:* melvillesociety.org, pg 610

McGrane, Marilyn, Krause Publications Inc, 700 E State St, Iola, WI 54990 *Tel:* 715-445-2214 *Toll Free Tel:* 800-258-0929 (cust serv); 888-457-2873 (orders) *Fax:* 715-445-4087 *E-mail:* bookorders@krause.com *Web Site:* www.krausebooks.com, pg 133

McGrath, Erinn, Alfred A Knopf/Everyman's Library, c/o Random House Inc, 1745 Broadway, New York, NY 10019 *Tel:* 212-751-2600 *Toll Free Tel:* 800-638-6460 *Fax:* 212-572-2593 *Web Site:* www.knopfdoubleday.com, pg 132

McGrath, Mary, Penguin Group (USA) LLC Sales, 375 Hudson St, New York, NY 10014 *Tel:* 212-366-2000 *E-mail:* online@penguinputnam.com *Web Site:* us.penguingroup.com, pg 186

McGrath, Michael, LinguaText Ltd, 103 Walker Way, Newark, DE 19711 *Tel:* 302-453-8695 *Fax:* 302-453-8601 *Web Site:* www.linguatextltd.com, pg 140

McGrath, Sarah, Riverhead Books (Hardcover), 375 Hudson St, New York, NY 10014 *Tel:* 212-366-2000 *E-mail:* online@penguinputnam.com *Web Site:* www.penguinputnam.com; us.penguingroup.com, pg 209

McGraw, Delois, Ozark Creative Writers Inc Annual Conference, PO Box 9076, Fayetteville, AR 72703 *Tel:* 479-751-7246 *E-mail:* ozarkcreativewriters1@gmail.com *Web Site:* www.ozarkcreativewriters.org, pg 654

McGraw, Harold W (Terry) III, McGraw-Hill Financial, 1221 Avenue of the Americas, 50th fl, New York, NY 10020 *Tel:* 212-512-2000 *Web Site:* www.mhfi.com, pg 151

McGraw, Mary, Bookhaven Press LLC, 302 Scenic Ct, Moon Township, PA 15108 *Tel:* 412-494-6926 *E-mail:* info@bookhavenpress.com; orders@bookhavenpress.com *Web Site:* bookhavenpress.com, pg 42

McGray, Jo Anne, Multimedia Larga, 900 S Boardman Dr, No G72, Gallup, NM 87301, pg 161

McGuire, Beverly, Coastside Editorial, PO Box 181, Moss Beach, CA 94038 *E-mail:* bevjoe@pacific.net, pg 523

McGuire, Libby, Random House Publishing Group, 1745 Broadway, New York, NY 10019 *Toll Free Tel:* 800-200-3552 *Web Site:* atrandom.com, pg 204

McGuire, Margaret, Quirk Books, 215 Church St, Philadelphia, PA 19106 *Tel:* 215-627-3581 *Fax:* 215-627-5220 *E-mail:* general@quirkbooks.com *Web Site:* www.quirkbooks.com, pg 202

McGuire, Marilyn, Nautilus Awards, 378 Bromley Dr, Eastsound, WA 98245 *Tel:* 360-376-2001 *Web Site:* www.nautilusbookawards.com, pg 711

McGuire, Tim, W W Norton & Company Inc, 500 Fifth Ave, New York, NY 10110-0017 *Tel:* 212-354-5500 *Toll Free Tel:* 800-233-4830 (orders & cust serv) *Fax:* 212-869-0856 *Toll Free Fax:* 800-458-6515 *Web Site:* www.wwnorton.com, pg 171

McGuirk, George, Pearson Scott Foresman, 1900 E Lake Ave, Glenview, IL 60025 *Tel:* 847-729-3000 *Toll Free Tel:* 800-535-4391 (Midwest) *Fax:* 847-729-8910 *Web Site:* www.pearsonschool.com, pg 185

McGurgan, Diane, Council for the Advancement of Science Writing (CASW), PO Box 910, Hedgesville, WV 25427 *Tel:* 304-754-6786 *Web Site:* www.casw.org, pg 604

McGurk, John, Quirk Books, 215 Church St, Philadelphia, PA 19106 *Tel:* 215-627-3581 *Fax:* 215-627-5220 *E-mail:* general@quirkbooks.com *Web Site:* www.quirkbooks.com, pg 202

McHugh, Arianne, Saddleback Educational Publishing, 3120-A Pullman St, Costa Mesa, CA 92626 *Tel:* 714-640-5200 *Toll Free Tel:* 888-SDLBACK (735-2225); 800-637-8715 *Fax:* 714-640-5297 *Toll Free Fax:* 888-734-4010 *E-mail:* contact@sdlback.com *Web Site:* www.sdlback.com, pg 213

McHugh, Daniel, National Institute for Trial Advocacy (NITA), 1685 38 St, Suite 200, Boulder, CO 80301-2735 *Tel:* 720-890-4860 *Toll Free Tel:* 877-648-2632; 800-225-6482 (orders & returns) *Fax:* 720-890-7069 *E-mail:* info@nita.org *Web Site:* www.nita.org, pg 165

McHugh, John B, McHugh's Rights/Permissions Workshop™, PO Box 170665, Milwaukee, WI 53217-8056 *Tel:* 414-351-3056 *E-mail:* jack@johnbmchugh.com *Web Site:* www.johnbmchugh.com, pg 652

McIlroy, Randal, Pemmican Publications Inc, 150 Henry Ave, Winnipeg, MB R3B 0J7, Canada *Tel:* 204-589-6346 *Fax:* 204-589-2063 *E-mail:* pemmican@pemmican.mb.ca *Web Site:* www.pemmican.mb.ca, pg 494

McInerney, Paige, Penguin Group (USA) LLC, a Penguin Random House company, 375 Hudson St, New York, NY 10014 *Tel:* 212-366-2000 *Toll Free Tel:* 800-847-5515 (inside sales); 800-631-8571 (cust serv) *Fax:* 212-366-2666; 607-775-4829 (inside sales) *E-mail:* online@us.penguingroup.com *Web Site:* www.penguin.com; us.penguingroup.com, pg 186

McIntosh, Dorla, Columbia University School of the Arts, Creative Writing Program, 617 Kent Hall, New York, NY 10027 *Tel:* 212-854-3774 *Fax:* 212-854-7704 *E-mail:* writingprogram@columbia.edu *Web Site:* www.columbia.edu/cu/writing, pg 659

McIntosh, Joel, Prufrock Press, PO Box 8813, Waco, TX 76714-8813 *Tel:* 254-756-3337 *Toll Free Tel:* 800-998-2208 *Fax:* 254-756-3339 *Toll Free Fax:* 800-240-0333 *E-mail:* info@prufrock.com *Web Site:* www.prufrock.com, pg 199

McIntosh, Kelly, Barbour Publishing Inc, 1810 Barbour Dr, Uhrichsville, OH 44683 *Tel:* 740-922-6045 *Fax:* 740-922-5948 *E-mail:* info@barbourbooks.com *Web Site:* www.barbourbooks.com, pg 30

McIntosh, Madeline, Penguin Random House Inc, 1745 Broadway, New York, NY 10019 *Tel:* 212-782-9000 *Toll Free Tel:* 800-726-0600 *Web Site:* www.randomhouse.com, pg 187

McIntosh, Susan, McGill-Queen's University Press, 1010 Sherbrooke W, Suite 1720, Montreal, QC H3A 2R7, Canada *Tel:* 514-398-3750 *Fax:* 514-398-4333 *E-mail:* mqup@mqup.ca *Web Site:* www.mqup.ca, pg 491

McIntyre, Jennifer, South Dakota Historical Society Press, 900 Governors Dr, Pierre, SD 57501 *Tel:* 605-773-6009 *Fax:* 605-773-6041 *E-mail:* info@sdshspress.com *Web Site:* sdshspress.com, pg 231

McIntyre, Kheil, LearningExpress LLC, 2 Rector St, 26th fl, New York, NY 10006 *Tel:* 212-995-2566 *Toll Free Tel:* 800-295-9556 (ext 2) *Fax:* 212-995-5512 *E-mail:* customerservice@learningexpressllc.com (cust serv) *Web Site:* www.learningexpressllc.com, pg 136

McIntyre, Maury, Television Academy, 5220 Lankershim Blvd, North Hollywood, CA 91601-3109 *Tel:* 818-754-2800 *Fax:* 818-761-2827 *Web Site:* www.emmys.com, pg 620

McIntyre, Suzanne Ostiguy, Institute for Research on Public Policy (IRPP), 1470 Peel St, No 200, Montreal, QC H3A 1T1, Canada *Tel:* 514-985-2461 *Fax:* 514-985-2559 *E-mail:* irpp@irpp.org *Web Site:* www.irpp.org, pg 488

McIntyre, Tina, Little, Brown Books for Young Readers, 1290 Avenue of the Americas, New York, NY 10019 *Tel:* 212-364-1100 *Toll Free Tel:* 800-759-0190 (cust serv) *Web Site:* www.HachetteBookGroup.com, pg 141

McKay, Matt PhD, New Harbinger Publications Inc, 5674 Shattuck Ave, Oakland, CA 94609 *Tel:* 510-652-0215 *Toll Free Tel:* 800-748-6273 (orders only) *Fax:* 510-652-5472 *Toll Free Fax:* 800-652-1613 *E-mail:* nhhelp@newharbinger.com; customerservice@newharbinger.com *Web Site:* www.newharbinger.com, pg 167

McMillan, Sally Hill, Sally Hill McMillan LLC, 429 E Kingston Ave, Charlotte, NC 28203 *Tel:* 704-334-0897 *E-mail:* mcmagency@aol.com, pg 565

McMillen, Wendy, University of Notre Dame Press, 310 Flanner Hall, Notre Dame, IN 46556 *Tel:* 574-631-6346 *Fax:* 574-631-8148 *E-mail:* undpress@nd.edu *Web Site:* www.undpress.nd.edu, pg 258

McMullen, Shawn, Standard Publishing, 8805 Governors Hill Dr, Suite 400, Cincinnati, OH 45249 *Tel:* 513-931-4050 *Toll Free Tel:* 800-543-1353 *Fax:* 513-931-0950 *Toll Free Fax:* 877-867-5751 *E-mail:* customerservice@standardpub.com *Web Site:* www.standardpub.com, pg 233

McMurray, Debbie, Nilgiri Press, 3600 Tomales Rd, Tomales, CA 94971 *Tel:* 707-878-2369 *E-mail:* info@easwaran.org *Web Site:* www.easwaran.org, pg 170

McMurray, Heather, SBL Press, The Luce Ctr, Suite 350, 825 Houston Mill Rd, Atlanta, GA 30329 *Tel:* 404-727-3100 *Fax:* 404-727-3101 (corp) *E-mail:* sbl@sbl-site.org *Web Site:* www.sbl-site.org, pg 217

McNabb, Stephen, Vintage & Anchor Books, c/o Random House Inc, 1745 Broadway, New York, NY 10019 *Tel:* 212-572-2420 *E-mail:* vintageanchorpublicity@randomhouse.com *Web Site:* vintage-anchor.knopfdoubleday.com, pg 266

McNair, Shanna, Knightville Poetry Contest, PO Box 5101, Hanover, NH 03755 *E-mail:* info@newguardreview.com *Web Site:* www.newguardreview.com, pg 698

McNair, Shanna, Machigonne Fiction Contest, PO Box 5101, Hanover, NH 03755 *E-mail:* info@newguardreview.com *Web Site:* www.newguardreview.com, pg 704

McNally, Katie, Random House Publishing Group, 1745 Broadway, New York, NY 10019 *Toll Free Tel:* 800-200-3552 *Web Site:* atrandom.com, pg 204

McNaughton, Charlotte, American Society of Civil Engineers (ASCE), 1801 Alexander Bell Dr, Reston, VA 20191-4400 *Tel:* 703-295-6300 *Toll Free Tel:* 800-548-2723 *Fax:* 703-295-6278 *E-mail:* marketing@asce.org *Web Site:* www.asce.org, pg 16

McNeal, A Phil II, The National Endowment for the Arts, Nancy Hanks Ctr, Rm 703, 1100 Pennsylvania Ave NW, Washington, DC 20506-0001 *Tel:* 202-682-5400 *Web Site:* www.arts.gov; www.nea.gov, pg 623

McNeely, Joe, Brilliance Audio, 1704 Eaton Dr, Grand Haven, MI 49417 *Tel:* 616-846-5256 *Toll Free Tel:* 800-648-2312 (orders only) *Fax:* 616-846-0630 *E-mail:* customerservice@brillianceaudio.com *Web Site:* www.brillianceaudio.com, pg 46

McNeill, Doug, Wimmer Cookbooks, 4650 Shelby Air Dr, Memphis, TN 38118 *Tel:* 901-362-8900 *Toll Free Tel:* 800-363-1771 *E-mail:* wimmer@wimmerco.com *Web Site:* www.wimmerco.com, pg 273

McNeill, Timothy, Wisdom Publications Inc, 199 Elm St, Somerville, MA 02144 *Tel:* 617-776-7416 *Toll Free Tel:* 800-272-4050 (orders) *Fax:* 617-776-7841 *E-mail:* info@wisdompubs.org *Web Site:* www.wisdompubs.org, pg 274

McNeillie, Carolyn, House of Anansi Press Inc, 110 Spadina Ave, Suite 801, Toronto, ON M5V 2K4, Canada *Tel:* 416-363-4343 *Fax:* 416-363-1017 *E-mail:* customerservice@houseofanansi.com *Web Site:* www.houseofanansi.com, pg 488

McNulty, Heather, Astragal Press, 5995 149 St W, Suite 105, Apple Valley, MN 55124 *Tel:* 952-469-6699 *Toll Free Tel:* 866-543-3045 *Fax:* 952-469-1968 *Toll Free Fax:* 800-330-6232 *E-mail:* info@finneyco.com *Web Site:* www.astragalpress.com, pg 26

McParland, Connie, Guernica Editions Inc, 1569 Heritage Way, Oakville, ON L6M 2Z7, Canada *Fax:* 416-576-9403 *E-mail:* info@guernicaeditions.com *Web Site:* guernicaeditions.com, pg 486

McPartland, Pat, Albert Whitman & Co, 250 S Northwest Hwy, Suite 320, Park Ridge, IL 60068 *Tel:* 847-232-2800 *Toll Free Tel:* 800-255-7675 *Fax:* 847-581-0039 *E-mail:* mail@awhitmanco.com *Web Site:* www.albertwhitman.com, pg 7

McPherson, Bruce R, McPherson & Co, 148 Smith Ave, Kingston, NY 12401 *Tel:* 845-331-5807 *Fax:* 845-331-5807 *E-mail:* bmcphersonco@gmail.com *Web Site:* www.mcphersonco.com, pg 152

McPherson, Rachel, Beacon Hill Press of Kansas City, PO Box 419527, Kansas City, MO 64141-6527 *Tel:* 816-931-1900 *Toll Free Tel:* 800-877-0700 (cust serv) *Fax:* 816-753-4071 *Web Site:* www.beaconhillbooks.com, pg 32

McQuagge, Cassie, ARE Press, 215 67 St, Virginia Beach, VA 23451 *Tel:* 757-428-3588 *Toll Free Tel:* 800-333-4499 *Fax:* 757-491-0689 *Web Site:* www.edgarcayce.org, pg 22

McQuilkin, Robert Rennie, Antrim House, 21 Goodrich Rd, Simsbury, CT 06070-1804 *Tel:* 860-217-0023 *E-mail:* eds@antrimhousebooks.com *Web Site:* www.antrimhousebooks.com, pg 19

McSweeney, Prof Joyelle, The Ernest Sandeen & Richard Sullivan Prizes in Fiction & Poetry, 356 O'Shaughnessy Hall, Notre Dame, IN 46556 *Tel:* 574-631-7526 *Fax:* 574-631-4795 *E-mail:* creativewriting@nd.edu *Web Site:* creativewriting.nd.edu, pg 684

McVay, Barry, Panoptic Enterprises, PO Box 11220, Burke, VA 22009-1220 *Tel:* 703-451-5953 *Toll Free Tel:* 800-594-4766 *Fax:* 703-451-5953 *E-mail:* panoptic@fedgovcontracts.com *Web Site:* www.fedgovcontracts.com, pg 181

McVay, Vivina H, Panoptic Enterprises, PO Box 11220, Burke, VA 22009-1220 *Tel:* 703-451-5953 *Toll Free Tel:* 800-594-4766 *Fax:* 703-451-5953 *E-mail:* panoptic@fedgovcontracts.com *Web Site:* www.fedgovcontracts.com, pg 181

McWilliams, Skip, Teacher's Discovery, 2741 Paldan Dr, Auburn Hills, MI 48326 *Toll Free Tel:* 800-832-2437 *Toll Free Fax:* 800-287-4509 *E-mail:* foreignlanguage@teachersdiscovery.com, pg 242

Mdhlongwa, Ndaba, OUT OF YOUR MIND...AND INTO THE MARKETPLACE™, 13381 White Sand Dr, Tustin, CA 92780-4565 *Tel:* 714-544-0248 *Toll Free Tel:* 800-419-1513 *Fax:* 714-730-1414 *Web Site:* www.business-plan.com, pg 178

Meacham, Beth, Tom Doherty Associates, LLC, 175 Fifth Ave, 14th fl, New York, NY 10010 *Tel:* 646-307-5151 *Toll Free Tel:* 800-455-0340 *Fax:* 212-388-0191 *E-mail:* firstname.lastname@tor.com *Web Site:* www.tor-forge.com, pg 75

Meader, James, Picador, 175 Fifth Ave, 19th fl, New York, NY 10010 *Tel:* 646-307-5151 *Fax:* 212-253-9627 *E-mail:* firstname.lastname@picadorusa.com *Web Site:* www.picadorusa.com, pg 191

Meadows, Laura, Carl Vinson Institute of Government, University of Georgia, 201 N Milledge Ave, Athens, GA 30602 *Tel:* 706-542-2736 *Fax:* 706-542-9301 *Web Site:* www.cviog.uga.edu, pg 265

Meadows, Rob, Bear & Co Inc, One Park St, Rochester, VT 05767 *Tel:* 802-767-3174 *Toll Free Tel:* 800-932-3277 *Fax:* 802-767-3726 *E-mail:* customerservice@InnerTraditions.com *Web Site:* InnerTraditions.com, pg 33

Meakin, Jonathan, Atlantic Poetry Prize, 1113 Marginal Rd, Halifax, NS B3H 4P7, Canada *Tel:* 902-423-8116 *Fax:* 902-422-0881 *E-mail:* contact@writers.ns.ca *Web Site:* writers.ns.ca, pg 669

Meakin, Jonathan, Thomas Head Raddall Atlantic Fiction Award, 1113 Marginal Rd, Halifax, NS B3H 4P7, Canada *Tel:* 902-423-8116 *Fax:* 902-422-0881 *E-mail:* contact@writers.ns.ca *Web Site:* www.writers.ns.ca, pg 723

Meakin, Jonathan, Evelyn Richardson Memorial Literary Trust Award, 1113 Marginal Rd, Halifax, NS B3H 4P7, Canada *Tel:* 902-423-8116 *Fax:* 902-422-0881 *E-mail:* contact@writers.ns.ca *Web Site:* writers.ns.ca, pg 724

Meakin, Jonathan, Writers' Federation of Nova Scotia, 1113 Marginal Rd, Halifax, NS B3H 4P7, Canada *Tel:* 902-423-8116 *Fax:* 902-422-0881 *E-mail:* contact@writers.ns.ca *Web Site:* writers.ns.ca, pg 621

Means, Lindsay, Simon & Schuster, 1230 Avenue of the Americas, New York, NY 10020 *Tel:* 212-698-7000 *Toll Free Tel:* 800-223-2348 (cust serv); 800-223-2336 (orders) *Toll Free Fax:* 800-943-9831 (orders) *Web Site:* www.simonandschuster.com, pg 225

Mechanic, Joline, Black Mountain Press, PO Box 9907, Asheville, NC 28815 *Tel:* 828-273-3332 *Web Site:* www.theblackmountainpress.com, pg 38

Mecklenborg, Mark, The American Ceramic Society, 600 N Cleveland Ave, Suite 210, Westerville, OH 43082 *Tel:* 240-646-7054 *Toll Free Tel:* 866-721-3322 *Fax:* 240-396-5637 *E-mail:* customerservice@ceramics.org *Web Site:* ceramics.org, pg 11

Medaille, Jessica, International Society for Technology in Education, 180 W Eighth Ave, Suite 300, Eugene, OR 97401-2916 *Tel:* 541-302-3777 (intl) *Toll Free Tel:* 800-336-5191 (US & CN) *Fax:* 541-302-3778 *E-mail:* iste@iste.org *Web Site:* www.iste.org; www.iste.org/bookstore (orders); www.isteconference.org, pg 125

Medeiros, Maria, Novalis Publishing, 10 Lower Spadina Ave, Suite 400, Toronto, ON M5V 2Z2, Canada *Tel:* 416-363-3303 *Toll Free Tel:* 877-702-7773 *Fax:* 416-363-9409 *Toll Free Fax:* 877-702-7775 *E-mail:* books@novalis.ca *Web Site:* www.novalis.ca, pg 493

Medeot, William, Orbis Books, Price Bldg, Box 302, Maryknoll, NY 10545-0302 *Tel:* 914-941-7636 *Toll Free Tel:* 800-258-5838 (orders) *Fax:* 914-941-7005 *E-mail:* orbisbooks@maryknoll.org *Web Site:* www.orbisbooks.com, pg 176

Medina, Kate, Random House Publishing Group, 1745 Broadway, New York, NY 10019 *Toll Free Tel:* 800-200-3552 *Web Site:* atrandom.com, pg 204

Meerdink, Jan, The Russell Meerdink Co Ltd, 1555 S Park Ave, Neenah, WI 54956 *Tel:* 920-725-0955 *Toll Free Tel:* 800-635-6499 *Fax:* 920-725-0709 *E-mail:* questions@horseinfo.com *Web Site:* www.horseinfo.com, pg 153

Meere, Selina, Workman Publishing Co Inc, 225 Varick St, 9th fl, New York, NY 10014-4381 *Tel:* 212-254-5900 *Toll Free Tel:* 800-722-7202 *Fax:* 212-254-8098 *E-mail:* info@workman.com *Web Site:* www.workman.com, pg 275

Meeropol, Ellen, Mt Chocorua Writing Workshop, PO Box 2280, Conway, NH 03818-2280 *Tel:* 603-447-2280 *E-mail:* reservations@worldfellowship.org *Web Site:* www.worldfellowship.org, pg 652

Meese, Allan, Macmillan, 175 Fifth Ave, New York, NY 10010 *Tel:* 646-307-5151 *Fax:* 212-420-9314 *E-mail:* firstname.lastname@macmillan.com *Web Site:* www.macmillan.com, pg 145

Megargee, Moira, Interlink Publishing Group Inc, 46 Crosby St, Northampton, MA 01060 *Tel:* 413-582-7054 *Toll Free Tel:* 800-238-LINK (238-5465) *Fax:* 413-582-7057 *E-mail:* info@interlinkbooks.com *Web Site:* www.interlinkbooks.com, pg 123

Megged, Semadar, Philomel, 345 Hudson St, New York, NY 10014 *Tel:* 212-366-2000, pg 191

Meglio, Leila, Houghton Mifflin Harcourt, 222 Berkeley St, Boston, MA 02116 *Tel:* 617-351-5000 *Toll Free Tel:* 800-225-5425 (K-12 educ materials); 800-323-9540 (assessment materials); 877-219-1537 (SkillsTutor); 888-242-6747 (Destination; Earobics; Edmark; Learning Village; Riverdeep); 800-225-3362 (Houghton Mifflin Harcourt Trade & Reference Publishers) *Toll Free Fax:* 800-269-5232 *E-mail:* customerservice@hmhpub.com *Web Site:* www.hmhco.com, pg 115

Mehta, Sonny, Doubleday/Nan A Talese, c/o Penguin Random House Inc, 1745 Broadway, New York, NY 10019 *Tel:* 212-751-2600 *Fax:* 212-572-2662 *E-mail:* ddaypub@randomhouse.com *Web Site:* knopfdoubleday.com, pg 76

Mehta, Sonny, Alfred A Knopf/Everyman's Library, c/o Random House Inc, 1745 Broadway, New York, NY 10019 *Tel:* 212-751-2600 *Toll Free Tel:* 800-638-6460 *Fax:* 212-572-2593 *Web Site:* www.knopfdoubleday.com, pg 132

Mehta, Sonny, Penguin Random House Inc, 1745 Broadway, New York, NY 10019 *Tel:* 212-782-9000 *Toll Free Tel:* 800-726-0600 *Web Site:* www.randomhouse.com, pg 187

Meier, Anna, Houghton Mifflin Harcourt Trade & Reference Division, 222 Berkeley St, Boston, MA 02116 *Tel:* 617-351-5000 *Toll Free Tel:* 800-225-3362 *Web Site:* www.hmhco.com, pg 115

Meier, Rachel, Crown Publishing Group, c/o Penguin Random House Inc, 1745 Broadway, New York, NY 10019 *Tel:* 212-782-9000 *Toll Free Tel:* 888-264-1745 *Fax:* 212-940-7408 *E-mail:* crownosm@penguinrandomhouse.com *Web Site:* crownpublishing.com, pg 68

Meinholz, Matt, American Society for Quality (ASQ), 600 N Plankinton Ave, Milwaukee, WI 53203 *Tel:* 414-272-8575 *Toll Free Tel:* 800-248-1946 (US & CN); 800-514-1564 (Mexico) *Fax:* 414-272-1734 *E-mail:* help@asq.org *Web Site:* www.asq.org, pg 16

Meisenheimer, Barbara, Pacific Northwest Young Reader's Choice Award, Vancouver Mall Community Library, 8700 NE Vancouver Mall Dr, Suite 285, Vancouver, WA 98662 *Tel:* 360-892-8256 *Web Site:* www.pnla.org/yrca, pg 716

Meissner, Bill, Mississippi River Creative Writing Workshop, 720 Fourth Ave S, B-151, Rm 100, St Cloud, MN 56301-4498 *Tel:* 320-308-4947 *Fax:* 320-308-5524 *Web Site:* www.stcloudstate.edu, pg 652

Meizlik, Shelby, HarperCollins General Books Group, 195 Broadway, New York, NY 10007 *Tel:* 212-207-7000 *Web Site:* www.harpercollins.com, pg 105

Mejias, Ricardo, Disney-Hyperion Books, 1101 Flower St, Glendale, CA 91201 *Web Site:* books.disney.com, pg 74

Melancon, Barry C, AICPA Professional Publications, 220 Leigh Farm Rd, Durham, NC 27707 *Tel:* 919-402-4500 *Toll Free Tel:* 888-777-7077 *Fax:* 919-402-4505 *Toll Free Fax:* 800-362-5066 *E-mail:* acquisitions@aicpa.org; service@aicpa.org *Web Site:* www.aicpa.org, pg 6

Melander, Nicole, Houghton Mifflin Harcourt, 222 Berkeley St, Boston, MA 02116 *Tel:* 617-351-5000 *Toll Free Tel:* 800-225-5425 (K-12 educ materials); 800-323-9540 (assessment materials); 877-219-1537 (SkillsTutor); 888-242-6747 (Destination; Earobics; Edmark; Learning Village; Riverdeep); 800-225-3362 (Houghton Mifflin Harcourt Trade & Reference Publishers) *Toll Free Fax:* 800-269-5232 *E-mail:* customerservice@hmhpub.com *Web Site:* www.hmhco.com, pg 115

Melando, Edward J, John Wiley & Sons Inc, 111 River St, Hoboken, NJ 07030-5774 *Tel:* 201-748-6000 *Toll Free Tel:* 800-225-5945 (cust serv) *Fax:* 201-748-6088 *E-mail:* info@wiley.com *Web Site:* www.wiley.com, pg 272

Mell, Prof Donald C, University of Delaware Press, 200A Morris Library, 181 S College Ave, Newark, DE 19717-5267 *Tel:* 302-831-1149 *Fax:* 302-831-6549 *E-mail:* ud-press@udel.edu *Web Site:* library.udel.edu/udpress, pg 256

Mello, Felice, W W Norton & Company Inc, 500 Fifth Ave, New York, NY 10110-0017 *Tel:* 212-354-5500 *Toll Free Tel:* 800-233-4830 (orders & cust serv) *Fax:* 212-869-0856 *Toll Free Fax:* 800-458-6515 *Web Site:* www.wwnorton.com, pg 171

Meloche, Luc, LexisNexis® Canada Inc, 123 Commerce Valley Dr E, Suite 700, Markham, ON L3T 7W8, Canada *Tel:* 905-479-2665 *Toll Free Tel:* 800-668-6481; 800-387-0899 (cust care) *Fax:* 905-479-2826 *Toll Free Fax:* 800-461-3275 *E-mail:* orders@lexisnexis.ca; service@lexisnexis.ca (cust serv) *Web Site:* www.lexisnexis.ca, pg 490

Melski, Michelle, Second Story Press, 20 Maud St, Suite 401, Toronto, ON M5V 2M5, Canada *Tel:* 416-537-7850 *Fax:* 416-537-0588 *E-mail:* info@secondstorypress.ca *Web Site:* secondstorypress.ca, pg 498

Melton, Dianne, Summerthought Publishing, PO Box 2309, Banff, AB T1L 1C1, Canada *Tel:* 403-762-0535 *Fax:* 403-762-3095 *Toll Free Fax:* 800-762-3095 (orders) *E-mail:* info@summerthought.com; sales@summerthought.com *Web Site:* summerthought.com, pg 500

Meltzer, Lauren, The Charles Press, Publishers, 230 N 21 St, Suite 202, Philadelphia, PA 19103 *Tel:* 215-561-2786 *Fax:* 215-561-0191 *E-mail:* mail@charlespresspub.com *Web Site:* www.charlespresspub.com, pg 55

Meltzer, Steve, Celebra, 375 Hudson St, New York, NY 10014 *Tel:* 212-366-2000 *Fax:* 212-366-2889, pg 53

Meltzer, Steve, Dial Books for Young Readers, 345 Hudson St, New York, NY 10014 *Tel:* 212-366-2000 *Fax:* 212-414-3396 *E-mail:* online@penguinputnam.com *Web Site:* www.penguinputnam.com; us.penguingroup.com, pg 74

Meltzer, Steven, Dutton Children's Books, 345 Hudson St, New York, NY 10014 *Tel:* 212-366-2000 *E-mail:* online@penguinputnam.com *Web Site:* www.penguinputnam.com; us.penguingroup.com, pg 78

Melville, Kirsty, Andrews McMeel Publishing LLC, 1130 Walnut St, Kansas City, MO 64106-2109 *Toll Free Tel:* 800-851-8923; 800-943-9839 (cust serv) *Toll Free Fax:* 800-943-9831 (orders) *Web Site:* www.andrewsmcmeel.com, pg 18

Melvin, Annette, Random House Publishing Group, 1745 Broadway, New York, NY 10019 *Toll Free Tel:* 800-200-3552 *Web Site:* atrandom.com, pg 204

Melvin, Terrence, The Brookings Institution Press, 1775 Massachusetts Ave NW, Washington, DC 20036-2188 *Tel:* 202-536-3600 *Toll Free Tel:* 800-537-5487 *Fax:* 202-536-3623 *E-mail:* permissions@brookings.edu *Web Site:* www.brookings.edu, pg 47

Menchaca, Frank, Gale, 27500 Drake Rd, Farmington Hills, MI 48331-3535 *Tel:* 248-699-4253 *Toll Free Tel:* 800-877-4253 *Fax:* 248-699-8049 *Toll Free Fax:* 800-414-5043 (orders) *E-mail:* gale.salesassistance@cengage.com *Web Site:* www.gale.cengage.com, pg 94

Menchaca, Frank, Macmillan Reference USA™, 12 Lunar Dr, Woodbridge, CT 06525 *Tel:* 203-397-2600 *Toll Free Tel:* 800-444-0799 *Fax:* 203-397-8296 *Web Site:* www.gale.cengage.com/macmillan/, pg 145

Mendel, Scott, Mendel Media Group LLC, 115 W 30 St, Suite 800, New York, NY 10001 *Tel:* 646-239-9896 *Fax:* 212-685-4717 *Web Site:* www.mendelmedia.com, pg 565

Mendelson, John, Candlewick Press, 99 Dover St, Somerville, MA 02144-2825 *Tel:* 617-661-3330 *Fax:* 617-661-0565 *E-mail:* bigbear@candlewick.com; salesinfo@candlewick.com *Web Site:* www.candlewick.com, pg 49

Mendoza, Sylvia, The University of Arizona Press, 1510 E University Blvd, Tucson, AZ 85721 *Tel:* 520-621-1441 *Toll Free Tel:* 800-426-3797 (orders) *Fax:* 520-621-8899 *Toll Free Fax:* 800-426-3797 *E-mail:* uap@uapress.arizona.edu *Web Site:* www.uapress.arizona.edu, pg 255

Menick, Jim, Reader's Digest USA Select Editions, 44 S Broadway, 7th fl, White Plains, NY 10601 *Tel:* 914-238-1000 *Toll Free Tel:* 800-304-2807 (cust serv) *Fax:* 914-831-1560 *Web Site:* www.rda.com/readers-digest-select-editions, pg 205

Menke, Dean, American Society of Health-System Pharmacists (ASHP), 7272 Wisconsin Ave, Bethesda, MD 20814 *Tel:* 301-657-3000; 301-664-8700 *Toll Free Tel:* 866-279-0681 (orders) *Fax:* 301-657-1251 (orders) *E-mail:* custserv@ashp.org *Web Site:* www.ashp.org, pg 16

Menn, Don, Immedium, 535 Rockdale Dr, San Francisco, CA 94127 *Tel:* 415-452-8546 *Fax:* 360-937-6272 *E-mail:* orders@immedium.com; sales@immedium.com *Web Site:* www.immedium.com, pg 119

Mennel, Timothy, APA Planners Press, 205 N Michigan Ave, Suite 1200, Chicago, IL 60601 *Tel:* 312-431-9100 *Fax:* 312-786-6700 *E-mail:* customerservice@planning.org *Web Site:* www.planning.org, pg 19

Mennel, Timothy, University of Chicago Press, 1427 E 60 St, Chicago, IL 60637-2954 *Tel:* 773-702-7700; 773-702-7600 *Toll Free Tel:* 800-621-2736 (orders) *Fax:* 773-702-9756; 773-660-2235 (orders); 773-702-2708 *E-mail:* custserv@press.uchicago.edu; marketing@press.uchicago.edu *Web Site:* www.press.uchicago.edu, pg 255

Menon, Pooja, Kimberley Cameron & Associates, 1550 Tiburon Blvd, Suite 704, Tiburon, CA 94920 *Tel:* 415-789-9191 *Fax:* 415-789-9177 *E-mail:* info@kimberleycameron.com *Web Site:* www.kimberleycameron.com, pg 559

Menzies, Tracey, HarperCollins Children's Books, 195 Broadway, New York, NY 10007 *Tel:* 212-207-7000 *Web Site:* www.harpercollins.com/childrens, pg 105

Menzies, Tracey, HarperCollins General Books Group, 195 Broadway, New York, NY 10007 *Tel:* 212-207-7000 *Web Site:* www.harpercollins.com, pg 105

Menzies, Tracey, HarperCollins Publishers, 195 Broadway, New York, NY 10007 *Tel:* 212-207-7000 *Fax:* 212-207-7145 *Web Site:* www.harpercollins.com, pg 106

Meradji, Ahmad, BookLogix, 1264 Old Alpharetta Rd, Alpharetta, GA 30005 *Tel:* 470-239-8547 *Toll Free Fax:* 888-564-7890 *E-mail:* sales@booklogix.com *Web Site:* www.booklogix.com, pg 42

Mercandetti, Susan, Random House Publishing Group, 1745 Broadway, New York, NY 10019 *Toll Free Tel:* 800-200-3552 *Web Site:* atrandom.com, pg 204

Merchant, Ann, National Academies Press (NAP), Lockbox 285, 500 Fifth St NW, Washington, DC 20001 *Tel:* 202-334-3313 *Toll Free Tel:* 888-624-8373 (cust serv) *Fax:* 202-334-2451 (cust serv); 202-334-2793 (mktg dept) *E-mail:* customer_service@nap.edu *Web Site:* www.nap.edu, pg 163

Merchant, Leigh, Random House Publishing Group, 1745 Broadway, New York, NY 10019 *Toll Free Tel:* 800-200-3552 *Web Site:* atrandom.com, pg 204

Mercy, Jon, ANR Publications University of California, 1301 S 46 St, Bldg 478 - MC 3580, Richmond, CA 94804 *Tel:* 510-665-2195 (cust serv) *Toll Free Tel:* 800-994-8849 *Fax:* 510-665-3427 *E-mail:* anrcatalog@ucdavis.edu *Web Site:* anrcatalog.ucanr.edu, pg 18

Meredith, Leslie, Atria Books, 1230 Avenue of the Americas, New York, NY 10020 *Tel:* 212-698-7000 *Fax:* 212-698-7007 *Web Site:* www.simonandschuster.com, pg 27

Meredith, Mimi, Society of Environmental Toxicology & Chemistry, 229 S Baylen St, 2nd fl, Pensacola, FL 32502 *Tel:* 850-469-1500 *Fax:* 850-469-9778 *E-mail:* setac@setac.org *Web Site:* www.setac.org, pg 229

Merkh, Jonathan, Howard Books, 216 Centerview Dr, Suite 303, Brentwood, TN 37027 *Tel:* 615-873-2080 *Fax:* 615-370-3834 *E-mail:* howardbooks@simonandschuster.com (info) *Web Site:* www.howardpublishing.com, pg 116

Merkh, Jonathan, Simon & Schuster, Inc, 1230 Avenue of the Americas, New York, NY 10020 *Tel:* 212-698-7000 *Fax:* 212-698-7007 *E-mail:* firstname.lastname@simonandschuster.com *Web Site:* www.simonandschuster.com, pg 226

Merkle, Dieter, Springer, 233 Spring St, New York, NY 10013-1578 *Tel:* 212-460-1500 *Toll Free Tel:* 800-SPRINGER (777-4643) *Fax:* 212-460-1575 *E-mail:* service-ny@springer.com *Web Site:* www.springer.com, pg 232

Merkle, Molly B, Menasha Ridge Press Inc, 2204 First Ave S, Suite 102, Birmingham, AL 35233 *Tel:* 205-322-0439 *Toll Free Tel:* 888-604-4537 *Fax:* 205-326-1012 *E-mail:* info@menasharidge.com *Web Site:* www.menasharidge.com, pg 154

Merola, Marianne, Brandt & Hochman Literary Agents Inc, 1501 Broadway, Suite 2310, New York, NY 10036 *Tel:* 212-840-5760 *Fax:* 212-840-5776 *Web Site:* brandthochman.com, pg 544

Merriam, Ray, Merriam Press, 133 Elm St, Suite 3R, Bennington, VT 05201-2250 *Tel:* 802-447-0313 *E-mail:* ray@merriam-press.com *Web Site:* www.merriam-press.com, pg 155

Merrill, Robert, Maisonneuve Press, 6423 Adelphi Rd, Hyattsville, MD 20782 *Tel:* 301-277-7505 *Fax:* 301-277-2467 *Web Site:* www.maisonneuvepress.com, pg 145

Mesecher, Kim, M Lee Smith Publishers LLC, 5201 Virginia Way, Brentwood, TN 37027 *Tel:* 615-373-7517 *Toll Free Tel:* 800-274-6774 *Fax:* 615-373-5183 *E-mail:* custserv@mleesmith.com *Web Site:* www.mleesmith.com, pg 228

Messer, Miwa, Discover Great New Writers Award, 122 Fifth Ave, New York, NY 10011 *Web Site:* www.barnesandnoble.com, pg 681

Messer, Randy, Perfection Learning Corp, 2680 Berkshire Pkwy, Clive, IA 50325 *Tel:* 515-278-0133 *Toll Free Tel:* 800-762-2999 *Fax:* 515-278-2980 *Web Site:* perfectionlearning.com, pg 189

Messerli, Douglas, Green Integer, 6210 Wilshire Blvd, Suite 211, Los Angeles, CA 90048 *Tel:* 323-857-1115 *Fax:* 323-857-0143 *Web Site:* www.greeninteger.com, pg 100

Messick, Mary K, Schoolhouse Network Inc, PO Box 17676, Fountain Hills, AZ 85269 *Tel:* 973-206-1389 *E-mail:* info@schoolhousenetwork.com *Web Site:* www.schoolhousenetwork.com, pg 534

Messina, Dyana, Crown Publishing Group, c/o Penguin Random House Inc, 1745 Broadway, New York, NY 10019 *Tel:* 212-782-9000 *Toll Free Tel:* 888-264-1745 *Fax:* 212-940-7408 *E-mail:* crownosm@penguinrandomhouse.com *Web Site:* crownpublishing.com, pg 68

Messina, Scott, Fine Creative Media, Inc, 322 Eighth Ave, 15th fl, New York, NY 10001 *Tel:* 212-595-3500 *Fax:* 212-595-3779, pg 88

Messitte, Anne, Alfred A Knopf/Everyman's Library, c/o Random House Inc, 1745 Broadway, New York, NY 10019 *Tel:* 212-751-2600 *Toll Free Tel:* 800-638-6460 *Fax:* 212-572-2593 *Web Site:* www.knopfdoubleday.com, pg 132

Messitte, Anne, Vintage & Anchor Books, c/o Random House Inc, 1745 Broadway, New York, NY 10019 *Tel:* 212-572-2420 *E-mail:* vintageanchorpublicity@randomhouse.com *Web Site:* vintage-anchor.knopfdoubleday.com, pg 266

Meszaros, Abel, Central European University Press, 224 W 57 St, New York, NY 10019 *Web Site:* www.ceupress.com, pg 54

Metcalfe, Heidi, HarperCollins General Books Group, 195 Broadway, New York, NY 10007 *Tel:* 212-207-7000 *Web Site:* www.harpercollins.com, pg 105

Meth, David L, Writers' Productions, PO Box 630, Westport, CT 06881-0630 *Tel:* 203-227-8199, pg 580

Metro, Judy, National Gallery of Art, Fourth St & Pennsylvania Ave NW, Washington, DC 20565 *Tel:* 202-737-4215; 202-842-6480 *Fax:* 202-842-6733 *E-mail:* casva@nga.gov *Web Site:* www.nga.gov, pg 165

Metsch, Amy, Random House Large Print, 1745 Broadway, New York, NY 10019 *Tel:* 212-782-9000 *Fax:* 212-782-9484, pg 204

Metz, Isabel, University Press of Mississippi, 3825 Ridgewood Rd, Jackson, MS 39211-6492 *Tel:* 601-432-6205 *Toll Free Tel:* 800-737-7788 (orders & cust serv) *Fax:* 601-432-6217 *E-mail:* press@mississippi.edu *Web Site:* www.upress.state.ms.us, pg 262

Metz, Mary, The Mountaineers Books, 1001 SW Klickitat Way, Suite 201, Seattle, WA 98134 *Tel:* 206-223-6303 *Toll Free Tel:* 800-553-4453 *Fax:* 206-223-6306 *Toll Free Fax:* 800-568-7604 *E-mail:* mbooks@mountaineersbooks.org *Web Site:* www.mountaineersbooks.org, pg 161

Meyer, Kathleen, Duquesne University Press, 600 Forbes Ave, Pittsburgh, PA 15282 *Tel:* 412-396-6610 *Fax:* 412-396-5984 *E-mail:* dupress@duq.edu *Web Site:* www.dupress.duq.edu, pg 77

Meyer, Laura, House of Anansi Press Inc, 110 Spadina Ave, Suite 801, Toronto, ON M5V 2K4, Canada *Tel:* 416-363-4343 *Fax:* 416-363-1017 *E-mail:* customerservice@houseofanansi.com *Web Site:* www.houseofanansi.com, pg 488

Meyer, Michael A, Hebrew Union College Press, 3101 Clifton Ave, Cincinnati, OH 45220 *Tel:* 513-221-1875 *Fax:* 513-221-0321 *Web Site:* press.huc.edu, pg 109

Meyer, Steve, LAMA Books, 2381 Sleepy Hollow Ave, Hayward, CA 94545-3429 *Tel:* 510-785-1091 *Toll Free Tel:* 888-452-6244 *Fax:* 510-785-1099 *Web Site:* www.lamabooks.com, pg 134

Meyering, Michelle, PEN Center USA, PO Box 6037, Beverly Hills, CA 90212 *Tel:* 323-424-4939 *Fax:* 323-424-4944 *E-mail:* pen@penusa.org *Web Site:* www.penusa.org, pg 616

Meyers, Amy, Yale Center for British Art, 1080 Chapel St, New Haven, CT 06510-2302 *Tel:* 203-432-2800 *Toll Free Tel:* 877-274-8278 *Fax:* 203-432-9628 *E-mail:* ycba.info@yale.edu *Web Site:* www.yale.edu/ycba; britishart.yale.edu, pg 278

Meyers, Bob, National Press Foundation, 1211 Connecticut Ave NW, Suite 310, Washington, DC 20036 *Tel:* 202-663-7280 *Web Site:* nationalpress.org, pg 613

Meyers, Dale, Standard Publishing, 8805 Governors Hill Dr, Suite 400, Cincinnati, OH 45249 *Tel:* 513-931-4050 *Toll Free Tel:* 800-543-1353 *Fax:* 513-931-0950 *Toll Free Fax:* 877-867-5751 *E-mail:* customerservice@standardpub.com *Web Site:* www.standardpub.com, pg 233

Meyers, Tona Pearce, New World Library, 14 Pamaron Way, Novato, CA 94949 *Tel:* 415-884-2100 *Toll Free Tel:* 800-227-3900 (ext 52, retail orders); 800-972-6657 *Fax:* 415-884-2199 *E-mail:* escort@newworldlibrary.com *Web Site:* www.newworldlibrary.com, pg 168

Mhoon, Jim, Focus on the Family, 8605 Explorer Dr, Colorado Springs, CO 80920-1051 *Tel:* 719-531-5181 *Toll Free Tel:* 800-A-FAMILY (232-6459) *Fax:* 719-531-3424 *Web Site:* www.focusonthefamily.com; www.facebook.com/focusonthefamily, pg 90

Micallef, Joseph, McGraw-Hill Education, 2 Penn Plaza, New York, NY 10121-2298 *Tel:* 212-904-2000 *E-mail:* customer.service@mcgraw-hill.com *Web Site:* www.mheducation.com; www.mheducation.com/custserv.html, pg 151

Miceli, Jaya, Plume, 375 Hudson St, New York, NY 10014 *Tel:* 212-366-2000 *Fax:* 212-366-2666 *E-mail:* online@penguinputnam.com *Web Site:* www.penguinputnam.com; us.penguingroup.com, pg 193

Miceli, Jaya, Scribner, 1230 Avenue of the Americas, New York, NY 10020, pg 220

Michaels, Ken, Macmillan Higher Education, 41 Madison Ave, 37th fl, New York, NY 10010 *Tel:* 212-576-9400 *Fax:* 212-689-2383 *Web Site:* www.macmillanhighered.com, pg 145

Michalicek, Steven S, Heuer Publishing LLC, PO Box 248, Cedar Rapids, IA 52406 *Tel:* 319-368-8008 *Toll Free Tel:* 800-950-7529 *Fax:* 319-368-8011 *E-mail:* editor@hitplays.com; customerservice@hitplays.com *Web Site:* www.hitplays.com, pg 111

Michalski, Chris, Ascension Press, PO Box 1990, West Chester, PA 19380 *Tel:* 610-696-7795 (ext 207, edit); 484-875-4550 (admin) *Toll Free Tel:* 800-376-0520 (sales & cust serv) *E-mail:* info@ascensionpress.com *Web Site:* ascensionpress.com, pg 24

Michaud, Jacques, Les Editions Vents d'Ouest, 109, rue Wright, bureau 202, Gatineau, QC J8X 2G7, Canada *Tel:* 819-770-6377 *Fax:* 819-770-0559 *E-mail:* info@ventsdouest.ca *Web Site:* www.ventsdouest.ca, pg 483

Michel, Christie, Other Press LLC, 2 Park Ave, 24th fl, New York, NY 10016 *Tel:* 212-414-0054 *Toll Free Tel:* 877-843-6843 *Fax:* 212-414-0939 *E-mail:* editor@otherpress.com; rights@otherpress.com *Web Site:* www.otherpress.com, pg 178

Michels, Dia L, Platypus Media LLC, 725 Eighth St SE, Washington, DC 20003 *Tel:* 202-546-1674 *Toll Free Tel:* 877-PLATYPS (752-8977) *Fax:* 202-546-2356 *E-mail:* info@platypusmedia.com *Web Site:* www.platypusmedia.com, pg 192

Michels, Dia L, Science, Naturally!™, 725 Eighth St SE, Washington, DC 20003 *Tel:* 202-465-4798 *Toll Free Tel:* 866-724-9876 *Fax:* 202-558-2132 *E-mail:* info@sciencenaturally.com *Web Site:* www.sciencenaturally.com, pg 220

Michels, Greg, Municipal Analysis Services Inc, PO Box 13453, Austin, TX 78711-3453 *Tel:* 512-327-3328 *E-mail:* munilysis@gmail.com *Web Site:* sites.google.com/site/gregmichels/home, pg 161

Miciak, Kate, Random House Publishing Group, 1745 Broadway, New York, NY 10019 *Toll Free Tel:* 800-200-3552 *Web Site:* atrandom.com, pg 204

Mickey, Kathy, Simba Information, 1266 E Main St, Suite 700, Stamford, CT 06902 *Tel:* 203-325-8193 *Toll Free Tel:* 888-297-4622 (cust serv) *E-mail:* customerservice@simbainformation.com *Web Site:* www.simbainformation.com, pg 225

Mickulas, Peter, Rutgers University Press, 106 Somerset St, 3rd fl, New Brunswick, NJ 08901 *Tel:* 848-445-7762 *Toll Free Tel:* 800-848-6224 (orders only) *Fax:* 732-745-4935 (acqs, edit, mktg, perms & prodn) *Toll Free Fax:* 800-272-6817 (fulfillment) *Web Site:* rutgerspress.rutgers.edu, pg 213

Middendorf, Sandy, Augsburg Fortress Publishers, Publishing House of the Evangelical Lutheran Church in America, 510 Marquette Ave S, Minneapolis, MN 55402 *Tel:* 612-330-3300 *Toll Free Tel:* 800-426-0115 (ext 639, subns); 800-328-4648 (orders) *Fax:* 612-330-3455 *E-mail:* info@augsburgfortress.org; copyright@augsburgfortress.org (reprint permission requests); customercare@augsburgfortress.org *Web Site:* www.augsburgfortress.org, pg 27

Middlebrook, Ron, Centerstream Publishing LLC, PO Box 17878, Anaheim Hills, CA 92817-7878 *Tel:* 714-779-9390 *E-mail:* centerstrm@aol.com *Web Site:* www.centerstream-usa.com, pg 54

Middleton, Jean F, IndexEmpire Indexing Services, 16740 Orville Wright Dr, Riverside, CA 92518 *Tel:* 951-697-2819 *E-mail:* indexempire@gmail.com, pg 528

Middleton, Kathy, Crabtree Publishing Co, 350 Fifth Ave, 59th fl, PMB 59051, New York, NY 10118 *Tel:* 212-496-5040 *Toll Free Tel:* 800-387-7650 *Toll Free Fax:* 800-355-7166 *E-mail:* custserv@crabtreebooks.com *Web Site:* www.crabtreebooks.com, pg 66

Middleton, Kathy, Crabtree Publishing Co Ltd, 616 Welland Ave, St Catharines, ON L2M-5V6, Canada *Tel:* 905-682-5221 *Toll Free Tel:* 800-387-7650 *Fax:* 905-682-7166 *Toll Free Fax:* 800-355-7166 *E-mail:* custserv@crabtreebooks.com; sales@crabtreebooks.com; orders@crabtreebooks.com *Web Site:* www.crabtreebooks.com, pg 478

Middleton, Maria, Harry N Abrams Inc, 115 W 18 St, 6th fl, New York, NY 10011 *Tel:* 212-206-7715 *Toll Free Tel:* 800-345-1359 *Fax:* 212-519-1210 *E-mail:* abrams@abramsbooks.com *Web Site:* www.abramsbooks.com, pg 3

Middleton, Stephanie, American Law Institute, 4025 Chestnut St, Philadelphia, PA 19104-3099 *Tel:* 215-243-1600 *Toll Free Tel:* 800-253-6397 *Fax:* 215-243-1664 *Web Site:* www.ali.org, pg 14

Middleton, Stephanie, American Law Institute Continuing Legal Education (ALI CLE), 4025 Chestnut St, Philadelphia, PA 19104 *Tel:* 215-243-1600 *Toll Free Tel:* 800-CLE-NEWS (253-6397) *Fax:* 215-243-1664; 215-243-1683 *Web Site:* www.ali-cle.org, pg 14

Miller, Matthew, The Toby Press LLC, PO Box 8531, New Milford, CT 06776-8531 *Tel:* 203-830-8508 *Fax:* 203-830-8512 *E-mail:* toby@tobypress.com *Web Site:* korenpub.com/toby/intusd/, pg 246

Miller, Melissa, American Society of Agricultural & Biological Engineers (ASABE), 2950 Niles Rd, St Joseph, MI 49085-9659 *Tel:* 269-429-0300 *Toll Free Tel:* 800-371-2723 *Fax:* 269-429-3852 *E-mail:* hq@asabe.org *Web Site:* www.asabe.org, pg 16

Miller, Melissa, HarperCollins Children's Books, 195 Broadway, New York, NY 10007 *Tel:* 212-207-7000 *Web Site:* www.harpercollins.com/childrens, pg 105

Miller, Meredith, Trident Media Group LLC, 41 Madison Ave, 36th fl, New York, NY 10010 *Tel:* 212-333-1511 *E-mail:* info@tridentmediagroup.com; press@tridentmediagroup.com *Web Site:* www.tridentmediagroup.com, pg 578

Miller, Peter, Global Lion Intellectual Property Management Inc, PO Box 669238, Pompano Beach, FL 33066 *Tel:* 754-222-6948 *Fax:* 754-222-6948 *E-mail:* queriesgloballionmgt@gmail.com *Web Site:* www.globallionmanagement.com, pg 554

Miller, Peter, The Institutes™, 720 Providence Rd, Suite 100, Malvern, PA 19355-3433 *Tel:* 610-644-2100 *Toll Free Tel:* 800-644-2101 *Fax:* 610-640-9576 *E-mail:* customerservice@theinstitutes.org *Web Site:* www.theinstitutes.org, pg 123

Miller, Richard K, Richard K Miller Associates, 4132 Atlanta Hwy, Suite 110, Loganville, GA 30052 *Tel:* 404-276-3376 *Toll Free Tel:* 888-928-RKMA (928-7562) *Toll Free Fax:* 877-928-7562 *Web Site:* rkma.com, pg 157

Miller, Robert, Enigma Books, 12 E 86 St, New York, NY 10028 *Tel:* 646-246-8010 *E-mail:* editor@enigmabooks.com *Web Site:* www.enigmabooks.com, pg 83

Miller, Robin, Business Forms Management Association (BFMA), 1147 Fleetwood Ave, Madison, WI 53716 *Toll Free Tel:* 888-367-3078 *E-mail:* bfma@bfma.org *Web Site:* www.bfma.org, pg 601

Miller, Sarah, Yale University Press, 302 Temple St, New Haven, CT 06511-8909 *Tel:* 203-432-0960; 203-432-0966 (sales); 401-531-2800 (cust serv) *Toll Free Tel:* 800-405-1619 (cust serv) *Fax:* 203-432-0948; 203-432-8485 (sales); 401-531-2801 (cust serv) *Toll Free Fax:* 800-406-9145 (cust serv) *E-mail:* sales.press@yale.edu (sales); customer.care@trilateral.org (cust serv) *Web Site:* www.yalebooks.com; yalepress.yale.edu/yupbooks, pg 278

Miller, Scott, David C Cook, 4050 Lee Vance View, Colorado Springs, CO 80918 *Tel:* 719-536-0100 *Toll Free Tel:* 800-708-5550; 800-323-7543 (orders & cust serv) *Toll Free Fax:* 800-430-0726 (cust serv) *Web Site:* www.davidccook.com, pg 62

Miller, Scott, Trident Media Group LLC, 41 Madison Ave, 36th fl, New York, NY 10010 *Tel:* 212-333-1511 *E-mail:* info@tridentmediagroup.com; press@tridentmediagroup.com *Web Site:* www.tridentmediagroup.com, pg 577

Miller, Shannon, SDP Publishing Solutions LLC, 36 Captain's Way, East Bridgewater, MA 02333 *Tel:* 617-775-0656 *Web Site:* www.sdppublishingsolutions.com, pg 534

Miller, Sid, Burnside Review Fiction Chapbook Competition, PO Box 1782, Portland, OR 97207 *Web Site:* burnsidereview.org, pg 674

Miller, Stephen M, Stephen M Miller Inc, 15727 S Madison Dr, Olathe, KS 66062 *Tel:* 913-768-7997 *Web Site:* www.stephenmillerbooks.com, pg 531

Miller, Sue, Boydell & Brewer Inc, 668 Mount Hope Ave, Rochester, NY 14620-2731 *Tel:* 585-275-0419 *Fax:* 585-271-8778 *E-mail:* boydell@boydellusa.net *Web Site:* www.boydellandbrewer.com, pg 43

Miller, Ted, Human Kinetics Inc, 1607 N Market St, Champaign, IL 61820 *Tel:* 217-351-5076 *Toll Free Tel:* 800-747-4457 *Fax:* 217-351-1549 (orders/cust serv) *E-mail:* info@hkusa.com *Web Site:* www.humankinetics.com, pg 117

Miller, Terri, Pentecostal Publishing House, 8855 Dunn Rd, Hazelwood, MO 63042 *Tel:* 314-837-7300 *Fax:* 314-336-1803 *E-mail:* pphordersdept@upci.org (orders) *Web Site:* www.pentecostalpublishing.com, pg 188

Miller, Tom, Sanford J Greenburger Associates Inc, 55 Fifth Ave, New York, NY 10003 *Tel:* 212-206-5600 *Fax:* 212-463-8718 *Web Site:* greenburger.com; www.sjga.com/, pg 555

Miller, Dr Yvette E, Latin American Literary Review Press, PO Box 7530, Pittsburgh, PA 15213 *Tel:* 412-824-7903 *E-mail:* lalrp.editor@gmail.com *Web Site:* www.lalrp.org, pg 135

Miller-Callihan, Courtney, Sanford J Greenburger Associates Inc, 55 Fifth Ave, New York, NY 10003 *Tel:* 212-206-5600 *Fax:* 212-463-8718 *Web Site:* greenburger.com; www.sjga.com/, pg 555

Miller-Castells, Diana, Palm Springs Writers Guild, PO Box 947, Rancho Mirage, CA 92270-0947 *Web Site:* www.palmspringswritersguild.org, pg 615

Miller-Vincent, Kristin, D4EO Literary Agency, 7 Indian Valley Rd, Weston, CT 06883 *Tel:* 203-544-7180 *Fax:* 203-544-7160 *Web Site:* www.d4eoliteraryagency.com, pg 548

Milligan, Bryce, Wings Press, 627 E Guenther, San Antonio, TX 78210-1134 *Tel:* 210-271-7805 *Fax:* 210-271-7805 *E-mail:* press@wingspress.com *Web Site:* www.wingspress.com, pg 273

Milliken, Jean Mellichamp, Lyric Poetry Prizes, PO Box 110, Jericho, VT 05465 *Tel:* 802-899-3993 *Fax:* 802-899-3993 *E-mail:* themuse@thelyricmagazine.com *Web Site:* thelyricmagazine.com, pg 704

Milliken, Leif, University of Nebraska Press, 1111 Lincoln Mall, Lincoln, NE 68588-0630 *Tel:* 402-472-3581; 919-966-7449 (cust serv & foreign orders) *Toll Free Tel:* 800-848-6224 (cust serv & US orders) *Fax:* 402-472-6214; 919-962-2704 (cust serv & foreign orders) *Toll Free Fax:* 800-526-2617 (cust serv & US orders) *E-mail:* pressmail@unl.edu *Web Site:* www.nebraskapress.unl.edu, pg 257

Millman, Norman N, Summit University Press, 63 Summit Way, Gardiner, MT 59030-9314 *Tel:* 406-848-9742; 406-848-9500 *Toll Free Tel:* 800-245-5445 (retail orders) *Fax:* 406-848-9650 *Toll Free Fax:* 800-221-8307 *E-mail:* info@summituniversitypress.com *Web Site:* www.summituniversitypress.com, pg 237

Mills, Craig N, CTB/McGraw-Hill, 20 Ryan Ranch Rd, Monterey, CA 93940-5703 *Tel:* 831-393-0700 *Toll Free Tel:* 800-538-9547 *Fax:* 831-393-7825 *Toll Free Fax:* 800-282-0266 *Web Site:* www.ctb.com, pg 69

Mills, Elizabeth M, Temporal Mechanical Press, 6760 Hwy 7, Estes Park, CO 80517-6404 *Tel:* 970-586-4706 *E-mail:* enosmillscbn@earthlink.net *Web Site:* www.enosmills.com, pg 242

Mills, Eryn, Temporal Mechanical Press, 6760 Hwy 7, Estes Park, CO 80517-6404 *Tel:* 970-586-4706 *E-mail:* enosmillscbn@earthlink.net *Web Site:* www.enosmills.com, pg 242

Mills, Kathleen, Kathleen Mills Editorial Services, PO Box 214, Chardon, OH 44024 *Tel:* 440-285-4347 *E-mail:* mills_edit@yahoo.com, pg 531

Mills, Kevin, The Tuesday Agency, 132 1/2 E Washington St, Iowa City, IA 52240 *Tel:* 319-338-7080 *E-mail:* trinity@tuesdayagency.com *Web Site:* tuesdayagency.com, pg 588

Mills, Nancy L, Pie in the Sky Publishing LLC, 8031 E Phillips Circle, Centennial, CO 80112 *Tel:* 303-773-0851 *Fax:* 303-773-0851 *E-mail:* pieintheskypublishing@msn.com *Web Site:* www.pieintheskypublishing.com, pg 191

Mills, Pamela, Association of Writers & Writing Programs (AWP), George Mason University, 4400 University Dr, MSN 1E3, Fairfax, VA 22030 *Tel:* 703-993-4301 *Fax:* 703-993-4302 *E-mail:* awp@awpwriter.org *Web Site:* www.awpwriter.org, pg 599

Mills, Pamela, AWP Award Series, George Mason University, 4400 University Dr, MSN 1E3, Fairfax, VA 22030 *Tel:* 703-993-4301 *Fax:* 703-993-4302 *E-mail:* awp@awpwriter.org *Web Site:* www.awpwriter.org, pg 669

Mills, Sharon, Texas A&M University Press, John H Lindsey Bldg, Lewis St, 4354 TAMU, College Station, TX 77843-4354 *Tel:* 979-845-1436 *Toll Free Tel:* 800-826-8911 (orders) *Fax:* 979-847-8752 *Toll Free Fax:* 888-617-2421 (orders) *E-mail:* tampress@tamu.edu *Web Site:* www.tamupress.com, pg 243

Milsten, Melissa, Random House Publishing Group, 1745 Broadway, New York, NY 10019 *Toll Free Tel:* 800-200-3552 *Web Site:* atrandom.com, pg 204

Milward, Andrew, Mississippi Review Prize, 118 College Dr, Box 5144, Hattiesburg, MS 39406-0001 *E-mail:* msreview@usm.edu *Web Site:* www.usm.edu/mississippi-review/contest.html, pg 708

Milward, Andrew, Mississippi Review/University of Southern Mississippi, Center for Writers, 118 College Dr 5144, Hattiesburg, MS 39406-0001 *Tel:* 601-266-5600 *Fax:* 601-266-5757 *Web Site:* www.usm.edu/english/c4w.html; www.usm.edu/english/mississippireview.html, pg 661

Minard, Jeff, William Carey Library Publishers, 1605 E Elizabeth St, Pasadena, CA 91104 *Tel:* 626-720-8210 *Toll Free Tel:* 866-732-6657 (orders & cust serv) *E-mail:* assistant@wclbooks.com *Web Site:* www.missionbooks.org, pg 272

Minchew, Laura, Thomas Nelson, 501 Nelson Place, Nashville, TN 37214 *Tel:* 615-889-9000 *Toll Free Tel:* 800-251-4000 *Fax:* 615-902-1548 *E-mail:* publicity@thomasnelson.com *Web Site:* www.thomasnelson.com, pg 245

Mindlin, Ivy, The Ivy League of Artists Inc, 7 Coventry Rd, Livingston, NJ 07039-5105 *Tel:* 973-992-4048 *Fax:* 973-992-4049 *E-mail:* ilartists@comcast.net, pg 584

Mingolello, Aggie, MDR, A D&B Co, 6 Armstrong Rd, Suite 301, Shelton, CT 06484 *Tel:* 203-926-4800 *Toll Free Tel:* 800-333-8802 *Fax:* 203-225-4603 *Toll Free Fax:* 866-532-7097 *E-mail:* mdrinfo@dnb.com *Web Site:* schooldata.com, pg 152

Mintcheva, Svetlana, National Coalition Against Censorship (NCAC), 19 Fulton St, Suite 407, New York, NY 10038 *Tel:* 212-807-6222 *Fax:* 212-807-6245 *E-mail:* ncac@ncac.org *Web Site:* www.ncac.org, pg 611

Mintz, Anna, Clarkson Potter Publishers, c/o Random House Inc, 1745 Broadway, New York, NY 10019 *Tel:* 212-782-9000 *Toll Free Tel:* 888-264-1745 *Fax:* 212-572-6181 *Web Site:* www.clarksonpotter.com; www.randomhouse.com/crown/clarksonpotter, pg 195

Miracle, Tracy, Candlewick Press, 99 Dover St, Somerville, MA 02144-2825 *Tel:* 617-661-3330 *Fax:* 617-661-0565 *E-mail:* bigbear@candlewick.com; salesinfo@candlewick.com *Web Site:* www.candlewick.com, pg 49

Miranda, Joe, Fairchild Books, 1385 Broadway, 5th fl, New York, NY 10018 *Tel:* 212-419-5300 *Toll Free Tel:* 800-932-4724; 888-330-8477 (orders) *Fax:* 212-704-5975 *Web Site:* bloomsbury.com/us/academic/fairchildbooks, pg 85

Miranda, Lori, Cognizant Communication Corp, 18 Peekskill Hollow Rd, Putnam Valley, NY 10597-3213 *Tel:* 845-603-6440; 845-603-6441 (warehouse & orders) *Fax:* 845-603-6442 *E-mail:* inquiries@cognizantcommunication.com; sales@cognizantcommunication.com *Web Site:* www.cognizantcommunication.com, pg 60

Miranda, Robert N, Cognizant Communication Corp, 18 Peekskill Hollow Rd, Putnam Valley, NY 10597-3213 *Tel:* 845-603-6440; 845-603-6441 (warehouse & orders) *Fax:* 845-603-6442 *E-mail:* inquiries@cognizantcommunication.com; sales@cognizantcommunication.com *Web Site:* www.cognizantcommunication.com, pg 60

Mirensky, Gabriela, AIGA 50 Books/50 Covers, 233 Broadway, 17th fl, New York, NY 10279 *Tel:* 212-807-1990 *Fax:* 212-807-1799 *E-mail:* competitions@aiga.org *Web Site:* www.aiga.org, pg 666

Mirkin, Cheryl, Markus Wiener Publishers Inc, 231 Nassau St, Princeton, NJ 08542 *Tel:* 609-921-1141 *Fax:* 609-921-1140 *E-mail:* publisher@markuswiener.com *Web Site:* www.markuswiener.com, pg 271

Mirolla, Michael, Guernica Editions Inc, 1569 Heritage Way, Oakville, ON L6M 2Z7, Canada *Fax:* 416-576-9403 *E-mail:* info@guernicaeditions.com *Web Site:* guernicaeditions.com, pg 486

Miron, Steve, John Wiley & Sons Inc, 111 River St, Hoboken, NJ 07030-5774 *Tel:* 201-748-6000 *Toll Free Tel:* 800-225-5945 (cust serv) *Fax:* 201-748-6088 *E-mail:* info@wiley.com *Web Site:* www.wiley.com, pg 272

Miron, Steve, John Wiley & Sons Inc Scientific, Technical, Medical & Scholarly (STMS), 111 River St, Hoboken, NJ 07030 *Tel:* 201-748-6000 *Toll Free Tel:* 800-225-5945 (cust serv) *Fax:* 201-748-6088 *E-mail:* info@wiley.com *Web Site:* www.wiley.com, pg 272

Mironov, Stacey, CRC Press LLC, 6000 Broken Sound Pkwy NW, Suite 300, Boca Raton, FL 33487 *Tel:* 561-994-0555 *Toll Free Tel:* 800-272-7737 (orders) *Toll Free Fax:* 800-643-9428 (sales); 800-374-3401 (orders) *E-mail:* orders@crcpress.com; orders@taylorandfrancis.com *Web Site:* www.crcpress.com, pg 66

Mirsky, Danielle, Scholastic Education, 524 Broadway, New York, NY 10012 *Tel:* 212-343-6100 *Fax:* 212-343-6189 *Web Site:* www.scholastic.com, pg 218

Mishkin, Daniel, The Toby Press LLC, PO Box 8531, New Milford, CT 06776-8531 *Tel:* 203-830-8508 *Fax:* 203-830-8512 *E-mail:* toby@tobypress.com *Web Site:* korenpub.com/toby/intusd/, pg 246

Mishra, Pradeep C, Arkansas State University Graphic Communications Program, PO Box 1930, Dept of Journalism & Graphic Communications, State University, AR 72467-1930 *Tel:* 870-972-3114 *Fax:* 870-972-3321 *Web Site:* www.astate.edu, pg 659

Miskin, Michael J, Tapestry Press Ltd, 19 Nashoba Rd, Littleton, MA 01460 *Tel:* 978-486-0200 *Toll Free Tel:* 800-535-2007 *Fax:* 978-486-0244 *E-mail:* publish@tapestrypress.com *Web Site:* www.tapestrypress.com, pg 240

Mitchard, Jacquelyn, F+W, A Content + eCommerce Company, 10151 Carver Rd, Suite 200, Blue Ash, OH 45242 *Tel:* 513-531-2690 *Toll Free Tel:* 800-289-0963 (trade accts); 800-258-0929 (orders) *E-mail:* contact_us@fwmedia.com *Web Site:* www.fwcommunity.com, pg 86

Mitchell, Barbara J, Mitchell Lane Publishers Inc, PO Box 196, Hockessin, DE 19707 *Tel:* 302-234-9426 *Toll Free Tel:* 800-814-5484 *Fax:* 302-234-4742 *Toll Free Fax:* 866-834-4164 *E-mail:* orders@mitchelllane.com *Web Site:* www.mitchelllane.com, pg 158

Mitchell, Carine, Cambridge University Press, 32 Avenue of the Americas, New York, NY 10013-2473 *Tel:* 212-924-3900; 212-337-5000 *Fax:* 212-691-3239 *E-mail:* newyork@cambridge.org *Web Site:* www.cambridge.org/us, pg 49

Mitchell, Chuck, The Conference Board Inc, 845 Third Ave, New York, NY 10022-6679 *Tel:* 212-759-0900; 212-339-0345 (cust serv) *Fax:* 212-980-7014; 212-836-9740 (cust serv) *E-mail:* info@conference-board.org *Web Site:* www.conference-board.org, pg 62

Mitchell, David, The Guilford Press, 72 Spring St, New York, NY 10012 *Tel:* 212-431-9800 *Toll Free Tel:* 800-365-7006 *Fax:* 212-966-6708 *E-mail:* info@guilford.com *Web Site:* www.guilford.com, pg 102

Mitchell, Debbie, WaterBrook Multnomah Publishing Group, 12265 Oracle Blvd, Suite 200, Colorado Springs, CO 80921 *Tel:* 719-590-4999 *Toll Free Tel:* 800-603-7051 (orders) *Fax:* 719-590-8977 *Toll Free Fax:* 800-294-5686 (orders) *E-mail:* info@waterbrookmultnomah.com *Web Site:* waterbrookmultnomah.com, pg 267

Mitchell, Douglas C, University of Chicago Press, 1427 E 60 St, Chicago, IL 60637-2954 *Tel:* 773-702-7700; 773-702-7600 *Toll Free Tel:* 800-621-2736 (orders) *Fax:* 773-702-9756; 773-660-2235 (orders); 773-702-2708 *E-mail:* custserv@press.uchicago.edu; marketing@press.uchicago.edu *Web Site:* www.press.uchicago.edu, pg 255

Mitchell, Dr Francis, New World Publishing (Canada), PO Box 36075, Halifax, NS B3J 3S9, Canada *Tel:* 902-576-2055 (inquiries) *Toll Free Tel:* 877-211-3334 (orders) *Fax:* 902-576-2095 *Web Site:* www.newworldpublishing.com, pg 492

Mitchell, Gary, Anne & Philip Yandle Best Article Award, PO Box 5254, Sta B, Victoria, BC V8R 6N4, Canada *E-mail:* info@bchistory.ca; recognition@bchistory.ca *Web Site:* www.bchistory.ca, pg 739

Mitchell, Gwendolyn, Third World Press, 7822 S Dobson Ave, Chicago, IL 60619 *Tel:* 773-651-0700 *Fax:* 773-651-7286 *E-mail:* twpress3@aol.com *Web Site:* www.thirdworldpressbooks.com, pg 245

Mitchell, Hellan, Michelin Maps & Guides, One Parkway S, Greenville, SC 29615-5022 *Tel:* 864-458-5565 *Fax:* 864-458-5665 *Toll Free Fax:* 866-297-0914; 888-773-7979 *E-mail:* orders@americanmap.com (orders) *Web Site:* www.michelintravel.com; www.michelinguide.com, pg 155

Mitchell, Jack, Lumina Datamatics, 4 Collins Ave, Plymouth, MA 02360 *Tel:* 508-746-0300 *Fax:* 508-746-3233 *E-mail:* info@luminadatamatics.com *Web Site:* luminadatamatics.com, pg 530

Mitchell, Nicole, University of Washington Press, 433 Brooklyn Ave NE, Seattle, WA 98195-9570 *Tel:* 206-543-4050 *Toll Free Tel:* 800-537-5487 (orders) *Fax:* 206-543-3932; 410-516-6998 (orders) *E-mail:* uwpress@u.washington.edu *Web Site:* www.washington.edu/uwpress/, pg 260

Mitchell, Patricia, The Pennsylvania State University Press, University Support Bldg 1, Suite C, 820 N University Dr, University Park, PA 16802-1003 *Tel:* 814-865-1327 *Toll Free Tel:* 800-326-9180 *Fax:* 814-863-1408 *Toll Free Fax:* 877-778-2665 *E-mail:* info@psupress.org *Web Site:* www.psupress.org, pg 188

Mitchell, Robert P, Mitchell Lane Publishers Inc, PO Box 196, Hockessin, DE 19707 *Tel:* 302-234-9426 *Toll Free Tel:* 800-814-5484 *Fax:* 302-234-4742 *Toll Free Fax:* 866-834-4164 *E-mail:* orders@mitchelllane.com *Web Site:* www.mitchelllane.com, pg 158

Mitchell, Scott, Chain Store Guide (CSG), 10117 Princess Palm Ave, Suite 375, Tampa, FL 33610 *Tel:* 813-627-6957 *Toll Free Tel:* 800-927-9292 (orders) *Fax:* 813-627-6888 *E-mail:* info@csgis.com *Web Site:* www.csgis.com, pg 54

Mitchell, Steven L, Prometheus Books, 59 John Glenn Dr, Amherst, NY 14228-2119 *Tel:* 716-691-0133 *Toll Free Tel:* 800-421-0351 *Fax:* 716-691-0137 *E-mail:* marketing@prometheusbooks.com; editorial@prometheusbooks.com *Web Site:* www.prometheusbooks.com, pg 199

Mitchell, Sue, University of Alaska Press, 794 University Ave, Suite 220, Fairbanks, AK 99709 *Tel:* 907-474-5831 *Toll Free Tel:* 888-252-6657 (US only) *Fax:* 907-474-5502 *E-mail:* fypress@uaf.edu *Web Site:* www.uaf.edu/uapress, pg 254

Mitchem, Gary, McFarland, 960 NC Hwy 88 W, Jefferson, NC 28640 *Tel:* 336-246-4460 *Toll Free Tel:* 800-253-2187 (orders) *Fax:* 336-246-5018; 336-246-4403 (orders) *E-mail:* info@mcfarlandpub.com *Web Site:* www.mcfarlandpub.com, pg 150

Mitchem, Terri, Rothstein Publishing, 4 Arapaho Rd, Brookfield, CT 06804-3104 *Tel:* 203-740-7400 *Toll Free Tel:* 888-768-4783 *Fax:* 203-740-7401 *E-mail:* info@rothstein.com *Web Site:* www.rothstein.com; www.rothsteinpublishing.com, pg 211

Mitchem, Terri, TotalRecall Publications Inc, 1103 Middlecreek, Friendswood, TX 77546 *Tel:* 281-992-3131 *E-mail:* sales@totalrecallpress.com *Web Site:* www.totalrecallpress.com, pg 247

Mitchner, Leslie, Rutgers University Press, 106 Somerset St, 3rd fl, New Brunswick, NJ 08901 *Tel:* 848-445-7762 *Toll Free Tel:* 800-848-6224 (orders only) *Fax:* 732-745-4935 (acqs, edit, mktg, perms & prodn) *Toll Free Fax:* 800-272-6817 (fulfillment) *Web Site:* rutgerspress.rutgers.edu, pg 212

Mitnick, Audrey, Sleeping Bear Press™, 315 Eisenhower Pkwy, Suite 200, Ann Arbor, MI 48108 *Toll Free Tel:* 800-487-2323 *Fax:* 734-794-0004 *E-mail:* sleepingbearpress@cengage.com *Web Site:* www.sleepingbearpress.com, pg 228

Mittelstadt, David J, New Canaan Publishing Co LLC, 2384 N Hwy 341, Rossville, GA 30741 *Tel:* 423-285-8672 *E-mail:* djm@newcanaanpublishing.com *Web Site:* www.newcanaanpublishing.com, pg 167

Mitzman, Melanie, Gallery Books, 1230 Avenue of the Americas, New York, NY 10020 *Toll Free Tel:* 800-456-6798 *Fax:* 212-698-7284 *E-mail:* consumer.customerservice@simonandschuster.com *Web Site:* www.simonsays.com, pg 94

Moberg, David, Thomas Nelson, 501 Nelson Place, Nashville, TN 37214 *Tel:* 615-889-9000 *Toll Free Tel:* 800-251-4000 *Fax:* 615-902-1548 *E-mail:* publicity@thomasnelson.com *Web Site:* www.thomasnelson.com, pg 245

Mock, Alishea, Dufour Editions Inc, PO Box 7, Chester Springs, PA 19425 *Tel:* 610-458-5005 *Fax:* 610-458-7103 *E-mail:* info@dufoureditions.com *Web Site:* www.dufoureditions.com, pg 77

Mockler, Emily, House of Anansi Press Inc, 110 Spadina Ave, Suite 801, Toronto, ON M5V 2K4, Canada *Tel:* 416-363-4343 *Fax:* 416-363-1017 *E-mail:* customerservice@houseofanansi.com *Web Site:* www.houseofanansi.com, pg 488

Modugno, Maria, Random House Children's Books, 1745 Broadway, New York, NY 10019 *Tel:* 212-782-9000 *Toll Free Tel:* 800-200-3552 *Fax:* 212-782-9452 *Web Site:* randomhousekids.com, pg 203

Modys, Rob, Florida Outdoor Writers Association Inc, 24 NW 33 Ct, Suite A, Gainesville, FL 32607 *Tel:* 352-284-1763 *E-mail:* info@fowa.org *Web Site:* www.fowa.org, pg 606

Modzelewski, Joe, EMC Publishing LLC, 875 Montreal Way, St Paul, MN 55102 *Tel:* 651-290-2800 (corp) *Toll Free Tel:* 800-328-1452 *Toll Free Fax:* 800-328-4564 *E-mail:* educate@emcp.com *Web Site:* www.emcp.com, pg 81

Moe, Jack, Black Mountain Press, PO Box 9907, Asheville, NC 28815 *Tel:* 828-273-3332 *Web Site:* www.theblackmountainpress.com, pg 38

Moeckel, Prof Thorpe, Hollins University-Jackson Center for Creative Writing, PO Box 9677, Roanoke, VA 24020 *Tel:* 540-362-6317 *Fax:* 540-362-6097 *E-mail:* creative.writing@hollins.edu *Web Site:* www.hollins.edu, pg 660

Moeller, Vanessa, Artist-in-Residence Program, 649 rue Queen, 2nd fl, Fredericton, NB E3B 1C3, Canada *Tel:* 506-444-4444 *Toll Free Tel:* 866-460-ARTS (460-2787) *Fax:* 506-444-5543 *E-mail:* nbabcanb@artsnb.ca *Web Site:* www.artsnb.ca, pg 668

Moeller, Vanessa, Arts Scholarships, 649 rue Queen, 2nd fl, Fredericton, NB E3B 1C3, Canada *Tel:* 506-444-4444 *Toll Free Tel:* 866-460-ARTS (460-2787) *Fax:* 506-444-5543 *E-mail:* nbabcanb@artsnb.ca *Web Site:* www.artsnb.ca, pg 668

Moeller, Vanessa, Atlantic Public Art Funders (APAF) Creative Residency, 649 rue Queen, 2nd fl, Fredericton, NB E3B 1C3, Canada *Tel:* 506-444-4444 *Toll Free Tel:* 866-460-ARTS (460-2787) *Fax:* 506-444-5543 *E-mail:* nbabcanb@artsnb.ca *Web Site:* www.artsnb.ca, pg 669

Moeller, Vanessa, Creation Grant Program, 649 rue Queen, 2nd fl, Fredericton, NB E3B 1C3, Canada *Tel:* 506-444-4444 *Toll Free Tel:* 866-460-ARTS (460-2787) *Fax:* 506-444-5543 *E-mail:* nbabcanb@artsnb.ca *Web Site:* www.artsnb.ca, pg 679

Moeller, Vanessa, Documentation Grant Program, 649 rue Queen, 2nd fl, Fredericton, NB E3B 1C3, Canada *Tel:* 506-444-4444 *Toll Free Tel:* 866-460-ARTS (460-2787) *Fax:* 506-444-5543 *E-mail:* nbabcanb@artsnb.ca *Web Site:* www.artsnb.ca, pg 681

Moeller, Vanessa, Grants for Literary Artists, 649 rue Queen, 2nd fl, Fredericton, NB E3B 1C3, Canada *Tel:* 506-444-4444 *Toll Free Tel:* 866-460-ARTS (460-2787) *Fax:* 506-444-5543 *E-mail:* nbabcanb@artsnb.ca *Web Site:* www.artsnb.ca, pg 690

Moeller, Vanessa, The Lieutenant-Governor's Awards for High Achievement in the Arts, 649 rue Queen, 2nd fl, Fredericton, NB E3B 1C3, Canada *Tel:* 506-444-4444 *Toll Free Tel:* 866-460-ARTS (460-2787) *Fax:* 506-444-5543 *E-mail:* nbabcanb@artsnb.ca *Web Site:* www.artsnb.ca, pg 701

Moen, Jeff, University of Minnesota Press, 111 Third Ave S, Suite 290, Minneapolis, MN 55401-2520 *Tel:* 612-627-1970 *Fax:* 612-627-1980 *E-mail:* ump@umn.edu *Web Site:* www.upress.umn.edu, pg 257

Moench, Dan, Gibbs Smith Publisher, 1877 E Gentile St, Layton, UT 84041 *Tel:* 801-544-9800 *Toll Free Tel:* 800-748-5439; 800-835-4993 (orders) *Fax:* 801-544-5582 *Toll Free Fax:* 800-213-3023 (orders only) *E-mail:* info@gibbs-smith.com; tradeorders@gibbs-smith.com *Web Site:* www.gibbs-smith.com, pg 96

Moench, David, Random House Publishing Group, 1745 Broadway, New York, NY 10019 *Toll Free Tel:* 800-200-3552 *Web Site:* atrandom.com, pg 204

Moersch, Sarah, Southern Playwrights Competition, 700 Pelham Rd N, Jacksonville, AL 36265-1602 *Tel:* 256-782-5498 *Fax:* 256-782-5441 *Web Site:* www.jsu.edu/english/southpla.html, pg 730

Moggy, Dianne, Harlequin Enterprises Ltd, 225 Duncan Mill Rd, Don Mills, ON M3B 3K9, Canada *Tel:* 416-445-5860 *Toll Free Tel:* 888-432-4879; 800-370-5838 (ebook inquiries) *E-mail:* customerservice@harlequin.com *Web Site:* www.harlequin.com, pg 487

Moghari, Francesca, National Academies Press (NAP), Lockbox 285, 500 Fifth St NW, Washington, DC 20001 *Tel:* 202-334-3313 *Toll Free Tel:* 888-624-8373 (cust serv) *Fax:* 202-334-2451 (cust serv); 202-334-2793 (mktg dept) *E-mail:* customer_service@nap.edu *Web Site:* www.nap.edu, pg 163

Mogus, Mary Ann, Ligonier Valley Writers Conference, PO Box B, Ligonier, PA 15658-1602 *Tel:* 724-238-3692, pg 652

Mohan, Joseph, The Art Institute of Chicago, 111 S Michigan Ave, Chicago, IL 60603-6404 *Tel:* 312-443-3600; 312-443-3540 (pubns) *Fax:* 312-443-1334 (pubns) *Web Site:* www.artic.edu; www.artinstituteshop.org, pg 22

Mohyde, Colleen, The Doe Coover Agency, PO Box 668, Winchester, MA 01890 *Tel:* 781-721-6000 *Fax:* 781-721-6727 *E-mail:* info@doecooveragency.com *Web Site:* www.doecooveragency.com, pg 547

Mojica, JoAnne, Scholastic Trade Division, 557 Broadway, New York, NY 10012 *Tel:* 212-343-6100; 212-343-4685 (export sales) *Fax:* 212-343-4714 (export sales) *Web Site:* www.scholastic.com, pg 219

Moldow, Susan, Scribner, 1230 Avenue of the Americas, New York, NY 10020, pg 220

Moldow, Susan, Simon & Schuster, Inc, 1230 Avenue of the Americas, New York, NY 10020 *Tel:* 212-698-7000 *Fax:* 212-698-7007 *E-mail:* firstname.lastname@simonandschuster.com *Web Site:* www.simonandschuster.com, pg 226

Moldow, Susan, Touchstone, 1230 Avenue of the Americas, New York, NY 10020, pg 247

Mole, Alan, American Literacy Council, 1441 Mariposa Ave, Boulder, CO 80302 *Tel:* 303-440-7385 *Web Site:* www.americanliteracy.com, pg 595

Molgat, Anne, Les Editions du Ble, 340 Provencher Blvd, St Boniface, MB R2H 0G7, Canada *Tel:* 204-237-8200 *Fax:* 204-233-8182 *E-mail:* direction@editionsduble.ca *Web Site:* ble.avoslivres.ca, pg 480

Molish, John, Tantor Media Inc, 2 Business Park, Old Saybrook, CT 06475 *Toll Free Tel:* 877-782-6867 *Toll Free Fax:* 888-782-7821 *Web Site:* www.tantor.com, pg 240

Moller, Marilyn, W W Norton & Company Inc, 500 Fifth Ave, New York, NY 10110-0017 *Tel:* 212-354-5500 *Toll Free Tel:* 800-233-4830 (orders & cust serv) *Fax:* 212-869-0856 *Toll Free Fax:* 800-458-6515 *Web Site:* www.wwnorton.com, pg 171

Molnar, Szilvia, Sterling Lord Literistic Inc, 65 Bleecker St, New York, NY 10012 *Tel:* 212-780-6050 *Fax:* 212-780-6095 *E-mail:* info@sll.com *Web Site:* www.sll.com, pg 575

Moltke, Nina von, Random House Publishing Group, 1745 Broadway, New York, NY 10019 *Toll Free Tel:* 800-200-3552 *Web Site:* atrandom.com, pg 204

Molyneaux, David G, SATW Foundation Lowell Thomas Travel Journalism Competition, 306 Summer Hill Dr, Fredericksburg, TX 78654 *Tel:* 713-973-9985 *E-mail:* awards@satwf.com *Web Site:* www.satwfoundation.org, pg 726

Molyneux, Beverly, AAPG (American Association of Petroleum Geologists), 1444 S Boulder Ave, Tulsa, OK 74119 *Tel:* 918-584-2555 *Toll Free Tel:* 800-364-AAPG (364-2274) *Fax:* 918-580-2665 *Toll Free Fax:* 800-898-2274 *E-mail:* info@aapg.org *Web Site:* www.aapg.org, pg 1

Mommer, Kerri, Open Court, 70 E Lake St, Suite 300, Chicago, IL 60601 *Tel:* 312-701-1720 *Toll Free Tel:* 800-815-2280 (orders only) *Fax:* 312-701-1728 *E-mail:* opencourt@caruspub.com *Web Site:* www.opencourtbooks.com, pg 175

Monacelli, Gianfranco, Crown Publishing Group, c/o Penguin Random House Inc, 1745 Broadway, New York, NY 10019 *Tel:* 212-782-9000 *Toll Free Tel:* 888-264-1745 *Fax:* 212-940-7408 *E-mail:* crownosm@penguinrandomhouse.com *Web Site:* crownpublishing.com, pg 68

Monacelli, Gianfranco, The Monacelli Press, 236 W 27 St, 4th fl, New York, NY 10001 *Tel:* 212-229-9925 *E-mail:* contact@monacellipress.com *Web Site:* www.monacellipress.com, pg 159

Monaco, Lauren, Penguin Group (USA) LLC, a Penguin Random House company, 375 Hudson St, New York, NY 10014 *Tel:* 212-366-2000 *Toll Free Tel:* 800-847-5515 (inside sales); 800-631-8571 (cust serv) *Fax:* 212-366-2666; 607-775-4829 (inside sales) *E-mail:* online@us.penguingroup.com *Web Site:* www.penguin.com; us.penguingroup.com, pg 186

Monaghan, Katie, Scribner, 1230 Avenue of the Americas, New York, NY 10020, pg 220

Monaghan, Kelly, The Intrepid Traveler, 152 Staltonstall Pkwy (rear entrance), East Haven, CT 06512 *Tel:* 203-469-0214 *E-mail:* admin@intrepidtraveler.com *Web Site:* www.intrepidtraveler.com, pg 125

Monaghan, Timothy, The Ledge Press Fiction Awards Competition, 40 Maple Ave, Bellport, NY 11713 *E-mail:* info@theledgemagazine.com *Web Site:* theledgemagazine.com, pg 699

Monaghan, Timothy, The Ledge Press Poetry Awards Competition, 40 Maple Ave, Bellport, NY 11713 *E-mail:* info@theledgemagazine.com *Web Site:* theledgemagazine.com, pg 699

Monaghan, Timothy, The Ledge Press Poetry Chapbook Competition, 40 Maple Ave, Bellport, NY 11713 *E-mail:* info@theledgemagazine.com *Web Site:* theledgemagazine.com, pg 699

Monahan, Sherry, Spur Awards, 271 CR 219, Encampment, WY 82325 *Tel:* 307-329-8942 *Fax:* 307-327-5465 *E-mail:* wwa.moulton@gmail.com *Web Site:* westernwriters.org, pg 730

Monahan, Sherry, Western Writers of America Inc (WWA), 271 CR 219, Encampment, WY 82325 *Tel:* 307-329-8942 *Fax:* 307-327-5465 *Web Site:* westernwriters.org, pg 621

Monfried, Andrea, Crown Publishing Group, c/o Penguin Random House Inc, 1745 Broadway, New York, NY 10019 *Tel:* 212-782-9000 *Toll Free Tel:* 888-264-1745 *Fax:* 212-940-7408 *E-mail:* crownosm@penguinrandomhouse.com *Web Site:* crownpublishing.com, pg 68

Monfried, Andrea, The Monacelli Press, 236 W 27 St, 4th fl, New York, NY 10001 *Tel:* 212-229-9925 *E-mail:* contact@monacellipress.com *Web Site:* www.monacellipress.com, pg 159

Monfried, Lucia, Dial Books for Young Readers, 345 Hudson St, New York, NY 10014 *Tel:* 212-366-2000 *Fax:* 212-414-3396 *E-mail:* online@penguinputnam.com *Web Site:* www.penguinputnam.com; us.penguingroup.com, pg 74

Monge, Sr Marlyn Evangelina, Pauline Books & Media, 50 St Paul's Ave, Boston, MA 02130 *Tel:* 617-522-8911 *Toll Free Tel:* 800-876-4463 (orders); 800-836-9723 (cust serv) *Fax:* 617-541-9805 *E-mail:* editorial@paulinemedia.com (ms submissions); orderentry@pauline.org (cust serv) *Web Site:* www.pauline.org, pg 184

Monk, Steve, Wolters Kluwer Ltd, 90 Sheppard Ave E, Suite 300, Toronto, ON M2N 6X1, Canada *Tel:* 416-224-2224 *Toll Free Tel:* 800-268-4522 (CN & US cust serv) *Fax:* 416-224-2243 *Toll Free Fax:* 800-461-4131 *E-mail:* cservice@cch.ca (cust serv) *Web Site:* www.cch.ca, pg 505

Monks, Julia, McGill-Queen's University Press, 1010 Sherbrooke W, Suite 1720, Montreal, QC H3A 2R7, Canada *Tel:* 514-398-3750 *Fax:* 514-398-4333 *E-mail:* mqup@mqup.ca *Web Site:* www.mqup.ca, pg 491

Monroe, Elvira, Wide World Publishing, PO Box 476, San Carlos, CA 94070-0476 *Tel:* 650-593-2839 *Fax:* 650-595-0802 *E-mail:* wwpbl@aol.com *Web Site:* wideworldpublishing.com, pg 271

Monson, Ander, Diagram Essay Contest, University of Arizona, ML-445, PO Box 210067, Tucson, AZ 85721 *E-mail:* editor@thediagram.com *Web Site:* www.thediagram.com/contest.html, pg 680

Monson, Cheryl, EMC Publishing LLC, 875 Montreal Way, St Paul, MN 55102 *Tel:* 651-290-2800 (corp) *Toll Free Tel:* 800-328-1452 *Toll Free Fax:* 800-328-4564 *E-mail:* educate@emcp.com *Web Site:* www.emcp.com, pg 81

Montagni, Patricia, International Council of Shopping Centers (ICSC), 1221 Avenue of the Americas, 41st fl, New York, NY 10020-1099 *Tel:* 646-728-3800 *Fax:* 732-694-1755 *E-mail:* icsc@icsc.org *Web Site:* www.icsc.org, pg 124

Montague, Larry N, Technical Association of the Pulp & Paper Industry (TAPPI), 15 Technology Pkwy S, Suite 115, Peachtree Corners, GA 30092 *Tel:* 770-446-1400 *Toll Free Tel:* 800-332-8686 (US); 800-446-9431 (CN) *Fax:* 770-446-6947 *E-mail:* memberconnection@tappi.org *Web Site:* www.tappi.org, pg 620

Montague, Michelle, Harry N Abrams Inc, 115 W 18 St, 6th fl, New York, NY 10011 *Tel:* 212-206-7715 *Toll Free Tel:* 800-345-1359 *Fax:* 212-519-1210 *E-mail:* abrams@abramsbooks.com *Web Site:* www.abramsbooks.com, pg 3

Montecel, Dr Maria "Cuca" Robledo, Intercultural Development Research Association (IDRA), 5815 Callaghan Rd, Suite 101, San Antonio, TX 78228 *Tel:* 210-444-1710 *Fax:* 210-444-1714 *E-mail:* contact@idra.org *Web Site:* www.idra.org, pg 123

Montefinise, Angela, New York Public Library, Publications Off, 2nd fl, 188 Madison Ave, New York, NY 10016-4314 *Tel:* 917-275-6975 *Web Site:* www.nypl.org, pg 169

Monteith, Barnas, Tumblehome Learning Inc, PO Box 171386, Boston, MA 02117 *E-mail:* info@tumblehomelearning.com *Web Site:* www.tumblehomelearning.com, pg 250

Montgomery, Michelle, Society for Industrial & Applied Mathematics, 3600 Market St, 6th fl, Philadelphia, PA 19104-2688 *Tel:* 215-382-9800 *Toll Free Tel:* 800-447-7426 *Fax:* 215-386-7999 *E-mail:* siambooks@siam.org *Web Site:* www.siam.org, pg 228

Monti, Joe, Simon & Schuster Children's Publishing, 1230 Avenue of the Americas, New York, NY 10020 *Tel:* 212-698-7000 *Web Site:* KIDS.SimonandSchuster.com; TEEN.SimonandSchuster.com; simonandschuster.net; simonandschuster.biz, pg 225

Montoya, Martha, National Association of Hispanic Publications Inc (NAHP), 529 14 St NW, Suite 1126, Washington, DC 20045 *Tel:* 202-662-7250 *Web Site:* www.nahp.org, pg 611

Montsma, Haley, Society of American Travel Writers (SATW), 11950 W Lake Park Dr, Suite 320, Milwaukee, WI 53224-3049 *Tel:* 414-359-1625 *Fax:* 414-359-1671 *E-mail:* info@satw.org *Web Site:* www.satw.org, pg 619

Moody, Douglas, Educational Directories Inc (EDI), 1025 W Wise Rd, Suite 101, Schaumburg, IL 60193 *Tel:* 847-891-1250 *Toll Free Tel:* 800-357-6183 *Fax:* 847-891-0945 *E-mail:* info@ediusa.com *Web Site:* www.ediusa.com, pg 79

Moody, Jeanne C, Beaver Wood Associates, 655 Alstead Center Rd, Alstead, NH 03602 *Tel:* 603-835-7900 *Web Site:* www.beaverwood.com, pg 521

Moody, Jessica, Grey House Publishing Inc™, 4919 Rte 22, Amenia, NY 12501 *Tel:* 518-789-8700 *Toll Free Tel:* 800-562-2139 *Fax:* 518-789-0556 *E-mail:* books@greyhouse.com; customerservice@greyhouse.com *Web Site:* www.greyhouse.com, pg 101

Moody, Julie, Disney-Hyperion Books, 1101 Flower St, Glendale, CA 91201 *Web Site:* books.disney.com, pg 74

Moody, Rodger, Gerald Cable Book Award, PO Box 3541, Eugene, OR 97403 *Tel:* 541-344-5060 *E-mail:* sfrpress@earthlink.net *Web Site:* www.silverfishreviewpress.com, pg 675

Moog, Bob, BePuzzled, 2030 Harrison St, San Francisco, CA 94110 *Tel:* 415-503-1600 *Toll Free Tel:* 800-347-4818 *Fax:* 415-503-0085 *E-mail:* info@ugames.com *Web Site:* www.ugames.com, pg 35

Mooney, Robert, Etruscan Press, Wilkes University, 84 W South St, Wilkes-Barre, PA 18766 *Tel:* 570-408-4546 *Fax:* 570-408-3333 *E-mail:* books@etruscanpress.org *Web Site:* www.etruscanpress.org, pg 84

Moore, Berwyn, Gannon University's High School Poetry Contest, Gannon University, Dept of English, 109 University Sq, Erie, PA 16541 *Tel:* 814-871-7504 *Web Site:* www.gannon.edu/departmental/english/poetry.asp, pg 688

Moore, Brian, Houghton Mifflin Harcourt, 222 Berkeley St, Boston, MA 02116 *Tel:* 617-351-5000 *Toll Free Tel:* 800-225-5425 (K-12 educ materials); 800-323-9540 (assessment materials); 877-219-1537 (SkillsTutor); 888-242-6747 (Destination; Earobics; Edmark; Learning Village; Riverdeep); 800-225-3362 (Houghton Mifflin Harcourt Trade & Reference Publishers) *Toll Free Fax:* 800-269-5232 *E-mail:* customerservice@hmhpub.com *Web Site:* www.hmhco.com, pg 115

Moore, Brian, Houghton Mifflin Harcourt Trade & Reference Division, 222 Berkeley St, Boston, MA 02116 *Tel:* 617-351-5000 *Toll Free Tel:* 800-225-3362 *Web Site:* www.hmhco.com, pg 115

Moore, Claudette, Moore Literary Agency, 10 State St, Suite 210, Newburyport, MA 01950 *Tel:* 978-465-9015 *Fax:* 978-465-6653, pg 566

Moore, Declan, National Geographic Books, 1145 17 St NW, Washington, DC 20036-4688 *Tel:* 202-857-7000 *Fax:* 202-857-7670 *Web Site:* books.nationalgeographic.com/books, pg 165

Moore, Declan, National Geographic Society, 1145 17 St NW, Washington, DC 20036-4688 *Tel:* 202-857-7000 *Fax:* 202-429-5727 *Web Site:* www.nationalgeographic.com, pg 165

Moore, Dinty W, Ohio University, English Dept, Creative Writing Program, Ohio University, English Dept, Ellis Hall, Athens, OH 45701 *Tel:* 740-593-2838 (English Dept) *Fax:* 740-593-2832 *E-mail:* english.department@ohio.edu *Web Site:* english.ohiou.edu, pg 662

Moore, George, Cengage Learning, 20 Channel Center St, Boston, MA 02210 *Tel:* 617-289-7700 *Toll Free Tel:* 800-354-9706 *Fax:* 617-289-7844 *Toll Free Fax:* 800-487-8488 *E-mail:* esales@cengage.com *Web Site:* www.cengage.com, pg 53

Moore, Heather, Sourcebooks Inc, 1935 Brookdale Rd, Suite 139, Naperville, IL 60563 *Tel:* 630-961-3900 *Toll Free Tel:* 800-432-7444 *Fax:* 630-961-2168 *E-mail:* info@sourcebooks.com; customersupport@sourcebooks.com *Web Site:* www.sourcebooks.com, pg 230

Moore, John, BNi Building News, 990 Park Center Dr, Suite E, Vista, CA 92081-8352 *Tel:* 760-734-1113 *Toll Free Tel:* 888-BNI-BOOK (264-2665) *Web Site:* www.bnibooks.com, pg 41

Moore, Karen, Literary Management Group LLC, 16970 San Carlos Blvd, Suite 160-100, Fort Myers, FL 33908 *Tel:* 615-812-4445 *Web Site:* www.literarymanagementgroup.com, pg 562

Moore, Kenneth, IEEE Press, 445 Hoes Lane, Piscataway, NJ 08854 *Tel:* 732-981-0060 *Fax:* 732-562-1746 *E-mail:* pressbooks@ieee.org (proposals & info) *Web Site:* www.ieee.org/press, pg 118

Moore, Lisa C, RedBone Press, PO Box 15571, Washington, DC 20003 *Tel:* 202-667-0392 *Fax:* 301-588-0588 *E-mail:* info@redbonepress.com *Web Site:* www.redbonepress.com, pg 206

Moore, Marie, Decker Intellectual Properties Publisher, 69 John St S, Suite 310, Hamilton, ON L8N 2B9, Canada *Tel:* 905-522-8526 *Toll Free Tel:* 855-647-6511 (CN & US) *Fax:* 905-522-9273 *E-mail:* customercare@deckerip.com *Web Site:* www.deckerpublishing.com, pg 478

Moore, Marvin, Pacific Press Publishing Association, 1350 N Kings Rd, Nampa, ID 83687-3193 *Tel:* 208-465-2500 *Toll Free Tel:* 800-447-7377 *Fax:* 208-465-2531 *Web Site:* www.pacificpress.com, pg 180

Moore, Mary-Alice, Boyds Mills Press, 815 Church St, Honesdale, PA 18431 *Tel:* 570-253-1164 *Toll Free Tel:* 800-490-5111 *Fax:* 570-253-0179 *E-mail:* contact@boydsmillspress.com *Web Site:* www.boydsmillspress.com, pg 43

Moore, Mary-Alice, Highlights for Children, 1800 Watermark Dr, Columbus, OH 43215 *Tel:* 614-486-0631 *Toll Free Tel:* 800-962-3661 (Highlights Club cust serv); 800-255-9517 (Highlights Magazine cust serv) *Web Site:* www.highlights.com, pg 111

Moore, Michael, Augsburg Fortress Publishers, Publishing House of the Evangelical Lutheran Church in America, 510 Marquette Ave S, Minneapolis, MN 55402 *Tel:* 612-330-3300 *Toll Free Tel:* 800-426-0115 (ext 639, subns); 800-328-4648 (orders) *Fax:* 612-330-3455 *E-mail:* info@augsburgfortress.org; copyright@augsburgfortress.org (reprint permission requests); customercare@augsburgfortress.org *Web Site:* www.augsburgfortress.org, pg 27

Moore, Michael, Steerforth Press, 45 Lyme Rd, Suite 208, Hanover, NH 03755-1222 *Tel:* 603-643-4787 *Fax:* 603-643-4788 *E-mail:* info@steerforth.com *Web Site:* www.steerforth.com, pg 234

Moore, Nancy, Gerald & Cullen Rapp, 420 Lexington Ave, New York, NY 10170 *Tel:* 212-889-3337 *Fax:* 212-889-3341 *E-mail:* info@rappart.com *Web Site:* www.rappart.com, pg 584

Moore, Richard, Marshall Cavendish Corp, 99 White Plains Rd, Tarrytown, NY 10591-9001 *Tel:* 914-332-8888 *Toll Free Tel:* 800-821-9881 *Fax:* 914-332-8102 *E-mail:* mce@marshallcavendish.com *Web Site:* www.mceducation.us, pg 148

Moore, Stacey, Zeig, Tucker & Theisen Inc, 3614 N 24 St, Phoenix, AZ 85016 *Tel:* 480-389-4342 *Toll Free Tel:* 800-666-2211 (orders) *Fax:* 602-944-8118 *E-mail:* marketing@zeigtucker.com *Web Site:* www.zeigtucker.com, pg 279

Moore, Stephen, Paul Kohner Agency, 9300 Wilshire Blvd, Suite 555, Beverly Hills, CA 90212 *Tel:* 310-550-1060 *Fax:* 310-276-1083, pg 560

Moore, Steve, Ram Publishing Co, 1881 W State St, Garland, TX 75042 *Tel:* 972-494-6151 *Toll Free Tel:* 800-527-4011 *Fax:* 972-494-1881 *E-mail:* sales@garrett.com *Web Site:* www.garrett.com, pg 203

Moore, Sylvia, Midmarch Arts Press, 300 Riverside Dr, New York, NY 10025-5239 *Tel:* 212-666-6990 *Web Site:* midmarchartspress.org, pg 156

Moore, Tim, Baha'i Publishing, 401 Greenleaf Ave, Wilmette, IL 60091 *Tel:* 847-425-7950 *Toll Free Tel:* 800-999-9019 (orders) *Fax:* 847-425-7951 *E-mail:* bds@usbnc.org *Web Site:* books.bahai.us; www.bahaibookstore.com, pg 29

Moore-Anderson, Sheryl, HarperCollins Children's Books, 195 Broadway, New York, NY 10007 *Tel:* 212-207-7000 *Web Site:* www.harpercollins.com/childrens, pg 105

Moore-Swafford, Angela, Southern Illinois University Press, 1915 University Press Dr, SIUC Mail Code 6806, Carbondale, IL 62901-4323 *Tel:* 618-453-2281 *Fax:* 618-453-1221 *E-mail:* custserv@press.uchicago.edu; rights@siu.edu *Web Site:* www.siupress.com, pg 231

Moorehead, Harold, Stanford University Press, 1450 Page Mill Rd, Palo Alto, CA 94304-1124 *Tel:* 650-723-9434 *Fax:* 650-725-3457 *E-mail:* info@sup.org *Web Site:* www.sup.org, pg 233

Moose, Christina, Davies Publishing Inc, 32 S Raymond Ave, Suites 4 & 5, Pasadena, CA 91105-1961 *Tel:* 626-792-3046 *Toll Free Tel:* 877-792-0005 *Fax:* 626-792-5308 *E-mail:* info@daviespublishing.com *Web Site:* daviespublishing.com, pg 71

Mooser, Stephen, The Don Freeman Memorial Grant-In-Aid, 4727 Wilshire Blvd, Suite 301, Los Angeles, CA 90010 *Tel:* 323-782-1010; 310-403-0675 (cell) *Fax:* 323-782-1892 *E-mail:* membership@scbwi.org; scbwi@scbwi.org *Web Site:* www.scbwi.org, pg 687

Mooser, Stephen, Golden Kite Awards, 4727 Wilshire Blvd, Suite 301, Los Angeles, CA 90010 *Tel:* 323-782-1010; 310-403-0675 (cell) *Fax:* 323-782-1892 *E-mail:* scbwi@scbwi.org; membership@scbwi.org *Web Site:* www.scbwi.org, pg 690

Mooser, Stephen, Magazine Merit Awards, 4727 Wilshire Blvd, Suite 301, Los Angeles, CA 90010 *Tel:* 323-782-1010; 310-403-0675 (cell) *Fax:* 323-782-1892 *E-mail:* membership@scbwi.org; scbwi@scbwi.org *Web Site:* www.scbwi.org, pg 704

Mooser, Stephen, SCBWI Work-In-Progress Grants, 4727 Wilshire Blvd, Suite 301, Los Angeles, CA 90010 *Tel:* 323-782-1010; 310-403-0675 (cell) *Fax:* 323-782-1892 *E-mail:* membership@scbwi.org; scbwi@scbwi.org *Web Site:* www.scbwi.org, pg 727

Mooser, Stephen, Society of Children's Book Writers and Illustrators (SCBWI), 4727 Wilshire Blvd, Suite 301, Los Angeles, CA 90010 *Tel:* 323-782-1010 *Fax:* 323-782-1892 *E-mail:* membership@scbwi.org; scbwi@scbwi.org *Web Site:* www.scbwi.org, pg 619

Mopsik, Eugene, American Society of Media Photographers (ASMP), 150 N Second St, Philadelphia, PA 19106 *Tel:* 215-451-2767 *Fax:* 215-451-0880 *E-mail:* info@asmp.org *Web Site:* asmp.org, pg 596

Moraleda, Lisa, Little, Brown Books for Young Readers, 1290 Avenue of the Americas, New York, NY 10019 *Tel:* 212-364-1100 *Toll Free Tel:* 800-759-0190 (cust serv) *Web Site:* www.HachetteBookGroup.com, pg 141

Morales, Lisa, Holiday House Inc, 425 Madison Ave, New York, NY 10017 *Tel:* 212-688-0085 *Fax:* 212-421-6134 *E-mail:* holiday@holidayhouse.com *Web Site:* www.holidayhouse.com, pg 113

Moran, Bruce, TotalRecall Publications Inc, 1103 Middlecreek, Friendswood, TX 77546 *Tel:* 281-992-3131 *E-mail:* sales@totalrecallpress.com *Web Site:* www.totalrecallpress.com, pg 247

Moran, James David, Fellowships for Creative & Performing Artists & Writers, 185 Salisbury St, Worcester, MA 01609-1634 *Tel:* 508-755-5221 *Fax:* 508-753-3311 *Web Site:* www.americanantiquarian.org, pg 685

Moran, James David, Fellowships for Historical Research, 185 Salisbury St, Worcester, MA 01609-1634 *Tel:* 508-471-2131 *Fax:* 508-754-9069 *Web Site:* www.americanantiquarian.org, pg 685

Moran, Michael, Gem Guides Book Co, 1275 W Ninth St, Upland, CA 91786 *Tel:* 626-855-1611 *Toll Free Tel:* 800-824-5118 (orders) *Fax:* 626-855-1610 *E-mail:* info@gemguidesbooks.com *Web Site:* www.gemguidesbooks.com, pg 95

Moran, Patrick R, Pro Lingua Associates Inc, 74 Cotton Mill Hill, Suite A-315, Brattleboro, VT 05301 *Tel:* 802-257-7779 *Toll Free Tel:* 800-366-4775 *Fax:* 802-257-5117 *E-mail:* info@prolinguaassociates.com *Web Site:* www.prolinguaassociates.com, pg 198

Moran, Viniita, Chronicle Books LLC, 680 Second St, San Francisco, CA 94107 *Tel:* 415-537-4200 *Toll Free Tel:* 800-759-0190 (cust serv) *Fax:* 415-537-4460 *Toll Free Fax:* 800-858-7787 (orders); 800-286-9471 (cust serv) *E-mail:* frontdesk@chroniclebooks.com *Web Site:* www.chroniclebooks.com, pg 58

Morean, Rebecca, Antioch Writers' Workshop, 900 Dayton St, Yellow Springs, OH 45387 *Tel:* 937-769-1803 *E-mail:* info@antiochwritersworkshop.com *Web Site:* www.antiochwritersworkshop.com, pg 649

Morehouse, Jim, Paradise Cay Publications Inc, 550 S "G" St, Suite 1, Arcata, CA 95521 *Tel:* 707-822-9063 *Toll Free Tel:* 800-736-4509 *Fax:* 707-822-9163 *E-mail:* info@paracay.com *Web Site:* www.paracay.com, pg 182

Morehouse, Matt, Paradise Cay Publications Inc, 550 S "G" St, Suite 1, Arcata, CA 95521 *Tel:* 707-822-9063 *Toll Free Tel:* 800-736-4509 *Fax:* 707-822-9163 *E-mail:* info@paracay.com *Web Site:* www.paracay.com, pg 182

Morel, Madeleine, 2M Communications Ltd, 19 W 21 St, Suite 501, New York, NY 10010 *Tel:* 212-741-1509 *Fax:* 212-691-4460 *Web Site:* www.2mcommunications.com, pg 578

Morello, Frank, Florida Outdoor Writers Association Inc, 24 NW 33 Ct, Suite A, Gainesville, FL 32607 *Tel:* 352-284-1763 *E-mail:* info@fowa.org *Web Site:* www.fowa.org, pg 606

Moreno, Luis Alberto, Inter-American Development Bank, 1300 New York Ave NW, Washington, DC 20577 *Tel:* 202-623-1000 *Fax:* 202-623-3096 *E-mail:* pic@iadb.org *Web Site:* www.iadb.org/pub, pg 123

Morgan, Cal, HarperCollins General Books Group, 195 Broadway, New York, NY 10007 *Tel:* 212-207-7000 *Web Site:* www.harpercollins.com, pg 105

Morgan, Charlotte, Napa Valley Writers' Conference, Upper Valley Campus, 1088 College Ave, St Helena, CA 94574 *Tel:* 707-967-2900 (ext 1611) *Fax:* 707-967-2909 *E-mail:* writecon@napavalley.edu *Web Site:* www.napawritersconf.org, pg 653

Morgan, Clay, The MIT Press, 55 Hayward St, Cambridge, MA 02142 *Tel:* 617-253-5255 *Toll Free Tel:* 800-207-8354 (orders) *Fax:* 617-258-6779; 617-577-1545 (orders) *Web Site:* mitpress.mit.edu, pg 158

Morgan, Dr Jean, Castle Connolly Medical Ltd, 42 W 24 St, 2nd fl, New York, NY 10010 *Tel:* 212-367-8400 *Fax:* 212-367-0964 *Web Site:* www.castleconnolly.com, pg 51

Morgan, Jill, Purple House Press, 8100 US Hwy 62 E, Cynthiana, KY 41031 *Tel:* 859-235-9970 *Web Site:* www.purplehousepress.com, pg 200

Morgan, Kathi, University of Georgia Press, Main Library, 3rd fl, 320 S Jackson St, Athens, GA 30602 *Tel:* 706-369-6130 *Fax:* 706-542-2558; 706-369-6162 *E-mail:* books@ugapress.uga.edu (orders) *Web Site:* www.ugapress.org, pg 256

Morgan, Kristina, Lynx House Press, 420 W 24 St, Spokane, WA 99203 *Tel:* 509-624-4894 *E-mail:* lynxhousepress@gmail.com *Web Site:* www.lynxhousepress.org, pg 144

Morgan, Lael, Epicenter Press Inc, 6524 NE 181 St, Suite 2, Kenmore, WA 98028 *Tel:* 425-485-6822 (edit, mktg, busn off) *Fax:* 425-481-8253 *E-mail:* info@epicenterpress.com *Web Site:* www.epicenterpress.com, pg 83

Morgan, Mary, Aegean Publishing Co, PO Box 6790, Santa Barbara, CA 93160 *Tel:* 805-964-6669 *Fax:* 805-683-4798 *E-mail:* info@aegeanpublishing.com *Web Site:* aegeanpublishing.com, pg 5

Morgan, Scott, Thomson Reuters Westlaw™, 610 Opperman Dr, Eagan, MN 55123 *Tel:* 651-687-7000 *Toll Free Tel:* 800-328-9352 (sales); 800-328-4880 (cust serv) *Fax:* 651-687-7302 *Web Site:* www.westlawnext.com; store.westlaw.com, pg 245

Morgan, Steven, Simon & Schuster Digital, 1230 Avenue of the Americas, New York, NY 10020 *Tel:* 212-698-7547 *Web Site:* www.simonandschuster.com; kids.simonandschuster.com; www.simonandschuster.ca; www.simonandschuster.co.uk; www.simonandschuster.net; www.simonandschuster.biz; www.tipsoncareerandmoney.com; www.tipsonhealthyliving.com; www.tipsonhomeandstyle.com; www.tipsonlifeandlove.com; www.offtheshelf.com; www.simonandschuster.com/teen, pg 225

Morgan, Tom, Little Bee Books, 853 Broadway, Suite 2014, New York, NY 10003 *E-mail:* info@littlebeebooks.com *Web Site:* www.littlebeebooks.com, pg 140

Morgen, Emmanuelle, The Stonesong Press LLC, 270 W 39 St, No 201, New York, NY 10018 *Tel:* 212-929-4600 *E-mail:* editors@stonesong.com *Web Site:* www.stonesong.com, pg 575

Morgenstein, Leslie, Alloy Entertainment LLC, 1700 Broadway, New York, NY 10019 *Web Site:* alloyentertainment.com, pg 8

Morgridge, Sally, Holiday House Inc, 425 Madison Ave, New York, NY 10017 *Tel:* 212-688-0085 *Fax:* 212-421-6134 *E-mail:* holiday@holidayhouse.com *Web Site:* www.holidayhouse.com, pg 113

Morhaim, Howard, Howard Morhaim Literary Agency Inc, 30 Pierrepont St, Brooklyn, NY 11201-3371 *Tel:* 718-222-8400 *Fax:* 718-222-5056 *E-mail:* info@morhaimliterary.com *Web Site:* www.morhaimliterary.com, pg 566

Moriarty, Amy, WordCo Indexing Services Inc, 49 Church St, Norwich, CT 06360 *Tel:* 860-886-2532 *Toll Free Tel:* 877-WORDCO-3 (967-3263) *Fax:* 860-886-1155 *E-mail:* office@wordco.com *Web Site:* www.wordco.com, pg 536

Moriarty, Kerry, Twenty-Third Publications, One Montauk Ave, Suite 200, New London, CT 06320 *Tel:* 860-437-3012 *Toll Free Tel:* 800-321-0411 (orders) *Toll Free Fax:* 800-572-0788 *E-mail:* 23ppweb@bayard-inc.com *Web Site:* www.twentythirdpublications.com, pg 251

Morin, Lise, Editions MultiMondes, 930 rue Pouliot, Quebec, QC G1V 3N9, Canada *Tel:* 418-651-3885 *Toll Free Tel:* 800-840-3029 *Fax:* 418-651-6822 *Toll Free Fax:* 888-303-5931 *E-mail:* multimondes@multim.com *Web Site:* www.multim.com, pg 482

Morin, Suzanne, Association pour l'Avancement des Sciences et des Techniques de la Documentation, 2065 rue Parthenais, Bureau 387, Montreal, QC H2K 3T1, Canada *Tel:* 514-281-5012 *Fax:* 514-281-8219 *E-mail:* info@asted.org *Web Site:* www.asted.org, pg 472, 599, 649

Morin-Spatz, Patrice, MedBooks, 101 W Buckingham Rd, Richardson, TX 75081-4802 *Tel:* 972-643-1809 *Fax:* 972-643-1859 *E-mail:* medbooks@medbooks.com *Web Site:* www.medbooks.com, pg 153

Morita, Joseph, Springer Publishing Co, 11 W 42 St, 15th fl, New York, NY 10036-8002 *Tel:* 212-431-4370 *Toll Free Tel:* 877-687-7476 *Fax:* 212-941-7842 *E-mail:* marketing@springerpub.com; cs@springerpub.com (orders); editorial@springerpub.com *Web Site:* www.springerpub.com, pg 232

Morley, Jane, Quirk Books, 215 Church St, Philadelphia, PA 19106 *Tel:* 215-627-3581 *Fax:* 215-627-5220 *E-mail:* general@quirkbooks.com *Web Site:* www.quirkbooks.com, pg 202

Morneau, Claude, Ulysses Travel Guides, 4176 Rue St-Denis, Montreal, QC H2W 2M5, Canada *Tel:* 514-843-9447 (bookstore); 514-843-9882 (ext 2232) *Toll Free Tel:* 800-748-9171 *Fax:* 514-843-9448 *E-mail:* info@ulysses.ca; st-denis@ulysses.ca *Web Site:* www.ulyssesguides.com, pg 502

Morphew, Jess, Watson-Guptill Publications, c/o Random House Inc, 1745 Broadway, New York, NY 10019 *Tel:* 212-782-9000 *Fax:* 212-940-7381 *E-mail:* crownbiz@randomhouse.com *Web Site:* www.randomhouse.com/crown/watsonguptill, pg 268

Morris, Beth, Tag & Label Manufacturers Institute Inc (TLMI), One Blackburn Ctr, Gloucester, MA 01930 *Tel:* 978-282-1400 *Fax:* 978-282-3238 *E-mail:* office@tlmi.com *Web Site:* tlmi.com, pg 620

Morris, Candice E, Mercer University Press, 368 Orange St, Macon, GA 31201 *Tel:* 478-301-2880 *Toll Free Tel:* 866-895-1472 *Fax:* 478-301-2585 *E-mail:* mupressorders@mercer.edu *Web Site:* www.mupress.org, pg 154

Morris, David, Zondervan, 3900 Sparks Dr, Grand Rapids, MI 49546 *Tel:* 616-698-6900 *Toll Free Tel:* 800-226-1122; 800-727-1309 (retail orders) *Fax:* 616-698-3350 *Toll Free Fax:* 800-698-3256 (retail orders) *E-mail:* zinfo@zondervan.com *Web Site:* www.zondervan.com, pg 280

Morris, Gary, David Black Agency, 335 Adams St, 27th fl, Suite 2707, Brooklyn, NY 11201 *Tel:* 718-852-5500 *Fax:* 718-852-5539 *Web Site:* www.davidblackagency.com, pg 542

Morris, Julie, Book Industry Study Group Inc (BISG), 145 W 45 St, Suite 601, New York, NY 10036 *Tel:* 646-336-7141 *Fax:* 646-336-6214 *E-mail:* info@bisg.org *Web Site:* www.bisg.org, pg 600

Morris, Marshall I, McGraw-Hill Ryerson Limited, 300 Water St, Whitby, ON L1N 9B6, Canada *Tel:* 905-430-5000 *Toll Free Tel:* 800-565-5758 (cust serv) *Fax:* 905-430-5020 *Toll Free Fax:* 800-463-5885 *Web Site:* www.mheducation.ca, pg 491

Morris, Michael A, Cornell University Press, Sage House, 512 E State St, Ithaca, NY 14850 *Tel:* 607-277-2338 *Fax:* 607-277-2374 *E-mail:* cupressinfo@cornell.edu; cupress-sales@cornell.edu *Web Site:* www.cornellpress.cornell.edu, pg 63

Morris, Paul, PEN American Center, 588 Broadway, Suite 303, New York, NY 10012 *Tel:* 212-334-1660 *Fax:* 212-334-2181 *E-mail:* info@pen.org *Web Site:* www.pen.org, pg 615

Morris, Paul, The PEN Award for Poetry in Translation, 588 Broadway, Suite 303, New York, NY 10012 *Tel:* 212-334-1660 *Fax:* 212-334-2181 *E-mail:* awards@pen.org *Web Site:* www.pen.org, pg 717

Morris, Paul, PEN/Bellwether Prize for Socially Engaged Fiction, 588 Broadway, Suite 303, New York, NY 10012 *Tel:* 212-334-1660 *E-mail:* awards@pen.org *Web Site:* www.pen.org, pg 717

Morris, Paul, PEN/Diamonstein-Spielvogel Award for the Art of the Essay, 588 Broadway, Suite 303, New York, NY 10012 *Tel:* 212-334-1660 *E-mail:* awards@pen.org *Web Site:* www.pen.org/literary-awards, pg 717

Morris, Paul, PEN/E O Wilson Literary Science Writing Award, 588 Broadway, Suite 303, New York, NY 10012 *Tel:* 212-334-1660 *E-mail:* awards@pen.org *Web Site:* www.pen.org/literary-awards, pg 717

Morris, Paul, PEN/ESPN Award for Literary Sports Writing, 588 Broadway, Suite 303, New York, NY 10012 *Tel:* 212-334-1660 *E-mail:* awards@pen.org *Web Site:* www.pen.org/literary-awards, pg 717

Morris, Paul, PEN/ESPN Lifetime Achievement Award for Literary Sports Writing, 588 Broadway, Suite 303, New York, NY 10012 *Tel:* 212-334-1660 *E-mail:* awards@pen.org *Web Site:* www.pen.org/literary-awards, pg 717

Morris, Paul, PEN/Fusion Emerging Writers Prize, 588 Broadway, Suite 303, New York, NY 10012 *Tel:* 212-334-1660 *E-mail:* awards@pen.org *Web Site:* www.pen.org/literary-awards, pg 717

Morris, Paul, PEN/Jacqueline Bograd Weld Award for Biography, 588 Broadway, Suite 303, New York, NY 10012 *Tel:* 212-334-1660 *E-mail:* awards@pen.org *Web Site:* www.pen.org/literary-awards, pg 717

Morris, Paul, PEN/Joyce Osterweil Award for Poetry, 588 Broadway, Suite 303, New York, NY 10012 *Tel:* 212-334-1660 *E-mail:* awards@pen.org *Web Site:* www.pen.org, pg 717

Morris, Paul, PEN Open Book Award, 588 Broadway, Suite 303, New York, NY 10012 *Tel:* 212-334-1660 *E-mail:* awards@pen.org *Web Site:* www.pen.org/literary-awards, pg 717

Morris, Paul, PEN/Phyllis Naylor Working Writer Fellowship, 588 Broadway, Suite 303, New York, NY 10012 *Tel:* 212-334-1660 *Fax:* 212-334-2181 *E-mail:* awards@pen.org *Web Site:* www.pen.org, pg 718

Morris, Paul, PEN/Ralph Manheim Medal for Translation, 588 Broadway, Suite 303, New York, NY 10012 *Tel:* 212-334-1660 *Fax:* 212-334-2181 *E-mail:* awards@pen.org *Web Site:* www.pen.org, pg 718

Morris, Paul, PEN/Robert Bingham Prize for Debut Fiction, 588 Broadway, Suite 303, New York, NY 10012 *Tel:* 212-334-1660 *Fax:* 212-334-2181 *E-mail:* awards@pen.org *Web Site:* www.pen.org, pg 718

Morris, Paul, PEN/Steven Kroll Award for Picture Book Writing, 588 Broadway, Suite 303, New York, NY 10012 *Tel:* 212-334-1660 *E-mail:* awards@pen.org *Web Site:* www.pen.org/literary-awards, pg 718

Morris, Paul, PEN Translation Prize, 588 Broadway, Suite 303, New York, NY 10012 *Tel:* 212-334-1660 *Fax:* 212-334-2181 *E-mail:* awards@pen.org *Web Site:* www.pen.org, pg 718

Morris, Paul, PEN/Voelcker Award, 588 Broadway, Suite 303, New York, NY 10012 *Tel:* 212-334-1660 *E-mail:* awards@pen.org *Web Site:* www.pen.org/literary-awards, pg 718

Morris, Paul, PEN Writers' Emergency Fund, 588 Broadway, Suite 303, New York, NY 10012 *Tel:* 212-334-1660 *Fax:* 212-334-2181 *Web Site:* www.pen.org, pg 718

Morris, Richard, Janklow & Nesbit Associates, 445 Park Ave, New York, NY 10022 *Tel:* 212-421-1700 *Fax:* 212-980-3671 *E-mail:* info@janklow.com *Web Site:* www.janklowandnesbit.com, pg 558

Morris, Sherine, Mary Ann Liebert Inc, 140 Huguenot St, 3rd fl, New Rochelle, NY 10801-5215 *Tel:* 914-740-2100 *Toll Free Tel:* 800-654-3237 *Fax:* 914-740-2101 *E-mail:* info@liebertpub.com *Web Site:* www.liebertonline.com, pg 139

Morris-Babb, Meredith, University Press of Florida, 15 NW 15 St, Gainesville, FL 32603-2079 *Tel:* 352-392-1351 *Toll Free Tel:* 800-226-3822 (orders only) *Fax:* 352-392-0590 *Toll Free Fax:* 800-680-1955 (orders only) *E-mail:* info@upf.com *Web Site:* www.upf.com, pg 261

Morrisey, Stephenie, McLemore Prize, PO Box 571, Jackson, MS 39205-0571 *Tel:* 601-576-6850 *Fax:* 601-576-6975 *E-mail:* mhs@mdah.state.ms.us *Web Site:* www.mdah.state.ms.us, pg 707

Morrison, Charles, Prometheus Awards, 650 Castro St, Suite 120-433, Mountain View, CA 94041 *Tel:* 650-968-6319 *E-mail:* info@lfs.org *Web Site:* www.lfs.org, pg 722

Morrison, Henry, Henry Morrison Inc, PO Box 235, Bedford Hills, NY 10507-0235 *Tel:* 914-666-3500 *Fax:* 914-241-7846 *E-mail:* hmorrison1@aol.com, pg 566

Morrison, Jeff, LexisNexis® Canada Inc, 123 Commerce Valley Dr E, Suite 700, Markham, ON L3T 7W8, Canada *Tel:* 905-479-2665 *Toll Free Tel:* 800-668-6481; 800-387-0899 (cust care) *Fax:* 905-479-2826 *Toll Free Fax:* 800-461-3275 *E-mail:* orders@lexisnexis.ca; service@lexisnexis.ca (cust serv) *Web Site:* www.lexisnexis.ca, pg 490

Morrison, Marg Anne, Ontario Book Publishers Organization (OBPO), 20 Maud St, No 401, Toronto, ON M5V 2M5, Canada *Tel:* 416-536-7584 *Fax:* 416-536-7692 *Web Site:* obpo.ca, pg 615

Morrison, Margaret, Harlequin Enterprises Ltd, 225 Duncan Mill Rd, Don Mills, ON M3B 3K9, Canada *Tel:* 416-445-5860 *Toll Free Tel:* 888-432-4879; 800-370-5838 (ebook inquiries) *E-mail:* customerservice@harlequin.com *Web Site:* www.harlequin.com, pg 487

Morrison, Michael, HarperCollins General Books Group, 195 Broadway, New York, NY 10007 *Tel:* 212-207-7000 *Web Site:* www.harpercollins.com, pg 105

Morrison, Paula, North Atlantic Books, 2526 Martin Luther King Jr Way, Berkeley, CA 94704 *Tel:* 510-549-4270 *Fax:* 510-549-4276 *Web Site:* www.northatlanticbooks.com, pg 170

Morrison, Richard, Fordham University Press, 2546 Belmont Ave, University Box L, Bronx, NY 10458 *Tel:* 718-817-4795 *Fax:* 718-817-4785 *Web Site:* www.fordhampress.com, pg 90

Morrison, Rusty, Omnidawn Publishing, 1632 Elm Ave, Richmond, CA 94805-1614 *Tel:* 510-237-5472 *Toll Free Tel:* 800-792-4957 *Fax:* 510-232-8525 *E-mail:* manager@omnidawn.com *Web Site:* www.omnidawn.com, pg 175

Morrison, Stephen, Picador, 175 Fifth Ave, 19th fl, New York, NY 10010 *Tel:* 646-307-5151 *Fax:* 212-253-9627 *E-mail:* firstname.lastname@picadorusa.com *Web Site:* www.picadorusa.com, pg 191

Morrissey, Jake, Riverhead Books (Hardcover), 375 Hudson St, New York, NY 10014 *Tel:* 212-366-2000 *E-mail:* online@penguinputnam.com *Web Site:* www.penguinputnam.com; us.penguingroup.com, pg 209

Morrissey, Robert, Resilient Publishing, 406 S Third St, Boise, ID 83702 *Tel:* 208-258-9544 *E-mail:* submissions@resilientpublishing.com *Web Site:* www.resilientpublishing.com, pg 208

Morrongiello, Brittany, Alfred A Knopf/Everyman's Library, c/o Random House Inc, 1745 Broadway, New York, NY 10019 *Tel:* 212-751-2600 *Toll Free Tel:* 800-638-6460 *Fax:* 212-572-2593 *Web Site:* www.knopfdoubleday.com, pg 132

Morrow, Diane, The Barnabas Agency, PO Box 3113, Corsicana, TX 75110-3113 *Toll Free Tel:* 800-927-0517 *E-mail:* info@barnabasagency.com *Web Site:* www.barnabasagency.com, pg 587

Morrow, Stephen, Dutton, 375 Hudson St, New York, NY 10014 *Tel:* 212-366-2000 *Fax:* 212-366-2262 *E-mail:* online@penguinputnam.com *Web Site:* www.penguinputnam.com; us.penguingroup.com, pg 78

Morse, John M, Merriam-Webster Inc, 47 Federal St, Springfield, MA 01102 *Tel:* 413-734-3134 *Toll Free Tel:* 800-828-1880 (orders & cust serv) *Fax:* 413-731-5979 (sales) *E-mail:* support@merriam-webster.com *Web Site:* www.merriam-webster.com, pg 155

Mortensen, Dee, Indiana University Press, Herman B Wells Library 350, 1320 E Tenth St, Bloomington, IN 47405-3907 *Tel:* 812-855-8817 *Toll Free Tel:* 800-842-6796 (orders only) *Fax:* 812-855-7931; 812-855-8507 *E-mail:* iupress@indiana.edu; iuporder@indiana.edu (orders) *Web Site:* www.iupress.indiana.edu, pg 120

Mortimer, Bryce, Cedar Fort Inc, 2373 W 700 S, Springville, UT 84663 *Tel:* 801-489-4084 *Toll Free Tel:* 800-SKY-BOOK (759-2665) *Fax:* 801-489-1097 *Toll Free Fax:* 800-388-3727 *Web Site:* cedarfort.com, pg 52

Mortimer, Frank, Oxford University Press USA, 198 Madison Ave, New York, NY 10016 *Tel:* 212-726-6000 *Toll Free Tel:* 800-451-7556 (orders); 800-445-9714 (cust serv) *Fax:* 919-677-1303 *E-mail:* custserv.us@oup.com *Web Site:* www.oup.com/us, pg 179

Mortimer, Lyle, Cedar Fort Inc, 2373 W 700 S, Springville, UT 84663 *Tel:* 801-489-4084 *Toll Free Tel:* 800-SKY-BOOK (759-2665) *Fax:* 801-489-1097 *Toll Free Fax:* 800-388-3727 *Web Site:* cedarfort.com, pg 52

Mortimer, Michele, Darhansoff & Verrill, 236 W 26 St, Suite 802, New York, NY 10001-6736 *Tel:* 917-305-1300 *Fax:* 917-305-1400 *E-mail:* info@dvagency.com *Web Site:* www.dvagency.com, pg 547

Mortis, Steffanie, Trinity University Press, One Trinity Place, San Antonio, TX 78212-7200 *Tel:* 210-999-8884 *Fax:* 210-999-8838 *E-mail:* books@trinity.edu *Web Site:* www.tupress.org, pg 249

Morton, David, Rizzoli International Publications Inc, 300 Park Ave S, 4th fl, New York, NY 10010-5399 *Tel:* 212-387-3400 *Toll Free Tel:* 800-522-6657 (orders only) *Fax:* 212-387-3535 *E-mail:* publicity@rizzoliusa.com *Web Site:* www.rizzoliusa.com, pg 209

Morton, Douglas, Morton Publishing Co, 925 W Kenyon Ave, Unit 12, Englewood, CO 80110 *Tel:* 303-761-4805 *Fax:* 303-762-9923 *E-mail:* contact@morton-pub.com *Web Site:* www.morton-pub.com, pg 160

Morton, Larry, Hal Leonard Corp, 7777 W Bluemound Rd, Milwaukee, WI 53213 *Tel:* 414-774-3630 *Toll Free Tel:* 800-524-4425 *Fax:* 414-774-3259 *E-mail:* halinfo@halleonard.com *Web Site:* www.halleonard.com, pg 103

Morton, Lisa, Horror Writers Association (HWA), 244 Fifth Ave, Suite 2767, New York, NY 10001 *E-mail:* hwa@horror.org *Web Site:* horror.org, pg 606

Mosberg, Stephen R, College Publishing, 12309 Lynwood Dr, Glen Allen, VA 23059 *Tel:* 804-364-8410 *Toll Free Tel:* 800-827-0723 *Fax:* 804-364-8408 *E-mail:* collegepub@mindspring.com *Web Site:* www.collegepublishing.us, pg 61

Mosbrook, Bill, Pathfinder Publishing Inc, 120 S Houghton Rd, Suite 138, Tucson, AZ 85748 *Tel:* 520-647-0158 *Toll Free Tel:* 800-977-2282 *Fax:* 520-647-0160 *Web Site:* www.pathfinderpublishing.com, pg 183

Mosbrook, Evelyn, Pathfinder Publishing Inc, 120 S Houghton Rd, Suite 138, Tucson, AZ 85748 *Tel:* 520-647-0158 *Toll Free Tel:* 800-977-2282 *Fax:* 520-647-0160 *Web Site:* www.pathfinderpublishing.com, pg 183

Moschovakis, Anna, Ugly Duckling Presse, The Old American Can Factory, 232 Third St, Suite E002, Brooklyn, NY 11215 *Tel:* 347-948-5170 *E-mail:* udp_mailbox@yahoo.com; info@uglyducklingpresse.org *Web Site:* www.uglyducklingpresse.org, pg 252

Moscovich, Rotem, Disney-Hyperion Books, 1101 Flower St, Glendale, CA 91201 *Web Site:* books.disney.com, pg 74

Moseley, Lauren, Algonquin Books, 400 Silver Cedar Ct, Suite 300, Chapel Hill, NC 27514-1585 *Tel:* 919-967-0108 *Fax:* 919-933-0272 *E-mail:* inquiry@algonquin.com *Web Site:* www.workman.com/algonquin, pg 8

Moselle, Ben, Craftsman Book Co, 6058 Corte Del Cedro, Carlsbad, CA 92011 *Tel:* 760-438-7828 *Toll Free Tel:* 800-829-8123 *Fax:* 760-438-0398 *Web Site:* www.craftsman-book.com, pg 66

Moselle, Gary, Craftsman Book Co, 6058 Corte Del Cedro, Carlsbad, CA 92011 *Tel:* 760-438-7828 *Toll Free Tel:* 800-829-8123 *Fax:* 760-438-0398 *Web Site:* www.craftsman-book.com, pg 66

Moses, James, Primary Research Group Inc, 2753 Broadway, Suite 156, New York, NY 10025 *Tel:* 212-736-2316 *Fax:* 212-412-9097 *E-mail:* primaryresearchgroup@gmail.com *Web Site:* www.primaryresearch.com, pg 197

Mosher, Jessica, Pearson Education Canada, 26 Prince Andrew Place, Don Mills, ON M3C 2T8, Canada *Tel:* 416-447-5101 *Toll Free Tel:* 800-263-9965 *Fax:* 416-443-0948 *Toll Free Fax:* 800-263-7733; 888-465-0536 *Web Site:* www.pearsoned.ca, pg 494

Moskow, Shirley, Boston Authors Club Inc, 33 Brayton Rd, Brighton, MA 02135 *Tel:* 617-783-1357 *E-mail:* bostonauthors@aol.com *Web Site:* www.bostonauthorsclub.org, pg 601

Moskowitz, Kenneth, Practising Law Institute, 1177 Avenue of the Americas, New York, NY 10036 *Tel:* 212-824-5700 *Toll Free Tel:* 800-260-4PLI (260-4754, cust serv) *Fax:* 212-265-4742 (intl) *Toll Free Fax:* 800-321-0093 (local) *E-mail:* info@pli.edu (cust serv) *Web Site:* www.pli.edu, pg 195

Mosley, Christine, Penguin Group (USA) LLC Sales, 375 Hudson St, New York, NY 10014 *Tel:* 212-366-2000 *E-mail:* online@penguinputnam.com *Web Site:* us.penguingroup.com, pg 187

Mosley, Jody, Harry N Abrams Inc, 115 W 18 St, 6th fl, New York, NY 10011 *Tel:* 212-206-7715 *Toll Free Tel:* 800-345-1359 *Fax:* 212-519-1210 *E-mail:* abrams@abramsbooks.com *Web Site:* www.abramsbooks.com, pg 3

Moss, Sr Mary Martha, Pauline Books & Media, 50 St Paul's Ave, Boston, MA 02130 *Tel:* 617-522-8911 *Toll Free Tel:* 800-876-4463 (orders); 800-836-9723 (cust serv) *Fax:* 617-541-9805 *E-mail:* editorial@paulinemedia.com (ms submissions); orderentry@pauline.org (cust serv) *Web Site:* www.pauline.org, pg 184

Moss, Stephanie, Random House Children's Books, 1745 Broadway, New York, NY 10019 *Tel:* 212-782-9000 *Toll Free Tel:* 800-200-3552 *Fax:* 212-782-9452 *Web Site:* randomhousekids.com, pg 203

Mostyn, Greg, Worthy & James Publishing, PO Box 362015, Milpitas, CA 95036 *Tel:* 408-945-3963 *E-mail:* worthy1234@sbcglobal.net; mail@worthyjames.com *Web Site:* www.worthyjames.com, pg 509

Mosure, Jeanne, Disney Publishing Worldwide, 1101 Flower St, Glendale, CA 91201 *Web Site:* books.disney.com, pg 74

Motyl, Steve, Ascension Press, PO Box 1990, West Chester, PA 19380 *Tel:* 610-696-7795 (ext 207, edit); 484-875-4550 (admin) *Toll Free Tel:* 800-376-0520 (sales & cust serv) *E-mail:* info@ascensionpress.com *Web Site:* ascensionpress.com, pg 24

Moul, Joyanne, Zumaya Publications LLC, 3209 S IH 35, Suite 1086, Austin, TX 78741 *Tel:* 512-402-5298 *Fax:* 253-660-2009 *E-mail:* acquisitions@zumayapublications.com *Web Site:* www.zumayapublications.com, pg 280

Moul, Marianne, Zumaya Publications LLC, 3209 S IH 35, Suite 1086, Austin, TX 78741 *Tel:* 512-402-5298 *Fax:* 253-660-2009 *E-mail:* acquisitions@zumayapublications.com *Web Site:* www.zumayapublications.com, pg 280

Moulden, Yolanda, American Academy of Environmental Engineers & Scientists™, 147 Old Solomons Island Rd, Suite 303, Annapolis, MD 21401 *Tel:* 410-266-3311 *Fax:* 410-266-7653 *E-mail:* info@aaees.org *Web Site:* www.aaees.org, pg 10

Moulton, Candy, Spur Awards, 271 CR 219, Encampment, WY 82325 *Tel:* 307-329-8942 *Fax:* 307-327-5465 *E-mail:* wwa.moulton@gmail.com *Web Site:* westernwriters.org, pg 730

Moulton, Candy, Western Writers of America Inc (WWA), 271 CR 219, Encampment, WY 82325 *Tel:* 307-329-8942 *Fax:* 307-327-5465 *Web Site:* westernwriters.org, pg 621

Moulton, Katie, Indiana Review Fiction Prize, Ballantine Hall 465, 1020 E Kirkwood Ave, Bloomington, IN 47405 *Tel:* 812-855-3439 *E-mail:* inreview@indiana.edu *Web Site:* indianareview.org, pg 694

Moulton, Stephen, Himalayan Institute Press, 952 Bethany Tpke, Honesdale, PA 18431 *Tel:* 570-253-5551 *Toll Free Tel:* 800-822-4547 *E-mail:* info@himalayaninstitute.org *Web Site:* www.himalayaninstitute.org, pg 112

Mousa, Ed, Wadsworth Publishing, 20 Davis Dr, Belmont, CA 94002 *Tel:* 650-595-2350 *Fax:* 650-592-3022 *Toll Free Fax:* 800-522-4923 *Web Site:* www.cengage.com, pg 266

Moushabeck, Hannah, Chronicle Books LLC, 680 Second St, San Francisco, CA 94107 *Tel:* 415-537-4200 *Toll Free Tel:* 800-759-0190 (cust serv) *Fax:* 415-537-4460 *Toll Free Fax:* 800-858-7787 (orders); 800-286-9471 (cust serv) *E-mail:* frontdesk@chroniclebooks.com *Web Site:* www.chroniclebooks.com, pg 58

Moushabeck, Michel, Interlink Publishing Group Inc, 46 Crosby St, Northampton, MA 01060 *Tel:* 413-582-7054 *Toll Free Tel:* 800-238-LINK (238-5465) *Fax:* 413-582-7057 *E-mail:* info@interlinkbooks.com *Web Site:* www.interlinkbooks.com, pg 123

Mousseau, Richard, Moose Hide Books, 684 Walls Rd, Prince Township, ON P6A 6K4, Canada *Tel:* 705-779-3331 *Fax:* 705-779-3331 *E-mail:* mooseenterprises@on.aibn.com *Web Site:* www.moosehidebooks.com, pg 492

Moyer, Christopher, The Pinch Writing Awards in Fiction, University of Memphis, English Dept, 435 Patterson Hall, Memphis, TN 38152 *Tel:* 901-678-4190 *Fax:* 901-678-2226 *E-mail:* editor@thepinchjournal.com *Web Site:* www.thepinchjournal.com, pg 719

Moyer, Christopher, The Pinch Writing Awards in Poetry, University of Memphis, English Dept, 435 Patterson Hall, Memphis, TN 38152 *Tel:* 901-678-4190 *Fax:* 901-678-2226 *E-mail:* editor@thepinchjournal.com *Web Site:* www.thepinchjournal.com, pg 719

Moyers, Scott, The Penguin Press, 375 Hudson St, New York, NY 10014, pg 187

Moynagh, Kerry, HarperCollins Publishers Sales, 195 Broadway, New York, NY 10007 *Fax:* 212-207-7000 *Web Site:* www.harpercollins.com, pg 106

Mroczkowski, Manfred, InterLicense Ltd, 110 Country Club Dr, Suite A, Mill Valley, CA 94941 *Tel:* 415-381-9780 *Fax:* 415-381-6485 *E-mail:* interlicense@sbcglobal.net; ilicense@aol.com, pg 557

Mrvos, Josh, Sterling Publishing Co Inc, 1166 Avenue of the Americas, 17th fl, New York, NY 10036 *Tel:* 212-532-7160 *Toll Free Tel:* 800-367-9692 *Fax:* 212-213-2495 *Web Site:* www.sterlingpublishing.com, pg 235

Mubarek, Stephen, Hachette Book Group, 1290 Avenue of the Americas, New York, NY 10019 *Tel:* 212-364-1100 *Toll Free Tel:* 800-759-0190 (cust serv) *Fax:* 212-364-0933 (intl orders) *Toll Free Fax:* 800-286-9471 (cust serv) *Web Site:* www.HachetteBookGroup.com, pg 102

Mudd, Gary, American Printing House for the Blind Inc, 1839 Frankfort Ave, Louisville, KY 40206 *Tel:* 502-895-2405 *Toll Free Tel:* 800-223-1839 (cust serv) *Fax:* 502-899-2274 *E-mail:* info@aph.org *Web Site:* www.aph.org; shop.aph.org, pg 15

Mudditt, Alison, University of California Press, 2120 Berkeley Way, Berkeley, CA 94704-1012 *Tel:* 510-642-4247 *Fax:* 510-643-7127 *E-mail:* askucp@ucpress.edu (books); customerservice@ucpressjournals.com *Web Site:* www.ucpress.edu, pg 255

Muehlmann, Rachel, Vermont College of Fine Arts, MFA in Writing Program, 36 College St, Montpelier, VT 05602 *Tel:* 802-828-8840; 802-828-8839 *Toll Free Tel:* 866-934-VCFA (934-8232) *Fax:* 802-828-8649 *Web Site:* www.vcfa.edu, pg 664

Mueller-Grote, Susanne, Philosophy Documentation Center, PO Box 7147, Charlottesville, VA 22906-7147 *Tel:* 434-220-3300 *Toll Free Tel:* 800-444-2419 *Fax:* 434-220-3301 *E-mail:* order@pdcnet.org *Web Site:* www.pdcnet.org, pg 191

Muhlenkamp, Monique, HJ Kramer Inc, PO Box 1082, Tiburon, CA 94920 *Tel:* 415-884-2100 (ext 10) *Toll Free Tel:* 800-972-6657 *Fax:* 415-435-5364 *E-mail:* hjkramer@jps.net *Web Site:* www.hjkramer.com; www.newworldlibrary.com, pg 133

Muhlenkamp, Monique, New World Library, 14 Pamaron Way, Novato, CA 94949 *Tel:* 415-884-2100 *Toll Free Tel:* 800-227-3900 (ext 52, retail orders); 800-972-6657 *Fax:* 415-884-2199 *E-mail:* escort@newworldlibrary.com *Web Site:* www.newworldlibrary.com, pg 168

Muhlig, Adam, McIntosh & Otis Inc, 353 Lexington Ave, New York, NY 10016-0900 *Tel:* 212-687-7400 *Fax:* 212-687-6894 *E-mail:* info@mcintoshandotis.com *Web Site:* www.mcintoshandotis.com, pg 565

Muir, Sharona, Bowling Green State University, Creative Writing Program, Dept of English, 211 East Hall, Bowling Green, OH 43403 *Tel:* 419-372-2576 *Fax:* 419-372-0333 *Web Site:* www.bgsu.edu/departments/creative-writing, pg 659

Muirhead, Lucy, The Century Foundation Press, One Whitehall St, 15th fl, New York, NY 10004 *Tel:* 212-452-7700 *Fax:* 212-535-7534 *E-mail:* info@tcf.org *Web Site:* www.tcf.org, pg 54

Mukalla, Doris, International Book Centre Inc, 2391 Auburn Rd, Shelby Township, MI 48317 *Tel:* 586-254-7230 *Fax:* 586-254-7230 *E-mail:* ibc@ibcbooks.com *Web Site:* www.ibcbooks.com, pg 123

Mulcahy, Mike, Business Forms Management Association (BFMA), 1147 Fleetwood Ave, Madison, WI 53716 *Toll Free Tel:* 888-367-3078 *E-mail:* bfma@bfma.org *Web Site:* www.bfma.org, pg 601

Mulder, David, American Products Publishing Co, 8260 SW Nimbus Ave, Beaverton, OR 97008 *Tel:* 503-672-7502 *Toll Free Tel:* 800-668-8181 *Fax:* 503-672-7104 *E-mail:* info@american-products.com *Web Site:* www.american-products.com, pg 15

Mulder, Gary, Protestant Church-Owned Publishers Association, 6631 Westbury Oaks Ct, Springfield, VA 22152 *Tel:* 703-220-5989 *Web Site:* www.pcpaonline.org, pg 617

Mulder, Jane, Christian Schools International, 3350 E Paris Ave SE, Grand Rapids, MI 49512-3054 *Tel:* 616-957-1070 *Toll Free Tel:* 800-635-8288 *Fax:* 616-957-5022 *E-mail:* info@csionline.org *Web Site:* www.csionline.org, pg 57

Mulder, Matt, Upstart Books™, 4810 Forest Run Rd, Madison, WI 53704 *Tel:* 608-241-1201 *Toll Free Tel:* 800-448-4887 (orders) *Toll Free Fax:* 800-448-5828 *E-mail:* custsvc@upstartpromotions.com *Web Site:* www.upstartbooks.com, pg 263

Mulford, Natalie, Crown Publishing Group, c/o Penguin Random House Inc, 1745 Broadway, New York, NY 10019 *Tel:* 212-782-9000 *Toll Free Tel:* 888-264-1745 *Fax:* 212-940-7408 *E-mail:* crownosm@penguinrandomhouse.com *Web Site:* crownpublishing.com, pg 68

Mulford, Natalie, Watson-Guptill Publications, c/o Random House Inc, 1745 Broadway, New York, NY 10019 *Tel:* 212-782-9000 *Fax:* 212-940-7381 *E-mail:* crownbiz@randomhouse.com *Web Site:* www.randomhouse.com/crown/watsonguptill, pg 268

Mulhall, Danielle, Kids Can Press Ltd, 25 Dockside Dr, Toronto, ON M5A 0B5, Canada *Tel:* 416-479-7000 *Toll Free Tel:* 800-265-0884 *Fax:* 416-960-5437 *E-mail:* info@kidscan.com; customerservice@kidscan.com *Web Site:* www.kidscanpress.com; www.kidscanpress.ca, pg 489

Mulhallen, Karen, The Winston Collins/Descant Prize for Best Canadian Poem, 50 Baldwin St, Toronto, ON M5T 1L4, Canada *Tel:* 416-593-2557 *Fax:* 416-593-9362 *E-mail:* info@descant.ca *Web Site:* www.descant.ca, pg 678

Mullapudi, Gayatri, Glitterati Inc, 630 Ninth Ave, Suite 603, New York, NY 10036 *Tel:* 212-362-9119 *Fax:* 646-607-4433 *E-mail:* info@glitteratiincorporated.com *Web Site:* glitteratiincorporated.com, pg 97

Mullen, Laura, Louisiana State University Creative Writing Program MFA, English Dept, 260 Allen Hall, Baton Rouge, LA 70803 *Tel:* 225-578-5922 *Fax:* 225-578-4129 *Web Site:* www.lsu.edu; www.english.lsu.edu/dept/programs/grad/creative_writing, pg 660

Mullen, Shawna, Harry N Abrams Inc, 115 W 18 St, 6th fl, New York, NY 10011 *Tel:* 212-206-7715 *Toll Free Tel:* 800-345-1359 *Fax:* 212-519-1210 *E-mail:* abrams@abramsbooks.com *Web Site:* www.abramsbooks.com, pg 3

Mullendore, Nick, Loretta Barrett Books Inc, 220 E 23 St, 11th fl, New York, NY 10010 *Tel:* 212-242-3420 *E-mail:* query@lorettabarrettbooks.com *Web Site:* www.lorettabarrettbooks.com, pg 542

Muller, Pete, Crown Publishing Group, c/o Penguin Random House Inc, 1745 Broadway, New York, NY 10019 *Tel:* 212-782-9000 *Toll Free Tel:* 888-264-1745 *Fax:* 212-940-7408 *E-mail:* crownosm@penguinrandomhouse.com *Web Site:* crownpublishing.com, pg 68

Mullick, Farah, Harlequin Enterprises Ltd, 225 Duncan Mill Rd, Don Mills, ON M3B 3K9, Canada *Tel:* 416-445-5860 *Toll Free Tel:* 888-432-4879; 800-370-5838 (ebook inquiries) *E-mail:* customerservice@harlequin.com *Web Site:* www.harlequin.com, pg 487

Mulligan, Ryan, Princeton University Press, 41 William St, Princeton, NJ 08540-5237 *Tel:* 609-258-4900 *Toll Free Tel:* 800-777-4726 (orders) *Fax:* 609-258-6305 *Toll Free Fax:* 800-999-1958 *E-mail:* orders@cpfsinc.com *Web Site:* press.princeton.edu, pg 197

Mullin, Melinda, HarperCollins General Books Group, 195 Broadway, New York, NY 10007 *Tel:* 212-207-7000 *Web Site:* www.harpercollins.com, pg 105

Mullins, Antoinette, Emerging Playwright Award, 555 Eighth Ave, Suite 1800, New York, NY 10018 *Tel:* 212-421-1380 *Fax:* 212-421-1387 *E-mail:* urbanstage@aol.com, pg 683

Mullins, Brighde, University of Southern California, Master of Professional Writing Program, Mark Taper Hall, THH 355, 3501 Trousedale Pkwy, Los Angeles, CA 90089-0355 *Tel:* 213-740-3252 *Fax:* 213-740-5002 *E-mail:* mpw@college.usc.edu *Web Site:* college.usc.edu/mpw, pg 664

Mulloy-Bonn, Nancy, American Law Institute Continuing Legal Education (ALI CLE), 4025 Chestnut St, Philadelphia, PA 19104 *Tel:* 215-243-1600 *Toll Free Tel:* 800-CLE-NEWS (253-6397) *Fax:* 215-243-1664; 215-243-1683 *Web Site:* www.ali-cle.org, pg 14

Mumford, Tracy, Milkweed Editions, 1011 Washington Ave S, Suite 300, Minneapolis, MN 55415-1246 *Tel:* 612-332-3192 *Toll Free Tel:* 800-520-6455 *Fax:* 612-215-2550 *Web Site:* www.milkweed.org, pg 157

Mumm, Anita, Nelson Literary Agency LLC, 1732 Wazee St, Suite 207, Denver, CO 80202-1284 *Tel:* 303-292-2805 *E-mail:* query@nelsonagency.com *Web Site:* www.nelsonagency.com, pg 566

Munce, Alayna, Brick Books, Box 20081, 431 Boler Rd, London, ON N6K 4G6, Canada *Tel:* 519-657-8579 *E-mail:* brick.books@sympatico.ca *Web Site:* www.brickbooks.ca, pg 473

Munk, Laurie, American Association of Blood Banks, 8101 Glenbrook Rd, Bethesda, MD 20814-2749 *Tel:* 301-907-6977 *Toll Free Tel:* 866-222-2498 (sales) *Fax:* 301-907-6895 *E-mail:* aabb@aabb.org; sales@aabb.org (ordering); publications1@aabb.org *Web Site:* www.aabb.org, pg 11

Munn, Duncan, C D Howe Institute, 67 Yonge St, Suite 300, Toronto, ON M5E 1J8, Canada *Tel:* 416-865-1904 *Fax:* 416-865-1866 *E-mail:* cdhowe@cdhowe.org *Web Site:* www.cdhowe.org, pg 488

Munro, Bob, Elsevier, Health Sciences Division, 1600 John F Kennedy Blvd, Suite 1800, Philadelphia, PA 19103-2899 *Tel:* 215-239-3900 *Toll Free Tel:* 800-523-1649 *Fax:* 215-239-3990 *Web Site:* www.elsevierhealth.com, pg 81

Munro, Susan, The Continuing Legal Education Society of British Columbia (CLEBC), 500-1155 W Pender St, Vancouver, BC V6E 2P4, Canada *Tel:* 604-669-3544; 604-893-2121 (cust serv) *Toll Free Tel:* 800-663-0437 (CN) *Fax:* 604-669-9260 *E-mail:* custserv@cle.bc.ca *Web Site:* www.cle.bc.ca, pg 478

Munson, Diane, Oakstone Publishing LLC, 100 Corporate Pkwy, Suite 600, Birmingham, AL 35242 *Toll Free Tel:* 800-633-4743 *Fax:* 205-995-1926 *E-mail:* service@oakstonemedical.com *Web Site:* www.oakstonepublishing.com; www.cmeonly.com; www.cdeonly.com, pg 173

Murach, Ben, Mike Murach & Associates Inc, 4340 N Knoll Ave, Fresno, CA 93722 *Tel:* 559-440-9071 *Toll Free Tel:* 800-221-5528 *Fax:* 559-440-0963 *E-mail:* murachbooks@murach.com *Web Site:* www.murach.com, pg 156

Muranaka, Royden, University of Hawaii Press, 2840 Kolowalu St, Honolulu, HI 96822 *Tel:* 808-956-8255 *Toll Free Tel:* 888-UHPRESS (847-7377) *Fax:* 808-988-6052 *Toll Free Fax:* 800-650-7811 *E-mail:* uhpbooks@hawaii.edu *Web Site:* www.uhpress.hawaii.edu, pg 256

Murari, Raj, Disney Publishing Worldwide, 1101 Flower St, Glendale, CA 91201 *Web Site:* books.disney.com, pg 74

Murgolo, Karen, Grand Central Publishing, 1290 Avenue of the Americas, New York, NY 10019 *Tel:* 212-364-1100 *Web Site:* www.hachettebookgroup.com, pg 99

Murguia de Ferrer, Mariana, Cantos Para Todos, 4749 Hillcrest St, Bel Aire, KS 67226 *Tel:* 316-239 6477 *Web Site:* www.cantos.org, pg 49

Murkette, Julie, Satya House Publications, 22 Turkey St, Hardwick, MA 01037 *Tel:* 413-477-8743 *E-mail:* info@satyahouse.com; orders@satyahouse.com *Web Site:* www.satyahouse.com, pg 217

Murphy, Christopher, Hachette Book Group, 1290 Avenue of the Americas, New York, NY 10019 *Tel:* 212-364-1100 *Toll Free Tel:* 800-759-0190 (cust serv) *Fax:* 212-364-0933 (intl orders) *Toll Free Fax:* 800-286-9471 (cust serv) *Web Site:* www.HachetteBookGroup.com, pg 102

Murphy, Colleen, Houghton Mifflin Harcourt, 222 Berkeley St, Boston, MA 02116 *Tel:* 617-351-5000 *Toll Free Tel:* 800-225-5425 (K-12 educ materials); 800-323-9540 (assessment materials); 877-219-1537 (SkillsTutor); 888-242-6747 (Destination; Earobics; Edmark; Learning Village; Riverdeep); 800-225-3362 (Houghton Mifflin Harcourt Trade & Reference Publishers) *Toll Free Fax:* 800-269-5232 *E-mail:* customerservice@hmhpub.com *Web Site:* www.hmhco.com, pg 115

Murphy, Jacqueline, FinePrint Literary Management, 115 W 29 St, 3rd fl, New York, NY 10001 *Tel:* 212-279-1282 *Web Site:* www.fineprintlit.com, pg 551

Murphy, Jacqueline, InkWell Management, 521 Fifth Ave, 26th fl, New York, NY 10175 *Tel:* 212-922-3500 *Fax:* 212-922-0535 *E-mail:* info@inkwellmanagement.com; submissions@inkwellmanagement.com *Web Site:* inkwellmanagement.com, pg 557

Murphy, John, St Martin's Press, LLC, 175 Fifth Ave, New York, NY 10010 *Tel:* 646-307-5151 *Fax:* 212-420-9314 *E-mail:* firstname.lastname@macmillan.com *Web Site:* www.stmartins.com, pg 215

Murphy, Kim, Coachlight Press LLC, 1704 Craig's Store Rd, Afton, VA 22920-2017 *Tel:* 434-823-1692 *E-mail:* sales@coachlightpress.com *Web Site:* www.coachlightpress.com, pg 60

Murphy, Megan, Canadian Energy Research Institute, 3512 33 St NW, Suite 150, Calgary, AB T2L 2A6, Canada *Tel:* 403-282-1231 *Fax:* 403-284-4181 *E-mail:* info@ceri.ca *Web Site:* www.ceri.ca, pg 475

Murphy, Michael, Jessie Bernard Award, c/o Governance Off, 1430 "K" St NW, Suite 600, Washington, DC 20005 *Tel:* 202-383-9005 *Fax:* 202-638-0882 *E-mail:* governance@asanet.org *Web Site:* www.asanet.org, pg 671

Murphy, Michael, Distinguished Book Award, c/o Governance Off, 1430 "K" St NW, Suite 600, Washington, DC 20005 *Tel:* 202-383-9005 *Fax:* 202-638-0882 *E-mail:* governance@asanet.org *Web Site:* www.asanet.org, pg 681

Murphy, Pat, James Tiptree Jr Award, 680 66 St, Oakland, CA 94609 *Tel:* 510-658-7176 *E-mail:* info@tiptree.org *Web Site:* tiptree.org, pg 732

Murphy, Patrick, Nimbus Publishing Ltd, 3731 Mackintosh St, Halifax, NS B3K 5A5, Canada *Tel:* 902-455-4286; 902-454-7404 *Toll Free Tel:* 800-NIMBUS9 (646-2879) *Fax:* 902-455-5440 *Toll Free Fax:* 888-253-3133 *E-mail:* customerservice@nimbus.ca *Web Site:* www.nimbus.ca, pg 492

Murphy, Paul, RAND Corp, 1776 Main St, Santa Monica, CA 90407-2138 *Tel:* 310-393-0411 *Fax:* 310-393-4818 *Web Site:* www.rand.org, pg 203

Murphy, Richard J, BPA Worldwide, 100 Beard Sawmill Rd, 6th fl, Shelton, CT 06484 *Tel:* 203-447-2800 *Fax:* 203-447-2900 *E-mail:* info@bpaww.com *Web Site:* www.bpaww.com, pg 601

Murphy, Robert, Higginson Book Co, 10 Colonial Rd, Salem, MA 01970 *Tel:* 978-745-7170 *Fax:* 978-745-8025 *Web Site:* www.higginsonbooks.com, pg 111

Murphy, Ross, Aberdeen Bay, 6285 Gentle Lane, Alexandria, VA 22310 *Tel:* 703-473-1392 *E-mail:* editor@aberdeenbay.com *Web Site:* www.aberdeenbay.com, pg 2

Murphy, Sarah, HarperCollins General Books Group, 195 Broadway, New York, NY 10007 *Tel:* 212-207-7000 *Web Site:* www.harpercollins.com, pg 106

Murphy, Sarah, Random House Publishing Group, 1745 Broadway, New York, NY 10019 *Toll Free Tel:* 800-200-3552 *Web Site:* atrandom.com, pg 204

Murphy, Suzanne, HarperCollins Children's Books, 195 Broadway, New York, NY 10007 *Tel:* 212-207-7000 *Web Site:* www.harpercollins.com/childrens, pg 105

Murphy, Trace, Crown Publishing Group, c/o Penguin Random House Inc, 1745 Broadway, New York, NY 10019 *Tel:* 212-782-9000 *Toll Free Tel:* 888-264-1745 *Fax:* 212-940-7408 *E-mail:* crownosm@penguinrandomhouse.com *Web Site:* crownpublishing.com, pg 68

Murphy, Trace, Paulist Press, 997 Macarthur Blvd, Mahwah, NJ 07430-9990 *Tel:* 201-825-7300 *Toll Free Tel:* 800-218-1903 *Fax:* 201-825-8345 *Toll Free Fax:* 800-836-3161 *E-mail:* info@paulistpress.com *Web Site:* www.paulistpress.com, pg 184

Murphy, Will, Random House Publishing Group, 1745 Broadway, New York, NY 10019 *Toll Free Tel:* 800-200-3552 *Web Site:* atrandom.com, pg 204

Murray, Brian, HarperCollins Publishers, 195 Broadway, New York, NY 10007 *Tel:* 212-207-7000 *Fax:* 212-207-7145 *Web Site:* www.harpercollins.com, pg 106

Murray, Cindy, Random House Publishing Group, 1745 Broadway, New York, NY 10019 *Toll Free Tel:* 800-200-3552 *Web Site:* atrandom.com, pg 204

Murray, David, Piano Press, 1425 Ocean Ave, Suite 5, Del Mar, CA 92014 *Tel:* 619-884-1401 *Fax:* 858-755-1104 *E-mail:* pianopress@pianopress.com *Web Site:* www.pianopress.com, pg 191

Murray, Lawrence A, Sts Judes imPress, 5537 Waterman Blvd, Suite 2-W, St Louis, MO 63112 *Tel:* 314-454-0064 *E-mail:* stjudes1@att.net, pg 215

Murray, Mary, McGraw-Hill Professional, 1221 Avenue of the Americas, New York, NY 10020 *Tel:* 212-512-2000 *Web Site:* www.mhprofessional.com, pg 152

Murray, Nancy, Artisan Books, 225 Varick St, New York, NY 10014-4381 *Tel:* 212-254-5900 *Toll Free Tel:* 800-722-7202 *Fax:* 212-677-6692 *E-mail:* artisaninfo@artisanbooks.com *Web Site:* www.workman.com/artisanbooks, pg 23

Murray, Phyllis, Nimbus Publishing Ltd, 3731 Mackintosh St, Halifax, NS B3K 5A5, Canada *Tel:* 902-455-4286; 902-454-7404 *Toll Free Tel:* 800-NIMBUS9 (646-2879) *Fax:* 902-455-5440 *Toll Free Fax:* 888-253-3133 *E-mail:* customerservice@nimbus.ca *Web Site:* www.nimbus.ca, pg 493

Murray, William D G, Type & Archetype Press, 846 Dupont Rd, Suite-C, Charleston, SC 29407 *Tel:* 843-406-9113 *Toll Free Tel:* 800-447-8973 *Fax:* 843-406-9118 *E-mail:* info@typetemperament.com *Web Site:* www.typetemperament.com; typenewsletter.com, pg 252

Murray-Urdaneta, Maria, Bear & Co Inc, One Park St, Rochester, VT 05767 *Tel:* 802-767-3174 *Toll Free Tel:* 800-932-3277 *Fax:* 802-767-3726 *E-mail:* customerservice@InnerTraditions.com *Web Site:* InnerTraditions.com, pg 33

Murray-Urdaneta, Maria, Inner Traditions International Ltd, One Park St, Rochester, VT 05767 *Tel:* 802-767-3174 *Toll Free Tel:* 800-246-8648 *Fax:* 802-767-3726 *E-mail:* customerservice@InnerTraditions.com *Web Site:* www.InnerTraditions.com, pg 122

Muscatel, David, Rand McNally, 9855 Woods Dr, Skokie, IL 60077 *Tel:* 847-329-8100 *Toll Free Tel:* 800-678-7263 *Fax:* 847-329-6139 *E-mail:* ctsales@randmcnally.com; mediarelations@randmcnally.com *Web Site:* www.randmcnally.com, pg 203

Muscato, Dave, American Atheist Press, PO Box 158, Cranford, NJ 07016 *Tel:* 908-276-7300 *Fax:* 908-276-7402 *Web Site:* www.atheists.org, pg 11

Nasaw, David, Francis Parkman Prize, 603 Fayerweather, MC 2538, New York, NY 10027 *Tel:* 212-854-6495 *E-mail:* amhistsociety@columbia.edu *Web Site:* sah.columbia.edu, pg 716

Nash, Leigh, Coach House Books, 80 bpNichol Lane, Toronto, ON M5S 3J4, Canada *Tel:* 416-979-2217 *Toll Free Tel:* 800-367-6360 (outside Toronto) *Fax:* 416-977-1158 *E-mail:* mail@chbooks.com *Web Site:* www.chbooks.com, pg 477

Nasitka, Deb, University of California Press, 2120 Berkeley Way, Berkeley, CA 94704-1012 *Tel:* 510-642-4247 *Fax:* 510-643-7127 *E-mail:* askucp@ucpress.edu (books); customerservice@ucpressjournals.com *Web Site:* www.ucpress.edu, pg 255

Nasrallah, Dimitri, Vehicule Press, PO Box 42094, CP Roy, Montreal, QC H2W-2T3, Canada *Tel:* 514-844-6073 *Fax:* 514-844-7543 *E-mail:* vp@vehiculepress.com; admin@vehiculepress.com *Web Site:* www.vehiculepress.com, pg 504

Nasta, Charles, New Horizon Press, PO Box 669, Far Hills, NJ 07931-0669 *Tel:* 908-604-6311 *Toll Free Tel:* 800-533-7978 (orders only) *Fax:* 908-604-6330 *E-mail:* nhp@newhorizonpressbooks.com *Web Site:* www.newhorizonpressbooks.com, pg 168

Nathan, Geeta, American Booksellers Association, 333 Westchester Ave, Suite S202, White Plains, NY 10604 *Tel:* 914-406-7500 *Toll Free Tel:* 800-637-0037 *Fax:* 914-410-6297 *E-mail:* info@bookweb.org *Web Site:* www.bookweb.org, pg 594

Nathan, Terry, Benjamin Franklin Awards™, 1020 Manhattan Beach Blvd, Suite 204, Manhattan Beach, CA 90266 *Tel:* 310-546-1818 *Fax:* 310-546-3939 *E-mail:* info@ibpa-online.org *Web Site:* www.ibpa-online.org; ibpabenjaminfranklinawards.com, pg 671

Nathan, Terry, The Independent Book Publishers Association (IBPA), 1020 Manhattan Beach Blvd, Suite 204, Manhattan Beach, CA 90266 *Tel:* 310-546-1818 *Fax:* 310-546-3939 *E-mail:* info@ibpa-online.org *Web Site:* www.ibpa-online.org, pg 607

Naughton, Diane, HarperCollins Children's Books, 195 Broadway, New York, NY 10007 *Tel:* 212-207-7000 *Web Site:* www.harpercollins.com/childrens, pg 105

Navaretta, Cynthia, Midmarch Arts Press, 300 Riverside Dr, New York, NY 10025-5239 *Tel:* 212-666-6990 *Web Site:* midmarchartspress.org, pg 156

Navarre, Randy, Roncorp Music, PO Box 517, Glenmoore, PA 19343 *Tel:* 610-942-2370 *Fax:* 610-942-0660 *E-mail:* info@nemusicpub.com *Web Site:* www.nemusicpub.com, pg 211

Nawalinski, Beth, United for Libraries, 109 S 13 St, Suite 117B, Philadelphia, PA 19107 *Tel:* 312-280-2161 *Toll Free Tel:* 800-545-2433 (ext 2161) *Fax:* 215-545-3821 *E-mail:* united@ala.org *Web Site:* www.ala.org/united, pg 620

Nawrocki, Sarah, Trinity University Press, One Trinity Place, San Antonio, TX 78212-7200 *Tel:* 210-999-8884 *Fax:* 210-999-8838 *E-mail:* books@trinity.edu *Web Site:* www.tupress.org, pg 249

Nayer, Rick, Berkley Books, 375 Hudson St, New York, NY 10014 *Tel:* 212-366-2000 *Fax:* 212-366-2666 *E-mail:* online@penguinputnam.com *Web Site:* www.penguinputnam.com; us.penguingroup.com, pg 35

Nayer, Rick, Berkley Publishing Group, 375 Hudson St, New York, NY 10014 *Tel:* 212-366-2000 *Fax:* 212-366-2385 *E-mail:* online@penguinputnam.com *Web Site:* us.penguingroup.com, pg 35

Nayer, Rick, NAL, 375 Hudson St, New York, NY 10014 *Tel:* 212-366-2000 *E-mail:* online@penguinputnam.com *Web Site:* www.penguinputnam.com; us.penguingroup.com, pg 162

Nayeri, Daniel, Workman Publishing Co Inc, 225 Varick St, 9th fl, New York, NY 10014-4381 *Tel:* 212-254-5900 *Toll Free Tel:* 800-722-7202 *Fax:* 212-254-8098 *E-mail:* info@workman.com *Web Site:* www.workman.com, pg 275

Nazarian, Vera, Norilana Books, PO Box 209, Highgate Center, VT 05459-0209 *E-mail:* service@norilana.com *Web Site:* www.norilana.com, pg 170

Neal, John Vincent, Neal-Schuman Publishers Inc, 100 William St, Suite 2004, New York, NY 10038 *Tel:* 212-925-8650 *Toll Free Tel:* 866-NS-BOOKS (672-6657) *Fax:* 212-219-8916 *Toll Free Fax:* 877-231-6980 *E-mail:* info@neal-schuman.com *Web Site:* www.neal-schuman.com, pg 166

Neal, Rae, Multicultural Publications Inc, 936 Slosson St, Akron, OH 44320 *Tel:* 330-865-9578 *Fax:* 330-865-9578 *E-mail:* multiculturalpub@prodigy.net *Web Site:* www.multiculturalpub.net, pg 161

Neaverth, Kate, Amherst Media Inc, 175 Rano St, Suite 200, Buffalo, NY 14207 *Tel:* 716-874-4450 *Toll Free Tel:* 800-622-3278 *Fax:* 716-874-4508 *E-mail:* marketing@amherstmedia.com *Web Site:* www.amherstmedia.com, pg 17

Necarsulmer, Edward IV, Dunow, Carlson & Lerner Literary Agency Inc, 27 W 20 St, Suite 1107, New York, NY 10011 *Tel:* 212-645-7606 *E-mail:* mail@dclagency.com *Web Site:* www.dclagency.com, pg 549

Nedelcu, Maria, Teora USA LLC, 505 Hampton Park Blvd, Unit G, Capitol Heights, MD 20743 *Tel:* 301-986-6990 *Toll Free Tel:* 800-974-2105 *Fax:* 301-350-5480 *Toll Free Fax:* 800-358-3754 *E-mail:* 2010@teora.com *Web Site:* www.teora.com, pg 243

Neel, David, Texas A&M University Press, John H Lindsey Bldg, Lewis St, 4354 TAMU, College Station, TX 77843-4354 *Tel:* 979-845-1436 *Toll Free Tel:* 800-826-8911 (orders) *Fax:* 979-847-8752 *Toll Free Fax:* 888-617-2421 (orders) *E-mail:* tampress@tamu.edu *Web Site:* www.tamupress.com, pg 243

Neel, Thomas Stephen, Ohio Genealogical Society, 611 State Rte 97 W, Bellville, OH 44813-8813 *Tel:* 419-886-1903 *Fax:* 419-886-0092 *E-mail:* ogs@ogs.org *Web Site:* www.ogs.org, pg 174

Neely, Judith Illov, F A Davis Co, 1915 Arch St, Philadelphia, PA 19103 *Tel:* 215-568-2270; 215-440-3001 *Toll Free Tel:* 800-523-4049 *Fax:* 215-568-5065; 215-440-3016 *E-mail:* info@fadavis.com; orders@fadavis.com *Web Site:* www.fadavis.com, pg 71

Neesemann, Cynthia, CS International Literary Agency, 43 W 39 St, New York, NY 10018 *Tel:* 212-921-1610; 212-391-9208 *E-mail:* query@csliterary.com; csliterary08@gmail.com *Web Site:* www.csliterary.com, pg 524

Neff, Amber, University of Chicago, Graham School of General Studies, 1427 E 60 St, Chicago, IL 60637 *Tel:* 773-702-1722 *Fax:* 773-702-6814 *Web Site:* www.grahamschool.uchicago.edu, pg 663

Nehmer, Kathy, Educators Progress Service Inc, 214 Center St, Randolph, WI 53956 *Tel:* 920-326-3126 *Toll Free Tel:* 888-951-4469 *Fax:* 920-326-3127 *E-mail:* epsinc@centurytel.net, pg 80

Neibauer,
Nathan, Neibauer Press & ChurchSupplier.com, 20 Industrial Dr, Warminster, PA 18974 *Tel:* 215-322-6200 *Toll Free Tel:* 800-322-6203 *Fax:* 215-322-2495 *E-mail:* sales@neibauer.com; sales@churchsupplier.com *Web Site:* www.churchsupplier.com, pg 167

Neidlinger, Amy, Financial Times Press, 225 River St, Hoboken, NJ 07030-4772 *Tel:* 201-236-7000 *Toll Free Tel:* 800-922-0579 (orders) *Web Site:* www.ftpress.com, pg 88

Neimark, Nina, Nina Neimark Editorial Services, 543 Third St, Brooklyn, NY 11215 *Tel:* 718-499-6804 *E-mail:* pneimark@hotmail.com, pg 531

Nellis, Muriel G, Literary & Creative Artists Inc, 3543 Albemarle St NW, Washington, DC 20008-4213 *Tel:* 202-362-4688 *Fax:* 202-362-8875 *E-mail:* lca9643@lcadc.com (queries, no attachments) *Web Site:* www.lcadc.com, pg 562

Nelson, Bonita K, BK Nelson Inc Lecture Bureau, 1565 Paseo Vida, Palm Springs, CA 92264 *Tel:* 760-778-8800 *Fax:* 760-778-6242 *E-mail:* bknelson4@cs.com *Web Site:* www.bknelson.com; www.bknelsonlecturebureau.com; www.nelsonbookmovielecture.com; www.bknelsonmovieproduction.com, pg 587

Nelson, Bonita K, BK Nelson Inc Literary Agency, 1565 Paseo Vida, Palm Springs, CA 92264 *Tel:* 760-778-8800 *Fax:* 760-778-6242 *E-mail:* bknelson4@cs.com *Web Site:* www.bknelson.com; www.bknelsonlecturebureau.com; www.nelsonbookmovielecture.com; www.bknelsonmovieproduction.com, pg 566

Nelson, Cassie, Basic Books, 250 W 57 St, 15th fl, New York, NY 10107 *Tel:* 212-340-8164; 212-340-8136 *Fax:* 212-340-8135 *E-mail:* perseus.promos@perseusbooks.com *Web Site:* www.basicbooks.com; perseusbooks.com, pg 31

Nelson, Dan, Visual Media Alliance (VMA), 665 Third St, Suite 500, San Francisco, CA 94107-1956 *Tel:* 415-489-7601 *Toll Free Tel:* 800-659-3363 *Toll Free Fax:* 800-824-1911 *E-mail:* info@vma.bz *Web Site:* main.vma.bz, pg 621

Nelson, David, Waterside Productions Inc, 2055 Oxford Ave, Cardiff, CA 92007 *Tel:* 760-632-9190 *Fax:* 760-632-9295 *E-mail:* admin@waterside.com *Web Site:* www.waterside.com, pg 579

Nelson, Diane, DC Entertainment, 2900 Alameda, Burbank, CA 91505 *Toll Free Tel:* 800-887-6789 *E-mail:* dccomics@cambeywest.com *Web Site:* www.dcentertainment.com; www.dccomics.com; www.madmag.com, pg 72

Nelson, Eric, Penguin Group (USA) LLC, a Penguin Random House company, 375 Hudson St, New York, NY 10014 *Tel:* 212-366-2000 *Toll Free Tel:* 800-847-5515 (inside sales); 800-631-8571 (cust serv) *Fax:* 212-366-2666; 607-775-4829 (inside sales) *E-mail:* online@us.penguingroup.com *Web Site:* www.penguin.com; us.penguingroup.com, pg 186

Nelson, Eric, Portfolio, 375 Hudson St, New York, NY 10014, pg 195

Nelson, Jandy, Manus & Associates Literary Agency Inc, 425 Sherman Ave, Suite 200, Palo Alto, CA 94306 *Tel:* 650-470-5151 *Fax:* 650-470-5159 *E-mail:* manuslit@manuslit.com *Web Site:* www.manuslit.com, pg 563

Nelson, Kristin, Nelson Literary Agency LLC, 1732 Wazee St, Suite 207, Denver, CO 80202-1284 *Tel:* 303-292-2805 *E-mail:* query@nelsonagency.com *Web Site:* www.nelsonagency.com, pg 566

Nelson, Patricia, Marsal Lyon Literary Agency LLC, 665 San Rodolfo Dr, Suite 124, PMB 121, Solana Beach, CA 92075 *Tel:* 760-814-8507 *Web Site:* www.marsallyonliteraryagency.com, pg 563

Nelson, Stephen R, Sheffield Publishing Co, 9009 Antioch Rd, Salem, WI 53168 *Tel:* 262-843-2281 *Fax:* 262-843-3683 *E-mail:* info@spcbooks.com *Web Site:* www.spcbooks.com, pg 223

Nemeth, Terence, Theatre Communications Group, 520 Eighth Ave, 24th fl, New York, NY 10018-4156 *Tel:* 212-609-5900 *Fax:* 212-609-5901 *E-mail:* tcg@tcg.org *Web Site:* www.tcg.org, pg 244

Nephew, John, Trident Inc, 885 Pierce Butler Rte, St Paul, MN 55104 *Tel:* 651-638-0077 *Fax:* 651-638-0084 *E-mail:* info@atlas-games.com *Web Site:* www.atlas-games.com, pg 249

Neptune, Alyssa, Alice James Books, 114 Prescott St, Farmington, ME 04938 *Tel:* 207-778-7071 *Fax:* 207-778-7766 *E-mail:* info@alicejamesbooks.org *Web Site:* alicejamesbooks.org, pg 8

Nericcio, Dr Bill, San Diego State University Press, Arts & Letters 283, 5500 Campanile Dr, San Diego, CA 92182-6020 *Tel:* 619-594-6220 (orders) *Web Site:* sdsupress.sdsu.edu, pg 216

Nerya, Javier, McGraw-Hill International Publishing Group, 2 Penn Plaza, New York, NY 10121 *Tel:* 212-904-2000 *Web Site:* www.mcgraw-hill.com, pg 152

Nesbit, Lynn, Janklow & Nesbit Associates, 445 Park Ave, New York, NY 10022 *Tel:* 212-421-1700 *Fax:* 212-980-3671 *E-mail:* info@janklow.com *Web Site:* www.janklowandnesbit.com, pg 558

Nesbitt, Bruce, Nesbitt Graphics Inc, 555 Virginia Dr, Fort Washington, PA 19034 *Tel:* 215-591-9125 *Fax:* 215-591-9093 *Web Site:* cenveopublisherservices.com, pg 531

O'Brien, Sandra, The Geoffrey Bilson Award for Historical Fiction for Young People, 40 Orchard View Blvd, Suite 217, Toronto, ON M4R 1B9, Canada *Tel:* 416-975-0010 *Fax:* 416-975-8970 *E-mail:* info@bookcentre.ca *Web Site:* www.bookcentre.ca, pg 672

O'Brien, Sandra, Canadian Children's Book Centre, 40 Orchard View Blvd, Suite 217, Toronto, ON M4R 1B9, Canada *Tel:* 416-975-0010 *Fax:* 416-975-8970 *E-mail:* info@bookcentre.ca *Web Site:* www.bookcentre.ca, pg 602

O'Brien, Sandra, Norma Fleck Award for Canadian Children's Non-Fiction, 40 Orchard View Blvd, Suite 217, Toronto, ON M4R 1B9, Canada *Tel:* 416-975-0010 *Fax:* 416-975-8970 *E-mail:* info@bookcentre.ca *Web Site:* www.bookcentre.ca, pg 686

O'Brien, Sandra, Monica Hughes Award for Science Fiction & Fantasy, 40 Orchard View Blvd, Suite 217, Toronto, ON M4R 1B9, Canada *Tel:* 416-975-0010 *Fax:* 416-975-8970 *E-mail:* info@bookcentre.ca *Web Site:* www.bookcentre.ca, pg 693

O'Brien, Sandra, Amy Mathers Teen Book Award, 40 Orchard View Blvd, Suite 217, Toronto, ON M4R 1B9, Canada *Tel:* 416-975-0010 *Fax:* 416-975-8970 *E-mail:* info@bookcentre.ca *Web Site:* www.bookcentre.ca, pg 706

O'Brien, Sandra, John Spray Mystery Award, 40 Orchard View Blvd, Suite 217, Toronto, ON M4R 1B9, Canada *Tel:* 416-975-0010 *Fax:* 416-975-8970 *E-mail:* info@bookcentre.ca *Web Site:* www.bookcentre.ca, pg 730

O'Brien, Sandra, TD Canadian Children's Literature Award, 40 Orchard View Blvd, Suite 217, Toronto, ON M4R 1B9, Canada *Tel:* 416-975-0010 *Fax:* 416-975-8970 *E-mail:* info@bookcentre.ca *Web Site:* www.bookcentre.ca, pg 732

O'Brien-Nicholson, Kathleen, Fordham University Press, 2546 Belmont Ave, University Box L, Bronx, NY 10458 *Tel:* 718-817-4795 *Fax:* 718-817-4785 *Web Site:* www.fordhampress.com, pg 90

O'Cain, Stephanie, Random House Children's Books, 1745 Broadway, New York, NY 10019 *Tel:* 212-782-9000 *Toll Free Tel:* 800-200-3552 *Fax:* 212-782-9452 *Web Site:* randomhousekids.com, pg 203

O'Callaghan, Katie, HarperCollins General Books Group, 195 Broadway, New York, NY 10007 *Tel:* 212-207-7000 *Web Site:* www.harpercollins.com, pg 105

O'Connell, Maureen, Scholastic Inc, 557 Broadway, New York, NY 10012 *Tel:* 212-343-6100 *Toll Free Tel:* 800-scholastic *Web Site:* www.scholastic.com, pg 218

O'Connell, Tim, Vintage & Anchor Books, c/o Random House Inc, 1745 Broadway, New York, NY 10019 *Tel:* 212-572-2420 *E-mail:* vintageanchorpublicity@randomhouse.com *Web Site:* vintage-anchor.knopfdoubleday.com, pg 266

O'Connor, Amanda, Trident Media Group LLC, 41 Madison Ave, 36th fl, New York, NY 10010 *Tel:* 212-333-1511 *E-mail:* info@tridentmediagroup.com; press@tridentmediagroup.com *Web Site:* www.tridentmediagroup.com, pg 577

O'Connor, Bland, Catholic Library Association, 8550 United Plaza Blvd, Suite 1001, Baton Rouge, LA 70809-2256 *Tel:* 225-408-4417 *E-mail:* cla2@cathla.org *Web Site:* www.cathla.org, pg 602

O'Connor, Brian, National Society of Newspaper Columnists Annual Conference, 1345 Fillmore St, Suite 507, San Francisco, CA 94115 *Tel:* 415-488-NCNC (488-6762) *Toll Free Tel:* 866-440-NSNC (440-6762) *Fax:* 484-297-0336 *Toll Free Fax:* 866-635-5759 *Web Site:* www.columnists.com, pg 653

O'Connor, Dan, The Experiment, 220 East 23 St, Suite 301, New York, NY 10010-4674 *Tel:* 212-889-1659 *E-mail:* info@theexperimentpublishing.com *Web Site:* www.theexperimentpublishing.com, pg 85

O'Connor, Erika, Damron Co, PO Box 422458, San Francisco, CA 94142-2458 *Tel:* 415-255-0404 *Toll Free Tel:* 800-462-6654 *Fax:* 415-703-9049 *E-mail:* info@damron.com *Web Site:* www.damron.com, pg 70

O'Connor, Eugene PhD, Ohio State University Press, 180 Pressey Hall, 1070 Carmack Rd, Columbus, OH 43210-1002 *Tel:* 614-292-6930 *Fax:* 614-292-2065 *Toll Free Fax:* 800-621-8476 *E-mail:* info@osupress.org *Web Site:* ohiostatepress.org, pg 174

O'Connor, Jane, Grosset & Dunlap, 345 Hudson St, New York, NY 10014 *Tel:* 212-366-2000 *Web Site:* www.penguinrandomhouse.com, pg 101

O'Connor, John, Eastland Press, 1240 Activity Dr, Suite D, Vista, CA 92081 *Tel:* 206-217-0204 (edit); 760-598-9695 (orders) *Toll Free Tel:* 800-453-3278 (orders) *Fax:* 760-598-6083 (orders) *Toll Free Fax:* 800-241-3329 (orders) *E-mail:* info@eastlandpress.com; orders@eastlandpress.com (credit card orders only) *Web Site:* www.eastlandpress.com, pg 78

O'Connor, John, H W Wilson, 2 University Plaza, Suite 310, Hackensack, NJ 07601 *Tel:* 201-968-0500 *Toll Free Tel:* 800-221-1592 *Fax:* 201-968-0511 *E-mail:* info@hwwilsoninprint.com; csr@hwwilsoninprint.com; information@ebscohost.com *Web Site:* www.hwwilsoninprint.com; www.ebscohost.com/wilson, pg 273

O'Connor, Mike, Insomniac Press, 520 Princess Ave, London, ON N6B 2B8, Canada *Tel:* 416-504-6270 *Web Site:* www.insomniacpress.com, pg 488

O'Connor, Nichole, Baker & Taylor/YALSA Conference Grants, 50 E Huron St, Chicago, IL 60611 *Tel:* 312-280-4390 *Toll Free Tel:* 800-545-2433 *Fax:* 312-280-5276; 312-664-7459 *E-mail:* yalsa@ala.org *Web Site:* www.ala.org/yalsa, pg 670

O'Connor, Nichole, Margaret A Edwards Award, 50 E Huron St, Chicago, IL 60611 *Tel:* 312-280-4390 *Toll Free Tel:* 800-545-2433 *Fax:* 312-280-5276 *E-mail:* yalsa@ala.org *Web Site:* www.ala.org/yalsa/edwards, pg 683

O'Connor, Nichole, Frances Henne YALSA/VOYA Research Grant, 50 E Huron St, Chicago, IL 60611 *Tel:* 312-280-4390 *Toll Free Tel:* 800-545-2433 *Fax:* 312-280-5276 *E-mail:* yalsa@ala.org *Web Site:* www.ala.org/yalsa, pg 687

O'Connor, Nichole, Michael L Printz Award, 50 E Huron St, Chicago, IL 60611 *Tel:* 312-280-4390 *Toll Free Tel:* 800-545-2433 *Fax:* 312-280-5276 *E-mail:* yalsa@ala.org *Web Site:* www.ala.org/yalsa/printz, pg 721

O'Connor, Patricia, Eastland Press, 1240 Activity Dr, Suite D, Vista, CA 92081 *Tel:* 206-217-0204 (edit); 760-598-9695 (orders) *Toll Free Tel:* 800-453-3278 (orders) *Fax:* 760-598-6083 (orders) *Toll Free Fax:* 800-241-3329 (orders) *E-mail:* info@eastlandpress.com; orders@eastlandpress.com (credit card orders only) *Web Site:* www.eastlandpress.com, pg 78

O'Connor, Siobhan, The Writers' Union of Canada (TWUC), 600-460 Richmond St W, Toronto, ON M5V 1Y1, Canada *Tel:* 416-703-8982 *Fax:* 416-504-9090 *E-mail:* info@writersunion.ca *Web Site:* www.writersunion.ca, pg 622

O'Donnell, Joan, Peabody Museum Press, 11 Divinity Ave, Cambridge, MA 02138 *Tel:* 617-495-4255 *Fax:* 617-495-7535 *E-mail:* peapub@fas.harvard.edu *Web Site:* www.peabody.harvard.edu/publications, pg 184

O'Donnell, Katy, Nation Books, 116 E 16 St, 8th fl, New York, NY 10003 *Tel:* 212–822–0250 *Fax:* 212-253-5356 *E-mail:* submissions@nationbooks.org *Web Site:* www.nationbooks.org, pg 163

O'Donnell, Kevin, William H Sadlier Inc, 9 Pine St, New York, NY 10005 *Tel:* 212-227-2120 *Toll Free Tel:* 800-221-5175 (cust serv) *Fax:* 212-312-6080 *E-mail:* customerservice@sadlier.com *Web Site:* www.sadlier.com, pg 213

O'Donnell, Noelle, Writers' League of Texas (WLT), 611 S Congress Ave, Suite 200 A-3, Austin, TX 78704 *Tel:* 512-499-8914 *E-mail:* wlt@writersleague.org *Web Site:* www.writersleague.org, pg 622

O'Donnell, Peg, Lonely Planet, 150 Linden St, Oakland, CA 94607 *Tel:* 510-893-8555 *Toll Free Tel:* 800-275-8555 (orders) *Fax:* 510-893-8572 *E-mail:* info@lonelyplanet.com *Web Site:* www.lonelyplanet.com, pg 142

O'Donnell, Rob, The Rockefeller University Press, 1114 First Ave, 3rd fl, New York, NY 10065-8325 *Tel:* 212-327-7938 *Fax:* 212-327-8587 *E-mail:* rupress@rockefeller.edu *Web Site:* www.rupress.org, pg 210

O'Farrell, Anne Marie, Denise Marcil Literary Agency LLC, 483 Westover Rd, Stamford, CT 06902 *Tel:* 203-327-9970 *Fax:* 203-327-9970 *E-mail:* dmla@denisemarcilagency.com *Web Site:* www.denisemarcilagency.com, pg 563

O'Gaea, Ashleen, The Society of Southwestern Authors Writing Contest, PO Box 30355, Tucson, AZ 85751-0355 *Tel:* 520-546-9382 *Fax:* 520-751-7877 *E-mail:* info@ssa-az.org *Web Site:* www.ssa-az.org, pg 729

O'Halloran, Paul, Gallery Books, 1230 Avenue of the Americas, New York, NY 10020 *Toll Free Tel:* 800-456-6798 *Fax:* 212-698-7284 *E-mail:* consumer.customerservice@simonandschuster.com *Web Site:* www.simonsays.com, pg 94

O'Halloran, Paul, Scribner, 1230 Avenue of the Americas, New York, NY 10020, pg 220

O'Halloran, Paul, Touchstone, 1230 Avenue of the Americas, New York, NY 10020, pg 247

O'Hanlon, Martin, CWA/SCA Canada, 2200 Prince of Wales Dr, Suite 301, Ottawa, ON K2E 6Z9, Canada *Tel:* 613-820-9777 *Toll Free Tel:* 877-486-4292 *Fax:* 613-820-8188 *E-mail:* info@cwa-scacanada.ca *Web Site:* www.cwa-scacanada.ca, pg 604

O'Hara, Lisa, Wilkinson Studios Inc, 1121 E Main St, Suite 310, St Charles, IL 60174 *Tel:* 630-549-0504 *Web Site:* www.wilkinsonstudios.com, pg 585

O'Hara, Mary, Chronicle Books LLC, 680 Second St, San Francisco, CA 94107 *Tel:* 415-537-4200 *Toll Free Tel:* 800-759-0190 (cust serv) *Fax:* 415-537-4460 *Toll Free Fax:* 800-858-7787 (orders); 800-286-9471 (cust serv) *E-mail:* frontdesk@chroniclebooks.com *Web Site:* www.chroniclebooks.com, pg 58

O'Hare, Joanne, University of Nevada Press, University of Nevada, M/S 0166, Reno, NV 89557-0166 *Tel:* 775-784-6573 *Fax:* 775-784-6200 *Web Site:* www.unpress.nevada.edu, pg 258

O'Leary, M J, John Wiley & Sons Inc Higher Education, 111 River St, Hoboken, NJ 07030-5774 *Tel:* 201-748-6000 *Toll Free Tel:* 800-225-5945 (cust serv) *Fax:* 201-748-6008 *E-mail:* info@wiley.com *Web Site:* www.wiley.com, pg 272

O'Leary, Sean, Newspaper Association of America (NAA), 4401 Wilson Blvd, Suite 900, Arlington, VA 22203 *Tel:* 571-366-1000 *Web Site:* www.naa.org, pg 614

O'Mara, Paul, American Society for Quality (ASQ), 600 N Plankinton Ave, Milwaukee, WI 53203 *Tel:* 414-272-8575 *Toll Free Tel:* 800-248-1946 (US & CN); 800-514-1564 (Mexico) *Fax:* 414-272-1734 *E-mail:* help@asq.org *Web Site:* www.asq.org, pg 16

O'Moore-Klopf, Katharine, KOK Edit, 15 Hare Lane, East Setauket, NY 11733-3606 *Tel:* 631-997-8191 *Fax:* 631-474-9849 *E-mail:* editor@kokedit.com *Web Site:* www.kokedit.com; twitter.com/kokedit; www.facebook.com/k.omooreklopf; www.linkedin.com/in/kokedit; www.editor-mom.blogspot.com, pg 529

O'Neal, David, Shambhala Publications Inc, Horticultural Hall, 300 Massachusetts Ave, Boston, MA 02115 *Tel:* 617-424-0030 *Toll Free Tel:* 866-424-0030 (off); 888-424-2329 (cust serv) *Fax:* 617-236-1563 *E-mail:* customercare@shambhala.com *Web Site:* www.shambhala.com, pg 223

O'Neal, Eilis, The Pablo Neruda Prize for Poetry, Nimrod International Journal, 800 S Tucker Dr, Tulsa, OK 74104 *Tel:* 918-631-3080 *Fax:* 918-631-3033 *E-mail:* nimrod@utulsa.edu *Web Site:* www.utulsa.edu/nimrod, pg 712

O'Neal, Eilis, Katherine Anne Porter Prize for Fiction, Nimrod International Journal, 800 S Tucker Dr, Tulsa, OK 74104 *Tel:* 918-631-3080 *Fax:* 918-631-3033 *E-mail:* nimrod@utulsa.edu *Web Site:* www.utulsa.edu/nimrod, pg 720

O'Neil, Casey, Milkweed Editions, 1011 Washington Ave S, Suite 300, Minneapolis, MN 55415-1246 *Tel:* 612-332-3192 *Toll Free Tel:* 800-520-6455 *Fax:* 612-215-2550 *Web Site:* www.milkweed.org, pg 157

O'Neil, Casey, Milkweed National Fiction Prize, 1011 Washington Ave S, Suite 300, Minneapolis, MN 55415-1246 *Tel:* 612-332-3192 *Toll Free Tel:* 800-520-6455 *Fax:* 612-215-2550 *E-mail:* submissions@milkweed.org *Web Site:* www.milkweed.org, pg 707

O'Neil, Michael, National Coalition Against Censorship (NCAC), 19 Fulton St, Suite 407, New York, NY 10038 *Tel:* 212-807-6222 *Fax:* 212-807-6245 *E-mail:* ncac@ncac.org *Web Site:* www.ncac.org, pg 611

O'Neill, Colleen, Canadian Publishers' Council (CPC), 250 Merton St, Suite 203, Toronto, ON M4S 1B1, Canada *Tel:* 416-322-7011 *Fax:* 416-322-6999 *Web Site:* www.pubcouncil.ca, pg 602

O'Neill, Jill, Miles Conrad Memorial Lecture, 801 Compass Way, Suite 201, Annapolis, MD 21401 *Tel:* 443-221-2980 *Fax:* 443-221-2981 *E-mail:* nfais@nfais.org *Web Site:* www.nfais.org, pg 679

O'Neill, Jill, National Federation of Advanced Information Services (NFAIS), 801 Compass Way, Suite 201, Annapolis, MD 21401 *Tel:* 443-221-2980 *Fax:* 443-221-2981 *E-mail:* nfais@nfais.org *Web Site:* www.nfais.org, pg 612

O'Neill, Mary Ellen, Workman Publishing Co Inc, 225 Varick St, 9th fl, New York, NY 10014-4381 *Tel:* 212-254-5900 *Toll Free Tel:* 800-722-7202 *Fax:* 212-254-8098 *E-mail:* info@workman.com *Web Site:* www.workman.com, pg 275

O'Neill, Michael, BMI®, 7 World Trade Ctr, 250 Greenwich St, New York, NY 10007-0030 *Tel:* 212-586-2000; 212-220-3000 *Toll Free Tel:* 888-689-5264 (sales); 800-925-8451 (cust rel) *Fax:* 212-246-2163 *E-mail:* foundation@bmi.com *Web Site:* www.bmi.com, pg 600

O'Neill, Robert J Jr, International City/County Management Association (ICMA), 777 N Capitol St NE, Suite 500, Washington, DC 20002-4201 *Tel:* 202-289-4262 *Toll Free Tel:* 800-745-8780 *Fax:* 202-962-3500 *E-mail:* customerservice@icma.org *Web Site:* icma.org, pg 123

O'Neill, Suzanne, Crown Publishing Group, c/o Penguin Random House Inc, 1745 Broadway, New York, NY 10019 *Tel:* 212-782-9000 *Toll Free Tel:* 888-264-1745 *Fax:* 212-940-7408 *E-mail:* crownosm@penguinrandomhouse.com *Web Site:* crownpublishing.com, pg 68

O'Reilly, James, Travelers' Tales, 2320 Bowdoin St, Palo Alto, CA 94306 *Tel:* 650-462-2110 *Fax:* 650-462-6305 *E-mail:* ttales@travelerstales.com *Web Site:* www.travelerstales.com, pg 249

O'Reilly, Sean, Travelers' Tales, 2320 Bowdoin St, Palo Alto, CA 94306 *Tel:* 650-462-2110 *Fax:* 650-462-6305 *E-mail:* ttales@travelerstales.com *Web Site:* www.travelerstales.com, pg 249

O'Reilly, Tim, O'Reilly Media Inc, 1005 Gravenstein Hwy N, Sebastopol, CA 95472 *Tel:* 707-827-7000; 707-827-7019 *Toll Free Tel:* 800-998-9938; 800-889-8969 *Fax:* 707-829-0104; 707-824-8268 *E-mail:* orders@oreilly.com *Web Site:* www.oreilly.com, pg 177

O'Rourke, T Patrick, TJ Publishers Inc, PO Box 702701, Dallas, TX 75370 *Toll Free Tel:* 800-999-1168 *Fax:* 972-416-0944 *E-mail:* TJPubinc@aol.com, pg 509

O'Shaughnessy, Caitlin, The Penguin Press, 375 Hudson St, New York, NY 10014, pg 187

O'Shea, Patti, University of Chicago Press, 1427 E 60 St, Chicago, IL 60637-2954 *Tel:* 773-702-7700; 773-702-7600 *Toll Free Tel:* 800-621-2736 (orders) *Fax:* 773-702-9756; 773-660-2235 (orders); 773-702-2708 *E-mail:* custserv@press.uchicago.edu; marketing@press.uchicago.edu *Web Site:* www.press.uchicago.edu, pg 255

O'Shea, Sheila, Crown Publishing Group, c/o Penguin Random House Inc, 1745 Broadway, New York, NY 10019 *Tel:* 212-782-9000 *Toll Free Tel:* 888-264-1745 *Fax:* 212-940-7408 *E-mail:* crownosm@penguinrandomhouse.com *Web Site:* crownpublishing.com, pg 68

O'Sullivan, Patty, Prospect Park Books, 2359 Lincoln Ave, Altadena, CA 91001 *Tel:* 626-793-9796 *E-mail:* info@prospectparkbooks.com *Web Site:* www.prospectparkbooks.com, pg 199

Oakes, Roger B, Adams & Ambrose Publishing, PO Box 259684, Madison, WI 53725-9684 *Tel:* 608-257-5700 *Fax:* 608-257-5700 *E-mail:* info@adamsambrose.com, pg 4

Oakley, Eric, Haynes Manuals Inc, 861 Lawrence Dr, Newbury Park, CA 91320 *Tel:* 805-498-6703 *Toll Free Tel:* 800-4-HAYNES (442-9637) *Fax:* 805-498-2867 *E-mail:* cstn@haynes.com *Web Site:* www.haynes.com, pg 108

Oates, Steve, Bethany House Publishers, 11400 Hampshire Ave S, Bloomington, MN 55438 *Tel:* 952-829-2500 *Toll Free Tel:* 800-877-2665 (orders) *Fax:* 952-829-2568 *Toll Free Fax:* 800-398-3111 (orders) *Web Site:* www.bethanyhouse.com; www.bakerpublishinggroup.com, pg 36

Obeng, Samuel, Indiana University African Studies Program, Indiana University, 221 Woodburn Hall, Bloomington, IN 47405 *Tel:* 812-855-8284 *Fax:* 812-855-6734 *E-mail:* afrist@indiana.edu *Web Site:* www.indiana.edu/~afrist, pg 120

Oberhelman, David, Mythopoeic Awards, Oklahoma State University, 306 Edmon Low Library, Stillwater, OK 74078 *Tel:* 405-744-9773 *E-mail:* awards@mythsoc.org *Web Site:* www.mythsoc.org, pg 710

Oberrender, Maggie, Random House Publishing Group, 1745 Broadway, New York, NY 10019 *Toll Free Tel:* 800-200-3552 *Web Site:* atrandom.com, pg 204

Oberweger, Lorin, Writers Retreat Workshop (WRW), PO Box 4236, Louisville, KY 40204 *E-mail:* wrw04@netscape.net *Web Site:* www.writersretreatworkshop.com, pg 657

Oblack, Linda, Indiana University Press, Herman B Wells Library 350, 1320 E Tenth St, Bloomington, IN 47405-3907 *Tel:* 812-855-8817 *Toll Free Tel:* 800-842-6796 (orders only) *Fax:* 812-855-7931; 812-855-8507 *E-mail:* iupress@indiana.edu; iuporder@indiana.edu (orders) *Web Site:* www.iupress.indiana.edu, pg 120

Obry, Carrie, Midwest Independent Booksellers Association (MIBA), 2355 Louisiana Ave N, Suite A, Golden Valley, MN 55427-3646 *Tel:* 763-544-2993 *Toll Free Tel:* 800-784-7522 *Fax:* 612-354-5728 *E-mail:* info@midwestbooksellers.org *Web Site:* midwestbooksellers.org, pg 610

Ocampo, Patricia, Simon & Schuster Canada, 166 King St E, Suite 300, Toronto, ON M5A 1J3, Canada *Tel:* 647-427-8882 *Toll Free Tel:* 800-387-0446; 800-268-3216 (orders) *Fax:* 647-430-9446 *Toll Free Fax:* 888-849-8151 (orders) *E-mail:* info@simonandschuster.ca *Web Site:* www.simonandschuster.ca, pg 499

Ochsner, Daniel, University of Minnesota Press, 111 Third Ave S, Suite 290, Minneapolis, MN 55401-2520 *Tel:* 612-627-1970 *Fax:* 612-627-1980 *E-mail:* ump@umn.edu *Web Site:* www.upress.umn.edu, pg 257

Ode, Jeanne, South Dakota Historical Society Press, 900 Governors Dr, Pierre, SD 57501 *Tel:* 605-773-6009 *Fax:* 605-773-6041 *E-mail:* info@sdshspress.com *Web Site:* sdshspress.com, pg 231

Oden, Kelly, Ballinger Publishing, 41 N Jefferson St, Suite 402, Pensacola, FL 32502 *Tel:* 850-433-1166 *Fax:* 850-435-9174 *E-mail:* info@ballingerpublishing.com *Web Site:* www.ballingerpublishing.com, pg 30

Odiseos, Nikko, Shambhala Publications Inc, Horticultural Hall, 300 Massachusetts Ave, Boston, MA 02115 *Tel:* 617-424-0030 *Toll Free Tel:* 866-424-0030 (off); 888-424-2329 (cust serv) *Fax:* 617-236-1563 *E-mail:* customercare@shambhala.com *Web Site:* www.shambhala.com, pg 223

Odom, Monica, Bradford Literary Agency, 5694 Mission Center Rd, Suite 347, San Diego, CA 92108 *Tel:* 619-521-1201 *E-mail:* queries@bradfordlit.com *Web Site:* www.bradfordlit.com, pg 543

Odu, Jude, Decent Hill Publishers LLC, 6100 Oak Tree Blvd, Suite 200, Cleveland, OH 44131 *Toll Free Tel:* 866-688-5325 *Toll Free Fax:* 866-688-5325 *E-mail:* support@decenthill.com *Web Site:* www.decenthill.com, pg 72

Oerlemans, Onno, Hamilton College, English/Creative Writing, English/Creative Writing Dept, 198 College Hill Rd, Clinton, NY 13323 *Tel:* 315-859-4370 *Fax:* 315-859-4390 *E-mail:* english@hamilton.edu *Web Site:* www.hamilton.edu, pg 660

Oestreich, Julia, University of Delaware Press, 200A Morris Library, 181 S College Ave, Newark, DE 19717-5267 *Tel:* 302-831-1149 *Fax:* 302-831-6549 *E-mail:* ud-press@udel.edu *Web Site:* library.udel.edu/udpress, pg 256

Oestreicher, Mark, Zondervan, 3900 Sparks Dr, Grand Rapids, MI 49546 *Tel:* 616-698-6900 *Toll Free Tel:* 800-226-1122; 800-727-1309 (retail orders) *Fax:* 616-698-3350 *Toll Free Fax:* 800-698-3256 (retail orders) *E-mail:* zinfo@zondervan.com *Web Site:* www.zondervan.com, pg 280

Oey, Eric, Tuttle Publishing, Airport Business Park, 364 Innovation Dr, North Clarendon, VT 05759-9436 *Tel:* 802-773-8930 *Toll Free Tel:* 800-526-2778 *Fax:* 802-773-6993 *Toll Free Fax:* 800-FAX-TUTL *E-mail:* info@tuttlepublishing.com *Web Site:* www.tuttlepublishing.com, pg 251

Offit, Sidney, The Authors League Fund, 31 E 32 St, 7th fl, New York, NY 10016 *Tel:* 212-268-1208 *Fax:* 212-564-5363 *E-mail:* staff@authorsleaguefund.org *Web Site:* www.authorsleaguefund.org, pg 599

Ogden, Abe, American Diabetes Association, 1701 N Beauregard St, Alexandria, VA 22311 *Toll Free Tel:* 800-342-2383 *E-mail:* booksinfo@diabetes.org *Web Site:* www.diabetes.org, pg 12

Ogilvie, June, Bookmakers Ltd, 32 Parkview Ave, Wolfville, NS B4P 2K8, Canada *Tel:* 902-697-2569 *Web Site:* bookmakersltd.com, pg 583

Ogilvie, Reg, Bookmakers Ltd, 32 Parkview Ave, Wolfville, NS B4P 2K8, Canada *Tel:* 902-697-2569 *Web Site:* bookmakersltd.com, pg 583

Ogle, Jim, F+W, A Content + eCommerce Company, 10151 Carver Rd, Suite 200, Blue Ash, OH 45242 *Tel:* 513-531-2690 *Toll Free Tel:* 800-289-0963 (trade accts); 800-258-0929 (orders) *E-mail:* contact_us@fwmedia.com *Web Site:* www.fwcommunity.com, pg 86

Ogle, Jim, Krause Publications Inc, 700 E State St, Iola, WI 54990 *Tel:* 715-445-2214 *Toll Free Tel:* 800-258-0929 (cust serv); 888-457-2873 (orders) *Fax:* 715-445-4087 *E-mail:* bookorders@krause.com *Web Site:* www.krausebooks.com, pg 133

Ognibene, Peter E, Breakthrough Publications Inc, 3 Iroquois St, Barn, Emmaus, PA 18049 *Toll Free Tel:* 800-824-5001 (ext 12) *Fax:* 610-928-4064 *E-mail:* dot@booksonhorses.com; ruth@booksonhorses.com *Web Site:* www.booksonhorses.com, pg 44

Ogorek, Keith, AuthorHouse, 1663 Liberty Dr, Bloomington, IN 47403 *Tel:* 812-339-6000 (outside US) *Toll Free Tel:* 888-519-5121 *E-mail:* authorsupport@authorhouse.com *Web Site:* www.authorhouse.com, pg 27

Ogorek, Keith, iUniverse, 1663 Liberty Dr, Bloomington, IN 47403 *Toll Free Tel:* 800-AUTHORS (288-4677) *Fax:* 812-355-4085 *Web Site:* www.iuniverse.com, pg 126

Ogorek, Keith, Trafford, 1663 Liberty Dr, Bloomington, IN 47403 *Toll Free Tel:* 888-232-4444 *E-mail:* customersupport@trafford.com *Web Site:* www.trafford.com, pg 248

Ogorek, Keith, Xlibris Corp, 1663 Liberty Dr, Suite 200, Bloomington, IN 47403 *Toll Free Tel:* 888-795-4274 *Fax:* 610-915-0294 *E-mail:* info@xlibris.com *Web Site:* www.xlibris.com, pg 277

Ohl, Helaine, Macmillan, 175 Fifth Ave, New York, NY 10010 *Tel:* 646-307-5151 *Fax:* 212-420-9314 *E-mail:* firstname.lastname@macmillan.com *Web Site:* www.macmillan.com, pg 145

Ohle, Heather, Encounter Books, 900 Broadway, Suite 601, New York, NY 10003 *Tel:* 212-871-6310 *Toll Free Tel:* 800-786-3839 *Fax:* 212-871-6311 *E-mail:* publicity@encounterbooks.com *Web Site:* www.encounterbooks.com, pg 82

Ohman, Jack, Association of American Editorial Cartoonists, 3899 N Front St, Harrisburg, PA 17110 *Tel:* 717-703-3003 *Fax:* 717-703-3008 *E-mail:* aaec@pa-news.org *Web Site:* www.editorialcartoonists.com, pg 598

Ojakli, Sumya, Simon & Schuster Sales Division, 1230 Avenue of the Americas, New York, NY 10020 *Tel:* 212-698-7000, pg 226

Olafsson, Johann G, Edda USA, 373 Park Ave S, 6th fl, New York, NY 10016 *Tel:* 646-755-9210 *Web Site:* eddausa.com, pg 79

Olafsson, Jon Axel, Edda USA, 373 Park Ave S, 6th fl, New York, NY 10016 *Tel:* 646-755-9210 *Web Site:* eddausa.com, pg 79

Oldsey, William F, McGraw-Hill Education, 2 Penn Plaza, New York, NY 10121-2298 *Tel:* 212-904-2000 *E-mail:* customer.service@mcgraw-hill.com *Web Site:* www.mheducation.com; www.mheducation.com/custserv.html, pg 151

Olenick, Michelle, Emmaus Road Publishing Inc, 1468 Parkview Cir, Steubenville, OH 43952 *Tel:* 740-283-2880 (outside US) *Toll Free Tel:* 800-398-5470 (orders) *Fax:* 740-283-4011 (orders) *E-mail:* questions@emmausroad.org *Web Site:* www.emmausroad.org, pg 82

Olinger, Chauncey G Jr, Metropolitan Editorial & Writing Service, 4455 Douglas Ave, Riverdale, NY 10471 *Tel:* 718-549-5518, pg 531

Oliver, Becka, Writers' League of Texas (WLT), 611 S Congress Ave, Suite 200 A-3, Austin, TX 78704 *Tel:* 512-499-8914 *E-mail:* wlt@writersleague.org *Web Site:* www.writersleague.org, pg 622

Oliver, Lin, The Don Freeman Memorial Grant-In-Aid, 4727 Wilshire Blvd, Suite 301, Los Angeles, CA 90010 *Tel:* 323-782-1010; 310-403-0675 (cell) *Fax:* 323-782-1892 *E-mail:* membership@scbwi.org; scbwi@scbwi.org *Web Site:* www.scbwi.org, pg 687

Oliver, Lin, Golden Kite Awards, 4727 Wilshire Blvd, Suite 301, Los Angeles, CA 90010 *Tel:* 323-782-1010; 310-403-0675 (cell) *Fax:* 323-782-1892 *E-mail:* scbwi@scbwi.org; membership@scbwi.org *Web Site:* www.scbwi.org, pg 690

Oliver, Lin, Magazine Merit Awards, 4727 Wilshire Blvd, Suite 301, Los Angeles, CA 90010 *Tel:* 323-782-1010; 310-403-0675 (cell) *Fax:* 323-782-1892 *E-mail:* membership@scbwi.org; scbwi@scbwi.org *Web Site:* www.scbwi.org, pg 704

Oliver, Lin, SCBWI Work-In-Progress Grants, 4727 Wilshire Blvd, Suite 301, Los Angeles, CA 90010 *Tel:* 323-782-1010; 310-403-0675 (cell) *Fax:* 323-782-1892 *E-mail:* membership@scbwi.org; scbwi@scbwi.org *Web Site:* www.scbwi.org, pg 727

Oliver, Lin, Society of Children's Book Writers and Illustrators (SCBWI), 4727 Wilshire Blvd, Suite 301, Los Angeles, CA 90010 *Tel:* 323-782-1010 *Fax:* 323-782-1892 *E-mail:* membership@scbwi.org; scbwi@scbwi.org *Web Site:* www.scbwi.org, pg 619

Oliver, Paul, Soho Press Inc, 853 Broadway, New York, NY 10003 *Tel:* 212-260-1900 *Fax:* 212-260-1902 *E-mail:* soho@sohopress.com; publicity@sohopress.com *Web Site:* www.sohopress.com, pg 229

Olivieri, John, Abbeville Publishing Group, 137 Varick St, Suite 504, New York, NY 10013 *Tel:* 212-366-5585 *Toll Free Tel:* 800-ART-BOOK (278-2665) *Fax:* 212-366-6966 *E-mail:* abbeville@abbeville.com; marketing@abbeville.com; sales@abbeville.com; rights@abbeville.com *Web Site:* www.abbeville.com, pg 2

Ollis, Emily, Random House Children's Books, 1745 Broadway, New York, NY 10019 *Tel:* 212-782-9000 *Toll Free Tel:* 800-200-3552 *Fax:* 212-782-9452 *Web Site:* randomhousekids.com, pg 204

Olsen, Charlie, InkWell Management, 521 Fifth Ave, 26th fl, New York, NY 10175 *Tel:* 212-922-3500 *Fax:* 212-922-0535 *E-mail:* info@inkwellmanagement.com; submissions@inkwellmanagement.com *Web Site:* inkwellmanagement.com, pg 557

Olsen, Eric, Twilight Times Books, PO Box 3340, Kingsport, TN 37664-0340 *Tel:* 423-323-0183 *Fax:* 423-323-0183 *E-mail:* publisher@twilighttimes.com *Web Site:* www.twilighttimesbooks.com, pg 251

Olsen, Kevin, W W Norton & Company Inc, 500 Fifth Ave, New York, NY 10110-0017 *Tel:* 212-354-5500 *Toll Free Tel:* 800-233-4830 (orders & cust serv) *Fax:* 212-869-0856 *Toll Free Fax:* 800-458-6515 *Web Site:* www.wwnorton.com, pg 172

Olsen, Lance, The FC2 Catherine Doctorow Innovative Fiction Prize, c/o Dept of English, Langs & Commun Bldg, 255 S Central Campus Dr, Rm 3500, Salt Lake City, UT 84112-0494 *Tel:* 773-702-7000 *Web Site:* www.fc2.org/prizes.html, pg 685

Olsen, Lance, Fiction Collective Two Inc (FC2), c/o Dept of English, Langs & Commun Bldg, 255 S Central Campus Dr, Rm 3500, Salt Lake City, UT 84112-0494 *Tel:* 773-702-7000 *E-mail:* fc2.cmu@gmail.com *Web Site:* www.fc2.org/prizes.html, pg 88

Olsen, Lance, Ronald Sukenick American Book Review Innovative Fiction Prize, c/o Dept of English, Langs & Commun Bldg, 255 S Central Campus Dr, Rm 3500, Salt Lake City, UT 84112-0494 *Tel:* 773-702-7000 *Web Site:* www.fc2.org/prizes.html, pg 731

Olsen, Marilyn, Oak Tree Press, 1820 W Lacey Blvd, Suite 220, Hanford, CA 93230 *Tel:* 217-824-6500 *E-mail:* publisher@oaktreebooks.com; info@oaktreebooks.com; query@oaktreebooks.com; pressdept@oaktreebooks.com; bookorders@oaktreebooks.com *Web Site:* www.oaktreebooks.com; www.otpblog.blogspot.com, pg 173

Olsen, William, The Green Rose Prize in Poetry, c/o Western Michigan University, 1903 W Michigan Ave, Kalamazoo, MI 49008-5463 *Tel:* 269-387-8185 *Fax:* 269-387-2562 *E-mail:* new-issues@wmich.edu *Web Site:* www.wmich.edu/newissues/sub-guide.html, pg 690

Olsen, William, New Issues Poetry & Prose, c/o Western Michigan University, 1903 W Michigan Ave, Kalamazoo, MI 49008-5463 *Tel:* 269-387-8185 *Fax:* 269-387-2562 *E-mail:* new-issues@wmich.edu *Web Site:* www.wmich.edu/newissues, pg 168

Olsen-Smith, Steven, The Melville Society, Johns Hopkins University Press, PO Box 19966, Baltimore, MD 21211-0966 *Web Site:* melvillesociety.org, pg 610

Olson, Carol, South Dakota Historical Society Press, 900 Governors Dr, Pierre, SD 57501 *Tel:* 605-773-6009 *Fax:* 605-773-6041 *E-mail:* info@sdshspress.com *Web Site:* sdshspress.com, pg 231

Olson, Georgine, Historical Novel Society North American Conference, 400 Dark Star Ct, Fairbanks, AK 99709 *Tel:* 217-581-7538 *Fax:* 217-581-7534 *Web Site:* www.historicalnovelsociety.org, pg 651

Olson, Kaitlin, Simon & Schuster, 1230 Avenue of the Americas, New York, NY 10020 *Tel:* 212-698-7000 *Toll Free Tel:* 800-223-2348 (cust serv); 800-223-2336 (orders) *Toll Free Fax:* 800-943-9831 (orders) *Web Site:* www.simonandschuster.com, pg 225

Olson, Larry, John Wiley & Sons Inc Professional/Trade Group, 111 River St, Hoboken, NJ 07030 *Tel:* 201-748-6000 *Toll Free Tel:* 800-225-5945 (cust serv) *Fax:* 201-748-6088 *E-mail:* info@wiley.com *Web Site:* www.wiley.com, pg 272

Olson, Neil, Donadio & Olson Inc, 121 W 27 St, Suite 704, New York, NY 10001 *Tel:* 212-691-8077 *Fax:* 212-633-2837 *E-mail:* mail@donadio.com *Web Site:* donadio.com, pg 548

Olson, Norman A, Regular Baptist Press, 1300 N Meacham Rd, Schaumburg, IL 60173-4806 *Tel:* 847-843-1600 *Toll Free Tel:* 800-727-4440 (orders only); 888-588-1600 *Fax:* 847-843-3757 *E-mail:* rbp@garbc.org *Web Site:* www.regularbaptistpress.org, pg 208

Onder, Catherine, Bloomsbury Publishing Inc, 1385 Broadway, 5th fl, New York, NY 10018 *Tel:* 212-419-5300 *E-mail:* marketingusa@bloomsbury.com; adultpublicityusa@bloomsbury.com; askacademic@bloomsbury.com *Web Site:* www.bloomsbury.com, pg 40

Onken, Janice, WendyLynn & Co, 504 Wilson Rd, Annapolis, MD 21401 *Tel:* 410-224-2729; 410-507-1059 *Web Site:* wendylynn.com, pg 585

Onstad-Latham, Hannah, Peachpit Press, 1249 Eighth St, Berkeley, CA 94710 *Tel:* 510-524-2178 *Toll Free Tel:* 800-283-9444 *Fax:* 510-524-2221 *E-mail:* info@peachpit.com *Web Site:* www.peachpit.com, pg 184

Oppel, Frank, Book Sales Inc, 142 W 36 St, 4th fl, New York, NY 10018 *Tel:* 212-779-4971; 212-779-4972 *Toll Free Tel:* 866-483-5456 *Fax:* 212-779-6058 *E-mail:* sales@quartous.com; customerservice@quartous.com *Web Site:* www.booksalesusa.com, pg 42

Opper, Lauren, W W Norton & Company Inc, 500 Fifth Ave, New York, NY 10110-0017 *Tel:* 212-354-5500 *Toll Free Tel:* 800-233-4830 (orders & cust serv) *Fax:* 212-869-0856 *Toll Free Fax:* 800-458-6515 *Web Site:* www.wwnorton.com, pg 172

Oria, Mary Beth, Association of Catholic Publishers Inc, 4725 Dorsey Hall Dr, Suite A, PMB 709, Elliott City, MD 21042 *Tel:* 410-988-2926 *Fax:* 410-571-4946 *Web Site:* www.catholicsread.org; www.catholicpublishers.org; www.midatlanticcongress.org, pg 598

Orlando, Kris, Hendrickson Publishers Inc, PO Box 3473, Peabody, MA 01961-3473 *Tel:* 978-532-6546 *Toll Free Tel:* 800-358-3111 *Fax:* 978-573-8111 *E-mail:* orders@hendrickson.com *Web Site:* www.hendrickson.com, pg 110

Ornstein, Michael, IET USA Inc, 379 Thornall St, Edison, NJ 08837 *Tel:* 732-321-5575 *Fax:* 732-321-5702 *E-mail:* ietusa@theiet.org *Web Site:* www.theiet.org, pg 118

Orphee, Mr Matanya, Editions Orphee Inc, 1240 Clubview Blvd N, Columbus, OH 43235-1226 *Tel:* 614-846-9517 *Fax:* 614-846-9794 *E-mail:* sales@editionsorphee.com *Web Site:* www.editionsorphee.com, pg 79

Orr, Allan, Wolters Kluwer Ltd, 90 Sheppard Ave E, Suite 300, Toronto, ON M2N 6X1, Canada *Tel:* 416-224-2224 *Toll Free Tel:* 800-268-4522 (CN & US cust serv) *Fax:* 416-224-2243 *Toll Free Fax:* 800-461-4131 *E-mail:* cservice@cch.ca (cust serv) *Web Site:* www.cch.ca, pg 505

Orr, John, Lynx House Press, 420 W 24 St, Spokane, WA 99203 *Tel:* 509-624-4894 *E-mail:* lynxhousepress@gmail.com *Web Site:* www.lynxhousepress.org, pg 144

Orr, Rachel, Prospect Agency, 285 Fifth Ave, PMB 445, Brooklyn, NY 11215 *Tel:* 718-788-3217 *Fax:* 718-360-9582 *Web Site:* www.prospectagency.com, pg 568

Ortberg, Barton, City & Regional Magazine Association, 1970 E Grand Ave, Suite 330, El Segundo, CA 90245 *Tel:* 310-364-0193 *Fax:* 310-364-0196 *E-mail:* admin@citymag.org *Web Site:* www.citymag.org, pg 603

Ortega, Juan, McGraw-Hill International Publishing Group, 2 Penn Plaza, New York, NY 10121 *Tel:* 212-904-2000 *Web Site:* www.mcgraw-hill.com, pg 152

Ortiz, Lukas, Philip G Spitzer Literary Agency Inc, 50 Talmage Farm Lane, East Hampton, NY 11937 *Tel:* 631-329-3650 *Fax:* 631-329-3651 *Web Site:* www.spitzeragency.com, pg 575

Ortiz, Shirley, Workman Publishing Co Inc, 225 Varick St, 9th fl, New York, NY 10014-4381 *Tel:* 212-254-5900 *Toll Free Tel:* 800-722-7202 *Fax:* 212-254-8098 *E-mail:* info@workman.com *Web Site:* www.workman.com, pg 275

Ortlund, Dane, Crossway, 1300 Crescent St, Wheaton, IL 60187 *Tel:* 630-682-4300 *Toll Free Tel:* 800-635-7993 (orders); 800-543-1659 (cust serv) *Fax:* 630-682-4785 *E-mail:* info@crossway.org *Web Site:* www.crossway.org, pg 67

Ortner, Renee, OPIS/STALSBY Directories & Databases, 3349 Hwy 138, Bldg D, Suite D, Wall, NJ 07719 *Tel:* 732-901-8800 *Toll Free Tel:* 800-275-0950 *Toll Free Fax:* 800-450-5864 *E-mail:* opisstalsbylistings@opisnet.com *Web Site:* www.opisnet.com, pg 175

Osborne, Mary, Matt Cohen Prize: In Celebration of a Writing Life, 460 Richmond St W, Suite 600, Toronto, ON M5V 1Y1, Canada *Tel:* 416-504-8222 *Toll Free Tel:* 877-906-6548 *Fax:* 416-504-9090 *E-mail:* info@writerstrust.com *Web Site:* www.writerstrust.com, pg 706

Osborne, Mary, Dayne Ogilvie Prize, 460 Richmond St W, Suite 600, Toronto, ON M5V 1Y1, Canada *Tel:* 416-504-8222 *Toll Free Tel:* 877-906-6548 *Fax:* 416-504-9090 *E-mail:* info@writerstrust.com *Web Site:* www.writerstrust.com, pg 714

Osborne, Mary, RBC Bronwen Wallace Award for Emerging Writers, 460 Richmond St W, Suite 600, Toronto, ON M5V 1Y1, Canada *Tel:* 416-504-8222 *Toll Free Tel:* 877-906-6548 *Fax:* 416-504-9090 *E-mail:* info@writerstrust.com *Web Site:* www.writerstrust.com, pg 723

Osborne, Mary, Rogers Writers' Trust Fiction Prize, 460 Richmond St W, Suite 600, Toronto, ON M5V 1Y1, Canada *Tel:* 416-504-8222 *Toll Free Tel:* 877-906-6548 *Fax:* 416-504-9090 *E-mail:* info@writerstrust.com *Web Site:* www.writerstrust.com, pg 724

Osborne, Mary, Shaughnessy Cohen Prize for Political Writing, 460 Richmond St W, Suite 600, Toronto, ON M5V 1Y1, Canada *Tel:* 416-504-8222 *Toll Free Tel:* 877-906-6548 *Fax:* 416-504-9090 *E-mail:* info@writerstrust.com *Web Site:* www.writerstrust.com, pg 727

Osborne, Mary, Vicky Metcalf Award for Literature for Young People, 460 Richmond St W, Suite 600, Toronto, ON M5V 1Y1, Canada *Tel:* 416-504-8222 *Toll Free Tel:* 877-906-6548 *Fax:* 416-504-9090 *E-mail:* info@writerstrust.com *Web Site:* www.writerstrust.com, pg 734

Osborne, Mary, Hilary Weston Writers' Trust Prize for Nonfiction, 460 Richmond St W, Suite 600, Toronto, ON M5V 1Y1, Canada *Tel:* 416-504-8222 *Toll Free Tel:* 877-906-6548 *Fax:* 416-504-9090 *E-mail:* info@writerstrust.com *Web Site:* www.writerstrust.com, pg 735

Osborne, Mary, Writers' Trust Engel/Findley Prize, 460 Richmond St W, Suite 600, Toronto, ON M5V 1Y1, Canada *Tel:* 416-504-8222 *Toll Free Tel:* 877-906-6548 *Fax:* 416-504-9090 *E-mail:* info@writerstrust.com *Web Site:* www.writerstrust.com, pg 738

Osborne, Mary, The Writers Trust/McClelland & Stewart Journey Prize, 460 Richmond St W, Suite 600, Toronto, ON M5V 1Y1, Canada *Tel:* 416-504-8222 *Toll Free Tel:* 877-906-6548 *Fax:* 416-504-9090 *E-mail:* info@writerstrust.com *Web Site:* www.writerstrust.com, pg 738

Osnos, Peter, PublicAffairs, 250 W 57 St, Suite 1321, New York, NY 10107 *Tel:* 212-397-6666 *Toll Free Tel:* 800-343-4499 (orders) *Fax:* 212-397-4277 *E-mail:* publicaffairs@perseusbooks.com *Web Site:* www.publicaffairsbooks.com, pg 200

Ostby, Kristin, Simon & Schuster Children's Publishing, 1230 Avenue of the Americas, New York, NY 10020 *Tel:* 212-698-7000 *Web Site:* KIDS.SimonandSchuster.com; TEEN.SimonandSchuster.com; simonandschuster.net; simonandschuster.biz, pg 225

Ostertag, Genny, ASCD, 1703 N Beauregard St, Alexandria, VA 22311-1714 *Tel:* 703-578-9600 *Toll Free Tel:* 800-933-2723 *Fax:* 703-575-5400 *E-mail:* member@ascd.org *Web Site:* www.ascd.org, pg 23

Ostfield, Sue, Redleaf Press, 10 Yorkton Ct, St Paul, MN 55117 *Tel:* 651-641-0508 *Toll Free Tel:* 800-423-8309 *Toll Free Fax:* 800-641-0115 *Web Site:* www.redleafpress.org, pg 207

Osuszek, Alex, Harlequin Enterprises Ltd, 225 Duncan Mill Rd, Don Mills, ON M3B 3K9, Canada *Tel:* 416-445-5860 *Toll Free Tel:* 888-432-4879; 800-370-5838 (ebook inquiries) *E-mail:* customerservice@harlequin.com *Web Site:* www.harlequin.com, pg 487

Oswald, Dan, Business & Legal Resources Inc, 100 Winners Circle, Suite 300, Brentwood, TN 37027 *Tel:* 860-510-0100 *Toll Free Tel:* 800-727-5257 *E-mail:* service@blr.com *Web Site:* www.blr.com, pg 48

Oswald, Dan, M Lee Smith Publishers LLC, 5201 Virginia Way, Brentwood, TN 37027 *Tel:* 615-373-7517 *Toll Free Tel:* 800-274-6774 *Fax:* 615-373-5183 *E-mail:* custserv@mleesmith.com *Web Site:* www.mleesmith.com, pg 228

Oswald, Denise, HarperCollins General Books Group, 195 Broadway, New York, NY 10007 *Tel:* 212-207-7000 *Web Site:* www.harpercollins.com, pg 105

Otter, Samuel, The Melville Society, Johns Hopkins University Press, PO Box 19966, Baltimore, MD 21211-0966 *Web Site:* melvillesociety.org, pg 610

Ou, Michelle, Editors' Association of Canada (Association canadienne des reviseurs), 27 Carlton St, Suite 502, Toronto, ON M5B 1L2, Canada *Tel:* 416-975-1379 *Toll Free Tel:* 866-CAN-EDIT (226-3348) *Fax:* 416-975-1637 *E-mail:* info@editors.ca; info@reviseurs.ca *Web Site:* www.editors.ca; www.reviseurs.ca, pg 605

Ou, Michelle, Tom Fairley Award for Editorial Excellence, 27 Carlton St, Suite 502, Toronto, ON M5B 1L2, Canada *Tel:* 416-975-1379 *Toll Free Tel:* 866-CAN-EDIT (226-3348) *Fax:* 416-975-1637 *E-mail:* fairley_award@editors.ca *Web Site:* www.editors.ca; www.reviseurs.ca, pg 684

Ovedovitz, Nancy, Yale University Press, 302 Temple St, New Haven, CT 06511-8909 *Tel:* 203-432-0960; 203-432-0966 (sales); 401-531-2800 (cust serv) *Toll Free Tel:* 800-405-1619 (cust serv) *Fax:* 203-432-0948; 203-432-8485 (sales); 401-531-2801 (cust serv) *Toll Free Fax:* 800-406-9145 (cust serv) *E-mail:* sales.press@yale.edu (sales); customer.care@trilateral.org (cust serv) *Web Site:* www.yalebooks.com; yalepress.yale.edu/yupbooks, pg 278

Overby, Jordan, Red Wheel/Weiser/Conari, 65 Parker St, Suite 7, Newburyport, MA 01950 *Tel:* 978-465-0504 *Toll Free Tel:* 800-423-7087 (orders) *Fax:* 978-465-0243 *E-mail:* info@rwwbooks.com *Web Site:* www.redwheelweiser.com, pg 206

Overman, Christopher, Copper Canyon Press, Fort Worden State Park, Bldg 313, Port Townsend, WA 98368 *Tel:* 360-385-4925 *Toll Free Tel:* 877-501-1393 (orders) *Fax:* 360-385-4985 *E-mail:* poetry@coppercanyonpress.org *Web Site:* www.coppercanyonpress.org, pg 63

Overstreet, Sheryl, Standard Publishing, 8805 Governors Hill Dr, Suite 400, Cincinnati, OH 45249 *Tel:* 513-931-4050 *Toll Free Tel:* 800-543-1353 *Fax:* 513-931-0950 *Toll Free Fax:* 877-867-5751 *E-mail:* customerservice@standardpub.com *Web Site:* www.standardpub.com, pg 233

Owen, Charlyce Jones, Pearson Humanities & Social Sciences, 225 River St, Hoboken, NJ 07030-4772 *Tel:* 201-236-7000 *Fax:* 201-236-3400, pg 185

Owen, Rebecca, Ingalls Publishing Group Inc (IPG), PO Box 2500, Banner Elk, NC 28604 *Tel:* 828-297-6884 *Fax:* 828-297-6880 *E-mail:* sales@ingallspublishinggroup.com *Web Site:* www.ingallspublishinggroup.com, pg 121

Owen, Richard C, Richard C Owen Publishers Inc, PO Box 585, Katonah, NY 10536-0585 *Tel:* 914-232-3903 *Toll Free Tel:* 800-336-5588 *Fax:* 914-232-3977 *Web Site:* www.rcowen.com, pg 179

Owens, Alexandra, American Society of Journalists and Authors (ASJA), 1501 Broadway, Suite 403, New York, NY 10036 *Tel:* 212-997-0947 *Fax:* 212-937-2315 *Web Site:* asja.org, pg 596

Owens, Alexandra, American Society of Journalists and Authors Annual Writers Conference, 1501 Broadway, Suite 403, New York, NY 10036 *Tel:* 212-997-0947 *Fax:* 212-937-2315 *Web Site:* asja.org, pg 649

Owens, Alexandra, ASJA Freelance Writer Search, 355 Lexington Ave, 15th fl, New York, NY 10017 *Tel:* 212-997-0947 *E-mail:* asjaoffice@asja.org *Web Site:* www.freelancewritersearch.com, pg 520

Owens, Katherine, Potomac Books Inc, 22841 Quicksilver Dr, Dulles, VA 20166 *Tel:* 703-661-1548 *Fax:* 703-661-1547 *E-mail:* pbimail@presswarehouse.com *Web Site:* www.potomacbooksinc.com, pg 195

Owens, Nancy L, National One-Act Playwriting Competition, 600 Wolfe St, Alexandria, VA 22314 *Tel:* 703-683-5778 *Fax:* 703-683-1378 *E-mail:* asklta@thelittletheatre.com *Web Site:* www.thelittletheatre.com, pg 711

Owens, William A Jr, North Carolina Office of Archives & History, Historical Publications Section, 4622 Mail Service Ctr, Raleigh, NC 27699-4622 *Tel:* 919-733-7442 (ext 225) *Fax:* 919-733-1439 *Web Site:* www.ncpublications.com; nc-historical-publications.stores.yahoo.net (online store), pg 170

Owles, John Paul, Joshua Tree Publishing, 190 S LaSalle St, Suite 2100, Chicago, IL 60603 *Tel:* 312-893-7525 *E-mail:* info@joshuatreepublishing.com *Web Site:* www.joshuatreepublishing.com; www.centaurbooks.com (imprint); www.chiralhouse.com (imprint), pg 128

Oxenreider, Ken, Simon & Schuster Audio, 1230 Avenue of the Americas, New York, NY 10020 *Web Site:* audio.simonandschuster.com, pg 225

Pace, John, ASTM International, 100 Barr Harbor Dr, West Conshohocken, PA 19428-2959 *Tel:* 610-832-9500; 610-832-9585 (intl) *Toll Free Tel:* 877-909-2786 (sales & cust support) *Fax:* 610-832-9555 *E-mail:* service@astm.org *Web Site:* www.astm.org, pg 26

Pace, Kaye, John Wiley & Sons Inc Higher Education, 111 River St, Hoboken, NJ 07030-5774 *Tel:* 201-748-6000 *Toll Free Tel:* 800-225-5945 (cust serv) *Fax:* 201-748-6008 *E-mail:* info@wiley.com *Web Site:* www.wiley.com, pg 272

Pace, Steven, Workman Publishing Co Inc, 225 Varick St, 9th fl, New York, NY 10014-4381 *Tel:* 212-254-5900 *Toll Free Tel:* 800-722-7202 *Fax:* 212-254-8098 *E-mail:* info@workman.com *Web Site:* www.workman.com, pg 275

Packard, Michael, Binding Industries Association (BIA), 200 Deer Run Rd, Sewickley, PA 15143 *Web Site:* www.printing.org/bia, pg 600

Padakis, Marina, Houghton Mifflin Harcourt Trade & Reference Division, 222 Berkeley St, Boston, MA 02116 *Tel:* 617-351-5000 *Toll Free Tel:* 800-225-3362 *Web Site:* www.hmhco.com, pg 115

Padberg, Fr John W, Institute of Jesuit Sources (IJS), 3601 Lindell Blvd, St Louis, MO 63108 *Tel:* 314-633-4622 *Fax:* 314-633-4623 *E-mail:* ijs@jesuitsources.com *Web Site:* www.jesuitsources.com, pg 122

Paddick, Christy, Institute of Public Administration of Canada, 1075 Bay St, Suite 401, Toronto, ON M5S 2B1, Canada *Tel:* 416-924-8787 *Fax:* 416-924-4992 *E-mail:* ntl@ipac.ca *Web Site:* www.ipac.ca; www.iapc.ca, pg 489

Paddio, Martin, Monthly Review Press, 146 W 29 St, Suite 6W, New York, NY 10001 *Tel:* 212-691-2555 *Toll Free Tel:* 800-670-9499 *Fax:* 212-727-3676 *E-mail:* mreview@igc.org *Web Site:* www.MonthlyReview.org, pg 159

Pagan, Zena, Advertising Research Foundation (ARF), 432 Park Ave S, 6th fl, New York, NY 10016-8013 *Tel:* 212-751-5656 *Fax:* 212-319-5265 *E-mail:* info@thearf.org; jar@thearf.org (edit) *Web Site:* www.thearf.org, pg 593

Page, Lisa, Jenny McKean Moore Writer-in-Washington, English Dept, Rome Hall, 801 22 St NW, Suite 760, Washington, DC 20052 *Tel:* 202-994-6180 *Fax:* 202-994-7915 *E-mail:* engldept@gwu.edu *Web Site:* www.gwu.edu/~english; departments.columbian.gwu.edu/english/openings (position details), pg 709

Page, Robert, Zaner-Bloser Inc, 1201 Dublin Rd, Columbus, OH 43215-1026 *Tel:* 614-486-0221 *Toll Free Tel:* 800-421-3018 (cust serv) *Toll Free Fax:* 800-992-6087 (orders) *E-mail:* zbcsd@zaner-bloser.com; international@zaner-bloser.com *Web Site:* www.zaner-bloser.com, pg 279

Paine, John, Joelle Delbourgo Associates Inc, 101 Park St, Montclair, NJ 07042 *Tel:* 973-773-0836 (call only during standard business hours) *Web Site:* www.delbourgo.com, pg 548

Paine, John, The Editors Circle, 462 Grove St, Montclair, NJ 07043 *Tel:* 973-783-5082 *E-mail:* query@theeditorscircle.com *Web Site:* www.theeditorscircle.com, pg 525

Painter, Benjamin, Schlager Group Inc, 325 N Saint Paul, Suite 3425, Dallas, TX 75201 *Toll Free Tel:* 888-416-5727 *Fax:* 214-347-9469 *E-mail:* info@schlagergroup.com *Web Site:* www.schlagergroup.com, pg 218

Painter, Jeannie, Mountain Press Publishing Co, 1301 S Third W, Missoula, MT 59801 *Tel:* 406-728-1900 *Toll Free Tel:* 800-234-5308 *Fax:* 406-728-1635 *E-mail:* info@mtnpress.com *Web Site:* www.mountain-press.com, pg 160

Painton, Priscilla, Simon & Schuster, 1230 Avenue of the Americas, New York, NY 10020 *Tel:* 212-698-7000 *Toll Free Tel:* 800-223-2348 (cust serv); 800-223-2336 (orders) *Toll Free Fax:* 800-943-9831 (orders) *Web Site:* www.simonandschuster.com, pg 225

Pakalik, Eugenia, W W Norton & Company Inc, 500 Fifth Ave, New York, NY 10110-0017 *Tel:* 212-354-5500 *Toll Free Tel:* 800-233-4830 (orders & cust serv) *Fax:* 212-869-0856 *Toll Free Fax:* 800-458-6515 *Web Site:* www.wwnorton.com, pg 171

Palassis, Neketas S, Saint Nectarios Press, 10300 Ashworth Ave N, Seattle, WA 98133-9410 *Tel:* 206-522-4471 *Toll Free Tel:* 800-643-4233 *Fax:* 206-523-0550 *E-mail:* orders@stnectariospress.com *Web Site:* www.stnectariospress.com, pg 215

Palazzo, Norma, Marshall Cavendish Corp, 99 White Plains Rd, Tarrytown, NY 10591-9001 *Tel:* 914-332-8888 *Toll Free Tel:* 800-821-9881 *Fax:* 914-332-8102 *E-mail:* mce@marshallcavendish.com *Web Site:* www.mceducation.us, pg 148

Palermo, Laura, Peachtree Publishers, 1700 Chattahoochee Ave, Atlanta, GA 30318-2112 *Tel:* 404-876-8761 *Toll Free Tel:* 800-241-0113 *Fax:* 404-875-2578 *Toll Free Fax:* 800-875-8909 *E-mail:* hello@peachtree-online.com *Web Site:* www.peachtree-online.com, pg 184

Palkovic, Mark, Miniature Book Society Inc, 702 Rosecrans St, San Diego, CA 92106-3013 *Tel:* 619-226-4441 *Fax:* 619-226-4441 *E-mail:* minibook@cox.net *Web Site:* www.mbs.org, pg 610

Palladino, Linda, Random House Children's Books, 1745 Broadway, New York, NY 10019 *Tel:* 212-782-9000 *Toll Free Tel:* 800-200-3552 *Fax:* 212-782-9452 *Web Site:* randomhousekids.com, pg 203

Palmer, Heather, Jane Addams Children's Book Award, 777 United Nations Plaza, 6th fl, New York, NY 10017 *Tel:* 212-682-8830 *E-mail:* japa@igc.org *Web Site:* www.janeaddamspeace.org, pg 665

Palmer, Jojo, World Vision Resources, 800 W Chestnut Ave, Monrovia, CA 91016-3198 *Tel:* 626-303-8811; 909-463-2998 (intl orders) *Toll Free Tel:* 800-777-7752 (US only) *Fax:* 909-463-2999 *E-mail:* wvresources@worldvision.org *Web Site:* www.worldvisionresources.com, pg 276

Palmer, Judd, Bayeux Arts Inc, 119 Stratton Crescent SW, Calgary, AB T3H 1T7, Canada *Tel:* 403-249-2477 *E-mail:* mail@bayeux.com *Web Site:* bayeux.com, pg 472

Palmer, Linda, Insomniac Press, 520 Princess Ave, London, ON N6B 2B8, Canada *Tel:* 416-504-6270 *Web Site:* www.insomniacpress.com, pg 488

Palmer, Michael, Business Marketing Association (BMA), 708 Third Ave, New York, NY 10017 *Tel:* 212-697-5950 *Fax:* 212-687-7310 *E-mail:* info@marketing.org *Web Site:* www.marketing.org, pg 601

Palmer, Paula, US Games Systems Inc, 179 Ludlow St, Stamford, CT 06902 *Tel:* 203-353-8400 *Toll Free Tel:* 800-54-GAMES (544-2637) *Fax:* 203-353-8431 *E-mail:* info@usgamesinc.com *Web Site:* www.usgamesinc.com, pg 264

Palmquist, Nancy K, W W Norton & Company Inc, 500 Fifth Ave, New York, NY 10110-0017 *Tel:* 212-354-5500 *Toll Free Tel:* 800-233-4830 (orders & cust serv) *Fax:* 212-869-0856 *Toll Free Fax:* 800-458-6515 *Web Site:* www.wwnorton.com, pg 171

Pan, Dr Hui, Information Gatekeepers Inc, 1340 Soldiers Field Rd, Suite 2, Boston, MA 02135 *Tel:* 617-782-5033 *Fax:* 617-507-8338 *E-mail:* info@igigroup.com *Web Site:* www.igigroup.com, pg 121

Panara, David, Information Today, Inc, 143 Old Marlton Pike, Medford, NJ 08055-8750 *Tel:* 609-654-6266 *Toll Free Tel:* 800-300-9868 (cust serv) *Fax:* 609-654-4309 *E-mail:* custserv@infotoday.com *Web Site:* www.infotoday.com, pg 121

Pancrazi, Elsbeth, Poetry Society of America (PSA), 15 Gramercy Park, New York, NY 10003 *Tel:* 212-254-9628 *Fax:* 212-673-2352 *Web Site:* www.poetrysociety.org, pg 616

Pandya, Ruchir, HarperCollins Publishers, 195 Broadway, New York, NY 10007 *Tel:* 212-207-7000 *Fax:* 212-207-7145 *Web Site:* www.harpercollins.com, pg 106

Panec, Don, Treasure Bay Inc, PO Box 119, Novato, CA 94948 *Tel:* 415-884-2888 *Fax:* 415-884-2840 *E-mail:* webothread@comcast.net *Web Site:* www.webothread.com, pg 249

Panepinto, Lauren, Orbit, 1290 Avenue of the Americas, New York, NY 10019 *Tel:* 212-364-1100 *Toll Free Tel:* 800-759-0190 *Web Site:* www.orbitbooks.net, pg 176

Pangburn, Michael, Artist Grants, 711 E Wells Ave, Pierre, SD 57501-3369 *Tel:* 605-773-3301 *Fax:* 605-773-5977 *E-mail:* sdac@state.sd.us *Web Site:* www.artscouncil.sd.gov/grants, pg 668

Panger, Bob, American Marketing Association, 311 S Wacker Dr, Suite 5800, Chicago, IL 60606 *Tel:* 312-542-9000 *Toll Free Tel:* 800-AMA-1150 (262-1150) *Fax:* 312-542-9001 *E-mail:* info@ama.org *Web Site:* www.ama.org, pg 595

Pangle, Noelle, Playhouse Publishing, PO Box 1962, Cleveland, OH 44106 *Tel:* 330-926-1313 *Fax:* 330-475-8579 *E-mail:* info@picturemepress.com *Web Site:* www.picturemepress.com, pg 193

Panico, Neil, The Dawn Horse Press, 10336 Loch Lomond Rd, No 305, Middletown, CA 95461 *Tel:* 707-928-6590 *Toll Free Tel:* 877-770-0772 *Fax:* 707-928-6590 *E-mail:* dhp@adidam.org *Web Site:* www.dawnhorsepress.com, pg 71

Panikian, Katherine Allnutt Esq, Standard Publishing Corp, 155 Federal St, 13th fl, Boston, MA 02110 *Tel:* 617-457-0600 *Toll Free Tel:* 800-682-5759 *Fax:* 617-457-0608 *Web Site:* www.spcpub.com, pg 233

Pannek, Lisa, Penguin Group (USA) LLC Sales, 375 Hudson St, New York, NY 10014 *Tel:* 212-366-2000 *E-mail:* online@penguinputnam.com *Web Site:* us.penguingroup.com, pg 187

Pantelo, Pam, Humanix Books LLC, PO Box 20989, West Palm Beach, FL 33416 *Tel:* 561-459-5997 *Toll Free Tel:* 855-371-7810 *Fax:* 561-241-6448 *Toll Free Fax:* 855-371-7809 *E-mail:* info@humanixbooks.com *Web Site:* www.humanixbooks.com, pg 117

Pantoliano, Matt, Simon & Schuster Children's Publishing, 1230 Avenue of the Americas, New York, NY 10020 *Tel:* 212-698-7000 *Web Site:* KIDS.SimonandSchuster.com; TEEN.SimonandSchuster.com; simonandschuster.net; simonandschuster.biz, pg 225

Panzer, Robert, Visual Artists & Galleries Association Inc (VAGA), 111 Broadway, Suite 1006, New York, NY 10006 *Tel:* 212-736-6666 *Fax:* 212-736-6767 *E-mail:* info@vagarights.com *Web Site:* vagarights.com, pg 621

Papademetriou, Dean, Somerset Hall Press, 416 Commonwealth Ave, Suite 612, Boston, MA 02215 *Tel:* 617-236-5126 *E-mail:* info@somersethallpress.com *Web Site:* www.somersethallpress.com, pg 230

Papadopoulos, Niki, Portfolio, 375 Hudson St, New York, NY 10014, pg 195

Paparozzi, Andrew D, Epicomm, 1800 Diagonal Rd, Suite 320, Alexandria, VA 22314-2862 *Tel:* 703-836-9200 *E-mail:* webmaster@epicomm.org *Web Site:* epicomm.org, pg 605

Papin, Jessica, Dystel & Goderich Literary Management, One Union Sq W, Suite 904, New York, NY 10003 *Tel:* 212-627-9100 *Fax:* 212-627-9313 *Web Site:* www.dystel.com, pg 549

Pappas, Evangeline A, ASIS International, 1625 Prince St, Alexandria, VA 22314 *Tel:* 703-519-6200 *Fax:* 703-519-6299 *E-mail:* asis@asisonline.org *Web Site:* www.asisonline.org, pg 25

Pappas, Joseph J, Consumer Press, 13326 SW 28 St, Suite 102, Fort Lauderdale, FL 33330-1102 *Tel:* 954-370-9153 *Fax:* 954-472-1008 *E-mail:* info@consumerpress.com *Web Site:* www.consumerpress.com, pg 62

Pappenheimer, Andrea, HarperCollins Children's Books, 195 Broadway, New York, NY 10007 *Tel:* 212-207-7000 *Web Site:* www.harpercollins.com/childrens, pg 105

Pappenheimer, Andrea, HarperCollins Publishers Sales, 195 Broadway, New York, NY 10007 *Fax:* 212-207-7000 *Web Site:* www.harpercollins.com, pg 106

Paprocki, Karin, Simon & Schuster Children's Publishing, 1230 Avenue of the Americas, New York, NY 10020 *Tel:* 212-698-7000 *Web Site:* KIDS.SimonandSchuster.com; TEEN.SimonandSchuster.com; simonandschuster.net; simonandschuster.biz, pg 225

Paradis, Anne, Chouette Publishing, 1001 Lenoir St, Suite B-238, Montreal, QC H4C 2Z6, Canada *Tel:* 514-925-3325 *Fax:* 514-925-3323 *E-mail:* info@editions-chouette.com *Web Site:* www.chouette-publishing.com, pg 477

Paradis, Lucille, Paulines Editions, 5610 rue Beaubien est, Montreal, QC H1T 1X5, Canada *Tel:* 514-253-5610 *Fax:* 514-253-1907 *E-mail:* fsp-paulines@videotron.ca *Web Site:* www.editions.paulines.qc.ca, pg 494

Paradise, Bridgett, Houghton Mifflin Harcourt, 222 Berkeley St, Boston, MA 02116 *Tel:* 617-351-5000 *Toll Free Tel:* 800-225-5425 (K-12 educ materials); 800-323-9540 (assessment materials); 877-219-1537 (SkillsTutor); 888-242-6747 (Destination; Earobics; Edmark; Learning Village; Riverdeep); 800-225-3362 (Houghton Mifflin Harcourt Trade & Reference Publishers) *Toll Free Fax:* 800-269-5232 *E-mail:* customerservice@hmhpub.com *Web Site:* www.hmhco.com, pg 115

Paraskevopoulos, D Jane, Forward Movement, 412 Sycamore St, Cincinnati, OH 45202-4110 *Tel:* 513-721-6659 *Toll Free Tel:* 800-543-1813 *Fax:* 513-721-0729 (orders) *E-mail:* orders@forwardmovement.org (orders & cust serv) *Web Site:* www.forwardmovement.org, pg 91

Parent, Gilles, Les Editions Vents d'Ouest, 109, rue Wright, bureau 202, Gatineau, QC J8X 2G7, Canada *Tel:* 819-770-6377 *Fax:* 819-770-0559 *E-mail:* info@ventsdouest.ca *Web Site:* www.ventsdouest.ca, pg 483

Parfrey, Adam, Feral House, 1240 W Sims Way, Suite 124, Port Townsend, WA 98368 *Tel:* 323-666-3311 *Fax:* 323-297-4331 *E-mail:* info@feralhouse.com *Web Site:* feralhouse.com, pg 88

Paris, Shirley, Carroll Publishing, 4701 Sangamore Rd, Suite S-155, Bethesda, MD 20816 *Tel:* 301-263-9800 *Toll Free Tel:* 800-336-4240 *Fax:* 301-263-9801 *E-mail:* info@carrollpub.com; customersvc@carrollpub.com *Web Site:* www.carrollpublishing.com, pg 51

Park, Drew, WingSpread Publishers, 2020 State Rd, Camp Hill, PA 17011 *Tel:* 717-761-7044 *Toll Free Tel:* 800-884-4571 *Fax:* 717-761-7273 *E-mail:* customerservice@echurchdepot.com *Web Site:* wingspreadpublishers.com, pg 273

Toll Free Fax: 800-858-7787 (orders); 800-286-9471 (cust serv) *E-mail:* frontdesk@chroniclebooks.com *Web Site:* www.chroniclebooks.com, pg 58

Patterson, David, Stuart Krichevsky Literary Agency Inc, 381 Park Ave South, Suite 428, New York, NY 10016 *Tel:* 212-725-5288 *Fax:* 212-725-5275 *E-mail:* query@skagency.com *Web Site:* skagency.com, pg 561

Patterson, Elaine, Maryland History Press, PO Box 206, Fruitland, MD 21826-0206 *Tel:* 410-742-2682 *E-mail:* sales@marylandhistorypress.com *Web Site:* www.marylandhistorypress.com, pg 148

Patterson, Emma, Brandt & Hochman Literary Agents Inc, 1501 Broadway, Suite 2310, New York, NY 10036 *Tel:* 212-840-5760 *Fax:* 212-840-5776 *Web Site:* brandthochman.com, pg 544

Patterson, Jean, Huntington Library Press, 1151 Oxford Rd, San Marino, CA 91108 *Tel:* 626-405-2172 *Fax:* 626-585-0794 *E-mail:* booksales@huntington.org *Web Site:* www.huntington.org, pg 117

Patterson, Karen, Adams Media, 57 Littlefield St, Avon, MA 02322 *Tel:* 508-427-7100 *Fax:* 508-427-6790 *E-mail:* orders@adamsmedia.com *Web Site:* www.adamsmedia.com, pg 4

Patterson, Karen, F+W, A Content + eCommerce Company, 10151 Carver Rd, Suite 200, Blue Ash, OH 45242 *Tel:* 513-531-2690 *Toll Free Tel:* 800-289-0963 (trade accts); 800-258-0929 (orders) *E-mail:* contact_us@fwmedia.com *Web Site:* www.fwcommunity.com, pg 86

Patterson, Kathleen, Optometric Extension Program Foundation, 1921 E Carnegie Ave, Suite 3-L, Santa Ana, CA 92705-5510 *Tel:* 949-250-8070 *Fax:* 949-250-8157 *E-mail:* oep@oep.org *Web Site:* www.oepf.org, pg 176

Patterson, Kellyn, Simon & Schuster, 1230 Avenue of the Americas, New York, NY 10020 *Tel:* 212-698-7000 *Toll Free Tel:* 800-223-2348 (cust serv); 800-223-2336 (orders) *Toll Free Fax:* 800-943-9831 (orders) *Web Site:* www.simonandschuster.com, pg 225

Patterson, Monique, St Martin's Press, LLC, 175 Fifth Ave, New York, NY 10010 *Tel:* 646-307-5151 *Fax:* 212-420-9314 *E-mail:* firstname.lastname@macmillan.com *Web Site:* www.stmartins.com, pg 215

Patterson, Tracy, Stackpole Books, 5067 Ritter Rd, Mechanicsburg, PA 17055 *Tel:* 717-796-0411 *Toll Free Tel:* 800-732-3669 *Fax:* 717-796-0412 *Web Site:* www.stackpolebooks.com, pg 233

Patukas, Jane, Fox Chapel Publishing Co Inc, 1970 Broad St, East Petersburg, PA 17520 *Tel:* 717-560-4703 *Toll Free Tel:* 800-457-9112 *Fax:* 717-560-4702 *E-mail:* customerservice@foxchapelpublishing.com *Web Site:* www.foxchapelpublishing.com, pg 91

Paul, Chris, Candlewick Press, 99 Dover St, Somerville, MA 02144-2825 *Tel:* 617-661-3330 *Fax:* 617-661-0565 *E-mail:* bigbear@candlewick.com; salesinfo@candlewick.com *Web Site:* www.candlewick.com, pg 49

Paul, Joseph, Hachette Nashville, 12 Cadillac Dr, Suite 480, Brentwood, TN 37027 *Tel:* 615-221-0996 *Fax:* 615-221-0962 *Web Site:* www.hachettebookgroup.com, pg 103

Paul, Nancy Gray, Woodbine House, 6510 Bells Mill Rd, Bethesda, MD 20817 *Tel:* 301-897-3570 *Toll Free Tel:* 800-843-7323 *Fax:* 301-897-5838 *E-mail:* info@woodbinehouse.com *Web Site:* www.woodbinehouse.com, pg 275

Paulding, Barbara, Peter Pauper Press, Inc, 202 Mamaroneck Ave, White Plains, NY 10601-5376 *Tel:* 914-681-0144 *Fax:* 914-681-0389 *E-mail:* customerservice@peterpauper.com; orders@peterpauper.com *Web Site:* www.peterpauper.com, pg 190

Paulsen, Nancy, GP Putnam's Sons (Children's), 345 Hudson St, New York, NY 10014 *Tel:* 212-366-2000 *Fax:* 212-414-3393 *E-mail:* online@penguinputnam.com *Web Site:* us.penguingroup.com, pg 201

Paulsen, Nancy Rose, Penguin Young Readers Group, 345 Hudson St, New York, NY 10014 *Tel:* 212-366-2000 *E-mail:* online@penguinputnam.com *Web Site:* www.penguinputnam.com; us.penguingroup.com, pg 187

Paulson, Jamis, Turnstone Press, Artspace Bldg, 206-100 Arthur St, Winnipeg, MB R3B 1H3, Canada *Tel:* 204-947-1555 *Toll Free Tel:* 888-363-7718 *Fax:* 204-942-1556 *E-mail:* info@turnstonepress.com *Web Site:* www.turnstonepress.com, pg 502

Paulson, Tim, Augsburg Fortress Publishers, Publishing House of the Evangelical Lutheran Church in America, 510 Marquette Ave S, Minneapolis, MN 55402 *Tel:* 612-330-3300 *Toll Free Tel:* 800-426-0115 (ext 639, subns); 800-328-4648 (orders) *Fax:* 612-330-3455 *E-mail:* info@augsburgfortress.org; copyright@augsburgfortress.org (reprint permission requests); customercare@augsburgfortress.org *Web Site:* www.augsburgfortress.org, pg 27

Paumen, Brandon, North Star Press of Saint Cloud Inc, PO Box 451, St Cloud, MN 56302-0451 *Tel:* 320-558-9062 *Toll Free Tel:* 888-820-1636 *Fax:* 320-558-9063 *E-mail:* info@northstarpress.com *Web Site:* www.northstarpress.com, pg 171

Pautz, Peter Dennis, World Fantasy Awards, PO Box 43, Mukilteo, WA 98275-0043 *Web Site:* www.worldfantasy.org, pg 738

Paverman, Lauren, Trident Media Group LLC, 41 Madison Ave, 36th fl, New York, NY 10010 *Tel:* 212-333-1511 *E-mail:* info@tridentmediagroup.com; press@tridentmediagroup.com *Web Site:* www.tridentmediagroup.com, pg 578

Pavia, Julian, Crown Publishing Group, c/o Penguin Random House Inc, 1745 Broadway, New York, NY 10019 *Tel:* 212-782-9000 *Toll Free Tel:* 888-264-1745 *Fax:* 212-940-7408 *E-mail:* crownosm@penguinrandomhouse.com *Web Site:* crownpublishing.com, pg 68

Pavlin, Jordan, Alfred A Knopf/Everyman's Library, c/o Random House Inc, 1745 Broadway, New York, NY 10019 *Tel:* 212-751-2600 *Toll Free Tel:* 800-638-6460 *Fax:* 212-572-2593 *Web Site:* www.knopfdoubleday.com, pg 132

Pavola, Tatiana, Ten Speed Press, 2625 Alcatraz Ave, Unit 505, Berkeley, CA 94705 *Tel:* 510-285-3000 *Toll Free Tel:* 800-841-BOOK (841-2665) *E-mail:* csorders@randomhouse.com *Web Site:* crownpublishing.com/imprint/ten-speed-press, pg 243

Pawlak, Mark, Hanging Loose Press, 231 Wyckoff St, Brooklyn, NY 11217 *Tel:* 347-529-4738 *Fax:* 347-227-8215 *E-mail:* print225@aol.com *Web Site:* www.hangingloosepress.com, pg 104

Pawlitz, Mr Loren, Concordia Publishing House, 3558 S Jefferson Ave, St Louis, MO 63118-3968 *Tel:* 314-268-1000; 314-268-1268 (bookshop) *Toll Free Tel:* 800-325-3040 (cust serv) *Toll Free Fax:* 800-490-9889 (cust serv) *E-mail:* order@cph.org *Web Site:* www.cph.org, pg 62

Pawluk, Justyna, Facts On File, 132 W 31 St, 17th fl, New York, NY 10001 *Tel:* 212-967-8800 *Toll Free Tel:* 800-322-8755 *Toll Free Fax:* 800-678-3633 *E-mail:* custserv@factsonfile.com *Web Site:* infobasepublishing.com, pg 85

Pawluk, Justyna, Ferguson Publishing, 132 W 31 St, 17th fl, New York, NY 10001 *Tel:* 212-967-8800 *Toll Free Tel:* 800-322-8755 *Fax:* 917-339-0323 *Toll Free Fax:* 800-678-3633 *E-mail:* custserv@factsonfile.com *Web Site:* infobasepublishing.com, pg 88

Payette, Jacques, Les Editions Heritage Inc, 1101, ave Victoria, St-Lambert, QC J4R 1P8, Canada *Tel:* 514-875-0327 *Toll Free Tel:* 800-561-3737 *Fax:* 450-672-5448, pg 482

Payette, Sylvie, Les Editions Heritage Inc, 1101, ave Victoria, St-Lambert, QC J4R 1P8, Canada *Tel:* 514-875-0327 *Toll Free Tel:* 800-561-3737 *Fax:* 450-672-5448, pg 482

Payne, Darwin, Carr P Collins Award, c/o 7748 Hwy 290 W, Austin, TX 78736-3202 *Tel:* 512-683-5640 *E-mail:* president@texasinstituteofletters.org *Web Site:* www.texasinstituteofletters.org, pg 678

Payne, Darwin, Soeurette Diehl Fraser Translation Award, c/o 7748 Hwy 290 W, Austin, TX 78736-3202 *Tel:* 512-683-5640 *E-mail:* president@texasinstituteofletters.org *Web Site:* www.texasinstituteofletters.org, pg 687

Payne, Darwin, Jesse H Jones Award, c/o 7748 Hwy 290 W, Austin, TX 78736-3202 *Tel:* 512-683-5640 *E-mail:* president@texasinstituteofletters.org *Web Site:* www.texasinstituteofletters.org, pg 697

Payne, Darwin, Most Significant Scholarly Book Award, c/o 7748 Hwy 290 W, Austin, TX 78736-3202 *Tel:* 512-683-5640 *E-mail:* president@texasinstituteofletters.org *Web Site:* www.texasinstituteofletters.org, pg 709

Payne, Darwin, Edwin "Bud" Shrake Award for Best Short Nonfiction, c/o 7748 Hwy 290 W, Austin, TX 78736-3202 *Tel:* 512-683-5640 *E-mail:* president@texasinstituteofletters.org *Web Site:* www.texasinstituteofletters.org, pg 728

Payne, Darwin, Helen C Smith Memorial Award, c/o 7748 Hwy 290 W, Austin, TX 78736-3202 *Tel:* 512-683-5640 *E-mail:* president@texasinstituteofletters.org *Web Site:* www.texasinstituteofletters.org, pg 729

Payne, Darwin, Texas Institute of Letters (TIL), c/o 7748 Hwy 290 W, Austin, TX 78736-3202 *E-mail:* president@texasinstituteofletters.org; secretary@texasinstituteofletters.org *Web Site:* www.texasinstituteofletters.org, pg 620

Payne, Darwin, Texas Institute of Letters Awards, c/o 7748 Hwy 290 W, Austin, TX 78736-3202 *Tel:* 512-683-5640 *E-mail:* president@texasinstituteofletters.org *Web Site:* www.texasinstituteofletters.org, pg 732

Payne, Jennifer, Bick Publishing House, 16 Marion Rd, Branford, CT 06405 *Tel:* 203-208-5253 *Fax:* 203-208-5253 *E-mail:* bickpubhse@aol.com *Web Site:* www.bickpubhouse.com, pg 37

Payne, Prof Johnny, University of Texas at El Paso, Department of Creative Writing, MFA/Department of Creative Writing, Liberal Arts 415 UTEP, 500 W University Ave, El Paso, TX 79968-9991 *Tel:* 915-747-5713 *Fax:* 915-747-5523 *Web Site:* www.utep.edu/cw, pg 664

Payne, Maribeth, W W Norton & Company Inc, 500 Fifth Ave, New York, NY 10110-0017 *Tel:* 212-354-5500 *Toll Free Tel:* 800-233-4830 (orders & cust serv) *Fax:* 212-869-0856 *Toll Free Fax:* 800-458-6515 *Web Site:* www.wwnorton.com, pg 171

Payton, Thomas, Trinity University Press, One Trinity Place, San Antonio, TX 78212-7200 *Tel:* 210-999-8884 *Fax:* 210-999-8838 *E-mail:* books@trinity.edu *Web Site:* www.tupress.org, pg 249

Peabody, William, GP Putnam's Sons (Hardcover), 375 Hudson St, New York, NY 10014 *Tel:* 212-366-2000 *E-mail:* online@penguinputnam.com *Web Site:* us.penguingroup.com, pg 201

Pearce, Anne, Simon & Schuster, 1230 Avenue of the Americas, New York, NY 10020 *Tel:* 212-698-7000 *Toll Free Tel:* 800-223-2348 (cust serv); 800-223-2336 (orders) *Toll Free Fax:* 800-943-9831 (orders) *Web Site:* www.simonandschuster.com, pg 225

Pearce, Beth, The Fairmont Press Inc, 700 Indian Trail, Lilburn, GA 30047 *Tel:* 770-925-9388 *Fax:* 770-381-9865 *Web Site:* www.fairmontpress.com, pg 85

Pearce, John, Westwood Creative Artists Ltd, 94 Harbord St, Toronto, ON M5S 1G6, Canada *Tel:* 416-964-3302 *Fax:* 416-975-9209 *E-mail:* wca_office@wcaltd.com *Web Site:* www.wcaltd.com, pg 579

Pearce, Dr Scott, Center for East Asian Studies (CEAS), Western Washington University, 516 High St, Bellingham, WA 98225 *Tel:* 360-650-3339 *Fax:* 360-650-6110 *E-mail:* easpress@wwu.edu *Web Site:* www.wwu.edu/eas, pg 53

Pearl, Allyson, Random House Publishing Group, 1745 Broadway, New York, NY 10019 *Toll Free Tel:* 800-200-3552 *Web Site:* atrandom.com, pg 204

Perel, Kimberly, Wendy Sherman Associates Inc, 27 W 24 St, Suite 700-B, New York, NY 10010 *Tel:* 212-279-9027 *E-mail:* submissions@wsherman.com *Web Site:* www.wsherman.com, pg 573

Perez, Danielle, NAL, 375 Hudson St, New York, NY 10014 *Tel:* 212-366-2000 *E-mail:* online@penguinputnam.com *Web Site:* www.penguinputnam.com; us.penguingroup.com, pg 162

Perez, Jeanette, HarperCollins General Books Group, 195 Broadway, New York, NY 10007 *Tel:* 212-207-7000 *Web Site:* www.harpercollins.com, pg 105

Perez, Joe, Random House Publishing Group, 1745 Broadway, New York, NY 10019 *Toll Free Tel:* 800-200-3552 *Web Site:* atrandom.com, pg 204

Perez, Minh L, Multimedia Larga, 900 S Boardman Dr, No G72, Gallup, NM 87301, pg 161

Perez, Nanette, John Phillip Immroth Memorial Award, 50 E Huron St, Chicago, IL 60611 *Tel:* 312-280-4223 *Toll Free Tel:* 800-545-2433 *Fax:* 312-280-4227 *E-mail:* oif@ala.org *Web Site:* www.ala.org/ifrt, pg 694

Perez, Nanette, Eli M Oboler Memorial Award, 50 E Huron St, Chicago, IL 60611 *Tel:* 312-280-4223 *Toll Free Tel:* 800-545-2433 *Fax:* 312-280-4227 *E-mail:* oif@ala.org *Web Site:* www.ala.org/ifrt, pg 714

Perez, Ruby, McSweeney's Publishing, 849 Valencia St, San Francisco, CA 94110 *Tel:* 415-642-5609 (cust serv) *Web Site:* www.mcsweeneys.net, pg 152

Perillo, Jennifer, Columbia University Press, 61 W 62 St, New York, NY 10023 *Tel:* 212-459-0600 *Toll Free Tel:* 800-944-8648 *Fax:* 212-459-3678 *E-mail:* cup_book@columbia.edu (orders & cust serv) *Web Site:* cup.columbia.edu, pg 61

Perkins, Dorothy, Diane Publishing Co, 330 Pusey Ave, Suite 3 (rear), Collingdale, PA 19023-0617 *Tel:* 610-461-6200 *Toll Free Tel:* 800-782-3833 *Fax:* 610-461-6130 *Web Site:* www.dianepublishing.net, pg 74

Perkins, Edie, Scholastic International, 557 Broadway, New York, NY 10012 *Tel:* 212-343-6100; 646-330-5288 (intl cust serv) *Toll Free Tel:* 800-SCHOLASTIC (800-724-6527) *Fax:* 646-837-7878 *E-mail:* international@scholastic.com, pg 218

Perkins, Gareth K, Berkeley Slavic Specialties, PO Box 3034, Oakland, CA 94609-0034 *Tel:* 510-653-8048 *Fax:* 510-653-6313 *E-mail:* 71034.456@compuserve.com *Web Site:* www.berkslav.com, pg 35

Perkins, Lori, Riverdale Avenue Books (RAB), 5676 Riverdale Ave, Bronx, NY 10471 *Tel:* 212-279-6418 *Web Site:* www.riverdaleavebooks.com, pg 209

Perkins, Mr Terry, Pflaum Publishing Group, 2621 Dryden Rd, Suite 300, Dayton, OH 45439 *Tel:* 937-293-1415 *Toll Free Tel:* 800-543-4383; 800-523-4625 (sales) *Fax:* 937-293-1310 *Toll Free Fax:* 800-370-4450 *E-mail:* service@pflaum.com *Web Site:* pflaum.com, pg 190

Perl, Liz, Simon & Schuster, Inc, 1230 Avenue of the Americas, New York, NY 10020 *Tel:* 212-698-7000 *Fax:* 212-698-7007 *E-mail:* firstname.lastname@simonandschuster.com *Web Site:* www.simonandschuster.com, pg 226

Perlee, Chris, McGraw-Hill Create, 501 Bell St, Dubuque, IA 52001 *Tel:* 563-584-6000 *Fax:* 563-584-6600 *E-mail:* first_last@mcgraw-hill.com *Web Site:* www.mhhe.com, pg 150

Perlee, Mr Christian, McGraw-Hill Contemporary Learning Series, 501 Bell St, Dubuque, IA 52001 *Toll Free Tel:* 800-243-6532 *Web Site:* www.mhcls.com, pg 150

Perlman Cohen, Susan, The Gersh Agency (TGA), 41 Madison Ave, 33rd fl, New York, NY 10010 *Tel:* 212-997-1818 *E-mail:* info@gershla.com *Web Site:* www.gershagency.com, pg 553

Perlman, Jim, Holy Cow! Press, PO Box 3170, Mount Royal Sta, Duluth, MN 55803 *Tel:* 218-724-1653 *E-mail:* holycow@holycowpress.org *Web Site:* www.holycowpress.org, pg 113

Perlman, Michael, Simon & Schuster Sales Division, 1230 Avenue of the Americas, New York, NY 10020 *Tel:* 212-698-7000, pg 226

Perlman, Victor, American Society of Media Photographers (ASMP), 150 N Second St, Philadelphia, PA 19106 *Tel:* 215-451-2767 *Fax:* 215-451-0880 *E-mail:* info@asmp.org *Web Site:* asmp.org, pg 596

Perlstein, Jill, American Booksellers Association, 333 Westchester Ave, Suite S202, White Plains, NY 10604 *Tel:* 914-406-7500 *Toll Free Tel:* 800-637-0037 *Fax:* 914-410-6297 *E-mail:* info@bookweb.org *Web Site:* www.bookweb.org, pg 594

Permingeat, Max, Les Editions de Mortagne, CP 116, Boucherville, QC J4B 5E6, Canada *Tel:* 450-641-2387 *Fax:* 450-655-6092 *E-mail:* info@editionsdemortagne.com *Web Site:* www.editionsdemortagne.com, pg 480

Perreault, Diane, Beliveau Editeur, 920, rue Jean-Neveu, Longueuil, QC J4G 2M1, Canada *Tel:* 450-679-1933; 514-253-0403 *Fax:* 450-679-6648 *E-mail:* info@beliveauediteur.com *Web Site:* www.beliveauediteur.com, pg 472

Perreault, Melanie, Les Editions Pierre Tisseyre, 155, rue Maurice, Rosemere, QC J7A 2S8, Canada *Tel:* 514-335-0777 *Fax:* 514-335-6723 *E-mail:* info@edtisseyre.ca *Web Site:* www.tisseyre.ca, pg 483

Perreault, Michel, Les Editions Fides, 7333 place des Roseraies, bureau 100, Anjou, QC H1M 2X6, Canada *Tel:* 514-745-4290 *Fax:* 514-745-4299 *E-mail:* editions@groupefides.com *Web Site:* www.editionsfides.com, pg 481

Perreault, Russell, Vintage & Anchor Books, c/o Random House Inc, 1745 Broadway, New York, NY 10019 *Tel:* 212-572-2420 *E-mail:* vintageanchorpublicity@randomhouse.com *Web Site:* vintage-anchor.knopfdoubleday.com, pg 266

Perrin, Brian, HarperCollins General Books Group, 195 Broadway, New York, NY 10007 *Tel:* 212-207-7000 *Web Site:* www.harpercollins.com, pg 105

Perrin, Christopher, Classical Academic Press, 2151 Market St, Camp Hill, PA 17011 *Tel:* 717-730-0711 *Fax:* 717-730-0721 *E-mail:* office@classicalsubjects.com *Web Site:* www.classicalsubjects.com, pg 59

Perrin, Christopher, Plum Tree Books, 2151 Market St, Camp Hill, PA 17011 *Tel:* 717-730-0711 *Fax:* 717-730-0721 *E-mail:* info@classicalsubjects.com *Web Site:* www.plumtreebooks.com, pg 193

Perrin, Dr James, American Academy of Pediatrics, 141 NW Point Blvd, Elk Grove Village, IL 60007-1098 *Tel:* 847-434-4000 *Toll Free Tel:* 888-227-1770 *Fax:* 847-434-8000 *E-mail:* pubs@aap.org *Web Site:* www.aap.org, pg 10

Perritt, Megan, Crown Publishing Group, c/o Penguin Random House Inc, 1745 Broadway, New York, NY 10019 *Tel:* 212-782-9000 *Toll Free Tel:* 888-264-1745 *Fax:* 212-940-7408 *E-mail:* crownosm@penguinrandomhouse.com *Web Site:* crownpublishing.com, pg 68

Perrizo, Mira, Johnson Books, 3005 Center Green Dr, Suite 225, Boulder, CO 80301 *Tel:* 303-443-9766 *Toll Free Tel:* 800-258-5830 *Fax:* 303-443-9687 *E-mail:* books@bigearthpublishing.com *Web Site:* www.bigearthpublishing.com; www.johnsonbooks.com, pg 128

Perrone, Madeline, Literary Artists Representatives, 575 West End Ave, Suite GRC, New York, NY 10024-2711 *Tel:* 212-679-7788 *Fax:* 212-595-2098 *E-mail:* litartists@aol.com, pg 562

Perry, Ava, Circlet Press Inc, 39 Hurlbut St, Cambridge, MA 02138 *Toll Free Tel:* 800-729-6423 *E-mail:* circletintern@gmail.com *Web Site:* www.circlet.com, pg 58

Perry, Bonnie, Beacon Hill Press of Kansas City, PO Box 419527, Kansas City, MO 64141-6527 *Tel:* 816-931-1900 *Toll Free Tel:* 800-877-0700 (cust serv) *Fax:* 816-753-4071 *Web Site:* www.beaconhillbooks.com, pg 32

Perry, Jack, Boyds Mills Press, 815 Church St, Honesdale, PA 18431 *Tel:* 570-253-1164 *Toll Free Tel:* 800-490-5111 *Fax:* 570-253-0179 *E-mail:* contact@boydsmillspress.com *Web Site:* www.boydsmillspress.com, pg 43

Perry, Jack W, Highlights for Children, 1800 Watermark Dr, Columbus, OH 43215 *Tel:* 614-486-0631 *Toll Free Tel:* 800-962-3661 (Highlights Club cust serv); 800-255-9517 (Highlights Magazine cust serv) *Web Site:* www.highlights.com, pg 111

Perry, Rochon, Cedar Grove Books, 2215 High Point Dr, Carrollton, TX 75007 *Tel:* 415-364-8292 *Fax:* 415-276-9858 *E-mail:* queries@cedargrovebooks.com *Web Site:* www.cedargrovebooks.com, pg 52

Perry, Ronald, Sheron Enterprises Inc, 1035 S Carley Ct, North Bellmore, NY 11710 *Tel:* 516-783-5885 *E-mail:* contact@longislandbookpublisher.com *Web Site:* www.longislandbookpublisher.com, pg 223

Perry, Shayla, SDP Publishing Solutions LLC, 36 Captain's Way, East Bridgewater, MA 02333 *Tel:* 617-775-0656 *Web Site:* www.sdppublishingsolutions.com, pg 534

Perry, Sheila M, Sophia Institute Press®, 522 Donald St, Unit 3, Bedford, NH 03110 *Tel:* 603-836-5505 *Toll Free Tel:* 800-888-9344 *Fax:* 603-641-8108 *Toll Free Fax:* 888-288-2259 *E-mail:* orders@sophiainstitute.com *Web Site:* www.sophiainstitute.com, pg 230

Perry, Sheryl, Sheron Enterprises Inc, 1035 S Carley Ct, North Bellmore, NY 11710 *Tel:* 516-783-5885 *E-mail:* contact@longislandbookpublisher.com *Web Site:* www.longislandbookpublisher.com, pg 223

Perry, Thomas, Random House Publishing Group, 1745 Broadway, New York, NY 10019 *Toll Free Tel:* 800-200-3552 *Web Site:* atrandom.com, pg 204

Pershing, John, Hackett Publishing Co Inc, 3333 Massachusetts Ave, Indianapolis, IN 46218 *Tel:* 317-635-9250 (orders & cust serv) *Fax:* 317-635-9292 *Toll Free Fax:* 800-783-9213 *E-mail:* customer@hackettpublishing.com *Web Site:* www.hackettpublishing.com, pg 103

Person, Hara, Central Conference of American Rabbis/CCAR Press, 355 Lexington Ave, 18th fl, New York, NY 10017 *Tel:* 212-972-3636 *E-mail:* info@ccarnet.org *Web Site:* www.ccarpress.org, pg 54

Persun, Terry, Whidbey Island Writers Conference, Old Bayview School, 5611 Bayview Rd, Langley, WA 98260 *Tel:* 360-331-0307 *E-mail:* info@nila.edu *Web Site:* www.nila.edu, pg 656

Peruzza, Albert L, The Reader's Digest Association Inc, 750 Third Ave, New York, NY 10017 *Tel:* 914-238-1000; 646-293-6284 *Toll Free Tel:* 800-310-6261 (cust serv) *Fax:* 914-238-4559 *Web Site:* www.rd.com; www.rda.com, pg 205

Pesch, Fran, Dayton Playhouse FutureFest, 1301 E Siebenthaler Ave, Dayton, OH 45414 *Tel:* 937-424-8477 *Fax:* 937-424-0062 *E-mail:* dp_futurefest@yahoo.com *Web Site:* www.daytonplayhouse.com, pg 680

Pesek, Cara, University of Nebraska Press, 1111 Lincoln Mall, Lincoln, NE 68588-0630 *Tel:* 402-472-3581; 919-966-7449 (cust serv & foreign orders) *Toll Free Tel:* 800-848-6224 (cust serv & US orders) *Fax:* 402-472-6214; 919-962-2704 (cust serv & foreign orders) *Toll Free Fax:* 800-526-2617 (cust serv & US orders) *E-mail:* pressmail@unl.edu *Web Site:* www.nebraskapress.unl.edu, pg 257

Peskin, Joy, Farrar, Straus & Giroux Books for Young Readers, 175 Fifth Ave, 7th fl, New York, NY 10010 *Tel:* 646-307-5151 *Fax:* 646-438-6150 *Web Site:* us.macmillan.com/mackids.aspx, pg 86

Pester, John, Living Stream Ministry (LSM), 2431 W La Palma Ave, Anaheim, CA 92801 *Tel:* 714-991-4681 *Fax:* 714-236-6005 *E-mail:* books@lsm.org *Web Site:* www.lsm.org, pg 142

Pestritto, Carrie, Prospect Agency, 285 Fifth Ave, PMB 445, Brooklyn, NY 11215 *Tel:* 718-788-3217 *Fax:* 718-360-9582 *Web Site:* www.prospectagency.com, pg 568

Peter, Judith, Stemmer House Publishers Inc, 4 White Brook Rd, Gilsum, NH 03448 *Tel:* 603-357-0236 *Toll Free Tel:* 800-345-6665 *Fax:* 603-357-2073 *E-mail:* pbs@pathwaybook.com *Web Site:* www.stemmer.com, pg 235

Peter, Steven, Princeton University Press, 41 William St, Princeton, NJ 08540-5237 *Tel:* 609-258-4900 *Toll Free Tel:* 800-777-4726 (orders) *Fax:* 609-258-6305 *Toll Free Fax:* 800-999-1958 *E-mail:* orders@cpfsinc.com *Web Site:* press.princeton.edu, pg 197

Peters, Barbara, Poisoned Pen Press, 6962 E First Ave, Suite 103, Scottsdale, AZ 85251 *Tel:* 480-945-3375 *Toll Free Tel:* 800-421-3976 *Fax:* 480-949-1707 *E-mail:* info@poisonedpenpress.com *Web Site:* www.poisonedpenpress.com, pg 194

Peters, Funda, Ohio Genealogical Society, 611 State Rte 97 W, Bellville, OH 44813-8813 *Tel:* 419-886-1903 *Fax:* 419-886-0092 *E-mail:* ogs@ogs.org *Web Site:* www.ogs.org, pg 174

Peters, Michelle, Association of Manitoba Book Publishers, 100 Arthur St, Suite 404, Winnipeg, MB R3B 1H3, Canada *Tel:* 204-947-3335 *Fax:* 204-956-4689 *E-mail:* ambp@mts.net *Web Site:* ambp.ca, pg 599

Peters, Simone, Tortuga Press, 2777 Yulupa Ave, PMB 181, Santa Rosa, CA 95405 *Tel:* 707-544-4720 *Toll Free Tel:* 866-4TORTUGA (486-7884) *Fax:* 707-544-5609 *E-mail:* info@tortugapress.com *Web Site:* www.tortugapress.com, pg 247

Peterson, Carol, Hoover Institution Press, Stanford University, 434 Galvez Mall, Stanford, CA 94305-6003 *Tel:* 650-725-7146; 650-723-3373 *Toll Free Tel:* 800-935-2882 *Fax:* 650-723-8626 *E-mail:* hooverpress@stanford.edu *Web Site:* www.hoover.org; www.hooverpress.org, pg 114

Peterson, Carol, Penguin Group (USA) LLC, a Penguin Random House company, 375 Hudson St, New York, NY 10014 *Tel:* 212-366-2000 *Toll Free Tel:* 800-847-5515 (inside sales); 800-631-8571 (cust serv) *Fax:* 212-366-2666; 607-775-4829 (inside sales) *E-mail:* online@us.penguingroup.com *Web Site:* www.penguin.com; us.penguingroup.com, pg 186

Peterson, Gabrielle, Annual Reviews, 4139 El Camino Way, Palo Alto, CA 94306 *Tel:* 650-493-4400 *Toll Free Tel:* 800-523-8635 *Fax:* 650-424-0910; 650-855-9815 *E-mail:* service@annualreviews.org *Web Site:* www.annualreviews.org, pg 18

Peterson, Gayla, Foil & Specialty Effects Association (FSEA), 2150 SW Westport Dr, Suite 101, Topeka, KS 66614 *Tel:* 785-271-5816 *Fax:* 785-271-6404 *E-mail:* info@fsea.com; fseamail@fsea.com *Web Site:* www.fsea.com, pg 606

Peterson, James, Coaches Choice, 514 Airport Way, Monterey, CA 93940 *Toll Free Tel:* 888-229-5745 *Fax:* 831-372-6075 *E-mail:* info@coacheschoice.com *Web Site:* www.coacheschoice.com, pg 60

Peterson, Jeff, Foil & Specialty Effects Association (FSEA), 2150 SW Westport Dr, Suite 101, Topeka, KS 66614 *Tel:* 785-271-5816 *Fax:* 785-271-6404 *E-mail:* info@fsea.com; fseamail@fsea.com *Web Site:* www.fsea.com, pg 606

Peterson, Kathryn, Atlantic Center for the Arts Artists-in-Residence Program, 1414 Art Center Ave, New Smyrna Beach, FL 32168 *Tel:* 386-427-6975 *Toll Free Tel:* 800-393-6975 *Fax:* 386-427-5669 *E-mail:* program@atlanticcenterforthearts.org *Web Site:* www.atlanticcenterforthearts.org, pg 649

Peterson, Kristina, Workman Publishing Co Inc, 225 Varick St, 9th fl, New York, NY 10014-4381 *Tel:* 212-254-5900 *Toll Free Tel:* 800-722-7202 *Fax:* 212-254-8098 *E-mail:* info@workman.com *Web Site:* www.workman.com, pg 275

Peterson, Laura Blake, Curtis Brown Ltd, 10 Astor Place, New York, NY 10003 *Tel:* 212-473-5400 *Web Site:* www.curtisbrown.com, pg 544

Peterson, Lowell, Writers Guild of America, East (WGAE), 250 Hudson St, Suite 700, New York, NY 10013 *Tel:* 212-767-7800 *Fax:* 212-582-1909 *Web Site:* www.wgaeast.org, pg 621

Peterson, Mike, The Child's World Inc, 1980 Lookout Dr, North Mankato, MN 56003-1705 *Tel:* 507-385-1044 *Toll Free Tel:* 800-599-READ (599-7323) *Toll Free Fax:* 888-320-2329 *E-mail:* sales@childsworld.com *Web Site:* childsworld.com, pg 57

Peterson, Tami, Meadowbrook Press, 6110 Blue Circle Dr, Suite 237, Minnetonka, MN 55343 *Toll Free Tel:* 800-338-2232 *Fax:* 952-930-1940 *E-mail:* info@meadowbrookpress.com *Web Site:* www.meadowbrookpress.com, pg 153

Peterson, Tom, The Creative Co, PO Box 227, Mankato, MN 56002 *Tel:* 507-388-6273 *Toll Free Tel:* 800-445-6209 *Fax:* 507-388-2746 *E-mail:* info@thecreativecompany.us; orders@thecreativecompany.us *Web Site:* www.thecreativecompany.us, pg 66

Peterson, Tony, The Society of Professional Journalists (SPJ), Eugene S Pulliam National Journalism Ctr, 3909 N Meridian St, Indianapolis, IN 46208 *Tel:* 317-927-8000 *Fax:* 317-920-4789 *E-mail:* spj@spj.org *Web Site:* www.spj.org, pg 620

Petilos, Randolph, University of Chicago Press, 1427 E 60 St, Chicago, IL 60637-2954 *Tel:* 773-702-7700; 773-702-7600 *Toll Free Tel:* 800-621-2736 (orders) *Fax:* 773-702-9756; 773-660-2235 (orders); 773-702-2708 *E-mail:* custserv@press.uchicago.edu; marketing@press.uchicago.edu *Web Site:* www.press.uchicago.edu, pg 255

Petit, Kim, T&T Clark International, 1385 Broadway, 5th fl, New York, NY 10018 *Tel:* 212-953-5858 *Toll Free Tel:* 800-561-7704 (orders) *Fax:* 212-953-5944 *Web Site:* www.continuumbooks.com, pg 240

Petitt, Tracey, Rizzoli International Publications Inc, 300 Park Ave S, 4th fl, New York, NY 10010-5399 *Tel:* 212-387-3400 *Toll Free Tel:* 800-522-6657 (orders only) *Fax:* 212-387-3535 *E-mail:* publicity@rizzoliusa.com *Web Site:* www.rizzoliusa.com, pg 209

Petrie, Jeremy, Willow Creek Press, 9931 Hwy 70 W, Minocqua, WI 54548 *Tel:* 715-358-7010 *Toll Free Tel:* 800-850-9453 *Fax:* 715-358-2807 *E-mail:* info@willowcreekpress.com *Web Site:* www.willowcreekpress.com, pg 272

Petrie, Tom, Willow Creek Press, 9931 Hwy 70 W, Minocqua, WI 54548 *Tel:* 715-358-7010 *Toll Free Tel:* 800-850-9453 *Fax:* 715-358-2807 *E-mail:* info@willowcreekpress.com *Web Site:* www.willowcreekpress.com, pg 272

Petrillo, Alan M, Excalibur Publications, PO Box 89667, Tucson, AZ 85752-9667 *Tel:* 520-575-9057 *E-mail:* excaliburpublications@centurylink.net, pg 84

Petrovich, Aaron, Akashic Books, 232 Third St, Suite A-115, Brooklyn, NY 11215 *Tel:* 718-643-9193 *Fax:* 718-643-9195 *E-mail:* info@akashicbooks.com *Web Site:* www.akashicbooks.com, pg 7

Pettigrew, Jean, Les Editions Alire, CP 67, Succursale B, Quebec, QC G1K 7A1, Canada *Tel:* 418-835-4441 *Fax:* 418-838-4443 *E-mail:* info@alire.com *Web Site:* www.alire.com, pg 479

Pettit, Kristen, HarperCollins Children's Books, 195 Broadway, New York, NY 10007 *Tel:* 212-207-7000 *Web Site:* www.harpercollins.com/childrens, pg 105

Pevner, Stephen, Stephen Pevner Inc, 382 Lafayette St, Suite 8, New York, NY 10003 *Tel:* 212-674-8403 *Fax:* 212-529-3692 *E-mail:* spidevelopment@gmail.com, pg 567

Pfaff, Eugene E Jr, Tudor Publishers Inc, 3109 Shady Lawn Dr, Greensboro, NC 27408 *Tel:* 336-288-5395 *E-mail:* tudorpublishers@triad.rr.com, pg 250

Pfeffer, Keith, Harvard Business Review Press, 300 N Beacon St, Watertown, MA 02472 *Tel:* 617-783-7400 *Fax:* 617-783-7489 *E-mail:* custserv@hbsp.harvard.edu *Web Site:* www.harvardbusiness.org, pg 106

Pfeiffer, Alice Randal, Syracuse University Press, 621 Skytop Rd, Suite 110, Syracuse, NY 13244-5290 *Tel:* 315-443-5534 *Toll Free Tel:* 800-365-8929 (cust serv) *Fax:* 315-443-5545 *E-mail:* supress@syr.edu *Web Site:* syracuseuniversitypress.syr.edu, pg 239

Pfeiffer, Douglas, Graphic Arts Books, 7820 NE Holman St, Suite B-9, Portland, OR 97218 *Tel:* 503-254-5591 *Fax:* 503-254-5609 *E-mail:* info-ga@graphicartsbooks.com *Web Site:* www.graphicartsbooks.com, pg 99

Pflum, Patricia, Young People's Press Inc (YPPI), 1527 Reed Ave, San Diego, CA 92109 *Tel:* 619-992-3258 (orders) *Toll Free Tel:* 800-231-9774 *E-mail:* admin@youngpeoplespress.com *Web Site:* www.youngpeoplespress.com, pg 279

Pfund, Niko, Oxford University Press USA, 198 Madison Ave, New York, NY 10016 *Tel:* 212-726-6000 *Toll Free Tel:* 800-451-7556 (orders); 800-445-9714 (cust serv) *Fax:* 919-677-1303 *E-mail:* custserv.us@oup.com *Web Site:* www.oup.com/us, pg 179

Phelan, James F, H W Wilson, 2 University Plaza, Suite 310, Hackensack, NJ 07601 *Tel:* 201-968-0500 *Toll Free Tel:* 800-221-1592 *Fax:* 201-968-0511 *E-mail:* info@hwwilsoninprint.com; csr@hwwilsoninprint.com; information@ebscohost.com *Web Site:* www.hwwilsoninprint.com; www.ebscohost.com/wilson, pg 273

Phelan, Shani, IACP Cookbook Awards, 1221 Avenue of the Americas, 42nd fl, New York, NY 10020 *Tel:* 646-358-4957 *Toll Free Tel:* 866-358-4951 *Toll Free Fax:* 866-358-2524 *E-mail:* info@iacp.com *Web Site:* www.iacp.com, pg 694

Phelan, Sheila, DK Publishing, 345 Hudson St, 2nd fl, New York, NY 10014 *Tel:* 646-674-4000 *Toll Free Tel:* 877-342-5357 (cust serv) *Web Site:* us.dk.com, pg 75

Phelps, Chad, F+W, A Content + eCommerce Company, 10151 Carver Rd, Suite 200, Blue Ash, OH 45242 *Tel:* 513-531-2690 *Toll Free Tel:* 800-289-0963 (trade accts); 800-258-0929 (orders) *E-mail:* contact_us@fwmedia.com *Web Site:* www.fwcommunity.com, pg 86

Phelps, Max, The Globe Pequot Press, 246 Goose Lane, Guilford, CT 06437 *Tel:* 203-458-4500 *Toll Free Tel:* 800-243-0495 (orders only); 888-249-7586 (cust serv) *Fax:* 203-458-4601 *Toll Free Fax:* 800-820-2329 (orders & cust serv) *E-mail:* editorial@globepequot.com; info@rowman.com; orders@rowman.com *Web Site:* rowman.com, pg 98

Phi, Bao, McKnight Artist Fellowship for Writers, Open Book, Suite 200, 1011 Washington Ave S, Minneapolis, MN 55415 *Tel:* 612-215-2575 *Fax:* 612-215-2576 *E-mail:* loft@loft.org *Web Site:* www.loft.org, pg 706

Phillips, Andrew, AuthorHouse, 1663 Liberty Dr, Bloomington, IN 47403 *Tel:* 812-339-6000 (outside US) *Toll Free Tel:* 888-519-5121 *E-mail:* authorsupport@authorhouse.com *Web Site:* www.authorhouse.com, pg 27

Phillips, Andrew, iUniverse, 1663 Liberty Dr, Bloomington, IN 47403 *Toll Free Tel:* 800-AUTHORS (288-4677) *Fax:* 812-355-4085 *Web Site:* www.iuniverse.com, pg 126

Phillips, Andrew, Trafford, 1663 Liberty Dr, Bloomington, IN 47403 *Toll Free Tel:* 888-232-4444 *E-mail:* customersupport@trafford.com *Web Site:* www.trafford.com, pg 248

Phillips, Andrew, Xlibris Corp, 1663 Liberty Dr, Suite 200, Bloomington, IN 47403 *Toll Free Tel:* 888-795-4274 *Fax:* 610-915-0294 *E-mail:* info@xlibris.com *Web Site:* www.xlibris.com, pg 277

Phillips, Andrew V, Windhaven®, 466 Rte 10, Orford, NH 03777 *Tel:* 603-483-0929 *E-mail:* info@windhaven.com *Web Site:* www.windhaven.com, pg 535

Phillips, Ashley, Clarkson Potter Publishers, c/o Random House Inc, 1745 Broadway, New York, NY 10019 *Tel:* 212-782-9000 *Toll Free Tel:* 888-264-1745 *Fax:* 212-572-6181 *Web Site:* www.clarksonpotter.com; www.randomhouse.com/crown/clarksonpotter, pg 195

Phillips, Barb, The Literary Press Group of Canada, 425 Adelaide St W, Suite 700, Toronto, ON M5V 3C1, Canada *Tel:* 416-483-1321 *Fax:* 416-483-2510 *Web Site:* www.lpg.ca, pg 609

Phillips, Betsy, Vanderbilt University Press, 2014 Broadway, Suite 320, Nashville, TN 37203 *Tel:* 615-322-3585 *Toll Free Tel:* 800-627-7377 (orders only) *Fax:* 615-343-8823 *Toll Free Fax:* 800-735-0476 (orders only) *E-mail:* vupress@vanderbilt.edu *Web Site:* www.vanderbiltuniversitypress.com, pg 264

Phillips, Kathleen, North American Agricultural Journalists (NAAJ), 6434 Hurta Lane, Bryan, TX 77808 *Tel:* 979-845-2872 *Web Site:* www.naaj.net, pg 614

Phillips, Kirsten, Portage & Main Press, 318 McDermot, Suite 100, Winnipeg, MB R3A 0A2, Canada *Tel:* 204-987-3500 *Toll Free Tel:* 800-667-9673 *Fax:* 204-947-0080 *Toll Free Fax:* 866-734-8477 *E-mail:* books@portageandmainpress.com *Web Site:* www.portageandmainpress.com, pg 495

Phillips, Peter, The 25 Most "Censored" Stories Annual, PO Box 571, Cotati, CA 94931 *Tel:* 707-874-2695 *Web Site:* www.projectcensored.org, pg 733

Phillips, Ted, United States Holocaust Memorial Museum, 100 Raoul Wallenberg Place SW, Washington, DC 20024-2126 *Tel:* 202-314-7837; 202-488-6144 (orders) *Toll Free Tel:* 800-259-9998 (orders) *Fax:* 202-479-9726; 202-488-0438 (orders) *E-mail:* cahs_publications@ushmm.org *Web Site:* www.ushmm.org, pg 253

Phillips, Tom, Jackie White Memorial National Children's Playwriting Contest, 1400 Forum Blvd, 1C No 214, Columbia, MO 65203 *E-mail:* jwmcontest@cectheatre.org *Web Site:* www.cectheatre.org, pg 696

Phillipson, Nicholas, Springer, 233 Spring St, New York, NY 10013-1578 *Tel:* 212-460-1500 *Toll Free Tel:* 800-SPRINGER (777-4643) *Fax:* 212-460-1575 *E-mail:* service-ny@springer.com *Web Site:* www.springer.com, pg 232

Philpott, Sandy, Dawn Publications Inc, 12402 Bitney Springs Rd, Nevada City, CA 95959 *Tel:* 530-274-7775 *Toll Free Tel:* 800-545-7475 *Fax:* 530-274-7778 *E-mail:* nature@dawnpub.com; orders@dawnpub.com *Web Site:* www.dawnpub.com, pg 71

Philps, Rebecca, Western Magazine Awards Foundation, 875 Prairie Ave, Port Coquitlam, BC V3B 1R9, Canada *Tel:* 604-945-3711 *E-mail:* wma@direct.ca *Web Site:* www.westernmagazineawards.ca, pg 735

Phinn, Jessica, Nelson Education Ltd, 1120 Birchmount Rd, Scarborough, ON M1K 5G4, Canada *Tel:* 416-752-9100 *Toll Free Tel:* 800-268-2222 (cust serv) *Fax:* 416-752-8101 *Toll Free Fax:* 800-430-4445 *E-mail:* peopleandengagement@nelson.com *Web Site:* www.nelson.com, pg 492

Phirmam, James, Houghton Mifflin Harcourt, 222 Berkeley St, Boston, MA 02116 *Tel:* 617-351-5000 *Toll Free Tel:* 800-225-5425 (K-12 educ materials); 800-323-9540 (assessment materials); 877-219-1537 (SkillsTutor); 888-242-6747 (Destination; Earobics; Edmark; Learning Village; Riverdeep); 800-225-3362 (Houghton Mifflin Harcourt Trade & Reference Publishers) *Toll Free Fax:* 800-269-5232 *E-mail:* customerservice@hmhpub.com *Web Site:* www.hmhco.com, pg 115

Phuna, K K, World Scientific Publishing Co Inc, 27 Warren St, Suite 401-402, Hackensack, NJ 07601 *Tel:* 201-487-9655 *Toll Free Tel:* 800-227-7562 *Fax:* 201-487-9656 *Toll Free Fax:* 888-977-2665 *E-mail:* wspc@wspc.com *Web Site:* www.wspc.com, pg 276

Piazzi, Remo D, The United Educators Inc, 900 N Shore Dr, Suite 279, Lake Bluff, IL 60044-2210 *Tel:* 847-234-3700 *Toll Free Tel:* 800-323-5875 *Fax:* 847-234-8705 *E-mail:* unitededucators@yahoo.com *Web Site:* www.theunitededucatorsinc.com, pg 253

Pichette, Sylvain, Beliveau Editeur, 920, rue Jean-Neveu, Longueuil, QC J4G 2M1, Canada *Tel:* 450-679-1933; 514-253-0403 *Fax:* 450-679-6648 *E-mail:* info@beliveauediteur.com *Web Site:* www.beliveauediteur.com, pg 472

Pickett, Patty, Accuity, 4709 W Golf Rd, Skokie, IL 60076 *Tel:* 847-676-9600 *Toll Free Tel:* 800-321-3373 *Fax:* 847-933-8101 *E-mail:* custserv@accuity.com; sales@accuity.com *Web Site:* www.accuity.com, pg 4

Pickett, Shumeca, John Phillip Immroth Memorial Award, 50 E Huron St, Chicago, IL 60611 *Tel:* 312-280-4223 *Toll Free Tel:* 800-545-2433 *Fax:* 312-280-4227 *E-mail:* oif@ala.org *Web Site:* www.ala.org/ifrt, pg 694

Pickett, Shumeca, Eli M Oboler Memorial Award, 50 E Huron St, Chicago, IL 60611 *Tel:* 312-280-4223 *Toll Free Tel:* 800-545-2433 *Fax:* 312-280-4227 *E-mail:* oif@ala.org *Web Site:* www.ala.org/ifrt, pg 714

Pientka, Cheryl, Jill Grinberg Literary Management LLC, 392 Vanderbilt Ave, Brooklyn, NY 11238 *Tel:* 212-620-5883 *E-mail:* info@jillgrinbergliterary.com *Web Site:* www.jillgrinbergliterary.com, pg 555

Pierce, Carol, National Federation of Press Women Inc (NFPW), PO Box 5556, Arlington, VA 22205-0798 *Tel:* 703-237-9804 *Fax:* 703-237-9808 *E-mail:* presswomen@aol.com *Web Site:* www.nfpw.org, pg 612

Pierce, Gregory, ACTA Publications, 4848 N Clark St, Chicago, IL 60640 *Tel:* 773-271-1030 *Toll Free Tel:* 800-397-2282 *Fax:* 773-271-7399 *Toll Free Fax:* 800-397-0079 *E-mail:* info@actapublications.com *Web Site:* www.actapublications.com, pg 4

Pierce, Jesse, Albert B Corey Prize, c/o American Historical Association, 400 "A" St SE, Washington, DC 20003-3889 *Tel:* 202-544-2422 *Fax:* 202-544-8307 *E-mail:* cha-shc@cha-shc.ca *Web Site:* www.historians.org/prizes; www.cha-shc.ca, pg 679

Pierce, Valerie, Sourcebooks Inc, 1935 Brookdale Rd, Suite 139, Naperville, IL 60563 *Tel:* 630-961-3900 *Toll Free Tel:* 800-432-7444 *Fax:* 630-961-2168 *E-mail:* info@sourcebooks.com; customersupport@sourcebooks.com *Web Site:* www.sourcebooks.com, pg 230

Piergies, Mary, Manning Publications Co, PO Box 761, Shelter Island, NY 11964 *Tel:* 203-626-1510 *E-mail:* sales@manning.com; support@manning.com (cust serv) *Web Site:* www.manning.com, pg 146

Pierpont, Amy, Grand Central Publishing, 1290 Avenue of the Americas, New York, NY 10019 *Tel:* 212-364-1100 *Web Site:* www.hachettebookgroup.com, pg 99

Pierre, Farah, Simba Information, 1266 E Main St, Suite 700, Stamford, CT 06902 *Tel:* 203-325-8193 *Toll Free Tel:* 888-297-4622 (cust serv) *E-mail:* customerservice@simbainformation.com *Web Site:* www.simbainformation.com, pg 225

Piersanti, Steven, Berrett-Koehler Publishers Inc, 1333 Broadway, Suite 1000, Oakland, CA 94612 *Tel:* 510-817-2277 *Fax:* 510-817-2278 *E-mail:* bkpub@bkpub.com *Web Site:* www.bkconnection.com, pg 35

Pierson, Caryl K, Math Teachers Press Inc, 4850 Park Glen Rd, Minneapolis, MN 55416 *Tel:* 952-545-6535 *Toll Free Tel:* 800-852-2435 *Fax:* 952-546-7502 *E-mail:* info@movingwithmath.com *Web Site:* www.movingwithmath.com, pg 149

Pierson, Jennifer, Rizzoli International Publications Inc, 300 Park Ave S, 4th fl, New York, NY 10010-5399 *Tel:* 212-387-3400 *Toll Free Tel:* 800-522-6657 (orders only) *Fax:* 212-387-3535 *E-mail:* publicity@rizzoliusa.com *Web Site:* www.rizzoliusa.com, pg 209

Pietsch, Michael, Hachette Book Group, 1290 Avenue of the Americas, New York, NY 10019 *Tel:* 212-364-1100 *Toll Free Tel:* 800-759-0190 (cust serv) *Fax:* 212-364-0933 (intl orders) *Toll Free Fax:* 800-286-9471 (cust serv) *Web Site:* www.HachetteBookGroup.com, pg 102

Pike, Bryan, The BC Book Prizes, 207 W Hastings St, Suite 901, Vancouver, BC V6B 1H7, Canada *Tel:* 604-687-2405 *Fax:* 604-687-2435 *E-mail:* info@bcbookprizes.ca *Web Site:* www.bcbookprizes.ca, pg 670

Pike, Nadyne, Sterling Lord Literistic Inc, 65 Bleecker St, New York, NY 10012 *Tel:* 212-780-6050 *Fax:* 212-780-6095 *E-mail:* info@sll.com *Web Site:* www.sll.com, pg 575

Pike, Paula, Emond Montgomery Publications Ltd, 60 Shaftesbury Ave, Toronto, ON M4T 1A3, Canada *Tel:* 416-975-3925 *Toll Free Tel:* 888-837-0815 *Fax:* 416-975-3924 *E-mail:* orders@emp.ca *Web Site:* www.emp.ca, pg 483

Pilguy, Natalya, Workman Publishing Co Inc, 225 Varick St, 9th fl, New York, NY 10014-4381 *Tel:* 212-254-5900 *Toll Free Tel:* 800-722-7202 *Fax:* 212-254-8098 *E-mail:* info@workman.com *Web Site:* www.workman.com, pg 275

Pillai, Devi, Orbit, 1290 Avenue of the Americas, New York, NY 10019 *Tel:* 212-364-1100 *Toll Free Tel:* 800-759-0190 *Web Site:* www.orbitbooks.net, pg 176

Pilon, Didier, University of Ottawa Press (Les Presses de l'Université d'Ottawa), 542 King Edward Ave, Ottawa, ON K1N 6N5, Canada *Tel:* 613-562-5246 *Fax:* 613-562-5247 *E-mail:* puo-oup@uottawa.ca *Web Site:* www.press.uottawa.ca, pg 503

Pimlott, Philip, Gravure Association of the Americas Inc, 8281 Pine Lake Rd, Denver, NC 28037 *Tel:* 201-523-6042 *Fax:* 201-523-6048 *E-mail:* gaa@gaa.org *Web Site:* www.gaa.org, pg 606

Pincus, Caroline, Caroline Pincus Book Midwife, 101 Wool St, San Francisco, CA 94110 *Tel:* 415-516-6206 *E-mail:* cpincus100@sbcglobal.net, pg 532

Pincus, Caroline, Red Wheel/Weiser/Conari, 65 Parker St, Suite 7, Newburyport, MA 01950 *Tel:* 978-465-0504 *Toll Free Tel:* 800-423-7087 (orders) *Fax:* 978-465-0243 *E-mail:* info@rwwbooks.com *Web Site:* www.redwheelweiser.com, pg 206

Pinder, Victoria, Fun in the Sun Conference, PO Box 480211, Fort Lauderdale, FL 33348 *E-mail:* frwfuninthesun@yahoo.com *Web Site:* www.frwriters.org/fun-in-the-sun-conference/; frwfuninthesunmain.blogspot.com/; www.frwriters.org, pg 651

Pine, Barbra, MIT List Visual Arts Center, MIT E 15-109, 20 Ames St, Cambridge, MA 02139 *Tel:* 617-253-4400; 617-253-4680 *Fax:* 617-258-7265 *E-mail:* mlinga@mit.edu *Web Site:* listart.mit.edu, pg 157

Pine, Ralph, Quite Specific Media Group Ltd, 7373 Pyramid Place, Hollywood, CA 90046 *Tel:* 323-851-5797 *Fax:* 323-851-5798 *E-mail:* info@quitespecificmedia.com *Web Site:* www.quitespecificmedia.com, pg 202

Pine, Richard S, InkWell Management, 521 Fifth Ave, 26th fl, New York, NY 10175 *Tel:* 212-922-3500 *Fax:* 212-922-0535 *E-mail:* info@inkwellmanagement.com; submissions@inkwellmanagement.com *Web Site:* inkwellmanagement.com, pg 557

Pinkney, Andrea, Scholastic Trade Division, 557 Broadway, New York, NY 10012 *Tel:* 212-343-6100; 212-343-4685 (export sales) *Fax:* 212-343-4714 (export sales) *Web Site:* www.scholastic.com, pg 219

Pinney, Marilyn R, EDC Publishing, 10302 E 55 Place, Tulsa, OK 74146-6515 *Tel:* 918-622-4522 *Toll Free Tel:* 800-475-4522 *Fax:* 918-665-7919 *Toll Free Fax:* 800-743-5660 *E-mail:* edc@edcpub.com *Web Site:* www.edcpub.com, pg 79

Pinsky, Prof Robert, Boston University, 236 Bay State Rd, Boston, MA 02215 *Tel:* 617-353-2510 *Fax:* 617-353-3653 *E-mail:* crwr@bu.edu *Web Site:* www.bu.edu/writing, pg 659

Pinson, Linda, OUT OF YOUR MIND...AND INTO THE MARKETPLACE™, 13381 White Sand Dr, Tustin, CA 92780-4565 *Tel:* 714-544-0248 *Toll Free Tel:* 800-419-1513 *Fax:* 714-730-1414 *Web Site:* www.business-plan.com, pg 178

Pintaudi-Jones, Rose, Oxford University Press USA, 198 Madison Ave, New York, NY 10016 *Tel:* 212-726-6000 *Toll Free Tel:* 800-451-7556 (orders); 800-445-9714 (cust serv) *Fax:* 919-677-1303 *E-mail:* custserv.us@oup.com *Web Site:* www.oup.com/us, pg 179

Pinter, Jason, Polis Books, 1201 Hudson St, No 211S, Hoboken, NJ 07030 *E-mail:* info@polisbooks.com; submissions@polisbooks.com *Web Site:* www.polisbooks.com; facebook.com/PolisBooks; twitter.com/PolisBooks, pg 194

Pinto, Matthew, Ascension Press, PO Box 1990, West Chester, PA 19380 *Tel:* 610-696-7795 (ext 207, edit); 484-875-4550 (admin) *Toll Free Tel:* 800-376-0520 (sales & cust serv) *E-mail:* info@ascensionpress.com *Web Site:* ascensionpress.com, pg 24

Pioreck, Richard, Summer Writers Program, CE, 250 Hofstra University, Hempstead, NY 11549-2500 *Tel:* 516-463-7200 *Fax:* 516-463-4833 *E-mail:* ce@hofstra.edu *Web Site:* ce.hofstra.edu, pg 656

Pires, Lauren, Simon & Schuster Audio, 1230 Avenue of the Americas, New York, NY 10020 *Web Site:* audio.simonandschuster.com, pg 225

Pitoniak, Anna, Random House Publishing Group, 1745 Broadway, New York, NY 10019 *Toll Free Tel:* 800-200-3552 *Web Site:* atrandom.com, pg 204

Pittman, Joseph, Riverdale Avenue Books (RAB), 5676 Riverdale Ave, Bronx, NY 10471 *Tel:* 212-279-6418 *Web Site:* www.riverdaleavebooks.com, pg 209

Pittman, Judith, Books We Love Ltd, 192 Lakeside Greens Dr, Chestermere, AB T1X 1C2, Canada *Tel:* 403-710-4869 *E-mail:* bookswelove@shaw.ca, pg 473

Pitts, John, Doubleday/Nan A Talese, c/o Penguin Random House Inc, 1745 Broadway, New York, NY 10019 *Tel:* 212-751-2600 *Fax:* 212-572-2662 *E-mail:* ddaypub@randomhouse.com *Web Site:* knopfdoubleday.com, pg 76

Pitts, Melissa, University of British Columbia Press, 2029 West Mall, Vancouver, BC V6T 1Z2, Canada *Tel:* 604-822-5959 *Toll Free Tel:* 877-377-9378 *Fax:* 604-822-6083 *Toll Free Fax:* 800-668-0821 *E-mail:* frontdesk@ubcpress.ca *Web Site:* www.ubcpress.ca, pg 502

Pitts, Stephanie, Random House Children's Books, 1745 Broadway, New York, NY 10019 *Tel:* 212-782-9000 *Toll Free Tel:* 800-200-3552 *Fax:* 212-782-9452 *Web Site:* randomhousekids.com, pg 204

Piver, Susan, Shambhala Publications Inc, Horticultural Hall, 300 Massachusetts Ave, Boston, MA 02115 *Tel:* 617-424-0030 *Toll Free Tel:* 866-424-0030 (off); 888-424-2329 (cust serv) *Fax:* 617-236-1563 *E-mail:* customercare@shambhala.com *Web Site:* www.shambhala.com, pg 223

Pizzo, Matthew, ZOVA Books, PO Box 21833, Long Beach, CA 90801 *Tel:* 805-426-9682 *Fax:* 562-394-9568 *Web Site:* www.zovabooks.com, pg 280

Plafsky, Danielle, Alfred A Knopf/Everyman's Library, c/o Random House Inc, 1745 Broadway, New York, NY 10019 *Tel:* 212-751-2600 *Toll Free Tel:* 800-638-6460 *Fax:* 212-572-2593 *Web Site:* www.knopfdoubleday.com, pg 132

Plantier, Paula, EditAmerica, 115 Jacobs Creek Rd, Ewing, NJ 08628 *Tel:* 609-882-5852 *Web Site:* www.editamerica.com; www.linkedin.com/in/PaulaPlantier, pg 525

Plata, Glory, Riverhead Books (Hardcover), 375 Hudson St, New York, NY 10014 *Tel:* 212-366-2000 *E-mail:* online@penguinputnam.com *Web Site:* www.penguinputnam.com; us.penguingroup.com, pg 209

Platkin, Charles, Diversion Books, 443 Park Ave S, Suite 1008, New York, NY 10016 *Tel:* 212-961-6390 *E-mail:* info@diversionbooks.com *Web Site:* www.diversionbooks.com, pg 74

Platt, Ben, Basic Books, 250 W 57 St, 15th fl, New York, NY 10107 *Tel:* 212-340-8164; 212-340-8136 *Fax:* 212-340-8135 *E-mail:* perseus.promos@perseusbooks.com *Web Site:* www.basicbooks.com; perseusbooks.com, pg 31

Platt, Julie M, SAS Publishing, 100 SAS Campus Dr, Cary, NC 27513-2414 *Tel:* 919-677-8000 *Fax:* 919-677-4444 *E-mail:* saspress@sas.com *Web Site:* www.sas.com/publishing, pg 216

Platter, Clara, PublicAffairs, 250 W 57 St, Suite 1321, New York, NY 10107 *Tel:* 212-397-6666 *Toll Free Tel:* 800-343-4499 (orders) *Fax:* 212-397-4277 *E-mail:* publicaffairs@perseusbooks.com *Web Site:* www.publicaffairsbooks.com, pg 200

Plikaitis, Kara, Ten Speed Press, 2625 Alcatraz Ave, Unit 505, Berkeley, CA 94705 *Tel:* 510-285-3000 *Toll Free Tel:* 800-841-BOOK (841-2665) *E-mail:* csorders@randomhouse.com *Web Site:* crownpublishing.com/imprint/ten-speed-press, pg 243

Plotnick, Stanley D, University Press of America Inc, 4501 Forbes Blvd, Suite 200, Lanham, MD 20706 *Tel:* 301-459-3366 *Toll Free Tel:* 800-462-6420 *Fax:* 301-429-5748 *Toll Free Fax:* 800-338-4550 *Web Site:* www.univpress.com, pg 261

Plunkett, Jack W, Plunkett Research Ltd, PO Drawer 541737, Houston, TX 77254-1737 *Tel:* 713-932-0000 *Fax:* 713-932-7080 *E-mail:* customersupport@plunkettresearch.com *Web Site:* www.plunkettresearch.com, pg 194

Poblocka, Joanna, Gerald Lampert Memorial Award, 192 Spadina Ave, Suite 312, Toronto, ON M5T 2C2, Canada *Tel:* 416-504-1657 *Fax:* 416-504-0096 *E-mail:* readings@poets.ca *Web Site:* poets.ca, pg 699

Poblocka, Joanna, The League of Canadian Poets, 192 Spadina Ave, Suite 312, Toronto, ON M5T 2C2, Canada *Tel:* 416-504-1657 *Fax:* 416-504-0096 *Web Site:* poets.ca, pg 608

Poblocka, Joanna, Pat Lowther Memorial Award, 192 Spadina Ave, Suite 312, Toronto, ON M5T 2C2, Canada *Tel:* 416-504-1657 *Fax:* 416-504-0096 *E-mail:* readings@poets.ca *Web Site:* poets.ca, pg 703

Poblocka, Joanna, Jessamy Stursberg Poetry Contest for Youth, 192 Spadina Ave, Suite 312, Toronto, ON M5T 2C2, Canada *Tel:* 416-504-1657 *Fax:* 416-504-0096 *E-mail:* readings@poets.ca *Web Site:* www.youngpoets.ca; poets.ca, pg 731

Pochron, J P, J P Pochron Writer for Hire, 830 Lake Orchid Circle, No 203, Vero Beach, FL 32962 *Tel:* 772-569-2967 *E-mail:* hotwriter15@hotmail.com, pg 532

Pocius, Jenna, Little Bee Books, 853 Broadway, Suite 2014, New York, NY 10003 *E-mail:* info@littlebeebooks.com *Web Site:* www.littlebeebooks.com, pg 140

Podrasky, Bob, Recorded Books LLC, 270 Skipjack Rd, Prince Frederick, MD 20678 *Tel:* 410-535-5590 *Toll Free Tel:* 800-638-1304; 877-732-2898 *Fax:* 410-535-5499 *E-mail:* customerservice@recordedbooks.com *Web Site:* www.recordedbooks.com, pg 206

Poehler, Leigh, No Starch Press Inc, 245 Eighth St, San Francisco, CA 94103 *Tel:* 415-863-9900 *Toll Free Tel:* 800-420-7240 *Fax:* 415-863-9950 *E-mail:* info@nostarch.com *Web Site:* www.nostarch.com, pg 170

Poelle, Barbara, Irene Goodman Literary Agency, 27 W 24 St, Suite 700B, New York, NY 10010 *Tel:* 212-604-0330 *E-mail:* queries@irenegoodman.com *Web Site:* www.irenegoodman.com, pg 554

Poggione, Mary, Minnesota Historical Society Press, 345 Kellogg Blvd W, St Paul, MN 55102-1906 *Tel:* 651-259-3205; 651-259-3000 *Toll Free Tel:* 800-621-2736 (warehouse) *Fax:* 651-297-1345 *Toll Free Fax:* 800-621-8476 (warehouse) *E-mail:* info-mnhspress@mnhs.org *Web Site:* www.mnhs.org/mnhspress, pg 157

Pogodzinski, Mark, No Frills Buffalo, 119 Dorchester Rd, Buffalo, NY 14213 *Tel:* 716-510-0520 *E-mail:* contact@nofrillsbuffalo.com *Web Site:* www.nofrillsbuffalo.com, pg 170

Pohland, Liz, Society for Technical Communication, 9401 Lee Hwy, Suite 300, Fairfax, VA 22031 *Tel:* 703-522-4114 *Fax:* 703-522-2075 *E-mail:* stc@stc.org *Web Site:* www.stc.org, pg 618

Pohlen, Jerome, Chicago Review Press, 814 N Franklin St, Chicago, IL 60610 *Tel:* 312-337-0747 *Toll Free Tel:* 800-888-4741 *Fax:* 312-337-5110 *E-mail:* frontdesk@chicagoreviewpress.com *Web Site:* www.chicagoreviewpress.com, pg 56

Pointer, Ryan, Annual Off Off Broadway Short Play Festival, 235 Park Ave S, 5th fl, New York, NY 10003 *Tel:* 212-206-8990 *Toll Free Tel:* 866-598-8449 *Fax:* 212-206-1429 *E-mail:* oobfestival@samuelfrench.com *Web Site:* oob.samuelfrench.com; www.samuelfrench.com, pg 668

Poirot, Henry M, Poirot & Co Literary Agency, 3887 Nimbus Rd, Longmont, CO 80503 *Tel:* 303-494-0668 *Fax:* 303-494-9396 *E-mail:* poirotco@comcast.net, pg 568

Pola, Matthew Dela, Piano Press, 1425 Ocean Ave, Suite 5, Del Mar, CA 92014 *Tel:* 619-884-1401 *Fax:* 858-755-1104 *E-mail:* pianopress@pianopress.com *Web Site:* www.pianopress.com, pg 191

Polansky, Debra, Studio Fun International Inc, 44 S Broadway, White Plains, NY 10601 *Tel:* 914-238-1000 *Toll Free Tel:* 800-934-0977 *Web Site:* www.rdtradepublishing.com, pg 237

Polcari, Beth, Scholastic Education, 524 Broadway, New York, NY 10012 *Tel:* 212-343-6100 *Fax:* 212-343-6189 *Web Site:* www.scholastic.com, pg 218

Polese, Richard, New Mexico Book Association (NMBA), 1219 Luisa St, Suite 1, Santa Fe, NM 87505 *Tel:* 505-660-6357 *E-mail:* admin@nmbook.org *Web Site:* www.nmbook.org, pg 614

Polese, Richard, Ocean Tree Books, 1325 Cerro Gordo Rd, Santa Fe, NM 87501 *Tel:* 505-983-1412 *Fax:* 505-983-0899 *Web Site:* www.oceantree.com, pg 173

Polin, Cathy, Manhattan Publishing Co, 670 White Plains Rd, Scarsdale, NY 10583 *Tel:* 914-472-4650 *Fax:* 914-472-4316 *E-mail:* coe@manhattanpublishing.com *Web Site:* www.manhattanpublishing.com, pg 146

Polin, Kenneth, Manhattan Publishing Co, 670 White Plains Rd, Scarsdale, NY 10583 *Tel:* 914-472-4650 *Fax:* 914-472-4316 *E-mail:* coe@manhattanpublishing.com *Web Site:* www.manhattanpublishing.com, pg 146

Poling, Jan A, American Forest Paper Association (AF&PA), 1101 "K" St NW, Suite 700, Washington, DC 20005 *Tel:* 202-463-2700 *E-mail:* info@afandpa.org *Web Site:* www.afandpa.org, pg 595

Poling, Victoria, Copper Canyon Press, Fort Worden State Park, Bldg 313, Port Townsend, WA 98368 *Tel:* 360-385-4925 *Toll Free Tel:* 877-501-1393 (orders) *Fax:* 360-385-4985 *E-mail:* poetry@coppercanyonpress.org *Web Site:* www.coppercanyonpress.org, pg 63

Polishuk, Paul PhD, Information Gatekeepers Inc, 1340 Soldiers Field Rd, Suite 2, Boston, MA 02135 *Tel:* 617-782-5033 *Fax:* 617-507-8338 *E-mail:* info@igigroup.com *Web Site:* www.igigroup.com, pg 121

Polivka, Raina, Indiana University Press, Herman B Wells Library 350, 1320 E Tenth St, Bloomington, IN 47405-3907 *Tel:* 812-855-8817 *Toll Free Tel:* 800-842-6796 (orders only) *Fax:* 812-855-7931; 812-855-8507 *E-mail:* iupress@indiana.edu; iuporder@indiana.edu (orders) *Web Site:* www.iupress.indiana.edu, pg 120

Polizzotti, Mark, The Metropolitan Museum of Art, 1000 Fifth Ave, New York, NY 10028 *Tel:* 212-879-5500; 212-570-3725 *Fax:* 212-396-5062 *E-mail:* editorial@metmuseum.org *Web Site:* www.metmuseum.org, pg 155

Polkinhorn, Prof Harry, San Diego State University Press, Arts & Letters 283, 5500 Campanile Dr, San Diego, CA 92182-6020 *Tel:* 619-594-6220 (orders) *Web Site:* sdsupress.sdsu.edu, pg 216

Poll, Michael R, Cornerstone Book Publishers, PO Box 24652, New Orleans, LA 70184 *E-mail:* info@cornerstonepublishers.com *Web Site:* www.cornerstonepublishers.com, pg 64

Pollak, Fran, Mews Books Ltd, 20 Bluewater Hill, Westport, CT 06880 *Tel:* 203-227-1836 *Fax:* 203-227-1144 *E-mail:* mewsbooks@aol.com, pg 565

Pollert, Annette, Sourcebooks Inc, 1935 Brookdale Rd, Suite 139, Naperville, IL 60563 *Tel:* 630-961-3900 *Toll Free Tel:* 800-432-7444 *Fax:* 630-961-2168 *E-mail:* info@sourcebooks.com; customersupport@sourcebooks.com *Web Site:* www.sourcebooks.com, pg 230

Pollock, Ben, National Society of Newspaper Columnists Annual Conference, 1345 Fillmore St, Suite 507, San Francisco, CA 94115 *Tel:* 415-488-NCNC (488-

Powers, Joan, Candlewick Press, 99 Dover St, Somerville, MA 02144-2825 *Tel:* 617-661-3330 *Fax:* 617-661-0565 *E-mail:* bigbear@candlewick.com; salesinfo@candlewick.com *Web Site:* www.candlewick.com, pg 49

Powers, Marcia, Wilshire Book Co, 9731 Variel Ave, Chatsworth, CA 91311-4315 *Tel:* 818-700-1522 *Fax:* 818-700-1527 *E-mail:* sales@mpowers.com *Web Site:* www.mpowers.com, pg 272

Powers, Retha, Publishing Certificate Program at City College, Division of Humanities NAC 5225, City College of New York, New York, NY 10031 *Tel:* 212-650-7925 *Fax:* 212-650-7912 *E-mail:* ccnypub@aol.com *Web Site:* www.ccny.cuny.edu/publishing_certificate/index.html, pg 662

Powers, Thomas, Steerforth Press, 45 Lyme Rd, Suite 208, Hanover, NH 03755-1222 *Tel:* 603-643-4787 *Fax:* 603-643-4788 *E-mail:* info@steerforth.com *Web Site:* www.steerforth.com, pg 234

Poynor, Jay, The Poynor Group, 13454 Yorktown Dr, Bowie, MD 20715 *Tel:* 301-805-6788, pg 568

Poynter, Dan, Global Ebook Awards, PO Box 8206-240, Santa Barbara, CA 93118-8206 *Tel:* 805-968-7277 *Fax:* 805-968-1379 *Web Site:* globalebookawards.com, pg 689

Poynter, Dan, Para Publishing LLC, PO Box 8206-240, Santa Barbara, CA 93118-8206 *Tel:* 805-968-7277 *Toll Free Tel:* 800-727-2782 *Fax:* 805-968-1379 *Web Site:* www.parapublishing.com, pg 181

Poynter, Dan, Santa Barbara Book Promotion Workshop, PO Box 8206-240, Santa Barbara, CA 93118-8206 *Tel:* 805-968-7277 *Toll Free Tel:* 800-727-2782 *Fax:* 805-968-1379 *E-mail:* info@parapublishing.com *Web Site:* www.parapublishing.com, pg 655

Pozier, Bernard, Ecrits des Forges, 992-A rue Royale, Trois-Rivieres, QC G9A 4H9, Canada *Tel:* 819-840-8492 *E-mail:* ecritsdesforges@gmail.com *Web Site:* www.ecritsdesforges.com, pg 479

Poznansky, Joel, Columbia Books & Information Services, 4340 East-West Hwy, Suite 300, Bethesda, MD 20814 *Tel:* 240-235-0266 *Toll Free Tel:* 888-265-0600 (cust serv) *Fax:* 202-464-1775 *E-mail:* info@columbiabooks.com *Web Site:* www.columbiabooks.com; www.lobbyists.info; www.associationexecs.com, pg 61

Pracher, Richard, Henry Holt and Company, LLC, 175 Fifth Ave, New York, NY 10010 *Tel:* 646-307-5151 *Toll Free Tel:* 888-330-8477 (orders) *Fax:* 646-307-5285 *E-mail:* firstname.lastname@hholt.com *Web Site:* www.henryholt.com, pg 113

Praded, Joni, Chelsea Green Publishing Co, 85 N Main St, Suite 120, White River Junction, VT 05001 *Tel:* 802-295-6300 *Toll Free Tel:* 800-639-4099 (cust serv, consumer & trade orders) *Fax:* 802-295-6444 *Web Site:* www.chelseagreen.com, pg 56

Praeger, Marta, Robert A Freedman Dramatic Agency Inc, 1501 Broadway, Suite 2310, New York, NY 10036 *Tel:* 212-840-5760 *Fax:* 212-840-5776, pg 553

Pratt, Darrin, University Press of Colorado, 5589 Arapahoe Ave, Suite 206-C, Boulder, CO 80303 *Tel:* 720-406-8849 *Toll Free Tel:* 800-621-2736 (orders) *Fax:* 720-406-3443 *Web Site:* www.upcolorado.com, pg 261

Precourt, Geoffrey, Advertising Research Foundation (ARF), 432 Park Ave S, 6th fl, New York, NY 10016-8013 *Tel:* 212-751-5656 *Fax:* 212-319-5265 *E-mail:* info@thearf.org; jar@thearf.org (edit) *Web Site:* www.thearf.org, pg 593

Prellwitz, Gwendolyn, Coretta Scott King Book Awards, 50 E Huron St, Chicago, IL 60611 *Toll Free Tel:* 800-545-2433 *E-mail:* olos@ala.org *Web Site:* www.ala.org/emiert/cskbookawards, pg 698

Prentis, Linn, Linn Prentis Literary, 6830 NE Bothell Way, PMB 496, Kenmore, WA 98028 *Tel:* 212-876-8557 *Fax:* 206-984-0837 *E-mail:* linn@linnprentis.com *Web Site:* www.linnprentis.com, pg 568

Prentiss, Winnie, Fair Winds Press, 100 Cummings Ctr, Suite 406-L, Beverly, MA 01915 *Tel:* 978-282-9590 *Fax:* 978-282-7765 *E-mail:* sales@quartos.com *Web Site:* www.quartoknows.com, pg 85

Prescott, Emily, Unicorn Writers' Conference, 17 Church Hill Rd, Redding, CT 06896 *Tel:* 203-938-7405 *Fax:* 203-938-7405 *E-mail:* unicornwritersconference@gmail.com *Web Site:* unicornwritersconference.com, pg 656

Presley, Ali, Chronicle Books LLC, 680 Second St, San Francisco, CA 94107 *Tel:* 415-537-4200 *Toll Free Tel:* 800-759-0190 (cust serv) *Fax:* 415-537-4460 *Toll Free Fax:* 800-858-7787 (orders); 800-286-9471 (cust serv) *E-mail:* frontdesk@chroniclebooks.com *Web Site:* www.chroniclebooks.com, pg 58

Presley, Ron, Florida Outdoor Writers Association Inc, 24 NW 33 Ct, Suite A, Gainesville, FL 32607 *Tel:* 352-284-1763 *E-mail:* info@fowa.org *Web Site:* www.fowa.org, pg 606

Presley, Todd, Chronicle Books LLC, 680 Second St, San Francisco, CA 94107 *Tel:* 415-537-4200 *Toll Free Tel:* 800-759-0190 (cust serv) *Fax:* 415-537-4460 *Toll Free Fax:* 800-858-7787 (orders); 800-286-9471 (cust serv) *E-mail:* frontdesk@chroniclebooks.com *Web Site:* www.chroniclebooks.com, pg 57

Prestia, Christina, Jane Rotrosen Agency LLC, 318 E 51 St, New York, NY 10022 *Tel:* 212-593-4330 *Fax:* 212-935-6985 *Web Site:* janerotrosen.com, pg 571

Preston, Mark, United States Tennis Association, 70 W Red Oak Lane, White Plains, NY 10604 *Tel:* 914-696-7000 *Fax:* 914-696-7027 *Web Site:* www.usta.com, pg 254

Preston, Michael L, John Wiley & Sons Inc, 111 River St, Hoboken, NJ 07030-5774 *Tel:* 201-748-6000 *Toll Free Tel:* 800-225-5945 (cust serv) *Fax:* 201-748-6088 *E-mail:* info@wiley.com *Web Site:* www.wiley.com, pg 272

Pricci, Linda, Rizzoli International Publications Inc, 300 Park Ave S, 4th fl, New York, NY 10010-5399 *Tel:* 212-387-3400 *Toll Free Tel:* 800-522-6657 (orders only) *Fax:* 212-387-3535 *E-mail:* publicity@rizzoliusa.com *Web Site:* www.rizzoliusa.com, pg 209

Price, B Byron, University of Oklahoma Press, 2800 Venture Dr, Norman, OK 73069-8216 *Tel:* 405-325-2000 *Toll Free Tel:* 800-627-7377 (orders) *Fax:* 405-364-5798 (orders) *Toll Free Fax:* 800-735-0476 (orders) *E-mail:* presscs@ou.edu *Web Site:* www.oupress.com, pg 258

Price, Bernadette B, Orbis Books, Price Bldg, Box 302, Maryknoll, NY 10545-0302 *Tel:* 914-941-7636 *Toll Free Tel:* 800-258-5838 (orders) *Fax:* 914-941-7005 *E-mail:* orbisbooks@maryknoll.org *Web Site:* www.orbisbooks.com, pg 176

Price, Bruce, Marathon Press, 1500 Square Turn Blvd, Norfolk, NE 68701 *Tel:* 402-371-5040 *Toll Free Tel:* 800-228-0629 *Fax:* 402-371-9382 *Web Site:* www.marathonpress.com, pg 147

Price, Chris, Graphic Arts Show Company (GASC), 1899 Preston White Dr, Reston, VA 20191 *Tel:* 703-264-7200 *Fax:* 703-620-9187 *E-mail:* info@gasc.org *Web Site:* www.gasc.org, pg 606

Price, Robert, Gatekeeper Press, 3971 Hoover Rd, Suite 77, Columbus, OH 43123-2839 *Toll Free Tel:* 866-535-0913 *Fax:* 216-403-1314 *E-mail:* info@gatekeeperpress.com *Web Site:* www.gatekeeperpress.com, pg 95

Price, Robert Esq, Price World Publishing, 3971 Hoover Rd, Suite 77, Columbus, OH 43123-2839 *Toll Free Tel:* 888-234-6896 *Fax:* 216-803-0350 *E-mail:* info@priceworldpublishing.com *Web Site:* www.priceworldpublishing.com, pg 196

Price, Todd Alan, Stanley Drama Award, One Campus Rd, Staten Island, NY 10301 *Tel:* 718-390-3223 *Fax:* 718-390-3323, pg 730

Price, Vince, ProQuest LLC, 789 E Eisenhower Pkwy, Ann Arbor, MI 48108-3218 *Tel:* 734-761-4700 *Toll Free Tel:* 800-521-0600 *Fax:* 734-975-6486 *Toll Free Fax:* 800-864-0019 *E-mail:* info@proquest.com *Web Site:* www.proquest.com, pg 199

Prichard, Rob, Penguin Group (Canada), 90 Eglinton Ave E, Suite 700, Toronto, ON M4P 2Y3, Canada *Tel:* 416-925-2249 *Fax:* 416-925-0068 *E-mail:* customerservicescanada@penguinrandomhouse.com *Web Site:* penguinrandomhouse.ca, pg 494

Priddis, Ronald L, Signature Books Publishing LLC, 564 W 400 N, Salt Lake City, UT 84116-3411 *Tel:* 801-531-1483 *Fax:* 801-531-1488 *E-mail:* people@signaturebooks.com *Web Site:* www.signaturebooks.com; www.signaturebookslibrary.org, pg 224

Priddle, Clive, PublicAffairs, 250 W 57 St, Suite 1321, New York, NY 10107 *Tel:* 212-397-6666 *Toll Free Tel:* 800-343-4499 (orders) *Fax:* 212-397-4277 *E-mail:* publicaffairs@perseusbooks.com *Web Site:* www.publicaffairsbooks.com, pg 200

Pride, Jean, ASCD, 1703 N Beauregard St, Alexandria, VA 22311-1714 *Tel:* 703-578-9600 *Toll Free Tel:* 800-933-2723 *Fax:* 703-575-5400 *E-mail:* member@ascd.org *Web Site:* www.ascd.org, pg 23

Priest, Aaron M, The Aaron M Priest Literary Agency Inc, 708 Third Ave, 23rd fl, New York, NY 10017-4201 *Tel:* 212-818-0344 *Fax:* 212-573-9417 *E-mail:* info@aaronpriest.com *Web Site:* www.aaronpriest.com, pg 568

Prieur, Richard, Association Nationale des Editeurs de Livres, 2514 boul Rosemont, Montreal, QC H1Y 1K4, Canada *Tel:* 514-273-8130 *Toll Free Tel:* 866-900-ANEL (900-2635) *E-mail:* info@anel.qc.ca *Web Site:* www.anel.qc.ca, pg 598

Primlani, Vijay, Science Publishers Inc, PO Box 699, Enfield, NH 03748-0699 *Tel:* 603-632-7377 *Fax:* 603-632-5611 *E-mail:* info@scipub.net *Web Site:* www.scipub.net, pg 220

Prince, Danforth, Blood Moon Productions Ltd, 75 Saint Marks Place, Staten Island, NY 10301-1606 *Tel:* 718-556-9410 *E-mail:* editors@bloodmoonproductions.com *Web Site:* bloodmoonproductions.com, pg 39

Pringle, Rebecca "Becky", National Education Association (NEA), 1201 16 St NW, Washington, DC 20036-3290 *Tel:* 202-833-4000 *Fax:* 202-822-7974 *Web Site:* www.nea.org, pg 164, 612

Prior, Robert, The MIT Press, 55 Hayward St, Cambridge, MA 02142 *Tel:* 617-253-5255 *Toll Free Tel:* 800-207-8354 (orders) *Fax:* 617-258-6779; 617-577-1545 (orders) *Web Site:* mitpress.mit.edu, pg 158

Proia, Brandon, PublicAffairs, 250 W 57 St, Suite 1321, New York, NY 10107 *Tel:* 212-397-6666 *Toll Free Tel:* 800-343-4499 (orders) *Fax:* 212-397-4277 *E-mail:* publicaffairs@perseusbooks.com *Web Site:* www.publicaffairsbooks.com, pg 200

Proia, Brandon, The University of North Carolina Press, 116 S Boundary St, Chapel Hill, NC 27514-3808 *Tel:* 919-966-3561 *Fax:* 919-966-3829 *E-mail:* uncpress@unc.edu *Web Site:* www.uncpress.unc.edu, pg 258

Pronk, Gord, Pronk Media Inc, PO Box 340, Beaverton, ON L0K 1A0, Canada *Tel:* 416-441-3760 *E-mail:* info@pronk.com *Web Site:* www.pronk.com, pg 532

Pronovost, Nita, Simon & Schuster Canada, 166 King St E, Suite 300, Toronto, ON M5A 1J3, Canada *Tel:* 647-427-8882 *Toll Free Tel:* 800-387-0446; 800-268-3216 (orders) *Fax:* 647-430-9446 *Toll Free Fax:* 888-849-8151 (orders) *E-mail:* info@simonandschuster.ca *Web Site:* www.simonandschuster.ca, pg 499

Proppe, Tinna, Edda USA, 373 Park Ave S, 6th fl, New York, NY 10016 *Tel:* 646-755-9210 *Web Site:* eddausa.com, pg 79

Prosser, Julia, Simon & Schuster, 1230 Avenue of the Americas, New York, NY 10020 *Tel:* 212-698-7000 *Toll Free Tel:* 800-223-2348 (cust serv); 800-223-2336 (orders) *Toll Free Fax:* 800-943-9831 (orders) *Web Site:* www.simonandschuster.com, pg 225

Prosser, Megan, Aptara Inc, 3110 Fairview Park Dr, Suite 900, Falls Church, VA 22042 *Tel:* 703-352-0001 *E-mail:* info@aptaracorp.com *Web Site:* www.aptaracorp.com, pg 520

Prost, Jennifer, Joelle Delbourgo Associates Inc, 101 Park St, Montclair, NJ 07042 *Tel:* 973-773-0836 (call only during standard business hours) *Web Site:* www.delbourgo.com, pg 548

Protano, Generosa Gina, GGP Publishing Inc, 105 Calvert St, Suite 201, Harrison, NY 10528-3138 *Tel:* 914-834-8896 *Fax:* 914-834-7566 *Web Site:* www.GGPPublishing.com, pg 526, 554

Proulx, Marc, Editions FouLire, 4339, rue des Becassines, Quebec, QC G1G 1V5, Canada *Tel:* 418-628-4029 *Toll Free Tel:* 877-628-4029 (CN & US) *Fax:* 418-628-4801 *E-mail:* info@foulire.com; edition@foulire.com *Web Site:* www.foulire.com, pg 481

Provost, Cherry, Medal of Honor for Literature, 15 Gramercy Park S, New York, NY 10003 *E-mail:* literary@thenationalartsclub.org *Web Site:* www.nationalartsclub.org, pg 707

Prudhomme, Jessica, Crown Publishing Group, c/o Penguin Random House Inc, 1745 Broadway, New York, NY 10019 *Tel:* 212-782-9000 *Toll Free Tel:* 888-264-1745 *Fax:* 212-940-7408 *E-mail:* crownosm@penguinrandomhouse.com *Web Site:* crownpublishing.com, pg 68

Pruett, Robert H, Brandylane Publishers Inc, 5 S First St, Richmond, VA 23219 *Tel:* 804-644-3090 *Fax:* 804-644-3092 *Web Site:* brandylanepublishers.com, pg 44

Prunty, Wyatt, Sewanee Writers' Conference, Stamler Ctr, 119 Gailor Hall, 735 University Ave, Sewanee, TN 37383-1000 *Tel:* 931-598-1141 *E-mail:* swc@sewanee.edu *Web Site:* www.sewaneewriters.org, pg 655

Prybylowski, Doug, Comex Systems Inc, 101 Pleasant Hill Rd, Chester, NJ 07930 *Tel:* 973-543-2862 *Toll Free Tel:* 800-543-6959 *Fax:* 973-543-9644 *E-mail:* mail@comexsystems.com *Web Site:* www.comexsystems.com, pg 62

Pryor, Victoria Gould, Arcadia, 31 Lake Place N, Danbury, CT 06810 *Tel:* 203-797-0993 *E-mail:* arcadialit@sbcglobal.net, pg 541

Psaltis, Elizabeth, Gallery Books, 1230 Avenue of the Americas, New York, NY 10020 *Toll Free Tel:* 800-456-6798 *Fax:* 212-698-7284 *E-mail:* consumer.customerservice@simonandschuster.com *Web Site:* www.simonsays.com, pg 94

Pucci, Cameron, Institute of Police Technology & Management, University Ctr, 12000 Alumni Dr, Jacksonville, FL 32224-2678 *Tel:* 904-620-4786 *Fax:* 904-620-2453 *E-mail:* info@iptm.org; orders@iptm.org *Web Site:* www.iptm.org, pg 123

Pucillo, Ann-Marie, Houghton Mifflin Harcourt Trade & Reference Division, 222 Berkeley St, Boston, MA 02116 *Tel:* 617-351-5000 *Toll Free Tel:* 800-225-3362 *Web Site:* www.hmhco.com, pg 115

Pugh, Marsha, Dog Writers' Association of America Inc (DWAA), 66 Adams St, Jamestown, NY 14701 *Tel:* 716-484-6155 *E-mail:* dogwriter@windstream.net *Web Site:* www.dwaa.org, pg 604

Pugh, Marsha, Dog Writers' Association of America Inc (DWAA) Annual Writing Competition, 2243 Kelmscott Ct, Westlake Village, CA 91361 *Tel:* 805-418-7899 *Fax:* 831-374-9231 *E-mail:* dogwriter@windstream.net *Web Site:* www.dwaa.org, pg 681

Puglisi, Jess, Fence Books, University at Albany, Science Library 320, 1400 Washington Ave, Albany, NY 12222 *Tel:* 518-591-8162 *E-mail:* fence.fencebooks@gmail.com *Web Site:* www.fenceportal.org, pg 87

Puglisi, Jess, Fence Modern Poets Series, University at Albany, Science Library 320, 1400 Washington Ave, Albany, NY 12222 *Tel:* 518-591-8162 *E-mail:* fence.fencebooks@gmail.com *Web Site:* www.fenceportal.org, pg 685

Puglisi, Jess, Ottoline Morrell Prize, University at Albany, Science Library 320, 1400 Washington Ave, Albany, NY 12222 *Tel:* 518-591-8162 *E-mail:* fence.fencebooks@gmail.com *Web Site:* www.fenceportal.org, pg 709

Puhalo, Archbishop Lazar, Synaxis Press, 37323 Hawkins Rd, Dewdney, BC V0M 1H0, Canada *Tel:* 604-826-9336 *E-mail:* synaxis@new-ostrog.org *Web Site:* synaxispress.ca, pg 500

Pujic, Anja, DC Canada Education Publishing (DCCED), 180 Metcalfe St, Suite 204, Ottawa, ON K2P 1P5, Canada *Tel:* 613-565-8885 *Toll Free Tel:* 888-565-0262 *Fax:* 613-565-8881 *E-mail:* info@dc-canada.ca *Web Site:* www.dc-canada.ca, pg 478

Pulice, Mario, Little, Brown and Company, 1290 Avenue of the Americas, New York, NY 10019 *Tel:* 212-364-1100 *Fax:* 212-364-0952 *E-mail:* firstname.lastname@hbgusa.com *Web Site:* www.HachetteBookGroup.com, pg 141

Pullano, Michelle, The MIT Press, 55 Hayward St, Cambridge, MA 02142 *Tel:* 617-253-5255 *Toll Free Tel:* 800-207-8354 (orders) *Fax:* 617-258-6779; 617-577-1545 (orders) *Web Site:* mitpress.mit.edu, pg 158

Pullen, Lindsey, The Perseus Books Group, 387 Park Ave S, 12th fl, New York, NY 10016 *Tel:* 212-340-8100 *Toll Free Tel:* 800-343-4499 (cust serv) *Fax:* 212-340-8105 *Web Site:* www.perseusbooksgroup.com, pg 189

Puls, Eloise, University of Rochester Press, 668 Mount Hope Ave, Rochester, NY 14620-2731 *Tel:* 585-275-0419 *Fax:* 585-271-8778 *E-mail:* boydell@boydellusa.net *Web Site:* www.urpress.com, pg 259

Pult, Richard, University Press of New England, One Court St, Suite 250, Lebanon, NH 03766 *Tel:* 603-448-1533 *Toll Free Tel:* 800-421-1561 (orders only) *Fax:* 603-448-7006; 603-643-1540 *E-mail:* university.press@dartmouth.edu *Web Site:* www.upne.com, pg 262

Pulver, Sarah, Ten Speed Press, 2625 Alcatraz Ave, Unit 505, Berkeley, CA 94705 *Tel:* 510-285-3000 *Toll Free Tel:* 800-841-BOOK (841-2665) *E-mail:* csorders@randomhouse.com *Web Site:* crownpublishing.com/imprint/ten-speed-press, pg 243

Punia, Katherine Fleming, Living Language, c/o Random House Inc, 1745 Broadway, New York, NY 10019 *Tel:* 212-782-9000 *Toll Free Tel:* 800-733-3000 (orders) *Toll Free Fax:* 800-659-2436 *E-mail:* livinglanguage@randomhouse.com *Web Site:* www.livinglanguage.com, pg 142

Puopolo, Kristine, Doubleday/Nan A Talese, c/o Penguin Random House Inc, 1745 Broadway, New York, NY 10019 *Tel:* 212-751-2600 *Fax:* 212-572-2662 *E-mail:* ddaypub@randomhouse.com *Web Site:* knopfdoubleday.com, pg 76

Puppa, Brian, TCP Press, Legacy Ctr, 9 Lobraico Lane, Whitchurch-Stouffville, ON L4A 7X5, Canada *Tel:* 905-640-8914 *Toll Free Tel:* 800-772-7765 *E-mail:* tcp@tcpnow.com *Web Site:* www.tcppress.com, pg 500

Purcell, Anita, CAA Award for Fiction, 6 West St N, Suite 203, Orillia, ON L3V 5B8, Canada *Tel:* 705-325-3926 *Toll Free Tel:* 866-216-6222 *E-mail:* admin@canadianauthors.org *Web Site:* www.canadianauthors.org, pg 675

Purcell, Anita, CAA Emerging Writer Award, 6 West St N, Suite 203, Orillia, ON L3V 5B8, Canada *Tel:* 705-325-3926 *Toll Free Tel:* 866-216-6222 *E-mail:* admin@canadianauthors.org *Web Site:* www.canadianauthors.org, pg 675

Purcell, Anita, CAA Lela Common Award for Canadian History, 6 West St N, Suite 203, Orillia, ON L3V 5B8, Canada *Tel:* 705-325-3926 *Toll Free Tel:* 866-216-6222 *E-mail:* admin@canadianauthors.org *Web Site:* www.canadianauthors.org, pg 675

Purcell, Anita, CAA Poetry Award, 6 West St N, Suite 203, Orillia, ON L3V 5B8, Canada *Tel:* 705-325-3926 *Toll Free Tel:* 866-216-6222 *E-mail:* admin@canadianauthors.org *Web Site:* www.canadianauthors.org, pg 675

Purcell, Anita, Canadian Authors Association (CAA), 6 West St N, Suite 203, Orillia, ON L3V 5B8, Canada *Tel:* 705-325-3926 *Toll Free Tel:* 866-216-6222 *E-mail:* admin@canadianauthors.org *Web Site:* www.canadianauthors.org, pg 601

Purcell, Jessica, Alfred A Knopf/Everyman's Library, c/o Random House Inc, 1745 Broadway, New York, NY 10019 *Tel:* 212-751-2600 *Toll Free Tel:* 800-638-6460 *Fax:* 212-572-2593 *Web Site:* www.knopfdoubleday.com, pg 132

Purcell, Nancy, Simon & Schuster Canada, 166 King St E, Suite 300, Toronto, ON M5A 1J3, Canada *Tel:* 647-427-8882 *Toll Free Tel:* 800-387-0446; 800-268-3216 (orders) *Fax:* 647-430-9446 *Toll Free Fax:* 888-849-8151 (orders) *E-mail:* info@simonandschuster.ca *Web Site:* www.simonandschuster.ca, pg 499

Purdy, C, Oxford University Press USA, 198 Madison Ave, New York, NY 10016 *Tel:* 212-726-6000 *Toll Free Tel:* 800-451-7556 (orders); 800-445-9714 (cust serv) *Fax:* 919-677-1303 *E-mail:* custserv.us@oup.com *Web Site:* www.oup.com/us, pg 179

Purelis, Eileen, Springer, 233 Spring St, New York, NY 10013-1578 *Tel:* 212-460-1500 *Toll Free Tel:* 800-SPRINGER (777-4643) *Fax:* 212-460-1575 *E-mail:* service-ny@springer.com *Web Site:* www.springer.com, pg 232

Purich, Donald, Purich Publishing Ltd, PO Box 23032, Market Mall Postal Outlet, Saskatoon, SK S7J 5H3, Canada *Tel:* 306-373-5311 *Fax:* 306-373-5315 *E-mail:* purich@sasktel.net *Web Site:* www.purichpublishing.com, pg 496

Puro, Nina, Persea Books, 277 Broadway, Suite 708, New York, NY 10007 *Tel:* 212-260-9256 *Fax:* 212-267-3165 *E-mail:* info@perseabooks.com *Web Site:* www.perseabooks.com, pg 189

Purple, Katherine, Purdue University Press, Stewart Ctr 370, 504 W State St, West Lafayette, IN 47907-2058 *Tel:* 765-494-2038 *Fax:* 765-496-2442 *E-mail:* pupress@purdue.edu *Web Site:* www.thepress.purdue.edu, pg 200

Purtell, April, Hewitt Homeschooling Resources, 2103 Main St, Washougal, WA 98671 *Tel:* 360-835-8708 *Toll Free Tel:* 800-348-1750 *Fax:* 360-835-8697 *E-mail:* sales@hewitthomeschooling.com *Web Site:* hewitthomeschooling.com, pg 111

Pusey, Stacey, AAP PreK-12 Learning Group, 325 Chestnut St, Suite 1110, Philadelphia, PA 19106 *Tel:* 267-351-4310 *Fax:* 267-351-4317 *E-mail:* prek12learning@publishers.org *Web Site:* www.aepweb.org, pg 593

Putnam, Richelle, MWG Writer Workshops, PO Box 3845, Meridian, MS 39303-3845 *Tel:* 601-880-1089 *Web Site:* www.mississippiwritersguild.com, pg 653

Pye, Michael, The Career Press Inc, 12 Parish Dr, Wayne, NJ 07470 *Tel:* 201-848-0310 *Toll Free Tel:* 800-CAREER-1 (227-3371) *Fax:* 201-848-1727 *E-mail:* sales@careerpress.com *Web Site:* www.careerpress.com, pg 50

Pyle, Ellie, DC Entertainment, 2900 Alameda, Burbank, CA 91505 *Toll Free Tel:* 800-887-6789 *E-mail:* dccomics@cambeywest.com *Web Site:* www.dcentertainment.com; www.dccomics.com; www.madmag.com, pg 72

Pyster, Phil, National Cartoonists Society (NCS), 341 N Maitland Ave, Suite 260, Maitland, FL 32751 *Tel:* 407-647-8839 *Fax:* 407-629-2502 *E-mail:* info@reuben.org *Web Site:* www.reuben.org, pg 611

Quach, Andrew, Standard Publishing, 8805 Governors Hill Dr, Suite 400, Cincinnati, OH 45249 *Tel:* 513-931-4050 *Toll Free Tel:* 800-543-1353 *Fax:* 513-931-0950 *Toll Free Fax:* 877-867-5751 *E-mail:* customerservice@standardpub.com *Web Site:* www.standardpub.com, pg 233

Qualben, Lois, LangMarc Publishing, PO Box 90488, Austin, TX 78709-0488 *Tel:* 512-394-0989 *Toll Free Tel:* 800-864-1648 (orders) *Fax:* 512-394-0829 *E-mail:* langmarc@booksails.com *Web Site:* www.langmarc.com, pg 134

Qualben, Michael, LangMarc Publishing, PO Box 90488, Austin, TX 78709-0488 *Tel:* 512-394-0989 *Toll Free Tel:* 800-864-1648 (orders) *Fax:* 512-394-0829 *E-mail:* langmarc@booksails.com *Web Site:* www.langmarc.com, pg 134

Quon, Felicia, Simon & Schuster Canada, 166 King St E, Suite 300, Toronto, ON M5A 1J3, Canada *Tel:* 647-427-8882 *Toll Free Tel:* 800-387-0446; 800-268-3216 (orders) *Fax:* 647-430-9446 *Toll Free Fax:* 888-849-8151 (orders) *E-mail:* info@simonandschuster.ca *Web Site:* www.simonandschuster.ca, pg 499

Raab, Jackie, Barron's Educational Series Inc, 250 Wireless Blvd, Hauppauge, NY 11788 *Tel:* 631-434-3311 *Toll Free Tel:* 800-645-3476 *Fax:* 631-434-3723 *E-mail:* barrons@barronseduc.com *Web Site:* www.barronseduc.com, pg 31

Raab, Jamie, Grand Central Publishing, 1290 Avenue of the Americas, New York, NY 10019 *Tel:* 212-364-1100 *Web Site:* www.hachettebookgroup.com, pg 99

Raab, Jamie, Hachette Book Group, 1290 Avenue of the Americas, New York, NY 10019 *Tel:* 212-364-1100 *Toll Free Tel:* 800-759-0190 (cust serv) *Fax:* 212-364-0933 (intl orders) *Toll Free Fax:* 800-286-9471 (cust serv) *Web Site:* www.HachetteBookGroup.com, pg 102

Raagas, Lorna, Financial Executives Research Foundation Inc (FERF), West Tower, 7th fl, 1250 Headquarters Plaza, Morristown, NJ 07960-6837 *Tel:* 973-765-1000 *Fax:* 973-765-1023 *Web Site:* www.financialexecutives.org, pg 88

Rab, Sharon, Dayton Literary Peace Prize, 25 Harman Terr, Dayton, OH 45419 *Tel:* 937-298-5072 *Web Site:* daytonliterarypeaceprize.org, pg 680

Rabberman, Kristine PhD, College of Liberal & Professional Studies, University of Pennsylvania, 3440 Market St, Suite 100, Philadelphia, PA 19104-3335 *Tel:* 215-898-7326 *Fax:* 215-573-2053 *E-mail:* lps@sas.upenn.edu *Web Site:* www.sas.upenn.edu; www.sas.upenn.edu/lps, pg 659

Rabiner, Susan, Susan Rabiner Literary Agency Inc, 315 W 39 St, Suite 1501, New York, NY 10018-3907 *Web Site:* RabinerLit.com, pg 569

Rabinovitch, Elana, Giller Prize, 543 Logan Ave, Toronto, ON M4K 3B6, Canada *Web Site:* www.scotiabankgillerprize.ca, pg 689

Rabinowitz, Jonathan D, Turtle Point Press, 233 Broadway, Rm 946, New York, NY 10279 *Tel:* 212-945-6622 *E-mail:* countomega@aol.com *Web Site:* www.turtlepointpress.com, pg 251

Raccah, Dominique, Cumberland House, 1935 Brookdale Rd, Suite 139, Naperville, IL 60563 *Tel:* 630-961-3900 *Toll Free Tel:* 800-43-BRIGHT (432-7444) *Fax:* 630-961-2168 *E-mail:* info@sourcebooks.com *Web Site:* www.sourcebooks.com, pg 69

Raccah, Dominique, Sourcebooks Inc, 1935 Brookdale Rd, Suite 139, Naperville, IL 60563 *Tel:* 630-961-3900 *Toll Free Tel:* 800-432-7444 *Fax:* 630-961-2168 *E-mail:* info@sourcebooks.com; customersupport@sourcebooks.com *Web Site:* www.sourcebooks.com, pg 230

Racette, Ann-Christine, Fordham University Press, 2546 Belmont Ave, University Box L, Bronx, NY 10458 *Tel:* 718-817-4795 *Fax:* 718-817-4785 *Web Site:* www.fordhampress.com, pg 90

Rach, Beverly, Fernwood Publishing, 32 Oceanvista Lane, Black Point, NS B0J 1B0, Canada *Tel:* 902-857-1388 *Fax:* 902-857-1328 *E-mail:* info@fernpub.ca; roseway@fernpub.ca *Web Site:* fernwoodpublishing.ca, pg 483

Rada, Monica, OCP, 5536 NE Hassalo St, Portland, OR 97213 *Tel:* 503-281-1191 *Toll Free Tel:* 800-548-8749 *Fax:* 503-282-3486 *Toll Free Fax:* 800-843-8181 *E-mail:* liturgy@ocp.org *Web Site:* www.ocp.org, pg 173

Radant, Cyndi, Carolrhoda Books, 241 First Ave N, Minneapolis, MN 55401 *Tel:* 612-332-3344 *Toll Free Tel:* 800-328-4929 *Fax:* 612-332-7615 *Toll Free Fax:* 800-332-1132 *E-mail:* info@lernerbooks.com *Web Site:* www.lernerbooks.com, pg 50

Radant, Cyndi, ediciones Lerner, 241 First Ave N, Minneapolis, MN 55401 *Tel:* 612-332-3344 *Toll Free Tel:* 800-328-4929 *Fax:* 612-332-7615 *Toll Free Fax:* 800-332-1132 *E-mail:* info@lernerbooks.com *Web Site:* www.lernerbooks.com, pg 79

Radant, Cyndi, First Avenue Editions, 241 First Ave N, Minneapolis, MN 55401 *Tel:* 612-332-3344 *Toll Free Tel:* 800-328-4929 *Fax:* 612-332-7615 *Toll Free Fax:* 800-332-1132 *E-mail:* info@lernerbooks.com *Web Site:* www.lernerbooks.com, pg 89

Radant, Cyndi, Graphic Universe™, 241 First Ave N, Minneapolis, MN 55401 *Tel:* 612-332-3344 *Toll Free Tel:* 800-328-4929 *Fax:* 612-332-7615 *Toll Free Fax:* 800-332-1132 *E-mail:* info@lernerbooks.com *Web Site:* www.lernerbooks.com, pg 99

Radant, Cyndi, Lerner Publications, 241 First Ave N, Minneapolis, MN 55401 *Tel:* 612-332-3344 *Toll Free Tel:* 800-328-4929 *Fax:* 612-332-7615 *Toll Free Fax:* 800-332-1132 *E-mail:* info@lernerbooks.com *Web Site:* www.lernerbooks.com, pg 137

Radant, Cyndi, Lerner Publishing Group Inc, 241 First Ave N, Minneapolis, MN 55401 *Tel:* 612-332-3344 *Toll Free Tel:* 800-328-4929 *Fax:* 612-332-7615 *Toll Free Fax:* 800-332-1132 *E-mail:* info@lernerbooks.com *Web Site:* www.lernerbooks.com, pg 137

Radant, Cyndi, LernerClassroom, 241 First Ave N, Minneapolis, MN 55401 *Tel:* 612-332-3344 *Toll Free Tel:* 800-328-4929 *Fax:* 612-332-7615 *Toll Free Fax:* 800-332-1132 *E-mail:* info@lernerbooks.com *Web Site:* www.lernerbooks.com, pg 137

Radant, Cyndi, Millbrook Press, 241 First Ave N, Minneapolis, MN 55401 *Tel:* 612-332-3344 *Toll Free Tel:* 800-328-4929 (US only) *Fax:* 612-332-7615 *Toll Free Fax:* 800-332-1132, pg 157

Radant, Cyndi, Twenty-First Century Books, 241 First Ave N, Minneapolis, MN 55401 *Tel:* 612-332-3344 *Toll Free Tel:* 800-328-4929 *Fax:* 612-332-7615 *Toll Free Fax:* 800-332-1132 *E-mail:* info@lernerbooks.com *Web Site:* www.lernerbooks.com, pg 251

Radcliffe, Barbara, Center for the Collaborative Classroom, 1250 53 St, Suite 3, Emeryville, CA 94608 *Tel:* 510-533-0213 *Toll Free Tel:* 800-666-7270 *Fax:* 510-464-3670 *E-mail:* info@collaborativeclassroom.org; clientsupport@collaborativeclassroom.org *Web Site:* www.collaborativeclassroom.org, pg 53

Rade, David, Swan Isle Press, 11030 S Langley Ave, Chicago, IL 60628 *Tel:* 773-728-3780 (edit); 773-702-7000 (cust serv) *Toll Free Tel:* 800-621-2736 (cust serv) *Fax:* 773-702-7212 (cust serv) *Toll Free Fax:* 800-621-8476 (cust serv) *E-mail:* info@swanislepress.com *Web Site:* www.swanislepress.com, pg 239

Radford, Deanna, Quebec Writers' Federation (QWF), 1200 Atwater Ave, Suite 3, Westmount, QC H3Z 1X4, Canada *Tel:* 514-933-0878 *E-mail:* info@qwf.org *Web Site:* www.qwf.org, pg 617

Radford, Deanna, QWF Literary Awards, 1200 Atwater Ave, Suite 3, Westmount, QC H3Z 1X4, Canada *Tel:* 514-933-0878 *E-mail:* info@qwf.org *Web Site:* www.qwf.org, pg 722

Radice, Neal, Maxim Mazumdar New Play Competition, One Curtain Up Alley, Buffalo, NY 14202-1911 *Tel:* 716-852-2600 *E-mail:* publicrelations@alleyway.com *Web Site:* alleyway.com, pg 706

Radich, Anthony, Western States Arts Federation, 1743 Wazee St, Suite 300, Denver, CO 80202 *Tel:* 303-629-1166 *Toll Free Tel:* 888-562-7232 *Fax:* 303-629-9717 *E-mail:* staff@westaf.org *Web Site:* www.westaf.org, pg 623

Radke, Linda F, Five Star Dragonfly Book Awards, 4696 W Tyson St, Chandler, AZ 85226-2903 *Tel:* 480-940-8182 *Fax:* 480-940-8787 *E-mail:* info@fivestarpublications.com *Web Site:* www.FiveStarBookAwards.com; www.FiveStarPublications.com, pg 686

Radke, Linda F, Five Star Publications Inc, 4696 W Tyson St, Chandler, AZ 85226-2903 *Tel:* 480-940-8182 *Fax:* 480-940-8787 *E-mail:* fivestarpublications@gmail.com *Web Site:* www.FiveStarPublications.com; www.FiveStarBookAwards.com; www.AuthorsandExperts.com, pg 89

Radke, Linda F, Five Star Publishing & Marketing Secrets, 4696 W Tyson St, Chandler, AZ 85226-2903 *Tel:* 480-940-8182 *Fax:* 480-940-8787 *E-mail:* info@fivestarpublications.com *Web Site:* www.FiveStarPublications.com, pg 650

Radler, Kyle, Scribner, 1230 Avenue of the Americas, New York, NY 10020, pg 220

Rados, Kate, Crown Publishing Group, c/o Penguin Random House Inc, 1745 Broadway, New York, NY 10019 *Tel:* 212-782-9000 *Toll Free Tel:* 888-264-1745 *Fax:* 212-940-7408 *E-mail:* crownosm@penguinrandomhouse.com *Web Site:* crownpublishing.com, pg 68

Raducanu, Teodor, Teora USA LLC, 505 Hampton Park Blvd, Unit G, Capitol Heights, MD 20743 *Tel:* 301-986-6990 *Toll Free Tel:* 800-974-2105 *Fax:* 301-350-5480 *Toll Free Fax:* 800-358-3754 *E-mail:* 2010@teora.com *Web Site:* www.teora.com, pg 243

Rae, Sonia, Vermont Arts Council Grants, 136 State St, Montpelier, VT 05602 *Tel:* 802-828-5425 *Fax:* 802-828-3363 *E-mail:* info@vermontartscouncil.org *Web Site:* www.vermontartscouncil.org, pg 734

Raeber, Rick, W W Norton & Company Inc, 500 Fifth Ave, New York, NY 10110-0017 *Tel:* 212-354-5500 *Toll Free Tel:* 800-233-4830 (orders & cust serv) *Fax:* 212-869-0856 *Toll Free Fax:* 800-458-6515 *Web Site:* www.wwnorton.com, pg 172

Rafal, Jane, Jane Rafal Editing Associates, 325 Forest Ridge Dr, Scottsville, VA 24590 *Tel:* 434-286-6949, pg 533

Rafer, Suzanne, Workman Publishing Co Inc, 225 Varick St, 9th fl, New York, NY 10014-4381 *Tel:* 212-254-5900 *Toll Free Tel:* 800-722-7202 *Fax:* 212-254-8098 *E-mail:* info@workman.com *Web Site:* www.workman.com, pg 275

Rafferty, Emily K, The Metropolitan Museum of Art, 1000 Fifth Ave, New York, NY 10028 *Tel:* 212-879-5500; 212-570-3725 *Fax:* 212-396-5062 *E-mail:* editorial@metmuseum.org *Web Site:* www.metmuseum.org, pg 155

Raffio, Michael, Pflaum Publishing Group, 2621 Dryden Rd, Suite 300, Dayton, OH 45439 *Tel:* 937-293-1415 *Toll Free Tel:* 800-543-4383; 800-523-4625 (sales) *Fax:* 937-293-1310 *Toll Free Fax:* 800-370-4450 *E-mail:* service@pflaum.com *Web Site:* pflaum.com, pg 190

Raft, Steven, Alfred Music Publishing, PO Box 10003, Van Nuys, CA 91410 *Tel:* 818-891-5999 (dealer sales (intl)); 818-891-2452 (cust serv) *Toll Free Tel:* 800-292-6122 (dealer sales (US & CN)) *Fax:* 818-893-5560 (dealer sales); 818-830-6252 (cust serv) *Toll Free Fax:* 800-632-1928 (dealer sales) *E-mail:* customerservice@alfred.com; sales@alfred.com *Web Site:* www.alfred.com, pg 7

Rafter, Katherine, Art of Living, PrimaMedia Inc, 1250 Bethlehem Pike, Suite 241, Hatfield, PA 19440 *Tel:* 215-660-5045 *E-mail:* primamedia4@yahoo.com, pg 23

Ragan, Lise B, Course Crafters Inc, 116 Pleasant Valley Rd, Amesbury, MA 01913 *Tel:* 978-372-3446 *E-mail:* info@coursecrafters.com *Web Site:* www.coursecrafters.com, pg 524

Ragan, Melissa, Course Crafters Inc, 116 Pleasant Valley Rd, Amesbury, MA 01913 *Tel:* 978-372-3446 *E-mail:* info@coursecrafters.com *Web Site:* www.coursecrafters.com, pg 524

Rager, Shari, American Medical Writers Association (AMWA), 30 W Gude Dr, Suite 525, Rockville, MD 20850-4357 *Tel:* 240-238-0940 *Fax:* 301-294-9006 *E-mail:* amwa@amwa.org *Web Site:* www.amwa.org, pg 595

Ragland, Kelley, St Martin's Press, LLC, 175 Fifth Ave, New York, NY 10010 *Tel:* 646-307-5151 *Fax:* 212-420-9314 *E-mail:* firstname.lastname@macmillan.com *Web Site:* www.stmartins.com, pg 215

Rago, Martha, Random House Children's Books, 1745 Broadway, New York, NY 10019 *Tel:* 212-782-9000 *Toll Free Tel:* 800-200-3552 *Fax:* 212-782-9452 *Web Site:* randomhousekids.com, pg 203

Rahaeuser, Alice, Random House Children's Books, 1745 Broadway, New York, NY 10019 *Tel:* 212-782-9000 *Toll Free Tel:* 800-200-3552 *Fax:* 212-782-9452 *Web Site:* randomhousekids.com, pg 204

Rahill, Hannah, Ten Speed Press, 2625 Alcatraz Ave, Unit 505, Berkeley, CA 94705 *Tel:* 510-285-3000 *Toll Free Tel:* 800-841-BOOK (841-2665) *E-mail:* csorders@randomhouse.com *Web Site:* crownpublishing.com/imprint/ten-speed-press, pg 243

Rahja, John, Augsburg Fortress Publishers, Publishing House of the Evangelical Lutheran Church in America, 510 Marquette Ave S, Minneapolis, MN 55402 *Tel:* 612-330-3300 *Toll Free Tel:* 800-426-0115 (ext 639, subns); 800-328-4648 (orders) *Fax:* 612-330-3455 *E-mail:* info@augsburgfortress.org; copyright@augsburgfortress.org (reprint permission requests); customercare@augsburgfortress.org *Web Site:* www.augsburgfortress.org, pg 27

Rahm, Willi, Alan Wofsy Fine Arts, 1109 Geary Blvd, San Francisco, CA 94109 *Tel:* 415-292-6500 *Toll Free Tel:* 800-660-6403 *Fax:* 415-292-6594 (off & cust serv); 510-251-1840 (acctg) *E-mail:* order@art-books.com (orders); editeur@earthlink.net (edit); beauxarts@earthlink.net (cust serv) *Web Site:* www.art-books.com, pg 274

Raihofer, Susan, David Black Agency, 335 Adams St, 27th fl, Suite 2707, Brooklyn, NY 11201 *Tel:* 718-852-5500 *Fax:* 718-852-5539 *Web Site:* www.davidblackagency.com, pg 542

Raim, Sam, Penguin Group (USA) LLC, a Penguin Random House company, 375 Hudson St, New York, NY 10014 *Tel:* 212-366-2000 *Toll Free Tel:* 800-847-5515 (inside sales); 800-631-8571 (cust serv) *Fax:* 212-366-2666; 607-775-4829 (inside sales) *E-mail:* online@us.penguingroup.com *Web Site:* www.penguin.com; us.penguingroup.com, pg 186

Rainer, Tom, B&H Publishing Group, One Lifeway Plaza, Nashville, TN 37234-0114 *Tel:* 615-251-2520 *Fax:* 615-251-5004 *Web Site:* www.bhpublishinggroup.com, pg 30

Raines, Joan, Raines & Raines, 103 Kenyon Rd, Medusa, NY 12120 *Tel:* 518-239-8311 *Fax:* 518-239-6029, pg 569

Rains, H Montgomery, Oakstone Publishing LLC, 100 Corporate Pkwy, Suite 600, Birmingham, AL 35242 *Toll Free Tel:* 800-633-4743 *Fax:* 205-995-1926 *E-mail:* service@oakstonemedical.com *Web Site:* www.oakstonepublishing.com; www.cmeonly.com; www.cdeonly.com, pg 173

Raissian, Katie, Grove Atlantic Inc, 154 W 14 St, 12th fl, New York, NY 10011 *Tel:* 212-614-7850 *Toll Free Tel:* 800-521-0178 *Fax:* 212-614-7886 *E-mail:* info@groveatlantic.com *Web Site:* www.groveatlantic.com, pg 101

Rajagopalan, Pari, PEN Canada, 24 Ryerson Ave, Suite 301, Toronto, ON M5T 2P3, Canada *Tel:* 416-703-8448 *Fax:* 416-703-3870 *E-mail:* queries@pencanada.ca *Web Site:* www.pencanada.ca, pg 616

Rajamani, Madhu, diacriTech Inc, 667 Boylston St, 5th fl, Boston, MA 02116 *Tel:* 617-236-7500 *Fax:* 617-848-2938 *Web Site:* www.diacritech.com, pg 524

Rak, Brian, Focus, PO Box 44937, Indianapolis, IN 46244-0937 *Tel:* 317-635-9250 *Fax:* 317-635-9292 *E-mail:* customer@hackettpublishing.com; editorial@hackettpublishing.com *Web Site:* focusbookstore.com, pg 90

Rambo, Cat, Science Fiction & Fantasy Writers of America Inc (SFWA), PO Box 3238, Enfield, CT 06083-3238 *E-mail:* office@sfwa.org *Web Site:* www.sfwa.org, pg 618

Rambo, Cat, SFWA Nebula Awards, PO Box 3238, Enfield, CT 06083-3238 *E-mail:* office@sfwa.org *Web Site:* www.sfwa.org, pg 727

Ramer, Susan, Don Congdon Associates Inc, 110 William St, Suite 2202, New York, NY 10038-3914 *Tel:* 212-645-1229 *Fax:* 212-727-2688 *E-mail:* dca@doncongdon.com *Web Site:* www.doncongdon.com, pg 546

Ramji, Shazia Hafiz, Anvil Press Publishers, 278 E First Ave, Vancouver, BC V5T 1A6, Canada *Tel:* 604-876-8710 *Fax:* 604-879-2667 *E-mail:* info@anvilpress.com *Web Site:* www.anvilpress.com, pg 471

Ramo, Roberta Cooper, American Law Institute, 4025 Chestnut St, Philadelphia, PA 19104-3099 *Tel:* 215-243-1600 *Toll Free Tel:* 800-253-6397 *Fax:* 215-243-1664 *Web Site:* www.ali.org, pg 14

Ramondo, Anthony, NAL, 375 Hudson St, New York, NY 10014 *Tel:* 212-366-2000 *E-mail:* online@penguinputnam.com *Web Site:* www.penguinputnam.com; us.penguingroup.com, pg 162

Ramos, Luis Arturo, University of Texas at El Paso, Department of Creative Writing, MFA/Department of Creative Writing, Liberal Arts 415 UTEP, 500 W University Ave, El Paso, TX 79968-9991 *Tel:* 915-747-5713 *Fax:* 915-747-5523 *Web Site:* www.utep.edu/cw, pg 664

Randall, Deidre C, Peter E Randall Publisher, 5 Greenleaf Woods Dr, Suite 102, Portsmouth, NH 03801 *Tel:* 603-431-5667 *Fax:* 603-431-3566 *E-mail:* media@perpublisher.com *Web Site:* www.perpublisher.com, pg 203

Randall, Michele E, Bibliographical Society of America, PO Box 1537, Lenox Hill Sta, New York, NY 10021-0043 *Tel:* 212-452-2710 *Fax:* 212-452-2710 *E-mail:* bsa@bibsocamer.org *Web Site:* www.bibsocamer.org, pg 600

Randolph, Carol, Akin & Randolph Agency, Literary Div, One Gateway Ctr, Suite 2600, Newark, NJ 07102 *Tel:* 973-353-8409; 973-623-6834 *Fax:* 973-353-8417 *E-mail:* info@akinandrandolph.com *Web Site:* www.akinandrandolph.com, pg 540

Randolph, Ladette, Ploughshares, Emerson College, 120 Boylston St, Boston, MA 02116 *Tel:* 617-824-3757 *E-mail:* pshares@pshares.org *Web Site:* www.pshares.org, pg 193

Raney, Candace, Watson-Guptill Publications, c/o Random House Inc, 1745 Broadway, New York, NY 10019 *Tel:* 212-782-9000 *Fax:* 212-940-7381 *E-mail:* crownbiz@randomhouse.com *Web Site:* www.randomhouse.com/crown/watsonguptill, pg 268

Ranger, Abby, Disney-Hyperion Books, 1101 Flower St, Glendale, CA 91201 *Web Site:* books.disney.com, pg 74

Ranger, Abby, HarperCollins Children's Books, 195 Broadway, New York, NY 10007 *Tel:* 212-207-7000 *Web Site:* www.harpercollins.com/childrens, pg 105

Rankin, Charles, University of Oklahoma Press, 2800 Venture Dr, Norman, OK 73069-8216 *Tel:* 405-325-2000 *Toll Free Tel:* 800-627-7377 (orders) *Fax:* 405-364-5798 (orders) *Toll Free Fax:* 800-735-0476 (orders) *E-mail:* presscs@ou.edu *Web Site:* www.oupress.com, pg 258

Rankin, Jada, Texas Tech University Press, 2903 Fourth St, Suite 201, Lubbock, TX 79409 *Tel:* 806-742-2982 *Toll Free Tel:* 800-832-4042 *Fax:* 806-742-2979 *E-mail:* ttup@ttu.edu *Web Site:* www.ttupress.org, pg 244

Rankin, Jenni, Annual Reviews, 4139 El Camino Way, Palo Alto, CA 94306 *Tel:* 650-493-4400 *Toll Free Tel:* 800-523-8635 *Fax:* 650-424-0910; 650-855-9815 *E-mail:* service@annualreviews.org *Web Site:* www.annualreviews.org, pg 18

Rankin, Samuel M III, American Mathematical Society, 201 Charles St, Providence, RI 02904-2294 *Tel:* 401-455-4000 *Toll Free Tel:* 800-321-4267 *Fax:* 401-331-3842; 401-455-4046 (cust serv) *E-mail:* ams@ams.org; cust-serv@ams.org *Web Site:* www.ams.org, pg 14

Raoult, Marie-Madeleine, Editions de la Pleine Lune, 223 34 Ave, Lachine, QC H8T 1Z4, Canada *Tel:* 514-634-7954 *Fax:* 514-637-6366 *E-mail:* editpllune@videotron.ca *Web Site:* www.pleinelune.qc.ca, pg 480

Raphel, Neil, Brigantine Media, 211 North Ave, St Johnsbury, VT 05819 *Tel:* 802-751-8802 *Fax:* 802-751-8804 *Web Site:* brigantinemedia.com, pg 46

Rapp, Alan, The Monacelli Press, 236 W 27 St, 4th fl, New York, NY 10001 *Tel:* 212-229-9925 *E-mail:* contact@monacellipress.com *Web Site:* www.monacellipress.com, pg 159

Rapson, Judith, Stephen Leacock Memorial Medal for Humour, RR2, 4223 Line 12 N, Coldwater, ON L0K 1E0, Canada *Tel:* 705-835-3218 *Fax:* 705-835-5171 *Web Site:* www.leacock.ca, pg 699

Rarick, Ethan, Institute of Governmental Studies, 109 Moses Hall, No 2370, Berkeley, CA 94720-2370 *Tel:* 510-642-1428 *Fax:* 510-642-3020; 510-642-5537 (orders) *E-mail:* igspress@berkeley.edu *Web Site:* www.igs.berkeley.edu, pg 122

Ras, Barbara, Trinity University Press, One Trinity Place, San Antonio, TX 78212-7200 *Tel:* 210-999-8884 *Fax:* 210-999-8838 *E-mail:* books@trinity.edu *Web Site:* www.tupress.org, pg 249

Rasanen, John P, American Geosciences Institute (AGI), 4220 King St, Alexandria, VA 22302-1502 *Tel:* 703-379-2480 (ext 246) *Fax:* 703-379-7563 *E-mail:* pubs@agiweb.org *Web Site:* www.agiweb.org, pg 13

Rasbury, Angeli, Akin & Randolph Agency, Literary Div, One Gateway Ctr, Suite 2600, Newark, NJ 07102 *Tel:* 973-353-8409; 973-623-6834 *Fax:* 973-353-8417 *E-mail:* info@akinandrandolph.com *Web Site:* www.akinandrandolph.com, pg 540

Rasenberger, Mary, The Authors Guild, 31 E 32 St, 7th fl, New York, NY 10016 *Tel:* 212-563-5904 *Fax:* 212-564-5363 *E-mail:* staff@authorsguild.org *Web Site:* www.authorsguild.org, pg 599

Raskin, Sherman, Pace University, Master of Science in Publishing, Dept of Publishing, Rm 805-E, 551 Fifth Ave, New York, NY 10176 *Tel:* 212-346-1431 *Toll Free Tel:* 877-284-7670 *Fax:* 212-346-1165 *Web Site:* www.pace.edu/dyson/mspub, pg 662

Raskin, Sherman, Pace University Press, Dept of Publishing, Rm 805-E, 551 Fifth Ave, New York, NY 10176 *Tel:* 212-346-1417 *Fax:* 212-346-1165 *Web Site:* www.pace.edu/press, pg 180

Rasmussen, Jim, Bethlehem Books, 10194 Garfield St S, Bathgate, ND 58216 *Toll Free Tel:* 800-757-6831 *Fax:* 701-265-3716 *E-mail:* contact@bethlehembooks.com *Web Site:* www.bethlehembooks.com, pg 36

Rath, Kristin, Big Apple Conference, 274 Madison Ave, Suite 1202, New York, NY 10016 *Tel:* 917-720-6959 *E-mail:* iwwgquestions@gmail.com *Web Site:* www.iwwg.org, pg 650

Rath, Kristin, The International Women's Writing Guild (IWWG), 274 Madison Ave, Suite 1202, New York, NY 10016 *Tel:* 917-720-6959 *E-mail:* iwwgquestions@gmail.com *Web Site:* www.iwwg.org, pg 608

Rath, Kristin, ReIMAGINE the MAGIC Annual Summer Conference, 274 Madison Ave, Suite 1202, New York, NY 10016 *Tel:* 917-720-6959 *E-mail:* iwwgquestions@gmail.com *Web Site:* www.iwwg.org, pg 654

Rath, Ronald, SAE (Society of Automotive Engineers International), 400 Commonwealth Dr, Warrendale, PA 15096-0001 *Tel:* 724-776-4841; 724-776-4970 (outside US & CN) *Toll Free Tel:* 877-606-7323 (cust serv) *Fax:* 724-776-0790 (cust serv) *E-mail:* publications@sae.org; customerservice@sae.org *Web Site:* www.sae.org, pg 213

Ratliff, Scott, Painted Pony Inc, 3 Ethete Rd, Fort Washakie, WY 82514 *Tel:* 307-335-7330 *Toll Free Tel:* 877-253-3824 *Fax:* 307-335-7332 *E-mail:* ppi@wrdf.org *Web Site:* www.paintedponyinc.com, pg 180

Ratliff, Therese, Twenty-Third Publications, One Montauk Ave, Suite 200, New London, CT 06320 *Tel:* 860-437-3012 *Toll Free Tel:* 800-321-0411 (orders) *Toll Free Fax:* 800-572-0788 *E-mail:* 23ppweb@bayard-inc.com *Web Site:* www.twentythirdpublications.com, pg 251

Ratzlaff, Marilyn, Rainbow Books Inc, PO Box 430, Highland City, FL 33846 *Tel:* 863-648-4420 *Fax:* 863-647-5951 *E-mail:* info@rainbowbooksinc.com *Web Site:* www.rainbowbooksinc.com, pg 202

Rawa, Lisa, Binding Industries Association (BIA), 200 Deer Run Rd, Sewickley, PA 15143 *Web Site:* www.printing.org/bia, pg 600

Rawa, Lisa, Premier Print Awards, 200 Deer Run Rd, Sewickley, PA 15143-2324 *Tel:* 412-741-6860 *Toll Free Tel:* 800-910-4283 *Fax:* 412-741-2311 *E-mail:* printing@printing.org *Web Site:* www.printing.org/premierprint, pg 721

Rawa, Lisa, Printing Industries of America, 200 Deer Run Rd, Sewickley, PA 15143-2324 *Tel:* 412-741-6860 *Toll Free Tel:* 800-910-4283 *Fax:* 412-741-2311 *E-mail:* printing@printing.org *Web Site:* www.printing.org, pg 617

Rawlings, Jeremy, HarperCollins Canada Ltd, 2 Bloor St E, 20th fl, Toronto, ON M4W 1A8, Canada *Tel:* 416-975-9334 *Fax:* 416-975-9884 *E-mail:* hcorder@harpercollins.com *Web Site:* www.harpercollins.ca, pg 487

Rawlings, Wendy, University of Alabama Program in Creative Writing, PO Box 870244, Tuscaloosa, AL 35487-0244 *Tel:* 205-348-5065 *Fax:* 205-348-1388 *E-mail:* english@ua.edu *Web Site:* www.as.ua.edu/english, pg 663

Rawlins, Chloe, Ten Speed Press, 2625 Alcatraz Ave, Unit 505, Berkeley, CA 94705 *Tel:* 510-285-3000 *Toll Free Tel:* 800-841-BOOK (841-2665) *E-mail:* csorders@randomhouse.com *Web Site:* crownpublishing.com/imprint/ten-speed-press, pg 243

Ray, Barbara F, Rayve Productions Inc, PO Box 726, Windsor, CA 95492 *Tel:* 707-838-6200 *Toll Free Tel:* 800-852-4890 *Fax:* 707-838-2220 *E-mail:* rayvepro@aol.com *Web Site:* www.rayveproductions.com; www.foodandwinebooks.com, pg 205

Ray, Jo-Anne, Canadian Institute for Studies in Publishing, Simon Fraser University at Harbour Centre, 515 W Hastings St, Suite 3576, Vancouver, BC V6B 5K3, Canada *Tel:* 778-782-5242 *Fax:* 778-782-5239 *E-mail:* ccsp-info@sfu.ca *Web Site:* publishing.sfu.ca, pg 602

Ray, Norm, Rayve Productions Inc, PO Box 726, Windsor, CA 95492 *Tel:* 707-838-6200 *Toll Free Tel:* 800-852-4890 *Fax:* 707-838-2220 *E-mail:* rayvepro@aol.com *Web Site:* www.rayveproductions.com; www.foodandwinebooks.com, pg 205

Ray, Robert, MWG Writer Workshops, PO Box 3845, Meridian, MS 39303-3845 *Tel:* 601-880-1089 *Web Site:* www.mississippiwritersguild.com, pg 653

Ray, Terresa, Quail Ridge Press, 101 Brooks Dr, Brandon, MS 39042 *Tel:* 601-825-2063 *Toll Free Tel:* 800-343-1583 *Fax:* 601-825-3091 *Toll Free Fax:* 800-864-1082 *E-mail:* info@quailridge.com *Web Site:* quailridge.com, pg 201

Ray, Trinity, The Tuesday Agency, 132 1/2 E Washington St, Iowa City, IA 52240 *Tel:* 319-338-7080 *E-mail:* trinity@tuesdayagency.com *Web Site:* tuesdayagency.com, pg 588

Raye, Janis, Brigantine Media, 211 North Ave, St Johnsbury, VT 05819 *Tel:* 802-751-8802 *Fax:* 802-751-8804 *Web Site:* brigantinemedia.com, pg 46

Rayfield, Trudy, North Carolina Office of Archives & History, Historical Publications Section, 4622 Mail Service Ctr, Raleigh, NC 27699-4622 *Tel:* 919-733-7442 (ext 225) *Fax:* 919-733-1439 *Web Site:* www.ncpublications.com; nc-historical-publications.stores.yahoo.net (online store), pg 170

Raymo, Margaret, Houghton Mifflin Harcourt Trade & Reference Division, 222 Berkeley St, Boston, MA 02116 *Tel:* 617-351-5000 *Toll Free Tel:* 800-225-3362 *Web Site:* www.hmhco.com, pg 115

Raymond, Andrea, Bear & Co Inc, One Park St, Rochester, VT 05767 *Tel:* 802-767-3174 *Toll Free Tel:* 800-932-3277 *Fax:* 802-767-3726 *E-mail:* customerservice@InnerTraditions.com *Web Site:* InnerTraditions.com, pg 33

Raymond, Andrea, Inner Traditions International Ltd, One Park St, Rochester, VT 05767 *Tel:* 802-767-3174 *Toll Free Tel:* 800-246-8648 *Fax:* 802-767-3726 *E-mail:* customerservice@InnerTraditions.com *Web Site:* www.InnerTraditions.com, pg 122

Raymond, Carl, The Lisa Ekus Group LLC, 57 North St, Hatfield, MA 01038 *Tel:* 413-247-9325 *Fax:* 413-247-9873 *Web Site:* lisaekus.com, pg 660

Raymond, Mary, Penguin Group (USA) LLC Sales, 375 Hudson St, New York, NY 10014 *Tel:* 212-366-2000 *E-mail:* online@penguinputnam.com *Web Site:* us.penguingroup.com, pg 187

Raymond, Melissa, PublicAffairs, 250 W 57 St, Suite 1321, New York, NY 10107 *Tel:* 212-397-6666 *Toll Free Tel:* 800-343-4499 (orders) *Fax:* 212-397-4277 *E-mail:* publicaffairs@perseusbooks.com *Web Site:* www.publicaffairsbooks.com, pg 200

Raymond, Midge, Ashland Creek Press, 2305 Ashland St, Suite C417, Ashland, OR 97520 *Tel:* 760-300-3620 *E-mail:* editors@ashlandcreekpress.com *Web Site:* www.ashlandcreekpress.com, pg 24

Raynor, Bruce, Hillman Prizes in Journalism, 12 W 31 St, 12th fl, New York, NY 10001 *Tel:* 646-448-6413 *Web Site:* www.hillmanfoundation.org, pg 692

Raynor, Jacqueline Hope, The Boston Mills Press, 50 Staples Ave, Unit 1, Richmond Hill, ON L4B 0A7, Canada *Tel:* 416-499-8412 *Toll Free Tel:* 800-387-6192 *Fax:* 416-499-8313 *Toll Free Fax:* 800-450-0391 *E-mail:* service@fireflybooks.com *Web Site:* www.fireflybooks.com, pg 473

Rea, Elizabeth R, The Rea Award for the Short Story, 53 W Church Hill Rd, Washington, CT 06794 *Web Site:* reaaward.org, pg 723

Reach, Anna Duke, The Writers Workshop, Finn House, 102 W Wiggin St, Gambier, OH 43022 *Tel:* 740-427-5207 *Fax:* 740-427-5417 *E-mail:* kenyonreview@kenyon.edu *Web Site:* www.kenyonreview.org, pg 657

Read, Mary, Washington State University Press, Cooper Publications Bldg, Grimes Way, Pullman, WA 99164 *Tel:* 509-335-3518; 509-335-7880 (order fulfillment) *Toll Free Tel:* 800-354-7360 *Fax:* 509-335-8568 *E-mail:* wsupress@wsu.edu *Web Site:* wsupress.wsu.edu, pg 267

Reade, Amy, Women Who Write Inc, PO Box 652, Madison, NJ 07940-0652 *E-mail:* info@womenwhowrite.org *Web Site:* womenwhowrite.org, pg 621

Ream, Robaire, Polebridge Press, c/o Willamette University, 900 State St, Salem, OR 97301 *Tel:* 503-375-5323 *E-mail:* orders@westarinstitute.org *Web Site:* www.polebridgepress.com, pg 194

Reaman, Micki, Oregon State University Press, 121 The Valley Library, Corvallis, OR 97331-4501 *Tel:* 541-737-3166 *Toll Free Tel:* 800-621-2736 (orders) *Web Site:* osupress.oregonstate.edu, pg 177

Reamer, Jodi Esq, Writers House, 21 W 26 St, New York, NY 10010 *Tel:* 212-685-2400 *Fax:* 212-685-1781 *Web Site:* www.writershouse.com, pg 580

Reardon, Lisa, Chicago Review Press, 814 N Franklin St, Chicago, IL 60610 *Tel:* 312-337-0747 *Toll Free Tel:* 800-888-4741 *Fax:* 312-337-5110 *E-mail:* frontdesk@chicagoreviewpress.com *Web Site:* www.chicagoreviewpress.com, pg 56

Reaume, Julie K, Michigan State University Press (MSU Press), 1405 S Harrison Rd, Suite 25, East Lansing, MI 48823 *Tel:* 517-355-9543 *Fax:* 517-432-2611 *Toll Free Fax:* 800-678-2120 *E-mail:* msupress@msu.edu *Web Site:* www.msupress.msu.edu, pg 156

Reback, Erin, Simon & Schuster, 1230 Avenue of the Americas, New York, NY 10020 *Tel:* 212-698-7000 *Toll Free Tel:* 800-223-2348 (cust serv); 800-223-2336 (orders) *Toll Free Fax:* 800-943-9831 (orders) *Web Site:* www.simonandschuster.com, pg 225

Rebhun, Elliot, Scholastic Education, 524 Broadway, New York, NY 10012 *Tel:* 212-343-6100 *Fax:* 212-343-6189 *Web Site:* www.scholastic.com, pg 218

Redd, Kimberly L, David H Clift Scholarship, 50 E Huron St, Chicago, IL 60611 *Toll Free Tel:* 800-545-2433 (ext 4279) *Fax:* 312-280-3256 *E-mail:* scholarships@ala.org *Web Site:* www.ala.org/scholarships, pg 678

Reddick, Alecia, The Vendome Press, 1334 York Ave, 3rd fl, New York, NY 10021 *Tel:* 212-737-5297 *Fax:* 212-737-5340 *E-mail:* info@vendomepress.com *Web Site:* www.vendomepress.com, pg 265

Redding, Jill, Brewers Publications, 1372 Spruce St, Boulder, CO 80302 *Tel:* 303-447-0816 *Toll Free Tel:* 888-822-6273 (CN & US) *Fax:* 303-447-2825 *E-mail:* info@brewersassociation.org *Web Site:* www.brewersassociation.org, pg 45

Redfern-West, Robert, Academica Press LLC, PO Box 60728, Cambridge Sta, Palo Alto, CA 94306 *Tel:* 650-329-0685 *Fax:* 650-329-0685 *E-mail:* academicapress@aol.com *Web Site:* www.academicapress.com, pg 3

Redford, Margie, Standard Publishing, 8805 Governors Hill Dr, Suite 400, Cincinnati, OH 45249 *Tel:* 513-931-4050 *Toll Free Tel:* 800-543-1353 *Fax:* 513-931-0950 *Toll Free Fax:* 877-867-5751 *E-mail:* customerservice@standardpub.com *Web Site:* www.standardpub.com, pg 233

Redkin, Andy, Alan Wofsy Fine Arts, 1109 Geary Blvd, San Francisco, CA 94109 *Tel:* 415-292-6500 *Toll Free Tel:* 800-660-6403 *Fax:* 415-292-6594 (off & cust serv); 510-251-1840 (acctg) *E-mail:* order@art-books.com (orders); editeur@earthlink.net (edit); beauxarts@earthlink.net (cust serv) *Web Site:* www.art-books.com, pg 274

Redmon, Hilary, HarperCollins General Books Group, 195 Broadway, New York, NY 10007 *Tel:* 212-207-7000 *Web Site:* www.harpercollins.com, pg 105

Redmond, Robert, Cold Spring Harbor Laboratory Press, 500 Sunnyside Blvd, Woodbury, NY 11797-2924 *Tel:* 516-422-4100 *Toll Free Tel:* 800-843-4388 *Fax:* 516-422-4097; 516-422-4092 (submissions) *E-mail:* cshpress@cshl.edu *Web Site:* www.cshlpress.com, pg 60

Reed, Adam, The Joy Harris Literary Agency Inc, 381 Park Ave S, Suite 428, New York, NY 10016 *Tel:* 212-924-6269 *Fax:* 212-725-5275 *E-mail:* contact@jhlitagent.com *Web Site:* www.joyharrisliterary.com, pg 556

Reed, Alyson, Linguistic Society of America, 1325 18 St NW, Suite 211, Washington, DC 20036-6501 *Tel:* 202-835-1714 *Fax:* 202-835-1717 *E-mail:* lsa@lsadc.org *Web Site:* www.linguisticsociety.org, pg 609

Reed, Corp, BK Nelson Inc Lecture Bureau, 1565 Paseo Vida, Palm Springs, CA 92264 *Tel:* 760-778-8800 *Fax:* 760-778-6242 *E-mail:* bknelson4@cs.com *Web Site:* www.bknelson.com; www.bknelsonlecturebureau.com; www.nelsonbookmovielecture.com; www.bknelsonmovieproduction.com, pg 587

Reed, Corp, BK Nelson Inc Literary Agency, 1565 Paseo Vida, Palm Springs, CA 92264 *Tel:* 760-778-8800 *Fax:* 760-778-6242 *E-mail:* bknelson4@cs.com *Web Site:* www.bknelson.com; www.bknelsonlecturebureau.com; www.nelsonbookmovielecture.com; www.bknelsonmovieproduction.com, pg 566

Reed, Derek, Crown Publishing Group, c/o Penguin Random House Inc, 1745 Broadway, New York, NY 10019 *Tel:* 212-782-9000 *Toll Free Tel:* 888-264-1745 *Fax:* 212-940-7408 *E-mail:* crownosm@penguinrandomhouse.com *Web Site:* crownpublishing.com, pg 68

Reed, Frances, The Blackburn Press, PO Box 287, Caldwell, NJ 07006-0287 *Tel:* 973-228-7077 *Fax:* 973-228-7276 *Web Site:* www.blackburnpress.com, pg 39

Reed, Ishmael, American Book Award, The Raymond House, 655 13 St, Suite 302, Oakland, CA 94612 *Tel:* 510-268-9775 *E-mail:* info@beforecolumbusfoundation.com *Web Site:* www.beforecolumbusfoundation.com, pg 667

Reed, Ishmael, Before Columbus Foundation, The Raymond House, 655 13 St, Suite 302, Oakland, CA 94612 *Tel:* 510-268-9775 *E-mail:* info@beforecolumbusfoundation.com *Web Site:* www.beforecolumbusfoundation.com, pg 600

Reed, Kathleen, Harlequin Enterprises Ltd, 233 Broadway, Suite 1001, New York, NY 10279 *Tel:* 212-553-4200 *Fax:* 212-227-8969 *E-mail:* CustomerService@harlequin.com *Web Site:* www.harlequin.com, pg 105

Reed, Mindy, Small Publishers, Artists & Writers Network (SPAWN), 323 E Matilija St, Suite 110, PMB 123, Ojai, CA 93023 *Tel:* 805-646-3045 *Fax:* 805-640-8213 *E-mail:* execdir@spawn.org *Web Site:* www.spawn.org, pg 618

Reed, Robert D, Robert D Reed Publishers, PO Box 1992, Bandon, OR 97411-1192 *Tel:* 541-347-9882 *Fax:* 541-347-9883 *E-mail:* 4bobreed@msn.com *Web Site:* www.rdrpublishers.com, pg 207

Reed, Sally Gardner, United for Libraries, 109 S 13 St, Suite 117B, Philadelphia, PA 19107 *Tel:* 312-280-2161 *Toll Free Tel:* 800-545-2433 (ext 2161) *Fax:* 215-545-3821 *E-mail:* united@ala.org *Web Site:* www.ala.org/united, pg 620

Reed, Sarah, Random House Publishing Group, 1745 Broadway, New York, NY 10019 *Toll Free Tel:* 800-200-3552 *Web Site:* atrandom.com, pg 204

Reed-Morrisson, Laura, The Pennsylvania State University Press, University Support Bldg 1, Suite C, 820 N University Dr, University Park, PA 16802-1003 *Tel:* 814-865-1327 *Toll Free Tel:* 800-326-9180 *Fax:* 814-863-1408 *Toll Free Fax:* 877-778-2665 *E-mail:* info@psupress.org *Web Site:* www.psupress.org, pg 188

Reel, Erin, WriteLife LLC, 2323 S 171 St, Suite 202, Omaha, NE 68130 *Tel:* 402-934-1412 *Toll Free Tel:* 877-974-8354 *E-mail:* info@writelife.com *Web Site:* www.writelife.com; www.facebook.com/WriteLife; twitter.com/WriteLifeLLC, pg 277

Rees, Mr Lorin, Rees Literary Agency, 14 Beacon St, Suite 710, Boston, MA 02108 *Tel:* 617-227-9014 *Fax:* 617-227-8762 *E-mail:* reesagency@reesagency.com *Web Site:* reesagency.com, pg 569

Reese, Bob, Aro Book Publishing Co, 130 S 800 W, Salt Lake City, UT 84104-1120 *Tel:* 801-953-1760 (office); 801-637-9115 (cell) *Fax:* 801-419-0125 *E-mail:* arobook@yahoo.com *Web Site:* www.arobookpublishing.com, pg 22

Reeve, William D, Virginia Kidd Agency Inc, 538 E Harford St, PO Box 278, Milford, PA 18337 *Tel:* 570-296-6205 *Web Site:* vk-agency.com, pg 559

Regan, Ann, Minnesota Historical Society Press, 345 Kellogg Blvd W, St Paul, MN 55102-1906 *Tel:* 651-259-3205; 651-259-3000 *Toll Free Tel:* 800-621-2736 (warehouse) *Fax:* 651-297-1345 *Toll Free Fax:* 800-621-8476 (warehouse) *E-mail:* info-mnhspress@mnhs.org *Web Site:* www.mnhs.org/mnhspress, pg 157

Regan, Bob, Thompson Mill Press LLC, 2865 S Eagle Rd, No 368, Newtown, PA 18940 *Tel:* 215-431-1424 *E-mail:* bob.regan@thompsonmillpress.com *Web Site:* www.thompsonmillpress.com; www.KobeeManatee.com, pg 509

Regan, Harold, H W Wilson, 2 University Plaza, Suite 310, Hackensack, NJ 07601 *Tel:* 201-968-0500 *Toll Free Tel:* 800-221-1592 *Fax:* 201-968-0511 *E-mail:* info@hwwilsoninprint.com; csr@hwwilsoninprint.com; information@ebscohost.com *Web Site:* www.hwwilsoninprint.com; www.ebscohost.com/wilson, pg 273

Regan, Harold, H W Wilson Foundation, 10 Estes St, Ipswich, MA 01938 *Tel:* 978-356-6500 *Toll Free Tel:* 800-653-2726 (US & CN) *Fax:* 978-356-6565 *E-mail:* information@ebscohost.com *Web Site:* www.ebscohost.com, pg 623

Reggio, Christopher T, TFH Publications Inc, One TFH Plaza, Third & Union Aves, Neptune City, NJ 07753 *Tel:* 732-988-8400 *Toll Free Tel:* 800-631-2188 *Fax:* 732-776-8763 *E-mail:* info@tfh.com *Web Site:* www.tfh.com, pg 244

Regier, Willis G, University of Illinois Press, 1325 S Oak St, MC-566, Champaign, IL 61820-6903 *Tel:* 217-333-0950 *Fax:* 217-244-8082 *E-mail:* uipress@uillinois.edu; journals@uillinois.edu *Web Site:* www.press.uillinois.edu, pg 256

Regis, Emily, Cider Mill Press Book Publishers LLC, 12 Spring St, Kennebunkport, ME 04046 *Tel:* 207-967-8232 *Fax:* 207-967-8233 *Web Site:* www.cidermillpress.com, pg 58

Rehl, Dr Beatrice, Cambridge University Press, 32 Avenue of the Americas, New York, NY 10013-2473 *Tel:* 212-924-3900; 212-337-5000 *Fax:* 212-691-3239 *E-mail:* newyork@cambridge.org *Web Site:* www.cambridge.org/us, pg 49

Rehm, Jerry, United States Holocaust Memorial Museum, 100 Raoul Wallenberg Place SW, Washington, DC 20024-2126 *Tel:* 202-314-7837; 202-488-6144 (orders) *Toll Free Tel:* 800-259-9998 (orders) *Fax:* 202-479-9726; 202-488-0438 (orders) *E-mail:* cahs_publications@ushmm.org *Web Site:* www.ushmm.org, pg 253

Rehou, Maja, WordForce Communications, 35 Ormskirk Ave, Suite 805, Toronto, ON M6S 1A8, Canada *Tel:* 416-534-9881 *E-mail:* info@wordforce.ca *Web Site:* www.wordforce.ca, pg 536

Reichert, Stephen, Erskine J Poetry Prize, PO Box 22161, Baltimore, MD 21203 *Web Site:* www.smartishpace.com, pg 684

Reichlin, Jennifer, University of Illinois Press, 1325 S Oak St, MC-566, Champaign, IL 61820-6903 *Tel:* 217-333-0950 *Fax:* 217-244-8082 *E-mail:* uipress@uillinois.edu; journals@uillinois.edu *Web Site:* www.press.uillinois.edu, pg 256

Reid, Daniel, InterVarsity Press, 430 Plaza Dr, Westmont, IL 60559-1234 *Tel:* 630-734-4000 *Toll Free Tel:* 800-843-9487 *Fax:* 630-734-4200 *E-mail:* email@ivpress.com *Web Site:* www.ivpress.com, pg 125

Reid, Daniel, Whiting Writers' Awards, 1133 Avenue of the Americas, 22nd fl, New York, NY 10036-6710 *Tel:* 212-336-2138 *E-mail:* info@whitingfoundation.org *Web Site:* www.whitingfoundation.org, pg 735

Reid, Don, Stephen Leacock Memorial Medal for Humour, RR2, 4223 Line 12 N, Coldwater, ON L0K 1E0, Canada *Tel:* 705-835-3218 *Fax:* 705-835-5171 *Web Site:* www.leacock.ca, pg 699

Reid, Janet, FinePrint Literary Management, 115 W 29 St, 3rd fl, New York, NY 10001 *Tel:* 212-279-1282 *Web Site:* www.fineprintlit.com, pg 551

Reid, Karen, Harlequin Enterprises Ltd, 225 Duncan Mill Rd, Don Mills, ON M3B 3K9, Canada *Tel:* 416-445-5860 *Toll Free Tel:* 888-432-4879; 800-370-5838 (ebook inquiries) *E-mail:* customerservice@harlequin.com *Web Site:* www.harlequin.com, pg 487

Reid, Lisa, Broadview Press, 280 Perry St, Unit 5, Peterborough, ON K9J 2J4, Canada *Tel:* 705-743-8990 *Fax:* 705-743-8353 *E-mail:* customerservice@broadviewpress.com *Web Site:* www.broadviewpress.com, pg 474

Reid, Rosalind, Council for the Advancement of Science Writing (CASW), PO Box 910, Hedgesville, WV 25427 *Tel:* 304-754-6786 *Web Site:* www.casw.org, pg 604

Reid, Rosalind, Rennie Taylor & Alton Blakeslee Fellowships in Science Writing, PO Box 910, Hedgesville, WV 25427 *Tel:* 304-754-6786 *Web Site:* www.casw.org, pg 731

Reidhead, Julia, W W Norton & Company Inc, 500 Fifth Ave, New York, NY 10110-0017 *Tel:* 212-354-5500 *Toll Free Tel:* 800-233-4830 (orders & cust serv) *Fax:* 212-869-0856 *Toll Free Fax:* 800-458-6515 *Web Site:* www.wwnorton.com, pg 171

Reidy, Carolyn K, Simon & Schuster, Inc, 1230 Avenue of the Americas, New York, NY 10020 *Tel:* 212-698-7000 *Fax:* 212-698-7007 *E-mail:* firstname.lastname@simonandschuster.com *Web Site:* www.simonandschuster.com, pg 226

Reidy, Sarah, Simon & Schuster, 1230 Avenue of the Americas, New York, NY 10020 *Tel:* 212-698-7000 *Toll Free Tel:* 800-223-2348 (cust serv); 800-223-2336 (orders) *Toll Free Fax:* 800-943-9831 (orders) *Web Site:* www.simonandschuster.com, pg 225

Reighard, Jessica, Brookes Publishing Co Inc, PO Box 10624, Baltimore, MD 21285-0624 *Tel:* 410-337-9580 (outside US & CN) *Toll Free Tel:* 800-638-3775 (US & CN) *Fax:* 410-337-8539 *E-mail:* custserv@brookespublishing.com *Web Site:* www.brookespublishing.com, pg 46

Reil, Doug, Frog Books, 2526 Martin Luther King Jr Way, Berkeley, CA 94704 *Tel:* 510-549-4270 *Fax:* 510-549-4276 *E-mail:* customerservice@northatlanticbooks.com *Web Site:* www.northatlanticbooks.com, pg 93

Reil, Doug, North Atlantic Books, 2526 Martin Luther King Jr Way, Berkeley, CA 94704 *Tel:* 510-549-4270 *Fax:* 510-549-4276 *Web Site:* www.northatlanticbooks.com, pg 170

Reilly, Edward T, American Management Association (AMA), 1601 Broadway, New York, NY 10019 *Tel:* 212-586-8100 *Toll Free Tel:* 877-566-9441 *Fax:* 212-903-8168; 518-891-0368 *E-mail:* customerservice@amanet.org *Web Site:* www.amanet.org, pg 595

Reilly, Jack, Pearson Higher Education, 225 River St, Hoboken, NJ 07030-4772 *Tel:* 201-236-7000 *Fax:* 201-236-3381 *Web Site:* www.pearsonhighered.com, pg 185

Reilly, Michael, American Association of Collegiate Registrars & Admissions Officers (AACRAO), One Dupont Circle NW, Suite 520, Washington, DC 20036 *Tel:* 202-293-9161 *Fax:* 202-872-8857 *Web Site:* www.aacrao.org, pg 11

Reimer, John, IEEE Computer Society, 2001 "L" St NW, Suite 700, Washington, DC 20036-4928 *Tel:* 202-371-0101 *Toll Free Tel:* 800-272-6657 (memb info) *Fax:* 202-728-9614 *E-mail:* help@computer.org *Web Site:* www.computer.org, pg 118

Reimnitz, Arlen, ASET - The Neurodiagnostic Society, 402 E Bannister Rd, Suite A, Kansas City, KS 64131-3019 *Tel:* 816-931-1120 *Fax:* 816-931-1145 *E-mail:* info@aset.org *Web Site:* www.aset.org, pg 24

Rein, Jody, Jody Rein Books Inc, 7741 S Ash Ct, Centennial, CO 80122 *Tel:* 303-694-9386 *Web Site:* www.jodyreinbooks.com, pg 558

Reina, Jeanne, HarperCollins General Books Group, 195 Broadway, New York, NY 10007 *Tel:* 212-207-7000 *Web Site:* www.harpercollins.com, pg 105

Reinertsen, Claire, W W Norton & Company Inc, 500 Fifth Ave, New York, NY 10110-0017 *Tel:* 212-354-5500 *Toll Free Tel:* 800-233-4830 (orders & cust serv) *Fax:* 212-869-0856 *Toll Free Fax:* 800-458-6515 *Web Site:* www.wwnorton.com, pg 172

Reis, Mike, Kids Can Press Ltd, 25 Dockside Dr, Toronto, ON M5A 0B5, Canada *Tel:* 416-479-7000 *Toll Free Tel:* 800-265-0884 *Fax:* 416-960-5437 *E-mail:* info@kidscan.com; customerservice@kidscan.com *Web Site:* www.kidscanpress.com; www.kidscanpress.ca, pg 489

Reisdorff, James J, South Platte Press, PO Box 163, David City, NE 68632-0163 *Tel:* 402-367-3554 *E-mail:* railroads@windstream.net *Web Site:* www.southplattepress.net, pg 231

Reiser, Annie M, Morton N Cohen Award for a Distinguished Edition of Letters, 26 Broadway, 3rd fl, New York, NY 10004-1789 *Tel:* 646-576-5141 *Fax:* 646-458-0030 *E-mail:* awards@mla.org *Web Site:* www.mla.org, pg 678

Reiser, Annie M, Katherine Singer Kovacs Prize, 26 Broadway, 3rd fl, New York, NY 10004-1789 *Tel:* 646-576-5141 *Fax:* 646-458-0030 *E-mail:* awards@mla.org *Web Site:* www.mla.org, pg 698

Reiser, Annie M, Fenia & Yaakov Leviant Memorial Prize in Yiddish Studies, 26 Broadway, 3rd fl, New York, NY 10004-1789 *Tel:* 646-576-5141 *Fax:* 646-458-0030 *E-mail:* awards@mla.org *Web Site:* www.mla.org, pg 700

Reiser, Annie M, James Russell Lowell Prize, 26 Broadway, 3rd fl, New York, NY 10004-1789 *Tel:* 646-576-5141 *Fax:* 646-458-0030 *E-mail:* awards@mla.org *Web Site:* www.mla.org, pg 703

Reiser, Annie M, Howard R Marraro Prize, 26 Broadway, 3rd fl, New York, NY 10004-1789 *Tel:* 646-576-5141 *Fax:* 646-458-0030 *E-mail:* awards@mla.org *Web Site:* www.mla.org, pg 705

Reiser, Annie M, Kenneth W Mildenberger Prize, 26 Broadway, 3rd fl, New York, NY 10004-1789 *Tel:* 646-576-5141 *Fax:* 646-458-0030 *E-mail:* awards@mla.org *Web Site:* www.mla.org, pg 707

Reiser, Annie M, MLA Prize for a Bibliography, Archive or Digital Project, 26 Broadway, 3rd fl, New York, NY 10004-1789 *Tel:* 646-576-5141 *Fax:* 646-458-0030 *E-mail:* awards@mla.org *Web Site:* www.mla.org, pg 708

Reiser, Annie M, MLA Prize for a First Book, 26 Broadway, 3rd fl, New York, NY 10004-1789 *Tel:* 646-576-5141 *Fax:* 646-458-0030 *E-mail:* awards@mla.org *Web Site:* www.mla.org, pg 708

Reiser, Annie M, MLA Prize for a Scholarly Edition, 26 Broadway, 3rd fl, New York, NY 10004-1789 *Tel:* 646-576-5141 *Fax:* 646-458-0030 *E-mail:* awards@mla.org *Web Site:* www.mla.org, pg 708

Reiser, Annie M, MLA Prize for Independent Scholars, 26 Broadway, 3rd fl, New York, NY 10004-1789 *Tel:* 646-576-5141 *Fax:* 646-458-0030 *E-mail:* awards@mla.org *Web Site:* www.mla.org, pg 708

Reiser, Annie M, MLA Prize for Studies in Native American Literatures, Cultures & Languages, 26 Broadway, 3rd fl, New York, NY 10004-1789 *Tel:* 646-576-5141 *Fax:* 646-458-0030 *E-mail:* awards@mla.org *Web Site:* www.mla.org, pg 708

Reiser, Annie M, MLA Prize in United States Latina & Latino & Chicana & Chicano Literary & Cultural Studies, 26 Broadway, 3rd fl, New York, NY 10004-1789 *Tel:* 646-576-5141 *Fax:* 646-458-0030 *E-mail:* awards@mla.org *Web Site:* www.mla.org, pg 708

Reiser, Annie M, Lois Roth Award, 26 Broadway, 3rd fl, New York, NY 10004-1789 *Tel:* 646-576-5141 *Fax:* 646-458-0030 *E-mail:* awards@mla.org *Web Site:* www.mla.org, pg 725

Reiser, Annie M, Aldo & Jeanne Scaglione Prize for a Translation of a Literary Work, 26 Broadway, 3rd fl, New York, NY 10004-1789 *Tel:* 646-576-5141 *Fax:* 646-458-0030 *E-mail:* awards@mla.org *Web Site:* www.mla.org, pg 726

Reiser, Annie M, Aldo & Jeanne Scaglione Prize for a Translation of a Scholarly Study of Literature, 26 Broadway, 3rd fl, New York, NY 10004-1789 *Tel:* 646-576-5141 *Fax:* 646-458-0030 *E-mail:* awards@mla.org *Web Site:* www.mla.org, pg 726

Reiser, Annie M, Aldo & Jeanne Scaglione Prize for Comparative Literary Studies, 26 Broadway, 3rd fl, New York, NY 10004-1789 *Tel:* 646-576-5141 *Fax:* 646-458-0030 *E-mail:* awards@mla.org *Web Site:* www.mla.org, pg 726

Reiser, Annie M, Aldo & Jeanne Scaglione Prize for French & Francophone Studies, 26 Broadway, 3rd fl, New York, NY 10004-1789 *Tel:* 646-576-5141 *Fax:* 646-458-0030 *E-mail:* awards@mla.org *Web Site:* www.mla.org, pg 726

Reiser, Annie M, Aldo & Jeanne Scaglione Prize for Italian Studies, 26 Broadway, 3rd fl, New York, NY 10004-1789 *Tel:* 646-576-5141 *Fax:* 646-458-0030 *E-mail:* awards@mla.org *Web Site:* www.mla.org, pg 726

Reiser, Annie M, Aldo & Jeanne Scaglione Prize for Studies in Germanic Languages & Literatures, 26 Broadway, 3rd fl, New York, NY 10004-1789 *Tel:* 646-576-5141 *Fax:* 646-458-0030 *E-mail:* awards@mla.org *Web Site:* www.mla.org, pg 726

Reiser, Annie M, Aldo & Jeanne Scaglione Prize for Studies in Slavic Languages & Literatures, 26 Broadway, 3rd fl, New York, NY 10004-1789 *Tel:* 646-576-5141 *E-mail:* awards@mla.org *Web Site:* www.mla.org, pg 726

Reiser, Annie M, Aldo & Jeanne Scaglione Publication Award for a Manuscript in Italian Literary Studies, 26 Broadway, 3rd fl, New York, NY 10004-1789 *Tel:* 646-576-5141 *Fax:* 646-458-0030 *E-mail:* awards@mla.org *Web Site:* www.mla.org, pg 726

Reiser, Annie M, William Sanders Scarborough Prize, 26 Broadway, 3rd fl, New York, NY 10004-1789 *Tel:* 646-576-5141 *Fax:* 646-458-0030 *E-mail:* awards@mla.org *Web Site:* www.mla.org, pg 727

Reiser, Annie M, Mina P Shaughnessy Prize, 26 Broadway, 3rd fl, New York, NY 10004-1789 *Tel:* 646-576-5141 *Fax:* 646-458-0030 *E-mail:* awards@mla.org *Web Site:* www.mla.org, pg 728

Reiser, Marc A, National Notary Association (NNA), 9350 De Soto Ave, Chatsworth, CA 91311 *Tel:* 818-739-4000 *Toll Free Tel:* 800-876-6827 *Toll Free Fax:* 800-833-1211 *E-mail:* nna@nationalnotary.org *Web Site:* www.nationalnotary.org, pg 165

Reiss, William, John Hawkins and Associates Inc, 71 W 23 St, Suite 1600, New York, NY 10010 *Tel:* 212-807-7040 *E-mail:* jha@jhalit.com *Web Site:* jhalit.com, pg 556

Reiter, Jendi, Tom Howard/John H Reid Fiction & Essay Contest, 351 Pleasant St, PMB 222, Northampton, MA 01060-3961 *Tel:* 413-320-1847 *Toll Free Tel:* 866-WINWRIT (946-9748) *Fax:* 413-280-0539 *Web Site:* www.winningwriters.com, pg 693

Reiter, Jendi, Tom Howard/Margaret Reid Poetry Contest, 351 Pleasant St, PMB 222, Northampton, MA 01060-3961 *Tel:* 413-320-1847 *Toll Free Tel:* 866-WINWRIT (946-9748) *Fax:* 413-280-0539 *Web Site:* www.winningwriters.com, pg 693

Reiter, Jendi, Wergle Flomp Humor Poetry Contest, 351 Pleasant St, PMB 222, Northampton, MA 01060-3961 *Tel:* 413-320-1847 *Toll Free Tel:* 866-WINWRIT (946-9748) *Fax:* 413-280-0539 *Web Site:* www.winningwriters.com, pg 735

Rekulak, Jason, Quirk Books, 215 Church St, Philadelphia, PA 19106 *Tel:* 215-627-3581 *Fax:* 215-627-5220 *E-mail:* general@quirkbooks.com *Web Site:* www.quirkbooks.com, pg 202

Rella, Susan, Gallery Books, 1230 Avenue of the Americas, New York, NY 10020 *Toll Free Tel:* 800-456-6798 *Fax:* 212-698-7284 *E-mail:* consumer.customerservice@simonandschuster.com *Web Site:* www.simonsays.com, pg 94

Remazeilles, Ingrid, Les Editions Goelette Inc, 1350 Marie-Victorin, St-Bruno-de-Montarville, Quebec, QC J3V 6B9, Canada *Tel:* 450-653-1337 *Toll Free Tel:* 800-463-4961 *Fax:* 450-653-9924 *E-mail:* info@boutiquegoelette.com *Web Site:* www.editionsgoelette.com, pg 481

Renaud, Alain-Nicolas, Les Editions de l'Hexagone, 1010 rue de la Gauchetiere E, Montreal, QC H2L 2N5, Canada *Tel:* 514-523-7993 *Fax:* 514-282-7530 *Web Site:* www.edhexagone.com, pg 480

Renaud, Alain-Nicolas, VLB Editeur Inc, 1010, Rue de la Gauchetiere Est, Montreal, QC H2L 2N5, Canada *Tel:* 514-523-7993 *Fax:* 514-282-7530 *Web Site:* www.edvlb.com, pg 504

Renaud, Marie-Lyne, Innis-Gerin Medal, Walter House, 282 Somerset W, Ottawa, ON K2P 0J6, Canada *Tel:* 613-991-6990 (ext 106) *Fax:* 613-991-6996 *E-mail:* nominations@rsc-src.ca *Web Site:* www.rsc-src.ca, pg 695

Renaud, Marie-Lyne, Lorne Pierce Medal, Walter House, 282 Somerset W, Ottawa, ON K2P 0J6, Canada *Tel:* 613-991-6990 (ext 106) *Fax:* 613-991-6996 *E-mail:* nominations@rsc-src.ca *Web Site:* www.rsc-src.ca, pg 719

Renaud, Michelle, Harlequin Enterprises Ltd, 225 Duncan Mill Rd, Don Mills, ON M3B 3K9, Canada *Tel:* 416-445-5860 *Toll Free Tel:* 888-432-4879; 800-370-5838 (ebook inquiries) *E-mail:* customerservice@harlequin.com *Web Site:* www.harlequin.com, pg 487

Renker, Jason, The Century Foundation, One Whitehall St, 15 fl, New York, NY 10004 *Tel:* 212-452-7700 *Fax:* 212-535-7534 *E-mail:* info@tcf.org *Web Site:* www.tcf.org, pg 623

Renker, Jason, The Century Foundation Press, One Whitehall St, 15th fl, New York, NY 10004 *Tel:* 212-452-7700 *Fax:* 212-535-7534 *E-mail:* info@tcf.org *Web Site:* www.tcf.org, pg 54

Renner, Georgene, Society for Mining, Metallurgy & Exploration, 12999 E Adam Aircraft Circle, Englewood, CO 80112 *Tel:* 303-948-4200 *Toll Free Tel:* 800-763-3132 *Fax:* 303-973-3845 *E-mail:* cs@smenet.org *Web Site:* www.smenet.org, pg 229

Rennert, Amy, The Amy Rennert Agency Inc, 1550 Tiburon Blvd, Suite 302, Tiburon, CA 94920 *Tel:* 415-789-8955 *E-mail:* queries@amyrennert.com *Web Site:* amyrennert.com, pg 569

Rennert, Richard S, United States Tennis Association, 70 W Red Oak Lane, White Plains, NY 10604 *Tel:* 914-696-7000 *Fax:* 914-696-7027 *Web Site:* www.usta.com, pg 254

Rens, Kristin, HarperCollins Children's Books, 195 Broadway, New York, NY 10007 *Tel:* 212-207-7000 *Web Site:* www.harpercollins.com/childrens, pg 105

Renzulli, Allison, Houghton Mifflin Harcourt Trade & Reference Division, 222 Berkeley St, Boston, MA 02116 *Tel:* 617-351-5000 *Toll Free Tel:* 800-225-3362 *Web Site:* www.hmhco.com, pg 115

Repas, Laura, Groundwood Books, 110 Spadina Ave, Suite 801, Toronto, ON M5V 2K4, Canada *Tel:* 416-363-4343 *Fax:* 416-363-1017 *E-mail:* genmail@groundwoodbooks.com *Web Site:* www.houseofanansi.com, pg 486

Repcheck, Jack, W W Norton & Company Inc, 500 Fifth Ave, New York, NY 10110-0017 *Tel:* 212-354-5500 *Toll Free Tel:* 800-233-4830 (orders & cust serv) *Fax:* 212-869-0856 *Toll Free Fax:* 800-458-6515 *Web Site:* www.wwnorton.com, pg 171

Reschke, Phil, Covenant Communications Inc, 920 E State Rd, Suite F, American Fork, UT 84003-0416 *Tel:* 801-756-1041 *E-mail:* info@covenant-lds.com *Web Site:* www.covenant-lds.com, pg 66

Rescigno, Don, Nystrom Herff Jones Education Division, 4719 W 62 St, Indianapolis, IN 46268-2593 *Tel:* 317-612-3901 *Toll Free Tel:* 800-621-8086 (cust serv) *Fax:* 317-329-3305 *E-mail:* info@nystromnet.com *Web Site:* www.nystromnet.com, pg 172

Resciniti, Nicole, Mary Sue Seymour, 475 Miner Street Rd, Canton, NY 13617 *Tel:* 315-386-1831 *Web Site:* www.theseymouragency.com, pg 573

Reshota, Olga, Boydell & Brewer Inc, 668 Mount Hope Ave, Rochester, NY 14620-2731 *Tel:* 585-275-0419 *Fax:* 585-271-8778 *E-mail:* boydell@boydellusa.net *Web Site:* www.boydellandbrewer.com, pg 43

Resnick, Marc, St Martin's Press, LLC, 175 Fifth Ave, New York, NY 10010 *Tel:* 646-307-5151 *Fax:* 212-420-9314 *E-mail:* firstname.lastname@macmillan.com *Web Site:* www.stmartins.com, pg 215

Restivo-Alessi, Chantal, HarperCollins Publishers, 195 Broadway, New York, NY 10007 *Tel:* 212-207-7000 *Fax:* 212-207-7145 *Web Site:* www.harpercollins.com, pg 106

Rettino, Lucille, Simon & Schuster Children's Publishing, 1230 Avenue of the Americas, New York, NY 10020 *Tel:* 212-698-7000 *Web Site:* KIDS.SimonandSchuster.com; TEEN.SimonandSchuster.com; simonandschuster.net; simonandschuster.biz, pg 225

Reue, Susan, LangMarc Publishing, PO Box 90488, Austin, TX 78709-0488 *Tel:* 512-394-0989 *Toll Free Tel:* 800-864-1648 (orders) *Fax:* 512-394-0829 *E-mail:* langmarc@booksails.com *Web Site:* www.langmarc.com, pg 134

Reveal, Judith, Just Creative Writing & Indexing Services (JCR), 301 Wood Duck Dr, Greensboro, MD 21639 *Tel:* 410-482-6337 *E-mail:* jreveal@verizon.net; support@justcreativewriting.com *Web Site:* www.justcreativewriting.com, pg 528

Revesz, Richard, American Law Institute Continuing Legal Education (ALI CLE), 4025 Chestnut St, Philadelphia, PA 19104 *Tel:* 215-243-1600 *Toll Free Tel:* 800-CLE-NEWS (253-6397) *Fax:* 215-243-1664; 215-243-1683 *Web Site:* www.ali-cle.org, pg 14

Revesz, Richard L, American Law Institute, 4025 Chestnut St, Philadelphia, PA 19104-3099 *Tel:* 215-243-1600 *Toll Free Tel:* 800-253-6397 *Fax:* 215-243-1664 *Web Site:* www.ali.org, pg 14

Reynolds, Dan, Storey Publishing LLC, 210 MASS MoCA Way, North Adams, MA 01247 *Tel:* 413-346-2100 *Toll Free Tel:* 800-441-5700 (orders); 800-793-9396 (edit) *Fax:* 413-346-2199; 413-346-2196 (edit) *E-mail:* sales@storey.com *Web Site:* www.storey.com, pg 236

Reynolds, Dan, Workman Publishing Co Inc, 225 Varick St, 9th fl, New York, NY 10014-4381 *Tel:* 212-254-5900 *Toll Free Tel:* 800-722-7202 *Fax:* 212-254-8098 *E-mail:* info@workman.com *Web Site:* www.workman.com, pg 275

Reynolds, Darlene, The Magni Co, 7106 Wellington Point Rd, McKinney, TX 75070 *Tel:* 972-540-2050 *Fax:* 972-540-1057 *E-mail:* sales@magnico.com; info@magnico.com *Web Site:* www.magnico.com, pg 145

Reynolds, Evan B, The Magni Co, 7106 Wellington Point Rd, McKinney, TX 75070 *Tel:* 972-540-2050 *Fax:* 972-540-1057 *E-mail:* sales@magnico.com; info@magnico.com *Web Site:* www.magnico.com, pg 145

Reynolds, Jen, Houghton Mifflin Harcourt, 222 Berkeley St, Boston, MA 02116 *Tel:* 617-351-5000 *Toll Free Tel:* 800-225-5425 (K-12 educ materials); 800-323-9540 (assessment materials); 877-219-1537 (SkillsTutor); 888-242-6747 (Destination; Earobics; Edmark; Learning Village; Riverdeep); 800-225-3362 (Houghton Mifflin Harcourt Trade & Reference Publishers) *Toll Free Fax:* 800-269-5232 *E-mail:* customerservice@hmhpub.com *Web Site:* www.hmhco.com, pg 115

Reynolds, Jill, The Linick Group Inc, Linick Bldg, 7 Putter Lane, Middle Island, NY 11953 *Tel:* 631-924-3888; 631-924-8555 *Fax:* 631-924-8555 *E-mail:* linickgroup@gmail.com; andrew@AskLinick.com *Web Site:* www.AndrewLinickDirectMarketing.com/Publishers-Advice.html; www.NewWorldPressBooks.com, pg 140

Reynolds, Laurie, Child's Play®, 250 Minot Ave, Auburn, ME 04210 *Tel:* 207-784-7252 *Toll Free Tel:* 800-639-6404 *Fax:* 207-784-7358 *Toll Free Fax:* 800-854-6989 *E-mail:* chpmaine@aol.com; cplay@earthlink.net *Web Site:* www.childs-play.com, pg 57

Reynolds, Laurie, Web Offset Association (WOA), 200 Deer Run Rd, Sewickley, PA 15143 *Tel:* 412-741-6860 *Toll Free Tel:* 800-910-4283 *Fax:* 412-741-2311 *E-mail:* printing@printing.org *Web Site:* www.printing.org/page/3419, pg 621

Reynolds, Margaret, Association of Book Publishers of British Columbia, 600-402 W Pender St, Vancouver, BC V6B 1T6, Canada *Tel:* 604-684-0228 *Fax:* 604-684-5788 *E-mail:* admin@books.bc.ca *Web Site:* www.books.bc.ca, pg 598

Reynolds, Michael, Europa Editions, 214 W 29 St, Suite 1003, New York, NY 10001 *Tel:* 212-868-6844 *Fax:* 212-868-6845 *E-mail:* info@europaeditions.com *Web Site:* www.europaeditions.com, pg 84

Rezek, Anthony, Emond Montgomery Publications Ltd, 60 Shaftesbury Ave, Toronto, ON M4T 1A3, Canada *Tel:* 416-975-3925 *Toll Free Tel:* 888-837-0815 *Fax:* 416-975-3924 *E-mail:* orders@emp.ca *Web Site:* www.emp.ca, pg 483

Rha, Alice, W W Norton & Company Inc, 500 Fifth Ave, New York, NY 10110-0017 *Tel:* 212-354-5500 *Toll Free Tel:* 800-233-4830 (orders & cust serv) *Fax:* 212-869-0856 *Toll Free Fax:* 800-458-6515 *Web Site:* www.wwnorton.com, pg 172

Rheaume, Claude, Les Editions Fides, 7333 place des Roseraies, bureau 100, Anjou, QC H1M 2X6, Canada *Tel:* 514-745-4290 *Fax:* 514-745-4299 *E-mail:* editions@groupefides.com *Web Site:* www.editionsfides.com, pg 481

Rhetts, Paul, LPD Press, 925 Salamanca NW, Los Ranchos de Albuquerque, NM 87107-5647 *Tel:* 505-344-9382 *Fax:* 505-345-5129 *E-mail:* info@nmsantos.com *Web Site:* nmsantos.com, pg 144

Rhie, Gene S, Hollym International Corp, 18 Donald Place, Elizabeth, NJ 07208 *Tel:* 908-353-1655 *Fax:* 908-353-0255 *E-mail:* contact@hollym.com *Web Site:* www.hollym.com, pg 113

Rhind-Tutt, Stephen, Alexander Street Press LLC, 3212 Duke St, Alexandria, VA 22314 *Tel:* 703-212-8520 *Toll Free Tel:* 800-889-5937 *Fax:* 703-940-6584 *E-mail:* sales@alexanderstreet.com; marketing@alexanderstreet.com; info@alexanderstreet.com *Web Site:* alexanderstreet.com, pg 7

Rhoades, Bishop Kevin C, Our Sunday Visitor Publishing, 200 Noll Plaza, Huntington, IN 46750 *Tel:* 260-356-8400 *Toll Free Tel:* 800-348-2440 (orders) *Fax:* 260-356-8472 *Toll Free Fax:* 800-498-6709 *E-mail:* osvbooks@osv.com (book orders) *Web Site:* www.osv.com, pg 178

Rhoads, Marilyn, Oregon Christian Writers (OCW), 1075 Willow Lake Rd N, Keizer, OR 97303 *Tel:* 503-393-3356 *E-mail:* contact@oregonchristianwriters.org *Web Site:* www.oregonchristianwriters.org, pg 615

Rhoads, Marilyn, Oregon Christian Writers Seminar, 1075 Willow Lake Rd N, Keizer, OR 97303 *Tel:* 503-393-3356 *E-mail:* contact@oregonchristianwriters.org *Web Site:* www.oregonchristianwriters.org, pg 653

Rhoda, Virginia, Crown Publishing Group, c/o Penguin Random House Inc, 1745 Broadway, New York, NY 10019 *Tel:* 212-782-9000 *Toll Free Tel:* 888-264-1745 *Fax:* 212-940-7408 *E-mail:* crownosm@penguinrandomhouse.com *Web Site:* crownpublishing.com, pg 68

Rhodes, Christopher, University of Chicago Press, 1427 E 60 St, Chicago, IL 60637-2954 *Tel:* 773-702-7700; 773-702-7600 *Toll Free Tel:* 800-621-2736 (orders) *Fax:* 773-702-9756; 773-660-2235 (orders); 773-702-2708 *E-mail:* custserv@press.uchicago.edu; marketing@press.uchicago.edu *Web Site:* www.press.uchicago.edu, pg 255

Rhodes, David R, Pyncheon House, 6 University Dr, Suite 105, Amherst, MA 01002, pg 201

Rhodes, Emilia, HarperCollins Children's Books, 195 Broadway, New York, NY 10007 *Tel:* 212-207-7000 *Web Site:* www.harpercollins.com/childrens, pg 105

Rhodes, Jodie, Jodie Rhodes Literary Agency, 8840 Villa La Jolla Dr, Suite 315, La Jolla, CA 92037 *E-mail:* jrhodesl@san.rr.com, pg 569

Rhone, Mitzi, The Aaland Agency, PO Box 849, Inyokern, CA 93527-0849 *Tel:* 760-384-3910 *Web Site:* www.the-aaland-agency.com, pg 539

Rhorer, Richard, Simon & Schuster, 1230 Avenue of the Americas, New York, NY 10020 *Tel:* 212-698-7000 *Toll Free Tel:* 800-223-2348 (cust serv); 800-223-2336 (orders) *Toll Free Fax:* 800-943-9831 (orders) *Web Site:* www.simonandschuster.com, pg 225

Ribas, Maria, The Stonesong Press LLC, 270 W 39 St, No 201, New York, NY 10018 *Tel:* 212-929-4600 *E-mail:* editors@stonesong.com *Web Site:* www.stonesong.com, pg 575

Ribble, Anne G, Bibliographical Society of the University of Virginia, c/o Alderman Library, University of Virginia, McCormick Rd, Charlottesville, VA 22904 *Tel:* 434-924-7013 *Fax:* 434-924-1431 *E-mail:* bibsoc@virginia.edu *Web Site:* bsuva.org, pg 600

Ribesky, Mary, University of Washington Press, 433 Brooklyn Ave NE, Seattle, WA 98195-9570 *Tel:* 206-543-4050 *Toll Free Tel:* 800-537-5487 (orders) *Fax:* 206-543-3932; 410-516-6998 (orders) *E-mail:* uwpress@u.washington.edu *Web Site:* www.washington.edu/uwpress/, pg 260

Ricca, Aimee, Society of Motion Picture & Television Engineers® (SMPTE®), 3 Barker Ave, 5th fl, White Plains, NY 10601 *Tel:* 914-761-1100 *Fax:* 914-761-3115 *Web Site:* www.smpte.org, pg 619

Ricci-Thode, Vanessa, Thodestool Fiction Editing, 40 McDougall Rd, Waterloo, ON N2L 2W5, Canada *Web Site:* www.thodestool.com, pg 535

Rice, Mark, Faith Alive Christian Resources, 1700 28 St SE, Grand Rapids, MI 49508-1407 *Tel:* 616-224-0728 *Toll Free Tel:* 800-333-8300 *Toll Free Fax:* 888-642-8606 *E-mail:* info@faithaliveresources.org; sales@faithaliveresources.org; orders@faithaliveresources.org *Web Site:* www.faithaliveresources.org, pg 86

Rice, Marnie, City of Vancouver Book Award, Woodward's Heritage Bldg, Suite 501, 111 W Hastings St, Vancouver, BC V6B 1H4, Canada *Tel:* 604-871-6634 *Fax:* 604-871-6005 *E-mail:* culture@vancouver.ca *Web Site:* vancouver.ca/bookaward, pg 677

Rich, Alison, Doubleday/Nan A Talese, c/o Penguin Random House Inc, 1745 Broadway, New York, NY 10019 *Tel:* 212-751-2600 *Fax:* 212-572-2662 *E-mail:* ddaypub@randomhouse.com *Web Site:* knopfdoubleday.com, pg 76

Rich, Daniel, Book Sales Inc, 142 W 36 St, 4th fl, New York, NY 10018 *Tel:* 212-779-4971; 212-779-4972 *Toll Free Tel:* 866-483-5456 *Fax:* 212-779-6058 *E-mail:* sales@quartous.com; customerservice@quartous.com *Web Site:* www.booksalesusa.com, pg 42

Richard, Barbara, Vintage & Anchor Books, c/o Random House Inc, 1745 Broadway, New York, NY 10019 *Tel:* 212-572-2420 *E-mail:* vintageanchorpublicity@randomhouse.com *Web Site:* vintage-anchor.knopfdoubleday.com, pg 266

Richard, Ronald B, The Anisfield-Wolf Book Awards, 1422 Euclid Ave, Suite 1300, Cleveland, OH 44115 *Tel:* 216-861-3810 *Fax:* 216-861-1729 *E-mail:* awinfo@clevefdn.org *Web Site:* www.anisfield-wolf.org; www.clevelandfoundation.org, pg 667

Richards, Maggie, Henry Holt and Company, LLC, 175 Fifth Ave, New York, NY 10010 *Tel:* 646-307-5151 *Toll Free Tel:* 888-330-8477 (orders) *Fax:* 646-307-5285 *E-mail:* firstname.lastname@hholt.com *Web Site:* www.henryholt.com, pg 113

Richards, Michael, University of Rochester Press, 668 Mount Hope Ave, Rochester, NY 14620-2731 *Tel:* 585-275-0419 *Fax:* 585-271-8778 *E-mail:* boydell@boydellusa.net *Web Site:* www.urpress.com, pg 259

Richards, Ramona, Abingdon Press, 201 Eighth Ave S, Nashville, TN 37203-3919 *Tel:* 615-749-6000 (academic books) *Toll Free Tel:* 800-251-3320 *Fax:* 615-749-6056 (academic books) *Toll Free Fax:* 800-836-7802 (orders) *E-mail:* orders@abingdonpress.com *Web Site:* www.abingdonpress.com, pg 2

Richards, Victor, Bookhaven Press LLC, 302 Scenic Ct, Moon Township, PA 15108 *Tel:* 412-494-6926 *E-mail:* info@bookhavenpress.com; orders@bookhavenpress.com *Web Site:* bookhavenpress.com, pg 42

Richardson, Anita, Morgan Reynolds Publishing, 620 S Elm St, Suite 387, Greensboro, NC 27406 *Tel:* 336-275-1311 *Toll Free Tel:* 800-535-1504 *Fax:* 336-275-1152 *Toll Free Fax:* 800-535-5725 *E-mail:* editorial@morganreynolds.com *Web Site:* www.morganreynolds.com, pg 160

Richardson, Ariel, Chronicle Books LLC, 680 Second St, San Francisco, CA 94107 *Tel:* 415-537-4200 *Toll Free Tel:* 800-759-0190 (cust serv) *Fax:* 415-537-4460

Toll Free Fax: 800-858-7787 (orders); 800-286-9471 (cust serv) *E-mail:* frontdesk@chroniclebooks.com *Web Site:* www.chroniclebooks.com, pg 58

Richardson, Elaina, Yaddo Artists Residency, 312 Union Ave, Saratoga Springs, NY 12866 *Tel:* 518-584-0746 *Fax:* 518-584-1312 *E-mail:* yaddo@yaddo.org *Web Site:* www.yaddo.org, pg 657

Richardson, Herbert, The Mellen Poetry Press, 240 Portage Rd, Lewiston, NY 14092 *Tel:* 716-754-2266; 716-754-1400 (mktg); 716-754-2788 (order fulfillment) *Fax:* 716-754-4056; 716-754-1860 (fulfillment) *E-mail:* cservice@mellenpress.com *Web Site:* www.mellenpress.com, pg 154

Richardson, Michael, Dark Horse Comics, 10956 SE Main St, Milwaukie, OR 97222 *Tel:* 503-652-8815 *Fax:* 503-654-9440 *E-mail:* dhcomics@darkhorse.com *Web Site:* www.darkhorse.com, pg 70

Richardson, Paul E, Russian Information Service Inc, PO Box 567, Montpelier, VT 05601 *Tel:* 802-223-4955 *E-mail:* editors@russianlife.com *Web Site:* www.russianlife.com, pg 212

Richardson, Sally, Macmillan, 175 Fifth Ave, New York, NY 10010 *Tel:* 646-307-5151 *Fax:* 212-420-9314 *E-mail:* firstname.lastname@macmillan.com *Web Site:* www.macmillan.com, pg 145

Richardson, Sally, St Martin's Press, LLC, 175 Fifth Ave, New York, NY 10010 *Tel:* 646-307-5151 *Fax:* 212-420-9314 *E-mail:* firstname.lastname@macmillan.com *Web Site:* www.stmartins.com, pg 214

Richardson, Tracy, Luminis Books Inc, 1950 E Greyhound Pass, Suite 18, PMB 280, Carmel, IN 46033 *Tel:* 317-840-5838 *E-mail:* editor@luminisbooks.com *Web Site:* www.luminisbooks.com, pg 144

Richason, Brad, Lerner Publishing Group Inc, 241 First Ave N, Minneapolis, MN 55401 *Tel:* 612-332-3344 *Toll Free Tel:* 800-328-4929 *Fax:* 612-332-7615 *Toll Free Fax:* 800-332-1132 *E-mail:* info@lernerbooks.com *Web Site:* www.lernerbooks.com, pg 137

Richer, Joss, Artist-in-Residence Program, 649 rue Queen, 2nd fl, Fredericton, NB E3B 1C3, Canada *Tel:* 506-444-4444 *Toll Free Tel:* 866-460-ARTS (460-2787) *Fax:* 506-444-5543 *E-mail:* nbabcanb@artsnb.ca *Web Site:* www.artsnb.ca, pg 668

Richer, Joss, Arts Scholarships, 649 rue Queen, 2nd fl, Fredericton, NB E3B 1C3, Canada *Tel:* 506-444-4444 *Toll Free Tel:* 866-460-ARTS (460-2787) *Fax:* 506-444-5543 *E-mail:* nbabcanb@artsnb.ca *Web Site:* www.artsnb.ca, pg 668

Richer, Joss, Atlantic Public Art Funders (APAF) Creative Residency, 649 rue Queen, 2nd fl, Fredericton, NB E3B 1C3, Canada *Tel:* 506-444-4444 *Toll Free Tel:* 866-460-ARTS (460-2787) *Fax:* 506-444-5543 *E-mail:* nbabcanb@artsnb.ca *Web Site:* www.artsnb.ca, pg 669

Richer, Joss, Creation Grant Program, 649 rue Queen, 2nd fl, Fredericton, NB E3B 1C3, Canada *Tel:* 506-444-4444 *Toll Free Tel:* 866-460-ARTS (460-2787) *Fax:* 506-444-5543 *E-mail:* nbabcanb@artsnb.ca *Web Site:* www.artsnb.ca, pg 679

Richer, Joss, Documentation Grant Program, 649 rue Queen, 2nd fl, Fredericton, NB E3B 1C3, Canada *Tel:* 506-444-4444 *Toll Free Tel:* 866-460-ARTS (460-2787) *Fax:* 506-444-5543 *E-mail:* nbabcanb@artsnb.ca *Web Site:* www.artsnb.ca, pg 681

Richer, Joss, Grants for Literary Artists, 649 rue Queen, 2nd fl, Fredericton, NB E3B 1C3, Canada *Tel:* 506-444-4444 *Toll Free Tel:* 866-460-ARTS (460-2787) *Fax:* 506-444-5543 *E-mail:* nbabcanb@artsnb.ca *Web Site:* www.artsnb.ca, pg 690

Richer, Joss, The Lieutenant-Governor's Awards for High Achievement in the Arts, 649 rue Queen, 2nd fl, Fredericton, NB E3B 1C3, Canada *Tel:* 506-444-4444 *Toll Free Tel:* 866-460-ARTS (460-2787) *Fax:* 506-444-5543 *E-mail:* nbabcanb@artsnb.ca *Web Site:* www.artsnb.ca, pg 701

Richie, Ross, Boom! Studios, 5670 Wilshire Blvd, Suite 450, Los Angeles, CA 90036 *Web Site:* www.boom-studios.com, pg 43

Richman, Howard, Sound Feelings Publishing, 18375 Ventura Blvd, No 8000, Tarzana, CA 91356 *Tel:* 818-757-0600 *E-mail:* information@soundfeelings.com *Web Site:* www.soundfeelings.com, pg 230

Richman, Jordan, Writers Anonymous Inc, 1302 E Coronado Rd, Phoenix, AZ 85006 *Tel:* 602-256-2830 *Fax:* 602-256-2830 *Web Site:* writersanonymousinc.blogspot.com, pg 536

Richman, Vita, Writers Anonymous Inc, 1302 E Coronado Rd, Phoenix, AZ 85006 *Tel:* 602-256-2830 *Fax:* 602-256-2830 *Web Site:* writersanonymousinc.blogspot.com, pg 536

Richmond, Tom, National Cartoonists Society (NCS), 341 N Maitland Ave, Suite 260, Maitland, FL 32751 *Tel:* 407-647-8839 *Fax:* 407-629-2502 *E-mail:* info@reuben.org *Web Site:* www.reuben.org, pg 611

Rickard, Joan, Author Author Literary Agency Ltd, 130-1005 Columbia St, PO Box 42522, Columbia Sq, New Westminster, BC V3M 6H5, Canada *Tel:* 604-415-0056 *Fax:* 604-415-0076, pg 541

Rico, Liz, Chronicle Books LLC, 680 Second St, San Francisco, CA 94107 *Tel:* 415-537-4200 *Toll Free Tel:* 800-759-0190 (cust serv) *Fax:* 415-537-4460 *Toll Free Fax:* 800-858-7787 (orders); 800-286-9471 (cust serv) *E-mail:* frontdesk@chroniclebooks.com *Web Site:* www.chroniclebooks.com, pg 58

Ridder, Myles, School Guide Publications, 210 North Ave, New Rochelle, NY 10801 *Tel:* 914-632-1220 *Toll Free Tel:* 800-433-7771 *Fax:* 914-632-3412 *E-mail:* info@religiousministries.com *Web Site:* www.graduateguide.com; www.schoolguides.com; www.religiousministries.com, pg 219

Ridgeway, Nichole, ASM Press, 1752 "N" St NW, Washington, DC 20036-2904 *Tel:* 202-737-3600 *Toll Free Tel:* 800-546-2416 *Fax:* 202-942-9342 *E-mail:* books@asmusa.org *Web Site:* estore.asm.org, pg 25

Riebe, Anna, Ambassador International, 427 Wade Hampton Blvd, Greenville, SC 29609 *Tel:* 864-235-2434 *Toll Free Tel:* 800-209-8570 *Fax:* 864-235-2491 *E-mail:* info@emeraldhouse.com; publisher@emeraldhouse.com (ms submissions); sales@emeraldhouse.com (orders/order inquiries) *Web Site:* ambassador-international.com; www.facebook.com/AmbassadorIntl; twitter.com/ambassadorintl, pg 10

Riegert, Ray, Ulysses Press, PO Box 3440, Berkeley, CA 94703-0440 *Tel:* 510-601-8301 *Toll Free Tel:* 800-377-2542 *Fax:* 510-601-8307 *E-mail:* ulysses@ulyssespress.com *Web Site:* www.ulyssespress.com, pg 252

Rielly, Emily, University of British Columbia Press, 2029 West Mall, Vancouver, BC V6T 1Z2, Canada *Tel:* 604-822-5959 *Toll Free Tel:* 877-377-9378 *Fax:* 604-822-6083 *Toll Free Fax:* 800-668-0821 *E-mail:* frontdesk@ubcpress.ca *Web Site:* www.ubcpress.ca, pg 502

Rienner, Lynne, Kumarian Press, 1800 30 St, Suite 314, Boulder, CO 80301 *Tel:* 303-444-6684 *Toll Free Tel:* 800-232-0223 (orders only) *Fax:* 303-444-0824 *E-mail:* questions@rienner.com *Web Site:* www.kpbooks.com, pg 133

Rienner, Lynne C, Lynne Rienner Publishers Inc, 1800 30 St, Suite 314, Boulder, CO 80301 *Tel:* 303-444-6684 *Fax:* 303-444-0824 *E-mail:* questions@rienner.com; cservice@rienner.com *Web Site:* www.rienner.com, pg 209

Rieselbach, Erik, New Directions Publishing Corp, 80 Eighth Ave, New York, NY 10011 *Tel:* 212-255-0230 *Fax:* 212-255-0231 *E-mail:* newdirections@ndbooks.com; editorial@ndbooks.com *Web Site:* ndbooks.com, pg 167

Riess, Jana, Westminster John Knox Press (WJK), 100 Witherspoon St, Louisville, KY 40202-1396 *Tel:* 502-569-5052 *Toll Free Tel:* 800-227-2872 (US only) *Fax:* 502-569-8308 *Toll Free Fax:* 800-541-5113 (US & CN) *E-mail:* wjk@wjkbooks.com; customer_service@wjkbooks.com *Web Site:* www.wjkbooks.com, pg 269

Rigas, Maia M, The Art Institute of Chicago, 111 S Michigan Ave, Chicago, IL 60603-6404 *Tel:* 312-443-3600; 312-443-3540 (pubns) *Fax:* 312-443-1334 (pubns) *Web Site:* www.artic.edu; www.artinstituteshop.org, pg 22

Riley, Elizabeth, W W Norton & Company Inc, 500 Fifth Ave, New York, NY 10110-0017 *Tel:* 212-354-5500 *Toll Free Tel:* 800-233-4830 (orders & cust serv) *Fax:* 212-869-0856 *Toll Free Fax:* 800-458-6515 *Web Site:* www.wwnorton.com, pg 171

Riley, Jocelyn, Her Own Words LLC, PO Box 5264, Madison, WI 53705-0264 *Tel:* 608-271-7083 *Fax:* 608-271-0209 *Web Site:* www.herownwords.com; www.nontraditionalcareers.com, pg 110

Riley, John, Morgan Reynolds Publishing, 620 S Elm St, Suite 387, Greensboro, NC 27406 *Tel:* 336-275-1311 *Toll Free Tel:* 800-535-1504 *Fax:* 336-275-1152 *Toll Free Fax:* 800-535-5725 *E-mail:* editorial@morganreynolds.com *Web Site:* www.morganreynolds.com, pg 160

Riley, Kate, Association of Opinion Journalists (AOJ), 2301 Vanderbilt Place, VU Sta B 351669, Nashville, TN 37235-1669 *E-mail:* opinionjounalists@gmail.com *Web Site:* www.opinionjournalists.org, pg 599

Rimas, Ruta, Simon & Schuster Children's Publishing, 1230 Avenue of the Americas, New York, NY 10020 *Tel:* 212-698-7000 *Web Site:* KIDS.SimonandSchuster.com; TEEN.SimonandSchuster.com; simonandschuster.net; simonandschuster.biz, pg 225

Rimel, John, Mountain Press Publishing Co, 1301 S Third W, Missoula, MT 59801 *Tel:* 406-728-1900 *Toll Free Tel:* 800-234-5308 *Fax:* 406-728-1635 *E-mail:* info@mtnpress.com *Web Site:* www.mountain-press.com, pg 160

Rinaldi, Angela, The Angela Rinaldi Literary Agency, PO Box 7877, Beverly Hills, CA 90212-7877 *Tel:* 310-842-7665 *Fax:* 310-837-8143 *E-mail:* info@rinaldiliterary.com (submissions) *Web Site:* www.rinaldiliterary.com, pg 570

Rinaldi, Karen, HarperCollins General Books Group, 195 Broadway, New York, NY 10007 *Tel:* 212-207-7000 *Web Site:* www.harpercollins.com, pg 105

Rinck, Gary M, John Wiley & Sons Inc, 111 River St, Hoboken, NJ 07030-5774 *Tel:* 201-748-6000 *Toll Free Tel:* 800-225-5945 (cust serv) *Fax:* 201-748-6088 *E-mail:* info@wiley.com *Web Site:* www.wiley.com, pg 272

Rinehart, Rebecca D, American Psychiatric Publishing (APP), 1000 Wilson Blvd, Suite 1825, Arlington, VA 22209 *Tel:* 703-907-7322 *Toll Free Tel:* 800-368-5777 *Fax:* 703-907-1091 *E-mail:* appi@psych.org *Web Site:* www.appi.org; www.psychiatryonline.org, pg 15

Rinehart, Rick, M Evans & Company, c/o Rowman & Littlefield Publishing Group, 4501 Forbes Blvd, Suite 200, Lanham, MD 20706 *Tel:* 301-459-3366 *Fax:* 301-429-5748 *Web Site:* rowman.com, pg 84

Ringer, Cheryl, McGraw-Hill Education, 2 Penn Plaza, New York, NY 10121-2298 *Tel:* 212-904-2000 *E-mail:* customer.service@mcgraw-hill.com *Web Site:* www.mheducation.com; www.mheducation.com/custserv.html, pg 151

Riordan, Caroline, Penguin Group (USA) LLC Sales, 375 Hudson St, New York, NY 10014 *Tel:* 212-366-2000 *E-mail:* online@penguinputnam.com *Web Site:* us.penguingroup.com, pg 186

Riordan, James C, Seven Locks Press, 3100 W Warner Ave, Suite 8, Santa Ana, CA 97204 *E-mail:* sevenlocks@aol.com *Web Site:* www.sevenlockspublishing.com, pg 222

Ripianzi, David, YMAA Publication Center, PO Box 480, Wolfeboro, NH 03894 *Tel:* 603-569-7988 *Toll Free Tel:* 800-669-8892 *Fax:* 603-569-1889 *E-mail:* ymaa@aol.com *Web Site:* www.ymaa.com, pg 278

Riske, Douglas, Manitoba Arts Council, 525-93 Lombard Ave, Winnipeg, MB R3B 3B1, Canada *Tel:* 204-945-2237 *Toll Free Tel:* 866-994-2787 *Fax:* 204-945-5925 *E-mail:* info@artscouncil.mb.ca *Web Site:* artscouncil.mb.ca, pg 609

Riske, Kris Brandt, American Federation of Astrologers Inc, 6535 S Rural Rd, Tempe, AZ 85283-3746 *Tel:* 480-838-1751 *Toll Free Tel:* 888-301-7630 *Fax:* 480-838-8293 *Web Site:* www.astrologers.com, pg 12

Riskey, Curtis, CBA: The Association for Christian Retail, 1365 Garden of the Gods Rd, Suite 105, Colorado Springs, CO 80907 *Tel:* 719-265-9895 *Toll Free Tel:* 800-252-1950 *Fax:* 719-272-3508 *E-mail:* info@cbaonline.org *Web Site:* cbaonline.org, pg 603

Rissi, Anica, HarperCollins Children's Books, 195 Broadway, New York, NY 10007 *Tel:* 212-207-7000 *Web Site:* www.harpercollins.com/childrens, pg 105

Ristau, Karen M PhD, National Catholic Educational Association, 1005 N Glebe Rd, Suite 525, Arlington, VA 22201 *Tel:* 571-257-0010 *Toll Free Tel:* 800-711-6232 *Fax:* 703-243-0025 *E-mail:* nceaadmin@ncea.org *Web Site:* www.ncea.org, pg 164

Ristau, Todd, Southeastern Theatre Conference New Play Project, 1175 Revolution Mill Dr, Suite 14, Greensboro, NC 27405 *Tel:* 336-272-3645 *Fax:* 336-272-8810 *E-mail:* info@setc.org *Web Site:* www.setc.org, pg 729

Ritchie, Adele, Canadian Newspaper Association, 890 Yonge St, Suite 200, Toronto, ON M4W 3P4, Canada *Tel:* 416-923-3567; 416-482-1090 *Toll Free Tel:* 877-305-2262 *Fax:* 416-923-7206; 416-482-1908 *E-mail:* info@newspaperscanada.ca *Web Site:* www.newspaperscanada.ca, pg 602

Ritchken, Deborah, Marsal Lyon Literary Agency LLC, 665 San Rodolfo Dr, Suite 124, PMB 121, Solana Beach, CA 92075 *Tel:* 760-814-8507 *Web Site:* www.marsallyonliteraryagency.com, pg 563

Ritt, Judith W, Professional Resource Press, 1958 Barber Rd, Sarasota, FL 34240 *Tel:* 941-343-9601 *Toll Free Tel:* 800-443-3364 (orders & cust serv) *Fax:* 941-343-9201 *Toll Free Fax:* 866-804-4843 (orders only) *E-mail:* cs.prpress@gmail.com *Web Site:* www.prpress.com, pg 198

Rittenberg, Ann, Ann Rittenberg Literary Agency Inc, 15 Maiden Lane, Suite 206, New York, NY 10038 *Tel:* 212-684-6936 *Fax:* 212-684-6929 *E-mail:* info@rittlit.com *Web Site:* www.rittlit.com, pg 570

Ritter, Carol, Romance Writers of America®, 14615 Benfer Rd, Houston, TX 77069 *Tel:* 832-717-5200 *Fax:* 832-717-5201 *E-mail:* info@rwa.org *Web Site:* www.rwa.org, pg 618

Ritter, Carol, Romance Writers of America Awards, 14615 Benfer Rd, Houston, TX 77069 *Tel:* 832-717-5200 *Fax:* 832-717-5201 *E-mail:* info@rwa.org *Web Site:* www.rwa.org, pg 724

Ritter, Emily, Bloomsbury Publishing Inc, 1385 Broadway, 5th fl, New York, NY 10018 *Tel:* 212-419-5300 *E-mail:* marketingusa@bloomsbury.com; adultpublicityusa@bloomsbury.com; askacademic@bloomsbury.com *Web Site:* www.bloomsbury.com, pg 40

Riva, Peter, International Transactions Inc, 28 Alope Way, Gila, NM 88038 *Tel:* 845-373-9696 *Fax:* 480-393-5162 *E-mail:* info@intltrans.com *Web Site:* www.intltrans.com, pg 557

Riva, Sandra Anne, International Transactions Inc, 28 Alope Way, Gila, NM 88038 *Tel:* 845-373-9696 *Fax:* 480-393-5162 *E-mail:* info@intltrans.com *Web Site:* www.intltrans.com, pg 557

Rivas, Laura, Candlewick Press, 99 Dover St, Somerville, MA 02144-2825 *Tel:* 617-661-3330 *Fax:* 617-661-0565 *E-mail:* bigbear@candlewick.com; salesinfo@candlewick.com *Web Site:* www.candlewick.com, pg 49

Rivas-Smith, Alexandra, William H Sadlier Inc, 9 Pine St, New York, NY 10005 *Tel:* 212-227-2120 *Toll Free Tel:* 800-221-5175 (cust serv) *Fax:* 212-312-6080 *E-mail:* customerservice@sadlier.com *Web Site:* www.sadlier.com, pg 213

Riven, Judith, Judith Riven Literary Agent LLC, 250 W 16 St, Suite 4F, New York, NY 10011 *Tel:* 212-255-1009 *Fax:* 212-255-8547 *E-mail:* rivenlitqueries@gmail.com *Web Site:* rivenlit.com, pg 533, 570

Rivers, Shana R, University of Alabama Press, 200 Hackberry Lane, 2nd fl, Tuscaloosa, AL 35487 *Tel:* 205-348-5180 *Fax:* 205-348-9201 *Web Site:* www.uapress.ua.edu, pg 254

Rizzo, Gina, HarperCollins Children's Books, 195 Broadway, New York, NY 10007 *Tel:* 212-207-7000 *Web Site:* www.harpercollins.com/childrens, pg 105

Rizzo, Mary, New Jersey Council for the Humanities Book Award, 28 W State St, 6th fl, Trenton, NJ 08608 *Tel:* 609-695-4838 *Toll Free Tel:* 888-FYI-NJCH (394-6524) *Fax:* 609-695-4929 *E-mail:* njch@njch.org *Web Site:* www.njch.org, pg 712

Roach, Brian, The Catholic University of America Press, 240 Leahy Hall, 620 Michigan Ave NE, Washington, DC 20064 *Tel:* 202-319-5052 *Toll Free Tel:* 800-537-5487 (orders only) *Fax:* 202-319-4985 *E-mail:* cua-press@cua.edu *Web Site:* cuapress.cua.edu, pg 52

Roach, Reginald, Palmetto Bug Books, 121 N Hibiscus Dr, Miami Beach, FL 33139 *Tel:* 305-531-9813 *Fax:* 305-604-1516 *E-mail:* palmettobugbooks@gmail.com, pg 181

Roane, Rick, Cherry Hill Publishing LLC, 24344 Del Amo Rd, Ramona, CA 92065 *Tel:* 858-829-5550 *Toll Free Tel:* 800-407-1072 *Fax:* 760-203-1200 *E-mail:* operations@cherryhillpublishing.com; sales@cherryhillpublishing.com *Web Site:* www.cherryhillpublishing.com, pg 56

Roane, Sharon, Cherry Hill Publishing LLC, 24344 Del Amo Rd, Ramona, CA 92065 *Tel:* 858-829-5550 *Toll Free Tel:* 800-407-1072 *Fax:* 760-203-1200 *E-mail:* operations@cherryhillpublishing.com; sales@cherryhillpublishing.com *Web Site:* www.cherryhillpublishing.com, pg 56

Robbins, B J, B J Robbins Literary Agency, 5130 Bellaire Ave, North Hollywood, CA 91607 *E-mail:* robbinsliterary@gmail.com, pg 570

Robbins, Caroline, Trafalgar Square Books, 388 Howe Hill Rd, North Pomfret, VT 05053 *Tel:* 802-457-1911 *Toll Free Tel:* 800-423-4525 *Fax:* 802-457-1913 *E-mail:* contact@trafalgarbooks.com *Web Site:* www.trafalgarbooks.com; www.horseandriderbooks.com, pg 248

Robbins, Fleetwood, Waxman Leavell Literary Agency, 443 Park Ave S, No 1004, New York, NY 10016 *Tel:* 212-675-5556 *Fax:* 212-675-1381 *Web Site:* www.waxmanleavell.com, pg 579

Robbins, Lara, Berkley Books, 375 Hudson St, New York, NY 10014 *Tel:* 212-366-2000 *Fax:* 212-366-2666 *E-mail:* online@penguinputnam.com *Web Site:* www.penguinputnam.com; us.penguingroup.com, pg 35

Robbins, Lara, Berkley Publishing Group, 375 Hudson St, New York, NY 10014 *Tel:* 212-366-2000 *Fax:* 212-366-2385 *E-mail:* online@penguinputnam.com *Web Site:* us.penguingroup.com, pg 35

Robbins-Butcher, Amanda, Jerome Fellowship, 2301 Franklin Ave E, Minneapolis, MN 55406-1099 *Tel:* 612-332-7481 *Fax:* 612-332-6037 *E-mail:* info@pwcenter.org *Web Site:* www.pwcenter.org, pg 697

Robbins-Butcher, Amanda, Many Voices Fellowships, 2301 Franklin Ave E, Minneapolis, MN 55406-1099 *Tel:* 612-332-7481 *Fax:* 612-332-6037 *E-mail:* info@pwcenter.org *Web Site:* www.pwcenter.org, pg 705

Robbins-Butcher, Amanda, McKnight Fellowships for Playwrights, 2301 Franklin Ave E, Minneapolis, MN 55406-1099 *Tel:* 612-332-7481 *Fax:* 612-332-6037 *E-mail:* info@pwcenter.org *Web Site:* www.pwcenter.org, pg 706

Robbins-Butcher, Amanda, McKnight National Residency & Commission, 2301 Franklin Ave E, Minneapolis, MN 55406-1099 *Tel:* 612-332-7481 *Fax:* 612-332-6037 *E-mail:* info@pwcenter.org *Web Site:* www.pwcenter.org, pg 706

Roberson, Nancy, AMACOM Books, 1601 Broadway, New York, NY 10019-7420 *Tel:* 212-586-8100 *Toll Free Tel:* 800-250-5308 (cust serv) *Fax:* 212-903-8083; 518-891-2372 (orders) *E-mail:* pubs_cust_serv@amanet.org *Web Site:* www.amacombooks.org, pg 9

Roberson, Nathan, Crown Publishing Group, c/o Penguin Random House Inc, 1745 Broadway, New York, NY 10019 *Tel:* 212-782-9000 *Toll Free Tel:* 888-264-1745 *Fax:* 212-940-7408 *E-mail:* crownosm@penguinrandomhouse.com *Web Site:* crownpublishing.com, pg 68

Roberson, Rick, The Barnabas Agency, PO Box 3113, Corsicana, TX 75110-3113 *Toll Free Tel:* 800-927-0517 *E-mail:* info@barnabasagency.com *Web Site:* www.barnabasagency.com, pg 587

Robert, Katie, American Industrial Hygiene Association - AIHA, 3141 Fairview Park Dr, Suite 777, Falls Church, VA 22042 *Tel:* 703-849-8888 *Fax:* 703-207-3561 *E-mail:* infonet@aiha.org *Web Site:* www.aiha.org, pg 13

Roberts, Claire, Trident Media Group LLC, 41 Madison Ave, 36th fl, New York, NY 10010 *Tel:* 212-333-1511 *E-mail:* info@tridentmediagroup.com; press@tridentmediagroup.com *Web Site:* www.tridentmediagroup.com, pg 578

Roberts, Conrad, University Press of Kansas, 2502 Westbrooke Circle, Lawrence, KS 66045-4444 *Tel:* 785-864-4154; 785-864-4155 (orders) *Fax:* 785-864-4586 *E-mail:* upress@ku.edu; upkorders@ku.edu (orders) *Web Site:* www.kansaspress.ku.edu, pg 261

Roberts, Jane F, Literary & Creative Artists Inc, 3543 Albemarle St NW, Washington, DC 20008-4213 *Tel:* 202-362-4688 *Fax:* 202-362-8875 *E-mail:* lca9643@lcadc.com (queries, no attachments) *Web Site:* www.lcadc.com, pg 562

Roberts, Janet, Centering Corp, 7230 Maple St, Omaha, NE 68134 *Tel:* 402-553-1200 *Toll Free Tel:* 866-218-0101 *Fax:* 402-553-0507 *E-mail:* orders@centering.org *Web Site:* www.centering.org, pg 54

Roberts, Jennifer, Candlewick Press, 99 Dover St, Somerville, MA 02144-2825 *Tel:* 617-661-3330 *Fax:* 617-661-0565 *E-mail:* bigbear@candlewick.com; salesinfo@candlewick.com *Web Site:* www.candlewick.com, pg 49

Roberts, Jill, Tachyon Publications, 1459 18 St, No 139, San Francisco, CA 94107 *Tel:* 415-285-5615 *E-mail:* tachyon@tachyonpublications.com *Web Site:* www.tachyonpublications.com, pg 240

Roberts, LaTisha, Texas Tech University Press, 2903 Fourth St, Suite 201, Lubbock, TX 79409 *Tel:* 806-742-2982 *Toll Free Tel:* 800-832-4042 *Fax:* 806-742-2979 *E-mail:* ttup@ttu.edu *Web Site:* www.ttupress.org, pg 244

Roberts, Marc, Centering Corp, 7230 Maple St, Omaha, NE 68134 *Tel:* 402-553-1200 *Toll Free Tel:* 866-218-0101 *Fax:* 402-553-0507 *E-mail:* orders@centering.org *Web Site:* www.centering.org, pg 54

Roberts, Megan, Sewanee Writers' Conference, Stamler Ctr, 119 Gailor Hall, 735 University Ave, Sewanee, TN 37383-1000 *Tel:* 931-598-1141 *E-mail:* swc@sewanee.edu *Web Site:* www.sewaneewriters.org, pg 655

Roberts, Michael, Fine Arts Work Center in Provincetown, 24 Pearl St, Provincetown, MA 02657 *Tel:* 508-487-9960 *Fax:* 508-487-8873 *E-mail:* general@fawc.org *Web Site:* www.fawc.org, pg 686

Roberts, Michele, Liberty Fund Inc, 8335 Allison Pointe Trail, Suite 300, Indianapolis, IN 46250-1684 *Tel:* 317-842-0880 *Toll Free Tel:* 800-955-8335; 800-866-3520; 800-368-7897 ext 6069 (cust serv) *Fax:* 317-577-9067; 317-579-6060 (cust serv); 708-534-7803 *E-mail:* books@libertyfund.org; info@libertyfund.org *Web Site:* www.libertyfund.org, pg 138

Roberts, Nancy, Pearson Humanities & Social Sciences, 225 River St, Hoboken, NJ 07030-4772 *Tel:* 201-236-7000 *Fax:* 201-236-3400, pg 185

Roberts, Nate, Emmaus Road Publishing Inc, 1468 Parkview Cir, Steubenville, OH 43952 *Tel:* 740-283-2880 (outside US) *Toll Free Tel:* 800-398-5470 (orders) *Fax:* 740-283-4011 (orders) *E-mail:* questions@emmausroad.org *Web Site:* www.emmausroad.org, pg 82

Roberts, Sherry, The Roberts Group, 12803 Eastview Curve, Apple Valley, MN 55124 *Tel:* 952-322-4005 *E-mail:* info@editorialservice.com *Web Site:* www.editorialservice.com, pg 533

Roberts, Stacie, Sovereign Award for Writing, Woodbine Sales Pavilion, 555 Rexdale Blvd, Rexdale, ON M9W 5L2, Canada *Tel:* 416-675-7756 *Fax:* 416-675-6378 *E-mail:* jockeyclub@bellnet.ca *Web Site:* www.jockeyclubcanada.com, pg 730

Roberts, Stuart, Simon & Schuster, 1230 Avenue of the Americas, New York, NY 10020 *Tel:* 212-698-7000 *Toll Free Tel:* 800-223-2348 (cust serv); 800-223-2336 (orders) *Toll Free Fax:* 800-943-9831 (orders) *Web Site:* www.simonandschuster.com, pg 225

Roberts, Tim, Counterpath Press, 613 22 St, Denver, CO 80205 *E-mail:* counterpath@counterpathpress.org; editors@counterpathpress.org *Web Site:* www.counterpathpress.org, pg 65

Roberts, Tony, The Roberts Group, 12803 Eastview Curve, Apple Valley, MN 55124 *Tel:* 952-322-4005 *E-mail:* info@editorialservice.com *Web Site:* www.editorialservice.com, pg 533

Roberts, U D, Brentwood Christian Press, 4000 Beallwood Ave, Columbus, GA 31904 *Toll Free Tel:* 800-334-8861 *E-mail:* brentwood@aol.com *Web Site:* www.brentwoodbooks.com, pg 45

Robertson, Michael, Specialty Graphic Imaging Association, 10015 Main St, Fairfax, VA 22031-3489 *Tel:* 703-385-1335 *Toll Free Tel:* 888-385-3588 *Fax:* 703-273-0456 *E-mail:* sgia@sgia.org *Web Site:* www.sgia.org, pg 620

Robertson, Randy, Susquehanna University, Department of English, 514 University Ave, Selinsgrove, PA 17870 *Tel:* 570-372-0101, pg 662

Robertson, Sarah, Schlager Group Inc, 325 N Saint Paul, Suite 3425, Dallas, TX 75201 *Toll Free Tel:* 888-416-5727 *Fax:* 214-347-9469 *E-mail:* info@schlagergroup.com *Web Site:* www.schlagergroup.com, pg 218

Robey, Annelise, Jane Rotrosen Agency LLC, 318 E 51 St, New York, NY 10022 *Tel:* 212-593-4330 *Fax:* 212-935-6985 *Web Site:* janerotrosen.com, pg 571

Robins, Jennifer, Prufrock Press, PO Box 8813, Waco, TX 76714-8813 *Tel:* 254-756-3337 *Toll Free Tel:* 800-998-2208 *Fax:* 254-756-3339 *Toll Free Fax:* 800-240-0333 *E-mail:* info@prufrock.com *Web Site:* www.prufrock.com, pg 199

Robinson, Alexa, Cricket Cottage Publishing LLC, 4409 Hoffner Ave, Unit 127, Orlando, FL 32812 *Tel:* 407-255-7785 *E-mail:* cricketcottage@att.net *Web Site:* www.thecricketpublishing.com, pg 67

Robinson, Andrea, Vintage & Anchor Books, c/o Random House Inc, 1745 Broadway, New York, NY 10019 *Tel:* 212-572-2420 *E-mail:* vintageanchorpublicity@randomhouse.com *Web Site:* vintage-anchor.knopfdoubleday.com, pg 266

Robinson, Andrew, Cricket Cottage Publishing LLC, 4409 Hoffner Ave, Unit 127, Orlando, FL 32812 *Tel:* 407-255-7785 *E-mail:* cricketcottage@att.net *Web Site:* www.thecricketpublishing.com, pg 67

Robinson, David, Linguistic Society of America, 1325 18 St NW, Suite 211, Washington, DC 20036-6501 *Tel:* 202-835-1714 *Fax:* 202-835-1717 *E-mail:* lsa@lsadc.org *Web Site:* www.linguisticsociety.org, pg 609

Robinson, Dino, Northwestern University Press, 629 Noyes St, Evanston, IL 60208-4210 *Tel:* 847-491-2046 *Toll Free Tel:* 800-621-2736 (orders only) *Fax:* 847-491-8150 *E-mail:* nupress@northwestern.edu *Web Site:* www.nupress.northwestern.edu, pg 171

Robinson, Eileen, Move Books, PO Box 183, Beacon Falls, CT 06403 *Web Site:* www.move-books.com, pg 508

Robinson, James J, The Minerals, Metals & Materials Society (TMS), 184 Thorn Hill Rd, Warrendale, PA 15086 *Tel:* 724-776-9000 *Toll Free Tel:* 800-759-4867 *Fax:* 724-776-3770 *E-mail:* publications@tms.org (orders) *Web Site:* www.tms.org (orders), pg 157

Robinson, Jennifer, Gallery Books, 1230 Avenue of the Americas, New York, NY 10020 *Toll Free Tel:* 800-456-6798 *Fax:* 212-698-7284 *E-mail:* consumer.customerservice@simonandschuster.com *Web Site:* www.simonsays.com, pg 94

Robinson, Jim, Harlequin Enterprises Ltd, 225 Duncan Mill Rd, Don Mills, ON M3B 3K9, Canada *Tel:* 416-445-5860 *Toll Free Tel:* 888-432-4879; 800-370-5838 (ebook inquiries) *E-mail:* customerservice@harlequin.com *Web Site:* www.harlequin.com, pg 487

Robinson, Jo Ann, Cricket Cottage Publishing LLC, 4409 Hoffner Ave, Unit 127, Orlando, FL 32812 *Tel:* 407-255-7785 *E-mail:* cricketcottage@att.net *Web Site:* www.thecricketpublishing.com, pg 67

Robinson, Joe, EEI Communications, 6301 Ivy Lane, Suite 250, Greenbelt, MD 20770 *Tel:* 410-309-8200 *Fax:* 410-630-3980 *E-mail:* info@eeicom.com *Web Site:* www.eeicom.com, pg 660

Robinson, Kelly, Milner Award, One Margaret Mitchell Sq NW, Atlanta, GA 30303 *Tel:* 404-730-1865 *E-mail:* info@themilneraward.org *Web Site:* www.themilneraward.org, pg 707

Robinson, Kim, University of California Press, 2120 Berkeley Way, Berkeley, CA 94704-1012 *Tel:* 510-642-4247 *Fax:* 510-643-7127 *E-mail:* askucp@ucpress.edu (books); customerservice@ucpressjournals.com *Web Site:* www.ucpress.edu, pg 255

Robinson, Marian, The Guilford Press, 72 Spring St, New York, NY 10012 *Tel:* 212-431-9800 *Toll Free Tel:* 800-365-7006 *Fax:* 212-966-6708 *E-mail:* info@guilford.com *Web Site:* www.guilford.com, pg 102

Robinson, Richard, Scholastic Inc, 557 Broadway, New York, NY 10012 *Tel:* 212-343-6100 *Toll Free Tel:* 800-scholastic *Web Site:* www.scholastic.com, pg 218

Robinson, Roxana, The Authors Guild, 31 E 32 St, 7th fl, New York, NY 10016 *Tel:* 212-563-5904 *Fax:* 212-564-5363 *E-mail:* staff@authorsguild.org *Web Site:* www.authorsguild.org, pg 599

Robinson, Sharon P, American Association of Colleges for Teacher Education (AACTE), 1307 New York Ave NW, Suite 300, Washington, DC 20005 *Tel:* 202-293-2450 *Fax:* 202-457-8095 *E-mail:* aacte@aacte.org *Web Site:* www.aacte.org, pg 11

Robson, William B P, C D Howe Institute, 67 Yonge St, Suite 300, Toronto, ON M5E 1J8, Canada *Tel:* 416-865-1904 *Fax:* 416-865-1866 *E-mail:* cdhowe@cdhowe.org *Web Site:* www.cdhowe.org, pg 488

Robyn, Chris, Long River Press, 360 Swift Ave, Suite 48, South San Francisco, CA 94080 *Tel:* 650-872-7718 (ext 312) *Fax:* 650-872-7808 *E-mail:* info@longriverpress.com *Web Site:* www.chinabooks.com, pg 143

Rocco, Renee, Kensington Publishing Corp, 119 W 40 St, New York, NY 10018 *Tel:* 212-407-1500 *Toll Free Tel:* 800-221-2647 *Fax:* 212-935-0699 *Web Site:* www.kensingtonbooks.com, pg 130

Roche, Art, Dubuque Fine Arts Players Annual One Act Play Festival, PO Box 1160, Dubuque, IA 52004-1160 *Tel:* 563-588-3438 *E-mail:* contact@dbqoneacts.org *Web Site:* www.dbqoneacts.org, pg 682

Roche, Mary Beth, Macmillan, 175 Fifth Ave, New York, NY 10010 *Tel:* 646-307-5151 *Fax:* 212-420-9314 *E-mail:* firstname.lastname@macmillan.com *Web Site:* www.macmillan.com, pg 145

Roche, Mary Beth, Macmillan Audio, 175 Fifth Ave, New York, NY 10010 *Tel:* 646-307-5151 *Toll Free Tel:* 888-330-8477 (cust serv) *Fax:* 917-534-0980 *Web Site:* www.macmillanaudio.com, pg 145

Rochefort, Jacques, Cheneliere Education Inc, 5800, rue St Denis, bureau 900, Montreal, QC H2S 3L5, Canada *Tel:* 514-273-1066 *Toll Free Tel:* 800-565-5531 *Fax:* 514-276-0324 *Toll Free Fax:* 800-814-0324 *E-mail:* info@cheneliere.ca *Web Site:* www.cheneliere.ca, pg 477

Rochefort, Jacques, Gaetan Morin Editeur, 5800, rue St-Denis, bureau 900, Montreal, QC H2S 3L5, Canada *Tel:* 514-273-1066 *Toll Free Tel:* 800-565-5531 *Fax:* 514-276-0324 *Toll Free Fax:* 800-814-0324 *E-mail:* info@cheneliere.ca *Web Site:* www.cheneliere.ca, pg 485

Rock, James A, James A Rock & Co Publishers, 900 S Irby St, Suite 508, Florence, SC 29501 *Toll Free Tel:* 800-411-2230 *Fax:* 843-395-5975 *E-mail:* jrock@rockpublishing.com *Web Site:* rockpublishing.com, pg 210

Rockefeller, Kirwan PhD, UCI Extension Writers' Program, PO Box 6050, Irvine, CA 92616-6050 *Tel:* 949-824-5990 *Fax:* 949-824-3651 *Web Site:* www.unex.uci.edu, pg 656

Rockmill, Jayne, Rockmill & Company, 647 Warren St, Brooklyn, NY 11217 *E-mail:* agentrockmill@yahoo.com, pg 570

Rockwell, Lew, Ludwig von Mises Institute, 518 W Magnolia Ave, Auburn, AL 36832 *Tel:* 334-321-2100 *Fax:* 334-321-2119 *E-mail:* info@mises.org *Web Site:* www.mises.org, pg 266

Roco, Mary, Krause Publications Inc, 700 E State St, Iola, WI 54990 *Tel:* 715-445-2214 *Toll Free Tel:* 800-258-0929 (cust serv); 888-457-2873 (orders) *Fax:* 715-445-4087 *E-mail:* bookorders@krause.com *Web Site:* www.krausebooks.com, pg 133

Rodale, Maria, Rodale Inc, 400 S Tenth St, Emmaus, PA 18098 *Tel:* 610-967-5171 *Web Site:* www.rodaleinc.com, pg 210

Rodenberger, Jean, F A Davis Co, 1915 Arch St, Philadelphia, PA 19103 *Tel:* 215-568-2270; 215-440-3001 *Toll Free Tel:* 800-523-4049 *Fax:* 215-568-5065; 215-440-3016 *E-mail:* info@fadavis.com; orders@fadavis.com *Web Site:* www.fadavis.com, pg 71

Rodengen, Jeffrey L, Write Stuff Enterprises LLC, 1001 S Andrews Ave, Suite 120, Fort Lauderdale, FL 33316 *Tel:* 954-462-6657 *Toll Free Tel:* 800-900-2665 *Fax:* 954-462-6023 *E-mail:* legends@writestuffbooks.com *Web Site:* www.writestuffbooks.com, pg 277

Roderick, Stacey, Kids Can Press Ltd, 25 Dockside Dr, Toronto, ON M5A 0B5, Canada *Tel:* 416-479-7000 *Toll Free Tel:* 800-265-0884 *Fax:* 416-960-5437 *E-mail:* info@kidscan.com; customerservice@kidscan.com *Web Site:* www.kidscanpress.com; www.kidscanpress.ca, pg 489

Rodgers, Emma, Second Story Press, 20 Maud St, Suite 401, Toronto, ON M5V 2M5, Canada *Tel:* 416-537-7850 *Fax:* 416-537-0588 *E-mail:* info@secondstorypress.ca *Web Site:* secondstorypress.ca, pg 498

Rodgers, Loren, National Center For Employee Ownership (NCEO), 1736 Franklin St, 8th fl, Oakland, CA 94612-3445 *Tel:* 510-208-1300 *Fax:* 510-272-9510 *E-mail:* customerservice@nceo.org *Web Site:* www.nceo.org, pg 164

Rodman, Howard, Writers Guild of America Awards, 7000 W Third St, Los Angeles, CA 90048 *Tel:* 323-951-4000; 323-782-4569 *Fax:* 323-782-4800 *Web Site:* www.wga.org, pg 738

Rodman, Howard, Writers Guild of America, West (WGAW), 7000 W Third St, Los Angeles, CA 90048 *Tel:* 323-951-4000 *Toll Free Tel:* 800-548-4532 *Fax:* 323-782-4800 *Web Site:* www.wga.org, pg 621

Rodmell, Emily, Love Inspired Books, 233 Broadway, Suite 1001, New York, NY 10279 *Tel:* 212-553-4200 *Fax:* 212-227-8969 *E-mail:* customer_service@harlequin.ca *Web Site:* www.harlequin.com, pg 143

Rodovsky, Jayson, Transcontinental Music Publications, 633 Third Ave, New York, NY 10017 *Tel:* 212-650-4101; 212-650-4120 *Toll Free Tel:* 888-489-8242 (orders) *Fax:* 212-650-4119 *E-mail:* tmp@urj.org; press@urj.org *Web Site:* www.transcontinentalmusic.com, pg 248

Rodrick, Scott, National Center For Employee Ownership (NCEO), 1736 Franklin St, 8th fl, Oakland, CA 94612-3445 *Tel:* 510-208-1300 *Fax:* 510-272-9510 *E-mail:* customerservice@nceo.org *Web Site:* www.nceo.org, pg 164

Roe, Rosanne, nursesbooks.org, The Publishing Program of ANA, 8515 Georgia Ave, Suite 400, Silver Spring, MD 20910-3492 *Tel:* 301-628-5000 *Toll Free Tel:* 800-924-9053; 800-637-0323 (orders) *Fax:* 301-628-5001 *E-mail:* anp@ana.org *Web Site:* www.nursesbooks.org; www.nursingworld.org, pg 172

Roeder, Taryn, Houghton Mifflin Harcourt Trade & Reference Division, 222 Berkeley St, Boston, MA 02116 *Tel:* 617-351-5000 *Toll Free Tel:* 800-225-3362 *Web Site:* www.hmhco.com, pg 115

Roehrig, Fr Matthew, St Pauls, 2187 Victory Blvd, Staten Island, NY 10314-6603 *Tel:* 718-761-0047 (edit & prodn); 718-698-2759 (mktg & billing) *Toll Free Tel:* 800-343-2522 *Fax:* 718-761-0057 *E-mail:* sales@stpauls.us; marketing@stpauls.us *Web Site:* www.stpauls.us, pg 215

Roetzheim, William, Level 4 Press Inc, 13518 Jamul Dr, Jamul, CA 91935-1635 *Fax:* 619-374-7311 *E-mail:* sales@level4press.com *Web Site:* www.level4press.com, pg 138

Rogatz, Mitch, Triumph Books, 814 N Franklin St, Chicago, IL 60610 *Toll Free Tel:* 800-888-4741 (orders only) *Fax:* 312-280-5470 *Web Site:* www.triumphbooks.com, pg 250

Rogen, Jessica, Boulevard Magazine Short Fiction Contest for Emerging Writers, 6614 Clayton Rd, PMB 325, Richmond Heights, MO 63117 *Tel:* 314-862-2643 *Web Site:* www.boulevardmagazine.org, pg 673

Rogers, Dr Amy, ScienceThrillers Media, PO Box 601392, Sacramento, CA 95860-1392 *Tel:* 916-712-3334 *E-mail:* query@sciencethrillersmedia.com *Web Site:* www.sciencethrillersmedia.com, pg 220

Rogers, Annette, Poisoned Pen Press, 6962 E First Ave, Suite 103, Scottsdale, AZ 85251 *Tel:* 480-945-3375 *Toll Free Tel:* 800-421-3976 *Fax:* 480-949-1707 *E-mail:* info@poisonedpenpress.com *Web Site:* www.poisonedpenpress.com, pg 194

Rogers, Christopher, Yale Series of Younger Poets, 302 Temple St, New Haven, CT 06511 *Tel:* 203-432-0960 *Fax:* 203-432-0948 *Web Site:* www.yalebooks.com, pg 739

Rogers, Christopher, Yale University Press, 302 Temple St, New Haven, CT 06511-8909 *Tel:* 203-432-0960; 203-432-0966 (sales); 401-531-2800 (cust serv) *Toll Free Tel:* 800-405-1619 (cust serv) *Fax:* 203-432-0948; 203-432-8485 (sales); 401-531-2801 (cust serv) *Toll Free Fax:* 800-406-9145 (cust serv) *E-mail:* sales.press@yale.edu (sales); customer.care@trilateral.org (cust serv) *Web Site:* www.yalebooks.com; yalepress.yale.edu/yupbooks, pg 278

Rogers, Kate, The Mountaineers Books, 1001 SW Klickitat Way, Suite 201, Seattle, WA 98134 *Tel:* 206-223-6303 *Toll Free Tel:* 800-553-4453 *Fax:* 206-223-6306 *Toll Free Fax:* 800-568-7604 *E-mail:* mbooks@mountaineersbooks.org *Web Site:* www.mountaineersbooks.org, pg 161

Rogers, Kelly, The Johns Hopkins University Press, 2715 N Charles St, Baltimore, MD 21218-4363 *Tel:* 410-516-6900; 410-516-6987 (journal orders outside US & CN) *Toll Free Tel:* 800-537-5487 (book orders & cust serv); 800-548-1784 (journal orders) *Fax:* 410-516-6968; 410-516-3866 (journal orders) *E-mail:* hfscustserv@press.jhu.edu (cust serv); jrnlcirc@press.jhu.edu (journal orders) *Web Site:* www.press.jhu.edu; muse.jhu.edu, pg 127

Rogers, Marian Hartman, Bibliogenesis, 152 Coddington Rd, Ithaca, NY 14850 *Tel:* 607-277-9660 *Web Site:* www.bibliogenesis.com, pg 521

Rogers, Tamara, Windbreak House Writing Retreat, PO Box 169, Hermosa, SD 57744-0169 *Tel:* 605-255-4064 *E-mail:* info@windbreakhouse.com *Web Site:* www.windbreakhouse.com, pg 656

Rogge, Robie, The Metropolitan Museum of Art, 1000 Fifth Ave, New York, NY 10028 *Tel:* 212-879-5500; 212-570-3725 *Fax:* 212-396-5062 *E-mail:* editorial@metmuseum.org *Web Site:* www.metmuseum.org, pg 155

Roghaar, Linda L, Linda Roghaar Literary Agency LLC, 133 High Point Dr, Amherst, MA 01002 *Tel:* 413-256-1921 *E-mail:* contact@lindaroghaar.com *Web Site:* www.lindaroghaar.com, pg 570

Roginsky, Gwen, The Metropolitan Museum of Art, 1000 Fifth Ave, New York, NY 10028 *Tel:* 212-879-5500; 212-570-3725 *Fax:* 212-396-5062 *E-mail:* editorial@metmuseum.org *Web Site:* www.metmuseum.org, pg 155

Roher, Lorna, Baywood Publishing Co Inc, 26 Austin Ave, Amityville, NY 11701 *Tel:* 631-691-1270 *Toll Free Tel:* 800-638-7819 *Fax:* 631-691-1770 *E-mail:* baywood@baywood.com *Web Site:* www.baywood.com, pg 32

Rohrbach, Lewis Bunker, Picton Press, 814 E Elkcam Circle, Marco Island, FL 34145-2558 *Tel:* 239-970-2442 *E-mail:* sales@pictonpress.com (orders) *Web Site:* www.pictonpress.com, pg 191

Roistacher, Robert E, The Roistacher Literary Agency, 545 W 111 St, Suite 7-J, New York, NY 10025 *Tel:* 212-222-1405, pg 571

Rokicki, Rachel, Crown Publishing Group, c/o Penguin Random House Inc, 1745 Broadway, New York, NY 10019 *Tel:* 212-782-9000 *Toll Free Tel:* 888-264-1745 *Fax:* 212-940-7408 *E-mail:* crownosm@penguinrandomhouse.com *Web Site:* crownpublishing.com, pg 68

Rolfs, Erin, Louisiana State University Press, 338 Johnston Hall, Baton Rouge, LA 70803 *Tel:* 225-578-6294 *Fax:* 225-578-6461 *E-mail:* lsupress@lsu.edu *Web Site:* lsupress.org, pg 143

Roliardi, Bob, Pearson Scott Foresman, 1900 E Lake Ave, Glenview, IL 60025 *Tel:* 847-729-3000 *Toll Free Tel:* 800-535-4391 (Midwest) *Fax:* 847-729-8910 *Web Site:* www.pearsonschool.com, pg 185

Rollans, Glenn, Brush Education Inc, 6531 111 St, Edmonton, AB T6H 4R5, Canada *Tel:* 780-989-0910 *Toll Free Tel:* 855-283-0900 *Fax:* 780-989-0930 *Toll Free Fax:* 855-283-6947 *E-mail:* contact@brusheducation.ca *Web Site:* www.brusheducation.ca, pg 474

Rollins, Danielle, Random House Children's Books, 1745 Broadway, New York, NY 10019 *Tel:* 212-782-9000 *Toll Free Tel:* 800-200-3552 *Fax:* 212-782-9452 *Web Site:* randomhousekids.com, pg 204

Rollins, John D, Yale University Press, 302 Temple St, New Haven, CT 06511-8909 *Tel:* 203-432-0960; 203-432-0966 (sales); 401-531-2800 (cust serv) *Toll Free Tel:* 800-405-1619 (cust serv) *Fax:* 203-432-0948; 203-432-8485 (sales); 401-531-2801 (cust serv) *Toll Free Fax:* 800-406-9145 (cust serv) *E-mail:* sales.press@yale.edu (sales); customer.care@trilateral.org (cust serv) *Web Site:* www.yalebooks.com; yalepress.yale.edu/yupbooks, pg 278

Rollins, Leslie, Getty Publications, 1200 Getty Center Dr, Suite 500, Los Angeles, CA 90049-1682 *Tel:* 310-440-7365 *Toll Free Tel:* 800-223-3431 (orders) *Fax:* 310-440-7758 *E-mail:* pubsinfo@getty.edu *Web Site:* www.getty.edu/publications, pg 96

Romanello, Jennifer, Simon & Schuster Children's Publishing, 1230 Avenue of the Americas, New York, NY 10020 *Tel:* 212-698-7000 *Web Site:* KIDS.SimonandSchuster.com; TEEN.SimonandSchuster.com; simonandschuster.net; simonandschuster.biz, pg 225

Romanello, Rosanne, HarperCollins Children's Books, 195 Broadway, New York, NY 10007 *Tel:* 212-207-7000 *Web Site:* www.harpercollins.com/childrens, pg 105

Romano, Maria, Chapter One Fiction Competition, 1738 Hone Ave, Bronx, NY 10461-1486 *Tel:* 718-931-9500 *Fax:* 718-409-6445 *E-mail:* info@bronxarts.org *Web Site:* www.bronxarts.org, pg 676

Romano, Rich, Random House Children's Books, 1745 Broadway, New York, NY 10019 *Tel:* 212-782-9000 *Toll Free Tel:* 800-200-3552 *Fax:* 212-782-9452 *Web Site:* randomhousekids.com, pg 203

Romano, Roger, Research & Education Association (REA), 61 Ethel Rd W, Piscataway, NJ 08854 *Tel:* 732-819-8880 *Fax:* 732-819-8808 (orders) *E-mail:* info@rea.com *Web Site:* www.rea.com, pg 208

Romano-Murray, Janet, Industrial Press Inc, 32 Haviland St, Unit 2C, Norwalk, CT 06854 *Tel:* 212-889-6330 *Toll Free Tel:* 888-528-7852 *Fax:* 212-545-8327 *E-mail:* info@industrialpress.com *Web Site:* new.industrialpress.com, pg 121

Rome, Dee, Piano Press, 1425 Ocean Ave, Suite 5, Del Mar, CA 92014 *Tel:* 619-884-1401 *Fax:* 858-755-1104 *E-mail:* pianopress@pianopress.com *Web Site:* www.pianopress.com, pg 191

Romero, Anthony D, American Civil Liberties Union, 125 Broad St, 18th fl, New York, NY 10004 *Tel:* 212-549-2500 *E-mail:* media@aclu.org *Web Site:* www.aclu.org, pg 594

Romero, Emily, Penguin Young Readers Group, 345 Hudson St, New York, NY 10014 *Tel:* 212-366-2000 *E-mail:* online@penguinputnam.com *Web Site:* www.penguinputnam.com; us.penguingroup.com, pg 188

Romero, Kim, Chronicle Books LLC, 680 Second St, San Francisco, CA 94107 *Tel:* 415-537-4200 *Toll Free Tel:* 800-759-0190 (cust serv) *Fax:* 415-537-4460 *Toll Free Fax:* 800-858-7787 (orders); 800-286-9471 (cust serv) *E-mail:* frontdesk@chroniclebooks.com *Web Site:* www.chroniclebooks.com, pg 58

Romig, Anna, The Putnam Publishing Group, 375 Hudson St, New York, NY 10014 *Tel:* 212-366-2000 *Toll Free Tel:* 800-631-8571 *Fax:* 212-366-2643 *E-mail:* online@penguinputnam.com *Web Site:* www.penguinputnam.com; us.penguingroup.com, pg 201

Romig, Anna, GP Putnam's Sons (Hardcover), 375 Hudson St, New York, NY 10014 *Tel:* 212-366-2000 *E-mail:* online@penguinputnam.com *Web Site:* us.penguingroup.com, pg 201

Rominger, Wray, Purple Mountain Press Ltd, 1060 Main St, Fleischmanns, NY 12430 *Tel:* 845-254-4062 *Toll Free Tel:* 800-325-2665 (orders) *Fax:* 845-254-4476 *E-mail:* purple@catskill.net *Web Site:* www.catskill.net/purple, pg 201

Romo, Terezita, Joseph Henry Jackson Literary Award, One Embarcadero Ctr, Suite 1400, San Francisco, CA 94111 *Tel:* 415-733-8500 *Fax:* 415-477-2783 *E-mail:* info@sff.org *Web Site:* www.sff.org, pg 696

Romo, Terezita, James D Phelan Literary Award, One Embarcadero Ctr, Suite 1400, San Francisco, CA 94111 *Tel:* 415-733-8500 *Fax:* 415-477-2783 *E-mail:* info@sff.org *Web Site:* www.sff.org, pg 718

Ronk, Bret, Gulf Publishing Co, 2 Greenway Plaza, Suite 1020, Houston, TX 77046 *Tel:* 713-529-4301 *Fax:* 713-520-4433 *E-mail:* store@gulfpub.com *Web Site:* www.gulfpub.com, pg 102

Ronnen, Lia, Artisan Books, 225 Varick St, New York, NY 10014-4381 *Tel:* 212-254-5900 *Toll Free Tel:* 800-722-7202 *Fax:* 212-677-6692 *E-mail:* artisaninfo@artisanbooks.com *Web Site:* www.workman.com/artisanbooks, pg 23

Roome, Hugh, Scholastic Education, 524 Broadway, New York, NY 10012 *Tel:* 212-343-6100 *Fax:* 212-343-6189 *Web Site:* www.scholastic.com, pg 218

Roome, Hugh, Scholastic Inc, 557 Broadway, New York, NY 10012 *Tel:* 212-343-6100 *Toll Free Tel:* 800-scholastic *Web Site:* www.scholastic.com, pg 218

Rooney, Linda, Oxford University Press USA, 198 Madison Ave, New York, NY 10016 *Tel:* 212-726-6000 *Toll Free Tel:* 800-451-7556 (orders); 800-445-9714 (cust serv) *Fax:* 919-677-1303 *E-mail:* custserv.us@oup.com *Web Site:* www.oup.com/us, pg 179

Rooney, Robert, National Association of Independent Publishers Representatives, 111 E 14 St, PMB 157, New York, NY 10003 *Tel:* 267-546-6561 *Toll Free Tel:* 888-624-7779 *Web Site:* naipr.org, pg 611

Root, Holly, Waxman Leavell Literary Agency, 443 Park Ave S, No 1004, New York, NY 10016 *Tel:* 212-675-5556 *Fax:* 212-675-1381 *Web Site:* www.waxmanleavell.com, pg 579

Root, William Pitt, Joy Harjo Poetry Award, PO Box 2414, Durango, CO 81302 *Tel:* 970-903-7914 *E-mail:* cutthroatmag@gmail.com *Web Site:* www.cutthroatmag.com, pg 691

Rosa-Mendoza, Gladys, me+mi publishing inc, 400 S Knoll St, Suite B, Wheaton, IL 60187 *Toll Free Tel:* 888-251-1444 *Fax:* 630-588-9804 *E-mail:* rw@rosawesley.com *Web Site:* www.memima.com, pg 153

Rosado, Darlene, BMI®, 7 World Trade Ctr, 250 Greenwich St, New York, NY 10007-0030 *Tel:* 212-586-2000; 212-220-3000 *Toll Free Tel:* 888-689-5264 (sales); 800-925-8451 (cust rel) *Fax:* 212-246-2163 *E-mail:* foundation@bmi.com *Web Site:* www.bmi.com, pg 600

Rosamilia, Michael, Kensington Publishing Corp, 119 W 40 St, New York, NY 10018 *Tel:* 212-407-1500 *Toll Free Tel:* 800-221-2647 *Fax:* 212-935-0699 *Web Site:* www.kensingtonbooks.com, pg 130

Rosati, Daniel, William S Hein & Co Inc, 2350 N Forest Rd, Getzville, NY 14068 *Tel:* 716-882-2600 *Toll Free Tel:* 800-828-7571 *Fax:* 716-883-8100 *E-mail:* mail@wshein.com; marketing@wshein.com *Web Site:* www.wshein.com, pg 110

Rosati, Miranda J, William S Hein & Co Inc, 2350 N Forest Rd, Getzville, NY 14068 *Tel:* 716-882-2600 *Toll Free Tel:* 800-828-7571 *Fax:* 716-883-8100 *E-mail:* mail@wshein.com; marketing@wshein.com *Web Site:* www.wshein.com, pg 110

Rose, Brad, Dreamscape Media LLC, 6940 Hall St, Holland, OH 43528 *Tel:* 419-867-6965 *Toll Free Tel:* 877-983-7326 *E-mail:* info@dreamscapeab.com *Web Site:* www.dreamscapeab.com, pg 77

Rose, Jean Anne, Gallery Books, 1230 Avenue of the Americas, New York, NY 10020 *Toll Free Tel:* 800-456-6798 *Fax:* 212-698-7284 *E-mail:* consumer.customerservice@simonandschuster.com *Web Site:* www.simonsays.com, pg 94

Rose, R Norman, Justin Winsor Prize for Library History Essay, 50 E Huron St, Chicago, IL 60611 *Tel:* 312-280-4283 *Toll Free Tel:* 800-545-2433 (ext 4283) *Fax:* 312-280-4392 *Web Site:* www.ala.org, pg 737

Rose, Rebecca, Breakwater Books Ltd, One Stamp's Lane, St John's, NL A1C 6E6, Canada *Tel:* 709-722-6680 *Toll Free Tel:* 800-563-3333 (orders) *Fax:* 709-753-0708 *E-mail:* info@breakwaterbooks.com; orders@breakwaterbooks.com *Web Site:* www.breakwaterbooks.com, pg 473

Rose, Rie Sheridan, Zumaya Publications LLC, 3209 S IH 35, Suite 1086, Austin, TX 78741 *Tel:* 512-402-5298 *Fax:* 253-660-2009 *E-mail:* acquisitions@zumayapublications.com *Web Site:* www.zumayapublications.com, pg 280

Rose, Verena, Agatha Awards, PO Box 8007, Gaithersburg, MD 20898-8007 *E-mail:* malicedomesticpr@gmail.com *Web Site:* www.malicedomestic.org, pg 665

Roselli, Leena, Financial Executives Research Foundation Inc (FERF), West Tower, 7th fl, 1250 Headquarters Plaza, Morristown, NJ 07960-6837 *Tel:* 973-765-1000 *Fax:* 973-765-1023 *Web Site:* www.financialexecutives.org, pg 88

Rosema, Randy, HarperCollins Children's Books, 195 Broadway, New York, NY 10007 *Tel:* 212-207-7000 *Web Site:* www.harpercollins.com/childrens, pg 105

Roseman, Karl-Heinz, McFarland, 960 NC Hwy 88 W, Jefferson, NC 28640 *Tel:* 336-246-4460 *Toll Free Tel:* 800-253-2187 (orders) *Fax:* 336-246-5018; 336-246-4403 (orders) *E-mail:* info@mcfarlandpub.com *Web Site:* www.mcfarlandpub.com, pg 150

Roseman, Mike, Thieme Medical Publishers Inc, 333 Seventh Ave, 18th fl, New York, NY 10001 *Tel:* 212-760-0888 *Toll Free Tel:* 800-782-3488 *Fax:* 212-947-1112 *E-mail:* customerservice@thieme.com *Web Site:* www.thieme.com, pg 245

Rosen, Joan, Charlotte Sheedy Literary Agency Inc, 928 Broadway, Suite 901, New York, NY 10010 *Tel:* 212-780-9800 *Web Site:* www.sheedylit.com, pg 573

Rosen, Roger, The Rosen Publishing Group Inc, 29 E 21 St, New York, NY 10010 *Tel:* 212-777-3017 *Toll Free Tel:* 800-237-9932 *Toll Free Fax:* 888-436-4643 *E-mail:* info@rosenpub.com *Web Site:* www.rosenpublishing.com, pg 211

Rosen, Sara, Glitterati Inc, 630 Ninth Ave, Suite 603, New York, NY 10036 *Tel:* 212-362-9119 *Fax:* 646-607-4433 *E-mail:* info@glitteratiincorporated.com *Web Site:* glitteratiincorporated.com, pg 97

Rosen, Selina, Yard Dog Press, 710 W Redbud Lane, Alma, AR 72921-7247 *Tel:* 479-632-4693 *Fax:* 479-632-4693 *Web Site:* www.yarddogpress.com, pg 278

Rosenberg, Barbara Collins, The Rosenberg Group, 23 Lincoln Ave, Marblehead, MA 01945 *Tel:* 781-990-1341 *Fax:* 781-990-1344 *Web Site:* www.rosenberggroup.com, pg 571

Rosenberg, Barr, Dorothy Sargent Rosenberg Poetry Prizes, PO Box 2306, Orinda, CA 94563 *Web Site:* www.dorothyprizes.org, pg 725

Rosenberg, Carol, Basic Health Publications Inc, 28812 Top of the World Dr, Laguna Beach, CA 92651 *Tel:* 949-715-7327 *Toll Free Tel:* 800-575-8890 (orders) *Fax:* 949-715-7328 *E-mail:* info@basichealthpub.com *Web Site:* www.basichealthpub.com, pg 32

Rosenberg, Gary, Basic Health Publications Inc, 28812 Top of the World Dr, Laguna Beach, CA 92651 *Tel:* 949-715-7327 *Toll Free Tel:* 800-575-8890 (orders) *Fax:* 949-715-7328 *E-mail:* info@basichealthpub.com *Web Site:* www.basichealthpub.com, pg 32

Rosenberg, Jessica, Harlequin Enterprises Ltd, 233 Broadway, Suite 1001, New York, NY 10279 *Tel:* 212-553-4200 *Fax:* 212-227-8969 *E-mail:* CustomerService@harlequin.com *Web Site:* www.harlequin.com, pg 105

Rosenberg, Leora, Objective Entertainment, 609 Greenwich St, 6th fl, New York, NY 10014 *Tel:* 212-431-5454 *Fax:* 917-464-6394 *Web Site:* www.objectiveent.com, pg 567

Rosenberg, Linda, GP Putnam's Sons (Hardcover), 375 Hudson St, New York, NY 10014 *Tel:* 212-366-2000 *E-mail:* online@penguinputnam.com *Web Site:* us.penguingroup.com, pg 201

Rosenberg, Liz, Binghamton University Creative Writing Program, c/o Dept of English, PO Box 6000, Binghamton, NY 13902-6000 *Tel:* 607-777-2168 *Fax:* 607-777-2408 *E-mail:* cwpro@binghamton.edu *Web Site:* english.binghamton.edu/cwpro, pg 659

Rosenberg, Mary, Dorothy Sargent Rosenberg Poetry Prizes, PO Box 2306, Orinda, CA 94563 *Web Site:* www.dorothyprizes.org, pg 725

Rosenberg, Tracy, Media Alliance, 2830 20 St, Suite 102, San Francisco, CA 94110 *Tel:* 415-746-9475 *E-mail:* information@media-alliance.org *Web Site:* www.media-alliance.org, pg 609

Rosenberry, Eliza, Blue Rider Press, 375 Hudson St, New York, NY 10014 *Tel:* 212-366-2000 *E-mail:* blueriderpublicity@us.penguingroup.com, pg 41

Rosenblum, Bruce, Television Academy, 5220 Lankershim Blvd, North Hollywood, CA 91601-3109 *Tel:* 818-754-2800 *Fax:* 818-761-2827 *Web Site:* www.emmys.com, pg 620

Rosenblum, Jill, Walch Education, 40 Walch Dr, Portland, ME 04103-1286 *Tel:* 207-772-2846 *Toll Free Tel:* 800-558-2846 *Fax:* 207-772-3105 *Toll Free Fax:* 888-991-5755 *E-mail:* customerservice@walch.com *Web Site:* www.walch.com, pg 266

Rosenbush, Ellen, Harper's Magazine Foundation, 666 Broadway, 11th fl, New York, NY 10012 *Tel:* 212-420-5720 *Toll Free Tel:* 800-444-4653 *Fax:* 212-228-5889 *E-mail:* harpers@harpers.org *Web Site:* www.harpers.org, pg 106

Rosenfeld, Dina, Hachai Publishing, 527 Empire Blvd, Brooklyn, NY 11225 *Tel:* 718-633-0100 *Fax:* 718-633-0103 *E-mail:* info@hachai.com *Web Site:* www.hachai.com, pg 102

Rosenfeld, Erv, BK Nelson Inc Lecture Bureau, 1565 Paseo Vida, Palm Springs, CA 92264 *Tel:* 760-778-8800 *Fax:* 760-778-6242 *E-mail:* bknelson4@cs.com *Web Site:* www.bknelson.com; www.bknelsonlecturebureau.com; www.nelsonbookmovielecture.com; www.bknelsonmovieproduction.com, pg 587

Rosenfeld, Erv, BK Nelson Inc Literary Agency, 1565 Paseo Vida, Palm Springs, CA 92264 *Tel:* 760-778-8800 *Fax:* 760-778-6242 *E-mail:* bknelson4@cs.com *Web Site:* www.bknelson.com; www.bknelsonlecturebureau.com; www.nelsonbookmovielecture.com; www.bknelsonmovieproduction.com, pg 566

Rosenfeld, Nancy, AAA Books Unlimited, 88 Greenbriar E Dr, Deerfield, IL 60015 *Tel:* 847-444-1220 *Fax:* 847-607-8335 *Web Site:* www.aaabooksunlimited.com, pg 539

Rosenfeld, Theodore D, Taplinger Publishing Co Inc, PO Box 175, Marlboro, NJ 07746-0175 *Tel:* 305-256-7880 *Fax:* 305-256-7816 *E-mail:* taplingerpub@yahoo.com (rts & perms, edit, corp only), pg 240

Rosenfelt, Rachel, Verso, 20 Jay St, Suite 1010, Brooklyn, NY 11201 *Tel:* 718-246-8160 *Fax:* 718-246-8165 *E-mail:* verso@versobooks.com *Web Site:* www.versobooks.com, pg 265

Rosengard, Alice, Words into Print, 57 Prince St, Suite 4R, New York, NY 10012 *Tel:* 212-741-1393 *Fax:* 419-441-1393 *E-mail:* query@wordsintoprint.org *Web Site:* www.wordsintoprint.org, pg 536

Rosengrave, Tracey, AuthorHouse, 1663 Liberty Dr, Bloomington, IN 47403 *Tel:* 812-339-6000 (outside US) *Toll Free Tel:* 888-519-5121 *E-mail:* authorsupport@authorhouse.com *Web Site:* www.authorhouse.com, pg 27

Rosenkranz, Randi, Penguin Random House Inc, 1745 Broadway, New York, NY 10019 *Tel:* 212-782-9000 *Toll Free Tel:* 800-726-0600 *Web Site:* www.randomhouse.com, pg 187

Rosenkranz, Rita, Rita Rosenkranz Literary Agency, 440 West End Ave, Suite 15D, New York, NY 10024-5358 *Tel:* 212-873-6333 *Fax:* 212-873-5225 *Web Site:* www.ritarosenkranzliteraryagency.com, pg 571

Rosenstein, Natalee, Berkley Books, 375 Hudson St, New York, NY 10014 *Tel:* 212-366-2000 *Fax:* 212-366-2666 *E-mail:* online@penguinputnam.com *Web Site:* www.penguinputnam.com; us.penguingroup.com, pg 35

Rosenstein, Natalee, Berkley Publishing Group, 375 Hudson St, New York, NY 10014 *Tel:* 212-366-2000 *Fax:* 212-366-2385 *E-mail:* online@penguinputnam.com *Web Site:* us.penguingroup.com, pg 35

Rosenthal, Carole, Hamilton Stone Editions, PO Box 43, Maplewood, NJ 07040 *Tel:* 973-378-8361 *E-mail:* hstone@hamiltonstone.org *Web Site:* www.hamiltonstone.org, pg 104

Rosenthal, David, Blue Rider Press, 375 Hudson St, New York, NY 10014 *Tel:* 212-366-2000 *E-mail:* blueriderpublicity@us.penguingroup.com, pg 40

Rosenthal, David, Penguin Group (USA) LLC, a Penguin Random House company, 375 Hudson St, New York, NY 10014 *Tel:* 212-366-2000 *Toll Free Tel:* 800-847-5515 (inside sales); 800-631-8571 (cust serv) *Fax:* 212-366-2666; 607-775-4829 (inside sales) *E-mail:* online@us.penguingroup.com *Web Site:* www.penguin.com; us.penguingroup.com, pg 186

Rosenthal, Elise, Rosenthal Represents, 3850 Eddingham Ave, Calabasas, CA 91302 *Tel:* 818-222-5445 *Fax:* 818-222-5650 *E-mail:* eliselicenses@earthlink.net *Web Site:* www.rosenthalrepresents.com, pg 584

Rosenwald, Robert, Poisoned Pen Press, 6962 E First Ave, Suite 103, Scottsdale, AZ 85251 *Tel:* 480-945-3375 *Toll Free Tel:* 800-421-3976 *Fax:* 480-949-1707 *E-mail:* info@poisonedpenpress.com *Web Site:* www.poisonedpenpress.com, pg 194

Rosenwasser, Rena, Kelsey Street Press, 2824 Kelsey St, Berkeley, CA 94705 *Tel:* 510-845-2260 *Fax:* 510-548-9185 *E-mail:* info@kelseyst.com *Web Site:* www.kelseyst.com, pg 130

Rosner, Annsley, Crown Publishing Group, c/o Penguin Random House Inc, 1745 Broadway, New York, NY 10019 *Tel:* 212-782-9000 *Toll Free Tel:* 888-264-1745 *Fax:* 212-940-7408 *E-mail:* crownosm@penguinrandomhouse.com *Web Site:* crownpublishing.com, pg 68

Rosokoff, Sylvie, Trident Media Group LLC, 41 Madison Ave, 36th fl, New York, NY 10010 *Tel:* 212-333-1511 *E-mail:* info@tridentmediagroup.com; press@tridentmediagroup.com *Web Site:* www.tridentmediagroup.com, pg 578

Ross, Andy, Andy Ross Literary Agency, 767 Santa Ray Ave, Oakland, CA 94610 *Tel:* 510-238-8965 *E-mail:* andyrossagency@hotmail.com *Web Site:* www.andyrossagency.com, pg 541

Ross, Bob, Pilgrim Publications, PO Box 66, Pasadena, TX 77501-0066 *Tel:* 713-477-4261 *Fax:* 713-477-7561 *E-mail:* pilgrimpub@aol.com *Web Site:* members.aol.com/pilgrimpub/; www.pilgrimpublications.com, pg 192

Ross, Carol, Hachette Book Group, 1290 Avenue of the Americas, New York, NY 10019 *Tel:* 212-364-1100 *Toll Free Tel:* 800-759-0190 (cust serv) *Fax:* 212-364-0933 (intl orders) *Toll Free Fax:* 800-286-9471 (cust serv) *Web Site:* www.HachetteBookGroup.com, pg 102

Ross, Franz H, Ross Books, PO Box 4340, Berkeley, CA 94704-0340 *Tel:* 510-841-2474 *Fax:* 510-295-2531 *E-mail:* sales@rossbooks.com *Web Site:* www.rossbooks.com, pg 211

Ross, Kim, Riverside Publishing, 3800 Golf Rd, Suite 200, Rolling Meadows, IL 60008 *Tel:* 630-467-7000 *Toll Free Tel:* 800-323-9540 *Fax:* 630-467-7192 (cust serv) *E-mail:* rpc_customer_service@hmhpub.com (cust serv) *Web Site:* www.riversidepublishing.com, pg 209

Ross, Marjory G, Regnery Publishing Inc, 300 New Jersey Ave NW, Washington, DC 20001 *Tel:* 202-216-0600 *Toll Free Tel:* 888-219-4747 *Fax:* 202-216-0612 *Web Site:* www.regnery.com, pg 208

Ross, Maureen, diacriTech Inc, 667 Boylston St, 5th fl, Boston, MA 02116 *Tel:* 617-236-7500 *Fax:* 617-848-2938 *Web Site:* www.diacritech.com, pg 524

Ross, Michael, Encyclopaedia Britannica Inc, 331 N La Salle St, Chicago, IL 60654 *Tel:* 312-347-7159 (all other countries) *Toll Free Tel:* 800-323-1229 (US & CN) *Fax:* 312-294-2104 *E-mail:* editor@eb.com *Web Site:* www.eb.com; www.britannica.com, pg 82

Ross, Michael, Macmillan, 175 Fifth Ave, New York, NY 10010 *Tel:* 646-307-5151 *Fax:* 212-420-9314 *E-mail:* firstname.lastname@macmillan.com *Web Site:* www.macmillan.com, pg 145

Ross, Mimi, Henry Holt and Company, LLC, 175 Fifth Ave, New York, NY 10010 *Tel:* 646-307-5151 *Toll Free Tel:* 888-330-8477 (orders) *Fax:* 646-307-5285 *E-mail:* firstname.lastname@hholt.com *Web Site:* www.henryholt.com, pg 113

Ross, Norman A, Ross Publishing LLC, 392 Central Park W, Suite 20-C, New York, NY 10025-5878 *Tel:* 212-765-8200 *E-mail:* info@rosspub.com *Web Site:* www.rosspub.com, pg 211

Ross, Rebecca, Livres Canada Books, One Nicholas, Suite 504, Ottawa, ON K1N 7B7, Canada *Tel:* 613-562-2324 *Fax:* 613-562-2329 *E-mail:* info@livrescanadabooks.com *Web Site:* www.livrescanadabooks.com, pg 609

Ross, Steve, Abrams Artists Agency, 275 Seventh Ave, 26th fl, New York, NY 10001 *Tel:* 646-486-4600 *Fax:* 646-486-2358 *E-mail:* literary@abramsartny.com *Web Site:* www.abramsartists.com, pg 539

Rossi, Janet, The MIT Press, 55 Hayward St, Cambridge, MA 02142 *Tel:* 617-253-5255 *Toll Free Tel:* 800-207-8354 (orders) *Fax:* 617-258-6779; 617-577-1545 (orders) *Web Site:* mitpress.mit.edu, pg 158

Rossi, Janice, Kensington Publishing Corp, 119 W 40 St, New York, NY 10018 *Tel:* 212-407-1500 *Toll Free Tel:* 800-221-2647 *Fax:* 212-935-0699 *Web Site:* www.kensingtonbooks.com, pg 130

Rossi, Stefani, Janet B McCabe Poetry Prize, 1041 N Taft Hill Rd, Fort Collins, CO 80521 *Tel:* 970-449-2726 *E-mail:* editor@ruminatemagazine.org *Web Site:* www.ruminatemagazine.com, pg 706

Rossi, Stefani, William Van Dyke Short Story Prize, 1041 N Taft Hill Rd, Fort Collins, CO 80521 *Tel:* 970-449-2726 *E-mail:* editor@ruminatemagazine.org *Web Site:* www.ruminatemagazine.com, pg 733

Rossi, Stefani, VanderMey Nonfiction Prize, 1041 N Taft Hill Rd, Fort Collins, CO 80521 *Tel:* 970-449-2726 *E-mail:* editor@ruminatemagazine.org *Web Site:* www.ruminatemagazine.com, pg 733

Rossi, Tony, The Christopher Awards, 5 Hanover Sq, 22nd fl, New York, NY 10004-2751 *Tel:* 212-759-4050 *Toll Free Tel:* 888-298-4050 (orders) *Fax:* 212-838-5073 *E-mail:* mail@christophers.org *Web Site:* www.christophers.org, pg 677

Rosso, Don, Waveland Press Inc, 4180 IL Rte 83, Suite 101, Long Grove, IL 60047-9580 *Tel:* 847-634-0081 *Fax:* 847-634-9501 *E-mail:* info@waveland.com *Web Site:* www.waveland.com, pg 268

Rostan, Stephanie, Levine|Greenberg|Rostan Literary Agency Inc, 307 Seventh Ave, Suite 2407, New York, NY 10001 *Tel:* 212-337-0934 *Fax:* 212-337-0948 *Web Site:* lgrliterary.com, pg 561

Rotenberg, Cliff, Houghton Mifflin Harcourt, 222 Berkeley St, Boston, MA 02116 *Tel:* 617-351-5000 *Toll Free Tel:* 800-225-5425 (K-12 educ materials); 800-323-9540 (assessment materials); 877-219-1537 (SkillsTutor); 888-242-6747 (Destination; Earobics; Edmark; Learning Village; Riverdeep); 800-225-3362 (Houghton Mifflin Harcourt Trade & Reference Publishers) *Toll Free Fax:* 800-269-5232 *E-mail:* customerservice@hmhpub.com *Web Site:* www.hmhco.com, pg 115

Roth, Jason, Springer Publishing Co, 11 W 42 St, 15th fl, New York, NY 10036-8002 *Tel:* 212-431-4370 *Toll Free Tel:* 877-687-7476 *Fax:* 212-941-7842 *E-mail:* marketing@springerpub.com; cs@springerpub.com (orders); editorial@springerpub.com *Web Site:* www.springerpub.com, pg 232

Roth, Jessica, Touchstone, 1230 Avenue of the Americas, New York, NY 10020, pg 247

Roth, Laurence, Susquehanna University, Department of English, 514 University Ave, Selinsgrove, PA 17870 *Tel:* 570-372-0101, pg 662

Roth, Maya E, Jane Chambers Playwriting Award, Georgetown University, 108 David Performing Arts Ctr, Box 571063, 37 & "O" St, NW, Washington, DC 20057-1063 *Tel:* 202-687-1327 *Web Site:* www.athe.org/?page=Jane_Chambers, pg 676

Roth, Melanie, Fulcrum Publishing Inc, 4690 Table Mountain Dr, Suite 100, Golden, CO 80403 *Tel:* 303-277-1623 *Toll Free Tel:* 800-992-2908 *Fax:* 303-279-7111 *Toll Free Fax:* 800-726-7112 *E-mail:* info@fulcrumbooks.com; orders@fulcrumbooks.com *Web Site:* www.fulcrumbooks.com, pg 93

Roth, Ruth Gleason, Society for Scholarly Publishing (SSP), 10200 W 44 Ave, Suite 304, Wheat Ridge, CO 80033-2840 *Tel:* 303-422-3914 *Fax:* 720-881-6101 *E-mail:* info@sspnet.org *Web Site:* www.sspnet.org, pg 618

Roth, Stefani, ASCD, 1703 N Beauregard St, Alexandria, VA 22311-1714 *Tel:* 703-578-9600 *Toll Free Tel:* 800-933-2723 *Fax:* 703-575-5400 *E-mail:* member@ascd.org *Web Site:* www.ascd.org, pg 23

Rothberg, Adam, Simon & Schuster, Inc, 1230 Avenue of the Americas, New York, NY 10020 *Tel:* 212-698-7000 *Fax:* 212-698-7007 *E-mail:* firstname.lastname@simonandschuster.com *Web Site:* www.simonandschuster.com, pg 226

Rothmeyer, Bob, Concordia Publishing House, 3558 S Jefferson Ave, St Louis, MO 63118-3968 *Tel:* 314-268-1000; 314-268-1268 (bookshop) *Toll Free Tel:* 800-325-3040 (cust serv) *Toll Free Fax:* 800-490-9889 (cust serv) *E-mail:* order@cph.org *Web Site:* www.cph.org, pg 62

Rothschild, Eileen, St Martin's Press, LLC, 175 Fifth Ave, New York, NY 10010 *Tel:* 646-307-5151 *Fax:* 212-420-9314 *E-mail:* firstname.lastname@macmillan.com *Web Site:* www.stmartins.com, pg 215

Rothschild, Richard, American Book Producers Association (ABPA), 31 W Eighth St, 2nd fl, New York, NY 10011 *Tel:* 212-675-1363 *Fax:* 212-675-1364 *E-mail:* office@abpaonline.org *Web Site:* www.abpaonline.org, pg 594

Rothstein, Philip Jan, Rothstein Publishing, 4 Arapaho Rd, Brookfield, CT 06804-3104 *Tel:* 203-740-7400 *Toll Free Tel:* 888-768-4783 *Fax:* 203-740-7401 *E-mail:* info@rothstein.com *Web Site:* www.rothstein.com; www.rothsteinpublishing.com, pg 211

Rotor, Elda, Penguin Books, 375 Hudson St, New York, NY 10014 *Tel:* 212-366-2000 *E-mail:* online@penguinputnam.com *Web Site:* www.penguinputnam.com; www.penguinclassics.com; us.penguingroup.com, pg 186

Rotstein, David, St Martin's Press, LLC, 175 Fifth Ave, New York, NY 10010 *Tel:* 646-307-5151 *Fax:* 212-420-9314 *E-mail:* firstname.lastname@macmillan.com *Web Site:* www.stmartins.com, pg 215

Rouleau, Lauren, F+W, A Content + eCommerce Company, 10151 Carver Rd, Suite 200, Blue Ash, OH 45242 *Tel:* 513-531-2690 *Toll Free Tel:* 800-289-0963 (trade accts); 800-258-0929 (orders) *E-mail:* contact_us@fwmedia.com *Web Site:* www.fwcommunity.com, pg 86

Rouleau, Nicolas, La Courte Echelle, 160, rue St-Viateur E, bureau 404, Montreal, QC H2T 1A8, Canada *Tel:* 514-274-2004 *Fax:* 514-270-4160 *E-mail:* info@courteechelle.com *Web Site:* www.courteechelle.com, pg 478

Rounds, John, St Martin's Press, LLC, 175 Fifth Ave, New York, NY 10010 *Tel:* 646-307-5151 *Fax:* 212-420-9314 *E-mail:* firstname.lastname@macmillan.com *Web Site:* www.stmartins.com, pg 215

Rourke, Kathleen, Candlewick Press, 99 Dover St, Somerville, MA 02144-2825 *Tel:* 617-661-3330 *Fax:* 617-661-0565 *E-mail:* bigbear@candlewick.com; salesinfo@candlewick.com *Web Site:* www.candlewick.com, pg 49

Rourke, Stacey, Anchor Group Publishing, PO Box 551, Flushing, MI 48433 *E-mail:* anchorgrouppublishing@gmail.com *Web Site:* anchorgrouppublishing.com, pg 17

Rous, Bernard, Association for Computing Machinery, 2 Penn Plaza, Suite 701, New York, NY 10121-0701 *Tel:* 212-626-0500 *Toll Free Tel:* 800-342-6626 *Fax:* 212-944-1318 *E-mail:* acmhelp@acm.org *Web Site:* www.acm.org, pg 25

Rouse, William R, Capstone Publishers™, 1710 Roe Crest Dr, North Mankato, MN 56003 *Toll Free Tel:* 800-747-4992 (cust serv) *Toll Free Fax:* 888-262-0705 *Web Site:* www.capstonepress.com, pg 49

Roush, Sheryl, Solid Gold Marketing Design Workshops, PO Box 2373, La Mesa, CA 91943-2373 *Tel:* 858-569-6555 *Toll Free Tel:* 800-932-0973 *Web Site:* www.sparklepresentations.com, pg 655

Routon, Anne, Columbia University Press, 61 W 62 St, New York, NY 10023 *Tel:* 212-459-0600 *Toll Free Tel:* 800-944-8648 *Fax:* 212-459-3678 *E-mail:* cup_book@columbia.edu (orders & cust serv) *Web Site:* cup.columbia.edu, pg 61

Roux, Michael, University of Illinois Press, 1325 S Oak St, MC-566, Champaign, IL 61820-6903 *Tel:* 217-333-0950 *Fax:* 217-244-8082 *E-mail:* uipress@uillinois.edu; journals@uillinois.edu *Web Site:* www.press.uillinois.edu, pg 256

Rowe, Alan, Torah Aura Productions, 4423 Fruitland Ave, Los Angeles, CA 90058 *Tel:* 323-585-7312 *Toll Free Tel:* 800-238-6724 *Fax:* 323-585-0327 *E-mail:* misrad@torahaura.com; orders@torahaura.com *Web Site:* www.torahaura.com, pg 247

Rowe, Carol, Waveland Press Inc, 4180 IL Rte 83, Suite 101, Long Grove, IL 60047-9580 *Tel:* 847-634-0081 *Fax:* 847-634-9501 *E-mail:* info@waveland.com *Web Site:* www.waveland.com, pg 268

Rowe, Martin, Lantern Books, 128 Second Place, Garden Suite, Brooklyn, NY 11231 *Tel:* 212-414-2275 *E-mail:* editorial@lanternbooks.com; info@lanternmedia.net *Web Site:* lanternbooks.presswarehouse.com/Home/home.aspx, pg 134

Rowe, Neil, Waveland Press Inc, 4180 IL Rte 83, Suite 101, Long Grove, IL 60047-9580 *Tel:* 847-634-0081 *Fax:* 847-634-9501 *E-mail:* info@waveland.com *Web Site:* www.waveland.com, pg 268

Rowland, Damaris, Damaris Rowland, 115 Elm St, Unit 7b, Hatfield, MA 01038-3808 *Tel:* 413-247-6011 *E-mail:* nicholerowland5@mac.com, pg 571

Rowland, Melissa, Levine|Greenberg|Rostan Literary Agency Inc, 307 Seventh Ave, Suite 2407, New York, NY 10001 *Tel:* 212-337-0934 *Fax:* 212-337-0948 *Web Site:* lgrliterary.com, pg 561

Roy, Denise, Dutton, 375 Hudson St, New York, NY 10014 *Tel:* 212-366-2000 *Fax:* 212-366-2262 *E-mail:* online@penguinputnam.com *Web Site:* www.penguinputnam.com; us.penguingroup.com, pg 78

Roy, Denise, Plume, 375 Hudson St, New York, NY 10014 *Tel:* 212-366-2000 *Fax:* 212-366-2666 *E-mail:* online@penguinputnam.com *Web Site:* www.penguinputnam.com; us.penguingroup.com, pg 193

Roy, Mary Lou, University of Alberta Press, Ring House 2, Edmonton, AB T6G 2E1, Canada *Tel:* 780-492-3662 *Fax:* 780-492-0719 *Web Site:* www.uap.ualberta.ca, pg 502

Roy, Michael, American Psychiatric Publishing (APP), 1000 Wilson Blvd, Suite 1825, Arlington, VA 22209 *Tel:* 703-907-7322 *Toll Free Tel:* 800-368-5777 *Fax:* 703-907-1091 *E-mail:* appi@psych.org *Web Site:* www.appi.org; www.psychiatryonline.org, pg 15

Royall, John T, Gulf Publishing Co, 2 Greenway Plaza, Suite 1020, Houston, TX 77046 *Tel:* 713-529-4301 *Fax:* 713-520-4433 *E-mail:* store@gulfpub.com *Web Site:* www.gulfpub.com, pg 102

Royce, Adam, Penguin Young Readers Group, 345 Hudson St, New York, NY 10014 *Tel:* 212-366-2000 *E-mail:* online@penguinputnam.com *Web Site:* www.penguinputnam.com; us.penguingroup.com, pg 188

Royce, Michael, Artists' Fellowships, 20 Jay St, 7th fl, Brooklyn, NY 11201 *Tel:* 212-366-6900 *Fax:* 212-366-1778 *E-mail:* info@nyfa.org *Web Site:* www.nyfa.org, pg 668

Rozansky, David A, Flying Pen Press LLC, 1416 S Newport St, Denver, CO 80224 *Tel:* 303-375-0499 *Fax:* 303-375-0499 *E-mail:* directory@flyingpenpress.com *Web Site:* www.flyingpenpress.com, pg 90

Rozier, Cheryl, HarperCollins Children's Books, 195 Broadway, New York, NY 10007 *Tel:* 212-207-7000 *Web Site:* www.harpercollins.com/childrens, pg 105

Rubenstein, Ellis, New York Academy of Sciences, 7 World Trade, 40th fl, 250 Greenwich St, New York, NY 10007-2157 *Tel:* 212-298-8600 *Toll Free Tel:* 800-843-6927 *Fax:* 212-298-3644 *E-mail:* nyas@nyas.org; publications@nyas.org *Web Site:* www.nyas.org, pg 169

Rubenstein, Norm, Bram Stoker Awards®, 244 Fifth Ave, Suite 2767, New York, NY 10001 *E-mail:* hwa@horror.org *Web Site:* www.horror.org/awards/stokers.htm, pg 730

Rubie, Peter, FinePrint Literary Management, 115 W 29 St, 3rd fl, New York, NY 10001 *Tel:* 212-279-1282 *Web Site:* www.fineprintlit.com, pg 551

Rubin, Barry, Lederer Books, 6120 Day Long Lane, Clarksville, MD 21029 *Tel:* 410-531-6644 *Toll Free Tel:* 800-410-7367 (orders) *Fax:* 410-531-9440 *E-mail:* lederer@messianicjewish.net; customerservice@messianicjewish.net *Web Site:* www.messianicjewish.net, pg 136

Rubin, Barry, Messianic Jewish Publishers, 6120 Day Long Lane, Clarksville, MD 21029 *Tel:* 410-531-6644 *Toll Free Tel:* 800-410-7367 (orders) *Fax:* 410-531-9440 (no orders) *E-mail:* lederer@messianicjewish.net; rightsandpermissions@messianicjewish.net (rights & perms) *Web Site:* messianicjewish.net, pg 155

Rubin, Donald S, McGraw-Hill Financial, 1221 Avenue of the Americas, 50th fl, New York, NY 10020 *Tel:* 212-512-2000 *Web Site:* www.mhfi.com, pg 151

Rubin, Lisa, Messianic Jewish Publishers, 6120 Day Long Lane, Clarksville, MD 21029 *Tel:* 410-531-6644 *Toll Free Tel:* 800-410-7367 (orders) *Fax:* 410-531-9440 (no orders) *E-mail:* lederer@messianicjewish.net; rightsandpermissions@messianicjewish.net (rights & perms) *Web Site:* messianicjewish.net, pg 155

Rubin, Lorna, Triad Publishing Co, PO Box 13355, Gainesville, FL 32604 *Tel:* 352-373-5800 *Fax:* 352-373-1488 *Toll Free Fax:* 800-854-4947 *E-mail:* orders@triadpublishing.com *Web Site:* www.triadpublishing.com, pg 249

Rubin, Melvin L, Triad Publishing Co, PO Box 13355, Gainesville, FL 32604 *Tel:* 352-373-5800 *Fax:* 352-373-1488 *Toll Free Fax:* 800-854-4947 *E-mail:* orders@triadpublishing.com *Web Site:* www.triadpublishing.com, pg 249

Rubin, Stephen, Henry Holt and Company, LLC, 175 Fifth Ave, New York, NY 10010 *Tel:* 646-307-5151 *Toll Free Tel:* 888-330-8477 (orders) *Fax:* 646-307-5285 *E-mail:* firstname.lastname@hholt.com *Web Site:* www.henryholt.com, pg 113

Rubin, Stephen, Macmillan, 175 Fifth Ave, New York, NY 10010 *Tel:* 646-307-5151 *Fax:* 212-420-9314 *E-mail:* firstname.lastname@macmillan.com *Web Site:* www.macmillan.com, pg 145

Rubino, Victor J, Practising Law Institute, 1177 Avenue of the Americas, New York, NY 10036 *Tel:* 212-824-5700 *Toll Free Tel:* 800-260-4PLI (260-4754, cust serv) *Fax:* 212-265-4742 (intl) *Toll Free Fax:* 800-321-0093 (local) *E-mail:* info@pli.edu (cust serv) *Web Site:* www.pli.edu, pg 195

Rubinstein, Elizabeth Winick, McIntosh & Otis Inc, 353 Lexington Ave, New York, NY 10016-0900 *Tel:* 212-687-7400 *Fax:* 212-687-6894 *E-mail:* info@mcintoshandotis.com *Web Site:* www.mcintoshandotis.com, pg 565

Ruby, Brenda A, Woodbine House, 6510 Bells Mill Rd, Bethesda, MD 20817 *Tel:* 301-897-3570 *Toll Free Tel:* 800-843-7323 *Fax:* 301-897-5838 *E-mail:* info@woodbinehouse.com *Web Site:* www.woodbinehouse.com, pg 275

Ruby-Strauss, Jeremie, Gallery Books, 1230 Avenue of the Americas, New York, NY 10020 *Toll Free Tel:* 800-456-6798 *Fax:* 212-698-7284 *E-mail:* consumer.customerservice@simonandschuster.com *Web Site:* www.simonsays.com, pg 94

Rucci, Marysue, Simon & Schuster, 1230 Avenue of the Americas, New York, NY 10020 *Tel:* 212-698-7000 *Toll Free Tel:* 800-223-2348 (cust serv); 800-223-2336 (orders) *Toll Free Fax:* 800-943-9831 (orders) *Web Site:* www.simonandschuster.com, pg 225

Rucker, Sarah, Little Bee Books, 853 Broadway, Suite 2014, New York, NY 10003 *E-mail:* info@littlebeebooks.com *Web Site:* www.littlebeebooks.com, pg 140

Rudick, Nicole, The Plimpton Prize, 544 W 27 St, New York, NY 10001 *Tel:* 212-343-1333 *Fax:* 212-343-1988 *E-mail:* queries@theparisreview.org *Web Site:* www.theparisreview.org, pg 719

Rudin, Max, The Library of America, 14 E 60 St, New York, NY 10022-1006 *Tel:* 212-308-3360 *Fax:* 212-750-8352 *E-mail:* info@loa.org *Web Site:* www.loa.org, pg 139

Rudman, Michael P, National Learning Corp, 212 Michael Dr, Syosset, NY 11791 *Tel:* 516-921-8888 *Toll Free Tel:* 800-632-8888 *Fax:* 516-921-8743 *E-mail:* info@passbooks.com *Web Site:* www.passbooks.com, pg 165

Rudolph, Allyson, The Overlook Press, 141 Wooster St, Suite 4-B, New York, NY 10012 *Tel:* 212-673-2210; 845-679-6838 (orders & dist) *Fax:* 212-673-2296 *E-mail:* sales@overlookny.com (orders) *Web Site:* www.overlookpress.com, pg 178

Rudolph, Janet, Macavity Award, 7155 Marlborough Terr, Berkeley, CA 94705 *Tel:* 510-845-3600 *Web Site:* www.mysteryreaders.org, pg 704

Rudolph, John, Dystel & Goderich Literary Management, One Union Sq W, Suite 904, New York, NY 10003 *Tel:* 212-627-9100 *Fax:* 212-627-9313 *Web Site:* www.dystel.com, pg 549

Rudolph, Kelly, HarperCollins General Books Group, 195 Broadway, New York, NY 10007 *Tel:* 212-207-7000 *Web Site:* www.harpercollins.com, pg 105

Rudy, Bryan, Wolf Pirate Project Inc, 337 Lost Lake Dr, Divide, CO 80814 *Tel:* 305-333-3186 *E-mail:* contact@wolfpiratebooks.com; workshop@wolfpiratebooks.com *Web Site:* www.wolf-pirate.com, pg 535

Rudy, Caryn Karmatz, DeFiore and Company, LLC, 47 E 19 St, 3rd fl, New York, NY 10003 *Tel:* 212-925-7744 *Fax:* 212-925-9803 *E-mail:* submissions@defioreandco.com; info@defioreandco.com *Web Site:* www.defioreandco.com, pg 548

Rudy, Catherine, Wolf Pirate Project Inc, 337 Lost Lake Dr, Divide, CO 80814 *Tel:* 305-333-3186 *E-mail:* contact@wolfpiratebooks.com; workshop@wolfpiratebooks.com *Web Site:* www.wolf-pirate.com, pg 535

Rudzinski, Joel, Dramatists Play Service Inc, 440 Park Ave S, New York, NY 10016 *Tel:* 212-683-8960 *Fax:* 212-213-1539 *E-mail:* postmaster@dramatists.com; orders@dramatists.com; publications@dramatists.com *Web Site:* www.dramatists.com, pg 77

Rue, Robin, Writers House, 21 W 26 St, New York, NY 10010 *Tel:* 212-685-2400 *Fax:* 212-685-1781 *Web Site:* www.writershouse.com, pg 580

Ruebel, Donny, Willow Creek Press, 9931 Hwy 70 W, Minocqua, WI 54548 *Tel:* 715-358-7010 *Toll Free Tel:* 800-850-9453 *Fax:* 715-358-2807 *E-mail:* info@willowcreekpress.com *Web Site:* www.willowcreekpress.com, pg 272

Ruenzel, Nancy, Peachpit Press, 1249 Eighth St, Berkeley, CA 94710 *Tel:* 510-524-2178 *Toll Free Tel:* 800-283-9444 *Fax:* 510-524-2221 *E-mail:* info@peachpit.com *Web Site:* www.peachpit.com, pg 184

Ruffino, Dan, Simon & Schuster, Inc, 1230 Avenue of the Americas, New York, NY 10020 *Tel:* 212-698-7000 *Fax:* 212-698-7007 *E-mail:* firstname.lastname@simonandschuster.com *Web Site:* www.simonandschuster.com, pg 226

Ruffner, Frederick G Jr, Omnigraphics Inc, 155 W Congress, Suite 200, Detroit, MI 48226 *Tel:* 313-961-1340 *Toll Free Tel:* 800-234-1340 (cust serv) *Fax:* 313-961-1383 *Toll Free Fax:* 800-875-1340 (cust serv) *E-mail:* info@omnigraphics.com *Web Site:* www.omnigraphics.com, pg 175

Ruffner, Peter E, Omnigraphics Inc, 155 W Congress, Suite 200, Detroit, MI 48226 *Tel:* 313-961-1340 *Toll Free Tel:* 800-234-1340 (cust serv) *Fax:* 313-961-1383 *Toll Free Fax:* 800-875-1340 (cust serv) *E-mail:* info@omnigraphics.com *Web Site:* www.omnigraphics.com, pg 175

Ruggiero, Anthony, Pauline Books & Media, 50 St Paul's Ave, Boston, MA 02130 *Tel:* 617-522-8911 *Toll Free Tel:* 800-876-4463 (orders); 800-836-9723 (cust serv) *Fax:* 617-541-9805 *E-mail:* editorial@paulinemedia.com (ms submissions); orderentry@pauline.org (cust serv) *Web Site:* www.pauline.org, pg 184

Ruggiero, Greg, City Lights Publishers, 261 Columbus Ave, San Francisco, CA 94133 *Tel:* 415-362-8193 *Fax:* 415-362-4921 *E-mail:* staff@citylights.com *Web Site:* www.citylights.com, pg 58

Ruggiero, Vincenzo, Penguin Group (USA) LLC, a Penguin Random House company, 375 Hudson St, New York, NY 10014 *Tel:* 212-366-2000 *Toll Free Tel:* 800-847-5515 (inside sales); 800-631-8571 (cust serv) *Fax:* 212-366-2666; 607-775-4829 (inside sales) *E-mail:* online@us.penguingroup.com *Web Site:* www.penguin.com; us.penguingroup.com, pg 186

Ruhl, Maria, Regnery Publishing Inc, 300 New Jersey Ave NW, Washington, DC 20001 *Tel:* 202-216-0600 *Toll Free Tel:* 888-219-4747 *Fax:* 202-216-0612 *Web Site:* www.regnery.com, pg 208

Ruhl, Peter, American Catholic Press (ACP), 16565 S State St, South Holland, IL 60473 *Tel:* 708-331-5485 *Fax:* 708-331-5484 *E-mail:* acp@acpress.org *Web Site:* www.acpress.org, pg 11

Ruhlig, Steve, Human Kinetics Inc, 1607 N Market St, Champaign, IL 61820 *Tel:* 217-351-5076 *Toll Free Tel:* 800-747-4457 *Fax:* 217-351-1549 (orders/cust serv) *E-mail:* info@hkusa.com *Web Site:* www.humankinetics.com, pg 117

Ruiz, Jonathan, Velazquez Press, 9682 Telstar Ave, Suite 110, El Monte, CA 91731 *Tel:* 626-448-3448 *Fax:* 626-602-3817 *E-mail:* info@academiclearningcompany.com *Web Site:* www.velazquezpress.com, pg 265

Rukkila, Roy, Bagwyn Books, Lattie F Coor Hall, 4th fl, Rms 4426-4442, 975 S Myrtle Ave, Tempe, AZ 85281 *Tel:* 480-965-5900 *Fax:* 480-965-1681 *E-mail:* bagwynbooks@acmrs.org *Web Site:* acmrs.org/publications/bagwyn, pg 29

Rukkila, Roy, MRTS, PO Box 874402, Tempe, AZ 85287-4402 *Tel:* 480-727-6503 *Toll Free Tel:* 800-621-2736 (orders) *Fax:* 480-965-1681 *Toll Free Fax:* 800-621-8476 (orders) *E-mail:* mrts@asu.edu *Web Site:* www.acmrs.org/pubs, pg 161

Ruley, Meg, Jane Rotrosen Agency LLC, 318 E 51 St, New York, NY 10022 *Tel:* 212-593-4330 *Fax:* 212-935-6985 *Web Site:* janerotrosen.com, pg 571

Rumberger, Anne, Verso, 20 Jay St, Suite 1010, Brooklyn, NY 11201 *Tel:* 718-246-8160 *Fax:* 718-246-8165 *E-mail:* verso@versobooks.com *Web Site:* www.versobooks.com, pg 265

Rumble, Brant, Blue Rider Press, 375 Hudson St, New York, NY 10014 *Tel:* 212-366-2000 *E-mail:* blueriderpublicity@us.penguingroup.com, pg 41

Rummans, Tony, ProQuest LLC, 789 E Eisenhower Pkwy, Ann Arbor, MI 48108-3218 *Tel:* 734-761-4700 *Toll Free Tel:* 800-521-0600 *Fax:* 734-975-6486 *Toll Free Fax:* 800-864-0019 *E-mail:* info@proquest.com *Web Site:* www.proquest.com, pg 199

Rumsch, BreAnn, ABDO Publishing Group, 8000 W 78 St, Suite 310, Edina, MN 55439 *Tel:* 952-831-2120 *Toll Free Tel:* 800-800-1312 *Toll Free Fax:* 800-862-3480 *E-mail:* customerservice@abdopublishing.com *Web Site:* abdopublishing.com, pg 2

Rundall, Nick, Whitecap Books Ltd, 314 W Cordova St, Suite 210, Vancouver, BC V6B 1E8, Canada *Tel:* 604-681-6181 *Toll Free Tel:* 800-387-9776 *Toll Free Fax:* 800-260-9777 *Web Site:* www.whitecap.ca, pg 504

Runde, Kate, Vintage & Anchor Books, c/o Random House Inc, 1745 Broadway, New York, NY 10019 *Tel:* 212-572-2420 *E-mail:* vintageanchorpublicity@randomhouse.com *Web Site:* vintage-anchor.knopfdoubleday.com, pg 266

Rundle, Lisa, HarperCollins Canada Ltd, 2 Bloor St E, 20th fl, Toronto, ON M4W 1A8, Canada *Tel:* 416-975-9334 *Fax:* 416-975-9884 *E-mail:* hcorder@harpercollins.com *Web Site:* www.harpercollins.ca, pg 487

Runge, Gailen, C & T Publishing Inc, 1651 Challenge Dr, Concord, CA 94520-5206 *Tel:* 925-677-0377 *Toll Free Tel:* 800-284-1114 *Fax:* 925-677-0373 *E-mail:* support@ctpub.com *Web Site:* www.ctpub.com, pg 48

Runk, David, FaithWalk Publishing, 5450 N Dixie Hwy, Lima, OH 45807 *Tel:* 419-227-1818 *Toll Free Tel:* 800-537-1030 (orders: non-bookstore mkts) *Fax:* 419-224-9184 *E-mail:* orders@csspub.com *Web Site:* www.faithwalkpub.com, pg 86

Runyon, Joy, The New York Botanical Garden Press, 2900 Southern Blvd, Bronx, NY 10458-5126 *Tel:* 718-817-8721 *Fax:* 718-817-8842 *E-mail:* nybgpress@nybg.org *Web Site:* www.nybgpress.org, pg 169

Runyon, Nancy, McCutchan Publishing Corp, 2694 Ohart Rd, Richmond, CA 94806 *Tel:* 510-758-5510 *Toll Free Tel:* 800-227-1540 *Fax:* 510-758-6078 *E-mail:* mccutchanpublish@sbcglobal.net *Web Site:* www.mccutchanpublishing.com, pg 150

Rupnow, Dr John, The Mellen Poetry Press, 240 Portage Rd, Lewiston, NY 14092 *Tel:* 716-754-2266; 716-754-1400 (mktg); 716-754-2788 (order fulfillment) *Fax:* 716-754-4056; 716-754-1860 (fulfillment) *E-mail:* cservice@mellenpress.com *Web Site:* www.mellenpress.com, pg 154

Rupp, Katherine, American Quilter's Society, 5801 Kentucky Dam Rd, Paducah, KY 42003-9323 *Tel:* 270-898-7903 *Toll Free Tel:* 800-626-5420 (orders) *Fax:* 270-898-1173 *E-mail:* orders@americanquilter.com *Web Site:* www.americanquilter.com, pg 15

Ruppel, Philip, Phaidon Press Inc, 180 Varick St, 14th fl, New York, NY 10014 *Tel:* 212-652-5400 *Toll Free Tel:* 800-759-0190 (cust serv) *Fax:* 212-652-5410 *Toll Free Fax:* 800-286-9471 (cust serv) *E-mail:* ussales@phaidon.com *Web Site:* www.phaidon.com, pg 190

Rushall, Kathleen, Marsal Lyon Literary Agency LLC, 665 San Rodolfo Dr, Suite 124, PMB 121, Solana Beach, CA 92075 *Tel:* 760-814-8507 *Web Site:* www.marsallyonliteraryagency.com, pg 563

Rusin, William F, W W Norton & Company Inc, 500 Fifth Ave, New York, NY 10110-0017 *Tel:* 212-354-5500 *Toll Free Tel:* 800-233-4830 (orders & cust serv) *Fax:* 212-869-0856 *Toll Free Fax:* 800-458-6515 *Web Site:* www.wwnorton.com, pg 171

Russ, Brice, Linguistic Society of America, 1325 18 St NW, Suite 211, Washington, DC 20036-6501 *Tel:* 202-835-1714 *Fax:* 202-835-1717 *E-mail:* lsa@lsadc.org *Web Site:* www.linguisticsociety.org, pg 609

Russ, Susan Fraysse, The Reader's Digest Association Inc, 750 Third Ave, New York, NY 10017 *Tel:* 914-238-1000; 646-293-6284 *Toll Free Tel:* 800-310-6261 (cust serv) *Fax:* 914-238-4559 *Web Site:* www.rd.com; www.rda.com, pg 205

Russell, Cheryl, New Strategist Publications Inc, 120 W State St, 4th fl, Ithaca, NY 14850 *Tel:* 607-273-0913 *Toll Free Tel:* 800-848-0842 *Fax:* 607-277-5009 *E-mail:* demographics@newstrategist.com *Web Site:* newstrategist.com, pg 168

Russell, Christie, Peter Lampack Agency Inc, 350 Fifth Ave, Suite 5300, New York, NY 10118 *Tel:* 212-687-9106 *Fax:* 212-687-9109 *Web Site:* www.peterlampackagency.com, pg 561

Russell, Jim, Amy Writing Awards, PO Box 16091, Lansing, MI 48901-6091 *Tel:* 517-323-6233 *Toll Free Tel:* 877-727-4262 *Fax:* 517-321-2572 *E-mail:* amyawards@worldmag.com *Web Site:* www.worldmag.com/amyawards, pg 667

Russell, Kenn, Henry Holt and Company, LLC, 175 Fifth Ave, New York, NY 10010 *Tel:* 646-307-5151 *Toll Free Tel:* 888-330-8477 (orders) *Fax:* 646-307-5285 *E-mail:* firstname.lastname@hholt.com *Web Site:* www.henryholt.com, pg 113

Russell, Pam, Council for Advancement & Support of Education (CASE), 1307 New York Ave NW, Suite 1000, Washington, DC 20005-4701 *Tel:* 202-328-CASE (328-2273) *Fax:* 202-387-4973 *E-mail:* membersupportcenter@case.org *Web Site:* www.case.org, pg 604

Russell, Rick, Naval Institute Press, 291 Wood Rd, Annapolis, MD 21402-5034 *Tel:* 410-268-6110 *Toll Free Tel:* 800-233-8764 *Fax:* 410-295-1084; 410-571-1703 (cust serv) *E-mail:* webmaster@navalinstitute.org; customer@navalinstitute.org (cust serv); trade@usni.org *Web Site:* www.nip.org; www.usni.org, pg 166

Russell, Susan, The Aaland Agency, PO Box 849, Inyokern, CA 93527-0849 *Tel:* 760-384-3910 *Web Site:* www.the-aaland-agency.com, pg 539

Russell, Tom, The Princeton Review, c/o Random House Inc, 1745 Broadway, New York, NY 10019 *Toll Free Tel:* 800-733-3000 *Fax:* 212-782-9682 *E-mail:* princetonreview@randomhouse.com *Web Site:* www.princetonreview.com, pg 197

Russo, Carmine, Prevention Products & Services Inc dba The Bureau for At-Risk Youth, PO Box 170, Farmingville, NY 11738 *Toll Free Tel:* 800-99YOUTH (999-6884) *Fax:* 631-389-2511 *Web Site:* www.at-risk.com, pg 196

Russo, Ellyn, Crown Publishing Group, c/o Penguin Random House Inc, 1745 Broadway, New York, NY 10019 *Tel:* 212-782-9000 *Toll Free Tel:* 888-264-1745 *Fax:* 212-940-7408 *E-mail:* crownosm@penguinrandomhouse.com *Web Site:* crownpublishing.com, pg 68

Russo, Nicole, Harry N Abrams Inc, 115 W 18 St, 6th fl, New York, NY 10011 *Tel:* 212-206-7715 *Toll Free Tel:* 800-345-1359 *Fax:* 212-519-1210 *E-mail:* abrams@abramsbooks.com *Web Site:* www.abramsbooks.com, pg 3

Russo, Richard, The Authors Guild, 31 E 32 St, 7th fl, New York, NY 10016 *Tel:* 212-563-5904 *Fax:* 212-564-5363 *E-mail:* staff@authorsguild.org *Web Site:* www.authorsguild.org, pg 599

Russo, Sarah, John Leonard Award, 160 Varick St, 11th fl, New York, NY 10013 *E-mail:* info@bookcritics.org *Web Site:* bookcritics.org, pg 700

Russo, Mr Seth, Simon & Schuster Sales Division, 1230 Avenue of the Americas, New York, NY 10020 *Tel:* 212-698-7000, pg 226

Rust, Ned, Little, Brown and Company, 1290 Avenue of the Americas, New York, NY 10019 *Tel:* 212-364-1100 *Fax:* 212-364-0952 *E-mail:* firstname.lastname@hbgusa.com *Web Site:* www.HachetteBookGroup.com, pg 141

Rutenberg, Sara, Spark Award, 4727 Wilshire Blvd, Suite 301, Los Angeles, CA 90010 *Tel:* 323-782-1010 *Fax:* 323-782-1892 *E-mail:* grants@scbwi.org *Web Site:* www.scbwi.org, pg 730

Rutman, Jim, Sterling Lord Literistic Inc, 65 Bleecker St, New York, NY 10012 *Tel:* 212-780-6050 *Fax:* 212-780-6095 *E-mail:* info@sll.com *Web Site:* www.sll.com, pg 575

Rutsky, Alan, Rizzoli International Publications Inc, 300 Park Ave S, 4th fl, New York, NY 10010-5399 *Tel:* 212-387-3400 *Toll Free Tel:* 800-522-6657 (orders only) *Fax:* 212-387-3535 *E-mail:* publicity@rizzoliusa.com *Web Site:* www.rizzoliusa.com, pg 209

Rutter, Sandy, American Society of Agricultural & Biological Engineers (ASABE), 2950 Niles Rd, St Joseph, MI 49085-9659 *Tel:* 269-429-0300 *Toll Free Tel:* 800-371-2723 *Fax:* 269-429-3852 *E-mail:* hq@asabe.org *Web Site:* www.asabe.org, pg 16

Ryan, Amy, HarperCollins Children's Books, 195 Broadway, New York, NY 10007 *Tel:* 212-207-7000 *Web Site:* www.harpercollins.com/childrens, pg 105

Ryan, Anthony J, Ignatius Press, 1348 Tenth Ave, San Francisco, CA 94122-2304 *Toll Free Tel:* 800-651-1531 (orders); 888-615-3186 (cust serv) *E-mail:* info@ignatius.com *Web Site:* www.ignatius.com, pg 118

Ryan, Becky, DawnSignPress, 6130 Nancy Ridge Dr, San Diego, CA 92121-3223 *Tel:* 858-625-0600 *Toll Free Tel:* 800-549-5350 *Fax:* 858-625-2336 *E-mail:* info@dawnsign.com *Web Site:* www.dawnsign.com, pg 72

Ryan, Dawn, Random House Children's Books, 1745 Broadway, New York, NY 10019 *Tel:* 212-782-9000 *Toll Free Tel:* 800-200-3552 *Fax:* 212-782-9452 *Web Site:* randomhousekids.com, pg 203

Ryan, James, The Electrochemical Society (ECS), 65 S Main St, Bldg D, Pennington, NJ 08534-2839 *Tel:* 609-737-1902 *Fax:* 609-737-2743 *E-mail:* publications@electrochem.org; customerservice@electrochem.org *Web Site:* www.electrochem.org, pg 80

Ryan, Jane, RAND Corp, 1776 Main St, Santa Monica, CA 90407-2138 *Tel:* 310-393-0411 *Fax:* 310-393-4818 *Web Site:* www.rand.org, pg 203

Ryan, John R, Center for Creative Leadership LLC, One Leadership Place, Greensboro, NC 27410-9427 *Tel:* 336-545-2810; 336-288-7210 *Fax:* 336-282-3284 *E-mail:* info@ccl.org *Web Site:* www.ccl.org/publications, pg 53

Ryan, Matt, Eric Hoffer Award for Short Prose, PO Box 11, Titusville, NJ 08560 *Fax:* 609-964-1718 *E-mail:* info@hofferaward.com *Web Site:* www.hofferaward.com, pg 692

Ryan, Mike, McGraw-Hill Humanities, Social Sciences, Languages, 2 Penn Plaza, 21st fl, New York, NY 10121 *Tel:* 212-904-2000 *Toll Free Tel:* 800-338-3987 (cust serv) *Fax:* 614-755-5645 (cust serv) *Web Site:* www.mhhe.com, pg 151

Ryan, Regina, Regina Ryan Books, 251 Central Park W, Suite 7-D, New York, NY 10024 *Tel:* 212-787-5589 *E-mail:* queries@reginaryanbooks.com *Web Site:* www.reginaryanbooks.com, pg 571

Ryan, Regina Sara, Hohm Press, PO Box 4410, Chino Valley, AZ 86323 *Tel:* 928-636-3331 *Toll Free Tel:* 800-381-2700 *Fax:* 928-636-7519 *E-mail:* hppublisher@cableone.net; hohmpresseditor@gmail.com *Web Site:* www.hohmpress.com, pg 113

Ryan, Sean, McGraw-Hill School Education Group, 8787 Orion Place, Columbus, OH 43240 *Tel:* 614-430-4000 *Toll Free Tel:* 800-848-1567 *Web Site:* www.mheducation.com, pg 152

Ryan, Sean, SRA/McGraw-Hill, 8787 Orion Place, Columbus, OH 43240 *Tel:* 614-430-4000 *Fax:* 614-430-4303 *E-mail:* sra@mcgraw-hill.com *Web Site:* www.sraonline.com, pg 232

Ryan, Suzanne, Oxford University Press USA, 198 Madison Ave, New York, NY 10016 *Tel:* 212-726-6000 *Toll Free Tel:* 800-451-7556 (orders); 800-445-9714 (cust serv) *Fax:* 919-677-1303 *E-mail:* custserv.us@oup.com *Web Site:* www.oup.com/us, pg 179

Ryce, Chris, Pacific Printing Industries Association, 6825 SW Sandburg St, Portland, OR 97223 *Tel:* 503-221-3944 *Toll Free Tel:* 877-762-7742 *Fax:* 503-221-5691 *E-mail:* info@ppiassociation.org *Web Site:* www.ppiassociation.org, pg 615

Rykerd, Beverly, WaterBrook Multnomah Publishing Group, 12265 Oracle Blvd, Suite 200, Colorado Springs, CO 80921 *Tel:* 719-590-4999 *Toll Free Tel:* 800-603-7051 (orders) *Fax:* 719-590-8977 *Toll Free Fax:* 800-294-5686 (orders) *E-mail:* info@waterbrookmultnomah.com *Web Site:* waterbrookmultnomah.com, pg 267

Saada, Yves, Disney Publishing Worldwide, 1101 Flower St, Glendale, CA 91201 *Web Site:* books.disney.com, pg 74

Sabbagh, Julia, Reader's Digest Trade Books, 44 S Broadway, White Plains, NY 10601 *Tel:* 914-244-7503 *Fax:* 914-244-4841 *Web Site:* www.rd.com, pg 205

Sabbagh, Julia, Studio Fun International Inc, 44 S Broadway, White Plains, NY 10601 *Tel:* 914-238-1000 *Toll Free Tel:* 800-934-0977 *Web Site:* www.rdtradepublishing.com, pg 237

Sabia, Mary Ann, Charlesbridge Publishing Inc, 85 Main St, Watertown, MA 02472 *Tel:* 617-926-0329 *Toll Free Tel:* 800-225-3214 *Fax:* 617-926-5720 *Toll Free Fax:* 800-926-5775 *E-mail:* books@charlesbridge.com *Web Site:* www.charlesbridge.com, pg 55

Sablik, Filip, Boom! Studios, 5670 Wilshire Blvd, Suite 450, Los Angeles, CA 90036 *Web Site:* www.boom-studios.com, pg 43

Sablone, Frank, Tag & Label Manufacturers Institute Inc (TLMI), One Blackburn Ctr, Gloucester, MA 01930 *Tel:* 978-282-1400 *Fax:* 978-282-3238 *E-mail:* office@tlmi.com *Web Site:* tlmi.com, pg 620

Sablone, Julie, Tag & Label Manufacturers Institute Inc (TLMI), One Blackburn Ctr, Gloucester, MA 01930 *Tel:* 978-282-1400 *Fax:* 978-282-3238 *E-mail:* office@tlmi.com *Web Site:* tlmi.com, pg 620

Sabol, Richard, Springer, 233 Spring St, New York, NY 10013-1578 *Tel:* 212-460-1500 *Toll Free Tel:* 800-SPRINGER (777-4643) *Fax:* 212-460-1575 *E-mail:* service-ny@springer.com *Web Site:* www.springer.com, pg 232

Sabol, Stephanie, Penguin Group (USA) LLC Sales, 375 Hudson St, New York, NY 10014 *Tel:* 212-366-2000 *E-mail:* online@penguinputnam.com *Web Site:* us.penguingroup.com, pg 187

Sachdev, Dr Rachana, Susquehanna University Press, 514 University Ave, Selinsgrove, PA 17870 *Tel:* 570-372-4175 *Fax:* 570-372-4021 *E-mail:* supress@susqu.edu, pg 238

Sacher, Jay, Clarkson Potter Publishers, c/o Random House Inc, 1745 Broadway, New York, NY 10019 *Tel:* 212-782-9000 *Toll Free Tel:* 888-264-1745 *Fax:* 212-572-6181 *Web Site:* www.clarksonpotter.com; www.randomhouse.com/crown/clarksonpotter, pg 195

Sacilotto, Loriana, Harlequin Enterprises Ltd, 225 Duncan Mill Rd, Don Mills, ON M3B 3K9, Canada *Tel:* 416-445-5860 *Toll Free Tel:* 888-432-4879; 800-370-5838 (ebook inquiries) *E-mail:* customerservice@harlequin.com *Web Site:* www.harlequin.com, pg 487

Sacilotto, Loriana, Love Inspired Books, 233 Broadway, Suite 1001, New York, NY 10279 *Tel:* 212-553-4200 *Fax:* 212-227-8969 *E-mail:* customer_service@harlequin.ca *Web Site:* www.harlequin.com, pg 143

Sadler, Christy, The AEI Press, 1150 17 St NW, Washington, DC 20036 *Tel:* 202-862-5800 *Fax:* 202-862-7177 *Web Site:* www.aei.org, pg 5

Sadler, Kim Martin, The Pilgrim Press/United Church Press, 700 Prospect Ave, Cleveland, OH 44115-1100 *Toll Free Tel:* 800-537-3394 (cust serv-indivs); 800-654-5129 (cust serv-commercial accts) *Fax:* 216-736-2206 (orders) *E-mail:* proposals@thepilgrimpress.com *Web Site:* www.thepilgrimpress.com; www.unitedchurchpress.com, pg 192

Sadler, Tom, Outdoor Writers Association of America Annual Conference, 615 Oak St, Suite 201, Missoula, MT 59801 *Tel:* 406-728-7434 *Fax:* 406-728-7445 *E-mail:* info@owaa.org *Web Site:* www.owaa.org, pg 653

Sadlon, Annie, Unicorn Writers' Conference, 17 Church Hill Rd, Redding, CT 06896 *Tel:* 203-938-7405 *Fax:* 203-938-7405 *E-mail:* unicornwritersconference@gmail.com *Web Site:* unicornwritersconference.com, pg 656

Sadowski, Br Frank, St Pauls, 2187 Victory Blvd, Staten Island, NY 10314-6603 *Tel:* 718-761-0047 (edit & prodn); 718-698-2759 (mktg & billing) *Toll Free Tel:* 800-343-2522 *Fax:* 718-761-0057 *E-mail:* sales@stpauls.us; marketing@stpauls.us *Web Site:* www.stpauls.us, pg 215

Saenz, Benjamin Alire, University of Texas at El Paso, Department of Creative Writing, MFA/Department of Creative Writing, Liberal Arts 415 UTEP, 500 W University Ave, El Paso, TX 79968-9991 *Tel:* 915-747-5713 *Fax:* 915-747-5523 *Web Site:* www.utep.edu/cw, pg 664

Saffel, Than, West Virginia University Press, West Virginia University, PO Box 6295, Morgantown, WV 26506-6295 *Tel:* 304-293-8400 *Toll Free Tel:* 866-WVU-PRES (988-7737) *Fax:* 304-293-6585 *E-mail:* press@wvu.edu *Web Site:* www.wvupress.com, pg 269

Safon, Teresa, Corporation for Public Broadcasting (CPB), 401 Ninth St NW, Washington, DC 20004-2129 *Tel:* 202-879-9600 *Web Site:* www.cpb.org, pg 604

Safyan, Susan, Arsenal Pulp Press, 211 E Georgia St, No 202, Vancouver, BC V6A 1Z6, Canada *Tel:* 604-687-4233 *Toll Free Tel:* 888-600-PULP (600-7857) *Fax:* 604-687-4283 *E-mail:* info@arsenalpulp.com *Web Site:* www.arsenalpulp.com, pg 471

Sagalyn, Raphael, ICM/Sagalyn, 1250 Connecticut Ave, 7th fl, Washington, DC 20036 *Tel:* 202-419-1525 *E-mail:* query@sagalyn.com *Web Site:* www.sagalyn.com, pg 557

Sagan, Raymond, William H Sadlier Inc, 9 Pine St, New York, NY 10005 *Tel:* 212-227-2120 *Toll Free Tel:* 800-221-5175 (cust serv) *Fax:* 212-312-6080 *E-mail:* customerservice@sadlier.com *Web Site:* www.sadlier.com, pg 213

Sagnette, Lindsay, Crown Publishing Group, c/o Penguin Random House Inc, 1745 Broadway, New York, NY 10019 *Tel:* 212-782-9000 *Toll Free Tel:* 888-264-1745 *Fax:* 212-940-7408 *E-mail:* crownosm@penguinrandomhouse.com *Web Site:* crownpublishing.com, pg 68

Saidenberg, Julie, Shambhala Publications Inc, Horticultural Hall, 300 Massachusetts Ave, Boston, MA 02115 *Tel:* 617-424-0030 *Toll Free Tel:* 866-424-0030 (off); 888-424-2329 (cust serv) *Fax:* 617-236-1563 *E-mail:* customercare@shambhala.com *Web Site:* www.shambhala.com, pg 223

Saidenberg, Julie, Snow Lion Publications Inc, 300 Massachusetts Ave, Boston, MA 02115 *Tel:* 617-236-0030 *Fax:* 617-236-1563 *E-mail:* customercare@shambhala.com *Web Site:* www.shambhala.com/snowlion, pg 228

Saielli, Robert J, Young People's Press Inc (YPPI), 1527 Reed Ave, San Diego, CA 92109 *Tel:* 619-992-3258 (orders) *Toll Free Tel:* 800-231-9774 *E-mail:* admin@youngpeoplespress.com *Web Site:* www.youngpeoplespress.com, pg 279

Saielli, Zach, Young People's Press Inc (YPPI), 1527 Reed Ave, San Diego, CA 92109 *Tel:* 619-992-3258 (orders) *Toll Free Tel:* 800-231-9774 *E-mail:* admin@youngpeoplespress.com *Web Site:* www.youngpeoplespress.com, pg 279

Saikia-Wilson, Becky, Houghton Mifflin Harcourt Trade & Reference Division, 222 Berkeley St, Boston, MA 02116 *Tel:* 617-351-5000 *Toll Free Tel:* 800-225-3362 *Web Site:* www.hmhco.com, pg 115

Saint-Jean, Marie-Claire, Guy Saint-Jean Editeur Inc, 3440 Blvd Industriel, Laval, QC H7L 4R9, Canada *Tel:* 450-663-1777 *Fax:* 450-663-6666 *E-mail:* info@saint-jeanediteur.com *Web Site:* www.saint-jeanediteur.com, pg 498

Saint-Jean, Nicole, Guy Saint-Jean Editeur Inc, 3440 Blvd Industriel, Laval, QC H7L 4R9, Canada *Tel:* 450-663-1777 *Fax:* 450-663-6666 *E-mail:* info@saint-jeanediteur.com *Web Site:* www.saint-jeanediteur.com, pg 498

Saint-Laurent, Marthe, Beliveau Editeur, 920, rue Jean-Neveu, Longueuil, QC J4G 2M1, Canada *Tel:* 450-679-1933; 514-253-0403 *Fax:* 450-679-6648 *E-mail:* info@beliveauediteur.com *Web Site:* www.beliveauediteur.com, pg 472

Sakai, Miss Takako, Price World Publishing, 3971 Hoover Rd, Suite 77, Columbus, OH 43123-2839 *Toll Free Tel:* 888-234-6896 *Fax:* 216-803-0350 *E-mail:* info@priceworldpublishing.com *Web Site:* www.priceworldpublishing.com, pg 196

Sakalenka, Elvira, Mountain n' Air Books, 2947-A Honolulu Ave, La Crescenta, CA 91214 *Tel:* 818-248-9345 *Toll Free Tel:* 800-446-9696 *Toll Free Fax:* 800-303-5578 *Web Site:* www.mountain-n-air.com, pg 160

Sakamoto, Dawn, Watermark Publishing, 1088 Bishop St, Suite 310, Honolulu, HI 96813 *Tel:* 808-587-7766 *Toll Free Tel:* 866-900-BOOK (900-2665) *Fax:* 808-521-3461 *E-mail:* info@bookshawaii.net *Web Site:* www.bookshawaii.net, pg 267

Sakoian, Carol, Scholastic International, 557 Broadway, New York, NY 10012 *Tel:* 212-343-6100; 646-330-5288 (intl cust serv) *Toll Free Tel:* 800-SCHOLASTIC (800-724-6527) *Fax:* 646-837-7878 *E-mail:* international@scholastic.com, pg 218

Sakowski, Carolyn, John F Blair Publisher, 1406 Plaza Dr, Winston-Salem, NC 27103 *Tel:* 336-768-1374 *Toll Free Tel:* 800-222-9796 *Fax:* 336-768-9194 *Web Site:* www.blairpub.com, pg 39

Sakuda, Takashi, Kodansha USA Inc, 451 Park Ave S, 7th fl, New York, NY 10016 *Tel:* 917-322-6200 *Fax:* 212-935-6929 *E-mail:* info@kodansha-usa.com *Web Site:* www.kodanshausa.com, pg 132

Salane, Jeffrey, Simon & Schuster Children's Publishing, 1230 Avenue of the Americas, New York, NY 10020 *Tel:* 212-698-7000 *Web Site:* KIDS.SimonandSchuster.com; TEEN.SimonandSchuster.com; simonandschuster.net; simonandschuster.biz, pg 225

Salayi, Jill, Workman Publishing Co Inc, 225 Varick St, 9th fl, New York, NY 10014-4381 *Tel:* 212-254-5900 *Toll Free Tel:* 800-722-7202 *Fax:* 212-254-8098 *E-mail:* info@workman.com *Web Site:* www.workman.com, pg 275

Salazar, Kat, Red Wheel/Weiser/Conari, 65 Parker St, Suite 7, Newburyport, MA 01950 *Tel:* 978-465-0504 *Toll Free Tel:* 800-423-7087 (orders) *Fax:* 978-465-0243 *E-mail:* info@rwwbooks.com *Web Site:* www.redwheelweiser.com, pg 206

Salazar, Wesley, Plume, 375 Hudson St, New York, NY 10014 *Tel:* 212-366-2000 *Fax:* 212-366-2666 *E-mail:* online@penguinputnam.com *Web Site:* www.penguinputnam.com; us.penguingroup.com, pg 193

Salek, Tina, Playwrights Guild of Canada, 401 Richmond St W, Suite 350, Toronto, ON M5V 3A8, Canada *Tel:* 416-703-0201 *Fax:* 416-703-0059 *E-mail:* info@playwrightsguild.ca *Web Site:* www.playwrightsguild.ca, pg 616

Salerno, Carey, Alice James Books, 114 Prescott St, Farmington, ME 04938 *Tel:* 207-778-7071 *Fax:* 207-778-7766 *E-mail:* info@alicejamesbooks.org *Web Site:* alicejamesbooks.org, pg 8

Sales, Bethany, Nicholas Brealey Publishing, 20 Park Plaza, Suite 610, Boston, MA 02116 *Tel:* 617-523-3801 *Toll Free Tel:* 888-BREALEY (273-2539) *Fax:* 617-523-3708 *E-mail:* info@nicholasbrealey.com *Web Site:* www.nicholasbrealey.com, pg 45

Saletan, Rebecca, Riverhead Books (Hardcover), 375 Hudson St, New York, NY 10014 *Tel:* 212-366-2000 *E-mail:* online@penguinputnam.com *Web Site:* www.penguinputnam.com; us.penguingroup.com, pg 209

Salicup, Jim, Papercutz, 160 Broadway, E Wing, Suite 700, New York, NY 10038 *Tel:* 646-559-4681 *Toll Free Tel:* 800-886-1223 *Fax:* 212-643-1545 *E-mail:* papercutz@papercutz.com *Web Site:* www.papercutz.com, pg 181

Salisbury, Leila W, University Press of Mississippi, 3825 Ridgewood Rd, Jackson, MS 39211-6492 *Tel:* 601-432-6205 *Toll Free Tel:* 800-737-7788 (orders & cust serv) *Fax:* 601-432-6217 *E-mail:* press@mississippi.edu *Web Site:* www.upress.state.ms.us, pg 262

Salk, Judy, Elsevier Engineering Information (Ei), 360 Park Ave S, New York, NY 10010-1710 *Tel:* 212-989-5800 *Toll Free Tel:* 800-221-1044 *Fax:* 212-633-6380 *E-mail:* eicustomersupport@elsevier.com *Web Site:* www.ei.org, pg 81

Salo, Gay, Piano Press, 1425 Ocean Ave, Suite 5, Del Mar, CA 92014 *Tel:* 619-884-1401 *Fax:* 858-755-1104 *E-mail:* pianopress@pianopress.com *Web Site:* www.pianopress.com, pg 191

Salome, Adam, The Harvard Common Press, 535 Albany St, Boston, MA 02118 *Tel:* 617-423-5803 *Toll Free Tel:* 888-657-3755 *Fax:* 617-695-9794 *E-mail:* orders@harvardcommonpress.com; info@harvardcommonpress.com *Web Site:* www.harvardcommonpress.com, pg 107

Salomon, Jake, Caribe Betania Editores, PO Box 141000, Nashville, TN 37214-1000 *Tel:* 615-902-1893 *Fax:* 615-883-9376 *Web Site:* www.caribebetania.com, pg 50

Salomons, Elizabeth, Pacific Educational Press, c/o University of British Columbia, Faculty of Education, 411-2389 Health Sciences Mall, Vancouver, BC V6T 1Z4, Canada *Tel:* 604-822-5385 *Fax:* 604-822-6603 *E-mail:* pep.admin@ubc.ca; pep.sales@ubc.ca *Web Site:* www.pacificedpress.educ.ubc.ca, pg 494

Salser, Mark R, National Book Co, PO Box 8795, Portland, OR 97207-8795 *Tel:* 503-228-6345 *Fax:* 810-885-5811 *E-mail:* info@eralearning.com *Web Site:* www.eralearning.com, pg 163

Saltz, Carole, Teachers College Press, 1234 Amsterdam Ave, New York, NY 10027 *Tel:* 212-678-3929 *Toll Free Tel:* 800-575-6566 *Fax:* 212-678-4149; 802-864-7626 *E-mail:* tcpress@tc.columbia.edu; tcp.orders@aidcvt.com (orders) *Web Site:* www.teacherscollegepress.com, pg 241

Saltzman, Glenn, Georgetown University Press, 3240 Prospect St NW, Suite 250, Washington, DC 20007 *Tel:* 202-687-5889 (busn) *Fax:* 202-687-6340 (edit) *E-mail:* gupress@georgetown.edu *Web Site:* press.georgetown.edu, pg 96

Salva, Richard, Crystal Clarity Publishers, 14618 Tyler Foote Rd, Nevada City, CA 95959 *Tel:* 530-478-7600 *Toll Free Tel:* 800-424-1055 *Fax:* 530-478-7610 *E-mail:* clarity@crystalclarity.com *Web Site:* www.crystalclarity.com, pg 68

Salvador, Vanda, Paulines Editions, 5610 rue Beaubien est, Montreal, QC H1T 1X5, Canada *Tel:* 514-253-5610 *Fax:* 514-253-1907 *E-mail:* fsp-paulines@videotron.ca *Web Site:* www.editions.paulines.qc.ca, pg 494

Salvatore, Laurea, Oxford University Press USA, 198 Madison Ave, New York, NY 10016 *Tel:* 212-726-6000 *Toll Free Tel:* 800-451-7556 (orders); 800-445-9714 (cust serv) *Fax:* 919-677-1303 *E-mail:* custserv.us@oup.com *Web Site:* www.oup.com/us, pg 179

Salvatore, Ruth, Ucross Foundation Residency Program, 30 Big Red Lane, Clearmont, WY 82835 *Tel:* 307-737-2291 *Fax:* 307-737-2322 *E-mail:* info@ucross.org *Web Site:* www.ucrossfoundation.org, pg 733

Salzman, Rachel, W W Norton & Company Inc, 500 Fifth Ave, New York, NY 10110-0017 *Tel:* 212-354-5500 *Toll Free Tel:* 800-233-4830 (orders & cust serv) *Fax:* 212-869-0856 *Toll Free Fax:* 800-458-6515 *Web Site:* www.wwnorton.com, pg 171

Salzman, Richard, Salzman International, 1751 Charles Ave, Arcata, CA 95521 *Tel:* 415-285-8267; 212-997-0115 (NY) *Fax:* 707-822-5500 *Web Site:* www.salzint.com, pg 584

Salzmann, Oliver, Madison Press Books, 155 Edward St, Suite 1, Aurora, ON L4G 1W3, Canada *Tel:* 905-841-9300 *E-mail:* info@madisonpressbooks.com *Web Site:* www.madisonpressbooks.com, pg 491

Sametz, Peter, Saskatchewan Arts Board, 1355 Broad St, Regina, SK S4R 7V1, Canada *Tel:* 306-787-4056 *Toll Free Tel:* 800-667-7526 (Saskatchewan only) *Fax:* 306-787-4199 *E-mail:* info@artsboard.sk.ca *Web Site:* www.artsboard.sk.ca, pg 618

Sammon, Patricia, H E Francis Award Short Story Competition, UAH Huntsville Dept of English, Morton Hall 222, Huntsville, AL 35899 *Web Site:* www.uah.edu/la/departments/english/h-e-francis-contest, pg 687

Samms, June, Kids Can Press Ltd, 25 Dockside Dr, Toronto, ON M5A 0B5, Canada *Tel:* 416-479-7000 *Toll Free Tel:* 800-265-0884 *Fax:* 416-960-5437 *E-mail:* info@kidscan.com; customerservice@kidscan.com *Web Site:* www.kidscanpress.com; www.kidscanpress.ca, pg 489

Samuels, Gary, Metropolitan Lithographers Association Inc, c/o Pictorial Offset, 111 Amor Ave, Carlstadt, NJ 07072 *Tel:* 201-935-7100, pg 610

San Filippo, Karen, Association of Manitoba Book Publishers, 100 Arthur St, Suite 404, Winnipeg, MB R3B 1H3, Canada *Tel:* 204-947-3335 *Fax:* 204-956-4689 *E-mail:* ambp@mts.net *Web Site:* ambp.ca, pg 599

Sanborn, Geoffrey, The Melville Society, Johns Hopkins University Press, PO Box 19966, Baltimore, MD 21211-0966 *Web Site:* melvillesociety.org, pg 610

Sanborn, Kat, Llewellyn Publications, 2143 Wooddale Dr, Woodbury, MN 55125 *Tel:* 651-291-1970 *Toll Free Tel:* 800-843-6666 *Fax:* 651-291-1908 *E-mail:* publicity@llewellyn.com *Web Site:* www.llewellyn.com, pg 142

Sanchez, Irene, Liturgy Training Publications, 3949 S Racine Ave, Chicago, IL 60609-2523 *Tel:* 773-579-4900 *Toll Free Tel:* 800-933-1800 (US & CN only orders) *Fax:* 773-579-4929 *Toll Free Fax:* 800-933-7094 (US & CN only orders) *E-mail:* orders@ltp.org *Web Site:* www.ltp.org, pg 141

Sanchez, Wanda, Mary Ann Liebert Inc, 140 Huguenot St, 3rd fl, New Rochelle, NY 10801-5215 *Tel:* 914-740-2100 *Toll Free Tel:* 800-654-3237 *Fax:* 914-740-2101 *E-mail:* info@liebertpub.com *Web Site:* www.liebertonline.com, pg 139

Sand, Michael, Harry N Abrams Inc, 115 W 18 St, 6th fl, New York, NY 10011 *Tel:* 212-206-7715 *Toll Free Tel:* 800-345-1359 *Fax:* 212-519-1210 *E-mail:* abrams@abramsbooks.com *Web Site:* www.abramsbooks.com, pg 3

Sandell, Katie, Howard Books, 216 Centerview Dr, Suite 303, Brentwood, TN 37027 *Tel:* 615-873-2080 *Fax:* 615-370-3834 *E-mail:* howardbooks@simonandschuster.com (info) *Web Site:* www.howardpublishing.com, pg 116

Sanders, Bob, Mundania Press LLC, 6457 Glenway Ave, Suite 109, Cincinnati, OH 45211-5222 *Tel:* 513-490-2822 *Fax:* 513-598-9220 *Toll Free Fax:* 888-460-4752 *E-mail:* books@mundania.com; inquiry@mundania.com *Web Site:* www.mundania.com, pg 161

Sanders, Keith P PhD, Frank Luther Mott-Kappa Tau Alpha Research Award, University of Missouri, School of Journalism, 76 Gannett Hall, Columbia, MO 65211-1200 *Tel:* 573-882-7685 *Fax:* 573-884-1720 *E-mail:* umcjourkta@missouri.edu *Web Site:* www.kappataualpha.org, pg 709

Sanders, Meredith K, Goose River Press, 3400 Friendship Rd, Waldoboro, ME 04572-6337 *Tel:* 207-832-6665 *E-mail:* gooseriverpress@roadrunner.com *Web Site:* gooseriverpress.com, pg 98

Sanders, Michael, Alpha Books, 375 Hudson St, New York, NY 10014 *Tel:* 212-366-2000, pg 9

Sanders, Patricia, Manitoba Arts Council, 525-93 Lombard Ave, Winnipeg, MB R3B 3B1, Canada *Tel:* 204-945-2237 *Toll Free Tel:* 866-994-2787 *Fax:* 204-945-5925 *E-mail:* info@artscouncil.mb.ca *Web Site:* artscouncil.mb.ca, pg 609

Sanders, Ray, Purple House Press, 8100 US Hwy 62 E, Cynthiana, KY 41031 *Tel:* 859-235-9970 *Web Site:* www.purplehousepress.com, pg 200

Sanders, Rob, Greystone Books Ltd, 343 Railway St, Suite 201, Vancouver, BC V6A 1A4, Canada *Tel:* 604-875-1550 *Fax:* 604-875-1556 *E-mail:* info@greystonebooks.com *Web Site:* www.greystonebooks.com, pg 486

Sanders, Victoria, Victoria Sanders & Associates LLC, 241 Avenue of the Americas, Suite 11-H, New York, NY 10014 *Tel:* 212-633-8811 *Fax:* 212-633-0525 *E-mail:* queriesvsa@gmail.com *Web Site:* www.victoriasanders.com, pg 571

Sanders-Foege, Erica, Oxmoor House, 2100 Lakeshore Dr, Birmingham, AL 35209 *Tel:* 205-445-6000 *Toll Free Tel:* 800-366-4712; 888-891-8935 (cust serv); 800-765-6400 (orders) *Web Site:* www.oxmoorhouse.com, pg 179

Sandler, Neil, Rosenthal Represents, 3850 Eddingham Ave, Calabasas, CA 91302 *Tel:* 818-222-5445 *Fax:* 818-222-5650 *E-mail:* eliselicenses@earthlink.net *Web Site:* www.rosenthalrepresents.com, pg 584

Sandoz, Claude, Galaxy Press, 7051 Hollywood Blvd, Suite 200, Hollywood, CA 90028 *Tel:* 323-466-7815 *Toll Free Tel:* 877-8GALAXY (842-5299) *E-mail:* customers@galaxypress.com; info@galaxypress.com *Web Site:* www.galaxypress.com, pg 93

Sandri, Gianna, Crown Publishing Group, c/o Penguin Random House Inc, 1745 Broadway, New York, NY 10019 *Tel:* 212-782-9000 *Toll Free Tel:* 888-264-1745 *Fax:* 212-940-7408 *E-mail:* crownosm@penguinrandomhouse.com *Web Site:* crownpublishing.com, pg 68

Sands, Katharine, Sarah Jane Freymann Literary Agency LLC, 59 W 71 St, Suite 9-B, New York, NY 10023 *Tel:* 212-362-9277 *E-mail:* submissions@sarahjanefreymann.com *Web Site:* www.sarahjanefreymann.com, pg 553

Sanfilippo, Tony, The Pennsylvania State University Press, University Support Bldg 1, Suite C, 820 N University Dr, University Park, PA 16802-1003 *Tel:* 814-865-1327 *Toll Free Tel:* 800-326-9180 *Fax:* 814-863-1408 *Toll Free Fax:* 877-778-2665 *E-mail:* info@psupress.org *Web Site:* www.psupress.org, pg 188

Scagnetti, Jack, Jack Scagnetti Talent & Literary Agency, 5136 Vineland Ave, North Hollywood, CA 91601 *Tel:* 818-762-3871, pg 571

Scalerbio, Elena, ASM Press, 1752 "N" St NW, Washington, DC 20036-2904 *Tel:* 202-737-3600 *Toll Free Tel:* 800-546-2416 *Fax:* 202-942-9342 *E-mail:* books@asmusa.org *Web Site:* estore.asm.org, pg 25

Scalissi, Linda, 3 Seas Literary Agency, PO Box 8571, Madison, WI 53708 *Tel:* 608-834-9317, pg 577

Scanlan, Brian, Thieme Medical Publishers Inc, 333 Seventh Ave, 18th fl, New York, NY 10001 *Tel:* 212-760-0888 *Toll Free Tel:* 800-782-3488 *Fax:* 212-947-1112 *E-mail:* customerservice@thieme.com *Web Site:* www.thieme.com, pg 245

Scanlan, Peggy, Health Forum Inc, 155 N Wacker Dr, Suite 400, Chicago, IL 60606 *Tel:* 312-893-6800 *Toll Free Tel:* 800-242-2626 *Fax:* 312-422-4500 *E-mail:* hfcustsvc@healthforum.com *Web Site:* www.ahaonlinestore.com; www.healthforum.com, pg 109

Scanlon, Elizabeth, Honickman First Book Prize, University of the Arts (UARTS), Hamilton Hall, 320 S Broad St, Rm 313, Philadelphia, PA 19102-4901 *Tel:* 215-717-6801 *Fax:* 215-717-6805 *Web Site:* www.aprweb.org, pg 692

Scanlon, Jim, IHS Jane's, 110 N Royal St, Suite 200, Alexandria, VA 22314-1651 *Tel:* 703-683-3700 *Toll Free Tel:* 800-824-0768 (sales) *Fax:* 703-836-0297 *Toll Free Fax:* 800-836-0297 *E-mail:* customercare@ihs.com *Web Site:* www.ihs.com, pg 119

Scanlon, Sally, The Intrepid Traveler, 152 Staltonstall Pkwy (rear entrance), East Haven, CT 06512 *Tel:* 203-469-0214 *E-mail:* admin@intrepidtraveler.com *Web Site:* www.intrepidtraveler.com, pg 125

Scarpulla, Zina, Bloom's Literary Criticism, 132 W 31 St, 17th fl, New York, NY 10001 *Toll Free Tel:* 800-322-8755 *Toll Free Fax:* 800-678-3633 *E-mail:* custserv@factsonfile.com *Web Site:* www.infobasepublishing.com, pg 39

Scarpulla, Zina, Chelsea House Publishers, 132 W 31 St, 17th fl, New York, NY 10001 *Tel:* 212-967-8800 *Toll Free Tel:* 800-322-8755 *Fax:* 917-339-0325 *Toll Free Fax:* 800-678-3633 *E-mail:* custserv@factsonfile.com *Web Site:* www.infobasepublishing.com; www.infobaselearning.com, pg 56

Scarpulla, Zina, Facts On File, 132 W 31 St, 17th fl, New York, NY 10001 *Tel:* 212-967-8800 *Toll Free Tel:* 800-322-8755 *Toll Free Fax:* 800-678-3633 *E-mail:* custserv@factsonfile.com *Web Site:* infobasepublishing.com, pg 85

Scarpulla, Zina, Ferguson Publishing, 132 W 31 St, 17th fl, New York, NY 10001 *Tel:* 212-967-8800 *Toll Free Tel:* 800-322-8755 *Fax:* 917-339-0323 *Toll Free Fax:* 800-678-3633 *E-mail:* custserv@factsonfile.com *Web Site:* infobasepublishing.com, pg 88

Scartz-Montesano, Sara, Teton NewMedia, 90 E Simpson, Suite 110, Jackson, WY 83001 *Tel:* 307-732-0028 *Toll Free Tel:* 877-306-9793 *Fax:* 307-734-0841 *E-mail:* sales@tetonnm.com *Web Site:* www.tetonnm.com, pg 243

Scavotto, Marie, Sinauer Associates Inc, 23 Plumtree Rd, Sunderland, MA 01375 *Tel:* 413-549-4300 *Fax:* 413-549-1118 *E-mail:* publish@sinauer.com; orders@sinauer.com *Web Site:* www.sinauer.com, pg 226

Schade, Ms Rachel, Asta Publications LLC, PO Box 1735, Stockbridge, GA 30281 *Tel:* 678-814-1320 *Toll Free Tel:* 800-482-4190 *Fax:* 678-814-1370 *E-mail:* info@astapublications.com *Web Site:* www.astapublications.com, pg 26

Schademann, Beth, The Electrochemical Society (ECS), 65 S Main St, Bldg D, Pennington, NJ 08534-2839 *Tel:* 609-737-1902 *Fax:* 609-737-2743 *E-mail:* publications@electrochem.org; customerservice@electrochem.org *Web Site:* www.electrochem.org, pg 80

Schaefer, Peggy, Ideals Publications, a Guideposts Co, 6100 Tower Circle, Suite 210, Franklin, TN 37067 *Tel:* 615-932-7600 *Toll Free Tel:* 800-586-2572 (cust serv) *Fax:* 615-781-1447 *Web Site:* www.idealsbooks.com, pg 118

Schaefer, Rita, Houghton Mifflin Harcourt, 222 Berkeley St, Boston, MA 02116 *Tel:* 617-351-5000 *Toll Free Tel:* 800-225-5425 (K-12 educ materials); 800-323-9540 (assessment materials); 877-219-1537 (SkillsTutor); 888-242-6747 (Destination; Earobics; Edmark; Learning Village; Riverdeep); 800-225-3362 (Houghton Mifflin Harcourt Trade & Reference Publishers) *Toll Free Fax:* 800-269-5232 *E-mail:* customerservice@hmhpub.com *Web Site:* www.hmhco.com, pg 115

Schaeffer, Dave, Simon & Schuster, Inc, 1230 Avenue of the Americas, New York, NY 10020 *Tel:* 212-698-7000 *Fax:* 212-698-7007 *E-mail:* firstname.lastname@simonandschuster.com *Web Site:* www.simonandschuster.com, pg 226

Schaffer, Holly, The University of Arizona Press, 1510 E University Blvd, Tucson, AZ 85721 *Tel:* 520-621-1441 *Toll Free Tel:* 800-426-3797 (orders) *Fax:* 520-621-8899 *Toll Free Fax:* 800-426-3797 *E-mail:* uap@uapress.arizona.edu *Web Site:* www.uapress.arizona.edu, pg 255

Schanck, Denise, Garland Science Publishing, 711 Third Ave, 8th fl, New York, NY 10017 *Tel:* 212-216-7800; 212-281-4487 *Fax:* 212-947-3027 *E-mail:* science@garland.com *Web Site:* www.garlandscience.com, pg 95

Schang, Scott, Environmental Law Institute, 1730 "M" St NW, Suite 700, Washington, DC 20036 *Tel:* 202-939-3800 *Toll Free Tel:* 800-433-5120 *Fax:* 202-939-3868 *E-mail:* law@eli.org *Web Site:* www.eli.org, pg 83

Schaps, Eric, Center for the Collaborative Classroom, 1250 53 St, Suite 3, Emeryville, CA 94608 *Tel:* 510-533-0213 *Toll Free Tel:* 800-666-7270 *Fax:* 510-464-3670 *E-mail:* info@collaborativeclassroom.org; clientsupport@collaborativeclassroom.org *Web Site:* www.collaborativeclassroom.org, pg 53

Scharf, Dan, The Jim Henson Co, 1416 N La Brea Ave, Hollywood, CA 90028 *Tel:* 323-802-1500 *Fax:* 323-802-1825 *Web Site:* www.henson.com, pg 127

Scharlatt, Elisabeth, Algonquin Books, 400 Silver Cedar Ct, Suite 300, Chapel Hill, NC 27514-1585 *Tel:* 919-967-0108 *Fax:* 919-933-0272 *E-mail:* inquiry@algonquin.com *Web Site:* www.workman.com/algonquin, pg 8

Schaub, Patricia, University of Texas at Austin, Creative Writing Program, Dept of English, PAR 108, One University Sta, Mailcode B5000, Austin, TX 78712-1164 *Tel:* 512-471-5132; 512-471-4991 *Fax:* 512-471-4909 *Web Site:* www.utexas.edu/cola/depts/english/creative-writing, pg 664

Schaub, Prof Thomas, Chris O'Malley Fiction Prize, University of Wisconsin, 6193 Helen C White Hall, English Dept, 600 N Park St, Madison, WI 53706 *Tel:* 608-263-0566 *E-mail:* madisonrevw@gmail.com *Web Site:* www.english.wisc.edu/madisonreview, pg 715

Schaub, Prof Thomas, Phyllis Smart-Young Poetry Prize, University of Wisconsin, 6193 Helen C White Hall, English Dept, 600 N Park St, Madison, WI 53706 *Tel:* 608-263-0566 *E-mail:* madisonrevw@gmail.com *Web Site:* www.english.wisc.edu/madisonreview, pg 739

Schauer, David A, National Council on Radiation Protection & Measurements (NCRP), 7910 Woodmont Ave, Suite 400, Bethesda, MD 20814-3095 *Tel:* 301-657-2652 *Toll Free Tel:* 800-229-2652 *Fax:* 301-907-8768 *E-mail:* ncrppubs@ncrponline.org *Web Site:* www.ncrponline.org; www.ncrppublications.org, pg 164

Schaumberg, Jean, The Tony Hillerman Prize, 1063 Willow Way, Santa Fe, NM 87507 *Tel:* 505-471-1565 *E-mail:* wordharvest@wordharvest.com *Web Site:* www.wordharvest.com, pg 692

Schaumberg, Jean, Tony Hillerman Writers Conference, 1063 Willow Way, Santa Fe, NM 87507 *Tel:* 505-471-1565 *E-mail:* wordharvest@wordharvest.com *Web Site:* www.wordharvest.com, pg 656

Schaut, Diane, University of Notre Dame Press, 310 Flanner Hall, Notre Dame, IN 46556 *Tel:* 574-631-6346 *Fax:* 574-631-8148 *E-mail:* undpress@nd.edu *Web Site:* www.undpress.nd.edu, pg 258

Schear, Adam, DeFiore and Company, LLC, 47 E 19 St, 3rd fl, New York, NY 10003 *Tel:* 212-925-7744 *Fax:* 212-925-9803 *E-mail:* submissions@defioreandco.com; info@defioreandco.com *Web Site:* www.defioreandco.com, pg 548

Scheel, Joanne, CWA/SCA Canada, 2200 Prince of Wales Dr, Suite 301, Ottawa, ON K2E 6Z9, Canada *Tel:* 613-820-9777 *Toll Free Tel:* 877-486-4292 *Fax:* 613-820-8188 *E-mail:* info@cwa-scacanada.ca *Web Site:* www.cwa-scacanada.ca, pg 604

Scheeler, Rev Jeff OFM, Franciscan Media, 28 W Liberty St, Cincinnati, OH 45202 *Tel:* 513-241-5615 *Toll Free Tel:* 800-488-0488 *Fax:* 513-241-0399 *E-mail:* books@americancatholic.org *Web Site:* www.americancatholic.org; www.franciscanmedia.org, pg 92

Scheer, Andy, Hartline Literary Agency LLC, 123 Queenston Dr, Pittsburgh, PA 15235 *Web Site:* www.hartlineliterary.com, pg 556

Scheffers, Todd, Goodheart-Willcox Publisher, 18604 W Creek Dr, Tinley Park, IL 60477-6243 *Tel:* 708-687-5000 *Toll Free Tel:* 800-323-0440 *Fax:* 708-468-8692 *Toll Free Fax:* 888-409-3900 *E-mail:* custserv@g-w.com; orders@g-w.com *Web Site:* www.g-w.com, pg 98

Scheibling, Kathleen, Worldwide Library, 225 Duncan Mill Rd, Don Mills, ON M3B 3K9, Canada *Tel:* 416-445-5860 *Toll Free Tel:* 888-432-4879 *Fax:* 416-445-8655; 416-445-8736 *E-mail:* customerservice@harlequin.com *Web Site:* www.harlequin.com, pg 505

Scheiner, C J, C J Scheiner Books, 275 Linden Blvd, Suite B-2, Brooklyn, NY 11226 *Tel:* 718-469-1089 *Fax:* 718-469-1089, pg 534

Schenck, Gina, The Career Press Inc, 12 Parish Dr, Wayne, NJ 07470 *Tel:* 201-848-0310 *Toll Free Tel:* 800-CAREER-1 (227-3371) *Fax:* 201-848-1727 *E-mail:* sales@careerpress.com *Web Site:* www.careerpress.com, pg 50

Schenck, Linny, ASCSA Publications, American School of Classical Studies at Athens, 6-8 Charlton St, Princeton, NJ 08540-5232 *Tel:* 609-683-0800 *Fax:* 609-924-0578 *Web Site:* www.ascsa.edu.gr/publications, pg 24

Schenck, Nancy, Central Recovery Press (CRP), 3321 N Buffalo Dr, Suite 275, Las Vegas, NV 89129 *Tel:* 702-868-5830 *Fax:* 702-868-5831 *E-mail:* info@centralrecovery.com *Web Site:* centralrecoverypress.com, pg 54

Schenck, Robert B, F A Davis Co, 1915 Arch St, Philadelphia, PA 19103 *Tel:* 215-568-2270; 215-440-3001 *Toll Free Tel:* 800-523-4049 *Fax:* 215-568-5065; 215-440-3016 *E-mail:* info@fadavis.com; orders@fadavis.com *Web Site:* www.fadavis.com, pg 71

Schenk, Pamela W, Golden Cylindar Awards, 8281 Pine Lake Rd, Denver, NC 28037 *Tel:* 201-523-6042 *Fax:* 201-523-6048 *E-mail:* gaa@gaa.org *Web Site:* www.gaa.org, pg 689

Schenk, Pamela W, Gravure Association of the Americas Inc, 8281 Pine Lake Rd, Denver, NC 28037 *Tel:* 201-523-6042 *Fax:* 201-523-6048 *E-mail:* gaa@gaa.org *Web Site:* www.gaa.org, pg 606

Schepp, Brad, Waterside Productions Inc, 2055 Oxford Ave, Cardiff, CA 92007 *Tel:* 760-632-9190 *Fax:* 760-632-9295 *E-mail:* admin@waterside.com *Web Site:* www.waterside.com, pg 579

Scherer, Rebecca, Jane Rotrosen Agency LLC, 318 E 51 St, New York, NY 10022 *Tel:* 212-593-4330 *Fax:* 212-935-6985 *Web Site:* janerotrosen.com, pg 571

Scherman, Nosson, Mesorah Publications Ltd, 4401 Second Ave, Brooklyn, NY 11232 *Tel:* 718-921-9000 *Toll Free Tel:* 800-637-6724 *Fax:* 718-680-1875 *E-mail:* artscroll@mesorah.com *Web Site:* www.artscroll.com; www.mesorah.com, pg 155

Schiavone, Dr James, Schiavone Literary Agency Inc, 236 Trails End, West Palm Beach, FL 33413-2135 *Tel:* 561-966-9294 *Fax:* 561-966-9294 *E-mail:* profschia@aol.com *Web Site:* www.publishersmarketplace.com/members/profschia, pg 571

Schiekofer, Rich, Newspaper Association of America (NAA), 4401 Wilson Blvd, Suite 900, Arlington, VA 22203 *Tel:* 571-366-1000 *Web Site:* www.naa.org, pg 614

Schiff, Robbin, Random House Publishing Group, 1745 Broadway, New York, NY 10019 *Toll Free Tel:* 800-200-3552 *Web Site:* atrandom.com, pg 204

Schiffer, Nancy, Cornell Maritime Press Inc, 4880 Lower Valley Rd, Atglen, PA 19310 *Tel:* 610-593-1777 *Fax:* 610-593-2002 *E-mail:* info@schifferbooks.com *Web Site:* www.cmptp.com, pg 63

Schiffer, Nancy, Schiffer Publishing Ltd, 4880 Lower Valley Rd, Atglen, PA 19310 *Tel:* 610-593-1777 *Fax:* 610-593-2002 *E-mail:* schifferbk@aol.com *Web Site:* www.schifferbooks.com, pg 217

Schiffer, Pete, Cornell Maritime Press Inc, 4880 Lower Valley Rd, Atglen, PA 19310 *Tel:* 610-593-1777 *Fax:* 610-593-2002 *E-mail:* info@schifferbooks.com *Web Site:* www.cmptp.com, pg 63

Schiffer, Pete, Schiffer Publishing Ltd, 4880 Lower Valley Rd, Atglen, PA 19310 *Tel:* 610-593-1777 *Fax:* 610-593-2002 *E-mail:* schifferbk@aol.com *Web Site:* www.schifferbooks.com, pg 217

Schiller, David, Workman Publishing Co Inc, 225 Varick St, 9th fl, New York, NY 10014-4381 *Tel:* 212-254-5900 *Toll Free Tel:* 800-722-7202 *Fax:* 212-254-8098 *E-mail:* info@workman.com *Web Site:* www.workman.com, pg 275

Schiller, Howard, Hollywood Film Archive, 8391 Beverly Blvd, Los Angeles, CA 90048 *Tel:* 323-655-4968 *Web Site:* hfarchive.com, pg 113

Schivley, Caryl, Merriam-Webster Inc, 47 Federal St, Springfield, MA 01102 *Tel:* 413-734-3134 *Toll Free Tel:* 800-828-1880 (orders & cust serv) *Fax:* 413-731-5979 (sales) *E-mail:* support@merriam-webster.com *Web Site:* www.merriam-webster.com, pg 155

Schlachter, Gail PhD, Reference Service Press, 5000 Windplay Dr, Suite 4, El Dorado Hills, CA 95762-9319 *Tel:* 916-939-9620 *Fax:* 916-939-9626 *E-mail:* info@rspfunding.com *Web Site:* www.rspfunding.com, pg 207

Schlager, Neil, Schlager Group Inc, 325 N Saint Paul, Suite 3425, Dallas, TX 75201 *Toll Free Tel:* 888-416-5727 *Fax:* 214-347-9469 *E-mail:* info@schlagergroup.com *Web Site:* www.schlagergroup.com, pg 218

Schleifer, Lisa, SDP Publishing Solutions LLC, 36 Captain's Way, East Bridgewater, MA 02333 *Tel:* 617-775-0656 *Web Site:* www.sdppublishingsolutions.com, pg 534

Schlesinger, Edward, Gallery Books, 1230 Avenue of the Americas, New York, NY 10020 *Toll Free Tel:* 800-456-6798 *Fax:* 212-698-7284 *E-mail:* consumer.customerservice@simonandschuster.com *Web Site:* www.simonsays.com, pg 94

Schlesinger, Jeff, Barringer Publishing, 3259 Sundance Circle, Naples, FL 34109 *Tel:* 239-514-7364 *E-mail:* schlesadv@gmail.com *Web Site:* www.barringerpublishing.com, pg 31

Schlessiger, Charles, Brandt & Hochman Literary Agents Inc, 1501 Broadway, Suite 2310, New York, NY 10036 *Tel:* 212-840-5760 *Fax:* 212-840-5776 *Web Site:* brandthochman.com, pg 544

Schley, Jim, Dorset Prize, PO Box 1767, North Adams, MA 01247 *Tel:* 413-664-9611 *Fax:* 413-664-9711 *E-mail:* info@tupelopress.org *Web Site:* www.tupelopress.org, pg 682

Schley, Jim, Tupelo Press Inc, PO Box 1767, North Adams, MA 01247 *Tel:* 413-664-9611 *Fax:* 413-664-9711 *E-mail:* info@tupelopress.org *Web Site:* www.tupelopress.org, pg 250

Schley, Jim, Tupelo Press Poetry Contest for First or Second Books of Poetry, PO Box 1767, North Adams, MA 01247 *Tel:* 413-664-9611 *Fax:* 413-664-9711 *E-mail:* info@tupelopress.org *Web Site:* www.tupelopress.org, pg 733

Schley, Jim, Tupelo Press Snowbound Series Chapbook Award, PO Box 1767, North Adams, MA 01247 *Tel:* 413-664-9611 *Fax:* 413-664-9711 *E-mail:* info@tupelopress.org *Web Site:* www.tupelopress.org, pg 733

Schlichte, Dave, Amicus, PO Box 1329, Mankato, MN 56002 *Tel:* 507-388-9357 *Fax:* 507-388-1779 *E-mail:* info@amicuspublishing.us; orders@amicuspublishing.us *Web Site:* www.amicuspublishing.us, pg 17

Schline, John, Penguin Group (USA) LLC, a Penguin Random House company, 375 Hudson St, New York, NY 10014 *Tel:* 212-366-2000 *Toll Free Tel:* 800-847-5515 (inside sales); 800-631-8571 (cust serv) *Fax:* 212-366-2666; 607-775-4829 (inside sales) *E-mail:* online@us.penguingroup.com *Web Site:* www.penguin.com; us.penguingroup.com, pg 186

Schlorff, Brittany, Pauline Books & Media, 50 St Paul's Ave, Boston, MA 02130 *Tel:* 617-522-8911 *Toll Free Tel:* 800-876-4463 (orders); 800-836-9723 (cust serv) *Fax:* 617-541-9805 *E-mail:* editorial@paulinemedia.com (ms submissions); orderentry@pauline.org (cust serv) *Web Site:* www.pauline.org, pg 184

Schmalz, Wendy, Wendy Schmalz Agency, 402 Union St, Unit 831, Hudson, NY 12534 *Tel:* 518-672-7697 *E-mail:* wendy@schmalzagency.com *Web Site:* www.schmalzagency.com, pg 572

Schmid, Oona, American Anthropological Association (AAA), 2300 Clarendon Blvd, Suite 1301, Arlington, VA 22201 *Tel:* 703-528-1902 *Fax:* 703-528-3546 *Web Site:* www.aaanet.org, pg 10

Schmidt, Alfred, Windsor Books, 260 Montauk Hwy, Suite 5, Bayshore, NY 11706 *Tel:* 631-665-6688 *Toll Free Tel:* 800-321-5934 *E-mail:* windsor.books@att.net *Web Site:* www.windsorpublishing.com, pg 273

Schmidt, Anja, Oxmoor House, 2100 Lakeshore Dr, Birmingham, AL 35209 *Tel:* 205-445-6000 *Toll Free Tel:* 800-366-4712; 888-891-8935 (cust serv); 800-765-6400 (orders) *Web Site:* www.oxmoorhouse.com, pg 179

Schmidt, Eric A, University of California Press, 2120 Berkeley Way, Berkeley, CA 94704-1012 *Tel:* 510-642-4247 *Fax:* 510-643-7127 *E-mail:* askucp@ucpress.edu (books); customerservice@ucpressjournals.com *Web Site:* www.ucpress.edu, pg 255

Schmidt, Harold D, Harold Schmidt Literary Agency, 415 W 23 St, Suite 6-F, New York, NY 10011 *Tel:* 212-727-7473, pg 572

Schmidt, Helga, Steerforth Press, 45 Lyme Rd, Suite 208, Hanover, NH 03755-1222 *Tel:* 603-643-4787 *Fax:* 603-643-4788 *E-mail:* info@steerforth.com *Web Site:* www.steerforth.com, pg 234

Schmidt, Jeff, Windsor Books, 260 Montauk Hwy, Suite 5, Bayshore, NY 11706 *Tel:* 631-665-6688 *Toll Free Tel:* 800-321-5934 *E-mail:* windsor.books@att.net *Web Site:* www.windsorpublishing.com, pg 273

Schmidt, Jocelyn, Penguin Young Readers Group, 345 Hudson St, New York, NY 10014 *Tel:* 212-366-2000 *E-mail:* online@penguinputnam.com *Web Site:* www.penguinputnam.com; us.penguingroup.com, pg 188

Schmidt, Kathleen, The Perseus Books Group, 387 Park Ave S, 12th fl, New York, NY 10016 *Tel:* 212-340-8100 *Toll Free Tel:* 800-343-4499 (cust serv) *Fax:* 212-340-8105 *Web Site:* www.perseusbooksgroup.com, pg 189

Schmidt, Kathleen, Running Press Book Publishers, 2300 Chestnut St, Philadelphia, PA 19103-4399 *Tel:* 215-567-5080 *Toll Free Tel:* 800-343-4499 (cust serv & orders) *Fax:* 215-568-2919 *Toll Free Fax:* 800-453-2884 (cust serv & orders) *E-mail:* perseus.promos@perseusbooks.com *Web Site:* www.runningpress.com, pg 212

Schmidt, Randy, University of British Columbia Press, 2029 West Mall, Vancouver, BC V6T 1Z2, Canada *Tel:* 604-822-5959 *Toll Free Tel:* 877-377-9378 *Fax:* 604-822-6083 *Toll Free Fax:* 800-668-0821 *E-mail:* frontdesk@ubcpress.ca *Web Site:* www.ubcpress.ca, pg 502

Schmierer-Lee, Melonie PhD, Gorgias Press LLC, PO Box 6939, Piscataway, NJ 08854-6939 *Tel:* 732-885-8900 *Fax:* 732-885-8908 *E-mail:* helpdesk@gorgiaspress.com *Web Site:* www.gorgiaspress.com, pg 99

Schmitz, Doug, Redleaf Press, 10 Yorkton Ct, St Paul, MN 55117 *Tel:* 651-641-0508 *Toll Free Tel:* 800-423-8309 *Toll Free Fax:* 800-641-0115 *Web Site:* www.redleafpress.org, pg 206

Schmitz, Elisabeth, Grove Atlantic Inc, 154 W 14 St, 12th fl, New York, NY 10011 *Tel:* 212-614-7850 *Toll Free Tel:* 800-521-0178 *Fax:* 212-614-7886 *E-mail:* info@groveatlantic.com *Web Site:* www.groveatlantic.com, pg 101

Schneider, Bill, Etruscan Press, Wilkes University, 84 W South St, Wilkes-Barre, PA 18766 *Tel:* 570-408-4546 *Fax:* 570-408-3333 *E-mail:* books@etruscanpress.org *Web Site:* www.etruscanpress.org, pg 84

Schneider, Deborah, Gelfman/Schneider/ICM, 850 Seventh Ave, Suite 903, New York, NY 10019 *Tel:* 212-245-1993 *Fax:* 212-245-8678 *E-mail:* mail@gelfmanschneider.com *Web Site:* gelfmanschneider.com, pg 553

Schneider, James, Princeton University Press, 41 William St, Princeton, NJ 08540-5237 *Tel:* 609-258-4900 *Toll Free Tel:* 800-777-4726 (orders) *Fax:* 609-258-6305 *Toll Free Fax:* 800-999-1958 *E-mail:* orders@cpfsinc.com *Web Site:* press.princeton.edu, pg 197

Schneider, Naomi, University of California Press, 2120 Berkeley Way, Berkeley, CA 94704-1012 *Tel:* 510-642-4247 *Fax:* 510-643-7127 *E-mail:* askucp@ucpress.edu (books); customerservice@ucpressjournals.com *Web Site:* www.ucpress.edu, pg 255

Schneider, Sam, Encounter Books, 900 Broadway, Suite 601, New York, NY 10003 *Tel:* 212-871-6310 *Toll Free Tel:* 800-786-3839 *Fax:* 212-871-6311 *E-mail:* publicity@encounterbooks.com *Web Site:* www.encounterbooks.com, pg 82

Schneider, Sara, Chronicle Books LLC, 680 Second St, San Francisco, CA 94107 *Tel:* 415-537-4200 *Toll Free Tel:* 800-759-0190 (cust serv) *Fax:* 415-537-4460 *Toll Free Fax:* 800-858-7787 (orders); 800-286-9471 (cust serv) *E-mail:* frontdesk@chroniclebooks.com *Web Site:* www.chroniclebooks.com, pg 58

Schneider, Saundra K, Inter-University Consortium for Political & Social Research (ICPSR), 330 Packard St, Ann Arbor, MI 48104 *Tel:* 734-647-5000 *Fax:* 734-647-8200 *E-mail:* netmail@icpsr.umich.edu *Web Site:* www.icpsr.umich.edu, pg 123

Schneider, Wendy Caruso, New York Academy of Sciences, 7 World Trade, 40th fl, 250 Greenwich St, New York, NY 10007-2157 *Tel:* 212-298-8600 *Toll Free Tel:* 800-843-6927 *Fax:* 212-298-3644 *E-mail:* nyas@nyas.org; publications@nyas.org *Web Site:* www.nyas.org, pg 169

Schnell, Judith, Stackpole Books, 5067 Ritter Rd, Mechanicsburg, PA 17055 *Tel:* 717-796-0411 *Toll Free Tel:* 800-732-3669 *Fax:* 717-796-0412 *Web Site:* www.stackpolebooks.com, pg 233

Schnitzer, Adam, The Perseus Books Group, 387 Park Ave S, 12th fl, New York, NY 10016 *Tel:* 212-340-8100 *Toll Free Tel:* 800-343-4499 (cust serv) *Fax:* 212-340-8105 *Web Site:* www.perseusbooksgroup.com, pg 189

Schnitzler, Alex, Keller Media Inc, 578 Washington Blvd, No 745, Marina del Rey, CA 90292 *Toll Free Tel:* 800-278-8706 *E-mail:* query@kellermedia.com *Web Site:* kellermedia.com/query, pg 559

Schoenwald, Mark, Thomas Nelson, 501 Nelson Place, Nashville, TN 37214 *Tel:* 615-889-9000 *Toll Free Tel:* 800-251-4000 *Fax:* 615-902-1548 *E-mail:* publicity@thomasnelson.com *Web Site:* www.thomasnelson.com, pg 245

Schoenwald, Mark, Tommy Nelson, 501 Nelson Place, Nashville, TN 37214 *Tel:* 615-889-9000; 615-902-1485 (cust serv) *Toll Free Tel:* 800-251-4000 *Fax:* 615-391-5225 *Web Site:* www.tommynelson.com, pg 247

Schofield, William, Paul Dry Books, 1616 Walnut St, Suite 808, Philadelphia, PA 19103 *Tel:* 215-231-9939 *Fax:* 215-231-9942 *E-mail:* editor@pauldrybooks.com *Web Site:* www.pauldrybooks.com, pg 184

Scholl, Roger, Crown Publishing Group, c/o Penguin Random House Inc, 1745 Broadway, New York, NY 10019 *Tel:* 212-782-9000 *Toll Free Tel:* 888-264-1745 *Fax:* 212-940-7408 *E-mail:* crownosm@penguinrandomhouse.com *Web Site:* crownpublishing.com, pg 68

Scholl, Steve, White Cloud Press, 300 E Hersey St, Suite 11, Ashland, OR 97520 *Tel:* 541-488-6415 *Toll Free Tel:* 800-380-8286 *Fax:* 541-482-7708 *E-mail:* info@whitecloudpress.com *Web Site:* www.whitecloudpress.com, pg 270

Schoo, Julie, National Press Club (NPC), 529 14 St NW, 13th fl, Washington, DC 20045 *Tel:* 202-662-7500 *Fax:* 202-662-7569 *E-mail:* infocenter@npcpress.org *Web Site:* www.press.org, pg 613

Schooler, Marta, HarperCollins General Books Group, 195 Broadway, New York, NY 10007 *Tel:* 212-207-7000 *Web Site:* www.harpercollins.com, pg 105

Schor, Lynda, Hamilton Stone Editions, PO Box 43, Maplewood, NJ 07040 *Tel:* 973-378-8361 *E-mail:* hstone@hamiltonstone.org *Web Site:* www.hamiltonstone.org, pg 104

Schorr, Sari, Levy Creative Management LLC, 425 E 58 St, Suite 37F, New York, NY 10022 *Tel:* 212-687-6463 *Fax:* 212-661-4839 *E-mail:* info@levycreative.com *Web Site:* www.levycreative.com, pg 584

Schott, Abby, Allen A Knoll Publishers, 200 W Victoria St, Santa Barbara, CA 93101-3627 *Tel:* 805-564-3377 *Toll Free Tel:* 800-777-7623 *Fax:* 805-966-6657 *E-mail:* bookinfo@knollpublishers.com *Web Site:* www.knollpublishers.com, pg 132

Schotter, Prof Richard, Boston University, 236 Bay State Rd, Boston, MA 02215 *Tel:* 617-353-2510 *Fax:* 617-353-3653 *E-mail:* crwr@bu.edu *Web Site:* www.bu.edu/writing, pg 659

Schrader, Christopher, Xlibris Corp, 1663 Liberty Dr, Suite 200, Bloomington, IN 47403 *Toll Free Tel:* 888-795-4274 *Fax:* 610-915-0294 *E-mail:* info@xlibris.com *Web Site:* www.xlibris.com, pg 277

Schrader, Jenny, Kay Snow Literary Contest, 2108 Buck St, West Linn, OR 97068 *Tel:* 503-305-6729 *Fax:* 503-344-6174 *E-mail:* wilwrite@willamettewriters.com *Web Site:* www.willamettewriters.com, pg 729

Schrader, Jenny, Willamette Writers, 2108 Buck St, West Linn, OR 97068 *Tel:* 503-305-6729 *Fax:* 503-344-6174 *E-mail:* wilwrite@willamettewriters.com *Web Site:* www.willamettewriters.com, pg 621

Schrader, Jenny, Willamette Writers' Conference, 2108 Buck St, West Linn, OR 97068 *Tel:* 503-305-6729 *Fax:* 503-344-6174 *E-mail:* wilwrite@willamettewriters.com *Web Site:* www.willamettewriters.com, pg 656

Schrader, Rebecca, The MIT Press, 55 Hayward St, Cambridge, MA 02142 *Tel:* 617-253-5255 *Toll Free Tel:* 800-207-8354 (orders) *Fax:* 617-258-6779; 617-577-1545 (orders) *Web Site:* mitpress.mit.edu, pg 158

Schramer, Leslie, Oriental Institute Publications, 1155 E 58 St, Chicago, IL 60637 *Tel:* 773-702-5967 *Fax:* 773-702-9853 *E-mail:* oi-publications@uchicago.edu; oi-museum@uchicago.edu; oi-administration@uchicago.edu *Web Site:* oi.uchicago.edu, pg 177

Schrank, Ben, Razorbill, 345 Hudson St, New York, NY 10014 *Tel:* 212-366-2000, pg 205

Schrefer, Sally, Elsevier, Health Sciences Division, 1600 John F Kennedy Blvd, Suite 1800, Philadelphia, PA 19103-2899 *Tel:* 215-239-3900 *Toll Free Tel:* 800-523-1649 *Fax:* 215-239-3990 *Web Site:* www.elsevierhealth.com, pg 81

Schreiber, Laura, Disney-Hyperion Books, 1101 Flower St, Glendale, CA 91201 *Web Site:* books.disney.com, pg 74

Schreiber, Sarah, Glitterati Inc, 630 Ninth Ave, Suite 603, New York, NY 10036 *Tel:* 212-362-9119 *Fax:* 646-607-4433 *E-mail:* info@glitteratiincorporated.com *Web Site:* glitteratiincorporated.com, pg 97

Schreier, Carl, Homestead Publishing, Box 193, Moose, WY 83012-0193 *Tel:* 307-733-6248 *Fax:* 307-733-6248 *E-mail:* orders@homesteadpublishing.net *Web Site:* www.homesteadpublishing.net, pg 114

Schrier, Eric, Reader's Digest General Books, Reader's Digest Rd, Pleasantville, NY 10570-7000 *Tel:* 914-238-1000 *Toll Free Tel:* 800-304-2807 (cust serv) *Fax:* 914-244-7436, pg 205

Schroeder, Ben, Centering Corp, 7230 Maple St, Omaha, NE 68134 *Tel:* 402-553-1200 *Toll Free Tel:* 866-218-0101 *Fax:* 402-553-0507 *E-mail:* orders@centering.org *Web Site:* www.centering.org, pg 54

Schroeder, Dave, B&H Publishing Group, One Lifeway Plaza, Nashville, TN 37234-0114 *Tel:* 615-251-2520 *Fax:* 615-251-5004 *Web Site:* www.bhpublishinggroup.com, pg 30

Schroeder, Meredith, American Quilter's Society, 5801 Kentucky Dam Rd, Paducah, KY 42003-9323 *Tel:* 270-898-7903 *Toll Free Tel:* 800-626-5420 (orders) *Fax:* 270-898-1173 *E-mail:* orders@americanquilter.com *Web Site:* www.americanquilter.com, pg 15

Schroeder, Sandi, Schroeder Indexing Services, 23 Camilla Pink Ct, Bluffton, SC 29909 *Tel:* 843-705-9779 *E-mail:* sanindex@schroederindexing.com *Web Site:* www.schroederindexing.com, pg 534

Schroeder, Tim, Beyond Words Publishing Inc, 20827 NW Cornell Rd, Suite 500, Hillsboro, OR 97124-9808 *Tel:* 503-531-8700 *Fax:* 503-531-8773 *E-mail:* info@beyondword.com *Web Site:* www.beyondword.com, pg 36

Schryer, Chantal, Canadian Museum of History (Musee Canadien de l'Histoire), 100 Laurier St, Gatineau, QC K1A 0M8, Canada *Tel:* 819-776-7000 *Toll Free Tel:* 800-555-5621 (North American orders only) *Fax:* 819-776-7187 *Web Site:* www.historymuseum.ca, pg 475

Schubart, William H, Magic Hill Press LLC, 144 Magic Hill Rd, Hinesburg, VT 05461 *Tel:* 802-482-3287 *E-mail:* MagicHillPress@gmail.com *Web Site:* www.MagicHillPress.com, pg 508

Schube, Peter, The Jim Henson Co, 1416 N La Brea Ave, Hollywood, CA 90028 *Tel:* 323-802-1500 *Fax:* 323-802-1825 *Web Site:* www.henson.com, pg 127

Schubert, Lori, Quebec Writers' Federation (QWF), 1200 Atwater Ave, Suite 3, Westmount, QC H3Z 1X4, Canada *Tel:* 514-933-0878 *E-mail:* info@qwf.org *Web Site:* www.qwf.org, pg 617

Schubert, Lori, QWF Literary Awards, 1200 Atwater Ave, Suite 3, Westmount, QC H3Z 1X4, Canada *Tel:* 514-933-0878 *E-mail:* info@qwf.org *Web Site:* www.qwf.org, pg 722

Schuetz, Richard, University of New Mexico, One University of New Mexico, Albuquerque, NM 87131-0001 *Tel:* 505-277-2346; 505-272-7777 (cust serv) *Toll Free Tel:* 800-249-7737 (orders only) *Fax:* 505-277-3343; 505-272-7778 (cust serv) *Toll Free Fax:* 800-622-8667 (orders only) *E-mail:* unmpress@unm.edu; custserv@upress.unm.edu (order dept) *Web Site:* unmpress.com, pg 258

Schuh, Lynda, University of Illinois Press, 1325 S Oak St, MC-566, Champaign, IL 61820-6903 *Tel:* 217-333-0950 *Fax:* 217-244-8082 *E-mail:* uipress@uillinois.edu; journals@uillinois.edu *Web Site:* www.press.uillinois.edu, pg 256

Schuler, Rebecca Murray, University Press of Kansas, 2502 Westbrooke Circle, Lawrence, KS 66045-4444 *Tel:* 785-864-4154; 785-864-4155 (orders) *Fax:* 785-864-4586 *E-mail:* upress@ku.edu; upkorders@ku.edu (orders) *Web Site:* www.kansaspress.ku.edu, pg 261

Schulman, Scott, Rodale Inc, 400 S Tenth St, Emmaus, PA 18098 *Tel:* 610-967-5171 *Web Site:* www.rodaleinc.com, pg 210

Schulman, Susan, Susan Schulman Literary Agency LLC, 454 W 44 St, New York, NY 10036 *Tel:* 212-713-1633 *Fax:* 212-581-8830, pg 572

Schultz, Brandon, Glitterati Inc, 630 Ninth Ave, Suite 603, New York, NY 10036 *Tel:* 212-362-9119 *Fax:* 646-607-4433 *E-mail:* info@glitteratiincorporated.com *Web Site:* glitteratiincorporated.com, pg 97

Schultz, Jonathan D, Concordia Publishing House, 3558 S Jefferson Ave, St Louis, MO 63118-3968 *Tel:* 314-268-1000; 314-268-1268 (bookshop) *Toll Free Tel:* 800-325-3040 (cust serv) *Toll Free Fax:* 800-490-9889 (cust serv) *E-mail:* order@cph.org *Web Site:* www.cph.org, pg 62

Schultz, Patricia, The Mellen Poetry Press, 240 Portage Rd, Lewiston, NY 14092 *Tel:* 716-754-2266; 716-754-1400 (mktg); 716-754-2788 (order fulfillment) *Fax:* 716-754-4056; 716-754-1860 (fulfillment) *E-mail:* cservice@mellenpress.com *Web Site:* www.mellenpress.com, pg 154

Schultz, Thom, Group Publishing Inc, 1515 Cascade Ave, Loveland, CO 80538 *Tel:* 970-669-3836 *Toll Free Tel:* 800-447-1070 *Fax:* 970-292-4373 *E-mail:* info@group.com *Web Site:* www.group.com, pg 101

Schulz, Andrea, Penguin Group (USA) LLC, a Penguin Random House company, 375 Hudson St, New York, NY 10014 *Tel:* 212-366-2000 *Toll Free Tel:* 800-847-5515 (inside sales); 800-631-8571 (cust serv) *Fax:* 212-366-2666; 607-775-4829 (inside sales) *E-mail:* online@us.penguingroup.com *Web Site:* www.penguin.com; us.penguingroup.com, pg 186

Schulz, Andrea, Viking, 375 Hudson St, New York, NY 10014 *Tel:* 212-366-2000 *E-mail:* online@penguinputnam.com *Web Site:* www.penguinputnam.com; us.penguingroup.com, pg 265

Schulze, Karin, Harry N Abrams Inc, 115 W 18 St, 6th fl, New York, NY 10011 *Tel:* 212-206-7715 *Toll Free Tel:* 800-345-1359 *Fax:* 212-519-1210 *E-mail:* abrams@abramsbooks.com *Web Site:* www.abramsbooks.com, pg 3

Schumacher, George, Penguin Young Readers Group, 345 Hudson St, New York, NY 10014 *Tel:* 212-366-2000 *E-mail:* online@penguinputnam.com *Web Site:* www.penguinputnam.com; us.penguingroup.com, pg 188

Schumacher, Peg, RAND Corp, 1776 Main St, Santa Monica, CA 90407-2138 *Tel:* 310-393-0411 *Fax:* 310-393-4818 *Web Site:* www.rand.org, pg 203

Schumacher, Ryan, Texas State Historical Association, Stovall Hall 175, 1400 W Highland St, Denton, TX 76203 *Tel:* 940-369-5200 *Fax:* 940-369-5248 *Web Site:* www.tshaonline.org, pg 243

Schuman, Patricia Glass, Neal-Schuman Publishers Inc, 100 William St, Suite 2004, New York, NY 10038 *Tel:* 212-925-8650 *Toll Free Tel:* 866-NS-BOOKS (672-6657) *Fax:* 212-219-8916 *Toll Free Fax:* 877-231-6980 *E-mail:* info@neal-schuman.com *Web Site:* www.neal-schuman.com, pg 166

Schumer, Fran, Joelle Delbourgo Associates Inc, 101 Park St, Montclair, NJ 07042 *Tel:* 973-773-0836 (call only during standard business hours) *Web Site:* www.delbourgo.com, pg 548

Schuna, Jo Anne, The Schuna Group Inc, 1503 Briarknoll Dr, Arden Hills, MN 55112 *Tel:* 651-631-8480 *Web Site:* www.schunagroup.com, pg 584

Schuneman, Robert, ECS Publishing Corp, 615 Concord St, Framingham, MA 01702 *Tel:* 508-620-7400 *Fax:* 508-620-7401 *E-mail:* office@ecspub.com *Web Site:* ecspublishing.com, pg 79

Schustack, Margie, John Wiley & Sons Inc Professional/Trade Group, 111 River St, Hoboken, NJ 07030 *Tel:* 201-748-6000 *Toll Free Tel:* 800-225-5945 (cust serv) *Fax:* 201-748-6088 *E-mail:* info@wiley.com *Web Site:* www.wiley.com, pg 272

Schuster, Jennifer, NAL, 375 Hudson St, New York, NY 10014 *Tel:* 212-366-2000 *E-mail:* online@penguinputnam.com *Web Site:* www.penguinputnam.com; us.penguingroup.com, pg 162

Schutt, David L, SAE (Society of Automotive Engineers International), 400 Commonwealth Dr, Warrendale, PA 15096-0001 *Tel:* 724-776-4841; 724-776-4970 (outside US & CN) *Toll Free Tel:* 877-606-7323 (cust serv) *Fax:* 724-776-0790 (cust serv) *E-mail:* publications@sae.org; customerservice@sae.org *Web Site:* www.sae.org, pg 213

Schwab, Ann, Black Rabbit Books, 515 N Riverfront Dr, Suite 200, Mankato, MN 56001 *Tel:* 507-388-1609 *Fax:* 507-388-1364 *E-mail:* info@blackrabbitbooks.com; orders@blackrabbitbooks.com *Web Site:* www.blackrabbitbooks.com, pg 38

Schwabinger, Jennifer, Penguin Group (USA) LLC Sales, 375 Hudson St, New York, NY 10014 *Tel:* 212-366-2000 *E-mail:* online@penguinputnam.com *Web Site:* us.penguingroup.com, pg 186

Schwacke, Susanna Sharp, Bottom Dog Press, 813 Seneca Ave, Huron, OH 44839 *Tel:* 419-433-3573 *Fax:* 419-616-3966 *Web Site:* smithdocs.net, pg 43

Schwartz, Adam, The Career Press Inc, 12 Parish Dr, Wayne, NJ 07470 *Tel:* 201-848-0310 *Toll Free Tel:* 800-CAREER-1 (227-3371) *Fax:* 201-848-1727 *E-mail:* sales@careerpress.com *Web Site:* www.careerpress.com, pg 50

Schwartz, Andrew E, A E Schwartz & Associates, 13 Conversation Way, Stoughton, MA 02072 *Tel:* 781-436-5033 *E-mail:* info@aeschwartz.com *Web Site:* aeschwartz.com, pg 572

Schwartz, Anne, Random House Children's Books, 1745 Broadway, New York, NY 10019 *Tel:* 212-782-9000 *Toll Free Tel:* 800-200-3552 *Fax:* 212-782-9452 *Web Site:* randomhousekids.com, pg 203

Schwartz, Barry L, Jewish Publication Society, 2100 Arch St, Philadelphia, PA 19103 *Tel:* 215-832-0600 *Toll Free Tel:* 800-234-3151 *Fax:* 215-568-2017 *Web Site:* www.jps.org, pg 126

Schwartz, Eric, Columbia University Press, 61 W 62 St, New York, NY 10023 *Tel:* 212-459-0600 *Toll Free Tel:* 800-944-8648 *Fax:* 212-459-3678 *E-mail:* cup_book@columbia.edu (orders & cust serv) *Web Site:* cup.columbia.edu, pg 61

Schwartz, J Alex, Northern Illinois University Press, 2280 Bethany Rd, DeKalb, IL 60115 *Tel:* 815-753-1826; 815-753-1075 *Fax:* 815-753-1845 *Web Site:* www.niupress.niu.edu, pg 171

Schwartz, Jenny Wesselmann, AMACOM Books, 1601 Broadway, New York, NY 10019-7420 *Tel:* 212-586-8100 *Toll Free Tel:* 800-250-5308 (cust serv) *Fax:* 212-903-8083; 518-891-2372 (orders) *E-mail:* pubs_cust_serv@amanet.org *Web Site:* www.amacombooks.org, pg 9

Schwartz, Marilyn, University of California Press, 2120 Berkeley Way, Berkeley, CA 94704-1012 *Tel:* 510-642-4247 *Fax:* 510-643-7127 *E-mail:* askucp@ucpress.edu (books); customerservice@ucpressjournals.com *Web Site:* www.ucpress.edu, pg 255

Schwartz, Matt, Penguin Random House Inc, 1745 Broadway, New York, NY 10019 *Tel:* 212-782-9000 *Toll Free Tel:* 800-726-0600 *Web Site:* www.randomhouse.com, pg 187

Schwartz, Matt, Random House Publishing Group, 1745 Broadway, New York, NY 10019 *Toll Free Tel:* 800-200-3552 *Web Site:* atrandom.com, pg 204

Schwartz, Rick, HarperCollins Publishers, 195 Broadway, New York, NY 10007 *Tel:* 212-207-7000 *Fax:* 212-207-7145 *Web Site:* www.harpercollins.com, pg 106

Schwartz, Russ, Thomas Nelson, 501 Nelson Place, Nashville, TN 37214 *Tel:* 615-889-9000 *Toll Free Tel:* 800-251-4000 *Fax:* 615-902-1548 *E-mail:* publicity@thomasnelson.com *Web Site:* www.thomasnelson.com, pg 245

Schwartz, Sheryl, The Perseus Books Group, 387 Park Ave S, 12th fl, New York, NY 10016 *Tel:* 212-340-8100 *Toll Free Tel:* 800-343-4499 (cust serv) *Fax:* 212-340-8105 *Web Site:* www.perseusbooksgroup.com, pg 189

Schwartz, Steven, Sarah Jane Freymann Literary Agency LLC, 59 W 71 St, Suite 9-B, New York, NY 10023 *Tel:* 212-362-9277 *E-mail:* submissions@sarahjanefreymann.com *Web Site:* www.sarahjanefreymann.com, pg 553

Schwartz, Susan, Dutton, 375 Hudson St, New York, NY 10014 *Tel:* 212-366-2000 *Fax:* 212-366-2262 *E-mail:* online@penguinputnam.com *Web Site:* www.penguinputnam.com; us.penguingroup.com, pg 78

Schwartz, Susan, The Editors Circle, 462 Grove St, Montclair, NJ 07043 *Tel:* 973-783-5082 *E-mail:* query@theeditorscircle.com *Web Site:* www.theeditorscircle.com, pg 525

Schwartzman, Jill, Dutton, 375 Hudson St, New York, NY 10014 *Tel:* 212-366-2000 *Fax:* 212-366-2262 *E-mail:* online@penguinputnam.com *Web Site:* www.penguinputnam.com; us.penguingroup.com, pg 78

Schwarz, Helena, Susan Rabiner Literary Agency Inc, 315 W 39 St, Suite 1501, New York, NY 10018-3907 *Web Site:* RabinerLit.com, pg 569

Schwarze, Diane, Book Peddlers, 18330 Minnetonka Blvd, Deephaven, MN 55391 *Tel:* 952-544-1154 *Fax:* 206-339-6913 *E-mail:* bookpeddlers@aol.com *Web Site:* www.bookpeddlers.com, pg 42

Scinta, Sam, Fulcrum Publishing Inc, 4690 Table Mountain Dr, Suite 100, Golden, CO 80403 *Tel:* 303-277-1623 *Toll Free Tel:* 800-992-2908 *Fax:* 303-279-7111 *Toll Free Fax:* 800-726-7112 *E-mail:* info@fulcrumbooks.com; orders@fulcrumbooks.com *Web Site:* www.fulcrumbooks.com, pg 93

Sciortino, Joseph, Editions Mediaspaul, 3965, blvd Henri-Bourassa E, Montreal, QC H1H 1L1, Canada *Tel:* 514-322-7341 *Fax:* 514-322-4281 *E-mail:* editeur@mediaspaul.ca *Web Site:* mediaspaul.ca, pg 482

Scognamiglio, John, Kensington Publishing Corp, 119 W 40 St, New York, NY 10018 *Tel:* 212-407-1500 *Toll Free Tel:* 800-221-2647 *Fax:* 212-935-0699 *Web Site:* www.kensingtonbooks.com, pg 130

Scollans, Colleen, Oxford University Press USA, 198 Madison Ave, New York, NY 10016 *Tel:* 212-726-6000 *Toll Free Tel:* 800-451-7556 (orders); 800-445-9714 (cust serv) *Fax:* 919-677-1303 *E-mail:* custserv.us@oup.com *Web Site:* www.oup.com/us, pg 179

Scordato, Ellen, The Stonesong Press LLC, 270 W 39 St, No 201, New York, NY 10018 *Tel:* 212-929-4600 *E-mail:* editors@stonesong.com *Web Site:* www.stonesong.com, pg 575

Scott, Angel, CODiE Awards, 1090 Vermont Ave NW, 6th fl, Washington, DC 20005-4095 *Tel:* 202-289-7442 *Fax:* 202-289-7097 *E-mail:* info@siia.net *Web Site:* www.siia.net, pg 678

Scott, Ardy M, Twilight Times Books, PO Box 3340, Kingsport, TN 37664-0340 *Tel:* 423-323-0183 *Fax:* 423-323-0183 *E-mail:* publisher@twilighttimes.com *Web Site:* www.twilighttimesbooks.com, pg 251

Scott, Craig R, Heritage Books Inc, 5810 Ruatan St, Berwyn Heights, MD 20740 *Toll Free Tel:* 800-876-6103 *Toll Free Fax:* 800-876-6103 *E-mail:* orders@heritagebooks.com; submissions@heritagebooks.com *Web Site:* www.heritagebooks.com, pg 110

Scott, Debra Leigh, Hidden River Arts Playwriting Award, PO Box 63927, Philadelphia, PA 19147 *Tel:* 610-764-0813 *E-mail:* hiddenriverarts@gmail.com *Web Site:* www.hiddenriverarts.org, pg 692

Scott, Debra Leigh, The William Van Wert Memorial Fiction Award, PO Box 63927, Philadelphia, PA 19147 *Tel:* 610-764-0813 *E-mail:* hiddenriverarts@gmail.com *Web Site:* www.hiddenriverarts.org, pg 733

Scott, Katherine, Canadian Council on Social Development (Conseil canadien de developpement social), 190 O'Connor St, Suite 100, Ottawa, ON K2P 2R3, Canada *Tel:* 613-236-8977 *Fax:* 613-236-2750 *E-mail:* info@ccsd.ca *Web Site:* www.ccsd.ca, pg 475

Scott, Lisa W, Periodical & Book Association of America Inc (PBAA), 481 Eighth Ave, Suite 526, New York, NY 10001 *Tel:* 212-563-6502 *Fax:* 212-563-4098 *Web Site:* www.pbaa.net, pg 616

Scott, Marianne, The Canadian Writers' Foundation Inc (La Fondation des Ecrivains Canadiens), PO Box 13281, Kanata Sta, Ottawa, ON K2K 1X4, Canada *Tel:* 613-256-6937 *Fax:* 613-256-5457 *E-mail:* info@canadianwritersfoundation.org *Web Site:* www.canadianwritersfoundation.org, pg 623

Scott, Michael, Aptara Inc, 3110 Fairview Park Dr, Suite 900, Falls Church, VA 22042 *Tel:* 703-352-0001 *E-mail:* info@aptaracorp.com *Web Site:* www.aptaracorp.com, pg 520

Scott, Nathalie, Gotham Literary Agency, 170 E 83 St, New York, NY 10028 *Tel:* 212-249-2615, pg 555

Scott, Richard, Dorland Health, 4 Choke Cherry Rd, 2nd fl, Rockville, MD 20850 *Tel:* 301-354-2000 *Toll Free Tel:* 855-225-5341 *Fax:* 301-287-2535 *E-mail:* customer@decisionhealth.com *Web Site:* www.dorlandhealth.com, pg 75

Scott-Wiley, Dewey, Trustus Playwrights' Festival, 520 Lady St, Columbia, SC 29201 *Tel:* 803-254-9732 *Fax:* 803-771-9153 *E-mail:* trustus@trustus.org *Web Site:* www.trustus.org, pg 732

Scriver, Julie, Goose Lane Editions, 500 Beaverbrook Ct, Suite 330, Fredericton, NB E3B 5X4, Canada *Tel:* 506-450-4251 *Toll Free Tel:* 888-926-8377 *Fax:* 506-459-4991 *E-mail:* info@gooselane.com; customerservice@gooselane.com *Web Site:* www.gooselane.com, pg 485

Scudder, Dean, Sinauer Associates Inc, 23 Plumtree Rd, Sunderland, MA 01375 *Tel:* 413-549-4300 *Fax:* 413-549-1118 *E-mail:* publish@sinauer.com; orders@sinauer.com *Web Site:* www.sinauer.com, pg 226

Scully, Kate, Northeastern Graphic Inc, 33 Crystal Bay Ct, Palm Coast, FL 32137 *Tel:* 386-246-9942 *E-mail:* contact@northeasterngraphic.com *Web Site:* www.northeasterngraphic.com, pg 531

Scurlock, Bill, Scurlock Publishing Co Inc, 1293 Myrtle Springs Rd, Texarkana, TX 75503 *Tel:* 903-832-4726 *Toll Free Tel:* 800-228-6389 (US & CN) *Fax:* 903-831-3177 *E-mail:* custserv@scurlockpublishing.com *Web Site:* muzzleloadermag.com; www.scurlockpublishing.com, pg 221

Scurlock, Linda, Scurlock Publishing Co Inc, 1293 Myrtle Springs Rd, Texarkana, TX 75503 *Tel:* 903-832-4726 *Toll Free Tel:* 800-228-6389 (US & CN) *Fax:* 903-831-3177 *E-mail:* custserv@scurlockpublishing.com *Web Site:* muzzleloadermag.com; www.scurlockpublishing.com, pg 221

Seager, Deb, Grove Atlantic Inc, 154 W 14 St, 12th fl, New York, NY 10011 *Tel:* 212-614-7850 *Toll Free Tel:* 800-521-0178 *Fax:* 212-614-7886 *E-mail:* info@groveatlantic.com *Web Site:* www.groveatlantic.com, pg 101

Searls, Hank, Hank Searls Authors Workshop, 4435 Holly Lane NW, Gig Harbor, WA 98335 *Tel:* 253-851-9896 *Fax:* 253-851-9897 *E-mail:* hanksearls@comcast.net, pg 655

Sears, Rebecca, AIGA, the professional association for design, 233 Broadway, 17th fl, New York, NY 10279 *Tel:* 212-807-1990 *Fax:* 212-807-1799 *E-mail:* general@aiga.org *Web Site:* www.aiga.org, pg 593

Sears, Rene, Prometheus Books, 59 John Glenn Dr, Amherst, NY 14228-2119 *Tel:* 716-691-0133 *Toll Free Tel:* 800-421-0351 *Fax:* 716-691-0137 *E-mail:* marketing@prometheusbooks.com; editorial@prometheusbooks.com *Web Site:* www.prometheusbooks.com, pg 199

Seaton, Ann, Northern California Independent Booksellers Association (NCIBA), The Presidio, 1007 General Kennedy Ave, San Francisco, CA 94129 *Tel:* 415-561-7686 *Fax:* 415-561-7685 *E-mail:* office@nciba.com *Web Site:* www.nciba.com, pg 614

Seaton, Sharon, University of Missouri-Kansas City, New Letters Weekend Writers Conference, College of Arts & Sciences, Continuing Education Div, 5300 Rockhill Rd, Kansas City, MO 64110 *Tel:* 816-235-2736 *Fax:* 816-235-5279 *Web Site:* www.umkc.edu, pg 663

Seaver, Kathleen, Berkley Books, 375 Hudson St, New York, NY 10014 *Tel:* 212-366-2000 *Fax:* 212-366-2666 *E-mail:* online@penguinputnam.com *Web Site:* www.penguinputnam.com; us.penguingroup.com, pg 35

Seaver, Kathleen, Berkley Publishing Group, 375 Hudson St, New York, NY 10014 *Tel:* 212-366-2000 *Fax:* 212-366-2385 *E-mail:* online@penguinputnam.com *Web Site:* us.penguingroup.com, pg 35

Secara, Andrea, Algora Publishing, 222 Riverside Dr, 16th fl, New York, NY 10025-6809 *Tel:* 212-678-0232 *Fax:* 212-666-3682 *E-mail:* editors@algora.com *Web Site:* www.algora.com, pg 8

Secara, Claudiu A, Algora Publishing, 222 Riverside Dr, 16th fl, New York, NY 10025-6809 *Tel:* 212-678-0232 *Fax:* 212-666-3682 *E-mail:* editors@algora.com *Web Site:* www.algora.com, pg 8

Seco, Nina S, Saint Nectarios Press, 10300 Ashworth Ave N, Seattle, WA 98133-9410 *Tel:* 206-522-4471 *Toll Free Tel:* 800-643-4233 *Fax:* 206-523-0550 *E-mail:* orders@stnectariospress.com *Web Site:* www.stnectariospress.com, pg 215

Secondari, Linda, Oxford University Press USA, 198 Madison Ave, New York, NY 10016 *Tel:* 212-726-6000 *Toll Free Tel:* 800-451-7556 (orders); 800-445-9714 (cust serv) *Fax:* 919-677-1303 *E-mail:* custserv.us@oup.com *Web Site:* www.oup.com/us, pg 179

Sedgeley, Carlton, Royce Carlton Inc, 866 United Nations Plaza, Suite 587, New York, NY 10017-1880 *Tel:* 212-355-7700 *Toll Free Tel:* 800-LECTURE (532-8873) *Fax:* 212-888-8659 *E-mail:* info@roycecarlton.com *Web Site:* www.roycecarlton.com, pg 588

Sedita, Francesco, Grosset & Dunlap, 345 Hudson St, New York, NY 10014 *Tel:* 212-366-2000 *Web Site:* www.penguinrandomhouse.com, pg 101

Sedita, Francesco, Price Stern Sloan, 345 Hudson St, New York, NY 10014 *Tel:* 212-366-2000 *E-mail:* online@penguinputnam.com *Web Site:* www.penguinputnam.com; us.penguingroup.com, pg 196

See, Sandy, University of Oklahoma Press, 2800 Venture Dr, Norman, OK 73069-8216 *Tel:* 405-325-2000 *Toll Free Tel:* 800-627-7377 (orders) *Fax:* 405-364-5798 (orders) *Toll Free Fax:* 800-735-0476 (orders) *E-mail:* presscs@ou.edu *Web Site:* www.oupress.com, pg 259

Seelen, Michael, Unveiled Media LLC, PO Box 930463, Verona, WI 53593 *Tel:* 707-986-8345 *Web Site:* www.unveiledmedia.com, pg 263

Seely, Steve, Balance Sports Publishing LLC, 195 Lucero Way, Portola Valley, CA 94028 *Tel:* 650-561-9586 *Fax:* 650-391-9850 *E-mail:* info@balancesportspublishing.com *Web Site:* www.balancesportspublishing.com, pg 30

Seepersad, Ravi, Bisk Education, 9417 Princess Palm Ave, Suite 400, Tampa, FL 33619 *Tel:* 813-621-6200 *Toll Free Tel:* 800-280-9718 (cust serv) *E-mail:* customerservice@bisk.com *Web Site:* www.bisk.com, pg 37

Seesequasis, Paul, Theytus Books Ltd, RR 2, Green Mountain Rd, Site 50, Comp 8, Lot 45, Penticton, BC V2A 6J7, Canada *Tel:* 250-493-7181 *Fax:* 250-493-5302 *E-mail:* order@theytus.com *Web Site:* www.theytus.com, pg 500

Segal, Jonathan, Alfred A Knopf/Everyman's Library, c/o Random House Inc, 1745 Broadway, New York, NY 10019 *Tel:* 212-751-2600 *Toll Free Tel:* 800-638-6460 *Fax:* 212-572-2593 *Web Site:* www.knopfdoubleday.com, pg 132

Segal, Joyce, Pippin Press, 229 E 85 St, New York, NY 10028 *Tel:* 212-288-4920 *Fax:* 908-237-2407, pg 192

Segal, Melissa, The Jim Henson Co, 1416 N La Brea Ave, Hollywood, CA 90028 *Tel:* 323-802-1500 *Fax:* 323-802-1825 *Web Site:* www.henson.com, pg 127

Segel, Brenda, HarperCollins General Books Group, 195 Broadway, New York, NY 10007 *Tel:* 212-207-7000 *Web Site:* www.harpercollins.com, pg 105

Seger, Rebecca, Oxford University Press USA, 198 Madison Ave, New York, NY 10016 *Tel:* 212-726-6000 *Toll Free Tel:* 800-451-7556 (orders); 800-445-9714 (cust serv) *Fax:* 919-677-1303 *E-mail:* custserv.us@oup.com *Web Site:* www.oup.com/us, pg 179

Sehlinger, Robert W, Menasha Ridge Press Inc, 2204 First Ave S, Suite 102, Birmingham, AL 35233 *Tel:* 205-322-0439 *Toll Free Tel:* 888-604-4537 *Fax:* 205-326-1012 *E-mail:* info@menasharidge.com *Web Site:* www.menasharidge.com, pg 154

Seibel, Susan, Materials Research Society, 506 Keystone Dr, Warrendale, PA 15086-7537 *Tel:* 724-779-3003 *Fax:* 724-779-8313 *E-mail:* info@mrs.org *Web Site:* www.mrs.org, pg 149

Seibold, Doug, Surrey Books, 1328 Greenleaf St, Evanston, IL 60202 *Tel:* 847-475-4457 *Toll Free Tel:* 800-326-4430 *Web Site:* agatepublishing.com/surrey, pg 238

Seidlitz, Lauri, Brush Education Inc, 6531 111 St, Edmonton, AB T6H 4R5, Canada *Tel:* 780-989-0910 *Toll Free Tel:* 855-283-0900 *Fax:* 780-989-0930 *Toll Free Fax:* 855-283-6947 *E-mail:* contact@brusheducation.ca *Web Site:* www.brusheducation.ca, pg 474

Seidman, Brian, NewSouth Books, 105 S Court St, Montgomery, AL 36104 *Tel:* 334-834-3556 *Fax:* 334-834-3557 *E-mail:* info@newsouthbooks.com *Web Site:* www.newsouthbooks.com, pg 169

Seidman, Erika, Farrar, Straus & Giroux, LLC, 18 W 18 St, New York, NY 10011 *Tel:* 212-741-6900 *E-mail:* fsg.publicity@fsgbooks.com *Web Site:* us.macmillan.com/fsg.aspx, pg 86

Seidman, Erika, Hill & Wang, 18 W 18 St, New York, NY 10011 *Tel:* 212-741-6900 *Fax:* 212-633-9385 *E-mail:* fsg.publicity@fsgbooks.com; fsg.editorial@fsgbooks.com; sales@fsgbooks.com *Web Site:* us.macmillan.com/hillandwang.aspx, pg 111

Seidman, Erika, North Point Press, 18 W 18 St, 8th fl, New York, NY 10011 *Tel:* 212-741-6900 *Toll Free Tel:* 888-330-8477 *Fax:* 212-633-9385 *Web Site:* www.fsgbooks.com, pg 171

Seidman, Yishai, Dunow, Carlson & Lerner Literary Agency Inc, 27 W 20 St, Suite 1107, New York, NY 10011 *Tel:* 212-645-7606 *E-mail:* mail@dclagency.com *Web Site:* www.dclagency.com, pg 549

Seigel, Judy, Midmarch Arts Press, 300 Riverside Dr, New York, NY 10025-5239 *Tel:* 212-666-6990 *Web Site:* midmarchartspress.org, pg 156

Seiler, Gretchen, American Association for the Advancement of Science (AAAS), 1200 New York Ave NW, Washington, DC 20005 *Tel:* 202-326-6400 *Web Site:* www.aaas.org, pg 594

Seiler, Maggie, W D Hoard & Sons Co, 28 W Milwaukee Ave, Fort Atkinson, WI 53538 *Tel:* 920-563-5551 *Fax:* 920-563-7298 *E-mail:* hdbooks@hoards.com; editors@hoards.com *Web Site:* www.hoards.com; www.hoardprinting.com, pg 112

Seitter, David, CTB/McGraw-Hill, 20 Ryan Ranch Rd, Monterey, CA 93940-5703 *Tel:* 831-393-0700 *Toll Free Tel:* 800-538-9547 *Fax:* 831-393-7825 *Toll Free Fax:* 800-282-0266 *Web Site:* www.ctb.com, pg 69

Seitz, Don, AuthorHouse, 1663 Liberty Dr, Bloomington, IN 47403 *Tel:* 812-339-6000 (outside US) *Toll Free Tel:* 888-519-5121 *E-mail:* authorsupport@authorhouse.com *Web Site:* www.authorhouse.com, pg 27

Seitz, Don, iUniverse, 1663 Liberty Dr, Bloomington, IN 47403 *Toll Free Tel:* 800-AUTHORS (288-4677) *Fax:* 812-355-4085 *Web Site:* www.iuniverse.com, pg 126

Seitz, Don, Trafford, 1663 Liberty Dr, Bloomington, IN 47403 *Toll Free Tel:* 888-232-4444 *E-mail:* customersupport@trafford.com *Web Site:* www.trafford.com, pg 248

Selah, Stephanie, HarperCollins General Books Group, 195 Broadway, New York, NY 10007 *Tel:* 212-207-7000 *Web Site:* www.harpercollins.com, pg 105

Self, Robert, Baby Tattoo Books, 6045 Longridge Ave, Van Nuys, CA 91401 *Tel:* 818-416-5314 *E-mail:* info@babytattoo.com *Web Site:* www.babytattoo.com, pg 29

Self, Ron, Brick Road Poetry Book Contest, 513 Broadway, Columbus, GA 31901 *Tel:* 706-649-3080 *Web Site:* brickroadpoetrypress.com, pg 674

Seligman, Ellen, McClelland & Stewart Ltd, One Toronto St, Toronto, ON M5C 2V6, Canada *Tel:* 416-364-4449 *Fax:* 416-957-1587 *E-mail:* editorial@mcclelland.com *Web Site:* www.mcclelland.com, pg 491

Selkirk, Sara, WaterBrook Multnomah Publishing Group, 12265 Oracle Blvd, Suite 200, Colorado Springs, CO 80921 *Tel:* 719-590-4999 *Toll Free Tel:* 800-603-7051 (orders) *Fax:* 719-590-8977 *Toll Free Fax:* 800-294-5686 (orders) *E-mail:* info@waterbrookmultnomah.com *Web Site:* waterbrookmultnomah.com, pg 267

Selleck, Carol, Society of Manufacturing Engineers, One SME Dr, Dearborn, MI 48121 *Tel:* 313-425-3000 *Toll Free Tel:* 800-733-4763 (cust serv) *Fax:* 313-425-3400 *E-mail:* publications@sme.org *Web Site:* www.sme.org, pg 229

Selleck, Michael, Simon & Schuster, Inc, 1230 Avenue of the Americas, New York, NY 10020 *Tel:* 212-698-7000 *Fax:* 212-698-7007 *E-mail:* firstname.lastname@simonandschuster.com *Web Site:* www.simonandschuster.com, pg 226

Selleck, Michael, Simon & Schuster Sales Division, 1230 Avenue of the Americas, New York, NY 10020 *Tel:* 212-698-7000, pg 226

Sellers, Scott, Seal Books, One Toronto St, Suite 300, Toronto, ON M5C 2V6, Canada *Tel:* 416-364-4449 *Toll Free Tel:* 888-523-9292 (order desk) *Fax:* 416-364-6863 *Web Site:* www.randomhouse.ca, pg 498

Sells, Dianna, Texas A&M University Press, John H Lindsey Bldg, Lewis St, 4354 TAMU, College Station, TX 77843-4354 *Tel:* 979-845-1436 *Toll Free Tel:* 800-826-8911 (orders) *Fax:* 979-847-8752 *Toll Free Fax:* 888-617-2421 (orders) *E-mail:* tampress@tamu.edu *Web Site:* www.tamupress.com, pg 243

Selman, Edythea Ginis, Edythea Ginis Selman Literary Agency Inc, 14 Washington Place, New York, NY 10003 *Tel:* 212-473-1874 *Fax:* 212-473-1875, pg 572

Selman, Richard, Edythea Ginis Selman Literary Agency Inc, 14 Washington Place, New York, NY 10003 *Tel:* 212-473-1874 *Fax:* 212-473-1875, pg 572

Seltz, Martin, Augsburg Fortress Publishers, Publishing House of the Evangelical Lutheran Church in America, 510 Marquette Ave S, Minneapolis, MN 55402 *Tel:* 612-330-3300 *Toll Free Tel:* 800-426-0115 (ext 639, subns); 800-328-4648 (orders) *Fax:* 612-330-3455 *E-mail:* info@augsburgfortress.org; copyright@augsburgfortress.org (reprint permission requests); customercare@augsburgfortress.org *Web Site:* www.augsburgfortress.org, pg 27

Seltzer, Joyce, Harvard University Press, 79 Garden St, Cambridge, MA 02138-1499 *Tel:* 617-495-2600; 401-531-2800 (intl orders) *Toll Free Tel:* 800-405-1619 (orders) *Fax:* 617-495-5898 (general); 617-496-4677 (edit & rts); 401-531-2801 (intl orders) *Toll Free Fax:* 800-406-9145 (orders) *E-mail:* contact_hup@harvard.edu *Web Site:* www.hup.harvard.edu, pg 107

Selvaggio, Victoria, The Jennifer DeChiara Literary Agency, 31 E 32 St, Suite 300, New York, NY 10016 *Tel:* 212-481-8484 (ext 362) *Fax:* 212-481-9582 *Web Site:* www.jdlit.com, pg 547

Semens, Zak, Goodheart-Willcox Publisher, 18604 W Creek Dr, Tinley Park, IL 60477-6243 *Tel:* 708-687-5000 *Toll Free Tel:* 800-323-0440 *Fax:* 708-468-8692 *Toll Free Fax:* 888-409-3900 *E-mail:* custserv@g-w.com; orders@g-w.com *Web Site:* www.g-w.com, pg 98

Sen, Sharmila, Harvard University Press, 79 Garden St, Cambridge, MA 02138-1499 *Tel:* 617-495-2600; 401-531-2800 (intl orders) *Toll Free Tel:* 800-405-1619 (orders) *Fax:* 617-495-5898 (general); 617-496-4677 (edit & rts); 401-531-2801 (intl orders) *Toll Free Fax:* 800-406-9145 (orders) *E-mail:* contact_hup@harvard.edu *Web Site:* www.hup.harvard.edu, pg 107

Senechal, David, Les Editions Fides, 7333 place des Roseraies, bureau 100, Anjou, QC H1M 2X6, Canada *Tel:* 514-745-4290 *Fax:* 514-745-4299 *E-mail:* editions@groupefides.com *Web Site:* www.editionsfides.com, pg 481

Senftleben, Peter, Kensington Publishing Corp, 119 W 40 St, New York, NY 10018 *Tel:* 212-407-1500 *Toll Free Tel:* 800-221-2647 *Fax:* 212-935-0699 *Web Site:* www.kensingtonbooks.com, pg 130

Sengthavy, Khamla, Norma Epstein Foundation, 15 King's College Circle, UC 173, Toronto, ON M5S 3H7, Canada *Tel:* 416-978-8083 *Fax:* 416-971-2027 *Web Site:* www.utoronto.ca, pg 684

Sengupta, Shivaji, Lumina Datamatics, 4 Collins Ave, Plymouth, MA 02360 *Tel:* 508-746-0300 *Fax:* 508-746-3233 *E-mail:* info@luminadatamatics.com *Web Site:* luminadatamatics.com, pg 530

Sennholz, Lyn M, Center for Futures Education Inc, 345 Erie St, Grove City, PA 16127 *Tel:* 724-458-5860 *Fax:* 724-458-5962 *E-mail:* info@thectr.com *Web Site:* www.thectr.com, pg 53

Sensale, Danielle, JayJo Books LLC, One Huntington Quadrangle, Suite 1N03, Melville, NY 11747 *Tel:* 516-496-4863 *Toll Free Tel:* 800-999-6884 *Fax:* 516-496-4050 *Toll Free Fax:* 800-262-1886 *E-mail:* jayjobooks@guidance-group.com *Web Site:* www.guidance-group.com; www.jayjo.com, pg 126

Senturk, Huseyin, Tughra Books, 345 Clifton Ave, Clifton, NJ 07011 *Tel:* 973-777-2704 *Fax:* 973-457-7334 *E-mail:* info@tughrabooks.com *Web Site:* www.tughrabooks.com, pg 250

Senuta, Ann, ANR Publications University of California, 1301 S 46 St, Bldg 478 - MC 3580, Richmond, CA 94804 *Tel:* 510-665-2195 (cust serv) *Toll Free Tel:* 800-994-8849 *Fax:* 510-665-3427 *E-mail:* anrcatalog@ucdavis.edu *Web Site:* anrcatalog.ucanr.edu, pg 18

Senz, Lisa, St Martin's Press, LLC, 175 Fifth Ave, New York, NY 10010 *Tel:* 646-307-5151 *Fax:* 212-420-9314 *E-mail:* firstname.lastname@macmillan.com *Web Site:* www.stmartins.com, pg 214

Seo, Ginee, Chronicle Books LLC, 680 Second St, San Francisco, CA 94107 *Tel:* 415-537-4200 *Toll Free Tel:* 800-759-0190 (cust serv) *Fax:* 415-537-4460 *Toll Free Fax:* 800-858-7787 (orders); 800-286-9471 (cust serv) *E-mail:* frontdesk@chroniclebooks.com *Web Site:* www.chroniclebooks.com, pg 58

Seow, Jackie, Simon & Schuster, 1230 Avenue of the Americas, New York, NY 10020 *Tel:* 212-698-7000 *Toll Free Tel:* 800-223-2348 (cust serv); 800-223-2336 (orders) *Toll Free Fax:* 800-943-9831 (orders) *Web Site:* www.simonandschuster.com, pg 225

Sepehri, Amin, Mage Publishers Inc, 1408 35 St NW, Washington, DC 20007 *Tel:* 202-342-1642 *Fax:* 202-342-9269 *Web Site:* www.mage.com, pg 145

Seplow-Jolley, Elana, Other Press LLC, 2 Park Ave, 24th fl, New York, NY 10016 *Tel:* 212-414-0054 *Toll Free Tel:* 877-843-6843 *Fax:* 212-414-0939 *E-mail:* editor@otherpress.com; rights@otherpress.com *Web Site:* www.otherpress.com, pg 178

Serafimidis, Sarah, Frog Books, 2526 Martin Luther King Jr Way, Berkeley, CA 94704 *Tel:* 510-549-4270 *Fax:* 510-549-4276 *E-mail:* customerservice@northatlanticbooks.com *Web Site:* www.northatlanticbooks.com, pg 93

Serafimidis, Sarah, North Atlantic Books, 2526 Martin Luther King Jr Way, Berkeley, CA 94704 *Tel:* 510-549-4270 *Fax:* 510-549-4276 *Web Site:* www.northatlanticbooks.com, pg 170

Serafini, Julie, The Texas Bluebonnet Award, 3355 Bee Cave Rd, Suite 401, Austin, TX 78746 *Tel:* 512-328-1518 *Toll Free Tel:* 800-580-2852 *Fax:* 512-328-8852 *Web Site:* www.txla.org, pg 732

Seraphim, Joshua, Leilah Publications, 510 E University Dr, No 3413, Tempe, AZ 85281 *Tel:* 847-275-1657 *E-mail:* leilah@leilahpublications.com *Web Site:* facebook.com/leilahpublications, pg 137

Sergel, Christopher III, Dramatic Publishing Co, 311 Washington St, Woodstock, IL 60098-3308 *Tel:* 815-338-7170 *Toll Free Tel:* 800-448-7469 *Fax:* 815-338-8981 *Toll Free Fax:* 800-334-5302 *E-mail:* plays@dramaticpublishing.com; customerservice@dpcplays.com *Web Site:* www.dramaticpublishing.com, pg 76

Sergel, Gayle, Dramatic Publishing Co, 311 Washington St, Woodstock, IL 60098-3308 *Tel:* 815-338-7170 *Toll Free Tel:* 800-448-7469 *Fax:* 815-338-8981 *Toll Free Fax:* 800-334-5302 *E-mail:* plays@dramaticpublishing.com; customerservice@dpcplays.com *Web Site:* www.dramaticpublishing.com, pg 76

Sergel, Susan, Dramatic Publishing Co, 311 Washington St, Woodstock, IL 60098-3308 *Tel:* 815-338-7170 *Toll Free Tel:* 800-448-7469 *Fax:* 815-338-8981 *Toll Free Fax:* 800-334-5302 *E-mail:* plays@dramaticpublishing.com; customerservice@dpcplays.com *Web Site:* www.dramaticpublishing.com, pg 76

Sergio, Christopher, Portfolio, 375 Hudson St, New York, NY 10014, pg 195

Seroy, Jeff, Farrar, Straus & Giroux, LLC, 18 W 18 St, New York, NY 10011 *Tel:* 212-741-6900 *E-mail:* fsg.publicity@fsgbooks.com *Web Site:* us.macmillan.com/fsg.aspx, pg 86

Seroy, Jeff, Hill & Wang, 18 W 18 St, New York, NY 10011 *Tel:* 212-741-6900 *Fax:* 212-633-9385 *E-mail:* fsg.publicity@fsgbooks.com; fsg.editorial@fsgbooks.com; sales@fsgbooks.com *Web Site:* us.macmillan.com/hillandwang.aspx, pg 111

Seroy, Jeff, North Point Press, 18 W 18 St, 8th fl, New York, NY 10011 *Tel:* 212-741-6900 *Toll Free Tel:* 888-330-8477 *Fax:* 212-633-9385 *Web Site:* www.fsgbooks.com, pg 171

Sery, Douglas, The MIT Press, 55 Hayward St, Cambridge, MA 02142 *Tel:* 617-253-5255 *Toll Free Tel:* 800-207-8354 (orders) *Fax:* 617-258-6779; 617-577-1545 (orders) *Web Site:* mitpress.mit.edu, pg 158

Settle, Alicia B, Per Annum Inc, 555 Eighth Ave, Suite 203, New York, NY 10018 *Tel:* 212-647-8700 *Toll Free Tel:* 800-548-1108 *Fax:* 212-647-8716 *E-mail:* info@perannum.com *Web Site:* www.perannum.com, pg 189

Seum, Rebecca, Cup of Tea Books, PO Box 21133, Columbus, OH 43221 *Tel:* 614-264-5588 *E-mail:* sales@pagespringpublishing.com *Web Site:* www.cupofteabooks.com, pg 69

Severini, Giorgia, R Ross Annett Award for Children's Literature, 11759 Groat Rd, Edmonton, AB T5M 3K6, Canada *Tel:* 780-422-8174 *Toll Free Tel:* 800-665-5354 (AB only) *Fax:* 780-422-2663 (attn WGA) *E-mail:* mail@writersguild.ab.ca *Web Site:* www.writersguild.ab.ca, pg 667

Severini, Giorgia, Amber Bowerman Memorial Travel Writing Award, 11759 Groat Rd, Edmonton, AB T5M 3K6, Canada *Tel:* 780-422-8174 *Toll Free Tel:* 800-665-5354 (AB only) *Fax:* 780-422-2663 (attn WGA) *E-mail:* mail@writersguild.ab.ca *Web Site:* www.writersguild.ab.ca, pg 673

Severini, Giorgia, Georges Bugnet Award for Fiction, 11759 Groat Rd, Edmonton, AB T5M 3K6, Canada *Tel:* 780-422-8174 *Toll Free Tel:* 800-665-5354 (AB only) *Fax:* 780-422-2663 (attn WGA) *E-mail:* mail@writersguild.ab.ca *Web Site:* www.writersguild.ab.ca, pg 674

Severini, Giorgia, The City of Calgary W O Mitchell Book Prize, 11759 Groat Rd, Edmonton, AB T5M 3K6, Canada *Tel:* 780-422-8174 *Toll Free Tel:* 800-665-5354 (AB only) *Fax:* 780-422-2663 (attn WGA) *E-mail:* mail@writersguild.ab.ca *Web Site:* www.writersguild.ab.ca, pg 677

Severini, Giorgia, Wilfrid Eggleston Award for Nonfiction, 11759 Groat Rd, Edmonton, AB T5M 3K6, Canada *Tel:* 780-422-8174 *Toll Free Tel:* 800-665-5354 (AB only) *Fax:* 780-422-2663 (attn WGA) *E-mail:* mail@writersguild.ab.ca *Web Site:* www.writersguild.ab.ca, pg 683

Severini, Giorgia, James H Gray Award for Short Nonfiction, 11759 Groat Rd, Edmonton, AB T5M 3K6, Canada *Tel:* 780-422-8174 *Toll Free Tel:* 800-665-5354 (AB only) *Fax:* 780-422-2663 (attn WGA) *E-mail:* mail@writersguild.ab.ca *Web Site:* www.writersguild.ab.ca, pg 690

Severini, Giorgia, The Robert Kroetsch City of Edmonton Book Prize, 11759 Groat Rd, Edmonton, AB T5M 3K6, Canada *Tel:* 780-422-8174 *Toll Free Tel:* 800-665-5354 (AB only) *Fax:* 780-422-2663 (attn WGA) *E-mail:* mail@writersguild.ab.ca *Web Site:* www.writersguild.ab.ca, pg 698

Severini, Giorgia, Howard O'Hagan Award for Short Story, 11759 Groat Rd, Edmonton, AB T5M 3K6, Canada *Tel:* 780-422-8174 *Toll Free Tel:* 800-665-5354 (AB only) *Fax:* 780-422-2663 (attn WGA) *E-mail:* mail@writersguild.ab.ca *Web Site:* www.writersguild.ab.ca, pg 714

Severini, Giorgia, Gwen Pharis Ringwood Award for Drama, 11759 Groat Rd, Edmonton, AB T5M 3K6, Canada *Tel:* 780-422-8174 *Toll Free Tel:* 800-665-5354 (AB only) *Fax:* 780-422-2663 (attn WGA) *E-mail:* mail@writersguild.ab.ca *Web Site:* www.writersguild.ab.ca, pg 724

Severini, Giorgia, Stephan G Stephansson Award for Poetry, 11759 Groat Rd, Edmonton, AB T5M 3K6, Canada *Tel:* 780-422-8174 *Toll Free Tel:* 800-665-5354 (AB only) *Fax:* 780-422-2663 (attn WGA) *E-mail:* mail@writersguild.ab.ca *Web Site:* www.writersguild.ab.ca, pg 730

Severini, Giorgia, Jon Whyte Memorial Essay Prize, 11759 Groat Rd, Edmonton, AB T5M 3K6, Canada *Tel:* 780-422-8174 *Toll Free Tel:* 800-665-5354 (AB only) *Fax:* 780-422-2663 (attn WGA) *E-mail:* mail@writersguild.ab.ca *Web Site:* www.writersguild.ab.ca, pg 736

Severini, Giorgia, Writers' Guild of Alberta, 11759 Groat Rd, Edmonton, AB T5M 3K6, Canada *Tel:* 780-422-8174 *Toll Free Tel:* 800-665-5354 (AB only) *Fax:* 780-422-2663 (attn WGA) *E-mail:* mail@writersguild.ab.ca *Web Site:* www.writersguild.ab.ca, pg 621

Sevier, Ben, Dutton, 375 Hudson St, New York, NY 10014 *Tel:* 212-366-2000 *Fax:* 212-366-2262 *E-mail:* online@penguinputnam.com *Web Site:* www.penguinputnam.com; us.penguingroup.com, pg 78

Sevig, Mike, Skandisk Inc, 6667 W Old Shakopee Rd, Suite 109, Bloomington, MN 55438-2622 *Tel:* 952-829-8998 *Toll Free Tel:* 800-468-2424 *Fax:* 952-829-8992 *E-mail:* tomten@skandisk.com *Web Site:* www.skandisk.com, pg 227

Sewell, Emily, Bull Publishing Co, PO Box 1377, Boulder, CO 80306 *Tel:* 303-545-6350 *Toll Free Tel:* 800-676-2855 *Fax:* 303-545-6354 *E-mail:* bullpublishing@msn.com *Web Site:* www.bullpub.com, pg 47

Sewell, Vicki, University of South Carolina Press, 1600 Hampton St, Suite 544, Columbia, SC 29208 *Tel:* 803-777-5245 *Toll Free Tel:* 800-768-2500 (orders) *Fax:* 803-777-0160 *Toll Free Fax:* 800-868-0740 (orders) *Web Site:* www.sc.edu/uscpress, pg 259

Sexton, Kim, SDP Publishing Solutions LLC, 36 Captain's Way, East Bridgewater, MA 02333 *Tel:* 617-775-0656 *Web Site:* www.sdppublishingsolutions.com, pg 534

Sexton, Phil, F+W, A Content + eCommerce Company, 10151 Carver Rd, Suite 200, Blue Ash, OH 45242 *Tel:* 513-531-2690 *Toll Free Tel:* 800-289-0963 (trade accts); 800-258-0929 (orders) *E-mail:* contact_us@fwmedia.com *Web Site:* www.fwcommunity.com, pg 86

Sexton, Phil, Writer's Digest Books, 10151 Carver Rd, Suite 200, Blue Ash, OH 45242 *Tel:* 513-531-2690 *Toll Free Tel:* 800-289-0963 *E-mail:* writersdigest@fwmedia.com (edit) *Web Site:* www.writersdigest.com, pg 277

Seymour, Mary Sue, Mary Sue Seymour, 475 Miner Street Rd, Canton, NY 13617 *Tel:* 315-386-1831 *Web Site:* www.theseymouragency.com, pg 573

Shaak, Teresa, Association of American Editorial Cartoonists, 3899 N Front St, Harrisburg, PA 17110 *Tel:* 717-703-3003 *Fax:* 717-703-3008 *E-mail:* aaec@pa-news.org *Web Site:* www.editorialcartoonists.com, pg 598

Shabelman, Doug, Burns Entertainment & Sports Marketing, 820 Davis St, Suite 222, Evanston, IL 60201 *Tel:* 847-866-9400 *Fax:* 847-491-9778 *E-mail:* burnsl@burnsent.com *Web Site:* burnsent.com, pg 587

Shadek, Ed, Wildlife Education Ltd, 2418 Noyes St, Evanston, IL 60201 *Toll Free Tel:* 800-477-5034 *E-mail:* owls5@zoobooks.com; helpdesk@zoobooks.com *Web Site:* www.zoobooks.com; wildlife-ed.com, pg 272

Shafer, Emma, Crown Publishing Group, c/o Penguin Random House Inc, 1745 Broadway, New York, NY 10019 *Tel:* 212-782-9000 *Toll Free Tel:* 888-264-1745 *Fax:* 212-940-7408 *E-mail:* crownosm@penguinrandomhouse.com *Web Site:* crownpublishing.com, pg 68

Shafeyeva, Yelena, Begell House Inc Publishers, 50 North St, Danbury, CT 06810 *Tel:* 203-456-6161 *Fax:* 203-456-6167 *E-mail:* orders@begellhouse.com *Web Site:* www.begellhouse.com, pg 33

Shaffer, Bryan, Purdue University Press, Stewart Ctr 370, 504 W State St, West Lafayette, IN 47907-2058 *Tel:* 765-494-2038 *Fax:* 765-496-2442 *E-mail:* pupress@purdue.edu *Web Site:* www.thepress.purdue.edu, pg 200

Shaffer, Mike, New Readers Press, 1320 Jamesville Ave, Syracuse, NY 13210 *Tel:* 315-422-9121 *Toll Free Tel:* 800-448-8878 *Fax:* 315-422-6369 *Toll Free Fax:* 866-894-2100 *E-mail:* nrp@proliteracy.org *Web Site:* www.newreaderspress.com, pg 168

Shah, Monica, Harry N Abrams Inc, 115 W 18 St, 6th fl, New York, NY 10011 *Tel:* 212-206-7715 *Toll Free Tel:* 800-345-1359 *Fax:* 212-519-1210 *E-mail:* abrams@abramsbooks.com *Web Site:* www.abramsbooks.com, pg 3

Shah, Vijay, University Press of Mississippi, 3825 Ridgewood Rd, Jackson, MS 39211-6492 *Tel:* 601-432-6205 *Toll Free Tel:* 800-737-7788 (orders & cust serv) *Fax:* 601-432-6217 *E-mail:* press@mississippi.edu *Web Site:* www.upress.state.ms.us, pg 262

Shaine, Ilene, Foster City International Writers Contest, 650 Shell Blvd, Foster City, CA 94404 *Tel:* 650-286-3386 *E-mail:* fostercity_writers@yahoo.com *Web Site:* www.fostercity.org, pg 687

Shakely, Lauren, Crown Publishing Group, c/o Penguin Random House Inc, 1745 Broadway, New York, NY 10019 *Tel:* 212-782-9000 *Toll Free Tel:* 888-264-1745 *Fax:* 212-940-7408 *E-mail:* crownosm@penguinrandomhouse.com *Web Site:* crownpublishing.com, pg 68

Shaker, Anthony F PhD, AFS Wordstead, 1062 Vallee-a-Josaphat, Lac-des-Iles, QC J0W 1J0, Canada *Tel:* 819-597-4072 *Fax:* 819-597-4547 *Web Site:* www.wordstead.com, pg 519

Shakhashiri, Bassam Z, The American Chemical Society, 1155 16 St NW, Washington, DC 20036 *Tel:* 202-872-4600 *Toll Free Tel:* 800-227-5558 (US) *Fax:* 202-872-6067 *E-mail:* help@acs.org *Web Site:* www.acs.org, pg 12

Shallcross, Andrea, Hachette Book Group, 1290 Avenue of the Americas, New York, NY 10019 *Tel:* 212-364-1100 *Toll Free Tel:* 800-759-0190 (cust serv) *Fax:* 212-364-0933 (intl orders) *Toll Free Fax:* 800-286-9471 (cust serv) *Web Site:* www.HachetteBookGroup.com, pg 102

Shaloo, Sharon, Massachusetts Book Awards, Simons College - GSLIS, 300 The Fenway, Boston, MA 02115 *Tel:* 617-521-2719 *Fax:* 617-521-3035 *E-mail:* bookawards@massbook.org *Web Site:* www.massbook.org, pg 705

Shamroe, Amy, Axiom Business Book Awards, 1129 Woodmere Ave, Suite B, Traverse City, MI 49686 *Tel:* 231-933-0445 *Toll Free Tel:* 800-706-4636 *Fax:* 231-933-0448 *E-mail:* info@axiomawards.com *Web Site:* www.axiomawards.com, pg 669

Shamroe, Amy, Illumination Book Awards, 1129 Woodmere Ave, Suite B, Traverse City, MI 49686 *Tel:* 231-933-0445 *Toll Free Tel:* 800-706-4636 *Fax:* 231-933-0448 *E-mail:* awards@bookpublishing.com *Web Site:* www.illuminationawards.com, pg 694

Shamroe, Amy, The Independent Publisher Book Awards, 1129 Woodmere Ave, Suite B, Traverse City, MI 49686 *Tel:* 231-933-0445 *Toll Free Tel:* 800-706-4636 *Fax:* 231-933-0448 *E-mail:* awards@bookpublishing.com *Web Site:* www.independentpublisher.com/ipland/ipawards.php, pg 694

Shamroe, Amy, Living Now Book Awards, 1129 Woodmere Ave, Suite B, Traverse City, MI 49686 *Tel:* 231-933-0445 *Toll Free Tel:* 800-706-4636 *Fax:* 231-933-0448 *E-mail:* awards@bookpublishing.com *Web Site:* www.livingnowawards.com, pg 702

Shamroe, Amy, Moonbeam Children's Book Awards, 1129 Woodmere Ave, Suite B, Traverse City, MI 49686 *Tel:* 231-933-0445 *Toll Free Tel:* 800-706-4636 *Fax:* 231-933-0448 *E-mail:* info@moonbeamawards.com *Web Site:* www.moonbeamawards.com, pg 709

Shanahan, Charif, George Bogin Memorial Award, 15 Gramercy Park, New York, NY 10003 *Tel:* 212-254-9628 *Fax:* 212-673-2352 *Web Site:* www.poetrysociety.org, pg 673

Shanahan, Charif, Alice Fay Di Castagnola Award, 15 Gramercy Park, New York, NY 10003 *Tel:* 212-254-9628 *Fax:* 212-673-2352 *Web Site:* www.poetrysociety.org, pg 680

Shanahan, Charif, Norma Farber First Book Award, 15 Gramercy Park, New York, NY 10003 *Tel:* 212-254-9628 *Fax:* 212-673-2352 *Web Site:* www.poetrysociety.org, pg 685

Shanahan, Charif, Cecil Hemley Memorial Award, 15 Gramercy Park, New York, NY 10003 *Tel:* 212-254-9628 *Fax:* 212-673-2352 *Web Site:* www.poetrysociety.org, pg 692

Shanahan, Charif, Louise Louis/Emily F Bourne Student Poetry Award, 15 Gramercy Park, New York, NY 10003 *Tel:* 212-254-9628 *Fax:* 212-673-2352 *Web Site:* www.poetrysociety.org, pg 703

Shanahan, Charif, Lyric Poetry Award, 15 Gramercy Park, New York, NY 10003 *Tel:* 212-254-9628 *Fax:* 212-673-2352 *Web Site:* www.poetrysociety.org, pg 704

Shanahan, Charif, Lucille Medwick Memorial Award, 15 Gramercy Park, New York, NY 10003 *Tel:* 212-254-9628 *Fax:* 212-673-2352 *Web Site:* www.poetrysociety.org, pg 707

Shanahan, Charif, Poetry Society of America (PSA), 15 Gramercy Park, New York, NY 10003 *Tel:* 212-254-9628 *Fax:* 212-673-2352 *Web Site:* www.poetrysociety.org, pg 616

Shanahan, Charif, William Carlos Williams Award, 15 Gramercy Park, New York, NY 10003 *Tel:* 212-254-9628 *Fax:* 212-673-2352 *Web Site:* www.poetrysociety.org, pg 736

Shanahan, Charif, The Writer Magazine/Emily Dickinson Award, 15 Gramercy Park, New York, NY 10003 *Tel:* 212-254-9628 *Fax:* 212-673-2352 *Web Site:* www.poetrysociety.org, pg 738

Shandler, Geoff, HarperCollins General Books Group, 195 Broadway, New York, NY 10007 *Tel:* 212-207-7000 *Web Site:* www.harpercollins.com, pg 105

Shandler, Sara, Alloy Entertainment LLC, 1700 Broadway, New York, NY 10019 *Web Site:* alloyentertainment.com, pg 8

Shangle, Barbara, American Products Publishing Co, 8260 SW Nimbus Ave, Beaverton, OR 97008 *Tel:* 503-672-7502 *Toll Free Tel:* 800-668-8181 *Fax:* 503-672-7104 *E-mail:* info@american-products.com *Web Site:* www.american-products.com, pg 15

Shangle, Robert, American Products Publishing Co, 8260 SW Nimbus Ave, Beaverton, OR 97008 *Tel:* 503-672-7502 *Toll Free Tel:* 800-668-8181 *Fax:* 503-672-7104 *E-mail:* info@american-products.com *Web Site:* www.american-products.com, pg 15

Shank, Merna B, Christian Light Publications Inc, 1051 Mount Clinton Pike, Harrisonburg, VA 22802 *Tel:* 540-434-1003 *Toll Free Tel:* 800-776-0478 *Fax:* 540-433-8896 *E-mail:* info@clp.org; orders@clp.org *Web Site:* www.clp.org, pg 57

Shannon, Katya, Penguin Group (USA) LLC Sales, 375 Hudson St, New York, NY 10014 *Tel:* 212-366-2000 *E-mail:* online@penguinputnam.com *Web Site:* us.penguingroup.com, pg 186

Shannon, Kim, Penguin Random House Inc, 1745 Broadway, New York, NY 10019 *Tel:* 212-782-9000 *Toll Free Tel:* 800-726-0600 *Web Site:* www.randomhouse.com, pg 187

Shannon, Scott, Penguin Random House Inc, 1745 Broadway, New York, NY 10019 *Tel:* 212-782-9000 *Toll Free Tel:* 800-726-0600 *Web Site:* www.randomhouse.com, pg 187

Shannon, Scott, Random House Publishing Group, 1745 Broadway, New York, NY 10019 *Toll Free Tel:* 800-200-3552 *Web Site:* atrandom.com, pg 204

Shannon, Tom, Oxford University Press USA, 198 Madison Ave, New York, NY 10016 *Tel:* 212-726-6000 *Toll Free Tel:* 800-451-7556 (orders); 800-445-9714 (cust serv) *Fax:* 919-677-1303 *E-mail:* custserv.us@oup.com *Web Site:* www.oup.com/us, pg 179

Shapiro, Anita C, Practising Law Institute, 1177 Avenue of the Americas, New York, NY 10036 *Tel:* 212-824-5700 *Toll Free Tel:* 800-260-4PLI (260-4754, cust serv) *Fax:* 212-265-4742 (intl) *Toll Free Fax:* 800-321-0093 (local) *E-mail:* info@pli.edu (cust serv) *Web Site:* www.pli.edu, pg 195

Shapiro, Howard, Animal Media Group LLC, 100 First Ave, Suite 1100, Pittsburgh, PA 15222-1519 *Tel:* 412-566-5656 *Fax:* 412-566-5656 *E-mail:* info@animalmediagroup.com *Web Site:* www.animalmediagroup.com, pg 18

Shapiro, James, The Authors Guild, 31 E 32 St, 7th fl, New York, NY 10016 *Tel:* 212-563-5904 *Fax:* 212-564-5363 *E-mail:* staff@authorsguild.org *Web Site:* www.authorsguild.org, pg 599

Shapiro, Karen, Sourcebooks Inc, 1935 Brookdale Rd, Suite 139, Naperville, IL 60563 *Tel:* 630-961-3900 *Toll Free Tel:* 800-432-7444 *Fax:* 630-961-2168 *E-mail:* info@sourcebooks.com; customersupport@sourcebooks.com *Web Site:* www.sourcebooks.com, pg 230

Shapiro, Melvin, Book Sales Inc, 142 W 36 St, 4th fl, New York, NY 10018 *Tel:* 212-779-4971; 212-779-4972 *Toll Free Tel:* 866-483-5456 *Fax:* 212-779-6058 *E-mail:* sales@quartous.com; customerservice@quartous.com *Web Site:* www.booksalesusa.com, pg 42

Shapiro, Norman, Judaica Press Inc, 123 Ditmas Ave, Brooklyn, NY 11218 *Tel:* 718-972-6200 *Toll Free Tel:* 800-972-6201 *Fax:* 718-972-6204 *E-mail:* info@judaicapress.com; orders@judaicapress.com *Web Site:* www.judaicapress.com, pg 128

Shapiro, Norman, Soncino Press Ltd, 123 Ditmas Ave, Brooklyn, NY 11218 *Tel:* 718-972-6200 *Toll Free Tel:* 800-972-6201 *Fax:* 718-972-6204 *E-mail:* info@soncino.com *Web Site:* www.soncino.com, pg 230

Shapiro, Shelly, Random House Publishing Group, 1745 Broadway, New York, NY 10019 *Toll Free Tel:* 800-200-3552 *Web Site:* atrandom.com, pg 204

Shapland, Juliette, HarperCollins Publishers, 195 Broadway, New York, NY 10007 *Tel:* 212-207-7000 *Fax:* 212-207-7145 *Web Site:* www.harpercollins.com, pg 106

Share, Don, Ruth Lilly Poetry Prize, 61 W Superior St, Chicago, IL 60654 *Tel:* 312-787-7070 *Fax:* 312-787-6650 *E-mail:* editors@poetrymagazine.org *Web Site:* poetrymagazine.org, pg 701

Shareck, Michael, Macmillan, 175 Fifth Ave, New York, NY 10010 *Tel:* 646-307-5151 *Fax:* 212-420-9314 *E-mail:* firstname.lastname@macmillan.com *Web Site:* www.macmillan.com, pg 145

Sharma, Deven, McGraw-Hill Financial, 1221 Avenue of the Americas, 50th fl, New York, NY 10020 *Tel:* 212-512-2000 *Web Site:* www.mhfi.com, pg 151

Sharp, Sydney, Society for the History of Authorship, Reading & Publishing Inc (SHARP), c/o The Johns Hopkins University Press, Journals Publishing Div, PO Box 19966, Baltimore, MD 21211-0966 *Tel:* 410-

516-6987 *Toll Free Tel:* 800-548-1784 *Fax:* 410-516-3866 *E-mail:* members@sharpweb.org *Web Site:* www.sharpweb.org, pg 618

Sharpe, Carol, M E Sharpe Inc, 80 Business Park Dr, Suite 202, Armonk, NY 10504 *Tel:* 914-273-1800 *Toll Free Tel:* 800-541-6563 *Fax:* 914-273-2106 *E-mail:* info@mesharpe.com *Web Site:* www.mesharpe.com, pg 223

Sharpe, Errol, Fernwood Publishing, 32 Oceanvista Lane, Black Point, NS B0J 1B0, Canada *Tel:* 902-857-1388 *Fax:* 902-857-1328 *E-mail:* info@fernpub.ca; roseway@fernpub.ca *Web Site:* fernwoodpublishing.ca, pg 483

Sharpe, Jack, Bethlehem Books, 10194 Garfield St S, Bathgate, ND 58216 *Toll Free Tel:* 800-757-6831 *Fax:* 701-265-3716 *E-mail:* contact@bethlehembooks.com *Web Site:* www.bethlehembooks.com, pg 36

Sharpe, Myron E, M E Sharpe Inc, 80 Business Park Dr, Suite 202, Armonk, NY 10504 *Tel:* 914-273-1800 *Toll Free Tel:* 800-541-6563 *Fax:* 914-273-2106 *E-mail:* info@mesharpe.com *Web Site:* www.mesharpe.com, pg 223

Sharpton, Jeff, Resilient Publishing, 406 S Third St, Boise, ID 83702 *Tel:* 208-258-9544 *E-mail:* submissions@resilientpublishing.com *Web Site:* www.resilientpublishing.com, pg 208

Sharrar, Kim, McCutchan Publishing Corp, 2694 Ohart Rd, Richmond, CA 94806 *Tel:* 510-758-5510 *Toll Free Tel:* 800-227-1540 *Fax:* 510-758-6078 *E-mail:* mccutchanpublish@sbcglobal.net *Web Site:* www.mccutchanpublishing.com, pg 150

Sharrard, Robert, City Lights Publishers, 261 Columbus Ave, San Francisco, CA 94133 *Tel:* 415-362-8193 *Fax:* 415-362-4921 *E-mail:* staff@citylights.com *Web Site:* www.citylights.com, pg 58

Shaub, Ms Bobbett, Medical Physics Publishing Corp (MPP), 555 Helgesen Dr, Madison, WI 53718 *Tel:* 608-262-4021 *Toll Free Tel:* 800-442-5778 (cust serv) *E-mail:* mpp@medicalphysics.org *Web Site:* www.medicalphysics.org, pg 153

Shaughnessy, Sandy, Florida Individual Artist Fellowships, 500 S Bronough St, Tallahassee, FL 32399-0250 *Tel:* 850-245-6470 *Fax:* 850-245-6497 *E-mail:* info@florida-arts.org *Web Site:* www.florida-arts.org, pg 686

Shaw, Bruce P, The Harvard Common Press, 535 Albany St, Boston, MA 02118 *Tel:* 617-423-5803 *Toll Free Tel:* 888-657-3755 *Fax:* 617-695-9794 *E-mail:* orders@harvardcommonpress.com; info@harvardcommonpress.com *Web Site:* www.harvardcommonpress.com, pg 107

Shaw, Connie, Sentient Publications LLC, 1113 Spruce St, Boulder, CO 80302 *Tel:* 303-443-2188 *Fax:* 303-381-2538 *E-mail:* contact@sentientpublications.com *Web Site:* www.sentientpublications.com, pg 222

Shaw, Jeanette, Prentice Hall Press, 375 Hudson St, New York, NY 10014 *Tel:* 212-366-2000 *Fax:* 212-366-2666, pg 196

Shaw, Joe, Cypress House, 155 Cypress St, Fort Bragg, CA 95437 *Tel:* 707-964-9520 *Toll Free Tel:* 800-773-7782 *Fax:* 707-964-7531 *E-mail:* cypresshouse@cypresshouse.com *Web Site:* www.cypresshouse.com, pg 69, 524

Shaw, Kathy Ann, Individual Artist Fellowships, 25 State House Sta, 193 State St, Augusta, ME 04333-0025 *Tel:* 207-287-2726 *Fax:* 207-287-2725 *Web Site:* mainearts.maine.gov, pg 695

Shaw, Lisa, Corwin, a Sage Co, 2455 Teller Rd, Thousand Oaks, CA 91320 *Tel:* 805-499-9734 *Toll Free Tel:* 800-233-9936 *Fax:* 805-499-5323 *Toll Free Fax:* 800-417-2466 *E-mail:* info@corwin.com; order@corwin.com *Web Site:* www.corwin.com, pg 64

Shaw, Liz, Shambhala Publications Inc, Horticultural Hall, 300 Massachusetts Ave, Boston, MA 02115 *Tel:* 617-424-0030 *Toll Free Tel:* 866-424-0030 (off); 888-424-2329 (cust serv) *Fax:* 617-236-1563 *E-mail:* customercare@shambhala.com *Web Site:* www.shambhala.com, pg 223

Shaw, Marjorie, Wildlife Education Ltd, 2418 Noyes St, Evanston, IL 60201 *Toll Free Tel:* 800-477-5034 *E-mail:* owls5@zoobooks.com; helpdesk@zoobooks.com *Web Site:* www.zoobooks.com; wildlife-ed.com, pg 272

Shaw, Patricia, Crown Publishing Group, c/o Penguin Random House Inc, 1745 Broadway, New York, NY 10019 *Tel:* 212-782-9000 *Toll Free Tel:* 888-264-1745 *Fax:* 212-940-7408 *E-mail:* crownosm@penguinrandomhouse.com *Web Site:* crownpublishing.com, pg 68

Shay, Michael, Neltje Blanchan Memorial Award, 2320 Capitol Ave, Cheyenne, WY 82002 *Tel:* 307-777-5234 *Fax:* 307-777-5499 *Web Site:* wyoarts.state.wy.us, pg 672

Shay, Michael, Frank Nelson Doubleday Memorial Award, 2320 Capitol Ave, Cheyenne, WY 82002 *Tel:* 307-777-5234 *Fax:* 307-777-5499 *Web Site:* wyoarts.state.wy.us, pg 682

Shay, Michael, Wyoming Arts Council Literature Fellowships, 2320 Capitol Ave, Cheyenne, WY 82002 *Tel:* 307-777-5234 *Fax:* 307-777-5499 *Web Site:* wyoarts.state.wy.us, pg 739

Shea, Samantha, Georges Borchardt Inc, 136 E 57 St, New York, NY 10022 *Tel:* 212-753-5785 *E-mail:* georges@gbagency.com *Web Site:* www.gbagency.com, pg 543

Shea-Joyce, Tep, Appraisal Institute, 200 W Madison, Suite 1500, Chicago, IL 60606 *Tel:* 312-335-4100 *Toll Free Tel:* 888-756-4624 *Fax:* 312-335-4400 *Web Site:* www.appraisalinstitute.org, pg 20

Shealy, Dennis, Random House Children's Books, 1745 Broadway, New York, NY 10019 *Tel:* 212-782-9000 *Toll Free Tel:* 800-200-3552 *Fax:* 212-782-9452 *Web Site:* randomhousekids.com, pg 203

Sheanin, Wendy, Simon & Schuster, Inc, 1230 Avenue of the Americas, New York, NY 10020 *Tel:* 212-698-7000 *Fax:* 212-698-7007 *E-mail:* firstname.lastname@simonandschuster.com *Web Site:* www.simonandschuster.com, pg 226

Shear, Donna, University of Nebraska Press, 1111 Lincoln Mall, Lincoln, NE 68588-0630 *Tel:* 402-472-3581; 919-966-7449 (cust serv & foreign orders) *Toll Free Tel:* 800-848-6224 (cust serv & US orders) *Fax:* 402-472-6214; 919-962-2704 (cust serv & foreign orders) *Toll Free Fax:* 800-526-2617 (cust serv & US orders) *E-mail:* pressmail@unl.edu *Web Site:* www.nebraskapress.unl.edu, pg 257

Sheedy, Charlotte, Charlotte Sheedy Literary Agency Inc, 928 Broadway, Suite 901, New York, NY 10010 *Tel:* 212-780-9800 *Web Site:* www.sheedylit.com, pg 573

Sheedy, Rachel, Don Buchwald & Associates Inc, 10 E 44 St, New York, NY 10017 *Tel:* 212-867-1200 *Fax:* 212-867-2434 *E-mail:* info@buchwald.com *Web Site:* www.buchwald.com, pg 545

Sheehan, Katie, Berrett-Koehler Publishers Inc, 1333 Broadway, Suite 1000, Oakland, CA 94612 *Tel:* 510-817-2277 *Fax:* 510-817-2278 *E-mail:* bkpub@bkpub.com *Web Site:* www.bkconnection.com, pg 35

Sheinkopf, Barry, The Writing Center, 601 Palisade Ave, Englewood Cliffs, NJ 07632 *Tel:* 201-567-4017 *Fax:* 201-567-7202 *E-mail:* writingcenter@optonline.net *Web Site:* www.thewritingcenternj.com, pg 657

Shekari, Lauren, Other Press LLC, 2 Park Ave, 24th fl, New York, NY 10016 *Tel:* 212-414-0054 *Toll Free Tel:* 877-843-6843 *Fax:* 212-414-0939 *E-mail:* editor@otherpress.com; rights@otherpress.com *Web Site:* www.otherpress.com, pg 178

Shelley, Jessica, Marshall Cavendish Corp, 99 White Plains Rd, Tarrytown, NY 10591-9001 *Tel:* 914-332-8888 *Toll Free Tel:* 800-821-9881 *Fax:* 914-332-8102 *E-mail:* mce@marshallcavendish.com *Web Site:* www.mceducation.us, pg 148

Shelton, Darryl, Christian Schools International, 3350 E Paris Ave SE, Grand Rapids, MI 49512-3054 *Tel:* 616-957-1070 *Toll Free Tel:* 800-635-8288 *Fax:* 616-957-5022 *E-mail:* info@csionline.org *Web Site:* www.csionline.org, pg 57

Shelton, Otis, American Institute of Chemical Engineers (AIChE), 120 Wall St, 23rd fl, New York, NY 10005-4020 *Tel:* 203-702-7660 *Toll Free Tel:* 800-242-4363 *Fax:* 203-775-5177 *E-mail:* customerservice@aiche.org *Web Site:* www.aiche.org, pg 13

Shepard, Aaron, Shepard Publications, PO Box 280, Friday Harbor, WA 98250 *Web Site:* www.shepardpub.com, pg 223

Shepard, Christopher, Pimlico/Aurous Inc, PO Box 20490, New York, NY 10017 *Tel:* 212-628-9729 *Fax:* 212-535-7861, pg 568

Shepard, Diane, Bear & Co Inc, One Park St, Rochester, VT 05767 *Tel:* 802-767-3174 *Toll Free Tel:* 800-932-3277 *Fax:* 802-767-3726 *E-mail:* customerservice@InnerTraditions.com *Web Site:* InnerTraditions.com, pg 33

Shepard, Diane, Inner Traditions International Ltd, One Park St, Rochester, VT 05767 *Tel:* 802-767-3174 *Toll Free Tel:* 800-246-8648 *Fax:* 802-767-3726 *E-mail:* customerservice@InnerTraditions.com *Web Site:* www.InnerTraditions.com, pg 122

Shepard, Jean H, The Shepard Agency, 73 Kingswood Dr, Bethel, CT 06801 *Tel:* 203-790-4230; 203-790-1780 *Fax:* 203-798-2924 *E-mail:* shepardagcy@mindspring.com, pg 573

Shepard, Judith, The Permanent Press, 4170 Noyac Rd, Sag Harbor, NY 11963 *Tel:* 631-725-1101 *Fax:* 631-725-8215 *E-mail:* info@thepermanentpress.com *Web Site:* www.thepermanentpress.com, pg 189

Shepard, Judith, Second Chance Press, 4170 Noyac Rd, Sag Harbor, NY 11963 *Tel:* 631-725-1101 *E-mail:* info@thepermanentpress.com *Web Site:* www.thepermanentpress.com, pg 221

Shepard, Lance Hastings, The Shepard Agency, 73 Kingswood Dr, Bethel, CT 06801 *Tel:* 203-790-4230; 203-790-1780 *Fax:* 203-798-2924 *E-mail:* shepardagcy@mindspring.com, pg 573

Shepard, Martin, The Permanent Press, 4170 Noyac Rd, Sag Harbor, NY 11963 *Tel:* 631-725-1101 *Fax:* 631-725-8215 *E-mail:* info@thepermanentpress.com *Web Site:* www.thepermanentpress.com, pg 189

Shepard, Martin, Second Chance Press, 4170 Noyac Rd, Sag Harbor, NY 11963 *Tel:* 631-725-1101 *E-mail:* info@thepermanentpress.com *Web Site:* www.thepermanentpress.com, pg 221

Sheppard, Christine, Library Association of Alberta (LAA), 80 Baker Crescent NW, Calgary, AB T2L 1R4, Canada *Tel:* 403-284-5818 *Toll Free Tel:* 877-522-5550 *Fax:* 403-282-6646 *E-mail:* info@laa.ca *Web Site:* www.laa.ca, pg 608

Sheppard, Nancy, Penguin Group (USA) LLC, a Penguin Random House company, 375 Hudson St, New York, NY 10014 *Tel:* 212-366-2000 *Toll Free Tel:* 800-847-5515 (inside sales); 800-631-8571 (cust serv) *Fax:* 212-366-2666; 607-775-4829 (inside sales) *E-mail:* online@us.penguingroup.com *Web Site:* www.penguin.com; us.penguingroup.com, pg 186

Sheppard, Nancy, Viking, 375 Hudson St, New York, NY 10014 *Tel:* 212-366-2000 *E-mail:* online@penguinputnam.com *Web Site:* www.penguinputnam.com; us.penguingroup.com, pg 265

Sherer, John, The University of North Carolina Press, 116 S Boundary St, Chapel Hill, NC 27514-3808 *Tel:* 919-966-3561 *Fax:* 919-966-3829 *E-mail:* uncpress@unc.edu *Web Site:* www.uncpress.unc.edu, pg 258

Sheridan, John, William Allen White Children's Book Awards, 1200 Commercial St, Emporia, KS 66801-5092 *Tel:* 620-341-5208 *Toll Free Tel:* 877-613-7323 *Fax:* 620-341-6208 *E-mail:* wawbookaward@emporia.edu *Web Site:* waw.emporia.edu, pg 735

Sherk, Mary Lou, Galen Press Ltd, PO Box 64400-WB, Tucson, AZ 85728-4400 *Tel:* 520-577-8363 *Fax:* 520-529-6459 *E-mail:* sales@galenpress.com *Web Site:* www.galenpress.com, pg 94

Sherman, Ken, Ken Sherman & Associates, 1275 N Hayworth, Suite 103, Los Angeles, CA 90046 *Tel:* 310-273-8840 *E-mail:* kenshermanassociates@gmail.com *Web Site:* www.kenshermanassociates.com, pg 573

Sherman, Laura, American Institute of Aeronautics & Astronautics (AIAA), 1801 Alexander Bell Dr, Suite 500, Reston, VA 20191-4344 *Tel:* 703-264-7500 *Toll Free Tel:* 800-639-AIAA (639-2422) *Fax:* 703-264-7551 *E-mail:* custserv@aiaa.org *Web Site:* www.aiaa.org, pg 13

Sherman, Rebecca, Writers House, 21 W 26 St, New York, NY 10010 *Tel:* 212-685-2400 *Fax:* 212-685-1781 *Web Site:* www.writershouse.com, pg 580

Sherman, Stephen, Radix Press, 11715 Bandlon Dr, Houston, TX 77072 *Tel:* 281-879-5688 *Web Site:* www.specialforcesbooks.com, pg 202

Sherman, Susan, Charlesbridge Publishing Inc, 85 Main St, Watertown, MA 02472 *Tel:* 617-926-0329 *Toll Free Tel:* 800-225-3214 *Fax:* 617-926-5720 *Toll Free Fax:* 800-926-5775 *E-mail:* books@charlesbridge.com *Web Site:* www.charlesbridge.com, pg 55

Sherman, Wendy, Wendy Sherman Associates Inc, 27 W 24 St, Suite 700-B, New York, NY 10010 *Tel:* 212-279-9027 *E-mail:* submissions@wsherman.com *Web Site:* www.wsherman.com, pg 573

Sherr, Roger, Genealogical Publishing Co, 3600 Clipper Mill Rd, Suite 260, Baltimore, MD 21211 *Tel:* 410-837-8271 *Toll Free Tel:* 800-296-6687 *Fax:* 410-752-8492 *Toll Free Fax:* 800-599-9561 *E-mail:* sales@genealogical.com; info@genealogical.com *Web Site:* www.genealogical.com, pg 95

Sherrod, Tracy, HarperCollins General Books Group, 195 Broadway, New York, NY 10007 *Tel:* 212-207-7000 *Web Site:* www.harpercollins.com, pg 105

Sherry, Cynthia, Chicago Review Press, 814 N Franklin St, Chicago, IL 60610 *Tel:* 312-337-0747 *Toll Free Tel:* 800-888-4741 *Fax:* 312-337-5110 *E-mail:* frontdesk@chicagoreviewpress.com *Web Site:* www.chicagoreviewpress.com, pg 56

Sherry, Sophia, Other Press LLC, 2 Park Ave, 24th fl, New York, NY 10016 *Tel:* 212-414-0054 *Toll Free Tel:* 877-843-6843 *Fax:* 212-414-0939 *E-mail:* editor@otherpress.com; rights@otherpress.com *Web Site:* www.otherpress.com, pg 178

Sheu, Kimberly, The Monacelli Press, 236 W 27 St, 4th fl, New York, NY 10001 *Tel:* 212-229-9925 *E-mail:* contact@monacellipress.com *Web Site:* www.monacellipress.com, pg 159

Shiel, Lisa, Slipdown Mountain Publications LLC, 28151 Quarry Lake Rd, Lake Linden, MI 49945 *Tel:* 906-523-4118 *Toll Free Tel:* 866-341-3705 *Toll Free Fax:* 866-341-3705 *E-mail:* books@jacobsvillebooks.com *Web Site:* www.jacobsvillebooks.com, pg 228

Shiel, Walt, Slipdown Mountain Publications LLC, 28151 Quarry Lake Rd, Lake Linden, MI 49945 *Tel:* 906-523-4118 *Toll Free Tel:* 866-341-3705 *Toll Free Fax:* 866-341-3705 *E-mail:* books@jacobsvillebooks.com *Web Site:* www.jacobsvillebooks.com, pg 228

Shield, Nina, Random House Publishing Group, 1745 Broadway, New York, NY 10019 *Toll Free Tel:* 800-200-3552 *Web Site:* atrandom.com, pg 204

Shields, Colin, Simon & Schuster Sales Division, 1230 Avenue of the Americas, New York, NY 10020 *Tel:* 212-698-7000, pg 226

Shields, Duncan, Doubleday Canada, One Toronto St, Suite 300, Toronto, ON M5C 2V6, Canada *Tel:* 416-364-4449 *Fax:* 416-364-6863 *Web Site:* www.randomhouse.ca, pg 479

Shields, Duncan, Knopf Canada, One Toronto St, Suite 300, Toronto, ON M5C 2V6, Canada *Tel:* 416-364-4449 *Toll Free Tel:* 888-523-9292 *Fax:* 416-364-6863 *Web Site:* www.randomhouse.ca, pg 490

Shields, Duncan, Penguin Random House Canada Limited, 320 Front St W, Suite 1400, Toronto, ON M5V 3B6, Canada *Tel:* 416-364-4449 *Toll Free Tel:* 888-523-9292 (cust serv) *Fax:* 416-364-6863; 416-364-6653 (subs rts) *Web Site:* penguinrandomhouse.ca, pg 495

Shields, Duncan, Seal Books, One Toronto St, Suite 300, Toronto, ON M5C 2V6, Canada *Tel:* 416-364-4449 *Toll Free Tel:* 888-523-9292 (order desk) *Fax:* 416-364-6863 *Web Site:* www.randomhouse.ca, pg 498

Shigekawa, Joan, The National Endowment for the Arts, Nancy Hanks Ctr, Rm 703, 1100 Pennsylvania Ave NW, Washington, DC 20506-0001 *Tel:* 202-682-5400 *Web Site:* www.arts.gov; www.nea.gov, pg 623

Shih, Amanda, Perigee Books, 375 Hudson St, New York, NY 10014 *Tel:* 212-366-2000 *Fax:* 212-366-2365 *E-mail:* perigeebooks@us.penguingroup.com *Web Site:* www.penguin.com, pg 189

Shillingford, Gordon, J Gordon Shillingford Publishing Inc, PO Box 86, RPO Corydon Ave, Winnipeg, MB R3M 3S3, Canada *Tel:* 204-779-6967 *Web Site:* www.jgshillingford.com, pg 498

Shimkus, Tony, Concordia Publishing House, 3558 S Jefferson Ave, St Louis, MO 63118-3968 *Tel:* 314-268-1000; 314-268-1268 (bookshop) *Toll Free Tel:* 800-325-3040 (cust serv) *Toll Free Fax:* 800-490-9889 (cust serv) *E-mail:* order@cph.org *Web Site:* www.cph.org, pg 62

Shin, Ann, W W Norton & Company Inc, 500 Fifth Ave, New York, NY 10110-0017 *Tel:* 212-354-5500 *Toll Free Tel:* 800-233-4830 (orders & cust serv) *Fax:* 212-869-0856 *Toll Free Fax:* 800-458-6515 *Web Site:* www.wwnorton.com, pg 172

Shin, Jinna, Random House Children's Books, 1745 Broadway, New York, NY 10019 *Tel:* 212-782-9000 *Toll Free Tel:* 800-200-3552 *Fax:* 212-782-9452 *Web Site:* randomhousekids.com, pg 204

Shine, Deborah, Star Bright Books Inc, 13 Landsdowne St, Cambridge, MA 02139 *Tel:* 617-354-1300 *Fax:* 617-354-1399 *E-mail:* info@starbrightbooks.com; orders@starbrightbooks.com *Web Site:* www.starbrightbooks.com, pg 234

Shipman, Leslie, National Book Awards, 90 Broad St, Suite 604, New York, NY 10004 *Tel:* 212-685-0261 *Fax:* 212-213-6570 *E-mail:* nationalbook@nationalbook.org *Web Site:* www.nationalbook.org, pg 710

Shippy, Karen, Wm B Eerdmans Publishing Co, 2140 Oak Industrial Dr NE, Grand Rapids, MI 49505 *Tel:* 616-459-4591 *Toll Free Tel:* 800-253-7521 *Fax:* 616-459-6540 *E-mail:* customerservice@eerdmans.com; sales@eerdmans.com *Web Site:* www.eerdmans.com, pg 80

Shirzad, Mr Farhad, Ibex Publishers, PO Box 30087, Bethesda, MD 20824 *Tel:* 301-718-8188 *Toll Free Tel:* 888-718-8188 *Fax:* 301-907-8707 *E-mail:* info@ibexpub.com *Web Site:* www.ibexpublishers.com, pg 117

Shnookal, Deborah, Ocean Press, 511 Avenue of the Americas, Suite 96, New York, NY 10011-8436 *Tel:* 212-260-3690 *E-mail:* info@oceanbooks.com.au; orders@oceanbooks.com.au (orders only) *Web Site:* www.oceanbooks.com.au, pg 173

Shoemaker, Jack, Counterpoint Press LLC, 1919 Fifth St, Berkeley, CA 94710 *Tel:* 510-704-0230 *Fax:* 510-704-0268 *E-mail:* info@counterpointpress.com *Web Site:* counterpointpress.com; www.sierraclub.org/books; softskull.com, pg 65

Shokoff, Elisa, Simon & Schuster Audio, 1230 Avenue of the Americas, New York, NY 10020 *Web Site:* audio.simonandschuster.com, pg 225

Shook, Sharon, Harvest House Publishers Inc, 990 Owen Loop N, Eugene, OR 97402-9173 *Tel:* 541-343-0123 *Toll Free Tel:* 888-501-6991 *Fax:* 541-342-6410 *E-mail:* admin@harvesthousepublishers.com *Web Site:* harvesthousepublishers.com, pg 107

Shor, Deborah, Oxford University Press USA, 198 Madison Ave, New York, NY 10016 *Tel:* 212-726-6000 *Toll Free Tel:* 800-451-7556 (orders); 800-445-9714 (cust serv) *Fax:* 919-677-1303 *E-mail:* custserv.us@oup.com *Web Site:* www.oup.com/us, pg 179

Shore, Dr Linda, The Astronomical Society of the Pacific, 390 Ashton Ave, San Francisco, CA 94112 *Tel:* 415-337-1100 *Toll Free Tel:* 800-335-2624 *Fax:* 415-337-5205 *Web Site:* www.astrosociety.org, pg 26

Shorney, John, Hope Publishing Co, 380 S Main Place, Carol Stream, IL 60188 *Tel:* 630-665-3200 *Toll Free Tel:* 800-323-1049 *Fax:* 630-665-2552 *E-mail:* hope@hopepublishing.com *Web Site:* www.hopepublishing.com, pg 114

Shorney, Scott A, Hope Publishing Co, 380 S Main Place, Carol Stream, IL 60188 *Tel:* 630-665-3200 *Toll Free Tel:* 800-323-1049 *Fax:* 630-665-2552 *E-mail:* hope@hopepublishing.com *Web Site:* www.hopepublishing.com, pg 114

Shorney, Steve, Hope Publishing Co, 380 S Main Place, Carol Stream, IL 60188 *Tel:* 630-665-3200 *Toll Free Tel:* 800-323-1049 *Fax:* 630-665-2552 *E-mail:* hope@hopepublishing.com *Web Site:* www.hopepublishing.com, pg 114

Short, Mark, Houghton Mifflin Harcourt, 222 Berkeley St, Boston, MA 02116 *Tel:* 617-351-5000 *Toll Free Tel:* 800-225-5425 (K-12 educ materials); 800-323-9540 (assessment materials); 877-219-1537 (SkillsTutor); 888-242-6747 (Destination; Earobics; Edmark; Learning Village; Riverdeep); 800-225-3362 (Houghton Mifflin Harcourt Trade & Reference Publishers) *Toll Free Fax:* 800-269-5232 *E-mail:* customerservice@hmhpub.com *Web Site:* www.hmhco.com, pg 115

Short, Sharon, Antioch Writers' Workshop, 900 Dayton St, Yellow Springs, OH 45387 *Tel:* 937-769-1803 *E-mail:* info@antiochwritersworkshop.com *Web Site:* www.antiochwritersworkshop.com, pg 649

Shotts, Jeffrey, Graywolf Press, 250 Third Ave N, Suite 600, Minneapolis, MN 55401 *Tel:* 651-641-0077 *Fax:* 651-641-0036 *E-mail:* wolves@graywolfpress.org *Web Site:* www.graywolfpress.org, pg 100

Shoults, Janice, EDGE Science Fiction & Fantasy Publishing, PO Box 1714, Sta M, Calgary, AB T2P 2L7, Canada *Tel:* 403-254-0160 *Web Site:* www.edgewebsite.com, pg 479

Shoup, William, SSPC: The Society for Protective Coatings, 40 24 St, 6th fl, Pittsburgh, PA 15222-4656 *Tel:* 412-281-2331 *Toll Free Tel:* 877-281-7772 (US only) *Fax:* 412-281-9992 *E-mail:* info@sspc.org *Web Site:* www.sspc.org, pg 233

Shows, Dawn, Eric Hoffer Award for Independent Books, PO Box 11, Titusville, NJ 08560 *Fax:* 609-964-1718 *E-mail:* info@hofferaward.com *Web Site:* www.hofferaward.com, pg 692

Shrestha, Heather, Brookes Publishing Co Inc, PO Box 10624, Baltimore, MD 21285-0624 *Tel:* 410-337-9580 (outside US & CN) *Toll Free Tel:* 800-638-3775 (US & CN) *Fax:* 410-337-8539 *E-mail:* custserv@brookespublishing.com *Web Site:* www.brookespublishing.com, pg 46

Shreve, Jeff, W W Norton & Company Inc, 500 Fifth Ave, New York, NY 10110-0017 *Tel:* 212-354-5500 *Toll Free Tel:* 800-233-4830 (orders & cust serv) *Fax:* 212-869-0856 *Toll Free Fax:* 800-458-6515 *Web Site:* www.wwnorton.com, pg 172

Shughart, William II, Independent Institute, 100 Swan Way, Oakland, CA 94621-1428 *Tel:* 510-632-1366 *Toll Free Tel:* 800-927-8733 *Fax:* 510-568-6040 *E-mail:* orders@independent.org *Web Site:* www.independent.org, pg 120

Shukla, Ajay, McGraw-Hill International Publishing Group, 2 Penn Plaza, New York, NY 10121 *Tel:* 212-904-2000 *Web Site:* www.mcgraw-hill.com, pg 152

Shultz, Melissa, Jim Donovan Literary, 5635 SMU Blvd, Suite 201, Dallas, TX 75206 *Tel:* 214-696-9411 *E-mail:* jdlqueries@sbcglobal.net, pg 549

Shumaker, Bradley E, Center for Creative Leadership LLC, One Leadership Place, Greensboro, NC 27410-9427 *Tel:* 336-545-2810; 336-288-7210 *Fax:* 336-282-3284 *E-mail:* info@ccl.org *Web Site:* www.ccl.org/publications, pg 53

Shuman, Eric, Harcourt Achieve, 6277 Sea Harbor Dr, Orlando, FL 32887 *Tel:* 407-345-2000 *Toll Free Tel:* 800-531-5015 (cust serv/orders) *Toll Free Fax:* 800-699-9459 (cust serv/orders) *Web Site:* www.harcourtachieve.com, pg 104

Shuman, Eric, Harcourt Inc, 6277 Sea Harbor Dr, Orlando, FL 32887 *Tel:* 407-345-2000 *Toll Free Tel:* 800-225-5425 (cust serv/orders) *Toll Free Fax:* 800-269-5232 (cust serv/orders) *Web Site:* www.hmhco.com, pg 105

Shuman, Eric, Houghton Mifflin Harcourt, 222 Berkeley St, Boston, MA 02116 *Tel:* 617-351-5000 *Toll Free Tel:* 800-225-5425 (K-12 educ materials); 800-323-9540 (assessment materials); 877-219-1537 (SkillsTutor); 888-242-6747 (Destination; Earobics; Edmark; Learning Village; Riverdeep); 800-225-3362 (Houghton Mifflin Harcourt Trade & Reference Publishers) *Toll Free Fax:* 800-269-5232 *E-mail:* customerservice@hmhpub.com *Web Site:* www.hmhco.com, pg 115

Shumate, Tom, Association of Catholic Publishers Inc, 4725 Dorsey Hall Dr, Suite A, PMB 709, Elliott City, MD 21042 *Tel:* 410-988-2926 *Fax:* 410-571-4946 *Web Site:* www.catholicsread.org; www.catholicpublishers.org; www.midatlanticcongress.org, pg 598

Shumway, Sarah, Bloomsbury Publishing Inc, 1385 Broadway, 5th fl, New York, NY 10018 *Tel:* 212-419-5300 *E-mail:* marketingusa@bloomsbury.com; adultpublicityusa@bloomsbury.com; askacademic@bloomsbury.com *Web Site:* www.bloomsbury.com, pg 40

Shur, Rudy, Square One Publishers Inc, 115 Herricks Rd, Garden City Park, NY 11040 *Tel:* 516-535-2010 *Toll Free Tel:* 877-900-BOOK (900-2665) *Fax:* 516-535-2014 *E-mail:* sq1publish@aol.com *Web Site:* www.squareonepublishers.com, pg 232

Shurtleff, William, Soyinfo Center, PO Box 234, Lafayette, CA 94549-0234 *Tel:* 925-283-2991 *E-mail:* info@soyinfocenter.com *Web Site:* www.soyinfocenter.com, pg 231

Shuster, Todd, Zachary Shuster Harmsworth Agency, 1776 Broadway, Suite 1405, New York, NY 10019 *Tel:* 212-765-6900 *Fax:* 212-765-6490 *Web Site:* www.zshliterary.com, pg 580

Sibbald, Anne, Janklow & Nesbit Associates, 445 Park Ave, New York, NY 10022 *Tel:* 212-421-1700 *Fax:* 212-980-3671 *E-mail:* info@janklow.com *Web Site:* www.janklowandnesbit.com, pg 558

Sibley, Ellen, Barron's Educational Series Inc, 250 Wireless Blvd, Hauppauge, NY 11788 *Tel:* 631-434-3311 *Toll Free Tel:* 800-645-3476 *Fax:* 631-434-3723 *E-mail:* barrons@barronseduc.com *Web Site:* www.barronseduc.com, pg 31

Siciliano, John, Penguin Books, 375 Hudson St, New York, NY 10014 *Tel:* 212-366-2000 *E-mail:* online@penguinputnam.com *Web Site:* www.penguinputnam.com; www.penguinclassics.com; us.penguingroup.com, pg 186

Sickles, Danielle, Jane Rotrosen Agency LLC, 318 E 51 St, New York, NY 10022 *Tel:* 212-593-4330 *Fax:* 212-935-6985 *Web Site:* janerotrosen.com, pg 571

Sicoli, Dan, Slipstream Annual Poetry Chapbook Contest, PO Box 2071, Dept W-1, Niagara Falls, NY 14301 *Web Site:* www.slipstreampress.org, pg 729

Siconolfi, Marcie, Cold Spring Harbor Laboratory Press, 500 Sunnyside Blvd, Woodbury, NY 11797-2924 *Tel:* 516-422-4100 *Toll Free Tel:* 800-843-4388 *Fax:* 516-422-4097; 516-422-4092 (submissions) *E-mail:* cshpress@cshl.edu *Web Site:* www.cshlpress.com, pg 60

Siddiqui, Shereen, Dissertation.com, 23331 Water Circle, Boca Raton, FL 33486-8540 *Tel:* 561-750-4344 *Toll Free Tel:* 800-636-8329 *Fax:* 561-750-6797 *Web Site:* www.dissertation.com, pg 74

Sidi, Rafael, ProQuest LLC, 789 E Eisenhower Pkwy, Ann Arbor, MI 48108-3218 *Tel:* 734-761-4700 *Toll Free Tel:* 800-521-0600 *Fax:* 734-975-6486 *Toll Free Fax:* 800-864-0019 *E-mail:* info@proquest.com *Web Site:* www.proquest.com, pg 199

Siegel, Lois, National Press Club of Canada Foundation Inc, 17 York St, Suite 201, Ottawa, ON K1N 9J6, Canada *E-mail:* info@pressclubcanada.ca *Web Site:* pressclubcanada.ca, pg 613

Siegel, Maury, Associated Editors, 27 W 96 St, New York, NY 10025 *Tel:* 212-662-9703, pg 520

Siegel, Rosalie, Rosalie Siegel, International Literary Agent Inc, One Abey Dr, Pennington, NJ 08534 *Tel:* 609-737-1007 *Fax:* 609-737-3708 *Web Site:* www.rosaliesiegel.com, pg 573

Siegel, Roz, Fine Creative Media, Inc, 322 Eighth Ave, 15th fl, New York, NY 10001 *Tel:* 212-595-3500 *Fax:* 212-595-3779, pg 88

Sieger, Peter, Teachers College Press, 1234 Amsterdam Ave, New York, NY 10027 *Tel:* 212-678-3929 *Toll Free Tel:* 800-575-6566 *Fax:* 212-678-4149; 802-864-7626 *E-mail:* tcpress@tc.columbia.edu; tcp.orders@aidcvt.com (orders) *Web Site:* www.teacherscollegepress.com, pg 241

Siembieda, Kevin, Palladium Books Inc, 39074 Webb Ct, Westland, MI 48185 *Tel:* 734-721-2903 (orders) *Fax:* 734-721-1238 *Web Site:* www.palladiumbooks.com, pg 180

Siemens, John, Crabtree Publishing Co, 350 Fifth Ave, 59th fl, PMB 59051, New York, NY 10118 *Tel:* 212-496-5040 *Toll Free Tel:* 800-387-7650 *Toll Free Fax:* 800-355-7166 *E-mail:* custserv@crabtreebooks.com *Web Site:* www.crabtreebooks.com, pg 66

Siemens, John, Crabtree Publishing Co Ltd, 616 Welland Ave, St Catharines, ON L2M-5V6, Canada *Tel:* 905-682-5221 *Toll Free Tel:* 800-387-7650 *Fax:* 905-682-7166 *Toll Free Fax:* 800-355-7166 *E-mail:* custserv@crabtreebooks.com; sales@crabtreebooks.com; orders@crabtreebooks.com *Web Site:* www.crabtreebooks.com, pg 478

Sierra, Hector, National Geographic Books, 1145 17 St NW, Washington, DC 20036-4688 *Tel:* 202-857-7000 *Fax:* 202-857-7670 *Web Site:* books.nationalgeographic.com/books, pg 165

Sigfrids, Chris, Crown Publishing Group, c/o Penguin Random House Inc, 1745 Broadway, New York, NY 10019 *Tel:* 212-782-9000 *Toll Free Tel:* 888-264-1745 *Fax:* 212-940-7408 *E-mail:* crownosm@penguinrandomhouse.com *Web Site:* crownpublishing.com, pg 68

Sigfrids, Chris, WaterBrook Multnomah Publishing Group, 12265 Oracle Blvd, Suite 200, Colorado Springs, CO 80921 *Tel:* 719-590-4999 *Toll Free Tel:* 800-603-7051 (orders) *Fax:* 719-590-8977 *Toll Free Fax:* 800-294-5686 (orders) *E-mail:* info@waterbrookmultnomah.com *Web Site:* waterbrookmultnomah.com, pg 267

Signorino, Kathy, Individual Excellence Awards, 30 E Broad St, 33rd fl, Columbus, OH 43215 *Tel:* 614-466-2613 *Fax:* 614-466-4494 *Web Site:* www.oac.state.oh.us, pg 695

Sigona, Serena, Crown Publishing Group, c/o Penguin Random House Inc, 1745 Broadway, New York, NY 10019 *Tel:* 212-782-9000 *Toll Free Tel:* 888-264-1745 *Fax:* 212-940-7408 *E-mail:* crownosm@penguinrandomhouse.com *Web Site:* crownpublishing.com, pg 68

Silber, Blake, Bridge Publications Inc, 5600 E Olympic Blvd, Commerce City, CA 90022 *Tel:* 323-888-6200 *Toll Free Tel:* 800-722-1733 *Fax:* 323-888-6202 *E-mail:* info@bridgepub.com *Web Site:* www.bridgepub.com, pg 45

Silberfeld, Ms Heath Lynn, Enough Said, 3959 NW 29 Lane, Gainesville, FL 32606 *Tel:* 352-262-2971 *Fax:* 352-372-5747 (call first) *E-mail:* enoughsaid@cox.net *Web Site:* users.navi.net/~heathlynn, pg 525

Silberman, Karen, Federal Bar Association, 1220 N Filmore St, Suite 444, Arlington, VA 22201 *Tel:* 571-481-9100 *Fax:* 571-481-9090 *E-mail:* fba@fedbar.org *Web Site:* www.fedbar.org, pg 87

Silbersack, John, Philip K Dick Award, PO Box 3447, Hoboken, NJ 07030 *Tel:* 201-876-2551 *Web Site:* www.philipkdickaward.org, pg 681

Silbersack, John, Trident Media Group LLC, 41 Madison Ave, 36th fl, New York, NY 10010 *Tel:* 212-333-1511 *E-mail:* info@tridentmediagroup.com; press@tridentmediagroup.com *Web Site:* www.tridentmediagroup.com, pg 577

Sileno, Helen, LearningExpress LLC, 2 Rector St, 26th fl, New York, NY 10006 *Tel:* 212-995-2566 *Toll Free Tel:* 800-295-9556 (ext 2) *Fax:* 212-995-5512 *E-mail:* customerservice@learningexpressllc.com (cust serv) *Web Site:* www.learningexpressllc.com, pg 136

Silfin, Beth, HarperCollins General Books Group, 195 Broadway, New York, NY 10007 *Tel:* 212-207-7000 *Web Site:* www.harpercollins.com, pg 105

Sillah, Andrea, R S Means from The Gordian Group, 1099 Hingham St, Suite 201, Rockland, MA 02370 *Tel:* 781-422-5000 *Toll Free Tel:* 800-448-8182 *Fax:* 781-585-8814 *Toll Free Fax:* 800-632-6701 *Web Site:* www.rsmeans.com, pg 153

Silva, Daniel, ZOVA Books, PO Box 21833, Long Beach, CA 90801 *Tel:* 805-426-9682 *Fax:* 562-394-9568 *Web Site:* www.zovabooks.com, pg 280

Silver, David, YMAA Publication Center, PO Box 480, Wolfeboro, NH 03894 *Tel:* 603-569-7988 *Toll Free Tel:* 800-669-8892 *Fax:* 603-569-1889 *E-mail:* ymaa@aol.com *Web Site:* www.ymaa.com, pg 278

Silver, Janet, Zachary Shuster Harmsworth Agency, 1776 Broadway, Suite 1405, New York, NY 10019 *Tel:* 212-765-6900 *Fax:* 212-765-6490 *Web Site:* www.zshliterary.com, pg 580

Silver, Joanne S, Beach Lloyd Publishers LLC, 40 Cabot Dr, Wayne, PA 19087-5619 *Tel:* 610-407-9107 *Fax:* 775-254-0633 *E-mail:* beachlloyd@erols.com *Web Site:* www.beachlloyd.com, pg 32

Silver, Tom, Leadership Directories, 1407 Broadway, Suite 318, New York, NY 10018 *Tel:* 212-627-4140 *Fax:* 212-645-0931 *E-mail:* info@leadershipdirectories.com *Web Site:* www.leadershipdirectories.com, pg 135

Silverman, David, American Atheist Press, PO Box 158, Cranford, NJ 07016 *Tel:* 908-276-7300 *Fax:* 908-276-7402 *Web Site:* www.atheists.org, pg 11

Silverman, Erica Rand, Sterling Lord Literistic Inc, 65 Bleecker St, New York, NY 10012 *Tel:* 212-780-6050 *Fax:* 212-780-6095 *E-mail:* info@sll.com *Web Site:* www.sll.com, pg 575

Silverman, Leanne, Rowman & Littlefield Publishers Inc, 4501 Forbes Blvd, Suite 200, Lanham, MD 20706 *Tel:* 301-459-3366 *Toll Free Tel:* 800-462-6420 (cust serv) *Fax:* 301-429-5748 *Web Site:* www.rowmanlittlefield.com, pg 212

Silverstein, Clara, Chautauqua Writers' Workshop, PO Box 28, Chautauqua, NY 14722-0408 *Tel:* 716-357-6316; 716-357-6250 *Toll Free Tel:* 800-836-ARTS (836-2787) *Fax:* 716-269-7444 *Web Site:* writers.ciweb.org, pg 650

Silvestro, Denise, Berkley Books, 375 Hudson St, New York, NY 10014 *Tel:* 212-366-2000 *Fax:* 212-366-2666 *E-mail:* online@penguinputnam.com *Web Site:* www.penguinputnam.com; us.penguingroup.com, pg 35

Silvestro, Denise, Berkley Publishing Group, 375 Hudson St, New York, NY 10014 *Tel:* 212-366-2000 *Fax:* 212-366-2385 *E-mail:* online@penguinputnam.com *Web Site:* us.penguingroup.com, pg 35

Silvis, Carol, Pennwriters Conference, 5706 Sonoma Ridge, Missouri City, TX 77459 *Web Site:* www.pennwriters.org, pg 654

Simmons, Ann, McLemore Prize, PO Box 571, Jackson, MS 39205-0571 *Tel:* 601-576-6850 *Fax:* 601-576-6975 *E-mail:* mhs@mdah.state.ms.us *Web Site:* www.mdah.state.ms.us, pg 707

Simmons, Ann, Pie in the Sky Publishing LLC, 8031 E Phillips Circle, Centennial, CO 80112 *Tel:* 303-773-0851 *Fax:* 303-773-0851 *E-mail:* pieintheskypublishing@msn.com *Web Site:* www.pieintheskypublishing.com, pg 191

Simmons, Carolyn, Getty Publications, 1200 Getty Center Dr, Suite 500, Los Angeles, CA 90049-1682 *Tel:* 310-440-7365 *Toll Free Tel:* 800-223-3431 (orders) *Fax:* 310-440-7758 *E-mail:* pubsinfo@getty.edu *Web Site:* www.getty.edu/publications, pg 96

Simmons, Zoe, PAGE International Screenwriting Awards, 7510 Sunset Blvd, Suite 610, Hollywood, CA 90046 *E-mail:* info@pageawards.com *Web Site:* www.pageawards.com, pg 716

Simms, Maria K, Starcrafts LLC, 334-A Calef Hwy, Epping, NH 03042 *Tel:* 603-734-4300 *Toll Free Tel:* 866-953-8458 (24/7 message ctr) *Fax:* 603-734-4311 *E-mail:* astrosales@astrocom.com; starcrafts@comcast.net *Web Site:* www.astrocom.com; starcraftspublishing.com; acspublications.com, pg 234

Simon, Daniel, Neustadt International Prize for Literature, c/o University of Oklahoma, 630 Parrington Oval, Suite 110, Norman, OK 73019-4033 *Tel:* 405-325-4531 *Fax:* 405-325-7495 *Web Site:* www.worldliteraturetoday.org, pg 712

Simon, Daniel, NSK Neustadt Prize for Children's Literature, c/o University of Oklahoma, 630 Parrington Oval, Suite 110, Norman, OK 73019-4033 *Tel:* 405-325-4531 *Fax:* 405-325-7495 *Web Site:* www.worldliteraturetoday.org, pg 714

Simon, Daniel, Seven Stories Press, 140 Watts St, New York, NY 10013 *Tel:* 212-226-8760 *Toll Free Tel:* 800-733-3000 (orders) *Fax:* 212-226-1411 *E-mail:* info@sevenstories.com *Web Site:* www.sevenstories.com, pg 222

Simon, Elizabeth, Council on Social Work Education (CSWE), 1701 Duke St, Suite 200, Alexandria, VA 22314-3457 *Tel:* 703-683-8080 *Fax:* 703-683-8493 *E-mail:* publications@cswe.org; info@cswe.org *Web Site:* www.cswe.org, pg 65

Simon, Peter J, W W Norton & Company Inc, 500 Fifth Ave, New York, NY 10110-0017 *Tel:* 212-354-5500 *Toll Free Tel:* 800-233-4830 (orders & cust serv) *Fax:* 212-869-0856 *Toll Free Fax:* 800-458-6515 *Web Site:* www.wwnorton.com, pg 171

Simon, Rebecca, University of California Press, 2120 Berkeley Way, Berkeley, CA 94704-1012 *Tel:* 510-642-4247 *Fax:* 510-643-7127 *E-mail:* askucp@ucpress.edu (books); customerservice@ucpressjournals.com *Web Site:* www.ucpress.edu, pg 255

Simon, Robin, Berkley Books, 375 Hudson St, New York, NY 10014 *Tel:* 212-366-2000 *Fax:* 212-366-2666 *E-mail:* online@penguinputnam.com *Web Site:* www.penguinputnam.com; us.penguingroup.com, pg 35

Simon, Robin, Berkley Publishing Group, 375 Hudson St, New York, NY 10014 *Tel:* 212-366-2000 *Fax:* 212-366-2385 *E-mail:* online@penguinputnam.com *Web Site:* us.penguingroup.com, pg 35

Simon, Tami, Sounds True Inc, 413 S Arthur Ave, Louisville, CO 80027 *Tel:* 303-665-3151 *Toll Free Tel:* 800-333-9185 *E-mail:* customerservice@soundstrue.com *Web Site:* www.soundstrue.com, pg 230

Simonello, Lorraine, Morehouse Publishing, 19 E 34 St, New York, NY 10016 *Tel:* 212-592-1800 *Toll Free Tel:* 800-672-1789 (retail orders only); 800-251-3320 (wholesale orders only) *Web Site:* www.morehousepublishing.com; www.churchpublishing.org, pg 160

Simonoff, Eric, WME, 1325 Avenue of the Americas, New York, NY 10019 *Tel:* 212-586-5100 *Fax:* 212-246-3583 *E-mail:* wma@interport.net *Web Site:* www.wma.com, pg 579

Simons, D Brenton, Newbury Street Press, 101 Newbury St, Boston, MA 02116 *Tel:* 617-536-5740 *Toll Free Tel:* 888-296-3447 (NEHGS membership) *Fax:* 617-536-7307 *E-mail:* sales@nehgs.org *Web Site:* www.newenglandancestors.org, pg 169

Simons, Jasper, American Psychological Association, 750 First St NE, Washington, DC 20002-4242 *Tel:* 202-336-5510 *Toll Free Tel:* 800-374-2721 *Fax:* 202-336-5502 *E-mail:* order@apa.org *Web Site:* www.apa.org/books, pg 15

Simons, Jasper, American Psychological Association, 750 First St NE, Washington, DC 20002-4242 *Tel:* 202-336-5500 *Toll Free Tel:* 800-374-2721 *E-mail:* order@apa.org *Web Site:* www.apa.org, pg 596

Simonsen, Reka, Simon & Schuster Children's Publishing, 1230 Avenue of the Americas, New York, NY 10020 *Tel:* 212-698-7000 *Web Site:* KIDS.SimonandSchuster.com; TEEN.SimonandSchuster.com; simonandschuster.net; simonandschuster.biz, pg 225

Simpson, Amy, University of Alaska Press, 794 University Ave, Suite 220, Fairbanks, AK 99709 *Tel:* 907-474-5831 *Toll Free Tel:* 888-252-6657 (US only) *Fax:* 907-474-5502 *E-mail:* fypress@uaf.edu *Web Site:* www.uaf.edu/uapress, pg 254

Simpson, Erin, Penguin Random House Speakers Bureau, 1745 Broadway, Mail Drop 13-1, New York, NY 10019 *Tel:* 212-572-2013 *E-mail:* speakers@penguinrandomhouse.com *Web Site:* www.prhspeakers.com, pg 588

Simpson, Fiona, Simon & Schuster Children's Publishing, 1230 Avenue of the Americas, New York, NY 10020 *Tel:* 212-698-7000 *Web Site:* KIDS.SimonandSchuster.com; TEEN.SimonandSchuster.com; simonandschuster.net; simonandschuster.biz, pg 225

Simpson, Jenna, House of Anansi Press Inc, 110 Spadina Ave, Suite 801, Toronto, ON M5V 2K4, Canada *Tel:* 416-363-4343 *Fax:* 416-363-1017 *E-mail:* customerservice@houseofanansi.com *Web Site:* www.houseofanansi.com, pg 488

Simpson, Jennie, American Anthropological Association (AAA), 2300 Clarendon Blvd, Suite 1301, Arlington, VA 22201 *Tel:* 703-528-1902 *Fax:* 703-528-3546 *Web Site:* www.aaanet.org, pg 10

Simpson, Michael, Carter G Woodson Book Awards, 8555 16 St, Suite 500, Silver Spring, MD 20910 *Tel:* 301-588-1800 *Toll Free Tel:* 800-296-7840 *Fax:* 301-588-2049 *E-mail:* excellence@ncss.org; publications@ncss.org *Web Site:* www.socialstudies.org, pg 737

Simpson, Shayla, Western Heritage Awards (Wrangler Award), 1700 NE 63 St, Oklahoma City, OK 73111 *Tel:* 405-478-2250 *Fax:* 405-478-4714 *E-mail:* info@nationalcowboymuseum.org *Web Site:* www.nationalcowboymuseum.org, pg 735

Simpson-Vos, Mark, The University of North Carolina Press, 116 S Boundary St, Chapel Hill, NC 27514-3808 *Tel:* 919-966-3561 *Fax:* 919-966-3829 *E-mail:* uncpress@unc.edu *Web Site:* www.uncpress.unc.edu, pg 258

Simqu, Blaise, Pine Forge Press, 2455 Teller Rd, Thousand Oaks, CA 91320 *Tel:* 805-499-4224; 805-499-9774 (orders) *Fax:* 805-499-0871 (orders) *E-mail:* info@sagepub.com *Web Site:* www.sagepub.com; www.pineforge.com, pg 192

Simqu, Blaise R, SAGE Publications, 2455 Teller Rd, Thousand Oaks, CA 91320 *Toll Free Tel:* 800-818-7243 *Toll Free Fax:* 800-583-2665 *E-mail:* info@sagepub.com *Web Site:* www.sagepub.com, pg 214

Sims, Michael, The MIT Press, 55 Hayward St, Cambridge, MA 02142 *Tel:* 617-253-5255 *Toll Free Tel:* 800-207-8354 (orders) *Fax:* 617-258-6779; 617-577-1545 (orders) *Web Site:* mitpress.mit.edu, pg 158

Sims-Nichols, Rebecca, Cedar Grove Books, 2215 High Point Dr, Carrollton, TX 75007 *Tel:* 415-364-8292 *Fax:* 415-276-9858 *E-mail:* queries@cedargrovebooks.com *Web Site:* www.cedargrovebooks.com, pg 52

Sinasac, Joseph, Novalis Publishing, 10 Lower Spadina Ave, Suite 400, Toronto, ON M5V 2Z2, Canada *Tel:* 416-363-3303 *Toll Free Tel:* 877-702-7773 *Fax:* 416-363-9409 *Toll Free Fax:* 877-702-7775 *E-mail:* books@novalis.ca *Web Site:* www.novalis.ca, pg 493

Sinauer, Andrew D, Sinauer Associates Inc, 23 Plumtree Rd, Sunderland, MA 01375 *Tel:* 413-549-4300 *Fax:* 413-549-1118 *E-mail:* publish@sinauer.com; orders@sinauer.com *Web Site:* www.sinauer.com, pg 226

Sinclair, Stephanie, Transatlantic Agency, 2 Bloor St E, Suite 3500, Toronto, ON M4W 1A8, Canada *Tel:* 416-488-9214 *E-mail:* info@transatlanticagency.com *Web Site:* www.transatlanticagency.com, pg 577

Sindler, Jessica, Random House Publishing Group, 1745 Broadway, New York, NY 10019 *Toll Free Tel:* 800-200-3552 *Web Site:* atrandom.com, pg 204

Singerman, Jerome E, University of Pennsylvania Press, 3905 Spruce St, Philadelphia, PA 19104 *Tel:* 215-898-6261 *Fax:* 215-898-0404 *E-mail:* custserv@pobox.upenn.edu *Web Site:* www.pennpress.org, pg 259

Sinnett, Gina, Humanix Books LLC, PO Box 20989, West Palm Beach, FL 33416 *Tel:* 561-459-5997 *Toll Free Tel:* 855-371-7810 *Fax:* 561-241-6448 *Toll Free Fax:* 855-371-7809 *E-mail:* info@humanixbooks.com *Web Site:* www.humanixbooks.com, pg 117

Sinnett, William, Financial Executives Research Foundation Inc (FERF), West Tower, 7th fl, 1250 Headquarters Plaza, Morristown, NJ 07960-6837 *Tel:* 973-765-1000 *Fax:* 973-765-1023 *Web Site:* www.financialexecutives.org, pg 88

Sinocchi, Michael, Productivity Press, c/o Routledge, 711 Third Ave, New York, NY 10017 *Tel:* 212-216-7800 *Toll Free Tel:* 800-634-7064 (orders) *Fax:* 212-563-2269 *Toll Free Fax:* 800-248-4724 (orders) *E-mail:* info@productivitypress.com; orders@taylorandfrancis.com *Web Site:* www.productivitypress.com, pg 198

Sinon, Ines, Dreaming Publications LLC, 1938 Old Balsam Rd, Waynesville, NC 28786 *Tel:* 828-423-0226 *E-mail:* dreamingpublications@gmail.com *Web Site:* dreamingpublications.com, pg 507

Sinsheimer, Jessica, Sarah Jane Freymann Literary Agency LLC, 59 W 71 St, Suite 9-B, New York, NY 10023 *Tel:* 212-362-9277 *E-mail:* submissions@sarahjanefreymann.com *Web Site:* www.sarahjanefreymann.com, pg 553

Sioles, Lee, Louisiana State University Press, 338 Johnston Hall, Baton Rouge, LA 70803 *Tel:* 225-578-6294 *Fax:* 225-578-6461 *E-mail:* lsupress@lsu.edu *Web Site:* lsupress.org, pg 143

Sipe, Keith R, Carolina Academic Press, 700 Kent St, Durham, NC 27701 *Tel:* 919-489-7486 *Toll Free Tel:* 800-489-7486 *Fax:* 919-493-5668 *E-mail:* cap@cap-press.com *Web Site:* www.cap-press.com; www.caplaw.com, pg 50

Sipe, Scott, Carolina Academic Press, 700 Kent St, Durham, NC 27701 *Tel:* 919-489-7486 *Toll Free Tel:* 800-489-7486 *Fax:* 919-493-5668 *E-mail:* cap@cap-press.com *Web Site:* www.cap-press.com; www.caplaw.com, pg 50

Sippola, Carlene, Whole Person Associates Inc, 210 W Michigan St, Duluth, MN 55802-1908 *Tel:* 218-727-0500 *Toll Free Tel:* 800-247-6789 *Fax:* 218-727-0505 *E-mail:* books@wholeperson.com *Web Site:* www.wholeperson.com, pg 271

Sirabian, Karen, Manhattanville College Master of Arts in Writing Program, 2900 Purchase St, Purchase, NY 10577 *Tel:* 914-323-5239 *Fax:* 914-323-3122 *Web Site:* www.mville.edu/writing, pg 661

Siscoe, Nancy, Random House Children's Books, 1745 Broadway, New York, NY 10019 *Tel:* 212-782-9000 *Toll Free Tel:* 800-200-3552 *Fax:* 212-782-9452 *Web Site:* randomhousekids.com, pg 203

Sisk, Jonathan, Rowman & Littlefield Publishers Inc, 4501 Forbes Blvd, Suite 200, Lanham, MD 20706 *Tel:* 301-459-3366 *Toll Free Tel:* 800-462-6420 (cust serv) *Fax:* 301-429-5748 *Web Site:* www.rowmanlittlefield.com, pg 212

Sisler, William P, Harvard University Press, 79 Garden St, Cambridge, MA 02138-1499 *Tel:* 617-495-2600; 401-531-2800 (intl orders) *Toll Free Tel:* 800-405-1619 (orders) *Fax:* 617-495-5898 (general); 617-496-4677 (edit & rts); 401-531-2801 (intl orders) *Toll Free Fax:* 800-406-9145 (orders) *E-mail:* contact_hup@harvard.edu *Web Site:* www.hup.harvard.edu, pg 107

Sisson, Walter R, American Geosciences Institute (AGI), 4220 King St, Alexandria, VA 22302-1502 *Tel:* 703-379-2480 (ext 246) *Fax:* 703-379-7563 *E-mail:* pubs@agiweb.org *Web Site:* www.agiweb.org, pg 13

Sita, Joe, Move Books, PO Box 183, Beacon Falls, CT 06403 *Web Site:* www.move-books.com, pg 508

Sita, Joe, Octane Press, 808 Kinney Ave, Austin, TX 78704 *Tel:* 512-334-9441 *Fax:* 512-852-4737 *E-mail:* info@octanepress.com *Web Site:* www.octanepress.com, pg 174

Sitzes, Jason S, Writers Retreat Workshop (WRW), PO Box 4236, Louisville, KY 40204 *E-mail:* wrw04@netscape.net *Web Site:* www.writersretreatworkshop.com, pg 657

Sivasubramaniam, Jeevan, Berrett-Koehler Publishers Inc, 1333 Broadway, Suite 1000, Oakland, CA 94612 *Tel:* 510-817-2277 *Fax:* 510-817-2278 *E-mail:* bkpub@bkpub.com *Web Site:* www.bkconnection.com, pg 35

Skafidas, Mary, McGraw-Hill Education, 2 Penn Plaza, New York, NY 10121-2298 *Tel:* 212-904-2000 *E-mail:* customer.service@mcgraw-hill.com *Web Site:* www.mheducation.com; www.mheducation.com/custserv.html, pg 151

Skaj, Paul, ABDO Publishing Group, 8000 W 78 St, Suite 310, Edina, MN 55439 *Tel:* 952-831-2120 *Toll Free Tel:* 800-800-1312 *Toll Free Fax:* 800-862-3480 *E-mail:* customerservice@abdopublishing.com *Web Site:* abdopublishing.com, pg 2

Skeel, Joe, The Society of Professional Journalists (SPJ), Eugene S Pulliam National Journalism Ctr, 3909 N Meridian St, Indianapolis, IN 46208 *Tel:* 317-927-8000 *Fax:* 317-920-4789 *E-mail:* spj@spj.org *Web Site:* www.spj.org, pg 620

Skinker, Will, Counterpath Press, 613 22 St, Denver, CO 80205 *E-mail:* counterpath@counterpathpress.org; editors@counterpathpress.org *Web Site:* www.counterpathpress.org, pg 65

Skinner, Heather, University of Minnesota Press, 111 Third Ave S, Suite 290, Minneapolis, MN 55401-2520 *Tel:* 612-627-1970 *Fax:* 612-627-1980 *E-mail:* ump@umn.edu *Web Site:* www.upress.umn.edu, pg 257

Sklare, Rose, Textbook Writers Associates Inc, 25 Crescent St, Suite 733, Waltham, MA 02453 *Tel:* 781-209-0051 *Fax:* 781-899-2084 *Web Site:* www.textbookwriters.com, pg 535

Sklena, Jennifer, Institute of Environmental Sciences and Technology - IEST, 2340 S Arlington Heights Rd, Suite 620, Arlington Heights, IL 60005-4510 *Tel:* 847-981-0100 *Fax:* 847-981-4130 *E-mail:* publications@iest.org *Web Site:* www.iest.org, pg 122

Skokut, Joyce, Educational Book & Media Association (EBMA), 37 Main St, Suite 203, Warrenton, VA 20186 *Tel:* 540-318-7770 *Fax:* 202-962-3939 *E-mail:* info@edupaperback.org *Web Site:* www.edupaperback.org, pg 605

Skolkin, David, Museum of New Mexico Press, 725 Camino Lejo, Suite C, Santa Fe, NM 87505 *Tel:* 505-476-1155; 505-272-7777 (orders) *Toll Free Tel:* 800-249-7737 (orders) *Fax:* 505-476-1156 *Toll Free Fax:* 800-622-8667 (orders) *Web Site:* www.mnmpress.org, pg 162

Skolnick, Irene, Irene Skolnick Literary Agency, 27 W 20 St, Suite 305, New York, NY 10011 *Tel:* 212-727-3648 *Fax:* 212-352-2059 *E-mail:* office@skolnickliterary.com (queries) *Web Site:* www.skolnickagency.com, pg 573

Skrabek, Alison, Living Language, c/o Random House Inc, 1745 Broadway, New York, NY 10019 *Tel:* 212-782-9000 *Toll Free Tel:* 800-733-3000 (orders) *Toll Free Fax:* 800-659-2436 *E-mail:* livinglanguage@randomhouse.com *Web Site:* www.livinglanguage.com, pg 142

Skrabek, Alison, Random House Reference/Random House Puzzles & Games/House of Collectibles, 1745 Broadway, New York, NY 10019 *Toll Free Tel:* 800-733-3000 *Toll Free Fax:* 800-659-2436 *E-mail:* words@random.com; puzzles@random.com, pg 204

Skurnick, Victoria, Levine|Greenberg|Rostan Literary Agency Inc, 307 Seventh Ave, Suite 2407, New York, NY 10001 *Tel:* 212-337-0934 *Fax:* 212-337-0948 *Web Site:* lgrliterary.com, pg 561

Skutt, Alexander, McBooks Press Inc, ID Booth Bldg, 520 N Meadow St, Ithaca, NY 14850 *Tel:* 607-272-2114 *Fax:* 607-273-6068 *E-mail:* mcbooks@mcbooks.com *Web Site:* www.mcbooks.com, pg 150

Slabaugh, Gerri, Adventure Publications, 820 Cleveland St, Cambridge, MN 55008 *Tel:* 763-689-9800 *Toll Free Tel:* 800-678-7006 *Fax:* 763-689-9039 *Toll Free Fax:* 877-374-9016 *E-mail:* custservice@adventurepublications.net; orders@adventurepublications.net *Web Site:* www.adventurepublications.net, pg 5

Slabaugh, Gordon, Adventure Publications, 820 Cleveland St, Cambridge, MN 55008 *Tel:* 763-689-9800 *Toll Free Tel:* 800-678-7006 *Fax:* 763-689-9039 *Toll Free Fax:* 877-374-9016 *E-mail:* custservice@adventurepublications.net; orders@adventurepublications.net *Web Site:* www.adventurepublications.net, pg 5

Slachta, Pedro, Casa Bautista de Publicaciones, 7000 Alabama Ave, El Paso, TX 79904 *Tel:* 915-566-9656 *Toll Free Tel:* 800-755-5958 (cust serv & orders) *Fax:* 915-562-6502; 915-565-9008 (orders) *E-mail:* orders@editorialmh.org *Web Site:* www.editorialmh.org, pg 51

Sladek, Dan, Sunburst Digital Inc, 3150 W Higgins Rd, Suite 140, Hoffman Estates, IL 60169 *Toll Free Tel:* 800-321-7511 *Toll Free Fax:* 888-800-3028 *E-mail:* service@sunburst.com; sales@sunburst.com *Web Site:* sunburst.com; edresources.com, pg 238

Slager, Daniel, Milkweed Editions, 1011 Washington Ave S, Suite 300, Minneapolis, MN 55415-1246 *Tel:* 612-332-3192 *Toll Free Tel:* 800-520-6455 *Fax:* 612-215-2550 *Web Site:* www.milkweed.org, pg 157

Slager, Daniel, Milkweed National Fiction Prize, 1011 Washington Ave S, Suite 300, Minneapolis, MN 55415-1246 *Tel:* 612-332-3192 *Toll Free Tel:* 800-520-6455 *Fax:* 612-215-2550 *E-mail:* submissions@milkweed.org *Web Site:* www.milkweed.org, pg 707

Slater, Alex, Trident Media Group LLC, 41 Madison Ave, 36th fl, New York, NY 10010 *Tel:* 212-333-1511 *E-mail:* info@tridentmediagroup.com; press@tridentmediagroup.com *Web Site:* www.tridentmediagroup.com, pg 578

Slaughter, Joe, Nystrom Herff Jones Education Division, 4719 W 62 St, Indianapolis, IN 46268-2593 *Tel:* 317-612-3901 *Toll Free Tel:* 800-621-8086 (cust serv) *Fax:* 317-329-3305 *E-mail:* info@nystromnet.com *Web Site:* www.nystromnet.com, pg 172

Slavin, Michelle, United States Institute of Peace Press, 2301 Constitution Ave NW, Washington, DC 20037 *Tel:* 202-457-1700 (edit); 703-661-1590 (cust serv) *Toll Free Tel:* 800-868-8064 (cust serv) *Fax:* 202-429-6063; 703-661-1501 (cust serv) *Web Site:* bookstore.usip.org, pg 253

Slavitt, Andrew, OptumInsight™, 12125 Technology Dr, Eden Prairie, MN 55334 *Tel:* 952-833-7100 *Toll Free Tel:* 888-445-8745; 800-765-6713 *Fax:* 952-833-7201 *E-mail:* insight@optum.com *Web Site:* www.optuminsight.com, pg 176

Slawsky, Steve, United Nations Publications, 300 E 42 St, 9th fl, New York, NY 10017 *Tel:* 703-661-1571 *Fax:* 703-996-1010 *E-mail:* publications@un.org *Web Site:* un.org/publications, pg 253

Slayton, Phillip, PEN Canada, 24 Ryerson Ave, Suite 301, Toronto, ON M5T 2P3, Canada *Tel:* 416-703-8448 *Fax:* 416-703-3870 *E-mail:* queries@pencanada.ca *Web Site:* www.pencanada.ca, pg 616

Slesin, Suzanne, Pointed Leaf Press, 136 Baxter St, New York, NY 10013 *Tel:* 212-941-1800 *Fax:* 212-941-1822 *E-mail:* info@pointedleafpress.com *Web Site:* www.pointedleafpress.com, pg 194

Sleven, Paul, Macmillan, 175 Fifth Ave, New York, NY 10010 *Tel:* 646-307-5151 *Fax:* 212-420-9314 *E-mail:* firstname.lastname@macmillan.com *Web Site:* www.macmillan.com, pg 145

Sloan, Barbara Sachs, Global Authors Publications (GAP), 38 Bluegrass, Middleberg, FL 32068 *Tel:* 904-425-1608 *E-mail:* gapbook@yahoo.com *Web Site:* globalauthorspublications.com, pg 97

Sloan, Robert, Indiana University Press, Herman B Wells Library 350, 1320 E Tenth St, Bloomington, IN 47405-3907 *Tel:* 812-855-8817 *Toll Free Tel:* 800-842-6796 (orders only) *Fax:* 812-855-7931; 812-855-8507 *E-mail:* iupress@indiana.edu; iuporder@indiana.edu (orders) *Web Site:* www.iupress.indiana.edu, pg 120

Slopen, Beverley, Beverley Slopen Literary Agency, 131 Bloor St W, Suite 711, Toronto, ON M5S 1S3, Canada *Tel:* 416-964-9598 *Fax:* 416-921-7726 *Web Site:* www.slopenagency.com, pg 574

Slopianka, Sherri, Humanix Books LLC, PO Box 20989, West Palm Beach, FL 33416 *Tel:* 561-459-5997 *Toll Free Tel:* 855-371-7810 *Fax:* 561-241-6448 *Toll Free Fax:* 855-371-7809 *E-mail:* info@humanixbooks.com *Web Site:* www.humanixbooks.com, pg 117

Slovak, Paul, Penguin Books, 375 Hudson St, New York, NY 10014 *Tel:* 212-366-2000 *E-mail:* online@penguinputnam.com *Web Site:* www.penguinputnam.com; www.penguinclassics.com; us.penguingroup.com, pg 186

Slovak, Paul, Viking, 375 Hudson St, New York, NY 10014 *Tel:* 212-366-2000 *E-mail:* online@penguinputnam.com *Web Site:* www.penguinputnam.com; us.penguingroup.com, pg 265

Slutsky, Lorie, Oscar Williams/Gene Derwood Award, 909 Third Ave, New York, NY 10022 *Tel:* 212-686-0010 *Fax:* 212-532-8528 *E-mail:* info@nycommunitytrust.org *Web Site:* www.nycommunitytrust.org, pg 736

Smagler, Alan, Scholastic Trade Division, 557 Broadway, New York, NY 10012 *Tel:* 212-343-6100; 212-343-4685 (export sales) *Fax:* 212-343-4714 (export sales) *Web Site:* www.scholastic.com, pg 219

Small, Christopher, Sinauer Associates Inc, 23 Plumtree Rd, Sunderland, MA 01375 *Tel:* 413-549-4300 *Fax:* 413-549-1118 *E-mail:* publish@sinauer.com; orders@sinauer.com *Web Site:* www.sinauer.com, pg 226

Small, Ellen, Publishing Synthesis Ltd, 39 Crosby St, New York, NY 10013 *Tel:* 212-219-0135 *Fax:* 212-219-0136 *E-mail:* mainmail@pubsyn.com *Web Site:* www.pubsyn.com, pg 533

Small, Kim, Crown Publishing Group, c/o Penguin Random House Inc, 1745 Broadway, New York, NY 10019 *Tel:* 212-782-9000 *Toll Free Tel:* 888-264-1745 *Fax:* 212-940-7408 *E-mail:* crownosm@penguinrandomhouse.com *Web Site:* crownpublishing.com, pg 68

Small, Kim, Watson-Guptill Publications, c/o Random House Inc, 1745 Broadway, New York, NY 10019 *Tel:* 212-782-9000 *Fax:* 212-940-7381 *E-mail:* crownbiz@randomhouse.com *Web Site:* www.randomhouse.com/crown/watsonguptill, pg 268

Small, Rachael, Europa Editions, 214 W 29 St, Suite 1003, New York, NY 10001 *Tel:* 212-868-6844 *Fax:* 212-868-6845 *E-mail:* info@europaeditions.com *Web Site:* www.europaeditions.com, pg 84

Smallfield, Edward, Apogee Press, 2308 Sixth St, Berkeley, CA 94710 *E-mail:* editors.apogee@gmail.com *Web Site:* www.apogeepress.com, pg 19

Smart, Dan, Twenty-Third Publications, One Montauk Ave, Suite 200, New London, CT 06320 *Tel:* 860-437-3012 *Toll Free Tel:* 800-321-0411 (orders) *Toll Free Fax:* 800-572-0788 *E-mail:* 23ppweb@bayard-inc.com *Web Site:* www.twentythirdpublications.com, pg 251

Smathers, Parker, Wesleyan University Press, 215 Long Lane, Middletown, CT 06459-0433 *Tel:* 860-685-7711 *Fax:* 860-685-7712 *Web Site:* www.wesleyan.edu/wespress, pg 269

Smetanka, Dan, Counterpoint Press LLC, 1919 Fifth St, Berkeley, CA 94710 *Tel:* 510-704-0230 *Fax:* 510-704-0268 *E-mail:* info@counterpointpress.com *Web Site:* counterpointpress.com; www.sierraclub.org/books; softskull.com, pg 65

Smiley, Matt, Templeton Press, 300 Conshohocken State Rd, Suite 550, West Conshohocken, PA 19428 *Tel:* 484-531-8380 *Fax:* 484-531-8382 *E-mail:* tpinfo@templetonpress.org *Web Site:* www.templetonpress.org, pg 242

Smiley, Matt, University of Minnesota Press, 111 Third Ave S, Suite 290, Minneapolis, MN 55401-2520 *Tel:* 612-627-1970 *Fax:* 612-627-1980 *E-mail:* ump@umn.edu *Web Site:* www.upress.umn.edu, pg 257

Smist, Erik, The Johns Hopkins University Press, 2715 N Charles St, Baltimore, MD 21218-4363 *Tel:* 410-516-6900; 410-516-6987 (journal orders outside US & CN) *Toll Free Tel:* 800-537-5487 (book orders & cust serv); 800-548-1784 (journal orders) *Fax:* 410-516-6968; 410-516-3866 (journal orders) *E-mail:* hfscustserv@press.jhu.edu (cust serv); jrnlcirc@press.jhu.edu (journal orders) *Web Site:* www.press.jhu.edu; muse.jhu.edu, pg 127

Smith, Allan H, Success Advertising & Publishing, 3419 Dunham Rd, Warsaw, NY 14569 *Tel:* 585-786-5663, pg 237

Smith, Allyson, The Jim Henson Co, 1416 N La Brea Ave, Hollywood, CA 90028 *Tel:* 323-802-1500 *Fax:* 323-802-1825 *Web Site:* www.henson.com, pg 127

Smith, Andrew, Little, Brown Books for Young Readers, 1290 Avenue of the Americas, New York, NY 10019 *Tel:* 212-364-1100 *Toll Free Tel:* 800-759-0190 (cust serv) *Web Site:* www.HachetteBookGroup.com, pg 141

Smith, Betty, International Publishers Co Inc, 235 W 23 St, New York, NY 10011 *Tel:* 212-366-9816 *Fax:* 212-366-9820 *E-mail:* service@intpubnyc.com *Web Site:* www.intpubnyc.com, pg 124

Smith, Bradford K, The Foundation Center, 32 Old Slip, 24th fl, New York, NY 10005-3500 *Tel:* 212-620-4230 *Toll Free Tel:* 800-424-9836 *Fax:* 212-807-3677 *E-mail:* customerservice@foundationcenter.org *Web Site:* foundationcenter.org, pg 91

Smith, Bridget, Dunham Literary Inc, 110 William St, Suite 2202, New York, NY 10038 *Tel:* 212-929-0994 *Web Site:* dunhamlit.com, pg 549

Smith, Brigitte, Gallery Books, 1230 Avenue of the Americas, New York, NY 10020 *Toll Free Tel:* 800-456-6798 *Fax:* 212-698-7284 *E-mail:* consumer.customerservice@simonandschuster.com *Web Site:* www.simonsays.com, pg 94

Smith, Casey, American Printing History Association, PO Box 4519, Grand Central Sta, New York, NY 10163 *Tel:* 202-544-2422 *E-mail:* secretary@printinghistory.org *Web Site:* printinghistory.org, pg 596

Smith, Casey, American Printing History Association Award, PO Box 4519, Grand Central Sta, New York, NY 10163 *Tel:* 202-544-2422 *Web Site:* printinghistory.org, pg 667

Smith, Casey, SkillPath Publications, PO Box 2768, Mission, KS 66201-2768 *Tel:* 913-362-3900 *Toll Free Tel:* 800-873-7545 *Fax:* 913-362-4241 *E-mail:* customercare@skillpath.net; products@skillpath.net *Web Site:* www.skillpath.com, pg 227

Smith, Christopher, Cleveland State University Poetry Center Prizes, 2121 Euclid Ave, Cleveland, OH 44115-2214 *Tel:* 216-687-3986 *Fax:* 216-687-6943 *E-mail:* poetrycenter@csuohio.edu *Web Site:* www.csuohio.edu/poetrycenter, pg 678

Smith, David Cloyce, The Library of America, 14 E 60 St, New York, NY 10022-1006 *Tel:* 212-308-3360 *Fax:* 212-750-8352 *E-mail:* info@loa.org *Web Site:* www.loa.org, pg 139

Smith, David Hale, InkWell Management, 521 Fifth Ave, 26th fl, New York, NY 10175 *Tel:* 212-922-3500 *Fax:* 212-922-0535 *E-mail:* info@inkwellmanagement.com; submissions@inkwellmanagement.com *Web Site:* inkwellmanagement.com, pg 557

Smith, Dean J, Cornell University Press, Sage House, 512 E State St, Ithaca, NY 14850 *Tel:* 607-277-2338 *Fax:* 607-277-2374 *E-mail:* cupressinfo@cornell.edu; cupress-sales@cornell.edu *Web Site:* www.cornellpress.cornell.edu, pg 63

Smith, Deborah, BelleBooks, PO Box 300921, Memphis, TN 38130 *Tel:* 901-344-9024 *Fax:* 901-344-9068 *E-mail:* bellebooks@bellebooks.com, pg 34

Smith, Diane E, Baylor University Press, Baylor University, One Bear Place, Waco, TX 76798-7363 *Tel:* 254-710-3164 *Fax:* 254-710-3440 *Web Site:* www.baylorpress.com, pg 32

Smith, Edward, McGraw-Hill Financial, 1221 Avenue of the Americas, 50th fl, New York, NY 10020 *Tel:* 212-512-2000 *Web Site:* www.mhfi.com, pg 151

Smith, Eric, Quirk Books, 215 Church St, Philadelphia, PA 19106 *Tel:* 215-627-3581 *Fax:* 215-627-5220 *E-mail:* general@quirkbooks.com *Web Site:* www.quirkbooks.com, pg 202

Smith, Erica, Interweave Press LLC, 201 E Fourth St, Loveland, CO 80537 *Toll Free Tel:* 800-272-2193; 800-289-0963 *Fax:* 970-613-4656 *Toll Free Fax:* 888-590-4082 *Web Site:* www.interweave.com, pg 125

Smith, Frederick B, Two Thousand Three Associates, 4180 Saxon Dr, New Smyrna Beach, FL 32169 *Tel:* 386-690-2503 *E-mail:* ttta1@att.net *Web Site:* www.twothousandthree.com, pg 252

Smith, George D, Signature Books Publishing LLC, 564 W 400 N, Salt Lake City, UT 84116-3411 *Tel:* 801-531-1483 *Fax:* 801-531-1488 *E-mail:* people@signaturebooks.com *Web Site:* www.signaturebooks.com; www.signaturebookslibrary.org, pg 224

Smith, Ginger B, Success Advertising & Publishing, 3419 Dunham Rd, Warsaw, NY 14569 *Tel:* 585-786-5663, pg 237

Smith, Gordon H, National Association of Broadcasters (NAB), 1771 "N" St NW, Washington, DC 20036 *Tel:* 202-429-5300 *Fax:* 202-429-4199 *E-mail:* nab@nab.org *Web Site:* www.nab.org, pg 163, 611

Smith, Icy, East West Discovery Press, PO Box 3585, Manhattan Beach, CA 90266 *Tel:* 310-545-3730 *Fax:* 310-545-3731 *E-mail:* info@eastwestdiscovery.com *Web Site:* www.eastwestdiscovery.com, pg 78

Smith, James Clois Jr, Sunstone Press, PO Box 2321, Santa Fe, NM 87504-2321 *Tel:* 505-988-4418 *Toll Free Tel:* 800-243-5644 *Fax:* 505-988-1025 (orders only) *Web Site:* www.sunstonepress.com, pg 238

Smith, Jeffrey, Bridge to Asia, 1505 Juanita Way, Berkeley, CA 94702-1103 *Tel:* 510-665-3998 *E-mail:* asianet@bridge.org *Web Site:* www.bridge.org, pg 623

Smith, Jennifer, Howard Books, 216 Centerview Dr, Suite 303, Brentwood, TN 37027 *Tel:* 615-873-2080 *Fax:* 615-370-3834 *E-mail:* howardbooks@simonandschuster.com (info) *Web Site:* www.howardpublishing.com, pg 116

Smith, Jerome K, Gollehon Press Inc, 3655 Glenn Dr SE, Grand Rapids, MI 49546 *Tel:* 616-949-3515 *Fax:* 616-949-8674 *Web Site:* www.gollehonbooks.com, pg 98

Smith, Jill, University of Denver Publishing Institute, 2000 E Asbury Ave, Denver, CO 80208 *Tel:* 303-871-2570 *Fax:* 303-871-2501 *Web Site:* www.du.edu/publishinginstitute, pg 663

Smith, Joseph, Bisk Education, 9417 Princess Palm Ave, Suite 400, Tampa, FL 33619 *Tel:* 813-621-6200 *Toll Free Tel:* 800-280-9718 (cust serv) *E-mail:* customerservice@bisk.com *Web Site:* www.bisk.com, pg 37

Smith, Kelly, Bywater Books, PO Box 3671, Ann Arbor, MI 48106-3671 *Tel:* 734-662-8815 *Web Site:* bywaterbooks.com, pg 48

Smith, Kelly, Paintbox Press, 275 Madison Ave, Suite 600, New York, NY 10016 *Tel:* 212-878-6610 *Fax:* 212-202-6157 *E-mail:* info@paintboxpress.com *Web Site:* www.paintboxpress.com, pg 180

Smith, Lance, The Little Entrepreneur, c/o Harper-Arrington, 18701 Grand River, Suite 105, Detroit, MI 48223 *Toll Free Tel:* 888-435-9234 *Fax:* 248-281-0373 *E-mail:* info@harperarringtonmedia.com *Web Site:* www.thelittlee.com, pg 141

Smith, Larry, Bottom Dog Press, 813 Seneca Ave, Huron, OH 44839 *Tel:* 419-433-3573 *Fax:* 419-616-3966 *Web Site:* smithdocs.net, pg 43

Smith, Latoya, Samhain Publishing Ltd, 11821 Mason Montgomery Rd, Suite 4-B, Cincinnati, OH 45249 *Tel:* 513-453-4688 *Fax:* 513-583-0191 *E-mail:* support@samhainpublishing.com *Web Site:* www.samhainpublishing.com, pg 216

Smith, Laura, Bottom Dog Press, 813 Seneca Ave, Huron, OH 44839 *Tel:* 419-433-3573 *Fax:* 419-616-3966 *Web Site:* smithdocs.net, pg 43

Smith, Laurie, Krause Publications Inc, 700 E State St, Iola, WI 54990 *Tel:* 715-445-2214 *Toll Free Tel:* 800-258-0929 (cust serv); 888-457-2873 (orders) *Fax:* 715-445-4087 *E-mail:* bookorders@krause.com *Web Site:* www.krausebooks.com, pg 133

Smith, Lisa Garrett, Reader's Digest General Books, Reader's Digest Rd, Pleasantville, NY 10570-7000 *Tel:* 914-238-1000 *Toll Free Tel:* 800-304-2807 (cust serv) *Fax:* 914-244-7436, pg 205

Smith, Lisa Marie, University of Ottawa Press (Les Presses de l'Université d'Ottawa), 542 King Edward Ave, Ottawa, ON K1N 6N5, Canada *Tel:* 613-562-5246 *Fax:* 613-562-5247 *E-mail:* puo-oup@uottawa.ca *Web Site:* www.press.uottawa.ca, pg 503

Smith, Liz, Per Annum Inc, 555 Eighth Ave, Suite 203, New York, NY 10018 *Tel:* 212-647-8700 *Toll Free Tel:* 800-548-1108 *Fax:* 212-647-8716 *E-mail:* info@perannum.com *Web Site:* www.perannum.com, pg 189

Smith, Lyn, University of Missouri Press, 2910 Le Mone Blvd, Columbia, MO 65201 *Tel:* 573-882-7641 *Toll Free Tel:* 800-621-2736 (orders) *Fax:* 573-884-4498 *Web Site:* press.umsystem.edu, pg 257

Smith, M Lee, M Lee Smith Publishers LLC, 5201 Virginia Way, Brentwood, TN 37027 *Tel:* 615-373-7517 *Toll Free Tel:* 800-274-6774 *Fax:* 615-373-5183 *E-mail:* custserv@mleesmith.com *Web Site:* www.mleesmith.com, pg 228

Smith, Mary Dupuy, Teacher Created Resources Inc, 6421 Industry Way, Westminster, CA 92683 *Tel:* 714-891-7895 *Toll Free Tel:* 800-662-4321; 888-343-4335 *Fax:* 714-892-0283 *Toll Free Fax:* 800-525-1254 *E-mail:* custserv@teachercreated.com *Web Site:* www.teachercreated.com, pg 241

Smith, Mary P, Thorndike Press, 10 Water St, Suite 310, Waterville, ME 04901 *Toll Free Tel:* 800-233-1244 (ext 4, cust serv/orders) *Toll Free Fax:* 800-558-4676 (orders) *E-mail:* gale.printorders@cengage.com; international@cengage.com (cust orders outside US & CN) *Web Site:* thorndike.gale.com, pg 245

Smith, Meg Z, American Booksellers Association, 333 Westchester Ave, Suite S202, White Plains, NY 10604 *Tel:* 914-406-7500 *Toll Free Tel:* 800-637-0037 *Fax:* 914-410-6297 *E-mail:* info@bookweb.org *Web Site:* www.bookweb.org, pg 594

Smith, Michael, East West Discovery Press, PO Box 3585, Manhattan Beach, CA 90266 *Tel:* 310-545-3730 *Fax:* 310-545-3731 *E-mail:* info@eastwestdiscovery.com *Web Site:* www.eastwestdiscovery.com, pg 78

Smith, Monte, Eagle's View Publishing, 6756 North Fork Rd, Liberty, UT 84310 *Tel:* 801-393-4555; 801-745-0905 (edit) *Fax:* 801-745-0903 (edit); 801-393-4647 *E-mail:* sales@eaglefeathertrading.com *Web Site:* www.eaglesviewpub.com, pg 78

Smith, Nazaleem, Barbara Bradley Prize, 2 Farrar St, Cambridge, MA 02138 *Tel:* 617-744-6034 *E-mail:* contests@nepoetryclub.org *Web Site:* www.nepoetryclub.org, pg 673

Smith, Nazaleem, Der-Hovanessian Translation Prize, 2 Farrar St, Cambridge, MA 02138 *Tel:* 617-744-6034 *E-mail:* contests@nepoetryclub.org *Web Site:* www.nepoetryclub.org, pg 680

Smith, Nazaleem, Firman Houghton Prize, 2 Farrar St, Cambridge, MA 02138 *Tel:* 617-744-6034 *E-mail:* contests@nepoetryclub.org *Web Site:* www.nepoetryclub.org, pg 693

Smith, Nazaleem, Sheila Margaret Motton Prize, 2 Farrar St, Cambridge, MA 02138 *Tel:* 617-744-6034 *E-mail:* contests@nepoetryclub.org *Web Site:* www.nepoetryclub.org, pg 709

Smith, Nazaleem, Erika Mumford Prize, 2 Farrar St, Cambridge, MA 02138 *Tel:* 617-744-6034 *E-mail:* contests@nepoetryclub.org *Web Site:* www.nepoetryclub.org, pg 710

Smith, Nazaleem, May Sarton Award, 2 Farrar St, Cambridge, MA 02138 *Tel:* 617-744-6034 *E-mail:* contests@nepoetryclub.org *Web Site:* www.nepoetryclub.org, pg 726

Smith, Nazaleem, Daniel Varoujan Award, 2 Farrar St, Cambridge, MA 02138 *Tel:* 617-744-6034 *E-mail:* contests@nepoetryclub.org *Web Site:* www.nepoetryclub.org, pg 734

Smith, P David, Western Reflections Publishing Co, 951 N Hwy 149, Lake City, CO 81235 *Tel:* 970-944-0110 *Toll Free Tel:* 800-993-4490 *Fax:* 970-944-0273 *E-mail:* publisher@westernreflectionspublishing.com *Web Site:* www.westernreflectionspublishing.com, pg 269

Smith, Paige, Vintage & Anchor Books, c/o Random House Inc, 1745 Broadway, New York, NY 10019 *Tel:* 212-572-2420 *E-mail:* vintageanchorpublicity@randomhouse.com *Web Site:* vintage-anchor.knopfdoubleday.com, pg 266

Smith, Pat, Oolichan Books, PO Box 2278, Fernie, BC V0B 1M0, Canada *Tel:* 250-423-6113 *E-mail:* info@oolichan.com *Web Site:* www.oolichan.com, pg 493

Smith, Peggy Boulos, Jane Rotrosen Agency LLC, 318 E 51 St, New York, NY 10022 *Tel:* 212-593-4330 *Fax:* 212-935-6985 *Web Site:* janerotrosen.com, pg 571

Smith, Piper, Lindgren & Smith, 888C Eighth Ave, No 329, New York, NY 10019 *Tel:* 212-397-7330 *E-mail:* info@lindgrensmith.com *Web Site:* lindgrensmith.com, pg 584

Smith, R Bob III, Psychological Assessment Resources Inc (PAR), 16204 N Florida Ave, Lutz, FL 33549 *Tel:* 813-968-3003; 813-449-4065 *Toll Free Tel:* 800-331-8378 *Fax:* 813-968-2598; 813-961-2196 *Toll Free Fax:* 800-727-9329 *E-mail:* custsup@parinc.com *Web Site:* www4.parinc.com, pg 199

Smith, R T, The James Boatwright III Prize for Poetry, Washington & Lee University, Mattingly House, 204 W Washington St, Lexington, VA 24450-2116 *Tel:* 540-458-8765 *E-mail:* shenandoah@wlu.edu *Web Site:* shenandoahliterary.org; shenandoah.wlu.edu, pg 673

Smith, R T, The Carter Prize For The Essay, Washington & Lee University, Mattingly House, 204 W Washington St, Lexington, VA 24450-2116 *Tel:* 540-458-8765 *E-mail:* shenandoah@wlu.edu *Web Site:* shenandoahliterary.org; shenandoah.wlu.edu, pg 676

Smith, Robert Ellis, Privacy Journal, PO Box 28577, Providence, RI 02908 *Tel:* 401-274-7861 *Fax:* 401-274-4747 *E-mail:* orders@privacyjournal.net *Web Site:* www.privacyjournal.net, pg 197

Smith, Ronald, Oolichan Books, PO Box 2278, Fernie, BC V0B 1M0, Canada *Tel:* 250-423-6113 *E-mail:* info@oolichan.com *Web Site:* www.oolichan.com, pg 493

Smith, Ronnie L, Writer's Relief, Inc, 207 Hackensack St, Wood-Ridge, NJ 07075 *Tel:* 201-641-3003 *Toll Free Tel:* 866-405-3003 *Fax:* 201-641-1253 *E-mail:* info@wrelief.com *Web Site:* www.WritersRelief.com, pg 536

Smith, Sandy, Chronicle Books LLC, 680 Second St, San Francisco, CA 94107 *Tel:* 415-537-4200 *Toll Free Tel:* 800-759-0190 (cust serv) *Fax:* 415-537-4460 *Toll Free Fax:* 800-858-7787 (orders); 800-286-9471 (cust serv) *E-mail:* frontdesk@chroniclebooks.com *Web Site:* www.chroniclebooks.com, pg 58

Smith, Sarah, David Black Agency, 335 Adams St, 27th fl, Suite 2707, Brooklyn, NY 11201 *Tel:* 718-852-5500 *Fax:* 718-852-5539 *Web Site:* www.davidblackagency.com, pg 542

Smith, Sarah, The Experiment, 220 East 23 St, Suite 301, New York, NY 10010-4674 *Tel:* 212-889-1659 *E-mail:* info@theexperimentpublishing.com *Web Site:* www.theexperimentpublishing.com, pg 85

Smith, Scott, R S Means from The Gordian Group, 1099 Hingham St, Suite 201, Rockland, MA 02370 *Tel:* 781-422-5000 *Toll Free Tel:* 800-448-8182 *Fax:* 781-585-8814 *Toll Free Fax:* 800-632-6701 *Web Site:* www.rsmeans.com, pg 153

Smith, Serena, Stephens Press™, 1111 W Bonanza Rd, Las Vegas, NV 89106 *Tel:* 702-387-5260 *Toll Free Tel:* 888-951-2665 *Fax:* 702-387-2997 *E-mail:* info@stephenspress.com *Web Site:* www.stephenspress.com, pg 235

Smith, Shaelyn, Black Warrior Review Fiction, Nonfiction & Poetry Contest, Office of Student Media, University of Alabama, Tuscaloosa, AL 35486-0027 *Tel:* 205-348-4518 *Web Site:* www.bwr.ua.edu, pg 672

Smith, Stephen R, American Institute of Chemical Engineers (AIChE), 120 Wall St, 23rd fl, New York, NY 10005-4020 *Tel:* 203-702-7660 *Toll Free Tel:* 800-242-4363 *Fax:* 203-775-5177 *E-mail:* customerservice@aiche.org *Web Site:* www.aiche.org, pg 13

Smith, Steve, Steve Smith Autosports, PO Box 11631, Santa Ana, CA 92711-1631 *Tel:* 714-639-7681 *Fax:* 714-639-9741 *Web Site:* www.stevesmithautosports.com, pg 228

Smith, Steven Rathgeb, American Political Science Association, 1527 New Hampshire Ave NW, Washington, DC 20036-1203 *Tel:* 202-483-2512 *Fax:* 202-483-2657 *E-mail:* apsa@apsanet.org *Web Site:* www.apsanet.org, pg 595

Smith, Sue, Boydell & Brewer Inc, 668 Mount Hope Ave, Rochester, NY 14620-2731 *Tel:* 585-275-0419 *Fax:* 585-271-8778 *E-mail:* boydell@boydellusa.net *Web Site:* www.boydellandbrewer.com, pg 43

Smith, Sue, CBA: The Association for Christian Retail, 1365 Garden of the Gods Rd, Suite 105, Colorado Springs, CO 80907 *Tel:* 719-265-9895 *Toll Free Tel:* 800-252-1950 *Fax:* 719-272-3508 *E-mail:* info@cbaonline.org *Web Site:* cbaonline.org, pg 603

Smith, Sue, Eagle's View Publishing, 6756 North Fork Rd, Liberty, UT 84310 *Tel:* 801-393-4555; 801-745-0905 (edit) *Fax:* 801-745-0903 (edit); 801-393-4647 *E-mail:* sales@eaglefeathertrading.com *Web Site:* www.eaglesviewpub.com, pg 78

Smith, Sue, University of Rochester Press, 668 Mount Hope Ave, Rochester, NY 14620-2731 *Tel:* 585-275-0419 *Fax:* 585-271-8778 *E-mail:* boydell@boydellusa.net *Web Site:* www.urpress.com, pg 259

Smith, Summer, Bloomsbury Publishing Inc, 1385 Broadway, 5th fl, New York, NY 10018 *Tel:* 212-419-5300 *E-mail:* marketingusa@bloomsbury.com; adultpublicityusa@bloomsbury.com; askacademic@bloomsbury.com *Web Site:* www.bloomsbury.com, pg 40

Smith, Suzanne, Doubleday/Nan A Talese, c/o Penguin Random House Inc, 1745 Broadway, New York, NY 10019 *Tel:* 212-751-2600 *Fax:* 212-572-2662 *E-mail:* ddaypub@randomhouse.com *Web Site:* knopfdoubleday.com, pg 76

Smith, Suzanne, Alfred A Knopf/Everyman's Library, c/o Random House Inc, 1745 Broadway, New York, NY 10019 *Tel:* 212-751-2600 *Toll Free Tel:* 800-638-6460 *Fax:* 212-572-2593 *Web Site:* www.knopfdoubleday.com, pg 132

Smith, Suzanne, Pantheon Books/Schocken Books, c/o Random House Inc, 1745 Broadway, New York, NY 10019 *Tel:* 212-751-2600 *Toll Free Tel:* 800-638-6460 *Fax:* 212-572-6030, pg 181

Smith, Valerie, Valerie Smith, Literary Agent, 1746 Rte 44-55, Modena, NY 12548 *Tel:* 845-883-5848, pg 574

Smith, Virginia, The Penguin Press, 375 Hudson St, New York, NY 10014, pg 187

Smith, William, The MIT Press, 55 Hayward St, Cambridge, MA 02142 *Tel:* 617-253-5255 *Toll Free Tel:* 800-207-8354 (orders) *Fax:* 617-258-6779; 617-577-1545 (orders) *Web Site:* mitpress.mit.edu, pg 158

Smith-Eivemark, Sarah, Coach House Books, 80 bpNichol Lane, Toronto, ON M5S 3J4, Canada *Tel:* 416-979-2217 *Toll Free Tel:* 800-367-6360 (outside Toronto) *Fax:* 416-977-1158 *E-mail:* mail@chbooks.com *Web Site:* www.chbooks.com, pg 477

Smith-Herbst, Peggy, Houghton Mifflin Harcourt School Publishers, 9205 Southport Center Loop, Orlando, FL 32819 *Tel:* 407-345-2000 *Toll Free Tel:* 800-225-5425 (cust serv) *Fax:* 407-345-3016 (cust serv) *Toll Free Fax:* 800-874-6418; 800-269-5232 (cust serv) *Web Site:* www.hmhco.com, pg 115

Smith-Mandell, Barbara, Chariton Review Short Fiction Prize, 100 E Normal Ave, Kirksville, MO 63501-4221 *Tel:* 660-785-7336 *Toll Free Tel:* 800-916-6802 *Fax:* 660-785-4480 *E-mail:* tsup@truman.edu *Web Site:* tsup.truman.edu, pg 676

Smith-Mandell, Barbara, T S Eliot Prize for Poetry, 100 E Normal Ave, Kirksville, MO 63501-4221 *Tel:* 660-785-7336 *Toll Free Tel:* 800-916-6802 *Fax:* 660-785-4480 *E-mail:* tsup@truman.edu *Web Site:* tsup.truman.edu, pg 683

Smith-Mandell, Barbara, Truman State University Press, 100 E Normal Ave, Kirksville, MO 63501-4221 *Tel:* 660-785-7336 *Toll Free Tel:* 800-916-6802 *Fax:* 660-785-4480 *E-mail:* tsup@truman.edu *Web Site:* tsup.truman.edu, pg 250

Smithers, Westwood Jr, Corporation for Public Broadcasting (CPB), 401 Ninth St NW, Washington, DC 20004-2129 *Tel:* 202-879-9600 *Web Site:* www.cpb.org, pg 604

Smoley, Nicole, Theosophical Publishing House/Quest Books, 306 W Geneva Rd, Wheaton, IL 60187 *Tel:* 630-665-0130 (ext 347) *Toll Free Tel:* 800-669-9425 (ext 347) *Fax:* 630-665-8791 *E-mail:* customerservice@questbooks.net *Web Site:* www.questbooks.net, pg 244

Smoley, Richard, Theosophical Publishing House/Quest Books, 306 W Geneva Rd, Wheaton, IL 60187 *Tel:* 630-665-0130 (ext 347) *Toll Free Tel:* 800-669-9425 (ext 347) *Fax:* 630-665-8791 *E-mail:* customerservice@questbooks.net *Web Site:* www.questbooks.net, pg 244

Smolin, Ronald, Trans-Atlantic Publications Inc, 311 Bainbridge St, Philadelphia, PA 19147 *Tel:* 215-925-5083 *Fax:* 215-925-1912 *Web Site:* www.transatlanticpub.com; www.businesstitles.com, pg 248

Smyk, Dorothy, New Harbinger Publications Inc, 5674 Shattuck Ave, Oakland, CA 94609 *Tel:* 510-652-0215 *Toll Free Tel:* 800-748-6273 (orders only) *Fax:* 510-652-5472 *Toll Free Fax:* 800-652-1613 *E-mail:* nhhelp@newharbinger.com; customerservice@newharbinger.com *Web Site:* www.newharbinger.com, pg 167

Smyth, Sam, StarGroup International Inc, 1194 Old Dixie Hwy, Suite 201, West Palm Beach, FL 33413 *Tel:* 561-547-0667 *Fax:* 561-843-8530 *E-mail:* info@stargroupinternational.com *Web Site:* www.stargroupinternational.com, pg 234

Smythe, Lauren, InkWell Management, 521 Fifth Ave, 26th fl, New York, NY 10175 *Tel:* 212-922-3500 *Fax:* 212-922-0535 *E-mail:* info@inkwellmanagement.com; submissions@inkwellmanagement.com *Web Site:* inkwellmanagement.com, pg 557

Snavely, Sheri, W W Norton & Company Inc, 500 Fifth Ave, New York, NY 10110-0017 *Tel:* 212-354-5500 *Toll Free Tel:* 800-233-4830 (orders & cust serv) *Fax:* 212-869-0856 *Toll Free Fax:* 800-458-6515 *Web Site:* www.wwnorton.com, pg 172

Snead, Beth, The Flannery O'Connor Award for Short Fiction, Main Library, 3rd fl, 320 S Jackson St, Athens, GA 30602 *Fax:* 706-542-2558 *Web Site:* www.ugapress.org, pg 714

Snee, Charles, Scott Publishing Co, 911 S Vandemark Rd, Sidney, OH 45365 *Tel:* 937-498-0802 *Toll Free Tel:* 800-572-6885 (cust serv) *Fax:* 937-498-0807 *Toll Free Fax:* 800-488-5349 *E-mail:* cuserv@amospress.com *Web Site:* www.amosadvantage.com, pg 220

Snell, Michael, Michael Snell Literary Agency, PO Box 1206, Truro, MA 02666-1206 *Tel:* 508-349-3718 *Web Site:* www.michaelsnellagency.com, pg 574

Snell, Patricia, Michael Snell Literary Agency, PO Box 1206, Truro, MA 02666-1206 *Tel:* 508-349-3718 *Web Site:* www.michaelsnellagency.com, pg 574

Snider, Stephen, St Martin's Press, LLC, 175 Fifth Ave, New York, NY 10010 *Tel:* 646-307-5151 *Fax:* 212-420-9314 *E-mail:* firstname.lastname@macmillan.com *Web Site:* www.stmartins.com, pg 215

Snodgrass, Catherine, Amber Quill Press LLC, PO Box 265, Indian Hills, CO 80454 *E-mail:* business@amberquill.com; customer_service@amberquill.com *Web Site:* www.amberquill.com, pg 10

Snodgrass, Prof Kate, Boston University, 236 Bay State Rd, Boston, MA 02215 *Tel:* 617-353-2510 *Fax:* 617-353-3653 *E-mail:* crwr@bu.edu *Web Site:* www.bu.edu/writing, pg 659

Snodgrass, Kristine, Anhinga Press, PO Box 3665, Tallahassee, FL 32315 *Tel:* 850-577-0745 *E-mail:* info@anhinga.org *Web Site:* www.anhinga.org; www.facebook.com/anhingapress, pg 18

Snodgrass, Kristine, Robert Dana-Anhinga Prize for Poetry, PO Box 3665, Tallahassee, FL 32315 *Tel:* 850-577-0745 *E-mail:* info@anhinga.org *Web Site:* www.anhinga.org, pg 680

Snodgrass, Robert, Ascend Books LLC, 12710 Pflumm Rd, Suite 200, Olathe, KS 66062 *Tel:* 913-948-5500 *Web Site:* www.ascendbooks.com, pg 23

Snouck-Hurgronje, Jan W, The Nautical & Aviation Publishing Co of America Inc, 845-A Lowcountry Blvd, Mount Pleasant, SC 29464 *Tel:* 843-856-0561 *Fax:* 843-856-3164 *Web Site:* www.nauticalandaviation.com, pg 166

Snow, Todd, Maren Green Publishing Inc, 5630 Memorial Ave N, Suite 3, Oak Park Heights, MN 55082 *Tel:* 651-439-4500 *Toll Free Tel:* 800-287-1512 *Fax:* 651-439-4532 *E-mail:* info@marengreen.com *Web Site:* www.marengreen.com, pg 147

Snowden, Elizabeth Regina, Alan Wofsy Fine Arts, 1109 Geary Blvd, San Francisco, CA 94109 *Tel:* 415-292-6500 *Toll Free Tel:* 800-660-6403 *Fax:* 415-292-6594 (off & cust serv); 510-251-1840 (acctg) *E-mail:* order@art-books.com (orders); editeur@earthlink.net (edit); beauxarts@earthlink.net (cust serv) *Web Site:* www.art-books.com, pg 274

Snowden, Kelly, Ten Speed Press, 2625 Alcatraz Ave, Unit 505, Berkeley, CA 94705 *Tel:* 510-285-3000 *Toll Free Tel:* 800-841-BOOK (841-2665) *E-mail:* csorders@randomhouse.com *Web Site:* crownpublishing.com/imprint/ten-speed-press, pg 243

Snyder, Becky, ABC-CLIO, 130 Cremona Dr, Santa Barbara, CA 93117 *Tel:* 805-968-1911 *Toll Free Tel:* 800-368-6868 *Fax:* 805-685-9685 *Toll Free Fax:* 866-270-3856 *E-mail:* sales@abc-clio.com; customerservice@abc-clio.com *Web Site:* www.abc-clio.com, pg 2

Snyder, Courtney, Crown Publishing Group, c/o Penguin Random House Inc, 1745 Broadway, New York, NY 10019 *Tel:* 212-782-9000 *Toll Free Tel:* 888-264-1745 *Fax:* 212-940-7408 *E-mail:* crownosm@penguinrandomhouse.com *Web Site:* crownpublishing.com, pg 68

Snyder, Elizabeth, Pacific Northwest Children's Book Conference, 615 SW Harrison St, Portland, OR 97201 *Tel:* 503-725-9786 *Toll Free Tel:* 800-547-8887 (ext 9786) *Fax:* 503-725-5599 *Web Site:* www.pdx.edu/ceed/childrens-book-conference, pg 654

Snyder, Emma, PEN/Faulkner Award for Fiction, Folger Shakespeare Library, 201 E Capitol St SE, Washington, DC 20003 *Tel:* 202-898-9063 *Fax:* 202-675-0360 *Web Site:* www.penfaulkner.org, pg 717

Snyder, Jake, Dalkey Archive Press, University of Houston-Victoria, 3007 N Ben Wilson, Victoria, TX 77901 *E-mail:* contact@dalkeyarchive.com *Web Site:* www.dalkeyarchive.com, pg 70

Snyder, James, Celebrity Profiles Publishing, PO Box 344, Stony Brook, NY 11790 *Tel:* 631-862-8555 *Fax:* 631-862-0139 *E-mail:* celebpro4@aol.com *Web Site:* www.richardgrudens.com; richardgrudensblog.blogspot.com, pg 53

Snyder, Ruth L, InScribe Christian Writers' Fellowship (ICWF), PO Box 6201, Wetaskiwin, AB T9A 2E9, Canada *E-mail:* inscribe.mail@gmail.com *Web Site:* inscribe.org, pg 607

Snyder, Tanya, The Literary Press Group of Canada, 425 Adelaide St W, Suite 700, Toronto, ON M5V 3C1, Canada *Tel:* 416-483-1321 *Fax:* 416-483-2510 *Web Site:* www.lpg.ca, pg 609

So, Mark, Piano Press, 1425 Ocean Ave, Suite 5, Del Mar, CA 92014 *Tel:* 619-884-1401 *Fax:* 858-755-1104 *E-mail:* pianopress@pianopress.com *Web Site:* www.pianopress.com, pg 191

Soares, Manuela, Pace University Press, Dept of Publishing, Rm 805-E, 551 Fifth Ave, New York, NY 10176 *Tel:* 212-346-1417 *Fax:* 212-346-1165 *Web Site:* www.pace.edu/press, pg 180

Sobel, Nat, Sobel Weber Associates Inc, 146 E 19 St, New York, NY 10003-2404 *Tel:* 212-420-8585 *Fax:* 212-505-1017 *E-mail:* info@sobelweber.com *Web Site:* www.sobelweber.com, pg 574

Socha, Kenneth M, The Perseus Books Group, 387 Park Ave S, 12th fl, New York, NY 10016 *Tel:* 212-340-8100 *Toll Free Tel:* 800-343-4499 (cust serv) *Fax:* 212-340-8105 *Web Site:* www.perseusbooksgroup.com, pg 189

Soda, Tai, Industrial Press Inc, 32 Haviland St, Unit 2C, Norwalk, CT 06854 *Tel:* 212-889-6330 *Toll Free Tel:* 888-528-7852 *Fax:* 212-545-8327 *E-mail:* info@industrialpress.com *Web Site:* new.industrialpress.com, pg 121

Sogah, Esi, Kensington Publishing Corp, 119 W 40 St, New York, NY 10018 *Tel:* 212-407-1500 *Toll Free Tel:* 800-221-2647 *Fax:* 212-935-0699 *Web Site:* www.kensingtonbooks.com, pg 130

Soha, Yaniv, Doubleday/Nan A Talese, c/o Penguin Random House Inc, 1745 Broadway, New York, NY 10019 *Tel:* 212-751-2600 *Fax:* 212-572-2662 *E-mail:* ddaypub@randomhouse.com *Web Site:* knopfdoubleday.com, pg 76

Sokol, Dr Mick, Drury University One-Act Play Competition, 900 N Benton Ave, Springfield, MO 65802-3344 *Tel:* 417-873-6821 *Web Site:* www.drury.edu, pg 682

Sokoloski, Robin, Playwrights Guild of Canada, 401 Richmond St W, Suite 350, Toronto, ON M5V 3A8, Canada *Tel:* 416-703-0201 *Fax:* 416-703-0059 *E-mail:* info@playwrightsguild.ca *Web Site:* www.playwrightsguild.ca, pg 616

Solomon, Andrew, PEN American Center, 588 Broadway, Suite 303, New York, NY 10012 *Tel:* 212-334-1660 *Fax:* 212-334-2181 *E-mail:* info@pen.org *Web Site:* www.pen.org, pg 615

Solomon, Andrew, The PEN Award for Poetry in Translation, 588 Broadway, Suite 303, New York, NY 10012 *Tel:* 212-334-1660 *Fax:* 212-334-2181 *E-mail:* awards@pen.org *Web Site:* www.pen.org, pg 717

Solomon, Andrew, PEN/Phyllis Naylor Working Writer Fellowship, 588 Broadway, Suite 303, New York, NY 10012 *Tel:* 212-334-1660 *Fax:* 212-334-2181 *E-mail:* awards@pen.org *Web Site:* www.pen.org, pg 718

Solomon, Andrew, PEN/Ralph Manheim Medal for Translation, 588 Broadway, Suite 303, New York, NY 10012 *Tel:* 212-334-1660 *Fax:* 212-334-2181 *E-mail:* awards@pen.org *Web Site:* www.pen.org, pg 718

Solomon, Andrew, PEN/Robert Bingham Prize for Debut Fiction, 588 Broadway, Suite 303, New York, NY 10012 *Tel:* 212-334-1660 *Fax:* 212-334-2181 *E-mail:* awards@pen.org *Web Site:* www.pen.org, pg 718

Solomon, Andrew, PEN Translation Prize, 588 Broadway, Suite 303, New York, NY 10012 *Tel:* 212-334-1660 *Fax:* 212-334-2181 *E-mail:* awards@pen.org *Web Site:* www.pen.org, pg 718

Solomon, Andrew, PEN Writers' Emergency Fund, 588 Broadway, Suite 303, New York, NY 10012 *Tel:* 212-334-1660 *Fax:* 212-334-2181 *Web Site:* www.pen.org, pg 718

Solomon, Jeremy, Inkwater Press, 6750 SW Franklin St, Suite A, Portland, OR 97223 *Tel:* 503-968-6777 *Fax:* 503-968-6779 *E-mail:* orders@inkwaterbooks.com *Web Site:* www.inkwater.com, pg 122

Solorzano, Elsa, Global Training Center Inc, 550 S Mesa Hills Dr, Suite E4, El Paso, TX 79912 *Tel:* 915-534-7900 *Toll Free Tel:* 800-860-5030 *Fax:* 915-534-7903 *E-mail:* contact@globaltrainingcenter.com *Web Site:* www.globaltrainingcenter.com, pg 97

Somberg, Andrea, Harvey Klinger Inc, 300 W 55 St, Suite 11V, New York, NY 10019 *Tel:* 212-581-7068 *Fax:* 212-315-3823 *E-mail:* queries@harveyklinger.com *Web Site:* www.harveyklinger.com, pg 560

Somers, Evelyn, William Peden Prize in Fiction, 357 McReynolds Hall, Columbia, MO 65211 *Tel:* 573-882-4474 *Toll Free Tel:* 800-949-2505 *Fax:* 573-884-4671 *E-mail:* question@moreview.com *Web Site:* www.missourireview.com, pg 716

Somers, Evelyn, The Jeffrey E Smith Editors' Prize, 357 McReynolds Hall, Columbia, MO 65211 *Tel:* 573-882-4474 *Toll Free Tel:* 800-949-2505 *Fax:* 573-884-4671 *Web Site:* www.missourireview.com, pg 729

Somers, John, Reference Publications Inc, 218 Saint Clair River Dr, Algonac, MI 48001 *Tel:* 810-794-5722 *Fax:* 810-794-7463 *E-mail:* referencepub@sbcglobal.net, pg 207

Somers, Michelle, Pantheon Books/Schocken Books, c/o Random House Inc, 1745 Broadway, New York, NY 10019 *Tel:* 212-751-2600 *Toll Free Tel:* 800-638-6460 *Fax:* 212-572-6030, pg 181

Somers, Sandi, InScribe Christian Writers' Fellowship (ICWF), PO Box 6201, Wetaskiwin, AB T9A 2E9, Canada *E-mail:* inscribe.mail@gmail.com *Web Site:* inscribe.org, pg 607

Sommaruga, Rossana, QA International (QAI), 329 De la Commune W, 3rd fl, Montreal, QC H2Y 2E1, Canada *Tel:* 514-499-3000 *Fax:* 514-499-3010 *Web Site:* www.qa-international.com, pg 496

Sommer, John, Advance Publishing Inc, 6950 Fulton St, Houston, TX 77022 *Tel:* 713-695-0600 *Toll Free Tel:* 800-917-9630 *Fax:* 713-695-8585 *E-mail:* info@advancepublishing.com *Web Site:* www.advancepublishing.com, pg 5

Sommers, Kathleen, Liturgy Training Publications, 3949 S Racine Ave, Chicago, IL 60609-2523 *Tel:* 773-579-4900 *Toll Free Tel:* 800-933-1800 (US & CN only orders) *Fax:* 773-579-4929 *Toll Free Fax:* 800-933-7094 (US & CN only orders) *E-mail:* orders@ltp.org *Web Site:* www.ltp.org, pg 141

Sommers, Pam, Rizzoli International Publications Inc, 300 Park Ave S, 4th fl, New York, NY 10010-5399 *Tel:* 212-387-3400 *Toll Free Tel:* 800-522-6657 (orders only) *Fax:* 212-387-3535 *E-mail:* publicity@rizzoliusa.com *Web Site:* www.rizzoliusa.com, pg 209

Song, DongWon, Howard Morhaim Literary Agency Inc, 30 Pierrepont St, Brooklyn, NY 11201-3371 *Tel:* 718-222-8400 *Fax:* 718-222-5056 *E-mail:* info@morhaimliterary.com *Web Site:* www.morhaimliterary.com, pg 566

Sonnenfeld, Mark, Marymark Press, 45-08 Old Millstone Dr, East Windsor, NJ 08520 *Tel:* 609-443-0646, pg 148

Sonntag, Sue, FaithWalk Publishing, 5450 N Dixie Hwy, Lima, OH 45807 *Tel:* 419-227-1818 *Toll Free Tel:* 800-537-1030 (orders: non-bookstore mkts) *Fax:* 419-224-9184 *E-mail:* orders@csspub.com *Web Site:* www.faithwalkpub.com, pg 86

Soo Ping Chow, Frances, Running Press Book Publishers, 2300 Chestnut St, Philadelphia, PA 19103-4399 *Tel:* 215-567-5080 *Toll Free Tel:* 800-343-4499 (cust serv & orders) *Fax:* 215-568-

2919 *Toll Free Fax:* 800-453-2884 (cust serv & orders) *E-mail:* perseus.promos@perseusbooks.com *Web Site:* www.runningpress.com, pg 212

Sorce, Pat PhD, Rochester Institute of Technology, School of Print Media, 69 Lomb Memorial Dr, Rochester, NY 14623-5603 *Tel:* 585-475-2728; 585-475-5336 *Fax:* 585-475-5336 *E-mail:* spmofc@rit.edu *Web Site:* cias.rit.edu/printmedia, pg 662

Sorensen, Eric H, National Institute for Trial Advocacy (NITA), 1685 38 St, Suite 200, Boulder, CO 80301-2735 *Tel:* 720-890-4860 *Toll Free Tel:* 877-648-2632; 800-225-6482 (orders & returns) *Fax:* 720-890-7069 *E-mail:* info@nita.org *Web Site:* www.nita.org, pg 165

Sorensen, Nan, New England Book Awards, 1955 Massachusetts Ave, Cambridge, MA 02140 *Tel:* 617-547-3642 *Fax:* 617-547-3759 *Web Site:* www.newenglandbooks.org/bookawards, pg 712

Sorensen, Nan, New England Independent Booksellers Association Inc (NEIBA), 1955 Massachusetts Ave, Cambridge, MA 02140 *Web Site:* www.newenglandbooks.org, pg 613

Soroka-Dunn, Cynthia, Ariel Starr Productions Inc, PO Box 575, Woodstock, NY 12498 *Tel:* 201-784-9148 *E-mail:* arielstarrprod@aol.com *Web Site:* arielstarrprod.wix.com/arielstarr, pg 22

Sorsky, Richard, Linden Publishing Co Inc, 2006 S Mary St, Fresno, CA 93721 *Tel:* 559-233-6633 *Toll Free Tel:* 800-345-4447 (orders) *Fax:* 559-233-6933 *Web Site:* lindenpub.com, pg 139

Souksamrane, Santhana, Random House Children's Books, 1745 Broadway, New York, NY 10019 *Tel:* 212-782-9000 *Toll Free Tel:* 800-200-3552 *Fax:* 212-782-9452 *Web Site:* randomhousekids.com, pg 204

Soule, Susan, Cambridge University Press, 32 Avenue of the Americas, New York, NY 10013-2473 *Tel:* 212-924-3900; 212-337-5000 *Fax:* 212-691-3239 *E-mail:* newyork@cambridge.org *Web Site:* www.cambridge.org/us, pg 49

Soules, Gordon, Gordon Soules Book Publishers Ltd, 1359 Amble Side Lane, West Vancouver, BC V7T 2Y9, Canada *Tel:* 604-922-6588 *Fax:* 604-922-6574 *E-mail:* books@gordonsoules.com *Web Site:* www.gordonsoules.com, pg 499

Soules, Mike, Corwin, a Sage Co, 2455 Teller Rd, Thousand Oaks, CA 91320 *Tel:* 805-499-9734 *Toll Free Tel:* 800-233-9936 *Fax:* 805-499-5323 *Toll Free Fax:* 800-417-2466 *E-mail:* info@corwin.com; order@corwin.com *Web Site:* www.corwin.com, pg 64

Soussan, Lionel, Les Editions Phidal Inc, 5740 Ferrier, Montreal, QC H4P 1M7, Canada *Tel:* 514-738-0202 *Toll Free Tel:* 800-738-7349 *Fax:* 514-738-5102 *E-mail:* info@phidal.com; customer@phidal.com (sales & export), pg 482

Southern, Ed, North Carolina Writers' Network, PO Box 21591, Winston-Salem, NC 27120-1591 *Tel:* 336-293-8844 *Web Site:* www.ncwriters.org, pg 614

Southern, Ed, North Carolina Writers' Network Annual Fall Conference, PO Box 21591, Winston-Salem, NC 27120-1591 *Tel:* 336-293-8844 *E-mail:* mail@ncwriters.org *Web Site:* www.ncwriters.org, pg 653

Southern, Ed, Thomas Wolfe Fiction Prize, PO Box 21591, Winston-Salem, NC 27120-1591 *E-mail:* mail@ncwriters.org *Web Site:* www.ncwriters.org, pg 737

Soutor, Terri, Carolrhoda Books, 241 First Ave N, Minneapolis, MN 55401 *Tel:* 612-332-3344 *Toll Free Tel:* 800-328-4929 *Fax:* 612-332-7615 *Toll Free Fax:* 800-332-1132 *E-mail:* info@lernerbooks.com *Web Site:* www.lernerbooks.com, pg 50

Soutor, Terri, Carolrhoda Lab™, 241 First Ave N, Minneapolis, MN 55401 *Tel:* 612-332-3344 *Toll Free Tel:* 800-328-4929 *Fax:* 612-332-7615 *Toll Free Fax:* 800-332-1132 (US) *E-mail:* info@lernerbooks.com *Web Site:* www.lernerbooks.com, pg 51

Soutor, Terri, ediciones Lerner, 241 First Ave N, Minneapolis, MN 55401 *Tel:* 612-332-3344 *Toll Free Tel:* 800-328-4929 *Fax:* 612-332-7615 *Toll Free Fax:* 800-332-1132 *E-mail:* info@lernerbooks.com *Web Site:* www.lernerbooks.com, pg 79

Soutor, Terri, First Avenue Editions, 241 First Ave N, Minneapolis, MN 55401 *Tel:* 612-332-3344 *Toll Free Tel:* 800-328-4929 *Fax:* 612-332-7615 *Toll Free Fax:* 800-332-1132 *E-mail:* info@lernerbooks.com *Web Site:* www.lernerbooks.com, pg 89

Soutor, Terri, Graphic Universe™, 241 First Ave N, Minneapolis, MN 55401 *Tel:* 612-332-3344 *Toll Free Tel:* 800-328-4929 *Fax:* 612-332-7615 *Toll Free Fax:* 800-332-1132 *E-mail:* info@lernerbooks.com *Web Site:* www.lernerbooks.com, pg 99

Soutor, Terri, Lerner Publications, 241 First Ave N, Minneapolis, MN 55401 *Tel:* 612-332-3344 *Toll Free Tel:* 800-328-4929 *Fax:* 612-332-7615 *Toll Free Fax:* 800-332-1132 *E-mail:* info@lernerbooks.com *Web Site:* www.lernerbooks.com, pg 137

Soutor, Terri, Lerner Publishing Group Inc, 241 First Ave N, Minneapolis, MN 55401 *Tel:* 612-332-3344 *Toll Free Tel:* 800-328-4929 *Fax:* 612-332-7615 *Toll Free Fax:* 800-332-1132 *E-mail:* info@lernerbooks.com *Web Site:* www.lernerbooks.com, pg 137

Soutor, Terri, LernerClassroom, 241 First Ave N, Minneapolis, MN 55401 *Tel:* 612-332-3344 *Toll Free Tel:* 800-328-4929 *Fax:* 612-332-7615 *Toll Free Fax:* 800-332-1132 *E-mail:* info@lernerbooks.com *Web Site:* www.lernerbooks.com, pg 137

Soutor, Terri, Millbrook Press, 241 First Ave N, Minneapolis, MN 55401 *Tel:* 612-332-3344 *Toll Free Tel:* 800-328-4929 (US only) *Fax:* 612-332-7615 *Toll Free Fax:* 800-332-1132, pg 157

Soutor, Terri, Twenty-First Century Books, 241 First Ave N, Minneapolis, MN 55401 *Tel:* 612-332-3344 *Toll Free Tel:* 800-328-4929 *Fax:* 612-332-7615 *Toll Free Fax:* 800-332-1132 *E-mail:* info@lernerbooks.com *Web Site:* www.lernerbooks.com, pg 251

Sova, Kathy, Theatre Communications Group, 520 Eighth Ave, 24th fl, New York, NY 10018-4156 *Tel:* 212-609-5900 *Fax:* 212-609-5901 *E-mail:* tcg@tcg.org *Web Site:* www.tcg.org, pg 244

Sowards, Anne, Berkley Books, 375 Hudson St, New York, NY 10014 *Tel:* 212-366-2000 *Fax:* 212-366-2666 *E-mail:* online@penguinputnam.com *Web Site:* www.penguinputnam.com; us.penguingroup.com, pg 35

Sowards, Anne, Berkley Publishing Group, 375 Hudson St, New York, NY 10014 *Tel:* 212-366-2000 *Fax:* 212-366-2385 *E-mail:* online@penguinputnam.com *Web Site:* us.penguingroup.com, pg 35

Sox, A, Pacific Press Publishing Association, 1350 N Kings Rd, Nampa, ID 83687-3193 *Tel:* 208-465-2500 *Toll Free Tel:* 800-447-7377 *Fax:* 208-465-2531 *Web Site:* www.pacificpress.com, pg 180

Spagnuolo, Mary, Amy Writing Awards, PO Box 16091, Lansing, MI 48901-6091 *Tel:* 517-323-6233 *Toll Free Tel:* 877-727-4262 *Fax:* 517-321-2572 *E-mail:* amyawards@worldmag.com *Web Site:* www.worldmag.com/amyawards, pg 667

Spahr, Charles, The American Ceramic Society, 600 N Cleveland Ave, Suite 210, Westerville, OH 43082 *Tel:* 240-646-7054 *Toll Free Tel:* 866-721-3322 *Fax:* 240-396-5637 *E-mail:* customerservice@ceramics.org *Web Site:* ceramics.org, pg 11

Spain, Tom, Simon & Schuster Audio, 1230 Avenue of the Americas, New York, NY 10020 *Web Site:* audio.simonandschuster.com, pg 225

Spangler, Stephen, DEStech Publications Inc, 439 N Duke St, Lancaster, PA 17602-4967 *Tel:* 717-290-1660 *Toll Free Tel:* 877-500-4337 *Fax:* 717-509-6100 *E-mail:* info@destechpub.com *Web Site:* www.destechpub.com, pg 73

Sparhawk, Bud, Science Fiction & Fantasy Writers of America Inc (SFWA), PO Box 3238, Enfield, CT 06083-3238 *E-mail:* office@sfwa.org *Web Site:* www.sfwa.org, pg 618

Sparhawk, Bud, SFWA Nebula Awards, PO Box 3238, Enfield, CT 06083-3238 *E-mail:* office@sfwa.org *Web Site:* www.sfwa.org, pg 727

Sparkes, Kathy, Dumbarton Oaks, 1703 32 St NW, Washington, DC 20007 *Tel:* 202-339-6400 *Fax:* 202-339-6401; 202-298-8407 *E-mail:* doaksbooks@doaks.org *Web Site:* www.doaks.org, pg 77

Sparks, Kerry, Levine|Greenberg|Rostan Literary Agency Inc, 307 Seventh Ave, Suite 2407, New York, NY 10001 *Tel:* 212-337-0934 *Fax:* 212-337-0948 *Web Site:* lgrliterary.com, pg 561

Sparks, Lee Ann, Trinity University Press, One Trinity Place, San Antonio, TX 78212-7200 *Tel:* 210-999-8884 *Fax:* 210-999-8838 *E-mail:* books@trinity.edu *Web Site:* www.tupress.org, pg 249

Spassiani, Rachel, AMWA Medical Book Awards, 30 W Gude Dr, Suite 525, Rockville, MD 20850-4357 *Tel:* 240-238-0940 *Fax:* 301-294-9006 *E-mail:* amwa@amwa.org *Web Site:* www.amwa.org, pg 667

Spatz, Bruce, John Wiley & Sons Inc Higher Education, 111 River St, Hoboken, NJ 07030-5774 *Tel:* 201-748-6000 *Toll Free Tel:* 800-225-5945 (cust serv) *Fax:* 201-748-6008 *E-mail:* info@wiley.com *Web Site:* www.wiley.com, pg 272

Spear, Jody, Aaron-Spear, PO Box 42, Brooksville, ME 04617 *Tel:* 207-326-8764, pg 519

Spector, Jon, The Conference Board Inc, 845 Third Ave, New York, NY 10022-6679 *Tel:* 212-759-0900; 212-339-0345 (cust serv) *Fax:* 212-980-7014; 212-836-9740 (cust serv) *E-mail:* info@conference-board.org *Web Site:* www.conference-board.org, pg 62

Speer, Mark, Simon & Schuster, Inc, 1230 Avenue of the Americas, New York, NY 10020 *Tel:* 212-698-7000 *Fax:* 212-698-7007 *E-mail:* firstname.lastname@simonandschuster.com *Web Site:* www.simonandschuster.com, pg 226

Spellman-Silverman, Erica, Trident Media Group LLC, 41 Madison Ave, 36th fl, New York, NY 10010 *Tel:* 212-333-1511 *E-mail:* info@tridentmediagroup.com; press@tridentmediagroup.com *Web Site:* www.tridentmediagroup.com, pg 577

Spence, Bill, Information Today, Inc, 143 Old Marlton Pike, Medford, NJ 08055-8750 *Tel:* 609-654-6266 *Toll Free Tel:* 800-300-9868 (cust serv) *Fax:* 609-654-4309 *E-mail:* custserv@infotoday.com *Web Site:* www.infotoday.com, pg 121

Spence, Craig, Federation of BC Writers, PO Box 16028, 617 Belmont St, New Westminster, BC V3M 6W6, Canada *E-mail:* info@bcwriters.ca *Web Site:* bcwriters.ca, pg 605

Spencer, Denise, American Fisheries Society, 5410 Grosvenor Lane, Suite 110, Bethesda, MD 20814-2199 *Tel:* 301-897-8616; 703-661-1570 (book orders) *Fax:* 301-897-8096; 703-996-1010 (book orders) *E-mail:* main@fisheries.org *Web Site:* www.fisheries.org, pg 12

Spencer, Elaine, The Knight Agency Inc, 570 East Ave, Madison, GA 30650 *E-mail:* submissions@knightagency.net *Web Site:* www.knightagency.net, pg 560

Spengler-Jaffee, Pamela, HarperCollins General Books Group, 195 Broadway, New York, NY 10007 *Tel:* 212-207-7000 *Web Site:* www.harpercollins.com, pg 105

Sperling, Ehud C, Bear & Co Inc, One Park St, Rochester, VT 05767 *Tel:* 802-767-3174 *Toll Free Tel:* 800-932-3277 *Fax:* 802-767-3726 *E-mail:* customerservice@InnerTraditions.com *Web Site:* InnerTraditions.com, pg 33

Sperling, Ehud C, Inner Traditions International Ltd, One Park St, Rochester, VT 05767 *Tel:* 802-767-3174 *Toll Free Tel:* 800-246-8648 *Fax:* 802-767-3726 *E-mail:* customerservice@InnerTraditions.com *Web Site:* www.InnerTraditions.com, pg 122

Spicer, Charles, St Martin's Press, LLC, 175 Fifth Ave, New York, NY 10010 *Tel:* 646-307-5151 *Fax:* 212-420-9314 *E-mail:* firstname.lastname@macmillan.com *Web Site:* www.stmartins.com, pg 215

Spicer, Ed, The Pennsylvania State University Press, University Support Bldg 1, Suite C, 820 N University Dr, University Park, PA 16802-1003 *Tel:* 814-865-1327 *Toll Free Tel:* 800-326-9180 *Fax:* 814-863-1408 *Toll Free Fax:* 877-778-2665 *E-mail:* info@psupress.org *Web Site:* www.psupress.org, pg 188

Spiegel, Cindy, Random House Publishing Group, 1745 Broadway, New York, NY 10019 *Toll Free Tel:* 800-200-3552 *Web Site:* atrandom.com, pg 204

Spiegel, Lauren, Touchstone, 1230 Avenue of the Americas, New York, NY 10020, pg 247

Spiegelman, Willard, Morton Marr Poetry Prize, PO Box 750374, Dallas, TX 75275-0374 *Fax:* 214-768-1408 *E-mail:* swr@mail.smu.edu *Web Site:* www.smu.edu/southwestreview, pg 705

Spiegelman, Willard, John H McGinnis Memorial Award, PO Box 750374, Dallas, TX 75275-0374 *Fax:* 214-768-1408 *E-mail:* swr@mail.smu.edu *Web Site:* www.smu.edu/southwestreview, pg 706

Spiegelman, Willard, The David Nathan Meyerson Prize for Fiction, PO Box 750374, Dallas, TX 75275-0374 *Fax:* 214-768-1408 *E-mail:* swr@mail.smu.edu *Web Site:* www.smu.edu/southwestreview, pg 707

Spiegelman, Willard, Elizabeth Matchett Stover Memorial Award, PO Box 750374, Dallas, TX 75275-0374 *Fax:* 214-768-1408 *E-mail:* swr@mail.smu.edu *Web Site:* www.smu.edu/southwestreview, pg 731

Spieler, Joseph, The Spieler Agency, 27 W 20 St, Suite 305, New York, NY 10011 *Tel:* 212-757-4439 *Fax:* 212-333-2019 *E-mail:* spieleragency@spieleragency.com, pg 574

Spindler, Matt, The Karpfinger Agency, 357 W 20 St, New York, NY 10011-3379 *Tel:* 212-691-2690 *Fax:* 212-691-7129 *E-mail:* info@karpfinger.com (no queries or submissions) *Web Site:* karpfinger.com, pg 559

Spinelli, Melissa, Berghahn Books, 20 Jay St, Suite 512, Brooklyn, NY 11201 *Tel:* 212-233-6004 *Fax:* 212-233-6007 *E-mail:* info@berghahnbooks.com; salesus@berghahnbooks.com; editorial@journals.berghahnbooks.com *Web Site:* www.berghahnbooks.com, pg 35

Spinner, Dianna, The PRS Group Inc, 6320 Fly Rd, Suite 102, East Syracuse, NY 13057-9358 *Tel:* 315-431-0511 *Fax:* 315-431-0200 *E-mail:* custserv@prsgroup.com *Web Site:* www.prsgroup.com, pg 199

Spitkovsky, Neil, Crown Publishing Group, c/o Penguin Random House Inc, 1745 Broadway, New York, NY 10019 *Tel:* 212-782-9000 *Toll Free Tel:* 888-264-1745 *Fax:* 212-940-7408 *E-mail:* crownosm@penguinrandomhouse.com *Web Site:* crownpublishing.com, pg 68

Spittal, Robin, Writers' Federation of Nova Scotia, 1113 Marginal Rd, Halifax, NS B3H 4P7, Canada *Tel:* 902-423-8116 *Fax:* 902-422-0881 *E-mail:* contact@writers.ns.ca *Web Site:* writers.ns.ca, pg 621

Spitzer, Anne-Lise, Alfred A Knopf/Everyman's Library, c/o Random House Inc, 1745 Broadway, New York, NY 10019 *Tel:* 212-751-2600 *Toll Free Tel:* 800-638-6460 *Fax:* 212-572-2593 *Web Site:* www.knopfdoubleday.com, pg 132

Spitzer, Philip, Philip G Spitzer Literary Agency Inc, 50 Talmage Farm Lane, East Hampton, NY 11937 *Tel:* 631-329-3650 *Fax:* 631-329-3651 *Web Site:* www.spitzeragency.com, pg 575

Spizzirri, Linda, Spizzirri Publishing Inc, PO Box 9397, Rapid City, SD 57709-9397 *Tel:* 605-348-2749 *Toll Free Tel:* 800-325-9819 *Fax:* 605-348-6251 *Toll Free Fax:* 800-322-9819 *E-mail:* spizzpub@aol.com *Web Site:* www.spizzirri.com, pg 232

Spohn, Nancy, Lynne Rienner Publishers Inc, 1800 30 St, Suite 314, Boulder, CO 80301 *Tel:* 303-444-6684 *Fax:* 303-444-0824 *E-mail:* questions@rienner.com; cservice@rienner.com *Web Site:* www.rienner.com, pg 209

Spooner, Andrea, Little, Brown Books for Young Readers, 1290 Avenue of the Americas, New York, NY 10019 *Tel:* 212-364-1100 *Toll Free Tel:* 800-759-0190 (cust serv) *Web Site:* www.HachetteBookGroup.com, pg 141

Spooner, Michael, May Swenson Poetry Award, 3078 Old Main Hill, Logan, UT 84322-3078 *Tel:* 435-797-1362 *Fax:* 435-797-0313 *Web Site:* www.usupress.org, pg 731

Spooner, Michael, Utah State University Press, 3078 Old Main Hill, Logan, UT 84322-3078 *Tel:* 435-797-1362 *Fax:* 435-797-0313 *Web Site:* www.usupress.org, pg 264

Spraggins, Crystal, F A Davis Co, 1915 Arch St, Philadelphia, PA 19103 *Tel:* 215-568-2270; 215-440-3001 *Toll Free Tel:* 800-523-4049 *Fax:* 215-568-5065; 215-440-3016 *E-mail:* info@fadavis.com; orders@fadavis.com *Web Site:* www.fadavis.com, pg 71

Sprague, Peter, Piano Press, 1425 Ocean Ave, Suite 5, Del Mar, CA 92014 *Tel:* 619-884-1401 *Fax:* 858-755-1104 *E-mail:* pianopress@pianopress.com *Web Site:* www.pianopress.com, pg 191

Spring, Kathleen, Spring Time Writers Creative Writing & Journaling Workshop, PO Box 512, Lyons, CO 80540-0512 *Tel:* 303-823-0997 *E-mail:* writers@springtimewriters.com *Web Site:* www.springtimewriters.com, pg 655

Springer, Rebecca, Houghton Mifflin Harcourt Trade & Reference Division, 222 Berkeley St, Boston, MA 02116 *Tel:* 617-351-5000 *Toll Free Tel:* 800-225-3362 *Web Site:* www.hmhco.com, pg 115

Springstead, Phil, Triumph Books, 814 N Franklin St, Chicago, IL 60610 *Toll Free Tel:* 800-888-4741 (orders only) *Fax:* 312-280-5470 *Web Site:* www.triumphbooks.com, pg 250

Squires, Jeff, Riverside Publishing, 3800 Golf Rd, Suite 200, Rolling Meadows, IL 60008 *Tel:* 630-467-7000 *Toll Free Tel:* 800-323-9540 *Fax:* 630-467-7192 (cust serv) *E-mail:* rpc_customer_service@hmhpub.com (cust serv) *Web Site:* www.riversidepublishing.com, pg 209

Srivastava, Rahul, Simon & Schuster, Inc, 1230 Avenue of the Americas, New York, NY 10020 *Tel:* 212-698-7000 *Fax:* 212-698-7007 *E-mail:* firstname.lastname@simonandschuster.com *Web Site:* www.simonandschuster.com, pg 226

St John, Asia, Elderberry Press Inc, 1393 Old Homestead Dr, Oakland, OR 97462-9690 *Tel:* 541-459-6043 *Web Site:* www.elderberrypress.com, pg 80

St John, Max, Ransom Note Press, 143 E Ridgewood Ave, Box 419, Ridgewood, NJ 07451 *Tel:* 201-835-2790 *E-mail:* editorial@ransomnotepress.com *Web Site:* www.ransomnotepress.com, pg 509

St John, Valerie, Elderberry Press Inc, 1393 Old Homestead Dr, Oakland, OR 97462-9690 *Tel:* 541-459-6043 *Web Site:* www.elderberrypress.com, pg 80

St Lifer, Evan, Scholastic Education, 524 Broadway, New York, NY 10012 *Tel:* 212-343-6100 *Fax:* 212-343-6189 *Web Site:* www.scholastic.com, pg 218

St Pierre, Louisa, Bernstein & Andriulli Inc, 58 W 40 St, 6th fl, New York, NY 10018 *Tel:* 212-682-1490 *Fax:* 212-286-1890 *E-mail:* info@ba-reps.com *Web Site:* www.ba-reps.com, pg 583

St Thomasino, Carol, Palgrave Macmillan, 175 Fifth Ave, Suite 200, New York, NY 10010 *Tel:* 646-307-5151 *Fax:* 212-777-6359 *E-mail:* firstname.lastname@palgrave-usa.com *Web Site:* us.macmillan.com/Palgrave.aspx, pg 180

Stack, Deborah, Lark Crafts, 1166 Avenue of the Americas, New York, NY 10036 *Tel:* 212-532-7160 *E-mail:* customerservice@sterlingpublishing.com *Web Site:* larkcrafts.com; www.sterlingpublishing.com, pg 134

Stackler, Ed, Stackler Editorial Agency, 555 Lincoln Ave, Alameda, CA 94501 *Tel:* 510-814-9694 *Fax:* 510-814-9694 *E-mail:* stackler@aol.com *Web Site:* www.fictioneditor.com, pg 534

Stackpole, Kerry C, Printing & Graphics Association MidAtlantic (PGAMA), 9685 Gerwig Lane, Suite A, Columbia, MD 21046-1520 *Tel:* 410-319-0900 *Toll Free Tel:* 877-319-0906 *Fax:* 410-319-0905 *E-mail:* info@pgama.com *Web Site:* www.pgama.com, pg 616

Staff, Bruce, Blue Poppy Press, 1990 57 Ct, Unit A, Boulder, CO 80301 *Tel:* 303-447-8372 *Toll Free Tel:* 800-487-9296 *Fax:* 303-245-8362 *E-mail:* info@bluepoppy.com *Web Site:* www.bluepoppy.com, pg 40

Stafford, Greg, Chaosium Inc, 22568 Mission Blvd, Suite 423, Hayward, CA 94541-5116 *Tel:* 510-583-1000 *Fax:* 510-583-1101 *Web Site:* www.chaosium.com, pg 55

Staib, Erich, Duke University Press, 905 W Main St, Suite 18B, Durham, NC 27701 *Tel:* 919-688-5134 *Toll Free Tel:* 888-651-0122 (US) *Fax:* 919-688-2615 *Toll Free Fax:* 888-651-0124 *E-mail:* orders@dukeupress.edu; permissions@dukeupress.edu *Web Site:* www.dukeupress.edu, pg 77

Staines, Gail M PhD, Saint Louis Literary Award, Pius XII Memorial Library, 3650 Lindell Blvd, St Louis, MO 63108 *Tel:* 314-977-3100 *Fax:* 314-977-3587 *E-mail:* slula@slu.edu *Web Site:* www.slu.edu/libraries/associates, pg 725

Stakes, Robert, Texas Western Press, c/o University of Texas at El Paso, 500 W University Ave, El Paso, TX 79968-0633 *Tel:* 915-747-5688 *Toll Free Tel:* 800-488-3798 (orders only) *Fax:* 915-747-7515 *E-mail:* twpress@utep.edu *Web Site:* twp.utep.edu, pg 244

Stakes, Robert L, Carl Hertzog Award for Excellence in Book Design, c/o Dir of the Library, University of Texas at El Paso, University Library, El Paso, TX 79968-0582 *Tel:* 915-747-5683 *Fax:* 915-747-5345 *Web Site:* libraryweb.utep.edu/about/hertzog_call.php, pg 692

Stallings, A E, International Poetry Competition, PO Box 8248, Atlanta, GA 31106 *E-mail:* atlanta.review@yahoo.com *Web Site:* www.atlantareview.com, pg 695

Stamathis, George S, Brookes Publishing Co Inc, PO Box 10624, Baltimore, MD 21285-0624 *Tel:* 410-337-9580 (outside US & CN) *Toll Free Tel:* 800-638-3775 (US & CN) *Fax:* 410-337-8539 *E-mail:* custserv@brookespublishing.com *Web Site:* www.brookespublishing.com, pg 46

Stambaugh, Doug, Simon & Schuster, Inc, 1230 Avenue of the Americas, New York, NY 10020 *Tel:* 212-698-7000 *Fax:* 212-698-7007 *E-mail:* firstname.lastname@simonandschuster.com *Web Site:* www.simonandschuster.com, pg 226

Stampfel, Peter, DAW Books Inc, 375 Hudson St, New York, NY 10014 *Tel:* 212-366-2096 *Fax:* 212-366-2090 *E-mail:* daw@penguinrandomhouse.com *Web Site:* us.penguingroup.com; www.dawbooks.com, pg 71

Stanczyk, Ms Soki, New City Press, 202 Comforter Blvd, Hyde Park, NY 12538 *Tel:* 845-229-0335 *Toll Free Tel:* 800-462-5980 (orders only) *Fax:* 845-229-0351 *E-mail:* info@newcitypress.com *Web Site:* www.newcitypress.com, pg 167

Standafer, Ellen, The Quarasan Group Inc, 405 W Superior St, Chicago, IL 60654 *Tel:* 312-981-2500 *E-mail:* info@quarasan.com *Web Site:* www.quarasan.com, pg 533

Standley, Will, Wescott Cove Publishing Co, 1227 S Florida Ave, Rockledge, FL 32955 *Tel:* 321-690-2224 *Fax:* 321-690-0853 *E-mail:* customerservice@farhorizonsmedia.com *Web Site:* www.farhorizonsmedia.com, pg 268

Stanford, Elisa, Edit Resource LLC, 3578-E Hartsel Dr, Suite 387, Colorado Springs, CO 80920 *Tel:* 719-290-0757 *E-mail:* info@editresource.com (main) *Web Site:* www.editresource.com (main); www.inspirationalghostwriting.com, pg 525

Stanford, Eric, Edit Resource LLC, 3578-E Hartsel Dr, Suite 387, Colorado Springs, CO 80920 *Tel:* 719-290-0757 *E-mail:* info@editresource.com (main) *Web Site:* www.editresource.com (main); www.inspirationalghostwriting.com, pg 525

Stanford, Halle, The Jim Henson Co, 1416 N La Brea Ave, Hollywood, CA 90028 *Tel:* 323-802-1500 *Fax:* 323-802-1825 *Web Site:* www.henson.com, pg 127

Stanish, Charles, Cotsen Institute of Archaeology Press, 308 Charles E Young Dr N, Fowler A163, Box 951510, Los Angeles, CA 90024 *Tel:* 310-206-9384 *Fax:* 310-206-4723 *E-mail:* ioapubs@ioa.ucla.edu *Web Site:* www.ioa.ucla.edu, pg 64

Stanley, Cullen, Janklow & Nesbit Associates, 445 Park Ave, New York, NY 10022 *Tel:* 212-421-1700 *Fax:* 212-980-3671 *E-mail:* info@janklow.com *Web Site:* www.janklowandnesbit.com, pg 558

Stanley, George, John Wiley & Sons Inc Professional/Trade Group, 111 River St, Hoboken, NJ 07030 *Tel:* 201-748-6000 *Toll Free Tel:* 800-225-5945 (cust serv) *Fax:* 201-748-6088 *E-mail:* info@wiley.com *Web Site:* www.wiley.com, pg 272

Stanley, James, Xlibris Corp, 1663 Liberty Dr, Suite 200, Bloomington, IN 47403 *Toll Free Tel:* 888-795-4274 *Fax:* 610-915-0294 *E-mail:* info@xlibris.com *Web Site:* www.xlibris.com, pg 277

Stanley, Lindsay, Cengage Learning, 20 Channel Center St, Boston, MA 02210 *Tel:* 617-289-7700 *Toll Free Tel:* 800-354-9706 *Fax:* 617-289-7844 *Toll Free Fax:* 800-487-8488 *E-mail:* esales@cengage.com *Web Site:* www.cengage.com, pg 53

Stanley, Lindsay, Wadsworth Publishing, 20 Davis Dr, Belmont, CA 94002 *Tel:* 650-595-2350 *Fax:* 650-592-3022 *Toll Free Fax:* 800-522-4923 *Web Site:* www.cengage.com, pg 266

Stanley, Rex, Unicor Medical Inc, 4160 Carmichael Rd, Montgomery, AL 36106 *Tel:* 334-260-8150 *Toll Free Tel:* 800-825-7421 *Toll Free Fax:* 800-305-8030 *E-mail:* sales@unicormed.com *Web Site:* www.unicormed.com, pg 253

Stansfield, Gwyneth, Scribner, 1230 Avenue of the Americas, New York, NY 10020, pg 220

Stanton, Cheryl, Krieger Publishing Co, 1725 Krieger Dr, Malabar, FL 32950 *Tel:* 321-724-9542 *Toll Free Tel:* 800-724-0025 *Fax:* 321-951-3671 *E-mail:* info@krieger-publishing.com *Web Site:* www.krieger-publishing.com, pg 133

Stanulis, Roxanne, Delaware Division of the Arts, Carvel State Off Bldg, 4th fl, 820 N French St, Wilmington, DE 19801 *Tel:* 302-577-8278 *Fax:* 302-577-6561 *E-mail:* delarts@state.de.us *Web Site:* www.artsdel.org, pg 680

Staples, Debra, SynergEbooks, 948 New Hwy 7, Columbia, TN 38401 *Tel:* 931-548-2494 *E-mail:* synergebooks@aol.com *Web Site:* www.synergebooks.com, pg 239

Stapleton, Janet, Beacon Hill Press of Kansas City, PO Box 419527, Kansas City, MO 64141-6527 *Tel:* 816-931-1900 *Toll Free Tel:* 800-877-0700 (cust serv) *Fax:* 816-753-4071 *Web Site:* www.beaconhillbooks.com, pg 32

Stapleton, Jay, Law Tribune Books, 201 Ann Uccello St, 4th fl, Hartford, CT 06103 *Tel:* 860-527-7900 *Fax:* 860-527-7433 *E-mail:* lawtribune@alm.com *Web Site:* www.ctlawtribune.com, pg 135

Stapleton, Victoria, Little, Brown Books for Young Readers, 1290 Avenue of the Americas, New York, NY 10019 *Tel:* 212-364-1100 *Toll Free Tel:* 800-759-0190 (cust serv) *Web Site:* www.HachetteBookGroup.com, pg 141

Star, Brenda, StarGroup International Inc, 1194 Old Dixie Hwy, Suite 201, West Palm Beach, FL 33413 *Tel:* 561-547-0667 *Fax:* 561-843-8530 *E-mail:* info@stargroupinternational.com *Web Site:* www.stargroupinternational.com, pg 234

Staral, Christian, Springer, 233 Spring St, New York, NY 10013-1578 *Tel:* 212-460-1500 *Toll Free Tel:* 800-SPRINGER (777-4643) *Fax:* 212-460-1575 *E-mail:* service-ny@springer.com *Web Site:* www.springer.com, pg 232

Stark, Kate, Riverhead Books (Hardcover), 375 Hudson St, New York, NY 10014 *Tel:* 212-366-2000 *E-mail:* online@penguinputnam.com *Web Site:* www.penguinputnam.com; us.penguingroup.com, pg 209

Stark, Kate, Viking, 375 Hudson St, New York, NY 10014 *Tel:* 212-366-2000 *E-mail:* online@penguinputnam.com *Web Site:* www.penguinputnam.com; us.penguingroup.com, pg 265

Stark, Patty, John Wiley & Sons Inc Higher Education, 111 River St, Hoboken, NJ 07030-5774 *Tel:* 201-748-6000 *Toll Free Tel:* 800-225-5945 (cust serv) *Fax:* 201-748-6008 *E-mail:* info@wiley.com *Web Site:* www.wiley.com, pg 272

Starke, Alexis, History Publishing Co LLC, PO Box 700, Palisades, NY 10964 *Tel:* 845-398-8161 *E-mail:* info@historypublishingco.com *Web Site:* www.historypublishingco.com, pg 112

Starkman, Stanley, Chestnut Publishing Group Inc, 44 Stubbs Dr, Suite 207, Toronto, ON M2L 2R3, Canada *Tel:* 416-224-5824 *Fax:* 416-224-0595 *Web Site:* www.chestnutpublishing.com, pg 477

Starmer, Cate, Fodor's Travel Publications, 1745 Broadway, 15th fl, New York, NY 10019 *Toll Free Tel:* 800-733-3000 *E-mail:* fodorspublicity@randomhouse.com; editors@fodors.com *Web Site:* www.fodors.com, pg 90

Starnino, Carmine, Vehicule Press, PO Box 42094, CP Roy, Montreal, QC H2W-2T3, Canada *Tel:* 514-844-6073 *Fax:* 514-844-7543 *E-mail:* vp@vehiculepress.com; admin@vehiculepress.com *Web Site:* www.vehiculepress.com, pg 504

Starowitz, Todd, Tyndale House Publishers Inc, 351 Executive Dr, Carol Stream, IL 60188 *Tel:* 630-668-8300 *Toll Free Tel:* 800-323-9400 *Web Site:* www.tyndale.com, pg 252

Starr, Joshua, Phi Delta Kappa International®, 320 W Eighth St, Suite 216, Bloomington, IN 47404 *Tel:* 812-339-1156 *Toll Free Tel:* 800-766-1156 *Fax:* 812-339-0018 *E-mail:* customerservice@pdkintl.org *Web Site:* www.pdkintl.org, pg 190

Starr, Lara, Chronicle Books LLC, 680 Second St, San Francisco, CA 94107 *Tel:* 415-537-4200 *Toll Free Tel:* 800-759-0190 (cust serv) *Fax:* 415-537-4460 *Toll Free Fax:* 800-858-7787 (orders); 800-286-9471 (cust serv) *E-mail:* frontdesk@chroniclebooks.com *Web Site:* www.chroniclebooks.com, pg 58

Starr, Leslie, Wesleyan University Press, 215 Long Lane, Middletown, CT 06459-0433 *Tel:* 860-685-7711 *Fax:* 860-685-7712 *Web Site:* www.wesleyan.edu/wespress, pg 269

Starrett, Margaret, Branden Books, PO Box 812094, Wellesley, MA 02482-0013 *Tel:* 781-235-3347 *E-mail:* branden@brandenbooks.com *Web Site:* www.brandenbooks.com, pg 44

Stascavage, Anne, University Press of Mississippi, 3825 Ridgewood Rd, Jackson, MS 39211-6492 *Tel:* 601-432-6205 *Toll Free Tel:* 800-737-7788 (orders & cust serv) *Fax:* 601-432-6217 *E-mail:* press@mississippi.edu *Web Site:* www.upress.state.ms.us, pg 262

Staton, Cecil P Jr, Smyth & Helwys Publishing Inc, 6316 Peake Rd, Macon, GA 31210-3960 *Tel:* 478-757-0564 *Toll Free Tel:* 800-747-3016 (orders only); 800-568-1248 (orders only) *Fax:* 478-757-1305 *E-mail:* information@helwys.com *Web Site:* www.helwys.com, pg 228

Stebbins, Dr Chad, International Society of Weekly Newspaper Editors, Missouri Southern State University, 3950 E Newman Rd, Joplin, MO 64801-1595 *Tel:* 417-625-9736 *Fax:* 417-659-4445 *Web Site:* www.iswne.org, pg 608

Stech, Marko R, Canadian Institute of Ukrainian Studies Press, University of Toronto, 256 McCaul St, Rm 308, Toronto, ON M5T 1W5, Canada *Tel:* 416-978-6934 *Fax:* 416-978-2672 *E-mail:* cius@ualberta.ca *Web Site:* www.ciuspress.com, pg 475

Stecher, Leah, Basic Books, 250 W 57 St, 15th fl, New York, NY 10107 *Tel:* 212-340-8164; 212-340-8136 *Fax:* 212-340-8135 *E-mail:* perseus.promos@perseusbooks.com *Web Site:* www.basicbooks.com; perseusbooks.com, pg 31

Stecopoulos, Harilaos, The Iowa Review Award, 308 EPB, Iowa City, IA 52242-1408 *E-mail:* iowa-review@uiowa.edu *Web Site:* www.iowareview.org, pg 696

Steele, Alex, Gotham Writers' Workshop, 555 Eighth Ave, Suite 1402, New York, NY 10018-4358 *Tel:* 212-974-8377 *Toll Free Tel:* 877-974-8377 *E-mail:* office@write.org *Web Site:* www.writingclasses.com, pg 651

Steele, David Ramsay, Open Court, 70 E Lake St, Suite 300, Chicago, IL 60601 *Tel:* 312-701-1720 *Toll Free Tel:* 800-815-2280 (orders only) *Fax:* 312-701-1728 *E-mail:* opencourt@caruspub.com *Web Site:* www.opencourtbooks.com, pg 175

Steelman, Cheryl, Charles C Thomas Publisher Ltd, 2600 S First St, Springfield, IL 62704 *Tel:* 217-789-8980 *Toll Free Tel:* 800-258-8980 *Fax:* 217-789-9130 *E-mail:* books@ccthomas.com *Web Site:* www.ccthomas.com, pg 245

Steffen, Zach, North Country Books Inc, 220 Lafayette St, Utica, NY 13502-4312 *Tel:* 315-735-4877 *Toll Free Tel:* 800-342-7409 (orders) *Fax:* 315-738-4342 *E-mail:* ncbooks@verizon.net *Web Site:* www.northcountrybooks.com, pg 170

Stehlik, Liate, HarperCollins General Books Group, 195 Broadway, New York, NY 10007 *Tel:* 212-207-7000 *Web Site:* www.harpercollins.com, pg 105

Steidel, Lauren, Society for Industrial & Applied Mathematics, 3600 Market St, 6th fl, Philadelphia, PA 19104-2688 *Tel:* 215-382-9800 *Toll Free Tel:* 800-447-7426 *Fax:* 215-386-7999 *E-mail:* siambooks@siam.org *Web Site:* www.siam.org, pg 228

Steiger, Bill, American College of Physician Executives, 400 N Ashley Dr, Suite 400, Tampa, FL 33602 *Tel:* 813-287-2000 *Toll Free Tel:* 800-562-8088 *Fax:* 813-287-8993 *E-mail:* acpe@acpe.org *Web Site:* www.acpe.org, pg 12

Stein, Anna, Aitken Alexander Associates LLC, 30 Vandam St, Suite 5A, New York, NY 10013 *Tel:* 212-929-4100 *Web Site:* www.aitkenalexander.co.uk, pg 540

Stein, Anne Marie, Massachusetts College of Art & Design Writing Children's Literature, 621 Huntington Ave, Boston, MA 02115 *Tel:* 617-879-7200 *Fax:* 617-879-7171 *E-mail:* ce@massart.edu *Web Site:* www.massart.edu/ce, pg 661

Stein, Carol A, ASCSA Publications, American School of Classical Studies at Athens, 6-8 Charlton St, Princeton, NJ 08540-5232 *Tel:* 609-683-0800 *Fax:* 609-924-0578 *Web Site:* www.ascsa.edu.gr/publications, pg 24

Stein, Jonathan, Open Road Publishing, 32 Turkey Lane, Cold Spring Harbor, NY 11724 *Tel:* 631-692-7172 *E-mail:* jopenroad@aol.com *Web Site:* www.openroadguides.com, pg 175

Stein, Judith, The Author's Friend, 548 Ocean Blvd, No 12, Long Branch, NJ 07740 *Tel:* 732-571-8051, pg 521

Stein, Liz, Harlequin Enterprises Ltd, 233 Broadway, Suite 1001, New York, NY 10279 *Tel:* 212-553-4200 *Fax:* 212-227-8969 *E-mail:* CustomerService@harlequin.com *Web Site:* www.harlequin.com, pg 105

Stein, Lonny R, Barron's Educational Series Inc, 250 Wireless Blvd, Hauppauge, NY 11788 *Tel:* 631-434-3311 *Toll Free Tel:* 800-645-3476 *Fax:* 631-434-3723 *E-mail:* barrons@barronseduc.com *Web Site:* www.barronseduc.com, pg 31

Stein, Sarah, Penguin Books, 375 Hudson St, New York, NY 10014 *Tel:* 212-366-2000 *E-mail:* online@penguinputnam.com *Web Site:* www.penguinputnam.com; www.penguinclassics.com; us.penguingroup.com, pg 186

Stein, Sherry, The Fraser Institute, 1770 Burrard St, 4th fl, Vancouver, BC V6J 3G7, Canada *Tel:* 604-688-0221 *Toll Free Tel:* 800-665-3558 *Fax:* 604-688-8539 *E-mail:* info@fraserinstitute.org; sales@fraserinstitute.org *Web Site:* www.fraserinstitute.org, pg 485

Stein, Stephanie, HarperCollins Children's Books, 195 Broadway, New York, NY 10007 *Tel:* 212-207-7000 *Web Site:* www.harpercollins.com/childrens, pg 105

Steinberg, Andrew, Modern Publishing, 155 E 55 St, New York, NY 10022 *Tel:* 212-826-0850 *Fax:* 212-759-9069 *Web Site:* www.modernpublishing.com, pg 158

Steinberg, Michael, Michael Steinberg Literary Agent, PO Box 274, Glencoe, IL 60022-0274 *Tel:* 847-626-1000 *Fax:* 847-626-1002 *E-mail:* michael14steinberg@comcast.net, pg 575

Steinberger, David, Basic Books, 250 W 57 St, 15th fl, New York, NY 10107 *Tel:* 212-340-8164; 212-340-8136 *Fax:* 212-340-8135 *E-mail:* perseus.promos@perseusbooks.com *Web Site:* www.basicbooks.com; perseusbooks.com, pg 31

Steinberger, David, The Perseus Books Group, 387 Park Ave S, 12th fl, New York, NY 10016 *Tel:* 212-340-8100 *Toll Free Tel:* 800-343-4499 (cust serv) *Fax:* 212-340-8105 *Web Site:* www.perseusbooksgroup.com, pg 189

Steinberger, David, Westview Press, 2465 Central Ave, Boulder, CO 80301 *Tel:* 303-444-3541 *Fax:* 720-406-7336 *E-mail:* westview.orders@perseusbooks.com *Web Site:* www.perseusbooksgroup.com; www.westviewpress.com, pg 270

Steinbock, Steven, International Association of Crime Writers Inc, North American Branch, 243 Fifth Ave, Suite 537, New York, NY 10016 *Tel:* 212-243-8966 *Fax:* 815-361-1477 *E-mail:* info@crimewritersna.org *Web Site:* www.crimewritersna.org, pg 607

Steinecke, Anke, Penguin Random House Inc, 1745 Broadway, New York, NY 10019 *Tel:* 212-782-9000 *Toll Free Tel:* 800-726-0600 *Web Site:* www.randomhouse.com, pg 187

Steiner, Karen, Research Press, 2612 N Mattis Ave, Champaign, IL 61822 *Tel:* 217-352-3273 *Toll Free Tel:* 800-519-2707 *Fax:* 217-352-1221 *E-mail:* rp@researchpress.com; orders@researchpress.com *Web Site:* www.researchpress.com, pg 208

Steinert, Frank, Penguin Random House Inc, 1745 Broadway, New York, NY 10019 *Tel:* 212-782-9000 *Toll Free Tel:* 800-726-0600 *Web Site:* www.randomhouse.com, pg 187

Steinhardt, David J, IDEAlliance®, 1600 Duke St, Suite 420, Alexandria, VA 22314 *Tel:* 703-837-1070 *Fax:* 703-837-1072 *E-mail:* registrar@idealliance.org *Web Site:* www.idealliance.org, pg 607

Stelzig, Christopher, Entomological Society of America, 3 Park Place, Suite 307, Annapolis, MD 21401-3722 *Tel:* 301-731-4535 *Fax:* 301-731-4538 *E-mail:* esa@entsoc.org *Web Site:* www.entsoc.org, pg 83

Stender, Dr Uwe, TriadaUS Literary Agency, PO Box 561, Sewickley, PA 15143 *Tel:* 412-401-3376 *Fax:* 412-749-0842 *Web Site:* www.triadaus.com, pg 577

Stenger, Lisa, Kaeden Corp, PO Box 16190, Rocky River, OH 44116-0190 *Tel:* 440-617-1400 *Toll Free Tel:* 800-890-7323 *Fax:* 440-617-1403 *E-mail:* info@kaeden.com *Web Site:* www.kaeden.com, pg 129

Stenning, Blake, Marfield Prize, 2017 "I" St NW, Washington, DC 20006-1804 *E-mail:* award@artsclubofwashington.org *Web Site:* artsclubofwashington.org, pg 705

Stephanides, Myrsini, Carol Mann Agency, 55 Fifth Ave, New York, NY 10003 *Tel:* 212-206-5635 *Fax:* 212-675-4809 *E-mail:* submissions@carolmannagency.com *Web Site:* www.carolmannagency.com, pg 563

Stephens, Christopher P, Ultramarine Publishing Co Inc, 12 Washington Ave, Hastings-on-Hudson, NY 10706 *Tel:* 914-478-1339, pg 252

Stephens, Gavin, Presbyterian Publishing Corp (PPC), 100 Witherspoon St, Louisville, KY 40202 *Tel:* 502-569-5000 *Toll Free Tel:* 800-523-1631 (US only) *Fax:* 502-569-5113 *E-mail:* ppcmail@presbypub.com *Web Site:* www.ppcbooks.com, pg 196

Stephens, Gavin, Westminster John Knox Press (WJK), 100 Witherspoon St, Louisville, KY 40202-1396 *Tel:* 502-569-5052 *Toll Free Tel:* 800-227-2872 (US only) *Fax:* 502-569-8308 *Toll Free Fax:* 800-541-5113 (US & CN) *E-mail:* wjk@wjkbooks.com; customer_service@wjkbooks.com *Web Site:* www.wjkbooks.com, pg 269

Stephens, Michael, Manning Publications Co, PO Box 761, Shelter Island, NY 11964 *Tel:* 203-626-1510 *E-mail:* sales@manning.com; support@manning.com (cust serv) *Web Site:* www.manning.com, pg 146

Stephens, R David, Tradewind Books, 202-1807 Maritime Mews, Vancouver, BC V6H 3W7, Canada *Tel:* 604-662-4405 *E-mail:* tradewindbooks@yahoo.com *Web Site:* www.tradewindbooks.com, pg 501

Sterling, Jeremy, Spry Publishing, 2500 S State St, Ann Arbor, MI 48104 *Tel:* 734-913-1700 *Toll Free Tel:* 877-722-2264 *Fax:* 734-913-1249 *E-mail:* info@sprypub.com *Web Site:* www.sprypub.com, pg 232

Sterling, John, Macmillan, 175 Fifth Ave, New York, NY 10010 *Tel:* 646-307-5151 *Fax:* 212-420-9314 *E-mail:* firstname.lastname@macmillan.com *Web Site:* www.macmillan.com, pg 145

Stern, Amy, Sheldon Fogelman Agency Inc, 10 E 40 St, Suite 3205, New York, NY 10016 *Tel:* 212-532-7250 *Fax:* 212-685-8939 *E-mail:* info@sheldonfogelmanagency.com *Web Site:* sheldonfogelmanagency.com, pg 552

Stern, Chris, The Society of Southwestern Authors (SSA), PO Box 30355, Tucson, AZ 85751-0355 *Tel:* 520-546-9382 *Web Site:* www.ssa-az.org, pg 619

Stern, Ina, Algonquin Books, 400 Silver Cedar Ct, Suite 300, Chapel Hill, NC 27514-1585 *Tel:* 919-967-0108 *Fax:* 919-933-0272 *E-mail:* inquiry@algonquin.com *Web Site:* www.workman.com/algonquin, pg 8

Stern, Janet, Markus Wiener Publishers Inc, 231 Nassau St, Princeton, NJ 08542 *Tel:* 609-921-1141 *Fax:* 609-921-1140 *E-mail:* publisher@markuswiener.com *Web Site:* www.markuswiener.com, pg 271

Stern, Molly, Crown Publishing Group, c/o Penguin Random House Inc, 1745 Broadway, New York, NY 10019 *Tel:* 212-782-9000 *Toll Free Tel:* 888-264-1745 *Fax:* 212-940-7408 *E-mail:* crownosm@penguinrandomhouse.com *Web Site:* crownpublishing.com, pg 68

Stern, Walter B, Prayer Book Press Inc, 1363 Fairfield Ave, Bridgeport, CT 06605 *Tel:* 203-384-2284 *Fax:* 203-579-9109, pg 196

Sternlicht, Moshe, Moznaim Publishing Corp, 4304 12 Ave, Brooklyn, NY 11219 *Tel:* 718-438-7680 *Fax:* 718-438-1305 *E-mail:* sales@moznaim.com *Web Site:* www.moznaim.com, pg 161

Stets, Mary Anne, Mystic Seaport Museum Inc, PO Box 6000, Mystic, CT 06355-0990 *Tel:* 860-572-5302; 860-572-0711 (visitor serv) *Toll Free Tel:* 800-248-1066 (wholesale orders only); 800-331-2665 (retail orders only) *Fax:* 860-572-5321 *E-mail:* info@mysticseaport.org *Web Site:* www.mysticseaport.org, pg 162

Stetz, Jeffrey, Transaction Publishers Inc, 10 Corporate Place S, 35 Berrue Circle, Piscataway, NJ 08854 *Tel:* 732-445-2280; 732-445-1245 (orders) *Toll Free Tel:* 888-999-6778 (dist ctr) *Fax:* 732-445-3138 *E-mail:* trans@transactionpub.com; orders@transactionpub.com *Web Site:* www.transactionpub.com, pg 248

Steve, Betsy, New York University Press, 838 Broadway, 3rd fl, New York, NY 10003-4812 *Tel:* 212-998-2575 (edit) *Toll Free Tel:* 800-996-6987 (orders) *Fax:* 212-995-3833 (orders) *E-mail:* information@nyupress.org; customerservice@nyupress.org; orders@nyupress.org *Web Site:* www.nyupress.org, pg 169

Stevens, Drew, The Feminist Press at The City University of New York, 365 Fifth Ave, Suite 5406, New York, NY 10016 *Tel:* 212-817-7915 *Fax:* 212-817-1593 *E-mail:* info@feministpress.org *Web Site:* www.feministpress.org, pg 87

Stevens, Jacob, Verso, 20 Jay St, Suite 1010, Brooklyn, NY 11201 *Tel:* 718-246-8160 *Fax:* 718-246-8165 *E-mail:* verso@versobooks.com *Web Site:* www.versobooks.com, pg 265

Stevens, Karen, Novalis Publishing, 10 Lower Spadina Ave, Suite 400, Toronto, ON M5V 2Z2, Canada *Tel:* 416-363-3303 *Toll Free Tel:* 877-702-7773 *Fax:* 416-363-9409 *Toll Free Fax:* 877-702-7775 *E-mail:* books@novalis.ca *Web Site:* www.novalis.ca, pg 493

Stevens, Martin, Forum Publishing Co, 383 E Main St, Centerport, NY 11721 *Tel:* 631-754-5000 *Toll Free Tel:* 800-635-7654 *Fax:* 631-754-0630 *E-mail:* forumpublishing@aol.com *Web Site:* www.forum123.com, pg 91

Stevens, Paul, Quirk Books, 215 Church St, Philadelphia, PA 19106 *Tel:* 215-627-3581 *Fax:* 215-627-5220 *E-mail:* general@quirkbooks.com *Web Site:* www.quirkbooks.com, pg 202

Stevens, R Blake, Collector Grade Publications Inc, PO Box 1046, Cobourg, ON K9A 4W5, Canada *Tel:* 905-342-3434 *Fax:* 905-342-3688 *E-mail:* info@collectorgrade.com *Web Site:* www.collectorgrade.com, pg 477

Stevenson, Courtney, Pippin Properties Inc, 110 W 40 St, Suite 1704, New York, NY 10018 *Tel:* 212-338-9310 *Fax:* 212-338-9579 *E-mail:* info@pippinproperties.com *Web Site:* www.pippinproperties.com; www.facebook.com/pippinproperties, pg 568

Stevenson, Deborah, Scott O'Dell Award for Historical Fiction, c/o Horn Book Inc, 56 Roland St, Suite 200, Boston, MA 02129 *Tel:* 617-628-8471 *Toll Free Tel:* 800-325-1170 *Web Site:* www.scottodell.com/odellaward.html, pg 714

Stevenson, Dinah, Clarion Books, 215 Park Ave S, New York, NY 10003 *Tel:* 212-420-5889 *Toll Free Tel:* 800-225-3362 (orders) *Fax:* 212-420-5855 *Toll Free Fax:* 800-634-7568 (orders) *Web Site:* www.hmhco.com, pg 59

Stevenson, Dinah, Houghton Mifflin Harcourt Trade & Reference Division, 222 Berkeley St, Boston, MA 02116 *Tel:* 617-351-5000 *Toll Free Tel:* 800-225-3362 *Web Site:* www.hmhco.com, pg 115

Stevenson, Julie, Waxman Leavell Literary Agency, 443 Park Ave S, No 1004, New York, NY 10016 *Tel:* 212-675-5556 *Fax:* 212-675-1381 *Web Site:* www.waxmanleavell.com, pg 579

Steward, Carlos, Black Mountain Press, PO Box 9907, Asheville, NC 28815 *Tel:* 828-273-3332 *Web Site:* www.theblackmountainpress.com, pg 38

Steward, Scott C, Newbury Street Press, 101 Newbury St, Boston, MA 02116 *Tel:* 617-536-5740 *Toll Free Tel:* 888-296-3447 (NEHGS membership) *Fax:* 617-536-7307 *E-mail:* sales@nehgs.org *Web Site:* www.newenglandancestors.org, pg 169

Stewart, Amy, University of Texas at Austin, Creative Writing Program, Dept of English, PAR 108, One University Sta, Mailcode B5000, Austin, TX 78712-1164 *Tel:* 512-471-5132; 512-471-4991 *Fax:* 512-471-4909 *Web Site:* www.utexas.edu/cola/depts/english/creative-writing, pg 664

Stewart, Douglas, Sterling Lord Literistic Inc, 65 Bleecker St, New York, NY 10012 *Tel:* 212-780-6050 *Fax:* 212-780-6095 *E-mail:* info@sll.com *Web Site:* www.sll.com, pg 575

Stewart, James B, The Authors League Fund, 31 E 32 St, 7th fl, New York, NY 10016 *Tel:* 212-268-1208 *Fax:* 212-564-5363 *E-mail:* staff@authorsleaguefund.org *Web Site:* www.authorsleaguefund.org, pg 599

Stewart, Jenna, Chelsea Green Publishing Co, 85 N Main St, Suite 120, White River Junction, VT 05001 *Tel:* 802-295-6300 *Toll Free Tel:* 800-639-4099 (cust serv, consumer & trade orders) *Fax:* 802-295-6444 *Web Site:* www.chelseagreen.com, pg 56

Stewart, Joan, The Joan Stewart Agency, One Dag Hammarskjold Plaza, 35th fl, 885 Second Ave, New York, NY 10017 *Tel:* 212-418-7255 *Fax:* 212-832-3809, pg 575

Stewart, Robert, BkMk Press - University of Missouri-Kansas City, University House, 5101 Rockhill Rd, Kansas City, MO 64110-2499 *Tel:* 816-235-2558 *Fax:* 816-235-2611 *E-mail:* bkmk@umkc.edu *Web Site:* www.umkc.edu/bkmk, pg 38

Stewart, Robert, G S Sharat Chandra Prize for Short Fiction, University House, 5101 Rockhill Rd, Kansas City, MO 64110-2499 *Tel:* 816-235-2558 *Fax:* 816-235-2611 *E-mail:* bkmk@umkc.edu *Web Site:* www.umkc.edu/bkmk, pg 676

Stewart, Robert, John Ciardi Prize for Poetry, University House, 5101 Rockhill Rd, Kansas City, MO 64110-2499 *Tel:* 816-235-2558 *Fax:* 816-235-2611 *E-mail:* bkmk@umkc.edu *Web Site:* www.umkc.edu/bkmk, pg 677

Sticco, Maria, University of Pittsburgh Press, 7500 Thomas Blvd, Pittsburgh, PA 15260 *Tel:* 412-383-2456 *Fax:* 412-383-2466 *E-mail:* info@upress.pitt.edu *Web Site:* www.upress.pitt.edu, pg 259

Stiles, Lane, Mid-List Press, 6524 Brownlee Dr, Nashville, TN 37205-3038 *Tel:* 615-822-3777 *Fax:* 612-823-8387 *E-mail:* guide@midlist.org *Web Site:* www.midlist.org, pg 156

Stilson, Joyce, Maxim Mazumdar New Play Competition, One Curtain Up Alley, Buffalo, NY 14202-1911 *Tel:* 716-852-2600 *E-mail:* publicrelations@alleyway.com *Web Site:* alleyway.com, pg 706

Stilwell, Haleh Roshan, Dramatists Play Service Inc, 440 Park Ave S, New York, NY 10016 *Tel:* 212-683-8960 *Fax:* 212-213-1539 *E-mail:* postmaster@dramatists.com; orders@dramatists.com; publications@dramatists.com *Web Site:* www.dramatists.com, pg 77

Stilwell, Winston, Fitzhenry & Whiteside Limited, 195 Allstate Pkwy, Markham, ON L3R 4T8, Canada *Tel:* 905-477-9700 *Toll Free Tel:* 800-387-9776 *Fax:* 905-477-2834 *Toll Free Fax:* 800-260-9777 *E-mail:* bookinfo@fitzhenry.ca; godwit@fitzhenry.ca *Web Site:* www.fitzhenry.ca, pg 484

Stimola, Rosemary B, Stimola Literary Studio Inc, 308 Livingston Ct, Edgewater, NJ 07020 *Tel:* 201-945-9353 *Fax:* 201-945-9353; 201-490-5920 *E-mail:* info@stimolaliterarystudio.com *Web Site:* www.stimolaliterarystudio.com, pg 575

Stine, Jane, Parachute Publishing LLC, 322 Eighth Ave, Suite 702, New York, NY 10001 *Tel:* 212-691-1421 *Fax:* 212-647-9650 *Web Site:* www.parachutepublishing.com, pg 182

Stinnett, Barbara, Saint Johann Press, 315 Schraalenburgh Rd, Haworth, NJ 07641 *Tel:* 201-387-1529 *Fax:* 201-501-0698 *Web Site:* www.stjohannpress.com, pg 214

Stio, Stephanie, National Poetry Series Open Competition, 57 Mountain Ave, Princeton, NJ 08540 *Tel:* 609-430-0999 *Fax:* 609-430-9933 *Web Site:* www.pw.org/content/open_competition, pg 711

Stitzer, Tina, Fun in the Sun Conference, PO Box 480211, Fort Lauderdale, FL 33348 *E-mail:* frwfuninthesun@yahoo.com *Web Site:* www.frwriters.org/fun-in-the-sun-conference/; frwfuninthesunmain.blogspot.com/; www.frwriters.org, pg 651

Stiver, Kim, DeLorme Publishing Co Inc, 2 DeLorme Dr, Yarmouth, ME 04096 *Tel:* 207-846-7000; 207-846-7111 (sales) *Toll Free Tel:* 800-561-5105; 800-511-2459 (cust serv) *Fax:* 207-846-7051 *Toll Free Fax:* 800-575-2244 *E-mail:* reseller@delorme.com *Web Site:* www.delorme.com, pg 72

Stobaugh, Blair, Bisk Education, 9417 Princess Palm Ave, Suite 400, Tampa, FL 33619 *Tel:* 813-621-6200 *Toll Free Tel:* 800-280-9718 (cust serv) *E-mail:* customerservice@bisk.com *Web Site:* www.bisk.com, pg 37

Stocke, Todd, Sourcebooks Inc, 1935 Brookdale Rd, Suite 139, Naperville, IL 60563 *Tel:* 630-961-3900 *Toll Free Tel:* 800-432-7444 *Fax:* 630-961-2168 *E-mail:* info@sourcebooks.com; customersupport@sourcebooks.com *Web Site:* www.sourcebooks.com, pg 230

Stockland, Patricia M, Carolrhoda Books, 241 First Ave N, Minneapolis, MN 55401 *Tel:* 612-332-3344 *Toll Free Tel:* 800-328-4929 *Fax:* 612-332-7615 *Toll Free Fax:* 800-332-1132 *E-mail:* info@lernerbooks.com *Web Site:* www.lernerbooks.com, pg 50

Stockland, Patricia M, Carolrhoda Lab™, 241 First Ave N, Minneapolis, MN 55401 *Tel:* 612-332-3344 *Toll Free Tel:* 800-328-4929 *Fax:* 612-332-7615 *Toll Free Fax:* 800-332-1132 (US) *E-mail:* info@lernerbooks.com *Web Site:* www.lernerbooks.com, pg 51

Stockland, Patricia M, ediciones Lerner, 241 First Ave N, Minneapolis, MN 55401 *Tel:* 612-332-3344 *Toll Free Tel:* 800-328-4929 *Fax:* 612-332-7615 *Toll Free Fax:* 800-332-1132 *E-mail:* info@lernerbooks.com *Web Site:* www.lernerbooks.com, pg 79

Stockland, Patricia M, First Avenue Editions, 241 First Ave N, Minneapolis, MN 55401 *Tel:* 612-332-3344 *Toll Free Tel:* 800-328-4929 *Fax:* 612-332-7615 *Toll Free Fax:* 800-332-1132 *E-mail:* info@lernerbooks.com *Web Site:* www.lernerbooks.com, pg 89

Stockland, Patricia M, Graphic Universe™, 241 First Ave N, Minneapolis, MN 55401 *Tel:* 612-332-3344 *Toll Free Tel:* 800-328-4929 *Fax:* 612-332-7615 *Toll Free Fax:* 800-332-1132 *E-mail:* info@lernerbooks.com *Web Site:* www.lernerbooks.com, pg 99

Stockland, Patricia M, Lerner Publications, 241 First Ave N, Minneapolis, MN 55401 *Tel:* 612-332-3344 *Toll Free Tel:* 800-328-4929 *Fax:* 612-332-7615 *Toll Free Fax:* 800-332-1132 *E-mail:* info@lernerbooks.com *Web Site:* www.lernerbooks.com, pg 137

Stockland, Patricia M, Lerner Publishing Group Inc, 241 First Ave N, Minneapolis, MN 55401 *Tel:* 612-332-3344 *Toll Free Tel:* 800-328-4929 *Fax:* 612-332-7615 *Toll Free Fax:* 800-332-1132 *E-mail:* info@lernerbooks.com *Web Site:* www.lernerbooks.com, pg 137

Stockland, Patricia M, LernerClassroom, 241 First Ave N, Minneapolis, MN 55401 *Tel:* 612-332-3344 *Toll Free Tel:* 800-328-4929 *Fax:* 612-332-7615 *Toll Free Fax:* 800-332-1132 *E-mail:* info@lernerbooks.com *Web Site:* www.lernerbooks.com, pg 137

Stockland, Patricia M, Millbrook Press, 241 First Ave N, Minneapolis, MN 55401 *Tel:* 612-332-3344 *Toll Free Tel:* 800-328-4929 (US only) *Fax:* 612-332-7615 *Toll Free Fax:* 800-332-1132, pg 157

Stockland, Patricia M, Twenty-First Century Books, 241 First Ave N, Minneapolis, MN 55401 *Tel:* 612-332-3344 *Toll Free Tel:* 800-328-4929 *Fax:* 612-332-7615 *Toll Free Fax:* 800-332-1132 *E-mail:* info@lernerbooks.com *Web Site:* www.lernerbooks.com, pg 251

Stocks, John C, National Education Association (NEA), 1201 16 St NW, Washington, DC 20036-3290 *Tel:* 202-833-4000 *Fax:* 202-822-7974 *Web Site:* www.nea.org, pg 164, 612

Stockwell, Diane, Globo Libros Literary Agency, 402 E 64 St, Suite 6-C, New York, NY 10065 *Tel:* 212-888-4655 *Web Site:* www.globo-libros.com; publishersmarketplace.com/members/dstockwell, pg 554

Stockwell, Gail Provost, Writers Retreat Workshop (WRW), PO Box 4236, Louisville, KY 40204 *E-mail:* wrw04@netscape.net *Web Site:* www.writersretreatworkshop.com, pg 657

Stoddard, Andrew, WaterBrook Multnomah Publishing Group, 12265 Oracle Blvd, Suite 200, Colorado Springs, CO 80921 *Tel:* 719-590-4999 *Toll Free Tel:* 800-603-7051 (orders) *Fax:* 719-590-8977 *Toll Free Fax:* 800-294-5686 (orders) *E-mail:* info@waterbrookmultnomah.com *Web Site:* waterbrookmultnomah.com, pg 267

Stoddard, Bill, Prometheus Awards, 650 Castro St, Suite 120-433, Mountain View, CA 94041 *Tel:* 650-968-6319 *E-mail:* info@lfs.org *Web Site:* www.lfs.org, pg 722

Stoddard, Brooke C, Archon Editorial LLC, 815 King St, Suite 204, Alexandria, VA 22314 *Tel:* 703-838-1650, pg 520

Stoddard, Rebecca, Omnidawn Publishing, 1632 Elm Ave, Richmond, CA 94805-1614 *Tel:* 510-237-5472 *Toll Free Tel:* 800-792-4957 *Fax:* 510-232-8525 *E-mail:* manager@omnidawn.com *Web Site:* www.omnidawn.com, pg 175

Stokes, Susan S, Woodbine House, 6510 Bells Mill Rd, Bethesda, MD 20817 *Tel:* 301-897-3570 *Toll Free Tel:* 800-843-7323 *Fax:* 301-897-5838 *E-mail:* info@woodbinehouse.com *Web Site:* www.woodbinehouse.com, pg 275

Stokes-Peters, Natalie, Black Classic Press, 3921 Vero Rd, Suite F, Baltimore, MD 21203-3414 *Tel:* 410-242-6954 *Toll Free Tel:* 800-476-8870 *Fax:* 410-242-6959 *E-mail:* email@blackclassicbooks.com; blackclassicpress@yahoo.com *Web Site:* www.blackclassicbooks.com; www.bcpdigital.com, pg 38

Stolls, Amy, The National Endowment for the Arts, Nancy Hanks Ctr, Rm 703, 1100 Pennsylvania Ave NW, Washington, DC 20506-0001 *Tel:* 202-682-5400 *Web Site:* www.arts.gov; www.nea.gov, pg 623

Stoloff, Sam, Frances Goldin Literary Agency, Inc, 57 E 11 St, Suite 5-B, New York, NY 10003 *Tel:* 212-777-0047 *Fax:* 212-228-1660 *E-mail:* agency@goldinlit.com *Web Site:* www.goldinlit.com, pg 554

Stoltz, Jamison, Grove Atlantic Inc, 154 W 14 St, 12th fl, New York, NY 10011 *Tel:* 212-614-7850 *Toll Free Tel:* 800-521-0178 *Fax:* 212-614-7886 *E-mail:* info@groveatlantic.com *Web Site:* www.groveatlantic.com, pg 101

Stoltzfus, Alison, The Princeton Review, c/o Random House Inc, 1745 Broadway, New York, NY 10019 *Toll Free Tel:* 800-733-3000 *Fax:* 212-782-9682 *E-mail:* princetonreview@randomhouse.com *Web Site:* www.princetonreview.com, pg 197

Stone, Annie, Harlequin Enterprises Ltd, 233 Broadway, Suite 1001, New York, NY 10279 *Tel:* 212-553-4200 *Fax:* 212-227-8969 *E-mail:* CustomerService@harlequin.com *Web Site:* www.harlequin.com, pg 105

Stone, Judi, Artech House Inc, 685 Canton St, Norwood, MA 02062 *Tel:* 781-769-9750 *Toll Free Tel:* 800-225-9977 *Fax:* 781-769-6334 *E-mail:* artech@artechhouse.com *Web Site:* www.artechhouse.com, pg 23

Stone, Kevin, Cengage Learning, 20 Channel Center St, Boston, MA 02210 *Tel:* 617-289-7700 *Toll Free Tel:* 800-354-9706 *Fax:* 617-289-7844 *Toll Free Fax:* 800-487-8488 *E-mail:* esales@cengage.com *Web Site:* www.cengage.com, pg 53

Stone, Kris, Piano Press, 1425 Ocean Ave, Suite 5, Del Mar, CA 92014 *Tel:* 619-884-1401 *Fax:* 858-755-1104 *E-mail:* pianopress@pianopress.com *Web Site:* www.pianopress.com, pg 191

Stone, Michelle, McClanahan Publishing House Inc, 107 W Main, Princeton, KY 42445 *Tel:* 270-963-9005 *E-mail:* books@kybooks.com *Web Site:* kybooks.com, pg 150

Stone, Patricia, Chelsea Green Publishing Co, 85 N Main St, Suite 120, White River Junction, VT 05001 *Tel:* 802-295-6300 *Toll Free Tel:* 800-639-4099 (cust serv, consumer & trade orders) *Fax:* 802-295-6444 *Web Site:* www.chelseagreen.com, pg 56

Stone, Suezen, HJ Kramer Inc, PO Box 1082, Tiburon, CA 94920 *Tel:* 415-884-2100 (ext 10) *Toll Free Tel:* 800-972-6657 *Fax:* 415-435-5364 *E-mail:* hjkramer@jps.net *Web Site:* www.hjkramer.com; www.newworldlibrary.com, pg 133

Stonefield, Jeff, Apress Media LLC, 233 Spring St, New York, NY 10013 *Tel:* 212-460-1500 *Fax:* 212-460-1575 *E-mail:* editorial@apress.com *Web Site:* www.apress.com, pg 20

Storch, Maury, Gefen Books, c/o Storch, 255 Central Ave, B-206, Lawrence, NY 11559 *Tel:* 516-593-1234 *Toll Free Tel:* 800-477-5257 *Fax:* 516-295-2739 *E-mail:* gefenny@gefenpublishing.com; info@gefenpublishing.com *Web Site:* www.gefenpublishing.com; www.israelbooks.com, pg 95

Stordahl, Derek, Bloomsbury Academic, 1385 Broadway, 5th fl, New York, NY 10018 *Tel:* 212-419-5300 *Web Site:* www.bloomsbury.com, pg 39

Stordahl, Derek, Bloomsbury Publishing Inc, 1385 Broadway, 5th fl, New York, NY 10018 *Tel:* 212-419-5300 *E-mail:* marketingusa@bloomsbury.com; adultpublicityusa@bloomsbury.com; askacademic@bloomsbury.com *Web Site:* www.bloomsbury.com, pg 39

Storhoff, Tim, Florida Individual Artist Fellowships, 500 S Bronough St, Tallahassee, FL 32399-0250 *Tel:* 850-245-6470 *Fax:* 850-245-6497 *E-mail:* info@florida-arts.org *Web Site:* www.florida-arts.org, pg 686

Storm, Alison, Ambassador International, 427 Wade Hampton Blvd, Greenville, SC 29609 *Tel:* 864-235-2434 *Toll Free Tel:* 800-209-8570 *Fax:* 864-235-2491 *E-mail:* info@emeraldhouse.com; publisher@emeraldhouse.com (ms submissions); sales@emeraldhouse.com (orders/order inquiries) *Web Site:* ambassador-international.com; www.facebook.com/AmbassadorIntl; twitter.com/ambassadorintl, pg 10

Storrings, Michael, St Martin's Press, LLC, 175 Fifth Ave, New York, NY 10010 *Tel:* 646-307-5151 *Fax:* 212-420-9314 *E-mail:* firstname.lastname@macmillan.com *Web Site:* www.stmartins.com, pg 214

Story, Karin, Amber Quill Press LLC, PO Box 265, Indian Hills, CO 80454 *E-mail:* business@amberquill.com; customer_service@amberquill.com *Web Site:* www.amberquill.com, pg 10

Stoshak, Joe, Public Citizen, 1600 20 St NW, Washington, DC 20009 *Tel:* 202-588-1000 *Fax:* 202-588-7798 *E-mail:* public_citizen@citizen.org *Web Site:* www.citizen.org, pg 200

Stott, Phil, Vault.com Inc, 132 W 31 St, 17th fl, New York, NY 10001 *Tel:* 212-366-4212 *Toll Free Tel:* 800-535-2074 *Fax:* 212-366-6117 (cust serv) *E-mail:* editors@vault.com; customerservice@vault.com *Web Site:* www.vault.com, pg 265

Stouras, Tom, Macmillan, 175 Fifth Ave, New York, NY 10010 *Tel:* 646-307-5151 *Fax:* 212-420-9314 *E-mail:* firstname.lastname@macmillan.com *Web Site:* www.macmillan.com, pg 145

Stout, Christina, Penguin Group (USA) LLC Sales, 375 Hudson St, New York, NY 10014 *Tel:* 212-366-2000 *E-mail:* online@penguinputnam.com *Web Site:* us.penguingroup.com, pg 187

Stout, Rachel, Dystel & Goderich Literary Management, One Union Sq W, Suite 904, New York, NY 10003 *Tel:* 212-627-9100 *Fax:* 212-627-9313 *Web Site:* www.dystel.com, pg 549

Stoykova-Klemer, Katerina, Poetry Book Contest, PO Box 910456, Lexington, KY 40591-0456 *Web Site:* www.accents-publishing.com/contest.html, pg 720

Straatmann, Michael, Mari Sandoz Award, PO Box 21756, Lincoln, NE 68542-1756 *E-mail:* nebraskalibraries@gmail.com *Web Site:* www.nebraskalibraries.org, pg 725

Strachan, Glenn R, Jhpiego, 1615 Thames St, Baltimore, MD 21231-3492 *Tel:* 410-537-1800 *Fax:* 410-537-1473 *E-mail:* info@jhpiego.net *Web Site:* www.jhpiego.org, pg 126

Stranathan, Lynn, Yard Dog Press, 710 W Redbud Lane, Alma, AR 72921-7247 *Tel:* 479-632-4693 *Fax:* 479-632-4693 *Web Site:* www.yarddogpress.com, pg 278

Strand, Julie, Coffee House Press, 79 13 Ave NE, Suite 110, Minneapolis, MN 55413 *Tel:* 612-338-0125 *Fax:* 612-338-4004 *E-mail:* info@coffeehousepress.org *Web Site:* coffeehousepress.org, pg 60

Strand, Kurt, McGraw-Hill Contemporary Learning Series, 501 Bell St, Dubuque, IA 52001 *Toll Free Tel:* 800-243-6532 *Web Site:* www.mhcls.com, pg 150

Strand, Kurt, McGraw-Hill Higher Education, 1333 Burr Ridge Pkwy, Burr Ridge, IL 60527 *Tel:* 630-789-4000 *Toll Free Tel:* 800-338-3987 (cust serv) *Fax:* 614-755-5645 (cust serv) *Web Site:* www.mhhe.com, pg 151

Strand, Kurt, McGraw-Hill Humanities, Social Sciences, Languages, 2 Penn Plaza, 21st fl, New York, NY 10121 *Tel:* 212-904-2000 *Toll Free Tel:* 800-338-3987 (cust serv) *Fax:* 614-755-5645 (cust serv) *Web Site:* www.mhhe.com, pg 151

Strand, Kurt, McGraw-Hill/Irwin, 1333 Burr Ridge Pkwy, Burr Ridge, IL 60527 *Tel:* 630-789-4000 *Toll Free Tel:* 800-338-3987 (cust serv) *Fax:* 630-789-6942; 614-755-5645 (cust serv) *Web Site:* www.mhhe.com, pg 152

Strand, Kurt, McGraw-Hill Science, Engineering, Mathematics, 501 Bell St, Dubuque, IA 52001 *Tel:* 563-584-6000 *Toll Free Tel:* 800-338-3987 (cust serv) *Fax:* 614-755-5645 (cust serv) *Web Site:* www.mhhe.com, pg 152

Strand, Lisa K, Notable Wisconsin Authors, 4610 S Biltmore Lane, Madison, WI 53718 *Tel:* 608-245-3640 *Fax:* 608-245-3646 *Web Site:* www.wla.lib.wi.us, pg 713

Strand, Lisa K, WLA Literary Award, 4610 S Biltmore Lane, Madison, WI 53718 *Tel:* 608-245-3640 *Fax:* 608-245-3646 *Web Site:* www.wla.lib.wi.us, pg 737

Strang, Stephen, Charisma Media, 600 Rinehart Rd, Lake Mary, FL 32746 *Tel:* 407-333-0600 (all imprints) *Toll Free Tel:* 800-283-8494 (Charisma Media, Siloam Press, Creation House); 800-665-1468 *Fax:* 407-333-7100 (all imprints) *E-mail:* charisma@charismamedia.com *Web Site:* www.charismamedia.com, pg 55

Strang, Stephen, CharismaLife Publishers, 600 Rinehart Rd, Lake Mary, FL 32746 *Tel:* 407-333-0600 *Toll Free Tel:* 800-451-4598 *Fax:* 407-333-7100 *E-mail:* charismalife@charismamedia.com *Web Site:* www.charismamedia.com, pg 55

Strange, Nancy, Tudor Publishers Inc, 3109 Shady Lawn Dr, Greensboro, NC 27408 *Tel:* 336-288-5395 *E-mail:* tudorpublishers@triad.rr.com, pg 250

Strasbaugh, Joan, Abbeville Press, 137 Varick St, Suite 504, New York, NY 10013-1105 *Tel:* 212-366-5585 *Toll Free Tel:* 800-ARTBOOK (278-2665); 800-343-4499 (orders) *Fax:* 212-366-6966 *Toll Free Fax:* 800-351-5073 (orders) *E-mail:* abbeville@abbeville.com; sales@abbeville.com; marketing@abbeville.com; rights@abbeville.com *Web Site:* www.abbeville.com, pg 2

Straschnov, George, Bisk Education, 9417 Princess Palm Ave, Suite 400, Tampa, FL 33619 *Tel:* 813-621-6200 *Toll Free Tel:* 800-280-9718 (cust serv) *E-mail:* customerservice@bisk.com *Web Site:* www.bisk.com, pg 37

Stratton, Penny, Newbury Street Press, 101 Newbury St, Boston, MA 02116 *Tel:* 617-536-5740 *Toll Free Tel:* 888-296-3447 (NEHGS membership) *Fax:* 617-536-7307 *E-mail:* sales@nehgs.org *Web Site:* www.newenglandancestors.org, pg 169

Straub, Peter, The Authors League Fund, 31 E 32 St, 7th fl, New York, NY 10016 *Tel:* 212-268-1208 *Fax:* 212-564-5363 *E-mail:* staff@authorsleaguefund.org *Web Site:* www.authorsleaguefund.org, pg 599

Straus, Jonah, Straus Literary, 319 Lafayette St, Suite 220, New York, NY 10012 *Tel:* 646-843-9950 *Fax:* 646-390-3320 *Web Site:* www.strausliterary.com, pg 575

Straus, Robin, Robin Straus Agency Inc, 229 E 79 St, Suite 5A, New York, NY 10075 *Tel:* 212-472-3282 *E-mail:* info@robinstrausagency.com *Web Site:* www.robinstrausagency.com, pg 576

Straus, Robin, Wallace Literary Agency Inc, 229 E 79 St, No 5A, New York, NY 10075 *Tel:* 212-472-3282 *Fax:* 212-472-3833 *E-mail:* info@wallaceliteraryagency.com, pg 578

Strauss, Leslie R, Housing Assistance Council, 1025 Vermont Ave NW, Suite 606, Washington, DC 20005 *Tel:* 202-842-8600 *Fax:* 202-347-3441 *E-mail:* hac@ruralhome.org *Web Site:* www.ruralhome.org, pg 116

Strauss, Mark, Springer, 233 Spring St, New York, NY 10013-1578 *Tel:* 212-460-1500 *Toll Free Tel:* 800-SPRINGER (777-4643) *Fax:* 212-460-1575 *E-mail:* service-ny@springer.com *Web Site:* www.springer.com, pg 232

Strauss, Myra, Management Concepts Inc, 8230 Leesburg Pike, Suite 800, Vienna, VA 22182 *Tel:* 703-790-9595 *Toll Free Tel:* 800 506-4450 *Fax:* 703-790-1371 *E-mail:* info@managementconcepts.com *Web Site:* www.managementconcepts.com, pg 146

Strauss, Rebecca, DeFiore and Company, LLC, 47 E 19 St, 3rd fl, New York, NY 10003 *Tel:* 212-925-7744 *Fax:* 212-925-9803 *E-mail:* submissions@defioreandco.com; info@defioreandco.com *Web Site:* www.defioreandco.com, pg 548

Strauss-Gabel, Julie, Dutton Children's Books, 345 Hudson St, New York, NY 10014 *Tel:* 212-366-2000 *E-mail:* online@penguinputnam.com *Web Site:* www.penguinputnam.com; us.penguingroup.com, pg 78

Streckfus, Peter, University of Alabama Program in Creative Writing, PO Box 870244, Tuscaloosa, AL 35487-0244 *Tel:* 205-348-5065 *Fax:* 205-348-1388 *E-mail:* english@ua.edu *Web Site:* www.as.ua.edu/english, pg 663

Streetman, Ms Burgin, Trinity University Press, One Trinity Place, San Antonio, TX 78212-7200 *Tel:* 210-999-8884 *Fax:* 210-999-8838 *E-mail:* books@trinity.edu *Web Site:* www.tupress.org, pg 249

Streitfeld, Linda Topping, National Press Foundation, 1211 Connecticut Ave NW, Suite 310, Washington, DC 20036 *Tel:* 202-663-7280 *Web Site:* nationalpress.org, pg 613

Strickland, Albert Lee, Pacific Publishing Services, PO Box 1150, Capitola, CA 95010-1150 *Tel:* 831-476-8284 *Fax:* 831-476-8294 *E-mail:* pacpubs@attglobal.net, pg 532

Strickland, Jonathan, Black Rabbit Books, 515 N Riverfront Dr, Suite 200, Mankato, MN 56001 *Tel:* 507-388-1609 *Fax:* 507-388-1364 *E-mail:* info@blackrabbitbooks.com; orders@blackrabbitbooks.com *Web Site:* www.blackrabbitbooks.com, pg 38

Strickland, Kate, Milkweed Editions, 1011 Washington Ave S, Suite 300, Minneapolis, MN 55415-1246 *Tel:* 612-332-3192 *Toll Free Tel:* 800-520-6455 *Fax:* 612-215-2550 *Web Site:* www.milkweed.org, pg 157

Strickland, Kate, Milkweed National Fiction Prize, 1011 Washington Ave S, Suite 300, Minneapolis, MN 55415-1246 *Tel:* 612-332-3192 *Toll Free Tel:* 800-520-6455 *Fax:* 612-215-2550 *E-mail:* submissions@milkweed.org *Web Site:* www.milkweed.org, pg 707

Strickland, Sherri, University Press of New England, One Court St, Suite 250, Lebanon, NH 03766 *Tel:* 603-448-1533 *Toll Free Tel:* 800-421-1561 (orders only) *Fax:* 603-448-7006; 603-643-1540 *E-mail:* university.press@dartmouth.edu *Web Site:* www.upne.com, pg 262

Strickland, Tessa, Barefoot Books, 2067 Massachusetts Ave, 5th fl, Cambridge, MA 02140 *Tel:* 617-576-0660 *Toll Free Tel:* 866-215-1756 (cust serv); 866-417-2369 (orders) *Fax:* 617-576-0049 *E-mail:* help@barefootbooks.com *Web Site:* www.barefootbooks.com, pg 31

Strittmatter, Aimee, ALSC BWI/Summer Reading Program Grant, 50 E Huron St, Chicago, IL 60611-2795 *Tel:* 312-280-2163 *Toll Free Tel:* 800-545-2433 *Fax:* 312-440-9374 *E-mail:* alsc@ala.org *Web Site:* www.ala.org/alsc, pg 667

Strittmatter, Aimee, The May Hill Arbuthnot Honor Lecture Award, 50 E Huron St, Chicago, IL 60611-2795 *Tel:* 312-280-2163 *Toll Free Tel:* 800-545-2433 *Fax:* 312-440-9374 *E-mail:* alsc@ala.org *Web Site:* www.ala.org/alsc, pg 668

Strittmatter, Aimee, The Mildred L Batchelder Award, 50 E Huron St, Chicago, IL 60611-2795 *Tel:* 312-280-2163 *Toll Free Tel:* 800-545-2433 *Fax:* 312-440-9374 *E-mail:* alsc@ala.org *Web Site:* www.ala.org/alsc, pg 670

Strittmatter, Aimee, The Pura Belpre Award, 50 E Huron St, Chicago, IL 60611-2795 *Tel:* 312-280-2163 *Toll Free Tel:* 800-545-2433 *Fax:* 312-440-9374 *E-mail:* alsc@ala.org *Web Site:* www.ala.org/alsc, pg 671

Strittmatter, Aimee, Bound to Stay Bound Books Scholarship, 50 E Huron St, Chicago, IL 60611-2795 *Tel:* 312-280-2163 *Toll Free Tel:* 800-545-2433 *Fax:* 312-440-9374 *E-mail:* alsc@ala.org *Web Site:* www.ala.org/alsc, pg 673

Strittmatter, Aimee, The Randolph Caldecott Medal, 50 E Huron St, Chicago, IL 60611-2795 *Tel:* 312-280-2163 *Toll Free Tel:* 800-545-2433 *Fax:* 312-440-9374 *E-mail:* alsc@ala.org *Web Site:* www.ala.org/alsc, pg 675

Strittmatter, Aimee, Frederic G Melcher Scholarship, 50 E Huron St, Chicago, IL 60611-2795 *Tel:* 312-280-2163 *Toll Free Tel:* 800-545-2433 *Fax:* 312-440-9374 *E-mail:* alsc@ala.org *Web Site:* www.ala.org/alsc, pg 707

Strittmatter, Aimee, John Newbery Medal, 50 E Huron St, Chicago, IL 60611-2795 *Tel:* 312-280-2163 *Toll Free Tel:* 800-545-2433 *Fax:* 312-440-9374 *E-mail:* alsc@ala.org *Web Site:* www.ala.org/alsc, pg 713

Strittmatter, Aimee, Robert F Sibert Informational Book Award, 50 E Huron St, Chicago, IL 60611-2795 *Tel:* 312-280-2163 *Toll Free Tel:* 800-545-2433 *Fax:* 312-440-9374 *E-mail:* alsc@ala.org *Web Site:* www.ala.org/alsc, pg 728

Strittmatter, Aimee, The Laura Ingalls Wilder Medal, 50 E Huron St, Chicago, IL 60611-2795 *Tel:* 312-280-2163 *Toll Free Tel:* 800-545-2433 *Fax:* 312-440-9374 *E-mail:* alsc@ala.org *Web Site:* www.ala.org/alsc, pg 736

Strohbehn, Edward, Environmental Law Institute, 1730 "M" St NW, Suite 700, Washington, DC 20036 *Tel:* 202-939-3800 *Toll Free Tel:* 800-433-5120 *Fax:* 202-939-3868 *E-mail:* law@eli.org *Web Site:* www.eli.org, pg 83

Stromberg, Elizabeth, Ten Speed Press, 2625 Alcatraz Ave, Unit 505, Berkeley, CA 94705 *Tel:* 510-285-3000 *Toll Free Tel:* 800-841-BOOK (841-2665) *E-mail:* csorders@randomhouse.com *Web Site:* crownpublishing.com/imprint/ten-speed-press, pg 243

Strone, Daniel, Trident Media Group LLC, 41 Madison Ave, 36th fl, New York, NY 10010 *Tel:* 212-333-1511 *E-mail:* info@tridentmediagroup.com; press@tridentmediagroup.com *Web Site:* www.tridentmediagroup.com, pg 577

Strong, Marianne, Marianne Strong Literary Agency, 65 E 96 St, New York, NY 10128 *Tel:* 212-249-1000 *Fax:* 212-831-3241 *Web Site:* stronglit.com, pg 576

Stroschein, Steven, IBFD North America Inc (International Bureau of Fiscal Documentation), 8100 Boone Blvd, Suite 210, Vienna, VA 22182 *Tel:* 703-442-7757 *Fax:* 703-442-7758 *Web Site:* www.ibfd.org, pg 118

Strosnider, Ashley, Prairie Schooner Annual Strousse Award, University of Nebraska, 123 Andrews Hall, 625 N 14 St, Lincoln, NE 68508 *Tel:* 402-472-0911 *Fax:* 402-472-9771 *E-mail:* prairieschooner@unl.edu *Web Site:* prairieschooner.unl.edu, pg 720

Strosnider, Ashley, Prairie Schooner Bernice Slote Award, University of Nebraska, 123 Andrews Hall, 625 N 14 St, Lincoln, NE 68508 *Tel:* 402-472-0911 *E-mail:* prairieschooner@unl.edu *Web Site:* prairieschooner.unl.edu, pg 720

Strosnider, Ashley, Prairie Schooner Book Prize Contest in Fiction, University of Nebraska, 123 Andrews Hall, 625 N 14 St, Lincoln, NE 68508 *Tel:* 402-472-0911 *Fax:* 402-472-9771 *E-mail:* psbookprize@unl.edu *Web Site:* prairieschooner.unl.edu, pg 720

Strosnider, Ashley, Prairie Schooner Book Prize Contest in Poetry, University of Nebraska, 123 Andrews Hall, 625 N 14 St, Lincoln, NE 68508 *Tel:* 402-472-0911 *Fax:* 402-472-9771 *E-mail:* psbookprize@unl.edu *Web Site:* prairieschooner.unl.edu, pg 720

Strosnider, Ashley, Prairie Schooner Edward Stanley Award, University of Nebraska, 123 Andrews Hall, 625 N 14 St, Lincoln, NE 68508 *Tel:* 402-472-0911 *Fax:* 402-472-9771 *E-mail:* prairieschooner@unl.edu *Web Site:* prairieschooner.unl.edu, pg 720

Strosnider, Ashley, Prairie Schooner Glenna Luschei Award, University of Nebraska, 123 Andrews Hall, 625 N 14 St, Lincoln, NE 68508 *Tel:* 402-472-0911 *Fax:* 402-472-9771 *E-mail:* prairieschooner@unl.edu *Web Site:* prairieschooner.unl.edu, pg 721

Strosnider, Ashley, Prairie Schooner Hugh J Luke Award, University of Nebraska, 123 Andrews Hall, 625 N 14 St, Lincoln, NE 68508 *Tel:* 402-472-0911 *Fax:* 402-472-9771 *E-mail:* prairieschooner@unl.edu *Web Site:* prairieschooner.unl.edu, pg 721

Strosnider, Ashley, Prairie Schooner Jane Geske Award, University of Nebraska, 123 Andrews Hall, 625 N 14 St, Lincoln, NE 68508 *Tel:* 402-472-0911 *Fax:* 402-472-9771 *E-mail:* prairieschooner@unl.edu *Web Site:* prairieschooner.unl.edu, pg 721

Strosnider, Ashley, Prairie Schooner Lawrence Foundation Award, University of Nebraska, 123 Andrews Hall, 625 N 14 St, Lincoln, NE 68508 *Tel:* 402-472-0911 *Fax:* 402-472-9771 *E-mail:* prairieschooner@unl.edu *Web Site:* prairieschooner.unl.edu, pg 721

Strosnider, Ashley, Prairie Schooner Virginia Faulkner Award for Excellence in Writing, University of Nebraska, 123 Andrews Hall, 625 N 14 St, Lincoln, NE 68508 *Tel:* 402-472-0911 *Fax:* 402-472-9771 *E-mail:* prairieschooner@unl.edu *Web Site:* prairieschooner.unl.edu, pg 721

Strothman, Wendy, Strothman Agency LLC, 63 E Ninth St, 10X, New York, NY 10003 *E-mail:* info@strothmanagency.com *Web Site:* www.strothmanagency.com, pg 576

Stroud, Christine, Autumn House Press, 87 1/2 Westwood St, Pittsburgh, PA 15211 *Tel:* 412-381-4261 *Web Site:* www.autumnhouse.org, pg 28

Stroud, Christine, Coal Hill Review Poetry Chapbook Contest, c/o Autumn House Press, PO Box 60100, Pittsburgh, PA 15211 *E-mail:* reviewcoalhill@gmail.com *Web Site:* www.coalhillreview.com, pg 678

Stroud, Ward J, National Book Co, PO Box 8795, Portland, OR 97207-8795 *Tel:* 503-228-6345 *Fax:* 810-885-5811 *E-mail:* info@eralearning.com *Web Site:* www.eralearning.com, pg 163

Struckman, Dianne, Krieger Publishing Co, 1725 Krieger Dr, Malabar, FL 32950 *Tel:* 321-724-9542 *Toll Free Tel:* 800-724-0025 *Fax:* 321-951-3671 *E-mail:* info@krieger-publishing.com *Web Site:* www.krieger-publishing.com, pg 133

Stuart, Carole, Barricade Books Inc, 2037 LeMoine Ave, Fort Lee, NJ 07024 *Tel:* 201-944-7600 *E-mail:* customerservice@barricadebooks.com *Web Site:* www.barricadebooks.com, pg 31

Stuart, Kari, ICM Partners, 730 Fifth Ave, New York, NY 10019 *Tel:* 212-556-5600 *Web Site:* www.icmtalent.com, pg 557

Stuart, Kathryn, Writers House, 21 W 26 St, New York, NY 10010 *Tel:* 212-685-2400 *Fax:* 212-685-1781 *Web Site:* www.writershouse.com, pg 580

Stuart, Kelly, Center for the Collaborative Classroom, 1250 53 St, Suite 3, Emeryville, CA 94608 *Tel:* 510-533-0213 *Toll Free Tel:* 800-666-7270 *Fax:* 510-464-3670 *E-mail:* info@collaborativeclassroom.org; clientsupport@collaborativeclassroom.org *Web Site:* www.collaborativeclassroom.org, pg 53

Stuart, Nancy Rubin, Annual Cape Cod Writers' Center Conference, 919 Main St, Osterville, MA 02655 *Tel:* 508-420-0200 *E-mail:* writers@capecodwriterscenter.org *Web Site:* www.capecodwriterscenter.org, pg 650

Stuart, Nancy Rubin, Young Writers' Workshop, 919 Main St, Osterville, MA 02655 *Tel:* 508-420-0200 *E-mail:* writers@capecodwriterscenter.org *Web Site:* www.capecodwriterscenter.org, pg 657

Stubblefield, Terri, Neustadt International Prize for Literature, c/o University of Oklahoma, 630 Parrington Oval, Suite 110, Norman, OK 73019-4033 *Tel:* 405-325-4531 *Fax:* 405-325-7495 *Web Site:* www.worldliteraturetoday.org, pg 712

Stubblefield, Terri, NSK Neustadt Prize for Children's Literature, c/o University of Oklahoma, 630 Parrington Oval, Suite 110, Norman, OK 73019-4033 *Tel:* 405-325-4531 *Fax:* 405-325-7495 *Web Site:* www.worldliteraturetoday.org, pg 714

Stubbs, Peter, Fitzhenry & Whiteside Limited, 195 Allstate Pkwy, Markham, ON L3R 4T8, Canada *Tel:* 905-477-9700 *Toll Free Tel:* 800-387-9776 *Fax:* 905-477-2834 *Toll Free Fax:* 800-260-9777 *E-mail:* bookinfo@fitzhenry.ca; godwit@fitzhenry.ca *Web Site:* www.fitzhenry.ca, pg 484

Studer, Kate, Harlequin Enterprises Ltd, 225 Duncan Mill Rd, Don Mills, ON M3B 3K9, Canada *Tel:* 416-445-5860 *Toll Free Tel:* 888-432-4879; 800-370-5838 (ebook inquiries) *E-mail:* customerservice@harlequin.com *Web Site:* www.harlequin.com, pg 487

Stueve, Rev Dennis, Lutheran Braille Workers Inc, 13471 California St, Yucaipa, CA 92399 *Tel:* 909-795-8977 *Fax:* 909-795-8970 *E-mail:* lbw@lbwinc.org *Web Site:* www.lbwinc.org, pg 144

Stulack, Nancy, Herbert Warren Wind Book Award, 77 Liberty Corner Rd, Far Hills, NJ 07931-0708 *Tel:* 908-234-2300 *Fax:* 908-470-5013 *Web Site:* www.usga.org, pg 736

Stumpf, Becca, Prospect Agency, 285 Fifth Ave, PMB 445, Brooklyn, NY 11215 *Tel:* 718-788-3217 *Fax:* 718-360-9582 *Web Site:* www.prospectagency.com, pg 568

Sturgis, Randy, Copper Canyon Press, Fort Worden State Park, Bldg 313, Port Townsend, WA 98368 *Tel:* 360-385-4925 *Toll Free Tel:* 877-501-1393 (orders) *Fax:* 360-385-4985 *E-mail:* poetry@coppercanyonpress.org *Web Site:* www.coppercanyonpress.org, pg 63

Sturmer, Alan, Edward Elgar Publishing Inc, The William Pratt House, 9 Dewey Ct, Northampton, MA 01060-3815 *Tel:* 413-584-5551 *Toll Free Tel:* 800-390-3149 (orders) *Fax:* 413-584-9933 *E-mail:* elgarinfo@e-elgar.com; elgarsales@e-elgar.com; elgarsubmissions@e-elgar.com (edit) *Web Site:* www.e-elgar.com; www.elgaronline.com (ebooks & journals), pg 80

Stuve, Cathy, Amicus, PO Box 1329, Mankato, MN 56002 *Tel:* 507-388-9357 *Fax:* 507-388-1779 *E-mail:* info@amicuspublishing.us; orders@amicuspublishing.us *Web Site:* www.amicuspublishing.us, pg 17

Stvan, Beck, Random House Publishing Group, 1745 Broadway, New York, NY 10019 *Toll Free Tel:* 800-200-3552 *Web Site:* atrandom.com, pg 204

Styler, Lori, The Barbara Hogenson Agency Inc, 165 West End Ave, Suite 19-C, New York, NY 10023 *Tel:* 212-874-8084 *Fax:* 212-595-6748 *E-mail:* bhogenson@aol.com, pg 557

Styles, Bonnie, Illinois State Museum Society, 502 S Spring St, Springfield, IL 62706-5000 *Tel:* 217-782-7386 *Fax:* 217-782-1254 *E-mail:* editor@museum.state.il.us *Web Site:* www.museum.state.il.us, pg 119

Suarez, Kathryn, Neal-Schuman Publishers Inc, 100 William St, Suite 2004, New York, NY 10038 *Tel:* 212-925-8650 *Toll Free Tel:* 866-NS-BOOKS (672-6657) *Fax:* 212-219-8916 *Toll Free Fax:* 877-231-6980 *E-mail:* info@neal-schuman.com *Web Site:* www.neal-schuman.com, pg 166

Subba, Heather, Professional Publications Inc (PPI), 1250 Fifth Ave, Belmont, CA 94002 *Tel:* 650-593-9119 *Fax:* 650-592-4519 *E-mail:* info@ppi2pass.com *Web Site:* ppi2pass.com; feprep.com, pg 198

Subiyah, Camaren, Clarkson Potter Publishers, c/o Random House Inc, 1745 Broadway, New York, NY 10019 *Tel:* 212-782-9000 *Toll Free Tel:* 888-264-1745 *Fax:* 212-572-6181 *Web Site:* www.clarksonpotter.com; www.randomhouse.com/crown/clarksonpotter, pg 195

Subramanian, Uma, Fitzhenry & Whiteside Limited, 195 Allstate Pkwy, Markham, ON L3R 4T8, Canada *Tel:* 905-477-9700 *Toll Free Tel:* 800-387-9776 *Fax:* 905-477-2834 *Toll Free Fax:* 800-260-9777 *E-mail:* bookinfo@fitzhenry.ca; godwit@fitzhenry.ca *Web Site:* www.fitzhenry.ca, pg 484

Sweeney, Frances, PREP Publishing, 3528 Turnberry Circle, Fayetteville, NC 28303 *Tel:* 910-483-6611 *Toll Free Tel:* 800-533-2814 *E-mail:* preppub@aol.com *Web Site:* www.prep-pub.com, pg 196

Sweeney, Jillian, The Ned Leavitt Agency, 70 Wooster St, Suite 4-F, New York, NY 10012 *Tel:* 212-334-0999 *Web Site:* www.nedleavittagency.com, pg 561

Sweeney, Jon M, Franciscan Media, 28 W Liberty St, Cincinnati, OH 45202 *Tel:* 513-241-5615 *Toll Free Tel:* 800-488-0488 *Fax:* 513-241-0399 *E-mail:* books@americancatholic.org *Web Site:* www.americancatholic.org; www.franciscanmedia.org, pg 92

Sweeney, Katie, Fordham University Press, 2546 Belmont Ave, University Box L, Bronx, NY 10458 *Tel:* 718-817-4795 *Fax:* 718-817-4785 *Web Site:* www.fordhampress.com, pg 90

Sweet, Christopher, Thames & Hudson, 500 Fifth Ave, New York, NY 10110 *Tel:* 212-354-3763 *Toll Free Tel:* 800-233-4830 *Fax:* 212-398-1252 *E-mail:* bookinfo@thames.wwnorton.com *Web Site:* www.thamesandhudsonusa.com, pg 244

Sweeting, Kevin, Crown Publishing Group, c/o Penguin Random House Inc, 1745 Broadway, New York, NY 10019 *Tel:* 212-782-9000 *Toll Free Tel:* 888-264-1745 *Fax:* 212-940-7408 *E-mail:* crownosm@penguinrandomhouse.com *Web Site:* crownpublishing.com, pg 68

Sweeting, Kevin, Clarkson Potter Publishers, c/o Random House Inc, 1745 Broadway, New York, NY 10019 *Tel:* 212-782-9000 *Toll Free Tel:* 888-264-1745 *Fax:* 212-572-6181 *Web Site:* www.clarksonpotter.com; www.randomhouse.com/crown/clarksonpotter, pg 195

Sweetland, Helen, Sierra Club Books, 85 Second St, 2nd fl, San Francisco, CA 94105 *Tel:* 415-977-5500 *Fax:* 415-977-5794 *E-mail:* books.publishing@sierraclub.org *Web Site:* www.sierraclubbooks.org, pg 224

Swensen, Evan, Publication Consultants, 8370 Eleusis Dr, Anchorage, AK 99502 *Tel:* 907-349-2424 *Fax:* 907-349-2426 *E-mail:* books@publicationconsultants.com *Web Site:* www.publicationconsultants.com, pg 200

Swenson, Emily, Pearson Scott Foresman, 1900 E Lake Ave, Glenview, IL 60025 *Tel:* 847-729-3000 *Toll Free Tel:* 800-535-4391 (Midwest) *Fax:* 847-729-8910 *Web Site:* www.pearsonschool.com, pg 185

Swenson, Jamie, Wisconsin Annual Fall Conferencee, PO Box 259303, Madison, WI 53725 *Tel:* 608-278-0692 *Web Site:* www.scbwi.org; www.scbwi-wi.com, pg 657

Swenson, Tree, Raiziss/de Palchi Fellowship, 75 Maiden Lane, Suite 901, New York, NY 10038 *Tel:* 212-274-0343 *Fax:* 212-274-9427 *E-mail:* academy@poets.org *Web Site:* www.poets.org, pg 723

Swenson, Tree, Walt Whitman Award, 75 Maiden Lane, Suite 901, New York, NY 10038 *Tel:* 212-274-0343 *Fax:* 212-274-9427 *E-mail:* academy@poets.org *Web Site:* www.poets.org, pg 735

Swerdloff, Carolyn, Simon & Schuster Children's Publishing, 1230 Avenue of the Americas, New York, NY 10020 *Tel:* 212-698-7000 *Web Site:* KIDS.SimonandSchuster.com; TEEN.SimonandSchuster.com; simonandschuster.net; simonandschuster.biz, pg 225

Swetonic, Carrie, Dutton, 375 Hudson St, New York, NY 10014 *Tel:* 212-366-2000 *Fax:* 212-366-2262 *E-mail:* online@penguinputnam.com *Web Site:* www.penguinputnam.com; us.penguingroup.com, pg 78

Swetonic, Carrie, The Putnam Publishing Group, 375 Hudson St, New York, NY 10014 *Tel:* 212-366-2000 *Toll Free Tel:* 800-631-8571 *Fax:* 212-366-2643 *E-mail:* online@penguinputnam.com *Web Site:* www.penguinputnam.com; us.penguingroup.com, pg 201

Swetonic, Carrie, GP Putnam's Sons (Hardcover), 375 Hudson St, New York, NY 10014 *Tel:* 212-366-2000 *E-mail:* online@penguinputnam.com *Web Site:* us.penguingroup.com, pg 201

Swinwood, Craig, Harlequin Enterprises Ltd, 225 Duncan Mill Rd, Don Mills, ON M3B 3K9, Canada *Tel:* 416-445-5860 *Toll Free Tel:* 888-432-4879; 800-370-5838 (ebook inquiries) *E-mail:* customerservice@harlequin.com *Web Site:* www.harlequin.com, pg 487

Swinwood, Craig, Love Inspired Books, 233 Broadway, Suite 1001, New York, NY 10279 *Tel:* 212-553-4200 *Fax:* 212-227-8969 *E-mail:* customer_service@harlequin.ca *Web Site:* www.harlequin.com, pg 143

Swinwood, Susan, Harlequin Enterprises Ltd, 225 Duncan Mill Rd, Don Mills, ON M3B 3K9, Canada *Tel:* 416-445-5860 *Toll Free Tel:* 888-432-4879; 800-370-5838 (ebook inquiries) *E-mail:* customerservice@harlequin.com *Web Site:* www.harlequin.com, pg 487

Switzer, Kristi, Brewers Publications, 1372 Spruce St, Boulder, CO 80302 *Tel:* 303-447-0816 *Toll Free Tel:* 888-822-6273 (CN & US) *Fax:* 303-447-2825 *E-mail:* info@brewersassociation.org *Web Site:* www.brewersassociation.org, pg 45

Swope, Pamela K, Philosophy Documentation Center, PO Box 7147, Charlottesville, VA 22906-7147 *Tel:* 434-220-3300 *Toll Free Tel:* 800-444-2419 *Fax:* 434-220-3301 *E-mail:* order@pdcnet.org *Web Site:* www.pdcnet.org, pg 191

Sybert, Michelle, Indiana University Press, Herman B Wells Library 350, 1320 E Tenth St, Bloomington, IN 47405-3907 *Tel:* 812-855-8817 *Toll Free Tel:* 800-842-6796 (orders only) *Fax:* 812-855-7931; 812-855-8507 *E-mail:* iupress@indiana.edu; iuporder@indiana.edu (orders) *Web Site:* www.iupress.indiana.edu, pg 120

Sye, Stephen, ILA Children's & Young Adults' Book Awards, 800 Barksdale Rd, Newark, DE 19711-3204 *Tel:* 302-731-1600 *Toll Free Tel:* 800-336-7323 (US & CN) *Fax:* 302-731-1057 *E-mail:* committees@reading.org *Web Site:* www.literacyworldwide.org; www.reading.org, pg 694

Sygall, Susan, Mobility International USA, 132 E Broadway, Suite 343, Eugene, OR 97401 *Tel:* 541-343-1284 *Fax:* 541-343-6812 *E-mail:* info@miusa.org *Web Site:* www.miusa.org, pg 158

Sylbert, John, American Institute for Economic Research (AIER), 250 Division St, Great Barrington, MA 01230 *Tel:* 413-528-1216 *Toll Free Tel:* 888-528-1216 (orders) *E-mail:* info@aier.org, pg 13

Sylve, Elvira C, Clotilde's Secretarial & Management Services, PO Box 871926, New Orleans, LA 70187 *Tel:* 504-242-2912; 504-800-4853 (cell) *E-mail:* elcsy58@aol.com; elcsy58@att.net, pg 523

Sylvester, Marcia, Princeton Book Co Publishers, 614 Rte 130, Hightstown, NJ 08520 *Tel:* 609-426-0602 *Toll Free Tel:* 800-220-7149 *Fax:* 609-426-1344 *E-mail:* pbc@dancehorizons.com; elysian@princetonbookcompany.com *Web Site:* www.dancehorizons.com, pg 197

Symes, Peter D, Society of Motion Picture & Television Engineers® (SMPTE®), 3 Barker Ave, 5th fl, White Plains, NY 10601 *Tel:* 914-761-1100 *Fax:* 914-761-3115 *Web Site:* www.smpte.org, pg 619

Szakonyi, Mark, The JOC Group Inc, 2 Penn Plaza E, Newark, NJ 07105 *Tel:* 973-776-8660 *Web Site:* www.joc.com, pg 127

Szawiola, Kathleen, University of Nevada Press, University of Nevada, M/S 0166, Reno, NV 89557-0166 *Tel:* 775-784-6573 *Fax:* 775-784-6200 *Web Site:* www.unpress.nevada.edu, pg 258

Szekely, Peter, Deadline Club, c/o Salmagundi Club, 47 Fifth Ave, New York, NY 10003 *Tel:* 646-481-7584 *E-mail:* info@deadlineclub.org *Web Site:* www.deadlineclub.org, pg 604

Szost, Bernadette, Portfolio Solutions LLC, 136 Jameson Hill Rd, Clinton Corners, NY 12514 *Tel:* 845-266-1001 *Web Site:* www.portfoliosolutionsllc.com, pg 584

Szpyrka, Adrienne, Sky Pony Press, 307 W 36 St, 11th fl, New York, NY 10018 *Tel:* 212-643-6816 *Fax:* 212-643-6819 *E-mail:* skypony@skyhorsepublishing.com; submissions@skyhorsepublishing.com; info@skyhorsepublishing.com *Web Site:* www.skyponypress.com, pg 227

Tabian, Bob E, Robert E Tabian/Literary Agent, 229 Paterson Ave, Suite 2, East Rutherford, NJ 07073 *Tel:* 631-987-2293 *Fax:* 201-438-1327 *E-mail:* retlit@mindspring.com, pg 577

Tackett, Jessica, Bloomsbury Academic, 1385 Broadway, 5th fl, New York, NY 10018 *Tel:* 212-419-5300 *Web Site:* www.bloomsbury.com, pg 39

Tafura, Mariana, Editorial Unilit, 8167 NW 84 St, Medley, FL 33166 *Tel:* 305-592-6136 *Toll Free Tel:* 800-767-7726 *Fax:* 305-592-0087 *E-mail:* info@editorialunilit.com; customerservice@editorialunilit.com *Web Site:* www.editorialunilit.com, pg 253

Tager, Steve, Harry N Abrams Inc, 115 W 18 St, 6th fl, New York, NY 10011 *Tel:* 212-206-7715 *Toll Free Tel:* 800-345-1359 *Fax:* 212-519-1210 *E-mail:* abrams@abramsbooks.com *Web Site:* www.abramsbooks.com, pg 3

Tagler, John, Association of American Publishers (AAP), 71 Fifth Ave, 2nd fl, New York, NY 10003-3004 *Tel:* 212-255-0200 *Fax:* 212-255-7007 *E-mail:* info@publishers.org *Web Site:* publishers.org, pg 598

Tahirkheli, Sharon, American Geosciences Institute (AGI), 4220 King St, Alexandria, VA 22302-1502 *Tel:* 703-379-2480 (ext 246) *Fax:* 703-379-7563 *E-mail:* pubs@agiweb.org *Web Site:* www.agiweb.org, pg 13

Taillon, Peggy, Canadian Council on Social Development (Conseil canadien de developpement social), 190 O'Connor St, Suite 100, Ottawa, ON K2P 2R3, Canada *Tel:* 613-236-8977 *Fax:* 613-236-2750 *E-mail:* info@ccsd.ca *Web Site:* www.ccsd.ca, pg 475

Taintor, Declan, Picador, 175 Fifth Ave, 19th fl, New York, NY 10010 *Tel:* 646-307-5151 *Fax:* 212-253-9627 *E-mail:* firstname.lastname@picadorusa.com *Web Site:* www.picadorusa.com, pg 191

Tajima, Toni, Ten Speed Press, 2625 Alcatraz Ave, Unit 505, Berkeley, CA 94705 *Tel:* 510-285-3000 *Toll Free Tel:* 800-841-BOOK (841-2665) *E-mail:* csorders@randomhouse.com *Web Site:* crownpublishing.com/imprint/ten-speed-press, pg 243

Takes, Bill, Random House Publishing Group, 1745 Broadway, New York, NY 10019 *Toll Free Tel:* 800-200-3552 *Web Site:* atrandom.com, pg 204

Takoudes, Emily, Phaidon Press Inc, 180 Varick St, 14th fl, New York, NY 10014 *Tel:* 212-652-5400 *Toll Free Tel:* 800-759-0190 (cust serv) *Fax:* 212-652-5410 *Toll Free Fax:* 800-286-9471 (cust serv) *E-mail:* ussales@phaidon.com *Web Site:* www.phaidon.com, pg 190

Talbot, Greg, The Lawbook Exchange Ltd, 33 Terminal Ave, Clark, NJ 07066-1321 *Tel:* 732-382-1800 *Toll Free Tel:* 800-422-6686 *Fax:* 732-382-1887 *E-mail:* law@lawbookexchange.com *Web Site:* www.lawbookexchange.com, pg 135

Talbott, Strobe, The Brookings Institution Press, 1775 Massachusetts Ave NW, Washington, DC 20036-2188 *Tel:* 202-536-3600 *Toll Free Tel:* 800-537-5487 *Fax:* 202-536-3623 *E-mail:* permissions@brookings.edu *Web Site:* www.brookings.edu, pg 47

Talese, Nan A, Doubleday/Nan A Talese, c/o Penguin Random House Inc, 1745 Broadway, New York, NY 10019 *Tel:* 212-751-2600 *Fax:* 212-572-2662 *E-mail:* ddaypub@randomhouse.com *Web Site:* knopfdoubleday.com, pg 76

Tall, Asha, South End Press, PO Box 382132, Cambridge, MA 02238 *Tel:* 718-874-0089 *Toll Free Fax:* 800-960-0078 *E-mail:* southend@southendpress.org; info@southendpress.org *Web Site:* www.southendpress.org, pg 231

Tallberg, Anne Marie, St Martin's Press, LLC, 175 Fifth Ave, New York, NY 10010 *Tel:* 646-307-5151 *Fax:* 212-420-9314 *E-mail:* firstname.lastname@macmillan.com *Web Site:* www.stmartins.com, pg 214

Tallie, Ekere, Mt Chocorua Writing Workshop, PO Box 2280, Conway, NH 03818-2280 *Tel:* 603-447-2280 *E-mail:* reservations@worldfellowship.org *Web Site:* www.worldfellowship.org, pg 652

Tallon, Dr Andrew, Marquette University Press, 1415 W Wisconsin Ave, Milwaukee, WI 53233 *Tel:* 414-288-1564 *Toll Free Tel:* 800-247-6553 (cust serv) *Fax:* 414-288-7813 *Web Site:* www.marquette.edu/mupress, pg 147

Tamar, Rima, Dharma Publishing, 35788 Hauser Bridge Rd, Cazadero, CA 95421 *Tel:* 707-847-3717 *Toll Free Tel:* 800-873-4276 *Fax:* 707-847-3380 *E-mail:* contact@dharmapublishing.com; customerservice@dharmapublishing.com *Web Site:* www.dharmapublishing.com, pg 73

Tamarkin, Heather, David R Godine Publisher Inc, 15 Court Sq, Suite 320, Boston, MA 02108-4715 *Tel:* 617-451-9600 *Fax:* 617-350-0250 *E-mail:* info@godine.com *Web Site:* www.godine.com, pg 98

Tambeau, Renee, Museum of New Mexico Press, 725 Camino Lejo, Suite C, Santa Fe, NM 87505 *Tel:* 505-476-1155; 505-272-7777 (orders) *Toll Free Tel:* 800-249-7737 (orders) *Fax:* 505-476-1156 *Toll Free Fax:* 800-622-8667 (orders) *Web Site:* www.mnmpress.org, pg 162

Tambeau, Renee, University of Michigan Press, 839 Greene St, Ann Arbor, MI 48104-3209 *Tel:* 734-764-4388 *Fax:* 734-615-1540 *E-mail:* esladmin@umich.edu *Web Site:* www.press.umich.edu, pg 257

Tamminen, Suzanna L, Wesleyan University Press, 215 Long Lane, Middletown, CT 06459-0433 *Tel:* 860-685-7711 *Fax:* 860-685-7712 *Web Site:* www.wesleyan.edu/wespress, pg 269

Tan, Cecilia, Circlet Press Inc, 39 Hurlbut St, Cambridge, MA 02138 *Toll Free Tel:* 800-729-6423 *E-mail:* circletintern@gmail.com *Web Site:* www.circlet.com, pg 58

Tang, Adrienne, Kids Can Press Ltd, 25 Dockside Dr, Toronto, ON M5A 0B5, Canada *Tel:* 416-479-7000 *Toll Free Tel:* 800-265-0884 *Fax:* 416-960-5437 *E-mail:* info@kidscan.com; customerservice@kidscan.com *Web Site:* www.kidscanpress.com; www.kidscanpress.ca, pg 489

Tang, Albert, Atria Books, 1230 Avenue of the Americas, New York, NY 10020 *Tel:* 212-698-7000 *Fax:* 212-698-7007 *Web Site:* www.simonandschuster.com, pg 27

Tank, David, Planert Creek Press, E4843 395 Ave, Menomonie, WI 54751 *Tel:* 715-235-4110 *E-mail:* publisher@planertcreekpress.com *Web Site:* www.planertcreekpress.com, pg 192

Tannenbaum, Amy, Jane Rotrosen Agency LLC, 318 E 51 St, New York, NY 10022 *Tel:* 212-593-4330 *Fax:* 212-935-6985 *Web Site:* janerotrosen.com, pg 571

Tanner, Annette K, Michigan State University Press (MSU Press), 1405 S Harrison Rd, Suite 25, East Lansing, MI 48823 *Tel:* 517-355-9543 *Fax:* 517-432-2611 *Toll Free Fax:* 800-678-2120 *E-mail:* msupress@msu.edu *Web Site:* www.msupress.msu.edu, pg 156

Tanselle, G Thomas, Bibliographical Society of the University of Virginia, c/o Alderman Library, University of Virginia, McCormick Rd, Charlottesville, VA 22904 *Tel:* 434-924-7013 *Fax:* 434-924-1431 *E-mail:* bibsoc@virginia.edu *Web Site:* bsuva.org, pg 600

Tanzer, Steven, TripBuilder Media Inc, 180 Post Rd E, Suite 200, Westport, CT 06880 *Tel:* 203-227-1255 *Toll Free Tel:* 800-525-9745 *Fax:* 203-227-1257 *E-mail:* info@tripbuildermedia.com *Web Site:* www.tripbuildermedia.com, pg 249

Tapia, Miguel, Santillana USA Publishing Co Inc, 2023 NW 84 Ave, Doral, FL 33122 *Tel:* 305-591-9522 *Toll Free Tel:* 800-245-8584 *Fax:* 305-591-9145 *Toll Free Fax:* 888-248-9518 *E-mail:* customerservice@santillanausa.com *Web Site:* www.santillanausa.com; www.alfaguara.net, pg 216

Taplinger, Susan, Direct Marketing Association (DMA), 1120 Avenue of the Americas, New York, NY 10036-6700 *Tel:* 212-768-7277 *Fax:* 212-302-6714 *E-mail:* memberservices@the-dma.org *Web Site:* thedma.org, pg 74, 604

Tarquinio, J Alex, Deadline Club, c/o Salmagundi Club, 47 Fifth Ave, New York, NY 10003 *Tel:* 646-481-7584 *E-mail:* info@deadlineclub.org *Web Site:* www.deadlineclub.org, pg 604

Tart, Brian, Penguin Group (USA) LLC, a Penguin Random House company, 375 Hudson St, New York, NY 10014 *Tel:* 212-366-2000 *Toll Free Tel:* 800-847-5515 (inside sales); 800-631-8571 (cust serv) *Fax:* 212-366-2666; 607-775-4829 (inside sales) *E-mail:* online@us.penguingroup.com *Web Site:* www.penguin.com; us.penguingroup.com, pg 186

Tart, Brian, Viking, 375 Hudson St, New York, NY 10014 *Tel:* 212-366-2000 *E-mail:* online@penguinputnam.com *Web Site:* www.penguinputnam.com; us.penguingroup.com, pg 265

Tart, Brian, Viking Studio, 375 Hudson St, New York, NY 10014 *Tel:* 212-366-2000 *E-mail:* online@penguinputnam.com *Web Site:* www.penguinputnam.com; us.penguingroup.com, pg 265

Tart, David, Kendall Hunt Publishing Co, 4050 Westmark Dr, Dubuque, IA 52002-2624 *Tel:* 563-589-1000 *Toll Free Tel:* 800-228-0810 (orders) *Fax:* 563-589-1046 *Toll Free Fax:* 800-772-9165 *E-mail:* orders@kendallhunt.com *Web Site:* www.kendallhunt.com, pg 130

Tasman, Alice, Jean V Naggar Literary Agency Inc (JVNLA), 216 E 75 St, Suite 1-E, New York, NY 10021 *Tel:* 212-794-1082 *E-mail:* jvnla@jvnla.com *Web Site:* www.jvnla.com, pg 566

Tasse, Nathalie, Les Editions XYZ inc, 1815, ave De Lorimier, Montreal, QC H2K 3W6, Canada *Tel:* 514-525-2170 *Fax:* 514-525-7537 *E-mail:* info@editionsxyz.com *Web Site:* www.editionsxyz.com, pg 483

Tate, Corby, TotalRecall Publications Inc, 1103 Middlecreek, Friendswood, TX 77546 *Tel:* 281-992-3131 *E-mail:* sales@totalrecallpress.com *Web Site:* www.totalrecallpress.com, pg 247

Tate, Nancy E, League of Women Voters of the United States, 1730 "M" St NW, Suite 1000, Washington, DC 20036-4508 *Tel:* 202-429-1965 *Fax:* 202-429-0854; 202-429-4343 *E-mail:* lwv@lwv.org *Web Site:* www.lwv.org, pg 608

Taub, Daniel, National Association of Real Estate Editors (NAREE), 1003 NW Sixth Terr, Boca Raton, FL 33486-3455 *Tel:* 561-391-3599 *Fax:* 561-391-0099 *Web Site:* www.naree.org, pg 611

Tauber, Lisa, Clarkson Potter Publishers, c/o Random House Inc, 1745 Broadway, New York, NY 10019 *Tel:* 212-782-9000 *Toll Free Tel:* 888-264-1745 *Fax:* 212-572-6181 *Web Site:* www.clarksonpotter.com; www.randomhouse.com/crown/clarksonpotter, pg 195

Tauber, Mark, HarperCollins General Books Group, 195 Broadway, New York, NY 10007 *Tel:* 212-207-7000 *Web Site:* www.harpercollins.com, pg 105

Taublib, Nita, GP Putnam's Sons (Hardcover), 375 Hudson St, New York, NY 10014 *Tel:* 212-366-2000 *E-mail:* online@penguinputnam.com *Web Site:* us.penguingroup.com, pg 201

Taunton, Paul, Random House Publishing Group, 1745 Broadway, New York, NY 10019 *Toll Free Tel:* 800-200-3552 *Web Site:* atrandom.com, pg 204

Tavani, Mark, Random House Publishing Group, 1745 Broadway, New York, NY 10019 *Toll Free Tel:* 800-200-3552 *Web Site:* atrandom.com, pg 204

Tavarez, Yamberlie, The Feminist Press at The City University of New York, 365 Fifth Ave, Suite 5406, New York, NY 10016 *Tel:* 212-817-7915 *Fax:* 212-817-1593 *E-mail:* info@feministpress.org *Web Site:* www.feministpress.org, pg 87

Tavolacci, Joyce, Bearport Publishing Co Inc, 45 W 21 St, Suite 3B, New York, NY 10010 *Tel:* 212-337-8577 *Toll Free Tel:* 877-337-8577 *Fax:* 212-337-8557 *Toll Free Fax:* 866-337-8557 *E-mail:* service@bearportpublishing.com; info@bearportpublishing.com *Web Site:* www.bearportpublishing.com, pg 33

Taylor, Alex, McNeese State University, Writing Program, PO Box 92655, Lake Charles, LA 70609-0001 *Tel:* 337-475-5325; 337-475-5327 *Web Site:* www.mcneese.edu.com; www.mfa.mcneese.edu, pg 661

Taylor, Beth, American Marketing Association, 311 S Wacker Dr, Suite 5800, Chicago, IL 60606 *Tel:* 312-542-9000 *Toll Free Tel:* 800-AMA-1150 (262-1150) *Fax:* 312-542-9001 *E-mail:* info@ama.org *Web Site:* www.ama.org, pg 595

Taylor, Bob, The Quarasan Group Inc, 405 W Superior St, Chicago, IL 60654 *Tel:* 312-981-2500 *E-mail:* info@quarasan.com *Web Site:* www.quarasan.com, pg 533

Taylor, Christina, Robert F Kennedy Book Awards, 1300 19 St NW, Suite 750, Washington, DC 20036 *Tel:* 202-463-7575 *Fax:* 202-463-6606 *E-mail:* info@rfkcenter.org *Web Site:* www.rfkcenter.org, pg 698

Taylor, Elizabeth, Nelson Algren Awards, Chicago Tribune, TT200, 435 N Michigan Ave, Chicago, IL 60611 *Toll Free Tel:* 800-874-2863 *Fax:* 312-222-5816 *E-mail:* nelsonalgren@tribune.com *Web Site:* www.chicagotribune.com/about, pg 666

Taylor, Joe, Livingston Press, University of West Alabama, Sta 22, Livingston, AL 35470 *Tel:* 205-652-3470 *Web Site:* www.livingstonpress.uwa.edu, pg 142

Taylor, John, ProQuest LLC, 789 E Eisenhower Pkwy, Ann Arbor, MI 48108-3218 *Tel:* 734-761-4700 *Toll Free Tel:* 800-521-0600 *Fax:* 734-975-6486 *Toll Free Fax:* 800-864-0019 *E-mail:* info@proquest.com *Web Site:* www.proquest.com, pg 199

Taylor, John D, Bonasa Press, PO Box 340, Crosby, ND 58730 *Tel:* 701-965-3974 *E-mail:* new@bonasapress.com (inquiries) *Web Site:* www.bonasapress.com, pg 42

Taylor, Justin, Crossway, 1300 Crescent St, Wheaton, IL 60187 *Tel:* 630-682-4300 *Toll Free Tel:* 800-635-7993 (orders); 800-543-1659 (cust serv) *Fax:* 630-682-4785 *E-mail:* info@crossway.org *Web Site:* www.crossway.org, pg 67

Taylor, Keith, Page Davidson Clayton Prize for Emerging Poets, University of Michigan, 0576 Rackham Bldg, 915 E Washington St, Ann Arbor, MI 48109-1070 *Tel:* 734-764-9265 *E-mail:* mqr@umich.edu *Web Site:* www.umich.edu/~mqr, pg 678

Taylor, Keith, Laurence Goldstein Poetry Prize, University of Michigan, 0576 Rackham Bldg, 915 E Washington St, Ann Arbor, MI 48109-1070 *Tel:* 734-764-9265 *E-mail:* mqr@umich.edu *Web Site:* www.umich.edu/~mqr, pg 690

Taylor, Keith, Lawrence Foundation Prize, University of Michigan, 0576 Rackham Bldg, 915 E Washington St, Ann Arbor, MI 48109-1070 *Tel:* 734-764-9265 *E-mail:* mqr@umich.edu *Web Site:* www.umich.edu/~mqr, pg 699

Taylor, Marci, American Press, 60 State St, Suite 700, Boston, MA 02109 *Tel:* 617-247-0022 *E-mail:* americanpress@flash.net *Web Site:* www.americanpresspublishers.com, pg 15

Taylor, Mark, Standard Publishing, 8805 Governors Hill Dr, Suite 400, Cincinnati, OH 45249 *Tel:* 513-931-4050 *Toll Free Tel:* 800-543-1353 *Fax:* 513-931-0950 *Toll Free Fax:* 877-867-5751 *E-mail:* customerservice@standardpub.com *Web Site:* www.standardpub.com, pg 233

Taylor, Mark, Tyndale House Publishers Inc, 351 Executive Dr, Carol Stream, IL 60188 *Tel:* 630-668-8300 *Toll Free Tel:* 800-323-9400 *Web Site:* www.tyndale.com, pg 252

Taylor, Robert, The Colonial Williamsburg Foundation, PO Box 1776, Williamsburg, VA 23187-1776 *Tel:* 757-229-1000 *Toll Free Tel:* 800-HISTORY (447-8679) *Fax:* 757-220-7325 *E-mail:* cwres@cwf.org; geninfo@cwf.org *Web Site:* www.colonialwilliamsburg.org/publications, pg 61

Taylor, Robert PhD, Institute of Public Administration of Canada, 1075 Bay St, Suite 401, Toronto, ON M5S 2B1, Canada *Tel:* 416-924-8787 *Fax:* 416-924-4992 *E-mail:* ntl@ipac.ca *Web Site:* www.ipac.ca; www.iapc.ca, pg 489

Taylor, Sara, Dumbarton Oaks, 1703 32 St NW, Washington, DC 20007 *Tel:* 202-339-6400 *Fax:* 202-339-6401; 202-298-8407 *E-mail:* doaksbooks@doaks.org *Web Site:* www.doaks.org, pg 77

Taylor, Victor E, The Davies Group Publishers, PO Box 440140, Aurora, CO 80044-0140 *Tel:* 303-750-8374 *Fax:* 303-337-0952 *E-mail:* info@thedaviesgrouppublishers.com; daviesgroup@msn.com (orders) *Web Site:* www.thedaviesgrouppublishers.com, pg 71

Taylor, Yuval, Chicago Review Press, 814 N Franklin St, Chicago, IL 60610 *Tel:* 312-337-0747 *Toll Free Tel:* 800-888-4741 *Fax:* 312-337-5110 *E-mail:* frontdesk@chicagoreviewpress.com *Web Site:* www.chicagoreviewpress.com, pg 56

Tayman, William P Jr, Corporation for Public Broadcasting (CPB), 401 Ninth St NW, Washington, DC 20004-2129 *Tel:* 202-879-9600 *Web Site:* www.cpb.org, pg 604

Tebo, Meg, The Society of Midland Authors (SMA), PO Box 10419, Chicago, IL 60610 *E-mail:* info@midlandauthors.com *Web Site:* www.midlandauthors.com, pg 619

Tebo, Meg, The Society of Midland Authors Awards, 530 Michigan Ave, Evanston, IL 60202 *E-mail:* info@midlandauthors.com *Web Site:* www.midlandauthors.com, pg 729

Teehan, Tim, Columbia Books & Information Services, 4340 East-West Hwy, Suite 300, Bethesda, MD 20814 *Tel:* 240-235-0266 *Toll Free Tel:* 888-265-0600 (cust serv) *Fax:* 202-464-1775 *E-mail:* info@columbiabooks.com *Web Site:* www.columbiabooks.com; www.lobbyists.info; www.associationexecs.com, pg 61

Teeman, Hilary Rubin, Crown Publishing Group, c/o Penguin Random House Inc, 1745 Broadway, New York, NY 10019 *Tel:* 212-782-9000 *Toll Free Tel:* 888-264-1745 *Fax:* 212-940-7408 *E-mail:* crownosm@penguinrandomhouse.com *Web Site:* crownpublishing.com, pg 68

Teeple, Charlotte, Marilyn Baillie Picture Book Award, 40 Orchard View Blvd, Suite 217, Toronto, ON M4R 1B9, Canada *Tel:* 416-975-0010 *Fax:* 416-975-8970 *E-mail:* info@bookcentre.ca *Web Site:* www.bookcentre.ca, pg 669

Teeple, Charlotte, The Geoffrey Bilson Award for Historical Fiction for Young People, 40 Orchard View Blvd, Suite 217, Toronto, ON M4R 1B9, Canada *Tel:* 416-975-0010 *Fax:* 416-975-8970 *E-mail:* info@bookcentre.ca *Web Site:* www.bookcentre.ca, pg 672

Teeple, Charlotte, Canadian Children's Book Centre, 40 Orchard View Blvd, Suite 217, Toronto, ON M4R 1B9, Canada *Tel:* 416-975-0010 *Fax:* 416-975-8970 *E-mail:* info@bookcentre.ca *Web Site:* www.bookcentre.ca, pg 602

Teeple, Charlotte, Norma Fleck Award for Canadian Children's Non-Fiction, 40 Orchard View Blvd, Suite 217, Toronto, ON M4R 1B9, Canada *Tel:* 416-975-0010 *Fax:* 416-975-8970 *E-mail:* info@bookcentre.ca *Web Site:* www.bookcentre.ca, pg 686

Teeple, Charlotte, Monica Hughes Award for Science Fiction & Fantasy, 40 Orchard View Blvd, Suite 217, Toronto, ON M4R 1B9, Canada *Tel:* 416-975-0010 *Fax:* 416-975-8970 *E-mail:* info@bookcentre.ca *Web Site:* www.bookcentre.ca, pg 693

Teeple, Charlotte, Amy Mathers Teen Book Award, 40 Orchard View Blvd, Suite 217, Toronto, ON M4R 1B9, Canada *Tel:* 416-975-0010 *Fax:* 416-975-8970 *E-mail:* info@bookcentre.ca *Web Site:* www.bookcentre.ca, pg 706

Teeple, Charlotte, John Spray Mystery Award, 40 Orchard View Blvd, Suite 217, Toronto, ON M4R 1B9, Canada *Tel:* 416-975-0010 *Fax:* 416-975-8970 *E-mail:* info@bookcentre.ca *Web Site:* www.bookcentre.ca, pg 730

Teeple, Charlotte, TD Canadian Children's Literature Award, 40 Orchard View Blvd, Suite 217, Toronto, ON M4R 1B9, Canada *Tel:* 416-975-0010 *Fax:* 416-975-8970 *E-mail:* info@bookcentre.ca *Web Site:* www.bookcentre.ca, pg 732

Teer, Kaitlyn, Annie Dillard Award for Creative Nonfiction, Mail Stop 9053, Western Washington University, Bellingham, WA 98225 *Tel:* 360-650-4863 *E-mail:* bhreview@wwu.edu *Web Site:* www.bhreview.org, pg 681

Teer, Kaitlyn, 49th Parallel Poetry Award, Mail Stop 9053, Western Washington University, Bellingham, WA 98225 *Tel:* 360-650-4863 *E-mail:* bhreview@wwu.edu *Web Site:* www.bhreview.org, pg 687

Teer, Kaitlyn, Tobias Wolff Award for Fiction, Mail Stop 9053, Western Washington University, Bellingham, WA 98225 *Tel:* 360-650-4863 *E-mail:* bhreview@wwu.edu *Web Site:* www.bhreview.org, pg 737

Teicher, Oren, American Booksellers Association, 333 Westchester Ave, Suite S202, White Plains, NY 10604 *Tel:* 914-406-7500 *Toll Free Tel:* 800-637-0037 *Fax:* 914-410-6297 *E-mail:* info@bookweb.org *Web Site:* www.bookweb.org, pg 594

Teicher, Oren, Indies Choice Book Awards, 333 Westchester Ave, Suite S202, White Plains, NY 10604 *Tel:* 914-406-7500 *Toll Free Tel:* 800-637-0037 *Fax:* 914-410-6297 *Web Site:* www.bookweb.org, pg 694

Teichgraeber, Gretchen, Leadership Directories, 1407 Broadway, Suite 318, New York, NY 10018 *Tel:* 212-627-4140 *Fax:* 212-645-0931 *E-mail:* info@leadershipdirectories.com *Web Site:* www.leadershipdirectories.com, pg 135

Teigen, Rob, Bethany House Publishers, 11400 Hampshire Ave S, Bloomington, MN 55438 *Tel:* 952-829-2500 *Toll Free Tel:* 800-877-2665 (orders) *Fax:* 952-829-2568 *Toll Free Fax:* 800-398-3111 (orders) *Web Site:* www.bethanyhouse.com; www.bakerpublishinggroup.com, pg 36

Teitelbaum, Maura, Abrams Artists Agency, 275 Seventh Ave, 26th fl, New York, NY 10001 *Tel:* 646-486-4600 *Fax:* 646-486-2358 *E-mail:* literary@abramsartny.com *Web Site:* www.abramsartists.com, pg 539

Teixeira, Ian, Fine Creative Media, Inc, 322 Eighth Ave, 15th fl, New York, NY 10001 *Tel:* 212-595-3500 *Fax:* 212-595-3779, pg 88

Tell, David, Hudson Institute, 1015 15 St NW, 6th fl, Washington, DC 20005 *Tel:* 202-974-2400 *Fax:* 202-974-2410 *E-mail:* info@hudson.org *Web Site:* www.hudson.org, pg 116

Tell, Geoffery Crawford, Two Thousand Three Associates, 4180 Saxon Dr, New Smyrna Beach, FL 32169 *Tel:* 386-690-2503 *E-mail:* ttta1@att.net *Web Site:* www.twothousandthree.com, pg 252

Temertzoglou, Ted, Thompson Educational Publishing Inc, 20 Ripley Ave, Toronto, ON M6S 3N9, Canada *Tel:* 416-766-2763 (admin & orders) *Toll Free Tel:* 877-366-2763 *Fax:* 416-766-0398 (admin & orders) *E-mail:* info@thompsonbooks.com *Web Site:* www.thompsonbooks.com, pg 501

Tempest, Nephele, The Knight Agency Inc, 570 East Ave, Madison, GA 30650 *E-mail:* submissions@knightagency.net *Web Site:* www.knightagency.net, pg 560

Tempio, Robert, Princeton University Press, 41 William St, Princeton, NJ 08540-5237 *Tel:* 609-258-4900 *Toll Free Tel:* 800-777-4726 (orders) *Fax:* 609-258-6305 *Toll Free Fax:* 800-999-1958 *E-mail:* orders@cpfsinc.com *Web Site:* press.princeton.edu, pg 197

Temple, Jamey, Eric Hoffer Award for Short Prose, PO Box 11, Titusville, NJ 08560 *Fax:* 609-964-1718 *E-mail:* info@hofferaward.com *Web Site:* www.hofferaward.com, pg 692

Temple, John F, Guideposts Book & Inspirational Media, 16 E 34 St, 12th fl, New York, NY 10016 *Tel:* 212-251-8100 *Toll Free Tel:* 800-431-2344 (cust serv) *Fax:* 212-684-0689 *E-mail:* gpsprod@cdsfulfillment.com *Web Site:* guideposts.org, pg 102

Temple, Johnny, Akashic Books, 232 Third St, Suite A-115, Brooklyn, NY 11215 *Tel:* 718-643-9193 *Fax:* 718-643-9195 *E-mail:* info@akashicbooks.com *Web Site:* www.akashicbooks.com, pg 7

Tenforde, Thomas PhD, National Council on Radiation Protection & Measurements (NCRP), 7910 Woodmont Ave, Suite 400, Bethesda, MD 20814-3095 *Tel:* 301-657-2652 *Toll Free Tel:* 800-229-2652 *Fax:* 301-907-8768 *E-mail:* ncrppubs@ncrponline.org *Web Site:* www.ncrponline.org; www.ncrppublications.org, pg 164

Tenney, Craig, Harold Ober Associates Inc, 425 Madison Ave, New York, NY 10017 *Tel:* 212-759-8600 *Fax:* 212-759-9428 *Web Site:* www.haroldober.com, pg 567

Tepper, Michael, Genealogical Publishing Co, 3600 Clipper Mill Rd, Suite 260, Baltimore, MD 21211 *Tel:* 410-837-8271 *Toll Free Tel:* 800-296-6687 *Fax:* 410-752-8492 *Toll Free Fax:* 800-599-9561 *E-mail:* sales@genealogical.com; info@genealogical.com *Web Site:* www.genealogical.com, pg 95

TerBeek, Kendra, Bagwyn Books, Lattie F Coor Hall, 4th fl, Rms 4426-4442, 975 S Myrtle Ave, Tempe, AZ 85281 *Tel:* 480-965-5900 *Fax:* 480-965-1681 *E-mail:* bagwynbooks@acmrs.org *Web Site:* acmrs.org/publications/bagwyn, pg 29

Teresi, Christian, Association of Writers & Writing Programs (AWP), George Mason University, 4400 University Dr, MSN 1E3, Fairfax, VA 22030 *Tel:* 703-993-4301 *Fax:* 703-993-4302 *E-mail:* awp@awpwriter.org *Web Site:* www.awpwriter.org, pg 599

Teresi, Christian, AWP Award Series, George Mason University, 4400 University Dr, MSN 1E3, Fairfax, VA 22030 *Tel:* 703-993-4301 *Fax:* 703-993-4302 *E-mail:* awp@awpwriter.org *Web Site:* www.awpwriter.org, pg 669

Termine, Anna, Corwin, a Sage Co, 2455 Teller Rd, Thousand Oaks, CA 91320 *Tel:* 805-499-9734 *Toll Free Tel:* 800-233-9936 *Fax:* 805-499-5323 *Toll Free Fax:* 800-417-2466 *E-mail:* info@corwin.com; order@corwin.com *Web Site:* www.corwin.com, pg 64

Terraciano, Kevin, UCLA Latin American Center Publications, UCLA Latin American Institute, 10343 Bunche Hall, Los Angeles, CA 90095 *Tel:* 310-825-4571 *Fax:* 310-206-6859 *E-mail:* latinamctr@international.ucla.edu *Web Site:* www.international.ucla.edu/lai, pg 252

Terragni, Emilia, Phaidon Press Inc, 180 Varick St, 14th fl, New York, NY 10014 *Tel:* 212-652-5400 *Toll Free Tel:* 800-759-0190 (cust serv) *Fax:* 212-652-5410 *Toll Free Fax:* 800-286-9471 (cust serv) *E-mail:* ussales@phaidon.com *Web Site:* www.phaidon.com, pg 190

Terrell, Guy, Laura Day Boggs Bolling Memorial, 1194 Hume Rd, Hume, VA 22639-1806 *E-mail:* poetryinva@aol.com *Web Site:* www.poetrysocietyofvirginia.org, pg 673

Terrell, Guy, Joe Pendleton Campbell Narrative Contest, 1194 Hume Rd, Hume, VA 22639-1806 *E-mail:* poetryinva@aol.com *Web Site:* www.poetrysocietyofvirginia.org, pg 675

Terrell, Guy, Carleton Drewry Memorial, 1194 Hume Rd, Hume, VA 22639-1806 *E-mail:* poetryinva@aol.com *Web Site:* www.poetrysocietyofvirginia.org, pg 682

Terrell, Guy, Alfred C Gary Memorial, 1194 Hume Rd, Hume, VA 22639-1806 *E-mail:* poetryinva@aol.com *Web Site:* www.poetrysocietyofvirginia.org, pg 688

Terrell, Guy, Bess Gresham Memorial, 1194 Hume Rd, Hume, VA 22639-1806 *E-mail:* poetryinva@aol.com *Web Site:* www.poetrysocietyofvirginia.org, pg 690

Terrell, Guy, Loretta Dunn Hall Memorial, 1194 Hume Rd, Hume, VA 22639-1806 *E-mail:* poetryinva@aol.com *Web Site:* www.poetrysocietyofvirginia.org, pg 691

Terrell, Guy, Handy Andy Prize, 1194 Hume Rd, Hume, VA 22639-1806 *E-mail:* poetryinva@aol.com *Web Site:* www.poetrysocietyofvirginia.org, pg 691

Terrell, Guy, Brodie Herndon Memorial, 1194 Hume Rd, Hume, VA 22639-1806 *E-mail:* poetryinva@aol.com *Web Site:* www.poetrysocietyofvirginia.org, pg 692

Terrell, Guy, Judah, Sarah, Grace & Tom Memorial, 1194 Hume Rd, Hume, VA 22639-1806 *E-mail:* poetryinva@aol.com *Web Site:* www.poetrysocietyofvirginia.org, pg 697

Tijerina, Andres, Most Significant Scholarly Book Award, c/o 7748 Hwy 290 W, Austin, TX 78736-3202 *Tel:* 512-683-5640 *E-mail:* president@texasinstituteofletters.org *Web Site:* www.texasinstituteofletters.org, pg 709

Tijerina, Andres, Edwin "Bud" Shrake Award for Best Short Nonfiction, c/o 7748 Hwy 290 W, Austin, TX 78736-3202 *Tel:* 512-683-5640 *E-mail:* president@texasinstituteofletters.org *Web Site:* www.texasinstituteofletters.org, pg 728

Tijerina, Andres, Helen C Smith Memorial Award, c/o 7748 Hwy 290 W, Austin, TX 78736-3202 *Tel:* 512-683-5640 *E-mail:* president@texasinstituteofletters.org *Web Site:* www.texasinstituteofletters.org, pg 729

Tijerina, Andres, Texas Institute of Letters (TIL), c/o 7748 Hwy 290 W, Austin, TX 78736-3202 *E-mail:* president@texasinstituteofletters.org; secretary@texasinstituteofletters.org *Web Site:* www.texasinstituteofletters.org, pg 620

Tijerina, Andres, Texas Institute of Letters Awards, c/o 7748 Hwy 290 W, Austin, TX 78736-3202 *Tel:* 512-683-5640 *E-mail:* president@texasinstituteofletters.org *Web Site:* www.texasinstituteofletters.org, pg 732

Tiletnick, Michelle, Direct Marketing Association (DMA), 1120 Avenue of the Americas, New York, NY 10036-6700 *Tel:* 212-768-7277 *Fax:* 212-302-6714 *E-mail:* memberservices@the-dma.org *Web Site:* thedma.org, pg 74, 604

Tillman, Lillian Gail, Clotilde's Secretarial & Management Services, PO Box 871926, New Orleans, LA 70187 *Tel:* 504-242-2912; 504-800-4853 (cell) *E-mail:* elcsy58@aol.com; elcsy58@att.net, pg 523

Timberlake, Emily, Ten Speed Press, 2625 Alcatraz Ave, Unit 505, Berkeley, CA 94705 *Tel:* 510-285-3000 *Toll Free Tel:* 800-841-BOOK (841-2665) *E-mail:* csorders@randomhouse.com *Web Site:* crownpublishing.com/imprint/ten-speed-press, pg 243

Timbol, Christine, SDSU Writers' Conference, 5250 Campanile Dr, Rm 2503, San Diego, CA 92182-1920 *Tel:* 619-594-5821 *Fax:* 619-594-8566 *E-mail:* sdsuwritersconference@mail.sdsu.edu *Web Site:* www.neverstoplearning.net/writers, pg 655

Timmons, Barbara K, Management Sciences for Health, 200 Rivers Edge Dr, Medford, MA 02155 *Tel:* 617-250-9500 *Fax:* 617-250-9090 *E-mail:* bookstore@msh.org *Web Site:* www.msh.org, pg 146

Timony, Glenn, Penguin Group (USA) LLC Sales, 375 Hudson St, New York, NY 10014 *Tel:* 212-366-2000 *E-mail:* online@penguinputnam.com *Web Site:* us.penguingroup.com, pg 187

Tinari, Julianne, Jane Rotrosen Agency LLC, 318 E 51 St, New York, NY 10022 *Tel:* 212-593-4330 *Fax:* 212-935-6985 *Web Site:* janerotrosen.com, pg 571

Ting, Renee, Shen's Books, 1547 Palos Verdes Mall, Unit 291, Walnut Creek, CA 94597 *Tel:* 925-262-8108 *Toll Free Tel:* 800-456-6660 *Fax:* 925-415-6136 *Toll Free Fax:* 888-269-9092 *E-mail:* info@shens.com *Web Site:* www.shens.com, pg 223

Tingley, Megan, Hachette Book Group, 1290 Avenue of the Americas, New York, NY 10019 *Tel:* 212-364-1100 *Toll Free Tel:* 800-759-0190 (cust serv) *Fax:* 212-364-0933 (intl orders) *Toll Free Fax:* 800-286-9471 (cust serv) *Web Site:* www.HachetteBookGroup.com, pg 102

Tingley, Megan, Little, Brown Books for Young Readers, 1290 Avenue of the Americas, New York, NY 10019 *Tel:* 212-364-1100 *Toll Free Tel:* 800-759-0190 (cust serv) *Web Site:* www.HachetteBookGroup.com, pg 141

Tinker, Scott W, Bureau of Economic Geology, University of Texas at Austin, 10100 Burnet Rd, Bldg 130, Austin, TX 78758 *Tel:* 512-471-1534 *Fax:* 512-471-0140 *E-mail:* pubsales@beg.utexas.edu *Web Site:* www.beg.utexas.edu, pg 48

Tinsley, Tuck III, American Printing House for the Blind Inc, 1839 Frankfort Ave, Louisville, KY 40206 *Tel:* 502-895-2405 *Toll Free Tel:* 800-223-1839 (cust serv) *Fax:* 502-899-2274 *E-mail:* info@aph.org *Web Site:* www.aph.org; shop.aph.org, pg 15

Tipton, Virgil III, Liguori Publications, One Liguori Dr, Liguori, MO 63057-1000 *Tel:* 636-464-2500 *Toll Free Tel:* 866-848-2492; 800-325-9521 *Fax:* 636-464-8449 *Toll Free Fax:* 800-325-9526 (sales) *E-mail:* liguori@liguori.org (sales & cust serv) *Web Site:* www.liguori.org/contact-us.html, pg 139

Tirschwell, Peter, The JOC Group Inc, 2 Penn Plaza E, Newark, NJ 07105 *Tel:* 973-776-8660 *Web Site:* www.joc.com, pg 127

Tisseyre, Charles, Les Editions Pierre Tisseyre, 155, rue Maurice, Rosemere, QC J7A 2S8, Canada *Tel:* 514-335-0777 *Fax:* 514-335-6723 *E-mail:* info@edtisseyre.ca *Web Site:* www.tisseyre.ca, pg 482

Titen, Andrew, Bisk Education, 9417 Princess Palm Ave, Suite 400, Tampa, FL 33619 *Tel:* 813-621-6200 *Toll Free Tel:* 800-280-9718 (cust serv) *E-mail:* customerservice@bisk.com *Web Site:* www.bisk.com, pg 37

Tittiger, Peter, Phaidon Press Inc, 180 Varick St, 14th fl, New York, NY 10014 *Tel:* 212-652-5400 *Toll Free Tel:* 800-759-0190 (cust serv) *Fax:* 212-652-5410 *Toll Free Fax:* 800-286-9471 (cust serv) *E-mail:* ussales@phaidon.com *Web Site:* www.phaidon.com, pg 190

Tittle, Martin B, Barbara S Anderson, 706 W Davis Ave, Ann Arbor, MI 48103-4855 *Tel:* 734-995-0125 *E-mail:* bsa328@earthlink.net, pg 520

Tivnan, Maisie, Workman Publishing Co Inc, 225 Varick St, 9th fl, New York, NY 10014-4381 *Tel:* 212-254-5900 *Toll Free Tel:* 800-722-7202 *Fax:* 212-254-8098 *E-mail:* info@workman.com *Web Site:* www.workman.com, pg 275

Tjaden, Susan, WaterBrook Multnomah Publishing Group, 12265 Oracle Blvd, Suite 200, Colorado Springs, CO 80921 *Tel:* 719-590-4999 *Toll Free Tel:* 800-603-7051 (orders) *Fax:* 719-590-8977 *Toll Free Fax:* 800-294-5686 (orders) *E-mail:* info@waterbrookmultnomah.com *Web Site:* waterbrookmultnomah.com, pg 267

Tobey, Mary A, Brandylane Publishers Inc, 5 S First St, Richmond, VA 23219 *Tel:* 804-644-3090 *Fax:* 804-644-3092 *Web Site:* brandylanepublishers.com, pg 44

Tobin, Daniel, Barbara Bradley Prize, 2 Farrar St, Cambridge, MA 02138 *Tel:* 617-744-6034 *E-mail:* contests@nepoetryclub.org *Web Site:* www.nepoetryclub.org, pg 673

Tobin, Daniel, Der-Hovanessian Translation Prize, 2 Farrar St, Cambridge, MA 02138 *Tel:* 617-744-6034 *E-mail:* contests@nepoetryclub.org *Web Site:* www.nepoetryclub.org, pg 680

Tobin, Daniel, Golden Rose Award, 2 Farrar St, Cambridge, MA 02138 *Tel:* 617-744-6034 *E-mail:* contests@nepoetryclub.org *Web Site:* www.nepoetryclub.org, pg 690

Tobin, Daniel, Firman Houghton Prize, 2 Farrar St, Cambridge, MA 02138 *Tel:* 617-744-6034 *E-mail:* contests@nepoetryclub.org *Web Site:* www.nepoetryclub.org, pg 693

Tobin, Daniel, Sheila Margaret Motton Prize, 2 Farrar St, Cambridge, MA 02138 *Tel:* 617-744-6034 *E-mail:* contests@nepoetryclub.org *Web Site:* www.nepoetryclub.org, pg 709

Tobin, Daniel, Erika Mumford Prize, 2 Farrar St, Cambridge, MA 02138 *Tel:* 617-744-6034 *E-mail:* contests@nepoetryclub.org *Web Site:* www.nepoetryclub.org, pg 710

Tobin, Daniel, New England Poetry Club, 2 Farrar St, Cambridge, MA 02138 *Tel:* 617-744-6034 *E-mail:* info@nepoetryclub.org *Web Site:* www.nepoetryclub.org, pg 613

Tobin, Daniel, May Sarton Award, 2 Farrar St, Cambridge, MA 02138 *Tel:* 617-744-6034 *E-mail:* contests@nepoetryclub.org *Web Site:* www.nepoetryclub.org, pg 726

Tobin, Daniel, Daniel Varoujan Award, 2 Farrar St, Cambridge, MA 02138 *Tel:* 617-744-6034 *E-mail:* contests@nepoetryclub.org *Web Site:* www.nepoetryclub.org, pg 733

Tobin, Helen, Alfred A Knopf/Everyman's Library, c/o Random House Inc, 1745 Broadway, New York, NY 10019 *Tel:* 212-751-2600 *Toll Free Tel:* 800-638-6460 *Fax:* 212-572-2593 *Web Site:* www.knopfdoubleday.com, pg 132

Tod, Robert, AZ Books LLC, 320 Fifth Ave, New York, NY 10001 *Toll Free Tel:* 888-945-7723 *Toll Free Fax:* 888-945-7724 *Web Site:* www.azbooksusa.com, pg 29

Todd, Marissa, Jackie White Memorial National Children's Playwriting Contest, 1400 Forum Blvd, 1C No 214, Columbia, MO 65203 *E-mail:* jwmcontest@cectheatre.org *Web Site:* www.cectheatre.org, pg 696

Todd, Traci, Harry N Abrams Inc, 115 W 18 St, 6th fl, New York, NY 10011 *Tel:* 212-206-7715 *Toll Free Tel:* 800-345-1359 *Fax:* 212-519-1210 *E-mail:* abrams@abramsbooks.com *Web Site:* www.abramsbooks.com, pg 3

Todd, Trish, Simon & Schuster, 1230 Avenue of the Americas, New York, NY 10020 *Tel:* 212-698-7000 *Toll Free Tel:* 800-223-2348 (cust serv); 800-223-2336 (orders) *Toll Free Fax:* 800-943-9831 (orders) *Web Site:* www.simonandschuster.com, pg 225

Toke, Arun N, Skipping Stones Honor Awards, 166 W 12 Ave, Eugene, OR 97401 *Tel:* 541-342-4956 *E-mail:* info@skippingstones.org *Web Site:* www.skippingstones.org, pg 728

Toke, Arun N, The Youth Honor Awards, 166 W 12 Ave, Eugene, OR 97401 *Tel:* 541-342-4956 *E-mail:* info@skippingstones.org *Web Site:* www.skippingstones.org, pg 739

Tolen, Rebecca, Indiana University Press, Herman B Wells Library 350, 1320 E Tenth St, Bloomington, IN 47405-3907 *Tel:* 812-855-8817 *Toll Free Tel:* 800-842-6796 (orders only) *Fax:* 812-855-7931; 812-855-8507 *E-mail:* iupress@indiana.edu; iuporder@indiana.edu (orders) *Web Site:* www.iupress.indiana.edu, pg 120

Toler, Gloria, Women's National Book Association Award, PO Box 237, FDR Sta, New York, NY 10150-0231 *Tel:* 212-208-4629 *Fax:* 212-208-4629 *E-mail:* publicity@bookbuzz.com *Web Site:* www.wnba-books.org; www.NationalReadingGroupMonth.org, pg 737

Tolia, Shimul, Little Bee Books, 853 Broadway, Suite 2014, New York, NY 10003 *E-mail:* info@littlebeebooks.com *Web Site:* www.littlebeebooks.com, pg 140

Tolnay, Tom, Birch Brook Press, PO Box 81, Delhi, NY 13753-0081 *Tel:* 607-746-7453 (book sales & prodn) *Fax:* 607-746-7453 *E-mail:* birchbrook@copper.net *Web Site:* www.birchbrookpress.info, pg 37

Tolszczuk, Benoit, Les Editions Vents d'Ouest, 109, rue Wright, bureau 202, Gatineau, QC J8X 2G7, Canada *Tel:* 819-770-6377 *Fax:* 819-770-0559 *E-mail:* info@ventsdouest.ca *Web Site:* www.ventsdouest.ca, pg 483

Tomaselli, Valerie, American Book Producers Association (ABPA), 31 W Eighth St, 2nd fl, New York, NY 10011 *Tel:* 212-675-1363 *Fax:* 212-675-1364 *E-mail:* office@abpaonline.org *Web Site:* www.abpaonline.org, pg 594

Tomaselli, Valerie, Women's National Book Association Award, PO Box 237, FDR Sta, New York, NY 10150-0231 *Tel:* 212-208-4629 *Fax:* 212-208-4629 *E-mail:* publicity@bookbuzz.com *Web Site:* www.wnba-books.org; www.NationalReadingGroupMonth.org, pg 737

Tomasi, Prof Massimiliano, Center for East Asian Studies (CEAS), Western Washington University, 516 High St, Bellingham, WA 98225 *Tel:* 360-650-3339 *Fax:* 360-650-6110 *E-mail:* easpress@wwu.edu *Web Site:* www.wwu.edu/eas, pg 53

Tomasino, Christine K, The Tomasino Agency Inc, 70 Chestnut St, Dobbs Ferry, NY 10522 *Tel:* 914-674-9659 *Fax:* 914-693-0381 *E-mail:* info@tomasinoagency.com *Web Site:* www.tomasinoagency.com, pg 577

Tomassi, Noreen, The Center for Fiction, 17 E 47 St, New York, NY 10017 *Tel:* 212-755-6710 *Fax:* 212-826-0831 *E-mail:* info@centerforfiction.org *Web Site:* centerforfiction.org/awards, pg 603

Tomassi, Noreen, The Flaherty-Dunnan First Novel Prize, 17 E 47 St, New York, NY 10017 *Tel:* 212-755-6710 *Fax:* 212-826-0831 *E-mail:* info@centerforfiction.org *Web Site:* centerforfiction.org/awards, pg 686

Tomasulo, Christina, HarperCollins Publishers Sales, 195 Broadway, New York, NY 10007 *Fax:* 212-207-7000 *Web Site:* www.harpercollins.com, pg 106

Tombs, Greg, David C Cook, 4050 Lee Vance View, Colorado Springs, CO 80918 *Tel:* 719-536-0100 *Toll Free Tel:* 800-708-5550; 800-323-7543 (orders & cust serv) *Toll Free Fax:* 800-430-0726 (cust serv) *Web Site:* www.davidccook.com, pg 62

Tomkins, Paul, The Reader's Digest Association Inc, 750 Third Ave, New York, NY 10017 *Tel:* 914-238-1000; 646-293-6284 *Toll Free Tel:* 800-310-6261 (cust serv) *Fax:* 914-238-4559 *Web Site:* www.rd.com; www.rda.com, pg 205

Tomlin, Tiffany, Penguin Random House Speakers Bureau, 1745 Broadway, Mail Drop 13-1, New York, NY 10019 *Tel:* 212-572-2013 *E-mail:* speakers@penguinrandomhouse.com *Web Site:* www.prhspeakers.com, pg 587

Tomlinson, Mark, Society of Manufacturing Engineers, One SME Dr, Dearborn, MI 48121 *Tel:* 313-425-3000 *Toll Free Tel:* 800-733-4763 (cust serv) *Fax:* 313-425-3400 *E-mail:* publications@sme.org *Web Site:* www.sme.org, pg 229

Tompa, Andrea, Candlewick Press, 99 Dover St, Somerville, MA 02144-2825 *Tel:* 617-661-3330 *Fax:* 617-661-0565 *E-mail:* bigbear@candlewick.com; salesinfo@candlewick.com *Web Site:* www.candlewick.com, pg 49

Tompkins, Amy, Transatlantic Agency, 2 Bloor St E, Suite 3500, Toronto, ON M4W 1A8, Canada *Tel:* 416-488-9214 *E-mail:* info@transatlanticagency.com *Web Site:* www.transatlanticagency.com, pg 577

Tompkins, Bill, National Newspaper Publishers Association (NNPA), 1816 12 St NW, Washington, DC 20009 *Tel:* 202-588-8764 *Fax:* 202-588-8960 *E-mail:* info@nnpa.org *Web Site:* www.nnpa.org; www.blackpressusa.com, pg 613

Tonegutti, Marta, University of Chicago Press, 1427 E 60 St, Chicago, IL 60637-2954 *Tel:* 773-702-7700; 773-702-7600 *Toll Free Tel:* 800-621-2736 (orders) *Fax:* 773-702-9756; 773-660-2235 (orders); 773-702-2708 *E-mail:* custserv@press.uchicago.edu; marketing@press.uchicago.edu *Web Site:* www.press.uchicago.edu, pg 255

Toner, Joel, Sky Publishing, 90 Sherman St, Cambridge, MA 02140 *Tel:* 617-864-7360 *Toll Free Tel:* 866-644-1377 *Fax:* 617-864-6117 *E-mail:* info@skyandtelescope.com *Web Site:* www.skyandtelescope.com, pg 227

Toole, Jenny, Mercer University Press, 368 Orange St, Macon, GA 31201 *Tel:* 478-301-2880 *Toll Free Tel:* 866-895-1472 *Fax:* 478-301-2585 *E-mail:* mupressorders@mercer.edu *Web Site:* www.mupress.org, pg 154

Toraason, John O, Wildlife Education Ltd, 2418 Noyes St, Evanston, IL 60201 *Toll Free Tel:* 800-477-5034 *E-mail:* owls5@zoobooks.com; helpdesk@zoobooks.com *Web Site:* www.zoobooks.com; wildlife-ed.com, pg 272

Tortoroli, Melanie, Penguin Group (USA) LLC, a Penguin Random House company, 375 Hudson St, New York, NY 10014 *Tel:* 212-366-2000 *Toll Free Tel:* 800-847-5515 (inside sales); 800-631-8571 (cust serv) *Fax:* 212-366-2666; 607-775-4829 (inside sales) *E-mail:* online@us.penguingroup.com *Web Site:* www.penguin.com; us.penguingroup.com, pg 186

Tory, Caroline, Aspen Writers' Foundation, 110 E Hallam St, Suite 116, Aspen, CO 81611 *Tel:* 970-925-3122 *Fax:* 970-920-5700 *E-mail:* awfinfo@aspenwriters.org *Web Site:* www.aspenwriters.org, pg 597

Toth, AnnJanette, Tommy Nelson, 501 Nelson Place, Nashville, TN 37214 *Tel:* 615-889-9000; 615-902-1485 (cust serv) *Toll Free Tel:* 800-251-4000 *Fax:* 615-391-5225 *Web Site:* www.tommynelson.com, pg 247

Toth, Sarah, Galaxy Press, 7051 Hollywood Blvd, Suite 200, Hollywood, CA 90028 *Tel:* 323-466-7815 *Toll Free Tel:* 877-8GALAXY (842-5299) *E-mail:* customers@galaxypress.com; info@galaxypress.com *Web Site:* www.galaxypress.com, pg 93

Toto, Cheryl Cramer, Houghton Mifflin Harcourt Trade & Reference Division, 222 Berkeley St, Boston, MA 02116 *Tel:* 617-351-5000 *Toll Free Tel:* 800-225-3362 *Web Site:* www.hmhco.com, pg 115

Totten, Shay, Chelsea Green Publishing Co, 85 N Main St, Suite 120, White River Junction, VT 05001 *Tel:* 802-295-6300 *Toll Free Tel:* 800-639-4099 (cust serv, consumer & trade orders) *Fax:* 802-295-6444 *Web Site:* www.chelseagreen.com, pg 56

Touchie, Rodger, Heritage House Publishing Co Ltd, 1075 Pendergast St, No 103, Victoria, BC V8V 0A1, Canada *Tel:* 250-360-0829 *Fax:* 250-386-0829 *E-mail:* heritage@heritagehouse.ca *Web Site:* www.heritagehouse.ca, pg 487

Tourtlotte, Alan N, The Optical Society (OSA), 2010 Massachusetts Ave NW, Washington, DC 20036-1023 *Tel:* 202-223-8130 *Toll Free Tel:* 800-766-4672 *E-mail:* custserv@osa.org *Web Site:* www.osa.org, pg 175

Touvell, Anne, Thurber Prize for American Humor, 77 Jefferson Ave, Columbus, OH 43215 *Tel:* 614-464-1032 *Fax:* 614-280-3645 *E-mail:* thurberhouse@thurberhouse.org *Web Site:* www.thurberhouse.org, pg 732

Tower, Carol, Society of Manufacturing Engineers, One SME Dr, Dearborn, MI 48121 *Tel:* 313-425-3000 *Toll Free Tel:* 800-733-4763 (cust serv) *Fax:* 313-425-3400 *E-mail:* publications@sme.org *Web Site:* www.sme.org, pg 229

Townson, Donald, Townson Publishing Co Ltd, PO Box 1404, Sta A, Vancouver, BC V6C 2P7, Canada *Tel:* 604-886-0594 (CN) *E-mail:* townsonpublishing@gmail.com *Web Site:* generalpublishing.co.uk, pg 501

Tracten, Mark, Crown House Publishing Co LLC, 6 Trowbridge Dr, Bethel, CT 06801 *Tel:* 203-778-1300 *Toll Free Tel:* 877-925-1213 (cust serv); 866-272-8497 *Fax:* 203-778-9100 *E-mail:* info@chpus.com *Web Site:* www.crownhousepublishing.com, pg 67

Tracy, Bruce, Workman Publishing Co Inc, 225 Varick St, 9th fl, New York, NY 10014-4381 *Tel:* 212-254-5900 *Toll Free Tel:* 800-722-7202 *Fax:* 212-254-8098 *E-mail:* info@workman.com *Web Site:* www.workman.com, pg 275

Tracy, Reid, Hay House Inc, 2776 Loker Ave W, Carlsbad, CA 92010 *Tel:* 760-431-7695 (ext 2, intl) *Toll Free Tel:* 800-654-5126 (ext 2, US) *Toll Free Fax:* 800-650-5115 *E-mail:* info@hayhouse.com; editorial@hayhouse.com *Web Site:* www.hayhouse.com, pg 108

Trager, Katherine, Penguin Random House Inc, 1745 Broadway, New York, NY 10019 *Tel:* 212-782-9000 *Toll Free Tel:* 800-726-0600 *Web Site:* www.randomhouse.com, pg 187

Tramble, Madrid, ASM International, 9639 Kinsman Rd, Materials Park, OH 44073-0002 *Tel:* 440-338-5151 *Toll Free Tel:* 800-336-5152; 800-368-9800 (Europe) *Fax:* 440-338-4634 *E-mail:* memberservicecenter@asminternational.org *Web Site:* asmcommunity.asminternational.org, pg 25

Trammel, Madison, Zondervan, 3900 Sparks Dr, Grand Rapids, MI 49546 *Tel:* 616-698-6900 *Toll Free Tel:* 800-226-1122; 800-727-1309 (retail orders) *Fax:* 616-698-3350 *Toll Free Fax:* 800-698-3256 (retail orders) *E-mail:* zinfo@zondervan.com *Web Site:* www.zondervan.com, pg 280

Trandem, Bryan, Quarto Publishing Group USA Inc, 400 First Ave N, Suite 300, Minneapolis, MN 55401 *Tel:* 612-344-8100 *Toll Free Tel:* 800-328-0590 (sales); 800-458-0454 *Fax:* 612-344-8691 *E-mail:* sales@creativepub.com *Web Site:* quartoknows.com, pg 202

Tranfaglia, Frank, Piano Press, 1425 Ocean Ave, Suite 5, Del Mar, CA 92014 *Tel:* 619-884-1401 *Fax:* 858-755-1104 *E-mail:* pianopress@pianopress.com *Web Site:* www.pianopress.com, pg 191

Trank, Megan, Beaufort Books, 27 W 20 St, Suite 1102, New York, NY 10011 *Tel:* 212-727-0222 *Fax:* 212-727-0195 *E-mail:* info@beaufortbooks.com *Web Site:* www.beaufortbooks.com, pg 33

Trautner, Cris, Infusionmedia, 140 N Eighth St, Suite 214, The Apothecary, Lincoln, NE 68508-1353 *Tel:* 402-477-2065 *E-mail:* info@infusionmediadesign.com *Web Site:* www.infusionmediadesign.com, pg 508

Travers, Kate, Workman Publishing Co Inc, 225 Varick St, 9th fl, New York, NY 10014-4381 *Tel:* 212-254-5900 *Toll Free Tel:* 800-722-7202 *Fax:* 212-254-8098 *E-mail:* info@workman.com *Web Site:* www.workman.com, pg 275

Traversy, Nancy, Barefoot Books, 2067 Massachusetts Ave, 5th fl, Cambridge, MA 02140 *Tel:* 617-576-0660 *Toll Free Tel:* 866-215-1756 (cust serv); 866-417-2369 (orders) *Fax:* 617-576-0049 *E-mail:* help@barefootbooks.com *Web Site:* www.barefootbooks.com, pg 30

Travis, Jennifer, Storey Publishing LLC, 210 MASS MoCA Way, North Adams, MA 01247 *Tel:* 413-346-2100 *Toll Free Tel:* 800-441-5700 (orders); 800-793-9396 (edit) *Fax:* 413-346-2199; 413-346-2196 (edit) *E-mail:* sales@storey.com *Web Site:* www.storey.com, pg 236

Traynor, Karen, Tralco-Lingo Fun, 3909 Witmer Rd, Suite 856, Niagara Falls, NY 14305 *Tel:* 905-575-5717 *Toll Free Tel:* 888-487-2526 *Fax:* 905-575-1783 *Toll Free Fax:* 866-487-2527 *E-mail:* contact@tralco.com *Web Site:* www.tralco.com, pg 248

Treco, Stacy, Pearson Benjamin Cummings, 1301 Sansome St, San Francisco, CA 94111-1122 *Tel:* 415-402-2500 *Toll Free Tel:* 800-922-0579 (orders) *Fax:* 415-402-2590 *E-mail:* question@aol.com *Web Site:* www.pearsonhighered.com, pg 185

Treimel, Scott, S©ott Treimel NY, 434 Lafayette St, New York, NY 10003-6943 *Tel:* 212-505-8353 *E-mail:* general@scotttreimelny.com *Web Site:* scotttreimelny.com; scotttreimelny.blogspot.com, pg 572

Trelstad, Julie, Writers House, 21 W 26 St, New York, NY 10010 *Tel:* 212-685-2400 *Fax:* 212-685-1781 *Web Site:* www.writershouse.com, pg 580

Tress, Neil, Recorded Books LLC, 270 Skipjack Rd, Prince Frederick, MD 20678 *Tel:* 410-535-5590 *Toll Free Tel:* 800-638-1304; 877-732-2898 *Fax:* 410-535-5499 *E-mail:* customerservice@recordedbooks.com *Web Site:* www.recordedbooks.com, pg 206

Trevorrow, Elaine, Penguin Random House Speakers Bureau, 1745 Broadway, Mail Drop 13-1, New York, NY 10019 *Tel:* 212-572-2013 *E-mail:* speakers@penguinrandomhouse.com *Web Site:* www.prhspeakers.com, pg 588

Tribbey, Deb, Elite Books, PO Box 442, Fulton, CA 95439 *Tel:* 707-525-9292 *Toll Free Fax:* 800-330-9798 *E-mail:* books@authorspublishing.com *Web Site:* www.elitebooksonline.com, pg 81

Tribbey, Deb, Energy Psychology Press, 1490 Mark West Springs Rd, Santa Rosa, CA 95404 *Tel:* 707-237-6951 *Toll Free Fax:* 800-330-9798 *E-mail:* books@authorspublishing.com *Web Site:* www.energypsychologypress.com; www.elitebooksonline.com, pg 82

Tribble, Miriam, Harry N Abrams Inc, 115 W 18 St, 6th fl, New York, NY 10011 *Tel:* 212-206-7715 *Toll Free Tel:* 800-345-1359 *Fax:* 212-519-1210 *E-mail:* abrams@abramsbooks.com *Web Site:* www.abramsbooks.com, pg 3

Tribelli, Angela, HarperCollins General Books Group, 195 Broadway, New York, NY 10007 *Tel:* 212-207-7000 *Web Site:* www.harpercollins.com, pg 105

Tricarico, Joy Elton, Carol Bancroft & Friends, PO Box 2030, Danbury, CT 06813 *Tel:* 203-730-8270 *Fax:* 203-730-8275 *E-mail:* cb_friends8270@sbcglobal.net *Web Site:* www.carolbancroft.com, pg 583

Trimmer, Christian, Simon & Schuster Children's Publishing, 1230 Avenue of the Americas, New York, NY 10020 *Tel:* 212-698-7000 *Web Site:* KIDS.SimonandSchuster.com; TEEN.SimonandSchuster.com; simonandschuster.net; simonandschuster.biz, pg 225

Triplett, Rick, Prometheus Awards, 650 Castro St, Suite 120-433, Mountain View, CA 94041 *Tel:* 650-968-6319 *E-mail:* info@lfs.org *Web Site:* www.lfs.org, pg 722

Trippe, Bill, The MIT Press, 55 Hayward St, Cambridge, MA 02142 *Tel:* 617-253-5255 *Toll Free Tel:* 800-207-8354 (orders) *Fax:* 617-258-6779; 617-577-1545 (orders) *Web Site:* mitpress.mit.edu, pg 158

Tristan, Marina, Arte Publico Press, University of Houston, Bldg 19, Rm 10, 4902 Gulf Fwy, Houston, TX 77204-2004 *Tel:* 713-743-2998 (sales) *Toll Free Tel:* 800-633-2783 *Fax:* 713-743-2847 (sales) *E-mail:* appinfo@uh.edu; bkorders@uh.edu, pg 23

Triton, Jade, Teachers & Writers Collaborative, 520 Eighth Ave, Suite 2020, New York, NY 10018-4165 *Tel:* 212-691-6590 *Toll Free Tel:* 888-BOOKS-TW (266-5789) *Fax:* 212-675-0171 *E-mail:* info@twc.org *Web Site:* www.twc.org, pg 620

Troast, Bob, VanDam Inc, The VanDam Bldg, 121 W 27 St, New York, NY 10001 *Tel:* 212-929-0416 *Toll Free Tel:* 800-UNFOLDS (863-6537) *Fax:* 212-929-0426 *E-mail:* info@vandam.com *Web Site:* www.vandam.com, pg 264

Trocker, Dana, Simon & Schuster, 1230 Avenue of the Americas, New York, NY 10020 *Tel:* 212-698-7000 *Toll Free Tel:* 800-223-2348 (cust serv); 800-223-2336 (orders) *Toll Free Fax:* 800-943-9831 (orders) *Web Site:* www.simonandschuster.com, pg 225

Troha, Steve, Folio Literary Management LLC, The Film Center Bldg, 630 Ninth Ave, Suite 1101, New York, NY 10036 *Tel:* 212-400-1494 *Fax:* 212-967-0977 *Web Site:* www.foliolit.com, pg 552

Trombi, Liza Groen, Locus Awards, PO Box 13305, Oakland, CA 94661-0305 *Tel:* 510-339-9196 *Fax:* 510-339-9198 *E-mail:* locus@locusmag.com *Web Site:* www.locusmag.com, pg 702

Trombley, Dana, HarperCollins General Books Group, 195 Broadway, New York, NY 10007 *Tel:* 212-207-7000 *Web Site:* www.harpercollins.com, pg 105

Tropp, Sasha, The Experiment, 220 East 23 St, Suite 301, New York, NY 10010-4674 *Tel:* 212-889-1659 *E-mail:* info@theexperimentpublishing.com *Web Site:* www.theexperimentpublishing.com, pg 85

Trotti, Ricardo, Inter American Press Association (IAPA), Jules Dubois Bldg, 1801 SW Third Ave, Miami, FL 33129 *Tel:* 305-634-2465 *Fax:* 305-635-2272 *E-mail:* info@sipiapa.org *Web Site:* www.sipiapa.org, pg 607

Troutman, Karen, Dewey Publications Inc, 1840 Wilson Blvd, Suite 203, Arlington, VA 22201 *Tel:* 703-524-1355 *Fax:* 703-524-1463 *E-mail:* deweypublications@gmail.com *Web Site:* www.deweypub.com, pg 73

Truax, Denise, Prise de Parole Inc, 109 Elm St, Suite 205, Sudbury, ON P3C 1T4, Canada *Tel:* 705-675-6491 *Fax:* 705-673-1817 *E-mail:* info@prisedeparole.ca *Web Site:* www.prisedeparole.ca, pg 496

True, Nathan, Greenleaf Book Group LLC, Three Park Place, 4005 Banister Lane, Suite B, Austin, TX 78704 *Tel:* 512-891-6100 *Toll Free Tel:* 800-932-5420 *Fax:* 512-891-6150 *E-mail:* contact@greenleafbookgroup.com *Web Site:* www.greenleafbookgroup.com, pg 100

Trueblood, Marilyn, University of Washington Press, 433 Brooklyn Ave NE, Seattle, WA 98195-9570 *Tel:* 206-543-4050 *Toll Free Tel:* 800-537-5487 (orders) *Fax:* 206-543-3932; 410-516-6998 (orders) *E-mail:* uwpress@u.washington.edu *Web Site:* www.washington.edu/uwpress/, pg 260

Truitt, Sam, Barrytown/Station Hill Press, 120 Station Hill Rd, Barrytown, NY 12507 *Tel:* 845-758-5293 *E-mail:* publishers@stationhill.org *Web Site:* www.stationhill.org, pg 31

Trumbull, Jean, Impact Publishers Inc, PO Box 6016, Atascadero, CA 93423-6016 *Tel:* 805-466-5917 (opers & admin offs) *Toll Free Tel:* 800-246-7228 (orders) *Fax:* 805-466-5919 (opers & admin offs) *E-mail:* info@impactpublishers.com *Web Site:* www.impactpublishers.com; www.bibliotherapy.com, pg 119

Truong, Phuong, Second Story Press, 20 Maud St, Suite 401, Toronto, ON M5V 2M5, Canada *Tel:* 416-537-7850 *Fax:* 416-537-0588 *E-mail:* info@secondstorypress.ca *Web Site:* secondstorypress.ca, pg 498

Trupin, Jim, JET Literary Associates Inc, 941 Calle Mejia, Suite 507, Santa Fe, NM 87501 *Tel:* 212-971-2494 (NY voice mail); 505-780-0721 *E-mail:* query@jetliterary.com *Web Site:* www.jetliterary.wordpress.com, pg 558

Trupin-Pulli, Elizabeth, JET Literary Associates Inc, 941 Calle Mejia, Suite 507, Santa Fe, NM 87501 *Tel:* 212-971-2494 (NY voice mail); 505-780-0721 *E-mail:* query@jetliterary.com *Web Site:* www.jetliterary.wordpress.com, pg 558

Tryneski, John, University of Chicago Press, 1427 E 60 St, Chicago, IL 60637-2954 *Tel:* 773-702-7700; 773-702-7600 *Toll Free Tel:* 800-621-2736 (orders) *Fax:* 773-702-9756; 773-660-2235 (orders); 773-702-2708 *E-mail:* custserv@press.uchicago.edu; marketing@press.uchicago.edu *Web Site:* www.press.uchicago.edu, pg 255

Tsang, Erika, HarperCollins General Books Group, 195 Broadway, New York, NY 10007 *Tel:* 212-207-7000 *Web Site:* www.harpercollins.com, pg 105

Tsuchiya, Setsuko, Savant Books & Publications LLC, 2630 Kapiolani Blvd, Suite 1601, Honolulu, HI 96826 *Tel:* 808-941-3927 *Fax:* 808-941-3927 *E-mail:* savantbooks@gmail.com *Web Site:* www.savantbooksandpublications.com, pg 217

Tubach, Greg, Houghton Mifflin Harcourt Trade & Reference Division, 222 Berkeley St, Boston, MA 02116 *Tel:* 617-351-5000 *Toll Free Tel:* 800-225-3362 *Web Site:* www.hmhco.com, pg 115

Tucher, Andie, James Fenimore Cooper Prize, 603 Fayerweather, MC 2538, New York, NY 10027 *Tel:* 212-854-6495 *E-mail:* amhistsociety@columbia.edu *Web Site:* sah.columbia.edu, pg 679

Tucher, Andie, Allan Nevins Prize, 603 Fayerweather, MC 2538, New York, NY 10027 *Tel:* 212-854-6495 *E-mail:* amhistsociety@columbia.edu *Web Site:* sah.columbia.edu, pg 712

Tucher, Andie, Francis Parkman Prize, 603 Fayerweather, MC 2538, New York, NY 10027 *Tel:* 212-854-6495 *E-mail:* amhistsociety@columbia.edu *Web Site:* sah.columbia.edu, pg 716

Tucker, Jennifer, Center for Women Policy Studies, 4620 N Park Ave, Suite 302W, Chevy Chase, MD 20815 *Tel:* 301-986-0795 *E-mail:* cwps@centerwomenpolicy.org *Web Site:* www.centerwomenpolicy.org, pg 54

Tucker, Lloyd, Society for Technical Communication, 9401 Lee Hwy, Suite 300, Fairfax, VA 22031 *Tel:* 703-522-4114 *Fax:* 703-522-2075 *E-mail:* stc@stc.org *Web Site:* www.stc.org, pg 618

Tucker, Lloyd, Society for Technical Communication's Annual Conference, 9401 Lee Hwy, Suite 300, Fairfax, VA 22031 *Tel:* 703-522-4114 *Fax:* 703-522-2075 *E-mail:* stc@stc.org *Web Site:* www.stc.org, pg 655

Tucker, Memye Curtis, International Poetry Competition, PO Box 8248, Atlanta, GA 31106 *E-mail:* atlanta.review@yahoo.com *Web Site:* www.atlantareview.com, pg 695

Tudor, Jeannie, Square One Publishers Inc, 115 Herricks Rd, Garden City Park, NY 11040 *Tel:* 516-535-2010 *Toll Free Tel:* 877-900-BOOK (900-2665) *Fax:* 516-535-2014 *E-mail:* sq1publish@aol.com *Web Site:* www.squareonepublishers.com, pg 232

Tufariello, Frank, Data Trace Publishing Co (DTP), 110 West Rd, Suite 227, Towson, MD 21204-2316 *Tel:* 410-494-4994 *Toll Free Tel:* 800-342-0454 (orders only) *Fax:* 410-494-0515 *E-mail:* info@datatrace.com; salesandmarketing@datatrace.com; editorial@datatrace.com; info@datatrace.com *Web Site:* www.datatrace.com, pg 70

Tugeau, Christina, Christina A Tugeau Artist Agency LLC, 3009 Margaret Jones Lane, Williamsburg, VA 23185 *Tel:* 757-221-0666; 917-434-3141 *E-mail:* chris@catugeau.com *Web Site:* www.catugeau.com, pg 585

Tugeau, Nicole, Tugeau 2 Inc, 2231 Grandview Ave, Cleveland Heights, OH 44106 *Tel:* 216-707-0854 *Fax:* 216-795-8404 *Web Site:* www.tugeau2.com, pg 585

Tuller, Tamra, Chronicle Books LLC, 680 Second St, San Francisco, CA 94107 *Tel:* 415-537-4200 *Toll Free Tel:* 800-759-0190 (cust serv) *Fax:* 415-537-4460 *Toll Free Fax:* 800-858-7787 (orders); 800-286-9471 (cust serv) *E-mail:* frontdesk@chroniclebooks.com *Web Site:* www.chroniclebooks.com, pg 58

Tully, Nola, Encounter Books, 900 Broadway, Suite 601, New York, NY 10003 *Tel:* 212-871-6310 *Toll Free Tel:* 800-786-3839 *Fax:* 212-871-6311 *E-mail:* publicity@encounterbooks.com *Web Site:* www.encounterbooks.com, pg 82

Tumambing, Ryan, Hatherleigh Press Ltd, 62545 State Hwy 10, Hobart, NY 13788 *E-mail:* info@hatherleighpress.com; publicity@hatherleighpress.com *Web Site:* www.hatherleighpress.com, pg 108

Tuminelly, Nancy, Mighty Media Press, 1201 Currie Ave, Minneapolis, MN 55403 *Tel:* 612-455-0252 *Fax:* 612-338-4817 *E-mail:* info@mightymedia.com *Web Site:* www.mightymediapress.com, pg 156

Tung, Jennifer, Random House Publishing Group, 1745 Broadway, New York, NY 10019 *Toll Free Tel:* 800-200-3552 *Web Site:* atrandom.com, pg 204

Tunzelmann, Morgan, James Lorimer & Co Ltd, Publishers, 317 Adelaide St W, Suite 1002, Toronto, ON M5V 1P9, Canada *Tel:* 416-362-4762 *Fax:* 416-362-3939 *Web Site:* www.lorimer.ca, pg 490

Tupholme, Iris, HarperCollins Canada Ltd, 2 Bloor St E, 20th fl, Toronto, ON M4W 1A8, Canada *Tel:* 416-975-9334 *Fax:* 416-975-9884 *E-mail:* hcorder@harpercollins.com *Web Site:* www.harpercollins.ca, pg 487

Turner, Anne Marie, Kensington Publishing Corp, 119 W 40 St, New York, NY 10018 *Tel:* 212-407-1500 *Toll Free Tel:* 800-221-2647 *Fax:* 212-935-0699 *Web Site:* www.kensingtonbooks.com, pg 130

Turner, Emily, W W Norton & Company Inc, 500 Fifth Ave, New York, NY 10110-0017 *Tel:* 212-354-5500 *Toll Free Tel:* 800-233-4830 (orders & cust serv) *Fax:* 212-869-0856 *Toll Free Fax:* 800-458-6515 *Web Site:* www.wwnorton.com, pg 172

Turner, Erin, The Globe Pequot Press, 246 Goose Lane, Guilford, CT 06437 *Tel:* 203-458-4500 *Toll Free Tel:* 800-243-0495 (orders only); 888-249-7586 (cust serv) *Fax:* 203-458-4601 *Toll Free Fax:* 800-820-2329 (orders & cust serv) *E-mail:* editorial@globepequot.com; info@rowman.com; orders@rowman.com *Web Site:* rowman.com, pg 98

Turner, Jeffrey, US Government Publishing Office (GPO), Superintendent of Documents, 732 N Capitol St NW, Washington, DC 20401 *Tel:* 202-512-1800 *Toll Free Tel:* 866-512-1800 (orders) *Fax:* 202-512-2104 *E-mail:* contactcenter@gpo.gov *Web Site:* bookstore.gpo.gov (sales), pg 264

Turner, Monica, Printing Association of Florida Inc (PAF), 6250 Hazeltine National Dr, Suite 114, Orlando, FL 32822 *Tel:* 407-240-8009 *Toll Free Tel:* 800-331-0461 *Fax:* 407-240-8333 *Web Site:* www.flprint.org, pg 616

Turok, Katharine, Words into Print, 57 Prince St, Suite 4R, New York, NY 10012 *Tel:* 212-741-1393 *Fax:* 419-441-1393 *E-mail:* query@wordsintoprint.org *Web Site:* www.wordsintoprint.org, pg 536

Van Dyke, Brianna, William Van Dyke Short Story Prize, 1041 N Taft Hill Rd, Fort Collins, CO 80521 *Tel:* 970-449-2726 *E-mail:* editor@ruminatemagazine.org *Web Site:* www.ruminatemagazine.com, pg 733

Van Dyke, Brianna, VanderMey Nonfiction Prize, 1041 N Taft Hill Rd, Fort Collins, CO 80521 *Tel:* 970-449-2726 *E-mail:* editor@ruminatemagazine.org *Web Site:* www.ruminatemagazine.com, pg 733

Van Gelder, Gordon, Philip K Dick Award, PO Box 3447, Hoboken, NJ 07030 *Tel:* 201-876-2551 *Web Site:* www.philipkdickaward.org, pg 681

Van Hoof-Haines, Kristine, Hazelden Publishing, 15251 Pleasant Valley Rd, Center City, MN 55012-0011 *Tel:* 651-213-4200 *Toll Free Tel:* 800-257-7810 *Fax:* 651-213-4590 *E-mail:* info@hazelden.org *Web Site:* www.hazelden.org, pg 108

Van Hooft, Karen, Bilingual Press/Editorial Bilingue, Arizona State Univ, Hispanic Research Ctr, Tempe, AZ 85287-2702 *Tel:* 480-965-3867 *Toll Free Tel:* 866-965-3867 *Fax:* 480-965-0315 *E-mail:* brp@asu.edu *Web Site:* www.asu.edu/brp, pg 37

Van Huijstee, Ryan, McGill-Queen's University Press, 1010 Sherbrooke W, Suite 1720, Montreal, QC H3A 2R7, Canada *Tel:* 514-398-3750 *Fax:* 514-398-4333 *E-mail:* mqup@mqup.ca *Web Site:* www.mqup.ca, pg 491

van Hylckama Vlieg, Pam, D4EO Literary Agency, 7 Indian Valley Rd, Weston, CT 06883 *Tel:* 203-544-7180 *Fax:* 203-544-7160 *Web Site:* www.d4eoliteraryagency.com, pg 548

van Rheinberg, Brigitta, Princeton University Press, 41 William St, Princeton, NJ 08540-5237 *Tel:* 609-258-4900 *Toll Free Tel:* 800-777-4726 (orders) *Fax:* 609-258-6305 *Toll Free Fax:* 800-999-1958 *E-mail:* orders@cpfsinc.com *Web Site:* press.princeton.edu, pg 197

Van Roekel, Dennis, National Education Association (NEA), 1201 16 St NW, Washington, DC 20036-3290 *Tel:* 202-833-4000 *Fax:* 202-822-7974 *Web Site:* www.nea.org, pg 164, 612

Van Sant, Jules, Pacific Printing Industries Association, 6825 SW Sandburg St, Portland, OR 97223 *Tel:* 503-221-3944 *Toll Free Tel:* 877-762-7742 *Fax:* 503-221-5691 *E-mail:* info@ppiassociation.org *Web Site:* www.ppiassociation.org, pg 615

van Straaten, Tracy, Scholastic Trade Division, 557 Broadway, New York, NY 10012 *Tel:* 212-343-6100; 212-343-4685 (export sales) *Fax:* 212-343-4714 (export sales) *Web Site:* www.scholastic.com, pg 219

Van Wagner, CJ, Tyndale House Publishers Inc, 351 Executive Dr, Carol Stream, IL 60188 *Tel:* 630-668-8300 *Toll Free Tel:* 800-323-9400 *Web Site:* www.tyndale.com, pg 252

Van Woerden, Peter, American Psychiatric Publishing (APP), 1000 Wilson Blvd, Suite 1825, Arlington, VA 22209 *Tel:* 703-907-7322 *Toll Free Tel:* 800-368-5777 *Fax:* 703-907-1091 *E-mail:* appi@psych.org *Web Site:* www.appi.org; www.psychiatryonline.org, pg 15

Van Zandt, Christine, Write for Success (WFS), PO Box 292153, Los Angeles, CA 90029-8653 *Tel:* 323-356-8833 *E-mail:* writeforsuccess@yahoo.com *Web Site:* www.write-for-success.com, pg 536

Van't Haaf, Corey, Western Magazine Awards Foundation, 875 Prairie Ave, Port Coquitlam, BC V3B 1R9, Canada *Tel:* 604-945-3711 *E-mail:* wma@direct.ca *Web Site:* www.westernmagazineawards.ca, pg 735

Vance, Lisa Erbach, The Aaron M Priest Literary Agency Inc, 708 Third Ave, 23rd fl, New York, NY 10017-4201 *Tel:* 212-818-0344 *Fax:* 212-573-9417 *E-mail:* info@aaronpriest.com *Web Site:* www.aaronpriest.com, pg 568

Vance, V Ellis, Hans Christian Andersen Award, c/o V Ellis Vance, 5503 N El Adobe Dr, Fresno, CA 93711-2363 *Tel:* 559-351-6119 *E-mail:* executive.director@usbby.org *Web Site:* www.usbby.org, pg 667

Vance, V Ellis, US Board on Books For Young People (USBBY), c/o V Ellis Vance, 5503 N El Adobe Dr, Fresno, CA 93711-2363 *Tel:* 559-351-6119 *Web Site:* www.usbby.org, pg 620

Vandall, Jillian, Random House Children's Books, 1745 Broadway, New York, NY 10019 *Tel:* 212-782-9000 *Toll Free Tel:* 800-200-3552 *Fax:* 212-782-9452 *Web Site:* randomhousekids.com, pg 203

Vander Kam, Claire, Wm B Eerdmans Publishing Co, 2140 Oak Industrial Dr NE, Grand Rapids, MI 49505 *Tel:* 616-459-4591 *Toll Free Tel:* 800-253-7521 *Fax:* 616-459-6540 *E-mail:* customerservice@eerdmans.com; sales@eerdmans.com *Web Site:* www.eerdmans.com, pg 80

Vanderhart, Ruth, Faith Alive Christian Resources, 1700 28 St SE, Grand Rapids, MI 49508-1407 *Tel:* 616-224-0728 *Toll Free Tel:* 800-333-8300 *Toll Free Fax:* 888-642-8606 *E-mail:* info@faithaliveresources.org; sales@faithaliveresources.org; orders@faithaliveresources.org *Web Site:* www.faithaliveresources.org, pg 86

Vanderkooy, Diane, Firefly Books Ltd, 50 Staples Ave, Unit 1, Richmond Hill, ON L4B 0A7, Canada *Tel:* 416-499-8412 *Toll Free Tel:* 800-387-6192 (CN); 800-387-5085 (US) *Fax:* 416-499-8313 *Toll Free Fax:* 800-450-0391 (CN); 800-565-6034 (US) *E-mail:* service@fireflybooks.com *Web Site:* www.fireflybooks.com, pg 484

Vandewater, Cathy, Vault.com Inc, 132 W 31 St, 17th fl, New York, NY 10001 *Tel:* 212-366-4212 *Toll Free Tel:* 800-535-2074 *Fax:* 212-366-6117 (cust serv) *E-mail:* editors@vault.com; customerservice@vault.com *Web Site:* www.vault.com, pg 265

VanLangen, Mamie, Harry N Abrams Inc, 115 W 18 St, 6th fl, New York, NY 10011 *Tel:* 212-206-7715 *Toll Free Tel:* 800-345-1359 *Fax:* 212-519-1210 *E-mail:* abrams@abramsbooks.com *Web Site:* www.abramsbooks.com, pg 3

VanMeter, Joann, Standard Publishing, 8805 Governors Hill Dr, Suite 400, Cincinnati, OH 45249 *Tel:* 513-931-4050 *Toll Free Tel:* 800-543-1353 *Fax:* 513-931-0950 *Toll Free Fax:* 877-867-5751 *E-mail:* customerservice@standardpub.com *Web Site:* www.standardpub.com, pg 233

Vanterpool, Lisa, InkWell Management, 521 Fifth Ave, 26th fl, New York, NY 10175 *Tel:* 212-922-3500 *Fax:* 212-922-0535 *E-mail:* info@inkwellmanagement.com; submissions@inkwellmanagement.com *Web Site:* inkwellmanagement.com, pg 557

Vardanian, Carissa, Academy of Nutrition & Dietetics, 120 S Riverside Plaza, Suite 2000, Chicago, IL 60606-6995 *Tel:* 312-899-0040 (ext 5000) *Toll Free Tel:* 800-877-1600 *E-mail:* sales@eatright.org *Web Site:* www.eatright.org, pg 4

Vardigan, Mary, Inter-University Consortium for Political & Social Research (ICPSR), 330 Packard St, Ann Arbor, MI 48104 *Tel:* 734-647-5000 *Fax:* 734-647-8200 *E-mail:* netmail@icpsr.umich.edu *Web Site:* www.icpsr.umich.edu, pg 123

Varga, Lisa R, Jefferson Cup Award, c/o Virginia Library Association (VLA), PO Box 56312, Virginia Beach, VA 23456 *Tel:* 757-689-0594 *Fax:* 757-447-3478 *Web Site:* www.vla.org, pg 696

Vargas, Allison Astor, Nuestras Voces National Playwriting Competition, 138 E 27 St, New York, NY 10016 *Tel:* 212-225-9950 *Fax:* 212-225-9085 *Web Site:* www.repertorio.org, pg 714

Vargo, Linda, National Association of College Stores (NACS), 500 E Lorain St, Oberlin, OH 44074 *Tel:* 440-775-7777 *Toll Free Tel:* 800-622-7498 *Fax:* 440-775-4769 *Web Site:* www.nacs.org, pg 611

Vari, Frank, Cengage Learning, 20 Channel Center St, Boston, MA 02210 *Tel:* 617-289-7700 *Toll Free Tel:* 800-354-9706 *Fax:* 617-289-7844 *Toll Free Fax:* 800-487-8488 *E-mail:* esales@cengage.com *Web Site:* www.cengage.com, pg 53

Varma, Sarita, Farrar, Straus & Giroux, LLC, 18 W 18 St, New York, NY 10011 *Tel:* 212-741-6900 *E-mail:* fsg.publicity@fsgbooks.com *Web Site:* us.macmillan.com/fsg.aspx, pg 86

Varma, Sarita, North Point Press, 18 W 18 St, 8th fl, New York, NY 10011 *Tel:* 212-741-6900 *Toll Free Tel:* 888-330-8477 *Fax:* 212-633-9385 *Web Site:* www.fsgbooks.com, pg 171

Varner, William, Stenhouse Publishers, 480 Congress St, Portland, ME 04101-3451 *Tel:* 207-253-1600 *Toll Free Tel:* 888-363-0566 *Fax:* 207-253-5121 *Toll Free Fax:* 800-833-9164 *E-mail:* customerservice@stenhouse.com *Web Site:* www.stenhouse.com, pg 235

Varnum, Keith, New Dimensions Publishing, 11248 N 11 St, Phoenix, AZ 85020 *Tel:* 602-861-2631 *Toll Free Tel:* 800-736-7367 *Fax:* 602-944-1235 *E-mail:* info@thedream.com *Web Site:* www.thedream.com, pg 167

Varrette, Dan, Insomniac Press, 520 Princess Ave, London, ON N6B 2B8, Canada *Tel:* 416-504-6270 *Web Site:* www.insomniacpress.com, pg 488

Vasquez, Cynthia, Mike Murach & Associates Inc, 4340 N Knoll Ave, Fresno, CA 93722 *Tel:* 559-440-9071 *Toll Free Tel:* 800-221-5528 *Fax:* 559-440-0963 *E-mail:* murachbooks@murach.com *Web Site:* www.murach.com, pg 156

Vasquez-Perez, Carmen, Chain Store Guide (CSG), 10117 Princess Palm Ave, Suite 375, Tampa, FL 33610 *Tel:* 813-627-6957 *Toll Free Tel:* 800-927-9292 (orders) *Fax:* 813-627-6888 *E-mail:* info@csgis.com *Web Site:* www.csgis.com, pg 54

Vassallo, Nadine, Book Industry Study Group Inc (BISG), 145 W 45 St, Suite 601, New York, NY 10036 *Tel:* 646-336-7141 *Fax:* 646-336-6214 *E-mail:* info@bisg.org *Web Site:* www.bisg.org, pg 600

Vassilikos, Margaret, Newspaper Association of America (NAA), 4401 Wilson Blvd, Suite 900, Arlington, VA 22203 *Tel:* 571-366-1000 *Web Site:* www.naa.org, pg 614

Vaugeois, Denis, Les Editions du Septentrion, 1300 Maguire Ave, Sillery, QC G1T 1Z3, Canada *Tel:* 418-688-3556 *Fax:* 418-527-4978 *E-mail:* info@septentrion.qc.ca *Web Site:* www.septentrion.qc.ca, pg 481

Vaughan, Jeanne, Paladin Press, 5540 Central Ave, Suite 20, Boulder, CO 80301 *Tel:* 303-443-7250 *Toll Free Tel:* 800-392-2400 *Fax:* 303-442-8741 *E-mail:* service@paladin-press.com *Web Site:* www.paladin-press.com, pg 180

Vaughn, Ethan, Kimberley Cameron & Associates, 1550 Tiburon Blvd, Suite 704, Tiburon, CA 94920 *Tel:* 415-789-9191 *Fax:* 415-789-9177 *E-mail:* info@kimberleycameron.com *Web Site:* www.kimberleycameron.com, pg 559

Vaysbeyn, Elina, Simon & Schuster, 1230 Avenue of the Americas, New York, NY 10020 *Tel:* 212-698-7000 *Toll Free Tel:* 800-223-2348 (cust serv); 800-223-2336 (orders) *Toll Free Fax:* 800-943-9831 (orders) *Web Site:* www.simonandschuster.com, pg 225

Veach, Dan, International Poetry Competition, PO Box 8248, Atlanta, GA 31106 *E-mail:* atlanta.review@yahoo.com *Web Site:* www.atlantareview.com, pg 695

Vega, Javier, School of Visual Arts, 209 E 23 St, New York, NY 10010-3994 *Tel:* 212-592-2100 *Fax:* 212-592-2116 *Web Site:* www.sva.edu, pg 662

Vegso, Peter, Health Communications Inc, 3201 SW 15 St, Deerfield Beach, FL 33442 *Tel:* 954-360-0909 *Toll Free Tel:* 800-851-9100; 800-441-5569 (cust serv & orders) *Fax:* 954-360-0034 *Toll Free Fax:* 800-424-7652 (cust serv & orders) *Web Site:* www.hcibooks.com, pg 108

Veith, Richard, Cengage Learning, 20 Channel Center St, Boston, MA 02210 *Tel:* 617-289-7700 *Toll Free Tel:* 800-354-9706 *Fax:* 617-289-7844 *Toll Free Fax:* 800-487-8488 *E-mail:* esales@cengage.com *Web Site:* www.cengage.com, pg 53

Velasquez, Diana, Gallery Books, 1230 Avenue of the Americas, New York, NY 10020 *Toll Free Tel:* 800-456-6798 *Fax:* 212-698-7284 *E-mail:* consumer.customerservice@simonandschuster.com *Web Site:* www.simonsays.com, pg 94

Waldrep, G C, Bucknell Seminar for Younger Poets, Bucknell University, Bucknell Hall, Moore Ave, Lewisburg, PA 17837 *Tel:* 570-577-1853 *Fax:* 570-577-1885 *E-mail:* stadlercenter@bucknell.edu *Web Site:* www.bucknell.edu/stadlercenter, pg 650

Waldron, Laura, University of Pennsylvania Press, 3905 Spruce St, Philadelphia, PA 19104 *Tel:* 215-898-6261 *Fax:* 215-898-0404 *E-mail:* custserv@pobox.upenn.edu *Web Site:* www.pennpress.org, pg 259

Waldschmitt, Lisa, National Association of Black Journalists (NABJ), 1100 Knight Hall, Suite 3100, College Park, MD 20742 *Tel:* 301-405-0248 *Fax:* 301-314-1714 *E-mail:* nabj@nabj.org *Web Site:* www.nabj.org, pg 611

Walen, Audrey, American Federation of Arts, 305 E 47 St, 10th fl, New York, NY 10017 *Tel:* 212-988-7700 *Toll Free Tel:* 800-232-0270 *Fax:* 212-861-2487 *E-mail:* pubinfo@afaweb.org *Web Site:* www.afaweb.org, pg 12

Wales, Elizabeth, Wales Literary Agency Inc, 1508 Tenth Ave E, No 401, Seattle, WA 98102 *Tel:* 206-284-7114 *E-mail:* waleslit@waleslit.com *Web Site:* www.waleslit.com, pg 578

Walgren, Frank, NAL, 375 Hudson St, New York, NY 10014 *Tel:* 212-366-2000 *E-mail:* online@penguinputnam.com *Web Site:* www.penguinputnam.com; us.penguingroup.com, pg 162

Walhof, Karen, Kirk House Publishers, PO Box 390759, Minneapolis, MN 55439 *Tel:* 952-835-1828 *Toll Free Tel:* 888-696-1828 *Fax:* 952-835-2613 *E-mail:* publisher@kirkhouse.com *Web Site:* www.kirkhouse.com, pg 131

Walker, Alan, Penguin Group (USA) LLC Sales, 375 Hudson St, New York, NY 10014 *Tel:* 212-366-2000 *E-mail:* online@penguinputnam.com *Web Site:* us.penguingroup.com, pg 186

Walker, Alan, Ruth & Sylvia Schwartz Children's Book Award, c/o Ontario Arts Council, 151 Bloor St W, 5th fl, Toronto, ON M5S 1T6, Canada *Tel:* 416-961-1660 *Toll Free Tel:* 800-387-0058 (ON) *Fax:* 416-961-7447 *E-mail:* info@arts.on.ca *Web Site:* www.arts.on.ca, pg 727

Walker, Andrea, Random House Publishing Group, 1745 Broadway, New York, NY 10019 *Toll Free Tel:* 800-200-3552 *Web Site:* atrandom.com, pg 204

Walker, Bonnie G, National Council on Radiation Protection & Measurements (NCRP), 7910 Woodmont Ave, Suite 400, Bethesda, MD 20814-3095 *Tel:* 301-657-2652 *Toll Free Tel:* 800-229-2652 *Fax:* 301-907-8768 *E-mail:* ncrppubs@ncrponline.org *Web Site:* www.ncrponline.org; www.ncrppublications.org, pg 164

Walker, Brian, Charlesbridge Publishing Inc, 85 Main St, Watertown, MA 02472 *Tel:* 617-926-0329 *Toll Free Tel:* 800-225-3214 *Fax:* 617-926-5720 *Toll Free Fax:* 800-926-5775 *E-mail:* books@charlesbridge.com *Web Site:* www.charlesbridge.com, pg 55

Walker, Carol, Painted Hills Publishing, 16500 Dakota Ridge Rd, Longmont, CO 80503 *Tel:* 303-823-6642 *Fax:* 303-825-5119 *E-mail:* cw@livingimagescjw.com *Web Site:* www.wildhoofbeats.com; www.horsephotographyworkshops.com, pg 508

Walker, Chloe, Nicholas Ellison Agency, 55 Fifth Ave, 15th fl, New York, NY 10003 *Tel:* 212-206-5600 *Fax:* 212-463-8718 *Web Site:* greenburger.com/agent/nick-ellison, pg 551

Walker, David, The Field Poetry Prize, 50 N Professor St, Oberlin, OH 44074-1091 *Tel:* 440-775-8408 *Fax:* 440-775-8124 *E-mail:* oc.press@oberlin.edu *Web Site:* www.oberlin.edu/ocpress; www.oberlin.edu/ocpress/prize.htm (guidelines), pg 685

Walker, David, Oberlin College Press, 50 N Professor St, Oberlin, OH 44074-1091 *Tel:* 440-775-8408 *Fax:* 440-775-8124 *E-mail:* oc.press@oberlin.edu *Web Site:* www.oberlin.edu/ocpress, pg 173

Walker, James R Jr, Walch Education, 40 Walch Dr, Portland, ME 04103-1286 *Tel:* 207-772-2846 *Toll Free Tel:* 800-558-2846 *Fax:* 207-772-3105 *Toll Free Fax:* 888-991-5755 *E-mail:* customerservice@walch.com *Web Site:* www.walch.com, pg 266

Walker, Janet, The Brookings Institution Press, 1775 Massachusetts Ave NW, Washington, DC 20036-2188 *Tel:* 202-536-3600 *Toll Free Tel:* 800-537-5487 *Fax:* 202-536-3623 *E-mail:* permissions@brookings.edu *Web Site:* www.brookings.edu, pg 47

Walker, Jerald, Emerson College Department of Writing, Literature & Publishing, 180 Tremont St, 10th fl, Boston, MA 02116 *Tel:* 617-824-8750 *Fax:* 617-824-7856 *Web Site:* www.emerson.edu, pg 660

Walker, Joe, American Society of Agricultural & Biological Engineers (ASABE), 2950 Niles Rd, St Joseph, MI 49085-9659 *Tel:* 269-429-0300 *Toll Free Tel:* 800-371-2723 *Fax:* 269-429-3852 *E-mail:* hq@asabe.org *Web Site:* www.asabe.org, pg 16

Walker, Kathy, MidWest Plan Service (MWPS), Iowa State University, 122 Davidson Hall, Ames, IA 50011-3080 *Tel:* 515-294-4337 *Toll Free Tel:* 800-562-3618 *Fax:* 515-294-9589 *E-mail:* mwps@iastate.edu *Web Site:* www.mwps.org, pg 156

Walker, Kirsty, Hobblebush Books, 17-A Old Milford Rd, Brookline, NH 03033 *Tel:* 603-672-4317 *Fax:* 603-672-4317 *E-mail:* hobblebush@charter.net; info@hobblebush.com *Web Site:* www.hobblebush.com, pg 112

Walker, Laura, University of Alaska Press, 794 University Ave, Suite 220, Fairbanks, AK 99709 *Tel:* 907-474-5831 *Toll Free Tel:* 888-252-6657 (US only) *Fax:* 907-474-5502 *E-mail:* fypress@uaf.edu *Web Site:* www.uaf.edu/uapress, pg 254

Walker, Margaret, Taylor & Francis Inc, 325 Chestnut St, Suite 800, Philadelphia, PA 20036-1802 *Tel:* 215-625-8900 *Toll Free Tel:* 800-354-1420 *Fax:* 215-625-2940 *E-mail:* customer.service@taylorandfrancis.com *Web Site:* www.taylorandfrancis.com, pg 241

Walker, Matthew, Recorded Books LLC, 270 Skipjack Rd, Prince Frederick, MD 20678 *Tel:* 410-535-5590 *Toll Free Tel:* 800-638-1304; 877-732-2898 *Fax:* 410-535-5499 *E-mail:* customerservice@recordedbooks.com *Web Site:* www.recordedbooks.com, pg 206

Walker, Scott, Empire Press Media/Avant-Guide, 244 Fifth Ave, Suite 2053, New York, NY 10001-7604 *Tel:* 917-512-3881 *Fax:* 212-202-7757 *E-mail:* info@avantguide.com; communications@avantguide.com; editor@avantguide.com *Web Site:* www.avantguide.com, pg 82

Walker, Tara, Tundra Books, One Toronto St, Suite 300, Toronto, ON M5C 2V6, Canada *Tel:* 416-364-4449 *Toll Free Tel:* 888-523-9292 (orders); 800-588-1074 *Fax:* 416-598-0247 *Toll Free Fax:* 888-562-9924 (orders) *E-mail:* tundra@mcclelland.com *Web Site:* www.tundrabooks.com, pg 501

Walker, Theresa, The Catholic University of America Press, 240 Leahy Hall, 620 Michigan Ave NE, Washington, DC 20064 *Tel:* 202-319-5052 *Toll Free Tel:* 800-537-5487 (orders only) *Fax:* 202-319-4985 *E-mail:* cua-press@cua.edu *Web Site:* cuapress.cua.edu, pg 52

Wall, Patrick, A-R Editions Inc, 1600 Aspen Commons, Suite 100, Middleton, WI 53562 *Tel:* 608-836-9000 *Toll Free Tel:* 800-736-0070 (North America book orders only) *Fax:* 608-831-8200 *E-mail:* info@areditions.com; orders@areditions.com *Web Site:* www.areditions.com, pg 1

Wall, Rob, Little Bee Books, 853 Broadway, Suite 2014, New York, NY 10003 *E-mail:* info@littlebeebooks.com *Web Site:* www.littlebeebooks.com, pg 140

Wallace, Ivey P, Gallaudet University Press, 800 Florida Ave NE, Washington, DC 20002-3695 *Tel:* 202-651-5488; 773-568-1550 (orders) *Toll Free Tel:* 800-621-2736 (orders) *Fax:* 202-651-5489; 773-660-2235 (orders) *Toll Free Fax:* 800-621-8476 (orders) *E-mail:* gupress@gallaudet.edu *Web Site:* gupress.gallaudet.edu, pg 94

Wallace, Kristin, Fun in the Sun Conference, PO Box 480211, Fort Lauderdale, FL 33348 *E-mail:* frwfuninthesun@yahoo.com *Web Site:* www.frwriters.org/fun-in-the-sun-conference/; frwfuninthesunmain.blogspot.com/; www.frwriters.org, pg 651

Wallace, Ronald, Brittingham & Pollak Prizes in Poetry, Dept of English, 600 N Park St, Madison, WI 53706 *Web Site:* www.wisc.edu/wisconsinpress, pg 674

Wallace, Sharah, Hospital & Healthcare Compensation Service, 3 Post Rd, Suite 3, Oakland, NJ 07436 *Tel:* 201-405-0075 *Fax:* 201-405-2110 *E-mail:* allinfo@hhcsinc.com *Web Site:* www.hhcsinc.com, pg 114

Wallek, Daniel, Carolrhoda Books, 241 First Ave N, Minneapolis, MN 55401 *Tel:* 612-332-3344 *Toll Free Tel:* 800-328-4929 *Fax:* 612-332-7615 *Toll Free Fax:* 800-332-1132 *E-mail:* info@lernerbooks.com *Web Site:* www.lernerbooks.com, pg 50

Wallek, Daniel, Carolrhoda Lab™, 241 First Ave N, Minneapolis, MN 55401 *Tel:* 612-332-3344 *Toll Free Tel:* 800-328-4929 *Fax:* 612-332-7615 *Toll Free Fax:* 800-332-1132 (US) *E-mail:* info@lernerbooks.com *Web Site:* www.lernerbooks.com, pg 51

Wallek, Daniel, ediciones Lerner, 241 First Ave N, Minneapolis, MN 55401 *Tel:* 612-332-3344 *Toll Free Tel:* 800-328-4929 *Fax:* 612-332-7615 *Toll Free Fax:* 800-332-1132 *E-mail:* info@lernerbooks.com *Web Site:* www.lernerbooks.com, pg 79

Wallek, Daniel, First Avenue Editions, 241 First Ave N, Minneapolis, MN 55401 *Tel:* 612-332-3344 *Toll Free Tel:* 800-328-4929 *Fax:* 612-332-7615 *Toll Free Fax:* 800-332-1132 *E-mail:* info@lernerbooks.com *Web Site:* www.lernerbooks.com, pg 89

Wallek, Daniel, Graphic Universe™, 241 First Ave N, Minneapolis, MN 55401 *Tel:* 612-332-3344 *Toll Free Tel:* 800-328-4929 *Fax:* 612-332-7615 *Toll Free Fax:* 800-332-1132 *E-mail:* info@lernerbooks.com *Web Site:* www.lernerbooks.com, pg 99

Wallek, Daniel, Lerner Publications, 241 First Ave N, Minneapolis, MN 55401 *Tel:* 612-332-3344 *Toll Free Tel:* 800-328-4929 *Fax:* 612-332-7615 *Toll Free Fax:* 800-332-1132 *E-mail:* info@lernerbooks.com *Web Site:* www.lernerbooks.com, pg 137

Wallek, Daniel, Lerner Publishing Group Inc, 241 First Ave N, Minneapolis, MN 55401 *Tel:* 612-332-3344 *Toll Free Tel:* 800-328-4929 *Fax:* 612-332-7615 *Toll Free Fax:* 800-332-1132 *E-mail:* info@lernerbooks.com *Web Site:* www.lernerbooks.com, pg 137

Wallek, Daniel, LernerClassroom, 241 First Ave N, Minneapolis, MN 55401 *Tel:* 612-332-3344 *Toll Free Tel:* 800-328-4929 *Fax:* 612-332-7615 *Toll Free Fax:* 800-332-1132 *E-mail:* info@lernerbooks.com *Web Site:* www.lernerbooks.com, pg 137

Wallek, Daniel, Millbrook Press, 241 First Ave N, Minneapolis, MN 55401 *Tel:* 612-332-3344 *Toll Free Tel:* 800-328-4929 (US only) *Fax:* 612-332-7615 *Toll Free Fax:* 800-332-1132, pg 157

Wallek, Daniel, Twenty-First Century Books, 241 First Ave N, Minneapolis, MN 55401 *Tel:* 612-332-3344 *Toll Free Tel:* 800-328-4929 *Fax:* 612-332-7615 *Toll Free Fax:* 800-332-1132 *E-mail:* info@lernerbooks.com *Web Site:* www.lernerbooks.com, pg 251

Wallentine, Lois, Carolrhoda Books, 241 First Ave N, Minneapolis, MN 55401 *Tel:* 612-332-3344 *Toll Free Tel:* 800-328-4929 *Fax:* 612-332-7615 *Toll Free Fax:* 800-332-1132 *E-mail:* info@lernerbooks.com *Web Site:* www.lernerbooks.com, pg 50

Wallentine, Lois, Carolrhoda Lab™, 241 First Ave N, Minneapolis, MN 55401 *Tel:* 612-332-3344 *Toll Free Tel:* 800-328-4929 *Fax:* 612-332-7615 *Toll Free Fax:* 800-332-1132 (US) *E-mail:* info@lernerbooks.com *Web Site:* www.lernerbooks.com, pg 51

Wallentine, Lois, ediciones Lerner, 241 First Ave N, Minneapolis, MN 55401 *Tel:* 612-332-3344 *Toll Free Tel:* 800-328-4929 *Fax:* 612-332-7615 *Toll Free Fax:* 800-332-1132 *E-mail:* info@lernerbooks.com *Web Site:* www.lernerbooks.com, pg 79

Wallentine, Lois, First Avenue Editions, 241 First Ave N, Minneapolis, MN 55401 *Tel:* 612-332-3344 *Toll Free Tel:* 800-328-4929 *Fax:* 612-332-7615 *Toll Free Fax:* 800-332-1132 *E-mail:* info@lernerbooks.com *Web Site:* www.lernerbooks.com, pg 89

Wallentine, Lois, Graphic Universe™, 241 First Ave N, Minneapolis, MN 55401 *Tel:* 612-332-3344 *Toll Free Tel:* 800-328-4929 *Fax:* 612-332-7615 *Toll Free Fax:* 800-332-1132 *E-mail:* info@lernerbooks.com *Web Site:* www.lernerbooks.com, pg 99

Wallentine, Lois, Lerner Publications, 241 First Ave N, Minneapolis, MN 55401 *Tel:* 612-332-3344 *Toll Free Tel:* 800-328-4929 *Fax:* 612-332-7615 *Toll Free Fax:* 800-332-1132 *E-mail:* info@lernerbooks.com *Web Site:* www.lernerbooks.com, pg 137

Wallentine, Lois, Lerner Publishing Group Inc, 241 First Ave N, Minneapolis, MN 55401 *Tel:* 612-332-3344 *Toll Free Tel:* 800-328-4929 *Fax:* 612-332-7615 *Toll Free Fax:* 800-332-1132 *E-mail:* info@lernerbooks.com *Web Site:* www.lernerbooks.com, pg 137

Wallentine, Lois, LernerClassroom, 241 First Ave N, Minneapolis, MN 55401 *Tel:* 612-332-3344 *Toll Free Tel:* 800-328-4929 *Fax:* 612-332-7615 *Toll Free Fax:* 800-332-1132 *E-mail:* info@lernerbooks.com *Web Site:* www.lernerbooks.com, pg 137

Wallentine, Lois, Millbrook Press, 241 First Ave N, Minneapolis, MN 55401 *Tel:* 612-332-3344 *Toll Free Tel:* 800-328-4929 (US only) *Fax:* 612-332-7615 *Toll Free Fax:* 800-332-1132, pg 157

Wallentine, Lois, Twenty-First Century Books, 241 First Ave N, Minneapolis, MN 55401 *Tel:* 612-332-3344 *Toll Free Tel:* 800-328-4929 *Fax:* 612-332-7615 *Toll Free Fax:* 800-332-1132 *E-mail:* info@lernerbooks.com *Web Site:* www.lernerbooks.com, pg 251

Walling, Bonnie, OPIS/STALSBY Directories & Databases, 3349 Hwy 138, Bldg D, Suite D, Wall, NJ 07719 *Tel:* 732-901-8800 *Toll Free Tel:* 800-275-0950 *Toll Free Fax:* 800-450-5864 *E-mail:* opisstalsbylistings@opisnet.com *Web Site:* www.opisnet.com, pg 175

Walling, Lori, Tyndale House Publishers Inc, 351 Executive Dr, Carol Stream, IL 60188 *Tel:* 630-668-8300 *Toll Free Tel:* 800-323-9400 *Web Site:* www.tyndale.com, pg 252

Wallman, Keith, The Lyons Press, 246 Goose Lane, Guilford, CT 06437 *Tel:* 203-458-4500 *Fax:* 203-458-4668 *E-mail:* info@rowman.com *Web Site:* www.lyonspress.com; rowman.com, pg 144

Walls, Kathleen, Global Authors Publications (GAP), 38 Bluegrass, Middleberg, FL 32068 *Tel:* 904-425-1608 *E-mail:* gapbook@yahoo.com *Web Site:* globalauthorspublications.com, pg 97

Walsh, Barbara A, Holiday House Inc, 425 Madison Ave, New York, NY 10017 *Tel:* 212-688-0085 *Fax:* 212-421-6134 *E-mail:* holiday@holidayhouse.com *Web Site:* www.holidayhouse.com, pg 113

Walsh, Bruce, University of Regina Press, 2 Research Dr, Suite 246, Regina, SK S4S 7H9, Canada *Tel:* 306-585-4758 *Toll Free Tel:* 866-874-2257 *Fax:* 306-585-4699 *E-mail:* uofrpress@uregina.ca *Web Site:* uofrpress.ca, pg 503

Walsh, Jennifer Rudolph, WME, 1325 Avenue of the Americas, New York, NY 10019 *Tel:* 212-586-5100 *Fax:* 212-246-3583 *E-mail:* wma@interport.net *Web Site:* www.wma.com, pg 579

Walsh, Karen, Houghton Mifflin Harcourt Trade & Reference Division, 222 Berkeley St, Boston, MA 02116 *Tel:* 617-351-5000 *Toll Free Tel:* 800-225-3362 *Web Site:* www.hmhco.com, pg 115

Walsh, Lillie, HarperCollins Publishers Sales, 195 Broadway, New York, NY 10007 *Fax:* 212-207-7000 *Web Site:* www.harpercollins.com, pg 106

Walsh, Mark E, Artech House Inc, 685 Canton St, Norwood, MA 02062 *Tel:* 781-769-9750 *Toll Free Tel:* 800-225-9977 *Fax:* 781-769-6334 *E-mail:* artech@artechhouse.com *Web Site:* www.artechhouse.com, pg 23

Walsh, Mary Lou, The PRS Group Inc, 6320 Fly Rd, Suite 102, East Syracuse, NY 13057-9358 *Tel:* 315-431-0511 *Fax:* 315-431-0200 *E-mail:* custserv@prsgroup.com *Web Site:* www.prsgroup.com, pg 199

Walsh, Mike, LexisNexis®, 701 E Water St, Charlottesville, VA 22902 *Tel:* 434-972-7600 *Toll Free Tel:* 800-446-3410 *Fax:* 434-961-5576 *E-mail:* customer.support@lexisnexis.com *Web Site:* www.lexisnexis.com, pg 138

Walsh, Ryan, Vermont Studio Center Writer's Program Fellowships, 80 Pearl St, Johnson, VT 05656 *Tel:* 802-635-2727 *Fax:* 802-635-2730 *E-mail:* writing@vermontstudiocenter.org; info@vermontstudiocenter.org *Web Site:* www.vermontstudiocenter.org, pg 734

Walsh, Warren, Emerald Books, PO Box 55787, Seattle, WA 98155 *Tel:* 425-771-1153 *Toll Free Tel:* 800-922-2143 *Fax:* 425-775-2383 *E-mail:* books@ywampublishing.com *Web Site:* www.ywampublishing.com, pg 81

Walter, Hugh, Global Lion Intellectual Property Management Inc, PO Box 669238, Pompano Beach, FL 33066 *Tel:* 754-222-6948 *Fax:* 754-222-6948 *E-mail:* queriesglobalionmgt@gmail.com *Web Site:* www.globallionmanagement.com, pg 554

Walter, Joellen, Scott Publishing Co, 911 S Vandemark Rd, Sidney, OH 45365 *Tel:* 937-498-0802 *Toll Free Tel:* 800-572-6885 (cust serv) *Fax:* 937-498-0807 *Toll Free Fax:* 800-488-5349 *E-mail:* cuserv@amospress.com *Web Site:* www.amosadvantage.com, pg 220

Walter, Timothy M, Catholic Book Awards, 205 W Monroe St, Suite 470, Chicago, IL 60606 *Tel:* 312-380-6789 *Fax:* 312-361-0256 *E-mail:* cathjourn@catholicpress.org *Web Site:* www.catholicpress.org, pg 676

Walter, Timothy M, Catholic Press Association of the United States & Canada, 205 W Monroe St, Suite 470, Chicago, IL 60606 *Tel:* 312-380-6789 *Fax:* 312-361-0256 *E-mail:* cathjourn@catholicpress.org *Web Site:* www.catholicpress.org, pg 602

Walter, Timothy M, Catholic Press Awards, 205 W Monroe St, Suite 470, Chicago, IL 60606 *Tel:* 312-380-6789 *Fax:* 312-361-0256 *E-mail:* cathjourn@catholicpress.org *Web Site:* www.catholicpress.org, pg 676

Walters, Carolyn, Indiana University Press, Herman B Wells Library 350, 1320 E Tenth St, Bloomington, IN 47405-3907 *Tel:* 812-855-8817 *Toll Free Tel:* 800-842-6796 (orders only) *Fax:* 812-855-7931; 812-855-8507 *E-mail:* iupress@indiana.edu; iuporder@indiana.edu (orders) *Web Site:* www.iupress.indiana.edu, pg 120

Walters, Ed, Tuttle Publishing, Airport Business Park, 364 Innovation Dr, North Clarendon, VT 05759-9436 *Tel:* 802-773-8930 *Toll Free Tel:* 800-526-2778 *Fax:* 802-773-6993 *Toll Free Fax:* 800-FAX-TUTL *E-mail:* info@tuttlepublishing.com *Web Site:* www.tuttlepublishing.com, pg 251

Walters, John P, Hudson Institute, 1015 15 St NW, 6th fl, Washington, DC 20005 *Tel:* 202-974-2400 *Fax:* 202-974-2410 *E-mail:* info@hudson.org *Web Site:* www.hudson.org, pg 116

Walters, Linda, George Orwell Award, 1111 W Kenyon Rd, Urbana, IL 61801-1096 *Tel:* 217-328-3870 *Toll Free Tel:* 877-369-6283 (cust serv) *Fax:* 217-328-0977 *E-mail:* publiclangawards@ncte.org *Web Site:* www.ncte.org, pg 715

Walters, Maureen, Curtis Brown Ltd, 10 Astor Place, New York, NY 10003 *Tel:* 212-473-5400 *Web Site:* www.curtisbrown.com, pg 544

Walther, LuAnn, Alfred A Knopf/Everyman's Library, c/o Random House Inc, 1745 Broadway, New York, NY 10019 *Tel:* 212-751-2600 *Toll Free Tel:* 800-638-6460 *Fax:* 212-572-2593 *Web Site:* www.knopfdoubleday.com, pg 132

Walther, Luann, Vintage & Anchor Books, c/o Random House Inc, 1745 Broadway, New York, NY 10019 *Tel:* 212-572-2420 *E-mail:* vintageanchorpublicity@randomhouse.com *Web Site:* vintage-anchor.knopfdoubleday.com, pg 266

Walther, Stevia, Rocky Mountain Mineral Law Foundation, 9191 Sheridan Blvd, Suite 203, Westminister, CO 80031 *Tel:* 303-321-8100 *Fax:* 303-321-7657 *E-mail:* info@rmmlf.org *Web Site:* www.rmmlf.org, pg 210

Waltman, Fran, Edward Lewis Wallant Book Award, 3 Brighton Rd, West Hartford, CT 06117 *Tel:* 860-232-1421, pg 734

Waltman, Irving, Edward Lewis Wallant Book Award, 3 Brighton Rd, West Hartford, CT 06117 *Tel:* 860-232-1421, pg 734

Walton, Diane, SF Canada, 7433 E River Rd, Washago, ON L0K 2B0, Canada *Web Site:* www.sfcanada.org, pg 618

Walton, Kathy S, Texas Christian University Press, 3000 Sandage Ave, Fort Worth, TX 76109 *Tel:* 817-257-7822 *Toll Free Tel:* 800-826-8911 *Fax:* 817-257-5075 *Web Site:* www.prs.tcu.edu, pg 243

Wang, Xin, China Books, 360 Swift Ave, Suite 48, South San Francisco, CA 94080 *Tel:* 650-872-7076 *Toll Free Tel:* 800-818-2017 (US only) *Fax:* 650-872-7808 *E-mail:* info@chinabooks.com *Web Site:* www.chinabooks.com, pg 57

Wang-Iverson, Jeremy, Berghahn Books, 20 Jay St, Suite 512, Brooklyn, NY 11201 *Tel:* 212-233-6004 *Fax:* 212-233-6007 *E-mail:* info@berghahnbooks.com; salesus@berghahnbooks.com; editorial@journals.berghahnbooks.com *Web Site:* www.berghahnbooks.com, pg 35

Wanger, Shelley, Pantheon Books/Schocken Books, c/o Random House Inc, 1745 Broadway, New York, NY 10019 *Tel:* 212-751-2600 *Toll Free Tel:* 800-638-6460 *Fax:* 212-572-6030, pg 181

Waniewski, Elizabeth, Dial Books for Young Readers, 345 Hudson St, New York, NY 10014 *Tel:* 212-366-2000 *Fax:* 212-414-3396 *E-mail:* online@penguinputnam.com *Web Site:* www.penguinputnam.com; us.penguingroup.com, pg 74

Wanner, Eric, Russell Sage Foundation, 112 E 64 St, New York, NY 10065 *Tel:* 212-750-6000 *Toll Free Tel:* 800-524-6401 *Fax:* 212-371-4761 *E-mail:* info@rsage.org *Web Site:* www.russellsage.org, pg 212

Wantland, Clydette, University of Illinois Press, 1325 S Oak St, MC-566, Champaign, IL 61820-6903 *Tel:* 217-333-0950 *Fax:* 217-244-8082 *E-mail:* uipress@uillinois.edu; journals@uillinois.edu *Web Site:* www.press.uillinois.edu, pg 256

Wapner, Jenny, Ten Speed Press, 2625 Alcatraz Ave, Unit 505, Berkeley, CA 94705 *Tel:* 510-285-3000 *Toll Free Tel:* 800-841-BOOK (841-2665) *E-mail:* csorders@randomhouse.com *Web Site:* crownpublishing.com/imprint/ten-speed-press, pg 243

Ward, Andy, Random House Publishing Group, 1745 Broadway, New York, NY 10019 *Toll Free Tel:* 800-200-3552 *Web Site:* atrandom.com, pg 204

Ward, Anne C, High Tide Press, 301 Veterans Pkwy, New Lenox, IL 60451 *Web Site:* cherryhillhightide.com/high-tide-press/, pg 111

Warden, Yorke, Living Stream Ministry (LSM), 2431 W La Palma Ave, Anaheim, CA 92801 *Tel:* 714-991-4681 *Fax:* 714-236-6005 *E-mail:* books@lsm.org *Web Site:* www.lsm.org, pg 142

Wareing, Tracy, American Public Human Services Association, 1133 19 St NW, Suite 400, Washington, DC 20036 *Tel:* 202-682-0100 *Fax:* 202-289-6555 *Web Site:* www.aphsa.org, pg 596

Waricha, Joan, Parachute Publishing LLC, 322 Eighth Ave, Suite 702, New York, NY 10001 *Tel:* 212-691-1421 *Fax:* 212-647-9650 *Web Site:* www.parachutepublishing.com, pg 182

Warinner, J M, Professional Resource Press, 1958 Barber Rd, Sarasota, FL 34240 *Tel:* 941-343-9601 *Toll Free Tel:* 800-443-3364 (orders & cust serv) *Fax:* 941-343-9201 *Toll Free Fax:* 866-804-4843 (orders only) *E-mail:* cs.prpress@gmail.com *Web Site:* www.prpress.com, pg 198

Wark, Lee, Mason Crest Publishers, 450 Parkway Dr, Suite D, Broomall, PA 19008 *Tel:* 610-543-6200 *Toll Free Tel:* 866-MCP-BOOK (627-2665) *Fax:* 610-543-3878 *Web Site:* www.masoncrest.com, pg 149

Warlick, Dottie, Oxford University Press USA, 198 Madison Ave, New York, NY 10016 *Tel:* 212-726-6000 *Toll Free Tel:* 800-451-7556 (orders); 800-445-9714 (cust serv) *Fax:* 919-677-1303 *E-mail:* custserv.us@oup.com *Web Site:* www.oup.com/us, pg 179

Warner, Matt, Gem Guides Book Co, 1275 W Ninth St, Upland, CA 91786 *Tel:* 626-855-1611 *Toll Free Tel:* 800-824-5118 (orders) *Fax:* 626-855-1610 *E-mail:* info@gemguidesbooks.com *Web Site:* www.gemguidesbooks.com, pg 95

Warner, Nakeesha, Standard Publishing Corp, 155 Federal St, 13th fl, Boston, MA 02110 *Tel:* 617-457-0600 *Toll Free Tel:* 800-682-5759 *Fax:* 617-457-0608 *Web Site:* www.spcpub.com, pg 233

Warner, Sharon Oard, Taos Summer Writers' Conference, One University of New Mexico, Albuquerque, NM 87131-0001 *Tel:* 505-277-5572 *E-mail:* taosconf@unm.edu *Web Site:* taosconf.unm.edu, pg 656

Warnock, Colin, Fine Creative Media, Inc, 322 Eighth Ave, 15th fl, New York, NY 10001 *Tel:* 212-595-3500 *Fax:* 212-595-3779, pg 88

Warren, Bruce, Abrams Learning Trends, 16310 Bratton Lane, Suite 250, Austin, TX 78728-2403 *Toll Free Tel:* 800-227-9120 *Toll Free Fax:* 800-737-3322 *E-mail:* customerservice@abramslearningtrends.com (orders, cust serv); contactus@abramslearningtrends.com *Web Site:* www.abramslearningtrends.com (orders, cust serv), pg 3

Warren, Daniel, Warren Communications News Inc, 2115 Ward Ct NW, Washington, DC 20037 *Tel:* 202-872-9200 *Toll Free Tel:* 800-771-9202 *Fax:* 202-293-3435; 202-318-8350 *E-mail:* info@warren-news.com; newsroom@warren-news.com *Web Site:* www.warren-news.com, pg 267

Warren, Julie, RockBench Publishing Corp, 6101 Stillmeadow Dr, Nashville, TN 37211-6518 *Tel:* 615-831-2277 *Fax:* 615-831-2212 *E-mail:* info@rockbench.com *Web Site:* www.rockbench.com, pg 210

Warren, Lissa, Da Capo Press & Lifelong Books, 44 Farnsworth St, 3rd fl, Boston, MA 02210 *Tel:* 617-252-5200 *Toll Free Tel:* 800-343-4499 (orders) *Fax:* 617-252-5285 *Web Site:* www.perseusbooksgroup.com/dacapo, pg 69

Warren, Paul, Warren Communications News Inc, 2115 Ward Ct NW, Washington, DC 20037 *Tel:* 202-872-9200 *Toll Free Tel:* 800-771-9202 *Fax:* 202-293-3435; 202-318-8350 *E-mail:* info@warren-news.com; newsroom@warren-news.com *Web Site:* www.warren-news.com, pg 267

Warren, Prof Rosanna, Boston University, 236 Bay State Rd, Boston, MA 02215 *Tel:* 617-353-2510 *Fax:* 617-353-3653 *E-mail:* crwr@bu.edu *Web Site:* www.bu.edu/writing, pg 659

Warren, Wenche, YWAM Publishing, PO Box 55787, Seattle, WA 98155-0787 *Tel:* 425-771-1153 *Toll Free Tel:* 800-922-2143 *Fax:* 425-775-2383 *E-mail:* books@ywampublishing.com *Web Site:* www.ywampublishing.com, pg 279

Warren, Wenke, Emerald Books, PO Box 55787, Seattle, WA 98155 *Tel:* 425-771-1153 *Toll Free Tel:* 800-922-2143 *Fax:* 425-775-2383 *E-mail:* books@ywampublishing.com *Web Site:* www.ywampublishing.com, pg 81

Warren-Lynch, Isabel, Random House Children's Books, 1745 Broadway, New York, NY 10019 *Tel:* 212-782-9000 *Toll Free Tel:* 800-200-3552 *Fax:* 212-782-9452 *Web Site:* randomhousekids.com, pg 203

Warshaw, Hallie, Zest Books, 35 Stillman St, Suite 121, San Francisco, CA 94107 *Tel:* 415-777-8654 *Fax:* 415-777-8653 *E-mail:* info@zestbooks.net; publicity@zestbooks.net *Web Site:* zestbooks.net, pg 279

Warwick-Smith, Simon, Dunhill Publishing, 18340 Sonoma Hwy, Sonoma, CA 95476 *Tel:* 707-939-0570 *Fax:* 707-938-3515 *E-mail:* dunhill@vom.com *Web Site:* www.dunhillpublishing.com, pg 77

Warwick-Smith, Simon, Warwick Associates, 18340 Sonoma Hwy, Sonoma, CA 95476 *Tel:* 707-939-9212 *Fax:* 707-938-3515 *E-mail:* warwick@vom.com *Web Site:* www.warwickassociates.com, pg 578

Wasch, Kenneth, CODiE Awards, 1090 Vermont Ave NW, 6th fl, Washington, DC 20005-4095 *Tel:* 202-289-7442 *Fax:* 202-289-7097 *E-mail:* info@siia.net *Web Site:* www.siia.net, pg 678

Wasch, Kenneth, Software & Information Industry Association (SIIA), 1090 Vermont Ave NW, 6th fl, Washington, DC 20005-4095 *Tel:* 202-289-7442 *Fax:* 202-289-7097 *Web Site:* www.siia.net, pg 619

Wasdyke, Rachel, Houghton Mifflin Harcourt Trade & Reference Division, 222 Berkeley St, Boston, MA 02116 *Tel:* 617-351-5000 *Toll Free Tel:* 800-225-3362 *Web Site:* www.hmhco.com, pg 115

Washam, Alexis, Crown Publishing Group, c/o Penguin Random House Inc, 1745 Broadway, New York, NY 10019 *Tel:* 212-782-9000 *Toll Free Tel:* 888-264-1745 *Fax:* 212-940-7408 *E-mail:* crownosm@penguinrandomhouse.com *Web Site:* crownpublishing.com, pg 68

Wasielewski, Leah, HarperCollins General Books Group, 195 Broadway, New York, NY 10007 *Tel:* 212-207-7000 *Web Site:* www.harpercollins.com, pg 105

Wasserman, Marlie, Rutgers University Press, 106 Somerset St, 3rd fl, New Brunswick, NJ 08901 *Tel:* 848-445-7762 *Toll Free Tel:* 800-848-6224 (orders only) *Fax:* 732-745-4935 (acqs, edit, mktg, perms & prodn) *Toll Free Fax:* 800-272-6817 (fulfillment) *Web Site:* rutgerspress.rutgers.edu, pg 212

Wasserman, Steve, Yale University Press, 302 Temple St, New Haven, CT 06511-8909 *Tel:* 203-432-0960; 203-432-0966 (sales); 401-531-2800 (cust serv) *Toll Free Tel:* 800-405-1619 (cust serv) *Fax:* 203-432-0948; 203-432-8485 (sales); 401-531-2801 (cust serv) *Toll Free Fax:* 800-406-9145 (cust serv) *E-mail:* sales.press@yale.edu (sales); customer.care@trilateral.org (cust serv) *Web Site:* www.yalebooks.com; yalepress.yale.edu/yupbooks, pg 278

Wasserman, Veronica, Harry N Abrams Inc, 115 W 18 St, 6th fl, New York, NY 10011 *Tel:* 212-206-7715 *Toll Free Tel:* 800-345-1359 *Fax:* 212-519-1210 *E-mail:* abrams@abramsbooks.com *Web Site:* www.abramsbooks.com, pg 3

Waterman, Hilary, The AEI Press, 1150 17 St NW, Washington, DC 20036 *Tel:* 202-862-5800 *Fax:* 202-862-7177 *Web Site:* www.aei.org, pg 5

Waterman, Susan, New Mexico Book Association (NMBA), 1219 Luisa St, Suite 1, Santa Fe, NM 87505 *Tel:* 505-660-6357 *E-mail:* admin@nmbook.org *Web Site:* www.nmbook.org, pg 614

Waters, Christian, Osprey Publishing Inc, 4301 21 St, Suite 220B, Long Island City, NY 11101 *Tel:* 718-433-4402 *Fax:* 718-433-4497 *E-mail:* ospreyusa@ospreypublishing.com *Web Site:* www.ospreypublishing.com, pg 178

Waters, Lindsay, Harvard University Press, 79 Garden St, Cambridge, MA 02138-1499 *Tel:* 617-495-2600; 401-531-2800 (intl orders) *Toll Free Tel:* 800-405-1619 (orders) *Fax:* 617-495-5898 (general); 617-496-4677 (edit & rts); 401-531-2801 (intl orders) *Toll Free Fax:* 800-406-9145 (orders) *E-mail:* contact_hup@harvard.edu *Web Site:* www.hup.harvard.edu, pg 107

Waters, Michele, New Harbinger Publications Inc, 5674 Shattuck Ave, Oakland, CA 94609 *Tel:* 510-652-0215 *Toll Free Tel:* 800-748-6273 (orders only) *Fax:* 510-652-5472 *Toll Free Fax:* 800-652-1613 *E-mail:* nhhelp@newharbinger.com; customerservice@newharbinger.com *Web Site:* www.newharbinger.com, pg 167

Waters, Mitchell, Curtis Brown Ltd, 10 Astor Place, New York, NY 10003 *Tel:* 212-473-5400 *Web Site:* www.curtisbrown.com, pg 544

Watkins, Anne Dean, The University Press of Kentucky, 663 S Limestone St, Lexington, KY 40508-4008 *Tel:* 859-257-8400 *Fax:* 859-257-8481 *Web Site:* www.kentuckypress.com, pg 261

Watkinson, Charles, University of Michigan Press, 839 Greene St, Ann Arbor, MI 48104-3209 *Tel:* 734-764-4388 *Fax:* 734-615-1540 *E-mail:* esladmin@umich.edu *Web Site:* www.press.umich.edu, pg 257

Watson, Ben, Chelsea Green Publishing Co, 85 N Main St, Suite 120, White River Junction, VT 05001 *Tel:* 802-295-6300 *Toll Free Tel:* 800-639-4099 (cust serv, consumer & trade orders) *Fax:* 802-295-6444 *Web Site:* www.chelseagreen.com, pg 56

Watson, Elisabeth, Touchstone, 1230 Avenue of the Americas, New York, NY 10020, pg 247

Watson, James, Gordon W Dillon/Richard C Peterson Memorial Essay Prize, Fairfield Tropical Botanic Gardens, 10901 Old Cutler Rd, Coral Gables, FL 33156 *Tel:* 305-740-2010 *Fax:* 305-740-2011 *E-mail:* theaos@aos.org *Web Site:* www.aos.org, pg 681

Watson, Kara, Scribner, 1230 Avenue of the Americas, New York, NY 10020, pg 220

Watson, Kate, Hackmatack Children's Choice Book Award, PO Box 34055, Scotia Square RPO, Halifax, NS B3J 3S1, Canada *Tel:* 902-424-3774 *Fax:* 902-424-0613 *E-mail:* hackmatack@hackmatack.ca *Web Site:* www.hackmatack.ca, pg 691

Watson, Kent, Publishers Association of the West (PubWest), 17501 Hill Way, Lake Oswego, OR 97035 *Tel:* 503-901-9865 *Web Site:* pubwest.org, pg 617

Watson, Kent, PubWest Book Design Awards, 17501 Hill Way, Lake Oswego, OR 97035 *Tel:* 503-901-9865 *Fax:* 602-234-3062 *Web Site:* pubwest.org, pg 722

Watson, Kent, Jack D Rittenhouse Award, 17501 Hill Way, Lake Oswego, OR 97035 *Tel:* 503-901-9865 *Web Site:* pubwest.org, pg 724

Watson, Lucia, Avery, 375 Hudson St, New York, NY 10014 *Tel:* 212-366-2000 *Fax:* 212-366-2643 *E-mail:* online@penguinputnam.com *Web Site:* www.penguinputnam.com; us.penguingroup.com, pg 28

Watson, Mary, Shenanigan Books, 84 River Rd, Summit, NJ 07901 *Tel:* 908-219-4275 *Fax:* 908-219-4485 *E-mail:* info@shenaniganbooks.com *Web Site:* www.shenaniganbooks.com, pg 223

Watson, Neale W Esq, Watson Publishing International LLC, PO Box 1240, Sagamore Beach, MA 02562-1240 *Tel:* 508-888-9113 *Fax:* 508-888-3733 *E-mail:* orders@watsonpublishing.com; orders@shpusa.com *Web Site:* www.shpusa.com; www.watsonpublishing.com, pg 268

Watson, Warren, Society of American Business Editors & Writers Inc (SABEW), Walter Cronkite School of Journalism & Mass Communication, Arizona State University, 555 N Central Ave, Suite 406 E, Phoenix, AZ 85004-1248 *Tel:* 602-496-7862 *Fax:* 602-496-7041 *E-mail:* sabew@sabew.org *Web Site:* sabew.org, pg 619

Wattendorf, Bob, Florida Outdoor Writers Association Inc, 24 NW 33 Ct, Suite A, Gainesville, FL 32607 *Tel:* 352-284-1763 *E-mail:* info@fowa.org *Web Site:* www.fowa.org, pg 606

Watters, Ron, National Outdoor Book Awards, 921 S Eighth Ave, Stop 8128, Pocatello, ID 83209-8128 *Tel:* 208-282-3912 *Fax:* 208-282-2127 *Web Site:* www.noba-web.org, pg 711

Watterson, Jessica, Sandra Dijkstra Literary Agency, 1155 Camino del Mar, PMB 515, Del Mar, CA 92014-2605 *E-mail:* queries@dijkstraagency.com *Web Site:* dijkstraagency.com, pg 548

Watts, Benjamin, Stipes Publishing LLC, 204 W University, Champaign, IL 61820 *Tel:* 217-356-8391 *Fax:* 217-356-5753 *E-mail:* stipes01@sbcglobal.net *Web Site:* www.stipes.com, pg 236

Waugh, Rebecca, Books on Tape®, 1745 Broadway, New York, NY 10019 *Toll Free Tel:* 800-733-3000 (cust serv) *Toll Free Fax:* 800-940-7046 *Web Site:* www.booksontape.com, pg 43

Waxman, Scott, Diversion Books, 443 Park Ave S, Suite 1008, New York, NY 10016 *Tel:* 212-961-6390 *E-mail:* info@diversionbooks.com *Web Site:* www.diversionbooks.com, pg 74

Waxman, Scott, Waxman Leavell Literary Agency, 443 Park Ave S, No 1004, New York, NY 10016 *Tel:* 212-675-5556 *Fax:* 212-675-1381 *Web Site:* www.waxmanleavell.com, pg 579

Wayne, Alan, Imagination Publishing Group, PO Box 1304, Dunedin, FL 34697 *Toll Free Tel:* 888-701-6481 *Fax:* 727-361-0584 *E-mail:* info@imaginationpublishinggroup.com *Web Site:* www.imaginationpublishinggroup.com, pg 119

Wayne, Andrew, Canadian Scholars' Press Inc, 425 Adelaide St W, Suite 200, Toronto, ON M5V 3C1, Canada *Tel:* 416-929-2774 *Toll Free Tel:* 800-463-1998 *Fax:* 416-929-1926 *E-mail:* info@cspi.org; editorial@cspi.org; orders@cspi.org *Web Site:* www.cspi.org; womenspress.cspi.org, pg 475

Wayne, Sarah, Sumach Press, 425 Adelaide St W, Suite 200, Toronto, ON M5V 3C1, Canada *Tel:* 416-929-2964 *Fax:* 416-929-1926 *E-mail:* info@threeoclockpress.com *Web Site:* www.threeoclockpress.com, pg 500

Weaver, Kyle, Stackpole Books, 5067 Ritter Rd, Mechanicsburg, PA 17055 *Tel:* 717-796-0411 *Toll Free Tel:* 800-732-3669 *Fax:* 717-796-0412 *Web Site:* www.stackpolebooks.com, pg 233

Weaver, Michael, Chelsea Green Publishing Co, 85 N Main St, Suite 120, White River Junction, VT 05001 *Tel:* 802-295-6300 *Toll Free Tel:* 800-639-4099 (cust serv, consumer & trade orders) *Fax:* 802-295-6444 *Web Site:* www.chelseagreen.com, pg 56

Weaver, Muffy, Dawn Publications Inc, 12402 Bitney Springs Rd, Nevada City, CA 95959 *Tel:* 530-274-7775 *Toll Free Tel:* 800-545-7475 *Fax:* 530-274-7778 *E-mail:* nature@dawnpub.com; orders@dawnpub.com *Web Site:* www.dawnpub.com, pg 71

Weaver-Smith, Heidi, Forward Movement, 412 Sycamore St, Cincinnati, OH 45202-4110 *Tel:* 513-721-6659 *Toll Free Tel:* 800-543-1813 *Fax:* 513-721-0729 (orders) *E-mail:* orders@forwardmovement.org (orders & cust serv) *Web Site:* www.forwardmovement.org, pg 91

Webb, Dorothy, Write Now, 140 W Washington St, Indianapolis, IN 46204-3465 *Tel:* 317-635-5277 *Fax:* 317-236-0767 *E-mail:* info@writenow.co *Web Site:* www.writenow.co, pg 738

Webb, James T, Great Potential Press Inc, 1325 N Wilmot Ave, Suite 300, Tucson, AZ 85712 *Tel:* 520-777-6161 *Fax:* 520-777-6217 *Web Site:* www.greatpotentialpress.com, pg 100

Webb, Tom, Doug Fir Fiction Award, 240 N Broadway, Suite 112, Portland, OR 97227 *E-mail:* bear@orlo.org *Web Site:* www.orlo.org, pg 686

Weber, Johann, AIMS Education Foundation, 1595 S Chestnut Ave, Fresno, CA 93702-4706 *Tel:* 559-255-4094 *Toll Free Tel:* 888-733-2467 *Fax:* 559-255-6396 *E-mail:* aimsed@aimsedu.org *Web Site:* www.aimsedu.org, pg 6

Weber, John, Welcome Rain Publishers LLC, 217 Thompson St, Suite 473, New York, NY 10012 *Tel:* 212-686-1909 *Web Site:* welcomerain.com, pg 268

Weber, Judith, Sobel Weber Associates Inc, 146 E 19 St, New York, NY 10003-2404 *Tel:* 212-420-8585 *Fax:* 212-505-1017 *E-mail:* info@sobelweber.com *Web Site:* www.sobelweber.com, pg 574

Weber, Louis, Publications International Ltd, 7373 N Cicero Ave, Lincolnwood, IL 60712 *Tel:* 847-676-3470 *Fax:* 847-676-3671 *E-mail:* customer_service@pubint.com *Web Site:* www.pilbooks.com, pg 200

Weber, Mark, The Noontide Press, PO Box 2719, Newport Beach, CA 92659-1319 *Tel:* 714-593-9725 *Fax:* 714-593-9731 *E-mail:* orders@noontidepress.com *Web Site:* www.noontidepress.com, pg 170

Weber, Nicole, Vault.com Inc, 132 W 31 St, 17th fl, New York, NY 10001 *Tel:* 212-366-4212 *Toll Free Tel:* 800-535-2074 *Fax:* 212-366-6117 (cust serv) *E-mail:* editors@vault.com; customerservice@vault.com *Web Site:* www.vault.com, pg 265

Weberg, Inga, Redleaf Press, 10 Yorkton Ct, St Paul, MN 55117 *Tel:* 651-641-0508 *Toll Free Tel:* 800-423-8309 *Toll Free Fax:* 800-641-0115 *Web Site:* www.redleafpress.org, pg 207

Weberman, Alisa, Listen & Live Audio Inc, PO Box 817, Roseland, NJ 07068-0817 *Tel:* 201-558-9000 *Toll Free Tel:* 800-653-9400 (orders) *Fax:* 201-558-9800 *Web Site:* www.listenandlive.com, pg 140

Weckbaugh, Patty, Book Publicists of Southern California, 714 Crescent Dr, Beverly Hills, CA 90210 *Tel:* 323-461-3921 *Fax:* 323-461-0917 *Web Site:* www.bookpublicists.org, pg 600

Wedge, Phil, Cottonwood Press, University of Kansas, Kansas Union, Rm 400, 1301 Jayhawk Blvd, Lawrence, KS 66045 *Tel:* 785-864-4520 *Web Site:* www.englishcw.ku.edu/cottonwood, pg 64

Weed, Susun, Ash Tree Publishing, PO Box 64, Woodstock, NY 12498 *Tel:* 845-246-8081 *Fax:* 845-246-8081 *E-mail:* info@ashtreepublishing.com *Web Site:* www.ashtreepublishing.com, pg 24

Weeks, Robin, Dancing Dakini Press, 77 Morning Sun Dr, Sedona, AZ 86336 *Tel:* 928-852-0129 *E-mail:* editor@dancingdakinipress.com *Web Site:* www.dancingdakinipress.com, pg 70

Weeren, Scott, Aptara Inc, 3110 Fairview Park Dr, Suite 900, Falls Church, VA 22042 *Tel:* 703-352-0001 *E-mail:* info@aptaracorp.com *Web Site:* www.aptaracorp.com, pg 520

Wegendt, Sr Christina, Pauline Books & Media, 50 St Paul's Ave, Boston, MA 02130 *Tel:* 617-522-8911 *Toll Free Tel:* 800-876-4463 (orders); 800-836-9723 (cust serv) *Fax:* 617-541-9805 *E-mail:* editorial@paulinemedia.com (ms submissions); orderentry@pauline.org (cust serv) *Web Site:* www.pauline.org, pg 184

Wegner, Gregory R, GLCA New Writers Awards, 535 W William St, Suite 301, Ann Arbor, MI 48103 *Tel:* 734-661-2350 *Fax:* 734-661-2349 *Web Site:* www.glca.org, pg 689

Wehmueller, Jacqueline C, The Johns Hopkins University Press, 2715 N Charles St, Baltimore, MD 21218-4363 *Tel:* 410-516-6900; 410-516-6987 (journal orders outside US & CN) *Toll Free Tel:* 800-537-5487 (book orders & cust serv); 800-548-1784 (journal orders) *Fax:* 410-516-6968; 410-516-3866 (journal orders) *E-mail:* hfscustserv@press.jhu.edu (cust serv); jrnlcirc@press.jhu.edu (journal orders) *Web Site:* www.press.jhu.edu; muse.jhu.edu, pg 127

Wehner, Aaron, Crown Publishing Group, c/o Penguin Random House Inc, 1745 Broadway, New York, NY 10019 *Tel:* 212-782-9000 *Toll Free Tel:* 888-264-1745 *Fax:* 212-940-7408 *E-mail:* crownosm@penguinrandomhouse.com *Web Site:* crownpublishing.com, pg 68

Wehner, Aaron, Clarkson Potter Publishers, c/o Random House Inc, 1745 Broadway, New York, NY 10019 *Tel:* 212-782-9000 *Toll Free Tel:* 888-264-1745 *Fax:* 212-572-6181 *Web Site:* www.clarksonpotter.com; www.randomhouse.com/crown/clarksonpotter, pg 195

Wehner, Aaron, Ten Speed Press, 2625 Alcatraz Ave, Unit 505, Berkeley, CA 94705 *Tel:* 510-285-3000 *Toll Free Tel:* 800-841-BOOK (841-2665) *E-mail:* csorders@randomhouse.com *Web Site:* crownpublishing.com/imprint/ten-speed-press, pg 243

Weidemann, Jason, University of Minnesota Press, 111 Third Ave S, Suite 290, Minneapolis, MN 55401-2520 *Tel:* 612-627-1970 *Fax:* 612-627-1980 *E-mail:* ump@umn.edu *Web Site:* www.upress.umn.edu, pg 257

Weidknecht, Katrina, Stewart, Tabori & Chang, 115 W 18 St, 6th fl, New York, NY 10011 *Tel:* 212-519-1200 *Fax:* 212-519-1210 *Web Site:* www.abramsbooks.com, pg 236

Weidman, Anna, University of California Press, 2120 Berkeley Way, Berkeley, CA 94704-1012 *Tel:* 510-642-4247 *Fax:* 510-643-7127 *E-mail:* askucp@ucpress.edu (books); customerservice@ucpressjournals.com *Web Site:* www.ucpress.edu, pg 255

Weight, Alden PhD, Sourced Media Books, 29 Via Regalo, San Clemente, CA 92673 *Tel:* 949-813-0182 *E-mail:* info@sourcedmediabooks.com *Web Site:* sourcedmediabooks.com, pg 231

Weigl, Linda, Weigl Educational Publishers Ltd, 6325 Tenth St SE, Calgary, AB T2H 2Z9, Canada *Tel:* 403-233-7747 *Toll Free Tel:* 800-668-0766 *Fax:* 403-233-7769 *Toll Free Fax:* 866-449-3445 *E-mail:* info@weigl.com; orders@weigl.com *Web Site:* www.weigl.ca; av2books.com, pg 504

Weikart, Jim, International Association of Crime Writers Inc, North American Branch, 243 Fifth Ave, Suite 537, New York, NY 10016 *Tel:* 212-243-8966 *Fax:* 815-361-1477 *E-mail:* info@crimewritersna.org *Web Site:* www.crimewritersna.org, pg 607

Weikersheimer, Joshua R, ASCP Press, 33 W Monroe St, Suite 1600, Chicago, IL 60603 *Tel:* 312-541-4999 *Toll Free Tel:* 800-267-2727 *Fax:* 312-541-4998 *Web Site:* www.ascp.org, pg 24

Weil, Gideon, HarperCollins General Books Group, 195 Broadway, New York, NY 10007 *Tel:* 212-207-7000 *Web Site:* www.harpercollins.com, pg 105

Weil, Joe, Binghamton University Creative Writing Program, c/o Dept of English, PO Box 6000, Binghamton, NY 13902-6000 *Tel:* 607-777-2168 *Fax:* 607-777-2408 *E-mail:* cwpro@binghamton.edu *Web Site:* english.binghamton.edu/cwpro, pg 659

Weil, Robert, W W Norton & Company Inc, 500 Fifth Ave, New York, NY 10110-0017 *Tel:* 212-354-5500 *Toll Free Tel:* 800-233-4830 (orders & cust serv) *Fax:* 212-869-0856 *Toll Free Fax:* 800-458-6515 *Web Site:* www.wwnorton.com, pg 171

Weiland, Matt, W W Norton & Company Inc, 500 Fifth Ave, New York, NY 10110-0017 *Tel:* 212-354-5500 *Toll Free Tel:* 800-233-4830 (orders & cust serv) *Fax:* 212-869-0856 *Toll Free Fax:* 800-458-6515 *Web Site:* www.wwnorton.com, pg 172

Weimann, Frank, Folio Literary Management LLC, The Film Center Bldg, 630 Ninth Ave, Suite 1101, New York, NY 10036 *Tel:* 212-400-1494 *Fax:* 212-967-0977 *Web Site:* www.foliolit.com, pg 552

Wein, Lauren, Houghton Mifflin Harcourt Trade & Reference Division, 222 Berkeley St, Boston, MA 02116 *Tel:* 617-351-5000 *Toll Free Tel:* 800-225-3362 *Web Site:* www.hmhco.com, pg 115

Weinbaum, Robyn, Florida Writers Association Conference, PO Box 66069, St Pete Beach, FL 33736-6069 *Web Site:* www.floridawriters.net, pg 651

Weinbaum, Robyn, Florida Writers Association Inc, PO Box 66069, St Pete Beach, FL 33736-6069 *Web Site:* www.floridawriters.net, pg 606

Weinberg, Jeffrey H, Water Row Press, PO Box 438, Sudbury, MA 01776 *Tel:* 508-485-8515 *Fax:* 508-229-0885 *E-mail:* contact@waterrowbooks.com *Web Site:* www.waterrowbooks.com, pg 267

Weinberg, Susan, Basic Books, 250 W 57 St, 15th fl, New York, NY 10107 *Tel:* 212-340-8164; 212-340-8136 *Fax:* 212-340-8135 *E-mail:* perseus.promos@perseusbooks.com *Web Site:* www.basicbooks.com; perseusbooks.com, pg 31

Weinberg, Susan, Nation Books, 116 E 16 St, 8th fl, New York, NY 10003 *Tel:* 212–822–0250 *Fax:* 212-253-5356 *E-mail:* submissions@nationbooks.org *Web Site:* www.nationbooks.org, pg 163

Weinberg, Susan, The Perseus Books Group, 387 Park Ave S, 12th fl, New York, NY 10016 *Tel:* 212-340-8100 *Toll Free Tel:* 800-343-4499 (cust serv) *Fax:* 212-340-8105 *Web Site:* www.perseusbooksgroup.com, pg 189

Weinberg, Susan, PublicAffairs, 250 W 57 St, Suite 1321, New York, NY 10107 *Tel:* 212-397-6666 *Toll Free Tel:* 800-343-4499 (orders) *Fax:* 212-397-4277 *E-mail:* publicaffairs@perseusbooks.com *Web Site:* www.publicaffairsbooks.com, pg 200

Weinberger, Russell, Brockman Inc, 260 Fifth Ave, 10th fl, New York, NY 10001 *Tel:* 212-935-8900 *Fax:* 212-935-5535 *E-mail:* rights@brockman.com *Web Site:* www.brockman.com, pg 544

Weiner, Allison, Chronicle Books LLC, 680 Second St, San Francisco, CA 94107 *Tel:* 415-537-4200 *Toll Free Tel:* 800-759-0190 (cust serv) *Fax:* 415-537-4460

Wells, Vicky, The University of North Carolina Press, 116 S Boundary St, Chapel Hill, NC 27514-3808 *Tel:* 919-966-3561 *Fax:* 919-966-3829 *E-mail:* uncpress@unc.edu *Web Site:* www.uncpress.unc.edu, pg 258

Welsh, Jill, Chicago Women in Publishing, PO Box 268107, Chicago, IL 60626 *Tel:* 773-508-0351 *Fax:* 435-604-6049 *E-mail:* info@cwip.org *Web Site:* www.cwip.org, pg 603

Welsh, Kara, NAL, 375 Hudson St, New York, NY 10014 *Tel:* 212-366-2000 *E-mail:* online@penguinputnam.com *Web Site:* www.penguinputnam.com; us.penguingroup.com, pg 162

Welsh, Sara, Naomi Berber Memorial Award, 200 Deer Run Rd, Sewickley, PA 15143-2324 *Tel:* 412-259-1705 *Toll Free Tel:* 800-910-4283 (ext 705) *Fax:* 412-749-9890 *E-mail:* printing@printing.org *Web Site:* www.printing.org/berberaward, pg 671

Welsh, Sara, Education Awards of Excellence, 200 Deer Run Rd, Sewickley, PA 15143-2324 *Tel:* 412-259-1705 *Toll Free Tel:* 800-910-4283 (ext 705) *Fax:* 412-749-9890 *E-mail:* printing@printing.org *Web Site:* www.printing.org/educationaward, pg 683

Welsh, Sara, Frederick D Kagy Education Award of Excellence, 200 Deer Run Rd, Sewickley, PA 15143-2324 *Tel:* 412-259-1705 *Toll Free Tel:* 800-910-4283 (ext 705) *Fax:* 412-749-9890 *E-mail:* printing@printing.org *Web Site:* www.printing.org/page/3630, pg 697

Welsh, Sara, Robert F Reed Technology Medal, 200 Deer Run Rd, Sewickley, PA 15143-2324 *Tel:* 412-259-1705 *Toll Free Tel:* 800-910-4283 (ext 705) *Fax:* 412-749-9890 *E-mail:* printing@printing.org *Web Site:* www.printing.org/reedaward, pg 723

Welsh, Sara, William D Schaeffer Environmental Award, 200 Deer Run Rd, Sewickley, PA 15143-2324 *Tel:* 412-259-1705 *Toll Free Tel:* 800-910-4283 (ext 705) *Fax:* 412-749-9890 *E-mail:* printing@printing.org *Web Site:* www.printing.org/page/3783, pg 727

Weltz, Jennifer, Jean V Naggar Literary Agency Inc (JVNLA), 216 E 75 St, Suite 1-E, New York, NY 10021 *Tel:* 212-794-1082 *E-mail:* jvnla@jvnla.com *Web Site:* www.jvnla.com, pg 566

Wender, Phyllis, The Gersh Agency (TGA), 41 Madison Ave, 33rd fl, New York, NY 10010 *Tel:* 212-997-1818 *E-mail:* info@gershla.com *Web Site:* www.gershagency.com, pg 553

Wengerd, Marvin, Carlisle Press - Walnut Creek, 2673 Township Rd 421, Sugarcreek, OH 44681 *Tel:* 330-852-1900 *Toll Free Tel:* 800-852-4482 *Fax:* 330-852-3285, pg 50

Wentworth, K D, L Ron Hubbard's Writers of the Future Contest, PO Box 1630, Los Angeles, CA 90078 *Tel:* 323-466-3310 *Fax:* 323-466-6474 *E-mail:* contests@authorservicesinc.com *Web Site:* www.writersofthefuture.com, pg 693

Werk, Dawn, Alpha Books, 375 Hudson St, New York, NY 10014 *Tel:* 212-366-2000, pg 9

Werksman, Deb, Sourcebooks Inc, 1935 Brookdale Rd, Suite 139, Naperville, IL 60563 *Tel:* 630-961-3900 *Toll Free Tel:* 800-432-7444 *Fax:* 630-961-2168 *E-mail:* info@sourcebooks.com; customersupport@sourcebooks.com *Web Site:* www.sourcebooks.com, pg 230

Werner, Doug, Tracks Publishing, 140 Brightwood Ave, Chula Vista, CA 91910 *Tel:* 619-476-7125 *Toll Free Tel:* 800-443-3570 *Fax:* 619-476-8173 *E-mail:* tracks@cox.net *Web Site:* www.startupsports.com, pg 247

Werner, George, Pearson Higher Education, 225 River St, Hoboken, NJ 07030-4772 *Tel:* 201-236-7000 *Fax:* 201-236-3381 *Web Site:* www.pearsonhighered.com, pg 185

Werner, Rich, F+W, A Content + eCommerce Company, 10151 Carver Rd, Suite 200, Blue Ash, OH 45242 *Tel:* 513-531-2690 *Toll Free Tel:* 800-289-0963 (trade accts); 800-258-0929 (orders) *E-mail:* contact_us@fwmedia.com *Web Site:* www.fwcommunity.com, pg 86

Werstler, Larisa, Dufour Editions Inc, PO Box 7, Chester Springs, PA 19425 *Tel:* 610-458-5005 *Fax:* 610-458-7103 *E-mail:* info@dufoureditions.com *Web Site:* www.dufoureditions.com, pg 77

Wertheimer, Neil, The Reader's Digest Association Inc, 750 Third Ave, New York, NY 10017 *Tel:* 914-238-1000; 646-293-6284 *Toll Free Tel:* 800-310-6261 (cust serv) *Fax:* 914-238-4559 *Web Site:* www.rd.com; www.rda.com, pg 205

Werts, Lynn, University Press of Florida, 15 NW 15 St, Gainesville, FL 32603-2079 *Tel:* 352-392-1351 *Toll Free Tel:* 800-226-3822 (orders only) *Fax:* 352-392-0590 *Toll Free Fax:* 800-680-1955 (orders only) *E-mail:* info@upf.com *Web Site:* www.upf.com, pg 261

Werz, Ed, JayJo Books LLC, One Huntington Quadrangle, Suite 1N03, Melville, NY 11747 *Tel:* 516-496-4863 *Toll Free Tel:* 800-999-6884 *Fax:* 516-496-4050 *Toll Free Fax:* 800-262-1886 *E-mail:* jayjobooks@guidance-group.com *Web Site:* www.guidance-group.com; www.jayjo.com, pg 126

Weschcke, Carl L, Llewellyn Publications, 2143 Wooddale Dr, Woodbury, MN 55125 *Tel:* 651-291-1970 *Toll Free Tel:* 800-843-6666 *Fax:* 651-291-1908 *E-mail:* publicity@llewellyn.com *Web Site:* www.llewellyn.com, pg 142

Wesley, Mark, me+mi publishing inc, 400 S Knoll St, Suite B, Wheaton, IL 60187 *Toll Free Tel:* 888-251-1444 *Fax:* 630-588-9804 *E-mail:* rw@rosawesley.com *Web Site:* www.memima.com, pg 153

Wessels, Cindy, University of Pittsburgh Press, 7500 Thomas Blvd, Pittsburgh, PA 15260 *Tel:* 412-383-2456 *Fax:* 412-383-2466 *E-mail:* info@upress.pitt.edu *Web Site:* www.upress.pitt.edu, pg 259

Wessler, Derek, McGraw-Hill Education, 2 Penn Plaza, New York, NY 10121-2298 *Tel:* 212-904-2000 *E-mail:* customer.service@mcgraw-hill.com *Web Site:* www.mheducation.com; www.mheducation.com/custserv.html, pg 151

West, Ann, Mazda Publishers Inc, One Park Plaza, Suite 600, Irvine, CA 92614 *Tel:* 714-751-5252 *Fax:* 714-751-4805 *E-mail:* mazdapub@aol.com *Web Site:* www.mazdapub.com, pg 150

West, J C, Abaris Books, 64 Wall St, Norwalk, CT 06850 *Tel:* 203-838-8402 *Fax:* 203-857-0730 *E-mail:* abaris@abarisbooks.com *Web Site:* abarisbooks.com, pg 2

West, J C, EastBridge, 70 New Canaan Ave, Norwalk, CT 06850 *Tel:* 203-855-9125 *Fax:* 203-857-0730 *E-mail:* asia@eastbridgebooks.org; ask@eastbridgebooks.org *Web Site:* www.eastbridgebooks.org, pg 78

West, Salem, Bywater Books, PO Box 3671, Ann Arbor, MI 48106-3671 *Tel:* 734-662-8815 *Web Site:* bywaterbooks.com, pg 48

Westberg, Phyllis, Harold Ober Associates Inc, 425 Madison Ave, New York, NY 10017 *Tel:* 212-759-8600 *Fax:* 212-759-9428 *Web Site:* www.haroldober.com, pg 567

Westermann, Christian, Europa Editions, 214 W 29 St, Suite 1003, New York, NY 10001 *Tel:* 212-868-6844 *Fax:* 212-868-6845 *E-mail:* info@europaeditions.com *Web Site:* www.europaeditions.com, pg 84

Westfall, William, Barbour Publishing Inc, 1810 Barbour Dr, Uhrichsville, OH 44683 *Tel:* 740-922-6045 *Fax:* 740-922-5948 *E-mail:* info@barbourbooks.com *Web Site:* www.barbourbooks.com, pg 30

Westlund, Laura, University of Minnesota Press, 111 Third Ave S, Suite 290, Minneapolis, MN 55401-2520 *Tel:* 612-627-1970 *Fax:* 612-627-1980 *E-mail:* ump@umn.edu *Web Site:* www.upress.umn.edu, pg 257

Westmoreland, Lisa, Ten Speed Press, 2625 Alcatraz Ave, Unit 505, Berkeley, CA 94705 *Tel:* 510-285-3000 *Toll Free Tel:* 800-841-BOOK (841-2665) *E-mail:* csorders@randomhouse.com *Web Site:* crownpublishing.com/imprint/ten-speed-press, pg 243

Weston, Pamela, Research & Education Association (REA), 61 Ethel Rd W, Piscataway, NJ 08854 *Tel:* 732-819-8880 *Fax:* 732-819-8808 (orders) *E-mail:* info@rea.com *Web Site:* www.rea.com, pg 208

Westwood, Bruce, Westwood Creative Artists Ltd, 94 Harbord St, Toronto, ON M5S 1G6, Canada *Tel:* 416-964-3302 *Fax:* 416-975-9209 *E-mail:* wca_office@wcaltd.com *Web Site:* www.wcaltd.com, pg 579

Wetstein, Rachel, Transcontinental Music Publications, 633 Third Ave, New York, NY 10017 *Tel:* 212-650-4101; 212-650-4120 *Toll Free Tel:* 888-489-8242 (orders) *Fax:* 212-650-4119 *E-mail:* tmp@urj.org; press@urj.org *Web Site:* www.transcontinentalmusic.com, pg 248

Wexler, David, Carolrhoda Books, 241 First Ave N, Minneapolis, MN 55401 *Tel:* 612-332-3344 *Toll Free Tel:* 800-328-4929 *Fax:* 612-332-7615 *Toll Free Fax:* 800-332-1132 *E-mail:* info@lernerbooks.com *Web Site:* www.lernerbooks.com, pg 50

Wexler, David, Carolrhoda Lab™, 241 First Ave N, Minneapolis, MN 55401 *Tel:* 612-332-3344 *Toll Free Tel:* 800-328-4929 *Fax:* 612-332-7615 *Toll Free Fax:* 800-332-1132 (US) *E-mail:* info@lernerbooks.com *Web Site:* www.lernerbooks.com, pg 50

Wexler, David, ediciones Lerner, 241 First Ave N, Minneapolis, MN 55401 *Tel:* 612-332-3344 *Toll Free Tel:* 800-328-4929 *Fax:* 612-332-7615 *Toll Free Fax:* 800-332-1132 *E-mail:* info@lernerbooks.com *Web Site:* www.lernerbooks.com, pg 79

Wexler, David, First Avenue Editions, 241 First Ave N, Minneapolis, MN 55401 *Tel:* 612-332-3344 *Toll Free Tel:* 800-328-4929 *Fax:* 612-332-7615 *Toll Free Fax:* 800-332-1132 *E-mail:* info@lernerbooks.com *Web Site:* www.lernerbooks.com, pg 89

Wexler, David, Graphic Universe™, 241 First Ave N, Minneapolis, MN 55401 *Tel:* 612-332-3344 *Toll Free Tel:* 800-328-4929 *Fax:* 612-332-7615 *Toll Free Fax:* 800-332-1132 *E-mail:* info@lernerbooks.com *Web Site:* www.lernerbooks.com, pg 99

Wexler, David, Lerner Publications, 241 First Ave N, Minneapolis, MN 55401 *Tel:* 612-332-3344 *Toll Free Tel:* 800-328-4929 *Fax:* 612-332-7615 *Toll Free Fax:* 800-332-1132 *E-mail:* info@lernerbooks.com *Web Site:* www.lernerbooks.com, pg 137

Wexler, David, Lerner Publishing Group Inc, 241 First Ave N, Minneapolis, MN 55401 *Tel:* 612-332-3344 *Toll Free Tel:* 800-328-4929 *Fax:* 612-332-7615 *Toll Free Fax:* 800-332-1132 *E-mail:* info@lernerbooks.com *Web Site:* www.lernerbooks.com, pg 137

Wexler, David, LernerClassroom, 241 First Ave N, Minneapolis, MN 55401 *Tel:* 612-332-3344 *Toll Free Tel:* 800-328-4929 *Fax:* 612-332-7615 *Toll Free Fax:* 800-332-1132 *E-mail:* info@lernerbooks.com *Web Site:* www.lernerbooks.com, pg 137

Wexler, David, Millbrook Press, 241 First Ave N, Minneapolis, MN 55401 *Tel:* 612-332-3344 *Toll Free Tel:* 800-328-4929 (US only) *Fax:* 612-332-7615 *Toll Free Fax:* 800-332-1132, pg 157

Wexler, David, Twenty-First Century Books, 241 First Ave N, Minneapolis, MN 55401 *Tel:* 612-332-3344 *Toll Free Tel:* 800-328-4929 *Fax:* 612-332-7615 *Toll Free Fax:* 800-332-1132 *E-mail:* info@lernerbooks.com *Web Site:* www.lernerbooks.com, pg 251

Wexler, Pearl, Paul Kohner Agency, 9300 Wilshire Blvd, Suite 555, Beverly Hills, CA 90212 *Tel:* 310-550-1060 *Fax:* 310-276-1083, pg 560

Weyenberg, Patricia, Penguin Group (USA) LLC Sales, 375 Hudson St, New York, NY 10014 *Tel:* 212-366-2000 *E-mail:* online@penguinputnam.com *Web Site:* us.penguingroup.com, pg 186

Whalen, Bill, BCFL, 4806 Martinique Way, Naples, FL 34119 *Tel:* 908-447-3553 *Fax:* 239-596-8611 *E-mail:* BCFLGroup@gmail.com *Web Site:* judgingfloraldesign.com, pg 507

Whalen, Casey, Rizzoli International Publications Inc, 300 Park Ave S, 4th fl, New York, NY 10010-5399 *Tel:* 212-387-3400 *Toll Free Tel:* 800-522-6657 (orders only) *Fax:* 212-387-3535 *E-mail:* publicity@rizzoliusa.com *Web Site:* www.rizzoliusa.com, pg 209

Whalen, John F Jr, Cider Mill Press Book Publishers LLC, 12 Spring St, Kennebunkport, ME 04046 *Tel:* 207-967-8232 *Fax:* 207-967-8233 *Web Site:* www.cidermillpress.com, pg 58

Whalen, Kimberly, Trident Media Group LLC, 41 Madison Ave, 36th fl, New York, NY 10010 *Tel:* 212-333-1511 *E-mail:* info@tridentmediagroup.com; press@tridentmediagroup.com *Web Site:* www.tridentmediagroup.com, pg 577

Whalen, Lindsay, The Penguin Press, 375 Hudson St, New York, NY 10014, pg 187

Whalen, Stasia, Penguin Random House Speakers Bureau, 1745 Broadway, Mail Drop 13-1, New York, NY 10019 *Tel:* 212-572-2013 *E-mail:* speakers@penguinrandomhouse.com *Web Site:* www.prhspeakers.com, pg 588

Whalen, Will, Alexander Street Press LLC, 3212 Duke St, Alexandria, VA 22314 *Tel:* 703-212-8520 *Toll Free Tel:* 800-889-5937 *Fax:* 703-940-6584 *E-mail:* sales@alexanderstreet.com; marketing@alexanderstreet.com; info@alexanderstreet.com *Web Site:* alexanderstreet.com, pg 7

Whaley, Glenn, STM Learning Inc, 55 Westport Plaza, Suite 455, St Louis, MO 63146 *Tel:* 314-434-2424 *Toll Free Tel:* 800-600-0330 *Fax:* 314-434-2425 *E-mail:* info@stmlearning.com; orders@stmlearning.com *Web Site:* www.stmlearning.com, pg 236

Whaley, Marianne, STM Learning Inc, 55 Westport Plaza, Suite 455, St Louis, MO 63146 *Tel:* 314-434-2424 *Toll Free Tel:* 800-600-0330 *Fax:* 314-434-2425 *E-mail:* info@stmlearning.com; orders@stmlearning.com *Web Site:* www.stmlearning.com, pg 236

Whaley, Marika, Harvard Ukrainian Research Institute, 34 Kirkland St, Cambridge, MA 02138 *Tel:* 617-495-4053 *Fax:* 617-495-8097 *E-mail:* huri@fas.harvard.edu *Web Site:* www.huri.harvard.edu, pg 107

Wharton, Campbell, Crown Publishing Group, c/o Penguin Random House Inc, 1745 Broadway, New York, NY 10019 *Tel:* 212-782-9000 *Toll Free Tel:* 888-264-1745 *Fax:* 212-940-7408 *E-mail:* crownosm@penguinrandomhouse.com *Web Site:* crownpublishing.com, pg 68

Wharton, Sarah, Random House Children's Books, 1745 Broadway, New York, NY 10019 *Tel:* 212-782-9000 *Toll Free Tel:* 800-200-3552 *Fax:* 212-782-9452 *Web Site:* randomhousekids.com, pg 204

Whatley, Chris, United Nations Association of the United States of America, 1750 Pennsylvania Ave NW, Suite 300, Washington, DC 20006 *Tel:* 202-887-9040 *Fax:* 202-887-9021 *Web Site:* www.unausa.org, pg 620

Wheaton, Robert, Doubleday Canada, One Toronto St, Suite 300, Toronto, ON M5C 2V6, Canada *Tel:* 416-364-4449 *Fax:* 416-364-6863 *Web Site:* www.randomhouse.ca, pg 479

Wheaton, Robert, Knopf Canada, One Toronto St, Suite 300, Toronto, ON M5C 2V6, Canada *Tel:* 416-364-4449 *Toll Free Tel:* 888-523-9292 *Fax:* 416-364-6863 *Web Site:* www.randomhouse.ca, pg 490

Wheaton, Robert, Penguin Random House Canada Limited, 320 Front St W, Suite 1400, Toronto, ON M5V 3B6, Canada *Tel:* 416-364-4449 *Toll Free Tel:* 888-523-9292 (cust serv) *Fax:* 416-364-6863; 416-364-6653 (subs rts) *Web Site:* penguinrandomhouse.ca, pg 495

Wheeler, Betsy, Juniper Summer Writing Institute, c/o University Conference Services, 810 Campus Ctr, One Campus Ctr Way, Amherst, MA 01003 *Tel:* 413-545-5510 *E-mail:* juniperinstitute@hfa.umass.edu *Web Site:* www.umass.edu/juniperinstitute, pg 652

Wheeler, Diane, Kalmbach Publishing Co, 21027 Crossroads Circle, Waukesha, WI 53186 *Tel:* 262-796-8776 *Toll Free Tel:* 800-533-6644 (cust serv & orders) *Fax:* 262-796-1615 (sales & cust serv); 262-798-6468 (edit) *E-mail:* customerservice@kalmbach.com *Web Site:* www.kalmbach.com; www.kalmbachstore.com, pg 129

Wheeler, John, Lumina Datamatics, 4 Collins Ave, Plymouth, MA 02360 *Tel:* 508-746-0300 *Fax:* 508-746-3233 *E-mail:* info@luminadatamatics.com *Web Site:* luminadatamatics.com, pg 530

Whelan, Maria, Touchstone, 1230 Avenue of the Americas, New York, NY 10020, pg 247

Whelan, Michael F, The Baker Street Irregulars (BSI), 7938 Mill Stream Circle, Indianapolis, IN 46278 *Tel:* 317-293-2212; 317-956-6666 (cell) *Web Site:* bakerstreetjournal.com, pg 600

Whelchel, Sandy, Associated Business Writers of America Inc, 10940 S Parker Rd, Suite 508, Parker, CO 80134 *Tel:* 303-841-0246 *E-mail:* natlwritersassn@hotmail.com *Web Site:* www.nationalwriters.com, pg 597

Whelchel, Sandy, National Writers Association, 10940 S Parker Rd, Suite 508, Parker, CO 80134 *Tel:* 303-841-0246 *E-mail:* natlwritersassn@hotmail.com *Web Site:* www.nationalwriters.com, pg 613

Whelchel, Sandy, National Writers Association Novel Contest, 10940 S Parker Rd, Suite 508, Parker, CO 80134 *Tel:* 303-841-0246 *E-mail:* natlwritersassn@hotmail.com *Web Site:* www.nationalwriters.com, pg 711

Whitaker, Laura, Bloomsbury Publishing Inc, 1385 Broadway, 5th fl, New York, NY 10018 *Tel:* 212-419-5300 *E-mail:* marketingusa@bloomsbury.com; adultpublicityusa@bloomsbury.com; askacademic@bloomsbury.com *Web Site:* www.bloomsbury.com, pg 40

Whitbread, Thomas, University of Texas at Austin, Creative Writing Program, Dept of English, PAR 108, One University Sta, Mailcode B5000, Austin, TX 78712-1164 *Tel:* 512-471-5132; 512-471-4991 *Fax:* 512-471-4909 *Web Site:* www.utexas.edu/cola/depts/english/creative-writing, pg 664

White, Craig M, EDC Publishing, 10302 E 55 Place, Tulsa, OK 74146-6515 *Tel:* 918-622-4522 *Toll Free Tel:* 800-475-4522 *Fax:* 918-665-7919 *Toll Free Fax:* 800-743-5660 *E-mail:* edc@edcpub.com *Web Site:* www.edcpub.com, pg 79

White, Darrin, Milton Acorn Poetry Award, 115 Richmond St, Charlottetown, PE C1A 1H7, Canada *Tel:* 902-368-4410 *Toll Free Tel:* 888-734-2784 *Fax:* 902-368-4418 *E-mail:* peiwritersguild@gmail.com *Web Site:* www.peiwritersguild.com, pg 665

White, Darrin, The Aliant Creative Writing Award for Young People, 115 Richmond St, Charlottetown, PE C1A 1H7, Canada *Tel:* 902-368-4410 *Toll Free Tel:* 888-734-2784 *Fax:* 902-368-4418 *E-mail:* peiwritersguild@gmail.com *Web Site:* www.peiwritersguild.com, pg 666

White, Darrin, Lucy Maud Montgomery Literature for Children Prize, 115 Richmond St, Charlottetown, PE C1A 1H7, Canada *Tel:* 902-368-4410 *Toll Free Tel:* 888-734-2784 *Fax:* 902-368-4418 *E-mail:* peiwritersguild@gmail.com *Web Site:* www.peiwritersguild.com, pg 708

White, Darrin, Short Story Award, 115 Richmond St, Charlottetown, PE C1A 1H7, Canada *Tel:* 902-368-4410 *Toll Free Tel:* 888-734-2784 *Fax:* 902-368-4418 *E-mail:* peiwritersguild@gmail.com *Web Site:* www.peiwritersguild.com, pg 728

White, Doug, Bloomsbury Publishing Inc, 1385 Broadway, 5th fl, New York, NY 10018 *Tel:* 212-419-5300 *E-mail:* marketingusa@bloomsbury.com; adultpublicityusa@bloomsbury.com; askacademic@bloomsbury.com *Web Site:* www.bloomsbury.com, pg 40

White, Elizabeth, The Monacelli Press, 236 W 27 St, 4th fl, New York, NY 10001 *Tel:* 212-229-9925 *E-mail:* contact@monacellipress.com *Web Site:* www.monacellipress.com, pg 159

White, Emily, The Mountaineers Books, 1001 SW Klickitat Way, Suite 201, Seattle, WA 98134 *Tel:* 206-223-6303 *Toll Free Tel:* 800-553-4453 *Fax:* 206-223-6306 *Toll Free Fax:* 800-568-7604 *E-mail:* mbooks@mountaineersbooks.org *Web Site:* www.mountaineersbooks.org, pg 161

White, Howard, Douglas & McIntyre (2013) Ltd, 4437 Rondeview Rd, Madeira Park, BC V0N 2H1, Canada *Toll Free Tel:* 800-667-2988 *E-mail:* info@douglas-mcintyre.com *Web Site:* www.douglas-mcintyre.com, pg 479

White, Howard, Harbour Publishing Co Ltd, 4437 Rondeview Rd, Madeira Park, BC V0N 2H0, Canada *Tel:* 604-883-2730 *Toll Free Tel:* 800-667-2988 *Fax:* 604-883-9451 *E-mail:* info@harbourpublishing.com *Web Site:* www.harbourpublishing.com, pg 487

White, Hudson, Ocean Tree Books, 1325 Cerro Gordo Rd, Santa Fe, NM 87501 *Tel:* 505-983-1412 *Fax:* 505-983-0899 *Web Site:* www.oceantree.com, pg 173

White, Jodi, Libris Award for Author of the Year, 1881 Yonge St, Suite 800, Toronto, ON M4S 3C4, Canada *Tel:* 416-922-6678 *Toll Free Tel:* 888-373-8245 *Fax:* 416-467-7886 *E-mail:* info@retailcouncil.org *Web Site:* www.retailcouncil.org, pg 700

White, Jodi, Libris Children's Picture Book of the Year, 1881 Yonge St, Suite 800, Toronto, ON M4S 3C4, Canada *Tel:* 416-922-6678 *Toll Free Tel:* 888-373-8245 *Fax:* 416-467-7886 *E-mail:* info@retailcouncil.org *Web Site:* www.retailcouncil.org, pg 700

White, Jodi, Libris Distributor of the Year, 1881 Yonge St, Suite 800, Toronto, ON M4S 3C4, Canada *Tel:* 416-922-6678 *Toll Free Tel:* 888-373-8245 *Fax:* 416-467-7886 *E-mail:* info@retailcouncil.org *Web Site:* www.retailcouncil.org, pg 701

White, Jodi, Libris Editor of the Year, 1881 Yonge St, Suite 800, Toronto, ON M4S 3C4, Canada *Tel:* 416-922-6678 *Toll Free Tel:* 888-373-8245 *Fax:* 416-467-7886 *E-mail:* info@retailcouncil.org *Web Site:* www.retailcouncil.org, pg 701

White, Jodi, Libris Fiction Book of the Year, 1881 Yonge St, Suite 800, Toronto, ON M4S 3C4, Canada *Tel:* 416-922-6678 *Toll Free Tel:* 888-373-8245 *Fax:* 416-467-7886 *E-mail:* info@retailcouncil.org *Web Site:* www.retailcouncil.org, pg 701

White, Jodi, Libris Publisher of the Year, 1881 Yonge St, Suite 800, Toronto, ON M4S 3C4, Canada *Tel:* 416-922-6678 *Toll Free Tel:* 888-373-8245 *Fax:* 416-467-7886 *E-mail:* info@retailcouncil.org *Web Site:* www.retailcouncil.org, pg 701

White, Jodi, Libris Sales Rep of the Year, 1881 Yonge St, Suite 800, Toronto, ON M4S 3C4, Canada *Tel:* 416-922-6678 *Toll Free Tel:* 888-373-8245 *Fax:* 416-467-7886 *E-mail:* info@retailcouncil.org *Web Site:* www.retailcouncil.org, pg 701

White, Jodi, Libris Small Press Publisher of the Year, 1881 Yonge St, Suite 800, Toronto, ON M4S 3C4, Canada *Tel:* 416-922-6678 *Toll Free Tel:* 888-373-8245 *Fax:* 416-467-7886 *E-mail:* info@retailcouncil.org *Web Site:* www.retailcouncil.org, pg 701

White, Nancy, Word Works Washington Prize, Adirondack Community College, Dearlove Hall, 640 Bay Rd, Queensbury, NY 12804 *Fax:* 301-581-9443 *E-mail:* editor@wordworksbooks.org *Web Site:* www.wordworksbooks.org, pg 737

White, Pam, Random House Children's Books, 1745 Broadway, New York, NY 10019 *Tel:* 212-782-9000 *Toll Free Tel:* 800-200-3552 *Fax:* 212-782-9452 *Web Site:* randomhousekids.com, pg 203

White, Peter, Begell House Inc Publishers, 50 North St, Danbury, CT 06810 *Tel:* 203-456-6161 *Fax:* 203-456-6167 *E-mail:* orders@begellhouse.com *Web Site:* www.begellhouse.com, pg 33

White, Randall, EDC Publishing, 10302 E 55 Place, Tulsa, OK 74146-6515 *Tel:* 918-622-4522 *Toll Free Tel:* 800-475-4522 *Fax:* 918-665-7919 *Toll Free Fax:* 800-743-5660 *E-mail:* edc@edcpub.com *Web Site:* www.edcpub.com, pg 79

White, Stephen C, Mystic Seaport Museum Inc, PO Box 6000, Mystic, CT 06355-0990 *Tel:* 860-572-5302; 860-572-0711 (visitor serv) *Toll Free Tel:* 800-248-1066 (wholesale orders only); 800-331-2665 (retail orders only) *Fax:* 860-572-5321 *E-mail:* info@mysticseaport.org *Web Site:* www.mysticseaport.org, pg 162

Wiesepape, Betty, Texas Institute of Letters (TIL), c/o 7748 Hwy 290 W, Austin, TX 78736-3202 *E-mail:* president@texasinstituteofletters.org; secretary@texasinstituteofletters.org *Web Site:* www.texasinstituteofletters.org, pg 620

Wiesepape, Betty, Texas Institute of Letters Awards, c/o 7748 Hwy 290 W, Austin, TX 78736-3202 *Tel:* 512-683-5640 *E-mail:* president@texasinstituteofletters.org *Web Site:* www.texasinstituteofletters.org, pg 732

Wiewora, Kristen, Running Press Book Publishers, 2300 Chestnut St, Philadelphia, PA 19103-4399 *Tel:* 215-567-5080 *Toll Free Tel:* 800-343-4499 (cust serv & orders) *Fax:* 215-568-2919 *Toll Free Fax:* 800-453-2884 (cust serv & orders) *E-mail:* perseus.promos@perseusbooks.com *Web Site:* www.runningpress.com, pg 212

Wigg, Carol J, Sinauer Associates Inc, 23 Plumtree Rd, Sunderland, MA 01375 *Tel:* 413-549-4300 *Fax:* 413-549-1118 *E-mail:* publish@sinauer.com; orders@sinauer.com *Web Site:* www.sinauer.com, pg 226

Wight, Katy, Edward Elgar Publishing Inc, The William Pratt House, 9 Dewey Ct, Northampton, MA 01060-3815 *Tel:* 413-584-5551 *Toll Free Tel:* 800-390-3149 (orders) *Fax:* 413-584-9933 *E-mail:* elgarinfo@e-elgar.com; elgarsales@e-elgar.com; elgarsubmissions@e-elgar.com (edit) *Web Site:* www.e-elgar.com; www.elgaronline.com (ebooks & journals), pg 80

Wikey, Daniel, Crown Publishing Group, c/o Penguin Random House Inc, 1745 Broadway, New York, NY 10019 *Tel:* 212-782-9000 *Toll Free Tel:* 888-264-1745 *Fax:* 212-940-7408 *E-mail:* crownosm@penguinrandomhouse.com *Web Site:* crownpublishing.com, pg 68

Wikey, Daniel, Ten Speed Press, 2625 Alcatraz Ave, Unit 505, Berkeley, CA 94705 *Tel:* 510-285-3000 *Toll Free Tel:* 800-841-BOOK (841-2665) *E-mail:* csorders@randomhouse.com *Web Site:* crownpublishing.com/imprint/ten-speed-press, pg 243

Wikey, Daniel, Watson-Guptill Publications, c/o Random House Inc, 1745 Broadway, New York, NY 10019 *Tel:* 212-782-9000 *Fax:* 212-940-7381 *E-mail:* crownbiz@randomhouse.com *Web Site:* www.randomhouse.com/crown/watsonguptill, pg 268

Wilcox, Alana, Coach House Books, 80 bpNichol Lane, Toronto, ON M5S 3J4, Canada *Tel:* 416-979-2217 *Toll Free Tel:* 800-367-6360 (outside Toronto) *Fax:* 416-977-1158 *E-mail:* mail@chbooks.com *Web Site:* www.chbooks.com, pg 477

Wilcox, Bruce, University of Massachusetts Press, East Experiment Sta, 671 N Pleasant St, Amherst, MA 01003 *Tel:* 413-545-2217 *Fax:* 413-545-1226 *E-mail:* info@umpress.umass.edu *Web Site:* www.umass.edu/umpress, pg 257

Wilcox, Jeanne, Quincannon Publishing Group, PO Box 8100, Glen Ridge, NJ 07028-8100 *Tel:* 973-380-9942 *E-mail:* editors@quincannongroup.com *Web Site:* www.quincannongroup.com, pg 202

Wilcox, Lynn, Syracuse University Press, 621 Skytop Rd, Suite 110, Syracuse, NY 13244-5290 *Tel:* 315-443-5534 *Toll Free Tel:* 800-365-8929 (cust serv) *Fax:* 315-443-5545 *E-mail:* supress@syr.edu *Web Site:* syracuseuniversitypress.syr.edu, pg 239

Wilcox, Mary, Houghton Mifflin Harcourt Trade & Reference Division, 222 Berkeley St, Boston, MA 02116 *Tel:* 617-351-5000 *Toll Free Tel:* 800-225-3362 *Web Site:* www.hmhco.com, pg 115

Wilcoxon, Deborah, Research Press, 2612 N Mattis Ave, Champaign, IL 61822 *Tel:* 217-352-3273 *Toll Free Tel:* 800-519-2707 *Fax:* 217-352-1221 *E-mail:* rp@researchpress.com; orders@researchpress.com *Web Site:* www.researchpress.com, pg 208

Wilde, Michael, Words into Print, 57 Prince St, Suite 4R, New York, NY 10012 *Tel:* 212-741-1393 *Fax:* 419-441-1393 *E-mail:* query@wordsintoprint.org *Web Site:* www.wordsintoprint.org, pg 536

Wilderson, Joe, Rocky Mountain Books Ltd (RMB), 103-1075 Pendergast St, Victoria, BC V8V 0A1, Canada *Tel:* 250-360-0829 *Fax:* 250-386-0829 *Web Site:* www.rmbooks.com, pg 497

Wildfong, Kathryn, Wayne State University Press, Leonard N Simons Bldg, 4809 Woodward Ave, Detroit, MI 48201-1309 *Tel:* 313-577-6120 *Toll Free Tel:* 800-978-7323 *Fax:* 313-577-6131 *Web Site:* www.wsupress.wayne.edu, pg 268

Wiley, Jennie, Annual Cape Cod Writers' Center Conference, 919 Main St, Osterville, MA 02655 *Tel:* 508-420-0200 *E-mail:* writers@capecodwriterscenter.org *Web Site:* www.capecodwriterscenter.org, pg 650

Wiley, Jennie, Young Writers' Workshop, 919 Main St, Osterville, MA 02655 *Tel:* 508-420-0200 *E-mail:* writers@capecodwriterscenter.org *Web Site:* www.capecodwriterscenter.org, pg 657

Wiley, Peter Booth, John Wiley & Sons Inc, 111 River St, Hoboken, NJ 07030-5774 *Tel:* 201-748-6000 *Toll Free Tel:* 800-225-5945 (cust serv) *Fax:* 201-748-6088 *E-mail:* info@wiley.com *Web Site:* www.wiley.com, pg 272

Wilhelm, Le, Love Creek Annual Short Play Festival, 2144 45 Ave, Long Island City, NY 11101 *Tel:* 718-786-9397 *E-mail:* lovecreekle@aol.com; squaank@yahoo.com (submissions), pg 703

Wilkes, Deborah, Focus, PO Box 44937, Indianapolis, IN 46244-0937 *Tel:* 317-635-9250 *Fax:* 317-635-9292 *E-mail:* customer@hackettpublishing.com; editorial@hackettpublishing.com *Web Site:* focusbookstore.com, pg 90

Wilkes, Deborah, Hackett Publishing Co Inc, 3333 Massachusetts Ave, Indianapolis, IN 46218 *Tel:* 317-635-9250 (orders & cust serv) *Fax:* 317-635-9292 *Toll Free Fax:* 800-783-9213 *E-mail:* customer@hackettpublishing.com *Web Site:* www.hackettpublishing.com, pg 103

Wilkie, Craig, The University Press of Kentucky, 663 S Limestone St, Lexington, KY 40508-4008 *Tel:* 859-257-8400 *Fax:* 859-257-8481 *Web Site:* www.kentuckypress.com, pg 261

Wilkins, Timothy, Princeton University Press, 41 William St, Princeton, NJ 08540-5237 *Tel:* 609-258-4900 *Toll Free Tel:* 800-777-4726 (orders) *Fax:* 609-258-6305 *Toll Free Fax:* 800-999-1958 *E-mail:* orders@cpfsinc.com *Web Site:* press.princeton.edu, pg 197

Wilkinson, Christine, Wilkinson Studios Inc, 1121 E Main St, Suite 310, St Charles, IL 60174 *Tel:* 630-549-0504 *Web Site:* www.wilkinsonstudios.com, pg 585

Wilkinson, Jamie, F+W, A Content + eCommerce Company, 10151 Carver Rd, Suite 200, Blue Ash, OH 45242 *Tel:* 513-531-2690 *Toll Free Tel:* 800-289-0963 (trade accts); 800-258-0929 (orders) *E-mail:* contact_us@fwmedia.com *Web Site:* www.fwcommunity.com, pg 86

Wilkinson, Marco, The Field Poetry Prize, 50 N Professor St, Oberlin, OH 44074-1091 *Tel:* 440-775-8408 *Fax:* 440-775-8124 *E-mail:* oc.press@oberlin.edu *Web Site:* www.oberlin.edu/ocpress; www.oberlin.edu/ocpress/prize.htm (guidelines), pg 685

Wilkinson, Marco, Oberlin College Press, 50 N Professor St, Oberlin, OH 44074-1091 *Tel:* 440-775-8408 *Fax:* 440-775-8124 *E-mail:* oc.press@oberlin.edu *Web Site:* www.oberlin.edu/ocpress, pg 173

Wilkinson, Thomas, Maisonneuve Press, 6423 Adelphi Rd, Hyattsville, MD 20782 *Tel:* 301-277-7505 *Fax:* 301-277-2467 *Web Site:* www.maisonneuvepress.com, pg 145

Wilkofsky, Roth, Pearson Arts & Sciences, 330 Hudson St, 9th fl, New York, NY 10013-1048 *Tel:* 917-981-2200 *Web Site:* www.pearsonhighered.com, pg 184

Wilks, Rick, Annick Press Ltd, 15 Patricia Ave, Toronto, ON M2M 1H9, Canada *Tel:* 416-221-4802 *Fax:* 416-221-8400 *E-mail:* annickpress@annickpress.com *Web Site:* www.annickpress.com, pg 471

Will, Julie, HarperCollins General Books Group, 195 Broadway, New York, NY 10007 *Tel:* 212-207-7000 *Web Site:* www.harpercollins.com, pg 105

Willcox, Clair, University of Missouri Press, 2910 Le Mone Blvd, Columbia, MO 65201 *Tel:* 573-882-7641 *Toll Free Tel:* 800-621-2736 (orders) *Fax:* 573-884-4498 *Web Site:* press.umsystem.edu, pg 257

Willett, Bryce, Ulysses Press, PO Box 3440, Berkeley, CA 94703-0440 *Tel:* 510-601-8301 *Toll Free Tel:* 800-377-2542 *Fax:* 510-601-8307 *E-mail:* ulysses@ulyssespress.com *Web Site:* www.ulyssespress.com, pg 252

Willey, Paul, The Book Tree, 3316 Adams Ave, Suite A, San Diego, CA 92116 *Tel:* 619-280-1263 *Toll Free Tel:* 800-700-8733 (orders) *Fax:* 619-280-1285 *E-mail:* orders@thebooktree.com; titles@thebooktree.com; info@thebooktree.com *Web Site:* thebooktree.com, pg 42

Willey, Susan, New Readers Press, 1320 Jamesville Ave, Syracuse, NY 13210 *Tel:* 315-422-9121 *Toll Free Tel:* 800-448-8878 *Fax:* 315-422-6369 *Toll Free Fax:* 866-894-2100 *E-mail:* nrp@proliteracy.org *Web Site:* www.newreaderspress.com, pg 168

Williams, Bob, Burns Entertainment & Sports Marketing, 820 Davis St, Suite 222, Evanston, IL 60201 *Tel:* 847-866-9400 *Fax:* 847-491-9778 *E-mail:* burnsl@burnsent.com *Web Site:* burnsent.com, pg 587

Williams, Bryan C, Abingdon Press, 201 Eighth Ave S, Nashville, TN 37203-3919 *Tel:* 615-749-6000 (academic books) *Toll Free Tel:* 800-251-3320 *Fax:* 615-749-6056 (academic books) *Toll Free Fax:* 800-836-7802 (orders) *E-mail:* orders@abingdonpress.com *Web Site:* www.abingdonpress.com, pg 2

Williams, Carlene H, Cantos Para Todos, 4749 Hillcrest St, Bel Aire, KS 67226 *Tel:* 316-239 6477 *Web Site:* www.cantos.org, pg 49

Williams, Carolyn C, Africana Homestead Legacy Publishers Inc, 811 Church Rd, Suite 105, Cherry Hill, NJ 08002 *Tel:* 856-773-0694 *Fax:* 856-486-1135 *E-mail:* customer-service@ahlpub.com; sales@ahlpub.com; editors@ahlpub.com *Web Site:* www.ahlpub.com, pg 6

Williams, Dan, Baskerville Publishers Poetry Award, Texas Christian University, Dept of English, TCU Box 297270, Fort Worth, TX 76129 *Tel:* 817-257-5907 *Fax:* 817-257-7709 *E-mail:* descant@tcu.edu *Web Site:* www.descant.tcu.edu, pg 670

Williams, Dan, Betsy Colquitt Award for Poetry, Texas Christian University, Dept of English, TCU Box 297270, Fort Worth, TX 76129 *Tel:* 817-257-5907 *Fax:* 817-257-7709 *E-mail:* descant@tcu.edu *Web Site:* www.descant.tcu.edu, pg 679

Williams, Dan, Frank O'Connor Prize for Fiction, Texas Christian University, Dept of English, TCU Box 297270, Fort Worth, TX 76129 *Tel:* 817-257-5907 *Fax:* 817-257-7709 *E-mail:* descant@tcu.edu *Web Site:* www.descant.tcu.edu, pg 714

Williams, Dan, Texas Christian University Press, 3000 Sandage Ave, Fort Worth, TX 76109 *Tel:* 817-257-7822 *Toll Free Tel:* 800-826-8911 *Fax:* 817-257-5075 *Web Site:* www.prs.tcu.edu, pg 243

Williams, Dan, Gary Wilson Award for Short Fiction, Texas Christian University, Dept of English, TCU Box 297270, Fort Worth, TX 76129 *Tel:* 817-257-5907 *Fax:* 817-257-7709 *E-mail:* descant@tcu.edu *Web Site:* www.descant.tcu.edu, pg 736

Williams, Heather, Arbordale Publishing, 612 Johnnie Dodds Blvd, Suite A2, Mount Pleasant, SC 29464 *Tel:* 843-971-6722 *Toll Free Tel:* 877-243-3457 *Fax:* 843-216-3804 *E-mail:* customerservice@arbordalepublishing.com; info@arbordalepublishing.com *Web Site:* www.arbordalepublishing.com, pg 21

Williams, Isabel, Texas Tech University Press, 2903 Fourth St, Suite 201, Lubbock, TX 79409 *Tel:* 806-742-2982 *Toll Free Tel:* 800-832-4042 *Fax:* 806-742-2979 *E-mail:* ttup@ttu.edu *Web Site:* www.ttupress.org, pg 243

Williams, Jan, Jan Williams Indexing Services, 300 Dartmouth College Hwy, Lyme, NH 03768-3207 *Tel:* 603-795-4924 *Web Site:* www.janwilliamsindexing.com, pg 528

Williams, Jane A, Bluestocking Press, 3045 Sacramento St, No 1014, Placerville, CA 95667-1014 *Tel:* 530-622-8586 *Toll Free Tel:* 800-959-8586 *Fax:* 530-642-9222 *E-mail:* customerservice@bluestockingpress.com; orders@bluestockingpress.com *Web Site:* www.bluestockingpress.com, pg 41

Williams, Jessica, HarperCollins General Books Group, 195 Broadway, New York, NY 10007 *Tel:* 212-207-7000 *Web Site:* www.harpercollins.com, pg 106

Williams, John J, Consumertronics, PO Box 23097, Albuquerque, NM 87192 *Tel:* 505-321-1034 *E-mail:* wizguru@consumertronics.net *Web Site:* www.consumertronics.net, pg 62

Williams, John Taylor "Ike", Kneerim & Williams Agency, 90 Canal St, Boston, MA 02114 *Tel:* 617-303-1650 *Web Site:* www.kwblit.com, pg 560

Williams, Kathy, Brown Books Publishing Group, 16250 Knoll Trail, Suite 205, Dallas, TX 75248 *Tel:* 972-381-0009 *Fax:* 972-248-4336 *E-mail:* publishing@brownbooks.com *Web Site:* www.brownbooks.com, pg 47

Williams, Kim, Princeton University Press, 41 William St, Princeton, NJ 08540-5237 *Tel:* 609-258-4900 *Toll Free Tel:* 800-777-4726 (orders) *Fax:* 609-258-6305 *Toll Free Fax:* 800-999-1958 *E-mail:* orders@cpfsinc.com *Web Site:* press.princeton.edu, pg 197

Williams, Laura, Oak Knoll Press, 310 Delaware St, New Castle, DE 19720 *Tel:* 302-328-7232 *Toll Free Tel:* 800-996-2556 *Fax:* 302-328-7274 *E-mail:* oakknoll@oakknoll.com *Web Site:* www.oakknoll.com, pg 172

Williams, Laurencia, Consumertronics, PO Box 23097, Albuquerque, NM 87192 *Tel:* 505-321-1034 *E-mail:* wizguru@consumertronics.net *Web Site:* www.consumertronics.net, pg 62

Williams, Leslie, Twenty-Third Publications, One Montauk Ave, Suite 200, New London, CT 06320 *Tel:* 860-437-3012 *Toll Free Tel:* 800-321-0411 (orders) *Toll Free Fax:* 800-572-0788 *E-mail:* 23ppweb@bayard-inc.com *Web Site:* www.twentythirdpublications.com, pg 251

Williams, Lindsay, ASM Press, 1752 "N" St NW, Washington, DC 20036-2904 *Tel:* 202-737-3600 *Toll Free Tel:* 800-546-2416 *Fax:* 202-942-9342 *E-mail:* books@asmusa.org *Web Site:* estore.asm.org, pg 25

Williams, Margaret K, Standard Publishing, 8805 Governors Hill Dr, Suite 400, Cincinnati, OH 45249 *Tel:* 513-931-4050 *Toll Free Tel:* 800-543-1353 *Fax:* 513-931-0950 *Toll Free Fax:* 877-867-5751 *E-mail:* customerservice@standardpub.com *Web Site:* www.standardpub.com, pg 233

Williams, Matt, Groundwood Books, 110 Spadina Ave, Suite 801, Toronto, ON M5V 2K4, Canada *Tel:* 416-363-4343 *Fax:* 416-363-1017 *E-mail:* genmail@groundwoodbooks.com *Web Site:* www.houseofanansi.com, pg 486

Williams, Matt, House of Anansi Press Inc, 110 Spadina Ave, Suite 801, Toronto, ON M5V 2K4, Canada *Tel:* 416-363-4343 *Fax:* 416-363-1017 *E-mail:* customerservice@houseofanansi.com *Web Site:* www.houseofanansi.com, pg 488

Williams, Paul, American Society of Composers, Authors & Publishers (ASCAP), 1900 Broadway, New York City, NY 10023 *Tel:* 212-621-6000 *Toll Free Tel:* 800-952-7227 *Fax:* 212-612-8453 *E-mail:* info@ascap.com *Web Site:* www.ascap.com, pg 596

Williams, Rachel, Mount Hermon Christian Writers Conference, c/o Mount Hermon Association Inc, 37 Conference Dr, Felton, CA 95018 *Tel:* 831-335-4466 *Toll Free Tel:* 888-MH-CAMPS (642-2677 - registration) *Fax:* 831-335-9218 *E-mail:* info@mounthermon.org *Web Site:* www.mounthermon.org/writers, pg 653

Williams, Randall, NewSouth Books, 105 S Court St, Montgomery, AL 36104 *Tel:* 334-834-3556 *Fax:* 334-834-3557 *E-mail:* info@newsouthbooks.com *Web Site:* www.newsouthbooks.com, pg 169

Williams, Rob, Mountain Press Publishing Co, 1301 S Third W, Missoula, MT 59801 *Tel:* 406-728-1900 *Toll Free Tel:* 800-234-5308 *Fax:* 406-728-1635 *E-mail:* info@mtnpress.com *Web Site:* www.mountain-press.com, pg 160

Williams, Robert A, Optometric Extension Program Foundation, 1921 E Carnegie Ave, Suite 3-L, Santa Ana, CA 92705-5510 *Tel:* 949-250-8070 *Fax:* 949-250-8157 *E-mail:* oep@oep.org *Web Site:* www.oepf.org, pg 176

Williams, Roberta, American Printing House for the Blind Inc, 1839 Frankfort Ave, Louisville, KY 40206 *Tel:* 502-895-2405 *Toll Free Tel:* 800-223-1839 (cust serv) *Fax:* 502-899-2274 *E-mail:* info@aph.org *Web Site:* www.aph.org; shop.aph.org, pg 15

Williams, Dr Roger L MD, United States Pharmacopeia, 12601 Twinbrook Pkwy, Rockville, MD 20852-1790 *Tel:* 301-881-0666 *Toll Free Tel:* 800-227-8772 *Fax:* 301-816-8237 (mktg) *E-mail:* marketing@usp.org *Web Site:* www.usp.org, pg 253

Williams, Roger S, New England Publishing Associates Inc, One Carver Place, Lawrenceville, NJ 08648 *Tel:* 860-973-2439 *Web Site:* www.nepagency.com, pg 567

Williams, Sakina, Kensington Publishing Corp, 119 W 40 St, New York, NY 10018 *Tel:* 212-407-1500 *Toll Free Tel:* 800-221-2647 *Fax:* 212-935-0699 *Web Site:* www.kensingtonbooks.com, pg 130

Williams, Sandra, Mountain Writers Series, 2804 SE 27 Ave, Suite 2, Portland, OR 97202 *Tel:* 503-232-4517 *Fax:* 503-232-4517 *E-mail:* pdxmws@mountainwriters.org *Web Site:* www.mountainwriters.org, pg 653

Williams, Sarah, Chronicle Books LLC, 680 Second St, San Francisco, CA 94107 *Tel:* 415-537-4200 *Toll Free Tel:* 800-759-0190 (cust serv) *Fax:* 415-537-4460 *Toll Free Fax:* 800-858-7787 (orders); 800-286-9471 (cust serv) *E-mail:* frontdesk@chroniclebooks.com *Web Site:* www.chroniclebooks.com, pg 57

Williams, Stacie, Coffee House Press, 79 13 Ave NE, Suite 110, Minneapolis, MN 55413 *Tel:* 612-338-0125 *Fax:* 612-338-4004 *E-mail:* info@coffeehousepress.org *Web Site:* coffeehousepress.org, pg 60

Williams, Suzanne, The Canadian Writers' Foundation Inc (La Fondation des Ecrivains Canadiens), PO Box 13281, Kanata Sta, Ottawa, ON K2K 1X4, Canada *Tel:* 613-256-6937 *Fax:* 613-256-5457 *E-mail:* info@canadianwritersfoundation.org *Web Site:* www.canadianwritersfoundation.org, pg 623

Williams, Ta-Tanisha, Crown Publishing Group, c/o Penguin Random House Inc, 1745 Broadway, New York, NY 10019 *Tel:* 212-782-9000 *Toll Free Tel:* 888-264-1745 *Fax:* 212-940-7408 *E-mail:* crownosm@penguinrandomhouse.com *Web Site:* crownpublishing.com, pg 68

Williams, Thomas A PhD, Williams & Company Book Publishers, 1317 Pine Ridge Dr, Savannah, GA 31406 *Tel:* 912-352-0404 *E-mail:* bookpub@comcast.net *Web Site:* www.pubmart.com, pg 272

Williams, Tim, Edward Elgar Publishing Inc, The William Pratt House, 9 Dewey Ct, Northampton, MA 01060-3815 *Tel:* 413-584-5551 *Toll Free Tel:* 800-390-3149 (orders) *Fax:* 413-584-9933 *E-mail:* elgarinfo@e-elgar.com; elgarsales@e-elgar.com; elgarsubmissions@e-elgar.com (edit) *Web Site:* www.e-elgar.com; www.elgaronline.com (ebooks & journals), pg 80

Williams, Tracy, Little, Brown and Company, 1290 Avenue of the Americas, New York, NY 10019 *Tel:* 212-364-1100 *Fax:* 212-364-0952 *E-mail:* firstname.lastname@hbgusa.com *Web Site:* www.HachetteBookGroup.com, pg 141

Williamson, Alain, Editions Le Dauphin Blanc Inc, 825, boul Lebourgneuf, Suite 125, Quebec, QC G2J 0B9, Canada *Tel:* 418-845-4045 *Fax:* 418-845-1933 *E-mail:* info@dauphinblanc.com *Web Site:* www.dauphinblanc.com, pg 482

Williamson, Heather, Crown Publishing Group, c/o Penguin Random House Inc, 1745 Broadway, New York, NY 10019 *Tel:* 212-782-9000 *Toll Free Tel:* 888-264-1745 *Fax:* 212-940-7408 *E-mail:* crownosm@penguinrandomhouse.com *Web Site:* crownpublishing.com, pg 68

Williamson, Iain, Productive Publications, 7-B Pleasant Blvd, Unit 1210, Toronto, ON M4T 1K2, Canada *Tel:* 416-483-0634 *Toll Free Tel:* 877-879-2669 (orders) *Fax:* 416-322-7434 *E-mail:* productivepublications@rogers.com *Web Site:* www.productivepublications.ca, pg 496

Williamson, Lesley, Artists & Writers Summer Fellowships, 435 Ellis Hollow Creek Rd, Ithaca, NY 14850 *Tel:* 607-539-3146 *E-mail:* artscolony@saltonstall.org *Web Site:* www.saltonstall.org, pg 649

Williamson, Maureen, Roman Catholic Books, PO Box 2286, Fort Collins, CO 80522-2286 *Tel:* 970-490-2735 *Fax:* 904-212-1287 *Web Site:* www.booksforcatholics.com, pg 211

Williford, Lex, University of Texas at El Paso, Department of Creative Writing, MFA/Department of Creative Writing, Liberal Arts 415 UTEP, 500 W University Ave, El Paso, TX 79968-9991 *Tel:* 915-747-5713 *Fax:* 915-747-5523 *Web Site:* www.utep.edu/cw, pg 664

Willig, Alan, Don Buchwald & Associates Inc, 10 E 44 St, New York, NY 10017 *Tel:* 212-867-1200 *Fax:* 212-867-2434 *E-mail:* info@buchwald.com *Web Site:* www.buchwald.com, pg 545

Willig, Christine, Math Solutions®, One Harbor Dr, Suite 101, Sausalito, CA 94965 *Tel:* 415-332-4181 *Toll Free Tel:* 800-868-9092 *Fax:* 415-331-1931 *Toll Free Fax:* 877-942-8837 *E-mail:* info@mathsolutions.com; orders@mathsolutions.com *Web Site:* www.mathsolutions.com, pg 149

Willig, Christine, McGraw-Hill School Education Group, 8787 Orion Place, Columbus, OH 43240 *Tel:* 614-430-4000 *Toll Free Tel:* 800-848-1567 *Web Site:* www.mheducation.com, pg 152

Willinger, James L, Wide World of Maps Inc, 2626 W Indian School Rd, Phoenix, AZ 85017 *Tel:* 602-279-2324 *Toll Free Tel:* 800-279-7654 *Fax:* 602-279-2350 *E-mail:* sales@maps4u.com *Web Site:* www.maps4u.com, pg 271

Willis, Meredith Sue, Hamilton Stone Editions, PO Box 43, Maplewood, NJ 07040 *Tel:* 973-378-8361 *E-mail:* hstone@hamiltonstone.org *Web Site:* www.hamiltonstone.org, pg 104

Willoughby, Bruce E, University of Michigan Center for Japanese Studies, 1007 E Huron St, Ann Arbor, MI 48104-1690 *Tel:* 734-647-8885 *Fax:* 734-647-8886 *E-mail:* ii.cjspubs@umich.edu *Web Site:* www.cjspubs.lsa.umich.edu, pg 257

Willoughby-Harris, H Lee, Duke University Press, 905 W Main St, Suite 18B, Durham, NC 27701 *Tel:* 919-688-5134 *Toll Free Tel:* 888-651-0122 (US) *Fax:* 919-688-2615 *Toll Free Fax:* 888-651-0124 *E-mail:* orders@dukeupress.edu; permissions@dukeupress.edu *Web Site:* www.dukeupress.edu, pg 77

Wills, Juliet, Galaxy Press, 7051 Hollywood Blvd, Suite 200, Hollywood, CA 90028 *Tel:* 323-466-7815 *Toll Free Tel:* 877-8GALAXY (842-5299) *E-mail:* customers@galaxypress.com; info@galaxypress.com *Web Site:* www.galaxypress.com, pg 93

Wilmot, Jodie, National Association of College Stores (NACS), 500 E Lorain St, Oberlin, OH 44074 *Tel:* 440-775-7777 *Toll Free Tel:* 800-622-7498 *Fax:* 440-775-4769 *Web Site:* www.nacs.org, pg 611

Wilmoth, Anna, Gryphon House Inc, 6848 Leon's Way, Lewisville, NC 27023 *Toll Free Tel:* 800-638-0928 *Toll Free Fax:* 877-638-7576 *E-mail:* info@ghbooks.com *Web Site:* www.gryphonhouse.com, pg 101

Wilson, Adam, Gallery Books, 1230 Avenue of the Americas, New York, NY 10020 *Toll Free Tel:* 800-456-6798 *Fax:* 212-698-7284 *E-mail:* consumer.customerservice@simonandschuster.com *Web Site:* www.simonsays.com, pg 94

Wilson, Amy M, SkyLight Paths Publishing, Sunset Farm Offices, Rte 4, Woodstock, VT 05091 *Tel:* 802-457-4000 *Toll Free Tel:* 800-962-4544 *Fax:* 802-457-4004 *E-mail:* sales@skylightpaths.com *Web Site:* www.skylightpaths.com, pg 227

Wilson, Bev, Information Gatekeepers Inc, 1340 Soldiers Field Rd, Suite 2, Boston, MA 02135 *Tel:* 617-782-5033 *Fax:* 617-507-8338 *E-mail:* info@igigroup.com *Web Site:* www.igigroup.com, pg 121

Wilson, Edward E, Absey & Co Inc, 23011 Northcrest Dr, Spring, TX 77389 *Tel:* 281-257-2340 *Toll Free Tel:* 888-41-ABSEY (412-2739) *Fax:* 281-251-4676 *E-mail:* info@absey.biz *Web Site:* www.absey.biz, pg 3

Wilson, Elaine, Touchstone, 1230 Avenue of the Americas, New York, NY 10020, pg 247

Wilson, Gary, Green Dragon Books, 2875 S Ocean Blvd, Suite 200, Palm Beach, FL 33480 *Tel:* 561-533-6231 *Toll Free Tel:* 800-874-8844 *Fax:* 561-533-6233 *Toll Free Fax:* 888-874-8844 *E-mail:* info@greendragonbooks.com *Web Site:* greendragonbooks.com, pg 100

Wilson, J D, University of Alabama Press, 200 Hackberry Lane, 2nd fl, Tuscaloosa, AL 35487 *Tel:* 205-348-5180 *Fax:* 205-348-9201 *Web Site:* www.uapress.ua.edu, pg 254

Wilson, James, University of Louisiana at Lafayette Press, PO Box 40831, UL, Lafayette, LA 70504-0831 *Tel:* 337-482-6027 *Fax:* 337-482-6028 *E-mail:* cls@louisiana.edu *Web Site:* www.ulpress.org, pg 256

Wilson, Jeff, Simon & Schuster, Inc, 1230 Avenue of the Americas, New York, NY 10020 *Tel:* 212-698-7000 *Fax:* 212-698-7007 *E-mail:* firstname.lastname@simonandschuster.com *Web Site:* www.simonandschuster.com, pg 226

Wilson, Jennifer, Humanix Books LLC, PO Box 20989, West Palm Beach, FL 33416 *Tel:* 561-459-5997 *Toll Free Tel:* 855-371-7810 *Fax:* 561-241-6448 *Toll Free Fax:* 855-371-7809 *E-mail:* info@humanixbooks.com *Web Site:* www.humanixbooks.com, pg 117

Wilson, Jennifer, Kentucky Writers Conference, 1906 College Heights Blvd, Suite 11067, Bowling Green, KY 42101-1067 *Tel:* 270-745-4502 *Web Site:* www.sokybookfest.org, pg 652

Wilson, Kell, DK Publishing, 345 Hudson St, 2nd fl, New York, NY 10014 *Tel:* 646-674-4000 *Toll Free Tel:* 877-342-5357 (cust serv) *Web Site:* us.dk.com, pg 75

Wilson, Lance, Top of the Mountain Publishing, PO Box 2244, Pinellas Park, FL 33780-2244 *Tel:* 727-391-3958 *E-mail:* tag@abcinfo.com; info@abcinfo.com *Web Site:* abcinfo.com; www.topofthemountain.com, pg 247

Wilson, Laura, Macmillan Audio, 175 Fifth Ave, New York, NY 10010 *Tel:* 646-307-5151 *Toll Free Tel:* 888-330-8477 (cust serv) *Fax:* 917-534-0980 *Web Site:* www.macmillanaudio.com, pg 145

Wilson, Leah, BenBella Books Inc, 10300 N Central Expwy, Suite 400, Dallas, TX 75231 *Tel:* 214-750-3600 *Fax:* 214-750-3645 *E-mail:* feedback@benbellabooks.com *Web Site:* www.benbellabooks.com; www.smartpopbooks.com, pg 34

Wilson, Mary Ellen, Quirk Books, 215 Church St, Philadelphia, PA 19106 *Tel:* 215-627-3581 *Fax:* 215-627-5220 *E-mail:* general@quirkbooks.com *Web Site:* www.quirkbooks.com, pg 202

Wilson, Meredith, Houghton Mifflin Harcourt Trade & Reference Division, 222 Berkeley St, Boston, MA 02116 *Tel:* 617-351-5000 *Toll Free Tel:* 800-225-3362 *Web Site:* www.hmhco.com, pg 115

Wilson, Miriam J, Rocky River Publishers LLC, PO Box 1679, Shepherdstown, WV 25443-1679 *Tel:* 304-876-1868 *Fax:* 304-263-2949 *E-mail:* rockyriverpublishers@citlink.net *Web Site:* www.rockyriver.com, pg 210

Wilson, Pamela, University of Hawaii Press, 2840 Kolowalu St, Honolulu, HI 96822 *Tel:* 808-956-8255 *Toll Free Tel:* 888-UHPRESS (847-7377) *Fax:* 808-988-6052 *Toll Free Fax:* 800-650-7811 *E-mail:* uhpbooks@hawaii.edu *Web Site:* www.uhpress.hawaii.edu, pg 256

Wilson, Rick, Berrett-Koehler Publishers Inc, 1333 Broadway, Suite 1000, Oakland, CA 94612 *Tel:* 510-817-2277 *Fax:* 510-817-2278 *E-mail:* bkpub@bkpub.com *Web Site:* www.bkconnection.com, pg 35

Wilson, Sharon, University of Alberta Press, Ring House 2, Edmonton, AB T6G 2E1, Canada *Tel:* 780-492-3662 *Fax:* 780-492-0719 *Web Site:* www.uap.ualberta.ca, pg 502

Wilson, Stefanya, The Jack London Award, Box 17897, Encino, CA 91416-7897 *E-mail:* cwcsfv@gmail.com, pg 703

Wilson, Stefanya, Masters Literary Awards, PO Box 17897, Encino, CA 91416-7897 *Tel:* 818-377-4006 *E-mail:* titan91416@yahoo.com, pg 706

Wilson, Steve, McFarland, 960 NC Hwy 88 W, Jefferson, NC 28640 *Tel:* 336-246-4460 *Toll Free Tel:* 800-253-2187 (orders) *Fax:* 336-246-5018; 336-246-4403 (orders) *E-mail:* info@mcfarlandpub.com *Web Site:* www.mcfarlandpub.com, pg 150

Wilson, Steven, Book Sales Inc, 142 W 36 St, 4th fl, New York, NY 10018 *Tel:* 212-779-4971; 212-779-4972 *Toll Free Tel:* 866-483-5456 *Fax:* 212-779-6058 *E-mail:* sales@quartous.com; customerservice@quartous.com *Web Site:* www.booksalesusa.com, pg 42

Wilson, Victoria, Alfred A Knopf/Everyman's Library, c/o Random House Inc, 1745 Broadway, New York, NY 10019 *Tel:* 212-751-2600 *Toll Free Tel:* 800-638-6460 *Fax:* 212-572-2593 *Web Site:* www.knopfdoubleday.com, pg 132

Wiltshire, Betty C, Pioneer Publishing Co, Hwy 82 E, Carrolton, MS 38917 *Tel:* 662-237-6010 *E-mail:* pioneerse@tecinfo.com *Web Site:* www.pioneersoutheast.com, pg 192

Wimmer, Sandy, Standard Publishing, 8805 Governors Hill Dr, Suite 400, Cincinnati, OH 45249 *Tel:* 513-931-4050 *Toll Free Tel:* 800-543-1353 *Fax:* 513-931-0950 *Toll Free Fax:* 877-867-5751 *E-mail:* customerservice@standardpub.com *Web Site:* www.standardpub.com, pg 233

Winebarger, Albert, Penguin Group (USA) LLC Sales, 375 Hudson St, New York, NY 10014 *Tel:* 212-366-2000 *E-mail:* online@penguinputnam.com *Web Site:* us.penguingroup.com, pg 187

Wing, Eric, Carolyn Jenks Agency, 30 Cambridge Park Dr, Suite 3140, Cambridge, MA 02140 *Tel:* 617-354-5099 *Fax:* 617-354-5099 *E-mail:* queries@carolynjenksagency.com (submissions) *Web Site:* www.carolynjenksagency.com, pg 558

Wing, Frank, APA Talent & Literary Agency, 405 S Beverly Dr, Beverly Hills, CA 90212 *Tel:* 310-888-4200 *Fax:* 310-888-4242 *Web Site:* www.apa-agency.com, pg 541

Winge, Sara, O'Reilly Media Inc, 1005 Gravenstein Hwy N, Sebastopol, CA 95472 *Tel:* 707-827-7000; 707-827-7019 *Toll Free Tel:* 800-998-9938; 800-889-8969 *Fax:* 707-829-0104; 707-824-8268 *E-mail:* orders@oreilly.com *Web Site:* www.oreilly.com, pg 177

Winick, Eugene H, McIntosh & Otis Inc, 353 Lexington Ave, New York, NY 10016-0900 *Tel:* 212-687-7400 *Fax:* 212-687-6894 *E-mail:* info@mcintoshandotis.com *Web Site:* www.mcintoshandotis.com, pg 565

Winicour, Mike, Writers of the Round Table Press, 990 Bob-O-Link Rd, Highland Park, IL 60035 *Tel:* 949-375-1006 *Fax:* 815-346-2398 *Web Site:* www.roundtablecompanies.com, pg 277

Winnette, Andi, McSweeney's Publishing, 849 Valencia St, San Francisco, CA 94110 *Tel:* 415-642-5609 (cust serv) *Web Site:* www.mcsweeneys.net, pg 152

Winningham, Sharon, School Zone Publishing Co, 1819 Industrial Dr, Grand Haven, MI 49417 *Tel:* 616-846-5030 *Toll Free Tel:* 800-253-0564 *Fax:* 616-846-6181 *Toll Free Fax:* 800-550-4618 (orders only) *Web Site:* www.schoolzone.com, pg 219

Winns, Nadine, Abbeville Press, 137 Varick St, Suite 504, New York, NY 10013-1105 *Tel:* 212-366-5585 *Toll Free Tel:* 800-ARTBOOK (278-2665); 800-343-4499 (orders) *Fax:* 212-366-6966 *Toll Free Fax:* 800-351-5073 (orders) *E-mail:* abbeville@abbeville.com; sales@abbeville.com; marketing@abbeville.com; rights@abbeville.com *Web Site:* www.abbeville.com, pg 2

Winns, Nadine, Abbeville Publishing Group, 137 Varick St, Suite 504, New York, NY 10013 *Tel:* 212-366-5585 *Toll Free Tel:* 800-ART-BOOK (278-2665) *Fax:* 212-366-6966 *E-mail:* abbeville@abbeville.com; marketing@abbeville.com; sales@abbeville.com; rights@abbeville.com *Web Site:* www.abbeville.com, pg 2

Winslow, Anne, Algonquin Books, 400 Silver Cedar Ct, Suite 300, Chapel Hill, NC 27514-1585 *Tel:* 919-967-0108 *Fax:* 919-933-0272 *E-mail:* inquiry@algonquin.com *Web Site:* www.workman.com/algonquin, pg 8

Winslow, Susan, Macmillan Higher Education, 41 Madison Ave, 37th fl, New York, NY 10010 *Tel:* 212-576-9400 *Fax:* 212-689-2383 *Web Site:* www.macmillanhighered.com, pg 145

Winsor, Hugh, National Press Club of Canada Foundation Inc, 17 York St, Suite 201, Ottawa, ON K1N 9J6, Canada *E-mail:* info@pressclubcanada.ca *Web Site:* pressclubcanada.ca, pg 613

Winstanley, Nicole, Penguin Group (Canada), 90 Eglinton Ave E, Suite 700, Toronto, ON M4P 2Y3, Canada *Tel:* 416-925-2249 *Fax:* 416-925-0068 *E-mail:* customerservicescanada@penguinrandomhouse.com *Web Site:* penguinrandomhouse.ca, pg 494

Winstanley, Nicole, Penguin Random House Canada Limited, 320 Front St W, Suite 1400, Toronto, ON M5V 3B6, Canada *Tel:* 416-364-4449 *Toll Free Tel:* 888-523-9292 (cust serv) *Fax:* 416-364-6863; 416-364-6653 (subs rts) *Web Site:* penguinrandomhouse.ca, pg 495

Winston, Lois, Ashley Grayson Literary Agency, 1342 W 18 St, San Pedro, CA 90732 *Tel:* 310-548-4672 *E-mail:* graysonagent@earthlink.net; rights@graysonagency.com *Web Site:* graysonagency.com/blog/, pg 555

Winter, Carolyn Doyle, History Publishing Co LLC, PO Box 700, Palisades, NY 10964 *Tel:* 845-398-8161 *E-mail:* info@historypublishingco.com *Web Site:* www.historypublishingco.com, pg 112

Winter, Kel, Marion Street Press LLC, 4207 SE Woodstock Blvd, No 168, Portland, OR 97206 *Tel:* 503-888-4624 *Toll Free Fax:* 866-571-8359 *E-mail:* marionbooks@outlook.com *Web Site:* www.marionstreetpress.com, pg 147

Winter, Maureen, Hachette Books, 1290 Avenue of the Americas, New York, NY 10019 *Tel:* 212-364-1100 *Web Site:* www.hachettebookgroup.com, pg 102

Winters, Dawn B, FPMI Solutions Inc, 689 Discovery Dr, Suite 300, Huntsville, AL 35806 *Toll Free Tel:* 888-644-3764 *E-mail:* info@fpmi.com *Web Site:* www.fpmisolutions.com; www.fpmi.com, pg 92

Winters, Mr Tracy, Winters Publishing, 705 E Washington St, Greensburg, IN 47240 *Tel:* 812-663-4948 *Toll Free Tel:* 800-457-3230 *Fax:* 812-663-4948 *E-mail:* winterspublishing@gmail.com *Web Site:* www.winterspublishing.com, pg 273

Winton, Charlie, Counterpoint Press LLC, 1919 Fifth St, Berkeley, CA 94710 *Tel:* 510-704-0230 *Fax:* 510-704-0268 *E-mail:* info@counterpointpress.com *Web Site:* counterpointpress.com; www.sierraclub.org/books; softskull.com, pg 65

Winton, Helen M, The Reading Component, 3900 Parkview Lane, 3B, Irvine, CA 92612-2003 *Tel:* 949-387-6330, pg 533

Wirth, Jerry D, American Association of Colleges for Teacher Education (AACTE), 1307 New York Ave NW, Suite 300, Washington, DC 20005 *Tel:* 202-293-2450 *Fax:* 202-457-8095 *E-mail:* aacte@aacte.org *Web Site:* www.aacte.org, pg 11

Wise, Jay, Peace Hill Press, 18021 The Glebe Lane, Charles City, VA 23030 *Tel:* 804-829-5043 *Toll Free Tel:* 877-322-3445 (orders) *Fax:* 804-829-5704 *E-mail:* info@peacehillpress.com *Web Site:* www.peacehillpress.com, pg 184

Wise, Tomas, Schirmer Trade Books, 180 Madison Ave, 24th fl, New York, NY 10016 *Tel:* 212-254-2100 *Toll Free Tel:* 800-431-7187 (orders) *Fax:* 212-254-2013 *Web Site:* www.musicsales.com, pg 218

Wiseman, Charles, Peninsula Publishing, 26666 Birch Hill Way, Los Altos Hills, CA 94022 *Tel:* 650-948-2511 *Fax:* 650-948-5004 *E-mail:* sales@peninsulapublishing.com *Web Site:* www.peninsulapublishing.com, pg 188

Wiseman, Hannah, Peninsula Publishing, 26666 Birch Hill Way, Los Altos Hills, CA 94022 *Tel:* 650-948-2511 *Fax:* 650-948-5004 *E-mail:* sales@peninsulapublishing.com *Web Site:* www.peninsulapublishing.com, pg 188

Wiseman, Paula, Simon & Schuster Children's Publishing, 1230 Avenue of the Americas, New York, NY 10020 *Tel:* 212-698-7000 *Web Site:* KIDS.SimonandSchuster.com; TEEN.SimonandSchuster.com; simonandschuster.net; simonandschuster.biz, pg 225

Wisenthal, Paul, The Professional Writer, 175 W 12 St, Suite 6D, New York, NY 10011 *Tel:* 212-414-0188; 917-658-1946 (cell) *E-mail:* paul@theprofessionalwriter.com *Web Site:* www.theprofessionalwriter.com, pg 532

Wishard, Tammy, Anson Jones MD Award, 401 W 15 St, Austin, TX 78701 *Tel:* 512-370-1300 *Fax:* 512-370-1630 *Web Site:* www.texmed.org, pg 697

Wispelwey, June C, American Institute of Chemical Engineers (AIChE), 120 Wall St, 23rd fl, New York, NY 10005-4020 *Tel:* 203-702-7660 *Toll Free Tel:* 800-242-4363 *Fax:* 203-775-5177 *E-mail:* customerservice@aiche.org *Web Site:* www.aiche.org, pg 13

Wissoker, Ken, Duke University Press, 905 W Main St, Suite 18B, Durham, NC 27701 *Tel:* 919-688-5134 *Toll Free Tel:* 888-651-0122 (US) *Fax:* 919-688-2615 *Toll Free Fax:* 888-651-0124 *E-mail:* orders@dukeupress.edu; permissions@dukeupress.edu *Web Site:* www.dukeupress.edu, pg 77

Witcraft, Stacey, Random House Publishing Group, 1745 Broadway, New York, NY 10019 *Toll Free Tel:* 800-200-3552 *Web Site:* atrandom.com, pg 204

Witherell, Jennifer, InkWell Management, 521 Fifth Ave, 26th fl, New York, NY 10175 *Tel:* 212-922-3500 *Fax:* 212-922-0535 *E-mail:* info@inkwellmanagement.com; submissions@inkwellmanagement.com *Web Site:* inkwellmanagement.com, pg 557

Withers, Laurel, Playwrights Project, 3675 Ruffin Rd, Suite 330, San Diego, CA 92123 *Tel:* 858-384-2970 *Fax:* 858-384-2974 *E-mail:* write@playwrightsproject.org *Web Site:* www.playwrightsproject.org, pg 719

Witherspoon, Kim, InkWell Management, 521 Fifth Ave, 26th fl, New York, NY 10175 *Tel:* 212-922-3500 *Fax:* 212-922-0535 *E-mail:* info@inkwellmanagement.com; submissions@inkwellmanagement.com *Web Site:* inkwellmanagement.com, pg 557

Withington, Charles, Elsevier Inc, 225 Wyman St, Waltham, MA 02144 *Tel:* 781-663-5200 *Fax:* 781-663-2262 *E-mail:* bookscustomerservice-usa@elsevier.com *Web Site:* www.elsevier.com, pg 81

Withington, Marcy, Mystic Seaport Museum Inc, PO Box 6000, Mystic, CT 06355-0990 *Tel:* 860-572-5302; 860-572-0711 (visitor serv) *Toll Free Tel:* 800-248-1066 (wholesale orders only); 800-331-2665 (retail orders only) *Fax:* 860-572-5321 *E-mail:* info@mysticseaport.org *Web Site:* www.mysticseaport.org, pg 162

Witkin, Karrie, Harry N Abrams Inc, 115 W 18 St, 6th fl, New York, NY 10011 *Tel:* 212-206-7715 *Toll Free Tel:* 800-345-1359 *Fax:* 212-519-1210 *E-mail:* abrams@abramsbooks.com *Web Site:* www.abramsbooks.com, pg 3

Witlox, Cathy, WordWitlox, 70 Grainger Crescent, Ajax, ON L1T 4Y6, Canada *Tel:* 647-505-9673 *Web Site:* www.wordwitlox.com, pg 536

Witmore, Dr Michael, National Endowment for the Humanities, Mellon Foundation & Folger Long-term Fellowships, c/o Fellowship Committee, 201 E Capitol St SE, Washington, DC 20003 *Tel:* 202-544-4600 *Fax:* 202-544-4623 *E-mail:* institute@folger.edu *Web Site:* www.folger.edu, pg 710

Witt, Joseph W, Empire Publishing Service, PO Box 1344, Studio City, CA 91614-0344 *Tel:* 818-784-8918 *E-mail:* empirepubsvc@att.net *Web Site:* www.ppeps.com, pg 82

Witte, George, St Martin's Press, LLC, 175 Fifth Ave, New York, NY 10010 *Tel:* 646-307-5151 *Fax:* 212-420-9314 *E-mail:* firstname.lastname@macmillan.com *Web Site:* www.stmartins.com, pg 215

Witte, Steve, South Dakota Historical Society Press, 900 Governors Dr, Pierre, SD 57501 *Tel:* 605-773-6009 *Fax:* 605-773-6041 *E-mail:* info@sdshspress.com *Web Site:* sdshspress.com, pg 231

Woehlbier, Fred, Trans Tech Publications, c/o Enfield Distribution Co, 234 May St, Enfield, NH 03748 *Tel:* 603-632-7377 *Fax:* 603-632-5611 *E-mail:* usa-ttp@ttp.net; info@enfieldbooks.com *Web Site:* www.ttp.net, pg 248

Woehlbier, Thomas, Trans Tech Publications, c/o Enfield Distribution Co, 234 May St, Enfield, NH 03748 *Tel:* 603-632-7377 *Fax:* 603-632-5611 *E-mail:* usa-ttp@ttp.net; info@enfieldbooks.com *Web Site:* www.ttp.net, pg 248

Woerheide, Walt PhD, American College, 270 S Bryn Mawr Ave, Bryn Mawr, PA 19010 *Tel:* 610-526-1000 *Toll Free Tel:* 888-263-7265 *Fax:* 610-526-1310 *Web Site:* www.theamericancollege.edu, pg 12

Woessner, Steve, Brilliance Audio, 1704 Eaton Dr, Grand Haven, MI 49417 *Tel:* 616-846-5256 *Toll Free Tel:* 800-648-2312 (orders only) *Fax:* 616-846-0630 *E-mail:* customerservice@brillianceaudio.com *Web Site:* www.brillianceaudio.com, pg 46

Wofsy, Alan, Alan Wofsy Fine Arts, 1109 Geary Blvd, San Francisco, CA 94109 *Tel:* 415-292-6500 *Toll Free Tel:* 800-660-6403 *Fax:* 415-292-6594 (off & cust serv); 510-251-1840 (acctg) *E-mail:* order@art-books.com (orders); editeur@earthlink.net (edit); beauxarts@earthlink.net (cust serv) *Web Site:* www.art-books.com, pg 274

Wojcik, Tim, Levine|Greenberg|Rostan Literary Agency Inc, 307 Seventh Ave, Suite 2407, New York, NY 10001 *Tel:* 212-337-0934 *Fax:* 212-337-0948 *Web Site:* lgrliterary.com, pg 561

Wojtyla, Karen, Simon & Schuster Children's Publishing, 1230 Avenue of the Americas, New York, NY 10020 *Tel:* 212-698-7000 *Web Site:* KIDS.SimonandSchuster.com; TEEN.SimonandSchuster.com; simonandschuster.net; simonandschuster.biz, pg 225

Wolf, Maria, Institute of Governmental Studies, 109 Moses Hall, No 2370, Berkeley, CA 94720-2370 *Tel:* 510-642-1428 *Fax:* 510-642-3020; 510-642-5537 (orders) *E-mail:* igspress@berkeley.edu *Web Site:* www.igs.berkeley.edu, pg 122

Wolf, Wendy, Viking, 375 Hudson St, New York, NY 10014 *Tel:* 212-366-2000 *E-mail:* online@penguinputnam.com *Web Site:* www.penguinputnam.com; us.penguingroup.com, pg 265

Wolfe, Alexander, University of Pittsburgh Press, 7500 Thomas Blvd, Pittsburgh, PA 15260 *Tel:* 412-383-2456 *Fax:* 412-383-2466 *E-mail:* info@upress.pitt.edu *Web Site:* www.upress.pitt.edu, pg 259

Wolfe, Gary, New Author Publishing, 4 E Fulford Place, Brockville, ON K6V 2Z8, Canada *Tel:* 613-865-7471 *Web Site:* www.newauthorpublishing.com, pg 492

Wolfe, Jaymie Stuart, Pauline Books & Media, 50 St Paul's Ave, Boston, MA 02130 *Tel:* 617-522-8911 *Toll Free Tel:* 800-876-4463 (orders); 800-836-9723 (cust serv) *Fax:* 617-541-9805 *E-mail:* editorial@paulinemedia.com (ms submissions); orderentry@pauline.org (cust serv) *Web Site:* www.pauline.org, pg 184

Wolfe, Leslie R PhD, Center for Women Policy Studies, 4620 N Park Ave, Suite 302W, Chevy Chase, MD 20815 *Tel:* 301-986-0795 *E-mail:* cwps@centerwomenpolicy.org *Web Site:* www.centerwomenpolicy.org, pg 54

Wolfe, Margie, Second Story Press, 20 Maud St, Suite 401, Toronto, ON M5V 2M5, Canada *Tel:* 416-537-7850 *Fax:* 416-537-0588 *E-mail:* info@secondstorypress.ca *Web Site:* secondstorypress.ca, pg 498

Wolff, Doug, Workman Publishing Co Inc, 225 Varick St, 9th fl, New York, NY 10014-4381 *Tel:* 212-254-5900 *Toll Free Tel:* 800-722-7202 *Fax:* 212-254-8098 *E-mail:* info@workman.com *Web Site:* www.workman.com, pg 275

Wolff, Rebecca, Fence Books, University at Albany, Science Library 320, 1400 Washington Ave, Albany, NY 12222 *Tel:* 518-591-8162 *E-mail:* fence.fencebooks@gmail.com *Web Site:* www.fenceportal.org, pg 87

Wolff, Rebecca, Fence Modern Poets Series, University at Albany, Science Library 320, 1400 Washington Ave, Albany, NY 12222 *Tel:* 518-591-8162 *E-mail:* fence.fencebooks@gmail.com *Web Site:* www.fenceportal.org, pg 685

Wolff, Rebecca, Ottoline Morrell Prize, University at Albany, Science Library 320, 1400 Washington Ave, Albany, NY 12222 *Tel:* 518-591-8162 *E-mail:* fence.fencebooks@gmail.com *Web Site:* www.fenceportal.org, pg 709

Wolff, Rick, Houghton Mifflin Harcourt Trade & Reference Division, 222 Berkeley St, Boston, MA 02116 *Tel:* 617-351-5000 *Toll Free Tel:* 800-225-3362 *Web Site:* www.hmhco.com, pg 115

Wolford, Henry, Easy Money Press, 5419 87 St, Lubbock, TX 79424 *Tel:* 806-543-5215 *E-mail:* easymoneypress@yahoo.com, pg 79

Wolfsthal, Bill, Arcade Publishing Inc, 307 W 36 St, 11th fl, New York, NY 10018 *Tel:* 212-643-6816 *Fax:* 212-643-6819 *E-mail:* info@skyhorsepublishing.com (subs & foreign rts) *Web Site:* www.arcadepub.com, pg 21

Wollheim, Elizabeth R, DAW Books Inc, 375 Hudson St, New York, NY 10014 *Tel:* 212-366-2096 *Fax:* 212-366-2090 *E-mail:* daw@penguinrandomhouse.com *Web Site:* us.penguingroup.com; www.dawbooks.com, pg 71

Wolny, Karen, Palgrave Macmillan, 175 Fifth Ave, Suite 200, New York, NY 10010 *Tel:* 646-307-5151 *Fax:* 212-777-6359 *E-mail:* firstname.lastname@palgrave-usa.com *Web Site:* us.macmillan.com/Palgrave.aspx, pg 180

Wolny, Karen, St Martin's Press, LLC, 175 Fifth Ave, New York, NY 10010 *Tel:* 646-307-5151 *Fax:* 212-420-9314 *E-mail:* firstname.lastname@macmillan.com *Web Site:* www.stmartins.com, pg 215

Wolterstorff, Klaas, Wm B Eerdmans Publishing Co, 2140 Oak Industrial Dr NE, Grand Rapids, MI 49505 *Tel:* 616-459-4591 *Toll Free Tel:* 800-253-7521 *Fax:* 616-459-6540 *E-mail:* customerservice@eerdmans.com; sales@eerdmans.com *Web Site:* www.eerdmans.com, pg 80

Woltman, Kate, Kindred Productions, 1310 Taylor Ave, Winnipeg, MB R3M 3Z6, Canada *Tel:* 204-669-6575 *Toll Free Tel:* 800-545-7322 *Fax:* 204-654-1865 *E-mail:* custserv@kindredproductions.com; kindred@mbchurches.ca *Web Site:* www.kindredproductions.com, pg 490

Wolverton, Peter, St Martin's Press, LLC, 175 Fifth Ave, New York, NY 10010 *Tel:* 646-307-5151 *Fax:* 212-420-9314 *E-mail:* firstname.lastname@macmillan.com *Web Site:* www.stmartins.com, pg 215

Wolverton, Susan, Coe College Playwriting Festival, 1220 First Ave NE, Cedar Rapids, IA 52402 *Tel:* 319-399-8624 *Fax:* 319-399-8557 *Web Site:* www.theatre.coe.edu; www.coe.edu/academics/theatrearts/theatrearts_playwritingfestival, pg 678

Womack, Debra A MA, Whiskey Creek Press LLC, 541 Long Lane, Casper, WY 82609 *Tel:* 307-265-8585 *Fax:* 307-265-4640 *E-mail:* publisher@whiskeycreekpress.com; whiskeycreekpress@bresnan.net *Web Site:* www.whiskeycreekpress.com; www.torridbooks.com; www.weecreekpress.com, pg 270

Womack, Steven D PhD, Whiskey Creek Press LLC, 541 Long Lane, Casper, WY 82609 *Tel:* 307-265-8585 *Fax:* 307-265-4640 *E-mail:* publisher@whiskeycreekpress.com; whiskeycreekpress@bresnan.net *Web Site:* www.whiskeycreekpress.com; www.torridbooks.com; www.weecreekpress.com, pg 270

Wong, Betty, Watson-Guptill Publications, c/o Random House Inc, 1745 Broadway, New York, NY 10019 *Tel:* 212-782-9000 *Fax:* 212-940-7381 *E-mail:* crownbiz@randomhouse.com *Web Site:* www.randomhouse.com/crown/watsonguptill, pg 268

Wong, Ms Chi-Li, AEI (Atchity Entertainment International Inc), 9601 Wilshire Blvd, Unit 1202, Beverly Hills, CA 90210 *Tel:* 323-932-0407 *Fax:* 323-932-0321 *E-mail:* submissions@aeionline.com *Web Site:* www.aeionline.com, pg 540

Wong, Clarissa, The Feminist Press at The City University of New York, 365 Fifth Ave, Suite 5406, New York, NY 10016 *Tel:* 212-817-7915 *Fax:* 212-817-1593 *E-mail:* info@feministpress.org *Web Site:* www.feministpress.org, pg 87

Wong, Collin, University of Hawaii Press, 2840 Kolowalu St, Honolulu, HI 96822 *Tel:* 808-956-8255 *Toll Free Tel:* 888-UHPRESS (847-7377) *Fax:* 808-988-6052 *Toll Free Fax:* 800-650-7811 *E-mail:* uhpbooks@hawaii.edu *Web Site:* www.uhpress.hawaii.edu, pg 256

Wong, Gay, Mutual Publishing, 1215 Center St, Suite 210, Honolulu, HI 96816 *Tel:* 808-732-1709 *Fax:* 808-734-4094 *E-mail:* info@mutualpublishing.com *Web Site:* www.mutualpublishing.com, pg 162

Wong, Harry L III, Kumu Kahua/UHM Theatre & Dance Department Playwriting Contest, 46 Merchant St, Honolulu, HI 96813 *Tel:* 808-536-4441 (box off); 808-536-4222 *Fax:* 808-536-4226 *E-mail:* kumukahuatheatre@hawaiiantel.net *Web Site:* www.kumukahua.org, pg 699

Wong, Jaime, Chronicle Books LLC, 680 Second St, San Francisco, CA 94107 *Tel:* 415-537-4200 *Toll Free Tel:* 800-759-0190 (cust serv) *Fax:* 415-537-4460 *Toll Free Fax:* 800-858-7787 (orders); 800-286-9471 (cust serv) *E-mail:* frontdesk@chroniclebooks.com *Web Site:* www.chroniclebooks.com, pg 58

Wong, Jessica, Thomas Nelson, 501 Nelson Place, Nashville, TN 37214 *Tel:* 615-889-9000 *Toll Free Tel:* 800-251-4000 *Fax:* 615-902-1548 *E-mail:* publicity@thomasnelson.com *Web Site:* www.thomasnelson.com, pg 245

Wong, May, NBM Publishing Inc, 160 Broadway, E Wing, Suite 700, New York, NY 10038 *Tel:* 646-559-4681 *Toll Free Tel:* 800-886-1223 *Fax:* 212-643-1545 *E-mail:* admin@nbmpub.com *Web Site:* www.nbmpub.com, pg 166

Wong, Stephanie, Chronicle Books LLC, 680 Second St, San Francisco, CA 94107 *Tel:* 415-537-4200 *Toll Free Tel:* 800-759-0190 (cust serv) *Fax:* 415-537-4460 *Toll Free Fax:* 800-858-7787 (orders); 800-286-9471 (cust serv) *E-mail:* frontdesk@chroniclebooks.com *Web Site:* www.chroniclebooks.com, pg 58

Woo, Wei-Ling, PEN American Center, 588 Broadway, Suite 303, New York, NY 10012 *Tel:* 212-334-1660 *Fax:* 212-334-2181 *E-mail:* info@pen.org *Web Site:* www.pen.org, pg 616

Woo-Lun, Marlene, Linworth Publishing, 130 Cremona Dr, Santa Barbara, CA 93117 *Tel:* 805-968-1911 *Toll Free Tel:* 800-368-6868 *Fax:* 805-685-9685 *Toll Free Fax:* 866-270-3856 *E-mail:* customerservice@abc-clio.com *Web Site:* www.abc-clio.com, pg 140

Wood, Ann, Penguin Group (Canada), 90 Eglinton Ave E, Suite 700, Toronto, ON M4P 2Y3, Canada *Tel:* 416-925-2249 *Fax:* 416-925-0068 *E-mail:* customerservicescanada@penguinrandomhouse.com *Web Site:* penguinrandomhouse.ca, pg 495

Wood, Denise, AIGA, the professional association for design, 233 Broadway, 17th fl, New York, NY 10279 *Tel:* 212-807-1990 *Fax:* 212-807-1799 *E-mail:* general@aiga.org *Web Site:* www.aiga.org, pg 593

Wood, Eleanor, Spectrum Literary Agency, 320 Central Park W, Suite 1-D, New York, NY 10025 *Tel:* 212-362-4323 *Fax:* 212-362-4562 *Web Site:* www.spectrumliteraryagency.com, pg 574

Wood, Emily, American Academy of Political & Social Science, 202 S 36 St, Philadelphia, PA 19104-3806 *Tel:* 215-746-6500 *Fax:* 215-573-2667 *Web Site:* www.aapss.org, pg 594

Wood, Juliana, National Information Standards Organization, 3600 Clipper Mill Rd, Suite 302, Baltimore, MD 21211 *Tel:* 301-654-2512 *Fax:* 410-685-5278 *E-mail:* nisohq@niso.org *Web Site:* www.niso.org, pg 612

Wood, Laura, FinePrint Literary Management, 115 W 29 St, 3rd fl, New York, NY 10001 *Tel:* 212-279-1282 *Web Site:* www.fineprintlit.com, pg 551

Wood, Leighann, Andrew Carnegie Medals for Excellence in Fiction & Nonfiction, 50 E Huron St, Chicago, IL 60611 *Tel:* 312-944-6780 *Toll Free Tel:* 800-545-2433 *Fax:* 312-440-9374 *E-mail:* ala@ala.org *Web Site:* www.ala.org/awardsgrants/carnegieadult, pg 676

Wood, Marian, GP Putnam's Sons (Hardcover), 375 Hudson St, New York, NY 10014 *Tel:* 212-366-2000 *E-mail:* online@penguinputnam.com *Web Site:* us.penguingroup.com, pg 201

Wood, Michael, Anna Zornio Memorial Children's Theatre Playwriting Award, D22 Paul Creative Arts Center, 30 Academic Way, Durham, NH 03824 *Tel:* 603-862-2919 *Fax:* 603-862-0298 *Web Site:* cola.unh.edu/theatre-dance/resource/zornio, pg 740

Wood, Rocky, Horror Writers Association (HWA), 244 Fifth Ave, Suite 2767, New York, NY 10001 *E-mail:* hwa@horror.org *Web Site:* horror.org, pg 606

Wood, William, Publishers Information Bureau (PIB)®, 757 Third Ave, 11th fl, New York, NY 10017 *Tel:* 212-872-3745; 212-872-3700 (MPA) *E-mail:* infocenter@magazine.org *Web Site:* www.magazine.org, pg 617

Woodall, Amy, Printing Industries of America, 200 Deer Run Rd, Sewickley, PA 15143-2324 *Tel:* 412-741-6860; 412-259-1770 *E-mail:* membercentral@printing.org (orders) *Web Site:* www.printing.org, pg 197

Woodcheke, Lorraine, Ten Speed Press, 2625 Alcatraz Ave, Unit 505, Berkeley, CA 94705 *Tel:* 510-285-3000 *Toll Free Tel:* 800-841-BOOK (841-2665) *E-mail:* csorders@randomhouse.com *Web Site:* crownpublishing.com/imprint/ten-speed-press, pg 243

Wooden, Heather, Institute of Environmental Sciences and Technology - IEST, 2340 S Arlington Heights Rd, Suite 620, Arlington Heights, IL 60005-4510 *Tel:* 847-981-0100 *Fax:* 847-981-4130 *E-mail:* publications@iest.org *Web Site:* www.iest.org, pg 122

Woodfolk, Ashley, Random House Children's Books, 1745 Broadway, New York, NY 10019 *Tel:* 212-782-9000 *Toll Free Tel:* 800-200-3552 *Fax:* 212-782-9452 *Web Site:* randomhousekids.com, pg 204

Woodford, Charles, Princeton Book Co Publishers, 614 Rte 130, Hightstown, NJ 08520 *Tel:* 609-426-0602 *Toll Free Tel:* 800-220-7149 *Fax:* 609-426-1344 *E-mail:* pbc@dancehorizons.com; elysian@princetonbookcompany.com *Web Site:* www.dancehorizons.com, pg 197

Woodford, Connie, Princeton Book Co Publishers, 614 Rte 130, Hightstown, NJ 08520 *Tel:* 609-426-0602 *Toll Free Tel:* 800-220-7149 *Fax:* 609-426-1344 *E-mail:* pbc@dancehorizons.com; elysian@princetonbookcompany.com *Web Site:* www.dancehorizons.com, pg 197

Woodhouse, Sharon, Everything Goes Media LLC, PO Box 1524, Milwaukee, WI 53201 *Tel:* 312-226-8400 *E-mail:* info@everythinggoesmedia.com *Web Site:* www.everythinggoesmedia.com, pg 84

Woodhouse, Sharon, Lake Claremont Press, PO Box 711, Chicago, IL 60690 *Tel:* 312-226-8400 *Fax:* 312-226-8420 *Web Site:* www.lakeclaremont.com, pg 134

Woods, Brian, Liturgical Press, PO Box 7500, St John's Abbey, Collegeville, MN 56321-7500 *Tel:* 320-363-2213 *Toll Free Tel:* 800-858-5450 *Fax:* 320-363-3299 *Toll Free Fax:* 800-445-5899 *E-mail:* sales@litpress.org *Web Site:* www.litpress.org, pg 141

Woods, Caroline, Boston University, 236 Bay State Rd, Boston, MA 02215 *Tel:* 617-353-2510 *Fax:* 617-353-3653 *E-mail:* crwr@bu.edu *Web Site:* www.bu.edu/writing, pg 659

Woods, Ned, Springer, 233 Spring St, New York, NY 10013-1578 *Tel:* 212-460-1500 *Toll Free Tel:* 800-SPRINGER (777-4643) *Fax:* 212-460-1575 *E-mail:* service-ny@springer.com *Web Site:* www.springer.com, pg 232

Woods, Ryan, Newbury Street Press, 101 Newbury St, Boston, MA 02116 *Tel:* 617-536-5740 *Toll Free Tel:* 888-296-3447 (NEHGS membership) *Fax:* 617-536-7307 *E-mail:* sales@nehgs.org *Web Site:* www.newenglandancestors.org, pg 169

Woodward, Charlene, Dogwise Publishing, 403 S Mission St, Wenatchee, WA 98801 *Tel:* 509-663-9115 *Toll Free Tel:* 800-776-2665 *E-mail:* mail@dogwise.com *Web Site:* www.dogwise.com, pg 75

Woodward, Debra, Red Wheel/Weiser/Conari, 65 Parker St, Suite 7, Newburyport, MA 01950 *Tel:* 978-465-0504 *Toll Free Tel:* 800-423-7087 (orders) *Fax:* 978-465-0243 *E-mail:* info@rwwbooks.com *Web Site:* www.redwheelweiser.com, pg 206

Woodward, Larry, Dogwise Publishing, 403 S Mission St, Wenatchee, WA 98801 *Tel:* 509-663-9115 *Toll Free Tel:* 800-776-2665 *E-mail:* mail@dogwise.com *Web Site:* www.dogwise.com, pg 75

Woodward, Steve, Graywolf Press, 250 Third Ave N, Suite 600, Minneapolis, MN 55401 *Tel:* 651-641-0077 *Fax:* 651-641-0036 *E-mail:* wolves@graywolfpress.org *Web Site:* www.graywolfpress.org, pg 100

Woodward, Tessa, HarperCollins General Books Group, 195 Broadway, New York, NY 10007 *Tel:* 212-207-7000 *Web Site:* www.harpercollins.com, pg 106

Woodworth, Amy L, Crystal Productions, 5320 Carpinteria Ave, Suite K, Carpinteria, CA 93013-2107 *Tel:* 847-657-8144 *Toll Free Tel:* 800-255-8629 *Fax:* 847-657-8149 *Toll Free Fax:* 800-657-8149 *E-mail:* custserv@crystalproductions.com *Web Site:* www.crystalproductions.com, pg 69

Woodworth, Neil, Adirondack Mountain Club (ADK), 814 Goggins Rd, Lake George, NY 12845-4117 *Tel:* 518-668-4447 *Toll Free Tel:* 800-395-8080 *Fax:* 518-668-3746 *E-mail:* info@adk.org *Web Site:* www.adk.org, pg 5

Woodworth, Robert, Flanker Press Ltd, 1243 Kenmount Rd, Unit A, Paradise, NL A1L 0V8, Canada *Tel:* 709-739-4477 *Toll Free Tel:* 866-739-4420 *Fax:* 709-739-4420 *E-mail:* info@flankerpress.com *Web Site:* www.flankerpress.com, pg 484

Wooldridge, Andrew, Orca Book Publishers, PO Box 468, Custer, WA 98240-0468 *Tel:* 250-380-1229 *Toll Free Tel:* 800-210-5277 *Fax:* 250-380-1892 *Toll Free Fax:* 877-408-1551 *E-mail:* orca@orcabook.com *Web Site:* www.orcabook.com, pg 176

Worchte, Allison, Random House Children's Books, 1745 Broadway, New York, NY 10019 *Tel:* 212-782-9000 *Toll Free Tel:* 800-200-3552 *Fax:* 212-782-9452 *Web Site:* randomhousekids.com, pg 203

Worin, Melinda Sue, Book Publicists of Southern California, 714 Crescent Dr, Beverly Hills, CA 90210 *Tel:* 323-461-3921 *Fax:* 323-461-0917 *Web Site:* www.bookpublicists.org, pg 600

Workman, Carolan, Workman Publishing Co Inc, 225 Varick St, 9th fl, New York, NY 10014-4381 *Tel:* 212-254-5900 *Toll Free Tel:* 800-722-7202 *Fax:* 212-254-8098 *E-mail:* info@workman.com *Web Site:* www.workman.com, pg 275

Zingarelli, Vito, Hedgebrook VORTEXT, PO Box 1231, Freeland, WA 98249 *Tel:* 360-321-4786 *Fax:* 360-321-2171 *E-mail:* hedgebrook@hedgebrook.org *Web Site:* www.hedgebrook.org; www.facebook.com/hedgebrook, pg 651

Zingarelli, Vito, Hedgebrook Winter Salon, PO Box 1231, Freeland, WA 98249 *Tel:* 360-321-4786 *Fax:* 360-321-2171 *E-mail:* hedgebrook@hedgebrook.org *Web Site:* www.hedgebrook.org; www.facebook.com/hedgebrook, pg 651

Zingarelli, Vito, Hedgebrook Writers in Residence Program, PO Box 1231, Freeland, WA 98249 *Tel:* 360-321-4786 *Fax:* 360-321-2171 *E-mail:* hedgebrook@hedgebrook.org *Web Site:* www.hedgebrook.org; www.facebook.com/hedgebrook, pg 651

Zink, Seta, Running Press Book Publishers, 2300 Chestnut St, Philadelphia, PA 19103-4399 *Tel:* 215-567-5080 *Toll Free Tel:* 800-343-4499 (cust serv & orders) *Fax:* 215-568-2919 *Toll Free Fax:* 800-453-2884 (cust serv & orders) *E-mail:* perseus.promos@perseusbooks.com *Web Site:* www.runningpress.com, pg 212

Zinna, Diane, Association of Writers & Writing Programs (AWP), George Mason University, 4400 University Dr, MSN 1E3, Fairfax, VA 22030 *Tel:* 703-993-4301 *Fax:* 703-993-4302 *E-mail:* awp@awpwriter.org *Web Site:* www.awpwriter.org, pg 599

Zinna, Diane, AWP Award Series, George Mason University, 4400 University Dr, MSN 1E3, Fairfax, VA 22030 *Tel:* 703-993-4301 *Fax:* 703-993-4302 *E-mail:* awp@awpwriter.org *Web Site:* www.awpwriter.org, pg 669

Zinner, Eric, New York University Press, 838 Broadway, 3rd fl, New York, NY 10003-4812 *Tel:* 212-998-2575 (edit) *Toll Free Tel:* 800-996-6987 (orders) *Fax:* 212-995-3833 (orders) *E-mail:* information@nyupress.org; customerservice@nyupress.org; orders@nyupress.org *Web Site:* www.nyupress.org, pg 169

Zion, Claire, NAL, 375 Hudson St, New York, NY 10014 *Tel:* 212-366-2000 *E-mail:* online@penguinputnam.com *Web Site:* www.penguinputnam.com; us.penguingroup.com, pg 162

Zissimos, Mary Ann, Disney Publishing Worldwide, 1101 Flower St, Glendale, CA 91201 *Web Site:* books.disney.com, pg 74

Zitt, Dan, Penguin Random House Audio, 1745 Broadway, New York, NY 10019 *E-mail:* audio@randomhouse.com *Web Site:* www.randomhouse.com/audio, pg 187

Zitwer, Barbara J, Barbara J Zitwer Agency, 525 West End Ave, Unit 11-H, New York, NY 10024 *Tel:* 212-501-8423 *Fax:* 646-514-0497 *E-mail:* zitwer@gmail.com, pg 580

Ziv, Maya, HarperCollins General Books Group, 195 Broadway, New York, NY 10007 *Tel:* 212-207-7000 *Web Site:* www.harpercollins.com, pg 105

Zline, Patricia, Jason Aronson Inc, 4501 Forbes Blvd, Suite 200, Lanham, MD 20706 *Tel:* 301-459-3366 *Toll Free Tel:* 800-462-6420 (orders) *Fax:* 301-429-5748 *Web Site:* www.rowman.com, pg 22

Zlotowitz, Meir, Mesorah Publications Ltd, 4401 Second Ave, Brooklyn, NY 11232 *Tel:* 718-921-9000 *Toll Free Tel:* 800-637-6724 *Fax:* 718-680-1875 *E-mail:* artscroll@mesorah.com *Web Site:* www.artscroll.com; www.mesorah.com, pg 155

Zock, Jim, Atlantic Center for the Arts Artists-in-Residence Program, 1414 Art Center Ave, New Smyrna Beach, FL 32168 *Tel:* 386-427-6975 *Toll Free Tel:* 800-393-6975 *Fax:* 386-427-5669 *E-mail:* program@atlanticcenterforthearts.org *Web Site:* www.atlanticcenterforthearts.org, pg 649

Zollshan, Ronald P, Kirchoff/Wohlberg Inc, 897 Boston Post Rd, Madison, CT 06443 *Tel:* 203-245-7308 *Fax:* 203-245-3218 *Web Site:* www.kirchoffwohlberg.com, pg 560

Zoni, Matthew, American Booksellers Association, 333 Westchester Ave, Suite S202, White Plains, NY 10604 *Tel:* 914-406-7500 *Toll Free Tel:* 800-637-0037 *Fax:* 914-410-6297 *E-mail:* info@bookweb.org *Web Site:* www.bookweb.org, pg 594

Zoro, Theresa, Random House Publishing Group, 1745 Broadway, New York, NY 10019 *Toll Free Tel:* 800-200-3552 *Web Site:* atrandom.com, pg 204

Zoss, Bernadette, Indiana University Press, Herman B Wells Library 350, 1320 E Tenth St, Bloomington, IN 47405-3907 *Tel:* 812-855-8817 *Toll Free Tel:* 800-842-6796 (orders only) *Fax:* 812-855-7931; 812-855-8507 *E-mail:* iupress@indiana.edu; iuporder@indiana.edu (orders) *Web Site:* www.iupress.indiana.edu, pg 120

Zrioka, Pete, Poisoned Pen Press, 6962 E First Ave, Suite 103, Scottsdale, AZ 85251 *Tel:* 480-945-3375 *Toll Free Tel:* 800-421-3976 *Fax:* 480-949-1707 *E-mail:* info@poisonedpenpress.com *Web Site:* www.poisonedpenpress.com, pg 194

Zschock, Heather, Peter Pauper Press, Inc, 202 Mamaroneck Ave, White Plains, NY 10601-5376 *Tel:* 914-681-0144 *Fax:* 914-681-0389 *E-mail:* customerservice@peterpauper.com; orders@peterpauper.com *Web Site:* www.peterpauper.com, pg 190

Zubal, John T, USBE: United States Book Exchange, 2969 W 25 St, Cleveland, OH 44113 *Tel:* 216-241-6960 *Fax:* 216-241-6966 *E-mail:* usbe@usbe.com *Web Site:* www.usbe.com, pg 621

Zubal, Marilyn, USBE: United States Book Exchange, 2969 W 25 St, Cleveland, OH 44113 *Tel:* 216-241-6960 *Fax:* 216-241-6966 *E-mail:* usbe@usbe.com *Web Site:* www.usbe.com, pg 621

Zucca, Damon, Oxford University Press USA, 198 Madison Ave, New York, NY 10016 *Tel:* 212-726-6000 *Toll Free Tel:* 800-451-7556 (orders); 800-445-9714 (cust serv) *Fax:* 919-677-1303 *E-mail:* custserv.us@oup.com *Web Site:* www.oup.com/us, pg 179

Zuccarello, Dasya Anthony, Hohm Press, PO Box 4410, Chino Valley, AZ 86323 *Tel:* 928-636-3331 *Toll Free Tel:* 800-381-2700 *Fax:* 928-636-7519 *E-mail:* hppublisher@cableone.net; hohmpresseditor@gmail.com *Web Site:* www.hohmpress.com, pg 113

Zuccarello, Joe Bala, Hohm Press, PO Box 4410, Chino Valley, AZ 86323 *Tel:* 928-636-3331 *Toll Free Tel:* 800-381-2700 *Fax:* 928-636-7519 *E-mail:* hppublisher@cableone.net; hohmpresseditor@gmail.com *Web Site:* www.hohmpress.com, pg 113

Zuccarini, Margaret, Springer Publishing Co, 11 W 42 St, 15th fl, New York, NY 10036-8002 *Tel:* 212-431-4370 *Toll Free Tel:* 877-687-7476 *Fax:* 212-941-7842 *E-mail:* marketing@springerpub.com; cs@springerpub.com (orders); editorial@springerpub.com *Web Site:* www.springerpub.com, pg 232

Zuch, Franklin Jon, George T Bisel Co Inc, 710 S Washington Sq, Philadelphia, PA 19106-3519 *Tel:* 215-922-5760 *Toll Free Tel:* 800-247-3526 *Fax:* 215-922-2235 *E-mail:* gbisel@bisel.com *Web Site:* www.bisel.com, pg 37

Zucker, Irwin, Book Publicists of Southern California, 714 Crescent Dr, Beverly Hills, CA 90210 *Tel:* 323-461-3921 *Fax:* 323-461-0917 *Web Site:* www.bookpublicists.org, pg 600

Zucker, Joel, Harcourt Achieve, 6277 Sea Harbor Dr, Orlando, FL 32887 *Tel:* 407-345-2000 *Toll Free Tel:* 800-531-5015 (cust serv/orders) *Toll Free Fax:* 800-699-9459 (cust serv/orders) *Web Site:* www.harcourtachieve.com, pg 104

Zucker, Joel, Harcourt Inc, 6277 Sea Harbor Dr, Orlando, FL 32887 *Tel:* 407-345-2000 *Toll Free Tel:* 800-225-5425 (cust serv/orders) *Toll Free Fax:* 800-269-5232 (cust serv/orders) *Web Site:* www.hmhco.com, pg 105

Zuckerman, Albert, Writers House, 21 W 26 St, New York, NY 10010 *Tel:* 212-685-2400 *Fax:* 212-685-1781 *Web Site:* www.writershouse.com, pg 580

Zuckerman, Kathryn, Alfred A Knopf/Everyman's Library, c/o Random House Inc, 1745 Broadway, New York, NY 10019 *Tel:* 212-751-2600 *Toll Free Tel:* 800-638-6460 *Fax:* 212-572-2593 *Web Site:* www.knopfdoubleday.com, pg 132

Zuckerman, Mark, The Century Foundation, One Whitehall St, 15 fl, New York, NY 10004 *Tel:* 212-452-7700 *Fax:* 212-535-7534 *E-mail:* info@tcf.org *Web Site:* www.tcf.org, pg 623

Zuckerman, Mark, The Century Foundation Press, One Whitehall St, 15th fl, New York, NY 10004 *Tel:* 212-452-7700 *Fax:* 212-535-7534 *E-mail:* info@tcf.org *Web Site:* www.tcf.org, pg 54

Zuckerman, Phil, Applewood Books Inc, One River Rd, Carlisle, MA 01741 *Tel:* 781-271-0055 *Toll Free Tel:* 800-277-5312 (orders) *Fax:* 781-271-0056 *E-mail:* bookorder@awb.com; customercare@awb.com *Web Site:* www.awb.com, pg 20

Zuckerman, Phil, Commonwealth Editions, One River Rd, Carlisle, MA 01741 *Tel:* 781-271-0055 *Toll Free Tel:* 800-277-5312 *Fax:* 781-271-0056 *E-mail:* customercare@awb.com *Web Site:* www.awb.com, pg 62

Zukowski, Steve, Great Source Education Group, 181 Ballardvale St, Wilmington, MA 01887 *Toll Free Tel:* 800-289-4490 *Toll Free Fax:* 800-289-3994; 800-269-5232 *Web Site:* www.hmhco.com, pg 100

Zulli, Jessica, Sourcebooks Inc, 1935 Brookdale Rd, Suite 139, Naperville, IL 60563 *Tel:* 630-961-3900 *Toll Free Tel:* 800-432-7444 *Fax:* 630-961-2168 *E-mail:* info@sourcebooks.com; customersupport@sourcebooks.com *Web Site:* www.sourcebooks.com, pg 230

Zwarenstein, Lianne, Tom Fairley Award for Editorial Excellence, 27 Carlton St, Suite 502, Toronto, ON M5B 1L2, Canada *Tel:* 416-975-1379 *Toll Free Tel:* 866-CAN-EDIT (226-3348) *Fax:* 416-975-1637 *E-mail:* fairley_award@editors.ca *Web Site:* www.editors.ca; www.reviseurs.ca, pg 684

Zwart, Jeanette, Book Industry Study Group Inc (BISG), 145 W 45 St, Suite 601, New York, NY 10036 *Tel:* 646-336-7141 *Fax:* 646-336-6214 *E-mail:* info@bisg.org *Web Site:* www.bisg.org, pg 600

Zychowicz, James L, A-R Editions Inc, 1600 Aspen Commons, Suite 100, Middleton, WI 53562 *Tel:* 608-836-9000 *Toll Free Tel:* 800-736-0070 (North America book orders only) *Fax:* 608-831-8200 *E-mail:* info@areditions.com; orders@areditions.com *Web Site:* www.areditions.com, pg 1

Publishers Toll Free Directory

A-R Editions Inc, Middleton, WI *Toll Free Tel:* 800-736-0070 (North America book orders only), pg 1

AAPG (American Association of Petroleum Geologists), Tulsa, OK *Toll Free Tel:* 800-364-AAPG (364-2274) *Toll Free Fax:* 800-898-2274, pg 1

Abbeville Press, New York, NY *Toll Free Tel:* 800-ARTBOOK (278-2665); 800-343-4499 (orders) *Toll Free Fax:* 800-351-5073 (orders), pg 2

Abbeville Publishing Group, New York, NY *Toll Free Tel:* 800-ART-BOOK (278-2665), pg 2

ABC-CLIO, Santa Barbara, CA *Toll Free Tel:* 800-368-6868 *Toll Free Fax:* 866-270-3856, pg 2

ABDO Publishing Group, Edina, MN *Toll Free Tel:* 800-800-1312 *Toll Free Fax:* 800-862-3480, pg 2

Abingdon Press, Nashville, TN *Toll Free Tel:* 800-251-3320 *Toll Free Fax:* 800-836-7802 (orders), pg 2

Harry N Abrams Inc, New York, NY *Toll Free Tel:* 800-345-1359, pg 2

Abrams Learning Trends, Austin, TX *Toll Free Tel:* 800-227-9120 *Toll Free Fax:* 800-737-3322, pg 3

Absey & Co Inc, Spring, TX *Toll Free Tel:* 888-41-ABSEY (412-2739), pg 3

Academy of Nutrition & Dietetics, Chicago, IL *Toll Free Tel:* 800-877-1600, pg 3

Accuity, Skokie, IL *Toll Free Tel:* 800-321-3373, pg 4

Acres USA, Austin, TX *Toll Free Tel:* 800-355-5313, pg 4

ACTA Publications, Chicago, IL *Toll Free Tel:* 800-397-2282 *Toll Free Fax:* 800-397-0079, pg 4

ACU Press, Abilene, TX *Toll Free Tel:* 877-816-4455, pg 4

Adams-Pomeroy Press, Albany, WI *Toll Free Tel:* 877-862-3645, pg 507

Adirondack Mountain Club (ADK), Lake George, NY *Toll Free Tel:* 800-395-8080, pg 5

Adler Publishing Inc, Parker, CO *Toll Free Tel:* 800-660-5107 (sales & orders), pg 5

Advance Publishing Inc, Houston, TX *Toll Free Tel:* 800-917-9630, pg 5

Adventure Publications, Cambridge, MN *Toll Free Tel:* 800-678-7006 *Toll Free Fax:* 877-374-9016, pg 5

AFB Press, New York, NY *Toll Free Tel:* 800-232-5463; 800-232-3044 (orders) *Toll Free Fax:* 888-545-8331, pg 5

African American Images, Chicago Heights, IL *Toll Free Tel:* 800-552-1991 (orders), pg 6

AHA Press, Chicago, IL *Toll Free Tel:* 800-821-2039 *Toll Free Fax:* 866-516-5817 (orders), pg 6

AICPA Professional Publications, Durham, NC *Toll Free Tel:* 888-777-7077 *Toll Free Fax:* 800-362-5066, pg 6

AIMS Education Foundation, Fresno, CA *Toll Free Tel:* 888-733-2467, pg 6

Air Conditioning Contractors of America, Arlington, VA *Toll Free Tel:* 888-290-2220, pg 6

Albert Whitman & Co, Park Ridge, IL *Toll Free Tel:* 800-255-7675, pg 7

The Alexander Graham Bell Association for the Deaf & Hard of Hearing, Washington, DC *Toll Free Tel:* 866-337-5220 (orders), pg 7

Alexander Street Press LLC, Alexandria, VA *Toll Free Tel:* 800-889-5937, pg 7

Alfred Music Publishing, Van Nuys, CA *Toll Free Tel:* 800-292-6122 (dealer sales (US & CN)) *Toll Free Fax:* 800-632-1928 (dealer sales), pg 7

Allyn & Bacon, Boston, MA *Toll Free Tel:* 800-428-4466, pg 9

ALPHA Publications of America Inc, Tucson, AZ *Toll Free Tel:* 800-528-3494 *Toll Free Fax:* 800-770-4329, pg 9

Alpine Publications Inc, Crawford, CO *Toll Free Tel:* 800-777-7257, pg 9

AltaMira Press, Lanham, MD *Toll Free Tel:* 800-462-6420 (cust serv), pg 9

AMACOM Books, New York, NY *Toll Free Tel:* 800-250-5308 (cust serv), pg 9

Amadeus Press/Hal Leonard Performing Arts Publishing Group, Montclair, NJ *Toll Free Tel:* 800-524-4425, pg 9

Frank Amato Publications Inc, Milwaukie, OR *Toll Free Tel:* 800-541-9498, pg 9

Ambassador International, Greenville, SC *Toll Free Tel:* 800-209-8570, pg 9

Amber Lotus Publishing, Portland, OR *Toll Free Tel:* 800-326-2375 (orders only), pg 10

America West Publishers, Hayden, ID *Toll Free Tel:* 800-729-4131, pg 10

American Academy of Orthopaedic Surgeons (AAOS), Rosemont, IL *Toll Free Tel:* 800-346-2267, pg 10

American Academy of Pediatrics, Elk Grove Village, IL *Toll Free Tel:* 888-227-1770, pg 10

American Association of Blood Banks, Bethesda, MD *Toll Free Tel:* 866-222-2498 (sales), pg 11

American Bar Association, Chicago, IL *Toll Free Tel:* 800-285-2221 (orders), pg 11

American Bible Society, New York, NY *Toll Free Tel:* 800-322-4253; 888-596-6296, pg 11

American Carriage House Publishing, Nevada City, CA *Toll Free Tel:* 866-986-2665, pg 11

The American Ceramic Society, Westerville, OH *Toll Free Tel:* 866-721-3322, pg 11

The American Chemical Society, Washington, DC *Toll Free Tel:* 800-227-5558 (US), pg 12

American College, Bryn Mawr, PA *Toll Free Tel:* 888-263-7265, pg 12

American College of Physician Executives, Tampa, FL *Toll Free Tel:* 800-562-8088, pg 12

American Correctional Association, Alexandria, VA *Toll Free Tel:* 800-222-5646, pg 12

American Counseling Association, Alexandria, VA *Toll Free Tel:* 800-422-2648 (ext 222, book orders); 800-347-6647 *Toll Free Fax:* 800-473-2329, pg 12

American Diabetes Association, Alexandria, VA *Toll Free Tel:* 800-342-2383, pg 12

American Federation of Arts, New York, NY *Toll Free Tel:* 800-232-0270, pg 12

American Federation of Astrologers Inc, Tempe, AZ *Toll Free Tel:* 888-301-7630, pg 12

American Geophysical Union (AGU), Washington, DC *Toll Free Tel:* 800-966-2481 (North America), pg 13

American Girl Publishing, Middleton, WI *Toll Free Tel:* 800-233-0264; 800-360-1861; 800-845-0005 (US & CN), pg 13

American Institute for Economic Research (AIER), Great Barrington, MA *Toll Free Tel:* 888-528-1216 (orders), pg 13

American Institute of Aeronautics & Astronautics (AIAA), Reston, VA *Toll Free Tel:* 800-639-AIAA (639-2422), pg 13

American Institute of Chemical Engineers (AIChE), New York, NY *Toll Free Tel:* 800-242-4363, pg 13

American Law Institute, Philadelphia, PA *Toll Free Tel:* 800-253-6397, pg 14

American Law Institute Continuing Legal Education (ALI CLE), Philadelphia, PA *Toll Free Tel:* 800-CLE-NEWS (253-6397), pg 14

The American Library Association (ALA), Chicago, IL *Toll Free Tel:* 800-545-2433, pg 14

American Map Corp, Long Island City, NY *Toll Free Tel:* 888-774-7979, pg 14

American Marketing Association, Chicago, IL *Toll Free Tel:* 800-AMA-1150 (262-1150), pg 14

American Mathematical Society, Providence, RI *Toll Free Tel:* 800-321-4267, pg 14

American Medical Association, Chicago, IL *Toll Free Tel:* 800-621-8335, pg 14

The American Occupational Therapy Association Inc (AOTA), Bethesda, MD *Toll Free Tel:* 800-377-8555 (TDD); 877-404-AOTA (404-2682, orders), pg 14

American Printing House for the Blind Inc, Louisville, KY *Toll Free Tel:* 800-223-1839 (cust serv), pg 15

American Products Publishing Co, Beaverton, OR *Toll Free Tel:* 800-668-8181, pg 15

American Psychiatric Publishing (APP), Arlington, VA *Toll Free Tel:* 800-368-5777, pg 15

American Psychological Association, Washington, DC *Toll Free Tel:* 800-374-2721, pg 15

American Public Works Association (APWA), Kansas City, MO *Toll Free Tel:* 800-848-APWA (848-2792), pg 15

American Quilter's Society, Paducah, KY *Toll Free Tel:* 800-626-5420 (orders), pg 15

American Society for Nondestructive Testing, Columbus, OH *Toll Free Tel:* 800-222-2768, pg 15

American Society for Quality (ASQ), Milwaukee, WI *Toll Free Tel:* 800-248-1946 (US & CN); 800-514-1564 (Mexico), pg 16

American Society of Agricultural & Biological Engineers (ASABE), St Joseph, MI *Toll Free Tel:* 800-371-2723, pg 16

American Society of Civil Engineers (ASCE), Reston, VA *Toll Free Tel:* 800-548-2723, pg 16

American Society of Health-System Pharmacists (ASHP), Bethesda, MD *Toll Free Tel:* 866-279-0681 (orders), pg 16

American Society of Mechanical Engineers (ASME), New York, NY *Toll Free Tel:* 800-843-2763 (cust serv-US, CN & Mexico), pg 16

American Technical Publishers Inc, Orland Park, IL *Toll Free Tel:* 800-323-3471, pg 16

American Water Works Association (AWWA), Denver, CO *Toll Free Tel:* 800-926-7337, pg 17

Amherst Media Inc, Buffalo, NY *Toll Free Tel:* 800-622-3278, pg 17

Ancient Faith Publishing, University Park, IL *Toll Free Tel:* 800-967-7377 *Toll Free Fax:* 866-599-5208, pg 17

Andrews McMeel Publishing LLC, Kansas City, MO *Toll Free Tel:* 800-851-8923; 800-943-9839 (cust serv) *Toll Free Fax:* 800-943-9831 (orders), pg 18

Andrews University Press, Berrien Springs, MI *Toll Free Tel:* 800-467-6369 (Visa, MC & American Express orders only), pg 18

Angel City Press, Santa Monica, CA *Toll Free Tel:* 800-949-8039, pg 18

Angelus Press, Kansas City, MO *Toll Free Tel:* 800-966-7337, pg 18

Annual Reviews, Palo Alto, CA *Toll Free Tel:* 800-523-8635, pg 18

ANR Publications University of California, Richmond, CA *Toll Free Tel:* 800-994-8849, pg 18

Antique Collectors' Club Ltd, East Hampton, MA *Toll Free Tel:* 800-252-5231, pg 18

Antique Trader, Iola, WI *Toll Free Tel:* 888-457-2873, pg 19

Aperture Books, New York, NY *Toll Free Tel:* 800-929-2323, pg 19

The Apex Press, Lanham, MD *Toll Free Tel:* 800-462-6420 *Toll Free Fax:* 800-388-4450, pg 19

Appalachian Mountain Club Books, Boston, MA *Toll Free Tel:* 800-262-4455 (orders), pg 20

Appalachian Trail Conservancy, Harpers Ferry, WV *Toll Free Tel:* 888-287-8673 (orders only), pg 20

Applause Theatre & Cinema Books, Montclair, NJ *Toll Free Tel:* 800-637-2852, pg 20

Appletree Press Inc, Mankato, MN *Toll Free Tel:* 800-322-5679, pg 20

Applewood Books Inc, Carlisle, MA *Toll Free Tel:* 800-277-5312 (orders), pg 20

Appraisal Institute, Chicago, IL *Toll Free Tel:* 888-756-4624, pg 20

APS PRESS, St Paul, MN *Toll Free Tel:* 800-328-7560, pg 21

Aqua Quest Publications Inc, Locust Valley, NY *Toll Free Tel:* 800-933-8989, pg 21

Aquila Communications Inc, Montreal, QC Canada *Toll Free Tel:* 800-667-7071 *Toll Free Fax:* 866-338-1948, pg 471

Arbordale Publishing, Mount Pleasant, SC *Toll Free Tel:* 877-243-3457, pg 21

Arcadia Publishing Inc, Mount Pleasant, SC *Toll Free Tel:* 888-313-2665 (orders only), pg 21

ARE Press, Virginia Beach, VA *Toll Free Tel:* 800-333-4499, pg 22

Ariel Press, Canal Winchester, OH *Toll Free Tel:* 800-336-7769, pg 22

Jason Aronson Inc, Lanham, MD *Toll Free Tel:* 800-462-6420 (orders), pg 22

Arsenal Pulp Press, Vancouver, BC Canada *Toll Free Tel:* 888-600-PULP (600-7857), pg 471

Art Image Publications, Derby Line, VT *Toll Free Tel:* 800-361-2598 *Toll Free Fax:* 800-559-2598, pg 22

ArtAge Publications, Portland, OR *Toll Free Tel:* 800-858-4998, pg 23

Arte Publico Press, Houston, TX *Toll Free Tel:* 800-633-2783, pg 23

Artech House Inc, Norwood, MA *Toll Free Tel:* 800-225-9977, pg 23

Artisan Books, New York, NY *Toll Free Tel:* 800-722-7202, pg 23

ASCD, Alexandria, VA *Toll Free Tel:* 800-933-2723, pg 23

Ascension Press, West Chester, PA *Toll Free Tel:* 800-376-0520 (sales & cust serv), pg 24

ASCP Press, Chicago, IL *Toll Free Tel:* 800-267-2727, pg 24

Ashgate Publishing Co, Burlington, VT *Toll Free Tel:* 800-535-9544, pg 24

ASM International, Materials Park, OH *Toll Free Tel:* 800-336-5152; 800-368-9800 (Europe), pg 25

ASM Press, Washington, DC *Toll Free Tel:* 800-546-2416, pg 25

Aspatore Books, Eagan, MN *Toll Free Tel:* 866-ASPATORE (277-2867); 888-728-7677; 800-328-4880, pg 25

Association for Computing Machinery, New York, NY *Toll Free Tel:* 800-342-6626, pg 25

Association for Talent Development (ATD), Alexandria, VA *Toll Free Tel:* 800-628-2783, pg 25

Association of College & Research Libraries (ACRL), Chicago, IL *Toll Free Tel:* 800-545-2433 (ext 2523), pg 26

Association of School Business Officials International, Reston, VA *Toll Free Tel:* 866-682-2729, pg 26

Asta Publications LLC, Stockbridge, GA *Toll Free Tel:* 800-482-4190, pg 26

ASTM International, West Conshohocken, PA *Toll Free Tel:* 877-909-2786 (sales & cust support), pg 26

Astragal Press, Apple Valley, MN *Toll Free Tel:* 866-543-3045 *Toll Free Fax:* 800-330-6232, pg 26

The Astronomical Society of the Pacific, San Francisco, CA *Toll Free Tel:* 800-335-2624, pg 26

Athletic Guide Publishing, Flagler Beach, FL *Toll Free Tel:* 800-255-1050, pg 26

Atlantic Law Book Co, West Hartford, CT *Toll Free Tel:* 800-259-5534, pg 26

Atlantic Publishing Group Inc, Ocala, FL *Toll Free Tel:* 800-814-1132, pg 26

Atwood Publishing, Madison, WI *Toll Free Tel:* 888-242-7101, pg 27

Augsburg Fortress Publishers, Publishing House of the Evangelical Lutheran Church in America, Minneapolis, MN *Toll Free Tel:* 800-426-0115 (ext 639, subns); 800-328-4648 (orders), pg 27

August House Inc, Atlanta, GA *Toll Free Tel:* 800-284-8784, pg 27

AuthorHouse, Bloomington, IN *Toll Free Tel:* 888-519-5121, pg 27

Autism Asperger Publishing Co, Lenexa, KS *Toll Free Tel:* 877-277-8254, pg 27

Ave Maria Press, Notre Dame, IN *Toll Free Tel:* 800-282-1865 *Toll Free Fax:* 800-282-5681, pg 28

Avery Color Studios, Gwinn, MI *Toll Free Tel:* 800-722-9925, pg 28

AVKO Educational Research Foundation Inc, Birch Run, MI *Toll Free Tel:* 866-AVKO612 (285-6612), pg 28

Awe-Struck Publishing, Cincinnati, OH *Toll Free Tel:* 888-402-6657 *Toll Free Fax:* 888-460-4752, pg 28

AZ Books LLC, New York, NY *Toll Free Tel:* 888-945-7723 *Toll Free Fax:* 888-945-7724, pg 29

Babalu Inc, Santa Barbara, CA *Toll Free Tel:* 877-522-2258, pg 29

Backbeat Books, Montclair, NJ *Toll Free Tel:* 800-637-2852 (Music Dispatch), pg 29

Baha'i Publishing, Wilmette, IL *Toll Free Tel:* 800-999-9019 (orders), pg 29

Baker Books, Grand Rapids, MI *Toll Free Tel:* 800-877-2665; 800-679-1957 *Toll Free Fax:* 800-398-3111, pg 29

Banner of Truth, Carlisle, PA *Toll Free Tel:* 800-263-8085 (orders), pg 30

Barefoot Books, Cambridge, MA *Toll Free Tel:* 866-215-1756 (cust serv); 866-417-2369 (orders), pg 30

Barnhardt & Ashe Publishing Inc, Miami, FL *Toll Free Tel:* 800-283-6360 (orders), pg 31

Barron's Educational Series Inc, Hauppauge, NY *Toll Free Tel:* 800-645-3476, pg 31

Bartleby Press, Savage, MD *Toll Free Tel:* 800-953-9929, pg 31

Basic Health Publications Inc, Laguna Beach, CA *Toll Free Tel:* 800-575-8890 (orders), pg 32

Bay Tree Publishing LLC, Point Richmond, CA *Toll Free Fax:* 866-552-7329, pg 32

Baywood Publishing Co Inc, Amityville, NY *Toll Free Tel:* 800-638-7819, pg 32

Beacon Hill Press of Kansas City, Kansas City, MO *Toll Free Tel:* 800-877-0700 (cust serv), pg 32

Bear & Co Inc, Rochester, VT *Toll Free Tel:* 800-932-3277, pg 33

Bearport Publishing Co Inc, New York, NY *Toll Free Tel:* 877-337-8577 *Toll Free Fax:* 866-337-8557, pg 33

Bedford/St Martin's, Boston, MA *Toll Free Tel:* 800-779-7440, pg 33

Behrman House Inc, Springfield, NJ *Toll Free Tel:* 800-221-2755, pg 33

Bella Books, Tallahassee, FL *Toll Free Tel:* 800-729-4992, pg 34

Bellerophon Books, Santa Barbara, CA *Toll Free Tel:* 800-253-9943, pg 34

John Benjamins Publishing Co, Philadelphia, PA *Toll Free Tel:* 800-562-5666 (orders), pg 34

Bentley Publishers, Cambridge, MA *Toll Free Tel:* 800-423-4595, pg 35

BePuzzled, San Francisco, CA *Toll Free Tel:* 800-347-4818, pg 35

Bethany House Publishers, Bloomington, MN *Toll Free Tel:* 800-877-2665 (orders) *Toll Free Fax:* 800-398-3111 (orders), pg 36

Bethlehem Books, Bathgate, ND *Toll Free Tel:* 800-757-6831, pg 36

Betterway Books, Blue Ash, OH *Toll Free Tel:* 800-666-0963 *Toll Free Fax:* 888-590-4082, pg 36

Between the Lines (BTL), Toronto, ON Canada *Toll Free Tel:* 800-718-7201, pg 472

Bhaktivedanta Book Trust (BBT), Los Angeles, CA *Toll Free Tel:* 800-927-4152, pg 36

Big Guy Books Inc, Encinitas, CA *Toll Free Tel:* 800-536-3030 (booksellers' cust serv), pg 37

Bilingual Press/Editorial Bilingue, Tempe, AZ *Toll Free Tel:* 866-965-3867, pg 37

George T Bisel Co Inc, Philadelphia, PA *Toll Free Tel:* 800-247-3526, pg 37

Bisk Education, Tampa, FL *Toll Free Tel:* 800-280-9718 (cust serv), pg 37

BJU Press, Greenville, SC *Toll Free Tel:* 800-845-5731, pg 38

Black Classic Press, Baltimore, MD *Toll Free Tel:* 800-476-8870, pg 38

Black Rose Books Ltd, Montreal, QC Canada *Toll Free Tel:* 800-565-9523 (orders) *Toll Free Fax:* 800-221-9985 (orders), pg 472

John F Blair Publisher, Winston-Salem, NC *Toll Free Tel:* 800-222-9796, pg 39

Bloom's Literary Criticism, New York, NY *Toll Free Tel:* 800-322-8755 *Toll Free Fax:* 800-678-3633, pg 39

Blue Apple Books, Maplewood, NJ *Toll Free Tel:* 800-283-3572 (orders), pg 40

Blue Book Publications Inc, Minneapolis, MN *Toll Free Tel:* 800-877-4867, pg 40

Blue Dolphin Publishing Inc, Grass Valley, CA *Toll Free Tel:* 800-643-0765 (orders), pg 40

Blue Mountain Arts Inc, Boulder, CO *Toll Free Tel:* 800-525-0642 *Toll Free Fax:* 800-545-8573, pg 40

Blue Note Publications Inc, Melbourne, FL *Toll Free Tel:* 800-624-0401 (orders), pg 40

Blue Poppy Press, Boulder, CO *Toll Free Tel:* 800-487-9296, pg 40

Bluestocking Press, Placerville, CA *Toll Free Tel:* 800-959-8586, pg 41

BNA Books, Arlington, VA *Toll Free Tel:* 800-372-1033; 800-960-1220, pg 41

BNi Building News, Vista, CA *Toll Free Tel:* 888-BNI-BOOK (264-2665), pg 41

BoardSource, Washington, DC *Toll Free Tel:* 877-892-6273, pg 41

Bolchazy-Carducci Publishers Inc, Mundelein, IL *Toll Free Tel:* 800-392-6453, pg 41

Book Sales Inc, New York, NY *Toll Free Tel:* 866-483-5456, pg 42

The Book Tree, San Diego, CA *Toll Free Tel:* 800-700-8733 (orders), pg 42

BookLogix, Alpharetta, GA *Toll Free Fax:* 888-564-7890, pg 42

Books In Motion, Spokane Valley, WA *Toll Free Tel:* 800-752-3199, pg 42

Books on Tape®, New York, NY *Toll Free Tel:* 800-733-3000 (cust serv) *Toll Free Fax:* 800-940-7046, pg 43

Borealis Press Ltd, Nepean, ON Canada *Toll Free Tel:* 877-696-2585, pg 473

The Boston Mills Press, Richmond Hill, ON Canada *Toll Free Tel:* 800-387-6192 *Toll Free Fax:* 800-450-0391, pg 473

Eddie Bowers Publishing Co Inc, Peosta, IA *Toll Free Tel:* 800-747-2411, pg 43

R R Bowker LLC, New Providence, NJ *Toll Free Tel:* 888-269-5372 (edit & cust serv, press 2 for returns) *Toll Free Fax:* 877-337-7015 (US & CN), pg 43

Boyds Mills Press, Honesdale, PA *Toll Free Tel:* 800-490-5111, pg 43

Boynton/Cook Publishers, Portsmouth, NH *Toll Free Tel:* 800-225-5800 *Toll Free Fax:* 877-231-6980, pg 44

Boys Town Press, Boys Town, NE *Toll Free Tel:* 800-282-6657, pg 44

Bradford Publishing Co, Denver, CO *Toll Free Tel:* 800-446-2831, pg 44

BradyGames, Indianapolis, IN *Toll Free Tel:* 800-545-5912; 800-571-5840 (cust serv), pg 44

Brault & Bouthillier, Montreal, QC Canada *Toll Free Tel:* 800-361-0378 *Toll Free Fax:* 800-361-0378, pg 473

Breakthrough Publications Inc, Emmaus, PA *Toll Free Tel:* 800-824-5001 (ext 12), pg 44

Breakwater Books Ltd, St John's, NL Canada *Toll Free Tel:* 800-563-3333 (orders), pg 473

Nicholas Brealey Publishing, Boston, MA *Toll Free Tel:* 888-BREALEY (273-2539), pg 44

Brenner Information Group, San Diego, CA *Toll Free Tel:* 800-811-4337 (orders), pg 45

Brentwood Christian Press, Columbus, GA *Toll Free Tel:* 800-334-8861, pg 45

Brethren Press, Elgin, IL *Toll Free Tel:* 800-323-8039 *Toll Free Fax:* 800-667-8188, pg 45

Brewers Publications, Boulder, CO *Toll Free Tel:* 888-822-6273 (CN & US), pg 45

Brick Tower Press, New York, NY *Toll Free Tel:* 800-68-BRICK (682-7425), pg 45

Bridge-Logos Inc, Alachua, FL *Toll Free Tel:* 800-631-5802 (orders) *Toll Free Fax:* 800-935-6467, pg 45

Bridge Publications Inc, Commerce City, CA *Toll Free Tel:* 800-722-1733, pg 45

Brill Inc, Boston, MA *Toll Free Tel:* 800-962-4406, pg 46

Brilliance Audio, Grand Haven, MI *Toll Free Tel:* 800-648-2312 (orders only), pg 46

Brookes Publishing Co Inc, Baltimore, MD *Toll Free Tel:* 800-638-3775 (US & CN), pg 46

Brookhaven Press, La Crosse, WI *Toll Free Tel:* 800-236-0850, pg 46

The Brookings Institution Press, Washington, DC *Toll Free Tel:* 800-537-5487, pg 47

Brookline Books, Northampton, MA *Toll Free Tel:* 800-666-2665 (orders), pg 47

Brooklyn Publishers LLC, Cedar Rapids, IA *Toll Free Tel:* 888-473-8521, pg 47

Brush Education Inc, Edmonton, AB Canada *Toll Free Tel:* 855-283-0900 *Toll Free Fax:* 855-283-6947, pg 474

BuilderBooks.com, Washington, DC *Toll Free Tel:* 800-223-2665, pg 47

Bull Publishing Co, Boulder, CO *Toll Free Tel:* 800-676-2855, pg 47

Burford Books, Ithaca, NY *Toll Free Fax:* 866-212-7750, pg 48

Business & Legal Resources Inc, Brentwood, TN *Toll Free Tel:* 800-727-5257, pg 48

Business Research Services Inc, Bethesda, MD *Toll Free Tel:* 800-845-8420 *Toll Free Fax:* 877-516-0818, pg 48

Butte Publications Inc, Hillsboro, OR *Toll Free Tel:* 866-312-8883 *Toll Free Fax:* 866-412-8883 (orders only), pg 48

C & T Publishing Inc, Concord, CA *Toll Free Tel:* 800-284-1114, pg 48

Cambridge Educational, New York, NY *Toll Free Tel:* 800-322-8755 *Toll Free Fax:* 800-329-6687, pg 48

Campfield & Campfield Publishing, Philadelphia, PA *Toll Free Tel:* 888-518-2440, pg 49

Canada Law Book®, Toronto, ON Canada *Toll Free Tel:* 800-387-5351 (cust rel, CN & US only); 800-347-5164 (cust rel & orders, CN & US) *Toll Free Fax:* 877-750-9041 (cust rel & orders, CN only), pg 474

Canadian Bible Society, Toronto, ON Canada *Toll Free Tel:* 866-946-1711, pg 474

Canadian Institute of Chartered Accountants-CICA (L'Institut Canadien des Comptables Agrees), Toronto, ON Canada *Toll Free Tel:* 800-268-3793 (CN orders), pg 475

Canadian Museum of History (Musee Canadien de l'Histoire), Gatineau, QC Canada *Toll Free Tel:* 800-555-5621 (North American orders only), pg 475

Canadian Scholars' Press Inc, Toronto, ON Canada *Toll Free Tel:* 800-463-1998, pg 475

Capital Enquiry Inc, South Lake Tahoe, CA *Toll Free Tel:* 800-922-7486, pg 49

Capstone Publishers™, North Mankato, MN *Toll Free Tel:* 800-747-4992 (cust serv) *Toll Free Fax:* 888-262-0705, pg 49

Cardoza Publishing, Las Vegas, NV *Toll Free Tel:* 800-577-WINS (577-9467), pg 50

The Career Press Inc, Wayne, NJ *Toll Free Tel:* 800-CAREER-1 (227-3371), pg 50

Carlisle Press - Walnut Creek, Sugarcreek, OH *Toll Free Tel:* 800-852-4482, pg 50

Carolina Academic Press, Durham, NC *Toll Free Tel:* 800-489-7486, pg 50

Carolrhoda Books, Minneapolis, MN *Toll Free Tel:* 800-328-4929 *Toll Free Fax:* 800-332-1132, pg 50

Carolrhoda Lab™, Minneapolis, MN *Toll Free Tel:* 800-328-4929 *Toll Free Fax:* 800-332-1132 (US), pg 50

Carroll Publishing, Bethesda, MD *Toll Free Tel:* 800-336-4240, pg 51

Carson-Dellosa Publishing LLC, Greensboro, NC *Toll Free Tel:* 800-321-0943 *Toll Free Fax:* 800-535-2669, pg 51

Carswell, Toronto, ON Canada *Toll Free Tel:* 800-387-5164 (CN & US) *Toll Free Fax:* 877-750-9041 (CN only), pg 476

CarTech Inc, North Branch, MN *Toll Free Tel:* 800-551-4754, pg 51

Casa Bautista de Publicaciones, El Paso, TX *Toll Free Tel:* 800-755-5958 (cust serv & orders), pg 51

Cascade Pass Inc, Marina Del Rey, CA *Toll Free Tel:* 888-837-0704, pg 51

Catholic Book Publishing Corp, Totowa, NJ *Toll Free Tel:* 877-228-2665, pg 51

The Catholic University of America Press, Washington, DC *Toll Free Tel:* 800-537-5487 (orders only), pg 52

Cato Institute, Washington, DC *Toll Free Tel:* 800-767-1241, pg 52

Caxton Press, Caldwell, ID *Toll Free Tel:* 800-657-6465, pg 52

Cedar Fort Inc, Springville, UT *Toll Free Tel:* 800-SKY-BOOK (759-2665) *Toll Free Fax:* 800-388-3727, pg 52

CEF Press, Warrenton, MO *Toll Free Tel:* 800-748-7710 (cust serv); 800-300-4033 (USA ministries), pg 52

Cengage Learning, Boston, MA *Toll Free Tel:* 800-354-9706 *Toll Free Fax:* 800-487-8488, pg 53

The Center for Learning, Culver City, CA *Toll Free Tel:* 800-421-4246 *Toll Free Fax:* 800-944-5432, pg 53

Center for the Collaborative Classroom, Emeryville, CA *Toll Free Tel:* 800-666-7270, pg 53

Centering Corp, Omaha, NE *Toll Free Tel:* 866-218-0101, pg 54

Centre Franco-Ontarien de Ressources en Alphabetisation (Centre FORA), Sudbury, ON Canada *Toll Free Tel:* 888-814-4422 (orders, CN only), pg 476

Chain Store Guide (CSG), Tampa, FL *Toll Free Tel:* 800-927-9292 (orders), pg 54

Chalice Press, St Louis, MO *Toll Free Tel:* 800-366-3383, pg 54

Charisma Media, Lake Mary, FL *Toll Free Tel:* 800-283-8494 (Charisma Media, Siloam Press, Creation House); 800-665-1468, pg 55

CharismaLife Publishers, Lake Mary, FL *Toll Free Tel:* 800-451-4598, pg 55

Charles River Media, Boston, MA *Toll Free Tel:* 800-354-9706 *Toll Free Fax:* 800-487-8488, pg 55

Charles Scribner's Sons®, Farmington Hills, MI *Toll Free Tel:* 800-877-4253 *Toll Free Fax:* 800-414-5043, pg 55

Charlesbridge Publishing Inc, Watertown, MA *Toll Free Tel:* 800-225-3214 *Toll Free Fax:* 800-926-5775, pg 55

The Charlton Press, North York, ON Canada *Toll Free Tel:* 800-442-6042 (North America) *Toll Free Fax:* 800-442-1542 (North America), pg 476

Chelsea Green Publishing Co, White River Junction, VT *Toll Free Tel:* 800-639-4099 (cust serv, consumer & trade orders), pg 56

Chelsea House Publishers, New York, NY *Toll Free Tel:* 800-322-8755 *Toll Free Fax:* 800-678-3633, pg 56

Cheneliere Education Inc, Montreal, QC Canada *Toll Free Tel:* 800-565-5531 *Toll Free Fax:* 800-814-0324, pg 477

Cheng & Tsui Co Inc, Boston, MA *Toll Free Tel:* 800-554-1963, pg 56

Cherry Hill Publishing LLC, Ramona, CA *Toll Free Tel:* 800-407-1072, pg 56

Chicago Review Press, Chicago, IL *Toll Free Tel:* 800-888-4741, pg 56

Child's Play®, Auburn, ME *Toll Free Tel:* 800-639-6404 *Toll Free Fax:* 800-854-6989, pg 57

The Child's World Inc, North Mankato, MN *Toll Free Tel:* 800-599-READ (599-7323) *Toll Free Fax:* 888-320-2329, pg 57

Childswork/Childsplay LLC, Woodbury, NY *Toll Free Tel:* 800-962-1141 (cust serv) *Toll Free Fax:* 800-262-1886 (orders), pg 57

China Books, South San Francisco, CA *Toll Free Tel:* 800-818-2017 (US only), pg 57

Chosen Books, Bloomington, MN *Toll Free Tel:* 800-877-2665 (orders only) *Toll Free Fax:* 800-398-3111 (orders only), pg 57

Christian Liberty Press, Arlington Heights, IL *Toll Free Tel:* 800-832-2741 (cust serv), pg 57

Christian Light Publications Inc, Harrisonburg, VA *Toll Free Tel:* 800-776-0478, pg 57

Christian Schools International, Grand Rapids, MI *Toll Free Tel:* 800-635-8288, pg 57

The Christian Science Publishing Society, Boston, MA *Toll Free Tel:* 800-288-7090, pg 57

Chronicle Books LLC, San Francisco, CA *Toll Free Tel:* 800-759-0190 (cust serv) *Toll Free Fax:* 800-858-7787 (orders); 800-286-9471 (cust serv), pg 57

Cinco Puntos Press, El Paso, TX *Toll Free Tel:* 800-566-9072, pg 58

Circlet Press Inc, Cambridge, MA *Toll Free Tel:* 800-729-6423, pg 58

Cistercian Publications, Collegeville, MN *Toll Free Tel:* 800-436-8431 *Toll Free Fax:* 800-445-5899, pg 58

Clarion Books, New York, NY *Toll Free Tel:* 800-225-3362 (orders) *Toll Free Fax:* 800-634-7568 (orders), pg 59

Clarity Press Inc, Atlanta, GA *Toll Free Tel:* 877-613-1495 (edit) *Toll Free Fax:* 877-613-7868, pg 59

CLC Ministries, Fort Washington, PA *Toll Free Tel:* 800-659-1240, pg 59

Clear Light Publishers, Santa Fe, NM *Toll Free Tel:* 800-253-2747 (orders), pg 59

Clearfield Co Inc, Baltimore, MD *Toll Free Tel:* 800-296-6687 (orders & cust serv), pg 59

Cleis Press, Berkeley, CA *Toll Free Tel:* 800-780-2279 (US), pg 59

Clerisy Press, Covington, KY *Toll Free Tel:* 800-913-9563, pg 59

Clinical Laboratory & Standards Institute (CLSI), Wayne, PA *Toll Free Tel:* 877-447-1888 (orders), pg 59

Close Up Publishing, Alexandria, VA *Toll Free Tel:* 800-CLOSE-UP (256-7387), pg 60

Coach House Books, Toronto, ON Canada *Toll Free Tel:* 800-367-6360 (outside Toronto), pg 477

Coaches Choice, Monterey, CA *Toll Free Tel:* 888-229-5745, pg 60

Cold Spring Harbor Laboratory Press, Woodbury, NY *Toll Free Tel:* 800-843-4388, pg 60

College & University Professional Association for Human Resources (CUPA-HR), Knoxville, TN *Toll Free Tel:* 877-CUPA-HR4 (287-2474), pg 60

College Publishing, Glen Allen, VA *Toll Free Tel:* 800-827-0723, pg 61

The Colonial Williamsburg Foundation, Williamsburg, VA *Toll Free Tel:* 800-HISTORY (447-8679), pg 61

Columbia Books & Information Services, Bethesda, MD *Toll Free Tel:* 888-265-0600 (cust serv), pg 61

Columbia University Press, New York, NY *Toll Free Tel:* 800-944-8648, pg 61

Comex Systems Inc, Chester, NJ *Toll Free Tel:* 800-543-6959, pg 61

Common Courage Press, Monroe, ME *Toll Free Tel:* 800-497-3207, pg 62

Commonwealth Editions, Carlisle, MA *Toll Free Tel:* 800-277-5312, pg 62

Company's Coming Publishing Ltd, Vancouver, BC Canada *Toll Free Tel:* 800-661-9017 (CN); 800-518-3541 (US), pg 477

Concordia Publishing House, St Louis, MO *Toll Free Tel:* 800-325-3040 (cust serv) *Toll Free Fax:* 800-490-9889 (cust serv), pg 62

The Continuing Legal Education Society of British Columbia (CLEBC), Vancouver, BC Canada *Toll Free Tel:* 800-663-0437 (CN), pg 478

David C Cook, Colorado Springs, CO *Toll Free Tel:* 800-708-5550; 800-323-7543 (orders & cust serv) *Toll Free Fax:* 800-430-0726 (cust serv), pg 62

Copley Custom Textbooks, Acton, MA *Toll Free Tel:* 800-562-2147, pg 62

Copper Canyon Press, Port Townsend, WA *Toll Free Tel:* 877-501-1393 (orders), pg 63

Cortina Institute of Languages, Wilton, CT *Toll Free Tel:* 800-245-2145, pg 64

Cortina Learning International Inc (CLI), Wilton, CT *Toll Free Tel:* 800-245-2145, pg 64

Corwin, a Sage Co, Thousand Oaks, CA *Toll Free Tel:* 800-233-9936 *Toll Free Fax:* 800-417-2466, pg 64

Coteau Books, Regina, SK Canada *Toll Free Tel:* 800-440-4471 (CN only), pg 478

Council for Exceptional Children (CEC), Arlington, VA *Toll Free Tel:* 888-232-7733 (memb servs); 866-509-0219, pg 64

Council Oak Books LLC, San Francisco, CA *Toll Free Tel:* 888-275-2596, pg 65

Council of State Governments, Lexington, KY *Toll Free Tel:* 800-800-1910, pg 65

CQ Press, Washington, DC *Toll Free Tel:* 866-4CQ-PRESS (427-7737) *Toll Free Fax:* 800-380-3810, pg 66

Crabtree Publishing Co, New York, NY *Toll Free Tel:* 800-387-7650 *Toll Free Fax:* 800-355-7166, pg 66

Crabtree Publishing Co Ltd, St Catharines, ON Canada *Toll Free Tel:* 800-387-7650 *Toll Free Fax:* 800-355-7166, pg 478

Craftsman Book Co, Carlsbad, CA *Toll Free Tel:* 800-829-8123, pg 66

CRC Press LLC, Boca Raton, FL *Toll Free Tel:* 800-272-7737 (orders) *Toll Free Fax:* 800-643-9428 (sales); 800-374-3401 (orders), pg 66

The Creative Co, Mankato, MN *Toll Free Tel:* 800-445-6209, pg 66

Creative Homeowner, East Petersburg, PA *Toll Free Tel:* 800-475-9112 *Toll Free Fax:* 888-369-2885, pg 66

The Crossroad Publishing Co, Chestnut Ridge, NY *Toll Free Tel:* 800-888-4741 (orders), pg 67

Crossway, Wheaton, IL *Toll Free Tel:* 800-635-7993 (orders); 800-543-1659 (cust serv), pg 67

Crown House Publishing Co LLC, Bethel, CT *Toll Free Tel:* 877-925-1213 (cust serv); 866-272-8497, pg 67

Crown Publishing Group, New York, NY *Toll Free Tel:* 888-264-1745, pg 68

Crystal Clarity Publishers, Nevada City, CA *Toll Free Tel:* 800-424-1055, pg 68

Crystal Productions, Carpinteria, CA *Toll Free Tel:* 800-255-8629 *Toll Free Fax:* 800-657-8149, pg 68

CTB/McGraw-Hill, Monterey, CA *Toll Free Tel:* 800-538-9547 *Toll Free Fax:* 800-282-0266, pg 69

Cumberland House, Naperville, IL *Toll Free Tel:* 800-43-BRIGHT (432-7444), pg 69

Cypress House, Fort Bragg, CA *Toll Free Tel:* 800-773-7782, pg 69

Da Capo Press & Lifelong Books, Boston, MA *Toll Free Tel:* 800-343-4499 (orders), pg 69

Damron Co, San Francisco, CA *Toll Free Tel:* 800-462-6654, pg 70

John Daniel & Co, McKinleyville, CA *Toll Free Tel:* 800-662-8351, pg 70

The Dartnell Corporation, Durham, NC *Toll Free Tel:* 800-223-8720; 800-472-0148 (cust serv) *Toll Free Fax:* 800-508-2592, pg 70

Data Trace Publishing Co (DTP), Towson, MD *Toll Free Tel:* 800-342-0454 (orders only), pg 70

Davies Publishing Inc, Pasadena, CA *Toll Free Tel:* 877-792-0005, pg 71

F A Davis Co, Philadelphia, PA *Toll Free Tel:* 800-523-4049, pg 71

The Dawn Horse Press, Middletown, CA *Toll Free Tel:* 877-770-0772, pg 71

Dawn Publications Inc, Nevada City, CA *Toll Free Tel:* 800-545-7475, pg 71

DawnSignPress, San Diego, CA *Toll Free Tel:* 800-549-5350, pg 71

Day Owl Press Corp, Lantana, FL *Toll Free Tel:* 888-806-6981 *Toll Free Fax:* 866-854-4375, pg 72

dbS Productions, Charlottesville, VA *Toll Free Tel:* 800-745-1581, pg 72

DC Canada Education Publishing (DCCED), Ottawa, ON Canada *Toll Free Tel:* 888-565-0262, pg 478

DC Entertainment, Burbank, CA *Toll Free Tel:* 800-887-6789, pg 72

DC Press LLC, Lake Mary, FL *Toll Free Tel:* 877-203-1895, pg 72

De Vorss & Co, Camarillo, CA *Toll Free Tel:* 800-843-5743, pg 72

Decent Hill Publishers LLC, Cleveland, OH *Toll Free Tel:* 866-688-5325 *Toll Free Fax:* 866-688-5325, pg 72

Decker Intellectual Properties Publisher, Hamilton, ON Canada *Toll Free Tel:* 855-647-6511 (CN & US), pg 478

DeLorme Publishing Co Inc, Yarmouth, ME *Toll Free Tel:* 800-561-5105; 800-511-2459 (cust serv) *Toll Free Fax:* 800-575-2244, pg 72

Delta Publishing Co, McHenry, IL *Toll Free Tel:* 800-323-8270 (orders) *Toll Free Fax:* 800-909-9901, pg 73

Deseret Book Co, Salt Lake City, UT *Toll Free Tel:* 800-453-4532 (orders); 888-846-7302 (orders), pg 73

DEStech Publications Inc, Lancaster, PA *Toll Free Tel:* 877-500-4337, pg 73

Destiny Image Inc, Shippensburg, PA *Toll Free Tel:* 800-722-6774 (orders only), pg 73

Dharma Publishing, Cazadero, CA *Toll Free Tel:* 800-873-4276, pg 73

Diane Publishing Co, Collingdale, PA *Toll Free Tel:* 800-782-3833, pg 74

Discovery House Publishers, Grand Rapids, MI *Toll Free Tel:* 800-653-8333 (cust serv), pg 74

Dissertation.com, Boca Raton, FL *Toll Free Tel:* 800-636-8329, pg 74

DK Publishing, New York, NY *Toll Free Tel:* 877-342-5357 (cust serv), pg 75

Dogwise Publishing, Wenatchee, WA *Toll Free Tel:* 800-776-2665, pg 75

Tom Doherty Associates, LLC, New York, NY *Toll Free Tel:* 800-455-0340, pg 75

Dominie Press, Lebanon, IN *Toll Free Tel:* 800-321-3106 (Pearson Cust Serv); 800-848-9500 *Toll Free Fax:* 877-260-2530, pg 75

The Donning Company Publishers, Virginia Beach, VA *Toll Free Tel:* 800-296-8572, pg 75

Dordt College Press, Sioux Center, IA *Toll Free Tel:* 800-343-6738, pg 75

Dorland Health, Rockville, MD *Toll Free Tel:* 855-225-5341, pg 75

Dorrance Publishing Co Inc, Pittsburgh, PA *Toll Free Tel:* 800-695-9599; 800-788-7654 (gen cust orders), pg 75

Dorset House Publishing Co Inc, New York, NY *Toll Free Tel:* 800-DHBOOKS (342-6657, orders only), pg 76

Douglas & McIntyre (2013) Ltd, Madeira Park, BC Canada *Toll Free Tel:* 800-667-2988, pg 479

Dover Publications Inc, Mineola, NY *Toll Free Tel:* 800-223-3130 (orders), pg 76

Down East Books, Rockport, ME *Toll Free Tel:* 800-685-7962 (US only orders); 800-766-1670, pg 76

Dragon Door Publications, Little Canada, MN *Toll Free Tel:* 800-899-5111 (orders & cust serv), pg 76

Dramatic Publishing Co, Woodstock, IL *Toll Free Tel:* 800-448-7469 *Toll Free Fax:* 800-334-5302, pg 76

Dreamscape Media LLC, Holland, OH *Toll Free Tel:* 877-983-7326, pg 77

Duke University Press, Durham, NC *Toll Free Tel:* 888-651-0122 (US) *Toll Free Fax:* 888-651-0124, pg 77

Dun & Bradstreet, Short Hills, NJ *Toll Free Tel:* 800-526-0651; 800-234-3867 (cust serv), pg 77

Eagan Press, St Paul, MN *Toll Free Tel:* 800-328-7560, pg 78

Eakin Press, Fort Worth, TX *Toll Free Tel:* 888-982-8270, pg 78

Eastland Press, Vista, CA *Toll Free Tel:* 800-453-3278 (orders) *Toll Free Fax:* 800-241-3329 (orders), pg 78

Ecopress, Apple Valley, MN *Toll Free Tel:* 800-846-7027 *Toll Free Fax:* 800-330-6232, pg 79

EDC Publishing, Tulsa, OK *Toll Free Tel:* 800-475-4522 *Toll Free Fax:* 800-743-5660, pg 79

ediciones Lerner, Minneapolis, MN *Toll Free Tel:* 800-328-4929 *Toll Free Fax:* 800-332-1132, pg 79

Editions Marcel Didier Inc, Montreal, QC Canada *Toll Free Tel:* 800-361-1664 (Ontario to Maritimes), pg 480

Editions FouLire, Quebec, QC Canada *Toll Free Tel:* 877-628-4029 (CN & US), pg 481

Les Editions Goelette Inc, Quebec, QC Canada *Toll Free Tel:* 800-463-4961, pg 481

Les Editions Heritage Inc, St-Lambert, QC Canada *Toll Free Tel:* 800-561-3737, pg 482

Editions Hurtubise, Montreal, QC Canada *Toll Free Tel:* 800-361-1664, pg 482

Editions Marie-France, Montreal, QC Canada *Toll Free Tel:* 800-563-6644 (CN), pg 482

Editions MultiMondes, Quebec, QC Canada *Toll Free Tel:* 800-840-3029 *Toll Free Fax:* 888-303-5931, pg 482

Les Editions Phidal Inc, Montreal, QC Canada *Toll Free Tel:* 800-738-7349, pg 482

Les Editions Un Monde Different, Brossard, QC Canada *Toll Free Tel:* 800-443-2582, pg 483

Editions Yvon Blais, Cowansville, QC Canada *Toll Free Tel:* 800-363-3047, pg 483

Editorial Bautista Independiente, Sebring, FL *Toll Free Tel:* 800-398-7187 (US), pg 79

Editorial Portavoz, Grand Rapids, MI *Toll Free Tel:* 877-733-2607 (ext 206), pg 79

Educational Directories Inc (EDI), Schaumburg, IL *Toll Free Tel:* 800-357-6183, pg 79

Educational Impressions Inc, Franklin Lakes, NJ *Toll Free Tel:* 800-451-7450, pg 79

Educational Insights, Gardena, CA *Toll Free Tel:* 800-995-4436 *Toll Free Fax:* 888-892-8731, pg 80

Educators Progress Service Inc, Randolph, WI *Toll Free Tel:* 888-951-4469, pg 80

Edupress Inc, Madison, WI *Toll Free Tel:* 800-835-7978 *Toll Free Fax:* 800-558-9332, pg 80

Wm B Eerdmans Publishing Co, Grand Rapids, MI *Toll Free Tel:* 800-253-7521, pg 80

Edward Elgar Publishing Inc, Northampton, MA *Toll Free Tel:* 800-390-3149 (orders), pg 80

Elite Books, Fulton, CA *Toll Free Fax:* 800-330-9798, pg 81

Elsevier Engineering Information (Ei), New York, NY *Toll Free Tel:* 800-221-1044, pg 81

Elsevier, Health Sciences Division, Philadelphia, PA *Toll Free Tel:* 800-523-1649, pg 81

EMC Publishing LLC, St Paul, MN *Toll Free Tel:* 800-328-1452 *Toll Free Fax:* 800-328-4564, pg 81

Emerald Books, Seattle, WA *Toll Free Tel:* 800-922-2143, pg 81

Emmaus Road Publishing Inc, Steubenville, OH *Toll Free Tel:* 800-398-5470 (orders), pg 81

Emond Montgomery Publications Ltd, Toronto, ON Canada *Toll Free Tel:* 888-837-0815, pg 483

Encounter Books, New York, NY *Toll Free Tel:* 800-786-3839, pg 82

Encyclopaedia Britannica Inc, Chicago, IL *Toll Free Tel:* 800-323-1229 (US & CN), pg 82

Energy Psychology Press, Santa Rosa, CA *Toll Free Fax:* 800-330-9798, pg 82

Enslow Publishing LLC, New York, NY *Toll Free Tel:* 800-398-2504 *Toll Free Fax:* 877-980-4454, pg 83

Environmental Law Institute, Washington, DC *Toll Free Tel:* 800-433-5120, pg 83

EPS/School Specialty Literacy & Intervention, Cambridge, MA *Toll Free Tel:* 800-225-5750 *Toll Free Fax:* 888-440-2665, pg 83

Evan-Moor Educational Publishers, Monterey, CA *Toll Free Tel:* 800-777-4362 (orders) *Toll Free Fax:* 800-777-4332 (orders), pg 84

Excelsior Editions, Albany, NY *Toll Free Tel:* 866-430-7869, pg 84

Eye in the Ear Children's Audio, Portland, ME *Toll Free Tel:* 855-99-STORY (997-8679), pg 85

Facts On File, New York, NY *Toll Free Tel:* 800-322-8755 *Toll Free Fax:* 800-678-3633, pg 85

Fairchild Books, New York, NY *Toll Free Tel:* 800-932-4724; 888-330-8477 (orders), pg 85

Faith Alive Christian Resources, Grand Rapids, MI *Toll Free Tel:* 800-333-8300 *Toll Free Fax:* 888-642-8606, pg 85

Faith & Fellowship Publishing, Fergus Falls, MN *Toll Free Tel:* 800-332-9232, pg 86

Faith Library Publications, Tulsa, OK *Toll Free Tel:* 888-258-0999 (orders), pg 86

Faithlife Corp, Bellingham, WA *Toll Free Tel:* 800-875-6467, pg 86

FaithWalk Publishing, Lima, OH *Toll Free Tel:* 800-537-1030 (orders: non-bookstore mkts), pg 86

F+W, A Content + eCommerce Company, Blue Ash, OH *Toll Free Tel:* 800-289-0963 (trade accts); 800-258-0929 (orders), pg 86

Father & Son Publishing Inc, Tallahassee, FL *Toll Free Tel:* 800-741-2712 (orders only), pg 87

FC&A Publishing, Peachtree City, GA *Toll Free Tel:* 800-226-8024, pg 87

Federal Street Press, Darien, CT *Toll Free Tel:* 877-886-2830, pg 87

Feldheim Publishers (Philipp Feldheim Inc), Nanuet, NY *Toll Free Tel:* 800-237-7149 (orders), pg 87

Ferguson Publishing, New York, NY *Toll Free Tel:* 800-322-8755 *Toll Free Fax:* 800-678-3633, pg 88

Fifth Estate Publishing, Blounstville, AL *Toll Free Tel:* 855-299-2160, pg 88

Fifth House Publishers, Markham, ON Canada *Toll Free Tel:* 800-387-9776 *Toll Free Fax:* 800-260-9777, pg 484

Filter Press LLC, Palmer Lake, CO *Toll Free Tel:* 888-570-2663, pg 88

Financial Times Press, Hoboken, NJ *Toll Free Tel:* 800-922-0579 (orders), pg 88

Finney Company Inc, Apple Valley, MN *Toll Free Tel:* 800-846-7027 *Toll Free Fax:* 800-330-6232, pg 89

Fire Engineering Books & Videos, Tulsa, OK *Toll Free Tel:* 800-752-9764, pg 89

Firefly Books Ltd, Richmond Hill, ON Canada *Toll Free Tel:* 800-387-6192 (CN); 800-387-5085 (US) *Toll Free Fax:* 800-450-0391 (CN); 800-565-6034 (US), pg 484

First Avenue Editions, Minneapolis, MN *Toll Free Tel:* 800-328-4929 *Toll Free Fax:* 800-332-1132, pg 89

Fitzhenry & Whiteside Limited, Markham, ON Canada *Toll Free Tel:* 800-387-9776 *Toll Free Fax:* 800-260-9777, pg 484

FJH Music Co Inc, Fort Lauderdale, FL *Toll Free Tel:* 800-262-8744, pg 89

Flanker Press Ltd, Paradise, NL Canada *Toll Free Tel:* 866-739-4420, pg 484

FleetSeek, Atlanta, GA *Toll Free Tel:* 888-ONLY-TTS (665-9887), pg 89

Focus on the Family, Colorado Springs, CO *Toll Free Tel:* 800-A-FAMILY (232-6459), pg 90

Fodor's Travel Publications, New York, NY *Toll Free Tel:* 800-733-3000, pg 90

Forum Publishing Co, Centerport, NY *Toll Free Tel:* 800-635-7654, pg 91

Forward Movement, Cincinnati, OH *Toll Free Tel:* 800-543-1813, pg 91

Walter Foster Publishing Inc, Lake Forest, CA *Toll Free Tel:* 800-426-0099; 800-759-0190 (orders), pg 91

The Foundation Center, New York, NY *Toll Free Tel:* 800-424-9836, pg 91

Foundation Press, St Paul, MN *Toll Free Tel:* 877-888-1330, pg 91

Foundation Publications, La Habra, CA *Toll Free Tel:* 800-257-6272, pg 91

Fox Chapel Publishing Co Inc, East Petersburg, PA *Toll Free Tel:* 800-457-9112, pg 91

FPMI Solutions Inc, Huntsville, AL *Toll Free Tel:* 888-644-3764, pg 91

Franciscan Media, Cincinnati, OH *Toll Free Tel:* 800-488-0488, pg 92

Franklin, Beedle & Associates Inc, Portland, OR *Toll Free Tel:* 800-322-2665, pg 92

The Fraser Institute, Vancouver, BC Canada *Toll Free Tel:* 800-665-3558, pg 485

Free Spirit Publishing Inc, Minneapolis, MN *Toll Free Tel:* 800-735-7323 *Toll Free Fax:* 866-419-5199, pg 92

Samuel French Inc, New York, NY *Toll Free Tel:* 866-598-8449, pg 92

Fresh Air Books, Nashville, TN *Toll Free Tel:* 800-972-0433 (orders), pg 93

Fulcrum Publishing Inc, Golden, CO *Toll Free Tel:* 800-992-2908 *Toll Free Fax:* 800-726-7112, pg 93

FurnitureCore, Atlanta, GA *Toll Free Tel:* 800-826-8868, pg 93

Future Horizons Inc, Arlington, TX *Toll Free Tel:* 800-489-0727, pg 93

Gaetan Morin Editeur, Montreal, QC Canada *Toll Free Tel:* 800-565-5531 *Toll Free Fax:* 800-814-0324, pg 485

Galaxy Press, Hollywood, CA *Toll Free Tel:* 877-8GALAXY (842-5299), pg 93

Galde Press Inc, Lakeville, MN *Toll Free Tel:* 800-777-3454, pg 93

Gale, Farmington Hills, MI *Toll Free Tel:* 800-877-4253 *Toll Free Fax:* 800-414-5043 (orders), pg 94

Gallaudet University Press, Washington, DC *Toll Free Tel:* 800-621-2736 (orders) *Toll Free Fax:* 800-621-8476 (orders), pg 94

Gallery Books, New York, NY *Toll Free Tel:* 800-456-6798, pg 94

Gallopade International Inc, Peachtree City, GA *Toll Free Tel:* 800-536-2GET (536-2438) *Toll Free Fax:* 800-871-2979, pg 94

Gareth Stevens Publishing, New York, NY *Toll Free Tel:* 800-542-2595 *Toll Free Fax:* 877-542-2596 (cust serv), pg 94

Gatekeeper Press, Columbus, OH *Toll Free Tel:* 866-535-0913, pg 95

Gateways Books & Tapes, Nevada City, CA *Toll Free Tel:* 800-869-0658, pg 95

Gefen Books, Lawrence, NY *Toll Free Tel:* 800-477-5257, pg 95

Gem Guides Book Co, Upland, CA *Toll Free Tel:* 800-824-5118 (orders), pg 95

Genealogical Publishing Co, Baltimore, MD *Toll Free Tel:* 800-296-6687 *Toll Free Fax:* 800-599-9561, pg 95

General Store Publishing House (GSPH), Renfrew, ON Canada *Toll Free Tel:* 800-465-6072, pg 485

Genesis Press Inc, Columbus, MS *Toll Free Tel:* 888-463-4461 (orders only), pg 95

GeoLytics Inc, Branchburg, NJ *Toll Free Tel:* 800-577-6717, pg 96

Getty Publications, Los Angeles, CA *Toll Free Tel:* 800-223-3431 (orders), pg 96

GIA Publications Inc, Chicago, IL *Toll Free Tel:* 800-GIA-1358 (442-1358), pg 96

Gibbs Smith Publisher, Layton, UT *Toll Free Tel:* 800-748-5439; 800-835-4993 (orders) *Toll Free Fax:* 800-213-3023 (orders only), pg 96

Gilpin Publishing, Alliston, ON Canada *Toll Free Tel:* 800-867-3281, pg 485

Glenbridge Publishing Ltd, Centennial, CO *Toll Free Tel:* 800-986-4135 (orders), pg 97

Global Training Center Inc, El Paso, TX *Toll Free Tel:* 800-860-5030, pg 97

The Globe Pequot Press, Guilford, CT *Toll Free Tel:* 800-243-0495 (orders only); 888-249-7586 (cust serv) *Toll Free Fax:* 800-820-2329 (orders & cust serv), pg 98

Gold Eagle, Don Mills, ON Canada *Toll Free Tel:* 888-432-4879, pg 485

Golden West Cookbooks, Phoenix, AZ *Toll Free Tel:* 800-521-9221, pg 98

Goodheart-Willcox Publisher, Tinley Park, IL *Toll Free Tel:* 800-323-0440 *Toll Free Fax:* 888-409-3900, pg 98

Goose Lane Editions, Fredericton, NB Canada *Toll Free Tel:* 888-926-8377, pg 485

Goosebottom Books, Foster City, CA *Toll Free Fax:* 888-407-5286, pg 98

Gospel Publishing House (GPH), Springfield, MO *Toll Free Tel:* 800-641-4310 *Toll Free Fax:* 800-328-0294, pg 99

Government of Canada Publications, Ottawa, ON Canada *Toll Free Tel:* 800-635-7943 *Toll Free Fax:* 800-565-7757, pg 485

Graphic Universe™, Minneapolis, MN *Toll Free Tel:* 800-328-4929 *Toll Free Fax:* 800-332-1132, pg 99

Gray & Company Publishers, Cleveland, OH *Toll Free Tel:* 800-915-3609, pg 99

Great Quotations Inc, Downers Grove, IL *Toll Free Tel:* 800-830-3020, pg 100

Great Source Education Group, Wilmington, MA *Toll Free Tel:* 800-289-4490 *Toll Free Fax:* 800-289-3994; 800-269-5232, pg 100

Green Dragon Books, Palm Beach, FL *Toll Free Tel:* 800-874-8844 *Toll Free Fax:* 888-874-8844, pg 100

Greenhaven Press®, Farmington Hills, MI *Toll Free Tel:* 800-877-GALE (877-4253 - cust serv & orders) *Toll Free Fax:* 800-414-5043 (orders only), pg 100

Greenleaf Book Group LLC, Austin, TX *Toll Free Tel:* 800-932-5420, pg 100

Grey House Publishing Inc™, Amenia, NY *Toll Free Tel:* 800-562-2139, pg 101

Group Publishing Inc, Loveland, CO *Toll Free Tel:* 800-447-1070, pg 101

Groupe Educalivres Inc, Laval, QC Canada *Toll Free Tel:* 800-567-3671 (info serv), pg 486

Groupe Modulo, Montreal, QC Canada *Toll Free Tel:* 800-565-5531 *Toll Free Fax:* 800-814-0324, pg 486

Grove Atlantic Inc, New York, NY *Toll Free Tel:* 800-521-0178, pg 101

Gryphon Editions, Omaha, NE *Toll Free Tel:* 888-655-0134 (US & CN), pg 101

Gryphon House Inc, Lewisville, NC *Toll Free Tel:* 800-638-0928 *Toll Free Fax:* 877-638-7576, pg 101

Guideposts Book & Inspirational Media, New York, NY *Toll Free Tel:* 800-431-2344 (cust serv), pg 102

The Guilford Press, New York, NY *Toll Free Tel:* 800-365-7006, pg 102

Hachette Book Group, New York, NY *Toll Free Tel:* 800-759-0190 (cust serv) *Toll Free Fax:* 800-286-9471 (cust serv), pg 102

Hackett Publishing Co Inc, Indianapolis, IN *Toll Free Fax:* 800-783-9213, pg 103

Hagstrom Map, Wilmington, DE *Toll Free Tel:* 800-432-MAPS (432-6277) *Toll Free Fax:* 888-210-9654, pg 103

Hal Leonard Books, Montclair, NJ *Toll Free Tel:* 800-637-2852, pg 103

Hal Leonard Corp, Milwaukee, WI *Toll Free Tel:* 800-524-4425, pg 103

Hamilton Books, Lanham, MD *Toll Free Tel:* 800-462-6420 (cust serv) *Toll Free Fax:* 800-388-4550 (cust serv), pg 103

Hampton Press Inc, New York, NY *Toll Free Tel:* 800-894-8955, pg 104

Hampton Roads Publishing Co, Newburyport, MA *Toll Free Tel:* 800-423-7087 (orders) *Toll Free Fax:* 877-337-3309, pg 104

Hancock House Publishers, Blaine, WA *Toll Free Tel:* 800-938-1114 *Toll Free Fax:* 800-983-2262, pg 104

Hancock House Publishers Ltd, Surrey, BC Canada *Toll Free Tel:* 800-938-1114 *Toll Free Fax:* 800-983-2262, pg 487

Handprint Books Inc, Brooklyn, NY *Toll Free Tel:* 800-722-6657 (orders) *Toll Free Fax:* 800-858-7787 (orders), pg 104

Hanser Publications LLC, Cincinnati, OH *Toll Free Tel:* 800-950-8977; 877-751-5052 (orders) *Toll Free Fax:* 800-527-8801, pg 104

Harbour Publishing Co Ltd, Madeira Park, BC Canada *Toll Free Tel:* 800-667-2988, pg 487

Harcourt Achieve, Orlando, FL *Toll Free Tel:* 800-531-5015 (cust serv/orders) *Toll Free Fax:* 800-699-9459 (cust serv/orders), pg 104

Harcourt Inc, Orlando, FL *Toll Free Tel:* 800-225-5425 (cust serv/orders) *Toll Free Fax:* 800-269-5232 (cust serv/orders), pg 104

Hard Shell Word Factory, Cincinnati, OH *Toll Free Tel:* 888-232-0808 *Toll Free Fax:* 888-460-4752, pg 105

Harlequin Enterprises Ltd, Don Mills, ON Canada *Toll Free Tel:* 888-432-4879; 800-370-5838 (ebook inquiries), pg 487

Harper's Magazine Foundation, New York, NY *Toll Free Tel:* 800-444-4653, pg 106

Harrison House Publishers, Tulsa, OK *Toll Free Tel:* 800-888-4126 *Toll Free Fax:* 800-830-5688, pg 106

Hartman Publishing Inc, Albuquerque, NM *Toll Free Tel:* 800-999-9534 *Toll Free Fax:* 800-474-6106, pg 106

The Harvard Common Press, Boston, MA *Toll Free Tel:* 888-657-3755, pg 107

Harvard Education Publishing Group, Cambridge, MA *Toll Free Tel:* 800-513-0763 (subns); 888-437-1437 (orders), pg 107

Harvard University Press, Cambridge, MA *Toll Free Tel:* 800-405-1619 (orders) *Toll Free Fax:* 800-406-9145 (orders), pg 107

Harvest House Publishers Inc, Eugene, OR *Toll Free Tel:* 888-501-6991, pg 107

Hay House Inc, Carlsbad, CA *Toll Free Tel:* 800-654-5126 (ext 2, US) *Toll Free Fax:* 800-650-5115, pg 108

Haynes Manuals Inc, Newbury Park, CA *Toll Free Tel:* 800-4-HAYNES (442-9637), pg 108

Hazelden Publishing, Center City, MN *Toll Free Tel:* 800-257-7810, pg 108

HCPro Inc, Danvers, MA *Toll Free Tel:* 800-650-6787 *Toll Free Fax:* 800-785-9212, pg 108

Health Communications Inc, Deerfield Beach, FL *Toll Free Tel:* 800-851-9100; 800-441-5569 (cust serv & orders) *Toll Free Fax:* 800-424-7652 (cust serv & orders), pg 108

Health Forum Inc, Chicago, IL *Toll Free Tel:* 800-242-2626, pg 109

Health Professions Press, Towson, MD *Toll Free Tel:* 888-337-8808, pg 109

Health Research Books, Pomeroy, WA *Toll Free Tel:* 888-844-2386, pg 109

HeartMath LLC, Boulder Creek, CA *Toll Free Tel:* 800-450-9111, pg 109

Hearts & Tummies Cookbook Co, Wever, IA *Toll Free Tel:* 800-571-2665, pg 109

Heian, Albany, CA *Toll Free Fax:* 888-411-8527, pg 109

William S Hein & Co Inc, Getzville, NY *Toll Free Tel:* 800-828-7571, pg 109

Heinemann, Portsmouth, NH *Toll Free Tel:* 800-225-5800 (US) *Toll Free Fax:* 877-231-6980 (US), pg 110

Hellgate Press, Ashland, OR *Toll Free Tel:* 800-795-4059, pg 110

Hendrickson Publishers Inc, Peabody, MA *Toll Free Tel:* 800-358-3111, pg 110

Herald Press, Harrisonburg, VA *Toll Free Tel:* 800-245-7894 (orders-US); 800-631-6535 (orders-CN) *Toll Free Fax:* 877-271-0760, pg 110

Herald Press, Kitchener, ON Canada *Toll Free Tel:* 800-631-6535 (CN), pg 487

Herald Publishing House, Independence, MO *Toll Free Tel:* 800-767-8181, pg 110

Heritage Books Inc, Berwyn Heights, MD *Toll Free Tel:* 800-876-6103 *Toll Free Fax:* 800-876-6103, pg 110

The Heritage Foundation, Washington, DC *Toll Free Tel:* 800-544-4843, pg 110

Heuer Publishing LLC, Cedar Rapids, IA *Toll Free Tel:* 800-950-7529, pg 110

Hewitt Homeschooling Resources, Washougal, WA *Toll Free Tel:* 800-348-1750, pg 111

High Plains Press, Glendo, WY *Toll Free Tel:* 800-552-7819, pg 111

Highlights for Children, Columbus, OH *Toll Free Tel:* 800-962-3661 (Highlights Club cust serv); 800-255-9517 (Highlights Magazine cust serv), pg 111

Hillsdale College Press, Hillsdale, MI *Toll Free Tel:* 800-437-2268, pg 111

Himalayan Institute Press, Honesdale, PA *Toll Free Tel:* 800-822-4547, pg 112

Hobar Publications, Apple Valley, MN *Toll Free Tel:* 800-846-7027 *Toll Free Fax:* 800-330-6232, pg 112

Hogrefe Publishing, Boston, MA *Toll Free Tel:* 866-823-4726, pg 112

Hohm Press, Chino Valley, AZ *Toll Free Tel:* 800-381-2700, pg 113

Henry Holt and Company, LLC, New York, NY *Toll Free Tel:* 888-330-8477 (orders), pg 113

Homa & Sekey Books, Paramus, NJ *Toll Free Tel:* 800-870-HOMA (870-4662 orders), pg 114

Hoover Institution Press, Stanford, CA *Toll Free Tel:* 800-935-2882, pg 114

Hoover's Inc, Austin, TX *Toll Free Tel:* 866-486-8666, pg 114

Hope Publishing Co, Carol Stream, IL *Toll Free Tel:* 800-323-1049, pg 114

Houghton Mifflin Harcourt, Boston, MA *Toll Free Tel:* 800-225-5425 (K-12 educ materials); 800-323-9540 (assessment materials); 877-219-1537 (SkillsTutor); 888-242-6747 (Destination; Earobics; Edmark; Learning Village; Riverdeep); 800-225-3362 (Houghton Mifflin Harcourt Trade & Reference Publishers) *Toll Free Fax:* 800-269-5232, pg 114

Houghton Mifflin Harcourt K-12 Publishers, Boston, MA *Toll Free Tel:* 800-225-5425 (cust serv), pg 115

Houghton Mifflin Harcourt School Publishers, Orlando, FL *Toll Free Tel:* 800-225-5425 (cust serv) *Toll Free Fax:* 800-874-6418; 800-269-5232 (cust serv), pg 115

Houghton Mifflin Harcourt Trade & Reference Division, Boston, MA *Toll Free Tel:* 800-225-3362, pg 115

House to House Publications, Lititz, PA *Toll Free Tel:* 800-848-5892, pg 116

HRD Press, Amherst, MA *Toll Free Tel:* 800-822-2801, pg 116

Human Kinetics Inc, Champaign, IL *Toll Free Tel:* 800-747-4457, pg 116

Humanix Books LLC, West Palm Beach, FL *Toll Free Tel:* 855-371-7810 *Toll Free Fax:* 855-371-7809, pg 117

Huntington Press Publishing, Las Vegas, NV *Toll Free Tel:* 800-244-2224, pg 117

I-5 Publishing LLC, Irvine, CA *Toll Free Tel:* 888-738-2665, pg 117

Ibex Publishers, Bethesda, MD *Toll Free Tel:* 888-718-8188, pg 117

Iconografix Inc, Hudson, WI *Toll Free Tel:* 800-289-3504 (orders only), pg 118

Idaho Center for the Book, Boise, ID *Toll Free Tel:* 800-992-8398 (outside ID), pg 118

Ideals Publications, a Guideposts Co, Franklin, TN *Toll Free Tel:* 800-586-2572 (cust serv), pg 118

IEEE Computer Society, Washington, DC *Toll Free Tel:* 800-272-6657 (memb info), pg 118

Ignatius Press, San Francisco, CA *Toll Free Tel:* 800-651-1531 (orders); 888-615-3186 (cust serv), pg 118

IHS Jane's, Alexandria, VA *Toll Free Tel:* 800-824-0768 (sales) *Toll Free Fax:* 800-836-0297, pg 119

IHS Press, Norfolk, VA *Toll Free Tel:* 877-447-7737 *Toll Free Fax:* 877-447-7737, pg 119

Imagination Publishing Group, Dunedin, FL *Toll Free Tel:* 888-701-6481, pg 119

ImaJinn Books Inc, Phoenix, AZ *Toll Free Tel:* 877-625-3592 (US & CN), pg 119

Impact Publications/Development Concepts Inc, Manassas Park, VA *Toll Free Tel:* 800-361-1055 (cust serv), pg 119

Impact Publishers Inc, Atascadero, CA *Toll Free Tel:* 800-246-7228 (orders), pg 119

Incentive Publications by World Book, Chicago, IL *Toll Free Tel:* 800-967-5325, pg 120

Independent Institute, Oakland, CA *Toll Free Tel:* 800-927-8733, pg 120

Indiana Historical Society Press (IHS Press), Indianapolis, IN *Toll Free Tel:* 800-447-1830 (orders), pg 120

Indiana University Press, Bloomington, IN *Toll Free Tel:* 800-842-6796 (orders only), pg 120

Industrial Press Inc, Norwalk, CT *Toll Free Tel:* 888-528-7852, pg 121

Information Today, Inc, Medford, NJ *Toll Free Tel:* 800-300-9868 (cust serv), pg 121

Inner Traditions International Ltd, Rochester, VT *Toll Free Tel:* 800-246-8648, pg 122

Insight Editions, San Rafael, CA *Toll Free Tel:* 800-809-3792 *Toll Free Fax:* 866-509-0515, pg 122

Institute of Continuing Legal Education, Ann Arbor, MI *Toll Free Tel:* 877-229-4350 *Toll Free Fax:* 877-229-4351, pg 122

Institute of Psychological Research, Inc., Montreal, QC Canada *Toll Free Tel:* 800-363-7800 *Toll Free Fax:* 888-382-3007, pg 488

The Institutes™, Malvern, PA *Toll Free Tel:* 800-644-2101, pg 123

Intercultural Press Inc, Boston, MA *Toll Free Tel:* 888-273-2539, pg 123

Interlink Publishing Group Inc, Northampton, MA *Toll Free Tel:* 800-238-LINK (238-5465), pg 123

International City/County Management Association (ICMA), Washington, DC *Toll Free Tel:* 800-745-8780, pg 123

International Code Council Inc, Whittier, CA *Toll Free Tel:* 888-422-7233, pg 124

International Foundation of Employee Benefit Plans, Brookfield, WI *Toll Free Tel:* 888-334-3327, pg 124

International Linguistics Corp, Grandview, MO *Toll Free Tel:* 800-237-1830 (orders), pg 124

International Literacy Association (ILA), Newark, DE *Toll Free Tel:* 800-336-7323 (US & CN), pg 124

International Society for Technology in Education, Eugene, OR *Toll Free Tel:* 800-336-5191 (US & CN), pg 125

International Wealth Success Inc, Merrick, NY *Toll Free Tel:* 800-323-0548, pg 125

InterVarsity Press, Westmont, IL *Toll Free Tel:* 800-843-9487, pg 125

Interweave Press LLC, Loveland, CO *Toll Free Tel:* 800-272-2193; 800-289-0963 *Toll Free Fax:* 888-590-4082, pg 125

Irwin Law Inc, Toronto, ON Canada *Toll Free Tel:* 888-314-9014, pg 489

ISI Books, Wilmington, DE *Toll Free Tel:* 800-526-7022, pg 125

Island Press, Washington, DC *Toll Free Tel:* 800-828-1302, pg 126

iUniverse, Bloomington, IN *Toll Free Tel:* 800-AUTHORS (288-4677), pg 126

Richard Ivey School of Business, London, ON Canada *Toll Free Tel:* 800-649-6355, pg 489

JayJo Books LLC, Melville, NY *Toll Free Tel:* 800-999-6884 *Toll Free Fax:* 800-262-1886, pg 126

Jewish Lights Publishing, Woodstock, VT *Toll Free Tel:* 800-962-4544 (orders only), pg 126

Jewish Publication Society, Philadelphia, PA *Toll Free Tel:* 800-234-3151, pg 126

JIST Publishing, St Paul, MN *Toll Free Tel:* 800-328-1452 *Toll Free Fax:* 800-328-4564, pg 127

John Deere Publishing, Davenport, IA *Toll Free Tel:* 800-522-7448 (orders), pg 127

The Johns Hopkins University Press, Baltimore, MD *Toll Free Tel:* 800-537-5487 (book orders & cust serv); 800-548-1784 (journal orders), pg 127

Johnson Books, Boulder, CO *Toll Free Tel:* 800-258-5830, pg 127

Jones & Bartlett Learning LLC, Burlington, MA *Toll Free Tel:* 800-832-0034, pg 128

Jones McClure Publishing, Houston, TX *Toll Free Tel:* 800-626-6667, pg 128

Jossey-Bass, San Francisco, CA *Toll Free Tel:* 800-956-7739, pg 128

Joy Publishing Co, Fountain Valley, CA *Toll Free Tel:* 800-454-8228, pg 128

Judaica Press Inc, Brooklyn, NY *Toll Free Tel:* 800-972-6201, pg 128

Judson Press, King of Prussia, PA *Toll Free Tel:* 800-458-3766, pg 128

Kaeden Corp, Rocky River, OH *Toll Free Tel:* 800-890-7323, pg 129

Kalmbach Publishing Co, Waukesha, WI *Toll Free Tel:* 800-533-6644 (cust serv & orders), pg 129

Kar-Ben Publishing, Minneapolis, MN *Toll Free Tel:* 800-4-KARBEN (452-7236) *Toll Free Fax:* 800-332-1132, pg 129

J J Keller & Associates, Inc, Neenah, WI *Toll Free Tel:* 877-564-2333 *Toll Free Fax:* 800-727-7516, pg 130

Kendall Hunt Publishing Co, Dubuque, IA *Toll Free Tel:* 800-228-0810 (orders) *Toll Free Fax:* 800-772-9165, pg 130

Kennedy Information Inc, Keene, NH *Toll Free Tel:* 800-531-0140, pg 130

Kensington Publishing Corp, New York, NY *Toll Free Tel:* 800-221-2647, pg 130

Kids Can Press Ltd, Toronto, ON Canada *Toll Free Tel:* 800-265-0884, pg 489

Kindred Productions, Winnipeg, MB Canada *Toll Free Tel:* 800-545-7322, pg 489

Jessica Kingsley Publishers Inc, Philadelphia, PA *Toll Free Tel:* 866-416-1078 (cust serv), pg 131

Kirk House Publishers, Minneapolis, MN *Toll Free Tel:* 888-696-1828, pg 131

Kirkbride Bible Co Inc, Indianapolis, IN *Toll Free Tel:* 800-428-4385, pg 131

Wolters Kluwer Law & Business, New York, NY *Toll Free Tel:* 800-234-1660 (cust serv), pg 131

Allen A Knoll Publishers, Santa Barbara, CA *Toll Free Tel:* 800-777-7623, pg 132

Alfred A Knopf/Everyman's Library, New York, NY *Toll Free Tel:* 800-638-6460, pg 132

Knopf Canada, Toronto, ON Canada *Toll Free Tel:* 888-523-9292, pg 490

Koho Pono LLC, Clackamas, OR *Toll Free Tel:* 800-937-8000 (orders) *Toll Free Fax:* 800-876-0186 (orders), pg 132

HJ Kramer Inc, Tiburon, CA *Toll Free Tel:* 800-972-6657, pg 133

Krause Publications Inc, Iola, WI *Toll Free Tel:* 800-258-0929 (cust serv); 888-457-2873 (orders), pg 133

Kregel Publications, Grand Rapids, MI *Toll Free Tel:* 800-733-2607, pg 133

Krieger Publishing Co, Malabar, FL *Toll Free Tel:* 800-724-0025, pg 133

Kumarian Press, Boulder, CO *Toll Free Tel:* 800-232-0223 (orders only), pg 133

LadybugPress, Sonora, CA *Toll Free Tel:* 888-892-5000, pg 133

Lake Superior Port Cities Inc, Duluth, MN *Toll Free Tel:* 888-BIG-LAKE (244-5253), pg 134

LAMA Books, Hayward, CA *Toll Free Tel:* 888-452-6244, pg 134

Lanahan Publishers Inc, Baltimore, MD *Toll Free Tel:* 866-345-1949, pg 134

Landauer Corp, Urbandale, IA *Toll Free Tel:* 800-557-2144, pg 134

Peter Lang Publishing Inc, New York, NY *Toll Free Tel:* 800-770-5264 (cust serv), pg 134

LangMarc Publishing, Austin, TX *Toll Free Tel:* 800-864-1648 (orders), pg 134

Larson Publications, Burdett, NY *Toll Free Tel:* 800-828-2197, pg 134

Laughing Elephant, Seattle, WA *Toll Free Tel:* 800-354-0400, pg 135

Laurier Books Ltd, Ottawa, ON Canada *Toll Free Fax:* 855-736-9160, pg 490

The Lawbook Exchange Ltd, Clark, NJ *Toll Free Tel:* 800-422-6686, pg 135

Lawyers & Judges Publishing Co Inc, Tucson, AZ *Toll Free Tel:* 800-209-7109 *Toll Free Fax:* 800-330-8795, pg 135

Leadership Ministries Worldwide/OBR, Chattanooga, TN *Toll Free Tel:* 800-987-8790, pg 135

THE Learning Connection®, Orlando, FL *Toll Free Tel:* 800-218-8489, pg 136

Learning Links Inc, Cranbury, NJ *Toll Free Tel:* 800-724-2616, pg 136

LearningExpress LLC, New York, NY *Toll Free Tel:* 800-295-9556 (ext 2), pg 136

Lectorum Publications Inc, Lyndhurst, NJ *Toll Free Tel:* 800-345-5946 *Toll Free Fax:* 877-532-8676, pg 136

Lederer Books, Clarksville, MD *Toll Free Tel:* 800-410-7367 (orders), pg 136

Lee & Low Books Inc, New York, NY *Toll Free Tel:* 888-320-3190 (ext 28, orders only), pg 136

Leisure Arts Inc, Maumelle, AR *Toll Free Tel:* 800-643-8030, pg 137

Lerner Publications, Minneapolis, MN *Toll Free Tel:* 800-328-4929 *Toll Free Fax:* 800-332-1132, pg 137

Lerner Publishing Group Inc, Minneapolis, MN *Toll Free Tel:* 800-328-4929 *Toll Free Fax:* 800-332-1132, pg 137

LernerClassroom, Minneapolis, MN *Toll Free Tel:* 800-328-4929 *Toll Free Fax:* 800-332-1132, pg 137

Lessiter Publications, Brookfield, WI *Toll Free Tel:* 800-645-8455, pg 138

LexisNexis®, Charlottesville, VA *Toll Free Tel:* 800-446-3410, pg 138

LexisNexis® Canada Inc, Markham, ON Canada *Toll Free Tel:* 800-668-6481; 800-387-0899 (cust care) *Toll Free Fax:* 800-461-3275, pg 490

Liberty Fund Inc, Indianapolis, IN *Toll Free Tel:* 800-955-8335; 800-866-3520; 800-368-7897 ext 6069 (cust serv), pg 138

Libraries Unlimited, Santa Barbara, CA *Toll Free Tel:* 800-368-6868 *Toll Free Fax:* 866-270-3856, pg 138

Lidec Inc, Montreal, QC Canada *Toll Free Tel:* 800-350-5991 (CN only), pg 490

Mary Ann Liebert Inc, New Rochelle, NY *Toll Free Tel:* 800-654-3237, pg 139

Life Cycle Books, Fort Collins, CO *Toll Free Tel:* 800-214-5849 *Toll Free Fax:* 888-690-8532, pg 139

Life Cycle Books Ltd, Toronto, ON Canada *Toll Free Tel:* 866-880-5860 *Toll Free Fax:* 866-260-8172, pg 490

Light Technology Publishing, Flagstaff, AZ *Toll Free Tel:* 800-450-0985, pg 139

Liguori Publications, Liguori, MO *Toll Free Tel:* 866-848-2492; 800-325-9521 *Toll Free Fax:* 800-325-9526 (sales), pg 139

Linden Publishing Co Inc, Fresno, CA *Toll Free Tel:* 800-345-4447 (orders), pg 139

Linworth Publishing, Santa Barbara, CA *Toll Free Tel:* 800-368-6868 *Toll Free Fax:* 866-270-3856, pg 140

Lippincott Williams & Wilkins, New York, NY *Toll Free Tel:* 800-950-2035, pg 140

Listen & Live Audio Inc, Roseland, NJ *Toll Free Tel:* 800-653-9400 (orders), pg 140

Little, Brown Books for Young Readers, New York, NY *Toll Free Tel:* 800-759-0190 (cust serv), pg 141

The Little Entrepreneur, Detroit, MI *Toll Free Tel:* 888-435-9234, pg 141

Liturgical Press, Collegeville, MN *Toll Free Tel:* 800-858-5450 *Toll Free Fax:* 800-445-5899, pg 141

Liturgy Training Publications, Chicago, IL *Toll Free Tel:* 800-933-1800 (US & CN only orders) *Toll Free Fax:* 800-933-7094 (US & CN only orders), pg 141

Living Language, New York, NY *Toll Free Tel:* 800-733-3000 (orders) *Toll Free Fax:* 800-659-2436, pg 142

Llewellyn Publications, Woodbury, MN *Toll Free Tel:* 800-843-6666, pg 142

The Local History Co, Pittsburgh, PA *Toll Free Tel:* 866-362-0789 (orders), pg 142

Lone Pine Publishing, Edmonton, AB Canada *Toll Free Tel:* 800-661-9017 *Toll Free Fax:* 800-424-7173, pg 490

Lonely Planet, Oakland, CA *Toll Free Tel:* 800-275-8555 (orders), pg 142

Looseleaf Law Publications Inc, Flushing, NY *Toll Free Tel:* 800-647-5547, pg 143

Lorenz Educational Press, Dayton, OH *Toll Free Tel:* 800-444-1144, pg 143

Lotus Press, Twin Lakes, WI *Toll Free Tel:* 800-824-6396 (orders), pg 143

Love Publishing Co, Denver, CO *Toll Free Tel:* 877-240-6396, pg 143

Loving Healing Press Inc, Ann Arbor, MI *Toll Free Tel:* 888-761-6268 (US & CN), pg 143

Loyola Press, Chicago, IL *Toll Free Tel:* 800-621-1008, pg 144

LRP Publications, Palm Beach Gardens, FL *Toll Free Tel:* 800-341-7874, pg 144

LRS, Torrance, CA *Toll Free Tel:* 800-255-5002, pg 144

Macmillan Audio, New York, NY *Toll Free Tel:* 888-330-8477 (cust serv), pg 145

Macmillan Reference USA™, Woodbridge, CT *Toll Free Tel:* 800-444-0799, pg 145

Madonna House Publications, Combermere, ON Canada *Toll Free Tel:* 888-703-7110 *Toll Free Fax:* 877-717-2888, pg 491

Maharishi University of Management Press, Fairfield, IA *Toll Free Tel:* 800-831-6523, pg 145

Management Concepts Inc, Vienna, VA *Toll Free Tel:* 800 506-4450, pg 146

Mandala Earth, San Rafael, CA *Toll Free Fax:* 866-509-0515, pg 146

MapEasy Inc, Wainscott, NY *Toll Free Tel:* 888-627-3279, pg 146

MAR*CO Products Inc, Warminster, PA *Toll Free Tel:* 800-448-2197, pg 147

Marathon Press, Norfolk, NE *Toll Free Tel:* 800-228-0629, pg 147

Maren Green Publishing Inc, Oak Park Heights, MN *Toll Free Tel:* 800-287-1512, pg 147

Marion Street Press LLC, Portland, OR *Toll Free Fax:* 866-571-8359, pg 147

Marquette University Press, Milwaukee, WI *Toll Free Tel:* 800-247-6553 (cust serv), pg 147

Marquis Who's Who LLC, New Providence, NJ *Toll Free Tel:* 800-473-7020, pg 148

Marshall & Swift, Los Angeles, CA *Toll Free Tel:* 800-544-2678, pg 148

Marshall Cavendish Corp, Tarrytown, NY *Toll Free Tel:* 800-821-9881, pg 148

Martindale LLC, New Providence, NJ *Toll Free Tel:* 800-526-4902, pg 148

Martingale®, Bothell, WA *Toll Free Tel:* 800-426-3126, pg 148

Mason Crest Publishers, Broomall, PA *Toll Free Tel:* 866-MCP-BOOK (627-2665), pg 149

Math Solutions®, Sausalito, CA *Toll Free Tel:* 800-868-9092 *Toll Free Fax:* 877-942-8837, pg 149

Math Teachers Press Inc, Minneapolis, MN *Toll Free Tel:* 800-852-2435, pg 149

The Mathematical Association of America, Washington, DC *Toll Free Tel:* 800-741-9415, pg 149

Maven House Press, Palmyra, VA *Toll Free Fax:* 888-894-3403, pg 149

McCutchan Publishing Corp, Richmond, CA *Toll Free Tel:* 800-227-1540, pg 150

The McDonald & Woodward Publishing Co, Newark, OH *Toll Free Tel:* 800-233-8787, pg 150

McFarland, Jefferson, NC *Toll Free Tel:* 800-253-2187 (orders), pg 150

McGraw-Hill Career Education, Burr Ridge, IL *Toll Free Tel:* 800-338-3987 (cust serv), pg 150

McGraw-Hill Contemporary Learning Series, Dubuque, IA *Toll Free Tel:* 800-243-6532, pg 150

McGraw-Hill Higher Education, Burr Ridge, IL *Toll Free Tel:* 800-338-3987 (cust serv), pg 151

McGraw-Hill Humanities, Social Sciences, Languages, New York, NY *Toll Free Tel:* 800-338-3987 (cust serv), pg 151

McGraw-Hill/Irwin, Burr Ridge, IL *Toll Free Tel:* 800-338-3987 (cust serv), pg 152

McGraw-Hill Ryerson Limited, Whitby, ON Canada *Toll Free Tel:* 800-565-5758 (cust serv) *Toll Free Fax:* 800-463-5885, pg 491

McGraw-Hill School Education Group, Columbus, OH *Toll Free Tel:* 800-848-1567, pg 152

McGraw-Hill Science, Engineering, Mathematics, Dubuque, IA *Toll Free Tel:* 800-338-3987 (cust serv), pg 152

MDR, A D&B Co, Shelton, CT *Toll Free Tel:* 800-333-8802 *Toll Free Fax:* 866-532-7097, pg 152

Meadowbrook Press, Minnetonka, MN *Toll Free Tel:* 800-338-2232, pg 153

me+mi publishing inc, Wheaton, IL *Toll Free Tel:* 888-251-1444, pg 153

R S Means from The Gordian Group, Rockland, MA *Toll Free Tel:* 800-448-8182 *Toll Free Fax:* 800-632-6701, pg 153

Medical Group Management Association (MGMA), Englewood, CO *Toll Free Tel:* 877-275-6462, pg 153

Medical Physics Publishing Corp (MPP), Madison, WI *Toll Free Tel:* 800-442-5778 (cust serv), pg 153

MedMaster Inc, Fort Lauderdale, FL *Toll Free Tel:* 800-335-3480, pg 153

The Russell Meerdink Co Ltd, Neenah, WI *Toll Free Tel:* 800-635-6499, pg 153

Mel Bay Publications Inc, Pacific, MO *Toll Free Tel:* 800-863-5229 *Toll Free Fax:* 800-660-9818, pg 154

Menasha Ridge Press Inc, Birmingham, AL *Toll Free Tel:* 888-604-4537, pg 154

MennoMedia, Harrisonburg, VA *Toll Free Tel:* 800-245-7894 (orders & cust serv US); 800-631-6535 (orders & cust serv CN), pg 154

Mercer University Press, Macon, GA *Toll Free Tel:* 866-895-1472, pg 154

Meriwether Publishing, Englewood, CO *Toll Free Tel:* 800-333-7262, pg 155

Merriam-Webster Inc, Springfield, MA *Toll Free Tel:* 800-828-1880 (orders & cust serv), pg 155

Mesorah Publications Ltd, Brooklyn, NY *Toll Free Tel:* 800-637-6724, pg 155

Messianic Jewish Publishers, Clarksville, MD *Toll Free Tel:* 800-410-7367 (orders), pg 155

MGI Management Institute Inc, Hawthorne, NY *Toll Free Tel:* 800-932-0191, pg 155

Michelin Maps & Guides, Greenville, SC *Toll Free Fax:* 866-297-0914; 888-773-7979, pg 155

Michigan Municipal League, Ann Arbor, MI *Toll Free Tel:* 800-653-2483, pg 155

Michigan State University Press (MSU Press), East Lansing, MI *Toll Free Fax:* 800-678-2120, pg 155

Microsoft Press, Redmond, WA *Toll Free Tel:* 800-677-7377, pg 156

MidWest Plan Service (MWPS), Ames, IA *Toll Free Tel:* 800-562-3618, pg 156

Mike Murach & Associates Inc, Fresno, CA *Toll Free Tel:* 800-221-5528, pg 156

Milady, Clifton Park, NY *Toll Free Tel:* 800-998-7498, pg 156

Military Living Publications, Vienna, VA *Toll Free Tel:* 877-363-4677 (ext 1), pg 157

Milkweed Editions, Minneapolis, MN *Toll Free Tel:* 800-520-6455, pg 157

Millbrook Press, Minneapolis, MN *Toll Free Tel:* 800-328-4929 (US only) *Toll Free Fax:* 800-332-1132, pg 157

Richard K Miller Associates, Loganville, GA *Toll Free Tel:* 888-928-RKMA (928-7562) *Toll Free Fax:* 877-928-7562, pg 157

Milliken Publishing Co, Dayton, OH *Toll Free Tel:* 800-444-1144, pg 157

The Minerals, Metals & Materials Society (TMS), Warrendale, PA *Toll Free Tel:* 800-759-4867, pg 157

Minnesota Historical Society Press, St Paul, MN *Toll Free Tel:* 800-621-2736 (warehouse) *Toll Free Fax:* 800-621-8476 (warehouse), pg 157

The MIT Press, Cambridge, MA *Toll Free Tel:* 800-207-8354 (orders), pg 158

Mitchell Lane Publishers Inc, Hockessin, DE *Toll Free Tel:* 800-814-5484 *Toll Free Fax:* 866-834-4164, pg 158

Mondo Publishing, Farmingdale, NY *Toll Free Tel:* 888-88-MONDO (886-6636) *Toll Free Fax:* 888-532-4492, pg 159

Money Market Directories, Charlottesville, VA *Toll Free Tel:* 800-446-2810, pg 159

Montana Historical Society Press, Helena, MT *Toll Free Tel:* 800-243-9900, pg 159

Monthly Review Press, New York, NY *Toll Free Tel:* 800-670-9499, pg 159

Moody Publishers, Chicago, IL *Toll Free Tel:* 800-678-8812 (cust serv), pg 159

Morehouse Publishing, New York, NY *Toll Free Tel:* 800-672-1789 (retail orders only); 800-251-3320 (wholesale orders only), pg 160

Morgan James Publishing, New York, NY *Toll Free Tel:* 800-485-4943, pg 160

Morgan Kaufmann, Waltham, MA *Toll Free Tel:* 866-607-1417, pg 160

Morgan Reynolds Publishing, Greensboro, NC *Toll Free Tel:* 800-535-1504 *Toll Free Fax:* 800-535-5725, pg 160

Mountain n' Air Books, La Crescenta, CA *Toll Free Tel:* 800-446-9696 *Toll Free Fax:* 800-303-5578, pg 160

Mountain Press Publishing Co, Missoula, MT *Toll Free Tel:* 800-234-5308, pg 160

The Mountaineers Books, Seattle, WA *Toll Free Tel:* 800-553-4453 *Toll Free Fax:* 800-568-7604, pg 161

MRTS, Tempe, AZ *Toll Free Tel:* 800-621-2736 (orders) *Toll Free Fax:* 800-621-8476 (orders), pg 161

Mundania Press LLC, Cincinnati, OH *Toll Free Fax:* 888-460-4752, pg 161

Museum of New Mexico Press, Santa Fe, NM *Toll Free Tel:* 800-249-7737 (orders) *Toll Free Fax:* 800-622-8667 (orders), pg 162

Mystic Seaport Museum Inc, Mystic, CT *Toll Free Tel:* 800-248-1066 (wholesale orders only); 800-331-2665 (retail orders only), pg 162

NACE International, Houston, TX *Toll Free Tel:* 800-797-NACE (797-6223), pg 162

National Academies Press (NAP), Washington, DC *Toll Free Tel:* 888-624-8373 (cust serv), pg 163

The National Alliance Research Academy, Austin, TX *Toll Free Tel:* 800-633-2165, pg 163

National Association for Music Education (NAfME), Reston, VA *Toll Free Tel:* 800-462-6420 (orders & returns); 800-336-3768, pg 163

National Association of Secondary School Principals (NASSP), Reston, VA *Toll Free Tel:* 800-253-7746, pg 163

National Braille Press, Boston, MA *Toll Free Tel:* 800-548-7323 (cust serv); 888-965-8965, pg 164

National Catholic Educational Association, Arlington, VA *Toll Free Tel:* 800-711-6232, pg 164

National Council of Teachers of English (NCTE), Urbana, IL *Toll Free Tel:* 877-369-6283 (cust serv), pg 164

National Council of Teachers of Mathematics (NCTM), Reston, VA *Toll Free Tel:* 800-235-7566, pg 164

National Council on Radiation Protection & Measurements (NCRP), Bethesda, MD *Toll Free Tel:* 800-229-2652, pg 164

National Golf Foundation, Jupiter, FL *Toll Free Tel:* 888-275-4643, pg 165

National Institute for Trial Advocacy (NITA), Boulder, CO *Toll Free Tel:* 877-648-2632; 800-225-6482 (orders & returns), pg 165

National Learning Corp, Syosset, NY *Toll Free Tel:* 800-632-8888, pg 165

National Notary Association (NNA), Chatsworth, CA *Toll Free Tel:* 800-876-6827 *Toll Free Fax:* 800-833-1211, pg 165

National Register Publishing, New Providence, NJ *Toll Free Tel:* 800-473-7020, pg 166

National Resource Center for Youth Services (NRCYS), Tulsa, OK *Toll Free Tel:* 800-274-2687, pg 166

National Science Teachers Association (NSTA), Arlington, VA *Toll Free Tel:* 800-277-5300 (orders) *Toll Free Fax:* 888-433-0526 (orders), pg 166

The National Underwriter Co, Erlanger, KY *Toll Free Tel:* 800-543-0874, pg 166

Naval Institute Press, Annapolis, MD *Toll Free Tel:* 800-233-8764, pg 166

NavPress Publishing Group, Colorado Springs, CO *Toll Free Tel:* 800-366-7788 *Toll Free Fax:* 800-343-3902, pg 166

NBM Publishing Inc, New York, NY *Toll Free Tel:* 800-886-1223, pg 166

Neal-Schuman Publishers Inc, New York, NY *Toll Free Tel:* 866-NS-BOOKS (672-6657) *Toll Free Fax:* 877-231-6980, pg 166

Neibauer Press & ChurchSupplier.com, Warminster, PA *Toll Free Tel:* 800-322-6203, pg 167

Nelson Education Ltd, Scarborough, ON Canada *Toll Free Tel:* 800-268-2222 (cust serv) *Toll Free Fax:* 800-430-4445, pg 492

New City Press, Hyde Park, NY *Toll Free Tel:* 800-462-5980 (orders only), pg 167

New Dimensions Publishing, Phoenix, AZ *Toll Free Tel:* 800-736-7367, pg 167

New Forums Press Inc, Stillwater, OK *Toll Free Tel:* 800-606-3766, pg 167

New Harbinger Publications Inc, Oakland, CA *Toll Free Tel:* 800-748-6273 (orders only) *Toll Free Fax:* 800-652-1613, pg 167

New Horizon Press, Far Hills, NJ *Toll Free Tel:* 800-533-7978 (orders only), pg 167

New Leaf Press Inc, Green Forest, AR *Toll Free Tel:* 800-999-3777, pg 168

The New Press, New York, NY *Toll Free Tel:* 800-343-4489 (orders) *Toll Free Fax:* 800-351-5073 (orders), pg 168

New Readers Press, Syracuse, NY *Toll Free Tel:* 800-448-8878 *Toll Free Fax:* 866-894-2100, pg 168

New Strategist Publications Inc, Ithaca, NY *Toll Free Tel:* 800-848-0842, pg 168

New World Library, Novato, CA *Toll Free Tel:* 800-227-3900 (ext 52, retail orders); 800-972-6657, pg 168

New World Publishing (Canada), Halifax, NS Canada *Toll Free Tel:* 877-211-3334 (orders), pg 492

New York Academy of Sciences, New York, NY *Toll Free Tel:* 800-843-6927, pg 169

New York State Bar Association, Albany, NY *Toll Free Tel:* 800-582-2452, pg 169

New York University Press, New York, NY *Toll Free Tel:* 800-996-6987 (orders), pg 169

Newbury Street Press, Boston, MA *Toll Free Tel:* 888-296-3447 (NEHGS membership), pg 169

NeWest Press, Edmonton, AB Canada *Toll Free Tel:* 866-796-5473, pg 492

Nightingale-Conant, Niles, IL *Toll Free Tel:* 800-572-2770; 800-557-1660 (sales); 800-560-6081 (cust serv), pg 169

Nimbus Publishing Ltd, Halifax, NS Canada *Toll Free Tel:* 800-NIMBUS9 (646-2879) *Toll Free Fax:* 888-253-3133, pg 492

No Starch Press Inc, San Francisco, CA *Toll Free Tel:* 800-420-7240, pg 170

North Country Books Inc, Utica, NY *Toll Free Tel:* 800-342-7409 (orders), pg 170

North Point Press, New York, NY *Toll Free Tel:* 888-330-8477, pg 171

North River Press Publishing Corp, Great Barrington, MA *Toll Free Tel:* 800-486-2665 *Toll Free Fax:* 800-BOOK-FAX (266-5329), pg 171

North Star Press of Saint Cloud Inc, St Cloud, MN *Toll Free Tel:* 888-820-1636, pg 171

Northstone Publishing, Kelowna, BC Canada *Toll Free Tel:* 800-299-2926; 800-663-2775 (orders) *Toll Free Fax:* 888-841-9991, pg 493

Northwestern University Press, Evanston, IL *Toll Free Tel:* 800-621-2736 (orders only), pg 171

W W Norton & Company Inc, New York, NY *Toll Free Tel:* 800-233-4830 (orders & cust serv) *Toll Free Fax:* 800-458-6515, pg 171

Norwood House Press, Chicago, IL *Toll Free Tel:* 866-565-2900 *Toll Free Fax:* 866-565-2901, pg 172

Nova Press, West Hollywood, CA *Toll Free Tel:* 800-949-6175, pg 172

Novalis Publishing, Toronto, ON Canada *Toll Free Tel:* 877-702-7773 *Toll Free Fax:* 877-702-7775, pg 493

nursesbooks.org, The Publishing Program of ANA, Silver Spring, MD *Toll Free Tel:* 800-924-9053; 800-637-0323 (orders), pg 172

Nystrom Herff Jones Education Division, Indianapolis, IN *Toll Free Tel:* 800-621-8086 (cust serv), pg 172

OAG Worldwide, Downers Grove, IL *Toll Free Tel:* 800-342-5624 (cust serv), pg 172

Oak Knoll Press, New Castle, DE *Toll Free Tel:* 800-996-2556, pg 172

Oakstone Publishing LLC, Birmingham, AL *Toll Free Tel:* 800-633-4743, pg 173

OCP, Portland, OR *Toll Free Tel:* 800-548-8749 *Toll Free Fax:* 800-843-8181, pg 173

Ohio State University Foreign Language Publications, Columbus, OH *Toll Free Tel:* 800-678-6999, pg 174

Ohio State University Press, Columbus, OH *Toll Free Fax:* 800-621-8476, pg 174

The Oliver Press Inc, Minneapolis, MN *Toll Free Tel:* 800-8-OLIVER (865-4837), pg 174

Omnibus Press, New York, NY *Toll Free Tel:* 800-431-7187 *Toll Free Fax:* 800-345-6842, pg 174

Omnidawn Publishing, Richmond, CA *Toll Free Tel:* 800-792-4957, pg 175

Omnigraphics Inc, Detroit, MI *Toll Free Tel:* 800-234-1340 (cust serv) *Toll Free Fax:* 800-875-1340 (cust serv), pg 175

OneSource, Concord, MA *Toll Free Tel:* 866-354-6936, pg 175

Online Training Solutions Inc (OTSI), Redmond, WA *Toll Free Tel:* 888-308-6874 *Toll Free Fax:* 888-308-6875, pg 175

Open Court, Chicago, IL *Toll Free Tel:* 800-815-2280 (orders only), pg 175

OPIS/STALSBY Directories & Databases, Wall, NJ *Toll Free Tel:* 800-275-0950 *Toll Free Fax:* 800-450-5864, pg 175

The Optical Society (OSA), Washington, DC *Toll Free Tel:* 800-766-4672, pg 175

OptumInsight™, Eden Prairie, MN *Toll Free Tel:* 888-445-8745; 800-765-6713, pg 176

Orange Frazer Press Inc, Wilmington, OH *Toll Free Tel:* 800-852-9332 (orders), pg 176

Orbis Books, Maryknoll, NY *Toll Free Tel:* 800-258-5838 (orders), pg 176

Orbit, New York, NY *Toll Free Tel:* 800-759-0190, pg 176

Orca Book Publishers, Custer, WA *Toll Free Tel:* 800-210-5277 *Toll Free Fax:* 877-408-1551, pg 176

Oregon State University Press, Corvallis, OR *Toll Free Tel:* 800-621-2736 (orders), pg 177

O'Reilly Media Inc, Sebastopol, CA *Toll Free Tel:* 800-998-9938; 800-889-8969, pg 177

Organization for Economic Cooperation & Development, Washington, DC *Toll Free Tel:* 800-456-6323 (dist ctr/pubns orders), pg 177

Original Publications, Old Beth Page, NY *Toll Free Tel:* 888-622-8581, pg 178

Other Press LLC, New York, NY *Toll Free Tel:* 877-843-6843, pg 178

OTTN Publishing, Stockton, NJ *Toll Free Tel:* 866-356-6886, pg 178

Our Sunday Visitor Publishing, Huntington, IN *Toll Free Tel:* 800-348-2440 (orders) *Toll Free Fax:* 800-498-6709, pg 178

OUT OF YOUR MIND...AND INTO THE MARKETPLACE™, Tustin, CA *Toll Free Tel:* 800-419-1513, pg 178

The Overmountain Press, Johnson City, TN *Toll Free Tel:* 800-992-2691 (orders), pg 179

Richard C Owen Publishers Inc, Katonah, NY *Toll Free Tel:* 800-336-5588, pg 179

Oxbridge® Communications Inc, New York, NY *Toll Free Tel:* 800-955-0231, pg 179

Oxford University Press USA, New York, NY *Toll Free Tel:* 800-451-7556 (orders); 800-445-9714 (cust serv), pg 179

Oxmoor House, Birmingham, AL *Toll Free Tel:* 800-366-4712; 888-891-8935 (cust serv); 800-765-6400 (orders), pg 179

Ozark Mountain Publishing Inc, Huntsville, AR *Toll Free Tel:* 800-935-0045, pg 179

Ozark Publishing Inc, Prairie Grove, AR *Toll Free Tel:* 800-321-5671, pg 179

P & R Publishing Co, Phillipsburg, NJ *Toll Free Tel:* 800-631-0094, pg 180

P S M J Resources Inc, Newton, MA *Toll Free Tel:* 800-537-7765, pg 180

Pacific Press Publishing Association, Nampa, ID *Toll Free Tel:* 800-447-7377, pg 180

Painted Pony Inc, Fort Washakie, WY *Toll Free Tel:* 877-253-3824, pg 180

Paladin Press, Boulder, CO *Toll Free Tel:* 800-392-2400, pg 180

Panoptic Enterprises, Burke, VA *Toll Free Tel:* 800-594-4766, pg 181

Pantheon Books/Schocken Books, New York, NY *Toll Free Tel:* 800-638-6460, pg 181

Papercutz, New York, NY *Toll Free Tel:* 800-886-1223, pg 181

Para Publishing LLC, Santa Barbara, CA *Toll Free Tel:* 800-727-2782, pg 181

Parabola Books, New York, NY *Toll Free Tel:* 800-592-2521 (subns), pg 181

Paraclete Press Inc, Brewster, MA *Toll Free Tel:* 800-451-5006, pg 182

Paradigm Publications, Taos, NM *Toll Free Tel:* 800-873-3946 (US); 888-873-3947 (CN), pg 182

Paradise Cay Publications Inc, Arcata, CA *Toll Free Tel:* 800-736-4509, pg 182

Paragon House, St Paul, MN *Toll Free Tel:* 800-447-3709, pg 182

Parallax Press, Berkeley, CA *Toll Free Tel:* 800-863-5290 (orders), pg 182

Paramount Market Publishing Inc, Ithaca, NY *Toll Free Tel:* 888-787-8100, pg 182

Parenting Press Inc, Seattle, WA *Toll Free Tel:* 800-99-BOOKS (992-6657), pg 183

Parlay Press, Hilton Head, SC *Toll Free Fax:* 888-301-3116, pg 183

Pastoral Press, Portland, OR *Toll Free Tel:* 800-548-8749 *Toll Free Fax:* 800-462-7329, pg 183

Pathfinder Publishing Inc, Tucson, AZ *Toll Free Tel:* 800-977-2282, pg 183

Pauline Books & Media, Boston, MA *Toll Free Tel:* 800-876-4463 (orders); 800-836-9723 (cust serv), pg 184

Paulist Press, Mahwah, NJ *Toll Free Tel:* 800-218-1903 *Toll Free Fax:* 800-836-3161, pg 184

Peace Hill Press, Charles City, VA *Toll Free Tel:* 877-322-3445 (orders), pg 184

Peachpit Press, Berkeley, CA *Toll Free Tel:* 800-283-9444, pg 184

Peachtree Publishers, Atlanta, GA *Toll Free Tel:* 800-241-0113 *Toll Free Fax:* 800-875-8909, pg 184

Pearson Benjamin Cummings, San Francisco, CA *Toll Free Tel:* 800-922-0579 (orders), pg 184

Pearson Education Canada, Don Mills, ON Canada *Toll Free Tel:* 800-263-9965 *Toll Free Fax:* 800-263-7733; 888-465-0536, pg 494

Pearson ERPI, St-Laurent, QC Canada *Toll Free Tel:* 800-263-3678 *Toll Free Fax:* 800-643-4720, pg 494

Pearson Learning Solutions, Boston, MA *Toll Free Tel:* 800-428-4466 (orders), pg 185

Pearson Scott Foresman, Glenview, IL *Toll Free Tel:* 800-535-4391 (Midwest), pg 185

Peel Productions Inc, Vancouver, WA *Toll Free Tel:* 800-345-6665, pg 185

Pelican Publishing Co, Gretna, LA *Toll Free Tel:* 800-843-1724, pg 185

Pembroke Publishers Ltd, Markham, ON Canada *Toll Free Tel:* 800-997-9807 *Toll Free Fax:* 800-339-5568, pg 494

Pendragon Press, Hillsdale, NY *Toll Free Tel:* 877-656-6381 (orders), pg 185

Penfield Books, Iowa City, IA *Toll Free Tel:* 800-728-9998, pg 185

Penguin Group (USA) LLC, a Penguin Random House company, New York, NY *Toll Free Tel:* 800-847-5515 (inside sales); 800-631-8571 (cust serv), pg 186

Penguin Random House Canada Limited, Toronto, ON Canada *Toll Free Tel:* 888-523-9292 (cust serv), pg 495

Penguin Random House Inc, New York, NY *Toll Free Tel:* 800-726-0600, pg 187

Pennsylvania Historical & Museum Commission, Harrisburg, PA *Toll Free Tel:* 800-747-7790, pg 188

The Pennsylvania State University Press, University Park, PA *Toll Free Tel:* 800-326-9180 *Toll Free Fax:* 877-778-2665, pg 188

PennWell Books, Tulsa, OK *Toll Free Tel:* 800-752-9764, pg 188

Penton Media, Overland Park, KS *Toll Free Tel:* 800-262-1954 (cust serv) *Toll Free Fax:* 800-633-6219, pg 188

Peoples Education Inc, Saddle Brook, NJ *Toll Free Tel:* 800-822-1080, pg 188

Per Annum Inc, New York, NY *Toll Free Tel:* 800-548-1108, pg 189

Perfection Learning Corp, Clive, IA *Toll Free Tel:* 800-762-2999, pg 189

The Perseus Books Group, New York, NY *Toll Free Tel:* 800-343-4499 (cust serv), pg 189

Peterson Institute for International Economics (PIIE), Washington, DC *Toll Free Tel:* 800-522-9139 (orders), pg 190

Petroleum Extension Service (PETEX), Austin, TX *Toll Free Tel:* 800-687-4132 *Toll Free Fax:* 800-687-7839, pg 190

Pflaum Publishing Group, Dayton, OH *Toll Free Tel:* 800-543-4383; 800-523-4625 (sales) *Toll Free Fax:* 800-370-4450, pg 190

Phaidon Press Inc, New York, NY *Toll Free Tel:* 800-759-0190 (cust serv) *Toll Free Fax:* 800-286-9471 (cust serv), pg 190

Phi Delta Kappa International®, Bloomington, IN *Toll Free Tel:* 800-766-1156, pg 190

Philosophy Documentation Center, Charlottesville, VA *Toll Free Tel:* 800-444-2419, pg 191

Phoenix Society for Burn Survivors, Grand Rapids, MI *Toll Free Tel:* 800-888-BURN (888-2876), pg 191

Pictorial Histories Publishing Co, Missoula, MT *Toll Free Tel:* 888-763-8350, pg 191

Pieces of Learning, Marion, IL *Toll Free Tel:* 800-729-5137 *Toll Free Fax:* 800-844-0455, pg 191

The Pilgrim Press/United Church Press, Cleveland, OH *Toll Free Tel:* 800-537-3394 (cust serv-indivs); 800-654-5129 (cust serv-commercial accts), pg 192

Pineapple Press Inc, Sarasota, FL *Toll Free Tel:* 866-766-3850 (orders) *Toll Free Fax:* 800-838-1149 (orders), pg 192

Pippin Publishing, Toronto, ON Canada *Toll Free Tel:* 800-565-9523 (CN warehouse) *Toll Free Fax:* 800-221-9985 (CN warehouse), pg 495

Platypus Media LLC, Washington, DC *Toll Free Tel:* 877-PLATYPS (752-8977), pg 192

Plough Publishing House, Walden, NY *Toll Free Tel:* 800-521-8011, pg 193

Pocket Press Inc, Portland, OR *Toll Free Tel:* 888-237-2110 *Toll Free Fax:* 877-643-3732, pg 194

Pogo Press Inc, Apple Valley, MN *Toll Free Tel:* 800-846-7027 *Toll Free Fax:* 800-330-6232, pg 194

Poisoned Pen Press, Scottsdale, AZ *Toll Free Tel:* 800-421-3976, pg 194

Pomegranate Communications Inc, Portland, OR *Toll Free Tel:* 800-227-1428 *Toll Free Fax:* 800-848-4376, pg 195

Portage & Main Press, Winnipeg, MB Canada *Toll Free Tel:* 800-667-9673 *Toll Free Fax:* 866-734-8477, pg 495

Clarkson Potter Publishers, New York, NY *Toll Free Tel:* 888-264-1745, pg 195

Pottersfield Press, East Lawrencetown, NS Canada *Toll Free Fax:* 888-253-3133, pg 495

Practice Management Information Corp (PMIC), Los Angeles, CA *Toll Free Fax:* 800-633-6556 (orders), pg 195

Practising Law Institute, New York, NY *Toll Free Tel:* 800-260-4PLI (260-4754, cust serv) *Toll Free Fax:* 800-321-0093 (local), pg 195

PrairieView Press, Rosenort, MB Canada *Toll Free Tel:* 800-477-7377, pg 496

PREP Publishing, Fayetteville, NC *Toll Free Tel:* 800-533-2814, pg 196

Presbyterian Publishing Corp (PPC), Louisville, KY *Toll Free Tel:* 800-523-1631 (US only), pg 196

Prestel Publishing, New York, NY *Toll Free Tel:* 888-463-6110 (cust serv), pg 196

Prevention Products & Services Inc dba The Bureau for At-Risk Youth, Farmingville, NY *Toll Free Tel:* 800-99YOUTH (999-6884), pg 196

Price World Publishing, Columbus, OH *Toll Free Tel:* 888-234-6896, pg 196

Princeton Architectural Press, New York, NY *Toll Free Tel:* 800-722-6657 (dist); 800-759-0190 (sales), pg 197

Princeton Book Co Publishers, Hightstown, NJ *Toll Free Tel:* 800-220-7149, pg 197

The Princeton Review, New York, NY *Toll Free Tel:* 800-733-3000, pg 197

Princeton University Press, Princeton, NJ *Toll Free Tel:* 800-777-4726 (orders) *Toll Free Fax:* 800-999-1958, pg 197

PRO-ED Inc, Austin, TX *Toll Free Tel:* 800-897-3202 *Toll Free Fax:* 800-397-7633, pg 198

Pro Lingua Associates Inc, Brattleboro, VT *Toll Free Tel:* 800-366-4775, pg 198

Productive Publications, Toronto, ON Canada *Toll Free Tel:* 877-879-2669 (orders), pg 496

Productivity Press, New York, NY *Toll Free Tel:* 800-634-7064 (orders) *Toll Free Fax:* 800-248-4724 (orders), pg 198

Professional Communications Inc, Caddo, OK *Toll Free Tel:* 800-337-9838, pg 198

The Professional Education Group Inc (PEG), Minnetonka, MN *Toll Free Tel:* 800-229-2531, pg 198

Professional Resource Press, Sarasota, FL *Toll Free Tel:* 800-443-3364 (orders & cust serv) *Toll Free Fax:* 866-804-4843 (orders only), pg 198

Prometheus Books, Amherst, NY *Toll Free Tel:* 800-421-0351, pg 199

ProQuest LLC, Ann Arbor, MI *Toll Free Tel:* 800-521-0600 *Toll Free Fax:* 800-864-0019, pg 199

ProStar Publications Inc, Annapolis, MD *Toll Free Tel:* 800-481-6277 *Toll Free Fax:* 800-487-6277, pg 199

Prufrock Press, Waco, TX *Toll Free Tel:* 800-998-2208 *Toll Free Fax:* 800-240-0333, pg 199

Psychological Assessment Resources Inc (PAR), Lutz, FL *Toll Free Tel:* 800-331-8378 *Toll Free Fax:* 800-727-9329, pg 199

Psychology Press, New York, NY *Toll Free Tel:* 800-634-7064, pg 199

PublicAffairs, New York, NY *Toll Free Tel:* 800-343-4499 (orders), pg 200

Les Publications du Quebec, Quebec, QC Canada *Toll Free Tel:* 800-463-2100 (Quebec province only) *Toll Free Fax:* 800-561-3479, pg 496

Purple Mountain Press Ltd, Fleischmanns, NY *Toll Free Tel:* 800-325-2665 (orders), pg 201

The Putnam Publishing Group, New York, NY *Toll Free Tel:* 800-631-8571, pg 201

Quackenworth Publishing, Culver City, CA *Toll Free Tel:* 888-701-4991 *Toll Free Fax:* 888-892-6339, pg 201

Quail Ridge Press, Brandon, MS *Toll Free Tel:* 800-343-1583 *Toll Free Fax:* 800-864-1082, pg 201

Quality Medical Publishing Inc, St Louis, MO *Toll Free Tel:* 800-348-7808, pg 201

Quarto Publishing Group USA Inc, Minneapolis, MN *Toll Free Tel:* 800-328-0590 (sales); 800-458-0454, pg 201

Quicksilver Productions, Ashland, OR *Toll Free Fax:* 888-974-6462, pg 202

Quintessence Publishing Co Inc, Hanover Park, IL *Toll Free Tel:* 800-621-0387, pg 202

Quixote Press, Wever, IA *Toll Free Tel:* 800-571-2665, pg 202

Rainbow Publishers, San Diego, CA *Toll Free Tel:* 800-323-7337 *Toll Free Fax:* 800-331-0297, pg 203

Ram Publishing Co, Garland, TX *Toll Free Tel:* 800-527-4011, pg 203

Rand McNally, Skokie, IL *Toll Free Tel:* 800-678-7263, pg 203

Random House Children's Books, New York, NY *Toll Free Tel:* 800-200-3552, pg 203

Random House Publishing Group, New York, NY *Toll Free Tel:* 800-200-3552, pg 204

Random House Reference/Random House Puzzles & Games/House of Collectibles, New York, NY *Toll Free Tel:* 800-733-3000 *Toll Free Fax:* 800-659-2436, pg 204

Raven Publishing Inc, Norris, MT *Toll Free Tel:* 866-685-3545, pg 205

Raven Tree Press, McHenry, IL *Toll Free Tel:* 800-323-8270; 877-256-0579 *Toll Free Fax:* 800-909-9901, pg 205

Rayve Productions Inc, Windsor, CA *Toll Free Tel:* 800-852-4890, pg 205

Reader's Digest Association Canada ULC (Selection du Reader's Digest Canada SRL), Montreal, QC Canada *Toll Free Tel:* 866-236-7789 (cust serv), pg 497

The Reader's Digest Association Inc, New York, NY *Toll Free Tel:* 800-310-6261 (cust serv), pg 205

Reader's Digest General Books, Pleasantville, NY *Toll Free Tel:* 800-304-2807 (cust serv), pg 205

Reader's Digest USA Select Editions, White Plains, NY *Toll Free Tel:* 800-304-2807 (cust serv), pg 205

Recorded Books LLC, Prince Frederick, MD *Toll Free Tel:* 800-638-1304; 877-732-2898, pg 206

Red Chair Press, South Egremont, MA *Toll Free Tel:* 888-327-2141 (ext 110) *Toll Free Fax:* 888-533-4037, pg 206

Red Deer Press Inc, Markham, ON Canada *Toll Free Tel:* 800-387-9776 (orders) *Toll Free Fax:* 800-260-9777 (orders), pg 497

Red Wheel/Weiser/Conari, Newburyport, MA *Toll Free Tel:* 800-423-7087 (orders), pg 206

Redleaf Press, St Paul, MN *Toll Free Tel:* 800-423-8309 *Toll Free Fax:* 800-641-0115, pg 206

Reedswain Inc, Spring City, PA *Toll Free Tel:* 800-331-5191, pg 207

Referee Books, Racine, WI *Toll Free Tel:* 800-733-6100, pg 207

ReferencePoint Press Inc, San Diego, CA *Toll Free Tel:* 888-479-6436, pg 207

Regal Books, Ventura, CA *Toll Free Tel:* 800-446-7735 (orders), pg 207

Regal Crest Enterprises LLC, Belton, TX *Toll Free Fax:* 866-294-9628, pg 207

Regnery Publishing Inc, Washington, DC *Toll Free Tel:* 888-219-4747, pg 208

Regular Baptist Press, Schaumburg, IL *Toll Free Tel:* 800-727-4440 (orders only); 888-588-1600, pg 208

Research Press, Champaign, IL *Toll Free Tel:* 800-519-2707, pg 208

Revell, Grand Rapids, MI *Toll Free Tel:* 800-877-2665; 800-679-1957, pg 208

Review & Herald Publishing Association, Hagerstown, MD *Toll Free Tel:* 800-234-7630, pg 208

Rio Nuevo Publishers, Tucson, AZ *Toll Free Tel:* 800-969-9558 *Toll Free Fax:* 800-715-5888, pg 209

Rising Sun Publishing, Marietta, GA *Toll Free Tel:* 800-524-2813, pg 209

Riverside Publishing, Rolling Meadows, IL *Toll Free Tel:* 800-323-9540, pg 209

Rizzoli International Publications Inc, New York, NY *Toll Free Tel:* 800-522-6657 (orders only), pg 209

James A Rock & Co Publishers, Florence, SC *Toll Free Tel:* 800-411-2230, pg 210

Rod & Staff Publishers Inc, Crockett, KY *Toll Free Fax:* 800-643-1244 (ordering in US), pg 210

The Rosen Publishing Group Inc, New York, NY *Toll Free Tel:* 800-237-9932 *Toll Free Fax:* 888-436-4643, pg 211

Rothstein Publishing, Brookfield, CT *Toll Free Tel:* 888-768-4783, pg 211

Rough Guides, New York, NY *Toll Free Tel:* 800-631-8571, pg 211

The Rough Notes Co Inc, Carmel, IN *Toll Free Tel:* 800-428-4384 (cust serv) *Toll Free Fax:* 800-321-1909, pg 211

Routledge/Taylor & Francis, New York, NY *Toll Free Tel:* 800-634-7064 (orders), pg 211

Rowman & Littlefield Publishers Inc, Lanham, MD *Toll Free Tel:* 800-462-6420 (cust serv), pg 212

Running Press Book Publishers, Philadelphia, PA *Toll Free Tel:* 800-343-4499 (cust serv & orders) *Toll Free Fax:* 800-453-2884 (cust serv & orders), pg 212

Russell Sage Foundation, New York, NY *Toll Free Tel:* 800-524-6401, pg 212

Rutgers University Press, New Brunswick, NJ *Toll Free Tel:* 800-848-6224 (orders only) *Toll Free Fax:* 800-272-6817 (fulfillment), pg 212

Saddleback Educational Publishing, Costa Mesa, CA *Toll Free Tel:* 888-SDLBACK (735-2225); 800-637-8715 *Toll Free Fax:* 888-734-4010, pg 213

William H Sadlier Inc, New York, NY *Toll Free Tel:* 800-221-5175 (cust serv), pg 213

SAE (Society of Automotive Engineers International), Warrendale, PA *Toll Free Tel:* 877-606-7323 (cust serv), pg 213

Safari Press, Huntington Beach, CA *Toll Free Tel:* 800-451-4788, pg 213

Sagamore Publishing LLC, Urbana, IL *Toll Free Tel:* 800-327-5557 (orders), pg 213

SAGE Publications, Thousand Oaks, CA *Toll Free Tel:* 800-818-7243 *Toll Free Fax:* 800-583-2665, pg 214

St Augustine's Press Inc, South Bend, IN *Toll Free Tel:* 888-997-4994, pg 214

St James Press®, Farmington Hills, MI *Toll Free Tel:* 800-877-4253 (orders) *Toll Free Fax:* 800-414-5043 (orders), pg 214

Saint Mary's Press, Winona, MN *Toll Free Tel:* 800-533-8095 *Toll Free Fax:* 800-344-9225, pg 215

Saint Nectarios Press, Seattle, WA *Toll Free Tel:* 800-643-4233, pg 215

St Pauls, Staten Island, NY *Toll Free Tel:* 800-343-2522, pg 215

Salem Press Inc, Hackensack, NJ *Toll Free Tel:* 800-221-1592; 800-221-1592, pg 215

Salina Bookshelf Inc, Flagstaff, AZ *Toll Free Tel:* 877-527-0070, pg 215

SAMS Technical Publishing LLC, Indianapolis, IN *Toll Free Tel:* 800-428-7267 *Toll Free Fax:* 800-552-3910, pg 216

Sandlapper Publishing Inc, Orangeburg, SC *Toll Free Tel:* 800-849-7263 (orders only) *Toll Free Fax:* 800-337-9420, pg 216

Santa Monica Press LLC, Solana Beach, CA *Toll Free Tel:* 800-784-9553, pg 216

Santillana USA Publishing Co Inc, Doral, FL *Toll Free Tel:* 800-245-8584 *Toll Free Fax:* 888-248-9518, pg 216

Sara Jordan Publishing, St Catharines, ON Canada *Toll Free Tel:* 800-567-7733 *Toll Free Fax:* 800-229-3855, pg 498

Sasquatch Books, Seattle, WA *Toll Free Tel:* 800-775-0817, pg 217

Scepter Publishers, New York, NY *Toll Free Tel:* 800-322-8773, pg 217

Schiel & Denver Book Publishers, Houston, TX *Toll Free Tel:* 888-629-4449 *Toll Free Fax:* 888-224-2721, pg 217

Schirmer Trade Books, New York, NY *Toll Free Tel:* 800-431-7187 (orders), pg 218

Schlager Group Inc, Dallas, TX *Toll Free Tel:* 888-416-5727, pg 218

Scholastic Canada Ltd, Toronto, ON Canada *Toll Free Tel:* 800-268-3860 (CN) *Toll Free Fax:* 866-387-4944, pg 498

Scholastic Inc, New York, NY *Toll Free Tel:* 800-scholastic, pg 218

Scholastic International, New York, NY *Toll Free Tel:* 800-SCHOLASTIC (800-724-6527), pg 218

Schonfeld & Associates Inc, Libertyville, IL *Toll Free Tel:* 800-205-0030, pg 219

School for Advanced Research Press, Santa Fe, NM *Toll Free Tel:* 888-390-6070, pg 219

School Guide Publications, New Rochelle, NY *Toll Free Tel:* 800-433-7771, pg 219

School Zone Publishing Co, Grand Haven, MI *Toll Free Tel:* 800-253-0564 *Toll Free Fax:* 800-550-4618 (orders only), pg 219

Schreiber Publishing Inc, Rockville, MD *Toll Free Tel:* 800-296-1961 (sales), pg 219

Science, Naturally!™, Washington, DC *Toll Free Tel:* 866-724-9876, pg 219

Scobre Press Corp, La Jolla, CA *Toll Free Tel:* 877-726-2734, pg 220

Scott Publishing Co, Sidney, OH *Toll Free Tel:* 800-572-6885 (cust serv) *Toll Free Fax:* 800-488-5349, pg 220

Scurlock Publishing Co Inc, Texarkana, TX *Toll Free Tel:* 800-228-6389 (US & CN), pg 220

Seal Books, Toronto, ON Canada *Toll Free Tel:* 888-523-9292 (order desk), pg 498

Search Institute Press®, Minneapolis, MN *Toll Free Tel:* 800-888-7828, pg 221

Seedling Publications Inc, Elizabethtown, PA *Toll Free Tel:* 800-233-0759 *Toll Free Fax:* 888-834-1303, pg 221

Self-Counsel Press Ltd, Bellingham, WA *Toll Free Tel:* 800-663-3007, pg 221

Self-Realization Fellowship Publishers, Los Angeles, CA *Toll Free Tel:* 888-773-8680, pg 222

Seven Stories Press, New York, NY *Toll Free Tel:* 800-733-3000 (orders), pg 222

Shambhala Publications Inc, Boston, MA *Toll Free Tel:* 866-424-0030 (off); 888-424-2329 (cust serv), pg 223

M E Sharpe Inc, Armonk, NY *Toll Free Tel:* 800-541-6563, pg 223

Shen's Books, Walnut Creek, CA *Toll Free Tel:* 800-456-6660 *Toll Free Fax:* 888-269-9092, pg 223

Show What You Know® Publishing, A Lorenz Company, Dayton, OH *Toll Free Tel:* 877-PASSING (727-7464), pg 224

Signalman Publishing, Kissimmee, FL *Toll Free Tel:* 888-907-4423, pg 224

Silman-James Press, Los Angeles, CA *Toll Free Tel:* 877-SJP-BOOK (757-2665), pg 224

Silver Moon Press, New York, NY *Toll Free Tel:* 800-874-3320, pg 224

Simba Information, Stamford, CT *Toll Free Tel:* 888-297-4622 (cust serv), pg 224

Simcha Press, Deerfield Beach, FL *Toll Free Tel:* 800-851-9100 ext 212 *Toll Free Fax:* 800-424-7652, pg 225

Simon & Schuster, New York, NY *Toll Free Tel:* 800-223-2348 (cust serv); 800-223-2336 (orders) *Toll Free Fax:* 800-943-9831 (orders), pg 225

Simon & Schuster Canada, Toronto, ON Canada *Toll Free Tel:* 800-387-0446; 800-268-3216 (orders) *Toll Free Fax:* 888-849-8151 (orders), pg 499

Skandisk Inc, Bloomington, MN *Toll Free Tel:* 800-468-2424, pg 227

SkillPath Publications, Mission, KS *Toll Free Tel:* 800-873-7545, pg 227

Sky Publishing, Cambridge, MA *Toll Free Tel:* 866-644-1377, pg 227

SkyLight Paths Publishing, Woodstock, VT *Toll Free Tel:* 800-962-4544, pg 227

Slack Incorporated, Thorofare, NJ *Toll Free Tel:* 800-257-8290, pg 227

Sleeping Bear Press™, Ann Arbor, MI *Toll Free Tel:* 800-487-2323, pg 227

Slipdown Mountain Publications LLC, Lake Linden, MI *Toll Free Tel:* 866-341-3705 *Toll Free Fax:* 866-341-3705, pg 228

Smith & Kraus Publishers Inc, Portland, ME *Toll Free Tel:* 877-668-8680, pg 228

M Lee Smith Publishers LLC, Brentwood, TN *Toll Free Tel:* 800-274-6774, pg 228

Smyth & Helwys Publishing Inc, Macon, GA *Toll Free Tel:* 800-747-3016 (orders only); 800-568-1248 (orders only), pg 228

Society for Human Resource Management (SHRM), Alexandria, VA *Toll Free Tel:* 800-444-5006 (orders), pg 228

Society for Industrial & Applied Mathematics, Philadelphia, PA *Toll Free Tel:* 800-447-7426, pg 228

Society for Mining, Metallurgy & Exploration, Englewood, CO *Toll Free Tel:* 800-763-3132, pg 229

Society of American Archivists, Chicago, IL *Toll Free Tel:* 866-722-7858, pg 229

Society of Manufacturing Engineers, Dearborn, MI *Toll Free Tel:* 800-733-4763 (cust serv), pg 229

The Society of Naval Architects & Marine Engineers, Jersey City, NJ *Toll Free Tel:* 800-798-2188, pg 229

Solano Press Books, Point Arena, CA *Toll Free Tel:* 800-931-9373, pg 229

Solution Tree, Bloomington, IN *Toll Free Tel:* 800-733-6786, pg 230

Soncino Press Ltd, Brooklyn, NY *Toll Free Tel:* 800-972-6201, pg 230

Sophia Institute Press®, Bedford, NH *Toll Free Tel:* 800-888-9344 *Toll Free Fax:* 888-288-2259, pg 230

Sopris West Educational Services, Dallas, TX *Toll Free Tel:* 800-547-6747 *Toll Free Fax:* 888-819-7767, pg 230

Sounds True Inc, Louisville, CO *Toll Free Tel:* 800-333-9185, pg 230

Sourcebooks Inc, Naperville, IL *Toll Free Tel:* 800-432-7444, pg 230

South Carolina Bar, Columbia, SC *Toll Free Tel:* 800-768-7787, pg 231

South End Press, Cambridge, MA *Toll Free Fax:* 800-960-0078, pg 231

Southern Historical Press Inc, Greenville, SC *Toll Free Tel:* 800-233-0152, pg 231

Specialty Press Inc, Plantation, FL *Toll Free Tel:* 800-233-9273, pg 231

SPIE, Bellingham, WA *Toll Free Tel:* 888-504-8171, pg 231

Spizzirri Publishing Inc, Rapid City, SD *Toll Free Tel:* 800-325-9819 *Toll Free Fax:* 800-322-9819, pg 232

Springer, New York, NY *Toll Free Tel:* 800-SPRINGER (777-4643), pg 232

Springer Publishing Co, New York, NY *Toll Free Tel:* 877-687-7476, pg 232

Spry Publishing, Ann Arbor, MI *Toll Free Tel:* 877-722-2264, pg 232

Square One Publishers Inc, Garden City Park, NY *Toll Free Tel:* 877-900-BOOK (900-2665), pg 232

SSPC: The Society for Protective Coatings, Pittsburgh, PA *Toll Free Tel:* 877-281-7772 (US only), pg 233

ST Media Group Book Division, Cincinnati, OH *Toll Free Tel:* 866-265-0954, pg 233

Stackpole Books, Mechanicsburg, PA *Toll Free Tel:* 800-732-3669, pg 233

Standard International Media Holdings, Naples, FL *Toll Free Fax:* 866-948-7883, pg 233

Standard Publishing, Cincinnati, OH *Toll Free Tel:* 800-543-1353 *Toll Free Fax:* 877-867-5751, pg 233

Standard Publishing Corp, Boston, MA *Toll Free Tel:* 800-682-5759, pg 233

Starcrafts LLC, Epping, NH *Toll Free Tel:* 866-953-8458 (24/7 message ctr), pg 234

Stargazer Publishing Co, Corona, CA *Toll Free Tel:* 800-606-7895 (orders), pg 234

State University of New York Press, Albany, NY *Toll Free Tel:* 877-204-6073 (orders) *Toll Free Fax:* 877-204-6074 (orders), pg 234

Statistics Canada, Ottawa, ON Canada *Toll Free Tel:* 800-263-1136 (CN & US, gen inquiries); 800-267-6677 (prods & servs) *Toll Free Fax:* 877-287-4369 (orders), pg 500

Stemmer House Publishers Inc, Gilsum, NH *Toll Free Tel:* 800-345-6665, pg 235

Stenhouse Publishers, Portland, ME *Toll Free Tel:* 888-363-0566 *Toll Free Fax:* 800-833-9164, pg 235

Stephens Press™, Las Vegas, NV *Toll Free Tel:* 888-951-2665, pg 235

Sterling Publishing Co Inc, New York, NY *Toll Free Tel:* 800-367-9692, pg 235

STM Learning Inc, St Louis, MO *Toll Free Tel:* 800-600-0330, pg 236

Stone Bridge Press Inc, Albany, CA *Toll Free Tel:* 800-947-7271 (orders), pg 236

Stoneydale Press Publishing Co, Stevensville, MT *Toll Free Tel:* 800-735-7006, pg 236

Storey Publishing LLC, North Adams, MA *Toll Free Tel:* 800-441-5700 (orders); 800-793-9396 (edit), pg 236

Strategic Book Publishing & Rights Agency (SBPRA), Houston, TX *Toll Free Tel:* 888-808-6190, pg 237

Stress Free Kids®, Marietta, GA *Toll Free Tel:* 800-841-4204 *Toll Free Fax:* 866-302-2759, pg 237

Studio Fun International Inc, White Plains, NY *Toll Free Tel:* 800-934-0977, pg 237

Stylus Publishing LLC, Sterling, VA *Toll Free Tel:* 800-232-0223 (orders & cust serv), pg 237

Summerthought Publishing, Banff, AB Canada *Toll Free Fax:* 800-762-3095 (orders), pg 500

Summit University Press, Gardiner, MT *Toll Free Tel:* 800-245-5445 (retail orders) *Toll Free Fax:* 800-221-8307, pg 237

Sun Publishing Company, Santa Fe, NM *Toll Free Tel:* 877-849-0051, pg 238

Sunbelt Publications Inc, El Cajon, CA *Toll Free Tel:* 800-626-6579 (cust serv), pg 238

Sunburst Digital Inc, Hoffman Estates, IL *Toll Free Tel:* 800-321-7511 *Toll Free Fax:* 888-800-3028, pg 238

Sundance/Newbridge Publishing, Marlborough, MA *Toll Free Tel:* 888-200-2720; 800-343-8204 (Sundance cust serv & orders); 800-867-0307 (Newbridge cust serv & orders) *Toll Free Fax:* 800-456-2419 (orders), pg 238

Sunrise River Press, North Branch, MN *Toll Free Tel:* 800-895-4585, pg 238

Sunstone Press, Santa Fe, NM *Toll Free Tel:* 800-243-5644, pg 238

Surrey Books, Evanston, IL *Toll Free Tel:* 800-326-4430, pg 238

Swan Isle Press, Chicago, IL *Toll Free Tel:* 800-621-2736 (cust serv) *Toll Free Fax:* 800-621-8476 (cust serv), pg 239

Swedenborg Foundation, West Chester, PA *Toll Free Tel:* 800-355-3222 (cust serv), pg 239

Synapse Information Resources Inc, Endicott, NY *Toll Free Tel:* 888-SYN-CHEM (796-2436), pg 239

Syracuse University Press, Syracuse, NY *Toll Free Tel:* 800-365-8929 (cust serv), pg 239

TAN Books, Charlotte, NC *Toll Free Tel:* 800-437-5876, pg 240

T&T Clark International, New York, NY *Toll Free Tel:* 800-561-7704 (orders), pg 240

Tanglewood Press, Terre Haute, IN *Toll Free Tel:* 800-836-4994 (orders), pg 240

Tantor Media Inc, Old Saybrook, CT *Toll Free Tel:* 877-782-6867 *Toll Free Fax:* 888-782-7821, pg 240

Tapestry Press Ltd, Littleton, MA *Toll Free Tel:* 800-535-2007, pg 240

Taschen America, Los Angeles, CA *Toll Free Tel:* 888-TASCHEN (827-2436), pg 241

The Taunton Press Inc, Newtown, CT *Toll Free Tel:* 800-477-8727 (cust serv); 800-888-8286 (orders), pg 241

Taylor & Francis Inc, Philadelphia, PA *Toll Free Tel:* 800-354-1420, pg 241

TCP Press, Whitchurch-Stouffville, ON Canada *Toll Free Tel:* 800-772-7765, pg 500

Teach Me Tapes Inc, Minnetonka, MN *Toll Free Tel:* 800-456-4656, pg 241

Teacher Created Resources Inc, Westminster, CA *Toll Free Tel:* 800-662-4321; 888-343-4335 *Toll Free Fax:* 800-525-1254, pg 241

Teachers College Press, New York, NY *Toll Free Tel:* 800-575-6566, pg 241

Teacher's Discovery, Auburn Hills, MI *Toll Free Tel:* 800-832-2437 *Toll Free Fax:* 800-287-4509, pg 242

Teachers of English to Speakers of Other Languages Inc (TESOL), Alexandria, VA *Toll Free Tel:* 888-547-3369, pg 242

Teaching & Learning Co, Dayton, OH *Toll Free Tel:* 800-444-1144, pg 242

Teaching Strategies, Bethesda, MD *Toll Free Tel:* 800-637-3652, pg 242

Temple University Press, Philadelphia, PA *Toll Free Tel:* 800-621-2736, pg 242

Templegate Publishers, Springfield, IL *Toll Free Tel:* 800-367-4844 (orders only), pg 242

Ten Speed Press, Berkeley, CA *Toll Free Tel:* 800-841-BOOK (841-2665), pg 243

Teora USA LLC, Capitol Heights, MD *Toll Free Tel:* 800-974-2105 *Toll Free Fax:* 800-358-3754, pg 243

Teton NewMedia, Jackson, WY *Toll Free Tel:* 877-306-9793, pg 243

Tetra Press, Blacksburg, VA *Toll Free Tel:* 800-526-0650, pg 243

Texas A&M University Press, College Station, TX *Toll Free Tel:* 800-826-8911 (orders) *Toll Free Fax:* 888-617-2421 (orders), pg 243

Texas Christian University Press, Fort Worth, TX *Toll Free Tel:* 800-826-8911, pg 243

Texas Tech University Press, Lubbock, TX *Toll Free Tel:* 800-832-4042, pg 243

Texas Western Press, El Paso, TX *Toll Free Tel:* 800-488-3798 (orders only), pg 244

TFH Publications Inc, Neptune City, NJ *Toll Free Tel:* 800-631-2188, pg 244

Thames & Hudson, New York, NY *Toll Free Tel:* 800-233-4830, pg 244

Theosophical Publishing House/Quest Books, Wheaton, IL *Toll Free Tel:* 800-669-9425 (ext 347), pg 244

Thieme Medical Publishers Inc, New York, NY *Toll Free Tel:* 800-782-3488, pg 245

Charles C Thomas Publisher Ltd, Springfield, IL *Toll Free Tel:* 800-258-8980, pg 245

Thomas Geale Publications Inc, Montara, CA *Toll Free Tel:* 800-554-5457, pg 245

Thomas Nelson, Nashville, TN *Toll Free Tel:* 800-251-4000, pg 245

Thomas Publications, Gettysburg, PA *Toll Free Tel:* 800-840-6782, pg 245

Thompson Educational Publishing Inc, Toronto, ON Canada *Toll Free Tel:* 877-366-2763, pg 501

Thomson Reuters Westlaw™, Eagan, MN *Toll Free Tel:* 800-328-9352 (sales); 800-328-4880 (cust serv), pg 245

Thorndike Press, Waterville, ME *Toll Free Tel:* 800-233-1244 (ext 4, cust serv/orders) *Toll Free Fax:* 800-558-4676 (orders), pg 245

Tide-mark Press, East Hartford, CT *Toll Free Tel:* 800-338-2508, pg 246

Tilbury House Publishers, Thomaston, ME *Toll Free Tel:* 800-582-1899 (orders), pg 246

Timber Press Inc, Portland, OR *Toll Free Tel:* 800-327-5680, pg 246

TJ Publishers Inc, Dallas, TX *Toll Free Tel:* 800-999-1168, pg 509

Tommy Nelson, Nashville, TN *Toll Free Tel:* 800-251-4000, pg 247

Torah Aura Productions, Los Angeles, CA *Toll Free Tel:* 800-238-6724, pg 247

Tortuga Press, Santa Rosa, CA *Toll Free Tel:* 866-4TORTUGA (486-7884), pg 247

Tower Publishing Co, Standish, ME *Toll Free Tel:* 800-969-8693, pg 247

Tracks Publishing, Chula Vista, CA *Toll Free Tel:* 800-443-3570, pg 247

Trafalgar Square Books, North Pomfret, VT *Toll Free Tel:* 800-423-4525, pg 248

Trafford, Bloomington, IN *Toll Free Tel:* 888-232-4444, pg 248

Trails Books, Boulder, CO *Toll Free Tel:* 800-258-5830, pg 248

Training Resource Network Inc (TRN), St Augustine, FL *Toll Free Tel:* 800-280-7010 (orders), pg 248

Tralco-Lingo Fun, Niagara Falls, NY *Toll Free Tel:* 888-487-2526 *Toll Free Fax:* 866-487-2527, pg 248

Transaction Publishers Inc, Piscataway, NJ *Toll Free Tel:* 888-999-6778 (dist ctr), pg 248

Transcontinental Music Publications, New York, NY *Toll Free Tel:* 888-489-8242 (orders), pg 248

Treehaus Communications Inc, Loveland, OH *Toll Free Tel:* 800-638-4287 (orders), pg 249

Triad Publishing Co, Gainesville, FL *Toll Free Fax:* 800-854-4947, pg 249

TripBuilder Media Inc, Westport, CT *Toll Free Tel:* 800-525-9745, pg 249

TriQuarterly Books, Evanston, IL *Toll Free Tel:* 800-621-2736 (orders only), pg 249

TRISTAN Publishing, Minneapolis, MN *Toll Free Tel:* 866-545-1383, pg 250

Triumph Books, Chicago, IL *Toll Free Tel:* 800-888-4741 (orders only), pg 250

Triumph Learning LLC, New York, NY *Toll Free Tel:* 800-338-6519 (cust serv) *Toll Free Fax:* 866-805-5723, pg 250

Truman State University Press, Kirksville, MO *Toll Free Tel:* 800-916-6802, pg 250

Tundra Books, Toronto, ON Canada *Toll Free Tel:* 888-523-9292 (orders); 800-588-1074 *Toll Free Fax:* 888-562-9924 (orders), pg 501

Turnstone Press, Winnipeg, MB Canada *Toll Free Tel:* 888-363-7718, pg 502

Tuttle Publishing, North Clarendon, VT *Toll Free Tel:* 800-526-2778 *Toll Free Fax:* 800-FAX-TUTL, pg 251

Twayne Publishers™, Farmington Hills, MI *Toll Free Tel:* 800-877-4253; 800-363-4253 *Toll Free Fax:* 800-414-5043, pg 251

Twenty-First Century Books, Minneapolis, MN *Toll Free Tel:* 800-328-4929 *Toll Free Fax:* 800-332-1132, pg 251

Twenty-Third Publications, New London, CT *Toll Free Tel:* 800-321-0411 (orders) *Toll Free Fax:* 800-572-0788, pg 251

Tyndale House Publishers Inc, Carol Stream, IL *Toll Free Tel:* 800-323-9400, pg 252

Type & Archetype Press, Charleston, SC *Toll Free Tel:* 800-447-8973, pg 252

ULI-The Urban Land Institute, Washington, DC *Toll Free Tel:* 800-321-5011 (cust serv) *Toll Free Fax:* 800-248-4585, pg 252

Ulysses Press, Berkeley, CA *Toll Free Tel:* 800-377-2542, pg 252

Ulysses Travel Guides, Montreal, QC Canada *Toll Free Tel:* 800-748-9171, pg 502

Unarius Academy of Science Publications, El Cajon, CA *Toll Free Tel:* 800-475-7062, pg 252

Unicor Medical Inc, Montgomery, AL *Toll Free Tel:* 800-825-7421 *Toll Free Fax:* 800-305-8030, pg 253

Editorial Unilit, Medley, FL *Toll Free Tel:* 800-767-7726, pg 253

The United Educators Inc, Lake Bluff, IL *Toll Free Tel:* 800-323-5875, pg 253

United States Holocaust Memorial Museum, Washington, DC *Toll Free Tel:* 800-259-9998 (orders), pg 253

United States Institute of Peace Press, Washington, DC *Toll Free Tel:* 800-868-8064 (cust serv), pg 253

United States Pharmacopeia, Rockville, MD *Toll Free Tel:* 800-227-8772, pg 253

United Synagogue Book Service, New York, NY *Toll Free Tel:* 800-594-5617 (warehouse only), pg 254

Universal-Publishers Inc, Boca Raton, FL *Toll Free Tel:* 800-636-8329, pg 254

University of Alaska Press, Fairbanks, AK *Toll Free Tel:* 888-252-6657 (US only), pg 254

The University of Arizona Press, Tucson, AZ *Toll Free Tel:* 800-426-3797 (orders) *Toll Free Fax:* 800-426-3797, pg 254

The University of Arkansas Press, Fayetteville, AR *Toll Free Tel:* 800-626-0090, pg 255

University of British Columbia Press, Vancouver, BC Canada *Toll Free Tel:* 877-377-9378 *Toll Free Fax:* 800-668-0821, pg 502

University of Chicago Press, Chicago, IL *Toll Free Tel:* 800-621-2736 (orders), pg 255

University of Hawaii Press, Honolulu, HI *Toll Free Tel:* 888-UHPRESS (847-7377) *Toll Free Fax:* 800-650-7811, pg 256

University of Iowa Press, Iowa City, IA *Toll Free Tel:* 800-621-2736 (orders only) *Toll Free Fax:* 800-621-8476 (orders only), pg 256

University of Missouri Press, Columbia, MO *Toll Free Tel:* 800-621-2736 (orders), pg 257

University of Nebraska Press, Lincoln, NE *Toll Free Tel:* 800-848-6224 (cust serv & US orders) *Toll Free Fax:* 800-526-2617 (cust serv & US orders), pg 257

University of New Mexico, Albuquerque, NM *Toll Free Tel:* 800-249-7737 (orders only) *Toll Free Fax:* 800-622-8667 (orders only), pg 258

University of Oklahoma Press, Norman, OK *Toll Free Tel:* 800-627-7377 (orders) *Toll Free Fax:* 800-735-0476 (orders), pg 258

University of Puerto Rico Press, San Juan, PR *Toll Free Tel:* 877-338-7788, pg 259

University of Regina Press, Regina, SK Canada *Toll Free Tel:* 866-874-2257, pg 503

University of South Carolina Press, Columbia, SC *Toll Free Tel:* 800-768-2500 (orders) *Toll Free Fax:* 800-868-0740 (orders), pg 259

University of Tennessee Press, Knoxville, TN *Toll Free Tel:* 800-621-2736 (orders) *Toll Free Fax:* 800-621-8476 (orders), pg 260

The University of Utah Press, Salt Lake City, UT *Toll Free Tel:* 800-621-2736 (orders) *Toll Free Fax:* 800-621-8471, pg 260

The University of Virginia Press, Charlottesville, VA *Toll Free Tel:* 800-831-3406 (orders) *Toll Free Fax:* 877-288-6400, pg 260

University of Washington Press, Seattle, WA *Toll Free Tel:* 800-537-5487 (orders), pg 260

University of Wisconsin Press, Madison, WI *Toll Free Tel:* 800-621-2736 (orders) *Toll Free Fax:* 800-621-2736 (orders), pg 260

University Press of America Inc, Lanham, MD *Toll Free Tel:* 800-462-6420 *Toll Free Fax:* 800-338-4550, pg 261

University Press of Colorado, Boulder, CO *Toll Free Tel:* 800-621-2736 (orders), pg 261

University Press of Florida, Gainesville, FL *Toll Free Tel:* 800-226-3822 (orders only) *Toll Free Fax:* 800-680-1955 (orders only), pg 261

University Press of Mississippi, Jackson, MS *Toll Free Tel:* 800-737-7788 (orders & cust serv), pg 261

University Press of New England, Lebanon, NH *Toll Free Tel:* 800-421-1561 (orders only), pg 262

University Publishing Group, Hagerstown, MD *Toll Free Tel:* 800-654-8188, pg 262

W E Upjohn Institute for Employment Research, Kalamazoo, MI *Toll Free Tel:* 888-227-8569, pg 263

Upper Access Inc, Hinesburg, VT *Toll Free Tel:* 800-310-8320 (orders), pg 263

Upper Room Books, Nashville, TN *Toll Free Tel:* 800-972-0433, pg 263

Upstart Books™, Madison, WI *Toll Free Tel:* 800-448-4887 (orders) *Toll Free Fax:* 800-448-5828, pg 263

Urban Land Institute, Washington, DC *Toll Free Tel:* 800-321-5011 (cust serv), pg 263

US Conference of Catholic Bishops, Washington, DC *Toll Free Tel:* 800-235-8722 (orders only), pg 264

US Games Systems Inc, Stamford, CT *Toll Free Tel:* 800-54-GAMES (544-2637), pg 264

US Government Publishing Office (GPO), Washington, DC *Toll Free Tel:* 866-512-1800 (orders), pg 264

Utah Geological Survey, Salt Lake City, UT *Toll Free Tel:* 888-UTAH-MAP (882-4627 bookstore), pg 264

VanDam Inc, New York, NY *Toll Free Tel:* 800-UNFOLDS (863-6537), pg 264

Vandamere Press, St Petersburg, FL *Toll Free Tel:* 800-551-7776, pg 264

Vanderbilt University Press, Nashville, TN *Toll Free Tel:* 800-627-7377 (orders only) *Toll Free Fax:* 800-735-0476 (orders only), pg 264

Vault.com Inc, New York, NY *Toll Free Tel:* 800-535-2074, pg 264

Vedanta Press, Hollywood, CA *Toll Free Tel:* 800-816-2242, pg 265

Victory in Grace Press, Lake Zurich, IL *Toll Free Tel:* 800-78-GRACE (784-7223), pg 265

Volcano Press, Volcano, CA *Toll Free Tel:* 800-879-9636, pg 266

Wadsworth Publishing, Belmont, CA *Toll Free Fax:* 800-522-4923, pg 266

Walch Education, Portland, ME *Toll Free Tel:* 800-558-2846 *Toll Free Fax:* 888-991-5755, pg 266

Warner Press, Anderson, IN *Toll Free Tel:* 800-741-7721 (orders) *Toll Free Fax:* 800-347-6411, pg 267

Warren Communications News Inc, Washington, DC *Toll Free Tel:* 800-771-9202, pg 267

Washington State University Press, Pullman, WA *Toll Free Tel:* 800-354-7360, pg 267

Water Environment Federation, Alexandria, VA *Toll Free Tel:* 800-666-0206, pg 267

Water Resources Publications LLC, Highlands Ranch, CO *Toll Free Tel:* 800-736-2405 *Toll Free Fax:* 800-616-1971, pg 267

WaterBrook Multnomah Publishing Group, Colorado Springs, CO *Toll Free Tel:* 800-603-7051 (orders) *Toll Free Fax:* 800-294-5686 (orders), pg 267

Watermark Publishing, Honolulu, HI *Toll Free Tel:* 866-900-BOOK (900-2665), pg 267

Wayne State University Press, Detroit, MI *Toll Free Tel:* 800-978-7323, pg 268

Wayside Publishing, Sandwich, MA *Toll Free Tel:* 888-302-2519, pg 268

Weigl Educational Publishers Ltd, Calgary, AB Canada *Toll Free Tel:* 800-668-0766 *Toll Free Fax:* 866-449-3445, pg 504

Wesleyan Publishing House, Fishers, IN *Toll Free Tel:* 800-493-7539 *Toll Free Fax:* 800-788-3535, pg 269

West Academic Publishing, St Paul, MN *Toll Free Tel:* 877-888-1330, pg 269

West Virginia University Press, Morgantown, WV *Toll Free Tel:* 866-WVU-PRES (988-7737), pg 269

Westcliffe Publishers Inc, Boulder, CO *Toll Free Tel:* 800-258-5830, pg 269

Western Reflections Publishing Co, Lake City, CO *Toll Free Tel:* 800-993-4490, pg 269

Westminster John Knox Press (WJK), Louisville, KY *Toll Free Tel:* 800-227-2872 (US only) *Toll Free Fax:* 800-541-5113 (US & CN), pg 269

White Cloud Press, Ashland, OR *Toll Free Tel:* 800-380-8286, pg 270

White Wolf Publishing Inc, Decatur, GA *Toll Free Tel:* 800-454-9653, pg 270

Whitecap Books Ltd, Vancouver, BC Canada *Toll Free Tel:* 800-387-9776 *Toll Free Fax:* 800-260-9777, pg 504

Whitehorse Press, Center Conway, NH *Toll Free Tel:* 800-531-1133, pg 271

Whittier Publications Inc, Oceanside, NY *Toll Free Tel:* 800-897-TEXT (897-8398), pg 271

Whole Person Associates Inc, Duluth, MN *Toll Free Tel:* 800-247-6789, pg 271

Wide World of Maps Inc, Phoenix, AZ *Toll Free Tel:* 800-279-7654, pg 271

Michael Wiese Productions, Studio City, CA *Toll Free Tel:* 800-833-5738 (orders), pg 271

Wilderness Adventures Press Inc, Belgrade, MT *Toll Free Tel:* 866-400-2012, pg 271

Wildlife Education Ltd, Evanston, IL *Toll Free Tel:* 800-477-5034, pg 271

John Wiley & Sons Canada Ltd, Toronto, ON Canada *Toll Free Tel:* 800-467-4797 (orders only) *Toll Free Fax:* 800-565-6802 (orders), pg 505

John Wiley & Sons Inc, Hoboken, NJ *Toll Free Tel:* 800-225-5945 (cust serv), pg 272

John Wiley & Sons Inc Higher Education, Hoboken, NJ *Toll Free Tel:* 800-225-5945 (cust serv), pg 272

John Wiley & Sons Inc Professional/Trade Group, Hoboken, NJ *Toll Free Tel:* 800-225-5945 (cust serv), pg 272

John Wiley & Sons Inc Scientific, Technical, Medical & Scholarly (STMS), Hoboken, NJ *Toll Free Tel:* 800-225-5945 (cust serv), pg 272

Wilfrid Laurier University Press, Waterloo, ON Canada *Toll Free Tel:* 866-836-5551 (CN & US), pg 505

William Carey Library Publishers, Pasadena, CA *Toll Free Tel:* 866-732-6657 (orders & cust serv), pg 272

Willow Creek Press, Minocqua, WI *Toll Free Tel:* 800-850-9453, pg 272

H W Wilson, Hackensack, NJ *Toll Free Tel:* 800-221-1592, pg 273

Wimmer Cookbooks, Memphis, TN *Toll Free Tel:* 800-363-1771, pg 273

Wind Canyon Books, Stockton, CA *Toll Free Tel:* 800-952-7007 *Toll Free Fax:* 888-289-7086, pg 273

Windsor Books, Bayshore, NY *Toll Free Tel:* 800-321-5934, pg 273

Windward Publishing, Apple Valley, MN *Toll Free Tel:* 800-846-7027 *Toll Free Fax:* 800-330-6232, pg 273

The Wine Appreciation Guild Ltd, South San Francisco, CA *Toll Free Tel:* 800-231-9463, pg 273

WingSpread Publishers, Camp Hill, PA *Toll Free Tel:* 800-884-4571, pg 273

Winters Publishing, Greensburg, IN *Toll Free Tel:* 800-457-3230, pg 273

Winterthur Museum & Country Estate, Wilmington, DE *Toll Free Tel:* 800-448-3883, pg 274

Wisconsin Department of Public Instruction, Madison, WI *Toll Free Tel:* 800-441-4563, pg 274

Wisdom Publications Inc, Somerville, MA *Toll Free Tel:* 800-272-4050 (orders), pg 274

Wittenborn Art Books, San Francisco, CA *Toll Free Tel:* 800-660-6403, pg 274

Alan Wofsy Fine Arts, San Francisco, CA *Toll Free Tel:* 800-660-6403, pg 274

Wolters Kluwer Ltd, Toronto, ON Canada *Toll Free Tel:* 800-268-4522 (CN & US cust serv) *Toll Free Fax:* 800-461-4131, pg 505

Wood Lake Publishing Inc, Kelowna, BC Canada *Toll Free Tel:* 800-663-2775 (orders & cust serv) *Toll Free Fax:* 888-841-9991 (orders & cust serv), pg 505

Woodbine House, Bethesda, MD *Toll Free Tel:* 800-843-7323, pg 274

Woodland Publishing Inc, Salt Lake City, UT *Toll Free Tel:* 800-277-3243, pg 275

Workman Publishing Co Inc, New York, NY *Toll Free Tel:* 800-722-7202, pg 275

World Almanac®, New York, NY *Toll Free Tel:* 800-322-8755, pg 275

World Bank Publications, Washington, DC *Toll Free Tel:* 800-645-7247 (cust serv), pg 275

World Book Inc, Chicago, IL *Toll Free Tel:* 800-967-5325 (consumer sales, US); 800-463-8845 (consumer sales, CN); 800-975-3250 (school & lib sales, US); 800-837-5365 (school & lib sales, CN); 866-866-5200 (web sales) *Toll Free Fax:* 800-433-9330 (school & lib sales, US); 888-690-4002 (school lib sales, CN), pg 276

World Citizens, Mill Valley, CA *Toll Free Tel:* 800-247-6553 (orders only), pg 276

World Scientific Publishing Co Inc, Hackensack, NJ *Toll Free Tel:* 800-227-7562 *Toll Free Fax:* 888-977-2665, pg 276

World Trade Press, Petaluma, CA *Toll Free Tel:* 800-833-8586, pg 276

World Vision Resources, Monrovia, CA *Toll Free Tel:* 800-777-7752 (US only), pg 276

WorldTariff, San Francisco, CA *Toll Free Tel:* 800-556-9334, pg 276

Worldwide Library, Don Mills, ON Canada *Toll Free Tel:* 888-432-4879, pg 505

Wright Group/McGraw-Hill, Columbus, OH *Toll Free Tel:* 800-537-4740, pg 276

Write Stuff Enterprises LLC, Fort Lauderdale, FL *Toll Free Tel:* 800-900-2665, pg 277

WriteLife LLC, Omaha, NE *Toll Free Tel:* 877-974-8354, pg 277

Writer's Digest Books, Blue Ash, OH *Toll Free Tel:* 800-289-0963, pg 277

Wyndham Hall Press, Lima, OH *Toll Free Tel:* 866-895-0977, pg 277

Xlibris Corp, Bloomington, IN *Toll Free Tel:* 888-795-4274, pg 277

Yale Center for British Art, New Haven, CT *Toll Free Tel:* 877-274-8278, pg 278

Yale University Press, New Haven, CT *Toll Free Tel:* 800-405-1619 (cust serv) *Toll Free Fax:* 800-406-9145 (cust serv), pg 278

YMAA Publication Center, Wolfeboro, NH *Toll Free Tel:* 800-669-8892, pg 278

Young People's Press Inc (YPPI), San Diego, CA *Toll Free Tel:* 800-231-9774, pg 279

YWAM Publishing, Seattle, WA *Toll Free Tel:* 800-922-2143, pg 279

Zagat Survey LLC, New York, NY *Toll Free Tel:* 866-817-9947 (orders); 800-540-9609, pg 279

Zaner-Bloser Inc, Columbus, OH *Toll Free Tel:* 800-421-3018 (cust serv) *Toll Free Fax:* 800-992-6087 (orders), pg 279

Zeig, Tucker & Theisen Inc, Phoenix, AZ *Toll Free Tel:* 800-666-2211 (orders), pg 279

Zondervan, Grand Rapids, MI *Toll Free Tel:* 800-226-1122; 800-727-1309 (retail orders) *Toll Free Fax:* 800-698-3256 (retail orders), pg 280

Zone Books dba Urzone Inc, Brooklyn, NY *Toll Free Tel:* 800-405-1619 (orders & cust serv) *Toll Free Fax:* 800-406-9145 (orders), pg 280

Index to Sections

D

E

F

R

S

T

Index to Advertisers